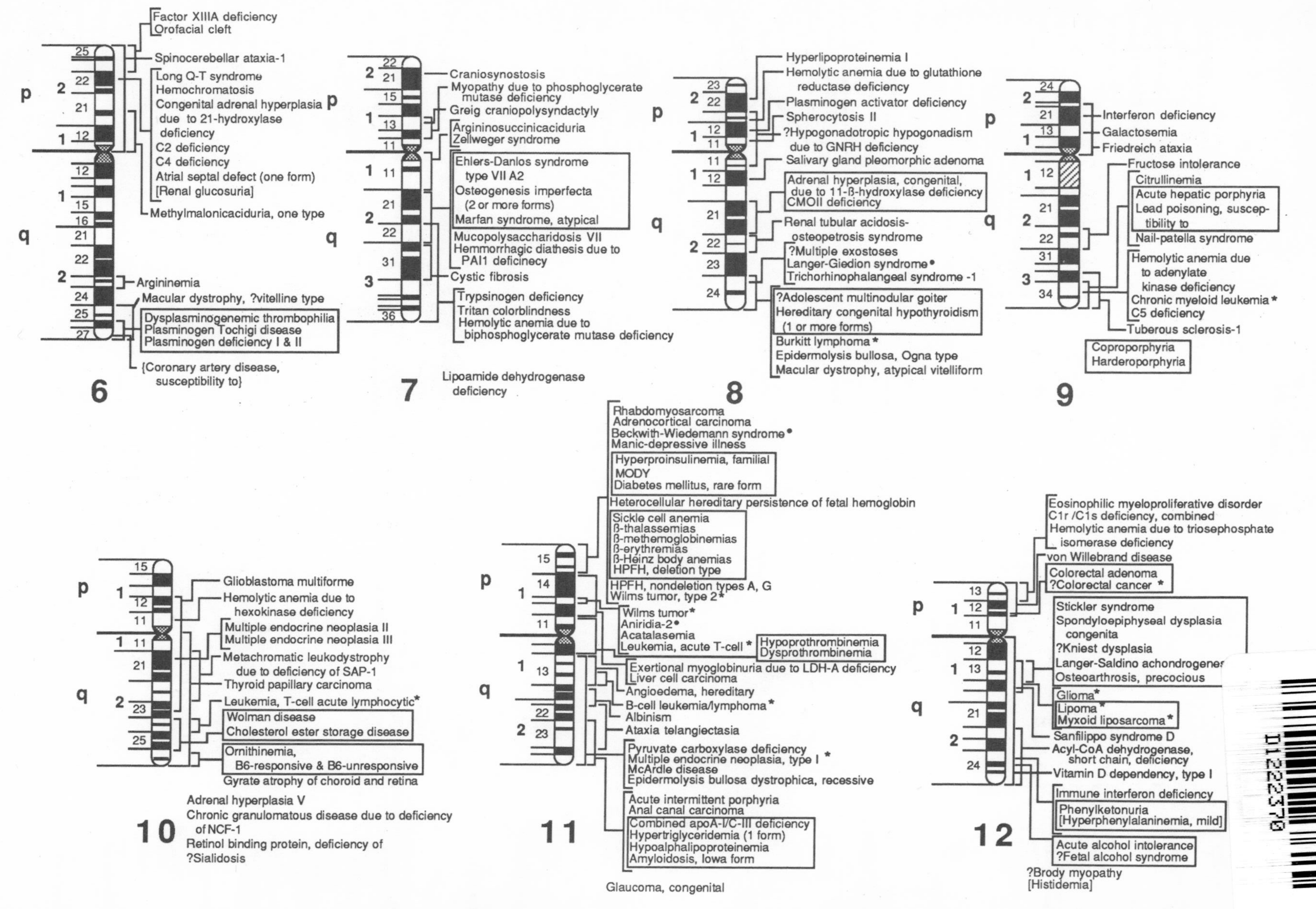

Factor XIIIA deficiency
Orofacial cleft
Spinocerebellar ataxia-1
Long Q-T syndrome
Hemochromatosis
Congenital adrenal hyperplasia due to 21-hydroxylase deficiency
C2 deficiency
C4 deficiency
Atrial septal defect (one form)
[Renal glucosuria]
Methylmalonicaciduria, one type
Argininemia
Macular dystrophy, ?vitelline type
Dysplasminogenemic thrombophilia
Plasminogen Tochigi disease
Plasminogen deficiency I & II
{Coronary artery disease, susceptibility to}
6
Craniosynostosis
Myopathy due to phosphoglycerate mutase deficiency
Greig craniopolysyndactyly
Argininosuccinicaciduria
Zellweger syndrome
Ehlers-Danlos syndrome type VII A2
Osteogenesis imperfecta (2 or more forms)
Marfan syndrome, atypical
Mucopolysaccharidosis VII
Hemmorrhagic diathesis due to PAI1 deficiency
Cystic fibrosis
Trypsinogen deficiency
Tritan colorblindness
Hemolytic anemia due to biphosphoglycerate mutase deficiency
7
Lipoamide dehydrogenase deficiency
Hyperlipoproteinemia I
Hemolytic anemia due to glutathione reductase deficiency
Plasminogen activator deficiency
Spherocytosis II
?Hypogonadotropic hypogonadism due to GNRH deficiency
Salivary gland pleomorphic adenoma
Adrenal hyperplasia, congenital, due to 11-ß-hydroxylase deficiency
CMOII deficiency
Renal tubular acidosis-osteopetrosis syndrome
?Multiple exostoses
Langer-Giedion syndrome•
Trichorhinophalangeal syndrome -1
?Adolescent multinodular goiter
Hereditary congenital hypothyroidism (1 or more forms)
Burkitt lymphoma*
Epidermolysis bullosa, Ogna type
Macular dystrophy, atypical vitelliform
8
Interferon deficiency
Galactosemia
Friedreich ataxia
Fructose intolerance
Citrullinemia
Acute hepatic porphyria
Lead poisoning, susceptibility to
Nail-patella syndrome
Hemolytic anemia due to adenylate kinase deficiency
Chronic myeloid leukemia*
C5 deficiency
Tuberous sclerosis-1
Coproporphyria
Harderoporphyria
9
Glioblastoma multiforme
Hemolytic anemia due to hexokinase deficiency
Multiple endocrine neoplasia II
Multiple endocrine neoplasia III
Metachromatic leukodystrophy due to deficiency of SAP-1
Thyroid papillary carcinoma
Leukemia, T-cell acute lymphocytic*
Wolman disease
Cholesterol ester storage disease
Ornithinemia, B6-responsive & B6-unresponsive
Gyrate atrophy of choroid and retina
Adrenal hyperplasia V
Chronic granulomatous disease due to deficiency of NCF-1
Retinol binding protein, deficiency of
?Sialidosis
10
Rhabdomyosarcoma
Adrenocortical carcinoma
Beckwith-Wiedemann syndrome•
Manic-depressive illness
Hyperproinsulinemia, familial
MODY
Diabetes mellitus, rare form
Heterocellular hereditary persistence of fetal hemoglobin
Sickle cell anemia
ß-thalassemias
ß-methemoglobinemias
ß-erythremias
ß-Heinz body anemias
HPFH, deletion type
HPFH, nondeletion types A, G
Wilms tumor, type 2*
Wilms tumor*
Aniridia-2•
Acatalasemia
Leukemia, acute T-cell *
Hypoprothrombinemia
Dysprothrombinemia
Exertional myoglobinuria due to LDH-A deficiency
Liver cell carcinoma
Angioedema, hereditary
B-cell leukemia/lymphoma*
Albinism
Ataxia telangiectasia
Pyruvate carboxylase deficiency
Multiple endocrine neoplasia, type I *
McArdle disease
Epidermolysis bullosa dystrophica, recessive
Acute intermittent porphyria
Anal canal carcinoma
Combined apoA-I/C-III deficiency
Hypertriglyceridemia (1 form)
Hypoalphalipoproteinemia
Amyloidosis, Iowa form
11
Glaucoma, congenital
Eosinophilic myeloproliferative disorder
C1r /C1s deficiency, combined
Hemolytic anemia due to triosephosphate isomerase deficiency
von Willebrand disease
Colorectal adenoma
?Colorectal cancer *
Stickler syndrome
Spondyloepiphyseal dysplasia congenita
?Kniest dysplasia
Langer-Saldino achondrogenes
Osteoarthrosis, precocious
Glioma*
Lipoma*
Myxoid liposarcoma*
Sanfilippo syndrome D
Acyl-CoA dehydrogenase, short chain, deficiency
Vitamin D dependency, type I
Immune interferon deficiency
Phenylketonuria
[Hyperphenylalaninemia, mild]
Acute alcohol intolerance
?Fetal alcohol syndrome
12
?Brody myopathy
[Histidemia]

(*Continued*)

SIXTH EDITION

THE METABOLIC BASIS OF INHERITED DISEASE

Editors

Charles R. Scriver, M.D.C.M.
Professor of Biology, Human Genetics and Pediatrics, Departments of Biology and Pediatrics and Center for Human Genetics, McGill University, Montreal, Canada

Arthur L. Beaudet, M.D.
Investigator, Howard Hughes Medical Institute; Professor, Institute for Molecular Genetics and Departments of Pediatrics and Cell Biology, Baylor College of Medicine, Houston, Texas

William S. Sly, M.D.
Alice A. Doisy Professor of Biochemistry and Professor of Pediatrics; Chairman, Edward A. Doisy Department of Biochemistry and Molecular Biology, St. Louis University School of Medicine, St. Louis, Missouri

David Valle, M.D.
Investigator, Howard Hughes Medical Institute; Professor of Pediatrics, Medicine, and Molecular Biology & Genetics, The Johns Hopkins University School of Medicine, Baltimore, Maryland

Consulting Editors

John B. Stanbury, M.D.
Honorary Physician, Massachusetts General Hospital; Division of Health Science and Technology, Massachusetts Institute of Technology, Boston, Massachusetts

James B. Wyngaarden, M.D.
Director, National Institutes of Health, Bethesda, Maryland

Donald S. Fredrickson, M.D.
Researcher, Molecular Disease Branch, National Heart, Lung and Blood Institute; Scholar, National Library of Medicine, National Institutes of Health, Bethesda, Maryland

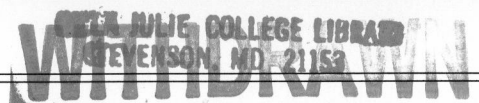

SIXTH EDITION

THE METABOLIC BASIS OF INHERITED DISEASE

I

Editors

Charles R. Scriver, M.D.C.M.
Arthur L. Beaudet, M.D.
William S. Sly, M.D.
David Valle, M.D.

Consulting Editors

John B. Stanbury, M.D.
James B. Wyngaarden, M.D.
Donald S. Fredrickson, M.D.

McGRAW-HILL INFORMATION SERVICES COMPANY
Health Professions Division
New York St Louis San Francisco Colorado Springs Auckland
Bogotá Caracas Hamburg Lisbon London Madrid Mexico Milan Montreal
New Delhi Panama Paris San Juan São Paulo Singapore Sydney Tokyo Toronto

THE METABOLIC BASIS OF INHERITED DISEASE

234567890HALHAL8932109

ISBN 0-07-909254-3 (set)
ISBN 0-07-060727-3 (v. 1)
ISBN 0-07-060728-1 (v. 2)

This book was set in Plantin by The Clarinda Company.
The editors were J. Dereck Jeffers and Gail Gavert.
The production supervisor was Robert R. Laffler.
The designer was Charles A. Carson.
The cover was designed by M N' O Production Services, Inc.
Arcata Graphics/Halliday was printer and binder.

Library of Congress Cataloging-in-Publication Data

The Metabolic basis of inherited disease/editors, Charles R. Scriver
. . . [et al.]; consulting editors, John B. Stanbury, James B.
Wyngaarden, Donald S. Fredrickson.—6th ed.
p. cm.
Includes bibliographies and index.
1. Metabolism, Inborn errors of. I. Scriver, Charles R.
[DNLM: 1. Hereditary Diseases. 2. Metabolic Diseases.
3. Metabolism, Inborn Errors. WD 2300 M587]
RC627.8.M47 1989
616.3'9042—dc19
DNLM/DLC
for Library of Congress 88-39722
CIP

NOTICE

CONTENTS

Part 19 SKIN

Part 20 INTESTINE

LIST OF CONTRIBUTORS

Milton B. Adesnik, Ph.D. [3]
Professor, Department of Cell Biology, New York University School of Medicine, New York, New York

Björn A. Afzelius, Ph.D. [112]
Professor, Wenner-Gren Institute, University of Stockholm, Stockholm, Sweden

Robert J. Alpern, M.D. [103]
Associate Professor of Medicine; Chief, Division of Nephrology, University of Texas Southwestern Medical Center, Dallas, Texas

D. Bernard Amos, M.D. [4]
James B. Duke Professor of Immunology and Experimental Surgery; Chief, Division of Immunology, Department of Microbiology and Immunology, Duke University Medical Center, Durham, North Carolina

Donald C. Anderson, M.D. [113]
Professor of Pediatrics, Microbiology and Immunology and Cell Biology; Head, Section of Leukocyte Biology, Baylor College of Medicine, Houston, Texas

Thomas E. Andreoli, M.D. [78]
Professor and Chairman, Department of Internal Medicine, University of Arkansas for Medical Sciences, Little Rock, Arkansas

Irwin M. Arias, M.D. [53]
Chairman of Physiology, Department of Physiology and Medicine, Tufts University Medical School, Boston, Massachusetts

Gerd Assmann, M.D. [50, 64]
Professor of Clinical Chemistry; Director of the Institute for Clinical Chemistry and Laboratory Medicine, Central Laboratory; Director of the Institute for Arteriosclerosis Research, Westphalian-Wilhelms University, Münster, West Germany

Salvatore Auricchio, M.D. [121]
Professor of Pediatrics, Department of Pediatrics, and 2nd Faculty of Medicine, University of Naples, Naples, Italy

John A. Barranger, M.D., Ph.D. [67]
Professor of Pediatrics and Biochemistry, University of Southern California; Head, Division of Medical Genetics, Children's Hospital of Los Angeles, Los Angeles, California

Arthur L. Beaudet, M.D. [1, 63, 108]
Investigator, Howard Hughes Medical Institute; Professor, Institute for Molecular Genetics and Department of Pediatrics, Baylor College of Medicine, Houston, Texas

David M. O. Becroft, M. D. [43]
Pathologist in Charge, Princess Mary Hospital for Children, Auckland, New Zealand

Pamela S. Becker, M.D., Ph.D. [95]
Fellow in Hematology, Yale University, School of Medicine, New Haven, Connecticut

Merrill D. Benson, M.D. [97]
Professor of Medicine and Medical Genetics, Indiana University School of Medicine, Indianapolis, Indiana

Michel Bergeron, M.D. [104]
Professor and Chairman, Department of Physiology, Faculty of Medicine, University of Montreal, Montreal, Canada

David F. Bishop, Ph.D. [70]
Associate Professor of Pediatrics and Genetics, Mount Sinai School of Medicine, New York, New York

Ingemar Bjorkhem, M.D., Ph.D. [51]
Professor, Department of Clinical Chemistry at Huddinge Hospital, Karolinska Institutet, Stockholm, Sweden

R. Michael Blaese, M.D. [110]
Deputy Chief, Metabolism Branch, National Cancer Institute, National Institutes of Health, Bethesda, Maryland

Thomas F. Boat, M.D. [108]
Professor and Chairman, Department of Pediatrics, University of North Carolina at Chapel Hill, Chapel Hill, North Carolina

Thomas H. Bothwell, M.D., D.Sc. [55]
Professor and Head of Department of Medicine, University of the Witwatersrand Medical School; Director, Medical Research Council Iron and Red Cell Metabolism Unit, Johannesburg, South Africa

Jan L. Breslow, M.D. [49]
Frederick Henry Leonhardt Professor, The Rockefeller University, New York, New York

H. Bryan Brewer, Jr., M.D. [50]
Chief, Molecular Disease Branch, National Heart, Lung, and Blood Institute, Bethesda, Maryland

Michael S. Brown, M.D. [48]
Paul J. Thomas Professor of Medicine and Genetics, University of Texas Southwestern Medical Center, Dallas, Texas

John D. Brunzell, M.D. [45]
Professor of Medicine, Division of Metabolism, Endocrinology and Nutrition, University of Washington, Seattle, Washington

Saul W. Brusilow, M.D. [20]
Professor of Pediatrics, The Johns Hopkins University School of Medicine, Baltimore, Maryland

Joseph L. Butler, M.D. [109]
Associate Professor of Pediatrics and Medicine, Division of Developmental and Clinical Immunology, Departments of Medicine, Pediatrics and Microbiology and The Comprehensive Cancer Center, University of Alabama at Birmingham, Birmingham, Alabama

Peter H. Byers, M.D. [115]
Professor, Departments of Pathology and Medicine (Medical Genetics), Center for Inherited Disease, University of Washington, Seattle, Washington

John W. Callahan, Ph.D. [66]
Associate Professor of Biochemistry and Pediatrics, Hospital for Sick Children, University of Toronto, Toronto, Canada

C. Thomas Caskey, M.D. [38]
Investigator, Howard Hughes Medical Institute; Professor and Director, Institute for Molecular Genetics, Baylor College of Medicine, Houston, Texas

Webster K. Cavenee, Ph.D. [9]
Director, Montreal Branch, Ludwig Institute for Cancer Research, Royal Victoria Hospital, Montreal, Canada

Robert W. Charlton, B.Sc., M.D. [55]
Senior Physician, Department of Medicine, University of the Witwatersrand Medical School, Johannesburg, South Africa

Winston W. Chen, Ph.D. [65]
Associate Professor of Neurology, The Johns Hopkins University, Baltimore, Maryland

Dominic Chung, Ph.D. [85]
Research Associate Professor, Department of Biochemistry, University of Washington, Seattle, Washington

James E. Cleaver, Ph.D. [120]
Professor of Radiology, Laboratory of Radiobiology and Environmental Health, University of California, San Francisco, California

J. B. Clegg, M.A., Ph.D. [93]
Reader, M. R. C. Molecular Haematology Unit, Nuffield Department of Clinical Medicine, University of Oxford, John Radcliffe Hospital, Oxford, England

Paul M. Coates, Ph.D. [33]
Research Associate Professor, Department of Pediatrics, University of Pennsylvania School of Medicine, Philadelphia, Pennsylvania

Harvey R. Colten, M.D. [111]
Harriet B. Spoehrer Professor and Chairman, Department of Pediatrics, Washington University School of Medicine, St. Louis, Missouri

Ernst Conzelmann, Ph.D. [72]
Wissenschaftlicher Assistant, Institute of Organic Chemistry and Biochemistry, Rheinische Friedrich-Wilhelms Universität, Bonn, Germany

David N. Cooper, B.Sc., Ph.D. [1]
Lecturer in Molecular Genetics, Haematology Department, King's College Hospital School of Medicine and Dentistry, University of London, London, England

Max D. Cooper, M.D., Ph.D [109]
Professor of Pediatrics and Microbiology, Division of Developmental and Clinical Immunology, Departments of Medicine, Pediatrics and Microbiology and The Comprehensive Cancer Center, University of Alabama at Birmingham, Birmingham, Alabama

Diane Wilson Cox, Ph.D. [96]
Professor, Research Institute, The Hospital for Sick Children; Departments of Paediatrics, Medical Genetics and Medical Biophysics, University of Toronto, Toronto, Canada

Rody P. Cox, M.D. [21]
Dean and Professor of Internal Medicine, University of Texas Southwest Medical Center at Dallas, Dallas, Texas

Joseph Dancis, M.D. [21]
Professor and Chairman, Department of Pediatrics, New York University School of Medicine, New York, New York

David M. Danks, M.D. [54]
Director, Murdoch Institute for Research into Birth Defects, Royal Children's Hospital; Professor of Pediatric Research, University of Melbourne, Melbourne, Australia

Dean J. Danner, Ph.D. [22]
Associate Professor, Division of Medical Genetics, Department of Pediatrics, Emory University School of Medicine, Atlanta, Georgia

Earl W. Davie, Ph.D. [84]
Professor of Biochemistry, University of Washington, Seattle, Washington

Thierry de Barsy, M.D. [12]
Professor, Laboratorire de Chimie Physiologique and Departement de Neuropsychiatrie, Faculté de Medecine, Université Catholique de Louvain, Brussels, Belgium

Jehan-François Desjeux, M.D. [98]
Chief, Research Unit on Intestinal Functions, Metabolism and Nutrition, Institut National de la Santé et de la Recherche Medicale, Paris, France

Robert J. Desnick, Ph.D., M.D. [70]
Arthur J. and Nellie Z. Cohen Professor of Pediatrics and Genetics; Chief, Division of Medical and Molecular Genetics, Mount Sinai School of Medicine, New York, New York

Thomas D. DuBose, Jr., M.D. [103]
Professor of Medicine, Physiology and Biophysics; Chief, Division of Nephrology, The University of Texas Medical Branch at Galveston, Galveston, Texas

J. E. Dumont, M.D., Ph.D. [73]
Professor of Biochemistry; Head, Institute of Interdisciplinary Research, School of Medicine, University of Brussels; Head, Euratom Radioprotection Contract, E.E.C., Brussels, Belgium

Bo Dupont, M.D. [74]
Professor of Immunology, Graduate School of Medicine; Director, Histocompatibility Testing Laboratory and Clinical Immunology Laboratory, Memorial Sloan-Kettering Cancer Center, New York, New York

John W. Eaton, Ph.D. [60]
Professor of Medicine, Laboratory Medicine and Pathology, Dight Laboratories, University of Minnesota, Minneapolis, Minnesota

Louis J. Elsas II, M.D. [22]
Professor, Division of Medical Genetics, Department of Pediatrics, Emory University School of Medicine, Atlanta, Georgia

Charles J. Epstein, M.D. [7]
Professor of Pediatrics and Biochemistry, University of California, San Francisco, California

Wayne A. Fenton, Ph.D. [29, 82]
Research Scientist in Human Genetics, Yale University School of Medicine, Department of Human Genetics, New Haven, Connecticut

Thomas B. Fitzpatrick, M.D., Ph.D., D.Sc. (Hon.) [119]
Wigglesworth Professor of Dermatology, Harvard Medical School, Massachusetts General Hospital, Boston, Massachusetts

Gebhard Flatz, M.D. [122]
Professor of Human Genetics, Department of Human Genetics, Medizinische Hochschule, Hannover, Germany

John R. Forehand, M.D. [114]
Assistant Professor, Department of Pediatrics, University of Pennsylvania School of Medicine and The Children's Hospital of Philadelphia, Philadelphia, Pennsylvania

Daniel W. Foster, M.D. [10]
The Jan and Henri Bromberg Professor and Chair, Internal Medicine, The University of Texas Southwestern Medical Center, Dallas, Texas

Irving H. Fox, M.D. [37]
Professor of Internal Medicine and Biological Chemistry; Director, Clinical Research Center, University of Michigan, University Hospital, Ann Arbor, Michigan

Frank E. Frerman, Ph.D. [30, 34]
Professor of Pediatrics and Microbiology, University of Colorado School of Medicine, Denver, Colorado

Kazuo Fujikawa, Ph.D. [88]
Research Professor, Department of Biochemistry, University of Washington School of Medicine, Seattle, Washington

William A. Gahl, M.D., Ph.D. [107]
Head, Section on Human Biochemical Genetics and Chief (Acting), Human Genetics Branch, National Institute of Child Health and Human Development, National Institutes of Health, Bethesda, Maryland

Richard A. Galbraith, M.D., Ph.D. [52]
Assistant Professor and Physician, The Rockefeller University, New York, New York

Edward I. Ginns, M.D., Ph.D. [67]
Head, Neurogenetics Section, Clinical Neuroscience Branch, National Institute of Mental Health, Bethesda, Maryland

Richard Gitzelmann, M.D. [11]
Professor, Division of Metabolism, University Pediatric Department, Kinderspital Zurich, Zurich, Switzerland

Egil Gjone, M.D. [46]
Professor, Department of Medicine, Rikshospitalet University Hospital, University of Oslo, Oslo, Norway

John A. Glomset, M.D. [46]
Professor, Howard Hughes Medical Institute Research Laboratories/Seattle, University of Washington School of Medicine, Seattle, Washington

Lowell A. Goldsmith, M.D. [16]
James H. Sterner Professor of Dermatology and Chairman, Department of Dermatology, University of Rochester School of Medicine and Dentistry, Rochester, New York

Joseph L. Goldstein, M.D. [48]
Paul J. Thomas Professor of Genetics and Chairman, Department of Molecular Genetics, University of Texas Southwestern Medical Center, Dallas, Texas

Stephen I. Goodman, M.D. [30, 34]
Professor of Pediatrics, University of Colorado School of Medicine, Denver, Colorado

André Gougoux, M.D. [104]
Professor, Department of Medicine and Department of Physiology, University of Montreal, Montreal, Canada

James E. Griffin, M.D. [75]
Associate Professor of Internal Medicine, The University of Texas Southwestern Medical Center, Dallas, Texas

Peter S. Harper, M.D. [118]
Professor and Consultant in Medical Genetics, Institute of Medical Genetics, University of Wales College of Medicine, Cardiff, Wales

Richard J. Havel, M.D. [44]
Director, Cardiovascular Research Institute and Professor of Medicine, University of California School of Medicine, San Francisco, California

Gregory S. Heard, Ph.D. [83]
Assistant Professor of Human Genetics, Department of Human Genetics, Medical College of Virginia, Richmond, Virginia

Ulla Hedner, M.D. [84]
Professor of Clinical Coagulation, University of Goteborg, Sweden; Director of Hematology Research, Novo Industri A/S, Bagsvaerd, Denmark

Henry-Géry Hers [12]
Professor of Biochemistry, Laboratoire de Chimie Physiologique, Université Catholique de Louvain and International Institute of Cellular and Molecular Pathology, Brussels, Belgium

Michael S. Hershfield, M.D. [40]
Associate Professor of Medicine and Assistant Professor of Biochemistry, Duke University Medical Center, Durham, North Carolina

Howard H. Hiatt, M.D. [14]
Professor of Medicine, Harvard Medical School; Professor of Medicine, Harvard School of Public Health; Senior Physician, Brigham & Women's Hospital, Boston, Massachusetts

D. R. Higgs, M.B., B.S. [93]
Honorary Consultant in Haematology, Nuffield Department of Clinical Medicine, University of Oxford, John Radcliffe Hospital, Oxford, England

Richard E. Hillman, M.D. [35]
Professor of Child Health and Biochemistry; Director of Metabolic Genetics, University of Missouri Hospital and Clinics, Columbia, Missouri

Edward W. Holmes, M.D. [41, 42]
Professor of Medicine, Associate Professor of Biochemistry, Division of Metabolism, Endocrinology and Genetics, Duke University Medical Center, Durham, North Carolina

Arthur L. Horwich, M.D. [20]
Associate Professor of Human Genetics and Pediatrics, Yale University School of Medicine, New Haven, Connecticut

Donald E. Hultquist, Ph.D. [92]
Professor of Biological Chemistry, University of Michigan Medical School, Ann Arbor, Michigan

Akitada Ichinose, M.D., Ph.D. [85]
Research Assistant Professor, Department of Biochemistry, University of Washington, Seattle, Washington

Ernst R. Jaffé, M.D. [92]
Distinguished University Professor of Medicine, Albert Einstein College of Medicine, Bronx, New York

Jean L. Johnson, Ph.D. [56]
Assistant Medical Research Professor, Department of Biochemistry, Duke University Medical Center, Durham, North Carolina

Richard B. Johnston, Jr., M.D. [114]
William H. Bennett Professor and Chairman, Department of Pediatrics, University of Pennsylvania School of Medicine and The Children's Hospital of Philadelphia, Philadelphia, Pennsylvania

Michael M. Kaback, M.D. [72]
Professor and Chairman, Department of Pediatrics, University of California San Diego School of Medicine, San Diego, California

John P. Kane, M.D., Ph.D. [44]
Professor of Medicine; Professor of Biochemistry and Biophysics, University of California, School of Medicine, San Francisco, California

Attallah Kappas, M.D. [52]
Sherman Fairchild Professor, Vice-President and Physician-in-Chief, The Rockefeller University, New York, New York

Seymour Kaufman, Ph.D. [15]
Chief, Laboratory of Neurochemistry, National Institute of Mental Health, Bethesda, Maryland

Richard A. King, M.D., Ph.D. [119]
Professor, Department of Medicine and Institute of Human Genetics, University of Minnesota School of Dentistry, Minneapolis, Minnesota

Edwin H. Kolodny, M.D. [69]
Professor of Neurology, Harvard Medical School, Boston; Director, Eunice Kennedy Shriver Center for Mental Retardation, Inc., Waltham, Massachusetts

Donna D. Kostyu, Ph.D. [4]
Assistant Medical Research Professor, Department of Microbiology and Immunology, Duke University Medical Center, Durham, North Carolina

Kenneth H. Kraemer, M.D. [120]
Research Scientist, Laboratory of Molecular Carcinogenesis, National Cancer Institute, National Institutes of Health, Bethesda, Maryland

Nicholas M. Kredich, M.D. [40]
Professor of Medicine and Biochemistry, Duke University Medical Center, Durham, North Carolina

Claude Laberge, M.D. [16]
Professor of Genetic Medicine, Laval University Medical Center, Department of Medicine, Quebec, Canada

Bert N. La Du, Jr., M.D., Ph.D. [27]
Professor, Department of Pharmacology, University of Michigan Medical School, Ann Arbor, Michigan

Jean Marc Lalouel, M.D., D.Sc. [6]
Professor, Department of Human Genetics; Investigator, Howard Hughes Medical Institute, University of Utah Medical Center, Salt Lake City, Utah

Agne Larsson, M.D. [31]
Department of Pediatrics, University Hospital, Uppsala, Sweden

Richard M. Lawn, Ph.D. [86]
Staff Scientist, Department of Cardiovascular Research, Genentech, Inc., South San Francisco, California

Paul B. Lazarow, Ph.D. [57]
Associate Professor, The Rockefeller University, New York, New York

David H. Ledbetter, Ph.D. [8, 9]
Associate Professor, Institute for Molecular Genetics, Baylor College of Medicine, Houston, Texas

Harvey L. Levy, M.D. [17, 23, 101]
Associate Professor of Neurology, Harvard Medical School; Assistant Neurologist and Pediatrician, Massachusetts General Hospital, Boston, Massachusetts

Samuel E. Lux, M.D. [95]
Chief, Division of Hematology and Oncology, The Children's Hospital, Boston, Massachusetts

Lucio Luzzatto, M.D. [91]
Professor of Hematology, Royal Postgraduate Medical School; Consultant Hematologist, Hammersmith Hospital, University of London, London, England

Robert W. Mahley, M.D., Ph.D. [47]
Director, Gladstone Foundation Laboratories for Cardiovascular Disease, Cardiovascular Research Institute, Departments of Pathology and Medicine, University of California, San Francisco, California

Philip W. Majerus, M.D. [90]
Professor of Medicine and Biological Chemistry, Washington University School of Medicine, St. Louis, Missouri

Stephen J. Marx, M.D. [80]
Chief, Mineral Metabolism Section, National Institute of Diabetes, and Digestive and Kidney Diseases, National Institutes of Health, Bethesda, Maryland

Edward R. B. McCabe, M.D., Ph.D. [36]
Associate Professor of Molecular Genetics and Pediatrics; Director, Robert J. Kleberg, Jr., Clinical Center, Institute for Molecular Genetics, Baylor College of Medicine, Houston, Texas

Rodger P. McEver, M.D. [90]
Investigator, St. Francis Medical Research Institute and Associate Professor of Medicine, University of Oklahoma Health Sciences Center; Affiliated Associate Member, Oklahoma Medical Research Foundation, Oklahoma City, Oklahoma

Victor A. McKusick, M.D. [1]
University Professor of Medical Genetics, The Johns Hopkins University School of Medicine; Physician, The Johns Hopkins Hospital, Baltimore, Maryland

Atul Mehta, M.D. [91]
Consultant Hematologist, Department of Hematology, Royal Free Hospital, University of London, London, England

Alton Meister, M.D. [31]
Professor and Chairman, Department of Biochemistry, Cornell University Medical College, New York, New York

Ann B. Moser, A.B. [58, 65]
Assistant in Neurology, The Johns Hopkins University, Baltimore, Maryland

Hugo W. Moser, M.D. [57, 58, 65]
University Professor of Neurology and Pediatrics, The Johns Hopkins University; Director, Neurogenetics Unit, John F. Kennedy Institute for Handicapped Children, Baltimore, Maryland

Björn Mossberg, M.D. [112]
Associate Professor, Department of Medicine 1, South Hospital, Stockholm, Sweden

Arno G. Motulsky, M.D., Sc.D. [55]
Professor of Medicine and Genetics; Director, Center for Inherited Diseases, University of Washington, Seattle, Washington

S. Harvey Mudd, M.D. [23]
Chief, Section on Alkaloid Biosynthesis, Laboratory of General and Comparative Biochemistry, National Institute of Mental Health, Bethesda, Maryland

Joseph Muenzer, M.D., Ph.D. [61]
Assistant Professor, Department of Pediatrics, The University of Michigan Medical School, Ann Arbor, Michigan

William M. Nauseef, M.D. [114]
Associate Professor, Department of Internal Medicine, College of Medicine, University of Iowa, Iowa City, Iowa

Elizabeth F. Neufeld, Ph.D. [61, 72]
Professor and Chair, Department of Biological Chemistry, University of California Los Angeles School of Medicine, Los Angeles, California

Maria I. New, M.D. [74]
Harold and Percy Uris Professor of Pediatric Endocrinology and Metabolism; Chief of Pediatric Endocrinology; Chairman, Department of Pediatrics, The New York Hospital–Cornell Medical Center, New York, New York

Catherine M. Nolan, Ph.D. [62]
Research Associate, Edward A. Doisy Department of Biochemistry and Molecular Biology, St. Louis University School of Medicine, St. Louis, Missouri

Yves Nordmann, M.D. [52]
Professor and Chief, French Center of Porphyria (Hospital Louis Mourier), Faculty Xavier Bichat University, Paris, France

Kaare R. Norum, M.D. [46]
Professor, Institute for Nutrition Research, School of Medicine, University of Oslo, Oslo, Norway

Robert L. Nussbaum, M.D. [8]
Associate Investigator, Howard Hughes Medical Institute; Assistant Professor, Departments of Human Genetics and Pediatrics, University of Pennsylvania School of Medicine, Philadelphia, Pennsylvania

William L. Nyhan, M.D., Ph.D. [25]
Professor, Department of Pediatrics, University of California, San Diego School of Medicine, La Jolla, California

John S. O'Brien, M.S., M.D. [71]
Professor, Department of Neurosciences, University of California, San Diego School of Medicine, La Jolla, California

Stuart H. Orkin, M.D. [2]
Leland Fikes Professor of Pediatric Medicine, Harvard Medical School; Investigator, Howard Hughes Medical Institute, Boston, Massachusetts

Donald E. Paglia, M.D. [94]
Professor, Department of Pathology, University of California School of Medicine, Los Angeles, California

Thomas D. Palella, M.D. [37]
Assistant Professor of Internal Medicine; Chief, Division of Rheumatology; Director, Rackham Arthritis Research Unit, University of Michigan School of Medicine, Ann Arbor, Michigan

Songya Pang, M.D. [74]
Professor of Pediatrics, Division of Pediatric Endocrinology, University of Illinois School of Medicine, Chicago, Illinois

Morag Park, Ph.D. [5]
Head of Molecular Oncology Section, Ludwig Institute for Cancer Research, Montreal, Canada

Thomas L. Perry, M.D. [26]
Professor, Department of Pharmacology and Therapeutics, University of British Columbia, Vancouver, Canada

James M. Phang, M.D. [18]
Chief, Endocrinology Section, Metabolism Branch, National Cancer Institute, National Institutes of Health, Bethesda, Maryland

John A. Phillips, III, M.D. [77]
Professor of Pediatrics and Biochemistry; Director, Division of Genetics, Vanderbilt University School of Medicine, Nashville, Tennessee

Walter C. Quevedo, Jr., Ph.D. [119]
Professor of Biology, Division of Biology and Medicine, Brown University, Providence, Rhode Island

Stanley C. Rall, Jr., Ph.D. [47]
Senior Scientist, Gladstone Foundation Laboratories for Cardiovascular Disease, Cardiovascular Research Institute, University of California, San Francisco, California

Howard Rasmussen, M.D., Ph.D. [105]
Professor of Medicine, Cell Biology and Physiology, Department of Internal Medicine, Yale University School of Medicine, New Haven, Connecticut

W. Brian Reeves, M.D. [78]
Assistant Professor, Department of Internal Medicine, Division of Nephrology, University of Arkansas for Medical Sciences, Little Rock, Arkansas

Samuel Refetoff, M.D. [73]
Professor of Medicine and Pediatrics, University of Chicago, Chicago, Illinois

Martin Renlund, M.D. [107]
Attending Neonatologist, Department of Obstetrics, Helsinki University Hospital; Researcher, Finnish Academy of Science, Helsinki, Finland

Brian H. Robinson, Ph.D. [32]
Professor, Departments of Biochemistry and Pediatrics, University of Toronto and Research Institute, The Hospital for Sick Children, Toronto, Canada

Charles R. Roe, M.D. [33]
Professor, Department of Pediatrics, Duke University School of Medicine, Durham, North Carolina

Leon E. Rosenberg, M.D. [29, 82]
Dean, School of Medicine; C. N. H. Long Professor of Human Genetics, Professor of Pediatrics and Internal Medicine, Yale University School of Medicine, New Haven, Connecticut

David S. Rosenblatt, M.D. [81]
Director, Division of Medical Genetics, Department of Medicine, McGill University; Principal Investigator, Medical Research Council of Canada Genetics Group; Professor, Medicine and Pediatrics, McGill University, Montreal, Canada

Jayanta Roy Chowdhury, M.D. [53]
Professor of Medicine and Director, Division of Gastroenterology, Albert Einstein College of Medicine, Bronx, New York

David D. Sabatini, M.D., Ph.D. [3]
Frederick L. Ehrman Professor and Chairman, Department of Cell Biology, New York University School of Medicine, New York, New York

Richard L. Sabina, Ph.D. [41]
Assistant Professor, Department of Anatomy and Cellular Biology, Medical College of Wisconsin, Milwaukee, Wisconsin

J. Evan Sadler, M.D., Ph.D. [87]
Associate Investigator, Howard Hughes Medical Institute and Departments of Medicine and Biological Chemistry, Washington University School of Medicine, St. Louis, Missouri

Amrik S. Sahota, Ph.D. [39]
Research Associate, Department of Medical Genetics, Indiana University Medical Center, Indianapolis, Indiana

Hidehiko Saito, M.D. [88]
Professor, First Department of Internal Medicine, Nagoya University School of Medicine, Nagoya, Japan

Konrad Sandhoff, Ph.D. [72]
Professor and Director, Institute of Organic Chemistry and Biochemistry, Rheinische Friedrich-Wilhelms Universität, Bonn, Germany

Shigeru Sassa, M.D., Ph.D. [52]
Associate Professor and Physician, The Rockefeller University, New York, New York

Jörg Schmidke, M.D. [1]
Professor, Institute of Human Genetics, University of Gottingen, Gottingen, West Germany

Gerd Schmitz, M.D. [50, 64]
Privatdozent, Institut für Klinische Chemie und Laboratoriumsmedizin, Westphalian-Wilhelms University, Münster, West Germany

Andre W. Schram, Ph.D. [65]
Senior Scientific Officer, Department of Biochemistry, Academic Medical Center, Amsterdam, The Netherlands

C. Ronald Scott, M.D. [24]
Professor, Department of Pediatrics, University of Washington School of Medicine, Seattle, Washington

Charles R. Scriver, M.D.C.M. [1, 15, 18, 26, 102]
Professor of Biology, Human Genetics and Pediatrics, Departments of Biology and Pediatrics and Center for Human Genetics, McGill University, Montreal, Canada

Stanton Segal, M.D. [13, 99]
Professor of Pediatrics and Medicine, University of Pennsylvania School of Medicine; Director, Division of Biochemical Development and Molecular Diseases, Children's Hospital of Philadelphia, Philadelphia, Pennsylvania

Giorgio Semenza, M.D. [121]
Professor of Biochemistry, Co-chairman, Department of Biochemistry, ETH, Zurich, Switzerland

Larry J. Shapiro, M.D. [76]
Professor of Pediatrics and Biological Chemistry, UCLA School of Medicine; Investigator, Howard Hughes Medical Institute; Chief, Division of Medical Genetics, Harbor/UCLA Medical Center, Torrance, California

Olli Simell, M.D. [19, 100]
Professor and Chairman, Department of Pediatrics, University of Turku Hospital, Turku, Finland

H. Anne Simmonds, Ph.D. [39]
Director, Purine Research Laboratory, UMDS Guy's & St. Thomas' Hospitals, London, England

Flemming Skovby, M.D. [23]
Associate Professor of Pediatrics, Section of Clinical Genetics, Department of Pediatrics, Rigshospitalet, University of Copenhagen, Copenhagen, Denmark

Sverre Skrede, M.D. [51]
(Deceased, March 10, 1987) Institute of Clinical Biochemistry, Rikshospitalet, University of Oslo, Oslo, Norway

William S. Sly, M.D. [1, 62, 117]
Alice A. Doisy Professor of Biochemistry and Professor of Pediatrics; Chairman, Edward A. Doisy Department of Biochemistry and Molecular Biology, St. Louis University School of Medicine, St. Louis, Missouri

C. Wayne Smith, M.D. [113]
Associate Professor of Pediatrics, Baylor College of Medicine, Houston, Texas

Phyllis W. Speiser, M.D. [74]
Assistant Professor of Pediatrics, Division of Pediatric Endocrinology; Associate Program Director of the Pediatric Clinical Research Center, The New York Hospital–Cornell Medical Center, New York, New York

Matthew W. Spence, M.D., Ph.D. [66]
Director, Atlantic Research Centre for Mental Retardation; Professor of Pediatrics and Biochemistry, Dalhousie University, Halifax, Nova Scotia, Canada

Oded Sperling, Ph.D. [106]
Professor of Chemical Pathology and Chairman of the Department of Chemical Pathology, Sackler School of Medicine, Tel-Aviv University; Director of Clinical Biochemistry and Chairman of the Division of Laboratories, Beilinson Medical Center, Petah Tekva, Israel

Allen M. Spiegel, M.D. [79]
Chief, Molecular Pathophysiology Branch, National Institute of Diabetes, Digestive, and Kidney Diseases, National Institutes of Health, Bethesda, Maryland

Timothy A. Springer, Ph.D. [113]
Associate Professor of Pathology, Center for Blood Research, Harvard Medical School, Boston, Massachusetts

Daniel Steinberg, M.D., Ph.D [59]
Professor, Department of Medicine and Head, Division of Endocrinology and Metabolism, University of California, San Diego, School of Medicine, La Jolla, California

Beat Steinmann, M.D. [11]
Privatdozent, Division of Metabolism, Department of Pediatrics, University of Zurich, Kinderspital Zurich, Zurich, Switzerland

J. Timothy Stout, Ph.D. [38]
Institute for Molecular Genetics, Baylor College of Medicine, Houston, Texas

D. Parker Suttle, Ph.D. [43]
Assistant Member, Division of Biochemical and Clinical Pharmacology, St. Jude's Children's Research Hospital, Memphis, Tennessee

Kinuko Suzuki, M.D. [72]
Professor, Department of Pathology, School of Medicine, University of North Carolina, Chapel Hill, North Carolina

Kunihiko Suzuki, M.D. [68]
Professor of Neurology and Psychiatry; Director, Biological Sciences Research Center, University of North Carolina School of Medicine, Chapel Hill, North Carolina

Yoshiyuki Suzuki, M.D. [68]
Vice Director, The Tokyo Metropolitan Institute of Medical Science, Tokyo, Japan

Judith L. Swain, M.D. [41]
Associate Professor of Medicine, Assistant Professor of Microbiology, Duke University Medical Center, Durham, North Carolina

Lawrence Sweetman, Ph.D. [28]
Professor of Pediatrics, Department of Pediatrics, University of California School of Medicine, San Diego, La Jolla, California

Kouichi R. Tanaka, M.D. [94]
Professor of Medicine, University of California School of Medicine, Los Angeles, California; Chief, Division of Hematology, Department of Medicine, Harbor-UCLA Medical Center, Torrance, California

Harriet S. Tenenhouse, Ph.D. [105]
Associate Professor of Pediatrics, McGill University; Associate Professor, McGill Center for Human Genetics; Auxiliary Professor of Biology, McGill University, Montreal, Canada

Samuel O. Thier, M.D. [99]
President, Institute of Medicine, National Academy of Sciences, Washington, D.C.

Jess G. Thoene, M.D. [107]
Professor, Departments of Pediatrics and Biological Chemistry, University of Michigan Medical School, Ann Arbor, Michigan

George H. Thomas, Ph.D. [63]
Associate Professor of Pediatrics, The Johns Hopkins University School of Medicine; Director, The Kennedy Institute Genetics Laboratory, Baltimore, Maryland

Douglas M. Tollefsen, M.D., Ph.D. [89]
Associate Professor of Medicine, Hematology-Oncology Division, Washington University Medical School, St. Louis, Missouri

Edward G. D. Tuddenham, M.D. [86]
Director, Haemostasis Research Group, Medical Research Council (U.K.) Clinical Research Centre, Harrow, Middlesex, England

William N. Valentine, M.D. [94]
Professor Emeritus, Department of Medicine, University of California Center for Health Sciences, Los Angeles, California

David Valle, M.D. [1, 19]
Investigator, Howard Hughes Medical Institute; Professor of Pediatrics, Medicine, and Molecular Biology & Genetics, The Johns Hopkins University School of Medicine, Baltimore, Maryland

Karel J. Van Acker, M.D. [39]
Professor, Department of Pediatrics, University of Antwerp, Wilrijk, Belgium

Georges Van den Berghe, M.D. [11]
Research Director, Laboratory of Physiological Chemistry, International Institute of Cellular and Molecular Pathology, Brussels; Consultant Physician, Department of Pediatrics, University of Leuven, Leuven, Belgium

George F. Vande Woude, Ph.D. [5]
Director, BRI-Basic Research Program, NCI-Frederick Cancer Research Facility, Frederick, Maryland

François Van Hoof, M.D. [12]
Professor of Biochemistry, Laboratoire de Chimie Physiologique, Université Catholique de Louvain and International Institute of Cellular and Molecular Pathology, Brussels, Belgium

Gilbert Vassart, M.D., Ph.D. [73]
Head, Molecular Genetics, Institute of Interdisciplinary Research and Department of Medical Genetics, Hospital Erasme, University of Brussels, Belgium

Gordon A. Vehar, Ph.D. [86]
Director, Department of Cardiovascular Research, Genentech, Inc., South San Francisco, California

Sybe K. Wadman, Ph.D. [56]
Professor of Biochemistry of Inherited Metabolic Disease, University Children's Hospital, Het Wilhelmina Kinderziekenhuis, Utrecht, The Netherlands

Margaret R. Wallace, Ph.D. [97]
Associate, Howard Hughes Medical Institute, University of Michigan, Ann Arbor, Michigan

D. J. Weatherall, M.D. [93]
Nuffield Professor of Medicine, Nuffield Department of Clinical Medicine, University of Oxford, John Radcliffe Hospital, Oxford, England

Dianne R. Webster, Ph.D. [43]
Deputy Director, National Testing Center, Auckland, New Zealand

Michael Welsh, M.D. [108]
Professor, Pulmonary Disease Division, Department of Internal Medicine, University of Iowa College of Medicine, Iowa City, Iowa

Perrin C. White, M.D. [74]
Assistant Professor of Pediatrics, Division of Pediatric Endocrinology; Director, Laboratory of Molecular Endocrinology, The New York Hospital–Cornell Medical Center, New York, New York

Ray White, Ph.D. [6]
Professor and Co-Chairman, Department of Human Genetics; Investigator, Howard Hughes Medical Institute, University of Utah Medical Center, Salt Lake City, Utah

Michael P. Whyte, M.D. [116]
Associate Professor of Medicine, Division of Bone and Mineral Diseases, Departments of Medicine and Pediatrics, The Jewish Hospital of St. Louis, Washington University School of Medicine; Director, Metabolic Research Unit, Shriners Hospital for Crippled Children, St. Louis, Missouri

Jean D. Wilson, M.D. [75]
Professor of Internal Medicine, The University of Texas Southwestern Medical Center, Dallas, Texas

Jerry Winkelstein, M.D. [111]
Eudowood Professor of Pediatrics, Director, Division of Allergy and Immunology, The Department of Pediatrics, The Johns Hopkins University School of Medicine, Baltimore, Maryland

Carl J. Witkop, Jr., D.D.S., M.S. [119]
Professor and Chairman, Division of Human Genetics, University of Minnesota School of Dentistry, Minneapolis, Minnesota

Barry Wolf, M.D., Ph.D. [83]
Professor, Departments of Human Genetics and Pediatrics, Medical College of Virginia, Richmond, Virginia

Allan W. Wolkoff, M.D. [53]
Professor of Medicine, Albert Einstein College of Medicine, Bronx, New York

Savio L. C. Woo, Ph.D. [15]
Professor, Department of Cell Biology and Molecular Genetics; Investigator, Howard Hughes Medical Institute, Baylor College of Medicine, Houston, Texas

W. G. Wood, Ph.D. [93]
Senior Scientist, M.R.C. Molecular Haematology Unit, Nuffield Department of Clinical Medicine, University of Oxford, John Radcliffe Hospital, Oxford, England

William I. Wood, Ph.D. [86]
Senior Scientist, Department of Development Biology, Genentech, Inc., South San Francisco, California

James B. Wyngaarden, M.D. [42]
Director, National Institutes of Health, Bethesda, Maryland

PREFACE

This edition of *The Metabolic Basis of Inherited Disease* marks a transition, a changing of the guard, as it were, among the editors. The sixth edition also reflects a transformation in the field of endeavor it encompasses; and there is a challenge too—for future editions. Transitions can be difficult and transformations sometimes produce unhappy results; neither need be the case here. Challenges can invigorate.

THE TRANSITION

Stanbury-Wyngaarden-'n-Fredrickson, collectively, were one famous "author" known to everyone in the field. This extraordinary editorial organism piloted the novel and timely book they had introduced and then edited through four successful editons. By a remarkable fision—or was it fusion?—the fifth edition was placed under the care of Stanbury-Wyngaarden-'n-Fredrickson, Goldstein 'n Brown. Now that giant has stepped aside, handing the challenge to a new team. The new editors have discovered how great the former ones were—if they hadn't known it before. Very large shoes had to be filled!

THE TRANSFORMATION

The sixth edition has many new features, notably the evidence of molecular genetics in one chapter after another. If *The Metabolic Basis of Inherited Disease* has had an abiding rationale, it was that the cause of all diseases listed in it was Mendelian and the diseases (so-called inborn errors of metabolism) were exceptions to be treasured for their illumination of human biology and for the insight they gave into pathogenesis of disease. But always there was a feeling that one did not understand cause as well as one should because not much was known about the genes. That situation is changing. There are new data about loci and structure of numerous normal genes and about the mutations affecting the phenotype encoded by them.

With 31 new chapters, the book is approximately one third larger than it was. Accordingly this edition appears for the first time in a two-volume format. It is a change undertaken with reluctance, but size of type, weight of paper, and the like had been adapted to the limit in the previous edition to accommodate the mass of information presented there. We elected to revise and print all chapters instead of using a précis of some, as in the last edition. Authors were encouraged to focus on up-to-date material and to use previous editions as archives of older material. But the wealth of new information neutralized contraction of the old. Hence the option taken here; to divide the book into two volumes, between separate covers.

New topics in the sixth edition include the following: There is a formal discussion of gene mapping and the medical use of genome markers (Chap. 6). Down syndrome (Chap. 7) and fragile X syndrome (Chap. 8) illustrate how any genetic disorder can eventually accommodate to our views of molecular genetics. They are the thin edge of the wedge toward understanding a great deal about human genetic disease and the editors introduce these chapters with some trepidation, realizing they could well be the very thin edge of a very big wedge—one of our challenges for future editions. One new chapter (122) covers the lactase deficiency polymorphism in whites. This disorder does not fit the paradigm of a rare inborn error because it is so common; on the other hand, it does represent a Mendelian disadaptive phenotype for some individuals. There is a whole new section on peroxisomal diseases (Chaps. 57-60) and Chap. 3 covers organelle biogenesis. Contiguous gene syndromes appear in this edition for the first time. The retinoblastoma story (Chap. 9) began as a contiguous gene syndrome; the new chapter encompasses this and analogous phenomena. Chap. 5 on oncogenes is new. The genes for retinoblastoma, chronic granulomatosus disease, and Duchenne muscular dystrophy are now known through techniques of "reverse" or "indirect" genetics. They are harbingers of what is to come in other diseases and they are topics developed at some length in this edition. Two appendices to Chap. 1, experiments in this edition, list: (1) the Mendelian disorders that can be diagnosed at the DNA level through oligonucleotide probes or by tightly linked markers that associate with alleles encoding mutant gene products; useful probes and their sources are catalogued in this appendix and (2) the mapped loci and their chromosomal assignments, the most current version of Victor McKusick's famous catalog available as we went to press. Perhaps a future edition will also catalog what we know about the mutant alleles at the loci encoding disease. Meanwhile the summary table grows in Chapter 1. It was introduced for the first time in the fifth edition and it is continued here for two reasons: first to show, in a simple manner, the growth of subject material between the last and present editions; second, to show how the white spaces in the fifth edition table are being filled in.

THE CHALLENGE

The future holds the potential for a separate chapter delineating the biochemical basis of each variant listed in *McKusick's Mendelian Inheritance in Man*. If this is the case, there will be many hundred chapters in subsequent editions of MBID. In addition, most monogenic disorders are not monogenic but modified through other loci by definable biochemical mechanisms; and most diseases are caused by polygenic and multifactorial mechanisms which also have a biochemical basis. Cytogenetic disorders have a biochemical basis as well, and in some instances the phenotypes may be determined by one or a few loci. These all represent effects of the constitutional genotype on the phenotype, but there is also the role of somatic mutation in the pathogenesis of malignancies whether inherited or sporadic. With the explosion of information virtually assured, the challenge of how to focus and mold future editions is a daunting one.

This book has not grown unattended. In addition to the herculean efforts of some 200 authors and their assistants, others assured a safe passage during the development of the book, notably Dereck Jeffers and Gail Gavert at McGraw-Hill; Loy Denis, who served as coordinator for the editors and authors; and our own assistants: Lynne Prevost and Huguette Rizziéro (CRS), Grace Watson (AB), Elizabeth Torno (WS), and Sandy Muscelli (DV). But especially we thank our extraordinary predecessors for their nurture and care of a book many of us have come to admire and need. If this edition meets with the approval of its former editors, we will have partially done the job we acquired; the readers will ultimately decide whether it was done satisfactorily.

Last, an acknowledgement to our families; they know more about this book than they bargained for. . . !

Charles R. Scriver
Arthur L. Beaudet
William S. Sly
David Valle

SIXTH EDITION

THE METABOLIC BASIS OF INHERITED DISEASE

PART 1

GENERAL THEMES

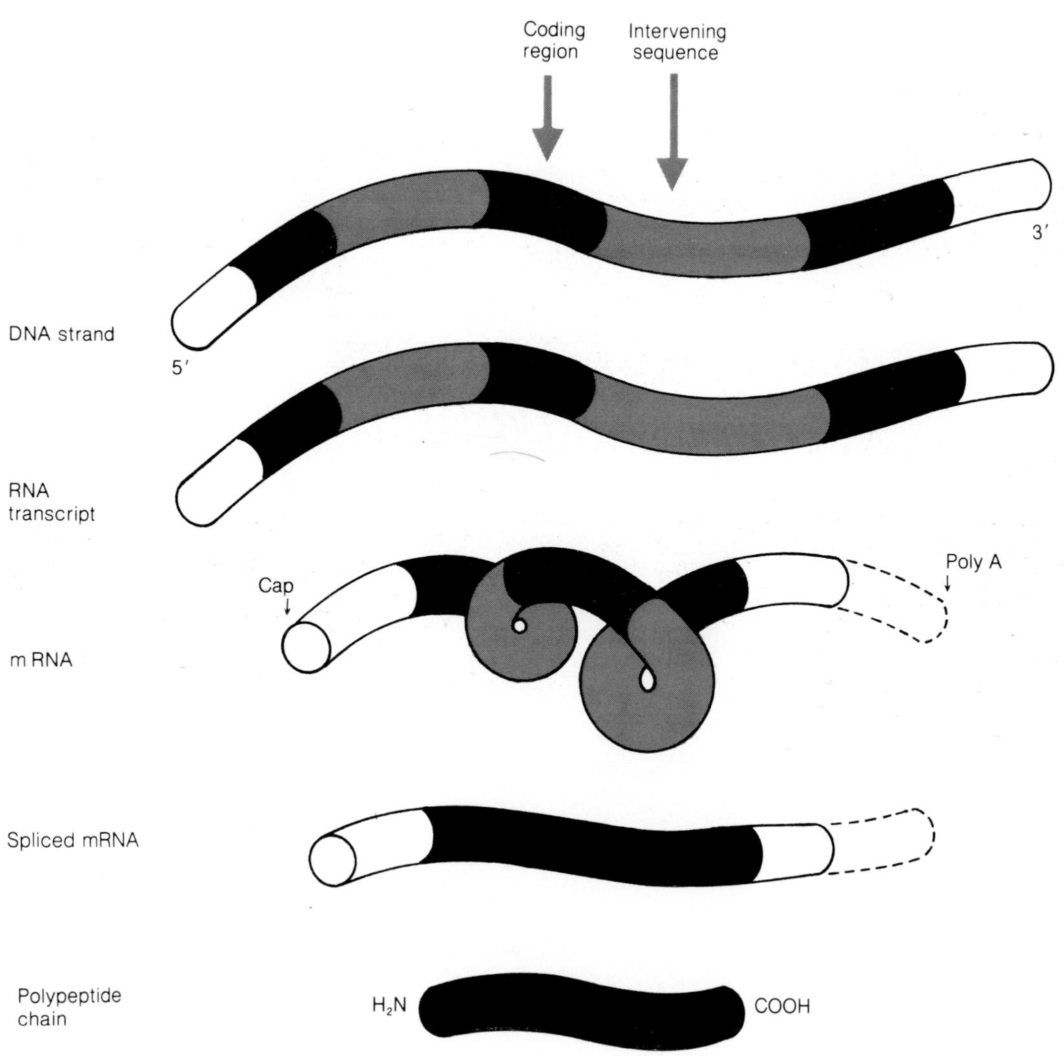

Gene splicing

CHAPTER 1

GENETICS AND BIOCHEMISTRY OF VARIANT HUMAN PHENOTYPES

ARTHUR L. BEAUDET*
CHARLES R. SCRIVER
WILLIAM S. SLY
DAVID VALLE
DAVID N. COOPER
VICTOR A. McKUSICK
JÖRG SCHMIDKE

The medical model of disease holds that *manifestations* are the result of a *process* which has a *cause*. The manifestations of disease are assembled in *diagnosis* and they constitute a *taxonomy*. The process which underlies them is the *pathogenesis* of disease. The cause of disease is either an event that overwhelms homeostatic mechanisms (an *extrinsic* cause) or one that undermines them (an *intrinsic* cause). Most diseases involve a combination of both (a multifactorial cause).

This text has three unifying themes, the first and central one being that the causes of the diseases described are mutations (intrinsic). Because these mutations are usually expressed as *disadaptive phenotypes* (i.e., clinical manifestations) in the universal environment, they are simply inherited and classified as *Mendelian disorders*. Some chapters describe more complex causes with non-Mendelian inheritance as in the case of Down syndrome (Chap. 7, a chromosomal disease) and diabetes mellitus (Chap. 10, a multifactorial disease). The discussion of LDL receptor deficiency (Chap. 48) and other lipoprotein disorders illustrates how a disease of heterogeneous etiology (coronary artery disease) is being broken down into its component causes, some cases being caused by single gene defects and some cases being of multifactorial etiology. This edition, when compared with earlier editions, reveals an enormous increase in our knowledge about genetic cause at the molecular level. This knowledge is applied increasingly through the use of recombinant DNA methods in clinical counseling.

This text's second unifying theme deals with pathogenesis in great detail. Knowledge of the pathophysiology of a disease explains its manifestations, is necessary for rational treatment, and may even suggest that treatment is not feasible.[1] It can be taken for granted that at least partial knowledge of pathogenesis is important for the treatment of most inborn errors of metabolism. Successive editions document the expansion of knowledge about cause and pathogenesis of inherited diseases. In due course, this text, or one like it, should become a fundamental textbook for the theory and practice of medicine, since most diseases in developed societies have a genetic determinant. Every individual is a deviant in terms of biochemical individuality,[2] meaning that every person has an inherited predisposition to disease (diathesis) in a particular circumstance. This is no new idea; Garrod expounded it thoroughly and clearly in his second book.[3] The difference between then and now is simply that molecular methods have made it possible to see in our DNA our inherited predispositions. We can either avoid the occurrence of serious disease genotypes through genetic counseling procedures or ameliorate symptoms through treatment. Therapy of inherited diseases constitutes the third unifying theme of this text.

The power of current cellular, molecular, and metabolic techniques is that they provide a vast amount of new information. There is the astounding prospect of identifying the biochemical defects for a large proportion of the thousands of disease phenotypes catalogued by McKusick in *Mendelian Inheritance in Man*.[4] At the Human Gene Mapping conference held in 1987, the chromosomal location of more than 1300 genes and 2000 anonymous DNA segments had been identified.[5] A detailed map of the human genome is becoming a reality (see Appendix 1-2 below and Chap. 6), and there are serious proposals to sequence the entire human genome.[6]

This avalanche of new information brings with it important new perspectives and goals. Metabolic, molecular, and genetic details are now available for hemoglobinopathies, phenylketonuria, Tay-Sachs disease, and many other disorders included in the chapters of this volume. Diseases such as cystic fibrosis, Duchenne muscular dystrophy, Huntington disease, adult polycystic kidney disease, and hereditary retinoblastoma, which have long resisted definition of the biochemical defect, are now yielding to investigation. Several gaps in current knowledge are likely to be the focus of future endeavors. Studies of inherited disorders of morphogenesis (which are often autosomal dominant) and of the function of the central nervous system (for which, it is said, a third of our genes are dedicated) will facilitate the understanding of these complex biologic processes. Elucidation of the biochemial basis of phenotypes caused by interaction between nongenetic factors and genetic variation at multiple loci will become increasingly feasible. We can hope to achieve an increased understanding of the homeostatic disturbances which underlie the clinical phenotypes of disorders whose molecular and biochemical lesions are already known. Challenges are posed to our understanding of pathogenesis both by classic questions such as what mechanism causes mental retardation in phenylketonuria and when

*The authors wish to acknowledge the substantial contributions of previous editors to this chapter.

new genes are cloned before we comprehend their biochemistry, as in the case of hereditary retinoblastoma (Chap. 9). Efforts to understand the molecular and biochemical bases underlying human genetic variation are more vigorous than ever. New techniques allow for the study of unique individuals in great detail. Garrod[7] quoted a letter written by William Harvey in 1657 to emphasize the value of studying human variants:

> Nature is nowhere accustomed more openly to display her secret mysteries than in cases where she shows traces of her workings apart from the beaten path; nor is there any better way to advance the proper practice of medicine than to give our minds to discovery of the usual law of nature by careful investigation of cases of rarer forms of disease. For it has been found, in almost all things, that what they contain of useful or applicable is hardly perceived unless we are deprived of them, or they become deranged in some way.

This thesis has many modern proponents. Basic scientists are attracted to the study of human genetic diseases in increasing numbers, and the most prestigious scientific journals vie to report the latest accomplishments. Reports such as the identification of the human gene determining sex[8] and of the product of the Duchenne muscular dystrophy gene[9] are prominently reported in leading newspapers. This is a golden era for the study of inherited metabolic disease.

DEVELOPMENT OF THE CONCEPT OF INHERITED METABOLIC DISEASE

Inborn Error Concept (Garrod)

The history of human biochemical genetics began at the turn of the twentieth century, when Sir Archibald Garrod initiated the brilliant studies of alkaptonuria that were to culminate in his Croonian Lectures in 1908[10] and in his monograph, *Inborn Errors of Metabolism,* which appeared in 1909 and in modified form in 1923.[11]

Garrod had observed that patients with alkaptonuria excreted large, rather constant quantities of homogentisic acid throughout their lifetimes, whereas other persons excreted none at all.[12] He observed that this condition had a familial distribution and that, while frequently one or more sibs were involved, parents and more distant relatives were normal. There was a high incidence of consanguineous marriages in the parents of his patients, as well as in the parents of similar patients studied elsewhere. On conferring with Bateson, one of the earliest of the great school of British geneticists, Garrod learned that these observations could readily be explained if the defect were inherited as a recessive condition in terms of the recently rediscovered laws of Mendel.[13,14]

From his observations of patients with alkaptonuria, albinism, cystinuria, and pentosuria, Garrod developed the concept that certain diseases of lifelong duration arise because an enzyme governing a single metabolic step is reduced in activity or missing altogether.[15] Garrod viewed the accumulation of homogentisic acid in alkaptonuria as evidence that this substance is a normal metabolite in the dissimulation of tyrosine, and he correctly attributed its accumulation to a failure of oxidation of homogentisic acid. A half-century later, Garrod's hypothesis was proved by the demonstration of deficient activity of homogentisic acid oxidase in the liver of a patient with alkaptonuria.[16]

Similarly, the failure of pigment formation in the skin in albinism, the excretion of large amounts of cystine in the urine in cystinuria, and the appearance of pentose in the urine in essential pentosuria were viewed by Garrod as the results of blocks in normal metabolic pathways. He attributed the first instance to failure of melanin formation and the other two to excretion of metabolites accumulating proximal to a metabolic block.

One Gene–One Enzyme Concept (Beadle and Tatum)

The term *gene* was first applied to the hereditary determinant of a unit characteristic by Johannsen in 1911.[17] The relation between gene and enzyme attained clear definition in the one gene–one enzyme principle, first succinctly stated by Beadle in 1945.[18] This formulation, now a biologic precept, emerged gradually from studies of eye color in the fruit fly, *Drosophila,* by Beadle and Tatum[19,20] and Ephrussi.[21] It received extensive support from the classic studies of Beadle and Tatum on induced mutants of *Neurospora crassa,* in which acquisitions of requirements for specific metabolites in the culture medium were traced to losses of single chemical transformations, each dependent on a different enzyme.[22,23]

The one gene–one enzyme concept that developed from these experiments has been well expressed by Tatum[23] as follows:

1. All biochemical processes in all organisms are under genetic control.
2. These biochemical processes are resolvable into series of individual stepwise reactions.
3. Each biochemical reaction is under the ultimate control of a different single gene.
4. Mutation of a single gene results only in an alteration in the ability of the cell to carry out a single primary chemical reaction.

The one gene–one enzyme hypothesis has since been refined[24] and extended to cover proteins that are not enzymes, as well as complex proteins composed of nonidentical polypeptide chains linked in various ways. The functional unit of DNA which controls the structure of a single polypeptide chain is frequently called a *cistron.*[25] The one gene–one enzyme principle has been redefined as the one cistron–one polypeptide concept. Posttranslational cleavage to generate multiple peptides, alternative splicing, and alternative promoter sequences contribute to complexities of the concept. Some examples of the complexity and variations involved in the one gene–one enzyme concept are presented in Table 1-1.

The one gene–one enzyme concept had immediate explanatory potential for the inborn errors of metabolism that Garrod had described. It appeared that inherited diseases such as alkaptonuria were produced by mutations in genes encoding enzymes in the same way that vitamin-dependent mutants of *Neurospora* lacked single enzymes required for vitamin synthesis. It was not until 1948 that the first enzyme defect in a human genetic disease was demonstrated by Gibson. This was the deficiency of the NADH-dependent enzyme required for

Table 1-1 Complexity and Variations in the One Gene–One Enzyme Concept

Concept	*Examples*	*Chapter or (Reference)*
One gene–one enzyme	Phenylalanine hydroxylase	15
	Hypoxanthine-guanine phosphoribosyl-transferase	38
One gene–nonenzymatic protein	Collagens	115
	Spectrin	95
One gene–RNA product	Transfer RNA, ribosomal RNA	1,2
One enzyme activity requires multiple subunits from separate genes	Propionyl CoA carboxylase	29
	Hexosaminidase A	72
One subunit functions in multiple enzymes	Hexosaminidases A and B	72
	E_3 subunit of dehydrogenases	22,32
One polypeptide chain with multiple enzyme activities	Orotate phosphoribosyl transferase and orotidine-5′-phosphate decarboxylase	43
	CAD tri-enzyme protein	(Ref. 26)
Deficiency of one enzyme causes multiple secondary enzyme deficiencies	Cobalamin C and D	82
	UDP-*N*-acetylglucosamine (GlcNAc): glycoprotein GlcNAc 1-phosphotransferase	62
Posttranslational cleavage of a peptide	ACTH (adrenocorticotrophic hormone), endorphins	(Ref. 27,28)
Alternative promoters for transcription	Amylase	(Ref. 29)
Alternative splicing of pre-mRNA	Calcitonin	(Ref. 30)
	Muscle proteins	(Ref. 31,32)
DNA rearrangements prior to transcription	Immunoglobulins	109
	T-cell receptors	110
Posttranscriptional modification of mRNA	Apolipoproteins B-100 and B-48	44B
Overlapping reading frames in DNA and RNA, suppression, frameshifting	Bacterial release factor	(Ref. 33)
	Retroviruses	(Ref. 34)

the reduction of methemoglobin in recessive methemoglobinemia.[35] This was soon followed by the description in 1952 by Cori and Cori of glucose-6-phosphatase deficiency in von Gierke disease (glycogen storage disease, type I)[36] and in 1953 by Jervis of phenylalanine hydroxylase deficiency in phenylketonuria.[37]

Molecular Disease Concept (Pauling and Ingram)

Direct evidence that human mutations actually produce an alteration in the primary structure of proteins was first obtained in 1949 by Pauling and his associates.[38] Studying hemoglobin extracted from erythrocytes of patients with sickle-cell anemia, Pauling showed that sickle hemoglobin migrated differently in an electric field than did normal hemoglobin. Heterozygotes for the sickle-cell trait produced both normal and abnormal hemoglobin molecules. The subsequent studies of Ingram established that the electrophoretic abnormality arose because sickle-cell hemoglobin had a valine substituted for a glutamic acid residue at a particular point in the amino acid sequence.[39] This finding closed one era of discovery in human biochemical genetics: Inborn errors of metabolism were caused by mutant genes that produced abnormal proteins whose functional activities were altered.

Reverse Genetics

With the identification of a restriction fragment length polymorphism (RFLP) at the β-globin locus by Kan and Dozy,[40] the concept of a new and virtually inexhaustible source of genetic markers for the exploration of inherited human disease became a reality. Quickly thereafter, Botstein et al.[41] proposed the feasibility of creating a linkage map of the human genome using RFLPs. Following these strategies, it became possible using genetic linkage analysis to identify DNA markers close to human disease loci.

"Reverse genetics" has been used to describe a variety of investigative approaches but is used here to describe the strategy of mapping and cloning genes prior to the identification of their products[42] (Chap. 2). For the great majority of disorders described in this volume, the gene product and its general function were identified long before the molecular characterization of the gene as exemplified for hemoglobin and phenylalanine hydroxylase. The reverse genetic strategy utilizes genetic information to clone a gene prior to the identification of the product. This approach was developed in bacterial genetics and has been extended in recent years to the study of *Drosophila* as exemplified by the characterization of homeotic genes which are involved in development.[43] The construction of a genomic map of the location of RFLPs is allowing for the extension of this approach to human diseases. Information gained from rare patients with visible cytogenetic abnormalities in association with single gene disorders, so-called contiguous gene syndromes, also has played a major role in early successes using reverse genetics (Chap. 9). The genes for chronic granulomatous disease[44] (Chap. 114), Duchenne muscular dystrophy[45] (Chap. 118), and hereditary retinoblastoma[46] (Chap. 9) were cloned by these approaches. The genes for Huntington disease,[47] adult polycystic kidney disease,[48] neurofibromatosis,[49] Von Hippel-Lindau disease,[50] polyposis of the colon,[51] and others have been mapped to specific sites in the human genome and are likely to be cloned in the foreseeable future. The continuing value of individual patients as experiments of nature was exemplified by the identification of a single patient with a deletion of chromosome 5 in association with polyposis of the colon leading to the mapping of the polyposis locus using RFLPs.[51,52]

The practice and performance of investigation of inherited disease are changing with this explosion of techniques. While the role of the individual laboratory remains prominent, often multiple laboratories, each with particular areas of expertise, contribute to the investigation of a disorder. As part of efforts to map the human genome, a massive international collaboration has been organized under the auspices of Centre d'Étude du Polymorphisme Humain (CEPH) (Chap. 6).[53] DNA samples on over 500 individuals from 40 large sibships have been prepared and are being analyzed for RFLPs by laboratories around the world. The data are returned to a computerized data base for collaborative analysis to construct a human gene map.

Recent molecular studies of cystic fibrosis represent another example of international collaboration and interaction (Chap. 108). Laboratories around the world collected samples from cystic fibrosis families for the purposes of linkage analysis. The first linkage to a protein polymorphism was reported from Copenhagen,[54] while the first DNA linkage which allowed chromosomal assignment was discovered in Toronto using a DNA probe isolated by a laboratory in Boston.[55] With the assignment of the cystic fibrosis locus to chromosome 7, more closely linked DNA markers were identified in Salt Lake City[56] and London.[57] A collaboration of nine laboratories provided detailed linkage data for 211 families in a short time.[58] The expansion of collaborative efforts has been accompanied by an increasing role of commercial laboratories in the investigation of inherited disease, which was once the almost exclusive purview of academic investigators.

With international proposals to map and sequence the human genome, it is possible that most human genes will be identified before any relationship to product or phenotype is established. This rather anonymous genetics has been experienced to some extent with the availability of the entire sequence for human mitochondrial DNA and the identification of open reading frames (coding segments) prior to information regarding the products or phenotypes which might be associated with these genes. While "anonymous" genetics may not seem attractive as an intellectual pursuit, its impact on the study of inherited disease is certain to be great.

MOLECULAR BASIS OF GENE EXPRESSION

The human genome is estimated to contain about 50,000 to 100,000 genes, each of which is composed of a linear polymer of DNA. The genes are assembled into lengthy linear arrays that together with certain proteins form rod-shaped bodies called *chromosomes*. All normal nucleated human cells other than sperm or ova contain 46 chromosomes, arrayed in 23 pairs, one of each pair derived from each of the individual's parents. The striking discovery that genes are not continuous sequences of DNA but consist of coding sequences (exons) interrupted by intervening sequences (introns) led to a new and more complex view of gene expression.

Some approximations regarding the magnitude and organization of the human genome are presented in Fig. 1-1. The estimated 50,000 to 100,000 genes are distributed within the 3 billion base pairs of DNA which constitute a haploid genome.

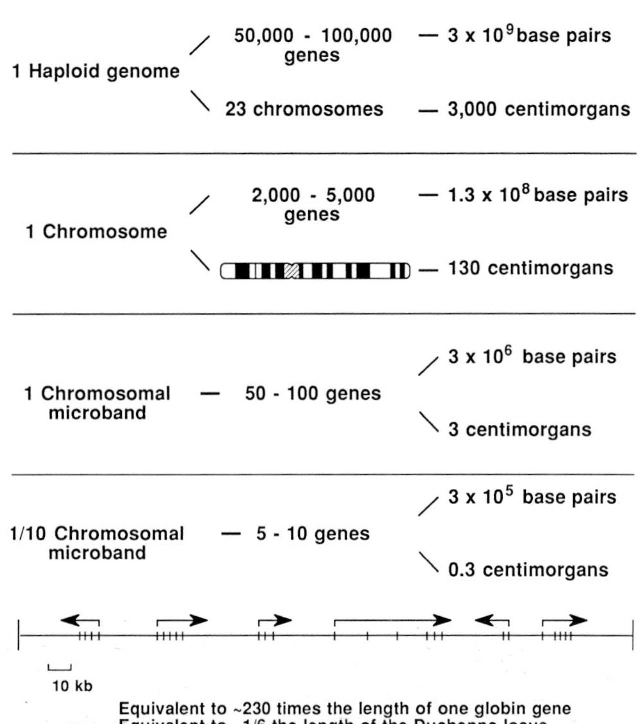

Fig. 1-1 Perspectives on the amount of DNA, number of genes, and genetic distance in the human genome. The arrows in the lowest panel indicate hypothetical transcripts with vertical lines indicating exons within genes.

Linkage studies indicate that the human genome comprises approximately 3000 centimorgans (cM) in recombination distance. A centimorgan (1/100 of a Morgan) is a measure of genetic distance reflecting the probability of a crossover between two loci during meiosis. One centimorgan approximately equals a recombination fraction of 0.01 or a 1 percent chance of a crossover during meiosis. Thus an average chromosome would contain 2000 to 5000 genes within 130 million base pairs of DNA and would be equivalent to about 130 cM of genetic material. A typical microband on a stained chromosome contains 3 to 5 million base pairs and 50 to 100 genes. This representation oversimplifies many issues. Estimates of the total number of genes are imprecise. Although the average recombination distance is estimated to be approximately 1 cM per million base pairs of DNA, there is wide variation in this rate over shorter distances, as well as differences in recombination distance according to sex (Chap. 6). Genes range in size from very small (1.5 kb for a globin gene) to very large (perhaps 2000 kb for the Duchenne muscular dystrophy locus). Cis-acting regulatory elements (i.e., on the contiguous DNA strand) may occur at a considerable distance from the coding region, e.g., 50 kb 5′ and 20 kb 3′ to the β-globin gene,[59] thus extending the functional domains of genes and complicating the definition of boundaries.

The human genome also includes numerous nonfunctional sequences and highly reiterated sequences.[60] There are 300,000 to 500,000 copies of the *Alu* repeat sequence (the most reiterated sequence which derives its name from the frequency with which it is cut by the restriction enzyme *Alu*I) in the human genome. Many other reiterated sequences occur with lesser frequency. Many genes have additional nonfunctional copies (pseudogenes), and the sequence distribution of human DNA is not uniform. For example, HTF (*Hpa*I tiny fragment) islands are G-plus-C-rich regions which occur near the 5′ end of constitutive genes and are thought to have some relationship to regulation of gene expression.[61] The functional significance of the majority of DNA which occurs outside coding regions remains to be determined.

The Molecular Flow of Information

Much is known about how living organisms store, transmit, and utilize their genetic information. The picture is most detailed for prokaryotic organisms, but information is being acquired rapidly for the more complex eukaryotic organisms. Two excellent textbooks[62,63] provide a more systematic and comprehensive treatment of cellular and molecular biology than is included here. The fourth edition of *Molecular Biology of the Gene* by Watson and colleagues[64] provides a detailed view of the molecular flow of information in prokaryotic and eukaryotic organisms.

The genetic information carried on chromosomes is transmitted to daughter cells under two different sets of circumstances. One of these occurs whenever a somatic cell (i.e., a nongerm cell) divides. This process, called *mitosis,* functions to transmit two identical copies of each gene to each daughter cell, thus maintaining a uniform genetic makeup in all cells of a single organism. The other set of circumstances prevails when genetic information is to be transmitted from one individual to an offspring. This process, called *meiosis,* functions to produce germ cells (i.e., ova or spermatozoa) that possess only one copy of each parental chromosome, thus allowing for new combinations of chromosomes to occur when the ovum and sperm cell fuse during fertilization and restoring the *diploid* state.

During the process of meiosis, the 46 chromosomes of an immature germ cell arrange themselves in 23 pairs at the center of the nucleus, each pair being composed of one chromosome derived from the mother and its homologous chromosome derived from the father. At a specified point in the meiotic process, the two partner chromosomes separate, only one of each pair going into each daughter cell, or gamete. Thus, meiosis produces gametes with a reduction in the number of chromosomes from 46 to 23, each gamete having received one chromosome from each of the 23 pairs. The assortment of the chromosomes within each pair is random, so that each germ cell receives a different combination of maternal and paternal chromosomes. During the process of fertilization the fusion of ovum and sperm cell, each of which has 23 chromosomes, results ultimately in an individual with 46 chromosomes.

The independent assortment of chromosomes into gametes during meiosis produces an enormous diversity among the possible genotypes of the progeny. For each 23 pairs of chromosomes, there are 2^{23} different combinations of chromosomes that could occur in a gamete, and the likelihood that one set of parents will produce two offspring with the identical complement of chromosomes is one in 2^{23} or one in 8.4 million (assuming no monozygotic twins). Adding even further to the enormous genetic diversity in humans is the phenomenon of *genetic recombination* (see "Genetic Linkage and the Human Gene Map," below, and Chap. 6).

The Structure of DNA

Most organisms store their genetic information in *deoxyribonucleic acid (DNA).* DNA is a linear polymer of four different monomeric units, collectively called *deoxyribonucleotides* or simply *nucleotides,* that are linked together in a chain by phosphodiester bonds (Fig. 1-2). A typical DNA molecule consists of two interwound polynucleotide chains, each containing several thousand to several million monomers (Fig. 1-3). Each nucleotide in one chain is specifically linked by hydrogen bonds to a nucleotide in the other chain. Only two nucleotide pairings are found in DNA: deoxyadenosine monophosphate with thymidine monophosphate (or A-T) and deoxyguanosine monophosphate with deoxycytidine monophosphate (or G-C). Thus, the sequence of nucleotides of one chain fixes the sequence of the other, and the two chains are therefore said to be *complementary* to each other.

The sequence of the four nucleotides along a polynucleotide chain varies among the DNAs of unrelated organisms and in-

Fig. 1-2 A polynucleotide chain. One of each of the four different monomeric units of DNA is present in this tetranucleotide. The monomers of DNA are, from top to bottom, deoxyguanosine monophosphate (or G), deoxycytidine monophosphate (or C), deoxyadenosine monophosphate (or A), and thymidine monophosphate (or T). Each nucleotide consists of a phosphate group, a deoxyribose moiety, and a heterocyclic base. G and A have purine bases, and C and T have pyrimidine bases. The phosphodiester bonds that link adjacent nucleotides extend from the 3′ position of one deoxyribose moiety to the 5′ position of the next; this gives the chain a chemical polarity. An abbreviated way of writing the same sequence is shown at the top right. In RNA (see text) ribose, which contains a 2′-hydroxyl group, replaces deoxyribose, and uridine monophosphate (or U) replaces T. U differs from T in the substitution of ribose for deoxyribose and in the loss of the 5-methyl group.

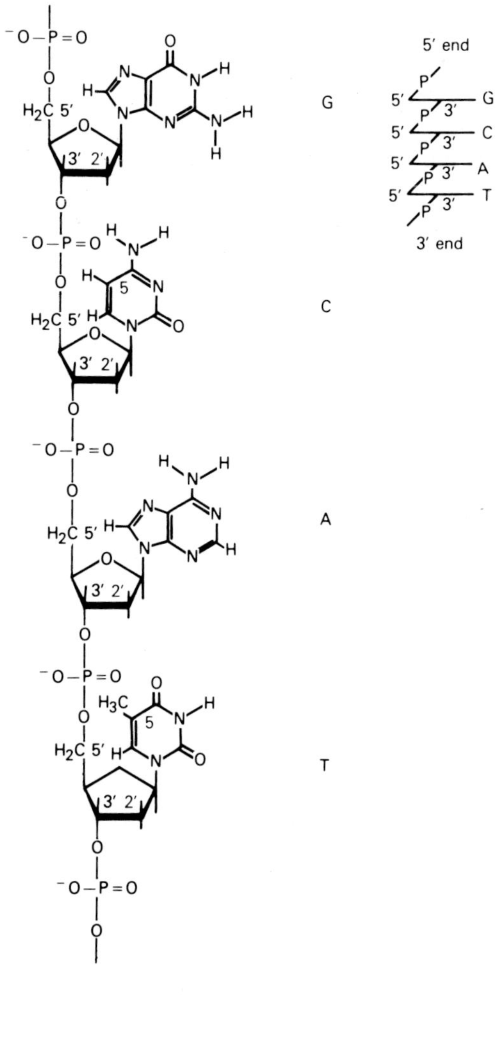

G

C

A

T

5′ end

3′ end

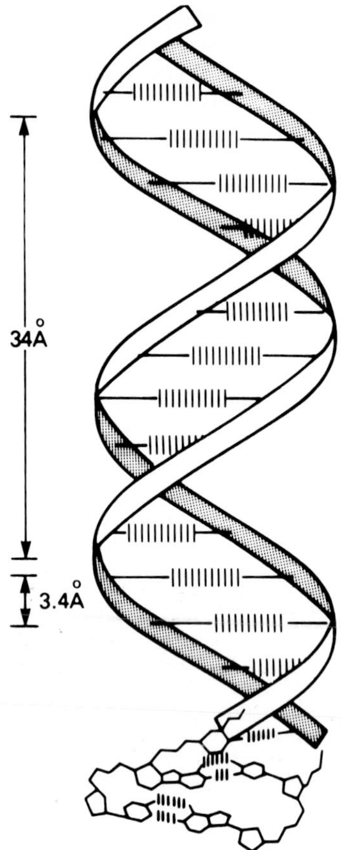

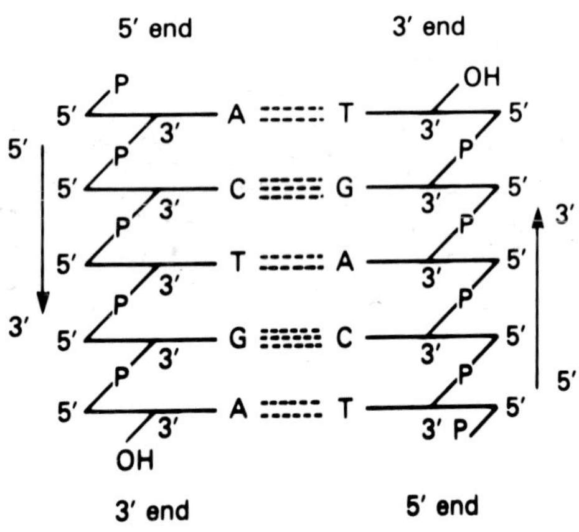

Fig. 1-3 The structure of DNA. *Top.* The two interwound hydrogen-bonded polynucleotide chains of DNA are shown. The hydrogen bonds are indicated by vertical hatches. The distance between adjacent nucleotide pairs is 3.4 Å. The distance between adjacent turns of the double helix is 34 Å or about 10 nucleotide pairs. *Bottom.* An alternative representation in which the opposite chemical polarities of the two chains can be clearly seen. *(From Kornberg.[65] Used by permission.)*

deed is the molecular basis of their genetic diversity. Because most genetic characteristics are stably transmitted from parent to progeny, the sequence of nucleotides in DNA must be faithfully copied or replicated as the organism reproduces itself. This occurs by unwinding of the two chains and polymerization of two daughter chains along the separated parental strands. The nucleotide sequence and hence the genetic information is conserved during this process because each nucleotide in the daughter chains is paired specifically with its complement in the parental or template chains before polymerization occurs.

The DNA of higher organisms, separated from the great bulk of cellular components by a nuclear membrane, is wound into a tightly and regularly packed chromosomal structure consisting of nucleoprotein elements called *nucleosomes.* Each of these nucleosomal elements is in turn composed of four (sometimes five) protein subunits, *histones,* that form a core structure about which are wound approximately 140 nucleotide pairs of genomic DNA. Histone structure is remarkably well conserved throughout the eukaryotic kingdom. Such conservation argues strongly that strict functional requirements, presumably related to the detailed architecture of the nucleosome, impede divergent evolution. The nucleosomes, arranged as "beads on a string," become further organized into more highly ordered structures consisting of coils of many closely packed nucleosomes that in turn must form fundamental organization units of the eukaryotic chromosome.

Nucleosomal structure may serve a variety of purposes, for example, in simply compacting the enormous amount of DNA (about 6×10^9 base pairs) comprising the human diploid genome. Aside from such a packing function, this ubiquitous structure must also be reconciled with a train of enzymes that acts upon DNA to permit its orderly replication and transcription. Undoubtedly, these functions are subserved and modulated by other proteins that little resemble the monotonous structure of the histones and that recognize specific structural features of a DNA sequence. A fundamental question in eukaryotic molecular biology is how this nucleoprotein structure permits access to specific proteins and is differentially made available in the course of cellular growth and development.

The double-helical model of DNA immediately suggested the manner in which genes could be replicated for transmission to offspring. The actual replication process is mechanically complex but conceptually simple. The two strands of DNA separate, and each is copied by a series of enzymes that inserts a complementary base opposite each base on the original strand of DNA. Thus, two identical double helices are generated from one.[64–66] Details of the mechanisms of DNA replication in *Escherichia coli* are becoming known.[65,67–69]

The Genetic Code

DNA makes RNA (transcription) makes protein (translation) in the accepted paradigm (Fig. 1-4). The sequence of bases in a specific gene ultimately dictates the sequence of amino acids in a specific protein. This collinearity between the DNA molecule and the protein sequence is achieved by means of the *genetic code.*[64] The four types of bases in DNA are arranged in groups of three, each triplet forming a code word or *codon* that signifies a single amino acid.

In this manner, triplet codons exist for each of the 20 amino acids which occur in proteins (Fig. 1-5). Inasmuch as 64 different triplets can be generated from the four bases and only 20 amino acids exist, the genetic code is said to be *degenerate.* That is, most amino acids are specified by more than one codon. Each codon, however, is completely specific. Thus, the double-stranded sequence adenine-adenine-adenine (or AAA) in the transcribed (antisense) strand and thymine-thymine-thymine (or TTT) in the nontranscribed (sense) strand of DNA codes for uridine-uridine-uridine (or UUU) in mRNA, which is translated to phenylalanine in protein (Fig. 1-4).

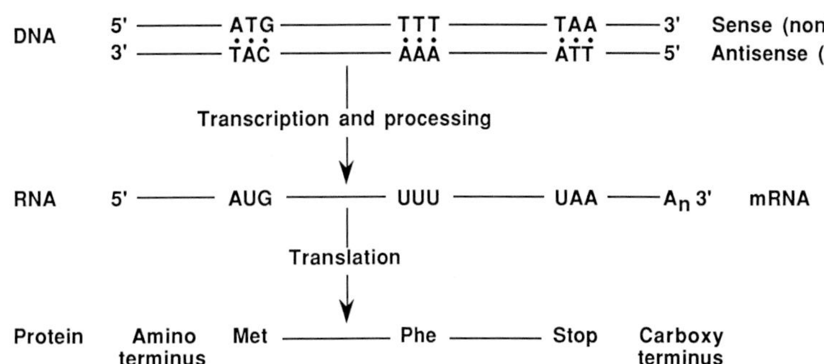

Fig. 1-4 DNA is transcribed and processed to yield mRNA which is translated to yield protein.

DNA-RNA Protein

To translate its genetic information into a protein, a segment of DNA is first transcribed into messenger ribonucleic acid (messenger RNA). The messenger RNA contains a sequence of purine and pyrimidine bases that is complementary to the bases of the transcribed (antisense) strand of the DNA. By this mechanism each adenine of DNA becomes a uridine of RNA, each cytosine of DNA becomes a guanine of RNA, each thymine of DNA becomes an adenine of RNA, and each guanine of DNA becomes a cytosine of RNA. Thus, each DNA triplet codon is translated into a corresponding RNA triplet codon.

The messenger RNA for each gene is processed extensively by modifying enzymes within the cell nucleus. It then crosses the nuclear membrane and enters the cytoplasm, where it serves as a template for the synthesis of a specific protein.[64] To translate the messenger RNA code into a protein, the messenger RNA binds to a complex structure called a *ribosome,* which is composed of a different type of RNA (ribosomal RNA) and a large number of proteins. In order to be inserted into its proper place in the protein sequence, each of the 20 amino acids is attached in the cytoplasm to an additional type of RNA (transfer RNA). Each amino acid is attached to a specific set of transfer RNAs (Fig. 1-6). Each transfer RNA contains an "anticodon loop," which includes a sequence of three bases that is complementary to a specific codon in the corresponding messenger RNA. For example, phenylalanine is attached specifically to a transfer RNA whose anticodon loop contains the sequence AAA, which is complimentary to the messenger RNA codon UUU, which codes for phenylalanine.

Under the influence of a host of cytoplasmic factors (initiation factors, elongation factors, and termination factors), peptide bonds are formed between the various amino acids that are aligned along the messenger RNA chain (Fig. 1-7). Eventually, a terminator codon is reached and the completed polypeptide is released from the ribosome. Inasmuch as the primary sequence of bases in the coding regions of the DNA determines the corresponding primary sequence of amino acids in the protein, the gene and its protein are said to be *collinear.* This means that any alteration of the sequence of bases in the gene will result in an alteration of the protein at a specific point in its sequence.

Control of Gene Expression

The proper rate and timing for transcription and translation are subject to complex controls. Cis-acting sequences are DNA regions at a distance but on the same duplex DNA molecule, and trans-acting factors (usually proteins) are encoded by other genes (usually unlinked). The trans-acting factors interact with the cis sequences to control the process of transcription. Many of the cis-acting transcriptional control elements occur short distances upstream from the initiation site for transcription (see Chap. 2), but some have been described at greater distances upstream and downstream from the initiation site for transcription (e.g., 5 to 50 kb). Regulation of gene expression also occurs posttranscriptionally involving RNA processing, translational control, and posttranslational control.

Some of our understanding about interactions between trans-acting factors and cis-acting sequences in mammalian cells comes from prokaryotes, especially studies of the *lac* and lambda repressors.[71] The mammalian cis-acting sequences include the TATA consensus, the CAAT consensus, Spl binding sites, enhancers, upstream activating sequences (UAS), hormone responsive elements, and others.[72–75] The TATA and CAAT consensus sequences occur upstream of the start site for transcription in many genes and bind transcription factors. There is evidence for multiple types of DNA binding proteins. Some DNA binding proteins, such as the λ repressor and the tryptophan repressor,[76] contain a "helix-turn-helix" motif, while others have a "zinc finger" motif which binds to DNA.[75] More recently, a third DNA binding motif, the "leucine zipper," has been suggested.[77] The DNA binding finger proteins contain Zn^{2+} molecules bound to amino acid residues. Proteins suggested to represent DNA binding proteins with Zn^{2+} fingers include transcription factor Spl, transcription factor TFIIIA, numerous *Drosophila* proteins (e.g., the *Kruppel* gene product), and yeast transcription factor ADR1.[74,75] In addition mammalian and avian proteins suggested to have DNA binding Zn^{2+} finger motifs include the glucocorticoid receptor, the estrogen receptor, the progesterone receptor, the c-*erb*-A protein, the vitamin D receptor, the mineralocorticoid receptor, and the product of the sex determining gene.[8,74,75] A strategy for cloning DNA binding proteins by screening expression DNA libraries with oligonucleotides has been described.[78] Studies of the control of mammalian gene expression are progressing rapidly, and human mutations already are identified in the cis regulatory sequences (e.g., globin genes, Chap. 93) and are likely to be identified in trans-acting factors.

MUTATION AS THE ORIGIN OF NORMAL VARIATION AND GENETIC DISEASE

Broadly defined, a *mutation* is a stable, heritable alteration in DNA which can be passed from cell to progeny. Some mutations are genetically lethal and cannot be passed from one gen-

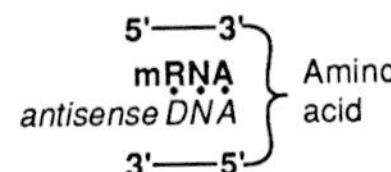

Second RNA nucleotide (columns); **First RNA nucleotide** (left); **Third RNA nucleotide** (right)

First	U	C	A	G	Third
U	**UUU** *AAA* Phe	**UCU** *AGA* Ser	**UAU** *ATA* Tyr	**UGU** *ACA* Cys	U
U	**UUC** *AAG* Phe	**UCC** *AGG* Ser	**UAC** *ATG* Tyr	**UGC** *ACG* Cys	C
U	**UUA** *AAT* Leu	**UCA** *AGT* Ser	**UAA** *ATT* Stop	**UGA** *ACT* Stop	A
U	**UUG** *AAC* Leu	**UCG** *AGC* Ser	**UAG** *ATC* Stop	**UGG** *ACC* Trp	G
C	**CUU** *GAA* Leu	**CCU** *GGA* Pro	**CAU** *GTA* His	**CGU** *GCA* Arg	U
C	**CUC** *GAG* Leu	**CCC** *GGG* Pro	**CAC** *GTG* His	**CGC** *GCG* Arg	C
C	**CUA** *GAT* Leu	**CCA** *GGT* Pro	**CAA** *GTT* Gln	**CGA** *GCT* Arg	A
C	**CUG** *GAC* Leu	**CCG** *GGC* Pro	**CAG** *GTC* Gln	**CGG** *GCC* Arg	G
A	**AUU** *TAA* Ile	**ACU** *TGA* Thr	**AAU** *TTA* Asn	**AGU** *TCA* Ser	U
A	**AUC** *TAG* Ile	**ACC** *TGG* Thr	**AAC** *TTG* Asn	**AGC** *TCG* Ser	C
A	**AUA** *TAT* Ile	**ACA** *TGT* Thr	**AAA** *TTT* Lys	**AGA** *TCT* Arg	A
A	**AUG** *TAC* Met	**ACG** *TGC* Thr	**AAG** *TTC* Lys	**AGG** *TCC* Arg	G
G	**GUU** *CAA* Val	**GCU** *CGA* Ala	**GAU** *CTA* Asp	**GGU** *CCA* Gly	U
G	**GUC** *CAG* Val	**GCC** *CGG* Ala	**GAC** *CTG* Asp	**GGC** *CCG* Gly	C
G	**GUA** *CAT* Val	**GCA** *CGT* Ala	**GAA** *CTT* Glu	**GGA** *CCT* Gly	A
G	**GUG** *CAC* Val	**GCG** *CGC* Ala	**GAG** *CTC* Glu	**GGG** *CCC* Gly	G

Fig. 1-5 The genetic code. The RNA codons appear in boldface type; the complementary DNA codons are in italics. A = adenine; C = cytosine; G = guanine; T = thymine; U = uridine (replaces thymine in RNA). In RNA, adenine is complementary to thymine of DNA; uridine is complementary to adenine of DNA; cytosine is complementary to guanine and vice versa. "Stop" = punctuation. The three-letter and single-letter abbreviations for the amino acids are as follows: Ala (A) = alanine; Arg (R) = arginine; Asn (N) = asparagine; Asp (D) = aspartic acid; Cys (C) = cysteine; Gln (Q) = glutamine; Glu (E) = glutamic acid; Gly (G) = glycine; His (H) = histidine; Ile (I) = isoleucine; Leu (L) = leucine; Lys (K) = lysine; Met (M) = methionine; Phe (F) = phenylalanine; Pro (P) = proline; Ser (S) = serine; Thr (T) = threonine; Trp (W) = tryptophan; Tyr (Y) = tyrosine; Val (V) = valine.

eration to the next, while others are less deleterious and are tolerated in the descendants under permissive conditions. From the viewpoint of evolution, mutations are essential for the generation of sufficient genetic diversity to permit species to adapt to their environment through the mechanism of natural selection.

Mutations involving gross alterations (millions of base pairs) in the structure of a chromosome include duplications, deletions, and translocations of a portion of one chromosome to another. Mutations can involve even the entire genome (3 billion base pairs) as in triploidy where there is a third copy of the whole chromosome constitution. On the other hand, mutations can be minute, involving a deletion, insertion, or replacement of a single base. Single-base or very small mutations are called *point mutations*. If deletions or insertions of a single base occur in a coding region, they give rise to *frameshift mutations* because they alter the reading frame of the genetic code such that every triplet distal to the mutation in the same gene is altered. Frameshift mutations grossly alter the protein sequence and frequently result in termination of the peptide chain shortly beyond the mutation site because of the occurrence of a termination codon in the altered reading frame. Small deletions or insertions can also affect transcription, splicing, or RNA processing, depending on their location.

When one base is replaced by another in the coding region, the point mutations may be of three types: (1) a *synonymous mutation* (constituting about 23 percent of random base substitutions in coding regions), in which the base replacement does not lead to a change in the amino acid but only to the substitution of a different codon for the same amino acid (e.g., a replacement of a single base pair in the DNA so that a RNA codon for phenylalanine will be transcribed into RNA not as UUU but as UUC, which still codes for phenylalanine); (2) a *missense mutation* (about 73 percent of base substitutions in coding regions), in which the base replacement changes the codon for one amino acid to another (e.g., the replacement of a base pair in DNA in the codon for phenylalanine such that it will be transcribed into RNA not as UUU but as UUA, which would change the codon to leucine); and (3) a *nonsense mutation* (about 4 percent of base substitutions in coding regions), in which the base replacement changes the codon to one of the termination codons (e.g., the replacement of a base pair in the codon for tyrosine such that it is transcribed into RNA not as UAU but as the stop codon UAA).[79]

In addition to these point mutations, there are larger deletions which may affect a portion of a gene, an entire gene, or

Fig. 1-6 A diagrammatic representation of a tRNA molecule. Each base in the tRNA is represented by a box. The structure is shown with interacting complementary sequences indicated by a row of dots. Each conserved loop is shown (DHU = dehydrouridylic acid loop; TψC = thymidylic acid-pseudouridylic acid-cytidylic acid loop). The anticodon position is indicated. All tRNAs end with a CCA sequence at their 3′ terminus that serves as the amino acid acceptor portion of the molecule. *(After L. Stryer.[70])*

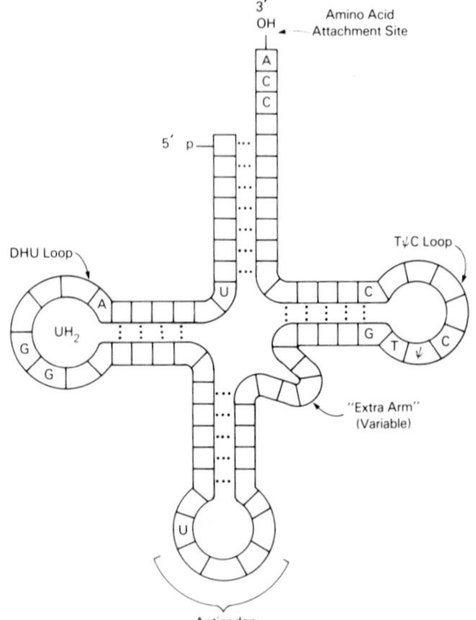

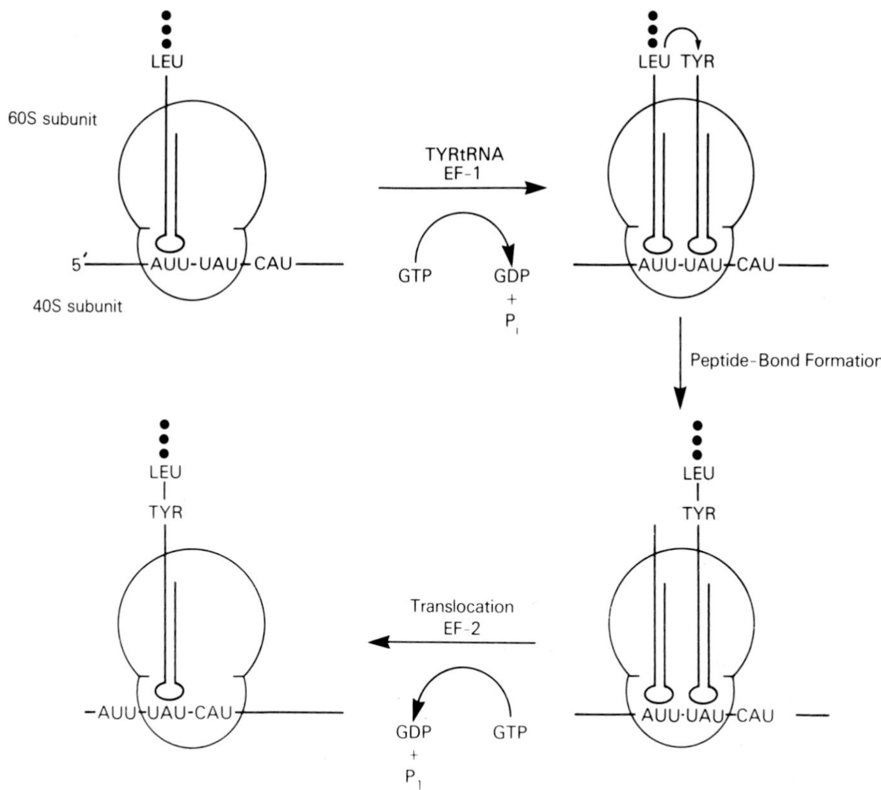

Fig. 1-7 The elongation reactions in protein synthesis. The figure diagrammatically represents the ribosome (60 S and 40 S subunits), the tRNA moieties (hairpinlike structures), and the associated mRNAs. The first elongation intermediate *(upper left)* shows a peptidyl tRNA, the peptide portion of which is represented by leucine and three dots, at the donor site on the ribosome interacting with a leucine codon, AUU. In the presence of GTP and elongation factor 1 (EF-1), tyr-tRNA binds to the next available codon at the receptor site. The peptide is transferred to the oncoming tyr-tRNA by an enzymatic activity associated with the 60 S subunit of the ribosome. The next step involves release of the deacylated tRNA (leucine) and the translocation of the mRNA and the newly elongated peptidyl tRNA to the donor site, exposing the next available codon, CAU, for recognition. The later reaction requires elongation factor 2 (EF-2) and consumes GTP. The entire process is repeated until a termination codon is encountered, and the finished peptide is released in the presence of appropriate termination factors.

a set of contiguous genes. Such deletion mutations may interrupt or remove the coding region of a gene causing the absence of its protein product. Alternatively, a deletion can bridge between the coding regions of two genes and produce a fusion resulting in the production of a hybrid protein containing the initial sequence of one protein followed by the terminal sequence of another protein. This latter type of mutation may occur particularly by unequal crossing over between tandemly repeated homologous genes such as the globin genes (Chap. 93). The range of mutations seen at the human β-globin locus provides a good perspective on the extent of heterogeneity of mutations that can occur (Chap. 93). Over 200 missense mutations causing amino acid substitutions with various phenotypes are known at the β-globin locus.[4] Various δ-β and β-δ fusions are known. Numerous transcriptional, splicing, and RNA processing mutations cause β thalassemia[80] as depicted in Fig. 1-8.

The type and frequency of human mutations is a very complex topic. Mutations causing chromosomal aneuploidy occur at increasing frequency with advancing age of the mother. Smaller mutations occur with increased frequency with advancing age of the father, although the molecular nature of the mutations seen with advanced paternal age is just becoming known. Some loci, such as those for Duchenne muscular dystrophy and achondroplasia, are subject to very high rates of new mutation. In the instance of Duchenne dystrophy, this may be related in part to the unusually large size of the gene. The structure of the gene, its position within the genome, and the constraints on the gene product may contribute along with other factors to the frequency of new mutations causing phenotypic effects at a locus. The occurrence of 5-methylcytosine, particularly at the sites of CpG base pairs, provides sites of increased mutational frequency, apparently due to spontaneous deamination of 5-methylcytosine yielding a thymine base. An enzymatic mechanism exists for selective methylation of cytosine residues after replication. The propensity for deamination of 5-methylcytosine leads to increased frequency of RFLPs for at least some restriction enzymes, which include CpG pairs in the recognition site,[81] and accounts for certain mutational hot spots causing hemophilia A (Chap. 86) and other human disorders. The availability of recombinant DNA techniques is leading to an increasing definition of the exact

Fig. 1-8 Location of 30 mutations causing β thalassemia. Symbols are △ = frameshift and nonsense mutations; ◇ = RNA splicing mutants; ● = transcription mutants; ○ = RNA cleavage mutant. *(From S. E. Antonarakis et al.[80] Used by permission.)*

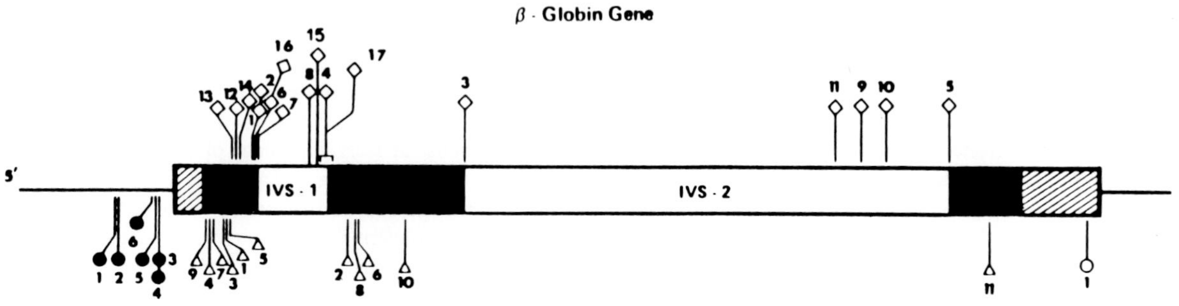

nature of new mutations, determination of whether they arose from a maternal gamete or from a paternal gamete, and identification of whether the mutation is of recent or ancient origin. Mutations which are widespread in the population but are descended from a single event can be recognized by the occurrence of specific haplotypes of RFLPs surrounding the mutations (see discussions of thalassemia, phenylalanine hydroxylase, and cystic fibrosis in various chapters). A haplotype is a group of genetic markers linked together on a single chromosome such as a group of close RFLP markers[80] or a group of HLA alleles (see Chap. 4).

When mutations occur in germ cells, the altered expression of the mutant gene does not affect the phenotype of the individual in whom the mutation occurs but is manifest only in subsequent generations. Usually such *new mutations* are recognized as sporadic events in human populations. On the other hand, when a mutation occurs in somatic cells at an early development stage, it may affect the individual harboring the mutation, but is not passed to subsequent generations. The individual harboring such a somatic cell mutation is said to be a *mosaic* because two populations of cells are present: normal cells and cells harboring the mutant gene. Mutations occurring in an early germ line cell can give rise to gonadal mosaicism so that numerous mutant gametes may be descended from a single event.

GENETIC DIVERSITY IN HUMANS: GARROD'S CHEMICAL INDIVIDUALITY AND THE CONCEPT OF POLYMORPHISM

Garrod recognized that the aberrant metabolism seen in a condition such as alkaptonuria might imply far more extensive chemical individuality, and he wrote[13]:

> If it be, indeed, the case that in alkaptonuria and the other conditions mentioned we are dealing with individualities of metabolism and not with the results of morbid processes the thought naturally presents itself that these are merely extreme examples of variations of chemical behaviour which are probably everywhere present in minor degrees and that just as no two individuals of a species are absolutely identical in bodily structure neither are their chemical processes carried out on exactly the same lines.

Garrod further said that "diathesis is nothing else but *chemical individuality*" which he described as follows[3]:

> . . . the factors which confer upon us our predispositions to and immunities from the various mishaps which are spoken of as diseases, are inherent in our very chemical structure; and even in the molecular groupings which confer upon us our individualities, and which went to the making of the chromosomes from which we sprang.

It becomes increasingly apparent that individuals have a molecular and biochemical individuality which is extraordinary. While there is often a tendency in medicine to regard patient populations as a homogeneous group of "wild-type individuals" or normal humans with "normal values" for all determinants, this is an erroneous conception. The aggregate of our genes determines who dies of myocardial infarction on a high fat diet, who develops cancer upon smoking, who only carries *Meningococcus* in the nasopharynx while another develops meningitis, who develops postoperative thromboembolism, and, perhaps, who is suceptible to alcoholism. These are risks that are substantially influenced by the genotype of the individual. Williams[2] emphasized the hypothesis that "everyone is a deviate" as follows:

> The existence in every human being of a vast array of attributes which are potentially measurable (whether by present methods or not), and probably often uncorrelated mathematically, makes quite tenable the hypothesis that *practically every human being is a deviate in some respects*.

Garrod's concept of chemical individuality has found its explanation over the past two decades with the realization that the gene for a given protein frequently exists in different forms in different normal individuals. Subsequently it was recognized that even more extensive variation exists in the DNA sequence of genomes between individuals. The widespread nature of this genetic diversity first became apparent when it became possible to study enzymes by electrophoresis of crude cell extracts and thereby to detect structurally variant forms of enzymes without the necessity of purification. With the use of this technique, studies by Harris in humans[82] and by Lewontin and Hubby in *Drosophila*[83] demonstrated that many proteins existed in two or more forms in the population. These multiple forms are due to the existence in the population of multiple genes (called *alleles*) at the same genetic locus coding for the same protein. At each genetic locus, each individual possesses two alleles, one derived from each parent. If the two alleles are identical, the individual is said to be *homozygous;* if they differ, the individual is *heterozygous*. The various alleles have been derived from a single precursor allele by mutations that have occurred during the evolution of the species; in general, they differ from each other only in the substitution of one base for another (missense mutations). In the vast majority of cases, the proteins produced by both alleles at a given locus are equally functional, i.e., the amino acid difference is "neutral" or nearly so from the standpoint of natural selection.

Based on population studies of 71 enzymes and other proteins that lend themselves to analysis by electrophoresis or other techniques, Harris has found that 28 percent of genetic loci show multiple alleles in the population.[79] Moreover, the average individual is detectably heterozygous at 7 percent of his or her loci. Since most detection methods require a change in the charge of the protein, they can detect only about one-third of the actual base changes that are possible, since only one-third result in a substitution of an amino acid with a different charge. Thus, all individuals may actually be heterozygous at as many as 20 percent of their loci.

At most genetic loci (such as that for the β chain of hemoglobin), there is one standard allele that accounts for the vast majority of the alleles in the population, whereas the alternate alleles are rare. At other genetic loci (such as that for the α chain of haptoglobin, a plasma protein), no single allele occurs with sufficient frequency to be designated as standard or normal. This latter situation represents an extreme example of genetic polymorphism. In strict terms, *polymorphism* is said to exist in a given population when the most common allele at a given locus accounts for fewer than 99 percent of the alleles in the population. By definition, when a polymorphism exists at a genetic locus, at least 2 percent of the population must be heterozygous at that locus.[79] Table 1-2 lists some plasma proteins and cellular enzymes for which electrophoretically determined polymorphisms have been demonstrated.

Harris' estimate that at least 28 percent of the genes for soluble blood proteins in humans show polymorphism is dis-

Table 1-2 Plasma Proteins and Cellular Enzymes that Exhibit Electrophoretically Detectable Polymorphisms

Protein	*Locus symbol*
Plasma proteins	
Haptoglobin (α chain)	HP
Transferrin	TF
Vitamin D-binding protein	GC (for group-specific component)
Ceruloplasmin	CP
α_1-Antitrypsin	PI (for protease inhibitor)
α_1-Acid glycoprotein	ORM (for orosomucoid)
β_2-Glycoprotein I	BG
Properdin factor B	BF
Complement	
Second component	C2
Third component	C3
Fourth component	C4
Sixth component	C6
Enzymes	
Pancreatic amylase	AMY2
Cholinesterase	CHE2
Red blood cell enzymes	
Acid phosphatase 1	ACP1
Adenosine deaminase	ADA
Adenylate kinase	AK1
Carbonic anhydrase 2	CA2
Diaphorase (NADPH-dependent)	DIA2
Esterase D	ESD
Galactose-1-uridyl transferase	GALT
Glucose-6-phosphate dehydrogenase	G6PD
Glutamic-pyruvic transaminase	GPT
Glutathione peroxidase	GPX1
Glutathione reductase	GSR
Glyoxalase I	GLO
Peptidase A	PEPA
Peptidase C	PEPC
Peptidase D	PEPD
Phosphoglucomutase 1	PGM1
Phosphoglucomutase 2	PGM2
Phosphogluconate dehydrogenase	PGD
Uridine monophosphate kinase	UMPK
White blood cell enzymes	
Aconitase (soluble)	ACO1
Cytidine deaminase	CDA
α-L-Fucosidase	FUCA2
α-Glucosidase	GAA
Glutamic-oxaloacetic transaminase (mitochondrial)	GOT2
Hexokinase 3	HK3
Malic enzyme (mitochondrial)	ME2
Phosphoglucomutase 3	PGM3

SOURCE: Data from Giblett[84] with updated gene symbols.

crepant with estimates for total cellular (fibroblast) proteins[85,86] where the variation is less for several possible reasons. Despite these differences, the frequency of protein polymorphism is high. The appreciation of polymorphism has been extended by the discovery of extraordinary variation at the DNA sequence level. Attention was focused on DNA polymorphism by the discovery of RFLPs by Kan and Dozy.[40] Extensive subsequent data suggest that approximately 1 in 100 to 1 in 200 bp in the human genome is polymorphic; this is consistent with heterozygosity at 1 in 250 to 1 in 500 bp.[87] A site is defined as polymorphic when at least 1 percent of the chromosomes have a sequence different from the majority. Although perhaps not an ideal usage, the term *allele* is now often extended to describe any nucleotide variation such as DNA fragment size differences detected as RFLPs even when these are not associated with an expressed gene locus. It is possible to detect single base DNA polymorphisms that represent synonymous differences or amino acid polymorphisms in coding regions, but polymorphism at a DNA level occurs with even greater frequency outside coding regions in parts of the genome which may have little or no effect on gene expression. The polymorphism within the genome extends beyond single base differences to include insertions, deletions, and variation in numbers of short tandemly repeated sequences. The latter types of variation provide highly polymorphic sites due to the variable number of tandem repeats (VNTR) as discussed in Chap. 6.

With the recognition of the extensive amount of polymorphism in DNA (millions of nucleotide differences between two random haploid genomes), including variation in nonexpressed sequences, it becomes obvious that the majority of DNA polymorphism is not associated with phenotypic effects. Presumably a modest fraction of genomic polymorphism is associated with effects on the phenotype that account for variation such as racial differences and human individuality without a significant effect on health or disease. Another proportion of polymorphism would be associated with phenotypic variation that might have relatively subtle and complex effects on susceptibility to disease. These variations would include genes affecting susceptibility to hypertension, atherosclerosis, malignancy, psychiatric illness, and infection. These genetic differences would provide the basis for polygenic and multifactorial disorders to be discussed below. Finally, a few genetic variations have such profound effect on the phenotype that they give rise to a disease condition in a relatively consistent manner (i.e., in the universal environment with minimal modifying effect from the remainder of the genome). These few genetic variations are referred to as *single gene* or *monogenic* disorders, and they constitute the basis for most of the diseases discussed in this volume. However, even the phenotype caused by these single gene disorders is often subject to modification by the genotype at other loci and by environmental factors. As knowledge increases, this becomes clearer and is exemplified by the effect of the number of α-globin loci on the phenotype when the β-globin locus is mutant in sickle-cell anemia.[88,89] Other examples can be found in the disorders of apolipoproteins where the phenotype is affected by the genotype at other loci and by environmental factors (Chaps. 44 to 51); the determinants of Hartnup disease versus Hartnup disorder are another illustration (Chap. 101).

GENETIC LINKAGE AND THE HUMAN GENE MAP

The most recent update of McKusick's catalog of *Mendelian Inheritance in Man*[4] lists 4344 loci, of which about 75 percent are associated with a disease phenotype,[90] indicating that over 3000 single-gene-determined human diseases are known to exist. This implies that at least 3000 of the 50,000 or so human genes have undergone mutation so as to cause human disease. The chromosomal location of more than 1300 of these genes is now known (Fig. 1-9).

The ability to locate genes relative to each other on the human chromosomes grew out of the pioneering studies of Morgan and his school in the first two decades of this century.[91] Using the fruit fly *D. melanogaster*, Morgan demonstrated that genes are aligned in a linear manner on the chromosomes and

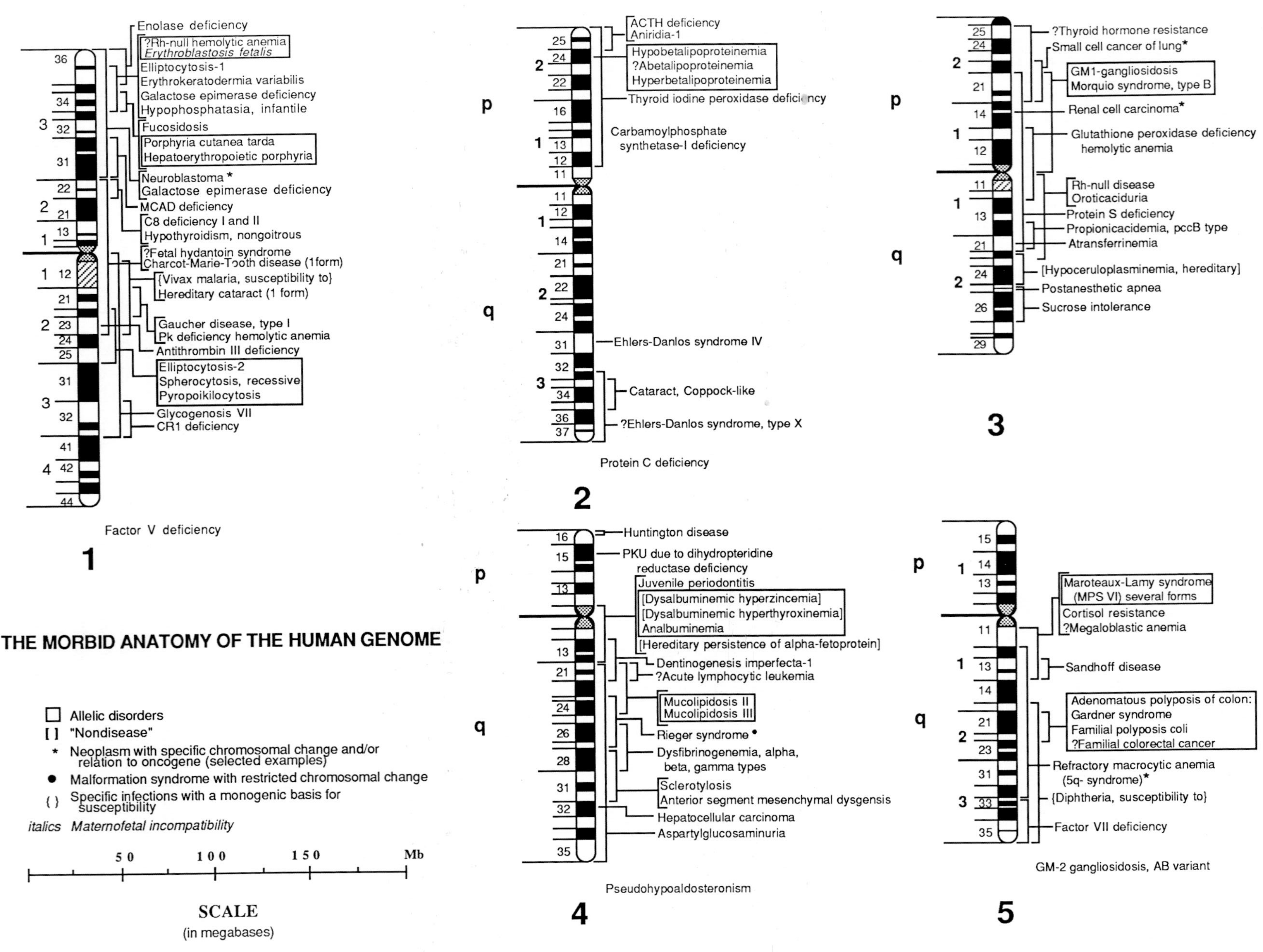

Fig. 1-9 The morbid anatomy of the human genome as of March 25, 1988 (generously provided by Victor A. McKusick). See Appendix 1-2 for details by individual chromosomes, disease and adjacent normal loci, location by banding pattern, gene symbol, McKusick number, and corresponding locus in mouse genome.

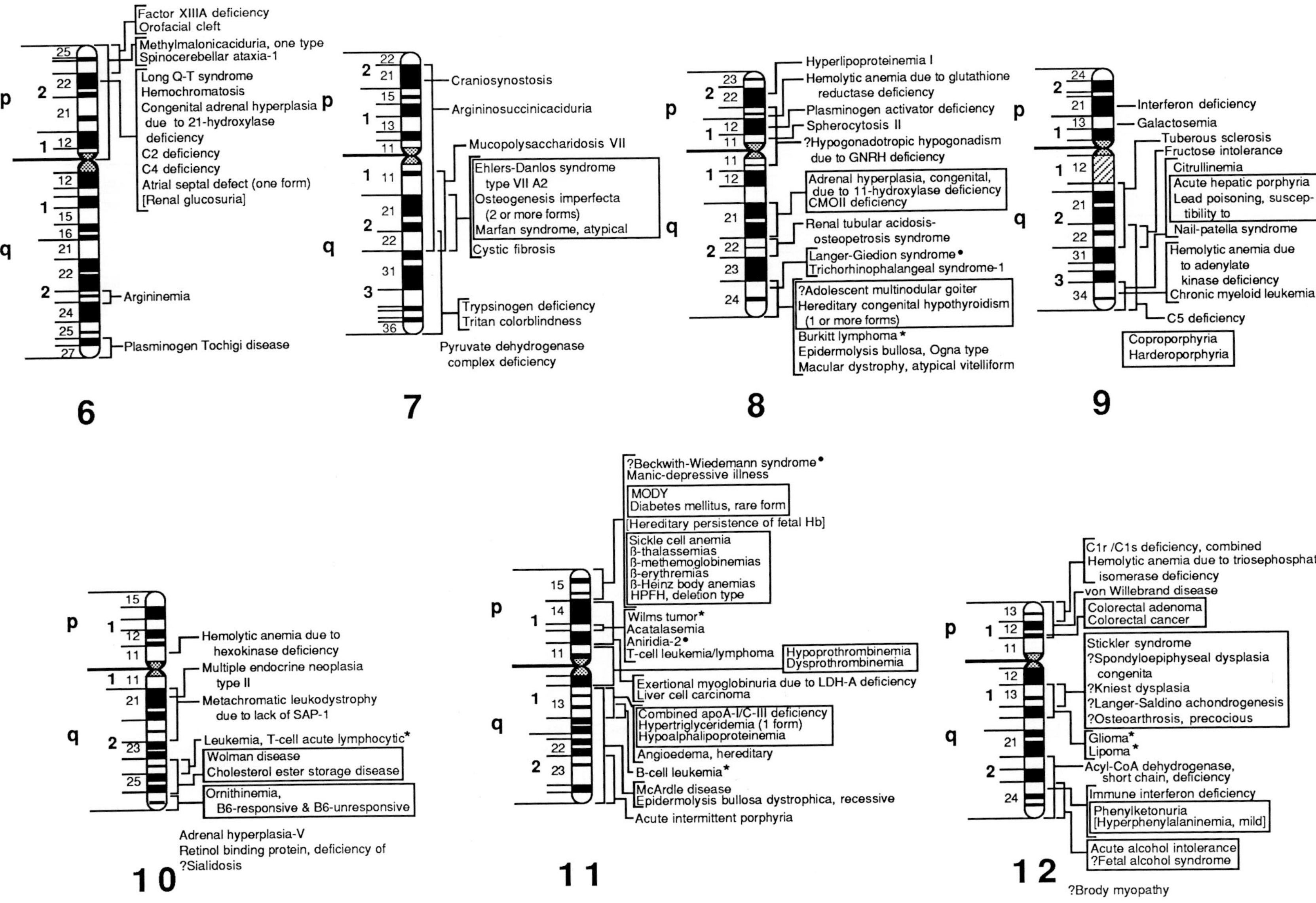

Fig. 1-9 (*Continued*)

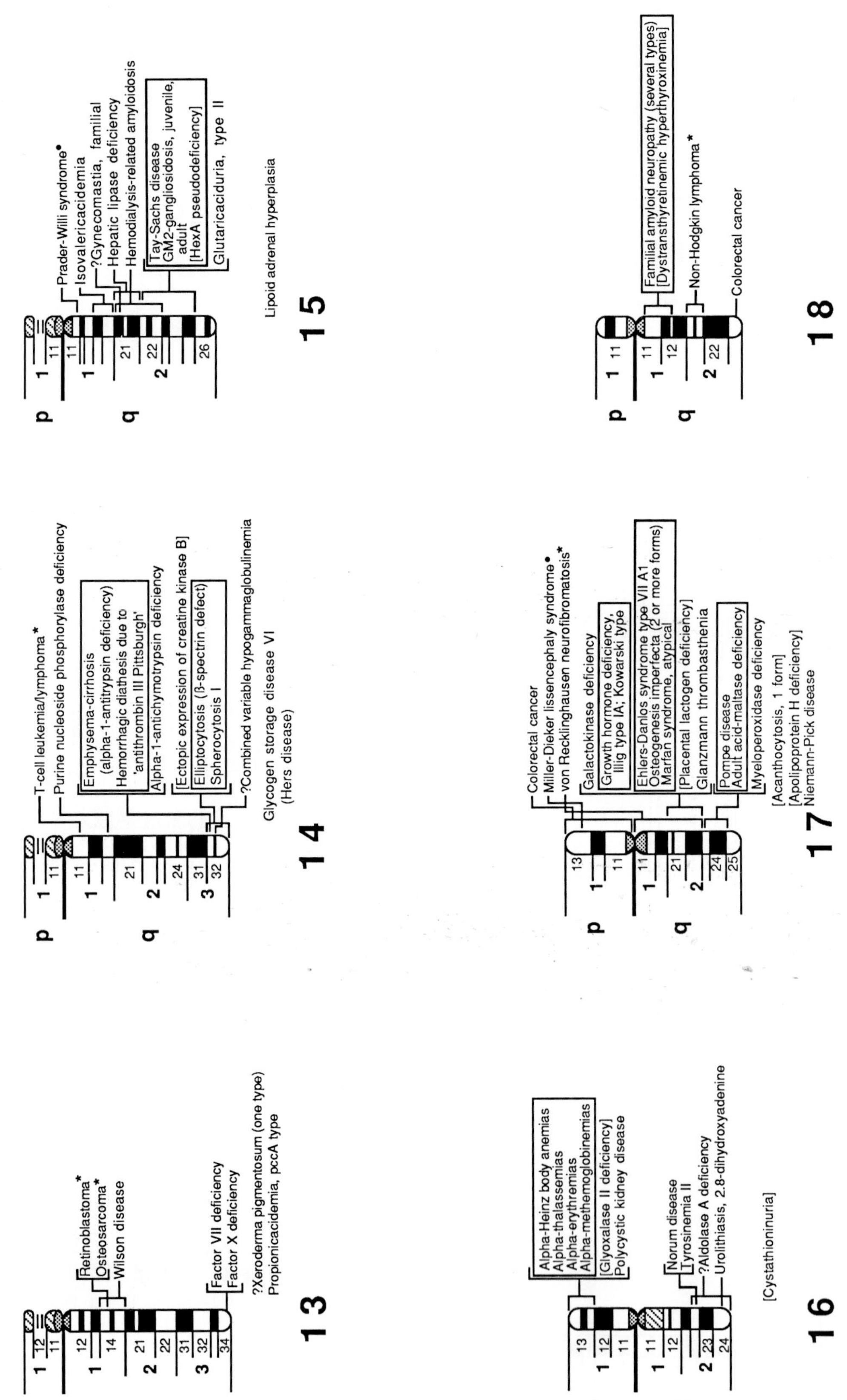

Fig. 1-9 (*Continued*)

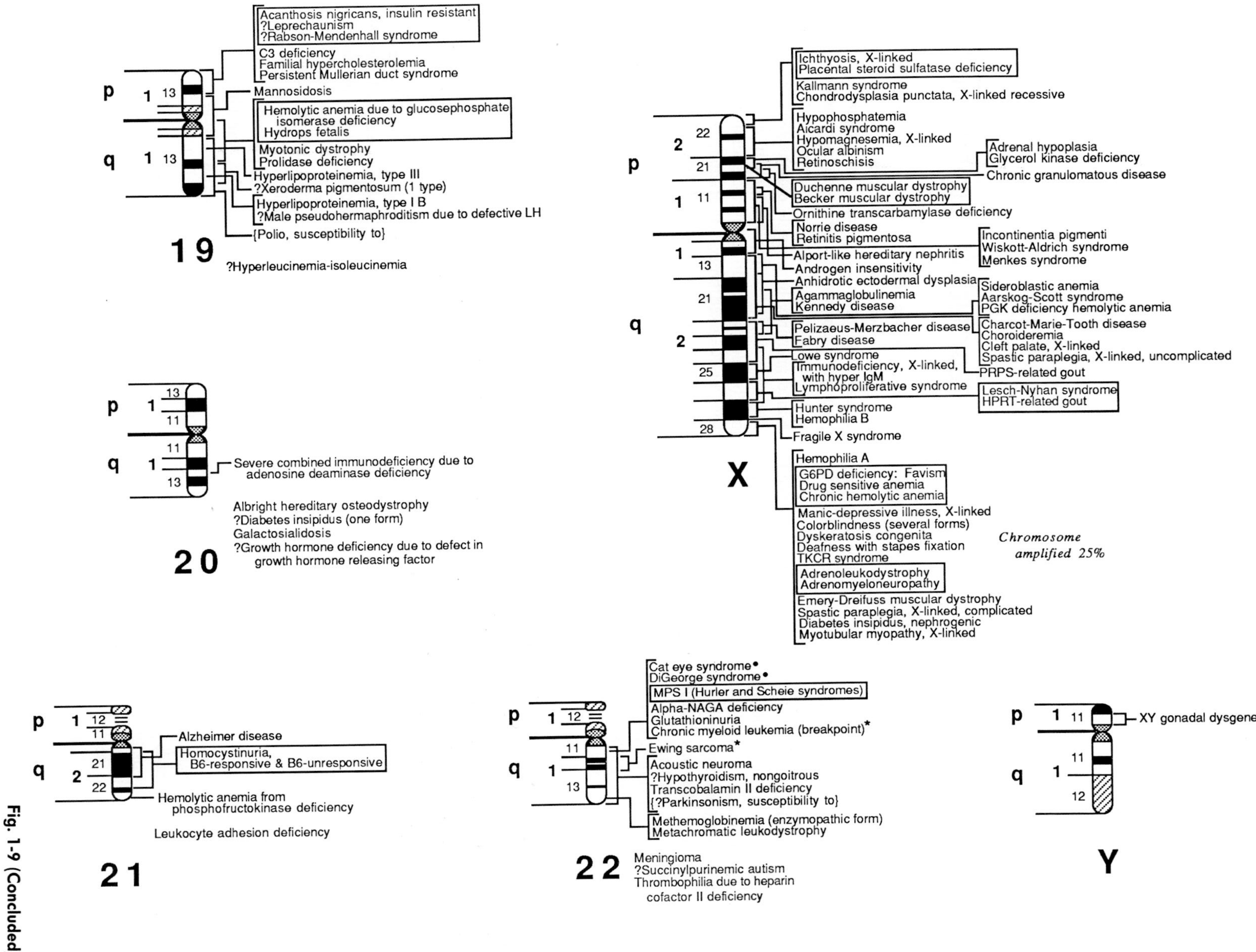

Fig. 1-9 (Concluded)

that if two genes are close together on the same chromosome, they do not assort independently at meiosis but are transmitted to the same gamete more than 50 percent of the time. Such genes are said to be *linked*. When two genes on a single chromosome are far apart, they are not genetically linked, even though they are physically linked by being on the same continuous chromosome. This lack of linkage is due to the phenomenon of *crossing-over*.

During the process of meiosis when homologous chromosomes are paired, bridges frequently form between corresponding regions of the chromosome pair. These bridges, or *chiasmas*, are regions in which the two chromosomes break at identical points along their length and subsequently rejoin, the distal segments having been switched from one homologous chromosome to the other. During this process of crossing-over, no net change in the amount of genetic material occurs. However, a *recombination* of genes does occur. For example, consider a chromosome with two loci, A and B, located at opposite ends of the same chromosome. On this particular chromosome, the A locus has a rare *x* allele and the B locus has a rare *y* allele. Without the phenomenon of recombination, every offspring that inherited the *x* allele at the A locus would also inherit the *y* allele at the B locus. However, if recombination occurs, the A locus with the *x* allele would then be on the opposite chromosome from the B locus with the *y* allele. In this case, any offspring that inherited the *x* allele at the A locus could not inherit the *y* allele at the B locus.

Crossing-over in humans occurs with great frequency in every meiosis, and the resultant recombination of genes may occur at any point on a chromosome. The farther apart two genes are on the same chromosome, the greater is the likelihood that a crossing-over will occur in the space between them. When two genes are on the opposite ends of a long chromosome, the probability of recombination is so great that their respective alleles are transmitted to offspring almost independently of one another, just as if the two gene loci were on different chromosomes. On the other hand, gene loci that are close together on the same chromosome are said to be *linked*, so that there is a great likelihood that offspring will inherit the same combination of alleles that is present on the parental chromosome.

Figure 1-9 and its accompanying key give the chromosomal assignments of hundreds of autosomal loci, with indications of the confidence of the assignment. In addition, some 120 loci are known from pedigree studies to be located on the X chromosome. As illustrated in Fig. 1-9, the mapping of genes on virtually all the chromosomes is now quite extensive, and an entire introductory chapter is devoted to how the human gene map can be used in medicine (Chap. 6).

Assignment of a locus to a specific chromosome is based on a variety of methods that have been reviewed in detail by McKusick and Ruddle.[92–94] Many genes have been mapped by linkage of traits in large families with multiple alleles at two loci (e.g., linkage of the nail-patella syndrome and the ABO blood group). Somatic cell hybrids have been used extensively to assign genes to particular chromosomes based on the concordance of the presence of the human gene product with the presence of the human chromosome (e.g., thymidine kinase segregates with chromosome 17). More recently many genes are mapped following the isolation of cDNA or genomic DNA clones. The cloned DNA can be used with a hybrid cell panel to assess the concordance of the DNA hybridizing sequence with a particular chromosome. Alternatively, the cloned DNA can be used for synthesis of probes to be used for *in situ* hybridization with human chromosomes. The opportunity for linkage studies has been greatly enhanced by the availability of numerous polymorphic DNA probes, and the genes for many common human diseases have been mapped to specific chromosomes using this strategy (e.g., assignment of Huntington disease to chromosome 4 using an anonymous probe to detect an RFLP.[47] A very large number of the disorders discussed in this text have been mapped to specific human chromosomes. Examples can be found in the summary table at the end of this chapter.

CATEGORIES OF GENETIC DISORDERS

Genetic diseases generally fall into one of three categories. (1) *Chromosomal disorders* involve the lack, excess, or abnormal arrangement of one or more chromosomes, producing large amounts of excessive or deficient genetic material and affecting many genes. (2) *Mendelian or monogenic disorders* are determined primarily by a single mutant gene. Accordingly, these disorders display simple (Mendelian) inheritance patterns that can be classified into autosomal dominant, autosomal recessive, or X-linked types. (3) *Multifactorial disorders* are caused by an interaction of multiple genes and multiple exogenous or environmental factors. Although many of these multifactorial disorders, such as diabetes mellitus, gout, and cleft lip and palate, are said to run in families, the inheritance pattern is complex and the risk to relatives is much less than that seen in the single gene (Mendelian) disorders. Each of the above three categories of genetic disease presents different problems with respect to causation, prevention, diagnosis, genetic counseling, and treatment.[95]

Although it is useful to consider these categories of genetic disorders, this classification necessarily represents an oversimplification. For example, small chromosomal deletions may cause the simultaneous presence of multiple Mendelian or monogenic disorders (contiguous gene syndromes). This is exemplified by the occurrence of patients with visible deletions in the short arm of the X chromosome in association with Duchenne muscular dystrophy, chronic granulomatous disease, retinitis pigmentosa, and the McLeod phenotype.[96] These deletions may be submicroscopic and yet be large enough to cause the simultaneous presence of phenotypes such as Duchenne muscular dystrophy, ornithine transcarbamylase deficiency, and glycerol kinase deficiency (Chaps. 9 and 36). Deletions of the retinoblastoma locus on chromosome 13 may be visible or submicroscopic and may extend to nearby loci such as esterase D (Chap. 9). Thus, these defects bridge the gap between chromosomal and monogenic disorders. The phenotype caused by chromosomal disorders obviously is due to the altered expression of single genes within the abnormal region. Chromosomal translocations may interrupt single genes as exemplified by some females with X autosomal translocations causing Duchenne muscular dystrophy (see Chaps. 9 and 118).

The phenotypes of many of the monogenic disorders discussed in this text are modified by the genes at other loci and by environmental factors. Figure 1-10 emphasizes the effect of nongenetic factors and modifying genes on monogenic phenotypes. There are relatively few monogenic disorders where the single locus *entirely* determines the disease phenotype. Simi-

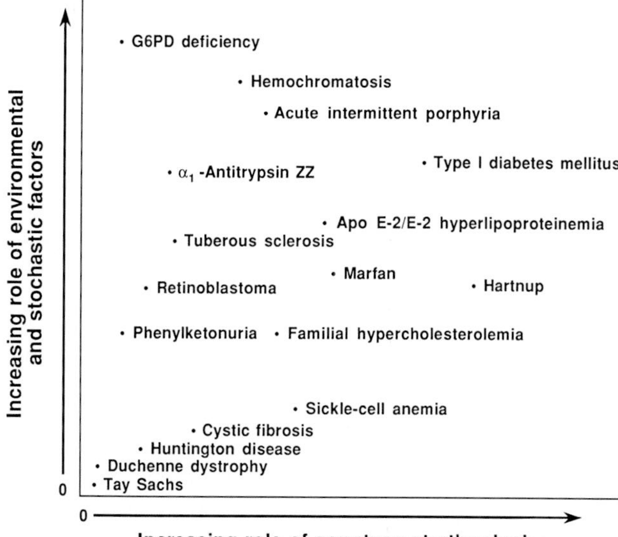

Fig. 1-10 Depiction of estimated roles of modifier genes and nongenetic factors in influencing the phenotypes for "monogenic" disorders. These are crude estimates meant to depict the range of contributions which might occur.

larly, there are relatively few environmental insults where the genotype does not in some way modify the risk. For example, the genotype undoubtedly influences which infants will survive in a famine. In theory, some disorders might be polygenic, which would imply an effect of multiple genes without a major contribution by exogenous or environmental factors. In practice, the majority of polygenic disorders are very likely to be subject to exogenous factors and are therefore multifactorial. The monogenic disorders have provided an excellent starting point for attempts to understand human genetic disease. The future will increasingly involve the greater challenge of understanding the much more common multifactorial disorders.

Frequency of Genetic Disease

Genetic disease accounts for a significant proportion of hospitalized children in referral centers. In studies in Montreal, Baltimore, and Newcastle, from 6 to 8 percent of diseases among hospitalized children were attributable to single gene defects and from 0.4 to 2.5 percent to chromosomal abnormalities; another 22 to 31 percent were considered gene influenced.[97,98] The overall frequency of monogenic disorders is about 1 percent.[97] About 5.3 percent of live-born individuals below age 25 can be expected to have disease with an important genetic component (single gene, chromosomal, and multifactorial).[99] If multifactorial disorders of late onset are included, about 60 percent of individuals have genetically influenced diseases.[99,100] One recent study[101] evaluated survival of adoptees relative to the survival of their biologic and adoptive parents. The results indicated that premature death in adults has a strong genetic component for death from all causes, for natural causes, for infections, and for cardiovascular causes. Premature death of a biologic parent (less than age 50) resulted in a relative risk of death in the adoptees of 1.71 (95 percent confidence interval, 1.14 to 2.57). More detailed information on the frequency of diseases within categories is provided below.

Chromosomal Disorders

The *karyotype* of an individual (i.e., the number and structure of the chromosomes) can be ascertained from readily accessible body cells, such as peripheral blood lymphocytes or skin fibroblasts, by growing them in tissue culture until active proliferation occurs and then preparing single metaphase cells for examination of chromosomes by microscopy. By the 1970s it became possible to identify each individual chromosome by special staining of DNA sequences, by the affinity of fluorescent dyes (such as quinacrine hydrochloride) for certain chromosomal segments that can be visualized by fluorescence microscopy, and by treatment of the chromosomes with dyes (Giemsa) after treatment with proteolytic enzymes (trypsin). These techniques produce characteristic *banding patterns* for each chromosome (Fig. 1-11). The number of chromosomes in normal individuals is 46, of which 44 are the 22 pairs of *autosomes* and the other 2 are the *sex chromosomes*. Females have two X chromosomes (XX), and males have one X chromosome and one Y chromosome (XY). Each of the 22 pairs of autosomes and the 2 sex chromosomes can be distinguished on the basis of size, location of the centromere (which divides the chromosome into arms of equal or unequal length), and the unique banding pattern (Fig. 1-11). More details regarding cytogenetic methodology are available elsewhere.[95]

Most chromosomal disorders found in humans can be classified into one of four groups: (1) excess or loss of one or more chromosomes *(aneuploidy)*; (2) breakage and loss of a piece of a chromosome *(deletion)*; (3) breakage of two chromosomes, with transfer and fusion of parts of the broken fragments onto each other *(translocation)*; and (4) abnormal splitting of the centromere during mitosis so that one arm is lost and the other is duplicated to form one symmetric chromosome with two genetically identical arms *(isochromosome formation)*. In addition, chromosomal *mosaicism* may occur such that a single individual may possess two cell lines, or *clones*, each differing in its chromosomal constitution. For example, many patients with the Turner syndrome have been shown to possess some

Fig. 1-11 A trypsin G-banded normal human female karyotype. *(Courtesy of David H. Ledbetter.)*

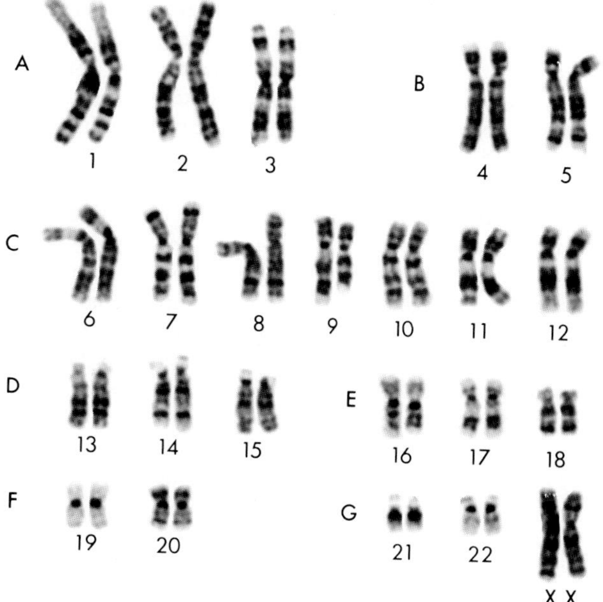

cells with a 45,X constitution and other cells with a normal 46,XX. Their karotype is symbolized 45,X/46,XX

The *autosomal* trisomies responsible for specific clinical syndromes include: (1) trisomy 21 (Down syndrome or mongolism, Chap. 7), characterized by mental retardation, a characteristic facies, marked hypotonia, and many other abnormalities; (2) trisomy 13, characterized by ocular defects, cleft lip and palate, polydactyly, and an average life span of less than 1 year; and (3) trisomy 18, characterized by micrognathia, severe failure to thrive, multiple malformations, and a life span of less than 3 months.

The numeric aberrations of the sex chromosomes include three disorders with 47 chromosomes (47,XXY; 47,XYY; and 47,XXX) and one disorder with 45 chromosomes (45,X). The XXY karyotype is found in patients with the Klinefelter syndrome, who are phenotypic males with testicular dysgenesis, infertility, gynecomastia, tall stature, and behavioral changes. Most individuals with a 47,XYY karyotype are normal fertile males; however, some may be unusually tall and show tendencies to criminality or other behavior abnormalities. Most individuals with the 47,XXX karyotype are clinically normal females, but some may be mentally retarded and deficient in secondary sexual development. The 45,X karyotype is found in about one-half of patients with the Turner syndrome, who are phenotypic females with ovarian dysgenesis, failure of secondary sexual development, short stature, renal anomalies, and pterygium colli. Patients with the Turner syndrome who do not have a 45,X karyotype may have either mosaicism (45,X/46,XX or 45,X/46,XY) or a structural abnormality of the X chromosome, such as an isochromosome X.

Little is known about the factors that cause chromosomal disorders in humans. The most important finding is the association between increasing maternal age and nondisjunction syndromes such as Down syndrome (trisomy 21) and the other autosomal trisomies. A possible etiologic role for other factors, such as genetic predisposition, autoimmune disorders (involving the thyroid gland, in particular), viruses, chemical mutagens, and radiation, has also been suggested.[95]

Chromosomal aberrations are common. The detected frequency of chromosomal aberrations in karyotypes of unselected newborn infants is 1 in 200 (0.5 percent), while among recognized first-trimester spontaneous abortions the frequency of chromosomal defects is as high as 50 percent. Given a 20 percent rate of spontaneous abortion in recognized conceptions, at least 10 percent of all conceptions result in chromosomal aberrations. The vast majority of affected fetuses do not survive the apparently intense in utero selection and are lost early in gestation. Despite this, a high frequency of chromosomal aberrations has been observed in patients with several clinical abnormalities, including (1) multiple congenital malformations (2 to 20 percent); (2) infertility and sterility (1 to 10 percent); (3) mental retardation (1 to 3 percent); and (4) certain forms of malignancy, such as chronic myelogenous leukemia, in which the long arm of chromosome 22 is translocated to one of the larger chromosomes, most often to the long arm of chromosome 9, producing the so-called *Philadelphia* chromosome (a shortened chromosome 22).

Chromosomal aberrations occur with extremely high frequency in various malignancies. In these instances, the constitutional karyotype is usually normal, but the tumor cells show abnormal findings as mentioned above for the Philadelphia chromosome. Numerous chromosomal translocations are now known to be found with some specificity for a variety of tumors.[102–104] In some instances, a constitutional genetic abnormality may represent a first step in a two-step process leading to malignancy. The second step in this process occurs in a single somatic cell and may often be a gross chromosomal aberration which contributes to the development of a tumor. This is best documented for retinoblastoma (Chap. 9), but also occurs in Wilms tumor (Chap. 9), polyposis of the colon,[105] Von Hippel-Lindau disease,[50] and other disorders. The locus involved in hereditary tumors is often also involved in sporadic tumors, as documented for colon tumors, retinoblastoma, renal cell carcinoma, and other tumors (Chap. 9).[106–107]

Chromosomal disorders often occur as new mutations. Both parents are usually normal, and the risk of recurrence in sibs is low. However, when the aberration involves an unbalanced translocation, one parent is a balanced translocation carrier in about a third of the cases. In this instance the recurrence risk for subsequent children may be as high as 20 percent, and additional members of the extended family may also be carriers at high risk for having an offspring with an unbalanced chromosomal complement. Table 1-3 lists the most frequently encountered chromosomal abnormalities occurring among live-born infants.

One important disorder involving a fragile site on the X chromosome is often considered with chromosomal abnormalities, although it may represent a monogenic disorder. Fragile sites are regions of chromosomes which are subject to narrowing or breakage when cells are cultured under conditions which slow or inhibit DNA replication. The fragile X mental retardation syndrome is a common important form of mental retardation associated with the occurrence of a fragile site at Xq28. The disorder has come to attention relatively recently, but enough has been learned to justify a chapter on the subject in this edition (Chap. 8). The disorder shows unusual features of inheritance (see Chap. 8 for details) with a high frequency of clinical expression in hemizygous males and a lower frequency of clinical expression in heterozygous females.

The indications for complete chromosomal analysis have expanded with the growth of information and with the improved resolution of the analysis. Chromosome analysis is clinically indicated in the following situations: (1) in children with two or more major malformations including prenatal or postnatal growth failure as a major malformation; (2) in children with

Table 1-3 Frequency of Chromosomal Disorders among Live-born Infants

Disorders	*Frequency*
Autosomal abnormalities	
Trisomy 21 (Down syndrome)	1 in 600
Trisomy 18	1 in 5000
Trisomy 13	1 in 15,000
Sex chromosome abnormalities	
Klinefelter syndrome (47,XXY)	1 in 700 males
XYY syndrome (47,XYY)	1 in 800 males
Triple-X syndrome (47,XXX)	1 in 1000 females
Turner syndrome (45,X or 45X/46XX or 45X/46,XY or isochromosome Xq)	1 in 1500 females
Fragile X mental retardation	1 in 2000 males 1 in 3000 females

SOURCE: Data modified from Vogel and Motulsky,[95] Galjaard,[97] and Chap. 8.

mental retardation of unknown cause with or without malformations; (3) in all children with features of recognized chromosomal syndromes including trisomies, fragile X, and deletions; (4) in couples with a poor reproductive history (infertility, increased numbers of spontaneous abortions, or stillbirths); (5) in antecendents and offspring of individuals with chromosomal translocations; (6) in individuals with sexual malformations or abnormalities of sexual development; and (7) in patients with various malignancies (analysis of tumor cells). The quality of chromosome analysis is important, and attention must be given to special conditions required for detection of the fragile X abnormality. Subtle deletions occur in conditions such as hereditary retinoblastoma, Prader-Willi syndrome, Miller-Dieker syndrome, and other conditions, such that high resolution analysis for a specific region can be requested if particular diagnoses are suspected (see Chap. 9). Analysis of malignancies also requires the use of special techniques. The role of chromosomal analysis in malignancy is growing rapidly.[102–104] Cytogenetic changes in tumors may assist in establishing diagnostic categories, in devising treatment protocols, and in long term follow-up. The role of chromosome analysis in prenatal diagnosis has grown such that the number of analyses performed on prenatal samples now exceeds the number of analyses performed on postnatal samples in most western countries. While prenatal cytogenetic analysis may be performed because of the previous occurrence of cytogenetic abnormalities or because of known familial translocations, the majority of studies are performed for advanced maternal age. There is a progressive trend toward increased utilization of cytogenetic analysis for prenatal diagnosis which can now be carried out using amniocentesis or chorionic villus sampling as discussed below.

For a more complete discussion of the etiology and clinical features of chromosome abnormalities affecting humans, refer to the *Clinical Atlas of Human Chromosomes*[108] and the *Catalogue of Unbalanced Chromosome Aberrations in Man.*[109]

Table 1-4 Frequency of Some Common Monogenic Disorders among Live-born Infants

Disorder	*Estimated frequency**
Autosomal dominant	
Familial hypercholesterolemia	1 in 500
Adult polycystic kidney disease	1 in 1250
Huntington chorea	1 in 2500
Hereditary spherocytosis	1 in 5000
von Willebrand disease	1 in 8000
Marfan syndrome	1 in 20,000
Achondroplasia	1 in 50,000
Autosomal recessive	
Sickle-cell anemia	1 in 655 (U.S. blacks)
Cystic fibrosis	1 in 2500 (Caucasians)
Tay-Sachs disease	1 in 3000 (Ashkenazi Jews)
α_1-Antitrypsin ZZ genotype	1 in 3500
Phenylketonuria	1 in 12,000 (average)
Mucopolysaccharidoses (all types together)	1 in 25,000
Glycogen storage diseases (all types together)	1 in 50,000
X-linked	
Duchenne muscular dystrophy	1 in 7000 males
Hemophilia A	1 in 10,000 males
Fragile X mental retardation	See Table 1-3

*The frequency of some disorders varies widely between ethnic groups (e.g., sickle-cell anemia, cystic fibrosis, Tay-Sachs, α_1-antitrypsin, and phenylketonuria) but is less variant for others, perhaps particularly when new mutations are frequent (e.g., achondroplasia, Duchenne dystrophy, and hemophilia A).

SOURCE: Data modified from Galjaard,[97] Carter,[110] Motulsky,[111] and various chapters in this book.

Monogenic Disorders

Having already acknowledged that very few phenotypes are entirely determined by a single locus, it is still very useful to discuss so-called monogenic disorders. Disorders caused by single mutant genes show one of three simple (or Mendelian) patterns of inheritance: (1) autosomal dominant, (2) autosomal recessive, or (3) X-linked. With few exceptions, each of the approximately 3000 Mendelian diseases is rare. As a group, these disorders constitute an important cause of morbidity and death, accounting directly for more than 5 percent of all pediatric hospital admissions.[97] The overall population frequency of monogenic disorders is about 10 per 1000 livebirths, with about 7 in 1000 dominants, about 2.5 in 1000 recessives, and about 0.4 in 1000 X-linked conditions.[97] Table 1-4 lists some of the most common Mendelian disorders.

If a particular disease shows one of the three Mendelian patterns of inheritance, its pathogenesis, no matter how complex, must be due to an abnormality in a single protein molecule. For example, in sickle-cell anemia, the entire clinical syndrome, including such seemingly unrelated disturbances as anemia, pain crises, nephropathy, and predisposition to pneumococcal infections, is the physiological consequence of having a single base change at a specific site in the gene that codes for the β chain of hemoglobin, producing a substitution of a valine for a glutamic acid in the sixth amino acid position in the protein sequence.

In many Mendelian disorders, it is not yet possible to demonstrate directly the protein that is altered by the mutation. In such cases only the distal physiological effects of the mutation are recognizable. Nevertheless, it is safe to assume that a single primary defect exists whenever a disease is transmitted by a single gene mechanism, and the various manifestations of the disease can all be related to the mutational event by a more or less complicated "pedigree of causes." In recent years, reverse genetic techniques and other molecular methods have led to the cloning of many disease genes, in all cases confirming the monogenic interpretation.

The basic biochemical lesions in monogenic disorders involve defects in a wide variety of proteins, including enzymes, receptors, transport proteins, peptide hormones, immunoglobulins, collagens, and coagulation factors. There are now over 300 human diseases whose biochemical defects have been defined. The majority involve abnormalities in enzymes, but the ability to identify defects in other types of proteins is improving. Most of these disorders are discussed in detail in this book and are tabulated at the end of this chapter. Although genetic defects could involve genes which do not encode a protein (e.g., defects in genes for transfer RNA), none has been identified in humans to date.

The impact of Mendelian disease on human health has been reviewed in detail.[90] It was found that 25 percent of disadaptive Mendelian phenotypes were apparent at birth and over 90 percent by the end of puberty. Slightly more than half of phenotypes involved more than one anatomic or functional sys-

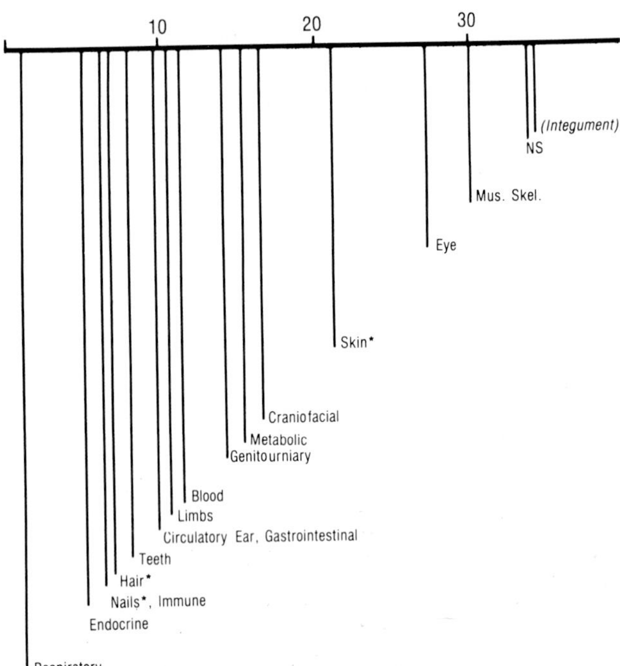

Fig. 1-12 Rank order (abscissa is percentage of phenotypes involving system) for the involvement of a particular anatomic/functional system by Mendelian disease in humans (see Ref. 90 for likelihood that more than one system is involved). Skin, hair, and nails are shown both individually and as a group designated *integument.* Mus Skel = musculo-skeletal; NS = nervous system. *(From T. Costa et al.[90] Used by permission.)*

tem. Life span was reduced in 57 percent of disorders, more often in autosomal recessive and X-linked diseases. Reproductive capacity was reduced in 69 percent of phenotypes. Most phenotypes compatible with prolonged survival were associated with handicaps which limited access to schooling and work. The distribution of phenotypes by systems affected is presented in Fig. 1-12, which indicates, in particular, a high frequency of central nervous system involvement.

Significance of Dominant or Recessive. The distinction between *dominant* and *recessive* is very useful for pedigree analysis but does not imply a fundamental difference in genetic mechanism. The terms are used slightly differently in descriptions of medical disorders than in classical genetics. In classical genetics, alleles are dominant or recessive only if the heterozygote is phenotypically indistinguishable from one or the other homozygote. The dominant allele is the one whose phenotype prevails in the heterozygote. Alleles are codominant if the heterozygote shows an intermediate phenotype. In medicine, the term *dominant* implies that a clinical phenotype will be manifest when an individual has a single copy of the mutant allele (i.e., is *heterozygous* for it), while *recessive* implies that a clinical phenotype occurs only when both alleles are defective (i.e., *homozygosity* or *compound heterozygosity*). These distinctions are extremely useful for clinical diagnosis, for genetic linkage analysis, and for genetic counseling. However, a number of subtleties about the use of the terms dominant and recessive to describe human disorders must be recognized. There is usually no requirement that the phenotype of the heterozygote resemble that of either homozygote particularly in the case of dominant disorders. Homozygotes for dominant disorders are identified relatively rarely, but when recognized, their disease is often much more severe than for heterozygotes (e.g., familial hypercholesterolemia, achondroplasia, and some forms of porphyria). When homozygotes are clinically indistinguishable from heterozygotes for dominant disorders, the condition may be described as a *true dominant.* Huntington disease has been suggested as such an example.[112] The terms *homozygous* or *homozygote* are widely used in reference to the phenotype and in a loose sense to imply an individual with two mutant alleles at a locus without knowledge of whether the two mutations are identical. In a strict sense the term implies that an individual has two identical alleles at a particular locus and should be distinguished from a compound heterozygote who is an individual with two different mutant alleles at the locus.

While the distinction of dominant disorders and recessive disorders is useful for classifying clinical phenotypes, there are additional subtleties and complexities to consider. The implication that heterozygotes for a recessive disorder are asymptomatic is an oversimplification. Heterozygotes for at least some recessive disorders may have subtle differences in phenotype which may be accentuated by environmental factors. These subtle phenotypic consequences may be advantageous or disadvantageous. Despite their overall clinical "normality," individuals who are heterozygous for recessive genes often have demonstrable biochemical differences. Many of these complexities are exemplified by sickle-cell anemia, which is best considered to be a recessive disorder for clinical purposes in that the heterozygotes are essentially normal healthy individuals. At a molecular level, the genes are not dominant or recessive, but both genes express their product in what might be described as a *codominant* manner. Both gene products can be demonstrated by hemoglobin electrophoresis in heterozygotes. Despite the general lack of phenotypic effect in heterozygotes, a selective advantage for resistance to malaria is well documented in heterozygotes (Chap. 93). Heterozygotes are also known to have subtle physiological abnormalities affecting renal concentrating ability and cardiopulmonary physiology at high altitudes (Chap. 93). These phenotypic effects in heterozygotes for recessive disorders may be more common than is generally recognized and may contribute to phenotypes more often considered to be of multifactorial etiology. It has been suggested that heterozygotes for ataxia telangectasia are at increased risk of malignancy.[113] Heterozygosity for known recessive disorders contributes to the biochemical and medical individuality of humans.

In other instances, the phenotypic consequences of being heterozygous may be inconsistent, resulting in uncertainty as to whether a disorder is better considered as dominant or recessive. If occasional heterozygotes show clear disease manifestations, a disorder is generally considered dominant. There are dominant disorders where a substantial proportion of heterozygous individuals are asymptomatic as exemplified by some forms of von Willebrand disease (Chap. 87) and some forms of porphyria (Chap. 52). In these instances, homozygous individuals may have heterozygous asymptomatic parents giving rise to an apparent recessive disorder, but these are probably best classified as examples of homozygous dominant disorders. *This exemplifies that the distinction between dominant and recessive disorders is an arbitrary division of a continuum rather than a sharp demarcation.* Clinicians tend to classify a disorder as dominant if most of the symptomatic individuals coming to attention are heterozygotes and as recessive if most of the symptomatic individuals are homozygotes. The distinction of dominant and recessive disorders is additionally complicated for X-linked loci by the mechanism of random X inactivation as discussed under X-linked disorders below.

Whether a mutation generates a dominant or recessive disorder is determined by two factors: (1) the effect of the mutation on the function of the gene product, and (2) the tolerance of the biologic system to a functional perturbation of that particular gene product. In this reductionist time, it is important to realize that gene products work in systems and that the phenotype—be it normal development and physiological homeostasis or maldevelopment and dyshomeostasis—is, at first approximation, the result of the normal or abnormal function of the systems (e.g., the blood glucose homeostatic system or the connective tissue extracellular matrix system). Tolerant systems tend to result in recessive phenotypes; less tolerant systems tend to result in dominant phenotypes. Loci which encode enzymes usually result in recessive phenotypes because of the catalytic nature of enzymes and because enzymes are usually present in amounts considerably in excess of that required to maintain a relatively normal phenotype. Kacser and Burns[114] described the sensitivity coefficient as the fractional change in flux in a pathway over the fractional change in enzyme activity. This quantitative approach demonstrates that a large change in enzyme activity results in a negligible change in flux for most pathways, explaining why most enzyme mutants are recessive. Some mutations at loci encoding enzymes generate dominant phenotypes (many porphyrias, see Chap. 52). Dominant negative mutations can result when a mutant gene product interferes with function of normal molecules produced by the normal allele in a heterozygote.[115] In this way, a product deficiency which might usually be associated with a recessive disorder might occur as a dominant disorder. Different mutations at the same locus may give rise to dominant or recessive disorders depending on the exact nature of the mutation as exemplified by the osteogenesis imperfecta phenotypes resulting from mutations at the loci for the chains of type I collagen (Chap. 115). Although we refer to dominant or recessive "disorders," in reality it is the mutation or allele which is dominant or recessive. Thus, it is possible to have different mutations at a single locus causing a phenotype which is dominant in some families and recessive in others. Some additional aspects of the mechanisms underlying dominant and recessive phenotypes are discussed under the specific categories below. All these complexities notwithstanding, it remains extremely useful to discuss monogenic disorders under separate patterns of inheritance.

Autosomal Dominant Disorders. Dominant diseases are manifest in the heterozygous state, i.e., when only one abnormal gene *(mutant allele)* is present and the corresponding partner allele on the homologous chromosome is normal. By definition, the gene responsible for an autosomal dominant disorder must be located on one of the 22 autosomes; hence, both males and females can be affected. Since alleles segregate independently at meiosis, there is a 1 in 2 chance that the offspring of an affected heterozygote will inherit the mutant allele.

Figure 1-13 shows typical pedigrees involving an autosomal dominant trait. The following features are characteristic: (1) each affected individual has an affected parent (unless the condition arose by a new mutation in the sperm or ovum that formed the individual or unless the mutant allele is present but without phenotypic effect in the affected parent as discussed under penetrance, below); (2) an affected individual will bear, on the average, both normal and affected offspring in equal proportions; (3) normal children of an affected individual will have only normal offspring; (4) males and females are affected in equal proportions; (5) each sex is equally likely to transmit the condition to male and female offspring, with male-to-male transmission occurring; and (6) vertical transmission of the condition through successive generations occurs, especially when the trait does not impair the reproductive capacity.

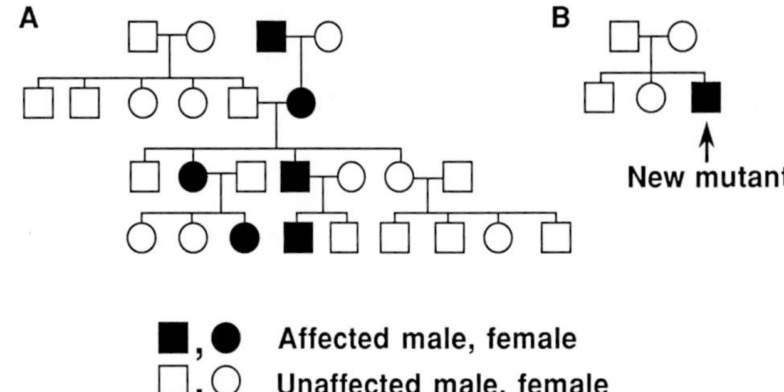

Fig. 1-13 Pedigree pattern for an autosomal dominant trait. Note the *vertical* pattern of inheritance; compare new mutation and inherited pedigrees.

NEW MUTATIONS. While there is a 50 percent risk that the offspring of an individual with an autosomal dominant condition will inherit the disease, it is not necessarily true that each affected person must have an affected parent. In every autosomal dominant disease, a certain proportion of affected persons owe their disorder to a new mutation rather than to an inherited one. Since a rough estimate of the frequency of mutation is 5×10^{-6} mutations per gene per generation and since a dominant trait, by definition, requires a mutation in only one of a pair of alleles, one would expect that about 1 in 100,000 newborn persons would possess a new mutation at any given genetic locus. Many of these mutations either will not impair the function of the gene product or will involve a recessive function, so that the mutation will be clinically silent. Others, however, will cause a defective gene product that gives rise to a dominant trait. The parent in whose germ cells the mutation arose will be clinically normal. The sibs of the affected individual usually will be normal since the mutation will affect one or only a few of the germ cells. Given the nature of germ cell proliferation, it is most probable that a mutation will occur at one of the later cell divisions since they are more numerous, but there may be variable numbers of gametes descended from a single mutational event. Since these mutant gametes still are likely to represent a small minority, and since humans have few offspring, the probability of a recurrence of the disorder among the siblings of a new mutation individual is quite low. Sibs with new mutations can occur, and it is now feasible to document these at a molecular level. The presence of the identical mutation in sibs when neither parent has the mutation in somatic cells can occur (see discussions of osteogenesis imperfecta and Duchenne muscular dystrophy in Chaps. 115 and 118). It will be possible to assess the proportion of gonadal mosaicism by molecular analysis of sperm in some cases. Individuals affected with new mutations are able to transmit the disease, and their offspring are at 50 percent risk for the condition.

The proportion of patients with dominant disorders that represent new mutations is inversely proportional to the effect of the disease on biologic fitness. The term *biologic fitness* refers to the ability of an affected individual to produce children who survive to adult life and reproduce. In the extreme case, if a dominant mutation produced absolute infertility, then all observed cases would, of necessity, represent new mutations, and it would be impossible to prove the genetic transmission of the trait. Molecular analysis could document such mutations. In less severe disorders, as in tuberous sclerosis, the severe mental retardation reduces biologic fitness to about 20 percent of normal, and the proportion of cases due to new mutations is about 80 percent.[116] In dominant disorders such as familial hypercholesterolemia, in which there is negligible if any reduction in biologic fitness, virtually all affected persons have a family pedigree showing classic vertical transmission (Chap. 48). The incidence of a dominant disorder is dependent on the biologic fitness and on the mutation frequency for the locus, which is widely variable. Although the proportion of cases due to new mutation is directly related to biologic fitness, genetic counseling and reproductive planning now can alter this proportion.

Many new mutations appear to occur in the germ cells of fathers who are of relatively advanced age.[95,117] Such a "paternal age effect" is seen, for example, in Marfan syndrome, in which the average age of fathers of sporadic or "new mutation" cases (37 years) is in excess of the mean age of fathers generally (30 years) and also in excess of the age of fathers who transmit Marfan disease due to an inherited mutation (30 years).[118] The increased mutation rate associated with advanced paternal age may be due to the large number of gene replications required for sperm production over many years. Differences in mutation rates for male and female gametes are discussed further below under X-linked disorders.

Before one concludes that a dominant disorder in a given patient with unaffected parents is the result of a new mutation, it is important to consider two other possibilities: (1) the gene may be carried by one parent, in whom the mutant allele is not penetrant (discussed below), and (2) nonpaternity may have occurred (i.e., the father is someone other than the putative father), since this is found in about 3 to 5 percent of randomly studied children in many cultures.

PENETRANCE AND EXPRESSIVITY. These terms are frequently the subject of confusion and slight variations in usage. In the autosomal dominant medical context, penetrance is the proportion of heterozygotes for a given mutation that present with *any* of the phenotypic features of the disorder induced by the mutation. In the medical context, the concept of penetrance can be usefully distinguished in both a clinical and a molecular way. Penetrance is the question at issue when the apparently unaffected offspring of an affected individual wishes to know the probability that they might still carry the mutant gene and bear an affected offspring. The mutant gene is not penetrant if an individual carrying the mutant gene shows absolutely no phenotypic effects. In molecular terms, the presence or absence of the mutant gene can be determined, and a person without the mutant gene can be distinguished from one carrying the mutant gene with lack of penetrance. In this medical and genetic counseling context, the ability to determine penetrance is dependent on diagnostic methods. For example, a new magnetic resonance imaging technique might demonstrate findings not previously recognizable. In the biologic context, the gene can be considered penetrant if it affects the function of the individual.

Expressivity or variability in clinical expression is a concept which describes the range of phenotypic effects in individuals with a mutant genotype. This variability can include the type and severity of symptoms and also can include variation in the age of onset of symptoms. Variability in clinical expression is illustrated dramatically by the multiple endocrine adenoma-peptic ulcer syndrome.[119] Patients in the same family inheriting the same abnormal gene may have hyperplasia or neoplasia of one or all of a wide variety of endocrine tissues, such as the pancreas, parathyroid glands, pituitary gland, or adipose tissue. The resulting clinical manifestations are extremely diverse; different members of the same family may develop peptic ulcers, hypoglycemia, kidney stones, multiple lipomas of the skin, or bitemporal hemianopsia. Because of this variability, the recognition that each family member suffers from the same genetic abnormality can be difficult. There is evidence that some of the variability in this disorder can be explained by chance second somatic mutations at the locus for the disorder on chromosome 11.[120]

Variation in age of onset is seen in disorders such as Huntington chorea and adult polycystic kidney disease. These disorders often do not become manifest clinically until adult life, even though the mutant gene is present from the time of conception. Consideration of variation in age of onset as one form of variation in expression is somewhat arbitrary. In one sense, it cannot be said finally that the mutant gene was never penetrant in an individual until the individual has had a maximal clinical evaluation, completed life, and died from other causes. Lack of penetrance can be considered as the absolute mildest end of the spectrum of expression such that no phenotypic effects whatsoever are observed. In the clinical context, variation in expression can be distinguished from penetrance as the question at issue when an affected individual wishes to know whether his or her offspring will have mild or severe symptoms if born affected. In molecular terms, analysis of the single gene locus will not answer this (i.e., predict variation in expression within a family) but can determine whether the mutant gene is present and not penetrant. Thus, molecular and biochemical analysis of the monogenic locus can uncover lack of penetrance but cannot predict variability in expression within a family with a dominant disorder. Variability in clinical expression between families may be due to allelic heterogeneity which can be defined by molecular methods.

The factors underlying lack of penetrance and variability in expression are similar and fall into three main categories: (1) the genotype at other loci, (2) exogenous or environmental factors, and (3) stochastic factors. The relevant genes at other loci are sometimes called *modifier genes* and probably play a large role in determining phenotypic expression. Despite their presumed importance, good examples are difficult to cite among dominant disorders, although the genotype at the α-globin locus affecting the sickle cell anemia phenotype[88,89] and the genotype at various loci affecting the monogenic hyperlipidemias (see Chap. 47) are examples of effects by modifier genes. The phenotypes in monogenic hyperlipidemias, the porphyrias, and hemochromatosis are affected by diet, alcohol use, smoking, and exercise; these are examples of the impact of environmental and exogenous factors. Stochastic factors are important in at least some instances as exemplified by the severity and distribution of lesions among identical twins with disorders such as retinoblastoma, neurofibromatosis, or tuberous sclerosis. Differences in phenotypic expression due to variable X inactivation among identical twin females heterozygous for an X-linked disorder represent another example of a stochastic effect. Although the issues of penetrance and expressivity are most easily discussed in the context of autosomal dominant disorders, these principles are relevant to chromosomal disorders, autosomal recessive disorders, X-linked disorders, and multifactorial disorders as well.

BIOCHEMICAL BASIS OF DOMINANT TRAITS. Historically, the biochemical bases for recessive disorders were frequently identified as enzyme deficiencies, while the biochemical defects for dominant disorders remained enigmatic. Subsequently, this has changed as the biochemical defects for disorders such as familial hypercholesterolemia, amyloidosis, hereditary spherocytosis, osteogenesis imperfecta, and hereditary retinoblastoma are being determined. A number of mechanisms can account for an abnormal phenotype in the presence of one normal gene and one mutant gene. One mechanism is simply that a half-normal level of gene product is insufficient to maintain a normal phenotype. This is likely to be true when the gene product is a major determinant of the metabolic phenotype in a complex network,[114] such as membrane receptors and rate limiting enzymes in biosynthetic pathways under feedback control (e.g., familial hypercholesterolemia and dominant porphyrias, Chaps. 48 and 52). Another mechanism involves abnormalities of structural proteins where a complex network of direct protein interactions is involved (e.g., collagens in osteogenesis imperfecta and erythrocyte cytoskeleton proteins in spherocytosis and elliptocytosis, Chaps. 95 and 115). Dominant negative mutations are instances where the molecules of mutant gene product interfere with the function of the molecules of normal gene product.[115] Although specific human examples are not well identified, this mechanism may occur for some collagen abnormalities (Chap. 115). In transgenic mice, as little as 10 percent gene expression of a mutant collagen gene can disrupt normal collagen function.[121] Another mechanism for dominant phenotypic effects results when heterozygous defects become homozygous at a single cell level owing to second somatic mutations (e.g., hereditary retinoblastoma, Chap. 9). These defects may be considered dominant at pedigree level and recessive at the single cell level. Conceptually, it is useful to distinguish dominant mutations which generate a product with a new biologic property creating a harmful effect (e.g., amyloidosis, Chap. 97) from those which merely represent a deficiency of normal gene product (e.g., familial hypercholesterolemia and porphyrias, Chaps. 48 and 52). In the former group, restoration of a normal level of gene product would not negate the effect of the mutant gene.

Autosomal Recessive Disorders. Autosomal recessive conditions are those that are clinically apparent only in the homozygous or compound heterozygous state, i.e., when both alleles at a particular genetic locus are mutant alleles. By definition, the gene responsible for an autosomal recessive disorder must be located on one of the 22 autosomes; thus, both males and females can be affected.

Figure 1-14 shows two pedigrees for families with an autosomal recessive trait. Monoplex families (pedigree A) are the most common, but families with multiple affected individuals occur, and the following features are characteristic: (1) the parents are clinically normal; (2) only sibs are affected, and vertical transmission does not occur; and (3) males and females are affected in equal proportions.

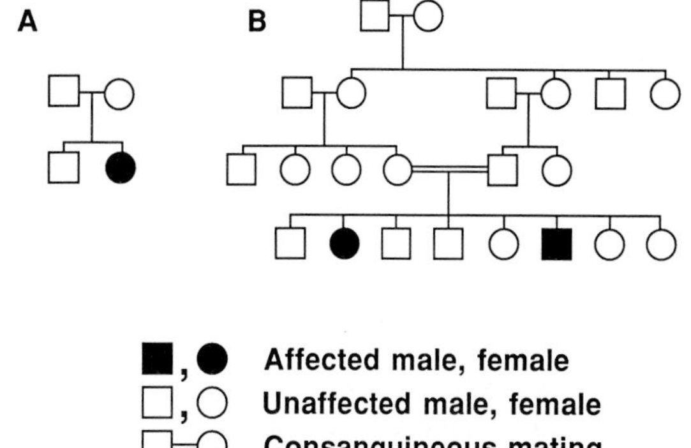

Fig. 1-14 Pedigree pattern for an autosomal recessive trait. Note the *horizontal* pattern of inheritance and consanguinity in the multiplex pedigree *(B)* in comparison to the more common monoplex pedigree *(A)*.

CHARACTERISTICS OF AUTOSOMAL RECESSIVE TRAITS. The relative infrequency of recessive genes in the population and the requirement for two abnormal genes for clinical expression combine to create special conditions for autosomal recessive inheritance: (1) the less frequent the mutant gene in the population, the stronger the likelihood that affected individuals are the product of consanguineous matings (see "Consanguinity," below); (2) if both parents are carriers for the same autosomal recessive gene, the probability for disease is 0.25, for a heterozygote (carrier) is 0.50, and for a noncarrier normal is 0.25; (3) if an affected individual mates with a heterozygote (as may occur with a common mutant gene or a consanguineous marriage), there is a 50 percent probability of disease for each child, and a pedigree simulating dominant inheritance will result; and (4) if two individuals with the same recessive disease mate, all their children will be affected.

The clinical picture in autosomal recessive disorders tends to be more uniform than that of dominant diseases, and onset often occurs early in life. As a general rule, recessive disorders are more commonly diagnosed in children, while dominant diseases have a trimodal age of symptomatology and are more frequently encountered in adults.[90]

In recessive inheritance the probability is that only one in four children in a sibship will be affected; hence, multiple cases in a family may not occur. This is especially true in a society in which small families are common. Consider, for example, 16 families in which both parents are heterozygous for the same recessive disorder, such as cystic fibrosis. If each family has 2 children, the probability is that 9 of the 16 families will have no affected children, 6 will have 1 affected and 1 normal child, and only 1 of the 16 families will have 2 affected children. Because of the tendency toward small families in many contemporary societies, physicians usually see sporadic or isolated cases of a recessive disease without an affected sib to alert them to the possibility of a genetic disorder. Fortunately, because of the relatively uniform clinical picture of recessive disorders and because many can be diagnosed directly by biochemical tests, the diagnosis of a genetic disease can usually be made even when no other members of a family are clinically affected.

BIOCHEMICAL DEFECTS. Basic biochemical lesions underlying many autosomal recessive disorders have been identified. Mutations that give rise to recessive diseases often involve enzymatic proteins, as opposed to nonenzymatic proteins. In these conditions, recessive inheritance occurs because a mutation that destroys the catalytic activity of an enzyme generally does not impair the health of a heterozygote (i.e., an individual who has one mutant allele specifying a functionless enzyme and one normal allele on the partner chromosome specifying a normal enzyme). In this situation, each cell in the body usually produces about 50 percent of the normal number of active enzyme molecules. However, normal regulatory mechanisms function to avert any clinical consequences of this 50 percent deficiency, and so heterozygotes for enzyme defects usually are clinically normal.[122] Frequently such compensation involves nothing more complicated than a simple two- to threefold increase in the substrate concentration for the enzyme. The concentration of a substrate is usually maintained at a point below saturation for the enzyme that metabolizes it. When the enzyme level is reduced 50 percent, as in a heterozygote for a functionless gene at that locus, the residual 50 percent of enzyme molecules can be made to function twice as fast as normal, simply by allowing the substrate concentration to increase twofold. If the twofold increase in substrate does not otherwise affect metabolism adversely, the heterozygote is clinically normal. On the other hand, when an individual inherits functionless alleles at both loci specifying an enzyme, the reduction in enzyme activity is too great for a compensatory mechanism to overcome the deficiency, and a disease results.

The genetic enzyme deficiencies that produce recessive diseases tend to involve enzymes that participate in catabolic pathways. Frequently these enzymes degrade organic molecules that are ingested in the diet, such as galactose (galactosemia), phenylalanine (PKU), and phytanic acid (Refsum syndrome). A special class of such catabolic diseases is one in which the deficiency affects an acid hydrolase that occurs within lysosomes. In these *lysosomal storage disorders,*[123–125] the substrate, usually a complex lipid or polysaccharide, accumulates within swollen lysosomes in specific organs, giving the cells a foamy appearance. Examples of such lysosomal diseases include the mucopolysaccharidoses such as Hurler syndrome (α-iduronidase deficiency) and the sphingolipidoses such as Gaucher disease (glucocerebrosidase deficiency).

POPULATION GENETICS. In general, recessive diseases are rare because the reduced biologic fitness of homozygotes acts to remove the mutant gene from the population. A few lethal recessive disorders, such as cystic fibrosis and sickle-cell anemia, are common. To explain this paradox, it has been postulated that the biologic fitness of heterozygotes is greater than that of noncarriers for these genes. In such a case, the frequency of the gene in the population depends on the balance between the increased fitness of the relatively numerous heterozygotes and the reduced fitness of the less common homozygotes. A small selective advantage of the heterozygote over the normal person results in a high gene frequency and hence a high birth frequency of homozygotes even when the disease is lethal.[126] Thus, about 1 in 20 to 25 Caucasians is heterozygous (a carrier) for the genetically lethal disease cystic fibrosis, and the disease occurs in about 1 in 2500 Caucasian births. In order to maintain such a high gene frequency, heterozygotes for cystic fibrosis may have a selective advantage over noncarriers, but the nature of such a potential advantage is unknown. A selective advantage for the mutant gene might involve the viability of heterozygotes for a reproductive advantage. There could be a slight meiotic drive, i.e., gametes carrying the mutant gene could have a slightly greater probability of achieving fertilization compared to gametes with the normal gene.[127] It has been argued that disorders might achieve a frequency as high as that seen with cystic fibrosis occasionally without a selective advantage, i.e., by chance. There is evidence from linkage disequilibrium that most or all cystic fibrosis genes are descended from a single mutational event,[128] but this does not resolve why the mutant gene is so frequent. In sickle-cell anemia, another recessive disorder with high frequency among certain populations, heterozygotes are known to have increased resistance to malaria (Chap. 93).

CONSANGUINITY. By definition, a recessive disease requires the inheritance of a mutant allele at the same genetic locus from each parent. When the genes are rare, the likelihood of any two parents being carriers for the same defect is small. If the parents have a common ancestor who carried a recessive gene, then the likelihood that two of the descendants would each have inherited the gene becomes relatively great. The less frequent the recessive gene, the stronger becomes the likelihood that an affected individual may have resulted from such a consanguineous mating. On the other hand, certain recessive genes are so common in the population that the likelihood of two random parents being carriers is great enough to minimize the role of consanguinity. For common traits such as sickle-cell anemia, PKU, cystic fibrosis, and Tay-Sachs disease, all of which have a high carrier frequency in certain populations, consanguinity is usually not present in the parents.

NEW MUTATION. Although new mutations for recessive disorders occur, they rarely can be identified in a clinical setting. This is because a new mutation usually will generate only an asymptomatic heterozygote. Only generations later will the descendants of that mutation be involved in a mating where both parents are heterozygotes. In addition, the selective pressure to eliminate deleterious recessive traits from the population is less because these traits are easily passed on in heterozygous form. A large portion of recessive disease is due to mutations that occurred many, many generations ago; this is becoming clear from studies of phenylketonuria, β thalassemia, and cystic fibrosis (see Chaps. 15, 93, and 108).

X-Linked Disorders. The genes responsible for X-linked disorders are located on the X chromosome; therefore, the clinical risk and severity of the disease are different for the two sexes. Since a female has two X chromosomes, she may be either heterozygous or homozygous for a mutant gene, and the trait may therefore demonstrate either recessive or dominant expression. Expression in females is often variable and heavily influenced by random X inactivation. Males, on the other hand, have only one X chromosome, so they can be expected to display the full syndrome whenever they inherit the gene regardless of whether the gene produces a recessive or dominant trait in the female. Thus, the terms *X-linked dominant* and *X-linked recessive* refer only to the expression of the gene in women.

The distinction of dominant and recessive X-linked disorders is complicated by the effect of X inactivation. This has led to some arbitrary and inconsistent assignments. Ornithine transcarbamylase deficiency (Chap. 20) has often been described as an X-linked dominant, while Fabry disease (Chap. 70) has often been described as an X-linked recessive. Phenotypic abnormalities occur relatively frequently in heterozygotes for either disorder, particularly if the heterozygotes are examined in an informed manner. Since there is no clear convention, it may be best to consider such disorders as simply X-linked without a dominant or recessive designation. The recessive or dominant descriptors are more useful for X-linked disorders where, respectively, heterozygotes are quite consistently asymptomatic (e.g., X-linked recessive Hunter disease, Chap. 61) or are quite consistently symptomatic in a manner similar to hemizygous males (e.g., X-linked dominant hypophosphatemic rickets, Chap. 105).

An important feature of all X-linked inheritance is the absence of male-to-male (i.e., father-to-son) transmission of the trait. This follows because a male must always contribute his Y chromosome to his sons; hence, he can never contribute his X chromosome. On the other hand, a male contributes his sole X chromosome to all his daughters, and so all daughters of a male with an X-linked trait must inherit the mutant gene.

X-LINKED PEDIGREES. The pedigrees in Fig. 1-15 illustrate some of the characteristic features of X-linked inheritance. (1) In contrast to the vertical distribution in dominant traits (parents and children affected) and the horizontal distribution in autosomal recessive traits (sibs affected), the pedigree pattern in X-linked recessive traits tends to be oblique; that is, the trait occurs in the maternal uncles of affected males and in male cousins who are descended from the mother's sisters who are carriers (Fig. 1-15*A*). (2) Male offspring of carrier females have a 50 percent chance of being affected. (3) All female offspring of affected males are carriers, and affected males do not transmit the disease to their sons. (4) Unaffected males do not transmit the trait to any offspring. (5) Affected homozygous females occur only when an affected male fathers the child of a carrier female.

Examples of X-linked recessive disorders in humans include the Lesch-Nyhan syndrome, glucose-6-phosphate dehydrogenase deficiency, testicular feminization, and Hunter mucopolysaccharidosis. Color blindness is also inherited as an X-linked recessive trait, but it is sufficiently frequent (occurring in about 8 percent of Caucasian males) that the occurrence of homozygous color-blind females is no rarity.

A pedigree for an X-linked disorder with variable symptomatology in females is depicted in Fig. 1-15*B*. Heterozygous females with and without symptoms occur in the same family. X-linked diseases may occur on the basis of new mutation as shown by the pedigree in Fig. 1-15*C* (see "New Mutation and Heterozygote Detection," below).

Fig. 1-15 Pedigree pattern for an X-linked trait. *A*. Note the oblique pattern of inheritance. *B*. Note the occurrence of symptomatic and asymptomatic heterozygous females in the same pedigree. Heterozygotes are consistently asymptomatic in some disorders (recessive) and are variably symptomatic in other disorders (see text). *C*. New mutations can give rise to affected males and can give rise to heterozygous females.

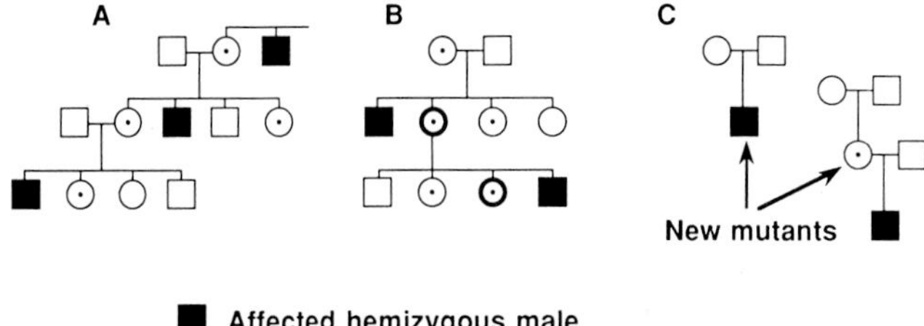

■ Affected hemizygous male
⊙ Asymptomatic heterozygous female
⊙ Symptomatic heterozygous female
□ Unaffected male
○ Noncarrier female

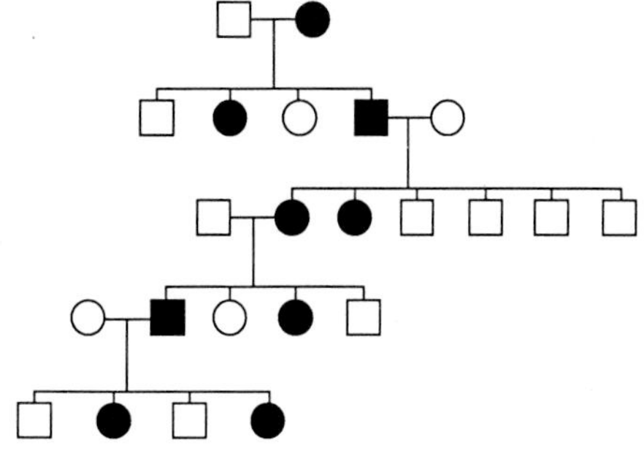

■ Affected hemizygous male
● Affected heterozygous female
□, ○ Unaffected male, female

Fig. 1-16 Pedigree pattern of an X-linked dominant trait.

X-linked dominant inheritance is illustrated by the pedigree in Fig. 1-16. Its characteristic features are as follows: (1) females are affected about twice as often as males; (2) an affected female has a 50 percent probability of transmitting the disorder to her sons or daughters; (3) an affected male transmits the disorder to all his daughters and to none of his sons; and (4) the syndrome may be more variable and less severe in heterozygous affected females than in hemizygous affected males. One common trait, the Xg(a+) blood group, is inherited as an X-linked dominant trait, as are a few diseases, such as hypophosphatemic rickets.

Some rare conditions may be inherited as X-linked dominant traits in which there is lethality in the hemizygous male. The characteristics of this form of inheritance are illustrated by the pedigree in Fig. 1-17. (1) The disorder occurs only in females who are heterozygous for the mutant gene; (2) an affected mother has a 50 percent probability of transmitting the trait to her daughters; (3) an increased frequency of abortions occurs in affected women, the abortions representing affected male fetuses. An example of a condition that is transmitted by this mode of inheritance is incontinentia pigmenti.

X-LINKED DISORDERS AND X INACTIVATION. Understanding of the mechanisms of expression of X-linked traits in females has been greatly advanced by knowledge of the phenomenon of random X inactivation, or the so-called Lyon effect.[129] Early in embryonic development, one of the two X chromosomes in each somatic cell of a female is irreversibly inactivated. The inactivation process is random, so that for each cell there is an equal probability that the paternally or maternally derived X chromosome will be inactivated. The inactivated X chromosome is rendered permanently nonfunctional, so that all progeny of the initial cell inherit the same active and inactive X chromosomes. Thus, each female is a mosaic; on the average, half of her cells express the X chromosome of the father, and half express the X chromosome of the mother. If a mutation in a gene is carried on one of her X chromosomes, about one-half of the cells in each tissue will be normal and the other half will manifest the mutant phenotype. Chance or preferential survival of one clone of cells may disturb these proportions in any given individual. Depending on the proportions of mutant and normal X chromosomes that are active in each tissue, a genetically heterozygous female may be clinically normal or she may have mild or severe manifestations of the disease.

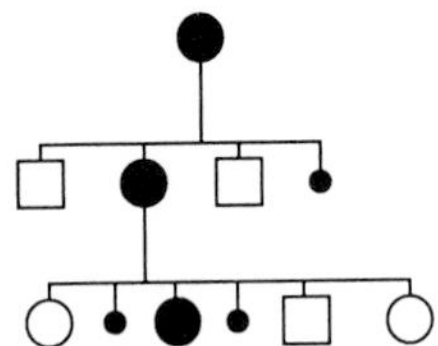

Fig. 1-17 Pedigree pattern of an X-linked dominant trait lethal in the hemizygous male.

In each female cell the nonfunctional X chromosome can be identified as a condensed clump of chromatin—the Barr body. The inactive X chromosome is late replicating, and its DNA is more highly methylated. Methylation of DNA is thought to play a role in maintenance of X inactivation.[130]

Random X inactivation appears to be the single most important determinant of expression in females for many X-linked disorders. There can be a wide range of expression in females with many individuals being asymptomatic, while other individuals have only mild symptoms, and other individuals have very severe symptoms. The recognized frequency of detectable phenotypic alterations in the heterozygote depends on how carefully the women are examined and in some instances on the age at examination. Ornithine transcarbamylase deficiency represents an excellent example of a highly variable phenotype in heterozygotes. Many heterozygous females are asymptomatic, some have minimal protein intolerance, and others experience intermittent episodes of hyperammonemic coma with numerous examples of fatal outcome. For many of these disorders, the hemizygous males are more consistently and more seriously symptomatic than are heterozygous females. Other examples where clinical expression occurs only occasionally in females include Duchenne muscular dystrophy and hemophilia A, while symptoms occur with higher frequency in Fabry disease. As discussed above, it may be easier to describe these as X-linked disorders without applying the dominant or recessive descriptor since the literature has been inconsistent.

NEW MUTATION AND HETEROZYGOTE DETECTION. New mutation in X-linked genes is a particularly important problem in families ascertained because of an isolated affected male (monoplex families). In these families, the mother may be a noncarrier and may have contributed an egg with a new mutation. The father cannot contribute the new mutation, since he contributes a Y chromosome. Alternatively, the mother may be a carrier and may have herself been conceived from a gamete with a new mutation from either her father or her mother. If the new mutation rate for male gametes is greater than for female gametes, as seems likely in some instances, then a larger fraction of mothers of isolated male patients will be carriers. This is because male gametes carrying a new mutation can only give rise to carriers and cannot be contributed to a male offspring. If the mutation rates for male and female gametes are identical, approximately two-thirds of mothers of isolated male patients are expected to be carriers. This proportion increases, if the mutation rate for male gametes exceeds that for female gametes. There is evidence of advanced paternal age in the maternal grandfathers of isolated male patients of some X-linked disorders such as hemophilia A.[131]

Detection of heterozygous females can sometimes be achieved using biochemical methods. These methods have varying degrees of accuracy and are useful in Lesch-Nyhan syndrome, Fabry disease, Hunter syndrome, hemophilia A, hemophilia B, ornithine transcarbamylase deficiency, and Duchenne muscular dystrophy. These biochemical methods are seldom completely accurate because random X inactivation may lead to a relatively normal biochemical result. Accuracy can be increased to some extent by sampling relatively clonal cell sources such as hair roots or cloned skin fibroblasts. Molecular methods can circumvent some of the problems of biochemical analysis of the gene product, particularly when the mutation can be detected directly. Detection of gene deletions or of mutations which alter restriction enzyme sites is very powerful in this regard. RFLP analysis without direct detection of the mutation generally will indicate whether descendants of carriers are themselves carriers or not but generally will not determine whether antecedent individuals in the pedigree are carriers or not (see "Molecular Techniques for Clinical Diagnosis," below). For Duchenne muscular dystrophy, molecular techniques currently allow for detection of gene deletions in the majority of families, making this the preferred method for prenatal diagnosis and carrier detection when informative.[45]

GENETIC HETEROGENEITY

Genetic heterogeneity may result from the existence of a series of different mutations at a single locus *(allelic heterogeneity)* or from mutations at different genetic loci *(nonallelic heterogeneity)*. For example, phenotypes such as Charcot-Marie-Tooth neurogenic atrophy, congenital sensorineural deafness, and retinitis pigmentosa all have autosomal dominant, autosomal recessive, and X-linked forms (nonallelic heterogeneity). A clinically similar bleeding disorder can be caused by mutations at either of two loci on the X chromosome, one leading to a deficiency of factor VIII (classic hemophilia, hemophilia A) and the other causing a deficiency of factor IX (Christmas disease, hemophilia B). That both allelic and nonallelic heterogeneity may underlie a clinical phenotype is exemplified by the syndrome of hereditary methemoglobinemia, which was once regarded as a homogeneous clinical entity. The disorder is the result of at least 10 different mutations occurring at three distinct gene loci: two at the locus coding for the α chain of hemoglobin, three at the locus coding for the β chain of hemoglobin, and at least five at the NADH dehydrogenase locus (Chaps. 92 and 93). It is likely that most, if not all, hereditary diseases, when carefully analyzed, will be shown to be genetically heterogeneous.[132,133]

The extent of allelic heterogeneity is particularly impressive and is being rapidly defined at a molecular level. As discussed in the section on mutations above, hundreds of different mutations (hemoglobinopathy and thalassemia) have been described at the β-globin locus, and similar molecular heterogeneity may exist at many if not most loci. Numerous different mutations have been delineated for the low density lipoprotein receptor (Chap. 48) and for phenylalanine hydroxylase (Chap. 15). Considerable clinical heterogeneity can be explained by the occurrence of different mutations at a single locus. With detailed molecular information, it becomes clear that many, if not most, patients with autosomal recessive disorders are in fact compound heterozygotes rather than true homozygotes in the strict sense. Compound heterozygotes have different mutations in the two abnormal genes as exemplified by an individual with SC hemoglobinopathy. Exceptions to this generalization would be when a patient is the product of a consanguineous mating or when a particular mutant allele achieves a high frequency in the population, e.g., sickle-cell anemia.

The extent of clinical heterogeneity that can occur secondary to allelic heterogeneity is particularly impressive for autosomal recessive disorders. For example, Hurler mucopolysaccharidosis and Scheie mucopolysaccharidosis were judged to be different genetic conditions based on the severe, lethal phenotype in Hurler disease compared with the much milder phenotype of bone and joint disease in Scheie disease (Chap. 61). These conditions were ultimately found both to be due to deficiency of L-iduronidase. Description of presumed Hurler-Scheie compound heterozygotes based on the existence of intermediate phenotypes served to emphasize the phenomenon of compound heterozygotes in the 1970s. Similarly the severe Duchenne muscular dystrophy and milder Becker muscular dystrophy are now known to be allelic disorders, both of which, surprisingly, can be caused by sizable gene deletions. Numerous other examples of widely different clinical phenotypes due to allelic heterogeneity are found throughout this text. In many instances there is a classic phenotype in which no functional gene product is produced. Many different alleles (presumably all those which encode no functional gene product) may cause this most severe phenotype. There is frequently a continuum of milder expression arising from mutations which do not totally eliminate the functional gene product. The complexity of the clinical continuum is contributed to by the occurrence of compound heterozygotes. At the mild end of the continuum are those mutant alleles which encode a product which leads to a nearly normal clinical phenotype or to one which is normal under most environmental circumstances. This continuum then extends into detectable biochemical variation which is ordinarily not associated with clinical effect. Hyperphenylalaninemia of mild degree (Chap. 15), mild ("benign") methylmalonic acidemia,[134] and Hartnup disorder (Chap. 101) are examples of this mild biochemical phenotype. Obviously the amount of functional gene product required to prevent clinical symptoms is dependent on other genetic factors and on exogenous factors such as diet and catabolic events. An individual with benign methylmalonic acidemia must be considered to be at greater risk than other individuals in the face of major catabolic episodes so that the benign designation is merely conditional. The individual with Hartnup disorder is at some risk for a "pellagra" complication, and even that risk can be anticipated (Chap. 101). This type of genetic heterogeneity forms one part of the border between monogenic disorders and multifactorial diseases.

MULTIFACTORIAL GENETIC DISEASES

The common chronic diseases of adults (such as essential hypertension, gout, coronary heart disease, diabetes mellitus, peptic ulcer disease, and schizophrenia), as well as the common birth defects (such as cleft lip and palate, spina bifida, and congenital heart disease), have long been known to "run in families." These disorders are described as *multifactorial genetic diseases*. It is useful to distinguish first, however, the existence of heterogeneity within the etiology for these disorders. For cleft lip and palate, some cases are due to single gene defects, some cases are due to chromosome abnormalities, and the majority of cases appear to be due to multiple genetic and environmental factors. The implication is that multiple factors enter into the etiology of a *single case* in the majority of circumstances. Similarly the etiology of coronary artery disease can be considered to be heterogeneous with a small proportion due primarily to single gene defects (e.g., familial hypercholesterolemia) while the majority of cases are multifactorial (i.e., multiple factors contribute to the etiology of individual cases). Multifactorial etiology implies the interaction of multiple genes with multiple environmental factors in the etiology of individual cases to produce familial aggregation without a simple Mendelian pattern.[135,136]

In the multifactorial genetic diseases, there are *constitutional (polygenic) components* consisting of multiple genes at independent loci whose effects interact in a cumulative fashion. An individual who inherits a particular combination of these genes has a relative risk which may combine with an *environmental component* to cross a "threshold" of biologic significance such that an individual is affected with a multifactorial disease.[135,136] In order for another individual in the same family to express the same syndrome, a similar combination of genes must be inherited. Since sibs share half of their genes, the probability of a sib inheriting the same combination of genes is $(\frac{1}{2})^n$, where n is the number of genes required to express the trait (assuming that none of the genes is linked).

Inasmuch as the precise number of genes responsible for polygenic traits is unknown, the risk of inheritance for a relative of an affected individual is difficult to calculate, and the standard is based on empiric risk figures (i.e., a direct tally of the proportion of affected relatives in previously reported families). In contrast to the monogenic disorders, in which 25 or 50 percent of the first-degree relatives of an affected proband are at genetic risk, multifactorial genetic disorders are generally observed empirically to affect no more than 5 to 10 percent of first-degree relatives. Moreover, in contrast to Mendelian traits, the recurrence risk of multifactorial conditions varies from family to family, and its estimation is significantly influenced by two factors: (1) the number of affected persons already present in the family, and (2) the severity of the disorder in the index case. The greater number of affected relatives and the more severe their disease, the higher the risk to other relatives. For example, the risk of cleft lip in the sibs of a child with unilateral cleft lip is about 2.5 percent, but if the lesion in the index case is bilateral, the risk in the sibs rises to 6 percent.[135,136]

Multifactorial etiology is thought to be important for many diseases which occur beyond adolescence, and diseases with later age of onset may have decreased heritability on average.[137] Review of nine multifactorial diseases provided evidence compatible with a decline in the impact of the genes on disease with increasing age.

The hypothesis of a polygenic component in the inheritance of multifactorial diseases has been given a sound basis in recent years by the demonstration that at least 28 percent of all gene loci harbor polymorphic alleles that vary among individuals (discussed above). Such a large degree of variation in normal genes undoubtedly provides the substrate for variations in genetic predisposition with which environmental factors can interact. So far, the genetic loci most strikingly associated with predisposition to specific diseases are those that constitute the major histocompatibility locus or HLA (human leukocyte antigens) system (Chap. 4). The HLA gene complex is located on the short arm of chromosome 6. It consists of multiple closely linked but distinct loci (A, B, DR, DQ, and DP). The products of these genes are proteins that are found on the surface of body cells and that enable an individual's immune system to distinguish its own cells from those of someone else. Each HLA locus in the population consists of multiple alleles, each of which produces an immunologically distinct protein. For example, an individual may inherit any 2 of 36 alleles at the HLA-B locus. The inheritance of certain alleles predisposes to the development of certain diseases when the individual is exposed to an environmental challenge. For a more detailed discussion of the HLA locus and its role in disease suceptibility, the reader is referred to Chap. 4.

Multifactorial disorders are heterogeneous in etiology in the sense that the relative contribution of the polygenic factors ("risk genes") and environmental factors will vary greatly from patient to patient. As discussed above, among common phenotypes which are largely multifactorial, a small proportion of cases may be due to monogenic or chromosomal abnormalities. For example, although coronary heart disease is usually of multifactorial etiology, about 5 percent of subjects with premature myocardial infarctions are heterozygotes for familial hypercholesterolemia, a single-gene disorder that produces atherosclerosis in the absence of an extraordinary environmental factor (Chap. 48). However, even in a single gene disorder such as familial hypercholesterolemia, other loci (e.g., the genes for apolipoprotein B and apolipoprotein E) could easily influence the phenotype, and nongenetic factors (diet and smoking) certainly modify the risk. The complexity of the etiology for coronary artery disease is detailed in part in Table 1-5. Numerous interrelated biochemical and genetic factors, as well as numerous nongenetic factors, affect the risk. An appreciation of this etiologic heterogeneity and careful investigation of each patient are necessary prerequisites for counseling families at risk for these disorders.

INTERACTION BETWEEN SINGLE GENETIC AND ENVIRONMENTAL FACTORS

In addition to polygenic states, many single-gene mutations are known to create abnormal responses to environmental factors. Some of the best examples of this interaction between genes and environmental factors are those monogenic disorders which produce clinically significant and often life-threatening idiosyncratic responses to drugs.

Table 1-5 Risk Factors for Atherosclerosis and Coronary Artery Disease

LDL receptor genotype	Aging
Apolipoprotein E genotype	Male sex
Familial hypertriglyceridemia	Smoking
Familial combined hyperlipidemia	Hypertension
Lipoprotein Lp(a)	Obesity
Apolipoprotein RFLP associations?	Diet
Rarer gene disorders	Diabetes mellitus
Increased LDL	Inactivity?
Decreased HDL	Stress?

NOTE: See Chapters 10, 44 to 51, 64, and 70 for discussion of various genetic risk factors.

Table 1-6 lists the most important of these *pharmacogenetic* disorders, which encompass all three of the Mendelian modes of inheritance.[95,138] Perhaps the most common is glucose-6-phosphate dehydrogenase deficiency, an X-linked trait in which a variety of drugs may precipitate a hemolytic anemia (Chap. 91). Plasma pseudocholinesterase deficiency and hepatic transacetylase deficiency are examples of autosomal recessive traits that alter drug catabolism so that when the muscle relaxant suxamethonium or the antituberculous drug isoniazid is administered, apnea or peripheral neuropathy, respectively, may ensue. Malignant hyperthermia is an autosomal dominant trait in which acute hyperpyrexia, muscle rigidity, and hyperkalemic cardiac arrest may be induced by administration of any one of several anesthetic agents. Acute intermittent prophyria is another example of a single-gene disorder that is exacerbated by drugs such as barbiturates (Chap. 52).

Misinterpretation of adverse drug reactions may result in serious harm to patients. In general, all unusual idiosyncratic reactions should be considered to be genetically determined until proven otherwise. Fortunately, the pharmacogenetic disorders are a group of diseases for which therapy is straightforward: avoidance of the noxious drug by the patient and relatives.

In addition to drugs, other factors in the environment may aggravate specific genetic traits. Cigarette smoke may have deleterious effects on persons homozygous (and possibly heterozygous) for α_1-antitrypsin deficiency, who are predisposed to the development of emphysema (Chap. 96). Patients with xeroderma pigmentosum are unusually sensitive to sunlight and high temperatures (Chap. 120). Avoidance of milk at an early age prevents many of the complications ordinarily seen in persons with galactosemia (Chap. 13). Unfortunately a modern society is also subjected to an endless array of novel environmental exposures. The recent widespread utilization of aspartame is an example of a special risk for PKU patients (Chap. 15).

Genetic-environmental interactions are particularly important in pregnancy. Women who are affected with PKU may develop high plasma phenylalanine levels during pregnancy, and thus their offspring may suffer from phenylalanine-induced birth defects even though the offspring may not themselves have PKU (Chap. 15). Other examples of diseases resulting from an adverse genetic relation between the mother and fetus include erythroblastosis caused by Rh incompatibility and diabetic embryopathy, a series of major birth defects occurring in about 5 percent of the offspring of women who are clinially diabetic during pregnancy.

PATHOGENESIS OF GENETIC DISEASES

Every genetic disease results from a primary alteration in DNA structure. This DNA change leads to the production of an abnormal mRNA or to a change in the amount of normal mRNA. The alteration in mRNA produces a disturbance in the amount of protein or in protein structure and function. This disturbance in turn leads to a disruption of cell and organ function. Three general mechanisms of pathogenesis can be distinguished: (1) Proteins may have a relatively direct effect on a biologic system, often by affecting functionally related proteins. (2) Proteins may affect the metabolism of other molecules (often small metabolites) which are intermediates in the

Table 1-6 Examples of Pharmacogenetic Disorders

Disorder	*Abnormal protein*	*Mode of inheritance*	*Frequency*	*Drugs producing the abnormal response*	*Clinical effect*
Slow inactivation of isoniazid	Isoniazid acetylase in liver	Autosomal recessive	Approximately 50% of U.S. population	Isoniazid, sulfamethazine, sulfamaprine, phenelzine, dapsone, hydralazine, procainamide	Polyneuritis (isoniazid); lupuslike reaction (hydralazine)
Suxamethonium sensitivity or atypical pseudocholinesterase	Pseudocholinesterase in plasma	Autosomal recessive	Several mutant alleles; most common allele occurs 1 in 2500	Suxamethonium or succinylcholine	Apnea
Warfarin resistance	? Altered receptor or enzyme in liver with increased affinity for vitamin K	Autosomal dominant	Rare	Warfarin (coumadin)	Inability to achieve anticoagulation with usual doses of drug
Glucose-6-phosphate dehydrogenase deficiency	Glucose-6-phosphate dehydrogenase in erythrocytes	X-linked recessive	Approximately 100 million affected in world; occurs in high frequency where malaria is endemic; multiple alleles	Analgesics, sulfonamides, antimalarials, nitrofurantoin, other drugs	Hemolysis
Malignant hyperthermia	Unknown	Autosomal dominant	Approximately 1 in 20,000	Various anesthetics, especially halothane	Severe hyperpyrexia, muscle rigidity, death
		Drug-sensitive hemoglobins			
Hemoglobin Zurich	Arginine substitution chain histidine at the 63d position of the β of hemoglobin	Autosomal dominant	Rare	Sulfonamides	Hemolysis
Hemoglobin H	Hemoglobin composed of four β chains; α chains missing	Autosomal dominant	Rare	Many different drugs	Hemolysis

SOURCE: Data modified from Vesell.[138]

pathogenesis. (3) Proteins may regulate the expression of other genes. These conceptual separations may not always be complete. In addition there is great heterogeneity in the exact nature of the structural and functional abnormalities of individual proteins. Some examples of mechanisms of pathogenesis are listed in Table 1-7.

Proteins with Direct Actions

Even in instances where the pathogenesis involves a direct action of the protein, proteins are interacting in complex systems, and there will be secondary effects on other molecules. Disorders of globin chains may lead to direct effects on the ability to transport oxygen, as in the case of certain hemoglobinopathies, or may lead to abnormalities of red cell maturation or stability, as occurs in the thalassemias and in sickle-cell anemia (Chap. 93). Disorders of the plasma proteins involved in the coagulation system also lead to relatively direct biologic effects, but these proteins do act in a cascade which leads ultimately to a carefully regulated coagulation process (Chaps. 84 to 90). Inherited abnormalities of α_1-antitrypsin cause a series of relatively direct defects which are due in part to hepatic injury secondary to accumulation of abnormal protein in hepatocytes and in part to the lack of action of the protein at peripheral sites such as the lung, but this is an example where understanding of pathogenesis is incomplete (Chap. 96). Abnormalities of the red cell cytoskeleton are thought to have a direct effect on red cell shape and function (Chap. 95). For amyloidosis, the presence of an altered peptide chain leads to extracellular deposition with distortion of architecture within various organs (Chap. 97). Abnormalities of surface proteins are thought to lead directly to the cellular dysfunction in leukocyte adhesion deficiency (Chap. 114). Abnormalities of collagen chains lead to relatively direct effects on extracellular matrix, but clearly there are associated secondary effects involving calcium and bone density in osteogenesis imperfecta (Chap. 115).

Proteins Affecting the Metabolism of Small Molecules

The pathogenesis of the majority of disorders discussed in this book involves secondary effects on metabolism of small molecules. In some instances, the pathogenesis involves *deficiency of products* whose synthesis or transport is impaired. In other instances the pathogenesis involves the harmful *accumulation of metabolites* due to impaired metabolism or transport. The details of pathogenesis are often poorly understood as in phenylketonuria, where it is clear that lowering phenylalanine intake is an effective form of treatment, but the biochemical mechanisms by which phenylalanine accumulation causes mental retardation are incompletely understood (Chap. 15). In the glycogen storage diseases, the phenotypes represent mixed effects of accumulation of excessive and/or abnormal glycogen in the tissues and deficiency of glucose to be derived from glycogen (Chap. 12). For many of the amino acid and organic

Table 1-7 Examples of Pathogenesis of Genetic Disease

Disorder	*Mechanism*	*Chapter*
A. Proteins with relatively direct biologic effects		
1. Globin abnormalities	Altered oxygen transport Alteration of cell shape or viability	93
2. Coagulation factor abnormalities	Increased or decreased coagulation cascade	84–90
3. Spherocytosis	Altered cell shape and membrane stability	95
4. Amyloidosis	Deposition of abnormal peptide in extracellular spaces	97
5. Leukocyte adhesion deficiency	Absence of cell adhesion protein impairs leukocyte motility and attachment	114
6. Osteogenesis imperfecta	Abnormal collagen chains impair extracellular matrix function	115
7. Kartagener syndrome	Alteration of organelle structure	112
B. Proteins affecting the metabolism of other (often small) molecules		
1. Altered flux through metabolic pathways		
a. Phenylketonuria	Accumulation of toxic precursor (catabolic pathway)	15
b. Lysosomal storage diseases	Accumulation of toxic precursor (catabolic pathway)	61–72
c. Thyroxine synthetic defects	Deficiency of product (anabolic pathway)	73
d. Gout with altered PP-ribose-P synthetase	Overproduction of product (anabolic pathway)	37
2. Disordered feedback regulation of synthetic pathways		
a. Acute intermittent porphyria	Overproduction of products owing to decreased synthesis or availability of feedback regulator	52
b. Lesch-Nyhan	Overproduction of products owing to decreased synthesis or availability of feedback regulator	38
c. Familial hypercholesterolemia	Overproduction of products owing to decreased synthesis or availability of feedback regulator	48
3. Disordered transport		
a. Cystinuria	Impaired renal reabsorption	99
b. Glucose-galactose malabsorption	Impaired gastrointestinal absorption	98
c. Cystinosis	Impaired lysosomal transport	107
4. Effects on other proteins		
a. Mucolipidosis II	Abnormal processing of lysosomal enzymes	62
b. Biotinidase deficiency	Deficiency of cofactor for various enzymes	83
C. Proteins regulating the expression of other genes (possible)		
1. XY females	Deficiency of sex-determining factor, ? failure of product to regulate other genes	(Ref. 8)
2. Testicular feminization	? Failure of testosterone receptor to regulate other genes	75

acid disorders, the pathogenesis appears to involve accumulation of substrates and their metabolites secondary to an enzyme deficiency rather than to lack of products of the reactions. This is reflected by the fact that many of these disorders can be treated by restriction of dietary products which feed into the pathway which is blocked. Disorders of vitamin metabolism often have secondary effects on multiple enzymes which function in the amino acid and organic acid pathways.

Other examples of secondary involvement of small molecules include the porphyrias and disorders of bilirubin metabolism, where the toxic effects of accumulated substrates and related metabolites appear to represent a major pathogenic mechanism, although product deficiency may also be important in some porphyrias. Disorders of copper and iron metabolism also appear to involve toxic effects of accumulated metals in some instances, but the details of pathogenesis are often poorly delineated. The lysosomal storage diseases represent a group of disorders where accumulation of various macromolecules is thought to have a detrimental effect on cell and organ function (Chaps. 61 to 72). Again the details of the biochemical mechanisms underlying these cellular disturbances are incompletely understood.

The disorders of hormone synthesis provide a contrast in that these usually involve deficiencies of the products of reactions rather than harmful effects of accumulated substrates (Chaps. 73 to 80). The details of pathogenesis in these instances are largely related to the understanding of the action of the various hormones. This mechanism of pathogenesis lends itself to treatment by replacement of the deficient hormone.

Disorders of membrane transport affect the compartmentation of small molecules (Chaps. 98 to 108). This can lead to gastrointestinal malabsorption, excessive urinary losses, or abnormalities of transport within cells as in the case of cystinosis. The pathogenesis of lipoprotein disorders is complex and variable. Even in instances such as LDL receptor deficiency where considerable information is available, the details of how excessive LDL accumulation leads to increased atherosclerosis are not entirely clear. These mechanisms certainly involve secondary effects on lipoproteins and lipid metabolism.

Regulatory Proteins

Although human mutations have yet to be definitively identified in proteins which regulate other genes, it seems likely that they exist. DNA is the "substrate" for these variant proteins. There are extensive data indicating that trans-acting proteins bind to DNA sequences which are cis to the structural genes, as discussed under "Control of Gene Expression," above. There is ample evidence that many hormone and ligand binding proteins represent regulatory gene products including the glucocorticord receptor, the estrogen receptor, the progesterone receptor, the thyroid hormone receptor (c-*erb*-A), the vitamin D receptor, and the mineralocorticoid receptor.[74,75] Human defects in some of these genes may ultimately prove to represent control gene mutations. In fact, deletion of the sex-determining region of the Y chromosome in XY females may prove to be a good example.[8] There is evidence that the sex-determining region encodes a protein which binds to DNA in a sequence specific manner, and may regulate transcription. Disorders of the androgen receptor (Chap. 75) may prove to represent defects in a protein which regulates transcription.

The Nature of Protein Abnormalities

The pathogenesis of a disease may be influenced by the exact nature of the mutation. A protein may be totally absent, may be produced but have no functional activity, or may be produced and have altered functional properties. In the case of enzymes, residual activity may be associated with decreased affinity for substrates or cofactors. Reduced activity may also result from instability of the protein. In other instances, a reduced amount of normal protein may be synthesized, as in the case of a splicing mutation where a small proportion of mRNA molecules is spliced normally. Often, residual levels of protein function or enzyme activity can be correlated with milder phenotypes, but lack of correlation between in vitro and in vivo activity frequently prevents reliable prognostication based on in vitro results. Proteins may be defective in posttranslational modification as in the case of the Z allele for α_1-antitrypsin deficiency. Many proteins are targeted to mitochondria, lysosomes, other compartments, or the extracellular space, and they may be mutated in ways that affect the targeting mechanisms (Chap. 3). Thus a mutation in the locus for a lysosomal enzyme may lead to no protein production, to production of a protein which never reaches the lysosome, or to production of a protein which reaches the lysosome but is unstable or catalytically impaired. Nonenzymatic proteins may show a variety of defects including an enhanced tendency to aggregation (sickle-cell disease) or defective ligand binding (familial hypercholesterolemia and testicular feminization).

TECHNIQUES FOR STUDYING METABOLIC DISEASES

Originally, inborn errors of metabolism attracted Garrod's attention because of the deficiency of a product (melanin in albinism) or the urinary excretion of an excess amount of a precursor (pentosuria, cystinuria, and alkaptonuria). Identification of the specific metabolite depended on the existence of qualitative chemical tests. This approach is still the basis for the detection of most biochemical genetic defects, although more complex analytic methods have been introduced. The reverse genetics approach is an entirely different strategy which is assuming a prominent role.

Initial Biochemical Clues: Accumulated or Missing Metabolites, Histochemistry, and Clinical Features

The majority of biochemical genetic defects are known today because of initial observations made with simple chemical tests or because a biochemical or medical test which was in widespread use detected unusual results in some individuals. Typical examples would include the detection of abnormal phenylalanine metabolites in PKU, elevated uric acid in Lesch-Nyhan syndrome, and elevated cholesterol in familial hypercholesterolemia. Simple screening procedures such as the ferric chloride test for detection of phenylalanine metabolites, the use of nitrosonaphthol for detection of tryosyl compounds, tests for reducing agents, and the dinitrophenylhydrazine reaction for detection of keto acids were very useful in the past. Screening tests for detection of mucopolysaccharides and the use of nitroprusside for detection of disulfides such as cystine or homocystine remain valuable. Paper chromatography and subsequently thin layer chromatography were used to identify the majority of amino acid disorders known presently. Currently, quantitative analysis of amino acids using ion-exchange chromatography, high performance liquid chromatography (HPLC), or gas chromatography has replaced the semiquantitative methods for analysis of plasma, serum, urine, or cerebrospinal fluid in most metabolic centers. The use of gas chromatography and mass spectroscopy (GC/MS) for detection of organic acids has been applied primarily to the urine for detection of numerous new biochemical genetic disorders (see organic acidemias, Chaps. 27 to 36). Fast atom bombardment has proven particularly useful for analysis of acyl carnitines in the urine (Chap. 33). Analysis of very long chain fatty acids in the plasma has contributed to the recognition of a number of peroxisomal disorders (Chaps. 57 to 60). With the application of each new technology, new classes of disorders are detected. Hence there are separate sections in this text for organic acidemias and for peroxisomal disorders.

Other conditions have been recognized as part of routine medical procedures. The presence of jaundice, excessive bleeding, recurrent infections, muscle weakness, fragile connective tissues, or evidence of hormonal insufficiency may offer broad clues to the underlying biochemical genetic defect. When electrophoretic procedures were adopted, direct detection of protein abnormalities occurred relatively incidentally, as in the case of many hemoglobinopathies, α_1-antitrypsin deficiency, analbuminemia, and adenosine deaminase deficiency. Accumulated metabolites were discovered for many disorders using pathologic and histochemical analyses as exemplified by the detection of glycogen in the glycogen storage diseases, the recognition of various lipids and glycoproteins in many lysosomal storage diseases, the presence of excess iron in hemochromatosis, and the unusual staining properties of tissues in amyloidosis.

In contrast to the examples where phenotypic features may suggest a particular biochemical area, the current level of knowledge frequently does not allow for any anticipation of the biochemical defect which might underlie a phenotype as exemplified by the Lesch-Nyhan syndrome, galactosemia, gyrate atrophy of the retina, and many other disorders. This inability to suspect the biochemical defect in the majority of monogenic disorders presumably will be increasingly circumvented by the reverse genetic approach. Despite the many mechanisms for identifying biochemical defects, the underlying abnormality in the majority of disorders listed in McKusick's *Mendelian Inheritance in Man*[4] remains unknown.

The clinical approach to diagnosis of inborn errors of metabolism relies heavily on a large fund of knowledge on the part of the diagnostician because of the large number of disorders. Some phenotypes are very distinctive (e.g., self-mutilation in Lesch-Nyhan syndrome), and some are very nonspecific (e.g., developmental delay in PKU). Good detection of inborn errors of metabolism relies in part on screening programs but depends primarily on a high index of suspicion and access to expert laboratory services. Detailed strategies for diagnosis and selection of laboratory tests are available.[139]

Direct Analysis of Enzymes and Proteins

When a biochemical pathway is known, chemical identification of an accumulated metabolite frequently leads directly to recognition of the site of the metabolic derangement and to confirmation by direct assay for activity of the suspect enzyme. When the steps in a metabolic pathway are not well understood, full disclosure of the biochemical abnormality frequently has to await the elucidation of the normal pathways of synthesis and degradation of the compound. Indeed, metabolic errors have served as a stimulus and a source of insight for biochemists in defining pathways of normal metabolism, as in the case of the gangliosidoses. In many cases, the accumulation of a metabolite in a patient with an enzyme deficiency provides the first clue to the existence or importance of a pathway.

Diagnosis of an enzymatic defect may be made by direct assay of blood or tissue obtained by biopsy. Direct demonstration of abnormality or deficiency of the gene or gene product is the preferred diagnostic approach. This can frequently be accomplished using blood samples. A particularly useful technique is enzyme assay using white blood cells which are easily isolated from normal and affected individuals. Leukocytes can be used to demonstrate the defect in a variety of disorders, such as maple syrup urine disease, methylmalonic acidemia, some forms of glycogen storage disease, and almost all lysosomal storage diseases. Plasma or serum may be used for many enzyme diagnoses as exemplified by Tay-Sachs disease and biotinidase deficiency. Erythrocytes provide a convenient source of enzyme for analysis as in Lesch-Nyhan syndrome, galactosemia, and deficiencies in many of the enzymes involving glycolytic and oxidative pathways of glucose metabolism. In some instances, cultured skin fibroblasts or cultured lymphoblasts may be the preferred tissue for enzymatic diagnosis or may represent a convenient source of viable cells which can be sent to consultant laboratories. Of course, abnormalities of coagulation and of hemoglobin can be studied using blood samples. In some instances, electrophoretic abnormalities of proteins rather than measurement of enzyme activity provide the diagnosis, as in the case of α_1-antitrypsin deficiency.

Samples from blood and cultured skin fibroblasts are preferred for diagnosis because of the less invasive nature of the sampling process, although tissue biopsy is necessary in some circumstances. Biopsies of liver, intestinal mucosa, muscle, and thyroid may usually be obtained at low risk and can provide critical information in some instances in which such information would have been unobtainable in any other way. In many instances, it is possible to use blood samples for enzymatic assay even though the major pathology involves specialized tissues as in Tay-Sachs disease. An important aspect of the clinical practice of metabolic disease involves the proper selection of diagnostic samples. If diagnosis can be accomplished by DNA analysis as discussed below, any source of DNA such as that from leukocytes can avoid the need for more invasive procedures. This is true for Duchenne muscular dystrophy where gross deletions can be demonstrated by DNA analysis in the majority of patients,[45] thus circumventing any need for muscle biopsy in the diagnosis of many patients.

Cell Culture Studies

The technology of cell culture has been standardized so that it is routine to grow somatic cells in vitro. The most readily cultured cells, skin fibroblasts and Epstein-Barr (EB) virus transformed lymphoblasts, have been exploited widely in the study of human genetic disorders. Single cells can be isolated and cloned. Biochemical studies of varying levels of complexity can be performed on the cells. Important advantages of cultured cells include: (1) the ability to incorporate radioactive precursors, (2) the ability to perform repeated studies without recourse to the patient, and (3) relative ease with which comparative studies can be done on different patients. Radioisotopic precursors can be used to follow the fate of metabolites in pathways. Studies of biosynthesis and posttranslational processing can be accomplished by incorporation of radioactive amino acids into newly synthesized proteins followed by immunoprecipitation and polyacrylamide gel electrophoresis. Such studies have been very valuable for analysis of lysosomal storage diseases (e.g., Tay-Sachs), mitochondrial protein disorders (e.g., ornithine transcarbamylase deficiency), and disorders of cell surface proteins (e.g., familial hypercholesterolemia and leukocyte adhesion deficiency). Hundreds of strains of mutant human fibroblasts and lymphoblasts are available on request from repositories around the world. A very large proportion of all biochemical genetic research conducted during the 1970s and 1980s has used cultured fibroblasts or lymphoblasts as a primary methodology.

The use of cell culture proved essential in the elucidation of the biochemical defects for several metabolic disorders. The underlying defects in the mucopolysaccharidoses were first revealed in the now classic "cross-correction" studies of Neufeld and Fratantoni.[140] These workers found that the medium in which fibroblasts from a patient with the Hurler syndrome had grown was able to correct the defect in the cells from a patient with the Hunter syndrome. This was because the Hurler cells excreted induronate sulfatase, the lysosomal enzyme that was deficient in the Hunter cells. Conversely, the medium from the Hunter cells contained α-iduronidase, which corrected the defect of the Hurler cells. These observations were the first to indicate the nature of the biochemical defects in these two syndromes, viz., in each case a deficiency of a different enzyme involved in mucopolysaccharide catabolism (Chap. 61). Moreover, these experiments provided the first indication that lysosomal enzymes could exchange between cells, a finding that later led to the elucidation of the pathway for receptor-mediated endocytosis of lysosomal enzymes (Chap. 62).

In addition to the mucopolysaccharidoses, the use of cultured cells provided the first clue to the elucidation of the biochemical defects in several other genetic disorders, including familial hypercholesterolemia (Chap. 48), I-cell disease (Chap. 62), and xeroderma pigmentosum (Chap. 120).

The fibroblast culture technique, unfortunately, is not applicable to the study of all inborn errors, since the metabolic activity at fault may not be expressed in the fibroblast. For example, phenylalanine hydroxylase activity is confined to the hepatic parenchymal cell. However, many specialized cell culture systems have proven useful for study of genetic disorders. The gene for chronic granulomatous disease was cloned using a myeloid leukemia cell line (HL-60 cells).[44] The Duchenne muscular dystrophy gene product is expressed in cultured myoblasts.[141] T-cell receptors were cloned using established T-cell lines. The ion channel abnormalities in cystic fibrosis are being studied using primary tracheal epithelial cultures and primary sweat gland cultures (Chap. 108). Many other specialized cell cultures are of use including erythroleukemia cells and hepatoma cell lines. Cultured embryonic stem cells from mice have been used to select mutations in vitro and then generate a mouse from these mutant cells.[142,143] Hypoxanthine-guanine phosphoribosyltransferase (HPRT)-deficient mice have been obtained in this manner.

With the techniques of molecular biology, it is possible to analyze genomic DNA in cultured cells, even when the gene product is not synthesized in the cells (see below and Chap. 2). Although cultured fibroblasts are adequate for isolation of DNA, cultured lymphoblasts are even more attractive because the cell lines are immortal, large numbers of cells are easily grown, and only a blood sample rather than a tissue biopsy is required to initiate the culture.

Cells in culture offer unique opportunities for testing genetic mechanisms. X-linked mutations have been used in cell cultures to text the X-inactivation hypothesis of Lyon. Studies of at least five X-linked loci, including the loci for glucose-6-phosphate dehydrogenase, hypoxanthine-guanine phosphoribosyltransferase (Lesch-Nyhan syndrome), phosphoglycerate kinase, ceramide trihexose α-galactosidase (Fabry disease), and phosphorylase-b-kinase (glycogen storage disease, type VIII), have shown random X inactivation of the paternal or maternal X chromosome in each cell of heterozygous females.[144] Similar inactivation does not occur in autosomal loci. Nor does it appear that inactivation of one X is necessarily complete at all loci. Present evidence suggests that in the case of at least three X-linked loci—the Xg(a) locus,[145] the steroid sulfatase locus,[146] and the MIC2X locus[147]—both alleles are expressed in cells of heterozygous females.

Somatic cell hybrids whose nuclei contain genomes from different species, including serially propagated hybrids of mouse and human fibroblast cells, have been prepared in a number of laboratories.[148–150] Following hybridization, there is a gradual reduction in chromosome number in which human chromosomes are preferentially eliminated. As mentioned earlier, this technology has been responsible for much of the genetic mapping of the human autosomes.

The cell hybridization technique has also been useful in defining heterogeneity of a number of inborn errors by complementation analysis.[149,150] Cultured fibroblasts from two affected individuals with a similar phenotype are fused to form heterokaryons with the use of either Sendai virus or polyethylene glycol. Generally, if the abnormal phenotype of the two parental strains is corrected in the heterokaryon, the defects must involve different genes, although intraallelic complementation also can occur. On the other hand, a negative complementation test suggests that the defects in the two parental strains involve allelic mutations that are not mutually corrective. This approach has been skillfully used in the analysis of heterogeneity in several inborn errors, including xeroderma pigmentosum (Chap. 120), the methylmalonic acidemias (Chap. 29), the propionic acidemias (Chap. 29), the G_{M2} gangliosidoses (Chap. 72), and galactosialidosis (Chap. 71).

Recombinant DNA Techniques

The most powerful new techniques for studying human biochemical genetics are those of recombinant DNA technology. They are described in broad terms in Chap. 2 and in specific detail in relevant chapters. These techniques include restriction enzyme digestion, cDNA cloning, genomic DNA cloning, DNA sequencing, Southern blotting for analysis of DNA, Northern blotting for analysis of RNA, and the polymerase chain reaction for amplification of DNA and RNA sequences. Molecular techniques allowed initially for the cloning of cDNAs and genomic DNAs for numerous well characterized gene products such as globin chains, phenylalanine hydroxylase, and HPRT (Chaps. 93, 15, and 38 respectively). Innumerable mutations were characterized at a nucleic acid level, and RNA splicing mutations were identified. The ability to associate unique mutations with haplotypes of RFLPs has provided insight into the history of the mutations currently contributing to allelic heterogeneity (e.g., thalassemia, PKU, and cystic fibrosis). This analysis of the gene and of mutations has been extended to most of the clotting factors (Chaps. 84 to 90), to the collagen genes (Chap. 115), and to most of the lipoprotein disorders (Chaps. 44 to 49). Study of mutations often contributes to the understanding of functional aspects of the corresponding gene product, as exemplified by the LDL receptor where mutations in various domains affect processes such as LDL binding or receptor internalization (Chap. 48). Molecular studies of apolipoprotein B allowed for determination of the structure of this gene product which was extremely difficult to analyze at a protein level. In addition, a remarkable new mechanism probably involving a single base alteration in mature mRNA to produce two mRNAs and two polypeptide products (apo B-48 and apo B-100) from a single gene was identified (Chap. 44B). Classic mutations in disorders such as Gaucher disease and Tay-Sachs disease are being delineated at the molecular level (Chaps. 67 and 72). In some cases, the molecular definition and biologic definition of conditions are approximately concurrent, as in the case of deficiency of a leukocyte adhesion subunit in leukocyte adhesion deficiency (Chap. 113).

Recombinant DNA techniques have opened the possibility for major new adventures such as reverse genetics as described in Chap. 2. The genes for retinoblastoma, chronic granulomatous disease, and Duchenne muscular dystrophy[44–46] (Chaps. 9, 114, and 118, respectively) have been cloned without prior knowledge of the gene product. Recombinant DNA techniques allowed the unraveling of the complex processes of genomic DNA recombination for production of immunoglobulins and T-cell receptors. The feasibility of a detailed human gene map based on RFLPs (Chap. 6) was a direct outgrowth of recombinant DNA techniques.

The use of a polymerase chain reaction technique (PCR) for amplification of DNA or RNA has become a powerful new tool. Using this technique, a small amount of genomic DNA, mRNA, or other nucleic acid can be amplified thousands or even millions of times to yield an abundant product for easy analysis.[151–153] The procedure can be automated using a heat stable *Taq* (from *Thermus aquaticus*) polymerase which survives the series of temperature changes necessary for the cycles of polymerization, denaturation, and oligonucleotide hybridization. The advantage of this procedure is the ability to prepare DNA within a single day from tiny amounts of whole blood or even dried blood.[153,154] The amplified product can be analyzed rapidly using restriction enzymes, hybridization with oligonucleotides, or direct DNA sequencing. This method has been used for rapid prenatal diagnosis of sickle-cell anemia[153] and hemophilia A.[155] The method has also been used for direct sequencing of mutations in genomic DNA.[156–158] It is now practical to use this method to sequence directly amplified cDNA, as has been demonstrated for HLA gene products beginning with RNA from peripheral leukocytes. This has been done for a number of individuals with insulin dependent diabetes and for controls.[159] The ability to automate the PCR method may allow for major new applications for population screening for human genetic variation.

Molecular Techniques for Clinical Diagnosis

Biochemical analysis in the form of enzyme assay and protein electrophoresis is a long-standing method for clinical diagnosis and heterozygote detection. Molecular diagnostic techniques gather small bits of genotypic information, and the interpretation of results is usually quite straightforward. The strategies for family analysis and interpretation are sometimes more complex. Multiple approaches for clinical application of molecular techniques should be clearly distinguished: (1) Molecular methods can be used to achieve *direct detection of the mutation.* (2) Diagnosis can be established using *linkage with negligible recombination,* usually using the cloned gene as the probe. (3) Diagnosis can also be achieved using *linkage with detectable recombination,* usually using linked RFLPs. (4) Although less common, diagnostic information can be based on *linkage disequilibrium* between genetic markers and a disease mutation.

Direct Detection of Mutations. Direct detection of mutations can be carried out if a restriction enzyme detects the gain or loss of a cutting site due to the mutation. Direct detection of a mutation can also be accomplished using standard Southern blotting analysis in combination with oligonucleotide probes which specifically hybridize with the normal or mutant sequence (allele specific oligonucleotides or ASOs).[160] The restriction enzyme method and the oligonucleotide method can be combined with the polymerase chain reaction to shorten the time required and increase the sensitivity of these methods. All these methods have been applied for detection of the sickle-cell mutation.[153,160,161] Direct detection of mutations is also possible in the instance of deletions or major gene rearrangements. This is particularly simple in instances where a probe is available which detects an abnormal junction fragment at the site of the rearrangement. In the instance where an entire gene is deleted and no junctional probe is available, dosage analysis may be required to identify heterozygotes for the deletion.[162] Dosage analysis requires great caution and appropriate use of control probes, and should be supplemented by use of RFLPs and junctional probes where possible. In general, direct detection of mutations is amenable to simple interpretation because the genotype of each individual is determined in regard to the mutation in the family. The only disadvantage of direct detection of mutations is the specificity of the process which means that slightly different tests must be used to detect alleleic heterogeneity from family to family or even from chromosome to chromosome in a compound heterozygote. Direct detection of a mutation is particularly powerful when the same mutation affects very large numbers of individuals in the population, as in the case of the sickle-cell mutation and as may prove to be the case for disorders such as cystic fibrosis and Huntington disease.

Linkage with Negligible Recombination. The general concepts for genetic recombination and linkage are discussed earlier in this chapter and in Chap. 6. Genetic diagnosis by linkage is utilized when it is not possible to demonstrate by direct analysis the mutation or the mutant gene product. For clinical linkage analysis, it is essential that some genetic marker near the disease locus (or near the mutation if the locus is very large) be *informative.* The genetic marker is informative if an individual who is heterozygous for the disease locus is also heterozygous for the marker. Linkage analysis is appropriate when an individual carries one mutant gene and one normal gene, and the goal is to determine which has been transmitted to the next generation. Most analyses can be made informative since RFLPs are frequent, and since it is usually possible to identify useful polymorphisms near genes causing diseases. A second requirement for linkage analysis is that of *phase* information between the two loci for genetic analysis. If an individual is heterozygous for an RFLP (genotype 1/2) which is tightly linked to a mutation, it must be determined whether allele 1 for the RFLP is on the chromosome with the disease gene or on the chromosome with the normal gene, assuming that allele 2 for the RFLP would be on the chromosome with the alternate gene. When the genetic marker is informative and the phase is known, genetic diagnosis can be carried out in the form of heterozygote detection, presymptomatic diagnosis, detection of lack of penetrance, and prenatal diagnosis. When the DNA probe is a portion of the gene which is mutated, crossing-over between the genetic marker (often an RFLP) and a mutation is usually negligible. Duchenne muscular dystrophy is an exception with an extremely large gene where crossing-over within the gene does occur at a detectable frequency.

A hypothetical series of families with a recessive disorder is illustrated in Fig. 1-18 demonstrating some questions of informativeness and phase. For these examples, it is assumed that the cloned gene is available as a probe. For family 1 the analysis is informative, and the phase can be deduced; both parents are heterozygous for an RFLP, and the first affected child indicates that the 5-kb fragment is on the same chromosome as the disease gene in both parents. For family 2, the analysis is informative only for the father. For family 3, both parents are heterozygous for the RFLP, but the phase cannot be determined adequately, and the analysis is only partially informative. Family 3 is described as having an intercross result. For families 2 and 3, prenatal diagnosis can still be of some value since there is a 50 percent probability that a fetus will be predicted to be unaffected and a 50 percent probability that a fetus will be predicted to be at 50 percent risk. For family 4, the analysis is entirely uninformative, since both parents are homozygous for the RFLP. For family 5, complete information can be obtained using two RFLPs, since the father is informative for one analysis and the mother is informative for the other analysis. Because more than one RFLP is potentially informative, most families are fully informative, and prenatal diagnosis can be provided to the majority of families with a previously affected child.

Numerous examples of molecular diagnosis by linkage, where there is negligible recombination between the loci, are presented in Fig. 1-19. Genetic marker data are presented as letters which might represent simple RFLP alleles or haplotypes of RFLPs. Phase can usually be determined from a single index case for autosomal recessive disorders (Fig. 1-19*A*).

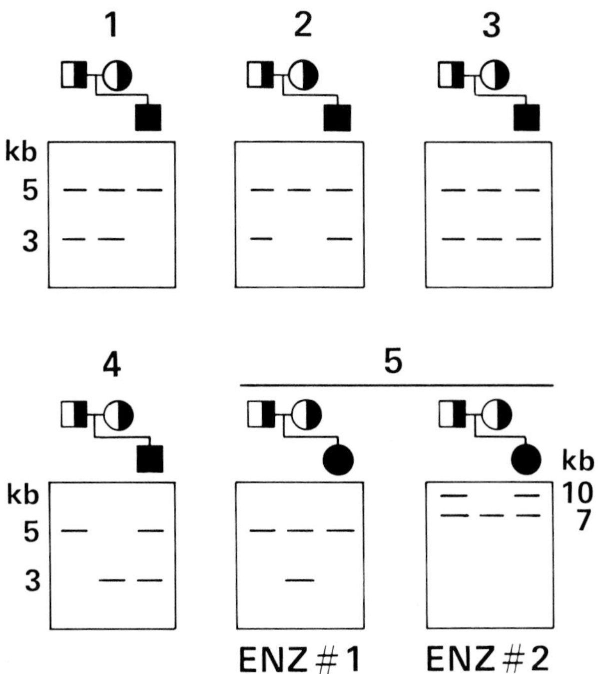

Fig. 1-18 Hypothetical families with a child affected with an autosomal recessive disorder. Simplified but realistic examples of Southern blot analysis using the cloned cDNA for the mutant gene are depicted. Families are numbered above, and restriction fragment sizes are indicated in kilobases; see text. *(From A. Beaudet.[217] Used by permission.)*

Phase can also be determined for recessive disorders in the absence of an index case if a reliable biologic or biochemical heterozygote test is available as might occur for β thalassemia (Fig. 1-19*B*). Fetuses of AA genotype are predicted to be affected for panels *A* and *B*. For autosomal dominant disorders, linkage phase usually cannot be determined from a single affected individual (Fig. 1-19*C*). Exceptions would occur in retinoblastoma or polyposis of the colon, when analysis of tumor DNA may distinguish the allele on the abnormal chromosome (often retained in the tumor) from the allele on the normal chromosome (often lost in the tumor). Linkage phase for autosomal dominant disorders can be determined from two appropriate individuals; it is not essential that both be affected (Fig. 1-19*D* and *E*). Fetuses of AB genotype are predicted to be affected for panels *D* and *E*. For X-linked disorders, phase information is most readily obtained from a single affected male individual (Fig. 1-19*F*). In general, linkage information can be used to determine the genotype of offspring of individuals of known genotype. Linkage information generally cannot be used consistently to determine the genotype of antecedents of individuals of known genotypes because of the possibility of new mutation from one generation to the next. This is exemplified for an X-linked disorder where linkage information will not clarify if the mother of an isolated affected male is a heterozygote or not (Fig. 1-19*G*). This represents an important difference between direct detection of a mutation and linkage analysis. Occasionally, linkage analysis can suggest the genotype of an antecedent. Note for panel *G* that the mutation arose on the chromosome from the unaffected maternal grandfather, and it can be stated that the maternal grandmother and the maternal aunt of the index case do not carry the mutation and that either the mother or the index case is the recipient of the new mutation. The situation is similar in panel *H*, except that the mutation is on the chromosome from the maternal grandmother, and the site of the new mutation is unknown and could go back further in the family. Still by linkage analysis, the maternal aunt is not a carrier of the mutation. The genotype of an antecedent also can be inferred when a woman has two sons with the same DNA marker, one son being affected and one son being unaffected with the X-linked disorder (Fig. 1-19*I*). In this instance, the data indicate that the mother is not a heterozygote for the X-linked disorder, although the possibility of gonadal mosaicism is not eliminated.

Linkage with Detectable Recombination. Linkage analysis using a genetic marker which shows detectable recombination with a disease mutation has the same requirements for informativeness and phase as discussed above. However, the analysis is further complicated by the possibility of recombination at each meiosis in the family. For purposes of discussion, it is convenient to consider a genetic marker which has a recombination fraction of 0.1 with a disease mutation (Fig. 1-20). The immediate implication is that genetic diagnosis will be only 90 percent accurate using this single marker, even if complete informativeness and phase are available. If a second genetic marker is available at a similar distance on the *opposite* side of the disease mutation (flanking markers), the two can be used to increase greatly the accuracy of diagnosis, if no crossover occurs between the two markers. However, the information would be almost useless in about 20 percent of fam-

Fig. 1-19 Examples of molecular diagnosis by genetic linkage with negligible recombination between the DNA probe and the disease locus. Letters indicate haplotypes for RFLPs. Panels *A* and *B* depict autosomal recessive disorders; *C* through *E* depict autosomal dominant disorders; and *F* through *I* depict X-linked disorders. The phase is presented with the A haplotype on the same chromosome as the mutant allele in all cases where it can be determined; see text for discussion.

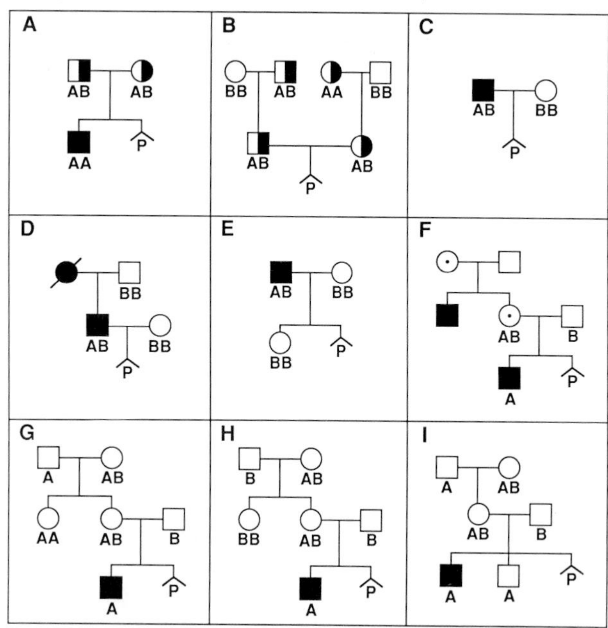

■,● Affected phenotype; male, female
◧,◑ Heterozygote for autosomal recessive disorder
⊙ Obligate heterozygote for X-linked disorder
□,○ Normal phenotype

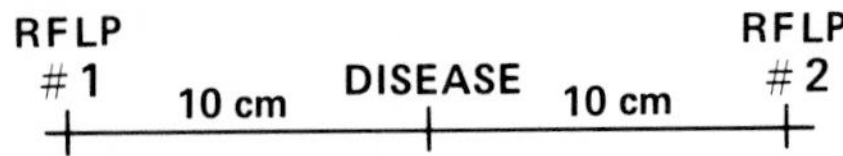

ONE MARKER INFORMATIVE

- 100% OF FAMILIES, 90% ACCURATE

TWO MARKERS INFORMATIVE

- 81% OF FAMILIES, 99% ACCURATE
- 19% OF FAMILIES, NO DIAGNOSIS

Fig. 1-20 Demonstration of the effect of flanking linked genetic markers; see text for discussion. *(From A. Beaudet.[217] Used by permission.)*

ilies who would have at least one crossover between the flanking markers. The determination of phase is also complicated by the possibility of recombination. If phase is deduced from the offspring of an affected individual, a larger number of offspring increases the certainty of the phase information. Continuing to assume a recombination fraction of 0.1 between a genetic marker and a disease mutation, the phase in an individual with a dominant disorder can be deduced with a probability of 0.90 from a single offspring but with a probability of 0.99 from two offspring of affected or unaffected status (Fig. 1-21, compare panels *A* and *B*). In some families with a dominant disorder, the phase can be deduced with complete certainty from antecedent data such as when an affected individual must have inherited the disease gene and a particular genetic marker from an affected parent (Fig. 1-21*C*). Fetuses of the AB genotype have probabilities of being affected of approximately 0.81, 0.89, and 0.90 for panels *A*, *B*, and *C*, respectively, since crossovers may occur in the meioses leading to conception of the fetus. For autosomal recessive disorders, the considerations are analogous. If prenatal diagnosis is based on phase data from a single previous affected offspring, there are four meioses which would affect the prediction (Fig. 1-21*D*). For example, using a single genetic marker at a recombination fraction of 0.02, there would be approximately an 8 percent chance that a prediction of an affected fetus would be erroneous, since a single crossover at any of the four meioses would cause a diagnostic error. For X-linked disorders phase can be deduced from offspring of heterozygous females, but more definitive phase information can often be obtained by analysis of the fathers of heterozygous females. In Fig. 1-21*E* and *F*, the same family is depicted with and without data from the maternal grandfather. If an unwise counselor (panel *E*) fails to obtain a sample from the maternal grandfather, the data suggest that the A marker is on the chromosome with the disease gene in the pregnant woman. The phase is known with only 90 percent certainty, and prenatal diagnosis would provide accuracy of approximately 81 percent because of the possibility of crossing-over in either of the meioses leading to the offspring of the heterozygous mother. If a wiser counselor (panel *F*) recognizes the absolute necessity of a sample from the maternal grandfather, the phase in the heterozygous mother becomes known with certainty, and it becomes obvious that the affected son represents a crossover between the genetic marker and the disease mutation. Prenatal diagnosis now becomes 90 percent accurate, but, more important, the prediction of disease or nondisease has been reversed for the presence of a given marker in a male fetus. If phase is to be determined for heterozygous females based on their offspring, the accuracy of phase information increases with increasing numbers of offspring as for the autosomal disorders.

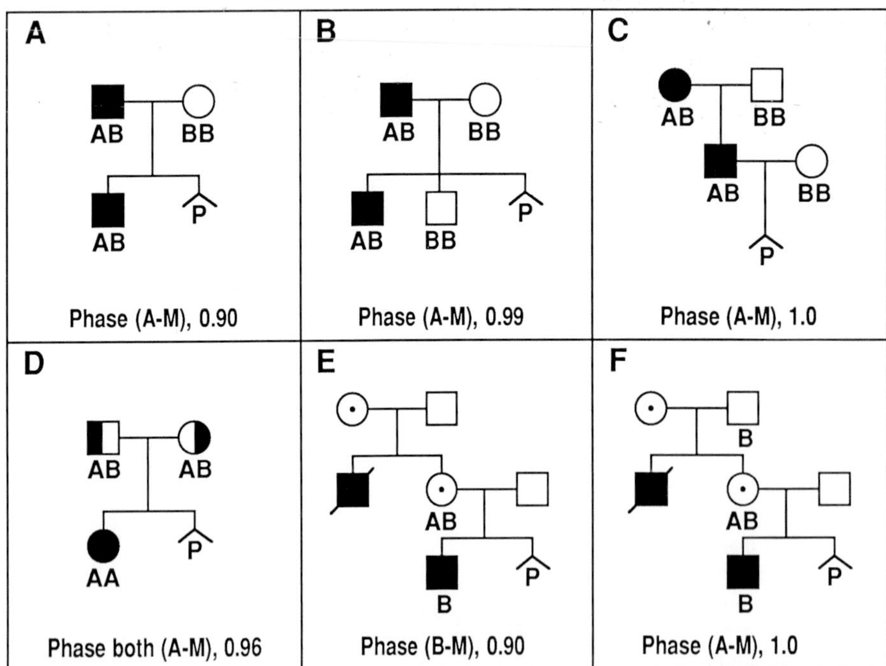

■,● Affected phenotype; male, female
◧,◑ Heterozygote for autosomal recessive disorder
⊙ Obligate heterozygote for X-linked disorder
□,○ Normal phenotype

Fig. 1-21 Examples of molecular diagnosis using genetic linkage with detectable recombination between the DNA probe and the disease locus. Letters indicate haplotypes detected with RFLPs. Panels *A* through *C* depict autosomal dominant disorders; panel *D* depicts an autosomal recessive disorder; and panels *E* and *F* depict X-linked disorders. The probability of phase at the bottom of each panel indicates the probability that a given haplotype is on the chromosome with the mutant allele (M) in the parent(s) of the pregnancy (P). For example, phase (A-M), 0.90, in panel *A* indicates that the probability is 0.90 that the A haplotype is on the chromosome with the mutant allele and the B haplotype is on the chromosome with the normal allele in the father of the pregnancy. The recombination fraction is presented as 0.1 for all cases except in panel *D* where a recombination fraction of 0.02 is assumed; see text for discussion.

Linkage Disequilibrium. Linkage disequilibrium refers to the fact that certain alleles at two nearby loci may be found together more often than would be predicted from their frequency in the general population. For purposes of genetic diagnosis, this is most readily discussed in terms of a genetic marker and a disease mutation. Linkage disequilibrium reflects the rarity of crossing-over in the historical meioses between the present and the origin of the more recent of the two genetic variations under study. For linkage disequilibrium to be present, the two genetic markers must be quite tightly linked. In addition, there must be one or only a few origins for the disease mutations, or the mutations will be found relatively randomly with various alleles for the marker gene. Either extensive crossing-over or frequent occurrence of new mutations would lead to relatively random occurrence of the mutation with marker genotypes.

Linkage disequilibrium is extensive within the HLA complex, and numerous diseases are found in association with various HLA haplotypes (see Chap. 4). Although it is unclear whether some associations such as that with ankylosing spondylitis represent causation by genetic variation in the HLA loci themselves or represent linkage disequilibrium, it is more definite that the finding of certain HLA haplotypes with mutant genes for 21 hydroxylase deficiency represents linkage disequilibrium (Chap. 74). It is also likely that the association of particular HLA haplotypes with hemochromatosis also represents linkage disequilibrium (Chap. 55). For offspring of individuals with hemochromatosis, one mutant gene is inherited from the affected parent, since this is a recessive disorder. The possibility that the unaffected parent has contributed the hemochromatosis gene can be calculated taking into account the HLA haplotypes inherited from the unaffected parent and the appropriate data on linkage disequilibrium. A striking example of linkage disequilibrium is found for the Z allele at the α_1-antitrypsin locus where a particular allele for an RFLP is found almost uniquely with the Z allele (Chap. 96). This instance is unusual, since the presence of the allele at the RFLP and the presence of the Z allele correlate almost completely. This is different from the usual circumstance where a particular mutation is often found with a unique haplotype of RFLPs, but the RFLP haplotype associated with the mutation may also be found with normal copies of the gene (PKU and β thalassemia).

Recently, RFLPs showing strong linkage disequilibrium with cystic fibrosis were identified. This result indicates that the DNA markers are extremely close to the cystic fibrosis (CF) locus and that a single mutation accounts for most or all of the mutant CF genes in the population. The linkage disequilibrium information can be used in a variety of ways for genetic counseling in cystic fibrosis. Linkage disequilibrium can be used to estimate phase in parents who have an affected but deceased offspring. Linkage disequilibrium can be used to adjust the probability of a cystic fibrosis mutation on a chromosome contributed by an individual with no prior family history of CF. This can be used to modify risk calculations for pregnancies of aunts, uncles, and sibs of CF patients in defined populations. Linkage disequilibrium has played a limited role in genetic diagnosis in the past, and its role is likely to remain limited, since it is found with unique mutations which could be directly detected once they are characterized.

Molecular diagnosis is assuming an increasingly important role in medical genetics. Selected examples of current applications are listed in Table 1-8, and a more detailed list is provided by Cooper and Schmidtke in Appendix 1-1 to this chapter.

DIAGNOSIS AND PREVENTION OF GENETIC METABOLIC DISEASES

The present trend for couples to have smaller families has heightened the concern that children should be healthy and free of genetic diseases. Primary-care physicians are called upon to play a more active role in the prevention and treatment of hereditary diseases. In many clinical situations, genetic advice can be given by the primary physician once the relatively simple principles of medical genetics and genetic

Table 1-8 Examples of Role of Molecular Analysis for Diagnosis of Genetic Disease

Disease	*Detection of mutation**	*RFLPs with gene probe*	*RFLPs with linked marker*	*Comments*
Sickle-cell anemia	+ + + +			*Mst* II analysis
β Thalassemia	+ +	+ +		Very heterogeneous
α Thalassemia	+ + +	+		Many deletions
Hemophilia A	+	+ +	+	
Hemophilia B	+	+ +	+	
Phenylketonuria	+	+ + +		
α_1-Antitrypsin ZZ	+ + +	+		
Antithrombin III deficiency	+	+ +		Biologic tests valuable
Familial hypercholesterolemia	+ +	+ +		Biologic tests valuable
Growth hormone deficiency	+			Rare form
Lesch-Nyhan syndrome	+ +	+ +		Heterozygote detection
Retinoblastoma	+ + +	+		Inherited form
Huntington disease			+ + +	Delay over ethical concerns
Myotonic dystrophy			+ +	
Adult polycystic kidney disease			+ + +	
Ornithine transcarbamylase deficiency	+	+ + +		Prenatal and heterozygote
Tay-Sachs disease	+ +	+ +		Enzyme diagnosis
X-linked retinitis pigmentosa			+ + +	
Fragile X syndrome			+ + +	
Cystic fibrosis			+ + +	

*+ = relative importance of an approach as of early 1988, and the status for disorders could change rapidly.
NOTE: See Appendix 1-1 for greater detail.

counseling have been mastered. In other situations, the complexities may make referral to a genetic specialist a necessity, but a good genetic history is essential even for identification of families for appropriate referral. For a more in-depth discussion of these principles, the reader is referred to Vogel and Motulsky's textbook *Human Genetics: Problems and Approaches.*[95] Genetic counseling may be provided because of the occurrence of an affected individual (index case) in a family. Other types of programs are population based and may include newborn screening, heterozygote screening, prenatal screening, and screening for disease in later life.

Genetic Counseling with an Index Case

The prevention of genetic diseases requires the advance identification of matings that are capable of producing genotypes associated with medical disorders. These may involve matings in which one of the two individuals is carrying a dominant or X-linked gene mutation or a balanced translocation, or matings in which both individuals carry a deleterious recessive gene at the same locus. Such individuals are usually identified through the birth of an affected child or near relative, in which case retrospective genetic counseling can be provided.

When advising family members about the risk of transmitting a disorder that has already affected someone in the family, the counselor's first step is to be certain of the *correct diagnosis*—in particular, to make certain that the problem in question is really of genetic origin. This is especially important in disorders that may have either a genetic or a nongenetic etiology, such as deafness or mental retardation. Second, if the disease has a hereditary element, the possibility of genetic heterogeneity must be considered.

Estimation of the *recurrence risk* of a disease requires knowledge of the genetic mechanisms controlling the relevant disorder. When more than one genetic mechanism exists, or when environmental factors can cause clinically indistinguishable traits, the *relative probabilities* of the different mechanisms operating in the particular family are computed. For conditions determined by simple Mendelian inheritance, there is no difficulty in predicting the probability of an offspring's being affected, provided the genotypes of the parents can be recognized. Identification of the parental genotype is easiest if a biochemical or molecular test is available to detect the mutant gene.

For autosomal dominant disorders, identification of the parental genotype is often more difficult because of the occurrence of *lack of penetrance* and *variation in expression.* In counseling a family in which one relative is affected with a dominant disorder, it is important that appropriate clinical examination of all first-degree relatives and appropriately selected distant relatives be carried out. If relatives appear unaffected, there is the possibility that the gene is present but not penetrant or the possibility of delayed age of onset or mild expression. When no relatives are affected, the possibility of a new dominant mutation must be entertained. Presumably it will become increasingly feasible to determine genotypes using biochemical and molecular methods in such circumstances.

When advising families about multifactorial genetic diseases, such as diabetes mellitus, in which the inheritance pattern is not clear-cut, the physician must resort to empiric risk estimates that have been derived from retrospectively assembled data.[95]

Once the parental genotypes are determined, the genetic prognosis is usually presented in terms of probability that a given couple will produce an affected offspring. The physician providing genetic counseling must make certain that the couple understands not only the meaning of such absolute risk figures but also the severity of the disease and the variability in clinical expression. In other words, in dealing with a disorder such as α_1-antitrypsin deficiency, it is important for the parents to realize not only that they have a 25 percent risk of producing a child with this disorder but also that a certain proportion of children with the disorder have severe disease with both liver and pulmonary manifestations, a certain portion have mild disease with only pulmonary manifestations, etc. They should also have an understanding of the potential impact of the disease on their family. A disease that is lethal at birth might be classified by some as more "severe" than one that is lethal at age 16, but the latter is likely to have a much more profound impact on the family. There is evidence that the relative burden of a disorder is an important factor in the decision-making process for couples with increased genetic risks.[163]

Heterozygote Detection

Heterozygote testing is one form of genetic screening. The efficiency of a genetic screening test is related to its sensitivity (detection rate) and its false positive rate (equivalent to 1 minus specificity).[164] *Sensitivity* is defined as the ability of the test to identify those with the mutant phenotype. Such persons yield either a positive test (with frequency a) or a normal (false negative) test (with frequency b). Sensitivity (detection rate) is thus $a/(a + b)$. *Specificity* is defined as the ability to exclude those with the normal genotype (with frequency d) from a false positive classification (with frequency c); specificity of the screening test is thus $d/(c + d)$ [the false-positive rate is 1 minus specificity or $c/(c + d)$]. Binary discrimination yields perfect specificity and sensitivity (value = 1 for each). In practice, discrimination of most tests is statistical (i.e., dependent on the distribution of metric parameters); hence specificity and sensitivity are less than perfect. There is thus no overlap of values between classes (e.g., heterozygotes and normals) for a binary test, but there are overlapping values for a statistical test.

Detection of heterozygotes is an important part of counseling families where a known genetic disorder has occurred. This arises most frequently in the case of X-linked disorders or autosomal recessive traits, but analogous questions arise in the case of autosomal dominant disorders where an enzyme assay is available, and the phenotype is not always obvious clinically (e.g., acute intermittent porphyria). The ideal method for heterozygote detection is the direct demonstration of the mutant gene or gene product (i.e., binary discrimination with a specificity and sensitivity both with a value of 1). This is possible for some disorders using protein electrophoresis as for hemoglobin or α_1-antitrypsin. This is also possible when the disease mutation can be directly detected by molecular techniques. As discussed above, heterozygote detection is also possible using linkage analysis, in which case the accuracy will depend on the possibility of recombination between the linked marker and the disease mutation.

Another method for heterozygote detection involves the detection of half-normal levels of the mutant gene product. In such a statistical discrimination, the values for specificity and sensitivity are both less than 1. This approach usually involves enzyme assay on blood or tissue samples. The ability to separate heterozygotes from normal individuals is extremely dependent on the coefficient of variation for the determination in question, as demonstrated in Fig. 1-22. A high degree of variation may be due to unavoidable biologic variation in the human population. In many instances the variation can be reduced by appropriate strategies. For example analysis of mixed leukocytes may give a wide variation because of heterogeneity in differential white blood cell count, while analysis of a specific leukocyte population such as granulocytes or lymphocytes may reduce the variation. For many enzyme assays causing inborn errors of metabolism, the data sets for determining the normal and heterozygote ranges are suboptimal, in part due to lack of adequate numbers of obligate heterozygote samples and in part due to infrequent demand for the procedures. In the case of Tay-Sachs disease, the ability to distinguish heterozygotes by enzyme assay is unusually good. This is due in part to the excellent data sets available, but perhaps also in part to the intrinsic circumstances where the deficiency of α subunits both reduces hexosaminidase A activity and increases hexosaminidase B activity through the formation of β_2 dimers. Heterozygote detection tests are frequently interpreted as positive or negative, and this is appropriate for a relatively absolute or binary test such as hemoglobin electrophoresis. When significant doubt is present, it would be preferable to use the results to modify the probability that an individual is a carrier based on the range of values observed in heterozygotes and normal individuals.[165] Again, the data are frequently inadequate to pursue this optimal approach, but it should be recognized that many enzyme determinations for heterozygote detection do not provide absolute diagnoses. These same issues apply when diagnosing affected individuals with autosomal dominant enzyme disorders such as acute intermittent porphyria. As more molecular tests become available, heterozygote detection may move increasingly from a statistical to a binary discrimination.

In the case of X-linked disorders, heterozygote detection is complicated by the Lyon mechanism for random X inactivation as discussed above. Strategies for circumventing the problems of X inactivation include analysis of clonal cell populations which can include individual hair roots, randomly isolated cultured cell clones, and cell clones isolated by selection methods. In the case of the Lesch-Nyhan syndrome, toxic purine antimetabolites such as thioguanine or azaguanine can be used to select for, and thereby demonstrate the presence of, deficient cells in a mixed population from a heterozygote female.

Fig. 1-22 The relevance of the coefficient of variation using a quantitative trait such as enzyme activity for diagnosis of heterozygotes and homozygotes.

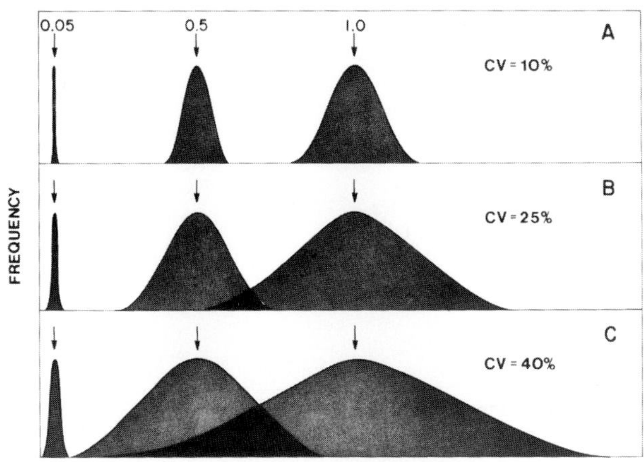

Heterozygote detection can also be based on various metabolic studies. In general, these tests (again statistical discriminations) which are more removed from the defective gene are less reliable. For example, in heterozygotes for cystinuria, the excretion of dibasic amino acids in the urine is elevated, but not as much as in the patient with the homozygous disease (Chap. 99). Appropriate measurements of the ratio of blood phenylalanine to tyrosine provide a useful heterozygote test for phenylketonuria (Chap. 15). In the case of ornithine transcarbamylase deficiency, urinary excretion of orotic acid and orotidine is significantly increased in heterozygotes after a protein loading test or after administration of allopurinol (Chap. 20). These metabolic heterozygote tests for ornithine transcarbamylase deficiency are quite accurate, although molecular data offer a binary discrimination when informative.

Antenatal Diagnosis of Genetic Disease

During the 1960s, transabdominal amniocentesis came into widespread use for the purpose of diagnosis of certain genetic diseases at a stage early enough to permit parents the option of terminating the pregnancy and preventing the birth of a defective child. This procedure gives high-risk couples the opportunity to have unaffected children provided they are willing for the pregnancy to be terminated in the event that an abnormal fetus is detected. Since the 1960s, there has been a progressive expansion of prenatal diagnostic techniques with improved resolution by prenatal ultrasound, measurement of amniotic fluid α-fetoprotein, fetal blood sampling, and the development of transcervical and transabdominal chorionic villus sampling.

Amniocentesis consists of the transabdominal aspiration of amniotic fluid from the uterus. The procedure involves minimal risk. Maternal mortality has not been observed, and morbidity has been minor. Fetal loss (due to death or spontaneous abortion) is minimally different from that in controls matched for maternal age, gravidity, parity, race, religion, socioeconomic group, gestational age, and other features.[95,166–169] If a diagnostic amniocentesis is performed at the fifteenth week of gestation, the 4-week delay required for culture of an adequate number of cells for biochemical or cytogenetic study brings one only to the twentieth week, when pregnancy may still be terminated safely.

Direct examination of the amniotic fluid itself may be diagnostic. For example, an elevated level of α-fetoprotein is a relatively good indicator of the presence of spina bifida or some other related neural tube abnormality.[170] More frequently, prenatal diagnosis requires culture of the fetal cells in vitro, as mentioned above. By this means, the karyotype of the fetus can be determined to ascertain fetal sex and to detect various chromosomal aberrations such as Down syndrome.

Transcervical or transabdominal chorionic villus sampling (CVS) can be used to obtain tissue of fetal origin.[171–174] Transcervical CVS can be performed at 9 to 12 weeks gestation (only 5 to 8 weeks after the first missed menstrual period), and transabdominal CVS can be performed similarly early in gestation. Chorionic villi can be analyzed directly using cytogenetic, biochemical, or molecular techniques. In addition, cells can be cultured from chorionic villi and again subjected to any of these forms of analysis. The major advantage of CVS is the earlier sampling time and the availability of larger amounts of tissue which allow for direct analysis, so that a woman undergoing CVS at 9 weeks gestation might have final diagnostic information at 10 weeks gestation in comparison to approximately 20 weeks gestation for amniocentesis. The earlier results are substantially more attractive to many high-risk families. The safety of CVS is still under evaluation through collaborative studies in various countries, but the risk of fetal loss above the background risk appears to be between 1 and 3 percent, which may be acceptable to families facing a high genetic risk.

Virtually all cytogenetic disorders can be detected using either amniocentesis or CVS. Many biochemical genetic disorders can be detected by suitable assays of specific enzyme activities in cultured fetal cells or in chorionic villi. In general, most of the disorders which can be detected by enzyme assay in cultured amniotic fluid cells can also be detected using CVS, but the relative expression of genes in these tissues differs slightly, and the reliability of each cell type for each enzymatic assay must be documented carefully.[175] DNA can be obtained from any of the cell sources, and molecular diagnosis is assuming an expanding role using direct detection of the mutation, linkage where recombination is negligible, and linkage where recombination is measurable. Increasingly, the cloned gene itself is used as the diagnostic molecular probe. Molecular diagnosis does not require that the gene product be expressed in the fetal cells. Table 1-9 lists numerous biochemical genetic disorders for which prenatal diagnosis is currently feasible. Many different circumstances are included in Table 1-9. For some disorders, such as Tay-Sachs disease, Lesch-Nyhan syndrome and sickle cell anemia, prenatal diagnosis is extremely reliable. In some instances, diagnosis has traditionally been accomplished by enzyme assay, and molecular diagnosis is becoming a useful alternative. In some instances, molecular diagnosis may be available only for a proportion of families, because of incomplete informativeness and inability to detect all possible mutations directly (currently exemplified by hemophilia A). Fetal blood sampling is useful for prenatal diagnosis of hemophilia if molecular analysis is not informative (Chap. 86). In other instances, prenatal diagnosis is complex, as in the case of fragile X syndrome where cytogenetic diagnosis is of partial value, and linkage analysis is complicated by incomplete information and crossing-over in some cases. It is virtually certain that the range of disorders which can be diagnosed will continue to expand rapidly and that the accuracy of diagnosis will improve in instances where it is still troublesome. Specific details for prenatal diagnosis can be found in chapters throughout this book.

Population Based Genetic Screening

Genetic screening represents the search in a population for persons possessing certain genotypes that are known to be associated with or to predispose to disease in the individuals or their descendants.[164,176] Screening is also employed for research purposes in order to ascertain distributions of traits, e.g., polymorphisms, not known to be associated with disease. In this section, we are concerned only with the identification of deleterious genes in individual members of populations.

Population based genetic screening will be considered under the headings of newborn screening (usually for disease), heterozygote screening, prenatal screening, and screening for disease later in life. Newborn screening involves the identification of genetic disease in an infant to allow the institution of a

Table 1-9 Overview of Prenatal Diagnosis of Genetic Disorders

Chromosomal
- Most routine cytogenetic analysis
- Fragile X, possible but complex, cytogenetic and linkage

Carbohydrate disorders
- Glycogen storage II, III, and IV by enzyme
- Galactosemia by enzyme

Amino acid disorders
- Majority possible by enzyme, e.g., maple syrup urine disease, citrullinemia, ornithinemia
- Some by DNA, e.g., PKU, ornithine transcarbamylase

Organic acidemia
- Most possible by enzyme, e.g., methylmalonic acidemia, isovaleric acidemia

Purine and pyrimidine disorders
- Most possible by enzyme with DNA possible also, e.g., HPRT, adenosine deaminase

Lipoprotein disorders
- Familial hypercholesterolemia by receptor assay or DNA
- DNA increasingly feasible for apolipoproteins

Porphyrias and heme disorders
- Many porphyrias by enzyme, DNA feasible

Disorders of metal metabolism
- Menkes by copper in cells

Peroxisomal disorders
- Most possible by lipid and enzyme analysis

Lysosomal disorders
- Virtually all possible by enzyme assay, DNA increasingly feasible, e.g., Tay-Sachs deletions and mutations

Disorders of hormone synthesis
- 21-Hydroxylase deficiency by metabolites, HLA linkage, and DNA
- Steroid sulfatase by enzyme and DNA
- Testicular feminization by receptor assay

Vitamin disorders
- Biotinidase by enzyme
- Cobalamins by bioassays

Blood disorders
- Most proteins by DNA, e.g., hemophilias, α_1-antitrypsin, amyloidosis
- Most hemoglobins by DNA

Disorders of membrane transport
- Cystinosis by cystine content
- Cystic fibrosis by DNA

Disorders of immune defense
- Many feasible by fetal blood analysis
- Chronic granulomatous disease and leukocyte adhesion deficiency by DNA

Disorders of connective tissue
- Hypophosphatasia and carbonic anhydrase II deficiency by enzyme, DNA feasible for latter
- Collagen disorders by protein analysis and DNA

Muscle disorders
- Duchenne dystrophy by DNA
- Myotonic dystrophy by linkage

Skin disorders
- Xeroderma pigmentosa by bioassay

Intestinal disorders
- Analysis of enzymes in amniotic fluid feasible

prophylactic or therapeutic program to prevent injury to the child. Heterozygote screening and prenatal screening are designed to identify couples at high risk of transmitting a serious genetic disease in order to provide the couple with the option to forestall the birth of affected children. Reproductive options for carrier couples detected by heterozygote screening are numerous and include avoidance of pregnancy, adoption, artificial insemination by noncarrier donor, selective abortion after prenatal diagnosis, and acceptance of the birth of affected infants. Screening for disease is designed to detect individuals in the population under circumstances where some prophylactic or therapeutic program may avert or reduce the burden of the disease. This strategy is similar to newborn screening but is applied later in life.

Detailed discussions of genetic screening are available in a report published by the United States National Academy of Sciences in 1975[176] and in the report of an international workshop held in 1982.[164] Recommendations from the workshop are:[164]

1. The specific rationale for genetic screening should be defined, namely, whether the goal is medical intervention, family planning, or research.
2. Population screening for medical intervention should not be performed outside an integrated program capable of information dispersal, screening, retrieval of persons with positive tests, diagnosis, counseling, medical management, and outcome evaluation.
3. The screening procedure should maximize specificity (by counting false positive tests), sensitivity (by counting false negative tests), and predictive efficiency (ratio of true positive to false positive tests) of the test. Proficiency testing should be implemented to monitor performance. (See explanation of specificity and sensitivity, above, under "Heterozygote Detection.")
4. The contribution of ethnic and geographic factors to variation of phenotype should be considered when designing and implementing programs.
5. Participation should be informed and in keeping with the relevant mores of the society; participants should acquire accurate information relevant to their needs.
6. Information about the rationale and goal of the program and the meaning of test results should be available to participants, physicians, and all other personnel affected by the program.
7. Outcome and impact of the program, whether for service or research in medical, economic, social, and legal contexts, should be evaluated. Policy should be sufficiently flexible so that practice can be modified in keeping with developments and findings.

Newborn Screening. The goal of newborn screening is almost always to make a specific diagnosis for the purpose of providing medical intervention to avoid or ameliorate symptoms. Newborn screening first evolved to identify PKU in infants in time to institute a low phenylalanine diet and thus prevent the devastating effects of the untreated disease.[177] Newborn screening for PKU is discussed in detail in Chap. 15. Subsequently newborn screening has been implemented for many other disorders including aminoacidopathies, galactosemia, congenital hypothyroidism, sickle-cell anemia, cystic fibrosis, α_1-antitrypsin deficiency, and Duchenne muscular dystrophy. Almost all disorders detected by newborn screening represent Mendelian conditions, except congenital hypothyroidism, which has a heterogeneous etiology. For some disorders, the evidence for efficacy of medical intervention is overwhelming as in the cases of PKU, galactosemia, and congenital hypothyroidism. In other instances, the benefits of medical intervention are less dramatic but probably significant. Examples include sickle-cell anemia, cystic fibrosis, and α_1-antitrypsin deficiency. In the case of Duchenne muscular dystrophy, no significant medical intervention is available. Prenatal diagnosis is more widely accepted and practiced for the disorders where intervention is most beneficial (Table 1-10). There are some genetic counseling benefits for early detection of disorders such as Duchenne muscular dystrophy.

Heterozygote Screening. The general recommendations for genetic screening in populations cited above apply to heterozygote screening as well. The usual goal for heterozygote screening in this context is to provide options for family planning. The specificity and sensitivity of the heterozygote test are important variables. Qualitative or binary tests such as hemoglobin electrophoresis for sickle-cell anemia provide relatively absolute diagnosis, while quantitative or statistical tests may provide lower specificity and sensitivity as discussed under "Heterozygote Detection," above.

TAY-SACHS DISEASE. The carrier frequency of this lethal disorder is 1 in 30 to 1 in 60 in the Jewish population of northeastern European ancestry, approximately tenfold higher than in the population at large. Detection of Tay-Sachs heterozygotes is accomplished by quantitative analysis of hexosaminidase A in serum, plasma, or leukocytes using a ratio to hexosaminidase B (Chap. 72). Tay-Sachs disease is an ideal disorder for screening for reproductive counseling for the following reasons: (1) it is limited mainly to a defined population; (2) there is a simple, reliable, automated, and relatively inexpensive test for identifying the carrier state; (3) there are positive reproductive alternatives for couples, both of whom are carriers, because the disorder can be diagnosed antenatally at a time when induced abortion can be safely performed. Thus, such couples can plan to have unaffected children while avoiding having children with the disease. Heterozygote screening has led to a marked reduction of the frequency of Tay-Sachs

Table 1-10 Frequency of Some Inborn Errors of Metabolism for Which Newborn Screening Tests Are Available

Disorder	*Average frequency in liveborn infants**
Cystic fibrosis	1 in 2500
Congenital hypothyroidism	1 in 6000
Cystinuria	1 in 7000
α_1-Antitrypsin deficiency	1 in 8000
Phenylketonuria	1 in 12,000
Histidinemia	1 in 17,000
Iminoglycinuria	1 in 20,000
Hartnup disorder	1 in 26,000
Hyperprolinemia	1 in 40,000
Galactosemia	1 in 57,000
Biotinidase deficiency	1 in 60,000
Adenosine deaminase deficiency	<1 in 100,000
Maple syrup urine disease	1 in 200,000
Homocystinuria	1 in 200,000

*These frequencies often vary widely among ethnic groups, e.g., about 1 in 5000 in Dublin compared with 1 in 200,000 in Japan for phenylketonuria (see Ref. 164 for details).
SOURCE: Data from Galjaard[97] and various chapters in this text.

disease in the Jewish and French Canadian populations as detailed in Chap. 72.

The advent of reliable screening procedures for heterozygote detection and antenatal diagnosis is particularly valuable in Tay-Sachs disease, in which 80 percent of cases are first cases. But amniocentesis also enables the prevention of the birth of a second affected child in a family in which one Tay-Sachs case has appeared and in which both parents are therefore known heterozygotes.

SICKLE-CELL DISEASE. Many heterozygotes for sickle-cell anemia are being diagnosed as a relatively incidental component of newborn screening programs designed to detect homozygotes. In addition, heterozygote screening programs are being offered in many cities in the United States and elsewhere.[178] The most reliable procedure for heterozygote detection is hemoglobin electrophoresis, which will also screen for other hemoglobinopathies. Molecular techniques have made prenatal diagnosis for sickle-cell anemia completely reliable. The three favorable features of screening for Tay-Sachs disease listed above apply here also. There is a major difference however in regard to the severity and burden of sickle-cell anemia in comparison to Tay-Sachs disease. There is considerable variation in expression for sickle-cell disease, and some individuals experience mild disease which is compatible with a long and productive life. In addition, there are major cultural, educational, and socioeconomic differences between the Jewish population and the black population in the United States and elsewhere. Because of some combination of these reasons, perhaps primarily due to the milder expression, heterozygote screening and prenatal diagnosis have not been used in combination to reduce the frequency of sickle-cell anemia to anywhere near the extent that this approach has been applied for Tay-Sachs disease. While heterozygote screening for sickle-cell anemia may be successful at an educational level or for individual couples, it has not reduced substantially the burden of disease in the population up to the present time. This may provide important lessons for milder disorders such as α_1-antitrypsin deficiency and familial hypercholesterolemia where individuals in the population may be more attracted to therapeutic strategies and may show little interest in preventive approaches which make extensive use of selective abortion.

OTHER DISEASES. Heterozygote screening programs for β thalassemia have been extremely successful in various parts of the Mediterranean and North America. Major reductions in the frequency of β thalassemia have been achieved.[179,180] Heterozygote screening programs for β thalassemia and α thalassemia may be appropriate in various parts of Asia as other health care needs are met with further economic development. The prospects for population based heterozygote screening for cystic fibrosis appear excellent, since there is now evidence from linkage disequilibrium that the majority of heterozygotes carry the same mutation. Reproductive decisions regarding risks for cystic fibrosis will be complex, since the disorder has a wide range of expression, intelligence is normal, and supportive treatment continues to improve. It is possible that further developments involving the automation of molecular diagnosis, particularly using the polymerase chain reaction, could increase the technical feasibility for heterozygote detection for disorders such as PKU, cystic fibrosis, α_1-antitrypsin deficiency, and other conditions. It is difficult to predict which programs will be widely accepted by populations for avoidance of affected individuals.

Prenatal Screening. Major forms of population based prenatal screening in use today include cytogenetic prenatal diagnosis for advanced maternal age, maternal serum α-fetoprotein analysis, and routine prenatal ultrasound. These methods represent a growing approach to monitor the health of the fetus prior to delivery, usually in conjunction with the option of elective abortion of abnormal fetuses. Utilization of cytogenetic prenatal diagnosis for women of advanced maternal age has grown steadily since it became generally available in the 1960s. The procedure is widely used, but utilization is quite variable depending on urban compared to rural location, educational level, and religious preference.[181] Maternal serum α-fetoprotein screening was instituted with the goal of prenatal detection of anencephaly and meningomyelocele.[170,182] Subsequently it was recognized that low levels of maternal serum α-fetoprotein may be associated with increased risk of Down syndrome. This has led to strategies which calculate the risk of Down syndrome based on maternal age in combination with the maternal serum α-fetoprotein level to determine who should be offered cytogenetic prenatal diagnosis.[183] Fetal ultrasound studies during the second trimester have become widespread and are routine in some settings. Careful ultrasound evaluation can detect a very broad range of fetal anatomic abnormalities.[184] Although heterozygote screening would optimally be implemented prior to conception, such testing is frequently delayed until the time of pregnancy. Strategies for prenatal screening are likely to continue to expand.

Screening for Disease in Later Life. Screening for genotypes that are associated with increased risk of disease in the individual or in their offspring or relatives is assuming many different forms. Newborn screening programs are detecting individuals who will have major disease risks later in life (e.g., sickle-cell anemia and cystic fibrosis). Screening institutionalized populations for genetic disorders can lead to genetic counseling for relatives. For example, detection of fragile X syndrome, chromosomal translocations, or Lesch-Nyhan syndrome can lead to anticipatory genetic counseling for numerous relatives.

However, the primary focus of screening for disease later in life would be to detect adults or children for whom medical intervention would be beneficial. Widespread use of laboratory screening in adult populations is leading to the identification of numerous individuals with disorders such as hyperlipidemia. Identification of disorders such as heterozygous familial hypercholesterolemia has both major therapeutic implications for the individual detected and implications for disease risk in offspring. The impetus to screen for diseases increases as therapeutic options improve. Genetic screening of individuals in the workplace is beginning to occur and may become more frequent. It is appropriate to consider whether individuals with heterozygous or homozygous α_1-antitrypsin deficiency should work in environments with pulmonary risks (e.g., coal mines). Genetic screening of populations carries many potential risks and benefits for the future.

TREATMENT OF GENETIC DISEASE

Genetic disease is the result of inherited abnormalities in the complex systems which program normal development and physiological homeostasis. Environmental factors contribute variably to the disease phenotype by stressing these defective systems. Treatment of genetic disorders requires accurate diagnosis, early intervention, and knowledge of the biochemical basis of the disorder, i.e., the pathophysiology. The current explosion of information concerning the molecular basis of genetic diseases plus continued technological advances in the analysis of biological samples (e.g., gas chromatography/mass spectrometry and fast-atom bombardment mass spectrometry) have greatly enhanced the capabilities for rapid and specific diagnosis.

While our understanding of the corresponding pathophysiology is increasing more slowly, the development of noninvasive metabolic monitoring techniques, such as positron emission tomography[185] and topical nuclear magnetic resonance spectrometry,[186] offer promising new approaches to this problem. Meanwhile, incomplete knowledge of pathophysiology hampers our attempts at therapeutics. For example, we still lack a clear understanding of the mechanism(s) and developmental timetable of the neural damage in phenylketonuria, and we are unsure if toxic precusors and/or deficiencies of downstream metabolites are the major pathologic factor(s) in the defects of fatty acid oxidation.

Evaluation of therapy of genetic disease is another difficult problem. Two general questions must be asked: (1) does the treatment improve the patients' condition and (2) does the treatment restore the patients to full physiological normality—as if they did not have the disease. These questions are relevant to the treatment of any medical disorder, but they have special significance for genetic diseases which often are predictable and preventable.

A recent study systematically evaluated the impact of therapy of 351 representative monogenic disorders on three basic variables: life span, reproductive capability, and social adaptation.[1,90] The results showed that available therapy normalized life span in 15 percent of the patients, reproductive capability in 11 percent, and social adaptation in only 6 percent. Only slightly better outcomes were found with a subset of 65 diseases in which the basic defect was known.[1] Because more severe diseases are more quickly recognized, this sample of currently known diseases may be skewed toward the worst. Nevertheless, the results are disappointing, and they highlight both the difficulty in developing effective therapies for genetic diseases and the need for continued work in this area. The results also underscore the value of preventive measures (genetic screening, genetic counseling, and prenatal diagnosis) in the management of genetic disease.

Conventional approaches to therapy of genetic disease can be viewed as a biologic model starting from the clinical phenotype and working back to the level of the defective gene.[187,187a] Table 1-11 lists some therapies currently used.

Table 1-11 Some Examples of Proven and Experimental Treatments for Inborn Errors of Metabolism

Level of treatment and method	*Disorder*
Clinical phenotype	
Patient education	
Avoidance of certain drugs	Pharmacogenetic disorders
Avoidance of sun exposure	Albinism Xeroderma pigmentosa
Pharmacologic	
β-Blockers	Marfan syndrome
Anticonvulsants	Neurodegenerative disorders
Surgical	
Orthopedic reconstruction	Chondrodystrophies
Colectomy	Familial polyposis coli
Metabolite	
Substrate restriction	
Phenylalanine	Phenylketonuria
Branched chain amino acids	Maple syrup urine disease
Galactose	Galactosemia and galactokinase deficiency
Alternative pathway	
Benzoate and phenylacetate	Urea cycle disorders
Glycine	Isovaleric acidemia
Carnitine	Organic acidemias
Cysteamine	Cystinosis
Penicillamine	Wilson disease
Metabolic inhibition	
Allopurinol	Gout
Mevinolin	Familial hypercholesterolemia
Replacement of deficient product	
Glucose polymers (cornstarch)	Glycogen storage disease, types I and III
Uridine	Hereditary orotic aciduria
Corticosteroids	Adrenogenital syndromes
Thyroxine	Familial goiter
Biotin	Biotinidase deficiency
Dysfunctional protein	
Activation	
Pyridoxine (Vitamin B_6)	Homocystinuria
Thiamine	Maple syrup urine disease
Protein replacement	
Growth hormone	Growth hormone deficiency
Factor VIII	Classic hemophilia
α_1-Antitrypsin	α_1-Antitrypsin deficiency
Polyethylene glycol–adenosine deaminase	Adenosine deaminase deficiency
Organ transplantation	
As a source for a specific protein	
Allogenic bone marrow	Lysosomal storage diseases β-Thalassemia
Liver	Glycogen storage disease, type 1 Familial hypercholesterolemia Ornithine transcarbamylase deficiency
As a protein source and replacement of a damaged organ	
Liver	α_1-Antitrypsin deficiency Hepatorenal tyrosinemia
Kidney	Cystinosis

Treatment at the Clinical Phenotype Level

Therapy at this level covers a variety of conventional medical practices and depends on a thorough understanding of the natural history of the particular disorder. The basic genetic defect is not corrected, but the patients' problems often are ameliorated. Examples include education of patients with pharmacogenetic susceptibilities, instruction to limit sun exposure for patients with the various forms of albinism and xeroderma pigmentosa, administration of β-adrenergic blocking agents to patients with Marfan syndrome to prevent or slow dilatation of the aortic root, and use of anticonvulsants for a variety of patients with neurogenetic disorders. In addition, a host of surgical interventions can benefit patients with malformations, chondrodystrophies, and disorders with increased risk of malignancy in a particular organ.

Treatment at the Metabolite Level

Therapy at this level often involves nutritional or pharmacological approaches. It is absolutely dependent on some understanding of pathophysiology (Fig. 1-23). Deficient function of a mutant enzyme may cause a disease phenotype because (1) a substrate accumulates to toxic levels (precursor toxicity), (2) an alternative metabolite is produced in excessive amounts (alternative pathway overflow), (3) there is reduced formation of the reaction product or some downstream metabolite (product deficiency), or (4) some combination of these possibilities coexists. Although this paradigm is most easily visualized for enzymes in a metabolic pathway, it holds for all proteins which participate in biochemical interactions with small molecules.

Substrate Restriction. Dietary alterations designed to restrict intake of a particular substrate may be effective if the pathophysiology involves accumulation of a toxic precursor whose major source is nutritional. Inborn errors of essential amino acids and certain sugars are the best examples of this approach. Diets restricted in phenylalanine or the branched chain amino acids are effective in preventing the mental retardation associated with phenylketonuria and maple syrup urine disease, respectively, if the diets are started soon after birth and monitored in such a way that amounts of these substances just sufficient for normal growth are supplied[188] (see Chaps. 15 and 22). Episodes of net protein catabolism (e.g., associated with intercurrent infections or trauma) complicate this therapy by providing large amounts of the offending amino acids from endogenous sources. In the case of maple syrup urine disease, these episodes may rquire hospitalization for administration of intravenous fluids and even dialysis. In a similar fashion, lifetime restriction of dietary galactose in patients with galactosemia due to deficiency of galactose 1-phosphate uridyl transferase corrects growth failure, prevents cataracts, and reduces but does not seem to prevent completely the impairment of cognitive development (Chap. 13). Despite this improved outcome, the observation that treated galactosemic females exhibit ovarian failure as a long-term complication of their disease[189] indicates that the efficacy of therapy is only partial.

Utilization of Alternative Pathways to Remove Toxic Metabolites. For disorders in which the pathophysiology involves accumulation of a toxic precursor or alternative pathway overflow, it is sometimes possible to promote conversion of the offending metabolite to a readily eliminated substance.[190] The effectiveness of this approach may be limited by the capacity of the converting system and often it must be combined with

Fig. 1-23 Pathophysiological consequences of a genetic defect in a metabolic pathway. Substrate A is converted via a series of intermediates to a final product, D. The enzymes catalyzing these reactions are indicated by the horizontal arrows. A also is converted to F in an alternative pathway. A genetic deficiency in the enzyme converting A to B (indicated by the hatched rectangle) may have pathophysiological consequences related to accumulation of A (precursor toxicity), overflow to F (alternative pathway overflow), reduced formation of D (product deficiency), or some combination of these possibilities.

$$\rightarrow \Uparrow A \dashv\vdash B \longrightarrow C \longrightarrow \Downarrow D$$

$$\hookrightarrow E \longrightarrow \Uparrow F$$

some dietary restriction of the offending substrate. Administration of benzoate and phenylacetate to patients with inborn errors of ureagenesis is a good example of this approach[191] (Chap. 20). Benzoate and phenylacetate undergo conjugation reactions with glycine and glutamine, respectively, forming hippurate and phenylacetylglutamine. These conjugates are readily excreted and contain more nitrogen than their precursors, thereby providing a means to eliminate excess nitrogen. When used in conjunction with restrictions of dietary protein, this therapy reduces the accumulation of the toxic precursor (ammonium) characteristic of the urea cycle disorders. Similar approaches include the use of glycine to conjugate with isovaleryl CoA in isovaleric acidemia, carnitine to conjugate with accumulated CoA esters in various defects of fatty acid and organic acid metabolism, cysteamine to help eliminate cystine in cystinosis, penicillamine to remove stored copper in Wilson disease, and phlebotomy to remove iron in hemochromatosis (see Chaps. 28, 33, 107, 54, and 55, respectively).

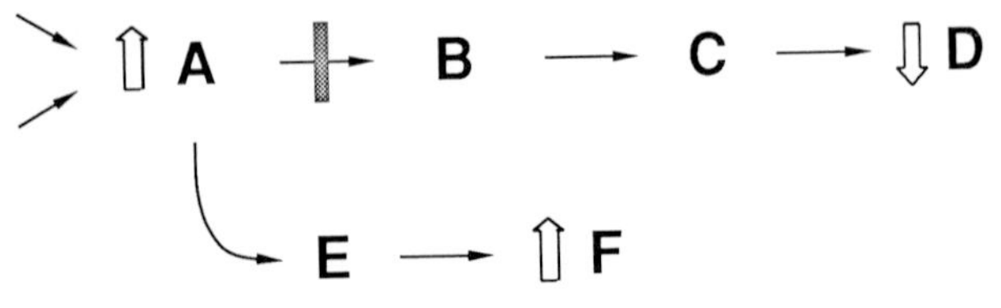

Metabolic Inhibitors. In certain disorders, often those in which the alternative pathway produces a toxic level of a particular metabolite, it is possible to reduce the accumulation by inhibiting a step in the pathway. This may lead to accumulation of upstream substrates which may be better tolerated if this approach is to be successful. Allopurinol, for example, is used to inhibit xanthine oxidase in gout and in a variety of situations characterized by excessive purine degradation and uric acid accumulation (Chaps. 37 and 38). Inhibition of xanthine oxidase lowers the level of uric acid and reduces the risk of uric acid nephropathy and gouty arthritis. Accumulation of xanthine is the biochemical consequence of xanthine oxidase inhibition but, because of its greater aqueous solubility, xanthine accumulation usually is well tolerated. Similarly, heterozygotes for mutations at the LDL receptor locus experience significant reductions in plasma cholesterol when treated with mevinolin, a potent inhibitor of 3-hydroxy-3-methyglutaryl-CoA reductase, which catalyzes an important early and rate limiting step in the synthesis of cholesterol[192] (Chap. 48).

Replacement of Deficient Product. For disorders in which the pathophysiology involves product deficit, nutritional or pharmacological approaches to replenishing this product may be effective. For example, deficient hepatic glucose production in patients with deficiency of glucose 6-phosphatase (glycogen storage disease, type Ia) is treated by frequent feeding with glucose or glucose polymers (Chap. 12). Cornstarch, a slowly digested glucose polymer, acts as a timed-release source of glucose and is helpful to these patients.[193] Similarly, administration of uridine to patients with impaired pyrimidine synthesis due to hereditary orotic aciduria provides a source for the deficient product and corrects the macrocytic anemia caused by pyrimidine deficiency (Chap. 43). Furthermore, the products depress the stimuli for pyrimidine biosynthesis, reducing orotic acid production and decreasing episodes of orotic acid nephrolithiasis.

Many of the inborn errors in hormone biosynthesis respond well to pharmacologic replacement of the deficient hormone. Thyroid hormone replacement for patients with cretinism (Chap. 73), corticosteroid administration to patients with the adrenogenital syndrome (Chap. 74), and biotin treatment of biotinidase deficient patients (Chap. 83) are examples of product replacement therapy. Biotinidase deficiency disrupts recovery of biotin from biotinylated proteins, resulting in increased biotin losses and eventually biotin deficiency and impairment of the biotin-dependent carboxylases. The recognition of this cause of mental retardation by Wolf and his colleagues,[194] the development of a presymptomatic screening test,[195] and the ease of replacement therapy with biotin all augur for this being one of the most successfully treated genetic disorders.

Treatment at the Dysfunctional Protein Level

Therapy at this level involves either activation or replenishment of the mutant protein.

Activation with Vitamin Cofactors. Enhancement of the activity of a dysfunctional enzyme may be possible when the protein utilizes a vitamin cofactor which is tolerated by the patient in amounts far exceeding normal. Furthermore, not all mutations of a vitamin-dependent protein will respond. Those that do are likely to be missense mutations which either decrease the affinity of the enzyme for its cofactor or destabilize the protein in a way that can be partially overcome by substantial increments in cofactor concentration in the surrounding milieu. For example, about one-third of the cases of homocystinuria due to deficiency of cystathione β-synthase recover a functionally significant amount of enzyme activity when treated with large doses (50–500 mg/day) of pyridoxine (vitamin B_6) (Chap. 23). The actual increment in enzyme activity is often small but is sufficient to improve or even normalize metabolic flux in the transsulfuration pathway. Since activation of residual activity both reduces precursor accumulation and increases product formation, knowledge of the pathophysiological mechanism is less critical. Other examples of this type of therapy include the use of thiamine in some cases of maple syrup urine disease and thiamine, biotin, or riboflavin for certain forms of lactic acidosis. Thus, vitamin responsive disorders may represent either examples of inborn errors of vitamin metabolism with replacement of deficient product as described for biotinidase deficiency above or examples of enhancement of apoprotein function as described for cystathionine β-synthase deficiency.

Protein Replacement Therapies. Replacement of the mutant protein continues to be an active area of research. To have some hope of succeeding, the protein must be administered directly into or eventually reach its appropriate physiological compartment. Thus, blood proteins or proteins which transverse the vascular compartment (peptide hormones) are good candidates for this approach. Other considerations include the availability, stability, and immunogenicity of the administered protein. In a few instances, recombinant DNA technology is being utilized to supply sufficient amounts of pure protein (e.g., human growth hormone). Other proteins, including factor VIII for the treatment of hemophilia A and α_1-antitrypsin for the treatment of its deficiency,[196] are still being purified from natural sources but may soon be produced by recombinant DNA technology. This advance would ensure adequate supplies and avoid the risk of transmission of contaminating viruses to the recipients.

An innovative approach to the problems of stability and avoidance of immunological recognition has been reported by Hershfield et al.[197] in the treatment of severe combined immunodeficiency caused by adenosine deaminase deficiency (Chap. 40). These investigators used polyethylene glycol (PEG) cross-linked to bovine adenosine deaminase and administered the product by intramuscular injection to adenosine deaminase deficient patients. The bulky hydrophilic PEG molecules coat the surface of the enzyme and prevent immunologic recognition and rapid clearance of it from the vascular space. Substrates and products diffuse through the PEG layer and reach the active site of the protein. Weekly intramuscular injections are sufficient to maintain high blood adenosine deaminase levels and have resulted in gradual improvement in immunologic function over several months. The long-term consequences of continued exposure to PEG and the feasibility of this sort of approach in patients who are not immunocompromised will require additional study.

Organ Transplantation

Organ transplantation lies on the borderline between therapy at the level of the dysfunctional protein and gene therapy. On the one hand a transplanted organ supplies a deficient protein; on the other, the transplanted tissue also brings new genetic information, although this is not integrated into the recipient's genome. Without resolving the semantic question, transplantation of kidneys, bone marrow, and livers is being applied increasingly to a variety of genetic diseases. The development of more effective and specific immunosuppressants (particularly cyclosporine) and inadequacies of more conventional therapies contribute to the increased interest in this form of treatment. The long-term efficacy and consequences of organ transplantation are unknown.

In some instances, transplantation is done strictly to supply the recipient with a tissue which can provide a missing protein; in others, the transplant also replaces a damaged organ. Examples of the former include bone marrow transplants for lysosomal storage diseases[198] as well as β thalassemia[199] and liver transplantation for type I glycogen storage disease,[200] familial hypercholesterolemia[201] and ornithine transcarbamylase deficiency.[202] Examples of the latter include liver transplants in α_1-antitrypsin deficiency and hepatorenal tyrosinemia[203] as well as kidney transplants in cystinosis. In the future, the distinction may be relevant because, when the intent is simply to provide a source for a deficient protein, it may be possible to perform partial liver transplants or even to infuse hepatocytes into the portal vein or peritoneal cavity. The recipient's liver, which is normal except for the specific deficiency, can then remain in place. Promising results with hepatocytes bound to inert beads injected into the peritoneal cavity of rats with analbuminemia or UDP-glucuronyltransferase deficiency have been reported.[204] Immunosuppression still is required, but the procedure is much less involved than liver transplantation. Perhaps this technique will be improved in the future and combined with a method of storing the donor cells indefinitely (as is done with tissue culture cells) so that frozen normal hepatocytes would be immediately available as a reagent to treat, at least temporarily, a variety of liver specific deficiencies.

A second major consideration when transplantation is performed to provide a tissue source for a deficient protein is whether or not the protein will reach the tissue or organelle of pathophysiological significance. This is of special concern for bone marrow transplantation in the lysosomal storage diseases. The rationale is that the transplanted marrow will provide cells capable of repopulating the recipient's reticuloendothelial system, and the lysosomal enzymes released from the donor cells will enter host cells by systems which deliver the enzyme to the proper subcellular compartments (i.e., lysosomes). Evidence from marrow transplants in patients with mucopolysaccharidosis indicates that both of these desired results occur. It is not clear, however if either transplant derived cells or enzymes can cross the blood-brain barrier. Since central nervous system involvement is a prominent feature of most lysosomal storage diseases, failure to reach this tissue would severely limit the applicability of bone marrow transplantation, particularly in iew of the attendant morbidity and mortality. Clinical trials in patients with a variety of lysosomal storage diseases provide no evidence of transfer of donor cells or enzymes across the blood-brain barrier.[198] The one exception is a study done in dogs with α-iduronidase deficiency and a Hurler-Scheie phenotype who had some biochemical and ultrastructural evidence for improvement in the central nervous system 3 to 9 months after transplant.[205] This tantalyzing observation requires additional investigation.

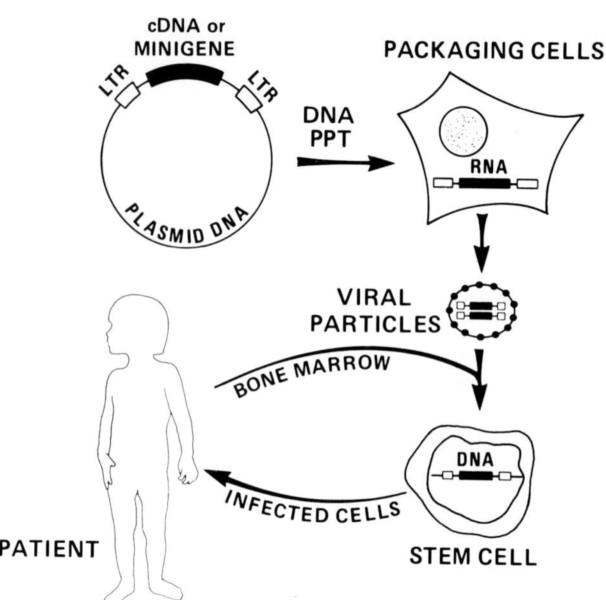

Fig. 1-24 One strategy for attempting gene replacement therapy for bone marrow derived cells. *(From A. Beaudet.[217] Used by permission.)*

Somatic Gene Therapy

While there is great hope that patients with genetic disorders can be treated by somatic gene replacement (Chap. 2), as of early 1988, no patient has benefited from such an approach. Most of the interest has focused on introduction of a competent replacement gene into tissues such as bone marrow stem cells, hepatocytes, or fibroblasts. A number of biologic considerations enter into the feasibility of somatic gene replacement therapy, including the question of whether the addition of normal gene product will be therapeutic. Presumably this would be the case for many or most disorders, but it might not be adequate for a "true dominant" disorder where a mutant gene can negate the presence of normal gene product. The latter instance might require gene specific correction or elimination of the dominant mutation. And how much gene product would indeed be required to ameliorate or totally correct the disease phenotype? In some instances, as little as 1 to 5 percent of normal gene product activity might be virtually curative (e.g., some enzyme activities or clotting factors). The need for tissue specific expression and gene regulation are also important, as are several ethical considerations. Many reviews and commentaries on the potential for somatic gene replacement therapy are available.[206–208] Early efforts at gene therapy have focused attention on tissue which can be removed for purposes of infection and then restored to the patient (Fig. 1-24). This approach is feasible for bone marrow and fibroblasts and perhaps for hepatocytes, epithelial cells, and some other cell types. Disorders which affect bone marrow derived cells merit particular attention, including sickle-cell anemia, thalassemias, adenosine deaminase deficiency, chronic granulomatous disease, and leukocyte adhesion deficiency. It may be possible to use bone marrow–derived cells to achieve expression of gene products which ordinarily would be produced by other tissues. Production of clotting factors, hormones, or enzymes that utilize circulating metabolites might be therapeutic in bone marrow cells even if this were not the natural site for expression. Similar use might be made of cultured fibroblasts or epithelial cells. The feasibility of infecting bone marrow–derived cells, fibroblasts, or hepatocytes in vitro followed by reintroduction of the infected cells into the organism is being explored in various rodents and other animal models.[209–211] Eventually, one goal might be to obtain adequate viral titers and targeting ability to allow direct injection of viral preparations into humans. At the moment, diseases which would require introduction of DNA sequences into the central nervous system would seem to be the most challenging and least feasible.

The need for proper gene regulation is likely to vary considerably from disease to disease. In many instances where there is total absence of gene product, it is probable that any level of expression—from very low to even excessive—would be beneficial. In other instances, relatively precise levels of expression and tissue specificity would be required as in the case of hemoglobin disorders.

Most of the work up to the present has focused on the use of retroviral vectors (derived from components of retroviral genomes). Typically, a cloned cDNA for a human gene product is inserted into a retroviral vector using the long terminal repeat (LTR) of the retrovirus or a regulatory element from another gene as a promoter. Pseudovirus particles are produced by introduction of the vector sequences into packaging cell lines, which are designed to provide the necessary viral gene products in trans without leading to the production of infectious retrovirus particles. Pseudovirus particles encoding the following human gene products have been demonstrated: adenosine deaminase, HPRT, phenylalanine hydroxylase, α_1-antitrypsin, β-glucocerebrosidase, LDL receptor, β globin, and others (see chapters in gene therapy section in Ref. 212). There have been difficulties in obtaining good gene expression after reimplantation of cells into animals, but some limited expression in intact animals is being reported.[209]

Many different diseases have been discussed as candidates for somatic gene therapy. The relative feasibility for disorders being considered takes into account the burden of the disease, the availability of alternative treatment, the disease frequency, the requirement for tissue specificity, the possible need for gene regulation, and the availability of the cloned gene. Some widely discussed examples are listed in Table 1-12, including some examples where feasibility appears quite poor because of the need to reach the central nervous system (e.g., Huntington disease and Tay-Sachs disease).

Table 1-12 Human Diseases as Candidates for Gene Replacement Therapy

Disorders	*Burden of disease*	*Alternative treatment*	*Disease frequency*	*Requirement for tissue specificity*	*Regulation*	*Relative feasibility**
Hemoglobinopathies	Great	Transfusion, fair to poor	1 in 600 in ethnic groups	Erythroid	Required	+ +
Lesch-Nyhan	Great	Poor	Rare	Brain, ?other	?Not essential	+ +
Adenosine deaminase and nucleoside phosphorylase	Great	Transplant, enzyme replacement, fair to good	Very rare	Bone marrow	?Not essential	+ + +
Leukocyte adhesion deficiency	Great	Transplant, fair to poor	Very rare	Bone marrow	?Not essential	+ + + +
Phenylketonuria	Small to moderate	Diet, good	1 in 11,000	Liver, ?other	?Not essential	+ +
Urea cycle disorders	Moderate to great	Diet, drug, good to poor	1 in 30,000 for all types	Liver, ?other	?Not essential	+ + +
α_1-Antitrypsin	Moderate	Poor	1 in 3500	Liver, ?other	?Not essential	+ + +
Hemophilia A & B	Moderate to great	Replacement, fair (AIDS)	1 in 10,000 males	?Any organ, factor VIII	?Not essential	+ + + +
Lysosomal storage diseases	Great	Poor	1 in 1500 for all types	Brain for many	?Not essential	+
Familial hypercholesterolemia	Great	Diet, drug, fair	1 in 500 heterozygotes	Liver, ?other	Some importance	+ +
Cystic fibrosis	Great	Supportive, fair to poor	1 in 2500 whites	?	?	?
Duchenne muscular dystrophy	Great	Poor	1 in 10,000 males	?Muscle	?	?Poor
Tay-Sachs disease	Great	Poor	1 in 3000 Jews	?Brain	?Not essential	?Poor
Huntington disease	Great	Poor	1 in 20,000	?Brain	?	?Poor

*Relative feasibility attempts to take into account requirements for regulation, accessibility of target organ, alternative treatment, and risk-benefit considerations.

ANIMAL MODELS

Numerous examples of genetic diseases in animals are cited throughout this text and elsewhere,[213] including diseases in mice, rats, dogs, cats, sheep, and cattle, among others. Exactly analogous enzyme deficiencies and gene defects are known as well as similar clinical phenotypes such as albinism. Available models include amino acid disorders, urea cycle disorders, numerous lysosomal enzyme deficiencies, receptor deficiencies, bilirubin disorders, and clotting disorders. For example, a mutated canine guanosine triphosphate cyclohydrolase deficiency mimics the human counterpart variant of PKU (Chap. 15). These animal models are likely to become of increasing importance because they facilitate the study of two areas which are particularly poorly developed in biochemical genetics: (1) treatment and (2) understanding of pathogenesis.

Another perspective occurs when diseases are discovered first in animals, and analogous human disorders are then sought. Defects in the gene for myelin basic protein cause the *shiverer* phenotype in mice, and this disorder has been characterized at a nucleic acid and protein level.[214] The discovery of homeotic mutations in *Drosophila* has led to the identification of homologous regions in homeotic genes in mice and humans.[215] Perhaps this will lead to the identification of human genetic disorders involving these homeotic loci.

Animal models are also receiving new impetus from two quarters. First there is the great potential value for trials of somatic gene replacement therapy. Prior to human treatment, there is a need to demonstrate both the safety and efficacy of such procedures. Efficacy can best be judged by correcting an analogous defect in an animal prior to human trials. The second impetus is coming from the potential to generate animal models for human mutations, particularly in mice, rather than simply discovering naturally occurring mutants. This has been achieved in part by intensely mutagenizing mice and screening them for biochemical defects. This has led to the discovery of a series of mutations at the mouse *mdx* locus,[216] which is homologous with the Duchenne muscular dystrophy locus.[9] Another strategy has been to take advantage of the availability of embryonic stem cells which can be cultured and then used to generate chimeric animals and introduce new genotypes into the germ line. This strategy has been used to obtain HPRT deficient mice.[142,143] Many animal models have exactly analogous biochemical defects and phenotypes compared to the human diseases. Interestingly, for the *mdx* mouse and for the HPRT deficient mouse, this is not the case. The *mdx* mouse has no significant muscular disability and the HPRT deficient mouse does not show self-mutilation or obvious neurologic symptoms. While one might be concerned that these then represent poor animal models, they may represent very good models in terms of the potential for understanding pathogenesis and developing therapy, if one can understand the different consequences of the mutations in different species. Attempts to analyze the homeostatic differences between the mouse and human diseases are likely to focus attention on those factors which are instrumental in the primary genetic defect generating the phenotypic abnormalities (i.e., pathophysiology). Understanding the basis of these differences might provide the insights to modify the human circumstance so that it is less symptomatic and more similar to the *mdx* mouse or HPRT deficient mouse.

REFERENCES

1. HAYES A, COSTA, T, SCRIVER CR, CHILDS B: The effect of Mendelian disease on human health. II: Response to treatment. *Am J Med Genet* 21:243, 1985.
2. WILLIAMS RJ: *Biochemical Individuality*. New York, Wiley, 1956.
3. GARROD AE: *Inborn Factors in Disease*. London, Oxford University Press, 1931.

4. MCKUSICK VA: *Mendelian Inheritance in Man*, 8th ed. Baltimore, Johns Hopkins University Press, 1988.
5. FREZAL J: Human gene mapping 9. *Cytogenet Cell Genet* 46:1, 1988.
6. *Mapping and Sequencing the Human Genome*. Washington, DC, National Academy of Sciences, 1988.
7. GARROD A: The lessons of rare maladies. *Lancet* 1:1055, 1928.
8. PAGE DC, MOSHER R, SIMPSON EM, FISHER EM, MARDON G, POLLACK J, MCGILLIVRAY B, de la CHAPPELE A, BROWN LG: The sex-determining region of the human Y chromosome encodes a finger protein. *Cell* 51:1091, 1987.
9. HOFFMAN EP, BROWN RH, KUNKEL LM: Dystrophin: The protein product of the Duchenne muscular dystrophy locus. *Cell* 51:919, 1987.
10. GARROD AE: Inborn errors of metabolism (Croonian Lectures). *Lancet* 2:1, 73, 142, 214, 1908.
11. GARROD AE: *Inborn Errors of Metabolism*, 2d ed. London, Oxford University Press, 1923.
12. GARROD AE: A contribution to the study of alkaptonuria. *Proc R Med Chir Soc* 2:130, 1899.
13. GARROD AE: The incidence of alkaptonuria: A study in chemical individuality. *Lancet* 2:1616, 1902.
14. MENDEL G: *Versuche über Pflanzenhybriden*. Leipzig, Engelmann, 1901.
15. BEARN AG, MILLER ED: Archibald Garrod and the development of the concept of inborn errors of metabolism. *Bull Hist Med* 53:315, 1979.
16. LaDU BN, ZANNONI VA, LASTER L, SEEGMILLER JE: The nature of the defect in tyrosine metabolism in alcaptonuria. *J Biol Chem* 230:251, 1958.
17. JOHANNSEN W: The genotype conception of heredity. *Am Nat* 45:129, 1911.
18. BEADLE GW: Biochemical genetics. *Chem Rev* 37:15, 1945.
19. BEADLE GW, TATUM EL: Experimental control of developmental reactions. *Am Nat* 75:107, 1941.
20. BEADLE GW, TATUM EL: Genetic control of biochemical reactions in *Neurospora*. *Proc Natl Acad Sci USA* 27:499, 1941.
21. EPHRUSSI B: Chemistry of "eye color hormones" of *Drosophila*. *Q Rev Biol* 17:327, 1942.
22. BEADLE GW: Genes and chemical reactions in *Neurospora*. *Science* 129:1715, 1959.
23. TATUM EL: A case history of biological research. *Science* 129:1711, 1959.
24. HOROWITZ NH, LEUPOLD U: Some recent studies bearing on the one gene one enzyme hypothesis. *Cold Spring Harbor Symp Quant Biol* 16:65, 1951.
25. BENZER S: The elementary units of heredity, in McElroy WD, Glass B (eds): *The Chemical Basis of Heredity*. Baltimore, Johns Hopkins University Press, 1957, p 70.
26. JONES ME: Pyrimidine nucleotide biosynthesis in animals: Genes, enzymes, and regulation of UMP biosynthesis. *Annu Rev Biochem* 49:253, 1980.
27. DOUGLASS J, CIVELLI O, HERBERT E: Polyprotein gene expression: Generation of diversity of neuroendocrine peptides. *Annu Rev Biochem* 53:665, 1984.
28. LYNCH DR, SNYDER SH: Neuropeptides: Multiple molecular forms, metabolic pathways, and receptors. *Annu Rev Biochem* 55:773, 1986.
29. SCHIBLER U, SIERRA F: Alternative promoters in developmental gene expression. *Annu Rev Genet* 21:237, 1987.
30. AMARA SG, JONAS V, ROSENFELD MG, ONG ES, EVANS RM: Alternative RNA processing in calcitonin gene expression generates mRNAs encoding different polypeptide products. *Nature* 298:240, 1982.
31. NABESHIMA Y, FUJII-KURIYAMA Y, MURAMATSU M, OGATA K: Alternative transcription and two modes of splicing result in two myosin light chains from one gene. *Nature* 308:333, 1984.
32. BREITBART RE, ANDREADIA A, NADAL-GINARD B: Alternative splicing: A ubiquitous mechanism for the generation of multiple protein isoforms from single genes. *Annu Rev Biochem* 56:467, 1987.
33. CRAIGEN WJ, CASKEY CT: Translational frameshifting: Where will it stop? *Cell* 50:1, 1987.
34. JACKS T, POWER MD, MASIARZ FR, LUCIW PA, BARR PJ, VARMUS HE: Characterization of ribosomal frameshifting in HIV-1 *gag-pol* expression. *Nature* 331:280, 1988.
35. GIBSON QH: The reduction of methaemoglobin in red blood cells and studies on the cause of idiopathic methaemoglobinaemia. *Biochem J* 42:13, 1948.
36. CORI GT, CORI CF: Glucose-6-phosphatase of the liver in glycogen storage disease. *J Biol Chem* 199:661, 1952.
37. JERVIS GA: Phenylpyruvic oligophrenia: Deficiency of phenylalanine oxidizing system. *Proc Soc Exp Biol Med* 82:514, 1953.
38. PAULING L, ITANO HA, SINGER SJ, WELLS IC: Sickle cell anemia: A molecular disease. *Science* 110:543, 1949.
39. INGRAM VM: A specific chemical difference between the globins of normal human and sickle cell anaemia haemoglobin. *Nature* 178:792, 1956.
40. KAN YW, DOZY AM: Polymorphism of DNA sequence adjacent to human β-globin structural gene: Relationship to sickle mutation. *Proc Natl Acad Sci USA* 75:5631, 1978.
41. BOTSTEIN D, WHITE RL, SKOLNICK M, DAVIS RW: Construction of a genetic linkage map in man using restriction fragment length polymorphisms. *Am J Hum Genet* 32:314, 1980.
42. ORKIN SH: Reverse genetics and human disease. *Cell* 47:845, 1986.
43. GEHRING WH, HIROMI Y: Homeotic genes and the homeobox. *Annu Rev Genet* 20:147, 1986.
44. ROYER-POKORA B, KUNKEL LM, MONACO AP, GOFF SC, NEWBURGER PE, BAEHNER RL, COLE FS, CURNUTTE JT, ORKIN SH: Cloning the gene for an inherited human disorder—chronic granulomatous disease—on the basis of its chromosomal location. *Nature* 322:32, 1986.
45. KOENIG M, HOFFMAN EP, BERTELSON CJ, MONACO AP, FEENER C, KUNKEL LM: Complete cloning of the Duchenne muscular dystrophy (DMD) cDNA and preliminary genomic organization of the DMD gene in normal and affected individuals. *Cell* 50:509, 1987.
46. FRIEND SH, BERNARDS R, ROGELJ S, WEINBERG RA, RAPAPORT JM, ALBERT DM, DRYJA TP: A human DNA segment with properties of the gene that predisposes to retinoblastoma and osteosarcoma. *Nature* 323:643, 1986.
47. GILLIAM TC, TANZI RE, HAINES JL, BONNER TI, FARYNIARZ AG, HOBBS WJ, MacDONALD ME, CHENG SV, FOLSTEIN SE, CONNEALLY PM, WEXLER NS, GUSELLA JF: Localization of the Huntington's disease gene to a small segment of chromosome 4 flanked by D4S10 and the telomere. *Cell* 50:565, 1987.
48. REEDERS ST, BREUNING MH, DAVIES KE, NICHOLLS RD, JARMAN AP, HIGGS DR, PEARSON PL, WEATHERALL DJ: A highly polymorphic DNA marker linked to adult polycystic kidney disease on chromosome 16. *Nature* 317:542, 1985.
49. SEIZINGER BR, ROULEAU GA, OZELIUS LJ, LANE AH, FARYNIARZ AG, CHAO MV, HUSON S, KORF BR, PARRY DM, PERICAK-VANCE MA, COLLINS FS, HOBBS WJ, FALCONE BG, IANNAZZI JA, ROY JC, ST. GEORGE-HYSLOP PH, TANZI RE, BOTHWELL MA, UPADHYAYA M, HARPER P, GOLDSTEIN AE, HOOVER DL, BADER JL, SPENCE MA, MULVIHILL JJ, AYLSWORTH AS, VANCE JM, ROSSENWASSER GOD, GASKELL PC, ROSEO AD, MARTUZA RL, BREAKEFIELD XO, GUSELLA JF: Genetic linkage of von Recklinghausen neurofibromatosis to the nerve growth factor receptor gene. *Cell* 49:589, 1987.
50. SEIZINGER BR, ROULEAU GA, OZELIUS LJ, LANE AH, FARMER GE, LAMIELL JM, HAINES J, YUEN JWM, COLLINS D, MAJOOR-KRAKAUER D, BONNER T, MATHEW C, RUBENSTEIN A, HALPERIN J, McCONKIE-ROSELL A, GREEN JS, TROFATTER JA, PONDER BA, EIERMAN L, BOWMER MI, SCHIMKE R, OOSTRA B, ARONIN N, SMITH DI, DRABKIN H, WAZIRI MH, HOBBS WJ, MARTUZA RL, CONNEALLY PM, HSIA YE, GUSELLA JF: Von Hippel-Lindau disease maps to the region of chromosome 3 associated with renal cell carcinoma. *Nature* 332:268, 1988.
51. BODMER WF, BAILEY CJ, BODMER J, BUSSEY HJR, ELLIS A, GORMAN P, LUCIBELLO FC, MURDAY VA, RIDER SH, SCAMBLER P, SHEER D, SOLOMON E, SPURR NK: Localization of the gene for familial adenomatous polyposis on chromosome 5. *Nature* 328:614, 1987.
52. HERRERA L, KAKATI S, GIBAS L, PIETRZAK E, SANDBERG AA: Brief clinical report: Gardner syndrome in a man with an interstitial deletion of 5q. *Am J Med Genet* 25:473, 1986.
53. MARX JL: Putting the human genome on the map. *Science* 229:150, 1985.
54. EIBERG H, MOHR J, SCHMIEGELOW K, NIELSEN LS, WILLIAMSON R: Linkage relationships of paraoxonase (PON) with other markers: Indication of PON-cystic fibrosis synteny. *Clin Genet* 28:265, 1985.
55. TSUI L-P, BUCHWALD M, BARKER D, BRAMAN JC, KNOWLTON R, SCHUMM JW, EIBERT H, MOHR J, KENNEDY D, PLAVSIC N, ZSIGA M, MARKIEWICZ D, AKOTS G, BROWN V, HELMS C, GRAVIUS T, PARKER C, REDIKER K, DONIS-KELLER H: Cystic fibrosis locus defined by a genetically linked polymorphic DNA marker. *Science* 230:1054, 1985.
56. WHITE R, WOODWARD C, LEPPERT M, O'CONNELL P, HOFF M, HERBST J, LALOUEL J-M, DEAN M, VANDE WOUDE G: A closely linked genetic marker for cystic fibrosis. *Nature* 318:382, 1985.
57. WAINWRIGHT BJ, SCAMBLER PG, SCHMIDTKE J, WATSON EA, LAW H-Y, FARRALL M, COOKE HJ, EIBERT H, WILLIAMSON R: Localization of cystic fibrosis locus to human chromosome 7cen-q22. *Nature* 318:384, 1985.
58. BEAUDET A, BOWCOCK A, BUCHWALD M, CAVALLI-SFORZA L, FARRALL M, KING M-C, KLINGER K, LALOUEL J-M, LATHROP G, NAYLOR S, OTT J, TSUI L-C, WAINWRIGHT B, WATKINS P, WHITE R, WILLIAMSON R: Linkage of cystic fibrosis to two tightly linked DNA markers: Joint report from a collaborative study. *Am J Hum Genet* 39:681, 1986.
59. GROSVELD F, van ASSENDELFT GB, GREAVES DR, KOLLIAS G: Position independent, high level expression of the human β-globin gene in transgenic mice. *Cell* 51:975, 1987.
60. JELINEK WR, SCHMID CW: Repetitive sequences in eukaryotic DNA and their expression. *Annu Rev Biochem* 51:813, 1982.
61. BIRD AP: CpG-rich islands and the function of DNA methylation. *Nature* 321:209, 1986.

62. ALBERTS B, BRAY D, LEWIS J, RAFF M, ROBERTS K, WATSON JD: *Molecular Biology of the Cell.* New York, Garland, 1983.
63. DARNELL J, LODISH H, BALTIMORE D: *Molecular Cell Biology.* New York, Scientific American Books, 1986.
64. WATSON JD, HOPKINS NH, ROBERTS JW, STEITZ JA, WEINER AM: *Molecular Biology of the Gene.* Menlo Park, Benjamin/Cummings, 1987.
65. KORNBERG A: *DNA Replication.* San Francisco, Freeman, 1980.
66. WATSON JD, CRICK FHC: Molecular structure of nucleic acids. *Nature* 171:737, 1953.
67. KORNBERG A: *Supplement to DNA Replication.* San Francisco, Freeman, 1982.
68. MCMACKEN R, KELLY TJ: *Replication and Recombination: UCLA Symposia on Molecular and Cellular Biology, New Series.* New York, AR Liss, 1987.
69. KORNBERG A: DNA replication. *J Biol Chem* 263:1, 1988.
70. STRYER L: *Biochemistry.* San Francisco, Freeman, 1981.
71. PTASHNE M: *A Genetic Switch: Gene Control and Phage λ.* Cambridge, Cell Press, 1986.
72. MANIATIS T, GOODBOURN S, FISCHER JA: Regulation of inducible and tissue-specific gene expression. *Science* 236:1237, 1987.
73. GUARENTE L: UASs and enhancers: Common mechanism of transcriptional activation in yeast and mammals. *Cell* 52:303, 1988.
74. BERG JM: Potential metal-binding domains in nucleic acid binding proteins. *Science* 232:485, 1986.
75. EVANS RM, HOLLENBERG SM: Zinc fingers: Gilt by association. *Cell* 52:1, 1988.
76. SCHEVITZ RW, OTWINOWSKI Z, JOACHIMIAK A, LAWSON CL, SIGLER PB: The three-dimensional structure of *trp* repressor. *Nature* 317:782, 1985.
77. LANDSCHULZ WH, JOHNSON PF, MCKNIGHT SL: Leucine zipper: A hypothetical structure common to a new class of DNA binding proteins. *Science* 240:1759, 1988.
78. SINGH H, LEBOWITZ JH, BALDWIN AS, SHARP PA: Molecular cloning of an enhancer binding protein: Isolation by screening of an expression library with a recognition site DNA. *Cell* 52:415, 1988.
79. HARRIS H: *The Principles of Human Biochemical Genetics,* 3d ed. Amsterdam, North-Holland, 1980.
80. ANTONARAKIS SE, KAZAZIAN HH, ORKIN SH: DNA polymorphism and molecular pathology of the human globin gene clusters. *Hum Genet* 69:1, 1985.
81. BARKER D, SCHAFER M, WHITE R: Restriction sites containing CpG show a higher frequency of polymorphism in human DNA. *Cell* 36:131, 1984.
82. HARRIS H: Enzyme polymorphisms in man. *Proc R Soc Lond (Biol)* 174:1, 1966.
83. LEWONTIN RC, HUBBY JL: A molecular approach to the study of genetic heterozygosity in natural populations. II. Amount of variation and degree of heterozygosity in natural population of *Drosophila pseudoobscura. Genetics* 54:595, 1966.
84. GIBLETT ER: Genetic polymorphisms in human blood. *Annu Rev Genet* 11:13, 1977.
85. WALTON KE, STYER D, GRUENSTEIN EI: Genetic polymorphism in normal human fibroblasts as analyzed by two-dimensional polyacrylamide gel electrophoresis. *J Biol Chem* 254:7951, 1979.
86. MCCONKEY EH, TAYLOR BJ, PHAN D: Human heterozygosity: A new estimate. *Proc Natl Acad Sci USA* 76:6500, 1979.
87. COOPER DN, SMITH BA, BOOKE HJ, NIEMANN S, SCHMIDTKE J: An estimate of unique DNA sequence heterozygosity in the human genome. *Hum Genet* 69:201, 1985.
88. EMBURY SH, DOZY AJ, MILLER J, DAVIS JR, KLEMAN KM, PRESILER H, VICHINSKY E, LANDE WN, LUBIN B, KAN YW, MENTZER WC: Concurrent sickle cell anemia and α-thalassemia. Effect on severity of anemia. *N Engl J Med* 306:270, 1982.
89. HIGGS DR, ALDRIDGE BE, LAMB J, CLEGG JB, WEATHERALL DJ, HAYES RJ, GRANDISON Y, LOWRIE Y, MAON KP, SERJEANT BE, SERJEANT GR: The interaction of α-thalassemia and homozygous sickle cell disease. *N Engl Med* 306:1441, 1982.
90. COSTA T, SCRIVER CR, CHILDS B: The effect of Mendelian disease on human health: A measurement. *Am J Med Genet* 21:231, 1985.
91. MORGAN TH: The relation of genetics to physiology and medicine, in Baltimore D (ed): *Nobel Lectures in Molecular Biology 1933–1975.* New York, Elsevier North-Holland, 1977, p 3.
92. MCKUSICK VA, RUDDLE FH: The status of the gene map of the human chromosomes. *Science* 196:390, 1977.
93. RUDDLE FH: A new era in mammalian gene mapping: Somatic cell genetics and recombinant DNA methodologies. *Nature* 294:115, 1981.
94. RUDDLE FH: The William Allan Memorial Award address: Reverse genetics and beyond. *Am J Hum Genet* 36:944, 1984.
95. VOGEL F, MOTULSKY AG: *Human Genetics: Problems and Approaches,* 2d ed. Berlin, Springer-Verlag, 1986.
96. FRANCKE U, OCHS HD, deMARTINVILLE B, GIACALONE J, LINDGREN V, DISTÈCHE C, PAGON RA, HOFKER MH, van OMMEN G-JB, PEARSON PL, WEDGWOOD RJ: Minor Xp21 chromosome deletion in a male associated with expression of Duchenne muscular dystrophy, chronic granulomatous disease, retinitis pigmentosa, and McLeod syndrome. *Am J Hum Genet* 37:250, 1985.
97. GALJAARD H: *Genetic Metabolic Diseases: Early Diagnosis and Prenatal Analysis.* Amsterdam, Elsevier North-Holland, 1980.
98. SCRIVER CR, NEAL JL, SAGINUR R, CLOW A: The frequency of genetic disease and congenital malformation among patients in a pediatric hospital. *Can Med Assoc J* 108:1111, 1973.
99. BAIRD PA, ANDERSON TW, NEWCOMBE HB, LOWRY RB: Genetic disorders in children and young adults: A population study. *Am J Hum Genet* 42:677, 1988.
100. UNSCEAR: Genetic and somatic effects of ionizing radiation. New York, United Nations, 1986.
101. SORENSEN TIA, NIELSEN GG, ANDERSEN PK, TEASDALE TW: Genetic and environmental influences on premature death in adult adoptees. *N Engl J Med* 318:727, 1988.
102. YUNIS JJ: The chromosomal basis of human neoplasia. *Science* 221:227, 1983.
103. LE BEAU MM, ROWLEY JD: Chromosomal abnormalities in leukemia and lymphoma: Clinical and biological significance. *Adv Hum Genet* 15:1, 1986.
104. HALUSKA FG, TSUJIMOTO Y, CROCE CM: Oncogene activation by chromosome translocation in human malignancy. *Annu Rev Genet* 21:321, 1987.
105. OKAMOTO M, SASAKI M, SUGIO K, SATO C, IWAMA T, IKEUCHI T, TONOMURA A, SASAZUKI T, MIYAKI M: Loss of constitutional heterozygosity in colon carcinoma from patients with familial polyposis coli. *Nature* 331:273, 1988.
106. SOLOMON E, VOSS R, HALL V, BODMER WF, JASS JR, JEFFREYS AJ, LUCIBELLO FC, PATEL I, RIDER SH: Chromosome 5 allele loss in human colorectal carcinomas. *Nature* 328:616, 1987.
107. KOVACS G, ERLANDSSON R, BOLDOG F, INGVARSSON S, MÜLLER-BRECHLIN R, KLEIN G, SÜMEGI J: Consistent chromosome 3p deletion and loss of heterozygosity in renal cell carcinoma. *Proc Natl Acad Sci USA* 85:1571, 1988.
108. DE GROUCHY J, TURLEAU C: *Clinical Atlas of Human Chromosomes,* 2d ed. New York, Wiley, 1984.
109. SCHINZEL A: *Catalogue of Unbalanced Chromosome Aberrations in Man.* New York, Walter de Gruyter, 1983.
110. CARTER CO: Monogenic disorders. *J Med Genet* 14:316, 1977.
111. MOTULSKY AG: Frequency of sickling disorders in US blacks. *N Engl J Med* 288:31, 1973.
112. WEXLER NS, YOUNG AB, TANZI RE, TRAVERS H, STAROSTA-RUBINSTEIN S, PENNEY JB, SNODGRASS SR, SHOULSON I, GOMEZ F, RAMOS ARROYO MA, PENCHASZADEH GK, MORNEO H, GIBBONS K, FARYNIARZ A, HOBBS W, ANDERSON MA, BONILLA E, CONNEALLY PM, GUSELLA JF: Homozygotes for Huntington's disease. *Nature* 326:194, 1987.
113. SWIFT M, REITNAUER PJ, MORRELL D, CHASE CL: Breast and other cancers in families with ataxia-telangiectasia. *N Engl J Med* 316:1289, 1987.
114. KACSER H, BURNS JA: The molecular basis of dominance. *Genetics* 97:639, 1981.
115. HERSKOWITZ I: Functional inactivation of genes by dominant negative mutations. *Nature* 329:219, 1987.
116. BUNDEY S, EVANS K: Tuberous sclerosis—A genetic study. *J Neurol Neurosurg Psychiatry* 32:591, 1969.
117. JONES KL, SMITH DW, HARVEY MAS, HALL BD, QUAN L: Older paternal age and fresh gene mutation: Data on additional disorders. *J Pediatr* 86:84, 1975.
118. MURDOCH JL, WALKER BA, MCKUSICK VA: Parental age effects on the occurrence of new mutations for the Marfan syndrome. *Ann Hum Genet* 35:331, 1972.
119. BALLARD HS, FRAME B, HARTSOCK RJ: Familial multiple endocrine adenoma-peptic ulcer complex. *Medicine* 43:481, 1964.
120. LARSSON C, SKOGSEID B, ÖBERG K, NAKAMURA Y, NORDENSKJÖLD M: Multiple endocrine neoplasia type 1 gene maps to chromosome 11 and is lost in insulinoma. *Nature* 332:85, 1988.
121. STACEY A, BATEMAN J, CHOI T, MASCARA T, COLE W, JAENISCH R: Perinatal lethal osteogenesis imperfecta in transgenic mice bearing an engineered mutant pro-α1 (I) collagen gene. *Nature* 332:131, 1988.
122. BROWN MS, GOLDSTEIN JL: New directions in human biochemical genetics: Understanding the manifestations of receptor deficiency disorders. *Prog Med Genet* 1 (new series):103, 1976.
123. HERS HG: Inborn lysosomal diseases. *Gastroenterology* 48:625, 1965.
124. NEUFELD EF, TIMPLE WL, SHAPIRO LJ: Inherited disorders of lysosomal metabolism. *Annu Rev Biochem* 44:357, 1975.
125. VON FIGURA K, HASILIK A: Lysosomal enzymes and their receptors. *Annu Rev Biochem* 55:167, 1986.

126. CAVALLI-SFORZA LL, BODMER WF: *The Genetics of Human Populations.* San Francisco, Freeman, 1971.

127. CHARLESWORTH B: Driving genes and chromosomes. *Nature* 332:394, 1988.

128. ESTIVILL X, FARRALL M, SCAMBLER PJ, BELL GM, HAWLEY KMF, LENCH NJ, BATES GP, KRUYER HC, FREDERICK PA, STANIER P, WATSON EK, WILLIAMSON R, WAINWRIGHT BJ: A candidate for the cystic fibrosis locus isolated by selection for methylation-free islands. *Nature* 326:840, 1987.

129. LYON MF: X-Chromosome inactivation and developmental patterns in mammals. *Biol Rev* 47:1, 1972.

130. GARTLER SM, RIGGS AD: Mammalian X-chromosome inactivation. *Annu Rev Genet* 17:155, 1983.

131. VOGEL F, RATHENBERG R: Spontaneous mutation in man. *Adv Hum Genet* 5:223, 1975.

132. CHILDS B, DER KALOUSTIAN VM: Genetic heterogeneity. *N Engl J Med* 279:1205, 1267, 1968.

133. HARRIS H: Genetic heterogeneity in inherited disease. *J Clin Pathol (Suppl)* 27:32, 1974.

134. LEDLEY FD, LEVY HL, SHIH VE, BENJAMIN R, MAHONEY MJ: Benign methylmalonic aciduria. *N Engl J Med* 311:1015, 1984.

135. CARTER CO: Genetics of common disorders. *Br Med Bull* 25:52, 1972.

136. CARTER CO: Principles of polygenic inheritance. *Birth Defects* 13:69, 1977.

137. CHILDS B, SCRIVER CR: Age at onset and causes of disease. *Perspect Biol Med* 29:437, 1986.

138. VESELL ES: Pharmacogenetics: Multiple interactions between genes and environment as determinants of drug response. *Am J Med* 66:183, 1979.

139. BURTON BK: Inborn errors of metabolism: The clinical diagnosis in early infancy. *Pediatrics* 79:359, 1987.

140. NEUFELD EF, FRATANTONI JC: Inborn errors of mucopolysaccharide metabolism. *Science* 169:141, 1970.

141. NUDEL U, ROBZYK K, YAFFE D: Expression of the putative Duchenne muscular dystrophy gene in differentiated myogenic cell cultures and in the brain. *Nature* 331:635, 1988.

142. HOOPER M, HARDY K, HANDYSIDE A, HUNTER S, MONK M: HPRT-deficient (Lesch-Nyhan) mouse embryos derived from germline colonization by cultured cells. *Nature* 326:292, 1987.

143. KUEHN MR, BRADLEY A, ROBERTSON EJ, EVANS MJ: A potential animal model for Lesch-Nyhan syndrome through introduction of HPRT mutations into mice. *Nature* 326:295, 1987.

144. BERG K: Inactivation of one of the X chromosomes in females is a biological phenomenon of clinical importance. *Acta Med Scand* 206:1, 1979.

145. FIALKOW PJ, LISKER R, GIBLETT ER, ZAVALA C: Xg locus: Failure to detect inactivation in females with chronic myelocytic leukaemia. *Nature* 226:367, 1970.

146. SHAPIRO LJ, MOHANDAS T, WEISS R: Non-inactivation of an X-chromosome locus in man. *Science* 204:1224, 1979.

147. GOODFELLOW P, PYM B, MOHANDAS T, SHAPIRO LJ: The *MIC2X* locus escapes X inactivation. *Am J Hum Genet* 36:777, 1984.

148. MIGEON BR, CHILDS B: Hybridization of mammalian somatic cells. *Prog Med Genet* 7 (old series):1, 1970.

149. SAUNDERS M, SWEETMAN L, ROBINSON B, ROTH K, COHN R, GRAVEL RA: Biotin-response organicaciduria: Multiple carboxylase defects and complementation studies with propionicacidemia in cultured fibroblasts. *J Clin Invest* 64:1695, 1979.

150. GRAVEL RA, LEUNG A, SAUNDERS M, HOSLI P: Analysis of genetic complementation by whole-cell microtechniques in fibroblast heterokaryons. *Proc Natl Acad Sci USA* 76:6520, 1979.

151. SAIKI RK, SCHARF S, FALOONA F, MULLIS KB, HORN GT, ERLICH HA, ARNHEIM M: Enzymatic amplification of β-globin genomic sequences and restriction site analysis for diagnosis of sickle cell anemia. *Science* 230:1350, 1985.

152. SCHARF SJ, HORN GT, ERLICH HA: Direct cloning and sequence analysis of enzymatically amplified genomic sequences. *Science* 233:1076, 1986.

153. EMBURY SH, SCHARF SJ, SAIKI RK, GHOLSON MA, GOLBUS M, ARNHEIM N, ERLICH H: Rapid prenatal diagnosis of sickle cell anemia by a new method of DNA analysis. *N Engl J Med* 316:656, 1987.

154. MCCABE ERB, HUANG S-Z, SELTZER WK, LAW ML: DNA microextraction from dried blood spots on filter paper blotters: Potential applications to newborn screening. *Hum Genet* 75:213, 1987.

155. KOGAN SC, DOHERTY M, GITSCHIER J: An improved method for prenatal diagnosis of genetic diseases by analysis of amplified DNA sequences: Application to hemophilia A. *N Engl J Med* 317:985, 1987.

156. STOFLET ES, KOEBERL DD, SARKAR G, SOMMER SS: Genomic amplification with transcript sequencing. *Science* 239:491, 1988.

157. WONG C, DOWLING CE, SAIKI RK, HIGUCHI RG, ERLICH HA, KAZAZIAN HH JR: Characterization of β-thalassaemia mutations using direct genomic sequencing of amplified single copy DNA. *Nature* 330:384, 1987.

158. ENGELKE DR, HOENER PA, COLLINS FS: Direct sequencing of enzymatically amplified human genomic DNA. *Proc Natl Acad Sci USA* 85:544, 1988.

159. TODD JA, BELL JI, MCDEVITT HO: HLA-DQβ gene contributes to susceptibility and resistance to insulin-dependent diabetes mellitus. *Nature* 329:599, 1987.

160. CONNER BJ, REYES AA, MORIN C, ITAKURA K, TEPLITZ RL, WALLACE RB: Detection of sickle cell β^s-globin allele by hybridization with synthetic oligonucleotides. *Proc Natl Acad Sci USA* 80:278, 1983.

161. CHANG JC, KAN YW: A sensitive new prenatal test for sickle-cell anemia. *N Engl J Med* 307:30, 1982.

162. LATT SA, KURNIT DM, BRUNS GP, SCHRECK RR, MORTON CC, KUNKEL LM, LALANDE M, ALDRIDGE J, NEVE R, TANTRAVAHI U, KANDA N, LINDNER G, MERYASH D: Molecular genetic approaches to human diseases involving mental retardation. *Am J Ment Defic* 88:561, 1984.

163. LEONARD CO, CHASE GA, CHILDS B: Genetic counseling: A consumers' view. *N Engl J Med* 287:433, 1972.

164. SCRIVER CR AND COMMITTEE: in Marois M, Bennett HS, Klingberg MS, Brent RL, Lauder J, Saxen L (eds): *Population Screening: Report of a Workshop in Prevention of Physical and Mental Congenital Defects: Part B: Epidemiology. Early Detection and Therapy, and Environmental Factors.* New York, AR Liss, 1985, p 89.

165. KABACK MM, RIMOIN DL, O'BRIEN JS: *Tay-Sachs Disease: Screening and Prevention.* New York, AR Liss, 1977.

166. MILUNSKY A: Prenatal diagnosis of genetic disorders. *N Engl J Med* 300:157, 1976.

167. EPSTEIN CJ, GOLBUS MS: Prenatal diagnosis of genetic diseases. *Am Sci* 65:703, 1977.

168. NICHD NATIONAL REGISTRY FOR AMNIOCENTESIS STUDY GROUP: Midtrimester amniocentesis for prenatal diagnosis. *JAMA* 236:1471, 1976.

169. TABOR A, MADSEN M, OBEL EB, PHILIP J, BANG J, NØRGAARD-PEDERSEN B: Randomised controlled trial of genetic amniocentesis in 4606 low risk women. *Lancet* 1:1287, 1986.

170. BROCK DJH: Biochemical and cytological methods in the diagnosis of neural tube defects. *Prog Med Genet* 2(new series):1, 1977.

171. BRAMBATI B, OLDRINI A, FERRAZZI E, LANZANI A: Chorionic villus sampling: An analysis of the obstetric experience of 1000 cases. *Prenat Diagn* 7:157, 1987.

172. HOGGE WA, SCHONBERG SA, GOLBUS MS: Chorionic villus sampling: Experience of the first 1000 cases. *Am J Obstet Gynecol* 154:1249, 1986.

173. SMIDT-JENSEN S, HAHNEMANN N: Transabdominal chorionic villus sampling for fetal genetic diagnosis. Technical and obstetrical evaluation of 100 cases. *Prenat Diagn* 8:7, 1988.

174. PESCIA G, NGUYEN THE H: *Chorionic Villi Sampling (CVS).* New York, Karger, 1986.

175. POENARU L: First trimester prenatal diagnosis of metabolic diseases: A survey in countries from the European community. *Prenat Diagn* 7:333, 1987.

176. *Genetic Screening: Programs, Principles and Research.* Washington, DC, National Academy of Sciences, 1975.

177. MacCREADY RA, HUSSEY MG: Newborn phenylketonuria detection program in Massachusetts. *Am J Public Health* 54:2075, 1964.

178. RUCKNAGEL DL: A decade of screening in the hemoglobinopathies: Is a national program to prevent sickle cell anemia possible? *Am J Pediatr Hematol Oncol* 5:373, 1983.

179. Annotation: The prenatal diagnosis of thalassaemia. *Br J Haematol* 63:215, 1986.

180. SCRIVER CR, BARDANIS M, CARTIER L, CLOW CL, LANCASTER GA, OSTROWSKY JT: β-Thalassemia disease prevention: Genetic medicine applied. *Am J Hum Genet* 36:1024, 1984.

181. SOKAL DC, BYRD JR, CHEN ATL, GOLDBERG MF, OAKLEY GP: Prenatal chromosomal diagnosis: Racial and geographic variation for older women in Georgia. *JAMA* 244;1355, 1980.

182. UK collaborative study on α-fetoprotein in relation to neural tube defects: Maternal serum α-fetoprotein measurement in antenatal screening for anencephaly and spina bifida in early pregnancy. *Lancet* 1:1323, 1977.

183. DiMAIO MS, BAUMGARTEN A, GREENSTEIN RM, SAAL HM, MAHONEY MJ: Screening for fetal Down's syndrome in pregnancy by measuring maternal serum α-fetoprotein levels. *N Engl J Med* 317:342, 1987.

184. ROMERO R, PILU G, JEANTY P, GHIDINI A, HOBBINS JC: *Prenatal Diagnosis of Congenital Anomalies.* Norwalk, Appleton & Lange, 1988.

185. KUHL DE: Imaging local brain function with emission computed tomograpy. *Radiology* 150:625, 1984.

186. CHANCE B: Application of ^{31}P-NMR to clinical biochemistry. *Ann NY Acad Sci* 428:318, 1984.

187. VALLE D: Genetic disease: An overview of current therapy. *Hosp Pract* 22:167, 1987.

187a. SCRIVER CR: Treatment in medical genetics, in Crow JF, Neel JV (eds): *Proceedings of the Third International Congress on Human Genetics.* Baltimore, Johns Hopkins University Press, 1967, p 45.

188. HOLTZMAN NA, DRONMAL RA, VAN DOORNINCK W, AZEN C, KOCH R: Effect of age at loss of dietary control on intellectual performance and behavior on children with phenylketonuria. *N Engl J Med* 314:593, 1986.

189. KAUFMAN FR, DONNELL GN, ROE TF, KOGUT MD: Gonadal function in patients with galactosemia. *J Inherited Metab Dis* 9:140, 1986.

190. BRUSILOW SW, VALLE D, BATSHAW ML: New pathways of waste nitrogen excretion in inborn errors of urea synthesis. *Lancet* 2:452, 1979.

191. BRUSILOW SW: Inborn errors of urea synthesis, in Lloyd JK, Scriver CR (eds): *Genetic and Metabolic Disease in Pediatrics.* Borough Green, Butterworths, 1985, p 140.

192. HAVEL RJ, HUNNINHAKE DB, ILLINGWORTH DR, LEES RS, STEIN EA, TOBERT JA, BACON SR, BOLOGNESE JA, FROST PH, LAMKIN GE, LEES AM, LEON AS, GARDNER K, JOHNSON G, MELLIES MK, RHYMER PA, TUN P: Lovastatin (Mevinolin) in the treatment of heterozygous familial hypercholesterolemia. *Ann Intern Med* 107:609, 1987.

193. CHEN YT, CORNBLATH M, SIDBURY JB: Cornstarch therapy in type I glycogen storage disease. *N Engl J Med* 310:171, 1984.

194. WOLF B, GRIER RE, SECOR-MCVOY JR, HEARD GS: Biotinidase deficiency: A novel vitamin recycling defect. *J Inherited Metab Dis (Suppl)* 8:53, 1985.

195. HEARD GS, WOLF B, JEFFERSON LG, WEISSBECKER KA, NANCE WE, SECOR-MCVOY JR, NAPOLITANO A, MITCHELL PL, LAMBERT FW, LINYEAR AS: Neonatal screening for biotinidase deficiency: Results of a 1 year pilot study. *J Pediatr* 108:40, 1986.

196. WEWERS MD, CASOLARO MA, SELLERS SE, SWAYZE SC, MCPHAUL KM, WITTES JT, CRYSTAL RG: Replacement therapy for α_1-antitrypsin deficiency associated with emphysema. *N Engl J Med* 316:1055, 1987.

197. HERSHFIELD MS, BUCKLEY RH, GREENBERG ML, MELTON AL, SCHIFF R, HATEM C, KURTZBERG J, MARKERT ML, KOBAYASHI RH, KOBAYASHI AL, ABUCHOWSKI A: Treatment of adenosine deaminase deficiency with polyethylene glycol-modified adenosine deaminase. *N Engl J Med* 316:589, 1987.

198. KRIVIT W, WHITLEY CB: Bone marrow transplantation for genetic diseases. *N Engl J Med* 3165:1085, 1987.

199. LUCARELLI G, GALIMBERTI M, POLCHI P, GIARDINI C, POLITI P, BARONCIANI D, ANGELUCCI E, MANENTI F, DELFINI C, AURELLI G, MURETTO P: Marrow transplantation in patients with advanced thalassemia. *N Engl J Med* 316:1050, 1987.

200. MALATACK JJ, FINEGOLD DN, IWATSUKI S, SHAW BW, GARTNER JC, ZITELLI BJ, ROE T, STARZL TE: Liver transplantation for type I glycogen storage disease. *Lancet* 1:1073, 1983.

201. BILHEIMER DW, GOLDSTEIN JL, GRUNDY SM, STARZL TE, BROWN MS: Liver transplantation to provide low-density lipoprotein receptors and lower plasma cholesterol in a child with homozygous familial hypercholesterolemia. *N Engl J Med* 311:1658, 1984.

202. DOWTON SB: Presented at the annual meeting of the Society for Inherited Metabolic Disorders, March 1988.

203. STARZL TE: Changing concepts: Liver replacement for hereditary tyrosinemia and hepatoma. *J Pediatr* 106:604, 1985.

204. DEMETRIOUS AA, WHITING JF, FELDMAN D, LEVENSON SM, CHOWDHURY NR, MOSCIONI AD, KRAM M, CHOWDHURY JR: Replacement of liver function in rats by transplantation of microcarrier-attached hepatocytes. *Science* 233:1090, 1986.

205. SHULL RM, HASTINGS NE, SELCER RR, JONES JB, SMITH JR, CULLEN WC, CONSTANTOPOULOS G: Bone marrow transplantation in canine mucopolysaccharidosis. I: Effects with the central nervous system. *J Clin Invest* 79:435, 1987.

206. ANDERSON WF: Prospects for human gene therapy. *Science* 226:401, 1984.

207. WILLIAMS DA, ORKIN SH: Somatic gene therapy: Current status and future prospects. *J Clin Invest* 77:1053, 1986.

208. CLINE MJ: Gene therapy: Current status. *Am J Med* 83:291, 1987.

209. DZIERZAK EA, PAPAYANNOPOULOU T, MULLIGAN RC: Lineage-specific expression of a human β-globin gene in murine bone marrow transplant recipients reconstituted with retrovirus-transduced stem cells. *Nature* 331:35, 1988.

210. WILSON JM, JOHNSTON DE, JEFFERSON DM, MULLIGAN RC: Correction of the genetic defect in hepatocytes from the Watanabe heritable hyperlipidemic rabbit. *Proc Natl Acad Sci USA,* 85:4421, 1988.

211. ST. LOUIS D, VERMA IM: An alternative approach to somatic cell gene therapy. *Proc Natl Acad Sci USA* 85:3150, 1988.

212. Molecular biology of *Homo sapiens. Cold Spring Harbor Symp Quant Biol* 51:1, 1986.

213. DESNICK RJ, PATTERSON DF, SCARPELLI DG: Animal models of inherited metabolic diseases. *Prog Clin Biol Res* 94:1, 1982.

214. POPKO B, PUCKETT C, LAI E, SHINE HD, READHEAD C, TAKAHASHI N, HUNT SW, SIDMAN RL, HOOD L: Myelin deficient mice: Expression of myelin basic protein and generation of mice with varying levels of myelin. *Cell* 48:713, 1987.

215. LEVINE M, RUBIN G, TJIAN R: Human DNA sequences homologous to a protein coding region conserved between homeotic genes of *Drosophila. Cell* 38:667, 1984.

216. CHAPMAN VM, MILLER DR, ARMSTRONG D, CASKEY CT: Recovery of induced mutations for X chromosome-linked muscular dystrophy in mice. *Proc Natl Acad Sci USA,* in press.

217. BEAUDET AL: Molecular genetics and medicine, in Braunwald E, Isselbacher KJ, Petersdorf RG, Wilson JD, Martin JB, Fauci AS (eds): *Harrison's Principles of Internal Medicine.* New York, McGraw-Hill, 1987, p 296.

APPENDIX 1-1

Analysis and Diagnosis of Human Inherited Disease by Recombinant DNA Methods

David N. Cooper* and Jörg Schmidtke†

This database is primarily a list of publications detailing the analysis and diagnosis of human inherited disease using recombinant DNA methods. It is intended to serve both the clinical geneticist and diagnostic laboratories as a quick and up-to-date reference source to current possibilities in this field. Earlier versions of this compilation have appeared in *Hum. Genet.* 73,1-11 (1986) and 77, 66-75 (1987), and we are prepared to continue publishing this list annually. Updates of the list will however be sent out quarterly to those requesting it (*Gene Diagnosis Newsletter*). This newsletter therefore complements the *GENE COMMUNICATIONS* database, which provides a reference source to primary reports on the cloning of DNA sequences from the human genome.

The *Gene Diagnosis Newsletter* will present not only the raw reference data [AUTHOR, JOURNAL, VOL(UME), PAGE, Y(EA)R] but also relevant data extracted from each report:

DISEASE: The disease nomenclature follows that of the McKusick catalogue (V. A. McKusick, *Mendelian Inheritance in Man*, 8th edition, 1988, Johns Hopkins University, Baltimore), wherever possible. To facilitate the one-line entry format, we have sometimes abbreviated the disease description. The mode of genetic transmission is given by the McKusick catalogue number.

McK-#: McKusick catalogue number.

GENE/DNA SEGMENT: This entry refers to the gene or DNA segment that has been used to analyze directly or indirectly the mutational change underlying the disease.

PROBE: Laboratory acronym for the recombinant DNA clone.

DISTANCE: This entry refers to the genetic, and occasionally to the physical, distance between the disease and marker loci. The reliability of the figures given will vary considerably due to variable data quality. In the present state of the list, "—" denotes direct analysis using either a probe corresponding to the site of the mutation or one derived from the disease locus itself which does not exhibit recombination. For reports detailing indirect analysis, "—" denotes a lack of linkage data in the article. A single real number refers to the maximum likelihood estimate of the genetic distance in centimorgans (cM). A number preceded by "<" denotes the upper limit of the so-called one-unit-down confidence interval. Lod scores are given in brackets whenever reported in the article referred to.

DETECT.: The following abbreviations are used to define the detection method:

RE.: restriction enzyme analysis of the gene

SEQU.: analysis of the gene by DNA sequencing

OLIGO.: detection of a mutation by differential oligonucleotide hybridization

RFLP.: indirect analysis of the disease using a linked restriction fragment length polymorphism (RFLP) as a genetic marker

MMP.: mismatch-pairing analysis

MUT.: The following abbreviations are used to define the nature of the mutation responsible for the disease:

DEL.: deletion	*LH.:* loss of heterozygosity
INS.: insertion	*AN.:* aneuploidy
REAR.: rearrangement	*DUP.:* gene duplication
PM.: point mutation	*INV.:* inversion

Reports of the analysis/diagnosis of the hemoglobinopathies/thalassemias are now too numerous to list in full and require special treatment. The reader is therefore referred to reviews of this subject area [Antonarakis et al., *Hum. Genet.*, 69, 1-14 (1985); Spritz and Forget, *Am. J. Hum. Genet.* 35, 333-361 (1983); Weatherall et al., *J. Med. Genet.* 22, 422-430 (1985); Cao et al., *J. Genet. Hum.* 34, 413-424 (1986); Weatherall et al., this edition of *Metabolic Basis of Inherited Disease*; McKusick (op. cit.)]

The database does not include reports of the exclusion of candidate genes, nor does it list reports where no defect was detected or no linkage established using genes or DNA segments as probes. Also excluded are studies of disease association using RFLPs; this topic is reviewed elsewhere [D. N. Cooper and J. R. Clayton, *Hum. Genet.* 78; 299-312 (1988)].

Gene alterations in neoplasia are covered only in part and only when they involve loss of heterozygosity. Also omitted

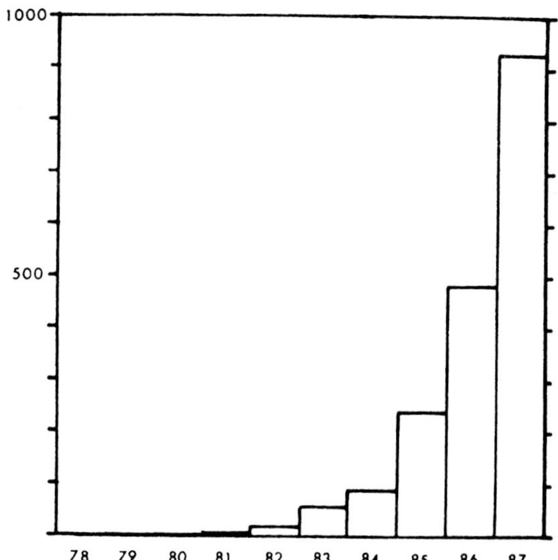

Fig. A1-1. Cumulative number of reports on the analysis and diagnosis of human genetic disease 1978–1987 (globin gene defects covered only in part, see text).

*Haematology Department, King's College Hospital School of Medicine and Dentistry, Denmark Hill, London SE5 BRX, UK.
†Institute of Human Genetics, University of Göttingen, Gosslerstrasse 12d, D-3400 Göttingen, West Germany.

are reports in which a molecular defect was inferred solely from abnormal or absent mRNA expression in the absence of the demonstration of a structural gene alteration. Reports detailing allele and/or haplotype frequencies only are similarly not included.

The recent dramatic increase in the numbers of reports describing human disease analysis/diagnosis is depicted in Fig. A1-1. Almost exactly half of the total number of reports logged to date were published during 1987. This literature explosion parallels that described by Schmidtke et al., 1986 (*Nature* 322:119), for the cloning of human DNA sequences and is clearly related to it. Other factors responsible probably include the increased awareness among scientists and clinicians alike of the potential applications of newly emergent technology to diagnostic medicine.

Altogether, nearly 1000 reports logged before January 6, 1988, are listed in the database presented here. This represents the potential to analyze over 165 different human conditions and disease states. A total of 337 reports describe the direct analysis of a disease state using a gene probe corresponding to the locus of interest; the most common lesions described were deletions (53 percent) and point mutations (30 percent), while loss of heterozygosity (10 percent), rearrangements (5 percent), insertions (1 percent), and aneuploidies (1 percent) made up the remainder. Of the 66 disease states analyzed indirectly by tracking the disease locus with RFLPs around a linked anonymous DNA segment (marker locus), 19 were autosomal (29 percent) while 47 (71 percent) were located on the X chromosome. This disparity is probably due to the easily recognized mode of inheritance in X-linked conditions and also to the large number of polymorphic DNA segments from the X chromosome which are available for use as genetic markers.

We welcome additions and corrections to this list to enable us to keep it as accurate and up to date as possible.

Disease	*McK-#*	*Gene/DNA segment*	*Probe*	*Distance*	*Detect.*	*Mut.*	*Author*	*Journal*	*Vol.*	*Page*	*Yr.*
17p Deletion	—	D17S	pYN222	—	RE	DEL	Fearon	Science	238	193	87
18p Syndrome	—	D18	ar	—	RE	DEL	Vorsanova	Hum. Genet.	72	185	86
5p Deletion	—	D5(sev.)		—	RE	DEL	Overhauser	AJHG	39	1	86
5q Syndrome	—	CSF1		—	RE	DEL	Pettanati	PNAS	84	2970	87
5q Syndrome	—	FMS		—	RE	DEL	Bartram	Leukemia	1	146	87
5q Syndrome	—	FMS		—	RE	DEL	LeBeau	Science	231	984	86
5q Syndrome	—	FMS		—	RE	DEL	Nienhuis	Cell	42	421	85
5q Syndrome	—	GMCSF		—	RE	DEL	Huebner	Science	230	1282	85
5q Syndrome	—	GMCSF		—	RE	DEL	LeBeau	Science	231	984	86
5q Syndrome	—	IL3		—	RE	DEL	LeBeau	PNAS	84	5913	87
7q Deletion	—	D7S18		—	RE	DEL	Wainwright	CCG	44	101	87
7q Deletion	—	D7S8		—	RE	DEL	Wainwright	CCG	44	101	87
7q Deletion	—	MET		—	RE	DEL	Wainwright	CCG	44	101	87
APRT deficiency	10260	APRT	p46	—	SEQU	DEL	Hidaka	JCI	80	1409	87
APRT deficiency	10260	APRT	p9B12	—	SEQU	INS	Hidaka	JCI	80	1409	87
Acoustic neuroma	10100	D22(sev.)		—	RE	LH	Seizinger	Nature	322	644	86
Adenomatous polyposis	17510	D5S	C11p11	0(3.3)	RFLP		Bodmer	Nature	328	614	87
Adenomatous polyposis	17510	D5(sev.)	sev.	var.	RFLP		Leppert	Science	238	1411	87
Adenosine deaminase deficiency	10270	ADA		—	SEQU	PM	Akeson	PNAS	84	5947	87
Adenosine deaminase deficiency	10270	ADA		—	RE	DEL	Berkvens	NAR	15	9365	87
Adenosine deaminase deficiency	10270	ADA		—	SEQU	PM	Bonthron	JCI	76	894	85
Adenosine deaminase deficiency	10270	ADA		—	SEQU	PM	Valerio	EMBO J	5	113	86
Adrenal hyperplasia	20191	C4B	550/1.4	40 kb	RFLP		Strachan	Lancet	2	1272	87
Adrenal hyperplasia	20191	CA21HA		—	RE	DEL	Boehm	Blood	67	1185	86
Adrenal hyperplasia	20191	CA21HA		—	RE	DEL	Caroll	EMBO J	4	2547	85
Adrenal hyperplasia	20191	CA21HA	pC21/3c	—	RE	REAR	Dawkins	JIMMG	14	89	87
Adrenal hyperplasia	20191	CA21HA		—	RE	DEL	Harada	PNAS	84	8091	87
Adrenal hyperplasia	20191	CA21HA		—	RE	DEL	Keller	IMG	25	123	87
Adrenal hyperplasia	20191	CA21HA		—	RE	PM	Matteson	PNAS	84	5858	87
Adrenal hyperplasia	20191	CA21HA		—	RE	REAR	Matteson	PNAS	84	5858	87
Adrenal hyperplasia	20191	CA21HA		—	RE	DEL	Miki	AICHG		648	86
Adrenal hyperplasia	20191	CA21HA		—	RE	REAR	Mornet	Hum. Genet.	74	402	86
Adrenal hyperplasia	20191	CA21HA		—	RE	DEL	Schneider	JCI	78	650	86
Adrenal hyperplasia	20191	CA21HA	21A-1.8	—	RE	REAR	Strachan	Lancet	2	1272	87
Adrenal hyperplasia	20191	CA21HA		—	RE	DEL	White	PNAS	81	7505	84
Adrenal hyperplasia	20191	CA21HA		—	RE	DEL	White	PNAS	82	1089	85
Adrenal hyperplasia	20191	CA21HB		—	RE	DEL	Jospe	BBRC	142	798	87
Adrenal hyperplasia	20191	CA21HB		—	SEQU	PM	Rodrigues	EMBO J	6	1653	87
Adrenal hyperplasia	20191	CA21HB		—	RE	DEL	Werkmeister	AJHG	39	461	86
Adrenal hyperplasia	20191	HLA	sev.	0	RFLP		Mornet	Hum. Genet.	73	358	86
Adrenal hyperplasia	20191	HLAB	pB250	—	RFLP		Strachan	Lancet	2	1272	87
Adrenal hyperplasia	20191	HLADR	pRTV1	—	RFLP		Strachan	Lancet	2	1272	87
Adrenal hyperplasia-classic	20191	CA21HA		—	RE	DEL	Boehm	MBM	3	437	86
Adrenal hyperplasia-classic form	20191	CA21HA		—	RE	DEL	Mornet	Hum. Genet.	74	402	86
Adrenal hyperplasia-late onset	20191	CA21HA		—	RE	DUP	Mornet	Hum. Genet.	74	402	86
Adrenal hyperplasia-non-classic	20191	CA21HA		—	RE	REAR	Boehm	MBM	3	437	86

Disease	*McK-#*	*Gene/DNA segment*	*Probe*	*Distance*	*Detect.*	*Mut.*	*Author*	*Journal*	*Vol.*	*Page*	*Yr.*
Adrenal hypoplasia	30020	DX(sev.)		—	RE	DEL	Clarke	JMG	23	473	86
Adrenal hypoplasia	30020	DX(sev.)		—	RE	DEL	Francke	AJHG	40	212	87
Adrenal hypoplasia	30020	DXS28	C7	—	RE	DEL	Yates	HGM9		117	87
Adrenal hypoplasia	30020	DXS67	pB24	—	RE	DEL	Yates	HGM9		117	87
Adrenal hypoplasia	30020	DXS68	pL1	—	RE	DEL	Yates	HGM9		117	87
Adrenoleukodystrophy	30010	DXS52	St14	0(13.8)	RFLP		Aubourg	Ann. Neurol.	21	349	87
Adrenoleukodystrophy	30010	DXS52	St14	<10	RFLP		Boue	Hum. Genet.	69	272	85
Adrenoleukodystrophy	30010	DXS52	St14	0(4.2)	RFLP		van Oost	HGM9		308	87
Agammaglobulinemia	30030	DX(sev.)		var.	RFLP		Ott	Hum. Genet.	74	280	86
Agammaglobulinemia	30030	DXS17	S21	0(2.2)	RFLP		Kwan	JCI	77	649	86
Agammaglobulinemia	30030	DXS17	S21	0(4.4)	RFLP		Malcolm	Hum. Genet.	77	172	87
Agammaglobulinemia	30030	DXS3	p19-2	4(3.7)	RFLP		Kwan	JCI	77	649	86
Agammaglobulinemia	30030	DXS3	19.2	5(3.6)	RFLP		Malcolm	Hum. Genet.	77	172	87
Agammaglobulinemia	30030	DXS3	p19-2	6(3.3)	RFLP		Mensink	Hum. Genet.	73	327	86
Agammaglobilunemia	30030	DXS94	pXG12	0(6.6)	RFLP		Malcolm	Hum. Genet.	77	172	87
Albinism-Deafness syndrome	30070	DXS37	RIb	18(1.5)	RFLP		Litvak	HGM9		238	87
Albinism-Deafness syndrome	30070	DXS91	DXG-17	18(2.2)	RFLP		Litvak	HGM9		238	87
α_1-Antitrypsin deficiency	10740	PI		—	RFLP		Abbott	Lancet	1	1425	87
α_1-Antitrypsin deficiency	10740	PI		—	RFLP		Cox	Lancet	1	230	85
α_1-Antitrypsin deficiency	10740	PI		—	RE	PM	Cox	Lancet	2	741	86
α_1-Antitrypsin deficiency	10740	PI		—	RFLP		Cox	JMG	24	52	87
α_1-Antitrypsin deficiency	10740	PI		—	RFLP		Garver	NEJM	314	762	86
α_1-Antitrypsin deficiency	10740	PI		—	OLIGO	PM	Hejtmancik	Lancet	2	767	86
α_1-Antitrypsin deficiency	10740	PI		—	RFLP		Hejtmancik	Lancet	2	767	86
α_1-Antitrypsin deficiency	10740	PI		—	OLIGO	PM	Kidd	Nature	304	230	83
α_1-Antitrypsin deficiency	10740	PI		—	OLIGO	PM	Kidd	NEJM	310	639	84
α_1-Antitrypsin deficiency	10740	PI		—	OLIGO	PM	Nukiwa	JBC	261	15989	86
α_1-Antitrypsin deficiency	10740	PI	LAMBDA A	—	RE	DEL	Nukiwa	JBC	262	11999	87
α_1-Antitrypsin deficiency	10740	PI		—	SEQU	PM	Nukiwa	JBC	262	11999	87
Alport syndromelike hered. neph.	30105	DXS1	8EA	25(2.6)	RFLP		Menlove	HGM8		697	86
Alport syndromelike hered. neph.	30105	DXS17		5(4.1)	RFLP		Brunner	AICHG		629	86
Alport syndromelike hered. neph.	30105	DSX3	19-2	22(7.7)	RFLP		Menlove	HGM8		697	86
Alzheimer disease	10430	D21S1		8(2.3)	RFLP		Haines	HGM9		318	87
Alzheimer disease	10430	D21S16		0(2.5)	RFLP		St. George-Hyslop	Science	235	885	87
Anderson-Fabry disease	30150	DXS17	S21/S9	0(5.8)	RFLP		MacDermot	Hum. Genet.	77	263	87
Anderson-Fabry disease	30150	DXS17		0(5.8)	RFLP		Morgan	HGM9		215	87
Anderson-Fabry disease	30150	DXS3	p19.2	10(2.9)	RFLP		MacDermot	Hum. Genet.	77	263	87
Anderson-Fabry disease	30150	DXS3	p19.2	10(2.9)	RFLP		MacDermot	JMG	24	635	87
Anderson-Fabry disease	30150	DXS3		10(2.9)	RFLP		Morgan	HGM9		215	87
Anderson-Fabry disease	30150	DXS87	pA13.RI	0(6.4)	RFLP		MacDermot	Hum. Genet.	77	263	87
Anderson-Fabry disease	30150	DXS87	pA13.RI	0(6.4)	RFLP		MacDermot	JMG	24	635	87
Anderson-Fabry disease	30150	DXS87		0(6.4)	RFLP		Morgan	HGM9		215	87
Anderson-Fabry disease	30150	DXS88	G3.1	0(6.4)	RFLP		MacDermot	Hum. Genet.	77	263	87
Anderson-Fabry disease	30150	DXS88	G3-1	0(5.8)	RFLP		MacDermot	JMG	24	635	87
Anderson-Fabry disease	30150	DXS88		0(6.4)	RFLP		Morgan	HGM9		215	87
Androgen-resistance syndromes	31370	DXS1	p8	0(3.5)	RFLP		Wieacker	Hum. Genet.	76	248	87
Angioneurotic edema	10610	C1I	pCI-INHI	—	RFLP		Cicardi	JCI	80	1640	87
Angioneurotic edema-hereditary type I	10610	C1I		—	RE	REAR	Stoppa-Lyonne	NEJM	317	1	87
Anhidrotic ectodermal dysplasia	30510	DXS1	p8	0(2.0)	RFLP		MacDermot	HGM9		216	87
Anhidrotic ectodermal dysplasia	30510	DXS14	p58-1	0(3.3)	RFLP		MacDermot	HGM9		216	87
Anhidrotic ectodermal dysplasia	30510	DXS146	pTAK8	0	RFLP		Bolund	Clin. Genet.	29	458	86
Anhidrotic ectodermal dysplasia	30510	DXS146	pTAK8	0(2.4)	RFLP		Koelvraa	Hum. Genet.	74	284	86
Aniridia	10621	CAT		—	RE	DEL	Boyd	Hum. Genet.	73	171	86
Aniridia	10621	CAT		—	RE	DEL	Mannens	HGM9		28	87
Antithrombin III deficiency	10730	AT3		—	SEQU	PM	Bock	AJHG	37	A145	85
Antithrombin III deficiency	10730	AT3		0(3.4)	RFLP		Bock	AJHG	37	32	85
Antithrombin III deficiency	10730	AT3		—	RE	DEL	Bock	Blood	70	1273	87
Antithrombin III deficiency	10730	AT3		—	SEQU	PM	Brunel	AJH	25	223	87
Antithrombin III deficiency	10730	AT3		—	SEQU	PM	Duchange	NAR	14	2408	86
Antithrombin III deficiency	10730	AT3		—	RE	DEL	Prochownik	NEJM	308	1549	83
Apolipoprotein A deficiency	10766	APOA1		—	SEQU	PM	Law	JBC	260	12810	85
Apolipoprotein A-1 deficiency	10766	APOA1		—	RE	INS	Karathanasis	Nature	305	823	83
Apolipoprotein A-1 deficiency	10766	APOA1		—	RFLP		Karathanasis	Nature	301	718	83
Apolipoprotein A-1 deficiency	10766	APOA1		—	RE	INV	Karathanasis	PNAS	84	7198	87
Apolipoprotein B deficiency	20010	APOB		—	SEQU	PM	Hospattankar	BBRC	148	279	87

Disease	*McK-#*	*Gene/DNA segment*	*Probe*	*Distance*	*Detect.*	*Mut.*	*Author*	*Journal*	*Vol.*	*Page*	*Yr.*
Apolipoprotein C-2 deficiency	20775	APOC2		—	RFLP		Humphries	Hum. Genet.	67	151	84
Apolipoprotein E deficiency	14450	APOE		—	SEQU	PM	Cladaras	JBC	262	2310	87
Apolipoprotein E deficiency	14450	APOE		—	SEQU	PM	Cladaras	JBC	262	2310	87
Ataxia/adult onset dementia	—	DXS95		10(2.4)	RFLP		Dlouhy	AJHG	41	A164	87
Ataxia/adult onset dementia	—	DXYS1		0(2.3)	RFLP		Dlouhy	AJHG	41	A164	87
Beckwith-Wiedemann syndrome	13065	D11(sev.)		—	RE	LH	Jeanpierre	HGM8		661	86
Beckwith-Wiedemann syndrome	13065	D11(sev.)	sev.	—	RE	LH	Mannens	HGM9		28	87
Bladder cancer	19002	HRAS1		—	RE	LH	Fearon	Nature	318	377	85
Bladder cancer	17673	INS		—	RE	LH	Fearon	Nature	318	377	85
Blue cone monochromacy	30370	CBP/D	hs?		RE	REAR	Lewis	AJHG	41	A102	87
Blue cone monochromacy	30370	DXS15	DX13	5(3.6)	RFLP		Lewis	Arch. Ophth.	105	1055	87
Blue cone monochromacy	30370	DXS52	St14	7(2.4)	RFLP		Lewis	Arch. Ophth.	105	1055	87
Breast cancer	—	D11S(sev.)		—	RE	LH	Ali	Science	238	185	87
Breast cancer	—	D13S(sev.)		—	RE	LH	Lund	PNAS	84	2372	87
Bulbospinal neuronopathy		DXYS1		15(1.2)	RFLP		Kelly	HGM9		418	87
Carbamyl phosphate synthesis I deficiency	23730	CPS1		—	RFLP		Fearon	Hum. Genet.	70	207	85
Cat-eye syndrome	11547	D22S9		—	RE	AN	McDermid	Science	232	646	86
Cataract-Coppock-like	12366	CRYG		0(7.6)	RFLP		Lubsen	PNAS	84	489	87
Charcot-Marie-Tooth disease	30280	DXS1	p8	15(2.5)	RFLP		Kelly	JMG	24	639	87
Charcot-Marie-Tooth disease	30280	DXYS1	pDP34	6(2.9)	RFLP		Beckett	J. Neurogenet	3	225	86
Charcot-Marie-Tooth disease	30280	DXYS1	pDP34	0(1.4)	RFLP		Gal	Hum. Genet.	70	38	85
Charcot-Marie-Tooth disease	30280	DXYS1		0(5.1)	RFLP		Goon	HGM9		296	87
Charcot-Marie-Tooth disease	30280	DXYS1		15(2.5)	RFLP		Kelly	HGM9		418	87
Chorionic somatomammotropin deficiency	15020	CSH		—	RE	DEL	Parks	JCEM	60	994	85
Chorionic somatomammotropin deficiency	15020	CSH		—	RE	DEL	Simon	AICHG		652	86
Chorionic somatomammotropin deficiency	15020	CSH		—	RE	DEL	Simon	Hum. Genet.	74	235	86
Chorionic somatomammotropin deficiency	15020	CSH		—	RE	DEL	Wurzel	DNA	1	251	82
Choroideremia	30310	DX(sev.)	sev.	—	RE	DEL	Nussbaum	HGM9		258	87
Choroideremia	30310	DX(sev.)	sev.	—	RE	DEL	Schwartz	HGM9		401	87
Choroideremia	30310	DXS(sev.)	sev.	—	RE	DEL	Nussbaum	PNAS	84	6521	87
Choroideremia	30310	DXS11	52d	0	RFLP		Gal	Hum. Genet.	73	123	86
Choroideremia	30310	DXS11	52d	0(1.5)	RFLP		Lewis	Ophthalmology	92	800	85
Choroideremia	30310	DXS165	p1bD5	—	RE	DEL	Cremers	Clin. Genet.	32	421	87
Choroideremia	30310	DXS3	19.2	—	RE	DEL	Hodgson	Hum. Genet.	75	286	87
Choroideremia	30310	DXS3		3(7.7)	RFLP		Lesko	AJHG	37	A65	85
Choroideremia	30310	DXS3	p19-2	14(4.0)	RFLP		MacDonald	Hum. Genet.	77	233	87
Choroideremia	30310	DXS1	pDP34	0	RFLP		Gal	Hum. Genet.	73	123	86
Choroideremia	30310	DXS1	pDP34	—	RE	DEL	Hodgson	Hum. Genet.	75	286	87
Choroideremia	30310	DXS1	pDP34	0(5.0)	RFLP		Jay	OPG	7	201	86
Choroideremia	30310	DXS1	var.	<4	RFLP		Lesko	AJHG	40	303	87
Choroideremia	30310	DXS1	pDP34	0(5.8)	RFLP		Lewis	Ophthalmology	92	800	85
Choroideremia	30310	DXS1	pDP34	5(5.2)	RFLP		MacDonald	Hum. Genet.	77	233	87
Choroideremia	30310	DXS1	pDP34	0(5.8)	RFLP		Nussbaum	AJHG	37	473	85
Choroideremia	30310	DXS1	pDP34	—	RE	DEL	Robertson	JMG	23	472	86
Choroideremia	30310	DXS1	pDP34	—	RE	DEL	Rosenberg	OPG	7	205	86
Choroideremia	30310	DXYS1	pDP34	0(11.4)	RFLP		Sankila	Clin. Genet.	31	315	87
Choroideremia	30310	DXYS12	St25-1	0(3.3)	RFLP		Sankila	Clin. Genet.	31	315	87
Chronic granulomatous disease	30640	CGD		—	RE	DEL	Royer-Pokora	Nature	322	32	86
Chronic granulomatous disease	30640	DX(sev.)		—	RE	DEL	Francke	AJHG	37	250	85
Chronic granulomatous disease	30640	DX(sev.)	var.	var.	RFLP		Lind	Genomics	1	87	87
Chronic granulomatous disease	30640	DXS164	pERT84	0(2.1)	RFLP		Baehner	PNAS	83	3398	86
Chronic granulomatous disease	30640	DXS84	754	8(3.7)	RFLP		Baehner	PNAS	83	3398	86
Cleft palate	30340	DX(sev.)	sev.	—	RE	DEL	Ivens	HGM9		191	87
Cleft palate-with/without cleft lip	—	F13A		0/26(3.7)	RFLP		Eiberg	Clin. Genet.	32	129	87
Cleft palate/ankyloglossia	30340	DXYS1	pDP34	0(3.1)	RFLP		Moore	Nature	326	91	87
Coffin-Lowry syndrome	30360	DXS16	pXUT23	0(0.9)	RFLP		Hanauer	HGM9		409	87
Colorectal carcinoma	17510	D5S	Minisat.	—	RE	LH	Solomon	Nature	328	616	87
Color blindness—anomalous trichromacy	30400	—	GCP	—	RE	DEL	Nathans	Science	232	203	86
Color blindness—deutan	30380	CBD	GCP	—	RE	DEL	Nathans	Science	232	203	86
Color blindness-protan	30390	CDP	RCP	—	RE	DEL	Nathans	Science	232	203	86
Cri du Chat syndrome	—	D5(sev.)		—	RE	AN	Carlock	SCMG	11	267	85
Cri du Chat syndrome	—	DY(sev.)	sev.	—	RE	REAR	Gal	HGM9		397	87

Disease	*McK-#*	*Gene/DNA segment*	*Probe*	*Distance*	*Detect.*	*Mut.*	*Author*	*Journal*	*Vol.*	*Page*	*Yr.*
Cystic fibrosis	21970	COL1A2		16(4.4)	RFLP		Buchwald	CCG	41	234	86
Cystic fibrosis	21970	COL1A2		8(3.3)	RFLP		Scambler	Lancet	2	1241	85
Cystic fibrosis	21970	D758	pJ3.11	—	RFLP		Law	PND	7	215	87
Cystic fibrosis	21970	D7S23	XV2c	—	RFLP		Farrall	Lancet	2	156	87
Cystic fibrosis	21970	D7S23	CS.7	0	RFLP		Farrall	Lancet	2	156	87
Cystic fibrosis	21970	D7S(sev.)	sev.	var.	RFLP		Berger	Hum. Genet.	77	197	87
Cystic fibrosis	21970	D7S13	pB79a	8(12.6)	RFLP		Wainwright	AJHG	41	944	87
Cystic fibrosis	21970	D7S15	LAM4-917		RFLP		Knowlton	Nature	318	380	85
Cystic fibrosis	21970	D7S15	LAM4-917	14(4.0)	RFLP		Tsui	Science	230	1054	85
Cystic fibrosis	21970	D7S16	7c22	2.5(35.9)	RFLP		Farrall	AJHG	41	286	87
Cystic fibrosis	21970	D7S16	7c22	0(3.4)	RFLP		Klinger	NAR	14	8681	86
Cystic fibrosis	21970	D7S16	7c22	5(4.5)	RFLP		Scambler	NAR	14	1951	86
Cystic fibrosis	21970	D7S16	7c22	0(5.7)	RFLP		Schmidtke	Hum. Genet.	76	337	87
Cystic fibrosis	21970	D7S16	7c22	0(6.6)	RFLP		Watkins	AJHG	39	735	86
Cystic fibrosis	21970	D7S8	pJ3.11	0.3(71.3)	RFLP		Beaudet	AJHG	39	681	86
Cystic fibrosis	21970	D7S8	pJ3.11	0.1(10.0)	RFLP		Bowcock	AJHG	39	699	86
Cystic fibrosis	21970	D7S8	p3H-3	—	RFLP		Dean	J. Pediatr.	111	490	87
Cystic fibrosis	21970	D7S8	pJ3.11	1.25(>65)	RFLP		Farrall	Lancet	1	1402	86
Cystic fibrosis	21970	D7S8	pJ3.11	—	RFLP		Farrall	JMG	23	295	86
Cystic fibrosis	21970	D7S8	pJ3.11	2(6.8)	RFLP		Farrall	AJHG	39	713	86
Cystic fibrosis	21970	D7S8	pJ3.11	0(4.9)	RFLP		Klinger	NAR	14	8681	86
Cystic fibrosis	21970	D7S8	pJ3.11	0.1(3.9)	RFLP		Naylor	AJHG	39	707	86
Cystic fibrosis	21970	D7S8	pJ3.11	1.6(11.0)	RFLP		Schmidtke	Hum. Genet.	76	337	87
Cystic fibrosis	21970	D7S8	pJ3.11	0(12.1)	RFLP		Spence	AJHG	39	729	86
Cystic fibrosis	21970	D7S8	pJ3.11	—	RFLP		Spence	Hum. Genet.	76	5	87
Cystic fibrosis	21970	D7S8	pJ3.11	10(4.0)	RFLP		Tsui	AJHG	39	720	86
Cystic fibrosis	21970	D7S8	pJ3.11	0(5.2)	RFLP		Wainwright	Nature	318	384	85
Cystic fibrosis	21970	D7S8	pJ3.11	0(10.0)	RFLP		Watkins	AJHG	39	735	86
Cystic fibrosis	21970	D7S8	pJ3.11	1.4(10.9)	RFLP		White	AJHG	39	694	86
Cystic fibrosis	21970	MET		0.4(91.0)	RFLP		Beaudet	AJHG	39	681	86
Cystic fibrosis	21970	MET		0.1(9.3)	RFLP		Bowcock	AJHG	39	699	85
Cystic fibrosis	21970	MET		—	RFLP		Dean	J. Pediatr.	111	490	87
Cystic fibrosis	21970	MET		1.5(>70.0)	RFLP		Farrall	Lancet	1	1402	86
Cystic fibrosis	21970	MET		—	RFLP		Farrall	JMG	23	295	86
Cystic fibrosis	21970	MET		2(6.8)	RFLP		Farrall	AJHG	39	713	86
Cystic fibrosis	21970	MET		—	RFLP		Law	PND	7	215	87
Cystic fibrosis	21970	MET		0.7(2.6)	RFLP		Mathy	Hum. Genet.	75	359	87
Cystic fibrosis	21970	MET		0.1(7.2)	RFLP		Naylor	AJHG	39	707	86
Cystic fibrosis	21970	MET		—	RFLP		Patton	Lancet	2	155	87
Cystic fibrosis	21970	MET		0.7(18.3)	RFLP		Schmidtke	Hum. Genet.	76	337	87
Cystic fibrosis	21970	MET		0.9(18.2)	RFLP		Spence	AJHG	39	729	86
Cystic fibrosis	21970	MET		—	RFLP		Spence	Hum. Genet.	76	5	87
Cystic fibrosis	21970	MET		10(4.2)	RFLP		Tsui	AJHG	39	720	86
Cystic fibrosis	21970	MET		0(15.5)	RFLP		Watkins	AJHG	39	735	86
Cystic fibrosis	21970	MET		0(8.7)	RFLP		White	Nature	318	382	85
Cystic fibrosis	21970	MET		1(16.8)	RFLP		White	AJHG	39	694	86
Cystic fibrosis	21970	TCRB		10(2.1)	RFLP		Wainwright	Nature	318	384	85
Diabetes insipidus—nephrogenic	30480	DXS52	St14	0(3.5)	RFLP		Knoerts	HGM9		515	87
Diabetes mellitus (Mody)	17673	INS		—	RE	PM	Haneda	PNAS	80	6366	83
Diabetes mellitus (Mody)	17673	INS		—	RE	PM	Shoelson	Nature	302	540	83
Diabetes mellitus type II	17673	INS		—	RFLP		Bell	Diabetes	33	176	84
Diabetes mellitus type II	17673	INS		—	RFLP		Rotwein	Science	213	1117	81
Diabetes mellitus type II	17673	INS		—	RFLP		Rotwein	NEJM	308	65	83
Displasia gigantism		DXYS1	pDP34	10(0.8)	RFLP		Gal	HGM9		396	87
Down syndrome	—	D21S13	D21K9	—	RE	AN	Davies	Hum. Genet.	66	54	84
Down syndrome	—	D21S73	DS21D1	—	RE	AN	Devine	ANYAS	450	85	85
Down syndrome	—	SOD1		—	RE	AN	Huret	Hum. Genet.	75	251	87
Ductal breast cancer	21141	D13(sev.)		—	RE	LH	Lundberg	PNAS	84	2372	87
Dyskeratosis congenita	30500	DXS15	DX13	0(1.6)	RFLP		Connor	Hum. Genet.	72	348	86
Dyskeratosis congenita	30500	DXS52	ST14	0(3.3)	RFLP		Connor	Hum. Genet.	72	348	86
Dyskeratosis congenita	30500	F8		0(1.2)	RFLP		Connor	Hum. Genet.	72	348	86
Ectodermal dysplasia hypohidrotic	30510	DXS14	58-1	7(3.6)	RFLP		Clarke	JMG	23	473	86
Ectodermal dysplasia hypohidrotic	30510	DXS14	58-1	7(3.6)	RFLP		Clarke	Hum. Genet.	75	378	87
Ectodermal dysplasia hypohidrotic	30510	DXS159	cpX73	5(4.3)	RFLP		Hanauer	HGM9		410	87
Ectodermal dysplasia hypohidrotic	30510	DXS3	19-2	9(4.3)	RFLP		Clarke	JMG	23	473	86
Ectodermal dysplasia hypohidrotic	30510	DXS3	19-2	22(2.3)	RFLP		Clarke	Hum. Genet.	75	378	87
Ectodermal dysplasia hypohidrotic	30510	DXS3	19-2	20(3.1)	RFLP		Clarke	HGM9		422	87

Disease	*McK-#*	*Gene/DNA segment*	*Probe*	*Distance*	*Detect.*	*Mut.*	*Author*	*Journal*	*Vol.*	*Page*	*Yr.*
Ectodermal dysplasia hypohidrotic	30510	DXYS1	pDP34	5(5.2)	RFLP		Clarke	Hum. Genet.	75	378	87
Ectodermal dysplasia hypohidrotic	30510	DXYS1	pDP34	12(3.9)	RFLP		Clarke	HGM9		422	87
Ectodermal dysplasia hypohidrotic	30510	DXYS1	pDP34	5(3.5)	RFLP		Hanauer	HGM9		410	87
Ectodermal dysplasia hypohidrotic	30510	DXYS1	pDP34	6(2.7)	RFLP		MacDermot	Hum. Genet.	74	172	86
Ectodermal dysplasia hypohidrotic	30510	DXYS2		13(5.8)	RFLP		Clarke	HGM9		422	87
Ectodermal dysplasia hypohidrotic	30510	PGK1		2(13.3)	RFLP		Clarke	HGM9		422	87
Ehlers-Danlos syndrome (type II)	13001	COL1A1		—	RE	DEL	Pope	Clin. Genet.	24	303	83
Ehlers-Danlos syndrome (type IV)	13005	COL3A1		—	RFLP		DePaepe	AICHG		712	86
Ehlers-Danlos syndrome (type IV)	13005	COL3A1		—	RFLP		Tsipouras	Hum. Genet.	74	41	86
Elliptocytosis-hereditary	13050	EL1		—	RE	REAR	Conboy	NEJM	315	680	86
Emery-Dreifuss muscular dystrophy	31030	CBD		14(3.4)	RFLP		Thomas	HGM9		419	87
Emery-Dreifuss muscular dystrophy	31030	DXS15	DX13	15(1.1)	RFLP		Hodgson	Hum. Genet.	74	409	86
Emery-Dreifuss muscular dystrophy	31030	DXS15	DX13	10(2.9)	RFLP		Thomas	JMG	23	471	86
Emery-Dreifuss muscular dystrophy	31030	DXS15	DX13	10(2.9)	RFLP		Thomas	JMG	23	596	86
Emery-Dreifuss muscular dystrophy	31030	DXS15	DX13	9(3.0)	RFLP		Thomas	HGM9		419	87
Emery-Dreifuss muscular dystrophy	31030	DXS15	DX13	0(2.5)	RFLP		Yates	JMG	23	587	86
Emery-Dreifuss muscular dystrophy	31030	DXS52	St14	6(7.0)	RFLP		Thomas	HGM9		419	87
Emery-Dreifuss muscular dystrophy	31030	F8		0(4.3)	RFLP		Thomas	JMG	23	471	86
Emery-Dreifuss muscular dystrophy	31030	F8		0(4.3)	RFLP		Thomas	JMG	23	596	86
Emery-Dreifuss muscular dystrophy	31030	F8		0(6.1)	RFLP		Thomas	HGM9		419	87
Emery-Dreifuss muscular dystrophy	31030	F8		0(3.5)	RFLP		Yates	JMG	23	587	86
Factor X deficiency	22760	F10		—	RE	DEL	Scambler	CCG	39	231	85
Factor XII deficiency	23400	F12		—	RE	RM	Bernardi	Blood	69	1421	87
Fragile X mental retardation syndrome	30955	F9		20(2.8)	RFLP		Forster-G.	J. Neurogenet	2	231	85
Fragile X mental retardation syndrome	30955	DXS98	4D8	5(3.4)	RFLP		Brown	Lancet	1	280	87
Fragile X mental retardation syndrome	30955	DX(sev.)	sev.	var.	RFLP		Brown	HGM9		353	87
Fragile X mental retardation syndrome	30955	DX(sev.)	sev.	var.	RFLP		Brown	Lancet	1	280	87
Fragile X mental retardation syndrome	30955	DX(sev.)	sev.	var.	RFLP		Connor	JMG	24	14	87
Fragile X mental retardation syndrome	30955	DX(sev.)		var.	RFLP		Mulligan	AJHG	37	463	85
Fragile X mental retardation syndrome	30955	DXS(sev.)	sev.	var.	RFLP		Oberle	Hum. Genet.	77	60	87
Fragile X mental retardation syndrome	30955	DXS105	CX55-7	4(5.0)	RFLP		Carpenter	AJMG	27	731	87
Fragile X mental retardation syndrome	30955	DXS105	CX55-7	5(4.2)	RFLP		Connor	JMG	24	635	87
Fragile X mental retardation syndrome	30955	DXS105	CX55-7	5(4.2)	RFLP		Connor	HGM9		80	87
Fragile X mental retardation syndrome	30955	DXS105	CX55-7	4(5.0)	RFLP		Veenema	JMG	24	413	87
Fragile X mental retardation syndrome	30955	DXS15	DX13	13(2.3)	RFLP		Buchanan	Hum. Genet.	76	165	87
Fragile X mental retardation syndrome	30955	DXS15	DX13	0(3.1)	RFLP		Gosden	HGM9		53	87
Fragile X mental retardation syndrome	30955	DXS15	DX13	12	RFLP		Holden	HGM8		653	85
Fragile X mental retardation syndrome	30955	DXS15	DX13	6(0.4)	RFLP		Mulley	AJMG	27	435	87
Fragile X mental retardation syndrome	30955	DXS51	52A	23(3.9)	RFLP		Brown	Hum. Genet.	75	311	87

Disease	McK-#	Gene/DNA segment	Probe	Distance	Detect.	Mut.	Author	Journal	Vol.	Page	Yr.
Fragile X mental retardation syndrome	30955	DXS51	52A	26(2.7)	RFLP		Buchanan	Hum. Genet.	76	165	87
Fragile X mental retardation syndrome	30955	DXS51	52A	30(1.0)	RFLP		Davies	Hum. Genet.	70	249	85
Fragile X mental retardation syndrome	30955	DXS51	52A	—	RFLP		Giannelli	AHG	51	107	87
Fragile X mental retardation syndrome	30955	DXS51	52A	10(1.2)	RFLP		Gosden	HGM9		53	87
Fragile X mental retardation syndrome	30955	DXS51	52A	11(3.5)	RFLP		Mulley	AJMG	27	435	87
Fragile X mental retardation syndrome	30955	DXS52	St14	12(12.4)	RFLP		Brown	Hum. Genet.	75	311	87
Fragile X mental retardation syndrome	30955	DXS52	St14	12(8.9)	RFLP		Brown	Lancet	1	280	87
Fragile X mental retardation syndrome	30955	DXS52	St14	8(16.0)	RFLP		Buchanan	Hum. Genet.	76	165	87
Fragile X mental retardation syndrome	30955	DXS52	St14	10(9.5)	RFLP		Goonewardena	HGM8		715	86
Fragile X mental retardation syndrome	30955	DXS52	St14	10(1.8)	RFLP		Gosden	HGM9		53	87
Fragile X mental retardation syndrome	30955	DXS52	St14	11(3.6)	RFLP		Mulley	AJMG	27	435	87
Fragile X mental retardation syndrome	30955	DXS52	St14	10(8.2)	RFLP		Oberle	PNAS	83	1016	86
Fragile X mental retardation syndrome	30955	DXS52	St14	8(4.0)	RFLP		Veenema	JMG	24	413	87
Fragile X mental retardation syndrome	30955	F9		—	RFLP		Brown	Hum. Genet.	71	11	85
Fragile X mental retardation syndrome	30955	F9		21(7.6)	RFLP		Brown	Hum. Genet.	75	311	87
Fragile X mental retardation syndrome	30955	F9		15(6.2)	RFLP		Brown	Lancet	1	280	87
Fragile X mental retardation syndrome	30955	F9		26(4.6)	RFLP		Buchanan	Hum. Genet.	76	165	87
Fragile X mental retardation syndrome	30955	F9		0(5.1)	RFLP		Camerino	Nature	306	701	83
Fragile X mental retardation syndrome	30955	F9		23(0.6)	RFLP		Choo	Lancet	2	349	84
Fragile X mental retardation syndrome	30955	F9		—	RFLP		Davies	Hum. Genet.	70	249	85
Fragile X mental retardation syndrome	30955	F9		20(2.7)	RFLP		Davies	Hum. Genet.	70	249	85
Fragile X mental retardation syndrome	30955	F9		—	RFLP		Giannelli	AHG	51	107	87
Fragile X mental retardation syndrome	30955	F9		12(6.2)	RFLP		Goonewardena	HGM8		715	86
Fragile X mental retardation syndrome	30955	F9		—	RFLP		Landoulski	Ann. Genet.	28	201	85
Fragile X mental retardation syndrome	30955	F9		9(3.2)	RFLP		Mulley	AJMG	27	435	87
Fragile X mental retardation syndrome	30955	F9		12.5(5.0)	RFLP		Oberle	PNAS	83	1016	86
Fragile X mental retardation syndrome	30955	F9		16(1.9)	RFLP		Veenema	JMG	24	413	87
Fragile X mental retardation syndrome	30955	F9		35(0.0)	RFLP		Warren	Hum. Genet.	69	44	85
Fragile X mental retardation syndrome	30955	F9		25(0.0)	RFLP		Zoll	Hum. Genet.	71	122	85
Fucosidosis	23000	FUCA1		—	RE	REAR	O'Brien	AJHG	41	A231	87
Gangliosidosis-GM2-B1 variant	23071	HEXB		—	SEQU	PM	Ohno	AJHG	41	A231	87
Gaucher disease type 2	23080	GBA		—	SEQU	PM	Tsuji	NEJM	316	570	87
Gerbich blood group deficiency	11075	GPC		—	RE	DEL	Le Van Kim	EJB	165	571	87
Glycerol kinase deficiency	30703	DX(sev.)		—	RE	DEL	Clarke	JMG	23	473	86
Glycerol kinase deficiency	30703	DX(sev.)	sev.	—	RE	DEL	Forrest	HGM9		118	87
Glycerol kinase deficiency	30703	DX(sev.)		—	RE	DEL	Francke	AJHG	40	212	87
Glycerol kinase deficiency	30703	DX(sev.)		—	RE	DEL	Goonewardena	HGM9		295	87
Glycerol kinase deficiency	30703	DX(sev.)	sev.	—	RE	DEL	Matsumoto	HGM9		3	87
Glycerol kinase deficiency	30703	DXS28	C7	—	RE	DEL	Boerresen	Clin. Genet	32	254	87
Glycerol kinase deficiency	30703	DXS68	L1.4	—	RE	DEL	Boerresen	Clin. Genet	32	254	87
Glycerol kinase deficiency	30703	DXS84		—	RE	DEL	Wieringa	HGM8		777	86
Growth hormone deficiency	13929	GH		—	RE	DEL	Orlando	AJHG	41	A105	87
Growth hormone deficiency (type A)	13929	GH		—	RE	DEL	Braga	AJMG	25	443	86
Growth hormone deficiency (type A)	13929	GH		—	RE	DEL	Phillips	PNAS	78	6372	81

Disease	*McK-#*	*Gene/DNA segment*	*Probe*	*Distance*	*Detect.*	*Mut.*	*Author*	*Journal*	*Vol.*	*Page*	*Yr.*
Growth hormone deficiency type I	13925	GH		—	RFLP		Phillips	JCI	70	489	82
Gyrate atrophy	25887	OAT		—	SEQU	PM	Mitchell	AJHG	41	A103	87
Gyrate atrophy	25887	OAT		—	RFLP		Ramesh	AJHG	41	A235	87
HPRT deficiency	30800	HPRT		—	SEQU	PM	Fujimori	AJHG	41	A214	87
HPRT deficiency	30800	HPRT		—	RE	DEL	Ishii	JJHG	31	204	86
HPRT deficiency	30800	HPRT		—	RE	DEL	Wilson	NEJM	309	900	83
HPRT deficiency	30800	HPRT		—	RE	PM	Wilson	NEJM	309	900	83
HPRT deficiency	30800	HPRT		—	RE	PM	Wilson	JCI	72	767	83
HPRT deficiency	30800	HPRT		—	RE	REAR	Wilson	JCI	77	188	86
Hemochromatosis	23520	HLAA		—	RE	REAR	David	HGM9		407	87
Hemoglobin C & SC disease	14190	HBB		—	OLIGO	PM	Saiki	Nature	324	163	86
Hemoglobin C & SC disease	14190	HBB		—	OLIGO	PM	Studencki	AJHG	37	42	85
Hemoglobin H disease	14175	HBA		—	SEQU	PM	Olivieri	Blood	70	729	87
Hemoglobin H disease	14175	HBA	pHPzeta	—	RFLP		Safaya	AJH	26	329	87
Hemophilia A	30670	DXS15	DX13		RFLP		Bernardi	Hum. Genet.	76	253	87
Hemophilia A	30670	DXS15	DX13	9(1.3)	RFLP		Bhattacharya	HGM9		226	87
Hemophilia A	30670	DXS15	DX13		RFLP		Broecker-Vrie	Thromb. Hae.	54	506	85
Hemophilia A	30670	DXS15	DX13		RFLP		Broecker-Vrie	Thromb. Hae.	57	131	87
Hemophilia A	30670	DXS15	DX13		RFLP		Delpech	Hum. Genet.	74	316	86
Hemophilia A	30670	DXS15	DX13		RFLP		Din	Lancet	1	1446	85
Hemophilia A	30670	DXS15	DX13		RFLP		Grover	Clin. Genet.	32	10	87
Hemophilia A	30670	DXS15	DX13	0(5.4)	RFLP		Harper	Lancet	2	6	84
Hemophilia A	30670	DXS15	DX13		RFLP		Janco	Lancet	1	148	86
Hemophilia A	30670	DXS15	DX13		RFLP		Lehesjoki	Lancet	2	280	86
Hemophilia A	30670	DXS15	DX13	15(1.1)	RFLP		Lehesjoki	HGM9		43	87
Hemophilia A	30670	DXS15	DX13		RFLP		Peake	Lancet	2	1003	85
Hemophilia A	30670	DXS15	DX13	4.5	RFLP		Peake	Lancet	1	1335	86
Hemophilia A	30670	DXS15	DX13	4.5(2.1)	RFLP		Pecorara	Blood	70	531	87
Hemophilia A	30670	DXS15	DX13		RFLP		Toennesen	Lancet	2	1269	84
Hemophilia A	30670	DXS15	DX13		RFLP		Winter	BMJ	291	765	85
Hemophilia A	30670	DXS15	DX13	4.7(6.1)	RFLP		Winter	HGM8		780	85
Hemophilia A	30670	DXS52	St14		RFLP		Bernardi	Hum. Genet.	76	253	87
Hemophilia A	30670	DXS52	St14	9(3.4)	RFLP		Bhattacharya	HGM9		226	87
Hemophilia A	30670	DXS52	St14		RFLP		Broecker-Vrie	Thromb. Hae.	57	131	87
Hemophilia A	30670	DXS52	St14		RFLP		Delpech	Hum. Genet.	74	316	86
Hemophilia A	30670	DXS52	St14		RFLP		Driscoll	Lancet	2	279	86
Hemophilia A	30670	DXS52	St14		RFLP		Grover	Clin. Genet.	32	10	87
Hemophilia A	30670	DXS52	St14		RFLP		Janco	Lancet	1	148	86
Hemophilia A	30670	DXS52	St14		RFLP		Kirk	Lancet	1	560	87
Hemophilia A	30670	DXS52	St14		RFLP		Lehesjoki	Lancet	2	280	86
Hemophilia A	30670	DXS52	St14	5(4.7)	RFLP		Lehesjoki	HGM9		43	87
Hemophilia A	30670	DXS52	St14	0(9.7)	RFLP		Oberle	NEJM	312	682	85
Hemophilia A	30670	DXS52	St14	0(4.2)	RFLP		Pecorara	Blood	70	531	87
Hemophilia A	30670	F8		—	RFLP		Antonarakis	Lancet	1	1407	85
Hemophilia A	30670	F8		—	RFLP		Antonarakis	NEJM	313	842	85
Hemophilia A	30670	F8		—	RE	DEL	Antonarakis	NEJM	313	842	85
Hemophilia A	30670	F8		—	RE	PM	Antonarakis	NEJM	313	842	85
Hemophilia A	30670	F8		—	OLIGO	PM	Antonarakis	NEJM	313	842	85
Hemophilia A	30670	F8		—	RFLP		Baty	Lancet	1	207	86
Hemophilia A	30670	F8		—	RFLP		Bernardi	Hum. Genet.	76	253	87
Hemophilia A	30670	F8		—	RFLP		Broecker-Vrie	Thromb. Hae.	57	131	87
Hemophilia A	30670	F8		—	RFLP		Delpech	Hum. Genet.	74	316	86
Hemophilia A	30670	F8		—	RFLP		Din	Lancet	1	1446	85
Hemophilia A	30670	F8		—	RFLP		Driscoll	Lancet	2	279	86
Hemophilia A	30670	F8		—	RE	DEL	Gitschier	Nature	315	427	85
Hemophilia A	30670	F8		—	RE	PM	Gitschier	Nature	315	427	85
Hemophilia A	30670	F8		—	RFLP		Gitschier	Nature	314	738	85
Hemophilia A	30670	F8		—	RFLP		Gitschier	Lancet	1	1093	85
Hemophilia A	30670	F8		—	RE	DEL	Gitschier	Science	232	1415	86
Hemophilia A	30670	F8		—	RE	PM	Gitschier	Science	232	1415	86
Hemophilia A	30670	F8		—	RE	DEL	Grover	Clin. Genet.	32	10	87
Hemophilia A	30670	F8		—	RFLP		Grover	Clin. Genet.	32	10	87
Hemophilia A	30670	F8		—	RFLP		Janco	Lancet	1	148	86
Hemophilia A	30670	F8		—	RFLP		Janco	Blood	69	1539	87
Hemophilia A	30670	F8		—	RFLP		Kirk	Lancet	1	560	87
Hemophilia A	30670	F8		—	OLIGO	PM	Kogan	NEJM	317	985	87
Hemophilia A	30670	F8		—	RFLP		Lehesjoki	Lancet	2	280	86
Hemophilia A	30670	F8		—	RFLP		Peake	Lancet	2	1003	85
Hemophilia A	30670	F8	var.	—	RFLP		Pecorara	Blood	70	531	87
Hemophilia A	30670	F8		—	RFLP		Schwartz	Clin. Genet.	29	472	86
Hemophilia A	30670	F8		—	RE	DEL	Wion	NAR	14	4535	86
Hemophilia A	30670	F8		—	RFLP		Wion	NAR	14	4535	86
Hemophilia A	30670	F8		—	RE	DEL	Youssoufian	AICHG		656	86
Hemophilia A	30670	F8		—	RE	PM	Youssoufian	AICHG		656	86

Disease	*McK-#*	*Gene/DNA segment*	*Probe*	*Distance*	*Detect.*	*Mut.*	*Author*	*Journal*	*Vol.*	*Page*	*Yr.*
Hemophilia B	30680	DXS100	p4S	—	RFLP		Poon	JCI	79	1204	87
Hemophilia B	30680	DXS51	52a	—	RFLP		Poon	JCI	79	1204	87
Hemophilia B	30680	F9		—	SEQU	PM	Bentley	Cell	45	343	86
Hemophilia B	30680	F9		—	RE	DEL	Bernardi	JMG	22	305	85
Hemophilia B	30680	F9		—	RFLP		Broecker-Vrie	Thromb. Hae.	54	506	85
Hemophilia B	30680	F9		—	RE	DEL	Chen	AJHG	37	A7	85
Hemophilia B	30680	F9		—	RE	PM	Chen	AJHG	37	A7	85
Hemophilia B	30680	F9		—	RE	DEL	Chen	AICHG		655	86
Hemophilia B	30680	F9		—	RE	PM	Chen	AICHG		655	86
Hemophilia B	30680	F9		—	OLIGO	PM	Chen	AICHG		655	86
Hemophilia B	30680	F9		—	RFLP		Connor	JMG	22	441	85
Hemophilia B	30680	F9		—	RFLP		Connor	JMG	23	300	86
Hemophilia B	30680	F9		—	SEQU	PM	Davis	Blood	69	140	87
Hemophilia B	30680	F9		—	RE	DEL	Giannelli	Nature	303	181	83
Hemophilia B	30680	F9		—	RFLP		Giannelli	Lancet	1	239	84
Hemophilia B	30680	F9		—	RFLP		Grunebaum	JCI	73	1491	84
Hemophilia B	30680	F9		—	RE	DEL	Hassan	Blood	66	728	85
Hemophilia B	30680	F9		—	RFLP		Hay	Blood	67	1508	86
Hemophilia B	30680	F9		—	RFLP		Lillicrap	BJH	62	557	86
Hemophilia B	30680	F9		—	RE	DEL	Ludwig	AICHG		653	86
Hemophilia B	30680	F9		—	RE	DEL	Matthews	JCI	79	746	87
Hemophilia B	30680	F9		—	RE	REAR	Matthews	JCI	79	746	87
Hemophilia B	30680	F9		—	RE	DEL	Mikami	JJHG	32	21	87
Hemophilia B	30680	F9		—	RE	DEL	Nisen	NEJM	315	1139	86
Hemophilia B	30680	F9		—	RE	DEL	Peake	Lancet	1	242	84
Hemophilia B	30680	F9		—	RFLP		Poon	JCI	79	1204	87
Hemophilia B	30680	F9		—	SEQU	PM	Rees	Nature	316	643	85
Hemophilia B	30680	F9		—	SEQU	DEL	Schach	JCI	80	1023	87
Hemophilia B	30680	F9		—	RFLP		Schwartz	Clin. Genet.	29	472	86
Hemophilia B	30680	F9		—	RE	DEL	Vidaud	Blood	68	961	86
Hemophilia B	30680	F9		—	RE	DEL	Wadelius	AICHG		654	86
Hemophilia B	30680	F9		—	RFLP		Winship	NAR	12	8861	84
Hemophilia B	30680	F9		—	OLIGO	PM	Winship	Lancet	2	218	86
Heavy chain disease	14702	IGHM		—	RE	DEL	Bakhshi	PNAS	83	2689	86
Heavy chain disease	14702	IGHM		—	RE	INS	Bakhshi	PNAS	83	2689	86
Hepatocellular carcinoma	—	D4S(sev.)	sev.	—	RE	LH	Beutow	AJHG	41	A24	87
Hereditary persist. of fetal hemoglobin	14190	HBB		—	RE	DEL	Farquhar	AJHG	35	611	83
Hereditary persist. of fetal hemoglobin	14190	HBB		—	OLIGO	PM	Waber	Blood	67	551	86
Hereditary persist. of fetal hemoglobin	14190	HBG		—	RE	PM	Collins	Blood	64	1292	84
Hereditary persist. of fetal hemoglobin	14190	HBG		—	SEQU	PM	Collins	PNAS	81	4894	84
Hunter syndrome	30990	DXS15	DX13	10(3.0)	RFLP		Chase	AHG	50	349	86
Hunter syndrome	30990	DXS15	DX13	10	RFLP		Giannelli	AICHG		628	86
Hunter syndrome	30990	sev.	sev.	var.	RFLP		Upadhyaya	Hum. Genet.	74	391	86
Hunter syndrome	30990	sev.	sev.	var.	RFLP		Upadhyaya	HGM8		765	86
Huntington disease	14310	D4S10	G8	6(13.6)	RFLP		Folstein	Science	229	776	85
Huntington disease	14310	D4S10	G8	3(34.6)	RFLP		Gilliam	Cell	50	565	87
Huntington disease	14310	D4S10	G8	0(1.8)	RFLP		Gusella	Nature	306	234	83
Huntington disease	14310	D4S10	G8	2	RFLP		Gusella	Science	225	1320	84
Huntington disease	14310	D4S10	G8	4(87.2)	RFLP		Haines	HGM9		442	87
Huntington disease	14310	D4S10	G8	2(5.6)	RFLP		Harper	JMG	22	447	85
Huntington disease	14310	D4S10	G8	—	RFLP		Hayden	Lancet	1	1284	87
Huntington disease	14310	D4S10	G8	—	RFLP		Hayden	Neurology	37	1441	87
Huntington disease	14310	D4S10	G8	4	RFLP		Holmgren	Clin. Genet.	32	289	87
Huntington disease	14310	D4S10	G8	—	RFLP		Quarrell	Lancet	1	1281	87
Huntington disease	14310	D4S10	G8	4	RFLP		Skraastad	AICHG		680	86
Huntington disease	14310	D4S10	G8	4	RFLP		Wexler	Nature	326	194	87
Huntington disease	14310	D4S10	G8	2(17.6)	RFLP		Youngman	Hum. Genet.	73	333	86
Huntington disease	14310	D4S43	C9A/LCD	0(44.8)	RFLP		Gilliam	Science	238	950	87
Huntington disease	14310	D4S62		4(13.4)	RFLP		Gilliam	Cell	50	565	87
Huntington disease	14310	RAF2		32(1.1)	RFLP		Gilliam	Cell	50	565	87
Huntington disease (juvenile)	14310	D4S10	F5.52	4	RFLP		Hammer	Lancet	2	1088	87
Hypercholesterolemia	14389	LDLR		0(1.8)	RFLP		Berg	HGM8		581	86
Hypercholesterolemia	14389	LDLR		—	SEQU	PM	Davis	Cell	45	15	86
Hypercholesterolemia	14389	LDLR		—	RE	DEL	Hobbs	NEJM	317	734	87
Hypercholesterolemia	14389	LDLR		—	RE	DEL	Horsthemke	Hum. Genet.	71	75	85
Hypercholesterolemia	14389	LDLR		—	RE	DEL	Horsthemke	JMG	24	144	87
Hypercholesterolemia	14389	LDLR		—	RE	REAR	Horsthemke	EJB	164	77	87
Hypercholesterolemia	14389	LDLR		—	RFLP		Humphries	Lancet	1	1003	85
Hypercholesterolemia	14389	LDLR	pLDLR-2H	—	RFLP		Kotze	JMG	24	750	87
Hypercholesterolemia	14389	LDLR		—	RE	DEL	Langlois	AICHG		752	86
Hypercholesterolemia	14389	LDLR		—	RE	DEL	Lehrman	Science	227	140	85

Disease	*McK-#*	*Gene/DNA segment*	*Probe*	*Distance*	*Detect.*	*Mut.*	*Author*	*Journal*	*Vol.*	*Page*	*Yr.*
Hypercholesterolemia	14389	LDLR		—	SEQU	PM	Lehrman	Cell	41	735	85
Hypercholesterolemia	14389	LDLR		—	SEQU	DUP	Lehrman	Cell	41	735	85
Hypercholesterolemia	14389	LDLR		—	RE	DEL	Lehrman	PNAS	83	3679	86
Hypercholesterolemia	14389	LDLR		—	RE	PM	Lehrman	JBC	262	401	87
Hypercholesterolemia	14389	LDLR		—	RE	DUP	Lehrman	Cell	48	827	87
Hypercholesterolemia	14389	LDLR		0(7.5)	RFLP		Leppert	AJHG	39	300	86
Hyperlipidemia (type II)	10768	APOA1		—	RFLP		Vella	Hum. Genet.	69	275	85
Hyperlipidemia (type Ib)	20775	APOC2		—	RFLP		Humphries	ATS VII		143	86
Hyperproinsulinemia	17673	INS		—	SEQU	PM	Chan	PNAS	84	2194	87
Hyperproinsulinemia	17673	INS		—	RE	PM	Kwok	BBRC	98	844	81
Hyperproinsulinemia	17673	INS		—	RE	PM	Kwok	Diabetes	32	872	83
Hyperproinsulinemia	17673	INS		—	SEQU	PM	Kwok	Diabetes	32	872	83
Hyperproinsulinemia	17673	INS		—	SEQU	PM	Shibasaki	JCI	76	378	85
Hypertriglyceridemia	10768	APOA1		—	RFLP		Rees	Lancet	1	444	83
Hypertriglyceridemia	10768	APOA1		—	RFLP		Rees	JCI	76	1090	85
Hypoparathyroidism	16845	PTH		—	RFLP		Ahn	Medicine	65	73	86
Hypophosphatemia	30780	DX(sev.)	sev.	var.	RFLP		Thakker	HGM9		450	87
Hypophosphatemia	30780	DXS207	pPA4B	9(1.3)	RFLP		Albertsen	HGM9		317	87
Hypophosphatemia	30780	DXS41	99.6	16(1.1)	RFLP		Maechler	Hum. Genet.	73	271	86
Hypophosphatemia	30780	DXS41	99.6	10(4.8)	RFLP		Read	Hum. Genet.	73	267	86
Hypophosphatemia	30780	DXS41	99.6	9(7.4)	RFLP		Thakker	JMG	24	756	87
Hypophosphatemia	30780	DXS43	D2	6(2.5)	RFLP		Maechler	Hum. Genet.	73	271	86
Hypophosphatemia	30780	DXS43	D2	16(4.8)	RFLP		Thakker	JMG	24	756	87
Hypothyroidism	18845	TG		—	RFLP		Baas	Hum. Genet.	67	301	84
Ichthyosis	30810	DXS143	dic56	0(1.6)	RFLP		Ballabio	Hum. Genet.	72	237	86
Ichthyosis	30810	DXS143	dic56	6(3.1)	RFLP		Yates	Genomics	1	52	87
Ichthyosis	30810	DXS143	dic56	6(3.1)	RFLP		Yates	HGM9		120	87
Ichthyosis	30810	DXS237	GMGX9	—	RE	DEL	Gillard	NAR	15	3977	87
Ichthyosis	30810	DXS237	GMGX9	—	RE	DEL	Gillard	HGM9		84	87
Ichthyosis	30810	DXS237	GMGX9	0(8.7)	RE	DEL	Goudie	JMG	24	239	87
Ichthyosis	30810	DXS237	GMGX9	0(8.7)	RFLP		Yates	Genomics	1	52	87
Ichthyosis	30810	DXS237	GMGX9	0(8.7)	RFLP		Yates	HGM9		120	87
Ichthyosis	30810	DXS85	782	8(5.8)	RFLP		Goudie	JMG	24	239	87
Ichthyosis	30810	DXS85	782	8(6.1)	RFLP		Yates	Genomics	1	52	87
Ichthyosis	30810	DXS85	782	8(6.2)	RFLP		Yates	HGM9		120	87
Ichthyosis	30810	DXS9	RC8	25(0.5)	RFLP		Wieacker	Hum. Genet.	63	113	83
Ichthyosis	30810	STS		—	RE	DEL	Ballabio	PNAS	84	4519	87
Ichthyosis	30810	STS		—	RE	DEL	Conary	BBRC	144	1010	87
Ichthyosis	30810	STS		—	RE	DEL	Yen	Cell	49	443	87
Immunodeficiency with hyper-IgM	30823	DXS42	43-15	—	RFLP		Mensink	Hum. Genet.	76	96	87
Immunodeficiency—severe combined	30040	DXS1	p8	10(2.1)	RFLP		Saint Basile	PNAS	84	7576	87
Immunodeficiency—severe combined	30040	DXS159	CpX73	0(5.3)	RFLP		Saint Basile	PNAS	84	7576	87
Immunodeficiency—severe combined	30040	DXS3	19.2	11(5.5)	RFLP		Saint Basile	PNAS	84	7576	87
Immunodeficiency—severe combined	30040	DXYS1	pDP34	10(2.3)	RFLP		Saint Basile	PNAS	84	7576	87
Immunoglobulin H chain deficiency	14710	IGH		—	RE	DEL	Chaabani	AJHG	37	1164	86
Immunoglobulin K chain deficiency	14720	IGK		—	RE	DEL	Chaabani	AJHG	37	1164	85
Immunoglobulin K chain deficiency	14720	IGK		—	SEQU	PM	Stavnezer-Nor	Science	230	458	85
Kennedy disease	31320	DXYS1	pDP34	5(3.5)	RFLP		Fischbeck	Neurology	36	1595	86
Kennedy disease	31320	DXYS1	pDP34	0(1.4)	RFLP		Ionasescu	AJMG	25	722	86
Klinefelter syndrome	—	DS(sev.)	sev.	—	RE	AN	Patil	AJHG	37	A110	85
Lesch-Nyhan syndrome (HPRT-def.)	30800	HPRT		—	RFLP		Gibbs	JIMD	9	45	86
Lesch-Nyhan syndrome (HPRT-def.)	30800	HPRT		—	RE	DEL	Gibbs	Science	236	303	87
Lesch-Nyhan syndrome (HPRT-def.)	30800	HPRT		—	RE	PM	Nussbaum	PNAS	80	4035	83
Lesch-Nyhan syndrome (HPRT-def.)	30800	HPRT		—	RFLP		Nussbaum	PNAS	80	4035	83
Lesch-Nyhan syndrome (HPRT-def.)	30800	HPRT		—	RFLP		Yang	AJHG	35	185A	83
Lesch-Nyhan syndrome (HPRT-def.)	30800	HPRT		—	RE	DEL	Yang	Nature	310	412	84
Lesch-Nyhan syndrome (HPRT-def.)	30800	HPRT		—	RE	PM	Yang	Nature	310	412	84
Lowe oculocerebrorenal syndrome	30900	DXS10		0(6.5)	RFLP		Silver	JCI	79	282	87

Disease	McK-#	Gene/DNA segment	Probe	Distance	Detect.	Mut.	Author	Journal	Vol.	Page	Yr.
Lowe oculocerebrorenal syndrome	30900	DXS10		3(7.1)	RFLP		Silver	HGM9		257	87
Lowe oculocerebrorenal syndrome	30900	DXS42		0(5.1)	RFLP		Silver	JCI	79	282	87
Lowe oculocerebrorenal syndrome	30900	DXS42		0(6.6)	RFLP		Silver	HGM9		257	87
Lung cancer	—	D1S1	pH3H2	—	RE	LH	Kok	Nature	330	578	87
Lymphoproliferative syndrome	30824	DXS42		4(5.3)	RFLP		Skare	PNAS	84	2015	87
Manic depression	30920	F9		11(3.1)	RFLP		Mendlewicz	Lancet	1	1230	87
Manic depression	12548	HRAS1		0(<0.6)	RFLP		Egeland	Nature	325	783	87
Marfan syndrome	15470	COL1A2		—	RE	INS	Henke	JCB	Suppl	284	84
Marfan syndrome	12016	COL1A2		—	RFLP		Ahti	AICHG		713	86
McLeod syndrome	31458	DX(sev.)		—	RE	DEL	Francke	AJHG	37	250	85
Meningioma	15610	D22(sev.)	sev.	—	RE	LH	Cogen	AJHG	41	A25	87
Meningioma	15610	D22(sev.)	sev.	—	RE	LH	Dumanski	HGM9		90	87
Meningioma	15610	D22(sev.)		—	RE	LH	Seizinger	PNAS	84	5419	87
Meningioma	15610	D22S1		—	RE	DEL	Cogen	HGM9		134	87
Meningioma	15610	IGL		—	RE	DEL	Cogen	HGM9		134	87
Menke syndrome	30940	DXS7	L1.28	18(0.6)	RFLP		Wieacker	Hum. Genet.	64	139	83
Mental retardation X-linked	30953	DXS85	782	6(2.6)	RFLP		Arveiler	HGM9		411	87
Mental retardation X-linked	—	DXYS1	pDP34	0(2.2)	RFLP		Sutherland	HGM9		18B	87
Multiple endocrine neoplasia-type 2	17140	D1S7	Minisat.	—	RE	LH	Mathew	Nature	328	524	87
Multiple endocrine neoplasia-type 2A	17140	D10S5		19(3.6)	RFLP		Simpson	Nature	328	528	87
Multiple endocrine neoplasia-type 2A	17140	D22S9		—	RE	LH	Takai	JJCR	78	894	87
Multiple endocrine neoplasia-type 2A	17140	IRBP		4(3.9)	RFLP		Mathew	Nature	328	527	87
Multiple endocrine neoplasia-type 2A	17140	IRBP		11(8.0)	RFLP		Simpson	Nature	328	528	87
Muscular dystrophy (BMD)	31010	DXS206	pXJ1.1/2	—	RE	DEL	Leichti-Galla	Hum. Genet.	77	267	87
Muscular dystrophy (BMD)	31010	DMD		—	RE	DEL	Koenig	Cell	50	509	87
Muscular dystrophy (BMD)	31010	DXS164	pERT87	0	RFLP		Wood	Clin. Genet.	31	45	87
Muscular dystrophy (BMD)	31010	DXS28	C7	0	RFLP		Dorkins	Hum. Genet.	71	103	85
Muscular dystrophy (BMD)	31020	DXS43		15(1.2)			Fadda	Hum. Genet.	71	33	85
Muscular dystrophy (BMD)	31010	DXS7	L1.28	16(3.0)	RFLP		Kingston	JMG	20	255	83
Muscular dystrophy (BMD)	31010	DXS7	L1.28	—	RFLP		Roncuzzi	AJHG	37	407	85
Muscular dystrophy (BMD)	31010	DXS84	754	15(1.7)	RFLP		Brown	JMG	22	179	85
Muscular dystrophy (BMD)	31010	DXS84	754	18	RFLP		Kingston	Clin. Genet.	27	383	85
Muscular dystrophy (BMD)	31020	DXS9		10(1.1)			Fadda	Hum. Genet.	71	33	85
Muscular dystrophy (BMD)	31010	OTC		—	RFLP		Roncuzzi	AJHG	37	407	85
Muscular dystrophy (DMD)	31020		J-Bir	—	RE	DEL	Darras	Nature	329	556	87
Muscular dystrophy (DMD)	31020	DXS206	XJ1-1	—	RE	DEL	DenDunnen	Nature	329	640	87
Muscular dystrophy (DMD)	31020	DXS206	pXJ-1.1	—	RE	DEL	Greenberg	AJHG	41	128	87
Muscular dystrophy (DMD)	31020	DXS206	XJ1.1	0(6.4)	RFLP		Pericak-Vance	HGM9		63	87
Muscular dystrophy (DMD)	31020	DXS206	XJNCT	0(7.4)	RFLP		Pericak-Vance	HGM9		63	87
Muscular dystrophy (DMD)	31020	Breakp.		—	SEQU	DEL	Bodrug	Science	237	1620	87
Muscular dystrophy (DMD)	31020	DMD		—	RE	DEL	Doenig	Cell	50	509	87
Muscular dystrophy (DMD)	31020	DX(sev.)	—	—	RFLP		Darr	NEJM	316	985	87
Muscular dystrophy (DMD)	31020	DXS(sev.)	sev.	—	RE	DEL	Darras	Nature	329	556	87
Muscular dystrophy (DMD)	31020	DXS148	CX5	—	RE	DEL	Hofker	Hum. Genet.	74	275	86
Muscular dystrophy (DMD)	31020	DXS164	pERT87	—	RE	DEL	Bakker	Nature	329	554	87
Muscular dystrophy (DMD)	31020	DXS164	pERT87.8	—	RFLP		Boerresen	Clin. Genet.	32	187	87
Muscular dystrophy (DMD)	31020	DXS164	pERT84-1	—	RE	REAR	DenDunnen	Nature	329	640	87
Muscular dystrophy (DMD)	31020	DXS164	pERT87	0(17.2)	RFLP		Donald	Lancet	1	39	87
Muscular dystrophy (DMD)	31020	DXS164	pERT87.1	—	RE	DEL	Fuerst	FEBS Lett.	224	49	87
Muscular dystrophy (DMD)	31020	DXS164	pERT-87	—	RE	DEL	Greenberg	AJHG	41	128	87
Muscular dystrophy (DMD)	31020	DXS164	pERT87	—	RFLP		Hyser	Neurology	37	1476	87
Muscular dystrophy (DMD)	31020	DXS164	pERT-87	—	RE	DEL	Lanman	AJHG	41	138	87
Muscular dystrophy (DMD)	31020	DXS164	pERT87-1	2(7.8)	RFLP		Lindloef	AHG	51	317	87
Muscular dystrophy (DMD)	31020	DXS164	pERT-87	0(9.9)	RFLP		Pericak-Vance	HGM9		63	87
Muscular dystrophy (DMD)	31020	DXS28	C7	12(2.7)	RFLP		Dorkins	Hum. Genet.	71	103	85
Muscular dystrophy (DMD)	31020	DXS41	99-6	—	RFLP		Hyser	Neurology	37	1476	87
Muscular dystrophy (DMD)	31020	DXS41	99.6	30(1.5)	RFLP		Pericak-Vance	HGM9		63	87
Muscular dystrophy (DMD)	31020	DXS41	99.6	3(3.7)	RFLP		Wilcox	Hum. Genet.	70	365	85
Muscular dystrophy (DMD)	31020	DXS43	pD2	—	RFLP		Hyser	Neurology	37	1476	87
Muscular dystrophy (DMD)	31020	DXS67	B24	—	RFLP		Noerby	Clin. Genet	31	192	87
Muscular dystrophy (DMD)	31020	DXS7	L1.28	17(2.6)	RFLP		Davies	NAR	11	2303	83
Muscular dystrophy (DMD)	31020	DXS7	L1.28	22	RFLP		Hofker	Hum. Genet.	74	275	86
Muscular dystrophy (DMD)	31020	DXS84	754	3(6.2)	RFLP		Bakker	Lancet	1	655	85
Muscular dystrophy (DMD)	31020	DXS84	754	20(1.2)	RFLP		Brown	JMG	22	179	85
Muscular dystrophy (DMD)	31020	DXS84	754	12(2.7)	RFLP		Davies	NAR	13	3419	85
Muscular dystrophy (DMD)	31020	DXS84	754	—	RFLP		Hyser	Neurology	37	1476	87

Disease	McK-#	Gene/DNA segment	Probe	Distance	Detect.	Mut.	Author	Journal	Vol.	Page	Yr.
Muscular dystrophy (DMD)	31020	DXS84	754	10(3.4)	RFLP		Pericak-Vance	HGM9		63	87
Muscular dystrophy (DMD)	31020	DXS9	RC8	17(1.6)	RFLP		Davies	NAR	11	2303	83
Muscular dystrophy (DMD)	31020	DXS9	RC8	10(1.8)	RFLP		Murray	Nature	300	69	82
Muscular dystrophy (DMD)	31020	OTC		5(2.6)	RFLP		Davies	NAR	13	155	85
Muscular dystrophy (DMD)	31020	OTC		12	RFLP		Davies	NAR	13	3419	85
Muscular dystrophy (DMD)	31020	sev.	sev.	var.	RFLP		Bakker	Lancet	1	655	85
Muscular dystrophy (DMD)	31020	sev.	sev.	var.	RFLP		Darras	NEJM	316	985	87
Muscular dystrophy (DMD)	31020	sev.	sev.	var.	RFLP		Hejtmancik	Neurology	36	1553	86
Muscular dystrophy (DMD)	31020	sev.	sev.	var.	RFLP		Lavergne	Lancet	2	216	86
Muscular dystrophy (DMD/BMD)	31020	DXS164	pERT87-4	—	RE	DEL	Bartlett	HGM9		64	87
Muscular dystrophy (DMD/BMD)	31020	DXS206	pXJ1	—	RE	REAR	Boyd	Clin. Genet.	31	265	87
Muscular dystrophy (DMD/BMD)	31020	DXS206	XJ-1	0(12.5)	RFLP		Denton	HGM9		231	87
Muscular dystrophy (DMD/BMD)	31020		J-Bir	9(2.8)	RFLP		Denton	HGM9		231	87
Muscular dystrophy (DMD/BMD)	31020	DMD	Cal/Cf16	—	RE	DEL	Cross	EMBO J.	6	3277	87
Muscular dystrophy (DMD/BMD)	31020	DMD		—	RE	DEL	Forrest	Nature	329	638	87
Muscular dystrophy (DMD/BMD)	31010	DMD		—	RE	DUP	Hu	AJHG	41	A100	87
Muscular dystrophy (DMD/BMD)	31020	DMD		—	RE	DEL	Smith	NAR	15	9761	87
Muscular dystrophy (DMD/BMD)	31020	DX(sev.)	sev.	var.	RE	DEL	Bakker	HGM9		458	87
Muscular dystrophy (DMD/BMD)	31020	DX(sev.)		—	RE	DEL	Clarke	JMG	23	473	86
Muscular dystrophy (DMD/BMD)	31020	DX(sev.)	—	—	RE	DEL	Forrest	Lancet	2	1294	87
Muscular dystrophy (DMD/BMD)	31020	DX(sev.)		—	RE	DEL	Francke	AJHG	37	250	85
Muscular dystrophy (DMD/BMD)	31020	DX(sev.)		—	RE	DEL	Hart	JMG	23	516	86
Muscular dystrophy (DMD/BMD)	31020	DX(sev.)		—	RE	DEL	Hodgson	Lancet	1	918	86
Muscular dystrophy (DMD/BMD)	31020	DX(sev.)		—	RE	DEL	Ingle	AJHG	37	451	85
Muscular dystrophy (DMD/BMD)	31020	DX(sev.)		—	RE	DEL	Ionasescu	Neurology	36	1143	86
Muscular dystrophy (DMD/BMD)	31020	DX(sev.)		—	RE	DEL	Kenwrick	Cell	48	351	87
Muscular dystrophy (DMD/BMD)	31020	DX(sev.)		—	RE	DEL	Kunkel	PNAS	82	4778	85
Muscular dystrophy (DMD/BMD)	31020	DX(sev.)		—	RE	DEL	Kunkel	Nature	322	73	86
Muscular dystrophy (DMD/BMD)	31020	DX(sev.)	sev.		RE	DEL	Lindloef	HGM9		41	87
Muscular dystrophy (DMD/BMD)	31020	DX(sev.)		—	RE	DEL	Monaco	Nature	316	842	85
Muscular dystrophy (DMD/BMD)	31020	DX(sev.)		—	RE	DEL	Monaco	Nature	323	646	86
Muscular dystrophy (DMD/BMD)	31020	DX(sev.)		—	RE	DEL	Monaco	Hum. Genet.	75	221	87
Muscular dystrophy (DMD/BMD)	31020	DX(sev.)		—	RE	DEL	Wilcox	Hum. Genet.	73	175	86
Muscular dystrophy (DMD/BMD)	31020	DX(sev.)		—	RE	DEL	van Ommen	Cell	47	499	86
Muscular dystrophy (DMD/BMD)	31020	DXS148		—	RE	DEL	Hofker	Hum. Genet.	74	275	86
Muscular dystrophy (DMD/BMD)	31020	DXS164	pERT87	—	RE	DEL	Bartlett	Neurology	37	355	87
Muscular dystrophy (DMD/BMD)	31020	DXS164	pERT87	—	RE	REAR	Boyd	Clin. Genet.	31	265	87
Muscular dystrophy (DMD/BMD)	31020	DXS164		0(19.8)	RFLP		Denton	HGM9		231	87
Muscular dystrophy (DMD/BMD)	31020	DXS164	pERT87	6	RFLP		Fischbeck	Lancet	2	104	86
Muscular dystrophy (DMD/BMD)	31020	DXS164	pERT87-1		RE	DEL	Hart	Hum. Genet.	77	88	87
Muscular dystrophy (DMD/BMD)	31020	DXS164	pERT87	5	RFLP		Kunkel	Nature	322	73	86
Muscular dystrophy (DMD/BMD)	31020	DXS164	pERT87-1	2(7.8)	RFLP		Lindloef	HGM9		40	87

Disease	McK-#	Gene/DNA segment	Probe	Distance	Detect.	Mut.	Author	Journal	Vol.	Page	Yr.
Muscular dystrophy (DMD/BMD)	31020	DXS164	pERT87	—	RE	DEL	Thomas	JMG	23	509	86
Muscular dystrophy (DMD/BMD)	31020	DXS206		7(1.6)	RFLP		Lindloef	HGM9		40	87
Muscular dystrophy (DMD/BMD)	31010	DXS206		—	RE	DEL	Worton	HGM9		507	87
Muscular dystrophy (DMD/BMD)	31020	DXS28		14(2.0)	RFLP		Denton	HGM9		231	87
Muscular dystrophy (DMD/BMD)	31020	DXS28	C7	15(2.7)			Dorkins	Hum. Genet.	71	103	85
Muscular dystrophy (DMD/BMD)	31020	DXS41	99.6	15(3.4)	RFLP		Brown	Hum. Genet.	71	62	85
Muscular dystrophy (DMD/BMD)	31020	DXS7	L1.28	18(4.2)	RFLP		Brown	Hum. Genet.	71	62	85
Muscular dystrophy (DMD/BMD)	31020	DXS84	754	18(2.1)	RFLP		Brown	Hum. Genet.	71	62	85
Muscular dystrophy (DMD/BMD)	31020	DXS84	754	11(5.6)			Dorkins	Hum. Genet.	71	103	85
Muscular dystrophy (DMD/BMD)	31020	DXS85	782	20(1.3)	RFLP		Brown	Hum. Genet.	71	62	85
Muscular dystrophy (DMD/BMD)	31010	DXS9	RC8	19(0.8)	RFLP		Brown	Hum. Genet.	71	62	85
Muscular dystrophy (DMD/BMD)	31020	OTC		15(2.7)	RFLP		Brown	Hum. Genet.	71	62	85
Muscular dystrophy (DMD/BMD)	31020	sev.	sev.	var.	RFLP		Bakker	JMG	23	573	86
Muscular dystrophy (DMD/BMD)	31020	sev.	sev.	var.	RFLP		Hodgson	JMG	24	152	87
Muscular dystrophy (DMD/BMD)	31020	sev.	sev.	var.	RFLP		Hyser	Neurology	37	4	87
Muscular dystrophy (DMD/BMD)	31020	sev.	sev.	var.	RFLP		Lavergne	Lancet	2	216	86
Muscular dystrophy (DMD/BMD)	31020	sev.	sev.	var.	RFLP		Lindloef	JMG	23	560	86
Muscular dystrophy (DMD/BMD)	31020	sev.	sev.	var.	RFLP		Old	JMG	23	556	86
Muscular dystrophy (DMD/BMD)	31020	sev.	sev.	var.	RFLP		Read	JMG	23	581	86
Muscular dystrophy (DMD/BMD)	31020	sev.	sev.	var.	RFLP		Wilichowski	Hum. Genet.	75	32	87
Myotonic dystrophy	16090	APOC2		0(3.3)	RFLP		Bird	Arch. Neurol.	44	273	87
Myotonic dystrophy	16090	APOC2		2(16.3)	RFLP		Pericak-Vance	Neurology	36	1418	86
Myotonic dystrophy	16090	APOC2		2(23.8)	RFLP		Pericak-Vance	HGM9		62	87
Myotonic dystrophy	16090	APOC2		4(7.8)	RFLP		Shaw	Hum. Genet.	70	271	85
Myotonic dystrophy	16090	C3		10(0.9)	RFLP		Davies	JMG	20	259	83
Myotonic dystrophy	16090	D19(sev.)	sev.	var.	RFLP		Brunner	HGM9		305	87
Myotonic dystrophy	16090	D19(sev.)	sev.	var.	RFLP		Meredith	HGM8		698	85
Myotonic dystrophy	16090	D19(sev.)	sev.	var.	RFLP		Shaw	Hum. Genet.	74	262	86
Myotonic dystrophy	16090	D19(sev.)	sev.	var.	RFLP		Yamaoka	J Neurogenet	2	403	85
Myotonic dystrophy	16090	D19S15	pJSB6	6(4.5)	RFLP		Schepens	NAR	15	3193	87
Myotonic dystrophy	16090	D19S16	pJSB11	5(5.0)	RFLP		Schepens	NAR	15	3192	87
Myotonic dystrophy	16090	D19S19	LDR152	0(15.4)	RFLP		Bartlett	Science	235	1648	87
Myotonic dystrophy	16090	D19S19		0(17.3)	RFLP		Pericak-Vance	HGM9		62	87
Myotonic dystrophy	16090	D19S19	LDR152	0(11.0)	RFLP		Roses	NAR	14	5569	86
Myotubular myopathy	31040	DXS15	DX13	0(3.7)	RFLP		Thomas	HGM9		314	87
Myotubular myopathy	31040	DXS52	St14	0(2.7)	RFLP		Thomas	HGM9		314	87
Neurofibromatosis	16220	D17S	pA10-41	5(4.4)	RFLP		Barker	Science	236	1100	87
Neurofibromatosis	16220	D17S1	p3-6	4(4.2)	RFLP		Barker	Science	236	1100	87
Neurofibromatosis	16220	NGFR		14(4.4)	RFLP		Seizinger	Cell	49	589	87
Neurofibromatosis—bilateral acoustic	10100	D22S1	pMS3-18	0(3.4)	RFLP		Rouleau	Nature	329	246	87
Neuropathy	31049	DXS14	p58-1	5(3.2)	RFLP		Fischbeck	Ann. Neurol.	20	527	86
Neuropathy	31049	DXYS1	pDP34	10(4.5)	RFLP		Fischbeck	Ann. Neurol.	20	527	86
Norrie disease	31060	DXS7	L1.28	0(3.8)	RFLP		Bleeker-Wagem	Hum. Genet.	71	211	85
Norrie disease	31060	DXS7	L1.28	—	RE	DEL	De La Chapelle	Clin. Genet.	28	317	85
Norrie disease	31060	DXS7	L1.28	0(3.5)	RFLP		Gal	Clin. Genet.	27	282	85
Norrie disease	31060	DXS7	L1.28	—	RE	DEL	Gal	CCG	42	219	86
Ocular albinism	30050	DXS85		0(4.6)	RFLP		Kidd	HGM8		667	85
Ornithine transcarbamylase deficiency	31125	OTC		—	RFLP		Fox	NEJM	315	1205	86
Ornithine transcarbamylase deficiency	31125	OTC		—	RFLP		Fox	AJHG	38	841	86

Disease	*McK-#*	*Gene/DNA segment*	*Probe*	*Distance*	*Detect.*	*Mut.*	*Author*	*Journal*	*Vol.*	*Page*	*Yr.*
Ornithine transcarbamylase deficiency	31125	OTC		—	RFLP		McClead	AJMG	25	513	86
Ornithine transcarbamylase deficiency	31125	OTC		—	RFLP		Nussbaum	AJHG	38	149	86
Ornithine transcarbamylase deficiency	31125	OTC		—	RFLP		Old	Lancet	1	73	85
Ornithine transcarbamylase deficiency	31125	OTC		—	RFLP		Pembrey	JMG	22	462	85
Ornithine transcarbamylase deficiency	31125	OTC		—	RE	DEL	Rozen	Nature	313	815	85
Ornithine transcarbamylase deficiency	31125	OTC		—	RFLP		Rozen	Nature	313	815	85
Ornithine transcarbamylase deficiency	31125	OTC		—	RFLP		Schwartz	Clin. Genet.	29	449	86
Osteoarthrosis	12014	COL2A1		0(0.1–1.1)	RFLP		Vaisanen	HGM9		164	87
Osteogenesis imperfecta (type I)	12015	COL1A1		—	RFLP		Sykes	Lancet	2	69	86
Osteogenesis imperfecta (type I)	16221	COL1A1		—	SEQ	PM	Vogel	JBC	262	14737	87
Osteogenesis imperfecta (type I)	12016	COL1A2		—	RFLP		Sykes	Lancet	2	69	86
Osteogenesis imperfecta (type I)	12016	COL1A2		—	RFLP		Wallis	JMG	23	411	86
Osteogenesis imperfecta (type II)	16621	COL1A1		—	RE	DEL	Barsh	PNAS	82	2870	85
Osteogenesis imperfecta (type II)	16621	COL1A1		—	RE	DEL	Chu	Nature	304	78	83
Osteogenesis imperfecta (type II)	16621	COL1A1		—	RE	DEL	Chu	JBC	260	691	85
Osteogenesis imperfecta (type II)	16621	COL1A1		—	SEQU	PM	Cohn	PNAS	83	6045	86
Osteogenesis imperfecta (type II)	16621	COL1A1		—	RE	DEL	Pope	Clin. Genet.	24	303	83
Osteogenesis imperfecta (type II)	16621	COL1A1		—	RE	DEL	Pope	BMJ	288	431	84
Osteogenesis imperfecta (type II)	16621	COL1A2		—	RE	DEL	de Wet	JBC	261	3857	86
Osteogenesis imperfecta (type IV)	12016	COL1A2		—	RFLP		Tsipouras	JMG	24	406	87
Osteogenesis imperfecta (mild atyp.)	16621	COL1A2		—	RE	DEL	de Wet	JBC	261	3857	86
Osteogenesis imperfecta (types I–IV)	12016	COL1A1		0(7.5)	RFLP		Tsipouras	HGM9		207	87
Osteogenesis imperfecta types I & IV	12016	COL1A2		0(3.9)	RFLP		Grobler-Rabie	EMBO J.	4	1745	85
Osteogenesis imperfecta types I & IV	12016	COL1A2		—	RFLP		Tsipouras	AJHG	36	1172	84
Osteogenesis imperfecta types I & IV	12016	COL1A2		—	RFLP		Tsipouras	JMG	24	406	87
Osteosarcoma	25950	D13(sev.)		—	RE	LH	Dryja	AJHG	38	59	86
Osteosarcoma	25950	D13(sev.)		—	RE	LH	Hansen	PNAS	82	6216	85
Pelizaeus-Merzbacher disease	31160	DXS(sev.)	sev.	var.	RFLP		Cremers	Hum. Genet.	77	23	87
Pelizaeus-Merzbacher disease	31160	PLP		—	RE	REAR	Fahim	JNR	16	303	86
Pelizaeus-Merzbacher disease	31160	PLP		—	RE	DEL	Willard	HGM9		441	87
Phenylketonuria	26160	PAH		—	RE	DEL	Avigad	AJHG	41	A205	87
Phenylketonuria	26160	PAH		—	RFLP		Daiger	Lancet	1	229	86
Phenylketonuria	26160	PAH		—	RE	INS	Dilella	AJHG	37	A151	85
Phenylketonuria	26160	PAH		—	SEQU	PM	Dilella	Nature	322	799	86
Phenylketonuria	26160	PAH		—	OLIGO	PM	Dilella	Nature	327	333	87
Phenylketonuria	26160	PAH		—	SEQU	PM	Dilella	Nature	327	333	87
Phenylketonuria	26160	PAH		—	RFLP		Guttler	J. Pediatr.	110	68	87
Phenylketonuria	26160	PAH		—	RFLP		Ledley	NEJM	314	1276	86
Phenylketonuria	26160	PAH		—	RFLP		Lidsky	Lancet	1	549	85
Phenylketonuria	26160	PAH		—	RFLP		Lidsky	AJHG	37	619	85
Phenylketonuria	26160	PAH		—	SEQU	PM	Marvit	NAR	15	5613	87
Phenylketonuria	26160	PAH		—	RFLP		Riess	Clin. Genet.	32	209	87
Phenylketonuria	26160	PAH		—	RFLP		Speer	Clin. Genet.	29	491	86
Phenylketonuria	26160	PAH		—	RFLP		Speer	PND	6	447	86
Phenylketonuria	26160	PAH		—	RFLP		Woo	Nature	306	151	83
Polycystic kidney disease	17390	D16S	24-1	5(8.1)	RFLP		Breuning	Lancet	2	1359	87
Polycystic kidney disease	17390	D16S	090	6(6.3)	RFLP		Reeders	HGM9		133	87
Polycystic kidney disease	17390	D16S	0128	5(3.0)	RFLP		Reeders	HGM9		133	87
Polycystic kidney disease	17390	D16S(sev.)	sev.	var.	RFLP		Reeders	HGM9		133	87
Polycystic kidney disease	17390	HBA	ms	3(24.2)	RFLP		Lazarou	JMG	24	466	87
Polycystic kidney disease	17390	HBA	ms	5(25.8)	RFLP		Reeders	Nature	317	542	85

Disease	McK-#	Gene/DNA segment	Probe	Distance	Detect.	Mut.	Author	Journal	Vol.	Page	Yr.
Polycystic kidney disease	17390	HBA	ms	5(25.8)	RFLP		Reeders	BMJ	292	851	86
Polycystic kidney disease	17390	HBA	ms	5	RFLP		Reeders	Lancet	2	6	86
Polycystic kidney disease	17390	HBA	ms	5(59.7)	RFLP		Reeders	Hum. Genet.	76	348	87
Polycystic kidney disease	17390	HBA	ms	0(2.6)	RFLP		Ryynanen	JMG	24	462	87
Polycystic kidney disease	26320	HBA	ms	>20	RFLP		Wirth	Hum. Genet.	77	221	87
Porphyria	17610	UROD		—	SEQU	PM	De Verneuil	Science	234	732	86
Porphyria-acute intermittent	17600	PBGD		—	RFLP		Llewellyn	Lancet	2	706	87
Prader-Willi syndrome	17627	D15(sev.)		—	RE	DEL	Donlon	AJHG	37	A91	85
Prader-Willi syndrome	17627	D15(sev.)		—	RE	DEL	Donlon	PNAS	83	4408	86
Prealbumin amyloidoses	17630	PALB		—	SEQU	PM	Furuya	JCI	80	1706	87
Prealbumin amyloidoses	17630	PALB		—	RE	PM	Ide	Hum. Genet.	73	281	86
Prealbumin amyloidoses	17630	PALB		—	RE	PM	Maeda	MBM	3	329	86
Prealbumin amyloidoses	17630	PALB		—	SEQU	PM	Maeda	MBM	3	329	86
Prealbumin amyloidoses	17630	PALB		—	RE	PM	Mita	Neurology	36	298	86
Prealbumin amyloidoses	17630	PALB		—	RE	PM	Saraiva	Neurology	36	1413	86
Prealbumin amyloidoses	17630	PALB		—	RE	PM	Sasaki	Lancet	1	100	85
Prealbumin amyloidoses	17630	PALB		—	RE	PM	Wallace	AJMG	25	335	86
Prealbumin amyloidoses	17630	PALB		—	RE	PM	Wallace	JCI	78	6	86
Prealbumin amyloidoses	17630	PALB		—	RFLP		Wallace	AJMG	25	335	86
Prealbumin amyloidoses	17630	PALB		—	RE	PM	Whitehead	MBM	2	411	84
Prealbumin amyloidoses	17630	PALB		—	SEQU	PM	Yoshioka	MBM	3	319	86
Properdin deficiency	31206	DXS7		0	RFLP		Goonewardena	HGM9		294	87
Properdin deficiency	31206	OTC		0	RFLP		Goonewardena	HGM9		294	87
Purine nucleoside phosph. def.	16405	NP		—	SEQU	PM	Williams	JBC	262	2332	87
Renal cell carcinoma	14470	D3(sev.)		—	RE	LH	Zbar	Nature	327	721	87
Retinitis pigmentosa	31260	DX(sev.)		—	RE	DEL	Francke	AJHG	37	250	85
Retinitis pigmentosa	31260	DXS1	p8	0(2.1)	RFLP		Litt	HGM9		144	87
Retinitis pigmentosa	31260	DXS1	p8	7(2.1)	RFLP		Wright	AJHG	41	635	87
Retinitis pigmentosa	31260	DXS1	p8	14(1.6)	RFLP		Wright	HGM9		227	87
Retinitis pigmentosa	31260	DXS14	p58-1	22(1.2)	RFLP		Wirth	HGM9		395	87
Retinitis pigmentosa	31260	DXS14	58.1	20(2.5)	RFLP		Wright	AJHG	41	635	87
Retinitis pigmentosa	31260	DXS14	58.1	21(3.4)	RFLP		Wright	HGM9		227	87
Retinitis pigmentosa	31260	DXS164	pERT84	13(5.6)	RFLP		Chen	HGM9		230	87
Retinitis pigmentosa	31260	DXS7	L1.28	3(7.9)	RFLP		Bhattacharya	Nature	309	253	84
Retinitis pigmentosa	31260	DXS7	L1.28	9(3.8)	RFLP		Bhattacharya	BJO	69	340	85
Retinitis pigmentosa	31260	DXS7	L1.28	7(9.6)	RFLP		Chen	HGM9		230	87
Retinitis pigmentosa	31260	DXS7	L1.28	8(14.0)	RFLP		Clayton	Hum. Genet.	74	168	86
Retinitis pigmentosa	31260	DXS7	L1.28	0(3.4)	RFLP		Farrar	HGM9		345	87
Retinitis pigmentosa	31260	DXS7	L1.28	15(1.3)	RFLP		Friedrich	Hum. Genet.	71	93	85
Retinitis pigmentosa	31260	DXS7	L1.28	0(1.5)	RFLP		Litt	HGM9		144	87
Retinitis pigmentosa	31260	DXS7	L1.28	10(2.3)	RFLP		Mukai	AJO	100	225	85
Retinitis pigmentosa	31260	DXS7	L1.28	12.5(2.5)	RFLP		Nussbaum	Hum. Genet.	70	45	85
Retinitis pigmentosa	31260	DXS7	L1.28	14(1.8)	RFLP		Wirth	HGM9		395	87
Retinitis pigmentosa	31260	DXS7	L1.28	6(9.4)	RFLP		Wright	AJHG	41	635	87
Retinitis pigmentosa	31260	DXS7	L1.28	9(8.7)	RFLP		Wright	HGM9		227	87
Retinitis pigmentosa	31260	DXS84	754	3(8.4)	RFLP		Chen	HGM9		230	87
Retinitis pigmentosa	31260	DXS84	754	0(3.4)	RFLP		Farrar	HGM9		345	87
Retinitis pigmentosa	31260	DXS84	754	6(3.4)	RFLP		Musarella	HGM9		523	87
Retinitis pigmentosa	31260	DXS84	p754	0(4.8)	RFLP		Wirth	HGM9		395	87
Retinitis pigmentosa	31260	OTC		0(16.6)	RFLP		Chen	HGM9		230	87
Retinitis pigmentosa	31260	OTC		4(3.7)	RFLP		Musarella	HGM9		523	87
Retinitis pigmentosa	31260	OTC		0(2.7)	RFLP		Wirth	HGM9		395	87
Retinitis pigmentosa	31260	OTC		16(2.8)	RFLP		Wright	AJHG	41	635	87
Retinitis pigmentosa	31260	OTC		19(3.6)	RFLP		Wright	HGM9		227	87
Retinitis pigmentosa	31260	DXS206	XJ1.1	8(4.6)	RFLP		Chen	HGM9		230	87
Retinoblastoma	18020	D13	H3-8	—	RE	DEL	Horsthamke	Lancet	1	511	87
Retinoblastoma	18020	D13(sev.)		—	RE	LH	Cavenee	Nature	305	779	83
Retinoblastoma	18020	D13(sev.)		—	RE	LH	Cavenee	Science	228	501	85
Retinoblastoma	18020	D13(sev.)		—	RE	LH	Cavenee	NEJM	314	201	86
Retinoblastoma	18020	D13(sev.)		—	Re	LH	Dryja	NEJM	310	550	84
Retinoblastoma	18020	D13(sev.)		—	RE	DEL	Dryja	PNAS	83	7391	86
Retinoblastoma	18020	D13(sev.)		—	RE	DEL	Lalande	CGC	23	151	86
Retinoblastoma	18020	D13S22		5(2.3)	RFLP		Scheffer	HGM9		326	87
Retinoblastoma	18020	ESD		—	RE	DEL	Lee	Hum. Genet.	76	33	87
Retinoblastoma	18020	RB		—	RE	DEL	Friend	Nature	323	643	86
Retinoblastoma	18020	RB		—	RE	DEL	Gung	Science	236	1657	87
Retinoblastoma	18020	RB		—	RE	DEL	Horsthemke	Hum. Genet.	76	257	87
Retinoblastoma	18020	RB		—	RE	DEL	Lee	Science	235	1394	87
Retinoblastoma	18020	RB	sev.	0(9.0)	RFLP		Wiggs	HGM9		519	87
Retinoblastoma	18020	RB	VNTR	—	RFLP	—	Wiggs	AJHG	41	A40	87
Retinoschisis	31270	DX(sev.)	sev.	var.(<1.6)	RFLP		Goudie	HGM9		89	87
Retinoschisis	31270	DXS16	pXUT23	0(4.1)	RFLP		Alitalo	Clin. Genet.	32	192	87
Retinoschisis	31270	DXS16	pXUT23	4(5.2)	RFLP		Alitalo	HGM9		38	87
Retinoschisis	31270	DXS16	pXUT23	11(2.1)	RFLP		Gal	HGM8		634	85
Retinoschisis	31270	DXS207	pPA4B	8(2.9)	RFLP		Alitalo	HGM9		38	87

Disease	McK-#	Gene/DNA segment	Probe	Distance	Detect.	Mut.	Author	Journal	Vol.	Page	Yr.
Retinoschisis	31270	DXS41	p99-6	5(3.6)	RFLP		Alitalo	Clin. Genet.	32	192	87
Retinoschisis	31270	DXS41	p99-6	2(9.8)	RFLP		Alitalo	HGM9		38	87
Retinoschisis	31270	DXS41	p99-6	0(4.1)	RFLP		Dahl	HGM9		297	87
Retinoschisis	31270	DXS43	pD2	5(7.5)	RFLP		Alitalo	HGM9		38	87
Retinoschisis	31270	DXS43	pD2	0(5.0)	RFLP		Dahl	HGM9		297	87
Retinoschisis	31270	DXS85	782	16(3.2)	RFLP		Alitalo	HGM9		38	87
Retinoschisis	31270	DXS85	782	21(0.9)	RFLP		Gal	HGM8		634	85
Retinoschisis	31270	DXS9	RC8	0(2.7)	RFLP		Gellert	HGM9		474	87
Retinoschisis	31270	DXS9	RC8	15(1.7)	RFLP		Wieacker	Hum. Genet.	64	143	83
Sandhoff disease (type II)	26880	HEXB		—	RE	DEL	O'Dowd	JBC	261	12680	86
Sickle-cell anemia	14190	HBB		—	RFLP		Boehm	NEJM	308	1054	83
Sickle-cell anemia	14190	HBB		—	RE	PM	Chang	Lancet	2	1127	81
Sickle-cell anemia	14190	HBB		—	RE	PM	Chang	NEJM	307	30	82
Sickle-cell anemia	14190	HBB		—	OLIGO	PM	Conner	PNAS	80	278	83
Sickle-cell anemia	14190	HBB		—	RE	PM	Driscoll	AJHG	40	548	87
Sickle-cell anemia	14190	HBB		—	OLIGO	PM	Embury	NEJM	316	656	87
Sickle-cell anemia	14190	HBB		—	RFLP		Feldenzer	JCI	64	751	79
Sickle-cell anemia	14190	HBB		—	RE	PM	Geever	PNAS	78	5081	81
Sickle-cell anemia	14190	HBB		—	RE	PM	Goosens	NEJM	309	831	83
Sickle-cell anemia	14190	HBB		—	MMP	PM	Jones	Gene	39	77	85
Sickle-cell anemia	14190	HBB		—	RFLP		Kan	PNAS	75	5631	78
Sickle-cell anemia	14190	HBB		—	RFLP		Kan	Lancet	2	910	78
Sickle-cell anemia	14190	HBB		—	RE	PM	Orkin	NEJM	307	32	82
Sickle-cell anemia	14190	HBB		—	RFLP		Phillips	PNAS	77	2853	80
Sickle-cell anemia	14190	HBB		—	OLIGO	PM	Rabin	Hum. Genet.	75	120	87
Sickle-cell anemia	14190	HBB		—	RE	PM	Sheldon	Clin. Chem.	33	1368	87
Sickle-cell anemia	14190	HBB		—	OLIGO	PM	Studencki	DNA	3	7	84
Sickle-cell anemia	14190	HBB		—	OLIGO	PM	Studencki	AJHG	37	42	85
Sickle-cell anemia	14190	HBB		—	RE	PM	Wilson	PNAS	79	3628	82
Skeletal dysplasia X-linked		DXS15	DX13	0(3.1)	RFLP		Dlouhy	Hum. Genet.	75	136	87
Skeletal dysplasia X-linked		DXS52	St14	0(3.3)	RFLP		Dlouhy	Hum. Genet.	75	136	87
Small cell lung cancer	18228	D3	H3H2	—	RE	LH	Mooibroek	CGC	27	361	87
Small cell lung cancer	18228	D3(sev.)		—	RE	LH	Naylor	AICHG		560	86
Small cell lung cancer	18228	D3(sev.)	sev.	—	RE	LH	Naylor	HGM9		444	87
Small cell lung cancer	18228	D3S2	DNF1552	—	RE	LH	Brauch	NEJM	317	1109	87
Small cell lung cancer	18228	D3S(sev.)	sev.	—	RE	LH	Naylor	Nature	329	451	87
Small cell lung cancer	18228	D3S2	DNF1552	—	RE	LH	Brauch	NEJM	317	1109	87
Small cell lung cancer	18228	D3S3		—	RE	LH	Gerber	AJHG	37	A28	85
Spastic paraplegia	31290	—	pYNH3	0(4.5)	RFLP		Keppen	AJHG	41	933	87
Spastic paraplegia	31290	DXS15	DX13	0(3.2)	RFLP		Kenwrick	Hum. Genet.	73	264	86
Spastic paraplegia	31290	DXS17	S21	0(4.0)	RFLP		Keppen	AJHG	41	933	87
Spastic paraplegia	31290	DXS52	St14	0(3.3)	RFLP		Kenwrick	Hum. Genet.	73	264	86
Spinocerebellar ataxia	16440	D6(sev.)	sev.	var.	RFLP		Zoghbi	AICHG		608	86
Spinocerebellar ataxia	16440	D6S7	7H4	0(1.1)	RFLP		Rich	AJHG	41	524	87
Stickler syndrome	10830	COL2A1		0(4.0)	RFLP		Francomano	HGM9		447	87
Tangier disease	20540	APOA1		—	SEQU	PM	Law	JBC	260	12810	85
Tay-Sachs disease	27280	HEXB		—	RE	DEL	Myerowitz	JBC	262	15396	87
Testicular feminization syndrome	31370	DXS1	p8	—	RFLP		Wieacker	Dis. Marker	3	213	85
α Thalassemia	14180	HBA		—	RE	DEL	Chui	NEJM	314	76	86
α Thalassemia	14180	HBA		—	RE	DEL	Di Rienzo	AJHG	39	631	86
α Thalassemia	14180	HBA		—	RE	DEL	El-Hazmi	Hum. Genet.	74	219	86
α Thalassemia	14180	HBA		—			Griese	Hum. Genet.	71	134	85
α Thalassemia	14180	HBA		—	RFLP		Henni	Hum. Genet.	75	272	87
α Thalassemia	14180	HBA		—	RE	DEL	Horst	Hum. Genet.	68	260	84
α Thalassemia	14180	HBA		—			Horst	Hum. Genet.	75	53	87
α Thalassemia	14180	HBA		—	SEQU	PM	Liehaber	JCI	80	154	87
α Thalassemia	14180	HBA		—	RE	DEL	Liming	PND	6	89	86
α Thalassemia	14180	HBA		—	SEQU	PM	Moi	JCI	80	1416	87
α Thalassemia	14180	HBA		—	Re	PM	Whitelaw	EMBO J	5	2919	86
α Thalassemia	14180	HBA		—	RFLP		Zeng	Lancet	1	304	85
β Thalassemia	14190	HBB		—	SEQU	PM	Atweh	Blood	70	147	87
β Thalassemia	14190	HBB		—	RFLP		Boehm	NEJM	308	1054	83
β Thalassemia	14190	HBB		—	RE	PM	Boehm	Blood	67	1185	86
β Thalassemia	14190	HBB		—	RFLP		Carestia	BJH	67	231	87
β Thalassemia	14190	HBB		—	SEQU	PM	Chehab	Lancet	1	3	86
β Thalassemia	14190	HBB		—	RE	DEL	Efremov	Blood	68	971	86
β Thalassemia	14190	HBB		—	RE	DEL	Gilman	BJH	67	369	87
β Thalassemia	14190	HBB		—			Horst	BJH	54	643	83
β Thalassemia	14190	HBB		—			Horst	Hum. Genet.	64	263	83
β Thalassemia	14190	HBB		—			Horst	Blut	48	213	84
β Thalassemia	14190	HBB		—	OLIGO	PM	Horst	Blood	68	1175	86
β Thalassemia	14190	HBB		—	OLIGO	PM	Kazazian	Blood	68	964	86
β Thalassemia	14190	HBB		—	SEQU	PM	Lapoumer.	BBRC	139	709	87
β Thalassemia	14190	HBB		—	RFLP		Little	Nature	285	144	80

Disease	McK-#	Gene/DNA segment	Probe	Distance	Detect.	Mut.	Author	Journal	Vol.	Page	Yr.
β Thalassemia	14190	HBB		—	RE	PM	Metherall	EMBO J.	5	2551	86
β Thalassemia	14190	HBB		—	SEQU	PM	Moi	JCI	80	1416	87
β Thalassemia	14190	HBB		—	OLIGO	PM	Monni	PND	6	63	86
β Thalassemia	14190	HBB		—			Oehme	Hum. Genet.	71	219	85
β Thalassemia	14190	HBB		—	RFLP		Oggiano	BJH	67	225	87
β Thalassemia	14190	HBB		—	RFLP		Old	Lancet	2	1413	82
β Thalassemia	14190	HBB		—	RE	DEL	Orkin	NEJM	299	166	78
β Thalassemia	14190	HBB		—	OLIGO	PM	Orkin	JCI	71	775	83
β Thalassemia	14190	HBB		—	OLIGO	PM	Piratsu	Science	223	929	84
β Thalassemia	14190	HBB		—	RE	DEL	Popovich	AJHG	39	797	86
β Thalassemia	14190	HBB		—	OLIGO	PM	Rosatelli	Lancet	1	241	85
β Thalassemia	14190	HBB		—	OLIGO	PM	Rosatelli	JMG	24	97	87
β Thalassemia	14190	HBB		—	OLIGO	PM	Thein	Lancet	2	345	85
β Thalassemia	14190	HBB		—	RFLP		Wainscoat	BJH	62	495	86
δ-β Thalassemia	14190	HBB		—	SEQU	PM	Atweh	Blood	70	1470	87
γ-δ-β Thalassemia	14190	HBB		—	RE	DEL	Taramelli	NAR	14	7017	86
Thrombophilia—hereditary	17686	PROC		—	RE	PM	Romeo	PNAS	84	2829	87
Thrombophilia—hereditary	17686	PROC		—	SEQU	PM	Romeo	PNAS	84	2829	87
Triose phosphate isomerase deficiency	19045	TPI		—	SEQU	PM	Daar	PNAS	83	7903	86
Tuberous sclerosis	19110	ABL		0(3.2)	RFLP		Connor	JMG	24	544	87
Tyrosinemia type II	27660	TAT1		—	RE	DEL	Natt	AICHG		662	86
Uveal melanoma	15572	D2(sev.)		—	RE	LH	Mukai	CGC	22	45	86
Wieacker-Wolf syndrome	31458	DXYS1	pDP34	0(3.2)	RFLP		Wieacker	JMG	28	245	87
Wilms tumor	19407	CAT		—	RE	DEL	van Heyningen	PNAS	82	8592	85
Wilms tumor	19407	CAT	—	—	RE	DEL	van Heyningen	HGM9		24	87
Wilms tumor	19407	D11(sev.)		—	RE	LH	Dao	AJHG	41	202	87
Wilms tumor	19407	D11(sev.)		—	RE	LH	Fearon	Nature	309	176	84
Wilms tumor	19407	D11(sev.)		—	RE	LH	Koufos	Nature	309	170	84
Wilms tumor	19407	D11(sev.)		—	RE	DEL	Mannens	Hum. Genet.	75	180	87
Wilms tumor	19407	D11(sev.)		—	RE	LH	Michalopoulos	Hum. Genet.	70	157	85
Wilms tumor	19407	D11(sev.)		—	RE	LH	Orkin	Nature	309	172	84
Wilms tumor	19407	D11(sev.)		—	RE	LH	Reeve	Nature	309	174	84
Wilms tumor	19407	D11(sev.)		—	RE	DEL	Schroeder	AJHG	40	413	87
Wilms tumor	19407	D11S87	p2.3	—	RE	DEL	Lewis	HGM9		72	87
Wilms tumor	19407	FSHB	—	—	RE	DEL	van Heyningen	HGM9		24	87
Wilms tumor-aniridia	19407	FSHB		—	RE	DEL	Glaser	Nature	321	882	86
Wilson disease	27790	D13S10		3(5.0)	RFLP		Bonne-Tamir	AICHG		618	86
Wilson disease	27790	D13S10	7D2	7.5(4.7)	RFLP		Bowcock	AJGH	41	27	87
Wilson disease	27790	D13S4		7(2.3)	RFLP		Bonne-Tamir	AICHG		618	86
Wiskott-Aldrich syndrome	30100	DXS1	p8	0(2.4)	RFLP		Arveiler	HGM9		413	87
Wiskott-Aldrich syndrome	30100	DXS14		3(4.3)	RFLP		Peacocke	PNAS	84	3430	87
Wiskott-Aldrich syndrome	30100	DXS3	p19.2	10(2.1)	RFLP		Arveiler	HGM9		413	87
Wiskott-Aldrich syndrome	30100	DXS7	L1.28	0(4.1)	RFLP		Peacocke	PNAS	84	3430	87
Wolf-Hirschhorn syndrome	—	D4S10	G8	—	RE	DEL	MacDonald	Genomics	1	29	87
Wolf-Hirschhorn syndrome	—	D4S10	G8	—	RE	DEL	Gusella	Nature	318	75	85
Xq deletion	—	DXS15	DX13	—	RE	DEL	Schwartz	Hum. Genet.	76	54	87
Xq deletion	—	DXS52	St14	—	RE	DEL	Schwartz	Hum. Genet.	76	54	87
Xq deletion	—	F8		—	RE	DEL	Schwartz	Hum. Genet.	76	54	87
Yp deletion	—	DY(sev.)		—	RE	DEL	Disteche	PNAS	83	7841	86
Yq deletion	—	DY(sev.)	sev.	—	RE	DEL	Gilgenkrantz	PND	6	307	86
von Willebrand disease (type III)	19340	VWF		—	RE	DEL	Shelton-Inloe	JCI	79	1459	87
von Willebrand disease (autos. dom.)	19340	VWF		—	RFLP		Shiach	JMG	24	245	87

LIST OF ABBREVIATIONS:*

AHG	*Annals of Human Genetics*
AICHG	*Abstracts Int. Congress Hum. Genet. 7,* Berlin, 1986
AJH	*American Journal of Hematology*
AJHG	*American Journal of Human Genetics*
AJMG	*American Journal of Medical Genetics*
AJO	*American Journal of Ophthalmology*
ANYAS	*Annals of the New York Academy of Sciences*
Arch. Ophth.	*Archives of Ophthalmology*
Atheroscl r.	*Atherosclerosis*
ATS VII	*Atherosclerosis VII,* Fidge Nestel (eds.), Elsevier
BBRC	*Biochemical and Biophysical Research Communications*
BJH	*British Journal of Haematology*
BJO	*British Journal of Ophthalmology*
BMJ	*British Medical Journal*
CCG	*Cytogenetics and Cell Genetics*
CGC	*Cancer Genetics and Cytogenetics*
Dis. Markers	*Disease Markers*
EJB	*European Journal of Biochemistry*
HGM8	*Human Gene Mapping 8* (CCG 40:1, 1985)
HGM9	*Human Gene Mapping 9* (CCG 46:1, 1987)
HPRT	Hypoxanthine phosphoribosyltransferase
IMG	*Immunogenetics*
JBC	*Journal of Biological Chemistry*
JCB	*Journal of Cell Biology*
JCEM	*Journal of Clinical Endocrinology Metabolism*
JCI	*Journal of Clinical Investigation*
JIMD	*Journal of Inherited Metabolic Disease*
JIMMG	*Journal of Immunogenetics*
JJCR	*Japanese Journal of Cancer Research*
JJHG	*Japanese Journal of Human Genetics*
JMG	*Journal of Medical Genetics*
JNR	*Journal of Neuroscience Research*
MBM	*Molecular Biology and Medicine*
MODY	Maturity onset diabetes of the young
NAR	*Nucleic Acids Research*
NEJM	*New England Journal of Medicine*
OPG	*Ophthalmic Pediatrics and Genetics*
PNAS	*Proceedings of the National Academy of Sciences of the U.S.A.*

PND	*Prenatal Diagnosis*
SCMG	*Somatic Cell Molecular Genetics*
Thromb. Hae.	*Thrombosis and Haemostasis*
ar	alphoid repeat
atyp.	atypical
breakp.	break point
def.	deficiency
haem.	hemoglobin
hered.	hereditary
ms	minisatellite
neph.	nephritis
persist.	persistent
phosph.	phosphorylase
sev.	several
synth.	synthetase
var.	various

*Journal abbreviations are listed only if shortened from *Index Medicus* style.

APPENDIX 1-2

Genetic Map of the Human Genome Autosomes, and X, Y, and Mitochondrial Chromosomes

Victor A. McKusick

NOTE: Previous editions contained abbreviated maps of loci on human chromosomes. A new morbid anatomy map (Fig. 1-9) complements the disorders discussed in chapters in this edition. It is supplemented by this appendix which contains catelogues of the human gene map. We are very grateful to Dr. McKusick for providing us with up-to-date information from the on-line databases of *Mendelian Inheritance in Man* (OMIM) at the Johns Hopkins Hospital and the Howard Hughes Medical Institute's Human Gene Mapping Library (HGML) in New Haven (Yale University). *The Editors.*

Gene Map of the Autosomes

About 2100 loci are known with confidence to exist on autosomes, on the basis mainly of characteristic mendelian patterns of inheritance of alternative forms of particular traits. (Another 2000 loci have been less securely identified on autosomes.) As indicated by the following data, some mapping information is available concerning over half of the well confirmed autosomal loci. In addition to the loci listed here, anonymous DNA segments, antigens defined by monoclonal antibodies, surface antigens, some 'like' genes, and function-unknown electrophoretic (O'Farrell) protein spots have been assigned to individual autosomes, as cataloged by HGM9. The number in parentheses after the name of each item in the disorder field indicates whether the disorder was mapped by mapping of the 'wildtype' gene (1), by the disease phenotype itself (2), or by both approaches (3). Multiple allelic disorders in the disorder column are separated by semicolons. Brackets indicate 'nondisease' and braces indicate susceptibilities. (Note that HGM9 refers to information from the ninth Human Gene Mapping Workshop in Paris in September 1987. HGML refers to information from the Human Gene Mapping Library of the Howard Hughes Medical Institute in New Haven, March 1, 1988.)

Chromosome No. 1

Location	*Symbol*	*Status*	*Title*	*MIM #*	*Comments*	*Disorder*	*Mouse*
1pter-p36.13	A12M2	P	Adenovirus-12 chromosome modification site-1p	10292			
1pter-p36.13	ENO1, PPH	C	Enolase-1	17243		Enolase deficiency (1)	4(Eno-1)
1pter-p36.13	GDH	C	Glucose dehydrogenase	13809			
1pter-p36	HLM2	C	Oncogene HLM2	13119			
1pter-p32	GALE	C	UDP galactose-4-epimerase	23035		Galactose epimerase deficiency (1)	
1pter-p31	NB	P	Neuroblastoma	25670	?1p34	Neuroblastoma (2)	
1pter-p22.1	TFS1	P	Transformation suppressor-1	19019			
1p36.3	RNU1	C	RNA, U1 small nuclear	18068	?same as A12M2		
1p36.2	ANF, PND	C	Atrial natriuretic factor	10878			4(Pnd)
1p36.2-p36.13	PGD	C	6-Phosphogluconate dehydrogenase	17220			4(Pgd)
1p36.2-p36.1	FGR, SRC2	P	Oncogene FGR	16494	same as SRC2		
1p36.2-p34	ALPL, HOPS	C	Alkaline phosphatase, liver/bone form	17176		Hypophosphatasia, infantile 24150 (3); ?Hypophosphatasia, adult 14630 (1)	4(Akp-2)
1p36.2-p34	EL1	C	Elliptocytosis-1 (protein 4.1)	13050	linked to RH	Elliptocytosis-1 (3)	
1p36.2-p34	EKV	P	Erythrokeratodermia variabilis	13320	theta = 0.044 with RH	Erythrokeratodermia variabilis (2)	
1p36.2-p34	CMM, HCMM	L	Malignant melanoma, cutaneous	15560	linked to RH; lod = 2.0 at theta 0.30	Malignant melanoma, cutaneous (2)	
1p36.2-p34	RD	C	Radin blood group	11162			
1p36.2-p34	RH	C	Rhesus blood group	11170	Order: 1pter--D-C-E--cen	Erythroblastosis fetalis (1); ?Rh-null hemolytic anemia (1)	
1p36.2-p34	SC	C	Scianna blood group	11175			
1p36.1-p35	APNH	P	Antiporter, sodium-potassuim ion, amiloride-sensitive	10731			
1p35-p32	LCK	P	Lymphocyte-specific tyrosine kinase	15339			4(lck)
1p35-p31.3	GLUT	P	Glucose transporter protein	13814	probably in 1p33		
1p34	AK2	C	Adenylate kinase-2, mitochondrial	10302			4(Ak-2)
1p34	FUCA1, FUCA	C	Alpha-L-fucosidase-1	23000		Fucosidosis (1)	4(Fuca)
1p34	FUCT	L	Alpha-L-fucosidase regulator	13683	?very close to FUCA1		
1p34	UROD	C	Uroporphyrinogen decarboxylase	17610		Porphyria cutanea tarda (1); Porphyria, hepatoerythropoietic (1)	
1p32	BLYM1, BLYM	P	Oncogene BLYM1, chicken bursal lymphoma	16483			
1p32	MYCL, LMYC	P	Oncogene MYC, lung carcinoma-derived	16485			

1p32	UMPK	C	Uridine monophosphate kinase	19171			
1p31	ACADM, MCAD	P	Acyl-CoA dehydrogenase, medium chain	20145		Acyl-CoA dehydrogenase, medium chain, deficiency of (1)	
1p22.1-qter	SDH	P	Succinate dehydrogenase	18547	1 of 2 polypeptides		
1p22.1-p13.3	COL11A1	P	Collagen, type XI, alpha	12028			
1p22.1	PGM1	C	Phosphoglucomutase-1	17190			4(Pgm-2)
1p22	C8A	P	C8, alpha polypeptide	12095	close to PGM1; alpha and gamma coded by separate genes	C8 deficiency, type I (2)	
1p22	C8B	P	C8, beta polypeptide	12096	close to PGM1	C8 deficiency, type II (2)	
1p22	TSHB	C	Thyroid stimulating hormone, beta subunit	18854	same PFGE fragment as NGFB	Hypothyroidism, nongoitrous (1)	3(Tshb)
1p22	NRAS1	C	Oncogene NRAS1	16479	1p12-p11 by A; ?same as NGF		3(Nras)
1p22-p21	F3, TFA	C	Clotting factor III	13439			
1p22-q23	CMT1	C	Charcot-Marie-Tooth disease, slow nerve conduction type	11820	ca. 15cM from FY	Charcot-Marie-Tooth disease, slow nerve conduction type (2)	
1p22-qter	EPOX	P	Epoxide hydrolase	13281		?Fetal hydantoin syndrome (1)	
1p21	AMY2	C	Amylase, pancreatic	10465			3(Amy-2)
1p21	AMY1	C	Amylase, salivary	10470	multiple amylase genes		3(Amy-1)
1p21-q23	APOA2	C	Apolipoprotein A-II	10767			1(Alp-2)
1p21-qter	ACTA, ASMA	C	Actin, skeletal muscle alpha chains	10261	?near centromere suggested by mouse data		3(Acts)
1p13	ASG	L	Aspermiogenesis factor	10842	1q25 = conflicting localization		
1p13	CD2	P	T-cell surface CD2 antigen	18699			3(Cd-2)
1p13	NGFB	C	Nerve growth factor, beta	16203	same PFGE fragment as TSHB		3(Ngfb)
1p13-p11	ATP1A1	P	Sodium-potassium-ATPase, alpha-1 polypeptide	18231			3(Atpa-1)
1p	C1QA	P	Complement component, C1q, A chain	12055		?C1q deficiency (1)	
1p	C1QB	C	Complement component C1q, B chain	12057		?C1q deficiency (1)	
1p	FTHP	C	Ferritin, heavy chain	see 13477	presumably a pseudogene; q32.3-q42.3 by D		
1p	NBCCS, BCNS, NBCS	L	Nevoid basal cell carcinoma syndrome	10940		?Nevoid basal cell carcinoma syndrome (2)	
1cen-q32	ATP1A2	P	Sodium-potassium-ATPase, alpha-2 polypeptide	18234			1(Atpa-3)
1cen-q32	BCM1, BLAST1	P	B-cell activation marker	10953			
1cen-q32	PFKM	P	Phosphofructokinase, muscle type	23280		Glycogen storage disease, type VII (1)	
1q	ATP1B	P	Sodium-potassium ATPase, beta polypeptide	18233			1(Atpb)
1q	PPOL, PARP	P	Poly-ADP-ribose polymerase	17387	?processed pseudogenes on 13, 14		
1q11	D1Z1	C	Satellite DNA III	12637	1qh		
1q12-q21	FY	C	Duffy blood group	11070	distal to 1qh	{Vivax malaria, susceptibility to} (1)	
1q12-q22	CFAG, CFA	P	Cystic fibrosis antigen	21971			
1q12-q23	CRP	C	C-reactive protein	12326			

Location	*Symbol*	*Status*	*Title*	*MIM #*	*Comments*	*Disorder*	*Mouse*
1q12-q23	APCS, SAP	C	Amyloid P component, serum	10477	probably close to CRP	{?Amyloidosis, secondary, susceptibility to} (2)	1(Sap)
1q12-q32.3	F13B	P	Clotting factor XIII, B subunit	13458			
1q2	CAE	C	Cataract, zonular pulverulent	11620	close to FY	Cataract, zonular pulverulent (2)	
1q2	EL2	L	Elliptocytosis-2	13060	?linked to FY; ?same locus as alpha-spectrin	?Elliptocytosis-2 (2)	
1q2	HCB	P	HISTONE CLUSTER B: H3,H4	14278, 14275	100-200 histone genes; some on chromosome 6 and 12, as well as perhaps 7		
1q21	GBA	C	Acid beta-glucosidase (glucocerebrosidase)	23080		Gaucher disease (1)	
1q21	A12M3	P	Adenovirus-12 chromosome modification site-1q2	10294	class 1, U2 snRNA pseudogenes, 18069, at this site		
1q21	IVL	P	Involucrin	14736			
1q21-q22	PKLR, PK1, PKR	C	Pyruvate kinase, red cell type	26620		PK deficiency hemolytic anemia (1)	
1q21-q23	UGP1	C	Uridyl diphosphate glucose pyrophosphorylase-1	19175			
1q21-q24	PUM	P	Peanut lectin binding urinary mucins	15834			
1q21-q25	CACY	P	Calcyclin	11411			
1q21-q25	F5	P	Clotting factor V	22740		Factor V deficiency (1)	
1q22-q24	SK, D1S3, SKI	P	Oncogene Sloan-Kettering, chicken virus	16478			
1q22-q25	SPTA	P	Alpha-spectrin	18286	?same locus as EL2	Elliptocytosis-2 (2); Pyropoikilocytosis (1); Spherocytosis, recessive (1)	1(Spna-1)
1q23.1-q23.9	AT3	C	Antithrombin III	10730	ca. 10cM from FY	Antithrombin III deficiency (3)	1(At-3)
1q24-q25	ARG	P	Oncogene ARG	16469			1(Arg)
1q24-q31	CHR39A	P	Cholesterol repressible protein 39A	11846			
1q31	LAMB2	P	Laminin B2	15029			1(Lamb-2)
1q31-q32	CD45, LCA, T200	C	Leukocyte common antigen (T200)	15146			1(Ly-5)
1q31-q32.1	MCT	L	Microcephaly, true	25120	at junction	?Microcephaly, true (2)	
1q31-q41	TRK	P	Oncogene TRK	16497			
1q31-q41	TPM	P	Tropomyosin, nonmuscle	19103	NA2 protein in TRK oncogene		
1q32	RCAC	C	REGULATOR OF COMPLEMENT ACTIVATION CLUSTER		CR1, CR2, DAF, C4BP in 800kb segment		
1q32	C4BP, C4BR	C	Complement component-4 binding protein	12083	?same as CR1		1(C4bp)
1q32	CR1, C3BR	C	Complement component-3b, C3b, receptor	12062		CR1 deficiency (1); ?SLE (1)	
1q32	CR2, C3DR	C	Complement component-3d, C3d, receptor	12065			
1q32	HF, CFH	C	Complement factor H	13437			
1q32	DAF	C	Decay-accelerating factor of complement	12524			
1q32	REN	C	Renin	17982	q32.3-q42.3 excluded by D		1(Ren-1)
1q32-q41	LPS, PIT	L	Lip pits	11930	del (1q32-q41)	?van der Woude syndrome (2)	
1q32.1-q42	GUK1	C	Guanylate kinase-1	13927			

1q32.1-q42	GUK2	C	Guanylate kinase-2	13928	genetic independence of GUK1 and GUK2 unproved		
1q42	PEPC	C	Peptidase C	17000	1q25 = conflicting localization		1(Pep-3)
1q42-q43	RN5S	C	5S ribosomal RNA genes	18042	same site as A12M1		
1q42-q43	A12M1	P	Adenovirus-12 chromosome modification site-1q1	10293			
1q42-qter	XPA	P	Xeroderma pigmentosum A	27870	should be on 1p in light of mouse location	?Xeroderma pigmentosum A (1)	4(Xpa)
1q42.1	FH	C	Fumarate hydratase	13685		?Fumarase deficiency (1)	
Chr.1	CD1	P	Thymocyte antigens CD1	18837			
Chr.1	GNAI3	P	Guanine nucleotide binding protein, alpha inhibiting, polypeptide 3	13937			9(Gnai-3)
Chr.1	GNAT2	P	Guanine nucleotide binding protein, alpha transducing, polypeptide 2	13934			
Chr.1	GNB1	P	Guanine nucleotide binding protein, beta polypeptide 1	13938			19(Gnb-1)
Chr.1	LFA3	P	Lymphocyte function associated antigen-3	15342	?same as MSK1; gene cloned		
Chr.1	MTR	P	5-Methyltetrahydrofolate:L-homocysteine S-methyltransferase; tetrahydropteroyl-glutamate methyltransferase	15657			
Chr.1	RCC1	P	Regulator of chromosome condensation	17971			
Chr.1	TPR	P	Tumor potentiating region (translocated promoter region)	18994	fused with MET in chemically induced tumor		

In addition: 4 surface antigens, most defined by monoclonals, 4 O'Farrell protein spots, 11 'like' genes, 8 pseudogenes, and 9 fragile sites (HGM9) and 70 anonymous DNA segments (HGML).
The order of closely linked loci (of ENO1 and 6PGD; of EL1, RH, and FUCA; of UMPK and SC; and of FY and CAE) is uncertain. 'However, the following order of loosely linked segments seems established': 6PGD--RH--UMPK--PGM1--AMY--1qh12--FY--PEPC. (From Rao et al., Am. J. Hum. Genet. 31: 680-696, 1979.)

Chromosome No. 2

2pter-p25.1	COI	L	Coloboma of iris	12020		?Coloboma of iris (2)	
2pter-p12	TPX, TPO	C	Thyroid peroxidase	27450		Thyroid iodine peroxidase deficiency (1)	
2p25	AN1	P	Aniridia-1	10620	linked to ACP1	Aniridia-1 (2)	
2p25	CAP	L	Cataract, anterior polar	11565	see 14q24	?Cataract, anterior polar (2)	
2p25	ODC1	C	Ornithine decarboxylase-1	16564			12(Odc-1)
2p25	POMC	C	Proopiomelanocortin	17683	?close to ACP1	ACTH deficiency (1)	12(Pomc-1)
2p25-p24	RRM2	P	Ribonucleotide reductase, M2 subunit	18039	pseudogenes on 1p, 1q, Xp		4,7,12,13(Rrm-2)
2p24	APOB	C	Apolipoprotein B	10773	1 gene for liver apo-B100 and gut apo-B48	Hypobetalipoproteinemia (1); ?Abetalipoproteinemia (1); Hyperbetalipoproteinemia (1)	12(Apob)
2p24	MYCN, NMYC	C	Oncogene NMYC	16484	proximal to APOB		
2p23	MDH1	C	Malate dehydrogenase, soluble	15420	proximal to APOB		
2p23	ACP1	C	Acid phosphatase-1	17150	proximal to MDH1		12(Acp-1)

Location	*Symbol*	*Status*	*Title*	*MIM #*	*Comments*	*Disorder*	*Mouse*
2p23-qter	ERCC3	P	Excision-repair, complementing defective, in Chinese hamster, number 3	13351			
2p23-qter	IFNB3	C	Beta-3-interferon	see 14764			
2p22-p21	CAD	P	CAD trifunctional protein of pyrimidine biosynthesis	11401			
2p22-p11	GLAT	P	Galactose enzyme activator	13703			
2p13	TGFA	C	Transforming (or tumor) growth factor, alpha type	19017			
2p13-cen	REL	P	Oncogene REL, avian reticuloendotheliosis	16491			11(Rel)
2p12	IGK, KM	C	IMMUNOGLOBULIN KAPPA LIGHT CHAIN GENE CLUSTER	14697, 14698, 14720	2p11.2 by high resolution in situ mapping; order: pter-C-J-V-cen		6(Igk)
2p12	IGKV	C	Variable region of kappa light chain	14698	25+ genes in 4 classes		
2p12	IGKJ	C	J region of kappa light chain	14697	5 genes		
2p12	IGKC	C	Constant region of kappa light chain	14720	1 gene		
2p12	CD8, T8, LEU2	C	Leu-2 T-cell antigen (T8 lymphocyte antigen)	18691	distal to IGK		6(Lyt-3; ?Ly-2)
2p11	FABP1, FABPL	C	Fatty acid binding protein, liver	13465			6(Fabp-l; ?lvp-1)
2p	AKE	L	Acrokeratoelastoidosis	10185	?linked to ACP1, JK, IGKC	?Acrokeratoelastoidosis (2)	
2p	CPS1	P	Carbamoylphosphate synthetase I (mitochondrial CPS)	23730	urea cycle enzyme	Carbamoylphosphate synthetase I deficiency (1)	
2p	OAK	L	Optic atrophy, Kjer type	16550	?linked to JK; lod = 2.15 at theta 0.14 male, 0.27 female	?Optic atrophy, Kjer type (2)	
2cen-q13	INHBB	P	Inhibin, beta-2	14739			1(Inhbb)
2cen-q13	MAL	P	T-lymphocyte maturation-associated protein	18886			
2q	TUBA1	P	Tubulin, alpha, testis-specific	19111			
2q12-q13	HOX4	P	Homeo box-4	14298	linked to Km in mice		6(Hox-4)
2q13-q21	IL1A	P	Interleukin-1, alpha	14776	tight linkage to IL1B in mouse		2(Il-1a)
2q13-q21	IL1B	I	Interleukin-1, ?beta form	14772	?distal 18q		2(Il-1b)
2q14-q21	GYPC, GE, GPC	P	Blood group Gerbich (glycophorin C)	11075			
2q31	COL3A1	C	Collagen III, alpha-1 chain	12018		Ehlers-Danlos syndrome, type IV (3)	
2q31	COL5A2	C	Collagen V, alpha-2 chain	12019	about 5cM from COL3A1		
2q31-q32	NEB	C	Nebulin	16165			
2q31-qter	ELN	P	Elastin	13016			
2q32-qter	ACHRD, ACHRMD	P	Muscle nicotinic acetylcholine receptor, delta subunit	10072	linked to Idh-1 in mouse		1(Achr-d)
2q32-qter	ACHRG, ACHRMG	P	Muscle nicotinic acetylcholine receptor, gamma subunit	10073	tightly linked to ACHRMD?		1(Achr-g)
2q32-qter	RPE	C	Ribulose 5-phosphate 3-epimerase	18048			
2q32.1-qter	MYL1	P	Myosin light chain, skeletal fast	16078			1(Myl-1)
2q33-q35	CRYG, CCL	C	CRYSTALLIN, GAMMA POLYPEPTIDE CLUSTER	12366		Cataract, Coppock-like (3)	1(Cryg)
2q33-qter	INHA	P	Inhibin, alpha	14738			1(Inha)

2q33.3	IDH1	C	Isocitrate dehydrogenase, soluble	14770			
2q34-q35	MAP2	P	Microtubule-associated protein-2	15713			1(Idh-1)
2q34-q36	FN1	C	Fibronectin-1	13560	structural gene; see chr. 8, 11	?Ehlers-Danlos syndrome, type X (3)	1(Fn-1)
2q35-q36	VIL	P	Villin	19304			1(Vil)
2q36-q37	GCG	C	Glucagon	13803			2(Gcg)
2q37	ALPI	C	Alkaline phosphatase, adult intestinal	17174	close to ALPP		
2q37	ALPP, PLAP	C	Alkaline phosphatase, placental	17180			4(Akp-2)
2q37	COL6A3	P	Collagen VI, alpha-3 chain	12025	close to CRBP1		9(Crbp-2)
Chr.2	ADCP2	C	Adenosine deaminase complexing protein-2	10272			
Chr.2	DES	P	Desmin	12566			
Chr.2	GAD	P	Glutamate decarboxylase	26610		?Pyridoxine dependency with seizures (1)	
Chr.2	PROC	C	Protein C	17686		Protein C deficiency (1)	
Chr.2	RACH	P	Acetylcholinesterase regulator, or derepressor	10068			
Chr.2	SFTP2	P	Pulmonary surfactant-associated protein, 18kD	17864			
Chr.2	UGP2	P	Uridyl diphosphate glucose pyrophosphorylase-2	19176			
Chr.2	UV24	P	Ultraviolet damage, repair of, in UV24	19207			

In addition: 2 surface antigens, most defined by monoclonals, 1 O'Farrell protein spot, 6 'like' genes, 4 pseudogenes, and 10 fragile sites (HGM9) and 52 anonymous DNA segments (HGML).

Chromosome No. 3

3pter-p21	CCK	C	Cholecystokinin	11844			
3p25	RAF1	P	Oncogene RAF1	16476			6(Raf-1)
3p25-p21	THRB, THR1, ERBA2	C	Thyroid hormone receptor, beta (ERBA2)	19016		?Thyroid hormone resistance, 27430, 18857 (1)	
3p23-p21	SCCL	C	Small-cell cancer of lung	18228		Small-cell cancer of lung (2)	
3p21.1?	GCPS	L	Greig craniopolysyndactyly syndrome	17570	?or 7p13; balanced translocation	?Greig craniopolysyndactyly syndrome (2)	
3p21	ACY1	C	Aminoacylase-1	10462			9(Acy)
3p21-cen	GLB1	C	Beta-galactosidase-1	23050		GM1-gangliosidosis (1); Mucopolysaccharidosis IVB (1)	9(Bgl)
3p21-q21	PROS	C	Protein S	17688		Protein S deficiency (1)	
3p14.2	RCC	C	Renal cell carcinoma	14470	?related to RAF1; 3p13-p11.2	Renal cell carcinoma (2)	
3p14.2-qter	APOD	P	Apolipoprotein D	10774			
3p13-q12	GPX1	C	Glutathione peroxidase-1	23170		Hemolytic anemia due to glutathione peroxidase deficiency (1)	
3p	MYL3	P	Myosin light chain alkali, ventricular and skeletal slow	16079			9(Myl-3)
3p	VHL	P	von Hippel-Lindau syndrome	19330	linked to RAF1	von Hippel-Lindau syndrome (1)	
3cen-q13	AHSG	C	Alpha-2HS-glycoprotein	13868	linked to TF, CHE1; ?order = cen-TF-CHE1-AHSG		
3cen-q21	UMPS, OPRT	P	Orotate phosphoribosyltransferase/OMP decarboxylase (UMP synthase)	25890		Oroticaciduria (1)	

Location	Symbol	Status	Title	MIM #	Comments	Disorder	Mouse
3cen-q22	RHN	P	Rh-null, regulator type	26815	monoclonal ID8	Rh-null disease (1)	
3q13.3-q22	PCCB	C	Propionyl CoA carboxylase, beta polypeptide	23205	pccB complementation group	Propionicacidemia, type II or pccB type (1)	
3q21	TF	C	Transferrin	19000		Atransferrinemia (1)	9(Trf)
3q21-q23	LTF	P	Lactotransferrin	15021			9(Ltf)
3q21-q24	CP	C	Ceruloplasmin	11770	ca. 15cM from TF	[Hypoceruloplasminemia, hereditary] (1)	9(Cp)
3q21-qter	RBP1, CRBP1	C	Cellular retinol binding protein I	18026			9(Crbp-1)
3q21-qter	RBP2, CRBP2	P	Cellular retinol binding protein II	18028	close to CRBP1		9(Crbp-2)
3q21-qter	RHO	P	Rhodopsin	18038			
3q25-q26	SI	P	Sucrase-isomaltase	22290		Sucrose intolerance (1)	
3q25.2	CHE1	C	Pseudocholinesterase-1	17740	distal to CP, TF	Postanesthetic apnea (1)	
3q26.2	TFRC	C	Transferrin receptor	19001			
3q27	FIM3	P	Friend murine leukemia virus integration site 3, homolog of	13677			
3q28	SST	C	Somatostatin	18245			16(Smst)
3q29	MAP97, MFJ1, MFI2	P	Melanoma-associated antigen p97	15575	identical to TFRC		
Chr.3	AF8T	P	Temperature sensitive, tsAF8, complement	11695			
Chr.3	ALAS	P	Delta-aminolevulinate synthase	12529			
Chr.3	DHFRP4	C	Dihydrofolate reductase pseudogene-4	see 12606			
Chr.3	GNAI2	P	Guanine nucleotide binding protein, alpha inhibiting, polypeptide 2	13936			9(?Gai)
Chr.3	GNAT1	P	Guanine nucleotide binding protein, alpha transducing, polypeptide 1	13933			
Chr.3	HAP	P	HBV-activated protein	14243			
Chr.3	HV1S	I	Herpes virus sensitivity	14245	see chr. 11		
Chr.3	MOX2	P	MRC OX-2 antigen	15597			
Chr.3	RPN1	P	Ribophorin I	18047			6(Rpm-1)
Chr.3	TSP1	P	Testis-specific protein-1	18742			

In addition: 4 surface antigens, most defined by monoclonals, 4 'like' genes, 5 pseudogenes, and 3 fragile sites (HGM9) and 31 anonymous DNA segments (HGML).

Chromosome No. 4

Location	Symbol	Status	Title	MIM #	Comments	Disorder	Mouse
4pter-p15	RAF2	P	Oncogene RAF2	see 16476			
4pter-q21	PPAT	P	Phosphoribosylpyrophosphate amidotransferase	17245	processed pseudogene		6(Raf-2)
4p16.3	HD	C	Huntington disease	14310			
4p16.1	D4S10	C	G8 DNA segment	see 14310	distal to D4S10	Huntington disease (2)	
4p15.3	QDPR, DHPR	C	Quinoid dihydropteridine reductase	26163	theta .03-.05, vs. HD	Phenylketonuria due to dihydropteridine reductase deficiency (1)	
4p14-q12	PGM2	C	Phosphoglucomutase-2	17200			
4p11-q12	PEPS	C	Peptidase S	17025			5(Pgm-1)
4cen-q21	MT2P1	C	Metallothionein II processed pseudogene	see 15636			5(Pep-7)

4cen-q24	US, USS1	L	Usher syndrome	27690	?linked to GC	Usher syndrome (2)	
4q11-q12	KIT	C	Oncogene KIT	16492			5(Kit)
4q11-q13	ALB	C	Albumin	10360	linked to GC	Analbuminemia (1); [Dysalbuminemic hyperthyroxinemia] (1); [Dysalbuminemic hyperzincemia] (1)	5(Alb-1)
4q11-q13	AFP	C	Alpha-fetoprotein	10415	order: 5'-ALB-3'--5'-AFP-3'		5(Afp)
4q11-q13	HPAFP	P	Hereditary persistence of alpha-fetoprotein	10414	?same locus as AFP	[Hereditary persistence of alpha-fetoprotein] (3)	
4q11-q13	JP	P	Periodontitis, juvenile	17065	linked to GC, which is probably between DGI1 and JP	Periodontitis, juvenile	
4q11-q13	STATH, STR	P	Statherin	18447			
4q12	GC, DBP	C	Group-specific component (vitamin D binding protein)	13920	4q13-q21.1 by in situ hybridization		
4q12	PBT	L	Piebald trait	17280			
4q12-q21	PF4	P	Platelet factor 4	17346			
4q13-q21	DGI1	C	Dentinogenesis imperfecta-1	12549	ca. 11cM from GC	Dentinogenesis imperfecta-1 (2)	
4q21	INP10, IP10	C	Interferon-inducible cytokine IP-10	14731	?involved in monocytic leukemia with t(4;11)(q21;q23)		
4q21	JCH	P	J region of immunoglobulin heavy chain	14779		?Leukemia, acute lymphocytic, with 4/11 translocation (3)	5(Igj)
4q21-q23	GNPTA	P	N-acetyl-alpha-glucosaminylphosphotransferase	25250		Mucolipidosis II (1); Mucolipidosis III (1)	
4q21-q24	ADHC1	C	ALCOHOL DEHYDROGENASE, CLASS I, CLUSTER	10370, 10372, 10373	ADH1,ADH2,ADH3 loci for alpha, beta, and gamma chains		3(Adh-1,3)
4q21-q24	FDH	C	Formaldehyde dehydrogenase	13649	4q24-qter (M. Smith)		
4q21-q25	ADHX, ADH5	P	Alcohol dehydrogenase, class III	10371			
4q21-q31	LPC2A	P	Lipocortin IIa	15171			
4q21-qter	AGA	P	Aspartylglucosaminidase	20840		Aspartylglucosaminuria (1)	
4q23-q25	IF	C	Factor I	21703			
4q23-q27	RGS	P	Rieger syndrome	18050	chr.21 and others implicated in some cases; ?not in 4q26	Rieger syndrome (2)	
4q25-q27	EGF	C	Epidermal growth factor	13153	linked to ADH3; cen-ADH3-EGF-IL2-qter		3(Egf)
4q26-q27	IL2, TCGF	C	T-cell growth factor (interleukin-2)	14768			
4q26-q28	FGC	C	FIBRINOGEN GENE CLUSTER	13482-13485	likely order: gamma-alpha-beta		
4q26-q28	FGB	C	Fibrinogen, beta chain	13483	4q31 by A	Dysfibrinogenemia, beta types (1)	
4q26-q28	FGA	C	Fibrinogen, alpha chain	13482		Dysfibrinogenemia, alpha types (1)	

Location	Symbol	Status	Title	MIM #	Comments	Disorder	Mouse
4q26-q28	FGG	C	Fibrinogen, gamma chain	13485	linked to MN	Dysfibrinogenemia, hypofibrinogenemia, gamma types (1)	
4q28-q31	ASMD	P	Anterior segment mesenchymal dysgenesis	10725	linked to MN	Anterior segment mesenchymal dysgenesis (2)	
4q28-q31	FABP2	P	Fatty acid binding protein, intestinal	13464			3(Fabp-i)
4q28-q31	SS, GYPB	C	Ss blood group; glycophorin B	11174			
4q28-q31	MN, GYPA	C	MN blood group (glycophorin A)	11130	male lod = 3.79 at theta 0.32 vs. GC		
4q28-q31	TYS	C	Sclerotylosis	18160	tightly linked to MN	Sclerotylosis (2)	
4q28-q31	RHC, RHA	P	Red hair color	26630	see unassigned linkage groups, Ib4		
4q28-q31	SF	C	Stoltzfus blood group	11180	ca. 25cM from MNSs		
4q32.1	HCC2	P	Hepatocellular carcinoma-2 (hepatitis B virus integration site-2)	14238		Hepatocellular carcinoma (2)	
Chr.4	ATPBL1	P	Sodium-potassium-ATPase, beta-polypeptide-like	18237			
Chr.4	FGFB	P	Fibroblast growth factor, basic	13492	many alternate names		
Chr.4	GTB	I	Galactosyltransferase, 4-beta	13706	see chr.9		
Chr.4	LAG5	P	Leukocyte antigen group five	15145			
Chr.4	MCR, MR	P	Mineralocorticoid receptor	26435		Pseudohypoaldosteronism (1)	
Chr.4	TS13	P	Temperature sensitivity complementation, ts13	18732			

In addition: 1 antigen, 3 'like' genes, 3 pseudogenes, and 3 fragile sites (HGM9) and 118 anonymous DNA segments (HGML). Possible order: CEN--GC--DGI1--SS--MN--FGG. FGB--FGA--FGG in this order in 50kb segment.

Chromosome No. 5

Location	Symbol	Status	Title	MIM #	Comments	Disorder	Mouse
5pter-q11	RARS	P	Arginyl-tRNA synthetase	10782	very close to LARS		
5p14-p13	HMGCS	C	3-hydroxy-3-methylglutaryl coenzyme A synthase; HMG CoA synthase	14294	like HMGCR, regulated transcriptionally by steroid; ?2 genes closely situated		
5p13-cen	TARS	P	Threonyl-tRNA synthetase	18779	linked to LARS		
5cen-q11	LARS, RNTLS	C	Leucyl-tRNA synthetase	15135			
5q11	MFD1	L	Treacher Collins mandibulofacial dysostosis	15450	t(5;13)(q11;p11)	?Treacher Collins mandibulofacial dysostosis (2)	
5q11-q13	ARSB	C	Arylsulfatase B	25320		Maroteaux-Lamy syndrome (1)	13(As-1)
5q11-q13	GRL	C	Glucocorticoid receptor, lymphocyte	13804		Cortisol resistance (1)	18(Grl-1)
5q11.1-q13.2	DHFR	C	Dihydrofolate reductase	12606	5q23 = conflicting localization; to other chrs. with amplification	?Megaloblastic anemia (1)	13(Dhfr)
5q12-q32	MAR	P	Macrocytic anemia, refractory	15355	resulting from 5q-	Macrocytic anemia of 5q- syndrome, refractory (2)	
5q13	HEXB	C	Beta-hexosaminidase, beta chain	26880		Sandhoff disease (1)	13(Hex-2)

5q13.3-q14	HMGCR	C	3-hydroxy-3-methylglutaryl coenzyme A reductase; HMG CoA reductase	14291			
5q21-q22	APC, GS, FPC	C	Adenomatous polyposis of the colon (Gardner syndrome; familial polyposis coli)	17530		Gardner syndrome (2); Polyposis coli, familial (2);?Familial colorectal cancer (2)	
5q23	DTS	C	Diphtheria toxin sensitivity	12615		{Diphtheria, susceptibility to} (1)	
5q23-q31	CD14	P	Monocyte differentiation antigen CD14	15812			
5q23-q31	IL3	P	Interleukin-3	14774			11(Il-3)
5q23-q32	CSF2, GMCSF	C	Granulocyte-macrophage colony-stimulating factor	13896	order: cen-CSF2-CSF1-FMS-qter		11(Csfgm)
5q23.3-q32	IL5	P	Interleukin 5	14785			
5q31-q32	ADRB2R, BAR2	C	Beta-2-adrenergic receptor	10969			
5q31-q32	PDGFR	P	Platelet-derived growth factor receptor	17341	between GMCSF and FMS		
5q31-q33	EMTB, RPS14	C	Emetine resistance (ribosomal protein S14)	13062	see 18046		
5q31-q33	SPARC	P	Secreted protein, acidic, cysteine-rich (osteonectin)	18212			11(Sparc)
5q31.3-q33.2	ECGF	C	Endothelial cell growth factor	13122			
5q33-qter	F12, HAF	C	Clotting factor XII (Hageman factor)	23400		Factor XII deficiency (1)	
5q33.1?	CMD1	L	Campomelic dysplasia with sex reversal	21197	?or 8q21.4; balanced translocation	?Campomelic dysplasia with sex reversal (2)	
5q33.1	CSF1, MCSF	P	Macrophage colony stimulating factor	12042			11(Csfm)
5q33.2-q33.3	CSF1R, FMS	C	Oncogene FMS (McDonough feline sarcoma)	16477	= receptor for CSF1		18(Fms)
5q35	CHR	C	Chromate resistance (sulfate transport)	11884			
Chr.5	FGFA	P	Fibroblast growth factor, acidic	13491	same locus as ECGF		
Chr.5	GM2A	P	GM2-activator protein	27275		GM2-gangliosidosis, AB variant (1)	
Chr.5	HARS	P	Histidyl-tRNA synthetase	14281			
Chr.5	HFSP	P	Hanukah factor serine protease	14005			
Chr.5	HLADG, DHLAG	C	Histocompatibility class II antigens, gamma chain	14279	S, REb		18(Ii)
Chr.5	PSTI	P	Pancreatic secretory trypsin inhibitor	16779	REb		

In addition: 1 surface antigen, 1 O'Farrell protein spot, 5 'like' genes, 5 pseudogenes, and 3 fragile sites (HGM9) and 80 anonymous DNA segments (HGML). Critical segment in *cri du chat* syndrome near 5p15.3-p15.2 junction.

Chromosome No. 6

Location	Symbol	Status	Title	MIM #	Comments	Disorder	Mouse
6pter-p23	F13A	C	Clotting factor XIII, A component	13457	male theta = 0.17 vs. HLA	Factor XIII, A component deficiency (1)	
6pter-p23	ME2	P	Malic enzyme, mitochondrial	15427	10cM distal to F13A		7(Mod-2)
6pter-p23	OFC, CL	P	Orofacial cleft (cleft lip with or without cleft palate; isolated cleft palate)	11953	linked to F13A	Orofacial cleft (2)	
6pter-p21.1	PGC	P	Preprogastricsin	16974			
6pter-p21	TUBB	P	Tubulin, beta, M40	19113			
6pter-q12	PIM1	P	Oncogene PIM1	16496			17(Pim-1)
6p23-q12	HYS, MEA	P	H-Y antigen, structural gene for	14317	male enhanced antigen		
6p23-q12	INSL	P	Insulin-like DNA sequence	14749			
6p23-q12	RNTMI, TRM1	P	Initiator methionine tRNA	18062	2 of 12+ RNTMI genes are on chr. 6		
6p23-q12	PRL	C	Prolactin	17676	?between 6cen and GLO1		
6p22-p21.3	HSPA1, HSP70	C	Heat shock proteins-70	14055	also 14q22-q24, chr.21, and at least 1 other chromosome		
6p21.3	LQT	C	Long QT syndrome	19250	ca. 5cM from MHC; ?proximal or distal to MHC	Long QT syndrome (2)	
6p21.3	ASD2	P	Atrial septal defect, secundum type	10880	lod = 3.612 at theta 0.0 with HLA	Atrial septal defect, secundum type (2)	
6p21.3	GLUR	P	Renal glucosuria	23310	closer to HLA-A than HLA-B	[Renal glucosuria] (2)	
6p21.3	IS, ISCW, ISSCW	P	Immune suppression to streptococcal antigen	14685	HLA-linked		
6p21.3	NDF	P	Neutrophil differentiation factor	20270	?linkage disequilibrium with HLA-B12	?Kostmann agranulocytosis (2)	
6p21.3	IDDM	L	Insulin dependent diabetes mellitus	22210	?linkage or association, with HLA	?Diabetes mellitus, insulin dependent (2)	
6p21.3	PDB	L	Paget disease of bone	16725	?linkage or association, with HLA	?Paget disease of bone (2)	
6p21.3	RWS	L	Ragweed sensitivity	17945	?linkage or association, with HLA	?Ragweed sensitivity (2)	
6p21.3	MHC	C	MAJOR HISTOCOMPATIBILITY COMPLEX	14280	class I distal to class II		17(Mhc)
6p21.3	HLAA	C	HLA-A tissue type	14280	HLA-A, -B, -C = class I		17(H-2D)
6p21.3	HFE	C	Hemochromatosis	23520	close to HLA-A; between HLA-A and HLA-B or ?distal to HLA-A	Hemochromatosis (2)	
6p21.3	HLAC	C	HLA-C tissue type	14284			
6p21.3	HLAB	C	HLA-B tissue type	14283			
6p21.3	CYP21, CA21H, CAH1	C	Congenital adrenal hyperplasia due to 21-hydroxylase deficiency; P450C21	20191	linked to C2, C4, BF; 2 loci, A and B; only B active	Adrenal hyperplasia, congenital, due to 21-hydroxylase deficiency (3)	17(P450-21)

6p21.3	C2	C	Complement component-2	21700	no crossover with BF; 2% recombination with HLA-B	C2 deficiency (3)	17(C2)
6p21.3	C4S, C4A	C	Complement component-4S, or C4A	12081	on HLA-B side of C4B	C4 deficiency (3)	17(C4)
6p21.3	C4F, C4B	C	Complement component-4F, or C4B	12082	10kb from C4S	C4 deficiency (3)	17(C4)
6p21.3	BF	C	Properdin factor B	13847	no crossover with C2; less than 1kb from C2, 30kb from C4; C2, BF, C4A, C4B = class III		17(Bf)
6p21.3	HLADZ	C	HLA-DZ tissue type	14293	1 alpha, 1 beta chain; DZ, DR, etc. = class II		
6p21.3	HLADR	C	HLA-DR tissue type	14286	1 alpha, 3 different beta chains		
6p21.3	HLADQ	C	HLA-DQ tissue type	14688	1 Dx alpha, 1 Dx beta; 1 DC alpha, 1 DC beta chains		
6p21.3	HLADP	C	HLA-DP tissue type	14288	2 different alpha, 2 different beta chains		
6p21.3	IHG, ITG	P	Blastogenic response to synthetic polypeptides	14695, 14696	in A/B segment		
6p21.3	IPHEG, IGAT	P	Blastogenic response to synthetic polypeptides	14681, 14682	in B/D segment		
6p21.3	IGLP1	C	Immune response to synthetic polypeptides	14708			
6p21.3	IGLP2	C	Immune response to synthetic polypeptides	14709			
6p21.3	MLRW	P	Mixed lymphocyte reaction, weak	15786	near HLA-A end		
6p21.3	PLT1	C	Primed lymphocyte test-1	17668	near HLA-D		
6p21.3	NEU, NEU1	L	Neuraminidase-1; sialidosis	16205, 25655	?linked to HLA; see chr. 10	?Sialidosis (2)	17(Neu-1)
6p21.3-p21.2	LAP	L	Laryngeal adductor paralysis	15027	?linkage to HLA and GLO1	?Laryngeal adductor paralysis (2)	
6p21.3-p21.2	HMAA	P	Human monocyte antigen A	14307			
6p21.3-p21.2	HMAB	P	Human monocyte antigen B	14308	between HLADQ and GLO		
6p21.3-p21.2	GLO1	C	Glyoxalase I	13875	ca. 3cM proximal to HLA		17(Glo-1)
6p21.3-p21.2	CP20	L	Lymphocyte cytosolic protein, molecular weight 20kD	15342			
6p21.3-p21.1	TNFA, TNF1	P	Tissue necrosis factor, alpha	19116	5'-TNFB--TNFA-3' in 7kb segment (pter-cen)		17(Tnfa)
6p21.3-p21.1	TNFB, TNF2	P	Tissue necrosis factor, beta	15344	cen-DR-21OH-C4-BF-C2-TNFA-TNFB-HLA-B		17(Tnfb)
6p21.1-p12	PGK1P2	C	Phosphoglycerate kinase-1 pseudogene-2	17227	proximal to MHC		17(Pgk-2)
6p21	MAPT2	P	Microtubule-associated protein tau-2	see 15713	see 17q21		

6p12	GST2	P	Glutathione S-transferase-2	13836		
6p12-p11	RASK1, KRAS1	C	Oncogene, Kirsten rat sarcoma virus-1	19011	pseudogene		
6p	CSCI	L	Corticosterone side-chain isomerase	12255	?linked to MHC		
6p	EJM, JME	P	Epilepsy, juvenile myoclonic	25477	?linked to BF and HLA	?Epilepsy, juvenile myoclonic (2)	
6p	MUT, MCM	P	Methylmalonyl CoA mutase	25100		Methylmalonicaciduria, mutase deficiency type (1)	
6p	SCA1	C	Spinocerebellar ataxia-1	16440	telomeric to GLO1 and perhaps to HLA	Spinocerebellar ataxia-1 (2)	
6q	IFNGR1	I	Immune interferon, receptor for	10747	both 6 and 18 required		10(Ifgr)
6q12	ME1	C	Malic enzyme, cytoplasmic	15425			9(Mod-1)
6q12	PGM3	C	Phosphoglucomutase-3	17210			9(Pgm-3)
6q21	BKMA1	P	Banded krait minor satellite DNA-1	see 10978	related to heterogametic sex		
6q21	SOD2	C	Superoxide dismutase-2, mitochondrial	14746			17(Sod-2)
6q21	SYN	P	Oncogene SYN	16499			
6q21	SYR	C	SRC/YES-related oncogene	16499			
6q21.1-q23	CGA	P	Chorionic gonadotropin, alpha chain	11885	shared with LH, FSH, TSH		4(Tsha)
6q22	MYB	C	Oncogene, avian myeloblastosis virus	18999			10(Myb)
6q22	ROS, MCF3	C	Oncogene ROS (oncogene MCF3)	16502			
6q23	ARG1	P	Arginase, liver	20780		Argininemia (1)	
6q24	VIP	C	Vasoactive intestinal peptide	19232			
6q24-q27	ESR, ER	C	Estrogen receptor	13343			
6q24-q27	MAS1	P	Oncogene MAS1	16518	?same as ESR		
6q25-q27	TCP1	C	T-complex locus TCP-1	18698			17(Cp)
6q25-qter	FUCA2	C	Alpha-L-fucosidase-2	13682	linked to PLG		
6q25-qter	VMD2	L	Macular dystrophy, ?vitelline type	15370		Macular dystrophy, ?vitelline type (2)	
6q26-q27	PLG	C	Plasminogen	17335		Plasminogen Tochigi disease (1)	
6q27	LPA	P	Apolipoprotein Lp(a)	15220			
Chr.6	ADCP1	I	Adenosine deaminase complexing protein-1	10271			
Chr.6	AMD	P	S-adenosylmethionine decarboxylase	18098	sequences on Xq22-q28		
Chr.6	ASSP2	P	Argininosuccinate synthetase pseudogene-2	10784	others on 8 or more other chromosomes including X and Y		
Chr.6	BEVI	C	Baboon M7 virus replication	10918			
Chr.6	DHFRP2	P	Dihydrofolate reductase pseudogene-2	see 12606			
Chr.6	FEA	L	F9 embryonic antigen	13701			
Chr.6	MRBC	P	Monkey RBC receptor	15805			
Chr.6	P	P	P blood group globoside	11140			
Chr.6	TS546	P	Temperature sensitivity complementation, cell cycle specific, ts546 cells	18733			
Chr.6	YES2	P	Oncogene YES-2	16489			

In addition: 3 surface antigens, most defined by monoclonals, 2 O'Farrell protein spots, 5 'like' genes, 8 pseudogenes, and 5 fragile sites (HGM9) and 36 anonymous DNA segments (HGML). Order: 6cen--DR--C2--BF--C4A--CA21HA--C4B--CA21HB--HLA-B--pter (Wilton and Charlton, 1986). Order of class II subregions: 6cen--DP--DZalpha--DObeta--DX--DQ--DRbeta--DRalpha (Hardy et al., 1986). Order in region of class I genes: 6cen--DR--HLA--B--0.01--HLA--C--0.7--HLA-A--pter. HLADP shows relatively high recombination with DQ but the physical distance by molecular studies is about same as DQ-to-DR. Recombinational hotspots probably exist within the DQ subregion and between HLA-A and HLA-C (which molecular data suggest are as close as B and C). Family data show HLA-A to HLA-C = 0.7cM; HLA-C to HLA-B = 0.1cM. Disease/MHC associations of various strengths are probably indicative of pleiotropic effects of specific alleles or haplotypes, not linkage. Two of the strongest are ankylosing spondylitis (10630) with HLA-B27 and narcolepsy (16140) with HLA-DR2.

Chromosome No. 7

Location	Symbol	Status	Title	MIM #	Comments	Disorder	Mouse
7pter-p14	GCTG	P	Gamma-glutamylcyclotransferase	13717			
7pter-q22	ACTB	P	Actin, cytoskeletal beta	10263	ca. 20 pseudogenes also		5(Actb)
7pter-q22	NPY	P	Neuropeptide Y	16264			
7pter-q22	PSP	C	Phosphoserine phosphatase	17248			5(Psph)
7p22-q21	PDGFA	C	Platelet-derived growth factor, A chain	17343			
7p22-p15	RAL	P	RAS-like protein	17955			
7p21.3-p21.2	CRS, CSO	C	Craniosynostosis	12310		Craniosynostosis (2)	
7p21	IFNB2, IL6, BSF2	C	Interferon, beta-2	14762			
7p21-p14	HOX1	C	Homeo box-1	14295			6(Hox-1)
7p21-q22	ASL	C	Argininosuccinate lyase	20790		Argininosuccinicaciduria (1)	5(Asl)
7p15	TCRG	C	T-cell antigen receptor, gamma subunit	18697	multiple V genes, two J-C duplexes		13(Tcrg)
7p14-p12	ERBB	C	Oncogene ERBB	19014	?same as EGFR; similar sequences		11(Erbb)
7p14-cen	BLVR	C	Biliverdin reductase	10975			2(Blvr)
7p13?	GCPS	L	Greig craniopolysyndactyly syndrome	17570	?or 3p21.1; balanced translocation	?Greig craniopolysyndactyly syndrome (2)	
7p13-p11	EGFR	C	Epidermal growth factor receptor	13155			
7p13-q22	MDH2	C	Malate dehydrogenase, mitochondrial	15410			5(Mor-1)
7p13-qter	PKR1	P	Protein kinase, cAMP-dependent, type I regulatory subunit	17689	not in 7q22-q31.3		
7p11.4-q21	ARAF2	P	Oncogene ARAF2	16471			
7p11-q11	ASNS, AS	C	Asparagine synthetase	10837			
7p11-q11.2	PKS1	P	Oncogene PKS1	16501			
7p	GHS	L	Goldenhar syndrome	14140		?Goldenhar syndrome (2)	
7q11.2-q22	GUSB	C	Beta-glucuronidase	25322		Mucopolysaccharidosis VII (1)	5(Gus)
7q21-q22	EPO	C	Erythropoietin	13317	close to COL1A2; no recombination	?Erythremia (1)	
7q21-q22	NKNA	P	Neurokinin A (substance P)	16232			
7q21.1	PGY1, MDR1	C	P-glycoprotein-1 (multidrug resistance)	17105			5(Mdr-1)
7q21.1	PGY3, MDR3	P	P-glycoprotein-3 (multidrug resistance-3)	17106	within 500kb of MDR1		
7q21.3-q22	CYP3	C	Cytochrome P450C3 (nifedipine oxidase)	12401			6(Cyp-3)
7q21.3-q22	PLANH1, PAI1	C	Plasminogen activator inhibitor-1	17336		?Thrombophilia due to excessive plasminogen activator inhibitor (1)	
7q21.3-q22.1	COL1A2	C	Collagen I, alpha-2 chain	12016	ca. 17cM from CF	Osteogenesis imperfecta, 2 or more clinical forms (3); Ehlers-Danlos syndrome, type VIIA2 (3); Marfan syndrome, atypical (1)	16(Cola-2)
7q22	PON, ESA	C	Paraoxonase	16882	Order: COL1A2-D7S15-PON-CF		
7q22	HCA	I	HISTONE CLUSTER A: H1, H2A, H2B	14271, 14272, 14276	7q32-q36 = conflicting localization; others find none on 7		13(Hist-1)

Location	Symbol	Status	Title	MIM #	Comments	Disorder	Mouse
7q22-q31	PKR2	P	Protein kinase, cAMP-dependent, type II regulatory subunit	17691			
7q22-q34	BPGM	P	2,3-bisphosphoglycerate mutase	22280		Hemolytic anemia due to bisphosphoglycerate mutase deficiency (1)	
7q22-qter	ACTBP5	P	Actin, cytoskeletal beta, pseudogene-5	10264	ca. 20 in all; 1 on X chr.; 2 on chr. 5; 3 on chr. 18; 4 on chr. 5, etc.		
7q22-qter	BCP, CBT	P	Blue cone pigment	19090		Colorblindness, tritan (2)	
7q22-qter	CPA	P	Carboxypeptidase A	11485	both CPA and TRY1 = serine proteases		6(Cpa)
7q22-qter	GP130, NM	C	Neutrophil migration (granulocyte glycoprotein)	16282	formerly neutrophil chemotactic response, NCR		
7q22-qter	TRY1, TRP1	P	Trypsin-1	27600		Trypsinogen deficiency (1)	6(Try-1)
7q22.3-q23.1	MET	C	Oncogene MET	16486	ca. 1.2cM from CF		6(Met)
7q22.3-q23.1	CF	C	Cystic fibrosis	21970	ca. 22cM from TCRB	Cystic fibrosis (2)	
7q31-qter	ODC2	C	Ornithine decarboxylase-2	16565			
7q31.1-q31.3	LAMB1	C	Laminin B1	15024	7q22 = conflicting assignment		1(Lamb-1)
7q35	TCRB	C	T-cell antigen receptor, beta subunit	18693	7q32 by A; cluster of V, D, J, and C genes;many V, two D-J-C triplexes		6(Tcrb)
7q35-q36	MPB3	P	Membrane protein band 3, nonerythroid	10928			
Chr.7	DIA2	L	Diaphorase-2	12587			
Chr.7	ERV3	P	Endogenous retrovirus-3	13117			
Chr.7	GCF1	P	Growth rate controlling factor-1	13922			
Chr.7	GNAI1	P	Guanine nucleotide binding protein, alpha inhibiting, polypeptide-1	13931			
Chr.7	INHBA	P	Inhibin, beta-1	14729			13(Inhba)
Chr.7	INM7	P	Invasion-metastasis of neoplasms, chromosome 7 determined	14783			
Chr.7	HADH	P	Hydroxyacyl CoA dehydrogenase	14345			
Chr.7	NHCP2	P	Nonhistone chromosomal protein-2	11888			
Chr.7	UP	C	Uridine phosphorylase	19173			

In addition: 1 surface antigen, 2 O'Farrell protein spots, 5 'like' genes, 2 pseudogenes, and 8 fragile sites (HGM9) and 389 anonymous DNA segments (HGML).

Chromosome No. 8

8p22	CTSB, CPSB	P	Cathepsin B [EC 3.4.22.1]	11681			
8p22	LIPD	P	Lipoprotein lipase (lipase D)	23860		Hyperlipoproteinemia I (1)	
8p21.1	GSR	C	Glutathione reductase	13830		Hemolytic anemia due to glutathione reductase deficiency (1)	8(Gr-1)
8p21	NEFL, NFL	P	Neurofilament, light polypeptide	16228			
8p21-q11.2	GNRH, LHRH	P	Luteinizing hormone releasing hormone (gonadotropin releasing hormone)	15276		?Hypogonadotropic hypogonadism due to GNRH deficiency , 22720 (1)	
8p12	PLAT, TPA	C	Plasminogen activator, tissue type	17337		Plasminogen activator deficiency (1)	8(Plat)
8p12-p11	POLB	C	Polymerase, DNA, beta	17476			
8p11	SPH2	C	Spherocytosis	18290		Spherocytosis-2 (2)	
8q	F7E, F7R	P	Clotting factor VII expression, or regulator	13445			
8q	GPB	P	Beta-glycerol phosphatase	10964			
8q13	CRH	P	Corticotropin releasing hormone	12256			
8q13-qter	LYN	P	Oncogene Yamaguchi sarcoma viral related	16512			
8q21	CYP11B, P450C11	P	11-beta-hydroxylase	20201	multifunctional enzyme	Adrenal hyperplasia, congenital, due to 11-beta-hydroxylase deficiency (1)	
8q21.1-q23	MRS	P	Myeloid-related sequence	15956		?ANLL-M2 (1)	
8q21.1-qter	GLYB	P	Glycine auxotroph B, complementation of hamster	13848	gly(-)B		
8q21.4?	CMD1	L	Campomelic dysplasia with sex reversal	21197	?or 5q33.1; balanced translocation	?Campomelic dysplasia with sex reversal (2)	
8q22	CAC	C	CARBONIC ANHYDRASE CLUSTER	11475, 11480, 11481			
8q22	CA1	C	Carbonic anhydrase I	11480			3(Car-1)
8q22	CA2	C	Carbonic anhydrase II	11481	CA1, CA2 linked in monkey and mouse	Renal tubular acidosis-osteopetrosis syndrome (1)	3(Car-2)
8q22	CA3	C	Carbonic anhydrase III	11475			
8q22	MOS	C	Oncogene MOS, Moloney murine sarcoma virus	19006	8q11 = conflicting localization		4(Mos)
8q23-q24	PENK	P	Proenkephalin	13133			
8q23-q24.1?	EXT	L	Multiple exostoses	13370		?Multiple exostoses (2)	
8q24	EBS1	C	Epidermolysis bullosa, Ogna type	13195	closely linked to GPT	Epidermolysis bullosa, Ogna type (2)	
8q24	GPT	C	Glutamate-pyruvate transaminase	13820			15(Gpt-1)
8q24	PDS	L	Pendred syndrome	27460		?Pendred syndrome (2)	
8q24	PVT1	P	Oncogene PVT-1 (MYC activator)	16514			
8q24	VMD1	C	Macular dystrophy, atypical vitelliform	15384	5cm from GPT	Macular dystrophy, atypical vitelliform (2)	
8q24.1	MYC	C	Oncogene MYC, avian myelocytomatosis virus	19008	cen-5'-3'-ter	Burkitt lymphoma (3)	15(Myc)

Location	Symbol	Status	Title	MIM #	Comments	Disorder	Mouse
8q24.11-q24.13	LGCR, LGS, TRPS2	C	Langer-Giedion syndrome	15023	?deletion of both EXT and TRP1 in LGS; ?critical segment = 8q24.11-q24.12	Langer-Giedion syndrome (2)	
8q24.12	TRPS1	P	Trichorhinophalangeal syndrome, type I	19035		Trichorhinophalangeal syndrome, type I (2)	
8q24.2-q24.3	TG	C	Thyroglobulin	18845	distal to MYC	Hypothyroidism, hereditary congenital, 1 or more types (1); ?Goiter, adolescent multinodular, 13880 (1)	?15(Tg)
Chr.8	FNZ	L	Fibronectin	13560	?concerned with expression on cell surface		

In addition: 4 'like' genes, 2 pseudogenes, and 4 fragile sites (HGM9) and 34 anonymous DNA segments (HGML).

Chromosome No. 9

Location	Symbol	Status	Title	MIM #	Comments	Disorder	Mouse
9pter-q12	RLXH1, RLN1	P	Relaxin, H1	17973			
9pter-q12	RLXH2, RLN2	P	Relaxin, H2	17974			
9pter-q34	LPC2B	P	Lipocortin IIb	15172			
9p24-p13	AK3	C	Adenylate kinase-3, mitochondrial	10303			
9p22-p21	LALL	P	Lymphomatous acute lymphoblastic leukemia	24764			
9p22-p21	MTAP, MSAP	C	Methylthioadenosine phosphorylase	15654			
9p22-p13	ACO1	C	Aconitase, soluble	10088			4(Aco-1)
9p21	IFNB, IFNB1, IFF	C	Fibroblast interferon; beta-interferon	14764	distal to IFL; 9p23-p22 according to Rowley; IFF duplicate in some persons		4(Ifb)
9p21	IFNA, IFL, IFA	C	LEUKOCYTE INTERFERON GENE CLUSTER; ALPHA-INTERFERON	14766	very close to IFF by Fd, LD; 15-30 genes	Interferon, alpha, deficiency (1)	4(Ifa)
9p13	GALT	C	Galactose-1-phosphate uridyltransferase	23040		Galactosemia (1)	4(Galt)
9p13	GT1	I	Galactosyltransferase-1	13706	?relation to GTB on chr.4		4(Ggt-1)
9cen-q34	FPGS	P	Folylpolyglutamate synthetase	13651			2(Fpgs)
9cen-qter	GRP78	P	Glucose-regulated protein	13812			
9q11-q22	LPC1	P	Lipocortin I	15169			
9q11-q22	TSC, TS	P	Tuberous sclerosis	19110	linked to ABO	Tuberous sclerosis (2)	
9q12	DNCM	P	Cytoplasmic membrane DNA	12633	9qh		
9q21	ALDH1	P	Aldehyde dehydrogenase-1	10064			19(Ahd-1,2)
9q22	ALDOB	C	Aldolase B; fructose-1-phosphate aldolase	22960		Fructose intolerance (1)	
9q22-q34	C5	P	Complement component 5	12090		C5 deficiency (1)	
9q32-q34	GSN	P	Gelsolin	13735			
9q33-q34	SPTAN1, NEAS	P	Spectrin, alpha, nonerythrocytic 1 (alpha-fodrin)	18281			
9q33-qter	ITO	I	Hypomelanosis of Ito	14615	see chr.15	?Hypomelanosis of Ito (2)	

9q34	ABO	C	ABO blood group	11030	linked to AK1		
9q34	ASS	C	Argininosuccinate synthetase	21570	14 pseudogenes on 11 chromosomes	Citrullinemia (1)	2(Ass)
9q34	ALAD	C	Delta-aminolevulinate dehydratase	12527	linked to ABO; ORM-13-ALAD-11-AK-13-ABO	Porphyria, acute hepatic (1); {Lead poisoning, susceptibility to} (1)	4(Lv)
9q34	DBH	P	Dopamine-beta-hydroxylase	22336	tightly linked to ABO		
9q34	NPS1	C	Nail-patella syndrome	16120	linked to AK1, ABO; no recombination with AK1	Nail-patella syndrome (2)	
9q34.1	ABL	C	Oncogene ABL (Abelson strain, murine leukemia virus)	18998	fusion hybrid gene with BCR1 in CML	Leukemia, chronic myeloid (3)	2(Abl)
9q34.1	AK1	C	Adenylate kinase-1, soluble	10300	proximal to Ph1 break, 9q34.1; AK1 to ORM = 17cM	Hemolytic anemia due to adenylate kinase deficiency (1)	2(Ak-1)
9q34.3	ORM	C	Orosomucoid (alpha-1-acid glycoprotein)	13860	linked to ABO, AK1, ALAD; ORM to ABO = 27cM; 2nd ORM locus (13861)		4(Orm-1,2)
Chr.9	CPRO, CPO	P	Coproporphyrinogen oxidase	12130		Coproporphyria (1); Harderoporphyria (1)	
Chr.9	H142T	P	Temperature sensitivity complementation, H142	18729	?on 9p		
Chr.9	ITI, ITIL, HCP	P	Protein HC; inter-alpha-trypsin inhibitor, light chain	17687		?Familial Mediterranean fever (1)	
Chr.9	IGEP2	P	Immunoglobulin epsilon heavy chain pseudogene	14721			
Chr.9	VARS	P	Valyl-tRNA synthetase	19215			

In addition: 1 antigen, 4 O'Farrell protein spots, 2 'like' genes and 4 pseudogenes (HGM9) and 26 anonymous DNA segments (HGML).

Chromosome No. 10

10pter-p11.1	PFKF, PFKP	C	Phosphofructokinase, platelet type	17184			
10p15-p14	IL2R, TAK	C	Interleukin-2 receptor; T-cell growth factor receptor	14773			
10p13	VIM	C	Vimentin	19306			
10p11.2	HK1	C	Hexokinase-1	14260		Hemolytic anemia due to hexokinase deficiency (1)	10(Hk-1)
10p11.2-q11.2	RBP3, IRBP	C	Interstitial retinol-binding protein	18029			
10p	FRNB	P	Fibronectin receptor, beta subunit	13563			
10q11-q24	ADK	C	Adenosine kinase	10275			14(Adk)
10q11-qter	ALDOBP	P	Aldolase B pseudogene	see 22960			
10q11.1-q24	PP	C	Inorganic pyrophosphatase	17903			10(Pyp)
10q21-q22	LPC2C	P	Lipocortin IIc	15173			
10q21-q22	SAP1	C	Sphingolipid activator protein-1	24990		Metachromatic leukodystrophy due to deficiency of SAP-1 (1)	
10q21-q24	SFTP1, PSAP	P	Pulmonary surfactant-associated protein, 35kD	17863			
10q21.1	MEN2	C	Multiple endocrine neoplasia, type II	17140	19cM from D10S5 at 10q21.1	Multiple endocrine neoplasia II (2)	

Location	Symbol	Status	Title	MIM #	Comments	Disorder	Mouse
10q23-q24	GLUD	P	Glutamate dehydrogenase	13813			
10q23-q24	DNTT, TDT	C	Terminal deoxynucleotidyltransferase	18741			19(Tdt)
10q23-q25	ADRA2R	P	Alpha-2-adrenergic receptor	10421			
10q24	TCL3	P	T-cell leukemia-3	18677		Leukemia, T-cell acute lymphocytic (2)	
10q24-q25	LIPA	P	Lysosomal acid lipase-A	27800	?close to GOT	Wolman disease (1); Cholesterol ester storage disease (1)	19(Lip-1)
10q24-qter	PLAU, URK	C	Urokinase (plasminogen activator, urinary)	19184			9(Plau)
10q24.1-q24.3	CYP2C	P	Cytochrome P450, family II, subfamily C (mephenytoin 4-hydroxylase)	12402	7 genes at least		19(P450-2c)
10q25-q26	IFNAI1, RNM561	P	Interferon-inducible mRNA 561	14769			
10q25.3	GOT1	C	Glutamate oxaloacetate transaminase, soluble	13818	10q24.3 and 26.1 = conflicting localizations		19(Got-1)
10q25.3	PGAMA, PGAM1	P	Phosphoglycerate mutase A	17225			19(Pgam-1)
10q26	OAT	C	Ornithine aminotransferase	25887	pseudogene at Xp11.2	Gyrate atrophy of choroid and retina (1)	7(Oat)
Chr.10	ATPM, OMR	P	Mitochondrial ATPase (Oligomycin resistance)	16436			
Chr.10	CDC2	P	Cell cycle controller, CDC2	11694			
Chr.10	CYP2E	P	Cytochrome P450, family II, subfamily E	12404			
Chr.10	CYP17, P450C17	P	Steroid 17-alpha-hydroxylase / 17,20 lyase	20211	at least 2 genes	Adrenal hyperplasia V (1)	
Chr.10	FUSE	P	Polykaryocytosis inducer	17475			
Chr.10	GSAS	P	Glutamate-gamma-semialdehyde synthetase	13825	GOT1 and GSAS in same pathway		
Chr.10	HEP10	P	Hepatic protein 10	14239			
Chr.10	M130	P	External membrane protein-130	13371			
Chr.10	NEUG	P	Glycoprotein neuraminidase; sialidosis	25655	see 6p	?Sialidosis (1)	
Chr.10	PROA	P	Proline(-) auxotroph, complementation of	17677			
Chr.10	RBP4	P	Retinol binding protein, plasma	18025		Retinol binding protein, deficiency of (1)	
Chr.10	SAP2	P	Sphingolipid activator protein-2	18291			

In addition: 2 antigens, 2 O'Farrell protein spots and 1 pseudogene (HGM9) and 20 anonymous DNA segments (HGML).

Chromosome No. 11

11pter-p15.5	RMS	P	Rhabdomyosarcoma	26821		Rhabdomyosarcoma (2)	
11pter-p15.4	BWCR, BWS, WBS	C	Beckwith-Wiedemann syndrome	13065	partial trisomy	Beckwith-Wiedemann syndrome (2)	
11pter-p12	SAA	C	Serum amyloid A	10475		?Susceptibility to amyloid in FMF, 24910 (1)	7(Saa)
11p15.5	TYH, TH	C	Tyrosine hydroxylase	19129	distal to HRAS1		7(Th)
11p15.5	HRAS1, RASH1	C	Oncogene HRAS1, Harvey rat sarcoma-1	19002	pseudogene HRAS2 on X		7(Hras1)
11p15.5	INS	C	Insulin	17673	5'--INS-12.6kb-IGF2--3'; cen-HBBC-10cM-INS-2cM-HRAS1-3cM-TH	Diabetes mellitus, rare form (1); MODY, 12585 (3)	6(Ins-1); 7(Ins-2)
11p15.5	MAFD1, MD1	P	Manic-depressive illness (major affective disorder 1)	12548	linked to HRAS, INS; in some families, not linked	Manic-depressive illness (2)	
11p15.5	IGF2	C	Insulin-like growth factor II, or somatomedin A	14747	11p14.1 = conflicting localization; separate gene for variant, 14741		
11p15.5	NAGC, HBBC	C	NON-ALPHA GLOBIN CLUSTER (HEMOGLOBIN BETA CLUSTER)	14190-14225	11p12.08-p12.05 = conflicting localization; cen-5'-HBE-3'--////-5'-HBB-3'		
11p15.5	HBB	C	Hemoglobin beta	14190		Sickle cell anemia (1); Thalassemias, beta- (1); Methemoglobinemias, beta- (1); Erythremias, beta- (1); Heinz body anemias, beta- (1); HPFH, deletion type (1)	7(Hbb)
11p15.5	HBD	C	Hemoglobin delta	14200			
11p15.5	HBGR	C	Hb gamma regulator	14227		?Hereditary persistence of fetal hemoglobin (3)	
11p15.5	HBG1	C	Hemoglobin gamma 136 alanine	14220		HPFH, nondeletion type A (1)	
11p15.5	HBG2	C	Hemoglobin gamma 136 glycine	14225		HPFH, nondeletion type G (1)	
11p15.5	HBE	C	Hemoglobin epsilon	14210			
11p15.5-p15.4	HPX	C	Hemopexin	14229			
11p15.4	CALCA, CALC1	C	Calcitonin/calcitonin gene related peptide, alpha polypeptide	11413			7(Calc)
11p15	CTSD, CPSD	P	Cathepsin D	11684			
11p15	PTH	C	Parathyroid hormone	16845	ca.9cM distal to CALC1	?Hypoparathyroidism, familial (1)	7(Pth)
11p15	HPFH, FCP, HHPF	L	F-cell production	14247	ca.15cM from HBB; ?on Xq28	Heterocellular hereditary persistence of fetal hemoglobin (2)	
11p15	MER2	P	Red blood cell antigen MER2	17962			
11p15	RRM1	P	Ribonucleotide reductase, M1 subunit	18041			

Location	*Symbol*	*Status*	*Title*	*MIM #*	*Comments*	*Disorder*	*Mouse*
11p15	TCL2	P	T-cell leukemia/lymphoma-2	15139	involved in t(11;14)(p15;q11.2); between HRAS1 and INS/IGF2	Leukemia, acute T-cell (2)	
11p15-p14	LDHA	C	Lactate dehydrogenase A	15000		Exertional myoglobinuria due to deficiency of LDH-A (1)	7(Ldh-1)
?11p15-p14	LDHC	P	Lactate dehydrogenase C	15015	closely linked to LDHB in other species; in man syntenic with LDHA; ?close to LDHA		
11p15-p13	TRPH	P	Tryptophan hydroxylase	19106			
11p14.2-p12	CALCB, CALC2	C	Calcitonin gene related peptide beta	11416			
11p14-p13	HBVS1, HBVIS	C	Hepatitis B virus integration site-1	11455		Liver cell carcinoma (1)	
11p13	FSHB	C	Follicle stimulating hormone, beta polypeptide	13653	distal to AN2	?Male infertility, familial (1)	2(Fshb)
11p13	AN2	C	Aniridia-2	10621		Aniridia-2 (2)	
11p13	WAGR	C	Wilms tumor/aniridia/ gonadoblastoma/retardation complex	19407	actually clump of pter-FSHB-AN2-WT-CAT	Wilms tumor (2); Aniridia of WAGR syndrome (2); Gonadoblastoma (2); Mental retardation of WAGR (2)	
11p13	CAT	C	Catalase	11550	cen-CAT-WT-AN-pter	Acatalasemia (1)	2(Cas-1)
11p12-p11	ACP2	C	Acid phosphatase-2	17165		?Lysosomal acid phosphatase deficiency (1)	2(Acp-2)
11p11.2-q13	CINH, C1I, HANE	C	C1 inhibitor	10610		Angioedema, hereditary (1)	
11p11-q12	F2	C	Prothrombin (clotting factor II)	17693		Hypoprothrombinemia (1); Dysprothrombinemia (1)	
11p	ADCC	P	Adrenocortical carcinoma	20230		Adrenocortical carcinoma (2)	
11p	MDU3, INLU	P	Lutheran inhibitor, dominant (monoclonal antibody A3D8)	11115			
11q	NACAE, MDU1	C	Sodium-calcium exchanger	15807			
11q	PC	P	Pyruvate carboxylase	26615		Pyruvate carboxylase deficiency (1)	
11q11-q23	CLG, EBR1, CLGN	C	Collagenase (recessive epidermolysis bullosa dystrophica)	22660		Epidermolysis bullosa dystrophica, recessive (3)	
11q12.1-q13.5	FNL2	P	Fibronectin-like-2	13561			
11q13	INT2	P	Oncogene INT2	16495			7(Int-2)
11q13	PGA	C	PEPSINOGEN A CLUSTER	16970	about 20cM from CAT		
11q13	PGA3	C	Pepsinogen A3	16971			
11q13	PGA4	C	Pepsinogen A4	16972			
11q13	PGA5	C	Pepsinogen A5	16973	pter-5'HRAS--5'INS--cen		
11q13	SEA	P	Oncogene SEA (S13 avian erythroblastosis)	16511			
11q13-q14	BKMA	P	BKM, banded krait minor satellite, DNA	see 10978	related to heterogametic sex		
11q13-q22	ESA4	C	Esterase-A4	13322			9(Es-17)
11q13-q22	GST3	C	Glutathione S-transferase-3	13837	formerly called GST1		9(Gsta)
11q13-qter	MEN1	C	Multiple endocrine neoplasia-1	13110	linked to PYGM		

11q13-qter	PYGM, MGP	P	Muscle glycogen phosphorylase	23260		McArdle disease (1)	
11q13-qter	GANAB	P	Neutral alpha-glucosidase AB	10416			
11q13.3	BCL1	C	B-cell leukemia-1; chronic lymphocytic leukemia	15140	t(11;14)--(q13.3;q32.3)	Leukemia/lymphoma, B-cell, 1 (2)	
11q14-q21	TYR	P	Tyrosinase	20310		Albinism	7(c)
11q22	PGR	C	Progesterone receptor	26408	11q13 = earlier regionalization		
11q22-qter	ANC	L	Anal canal carcinoma	10558	3p22 also deleted	Anal canal carcinoma (2)	
11q22.3	THY1	C	Thy-1 T-cell antigen	18823	11q23 = conflicting localization		9(Thy-1)
11q23	CD3D, CD3, T3D	C	T3 T-cell antigen receptor, delta polypeptide	18679	3 CD3 genes in 300kb		9(T3d)
11q23	CD3G	C	T3 T-cell antigen receptor, gamma polypeptide	18674			9(T3g)
11q23	NCAM	P	Neural cell adhesion molecule	11693	defective in "staggerer," a form of cerebellar ataxia in mice		9(Ncam)
11q23	CD3E, T3E	P	T3 T-cell antigen receptor, epsilon polypeptide	18683			9(T3e)
11q23-qter	APOLP1	C	APOLIPOPROTEIN CLUSTER I	10768, 10772, 10769	11q13 = earlier assignment		
11q23-qter	APOA1	C	Apolipoprotein A-I	10768		ApoA-I and apoC-III deficiency, combined (1); Hypertriglyceridemia, 1 form (1); Hypoalphalipoproteinemia (1); Amyloidosis, Iowa form 10510 (1)	9(Apl-1)
11q23-qter	APOC3	C	Apolipoprotein C-III	10772	2.6kb 3' to APOA1		
11q23-qter	APOA4	C	Apolipoprotein A-IV	10769	12 kb 3' to APOA1		
11q23.1	EBVM1	P	Epstein-Barr virus modification site-1	13286			
11q23.2-qter	PBGD, UPS	C	Porphobilinogen deaminase (uroporphyrinogen I synthase)	17600		Porphyria, acute intermittent (1)	9(Ups)
11q24	ETS1	C	Oncogene ETS-1	16472	shown by HSR		9(Ets-1)
11q24-q25	SRPR	P	Signal recognition particle receptor	18218			
Chr.11	ADX	P	Adrenodoxin	10326	pseudogene on 20		
Chr.11	CD5, LEU1	P	Lymphocyte antigen CD5	15334			19(Ly-1)
Chr.11	FTH	P	Ferritin, heavy chain	13477			
Chr.11	GLAU1	L	Congenital glaucoma-1	231[illegible]		Glaucoma, congenital (2)	
Chr.11	HV1S	P	Herpes virus sensitivity	14245	see chr. 3		
Chr.11	LEU7, HNK1	P	Leu-7 antigen of natural killer lymphocytes, HNK-1	15129			
Chr.11	OIAS	I	2',5'-oligoisoadenylate synthetase	16435	see chr.12		
Chr.11	STMY	P	Stromelysin	18525			

In addition: 22 surface antigens, most defined by monoclonals, 1 O'Farrell protein spot, 2 'like' genes and 4 pseudogenes (HGM9) and 278 anonymous DNA segments (HGML). 11p physical map (HGM9): Cen--CAT--FSHB--LDHA--CALC1--PTH--HBBC--INS--HRAS1--pter. Genetic map (HGM9): Cen--CAT--18%--CALC1--8%--PTH--12%--HBBC--10%--INS--30%--HRAS1--pter; ?linkage heterogeneity (polymorphism) raised by some discrepant results. Map of apolipoprotein cluster I: ?11cen or 11qter 5'--APOA1--3'--(2.6kb)--3'--APOC3-5'--(4.5kb)--5'--APOA4--3'--?11cen or 11qter.

Location	Symbol	Status	Title	MIM #	Comments	Disorder	Mouse
Chromosome No. 12							
12pter-p12	F8VWF, VWF	C	von Willebrand factor	19340		von Willebrand disease (1)	
12pter-p12	CD4, T4, LEU3	C	CD4	18694	CD = 'cluster of differentiation' = nomenclature of leukocyte differentiation antigens		
12pter-q12	CD9, MIC3	C	Antigen CD9 identified by monoclonal antibodies 602-29, BA-2, et al.	14303			
12pter-q12	BCT1	C	Branched chain amino acid transaminase-1	11352		?Hyperleucinemia-isoleucinemia or hypervalinemia (1)	
12p13.31-p13.1	GAPD	C	Glyceraldehyde-3-phosphate dehydrogenase	13840	6 loci in 2 subfamilies		6(Gapd)
12p13.2	SPC, PRP	P	SALIVARY PROLINE-RICH PROTEIN COMPLEX	16871-16888	6 loci in 2 subfamilies; in 500 kb: PRH1, PRH2, PRB1, PRB2, PRB3, PRB4		8(Prp)
12p13.2	G1, PRB3	C	Parotid salivary glycoprotein	16884	= PRB3 in basic subfamily		
12p13.2	PE	P	Salivary protein Pe	18097			
12p13.2	PM	C	Parotid middle band protein	16878	linked to PRH1, PRH2, G1		
12p13.2	PRH1	C	Proline-rich acidic protein, HaeIII type, 1	16873	PA, DB, PIF alleles		
12p13.2	PRH2, PR	C	Proline-rich acidic protein, HaeIII type, 2	16879			
12p13.2	PS	C	Parotid size variant	16881			
12p13.2	PB	C	Parotid basic protein	16875			
12p13.2	PPB	C	Post-parotid basic protein	16876			
12p13.2	CON1	C	CON1	16887	close to PS; ?order: PS-PR-PM-G1-DB		
12p13.2	CON2	C	CON2	16888	close to PM		
12p13.2	PO	P	Salivary protein Po	18099	probably closely linked to CON2		
12p13.2	PCS, PC	P	Parotid proline-rich protein Pc	16871	linked to PS		
12p13	TPI1, TPI	C	Triosephosphate isomerase	19045		Hemolytic anemia due to triosephosphate isomerase deficiency (1)	6(Tpi-1)
12p13	C1R	C	Complement component C1r	21695		C1r/C1s deficiency, combined (1)	
12p13	C1S	C	Complement component C1s	12058		C1r/C1s deficiency, combined (1)	
12p12.2-p12.1	LDHB	C	Lactate dehydrogenase B	15010			6(Ldh-2)
12p12.1	KRAS2, RASK2	C	Oncogene Kras-2, Kirsten rat sarcoma virus	19007		Colorectal adenoma (1); Colorectal cancer (1)	6(Kras-2)
12p11-qter	CS	C	Citrate synthase, mitochondrial	11895			10(Cs)
12p11-qter	ENO2	C	Enolase-2	13136			
12p	KAR	L	Aromatic alpha-keto acid reductase	10792	?same as MDH1		

12p	ELA1	C	Elastase-1	13012	on proximal 12p		15(Ela-1)
12cen-q14	MIP	P	Major intrinsic protein of lens fiber	15405			
12q11-q21	KRTA	L	Keratin, acid or alpha-	13935	close to Hox-3 in mouse		15(Krta)
12q12-q13	INT1	P	Oncogene INT1, murine mammary cancer virus	16482			15(Int-1)
12q12-q14	SHMT, GLYA	C	Serine hydroxymethyltransferase	13845	glycine A auxotroph		
12q13	HOX3	C	Homeo box-3	14297	probably 1 gene		15(Hox-3)
12q13	LALBA	P	Lactalbumin, alpha	14975			
12q13-q14	BABL, LIPO	C	Lipoma (breakpoint in benign lipoma)	15190	?recombination 12q13 and 16p11 for myxoid liposarcoma	Lipoma (2)	
12q13-q14.3	GLI	P	Glioma oncogene GLI	13780		Glioma (3)	
12q13-q21	NKNB	P	Neurokinin B	16233			
12q13.1-q13.3	COL2A1	C	Collagen II, alpha-1 chain	12014	conflicting: 12q14.3	Stickler syndrome (3); ?Spondyloepiphyseal dysplasia congenita (1); ?Kniest dysplasia (1); ?Langer-Saldino achondrogenesis (1); ?Osteoarthrosis, precocious (3)	
12q21	PEPB	C	Peptidase B	16990			10(Pep-2)
12q22-q24.1	IGF1	C	Insulin-like growth factor I, or somatomedin C	14744			
12q22-qter	ACADS	P	Acyl-CoA dehydrogenase, short chain	20147		Acyl-CoA dehydrogenase, short chain, deficiency of (1)	
12q24	ALDH2	C	Aldehyde dehydrogenase, mitochondrial	10065		Acute alcohol intolerance (1); ?Fetal alcohol syndrome (1)	4(Aldh-2)
12q24.1	IFNG, IFI, IFG	C	Interferon, gamma or immune type	14757	3 introns; IFF, IFL none	Interferon, immune, deficiency (1)	10(Ifg)
12q24.1	PAH, PKU1	C	Phenylalanine hydroxylase	26160		Phenylketonuria (3); [Hyperphenylalaninemia, mild] (3)	10(Pah)
Chr.12	A2M	C	Alpha-2-macroglobulin	10395			
Chr.12	ATP2B	P	ATPase, CA++ dependent, slow twitch/cardiac muscle	10874		?Brody myopathy (1)	
Chr.12	CYK4	P	Cytokeratin 4	12394			
Chr.12	GNAIH	P	Guanine nucleotide binding protein, alpha inhibiting, polypeptide h	13918			
Chr.12	GPD1	P	Alpha-glycerophosphate dehydrogenase; glycerol-3-phosphate dehydrogenase	13842			15(Gdc-1)
Chr.12	MPRD	P	Mannose 6-phosphate receptor, cation-dependent	15454			
Chr.12	MTRNS, MARS, METRS	P	Methioninyl-tRNA synthetase	15656			
Chr.12	OIAS	I	2',5'-oligoisoadenylate synthetase	16435	see chr.11		
Chr.12	PFKX	P	Phosphofructokinase X	17188			15(Pfkx)
Chr.12	PPLA2	P	Phospholipase A2, pancreatic	17241			

In addition: 7 surface antigens, most defined by monoclonals, 3 O'Farrell protein spots and 1 pseudogene (HGM9) and 29 anonymous DNA segments (HGML). Probable order: 12pter--TPI1--GAPD--LDHB--ENO2--cen--SHMT--PEPB--12qter

Location	Symbol	Status	Title	MIM #	Comments	Disorder	Mouse
Chromosome No. 13							
13p12	RNR1	C	Ribosomal RNA	18045			
13q12	FRT, FLT	P	Oncogene FRT (FMS-related tyrosine kinase)	16507			
13q14	IGEL	L	Immunoglobulin E level	14705	very close to ESD		
13q14	WND, WD	C	Wilson disease	27790	vs. ESD, max. lod = 5.49, theta = 0.03	Wilson disease (2)	
13q14	XRS	L	X-ray sensitivity	19437			
13q14-q31	LSD	L	Letterer-Siwe disease	24640		?Letterer-Siwe disease (2)	
13q14-q34	ERCC5	P	Excision-repair, complementing defective, in Chinese hamster, number 5	13353			
13q14.1	RB1	C	Retinoblastoma-1	18020		Retinoblastoma (2)	
13q14.1	OSRC	P	Osteosarcoma	25950	probably same locus as retinoblastoma	Osteosarcoma, retinoblastoma-related (2)	
13q14.1-q14.3	LCP1	P	Lymphocyte cytosolic protein-1	15343			
13q14.11	ESD, FGH	C	Esterase D; S-formylglutathione hydrolase	13328	proximal to RB1, WND		14(Es-10)
13q21-q31	ATP1AL2	P	Sodium-potassium-ATPase, alpha-polypeptide-like	18236			
13q34	CBT1	L	Carotid body tumor-1	16800	?linked to factors VII and X		
13q34	DJS	L	Dubin-Johnson syndrome	23750	with factor VII deficiency	?Dubin-Johnson syndrome (2)	
13q34	F7	C	Clotting factor VII	22750		Factor VII deficiency (1)	
13q34	F10	C	Clotting factor X	22760		Factor X deficiency (1)	
13q34	COL4A1	C	Collagen IV, alpha-1 chain	12013			
13q34	COL4A2	C	Collagen IV, alpha-2 chain	12009			
13q34	HHHS	L	Hyperornithinemia-hyperammonemia-homocitrullinemia syndrome	23897	associated with deficiency of factors VII and X in 3 unrelated cases	?HHH syndrome (2)	
Chr.13	BRCD, DBC, BCDS1	P	Breast cancer, ductal, suppressor-1	21141		Breast cancer, ductal (2)	
Chr.13	PCCA	P	Propionyl CoA carboxylase, alpha subunit	23200		Propionicacidemia, type I or pccA type (1)	
Chr.13	UVDR, ERCM2	P	UV-damage, excision repair of (XP complementation group I)	19206	also called UV-135	?Xeroderma pigmentosum, one type (1)	

In addition: 1 O'Farrell protein spot, 1 'like' gene and 2 pseudogenes (HGM9) and 46 anonymous DNA segments (HGML).

Chromosome No. 14

14p12	RNR2	C	Ribosomal RNA	18045			
14q11.2	TCRA	C	T-cell antigen receptor, alpha subunit	18688	cen--V-C--ter	Leukemia/lymphoma, T-cell (3)	14(Tcra)
14q13.1	NP	C	Nucleoside phosphorylase	16405		Nucleoside phosphorylase deficiency, immunodeficiency due to (2)	14(Np-1,2)
14q21-q31	FOS	C	Oncogene FOS (FBJ murine osteosarcoma virus)	16481			12(Fos)
14q21-qter	WARS	C	Tryptophanyl-tRNA synthetase	19105			
14q22-qter	ADEB	P	Phosphoribosylformylglycinamidine synthetase (adenine (-)B auxotroph)	see 17246	?separate from ADEE locus		
14q22-qter	PGFT, ADEE	P	5,10-methenyltetrahydrofolate cyclohydrolase (adenine(-)E auxotroph)	17246			
14q23-q24.2	HOS	L	Holt-Oram syndrome	14290		?Holt-Oram syndrome (2)	
14q24	CAP	L	Cataract, anterior polar	11565	see 2p25	?Cataract, anterior polar (2)	
14q32	CKBB	C	Creatine kinase, brain type	12328	sequence also on 16		
14q32	CKBE	P	Creatine kinase, brain type, ectopic expression of	12327	linked to IGH, PI; ?same locus as CKBB	[Creatine kinase, brain type, ectopic expression of] (2)	
14q32	SPTB, SPH1	C	Beta-spectrin (spherocytosis-1)	18287		Elliptocytosis-3 (2); Spherocytosis-1 (3)	12(Sptb)
14q32.1	AACT	P	Alpha-1-antichymotrypsin	10728	gene cluster with PI	?Alpha-1-antichymotrypsin deficiency (1)	
14q32.1	PI, AAT	C	Protease inhibitor (alpha-1-antitrypsin)	10740		Emphysema-cirrhosis (1); Hemorrhagic diathesis due to 'antithrombin' Pittsburgh (1)	12(Aat)
14q32.3	AKT1	C	Oncogene AKT1	16473	proximal to IGH; ?identical to TCL1)		
14q32.3	TCL1	P	T-cell leukemia-1	18696			
14q32.33	IGH	C	IMMUNOGLOBULIN HEAVY CHAIN GENE CLUSTER	14690-14718		?Combined variable hypogammaglobulinemia (1)	12(Igh)
14q32.33	IGHV	C	V (variable) region of heavy chains	14707	ca. 250 genes; orientation: cen-PI-D14S1-IGH-IGHV--qter; 3' centromeric, 5' telomeric; IgM telomeric to IgG		
14q32.33	IGD1	C	D (diversity) region of heavy chains	14691	many genes; D = diversity		
14q32.33	IGHJ	C	J (joining) region of heavy chains	14701	more than 4 genes; J = joining		
14q32.33	IGHM, MU	C	Constant region of heavy chain of IgM	14702			
14q32.33	IGHD	C	Constant region of heavy chain of IgD	14717			
14q32.33	IGHG2	C	Constant region of heavy chain of IgG2	14711	5'-G2-17kb-G4-3'; closeness of IGG3 and IGG1 known from Lepore-like myeloma protein		
14q32.33	IGHG4	C	Constant region of heavy chain of IgG4	14713			

Location	Symbol	Status	Title	MIM #	Comments	Disorder	Mouse
14q32.33	IGHG3	C	Constant region of heavy chain of IgG3	14712			
14q32.33	IGHG1	C	Constant region of heavy chain of IgG1	14710			
14q32.33	IGHE	C	Constant region of heavy chain of IgE	14718			
14q32.33	IGHEP1	C	Constant region of heavy chain of IgEP1	14716	IGEP2 on chr. 9; 14721		
14q32.33	IGHA1	C	Constant region of heavy chain of IgA1	14690			
14q32.33	IGHA2	C	Constant region of heavy chain of IgA2	14700			
Chr.14	CHGA	P	Chromogranin A (parathyroid secretory protein 1)	11891			
Chr.14	ESAT	P	Esterase activator	13325			
Chr.14	K12T	P	Temperature sensitivity complementation, K12	18731			
Chr.14	LCH	C	Lentil agglutinin binding	15102			
Chr.14	M195	P	External membrane protein-195	13374			
Chr.14	MYHCA	C	Myosin, cardiac heavy chain, alpha	16071			?11(Myh)
Chr.14	MYHCB	P	Myosin, cardiac heavy chain, beta	16076			
Chr.14	PYGL, PPYL	P	Liver glycogen phosphorylase	23270		Hers disease, or glycogen storage disease VI (1)	
Chr.14	RIB1	L	Pancreatic ribonuclease	18044	?close to TCRA and NP		14(Rib-1)

In addition: 1 antigen defined by monoclonal, 3 'like' genes and 3 pseudogenes (HGM9) and 17 anonymous DNA segments (HGML). A Tunisian deletion indicates order: 5'--G3--G1--psi E1--A1--G2--G4--E--A2--3' (Lefranc et al., Nature 300: 760, 1982). 5'--E2--E1--E3--3' (Nishida et al., PNAS 79: 3833, 1982; E3 = ?pseudogene). Following information from J. J. Johnson and L. L. Cavalli-Sforza Stanford Univ., Nov., 1983: 5'(qter)--V--(7cM)--D--J--8kb--mu--5kb--delta--?--gamma-3--26kb--gamma-1--19kb--pseudo-epsilon-1(pseudo-epsilon-2 on chr. 9)--13kb--alpha--1--?--gamma-2--18kb--gamma-4--23kb--epsilon--10kb--alpha-2--3'(centromere). Pseudo-gamma between alpha-1 and gamma-2 (Bech-Hansen et al., PNAS 80:6952, 1983; Migone et al., PNAS 81: 5811, 1984).

Chromosome No. 15

Location	Symbol	Status	Title	MIM #	Comments	Disorder	Mouse
15p12	RNR3	C	Ribosomal RNA	18045			
15p12-q21	SORD	C	Sorbitol dehydrogenase	18250			2(Sdh-1)
15q11	DLX1	L	Dyslexia-1	12770	?near centromere; lod under 3.0 with HGM8 data	Dyslexia-1 (2)	
15q11	F11	L	Clotting factor XI	26490		?Factor XI deficiency (1)	
15q11	PWCR, PWS	C	Prader-Willi syndrome	17627		Prader-Willi syndrome (2)	
15q11-q12	IGD2	P	Immunoglobulin heavy chain diversity region-2	14699	?functional		
15q11-q12	MIC7	P	Attached cell antigen 28.3.7	10899			
15q11-q13	ITO	L	Hypomelanosis of Ito	14615	see chr.9	?Hypomelanosis of Ito (2)	
15q11-q13	MANA	C	Alpha-mannosidase-A, cytoplasmic	15458			
15q11-qter	ACTC	P	Actin, cardiac alpha	10254			17(Actc)
15q11-qter	CVS, HCVS	P	Coronavirus 229E sensitivity	12246			
15q13-q15	B2MR	C	Beta-2-microglobulin regulator	10971			
15q14-q15	IVD	P	Isovaleryl CoA dehydrogenase	24350		Isovalericacidemia (1)	
15q15-q21	CHR39B	P	Cholesterol repressible protein 39B	11848			
15q21	LIPH, HL	C	Hepatic lipase	15167		Hepatic lipase deficiency (1)	
15q21-q22	B2M	C	Beta-2-microglobulin	10970	on 15q+ in APL	Hemodialysis-related amyloidosis (1)	2(B2m)
15q21-q22	LPC2D	P	Lipocortin IId	15174			
15q21-qter	IDH2	C	Isocitrate dehydrogenase, mitochondrial	14765			7(Idh-2)
15q21.1	CYP19, ARO	P	Cytochrome P450 aromatization of androgen (aromatase)	10791		?Gynecomastia, familial, due to increased aromatase activity (1)	

15q22-q25.1	HEXA, TSD	C	Beta-hexosaminidase A, alpha chain	27280	on 15q+ in APL	Tay-Sachs disease (1); GM2-gangliosidosis, juvenile, adult (1); [Hex A pseudodeficiency] (1)	
15q22-qter	MPI	C	Mannosephosphate isomerase	15455			9(Mpi-1)
15q22-qter	CYP1A1, CYP1, P450C1	P	Dioxin-inducible P1-450 (TCDD-inducible P1-450)	10833	CYP2 = earlier symbol		9(P450-1)
15q22-qter	CYP1A2	P	Dioxin-inducible P3-450	12406	both CYP1 genes close to MPI in rodents		9(P450-1)
15q22-qter	PK3, PKM2	C	Pyruvate kinase-3	17905			9(Pk-3)
15q23-q25	ETFA, GA2	P	Electron transfer flavoprotein, alpha subunit	23168		Glutaricaciduria, type II (1)	
15q24-q25	CTSH	P	Cathepsin H	11682			
15q25-q26	FES	C	Oncogene FES, feline sarcoma virus	19003	?15q26; far from breakpoint in acute promyelocyte leukemia:t(15;17)(q22;q21)		7(Fes)
15q25-q26	FUR	C	Furin membrane associated receptor protein	13695	less than 1.1kb 5' to FES		
15q25-q26	IGF1R	P	Insulin-like growth factor-1 receptor	14737	?relation to FES		
15q25-q26	CD13, GP150	P	GP150,95 myeloid membrane antigen, alpha subunit	15151			
?Chr.15	ACHRA, ACHRMA	L	Muscle nicotinic acetylcholine receptor, alpha subunit	10069	linked to Actc in mouse		17(?Achr-?)
Chr.15	CSPG1	P	Chondroitin sulfate proteoglycan core protein	15576			
Chr.15	CYP11A, P450SCC, P450C11A1	P	P450 side chain cleavage enzyme (20,22 desmolase)	20171		Lipoid adrenal hyperplasia, congenital (1)	
Chr.15	GANC	P	Neutral alpha-glucosidase C	10418			

In addition: 5 surface antigens, most defined by monoclonals, 2 O'Farrell protein spots, and 1 pseudogene (HGM9) and 24 anonymous DNA segments (HGML). Hemodialysis-related amyloidosis is presumably not genetic in a specific sense.

Chromosome No. 16

16p13.33-p13.11	AGC, HBAC	C	ALPHA GLOBIN GENE CLUSTER	14180, 14185, 14231	order: cen-APKD-HBZ1--HBA1-3'HVR-pter; distal to PGP		
16p13.33-p13.11	HBA1, HBA2	C	Hemoglobin alpha-1, hemoglobin alpha-2	14180, 14185	1, 2, or 3 loci; 5'-zeta-pseudozeta-pseudoalpha-alpha-2-alpha-1-3'	Thalassemias, alpha- (1); Methemoglobinemias, alpha- (1); Erythremias, alpha- (1); Heinz body anemias, alpha- (1)	11(Hba)
16p13.33-p13.11	HBQ1	P	Hemoglobin theta-1	14224			
16p13.33-p13.11	HBZ1	C	Hemoglobin zeta pseudogene (formerly zeta-1)	see 14231			
16p13.33-p13.11	HBZ2	C	Hemoglobin zeta (formerly zeta-2)	14231			
16p13.33-p13.11	HBHR	L	Hb H mental retardation syndrome	14175		Hb H mental retardation syndrome (2)	
16p13.31-p13.12	PGP	C	Phosphoglycolate phosphatase	17228	no recombination with PKD1		
16p13.31-p13.12	PKD1, APKD	C	Adult polycystic kidney disease	17390	tightly linked to PGP	Polycystic kidney disease (2)	
16p13	HAGH, GLO2	C	Glyoxalase II; hydroxyacyl glutathione hydrolase	13876		[Glyoxalase II deficiency] (1)	

Location	Symbol	Status	Title	MIM #	Comments	Disorder	Mouse
16p12-q11.1	PKCB	P	Protein kinase C, beta form	17697			
16p11-q23	CHE2	P	Pseudocholinesterase-2	17750			
16cen-q22	GOT2	C	Glutamate oxaloacetic transaminase, mitochondrial	13815	on 16q by homology to mouse		8(Got-2)
16q11-q24	UVO	P	Uvomorulin	19209			8(?)
16q12-q22	DIA4	C	Diaphorase-4	12586			
16q21	CETP	P	Cholesterol ester transfer protein, plasma	11847			
16q22	MT1	C	METALLOTHIONEIN I CLUSTER	15635	multiple genes		8(Mt-1)
16q22	MT2	C	METALLOTHIONEIN II CLUSTER	15636	single gene		8(Mt-2)
16q22-q24	ALDOA, ALDA	C	Aldolase A	10385		?Aldolase A deficiency (1)	
16q22.1	CA4	P	Carbonic anhydrase IV	11476	not proved to be expressed		
16q22.1	CC	L	Congenital cataract	11670	?linked to HP; cataract with t(3;4)(p26.2;p15)	?Cataract, congenital (2)	
16q22.1	HP	C	Haptoglobin	14010	just distal to fra16q22.1		8(Hp)
16q22.1	HPR	C	Haptoglobin-related locus	14021	3' to HP; multiple tandem genes in blacks		
16q22.1	LCAT	C	Lecithin-cholesterol acyltransferase	24590	very close to HP	Norum disease (3)	
16q22.1-q22.3	TAT	C	Tyrosine aminotransferase, cytosolic	27660		Tyrosinemia, type II (1)	8(Tat-1)
16q22.2	CTRB	C	Chymotrypsinogen B	11889	HP-7cM-TAT-9cM-CTRB		8(Ctrb)
16q24	APRT	C	Adenine phosphoribosyltransferase	10260	distal to GOT2, DIA4; earlier mapped to 16q22.2-q22.3	Urolithiasis, 2,8-dihydroxyadenine (1)	8(Aprt)
Chr.16	ATP2A	P	ATPase, Ca++ transporting, fast-twitch, muscle	10873			
Chr.16	CD11A, LFA1A	C	Lymphocyte function associated antigen-1, alpha subunit	15337			
Chr.16	CRYA2	L	Crystallin, alpha-B	12359			
Chr.16	CTH	P	Cystathionase	21950		[Cystathioninuria] (1)	
Chr.16	DIPI, VDI	P	Vesicular stomatitis virus defective interfering particle repressor	12526			
Chr.16	ERCC4	P	Excision-repair, complementing defective, in Chinese hamster, number 4	13352			
Chr.16	ESB3	P	Esterase-B3	13329			
Chr.16	GCF2	P	Growth rate controlling factor-2	13923			
Chr.16	GRLL	P	Glucocorticoid receptor, lymphocyte, like	13806			
Chr.16	LIPB	P	Lysosomal acid lipase-B	24798			
Chr.16	MAC1A, CR3A	P	Macrophage antigen-1, Mac-1, alpha subunit	12098	?in same restriction fragment as LFA1A		
Chr.16	NHCP1	P	Nonhistone chromosomal protein-1	11887			
Chr.16	PRM1	P	Protamine 1	18288			
Chr.16	TK2	P	Thymidine kinase, mitochondrial	18825			

In addition: 1 O'Farrell protein spot, 4 'like' genes, and 3 pseudogenes (HGM9) and 90 anonymous DNA segments (HGML). Order: pter--PGP--0.25--16qh--0.17--GOT2--0.08--HP--qter (Jeremiah et al., Ann. Hum. Genet. 46: 145, 1982).

Chromosome No. 17

17p13.3	MDCR, MDLS, MDS	C	Miller-Dieker lissencephaly syndrome	24720		Miller-Dieker lissencephaly syndrome (2)	
17p13.105-p12	POLR2, RPOL2	C	RNA polymerase II, large subunit	18066			11(Rpol-2)
17p13.105-p12	TP53	C	Tumor protein p53	19117			11(Trp53)
17p13	MYH1	C	MYOSIN, HEAVY CHAIN CLUSTER	16073	a myosin gene cluster also on 7		11(Myh)
17p13	MYHSA1	C	Myosin heavy chain, adult-1	16073			
17p13	MYHSA2	C	Myosin heavy chain, adult-2	16074	17p13.105-p12		
17p13	MYHSE1	C	Myosin heavy chain, embryonic-1	16072			
17p11.2	SMCR	C	Smith-Magenis syndrome chromosome region	18229			
17p11.1-qter	PNP, PPY	P	Pancreatic polypeptide	16778			
?17p	ACHRB, ACHRMB	L	Muscle nicotinic acetylcholine receptor, beta subunit	10071	linked to Myh on mouse 11		11(?Achr-?)
17p	CRC	P	Colorectal cancer	11450		Colorectal cancer (1)	
17p	CRC17	P	Colorectal cancer-related sequence-17	12046		Colorectal cancer (1)	
17cen-q22	NF1, VRNF	C	Neurofibromatosis, von Recklinghausen type	16220		Neurofibromatosis, von Recklinghausen (2)	
17cen-qter	GAS	C	Gastrin	13725			
17q	UMPH2	P	Uridine 5'-monophosphate phosphohydrolase-2; uridine monophosphatase-2	19172			11(Umph-2)
17q11-q21	KRTB, CYK13	P	Keratin, basic or beta- (cytokeratin 13)	14803	tightly linked to Hox-2 in mouse		11(Krtb)
17q11-q22	HOX2, HU2	C	Homeo box-2	14296	5 or 6 genes		11(Hox-2)
17q11.2	ERBA1, THRA	C	Oncogene ERB-A1 (avian erythroblastic leukemia virus)	19012			11(Erba)
17q21	CRYB1	C	Crystallin, beta-B1	12361			
17q21	ERBB2	P	Oncogene ERB-B2	19015	(?same as NGL)		
17q21	GCSF, CSF3	C	Granulocyte colony-stimulating factor	13897	proximal to APL breakpoint		
17q21	MTBT1, MAPT1	P	Microtubule, beta, associated protein tau	15714	see 6p21		
17q21	RAR	P	Retinoic acid receptor	18024			
17q21-q22	NGFR	C	Nerve growth factor receptor	16201	distal to APL breakpoint, q21		
17q21-q22	NGL, NEU	P	Oncogene NGL (oncogene NEU, neuro- or glioblastoma derived)	16487			
17q21-q22	HER2, TKR1	P	Tyrosine kinase-type cell surface receptor	19131	?same as NGL		
17q21-q22	RNU2	C	U2 snRNA GENE CLUSTER	18069			
17q21.0-q22.0	A12M4	C	Adenovirus-12 chromosome modification site-17	10297			
17q21.0-q22.0	GALK	C	Galactokinase	23020	by CMGT, order = cen-GALK-TK1-COL1A1	Galactokinase deficiency (1)	11(Glk)
17q21.0-q22.0	GHC	C	GROWTH HORMONE/PLACENTAL LACTOGEN GENE CLUSTER	13925	17q22-q24		

Location	Symbol	Status	Title	MIM #	Comments	Disorder	Mouse
17q21.0-q22.0	GH1, GHN	C	Growth hormone, normal	13925	5'-GH1-CSHP1-CSH1-GH2-CSH2-3'	Isolated growth hormone deficiency, Illig type with absent GH and Kowarski type with bioinactive GH (3)	
17q21.0-q22.0	GH2, GHV	C	Growth hormone, variant	13924			
17q21.0-q22.0	CSHP1, CSL	C	Chorionic somatomammotropin pseudogene	see 15020			
17q21.0-q22.0	CSA, PL, CSH1	C	Chorionic somatomammotropin A	15020		[Placental lactogen deficiency] (1)	
17q21.0-q22.0	CSB, CSH2	C	Chorionic somatomammotropin B	11882	at 3' end		
17q21.0-q22.0	TK1	C	Thymidine kinase-1	18830	to chromosome 15 in APL; really in q23-qter		11(Tk-1)
17q21.1-q21.3	GP2B	C	Platelet glycoprotein IIb	27380		Glanzmann thrombasthenia (1)	
17q21.31-q22.05	COL1A1	C	Collagen I, alpha-1 chain	12015		Osteogenesis imperfecta, 2 or more clinical forms (3); Ehlers-Danlos syndrome, type VIIA1 (3); ?Marfan syndrome, atypical, 15470(1)	11(Cola-1)
17q22-q24	PKCA	P	Protein kinase C, alpha form	17696			11(Pkca)
17q23	GAA	C	Acid alpha-glucosidase	23230		Pompe disease (1); Acid-maltase deficiency, adult (1)	
17q23-q24	MPO	C	Myeloperoxidase	25460		Myeloperoxidase deficiency (1)	
17q23-q25	P4HB, PROHB	P	Prolyl-4-hydroxylase, beta subunit; disulfide isomerase	17679			
17q23-qter	PEPE	C	Peptidase E	17020			
Chr.17	ALDH3	P	Aldehyde dehydrogenase-3	10066			
Chr.17	ALDOC, ALDC	P	Aldolase C	10387			
Chr.17	ALPPL	P	Placental alkaline phosphatase-like gene	see 17180			
Chr.17	APOH	P	Apolipoprotein H (beta-2-glycoprotein I)	13870		[Apolipoprotein H deficiency] (1)	
Chr.17	CD7	P	T-cell antigen CD7	18682			
Chr.17	CKBB2	L	Creatine kinase, brain type, second locus	12331			
Chr.17	EMPB3	P	Erythroid membrane protein band 3	10927		[Acanthocytosis, 1 form] (1)	
Chr.17	G6PDL	P	Glucose-6 phosphate dehydrogenase-like	13811			
Chr.17	SMPD1, NPD	P	Sphingomylinase (Niemann-Pick disease)	25720		Niemann-Pick disease (1)	
Chr.17	TSE1	P	Tissue-specific extinguisher-1	18885			11(Tse-1)

In addition: 3 surface antigens, most defined by monoclonals, 4 'like' genes, and 3 pseudogenes (HGM9) and 68 anonymous DNA segments (HGML).

Chromosome No. 18

18p11.32	MCL	L	Multiple hereditary cutaneous leiomyomata	15080		?Leiomyomata, multiple hereditary cutaneous (2)	
18q11-q12	JK	P	Kidd blood group	11100	previous suggestion of chr.7 or chr.2		
18q11.2-q12.1	PALB, TTR, TBPA	C	Thyroxine-binding prealbumin (transthyretin)	17630		Amyloid neuropathy, familial, several allelic types (3); [Dystransthyretinemic hyperthyroxinemia](1)	
18q21	BCL3	P	B cell CLL/lymphoma 3	15142		Leukemia/lymphoma, B-cell, 3 (2)	
18q21	GRP	C	Gastrin releasing peptide	13726	mammalian equivalent of bombesin		
18q21.3	BCL2	C	Oncogene B-cell leukemia/lymphoma-2	15143	most frequent hematologic malignancy t(14;18)(q22;q21)	Leukemia/lymphoma, B-cell, 2 (2)	1(bcl-2)
18q21.3	YES1	C	Oncogene YES-1	16488			
18q21.31-qter	TS, TMS	C	Thymidylate synthase	18835			
18q22-q23	ERV1	C	Oncogene ERV1, endogenous retrovirus-1	13115			
18q22-qter	MBP	C	Myelin basic protein	15943	defective in "shiverer," neurologic mutant in mouse		18(Mbp)
18q22.1	GTS	L	Gilles de la Tourette syndrome	13758	t(7;18)(q22;q22.1)	?Tourette syndrome (2)	
18q23	PEPA	C	Peptidase A	16980			18(Pep-1)
18q23.3-qter	CRC18	P	Colorectal cancer-related sequence-18	12047		Colorectal cancer (1)	
Chr.18	DD	L	Diastrophic dysplasia	22260		?Diastrophic dysplasia (2)	
Chr.18	DHFRP1	P	Dihydrofolate reductase pseudogene-1	see 12606	shows +/- polymorphism		
Chr.18	IFNGR2	P	Interferon, gamma, receptor for	10747	both 6 and 18 required		
Chr.18	NARS, ASNRS	P	Asparaginyl-tRNA synthetase	10841			
Chr.18	PLANH2	P	Plasminogen activator inhibitor, type II	17339			

In addition: 2 'like' genes, and 2 pseudogenes (HGM9) and 20 anonymous DNA segments (HGML). Subband critical to trisomy 18 phenotype = 18q12.2.

Location	Symbol	Status	Title	MIM #	Comments	Disorder	Mouse
Chromosome No. 19							
19pter-p13.2	OK	P	Blood group OK	11138			
19pter-q13	CXB3S	P	Coxsackie virus B3 sensitivity	12005			
19pter-q12	EF2	C	Elongation factor-2	13061			
19p13.3-p13.2	AMH, MIF	P	Anti-Mullerian hormone	26155		Persistent Mullerian duct syndrome (1)	
19p13.3-p13.2	INSR	C	Insulin receptor	14767	1 gene for alpha and beta subunits	?Leprechaunism (1); ?Acanthosis nigricans, insulin-resistant (1); ?Rabson-Mendenhall syndrome (2)	8(Insr)
19p13.3-p13.2	C3	C	Complement component-3	12070	LE ca. 7cM in males vs. C3 RFLP	C3 deficiency (1)	17(C3)
19p13.2-p13.1	LDLR, FHC	C	Familial hypercholesterolemia (LDL receptor)	14389	ca. 20cM distal to C3	Hypercholesterolemia, familial (3)	9(Ldlr)
19p13.2-q12	MANB	C	Lysosomal alpha-D-mannosidase-B	24850		Mannosidosis (1)	
19p13.2-q13.2	MEL	P	Oncogene MEL	16504			
19p13.2-q13.4	DNL	P	Lysosomal DNA-ase	12635			
19p13.1-q13.11	LE, LES	C	Lewis blood group	11110	linked to C3; order:FHC-C3-LE-DM-SE-LU		
19p13.1-q13.11	H, HH	P	Bombay phenotype	21110	SE tightly linked		
19p13.1-q13.11	LW	C	LW (Landsteiner-Weiner) blood group	11125	close to C3, LU		
19p13.1-q13.11	SE	C	Secretor	18210	H, SE = alpha-L-fucosyltransferases; from common ancestral genes		
19p13.1-q13.11	BRHC	P	Brown hair color	11375			
19p13.1-q13.11	GEY	P	Green/blue eye color	22724	different locus for brown/blue		
19p13.1-q13.11	LU	C	Lutheran blood group	11120	linked to SE		
19cen-q12	GPI	C	Glucosephosphate isomerase	17240		Hemolytic anemia due to glucosephosphate isomerase deficiency (1); Hydrops fetalis (1)	7(Gpi-1)
19cen-q12	DM	C	Myotonic dystrophy	16090	ca. 5cM from PEPD	Myotonic dystrophy (2)	
19cen-q13.11	PEPD	C	Peptidase D (prolidase)	17010	closely linked to APOC2	?Prolidase deficiency, 26413 (1)	7(Pep-4)
19cen-q13.3	XRCC1	P	X-ray-repair, complementing defective, in Chinese hamster	19436			
19q12-q13.2	ATP1A3	C	Sodium-potassium-ATPase, alpha-3 polypeptide	18235			7(Atpa-2)
19q13	CKMM	P	Creatine kinase, muscle type	12331	downstream from APOE		
19q13-qter	PVS	C	Polio virus sensitivity	17385		{Polio, susceptibility to} (2)	
19q13.1	APOLP2	C	APOLIPOPROTEIN CLUSTER II	20775, 20776, 10771	5'--APOE-4.3kb-APOC1-6kb-APOC1 pseudogene-22kb-APOC2--3'		
19q13.1	APOE	C	Apolipoprotein E	20776		Hyperlipoproteinemia, type III (1)	7(Apoe)
19q13.1	APOC1	C	Apolipoprotein C-I	10771			

19q13.1	APOC2	C	Apolipoprotein C-II	20775		Hyperlipoproteinemia, type Ib (1)	7(Pkcc)
19q13.1-q13.3	CEA	P	Carcinoembryonic antigen	11489			
19q13.1-q13.3	TGFB	P	Transforming (or tumor) growth factor, beta form	19018			7(Tgfb)
19q13.1-q13.3	CYP2A, P450C2A	C	Phenobarbital-inducible cytochrome P450	12396	?another on 19p; CYP1 = earlier symbol		7(Coh)
19q13.1-qter	E11S	C	Echo 11 sensitivity	12915			
19q13.1-qter	M7V1, M7VS1, RDRC	C	Baboon M7 virus receptor (RD114 sensitivity)	10919	?same as virus RD114 receptor		
19q13.2-q13.4	PKCC	P	Protein kinase C, gamma form	17698			
19q13.3-q13.2	UV20, ERCC1	C	Complementation of CHO DNA-repair defect UV20	12638		?Xeroderma pigmentosum, 1 form (1)	
19q13.3-q13.4	FTL	C	Ferritin, light chain	13479			
19q13.32	CGB	C	CHORIONIC GONADOTROPIN, BETA CHAIN	11886	at least 5 genes		
19q13.32	LHB	C	Luteinizing hormone, beta chain	15278	beta chains of FSH, TSH on 11p, 1p, respectively	?Male pseudohermaphroditism due to defective LH (1)	7(Lhb)
Chr.19	BCT2	P	Branched chain amino acid transaminase-2	11353		?Hypervalinemia or hyperleucinemia-isoleucinemia (1)	
Chr.19	ERCC2, EM9	P	Complementation of CHO DNA-repair defect EM9	12634			
Chr.19	GUSM	P	Beta-glucuronidase, mouse, modifier of	23161			
Chr.19	MAG, GMA	P	Myelin-associated glycoprotein	15946			7(Gma)
Chr.19	PGK2	C	Phosphoglycerate kinase-2 (testicular PGK)	17227			
Chr.19	RPU1, U1AP	P	U1 snRNP-associated protein	18074			
Chr.19	RRAS	P	Oncogene RRAS	16509			7(Rras)
Chr.19	TRSP	P	Opal suppressor phosphoserine tRNA	16506	pseudogene on 22		

In addition: 4 surface antigens, most defined by monoclonals, 1 O'Farrell protein spot, and 1 pseudogene (HGM9) and 23 anonymous DNA segments (HGML). Map (HGM9): pter--LDLR--(C3--LE)--LW--(PEPD--DM)--(SE--APOC2)--APOE--LU--qter. LDLR, distal 19p; C3, mid 19p; APOE, 19q. Order (Eiberg et al., 1983): LE--C3--DM--(SE--PEPD)--LU. Order (Breslow, 1984):FHC--C3--APOE/APOC2. APOC1 6kb 3' to APOE. Location 19p13.1-q13.11 for LE, HH, LW, PEPD, SE, GEY, LU is estimated from collation of physical and meiotic data.

Location	Symbol	Status	Title	MIM #	Comments	Disorder	Mouse
Chromosome No. 20							
20pter-p12	SCG1, CHGB	P	Chromogranin B (secretogranin B)	11892			
20pter-p12	PDYN	P	Prodynorphin	13134			
20pter-p12	PRIP, PRNP	C	Prion protein	17664	related to kuru, CJD, etc.		2(Prn-p)
20p11.2	AHD	L	Arteriohepatic dysplasia	11845		?Arteriohepatic dysplasia (2)	
20p	ITPA	C	Inosine triphosphatase-A	14752			2(Itp)
20cen-q13.1	SAHH, AHCY	C	S-adenosylhomocysteine hydrolase	18096	~13cM from ADA		
20q11-q12	HCK	P	Hemopoietic cell kinase	14237			
20q12-q13	SRC, ASV, SRC1	C	Protooncogene SRC, Rous sarcoma	19009			2(Src)
20q13.11	ADA	C	Adenosine deaminase	10270		Severe combined immunodeficiency due to ADA deficiency (1)	2(Ada)
Chr.20	ARVP, VP	P	Arginine vasopressin-neurophysin II	19234		?Diabetes insipidus, neurohypophyseal, 12570 (1)	
Chr.20	DCE	P	Desmosterol-to-cholesterol enzyme	12565			
Chr.20	GHRF	C	Growth hormone releasing factor; somatocrinin	13919		?Isolated growth hormone deficiency due to defect in GHRF (1)	
Chr.20	GNAS, GPSA	P	G-protein, stimulatory, alpha subunit (Gs-alpha)	13932		Albright hereditary osteodystrophy	2(Gs-a)
Chr.20	GSL, NGBE	P	Neuraminidase/beta-galactosidase expression (galactosialidosis)	25654		Galactosialidosis (1)	
Chr.20	LEUT, HTL, HLT	P	Leucine transport, high	15131			
Chr.20	OT	P	Oxytocin-neurophysin I	16705	separated from VP by 12kb		
Chr.20	RPN2	P	Ribophorin II	18049			2(Rpn-2)
Chr.20	THRM	P	Thrombomodulin	18804			

In addition: 1 antigen and 2 'like' genes (HGM9) and 17 anonymous DNA segments (HGML).

Chromosome No. 21

21p12	RNR4	C	Ribosomal RNA	18045			
21q11.2-q21	AD1	C	Alzheimer disease	10430		Alzheimer disease (2)	
21q21	APP, AAA, CVAP	C	Amyloid beta A4 precursor protein	10476	proximal to SOD		16(Cvap)
21q21-q22.1	CBS	C	Cystathionine beta-synthase	23620	21q22	Homocystinuria, B6-responsive and nonresponsive types (1)	17(Cbs)
21q21-qter	IFNAR	C	Antiviral protein; alpha-interferon receptor	10745			16(Ifrc)
21q21-qter	IFNBR	C	Antiviral protein; beta-interferon receptor	10746			
21q22	S100	P	S100 protein, beta polypeptide	17699			
21q22.1	PGFT, PAIS, GART	C	Phosphoribosylaminoimidazole synthetase; phosphoribosylglycineamide synthetase; phosphoribosylglycineamide formyltransferase	13844	multifunctional protein: Ade(-)C, Ade(-)G, GART		16(Prgs)
21q22.1	SOD1	C	Superoxide dismutase-1, soluble	14745			16(Sod-1)
21q22.1-q22.3	ETS2	P	Oncogene ETS-2	16474	rearranged in Alzheimer disease		16(Ets-2)
21q22.3	BCEI	C	Breast cancer estrogen-inducible sequence	11371			
21q22.3	COL6A1	P	Collagen VI, alpha-1 chain	12022			10(Col6a1)
21q22.3	COL6A2	P	Collagen VI, alpha-2 chain	12024			10(Col6a2)
21q22.3	CRYA1	C	Crystallin, alpha A	12358	alpha B on another chr., ?chr. 16		17(Crya-1)
21q22.3	PFKL	C	Phosphofructokinase, liver type	17186		Hemolytic anemia due to phosphofructokinase deficiency (1)	17(Pfkl)
Chr.21	AABT	L	Beta-amino acids, renal transport of	10966			
Chr.21	BAS	L	Beta-adrenergic stimulation, response to	10967			
Chr.21	CD18, LCAMB, LAD	C	Cell adhesion molecule, leukocyte, beta subunit	11692	common subunit for CR3, LFA1, and P150,95	Leukocyte adhesion deficiency (2)	7(Ly-15)
Chr.21	ERG	P	Oncogene ERG	16508	related to ETS		
Chr.21	HTOR	L	5-hydroxytryptamine oxygenase regulator	14346			

In addition: 1 surface antigen and 5 O'Farrell protein spots (HGM9) and 107 anonymous DNA segments (HGML). Band critical to Down syndrome phenotype = 21q22. Hyperuricemia, leukemia, Alzheimer disease, and cataract of Down syndrome may be explained by the presence of specific genes on chromosome 21.

Location	Symbol	Status	Title	MIM #	Comments	Disorder	Mouse
Chromosome No. 22							
22pter-q11.2	PVALB	P	Parvalbumin	16889	?role in DiGeorge syndrome		
22p12	RNR5	C	Ribosomal RNA	18045			
22q11	IDUA, IDA	P	Alpha-L-iduronidase	25280	on Ph1 chr.	Hurler syndrome (1); Mucopolysaccharidosis I (1); Hurler-Scheie syndrome (1); Scheie syndrome (1)	
22q11	CECR, CES	C	Cat eye syndrome	11547	partial tetrasomy of 22q11	Cat eye syndrome (2)	
22q11	DGCR, DGS	C	DiGeorge syndrome	18840		DiGeorge syndrome (2)	
22q11	NAGA	C	N-acetyl-alpha-D-galactosaminidase (alpha-galactosidase B)	10417	proximal to Ph1 break	Alpha-NAGA deficiency (2)	
22q11-q13	TSHR	P	Thyroid stimulating hormone receptor	18846		?Hypothyroidism, nongoitrous (1)	
22q11.1-q11.2	GGT, GTG	P	Gamma-glutamyl transpeptidase	23195	minor peak, q13.1	Glutathioninuria (1)	
22q11.12	IGL	C	IMMUNOGLOBULIN LAMBDA LIGHT CHAIN GENE CLUSTER	14722-14724	on Ph1 chr.; order 5' to 3':cen-V-C-ter		
22q11.12	IGLV	C	Variable region of lambda light chains	14724	many genes		
22q11.12	IGLJ	C	J region of lambda light chains	14723	nine J-C duplexes		
22q11.12	IGLC	C	Constant region of lambda light chains	14722	several genes		16(Igl)
22q11.2-q12.2	CRYB2	P	Crystallin, beta-B2	12362			
22q11.2-q12.2	CRYB3	P	Crystallin, beta-B3	12363			
22q11.2-q12.2	CYP2D, P450C2D	P	Cytochrome P450, family II, subfamily D	12403	debrisoquine 4-hydroxylase	{?Parkinsonism, susceptibility to} (1)	
22q11.2-q13	MB	C	Myoglobin	16000			
22q11.2-qter	P1	P	P1 blood group	11141	?linked to DIA1 and SIS		
22q11.2-qter	TCN2, TC2	C	Transcobalamin II	27535	linked to P1	Transcobalamin II deficiency (1)	11(Tcn-2)
22q11.21	BCR, CML, PHL	C	Chronic myeloid leukemia; breakpoint cluster region-1	15141	distal to IGL; Ph1=t(9;22)(q34.1;q11.21); fusion gene with ABL in CML; cluster of 4 loci: cen-BCR2, BCR4, IGL-BCR1-BCR3-SIS	Leukemia, chronic myeloid (3)	
22q11.21-q13.1	NF2, ACN	C	Acoustic neuroma	10100	deletion of chr.22 markers	Acoustic neuroma (2)	
22q11.21-q13.31	ACO2	C	Aconitase, mitochondrial	10085	distal to Ph1 break		
22q12	ES	P	Ewing sarcoma	13345	(t11;22)(q24;q12)	Ewing sarcoma (2)	
22q12.3-q13.1	SIS, PDGFB	C	Oncogene SIS (platelet derived growth factor, B chain)	19004			15(Sis)
22q12.3-qter	MGCR, MGM	C	Meningioma	15610	?same determinant as ACN or allelic; ?q11-q12 critical	Meningioma (2)	
22q13-qter	GLB2, PPGB	C	Beta-galactosidase-2 (GLB protective protein)	10968			
22q13.31-qter	ARSA	C	Arylsulfatase A	25010		Metachromatic leukodystrophy (1)	15(As-2)
22q13.31-qter	DIA1	C	NADH-diaphorase-1 (cytochrome b/5)	25080		Methemoglobinemia, enzymopathic (1)	15(Dia-1)

Chr.22	ADSL, ADS	P	Adenylosuccinase (adenylosuccinate lyase)	10305	ade(-)I	?Succinylpurinemic autism (1)
Chr.22	ASLP	P	Argininosuccinate lyase pseudogene	see 20790		
Chr.22	COMT	P	Catechol-O-methyltransferase	11679		
Chr.22	HC2	P	Heparin cofactor II	14236		Thrombophilia due to heparin cofactor II deficiency (1)

In addition: 2 surface antigens, 2 'like' genes and 5 pseudogenes (HGM9) and 19 anonymous DNA segments (HGML).

Gene Map of the X Chromosome

Over 140 separate expressed genetic loci have been assigned to the X chromosome; for about an equal number of loci, X-chromosomal location has been suggested but not proved. Most of these loci have been placed on the X chromosome because of pedigree patterns and other characteristics of X-linked traits in families. Some have been assigned to the X chromosome by the same methods used in autosomal mapping: interspecies somatic cell hybridization (S, REa), *in situ* hybridization (A), or small, microscopically visible deletions (Ch). Some methods unique to the X chromosome have corroborated X-linkage or in some instances have given the first information on X-linkage or regional mapping: lyonization (L), Ohno's law of the evolutionary conservatism of the X chromosome in mammals (H), and X-autosome translocations in females affected by X-linked recessive disorders (X/A). The 'status' information in this case refers to certainty of regional assignment.

In addition: In addition: 3 surface antigens, 7 O'Farrell protein spots, 7 'like' genes and 8 pseudogenes (HGM9) and at least 277 anonymous DNA segments, many with known RFLPs, as well as 60 DNA segments shared by the X and Y (HGML).

Location	*Symbol*	*Status*	*Title*	*MIM #*	*Comments*	*Disorder*	*Mouse*
Xpter-p22.32	MIC2, MIC2X	C	MIC2 (monoclonal antibody 12E7)	31347	distal to STS		
Xpter-p22.32	STS, SSDD	C	Steroid sulfatase	30810	in nonlyonizing segment	Ichthyosis, X-linked (3); Placental steroid sulfatase deficiency (3)	X,Y(Sts)
Xpter-p22.32	XG	C	Xg blood group	31470	nonlyonizing		
Xpter-p22.32	KAL, KMS	C	Kallmann syndrome	30870	with ichthyosis in probable microdeletion syndrome	Kallmann syndrome (2)	
Xpter-p22.32	CPXR	P	Chondrodysplasia punctata, X-linked recessive	30295		Chondrodysplasia punctata, X-linked recessive (2)	
Xp22	HYP, HPDR1	C	Hereditary hypophosphatemia	30780	linked to DXS41	Hypophosphatemia, hereditary (2)	X(Hyp)
Xp22	AIC	P	Aicardi syndrome	30405		Aicardi syndrome (2)	
Xp22	GY	L	Hereditary hypophosphatemia II (gyro equivalent)	30781	close to hyp in mouse	?Hypophosphatemia with deafness (2)	
Xp22	HOMG, HSH, HMGX	C	Hypomagnesemia, X-linked primary	30760		Hypomagnesemia, X-linked primary (2)	
Xp22	MRX1	P	Mental retardation, X-linked nonspecific, I	30953	?11cM from XG	Mental retardation, X-linked nonspecific, I (2)	
Xp22	OA2	P	Ocular albinism, Forsius-Eriksson type	30060	?linked to XG	?Ocular albinism, Forsius-Eriksson type (2)	
Xp22	OA1	C	Ocular albinism, Nettleship-Falls type	30050	linked to XG	Ocular albinism, Nettleship-Falls type (2)	
Xp22	RS	C	Retinoschisis	31270	25cM from XG	Retinoschisis (2)	
Xp22	XLA2	L	X-linked agammaglobulinemia, type 2	30031		Agammaglobulinemia, type 2, X-linked (2)	X(xid)
Xp22-p21	GDXY, TDFX	P	Gonadal dysgenesis, XY female type	30610		Gonadal dysgenesis, XY female type (2)	
Xp22.3	HYR	P	H-Y regulator, or repressor	30697	structural HY locus on chr.6, 14317		
Xp22.3-p22.1	CLS	L	Coffin-Lowry syndrome	30360		Coffin-Lowry syndrome (2)	
Xp22.3-p21.1	POLA	C	Polymerase, DNA, alpha	31204			
Xp22.2-p22.1	CND	L	Corneal dermoids	30473	linked to DXS43		
Xp21.3-p21.2	AHC, AHX	C	Primary adrenal hypoplasia	30020	distal to GK	Adrenal hypoplasia, primary (2)	
Xp21.3-p21.2	GK	C	Glycerol kinase	30703	2Mb distal to DMD	Glycerol kinase deficiency (2)	
Xp21.2	DMD, BMD	C	Duchenne muscular dystrophy; Becker muscular dystrophy	31020	dystrophin gene; cen-5'-3'-pter; 2Mb	Duchenne muscular dystrophy (3); Becker muscular dystrophy (3)	X(mdx)
Xp21.2-q21.1	LUS, XS	L	Lutheran suppressor, X-linked	30905			

Xp21.2-p21.1	XK	C	Xk	31485	?deleted with CGD locus in some cases of CGD	[McLeod phenotype] (2)	
Xp21.1	CYBB, CGD	C	Chronic granulomatous disease	30640	proximal to DMD	Granulomatous disease, chronic (3)	
Xp21.1	OTC	C	Ornithine transcarbamylase	31125	proximal to DMD	Ornithine transcarbamylase deficiency (3)	X(spf)
Xp21.1-cen	BFD	P	Properdin deficiency	31206	?distal to DMD	Properdin deficiency, X-linked (2)	
Xp21	RP3	C	Retinitis pigmentosa 3	31261		Retinitis pigmentosa 3 (2)	
Xp21-p11	MAOA	C	Monoamine oxidase A	30985			
Xp21-p11	GAPDP1	C	Glyceraldehyde-3-phosphate dehydrogenase pseudogene-1	30598			
Xp13-p11	ARAF1, RAFA1	P	Oncogene ARAF1	31101			X(Araf)
Xp11.4	NDP, ND	C	Norrie disease	31060	close to DXS7	Norrie disease (2)	
Xp11.4	PKS2	P	Oncogene PKS2	31102			
Xp11.4-p11.1	EPA, TIMP	C	Erythroid-potentiating activity (tissue inhibitor of metalloproteinases)	30537	tissue inhibitor of metalloproteinases	?Menkes disease (1)	
Xp11.3	RP2	C	Retinitis pigmentosa 2	31260		Retinitis pigmentosa 2 (2)	
Xp11.2	SSRC	L	Sarcoma, synovial	31282		Sarcoma, synovial (2)	
Xp11.2	IP1, IP	L	Incontinentia pigmenti	30830	Xq21 = conflicting localization	Incontinentia pigmenti (2)	
Xp11	SYN1	P	Synapsin I	31344			
Xp11-q11	MNK, MK	C	Menkes disease	30940	?Xq13 by X/A	Menkes disease (2)	X(Mo)
Xp11-q12	IMD2, WAS	P	Wiskott-Aldrich syndrome	30100	t(18;X)(q11.2;p11.2)	Wiskott-Aldrich syndrome (2)	
Xp	A1S9T, A1S9	P	Temperature-sensitive mutation, mouse, complementation of (ts A1S9)	31366			
Xp	ALGN	P	Amelogenin	30120	distal Xp; ?also Y	?Amelogenesis imperfecta (1)	
Xcen-q11	DHTR, TFM	C	Testicular feminization (androgen receptor)	31370	B. Migeon thinks proximal Xq; close to DXS1	Testicular feminization (1); Reifenstein syndrome (1); Infertile male syndrome (1)	X(Tfm)
Xcen-q13	EDA	C	Anhidrotic ectodermal dysplasia	30510		Anhidrotic ectodermal dysplasia (2)	X(Ta)
Xq11-q12	MRX2	L	Mental retardation, X-linked nonspecific, II	30954		Mental retardation, X-linked nonspecific, II (2)	
Xq11-q13	PGK1P1	C	Phosphoglycerate kinase-1 pseudogene-1	31181			
Xq11.2-q21.1	XCE	P	X chromosome controlling element (X-inactivation center)	31467	q13-q21; metaphase bend, or fold, at q13.3-q21.1		X(Xce)
Xq12-q13	IMD4, SCIDX	P	Severe combined immunodeficiency, X-linked	30040	linked to DXS159	SCID, X-linked (2)	
Xq13	FGDY, AAS	P	Aarskog-Scott syndrome (faciogenital dysplasia)	30540		Aarskog-Scott syndrome (2)	
Xq13	PGKA, PGK1	C	Phosphoglycerate kinase-1	31180		Hemolytic anemia due to PGK deficiency (1)	X(Pgk-1)
Xq13	ANH1, SBA	P	Sideroblastic anemia	30130	somatic cell chromosome rearrangement	Anemia, sideroblastic/hypochromic (2)	
Xq13-q21	CHR39C	P	Cholesterol repressible protein 39C	30292			
Xq13-q21	CMTX, CMT2	C	Charcot-Marie-Tooth disease, X-linked	30280	linked to DXYS1	Charcot-Marie-Tooth disease, X-linked (2)	
Xq13-q21	SDYS, DGSX, GDS	L	Dysplasia-gigantism syndrome, X-linked	31287	?linked to DXYS1	Dysplasia-gigantism syndrome, X-linked (2)	
Xq13-q21	WWS	P	Wieacker-Wolff syndrome	31458	linked to DXYS1	Wieacker-Wolff syndrome (2)	
Xq13-q26	ADFN	L	Albinism-deafness syndrome	30070		Albinism-deafness syndrome (2)	

Location	*Symbol*	*Status*	*Title*	*MIM #*	*Comments*	*Disorder*	*Mouse*
Xq13-q27	BA2R, C1HR	C	Temperature sensitivity, mouse and hamster, complement	31365	?near HPRT		
Xq21	CPX	C	Cleft palate, X-linked	30340		Cleft palate, X-linked (2)	
Xq21	TCD	C	Choroideremia	30310	0.0 recombination with DXYS1, DXYS12	Choroideremia (2)	
Xq21-q22	SPG2, SPPX2	P	Spastic paraplegia, X-linked, uncomplicated	31292		Spastic paraplegia, X-linked, uncomplicated (2)	
Xq21-q22	TBG	P	Thyroxine-binding globulin	31420		[Euthyroidal hyper- and hypothyroxinemia] (1)	
Xq21.3-q22	SBMA, KD, SMAX1	C	Kennedy spinal muscular atrophy	31320	with DXYS1, lod=3.63, theta .05	Kennedy disease (2)	
Xq21.3-q22	IMD1, XLA	C	X-linked agammaglobulinemia	30030	?Ig V-D-J recombinase	Agammaglobulinemia, X-linked (2)	
Xq22	GLA	C	Alpha-galactosidase A	30150		Fabry disease (3)	X(Ags)
Xq22	PLP, PMD	C	Myelin proteolipid protein	31208		Pelizaeus-Merzbacher disease (3)	X(Plp(jp))
Xq22-q25	ASLN, ASLHN	C	Alport-syndrome-like hereditary nephritis	30105	distal to DXS3	Alport-syndrome-like hereditary nephritis (2)	
Xq22-q26	PRPS1	C	Phosphoribosylpyrophosphate synthetase	31185		Phosphoribosylpyrophosphate synthetase-related gout (1)	
Xq24-q26	GLUDP1	C	Glutamate dehydrogenase pseudogene-1	30591			
Xq24-q27	CDR	P	Cerebellar degeneration-related autoantigen	30265			
Xq24-q27	IMD3, XHM	P	X-linked immunodeficiency with hyper-IgM	30823		Immunodeficiency, X-linked, with hyper-IgM (2)	
Xq25	OCRL, LOCR	C	Lowe oculocerebrorenal syndrome	30900		Lowe syndrome (2)	
Xq26	IMD5, XLP, XLPD	P	Lymphoproliferative syndrome, X-linked	30824		Lymphoproliferative syndrome, X-linked (2)	
Xq26-q27	POF	L	Premature ovarian failure	31136		Ovarian failure, premature (2)	
Xq26-q27.2	HPRT	C	Hypoxanthine-guanine phosphoribosyltransferase	30800		Lesch-Nyhan syndrome (3); HPRT-related gout (1)	X(Hprt)
Xq26-q28	IDS, MPS2, SIDS	C	Hunter syndrome (sulfoiduronate sulfatase deficiency)	30990	?linked to XM	Hunter syndrome (1); Mucopolysaccharidosis II (1)	
Xq27	MCF2	P	Oncogene MCF2	31103	< 270kb from F9		
Xq27-qter	DFN3	P	Conductive deafness with stapes fixation	30440	linked to DXS51	Conductive deafness with stapes fixation (2)	
Xq27.1-q27.2	HEMB, F9	C	Hemophilia B; clotting factor IX	30690	distal to HPRT; proximal part of Xq27	Hemophilia B (3)	
Xq27.3	FRAXA	C	Fragile site Xq27.3 (Martin-Bell syndrome)	30955		Martin-Bell syndrome (2)	
Xq28	ALD	C	Adrenoleukodystrophy	30010	cone pigment gene deleted in some ALD males	Adrenoleukodystrophy (2)	
Xq28	CBBM, BCM	C	Blue-monochromatic colorblindness (blue cone monochromacy)	30370		Colorblindness, blue-monochromatic (3)	
Xq28	CBD, GCP	C	Deutan colorblindness (green cone pigment)	30380	linked to G6PD; multiple genes	Colorblindness, deutan (2)	
Xq28	CBP, RCP	C	Protan colorblindness (red cone pigment)	30390	linked to G6PD; 5' to CBD	Colorblindness, protan (2)	
Xq28	CPXD, CDPX, CPX	L	Chondrodysplasia punctata, X-linked dominant	30296	in mouse Bpa, bare-patches, close to G6pd and mdx	Chondrodysplasia punctata, X-linked dominant (2)	X(Bpa)

Xq28	DIR, DI1	C	Nephrogenic diabetes insipidus	30480		Diabetes insipidus, nephrogenic (2)	
Xq28	DKC	P	Dyskeratosis congenita	30500		Dyskeratosis congenita (2)	
Xq28	EMD	C	Emery-Dreifuss muscular dystrophy	31030	combined with ALD in some cases	Emery-Dreifuss muscular dystrophy (2)	X(Mdx)
Xq28	FCPX	L	F-cell production	30543		?Heterocellular hereditary persistence of fetal hemoglobin (2)	
Xq28	G6PD	C	Glucose-6-phosphate dehydrogenase	30590		G6PD deficiency (3); Favism (1); Hemolytic anemia due to G6PD deficiency (1)	X(G6pd)
Xq28	GDX	P	Protein GDX	31207	40kb 3' to G6PD		
Xq28	HEMA, F8C	C	Hemophilia A (clotting factor VIII)	30670	linked to G6PD, CB; proximal q28; DX13 and St14 distal	Hemophilia A (3)	
Xq28	MAFD2, MDX	P	Manic-depressive illness, X-linked	30920	linkage to G6PD,CB in non-Ashkenazi Jews	Manic-depressive illness, X-linked (2)	
Xq28	MRSD, CHRS	P	Mental retardation-skeletal dysplasia	30962		Mental retardation-skeletal dysplasia (2)	
Xq28	MTM1, MTMX	P	Myotubular myopathy, X-linked	31040		Myotubular myopathy, X-linked (2)	
Xq28	P3	P	Protein P3	31209	order: G6PD-3'-(7kb)-5'-P3-3'-(0.5kb)-5'-GDX		
Xq28	SEDL, SEDT	L	Spondyloepiphyseal dysplasia tarda, X-linked	31340	cosegregation with colorblindness	?SED tarda, X-linked (2)	
Xq28	SPG1, SPPX1	P	Spastic paraplegia, X-linked, complicated	31290	linked to DXS15 and DXS52	Spastic paraplegia, X-linked, complicated (2)	
Xq28	TKCR	C	Goeminne TKCR syndrome	31430	distal to G6PD	Goeminne TKCR syndrome (2)	
Xq28	XM	P	Xm	31490	linked to DCB, PCB		

GENE MAP OF THE Y CHROMOSOME

1. According to the classical model (using the term of Goodfellow et al., J. Med. Genet. 22: 329-344, 1985), the Y chromosome has been thought to have several subregions: (1) an X-Y homologous, meiotic-pairing region occupying most of Yp and perhaps including a pseudoautosomal region of X-Y exchange; (2) a pericentric region containing the sex determining gene(s); and (3) a long arm heterochromatic, genetically inert region. Some recent findings support the classical model, whereas others refute it. Molecular studies indicate that Yp contains many sequences not homologous to Xp but with homology to Yq, Xq, or an autosome.

2. From the study of normal males and females, of persons with abnormal numbers of sex chromosomes, and of those carrying variant Y chromosomes, a factor (or factors) that determines the differentiation of the indifferent gonads into testes is known to be located on the Y chromosome, probably on the short arm; this may be called testis determining factor (TDF). (*See Mendelian Inheritance in Man*, 4th edition, figure 1, p.lix, 1975.) Translocation of this locus to Xp as the cause of XX males was suggested by Ferguson-Smith (1966) and found confirmation in several observations. Location of TDF near the centromere was suggested by Davis (J. Med. Genet. 18: 161-195, 1981) and others; translocation to an X in XX males may indicate a somewhat more distal location, probably the junction of pseudoautosomal and Y-specific segments of Yp. Deletion of TDF in XY females was suggested by the observation of Disteche et al. (PNAS 83: 7841, 1986). Page et al. (Cell 51: 1091-1104, 1987) cloned part or all of the TDF gene, found that some sequences were highly conserved in mammals and even birds, and showed that the nucleotide sequence of the conserved DNA on the human Y chromosome corresponds to a protein with multiple 'finger' domains. The product probably binds to nucleic acids in a sequence-specific manner and may regulate transcription. TDF is probably located in band Yp11.2.

3. A pseudoautosomal segment (PAS) of distal Yp and distal Xp (between which crossing-over occurs) has been suspected from microscopic observations and has been confirmed by studies using polymorphic DNA markers. (See Fig. 1 of Polani, Hum. Genet. 60: 207, 1982, and of Burgoyne, Hum. Genet. 61: 95, 1982, for a suggested homologous segment of X and Y.) DNA polymorphisms in a homologous segment of X and Y show 'pseudoautosomal' inheritance (Cooke et al., Nature 317:687, 1985; Simmler et al., Nature 317: 692, 1985). It appears that TDF is just proximal to PAS and that in PAS there is one, but only one, obligatory crossingover. The following order has been observed with regard to recombination with sex: Ypter--DXYS14--(50% recombination with sex)--DXYS15--(35.5%)--DXYS17--(11.5%)--MIC2--(2.7%)--TDF. These values are strictly additive indicating no double crossovers. Thus, the sequence can be written: Ypter --DXYS14--14.5%--DXYS15--24%--DXYS17--8.8%--MIC2--2.7%--nonexchanging segment of Yp containing TDF.

4. Until identification of the TDF gene product, the only specific structural gene confidently identified on the Y chromosome was that homologous to the X-linked gene for surface antigen MIC2 (Goodfellow et al., Nature 298:346, 1983). The so-called MYC2Y (see 31347) gene is the first Y chromosome gene for which a gene product was identified, the first gene proved to have pseudoautosomal inheritance and the first gene proved to escape lyonization. The locus is in the Ypter-Yq11.2 segment. MIC2X (see 31347) is a homologous locus at Xp22.32 (Buckle et al., Nature 317:739, 1985).

5. Histocompatibility antigens determined by the Y chromosome were first found in the mouse (Eichwald, E. J. and Silmser, C. R., Transplant Bull. 2: 148-149, 1955; see review by Gasser, D. L. and Silver, W. K., Adv. Immun. 15:215-217, 1972) and later in the rat, guinea pig, and many other species. Their existence in man was first shown by the fact that mouse antisera react with human male lymphocytes but not with female lymphocytes (Wachtel et al., PNAS 71:1215-1218, 1974). The possibility that the locus that determines heterogametic sex determination and that for the H-Y antigen are one and the same was suggested by Wachtel et al. (New Engl. J. Med. 293:1070-1072, 1975). Subsequent evidence ruled out this possibility. (At the 1986 Cold Spring Harbor Symposium, 6 speakers discussed the Y chromosome at length, but H-Y was not once mentioned.) From the study of XX males and XY females, it can be concluded that the H-Y determinant on the Y (whatever its nature) and TDF was separate entities and not closely situated (Simpson, E., Cell 44: 813, 1986; Simpson et al., Nature 326: 876-878, 1987). H-Y (structural gene or regulator) is coded near the centromere, possibly on Yq.

6. The existence of factors controlling spermatogenesis on the nonfluorescent part of the long arm of Y (distal part of Yq11) was suggested by study of 6 men with deletion of this segment and azoospermia (Tiepolo, L. and Zuffardi, O., Hum. Genet. 34: 110-124, 1976). This has been called azoospermia third factor (symbolized Sp-3), or more recently (HGM9), AZF (for azoospermia factor). This might be identical to H-Y because it maps to the same region. In mice, H-Y or a closely linked gene has been implicated in spermatogenesis (Burgoyne et al., Nature 320: 170, 1986).

7. That one or more genes concerned with stature are on the Y chromosome is suggested by the comparative heights of the XX, XY and XYY genotypes; that the effect of the Y chromosome on stature is mediated through a mechanism other than androgen is suggested by the tall stature of persons with XY gonadal dysgenesis (30610). See also the argument, from XO and XXY cases, that genes determining slower maturation must be on the Y (Tanner et al., Lancet II: 141–144, 1959). The postulated locus is symbolized STA (for 'stature'). Yamada et al. (Hum. Genet. 58:268-270, 1981) found a correlation between the length of heterochromatic band Yq12 and height. The STA locus may be identical to the TSY (or GCY) locus (see later).

8. Alvesalo and de la Chapelle (Ann. Hum. Genet. 43:97-102, 1979; HGM5, Edinburgh, 1979) suggested, on the basis of tooth size in males of various Y chromosome constitutions, that a Y-chromosomal gene controlling tooth size is independent of the testis-determining gene and is carried by Yq11 (symbolized TS for 'tooth size,' or, more recently, in HGM8, GCY for 'growth control Y'. See Alvesalo and Portin, Am. J. Hum. Genet. 32:955-959, 1980;

Alvesalo and de la Chapelle, Ann. Hum. Genet. 54:49-54, 1981. The dental growth factors are thought to coincide with determinants of stature.

9. An argininosuccinate synthetase pseudogene is on the Y (Daiger et al., Nature 298: 682, 1982), as is also an actin pseudogene (Heilig et al., EMBO J. 3:1803, 1984).

10. The Howard Hughes Medical Institute's Human Gene Mapping Library (HGML) has cataloged 103 seemingly low copy number anonymous DNA segments mapped exclusively to specific regions of the Y chromosome, as well as at least 60 DNA segments that map to both the Y and the X. Some segments map to both the Y and an autosome, and some repetitive DNA segments map to the Y exclusively or to both the Y and the X.

11. Repetitive sequences located exclusively or predominantly to the Y chromosome (e.g., Kunkel, Smith and Boyer, Biochemistry 18:3343-3353, 1979) map to the heterochromatic portion of Yq and are presumably genetically inert because persons lacking these are phenotypically normal and normally fertile.

UNASSIGNED LINKAGE GROUPS (ULGs)

Linked autosomal loci for which assignment to a specific chromosome has not yet been achieved. The tightness of the linkage is stated in general terms defined as follows:

v = very close; recombination less than 2%
(NR = no recombinant observed)
c = close; recombination 2-6%
m = medium; recombination 6-22%
l = loose; recombination more than 22%
? = lods 2.0-3.0

1. Phenylthiocarbamide taste, PTC (17120) (m, F)
Kell blood group, K, KEL (11090)
Hyperreflexia, HRX (14529)
(Spence: Hum. Genet. 67: 183-186, 1984. All published data: lod = 8.94 at theta 0.14, but evidence of heterogeneity.)

2. Complement component-6, C6 (21705)
Complement component-7, C7 (21707) (v, F)
(C6 and C7 linked in dog, marmoset. Two C7 loci in dog. In man, C6 and C7 genes physically close by DNA studies (RE). Linkage supported by observation of combined deficiency.)

3. Ii blood group, II (11080)
Congenital cataract, CCAT (21250) (?c, F)

4. Epidermolysis bullosa progressiva, EBR3 (22650)
Hypoacusis (HOAC; a recessive partial deafness) (22070) (?c, F)
?Red hair, RHA (26630)—linked to MNS (11130) on chr.4
?Ataxia-deafness-retardation syndrome (20885)

5. Cerebellar ataxia, a recessive form, CPD3 (21320)
Tyrosinase-negative albinism, ATN (20310)(?c,F)
(From homology to tyrosine-negative albinism in the mouse, which is linked to the beta-globin cluster [8cM apart] and to malic enzyme, mitochondrial [4cM apart], on mouse chromosome 7, this linkage pair in man might be on either 11p or 6p.)

6. Marinesco-Sjogren syndrome, MSS (24880)
Hypergonadotropic hypogonadism, HRGHG (23832) (m, F)
(Lod score more than +30; however, HRGHG probably pleiotropic effect of MSS.)

7. Restriction mapping indicates that type I (14803) and type II (14804) keratin genes are linked as well as glycine-rich keratins and keratins without glycine-rich regions. All keratin genes (at least 20 in number) may be in one region of the genome. Some evidence points to chromosome 17 as the site of keratin gene(s) (see 14803) and weaker evidence indicates chromosome 12 (see 13935).

8. Xeroderma pigmentosum, group D, XPD (27873)
Trichothiodystrophy (24217) (?c,F)

For a collection and collation of published linkage data, see the following: Keats, B. J. B., Morton, N. E., Rao, C. C. and Williams, W. R.: *A Source Book for Linage in Man.* Baltimore: Johns Hopkins University Press, 1979; Keats, B. J. B.: *Linkage and Chromosome Mapping in Man.* Honolulu: University Press of Hawaii, 1981.

THE MITOCHONDRIAL CHROMOSOME (CHROMOSOME M OR CHROMOSOME 25)

Each mitochondrion contains several circular chromosomes. The most important function of the mitochondria is synthesis of ATP by the process of oxidative phosphorylation (OXPHOS). OXPHOS involves 5 multi-polypeptide enzyme complexes in the mitochondrial inner membrane. The biogenesis of 4 of these 5 complexes is under the combined control of nuclear DNA and mitochondrial DNA (mtDNA). At least 69 separate polypeptides are known to be required for OXPHOS; only 13 of them are coded by mtDNA.

The 16,569 basepairs of the mitochondrial chromosome are the equivalent of 5,523 codons. Most of the mtDNA serves a coding function. The genes contain no intervening sequences, and little in the way of flanking sequences is present. The ribosomal and transfer RNAs are those involved in the synthesis of protein in the mitochondrion. Of the 22 tRNAs, 14 are coded on the L (light) strand. For all 13 reading frames, the function of the specific protein coded is known. The mtDNA code differs from that of the nuclear DNA and the genetic code of any presentday prokaryote. UGA codes for tryptophan (not termination), AUA codes for methionine (not isoleucine), and AGA and AGG code for termination (not arginine). The mitochondrial genome is transcribed as a single mRNA transcript which is subsequently cleaved into its several component genes.

Mitochondrial inheritance ('cytoplasmic inheritance' the old terminology) is exclusively matrilineal. Restriction fragment length polymorphisms (RFLPs) are known in mitochondrial DNA as in nuclear DNA. Mitochondrial restriction patterns can be used to construct a biological history of the human species.

Whereas each nuclear chromosome is present in only 2 copies per cell at the most, the mitochondrial chromosome is present in thousands of copies. The behavior of a mitochondrial mutation in inheritance might be expected, therefore, to be galtonian rather than mendelian.

In cultured cells, chloramphenicol resistance is demonstrably the result of mutation in the mtDNA gene for 16S rRNA (see 21465). Indeed, the specific nucleotide changes have been identified. Disorders that are thought to involve mitochondrial mutation include Leber optic atrophy, which is often associated with 'neurodegenerative' disorders (see 30890), infantile bilateral striatal necrosis (IBSN), and myoclonic epilepsy with 'ragged red fibers' (MERRF). In cases of 'mitochondrial myopathy' (see 25190), partial deletion of the mitochondrial chromosome was found in some cases (Holt et al., Nature 331: 717-719, 1988). In muscle, both normal and partially deleted mtDNA ('heteroplasmy') was found, whereas circulating white cells, probably because of selection, had only normal mtDNA.

Fig. A1-2 The human mitochondrial genome.

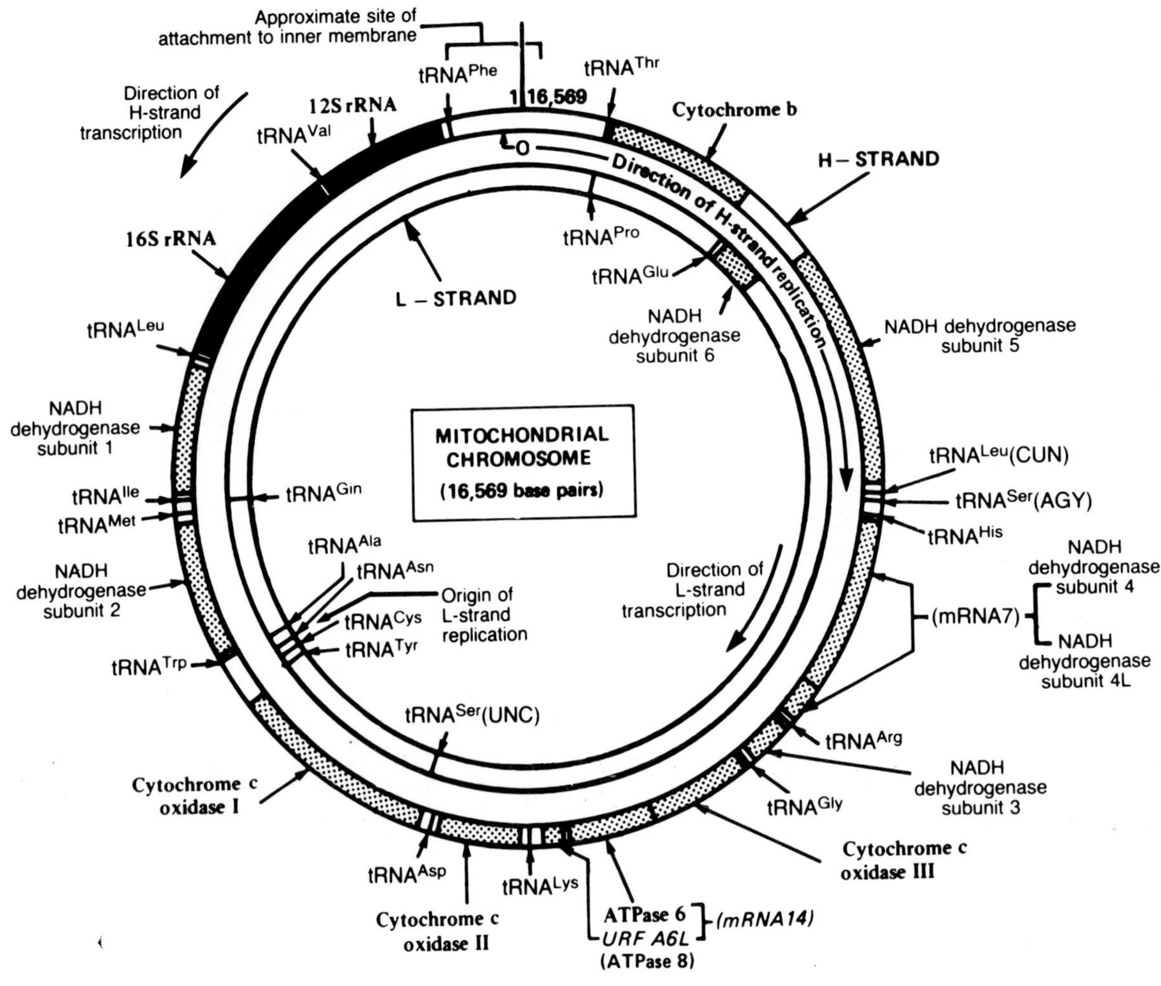

Gene	Location (nucleotide pair)	Gene	Location (nucleotide pair)
(L-strand promoter	about 392-435)	tRNA asparagine	7518-7585
(major H-strand promoter	about 545-567)	cytochrome c oxidase subunit II	7586-8262
(minor L-strand start site	561)	tRNA lysine	8295-8364
tRNA phenylalanine	577-647	ATPase subunit 8 (URF A-L)	8366-8572
(minor H-strand start site	about 645)	ATPase subunit 6	8527-9207
12S rRNA	648-1601	cytochrome c oxidase subunit III	9207-9990
tRNA valine	1602-1670	tRNA glycine	9991-10058
16S rRNA	1671-3229	NADH dehydrogenase subunit 3	10059-10404
tRNA leucine (UUR)	3230-3304	tRNA arginine	10405-10469
NADH dehydrogenase subunit 1	3307-4262	NADH dehydrogenase subunit 4L	10470-10766
tRNA isoleucine	4263-4331	NADH dehydrogenase subunit 4	10760-12137
tRNA glutamine	4329-4400	tRNA histidine	12138-12206
tRNA methionine (including fMET)	4402-4469	tRNA serine (AGY)	12207-12265
NADH dehydrogenase subunit 2	4470-5511	tRNA leucine (CUN)	12266-12336
tRNA tryptophan	5512-5576	NADH dehydrogenase subunit 5	12337-14148
tRNA alanine	5587-5655	NADH dehydrogenase subunit 6 (on L)	14149-14673
tRNA asparagine	5657-5729	tRNA glutamic acid (L-strand)	14674-14742
(origin of L-strand replication	5729-5805)	cytochrome b	14747-15887
tRNA cysteine	5761-5826	tRNA threonine	15888-15953
tRNA tyrosine	5826-5891	tRNA proline (L-strand)	15955-16023
cytochrome c oxidase subunit I	5904-7444	(membrane attachment site	about 15925-499)
tRNA serine	7445-7516		

SUMMARY TABLE

Name of disease	Chap. no.	Frequency	Mode of inheritance	Mutant gene product	Chromosomal location	Expression: Altered DNA structure	Expression: Disturbed protein function	Expression: Disrupted cell and organ function
Part 2: Chromosomes								
Down syndrome (Trisomy 21)	7	1:1000 live births (mean); increases with maternal age; higher rates in fetuses	Sporadic in most cases; translocation forms (<5% of total) may sometimes be inherited	Increased amounts of numerous normal gene products	Genes in 21q22 are implicated in dysmorphic features and heart disease; genes in other regions may be involved in mental retardation and other manifestations	Trisomy of chromosome 21 or duplication of part of chromosome 21	50% increase in synthesis and concentration of many gene products	Aberrant morphogenesis, short stature, fewer cortical neurons, mental retardation, hypotonia, immune deficiency, increased risk of leukemia, male infertility, reduced life span.
Fragile X syndrome	8	1–2:2600 males 1–2:4100 females	X-linked but with significant deviation	Unknown	Xq27	Unknown	Unknown	Primary: unknown. Secondary: mental retardation, mild facial dysmorphism, macroorchidism.
Retinoblastoma	9	1:14,000	Autosomal dominant	*RB1*	13q14.1	Deletion	Deficient	Retinal differentiation, retinal tumors, osteogenic tumors.
Wilms tumor	9	1:10,000	Autosomal dominant	*WT1* (locus, gene not yet isolated)	11p13	Unknown	Unknown	Unknown.
Beckwith-Wiedemann syndrome	9	1:100,000	Autosomal dominant	Unknown	11p15	Unknown	Unknown	Unknown.
Part 3: Carbohydrates								
Diabetes mellitus, type 1 (insulin-dependent diabetes mellitus)	10	1:400 whites and blacks Less in Hispanics, Indians	Unknown	*DQ* locus product?	6p21.3 HLA-DQ	Unknown	Substitution of residue 57	Immune-mediated destruction of pancreatic β cell resulting in insulin deficiency/glucagon excess. Major complications probably due to hyperglycemia-induced sorbitol accumulation in tissues.
Diabetes mellitus, type 2 (non-insulin-dependent diabetes mellitus)	10	1:133 whites and blacks Higher in Hispanics and Indians	Unknown except in maturity-onset diabetes of youth (MODY), which is Mendelian dominant	Unknown	Unknown	Unknown	Unknown	Impaired insulin release in response to glucose coupled with insulin resistance. Relative insulin deficiency/glucagon excess. Major complications probably due to hyperglycemia-induced sorbitol accumulation in tissues.

SUMMARY TABLE *(continued)*

Name of disease	Chap. no.	Frequency	Mode of inheritance	Mutant gene product	Chromosomal location	Expression: Altered DNA structure	Expression: Disturbed protein function	Expression: Disrupted cell and organ function
Part 3: Carbohydrates (continued)								
Essential fructosuria hepatic fructokinase deficiency	11	~1:130,000; more common in Jews	Autosomal recessive	Fructokinase	Unknown	Unknown	Deficient enzyme activity	Decreased phosphorylation of fructose to fructose 1-phosphate leads to alimentary hyperfructosemia and fructosuria. No clinical symptoms.
Hereditary fructose intolerance	11	1:20,000 in Switzerland	Autosomal recessive	Fructose 1,6-biphosphate aldolase B	9q13-q32	Unknown	Deficient enzyme activity	Ingestion of fructose causes the accumulation of fructose 1-phosphate and hence multiple dysfunctions in small intestine, liver, and kidneys.
Hereditary fructose 1,6-diphosphatase deficiency	11	85 cases	Autosomal recessive	Fructose 1,6-biphosphatase	Unknown	Unknown	Deficient enzyme activity	Gluconeogenesis is impaired, which during fasting leads to hypoglycemia, ketosis, lactic acidosis, and hyperalaninemia.
D-Glyceric aciduria	11	4 cases	Unknown	Unknown	Unknown	Unknown	Unknown	Metabolic acidosis.
Erythrocyte aldolase deficiency with nonspherocytic hemolytic anemia (aldolase A deficiency)	11	3 cases	? Autosomal recessive	Fructose 1,6-biphosphate aldolase A	Unknown	Point mutation	Deficient enzyme deficiency	Elevated fructose 1,6-biphosphate inhibits glucose 6-phosphate dehydrogenase and hence hexose monophosphate shunt activity in red cells.
Fructose malabsorption	11	Unknown (prevalence may be high)	Unknown	Unknown	Unknown	Unknown	Unknown	Oral fructose is incompletely absorbed causing abdominal symptoms and diarrhea.
Glycogen storage disease type Ia (von Gierke disease)	12	~1:100,000	Autosomal recessive	Glucose 6-phosphatase	Unknown	Unknown	Absent or deficient enzyme activity	Impaired gluconeogenesis, hypoglycemia, hyperlactic acidemia. Glycogen accumulation in liver & kidney.
Glycogen storage disease type Ib	12	~1:200,000	Autosomal recessive	Glucose 6-phosphate translocase	Unknown	Unknown	Deficient transport of glucose 6-phosphate across the membrane of endoplasmic reticulum	Same as type Ia plus leukocyte defect.
Glycogen storage disease type II	12	~1:175,000	Autosomal recessive	Lysosomal α-glucosidase	17q23	Unknown	Absent or deficient enzyme activity	Glycogen accumulates within lysosomes in all cells. Muscle weakness and heart failure are the main signs. Existence of infantile (Pompe disease), late infantile, and adult variants.

Glycogen storage disease type III	12	~1:125,000	Autosomal recessive	Amylo-1, 6-glucosidase (debrancher enzyme)	Unknown	Unknown	Absent or deficient enzyme activity	Generalized accumulation of a glycogen with shorter outer chains (limit-dextrin). Moderate hypoglycemia and lacticacidemia. Muscle weakness mostly in adults.
Glycogen storage disease type IV (Andersen disease)	12	~1:million	Autosomal recessive	Amylo-1, 4:1,6-glucantransferase (Brancher enzyme)	Unknown	Unknown	Deficient enzyme activity	Generalized accumulation of a poorly branched glycogen (amylopectin-like). Rapidly fatal cirrhosis.
Glycogen storage disease type V (McArdle disease)	12	~1:million	Autosomal recessive	Muscle glycogen phosphorylase	11q13-qter (provisional)	Unknown	Absent or deficient enzyme activity	Accumulation of glycogen in striated muscle. Abnormal fatigue and cramps on exercise; sometimes myoglobinuria.
Glycogen storage disease X-linked phosphorylase kinase deficiency	12	1:125,000	X-linked recessive	Phosphorylase b-kinase	X	Unknown	Deficient or absent enzyme activity function	Accumulation of glycogen in liver causes hepatomegaly.
Glycogen storage disease autosomal phosphorylase kinase deficiency	12	~1:175,000	Autosomal recessive	Phosphorylase b-kinase	Unknown	Unknown	Deficient enzyme activity	Accumulation of glycogen in liver and muscle. Relatively benign.
Glycogen storage disease liver phosphorylase deficiency	12	~1:million	Autosomal recessive	Liver phosphorylase	Unknown	Unknown	Deficient enzyme activity	Accumulation of glycogen in liver causes hepatomegaly.
Glycogen storage disease type VII (Tarui disease)	12	~1:million	Autosomal recessive	Muscle phosphofructokinase 1	1cen-q32	Unknown	Deficient enzyme activity	Accumulation of glycogen in muscle. Exercise intolerance, hemolysis, hyperuricemia.
Liver glycogen synthase deficiency	12	?2 cases	Autosomal recessive	Liver glycogen synthase	Unknown	Unknown	Unknown	Fasting hypoglycemia.
Phosphoglycerate kinase deficiency	12	<1:million	X-linked	Phosphoglycerate kinase	Xq13	Unknown	Deficient enzyme	Impaired glycolysis in most cells leading to hemolytic anemia and muscle exercise intolerance without glycogenosis.
Phosphoglycerate mutase deficiency	12	<1:million	Autosomal recessive	Phosphoglycerate mutase	10q25.3 (provisional)	Unknown	Deficient enzyme	Intolerance for strenuous exercise, cramps, myoglobinuria.
Muscle lactate dehydrogenase deficiency	12	<1:million	Autosomal recessive	Muscle-specific subunit of lactate dehydrogenase (LDH)	11 (provisional)	Unknown	Absence of M subunit of LDH. Muscle LDH is a tetramer of the heart-specific subunit.	Myoglobinuria after intense exercise.
Glucose phosphate isomerase deficiency	12	?(1 case)	? Autosomal recessive	Glucose phosphate isomerase	19cen-q13.2	Unknown	Unknown	Liver glycogenosis, muscular fatigue, hemolytic disorder, and mental retardation.
Transferase deficiency galactosemia	13	1:35,000–60,000	Autosomal recessive	Galactose 1-phosphate uridyltransferase	9p13	Probable missense mutation(s)	Deficient enzyme activity	Accumulation of galactitol, galactose 1-phosphate, and galactonate causes cataracts, mental retardation, and liver and kidney dysfunction.

SUMMARY TABLE *(continued)*

Name of disease	*Chap. no.*	*Frequency*	*Mode of inheritance*	*Mutant gene product*	*Chromosomal location*	*Expression:* *Altered DNA structure*	*Expression:* *Disturbed protein function*	*Expression:* *Disrupted cell and organ function*
Part 3: Carbohydrates (continued)								
Galactokinase deficiency galactosemia	13	1:40,000	Autosomal recessive	Galactokinase	17q21-q25	Unknown	Deficient enzyme activity	Accumulation of galactitol in lens results in cataracts.
Epimerase deficiency galactosemia	13	Unknown, rare	Autosomal recessive	Uridine diphosphate galactose-4-epimerase	1pter-p32	Unknown	Deficient enzyme action in blood cells only (benign) or more rarely, in all tissues (generalized)	In the benign form, galactose 1-phosphate accumulates in red cells without clinical significance. In the generalized form the clinical and biochemical abnormalities resemble transferase-deficient galactosemia.
Pentosuria	14	1:2500 Ashkenazi Jews	Autosomal recessive	L-Xylulose reductase	Unknown	Unknown	Deficient enzyme activity	Accumulation of substrate (L-xylulose) leads to its continuous excretion in the urine without apparent clinical dysfunction.
Part 4: Amino acids								
Phenylketonuria (PKU)	15	~1:10,000 births (considerable regional variation)	Autosomal recessive (homozygous or compound)	Phenylalanine hydroxylase (PAH)	12q22-q24.1	6 different mutations known so far: splicing defect, missense mutations, and partial deletion. Known associations between RFLP haplotypes and PKU alleles	Deficient or absent PAH activity (<1% normal)	Hepatic enzyme deficiency causes hyperphenylalaninemia; plasma values persistently above 1.3 m*M* cause impaired cognitive development.
Non-PKU hyperphenylalaninemia	15	<1:20,000 in most populations	Autosomal recessive (homozygous or compound)	Phenylalanine hydroxylase (PAH)	12q22-q24.1	Unknown. Associated with RFLP haplotypes 1 & 4 in northern Europeans	Deficient PAH activity (>1% normal)	Benign phenotype for proband. Risk of maternal hyperphenylalaninemia effect on fetus carried by female proband.
"Malignant" hyperphenylalaninemia: DHPR-deficient form	15	~1:million (~1% of hyperphenylalaninemia cases)	Autosomal recessive (homozygous or compound)	Dihydropteridine reductase (DHPR)	4p15.3	Unknown; informative RFLP markers available	Deficient or absent DHPR activity	Impaired regeneration of tetrahydrobiopterin (BH_4) from qBH_2 inhibits hydroxylation of phenylalanine tyrosine and tryptophan; associated neurotransmitter deficiencies affect brain function.

"Malignant" hyperphenylalaninemia: GTP-CH–deficient form	15	~1:million (<1% of hyperphenylalaninemia cases)	Autosomal recessive	Guanosine triphosphate cyclohydrolase (GTP-CH)	Unknown	Unknown	Deficient enzyme activity	Impairs tetrahydrobiopterin (BH_4) synthesis. BH_4 deficiency affects hydroxylation of phenylalanine, tyrosine, and tryptophan.
"Malignant" hyperphenylalaninemia: 6-PTS–deficient form	15	~1:million (~1% of hyperphenylalaninemia cases)	Autosomal recessive	6-Pyruvoyl tetrahydropterin synthase (6-PTS)	Unknown	Unknown	Deficient enzyme activity	Impairs tetrahydrobiopterin (BH_4) synthesis. BH_4 deficiency affects hydroxylation of phenylalanine, tyrosine, and tryptophan. "Complete" form affects brain, liver, etc. "Peripheral" form spares brain.
Tyrosinemia IA (fumarylacetoacetate hydrolase deficiency)	16	1:20,000 with significant ethnic/regional variation	Autosomal recessive	Fumarylacetoacetate hydrolyase	Unknown	Unknown	Deficient enzyme activity; greater deficiency in acute than in chronic form	Increased succinylacetone, which inhibits renal tubular transport and hepatic enzymes.
Tyrosinemia IB (tentative) (maleylacetoacetate isomerase deficiency)	16	1 case	Autosomal recessive (provisional)	Maleylacetoacetate isomerase	Unknown	Unknown	Deficient enzyme activity	No increase in succinylacetone; otherwise chemical and clinical findings are like type IA.
Tyrosinemia II (Tyrosine aminotransferase deficiency)	16	<100 cases	Autosomal recessive	Tyrosine aminotransferase (TAT)	16q22-q24	Unknown	Deficient enzyme activity	Tyrosine crystals in cornea, inflammation in palm and sole skin and in cornea.
Urocanic aciduria	17	? (perhaps 1:200,000)	Unknown	Urocanase	Unknown	Unknown	Absent urocanase activity	Increased substrate (urocanic acid); reduced products (imidazolonepropionate and FIGLU).
Histidinemia	17	1:10,000 general population	Autosomal recessive	Histidase (L-histidine ammonialyase)	Unknown	Unknown	Absent or markedly reduced enzyme activity	Increased substrate; reduced products (urocanic acid and FIGLU).
Hyperprolinemia types I and II	18	1:200,000	Autosomal recessive	Type I, proline oxidase Type II, Δ-pyrroline-5-carboxylate dehydrogenase	Unknown; two loci	Unknown	Deficient activity in types I and II	No apparent dysfunction; may have predisposition for neurological manifestations.
Hyperhydroxyprolinemia	18	Rare (<1:600,000)	Autosomal recessive	4-Hydroxy-L-proline oxidase	Unknown	Unknown	Deficient activity	No apparent dysfunction (benign).
Prolidase deficiency (hyperimidodipeptiduria) and prolidase polymorphisms	18	1:50,000 (rare phenotypes, 28 cases) >1:100 (polymorphisms)	Autosomal recessive for rare alleles, codominant for polymorphisms	Peptidase D (prolidase)	19p13-cen	Unknown	"Activity" mutations = prolidase deficiency "Structural" mutations = polymorphisms	Impaired imidodipeptide (X-Pro, X-Hypro) cleavage, (altered collagen metabolism ?), imidodipeptiduria, skin changes, impaired development, and other problems.

SUMMARY TABLE *(continued)*

Name of disease	*Chap. no.*	*Frequency*	*Mode of inheritance*	*Mutant gene product*	*Chromosomal location*	*Expression* — *Altered DNA structure*	*Expression* — *Disturbed protein function*	*Expression* — *Disrupted cell and organ function*
Part 4: Amino acids (continued)								
Gyrate atrophy of the choroid and retina	19	~150 cases; ~1:50,000 in Finland	Autosomal recessive	Ornithine-δ-aminotransferase	10q26	Several point mutations and at least one deletion	Absent or deficient enzyme activity	Accumulation of substrate (ornithine) and reduced synthesis of creatine due to inhibition by ornithine of glycine transaminidinase. Mechanism of chorioretinal degeneration and cataract formation not known.
Hyperornithinemia-hyperammonemia-homocitrullinuria syndrome	19	15 cases	Autosomal recessive	Unknown	Unknown	Unknown	Impaired ornithine transport into mitochondria	Decreased availability of ornithine within mitochondria leads to decreased citrulline synthesis and impaired ammonia detoxification, causing hyperammonemia.
Carbamyl phosphate synthetase deficiency	20	1:70,000–100,000	Autosomal recessive	Carbamyl phosphate synthetase I	2p	Unknown	Absent of deficient enzyme activity	Impaired urea formation leads to ammonia intoxication.
Ornithine transcarbamylase deficiency	20	1:70,000–100,000	X-linked	Ornithine transcarbamylase	Xp21.1	Deletions, missense & nonsense mutations	Absent or reduced enzyme activity	Impaired urea formation leads to ammonia intoxication.
Argininosuccinic acid synthetase deficiency	20	1:70,000–100,000	Autosomal recessive	Argininosuccinic acid synthetase	9q34	Abnormal intron splicing?	Deficient enzyme activity	Accumulation of citrulline in blood, urine, and CSF leads to neurologic dysfunction.
Argininosuccinase deficiency	20	1:70,000–100,000	Autosomal recessive	Argininosuccinate lyase	7p21-cen	Unknown	Deficient enzyme activity	Accumulation of argininosuccinate in blood, urine, & CSF leads to neurologic problems.
Arginase deficiency	20	<1:100,000	Autosomal recessive	Liver arginase	6q23	Unknown	Deficient enzyme activity	Accumulation of arginine in blood and CSF leads to neurologic dysfunction.
Familial hyperlysinemia (variant: saccharopinuria)	21	Unknown (rare)	Autosomal recessive	α-Aminoadipic semialdehyde synthase (bifunctional enzyme: lysine-ketoglutarate reductase and saccharopine dehydrogenase activities)	Unknown	Unknown	Deficient enzyme activity	Severe hyperlysinemia. Saccharopinuria is less constant and less severe. No recognizable disruption of function.
Maple syrup urine disease or branched chain ketoacidemia	22	1:100,000 with ethnic/ regional variation	Autosomal recessive	Multiple loci and subunits	Unknown	Unknown	Impaired dehydrogenase activity, absent E_2 and $E_1\beta$ subunits in rare variants	Enzyme deficiency causes accumulation of organic acids and amino acids; acute and chronic neurologic dysfunction occurs.

Cystathionine β-synthase deficiency	23	1:335,000	Autosomal recessive	Cystathionine β-synthase	21q21-q22.1	Unknown	Deficient enzyme activity	Vitamin B_6–responsive and –unresponsive forms. Vascular thrombosis, dislocation of ocular lens, and abnormal development.
α-Cystathionase deficiency	23	1:68,000–333,000	Autosomal recessive	α-Cystathionase	16	Unknown	Deficient enzyme activity	Benign.
Hepatic methionine adenosyltransferase deficiency	23	Unknown	? Autosomal recessive	Isoenzyme of methionine adenosyltransferase		Unknown	Deficient enzyme activity	Benign.
Sarcosinemia	24	1:350,000	Autosomal recessive	Sarcosine dehydrogenase ?	Unknown	Unknown	Deficient enzyme activity	Believed to be a benign condition without clinical symptoms.
Nonketotic hyperglycinemia	25	1:250,000 (U.S.) 1:12,000 (northern Finland)	Autosomal recessive	1 of several proteins of glycine cleavage system	Unknown	Unknown	Deficient enzyme activity	Substrate (glycine) accumulates in body fluids including CSF. Severe retardation may be related to glycine role as a neurotransmitter.
Hyperuracil thyminuria	26	5 cases	Autosomal recessive	Dihydropyrimidine dehydrogenase	Unknown	Unknown	Deficient enzyme activity	Impaired CNS function; impaired disposal of fluorouracil.
Hyper-β-alaninemia	26	1 case	Autosomal recessive	β-Alanine-pyruvate transaminase (putative)	Unknown	Unknown	Deficient enzyme activity (or coenzyme binding)	Impaired CNS function.
Hyper-β-aminoisobutyric aciduria	26	5–95% of population	Autosomal (incompletely recessive)	R-β-aminoisobutyrate-pyruvate transaminase	Unknown	Unknown	Deficient enzyme activity (liver)	Benign metabolic polymorphism.
Pyridoxine dependency with seizures	26	uncommon	Autosomal recessive	Brain (type 1) glutamic acid decarboxylase (putative)	Unknown	Unknown	Deficient coenzyme binding? (brain)	Seizures controlled only by pharmacologic doses of vitamin B_6.
GABA aminotransferase deficiency	26	3 cases	Autosomal recessive	GABA-α-ketoglutarate transaminase (form not specified)	Unknown	Unknown	Deficient enzyme activity	Impaired CNS function, accelerated somatic growth, elevated plasma growth hormone levels.
4-Hydroxybutyricaciduria	26	6 cases	Autosomal recessive	Succinic semialdehyde dehydrogenase	Unknown	Unknown	Deficient enzyme activity	Cerebellar signs, hypotonia, and mental retardation.
Serum carnosinase deficiency (and homocarnosinosis)	26	20 cases	Autosomal recessive	Serum carnosinase	Unknown	Unknown	Deficient enzyme activity	Probably benign.
Part 5: Organic acids								
Alcaptonuria	27	1:100,000–million	Autosomal recessive	Homogentisic acid oxidase	Unknown	Unknown	Absent or deficient enzyme activity	Homogentisic acid accumulates in the tissues and is excreted in the urine. Abnormal pigmentation of connective tissues (ochronosis) and arthritis commonly found in older alcaptonurics.

SUMMARY TABLE *(continued)*

Name of disease	Chap. no.	Frequency	Mode of inheritance	Mutant gene product	Chromosomal location	Expression: Altered DNA structure	Expression: Disturbed protein function	Expression: Disrupted cell and organ function
Part 5: Organic acids (continued)								
Isovaleric acidemia	28	>45 cases	Autosomal recessive	Isovaleryl-CoA dehydrogenase	15q14-q15	Unknown	Deficient enzyme activity	Accumulation of isovaleryl-CoA causes episodes of severe metabolic acidosis and ketosis, often with neutropenia and thrombocytopenia, precipitated by infections or high protein intake.
Isolated 3-methylcrotonyl-CoA carboxylase deficiency	28	4 cases	Autosomal recessive	3-Methylcrotonyl-CoA carboxylase	Unknown	Unknown	Deficient enzyme activity	Accumulation of 3-methyl-crotonyl-CoA causes episodes of severe metabolic acidosis and hypoglycemia.
3-Methylglutaconic aciduria	28	2 mild cases 7 severe cases	Mild form: autosomal or X-linked Severe form: autosomal recessive	Mild form: 3-methylglutaconyl-CoA hydratase Severe form: unknown	Unknown	Unknown	Mild form: deficient enzyme activity Severe form: unknown	Mild form: Delayed speech development. Severe form: Progressive neurologic degeneration, optic atrophy.
3-Hydroxy-3-methylglutaryl-CoA lyase deficiency	28	19 cases	Autosomal recessive	3-Hydroxy-3-methylglutaryl-CoA lyase	Unknown	Unknown	Deficient enzyme activity	Accumulated 3-hydroxy-3-methylglutaryl-CoA causes episodes of severe metabolic acidosis without ketosis. Deficiency of enzyme blocks ketogenic pathway, leading to hypoglycemia on fasting.
Mevalonic aciduria	28	4 cases	Autosomal recessive	Mevalonate kinase	Unknown	Unknown	Deficient enzyme activity	Deficiency of enzyme in cholesterol and isoprenoid biosynthesis causes failure to thrive, anemia, lack of development.
2-Methylacetoacetyl-CoA thiolase deficiency	28	14 cases	Autosomal recessive	2-Methylacetoacetyl-CoA thiolase	Unknown	Unknown	Deficient enzyme activity	Accumulation of 2-methy-lacetoacetyl-CoA causes episodes of severe metabolic acidosis and ketosis.
3-Hydroxyisobutyryl-CoA deacylase deficiency	28	1 case	Autosomal recessive	3-Hydroxyisobutyryl-CoA deacylase	Unknown	Unknown	Deficient enzyme activity	Causes congenital malformations of vertebra and heart, lack of neurologic development.
Propionic acidemia (2 nonallelic disorders designated *pccA* and *pccBC*)	29	Rare	Autosomal recessive	Propionyl-CoA carboxylase (PCC)	α subunit: 13 β subunit: 3q13.3-q22	Unknown	Deficient enzyme activity (nonallelic variants reflect mutations in nonidentical subunits of PCC)	Accumulation of propionate and alternate pathway metabolites (methylcitrate, hydroxypropionate, and propionylglycine) leads to ketoacidosis and developmental retardation.

Methylmalonic acidemia (two allelic variants designated *mut*° and *mut*$^{-}$)	29	1:20,000	Autosomal recessive	Methylmalonyl-CoA mutase (MUT) apoenzyme	6p12-p21.2	Unknown	Absent MUT activity in *mut*°, deficient MUT activity due to reduced affinity for cofactor (adenosylcobalamin) in *mut*$^{-}$	Accumulation of methylmalonate leading to metabolic ketoacidosis and developmental retardation.
Methylmalonic acidemia (two nonallelic variants designated *cblA* and *cblB*)	29, 82	1:20,000	Autosomal recessive	*cblA* form: unknown *cblB* form: ATP: cobalamin′ adenosyltransferase	Unknown	Unknown	Unknown in *cblA;* absent or deficient enzyme activity in *cblB*	Impaired adenosylcobalamin synthesis leads to deficient methylmalonyl-CoA mutase (MUT) activity; clinical and chemical findings resemble those in apoprotein MUT deficiency.
Methylmalonic acidemia and homocystinuria (two nonallelic forms designated *cblC* and *cblD*)	29, 82	Rare	Autosomal recessive	Unknown	Unknown	Unknown	Unknown	Impaired synthesis of adenosylcobalamin and methylcobalamin leads to deficient activities of two cobalamin-dependent enzymes, N^5-methyltetra-hydrofolate: homocysteine methyltransferase and methylmalonyl-CoA mutase. Hematologic and neurologic abnormalities predominate.
Methylmalonic acidemia (variant designated *cblF*)	29, 82	Rare	? Autosomal recessive	Unknown	Unknown	Unknown	Impaired efflux of cobalamin from lysosomes into the cell	Impaired synthesis of both cobalamin coenzymes leads to deficient activities of methylmalonyl-CoA mutase and N^5-methyltransferase in vitro. In the one case described, homocystinuria was not present in vivo.
Glutaric acidemia type I	30, 34	~50 patients 1:30,000 in Sweden	Autosomal recessive	Glutaryl-CoA dehydrogenase	Unknown	Unknown	Deficient enzyme activity	Accumulation of compounds (glutaric acid, 3-hydroxyglutaric acid, glutaconic acid) related to enzyme substrate. Relation between enzyme defect and neurologic dysfunction is not understood.
2-Ketoadipic acidemia	30	Unknown	Autosomal recessive	Probably 2-ketoadipic dehydrogenase E_1 or E_2	Unknown	Unknown	Deficient enzyme activity	Substrate accumulation possibly of no pathologic significance.

SUMMARY TABLE *(continued)*

Name of disease	Chap. no.	Frequency	Mode of inheritance	Mutant gene product	Chromosomal location	Expression: Altered DNA structure	Expression: Disturbed protein function	Expression: Disrupted cell and organ function
Part 5: Organic acids (continued)								
Glutathione synthetase deficiency	31	Rare	Autosomal recessive	Glutathione synthetase	Unknown	Unknown	Decreased enzyme activity. Two forms: A, severe, generalized deficiency of enzyme activity; B, a mild form, possibly due to an unstable enzyme, with deficient function manifested only in red cells	Both forms have decreased erythrocyte glutathione and increased rate of hemolysis. In the generalized form there is 5-oxoproline overproduction, metabolic acidosis, and progressive brain dysfunction.
5-Oxoprolinase deficiency	31	Rare	Autosomal recessive	5-Oxoprolinase	Unknown	Unknown	Decreased enzyme activity	Increased urinary excretion of 5-oxoproline.
γ-Glutamylcysteine synthetase deficiency	31	Rare	Unknown	γ-Glutamylcysteine synthetase	Unknown	Unknown	Decreased enzyme activity	Decreased cellular levels of glutathione. Two patients described have had hemolytic anemia, spinocerebellar degeneration, peripheral neuropathy, myopathy, and aminoaciduria.
δ-Glutamyl transpeptidase deficiency	31	Rare	Autosomal recessive	δ-Glutamyl transpeptidase	Unknown	Unknown	Decreased enzyme activity	Increased extracellular levels and urinary excretion of glutathione. All patients have had central nervous system involvement.
Cytochrome oxidase deficiency	32	Unknown	Autosomal recessive	Cytochrome oxidase polypeptides	Unknown	Unknown	Decreased activity of the cytochrome oxidase complex	Neuronal loss in brain leading to psychomotor retardation and neurodegenerative disease.
Fumarase deficiency/fumaric acidemia	32	5 cases	? Autosomal recessive	Fumarase	1q	Unknown	Decreased enzyme activity	Mental retardation.
Pyruvate dehydrogenase complex deficiency—E_1 decarboxylase component	32	<1:250,000	Autosomal recessive	Pyruvate decarboxylase, either $E_1\alpha$ or $E_1\beta$	Unknown	Unknown	Decreased enzyme activity	Neuronal loss in brain leading to psychomotor retardation. Muscular hypotonia.
Combined α-ketoacid dehydrogenase deficiency/lipoamide dehydrogenase deficiency	22, 32	6 cases	Autosomal recessive	Lipoamide dehydrogenase	Unknown	Unknown	Decreased enzyme activity	Neuronal loss in brain leads to psychomotor retardation.
NADH-CoQ reductase deficiency	32	Unknown	? Autosomal recessive	Any of the nuclear genes encoding the 25 complex I polypeptides of mitochondria	Unknown	Unknown	Decreased activity of the overall complex I	Overwhelming acidosis due to lactic acid production from many types especially those of the brain.

Pyruvate carboxylase deficiency	32	<1:250,000; higher in certain Amerindian groups	Autosomal recessive	Pyruvate carboxylase	11q	Unknown	Absent enzyme activity; seven cases absent enzyme, protein and mRNA	Neuronal loss in cerebral cortex leading to mental retardation.
Long-chain acyl-CoA dehydrogenase deficiency	33	Rare	Autosomal recessive	Long-chain acyl-CoA dehydrogenase	Unknown	Unknown	Deficient enzyme activity	Impaired β oxidation of long-chain fatty acids with recurrent episodes of coma, hypoglycemia, and inadequate ketogenesis. Hypotonia and cardiomyopathy occur.
Medium-chain acyl-CoA dehydrogenase deficiency	33	~1:10,000–25,000 (U.K.)	Autosomal recessive	Medium-chain acyl-CoA dehydrogenase	1p31	Unknown	Deficient enzyme activity	Impaired β oxidation of medium-chain fatty acids with recurrent episodes of coma, hypoglycemia, and inadequate ketogenesis.
Short-chain acyl-CoA dehydrogenase deficiency	33	Rare	Autosomal recessive	Short-chain acyl-CoA dehydrogenase	Unknown	Unknown	Deficient enzyme activity	Variable with some presenting in infancy with vomiting and lethargy; another case exhibited a proximal myopathy in otherwise asymptomatic adult.
Glutaric acidemia type I (See Chap. 30)	30, 34							
Glutaric acidemia type II	34	Unknown	Autosomal recessive	In some patients: electron transfer flavoprotein (ETF); in some patients: ETF: ubiquinone oxidoreductase	Unknown	Unknown	In some cases, no enzyme antigen; in others, no enzyme activity	Inability to oxidize fatty acids leads to lipid accumulation, hypoglycemia (nonketotic), myopathy, and cardiomyopathy. Cause of congenital anomalies is not known.
Primary hyperoxaluria type I	35	Unknown, rare	Autosomal recessive	Alanine: glyoxylate aminotransferase	Unknown	Unknown	Alteration of reaction rate	Glyoxylate leaves the peroxisome and is oxidized to oxalate.
Primary hyperoxaluria type II	35	Unknown, rare	Autosomal recessive	D-Glycerate dehydrogenase	Unknown	Unknown	Alteration of reaction rate	Glyoxylate leaves the peroxisome and is oxidized to oxalate.
Glycerol kinase deficiency (Gkd)	36	~30 cases	X-linked	Glycerol kinase and in microdeletion cases the products of linked loci, including *AHC*, *DMD*, and/or *OTC*	Xp21	Microdeletions in patients with complex phenotype. Less extensive mutations presumed in individuals with isolated Gkd	The microdeletion involves not only *GK* but also the other deleted loci: *AHC*, *DMD*, *OTC*, and other linked loci.	Disruption of adrenal, muscle, and/or liver and brain function as consequence of microdeletions in *AHC*, *DMD*, and/or *OTC* in patients with complex phenotypes. Not clear that isolated Gkd has any detrimental effect.

SUMMARY TABLE *(continued)*

Name of disease	Chap. no.	Frequency	Mode of inheritance	Mutant gene product	Chromosomal location	Expression: Altered DNA structure	Expression: Disturbed protein function	Expression: Disrupted cell and organ function
Part 6: Purines and pyrimidines								
Primary gout: idiopathic	37	1:500 in Western populations; 1:50 in American males by age 60; 1:10 males and 1:25 females in some Polynesian groups	Multifactorial	Unknown	Unknown	Unknown	Unknown	Mixed pathogenesis: increased biosynthesis and reduced renal clearance in most affected individuals.
Primary gout: superactive variant of phosphoribosyl-pyrophosphate (PP-ribose-P) synthetase	37	~20 families	X-linked recessive	PP-ribose-P synthetase	Xq	Unknown	Enhanced enzyme activity	Increased production of PP-ribose-P leads to increased purine synthesis de novo, causing gout.
Primary gout: partial deficiency of hypoxanthine-guanine phosphoribosyltransferase (HPRT)	37, 38	1:100,000 males	X-linked recessive	Hypoxanthine-guanine phosphoribosyltransferase (HPRT)	Xq26-q27	$Arg_{50} \rightarrow Gly$; $Ser_{109} \rightarrow Leu$; $Ser_{103} \rightarrow Arg$	Absent or deficient enzyme activity	Accumulation of substrate (phosphoribosylpyrophosphate) leads to enhanced purine biosynthesis de novo, causing gout.
Lesch Nyhan: deficiency of hypoxanthine-guanine phosphoribosyltransferase (HPRT)	38	1:10,000 males	X-linked recessive	Hypoxanthine-guanine phosphoribosyltransferase (HPRT)	Xq26-q27	$Arg_{193} \rightarrow Asn$ point mutations, deletions, insertions	Deficient enzyme activity	Increased PP-ribose-P leads to gout. Mechanism of neurologic dysfunction in Lesch-Nyhan unknown.
2,8-Dihydroxyadenine lithiasis (adenine phosphoribosyltransferase deficiency)	39	Type I: 32 cases; Type II: 31 cases	Autosomal recessive	Adenine phosphoribosyltransferase	16q	Unknown	Type I: Absent enzyme activity; Type II: Reduced affinity for PP-ribose-P	Adenine is metabolized through an alternative pathway leading to the formation of 2,8-dihydroxyadenine, a product that is insoluble in the kidney or urinary tract. Urolithiasis frequently results.
Adenosine deaminase deficiency with severe combined immunodeficiency disease	40	100 families	Autosomal recessive	Adenosine deaminase	20q13.11	Multiple missense mutations and exon deletions	Absent or greatly diminished enzyme activity	Accumulation of substrates (adenosine and deoxyadenosine) which are toxic to lymphoid cells leads to immunodeficiency.
Purine nucleoside phosphorylase deficiency with cellular immunodeficiency	40	21 cases	Autosomal recessive	Purine nucleoside phosphorylase	14q13	$Glu_{89} \rightarrow Lys$	Absent or greatly diminished enzyme activity	Accumulation of substrates (primarily deoxyguanosine) toxic to T lymphocytes causes cellular immunodeficiency.
Myoadenylate deaminase deficiency	41	1–2% of all muscle biopsies submitted for pathological evaluation	? Autosomal recessive	Myoadenylate deaminase	Unknown	Unknown	No enzyme activity; no immunoreactive protein	Only skeletal muscle is affected; all other tissues are normal.

Xanthinuria	42	1:45,000	Autosomal recessive	Xanthine dehydrogenase (xanthine oxidase)	Unknown	Unknown	Absent enzyme activity	Accumulated substrate (xanthine) crystallizes in urinary tract and muscle, causing nephrolithiasis and myopathy.
Hereditary orotic aciduria	43	13 cases	Autosomal recessive	UMP synthase	3q13	Unknown	Deficient enzyme activity (probably unstable protein)	Block in UMP biosynthesis leads to overproduction of orotic acid, megaloblastic anemia, failure to thrive, possible malformations.
Pyrimidine 5′-nucleotidase deficiency	43	~100 cases	Autosomal recessive	Pyrimidine 5′-nucleotidase	Unknown	Unknown	Absent or unstable enzyme	Accumulation of pyrimidine nucleotides leads to hemolytic anemia.
Dihydropyrimidine dehydrogenase deficiency	43	1 case	Autosomal recessive	Dihydropyrimidine dehydrogenase	Unknown	Unknown	Absent or unstable enzyme	Accumulation of uracil and thymine in blood and elevated urine excretion. Physiological consequences unclear.
Part 7: Lipoproteins and lipids								
Chylomicron retention disease	44B	~10 cases	? Autosomal recessive	Unknown	Unknown	Unknown	Apo B-48 retained in intestine and absent from plasma	Abnormality of release of apo B-48 from intestine associated with fat malabsorption.
Familial combined hyperlipidemia	44B	~1:100	Autosomal dominant	Unknown	Unknown	Unknown	Increased apo B in plasma	Increased LDL or VLDL or both. Increased risk of myocardial infarction.
Lp(a) hyperlipoproteinemia	44B	? major gene frequency of 0.10	? Autosomal dominant or polygenic	Unknown, ? Lp(a) protein	Unknown	Unknown	Increased Lp(a) in plasma	Increased LP(a) associated with increased risk of coronary disease by unknown mechanism.
Abetalipoproteinemia	44B	~50 cases	Autosomal recessive	Unknown, ? apo B in some	2p24 for apo B	Unknown, increased apo B mRNA in some	Apo B not detectable in some	Lack of synthesis and/or secretion of apoprotein B prevents formation of chylomicrons, VLDL, and LDL. This leads to decreased vitamin E transport, which in turn causes neurologic and retinal abnormalities. Heterozygotes have normal plasma levels of apoprotein B.
Familial hypobetalipoproteinemia	44B	~10 cases	Autosomal recessive	? Apo B in some	2p24 for apo B	Unknown, decreased mRNA for apo B in some	Decreased apo B in some	Homozygotes have syndrome similar to abetalipoproteinemia. Heterozygotes have one-half of the normal levels of apoprotein B in plasma and are asymptomatic.
Normotriglyceridemic abetalipoproteinemia	44B	1 case	? Autosomal recessive	Probably apo B	2p24	Unknown	Absent apo B-100, apo B-48 present	Absent LDL able to absorb fat and form chylomicrons.
Hypobetalipoproteinemia with apo B-37	44B	1 family	? Autosomal recessive	Apo B	2p24	Unknown	Truncated apo B-37 formed	Very low LDL, mild fat malabsorption, mild phenotype.

SUMMARY TABLE *(continued)*

Name of disease	Chap. no.	Frequency	Mode of inheritance	Mutant gene product	Chromosomal location	Expression: Altered DNA structure	Expression: Disturbed protein function	Expression: Disrupted cell and organ function
Part 7: Lipoproteins and lipids (continued)								
Familial lipoprotein lipase deficiency	45	~100 cases, 1:million	Autosomal recessive	Lipoprotein lipase	Unknown	Unknown	Nonfunctional protein in some, nondectable enzyme activity and protein in others	Accumulation of substrate (chylomicrons and VLDL) in plasma as triglyceride, associated with pancreatitis and eruptive xanthomas of skin.
Apolipoprotein C-II deficiency	45	~30 cases	Autosomal recessive	Apo C-II (activator of lipoprotein lipase)	19	Unknown	Decreased lipoprotein lipase activity due to absence of normal apo C-II	Same as familial lipoprotein lipase deficiency. Apo C-II activates lipoprotein lipase.
Familial lipoprotein lipase inhibitor	45	3 cases in one family	Autosomal dominant	Unknown	Unknown	Unknown	Decreased lipoprotein lipase activity	Same as familial lipoprotein lipase deficiency.
Familial chylomicronemia syndrome	45	~1:10,000	Complex, multiple loci	Unknown	Unknown	Unknown	Unknown	Same as familial lipoprotein lipase deficiency.
Familial lecithin: cholesterol acyltransterase deficiency	46	~50 cases	Autosomal recessive	Lecithin: cholesterol acyltransferase	16q	Unknown	Absent enzyme protein or deficient enzyme activity	Accumulation of unesterified cholesterol in plasma and tissues leads to anemia, dyslipoproteinemia, proteinuria, and renal failure and corneal opacities.
Familial type III hyperlipoproteinemia (dysbetalipoproteinemia)	47	1:1000–5000	Autosomal recessive (with modifiers)	Apolipoprotein E	19	Point mutation leading to single amino acid substitution in apolipoprotein E	Decreased binding to lipoprotein receptors	Accumulation in plasma of chylomicron and very low density lipoprotein remnants (collectively, β-very low density lipoproteins), leading to hyperlipidemia and atherosclerosis.
Familial hypercholesterolemia, multiple allelic types	48	1:500 in most populations; more frequent in Lebanese and Afrikaaners	Autosomal dominant	LDL receptor	19 p13.1-p13.3	13 different mutations characterized at DNA level; include deletion insertion, nonsense, frameshift, and missense mutations	Absent or deficient receptor activity (homozygotes); half normal receptor activity (heterozygotes)	Absent or deficient receptor-mediated endocytosis of LDL causes LDL to accumulate in plasma. Hypercholesterolemia and artherosclerosis results.
Hepatic triglyceride lipase (HGTL) deficiency	49	Rare; 3 families	Autosomal recessive	Unknown	Unknown	Unknown	Quantitative deficiency of HGTL	Hypercholesterolemia, hypertriglyceridemia, and increased susceptibility to arteriosclerosis.

Apolipoprotein A-I deficiency: Type I (apo A-I/apo C-III deficiency) Type II (apo A-I deficiency without xanthoma) Type III (apo A-I deficiency with xanthoma)	49	All rare	Autosomal recessive	Only known for type I; apo A-I and apo C-III both affected	11q23	5.5-kb inversion in 4th exon of apo A-I gene producing gene fusion of apo A-I and C-III genes	Deficiency of apo A-I and apo C-III	Low apo A-I level leads to low HDL levels, and accumulation of cholesteryl containing deposits in the cornea, the blood vessels. Xanthoma occurs in types I and III. Coronary insufficiency is the most serious disability.
Fish eye disease	49	2 families	Unknown	Unknown	Unknown	Unknown	Quantitative deficiency of lecithin-cholesterol acyltransferase, which esterifies free cholesterol in HDL	Low HDL cholesterol, corneal opacities.
Cholesteryl ester transport protein (CETP) deficiency	49	2 families from Japan	Unknown	Unknown	Unknown	Unknown	Quantitative deficiency of enzyme which transfers cholesteryl ester from HDL to VLDL and LDL	Hypercholesterolemia, hypertriglyceridemia, elevated HDL cholesterol levels. No arteriosclerotic heart disease or xanthoma.
Lipoprotein lipase deficiency	49	Covered in Chap. 45						
Tangier disease	50	Rare mutant	Autosomal codominant	Unknown	Unknown	Unknown	HDL-deficiency due to hypercatabolism of apo A-I–containing lipoproteins	Cholesteryl ester storage in histiocytes, Schwann cells, nevus cells, and others. Splenomegaly and hyperplastic orange-yellow tonsils.
Cerebrotendinous xanthomatosis	51	More than 100 but less than 150 cases	Autosomal recessive	Hepatic mitochondrial 26-hydroxylase involved in bile acid biosynthesis	Unknown	Unknown	Markedly reduced enzyme activity	Accumulation of cholesterol and intermediates in bile acid biosynthesis. Reduced biosynthesis of normal bile acids. Excretion of huge amounts of bile alcohols in feces and urine.
Phytosterolemia (sitosterolemia)	51	22 cases	? Autosomal recessive	Unknown	Unknown	Unknown	Unknown	Hyperabsorption of phytosterols and shellfish sterols leading to tendon and tuberous xanthoma and a strong predisposition for premature coronary atherosclerosis.
Part 8: Porphyrins and heme								
δ-Aminolevulinic acid dehydratase porphyria	52	3 cases	Autosomal recessive	δ-Aminolevulinic acid dehydratase	Unknown	Unknown	Minimal enzyme activity	Overproduction of δ-aminolevulinic acid, leading to neurologic disturbances.
Acute intermittent porphyria	52	1:10,000–20,000 (U.S.A.)	Autosomal dominant	Porphobilinogen deaminase	11q23-qter	Unknown	Decreased enzyme activity (~50%)	Overproduction of porphyrin precursors, leading to neurologic disturbances.

SUMMARY TABLE *(continued)*

Name of disease	Chap. no.	Frequency	Mode of inheritance	Mutant gene product	Chromosomal location	Expression: Altered DNA structure	Expression: Disturbed protein function	Expression: Disrupted cell and organ function
Part 8: Porphyrins and heme (continued)								
Congenital erythropoietic porphyria	52	<200 cases	Autosomal recessive	Uroporphyrinogen III cosynthase	Unknown	Unknown	Decreased enzyme activity	Overproduction of type I porphyrin isomers, leading to photosensitivity and hemolytic anemia.
Porphyria cutanea tarda (familial form)	52	Unknown	Autosomal dominant	Uroporphyrinogen decarboxylase	1pter-p21	Unknown	Decreased enzyme activity (~50%)	Excessive hepatic production of 8- and 7-carboxylate porphyrins, leading to photosensitivity.
Hepatoerythropoietic porphyria	52	16 cases	Autosomal recessive	Uroporphyrinogen decarboxylase	1pter-p21	$Gly_{281} \rightarrow Glu$ mutation (in one case)	Minimal enzyme activity	Excessive hepatic production of 8- and 7-carboxylate porphyrins, leading to photosensitivity.
Hereditary coproporphyria	52	1:500,000 (Denmark)	Autosomal dominant	Coproporphyrinogen oxidase	Unknown	Unknown	Decreased enzyme activity (~50%)	Overproduction of porphyrin precursors and coproporphyrin leading to neurologic disturbances ± photosensitivity.
Variegate porphyria	52	1:75,000 (Finland)	Autosomal dominant	Protoporphyrinogen oxidase	Unknown	Unknown	Decreased enzyme activity	Overproduction of porphyrin precursors and protoporphyrin, leading to neurologic disturbances ± photosensitivity.
Erythropoietic protoporphyria	52	300 cases (1961–1976)	Autosomal dominant	Ferrochelatase	Unknown	Unknown	Decreased enzyme activity	Overproduction of protoporphyrin leading to mild to moderate photosensitivity.
Crigler-Najjar syndrome type I	53	Over 70 cases	Autosomal recessive	Hepatic bilirubin UDPglucuronyl transferase	Unknown	Unknown	Absent enzyme activity	Substrate (unconjugated bilirubin) accumulates in brain, resulting in kernicterus.
Crigler-Najjar syndrome type II	53	Uncommon	? Autosomal recessive	Hepatic bilirubin UDPglucuronyl transferase	Unknown	Unknown	Reduced enzyme activity	Partial ability to conjugate bilirubin leads to mild unconjugated hyperbilirubinemia with increased proportion of bilirubin monoglucuronide in bile. Usually benign disorder.

Gilbert syndrome	53	~1:30	? Autosomal dominant	Unknown	Unknown	Unknown	Unknown	Impaired hepatic uptake of bilirubin and reduced activity of hepatic bilirubin uridine diphosphoglucuronyl transferase lead to mild unconjugated hyperbilirubinemia and increased proportion of bilirubin monoglucuronide in bile. Benign disorder.
Dubin-Johnson syndrome	53	Rare worldwide; 1:1300 in Persian Jews	Autosomal recessive	Unknown	Unknown	Unknown	Unknown	Failure of biliary excretion of conjugated bilirubin produces mild conjugated hyperbilirubinemia.
Rotor syndrome	53	Rare	Autosomal recessive	Unknown	Unknown	Unknown	Unknown	Partial failure of biliary excretion of conjugated bilirubin causes mild hyperbilirubinemia.
Part 9: Metals								
Menkes disease	54	1:100,000	X-linked recessive	Unknown	? Xq13	Unknown	Unknown	Defective intracellular transport of copper leads to deficiency of copper-containing enzymes and causes arterial and brain degeneration.
Occipital horn syndrome	54	Rare	X-linked recessive	Unknown	Unknown—? allelic to Menkes disease	Unknown	Unknown	Defective biliary excretion of copper leads to deficiency of lysyl oxidase and causes skin and joint laxity, hernias, and urinary tract diverticulas.
Wilson disease	54	1:50,000	Autosomal recessive	Unknown	13q14	Unknown	Unknown	Defective biliary excretion of copper leads to accumulation in liver (cirrhosis), cornea (Kayser-Fleischer rings), and basal ganglia (movement disorder).
Hereditary (idiopathic) hemochromatosis	55	~1:200–500 of European populations (males and females) are homozygous for hereditary hemochromatosis. A majority of cases are clinically unexpressed.	Autosomal	Unknown recessive	6p21.3	Unknown	Unknown	A greater proportion of the dietary iron taken up by the mucosal cells of the intestinal tract is absorbed into the body. When the body iron content reaches massive proportions (usually 15 g), many organs are severely damaged, including the liver, heart, and pancreas.

SUMMARY TABLE *(continued)*

Name of disease	Chap. no.	Frequency	Mode of inheritance	Mutant gene product	Chromosomal location	Expression: Altered DNA structure	Expression: Disturbed protein function	Expression: Disrupted cell and organ function
Part 9: Metals (continued)								
Molybdenum cofactor deficiency	56	15 cases	Autosomal recessive	Enzyme required for molybdenum cofactor biosynthesis	Unknown	Unknown	Absent or deficient activities of sulfite oxidase, xanthine dehydrogenase, and aldehyde oxidase	Sulfite, thiosulfate, *S*-sulfocysteine, hypoxanthine, and xanthine levels are elevated. Mental retardation, neurologic disturbances (seizures), and dislocated ocular lenses occur.
Part 10: Peroxisomes								
Peroxisome biogenesis, disorders of: Zellweger syndrome Neonatal adrenoleukodystrophy Infantile Refsum disease Hyperpipecolic acidemia	57	Combined incidence estimated at 1:25,000–50,000	Autosomal recessive for all	Unknown	Unknown	Unknown	Unknown for all	Failure of peroxisome assembly and deficiency of multiple peroxisomal enzymes in Zellweger syndrome. Impaired peroxisomal function, by any cause, results in accumulation of very long chain fatty acids, pipecolic acid, and phytanic acid and reduced synthesis of plasmalogens and bile acids. Biochemical alterations result in pathologic changes in brain, liver, kidney, eye, adrenal, bone, and other organs.
Adrenoleukodystrophy	58	1:100,000 minimum	X-linked	Unknown	Xq28	Unknown	Unknown	Accumulation of unbranched saturated very long chain fatty acids ($C_{24.0}$–$C_{26.0}$) occurs. How this relates to the clinical phenotype of progressive dementia, visual impairment, seizures, and adrenal insufficiency is not known.
Adrenomyeloneuropathy	58	1:50,000 minimum	X-linked	Unknown	Xq28	Unknown	Unknown	A milder phenotype of adrenoleukodystrophy which may occur in the same kindred. There is also accumulation of very long chain fatty acids, but the clinical phenotype is paraparesis and sphincter

Adrenomyeloneuropathy (continued)								disturbance progressing over several decades and adrenal insufficiency. From 10 to 15% female heterozygotes develop a phenotype resembling adrenomyeloneuropathy.
Refsum disease	59	~100 cases	Autosomal recessive	Phytanic acid α-hydroxylase	Unknown	Unknown	Deficient enzyme activity	Accumulation of substrate (phytanic acid) is associated with the development of retinitis pigmentosa, ataxia, and peripheral neuropathy in young adults.
Acatalasemia	60	1:25,000–250,000 (worldwide)	Autosomal recessive	Catalase (mutations probably multiple, all uncharacterized)	11p13	Unknown	Unstable enzyme or decreased enzyme synthesis	Deficiency most marked in red cells. Associated gum disease in some patients. Otherwise, affected subjects are normal.
Part 11: Lysosomal enzymes								
Mucopolysaccharidosis I & V (Hurler, Scheie, and Hurler-Scheie syndromes)	61	~1:100,000 for Hurler syndrome 1:600,000 for Scheie syndrome	Autosomal recessive; disorders are allelic.	α-L-iduronidase	22pter-q11	Unknown	Absent enzyme activity	Defective lysosomal degradation of dermatan sulfate and heparan sulfate leads to storage of the incompletely degraded glycosaminoglycans. Nearly all cells and organs are affected.
Mucopolysaccharidosis II (Hunter syndrome)	61	1:70,000 in Israel; rarer in British and British Columbian surveys	X-linked recessive	Iduronate sulfatase	Xq26-q28	Unknown	Absent enzyme activity	Defective lysosomal degradation of dermatan sulfate and heparan sulfate leads to storage of the incompletely degraded glycosaminoglycans. Nearly all cells and organs are affected.
Mucopolysaccharidosis III (Sanfilippo syndrome) types A–D	61	1:24,000 (all types combined) in the Netherlands IIIA and IIIB most common; A > B in northern Europe, B > A in southern Europe	Autosomal recessive Four types nonallelic	IIIA: heparan-*N*-sulfatase IIIB: α-*N*-acetylglucosaminidase IIIC: acetyl-CoA: α-glucosaminide acetyltransferase IIID: *N*-acetylglucosamine-6-sulfatase	Unknown	Unknown	Absent enzyme activity	Defective lysosomal degradation of heparan sulfate leads to lysosomal storage of the partially degraded glycosaminoglycan. Cellular function is disrupted primarily in the central nervous system.
Mucopolysaccharidosis IV (Morquio syndrome) types A and B	61	1:300,000	Autosomal recessive Two types nonallelic	IVA: galactose-6-sulfatase IVB: β-galactosidase	IVA: unknown IVB: 3p21-cen	Unknown	IVA: absent enzyme activity IVB: defective enzyme activity	Defective lysosomal degradation of keratan sulfate leads to lysosomal storage of the glycosaminoglycan. Cellular function is disrupted primarily in cornea, skeletal, and cardiovascular systems.

SUMMARY TABLE *(continued)*

Name of disease	Chap. no.	Frequency	Mode of inheritance	Mutant gene product	Chromosomal location	Expression: Altered DNA structure	Expression: Disturbed protein function	Expression: Disrupted cell and organ function
Part 11: Lysosomal enzymes (continued)								
Mucopolysaccharidosis VI (Maroteaux-Lamy syndrome)	61	Rare	Autosomal recessive	*N*-acetylgalactosamine-4-sulfatase (arylsulfatase B)	5p11-q13	Unknown	Absent enzyme activity	Defective lysosomal degradation of dermatan sulfate leads to lysosomal storage of the partially degraded glycosaminoglycan. Cellular function is disrupted in most tissues.
Mucopolysaccharidosis VII (Sly syndrome)	61	Very rare	Autosomal recessive	β-Glucuronidase	7q11.2-q22	Unknown	Absent or deficient enzyme activity	Defective lysosomal degradation of dermatan sulfate, heparan sulfate, and chondroitin sulfates leads to lysosomal storage of the partially degraded glycosaminoglycans. Cellular function is disrupted in most tissues.
I-cell disease (ML-II)	62	Rare (less rare in Japan ?)	Autosomal recessive	UDP-*N*-acetylglucosamine: lysosomal enzyme *N*-acetylglucosaminyl-1-phosphotransferase	Unknown	Unknown	Phosphorylation of many lysosomal enzymes	Impaired lysosomal function in mesenchymal cells, especially fibroblasts.
Pseudo-Hurler polydystrophy (ML III)	62	Rare	Autosomal recessive	UDP-*N*-acetylglucosamine: lysosomal enzyme *N*-acetylglucosaminyl-1-phosphotransferase	Unknown	Unknown	Phosphorylation of many lysosomal enzymes	Impaired lysosomal function in mesenchymal cells, especially fibroblasts.
Mannosidosis	63	50–100 cases	Autosomal recessive	Lysosomal α-D-mannosidase	19p13-q13	Unknown	Deficient or unstable enzyme activity	Accumulation of oligosaccharides causes tissue damage.
Sialidosis	63	50-100 cases	Autosomal recessive	Lysosomal α-neuraminidase (glycoprotein substrate)	10pter-q23	Unknown	Deficient enzyme activity	Accumulation of oligosaccharides causes tissue damage.
Aspartylglycosaminuria	63	70-100 cases in Finland; extremely rare elsewhere	Autosomal recessive	Lysosomal aspartylglycosaminidase	4q	Unknown	Deficient enzyme activity	Accumulation of glycopeptides causes tissue damage.
Fucosidosis	63	30-60 cases	Autosomal recessive	Lysosomal α-L-fucosidase	1p34	Unknown	Deficient enzyme activity	Accumulation of glycolipid, glycopeptides, and oligosaccharides causes tissue damage.

Wolman disease and cholesteryl ester storage disease	64	Wolman disease; 45 cases Cholesteryl ester storage disease; 25 cases	Autosomal recessive	Acid lipase	10q	Unknown	Deficient enzyme activity	Cholesteryl esters and triglycerides accumulate in lysosomes of body cells producing hepatic, intestinal, and adrenal dysfunction. Death in infancy in Wolman disease. Hyperlipidemia and atherosclerosis with survival to early adulthood in cholesteryl ester storage disease.
Ceramidase deficiency (Farber lipogranulomatosis)	65	Rare; 40 cases	Autosomal recessive	Lysosomal acid ceramidase	Unknown	Unknown	Deficient enzyme activity	Accumulation of substrate (ceramide) leads to granulomatous reaction in joints, subcutaneous tissues, larynx, and other tissues. Accumulation of ceramides and gangliosides in lysosomes of neurons leads to spinal cord and brain dysfunction.
Niemann-Pick disease type I (primary sphingomyelin storage)	66	Rare (regional variations)	Autosomal recessive	Type I: sphingomyelinase	Unknown	Unknown	Type I: deficient sphingomyelinase activity	Type I: Accumulation of sphingomyelin and cholesterol in cells leads to dysfunction.
Neimann-Pick disease type II: (secondary sphingomyelin storage)	66	Rare	Autosomal recessive	Type II: unknown	Unknown	Unknown	Type II: unknown	Type II: Accumulation of cholesterol, glycolipid, bis (monoacylglycero) phosphate, and some sphingomyelin.
Gaucher disease type 1 (nonneurologic)	67	1:600 among Ashkenazi Jews; rare in the general population	Autosomal recessive	Glucocerebrosidase	1q21	Probably many $Asn_{370} \rightarrow Ser$	Decreased catalytic activity and some instability of enzyme protein	Accumulation of glucosylceramide in lysosomes of macrophages leads to injury of it and surrounding cells (not including neurons).
Gaucher disease type 2 (infantile neurologic)	67	Rare; no ethnic predilection	Autosomal recessive	Glucocerebrosidase	1q21	Probably many $Leu_{444} \rightarrow Pro$	Small decrease in catalytic activity but major decrease in enzyme protein stability which results in little or no lysosomal glucocerebrosidase	Accumulation of glucosylceramide in lysosomes of macrophages which leads to injury of cell and surrounding cells (including neurons).
Gaucher disease type 3 (juvenile neurologic)	67	Rare; genetic isolate in Boden, Sweden	Autosomal recessive	Glucocerebrosidase	1q21	Unknown	Small decrease in catalytic activity and unstable enzyme protein result in significant decreased lysosomal glucocerebrosidase	Accumulation of glucosylceramide in lysosomes of macrophages which leads to injury of cell and surrounding cells (including neurons).

SUMMARY TABLE *(continued)*

Name of disease	*Chap. no.*	*Frequency*	*Mode of inheritance*	*Mutant gene product*	*Chromosomal location*	*Expression* *Altered DNA structure*	*Disturbed protein function*	*Disrupted cell and organ function*
Part 11: Lysosomal enzymes (continued)								
Globoid-cell leukodystrophy (Krabbe disease)	68	1:50,0000 in Sweden, much lower elsewhere 1:170 in unusual inbred Druze population in Israel	Autosomal recessive	Lysosomal galactosylceramidase (galactocerebroside β-galactosidase)	Unknown	Unknown	Absent enzyme activity	Accumulation of a toxic natural substrate (galactosylsphingosine-psychosine) leads to disappearance of oligodendroglia and cessation of myelination, resulting in destruction of CNS white matter and peripheral neuropathy.
Multiple sulfatase deficiency	69	40 cases	Autosomal recessive	6 lysosomal sulfatases and steroid sulfatase	Unknown	Unknown	Unstable enzyme proteins	Failure to hydrolyze sulfatides and sulfated mucopolysaccharides leads to their accumulation in neural and extraneural tissues causing demyelination with progressive CNS deterioration, facial and skeletal dysmorphism, hepatosplenomegaly, sulfatiduria, and mucopolysaccharidurria.
Metachromatic leukodystrophy	69	1:100,000	Autosomal recessive	Arylsulfatase A	22q13	Unknown	Deficient enzyme activity	Failure to hydrolyze sulfatides leads to their accumulation in the nervous system, kidney, gallbladder, and other organs, causing demyelination, progressive CNS deterioration, and sulfatiduria.
Fabry disease	70	1:40,000: panethnic	X-linked	α-Galactosidase A	Xq22	Partial deletions, partial duplications, missense mutations	Nonfunctional or unstable enzyme protein	Accumulation of substrates with terminal galactosyl moieties (globotriaosylceramide, galabiaosylceramide, blood group B substances) particularly in vascular endothelial lysosomes, leading to ischemia and infarction.

Schindler disease (α-*N*-acetylgalactosaminidase deficiency)	70	**Unknown, very rare**	**Autosomal recessive**	**α-*N*-acetylgalactos-aminidase**	**22q13-qter**	**Probable point mutations**	**Deficient activity of α-*N*-acetylgalactos-aminidase**	**Accumulation of glycoprotein, glycopeptide, glycosphingo-lipid, and mucopolysac-charide substrates with α-*N*-galactosaminyl residues. Major pathologic substrate deposition is the terminal axons primarily in gray matter.**
G_{M1} gangliosidosis	71	Unknown	Autosomal recessive	Acid β-galactosidase (GLB1)	3p21-cen	Unknown	Deficient enzyme activity	Lysosomal storage of ganglioside G_{M1} and galactosyl oligosaccharides.
Galactosialidosis	71	Uncommon but not rare in Japan; rare elsewhere	Autosomal recessive	20	Unknown	Unknown	Reduced to absent 32-kDa lysosomal protective protein which is required for realizing or stabilizing activities of β-galactosidase and oligosaccharide neuraminidase	Lysosomal accumulation of glycolipids and oligosaccharides producing dysostosis multiplex, some Hurler-like features, and CNS abnormalities including dementia.
G_{M2} gangliosidosis: hexosaminidase α-subunit deficiency (variant B, Tay-Sachs disease)	72	1:300,000; 100 times higher in Ashkenazi Jews	Autosomal recessive	α subunit of β-hexosaminidase	15q22-q25.1	Multiple alleles: deletion (French-Canadian) and non-deletion	Absent or defective hexosaminidase A (αβ) activity	Accumulation of ganglioside G_{M2} in lysosomes causes neuronal dysfunction.
G_{M2} gangliosidosis: hexosaminidase β-subunit deficiency (variant O, Sandhoff disease)	72	1:300,000	Autosomal recessive	β subunit of β-hexosaminidase	5q13	Multiple alleles: deletion and nondeletion	Absent hexosaminidase A (αβ) and B (ββ) activity	Accumulation of ganglioside G_{M2} and water-soluble substrates causes neuronal dysfunction and organomegaly.
G_{M2} gangliosidosis: G_{M2} activator deficiency	72	Very rare	Autosomal recessive	G_{M2} activator protein	5	Unknown	Absent or defective G_{M2} activator	Accumulation of ganglioside G_{M2} in lysosomes causes neuronal dysfunction.
Part 12: Hormones: synthesis and action								
Pendred syndrome	73	~1:15,000	Autosomal recessive	Unknown	Unknown	Unknown	Unknown	Defect of H_2O_2-generating system, hypothyroidism and goiter, deaf-mutism.
Hereditary hyperthyroidism	73	Very rare	Autosomal dominant	Unknown	Unknown	Unknown	Unknown	Constitutive stimulation of the thyrocytes with autonomy and hyperthyroidism, goiter.
Thyrotropin resistance, *see also* Pseudohypoparathyroidism Ia	73	Rare	Autosomal recessive	Unknown	Unknown	Unknown	Unknown	Unresponsiveness of thyrocytes to thyrotropin and consequent hypothyroidism.
Iodide transport defect	73	Rare	? Autosomal recessive	Unknown	Unknown	Unknown	Unknown	Absence of iodide transport; hypothyroidism and goiter.
Iodotyrosine deiodinase defect	73	Rare	Autosomal recessive	Unknown	Unknown	Unknown	Defect in iodotyrosine deiodinase	Loss of iodotyrosines, and consequently of iodine, from the thyroid and in the urine; hypothyroidism and goiter.

SUMMARY TABLE *(continued)*

Name of disease	Chap. no.	Frequency	Mode of inheritance	Mutant gene product	Chromosomal location	Expression: Altered DNA structure	Expression: Disturbed protein function	Expression: Disrupted cell and organ function
Part 12: Hormones: synthesis and action (continued)								
Thyroxine-binding globulin deficiency	73	~1:4000	X-linked	Unknown	Xq	Unknown	Absence of serum thyroxine-binding globulin	None, benign.
Thyroglobulin defect	73	Rare	Autosomal recessive with one exception	? Thyroglobulin in some	8q24 for thyroglobulin	Unknown	Possibly abnormal thyroglobulin, proven in cattle	Reduced or dysfunctional thyroglobulin leading to hypothyroidism.
Classic steroid 21-hydroxylase deficiency salt-wasting type	74	1:19,000	Autosomal recessive	Steroid 21-hydroxylase	6p23 (HLA complex)	Deletions, gene conversions, and nonsense mutations	Absent or truncated enzyme with no activity	Nearly absent synthesis of cortisol and aldosterone in zona fasciculata of adrenal cortex. Deficiency of these hormones leads to impaired salt and water homeostasis.
Classic steroid 21-hydroxylase deficiency simple virilizing type	74	1:58,000	Autosomal recessive	Steroid 21-hydroxylase	6p23 (HLA complex)	Multiple point mutations	Decreased enzyme activity	Markedly decreased synthesis of cortisol in zona fasciculata of adrenal cortex. Compensatory overproduction of cortisol precursors and adrenal androgens leads to virilization.
Nonclassic steroid 21-hydroxylase deficiency	74	1:100 in some ethnic groups	Autosomal recessive	Steroid 21-hydroxylase	6p23 (HLA complex)	Associated with duplicated CYP21A pseudogene; point mutations	Decreased enzyme activity	Decreased cortisol synthesis in zona fasciculata of adrenal cortex.
Disorders of the androgen receptor (complete testicular feminization, incomplete testicular feminization, Reifenstein syndrome, infertile male syndrome)	75	1:64,000 with 46XY (complete testicular feminization)	X-linked recessive	Androgen receptor protein	Xq	Unknown	Absent, unstable, or deficient protein	Abnormality of the androgen receptor complex in androgen target cells leads to defective androgen action in utero and in postembryonic life.
Steroid 5α-reductase deficiency	75	Rare	Autosomal recessive	Steroid 5α-reductase	Unknown	Unknown	Absent or unstable enzyme activity	Deficiency of product (dihydrotestosterone) leads to a form of male pseudohermaphroditism in which genetic males have male genitalia, but female external genitalia.

Steroid sulfatase deficiency (X-linked ichthyosis)	76	1:2000–6000 males	X-linked recessive	3 β-hydroxysteroid sulfatase	Xp22.3-pter	Gene deletion in 90% of cases	Absent immunoreactive and enzymatically active protein (both deletion and nondeletion patients)	Accumulation of cholesterol sulfate in stratum corneum is responsible for abnormal desquamation. Some patients have other abnormalities due to deletion of contiguous genes.
Isolated human chorionic somatomammotropin deficiency	77	Rare	Autosomal recessive	Chorionic somatomammotropin	17q22-q24	Gene deletion of both functional loci (type 1A) or of one locus (type 1B)	Absent (type 1A) or deficient (type 1B)	Absent or deficient chorionic somatomammotropin during pregnancy. Affected children have normal intrauterine and postnatal growth.
Rieger syndrome	77	Rare	Autosomal dominant	Unknown	Unknown	Unknown	Deficient human growth hormone and other anterior pituitary hormones (ACTH, FSH, LH, and TSH)	Deficiency of pituitary hormones causes dwarfism, adrenal insufficiency, hypothyroidism, and delayed sexual development.
Pituitary aplasia	77	Rare	Autosomal recessive or sporadic	Unknown	Unknown	Unknown	Absent or deficient human growth hormone and other anterior pituitary hormones (ACTH, FSH, LH, and TSH)	Aplasia of pituitary results in panhypopituitarism, dwarfism, and adrenal insufficiency.
Holoprosencephaly	77	Unknown	Autosomal dominant or recessive, associated with chromosomal defects, or sporadic	Unknown	Unknown	Unknown	Absent or deficient ACTH, FSH, LH, and TSH	Developmental defect associated with median cleft lip and palate. Associated anomalies of the hypothalamus can cause anterior pituitary hormone deficiencies.
Ectrodactyly-ectodermal dysplasia-clefting (EEC) syndrome	77	Unknown	Autosomal recessive	Unknown	Unknown	Unknown	Deficiency of growth hormone and other anterior pituitary hormone deficiency in associated with CNS malformations that occur in some of these patients	Defects of hands and feet; ectodermal dysplasia causes fair skin, anodontia, and cleft palate. Patients with dwarfism due to human growth hormone deficiency usually respond to human growth hormone.
Panhypopituitary dwarfism type II	77	Rare	X-linked	Unknown	X	Unknown	Deficient human growth hormone, ACTH, FSH, LH, and TSH	Deficiency of human growth hormone causes dwarfism. Associated endocrine deficiencies cause delayed sexual development, hypothyroidism, and adrenal insufficiency.
Panhypopituitary dwarfism type I	77	Rare	Autosomal recessive	Unknown	Unknown	Unknown GH1 locus does not cosegregate with disorder	Deficient human growth hormone, ACTH, FSH, LH, and TSH	Panhypopituitinism results in dwarfism, delayed sexual development, hypothyroidism, and adrenal insufficiency.

SUMMARY TABLE *(continued)*

Name of disease	Chap. no.	Frequency	Mode of inheritance	Mutant gene product	Chromosomal location	Expression: Altered DNA structure	Expression: Disturbed protein function	Expression: Disrupted cell and organ function
Part 12: Hormones: synthesis and action (continued)								
Laron dwarfism	77	Unknown	Autosomal recessive	Unknown	Unknown	Unknown	Deficient growth hormone receptor function?	Normal amounts of normal growth hormone are produced, but insulinlike growth factor 1 levels are low and do not respond to exogenous growth hormone. This defect in the mediator of growth hormone function results in dwarfism.
Isolated growth hormone deficiency type IA (IGHD1A)	77	25 cases	Autosomal recessive	Growth hormone	17q22-q24	Gene deletion	Growth hormone absent	Absence of human growth hormone results in severe dwarfism. Patients often produce anti-growth hormone antibodies when given growth hormone.
Isolated growth hormone deficiency type IB (IGHD1B)	77	Unknown	Autosomal recessive	Unknown	Unknown	Unknown	Growth hormone deficiency	Deficiency of human growth hormone results in dwarfism. Patients usually respond to exogenous growth hormone.
Isolated growth hormone deficiency type II	77	Unknown	Autosomal dominant	Unknown	Unknown	Unknown	Growth hormone deficiency	Deficiency of growth hormone results in dwarfism. Patients usually respond to exogenous growth hormone.
Isolated growth hormone deficiency type III	77	Rare	X-linked	Unknown	X	Unknown	Growth hormone deficiency	Deficiency of growth hormone results in dwarfism. Patients usually respond to exogenous growth hormone. Hypogammaglobulinemia (deficient IgG, IgA, IgM, and IgE) also occurs.
Nephrogenic diabetes insipidus	78	Uncommon but not rare	X-linked with mild and variable manifestations in females	Unknown	Xq28	Unknown	Unknown	Renal tubular cells fail to accumulate cyclic AMP in response to vasopressin. The resulting vasopressin unresponsiveness leads to polyuria, hyposthenuria, and polydipsia.

Pseudohypoparathyroidism type Ia	79	Unknown; over 100 cases	? Autosomal dominant	α Subunit of stimulatory guanine nucleotide–binding protein associated with adenylate cyclase (?)	Unknown	Unknown	Reduced synthesis of protein	Deficiency of protein leads to generalized hormone resistance with hypoparathyroidism, hypothyroidism, and hypogonadism most prominent clinically. Other abnormalities include: obesity, short stature, mental retardation, and bony anomalies collectively termed *Albright osteodystrophy*.
Pseudohypoparathyroidism type Ib	79	Unknown; over 50 cases	Unknown	Unknown	Unknown	Unknown	Unknown	Isolated resistance to parathyroidism hormone due to defect in receptor-adenylate cyclase complex leads to parathyroidism.
Hereditary simple and selective deficiency of $1,25(OH)_2D$ (pseudo-vitamin D deficiency type I, vitamin D dependency type I)	80	Unknown	Autosomal recessive	$25(OH)D_3$-1 α-hydroxylase (so far confirmed only in similar disease in pigs)	Unknown	Unknown	Deficient enzyme activity (putative and by analogy with pig model)	Deficient product $[1,25(OH)_2D]$ causes features of vitamin D deficiency.
Hereditary generalized resistance to $1,25(OH)_2D$ (pseudo-vitamin D deficiency type II, vitamin D dependency type II)	80	Unknown	Autosomal recessive	Receptor for $1,25(OH)_2D$	Unknown	Unknown several alleles, (at one or more loci ?)	1. Hormone binding negative 2. Decreased maximal capacity of hormone binding 3. Decreased affinity of hormone binding 4. Normal hormone binding but undetectable nuclear localization 5. Nuclear localization positive	Disrupted cell and organ Decreased or absent $1,25(OH)_2D$ action in all cells causes features of vitamin D deficiency. The most severely affected cases show alopecia.
Idiopathic hypercalcemia with supravalvular aortic stenosis (Williams-Beuren syndrome)	80	Unknown	Unknown	Unknown	Unknown	Unknown	Unknown	Hypercalcemia, supravalvular aortic stenosis, characteristic "elfin" facies.
Part 13: Vitamins								
Methylenetetrahydrofolate reductase deficiency	81	>25 cases	Autosomal recessive	Methylenetetrahydrofolate reductase	Unknown	Unknown	Absent or deficient enzyme activity	Lack of formation of methyltetrahydrofolate results in elevated levels of homocysteine and decreased levels of methionine. Considerable phenotypic heterogeneity, but most patients have severe neurologic disturbances.

SUMMARY TABLE *(continued)*

Name of disease	Chap. no.	Frequency	Mode of inheritance	Mutant gene product	Chromosomal location	Expression: Altered DNA structure	Expression: Disturbed protein function	Expression: Disrupted cell and organ function
Part 13: Vitamins (continued)								
cblG (functional methionine synthase deficiency)	81	3 cases	Autosomal recessive	Unknown	Unknown	Unknown	Decreased activity of vitamin B_{12}–dependent methionine synthase	Elevated homocysteine and low methionine levels; failure to regenerate tetrahydrofolate. Patients have megaloblastic anemia and neurologic abnormalities.
cblE (functional methionine synthase deficiency)	81	4 cases	? Autosomal recessive; all cases male	Unknown	Unknown	Unknown	Decreased activity of a reducing system associated with B_{12}-dependent methionine synthase	Impaired methylcobalamin formation results in elevated homocysteine levels, decreased methionine levels, and failure to regenerate tetrahydrofolate. Patients have megaloblastic anemia and neurologic abnormalities.
Glutamate formiminotransferase deficiency	81	Rare; 13 cases	Autosomal recessive	Glutamate formiminotransferase	Unknown	Unknown	Low levels of enzyme reported in liver and erythrocytes	Elevated levels of formiminoglutamic acid. Some patients have neurologic abnormalities; significance not clear.
Hereditary folate malabsorption	81	12 cases	? Autosomal recessive, excess of females	Unknown	Unknown	Unknown	Defective transport system for folates in intestine and choroid plexus	Deficiency of folate derivatives leading to megaloblastic anemia and neurologic abnormalities.
Homocystinuria (cobalamin-dependent) (two nonallelic forms designated *cblE* and *cblG*)	82	Rare (6 cases)	Unknown	Unknown	Unknown	Unknown	Unknown	Impaired cytoplasmic utilization of cobalamin results in decreased activity of N^5-methyltetrahydrofolate-homocysteine methyltransferase and deficient synthesis of methylcobalamin and methionine. Clinical findings include developmental delay and megaloblastic anemia.
Transcobalamin II deficiency	82	Rare	Autosomal recessive	Transcobalamin II (TC II)	22q	Unknown	Absent TC II protein; decreased binding of TC II–cobalamin to cellular receptors	Defective function of TC II leads to abnormal transport of cobalamin into cells and to functional cellular cobalamin deficiency. Megaloblastic anemia and eventual neurologic and immunologic dysfunction are important findings.

Enterocyte cobalamin malabsorption (Imerslünd-Grasbeck syndrome) (possibly multiple nonallelic forms)	82	Rare (more common in Finns and North African Jews)	? Autosomal recessive; others unknown	Enterocyte intrinsic factor receptor	Unknown	Unknown	Failure of specific enterocyte receptor to bind intrinsic factor–cobalamin complex; failure of transfer of cobalamin from intrinsic factor to transcobalamin II	Impaired transintestinal transport of cobalamin leads to functional cobalamin deficiency. Hematologic and neurologic abnormalities are major clinical findings.
Intrinsic factor deficiency	82	Rare	Autosomal recessive	Intrinsic factor (IF)	Unknown	Unknown	Absent IF protein; increased lability of IF; decreased binding of cobalamin to IF; decreased binding of IF to specific enterocyte receptors	Defective IF function leads to reduced intestinal cobalamin transport and functional cobalamin deficiency. Hematologic abnormalities, particularly megaloblastic anemia, and neurologic dysfunction are prominent.
Holocarboxylase synthetase deficiency	83	Rare	Autosomal recessive	Holocarboxylase synthetase ?	Unknown	Unknown	Deficient holocarboxylase synthetase activity	Failure to biotinylate enzymes causes secondary deficiency of four carboxylases causing organic acidemia.
Biotinidase deficiency	83	1:50,000–70,000 whites by newborn screening	Autosomal recessive	Biotinidase	Unknown	Unknown	Deficient biotinidase activity	Failure to absorb and recycle biotin causes secondary deficiency of four carboxylases causing organic acidemia.
Part 14: Blood and blood forming tissues								
Protein C deficiency	84	Rare ?	Autosomal dominant	Protein C	2	Missense and nonsense known	Decreased anticoagulant activity	Impaired regulation of blood coagulation.
Prothrombin deficiency	84	<50 cases	Autosomal recessive	Prothrombin	11p11-q12	Several, Barcelona $Arg_{271} \rightarrow Cys$; Tokushima $Arg_{98} \rightarrow Trp$	Barcelona prevents cleavage by factor Xa. Tokushima has 21% clotting activity.	Impaired blood coagulation.
Factor VII deficiency	84	Estimated 1:500,000	Autosomal recessive	Factor VII	13q34-qter	Not established	Decreased factor VII coagulant activity	Impaired blood coagulation.
Factor IX deficiency (hemophilia B)	84	1:70,000	X-linked	Factor IX	Xq26-q27	Deletions, splicing abnormalities, and missense	Absence of protein, protein with reduced coagulant activity or abnormal susceptibility to cleavage for activation	Impaired blood coagulation.
Factor X deficiency	84	About 50 families	Autosomal recessive	Factor X	13q34-qter	Not established	Decreased coagulation activity	Impaired blood coagulation.
Afibrinogenemia	85	150 cases	Autosomal recessive	Fibrinogen	4q23-q32	Unknown	Absence of fibrinogen	Absence of fibrinogen leads to defective platelet aggregation.

SUMMARY TABLE *(continued)*

Name of disease	Chap. no.	Frequency	Mode of inheritance	Mutant gene product	Chromosomal location	Expression: Altered DNA structure	Expression: Disturbed protein function	Expression: Disrupted cell and organ function
Part 14: Blood and blood forming tissues (continued)								
Dysfibrinogenemia	85	130 cases	Autosomal recessive (in several cases autosomal codominant)	Fibrinogen	4q23-q32	Point mutations	Defective fibrinogen	Dysfunction of fibrinogen can lead to hemorrhage, spontaneous abortion, or thromboembolism.
Factor XIII deficiency	85	1:5 million in U.K. and Japan	Autosomal recessive	The A subunit of factor XIII	6p24-p21	Not determined	Absent or deficient enzyme activity	Deficiency of factor XIII leads to delayed bleeding and wound healing and to habitual abortion.
Factor VIII deficiency (hemophilia A, classic hemophilia)	86	1:10,000 males	X-linked recessive	Factor VIII	Xq28	Missense, nonsense, deletion	Factor VIII deficiency or dysfunction	Factor VIII fails to function as a cofactor for activation of factor X and impairs clotting cascade.
Factor V deficiency (parahemophilia)	86	Extremely rare (<1:million)	Autosomal recessive	Factor V	1q21-q25	Unknown	Factor V deficiency	Factor V fails to function as a cofactor for activation of prothrombin and impairs clotting cascade.
von Willebrand disease	87	1:125 but only 1:8000 clinically significant	Variable mostly autosomal dominant	von Willebrand factor	12p12-pter	Unknown, very heterogeneous	Quantitative or qualitative binding protein deficiency	Abnormal platelet adhesion and mildly reduced factor VIII levels cause bleeding.
von Willebrand disease type III (severe)	87	1:200,000–2 million higher in Arabs	Autosomal recessive	von Willebrand factor	12p12-pter	Gene deletions in some; unknown and heterogenous in most	Total binding protein deficiency	Abnormal platelet adhesion and markedly reduced factor VIII levels cause severe bleeding.
Factor XI deficiency	88	~1:1000 in Ashkenazi Jews of Israel	Autosomal recessive	Factor XI	Unknown	Unknown	Decreased levels of factor XI	Deficiency of protein leads to impaired contact activation and mild bleeding tendency.
Antithrombin deficiency	89	~1:5000	Autosomal dominant	Antithrombin	1q23-q25	Deletions point mutations	Deficient or dysfunctional antithrombin	Impaired inhibition of coagulation factors IIa, IXa, and Xa in plasma causes recurrent venous thrombosis.
Glanzmann thrombasthenia	90	Uncommon, but not rare	Autosomal recessive	Platelet membrane glycoprotein IIb-IIIa complex	The genes for glycoproteins IIb and IIIa are both on chromosome 17	Unknown	Quantitative or qualitative defects in glycoprotein IIb-IIIa (receptor for fibrinogen, fibronectin, and von Willebrand factor)	Failure of activated platelets to interact with extracellular adhesive proteins and intracellular contractile proteins results in defective platelet aggregation, platelet spreading, and clot retraction, causing moderate bleeding.

Bernard-Soulier disease	90	<50 cases	Autosomal recessive	Platelet membrane glycoprotein Ib-IX-(V)	Unknown	Unknown	Absent or decreased platelet membrane glycoproteins Ib, IX, and V (receptor for von Willebrand factor)	Failure of platelets to bind plasma von Willebrand factor results in defective platelet adhesion to blood vessel subendothelium, causing moderate bleeding.
Glucose-6-phosphate dehydrogenase deficiency (favism; primaquine sensitivity)	91	Very variable; up to 30% in parts of Africa and Asia; about 13% in U.S. black males	X-linked	Glucose-6-phosphate dehydrogenase (G6PD)	Xq28	Point mutations (missense), about 300 different variants known	Some variants unstable; some with altered enzyme kinetics; some with both	Red cells tend to hemolyze because of inadequate NADPH production; very rarely, impaired granulocyte function.
Hereditary methemoglobinemia, secondary to cytochrome b_5 reductase deficiency, types I, II, and III	92	~300 cases	Autosomal recessive	Cytochrome b_5 reductase	22	Unknown	Deficient enzyme activity in erythrocyte cytosol only (type I), in all tissues (type II), and in all hematopoetic cells (type III)	Failure to reduce substrate cytochrome b_5 leads to accumulation of methemoglobin in erythrocytes and cyanosis (types I, II, and III). Patients with type II also have severe progressive neurologic dysfunction.
Hereditary methyemoglobinemia secondary to cytochrome b_5 deficiency	92	1 case	Unknown	Cytochrome b_5	Unknown	Unknown	Deficiency of this electron transferring protein	Defective transfer of electrons to methemoglobin results in methemoglobin accumulation and cyanosis.
Hemoglobinopathies (selected entries):								
α-Thalassemia, multiple allelic disorders	93	High frequency in Mediterranean, African, and Asian populations	Autosomal recessive	α-Globin	16p13	Deletion of both loci (α^0 thalassemia); deletion of one α locus (α^+ thalassemia); single nucleotide mutation of termination codon (HB Constant Spring); nondeletion defects due to (1) mutation within intervening sequence and (2) unknown mutations	Deficiency of α-globin	Decreased α-globin synthesis leads to uncombined β-globin chains, which disrupts erythroid cell maturation and function, causing microcytosis, ineffective erythropoiesis, and hemolysis.
β-Thalassemia, multiple allelic disorders	93	High frequency in Mediterranean and Asian populations	Autosomal recessive	β-Globin	11p15.5	Gene deletion; nonsense mutation; frame shift mutation; mutation in intervening sequence causing abnormal processing	Decreased or absent β-globin	Decreased β-globin leads to uncombined α-globin chains, which disrupts erythroid cell maturation and function, causing microcytosis, ineffective erythrocytosis, and hemolysis.

SUMMARY TABLE *(continued)*

Name of disease	*Chap. no.*	*Frequency*	*Mode of inheritance*	*Mutant gene product*	*Chromosomal location*	*Expression*		
						Altered DNA structure	*Disturbed protein function*	*Disrupted cell and organ function*
Part 14: Blood and blood forming tissues (continued)								
Sickle-cell anemia	93	High frequency in African, Mediterranean, and Middle Eastern populations	Autosomal recessive	β-Globin	11p15.5 single nucleotide change	(A→T) in 6th codon	Glu→Val substitution at 6th residue of β chain	Phenotype liable to tactoid formation and sickle deformation of RBC under reduced O_2 pressure with effect on microcirculation.
Pyruvate kinase deficiency hemolytic anemia	94	1:20,000 Caucasians	Autosomal recessive	Pyruvate kinase	Unknown	Unknown	Deficient enzyme activity	Deficiency of product (ATP) leads to hemolysis.
Hexokinase deficiency hemolytic anemia	94	~14 cases	Autosomal recessive	Hexokinase	10 for type I	Unknown	Deficient enzyme activity	Impaired glycolysis. Hemolysis.
Glucose phosphate isomerase deficiency hemolytic anemia	94	>40 severely deficient cases	Autosomal recessive	Glucosephosphate isomerase	19q12-q13.2	Unknown	Deficient enzyme activity	Hemolytic anemia. Rarely hydrops fetalis.
Phosphofructokinase hemolytic anemia	94	>20 kindreds	Autosomal recessive	Usually of M (muscle) subunit	1cen-q32	Unknown	Partial enzyme activity deficiency	Hemolytic anemia. Myopathy.
Aldolase deficiency hemolytic anemia	94	Very rare; two kindreds	Autosomal recessive	Aldolase	Unknown	Unknown	Enzyme activity deficiency	Hemolytic anemia? Other tissue disorders.
Triose-phosphate isomerase deficiency hemolytic anemia	94	25 cases	Autosomal recessive	Triosephosphate isomerase	12p13	Glu_{104}→Asp	Enzyme activity deficient in all tissues	Hemolytic anemia, severe neurologic deficits, multisystem disease.
Phosphoglycerate kinase deficiency hemolytic anemia	94	About 12 deficiency variants documented	X-linked	Phosphoglycerate kinase	Xq13	Four missense	Deficient enzyme activity in hemizygotes	Hemolytic anemia. Often neurologic abnormalities.
2,3-Diphosphoglyceromutase and phosphatase deficiency	94	One kindred unequivocally documented	Autosomal recessive	2,3-Diphosphoglyceromutase and phosphatase (one protein)	Unknown	Uncertain	Enzyme activity deficient	Mild erythrocytosis. Nearly absent 2,3-DPG in red cells.
Lactate dehydrogenase deficiency	94	2 kindreds	Autosomal recessive	1. H subunit 2. M subunit	H subunit 12q12.1-p12.2 M subunit 11p14-p15	Unknown	Enzyme activity deficiency	1. No manifestations. 2. Myopathy.
6-Phosphogluconate dehydrogenase deficiency	94	Unknown; severe deficiency detected in surveys	Autosomal recessive	6-Phosphogluconate dehydrogenase	Unknown	Unknown	Enzyme activity deficiency	None known.
Glutathione peroxidase deficiency	94	Uncertain; very rare	Autosomal recessive	Glutathione peroxidase	3q13-q12	Unknown	Diminished enzyme activity	Uncertain? Hemolytic syndrome under some circumstances.
Glutathione reductase deficiency	94	1 kindred with unequivocal apoenzyme deficiency	Autosomal recessive	Glutathione reductase	8p21.1	Unknown	Enzyme activity deficiency	Hemolysis with oxidant stress such as fava bean ingestion.
Glutathione synthetase deficiency hemolytic anemia	94	Rare; several kindreds	Autosomal recessive	Glutathione synthetase	Unknown	Unknown	Enzyme activity deficiency	Hemolysis. Pyroglutamic aciduria. Variable neurologic deficits.
γ-Glutamylcysteine deficiency hemolytic anemia	94	1 kindred	Autosomal recessive	γ-Glutamylcysteine synthetase	Unknown	Unknown	Enzyme activity deficiency	1. Hemolytic anemia exacerbated by oxidant stress. 2. Spinocerebellar ataxia.

Adenosine deaminase hyperactivity hemolytic anemia	94	3 families	Autosomal dominant	Adenosine deaminase	20q13-qter	Unknown	Overproduction of structurally normal enzyme protein mediated at mRNA translation level	Decreased erythrocyte ATP salvage via adenosine kinase.
Pyrimidine nucleotidase deficiency hemolytic anemia	94	Rare	Autosomal recessive	Pyrimidine nucleotidase	Unknown	Unknown	Deficient enzyme activity	Accumulation of pyrimidine degradation products of RNA normally cleared during reticulocyte maturation.
Hereditary spherocytosis	95	~1:5000 Caucasians	Autosomal dominant	1. Unknown 2. β-Spectrin 3. ? Ankyrin	1. Unknown 2. 14 3. 8 (?8q11.1)	1. Unknown 2. Unknown 3. ? Deletion	Common denominator: Spectrin deficiency (primary or secondary) 1. Unknown primary defect 2. Decreased binding of protein 4.1 by defective β-spectrin weakened spectrin-actin interaction 3. ? Ankyrin deficiency decreased spectrin binding	All forms: Membrane loss causes spherocytosis, splenic sequestration, and hemolytic anemia.
Hereditary spherocytosis	95	~1:20,000	? Autosomal recessive	Spectrin, probably α subunit	1q22-q25	Unknown	Spectrin deficiency	Membrane loss causes spherocytosis, splenic sequestration, and hemolytic anemia.
Hereditary elliptocytosis	95	~1:2500 (all forms)	Autosomal dominant	1. α-Spectrin 2. β-Spectrin 3. Protein 4.1 4. Glycophorin C	1. 1 2. 14 3. 1p34-p36 4. 2q14-q21	Unknown (all forms)	1 & 2: Defective spectrin self-association 3. Decreased protein 4.1 4. Decreased glycophorin C (and decreased Gerbich antigen)	All forms: Membrane cytoskeletal weakness and elliptocytosis (? mechanism). Severe forms only: Red cell fragmentation and hemolysis.
Hereditary pyropoikilocytosis	95	Unknown	Autosomal recessive	α-Spectrin	1q22-q25	Unknown	Defective spectrin self-association	Membrane weakness leads to red cell fragmentation and hemolytic anemia.

SUMMARY TABLE *(continued)*

Name of disease	Chap. no.	Frequency	Mode of inheritance	Mutant gene product	Chromosomal location	Expression: Altered DNA structure	Expression: Disturbed protein function	Expression: Disrupted cell and organ function
Part 14: Blood and blood forming tissues (continued)								
α_1-Antitrypsin deficiency (Z variant)	96	1:7000 northern Europeans 1:3000 Scandinavians	Autosomal recessive	α_1-Antitrypsin	14q32.1	Missense mutations	Z, ($Glu_{342} \rightarrow Lys$); S, ($Glu_{264} \rightarrow Val$). Aggregated, nonsecreted protein PI_Z. Other phenotypes unknown	Liver storage of polypeptide; plasma deficiency of enzyme.
Hereditary amyloidosis	97	1:100,000–million	Autosomal dominant	Prealbumin (Transthyretin) Several allelic disorders	18q11.2-q12.1	Seven missense identified	Abnormal prealbumin	Abnormal prealbumin is deposited extracellularly as amyloid; causes peripheral neuropathy, cardiomyopathy, and nephropathy.
Part 15: Membrane transport systems								
Renal glycosuria	98	? <5% of the glycosuria in children	Type A: autosomal dominant (autosomal recessive mode not excluded)	Unknown	6 ?	Unknown several alleles	Defect in glucose carrier in nephron	Glucosuria—no clinical significance.
Congenital selective glucose and galactose intestinal malabsorption	98	<50 cases	Autosomal recessive	Unknown	Unknown	Unknown	Defect in intestinal carrier shared by glucose and galactose	Unabsorbed substrates (glucose and galactose) accumulate in intestinal lumen and exert an osmotic effect. This in turn leads to abdominal fullness, cramping abdominal pain, and diarrhea. Failure to thrive.
Cystinuria (3 allelic types)	99	1:7000	Autosomal recessive	Unknown	Unknown	Unknown	Defect in shared transport system for cystine and diabasic amino acids (ornithine, arginine, lysine) in renal tubule and intestinal mucosa	Elevated urinary excretion of cystine causes urinary tract calculi. Intestinal transport defect causes no clinical dysfunction.

Lysinuric protein intolerance	100	~80 cases worldwide; 1:60,000 (Finland)	Autosomal recessive	Unknown	Unknown	Unknown	Deficient function of the dibasic amino acid transporter in the basolateral membranes of epithelial cells and the plasma membrane of parenchymal cells	Impaired gastrointestinal absorption and increased renal losses of lysine, arginine, and ornithine leads to growth failure, osteoporosis, and reduced function of the urea cycle with protein intolerance and hyperammonemia.
Hyperdibasic aminoaciduria	100	Rare	Autosomal recessive	Unknown	Unknown	Unknown	Deficient function of a dibasic amino acid transporter whose cellular distribution is not yet well delineated	Reduced gastrointestinal absorption and increased renal clearance of the dibasic amino acids, without protein intolerance of hyperammonemia. Heterozygotes have milder but demonstrable absorption defects.
Hartnup disorder	101	1:24,000	Autosomal recessive	Unknown	Unknown	Unknown; more than one allele	Defect in neutral amino acid transport in kidney and intestine	Increased neutral amino acid loss in urine and feces. Pellagralike episodes or delayed development in some probands.
Familial renal iminoglycinuria	102	1:15,000	Autosomal recessive homozygotes and compounds; completely and incompletely recessive heterozygous phenotypes	Unknown; several alleles	Unknown	Unknown; several alleles	Defect in shared transport system for imino acids and glycine in renal tubule and intestine (brush-border membrane)	Aminoaciduria without clinical significance.
Distal renal tubular acidosis type I	103	Not rare	Autosomal dominant	Unknown	Unknown	Unknown	Defect in acidification in collecting tubule of nephron as a result of impaired H^+secretion (H^+-ATPase) or abnormally high permeability of luminal membrane	Chronic hyperchloremic metabolic acidosis associated with inability to acidify urine below pH 5.5 Often associated with hypokalemia, hypercalciuria, hypocitriuria, and nephrolithiasis.

SUMMARY TABLE *(continued)*

Name of disease	Chap. no.	Frequency	Mode of inheritance	Mutant gene product	Chromosomal location	Expression: Altered DNA structure	Expression: Disturbed protein function	Expression: Disrupted cell and organ function
Part 15: Membrane transport systems (continued)								
Idiopathic Fanconi syndrome	104	Not rare	Autosomal recessive and dominant	Unknown	Unknown	Unknown	Unknown	Impaired renal tubular reabsorption of multiple solutes and ions and water. Primary Mendelian disorders that cause FS (e.g., cystinosis, hereditary fructose intolerance, galactosemia, hereditary tyrosinemia 1, Wilson disease, hereditary and vitamin D deficiency) have associated primary dysfunctions.
Oculocereborenal syndrome (Lowe syndrome)	104	Rare	X-linked	Unknown	Xq25	Unknown, most cases; deletion (contiguous gene syndrome) rare	Unknown	Fanconi-like tubular dysfunction plus ocular manifestations (cataracts, glaucoma) and mental retardation.
Familial hypophosphatemic rickets (vitamin D–resistant rickets, X-linked hypophosphatemia)	105	1:20,000	X-linked dominant	Unknown	Xp22	Unknown	Unknown	Defect in renal tubular phosphate reabsorption and in regulation of renal vitamin D metabolism.
Hereditary hypophosphatemic rickets with hypercalciuria	105	Rare	Autosomal dominant (probably) with variable expressivity	Unknown	Unknown	Unknown	Unknown	Defect in renal tubular phosphate reabsorption.
Hereditary renal hypouricemia	106	21 families	Autosomal recessive	Unknown	Unknown	Unknown	Unknown	Increased fractional clearance of urate (FC_{ur}) due to defective reabsorption of urate in the renal proximal tubule, manifested in hypouricemia.
Cystinosis	107	1:100,000	Autosomal recessive	Unknown	Unknown	Unknown	Transport of cystine across lysosomal membranes	Lysosomal cystine storage.
Salla disease	107	1:7000 (northern Finland)	Autosomal recessive	Unknown	Unknown	Unknown	Transport of free sialic acid across lysosomal membranes	Lysosomal storage of free sialic acid.

Cystic fibrosis	108	1:2000–3000 Caucasians; rare in other ethnic groups	Autosomal recessive	Unknown	7q31	Unknown	Impaired chloride transport: apical membrane of epithelium; primary defect unknown	Dysfunction of exocrine cells leads to pulmonary infections, exocrine pancreatic insufficiency, meconium ileus, and atrophy of the vas deferens.
Part 16: Defense and immune mechanisms								
X-linked agammaglobulinemia	109	Not rare	X-linked recessive	Unknown	Xq	Unknown	Unknown	Inadequate antibody synthesis due to an absence of mature B cells. Pre-B cell numbers are normal, indicating a developmental arrest in B cell maturation. Recurrent pyogenic infections occur.
X-linked agammaglobulinemia with growth hormone deficiency	109	Multiple members of a single family	X-linked	Unknown	X	Unknown	Unknown	Hypogammaglobulinemia and reduced numbers of B cells. Growth hormone levels reduced in response to provocative testing. Short stature, delayed puberty, and recurrent infections.
Common variable immunodeficiency	109	Not rare	Autosomal recessive in some families; no definite Mendelian pattern in most	Unknown	Unknown	Unknown	Unknown	Abnormal B-cell development; recurrent infections beginning at any age.
Selective IgA deficiency	109	~1:600	Unclear; patterns consistent with autosomal recessive and autosomal dominant observed in a few families	Probably several; all unknown	Unknown	Unknown	Markedly reduced or absent IgA	Immature IgA-bearing B cells. Most affected individuals asymptomatic; some with recurrent respiratory infections and/or gastrointestinal disease. Frequency of autoimmune disease increased.
IgG subclass deficiency	109	Rare	Unclear	Unknown	Unknown	Unknown	Reduced levels of one or more IgG subclasses	Defective heavy chain genes or an abnormality in the regulation of immunoglobulin isotype switching. Recurrent infections.
Immunodeficiency with elevated IgM	109	Uncommon	X-linked and autosomal recessive	Unknown	X in some families; in others unknown	Unknown	Unknown	Reduced IgG- and IgA-bearing B cells. Recurrent pyogenic infection.
Severe combined immunodeficiency	109	Uncommon	X-linked or autosomal recessive in some families	Adenosine deaminase and nucleoside phosphorylase are two so far identified	Variable	Unknown	Deficient enzyme activity in some	Impaired humoral and cellular immunity; survival beyond 1 year unusual without treatment.

SUMMARY TABLE *(continued)*

Name of disease	Chap. no.	Frequency	Mode of inheritance	Mutant gene product	Chromosomal location	Expression: Altered DNA structure	Expression: Disturbed protein function	Expression: Disrupted cell and organ function
Part 16: Defense and immune mechanisms (continued)								
Ataxia-telangiectasia	110	1:40,000	Autosomal recessive	Unknown	Unknown	Unknown	Unknown	Variable defects in humoral and cellular immunity associated with cerebellar dysfunction and telangiectasias. Endocrine abnormalities, malignancies, and infections occur with increased frequency. Chromosomal breakage following irradiation of cultured cells is increased and has been used to define multiple complementation groups.
Wiskott-Aldrich syndrome	110	~1:500,000	X-linked recessive	Unknown	Unknown	Unknown	Unknown	Selective defects in humoral and cellular immunity with thrombocytopenia and eczema. Autoimmune disease and malignancies occur with increased frequency. Heterozygous females are clinically normal but show a nonrandom pattern of X inactivation in their T and B lymphocytes, monocytes, and granulocytes.
Severe combined immunodeficiency (*see also* Adenosine Deaminase Deficiency)	110	Rare	Heterogeneous; best delineated subtypes listed below and in Chap. 40	Variable	Variable	Unknown	Unknown	Profound dual system immunodeficiency, usually fatal.
Severe combined immunodeficiency and with MHC class I and/or class II antigen deficiency ("bare lymphocyte syndrome")	110	Rare	Autosomal recessive	Unknown	Unknown	Unknown	Abnormal expression of major histocompatibility class I and/or class II antigens	Profound dual system immunodeficiency, usually fatal.
X-linked severe combined immunodeficiency	110	Rare	X-linked	Unknown	X	Unknown	Unknown	Profound dual system immunodeficiency usually fatal. Heterozygous females are asymptomatic but exhibit a nonrandom pattern of X inactivation in their T and B lymphocytes.

C1q deficiency/dysfunction	111	Rare	Autosomal recessive	Complement component C1q, B chain	1p	Unknown	Absence of C1q in some kindreds and presence of dysfunctional C1q in others	Markedly reduced activation of the classic pathway.
C1r/C1s deficiency	111	Rare	Autosomal recessive	Unknown	12p13	Unknown	Absent C1r and reduced C1s	Markedly reduced activation of the classic pathway.
C2 deficiency	111	~1:10,000	Autosomal recessive	Complement component 2	6p21.3	Unknown but no mRNA expressed	Absent C2	Markedly reduced activation of the classic pathway.
C3 deficiency	111	Rare	Autosomal recessive	Complement component 3	19q13	Unknown	Absent C3	Markedly reduced C3-dependent opsonization and reduced C3-dependent activation of C5–C9.
C4 deficiency	111	Rare	Autosomal recessive	Complement component 4	6q21.3	Some due to gene deletion; others unknown	Absent C4	Markedly reduced activation of the classic pathway.
C5 deficiency	111	Rare	Autosomal recessive	Complement component 5	9q22-q34	Unknown	Absent C5	Markedly reduced C5-dependent chemotaxis and reduced C5-dependent activation of C6–C9.
C6 deficiency	111	Rare	Autosomal recessive	Complement component 6	Unknown	Unknown	Absent C6	Markedly reduced C6-dependent serum bactericidal activity.
C7 deficiency	111	Rare	Autosomal recessive	Complement component 7	Unknown	Unknown	Absent C7	Markedly reduced C7-dependent serum bactericidal activity.
C8 deficiency	111	Rare	Autosomal recessive	Complement component 8	1q36-p22	Unknown	One form has absent α-γ subunit and the other absent β subunit	Markedly reduced C8-dependent serum bactericidal activity.
C9 deficiency	111	Rare	Autosomal	Complement component 9	Unknown	Unknown	Absent C9	Moderately reduced C9-dependent serum bactericidal activity.
Factor H deficiency	111	Rare	Autosomal recessive	Complement factor H	1q32	Unknown	Absent factor H	Lack of inhibition of the alternative pathway leading to continuous activation and consumption of C3.
Factor I deficiency	111	Rare	Autosomal recessive	Complement factor I	4q23-q25	Unknown	Absent factor I	Lack of inhibition of the alternative pathway leading to continuous activation and consumption of native C3.
C1 esterase inhibitor deficiency	111	Unknown	Autosomal dominant	C1 esterase inhibitor	11q12-q13	Genetic heterogeneity	Absence of C1 inhibitor in some kindreds and presence of dysfunctional C1 inhibitor in others	Lack of inhibition of C1r and C1s leading to uncontrolled activation of the classic pathway and edema.
Properdin deficiency	111	Rare	X-linked recessive	Properdin, complement factor B	Xp21-cen	Unknown	Absent properdin	Lack of stabilization of the alternative pathway C3-cleaning enzyme.

SUMMARY TABLE *(continued)*

Name of disease	Chap. no.	Frequency	Mode of inheritance	Mutant gene product	Chromosomal location	Expression: Altered DNA structure	Expression: Disturbed protein function	Expression: Disrupted cell and organ function
Part 16: Defense and immune mechanisms (continued)								
Immotile cilia syndrome (Kartagener syndrome)	112	~1:40,000	Autosomal recessive	Unknown	Unknown	Unknown	Absence of structural and enzymatic proteins of cilia (dynein arms or other structures)	Ciliary immotility or dyskinesis causes abnormalities of the respiratory tract (bronchiectasis) and spermatozoa (male sterility).
Leukocyte adhesion deficiency	113	50 cases	Autosomal recessive	β Subunit of CD18 adherence complex	21	Abnormal or absent mRNA in some	Deficient or defective β subunit of CD18 complex with secondary absence of α subunits	Abnormal leukocyte adherence complex disturbs leukocyte chemotaxis with bacterial infections; fatal in severe forms.
Myeloperoxidase deficiency	114	1:2000	Autosomal recessive	Myeloperoxidase	17q22-q23	Unknown	Absent or deficient enzyme activity	Deficiency of product (OCl^-, a potent antimicrobial oxidant) by neutrophils and monocytes leads to impaired bacterial killing.
Chronic granulomatous disease	114	Uncommon, but not rare	X-linked recessive Autosomal recessive	β Subunit of cytochrome b (X-linked) Autosomal recessive form, product unknown	Xp21.1 (X-linked form)	One partial deletion, one abnormal mRNA	Absent or deficient activity or enzyme responsible for respiratory burst	Deficiency of product (O_2^-) prevents neutrophils, macrophages, and monocytes from expressing respiratory burst. This in turn leads to impaired bacterial killing and chronic infections.
Leukocyte glucose 6-phosphate dehydrogenase (G6PD) deficiency	114	Rare	X-linked recessive	G6PD	Xq28	Unknown	Absent enzyme activity in neutrophils	Deficiency of product (NADPH) prevents neutrophils from expressing respiratory burst. Impaired bacterial killing promotes infections.
Part 17: Connective tissues								
Osteogenesis imperfecta type I	115	1:20,000–40,000	Autosomal dominant	COL1A1, COL1A2	COL1A1 at 17q21.3-q22 COL1A2 at 7q21.3-q22.1	1. Frame shift in COL1A1 2. Splice mutations in COL1A1	Synthesis of half normal amount of type I	Bone fragility.
Osteogenesis imperfecta type II	115	1:20,000–40,000	Autosomal dominant (new mutations) (Autosomal recessive—rare)	COL1A1, COL1A2	COL1A1 at 17q21-q22 COL1A2 at 7q21.3-q22.1	COL1A1: Missense for glycine; deletion in triple helix; insertion in triple helix COL1A2: Deletion in triple helix; small deletion on background of null allele	Decreased secretion and thermal stability of type I procollagen	Bone fragility.

Osteogenesis imperfecta type III	115	Rare (? 1:60,000)	Autosomal dominant (frequent new mutations) Autosomal recessive—rare in most populations	COL1A1, COL1A2 Unknown	COL1A1 at 17q21.3-q22, COL1A2 at 7q21.3-q22.1	COL1A1: Missense for glycine in triple helix	Poor secretion, decreased thermal stability Failure to incorporate pro 2(I) chains into type I procollagen	Bone fragility and deformity.
Osteogenesis imperfecta type IV	115	1:20,000–50,000	Autosomal dominant	COL1A1, COL1A2	COL1A1 at 17q21.3-q22 COL1A2 at 7q21.3-q22.1	COL1A1: Missense near end of triple-helical domain COL1A2: Missense for glycine; small deletions	Decreased secretion and thermal stability. Free sulfhydryl (due to unpaired cysteine in 1(I) or 2(1) chains.	Bone fragility.
Ehlers-Danlos syndrome type I	115	1:20,000–40,000	Autosomal dominant	Unknown	Unknown	Unknown	Unknown	Altered morphology of collagen in skin. Altered mechanical properties of skin.
Ehlers-Danlos syndrome type II	115	1:20,000–40,000	Autosomal dominant	Unknown	Unknown	Unknown	Unknown	Altered morphology of collagen in skin. Altered mechanical properties of skin.
Ehlers-Danlos syndrome type III	115	1:5000–10,000	Autosomal dominant	Unknown	Unknown	Unknown	Unknown	Altered morphology of collagen in skin. Altered mechanical properties of skin.
Ehlers-Danlos syndrome type IV	115	1:100,000	Autosomal dominant (possibly rare autosomal recessive)	COL3A1	2q31-q32.3	Point mutations, deletions, insertions	Type III procollagen, unstable, poor secretion, abnormal structure	Tissues rich in type III collagen—skin, vessels, GI tract, uterus.
Ehlers-Danlos syndrome type V	115	Very rare	X-linked recessive	Unknown	Unknown	Unknown	Unknown	Altered morphology of collagen in skin. Altered mechanical properties of skin.
Ehlers-Danlos syndrome type VI	115	Rare	Autosomal recessive	Lysyl hydroxylase	Unknown	Unknown	Lysyl hydroxylase enzyme deficiency	Lax ligaments, vessel and globe fragility.
Ehlers-Danlos syndrome type VII	115	Rare	Autosomal dominant	COL1A1, COL1A2	COL1A1 at 17q21.3-q22, COL1A2 at 7q21.3-q22.1	COL1A1, COL1A2: deletion of exon 6 by splice junction mutation	Failure to convert procollagen to collagen	Marked joint instability.
Ehlers-Danlos syndrome type VIII	115	Rare	Autosomal dominant	Unknown	Unknown	Unknown	Unknown	Abnormal collagen structure in dermis and severe periodontal disease.
Ehlers-Danlos syndrome type IX	115	Rare	X-linked recessive	Unknown	Unknown	Unknown	Intracellular copper accumulation and defective function of some copper enzymes	Bladder diverticula, skeletal dysplasia.
Ehlers-Danlos syndrome type X	115	Rare	? Autosomal recessive	Fibronectin	2q	Unknown	Defective platelet binding	Joint laxity, bruising.
Marfan syndrome	115	1:10,000	Autosomal dominant	Unknown (COL1A2, very rare)	(7q-COL1A2)	Small insertion in COL1A2	Insertion in pro 2(I) chains	Aortic dissection.

SUMMARY TABLE *(continued)*

Name of disease	Chap. no.	Frequency	Mode of inheritance	Mutant gene product	Chromosomal location	Expression: Altered DNA structure	Expression: Disturbed protein function	Expression: Disrupted cell and organ function
Part 17: Connective tissues (continued)								
Stickler syndrome	115	1:20,000	Autosomal dominant	COL1A2	7q21.3-q22.1	Unknown	Unknown	Early degenerative joint disease. Vitreal degeneration.
Achondrogenesis type II	115	Rare	New dominant mutation	COL2A1	12q14.3	Unknown (probably point mutations)	Thermal instability of type II collagen	Poor secretion of abnormal molecules.
Epidermolysis bullosa, recessive dystrophic form	115	1:50,000	Autosomal recessive	Collagenase	Unknown	Unknown	Increased activity	Blistering with scar formation.
Hypophosphatasia	116	1 in 100,000 live births for severe forms; mild forms more common	Autosomal recessive (severe forms) Autosomal dominant (mild forms)	Probably alkaline phosphatase (bone, liver, kidney isozyme)	1p (provisional)	Unknown; allelic variation likely	Deficient activity of the tissue nonspecific alkaline phosphatase isoenzyme	Decreased hydrolysis of phosphoethanolamine, inorganic pyrophosphate, and pyridoxal 5′-phosphate in extracellular fluid. Accumulation of inorganic pyrophosphate. Defective skeletal mineralization.
Carbonic anhydrase II deficiency syndrome (osteopetrosis with renal tubular acidosis)	117	Unknown; rare except in the Middle East	Autosomal recessive	Unknown	Unknown	Unknown	Quantitative deficiency of carbonic anhydrase II	Defect in bone resorption produces osteopetrosis, defect in urinary acidification produces metabolic acidosis; cerebral calcification is late consequence. Growth failure and mental retardation common.
Part 18: Muscle								
Duchenne-Becker muscular dystrophy	118	~1:3500–4000 male births	X-linked	Cloned; total length c. 2×10^6 base pairs, with around 60 exons	Xp21	Gene deletions of varying length account for at least half of all cases; duplication and disruption by translocation also recorded	Specific protein 'dystrophin' characterized by reverse genetics techniques. Absent in most classic Duchenne cases. Reduced in some milder cases with "Becker" phenotype	Skeletal and cardiac muscle primarily involved; to a lesser extent smooth muscle and CNS. Dystrophin is localized in sarcolemmal membrane (and perhaps in triad regions of myofibrils).

Emery-Dreifuss muscular dystrophy	118	Unknown	X-linked	Unknown (not allelic to DMD)	Xq28	Unknown	Unknown	Muscle involvement, in particular cardiac and skeletal.
Myotonic dystrophy	118	5–15:100,000	Autosomal dominant	Unknown	19q	Unknown	Unknown	No primary defect identified. Widespread involvement of many organ systems, in particular muscle (skeletal, cardiac, smooth) CNS, endocrine organs.
Facioscapulohumeral muscular dystrophy	118	Unknown	Autosomal dominant	Unknown	Unknown	Unknown	Unknown	Skeletal muscle principally involved.
Part 19: Skin								
Albinism, oculocutaneous, autosomal dominant type	119	Rare: 2 kindreds	Autosomal dominant	Unknown	Unknown	Unknown	Unknown	Decreased melanin. Secondary: decreased visual acuity. Susceptibility to solar-induced skin changes.
Albinism, ocular with deafness	119	Rare: 2 kindreds	X-linked recessive	Unknown	X	Unknown	Unknown	Decreased melanin in eye. Secondary: decreased visual acuity. Ear: sensorineural hearing loss.
Albinism, oculocutaneous, rufous type	119	? Caucasians; has been observed in U.S. Caucasians and blacks. Prevalent in New Guinea natives and African blacks	Autosomal recessive	Unknown	Unknown	Unknown	Unknown	Reduced eumelanin, increase in pheomelanin. Secondary reduced visual acuity.
Albinism, ocular, X-linked type	119	1:180,000 Caucasians occurs in U.S. blacks	X-linked recessive	Unknown	Xq22.1	Unknown	Unknown	Reduction of melanin in eye with abnormal melanin bodies in eye and skin. Secondary decreased visual acuity; decussation defects in optic neuronal tracts.
Albinism, oculocutaneous, tyrosinase-negative type	119	1:39,000 U.S. Caucasians 1:28,000 U.S. blacks 1:15,000 Irish	Autosomal recessive	Tyrosinase	Unknown	Unknown	Absent enzyme activity	Absence of melanin. Secondary decreased visual acuity. Decussation defects of optic and otic neuronal tracts. Susceptibility to squamous-cell carcinoma of skin.
Albinism, oculocutaneous, tyrosinase-positive type	119	1:36,000 U.S. Caucasians 1:15,000 U.S. blacks 1:3000–4000 African blacks 1:140–240 in S.W. Amerindians	Autosomal recessive	Unknown	Unknown	Unknown	Unknown	Reduced melanin formation. Secondary decreased visual acuity. Decussation defects in optic and otic neuronal tracts. Susceptibility to squamous-cell carcinoma of skin.

SUMMARY TABLE *(continued)*

Name of disease	Chap. no.	Frequency	Mode of inheritance	Mutant gene product	Chromosomal location	Expression: Altered DNA structure	Expression: Disturbed protein function	Expression: Disrupted cell and organ function
Part 19: Skin (continued)								
Chédiak-Higashi syndrome	119	? Reported in all major races	Autosomal recessive	Unknown	Unknown	Unknown	Unknown	Defect in lysosomes and lysosomal-like organelles including melanosomes. Secondary: susceptibility to infections and lymphoreticular malignancy. Decreased melanin and visual acuity. Abnormal decussation of optic and otic neuronal tracts.
Albinism, ocular with lentigines and deafness	119	Rare: 1 family	Autosomal dominant	Unknown	Unknown	Unknown	Unknown	Decreased melanin. Eye: decreased visual acuity. Ear: sensorineuronal deafness.
Albinism, ocular, autosomal recessive type	119	1:180,000 U.S. Caucasians	Autosomal recessive	Unknown	Unknown	Unknown	Unknown	Reduced melanin in eye. Secondary decreased visual acuity. Decussation defect in optic neuronal tracts.
Albinism, oculocutaneous, Hermansky-Pudlak syndrome	119	Unknown U.S. 1:2000 Puerto Ricans Prevalent in Indians from Madras, Dutch, and Swiss	Autosomal recessive	Unknown	Unknown	Unknown	Unknown	Reduced melanin, accumulation of ceroid in lysosomes with restrictive lung disease, granulomatous colitis, kidney failure, cardiomyopathy, and storage pool–deficient platelets. Secondary reduced visual acuity. Decussation defects in optic and otic neuronal tracts. Susceptibility to squamous-cell carcinoma.
Albinism, oculocutaneous, platinum type	119	1:200,000 U.S. Caucasians	Autosomal recessive	Tyrosinase	Unknown	Unknown	Reduced enzyme activity	Reduction of melanin. Secondary decreased visual acuity; decussation defects of optic and otic neuronal tracts. Susceptibility to squamous-cell carcinoma of skin.
Albinism, oculocutaneous, brown type	119	Occurs in Afro-Americans. 1:10,000 Ibos of Nigeria	Autosomal recessive	Unknown	Unknown	Unknown	Unknown	Moderate reduction in melanin. Secondary reduced visual acuity; decussation defect in optic neuronal tract.

Albinism, oculocutaneous, yellow mutant type	119	1:180,000 U.S. Caucasians Higher in Amish	Autosomal recessive	Tyrosinase	Unknown	Unknown	Reduced enzyme activity	Reduced eumelanin formation. Secondary decreased visual acuity; decussation defects in optic and otic neuronal tracts; susceptibility to solar skin damage.
Albinism, oculocutaneous, minimal pigment type	119	? 6 Caucasian families in U.S.	Autosomal recessive	Probably tyrosinase	Unknown	Unknown	Reduced tyrosinase activity	Decreased melanin formation. Secondary decreased visual acuity; decussation defects in optic and otic neuronal tracts. Susceptibility to solar skin damage.
Xeroderma pigmentosum	120	1:250,000	Autosomal recessive	Unknown	Unknown	Unknown	Unknown	Defective repair of ultraviolet and chemical carcinogen damage to DNA leading to actinic carcinogenesis and neurologic dysfunction.
Part 20: Intestine								
Congenital sucrase-isomaltase deficiency	121	~200 cases ~2% frequency of heterozygotes in white Americans 4–10% frequency of homozygotes in Greenland and among Canadian Eskimos and Indians	Autosomal recessive	Unknown	3q25-q26	Unknown	Absent or deficient sucrase and isomaltase activities; defective homing of pro-sucrase-isomaltase from the endoplasmic reticulum to the brush borders (polymorphism possible)	Deficient intestinal digestion of sucrose, of linear oligo-1,4-α-glucanes and of α-limit dextrins.
Congenital lactase deficiency	121	Not more than 40 cases	Autosomal recessive (?)	Lactase	Chromosome 2	Unknown	Absent or deficient enzyme activity	Deficient intestinal digestion of lactose. Severe manifestations.
Congenital (?) trehalase deficiency	121	10–15% among Greenland Eskimos; one or two families elsewhere	Autosomal recessive	Trehalase	Unknown	Unknown	Absent or deficient enzyme activity	Deficient intestinal digestion of trehalose.
Lactase persistence (LAC*P) and restriction (LAC*R) polymorphic phenotypes	122	5–90% for LAC*R depending on ethnic group	LAC*P autosomal dominant; LAC*R recessive	Lactase (or regulator of activity) LAC*P is the variant in *H. sapiens;* LAC*R is the variant in Caucasians.	Unknown (chromosome 2?)	Unknown	Decreased lactase activity in LAC*R	Deficient intestinal digestion of lactose, after weaning.

CHAPTER 2

MOLECULAR GENETICS AND INHERITED HUMAN DISEASE

STUART H. ORKIN

The essence of genetics is phenotypic variation, which is reflected either as normal polymorphism or by what is commonly viewed as inherited disease. Differences are encoded in cellular DNA (the genome), the reservoir of genetic information for both the individual and the species. Until recently the precise relationship between a trait or a disease and a specific alteration in DNA could only at best be inferred. For instance, where a protein was recognized to be structurally abnormal in association with a clinical condition, demonstration of an amino acid replacement in the mutant product would predict a substitution in the DNA sequence in light of the genetic code, which was elucidated more than 20 years ago. By this logic, the replacement of glutamic acid by valine at the sixth amino acid position of the β chain in sickle hemoglobin could be explained by a single base substitution in the cellular DNA.

Over the past decade the development of extraordinarily powerful methods, known collectively as recombinant DNA technology, has forged a radical departure in the way inherited genetic diseases may be considered and ultimately understood. With these tools of molecular genetics the relationship between a phenotype or disease and a specific gene, and an alteration in that gene, can be established with certainty. Reintroduction of genes into cells of animals provides a convenient and incisive approach to study gene expression, function, and consequences of specific mutations. With these methods, the products of cloned genes may be synthesized in virtually unlimited amounts for biochemical, structural, and physiological studies and for clinical administration. The implications of this revolution in biology for understanding normal cellular physiology, development, and human genetic diseases, as well as for the design of new approaches for treatment, are profound and just becoming fully appreciated.

In this chapter selected principles and methods of molecular genetics are presented as they specifically relate to the study of inherited human disease. For additional background material of a more general nature readers are referred to the excellent texts by Watson, Tooze, and Kurtz[1] and Lodish, Darnell, and Baltimore.[2]

THE COMPLEXITY OF THE HUMAN GENOME

The primary flow of genetic information is from cellular DNA to RNA to protein. As such, analysis of DNA provides the most fundamental insights. DNA is a linear polymer of four monomeric units, known as deoxyribonucleotides (nucleotides), abbreviated A, C, G, and T. DNA molecules are typically composed of two interwound chains (the double helix), often millions of nucleotides in length. The sequence of two DNA strands is complementary, owing to strict pairing of A to T and G to C. The precise sequence of the DNA represents the stored genetic information.

In humans cellular DNA is packaged with associated nucleoproteins in chromosomes, 22 autosomes and 2 sex chromosomes (X and Y). The complexity of the human genome is formidable: the DNA of an individual cell comprises some 6×10^9 nucleotides, or about 10^5 genes. To focus on one specific gene and its nucleotide sequence requires isolation of a segment free of unrelated genes but in sufficient quantities for direct analysis. Methods of gene cloning have made possible purification of this magnitude (10^5-fold or greater) and production of suitable amounts of isolated genes for analysis.

MOLECULAR CLONING

Cloning refers to the process by which a DNA molecule is joined to another DNA molecule (termed a vector) that can replicate autonomously in a specially designed host, usually a bacterium or yeast. Many variations on this general theme have been developed, some of which are described briefly below. A common feature of all methods is the use of restriction endonucleases,[3] enzymes that recognize specific sequences in double-stranded DNA and generate predictable cleavages at or near those sites. In addition to their usefulness in recognizing landmarks along the DNA by virtue of their sequence specificity (see below), many restriction enzymes have the additional property of generating "sticking ends" that permit efficient joining (annealing) of unrelated, but similarly digested, DNA molecules (see Fig. 2-1). Annealed molecules may be covalently joined with enzymes, known as DNA ligases. Restriction enzymes provide the basic reagents whereby human (or other) DNA fragments may be recombined to vector DNA as an initial step in molecular cloning.

Numerous inventive vector cloning systems have been developed in recent years. The precise details of each are beyond the scope of this presentation. In part, choice of the system is determined by the nature of the DNA clones desired. The sizes of DNA fragments accepted by particular vector systems vary from short molecules (few nucleotides to several thousand), to moderate size molecules (several thousand to tens of thousands), to large molecules (several million). To date most cloning has been performed in either plasmid or bacteriophage vectors, which are described briefly.

Given the large size of the human genome (6×10^9 nucleotides), cloning of moderately large DNA segments is experimentally advantageous, as it reduces the number of independent recombinant clones needed to encompass the

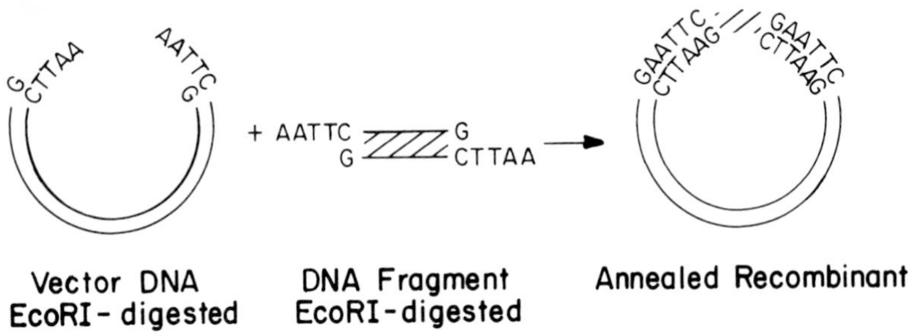

+ AATTC G / G CTTAA

Vector DNA EcoRI-digested

DNA Fragment EcoRI-digested

Annealed Recombinant

Fig. 2-1 Use of cohesive (or "sticky") ends to a form recombinant molecule.

entire genome. A collection of clones sufficient in number to include virtually all sequences in the starting tissue is often referred to as a "library." One of the most convenient, and most widely used, vectors for cloning mammalian genes has been bacteriophage λ[4] (Fig. 2-2). This double-stranded DNA virus contains approximately 50,000 nucleotides (50 kb) as its genetic information and infects and propagates efficiently in *Escherichia coli* as a host. The central portion of the viral DNA genome is expendable and can be replaced by foreign DNA sequences. Joining of vector DNA, specially designed with suitable restriction enzyme sites, and donor DNA can be performed by simple procedures, after which encapsidation of the recombinant DNA molecule (donor DNA linked to vector) into the viral protein coat can be accomplished in the test tube by a method known as in vitro packaging. Following infection of a bacterial lawn, recombinant phages generate plaques when lysis of host cells occurs. Efficient procedures for screening individual plaques have been developed, such that millions of independent clones may be readily examined in a matter of days. Most often, this screening process utilizes radiolabeled DNA fragments as hybridization probes, generated either from previously cloned segments or from chemically synthesized DNA. Phage DNA, transferred by adsorption to filters, is denatured *in situ* and allowed to anneal (or hybridize) to a complementary DNA strand of a probe. On average, each bacteriophage clone can accommodate roughly 15 to 20 kb of foreign DNA. Methods for the production of essentially random DNA fragments of this size permit assembly of a genomic library.[4] Approximately 5×10^5 independent clones represents a human library equivalent.

Plasmids are closed circular double-stranded DNA molecules that are most useful for cloning smaller DNA fragments.[5] Often segments initially isolated in bacteriophage clones are subcloned into plasmid vehicles. Plasmid vectors employed in cloning generally contain an origin of DNA replication to permit maintenance in bacterial cells, a selectable marker (usually an antibiotic resistance gene) to identify bacterial clones harboring the plasmid, and convenient restriction enzyme sites into which fragments are introduced. A typical scheme for cloning in a plasmid vector, such as the commonly used pBR322 and pUC 19 vectors, is illustrated in Fig. 2-3. In general, DNA fragments of fewer than 10,000 nucleotides (10 kb) are conveniently manipulated in these vectors.

For large-scale analysis of the human genome, the need exists for cloning considerably larger DNA fragments to complement chromosome mapping studies. Vectors known as cosmids, which have features in common with both bacteriophage and plasmid vectors, allow the cloning of DNA molecules roughly 40,000 (or 40 kb) in length, about twice the maximum contained in a bacteriophage. Very recently, a yeast artificial chromosome cloning system (YAC) has been developed that accepts much larger DNA fragments, approaching a million base pairs (a megabase)[6] (Fig. 2-4). This approach will extend the size of clonable DNA fragments by an order of magnitude.

Since only a subset of cellular DNA is eventually expressed

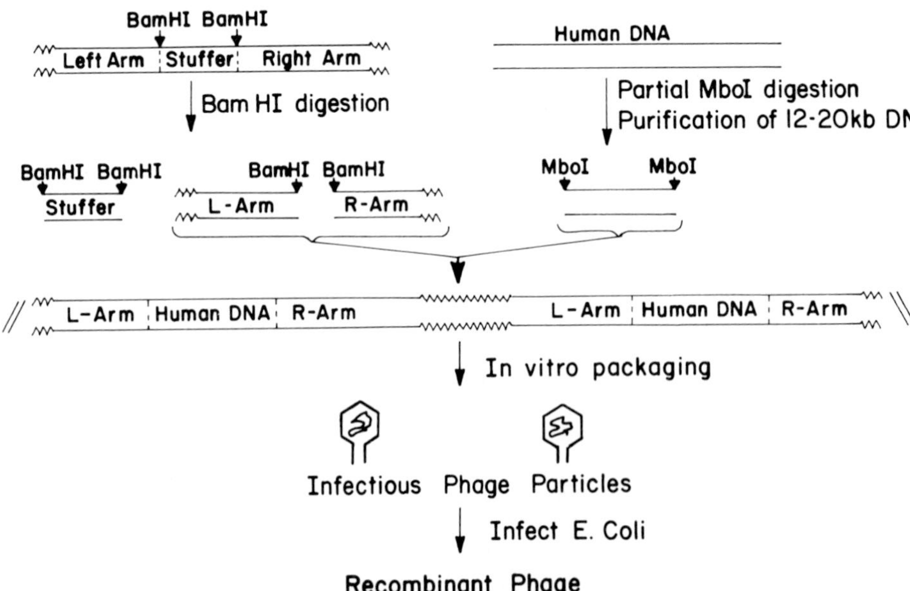

Fig. 2-2 Generation of a genomic "library" in bacteriophage. Phage DNA is depicted in the upper left. Digestion with *Bam*HI liberates a nonessential "stuffer" fragment which is discarded. Human DNA fragments of 12 to 20 kb in length resulting from partial digestion with *Mbo*I can be annealed and ligated into *Bam*HI sites of the bacteriophage arms. Since *Mbo*I cleaves at a four base recognition sequence (GATC), partial digestion approximates random DNA fragmentation. The overhang GATC resulting from *Mbo*I digestion anneals with the same overhang of *Bam*HI digested DNA.

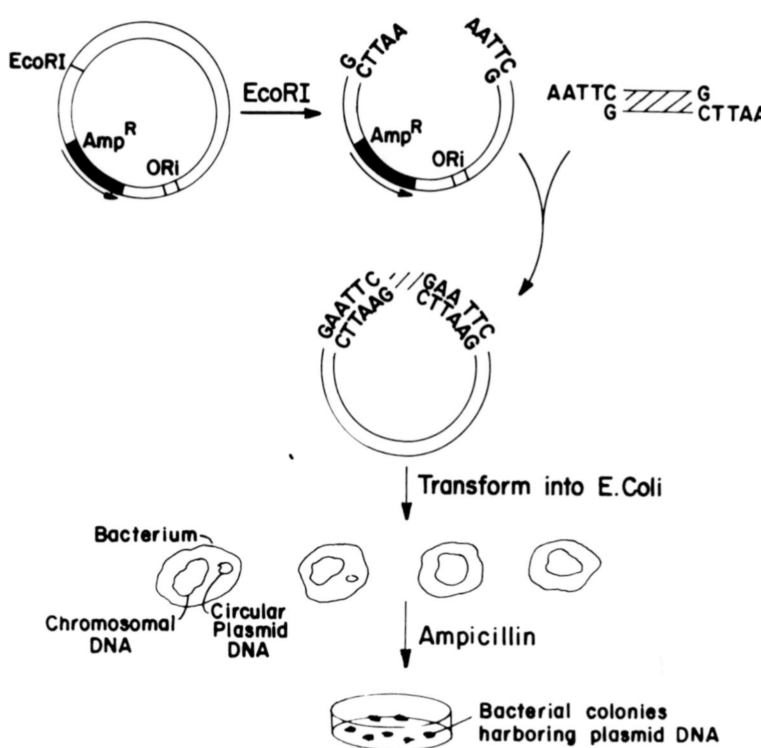

Fig. 2-3 Scheme for cloning a restriction fragment in a plasmid vector. The plasmid vector is depicted at the top left and the fragment to be subcloned at the top right. Amp^R is an ampicillin-resistant gene, and ORI is an origin of replication for the plasmid.

into messenger RNA (mRNA), cloning of mRNA, or its complementary copy known as cDNA, offers another strategy by which reagents for, and specific information about, particular genes may be obtained. The cloning of mRNA molecules rest on the use of the RNA-dependent DNA polymerase reverse transcriptase[7] to copy mRNA into cDNA.[8] Again, several procedures have been developed to clone in vitro synthesized cDNA, one of which is depicted in Fig. 2-5. cDNA may be cloned in plasmid or bacteriophage vectors which have been engineered to accept appropriately prepared cDNA molecules to express the encoded products, and to provide various convenience features for investigators.

Fig. 2-4 Yeast artificial chromosome cloning system (see Ref. 6). Blackened arrows refer to yeast telomeric sequences. Cen 4 = yeast centromere. TrpI and URA$_3$ = yeast selectable markers. Ars I = autonomous replication sequences.

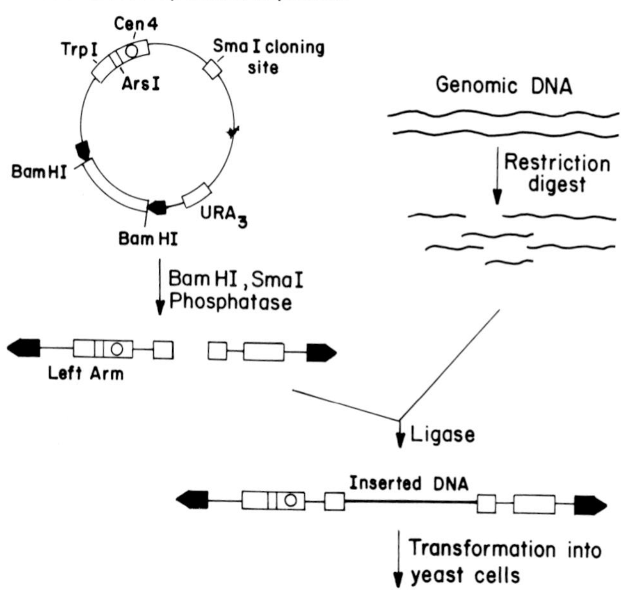

IDENTIFICATION OF RECOMBINANT CLONES

Many different strategies and methods may be used to identify and then isolate a desired recombinant among the numerous clones represented in a genomic or cDNA library (Table 2-1). In practice, the approach is usually dictated by the presumed abundance of the gene sequence under question (particularly if an mRNA is sought), the nature of its product,

Fig. 2-5 Protocol for cDNA cloning. The method outlined schematically above (see Ref. 63) is highly efficient and maximizes generation of full-length cDNA transcripts.

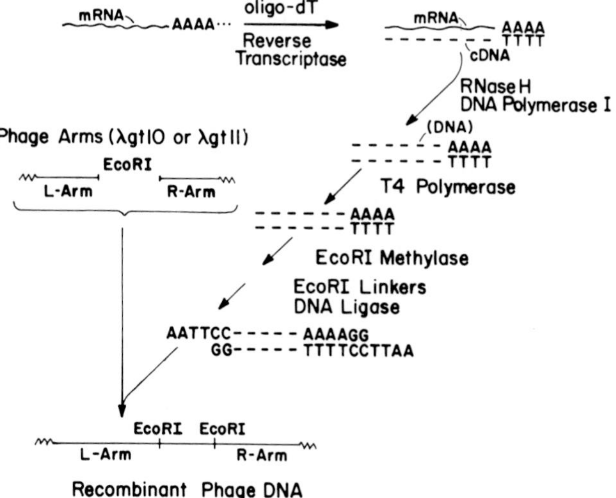

Table 2-1 Identification of Desired Recombinant Clone

1. Direct isolation and sequencing ("brute force")
2. Nucleic acid hybridization
3. Antibody screening of "expression library"
4. Functional assay
5. Genetic criteria (linkage, gene inactivation)

and the reagents and starting material available to the investigator.

In the simplest situation, where the desired product, for example, the messenger RNA for β-globin, constitutes the major portion of mRNA in a differentiated cell (a reticulocyte in this instance), it may be sufficient to isolate cDNA clones at random and subject each to direct DNA sequencing (see "The Study of Cloned Genes" below). More commonly, the abundance of the desired clone is much lower and precludes use of this as an efficient approach.

The most common screening approach employs nucleic acid hybridization, whereby replicas of plasmid colonies or phage plaques are lysed *in situ* on nitrocellulose or nylon paper, denatured, immobilized, and then incubated with radiolabeled DNA (or RNA) fragments specific for a desired gene sequence. If, for example, a cDNA clone for a specific RNA transcript has been previously isolated and a genomic clone is desired, the cDNA clone may be radiolabeled by a variety of enzymatic procedures and used to identify the desired gene within bacteriophage library. Related cDNA or genomic sequences can often be identified by using a previously cloned DNA as a probe, but with reduced stringency of hybridization (or washing) of the filters to permit isolation of homologous members. Often a short stretch of peptide sequence has been determined for a protein of interest, but its cDNA or genomic sequence has not been isolated. Synthetic oligonucleotides[9] encoding all possible mRNA sequences based on codon degeneracies or a so-called best guess sequence can be used as a hybridization probe to screen libraries. The success of such synthetic probes rests on the greatly favored stability of matched versus mismatched hybrid nucleic acids.[9]

Where no structural data are available for a protein, methods have been developed to identify the desired clone by expression of the protein within either bacterial or mammalian cells. In one of the most widely exploited and convenient methods, cDNAs are expressed as C-terminal fusions to *E. coli* β-galactosidase contained within a bacteriophage vector.[10] Upon induction of β-galactosidase synthesis, colonies are screened with antibody to the desired product. If the antibody is sufficiently specific and the epitope is available in the fusion protein made in *E. coli*, appropriate clones may be identified with few false positives. Generally, additional methods are required to establish that the antibody-selected clones, in fact, encode the desired product rather than another polypeptide bearing a related or shared epitope.

The function of a desired cDNA or genomic fragment may also be used to identify a recombinant clone. For example, if a biologic assay for a protein is available, such as a hormone or growth factor, a library or cDNA may be constructed in a vector that permits expression of the cDNA inserts when DNA is introduced (or transfected) into mammalian cells. Upon assay of culture media from transfected cells and subsequent sib selection of the clones from the positive pools, a single recombinant can be identified.[11] The success of this approach relies on the availability of a sensitive and reliable bioassay. Introduction of genomic DNA directly into mammalian cells by a process known as transfection has also been used successfully when the desired gene can be expressed in the host cells and manifested as a cell surface molecule detectable with an antibody or as a phenotypic alteration (such as malignant transformation) in the instance of an oncogene.[12] Several procedures have been devised to recover the mammalian cell clone harboring the foreign DNA of interest and to isolate this segment from the host cell.

Finally, the ability to map chromosomes and subregions by nkage analysis (see Chap. 6) and by newly developed gel electrophoresis procedures suitable for large DNA molecules combined with the availability of naturally occurring alterations in genes that lead to disease states offers the potential to identify genes responsible for diseases without prior protein data, homologous nucleic acid sequences, antiserums, or functional assays. This approach, often termed *reverse genetics*, is outlined later in this chapter.

GENE ORGANIZATION

For discussion of molecular genetics, particularly as related to human disease analysis, it is necessary to review explicitly the distinction between a "gene" and its messenger RNA (or its cDNA). As was first observed in the genes of animal viruses[13] and soon thereafter in mouse globin[14] and immunoglobulin genes,[15] the vast majority of cellular genes of higher eukaryotes (i.e., humans and mice) are larger in size than predicted from the mRNAs found in the cytoplasm of cells. The additional sequences are intervening sequences (or introns) that interrupt the gene in one or usually many locations. Although the precise role and function of introns remains a subject of considerable discussion, they often subdivide genes into apparent functional domains in the encoded proteins and may provide a mechanism by which coding blocks (or exons) are "shuffled" during evolution.[16] This provides an efficient means by which proteins may be developed (or modified) or useful domains dispersed to related (or unrelated) proteins. Although introns are present in the primary RNA transcript, they are removed by RNA processing and the interrupted exons precisely joined to assemble the mature, translatable mRNA.[17]

Cellular genes also contain important regulatory signals that are responsible for appropriate transcription into RNA and for processing of the primary RNA transcript. Some of these are schematically illustrated in Fig. 2-6. For exposition here *gene* refers to the cellular gene with its introns and other control sequences, whereas cDNA (or mRNA) refers to the processed, mature messenger RNA that encodes a protein product. The complexity of the steps involved in transfer of information from a cellular gene into a protein product is such that mutations may interfere with the process at virtually any step, as discussed below (see "The Array of Gene Mutations").

ANALYTIC METHODS

Development of highly sensitive and specific analytic methods has formed the basis for much of the experimental work that is fundamental to the analysis of human genes responsible for

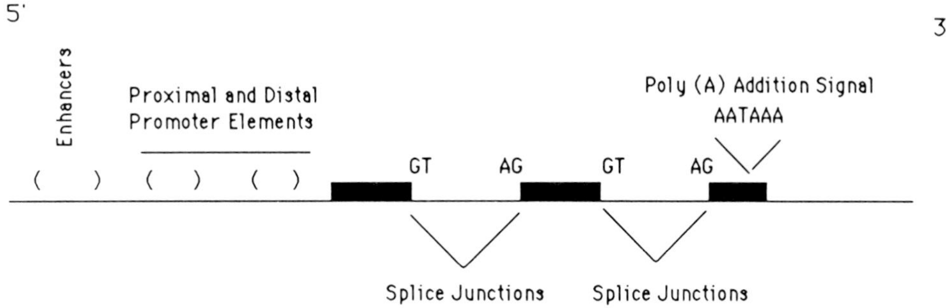

Fig. 2-6 Prototypical eukaryotic gene. In schematic form a cellular gene is depicted in which exons or coding regions (black boxes) are separated by intervening sequences (introns). Introns begin with the dinucleotide GT and end with AG. A short motif of AATAAA (or modified versions) direct endonucleolytic cleavage and polyadenylation of nascent RNAs. Promoter elements, shown as empty parentheses lie upstream of the start of gene and are often multiple in nature. Common promoter elements include motifs such as TATA and CCAAT (TATA and CAT boxes) and GGCGGG (the Spl nuclear factor binding site). Additional sequences, known as enhancers, augment transcription and can lie either before, within, or downstream from the gene.

disease. Two widely used procedures are known as Southern[18] and Northern blot[19] analysis.

The former, named after its originator, combines restriction endonuclease digestion of DNA, electrophoresis of the resultant fragments and their transfer to a solid paper support, and hybridization of nucleic acid to identify specific DNA fragments among a mixture (Fig. 2-7). Single genes or parts thereof can be detected within total human DNA, a collection of some 10^5 fragments. Information derived from Southern blots is of three sorts. First, the presence or absence of a specific fragment(s) can be determined. This often resolves whether a particular gene is present in the cellular DNA of a patient who cannot synthesize a given protein product. Second, the size(s) of detected DNA fragments provides information regarding the position of flanking restriction enzyme cleavage sites and directly reflects the physical "map" of the DNA region. Changes in restriction sites between individuals may reflect either normal variation (polymorphism) or a structural alteration in the gene or its flanking DNA. Restriction fragment length polymorphisms (RFLPs) (Fig. 2-8) provide useful genetic markers within families and populations and are the basis for genetic linkage analysis which permits construction of large-scale human gene maps (see Chap. 6).[20] Third, the copy number of a particular DNA fragment may be estimated by comparison with normal control samples. For an autosomal gene, the deletion of a single copy results in a signal of one-half normal intensity. Additional copies of a gene, either the result of the presence of additional chromosomes (for example, in XXY versus XY) or amplification of gene sequences (for example, in cancers associated with amplification of oncogenes), are similarly detectable by band intensity.

Northern blot analysis, a similar procedure in principle, involves electrophoresis of RNA under denaturing conditions, its subsequent transfer to a solid support, and detection of specific transcripts by hybridization (Fig. 2-7). This method yields information on the size and abundance of RNA transcripts and is especially useful in revealing the distribution of particular mRNAs in tissue or cell samples and structural or quantitative derangements in samples from affected patients.

Additional methods have greatly extended the analysis of

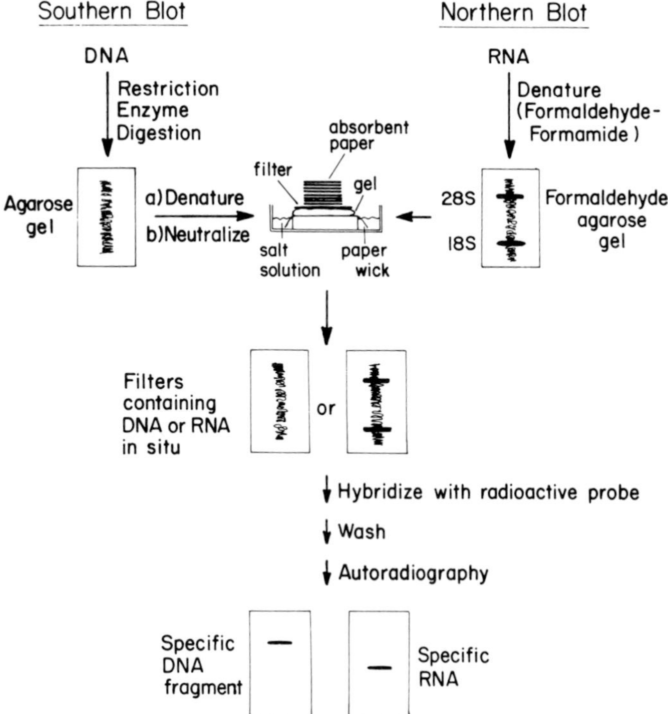

Fig. 2-7 Procedures for Southern and Northern blot analysis.

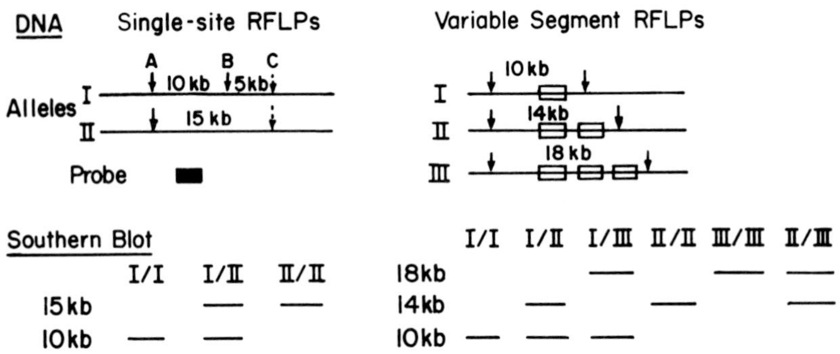

Fig. 2-8 Restriction-fragment length polymorphisms (RFLPs). Cleavage sites in genomic DNA are shown at the top with corresponding Southern blot patterns below. The variable (or polymorphic) site in the upper left is site B. In the upper right variable segments are denoted by boxes.

both cellular DNA and RNA. Conventional Southern blot analysis is most useful for DNA fragments fewer than 20 kb in length, principally due to limitations in resolution of conventional agarose gels. More recently, several methods have been developed that permit resolution of much larger DNA fragments, up to the megabase (10^6-bp or 10^3-kb) range. These techniques, known as pulsed-field gel electrophoresis (PFGE),[21] field inversion gels (FIG),[22] and contour-clamp homogeneous electric field electrophoresis (CHEF),[23] allow construction of restriction maps of DNA segments encompassing extended DNA regions. With these recent technologic advances, the resolution of physical mapping of DNA approaches that of contemporary cytogenetics (see Fig. 2-9). In conjunction with emerging methods for the cloning of large DNA fragments in artificial yeast chromosomes,[6] the assembly of physical maps for whole chromosomes becomes a realistic goal in the coming years. Such maps are likely to be the cornerstone for large scale DNA sequencing of the human genome.

In a similar fashion, RNA structure can be examined more precisely with various nuclease procedures (S1 nuclease and RNase mapping methods), in which a radiolabeled DNA or RNA strand is hybridized to mRNA and mismatched regions are removed by digestion with single strand specific nucleases or RNases.[24] Examination of the fragments of probe protected by hybridization can provide direct information regarding the structural integrity or organization of the mRNA. Refinements, as noted below (see "Detection of Gene Defects Associated with Disease"), permit recognition of single nucleotide alterations.

THE STUDY OF CLONED GENES

Acquisition of a cloned gene is the first step in the analysis of gene structure and function and in the definition of mutations that lead to disease. From this perspective a cloned DNA is analogous to a purified protein for a traditional biochemist. The most basic information obtainable from a cloned DNA segment is its nucleotide sequence. Two elegant methods, the dideoxy-chain termination procedure of Sanger[25] and the chemical degradation procedure of Maxam and Gilbert,[26] permit rapid, highly accurate determination of DNA sequence. In practice, 10,000 to 50,000 nucleotides of sequence can readily be acquired by a skilled worker in 1 year. Already several million nucleotides of human DNA sequence, but alas no more than 0.1 percent of the human genome, have been ascertained worldwide. With the advent of automated DNA sequencing,[27,28] it is anticipated that the volume of sequence in-

Fig. 2-9 Genome complexity versus current technologies. The horizontal axis represents base pairs of DNA in the haploid genome. As shown at the right, the human genome contains 3×10^9 bp. Genes can span from a few hundred to greater than a million base pairs of DNA. The approximate size range of human chromosomes in DNA content is also depicted. The horizontal rectangles (or portions thereof) denote the size range within which various methods are applicable. Cloning in plasmid is generally useful below 10^4 bp. Cloning in yeast artificial chromosome vectors is likely to be most useful in the 10^5- to 10^6-bp range, although the theoretical cloning range should extend higher. DNA linkage analysis is most useful in the 10^6- to several times 10^7-bp range. *In situ* analysis of chromosomes is most useful in the examination of larger DNA segments.

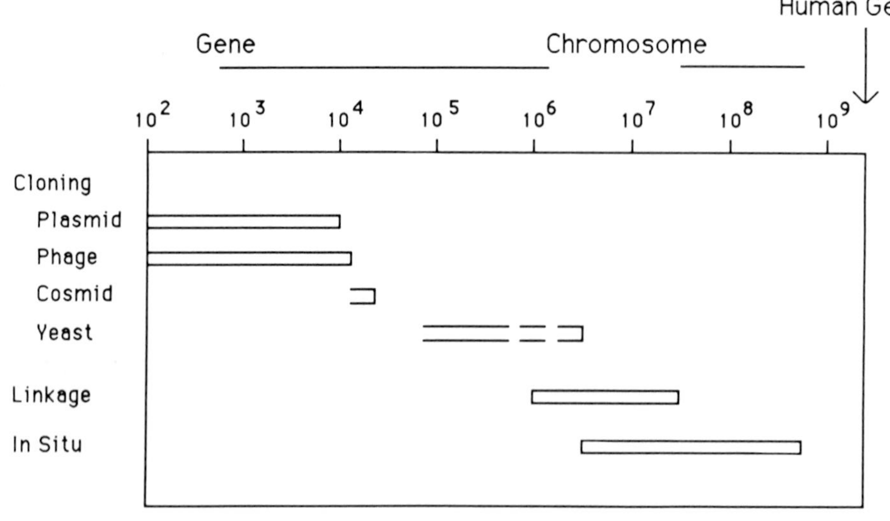

formation will greatly expand. In the opinion of some scientists, determination of the complete sequence of the human genome is an attainable, realistic goal in the next 20 to 30 years.

The nucleotide sequence of a gene, or its cDNA, provides a data base for further analysis. The coding potential of cDNA immediately predicts the amino acid sequence of the protein and may suggest relationships to previously sequenced polypeptides. From these similarities, domains of proteins may be placed into gene families that may suggest functions which were not readily apparent previously. Predictions of protein structure and function often, therefore, evolve from analysis of the linear protein sequence.

Within the cellular gene sequence are many short nucleotide sequences that provide important signals for RNA transcription and RNA processing. For example, sequence elements, such as those depicted in Fig. 2-6, constitute portions of promoters that interact with various nuclear proteins to direct transcription of the gene by RNA polymerase into RNA. Related elements, known as enhancers, often participate in restricted expression of genes in particular tissues or in specific developmental stages.[29] Often these transcriptional elements are strongly conserved across species or used in intricate ways in seemingly unrelated genes to control gene expression. Short nucleotide sequences at the boundaries of the intervening sequences and also within the intervening sequences are critical to normal RNA processing, as are sequences near the ends of genes that program cleavage of RNA transcripts and their subsequent polyadenylation. Although inspection and analysis of nucleotide sequences alone do not generally yield simple explanations for gene regulation or protein function, they are increasingly useful in providing clues for subsequent direct experimentation.

Were it not for the availability of methods for the systematic analysis of the function of cloned genes and their products, assignment of specific consequences of particular mutations would remain an inferential exercise. Predictions regarding the consequences of specific nucleotide substitutions in cloned genes can be tested experimentally in a variety of ways. In many instances the precise assay system chosen is tailored for the gene or its product that is under study. In order to compare a putative mutant cDNA with its normal counterpart, the cDNAs may be subcloned into bacterial or mammalian cell expression vectors and introduced into the respective host cells. Similarly, the effects of specific nucleotide substitutions or other alterations in a presumptive mutant gene on transcription, RNA processing, or mRNA stability may be examined by introduction of the gene into the appropriate mammalian cell hosts.[30] Such expression systems permit discrimination between phenotypically significant mutations and silent polymorphisms. The introduction of genes into the germ line of animals, particularly mice (transgenic mice),[31] offers another powerful strategy for correlation of gene structure and function.

THE ARRAY OF GENE MUTATIONS

What DNA lesions cause the mutations evident in human genes associated with disease? Quite simply, almost all alterations that are predicted to affect gene expression or function appear to exist in inherited disorders.[32]

Loss of gene function is readily accomplished by deletion of a gene (or deletion of a sufficient part) to render production of a stable mRNA impossible. Many examples of gene deletion causing disease have been described, as enumerated in Table 2-2. Biologically relevant deletions may be small, as a single nucleotide frameshift within a coding region, or large, such as extensive chromosome deletions. In many instances, specific sequences in the DNA mediate deletion by homologous recombination, whereas in others, deletions appear sporadically. Where short repeated sequences are present in the DNA, small deletions tend to be favored. Deletion of genes often leads to complete failure to produce the relevant protein product.

Commonly single nucleotide substitutions in the DNA are the mutations responsible for defective gene or protein function. These may occur spontaneously, but do appear more frequent at CpG dinucleotides in the DNA. The effects of single nucleotide changes can be quite dramatic. A classic example is that of the substitution of T for A in the sixth codon of the β-globin gene which directs the replacement of valine for glutamic acid in sickle cell anemia. The altered solubility of the sickle hemoglobin leads to the clinical sequelae. Rather than resulting in an amino acid substitution, a single base change may alter an amino acid codon to a stop signal for translation (termed a nonsense codon). Premature termination of protein synthesis thereby leads to a truncated polypeptide that is either nonfunctional or unstable in the cell. Single nucleotide substitutions at the junction between an exon and an intervening sequence (the splice junction) lead to profound disturbances of RNA processing, as evident in many forms of thalassemia.[33] Simple nucleotide substitutions also adversely affect RNA transcription and 3′-end formation of RNA. Virtually all types of gene defects that may be predicted from first principles have been observed as the basis for disease.

DETECTION OF GENE DEFECTS ASSOCIATED WITH DISEASE

Much of the impact of recent analysis of genetic disease by new DNA methods rests on detection of specific defects in uncloned DNA samples. The technical feasibility of assigning specific defects in limited DNA samples permits widespread analysis of the distribution of mutation in populations, carrier detection in families at risk or those possibly at risk, and prenatal diagnosis as early as the first trimester by chorion villus biopsy and later by amniocentesis.

Conventional Southern blot analysis using selected restriction enzymes has been a mainstay of detection methods. If a disorder is the result of an extensive DNA deletion, insertion, or rearrangement, its detection by blot analysis is usually quite straightforward.[34] Many examples have been described. If a single base change in the DNA is the underlying defect and either ablates or creates a recognition site for a restriction en-

Table 2-2 Some Diseases Associated with Gene Deletions

1. Thalassemia syndromes
2. Lesch-Nyhan syndrome (HPRT deficiency)
3. Hypercholesterolemia due to LDL receptor deficiency
4. Duchenne muscular dystrophy
5. Ornithine transcarbamylase deficiency
6. Hemophilia A or B

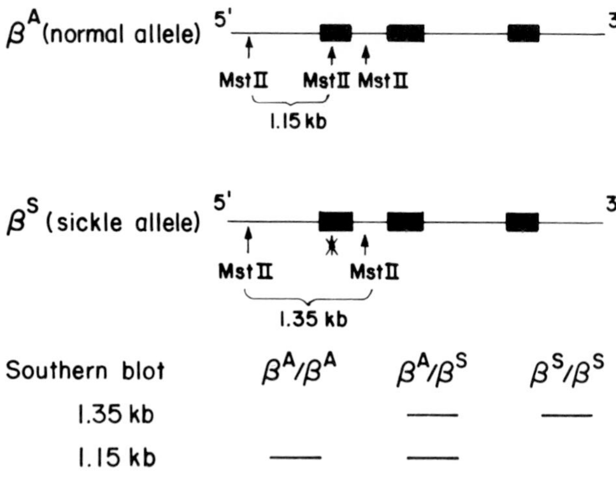

Fig. 2-10 Diagnosis of sickle cell anemia by restriction enzyme cleavage of DNA. The enzyme *Mst*II cleaves DNA at the sequence CCTNAGG. The mutation at codon 6 obliterates the normal cleavage site in exon 1 of the β-globin genes (indicated by the first black box to the left). The various genotypes (normal, sickle trait, and homozygous sickle cell anemia) are shown below with their corresponding blot patterns.

zyme, blot analysis with that enzyme and a suitable DNA probe spanning the region provides a simple diagnostic test. A classic example is illustrated by diagnosis of sickle cell anemia (Fig. 2-10). If a restriction fragment length polymorphism is closely linked to the defection gene within a family, it may be used in diagnosis. Most often, single base changes in genes are not associated with destruction or creation of a restriction enzyme cleavage site and, therefore, this approach, though successful in selected instances, is not generally useful.

Over the past several years methods to detect single base defects in uncloned DNA have evolved, such that virtually all may be identified with increased specificity and speed, and with less DNA as a substrate for the test. One of the first general methods developed employed synthetic DNA fragments (oligonucleotides) as specific probes.[35] Under carefully controlled experimental conditions perfectly matched DNA-DNA hybrids are substantially more stable than mismatched duplexes. With 19 to 20 nucleotide long fragments designed on the basis of either a normal or a mutant sequence, specific alleles can be detected and distinguished in uncloned DNA by Southern blot analysis. Although this approach can identify all mutations, it requires considerable experimental sophistication and, therefore, has had somewhat limited applicability in the clinical arena.

Two additional methods have been developed that allow detection of single base alterations, not necessarily known a priori, within a segment represented by a DNA (or labeled RNA probe). In these strategies, which rely on either the ability of RNase to cleave RNA-DNA hybrids at mismatches[36] or the differential melting of DNA duplexes under a gradient of denaturation,[37] not all mutations are detectable within a region. Although quite useful in selected instances, these methods have yet to have widespread clinical impact.

Within the past two years, a novel method has arisen that is likely to find increasing clinical application. This approach, called polymerase chain reaction (PCR), employs in vitro amplification of a DNA region with specific DNA primers and heat-stable DNA polymerase.[38] To use this strategy, the DNA sequences flanking a region of interest, perhaps an RFLP site or a mutation, must be known. With primers flanking the relevant DNA segment, it can be amplified in vitro more than a millionfold to provide abundant material for direct analysis either by restriction enzyme digestion, blot hybridization (for example, with synthetic DNA probes for the normal and mutant alleles), or direct DNA sequencing. Experimental protocols have also been devised, which employs exceedingly small samples of chorion villus biopsies or blood.[39] Amplification of DNA and its subsequent analysis requires less than a day. Improved automation, coupled with increased information regarding DNA sequences of clinically relevant genes and their mutations, will enhance the application of this ingenious approach in clinical medicine.[40]

DETERMINING THE MOLECULAR BASIS OF DISEASE

A full understanding of the pathophysiology of an inherited disease rests on knowledge of the primary genetic defect and, most specifically, the nature of the product encoded by the mutated gene. With increasing sophistication in biomedical science, an even expanding array of methods and approaches may be brought to bear on dissection of disease at the molecular level. Until recently, analysis of inherited disease in humans proceeded largely through identification and characterization of specific proteins and their corresponding genes. In the ensuing chapters in this book, many examples of this approach are evident. Particularly rewarding advances have been made in this manner in the molecular descriptions of the thalassemia syndromes[41] and familial hypercholesterolemia.[42] In these instances progress relied on recognition of the affected proteins.

For those disorders where the affected proteins may be identified by conventional biochemical purification or by generation of suitable antiserums or functional or selection assays, cloning of the cellular genes or cDNAs may be approached directly. With the putative normal and mutant genes or cDNAs in isolated form, structural and functional assays may be employed to characterize the specific mutations leading to the gene abnormalities associated with the disease. In many instances final assignment of the mutations involves demonstration that the putative mutation evident in the cloned gene or cDNA is, in fact, present in uncloned DNA of the patient. By this approach potential artifacts associated with gene cloning or errors in DNA sequencing can be eliminated.

Many inherited disorders, however, display phenotypes for which adequate biochemical explanations are lacking.[43] Very often no animal model that faithfully mimics the human condition is known. In these situations the relevant gene that is affected in a disorder may be identified and its product characterized by an approach which combines classic genetics and recombinant DNA methods. With DNA probes that recognize RFLPs within families afflicted with an inherited condition closely linked markers may be identified (see Chap. 6). By a variety of techniques the region of the relevant gene may be further delineated either by additional linkage mapping or by use of patient samples bearing DNA deletion or chromosomal translocations. The search for transcribed regions[44] or conserved DNA segments[45,46] that might denote potential exons may lead to identification of RNA transcripts derived from the appropriate locus. Alternatively, the search for unusually GC-rich DNA segments[47] often associated with the 5′ region of genes (called HTF, *Hpa*II tiny fragment, islands) constitutes another approach to identify expressed loci that may be related

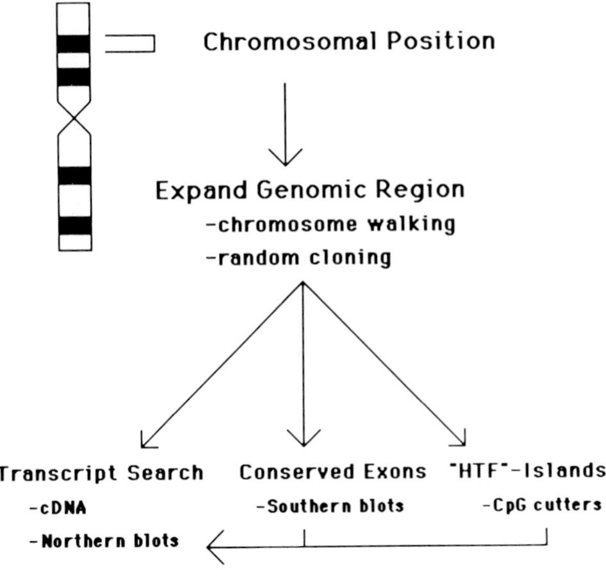

Fig. 2-11 Alternative approaches to identification of a locus responsible for a disease. By virtue of chromosome abbreviations (deletions or translocations) or DNA linkage analysis, the approximate position of a locus is first assigned. Recombinant DNA clones spanning a broader region are obtained by either chromosome walking or random cloning. The search for potentially transcribed regions (i.e., cellular genes) can be approached by direct transcript searches, by assessment of sequence conservation across species, or by identification of HTF islands.

to a disease. Some of the alternative methods that may be employed to identify a locus are illustrated in Fig. 2-11.

The general approach of characterizing the locus altered in a disease by molecular methods has recently been successful in the analysis of several inherited disorders and promises to contribute substantially to medical genetics in the ensuing years. Specifically, the genes mutated to produce Duchenne muscular dystrophy,[45] X-linked chronic granulomatous disease,[44] and retinoblastoma[46] have been identified and analyzed. With a cloned gene, and particularly its RNA transcript as cloned cDNA, reagents for encoded protein can be prepared by raising antibodies either to synthetic peptides or to polypeptides expressed in bacteria. By this route the nature of the encoded protein, its location and function in the cell, and its derangement in disease may be examined directly.[48–50]

CREATING NEW ANIMAL MODELS OF GENETIC DISEASE

For the majority of inherited human disorders, satisfactory animal models do not exist in which to examine the phenotypic consequences of specific biochemical defects. In-depth studies of pathogenesis often cannot be approached with human subjects, particularly in disorders affecting central nervous system function. Recent landmark research suggests that the tools are now at hand to engineer specific disorders in mice. This developing technology is likely to become an increasingly important component of future human molecular genetic investigation.

The emerging capacity to design mouse models of disease rests on the demonstration that embryonal stem (ES) cell lines established in tissue culture from preimplantation mouse blastocysts are able to colonize both the somatic and germlike cell lineages of chimeric mice upon injection into host blastocytes.[51] Introduction of a foreign gene sequence into ES cells offers a means to engineer specific mutations in mice. Using random integration of foreign DNA into the genome of ES cells, two groups of investigators have selected HPRT-deficient cells in culture and subsequently generated mice deficient in this enzyme.[52,53] This deficiency is the hallmark of the biochemical abnormality in the Lesch-Nyhan syndrome.

Since many biochemical phenotypes are not amenable to selection in cultured cells, as they may be manifested only in specific differentiated tissues, wide applicability of this system will require use of efficient methods for the identification of mutations at the DNA (rather than the phenotypic level) and/or improved approaches for directing integration of foreign DNA into specific gene regions (homologous recombination). Ingenious approaches to the identification of mutations are being explored in many laboratories. In addition, recent experiments have suggested that homologous recombination in mammalian cells can be achieved at frequencies that will be compatible with the envisioned screening procedures.[54–57]

Therefore, as new genes are characterized in relation to specific genetic diseases in humans, we can reasonably expect that mutations in the corresponding mouse genes may be created to provide convenient animal models with which to test hypotheses regarding pathophysiology. The findings of these approaches may suggest new research avenues to pursue, as well as yield animal models appropriate for the systematic testing of new therapies. Clues to disease pathogenesis may be derived from careful comparison of biochemical pathways in humans and mice. For example, although the engineered Lesch-Nyhan mice described above have the biochemical lesion found in the naturally occurring human disorder (see Chap. 38), the enzyme-deficient mice appear phenotypically normal, rather than affected by the behavioral abnormalities seen in humans.[52,53] Critical differences in other, interacting biochemical pathways very likely modify the effects of the biochemical deficit in mice. An understanding of the pathophysiology of the animal model may provide new insights into the human disease. In the ensuing years we can rightly expect these new technologies to yield invaluable information relating to the pathogenesis of genetic disease.

THE POTENTIAL FOR GENE THERAPY

The technology to clone genes and reintroduce them into cells and animals offers, in principle, prospects for correcting inherited disease by genetic means, often termed *gene therapy*.[58] The object of such an approach would be to treat only the affected individual (somatic gene therapy), rather than attempting to correct germline DNA. At present, somatic gene therapy strategies are being considered only for severe, life-threatening disorders for which conventional medical management is not entirely satisfactory.

Intensive research in laboratories worldwide has been devoted to developing methods and procedures that might be applicable to somatic therapy. Several alternative approaches are being explored. One promising avenue would use modified recombinant RNA viruses (retroviruses) to accomplish highly efficient transfer of genes into hematopoietic stem cells[59] or into specialized somatic cells (such as hepatocytes or fibroblasts).[60,61] Because correction of a mutant gene *in situ* would ensure regulated and appropriate expression of the corrected sequence in vivo, increasing attention is being directed to targeted gene insertion. It is premature to predict how soon genetic therapy might present itself as a reasonable and effective alternative to existing medical management. The disorders that would seem to be the best candidates for genetic therapy are immunodeficiencies (such as adenosine deaminase deficiency), hemoglobinopathies (thalassemia and sickle cell anemia), storage disorders (Gaucher disease), hepatic deficiencies (PKU and α_1-antitrypsin deficiency), and coagulation factor deficiencies (hemophilia A).

PROSPECTS FOR THE FUTURE: IMPLICATIONS FOR INHERITED DISEASES

Since the previous edition of this text, we have witnessed dramatic progress in understanding gene structure and regulation, the organization of the human genome, and the molecular basis for inherited disorders. From the continuing and accelerating application of recombinant DNA methods to research problems of biochemical concern we can be optimistic about future developments in unraveling the genetic components and pathophysiology of disease. From an understanding of pathology, new insights into normal biology will be acquired that may serve to stimulate design of new strategies for treatment and prevention of disease. Although humans have not traditionally been viewed as a convenient organism for genetic analysis, the techniques of gene cloning, DNA sequencing, and linkage analysis have combined to make the wealth of inherited genetic diseases an invaluable resource for biologic research. As the genetic map of humans is constructed with increasing resolution[62] and innovative approaches to cloning, mapping, and sequencing large DNA regions become fully mature, the determination of the complete DNA sequence of the human genome[64] becomes a more realistic and achievable goal. Although the benefits of knowing the complete sequence of a prototypical human genome may be debated, the impact of such research on the understanding, management, and prevention of disease may be the subject of subsequent introductory chapters in future editions.

REFERENCES

1. WATSON JD, TOOZE J, KURTZ DT: *Recombinant DNA—A Short Course.* New York, WH Freeman, 1983.
2. LODISH H, DARNELL J, BALTIMORE D: *Molecular Cell Biology.* New York, Scientific American Books, 1986.
3. ROBERT R: Restriction and modification enzymes and their recognition sequences. *Nucleic Acids Res* 10: 117, 1982.
4. MANIATIS T, HARDISON RC, LACY E, LAUER J, O'CONNELL C, QUON D, SIM DK, EFSTRATIADIS A: The isolation of structural genes from libraries of eucaryotic DNA. *Cell* 15: 587, 1978.
5. BOLIVAR F, BACKMAN K: Plasmids of E. coli as cloning vectors. *Methods Enzymol* 68: 245, 1979.
6. BURKE DT, CARLE GF, OLSON MV: Cloning of large segments of exogenous DNA in yeast using artificial chromosome vectors. *Science* 236: 806, 1987.
7. TEMIN H, BALTIMORE D: RNA-directed DNA synthesis and RNA tumor viruses. *Adv Virus Res* 17: 129, 1972.
8. EFSTRATIADIS A, KAFATOS FC, MAXAM AM, MANIATIS T: Enzymatic in vitro synthesis of globin genes. *Cell* 7: 279, 1976.
9. WALLACE RB, SCHOLD M, JOHNSON MJ, DEMBEK P, ITAKINA K: Oligonucleotide directed mutagenesis of the human beta-globin gene: a general method for producing specific point mutations in cloned DNA. *Nucleic Acids Res* 9: 1194, 1983.
10. YOUNG R, DAVIS RW: Efficient isolation of genes by using antibody probes. *Proc Natl Acad Sci USA* 92: 1194, 1983.
11. NAGATA S, TAIRA H, HALL A, JOHNSRUD L, STREULI M, ECSODI J, BOLL W, CANTELL K, WEISSMANN C: Synthesis in *E. coli* of a polypeptide with human leukocyte interferon activity. *Nature* 284: 316, 1980.
12. WEINBERG RA: Oncogenes of spontaneous and chemically induced tumors. *Adv Cancer Res* 36: 149, 1982.
13. BERGET SM, MOORE C, SHARP PA: Spliced segments at the 5′ terminus of adenovirus 2 late mRNA. *Proc Natl Acad Sci USA* 74: 3171, 1977.
14. KONKEL DA, TILGHMAN SM, LEDER P: Sequence of the chromosomal mouse β-globin major gene: Homologies in capping, splicing, and poly (A) sites. *Cell* 15: 1125, 1978.
15. TONEGAWA S, MAXAM AM, TIZARD R, BERNARD O, GILBERT W: Sequence of mouse germ-line gene for a variable region of an immunoglobulin light chain. *Proc Natl Acad Sci USA* 75: 1485, 1978.
16. GILBERT W: Why genes in pieces? *Nature* 271: 501, 1978.
17. TILGHMAN SM, CURTIS PJ, TIEMEIER DS, LEDER P, WEISSMANN C: The intervening sequence of a mouse β-globin mRNA precursor. *Proc Natl Acad Sci USA* 75: 1309, 1978.
18. SOUTHERN EM: Detection of specific sequences among DNA fragments separated by gel electrophoresis. *J Mol Biol* 98: 503, 1975.
19. THOMAS PS: Hybridization of denatured RNA and small DNA fragments transferred to nitrocellulose. *Proc Natl Acad Sci USA* 77: 5201, 1980.
20. BOTSTEIN D, WHITE RL, SKOLNICK M, DAVIS RW: Construction of a genetic linkage map in man using restriction fragment length polymorphisms. *Am J Hum Genet* 32: 314, 1980.
21. SCHWARTZ DC, CANTOR CR: Separation of yeast chromosome-sized DNAs by pulsed field gel electrophoresis. *Cell* 37: 67, 1984.
22. CARLE GF, FRANK F, OLSON MV: Electrophoretic separation of large DNA molecules by periodic inversion of the electric field. *Science* 232: 65, 1986.
23. CHU G, VOLLRATH D, DAVIS RW: Separation of large DNA molecules by contour-clamped homogeneous electric fields. *Science* 234: 1582, 1986.
24. MYERS RM, MANIATIS T: Detection of single base substitutions by ribonuclease cleavage of mismatches in RNA:DNA hybrids. *Science* 230: 1242, 1985.
25. SANGER F, NICKLEN S, COULSON AR: DNA sequencing with chain-terminating inhibitors. *Proc Natl Acad Sci USA* 74: 5463, 1977.
26. MAXAM AM, GILBERT W: A new method for sequencing DNA. *Proc Natl Acad Sci USA* 74: 560, 1977.
27. SMITH LM, SANDERS JZ, KAISER RJ, HUGHES P, DODD C, CONNELL CR, HEINER C, KENT SBH, HOOD LE: Fluorescence detection in automated DNA sequence analysis. *Nature* 321: 674, 1986.
28. PROBER JM, TRAINOR GL, DAIN RJ, HOBBS FW, ROBERTSON CW, ZAGENSKY RJ, COCUZZA AJ, JENSEN MA, KAUMERSTER K: A system for rapid sequencing with fluorescent chain-terminating dideoxynucleotides. *Science* 238: 336, 1987.
29. MANIATIS T, GOODBOURN S, FISCHER JA: Regulation of inducible and tissue-specific gene expression. *Science* 237: 1237, 1987.
30. TREISMAN R, ORKIN SH, MANIATIS T: Specific transcription and RNA splicing defects in five cloned beta-thalassemia genes. *Nature* 302: 591, 1983.
31. PALMITER RD, BRINSTER RL: Transgenic mice. *Cell* 41:343, 1985.
32. ORKIN SH: The use of cloned DNA segments in the analysis of human disease, in Setlow JA, Hollaender A (eds): *Genetic Engineering.* New York, Plenum Press, 1981, vol 3, p 189.
33. ORKIN SH, KAZAZIAN HH JR: The mutation and polymorphism of the human β-globin gene and its surrounding DNA. *Annu Rev Genet* 18:131, 1984.
34. ORKIN SH, ALTER BP, ALTAY C, MAHONEY MJ, LAZARUS H, HOBBINS JC, NATHAN DG: Application of endonuclease mapping to the analysis and prenatal diagnosis of thalassemias caused by globin gene-deletion. *N Engl J Med* 299:166, 1978.
35. CONNER BJ, REYES AA, MORIN C, ITAKURA K, TEPLITZ RL, WALLACE RB: Detection of sickle cell B-globin allele by hybridization with synthetic oligonucleotides. *Proc Natl Acad Sci USA* 80:278, 1983.
36. MYERS RM, LUMELSKY N, LERMAN LS, MANIATIS T: Detection of single base substitutions in total genomic DNA. *Nature* 313:495, 1985.
37. FISHER SG, LERMAN LS: DNA fragments differing by single base pair substitutions are separated in denaturing gradient gels: Correspondence with melting therapy. *Proc Natl Acad Sci USA* 80:1579, 1983.
38. SAIKI RK, SCHARF S, FALOONA F, ET AL: Enzymatic amplification of β-globin genomic sequences and restriction site analysis for diagnosis of sickle cell anemia. *Science* 230:1350, 1985.
39. KOGAN SC, DOHERTY M, GITSCHIER J: An improved method for prenatal diagnosis of genetic diseases by analysis of amplified DNA sequences: Application to hemophilia A. *N Engl J Med* 317:985, 1987.
40. WONG C, DOWLING CE, SAIKI RK, HIGUCHI RG, ERLICH HA, KAZAZIAN HH JR: Characterization of β-thalassemia mutations using direct genomic se-

quencing of amplified single copy DNA. *Nature* 330:384, 1987.

41. ORKIN SH: Disorders of hemoglobin synthesis: The thalassemias, in Stamatoyannopoulos G, Nienhuis AW, Leder P, Majerus PW (eds): *The Molecular Basis of Blood Diseases*. New York, Saunders, 1987, p 106.

42. BROWN MS, GOLDSTEIN JL: A receptor-mediated pathway for cholesterol homeostasis. *Science* 232:34, 1986.

43. ORKIN SH: Reverse genetics and human disease. *Cell* 47:845, 1986.

44. ROYER-POKORA B, KUNKEL LM, MONACO AP, GOFF SC, BAEHNER RL, COLE FS, CURNUTTE JT, NEWBURGER PE, ORKIN SH: Cloning the gene for the inherited human disorder (chronic granulomatous disease) on the basis of its chromosomal location. *Nature* 322:32, 1986.

45. MONACO AP, NEVE RL, COLLETTI-FEENER C, BERTELSON CJ, KURNIT DM, KUNKEL LM: Isolation of candidate cDNAs for positions of the Duchenne muscular dystrophy gene. *Nature* 323:646, 1986.

46. FRIEND SH, BERNARDS R, ROGELJ S, WINBERG RA, RAPAPORT JM, ALBERT DM, DRYJA TP: A human DNA segment with properties of the gene that predisposes to retinoblastoma and osteosarcoma. *Nature* 323:643, 1986.

47. ESTIVILL X, FARRALL M, SAMBLER PJ, BELL GM, HAWLEY KMF, LENCH NJ, BATES GP, KRUYER HC, FREDERICK PA, STANIER P, WATSON EK, WILLIAMSON R, WAINWRIGHT BJ: A candidate for the cystic fibrosis locus isolated by selection for methylation-free islands. *Nature* 326:840, 1987.

48. DINAUER MC, ORKIN SH, BROWN R, JESIATIS AJ, PARKOS CA: The glycoprotein encoded by the X-linked chronic granulomatous disease locus is a component of the neutrophil b-cytochrome complex. *Nature* 327:717, 1987.

49. HOFFMAN EP, BROWN ROBERT H, KUNKEL LM: Dystrophin: The protein product of the Duchenne muscular dystrophy locus. *Cell* 51:919, 1987.

50. LEE WH, SHEW JY, HONG FD, SERY TW, DONOSO LA, YOUNG LJ, BOOKSTEIN R, LEE YHP: The retinoblastoma susceptibility gene encodes a nuclear phosphoprotein associated with DNA binding activity. *Nature* 329:642, 1987.

51. ROBERTSON EJ (ed): *Teratocarcinomas and Embryonic Stem Cells: A Practical Approach*. Washington, IRL Press Oxford, 1987.

52. HOOPER M, HARDY K, HANDYSIDE A, HUNTER S, MONK M. HPRT-deficient (Lesch-Nyhan) mouse embryos derived from germline colonization by cultured cells. *Nature* 326:292, 1987.

53. KUEHN MR, BRADLEY A, ROBERTSON EJ, EVANS MJ: A potential animal model for Lesch-Nyhan syndrome through introduction of HPRT mutation in mice. *Nature* 326:295, 1987.

54. THOMAS KR, FOLGER KR, CAPECCHI MR: High frequency targeting of genes to specific sites in the mammalian genome. *Cell* 44:419, 1986.

55. SMITHIES O, GREGG RG, BOGGS SS, KORDEWSKI MA, KUCHERLAPATI RS: Insertion of DNA sequences into the human chromosomal beta-globin locus by homologous recombination. *Nature* 317:230, 1985.

56. THOMAS KR, CAPECCHI MR: Site-directed mutagenesis by gene targeting in mouse embryo-derived stem cells. *Cell* 51:503, 1987.

57. DOETSCHMAN T, GREGG RG, MAEDA N, HOOPER ML, MELTON DW, THOMPSON S, SMITHIES O: Targetted correction of a mutant HPRT gene in mouse embryonic stem cells. *Nature* 330:576, 1987.

58. WILLIAMS DA, ORKIN S: Somatic gene therapy: Current status and future prospects. *J Clin Invest* 77:1053, 1986.

59. WILLIAMS DA, LEMISCHKA IR, NATHAN DG, MULLIGAN RC: Introduction of new genetic material into pluripotent hematopoietic stem cells of the mouse. *Nature* 310:476, 1984.

60. SELDEN RF, SKOSKIEWICZ MJ, RUSSELL PS, GOODMAN HM: Regulation of insulin-gene expression: Implications for gene therapy. *N Engl J Med* 317:1067, 1987.

61. LEDLEY FD, DARLINGTON GJ, HAHN T, WOO SL: Retroviral gene transfer into primary hepatocytes: Implication for genetic therapy of liver-specific functions. *Proc Natl Acad Sci USA* 84:5335, 1987.

62. DONIS-KELLER H (and 32 others): A genetic linkage map of the human genome. *Cell* 51:319, 1987.

63. GUBLER U, HOFFMANN B: A simple and very efficient method for generating cDNA libraries. *Gene* 25:283, 1983.

64. Mapping and sequencing the human genome. *Report of the Committee on Mapping and Sequencing of the Human Genome*. Washington, National Academy of Sciences, 1988.

CHAPTER 3

THE BIOGENESIS OF MEMBRANES AND ORGANELLES

DAVID D. SABATINI
MILTON B. ADESNIK

THE ORGANIZATION OF THE EUKARYOTIC CELL

The eukaryotic cell shows an extraordinary degree of organizational complexity. Macromolecular components that carry out different metabolic processes are segregated in distinct subcellular compartments, and these must act in concert to sustain the various cellular functions. The membranes bounding all cellular organelles not only control the passage of substances between the various compartments and the surrounding cytoplasmic matrix but also provide a framework for the functional intregration and assembly of many of the organellar macromolecules into higher order complexes. This, of course, is also true for the *plasma membrane,* which surrounds the entire cell and regulates its interactions with the extracellular milieu.

The presence of a *nucleus,* a compartment limited by a membranous envelope, is the defining feature of the eukaryotic cell. In this compartment, the genome is stored and replicated and the process of decoding the genetic information begins. In the cytoplasm, several membrane-bounded organelles form an integrated *endomembrane system* (sometimes referred to as the "vacuolar system"[1]) which, together with the plasma membrane, is organized for the transfer of macromolecules and membrane components from one part of the cell to another, as well as to and from the cell's exterior. This transport takes place by means of *membrane vesicles* which bud from one organelle and fuse with another. The set of intercommunicating organelles that constitutes the endomembrane system (Fig. 3-1) includes: (1) the *endoplasmic reticulum* (ER), which may be regarded as an extension of the *nuclear envelope* and serves as a major site of protein synthesis and biosynthetic activity; (2) the *Golgi apparatus,* which modifies many of the proteins it receives from the ER and transfers them to other sites in the cell; (3) *secretory vesicles* and *granules,* which contain proteins that have traversed the Golgi apparatus and will be released at the cell surface; (4) *endosomes,* which receive materials taken in from the outside of the cell within plasma membrane invaginations; and (5) *lysosomes,* which degrade the exogenous material from the endosome as well as endogenous cellular components. Because the luminal cavities of the several membrane-bounded compartments of the endomembrane system can communicate with each other and with the extracellular space via transport vesicles, all luminal faces of the membranes in this system can be regarded as topologically equivalent to each other (Fig. 3-2).

Two other membrane-bounded organelles that do not directly communicate with the endomembrane system are found in animal cells. These are: (1) *mitochondria,* which generate most of the ATP required to sustain cellular activity but also play a major role in many aspects of intermediary metabolism, and (2) *peroxisomes,* in which several oxidative reactions that generate hydrogen peroxide take place, and in which important steps in the degradation of long-chain fatty acids and in the synthesis of plasmalogens and bile acids are carried out.

The portion of the cytoplasm that extends from the nuclear envelope to the plasma membrane and surrounds the membrane-bounded organelles is known as the *cytoplasmic matrix* (or *cytomatrix*). It contains filamentous elements such as *microtubules, microfilaments,* and *intermediate filaments* which constitute the *cytoskeleton.* This serves to organize the cytoplasm and controls the location and movement of the different organelles, and of the cell itself. The cytomatrix also contains *ribosomes* that function in protein synthesis, as well as numerous soluble enzymes that carry out a myriad of biochemical reactions. Several ribosomes are usually engaged in the translation of a single mRNA molecule, thus forming a *polyribosome* or *polysome.* The term *cytosol* is sometimes applied to the soluble components of the matrix which during cell fractionation are recovered in high speed supernatants.

Organization of Protein and Lipid Components in Membranes[2]

Membranes are lipoprotein structures that consist of amphipathic lipids disposed in a bilayer arrangement and proteins that penetrate the bilayer or are attached to its surfaces (Fig. 3-3). The most abundant lipid components of membranes are

Nonstandard abbreviations used in this chapter are: Bip = binding protein; CCCP = carbonylcyanide *m*-cholorophenolhydrazone; CURL = compartment of uncoupling of receptors and ligands; DHAP = dihydroxyacetone phosphate; DHFR = dihydrofolate reductase; EGF = epidermal growth factor; ER = endoplasmic reticulum; GERL = Golgi endoplasmic reticulum lysosome; HMG-CoA = 3-hydroxy-3-methylglutaryl-CoA; IMM = inner mitochondrial membrane; LDL = low density lipoprotein; NEM = *N*-ethylmaleimide; OMM = outer mitochondrial membrane; OTC = ornithine transcarbamylase; PC = phosphatidylcholine; PE = phosphatidylethanolamine; PIPLC = phosphoinositol-specific phospholipase C; POMC = pro-opiomelanocortin; PS = phosphatidylserine; SM = sphingomyelin; SRP = signal recognition particle; SSR = signal sequence receptor; TGN = trans Golgi network; VSG = variant surface glycoprotein; VSV = vesicular stomatitis virus.

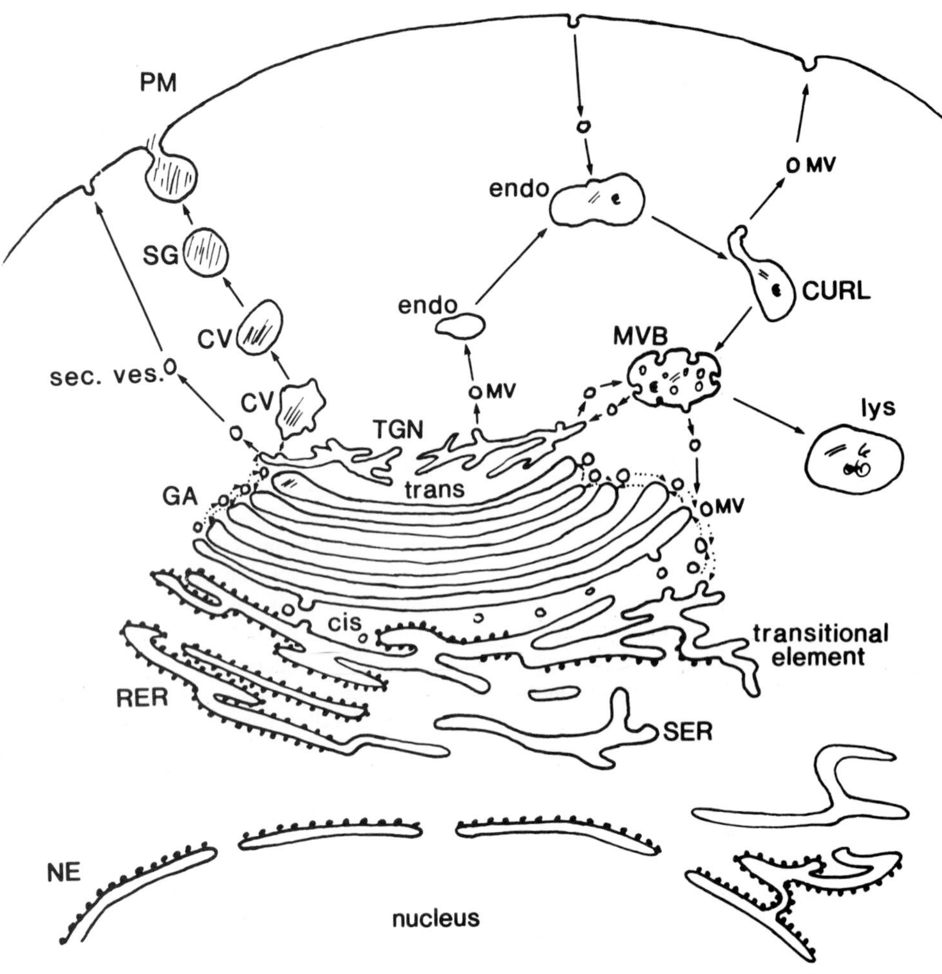

Fig. 3-1 Subcellular compartments that constitute the cellular endomembrane system. The major organelles of the endomembrane system are: the endoplasmic reticulum (ER), with its rough (RER) and smooth (SER) components; the Golgi apparatus (GA); endosomes (endo); lysosomes (lys); secretory granules (SG); and the plasma membrane (PM). The outer membrane of the nuclear envelope (NE) is studded with ribosomes and is continuous with the rough ER. The transitional element is a specialized ER cisterna from which membrane vesicles (MV) bud off that deliver materials from the ER to the cis region of the Golgi apparatus. Transport across the Golgi apparatus, from the cis to the trans face, is also mediated by membrane vesicles (MV). The trans-most cisterna of the Golgi apparatus is extended into a trans Golgi network (TGN) from which secretory materials are transferred to secretory vesicles (sec ves) or to condensing vacuoles (CV) that are converted into secretory granules (SG). Secretory vesicles and granules release their contents into the extracellular space by exocytosis, a process that involves the fusion of their membranes with the plasma membrane. Membrane proteins destined to the plasma membrane are also carried in vesicles that originate in the TGN. Materials taken into the cell by endocytosis are incorporated into membrane vesicles derived from the plasma membrane and transported to endosomes. The endosomal compartment is polymorphic and includes several classes of endosomes that represent stages in their development and their conversion into lysosomes. These include the CURL (compartment for uncoupling of receptors from ligands), from which membrane vesicles bud to return interiorized receptors to the cell surface, and multivesicular bodies (MVB), which receive lysosomal hydrolases and lysosome membrane components from the TGN and, after removal of the mannose-6-P receptors that delivered the lysosomal enzymes, are converted to lysosomes (lys). The interrelationships of the various endosomal compartments and lysosomes are depicted in greater detail in Fig. 3-21.

phospholipids, cholesterol, and glycolipids, all of which have their polar groups facing the aqueous environment on the membrane surfaces and their hydrophobic fatty acid chains (in phospholipids and glycolipids), or the sterol ring (in cholesterol), oriented toward the membrane interior. The hydrophobic interior of cellular membranes makes them effective barriers to the passage of highly polar or charged molecules from one compartment to another. The lipid molecules within the bilayer cannot easily flip-flop from one monolayer to the other, but can undergo extensive rotational and lateral translational movements. The resulting membrane fluidity permits the lateral displacement of proteins within the plane of the membrane, which is important in membrane function.

Proteins associated with membranes fall into two categories. Those that are embedded in the phospholipid bilayer and, therefore, interact directly with the hydrophobic lipid phase are known as *integral membrane proteins* (Fig. 3-3). They can only be removed from the membrane by procedures which disrupt the bilayer, such as treatment with detergents. Those proteins that do not interact directly with the membrane interior and are only bound to the surface of the membrane via interactions with other proteins or, possibly, with the polar groups of the lipids are known as *peripheral membrane proteins* (Fig. 3-3). They can be removed from membranes by treatment with media of high ionic strength or extreme pH, or that contain chelating or chaotropic agents.

In general, the membrane-embedded portions of integral membrane proteins consist of peptide segments that are rich in hydrophobic amino acids and are approximately 20 amino acids in length, just sufficient to span the thickness of the bilayer in an α-helical configuration. In some cases (see below) proteins are anchored in the membrane solely by a covalently bound lipid moiety. These may be the only integral membrane proteins that are exposed on only one membrane surface.

Proteins that fully traverse the lipid bilayer may cross the membrane only once and therefore have only one hydrophobic membrane-anchoring domain (Fig. 3-4). This is the case with several well-characterized hormone receptors of the plasma membrane, such as the epidermal growth factor (Refs. 4, 5; see Ref. 6) and insulin receptor (Refs. 7, 8; see Ref. 9) in which the ligand-binding portion of the molecule is exposed on the extracellular membrane surface while the signal-transducing domain is located in the cytoplasm. Integral membrane proteins which cross the membrane only once and have portions of their mass exposed on each surface are called *bitopic proteins*. Such proteins have one of two possible transmembrane orientations. *Type I proteins* (Fig. 3-4) have their C-terminal ends in the cytoplasm and their N-terminal ends exposed on the extracellular surface of the plasma membrane or on the (topologically equivalent) luminal surface of an organelle, such as the ER, within the endomembrane system. *Type II proteins* (Fig. 3-4) have the reverse disposition, traversing the membrane with an N-terminal cytoplasmic to C-terminal extracellular or luminal orientation. As explained in detail below, the different transmembrane orientations of the two classes of proteins can be explained as a consequence of the mechanism by which polypeptides are inserted into the ER membrane during their synthesis.

Some transmembrane proteins, in particular ion channels, cross the phospholipid bilayer several times (type III or *polytopic proteins*) (Fig. 3-4), and the N- and C-terminal ends of such proteins may be found on the same or opposite sides of the membrane. The transmembrane domains of these proteins may also be hydrophobic or may be capable of forming *amphipathic helices* whose existence within the membrane may be maintained by lateral interactions with other similar helices within the same polypeptide or within other subunits of a multimeric protein. In the final configuration, a hydrophilic channel is formed by several helices which have their hydrophobic faces interacting with the interior of the membrane bilayer.

Many membrane proteins are *glycoproteins* that contain carbohydrate moieties linked to the polypeptide backbone via either *N*-glycosidic bonds to asparagine residues, or *O*-glycosidic bonds to serine or threonine residues. Carbohydrate moieties may also be linked to membrane lipids (glycolipids). In all cases, the carbohydrates of membrane components are located only on the extracellular or luminal side of the mem-

Fig. 3-2 Topological equivalence of the membrane faces in the different compartments of the cellular endomembrane system. Intracellular traffic mediated by membrane vesicles (MV) first involves the generation of a vesicle from the membrane bounding one compartment by a budding process (also known as fission). The vesicle is then transported through the cytoplasm, and its membrane fuses with the membrane of the receiving compartment. During the fusion and fission processes, the integrity of the membrane barrier and the orientation of the luminal (thick line) and cytoplasmic (thin line) membrane faces are maintained.

Intracellular transport by membrane vesicles takes place from the ER to the Golgi apparatus and between this organelle and the plasma membrane. The route that begins with endocytosis also reaches the Golgi apparatus. Therefore, the luminal faces of ER and the Golgi membranes are topologically equivalent to the extracellular face of the plasma membrane.

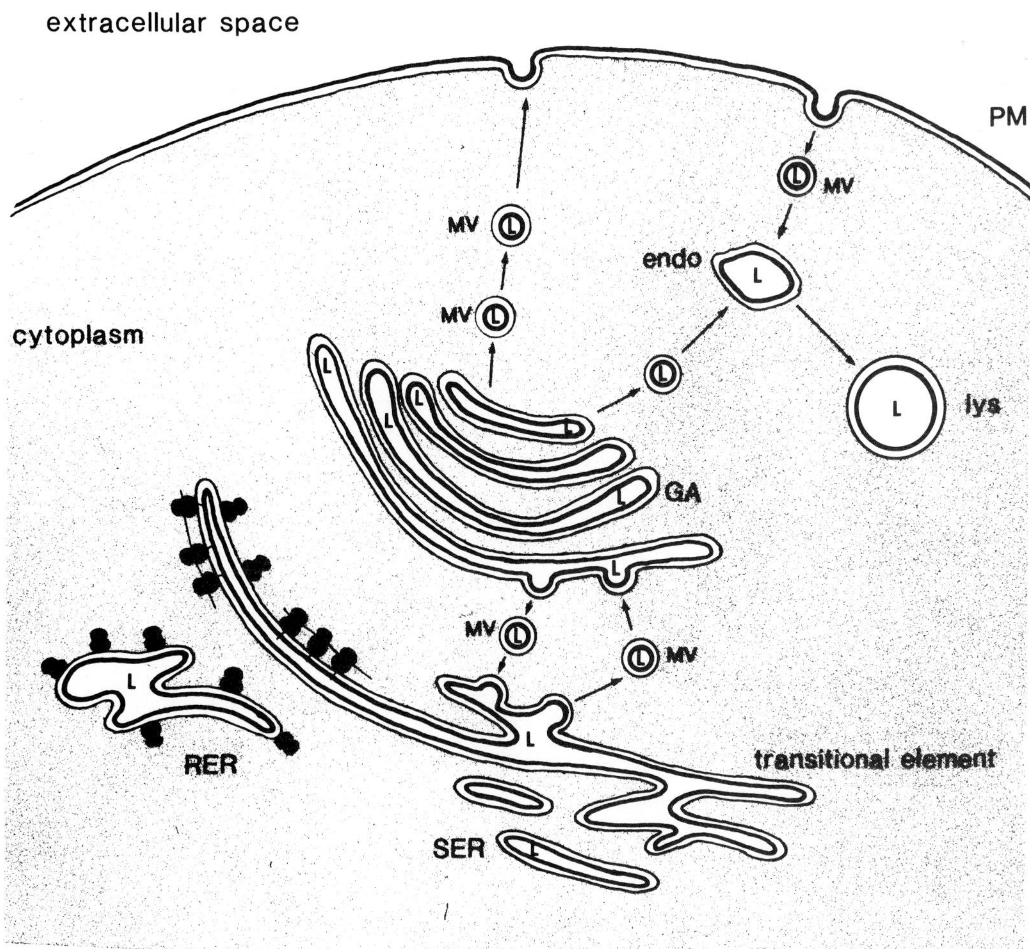

cytoplasmic side

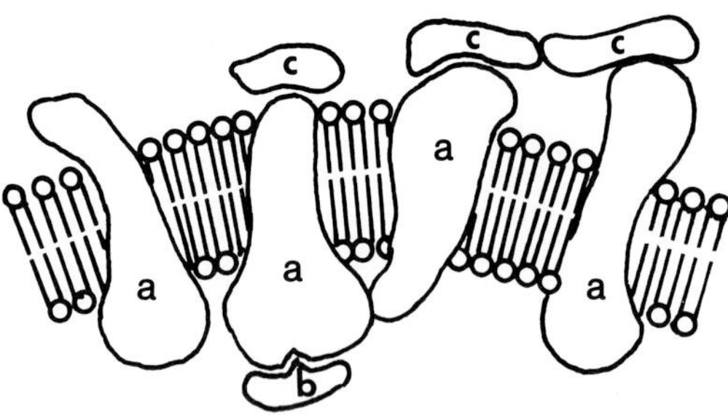

luminal or extracellular side

a) integral mb-protein

b) peripheral mb-protein of the luminal face

c) peripheral mb-protein of the cytoplasmic face

Fig. 3-3 Relationship of integral and peripheral membrane proteins to the membrane phospholipid bilayer. Integral membrane proteins (a) have portions of their mass embedded in the membrane that interact directly with the hydrophobic tails of the phospholipids. Other portions of these proteins are exposed on the cytoplasmic or luminal membrane faces. The extent of exposure on each side of the membrane may vary substantially from one protein to another. Peripheral membrane proteins (b and c) may interact with the exposed portions of integral membrane proteins, and are only associated with the membrane by virtue of these interactions. Exposed portions of integral membrane protein molecules may directly interact with each other or may be indirectly linked together via their association with interacting peripheral membrane proteins. On the cytoplasmic face, peripheral membrane proteins may provide a link between integral membrane proteins and the cellular cytoskeleton.

brane (Fig. 3-4). Since the enzymatic system responsible for the formation of *N*-glycosidic bonds is present only in the ER, only proteins that reside in this organelle or pass through it during their biosynthesis can bear asparagine-linked oligosaccharide chains.

An Overview of Organelle Biogenesis[10–12]

Because of the organizational complexity of eukaryotic cells, the implementation of their genetic programs requires not only the transcription of sets of specific genes and the translation of the resulting messenger RNAs but also the operation of mechanisms that ensure that the encoded polypeptides are transferred from their sites of synthesis to their sites of function, which may be in the cytomatrix, in a membrane, within a space enclosed by an organellar membrane, or outside the cell.

Aside from a very small number of polypeptides that are synthesized on special ribosomes found within mitochondria, the bulk of protein synthesis in mammalian cells takes place in the cytoplasmic matrix, either on ribosomes which appear to be free in the matrix, but could be associated with cytoskeletal elements, or on ribosomes which during their synthetic activity are attached to the membranes of the ER. The part of the endoplasmic reticulum to which these ribosomes are attached is called the *rough ER*, on account of its appearance in electron micrographs.

As previously noted, the universal structural feature of all cellular membranes is the presence of a phospholipid bilayer with a hydrophobic interior that constitutes a barrier to the passage of polar molecules. In particular, proteins, which normally fold with their charged and polar residues exposed on their surfaces, cannot freely traverse a phospholipid bilayer. Therefore, special mechanisms have evolved that facilitate the incorporation of polypeptides into specific membranes, and when necessary, assist them in their passage across the hydrophobic barrier.

Proteins destined for the nucleus, mitochondria, or peroxisomes are synthesized in ribosomes that are free in the cytoplasmic matrix and are directly targeted to their respective organelles (Fig. 3-5). Specific receptors for the newly synthesized organelle proteins are present in the surface of mitochondria and probably also in the surface of peroxisomes. Those receptors must recognize structural features of each polypeptide and participate in a process that leads either to its insertion into the membrane or its translocation across it. The latter process may require the expenditure of energy and entail conformational changes or extensive structural modifications of the polypeptides. Proteins destined for the interior of the nucleus must pass through the pores of the nuclear envelope.

Some proteins of the endoplasmic reticulum and of the plasma membrane are also synthesized on free polysomes and

Fig. 3-4 Transmembrane disposition of different types of integral membrane proteins. Types I and II membrane proteins cross the membrane only once. Type I proteins, such as red cell glycophorin, the LDL and EGF receptors, the heavy chain of the class I histocompatability antigen, and the viral envelope glycoproteins HA of influenza and G of VSV have their N-termini exposed on the extracellular (or luminal) face of the membrane and their C-termini on the cytoplasmic face. Type II proteins, such as the asialoglycoprotein and transferrin receptors, the sucrase-isomaltase of the intestinal brush border, and the neuraminidase of influenza virus, have the opposite transmembrane disposition. In both type I and type II proteins, the length of the segment exposed on each side of the membrane may be very short. Type III membrane proteins, such as rhodopsin, the β-adrenergic receptor, and the anion channel of the red cell membrane (band 3) cross the membrane several times. Depending on the specific protein, the N and C termini may be on either side of the membrane.

luminal or extracellular side

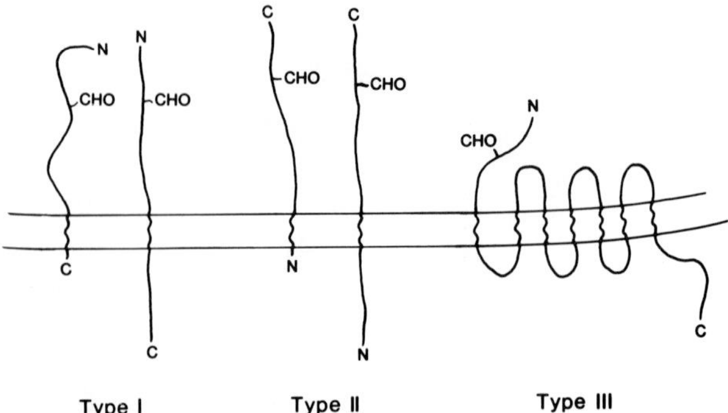

cytoplasmic side

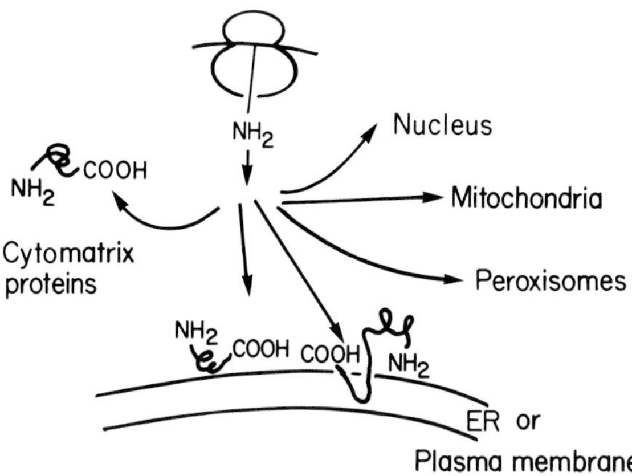

Fig. 3-5 Different fates of polypeptides synthesized on free polysomes. Upon release from the ribosome, these polypeptides may remain in the cytomatrix as soluble proteins or as components of the cytoskeleton, or they may be posttranslationally incorporated into different organelles.

become embedded in the membrane only after their synthesis is completed and they are discharged into the cytoplasm (Fig. 3-5). A similar mechanism could also, in principle, lead to the insertion of proteins in the cytoplasmic surfaces of other organelles.

In contrast to the direct targeting of nuclear, mitochondrial, and peroxisomal proteins to their sites of function, proteins destined for secretion or for incorporation into lysosomes, as well as most proteins of the plasma membrane and the Golgi apparatus, are initially incorporated into the ER and reach their sites of function by transfer through the cellular endomembrane system. Such proteins, like most proteins of the ER itself, are translocated across or inserted into the ER membrane cotranslationally, i.e., during the course of their synthesis in ribosomes bound to the rough endoplasmic reticulum membrane (Fig. 3-6). Although these proteins may later undergo extensive posttranslational modifications, it is during or immediately after their synthesis in bound polysomes that they are either transferred to the lumen of the endomembrane system or incorporated into the membrane with a characteristic disposition with respect to the phospholipid bilayer.

After discharge into the ER lumen or incorporation into the ER membrane, proteins synthesized in membrane-bound ribosomes are subjected to *sorting processes*, as yet poorly understood, which ensure that certain polypeptides are retained in the ER while others are transferred to the Golgi apparatus and from there to lysosomes, secretory vesicles or granules, or the plasma membrane. As already mentioned, transport within the endomembrane system and to and from the plasma membrane is effected by membrane vesicles that bud from one organelle and fuse with another. Throughout this movement, luminal proteins remain segregated within the successive organellar cavities and membrane proteins retain the characteristic transmembrane disposition that they acquired in the ER.

PROTEIN SYNTHESIS IN THE ROUGH ENDOPLASMIC RETICULUM[3,10–18]

The endoplasmic reticulum is a complex system of intercommunicating membrane-bounded flattened sacs *(cisternae)* and tubules that is present in all eukaryotic cells and in many cases permeates large regions of the cytoplasm. Membranes of the rough portions of the ER contain receptors for ribosomes and for nascent polypeptides, as well as enzymes that are involved in the cotranslational incorporation of these polypeptides into the organelle, or in their processing during or soon after their synthesis. In addition, both *rough* and *smooth ER* membranes contain enzymatic systems that carry out functions essential to all cells, such as steps in the synthesis of triglycerides, phospholipids, and cholesterol as well as systems that carry out specialized metabolic or biosynthetic functions and, therefore, are present only in specific cell types.

The rough ER is most prominent in cells that are engaged in protein secretion, such as pancreatic acinar cells and anterior pituitary cells, which synthesize digestive enzymes and polypeptide hormones, respectively, plasma cells, which produce immunoglobulins, or hepatocytes, which manufacture a wide variety of serum proteins. Because the rough ER plays a major role in the synthesis and assembly of membrane proteins, this organelle is prominent in cells, such as neurons, which maintain greatly expanded plasma membranes and undergo rapid expansion or turnover of membrane elements.

The degree of development of the smooth ER in different cell types usually reflects the participation of ER membrane enzymes in specialized activities of the cell. Thus, the smooth ER is very well developed in cells of steroid-secreting tissues, where it contains enzymes that catalyze several of the hydroxylation reactions that modify the steroid nucleus. It is also highly developed in skeletal muscle cells, where it is known as the "sarcoplasmic reticulum," an organelle equipped to sequester into its lumen calcium ions and to release them when the cells are stimulated to contract. In fact, the ER appears to have a widespread role in the control of cytoplasmic Ca^{2+} levels in many other cell types.

Although the membranes of the rough and smooth portions of the ER are continuous, they usually adopt within the same cell different morphologic configurations that must reflect differences in their protein and/or lipid composition. The rough cisternae are frequently arranged in stacks of interconnected flattened disks, whereas the smooth portions usually form an extensive system of thin convoluted tubules. Electron micrographs of grazing sections of rough cisternae reveal that the ribosomes attached to the membranes form rosettes, hairpins, or spiral patterns, which correspond to membrane-bound polysomes. Individual ribosomes within bound polysomes contact

Fig. 3-6 Different fates of polypeptides synthesized in ribosomes bound to the endoplasmic reticulum membrane. Proteins synthesized in membrane-bound ribosomes are inserted into the ER membranes or translocated into the ER lumen by a process that begins during their synthesis. After their synthesis is completed, these proteins either remain in the ER or are transferred to the membranes or luminal cavities of other organelles within the endomembrane system.

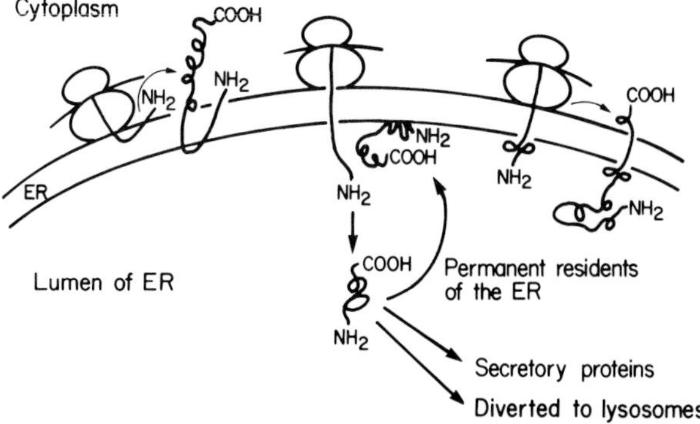

the membrane via their large subunits,[19] which are known to contain the nascent polypeptide chains.

Much information on the biochemical composition and function of the ER has come from the analysis of *rough* and *smooth microsomes,* subcellular fractions derived from rough and smooth portions of the endoplasmic reticulum, respectively. Extensive fragmentation of the ER takes place during the tissue homogenization that must be carried out before cell fractionation. The broken ER membranes, however, rapidly reseal to form microsomal vesicles that still contain a large part of the luminal content of the intact organelle.[20,21] The rough microsomes retain the ribosomes bound to their membranes and can be separated from the smooth microsomes on account of their greater density.

The structural and compositional differences between rough and smooth ER membranes have been best studied in liver cells, where both portions of the organelle are well developed and from which rough and smooth microsomes can be isolated with high yields and relative purity. Many of the most abundant ER membrane proteins are present in both rough and smooth membranes, but rough microsomes contain several specific membrane polypeptides that are likely to be involved in functions associated with the synthesis and processing of proteins made in bound ribosomes or with maintaining the characteristic structure of the rough cisternae.[22–23a]

Although cellular phospholipids are synthesized in the ER, the phospholipid composition of the ER membranes is not a simple reflection of their biosynthetic capacity. Thus, they are rich in phosphatidylcholine (PC), phosphatidylethanolamine (PE), phosphatidylserine (PS), and phosphatidylinositol (PI), but contain very small amounts of sphingomyelin (SM) and cholesterol, which are abundant in the plasma membrane. The fatty acids of ER phospholipids are usually highly unsaturated, and this accounts for the high fluidity of the ER membranes.

Cotranslational Insertion of Polypeptides into ER Membranes: Role of Insertion Signals in Determining the Association with the ER Membranes of Polysomes Synthesizing Specific Proteins

Ribosomes which are part of polysomes found free in the cytoplasmic matrix are structurally and functionally identical to those within polysomes bound to ER membranes.[24,25] Indeed, within the cell, after completion of each polypeptide chain, both polysomal populations may exchange ribosomal subunits.[26] The attachment to the ER membrane of those ribosomes that synthesize secretory, lysosomal, or certain classes of membrane proteins is determined by information contained within the nascent polypeptide chains.[27] Extensive studies with a wide variety of secretory proteins have demonstrated that, almost invariably, nascent secretory polypeptides contain N-terminal peptide segments that are not present in the mature proteins and serve to determine the attachment of the ribosome bearing the nascent chain to the ER membrane.[28–32] These segments consist of 15 to 30 amino acid residues and characteristically include a central hydrophobic core of at least 8 amino acids (see Refs. 33–36). Similar N-terminal peptides are found in nascent lysosomal proteins and in many membrane proteins. All these peptide segments are known as *transient insertion signals* or *signal sequences* or presequences. They serve to trigger the association of the ribosome with membrane and initiate the complete or partial translocation of the nascent polypeptide through it, but are removed by proteolytic cleavage before synthesis of the polypeptide is completed. The translocation of proteins across the ER membranes mediated by signal sequences (Fig. 3-7) is frequently referred to as the *vectorial discharge of nascent polypeptides.*[37]

The Process of Assembly of a Membrane-Bound Polysome

As is the case with the assembly of a free polysome, the assembly of a membrane-bound polysome begins in the cytoplasm with the binding of a small ribosomal subunit to the 5′ end of the mRNA (Fig. 3-8). After the large ribosomal subunit joins the small subunit, at the initiation codon of the mRNA, synthesis of the polypeptide begins. It is only after elongation is in course and the polypeptide is long enough for the signal segment to emerge from the large ribosomal subunit (which normally encloses a 40-amino acid segment of the nascent chain)[38,39] that the mechanism that leads to translocation begins to operate. This mechanism, illustrated schematically in Fig. 3-8, includes fail-safe features that ensure not only that the nascent polypeptide is inserted into the ER during its synthesis but also that, if insertion cannot take place, synthesis of the polypeptide is halted soon after the signal segment emerges from the ribosome.

The process of targeting the ribosome to the membrane begins with the recognition of the emerging signal by a soluble macromolecular complex, the *signal recognition particle* (SRP),[40–49] which consists of six distinct polypeptides and a small RNA molecule (7SL RNA) of approximately 300 nucleotides in length. The SRP interacts not only with the signal but also with the ribosome in such a way as to lead to a temporary block in polypeptide chain elongation. This block is only relieved in a subsequent step, when the SRP binds to its cognate *SRP receptor,*[45–47] also known as the *"docking protein,"* [48–51] which is an integral membrane protein exposed on the cytoplasmic surface of the ER. The pause in translation caused by SRP ensures that continued growth in the cytoplasm and subsequent folding of the polypeptide, which could prevent insertion in the membrane, do not take place.

Rough ER membranes also contain sites with high affinity for ribosomes that may be regarded as ribosome receptors.[52] Following docking of the SRP on the membrane, a firm attachment of the ribosome to its receptor takes place, which allows for the coupling of the processes of translation and membrane insertion. The exact sequence of events that occurs next is not known, but it is clear that binding of the SRP to its receptor displaces it from the signal and from the ribosome.[53] The signal sequence must then enter the membrane, where it interacts with a recently identified *signal sequence receptor* protein (SSR).[54]

Since neither the SRP nor its receptor appears to remain associated with the membrane-bound ribosome at the site of translocation (the number of SRP receptors in the ER membrane is much smaller than the number of active bound ribosomes), the essential role of the SRP-SRP receptor system appears to be simply to target the ribosome and its incipient chain to the endoplasmic reticulum, without participating in the translocation process itself.

It is not yet understood how the polypeptide actually traverses the ER membrane, and the models that have been proposed to explain this process fall into two major classes, ac-

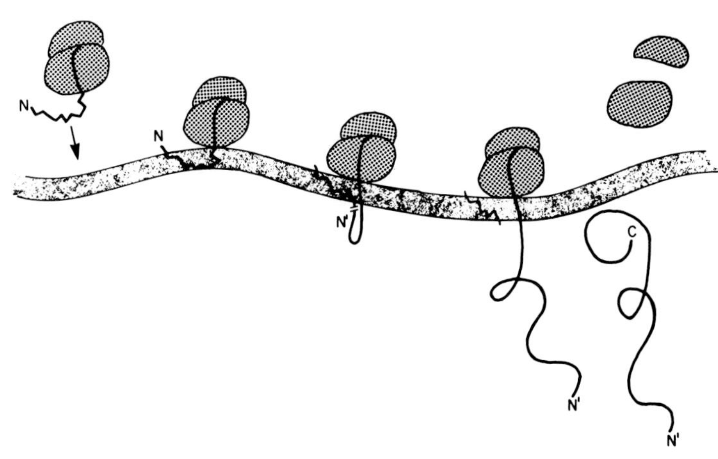

Fig. 3-7 Vectorial discharge of a secretory polypeptide across the ER membrane mediated by a cleavable N-terminal insertion signal. The cotranslational passage of a polypeptide, such as a secretory or lysosomal protein, into the ER lumen is represented in a simplified form that does not include any molecular components of the translocation machinery. The translocation is initiated by an N-terminal signal that is cleaved before polypeptide chain completion and is completed after polypeptide termination. The signal that has emerged from the ribosome leads to the association of the nascent chain and the ribosome with the membrane. The signal has been drawn as remaining in the membrane after it is cleaved. Its fate, however, has not yet been determined.

cording to whether or not they postulate that an interaction of the nascent chain with membrane proteins is necessary for translocation to occur. In one model, favored by many investigators, passage across the hydrophobic barrier within the membrane occurs through the aqueous environment of a proteinaceous channel.[31,37,55,56] In this model, a possible role of the insertion signal would be to trigger the assembly of the channel from dispersed membrane protein subunits; once assembled, the channel could be stabilized by the interaction of its components with the large ribosomal subunit. The channel would be disassembled following polypeptide chain termination or a halt in translocation caused by a halt transfer signal

Fig. 3-8 The process of assembly of a membrane-bounded polysome and the mechanism for the cotranslational translocation of a nascent polypeptide. An ordered series of molecular recognition events leads to the insertion of a nascent chain in the ER membrane. This involves an initial interaction of SRP with the ribosome (1) and with the emerging signal sequence (2 and 3), followed by binding of SRP to its receptor (4), which in turn leads to binding of the signal and the ribosome to their membrane receptors (5 and 6). See the text for the detailed description of the role of the different components of the translocation machinery illustrated in this figure. Note that SRP and its receptor function catalytically and are only transiently associated with the site of translocation. In this figure, only two cotranslational modifications, signal cleavage and core glycosylation, are shown, but several other modifications, such as disulfide exchange and hydroxylation of side chains, are also known to take place cotranslationally. Note that signal cleavage occurs relatively early in translocation so that covalent linkage of the signal to the remainder of the polypeptide is not required for the continuation of translocation. After chain termination (8), it is presumed that the translocation apparatus disassembles and the ribosome detaches from the membrane. Although the nature of the passageway for the nascent chain through the membrane is largely unknown, in this model translocation is depicted as taking place through a proteinaceous channel which becomes an extension of a tunnel within the large ribosomal subunit, where the nascent chain is contained. (*Based in part on Walter et al.*[47])

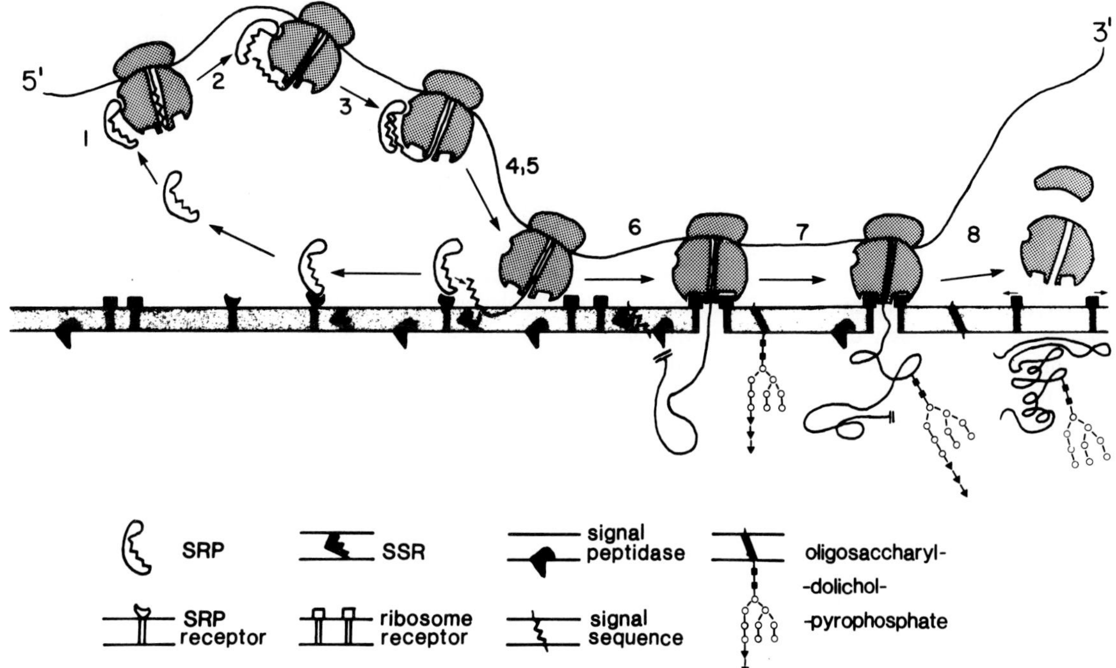

(see below). In alternative models,[57,58] The insertion signal and the nascent chain would interact directly with the membrane bilayer and no specific membrane proteins would be required to mediate translocation itself.

It is clear that whether or not proteins participate directly in the translocation process, several membrane enzymes located near the site of translocation interact with the growing chain to modify it as it emerges on the luminal side of the ER membrane. Thus, a *signal peptidase* cleaves off the signal, a *protein oligosaaccharyltransferase* links preformed mannose-rich oligosaccharide chains to selected asparagine residues within the nascent polypeptide, and a *protein disulfide exchange* enzyme catalyzes the formation of intramolecular disulfide bonds. These modifications, however, are not required for translocation to occur.

Experimental Analysis of Translocation[59]

The process of cotranslational insertion of nascent polypeptides into ER membranes has been best studied utilizing cell-free systems in which messenger RNAs from natural sources, or produced by in vitro transcription of cloned cDNA templates, are translated in the presence of rough microsomes. The most commonly used translation systems are derived from rabbit reticulocytes or wheat germ, and the most frequently used rough microsomal membranes are obtained from dog pancreas.[60]

When messenger RNAs encoding secretory proteins are translated in the absence of membranes, *primary translation products* are obtained which contain the signal sequences and are devoid of any modifications of their primary structure (Fig. 3-9*A*, lane a). Such artificial products of in vitro translation, which are generally not produced in vivo, are called *presecretory proteins* or *preproteins*. These are not true precursors of the secretory proteins, since, in vivo, their signals are actually removed before synthesis of the polypeptide is completed. When rough microsomal membranes are present during the in vitro translation, a large fraction of the product synthesized is translocated into the lumen of the microsomes and undergoes signal removal. If the translocated protein does not contain sites for *N*-linked glycosylation, its electrophoretic mobility is higher than that of the primary translation product (the presecretory protein) by the 2 to 3 kDa that corresponds to the cleaved signal (compare Fig. 3-9*A*, lanes a and b). The sequestration of the processed polypeptides in the lumen of the microsomes is demonstrated by the fact that they are protected from proteolysis when proteases are added to the reaction mixture after translation is completed (compare Fig. 3-9*A*, lanes b and c). On the other hand, the presecretory proteins (pre-GH in Fig. 3-9*A*, lane b), which remain outside the microsomes, are completely digested (Fig. 3-9*A*, lane c). Destruction of the membranes by detergent solubilization, of course, leads to digestion of the translocated products.

When the messenger RNA utilized for in vitro translation experiments encodes a protein with sites for *N*-glycosylation, translocation of the nascent chain is accompanied by both signal cleavage and addition of *N*-linked oligosaccharides (see below). In this case, the apparent size of the translocated product, when assessed by gel electrophoresis, may be higher than that of the primary translation product since the contribution of the added oligosaccharide chains may more than compensate for the size reduction resulting from signal cleavage (compare Fig. 3-9*B*, lanes a and b). Upon treatment with pro-

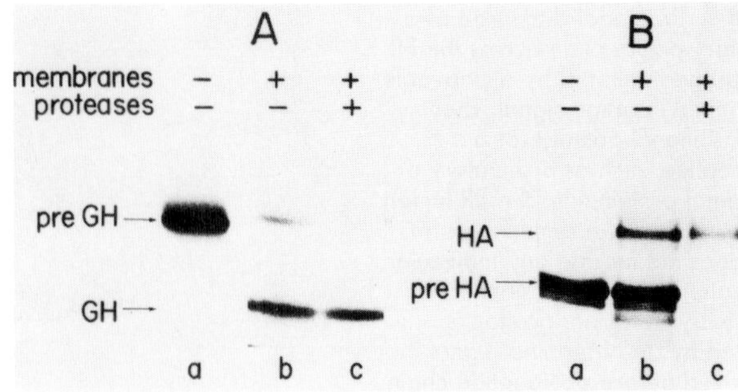

Fig. 3-9 Experimental analysis of the translocation of in vitro synthesized polypeptides: demonstration of signal cleavage, sequestration in the microsomal lumen, and glycosylation. Messenger RNAs encoding pregrowth hormone *(A)* or the hemagglutinin (HA) of influenza virus *(B)* were translated in vitro in the absence (a) or presence (b,c) of dog pancreas microsomal membranes, using a cell-free system for protein synthesis derived from wheat germ. In the absence of microsomal membranes, preproteins containing signal sequences are synthesized (*A*,a and *B*,a). When microsomes are present during translation, a large fraction of the products undergo signal cleavage. For growth hormone, this leads to an increase in electrophoretic mobility (compare *A*,a and *A*,b). In the case of HA, cleavage of the signal is accompanied by core glycosylation, and this results in a net increase in mass, which is reflected in a lower electrophoretic mobility (compare *B*,a and *B*,b). In both cases, only the cotranslationally processed products are translocated into the microsomal lumen since only they, and not the preproteins, are resistant to the degradative action of exogenous proteases (*A*,c and *B*,c). HA is a type I transmembrane glycoprotein, but only a very short segment at its C terminus (10 amino acids) is exposed on the exterior surface of the microsomes. Therefore, the protease treatment does not lead to a significant reduction in molecular weight and a concomitant increase in its electrophoretic mobility.

teases, only the glycosylated polypeptide remains undigested. The absence of the signal sequence in the translocated glycoproteins becomes apparent when, after dissolution of the microsomal membrane, they are treated with a glycosidase (endoglycosidase H) that removes the oligosaccharide chains (see below).

In vitro translocation experiments of the type just described, with mRNAs that encode lysosomal enzymes (most of which are glycoproteins) or type I transmembrane proteins, have demonstrated that these polypeptides, too, contain transient *N*-terminal signals which mediate their cotranslational insertion into the ER.

Characterization of Insertion Signals[33–36,61–63]

Insertion signals are necessary to initiate the translocation of nascent polypeptides across the ER membrane. Secretory polypeptides from which the signal is deleted by modification of the corresponding cloned gene can no longer be translocated across ER membranes, in vivo or in vitro. Moreover, in some cases, attachment of a cleavable insertion signal to the N terminus of a cytosolic protein has been shown to be sufficient to confer on it the capacity to be translocated. Although interaction of the signal with the membrane is necessary to initiate translocation, it is clear that covalent attachment of the signal to the rest of the polypeptide need not be maintained throughout translocation, since signal cleavage generally occurs much before elongation of the nascent chain is completed.[31] However, it is possible that the signal could, even after it is severed from the body of the nascent chain, be necessary for translocation to continue. If this were the case, degradation of the cleaved signal segments by the yet to be discovered *signal peptide peptidase,* would of course, occur only after translocation is completed.

Comparison of the amino acid sequences of different insertion signals shows that there is considerable variation in their primary structure. This suggests that general properties of the signals, including conformational features, rather than specific sequence information, are recognized by the various components of the translocation machinery (such as the SRP, the SSR, and the signal peptidase) that interact with the signal. Indeed many random sequences of the human genome that encode peptide segments of relatively high but varying degrees of hydrophobicity were shown to be capable of serving as a signal when linked to the yeast secretory protein invertase from which the N-terminal signal was removed.[64]

Insertion signals are, in general, 15 to 30 amino acids in length. Preprotein sequences are conventionally numbered so that the first residue after the cleavage site of the signal is designated +1 and the last residue of the signal is −1. Three segments can be recognized in all cleavable signals[35] (Fig. 3-10): (1) a hydrophobic core (the h region) 8 to 16 residues in length, which generally ends at residue −6, (2) a hydrophilic N-terminal segment that precedes the core (the n region) and usually contains, in addition to the positively charged N terminus, one basic amino acid, (3) an approximately five-residue-long C-terminal segment (the c region) which defines the cleavage site and usually begins with a helix-breaking glycine or proline residue. In some signals, such as the one in rat growth hormone, the amino terminal segment bears no net charge due to the presence of a negatively charged amino acid residue.

The charges in the n region of the signal are likely to play a role in initiating the association of the signal with the membrane that triggers the insertion of the nascent polypeptide. Deletion of the n region from prepropartathyroid hormone does not prevent the elongation arrest caused by SRP or its relief by the SRP receptor, but translocation of the nascent polypeptide is impaired.[65] These observations are in accord with the notion that, as the signal begins to enter the membrane itself, the charges in the n region associate directly with the polar head groups of the phospholipids.[66,67] If this association is maintained as translocation proceeds, the nascent chain would adopt a loop disposition in the membrane (Fig. 3-11), with its N terminus on the cytoplasmic face, the hydrophobic core of the signal within the membrane, and the cleavage site on the luminal surface. The formation of this loop would be facilitated by the helix-breaking nature of the residues immediately following the hydrophobic core.

From the analysis of numerous insertion signal sequences, certain rules have emerged that, with a fair degree of certainty, allow the prediction of the site of cleavage of the signal within the sequence of a preprotein. Most notably, the −1, −3 rule[34,63,68] states that the −1 position is almost always occupied by small neutral amino acids, such as alanine, glycine, or serine, and that the residue at −3 must not be aromatic (Phe, His, Tyr, Try), charged (Asp, Glu, Lys, Arg), or large and polar (Asn, Gln). It is also apparent that residues following the cleavage site may contribute to its recognition by the signal peptidase. Thus, some point mutations, produced by genetic engineering techniques, that affect residues following the cleavage site have been shown to prevent cleavage. A role of the sequence following the cleavage site in determining signal cleavage may account for the fact that some secretory proteins, such as parathyroid hormone and albumin, contain a second transient N-terminal peptide segment, the propiece, that is removed from the proprotein during or after passage through the Golgi apparatus. In these instances, the N-terminal sequence of the mature protein, which may be important for the function of the protein, might not have permitted cleavage of the signal had it been immediately adjacent to the −1 residue.[69] One function of the propiece could be, therefore, to satisfy the requirements for the creation of a signal peptidase cleavage site in the nascent preprotein.

The conformation that the signal segment attains within the

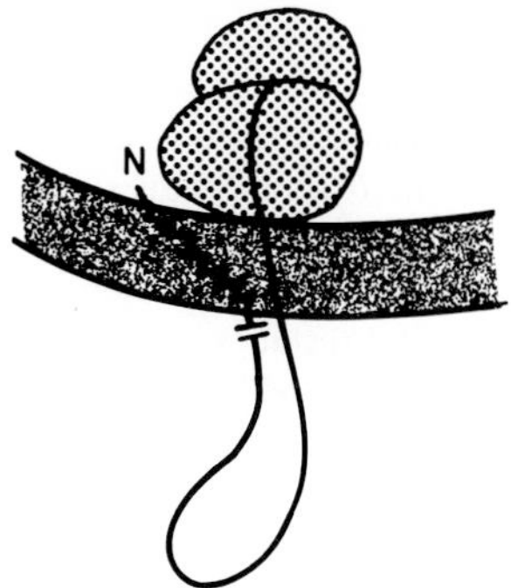

Fig. 3-11 Loop model for the disposition during translocation of the cleavable signal of a polypeptide synthesized in a membrane-bound ribosome. In this model, the extreme N terminus of the signal remains on the cytoplasmic face of the membrane and the nascent chain has a looped disposition during the initial stages of translocation. In most secretory, lysosomal, and type I transmembrane proteins, the signal is N-terminal and is cleaved during translocation, as depicted in this figure. In type II transmembrane proteins, the signal is not cleaved and the looped configuration would be maintained throughout translocation, until the extreme C terminus of the polypeptide is released into the lumen.

Fig. 3-10 Sequences of transient insertion signals of secretory proteins. The amino acid sequences of the transient insertion signals of numerous proteins are known, from which general consensus features for the signals have become apparent. The N-terminal portion of the sequences of three presecretory proteins are shown and the point of cleavage by the signal peptidase is indicated in each case by a downward arrow. The amino acid residue within the signal adjacent to the cleavage site is designated as −1 and the preceding residues in the signal are counted negatively from −1 toward the N terminus. The three segments in each signal, described in the text, are labeled n, h, and c. Hydrophobic amino acids are marked by filled-in circles, basic residues by squares, and acidic ones by triangles, all placed beneath the residue abbreviation. The residue designated +1 represents the new N terminus generated by signal cleavage. In the case of rat pregrowth hormone, the +1 residue corresponds to the N terminus of the mature protein. In the case of preproinsulin, this residue corresponds to the N terminus of the β chain of insulin. In the case of preproalbumin, a second cleavage near the n terminus takes place in the Golgi apparatus, at the site indicated by the arrowhead. This removes a hexapeptide propiece and leaves glutamic acid at the N terminus of the mature protein.

TRANSIENT INSERTION SIGNAL SEQUENCES OF SECRETORY PROTEINS

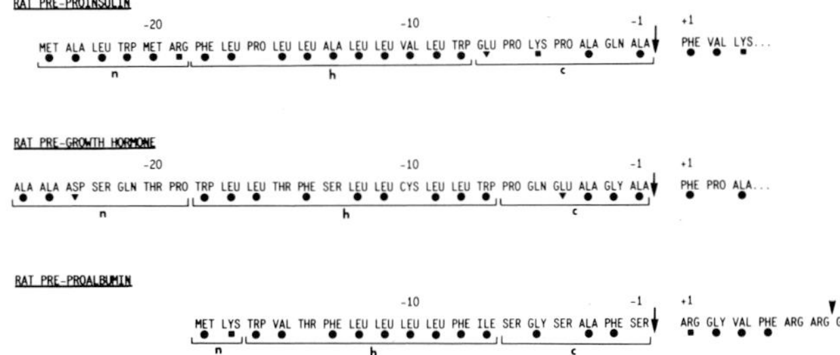

interior of the membrane has not been established. Within a hydrophobic environment, an α-helical conformation would be favored for the core region. However, the core is usually shorter than the approximately 20 amino acid residues that would be required for an α helix to completely span the membrane thickness of 2.5 to 3 nm, whereas in a fully extended configuration a peptide segment of only 8 residues could span the membrane. It has, therefore, been suggested[62] that within the membrane the hydrophobic core of the signal may exist partially as an α helix and partially as a fully extended structure. The important role played by the hydrophobicity of the central core of the signal in translocation is apparent from the deleterious effects of mutations which in bacterial secretory proteins replaced some of the hydrophobic residues by charged ones, or introduced partial deletions covering core residues.[70,71]

Even though insertion signals are usually removed by cleavage from nascent secretory and lysosomal polypeptides and from many nascent membrane proteins (see below), signal cleavage is not required for translocation. Indeed, one secretory protein, ovalbumin,[72–74] and several viral envelope glycoproteins[75–77] are known which contain signals near their amino termini that serve their function to mediate translocation but are not cleaved and are themselves transferred with adjacent portions of the polypeptide into the ER lumen.

The Signal Recognition Particle[15,17,18]

The signal recognition particle (SRP) plays a central role in selecting ribosomes for binding to the ER and in delivering the nascent chains to a receptor within the membrane. The distribution of SRP within the cell reflects its cyclic participation in these processes. SRP may be found free in the cytoplasm, weakly bound to inactive ribosomes, or attached to its receptor in the ER membranes[78] (Fig. 3-8). The affinity of SRP for ribosomes, however, increases at least 6000-fold when the ribosome contains a nascent chain with an exposed signal sequence, to which the SRP also binds.[42]

The most commonly used source of SRP for in vitro studies of its role in translocation is dog pancreas microsomes, from which SRP can be released by treatment with media of high salt concentration. Indeed, microsomes treated with high salt (KRM) are inactive in translocation unless supplemented with SRP.[40] The pause in translation caused by SRP is best observed when SRP is added to a wheat germ translation system, which lacks endogenous SRP. In the absence of added microsomes, SRP leads to an effective block in the elongation of nascent proteins that contain a signal peptide, such as preprolactin, but the synthesis of cytosolic proteins, such as globin, proceeds unaffected.[44] In several cases, it has been shown that in the presence of SRP, a ribosome-associated arrested fragment of the preprotein of approximately 80 amino acids accumulates in the translation system. The SRP-mediated arrest of polypeptide chain elongation is relieved by the addition of microsomes to the system, which leads to signal cleavage and translocation,[43,44] or even by the addition of purified SRP receptor.[46]

The SRP obtained from dog pancreas microsomes by washing with high salt is a particle with a sedimentation coefficient of 11 S that contains, in addition to the 7SL RNA molecule, six polypeptide chains of 9, 14, 19, 54, 68, and 72 kDa.[41,79] The 7SL RNA is an abundant and metabolically stable molecule which contains at its 5′ and 3′ ends sequences of the Alu family, one of the most highly repeated family of sequences in the genome, and in its middle region a core segment of 150 nucleotides, termed the *S sequence*, that is much less frequently repeated.[80] Both protein and RNA components of SRP have been shown to be required for its function. SRP has been disassembled into its RNA and protein components by the removal of Mg^{2+} ions, which normally stabilize its structure, and it has been possible to reassemble a functional particle from the dissociated components.[81] This has allowed studies on the role of the individual proteins in the different aspects of SRP function.[82,83]

It is noteworthy that 7SL RNAs from such evolutionarily distant species as *Drosophila melanogaster* and *Xenopus laevis* can replace the canine RNA in the reassembled particles. Reconstitution experiments have shown that the two smallest polypeptides of SRP are required for translational arrest but are not necessary for translocation which, of course, demonstrates that the arrest in translation is not essential for translocation to occur.[82] In fact, SRP may cause only a slowdown in the translation of certain mRNAs for which arrested peptides have not been detected in the wheat germ system.

Treatment of SRP with nucleases generates two subparticles that may correspond to domains exerting the functions of SRP.[80] One particle contains the two smallest polypeptides bound to the two ends of the 7SL RNA and the other, the four remaining ones bound to the central region of the RNA.

SRP can be purified by hydrophobic chromatography, suggesting that it interacts with the hydrophobic core of signal sequences. Indeed, replacement of leucine residues in a presecretory protein with β-hydroxyleucine, a polar analogue, abolishes the high affinity binding of SRP for the ribosome, and hence the translational arrest and subsequent translocation.[43] Moreover, it has recently been found that in a ribosome carrying SRP, the nascent chain is in close proximity to the 54-kDa polypeptide of SRP, since the two can be cross-linked through a photoactivatable group incorporated into the nascent chain.[84] In this case, the elongation arrest was maintained after cross-linking and was relieved upon binding to the SRP receptor, but translocation could not occur.

The Signal Recognition Particle Receptor or Docking Protein[45,46,48,49]

The SRP receptor is a protein complex exposed on the cytoplasmic surface of the ER membrane where it receives the SRP bound to a ribosome containing an exposed signal sequence (Fig. 3-8). This binding displaces the SRP from the ribosome and from the signal and allows the signal to insert into the membrane.[53] The SRP receptor is present in the ER in low amounts (0.1 percent of the total membrane protein) and functions catalytically, remaining associated with SRP for only the very brief period required to displace it from the ribosome and to establish the ribosome-membrane junction. These reactions can occur at 0°C in the absence of any polypeptide chain elongation.[53]

The SRP receptor has been purified from solubilized rough microsomal membranes by affinity chromatography to immobilized SRP, using the relief of the translation arrest of preprolactin as an assay to detect functional receptor.[45,46] The SRP receptor obtained in this manner consists of two subunits, a 69-kDa glycoprotein α subunit and a 30-kDa β subunit.[85] Treatment of rough microsomes with the protease elastase renders the membrane inactive in translocation and leads to the release of a 52-kDa fragment of the α subunit, which can be added back to the proteolyzed membranes at low ionic strength to restore translocation competence.[48,49]

The complete primary structure of the α subunit has been derived from the nucleotide sequence of a cDNA clone.[86] Comparison of this sequence with the N-terminal sequence of the 52-kDa fragment released by proteolysis shows that the protein is anchored to the membrane via a 155-amino acid N-terminal segment which contains two hydrophobic domains. The portion of the molecule exposed on the cytoplasmic surface contains three extremely hydrophilic regions rich in charged amino acids, with a predominance of basic residues that may interact directly with the 7SL RNA component of the SRP. This portion of the molecule also contains several additional hydrophobic segments which, clearly, do not interact permanently with the membrane and are probably buried within the protein.

Interaction of the Signal Sequence and the Nascent Polypeptide with Membrane Protein Components

After the displacement of the SRP from the ribosome induced by the SRP receptor, the insertion signal and the nascent chain enter the ER membrane, where they interact with protein components (Fig. 3-8). This was first demonstrated by the observation that partially translocated, incomplete nascent polypeptides could be removed from the microsomal membrane by treatment with agents, such as urea, that perturb protein-protein interactions but do not remove integral membrane proteins from membranes.[56] As was already mentioned, a signal receptor protein (SSR), to which a signal bearing a photoactivatable group can be cross-linked, has recently been identified in microsomal membranes.[54] The SSR is a 35-kDa glycoprotein that can interact with the signal in the absence of chain elongation (when the ribosomes are added to the membrane in the presence of the protein synthesis inhibitor cycloheximide). Its role in translocation is not yet clear, but its discovery definitively establishes that during translocation the nascent chain does not simply interact with membrane lipids. SSR could participate in the formation of a functional membrane channel through which the polypeptide could pass or, possibly mediate, an interaction of the signal sequence with membrane lipids.

The Signal Peptidase

The signal peptidase activity of microsomes can be demonstrated in detergent solubilized preparations,[87] using as substrates certain completed preproteins synthesized in vitro, such as preprolactin and pregrowth hormone. Most preproteins, however, cannot be processed posttranslationally by microsomal extracts, presumably because they are folded in such a way as to sequester the signal cleavage site. This sequestration of the signal may occur before synthesis of the preprotein is completed and the incapacity of the masked signals to interact with SRP when this is added late in translation would account for the fact that, beyond a certain length, nascent polypeptides are no longer "translocation competent."[88]

The solubilized signal peptidase is only active in the presence of phospholipids,[89] and its activity can be inhibited by agents such as chymostatin that inhibit zinc metallopeptidases.[90] Because the peptidase activity cannot be demonstrated without detergent solubilization, and it is not destroyed by proteolysis of intact microsomes,[87,91] it can be concluded that the active site of the signal peptidase is located on the luminal side of the ER membrane (Fig. 3-8). This location is consistent with the observation that signal cleavage does not take place before the polypeptide attains a minimal length of 70 to 90 residues, which are required to bring the cleavage site to the luminal face of the ER.

A protein complex with signal peptidase activity has recently been purified from solubilized dog pancreas microsomes.[92] It contains six polypeptide chains of apparent molecular weights ranging from 12,000 to 25,000 only two of which are glycosylated. It is likely that only one of these polypeptides carries out the signal cleavage and that the remaining ones participate in other aspects of the translocation process, such as the degradation of the cleaved signal peptide (signal peptide peptidase) or cotranslational modifications of the nascent chain. An intriguing possibility is that some of the polypeptides in the complex are constituents of a membrane pore through which translocation may take place. It is noteworthy that neither the signal sequence receptor (SSR) nor proteins that have been implicated in ribosome binding (see below) are part of the signal peptidase complex.

Ribosome Binding Sites on the ER Membrane

After displacement of the SRP by its receptor, binding of the ribosome to the ER membrane takes place (Fig. 3-8). During the subsequent translocation, the ribosome remains associated with the ER membrane via two types of bonds, direct ones between the large ribosomal subunit and a receptor in the membrane, and an indirect link that is provided by the nascent polypeptide chain.[93] The latter is broken upon termination of polypeptide growth or when a prematurely terminated polypeptide is released from the ribosome as a result of the incorporation of the chain-terminating peptidyl tRNA analogue puromycin at the c terminus of the nascent chain. Ribosomal subunits can then be detached from the membrane by exposure of the microsomes to media of high ionic strength, which disrupt electrostatic interactions between the large ribosomal subunit and its receptor. Ribosomes not containing nascent chains rebind in vitro and at low ionic strengths to rough microsomal membranes stripped of ribosomes but not to other cellular membranes, including those of smooth microsomes.[52,94,95] The number of ribosome binding sites detected by this method is equivalent to the number of ribosomes originally present in the rough microsomes.[96]

The ribosome receptors present in the rough ER contain proteinaceous components, since ribosome binding is abolished by mild proteolysis or heat treatment of the membranes.[52] The specific polypeptides involved in ribosome binding, however, have not been definitively identified. Two transmembrane glycoproteins, ribophorins I and II, present only in rough microsomes, where they are found in amounts stoichiometrically related to the number of ribosomes, appear to be associated with the binding sites.[22,23,97] Thus, these proteins, and only a few other membrane polypeptides, are recovered with the ribosomes when these are sedimented after certain nonionic detergents are used to solubilize the membranes. In this case, a membrane residue is obtained in which proteins appear to form a two-dimensional network bearing ribosomes. On this basis, it has been proposed[22,23] that the ribophorins also play a structural role in the rough ER, providing a scaffolding within the ER membrane that restricts the ribosome binding sites and their associated translocation apparatus to the rough domains and confers on the rough cisternae their characteristic morphology. The cDNAs for both ribophorins have recently been cloned,[98,99] and the primary structures of the polypeptides suggest that both proteins are type I monotopic proteins that cross the membrane only once and have C-terminal segments of 150 and 70 amino acids, respectively, exposed on the cytoplasmic face of the membrane. Proteins other than the ribophorins, however, are also likely to participate in the formation of the ribosome binding site, since mild proteolysis that does not appear to cleave the cytoplasmically exposed portions of the ribophorins abolishes the ribosome binding capacity of the membrane.[100,101]

BIOSYNTHESIS OF MEMBRANE PROTEINS: ROLE OF INSERTION AND HALT-TRANSFER SIGNALS IN DETERMINING THEIR TRANSMEMBRANE DISPOSITION[3,10,11,16,77]

All membrane glycoproteins and, indeed, all transmembrane proteins that are not contained within mitochondria or peroxisomes are synthesized in ribosomes bound to the rough ER and are cotranslationally inserted into the ER membrane.

Type I membrane proteins (Fig. 3-4), which cross the membrane only once and contain their N termini exposed on the extracellular or luminal surface of the membrane, such as the red cell glycophorin, the low density lipoprotein (LDL) and epidermal growth factor (EGF) receptors, the heavy chain of the histocompatibility antigen, and the much-studied hemagglutinin and G envelope glycoproteins of the influenza and vesicular stomatitis (VSV) viruses, respectively, are generally synthesized with transient N-terminal insertion signals that are totally equivalent to those in secretory proteins (Fig. 3-12*A*, *B*, and *C*). These signals, via their interaction with SRP, initiate passage of the polypeptides across the membrane, and their cleavage results in generation of new N termini exposed in the lumen of the ER. In contrast to secretory proteins (Fig. 3-12*D*), translocation of a type I membrane polypeptide is interrupted by a highly hydrophobic segment, the *halt-* or *stop-transfer signal,* that constitutes the sole transmembrane segment or *membrane-anchoring domain* in the mature protein (Fig. 3-12*E*). The relative lengths of the luminal and cytoplasmic domains of type I polypeptides are, therefore, determined by the position of the halt-transfer signal within the polypeptide. In rare instances, such as in the envelope glycoproteins of Sindbis[75] and Semliki Forest viruses (SFV),[76] type I proteins contain *uncleaved N-terminal insertion signals* which, after initiating translocation, are themselves translocated and form part of the luminal domain of the mature protein.

Segments that serve as halt-transfer signals consist of approximately 20 hydrophobic or uncharged amino acids that are usually followed by several basic residues (Fig. 3-13). In exerting its function, the halt-transfer signal must allow for the reutilization of the components of the translocation apparatus in other rounds of translocation. Therefore, if cotranslational translocation occurs through a channel, this must be disassembled by halt-transfer signals, which would then allow for their direct association with the membrane phospholipids. In many

Fig. 3-12 The transmembrane disposition of type I membrane polypeptides is established by the sequential action of a cleavable N-terminal insertion signal and an interior half-transfer signal. The early stages of insertion of a type I membrane protein into the ER membrane (a, b, c) are identical to those of a secretory protein. After signal cleavage takes place, translocation continues until a halt-transfer signal in the interior of the polypeptide reaches the membrane and stops further translocation (e). Secretory proteins (d) lack signals that stop transfer and, therefore, after completion of synthesis undergo complete vectorial discharge into the lumen of the ER.

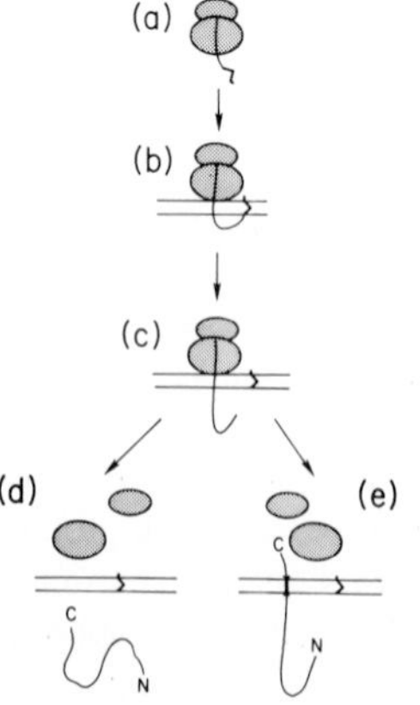

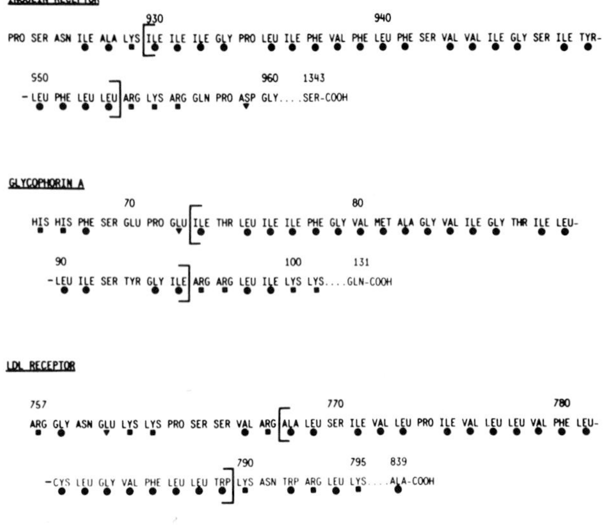

Fig. 3-13 Segments that contain the halt-transfer signal–membrane-anchoring domains of type I membrane proteins. The regions of four type I membrane proteins that contain the hydrophobic segments that are thought to traverse the phospholipid bilayer are presented. The exact borders of the transmembrane domains of these polypeptides have not been determined. Hydrophobic residues are marked with a circle, basic ones with a rectangle, and acidic residues with a triangle. Segments containing long stretches of hydrophobic amino acids uninterrupted by charged residues are enclosed within brackets. Note that these are followed by clusters of basic residues and are at varying distances from the C terminus of the protein. The numbers indicate the positions of the residues within each sequence.

instances, the halt-transfer segment is located so close to the C terminus that it must enter the membrane only after synthesis of the polypeptide has been completed and the chain released from the ribosome. In other cases, however, the halt-transfer signal is distant from the C terminus and elongation must continue in the cytoplasm after translocation has been halted. It is likely that in these instances the ribosome is dislodged from the membrane by the growing polypeptide chain.

The fact that the presence of the halt-transfer segment is the only feature of type I membrane proteins that distinguishes them from secretory proteins is strikingly demonstrated during B lymphocyte maturation, when the cells shift from the production of a membrane-bound form of IgM to a secretory form.[102,103] This shift simply involves a modification in the processing of the RNA transcript (primary transcript) from which the μ heavy chain messenger RNA is generated.[104] In pre-B cells, in which the immunoglobulin heavy chain (μ_m) is membrane-bound, the extreme 3′ portion of the coding region of the mRNA encodes the transmembrane and cytoplasmic domains of the polypeptide. At later stages, a different messenger RNA is generated from the same primary transcript. This mRNA encodes a polypeptide (μ_s) that does not contain the membrane-anchoring or cytoplasmic domains of μ_m but contains instead a short segment which includes the cysteine residue that within the pentameric secreted IgM forms a disulfide bond with the immunoglobulin J chain.

The exclusive role of the hydrophobic halt-transfer signal in maintaining the association of type I proteins with the membrane has been demonstrated experimentally. In fact, it has been possible to use genetic engineering techniques to convert membrane proteins into secretory proteins by deleting the region encoding the halt-transfer signal from the mRNA.[105,106] Moreover, in reciprocal experiments, secretory proteins have been converted into type I membrane proteins simply by introducing in them a halt-transfer signal.[107] Other genetic engineering experiments have shown that 12 to 16 consecutive hydrophobic residues suffice to maintain the anchoring of a type I protein to the membrane[108] and that the charges that follow the hydrophobic segment are not essential for this purpose.[109–111a]

The mechanism just described cannot, of course, account for the transmembrane disposition of type II membrane proteins, such as the asialoglycoprotein[111a] and transferrin receptors,[112,113] the sucrase-isomaltase of the intestinal brush border,[114] and the neuraminidase of influenza virus.[115–117] These proteins have their C termini exposed on the outer surface of the membrane and their N termini on the cytoplasmic side (Fig. 3-4). The biogenetic origin of the transmembrane disposition of these proteins can be understood, however, in the context of the loop model for the configuration of the signal and the nascent chain during translocation, as depicted in Fig. 3-14. In all these cases, the cotranslational insertion is initiated by a signal within the polypeptide which serves to mediate the translocation of downstream portions of the polypeptide but does not undergo cleavage and remains membrane-associated as the anchoring domain of the mature protein. The N-terminal portion of the polypeptide that precedes the signal, therefore, remains exposed on the cytoplasmic surface of the membrane. It should be clear that the process of insertion of a type II protein would be identical in all respects to that of a secretory protein, except that the signal does not undergo cleavage and is sufficiently hydrophobic to remain membrane-anchored after polypeptide chain termination. When the interior insertion signal-membrane anchoring domain of a type II protein is

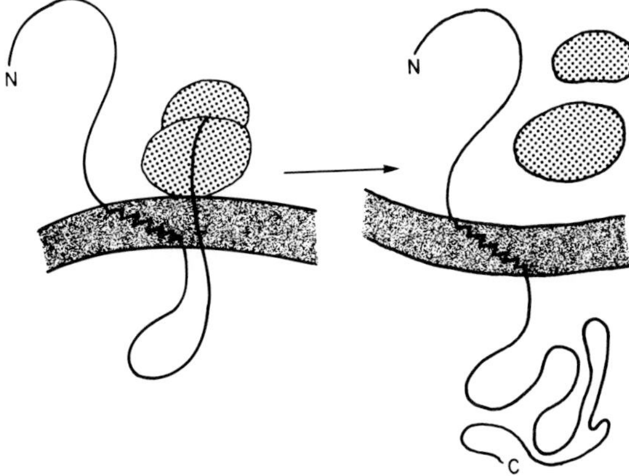

Fig. 3-14 The transmembrane disposition of a type II membrane protein results from the action of a permanent insertion signal that remains as a membrane anchor in the mature protein. The permanent insertion signal that initiates translocation of type II membrane proteins may be at the N terminus or, as shown in the figure, in the interior of the polypeptide. Insertion begins only after the signal emerges from the ribosome and, therefore, the portion of the polypeptide preceding the signal remains on the cytoplasmic side of the membrane as the signal establishes the looped disposition of the nascent chain within the membrane. The relative lengths of the polypeptide segments on each side of the membrane are determined by the location of the permanent insertion signal within the polypeptide.

located at some distance from the N-terminal end, it is, of course, necessary that folding of the N-terminal portion does not mask the signal and prevent its interaction with SRP.

Membrane-anchoring domains of type I and type II proteins differ, therefore, not only in their N-to-C orientation within the membrane, but also in that those in type I proteins enter the membrane as part of a translocating polypeptide and serve to arrest translocation, whereas those in type II proteins initiate the membrane insertion process and promote the translocation of following portions of the nascent polypeptide chain.

It should be apparent that a series of alternating insertion and halt-transfer signals within a single polypeptide chain, functioning in succession, could explain the transmembrane disposition of many type III (polytopic) proteins (Fig. 3-15). In these cases, the location of the N terminus would be determined by whether the first signal is N-terminal and transient (Fig. 3-15*B*) or internal and permanent (Fig. 3-15*A*), and the location of the C terminus by whether the last signal is an insertion (Fig. 3-15*A*) or a halt-transfer signal (Fig. 3-15*B*). It must be emphasized, however, that the two types of transmembrane domains could be, and frequently are, very similar in their primary structure, which is what determines the stability of their interaction with the phospholipid bilayer. Whether or not a sufficiently hydrophobic segment in a polypeptide functions as an insertion or as a halt-transfer signal could therefore depend on its relative position with respect to other signals within the primary translation product,[118,119] since this determines how the segment is presented to the membrane. If preceded by an insertion signal, cleaved or uncleaved, the hydrophobic segment would enter the membrane directly as it exits the ribosome and, therefore, would halt transfer of a translocating polypeptide. If, on the other hand, the segment is the first one in the polypeptide, or is preceded by a halt-transfer signal, it would emerge from the ribosome in the cytoplasm where it could be recognized by SRP and lead to insertion of downstream sequences. It should be noted, however, that the hydrophobicity of a typical cleavable insertion signal, such as that in the hemagglutinin of influenza, is

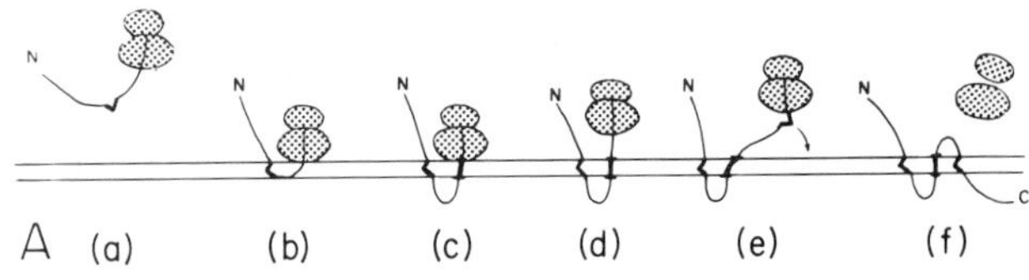

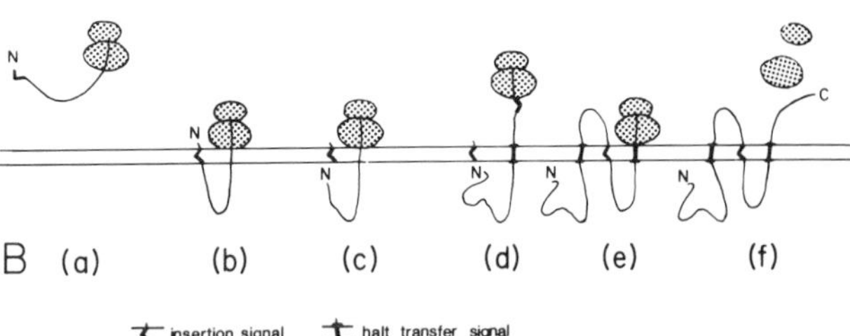

Fig 3-15 The transmembrane disposition of type II membrane proteins can result from the sequential action of a series of alternating insertion and halt-transfer signals. It is presumed that interior insertion signals can reinitiate translocation after this has been interrupted by the action of a halt-transfer signal. Consequently, a series of insertion and halt-transfer signals leads to multiple crossings of the membrane. In *A*, the first insertion signal is interior and noncleavable, so that the N terminus of the protein remains on the cytoplasmic side of the membrane. The last signal is an insertion signal and, therefore, the C-terminal portion of the polypeptide that follows that signal is translocated into the lumen. In *B*, the first insertion signal is cleavable and, therefore, the N terminus of the protein is on the luminal side of the membrane. The last signal is a halt-transfer signal and, therefore, the C terminus is on the cytoplasmic side. Note that, since elongation of the polypeptide continues after halt tranfer, the ribosomes (in *A*, d and *B*, d) have been depicted as being detached from the membrane, until another insertion signal reinitiates translocation and reestablishes their binding to the membrane (*B*, e).

not sufficient to halt transfer when the signal is placed in the interior of a translocating polypeptide.[120]

Combined Insertion–Halt-Transfer Signals in Membrane Proteins

Several polytopic membrane proteins have been characterized, such as rhodopsin[121] and the evolutionarily related β_2-adrenergic receptor,[122,123] that have glycosylated N-terminal segments located on the luminal side of the membrane and yet do not undergo signal removal during their membrane insertion. In the case of rhodopsin, it has been shown that the first transmembrane segment, which begins 35 residues from the N terminus, has the capacity to initiate the insertion of the nascent polypeptide into the membrane.[124,125] Although this segment can, therefore, be regarded as an insertion signal, it is clear from the disposition of the polypeptide with respect to the membrane that it must also act to halt translocation of following polypeptide sequences while, paradoxically, promoting the translocation of the preceding portion into the ER lumen. The first transmembrane domain of rhodopsin is, therefore, a combined insertion–halt transfer signal whose final orientation in the membrane is that characteristic of the regular halt transfer signals found in type I monotopic proteins, with its N terminus on the luminal surface of the membrane.

If, as is reasonable to assume, the signal in rhodopsin enters the membrane in a loop configuration, which would place the N-terminal portion of the protein in the cytoplasm, then the signal must later reorient to effect the transfer of the preceding peptide segment across the membrane, where its glycosylation occurs. This would lead to the dissipation of the loop, which may be responsible for the halt in translocation that leaves the amino acids following the signal on the cytoplasmic side of the membrane. Of course, the other membrane crossings in rhodopsin would require the action of a succession of subsequent insertion and halt transfer signals.

Signals with properties similar to that of the first transmembrane segment in rhodopsin are also present in several proteins of the ER membrane, such as cytochrome P_{450}[126,127] and its NADPH-dependent reductase,[128] which are synthesized in membrane-bound ribosomes and have uncleaved hydrophobic N-terminal segments, but remain almost completely exposed on the cytoplasmic surface of the ER. In the case of cytochrome P_{450}, the insertion–halt-transfer function of a segment that encompasses the first 20 amino acids has been directly demonstrated by genetic engineering experiments. When linked to the N terminus of a secretory protein, such as growth hormone, this segment confers upon the latter the same disposition with respect to the membrane as that of P_{450} itself.[127]

COTRANSLATIONAL MODIFICATIONS OF POLYPEPTIDES SYNTHESIZED IN THE ER[129–132]

Glycoproteins are characterized by the presence of oligosaccharide chains that are linked either to nitrogen atoms of asparagine residues or to oxygen atoms of serines and threonines. In collagen, hydroxylysine residues may also bear *O*-linked sugars. The attachment of *N*-linked oligosaccharide chains to proteins takes place during the course of polypeptide chain elongation, while the nascent chains are still traversing the ER membrane (Fig. 3-8). In this reaction, a preformed oligosaccharide ($Glc_3Man_9GlcNAc_2$) (Fig. 3-16) is transferred by an oligosaccharyltransferase from a membrane-bound dolicholpyrophosphate lipid carrier to asparagine residues in the polypeptide backbone. This enzyme is located on the luminal face of the ER membrane and recognizes asparagine residues within the triplet sequence Asn-X-Ser/Thr, where X can be any amino acid except proline or aspartic acid.[133,134]

The process by which the oligosaccharide is assembled on the dolicholpyrophosphate carrier involves enzymatic reactions that take place on both sides of the membrane.[132] The first seven sugar residues (two GlcNAc and five Man) are transferred directly in a stepwise fashion from the nucleotide sugars UDP-GlcNAc and GDP-Man to the membrane-bound dolichol phosphate, which has its acceptor site exposed on the cytoplasmic face of the membrane. The resulting intermediate ($Man_5GlcNAc_2$-PPDol) is then reoriented so that its acceptor site is exposed on the luminal side of the membrane, where it receives the remaining four mannose and three glucose residues from Dol-P-sugars that are formed on the cytoplasmic side but are capable of flipping across the membrane. The synthesis of the oligosaccharide chain on the lipid carrier can be inhibited by the drug tunicamycin, which thereby completely prevents the addition of oligosaccharides to asparagine residues.

In general, only approximately 30 percent of all the potential asparagine acceptor sites in a polypeptide actually carry oligosaccharide chains.[135] This may be due to the fact that glycosylation can only take place within a narrow window of time during polypeptide chain elongation, after the acceptor aspar-

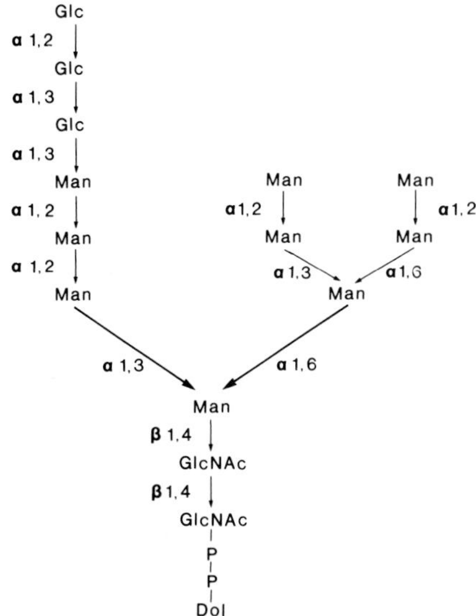

Fig. 3-16 Structure of the lipid-linked oligosaccharide precursor of oligosaccharides in glycoproteins. The lipid carrier dolichol phosphate consists of 22 five-carbon isoprene units that are embedded in the ER membrane. After the sugars are added to the lipid carrier, by a series of reactions that are mentioned in the text, the entire oligosaccharide is transferred *en bloc* to the nascent polypeptide chain. In this process, the *N*-acetylglucosamine (GlcNAc) moiety linked to the dolichol pyrophosphate becomes bound to an asparagine residue by an *N*-glycosidic bond (Glc = glucose; Man = mannose; Dol = dolichol).

agine reaches the luminal side of the membrane but before folding of the polypeptide may mask it. In addition, since it appears that certain asparagine-containing triplet sequences are better acceptors than others, depending on the X residue and the sequences flanking the triplet, the extent of glycosylation that could be achieved during the narrow window may vary considerably for different potential acceptor sequences.

Soon after its transfer to the polypeptide and even before the polypeptide is completed,[136] the oligosaccharide chain begins to undergo a trimming process in which the three glucose residues and one or two mannoses are removed (Fig. 3-17). These reactions are catalyzed by α1→2 and α1→3 glucosidases (glucosidases I and II) and by an α1→2 mannosidase, respectively, that are located in the ER membrane and are likely to be closely associated with the translocation apparatus. Oligosaccharides in glycoproteins that reside permanently in the ER, such as the ribophorins[137] or HMG-CoA reductase[138] or traverse it slowly on their way to the Golgi apparatus, may, over the course of time, lose two additional mannose residues in the ER. Oligosaccharides in proteins that are transferred to the Golgi apparatus usually undergo further trimming of mannose residues and the addition of terminal sugars in that organelle.

As a consequence of this biosynthetic pathway, which allows for different degrees of processing of individual oligosaccharides by the ER and Golgi enzymatic systems, *N*-linked oligosaccharide chains in the mature glycoproteins fall into three groups (Fig. 3-18). These all share a common *pentasaccharide core structure,*[131] Man(α1→3)[Man(α1→6)]Man(β1→4) GlcNAc(β1→4)GlcNAc-Asn, which reflects their derivation from the same high mannose precursor. One group, designated *high mannose type oligosaccharides,* consists of oligosaccharides that generally retain two to six mannose residues linked to the pentasaccharide core. Oligosaccharides in glycoproteins that are permanent residues of the ER belong to this group. A second group consists of *complex oligosaccharides,* in which the core is generally followed by two to four branches that most frequently consists of sialyllactosamine (SA(α2→3 or 6)Gal(β1→4)GlcNAc) sequences linked to the two outer mannoses of the core. In addition, in complex oligosaccharides, a "bisecting" GlcNAc residue may be bound to the first mannose in the core and a fucose may be linked to the innermost GlcNAc. The outer branches in complex oligosaccharides can vary significantly in length, and in many cases contain fucose residues and polysialic acid chains. A third group of oligosaccharides consists of *hybrid structures* in which one branch retains some of the outer mannose residues characteristic of the high mannose chains and other branches resemble those in complex oligosaccharides. In hybrid oligosaccharides, the bisecting GlcNAc may also be attached to the first mannose.

High mannose, but not complex or hybrid oligosaccharide chains, can be removed from glycoproteins by treatment with the enzyme endoglycosidase H,[139,140] which cleaves the core between the two GlcNAc residues. Another endoglycosidase, endo-D,[141,142] hydrolyzes the same bond only when the Man residue in the core that is linked by an α1→3 bond to the first mannose is unsubstituted in the 2 position, i.e., when the chain has been processed to the $Man_5GlcNAc_2$ species. However, all *N*-linked oligosaccharides can be removed by treatment with endoglycosidase F.[143] An increase in the electrophoretic mobility of a protein caused by treatment with any one of these enzymes demonstrates the presence of oligosaccharide chains. The acquisition of endo-D sensitivity can be used as a criterion to establish the transfer of a newly synthesized glycoprotein from the ER to the cis Golgi, where the α1→2 mannosidase I that reduces the number of mannoses to

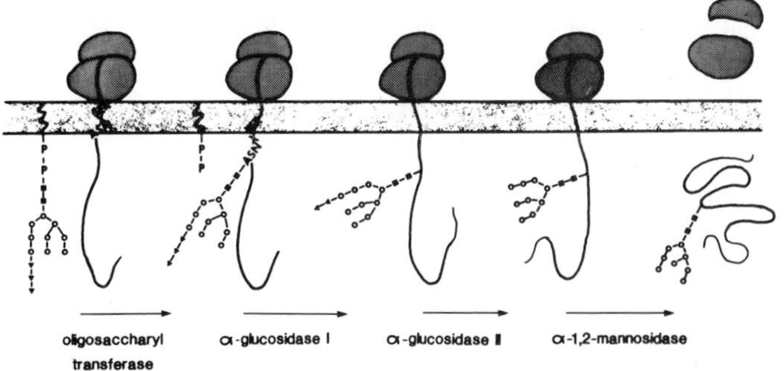

Fig. 3-17 Cotranslational transfer of an *N*-linked oligosaccharide to a nascent polypeptide and initial trimming in the ER. The oligosaccharyltransferase recognizes the triplet Asn-X-Ser in the nascent chain and transfers the high mannose oligosaccharide from the lipid donor to the asparagine residue. While the polypeptide chain is still growing, α-glucosidases and an α-mannosidase catalyze the sequential removal of the three glucose and one or two mannose residues. Although the glycoprotein is depicted as released into the ER lumen, the same reactions take place during the biosynthesis of membrane glycoproteins in the ER. (*Based on Kornfeld and Kornfeld.*[131])

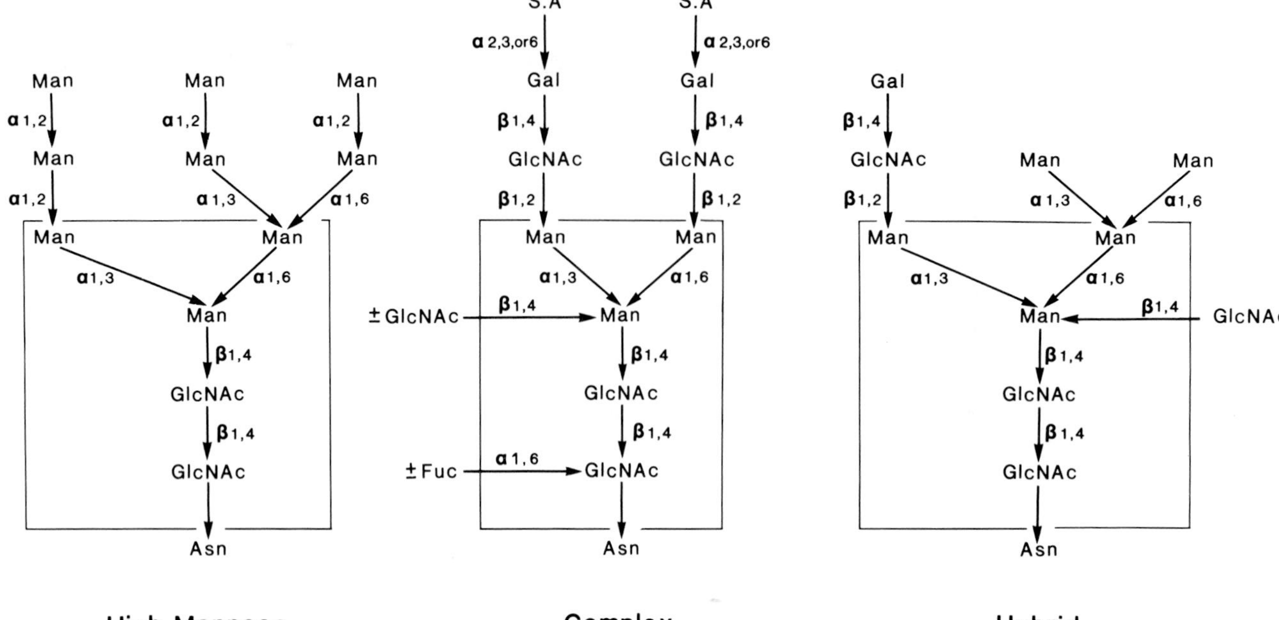

Fig. 3-18 Structures of representative high mannose, complex, and hybrid oligosaccharides that are N-linked to glycoproteins: A common pentasaccharide core is present in all types of chains. The high mannose oligosaccharide is found in glycoproteins after the glucose residues are removed in the ER. Some secreted products, such as bovine thyroglobulin, contain such chains. Other high mannose oligosaccharides contain up to four fewer mannose residues. The core pentasaccharide structure that is enclosed in the rectangles is the result of trimming in the Golgi apparatus and is present in all N-linked oligosaccharide chains. The complex type of oligosaccharide depicted has only two outer branches that consist of sialyl lactosamine sequences [SA(α2→3 or 6)Gal(β1→4)GlcNAc]. Other complex oligosaccharides may have additional outer branches, as well as extra sugar residues in the outer chains. A single purified glycoprotein may show considerable microheterogeneity in its oligosaccharide chains.

5 is located. The acquisition of endo-H resistance indicates that further progress of the protein through the Golgi apparatus has taken place to sites where the terminal sugars characteristic of complex oligosaccharides are added.

TRANSFER OF PROTEINS FROM THE ER TO THE GOLGI APPARATUS

Whereas some proteins synthesized in membrane-bound ribosomes remain as permanent residents of the ER, either as membrane or luminal proteins, others are transferred to the Golgi apparatus for incorporation into this organelle or for distribution to other sites of the cell. Transfer out of the ER takes place at specialized ER cisternae known as *transitional elements* or *transitional cisternae*, which are located close to the receiving (cis) face of the Golgi apparatus (Fig. 3-1). Transitional cisternae are partly "rough" and partly "smooth," and vesicles, which are coated with an as yet uncharacterized material, bud from their smooth portions. These vesicles are thought to serve as carriers that transport newly synthesized proteins to the Golgi apparatus.[13]

ER-to-Golgi transport was first demonstrated in pancreatic acinar cells, where the vast majority of the newly synthesized proteins are digestive enzymes to be stored in secretory granules (see Ref. 13). Autoradiographic analysis of pulse-labeled slices of pancreatic tissue and cell fractionation work first established that passage of the newly synthesized proteins to the Golgi apparatus takes place via the region of the transitional cisternae of the ER.[148,149] Cytochemical and immunocytochemical studies also demonstrated the presence of specific secretory proteins in the transitional elements and in vesicles located near the cis side of the Golgi apparatus.[150,151]

Transport from the ER to the Golgi apparatus is an energy-requiring process and, therefore, can be halted by anoxia or by drugs, such as azide or antimycin, that inhibit respiration, or by inhibitors of oxidative phosphorylation, such as dinitrophenol, oligomycin, or carbonylcyanide *m*-chlorophenolhydrazone (CCCP).[152–157] When the energy supply is exhausted, the proteins accumulate in the transitional elements or in vesicles between them and the cis face of the Golgi apparatus.

Experimental systems that utilize permeabilized cells, cell homogenates, or fractions derived from them, have been recently developed in which the ER-to-Golgi transfer of a viral envelope glycoprotein (G of VSV) can be achieved under controlled conditions.[158,159] This transfer has been shown to be directly dependent on the addition of ATP as well as cytosolic protein components.[158,159] Cell fractionation studies[160] have identified a vesicular fraction that differs in density from rough ER- and Golgi-derived fractions and in which secretory proteins unprocessed by Golgi enzymes can be detected soon after their synthesis. This fraction may contain the vesicular carriers that effect the ER-to-Golgi transport or may be derived by fragmentation from the transitional elements themselves.

The kinetics of transport of specific proteins from the ER to the Golgi apparatus has been followed in tissues and in cultured cells by analyzing the acquisition of endo-H resistance in polypeptides purified by immunoprecipitation with specific antibodies. Studies with both secretory and integral membrane proteins destined for the cell surface[161–164] have shown that different proteins are transported at different rates—anywhere from ½ to 1½ h—from the ER to the cell surface. The rate-limiting step appears to be passage from the ER to the Golgi apparatus, with transport from this organelle to the cell surface occurring at the same fast rate (20 min) for all proteins in a given cell. Using a temperature-sensitive virus, rapid transport through the Golgi apparatus has also been demonstrated directly. The envelope glycoproteins accumulate in the ER at the nonpermissive temperature, but become endo-H-resistant within 5 to 10 min after the infected cells are shifted to the permissive temperature.[165,166]

Two possible interpretations can be given to these observations. One, originally favored, is that the transport of proteins out of the ER requires their interaction with a common receptor or carrier and that those proteins with higher affinity for the receptor are transported more rapidly. This would imply that the transported proteins contain a sorting signal for interaction with the membrane-bound receptor and, hence, that the proteins that remain as permanent residents of the ER lack such signals. In this model, the secretory proteins that are transported at the lowest rates would be those that move by "bulk flow," i.e., that are carried in the fluid phase that exists within the transporting vesicles without interacting with the receptors. Such proteins would be free to diffuse within the luminal cavities of all the organelles within the endomembrane system to finally reach the cell surface.[167]

An alternative interpretation, suggested originally because of its parsimony[10] and recently supported experimentally, is that retention of both luminal and membrane proteins in the ER is an active process that results from the presence of specific signals *(retention signals)* within the polypeptides that lead them to interact with other components of the ER and prevent them from flowing into the vesicles that bud from the transitional cisternae. It has long been known (reviewed in Ref. 168) that in rodent liver the enzyme β-glucuronidase has a dual localization, being present in lysosomes as well as being a peripheral membrane protein in the lumen of the ER. The microsomal glycoprotein egasyn is responsible for retaining β-glucuronidase in the ER, and the enzyme is not detected in micorosmes of egasyn-deficient mutant animals.[169–171] Moreover, in vivo dissociation of the egasyn β-glucuronidase complex induced by organophosphorous compounds leads to massive and rapid secretion of glucuronidase into the plasma.[170] It can, therefore, be concluded that the microsomal β-glucuronidase has a retention signal that mediates its interaction with egasyn.

Exit from the ER would occur by default when proteins lack such retention signals. Experimental data supporting this notion include the finding that three different resident proteins of the ER lumen, the enzyme *protein disulfide isomerase* and two *glucose-regulated proteins* (Grp74, Grp 78), contain the same C-terminal tetrapeptide sequence (Lys-Asp-Glu-Leu) and the demonstration that the deletion of the tetrapeptide leads to the secretion of those proteins.[172,173] Moreover, addition of the tetrapeptide sequence to the C terminus of the secretory protein lysozyme leads to the retention of this protein in the ER.[173] Similarly, a short sequence in the C-terminal cytoplasmic domain of the adenovirus glycoprotein E19 is required for the retention of this membrane protein in the ER.[174] At early times during viral infection, the E19 glycoprotein helps the infected cells to escape from immune surveillance by cytotoxic cells. It does so by interacting in the ER with the newly synthesized class I histocompatability antigen molecules and preventing their transport out of the ER.[175]

The fact that specific information within a protein is not required for it to be secreted is strikingly demonstrated by the observation that β-lactamase, a protein of bacterial origin that, therefore, could not possibly contain information for passage out of the ER, is secreted when it is synthesized in amphibian oocytes that are microinjected with the corresponding mRNA.[176]

The rate at which molecules that contain no retention signals flow out of the ER appears to be quite high. Thus, certain simple synthetic peptides that contain the acceptor site for *N*-glycosylation are taken into cells, and traverse the membrane of the ER, where they are glycosylated. After glycosylation, however, the peptides can no longer traverse the membranes limiting the endomembrane system, but are discharged back into the medium within 10 min of being added to the cells.[167] This rapid rate of "bulk flow" through the cellular endomembrane system, presumably by a process that must involve diffusion of the peptides within the lumen of the various organelles and their random incorporation into the vesicles that bud from one compartment and fuse with another, must be contrasted with the much longer time it takes for a secretory protein to appear in the medium after its synthesis is completed. As previously noted, this time varies substantially for different proteins within a single cell type, from approximately 20 min to more than 1½ h. Given the high rate of bulk flow observed for unrestrained peptides, and the fact that transport from the Golgi to the cell surface is known to be a rapid process for proteins that are not stored intracellularly (see below), the different rates at which different proteins are secreted must be attributed to their differential retardation within the ER. This may be due to either specific or unspecific interactions of the secretory polypeptides with resident components of this organelle.

Clearly, the finding that "bulk flow" from the rough ER to the cell surface is a rapid process implies that no specific receptors are required to facilitate the transport of luminal and membrane proteins by mediating their incorporation into the vesicles that effect interorganellar transport within the endomembrane system. This reinforces the notion that specific retention signals must serve to restrict the location of proteins not only to the endoplasmic reticulum, but also to the different cisternae of the Golgi apparatus that lie along the pathway to the plasma membrane.

Even though transport of proteins out of the ER may be a default process, it nevertheless requires that the proteins to be transported have a "normal conformation." This is most strikingly demonstrated by the behavior of certain multimeric proteins when their assembly in the ER is perturbed (e.g., see Ref. 177). Thus, immunoglobulin heavy chains are not transported out of the ER unless the light chains are also present.[178] Similarly, in some cases, the heavy chain of the class I histocompatability antigen, which is a type I transmembrane protein, does not exit from the ER unless it becomes associated with β_2-microglobulin.[179,180] In addition, the influenza HA and the VSV G glycoproteins must undergo trimerization in the ER to be transported to the Golgi apparatus.[181–183] Numerous examples also exist of proteins that are normally secreted or transferred to the plasma membrane, but remain in the ER when altered by genetic engineering techniques. The fact that a "normal" conformation that makes the protein "soluble and transportable" is required for exit from the ER probably explains the accumulation in this organelle, and the failure to be secreted, of a mutant form of the human serum protein α_1-antitrypsin,[184] as well as of nonsecreting variants of immunoglobulin chains in certain myelomas.[185]

The retention in the ER of proteins with an improper conformation may not be simply due to their insolubility within the ER membrane or in the organellar lumen, but also to their specific recognition by a binding protein (Bip)[186] that is a resident component of the ER.[172] Normally, this 77-kDa protein binds to the free heavy chains or to incompletely assembled immunoglobulin molecules and prevents their premature exit from the ER and, therefore, their secretion from the cell.[187,188] In the *lymphoproliferative heavy-chain disease*, in which heavy chains are secreted in the absence of light chains, a deletion mutation in the heavy chain constant region gene reduces the affinity of the heavy chain for Bip.[188] Although Bip was first recognized in pre-B cell lines that do not yet synthesize light chains,[186–189] its presence has now been demonstrated in many other cell types, where it was found complexed to abnormal or incompletely assembled secretory and membrane proteins. It is worth noting that Bip may be identical or closely related to the Grp 78 previously mentioned that is retained in the ER through a C-terminal tetrapeptide.[172] This protein has been identified in fibroblasts and accumulates at high levels in the lumen of the ER when the cultured cells are submitted to the stress of glucose starvation or when they are treated with tunicamycin to prevent *N*-glycosylation.[172] By blocking the transport to the cell surface of abnormally folded polypeptides, the Grp 78, which is evolutionarily related to the heat-shock proteins, may play a role in protecting the organism from the adverse effects that could result if the immune system recognized denatured "self" polypeptides as foreign antigens.[183]

COVALENT LINKAGE OF LIPIDS TO CYTOPLASMIC, MEMBRANE, AND SECRETORY PROTEINS[190]

In recent years it has become evident that many proteins, some synthesized in free and others in bound polysomes, contain lipid moieties covalently linked to their polypeptide backbones. In some cases, the lipids serve as the sole means of anchoring the polypeptide to a membrane whereas, in others, they may only reinforce a membrane anchorage mediated by a hydrophobic segment of the protein. In addition, lipids may be found bound to cytoplasmic proteins or to proteins that are secreted from the cell.

Acylation of Proteins Synthesized on Free Polysomes[190,191]

Certain proteins synthesized in free polysomes, such as the catalytic subunit of the cyclic AMP–dependent protein kinase, NADH cytochrome b_5 reductase, and the phosphoprotein phosphatase, calcineurin, as well as a number of oncogene products, including the transforming protein of the Rous sarcoma virus ($p60^{v\text{-}src}$) and its corresponding cellular proto-oncogene ($p60^{c\text{-}src}$), have the 14-carbon saturated fatty acid, myristic acid, bound through an amide linkage to the α amino group of an N-terminal glycine. This type of acylation appears to be a cotranslational process by which, following removal of the initiator methionine, a myristyl group is transferred from acyl-CoA to the glycine which is exposed at the new N terminus of the nascent chain.[192] The amino acid sequence following the myristylated glycine varies significantly in different proteins, but in one instance at least, that of the $p60^{v\text{-}src}$, the signal recognized by the myristyl transferase, has been shown to be wholly contained within the first 14 residues of the protein.[193]

In the case of the $p60^{v\text{-}src}$, myristylation leads to the association of the protein with the inner, cytoplasmic face of the plasma membrane, and this association is an absolute requirement for the transforming activity of the protein.[194,195] Similarly, the lipid-mediated association of NADH cytochrome b_5 reductase with the cytoplasmic face of the ER membrane[196] may be important for the function of this enzyme in the electron transport chain that effects fatty acid desaturation in the ER.

It is not yet clear what factors determine the association of different myristylated proteins with different membranes, but it seems likely that specific interactions with other membrane proteins facilitate the incorporation of the acylated polypeptide into a given organelle. It is clear that, in some cases, the fatty acid moeity is insufficient to maintain the association of the protein with the membrane. This is apparent from the observation that the catalytic subunit of the cyclic AMP–dependent protein kinase is found associated with the regulatory subunit on the cytoplasmic face of the plasma membrane but is released into the cytoplasm when activated by cAMP.[197]

Some proteins synthesized in free polysomes, such as the *ras* oncogene product, which functions as a G protein in the regulation of adenyl cyclase activity, carry a palmitic acid moiety linked to a cysteine near the C terminus of the protein.[198] The presence of the fatty acid is required for the membrane association and transforming activity of this protein.[199] Ankyrin, a red cell cytoskeleton protein, has also been found to carry palmitate residues,[200] but the association of this polypeptide with the membrane is a peripheral one and is mediated by a high affinity binding to the anion transporter (band III) in the membrane.[201]

Lipid Attachment to Proteins Synthesized in the Endoplasmic Reticulum

C-Terminal Glypiation of Plasma Membrane Proteins.[202,203] Several membrane proteins have been identified which are located on the extracellular surface of the plasma membrane and can be released from the cell by treatment with a phosphoinositol-specific phospholipase C (PIPLC). These proteins include the variant surface glycoprotein (VSG) of the African trypanosome, the placental and intestinal alkaline phosphatases, acetylcholinesterase, 5′-nucleotidase, the Thy-1 antigen of T lymphocytes, one form of the neural adhesion molecule N-CAM, and the decay-accelerating factor (DAF) that protects host cells from complement-mediated lysis. These proteins are anchored in the membrane by the fatty acids of a diacylglycerol molecule that is part of a complex glycosylinositol phospholipid that is linked via a phosphorylethanolamine in an amide linkage to the C terminus of the polypeptide (Fig. 3-19). The structure of the glycan group has not been completely determined, but it contains galactosamine and mannose residues linked to the inositol via a nonacetylated glucosamine.

Proteins which undergo the glycosylphosphatidylinositolation, a process also known as *glypiation*, appear to be initially, or at least transiently, type I membrane proteins that are anchored in the ER membrane by a short hydrophobic (17 to 31 amino acids) peptide segment at the C terminus of the protein (see Refs. 202, 203). Glypiation seems to take place very soon after completion of translation and insertion of the

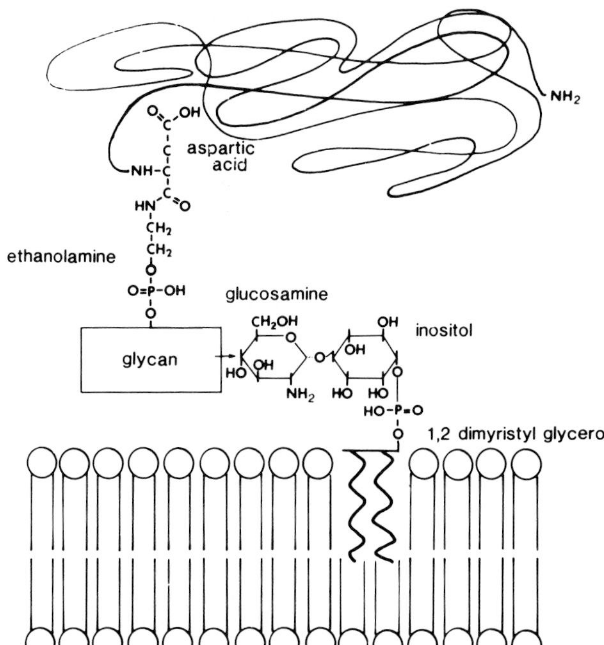

Fig. 3-19 Anchorage of proteins to membranes via a glycosylphosphatidylinositol. A glycan of variable structure that contains several mannose residues and a variable number of galactose residues is linked by a phosphodiester bond from the 6 carbon of a mannose residue to an ethanolamine, which is in turn linked in an amide bound to the α carbon of a C-terminal aspartic acid in the polypeptide. It is believed that even in a single type of protein there may be a significant variation in the structure and composition of the glycan. The glycan is also linked through a glucosamine residue, that is unsubstituted in its amino group, by a 1→4 linkage to the inositol residue in dimyristylphosphatidylinositol. Insertion of the myristyl fatty acid chains in the phospholipid bilayer serves to anchor the protein in the membrane.

protein in the ER membrane.[204] The reaction can be considered a pseudotranspeptidation in which the protein loses the C-terminal segment that served as membrane anchor while an amide linkage to the ethanolamine is established. Thus, it is most likely that the glycolipid is preformed in the ER membrane and then added to the new C terminus of the polypeptide. In the case of the DAF protein, in which glypiation involves removal of the last 17 amino acids, the information that determines this modification has been shown to be contained within the last 37 amino acids of the primary translation product.[205]

A defect in the pathway of glypiation may be the basis for *paroxysmal nocturnal hemoglobinuria*, in which DAF is absent from the surface of erythrocytes.[206,207] It is noteworthy that, in this disease, red cells also lack another glypiated protein, acetylcholinesterase.[208,209] Several possible functions for the anchoring of proteins to the cell surface via the glycosylated phosphoinositides have been proposed. These include an enhanced mobility of the protein within the plane of the bilayer, the possibility of regulating the release of the protein by the action of an extracellular phospholipase C, or of generating the intracellular "messenger" diacylglycerol that could serve to activate a protein kinase C.

Acylation of Membrane and Secretory Proteins.[190,191] Several transmembrane polypeptides, such as the envelope glycoproteins G of VSV, HA of influenza, and E2 of α viruses, and cellular proteins, such as the mammalian transferrin receptor and the HLA-B histocompatability antigen, contain a palmitate moiety linked in a thioester bond to a cysteine residue located within the cytoplasmic segment of the protein, near its membrane-anchoring domain.

Palmitylation is a posttranslational event which for viral envelope glycoproteins has been shown to occur approximately 20 min after synthesis of the polypeptide is completed[210] and probably takes place in the cis region of the Golgi apparatus, just before the high mannose *N*-linked oligosaccharides are converted into the complex chains. The incorporation of labeled palmitate into some membrane proteins, such as the transferrin receptor, has been shown to continue even several hours after synthesis of the polypeptide is completed,[211] but this may only represent the turnover of preexisting polypeptide-bound palmitate moieties.

The enzyme responsible for the acylation of polypeptides is not strictly specific for palmitic acid and in some cases it may add stearic acid residues. Because of the location of the modified amino acid residue, the enzyme must be located on the cytoplasmic side of the membrane and could conceivably be the same enzyme that catalyzes the palmitylation of some cytoplasmic proteins described above.

Some secretory proteins, such as the immunoglobulin heavy and light chains, have been shown to be acylated, in some cases with myristate and in others with palmitate or stearate. The myristate moieties in the membrane-bound and secreted forms of the immunoglobulin heavy chains, as well as in light chains, are probably bound in amide linkages to lysine side chains.[212] Similar linkages appear to be present in the α and β subunits of the insulin receptor, which also contains palmitate, probably linked in a thioester bond.[213]

The enzymes responsible for the fatty acylation of secretory proteins and luminal domains of membrane proteins have not been characterized, but clearly, they must be distinct from the enzyme(s) that add fatty acids to cytosolic proteins and to cytoplasmically exposed cysteine residues of membrane proteins.

THE GOLGI APPARATUS[144,214–216]

The Golgi apparatus is a complex organelle that receives both luminal and membrane proteins from the transitional elements of the ER. It effects a wide variety of posttranslational modifications on many of these proteins, including the processing of *N*-linked oligosaccharide chains in glycoproteins to complex oligosaccharides, the *O*-glycosylation of hydroxy amino acid residues, the phosphorylation of mannose residues in enzymes destined to lysosomes, the fatty acylation of some proteins, the sulfation of oligosaccharide chains, and the proteolytic processing of many precursor polypeptides. Whereas some of the proteins that reach the Golgi apparatus from the ER remain as permanent residents of its cisternae, others traverse the organelle and are either transported to the cell surface or are segregated within distal elements of the endomembrane system, such as secretory granules or lysosomes.

In secretory cells, and perhaps in all cell types, some membrane proteins that reach the cell surface by exocytosis are retrieved by endocytosis and returned to the Golgi apparatus for reutilization in the packaging of new secretory products.[217–222] The multiple destinations of proteins that emerge from the Golgi apparatus, as well as the role of this organelle in the recycling of plasma membrane proteins, make it the cell's center for the distribution and sorting of proteins addressed to various subcellular locations.

Structure of the Golgi Apparatus[214,223–226]

Characteristically, the Golgi apparatus consists of stacks of three to eight slightly curved, membranous cisternae or saccules that are platelike near their centers and dilated toward their rims. Several of these stacks may exist within a single cell, and they may be interconnected.[227–229] A Golgi stack shows a polarized organization. One side, the cis face (generally the convex one), is oriented toward the ER. The opposite, trans face is oriented toward secretory granules or the centrioles. The cis-most cisternae are usually fenestrated, and numerous vesicles that are believed to carry materials between the transitional elements of the ER and the Golgi apparatus are found between the two structures.

Vesicles that are thought to transport proteins from one Golgi cisterna to the next, in a cis-to-trans direction, are also found near the periphery of the Golgi stacks. They may be seen fusing with or budding from the cisternal rims. Both types of vesicles, those that mediate ER to Golgi transport and those that mediate transport within the Golgi itself, are coated by a material that has not yet been chemically characterized. It is not labeled with antibodies to *clathrin*,[230,231] the protein that forms the coat found in the endocytic vesicles that form at the cell surface during *receptor-mediated endocytosis* (see below), and in some of the vesicles that bud from the trans-Golgi region (see below).

In many cells, proteins to be packaged in secretory granules first accumulate in the dilated rims of the two or three trans-most Golgi cisternae.[214] In other cells, such as those in pancreatic acini, the concentration of secretory products takes place within separate dilated sacs, known as *condensing vacuoles*, that are adjacent to the trans face of the Golgi and appear to receive material from it by vesicular transport.[148,149]

In its trans-most region, the Golgi apparatus extends into a network of tubulovesicular structures that have somewhat thicker membranes and were originally known as GERL[224,225] but have recently received the names of *trans-Golgi network (TGN)*,[216] *trans-Golgi reticulum*,[232] or *transtubular network*.[227] It is in this region of the trans-Golgi that many of the proteins retrieved from the plasma membrane reach the organelle. Clathrin-coated vesicles that contain either lysosomal enzymes complexed to the Man-6-P receptor (see below) or secretory proteins destined to be stored in secretory granules, as well as vesicles with a nonclathrin coat that appear to mediate the constitutive bulk flow of secretory and membrane proteins to the cell surface, originate from the TGN.[216,233] Therefore, the trans-Golgi network is an important site of sorting for proteins with different destinations.

The polarized organization of the Golgi apparatus is also apparent morphologically from the progressive increase in the thickness of the cisternal membranes, from the cis to the trans side, seen in electron micrographs, and from the intense staining of the cis cisternae when cells are incubated for long times with OsO_4.[234] Cytochemically, the trans-most cisternae are characterized by a thiamine pyrophosphatase activity[229,235] that is not present in the TGN elements, which, however, do show acid phosphatase activity,[216] presumably reflecting the presence of this hydrolase "en route" to lysosomes.

Intercisternal Traffic Within the Golgi Apparatus[131,144,147]

The cis, medial, and trans Golgi cisternae represent a series of subcompartments with specific enzymatic complements that sequentially carry out posttranslational modifications on newly synthesized proteins that traverse the organelle unidirectionally. A combination of cytochemical, immunoelectron-microscopic, and cell fractionation studies has defined the pattern of organization within the golgi apparatus (Fig. 3-20) of the enzymes involved in the processing by *N*-linked oligosaccharide chains (see Refs. 236 to 240). The cis cisternae contain the *N*-acetylglucosaminylphosphotransferase and the *N*-acetylglucosamine-1-phosphodiester α-*N*-acetylglucosaminidase that add the phosphate marker to the mannose residues of newly synthesized lysosomal hydrolases (see below). The α-mannosidase I that reduces to 5 the number of mannose residues in oligo-

Fig. 3-20 Sequential modifications of oligosaccharide chains as glycoproteins move through the Golgi apparatus. A glycoprotein containing a high mannose oligosaccharide is transferred from the ER to a cis Golgi cisterna. If the protein is a lyosomal hydrolase, it acquires the mannose-6-phosphate marker in the cis Golgi by the sequential action of N-acetylglucosaminylphosphotransferase (phosphotransferase) and N-acetylglucosamine-1-phosphodiester α-N-acetylglucosaminidase (phosphodiesterase), as indicated by the leftward arrows. Other polypeptides undergo further removal of the outer mannose residues in the cis Golgi by the α-mannosidase I. The products of this reaction are transferred to medial Golgi cisternae, where N-acetylglucosaminyltransferase I adds an acetylglucosamine residue to provide the substrate from which the remaining outer mannose residues are removed by the α-mannosidase II. Formation of a complex oligosaccharide begins in medial cisternae by addition of fucosyl residues and is completed in the trans Golgi. *(Adapted from Kornfeld and Kornfeld.[131])*

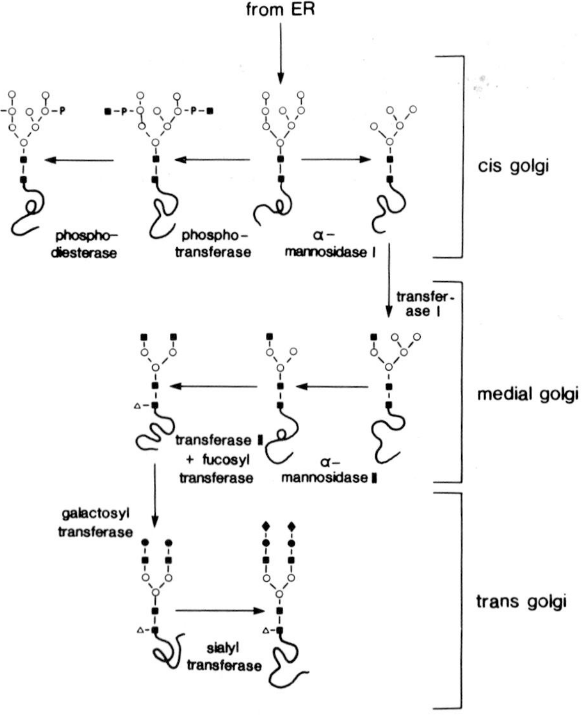

saccharides partially trimmed in the ER is also found in the cis and, possibly, the medial cisternae. Medial cisternae contain a number of enzymes, including the transferase I that adds the first outer GlcNAc residue in the formation of complex oligosaccharides, the α-mannosidase II that is responsible for the removal of the last two mannose residues, the transferase II that adds a second outer GlcNAc, and the fucosyltransferase that modifies the innermost GlcNAc. The glycosyltransferases that add galactose and sialic acid residues to the regrowing oligosaccharides have been localized to the trans-most cisternae as well as the TGN.

The sequential passage of a protein across the Golgi cisternae has been strikingly demonstrated in immunoelectron-microscopic studies with cells infected with a temperature-sensitive mutant of VSV, in which it is possible to synchronize the transport of the envelope glycoprotein G out of the ER.[165,166] It was clearly shown that the G protein enters the Golgi apparatus at the cis cisterna, traverses the organelle vectorially in approximately 10 min, and exits at the opposite face. When VSV-infected cells are incubated at low temperatures (20°C), large amounts of G protein accumulate in the TGN, which is greatly expanded. When the temperature is raised to 32°C, G protein molecules exit from the TGN toward the plasma membrane within coated vesicles that do not contain clathrin.[241] It is this observation that suggests that cellular plasma membrane proteins are also delivered from the TGN to the cell surface in non-clathrin-containing coated vesicles.

The demonstration that the transfer of newly synthesized proteins through the Golgi stack is a vectorial process involving vesicular carriers that bud from a donor cisterna and fuse with an acceptor one, rather than flowing along permanent physical connections between cisternae, has come from both cell fusion experiments[242,243] and the use of in vitro systems in which vectorial transfer between cisternae of different stacks has been obtained.[231,244–249]

These experiments have been possible because of the availability of mutant cell lines defective in some of the oligosaccharide processing enzymes.[250,251] In these cells, the processing of the oligosaccharide chains is arrested at specific points but the glycoproteins continue to be transferred to the cell surface. Transfer from the cis to medical cisternae was demonstrated when cells deficient in the medial Golgi enzyme GlcNAc transferase I were infected and fused with wild type cells.[242] The final mature G protein produced was shown to carry the normal terminal sugars and had therefore been transferred from the Golgi apparatus of the mutant infected cell to that of the uninfected wild type, where the normal transferase was found. In a similar experiment, transfer from the medial to the trans cisternae was inferred from the finding that a G protein synthesized in an infected mutant cell that lacked the trans Golgi enzyme galactosyltransferase was processed to the normal terminally glycosylated protein after the infected cell was fused with an uninfected cell containing the galactosyltransferase.[243] The unidirectionality of the transfer between the cisternae within a Golgi stack was demonstrated by the finding, in pulse chase experiments, that if cell fusion was carried out after the labeled protein was expected to have passed the appropriate subcompartment in the donor Golgi, processing by the wild-type Golgi apparatus enzyme did not occur.

The fact that vesicles mediate the intercisternal transfer has become evident from experiments in which the transfer of VSV G protein from the cis compartment of one Golgi apparatus to the medial compartment of another was achieved in a cell-free system, using as a donor a Golgi fraction isolated from mutant infected cells that lack GlcNAc transferase I.[244] Arrival of the G protein to the acceptor compartment was detected by its acquisition of [^{3}H]GlcNAc residues. In this system, intercisternal transport requires ATP, a cytosolic fraction, and the integrity of proteins that are exposed on the surface of the acceptor membrane and are, therefore, sensitive to proteases. The vesicle-mediated transfer appears to take place in a series of steps, all of which seem to require ATP but differ in their requirement for cytosolic components and in their sensitivity to inhibition by the SH reagent, *N*-ethylmaleimide (NEM).[245]

The first step, which can be visualized by electron microscopy,[244] is a "priming reaction" in which coated vesicles containing the G protein are seen to be budding from the donor stack. In the presence of the acceptor compartment, "prefusion complexes" are formed that probably represent stages in which the vesicles derived from the donor compartment become associated with the acceptor membrane in the recipient cisternae. Conversion of the final prefusion intermediate into the form in which GlcNAc addition takes place requires only ATP and is, probably, simply a membrane fusion event.[247]

The cytosolic fraction required for the in vitro transfer contains several chromatographically separable essential components. Remarkably, a cytosolic fraction from yeast can replace the mammalian components in the reconstitution of the inter Golgi transport of the G protein with fractions from infected and uninfected cultured cells.[249] An NEM-sensitive cytosolic component has been identified that appears to utilize fatty acyl-CoA as a cofactor, and this has raised the possibility that acylation-deacylation reactions play a role in permitting the transfer and recycling of the vesicular carriers between cisternae.[252]

In addition to the different sets of processing enzymes that they encounter as they move across the Golgi apparatus, newly synthesized proteins confront media of decreasing pH in their passage from the cis cisternae to the TGN. The presence of a *proton pump* has been demonstrated in isolated Golgi fractions.[253] Studies using a probe detectable by immunoelectron microscopy, whose accumulation within membrane-bound compartments is an inverse function of the pH, have revealed that the trans cisternae and the TGN are substantially more acidic than the cis Golgi cisternae.[254,255] Moreover, secretory vesicles in the trans Golgi region were found to have a low pH, comparable to that of the TGN from which they are derived.

The drug monensin, which is an ionophore that exchanges K^+ ions for protons and thus dissipates pH gradients across membranes,[256,257] inhibits the secretion of many proteins[258] and the passage of viral envelope glycoproteins through the Golgi apparatus. This drug leads to a remarkable swelling of Golgi cisternae, and the movement of the viral glycoproteins through the organelle is halted within the medial region.[259,260] Weak bases such as primaquine, chloroquine, and NH_4Cl traverse membranes in their uncharged forms and accumulate within acidic compartments in their protonated forms, raising the intravesicular pH.[261,262] Treatment of cells with these lysosomotropic drugs also affects the secretion of many proteins, albeit to different extents for different proteins within a given cell. These drugs appear to act at a late Golgi or post-Golgi stage. In fact, primaquine completely blocks the secretion of albumin from hepatoma cells, leading to its accumulation within vesicles in the trans side of the Golgi. It has a lesser effect on the secretion of other proteins, such as transferrin.[263] The acid pH of the Golgi apparatus may actually be required for some proteins to achieve a conformation that allows them to exit from the organelle. Conversely, the aberrant conformation of some abnormal proteins generated using recombinant DNA techniques may be manifested at the acidic pH of Golgi elements, which may account for their accumulation in this organelle.[264]

It has been suggested that a pH gradient may play a role in determining the unidirectional transport of proteins through the Golgi apparatus.[255] It is known that the low pH of endosomes (see below) mediates the dissociation of some ligands from their receptors, which allows for the return of interiorized receptors to the plasma membrane. One could imagine that vesicles that effect the successive transfer of proteins from cisternae to cisternae contain pH-sensitive receptors for these proteins that release their ligands at different pHs and that this is necessary for the vesicles to return to the cisternae of origin.

Sorting of Proteins that Exit from the Golgi Apparatus

Some of the proteins transferred from the ER to the Golgi apparatus must be retained within specific Golgi subcompartments or in the TGN, where they carry out their functions. Other proteins, however, traverse all Golgi cisternae and reach the TGN, where they are sorted into different classes that are either allowed to proceed to the plasma membrane or are addressed to developing secretory granules or lysosomes.

SECRETORY PATHWAYS IN EUKARYOTIC CELLS[13,265,266]

Direct passage of proteins from the Golgi apparatus to the cell surface is thought to be effected by a population of coated vesicles that do not contain clathrin which continuously emerge from the TGN and fuse with the plasma membrane.[231,241] The membrane proteins of these vesicles become incorporated into the plasma membrane, and their luminal contents are discharged into the extracellular medium. This would be the basis for the so-called *constitutive*, or *nonregulated, secretion* of proteins. The continuous discharge that takes place during constitutive secretion can be contrasted with the *regulated secretion* of proteins that takes place in many specialized cells. Regulated secretion requires the concentration and storage of proteins in secretory granules that release their content into the extracellular space only when an appropriate stimulation leads to fusion of the granule membrane with the plasma membrane (exocytosis).

Constitutive secretion is a generalized function of many cells. It represents the mechanism by which hepatocytes secrete a wide variety of serum proteins into the blood, fibroblasts secrete collagen and other components of the extracellular matrix, and plasma cells secrete immunoglobulins. The regulated secretory pathway, on the other hand, is utilized by many endocrine and exocrine cells, which must respond quickly to physiologic stimulation with a burst of secretory activity. For example, digestive enzymes are stored within zymogen granules of pancreatic acinar cells and, upon stimulation by a secretagogue, are released on the apical surfaces of the cells that confront the acinar lumen. Similarly, distinct cell types in the anterior pituitary gland store specific hormones that are released by exocytosis when the cells are stimulated by the appropriate hypothalamic releasing hormones. Some unicellular glands, such as mast cells, blood granulocytes, and platelets, also store their secretory products within granules which discharge their content at the cell surface after appropriate stimulation. Release of peptide neurotransmitters from neurons represents another example of regulated secretion. The extended processes of some neurosecretory cells, such as those that constitute the neurohypophysis may be packed with large amounts of secretory granules that are formed in the Golgi apparatus and then transferred to the nerve terminals.

The exocytotic event that represents regulated secretion results from the activation of a transducing mechanism that involves the interaction of a ligand with a plasma membrane receptor and, by a variety of mechanisms, leads to a transient rise in the cytoplasmic concentration of a "secondary messenger," such as Ca^{2+} or cyclic AMP (see Ref. 267).

The Biogenesis of Secretory Granules

Secretory granules are membrane-bounded structures that contain a dense core in which the secretory material is highly concentrated. In some granules, the dense core is a stable structure that remains intact even when the membrane is removed after isolation of the granules by cell fractionation.[268,269] The size and shape of a secretory granule is, in general, characteristic of the products that are stored in it. Frequently, different cell types can be identified by the morphologic characteristics of their granules, as in the pituitary, endocrine pancreas, and blood granulocyte population.

Many cells capable of regulated secretion are specialized for the production of one major secretory protein (e.g., pituitary thyrotrophs) or of several polypeptides that are derived from a single precursor (e.g., pituitary corticotrophs). Other cells, such as those in the exocrine pancreas, store a variety of independently produced secretory proteins within a single type of granule.[270–274] Such proteins are released together upon stimulation. However, some endocrine cells, such as the pituitary gonadotrophs, are able to store two different polypeptide hormones (i.e., LH and FSH) in separate granules, which may be easily identified by their different sizes.[275] It is not yet clear by what mechanism the segregation of the two hormones in gonadotrophs is effected, but it is reasonable to assume that the segregation is important to allow for the differential release of each gonadotrophin at different periods of the menstrual cycle. Still other cells, such as human neutrophils, segregate different sets of secretory products into distinct granule types[276–278] (e.g., azurophilic, specific, and secretory gelatinase-containing granules) and may be stimulated to differentially release the content of each type of granule.[278]

Studies with pancreatic exocrine[279–281] and endocrine[282] β cells and with cultured tumor cell lines[283] have shown that both the constitutive and regulated pathways can operate in a single cell. Cells of the AtT-20 rat cell line of pituitary origin are capable of forming secretory granules that contain ACTH and other derivatives of pro-opiomelanocortin (POMC). Upon stimulation with 8-Br-cAMP, they release the processed products of POMC in their granule contents by exocytosis. The segregation of the POMC to the secretory granules of these cells, however, is not very efficient and more than two-thirds of the newly synthesized POMC is also steadily released by the constitutive pathway. However, laminin, a component of the extracellular matrix, is secreted from the same cells essentially exclusively by the constitutive route[284] and a truncated secretory version of the VSV G protein, synthesized in AtT-20 cells transfected with the appropriate gene,[285] is also excluded from the regulated pathway.

These observations suggest that proteins incorporated into secretory granules contain specific information that leads to their segregation from the constitutively secreted polypeptides, which may follow a different pathway. In fact, proteins normally incorporated into the granules of endocrine cells, such as proinsulin,[286] growth hormone,[285] and trypsinogen,[284] an exocrine pancreatic product, when synthesized in transfected AtT-20 cells are as effectively incorporated into granules as the endogenous derivatives of POMC. Similar findings have been made with the pituitary-derived growth hormone–producing GH3 cells, which after transfection with a gene encoding proparathyroid hormone (pPTH), incorporate this polypeptide in the same granules that contain growth hormone.[287] Attempts to localize the putative sorting signal in trypsinogen showed that the signal is not found within the N-terminal region of the polypeptide, since deletion of the first 12 amino acids of the proprotein did not abolish its segregation into granules.[288]

In other experiments, a chimeric polypeptide consisting of the entire truncated secretory form of the G protein of VSV linked to the C terminus of human growth hormone was also found to be incorporated into granules, a finding which is consistent with the notion that a constitutively secreted protein does not contain specific sorting information, but specific signals are required for the incorporation of growth hormone into the granules.[289]

Mechanisms for the Sorting of Proteins into Secretory Granules

The sorting process responsible for the formation of secretory granules within cells that are also capable of constitutive secretion is likely to take place in the trans-most Golgi region or in the TGN. As previously mentioned, in many cell types that carry out regulated secretion, the condensation of secretory material that leads to the formation of a secretory granule is first detected in the dilated rims of the trans Golgi cisternae (see Ref. 214). In other cell types, such as the exocrine pancreatic cells, it appears to take place in condensing vacuoles which may, in fact, be specialized regions of the trans Golgi network. Electron microscopy suggests that condensation takes place progressively as material accumulates within the vesicles, which have been shown to have an acidic pH.[233,290] One possible mechanism would, therefore, involve membrane-bound pH-sensitive receptors. These would concentrate secretory proteins within regions of the Golgi complex that contain a proton pump capable of generating the acidic medium that leads to dissociation of the ligands from the receptors. After this takes place, the receptors could recycle to more proximal regions of the Golgi apparatus to bind additional ligand molecules. An alternative model for the segregation of proteins in secretory granules would not require the participation of receptors to effect the segregation, but simply involve the spontaneous aggregation of secretory molecules to be stored within the same type of granule. Such an aggregation may be triggered by conditions that prevail in the trans region of the Golgi (e.g., pH or Ca^{2+} concentration). It is also possible that the presence of specific granule matrix components, such as sulfated proteoglycans or glycoproteins (e.g., chromogranin A[291] and secretogranins I and II[292]), which have been shown to be present in many types of secretory granules, is required for the condensation process. Indeed, it has been shown[293] that chondroitin sulfate induces the aggregation of chymotrypsinogen A in vitro. In cases like this, the interaction between the polypeptide and the matrix component can, in fact, be viewed as one involving the binding of a sorting signal to its receptor. In some cell types, different proteins undergo condensation within different regions of a single granule. This is the case for prolactin and growth hormone in the granules of bovine somatomammotrophs,[294] and for glucagon and glycentin[295] in the α granules of pancreatic islet cells. These examples appear to clearly represent instances in which specific protein molecules undergo self-aggregation.

Immunoelectron-microscopic studies of the formation of proinsulin containing granules in β cells of pancreatic islets have shown that, within Golgi cisternae, proinsulin is found in close apposition to the membrane, which suggests that it interacts with a membrane receptor. Proinsulin, however, is found free in the lumen of developing (condensing vacuole–like) secretory granules. These granules are coated with clathrin,[230,296] which is thought to reflect their derivation from the TGN, a structure which displays a much higher concentration of clathrin associated with its cytoplasmic surface than cis or medial Golgi cisternal elements. These observations suggest that the transport of proinsulin to the condensing elements occurs by a receptor or carrier-dependent process, somewhat analogous to receptor-mediated endocytosis (see below), involving the segregation of the receptors in large areas of membrane of the trans cisternae or the TGN that are coated by clathrin and form the immature granule. The processing of proinsulin to insulin appears to take place in the clathrin-coated immature secretory granule. The maturation of the granule, with the elimination of the clathrin coat is dependent on the processing of the prohormone. When this is prevented by incorporation of an amino acid analogue into the polypeptide, the abnormal proinsulin remains within a clathrin-coated compartment.[296]

The presence of a clathrin coat in maturing secretory granules has also been observed in the cultured pituitary tumor cells (AtT-20) that secrete ACTH and other derivatives of proopiomelanocortin (POMC). In this case, serial sectioning electron microscopy showed that the condensing vacuoles partially coated by clathrin are still connected to the TGN.[269] Thus, it appears that the sorting processes that take place in the trans Golgi region or TGN involve the segregation of different groups of proteins to be incorporated either into clathrin-coated vesicles, or, in the examples cited earlier, into vesicles without a clathrin coat. In contrast to proteins secreted by the regulated pathway, plasma membrane proteins and constitutively secreted proteins emerge from the TGN in clathrin-coated vesicles. In addition, there may be at least two classes of clathrin-coated vesicles emerging from the TGN, since the vesicles that carry lysosomal hydrolases bound to mannose-6-phosphate receptors from the TGN to the incipient lysosome also contain a clathrin coat.

THE BIOGENESIS OF LYSOSOMES[1,297–302]

Lysosomes are membrane-bounded cytoplasmic organelles that contain a wide variety of hydrolytic enzymes that function at an acidic pH and together are capable of digesting essentially all types of biologic macromolecules. Both extracellular materials that are taken into the cell by *endocytosis* and intracellular components that undergo *autophagy* are broken down within lysosomes to their elementary constituents. These may then be transferred across the organellar membrane to the cytosol for further degradation or for reutilization in the synthesis of new macromolecules. A cell may contain several hundred lysosomes, and these may be quite variable in their size, shape, and morphologic appearance. This heterogeneity reflects the character of the material being digested within the lysosomes, as well as the various stages in the process of digestion that may be taking place. Some lysosomes may contain recently ingested materials whose origin is easily recognizable, while others, known as *residual bodies,* may contain only undigested remnants.*

The term *endocytosis* refers to a variety of cellular processes that lead to the interiorization of extracellular material. The essential feature of endocytosis is that extracellular fluid or solid particles become surrounded by a portion of the cell plasma membrane that ultimately pinches off from the cell surface to form a membrane-bounded cytoplasmic compartment.

The term *phagocytosis* is reserved for the internalization of large particles, such as bacteria, protozoa, cellular debris, carbon or silica grains, etc. In general, this process involves the formation of cytoplasmic extensions or pseudopodia that completely surround the particle being ingested to produce a *phagosome,* which later acquires lysosomal enzymes to become a *phagolysosome* in which digestion takes place. The process of phagocytosis requires the reorganization of a network of microfilaments located immediately beneath the plasma membrane and, therefore, can be inhibited by the drug cytochalasin D[303] which interferes with microfilament function. In multicellular organisms, phagocytosis is an activity reserved for "professional phagocytes," such as macrophages and polymorphonuclear leukocytes. Specific proteins in the plasma membrane of these cells serve as receptors that recognize ligands on the surface of the particle being taken in.[304]

Receptor-mediated endocytosis (see Ref. 301) is an important mechanism for the efficient uptake of extracellular substances, such as hormones, growth factors, and nutrient-carrier proteins, capable of binding to specific cell surface receptors that mediate their internalization (Fig. 3-21). The receptor-ligand complexes are concentrated in small invaginations of the plasma membrane which are known as *coated pits,* on account of their appearance in electron microscopy. The coat covering the region of the pit is composed primarily of *clathrin,*[305] a protein that consists of heavy (180 kDa) and light (35 kDa) chains and forms a lattice on the cytoplasmic face of the membrane. The formation of the coat is thought to result from the interaction of clathrin (and/or other minor components of the lattice) with the cytoplasmic portions of the receptor polypeptides. After pinching off into the cytoplasm, the pits generate *coated vesicles*[306] that are completely surrounded by a cage composed of clathrin and its associated proteins (see Ref. 307).

In receptor-mediated endocytosis, interaction of the ligands with their specific receptors markedly increases the efficiency of their uptake, since they are actually concentrated on the surface of the cell before being taken in. This process is responsible for the cellular uptake of some nutrients, such as vitamin B_{12} bound to transcobalamin II, cholesterol incorporated in low density lipoprotein (LDL) particles, and iron within transferrin molecules. After they bind to the cell surface receptors which mediate their function, polypeptide hormones and growth factors, such as insulin or epidermal growth factor (EGF), are also interiorized in coated vesicles. This leads to the removal of the hormones and factors from the extracellular fluid. It also provides a means to modulate the capacity of the cell to respond to these agents which control cellular metabolism and proliferation, since it reduces the number of receptors available at the cell surface (i.e., down-regulation). Some receptors internalized by endocytosis, such as the EGF receptor, are normally distributed over the surface of the cell (see Refs. 308, 309) and move to, or form, coated pits only after binding their ligands. Others, such as the LDL receptor, are continuously concentrated in coated pits, and internalized whether or not they contain a bound ligand.[310]

During the course of receptor-mediated endocytosis, solutes, such as albumin or horseradish peroxidase, that are present in the extracellular fluid but are not bound to specific receptors are, of course, also taken in and remain dissolved in the lumen of the endocytic vesicles. The intake of extracellular fluid, and of substances dissolved in it, which takes place continuously in this manner and occurs in all cells, is known as *fluid phase endocytosis* or *pinocytosis.* Kinetically, this is characterized by a strictly linear dependency on the concentration of the solute taken in. In contrast, receptor-mediated endocytosis can be saturated and shows typical Michaelis-Menten kinetics. It is not yet clear if pinocytosis may also be carried out independently of receptor-mediated endocytosis, by vesicles which are not coated by clathrin.

Soon after pinching off from the plasma membrane, coated vesicles lose their clathrin coat as they fuse with membrane-bounded tubulovesicular organelles known as *endosomes,*† to which they transfer the material adsorbed at the cell surface. Recent work[311] suggests that endosomes contain a distinct set of membrane proteins, and therefore that they are not entirely derived from the fusion of coated vesicles with each other. The biochemical individuality of endosomes must reflect their biogenetic derivation, at least in part, from other intracellular, presumably Golgi-derived, vesicles (Fig. 3-21).

Endosomes contain a membrane-associated ATPase that concentrates protons and, therefore, acidifies the lumen of the organelle.[312] At the acidic pH, many ligands are dissociated from their receptors[313] and released into the endosomal lumen (see Refs. 298, 314). The receptors are then segregated to a tubular region of the endosomal membrane from where vesicles are thought to pinch off to return the receptors to the cell surface so they can participate in further rounds of endocytosis (Fig. 3-21). An endosome with these features is known as CURL, for compartment of uncoupling of receptors and li-

*Lysosomes have been defined as membrane-bounded vacuoles rich in lysosomal hydrolases. The term *primary lysosome* was used to designate lysosomes that have not yet acquired the substrate for digestion, and the term *secondary lysosome* for those that have received these substrates subsequent to endocytosis or autophagy.[1] Primary lysosomes are prominent in polymorphonuclear leukocytes, where they are represented by the azurophilic granules.[150] In most other cells (see below), the term *primary lysosome* can only be applied to the small vesicles containing mannose-6-phosphate receptor molecules (see below) that carry newly synthesized hydrolases from the Golgi apparatus (or the TGN) to endosomes undergoing transformation into lysosomes.

†The term *receptosome* has also been proposed to designate this structure.[299]

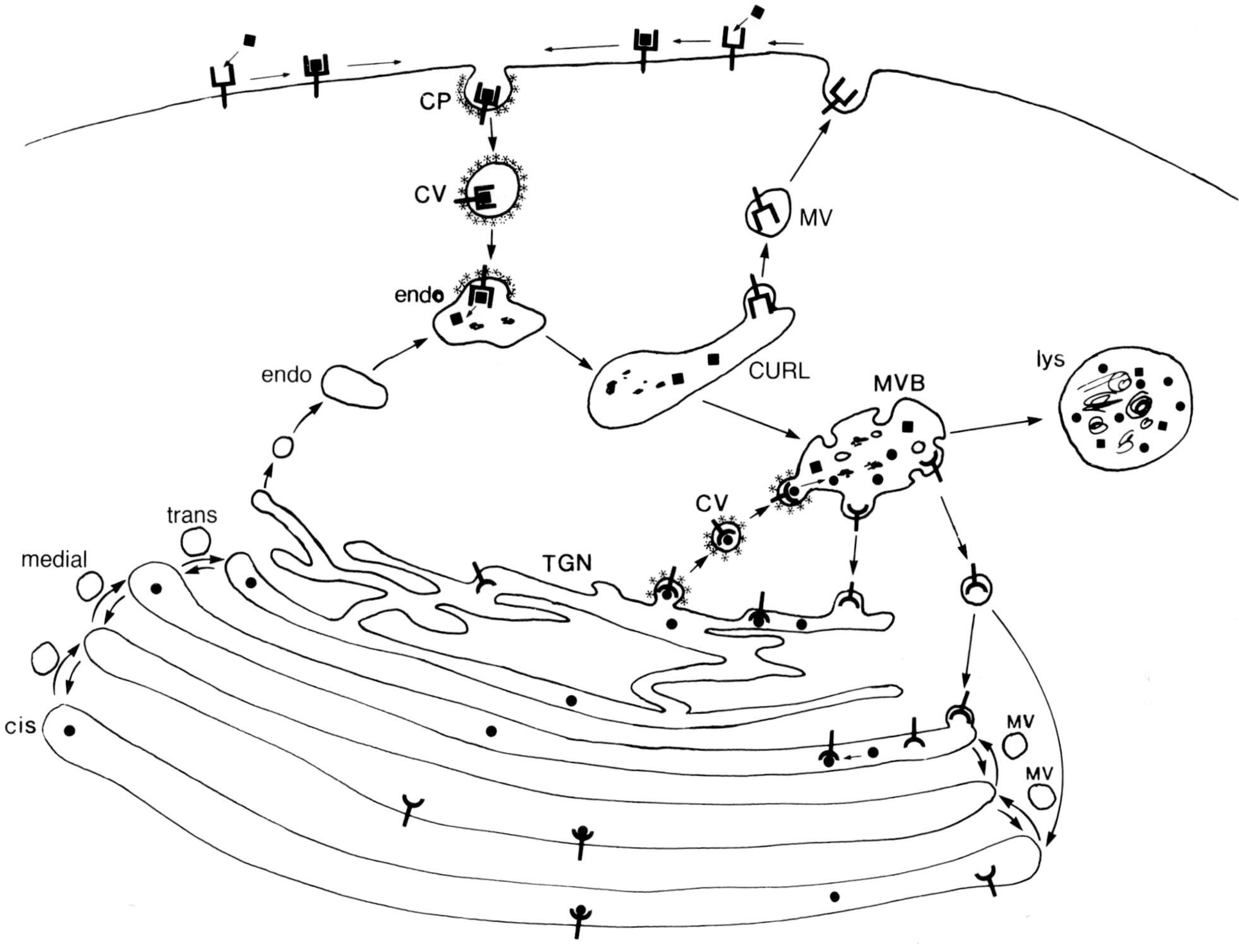

Fig. 3-21 Receptor-mediated endocytosis, membrane recycling, and biogenesis of lysosomes. After binding to its ligand (■) at the cell surface, a plasma membrane receptor is concentrated in a clathrin-coated pit (CP) which pinches off into the cytoplasm to form a coated vesicle (CV). The coated vesicle fuses with an endosome (endo) losing its coat, and, at the low pH in this compartment, the receptor releases its ligand into the endosomal lumen. The endosome itself is originally formed by vesicles that budded from the trans Golgi network (TGN). Within the endosomal membrane, the receptors become segregated to a region from where they become incorporated into membrane vesicles (MV) that bud and return to the cell surface. The endosomal compartment from which receptors return to the cell surface is labeled CURL. Endosomes containing the endocytosed material are further remodelled by acquisition of lysosomal hydrolases (●) which are transported from the TGN in coated vesicles containing the mannose 6-phosphate receptors. The membranes of this type of endosome show numerous invaginations and interiorized vesicles, thus accounting for the designation of the organelle as a multivesicular body (MVB). This organelle is defined not only by its morphologic appearance but also by the presence within it of lysosomal hydrolases, the mannose-6-phosphate receptor, and endocytosed material. The final step in the conversion of an endosome to a lysosome (lys) is the return in membrane vesicles (MV) of the mannose-6-phosphate receptor to the TGN and the Golgi apparatus, since the receptor is absent from the mature lysosome. Conversion into a lysosome also involves the acquisition of specific lysosomal membrane proteins that possibly arrive to the lysosome in the same coated vesicles that carry the mannose-6-phosphate receptors and their associated hydrolases.

gands.[315,316] The ligands released in the endosome and, in some cases, nondissociated receptor-ligand complexes, can subsequently undergo intralysosomal digestion. The endosome is, therefore, a functionally complex compartment in which sorting steps take place that control the flow of material into lysosomes or its return to the cell surface.

Several classes of endosomes that differ in their relative acidity, their receptor content, their biochemical composition, their morphologic appearance, and their closeness to the plasma membrane or to the Golgi apparatus have been recognized.[311,317–321] Although their functional differences are not yet completely clear, they are likely to represent different stages in the sorting process that takes place within endosomes and in the concomitant transfer of material to lysosomes. When endocytosis is allowed to proceed in cells incubated at temperatures between 16 and 20°C, transfer of the endocytosed material to lysosomes is inhibited. This provides a useful tool to study the elements involved in this process.[320,322] It was originally thought that the transfer of endosomal content to lysosomes takes place by fusion of the two organelles or with the participation of intervening transport vesicles. The current view, however, is that a subclass of endosomes located near the Golgi apparatus undergoes conversion into a lysosome by acquiring the necessary complement of lysosomal hydrolases and membrane proteins from clathrin-coated vesicles (Fig. 3-21) that originate from the trans Golgi region or trans Golgi network (TGN).[298,323,324] The presence of lysosomal hydrolases in *multivesicular bodies,* which are endosomes that contain invaginated membrane tubules or vesicles, suggests that these represent a transition stage in the conversion into a lysosome (Fig. 3-21).

The biogenesis of lysosomes is a complex process which requires that specific sets of soluble hydrolases and membrane proteins, which are synthesized in the ER, be segregated from proteins with other subcellular destinations and be transferred to developing or preexisting lysosomes. Whereas much progress has been made toward an understanding of the mechanism by which the newly synthesized hydrolases are sorted from secretory proteins, little is known of the sorting process that ensures the incorporation of specific proteins in the lysosomal membrane.

Biosynthesis of Lysosomal Enzymes[131,300,302,325]

With rare exceptions, lysosomal enzymes are glycoproteins that contain *N*-linked and sometimes *O-linked* oligosaccharide chains. Like secretory glycoproteins, lysosomal enzymes are synthesized in ribosomes bound to the ER membranes and the nascent ribosome-associated chains contain cleavable N-terminal insertion signals that lead to the cotranslational passage of the polypeptide into the lumen of the ER.[326–328] Translocation through the ER membrane is accompanied by the acquisition of *N*-linked high mannose oligosaccharide chains and cleavage of the signal sequence. These processes are indistinguishable from those that take place during the early stages of the biosynthesis of secretory glycoproteins.[326,327,329] Subsequently, however, the lysosomal polypeptides undergo modifications that introduce in some of their oligosaccharide chains the *lysosomal marker,* mannose-6-phosphate (Man-6-P). The Man-6-P distinguishes lysosomal from secretory glycoproteins and is responsible for addressing the former to their lysosomal destination (see below). The incorporation of a phosphate group at the C-6 position of some mannose residues is the result of two sequential reactions (Fig. 3-20) that are catalyzed by enzymes that appear to be concentrated in the cis region of the Golgi apparatus.[238] The first step is the transfer by a phosphotransferase of *N*-acetylglucosaminyl-1-phosphate from UDP-*N*-acetylglucosamine to the C-6 hydroxyl group of a mannose residue in a partially trimmed high mannose oligosaccharide. This results in the formation of a phosphodiester bond linking the mannose to the *N*-acetylglucosamine.[330,331] In the second reaction, a specific phosphodiesterase removes the *N*-acetylglucosamine residue and thus uncovers the phosphate on the modified mannose residue.[332–334] A defect in the first enzyme in this modification pathway occurs in patients with I-cell disease (mucolipidosis II),[335–341] or pseudo-Hurler polydystrophy[336–340,342] (Chap. 12) and is responsible for the secretion of nonphosphorylated hydrolases from cultured fibroblasts derived from these patients and for the high levels of hydrolases in sera from these patients.

The specificity of the *N*-acetylglucosaminyl phosphotransferase for some features of the lysosomal polypeptides is the key factor responsible for the addition of the lysosomal marker only to those polypeptides destined to lysosomes. Partially purified transferase preparations modify the C-6 positions of mannose residues present in lysosomal enzymes more than those in the isolated high mannose oligosaccharide chains or in the monomeric sugar α-methylmannoside.[330,331] Moreover, these enzyme preparations do not phosphorylate mannose residues in nonlysosomal glycoproteins any more effectively than α-methylmannoside.[330,331] The transferase appears to contain a site that recognizes a specific feature of the lysosomal polypeptide and positions the acceptor oligosaccharide chain in proximity to the enzyme active site that modifies the mannose residue. Thus, deglycosylated hydrolases are specific inhibitors of the transferase when other lysosomal enzymes are used as acceptors but not when α-methylmannoside is the acceptor.[343] The fact that the acceptor activity of lysosomal enzymes is obliterated when they are denatured suggests that a conserved conformational feature of the protein represents the recognition site for the transferase.[330] Indeed, the amino acid sequences of more than a half a dozen lysosomal hydrolases have been determined from the nucleotide sequences of cDNA clones, but no significant homology between their primary sequences can be recognized (e.g., Refs. 344 to 351). Because most lysosomal hydrolases contain several oligosaccharide chains and mannose phosphorylation seems to take place randomly on one or more of these chains, it also appears that the transferase recognizes a global structural feature of each protein rather than a localized domain around each oligosaccharide chain. In some cases of mucolipidosis III, the phosphotransferase appears to be defective only in its ability to recognize the lysosomal enzymes as substrates at physiological concentrations (μ*M*), but is unaffected in its capacity to phosphorylate α-methylmannoside at concentrations near its K_m (200 m*M*).[342]

The phosphorylation of mannose residues in some of the oligosaccharide chains in lysosomal hydrolases does not prevent the processing of other chains, or branches of the same chain, by the set of trimming enzymes and glycosyltransferases that are present in the Golgi apparatus and lead to the formation of the complex oligosaccharides containing *N*-acetylglucosaminyl, galactosyl, and sialyl residues that are characteristic of many secretory proteins.[352–355]

Studies with cultured cells indicate that a fraction of newly synthesized phosphorylated hydrolases are normally secreted into the medium (see Refs. 327, 356). The presence of some lysosomal hydrolases in serum and urine also suggests that, to some extent, some cells in the intact organism normally secrete lysosomal hydrolases.[357] Some of the secreted molecules contain the Man-6-P marker, as well as complex oligosaccharide chains. It is likely that even those hydrolases that reach the lysosome acquire terminal sugars during their passage through the trans Golgi cisternae, but such sugars are later lost within the lysosome. In fact, the phosphate group itself is not present in the mature enzymes and is thought to be removed by lysosomal phosphatases.

Lysosomal hydrolases also undergo a maturation process that involves one or more proteolytic cleavage steps. These cleavages either reduce the molecular weight by loss of a C-terminal segment, as is the case with β-glucuronidase, or generate, by two successive cleavages, two polypeptides from a single precursor, as is the case with cathepsin D.[327,358,359] Lysosomal enzymes secreted from normal cells, as well as enzymes that are secreted when the lysosomal marker is not present, as is the case in I-cell disease, or when glycosylation is prevented by treatment of cells with tunicamycin,[360] do not undergo proteolytic processing.[327] These findings suggest that the proteolytic modifications take place in the lysosome itself.[361]

The Man-6-P Marker and the Targeting of Lysosomal Hydrolases to Lysosomes

The study of I-cell disease fibroblasts played an important role in the discovery of the Man-6-P lysosomal marker and of the receptors that recognize it and effect the segregation of newly synthesized hydrolases to the lysosomes. It was originally observed that cultured fibroblasts from I-cell disease patients are deficient in lysosomal hydrolases, and that the medium in which these cells are cultured contains higher levels of the hydrolase activities than the media from cultures of normal fibroblasts.[362] It was subsequently demonstrated that lysosomal hydrolases secreted by normal fibroblasts can be taken up by both normal cells and cells from I-cell disease patients.[356] This uptake was shown to be mediated by a saturable receptor that recognizes these proteins, whereas the enzymes secreted by the defective cells could not be taken up. These observations showed that, in I-cell disease, the enzymes themselves are defective and not the cellular apparatus that is necessary for their incorporation into lysosomes. It was, therefore, proposed[356] that the defect in I-cell disease is in the inability of the cells to equip the newly synthesized enzymes with the marker necessary for their interiorization by receptor-mediated endocytosis. The crucial marker present in the oligosaccharide chains of secreted enzymes recognized by the receptor was later shown to be the Man-6-P residue.[363]

Although the ability of cells to take up exogenous lysosomal hydrolases reflects the presence of the Man-6-P receptor in the plasma membrane, it is now well established tht most of the receptor molecules are located in intracellular membranes and that, in fact, some cells have very low amounts of receptor at their surface.[364–366]

Although it has been amply demonstrated that in cultured fibroblasts the presence of the Man-6-P marker is necessary for the targeting of newly synthesized lysosomal hydrolases to lysosomes, alternative mechanisms must operate in other cell types. Thus, hepatocytes, Kupffer cells, and leukocytes from patients with I-cell disease contain nearly normal levels of lysosomal enzymes despite their deficiency in phosphotransferase activity.[367] In addition, in fibroblasts of I-cell disease patients, acid phosphatase activity is present at normal levels,[368] even though normally this enzyme contains the Man-6-P marker.[369] A mechanism which recognizes a sorting signal within the polypeptide rather than in an oligosaccharide chain[370,371] operates in yeast to address digestive enzymes, such as procarboxypeptidase Y to the vacuole, an organelle which is regarded as analogous to the lysosome. Mutational studies on chimeric proteins indicate that only the first 10 amino acids of procarboxypeptidase Y are required to determine its vacuolar localization.[372]

The Man-6-P Receptors

Two different types of Man-6-P receptor molecules that differ in their binding properties and divalent cation requirements have been purified by affinity chromatography of solubilized cellular membranes on matrices containing immobilized ligands. The first receptor identified (MPR^{CI}) was a 215-kDa glycoprotein that does not require cations to bind ligand.[373] Specific antibodies to this receptor have allowed studies of its subcellular distribution and of the pathway it follows in effecting its sorting and carrier functions.[316,323,374–380] The amino acid sequence of this receptor, as determined from the nucleotide squence of a cDNA clone,[381] reveals that it is a type I transmembrane glycoprotein which has a small segment of 17 kDa exposed on the cytoplasmic side of the membrane.[382] The luminal domain of this protein, where the ligand-binding site(s) is found, is composed of 15 homologous segments, each approximately 145 amino acids in length. The amount of this receptor present on the surface of the cell varies with the cell type, but most of the receptor is found in intracellular membranes. By immunocytochemistry, the receptor has been shown to be present in coated vesicles, endosomes, and Golgi membranes, but not in mature lysosomes (see below).

The second Man-6-P receptor, (MPR^{CD}), is a 45-kDa glycoprotein that requires divalent cations, particularly Mn^{2+}, and a somewhat more acidic pH (pH 6.3) for ligand binding than the 215-kDa receptor, which has high affinity for the phosphorylated ligand at neutral pH.[383,384] The discovery of this receptor resulted from the observation that certain cell lines which lack the 215-kDa receptor[385] are nevertheless capable of sorting properly some of their lysosomal hydrolases. These cells were found to be incapable of taking up the exogenous lysosomal hydrolases administered under the conditions usually employed, that do not satisfy the cation and pH requirements for binding to the MPR^{CD}. Since the conformation of the hydrolases may be differentially affected by the pH, it is possible that different newly synthesized enzymes may be differentially partitioned between the two receptors, as they progress along the increasingly acid compartments of the Golgi apparatus.[385] The amino acid sequence of the MPR^{CD} derived from a cDNA clone[386,387] shows that this is also a type I transmembrane protein with a cytoplasmic domain of 69 residues and a luminal domain that shows homology with the repeated segments within the luminal domain of the MPR^{CI}. In particular, significant similarity is found within a pentadecapeptide limited by cysteine residues that is found in all the repeating domains of MPR^{CI}.

The critical function of the receptors that allows them to selectively transfer lysosomal enzymes bearing the Man-6-P marker to developing lysosomes is the pH dependence of their affinity for the ligands: the receptors bind strongly to phosphomannose-containing oligosaccharides or lysosomal hydrolases bearing the marker at neutral or slightly acidic pH but release these ligands quantitatively at the strong acid pH characteristic of endosomes or lysosomes.[355,384,388] Binding to the receptors requires removal of the GlcNAc group that initially covers the phosphate group on the C-6 of the mannose residue,[355,388] and high affinity binding requires at least two Man-6-P residues in the same molecule, although not necessarily on the same oligosaccharide chain.[384,389,390] Lysosomal hydrolases of the slime mold *Dictyostelium discoideum* bind effectively to their receptor even though their Man-6-P residues are covered by methyl groups.[391]

Delivery of Hydrolases to Incipient Lysosomes

As previously noted, the enzymes that synthesize the Man-6-P marker are located in the cis region of the Golgi apparatus, and the MPR^{CI} receptor has been shown to be present in Golgi cisternae, in the trans Golgi network (TGN) and endosomes but not in mature lysosomes.[323,374–380] After binding lysosomal enzymes, the occupied receptors are incorporated into clathrin-coated vesicles that exit from the trans Golgi cisternae or trans Golgi network (Fig. 3-21). These fuse with neighboring endosomes, and the ligand then dissociates from the receptor as a result of the low pH.[323,375,376,380,392,393] There is some controversy on whether movement of the receptor from the Golgi apparatus to the receiving endosome and back takes place only if the receptor is occupied by a ligand or whether the receptor moves constitutively. One group has reported that receptors accumulate in Golgi membranes and that endosomes are depleted of receptors when cells are treated with tunicamycin,[376] a drug that blocks core glycosylation in the ER and therefore prevents the acquisition of the Man-6-P marker by the newly synthesized hydrolases. The same group also observed that when dissociation of the receptors from their ligands is prevented by administration of lysomotropic drugs, such as chloroquine or NH_4Cl, that are concentrated in the lumen of acidic compartments and raise their pH, the receptors accumulate in the endosome.[376,380] These authors showed that under these conditions the failure of the receptor to return to the Golgi apparatus results from its inability to release the ligand and not from the altered pH of the endosome. When cells treated with chloroquine were incubated with Man-6-P, which enters the endosome compartment by fluid phase pinocytosis, this competing ligand led to dissociation of the complex, which in turn was followed by reappearance of the receptor in Golgi membranes.[380] However, other investigators[394,395] have concluded that the receptor recycles constitutively, i.e., even in the absence of the ligand. It was observed that the level of receptor in the endosome was not significantly reduced when the synthesis of new lysosomal hydrolases was blocked by the protein synthesis inhibitor cycloheximide. The failure of the Man-6-P receptor-ligand complexes to dissociate at the altered pH of the endosomes in cells treated with lysosomotropic drugs accounts for the original finding[396] that secretion of lysosomal enzymes is increased under these conditions, since all the receptors remain occupied and, therefore, inaccessible to the newly synthesized hydrolases.

At least some of the receptor molecules that undergo recycling between the Golgi apparatus and the endosome must reach the plasma membrane, since the presence of variable amounts of the receptor at the cell surface has been demonstrated in many cell types (see Ref. 302). In fact, the presence of surface receptors, as well as significant levels of lysosomal hydrolases in normal serum, suggests that secretion and uptake of lysosomal enzymes is a physiological process. Indeed, there are conditions in which the secretion of enzymes from some cells and their uptake by others corrects a genetic defect. Thus, in female carriers of Hunter disease, an X-linked lysosomal disorder that is characterized by a deficiency in iduronate sulfatase, cells that cannot synthesize the normal enzyme because of inactivation of the normal X chromosome appear to be phenotypically normal. Presumably this is the result of cross-feeding by cells in which only the affected X chromosome was inactivated.[397]

THE LYSOSOMAL MEMBRANE[398]

The lysosomal membrane is a selective permeability barrier between the lysosomal lumen and the cytoplasm. It is equipped with carriers and transport systems that control the passage of substances between both compartments and with a proton pump that creates the acidic environment necessary for intralysosomal digestion. The lysosomal membrane prevents the egress of macromolecules brought into the lysosome by endocytosis or autophagy and only allows the escape of the end products of their digestion. The amino acids, dipeptides, nucleosides, small monomeric sugars, phosphate or sulfate ions, and other molecules released by active or passive transport may be utilized for biosynthetic reactions in the cytoplasm. Certain nutrients, such as cholesterol, released from cholesterol esters brought into lysosomes by endocytosis of LDL particles[399] (Chap. 48), and cobalamin (vitamin B_{12}), taken up complexed to transcobalamin II[400,401] (Chap. 82), are delivered to the cytoplasm by transport through the lysosomal membrane.

Several carrier-mediated transport systems specific for cystine,[402–407] cationic amino acids,[408,409] small neutral amino acids,[410] or tyrosine and other bulky neutral amino acids[411] have been identified in the lysosomal membrane, and knowledge of their function is rapidly increasing. In the recessively inherited disease *nephropathic cystinosis* (Chap. 107), a defect in the carrier that mediates the transport of cystine leads to the accumulation of large amounts of this disulfide amino acid within the lysosome.[402–404,406] Although cystine accumulates within the lysosomal compartment, it could not exist in the cytoplasm where strongly reducing conditions prevail. The therapeutic administration of the aminothiol cysteamine reduces the accumulation of cystine through the formation within the lysosome of the mixed disulfide of cysteine and cysteamine, which behaves as a lysine analogue and is recognized by the system that transports cationic amino acids.[403,412] Certain compounds, such as the acidotropic amines chloroquine and primaquine, as well as amino acid esters, dipeptides, and oligopeptides (particularly if rich in hydrophobic amino acids) traverse the lysosomal membrane from the cytoplasm to the luminal side. The protonated amines, as well as the free amino acids generated by hydrolysis of the ester and peptide bonds, accumulate within the lysosomes and exit only slowly through the lysosomal membrane. Monosaccharides seem to cross the lysosomal membrane by facilitated diffusion, and a carrier has been identified that mediates transfer of sialic acid. This carrier appears to be defective in Salla disease,[413,414] in which an intralysosomal accumulation of sialic acid occurs.

A membrane-associated enzyme, acetyl-CoA:α-glucosaminide N-acetyltransferase, transfers acetyl groups from acetyl-CoA in the cytoplasm to acceptor glucosamine moieties linked in terminal α linkages to heparan sulfate molecules within the lysosome.[415] The acetylation of heparan sulfate appears to be necessary for its degradation. A deficiency in the transferase produces the Sanfilippo C syndrome[416] (Chap. 61), resulting from intralysosomal accumulation of this mucopolysaccharide.

In the lysosomal membrane, there is a proton pump that creates and maintains an acid environment (pH 5) within the lysosomal lumen (see Refs. 417, 418). The pump utilizes cytoplasmic ATP and functions in an electrogenic[419,420] or electroneutral[421] manner, although it operates most effectively in the presence of chloride ions, which also accumulate in the lysosomal lumen. In its sensitivity to inhibitors[419,420] the lysosomal pump strongly resembles other proton ATPases (known as vacuolar ATPases) that have been identified in the ER,[422] the Golgi apparatus,[253] and endocytic and secretory vesicles (see Refs. 418, 423). These proton ATPases are responsible for the progressive acidification of the lumen of the organelles that constitute the endomembrane system. The vacuolar pumps are insensitive to oligomycin, an inhibitor that blocks the function of the mitochondrial F_OF_1 ATPase, and to vanadate, which inhibits the E_1E_2 phosphoenzyme-type ATPases (such as the Na^+/K^+ ATPase of the plasma membrane). On the other hand, levels of the sulfhydryl reagent *N*-ethylmaleimide (NEM) that inhibit the function of vacuolar ATPases do not affect the other ion-motive enzymes (the F_0F_1 and E_1E_2 ATPases).

The luminal surface of the lysosomal membrane is thought to be protected from the attack of lysosome hydrolases by complex oligosaccharides rich in sialic acid which appear to be characteristic of lysosomal membrane glycoproteins (see below). Acting as immobilized polyanions, the sialic acid moieties may also play an important role in establishing a Donnan potential for protons that contributes to the internal low pH of lysosomes.[424]

Almost nothing is known of the cytoplasmic surface of the lysosomal membrane, although it is clear that it must possess receptors that mediate the fusion of lysosomes between themselves or with phagosomes or endosomes to which lysosomal enzymes must be made available. This surface must also interact with the cytoskeletal elements responsible for lysosomal movement.[425,426]

Through the use of polyclonal and monoclonal antibodies prepared against lysosomal membranes, several lysosomal membrane proteins have been identified.[427–432] By immunocytochemical methods, they colocalize with cytoplasmic vesicles identified as lysosomes because of their content of lysosomal hydrolases and their capacity to accumulate the dye acridine orange.[433] Although their function remains unknown, these proteins have become useful models to study the biosynthesis of the lysosomal membrane. They are glycoproteins rich in *N*-linked oligosaccharides, most of which are of the complex type and are, therefore, synthesized and glycosylated in the ER and modified in the Golgi apparatus. Some lysosomal membrane proteins[427–429] are found in significant amounts only in mature or developing lysosomes and are absent from endosomes or the plasma membrane, whereas others appear to undergo a constant circulation through the three compartments.[431]

In contrast to the situation with the lysosomal hydrolases, the sorting of the lysosomal membrane proteins to the lysosome is not mediated by a carbohydrate marker. Thus, the membrane-associated enzymes β-glucocerebrosidase and acetyl-CoA:α-D-glucosaminide *N*-acetyltransferase are present at normal levels in I-cell disease fibroblasts. The former enzyme has been directly shown not to be phosphorylated in normal cells.[434] Moreover, the oligosaccharides of some of the previously mentioned purified lysosomal membrane proteins identified with antibodies to the lysosomal membrane do not appear to contain phosphate groups. In pulse-labeling and cell fractionation experiments with tunicamycin-treated cultured cells, some of these newly synthesized membrane proteins lacking *N*-linked oligosaccharides were shown nevertheless to be transported to the lysosome with a rapid kinetics.[432] These studies with tunicamycin also indicate that the transport of membrane proteins to lysosomes is not coupled obligatorily to the transport of lysosomal hydrolases, which takes place via the Man-6-P receptor and is interrupted under these conditions.

The oligosaccharide chains in the lysosomal membrane proteins appear to play a role in protecting the exposed portions of the polypeptides from the attack of lysosomal proteases, since in tunicamycin-treated cells the proteins have shorter than normal half-lives.[432]

MITOCHONDRIAL BIOGENESIS[435–443]

Mitochondria are cytoplasmic organelles that carry out cellular respiration and generate most of the cellular ATP. They contain a vast array of enzymes reflecting their central role in various aspects of cellular biochemistry. Mitochondria are also capable of storing and releasing calcium ions, and it is thought that this enables them, together with the endoplasmic reticulum, to serve as regulators of cytoplasmic calcium levels.

Structurally, mitochondria are characterized by the presence of two concentric lipoprotein membranes and two internal compartments (Fig. 3-22). The *outer mitochondrial membrane* (OMM) completely surrounds the organelle and all molecules entering or leaving the mitochondrion must pass through it. The *inner mitochondrial membrane* (IMM) is separated from the outer by an *intermembrane space* and encloses the major intramitochondrial compartment, known as the *matrix* space or stroma. The surface area of the inner membrane is greatly increased by the presence of numerous infoldings, known as *cristae*, that vary in number and configuration depending on the type of cell and its physiological state. Regions of close contact between the inner and outer membranes are frequently observed. Importation of proteins into the mitochondria is thought to take place at these sites.[444–447]

Specific mitochondrial proteins are found in each one of the four submitochondrial compartments (i.e., the two membranes and the intermembrane and matrix spaces). The outer membrane has a relatively low protein content and is characterized by large amounts of the transmembrane protein "porin," which forms channels through which small molecules can pass freely.[448] Several other proteins have been localized in this membrane, including monoamine oxidase and two proteins, cytochrome b_5 and cytochrome b_5 reductase, that have corresponding, but not identical, counterparts, in the ER.

In contrast to the outer membrane, the inner mitochondrial membrane is impermeable and contains specialized transport systems for small molecules. Most importantly, this membrane contains the components of the electron transport chain that receives electrons generated by dehydrogenation of the citric acid cycle substrates. It also contains the ATP synthetase (F_1F_0 ATPase) that carries out oxidative phosphorylation (see Ref. 440).

The intermembrane space contains enzymes such as myokinase (adenylate kinase) which functions to equilibrate ATP

Fig. 3-22 Mitochondrial subcompartments. A mitochondrion contains two concentric membranes, an inner (IM) and an outer one (OM), separated by an intermembrane space. The matrix represents the space completely surrounded by the inner membrane. Contact points between the two membranes (marked by arrows) appear to be the sites for the incorporation into the organelle of polypeptides synthesized in the cytoplasm. The cristae are platelike invaginations of the inner membrane. See the text for the characteristic protein contents of the various mitochondrial subcompartments.

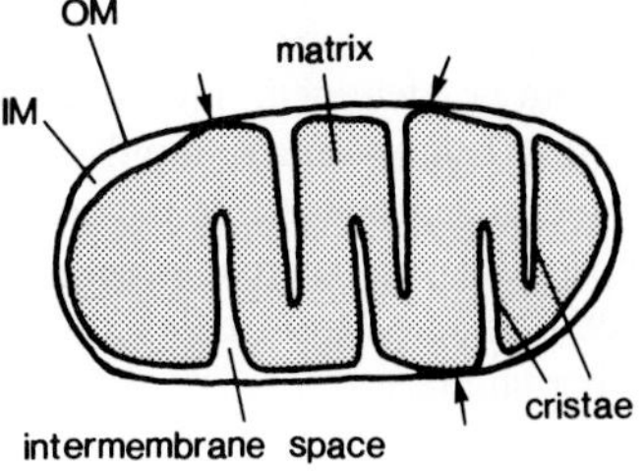

and AMP with ADP. These enzymes can be released relatively easily from isolated mitochondria by osmotic shock or sonication. The mitochondrial matrix houses enzymes of the citric acid cycle as well as those that carry out β oxidation of fatty acids. In the hepatocyte, the matrix is also the site of some of the enzymes of the urea cycle (Chap. 20).

The mitochondrial membranes contain both peripheral and integral proteins, and each membrane polypeptide has a characteristic disposition relative to the phospholipid bilayer. For example, cytochrome oxidase, a protein that consists of several subunits and serves as the terminal member of the electron transport chain that carries out the reduction of oxygen, is an integral component of the inner membrane and is exposed on both sides of this membrane. On the other hand, cytochrome c, which delivers electrons to cytochrome oxidase, is a peripheral membrane protein bound to the outer face of the inner membrane. The ATP synthetase that is driven by a proton gradient to effect ATP synthesis is also a complex protein that in yeast contains nine subunits. Four of these form the F_0, or stalk portion of the complex, which is embedded in the inner membrane. The other subunits form a round particle, the F_1 ATPase, which protrudes into the matrix space and is held onto the membrane by the stalk (see Ref. 440 for organization of components of the electron transport chain).

Mitochondria are the only organelles of mammalian cells that possess a separate genome and the enzymatic machinery necessary for its replication and expression. The mitochondrial genes are contained in a circular double-stranded DNA molecule that in the human consists of 16,569 nucleotides whose sequence has been determined.[449]

The mitochondrial DNA encodes the ribosomal RNA of the mitochondrial ribosomes as well as 22 different transfer RNA molecules. Although mitochondria contain at least several hundred different polypeptides, only a small fraction of these are encoded in the organellar genome and are synthesized within the mitochondria. These include some, but not all, of the subunits of the cytochrome oxidase and of the ATPase, as well as subunits of the coenzyme QH_2-cytochrome c reductase, another member of the electron transfer chain. The polypeptides synthesized in mitochondria contain hydrophobic segments and are, in general, components of the inner membrane. Almost all other mitochondrial proteins, including the remaining subunits of the ATPase and cytochrome oxidase, are encoded in nuclear genes and are synthesized outside the mitochondria. They are subsequently taken up into the organelle and sorted into one of the four mitochondrial subcompartments (see Ref. 442 for genetic aspects of mitochondrial biogenesis).

Incorporation of Proteins into Mitochondria

Much has been learned about this process from studies carried out with yeast and *Neurospora*. These unicellular eukaryotic organisms are suitable for both genetic analysis and in vivo pulse-chase experiments in which the precursors of polypeptides destined to mitochondria can be identified. The study of protein transfer into mitochondria has also made rapid progress because it has been possible to reproduce this phenomenon in vitro by adding polypeptides synthesized in cell-free systems to isolated mitochondria obtained from either unicellular organisms or cells of higher animals.

Mitochondrial proteins encoded in the nuclear genome are synthesized in polyribosomes that are not bound to endoplasmic reticulum membranes. Most, but not all, proteins destined to the interior of the mitochondrion are synthesized as larger precursors containing N-terminal extensions or *presequences* that are removed by intramitochondrial proteases[450] whose function is essential for normal mitochondrial biogenesis.[451] Each presequence contains an addressing or a *targeting signal* that is responsible for the incorporation of the polypeptide into the organelle. The presequence may also contain a sorting or *localization signal* that determines the intramitochondrial location of the polypeptide. Proteins of the outer mitochondrial membrane, such as porin[452] and a 70-kDa polypeptide,[453] and some proteins of the interior mitochondrial subcompartments, such as cytochrome c_1 of the intermembrane space[454,455] and the ADP-ATP translocator[456] of the inner membrane, are synthesized without cleavable presequences.

The polypeptides to be incorporated into mitochondria appear to be recognized by receptors present in the outer mitochondrial membrane.[436,457–461] Since polysomes synthesizing certain mitochondrial proteins are recovered selectively with sedimentable mitochondria,[462] it appears that, within the cell, interaction of precursors of mitochondrial proteins with their receptors may take place, albeit somewhat inefficiently, before translation of the polypeptide precursor is completed. The mitochondrial surface receptors are proteinaceous in nature since the in vitro uptake of the precursors is abolished by brief treatment of intact mitochondria with low concentrations of proteases.[455,457,459] Since several hundred different polypeptides must be imported into the mitochondria, it is inconceivable that separate receptors exist in the organelle surface for each mitochondrial polypeptide. It is likely, however, that there are multiple receptors each of which recognizes different sets of proteins. Indeed, the addition of a synthetic presequence peptide[463] or of a purified unfolded mitochondrial protein[455,464] to an in vitro uptake system or a mild protease treatment of the mitochondria[460] selectively blocked the incorporation of some precursors, but not others, into the organelle.

The insertion of outer membrane polypeptides into the membrane and the passage of apocytochrome c into the intermembrane space are processes which apear to occur spontaneously without the requirement of energy.[457,464–466] Cytochrome c seems to utilize a unique route to reach the intermembrane space, since the incorporation of other proteins of the intermembrane space requires energy and involves an initial incorporation into the inner membrane (see below). Once in the intermembrane space, apocytochrome c acquires the covalently bound heme, and this leads to a conformational change that renders the uptake process irreversible.[455,458,461]

However, uptake of other polypeptides or their precursors into the inner mitochondrial compartments (i.e., matrix, inner membrane, and intermembrane space), is an energy-dependent process that requires the existence of an electrochemical potential across the inner membrane. Thus, uptake of such polypeptides is blocked by the addition of respiratory inhibitors, uncouplers of oxidative phosphorylation, or the ionophore valinomycin, which eliminates the membrane potential by allowing for the equilibration of the K^+ ion concentrations on both sides of the membrane.[459,467–469]

Signals for Targeting of Proteins to Mitochondria

The presence of cleavable N-terminal presequences in newly synthesized mitochondrial polypeptides has been demonstrated by analysis of polypeptides synthesized in vitro in cell-free systems (see, for example, Refs. 470, 471), as well as in intact cells labeled during a brief pulse with radioactive amino acids.[472–475] Moreover, the sequences of mRNAs for many mitochondrial proteins, which have been determined by analysis of cloned cDNAs, demonstrate the presence of coding regions that precede those encoding the N-terminal sequences of the mature proteins. These mitochondrial precursor presequences are of variable length but generally contain N-terminal regions that are rich in basic and hydroxylated amino acids and usually lack acidic amino acids and extensive stretches of hydrophobic residues.[476] These segments appear to be able to form amphipathic helices that contain charged or polar residues on one side of the helix and hydrophobic residues on the other.[439,476,477] The structure of the mitochondrial presequences is, therefore, fundamentally different from that of the signal sequences characteristic of polypeptides synthesized in the endoplasmic reticulum.

The fact that the presequences, indeed, contain true targeting signals for incorporation of the polypeptides into mitochondria was definitively established by experiments that employed recombinant DNA methods to link the presequences, or portions thereof, to segments of other polypeptides that are not normally targeted to the mitochondria. Thus, when gene segments encoding the presequences of the yeast cytochrome oxidase subunit IV,[478,479] alcohol dehydrogenase III,[480] or rat liver ornithine transcarbamylase (OTC)[481,482] were fused with a sequence encoding dihydrofolate reductase (DHFR), a cytosolic enzyme, the resulting hybrid polypeptides were incorporated into mitochondria, both in vivo and in vitro. Experiments of this type showed that, although the presequence (i.e., the cleaved segment) of the yeast cytochrome oxidase subunit IV is 25 residues in length, only its first 12 amino acids serve as the targeting signal and are required for incorporation of the chimera into the mitochondria. With such a shortened presequence, however, proteolytic removal does not take place.[479] The importance of presequences in the uptake of mitochondrial proteins is highlighted by the existence of a natural mutation in patients with methylmalonic acidemia in which a short, apparently N-terminal deletion within the precursor of methylmalonyl-CoA mutase prevents the incorporation of the enzyme into the mitochondria (Chap. 29).[483]

The efficacy of shortened presequences of only 9 to 12 amino acids in length has also been demonstrated for other mitochondrial proteins, such as δ-aminolevulinate synthase.[484] Moreover, it has also become apparent that the targeting sequence need not be at the extreme N terminus of the polypeptide, since in ornithine transcarbamylase (OTC), which contains a 32-residue cleavable presequence, only residues 8 to 23 were found to be essential for uptake.[482,485] The targeting signal, however, must remain exposed after the polypeptide is discharged from the ribosome and folds in the cytoplasm. Thus, the cytosolic protein dihydrofolate reductase (DHFR) contains a cryptic targeting signal located between residues 26 to 85.[486] This signal does not normally operate to bring the polypeptide into the mitochondria, apparently because it is "masked" in the folded protein. However, when the first 85 residues of DHFR are linked to the N terminus of an intact DHFR sequence or to subunit IV of cytochrome oxidase lacking its own targeting sequence, the chimeric polypeptides were efficiently incorporated into mitochondria.[486]

The targeting signal initiates importation into the mitochondrion, presumably by binding to its receptor. However, this is insufficient for entry, which not only requires the transmembrane potential of an energized inner membrane, but also the unfolded state of the precursor polypeptide. Thus, a fusion protein containing a mitochondrial targeting signal attached to DHFR cannot be incorporated in the presence of methotrexate, a ligand that binds to DHFR and stabilizes its folded conformation.[487] The methotrexate block in uptake is not due to a "masking" of the presequence, since the protein still associates with the mitochondria in the presence of this analogue but is not translocated across the membrane. Evidence has been presented that, in addition to the transmembrane potential, hydrolysis of extramitochondrial ATP is necessary to provide the energy required for the unfolding of the polypeptide.[488–491] The participation of a cytosolic protein factor in the import of some proteins into mitochondria has also been demonstrated,[492] but the role of the factor remains to be elucidated. It is possible that it functions as an adaptor to bring the targeting signal to its receptor.

Signals for Submitochondrial Localization

Experiments with a variety of chimeric proteins bearing different natural or modified presequences have demonstrated that the targeting signals serve to direct the proteins across both the inner and outer mitochondrial membranes so that, in the absence of other specific signals, the polypeptide is incorporated into the mitochondrial matrix.[480,493–495] Sorting of a protein to other subcompartments, i.e., the outer membrane, the inner membrane, or the intermembrane space, results from the operation of other signals, designated *localization signals,* which are distal from the targeting signal but may be contained within the presequence.

A plausible pathway by which polypeptides containing targeting signals are incorporated into the matrix is schematically represented in Fig. 3-23*A*. The N-terminal targeting signal within the presequence first binds to the mitochondrial surface, presumably because it is recognized by a receptor not represented in the figure. This recognition step either leads to the formation of a special junction that involves the localized fusion of the inner and outer membranes or takes place near a preexisting junction.[446,447] The targeting signal then inserts in the inner membrane in a process which requires a transmembrane potential ($\Delta \Psi$) and leads to the translocation of the polypeptide across this membrane. Cleavage of the signal by the matrix metalloprotease[450] then takes place, but this step is not required for the completion of translocation.[479,496] Intermediate stages in the uptake process, in which the polypeptide is exposed both within the matrix and on the surface of the mitochondria, have been observed in experiments in which the completion of translocation of the β subunit of the *Neurospora* F_1 ATPase was interrupted by carrying out the importation at low temperatures.[446] These experiments have also shown that after insertion into the inner membrane has been initiated, completion of translocation is a process that does not require the transmembrane potential.

Although polypeptides destined to the outer mitochondrial

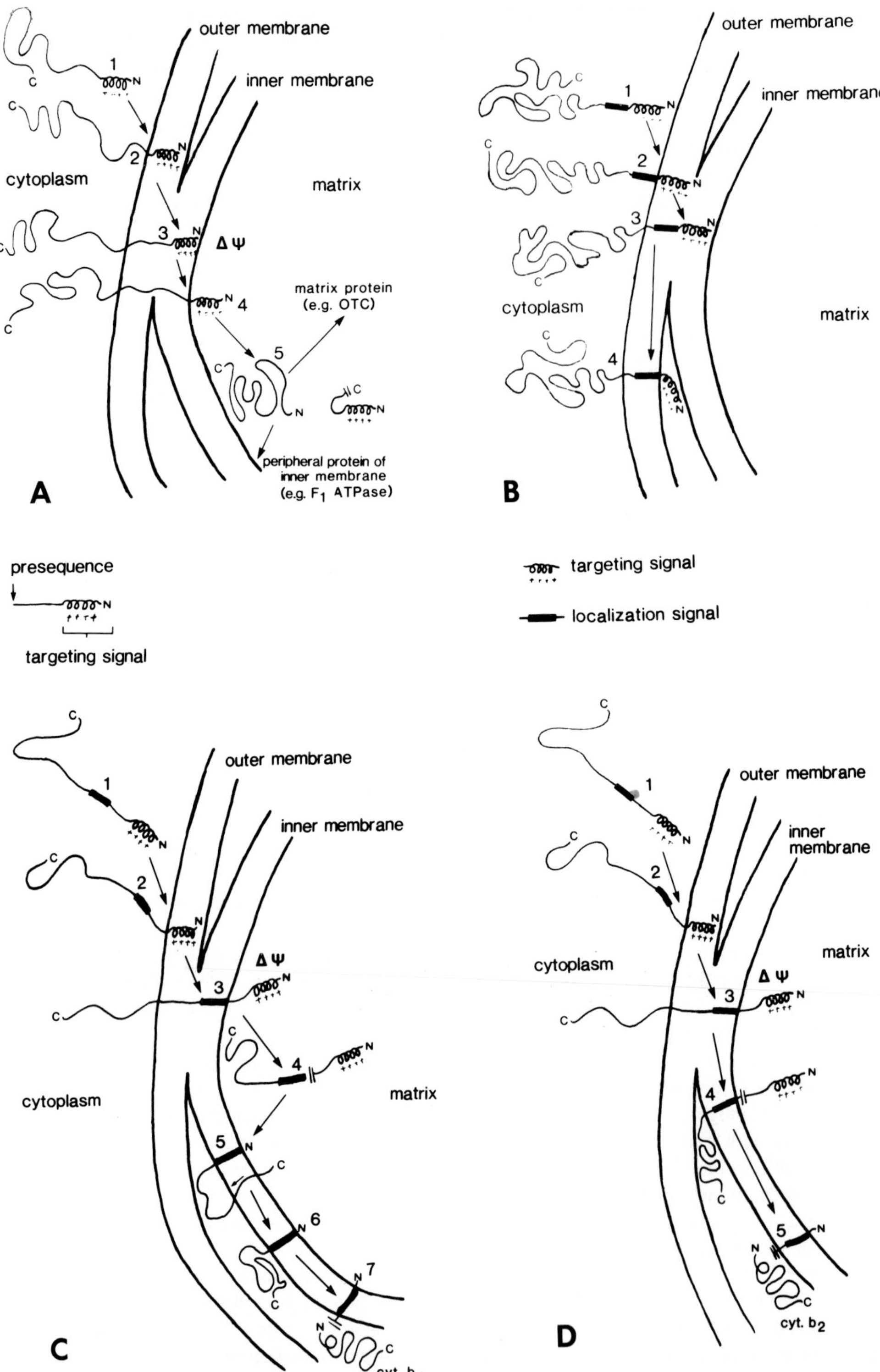

Fig. 3-23 Pathways for the incorporation of polypeptides into mitochondria. A. Incorporation of matrix proteins. A targeting signal located within a cleavable presequence at the N terminus of the polypeptide (1) leads to the association of the polypeptide first with the outer membrane (2) and then, in the presence of a transmembrane potential (3) ($\Delta\Psi$), to the passage of the polypeptide into the matrix through a point of contact between the two membranes. In an intermediate stage (4), parts of the polypeptide have reached the matrix while others are still exposed on the mitochondrial surface. The presequence is removed by a matrix metalloprotease, and (5) the final product may remain in the matrix (as is the case with ornithine transcarbamylase, OTC) or become peripherally associated with the inner membrane (as is the case with the β subunit of the F_1 ATPase).

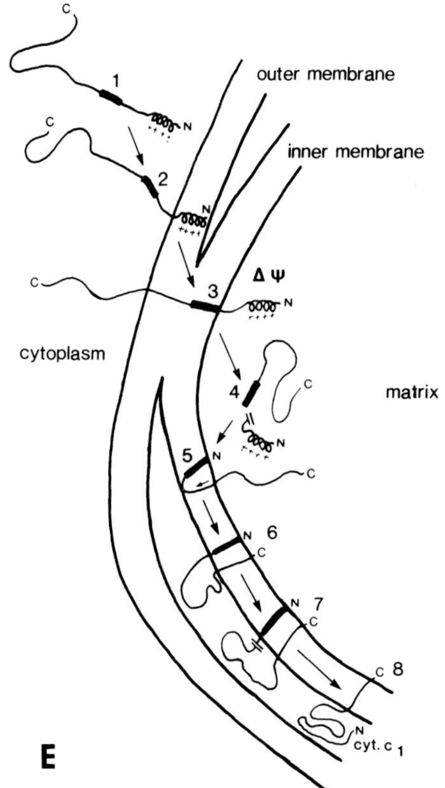

F

Fig. 3-23 (*Continued*) *B.* Incorporation of a protein into the outer membrane. The polypeptide contains an N-terminal targeting signal which is immediately followed by a localization signal (1). As in *A,* the targeting signal leads to association of the polypeptide with the outer membrane (2), but the localization signal prevents passage through the inner membrane at the contact point (3, 4). The localization signal is a hydrophobic segment similar to the halt-transfer signal of type I membrane proteins. In the figure, the targeting signal of the mature protein is depicted as exposed in the intermembrane space, but this has not been shown, and that part of the protein which forms an amphipatic helix may also be embedded in the outer membrane. The model is based on experimental data obtained for a 70-kDa outer membrane protein (OMP). *C, D.* Two alternative pathways for the incorporation of a protein (such as cytochrome b_2) into the intermembrane space. *C.* In this case, the targeting signal leads to complete translocation of the polypeptide into the matrix, where it is cleaved by the metalloprotease (1–4). This exposes a hydrophobic localization signal which serves as an insertion signal to mediate translocation of the polypeptide across the inner membrane from the matrix to the intermembrane space (4–6). The protein is discharged into the intermembrane space as a result of cleavage of the localization-insertion signal by a second protease that is located on the outer surface of the inner membrane (7). *D.* In this model, the localization signal serves to halt transfer of the polypeptide across the inner membrane (4), which is initiated by the targeting signal (1–3). The polypeptide is discharged into the intermembrane space after cleavage by the second protease (5), as in *C. E, F.* Alternative pathways for the incorporation into mitochondria of a protein such as cytochrome c_1, which is associated with the inner membrane but is largely exposed in the intermembrane space. *E.* The mechanism operates as in *C,* but translocation from the matrix into the intermembrane space is halted (7) before completion by a segment located near the C terminus of the protein. *F.* As in *D,* the localization signal halts translocation into the matrix (4). Before cleavage by the second protease (6), however, the C-terminal region of the polypeptide inserts into the inner membrane (5). (*Based in part on Hager*[436] *and Douglas et al.*[439])

membrane do not contain a cleavable presequence, they appear to contain tandemly arranged targeting and localization signals. In the 70-kDa outer membrane protein of yeast mitochondria, the targeting signal is N-terminal and consists of the first 12 residues which, in chimeric proteins, were capable of targeting a linked polypeptide to the mitochondrial matrix.[493] In this protein, the localization signal seems to consist of a hydrophobic segment that immediately follows the targeting signal and exerts its function by halting transfer of the polypeptide across the outer membrane, preventing its insertion into the inner membrane, as depicted in Fig. 3-23*B*. When the hydrophobic segment was deleted, the resulting modified polypeptide was translocated into the matrix.[453]

Proteins destined to the intermembrane space also contain distinct targeting and localization signals that serve to determine their uptake into the organelle and their subsequent submitochondrial location. The precursors of three proteins of the intermembrane space, cytochrome c peroxidase,[497] cytochrome b_2,[498] and cytochrome c_1,[499] have been characterized and found to contain long presequences that appear to be cleaved off in two steps.[475,500,501] The first cleavage, carried out by the matrix metalloprotease, removes the N-terminal targeting signal. The remainder of the presequence, where the localization signal appears to be contained, is cleaved by an as yet uncharacterized enzyme that is located in the intermembrane space or on the outer face of the inner membrane, and is resistant to chelating agents.[500] The putative localization signals within the presequences of these proteins appear to consist of a stretch of approximately 20 hydrophobic amino acids that are flanked by basic residues.[497–499] These hydrophobic segments could, conceivably, serve as cleavable stop-transfer signals that halt translocation through the inner membrane[480,495] or as insertion signals that, after the proteins are discharged into the matrix, initiate their reexportation to the intermembrane space.[502] These two possibilities are represented in Fig. 3-23*C* to *F*. It is clear tht during the uptake of these proteins into mitochondria, an intermediate precursor is generated that appears to be anchored in the inner membrane by the hydrophobic segment within the presequence, but is largely exposed in the intermembrane space.[475,500] From this precursor, the mature protein is generated by the second cleavage. In the case of cytochrome b_2 (Fig. 3-23*C* and *D*) and the cytochrome c peroxidase, the mature proteins remain free in the intermembrane space. On the other hand, cytochrome c_1 (Fig. 3-23*E* and *F*) is found associated with the outer face of the inner membrane, probably by a second hydrophobic segment near its C terminus.[499,503]

In the case of cytochrome c_1, the targeting and localization domains, located within the 61-amino acid presequence, have been defined by genetic engineering experiments. The N-terminal 16 residues of the presequence were shown to be sufficient to direct other linked polypeptide segments into the matrix.[494] The localization signal was found to occupy the C-terminal region of the presequence, although its boundaries were not strictly defined.

The incorporation of cytochrome b_2 into the intermembrane space was shown to take place in two stages.[475,500] The first stage requires an electrochemical gradient across the inner membrane and leads to cleavage of the targeting signal by the matrix protease. In a subsequent stage a membrane-associated intermediate is exposed on the outer face of the inner membrane, and it is discharged into the intermembrane space as a soluble protein following the second cleavage, which does not require an energized inner membrane.

Although there is disagreement as to whether cytochrome c_1 is first discharged into the matrix space and then reexported[502] or whether its localization signals seem to halt translocation into the matrix,[495] it is well-established that, during its importation into the mitochondrion, the Fe-S protein of the ubiquinol–cytochrome c reductase is indeed first translocated into the matrix.[495,504] This translocation is accompanied by the removal of the N-terminal 24 residues from the 32-residue-long presequence by the chelator-sensitive matrix endoprotease. When this cleavage is prevented, reexportation does not take place, indicating that the localization signal can only operate after the targeting signal is removed. The second cleavage takes place after the protein is exposed on the outer face of the inner membrane.[504]

From a biogenetic perspective, some proteins peripherally associated with the inner mitochondrial membrane, such as subunit IV of cytochrome oxidase or the β subunit of the F_1F_0 ATPase, can be regarded as matrix proteins. After undergoing cleavage of their presequences these polypeptides become part of multimeric complexes that include subunits that are integral components of the inner membrane. As previously mentioned, some of these integral membrane polypeptides are synthesized in mitochondrial ribosomes. However, some proteins of the inner membrane synthesized in cytoplasmic ribosomes are true integral membrane proteins that contain transmembrane hydrophobic segments. This is the case with the ADP-ATP translocator,[456] and with subunit 9 of the F_0F_1 ATPase.[496,505] The former polypeptide is synthesized without a cleavable presequence,[456] whereas the latter undergoes two successive cleavages carried out by matrix proteases.[506]

The ADP-ATP translocator contains several potential transmembrane domains, and there is good evidence that the first of these sequences, located between residues 78 and 98, actually spans the inner membrane in an N (matrix)–to–C (intermembrane space) direction. Chimeric polypeptides containing the first 115 residues of the translocator linked to β-galactosidase are incorporated into the organelle and appear to be associated with the membrane. It has been suggested[456] that a permanent targeting signal is present near the N terminus of the ADP-ATP translocator and that the first hydrophobic segment does not halt translocation in the outer membrane because it is sufficiently distal from the targeting signal as to not prevent the latter from entering the inner membrane. The hydrophobic segment, however, would halt translocation through the inner membrane. This notion is supported by the finding[507] that the stop-transfer signal (transmembrane domain) of the G protein of vesicular stomatitis virus (VSV) halts translocation through the inner mitochondrial membrane, but not through the outer membrane, when it is included in a chimera whose incorporation into the mitochondria is initiated by the targeting signal of ornithine transcarbamylase.

Many important questions remain to be answered concerning the import of proteins into mitochondria, including the identification and characterization of the surface receptors that recognize mitochondrial protein precursors and of the components that effect the translocation process. This may be facilitated in simple eukaryotes by the possibility of obtaining pleiotropic mutants with defects in the importation machinery. The availability of such mutants will permit the cloning of the respective genes. The identification of suppressor mutations in other genes that correct the pleiotropic defects may disclose genes encoding still unrecognized components of the apparatus that effects the uptake and suborganellar sorting of mitochondrial polypeptides.

BIOGENESIS OF PEROXISOMES[508–514]

Peroxisomes are small, membrane-bounded organelles that are present in all eukaryotic cells. They carry out oxidative reactions that generate hydrogen peroxide, and contain the hemoprotein enzyme catalase, which breaks down this reactive product. Peroxisomes were first recognized in electron micrographs as small dense bodies (microbodies) that are surrounded by a single membrane and contain a dense granular matrix. Histochemically, peroxisomes are easily identified by their catalase activity which, during incubation with diaminobenzidine, generates an electron-dense polymerized product. With this reaction, it is apparent that all cells contain small peroxisomes (0.1 to 0.2 μm) (named *microperoxisomes*)[515,516] and that only some cell types, such as hepatocytes and kidney tubule cells, contain large peroxisomes. In many species, peroxisomes are also characterized morphologically by the presence of a crystalline core that is composed of the enzyme urate oxidase (uricase). This enzyme, which functions in the purine degradative pathway to oxidize uric acid to allantoin, is not present in human beings and in other higher primates.

In the thin tissue sections that are examined by transmission electron microscopy, peroxisomes appear as rounded, ovoid, pear-like, or dumbbell-shaped individual bodies. However, three-dimensional reconstructions from serial sections indicate that, within the cell, peroxisomes are interconnected and form an extended network.[517] The existence of a *peroxisomal reticulum*[518] that may undergo a constant remodeling process involving membrane fusion and fission events would have important biogenetic implications since it could easily allow for the redistribution of proteins newly incorporated into the system.

After routine cell fractionation procedures, peroxisomes are recovered in subcellular fractions that are enriched in lysosomes and were known as "light mitochondrial fractions." When animals receive injections of the detergent Triton WX1339 shortly before sacrifice, lysosomes become significantly lighter in density so they can be separated from peroxisomes by isopyknic centrifugation.[519] Methods using sedimentation in metrizamide gradients have yielded highly purified peroxisomes from the livers of untreated animals.[520,521] Such fractions are essential for the rigorous biochemical characterization of the organelle, as well as for studies on its biogenesis.

Mitochondria and peroxisomes play an important role in the metabolism of fatty acids that are taken into the cell or are released from the triglycerides that are stored in cytoplasmic fat droplets. The degradation of fatty acids takes place by the process of β oxidation, which involves the successive removal of acetyl groups from their carboxyl ends.

The mitochondrial and peroxisomal β-oxidation systems carry out similar biochemical reactions but employ different enzymatic components.[522,523] The peroxisomal system consists of three enzymes that carry out four distinct reactions (see Ref. 524). The first reaction is catalyzed by a flavin oxidase (an FAD-containing enzyme), acyl-CoA oxidase, which uses molecular oxygen and generates H_2O_2 as a product. The second and third reactions are carried out by a single bifunctional protein that has enoyl-CoA hydratase and β-hydroxyacyl-CoA dehydrogenase activities. The final reaction in peroxisomal β oxidation involves the cleavage of 3-ketoacyl-CoA by 3-ketoacyl-CoA thiolase to yield acetyl-CoA and a saturated acyl-CoA that has two fewer carbons than the original substrate. It is believed that the peroxisomal β-oxidation system is primarily responsible for the oxidation of very long chain fatty acids and that the shortened products generated in the peroxisome are then efficiently degraded in mitochondria. High levels of the peroxisomal β-oxidation system are induced by various hypolipidemic agents, such as clofibrate,[522] which also lead to an increase in the number of peroxisomes.[525]

Peroxisomes also contain enzymes of the acyl-dihydroxyacetone phosphate (DHAP) pathway (DHAP acyltransferase, alkyl-DHAP synthase, and acyl*L*/alkyl-DHAP oxidoreductase) that catalyze the initial steps in the biosynthesis of glycerol-ether lipids (plasmalogens) (see Ref. 526). Both the β-oxidation enzymes[527,528] and the glycerol-ether lipid biosynthetic enzymes[529] are markedly diminished in patients with the Zellweger syndrome (see below, and Chap. 57), a disease in which the absence in the liver of morphologically distinct peroxisomes has been reported.[530]

The peroxisomes also appear to play an important role in the synthesis of bile acids. They carry out the conversion of 3α,7α,12α-trihydroxy-5β-cholestanoic acid (THCA) into cholic acid and 3α,7α-dihydro-5β-cholestanoic acid into chenodeoxycholic acid.[531,532] The importance of the peroxisomal pathway in bile acid synthesis accounts for the accumulation of THCA and various of its polar metabolites in the serum and bile of patients with Zellweger syndrome.

The Synthesis of Peroxisomal Proteins and Their Incorporation into the Organelle

Early electron-microscopic studies suggested that peroxisomes form by budding from the membranes of smooth endoplasmic reticulum cisternae.[533,534] However, studies on the biosynthesis of liver catalase, utilizing rats in which the newly synthesized catalase polypeptides were labeled in vivo,[535,536] indicated that these are released into the cytosol and only subsequently are taken up into the peroxisomal matrix, without passage through the endoplasmic reticulum. It was shown that, after a brief labeling period, the apomonomer of this hemoprotein was recovered in a nonsedimentable subcellular fraction and that only later did it appear in the peroxisomes. Incorporation of heme and tetramerization into the mature form of catalase took place upon incorporation of the polypeptides into the organelle.[536]

The notion that newly synthesized peroxisomal proteins are incorporated into the peroxisome posttranslationally has received strong support from the finding that several enzymes of the peroxisomal matrix, including urate oxidase,[537] catalase,[538] and the three proteins involved in β oxidation[538–540] are synthesized on free polysomes. The posttranslational incorporation into isolated peroxisomes of catalase and fatty acyl-CoA oxidase synthesized in mRNA-dependent cell-free systems has been achieved and found to be stimulated by the addition of a rat liver cytosolic fraction.[541] Only in the cases of the β-ketoacyl-CoA thiolase[528,540] and acyl-CoA oxidase[541] has the primary translation product been found to be larger than the mature proteins. Comparison of the sequences of the thiolase and of the mature bifunctional protein that effects the second and third reactions of β oxidation with those encoded in cDNA clones for these proteins, definitively established the absence of a cleavable N-terminal extension in the primary translation products.[542,543] Thus, most peroxisomal enzymes do not appear to contain cleavable presequences that could serve as transient signals for the organellar uptake of the polypeptides released from free polysomes.

Although these studies definitively established that proteins of the peroxisomal matrix are synthesized on free polysomes and subsequently transported directly into the organelle, it remained to be determined whether this was also true for proteins of the peroxisomal membrane. In principle, these could be synthesized in the ER by membraned-bound ribosomes, and their incorporation into the peroxisome could involve the budding of vesicles from the endoplasmic reticulum, as suggested by early electron-microscopic studies. The polypeptide composition of rat liver peroxisomal membranes is totally different from those of microsomes and mitochondria,[544] and it has been shown that the three major integral membrane polypeptides of the peroxisome, of as yet unknown function, are synthesized in free polysomes, as products which, apparently, do not undergo posttranslational proteolytic processing.[545–547] In this regard, it is worth noting that the notion that all peroxisomal proteins are synthesized in free polysomes, without the participation of the endoplasmic reticulum, is consistent with the fact that no peroxisomal membrane or matrix protein has been shown to be a glycoprotein. Therefore, it is quite puzzling that, in immunoelectron-microscopic studies, monoclonal antibodies to 3-hydroxy-3-methylglutaryl-CoA (HMG-CoA) reductase, a key glycoprotein enzyme of the cholesterol biosynthetic pathway, label the peroxisomal matrix[548,549] and that substantial levels of HMG-CoA reductase activity can be detected biochemically in the peroxisomal fraction.[549] Moreover, it has been reported that the specific activity of HMG-CoA reductase in the peroxisomal fraction increases markedly after the administration of cholestyramine, a treatment which also raises the levels of the microsomal enzyme, albeit to a lesser extent. The glycoprotein nature of the HMG-CoA reductase found in the endoplasmic reticulum, the major site of the enzyme within the hepatocyte, is well established, but the protein responsible for the peroxisomal activity has not been characterized in this regard. It also remains to be determined whether the monoclonal antibody used to localize the enzyme in peroxisomes was truly specific. If this is the case, the mechanism accounting for the dual localization of HMG-CoA reductase deserves considerable attention.

The incorporation of peroxisomal polypeptides into the organelle, after their discharge from free polysomes into the cytosol, must be determined by specific *targeting signals* within the polypeptides that are recognized by receptors on the organellar surface. The identification of the targeting signal responsible for the incorporation into peroxisomes of the firefly luciferase has recently been accomplished by genetic engineering experiments.[550] It was first shown[551] that the firefly enzyme, which is normally present in the lantern organ of the insect, when synthesized in transfected cultured monkey kidney cells, is incorporated into peroxisomes. This demonstrates the extraordinary degree of evolutionary conservation of the mechanism that effects the sorting of peroxisomal proteins. In subsequent experiments,[550] it was demonstrated that the C-terminal 12 amino acids of luciferase are both necessary and sufficient to ensure the targeting of luciferase or of linked polypeptides to peroxisomes.

Studies on peroxisome biogenesis in yeast, in which the synthesis of peroxisomal enzymes can be induced under conditions that also markedly increase the number of peroxisomes, have been particularly informative. Thus, in the methylotropic yeast *Candida boidinii,* peroxisomes are hardly detectable when the cells are grown on glucose. However, within 15 h after they are transferred to a medium containing methanol,[552] peroxisomes occupy 20 to 80 percent of the cytoplasmic volume. This induction leads to a marked accumulation of peroxisomal enzymes and, in particular, of two enzymes involved in the early steps of methanol metabolism, alcohol oxidase,[553] a homo-octamer flavin-containing enzyme, and dihydroxyacetone synthase.[554] Alcohol oxidase has been shown to be synthesized in free polysomes[555] and pulse-labeling experiments indicate that the monomeric polypeptide is released into the cytosol.[556] Assembly into the octamer and incorporation into the peroxisome occur posttranslationally. Studies within this system[557] have revealed two important features of peroxisomal biogenesis. First, incorporation of the matrix protein alcohol oxidase into the organelle requires the maintenance of a proton gradient, since it is prevented by treatment of the cells with the proton ionophore CCCP. Second, the formation of a complex containing several different peroxisomal polypeptides, including subunits of alcohol oxidase and dihydroxyacetone synthase, may be involved in the incorporation of the matrix proteins into the organelle. Such a complex has been found to be associated with the outer surface of the peroxisome and to accumulate there in cells treated with CCCP.

There is considerable current interest in the process of peroxisome biogenesis because several genetic diseases have been recognized in which the formation of this organelle is either impaired or absent (Chaps. 57 to 60). In some conditions—such as Zellweger cerebrohepatorenal syndrome, neonatal adrenoleukodystrophy, infantile Refsum disease, and hyperpipecolic acidemia—known as generalized *peroxisomal disorders* (see Refs. 558, 559), peroxisomes are lacking or markedly reduced in number and the patients show metabolic defects in all the major biosynthetic peroxisomal pathways. In particular, they fail to synthesize ether lipids or to oxidize long-chain fatty acids and, as previously noted, accumulate bile acid precursors.

The Zellweger syndrome is an autosomal recessive condition, and the generalized disorders are likely to be manifestations of single defects in peroxisomal components essential for normal assembly of the organelle. Thus, fibroblasts from patients with Zellweger syndrome or with the infantile form of Refsum disease appear to synthesize several peroxisomal enzymes at normal rates, including acyl-CoA oxidase and keto-acyl-CoA thiolase, but fail to process normally the precursors of these enzymes, which are rapidly degraded in the cytoplasm.[528] In Zellweger cells, newly synthesized catalase appears to accumulate at normal levels, but remains exclusively cytosolic.[527] Although the existence of a peroxisomal endoprotease has not been directly demonstrated, these observations indicate that the processing of precursors of the peroxisomal matrix proteins normally takes place after their uptake into the organelle.

The finding that in the liver of Zellweger patients a major integral membrane protein normally found in peroxisomes is present in normal amounts and is integrally associated with as yet unidentified membranes[560] has led to the suggestion that the defect in this disease is in the machinery for the importation of matrix proteins. Therefore, the undeveloped organelles lacking their enzymatic content would be morphologically unrecognizable.

In other peroxisomal defects, such as acatalasemia[561] and X-linked adrenoleukodystrophy,[562] specific mutations lead to deficiencies in single enzymatic activities, but peroxisomes are present and appear normal in other functions. Although the recently described pseudo-Zellweger syndrome[563] displays many of the biochemical defects of Zellweger, this condition appears to result from the absence of 3-ketoacyl thiolase. The fact that both long chain fatty acids and abnormal bile acids accumulate in these patients indicates that a single metabolic step involving the thiolase is common to both pathways involved.[564]

Future studies on peroxisome biogenesis are likely to focus on the mechanism for the uptake of proteins into the organelle and on the identification of receptors and soluble factors that participate in this process.

REFERENCES

1. STEINMAN RM, MELLMAN I, MULLER WA, COHN ZA: Endocytosis and the recycling of plasma membrane. *J Cell Biol* 96:1, 1983.
2. SINGER SJ: The fluid mosaic model of membrane structure, in Abrahamsson S, Pascher I (eds): *Structure of Biological Membranes.* New York, Plenum, 1976, p 443.
3. BLOBEL G: Intracellular protein topogenesis. *Proc Natl Acad Sci USA* 77:1496, 1980.
4. ULLRICH A, COUSSENS L, HAYFLICK JS, DULL TJ, GRAY A, TAM AW, LEE J, YARDEN Y, LIBERMANN TA, SCHLESSINGER J, DOWNWARD J, MAYES ELV, WHITTLE N, WATERFIELD MD, SEEBURG PH: Human epidermal growth factor receptor cDNA sequence and aberrant expression of the amplified gene in A431 epidermoid carcinoma cells. *Nature* 309:418, 1984.
5. DOWNWARD J, YARDEN Y, MAYES E, SCRACE G, TOTTY N, STOCKWELL P, ULLRICH A, SCHLESSINGER J, WATERFIELD MD: Close similarity of epidermal growth factor receptor and v-erb B oncogene protein sequences. *Nature* 307:521, 1984.
6. GILL GN, BERTICS PJ, SANTON JB: Epidermal growth factor and its receptor. *Mol Cell Endocrinol* 51:169, 1987.
7. ULLRICH A, BELL JR, CHEN EY, HERRERA R, PETRUZELLI LM, DULL TJ, GRAY A, COUSSENS L, LIAO Y-C, TSUBOKAWA M, MASON A, SEEBURG PH, GRUNFELD C, ROSEN OM, RAMACHANDRAN J: Human insulin receptor and its relationship to the tyrosine kinase family of oncogenes. *Nature* 313:756, 1985.
8. EBINA Y, ELLIS L, JARNAGIN K, EDERY M, GRAF L, CLAUSER E, OU J-H, MASIARZ F, KAN YW, GOLDFINE ID, ROTH RA, RUTTER WJ: The human insulin receptor cDNA: The structural basis for hormone-activated transmembrane signalling. *Cell* 40:747, 1985.

9. ROSEN OM: After insulin binds. *Science* 237:1452, 1987.
10. SABATINI DD, KREIBICH G, MORIMOTO T, ADESNIK M: Mechanisms for incorporation of proteins in membranes and organelles. *J Cell Biol* 92:1, 1982.
11. RAPOPORT TA: Protein translocation across and integration into membranes. *CRC Crit Rev Biochem* 20:73, 1986.
12. STRAUSS AW, BOIME I, KREIL G (eds): *Protein Compartmentalization.* New York, Springer-Verlag, 1986.
13. PALADE G: Intracellular aspects of the process of protein synthesis. *Science* 189:347, 1975.
14. KREIL G: Transfer of proteins across membranes. *Annu Rev Biochem* 50:317, 1981.
15. HORTSCH M, MEYER DI: Pushing the signal hypothesis: What are the limits? *Biol Cell* 52:1, 1984.
16. WICKNER WT, LODISH HF: Multiple mechanisms of protein insertion into and across membranes. *Science* 230:400, 1985.
17. HORTSCH M, MEYER DI: Transfer of secretory proteins through the membrane of the endoplasmic reticulum. *Int Rev Cytol* 102:215, 1986.
18. WALTER P, LINGAPPA VR: Mechanism of protein translocation across the endoplasmic reticulum membrane. *Annu Rev Cell Biol* 2:499, 1986.
19. SABATINI DD, TASHIRO Y, PALADE GE: On the attachment of ribosomes to microsomal membranes. *J Mol Biol* 19:503, 1966.
20. KREIBICH G, DEBEY P, SABATINI DD: Selective release of content from microsomal vesicles without membrane disassembly. I. Permeability changes induced by low detergent concentrations. *J Cell Biol* 58:436, 1973.
21. KREIBICH G, SABATINI DD: Selective release of content from microsomal vesicles without membrane disassembly. II. Electrophoretic and immunological chracterization of microsomal subfractions. *J Cell Biol* 61:789, 1974.
22. KREIBICH G, ULRICH BL, SABATINI DD: Proteins of rough microsomal membranes related to ribosome binding. I. Identification of ribophorins I and II, membrane proteins characteristic of rough microsomes. *J Cell Biol* 77:464, 1978.
23. KREIBICH G, FREIENSTEIN CM, PEREYRA BN, ULRICH BL, SABATINI DD: Proteins of rough microsomal membranes related to ribosome binding. II. Cross-linking of bound ribosomes to the specific membrane proteins exposed at the binding sites. *J Cell Biol* 77:488, 1978.
23a. HORTSCH M, MEYER DI: Immunochemical analysis of rough and smooth microsomes from rat liver. Segregation of docking protein in rough membranes. *Eur J Biochem* 150:559, 1985.
24. LEWIS JA, SABATINI DD: Accessibility of proteins in rat liver-free and membrane-bound ribosomes to lactoperoxidase-catalyzed iodination. *J Biol Chem* 252:5547, 1977.
25. LEWIS JA, SABATINI DD: Proteins of rat liver free and membrane-bound ribosomes: Modification of two large subunit proteins by a factor detached from ribosomes at high ionic strength. *Biochim Biophys Acta* 478:33, 1977.
26. BORGESE D, BLOBEL G, SABATINI DD: In vitro exchange of ribosomal subunits between free and membrane-bound ribosomes. *J Mol Biol* 74:415, 1973.
27. BLOBEL G, SABATINI DD: Ribosome-membrane interaction in eukaryotic cells, in Manson LA (ed): *Biomembranes.* New York, Plenum, 1971, vol 2, p 193.
28. MILSTEIN C, BROWNLEE GG, HARRISON TM, MATHEWS MB: A possible precursor of immunoglobulin light chains. *Nature* 239:117, 1972.
29. SWAN D, AVIV H, LEDER P: Purification and properties of biologically active messenger RNA for a myeloma light chain. *Proc Natl Acad Sci USA* 69:1967, 1972.
30. SCHECHTER I: Biologically and chemically pure mRNA coding for a mouse immunoglobulin L-chain prepared with the aid of antibodies and immobilized oligothymidine. *Proc Natl Acad Sci USA* 70:2256, 1973.
31. BLOBEL G, DOBBERSTEIN B: Transfer of proteins across membranes. I. Presence of proteolytically processed and unprocessed nascent immunoglobulin light chains on membrane-bound ribosomes of murine myeloma. *J Cell Biol* 67:835, 1975.
32. BLOBEL G, DOBBERSTEIN B: Transfer of proteins across membranes. II. Reconstitution of functional rough microsomes from heterologous components. *J Cell Biol* 67:852, 1975.
33. PERLMAN D, HALVORSON HO: A putative signal peptidase recognition site and sequence in eukaryotic and prokaryotic signal peptides. *J Mol Biol* 167:391, 1983.
34. von HEIJNE G: Towards a comparative anatomy of N-terminal topogenic protein sequences. *J Mol Biol* 189:239, 1986.
35. von HEIJNE G: Signal sequences: The limits of variation. *J Mol Biol* 184:99, 1985.
36. WATSON MEE: Compilation of published signal sequences. *Nucleic Acids Res* 12:5145, 1984.
37. REDMAN CM, SABATINI DD: Vectorial discharge of peptides released by puromycin from attached ribosomes. *Proc Natl Acad Sci USA* 56:608, 1966.
38. MALKIN LI, RICH A: Partial resistance of nascent polypeptide chains to proteolytic digestion due to ribosomal shielding. *J Mol Biol* 26:329, 1967.
39. BLOBEL G, SABATINI DD: Controlled proteolysis of nascent polypeptides in rat liver cell fractions. I. Location of the polypeptides within ribosomes. *J Cell Biol* 45:130, 1970.
40. WARREN G, DOBBERSTEIN B: Protein transfer across microsomal membranes reassembled from separated membrane components. *Nature* 273:569, 1978.
41. WALTER P, BLOBEL G: Purification of a membrane-associated protein complex required for protein translocation across the endoplasmic reticulum. *Proc Natl Acad Sci USA* 77:7112, 1980.
42. WALTER P, IBRAHIMI I, BLOBEL G: Translocation of proteins across the endoplasmic reticulum. I. Signal recognition protein (SRP) binds to in vitro assembled polysomes synthesizing secretory proteins. *J Cell Biol* 91:545, 1981.
43. WALTER P, BLOBEL G: Translocation of proteins across the endoplasmic reticulum. II. Signal recognition protein (SRP) mediates the selected binding to microsomal membranes of in-vitro-assembled polysomes synthesizing secretory proteins. *J Cell Biol* 91:551, 1981.
44. WALTER P, BLOBEL G: Translocation of proteins across the endoplasmic reticulum. III. Signal recognition protein (SRP) causes signal sequence-dependent and site-specific arrest of chain elongation that is released by microsomal membranes. *J Cell Biol* 91:557, 1981.
45. GILMORE R, BLOBEL G, WALTER P: Protein translocation across the endoplasmic reticulum. I. Detection in the microsomal membrane of a receptor for a signal recognition particle. *J Cell Biol* 95:463, 1982.
46. GILMORE R, WALTER P, BLOBEL G: Protein translocation across the endoplasmic reticulum. II. Isolation and characterization of the signal recognition particle receptor. *J Cell Biol* 95:477, 1982.
47. WALTER P, GILMORE R, BLOBEL G: Protein translocation across the endoplasmic reticulum. *Cell* 38:5, 1984.
48. MEYER DI, DOBBERSTEIN B: Identification and characterization of a membrane component essential for the translocation of proteins across the membrane of the endoplasmic reticulum. *J Cell Biol* 87:503, 1980.
49. MEYER DI, DOBBERSTEIN B: A membrane component essential for vectorial translocation of nascent proteins across the endoplasmic reticulum: Requirements for its extraction and reassociation with the membrane. *J Cell Biol* 87:498, 1980.
50. MEYER DI, KRAUSE E, DOBBERSTEIN B: Secretory protein translocation across membranes—The role of the "docking protein." *Nature* 297:647, 1982.
51. MEYER DI, LOUVARD D, DOBBERSTEIN B: Characterization of molecules involved in protein translocation using specific antibodies. *J Cell Biol* 92:579, 1982.
52. BORGESE N, MOK W, KREIBICH G, SABATINI DD: Ribosomal-membrane interaction: In vitro binding of ribosomes to microsomal membranes. *J Mol Biol* 88:559, 1974.
53. GILMORE R, BLOBEL G: Transient involvement of signal recognition particle and its receptor in the microsomal membrane prior to protein translocation. *Cell* 35:677, 1983.
54. WIEDMAN M, KURZCHALIA TV, HARTMANN E, RAPOPORT TA: A signal sequence receptor in the endoplasmic reticulum membrane. *Nature* 328:830, 1987.
55. SABATINI DD, BLOBEL G: Controlled proteolysis of nascent polpeptides in rat liver cell fractions II. Location of the polypeptides in rough microsomes. *J Cell Biol* 45:146, 1970.
56. GILMORE R, BLOBEL G: Translocation of secretory proteins across the microsomal membrane occurs through an environment accessible to aqueous perturbants. *Cell* 42:497, 1985.
57. von HEIJNE G, BLOMBERG C: Trans-membrane translocation of proteins (the direct transfer model). *Eur J Biochem* 97:175, 1973.
58. ENGELMAN DM, STEITZ TA: The spontaneous insertion of proteins into and across membranes: The helical hairpin hypothesis. *Cell* 23:411, 1981.
59. FLEISHER S, FLEISHER B (eds): *Membrane Biogenesis: Assembly and Targeting. Methods in Enzymology,* New York, Academic, 1983, vol 96, part J.
60. SCHEELE G: Methods for the study of protein translocation across the RER membrane using the reticulocyte lysate translocation system and canine pancreatic microsomal membranes. *Methods Enzymol* 96:94, 1983.
61. von HEIJNE G: How signal sequences maintain cleavage specificity. *J Mol Biol* 173:243, 1984.
62. von HEIJNE G: Structural and thermodynamic aspects of the transfer of proteins into and across membranes, in Knauf PA, Cook JS (eds): *Current Topics in Membranes and Transport.* New York, Academic, 1985, vol 24, p 151.

63. von HEIJNE G: A new method for predicting signal sequence cleavage sites. *Nucleic Acid Res* 14:4683, 1986.

64. KAISER CA, PREUSS D, GRISAFI P, BOTSTEIN D: Many random sequences functionally replace the secretion signal sequence of yeast invertase. *Science* 235:312, 1987.

65. SZCZESNA-SKORUPA E, MEAD DA, KEMPER B: Mutations in the NH_2-terminal domain of the signal peptide of preproparathyroid hormone inhibit translocation without affecting interaction with signal recognition particle. *J Biol Chem* 262:8896, 1987.

66. INOUYE M, HALEGOUA S: Secretion and membrane localization of proteins in Escherichia coli. *CRC Crit Rev Biochem* 7:339, 1980.

67. INOUYE S, SOBERON X, FRANCESCHINI T, NAKAMURA K, ITAKURA K, INOUYE M: Role of positive charge on the amino-terminal region of the signal peptide in protein secretion across the membrane. *Proc Natl Acad Sci USA* 79:3438, 1982.

68. von HEIJNE G: Patterns of amino acids near signal sequence cleavage sites. *Eur J Biochem* 133:17, 1983.

69. WIREN KM, FREEMAN MW, POTTS JT Jr KRONENBERG HM: Preproparathyroid hormone: A model for analyzing the secretory pathway. *Recent Prog Horm Res* 42:641, 1986.

70. EMR SD, SILHAVY TJ: Molecular components of the signal sequences that function in the initiation of protein export. *J Cell Biol* 95:689, 1982.

71. BEDOUELLE H, BASSFORD PJ Jr, FOWLER AV, ZABIN I, BECKWITH J, HOFNUNG M: Mutations which alter the function of the signal of the maltose binding protein of Escherichia coli. *Nature* 285:78, 1980.

72. PALMITER RD, GAGNON J, WALSH KA: Ovalbumin: A secreted protein without a transient hydrophobic leader sequence. *Proc Natl Acad Sci US* 75:94, 1978.

73. MEEK RL, WALSH K, PALMITER RD: The signal sequence of ovalbumin is located near the NH_2-terminus. *J Biol Chem* 257:12245, 1982.

74. TABE L, KRIEG P, STRACHAN R, JACKSON D, WALLIS E, COLMAN A: Segregation of mutant ovalbumins and ovalbumin-globin fusion proteins in Xenopus oocytes. Identification of an ovalbumin signal sequence. *J Mol Biol* 180:645, 1984.

75. BONATTI S, BLOBEL G: Absence of a cleavable signal sequence in Sindbis virus glycoproteins PE2. *J Biol Chem* 254:12261, 1979.

76. GAROFF H, FRISCHAUF AM, SIMONS K, LEHRACH H, DELIUS H: Nucleotide sequence of cDNA coding for Semliki Forest Virus membrane glycoproteins. *Nature* 288:236, 1980.

77. GAROFF H: Using recombinant DNA techniques to study protein targeting in the eucaryotic cell. *Annu Rev Cell Biol* 1:403, 1985.

78. WALTER P, BLOBEL G: Subcellular distribution of signal recognition particle and 7SL-RNA determined with polypeptide-specific antibodies and complementary DNA probe. *J Cell Biol* 97:1693, 1983.

79. WALTER P, BLOBEL G: Signal recognition particle contains a 7S RNA essential for protein translocation across the endoplasmic reticulum. *Nature* 299:691, 1982.

80. GUNDELFINGER ED, KRAUSE E, MELLI M, DOBBERSTEIN B: The organization of the 7SL RNA in the signal recognition particle. *Nucleic Acids Res* 11:7363, 1983.

81. WALTER P, BLOBEL G: Disassembly and reconstitution of signal recognition particle. *Cell* 34:525, 1983.

82. SIEGEL V, WALTER P: Elongation arrest is not a prerequisite for secretory protein translocation across the microsomal membrane. *J Cell Biol* 100:1913, 1985.

83. SIEGEL V, WALTER P: Each of the activities of signal recognition particle (SRP) is contained within a distinct domain: Analysis of biochemical mutants of SRP. *Cell* 52:39, 1988.

84. WIEDMANN M, KURZCHALIA TV, BIELKA H, RAPOPORT TA: Direct probing of the interaction between the signal sequence of nascent preprolactin and the signal recognition particle by specific cross-linking. *J Cell Biol* 104:201, 1987.

85. TAJIMA S, LAUFFER L, RATH VL, WALTER P: The signal recognition particle receptor is a complex that contains two distinct polypeptide chains. *J Cell Biol* 103:1167, 1986.

86. LAUFFER L, GARCIA PD, HARKINS RN, COUSSENS L, ULLRICH A, WALTER P: Topology of signal recognition particle receptor in endoplasmic reticulum membrane. *Nature* 318:334, 1985.

87. JACKSON RC, BLOBEL G: Post-translational cleavage of presecretory proteins with an extract of rough microsomes from dog pancreas containing signal peptidase activity. *Proc Natl Acad Sci USA* 74:5598, 1977.

88. ROTHMAN JE, LODISH HF: Synchronized transmembrane insertion and glycosylation of a nascent membrane protein. *Nature* 269:775, 1977.

89. JACKSON RC, WHITE WR: Phospholipid is required for the processing of presecretory proteins by detergent-solubilized canine pancreatic signal peptidase. *J Biol Chem* 256:2545, 1981.

90. MUMFORD RA, STRAUSS AW, POWERS JC, PIERZCHALA PA, NISHINO N, ZIMMERMAN M: A zinc metalloendopeptidase associated with dog pancreatic membranes. *J Cell Biol* 255:2227, 1980.

91. WALTER P, JACKSON RC, MARCUS MM, LINGAPPA VR, BLOBEL G: Tryptic dissection and reconstitution of translocation activity for nascent presecretory proteins across microsomal membranes. *Proc Natl Acad Sci USA* 76:1795, 1979.

92. EVANS EA, GILMORE R, BLOBEL G: Purification of the microsomal signal peptidase as a complex. *Proc Natl Acad Sci USA* 83:581, 1986.

93. ADELMAN MR, SABATINI DD, BLOBEL G: Ribosome-membrane interaction: Non-destructive disassembly of rat liver rough microsomes into ribosomal and microsomal components. *J Cell Biol* 56:206, 1973.

94. SABATINI DD, OJAKIAN G, LANDE MA, LEWIS J, MOK W, ADESNIK M, KREIBICH G: Structural and functional aspects of the protein synthesizing apparatus in the rough endoplasmic reticulum, in Meints RS, Davies E (eds): *Control Mechanisms in Development*. New York, Plenum, 1975, p 151.

95. KREIBICH G, BAR-NUN S, CZAKO-GRAHAM M, MOK W, NACK E, OKADA Y, ROSENFELD MG, SABATINI DD: The role of free and membrane-bound polysomes in organelle biogenesis, in Bucher T, Sebald W, Weiss H (eds): *Biological Chemistry of Organelle Formation*. Colloquium der Gesellschaft für Biologische Chemie 14–19 April 1980, in Mosbach/Baden. Berlin, Heidelberg, Springer-Verlag, 1980, p 147.

96. AMAR-COSTESEC A, TODD JA, KREIBICH G: Segregation of the polypeptide translocation apparatus to regions of the endoplasmic reticulum containing ribophorins and ribosomes. I. Functional tests on rat liver microsomal subfractions. *J Cell Biol* 99:2247, 1984.

97. KREIBICH G, MARCANTONIO EE, SABATINI DD: Ribophorins I and II: Membrane proteins characteristic of the rough endoplasmic reticulum. *Methods Enzymol* 96:520, 1983.

98. HARNIK-ORT V, PRAKASH K, COLMAN DR, ROSENFELD MG, ADESNIK M, SABATINI DD, KREIBICH G: Isolation and characterization of cDNA clones for rat ribophorin I: Complete coding sequence and in vitro synthesis and insertion of the encoded product into endoplasmic reticulum membranes. *J Cell Biol* 104:885, 1987.

99. CRIMAUDO C, HORTSCH M, GAUSEPOHL H, MEYER DI: Human ribophorins I and II: The primary structure and membrane topology of two highly conserved rough endoplasmic reticulum-specific glycoproteins. *EMBO J* 6:75, 1987.

100. TODD JA, SABATINI DD, KREIBICH G: An 83 Kd polypeptide is a component of the protein translocation apparatus of the rough endoplasmic reticulum. *J Cell Biol* 99:2a, 1984.

101. HORTSCH M, AVOSSA D, MEYER DI: Characterization of secretory protein translocation: Ribosome-membrane interaction in endoplasmic reticulum. *J Cell Biol* 103:241, 1986.

102. ALT FW, BOTHWELL ALM, KNAPP M, SIDEN E, MATHER E, KOSHLAND M, BALTIMORE D: Synthesis of secreted and membrane-bound immunoglobulin Mu heavy chains is directed by mRNAs that differ at their 3′ ends. *Cell* 20:293, 1980.

103. ROGERS J, EARLY P, CARTER C, CALAME K, BOND M, HOOD L, WALL R: Two mRNAs with different 3′ ends encode membrane-bound and secreted forms of immunoglobulin Mu chain. *Cell* 20:303, 1980.

104. EARLY P, ROGERS J, DAVIS M, CALAME K, BOND M, WALL R, HOOD L: Two mRNAs can be produced from a single immunoglobulin u gene by alternative RNA processing pathways. *Cell* 20:313, 1980.

105. GETHING M-J, SAMBROOK J: Construction of influenza haemagglutinin genes that code for intracellular and secreted forms of the protein. *Nature* 300:598, 1982.

106. ROSE JK, BERGMANN JE: Expression from cloned cDNA of cell-surface secreted forms of the glycoprotein of vesicular stomatitis virus in eucaryotic cells. *Cell* 30:753, 1982.

107. RIZZOLO LJ, FINIDORI J, GONZALEZ A, ARPIN M, IVANOV IE, ADESNIK M, SABATINI DD: Biosynthesis and intracellular sorting of growth hormone-viral envelope glycoprotein hybrids. *J Cell Biol* 101:1351, 1985.

108. ADAMS GA, ROSE JK: Incorporation of a charged amino acid into the membrane-spanning domain blocks cell-surface transport but not membrane anchoring of a viral glycoprotein. *Mol Cell Biol* 5:14442, 1985.

109. CUTLER DF, GAROFF H: Mutants of the membrane-binding region of Semliki Forest Virus E2 protein. I. Cell surface transport and fusogenic activity. *J Cell Biol* 102:889, 1986.

110. CUTLER DF, MELANCON P, GAROFF H: Mutants of the membrane-binding region of Semliki Forest Virus E2 protein. II. Topology and membrane binding. *J Cell Biol* 102:902, 1986.

111. ZUNIGA MC, HOOD LE: Clonal variation in cell surface display of an H-2 protein lacking a cytoplasmic tail. *J Cell Biol* 102:1, 1986.

111a. SPIESS M, LODISH HF: An internal signal sequence: The aisaloglycoprotein receptor membrane anchor. *Cell* 44:177, 1986.

112. SCHNEIDER C, OWEN MJ, BANVILLE D, WILLIAMS JG: Primary structure of

human transferrin receptor deduced from the mRNA sequence. *Nature* 311:675, 1984.

113. ZERIAL M, MELANCON P, SCHNEIDER C, GAROFF H: The transmembrane segment of the human transferrin receptor functions as a signal peptide. *EMBO J* 5:1543, 1986.

114. HUNZIKER W, SPIESS M, SEMENZA G, LODISH HF: The sucrase-isomaltase complex: Primary structure, membrane-orientation, and evolution of a stalked, intrinsic brush border protein. *Cell* 46:227, 1986.

115. BLOK J, EAR GM, LAVER WG, WARD CW, LILLEY GG, WOODS EF, ROXBURGH CM, INGLIS AS: Studies on the size, chemical composition and partial sequence of the neuraminidase (NA) from type A influenza virus shows that the N-terminal region of the NA is not processed and serves to anchor the NA in the viral membrane. *Virology* 119:109, 1982.

116. FIELDS SG, WINTER G, BROWNLEE GG: Structure of the neuraminidase gene in human influenza virus. *Nature* 290:213, 1981.

117. BOS TJ, DAVIS AR, NAYAK DP: NH_2-terminal hydrophobic region of influenza virus neuraminidase provides the signal function in translocation. *Proc Natl Acad Sci USA* 81:2327, 1984.

118. MIZE NK, ANDREWS DW, LINGAPPA VR: A stop transfer sequence recognizes receptors for nascent chain translocation across the endoplasmic reticulum membrane. *Cell* 47:711, 1986.

119. ZERIAL M, HUYLEBROECK D, GAROFF H: Foreign transmembrane peptides replacing the internal signal sequence of transferrin receptor allow its translocation and membrane binding. *Cell* 48:147, 1987.

120. FINIDORI J, RIZZOLO L, GONZALEZ A, KREIBCH G, ADESNIK M, SABATINI DD: The influenza haemagglutinin insertion signal is not cleaved and does not halt translocation when presented to the endoplasmic reticulum membrane as part of a translocating polypeptide. *J Cell Biol* 104:1705, 1987.

121. NATHANS J, HOGNESS DS: Isolation, sequence analysis, and intron-exon arrangement of the gene encoding bovine rhodopsin. *Cell* 34:807, 1983.

122. DIXON RAF, KOBILKA BK, STRADER DJ, BENOVIC JL, DOHLMAN HG, FRIELLE T, BOLANOWSKI MA, BENNETT CD, RANDS E, DIEHL RE, MUMFORD RA, SLATER EE, SIGAL IS, CARON MG, LEFKOWITZ RJ, STRADER CD: Cloning of the gene and cDNA for mammalian β-adrenergic receptor and homology with rhodopsin. *Nature* 321:75, 1986.

123. YARDEN Y, RODRIGUEZ H, WONG SK-F, BRANDT DR, MAY DC, BURNIER J, HARKINS RN, CHEN EY, RAMACHANDRAN J, ULLRICH A, ROSS EM: The avian β-adrenergic receptor: Primary structure and membrane topology. *Proc Natl Acad Sci USA* 83:6795, 1986.

124. FRIEDLANDER M, BLOBEL G: Bovine opsin has more than one signal sequence. *Nature* 318:338, 1985.

125. AUDIGIER Y, FRIEDLANDER M, BLOBEL G: Multiple topogenic sequences in bovine opsin. *Proc Natl Acad Sci USA* 84:5783, 1987.

126. SAKAGUCHI M, MIHARA K, SATO R: A short amino terminal segment of microsomal cytochrome P-450 functions both as an insertion signal and a stop-transfer sequence. *EMBO J* 6:2425, 1987.

127. MONIER S, VAN LUC P, KREIBICH G, SABATINI DD, ADESNIK M: Signals for the incorporation and orientation of cytochrome P450 in the ER membrane. *J Cell Biol* (in press).

128. PORTER TD, KASPER CB: Coding nucleotide sequence of rat NADPH-cytochrome P-450 oxidoreductase cDNA and identification of flavin-binding domains. *Proc Natl Acad Sci USA* 82:973, 1985.

129. LENNARZ WJ (ed): *Biochemistry of Glycoproteins and Proteoglycans.* New York, Plenum, 1980.

130. HUBBARD SC, IVATT RJ: Synthesis and processing of asparagine-linked oligosaccharides. *Annu Rev Biochem* 50:555, 1981.

131. KORNFELD R, KORNFELD S: Assembly of asparagine-linked oligosaccharides. *Annu Rev Biochem* 54:664, 1985.

132. HIRSCHBERG CB, SNIDER MD: Topography of glycosylation in the rough endoplasmic reticulum and Golgi apparatus. *Annu Rev Biochem* 56:63, 1987.

133. MARSHALL RD: The nature and metabolism of the carbohydrate-peptide linkages of glycoproteins. *Biochem Soc Symp* 40:17, 1974.

134. STRUCK DK, LENNARZ WJ: The function of saccharide-lipids in synthesis of glycoproteins, in Lennarz W (ed): *The Biochemistry of Glycoproteins and Proteoglycans.* New York, Plenum, 1980, p 35.

135. KRONQUIST KE, LENNARZ WJ: Enzymatic conversions of proteins to glycoproteins by lipid-linked saccharides: A study of potential exogenous acceptor proteins. *J Supramolec Struct* 8:51, 1978.

136. ATKINSON PH, LEE JT: Co-translational excision of alpha-glucose and alpha-mannose in nascent vesicular stomatitis virus G protein. *J Cell Biol* 98:2245, 1984.

137. ROSENFELD MG, MARCANTONIO EE, HAKIMI J, ORT VM, ATKINSON PH, SABATINI DD, KREIBICH G: Biosynthesis and processing of ribophorins in the endoplasmic reticulum. *J Cell Biol* 99:1076, 1984.

138. LISCUM L, CUMMINGS RD, ANDERSON RG, DeMARTINO GN, GOLDSTEIN JL, BROWN MS: 3-Hydroxy-3-methyglutaryl-CoA reductase: A transmembrane glycoprotein of the endoplasmic reticulum with N-linked "high-mannose" oligosaccharides. *Proc Natl Acad Sci USA* 80:7165, 1983.

139. TARENTINO AL, MALEY F: Purification and properties of an endo-β-N-acetylglucosaminidase from Streptomyces griseus. *J Biol Chem* 249:811, 1974.

140. TARENTINO AL, PLUMMER TH, MALEY F: The release of intact oligosaccharides from specific glycoproteins by endo-β-N-acetylglucosaminidase H. *J Biol Chem* 249:818, 1974.

141. MURAMATSU T, ATKINSON PH, NATHENSON SG, CECCARINI C: Cell-surface glycopeptides: Growth-dependent changes in the carbohydrate-peptide linkage region. *J Mol Biol* 80:781, 1973.

142. MIZUOCHI T, AMANO J, KOBATA A: New evidence of the substrate specificity of endo-β1-N-acetylglucosaminidase D. *J Biochem (Tokyo)* 95:1209, 1984.

143. PLUMMER TH, ELDER JH, ALEXANDER S, PHELAN AW, TARENTINO AL: Demonstration of peptide: N-glycosidase F activity in endo-β-N-acetylglucosaminidase F preparations. *J Biol Chem* 259:10700, 1984.

144. FARQUHAR MG: Progress in unraveling pathways of Golgi traffic. *Annu Rev Cell Biol* 1:447, 1985.

145. PELHAM HRB: Speculations on the functions of the major heat shock and glucose-regulated proteins. *Cell* 46:959, 1986.

146. ROTHMAN JE: Protein sorting by selective retention by ER and Golgi stack. *Cell* 50:521, 1987.

147. PFEFFER SR, ROTHMAN JE: Biosynthetic protein transport and sorting by the endoplasmic reticulum and Golgi. *Annu Rev Biochem* 56:829, 1987.

148. JAMIESON JD, PALADE GE: Intracellular transport of secretory proteins in the pancreatic exocrine cell. I. Role of the peripheral elements of the Golgi complex. *J Cell Biol* 34:577, 1967.

149. JAMIESON JD, PALADE GE: Intracellular transport of secretory proteins in the pancreatic exocrine cell. II. Transport to condensing vacuoles and zymogen granules. *J Cell Biol* 34:597, 1967.

150. BAINTON DF, FARQUHAR MG: Segregation and packaging of granule enzymes in eosinophilic leukocytes. *J Cell Biol* 45:54, 1970.

151. GEUZE JJ, SLOT JW, TOKUYASU KT, GOEDEMANS WEM, GRIFFITH JM: Immunocytochemical localization of amylase and chymotrypsinogen in the exocrine pancreatic cell with special attention to the Golgi complex. *J Cell Biol* 82:697, 1979.

152. JAMIESON JD, PALADE GE: Intracellular transport of secretory proteins in the pancreatic exocrine cell. IV. Metabolic requirements. *J Cell Biol* 39:589, 1968.

153. TARTAKOFF A, VASSALLI P: Plasma cell immunoglobulin secretion: Arrest is accompanied by alterations of the Golgi complex. *J Exp Med* 146:1332, 1977.

154. GODELAINE D, SPIRO MJ, SPIRO RG: Processing of the carbohydrate units of thyroglobulin. *J Biol Chem* 256:10161, 1981.

155. BALCH WE, ELLIOT MM, KELLER DS: ATP-coupled transport of vesicular stomatitis virus G protein between the endoplasmic reticulum and the Golgi. *J Cell Biol* 261:14681, 1986.

156. BALCH WE, KELLER DS: ATP-coupled transport of vesicular stomatitis virus G protein: Functional boundaries of secretory compartments. *J Biol Chem* 261:14690, 1986.

157. TARTAKOFF AM: Temperature and energy dependence of secretory protein transport in the exocrine pancreas. *EMBO J* 5:1477, 1986.

158. BALCH WE, WAGNER KR, KELLER DS: Reconstitution of transport of vesicular stomatitis virus G protein from the endoplasmic reticulum to the Golgi complex using a cell-free system. *J Cell Biol* 104:749, 1987.

159. BECKERS CJM, KELLER DS, BALCH WE: Semi-intact cells permeable to macromolecules: Use in reconstitution of protein transport from the ER to the Golgi complex. *Cell* 50:523, 1987.

160. LODISH HF, KONG N, HIRANI S, RASMUSSEN J: A vesicular intermediate in the transport of hepatoma secretory proteins from the rough endoplasmic reticulum to the Golgi complex. *J Cell Biol* 104:221, 1987.

161. LODISH HF, KONG N, SNIDER M, STROUS GJAM: Hepatoma secretory proteins migrate from the rough endoplasmic reticulum to Golgi at characteristic rates. *Nature* 304:80, 1983.

162. FITTING T, KABAT D: Evidence for a glycoprotein "signal" involved in transport between subcellular organelles: Two membrane glycoproteins encoded by murine leukemia virus reach the cell surface at different rates. *J Biol Chem* 257:14011, 1982.

163. FRIES E, GUSTAFSSON L, PETERSON PA: Four secretory proteins synthesized by hepatocytes are transported from endoplasmic reticulum to Golgi complex at different rates. *EMBO J* 3:147, 1984.

164. SCHEELE G, TARTAKOFF A: Exit of nonglycosylated secretory proteins from the rough endoplasmic reticulum is asynchronous in the exocrine pancreas. *J Biol Chem* 260:926, 1985.

165. BERGMANN JE, TOKUYASU KT, SINGER SJ: Passage of an integral membrane protein, the vesicular stomatitis virus glycoprotein, through the

Golgi apparatus en route to the plasma membrane. *Proc Natl Acad Sci USA* 78:1746, 1981.

166. BERGMANN JE, SINGER SJ: Immuno-electron microscopic studies of the intracellular transport of the membrane glycoprotein (G) of vesicular stomatitis virus in infected Chinese hamster ovary cells. *J Cell Biol* 97:1777, 1983.

167. WIELAND FT, GLEASON ML, SERAFINI TA, ROTHMAN JE: The rate of bulk flow from the endoplasmic reticulum to the cell surface. *Cell* 50:289, 1987.

168. LUSIS AG, PAIGEN K: Mechanisms involved in the intracellular localization of mouse glucuronidase, in Ratazzi MC, Scandelius JG, Whitt JS (eds): *Isozymes: Current Topics in Biological and Medical Research.* New York, AR Liss, 1977, vol 2, p 63.

169. SWANK RT, PAIGEN K: Biochemical and genetic evidence for a macromolecular β-glucuronidase complex in microsomal membranes. *J Mol Biol* 77:371, 1973.

170. MEDDA S, STEVENS AM, SWANK RT: Involvement of the esterase active site of egasyn in compartmentalization of β-glucuronidase within the endoplasmic reticulum. *Cell* 50:301, 1987.

171. MEDDA S, TAKEUCHI K, DEVORE-CARTES D, von DEIMLING O, HEYMANN E, SWANK RT: An accessory protein identical to mouse egasyn is complexed with rat microsomal β-glucuronidase and is identical to rat esterase-3. *J Biol Chem* 262:7248, 1987.

172. MUNRO S, PELHAM HRB: An hsp70-like protein in the ER: Identity with the 78 kD glucose-regulated protein and immunoglobulin heavy chain-binding protein. *Cell* 46:291, 1986.

173. MUNRO S, PELHAM HRB: A C-terminal signal prevents secretion of luminal ER proteins. *Cell* 48:899, 1987.

174. PAABO S, BHAT BM, WOLD WSM, PETERSON PA: A short sequence in the COOH-terminus makes an adenovirus membrane glycoprotein a resident of the endoplasmic reticulum. *Cell* 50:311, 1987.

175. SEVERINSSON L, PETERSON PA: Abrogation of cell surface expression of human class I transplantation antigens by an adenovirus protein in Xenopus laevis oocytes. *J Cell Biol* 101:540, 1985.

176. WIEDMANN M, HUTH A, RAPOPORT TA: Xenopus oocytes can secrete bacterial beta-lactamase. *Nature* 309:637, 1984.

177. CARLIN BE, MERLIE JP: Assembly of multisubunit membrane proteins, in Strauss AW, Boime I, Kreil G (eds.): *Protein Compartmentalization.* New York, Springer-Verlag, 1986, p 71.

178. MAINS PE, SIBLEY CH: The requirement of light chain for the surface deposition of the heavy chain of immunoglobulin M. *J Biol Chem* 258:5027, 1982.

179. SEGE K, RASK L, PETERSON PA: Role of β_2-microglobulin in the intracellular processing of HLA antigens. *Biochemistry* 20:4523, 1981.

180. SEVERINSSON L, PETERSON PA: β_2-microglobulin induces intracellular transport of human class I transplantation antigen heavy chains in Xenopus laevis oocytes. *J Cell Biol* 99:226, 1984.

181. KREIS TE, LODISH HF: Oligomerization is essential for transport of vesicular stomatitis viral glycoprotein to the cell surface. *Cell* 46:929, 1986.

182. COPELAND CS, DORNS RW, BOLZAU EM, WEBSTER RG, HELENIUS A: Assembly of influenza hemagglutinin trimers and its role in intracellular transport. *J Cell Biol* 103:1179, 1986.

183. GETHING MJ, MCCAMMON K, SAMBROOK J: Expression of wild type and mutant forms of influenza haemagglutinin: The role of folding and intracellular transport. *Cell* 46:939, 1986.

184. PERLMUTTER DH, KAY RM, COLE FS, ROSSING TH, Van THIEL D, COLTEN HR: The cellular defect in alpha$_1$-proteinase inhibitor (alpha$_1$-PI) deficiency is expressed in human monocytes and in Xenopus oocytes injected with human liver mRNA. *Proc Natl Acad Sci USA* 82:6918, 1985.

185. MOSMANN TR, WILLIAMSON AR: Structural mutations in a mouse immunoglobulin light chain resulting in the failure to be secreted. *Cell* 20:283, 1980.

186. HAAS IG, WABL M: Immunoglobulin heavy chain binding protein. *Nature* 306:387, 1983.

187. BOLE DG, HENDERSHOT LM, KEARNEY JF: Posttranslational association of immunoglobulin heavy chain binding protein with nascent heavy chains in nonsecreting and secreting hybridomas. *J Cell Biol* 102:1558, 1986.

188. HENDERSHOT L, BOLE D, KOHLER G, KEARNEY JF: Assembly and secretion of heavy chains that do not associate postranslationally with immunoglobulin heavy chain-binding proteins. *J Cell Biol* 104:761, 1987.

189. MORRISON SL, SCHARFF MD: Heavy chain-producing variants of a mouse myeloma cell line. *J Immunol* 114:655, 1975.

190. SEFTON BM, BUSS JE: The covalent modification of eukaryotic proteins by lipids. *J Cell Biol* 104:1449, 1987.

191. OLSON EN: Structure, function and biosynthesis of fatty acid–acetylated proteins, in Strauss AW, Boime I, Kreil G, (eds): *Protein Compartmentalization.* New York, Springer-Verlag, 1986, p 87.

192. WILCOX C, HU JS, OLSON EN: Acylation of proteins with myristic acid occurs cotranslationally. *Science* 238:1275, 1987.

193. PELLMAN D, GARBER EA, CROSS FR, HANAFUSA H: An N-terminal peptide from p60^{src} can direct myristylation and plasma membrane localization when fused to heterologous proteins. *Nature* 314:374, 1985.

194. CROSS FR, GARBER EA, PELLMAN D, HANAFUSA H: A short sequence in the p60^{src} N terminus is required for p60^{src} myristylation and membrane association and for cell transformation. *Mol Cell Biol* 4:1834, 1984.

195. KAMPS MP, BUSS JE, SEFTON BM: Rous sarcoma virus transforming protein lacking myristic acid phosphorylates most known polypeptide substrates without inducing transformation. *Cell* 45:105, 1986.

196. OZOLS J, CARR SA, STRITTMATTER P: Identification of the NH_2-terminal blocking group of NADH-cytochrome b5 reductase as myristic acid and the complete amino acid sequence of the membrane binding domain. *J Biol Chem* 259:13349, 1984.

197. LOHMANN SM, WALTER U: Regulation of the cellular and subcellular concentrations and distribution of cyclic nucleotide-dependent protein kinases. *Adv Cyclic Nucleotide Protein Phosphorylation Res* 18:63, 1984.

198. BUSS JE, SEFTON BM: Direct identification of palmitic acid as the lipid attached to p21 ras. *Mol Cell Biol* 6:116, 1986.

199. WILLUMSEN BM, NORRIS K, PAPAGEORGE AG, HUBBERT NL, LOWRY DR: Harvey murine sarcoma virus p21^{ras} protein: Biological and biochemical significance of the cysteine nearest the carboxy terminus. *EMBO J* 3:2581, 1984.

200. STAUFENBIEL M, LAZARIDES E: Anchyrin is fatty acid acylated in erythrocytes. *Proc Natl Acad Sci USA* 83:318, 1986.

201. BENNETT V: The membrane skeleton of human erythrocytes and its implications for more complex cells. *Annu Rev Biochem* 54:273, 1985.

202. CROSS GAM: Eukaryotic protein modification and membrane attachment via phosphatidyl inositol. *Cell* 48:179, 1987.

203. LOW MG, SALTIEL AR: Structural and functional roles of glycosyl-phosphatidly inositol in membranes. *Science* 239:268, 1988.

204. BANGS JD, GIRALD D, KRAKOW JL, HART GW, ENGLUND PT: Rapid processing of the carboxyl terminus of a trypanosome variant surface glycoprotein. *Proc Natl Acad Sci USA* 82:3207, 1985.

205. CARAS IW, WEDDELL GN, DAVITZ MA, NUSSENZWEIG V, MARTIN DW: Signal for the attachment of a phospholipid membrane anchor in Decay Accelerating Factor. *Science* 238:1280, 1987.

206. PANGBURN MK, SCHREIBER RD, MULLER-EBERHARD HJ: Deficiency of an erythrocyte membrane protein with complement regulatory activity in paroxysmal nocturnal hemoglobinuria. *Proc Natl Acad Sci USA* 80:5430, 1983.

207. NICHOLSON-WELLER A, MARCH JP, ROSENFELD SI, AUSTEN KF: Affected erythrocytes of patients with paroxysmal nocturnal hemoglobinuria are deficient in the complement regulatory protein, decay accelerating factor. *Proc Natl Acad Sci USA* 80:5066, 1983.

208. CHOW F-L, HALL SE, ROSSE WF, TELEN MJ: Separation of the acetylcholinesterase-deficient red cells in paroxysmal nocturnal hemoglobinuria. *Blood* 67:893, 1986.

209. MEDOF ME, GOTTLIEB A, KINOSHITA T, HALL S, SILBER R, NUSSENZWEIG V, ROSSE WF: Relationship between decay acceleration factor deficiency, diminished acetyl cholinesterase activity, and defective terminal complement pathway restriction in paroxysmal nocturnal hemoglobinuria erythrocytes. *J Clin Invest* 80:165, 1987.

210. SCHMIDT MFG, SCHLESINGER MJ: Relation of fatty acid attachment to the translation and maturation of vesicular stomatitis and Sindbis virus membrane glycoproteins. *J Biol Chem* 255:3334, 1980.

211. OMARI MB, TROWBRIDGE IS: Biosynthesis of the human transferrin receptor in cultured cells: *J Biol Chem* 256:12888, 1981.

212. PILLAI S, BALTIMORE D: Myristylation and post-translational acquisition of hydrophobicity by the membrane immunoglobulin heavy chain polypeptide in B lymphocytes. *Proc Natl Acad Sci USA* 84:7654, 1987.

213. HEDO JA, COLLIER E, WATKINSON A: Myristyl and palmityl acylation of the insulin receptor. *J Biol Chem* 262:954, 1987.

214. FARQUHAR MG, PALADE GE: The Golgi apparatus (complex)—(1954–1981)—From artifact to center stage. *J Cell Biol* 91:77s, 1981.

215. TARTAKOFF AM: The confined function model of the Golgi complex: Center for ordered processing of biosynthetic products of the rough endoplasmic reticulum. *Int Rev Cytol* 85:221, 1983.

216. GRIFFITHS G, SIMONS K: The trans Golgi network: Sorting at the exit site of the Golgi complex. *Science* 234:438, 1986.

217. HERZOG V, FARQUHAR MG: Luminal membrane retrieved after exocytosis reaches most Golgi cisternae in secretory cells. *Proc Natl Acad Sci USA* 74:5073, 1977.

218. FARQUHAR MG: Recovery of surface membrane in anterior pituitary cells. Variations in traffic detected with anionic and cationic ferritin. *J Cell Biol* 77:R35, 1978.

219. FARQUHAR MG: Membrane recycling in secretory cells: Implications for traffic of products and specialized membranes within the Golgi complex. *Methods Cell Biol* 23:399, 1981.

220. FARQUHAR MG: Membrane recycling in secretory cells: Pathways to the Golgi complex. *Ciba Found Symp* 92:157, 1982.

221. FARQUHAR MG: Multiple pathways of exocytosis, endocytosis and membrane recycling: Validation of a Golgi route. *Fed Proc* 42:2407, 1983.

222. PATZAK A, WINKLER H: Exocytotic exposure and recycling of membrane antigens of chromaffin granules: Ultrastructural evaluation after immunolabeling. *J Cell Biol* 102:510, 1986.

223. DALTON AJ, FELIX MD: Cytologic and cytochemical characteristics of the Golgi substance of epithelial cells of the epididymis—in situ, in homogenates and after isolation. *Am J Anat* 94:171, 1954.

224. NOVIKOFF AB: GERL, its form and function in neurons of rat spinal ganglia. *Biol Bull* 127:358, 1964.

225. NOVIKOFF AB: The endoplasmic reticulum: A cytochemist's view (a review). *Proc Natl Acad Sci USA* 73:2781, 1976.

226. MOLLENHAUER HH, MORRE DJ: Structural compartmentation of the cytosol: Zones of exclusion, zones of adhesion, cytoskeletal and intercisternal elements. *Subcell Biochem* 5:327, 1978.

227. RAMBOURG A, CLERMONT Y, HERMO L: Three dimensional architecture of the Golgi apparatus in Sertoli cells of the rat. *Am J Anat* 159:455, 1979.

228. RAMBOURG A, CLERMONT Y, HERMO L: Three dimensional structure of the Golgi apparatus. *Methods Cell Biol* 23:155, 1981.

229. NOVIKOFF AB, NOVIKOFF PM: Cytochemical contributions to differentiating GERL from the Golgi apparatus. *Histochem J* 9:525, 1977.

230. ORCI L, RAVAZZOLA M, AMHERDT M, LOUVARD D, PERRELET A: Clathrin-immunoreactive sites in the Golgi apparatus are concentrated at the trans pole in polypeptide hormone-secreting cells. *Proc Natl Acad Sci USA* 82:5385, 1985.

231. ORCI L, GLICK BS, ROTHMAN JE: A new type of coated vesicular carrier that appears not to contain clathrin: Its possible role in protein transport within the Golgi stack. *Cell* 46:171, 1986.

232. WILLINGHAM MC, PASTAN IH: Endocytosis and exocytosis: Current concepts of vesicle traffic in animal cells. *Int Rev Cytol* 92:51, 1984.

233. ORCI L, RAVAZZOLA M, AMHERDT M, PERRELET A, POWELL SK, QUINN DL, MOORE HH: The trans-most cisternae of the Golgi complex: A compartment for sorting of secretory and plasma membrane proteins. *Cell* 51:1039, 1987.

234. FRIEND DS, MURRAY MJ: Osmium impregnation of the Golgi apparatus. *Am J Anat* 117:135, 1965.

235. NOVIKOFF AB, GOLDFISCHER S: Nucleoside diphosphatase activity in the Golgi apparatus and its usefulness for cytological studies. *Proc Natl Acad Sci USA* 47:802, 1961.

236. DUNPHY WG, FRIES E, URBANI LJ, ROTHMAN JE: Early and late functions associated with Golgi apparatus reside in distinct compartments. *Proc Natl Acad Sci USA* 78:7453, 1981.

237. ROTH J, BERGER EJ: Immunocytochemical localization of galactosyltransferase in HeLa cells: Codistribution with thiamine pyrophosphatase in trans-Golgi cisternae. *J Cell Biol* 93:223, 1982.

238. GOLDBERG DE, KORNFELD S: Evidence for extensive subcellular organization of asparagine-linked oligosaccharide processing and lyosomal enzyme phosphorylation. *J Biol Chem* 258:3159, 1983.

239. DUNPHY WG, ROTHMAN JE: Compartmentalization of asparagine-linked oligosaccharide processing in the Golgi apparatus. *J Cell Biol* 97:270, 1983.

240. DUNPHY W, ROTHMAN JE: Attachment of terminal N-acetlyglucosamine to asparagine-linked oligosaccharides occurrs in central cisternae of the Golgi stack. *Cell* 40:463, 1985.

241. GRIFFITHS G, PFEIFFER S, SIMONS K, MATLIN K: Exit of newly synthesized membrane proteins from trans cisternae of the Golgi complex to the plasma membrane. *J Cell Biol* 101:949, 1985.

242. ROTHMAN JE, URBANI LJ, BRANDS R: Transport of protein between cytoplasmic membranes of fused cells: Correspondence to processes reconstituted in a cell-free system. *J Cell Biol* 99:248, 1984.

243. ROTHMAN JE, MILLER RL, URBANI LJ: Intercompartmental transport in the Golgi complex is a dissociative process: Facile transfer of membrane protein between two Golgi populations. *J Cell Biol* 99:260, 1984.

244. BALCH WE, DUNPHY WG, BRAELL WA, ROTHMAN JE: Reconstitution of the transport of proteins between successive compartments of the Golgi measured by the coupled incorporation of N-acetyl glucosamine. *Cell* 39:405, 1984.

245. BALCH WE, GLICK BS, ROTHMAN JE: Sequential intermediates in the pathway of intercompartmental transport in a cell-free system. *Cell* 39:525, 1984.

246. BRAELL WA, BALCH WE, DOBBERSTEIN DC, ROTHMAN JE: The glycoprotein that is transported between successive compartments of the Golgi in a cell-free system resides in stacks of cisternae. *Cell* 39:511, 1984.

247. WATTENBERG BW, BALCH WE, ROTHMAN JE: A novel prefusion complex formed during protein transport between Golgi cisternae in a cell-free system. *J Biol Chem* 261:2202, 1986.

248. WATTENBERG BW, ROTHMAN JE: Multiple cytosolic components promote intra-Golgi protein transport. Resolution of a protein acting at a late stage, prior to membrane fusion. *J Biol Chem* 261:2208, 1986.

249. DUNPHY WG, PFEFFER SR, CLARY DL, WATTENBERG BW, GLICK BS, ROTHMAN JE: Yeast and mammals utilize similar cytosolic components to drive protein transport through the Golgi complex. *Proc Natl Acad Sci USA* 83:1622, 1986.

250. GOTTLIEB C, BAENZIGER J, KORNFELD S: Deficient uridine diphosphatase-N-acetylglucosamine glycoprotein N-acetylglucosamine tranferase activity in a clone of Chinese hamster ovary cells with altered surface glycoproteins. *J Biol Chem* 250:3303, 1975.

251. BRILES EB, LI E, KORNFELD S: Isolation of wheat germ agglutinin resistant clones of Chinese hamster ovary cells deficient in membrane sialic acid and galactose. *J Biol Chem* 252:1106, 1977.

252. GLICK BS, ROTHMAN JE: Possible role of fatty acyl–coenzyme A in intracellular protein transport. *Nature* 326:309:1987.

253. GLICKMAN J, CROEN K, KELLY S, AL-AWQATI Q: Golgi membranes contain an electrogenic H^+ pump in parallel to a chloride conductance. *J Cell Biol* 97:1303, 1983.

254. ANDERSON RGW, FALCK JR, GOLDSTEIN JL, BROWN MS: Visualization of acidic organelles in intact cells by electromicroscopy. *Proc Natl Acad Sci USA* 81:4838, 1984.

255. ANDERSON RGW, PATHAK RK: Vesicles and cisternae in the trans Golgi apparatus of human fibroblasts are acidic compartments. *Cell* 40:635, 1985.

256. PRESSMAN PC: Biological applications of ionophores. *Annu Rev Biochem* 45:501, 1976.

257. LEDGER PW, TANZER ML: Monensin—A perturbant of cellular physiology. *Trends Biochem Sci* 9:313, 1984.

258. TARTAKOFF AM: Perturbation of vesicular traffic with the carboxylic ionophore monensin. *Cell* 32:1026, 1983.

259. STROUS GJAM, WILLEMSEN R, van KERKOF P, SLOT GW, GEUZE HJ, LODISH HF: Vesicular stomatitis virus glycoprotein, albumin, and transferrin are transported to the cell surface via the same Golgi vesicles. *J Cell Biol* 97:1815, 1983.

260. GRIFFITHS G, QUINN P, WARREN G: Dissection of the Golgi complex. I. Monensin inhibits the transport of viral membrane proteins from medial to trans Golgi cisternae in baby hamster kidney cells infected with Semliki forest virus. *J Cell Biol* 96:835, 1983.

261. OHKUMA S, POOLE B: Fluorescence probe measurement of the intralysosomal pH in living cells and the perturbation of pH by various agents. *Proc Natl Acad Sci USA* 75:3327, 1978.

262. OHKUMA S, POOLE B: Cytoplasmic vacuolation of mouse peritoneal macrophages and the uptake into lysosomes of weakly basic substances. *J Cell Biol* 90:656, 1981.

263. STROUS GJAM, DUMAINE A, ZIJDERHAND-BLEEKEMOLEN JE, SLOT JW, SCHWARTZ AL: Effect of lysosomotropic amines on the secretory pathway and on the recycling of the asialoglycoprotein receptor pathway in human hepatoma cells. *J Cell Biol* 101:531, 1985.

264. GUAN J-L, ROSE JK: Conversion of a secretory protein into a transmembrane protein results in its transport to the Golgi complex but not to the cell surface. *Cell* 37:779, 1984.

265. BURGESS TL, KELLY RB: Constitutive and regulated secretion of proteins. *Annu Rev Cell Biol* 3:243, 1987.

266. KELLY RB: Pathways of protein secretion in eukaryotes. *Science* 230:25, 1985.

267. DeLISLE RC, WILLIAMS JAA: Regulation of membrane fusion in secretory exocytosis. *Annu Rev Physiol* 48:225, 1986.

268. ANDERSON P, SLORACH SA, UVNAS B: Sequential exocytosis of storage granules during antigen-induced histamine release from synthesized rat mast cells in vitro. An electronmicroscopic study. *Acta Physiol Scand* 88:359, 1973.

269. TOOZE J, TOOZE Z: Clathrin-coated vesicular tranport of secretory proteins during the formation of ACTH-containing secretory granules in AtT-20 cells. *J Cell Biol* 103:839, 1986.

270. BENDAYAN M, ROTH J, PERRELET A, ORCI L: Quantitative immunocytochemical localization of pancreatic secretory proteins in subcellular compartments of the rat acinar cell. *J Histochem Cytochem* 28:149, 1980.

271. MROZ EA, LECHENE C: Pancreatic zymogen granules differ markedly in protein composition. *Science* 232:871, 1986.

272. GIANNATTASIO G, ZANNI A, ROSA P, MELDOLESI J, MARGOLIS RK, MARGOLIS RU: Molecular organization of prolactin granules. III. Intracellular

transport of sulfated glycosaminoglycans and glycoproteins of the bovine prolactin granule matrix. *J Cell Biol* 86:260, 1980.

273. SLABY F, FARQUHAR MG: Characterization of rat somatotroph and mammotroph secretory granules: Presense of sulfated molecules. *Mol Cell Endocrinol* 18:33, 1980.

274. ZANNINI A, GIANNATTASIO G, NUSSDORFER G, MARGOLIS RK, MARGOLIS RU, MELDOLESI J: Molecular organization of prolactin granules II. Characterization of glucosoaminoglycans and glycoproteins of the bovine prolactin granule matrix. *J Cell Biol* 86:260, 1980.

275. INOUE K, KUROSUMI K: Ultrastructural immunocytochemical localization of LH and FSH in the pituitary of the untreated male rat. *Cell Tissue Res* 235:77, 1984.

276. BAINTON DF, FARQUHAR MG: Differences in enzyme content of specific granules of PMN leukocytes. I. Histochemical staining of bone marrow smears. *J Cell Biol* 39:286, 1968.

277. BAINTON DF, FARQUHAR MG: Differences in enzyme content of specific granules of PMN leukocytes. II. Cytochemistry and electron microscopy of bone marrow cells. *J Cell Biol* 39:299, 1968.

278. LEW PD, MONOD A, WALDVOGEL FA, DEWALD B, BAGGIOLINI M, PORZAN T: Quantitative analysis of the cytosolic free calcium dependency of exocytosis from the subcellular compartments in intact human neutrophils. *J Cell Biol* 102:2197, 1986.

279. BEAUDOIN AR, VACHEREAU A, St JEAN P: Evidence that amylase is released from two distinct pools of secretory proteins in the pancreas. *Biochim Biophys Acta* 757:302, 1983.

280. BEAUDOIN AR, St JEAN P, VACHEREAU A: Asynchronism between amylase secretion and packaging in the zymogen granules of pig pancreas. *Pancreas* 1:2, 1986.

281. ARVAN P, CASTLE JD: Phasic release of newly synthesized secretory proteins in the unstimulated rat exocrine pancreas. *J Cell Biol* 104:243, 1987.

282. RHODES CJ, HALBAN PA: Newly synthesized proinsulin-insulin as well as stored insulin are released from pancreatic B cells uniquely by a regulated nonconstitutive pathway. *J Cell Biol* 105:145, 1987.

283. GUMBINER B, KELLY RB: Two distinct intracellular pathways transport secretory and membrane glycoproteins to the surface of pituitary tumor cells. *Cell* 28:51, 1982.

284. BURGESS TL, CRAIK CS, KELLY RB: The exocrine protein trypsinogen is targeted into the secretory granules of an endocrine cell line. Studies by gene transfer. *J Cell Biol* 101:639, 1985.

285. MOORE HPH, KELLY RB: Secretory protein targeting in a pituitary cell line: Differential transport of foreign secretory proteins to distinct secretory pathways. *J Cell Biol* 101:1773, 1985.

286. MOORE HPH, WALKER MD, LEE F, KELLY RB: Expressing a human proinsulin cDNA in a mouse ACTH-secreting cell. Intracellular storage, proteolytic processing and secretion on stimulation. *Cell* 35:531, 1983.

287. HELLERMAN JG, CONE RC, POTTS JT JR, RICH A, MULLIGAN RC, KRONENBERG HM: Secretion of human parathyroid hormone from rat pituitary cells infected with a recombinant retrovirus encoding preproparathyroid hormone. *Proc Natl Acad Sci USA* 81:5340, 1984.

288. BURGESS TL, CRAIK CS, MATSUUCHI L, KELLY RB: In vitro mutagenesis of pretrypsinogen: The role of the amino terminus in intracellular protein targeting to secretory granules. *J Cell Biol* 105:659, 1987.

289. MOORE HPH, KELLY RB: Rerouting of a secretory protein by fusion with human hormone sequences. *Nature* 321:443, 1986.

290. ORCI L, RAVAZZOLA M, AMHERDT M, MADSEN O, PERRELET A, VASSALLI JD, ANDERSON RGW: Conversion of proinsulin to insulin occurs coordinately with acidification of maturing secretory vesicles. *J Cell Biol* 103, 2273, 1986.

291. O'CONNOR DT, FRIGON RP: Chromogranin A, the major cathecolamine storage vesicle soluble protein. *J Biol Chem* 259:3237, 1984.

292. ROSA P, HILLE A, LEE RWH, ZANINI A, DE CAMILLI P, HUTTNER WB: Secretogranins I and II: Two tyrosine-sulfated secretory proteins common to a variety of cells secreting peptides by the regulated pathway. *J Cell Biol* 101:1999, 1985.

293. REGGIO H, DAGORN JC: Ionic interactions between bovine chymotrypsinogen A and chondroitin sulfate A.B.C.: A possible model for molecular aggregation in zymogen granules. *J Cell Biol* 78:951, 1978.

294. FUMAGALLI G, ZANINI A: In cow anterior pituitary, growth hormone and prolactin can be packed in separate granules of the same cell. *J Cell Biol* 100:2019, 1985.

295. RAVAZZOLA M, ORCI L: Glucagon and glicentin immunoreactivity are topologically segregated in the alpha granule of the human pancreatic A cell. *Nature* 284:66, 1980.

296. ORCI L, HALBAN P, AMHERDT M, RAVAZZOLA M, VASSALI JD, PERRELET A: Nonconverted, amino acid analog-modified proinsulin stays in a Golgi-derived clathrin-coated membrane compartment. *J Cell Biol* 99:2187, 1984.

297. de DUVE C: Lysosomes revisited. *Eur J Biochem* 137:391, 1983.

298. HELENIUS A, MELLAMAN I, WALL D, HUBBARD A: Endosomes. *Trends Biochem Sci* 8:245, 1983.

299. PASTAN IH, WILLINGHAM MC: Receptor-mediated endocytosis: Coated pits, receptosomes and the Golgi. *Trends Biochem Sci* 8:250, 1983.

300. DINGLE JT, DEAN RT, SLY W: *Lysosomes in Biology and Pathology*. Amsterdam, Elsevier, 1984, vol 7.

301. GOLDSTEIN JL, BROWN MS, ANDERSON RGW, RUSSELL DW, SCHNEIDER WJ: Receptor-mediated endocytosis: Concepts emerging from the LDL receptor system. *Annu Rev Cell Biol* 1:1, 1985.

302. von FIGURA K, HASILIK A: Lysosomal enzymes and their receptors. *Ann Rev Biochem* 55:167, 1986.

303. WANG E, MICHL J, PFEFFER LM, SILVERSTEIN SC, TAMM I: Interferon suppresses pinocytosis but stimulates phagocytosis in mouse peritoneal macrophages: Related changes in cytoskeletal organization. *J Cell Biol* 98:1328, 1984.

304. SILVERSTEIN SC, MICHL J, SUNG S-SJ: Phagocytosis, in Silverstein SC (ed): *Transport of Macromolecules in Cellular Systems*. Berlin, Dahlem Konferenzen, 1978, p 245.

305. PEARSE BMF: Clathrin: A unique protein associated with intracellular transport of membrane by coated vesicles. *Proc Natl Acad Sci USA* 73:1255, 1976.

306. ROTH TF, PORTER KR: Yolk protein uptake in the oocyte of the mosquito Aedes aegypti L. *J Cell Biol* 20:313, 1964.

307. PEARSE BMF: Coated vesicles. *Trends Biochem Sci* 5:131, 1980.

308. SCHLESINGER J: The mechanism and role of hormone-induced clustering of membrane receptors. *Trends Biochem Sci* 5:210, 1980.

309. DUNN WA, HUBBARD AL: Receptor-mediated endocytosis of epidermal growth factor by hepatocytes in the perfused rat liver: Ligand and receptor dynamics. *J Cell Biol* 98:2148, 1984.

310. ANDERSON RGW, BROWN MS, BEISIEGEL U, GOLDSTEIN JL: Surface distribution and recycling of the LDL receptor as visualized by anti-receptor antibodies. *J Cell Biol* 93:523, 1982.

311. SCHMID SL, FUCHS R, MALE P, MELLMAN I: Two distinct subpopulations of endosomes involved in membrane recycling and transport to lysosomes. *Cell* 52:73, 1988.

312. TYCKO B, MAXFIELD FR: Rapid acidification of endocytic vesicles containing alpha-2-macroglobulin. *Cell* 228:643. 1982.

313. DI PAOLA M, MAXFIELD FR: Conformational changes in the receptors for epidermal growth factor and asialoglycoprotein induced by the mildly acidic pH found in endocytic vesicles. *J Biol Chem* 259:9164, 1984.

314. BROWN MS, ANDERSON RGW, GOLDSTEIN JL: Recycling receptors: The round trip itinerary of a migrant membrane protein. *Cell* 32:663, 1983.

315. GEUZE HJ, SLOT JW, STROUS GJAM, LODISH HF, SCHWARTZ AL: Intracellular site of asialoglycoprotein receptor-ligand uncoupling: Double-label immunoelectron microscopy during receptor-mediated endocytosis. *Cell* 32:277, 1983.

316. GEUZE HJ, SLOT JW, STROUS GJAM, PEPPARD J, von FIGURA K, HASILIK A, SCHWARTZ AL: Intracellular receptor sorting during endocytosis: Comparative immunoelectronmicroscopy of multiple receptors in rat liver. *Cell* 37:195, 1984.

317. YAMASHIRO DJ, MAXFIELD FR: Acidification of endocytic compartments and the intracellular pathways of ligands and receptors. *J Cell Biochem* 26:231, 1984.

318. YAMASHIRO DJ, TYCKO B, FLUSS SR, MAXFIELD FR: Segregation of transferrin to a mildly acidic (pH 6.5) para-Golgi compartment in the recycling pathway. *Cell* 37:789, 1984.

319. WALL DA, HUBBARD AL: Receptor-mediated endocytosis of asialoglycoprotein by rat liver hepatocytes: Biochemical characterization of the endosomal compartments. *J Cell Biol* 101:2104, 1985.

320. MARSH M, GRIFFITHS G, DEAN GE, MELLMAN I, HELENIUS A: Three-dimensional structure of endosomes in BHK-21 cells. *Proc Natl Acad Sci USA* 83:2899, 1986.

321. MUELLER SC, HUBBARD AL: Receptor-mediated endocytosis of asialoglycoproteins by rat hepatocytes: Receptor positive and receptor negative endosomes. *J Cell Biol* 102:932, 1986.

322. DUNN WA, HUBBARD AL, ARONSON NN JR: Low temperature selectively inhibits fusion between pinocytic vesicles and lysosomes during heterophagy of ^{125}I-asialofetuin by the perfused liver. *J Biol Chem* 255:5971, 1980.

323. BROWN WJ, FARQUHAR MG: The mannose-6-phosphate receptor for lysosomal enzymes is concentrated in cis Golgi cisternae. *Cell* 36:295, 1984.

324. GRIFFITHS G, HOFLACK B, SIMONS K, MELLMAN I, KORNFELD S: The mannose 6-phosphate receptor and the biogenesis of lysosomes. *Cell* 52:329, 1988.

325. KORNFELD S: Trafficking of lysosomal enzymes. *FASEB J* 1:462, 1987.

326. ERICKSON AH, BLOBEL G: Early events in the biosynthesis of the lysosomal enzyme cathepsin D. *J Biol Chem* 254:1171, 1979.

327. ROSENFELD MG, KREIBICH G, POPOV D, KATO K, SABATINI DD: Biosyn-

thesis of lysosomal hydrolases: Their synthesis in bound polysomes and the role of co- and post-translational processing in determining their subcellular distribution. *J Cell Biol* 93:135, 1982.

328. PROIA R, NEUFELD EF: Synthesis of β-hexosaminidase in cell-free translation and in intact fibroblasts: An insoluble precursor alpha chain in a rare form of Tay Sachs disease. *Proc Natl Acad Sci USA* 79:6360, 1982.

329. ERICKSON AH, WALTER P, BLOBEL G: Translocation of a lysosomal enzyme across the microsomal membrane requires the signal recognition particle. *Biochem Biophys Res Commun* 115:275, 1983.

330. REITMAN ML, KORNFELD S: Lysosomal enzyme targeting: N-acetylglucosaminyl-phosphotransferase selectively phosphorylates native lysosomal enzymes. *J Biol Chem* 256:11977, 1981.

331. WAHEED A, HASILIK A, von FIGURA K: UDP-N-acetylglucosamine: Lysosomal enzyme precursor N-acetylglucosamine-l-phosphotransferase: Partial purification and characterization of the rat liver Golgi enzyme. *J Biol Chem* 257:12322, 1982.

332. VARKI A, KORNFELD S: Identification of a rat liver alpha-N-acetyl-glucosaminyl phosphodiesterase capable of removing "blocking" alpha-N-acetylglucosamine residues from phosphorylated high mannose oligosaccharides of lysosomal enzymes. *J Biol Chem* 255:8398, 1980.

333. VARKI A, KORNFELD S: Purification and characterization of rat liver alpha-N-acetylglucosaminyl phosphodiesterase. *J Biol Chem* 256:9937, 1981.

334. WAHEED A, HASILIK A, von FIGURA K: Processing of the phosphorylated recognition marker in lysosomal enzymes: Characterization and partial purification of the microsomal alpha-N-acetylglucosaminyl phosphodiesterase. *J Biol Chem* 256:5717, 1981.

335. HASILIK A, WAHEED A, von FIGURA K: Enzymatic phosphorylation of lysosomal enzymes in the presence of UDP-N-acetylglucosamine. Absence of the activity in I-cell fibroblasts. *Biochem Biophys Res Commun* 98:761, 1981.

336. REITMAN ML, VARKI A, KORNFELD S: Fibroblasts from patients with I-cell disease and pseudo-Hurler polydystrophy are deficient in uridine 5′-diphosphate-N-acetylglucosamine: Glycoprotein N-acetylglucosaminylphosphotransferase activities. *J Clin Invest* 67:1574, 1981.

337. VARKI AP, REITMAN ML, VANNIER A, KORNFELD S, GRUBB JH, SLY WS: Demonstration of the heterozygous state for I-cell disease and pseudo-Hurler polydystrophy by assay of N-acetylglucosaminyl-phosphotransferase in white blood cells and fibroblasts. *Am J Hum Genet* 34:717, 1982.

338. MUELLER OT, HONEY NK, LITTLE LE, MILLER AL, SHOWS TB: Mucolipidosis II and III. The genetic relationships between two disorders of lysosomal enzyme biosynthesis. *J Clin Invest* 72:1016, 1983.

339. LANG L, TAKAHASHI T, TANG J, KORNFELD S: Lysosomal enzyme phosphorylation in human fibroblasts: Kinetic parameters offer a biochemical rationale for two distinct defects in the UDP-GlcNAc: Lysosomal enzyme precursor N-acetylglucosamine l-phosphotransferase. *J Clin Invest* 76:2191, 1985.

340. BEN-YOSEPH Y, PACK BA, MITCHELL DA, ELWELL DG, POTIOR M, MELANCON SB, NADLER HL: Characterization of the mutant N-acetylglucosaminyl-phosphotransferase in I-cell disease and pseudo-Hurler polydystrophy. Complementation analysis and kinetic studies. *Enzymology* 35:106, 1986.

341. WAHEED A, POHLMAN R, HASILIK A, von FIGURA K, van ELSEN A, LeROY JG: Deficiency of UDP-N-acetylglucosamine: Lysosomal enzyme N-acetylglucosamine 1-phosphotransferase in organs of I-cell patients. *Biochem Biophys Res Commun* 105:1052, 1982.

342. VARKI AP, REITMAN ML, KORNFELD S: Identification of a variant of mucolipidosis III (pseudo Hurler polydystrophy): A catalytically active N-acetylglucosaminylphosphotransferase that fails to phosphorylate lysosomal enzymes. *Proc Natl Acad Sci USA* 78:7773, 1981.

343. LANG L, REITMAN ML, TANG J, ROBERTS RM, KORNFELD S: Lysosomal enzyme phosphorylation. Recognition of a protein-dependent determinant allows specific phosphorylation of oligosaccharides present on lysosomal enzymes. *J Biol Chem* 259:14663, 1984.

344. FAUST PL, KORNFELD S, CHIRGWIN JM: Cloning and sequence analysis of cDNA for human cathepsin D. *Proc Natl Acad Sci USA* 82:4910, 1985.

345. FUKUSHIMA H, DE WET J, O'BRIEN JS: Molecular cloning of a cDNA for human alpha-fucosidase. *Proc Natl Acad Sci USA* 82:1262, 1985.

346. MYEROWITZ R, PIEKARZ R, NEUFELD EF, SHOWS TB, SUSUKI K: Human β-hexosaminidase alpha chain: Coding sequence and homology with β chain. *Proc Natl Acad Sci USA* 82:7830, 1985.

347. BISHOP DF, CALHOUN PH, BERNSTEIN HS, HANTZOPOULOS P, QUINN M, DESNICK RJ: Human alpha galactosidase A: Nucleotide sequence of a cDNA clone encoding the mature enzyme. *Proc Natl Acad Sci USA* 83:4859, 1986.

348. CHAN SJ, SEGUNDO BS, McCORMICK MB, STEINER DF: Nucleotide and predicted amino acid sequences of cloned human and mouse preprocathepsin B cDNAs. *Proc Natl Acad Sci USA* 83:772, 1986.

349. FONG D, CALHOUN DH, HSIEH WT, LEE B, WELLS RD: Isolation of a cDNA clone for the human lysosomal proteinase cathepsin D. *Proc Natl Acad Sci USA* 83:2909, 1986.

350. NISHIMURA Y, ROSENFELD MG, KREIBICH G, GUBLER U, SABATINI DD, ADESNIK M, ANDY R: Nucleotide sequence of rat preputial gland β-glucuronidase cDNA and in vitro insertion of its encoded polypeptide into microsomal membranes. *Proc Natl Acad Sci USA* 83:7292, 1986.

351. OSHIMA A, KYLE JW, MILLER RD, HOFFMANN JW, POWELL PP, GRUBB JH, SLY WS, TROPAK M, GUISE KS, GRAVEL RA: Cloning, sequencing, and expression of cDNA for human β-glucuronidase. *Proc Natl Acad Sci USA* 89:685, 1987.

352. HASILIK A, KLEIN U, WAHEED A, STRECKER G, von FIGURA K: Phosphorylated oligosaccharides in lysosomal enzymes: Identification of alpha-N-acetylglucosamine (1) phospho (6) mannose diester groups. *Proc Natl Acad Sci USA* 77:7074, 1980.

353. HASILIK A, von FIGURA K: Oligosaccharides in lysosomal enzymes: Distribution of high-mannose and complex oligosaccharides in cathepsin D and β-hexosaminidase. *Eur J Biochem* 121:125, 1981.

354. GIESELMAN V, POHLMANN R, HASILIK A, von FIGURA K: Biosynthesis and transport of cathepsin D in cultured human fibroblasts. *J Cell Biol* 97:1, 1983.

355. VARKI AP, KORNFELD S: The spectrum of anionic oligosaccharides released by endo-β-N-acetylglucosaminidase H from glycoproteins. Structural studies and interactions with the phosphomannosyl receptor. *J Biol Chem* 258:2808, 1983.

356. HICKMANN S, NEUFELD EF: A hypothesis for I-cell disease: Defective hydrolases that do not enter lysosomes. *Biochem Biophys Res Commun* 49:992, 1972.

357. ZUHLSDORF M, IMORT M, HASILIK A, von FIGURA K: Molecular forms of β-hexosaminidase and cathepsin D in serum and urine of healthy subjects and patients with elevated activity of lysosomal enzymes. *Biochem J* 213:733, 1983.

358. ERICKSON AH, BLOBEL G: Carboxyl-terminal proteolytic processing during biosynthesis of the lysosomal enzymes β-glucuronidase and cathepsin D. *Biochemistry* 22:5201, 1983.

359. HASILIK A, von FIGURA K: Processing of lysosomal enzymes in fibroblasts, in Dingle JT, Dean RT, Sly W (eds): *Lysosomes in Biology and Pathology*. Amsterdam, Elsevier, 1984, vol 7, p 3.

360. von FIGURA K, REY M, PRINZ R, VOSS B, ULLRICH K: Effect of tunicamycin on transport of lysosomal enzymes in cultured skin fibroblasts. *Eur J Biochem* 101:103, 1979.

361. HASILIK A, NEUFELD EF: Biosynthesis of lysosomal enzymes in fibroblasts: Phosphorylation of mannose residues. *J Biol Chem* 255:4946, 1980.

362. WIESMANN UN, LIGHTBODY J, VASSELLA F, HERSCHKOWITZ NN: Multiple lysosomal enzyme deficiency due to enzyme leakage? *N Engl J Med* 284:109, 1971.

363. KAPLAN A, ACHORD DT, SLY SF: Phosphohexosyl components of a lysosomal enzyme are recognized by pinocytosis receptors on human fibroblasts. *Proc Natl Acad Sci USA* 74:2026, 1977.

364. ROME LH, WEISSMANN B, NEUFELD EF: Direct demonstration of binding of a lysosomal enzyme, alpha-L-iduronidase, to receptors on cultured fibroblasts. *Proc Natl Acad Sci USA* 76:2331, 1979.

365. FISCHER HD, GONZALEZ-NORIEGA A, SLY WS: β-glucuronidase binding to human fibroblast membrane receptors. *J Biol Chem* 255:5069, 1980.

366. SLY WS, FISCHER HD: The phosphomannosyl recognition system for intracellular and intercellular transport of lysosomal enzymes. *J Cell Biochem* 18:67, 1982.

367. OWADA M, NEUFELD EF: Is there a mechanism for introducing acid hydrolases into liver lysosomes that is independent of mannose 6-phosphate recognition? Evidence from I cell disease. *Biochem Biophys Res Commun* 105:814, 1982.

368. MILLER AL, KRESS BC, STEIN R, KINNON C, KERN H, SCHNEIDER JA, HARMS E: Properties of N-acetyl-β-D-hexosaminidase from isolated normal and I-cell lysosomes. *J Biol Chem* 256:9352, 1981.

369. LEMANSKY P, GIESELMANN V, HASILIK A, von FIGURA K: Synthesis and transport of lysosomal acid phosphatase in normal and I-cell fibroblasts. *J Biol Chem* 260:9023, 1985.

370. SCHWAIGER H, HASILIK A, von FIGURA K, WIEMKEN A, TANNER W: Carbohydrate-free carboxypeptidase Y is transferred into the lysosome-like yeast vacuole. *Biochem Biophys Res Commun* 104:950, 1982.

371. JOHNSON LM, BANKAITIS VA, EMR SD: Distinct sequence determinants direct intracellular sorting and modification of a yeast vacuolar protease. *Cell* 48:875, 1987.

372. VALLS LA, HUNTER CP, ROTHMAN GH, STEVENS TH: Protein sorting in yeast: The localization determinant of yeast vacuolar carboxypeptidase Y resides in the propeptide. *Cell* 48:887, 1987.

373. SAHAGIAN GG, DISTLER J, JOURDIAN GW: Characterization of membrane-

associated receptor from bovine liver that binds phosphomannosyl residues of bovine testicular β-galactosidase. *Proc Natl Acad Sci USA* 78:4289, 1981.

374. WILLINGHAM MC, PASTAN IH, SAHAGIAN GG, JOURDIAN GW, NEUFELD EF: Morphologic study of the internalization of a lysosomal enzyme by the mannose-6-phosphate receptor in cultured Chinese hamster ovary cells. *Proc Natl Acad Sci USA* 78:6967, 1981.

375. BROWN WJ, FARQUHAR MG: Accumulation of coated vesicles bearing mannose 6-phosphate receptors for lysosomal enzymes in the Golgi region of I-cell fibroblasts. *Proc Natl Acad Sci USA* 81:5135, 1984.

376. BROWN WJ, CONSTANTINESCU E, FARQUHAR MG: Redistribution of mannose-6-phosphate receptors induced by tunicamycin and chloroquine. *J Cell Biol* 99:320, 1984.

377. GEUZE HG, SLOT JW, STROUS GJAM, HASILIK A, von FIGURA K: Ultrastructural localization of the mannose-6-phosphate receptor in rat liver. *J Cell Biol* 98:2047, 1984.

378. GEUZE HJ, SLOT JW, STROUS GJ, LUZIO JP, SCHWARTZ AL: A cycloheximide-resistant pool of receptors for asialoglycoproteins and mannose 6-phosphate residues in the Golgi complex of hepatocytes. *EMBO J* 3:2677, 1984.

379. GEUZE HG, SLOT JW, STROUS GJAM, HASILIK A, von FIGURA K: Possible pathways for lysosomal enzyme delivery. *J Cell Biol* 101:2253, 1985.

380. BROWN WJ, GOODHOUSE J, FARQUHAR MG: Mannose-6-phosphate receptors for lysosomal enzymes cycle between the Golgi complex and endosomes. *J Cell Biol* 103:1235, 1986.

381. LOBEL P, DAHMS NM, BREITMEYER J, CHIRGWIN JM, KORNFELD S: Cloning of the bovine 215-kDa cation-independent mannose 6-phosphate receptor. *Proc Natl Acad Sci USA* 84:2233, 1987.

382. SAHAGIAN GG, STEER CJ: Transmembrane orientation of the mannose-6-phosphate receptor in isolated clathrin-coated vesicles. *J Biol Chem* 260:9838, 1985.

383. HOFLACK B, KORNFELD S: Purification and characterization of a cation-dependent mannose 6-phosphate receptor from murine P388D$_1$ macrophages and bovine liver. *J Biol Chem* 260:12008, 1985.

384. HOFLACK B, FUJIMOTO K, KORNFELD S: The interaction of phosphorylated oligosaccarides and lysosomal enzymes with bovine liver cation-dependent mannose-6-phosphate receptor. *J Biol Chem* 262:123, 1987.

385. HOFLACK B, KORNFELD S: Lysosomal enzyme binding to mouse P388D$_1$ macrophage membranes lacking the 215-kDa mannose 6-phosphate receptor: Evidence for the existence of a second mannose 6-phosphate receptor. *Proc Natl Acad Sci USA* 82:4428, 1985.

386. DAHMS NM, LOBEL P, BREITMEYER J, CHIRGWIN JM, KORNFELD S: 46 kD mannose 6-phosphate receptor: Cloning, expression, and homology to the 215 kD mannose 6-phosphate receptor. *Cell* 50:181, 1987.

387. POHLMANN R, NAGEL G, SCHMIDT B, STEIN M, LORKOWSKI G, KRENTLER C, CULLY J, MEYER HE, GRZESCHIK K-H, MERSMANN G, HASILIK A, von FIGURA K: Cloning of a cDNA encoding the human cation-dependent mannose 6-phosphate-specific receptor. *Proc Natl Acad Sci USA* 84:5575, 1987.

388. FISCHER HD, CREEK KE, SLY WS: Binding of phosphorylated oligosaccharides to immobilized phosphomannosyl receptors. *J Biol Chem* 257:9938, 1982.

389. NATOWICZ M, HALLETT DW, FRIER C, CHI M, SCHLESINGER PH, BAENZIGER JU: Recognition and receptor-mediated uptake of phosphorylated high mannose-type oligosaccharides by cultured human fibroblasts. *J Cell Biol* 96:915, 1983.

390. TALKAD V, SLY WS: Human β-glucuronidase pinocytosis and binding to the immobilized phosphomannosyl receptor: Effects of treatment of the enzyme with alpha-N-acetylglucosaminyl phosphodiesterase. *J Biol Chem* 258:7345, 1983.

391. GABEL CA, COSTELLO CE, REINHOLD VN, KURZ L, KORNFELD S: Identification of methylphosphomannosyl residues as components of the high mannose oligosaccharides of Dictyostelium discoideum glycoproteins. *J Biol Chem* 259:13762, 1984.

392. SCHULZE-LOHOFF E, HASILIK A, von FIGURA K: Cathepsin D precursor in clathrin-coated organelles from human fibroblasts. *J Cell Biol* 101:824, 1985.

393. LEMANSKY P, HASILIK A, von FIGURA K, HELMY S, FISHMAN J, FINE RE, KEDERSHA NL, ROME LH: Lysosomal enzyme precursors in coated vesicles derived from the exocytic and endocytic pathways. *J Cell Biol* 104:1743, 1987.

394. PFEFFER SR: The endosomal concentration of a mannose-6-phosphate receptor is unchanged in the absence of ligand synthesis. *J Cell Biol* 105:229, 1987.

395. BRAULKE T, GARTUNG C, HASILIK A, von FIGURA K: Is movement of mannose 6-phosphate-specific receptor triggered by binding of lysosomal enzymes? *J Cell Biol* 104:1735, 1987.

396. GONZALEZ-NORIEGA A, GRUBB JH, TALKAD V, SLY WS: Chloroquine inhibits lysosomal enzyme pinocytosis and enhances lysosomal enzyme secretion by impairing receptor recycling. *J Cell Biol* 85:839, 1980.

397. MIGEON BR, SPRENKLE JA, LIBAERS I, SCOTT JF, NEUFELD EF: X-linked Hunter Syndrome: The heterozygous phenotype in cell culture. *Am J Hum Genet* 29:448, 1977.

398. LLOYD JB, FORSTER S: The lysosomal membrane. *Trends Biochem Sci* 11:129, 1986.

399. BROWN MS, GOLDSTEIN JL: Receptor-mediated control of cholesterol metabolism. *Science* 191:150, 1976.

400. YOUNGDAHL-TURNER P, MELLMAN IS, ALLEN RH, ROSENBERG LE: Protein-mediated vitamin uptake. Adsorptive endocytosis of the transcobalamin II-cobalamin complex by cultured human fibroblasts. *Exp Cell Res* 118:127, 1979.

401. ROSENBLATT DS, HOSACK A, MATIASZUK NV, COOPER BA, LAFRAMBOISE R: Defect in vitamin B_{12} release from lysosomes: Newly described inborn error of vitamin B_{12} metabolism. *Science* 228:1319, 1985.

402. GAHL WA, BASHAN N, TIETZE F, BERNARDINI I, SCHULMAN JD: Cystine transport is defective in isolated leukocyte lysosomes from patients with cystinosis. *Science* 217:1263, 1982.

403. GAHL WA, TIETZE F, BASHAN N, STEINHERZ R, SCHULMAN JD: Defective cystine exodus from isolated lysosome-rich fractions of cystinotic leucocytes. *J Biol Chem* 257:9570, 1982.

404. JONAS AJ, GREENE AA, SMITH ML, SCHNEIDER JA: Cystine accumulation and loss in normal, heterozygous, and cystinotic fibroblasts. *Proc Natl Acad Sci USA* 79:4442, 1982.

405. JONAS AJ, SMITH ML, ALLISON WS, LAIKIND PK, GREENE AA, SCHNEIDER JA: Proton-translocating ATPase and lysosomal cystine transport. *J Biol Chem* 258:11727, 1983.

406. GAHL WA, TIETZE F, BASHAN N, BERNARDINI I, RAIFORD D, SCHULMAN JD: Characteristics of cystine counter-transport in normal and cystinotic lysosome-rich leucocyte granular fractions. *Biochem J* 216:393, 1983.

407. JONAS AJ, SYMONS LJ, SPELLER RJ: Polyamines stimulate lysosomal cystine transport. *J Biol Chem* 262:16391, 1987.

408. PISONI RL, THOENE JG, CHRISTENSEN HN: Detection and characterization of carrier-mediated cationic amino acid transport in lysosomes of normal and cystinotic human fibroblasts. *J Biol Chem* 260:4791, 1985.

409. PISONI RL, THOENE JG, LEMONS RM, CHRISTENSEN HN: Important differences in cationic amino acid transport by lysosomal system c and system y^+ of the human fibroblast. *J Biol Chem* 262:15011, 1987.

410. PISONI RL, FLICKINGER KS, THOENE JG, CHRISTENSEN HN: Characterization of carrier-mediated transport systems for small neutral amino acids in human fibroblast lysosomes. *J Biol Chem* 262:6010, 1987.

411. BERNAR J, TIETZE F, KOHN LD, BERNARDINI I, HARPER GS, GROLLMAN EF, GAHL WA: Characteristics of a lysosomal membrane transport system for tyrosine and other neutral amino acids in rat thyroid cells. *J Biol Chem* 261:17107, 1986.

412. THOENE JG, OSHIMA RG, CRAWHALL JC, OLSON DL, SCHNEIDER JA: Intracellular cystine depletion by aminothiols in vitro and in vivo. *J Clin Invest* 58:180, 1976.

413. RENLUND M, KOVANEN PT, RAVIO KO, OULA P, GAHMBERG CG, EHNHOLM C: Studies on the defect underlying the lysosomal storage of sialic acid in Salla disease. *J Clin Invest* 77:568, 1986.

414. RENLUND M, TITZE F, GAHL WA: Defective sialic acid egress from isolated fibroblast lysosomes of patients with Salla disease. *Science* 232:759, 1986.

415. BAME KJ, ROME LH: Acetyl coenzyme A: Alpha-glucosaminide N-acetyltransferase. Evidence for a transmembrane acetylation mechanism. *J Biol Chem* 260:11293, 1985.

416. KLEIN U, KRESSE H, von FIGURA K: Sanfilippo syndrome type C: Deficiency of acetyl-CoA: Alpha-glucosaminide N-acetyltransferase in skin fibroblasts. *Proc Natl Acad Sci USA* 75:5185, 1978.

417. REEVES JP: The mechanism of lysosomal acidification, in Dingle JT, Dean RT, Sly WS (eds): *Lysosomes in Biology and Pathology*. Amsterdam, Elsevier, 1984, vol 7, p 175.

418. MELLMAN I, FUCHS R, HELENIUS A: Acidification of the endocytic and exocytic pathways. *Annu Rev Biochem* 55:663, 1986.

419. OHKUMA S, MORIYAMA Y, TAKANO T: Identification and characterization of a proton pump in lysosomes by fluorescein isothiocyanate-dextran fluorescence. *Proc Natl Acad Sci USA* 79:2758, 1982.

420. HARIKUMAR P, REEVES JP: The lysosomal proton pump is electrogenic. *J Biol Chem* 258:10403, 1983.

421. SCHNEIDER DL: ATP-dependent acidification of membrane vesicles isolated from purified rat liver lysosomes. *J Biol Chem* 258:1833, 1983.

422. REES-JONES R, AL-AWQATI Q: Proton-translocating adenosinetriphosphatase in rough and smooth microsomes from rat liver. *Biochemistry* 23:2236, 1984.

423. RUDNICK G: ATP-driven H^+ pumping into intracellular organelles. *Annu Rev Physiol* 48:403, 1986.

424. REIJNGOUD D-J, TAGER JM: The permeability of the lysosomal membrane. *Biochem Biophys Acta* 272:419, 1977.

425. MEHRABIAN M, BAME KJ, ROME LH: Interaction of rat liver lysosomal membranes with actin. *J Cell Biol* 99:680, 1984.

426. COLLOT M, LOUVARD D, SINGER SJ: Lysosomes are associated with microtubules and not with intermediate filaments in cultured fibroblasts. *Proc Natl Acad Sci USA* 81:788, 1984.

427. CHEN JW, MURPHY TL, WILLINGHAM MC, PASTAN I, AUGUST JT: Identification of two lysosomal membrane glycoproteins. *J Cell Biol* 101:85, 1985.

428. CHEN JW, PAN W, D'SOUZA MP, AUGUST JT: Lysosome-associated membrane proteins: Characterization of LAMP-1 of macrophage P388 and mouse embryo 3T3 cultured cells. *Arch Biochem Biophys* 289:574, 1985.

429. LEWIS V, GREEN JA, MARSH M, VIHKO P, HELENIUS A, MELLMAN I: Glycoproteins of the lysosomal membrane. *J Cell Biol* 100:1839, 1985.

430. LIPPINCOTT-SCHWARTZ J, FAMBROUGH DM: Lysosomal membrane dynamics: Structure and interorganellar movement of a major lysosomal membrane glycoprotein. *J Cell Biol* 102:1593, 1986.

431. LIPPINCOTT-SCHWARTZ J, FAMBROUGH DM: Cycling of the integral membrane glycoprotein, LEP100, between plasma membrane and lysosomes: Kinetic and morphological analysis. *Cell* 49:669, 1987.

432. BARRIOCANAL JG, BONIFACINO JS, YUAN L, SANDOVAL IV: Biosynthesis, glycosylation, movement through the Golgi system, and transport to lysosomes by an N-linked carbohydrate-independent mechanism of three lysosomal integral membrane proteins. *J Biol Chem* 261:16755, 1986.

433. MORIYAMA Y, TAKANO T, OHKUMA S: Acridine orange as a fluorescent probe for lysosomal proton pump. *J Biochem (Tokyo)* 92:1333, 1982.

434. ERICKSON AH, GINNS EI, BARRANGER JA: Biosynthesis of the lysosomal enzyme glucocerebrosidase. *J Biol Chem* 260:14319, 1985.

435. SCHATZ G, BUTOW RA: How are proteins imported into mitochondria? *Cell* 32:316, 1983.

436. HAY R, BOHNI P, GASSER S: How mitochondria import proteins. *Biochim Biophys Acta* 779:65, 1984.

437. RIED G: Transport of proteins into mitochondria, in Kanuf P, Cook J (ed): *Current Topics in Membranes and Transport. Membrane Protein Biosynthesis and Turnover.* New York, Academic, 1985, vol 24, p 295.

438. COLMAN A, ROBINSON C: Protein import into organelles: Hierarchical targeting signals. *Cell* 46:321, 1986.

439. DOUGLAS MG, MCCAMMON MT, VASSAROTTI A: Targeting proteins into mitochondria. *Microbiol Rev* 50:166, 1986.

440. HATEFI Y: The mitochondrial electron transport and oxidative phosphorylation system. *Annu Rev Biochem* 54:1015, 1985.

441. HURT EC, van LOON APGM: How proteins find mitochondria and intramitochondrial compartments. *Trends Biochem Sci* 11:204, 1986.

442. TZAGOLOFF A, MYERS AM: Genetics of mitochondrial biogenesis. *Annu Rev Biochem* 55:249, 1986.

443. ZIMMERMAN R: Import of proteins into mitochondria, in Strauss AM, Boime I, Kreil G (eds): *Protein Compartmentalization.* New York, Springer-Verlag, 1986, p 119.

444. KELLEMS R, ALLISON V, BUTOW R: Cytoplasmic type 80S ribosomes associated with yeast mitochondria. II. Evidence for the association of cytoplasmic ribosomes with the outer mitochondrial membrane in situ. *J Biol Chem* 249:3297, 1974.

445. KELLEMS RE, ALLISON VF, BUTOW RA: Cytoplasmic type 80S ribosomes associated with yeast mitochondria. IV. Attachment of ribosomes to the outer membrane of isolated mitochondria. *J Cell Biol* 65:1, 1975.

446. SCHLEYER M, NEUPERT W: Transport of proteins into mitochondria: Translocational intermediates spanning contact sites between outer and inner membranes. *Cell* 43:339, 1985.

447. SCHWAIGER M, HERZOG V, NEUPERT W: Characterization of translocation contact sites involved in the import of mitochondrial proteins. *J Cell Biol* 105:235, 1987.

448. BENZ R: Porin from bacterial and mitochondrial outer membranes. *CRC Crit Rev Biochem* 19:145, 1985.

449. ANDERSON S, BANKIER AT, BARRELL BG, de BRUIJN MHL, COULSON AR, DROUIN J, EPERON IC, NIERLICH DP, ROE BA, SANGER SF, SCHREIR PH, SMITH AJH, STADEN R, YOUNG IG: Sequence and organization of the human mitochondrial genome. *Nature* 290:457, 1981.

450. BOHNI P, DAUM G, SCHATZ G: Import of proteins into mitochondria. Partial purification of a matrix-located protease involved in cleavage of mitochondrial precursor polypeptides. *J Biol Chem* 258:4937, 1983.

451. YAFFE MP, OHTA S, SCHATZ G: A yeast mutant temperature-sensitive for mitochondrial assembly is deficient in a mitochondrial protease activity that cleaves imported precursor polypeptides. *EMBO J* 4:2069, 1985.

452. MIHARA K, SATO R: Molecular cloning and sequencing of cDNA for yeast porin, an outer mitochondrial membrane protein: A search for targeting signal in the primary structure. *EMBO J* 4:769, 1985.

453. HASE T, MULLER U, RIESMAN H, SCHATZ G: A 70-kd protein of the yeast mitochondrial outer membrane is targeted and anchored via its extreme amino terminus. *EMBO J* 3:3157, 1984.

454. ZIMMERMAN R, PALUCH U, NEUPERT W: Cell-free synthesis of cytochrome c. *FEBS Lett* 108:141, 1979.

455. MATSUURA A, ARPIN M, HAMMUM E, MARGOLIASH E, SABATINI DD, MORIMOTO T: *In vitro* synthesis and posttranslational uptake of cytochrome c into apocytochrome c. *Proc Natl Acad Sci USA* 78:4368, 1981.

456. ADRIAN GS, MCCAMMON MT, MONTGOMERY DL, DOUGLAS MG: Sequences required for delivery and localization of the ADP/ATP translocator to the mitochondrial inner membrane. *Mol Cell Biol* 6:626, 1986.

457. GASSER S, SCHATZ G: Import of proteins into mitochondria. In vitro studies on the biogenesis of the outer membrane. *J Biol Chem* 258:3427, 1983.

458. KORB H, NEUPERT W: Biogenesis of cytochrome c in Neurospora crassa. Synthesis of apocytochrome c, transfer to mitochondria and conversion to holocytochrome c. *Eur J Biochem* 91:609, 1978.

459. ZWIZINSKI C, SCHLEYER M, NEUPERT W: Transfer of proteins into mitochondria. Precursor to the ADP/ATP carrier binds to receptor sites on isolated mitochondria. *J Biol Chem* 258:4071, 1983.

460. ZWIZINSKI C, SCHLEYER M, NEUPERT W: Proteinaceous receptors for the import of mitochondrial precursors. *J Biol Chem* 259:7850, 1984.

461. HENNIG B, KOEHLER H, NEUPERT W: Receptor sites involved in posttranslational transport of apocytochrome c into mitochondria: Specificity, affinity, and number of sites. *Proc Natl Acad Aci USA* 80:4963, 1983.

462. SUISSA M, SCHATZ G: Import of proteins into mitochondria. Translatable mRNAs for imported mitochondrial proteins are present in free as well as mitochondria-bound cytoplasmic polysomes. *J Biol Chem* 257:13048, 1982.

463. GILLESPIE LL, ARGAN C, TANEJA AT, HODGES RS, FREEMAN KB, SHORE GC: A synthetic signal peptide blocks import of precursor proteins destined for the mitochondrial inner membrane or matrix. *J Biol Chem* 260:16045, 1985.

464. ZIMMERMANN R, HENNIG B, NEUPERT W: Different transport pathways of individual precursor proteins in mitochondria. *Eur J Biochem* 116:455, 1981.

465. MIHARA K, BLOBEL G, SATO R: In vitro synthesis and integration into mitochondria of porin, a major protein of the outer mitochondrial membrane of Saccharomyces cerevisiae. *Proc Natl Acad Sci USA* 79:7102, 1982.

466. FRIETAG H, JANES M, NEUPERT W: Biosynthesis of mitochondrial porin and insertion into the outer mitochondrial membrane of Neurospora crassa. *Eur J Biochem* 126:197, 1982.

467. NELSON N, SCHATZ G: Energy-dependent processing of cytoplasmically made precursors to mitochondrial proteins. *Proc Natl Acad Sci USA* 76:4365, 1979.

468. ZIMMERMAN R, NEUPERT W: Transport of proteins into mitochondria. Posttranslational transfer of ADP/ATP carrier into mitochondria in vitro. *Eur J Biochem* 109:217, 1980.

469. SCHLEYEER M, SCHMIDT B, NEUPERT W: Requirement of a membrane potential for the posttranslational transfer of proteins into mitochondria. *Eur J Biochem* 125:109, 1982.

470. SCHATZ G: How mitochondria import proteins from the cytoplasm. *FEBS Lett* 103:203, 1979.

471. MacCECCHINI M-L, RUDIN Y, BLOBEL G, SCHATZ G: Import of proteins into mitochondria: Precursor forms of the extramitochondrially made F_1-ATPase subunits in yeast. *Proc Natl Acad Sci USA* 76:343, 1979.

472. HALLERMAYER G, ZIMMERMAN R, NEUPERT W: Kinetic studies on the transport of cytoplasmically synthesized proteins into the mitochondria in intact cells of Neurospora crassa. *Eur J Biochem* 81:523, 1977.

473. REID GA, SCHATZ G: Import of proteins into mitochondria. Yeast cells grown in the presence of carbonyl cyanide m-chlorophenylhydrazone accumulate massive amounts of some mitochondrial precursor polypeptides. *J Biol Chem* 257:13056, 1982.

474. REID GA, SCHATZ G: Import of proteins into mitochondria. Extramitochondrial pools and post-translational import of mitochondrial protein precursors in vivo. *J Biol Chem* 257:13062, 1982.

475. REID GA, YONETANI T, SCHATZ G: Import of proteins into mitochondria. Import and maturation of the mitochondrial intermembrane space enzymes cytochrome b2 and cytochrome c peroxidase in intake yeast cells. *J Biol Chem* 257:13068, 1982.

476. von HEIJNE G: Mitochondrial targeting sequences may form amphiphilic helices. *EMBO J* 5:1335, 1986.

477. ROISE D, HORVATH SJ, TOMICH JM, RICHARDS JH, SCHATZ G: A chemically synthesized pre-sequence of an imported mitochondrial protein can form an amphiphilic helix and perturb natural and artificial phospholipid bilayers. *EMBO J* 5:1327, 1986.

478. HURT EC, PESOLD-HURT B, SCHATZ G: The amino-terminal region of an imported mitochondrial precursor polypeptide can direct cytoplasmic di-

hydrofolate reductase into the mitochondrial matrix. *EMBO J* 3:3149, 1984.

479. HURT EC, PESOLD-HURT B, SUDA K, OPPLIGER W, SCHATZ G: The first 12 amino acids (less than half of the pre-sequence) of an imported mitochondrial protein can direct mouse cytosolic dihydrofolate reductase into the yeast mitochondrial matrix. *EMBO J* 4:2061, 1985.

480. van LOON APGM, BRANDLI AW, SCHATZ G: The presequences of two imported mitochondrial proteins contain information for intracellular and intramitochondrial sorting. *Cell* 44:801, 1986.

481. HORWICH AL, KALOUSEK F, MELLMAN I, ROSENBERG LE: A leader peptide is sufficient to direct mitochondrial import of a chimeric protein. *EMBO J* 4:1129, 1985.

482. HORWICH AL, KALOUSEK F, FENTON WA, POLLOCK RA, ROSENBERG LE: Targeting of pre-ornithine transcarbamylase to mitochondria: Definition of critical regions and residues in the leader peptide. *Cell* 44:451, 1986.

483. FENTON WA, HACK AM, KRAUS JP, ROSENBERG LE: Immunochemical studies of fibroblasts from patients with methymalonyl-CoA mutase apoenzyme deficiency: Detection of a mutation interfering with mitochondrial import. *Proc Natl Acad Sci USA* 84:1421, 1987.

484. KENG T, ALANI E, GUARENTE L: The nine amino-terminal residues of delta-aminolevulinate synthase direct β-galactosidase into the mitochondrial matrix. *Mol Cell Biol* 6:355, 1986.

485. HORWICH AL, KALOUSEK F, FENTON WA, FURTAK K, POLLOCK RA, ROSENBERG LE: The orithine transcarbamylase leader peptide directs mitochondrial import through both its midportion structure and net positive charge. *J Cell Biol* 105:669, 1987.

486. HURT EC, SCHATZ G: A cytosolic protein contains a cryptic mitochondrial targeting signal. *Nature* 325:499, 1987.

487. EILERS M, SCHATZ G: Binding of a specific ligand inhibits import of a purified precursor protein into mitochondria. *Nature* 322:228, 1986.

488. CHEN W-J, DOUGLAS MG: Phosphodiester bond cleavage outside mitochondria is required for the completion of protein import into the mitochondrial matrix. *Cell* 49:651, 1987.

489. EILERS M, OPPLIGER W, SCHATZ G: Both ATP and an energized inner membrane are required to import a purified precursor protein into mitochondria. *EMBO J* 6:1073, 1987.

490. PFANNER N, TROPSCHUG M, NEUPERT W: Mitochondrial protein import: Nucleoside triphosphates are involved in conferring import-competence to precursors. *Cell* 49:815, 1987.

491. VERNER K, SCHATZ G: Import of an incompletely folded precursor protein into isolated mitochondria requires an energized inner membrane, but no added ATP. *EMBO J* 6:2449, 1987.

492. OHTA S, SCHATZ G: A purified precursor polypeptide requires a cytosolic protein fraction for import into mitochondria. *EMBO J* 3:651, 1984.

493. HURT EC, MUELLER U, SCHATZ G: The first twelve amino acids of a yeast mitochondrial outer membrane protein can direct a nuclear-encoded cytochrome oxidase subunit to the mitochondrial inner membrane. *EMBO J* 4:3509, 1985.

494. van LOON APGM, BRANDLI AW, PESOLT-HURT B, BLANK D, SCHATZ G: Transport of proteins to the mitochondrial intermembrane space: The "matrix-targeting" and the "sorting" domain in the cytochrome c_1 presequence. *EMBO J* 6:2433, 1987.

495. van LOON APGM, SCHATZ G: Transport of protein to the mitochondrial inter-membrane space: The "sorting" domain of the cytochrome c_1 presequence is a stop-transfer sequence specific for the mitochondrial inner membrane. *EMBO J* 6:2441, 1987.

496. ZWIZINSKI C, NEUPERT W: Precursor proteins are transported into mitochondria in the absence of proteolytic cleavage of the additional sequences. *J Biol Chem* 258:13340, 1983.

497. KAPUT J, GOLTZ S, BLOBEL G: Nucleotide sequence of the yeast nuclear gene for cytochrome c peroxidase precursor. Functional implications of the presequence for protein transport into mitochondria. *J Biol Chem* 257:15054, 1982.

498. GUIARD B: Structure, expression and regulation of a nuclear gene encoding a mitochondrial protein: The yeast L(+)-lactate cytochrome c oxidoreductase (cytochrome b_2). *EMBO J* 3:3157, 1985.

499. SADLER I, SUDA K, SCHATZ G, KAUDEWITZ F, HAID A: Sequencing of the nuclear gene for the yeast cytochrome c_1 precursor reveals an unusually complex amino-terminal presequence. *EMBO J* 3:2137, 1984.

500. DAUM G, GASSER SM, SCHATZ G: Import of proteins into mitochondria. Energy-dependent, two-step processing of the intermembrane space enzyme cytochrome b_2 by isolated yeast mitochondria. *J Biol Chem* 257:13075, 1982.

501. OHASHI A, GIBSON J, GREGOR R, SCHATZ G: Import of proteins into mitochondria. The precursor of cytochrome c_1 is processed in two steps, one of them heme dependent. *J Biol Chem* 257:13042, 1982.

502. HARTL F-U, OSTERMANN J, GUIARD B, NEUPERT W: Successive translocation into and out of the mitochondrial matrix: Targeting of proteins to the intermembrane space by a bipartite signal peptide. *Cell* 51:1027, 1987.

503. LI Y, LEONARD K, WEISS H: Membrane-bound and water-soluble cytochrome c_1 from neurospora mitochondria. *Eur J Biochem* 116:199, 1981.

504. HARTL F-U, SCHMIDT B, WACHTER E, WEISS H, NEUPERT W: Transport into mitochondria and intramitochondrial sorting of the Fe/S protein of Ubiquinol-Cytochrome c reductase. *Cell* 47:939, 1986.

505. VIEBROCK A, PERZ A, SEBALD W: The imported preprotein of the proteolipid subunit of the mitochondrial ATP synthase from neurospora crassa. Molecular cloning and sequencing of the mRNA. *EMBO J* 5:565, 1982.

506. SCHMIDT B, WACHTER E, SEBALD W, NEUPERT W: Processing peptidase of Neurospora mitochondria two-step cleavage of imported ATPase subunit 9. *Eur J Biochem* 144:581, 1984.

507. NGUYEN M, SHORE GC: Import of hybrid vesicular stomatitis G protein to the mitochondrial inner membrane. *J Biol Chem* 262:3929, 1987.

508. de DUVE C, BAUDHUIN P: Peroxisomes (microbodies and related particles). *Physiol Rev* 46:323, 1966.

509. TOLBERT NE: Metabolic pathways in peroxisomes and glyoxysomes. *Annu Rev Biochem* 50:133, 1981.

510. KINDL H: The biosynthesis of microbodies (peroxisomes, glyoxysomes). *Int Rev Cytol* 80:193, 1982.

511. KINDL H, LAZAROW PB (eds): Peroxisomes and glyoxysomes. *Ann NY Acad Aci* 386:1, 1982.

512. BORST P: Animal peroxisomes (microbodies), lipid biosynthesis and the Zellweger syndrome. *Trends Biochem* 8:269, 1983.

513. LAZAROW PB, FUJIKI Y: Biogenesis of peroxisomes. *Annu Rev Cell Biol* 1:489, 1985.

514. LAZAROW PB: The role of peroxisomes in mammalian cellular metabolism. *J Inherited Metab Dis (suppl)*10:11, 1987.

515. NOVIKOFF PM, NOVIKOFF AB: Peroxisomes in absorptive cells of mammalian small intestine. *J Cell Biol* 53:532, 1972.

516. NOVIKOFF PM, NOVIKOFF AB, QUINTANA N, DAVIS C: Studies on microperoxisomes. III. Observations on human and rat hepatocytes. *J Histochem Cytochem* 21:540, 1973.

517. GORGAS K: Peroxisomes in sebaceous glands. V. Complex peroxisomes in the mouse preputial gland: Serial sectioning and three-dimensional reconstruction studies. *Anat Embryol* 169:261, 1984.

518. LAZAROW PB, SHIO H, ROBBI M: Biogenesis of peroxisomes and the peroxisome reticulum hypothesis, in Bucher T, Sebald W, Weiss H (eds): *Organelle Formation*, 31st Mosbach Colloq. Biol. Chem. New York, Springer-Verlag, 1980, p 187.

519. LEIGHTON F, POOLE B, BEAUFAY H, BAUDHUIN P, COFFEY JW, FOWLER S, de DUVE C: The large-scale separation of peroxisomes, mitochondria, and lysosomes from the livers of rats injected with Triton WR-1339: Improved isolation procedures, automated analysis, biochemical and morphological properties of fractions. *J Cell Biol* 37:482, 1968.

520. WATTIAUX R, WATTIAUX-DE CONINCK S, RONVEAUX-DUPAL MF, DUBOIS F: Isolation of rat liver lysosomes by isopycnic centrifugation in a metrizamide gradient. *J Cell Biol* 78:349, 1978.

521. BRONFMAN M, INESTROSA NC, LEIGHTON F: Fatty acid oxidation by human liver peroxisomes. *Biochem Biophys Res Commun* 88:1030, 1979.

522. LAZAROW PB, de DUVE C: A fatty acyl–CoA oxidizing system in rat liver peroxisomes; enhancement by clofibrate, a hypolipidemic drug. *Proc Natl Acad Sci USA* 73:2043, 1976.

523. LAZAROW PB: Rat liver peroxisomes catalyze the β-oxidation of fatty acids. *J Biol Chem* 253:1522, 1978.

524. HASHIMOTO T: Individual peroxisomal β-oxidation enzymes. *Ann NY Acad Sci* 386:5, 1982.

525. SVOBODA DJ, AZARNOFF DL: Response of hepatic microbodies to a hypolipidemic agent, ethyl chlorophenoxyisobutyrate (CPIB). *J Cell Biol* 30:442, 1966.

526. HAJRA AK, BISHOP JE: Glycerolipid biosynthesis in peroxisomes via the acyl dihydroxyacetone phosphate pathway, in Kindl H, Lazarow PB (eds): Peroxisomes and glyoxysomes. *Ann NY Acad Sci* 386:170, 1982.

527. LAZAROW PB, BLACK V, SHIO H, FUJIKI Y, HAJRA AK, DATTA NS, BANGARU B, DANCIS J: Zellweger syndrome: Biochemical and morphological studies on two patients treated with clofibrate. *J Pediatr Res* 19:1356, 1985.

528. SCHRAM AW, STRIJLAND A, HASHIMOTO T, WANDERS RJA, SCHUTGENS RBH, van den BOSCH H, TAGER JM: Biosynthesis and maturation of peroxisomal β-oxidation enzymes in fibroblasts in relation to the Zellweger syndrome and infantile Refsum disease. *Proc Natl Acad Sci USA* 83:6158, 1986.

529. DATTA NS, WILSON GN, HAJRA AK: Deficiency of enzymes catalyzing the biosynthesis of glycerol-ether lipids in Zellweger syndrome. A new category of metabolic disease involving the absence of peroxisomes. *N Engl J Med* 17:1080, 1984.

530. GOLDFISCHER S, MOORE CL, JOHNSON AB, SPIRO AJ, VALSAMIS MP, WIS-

NIEWSKI HK, RITCH RH, NORTON WT, RAPIN I, GARTNER LM: Peroxisomal and mitochondrial defects in the cerebro-hepato-renal syndrome. *Science* 182:62, 1973.

531. BJORKHEM I, KASE BF, PEDERSEN JI: Role of peroxisomes in the biosynthesis of bile acids. *Scan J Clin Lab Invest* 177:23, 1985.

532. KASE BF, PRYDZ K, BJORKHEM I, PEDERSEN JI: In vitro formation of bile acids from di- and trihydroxy-5β-cholestanoic acid in human liver peroxisomes. *Biochim Biophys Acta* 877:37, 1986.

533. RHODIN J: Correlation of ultrastructural organization and function in normal and experimentally changed proximal convoluted tubule cells of the mouse kidney. PhD thesis. Aktiebolaget Godvil, Stockholm, 1954, p 76.

534. NOVIKOFF AB, SHIN W-Y: The endoplasmic reticulum in the Golgi zone and its relations to microbodies, Golgi apparatus and autophagic vacuoles in rat liver cells. *J Microsc* 3:187, 1964.

535. REDMAN CM, GRAB DJ, IRUKULLA R: The intracellular pathway of newly formed rat liver catalase. *Arch Biochem Biophys* 152:496, 1972.

536. LAZAROW PB, de DUVE C: The synthesis and turnover of rat liver peroxisomes. V. Intracellular pathway of catalase synthesis. *J Cell Biol* 59:507, 1973.

537. GOLDMAN BM, BLOBEL G: Biogenesis of peroxisomes: Intracellular site of synthesis of catalase and uricase. *Proc Natl Acad Sci USA* 75:5066, 1978.

538. RACHUBINSKI RA, FUJIKI Y, MORTENSEN RM, LAZAROW PB: Acyl-CoA oxidase and hydratase-dehydrogenase, two enzymes of the peroxisomal β-oxidation system, are synthesized on free polysomes of clofibrate-treated rat liver. *J Cell Biol* 99:2241, 1984.

539. MIURA S, MORI M, TAKIGUCHI M, TATIBANA M, FURUTA S, MIYAZAWA S, HASHIMOTO T: Biosynthesis and intracellular transport of enzymes of peroxisomal β-oxidation. *J Biol Chem* 259:6397, 1984.

540. FUJIKI Y, RACHUBINSKI RA, MORTENSEN RM, LAZAROW PB: Synthesis of 3-ketoacyl-CoA thiolase of rat liver peroxisomes on free polyribosomes as a larger precursor. Induction of thiolase mRNA activity by clofibrate. *Biochem J* 226:697, 1985.

541. FUJIKI Y, LAZAROW PB: Post-translational import of fatty acyl–CoA oxidase and catalase into peroxisomes of rat liver in vitro. *J Biol Chem* 260:5603, 1985.

542. OSUMI T, ISHII N, HIJIKATA M, KAMIJO K, OZASA H, FURUTA S, SHOKO M, KONDO K, INOUE K, KAGAMIYAMA H, HASHIMOTO T: Molecular cloning and nucleotide sequence of the cDNA for rat peroxisomal enoyl-CoA: Hydratase-3-hydroxyacyl-CoA dehydrogenase bifunctional enzyme. *J Biol Chem* 260:8905, 1985.

543. ARAKAWA H, TAKIGUCHI M, AMAYA Y, NAGATA S, HAYASHI H, MORI M: cDNA-derived amino acid sequence of rat mitochondrial 3-oxoacyl-CoA thiolase with no transient presequence: Structural relationship with peroxisomal isozyme. *EMBO J* 6:1361, 1987.

544. FUJIKI Y, FOWLER S, SHIO H, HUBBARD AL, LAZAROW PB: Polypeptide and phospholipid composition of the membrane of rat liver peroxisomes: Comparison with endoplasmic reticulum and mitochondrial membranes. *J Cell Biol* 93:103, 1982.

545. FUJIKI Y, RACHUBINSKI RA, LAZAROW PB: Synthesis of a major integral membrane polypeptide of rat liver peroxisomes on free polysomes. *Proc Natl Acad Sci USA* 81:7127, 1984.

546. KOSTER A, HEISIG M, HEINRICH PC, JUST WW: In vitro synthesis of peroxisomal membrane polypeptides. *Biochem Biophys Res Commun* 137:626, 1986.

547. SUZUKI Y, ORII T, TAKIGUCHI M, MORI M, HIJIKATA M, HASHIMOTO T: Biosynthesis of membrane polypeptides of rat liver peroxisomes. *J Biochem (Tokyo)* 101:491, 1987.

548. KELLER GA, BARTON MC, SHAPIRO DJ, SINGER SJ: 3-Hydroxy-3-methylglutaryl coenzyme A reductase is present in peroxisomes in normal rat liver cells. *Proc Natl Acad Sci USA* 82:770, 1985.

549. KELLER GA, PAZIRANDEH M, KRISANS S: 3-Hydroxy-methylglutaryl coenzyme A reductase localization in rat liver peroxisomes and microsomes of control and cholestyramine-treated animals: Quantitative biochemical and immunoelectron microscopical analyses. *J Cell Biol* 103:875, 1986.

550. GOULD SJ, KELLER GA, SUBRAMANI S: Identification of a peroxisomal targeting signal at the carboxy terminus of firefly luciferase. *J Cell Biol* 105:2923, 1987.

551. KELLER GA, GOULD S, DELUCA M, SUBRAMANI S: Firefly luciferase is targeted to peroxisomes in mammalian cells. *Proc Natl Acad Sci USA* 84:3264, 1987.

552. VEENHUIS M, VAN DIJKEN JP, HARDER W: The significance of peroxisomes in the metabolism of one-carbon compounds in yeast. *Adv Microb Physiol* 24:1, 1983.

553. ROGGENKAMP R, SAHM H, HINKELMANN W, WAGNER F: Alcohol oxidase and catalase in peroxisomes of methanol-grown Candida boidinii. *Eur J Biochem* 59:231, 1975.

554. GOODMAN JM: Dihydroxyacetone synthase is an abundant constituent of the methanol-induced peroxisome of Candida boidinii. *J Biol Chem* 260:7108, 1985.

555. ROA M, BLOBEL G: Biosynthesis of peroxisomal enzymes in the methylotrophic yeast Hansenula polymorpha. *Proc Natl Acad Sci USA* 80:6872, 1983.

556. GOODMAN JM, SCOTT CW, DONAHUE PN, ATHERTON JP: Alcohol oxidase assembles post-translationally into the peroxisome of Candida boidinii. *J Biol Chem* 259:8485, 1984.

557. BELLION E, GOODMAN JM: Proton ionophores prevent assembly of a peroxisomal protein. *Cell* 48:165, 1987.

558. MOSER HW: New approaches in peroxisomal disorders. *Dev Neurosci* 9:1, 1987.

559. SCHUTGENS RBH, WANDERS RJA, HEYMANS HSA, SCHRAM AW, TAGER JM, SCHRAKAMP G, van den BOSCH H: Zellweger syndrome: Biochemical procedures in diagnosis, prevention and treatment. *J Inherited Metab Dis* 10:33, 1987.

560. LAZAROW PB, FUJIKI Y, SMALL GM, WATKINS P, MOSER H: Presence of the peroxisomal 22-kDa integral membrane protein in the liver of a person lacking recognizable peroxisomes (Zellweger syndrome). *Proc Natl Acad Sci USA* 83:9193, 1986.

561. SCHROEDER WT, SAUNDERS GF: Localization of the human catalase and apolipoprotein A-I genes to chromosome 11. *Cytogenet Cell Genet* 44:231, 1987.

562. HASHMI M, STANLEY W, SINGH I: Lignoceroyl-CoASH ligase-enzyme defect in fatty acid beta-oxidation system in X-linked childhood adenoleukodystrophy. *FEBS Lett* 196:247, 1986.

563. GOLDFISHER SL, COLLINS J, RAPIN I, NEUMANN P, NEGLIA W, SPIRO AJ, ISHII T, ROELS F, VAMECQ J, VAN HOOF F: Pseudo-Zellweger syndrome: Deficiencies in several peroxisomal oxidative activities. *J Pediatr* 108:25, 1986.

564. SCHRAM AW, GOLDFISCHER S, van ROERMUND CWT, BROUWER-KELDER EM, COLLINS J, HASHIMOTO T, HEYMANS HSA, van den BOSCH H, SCHUTGENS RBH, TAGER JM, WANDERS RJA: Human peroxisomal 3-oxoacyl-coenzyme A thiolase deficiency. *Proc Natl Acad Sci USA* 84:2494, 1987.

CHAPTER **4**

THE HLA COMPLEX: Genetic Polymorphism and Disease Susceptibility

DONNA D. KOSTYU
D. BERNARD AMOS

1. HLA, the major histocompatibility complex (MHC) in humans, consists of a cluster of genes, the HLA haplotype, on chromosome 6. Best known are genes which determine serologically defined antigens. Others function in the generation and regulation of immune responsiveness, and genes throughout the cluster are associated with the mediation of interactions between cells of the immune system and thus with susceptibility or resistance to disease.

2. There are seven internationally recognized, highly polymorphic components of the human MHC. HLA-A, -B, and -C are transmembrane glycoproteins found on most nucleated cells and are collectively known as class I antigens. They have a molecular weight of 44,000 and are associated with a nonpolymorphic polypeptide with a molecular weight of 11,000 called β_2-microglobulin. The class II HLA-DR, -DQ, and -DP antigens consist of two tightly bound transmembrane glycoproteins with molecular weights of 34,000 and 29,000. Expression is restricted primarily to B lymphocytes, monocytes, macrophages, activated T cells, and endothelial cells. A functional activity designated HLA-D is recognized through the complex proliferative responses to allogeneic cells in mixed lymphocyte cultures. Many other class I and class II genes have been defined; some are pseudogenes and others may not be expressed.

3. The products of the MHC were originally defined serologically with alloantibodies and by the functional mixed lymphocyte culture assay. Further recognition of epitopes on both class I and class II molecules has come with cellular reagents (primed proliferative and primed cytotoxic T-cell lines) and biochemical approaches (isoelectric focusing, 2-D gels, amino acid sequencing) and at the DNA level (hybridization with known probes and Southern blotting).

4. Evidence for the involvement of the MHC in immune recognition and response came from studies with laboratory animals and is being confirmed in humans. The generation and control of an efficient immune response require specific cooperation between two or more subsets of lymphocytes which must share MHC antigens, especially class II antigens. In addition, the recognition of virally infected or chemically modified cells may depend on the modification of predominantly class I antigens and subsequent recognition of these altered self-MHC antigens.

5. Evidence for the involvement of the MHC in disease processes has been striking. Different alleles of different loci are associated with a wide variety of diseases. Examples include the association of HLA-DR and -DQ with type 1 insulin dependent diabetes mellitus, HLA-DR3 with endocrine disorders, HLA-DR2 with narcolepsy, HLA-B27 with ankylosing spondylitis, and HLA-A3 with hemochromatosis. While these associations have been made most often at the population level, formal linkage has been demonstrated for hemochromatosis and for 21-hydroxylase deficiency. Some diseases appear to be directly due to genetic variation in an HLA molecule (e.g., the involvement of DQ alleles in IDDM), while other diseases such as 21-hydroxylase deficiency are due to deletions or other abnormalities of genes closely linked to the HLA markers. Still other diseases appear to segregate with an HLA haplotype within families but show no association with a particular HLA allele at the population level. Different ethnic groups are often characterized both by antigens largely restricted to that population and by diseases which may be associated with those specificities.

6. There are different causes for disease associations with HLA. Malfunction or deletion of genes regulating enzymes and complement components, the modification of the HLA gene products by infectious agents, or cross-reactivity between HLA components and viruses or bacterial products are examples. Some genes in the MHC may determine predisposition to disease and some resistance. Thus, MHC genes determining the rates, levels, or balance of cellular and humoral immune responses may affect the prognosis or complications of a disease.

HLA, the designation given to a cluster of genes located on the short arm of chromosome 6 (Fig. 4-1), is the major histocompatibility complex (MHC) of humans.[1–4] The MHC genes specify a set of proteins that occupy the outer surfaces of cells. The genes at the MHC loci are highly polymorphic—that is, in the population at large there are many different alleles at each locus. Each individual in the population inherits two specific alleles at each locus and is thus genetically distinct. When exposed to cells from other individuals in the same species, responding individuals form antibodies (alloantibodies) and/or cytotoxic T cells against the antigens that are foreign.

All mammals and birds that have been adequately tested have an MHC which is surprisingly similar.[4,5] The evolution of a cluster of many genes into an MHC appears to have begun during the age of Amphibia and to have been well advanced by the development of Reptilia.[4,5] That it has important functions is evidenced by its conservation during the divergence of birds from mammals and the early death from immunodefi-

Nonstandard abbreviations used in this chapter are: TNF = tumor necrosis factor; GLO = glyoxalase locus; PGK = phosphoglycerate kinase; MHC = major histocompatibility complex; HLA = the major histocompatibility complex in humans; Ig = immunoglobulin; RFLP = restriction fragment length polymorphism; HTC = homozygous typing cells; MLR = mixed lymphocyte response; MLC = mixed lymphocyte culture; PLT = primed lymphocyte test; Ir = immune response; CTL = cytotoxic lymphocyte.

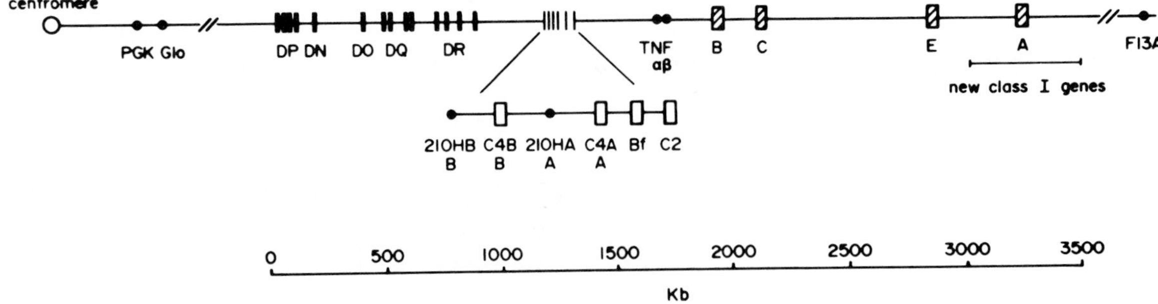

Fig. 4-1 Schematic diagram of the functional classes of HLA genes. The centromere is indicated by a circle. The MHC, from HLA-DP to HLA-A, spans approximately 3500 kb. The HLA-D region consists of three subregions (DR, DQ, and DP), each of which contains multiple genes; more detailed information on the D region is given in Fig. 4-6. New class I loci, similar to Qa, Tla in the mouse, will probably localize near HLA-A. Genes for the tumor necrosis factors are located midway between C2 and HLA-B. Genes for human phosphoglycerate kinase (PGK), glyoxalase (Glo), and coagulation factor F13A are linked to the MHC.

ciency of some few humans who lack MHC-specified antigens.[6,7] *Histocompatibility* refers to the involvement of the MHC in tissue or organ graft rejection. *Major* refers to the fact that rejection between two individuals of the same species who differ at the MHC is rapid and can be arrested only by extensive immune suppression of the recipient. This is in contrast to minor histocompatibility antigen involvement, in which incompatibility leads to a chronic rejection more easily controlled with immunosuppression. The system is *complex* because many genes of differing function are clustered together to form the MHC. Although the term *histocompatibility* is an old one, derived from allotransplants, it is entirely appropriate since MHC genes are intricately involved in self-recognition processes, in lymphocyte interactions, and in rejection of virally or chemically modified autologous cells, including transformed cells.

The term HLA is often regarded as an abbreviation for human leukocyte antigens. The first studies were prompted by searches for autoimmune antibodies in hemolytic anemia and leukopenia, and by investigations into tumor antigens responsible for skin and tissue rejection in the mouse, which led to the identification of the murine MHC H-2.[8] Mouse transplantation genetics were applied to human kidney transplantation and within a period of less than 10 years, the importance and complexity of HLA was realized. Only later was it recognized that genes in the HLA region are general regulators of the immune response and that the HLA antigens themselves, or genes linked to HLA, play a role in disease susceptibility.

This chapter describes the components of the HLA system, their biochemistry when known, their polymorphic nature, and their involvement in and regulation of the immune response. We then present some of the diseases known to be associated with these antigens and some of the problems in converting an association with HLA to genetic linkage to HLA.

OVERVIEW: HLA AS A SUPERGENE

The concept of a supergene originated in 1931 when Fischer[9] coined the term and defined it as a group of closely linked loci which have evolved together and function in concert. Selective interactions between the genes or their products maintain linkage. Cepellini introduced a helpful term, haplotype. This can be defined as the array of genes clustered together on a single chromosome that together constitute a functional unit, in this case HLA. The HLA supergene (Fig. 4-1) is found on the sixth chromosome in humans.

The human MHC contains three basic subregions, each coding for distinct products. Class I refers to the HLA-A, -B, and -C molecules found on most nucleated cells. Class II molecules (HLA-DR, -DQ, and -DP) are considered differentiation antigens restricted to particular cell lineages, while class III genes encode several complement components. The class I, II, and III families evolved from gene duplication. The primordial genes are similar to immunoglobulins, and it is thought that the MHC is part of the immunoglobulin supergene family (Fig. 4-2), a series of structures which functions at the cell surface and often interacts with others of the supergene family to control differentiation, cell movement, and cell-cell interactions. Other members include antigen recognition structures (e.g., immunoglobulins, T-cell receptor), T-cell-associated recognition units (e.g., CD4, CD8), immunoglobulin binding molecules (e.g., Fc receptor), neural cell adhesion molecules, myelin-associated glycoproteins, platelet derived growth factor receptor, and others.[9a]

The map order is as follows: centromere, the class II gene cluster or HLA-D region, the complement or class III cluster, the class I cluster, and telomere. The MHC spans approximately 3500 kb, a region 1/750th of the human genome and an area sufficient for 50 genes. The boundaries are not yet precise. Pulsed field gel electrophoresis and cosmid walking have produced long-range genomic restriction maps of the HLA region.[9b] The basic components of the HLA supergene are listed in the following sections.

HLA-A, -B, -C

These are the structural genes for three 44,000 molecular weight glycoproteins (gp44) found on most nucleated cells. Each is an integral component of the plasma membrane. Each gene contains one or more regions that exhibit polymorphism. Polymorphism leads to the production of proteins with differing antigenic sites, or epitopes, which are easily recognizable through antibody-dependent, complement-mediated lysis of peripheral blood lymphocytes, or other tests. The HLA-A, -B, -C antigens represent the most thoroughly understood and most easily detectable gene products of the HLA supergene.

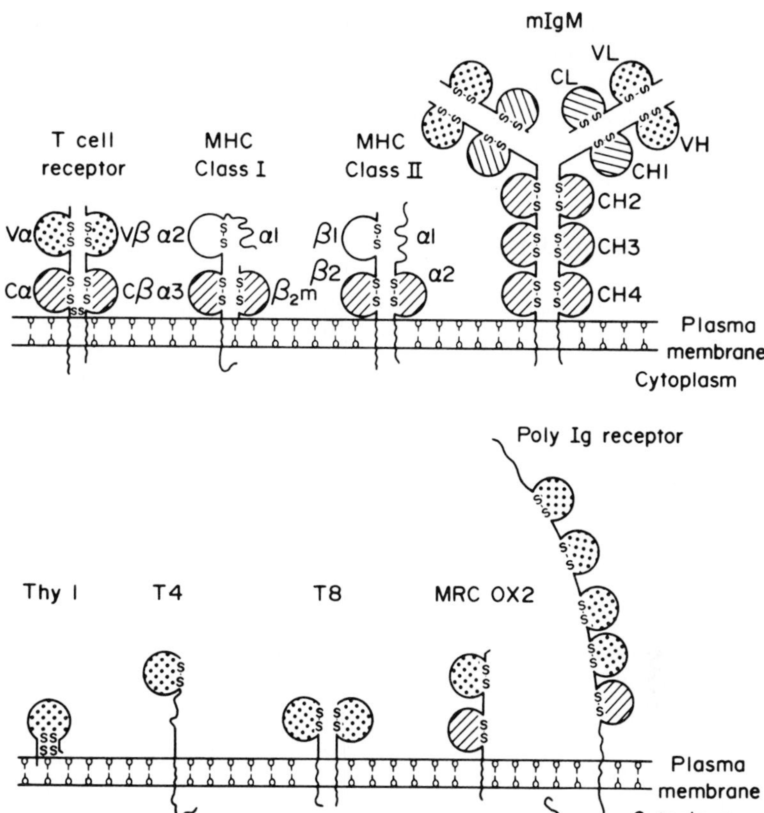

Fig. 4-2 Schematic representation of members of the immunoglobulin supergene family, including the MHC class I and class II antigens, T-cell receptor, and membrane IgM molecule. Domains with similarity to the immunoglobulin constant domains (hatched) and variable regions (dotted) are shaded. *(Reproduced from* The Journal of Clinical Investigation, *1986, volume 77, pages 1411-1415. By copyright permission of the American Society for Clinical Investigation.)*

HLA-D, -DR, -DQ, -DP

The HLA-D region molecules differ from the HLA-A, HLA-B, and HLA-C gene products functionally and structurally; they represent the second type (class II) of MHC antigen. Class II antigens are expressed on resting B cells, macrophages and macrophage-related cells, and possibly vascular endothelium. Some class II antigens are present on a wider variety of activated cells including activated T cells, thyroid parenchyma, and brain. They are formed of two chains, an α and β chain with molecular weights of 34,000 and 29,000, respectively. Both subunits span the membrane, and both chains are determined by closely linked genes within the MHC. The HLA-DR, -DQ, and -DP subregions have been extensively studied by serologic, biochemical, and molecular techniques. The molecular organization is quite complex, with presumptive evidence for other new class II molecules, e.g., DO and DN.

The original identification of "B-cell-specific antigens" through a functional test called the mixed lymphocyte culture, or MLC, led to the hypothesis of a genetic locus which was designated HLA-D. However, numerous class II molecules have been identified, and HLA-D is a term which is retained for occasional use in designating a segment of the chromosome and the functional MLC response.

Complement Components

Structural genes determining C2[10] and C4 (both C4A and C4B loci)[11] of the classic complement pathway and Bf of the alternate complement pathway[12] are closely associated with HLA (reviewed in Refs. 13 and 14) (see Chap. 111). These complement components have been designated class III products of the MHC. Receptors for C3b and C3d, the breakdown fragments of C3, have also been linked to the MHC,[15] as has a C8 deficiency in one study,[16] although other studies have shown no linkage.[17,18]

Other Genes within or near HLA

A locus determining alleles of the red cell enzyme glyoxalase is found approximately 5 centimorgans centromeric of HLA-D.[19] A similar gene is linked to the mouse MHC. This locus is designated GLO. A gene(s) for a human phosphoglycerate kinase (PGK) maps centromeric of GLO.[20] A structural locus for coagulation factor XIII A (F13A) of plasma and platelets maps telomeric to the HLA complex.[21]

Two steroid 21-hydroxylase genes (21-OHA and 21-OHB) map to the region between HLA-DR and HLA-B.[22] Only the 21-OHB is functional. Deletion or regulatory malfunction in the 21-OHB results in congenital adrenal hyperplasia.

Also within the MHC are genes for the two cytokines, α and β tumor necrosis factors (TNF).[9b,23] These cytokines, also called cachectin and lymphotoxin, are secreted by activated macrophages and activated lymphocytes, respectively, in response to stimuli. TNF can activate polymorphonuclear leukocytes and enhance class I gene transcription.

The HLA class I gene family may contain as many as 15 to 20 genes which are distinct from HLA-A, -B, and -C.[1-3] Only one of these, HLA-E, has been officially recognized. Although identification of these protein products by biochemical or serologic assays has been difficult, it seems likely that these genes code for differentiation antigens present on T cells and some leukemic cells and thus are similar to the murine Qa/Tla molecules. These are discussed in "New MHC Loci and Antigens: T-Cell-Specific Antigens," below.

Inheritance of the MHC

Although there are many alleles at the HLA loci, the pattern of inheritance is simple since the entire cluster of genes, or haplotype, usually is inherited as a unit. For convenience the two paternal chromosomes or haplotypes are often designated a and b and the maternal haplotypes c and d. The children must therefore be ac, ad, bc, or bd. This segregation of haplotypes is illustrated in Fig. 4-3. Two sibs inheriting the same haplotypes (e.g., ac and ac) are designated HLA identical, sibs and parents sharing one haplotype (e.g., bc and bd) are haploidentical, and sibs sharing neither haplotype (e.g., ac and bd) are haplodistinct. Recombination between loci occurs frequently (e.g., Fig. 4-3). These relationships have great relevance in kidney transplantation and in many immunologic reactions, including mixed lymphocyte stimulation.

The cluster of the four genes of the complement proteins (Bf, C2, C4A, C4B) on a haplotype is often described as a *complotype*. These complotypes are inherited in families, exhibit pronounced linkage disequilibrium, and are often associated with disease.

Definition of Antigens and Terminology

Current WHO terminology reflects the continuing definition of the serologic and MLC-defined antigens. The current listing of HLA antigens, as of the 1987 workshop, is presented in Table 4-1. There are 24 designated antigens at HLA-A, 52 at HLA-B, 11 at HLA-C, 26 at HLA-D, 20 at HLA-DR, 9 at HLA-DQ, and 6 at HLA-DP. Although DR and DQ are presented as single entities under this system of nomenclature, they actually represent subregions with multiple genes for α or β chains. Antigens may be localized to a particular α or β chain or to an $\alpha\beta$ combination, or they may be shared among several class II molecules. Note that although HLA-D specificities are listed as "antigens," there is no HLA-D locus as such. HLA-D alleles are defined by their function.

Refinements to and modification of the definition of these antigens is accomplished during the periodic International Histocompatibility Testing Workshops.[24-33] Such workshops have been held every 2 or 3 years since 1964. Nomenclature reports updating some antigens and assigning new antigens are published by the World Health Organization as a bulletin following each workshop. These reports are also included in the later *Histocompatibility Testing* volumes and in immunology journals such as *Tissue Antigens, Transplantation,* and *Human Immunology*.

The antigenic complexity of the MHC is striking. HLA antigens may be localized not only to an HLA molecule (e.g., DR), but also to a particular chain (e.g., DR β_1). Several epitopes may coexist on a single molecule (e.g., HLA-Bw4 and HLA-B51). Some alleles can be defined by cellular reagents (proliferative or cytotoxic responses of T cell clones), by biochemical techniques (isoelectric focusing, sequencing), or as restriction fragment length polymorphisms at the DNA level. Alleles defined by one technique may not correlate with those defined by a second technique.

Nomenclature in 1987 takes into account the definition of alleles and genes by conventional serology, new cellular techniques, and sequencing. In the D region, *genes* are prefixed by the letter D, followed by the letter of the subregion (e.g., R or Q or P), the letter A or B for an α or β chain, and then a number if there is more than one α or β chain. Thus, the gene for the DRα chain would be designated DRA and the gene for the DQβ_1 chain as DQB1. In order to delineate gene prod-

Fig. 4-3 Segregation of the HLA haplotypes in a family. The paternal haplotypes are designated a and b, while the maternal haplotypes are designated c and d. One individual is an HLA-A/HLA-B recombinant.

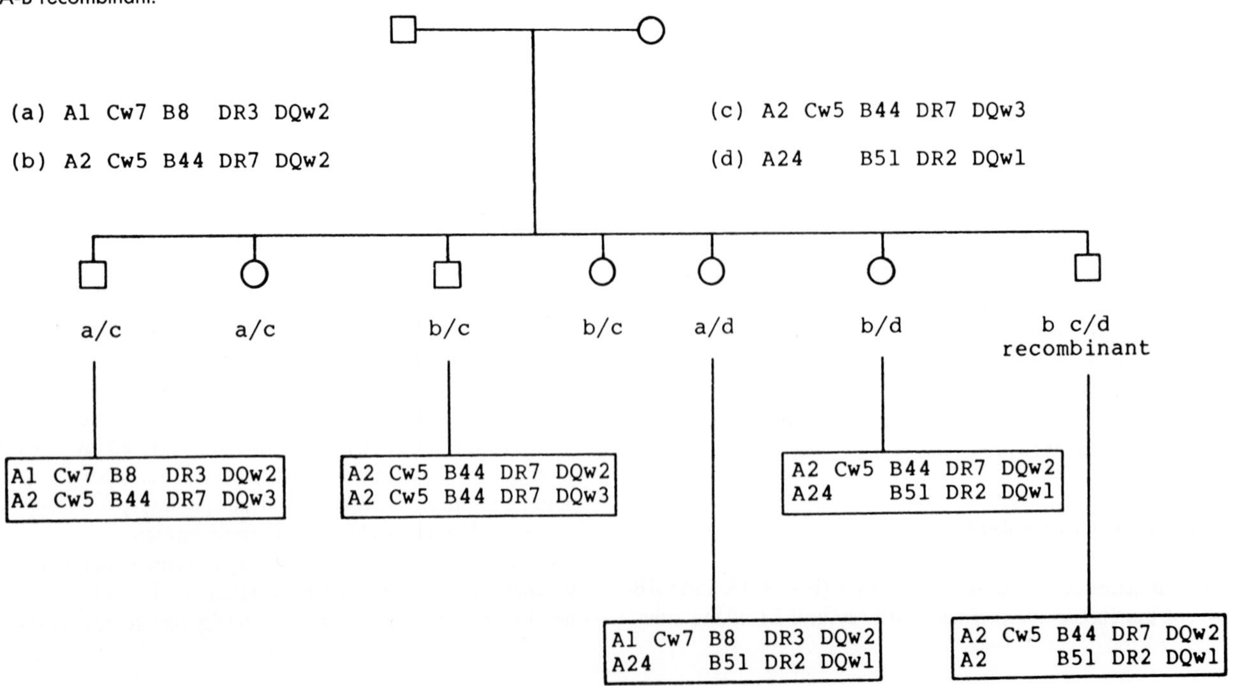

Table 4-1 Complete Listing of Recognized HLA Specificities as Determined by the WHO Terminology Committee, 1987

A	*B*	*C*	*D*	*DR*	*DQ*	*DP*
A1	B5	Cw1	Dw1	DR1	DQw1	DPw1
A2	B7	Cw2	Dw2	DR2	DQw2	DPw2
A3	B8	Cw3	Dw3	DR3	DQw3	DPw3
A9	B12	Cw4	Dw4	DR4	DQw4	DPw4
A10	B13	Cw5	Dw5	DR5	DQw5 (w1)	DPw5
A11	B14	Cw6	Dw6	DRw6	DQw6 (w1)	DPw6
Aw19	B15	Cw7	Dw7	DR7	DQw7 (w3)	
A23 (9)*	B16	Cw8	Dw8	DRw8	DQw8 (w3)	
A24 (9)	B17	Cw9 (w3)	Dw9	DR9	DQw9 (w3)	
A25 (10)	B18	Cw10 (w3)	Dw10	DRw10		
A26 (10)	B21	Cw11	Dw11 (w7)	DRw11 (5)		
A28	Bw22		Dw12	DRw12 (5)		
A29 (w19)	B27		Dw13	DRw13 (w6)		
A30 (w19)	B35		Dw14	DRw14 (w6)		
A31 (w19)	B37		Dw15	DRw15 (2)		
A32 (w19)	B38 (16)		Dw16	DRw16 (2)		
Aw33 (w19)	B39 (16)		Dw17 (w7)	DRw17 (3)		
Aw34 (10)	B40		Dw18 (w6)	DRw18 (3)		
Aw36	Bw41		Dw19 (w6)			
Aw43	Bw42		Dw20	DRw52		
Aw66 (10)	B44 (12)		Dw21	DRw53		
Aw68 (28)	B45 (12)		Dw22			
Aw69 (28)	Bw46		Dw23			
Aw74 (w19)	Bw47		Dw24			
	Bw48		Dw25			
	B49 (21)		Dw26			
	Bw50 (21)					
	B51 (5)					
	Bw52 (5)					
	Bw53					
	Bw54 (w22)					
	Bw55 (w22)					
	Bw56 (w22)					
	Bw57 (17)					
	Bw58 (17)					
	Bw59					
	Bw60 (40)					
	Bw61 (40)					
	Bw62 (15)					
	Bw63 (15)					
	Bw64 (14)					
	Bw65 (14)					
	Bw67					
	Bw70					
	Bw71 (w70)					
	Bw72 (w70)					
	Bw73					
	Bw75 (15)					
	Bw76 (15)					
	Bw77 (15)					
	Bw4					
	Bw6					

NOTE: The small "w" for workshop indicates an antigen that has been accepted provisionally at an international workshop as a specific HLA antigen. When the specificity of such an HLA antigen has been established, the w is deleted.

*Splits or variants of an antigen are listed with the primary antigen listed in parenthesis (e.g., A23 and A24 are variants of A9).

ucts which have been defined or confirmed by amino acid or nucleotide sequences, a unique four digit number is used. The first two numbers reflect the most closely related serologic specificity, the last two numbers the unique sequence. For example, variants of B27 defined by isoelectric focusing electrophoresis have been designated B*2701, B*2702, B*2703, etc., or *B2701* using italics and no asterisk for the combination of gene and allele. There is, at present, no standard terminology for the epitopes. For more information, see the 1987 WHO Nomenclature Report.[34]

HLA-A, -B, AND -C

The HLA-A, -B, and -C antigens are antigenic sites or epitopes on integral membrane glycoprotein molecules present on most nucleated cells. These molecules are believed to be indicative of gene duplication since they exhibit similar biochemical structures and have extensive amino acid homologies. The mutational frequency of HLA-A and HLA-B is unknown, but can be assumed to be high by analogy with the homologous

H-2D and H-2K genes of the mouse and from the extraordinary number of alleles (Table 4-1), a number that is increasing as new methods of detecting alleles become available.

As mentioned earlier, the conventional definition of HLA-A, -B, and -C antigens is serologic. A different set of antigens may be identified by other techniques. A prime example is B27, where at least six variants have been resolved by monoclonal antibodies,[35] amino acid sequencing,[36] class I restricted cytotoxic T cells,[37] isoelectric focusing,[38] and RFLP.[39] Variants of other antigens, for example, HLA-A2,[40,41] A3,[42,43] and B7,[44,45] have been identified by cellular reagents.

The HLA-B molecule carries at least two distinct antigenic sites, one highly polymorphic and the other diallelic (Bw4,Bw6).[46,47] New sites are implicated by patterns of reactivity given by some monoclonal and by many alloantiserums identifying such unusual patterns as HLA-A9, -A32, and -Bw4;[48,49] -Bw6 and -A11;[50] -Bw6 and -Cw3;[51] and -A2 and -B17.[52] The Aw69 antigen is a natural hybrid, presumably arising from intragenic recombination. It shares the α_1 domain of Aw68 and the α_2 and α_3 domains of A2.[53] The biochemical and molecular basis for "antigenicity" of class I antigens and the extensive cross-reactivity seen between particular antigens has been well documented (see, for example, Refs. 49, 52, and 54 to 56).

Tissue Distribution and Expression

The HLA-A, -B, and -C antigens are codominantly expressed on nearly all lymphocytes, macrophages, fibroblasts, platelets, endothelial cells, cells of the spleen, heart, liver, lung, intestine, and kidney, and most other nucleated human cells.[57] These antigens are also present in the placenta but are not on the trophoblast.[58] The red cell Bennett-Goodspeed antigens correlate with several known HLA antigens: Bg^a with HLA-B7, Bg^b with HLA-B17, and Bg^c with HLA-A28,[59] but chemical identity has not been established. The Rogers and Chido antigens represent the complement components C4A and C4B on the red cell surface.[11] Other HLA antigens on the red cell have been detected only through the use of the Auto Technicon and appear to be present in trace quantities, possibly on reticulocytes.

Peripheral blood T lymphocytes have approximately 10^3 to 10^4 HLA molecules per antigen per cell, while cultured B-lymphoblastoid cells may have 5 to 13 times as many.[60,61] HLA-A and -B antigens have been found in soluble form in saliva, serum, plasma,[57,62] urine,[63] seminal plasma,[64] and, in low concentration, in colostrum and milk.[65] For reasons as yet unknown, the concentration of soluble HLA-A9 is higher than that of other antigens. Other perturbations of HLA expression have been recorded, including several cases of HLA deficiency or "bare lymphocyte syndrome,"[6,7,66–68] where circulating lymphocytes lack all HLA-A, -B, and -C antigens. Many, but not all,[66,68] are associated with immunodeficiency. Sullivan and colleagues have traced one defect to a pretranslation regulatory defect of both class I antigens and β_2-microglobulin.[69] Ceppellini has described a chimeric individual who carried both HLA haplotypes of both parents and thus had twice as many antigens as normal.[70] Mayr et al.[71] have presented another example of abnormal heredity in a mother with apparent gonadal mosaicism. The HLA-A, -B, and -C antigens passed on to her children were not expressed on her circulating lymphocytes but were present in the maternal grandmother.

A more common and apparently benign absence of particular HLA-B and -C antigens is characteristic of platelets[72] and fibroblasts of some individuals.[73] This deficiency is not known to be related to any immunologic abnormality. Studies of membrane markers on early lymphoid stem cells have shown that the HLA-A, -B, and -C antigens are not present at detectable levels.[74]

A secondary deficiency of HLA-A, -B, and -C expression in vitro is due to the absence of β_2-microglobulin, since β_2-microglobulin is necessary for membrane transport of the HLA antigens and insertion into the membrane. The most notable example is that of the Daudi cell line.[75]

A number of immune response modulators are known to affect class I expression. For example, interferons (α, β, γ) increase the expression of class I on fibroblasts, T and B lymphocytes, and lymphoblastoid cells (reviewed Ref. 76). Tumor necrosis factor increases both RNA levels and cell surface expression in human tumor cells, vascular endothelial cells, and dermal fibroblasts.[77,78] Both sets of modulators may thus enhance cytolysis of virally infected cells by means of increasing MHC class I expression.

Biochemistry

The HLA-A, -B, and -C molecules are each composed of two noncovalently bound polypeptides, the larger of which is an integral membrane component (Fig. 4-2) (reviewed in Refs. 1 to 3 and 79). This larger, heavy chain determined by the HLA region is a glycoprotein with a molecular weight of 44,000 (gp44). The smaller, light chain is β_2-microglobulin, with a molecular weight of 11,600; it is encoded by a gene on chromosome 15. β_2-Microglobulin polymorphism has not been reported in humans; limited polymorphism occurs in mice.

Biochemical analysis of the HLA molecules required the introduction of several innovative techniques, e.g., the use of enzymes such as ficin or papain which selectively cleave the antigen-bearing portion of the molecules, the use of detergents to solubilize cell membranes, and lectin affinity purification. A number of molecules, including A3,[80] A32,[49] HLA-B7,[81] HLA-Bw58,[82] and HLA-A2[83] have been cloned and sequenced or their amino acid sequences inferred from the DNA sequences.

The class I heavy chains are composed of three extracellular domains, designated α_1, α_2, and α_3, each about 100 amino acids in length. There is a short hydrophobic transmembrane sequence of about 39 residues and a cytoplasmic domain of approximately 25 residues.

X-ray crystallographic analysis of HLA-A2 indicates that the class I molecules and, by analogy, class II molecules assume a most unusual form (see Fig. 4-4).[84,84a] The membrane-proximal portion consists of two domains (α_3 and β_2-microglobulin) with immunoglobulinlike folds; the pairing of these two domains is novel and not previously noted in immunoglobulin structures. The α_1 and α_2 domains constitute the portion of the molecule distal to the membrane. Each of these outer domains consists of four antiparallel β strands followed by a long helical region, together forming an eight-stranded β-pleated platform topped with two α helices and a long groove approximately 25 Å long and 10 Å wide. This groove is believed to be the recognition site for processed antigens and is lined with both polar and nonpolar side chains, some of which are known to be critical for T-cell recognition. The groove or antigen binding site would accommodate an α-heli-

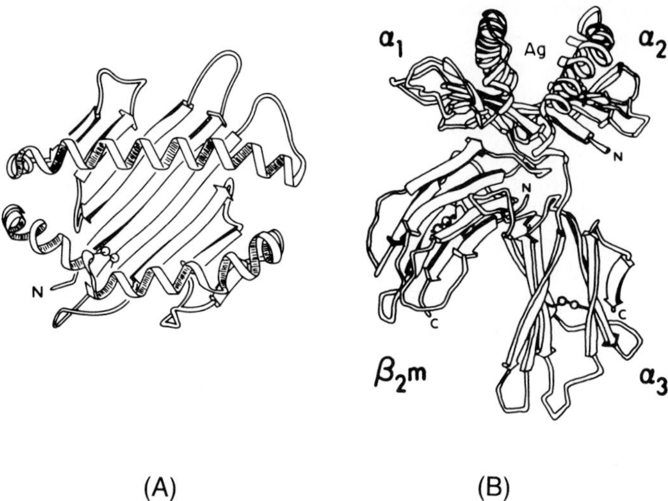

Fig. 4-4 Schematic drawing of the HLA-A2 molecule, derived by 3.5 Å x-ray crystallography (*A*, lateral view; *B*, top view). The α_3- and β_2-microglobulin domains constitute the membrane-proximal portion, while the α_1 and α_2 domains interact to form a single antigen-binding site distal to the membrane. This antigen binding site is formed by a platform of eight β strands, topped with two α helices. *(From Bjorkman et al.*[84a] *Used by permission.)*

cal peptide of approximately 20 residues or an extended chain of eight residues; one end of the groove is open. Significant polymorphism occurs in sequences in both the α helices and in the strands crossing below the helices.

Information on HLA-C is sketchy owing to the difficulties encountered in isolation and purification. While HLA-C has the same approximate molecular weight as HLA-A and HLA-B, the carbohydrate is reported to be more heterogeneous and the molecule less stable and more easily degraded. As noted earlier, fewer HLA-C antigens have been defined. This has prompted Ferrara et al., who extensively immunized human volunteers against HLA-C and failed to produce antibodies, to conclude that null genes or null antigens for HLA-C exist.[85] Inherent instability and low immunogenicity are other possibilities. RFLP analysis may ultimately help definition of HLA-C alleles.[86]

Typing Procedures

Serology: Antibody Mediated Assays. The traditional method for HLA typing has been serologic (reviewed in Ref. 4), although cellular, immunochemical, and molecular techniques are becoming more prevalent. The original cytotoxic assay was based on the reaction of lymphocytes with specific HLA antiserums in a complement-dependent lytic assay. This assay requires incubating 0.001 ml of a lymphocyte suspension with 0.001 ml human antiserum in the wells of a microtiter tray. After 30 min and an optional wash, 0.005 ml of rabbit serum is added as a source of complement. Then, 60 min later, cell viability is measured. The degree of cell death can be measured in several ways, such as by uptake of a vital dye (e.g., trypan blue or eosin), release of a fluorescent material (e.g., fluorescein diacetate), or release of a radioactive label (e.g., ^{51}Cr). The sensitivity of the complement-mediated test can be increased by washing the sensitized cells before adding complement, by adding an antiglobulin reagent, or by extending the incubation time. The latter two procedures tend to favor cross-reactivity.

Lymphocytes are obtained from peripheral blood by ficoll-hypaque density gradient sedimentation. They can be used immediately and can be depleted of macrophages or further divided into T and B lymphocytes. Other types of cells that may be tested in a complement-mediated assay include fibroblasts, B and T lymphoblastoid cell lines, macrophages, and possibly platelets. One very sensitive, albeit indirect, way to ascertain HLA antigens is by absorption of a single antiserum by the cell in question. The absorbed serum is then retested on a known positive lymphocyte to see if antibody activity has been removed.

HLA typing serums come from several sources, most commonly from multiparous women who have been sensitized to paternal antigens on the fetus during pregnancy. Other serum donors include individuals on dialysis, those who have received multiple blood transfusions, and those who have been experimentally immunized with human lymphocytes. The active immunoglobulin in most HLA alloantiserums is generally IgG. Titers are usually low, in the range of 1:1 or 1:16, depending on the method of testing. HLA antibodies are only rarely encountered in the absence of immunization with allogenic cells.

Other types of assays are used sporadically. These include direct or indirect immunofluorescence or incubation with ^{125}I-labeled protein A from *Staphylococcus aureus*, which binds to human IgG. Other older, less reproducible methods have included leukoagglutination and mixed hemagglutination. HLA typing in the future will probably be based on the reaction of monoclonal antibodies and new techniques, such as enzyme-linked immunoassay (ELISA), radioimmunoassay, and restriction fragment length polymorphism (RFLP).

Cellular Assays. Cytotoxic lymphocytes (CTLs) were at first directed against unmodified HLA antigens usually presented by intact cells. Only occasionally were these cells capable of giving specific reactions. Presently, the exquisite specificity of cytotoxic T lymphocytes focuses on class I molecules which serve as restricting elements for viral, chemical, or minor histocompatibility antigens.[87] In practice, peripheral blood lymphocytes are first "primed" to viral or chemically modified cells, then tested for cytolysis on a panel of target cells bearing the relevant foreign antigen and HLA antigens. The first studies of modified targets demonstrated that CTLs could recognize three subtypes of HLA-A2 on influenza-infected cells;[40,88] these A2 subtypes differed from the predominant A2 specificity by one to four amino acids. Variants of numerous other HLA antigens can now be discriminated by such primed cellular reagents.[89] In the future, a definition of HLA based on cellular typing may be of value for disease study. This is likely to be an interim measure, as the ultimate definition will almost certainly be base sequences (See "DNA Typing, below).

DNA Typing. Identification of HLA-A, -B, and -C genes at the molecular level is finding increased usage since restriction endonuclease digestion of genomic DNA detects polymorphisms in both coding and noncoding sequences. The technique identifying restriction fragment length polymorphisms is based on digestion, electrophoresis, Southern blotting, then identification of bands using cloned DNA hybridization probes. RFLP patterns can identify haplotypes in a family and can correlate with serologically detectable HLA-A,[90] HLA-B,[43,91] and HLA-C[86] antigens. RFLPs can also be analyzed from nonviable cells and nonlymphoid cells and have recently been used to identify haplotypes in a "bare lymphocyte" patient where HLA antigens were not expressed.[67]

There are two types of DNA polymorphism, each useful for a different purpose. One form involves polymorphic coding sequences, which may correlate with serologic, cellular, or biochemical assays if the substitution is for amino acids in an immunodominant part of the molecule (e.g., exposed as far as cellular or serologic recognition is concerned). The other involves the noncoding region. This type may have clinical relevance at some future time but at present is mainly useful for distinguishing haplotypes which would otherwise appear to be similar.

Molecular Organization

The class I genes consist of exons encoding the signal peptide, the three extracellular domains, the transmembrane and 3′ cytoplasmic region, with intervening, noncoding DNA segments (introns) (Fig. 4-5) (reviewed in Refs. 1 and 92). Multiple class I genes (possibly ≥20 in the human, ≥30 in the mouse) have been detected.[93] Although it is not yet known how many of the genes are expressed, the corresponding RNAs are now being identified and the gene products are expressed in transfection. It is possible that these genes are expressed in specific tissues during development. Some of them may be homologues of the murine Qa and Tla antigens, class I-like antigens which are restricted to thymocytes, some T-leukemic cells, or activated lymphocytes (see "New MHC Loci and Antigens: T-Cell-Specific Antigens," below). Regulatory genes which increase or depress the level of class I antigens are linked to HLA but have not been specifically localized.[76]

Fig. 4-5 Schematic representation of the gene structure of MHC class I and class II genes. L indicates leader exon, containing the 5′ untranslated region, the signal sequence, and the first amino acids of the mature protein. The α and β exons encode protein domains; TM = the transmembrane region; CY = the cytoplasmic domain.

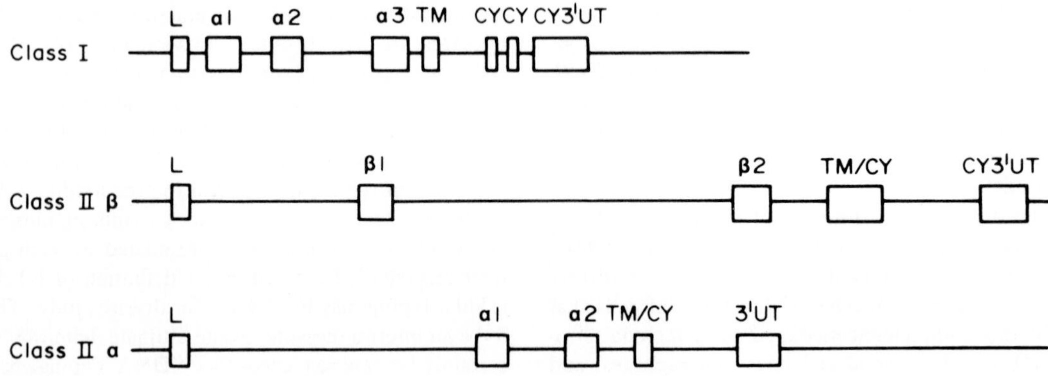

HLA-D REGION: DR, DQ, DP, DO, DN

The HLA-D region (Fig. 4-6) includes families of genes coding for cell surface antigens primarily found on B lymphocytes, macrophages, endothelial cells, and activated T cells (reviewed in Refs. 1 to 3, 92, 94, and 95). These antigens were originally known as B-cell antigens. The use of *Ia* and *class II* to designate antigens of this type has gained increasing acceptance and, in fact, transcends species designations. The genetics of the Ia antigens are particularly important, not only because of the complex molecular organization of these genes, but also because they play a critical role in immune responses and are associated with susceptibility to a number of diseases.

Identification of D-region genes and the molecules which they encode has required multiple approaches—serologic, biochemical, molecular, and functional. This point is particularly relevant, as the DR, DQ, and DP antigens can be identified and characterized by all approaches, whereas D is defined only by the functional assays of mixed lymphocyte reactions and primed lymphocyte testing.[96,97] Class II antigens share a common structure and have similar but nonidentical tissue distributions. It is still not known if the different antigens have identical functions. Some D-region genes, namely DO,[98,99] DQ$\alpha_2\beta_2$ (previously DX),[100,101] and DN,[102] have been identified only at the molecular level. Whether these are expressed on the cell surface and, if so, if they carry polymorphic epitopes is currently under study. The existence of other class II genes and cell surface molecules is suspected.[103]

Tissue Distribution and Expression

Since HLA-DR, -DQ, and -DP are restricted to particular cell types, they may be considered differentiation antigens. Besides being found on B lymphocytes, they are found on B lymphoblastoid cell lines, Langerhans cells of the skin, some monocytes and macrophages, endothelial cells, and activated but not resting T cells.[94,95,104–106] In addition, at least some class II antigens are present on normal tissues of differing embryonic origin, including the epithelium of both the gastrointestinal tract and mammary gland, urinary bladder, bronchial glands, thymic reticuloepithelial cells of entodermic origin, acinar cells of the parotid, astrocytes, Kupffer cells and endometrium,[107] and some malignant melanomas[108] and lymphomas.[109] These antigens may be inappropriately expressed in cells or tissues of patients with autoimmune disease, e.g., on enterocytes of children with celiac disease,[110] on thyrocytes in patients with autoimmune thyroid disease,[111] on β cells in diabetic pancreas,[112] and on alveolar macrophages in individuals

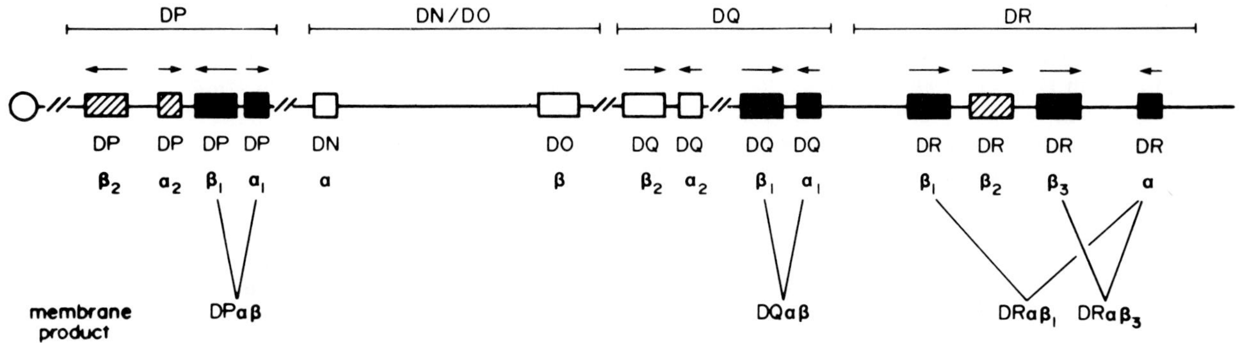

Fig. 4-6 Schematic map of the human HLA-D region. The DP region contains two expressed genes (DPα_1 and β_1) and two pseudogenes (DP$\alpha_2\beta_2$). The DN/DO region is least well studied, and no protein products have been detected to date. The DQ region consists of DQ$\alpha_1\beta_1$ genes and DQ$\alpha_2\beta_2$ genes. No identification of DQ$\alpha_2\beta_2$ protein products has been possible. The precise order of DN/DO and DN/DQ is not established, but the order indicated is consistent with biochemical and molecular data. The DR region is well characterized; the number and order of DRβ genes varies with the haplotype. ■ = expressed gene; ▨ = pseudogene; □ = undetermined.

with pulmonary sarcoidosis.[113] It has been suggested that such aberrant expression is due to the local inflammatory reaction of infiltrating lymphocytes, as class II is inducible on a number of normally negative tissues following exposure to γ-interferon,[114–116] tumor necrosis factor,[77] a combination of these,[117] and other unidentified factors.[118] Many proliferative stimuli also serve to induce class II expression.

Coordinate expression of DR, DQ, and DP is not always observed. Expression of DR and DP molecules, but not DQ, is evident in a subset of monocytes and macrophages,[119] in some leukemic cells,[120] and in multipotential, erythroid, and granulocyte/macrophage progenitor cells.[105] Although γ-interferon increases DR and DP expression above background levels and will induce *de novo* expression in certain cells, there is little increase in DQ in promyelocytic leukemias, monocytes, and fibroblasts, suggesting independent regulation of HLA-DQ.[121]

Biochemistry and Molecular Organization

The class II molecules are heterodimeric membrane glycoproteins consisting of a 33,000 to 34,000-dalton α chain and a 28,000 to 29,000-dalton β chain (Fig. 4-2) (reviewed in Refs. 1 and 94). Both the α and β chains of each DR, DQ, and DP molecule are encoded by the MHC, although during intracellular processing there is a transient association with an invariant polypeptide encoded for by a gene on chromosome 5, designated Ii or γ chain and with a more heavily glycosylated form of I chain. Each class II chain consists of two external domains, the domain closest to the membrane showing the greatest similarity to immunoglobulins. While the various class II molecules are members of the same gene family and arose from gene duplication, there are consistent differences between the genes of different regions that can be recognized by monoclonal antibodies, e.g., DRα versus DQα and DRβ versus DQβ. Oligonucleotide probes permit isolation of the corresponding genes. A complex battery of procedures including pulsed field gel electrophoresis,[122] isoelectric focusing,[123] transfection,[124] and DNA sequencing,[125] has been needed to separate individual genes and gene products from others in this large gene family.

Despite the similarity in protein products, DR, DQ, and DP differ in molecular organization.[1–3,92,94] The DR subregion consists of one α and as many as four β genes. Most chromosomes or haplotypes have two expressed β genes (β_1 and β_3), with the third (β_2) being a pseudogene. The DR1 and DR8 haplotypes, however, express only one DRβ chain while the DR4 and DR7 haplotypes may encode as many as four DRβ genes.[126] One DRβ chain is thought to carry the serologically detected DR alleles DR1, DR2, DR3, etc., while another DRβ is thought to carry the supertypic antigens DRw52 and DRw53.[127] This is probably an oversimplification.

In the DQ region, there are two α (DQα_1 and DQα_2) and two β (DQβ_1 and DQβ_2) genes.[100,101] Only the DQα_1 and β_1 form a functional membrane protein. These genes are oriented in opposite directions, approximately 12 kb apart. Since both chains are polymorphic, it is not known which chain carries the serologically determined DQ antigen, and both may contribute to an "interaction" antigen. At the DNA level, the DQ region appears to exhibit the most polymorphism of class II products, since both α and β chains can be found in numerous allelic forms by RFLP isoelectric focusing and sequencing.[1,123,128,129] Hybrid antigens arising by transcomplementation are likely.[130] Paradoxically, despite all this complexity few alleles have been defined serologically.[32]

The DQ$\alpha_2\beta_2$[100,101] are also oriented in opposite directions, about 8 kb apart. While probes for DQ$\alpha_2\beta_2$ cross-hybridize with DQ$\alpha_1\beta_1$ genes, no DQ$\alpha_2\beta_2$ mRNA or protein product has been identified to date.

The DP region covers over 100 kb and has been extensively mapped.[131] It encodes one expressed molecule DP$\alpha_1\beta_1$, while the DP$\alpha_2\beta_2$ genes are pseudogenes in the haplotypes studied to date.

Newly described subregions include genes for DOβ and DNα.[98,99,102] The DOβ gene exhibits little polymorphism, but it does have enhanced hydrophobicity at the amino-terminal end. Although the DOβ and DZα genes may be functional, since they are translated into mRNA, no protein product has been identified.

The gene structure of class II glycoproteins is well characterized. Each chain is determined by a 5′ untranslated region, a signal sequence, and exons for the two outer domains, the transmembrane region and the cytoplasmic tail and part of the 3′ untranslated region (Fig. 4-5). The sizes of the introns vary, and the DQα products differ in length of the mRNA and the 3′ untranslated region.[125] Alternative splicing patterns have been noted for both DPβ, and DQwlβ_1 genes.[94,125]

Class II gene transcription is under control of a complex series of regulatory elements in the 5′ flanking and intronic regions. These include tumor-associated transcriptional enhancer elements in intron 1, a promoter region consisting of TATA, octamer, X, Y, and Z boxes, and both tissue specific and nonspecific regulatory proteins.[131a] Cis-trans and positive-negative regulatory proteins are now being defined through study of mutant class II negative cell lines. Transcriptional regulation has been recently reviewed.[1,76,94,131a]

As is apparent from what has been said above, D region analysis is very complex. Not only are there many alleles at some loci, but there are many pairs or clusters of loci in strong linkage disequilibrium. For example: DR1 is always present with DQw2, DR4 usually with DQw3, DR3 with DQw2, and so on. This close relationship is complicated by varying degrees of cross-reactivity between gene products. Of the numerous "DR" antigens, most are considered "subtypic" and are encoded by a single DRβ chain on an $\alpha\beta_1$ molecule. The supertypic antigens, DRw52 and DRw53 (formerly MT2 and MT3), are carried on the DRβ_3 and DRβ_4 chains respectively.[127] Variants of the serologically detected DR antigens have been identified by isoelectric focusing;[132] RFLP;[133–135] cellular assays such as the mixed lymphocyte culture, primed lymphocyte test;[96,97] or alloreactive T-cell clones.[136–138]

An example of the antigenic complexity which is characteristic of the DR region and which extends to DQ is illustrated by DR4. DR4 is a serologically defined antigen present in about 13 percent of the Caucasian population. Three serologically defined subtypes of DR4 were identified at the Ninth International Histocompatibility Workshop in 1984 but were not officially recognized. Five DR4-associated antigens are recognized by mixed lymphocyte typing (Dw4, Dw10, Dw13, Dw14, and Dw15);[139] other subtypes can be discriminated by alloreactive T-cell clones,[137] by two-dimensional gel electrophoresis,[140] and by RFLP.[141,142]

The HLA-DQ region (formerly, unofficially designated MB, DC, DS, or LB-E) includes nine defined antigens. Some polymorphisms have been identified by cellular and molecular techniques.[123,128,129,143] It has been suggested that a single DQ molecule may carry as many multiple epitopes, localized to either the α_1 chain or the β_1 chain,[144] although some of the apparent heterogeneity at DQ may reflect reactions with products of the linked and homologous DQ$\alpha_2\beta_2$.[145]

The alleles of HLA-DP were originally identified by primed lymphocyte typing and are now being characterized by antibodies[146,147] and RFLP.[148]

Linkage disequilibrium between DR and DQ is particularly strong. Thus, DR1+, DR2+, and DRw6+ cells are almost invariably DQwl+ in Caucasians. Similarly, DR3+ and DR7+ cells are often DQw2+, and DR4+, DR5+, DR7+, and DR9+ cells are DQw3+. There are some exceptions, e.g., DR7 can be associated with DQw2 (usually these cells are also Dw7+) or with DQw3 (usually these cells are also Dw11+). It has been particularly difficult to assign some serologically or RFLP-generated patterns to DR or to DQ. This has clinical importance, as many of the diseases originally associated with DR are now being reassessed in light of the pronounced heterogeneity of DQ and close linkage with DR.

The DQ$\alpha_1\beta_1$ and DQ$\alpha_2\beta_2$ subregions do not exhibit the significant association seen between DR and DQ, prompting the suggestion of an area of high recombinational events or "hot spot" in the DQ region.[2] Such hot spots have been implicated in the murine MHC[149] and in human β-globin and insulin genes.[150,151] They may arise from repeat sequences or from specialized chromatin structures, both of which promote recombination.

Typing Procedures

Serology. Typing for HLA-DR and -DQ is in many ways similar to HLA-A, -B, and -C typing. Both rely heavily on human alloantibodies with rabbit serum as a source of complement. In HLA-DR typing, however, the target is the B lymphocyte, incubation times are sometimes lengthened, and the rabbit serum must be carefully selected to avoid the high background often seen when B cells or B-cell lines are tested. Only the B-cell subfraction of peripheral blood lymphocytes is used by most laboratories, and contaminating HLA-A, -B, and -C antibodies must be removed from the antiserums (see Ref. 31 for general techniques).

Both positive and negative selective measures can be used to isolate a pure B-cell population. B cells constitute less than 15 percent of the usual peripheral blood lymphocytes. Selective depletion of T cells can be performed by rosetting with sheep red blood cells.[152] Positive selection of B cells can be accomplished by taking advantage of their membrane receptor for the Fc portion of immunoglobulins,[153] their surface immunoglobulin,[154] their adherence to nylon fibers,[155] or their ability to form rosettes in the presence of a monoclonal anti-Ia antibody.[156]

Modification of the dye exclusion cytotoxicity assay is continually being attempted. Two-color fluorescence is one alternative[157] which is time-consuming but does not require separation of B cells from T cells. In this procedure, B cells are surface-labeled with a fluorescein-coupled Ig (green) before the cytotoxicity assay is performed. After cytotoxicity occurs, the dead cells are stained with ethidium bromide (red). The dead B cells can be identified by their content of both green and red fluorescence, as ascertained by the alternative use of ultraviolet and visible light.

The addition of an anti-β_2-microglobulin serum to B cells clears the surface of HLA-A, -B, and -C antigens and thereby eliminates reactivity with HLA-A, -B, and -C antiserums. Complement-mediated cytotoxicity to DR antigens proceeds unimpeded.[158] DR typing has also been performed on mitogen-activated peripheral blood lymphocytes.[159]

Human serum having anti-HLA-A, -B, or -C reactivity often includes antibodies to HLA-DR antigens. Since peripheral blood lymphocytes are usually mostly T cells which do not express DR antigens, the inclusion of anti-DR antibodies in a serum gives little trouble in ABC typing. In contrast, since B cells carry the HLA-A, -B, and -C antigens in addition to DR, the HLA-A, -B, and -C activity must be removed before DR typing. This is accomplished by platelet absorption (platelets carry HLA-A and generally HLA-B antigens, but not DR) or by T-cell lines. Absorption is a time-consuming and expensive procedure, and each absorbed serum must be retested to ensure that no antibodies to class I antigens remain.

Monoclonal antibodies come from cloned cells and do not require absorption. A wide array of monoclonal antibodies are available, most of them from the mouse. Most detect framework epitopes on DR, DQ, and DP. A few detect specific antigens such as DR3, DR5, DR7, and DQw1 while the remainder give complex patterns, e.g., reacting with all cells except those that are DR1 and DR3. The basis for these complex and often cross-reactive patterns is probably the sharing of molecular groupings or charges between otherwise different antigens. Many monoclonal antibodies will cross-react and recognize epitopes shared by other class II molecules; the extent of the cross-reactivity observed is often dependent on the cell line(s) tested.

Cellular Assays. The HLA-D and -DP antigens were first identified by the mixed lymphocyte culture (MLC), or mixed lymphocyte response (MLR). The MLR is a technically simple assay (reviewed in Refs. 96 and 97) in which 10^4 responding cells and 10^4 stimulating lymphocytes inactivated by γ irradiation or mitomycin C to prevent proliferation are cocultured for 5 to 7 days. During this time, class II disparity results in proliferation measured by incorporation of radiolabeled nucleotides such as [^{3}H]thymidine. Because of individual differences in stimulatory and in response capability between individuals, quite complex statistical treatments have been introduced to aid the analysis of MLR results. One of the most convenient is double normalization.[160]

HLA-D typing has become possible only through the use of lymphocytes from individuals who carry two identical HLA-D specificities. These lymphocytes are homozygous typing cells. HLA-D homozygous individuals occur very rarely in populations. They are more common in first-cousin marriages, in which the children have an appreciable chance of inheriting two copies of the same chromosome from the great-grandparent, or in incestuous matings. For HLA-D typing, a person is set up as a responder, with the stimulators being homozygous typing cells for Dw1, Dw2, etc. The responding cells will react with all stimulators except those carrying D alleles identical with the responder's. Thus, a person who fails to respond to the Dw2 and Dw3 homozygous typing cells but responds to all others would be considered Dw2,Dw3-positive.

The HLA-D antigens stimulating in the MLR are the equivalent of serologically and molecularly defined Ia antigens.[96,97,161,162] HLA-D typing roughly correlates with DR typing, e.g., Dw1+ cells are DR1+, Dw2+ cells are usually DR2+, etc. However, there are rare cells which are DR2+,Dw2− while as mentioned earlier, DR4 is associated with at least five separate Dw types.[139] Some D alleles appear to correlate more closely with DQ. For instance, D alleles associated with DR4 and DR7 differ at DQ (DR4-Dw10-DQw3 and DR4-Dw15-DQwx; DR7-Dw7-DQw2 and DR7-Dw11-DQw3). Perhaps the strongest evidence that DQ can be recognized in an MLR is that murine cells transfected with DQ genes alone will stimulate in mixed lymphocyte culture.[163] Thus, stimulation in MLR may be the composite result of incompatibility at any of several DR or DQ genes. The contributions of DO and DN are still unknown; DP will stimulate in secondary MLR but not in a primary MLR. D typing as now performed is laborious and requires cells from rare D homozygous individuals. It is slowly being discontinued as serological analysis with monoclonal antibodies and molecular typing give improved definition of D region antigens.

A modification of the MLR, the primed lymphocyte test (PLT) utilizes primed responder lymphocytes, e.g., those that have reacted in a primary MLR. These cells will then proliferate more rapidly upon secondary challenge (e.g., in 1 to 2 days rather than 5 to 7 days) with cells presenting the same antigen. Priming induces highly specific PLT-responding cells capable of recognizing D/DR antigens as well as DP antigens. The reason why DP stimulation is weak is not clear. It has been suggested that the DP antigens are less polymorphic or are expressed in lower number on the cell surface and so are less immunogenic or the number of T cells capable of recognizing these antigens is limited and requires expansion in a primary MLR. Few monoclonal antibodies have been found to specifically detect DP alleles.[146,147] Nevertheless, the DP antigens do function in antigen presentation, they are associated with disease, and they remain of great interest.

Molecular Typing. The greatest application of DNA typing has been in class II molecular organization, allele definition, and disease susceptibility. RFLPs have been widely used to characterize new DR, DQ, and DP alleles which are sometimes, but not always, equivalent to serologic or cellular defined antigens. The probes used to define HLA polymorphisms have routinely been labeled with ^{32}P and the bands identified by autoradiography. The method is highly sensitive, and the blots can be reused for more precise definition, but the radioactive probes require special handling and are short-lived. Nonisotopic DNA probes labeled with biotin are now available for class II genes.

Other molecular approaches include the use of oligomer DNA typing and amplified DNA. For example, 20- to 21-base synthetic oligonucleotide DNA probes help distinguish between different DRβ and different DQβ alleles on DR4+ haplotypes.[163a] Direct amplification of DNA for class II analysis can be accomplished using the polymerase chain reaction (PCR).[163b] In this method, DNA is enzymatically amplified using a thermostable DNA polymerase. PCR-amplified DNA has been used in dot blots with HLA-DP-specific β-oligonucleotide probes to identify 12 different allelic variants distinct from the standard DPw1-6 alleles[163c] and to identify DQβ alleles in type 1 insulin dependent diabetes mellitus patients.[163d]

NEW MHC LOCI AND ANTIGENS: T-CELL-SPECIFIC ANTIGENS

In the mouse, there are loci close to the MHC that also code for differentiation antigens which have a class I-like structure. These antigens, the Tla and Qa series, are expressed on T-cell subsets and on some leukemic cells. These genes are telomeric to H-2D/L in the mouse and are markers for what is known as the Tla region or TL and Qa2 subregions.[164]

Several searches for homologous molecules on human T cells have provided suggestive evidence that T-cell-specific antigens are determined by genes near or within HLA.[165,166] Molt 4, an "early" T-cell line, seems to express an antigen associated with β_2-microglobulin but distinct from HLA-A, -B, and -C.[167] Using quantitative binding assays, some but not all investigators[168,169] have found the concentration of β_2-microglobulin to be higher on these cells than can be accounted for by HLA-A, -B, and -C. Activity distinct from HLA-A, -B, -C, and -DR has been noted with peripheral blood T lymphocytes after mitogen stimulation, with EBV+ B-cell lines, and pre-B leukemic cells, but not with resting T cells, B cells, or thymocytes.[170–174] These new class I antigens are postulated to be members of a new family variously designated HT, HA, or TCA-TCB, near or telomeric to HLA-A. The HLA class I gene family is known from Southern blots to contain as many as 15 to 20 members. Recently, novel class I genes have been isolated which may be the equivalent of immune Qa antigens.[175,176] One gene, associated with a class I 6.2 kb *Hind*III fragment, has been designated HLA-E.

POPULATION GENETICS AND LINKAGE DISEQUILIBRIUM

As early as 1967, it was realized that the HLA antigens characteristic of one population could be completely absent from another. Consequently, the 1972 Histocompatibility Workshop was designed to "HLA type the populations of the world."[28] Included were Eskimos, American Indians, African pygmies, Nepalese Sherpas, Australian aborigines, Easter Islanders, and many more. Many extraordinary differences were encountered. Because of the intricacies of the Oriental HLA haplotypes and because of extreme differences in disease associations, three Asian Pan Oceanian histocompatibility testing workshops have since been held.[177]

Some antigens, such as A2 and Bw35, are found in nearly all populations. The A1, A3, B8, and B27 antigens are found in Caucasians and blacks, but seldom in Orientals. Where present, their introduction from the outside cannot be excluded. Conversely, certain antigens are found almost exclusively in blacks, e.g., Aw43 or Bw45, or in Chinese, e.g., Bw46. A summary of HLA gene frequencies in several ethnic groups is given in Table 4-2. As well as unique antigens,[178,179] unique haplotypes are characteristic of some populations, e.g., the A1-B8-DR3 haplotype in Caucasians, the A2-B35-DR4 haplotype in Mongoloids and A28-B38-DRw6 in African blacks.[180]

Bodmer and Thomson have calculated the number of possible arrangements of HLA alleles forming the Caucasian haplotype.[181] In 1975, based on 19 HLA-A antigens, 26 HLA-B antigens, 6 HLA-C antigens, and 8 HLA-D alleles, 26,676 haplotypes, 33,194,624 phenotypes, and 355,817,826 genotypes were theoretically possible. Of these, certain haplotypes, such as A1-B8-DR3 and A3-B7-DR2, are unduly frequent. The association of antigens more frequently than would be expected by chance is called linkage disequilibrium. It is given a numerical value referred to as Δ. The reasons for linkage disequilibrium are disputed.[182] It has been attributed to selective forces (e.g., infectious disease) acting either on the HLA antigens themselves or on the haplotype. Linkage disequilibrium has also been thought to be an artifact of population expansion, migration, and an admixture of heterogeneous populations (lack of time for equilibration).

Observations on the mouse suggest two further possibilities. (1) A series of semilethal genes (the T/t complex regulating embryonic differentiation and skeletal development) are present in the Qa and K regions of the mouse MHC; these effectively suppress recombination along the chromosome carrying H-2.[183] (2) Recombination in some hybrids is 200 times as frequent as recombination in other crosses.[184] Similar phenomena occur in the rat[185] and may occur in humans.[186] A locus regulating spinal development has been thought to map to the human sixth chromosome.[186] Several nuclear families include more than one intra-HLA recombinant; indeed, one 10-sib family includes no fewer than five recombinants in the HLA region, with a sixth recombination in the next generation.[187] Several HLA haplotypes are known to contain deletions in the complement genes between HLA-B and -DR (see "HLA and Disease," below). Oncogenes may also affect recombination and, hence, the stability of haplotypes. These all suggest close functional as well as organizational similarities between the MHCs of the two widely separated species. Some points in the analogy have been thought to support a selective advantage for

Table 4-2 Antigen Frequencies in Caucasians, Orientals, and Negroids

HLA-	*Caucasians*	*Orientals*	*Negroids*
A. Gene frequencies for HLA-A			
A1	14.2	1.0	8.1
A2	28.9	28.1	17.5
A3	13.2	1.5	6.7
A11	6.3	1.7	1.9
A23	1.4	0.1	8.0
A24	10.3	31.4	4.8
A25	2.4	0	0
A26	3.2	7.2	4.5
A28	4.7	2.1	9.9
A29	2.9	0.4	4.9
A30	3.5	2.3	11.0
A31	2.9	5.2	1.6
A32	3.9	0.4	2.3
Aw33	1.4	6.0	3.9
Aw34	0.1	0.3	5.1
Aw36	0.1	0.1	3.2
Aw43	0	0	1.3
Aw66	0.2	0.5	0.3
AX	0.4	1.7	5.0
Sample size*	2163	976	311
B. Gene frequencies for HLA-B			
B7	11.5	4.7	12.1
B8	9.6	0.2	5.5
B13	2.9	3.8	1.6
B18	5.5	0.3	4.2
B27	3.4	1.6	1.9
B35	10.5	10.2	7.1
B37	1.6	0.6	1.3
B38	2.5	0.7	1.6
B39	2.0	0.4	0
Bw41	0.9	0.1	2.3
Bw42	0.2	0.5	5.8
B44	12.3	6.0	7.7
B45	0.4	0.1	2.3
Bw46	0.1	3.6	0
Bw47	0.2	0.4	0
Bw48	0	1.6	0
B49	1.8	0.3	2.3
Bw50	1.1	0.3	0.6
B51	6.2	7.8	1.9
Bw52	2.0	7.3	0.6
Bw53	0.5	0.3	6.7
Bw54	0.1	6.7	0
Bw55	1.6	2.1	0
Bw56	1.1	1.5	0.3
Bw57	2.9	0.7	2.9
Bw58	0	1.2	0
Bw60	3.8	6.5	2.3
Bw61	2.1	11.7	1.5
Bw62	6.1	9.6	2.6
Bw63	0.7	0	1.9
Bw64	1.1	0	1.3
Bw65	2.6	0.2	1.6
Bw67	0	0.1	0
Bw71	0.1	0.4	0.8
Bw72	0.3	0.5	7.1
Bw73	0.1	0.2	0
B X	0.4	1.6	1.3
Sample size*	2132	968	311

Table 4-2 *(Continued)*

HLA-	*Caucasians*	*Orientals*	*Negroids*
C. Gene frequencies for HLA-C			
Cw1	3.3	16.3	1.0
Cw2	4.1	1.0	11.9
Cw3	12.6	27.3	8.3
Cw4	11.6	5.3	14.0
Cw5	6.9	0.6	3.0
Cw6	8.6	3.8	12.9
Cw7	24.3	12.1	24.1
Cw8	3.7	0.3	3.5
C X	24.9	33.3	21.3
Sample size*	2106	968	316
D. Gene frequencies for HLA-DR			
DR1	9.5	5.0	5.1
DR2	15.8	15.1	15.1
DR3	12.0	1.8	14.9
DR4	12.7	21.8	7.6
DR7	12.0	2.9	13.2
DRw8	3.0	7.3	0.8
DRw9	0.8	11.5	1.5
DRw10	0.8	0.5	2.3
DRw11	12.3	4.0	16.5
DRw12	2.0	7.2	3.4
DRw13	5.4	2.9	3.8
DRw14	5.8	6.8	10.7
DR X	7.9	13.2	5.3
Sample size*	1926	752	263
E. Gene frequencies for HLA-DQ			
DQw1	32.3	30.2	40.1
DQw2	18.1	5.0	23.1
DQw3	23.3	32.7	24.6
DQ X	26.3	32.1	12.2
Sample size*	2016	776	256

*Number of haplotypes counted.
SOURCE: From Albert et al.[32]

certain haplotypes. It is perhaps most interesting that certain "forbidden" haplotypes are excessively rare. It has also been suggested that certain forbidden gametic associations do not occur, but this is difficult to prove.

THE MHC AND IMMUNE RESPONSIVENESS

The simplest interpretation of the genetic basis of immune responsiveness is that the MHC antigens, which must interact with antigen before that antigen can be recognized by a T cell, are the products of immune response genes (reviewed in Refs. 87 and 188–188b). Best studied in this regard are the class II antigens, where immune responsiveness may be dominant or recessive. Dominance can be observed if the gene product of any class II locus is adequate for the presentation of a given antigen. Recessivity can be observed if the product of more than one locus is required for antigen presentation or if more than one allele is required. Hybrid antigens have been described between I-Aα and I-Eβ in the mouse and between DQα_1 of one haplotype and DQβ_1 of another haplotype in humans.[130] Because human HLA homozygotes are so rare and because only a limited range of suitable antigens is available, progress in unveiling this aspect of the immune response has been slow. Even in the mouse, the ability to respond to H-2-dependent antigens is rarely if ever an all or none phenomenon. Many other Ir loci have been postulated for the mouse. The ability to respond to other types of antigen such as those of erythocyte (Ea4) may be more sharply distinguished. Other loci, identified through susceptibility or resistance to viral infection, have sometimes been regarded as immune response loci but may really be loci regulating receptor development.

The measurement of immune responses in humans has been largely confined to T-cell proliferation in vitro or changes in antibody level following exposure to microbial antigens. This has given rise to some incomplete or unsatisfactory studies because of the complexity of the antigens used. However, Greenberg et al.[189] reported that individuals with the antigen HLA-B5 are high responders to streptococcal antigens. HLA-B5 individuals are also reported to have higher levels of immune complexes in acute rheumatic fever.[190] A28 has been associated with sperm autoantibodies[191] and DR4 with high responsiveness to mycobacteria in skin tests.[192] Certain HLA antigens have also been associated with acute poststreptococcal glomerulonephritis[193] and with high and low responses to schistosomal antigens.[194] Sensitivity to ragweed,[195] cellular responses in vitro to influenza[196] or rubella,[197] and responses in vitro to insulin[198] as a complication of insulin therapy in diabetics have also been reported to exhibit HLA associations. The opposite of Ir gene participation in stimulation has also been proposed in an interesting hypothesis that suggests that one important function of class II antigens is immunosuppression.[199]

Although recognition of the D-region antigens has proceeded at an exciting pace, there has been no such explosion of knowledge about the immune response capacities of the haplotypes. Lack of success in defining Ir gene functions, including those of many studies using synthetic polypeptides, vaccinia, influenza A, measles, and tetanus toxoid, can be attributed to many causes—failure to use a discriminating antigen dose, antigenic complexity, failure to use family members or unrelated subjects sharing an HLA-restricting antigen for the studies, and inability to control for sensitization from previous exposure. Multigenic effects may be especially difficult to deal with because of the small size of human families and the unknown segregation of alleles.

Other Ir gene effects have been localized to the Gm genes[200] and interaction and disease susceptibility may be noted only when both HLA and Gm are coordinately assessed.[201]

The interaction of MHC molecules with antigen is itself of considerable interest, since a major function of the MHC is to coordinate functional interaction between cells of the immune system. Thus, while B cells recognize antigens directly by means of surface immunoglobulin receptors, T cells recognize antigen only in context of MHC.[87,188a–188c] This phenomenon is termed MHC restriction (see Fig. 4-7). Both class I and class II function at different levels. The presence of self-class I antigens is an absolute requirement for CTLs to recognize and lyse virally infected cells. Class II compatibility is required for T-cell regulation, including interaction of Th, Ts, and T amplifier cells.

The functional "restricting" portions of the MHC molecule which interact with antigens correlate with the polymorphic areas of the MHC molecule. Thus, subtypes of A2 function in CTL recognition.[40,88,89,202] DR (both subtypic and the public DRw52, 53 antigens), DQ, and DP function in T-cell-macrophage or T-cell/B-cell interactions.[203–206] Increased density of DR and DQ on monocytes is associated with more efficient antigen presentation.[205,207] Transfection with DP$\alpha\beta$ genes

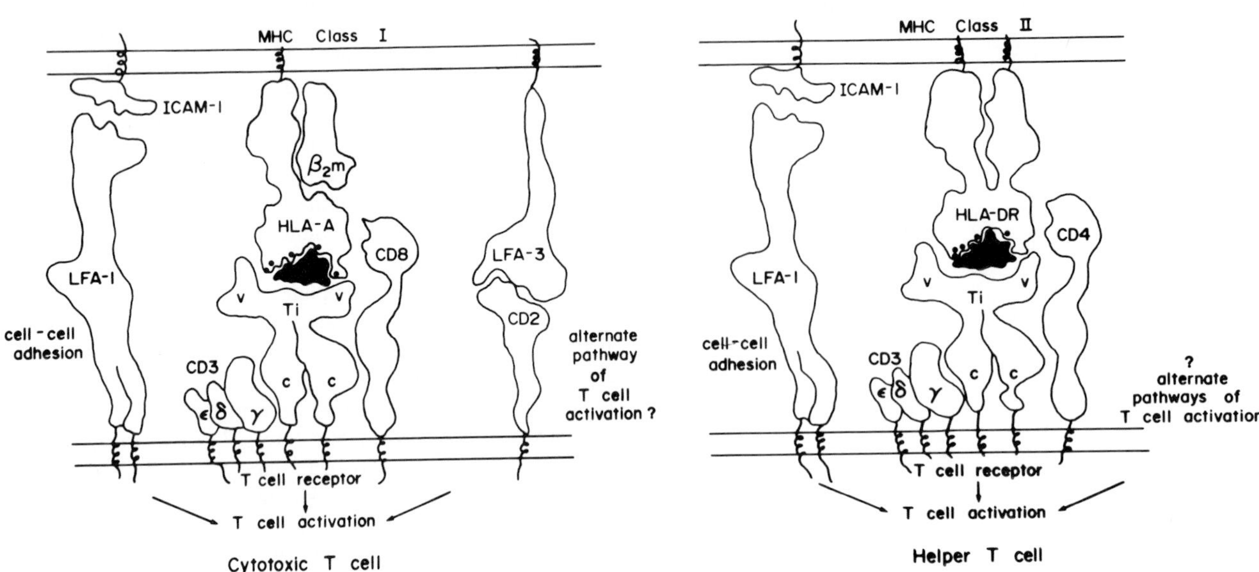

Fig. 4-7 Schematic representation of some structures involved in interactions between T cells and antigen-presenting or virally infected cells. In these models of *(A)* class I and *(B)* class II restriction, an antigen is bound simultaneously to an MHC molecule and to the T-cell $\alpha\beta$ heterodimer. The single T-cell receptor (designated Ti) responsible for both MHC and antigen recognition interacts further with CD3 subunits and with CD4 or CD8. MHC-restricting epitopes are designated as dots around the antigen-MHC boundary. The CD2/LFA-3 interaction is thought to constitute an alternate pathway for T-cell activation. LFA-1 functions in cell-cell adhesions; it binds to several ligands, ICAM-1 being shown here. Deficiencies of some of these recognition structures, e.g., HLA or LFA-1, can lead to recurrent infection or death. It should be noted that this figure is simplistic; the pathways for T-cell activation are exceedingly complex.[188,188a,188b]

yields cells which will react with DP specific monoclonal antibodies and will activate DP restricted clones in the presence of antigen.[208]

That T cell recognition depended on "self-MHC" and "antigen" was originally explained by two different models. The first, the dual receptor model, postulated two separate receptors on T cells, one for the MHC product and one for the antigen. The second model postulated a single T-cell receptor recognizing MHC and nominal antigen simultaneously. This altered self-hypothesis required a single T-cell receptor binding an antigen-MHC complex. The latter hypothesis is now well accepted.[87,188–188b] The T-cell receptor is a heterodimer of an α and a β chain and is minimally associated with several CD3 subunits; accessory molecules, namely CD4 and CD8, also contribute to the MHC/T-cell rerceptor interaction. Still other molecules, such as LFA-1/ICAM-1 and CD2/LFA-3, function in cell-cell adhesion or in alternate pathways of T-cell activation.[188–188b]

A three-dimensional view of the MHC/antigen interaction can be deduced from the x-ray crystallographic analysis of HLA-A2[84,84a] (see earlier discussion on biochemistry of HLA-A, -B, and -C). A single antigen binding site is located on the top surface of the class I molecule. This site faces away from the plane of the membrane and consequently would face toward the T-cell receptor. It can accommodate peptide ligands 8 to 20 amino acids long, depending on the degree of coiling or folding. Amino acid changes in the walls or floor of the groove forming this binding site may radically change the affinity for MHC/antigen interaction. The details of how and where the intracellular interaction of MHC and antigen occurs, and whether class I/antigen and class II/antigen interactions occur in different cellular compartments, are not yet known. Also unresolved is the contribution of CD8 (Lyt-2) and other accessory molecules to T-cell receptor/antigen/MHC interactions or to the part played by the T$\gamma\delta$ molecule.[208a]

HLA AND DISEASE

Efforts to show associations between HLA and disease were initiated because of the known relationship between H-2, the homologous system in the mouse, and various malignant diseases. Certain inbred strains of mice are highly sensitive to retrovirally induced leukemogenesis, while others are resistant.[209] This relationship is often complex. For example, resistance to Friend leukemia is polygenic. At least four unlinked genes are implicated, one of which is located at or close to H-2. A similar situation appeared likely for HLA. Amiel reported an increased frequency of the HLA antigen "4c" in Hodgkin's disease[210] and Rogentine and his colleagues reported an excess of HLA-A2 subjects in acute lymphocytic leukemia.[211] Despite intensive efforts since then, HLA associations with Hodgkin's disease[212] and leukemia[213] remain tenuous.

Whereas associations with malignancies (or even with retroviruses) are inconsistent, numerous other diseases show remarkably strong associations with HLA (see Table 4-3 for examples) (reviewed in Refs. 2 and 214 to 217). The first association to be reported was that with ankylosing spondylitis. In 1973, Schlosstein et al. and Brewerton et al. reported that over 90 percent of patients with the inflammatory rheumatoid disease ankylosing spondylitis carried the HLA-B27 al-

Table 4-3 Examples of HLA-Disease Associations

Antigen associated	*Disease*	*Relative risk*	*Comments*
A3	Hemochromatosis	4	Recessive inheritance with >95% penetrance; linked to HLA: most common haplotype A3-C-B14-BfF-DRw6
B27	Ankylosing spondylitis	90	Associated in all populations
Bw47	Steroid 21-hydroxylase deficiency	15	Late-onset 21-hydroxylase deficiency linked to B14-DR1 (see Table 4-4)
Cw6,DR7	Psoriasis	4	Association with DR7 in Caucasians and in Japanese, especially in early-onset disease; no clear linkage with HLA in 13 multiplex families
DR4 only	Diabetes mellitus	6	Possible DQ, GM associations; not simple dominant or recessive
DR3 only		3	
Both DR3 and DR4		33	
DR3,DQw2	Chronic active hepatitis	2	Especially in young females with autoantibodies
DR3,DQw2	Myasthenia gravis	3	HLA association varies with race; possible association with thymic disease and complications rather than susceptibility
DR3,DQw2	Celiac disease	17	Recessive inheritance; DR7 also associated
DR2,DQw1	Multiple sclerosis	4	Possible DQ, Gm association
DR4	Rheumatoid arthritis	4–6	Disease may be heterogeneous; other HLA antigens variably indicated
DR2	Narcolepsy	34	Nearly 100% affected DR2
DR2,DR3 C4A*QO	SLE		DR2 and C4A*QO effect may be independent and additive

lele.[218,219] Confirmation from other laboratories soon came and with it the additional finding that B27 was also frequent in Reiter syndrome and in anterior uveitis. Other early studies revealed associations with HLA-A or -B antigens, but as the HLA-D region became better characterized, more of the autoimmune-type diseases found a stronger association with HLA-DR, DQ, or with HLA-D. (The apparent associations with HLA-B alleles were due to linkage disequilibrium.) Relatively few conditions are associated with HLA-A, although one of these—hemochromatosis—is noteworthy since a recessive gene for hemochromatosis has been formally linked by family analysis to HLA-A.[220,221] As is discussed below, there is an important distinction between *association* and *linkage* to HLA.

The Search for HLA-Disease Associations

Since there are over 100 known HLA-A, -B, -C, -DR, -DQ, and -DP specificities, and there are multiple alleles of complement C4, the search for a new disease association is an expensive and time-consuming procedure. To demonstrate that an HLA association exists, lymphocytes from clinic patients are tested with as many typing serums defining HLA specificities as is practical. Once an association with a particular locus or antigen is suspected, in-depth characterization with additional alloantibodies and monoclonal antibodies, with molecular probes (RFLP analysis), with oligonucleotide typing, or with cytotoxic or proliferative T-cell clones leads to the positive identification of the gene. Sequencing of the gene responsible for the abnormality has been a lengthy and difficult procedure if the gene is many kilobases from the nearest HLA marker. However, sequencing selected genes using the polymerase chain reaction for DNA amplification may become very practical.[163b] There is an obvious reason to want to identify through simple procedures as many structural genes on the HLA haplotype as possible.

The diseased population to be typed should be as large as possible. While the sample size will be small in rare genetic abnormalities, every effort should be made to test at least 30 and preferably more than 50 patients. If there are fewer than 30 subjects with the disease but multicase families are available, then direct linkage within families can provide the required evidence.

Whenever a disease population is typed, a corresponding control population must be included. These controls should match for sex, age, and ethnic origin and should be free from selective bias. For the analysis, the differences in antigenic frequencies between subjects and controls are determined and the relative risk (RR) is calculated, the latter being the chance of developing a disease when the antigen is present relative to the risk when that antigen is absent.[222] The RR is expressed as

$$\frac{a \times d}{b \times c}$$

where a = number of patients with a given antigen
b = number of controls with the antigen
c = number of patients without the antigen
d = number of controls without the antigen

For type 1 insulin dependent diabetes mellitus and HLA-B8, typical figures are $a = 38$, $b = 467$, $c = 47$, and $d =$

1500. The RR is 38 × 1500/47 × 467 = 2.60. A significant increase of the antigen in the disease group as compared to controls can be determined by the classic chi square test, by Fisher's exact test, or under special circumstances by combining several sources of data.[222] The corrected p value (for the number of antigens tested) is obtained by multiplying the p value by the number of alleles at the appropriate locus, in the case above, HLA-B to exclude chance associations. Once a significant association has been found, the correction of p values is no longer indicated.

Association Versus Linkage

Using the above procedures, many associations between HLA and a particular disease have been found. Only rarely can linkage between HLA and a disease susceptibility gene be shown. One genetic disease in which both association and linkage have been demonstrated has been mentioned. This is the iron storage abnormality hemochromatosis (see Chap. 55). On a population basis, hemochromatosis has been associated with HLA-A3 in numerous studies.[223] There have been two genetic studies which show that there is a major gene for hemochromatosis, that this gene is recessive but highly penetrant in the homozygous state, that it is close to HLA-A, and that it is in linkage disequilibrium with HLA-A3.[220,221] The procedure for assigning linkage was based on Ott's method for the analysis of multigeneration families as modified by Elston and Sobel[224] and by Kravitz et al.[225] In brief, environmental, dominant, recessive, and intermediate models are tested; finally, lod (logarithm of the odds) scores are calculated at different recombinational frequencies. The demonstration of a major gene for a disease does not depend on the availability of HLA data. HLA data are, however, required to demonstrate that the gene is linked to HLA. The map position of the gene can then be determined if there is an informative recombinant in the pedigree.

Linkage analysis is difficult and expensive. It requires the availability of large multigeneration, multicase families and careful ascertainment of the disease status and the HLA haplotype of all family members. If critically important family members are unavailable, the study is greatly weakened. More and more geneticists have moved to sib pair analysis.[226] This is often more convenient, as large families are not required and age differences are less pronounced.

Diseases Associated with HLA-A

The only disease with consistent association with HLA-A is hemochromatosis, which is linked and strongly associated with the A3 allele. Genes for ragweed hypersensitivity are in linkage disequilibrium with A2, as first noticed by Marsh and Bias.[227] Mendell et al.[195] have found a complex interrelationship between responses to ragweed antigens Ra3, E5, and HLA-A2, suggesting the existence of an immune response gene near HLA-A and in linkage disequilibrium with the A2 allele (see Blumenthal and Amos[228] for a discussion of HLA and atopic disease). HLA-A1 and -A2 have been inconsistently associated with schizophrenia.[229] Whether this is because the association is weak or because of the difficulties of ascertainment and of working with the families of schizophrenics in linkage attempts is unclear.

Diseases Associated with HLA-B

The first unequivocal association between an HLA allele and a disease was the association between ankylosing spondylitis and HLA-B27. In many parts of the world, numerous other arthropathies, often postinfectious, also show a strong association with B27 (but not with the strongly cross-reactive specificity B7, thus demonstrating the validity of the split between these antigens). The RR is consistently about ninetyfold in Caucasians but leaps to 350-fold in Persians, in whom B27 was detected in 23 of 25 patients as compared with 12 of 400 controls.[223] Comparable figures are reported from Japan, where the frequency of B27 is also low. In contrast to association, linkage has been much more difficult to prove for the arthropathies, partly because of low penetrance in families, the greater frequency in males than females, and the lack of uniformity of environmental exposure.

Because many patients with anterior uveitis or arthropathies have a history of infection with gram-negative organisms (*Salmonella, Shigella, Yersinia*) or have antibodies to *Yersinia*, and because the patients are preponderantly male, it has been suggested that infections of the intestine or of the urogenital tract serve as triggers for what is probably an autoimmune response. Cross-reactivity between *Klebsiella* bacteria and B27+ cells has been suggested by several studies.[230,231] A brief commentary on the concept of molecular mimicry and autoimmune disease appeared recently.[231a]

There have been numerous attempts to distinguish differences in the B27 antigen present in ankylosing spondylitis patients from the B27 in normal individuals. Analysis of HLA-B27 by cellular, serologic, biochemical, or molecular techniques has not shown any subdivision into a form of the antigen that is more strongly disease associated.[232] This finding, as well as the unique strength of the B27 association in different ethnic groups, has been used to support the concept that the B27 antigen itself is modified by or cross-reacts with a bacterial product.

Diseases Associated with HLA-C

The diseases associated with particular HLA-C alleles include psoriasis (associated with Cw6)[217] and acute lymphoblastic and acute and chronic myelogenous leukemia (associated with Cw3 and Cw4).[213] The latter were found only in very large (>1000) patient studies.

Diseases Associated with HLA-D, -DR, -DQ, -DP

The majority of diseases associated with HLA have been associated with the HLA-D region. These include IDDM (assoicated with DR3, DR4, and a DQβ chain), a number of immunologically mediated diseases such as chronic active hepatitis, celiac disease (or gluten-sensitive enteropathy), dermatitis herpetiformis, and Graves disease (all associated with DR3), multiple sclerosis (DR2), rheumatoid arthritis (DR4), toxic reactions to D-pencillamine in rheumatoid arthritis patients (DR3), and acquired immunodeficiency (less constantly DR5). (See reviews on HLA and disease for further information.[2,214–217]) Many of the above diseases are clearly autoimmune. One of the more striking associations with no known etiology has been narcolepsy, where 26 of 28 patients in one study[233] and all 37 patients in another[234] were DR2. Of significant interest is the association of particular HLA-DR antigens in healthy individuals with abnormal immune or physiological responses, e.g., the association of DR2 with differential sleep patterns in normal individuals[235] or the association of B8, DR3 with defective Fc receptor function[236] and defective T-suppressor-cell function.[237,238]

Numerous DR associations are now being reevaluated in light of newly identified DQ polymorphisms. HLA-DQ associations were originally difficult to identify as only three alleles were serologically detectable. By restriction fragment polymorphism, however, additional DQ variants can be identified, and some of these are frequently associated with diseases such as Sjögren syndrome,[239] multiple sclerosis,[240] narcolepsy,[241] and both resistance[242] and susceptibility to IDDM.[163d,243] Narcolepsy, which has an overwhelming strong association with DR2, has an equally strong association with DQw1. There is no association with defective complement alleles.[244] More recent has been the suggestion that amino acid residue 57 of the DQβ chain determines the specificity and extent of regulation of autoimmune responses toward islet cell antigens in IDDM.[163d] To what degree these associations reflect an attribute of DQ and to what degree they reflect tight linkage between DR and DQ is not known. Further complexity in assessing DQ effects on disease susceptibility comes from DQαβ polymorphism, potential DQαβ transinteractions,[130] the possibility of DQ subregion associations,[245] and additive effects by non-HLA genes such as Gm.[200]

An increased risk of disease in HLA *heterozygous* individuals has been noted in IDDM, where the risk of DR3/DR4 heterozygotes is greater than individuals DR3+DR4− or DR3−DR4+[130] and in seropositive juvenile rheumatoid arthritis (Dw4/Dw14 heterozygotes).[246] There are two potential explanations. One is the presence of two disease susceptibility genes, one linked to each D/DR antigen. The other is transcomplementation and the formation of a hybrid DQ molecule. Nepom and coworkers have found DQαβ hybrid molecules in DR3/DR4 heterozygous IDDM patients. Hybrid antigens are also reported from nondiabetic sibs, so the hybrid molecule itself may not be the sole cause.[130]

Diseases Associated with Complement Components and 21-OH Genes

Hereditary deficiencies of several complement components within the HLA-B/DR region are associated with disease. Homozygous deficiencies of C2 and C4 are found in some systemic lupus erythematosis patients. The C4A null allele C4A*QO is associated with several autoimmune diseases.[247] Other associations include rheumatoid arthritis with the C4B*2.9 allotype,[248] progressive systemic sclerosis with C4B*QO,[249] multiple sclerosis with CA*4-C4B*2 haplotype,[250] subacute sclerosing panencephalitis with C4A*QO,[251] schizophrenia with C4B*QO, and sporadic Alzheimer's disease with C4B*2.[252] Many of these studies have been small and the complete HLA haplotypes not defined.

C2 and C4 deficiencies are often associated with a specific and extended HLA haplotype, e.g., C2 null occurs on an A25-B18-DR2 haplotype, C4A*QO on an A1-B8-DR3 haplotype, and C4B*QO on an A3-Bw47-DR7 haplotype.[13] Deletions and/or duplications in these complement genes may include the 21-OH genes as well (for review see Refs. 13 and 253).

The steroid 21-hydroxylase genes (21-OHA and 21-OHB) are tandemly duplicated loci between HLA-B and HLA-DR and alternate with the two genes for the fourth component of complement. Deletions in this area of the chromosome have been found in A3,Bw47,DR7+ patients with congenital adrenal hyperplasia and in some patients with the A1-B8-DR3 haplotype.[13,22,254] An attenuated form of congenital adrenal hyperplasia is associated with a B14-DR1 haplotype. The HLA-linked gene implicated in 21-hydroxylase deficiency is a structural gene for the cytochrome P_{450} specific for steroid 21-hydroxylation.[254]

Diseases Associated with an Extended HLA Haplotype

Some of the diseases associated with a specific sequence of genes on an HLA haplotype, or extended haplotype, have been mentioned previously, e.g., the occurrence of C2 deficiency with the A25-B18-DR2-Dw2 haplotype. Such haplotypes demonstrate pronounced linkage disequilibrium and may involve genes from HLA-A to genes as far away as GLO. Other examples are given in Table 4-4.

There are also diseases which co-segregate with an HLA haplotype in families, but the haplotypes in other families are different so that no one antigen or locus can be identified. In cases of loose linkage or polygenic diseases in which one gene is linked to HLA, any association with a particular HLA antigen may be slight and likely to be missed in a population study. An example is leprosy, in which the lepromatous and tuberculoid forms appeared to segregate with the HLA haplotype in families, but no association was found with a specific HLA antigen.[255] Recent studies indicate the class II genes control the type of leprosy developing upon infection as well as cell-mediated reactivity after skin testing.[256,257] Other haplotype associations have been noted with immune responses to allergens (reviewed in Ref. 228).

HLA and Malignancy

The early associations between the 4c antigen and Hodgkin's disease and HLA-A2 and acute lymphocytic leukemia were noted previously. Other HLA associations are reported in renal cell carcinoma,[258] testicular teratocarcinoma,[259] Burkitt lymphoma,[260] and metastasis of germ cell testicular tumors,[261] but not breast cancer or other malignancies.[262] In melanoma, prognosis is said to be better with tumors that are class I+,class II− than the reverse.[263]

Current interest lies in the genetic and molecular mechanisms which result in aberrant MHC expression on tumors and the consequences of this.[264] The expression of aberrant MHC-like antigens in tumors could be the result of DNA rearrangements, possibly involving normally silent class I genes. The contribution of environmental factors, radiation, and viruses to oncogenesis, and the role the MHC plays, is still unresolved. Certain adenoviruses are, however, known to depress class I MHC expression,[265] and this may affect the resistance of the tumor to natural killer cells.[266]

Speculations about the HLA-Disease Associations

HLA-disease associations can be grouped into the following categories: (1) malignant diseases, for which there is still little definitive evidence; (2) inflammatory diseases, such as ankylosing spondylitis and Reiter disease, which are strongly asso-

Table 4-4 Examples of Diseases Associated With an HLA Haplotype*

HLA haplotype									*Disease*
	DR7	C4B*QO	C4A*1	Bf*F	C2*C	Bw47	Cw6	A3	Salt wasting 210H deficiency (210HB, C4B deletion)
DQw1	DR1	C4B*1,2	C4A*2	Bf*S	C2*C	B14		Aw33	Nonclassic 210H deficiency (210HA, C4B duplication)
DQw1	DR2		C4A*2		C2*QO	B18		A25	C2 deficiency
DQw2	DR3	C4B*1	C4A*QO	Bf*S	C2*C	B8	Cw7	A1	IDDM; systemic lupus erythematosis; IgA deficiency
DQw2	DR3	C4B*QO	C4A*3			B18			IDDM
DQw3	DR4	C4B*2.9	C4A*3			Bw62	Cw3		Rheumatoid arthritis
		C4B*1,2	C4A*2	Bf*S		B14		A28	IgA deficiency
		C4B*1	C4A*6	Bf*S		Bw57		A1	IgA deficiency

*The term *haplotype* indicates a combination of antigens or genes inherited as a single unit on one chromosome. The haplotypes listed align the HLA class I, II, and III alleles as the genes occur on the chromosome (e.g., HLA-DQ, HLA-DR, -C4B, -C4A, -Bf, -C2, HLA-B, HLA-C, and HLA-A).

ciated with B27; (3) inborn errors of metabolism, such as hemochromatosis and steroid 21-hydroxylase deficiency; (4) complement-deficiency syndromes; (5) diseases of abnormal differentiation, e.g., congenital neutropenia; (6) autoaggressive and endocrine diseases associated with D/DR/DQ; and (7) other diseases, such as leprosy, which may be related only to the HLA haplotype and not to any specific allele. The contribution of the tumor necrosis factor genes to disease susceptibility is not yet known.

It is most unlikely that any unifying cause exists because of the variety of types of disease—from hemochromatosis to narcolepsy to IDDM—and because different regions of the haplotype appear to be central to certain types of disease (see Table 4-4). It is clear that some of the associations originally found indicate the segregation of a defective chromosome; sometimes a break or deletion can be followed. Molecular mimicry, a theory proposed for ankylosing spondylitis, may be more common than previously thought, since amino acid similarity has been noted between viral proteins and host cell proteins.[231a] Worth mentioning is the possibility that HLA-linked genes may affect the development of a disease or might even determine resistance. For example, retrospective studies of a lethal disease may include a high frequency of long-term survivors. Hence an HLA association would be for increased survival and not for disease susceptibility. Similarly, HLA may affect disease expression. As previously noted, certain adenoviruses can "turn off" HLA class I expression in infected cells, thus producing a method of escaping cytolytic T cells.[265] Thus, resistance to infection may be partially controlled by an HLA phenotype. Genes which control immunosuppression to streptococcal cell wall antigen, cedar pollen, and schistosomal antigens and are localized to the HLA region have been studied by Sasazuki and colleagues.[199,267] Further perturbations of the immune system may result from IgA deficiency, which may be associated with autoimmune disease, allergy, or possibly even neoplasia.[268]

Of possible significance is the induction and expression of class II determinants on a wide variety of cells that are normally class II-negative, including thyrocytes and pancreas cells, which become positive after exposure to γ interferon. These class II+, or Ia+, cells can present antigen and thus may be a contributory factor to autoimmune disease.

Studies of the mouse, rat, and human MHCs indicate that the MHC can have other unusual attributes (see Ref. 269), some of which may contribute to disease processes. Genes in or near the MHC interact with insulin,[270] glucagon and epidermal growth factor receptors,[271,272] and γ-type endorphins,[273] and they can affect hormone receptor binding.[274] Other genes appear to affect fluid excretion in the inflamed gut[275] and the production of sexually discriminating molecules.[276]

The murine H-2 complex includes a series a recessive lethal genes termed the T/t complex.[183] These genes cause sterility, segregation distortion in progeny, and abnormal embryonic development. Altered chromatin structure (inversions) appears to suppress recombination with normal chromosomes. A similar complex of genes controlling growth and reproduction (the grc genes) has been described in the rat.[185] T/t like genes have been implicated within the human MHC. Evidence includes an HLA haplotype association with spina bifida occulta and asymmetry of vertebral facets,[186] fetal wastage and neural tube defects,[277] and preferential transmission of HLA-DR3, DR4, and the A1-B8-DR3 haplotype in diabetic and healthy families.[278,279] Increased HLA compatibility in some couples is associated with propensity to spontaneous abortion,[280] prolonged birth intervals,[281] and increased risk of leukemia in the neonate.[282]

The influence of the MHC on aging is of new interest,[283] especially as it may be a regulatory system in developmental and antibiosenescent processes.

Some of the potential mechanisms which would account for observed HLA-disease associations or linkage are given in Table 4-5. Many associations appear to be the result of autoimmune phenomena or may be traced to deficient complement alleles. Some associations such as A3 with hemochromatosis or DR2 with narcolepsy remain a mystery and may be the result of the entrapment of a hitchhiker gene within the haplotype. Many other diseases, such as Hodgkin's disease,[212] juvenile rheumatoid arthritis,[284] and psoriatic arthritis,[285] have been associated with HLA class I and class II antigens, but no one allele is consistently implicated. Few associations are complete, e.g., concordance is always less than 100 percent, and inevitably other genes may play a role in susceptibility. HLA and Gm interactions have been widely noted and HLA/T-cell receptor gene interactions are possible.[286] The influence of environmental factors, sex hormones, and other genes is also likely.

For further detailed information, including many unsuc-

Table 4-5 Possible Mechanisms For HLA Disease Associations

Molecular mimicry—cross-reactivity between viruses, bacteria, or environmental agents and HLA antigens
Immune-response genes linked to HLA
Complement genes linked to HLA
Enzyme genes linked to HLA
HLA antigens functioning as virus, pathogen receptors
Linked genes determining or controlling differentiation processes
Alteration or modification of HLA antigen as a result of an infectious agent, drug, or environmental agent
Defective immunosuppression
Inappropriate expression of HLA class II antigens on normally Ia-negative cells

cessful attempts to demonstrate any relationship, the reader is referred to specific reviews on HLA and disease.[2,214–217,228,237]

Future

The last 10 years have produced dramatic changes in the analysis of the MHC, both in characterization of antigens and definition of function. Newly applied molecular and biochemical techniques include analysis with monoclonal antibodies, primed cellular reagents, pulsed field gel electrophoresis, isoelectric focusing, Southern and Northern blotting, cosmid cloning, amplification of DNA, and transfection of genes. The ability to measure transcription and translation and to correlate these with cell surface expression has allowed precise tracking of the HLA genes and their products. It is indeed remarkable that we can now identify genes such as DO and DN by molecular studies and secondarily trace their expression. Identification of regulatory elements in the HLA region is forthcoming.

We are closer to understanding the association of a particular HLA allele with disease susceptibility. It remains to be determined which diseases result from abnormal genes and which from abnormal function. Diseases such as hemochromatosis and narcolepsy, although governed by genes very close to the HLA genes, appear to have no relationship to the antigens themselves. For some, the etiology of a disease may be reconstructed in vitro by transfecting relevant genes into suitable cells and analyzing the interaction of these genes with T-cell clones. The specific protein or DNA sequence critical for antigen presentation, for autoimmune recognition, or cytolytic destruction can be identified. Direct sequencing of particular HLA-DR and -DQ antigens in both patient and control populations is now being accomplished. The usefulness of cloned genes in defining the structure and function of their products will bring a new dimension to HLA and disease.

There are undoubtedly many other genes in the HLA region which may be important in the etiology of disease, but their structure, function, and genetics are unknown. It is possible that the HLA genes themselves have functions other than antigen presentation and/or restriction. Their interaction with iron binding glycoproteins—lactoferrin, acidic isoferritins, and transferrin, for example—may indicate roles in intracellular transport and cell-cell communication as yet unknown.

The authors' work was supported by grants from the National Institutes of Health 5T32 CA09058-13, 5T32 AI07240-05, 5R01 AI08897-20, and HD21244.

REFERENCES

1. AUFFRAY C, STROMINGER JL: Molecular genetics of the human major histocompatibility complex. *Adv Hum Genet* 15:197, 1986.
2. BODMER WF: The HLA system: structure and function. *J Clin Pathol* 40:948, 1987.
3. THORSBY E: Structure and function of HLA molecules. *Transplant Proc* XIX: 29, 1987.
4. SNELL GD, DAUSSET J, NATHENSON S: *Histocompatibility*. New York, Academic, 1976, chap 9, pp 182–247.
5. KLEIN J: *Natural History of the Major Histocompatibility Complex*. New York, Wiley, 1986.
6. SCHURMANN RKB, VAN ROOD JJ, VOSSEN JM, SCHELLEKENS P TH A, FELTKAMP-VROOM TH M, DOYER E, GMELLING-MAYLING F, VISSNER HKA: Failure of lymphocyte-membrane HLA-A and B expression in two siblings with combined immunodeficiency. *Clin Immunol Immunopathol* 14:418, 1979.
7. BETUEL H, TOURAINE JL, SOUILLET G, JEUNE M: Absence of cell-membrane HLA antigens in an immunodeficient child. *Tissue Antigens* 11:68, 1978.
8. KLEIN J: The major histocompatibility complex of the mouse. *Science* 203:516, 1979.
9. FISHER RA: *Genetical Theory of Natural Selection*. New York, Dover, 1958.

9a. WILLIAMS AF, BARCLAY AN: The immunoglobulin supergene family—domains for cell surface recognition. *Ann Rev Immunol* 6:381, 1988.

9b. CARROLL MC, KATZMAN P, ALICOT EM, KOLLER BH, GERAGHTY DE, ORR HT, STROMINGER JL, SPIES T: Linkage map of the human major histocompatibility complex including the tumor necrosis factor genes. *Proc Natl Acad Sci USA* 84:8535, 1987.

10. WARD FE, LEVY SB, PINNELL SR: Mixed lymphocyte responses in a four generation C2 deficiency family. *Transplant Proc* 9:1733, 1977.
11. ROBINSON MA, CARROLL MC, JOHNSON AH, HARTZMAN RJ, BELT KT, KINDT TJ: Localization of C4 genes within the HLA complex by molecular genotyping. *Immunogenetics* 21:143, 1985.
12. ALBERT ED, RITTNER C, SCHOLZ S, KUNTZ B, MICKEY MR: Three point association of HLA-A, B, Bf haplotypes deduced in 200 parents of 100 families. *Scand J Immunol* 6:459, 1977.
13. CARROLL MC: Molecular genetics of the fourth component of human complement. *Fed Proc* 46:2457, 1987.
14. CAMPBELL RD, LAW SKA, REID KBM, SIM RB: Structure, organization and regulation of the complement genes. *Ann Rev Immunol* 6:161, 1988.
15. CURRY RA, DIERICH MP, PELLEGRINO MA, HOCH JA: Evidence for linkage between HLA antigens and receptors for complement components C3b and C3d in human-mouse hybrids. *Immunogenetics* 3:465, 1976.
16. MERRITT AD, PETERSEN BH, BIEGEL AA, MEYERS DA, BROOKES GF, HODES ME: Chromosome 6: Linkage of the eighth component of complement (C8) to the histocompatibility region (HLA) in Baltimore Conference (1975). *Third International Workshop on Human Gene Mapping, Birth Defects* 12:364, 1976.
17. GIRALDO G, DEGOS L, BETH E, SASPORTES M, MARCELLI A, GHARBI R, DAY NK: C8 deficiency in a family with xeroderma pigmentosum. Lack of linkage to the HLA region. *Clin Immunol Immunopathol* 8:377, 1977.
18. JERSILD C, RUBINSTEIN P, DAY NK: The HLA system and inherited deficiencies of the complement system. *Tranplant Rev* 32:43, 1976.
19. OLAISEN B, GEDDE-DAHL JR T, THORSBY E: Localization of the human GLO gene locus. *Humangenetik* 32:301, 1976.
20. MICHELSON AM, BRUNS GA, MORTON CC, ORKIN SH: The human phosphoglycerate kinase multigene family. *J Biol Chem* 260:6982, 1985.
21. OLAISEN B, GEDDE-DAHL T JR, TEISBERG P, THORSBY E, SIVERTS A, JONASSEN R, WILHELMY MC: A structural locus for coagulation factor XIIIA (F13A) is located distal to the HLA region chromosome 6p in man. *Am J Hum Genet* 37:220, 1985.
22. WHITE PC, WERKMEISTER J, NEW MI, DUPONT B: Steroid 21-hydroxylase deficiency and the major histocompatibility complex. *Hum Immunol* 15:404, 1986.
23. SPIES T, MORTON CC, NEDOSPASOV SA, FIERS W, PIOUS D, STROMINGER JL: Genes for the tumor necrosis factors alpha and beta are linked to the human major histocompatibility complex. *Proc Natl Acad Sci USA* 83:8699, 1986.
24. RUSSELL PS, WINN HJ (eds): *Histocompatibility Testing 1965*. Washington, DC, National Academy of Sciences of the USA, publ 1229, 1965.
25. BALNER H, CLETON FJ, EERNISSE JG (eds): *Histocompatibility Testing*. Baltimore, Williams & Wilkins, 1966.
26. CURTONI ES, MATTIUZ PL, TOSI RM (eds): *Histocompatibility Testing 1967*. Copenhagen, Munksgaard, 1967.

27. TERASAKI PI (ed): *Histocompatibility Testing 1970*. Copenhagen, Munksgaard, 1970.
28. DAUSSET J, COLOMBANI J (eds): *Histocompatibility Testing 1972*. Copenhagen, Munksgaard, 1973.
29. KISSMEYER-NIELSEN F (ed): *Histocompatibility Testing 1975*. Copenhagen, Munksgaard, 1976.
30. BODMER WF, BATCHELOR JR, BODMER JG, FESTENSTEIN H, MORRIS PJ (eds): *Histocompatibility Testing 1977*. Copenhagen, Munksgaard, 1977.
31. TERASAKI PI (ed): *Histocompatibility Testing 1980*. Los Angeles, UCLA Tissue Typing Laboratory, 1980.
32. ALBERT ED, BAUR MP, MAYR WR (eds): *Histocompatibility Testing 1984*. Copenhagen, Munksgaard, 1984.
33. DUPONT B (ed): *Immunobiology of HLA, Histocompatibility Testing 1987*. New York, Springer-Verlag, 1988, vol I.
34. Nomenclature for factors of the HLA system, 1987. *Human Immunology*, 1989, in press.
35. GRUMET FC, FENDLY BM, FISH L, FOUNG S, ENGLEMAN EG: A monoclonal antibody (B27M2) subdividing HLA-B27. *Hum Immunol* 5:61, 1982.
36. VEGA MA, EZQUERRA A, ROJO S, APARICIO P, BRAGADO R, LOPEZ DE CASTRO JA: Structural analysis of an HLA-B27 functional variant: Identification of residues that contribute to the specificity of recognition by cytolytic T lymphocytes. *Proc Natl Acad Sci USA* 82:7394, 1985.
37. TOUBERT A, GOMARD G, GRUMET FC, AMOR B, MULLER JY, LEVY JP: Identification of several functional subgroups of HLA-B27 by restriction of the activity of antiviral T killer lymphocytes. *Immunogenetics* 20:513, 1984.
38. CHOO SY, ANTONELLI P, NISPEROS B, NEPOM GT, HANSEN JA: Six variants of HLA-B27 identified by isoelectric focusing. *Immunogenetics* 23:24, 1986.
39. NESS DB, GRUMET FC: New polymorphisms of HLA-B27 and other B locus antigens detected by RFLP using a locus-specific probe. *Hum Immunol* 18:65, 1987.
40. BIDDISON WE, KOSTYU DD, STROMINGER JL, KRANGEL MS: Delineation of immunologically and biochemically distinct HLA-A2 antigens. *J Immunol* 129:730, 1982.
41. WALLACE LE, HOUGHTON MA, RICKINSON AB, EPSTEIN MA, BRADLEY BA: Allospecific T cell recognition of HLA-A2 antigens: Evidence for group-specific and subgroup-specific epitopes. *Immunogenetics* 21:201, 1985.
42. COWAN EP, JORDAN BR, COLIGAN JE: Molecular cloning and DNA sequence analysis of genes encoding cytotoxic T lymphocyte-defined HLA-A3 subtypes: The El subtype. *J Immunol* 135:2835, 1985.
43. VAN SCHRAVENDIJK MR, BIDDISON WE, BERGER AE, COLIGAN JE: Comparative structural analysis of HLA-A3 antigens distinguishable by cytotoxic T lymphocytes: Variant E1. *J Immunol* 134:410, 1985.
44. VAN SEVENTER GA, HUIS B, MELIEF CJ, IVANYI P: Fine specificity of human HLA-B7 specific cytotoxic T-lymphocyte clones. I. Identification of HLA-B7 subtypes and histotopes of the HLA-B7 cross-reacting group. *Hum Immunol* 16:375, 1986.
45. YANNELLI JR, MOORE LC, ENGELHARD VH: Multiple epitopes on human and murine cells expressing HLA-B7 as defined by specific murine cytotoxic T cell clones. *J Immunol* 135:900, 1985.
46. VAN ROOD JJ, VAN LEEUWEN A, ZWEERUS R: The 4a and 4b antigens, do they or don't they? in Terasaki PI (ed): *Histocompatibility Testing 1970*. Copenhagen, Munksgaard, 1970.
47. AYRES J, CRESSWELL P: HLA-B specificities and w4,w6 specificities are on the same polypeptide. *Eur J Immunol* 6:794, 1976.
48. KOSTYU DD, CRESSWELL P, AMOS DB: A public HLA antigen associated with HLA-A9, Aw32 and Bw4. *Immunogenetics* 10:433, 1980.
49. WAN AM, ENNIS P, PARHAM P, HOLMES N: The primary structure of HLA-A32 suggests a region involved in formation of the Bw4/Bw6 epitopes. *J Immunol* 137:3671, 1986.
50. BELVEDERE M, MATTIUZ P, CURTONI ES: An antibody cross-reacting with LA and FOUR antigens of the HL-A system. *Immunogenetics* 1:538, 1975.
51. LAYET C, DELOVITCH T, FERRIER P, CAILLOL DH, JORDAN BR, LEMONNIER FA: Expression of an HLA-Bw6-related specificity by the HLA-Cw3 molecule. *Immunogenetics* 21:469, 1985.
52. WAYS JP, ROTHBARD JB, PARHAM P: Amino acid residues 56 to 69 of HLA-A2 specify an antigenic determinant shared by HLA-A2 and HLA-B17. *J Immunol* 137:217, 1986.
53. HOLMES N, PARHAM P: Exon shuffling in vivo can generate novel HLA class I molecules. *EMBO J* 4:2849, 1985.
54. PARHAM P: In vitro production of a hybrid monoclonal antibody that preferentially binds to cells that express both HLA-A2 and HLA-B7. *Hum Immunol* 12:213, 1985.
55. PAUL P, LEPAGE V, SAYAGH B, METZGER JJ, PLA M, BOUMSELL L, COUAY C, COHEN D, COLOMBANI J, DAUSSET J: Serological expression after sequential double transfection with purified HLA-All gene of mouse fibroblasts carrying human beta-2 microglobulin. *Immunogenetics* 22:1, 1985.
56. SODOYER R, KAHN-PERLES B, STRACHAN T, SIRE J, SANTONI MJ, LAYET C, FERRIER P, JORDAN BR, LEMONNIER FA: Transfection of murine LMTK-cells with purified HLA class I genes. VII. Association of allele- and locus-specific serological reactivities with respectively the first and second domains of the HLA-B7 molecule. *Immunogenetics* 23:246, 1986.
57. ALBERT ED, GÖTZE D: The major histocompatibility system in man, in Götze D (ed): *The Major Histocompatibility System in Man and Animals*. New York, Springer-Verlag, 1977, p 7.
58. FAULK WP, SANDERSON AR, TEMPLE A: Distribution of MHC antigens in human placental chorionic villi. *Transplant Proc* 9:1379, 1977.
59. MORTON JA, PICKLES MM, SUTTON L, SKOV F: Identification of further antigens on red cells and lymphocytes: Association of Bg^b with w17 (Te57) and Bg^c with w28 (Da15,Ba*). *Vox Sang* 21:141, 1971.
60. BRODSKY FM, PARHAM P, BARNSTABLE CJ, CRUMPTON MJ, BODMER WF: Monoclonal antibodies for analysis of the HLA system. *Immunol Rev* 47:3, 1979.
61. TRUCCO M, DEPETRIS S, GAROTTA G, CEPPELLINI R: Quantitative analysis of cell surface HLA structures by means of monoclonal antibodies. *Hum Immunol* 1:233, 1980.
62. BILLING RJ, SAFANI M, PETERSON P: Soluble HLA antigens present in normal human serum. *Tissue Antigens* 10:75, 1977.
63. REISFELD RA, PELLEGRINO MA, FERRONE S: The immunologic and molecular profiles of HLA antigens isolated from urine. *J Immunol* 118:264, 1977.
64. MITTAL KK: Human histocompatibility (HL-A) antigens in semen and their role in reproduction. *Fertil Steril* 26:704, 1975.
65. DAWSON JR, SHASBY SS, AMOS DB: The serological detection of HL-A antigens in human milk. *Tissue Antigens* 4:76, 1974.
66. MAEDA H, HIRATA R, CHEN RF, SUZAKI H, KUDOH S, TOHYAMA H: Defective expression of HLA class I antigens: A case of the bare lymphocyte without immunodeficiency. *Immunogenetics* 21:549, 1985.
67. MARCADET A, COHEN D, DAUSSET J, FISCHER A, DURANDY A, GRISCELLI C: Genotyping with DNA probes in combined immunodeficiency syndrome with defective expression of HLA. *N Engl J Med* 312:1287, 1985.
68. PAYNE R, BRODSKY FM, PETERLIN M, YOUNG LM: "Bare lymphocytes" without immunodeficiency. *Hum Immunol* 6:219, 1983.
69. SULLIVAN KE, STOBO JD, PETERLIN BM: Molecular analysis of the bare lymphocyte syndrome. *J Clin Invest* 76:75, 1985.
70. CEPPELLINI R: Old and new facts and speculations about transplantation antigens of man. *Prog Immunol* 1:973, 1971.
71. MAYR MR, PAUSCH V, SCHNEDL W: Human chimaera detectable only by investigation of her progeny. *Nature* 277:210, 1979.
72. ASTER RH, SZATKOWSKI N, LIEBERT M, DUQUESNOY RJ: Expression of HLA-B12, HLA-B8, w4 and w6 on platelets. *Transplant Proc* 9:1695, 1977.
73. POLLACK MS, MAURER D, LEVINE LS, NEW MI, PANG S, DUCHON MA, OWENS RP, MERKATZ IR, NITOWSKY HM, SACHS G, DUPONT B: HLA typing of amniotic cells: The prenatal diagnosis of congenital adrenal hyperplasia (21-OH-deficiency type). *Transplant Proc* 11:1726, 1979.
74. BROWN G, BIBERFELD P, CHRISTENSSON B, MASON DY: The distribution of HLA on human lymphoid, bone barrow and peripheral blood cells. *Eur J Immunol* 9:272, 1979.
75. ARCE-GOMEZ B, JONES EA, BARNSTABLE CJ, SOLOMON E, BODMER WF: The genetic control of HLA-A and B antigens in somatic cell hybrids: Requirement for beta$_2$-microglobulin. *Tissue Antigens* 11:96, 1978.
76. CRESSWELL P: Regulation of HLA Class I and Class II antigen expression. *Br Med Bull* 43:66, 1987.
77. PFIZENMAIER K, SCHEURICH P, SCHLUTER C, KRONKE M: Tumor necrosis factor enhances HLA-A, B, C and HLA-DR gene expression in human tumor cells. *J Immunol* 138:975, 1987.
78. SCHEURICH P, KRONKE M, SCHLUTER C, UCER U, PFIZENMAIER K: Noncytocidal mechanisms of action of tumor necrosis factor-alpha on human tumor cells: Enhancement of HLA gene expression synergistic with interferon-gamma. *Immunobiology* 172:291, 1986.
79. STROMINGER JL: Structure of Class I and Class II HLA antigens. *Br Med Bull* 43:81, 1987.
80. STRACHAN T, SODOYER R, DAMOTTE M, JORDAN BR: Complete nucleotide sequence of a functional class I HLA gene, HLA-A3: implications for the evolution of HLA genes. *EMBO J* 3:887, 1984.
81. ORR HT, LOPEZ DE CASTRO JA, LANCET D, STROMINGER JL: Complete amino acid sequence of papain-solubilized human histocompatibility antigen, HLA-B7. II. Sequence determination and search for homologies. *Biochem* 18:5711, 1979.
82. WAYS JP, COPPIN HL, PARHAM P: The complete primary structure of HLA-Bw58. *J Biol Chem* 260:11924, 1985.

83. KOLLER BH, ORR HT: Cloning and complete sequence of an HLA-A2 gene: analysis of two HLA-A alleles at the nucleotide level. *J Immunol* 134:2727, 1985.

84. BJORKMAN PJ, SAPER MA, SAMRAOUI B, BENNETT WS, STROMINGER JL, WILEY DC: Structure of the human class I histocompatibility antigen, HLA-A2. *Nature* 329:506, 1987.

84a. BJORKMAN PJ, SAPER MA, SAMRAOUI B, BENNETT WS, STROMINGER JL, WILEY DC: The foreign antigen binding site and T cell recognition regions of class I histocompatibility antigens. *Nature* 329:512, 1987.

85. FERRARA G, TOSI R, LONGO A, CASTELLANI A, VIVIANI C, CARMINATI G: Silent alleles at the HLA-C locus. *J Immunol* 121:731, 1978.

86. SMEATON L, SUMMERS CW, HARRIS R, STRACHAN T: Restriction fragment length polymorphism at the HLA-C locus. *Immunogenetics* 25:179, 1987.

87. OWEN MJ, CRUMPTON MJ: The role of class I and class II antigens in T cell recognition. *Br Med Bull* 43:228, 1987.

88. KRANGEL MS, BIDDISON WE, STROMINGER JL: Comparative structural analysis of HLA-A2 antigens distinguishable by cytotoxic T lymphocytes. II. Variant DK1: Evidence for a discrete CTL recognition region. *J Immunol* 130:1856, 1983.

89. KRANGEL MS: Functional implications of structural variation in class I HLA antigens, in Schacter B, Brodsky F, Cresswell P, Kostyu D, and Sheehy M (eds): *Molecular and Cellular Biology of Histocompatibility Antigens.* New York, American Society for Histocompatibility and Immunogenetics, 1987, p 23.

90. KOLLER BH, WARD FE, DEMARS R, ORR HT: Comparison of multiple HLA-A alleles at the DNA level by using Southern blotting and HLA-A-specific probes. *J Immunol* 135:4229, 1985.

91. STEERE K, SIDWELL B, LEACH R, WARD FE, TAUROG JD, ORR HT: Use of DNA probes from the 5′ flanking region of the HLA-B gene to examine polymorphism at the HLA-B locus. *Hum Immunol* 16:137, 1986.

92. ORR HT: Molecular genetics of HLA, in Litwin SD, Scott D, Flaherty L, Reisfeld R, Marcus D (eds): *Human Immunogenetics: An Advanced Text,* New York, Marcel Dekker, Inc., 1988, chap. 15, in press.

93. ORR HT, DEMARS R: Class I-like HLA genes map telomeric to the HLA-A2 locus in human cells. *Nature* 302:534, 1983.

94. TROWSDALE J: Genetics and polymorphism: Class II antigens. *Br Med Bull* 43:15, 1987.

95. GILES RC, CAPRA JD: Structure, function and genetics of human class II molecules. *Adv Immunol* 37:1, 1975.

96. FESTENSTEIN H, COLLIER B: Cellular typing and functional heterogeneity of MHC-encoded products. *Br Med Bull* 43:122, 1987.

97. DUPONT B, HANSEN JA, YUNIS EJ: Human mixed lymphocyte culture reaction: Genetics, specificity and biological implications. *Adv Immunol* 23:108, 1976.

98. INOKO H, ANDO A, KIMURA M, TSUJI K: Isolation and characterization of the cDNA clone and genomic clones of a new HLA class II antigen heavy chain, DO alpha. *J Immunol* 135:2156, 1985.

99. SERVENIUS B, RASK L, PETERSON PA: Class II genes of the human major histocompatibility complex. The DO beta gene is a divergent member of the class II beta gene family. *J Biol Chem* 262:8759, 1987.

100. JONSSON A-K, HYLDIG-NIELSEN J-J, SERVENIUS B, LARHAMMAR D, ANDERSSON G, JORGENSEN F, PETERSON PA, RASK L: Class II genes of the human major histocompatibility complex. Comparisons of the DQ and DX alpha and beta genes. *J Biol Chem* 262:8767, 1987.

101. OKADA K, BOSS JM, PRENTICE H, SPIES T, MENGLER R, AUFFRAY C, LILLI J, GROSSBERGER D, STROMINGER JL: Gene organization of DC and DX subregions of the human major histocompatibility complex. *Proc Natl Acad Sci USA* 82:3410, 1985.

102. TROWSDALE J, KELLY A: The human HLA class II alpha chain gene DN alpha is distinct from genes in the DP, DQ and DR subregions. *EMBO J* 4:2231, 1985.

103. CARRA G, ACCOLLA RS: Structural analysis of human Ia antigens reveals the existence of a fourth molecular subset distinct from DP, DQ, and DR molecules. *J Exp Med* 165:47, 1987.

104. RADKA SF, CHARRON DJ, BRODSKY FM: Class II molecules of the major histocompatibility complex considered as differentiation markers. *Hum Immunol* 16:390, 1986.

105. BUSCH FW, LANGER M, PAWELEC G, ZIEGLER A, WERNET P, BUHRING HJ, MEYER P, MULLER C: HLA class II antigens on human hematopoietic progenitors. *Blut* 54:179, 1987.

106. ZIER KS: Expression of class II antigens by subsets of activated T cells. *Cell Immunol* 100:525, 1986.

107. NATALI PG, DE MARTINO C, QUARANTA V, NIRCOTRA MR, FREZZA F, PELLEGRINO MA, FERRONE S: Expression of Ia-like antigens in normal human nonlymphoid tissues. *Transplantation* 31:75, 1981.

108. NATALI P, BIGOTTI A, CAVALIERE R, LIAO SK, TANIGUCHI M, MATSUI M, FERRONE S: Heterogeneous expression of melanoma-associated antigens and HLA antigens by primary and multiple metastatic lesions removed from patients with melanoma. *Cancer Res* 45:2883, 1985.

109. SMITH ME, HOLGATE CS, WILLIAMSON JM, GRIGOR I, QUIRKE P, BIRD CC: Major histocompatibility complex class II antigen expression in B and T cell non-Hodgkin's lymphoma. *J Clin Pathol* 40:34, 1987.

110. ARNAUD-BATTANDIER F, CERF-BENSUSSAN N, AMSELLEM R, SCHMITZ J: Increased HLA-DR expression by enterocytes in children with celiac disease. *Gastroenterology* 91:1206, 1986.

111. HANAFUSA T, PUJOL-BORRELL R, CHIORATO L, RUSSELL RCG, DONLACH D, BOTTAZZO GF: Aberrant expression of HLA-DR antigen on thyrocytes in Graves' disease: Relevance for autoimmunity. *Lancet* 2:1111, 1983.

112. BOTTAZZO GF, DEAN BM, MCNALLY JM, MacKAY EH, SWIFT PG, GAMBLE DR: In situ characterization of autoimmune phenomena and expression of HLA molecules in the pancreas in diabetic insulitis. *N Engl J Med* 313:353, 1985.

113. CAMPBELL DA, DUBOIS RM, BUTCHER RG, POULTER LW: The density of HLA-DR antigen expression on alveolar macrophages is increased in pulmonary sarcoidosis. *Clin Exp Immunol* 65:165, 1986.

114. BERRIH S, ARENZANA-SEISDEDOS F, COHEN S, DEVOS R, CHARRON D, VIRELIZIER JL: Interferon-gamma modulates HLA class II antigen expression on cultured human thymic epithelial cells. *J Immunol* 135:1165, 1985.

115. HIRAYAMA M, YOKOCHI T, SHIMOKATA K, IIDA M, FUJIKI N: Induction of human leukocyte antigen -A,B,C and -DR on cultured human oligodendrocytes and astrocytes by human gamma interferon. *Neurosci Lett* 72:369, 1986.

116. SOLLID LM, GAUDERNACK G, MARKUSSEN G, KVALE D, BRANDTZAEG P, THORSBY E: Induction of various HLA class II molecules in a human colonic adenocarcinoma cell line. *Scand J Immunol* 25:175, 1987.

117. PUJOL-BORRELL R, TODD I, DOSHI M, BOTTAZZO GF, SUTTON R, GRAY D, ADOLF GR, FELDMANN M: HLA class II induction in human islet cells by interferon-gamma plus tumour necrosis factor or lymphotoxin. *Nature* 326:304, 1987.

118. PUJOL-BORRELL R, TODD I, DOSHI M, GRAY D, FELDMANN M: Differential expression and regulation of MHC products in the endocrine and exocrine cells of the human pancreas. *Clin Exp Immunol* 65:128, 1986.

119. GONWA TA, PICKER LJ, RAFF HV, GOYERT SM, SILVER J, STOBO JB: Antigen-presenting capabilities of human monocytes correlates with their expression of HLA-DS, an Ia determinant distinct from HLA-DR. *J Immunol* 130:706, 1983.

120. NAVARETTE C, FERNANDEZ N, ALONSO MC, FESTENSTEIN H: Ontogenic and functional implications of the differential expression of HLA-DQ antigens on leukemic cells. *Hum Immunol* 16:52, 1986.

121. WAKE C, FLAVELL RA: Multiple mechanisms regulate the expression of murine immune response genes. *Cell* 42:623, 1985.

122. LAWRENCE SK, SMITH CL, SRIVASTAVA R, CANTOR CR, WEISSMAN SM: Megabase-scale mapping of the HLA gene complex by pulsed field gel electrophoresis. *Science* 235:1387, 1987.

123. BONTROP RE, BAAS EJ, OTTING N, SCHREUDER GM, GIPHART MJ: Molecular diversity of HLA-DQ. DQ alpha and beta chain isoelectric point differences and their relation to serologically defined HLA-DQ allospecificities. *Immunogenetics* 25:305, 1987.

124. OKADA K, PRENTICE H, BOSS J, LEVY D, KAPPES D, SPIES T, RAGHUPATHY R, AUFFRAY C, STROMINGER JL: SB subregion of the human major histocompatibility complex: Gene organization, allelic polymorphism and expression in transformed cells. *EMBO J* 4:739, 1985.

125. TSUKAMOTO K, YASUNAMI M, KIMURA A, INOKO H, ANDO A, HIROSE T, INAYAMA S, SASAZUKI T: DQwl beta gene from HLA-DR2-Dw12 consists of six exons and expressed multiple DQwl beta polypeptides through alternative splicing. *Immunogenetics* 25:343, 1987.

126. ANDERSSON G, LARHAMMAR D, WIDMARK E, SERVENIUS B, PETERSON PA, RASK L: Class II genes of the human major histocompatibility complex. Organization and evolutionary relationship of the DR beta genes. *J Biol Chem* 262:8748, 1987.

127. GORSKI J, ROLLINI P, MACH B: Structural comparison of the genes of two HLA-DR supertypic groups: The loci encoding DRw52 and DRw53 are not truly allelic. *Immunogenetics* 25:397, 1987.

128. CASCINO I, ROSENSHINE S, TURCO E, MARRARI M, DUQUESNOY RJ, TRUCCO M: Relationship between DQ alpha and DQ beta RFLP and cell surface polymorphisms of class II HLA antigens. *J Immunogenet* 13:387, 1986.

129. BOSCH ML, FEI H, BONTROP RE, GERRETS R, TILANUS MGJ, TERMIJTELEN A, GIPHART MJ: Polymorphisms within the HLA-DRw6 haplotype. III. DQ alpha and DQ beta polymorphism, association with HLA-D. *Hum Immunol* 19:91, 1987.

130. NEPOM BS, SCHWARZ D, PALMER JP, NEPOM GT: Transcomplementation of

HLA genes in IDDM. HLA-DQ alpha- and beta-chains produce hybrid molecules in DR3/4 heterozygotes. *Diabetes* 36:114, 1987.

131. KELLY A, TROWSDALE J: Complete nucleotide sequence of a functional HLA-DP beta gene and the region between the DP beta 1 and DP alpha 1 genes: Comparison of the 5′ ends of HLA class II genes. *Nucleic Acids Res* 13:1607, 1985.

131a. SULLIVAN KE, CALMAN AF, NAKANISHI M, TSANG SY, WANG Y, PETERLIN BM: A model for the transcriptional regulation of MHC class II genes. *Immunology Today* 8:289, 1987.

132. RODRIGUEZ-DECORDOBA S, NUNEZ-ROLDAN A, WINCHESTER R, MARSHALL P, CARRIER C, MOLLEN N, WALKER M, GINSBERG-FELLNER F, RUBENSTEIN P: Molecular characterization by high resolution isoelectric focusing of the products encoded by the class II region loci of the major histocompatibility complex in humans. I. DR and DQ gene variants. *Hum Immunol* 20:71, 1987.

133. TILANUS MG, VAN EGGERMOND MC, VAN DER BIJL M, MOROLLI B, SCHREUDER GM, DE VRIES RR, GIPHART MJ: HLA class II DNA analysis by RFLP reveals novel class II polymorphism. *Hum Immunol* 18:265, 1987.

134. INOKO H, ANDO A, ITO M, TSUJI K: Southern hybridization analysis of DNA polymorphism in the HLA-D region. *Hum Immunol* 16:304, 1986.

135. HONGMING F, TILANUS M, VAN EGGERMOND M, GIPHART M: Reduced complexity of RFLP for HLA-Dr typing by the use of a DR beta 3′ cDNA probe. *Tissue Antigens* 28:129, 1986.

136. ECKELS DD, HARTZMAN RJ: Characterization of human T-lymphocyte clones (TLCs) specific for HLA-region gene products. *Immunogenetics* 16:117, 1982.

137. ZEEVI A, SCHEFFEL C, ANNEN K, BASS G, MARRARI M, DUQUESNOY RJ: Association of the PLT specificity of alloreactive lymphocyte clones with HLA-DR, MB and MT determinants. *Immunogenetics* 16:209, 1982.

138. ROSEN-BRONSON S, JOHNSON AH, HARTZMAN RJ, ECKELS DD: Human allospecific TLCs generated against HLA antigens associated with DR1 through DRw8. I. Growth and specificity analysis. *Immunogenetics* 24:368, 1986.

139. REINSMOEN NL, BACH FH: Five HLA-D clusters associated with DR4. *Hum Immunol* 4:249, 1982.

140. NEPOM BS, NEPOM GT, MICKELSON E, ANTONELLI P, HANSEN JA: Electrophoretic analysis of human HLA-DR antigens from HLA-DR4 homozygous cell lines: Correlation between beta chain diversity and HLA-D. *Proc Natl Acad Sci USA* 80:6962, 1983.

141. FESTENSTEIN H, AWAD J, HITMAN GA, CUTBUSH S, GROVES AV, CASSELL P, OLLIER W, SACHS JA: New HLA DNA polymorphisms associated with autoimmune diseases. *Nature* 322:64, 1986.

142. HOBLECK SL, KIM SJ, SILVER J, HANSEN JA, NEPOM GT: HLA-DR4 associated haplotypes are genotypically diverse within HLA. *J Immunol* 135:637, 1985.

143. ZEEVI A, CASCINO I, DI VECCHIA L, MARRARI M, DUQUESNOY RJ, TRUCCO M: Alloreactive T-cell recognition of two DQ beta allelic specificities associated with DQw1. *Hum Immunol* 18:225, 1987.

144. TANIGAKI N, TOSI R, COOPER J, STROMINGER JL: Immunochemistry of the HLA class II molecules isolated from a mouse cell lymphoma transfected with DQ alpha and beta genes from a DR4 haplotype. *Immunogenetics* 26:40, 1987.

145. AMAR A, MICKELSON E, HANSEN JA, NEPOM GI: HLA-DQ heterogeneity among HLA-DRw11 (5) haplotypes. *Tissue Antigens* 28:278, 1986.

146. JOHNSON AH, THORSBY E, NAKATSUJI T, FANG T, MOEN T, HARTZMAN RJ: Recognition of an HLA-DPw1 specific alloantiserum raised by planned immunization. *Hum Immunol* 17:21, 1986.

147. TANIGAKI N, TOSI R, PARODI B, SORRENTINO R, FERRARA GB, STROMINGER JL: Detection of HLA-DP serological allodeterminants by the use of radioiodinated DP molecules. *Eur J Immunol* 17:743, 1987.

148. HYLDIG-NIELSEN JJ, MORLING N, ODUM N, RYDER LP, PLATZ P, JAKOBSEN B, SVEJGAARD A: Restriction fragment length polymorphism of the HLA-DP subregion and correlations to HLA-DP phenotypes. *Proc Natl Acad Sci USA* 84:1644, 1987.

149. KOBORI JA, STRAUSS E, MINARD K, HOOD L: Molecular analysis of the hotspot of recombination in the murine major histocompatibility complex. *Science* 234:173, 1986.

150. LEBO RV, CHAKRAVARTI A, BUETOW KH, CHEUNG M-C, CANN H, CORDELL B, GOODMAN H: Recombination within and between the human insulin and beta globin gene loci. *Proc Natl Acad Sci USA* 80:4808, 1983.

151. BELL GI, SELBY MJ, RUTTER WJ: The highly polymorphic region near the human insulin gene is composed of simple tandemly repeating sequences. *Nature* 295:31, 1982.

152. MENDES NF, TOINAI MEA, SILVEIRA NPA, GILBERTSEN RB, METZGAR RS: Technical aspects of the rosette tests used to detect human complement receptor (B) and sheep erythrocyte-binding (T) lymphocytes. *J Immunol* 111:860, 1973.

153. MANN DL, ABELSON L, HARRIS S, AMOS DB: Detection of antigens specific for B-lymphoid cultured cell lines with human alloantisera. *J Exp Med* 142:84, 1975.

154. GRIER JO, ABELSON LA, MANN DL, AMOS DB, JOHNSON AH: Enrichment of B lymphocytes using goat anti-human $F(ab')_2$. *Tissue Antigens* 10:236, 1977.

155. LOWRY R, GOGUEN J, CARPENTER CB, STROM TB, GAROVOY MR: Improved B cell typing for HLA-DR using nylon wool column enriched B lymphocyte preparations. *Tissue Antigens* 14:325, 1979.

156. STOCKER JW, GAROTTA G, HAUSMAN B, TRUCCO M, CEPPELLINI R: Separation of human cells bearing HLA-DR antigens using a monoclonal antibody rosetting method. *Tissue Antigens* 13:212, 1979.

157. VAN ROOD JJ, VAN LEEUWEN A, PLOEM JS: A method to detect simultaneously two cell populations by two colour fluorescence. *Nature* 262:795, 1976.

158. HUNTER SV, BENSON JW, BULL RW, POULIK MD: Use of turkey anti-human $beta_2$-microglobulin antisera for identification of DR antibodies. *Transplant Proc* 10:853, 1978.

159. DEWOLF WC, SCHLOSSMAN SF, YUNIS EJ: DRw antisera react with activated T cells. *J Immunol* 122:1780, 1979.

160. JENSEN EB, KRISTENSEN T, JORGENSEN F, LAMM LU: HLA-D typing homozygous typing cells. A statistical analysis of experimental and biological variation. *Tissue Antigens* 10:83, 1977.

161. JARAQUEMADA D, NAVARRETTE C, OLLIER W, AWAD J, OKOYE R, FESTENSTEIN H: HLA-Dw specificity assignments are independent of HLA-DQ, HLA-DR, and other class II specificities and define a biologically important segregant series which strongly activates a functionally distinct T cell subset. *Hum Immunol* 16:259, 1986.

162. BACH FH, REINSMOEN NL: The role of HLA-DR and HLA-DQ products in T lymphocyte activation and in contributing to Dw specificities. *Hum Immunol* 16:271, 1986.

163. NAKATSUJI T, INOKO H, ANDO A, SATO T, KOIDE Y, TADAKUMA T, YOSHIDA TO, TSUJI K: The role of transfected HLA-DQ genes and the mixed lymphocyte reaction-like condition. *Immunogenetics* 25:1, 1987.

163a. NEPOM GT, SEYFRIED C, HOLBECK S, WILSKE K, PALMER J, BYERS P, KNITTER-JACK N, CUDAHY R, NEPOM B: Oligonucleotide probes identify allelic variation among individual disease-associated HLA class II genes, in Dupont B (ed): *Immunobiology of HLA*. New York, Springer-Verlag, 1989, in press.

163b. SAIKI RK, SCHARF S, FALOONA F, MULLIS KB, HORN GT, ERLICH HA, ARNHEIM N: Enzymatic amplification of beta-globin genomic sequences and restriction site analysis for diagnosis of sickle cell anemia. *Science* 230:1350, 1985.

163c. BUGAWAN T, HORN G, HANSEN J, MICKELSON E, ANGELINI G, FERRARA GB, LONG C, ERLICH H: Analysis of HLA-DP allelic sequence polymorphism using the in vitro enzymatic DNA amplification of DP alpha and DP beta loci, in Dupont B (ed): *Immunobiology of HLA*. New York, Springer-Verlag, 1989, in press.

163d. TODD JA, BELL JJ, MCDEVITT HO: HLA-DQ beta gene contributes to susceptibility and resistance to insulin-dependent diabetes mellitus. *Nature* 329:599, 1987.

164. FLAHERTY L: The TLA region antigens, in Dorf MD (ed): *Role of the Major Histocompatibility Complex in Immunobiology*. New York, Garland Press, 1980, p 33.

165. GAZIT E, TERHORST C, MAHONEY RJ, YUNIS EJ: Alloantigens of the human T (HT) genetic region of the HLA linkage group. *Hum Immunol* 1:97, 1980.

166. BILLING RJ, CLARK B, TERASAKI PI: Characterization of three different human T cell membrane antigens, two being present on T lymphocyte subpopulations. *Hum Immunol* 1:141, 1980.

167. TADA N, TANIGAKI N, PRESSMAN D: Human cell membrane components bound to $beta_2$-microglobulin in T cell type cell lines. *J Immunol* 120:513, 1978.

168. TRUCCO M, DEPETRIS S, GAROTTA G, CEPPELLINI R: Quantitative analysis of cell surface HLA structures by means of monoclonal antibodies. *Hum Immunol* 1:233, 1980.

169. BRODSKY FM, PARHAM P, BARNSTABLE CJ, CRUMPTON MJ, BODMER WF: Monoclonal antibodies for analysis of the HLA system. *Immunol Rev* 47:3, 1979.

170. KIM SJ, CHRISTIANSEN FT, GOSAR I, SILVER DM, POLLACK M, DUPONT B: Frequency of alloantibodies reacting with PHA-activated T lymphocytes, unexplainable by known HLA activities. *Hum Immunol* 1:347, 1980.

171. FAUCHET R, BOSCHER M, BOUHALLIER O, MERDRIGNAC G, GENETET B, TURMEL P, CHARRON DJ: New class I in man: Serological and molecular characterization. *Hum Immunol* 17:3, 1986.

172. LIMA G, WOLLMAN E, LEPAGE V, DEGOS L, DAUSSET J: Alloantigens expressed on activated human T cells different from HLA-A, -B, -C, and -DR antigens. *Immunogenetics* 13:529, 1981.

173. MITSUISHI Y, FALKENROOT A, TONGIO MM, MAYER S: New determinants expressed on activated lymphocytes and on human acute lymphoblastic leukemia cells closely linked to conventional HLA-A antigens, in Albert ED, Bauer MP, Mayr WR (eds): *Histocompatibility Testing 1984*. Berlin, Springer-Verlag, 1985.

174. VAN LEEUWEN A, GIPHART MJ, DE GROOT G, MOROLLI B, FESTENSTEIN H, NIJENHUIS LE, VAN ROOD JJ: Two different T cell systems in humans, one of which is probably equivalent to Qa or Tla in mice. *Hum Immunol* 12:235, 1985.

175. KOLLER BH, GERAGHTY D, ORR HT, SHIMIZU Y, DEMARS R: Organization of the human class I major histocompatibility complex genes. *Immunological Research* 6:1, 1987.

176. PAUL P, FAUCHET R, BOSCHER MY, SAYAGH B, MASSET M, MEDRIGNAC G, DAUSSET J, COHEN D: Isolation of a human major histocompatibility complex class I gene encoding a nonubiquitous molecule expressed on activated lymphocytes. *Proc Natl Acad Sci USA* 84:2872, 1987.

177. AIZAWA M (ed): *HLA in Asia-Oceania*. Sapporo, Japan, Hokkaido University Press, 1986.

178. WALFORD RL, HULETTE CM, EFFROS RB, ZEELER E: Unique restriction fragment within HLA-A2 of American Indians. *Tenth International Histocompatibility Workshop*, 1987.

179. BREUR-VRIESENDORP BS, NEEFJES JC, HUIS B, VAN SEVENTER GA, PLOEGH HL, IVANYI P: Identification of new B27 subtypes (B27C and B27D) prevalent in Oriental populations. *Hum Immunol* 16:163, 1986.

180. BODMER JG, KENNEDY LJ, LINDSAY J, WASIK AM: Applications of serology and the ethnic distribution of three locus HLA haplotypes. *Br Med Bull* 43:94, 1987.

181. BODMER WF: Evolutionary significance of the HL-A system. *Nature* 237:139, 1972.

182. BODMER WF, BODMER JG: Evolution and function of the HLA system. *Br Med Bull* 34:309, 1978.

183. ARTZT K: Genetic analysis of the T/t complex. *Hum Immunol* 15:374, 1986.

184. SHREFFLER DC, DAVID DS: Studies on recombination within the mouse H-2 complex. *Tissue Antigens* 2:232, 1972.

185. GILL TJ III, KUNZ HW, MISRA DN, HASSETT ALC: The major histocompatibility complex of the rat. *Transplantation*, 43:773, 1987.

186. AMOS DB, RUDERMAN RJ, MENDELL NP, JOHNSON AH: Linkage between HLA and spinal development. *Transplant Proc* 7:93, 1975.

187. ROSSEN RD, BREWER EJ, SHARP RM, YUNIS EJ, SCHANFIELD MS, BIRDSALL HH, FERRELL RE, TEMPLETON JW: Familial rheumatoid arthritis: A kindred identified through a proband with seronegative juvenile arthritis includes members with seropositive, adult-onset disease. *Hum Immunol* 4:183, 1982.

188. Entire issue. *Immunological Reviews* 98:5-171, 1987.

188a. ALLISON JP, LANIER LL: Structure, function and serology of the T-cell antigen receptor complex. *Ann Rev Immunol* 5:503, 1987.

188b. GOVERMAN J, HUNKAPILLER T, HOOD L: A speculative view of the multicomponent nature of T cell antigen recognition. *Cell* 45:475, 1986.

189. GREENBERG LJ, GRAY ED, YUNIS EJ: Association of HL-A 5 and immune responsiveness in vitro to streptococcal antigens. *J Exp Med* 141:935, 1975.

190. PATARROYO ME, WINCHESTER RJ, VEJERANO A, GIBOFSKY A, CHALEM F, ZABRISKIE JB, KUNKEL HG: Association of a B-cell alloantigen with susceptibility to rheumatic fever. *Nature* 278:173, 1979.

191. HANCOCK RJT, DUNCAN D, CAREY S, COCKETT ATK, MAY A: Anti-sperm antibodies, HLA and semen analysis. *Lancet* 2:847, 1983.

192. OTTENHOFF THM, TORRES P, DE LAS AGUAS JT, FERNANDEZ R, VAN EDEN W, DE VRIES RRP, STANFORD JL: Evidence for an HLA-DR4-associated immune response gene for mycobacterium tuberculosis. *Lancet* 2:310, 1986.

193. SASAZUKI T, HAYASE R, IWAMOTO I, TSUCHIDA H: HLA and acute post-streptococcal glomerulonephritis. *N Engl J Med* 301:1184, 1979.

194. SASAZUKI T, OHTA N, KANEOKA R, KOJIMA S: Association between HLA haplotype and low responsiveness to schistosomiasis worm antigen in man. *J Exp Med Suppl* 152:314, 1980.

195. MENDELL NR, AMOS DB, BLUMENTHAL MN, GLEICH GJ, YUNIS EJ: Ra3 skin test response and HLA-A2, Antigen E and IgE: Evidence of interactions between antigen E and HLA. *Hum Immunol* 4:63, 1982.

196. HENROTTE JG, HANNOUN C, BENECH A, DAUSSET J: Relationship between postvaccinal anti-influenza antibodies, blood magnesium levels, and HLA antigens. *Hum Immunol* 12:1, 1985.

197. ILONEN J, SALMI A: Comparison of HLA-Dw1 and -Dw2 positive adherent cells in antigen presentation to heterozygous T-cell lines and a low rubella antigen-specific response associated with HLA-Dw2. *Hum Immunol* 17:94, 1986.

198. ROSENTHAL AS: Regulation of the immune response—Role of the macrophage. *N Engl J Med* 303:1153, 1980.

199. SASAZUKI T, NISHIMURA Y, MUTO M, OHTA N: HLA-linked genes controlling immune response and disease susceptibility. *Immunol Rev* 70:52, 1983.

200. FRANCIS DA, BRAZIER DM, BATCHELOR JR, MCDONALD WI, DOWNIE AW, HERN JE: Gm allotypes in multiple sclerosis: Influence susceptibility in HLA-DQw1 positive patients from the Northeast of Scotland. *Clin Immunol Immunopathol* 41:409, 1986.

201. RICH SS, WEITKAMP LR, GUTTORMSEN S, BARBOSA J: Gm, Km and HLA in insulin-dependent Type 1 diabetes mellitus. *Diabetes* 35:927, 1986.

202. KENNEDY LJ, WALLACE LE, MADRIGAL JA, RICKINSON AB, BODMER JG: New HLA-A2 variants defined by monoclonal antibodies and cytotoxic T lymphocytes. *Immunogenetics* 26:155, 1987.

203. ECKELS D, LAKE P, LAMB J, SHAW S, WOODY J, HARTZMAN R: SB-restricted presentation of influenza and herpes virus antigens to human T-lymphocyte clones. *Nature* 301:716, 1983.

204. QUIGSTAD E, THORSBY E: Class II HLA restriction of antigen-specific human T-lymphocyte clones. Evidence of restriction elements of both DR and MT molecules. *Scand J Immunol* 18:299, 1983.

205. BALL EJ, STASTNY P: Antigen-specific HLA-restricted human T-cell lines. II. A GAT specific T cell line restricted by a determinant carried by an HLA-DQ molecule. *Immunogenetics* 20:547, 1984.

206. BENACERRAF B: Role of MHC gene products in immune regulation. *Science* 212:1229, 1981.

207. NUNEZ G, BALL EJ, STASTNY P: Antigen presentation by adherent cells from human peripheral blood. Correlation between T cell activation and expression of HLA-DQ and -DR antigens. *Hum Immunol* 19:29, 1987.

208. AUSTIN P, TROWSDALE J, RUDD C, BODMER W, FELDMAN M, LAMB J: Functional expression of HLA-DP genes transfected into mouse fibroblasts. *Nature* 313:61, 1985

208a. GABERT J, LANGLET C, ZAMOYSKA R, PARNES JR, SCHMITT-VERHULST A-M, MALISSEN B: Reconstitution of MHC class I specificity by transfer of the T cell receptor and Lyt-2 genes. *Cell* 50:545, 1987.

209. KLEIN J: *Biology of the Mouse Histocompatibility-2 Complex*. New York, Springer-Verlag, 1976, chap 16.

210. AMIEL JL: Study of the leucocyte phenotypes in Hodgkin's disease, in Curtoni ES, Mattiuz PL, Tosi RM (eds): *Histocompatibility Testing 1967*. Copenhagen, Munksgaard, 1967, p 79.

211. ROGENTINE GN, TRAPANI RJ, YANKEE RJ, MENDERRON ES: HLA antigens and acute lymphocytic leukemia: The nature of the HLA-A2 association. *Tissue Antigens* 3:470, 1973.

212. HORS J, BONAITI-PELLIE C, D'AGAY MF, RAPPAPORT H, ANDRIEUX JM, DEWAAL LP, DELANGE GG, FEINGOLD N: Hodgkin's disease, in Albert ED, Baur MP, Mayr WR (eds): *Histocompatibility Testing 1984*. New York, Springer-Verlag, 1984, p 411.

213. BORTIN MM, D'AMARO J, BACH FH, RIMM AA, VAN ROOD JJ: HLA associations with leukemia. *Blood* 70:227, 1987.

214. BATCHELOR JR, McMICHAEL AJ: Progress in understanding HLA and disease associations. *Br Med Bull* 43:156, 1987.

215. WARD FE, AMOS DB: Perspectives on HLA and Disease, in Litwin SD, Scott D, Flaherty L, Reisfeld R, Marcus D (eds): *Human Immunogenetics: An Advanced Text*. New York, Marcel Dekker, Inc., 1988, in press.

216. STROMINGER JL: Biology of the human histocompatibility leukocyte antigen (HLA) system and a hypothesis regarding the generation of autoimmune diseases. *J Clin Invest* 77:1411, 1986.

217. TIWARI JL, TERASAKI PI: *HLA and Disease Associations*. New York, Springer-Verlag, 1985.

218. SCHLOSSTEIN L, TERASAKI PI, BLUESTONE R, PEARSON CM: High association of an HLA-A antigen, w27, with ankylosing spondylitis. *N Engl J Med* 288:704, 1973.

219. BREWERTON DA, CAFFREY M, HART FD, JAMES DCO, NICHOLLS A, STURROCK RD: Ankylosing spondylitis and HL-A 27. *Lancet* 1:904, 1973.

220. EDWARDS CQ, CARTWRIGHT GE, SKOLNICK MH, AMOS DB: Genetic mapping of the hemochromatosis locus on chromosome six. *Hum Immunol* 1:19, 1980.

221. LIPINSKI M, HORS J, SALEUN JP, SADDI R, PASSA P, LAFAURIE S, FEINGOLD N, DAUSSET J: Idiopathic hemochromatosis: Linkage to HLA. *Tissue Antigens* 11:471, 1978.

222. SVEJGAARD A, RYDER LP: Associations between HLA and disease, in Dausset J, Svejgaard A (eds): *HLA and Disease*. Copenhagen, Munksgaard, 1977, p 46.

223. DAUSSET J, SVEJGAARD A (eds): *HLA and Disease*. Copenhagen, Munksgaard, 1977.

224. ELSTON RC, SOBEL E: Sampling considerations in the gathering and analysis of pedigree data. *Am J Hum Genet* 31:62, 1979.

225. KRAVITZ K, SKOLNICK M, CANNINGS C, CARMELLI D, BATY B, AMOS B, JOHNSON A, MENDELL N, EDWARDS C, CARTWRIGHT G: Genetic linkage between hereditary hemochromatosis and HLA. *Am J Hum Genet* 31:601, 1979.

226. MOTRO U, THOMPSON G: The affected sib method. I. Statistical features of the affected sib. *Genetics* 110:525, 1985.

227. MARSH DG, BIAS WB: Basal serum IgE levels and HLA antigen frequencies in allergic subjects. II. Studies in people sensitive to rye grass group I and ragweed antigen E and of postulated immune response (Ir) loci in the HLA region. *Immunogenetics* 5:235, 1977.

228. BLUMENTHAL MN, AMOS DB: Genetic and immunologic basis of atopic responses. *Chest* 91:176s, 1987.

229. ADLER S, VASILE RG, YUNIS E, SHAPIRO R: HLA in psychiatric and control subjects. A comparative study of HLA antigen frequencies in schizophrenic, schizoaffective and control subjects. *J Psychiatr Res* 19:573, 1985.

230. GECZY AF, VAN LEEUWEN A, VAN ROOD JJ, IVANYI P, BREUR BS, CATS A: Blind confirmation in Leiden of Geczy factor on the cells of Dutch patients with ankylosing spondylitis. *Hum Immunol* 17:239, 1986.

231. EBRINGER A, BAINES M, PTASZYNSKA T: Spondyloarthritis, uveitis, HLA-B27 and Klebsiella. *Immunol Rev* 86:101, 1985.

231a. OLDSTONE MBA: Molecular mimicry and autoimmune disease. *Cell* 50:819, 1987.

232. COPPIN HL, MCDEVITT HO: Absence of polymorphism between HLA-B27 genomic exon sequences isolated from normal donors and ankylosing spondylitis patients. *J Immunol* 137:2168, 1986.

233. CONFAVREUX C, GEBUHRER L, BETUEL H, FREIDEL C, BASTUJI H, AIMARD G, DEVIC M, JOUVET M: HLA-DR2 negative narcolepsy. *J Neurol Neurosurg Psychiatry* 50:635, 1987.

234. LANGDON N, VAN DAM M, WELSH KJ, VAUGHAN RW, PARKES D: Genetic markers in narcolepsy. *Lancet* 2:1178, 1984.

235. SCHULZ H, GEISLER P, POLLMAECHER T, ANDREAS-ZIETZ A, KELLER E, SCHOLZ S, ALBERT ED: HLA-DR2 correlates with rapid eye movement sleep latency in normal human subjects. *Lancet* 2:8510, 1986.

236. LAWLER TJ, HALL RP, FAUCI AS, KATZ SI, HAMBURGER MI, FRANK MM: Defective Fc-receptor functions associated with HLA-B8/DRw3 haplotype. Studies in patients with dermatitis herpetiformis and normal subjects. *N Engl J Med* 304:185, 1981.

237. POLLACK MS, RICH RR: The HLA complex and the pathogenesis of infectious diseases. *J Infect Dis* 151:1, 1985.

238. NOURI-ARIA KT, DONALDSON PT, HEGARTY JE, EDDLESTON AL, WILLIAM R: HLA A1-B8-DR3 and suppressor cell function in first-degree relatives of patients with autoimmune chronic active hepatitis. *J Hepatol* 1:235, 1985.

239. HARLEY J, REICHLIN M, ARNETT FC, ALEXANDER EL, BIAS WB, PROVOST TT: Gene interaction at HLA-DQ enhances autoantibody production in primary Sjogren's syndrome. *Science* 232:1145, 1986.

240. MARCADET A, MASSART C, SEMANA G, FAUCHET R, SABOURAUD O, MERIENNE M, DAUSSET J, COHEN D: Association of class II HLA-DQ beta chain DNA restriction fragments with multiple sclerosis. *Immunogenetics* 22:93, 1985.

241. INOKO H, ANDO A, TSUJI K, MATSUKI K, JUJI T, HONDA Y: HLA-DQ beta chain DNA restriction fragments can differentiate between healthy and narcoleptic individuals with HLA-DR2. *Immunogenetics* 23:126, 1986.

242. SCHREUDER GMTH, TILANUS MGH, BONTROP RE, BRUINING GJ, GIPHART MJ, VAN ROOD JJ, DE VRIES RRP: HLA-DQ polymorphism associated with resistance to type I diabetes detected with monoclonal antibodies, isoelectric point differences, and restriction fragment length polymorphism. *J Exp Med* 164:938, 1986.

243. BRUSERUD O, PAULSEN G, MARKUSSEN G, LUNDIN K, THORESEN AB, THORSBY E: Genomic HLA-DQ beta polymorphism associated with insulin-dependent diabetes mellitus. Analysis of possible functional significance. *Scand J Immunol* 25:235, 1987.

244. MUELLER-ECKHARDT G, MEIER-EWERT K, SCHENDEL DJ, REINECKER FB, MULTHOFF G, MUELLER-ECKHARDT C: HLA and narcolepsy in a German population. *Tissue Antigens* 28:163, 1986.

245. HITMAN GA, NIVEN MJ, FESTENSTEIN H, CASSELL PG, AWAD J, WALKER-SMITH J, LEONARD JM, FRY L, CICLITIRA P, KUMAR P, SACHS JA: HLA class II alpha chain gene polymorphisms in patients with insulin-dependent diabetes mellitus, dermatitis herpetiformis, and celiac disease. *J Clin Invest* 79:609, 1987.

246. NEPOM BS, NEPOM GT, MICKELSON E, SCHALLER JG, ANTONELLI P, HANSEN JA: Specific HLA-DR4 associated histocompatibility molecules characterize patients with seropositive juvenile rheumatoid arthritis. *J Clin Invest* 74:287, 1984.

247. HOWARD PF, HOCHBERG MC, BIAS WB, ARNETT FC JR, MCCLEAN RH: Relationship between C4 null genes, HLA-D region antigens and genetic susceptibility to systemic lupus erythematosus in Caucasian and Black Americans. *Am J Med* 81:187, 1986.

248. ONEILL GJ, NERL CW, KAY PH, CHRISTIANSEN GT, MCCUSKY J, DAWKINS RL: Complement C4 is a marker for adult rheumatoid arthritis. *Lancet* 2:214, 1982.

249. MOLLENHAUER E, SCHMIDT R, HEINRICHS M, RITTNER C: Scleroderma: Possible significance of silent alleles at the C4B locus. *Arthritis Rheum* 27:711, 1984.

250. SCHRODER R, ZANDER H, ANDREAS A, MAUFF G: Multiple sclerosis: Immunogenetic analysis of sib pair double case families. II. Studies on the association of multiple sclerosis with C2, C4, Bf, C3, C6 and GLO polymorphisms. *Immunobiology* 164:160, 1983.

251. RITTNER C, MEIER EMM, STRADMANN B, GILES CM, KOCHLING R, MOLLENHAUER E, KUTH HW: Partial C4 deficiency in subacute sclerosing panencephalitis. *Immunogenetics* 20:407, 1984.

252. HULETTE CM, WALFORD RL: Immunological aspects of Alzheimer's disease—A review, *Alzheimers Disease and Assoc Disorders* 1:72, 1987.

253. ALPER CA, AWDEH ZL, YUNIS EJ: Complotypes, extended haplotypes, male segregation distortion and disease markers. *Hum Immunol* 15:366, 1986.

254. WERKMEISTER JW, NEW MI, DUPONT B, WHITE PC: Frequent deletion and duplication of the steroid 21-hydroxylase genes. *Am J Hum Genet* 39:461, 1986.

255. DE VRIES RRP, NIJENHUIS LE, LAI A, FAT RFM, VAN ROOD JJ: HLA-linked genetic control of host response to Mycobacterium leprae. *Lancet* 2:1328, 1976.

256. OTTENHOFF TH, NEUTEBOOM S, ELFERINK DG, DE VRIES RR: Molecular localization and polymorphism of HLA class II restriction determinants defined by Mycobacterium leprae-reactive helper T cell clones from leprosy patients. *J Exp Med* 164:1923, 1986.

257. DE VRIES RR, OTTENHOFF TH, LI SG, YOUNG RA: HLA class II restricted helper and suppressor clones reactive with Mycobacterium leprae. *Lepr Rev* 57s:113, 1986.

258. DEWOLF WC, LANGE PH, SHEPHERD R, MARTIN-ALOSCO S, YUNIS EJ: Association of HLA and renal cell carcinoma. *Hum Immunol* 2:41, 1981.

259. DEWOLF WC, LANGE PH, EINARSON ME, YUNIS E: HLA and testicular cancer. *Nature* 277:216, 1979.

260. JONES EH, BIGGAR RJ, NKRUMAG FK, LAWLER SD: Study of the HLA system in Burkitt's lymphoma. *Hum Immunol* 3:207, 1980.

261. OLIVER RTD, STEPHENSON CA, PARKINSON MC, FORMAN D, ATKINSON A, BODMER J, BODMER WF: Germ cell tumors of the testicle as a model of MHC influence on human malignancy. *Lancet* 1:1506, 1986.

262. SIMONS MJ, AMIEL JL: HLA and malignant diseases, in Dausset J, Svejgaard A (eds): *HLA and Disease.* Copenhagen, Munksgaard, 1977, p 212.

263. RUITER DJ, BERMANN W, WELVAART K, SCHEFFER E, VAN VLOTEN WA, RUSSO C, FERRONE S: Immunohistochemical analysis of malignant melanomas and nevocellular nevi with monoclonal antibodies to distinct monomorphic determinants of HLA antigens. *Cancer Res* 44:3930, 1984.

264. FESTENSTEIN H: The biological consequences of altered MHC expression on tumours. *Br Med Bull* 43:217, 1987.

265. PAABO S, NILSSON T, PETERSON PA: Adenoviruses of subgenera B, C, D and E modulate cell-surface expression of MHC class I genes. *Proc Natl Acad Sci USA* 83:9665, 1986.

266. STORKUS WJ, HOWELL DN, SALTER RD, DAWSON JR, CRESSWELL P: NK susceptibility varies inversely with target cell class I HLA antigen expression. *J Immunol* 138:1657, 1987.

267. SASAZUKI T, OHTA N, KANEOKA R, KOJIMA S: Association between HLA haplotype and low responsiveness to schistosomal worm antigen in man. *J Exp Med Suppl* 152:314, 1980.

268. WILTON AN, COBAIN TJ, DAWKINS RL: Family studies of IgA deficiency. *Immunogenetics* 21:333, 1985.

269. Entire issue. *Human Immunology* 1986, vol 15, pp 347-426.

270. SIMONSEN M, OLSSON L: Possible roles of compound membrane receptors in the immune system. *Ann Immunol Inst Pasteur* 134D:85, 1983.

271. SCHREIBER AB, SCHLESSINGER J, EDIDIN M: Interaction between major histocompatibility complex antigens and epidermal growth factor receptors on human cells. *J Cell Biol* 98:725, 1984.

272. EDIDIN M: Major histocompatibility complex haplotypes and the cell physiology of peptide hormones. *Hum Immunol* 15:357, 1986.

273. CLAAS FHJ, VAN REE JM, VERHOEVEN WMA, VAN DER POEL JJ, VERDUYN W, DE WIED D, VAN ROOD JJ: The interaction between gamma-type endorphins and HLA class I antigens. *Hum Immunol* 15:347, 1986.

274. SHACKELFORD DA, TROWBRIDGE IS: Identification of lymphocyte integral membrane proteins as substrates for protein kinase C. Phosphorylation of the interleukin-2 receptor, class I HLA antigens, and T200 glycoprotein. *J Biol Chem* 261:8334, 1986.

275. RICHARDSON SH, GILES JC, KRUGER KS: Sealed adult mice: New model for enterotoxin evaluation. *Infect Immun* 43:482, 1984.

276. BOYSE EA: HLA and the chemical senses. *Hum Immunol* 15:391, 1986.

277. SCHACTER B, WEITKAMP LR, JOHNSON WE: Parental HLA compatibility, fetal wastage, and neural tube defects: Evidence for a T/t like locus in humans. *Am J Hum Genet* 36:1082, 1983.

278. VADHEIM CM, ROLTER JI, MacLAREN NK, RILEY WJ, ANDERSON CE: Pref-

erential transmission of diabetic alleles within the HLA gene complex. *N Engl J Med* 315:1314, 1986.

279. AWDEH ZL, RAUM D, YUNIS EJ, ALPER CA: Extended HLA/complement allele haplotypes: Evidence for T/t like complex in man. *Proc Natl Acad Sci USA* 80:259, 1983.

280. THOMAS ML, HARGER JH, WAGENER DK, RABIN BS, GILL TJ III: HLA sharing and spontaneous abortion in humans. *Am J Obstet Gynecol* 151:1053, 1985.

281. OBER CL, HAUCK WW, KOSTYU DD, O'BRIEN E, ELIAS S, SIMPSON JL, MARTIN AO: Adverse effects of human leukocyte antigen-DR sharing on fertility: A cohort study in a human isolate. *Fertil Steril* 44:227, 1985.

282. WERNER-FAVRE CH, JEANNET M: HLA compatibility in couples with children suffering from acute leukemia or aplastic anemia. *Tissue Antigens* 13:307, 1979.

283. WALFORD RL: MHC regulation of aging: An extension of the immunologic theory of aging, in Butler R (ed): *Modern Theories of Aging*. New York, Raven, 1987.

284. HOWARD JF, SIGSBEE A, GLASS DN: HLA genetics and inherited predisposition to JRA. *J Rheumatol* 12:7, 1985.

285. GLADMON DD, ANKORN KAB, SCHACTER RK, MERVART H: HLA antigens in psoriatic arthritis. *J Rheumatol* 13:586, 1986.

286. HOOVER ML, ANGELINI G, BALL E, STASTNY P, MARKS J, ROSENSTOCK J, RASKIN P, FERRARA GB, TOSI R, CAPRA JD: HLA-DQ and T cell receptor genes in insulin-dependent diabetes mellitus. *Cold Spring Harbor Symp Quant Biol* 51:803, 1986.

CHAPTER **5**

ONCOGENES: Genes Associated With Neoplastic Disease

MORAG PARK
GEORGE F. VANDE WOUDE

IDENTIFICATION OF ONCOGENES

In the last few years the study of oncogenes has considerably advanced our understanding of the molecular mechanisms leading to cancer. Oncogenes, or transforming genes, affect normal cell growth and differentiation, resulting in cells with an altered phenotype that can grow as tumors in animals. The majority of oncogenes are activated (altered) forms of cellular genes (c-*onc*) that have been acquired (transduced) by RNA tumor viruses (v-*onc*). Proto-oncogene is the name given to the normal cellular counterpart or unaltered form of an oncogene. Proto-oncogenes are highly conserved in evolution and, in contrast to oncogenes, appear to provide essential physiological functions in cell growth and differentiation in normal embryonic development. Molecular studies of oncogene structure, function, and regulation will elucidate not only the development of malignancy but also essential cellular and developmental processes. Moreover, the discovery of activated oncogenes in both animal and human tumors supported the concept that initiation, maintenance, and progression of cancerous growth is based on genetic alteration in the neoplastic cell.[1–4]

Retroviruses

The first advances in understanding the molecular basis of oncogenesis came from the study of RNA tumor viruses (retroviruses).[5,6] Retroviruses are RNA-containing animal viruses that replicate through a DNA intermediate. They have been isolated from many avian and mammalian sources and can be divided into two classes based on the latent period between infection and the appearance of a tumor.

Acute Transforming Retroviruses

Acute transforming retroviruses, rapidly produce tumors in newborn animals (often in less than 2 weeks).[7] This characteristic led early investigators to believe that they had identified agents responsible for neoplastic transformation. The acute transforming retroviruses are usually defective and lack a full complement of viral genes essential for replication. They possess, however, nucleic acid sequences, termed v-*onc*, acquired or transduced from the genetic information of the host cell,[8,9] and these sequences, acting in concert with the viral transcription control elements, termed long terminal repeats (LTR),[10] are responsible for the rapid transforming activity (Fig. 5-1). Approximately 20 acute transforming retroviral v-*onc* genes have been identified (Table 5-1).[11]

Leukemia and Leukosis Retroviruses

Leukemia and leukosis retroviruses produce disease in animals after latent periods of more than 3 months. These viruses generally produce leukemias and lymphomas[7] and do not contain transduced host or v-*onc* genes (Fig. 5-1). The leukemia retroviruses are competent for replication, contain only viral replication genes, and are prototypic retroviruses.

The leukemia and leukosis viruses induce disease by integrating during their normal replication cycle adjacent to or within a cellular proto-oncogene locus and as such, they represent a distinct class of movable genetic elements.[12] At each end of the proviral genome there is an LTR that contains transcription regulatory enhancer, promoter, and polyadenylation signals (Fig. 5-1).[13] The integration into the cellular genome of the retroviral provirus with its LTRs and their strong transcriptional enhancing action has been shown to induce the

Nonstandard abbreviations used in this chapter are: Ad = adenovirus; AEV = avian erythroblastosis virus; ALV = avian leukosis virus; bcr = break point cluster region or gene at 22q11 involved in translocations producing the Philadelphia chromosome; BLV = bovine leukemia virus; CML = chronic myelogenous leukemia; c-*onc* = cellular oncogene; CSF-1R = macrophage colony-stimulating factor-1 receptor; DMBA = dimethyl benzanthracene; EGFR = epidermal growth factor receptor; env = retroviral gene encoding virion envelope proteins; FGF = fibroblast growth factor; G × protein = one of a group of GTP-binding proteins which participate in signal transmission from cell surface receptors; gag = retroviral gene encoding protein components of the virion nucleoprotein core; HTLV = human T-cell leukemia virus; IL = interleukin; LTR = long terminal repeat sequences encoding retroviral transcriptional control elements; MLV = murine leukemia virus; MMTV = mouse mammary tumor virus; NMU = nitrosomethylurea; PDGFR = platelet-derived growth factor receptor; Ph = Philadelphia chromosome; pol = retroviral gene encoding reverse transcriptase; Py = polyoma virus; REF = rat embryo fibroblast; TGF = transforming growth factor; v-onc = viral oncogene. Other abbreviations used only in figures are presented in the figure legends. The various oncogenes and their abbreviated designations are listed in Table 5-1.

A

B

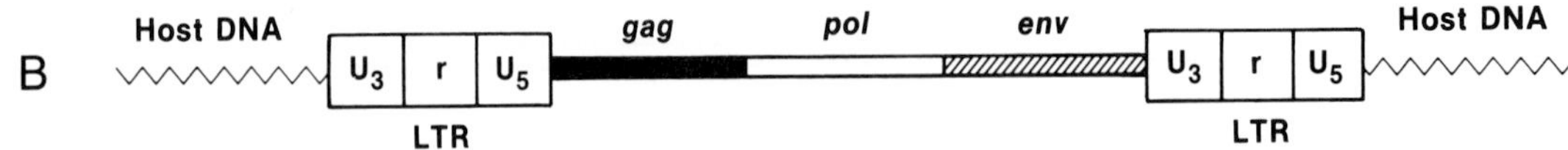

C

Fig. 5-1 Schematic representation of the general structure of leukemia and leukosis retroviral and acute transforming retroviral genomes. *A.* Genome of a nondefective leukemia or leukosis retrovirus. *B.* Genome of a nondefective integrated provirus. *C.* Genome of a replication-defective acute transforming retrovirus containing v-*onc* sequences. The *gag* region encodes the internal structural proteins of the virion, the *pol* region encodes the virion RNA-dependent DNA polymerase (reverse transcriptase), and the *env* region encodes the proteins found on the surface of the virion envelope. Although substantial portions of *gag, pol,* and/or *env* may be deleted in acute transforming retroviruses, they still retain the terminal noncoding regions R, U_5, and U_3. LTR is the long terminal repeat, a combination of U_3-R-U_5 that appears at each end of the unintegrated linear and proviral DNA forms. The R region is defined by DNA sequences, which at the 5′ end encode the initiation site for RNA transcription and at the 3′ end encode a poly A site where the viral RNA polyadenylation occurs. The U_5 region of the LTR encodes, in part, a portion of the untranslated leader sequence of the viral transcripts, and the U_3 region contains transcription enhancer sequences that result in the production of high levels of transcripts. The LTR elements provide all the necessary functions for eukaryotic transcription to take place and for the provirus to express genomic viral RNA.

unregulated expression of cellular homologues of known oncogenes resulting in or contributing to neoplastic transformation.[14,15] The long latent period for the development of neoplasia caused by these viruses is, in part, due to the low frequency of proviral integration adjacent to a host cellular gene in a fashion that can yield a product with transforming activity.

Oncogenes of DNA Tumor Viruses

Evidence derived mainly from epidemiologic studies suggested a possible role of some DNA viruses in the etiology of malignant disease in humans and other animals.[16] Unlike the v-*onc* genes of acute transforming retroviruses the oncogenes of certain DNA viruses are viral genes and are not transduced cellular genes (Table 5-2).[16] Most of the viral oncogenes are essential for virus infection and replication. Some act during the virus lytic cycle to stimulate transcription of other viral genes (Ela[17,18]; EBNA1[19]; SV40 large T[20]; Polyoma large T[21]) and/or are important for viral DNA replication (SV40 large T[20]; polyoma large T[21]; EBNA1[22,23]).

Detection of Oncogenes by DNA Transfection

The DNA transfection assay was developed to study and iden-
'ify the transforming genes of RNA or DNA tumor vi-
-s.[24,25] The cells used as recipients in most transfection ex-
-nts are NIH3T3 cells; these cells are mouse fibroblasts
-nd are maintained as contact-inhibited, nontumori-
-s. Transformation of these cells by gene transfer is monitored by changes in cell morphology in culture and loss of contact inhibition (where cells overgrow the monolayer and form focal areas of dense layers termed foci[26,27]) or by a modification of this technique in which the cells that have acquired transforming genes produce tumors in nude mice[28,29] (Fig. 5-2).

To assay for transforming genes, genomic DNA, prepared, for example, from human tumors or tumor cell lines, is transferred to recipient NIH3T3 cells. Transfer of DNA-containing activated oncogenes will occasionally give rise to foci of morphologically altered cells that have tumorigenic properties. Foci or tumors thus obtained contain NIH3T3 cells that are transformed as a result of incorporating human DNA containing an activated oncogene. Human repetitive DNA sequences located in the vicinity of the oncogene can be distinguished from mouse sequences,[30] and these can be used to molecularly clone and isolate the DNA segment responsible for transformation of the NIH3T3 cells[31–33] (Fig. 5-2). Many of the human transforming genes identified in this manner are related to the *ras* family of oncogenes. For instance, the transforming genes of a human bladder and lung carcinoma were shown to be homologous to the *ras* genes previously identified in the acute transforming retroviruses of the Harvey[34] and Kirsten[35] sarcoma viruses and were designated c-H-*ras*[36–38] and c-K-*ras*,[36–38] respectively. In addition, a third *ras* gene family member was initially identified in a human neuroblastoma tumor cell line[40] and human promyelocytic leukemia cell line[41] and was designated N-*ras* (Table 5-1).[42–44] Other human tumor cell lines have been shown to contain activated *ras* genes, including carcinomas of the lung, pancreas, colon, gallbladder, and urinary bladder and a rhabdomyosarcoma.[45] Approximately 15 percent of human tumor cell lines and fresh tumor

Table 5-1 Oncogenes

Ref.	*RNA tumor virus*	*Oncogene*	*Alternative method of identification*	*Species of origin*	*Source*	*Oncogene protein products, biochemical properties*
						I. Protein kinase
310	Rous sarcoma virus	v-*src*		Chicken	Sarcoma	Protein kinase (tyr)
310	Yamaguchi-79 sarcoma virus	v-*yes*		Chicken	Sarcoma	Protein kinase (tyr)
311	Gardner-Rasheed feline sarcoma virus	v-*fgr*		Cat	Sarcoma	Protein kinase (tyr)
310	Fujinami sarcoma virus	v-*fps*		Chicken	Sarcoma	Protein kinase (tyr)
312	Snyder-Theilen feline sarcoma virus	v-*fes*		Cat	Sarcoma	Protein kinase (tyr)
312	Abelson murine leukemia virus	v-*abl*		Mouse	Leukemia	Protein kinase (tyr)
313	Hardy Zuckerman 2 feline sarcoma virus	v-*abl*		Cat	Sarcoma	
310	UR2 avian sarcoma virus	v-*ros*		Chicken	Sarcoma	Protein kinase (tyr)
						Proto-onc structure characteristic of growth factor receptors
312	Susan McDonough feline sarcoma virus	v-*fms*		Cat	Sarcoma	Protein kinase (tyr) derived from CSF-1 receptor
314	Avian erythroblastosis virus	v-*erb*B		Chicken	Sarcoma/erythroblastosis	Protein kinase (tyr) derived from EGF receptor
315	HZ4 feline sarcoma virus	v-*kit*		Cat	Sarcoma	Protein kinase (tyr)
50		*neu*	DNA transfection	Rat	Neuroblastoma	Protein kinase (tyr)
51		*met*	DNA transfection	Human	MNNG-treated human osteo carcinoma cell line	Protein kinase (tyr)
52		*trk*	DNA transfection	Human	Colon carcinoma	Protein kinase (tyr)
316	Moloney murine sarcoma virus	v-*mos*		Mouse	Sarcoma	Protein kinase (ser/thr)
317	3611 murine sarcoma virus	*raf*		Mouse	Sarcoma	Protein kinase (ser/thr)
						II. GTP binding
34	Harvey murine sarcoma virus	v-H-*ras*		Rat	Erythroleukemia	GTPase
35	Kirsten murine sarcoma virus	v-K-*ras*		Rat	Sarcoma	GTPase
40		N-*ras*	DNA transfection	Human	Various	GTPase
						III. Nuclear localization
310	Myelocytomatosis-29 virus	v-*myc*		Chicken	Carcinoma myelocytomatosis	Binds DNA
175		N-*myc*	Gene amplification	Human	Neuroblastoma	?
323		L-*myc*	Gene amplification	Human	Small cell lung carcinoma	?
100	Avian myeloblastosis virus	v-*myb*		Chicken	Myeloblastosis	Binds DNA
318	FBJ murine sarcoma virus	v-*fos*		Mouse	Osteosarcoma	Binds DNA
319	Sloan-Kettering avian sarcoma virus	v-*ski*		Chicken	Carcinoma	?
287		v-*jun*		Chicken		Binds DNA
192		P53		Mouse/human	Expressed at high levels in transformed cells	Binds SV40 large T; binds Adenovirus E1B
						IV. Growth factors
320	Simian sarcoma virus	v-*sis*		Woolly monkey	Glioma/fibrosarcoma	B chain PDGF
102		*int* 2	Proviral insertion	Mouse	Mammary carcinoma	Member of FGF family
56		KS3	DNA transfection	Human	Kaposi's sarcoma	Member of FGF family
55		*hst*		Human	Stomach carcinoma	Member of FGF family
						V. Others
321	Reticuloendotheliosis virus, strain T	v-*rel*		Turkey	Lymphatic leukemia	
322	E26 avian leukemia virus	v-*ets*		Chicken		
314	Avian erythroblastosis virus	v-*erb*A		Chicken	Erythroblastosis	Derived from steroid receptor for thioredoxine
29		*mas*	DNA transfection	Human	Mammary carcinoma	Transmembrane protein
101		*int*-1	Proviral insertion	Mouse	Mammary carcinoma	

Table 5-2 Oncogenes of DNA tumor viruses

Virus	*Gene*	*Biochemical properties during lytic infection*	*Biochemical properties in transformed cells*
Adenoviruses	E1A (early region 1A)	Viral gene transactivator (TA)	Stimulates cellular DNA synthesis/TA
	E1B (early region 1B)	Negative regulator of viral genes	?
Polyomavirus	Large T	Viral DNA replication/TA	Binds DNA/TA ?
	Middle T	?	Complexed with c-*src* protein and phosphatidylinositol kinase
Simian virus 40	Large T	Viral DNA replication/TA	Binds DNA/TA ? Complexed with p53
Bovine papilloma virus	Early region 5,6	?	?
Epstein-Barr virus	EBNA 1,2,3 (EBV nuclear antigens)	EBNA 1, viral DNA replication	?

Fig. 5-2 NIH3T3 DNA transfection and/or transformation assay. High molecular weight DNA prepared from transformed cell or tumor DNA is precipitated with calcium phosphate and added to non-transformed mouse NH3T3 cells. These cells are then assayed for tumor production in nude mice or are assayed for the appearance of foci. DNA is prepared from either primary foci or tumors and is subjected to a second cycle of transfection to facilitate the loss of additional non-transforming sequences that are transferred with the transforming gene. After several cycles of transfection, the majority of the foreign DNA in the focus or tumor corresponds to the transforming gene and can be isolated by recombinant DNA technology.

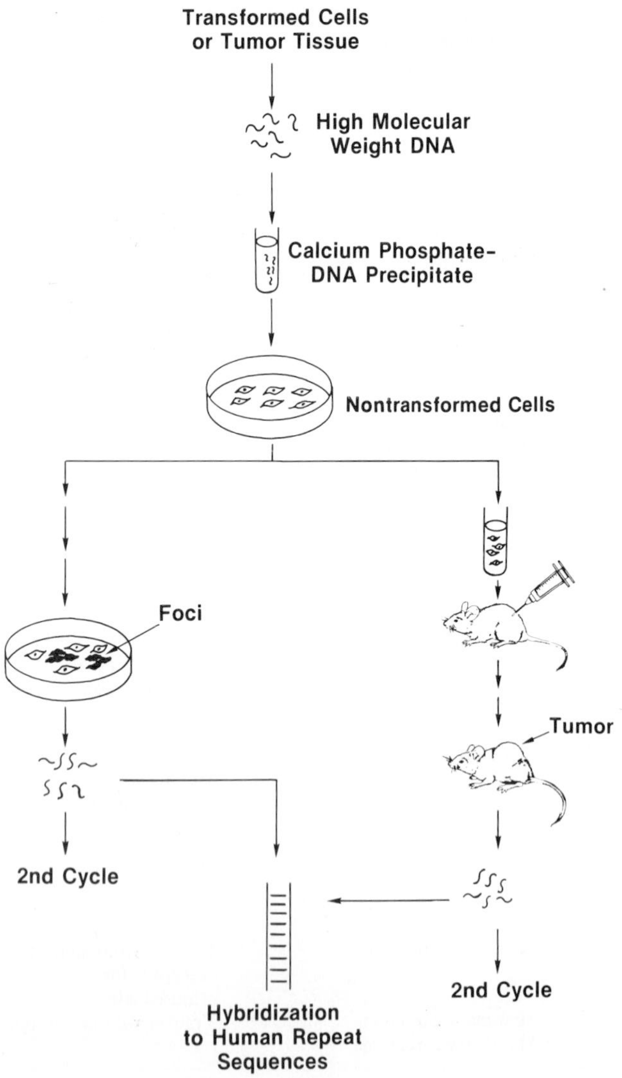

biopsies have activated *ras* oncogenes that can be detected using this assay.[45–47] This number may be much higher in human colorectal cancers.[48,49]

Gene transfer studies have led to the identification of a growing number of transforming genes that are not members of the *ras* gene family and have not been previously identified in a retrovirus. These include the *neu*,[50] *met*,[51] *trk*,[52] *mas*[29] *erb*B-2 (HER-2),[53,54] *hst*[55] and KS3 oncogenes[56] (Table 5-1).

Identification of Potential Oncogenes at Chromosomal Breakpoints

The chromosomal location of cellular proto-oncogenes determined by *in situ* hybridization (Table 5-3) has led to the iden-

Table 5-3 Chromosomal Location of Oncogenes

Chromosome	*Location*	*Proto-oncogene*	*Ref.*
1	1p36	*fgr*	324a
1	1p32	L-*myc*	323
1	1p11-13	N-*ras*	324b
1	1q22-qter	*ski*	325
1	1q32	*trk*	326
2	2p23-24	N-*myc*	175
2	2p11-12	*rel*	327
3	3p25	*raf*	328
5	5q34	*fms*	329
6	6p21	*pim*-1	330
6	6q21-22	*ros*	331
6	6q22-24	*myb*	332
6	6q24-27	*mas*	331
7	7p11-13	*erb*B	333
7	7q31	*met*	334
8	8q22	*mos*	335
8	8q24	*myc*	126
9	9q34.1	*abl*	144
11	11p14.1	H-*ras*	336
11	11q13	*int2*	337
11	11q23-24	*ets*-1	338
12	12p12.1	K-*ras*	339
12	12pter-q14	*int*-1	340
14	14q21-31	*fos*	341
15	15q26.1	*fes*	332
17	17p23	p53	342
17	17q12-22	*neu*	54
17	17q21-22	*erb*A	333
18	18q21.3	*yes*	343
20	20q12-13	*src*	344
21	21q22	*ets*-2	345
22	22q11	*bcr*	62
22	22q13.1	*sis*	346

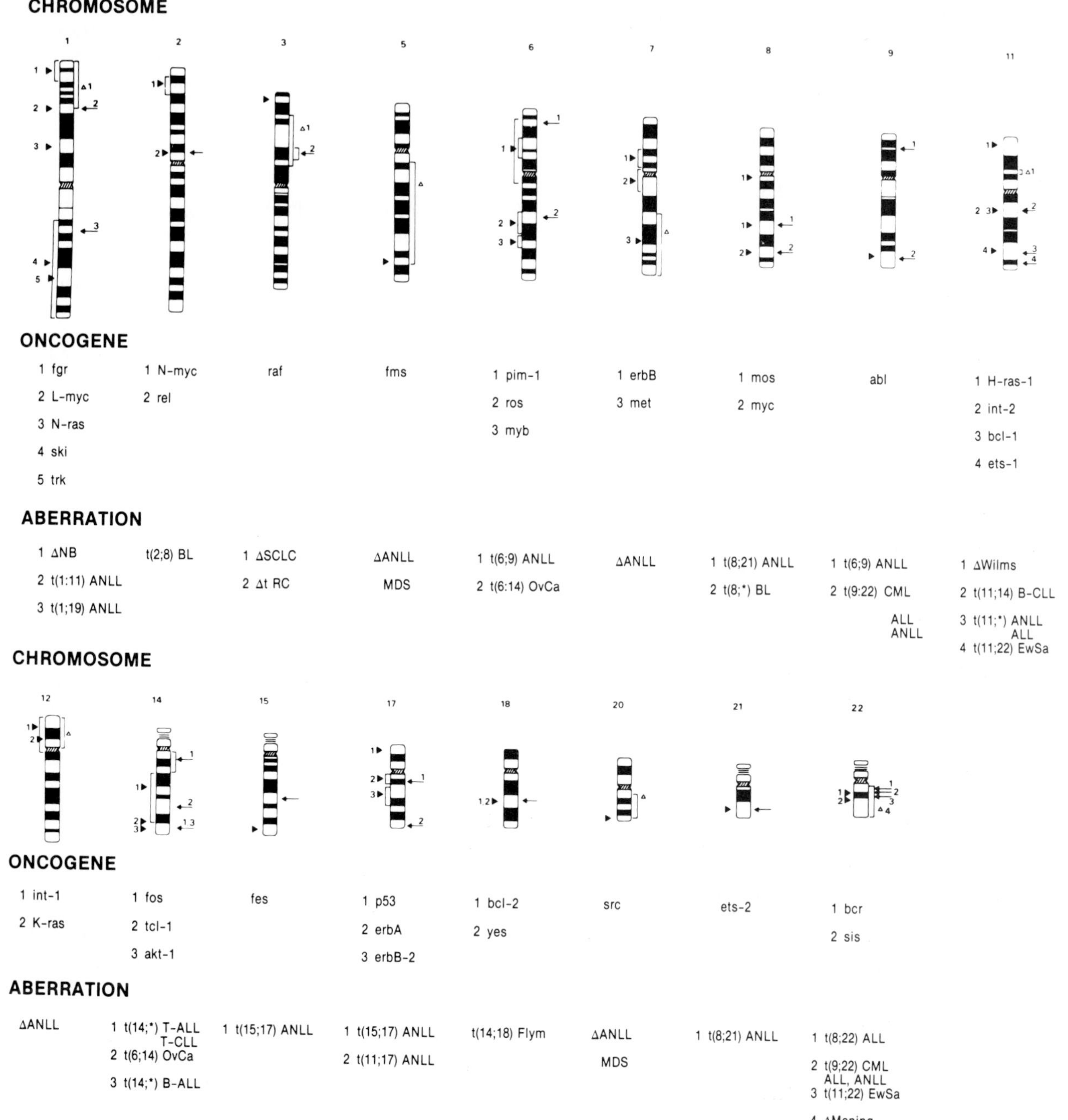

Fig. 5-3 Correlation between the position of proto-oncogenes on human chromosomes and the localization of breakpoints of consistent chromosomal aberrations. The position of proto-oncogenes is indicated by solid triangles; the chromosomal breakpoints of translocations by arrows; and deletions by open triangles. The diseases associated with the chromosomal aberrations shown are: NB = neuroblastoma; ANLL = acute nonlymphocytic leukemia; BL = Burkitt lymphoma; SCLC = small cell lung carcinoma; RLC = renal carcinoma; MDS = myelodysplastic syndrome; OvCa = ovarian carcinoma; CML = chronic myelocytic leukemia; ALL = acute lymphocytic leukemia; B-CLL = chronic lymphocyte leukemia, B cells; EwSa = Ewing sarcoma; T-ALL = acute lymphocytic leukemia, T cells; T-CLL = chronic lymphocytic leukemia, T cells; B-ALL = acute lymphocytic leukemia, B cells; F lym = follicular lymphoma.

tification of several proto-oncogenes at or near chromosomal translocation break points (Fig. 5-3).[57,58]

Nonrandom chromosome translocations are consistently associated with subtypes of leukemias, and myelodysplasias and are well documented (Fig. 5-3).[59,60] Where it has been possible to characterize and molecularly isolate the DNA adjoining the translocation breakpoint, candidate oncogenes implicated in the development of Burkitt lymphoma (c-*myc*),[61] chronic myelogenous leukemia (*bcr-abl*),[62] adult B-cell lymphomas (*bcl*1), and follicular lymphomas (*bcl2*)[63,64] have been isolated.

In contrast to leukemias and lymphomas, a relatively small number of solid tumors have been investigated cytogenetically. In the common childhood tumors such as retinoblastoma and Wilms,[65–67] chromosomal abnormalities have been described in patients that involve deletion of particular portions of a chromosome or involve chromosomal interchanges between specific regions of two chromosomes (see Chap. 9). Although the sizes of the deleted fragments among different patients are variable, a common deleted region involving chromosome 13 band q14[68] and chromosome 11 band p13[69] are observed in patients with retinoblastoma and Wilms tumor, respectively. Loss of DNA from these regions is thought to unmask a recessive mutation present in the remaining allele. These mutations are in genes with the phenotype of a recessive oncogene, and it has been suggested that these represent regulatory or tumor suppressor genes. A characterization of the genes in the vicinity of these chromosomal deletions has resulted in the identification of a candidate gene for retinoblastoma.[70,71]

CONSERVATION OF PROTO-ONCOGENES

Homologs of proto-oncogenes have been found in all multicellular animals studied thus far, and their widespread distribution in nature indicates that their protein products have essential biologic roles.[72] The more highly conserved domains of the protein are probably those that have a crucial structural and/or functional role, and characterization of their normal biochemical properties will provide insight into the contribution that an activated oncogene has on cell transformation. Of special interest are the proto-oncogene homologues found in organisms that have been well characterized genetically, such as *Drosophila* and yeast. The availability of well characterized mutants and the relative ease in generating new mutants and supressor mutations makes these organisms suitable model systems for studying proto-oncogene function.

The nucleotide sequence of the majority of viral oncogenes listed in Table 5-1 has been determined, and their RNA and protein products have been characterized. In many cases they have been compared with the nucleotide or predicted amino acid sequences of the host proto-oncogene from which they were derived as well as compared with the proto-oncogene homologues in other species, especially in humans. Conserved or related protein domains, crucial for biochemical function and for cellular localization of the oncogene or proto-oncogene protein product, have been used to classify them into distinct groups (Table 5-1.) The largest group, the *src* family, includes members that have tyrosine kinase activity. This family also includes members that have distant but distinct homology in domains essential for kinase function and have putative serine kinase activity (e.g., *mos*, *raf*)[73] The other major groups are the *ras* gene family of guanine nucleotide binding proteins; a group including *sis* and *int*, whose products are related to growth factors; and a group including *myc*, whose products are predominantly located in the nucleus.

MECHANISMS OF ONCOGENE ACTIVATION

Understanding the mechanism of activation of each oncogene requires characterization of the proto-oncogene, a comparison of the changes that have occurred, and systematic testing of changes influencing the transforming potential. Numerous mechanisms by which oncogenes are activated from proto-oncogenes have been identified; for example, an increase in the concentration of the oncogene (proto-oncogene) product can be sufficient for transformation. This increase can be mediated by proviral insertion adjacent to a proto-oncogene, by retroviral transduction of a proto-oncogene, or by amplification of a proto-oncogene locus. Unscheduled expression of a proto-oncogene in certain cell types or lineages can also result in transformation. Cellular proto-oncogenes can also become activated by structural changes that include a single point mutation or deletions of specific regulatory domains of the protein.

Activation of Cellular Proto-oncogenes via Retroviral Transduction

Once transduced into a virus, the v-*onc* sequence can rapidly undergo numerous mutational events that occur during viral replication.[74] Since the isolation of acute transforming viruses involves screening for tumor induction and the ability to transform cells in vitro, this can result in selection for virus isolates with increased transforming potential. Viral oncogenes are intronless and apparently are always incompletely or improperly processed forms of a normal proto-oncogene transcript. They usually contain multiple point mutations, are truncated (lack upstream or downstream exons), and are often fused with viral genes (*gag* or *env*) to produce *gag-onc* or *env-onc* fusion products.[11]

In general, all v-*onc* genes are expressed at high levels by retroviral enhancers.[11] Inappropriate cell type expression of v-*onc* genes can also occur, influenced by the target cell specificity of the virus. Some of the alterations in v-*onc* genes are involved in the maintenance of high level production of the v-*onc* product, for example, the absence of the first noncoding exon of c-*myc* removes a region that is important for regulating c-*myc* expression at the transcriptional level,[75,76] whereas deletion of the 3' noncoding region of c-*fos* that normally post-transcriptionally regulates c-*fos* expression[77,78] allows v-*fos* to be produced at high levels. Genetic alterations which may directly affect protein function also exist. For example, the v-*ras* genes are activated by a point mutation(s),[79] while v-*src* contains point mutations and a C-terminal deletion[80] and v-*myb* is missing extensive N- and C-terminal regions of c-*myb*.[81] Moreover, the formation of fusion proteins may serve to increase oncogenicity indirectly, where the presence of viral *gag* sequences has been shown to be necessary for transformation of lymphoid cells by v-*abl*.[82]

A careful characterization of the changes important for v-*onc* activation has shown that several of the members of the *src* gene family (Table 5-1) have deletions that result in the expression of a truncated protein. The products of the cellular and viral *src* genes possess intrinsic protein tyrosine kinase activity.[73] A major difference between the c-*src* proto-oncogene protein and the v-*src* product of Rous sarcoma virus is that the v-*src* product has a deletion of the 19 carboxy terminal amino acids of c-*src*, and this deletion causes the transforming activity of the v-*src*. The c-*src* product is normally phosphorylated on a tyrosine residue (*tyr* 527) that is deleted from the v-*src*.[83,84,85] This residue is thought to be a site important for down-regulating the intrinsic *src* tyrosine kinase activity (perhaps by transphosphorylation[84,86]). Thus, deletion of *tyr* 527 may render the v-*src* product constitutively active as a tyrosine kinase. Other nonintegral tyrosine kinase genes in the *src* family (c-*yes*, c-*fgr*, c-*fps*, c-*fes*, and c-*fms*) have similar C-terminal amino acid sequences (Table 5-1).[73] In the activated v-*yes*, v-*fgr*, and v-*fms* oncogenes, the C-termini are also deleted.[87–91] These contain a *tyr* codon thought to be equivalent in function to *tyr* 527 in c-*src*.

The v-*erb*B oncogene of avian erythroblastosis (AEV), in addition to a deletion at the C terminus, also has a deletion at the N terminus. The v-*erb*B oncogene is derived from the epidermal growth factor receptor (EGFR),[92] and the N-terminal deletion removes the ligand binding region but leaves the transmembrane and cytoplasmic tyrosine kinase domains intact (Fig. 5-4).[92] It is presumed that v-*erb*B functions as a constitutively activated growth factor receptor.[73,93,94] A hybrid protein expressed from the EGFR activated by proviral insertion (see below) contains the 32 C-terminal amino acids, and removal of the ligand binding domain is apparently sufficient for activating its transforming potential[94] (Fig. 5-4). However, the v-*erb*B product with the C-terminal deletion modification is more efficient as an oncogene. Thus AEV infection or EGFR activation by proviral insertion apparently results in the ectopic expression in erythroblasts of a modified EGFR.[95]

Similar rearrangements have been shown to activate several members of the tyrosine kinase growth factor receptor family. The v-*kit* gene (Table 5-1) has both N-terminal and C-terminal deletions and is derived from a proto-oncogene related to the platelet-derived growth factor receptor (PDGFR).[96] Two genes, *trk*[52] and *met*[97,98] (Table 5-1), identified by the NIH3T3 transfection assay were shown to represent activated forms of putative tyrosine kinase receptor genes. In both cases, genetic rearrangements resulted in the juxtaposition of two unrelated loci, with the concomitant deletion of the putative ligand binding domain of the receptor molecule.[52,98] In each case structural alterations in these oncogenes appears to deregulate the intrinsic kinase activity of the protein.

Oncogene Activiation by Proviral Insertion. Leukemia or leukosis retroviruses can cause neoplastic disease after long latent periods by insertional mutagenesis (provirus insertion into or adjacent to cellular proto-oncogenes). This activation mechanism was first demonstrated with avian leukosis virus (ALV)-induced bursal lymphomas. In these tumors transcription of the c-*myc* gene was elevated fifty- to one hundredfold as a result of a provirus insertion upstream from the c-*myc* proto-oncogene locus.[14] This is shown schematically in model A, Fig. 5-5. Several modes of oncogene activation by provirus insertion have been documented showing that integration of proviruses can also occur downstream of c-*myc* or upstream in the opposite orientation.[15] These latter transcriptional activation modes (Fig. 5-5*B*) involve viral transcription enhancers located in the viral LTR regions and are less confined with respect to the integration site, or viral orientation, since enhancers can mediate their effect bidirectionally over large genomic distances.[15] As described in the previous section and shown as the third model, in ALV-induced erythroleukemias, the provirus inserts into an intron of the c-*erb*B (EGFR) locus, which deletes protein-coding sequences of the EGFR extracellular ligand binding domain (Fig. 5-5*C*).[99] Another well-characterized example of a truncation activation mechanism occurs in murine leukemia virus-induced myeloid tumors. In these

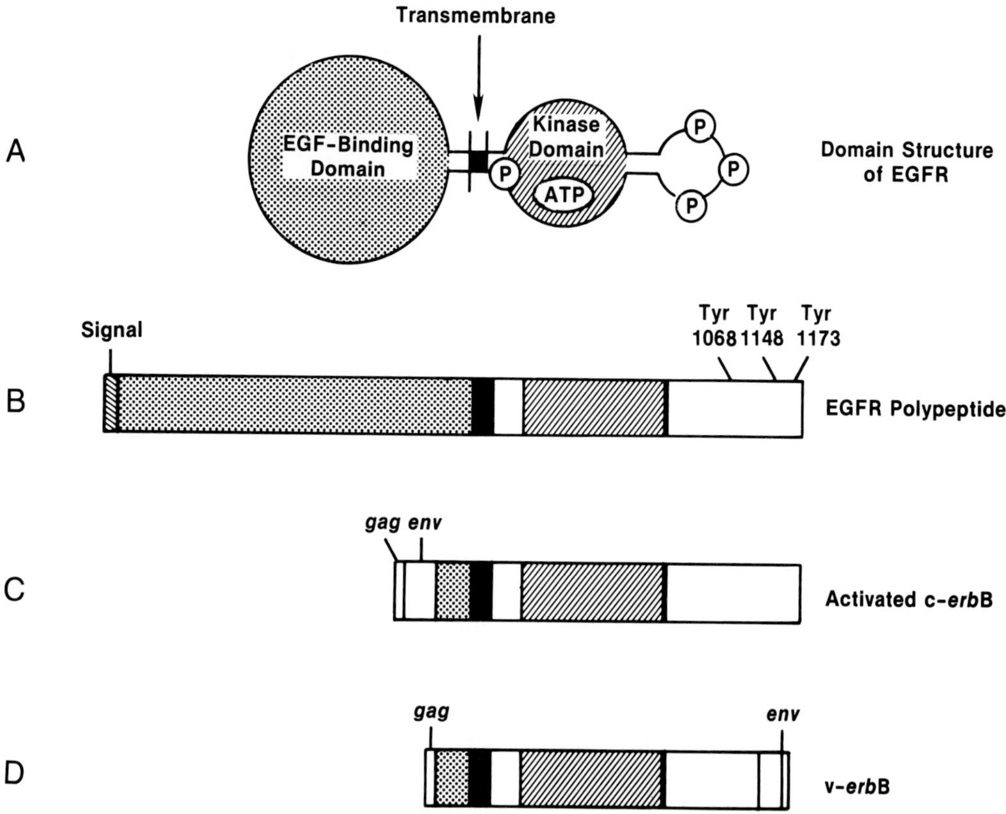

Fig. 5-4 Schematic diagram of the relationship between the epidermal growth factor receptor *(B)* (EGFR), v-*erb*B *(D)*, and c-*erb*B1 (C) activated by proviral insertion. The model for the domain structure of the EGFR *(A)* is based on that of Hunter.[357] The three tyrosine residues that are sites for phosphorylation (P) are shown. Tyr 1173 is deleted in v-*erb*B and substituted with *env* sequences from the provirus. In both v-*erb*B and activated c-*erb*B a large portion of the EGF (epidermal growth factor) binding domain is deleted, and chimeric proteins are formed between retroviral sequences (*gag, env*) and the EGFR transmembrane domain and tyrosine kinase domain.

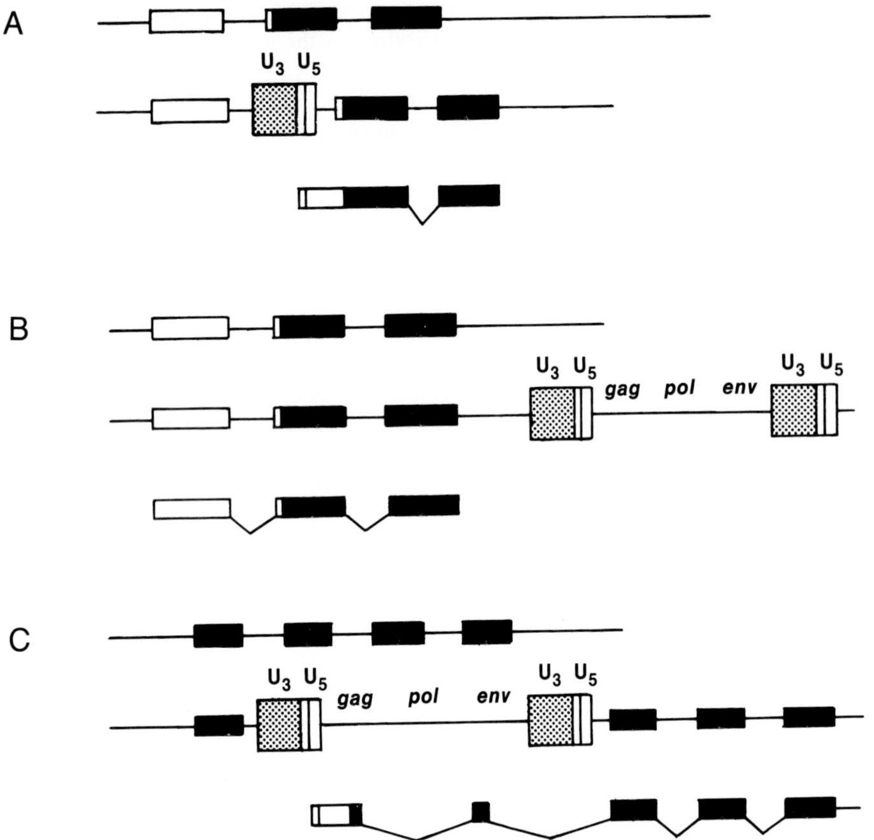

Fig. 5-5 Schematic diagrams for activation of a host gene by insertion of a provirus. Three different configurations of inserted proviral DNA are shown. The exons of the normal host gene (small rectangles) are shown in the upper line in each case, the position of the integrated provirus is shown on the second line, and the resulting transcript is shown on the third line. The protein coding domains are in solid black rectangles. A. Insertion of a proviral LTR (large box U_3-U_5) upstream of the first coding exon as observed with c-*myc*. This insertion results in a transcript that no longer contains the first exon of c-*myc*. B. Integration of an intact provirus downstream from, for example, the *int* genes. This form of integration may not alter the gene product but generally results in increased transcription of that gene promoted by the transcriptional enhancing activity of the retroviral LTR. C. Insertion of an intact provirus into the c-*erb*B1 gene (EGFR see Fig. 5-4C). This results in decapitation of the normal c-*erb*B1 transcript, and instead a hybrid transcript is generated that contains viral *gag* and *env* sequences in addition to c-*erb*B1 sequences.

tumors the provirus inserts into the N-terminal coding domain of the c-*myb* locus (Table 5-4).[100]

Retroviruses which lack v-*onc* sequences can induce many different types of tumors ranging from lymphoproliferative diseases to mammary carcinomas. The presence of a provirus integrated in the same region of the cellular genome in independently derived tumors of the same histiologic type has allowed investigators to identify new cellular genes which can be activated in specific tumor lineages. Following this strategy, many novel oncogenes have been discovered (Table 5-4). For example, mouse mammary tumor virus (MMTV) proviral insertions are frequently found near either of two genes, *int*-1 and *int*-2 (sometimes adjacent to both in the same tumor).[101,102] Several genes have been implicated in T-cell leukemias and lymphomas induced by murine leukemia virus (MLV) in mice or rats.[103–106] These are listed in Table 5-4 and include *Pim*-1 and *tck* genes, which are members of the *src* family of protein kinases.[106,107]

Table 5-4 Cellular Genes Activated by Proviral Insertion*

Gene	*Virus*	*Disease*	*Animal*	*Ref.*
c-*myc*	ALV, CSV, REV	Bursal lymphoma	Chicken	14,15
	MLV	T-cell lymphoma	Mouse	
	FeLV	T-cell lymphoma	Cat	347
c-*erb*B	ALV	Erythroleukemia	Chicken	99
c-*myb*	MLV	Lymphosarcoma	Mouse	348
c-H-*ras*	MAV	Nephroblastoma	Chicken	349
c-*mos*	IAP	Plasmacytoma cell line	Mouse	350
IL-2	GaLV	T-cell lymphoma cell line	Ape	112
IL-3	IAP	Myelomonocytic leukemia	Mouse	113
int-1	MMTV	Mammary carcinoma	Mouse	101
int-2	MMTV	Mammary carcinoma	Mouse	102
Pim-1	M-MLV	T-cell lymphoma	Mouse	106
tck(1skT)	M-MLV	Thymoma cell line	Mouse	105
pvt(mis-1)	M-MLV	T- or B-cell lymphoma	Mouse/rat	103,351
Mlvi-1	M-MLV	T-cell lymphoma	Rat	104
Mlvi-2	M-MLV	T-cell lymphoma	Rat	104
Mlvi-3	M-MLV	T-cell lymphoma	Rat	104
Evi-1	MCF-MLV	Myeloid lymphoma	Mouse	352
Evi-2	MCF-MLV	Myeloid lymphoma	Mouse	353

*ALV = avian leukosis virus; CSV = chick syncytial virus; REV = reticuloendotheliosis virus; MLV = murine leukemia virus; FeLV = feline leukemia virus; MAV = myeloblastosis-associated virus; IAP = intracisternal A particle; GaLV = gibbon ape leukemia virus; MMTV = mouse mammary tumor virus; M-MLV = Molony murine leukemia virus; MCF = mink cell focus forming virus.

The protein coding domain of many oncogenes activated by proviral insertion remains intact and unaltered. In these instances, activation occurs from inappropriate proto-oncogene expression. For example, *int*-1 and *int*-2 genes are normally only expressed transiently during mouse embryogenesis,[108,109] yet MMTV integration in mammary epithelial cells adjacent to *int*-1 and *int*-2 promotes a low level of expression of these genes that contributes to the development of mammary tumors. Some factor-independent T-cell lines were found to make their own growth factors as a consequence of proviral insertions near the interleukin 2 (IL-2) or interleukin 3 (IL-3) gene.[110,111] Similarly, introduction of the normal IL-2 or IL-3 genes in a retrovirus vector into certain factor-dependent cell lines causes these cells to become tumorigenic and factor-independent.[112,113] Thus, expression of IL-2 and IL-3 in cells containing appropriate receptors gives these cells a growth advantage through an autocrine stimulation mechanism (Fig. 5-6).

Human T-Cell Leukemia Retroviruses and Cell Transformation. Unlike the leukemia or leukosis viruses that induce tumors via proviral insertion, the human T-cell leukemia viruses HTLV-I and HTLV-II and the related bovine leukemia virus (BLV) are thought to transform cells via a different mechanism. HTLV-I and HTLV-II do not appear to contain a v-*onc* gene related to a cellular gene, and insertional mutagenesis by these viruses is unlikely since the site of proviral integration varies in different tumors.[114] HTLV-I and HTLV-II are associated with specific lymphoid malignancies in humans[115,116] that develop following an extremely long latent period >30 years,[117,118] whereas BLV is related in structure to HTLV and causes rare forms of B-cell leukosis in cattle.[119]

HTLV-I and HTLV-II share approximately 60 percent nucleic acid sequence homology, and the overall arrangement and structure of their genomes is similar to that of BLV.[114,120] Although the mechanism of cellular transformation by HTLV-I and HTLV-II is unknown, evidence points to a retroviral gene present in HTLV-I, HTLV-II, and BLV but not in other retroviruses. In addition to *gag*, *pol*, and *env* (found in all replication-competent retroviruses), HTLV viruses encode a fourth retroviral gene (*tat*, also referred to as X, or X-lor[121,122,123]). Like the oncogenes of some DNA transforming viruses the *tat* protein product is able to stimulate transcription of other viral genes by direct or indirect interaction with a transactivation-responsive region located within the viral LTR.[123,124] It has been proposed that the HTLV *tat* gene product induces malignant transformation of T cells by causing aberrant transcriptional regulation of specific cellular genes.[123,125] However, the long latent period required for the development of leukemias >30 years suggests that additional events are required.

Fig. 5-6 Diagrammatic representation of an autocrine model of growth stimulation. The figure shows a cell with nucleus that bears growth factor receptors on its surface. The cell produces and exports one of these factors (closed triangles) to the extracellular fluid. The normal growth factors and their corresponding oncogene are platelet-derived growth factor (PDGF) (v-*sis*); fibroblast growth factor (FGF) (*int*-2); transforming growth factor α (TGFα); and interleukin 2 and 3 (IL-2 and IL-3). Only cells that express a receptor specific for a particular growth factor will respond. For clarity, closed triangles are used to represent all the factors. In reality each growth factor has a characteristic structure and a specific receptor.

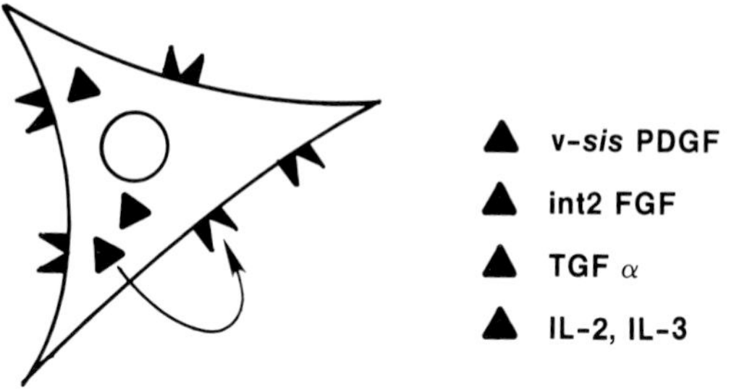

Oncogene Activation via Chromosomal Rearrangements

The most carefully characterized chromosomal rearrangements involving known oncogenes are in Burkitt lymphoma and in chronic myelogenous leukemia.

Burkitt Lymphoma. Eighty percent of Burkitt lymphomas involve activation of c-*myc* via a translocation between chromosomes 8 and 14. As a result of this translocation, c-*myc* is moved from its normal position at 8q24[126,127] distal to the immunoglobulin heavy chain locus at 14q32[128] (Fig. 5-7). The remaining 20 percent of Burkitt lymphoma translocations involve the κ (chromosome 2p11) (15 percent) or λ (chromosome 22q11) (5 percent) immunoglobulin light chain loci, respectively,[129–131] which are translocated to the vicinity of the c-*myc* locus on chromosome 8[130,132] (Fig. 5-7). Each c-*myc* translocation appears to be a unique DNA rearrangement that

Fig. 5-7 Schematic representation of the chromosomes involved in Burkitt lymphoma specific translocations: t(2;8) (p12;q24), t(8;14) (q24;q32) and t(8;22) (q24;q11). The position of the break points and the direction of transcription of the involved loci are shown. In the t(2;8) and the t(8;22), the c-*myc* gene remains on chromosome 8, whereas, on the t(2;8), the c-*myc* locus translocates to the immunoglobulin κ chain locus on chromosome 2.

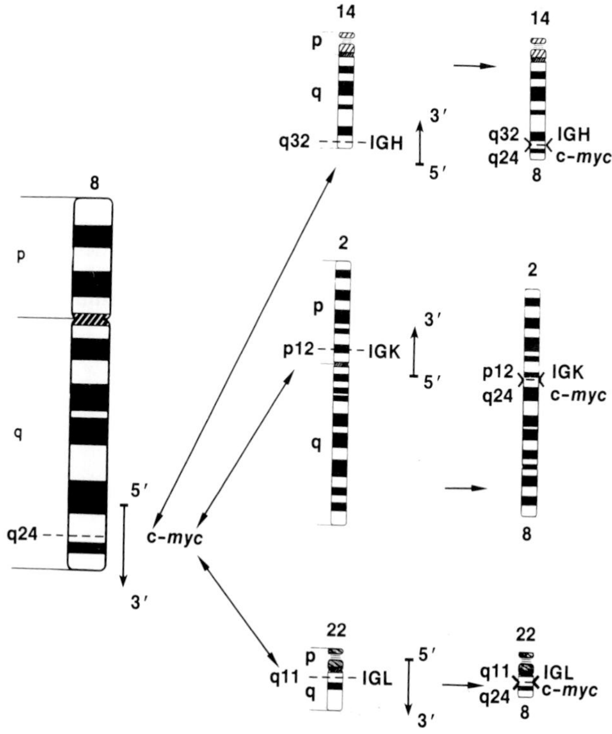

occurs during B-cell maturation between the immunoglobulin locus and cryptic sites in the c-*myc* locus. It is assumed that the translocations occur during the normal rearrangement of the immunoglobulin genes, which increase the risk of illegitimate recombination. In the most common Burkitt lymphoma translocation [t(8;14), Table 5-5] the c-*myc* locus is transposed to one of the immunoglobulin switch sites. The less frequent varient translocations involve one of the light chain loci. The switch regions of the immunoglobulin loci appear to be favored sites for translocation, although there are no such regions in the c-*myc* locus and the break points are variable.[133]

These variations suggest that the molecular mechanism for c-*myc* activation caused by translocation, cannot be explained by a single model. Normal c-*myc* expression is down-regulated during B-cell differentiation, and in Burkitt lymphoma tumors the nonrearranged c-*myc* allele is not expressed.[130,134,135] The rearranged c-*myc* gene, however, is expressed constitutively, and the c-*myc* protein appears to be unaltered and is either overexpressed or expressed at normal levels. Several mechanisms have been proposed to account for this expression: many translocation events alter the first exon of c-*myc*, where cis-acting transcription regulatory sequences are present (Fig. 5-8, region I)[136–139]; mutations are also found in these first exon cis-acting sequences, even when the translocation break point is distant from and does not interrupt this region (Fig. 5-8)[139–141]; moreover, the translocation of immunoglobulin enhancer cis-acting sequences into the vicinity of the c-*myc* locus has also been proposed as a transcriptional activation mechanism.[140,142] However, the exact mechanism involved in Burkitt lympoma translocations is not understood definitively. The most appealing model is a combination of the above; that is, structural alterations of the c-*myc* locus may inactivate cis-acting negative regulatory elements within the first exon, and/or regulatory elements of the juxtapositioned immunoglobulin locus may act to facilitate c-*myc* expression.

The Philadelphia Chromosome and Chronic Myelocytic Leukemia. Chronic myelogenous leukemia (CML) is a pluripotent stem cell disease that is characterized by the presence of the Philadelphia (Ph) chromosome in the leukemic cells of at least 95 percent of all CML patients.[57,143] The typical Ph chromosome results from a reciprocal translocation between chromosomes 9 and 22, t(9;22)(q34;q11).[57] The proto-oncogene c-*abl* is the normal cellular homologue of the oncogene v-*abl* of Abelson murine leukemic virus (A-MuLV). In the Ph chromosome, the c-*abl* proto-oncogene is translocated from chromosome 9, band q34, to chromosome 22 at band q11.[144,145] The break points in 9q34 in different patients vary and are spread over a considerable distance (>100 kb), while the break points in 22q11 are mostly clustered within a small region (5 kb) referred to as the break point cluster region (*bcr*). A transcription unit (gene) in this region is also called *bcr*.[146]

The Ph chromosome rearrangement results in the expression of a novel 8.5-kb *bcr-abl* hybrid mRNA[147,148] and encodes a novel fusion protein of 210 kDa.[149] The *bcr-abl* genomic DNA rearrangement, the expression of the 8.5-kb *bcr-abl* transcript, and the 210-kDa *bcr-abl* protein are diagnostic for Ph positive CML.[150] The 210-kDa *bcr-abl* protein is larger than the normal 145-kDa c-*abl* protein (Fig. 5-9), and in the fusion protein, the N-terminal c-*abl* residues [there are at least two alternative first exons of human c-*abl* (see Fig. 5-9)[151]] have been replaced by the N-terminal coding sequence of the first through the second or fourth exons of *bcr* (Fig. 5-9). The role of the *bcr* contribution in the c-*abl* activation is not completely understood. The normal c-*abl* product is believed to play a role in signal transduction,[149] and it is possible that, analogous to the c-*myc* immunoglobulin rearrangements in Burkitt lymphomas, the *bcr* contribution may result in unregulated expression of the hybrid *bcr-abl* gene. Alternatively, the substitution of *bcr* sequences at the amino terminus of c-*abl* could alter the substrate specificity of the tyrosine kinase and/or could confer a conformational change on the protein such that it is no longer subjected to normal regulation.[152] This could result in a constitutively active tyrosine kinase that would deliver a continuous signal to the cell. Consistent with this model, normal hematopoietic cells become growth-factor-independent after infection with a retrovirus expressing a hybrid p145 v-*gag-abl* protein (Table 5-1, Fig. 5-9).[153] Thus, the presence of the p210 *bcr-abl* protein may have similar growth-stimulating activity in human hematopoietic cells and may block terminal differentiation of these myeloid cells.

Oncogene Activation by Point Mutation

Direct comparison of the *ras* oncogene nucleotide sequence with the proto-oncogene sequence shows that *ras* genes acquire transformation-inducing properties by single point mutations in their coding sequences[47,79] (Fig. 5-10). For example, the c-H-*ras* gene isolated from a human bladder carcinoma cell line (EJ or T24) contained a single point mutation (G → T) resulting in a glycine → valine change in the 12th codon of the *ras* p21 protein.[154–156] Thus, conversion of c-*ras* to an oncogene occurs when the glycine residue at position 12 is changed (Fig. 5-10). Mutations in naturally occurring *ras* on-

Table 5-5 Chromosomal Translocations in Human Malignancies

Gene locus	*Human neoplasm*	*% tumors with translocation or gene rearrangement*	*Chromosome translocation*	*Ref.*
c-*myc*	Burkitt lymphoma	80	t(8;14)(q24;q32)	354
		15	t(8;22)(q34;q11)	355
		5	t(2;8)(q11;q24)	142
bcr-abl	Chronic myelogenous leukemia	90–95	t(9;22)(q34;q11)	146
	Acute lymphocytic leukemia	10–15	t(9;22)(q34;q11)	356
bcl-1	Chronic lymphocytic leukemia of B-cell type	10–20	t(11;14)(q13;q32)	63
bcl-2	Follicular lymphoma	85–95	t(14;18)(q32;q21)	64

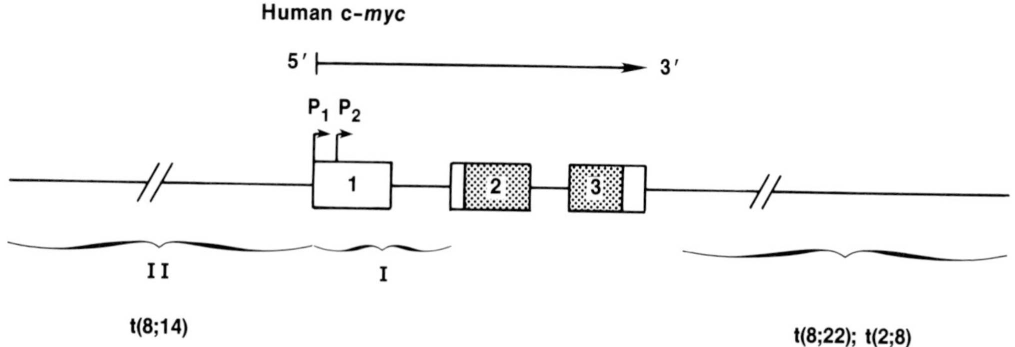

Fig. 5-8 Diagram of the human c-*myc* gene. The three exons are indicated as boxes, stippled areas indicate protein coding domains. The transcriptional orientation and the position of the alternative initiation sites for transcription (P1, P2) are shown. The position of the variant translocation break points t(8;22) and t(2;8) are shown, as well as the positions of break points in the t(8;14) translocations. I represents breakpoints within or between *myc* exon 1 and 2, and II represents breakpoints upstream of the c-*myc* gene.

cogenes have been identified in codons 12, 13, 59, and 61[79] and in vitro site-directed mutagenesis studies have also shown that mutations in codons 63, 116, and 119 can activate *ras* as a transforming gene in the DNA transfection assay.[79] All cellular *ras* oncogenes carry a single point mutation, whereas the retroviral v-H-*ras* and v-K-*ras* oncogenes contain the two activating mutations in codons 12 and 61.[49]

The *ras* proteins have been shown to bind guanine nucleotides and have GTPase activity.[157] This enzymatic activity is greatly reduced in the mutant *ras* oncogene proteins,[79] and it is proposed that codons 12 and 61 and the residues surrounding these codons contribute to the guanine nucleotide binding site. Thus, replacement of these amino acids may interfere with the GTPase activity of *ras* proteins. Evidence for the transforming ability of the altered *ras* protein has been obtained by microinjecting purified *ras* oncogene protein into NIH3T3 cells. These cells not only acquire a transformed morphology but also show a marked increase in mitotic activity.[158,159] Moreover, both phenotypes can be reversed by microinjection of monoclonal antibody directed against the *ras* protein.[160,161] These experiments suggest that the *ras* oncogenes transform established rodent cell lines in a dominant fashion.

Activation of *ras* Genes by Chemical Carcinogens. A role for *ras* genes in the multistep process of carcinogenesis has been shown in studies of carcinogen-induced animal tumor systems where the putative carcinogen-activiated *ras* oncogenes have the same type of activating mutations as those present in human tumors. Many carcinogens cause G→T base transversions and G→A base transitions, and these changes are often observed in activated *ras* genes.[162,163] Several laboratories have demonstrated that chemical carcinogens can activate the *ras* cellular oncogene. In one study, topical application of the carcinogen dimethyl benzanthracene (DMBA) (initiation) followed by treatment with tumor promoters (promotion) causes benign skin papillomas. These papillomas were shown to contain activated c-H-*ras* genes.[164] In a mammary carcinoma model system first described by Huggins, [165] treatment of newborn rats with a single dose of nitrosomethylurea (NMU) leads invariably to the development of mammary carcinomas 2 to 3 months after the animals reach sexual maturity. The majority (85 percent) of the tumors have an activated c-H-*ras* oncogene, and each oncogene contains the same G→A base transition in the 12th codon[166,167] (a preferred genotoxic alteration induced by NMU[162]). Since NMU is active for only approximately 15 min postinjection, these results demonstrate

Fig. 5-9 Structure of *abl*-related proteins. The Abelson murine leukemia virus *(A)* ($p160^{gag\text{-}abl}$), the two forms of the human cellular *(B)* ($p145^{c\text{-}abl}$), and the Philadelphia chromosome translocation derived ($p120^{bcr\text{-}abl}$) *(C)* proteins are shown. The filled boxes in *B* represent different amino terminal sequences for the human c-*abl* proteins. The filled box in *A* represents amino terminal sequences derived from retroviral *gag* sequences and in *C* represents amino terminal sequences derived from the *bcr* gene on chromosome 22 fused to the *abl* gene on chromosome 9 in the Philadelphia chromosome rearrangement found in patients with chronic myelogenous leukemia.

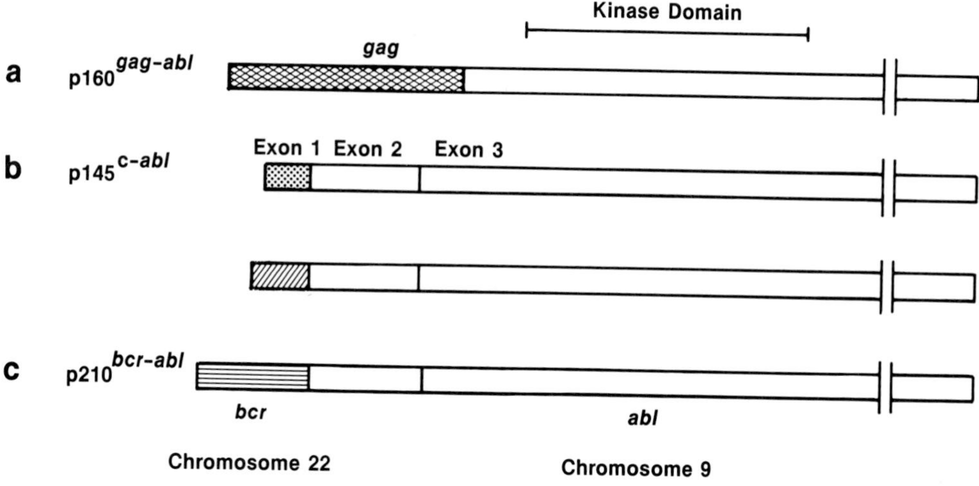

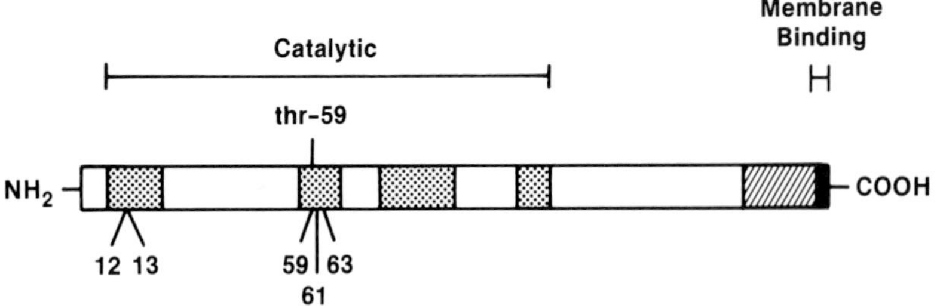

Fig. 5-10 Schematic of *ras* protein, p21. The proposed catalytic and membrane binding domains and the regions within the catalytic domain (stippled) that share homology with other GTP binding proteins are shown. The five residues (12,13,59,61,63) of which amino acid substitutions can activate the transforming potential of the protein are indicated.

that c-H-*ras* activation is the initiation step in this system. However, activation of *ras* is not sufficient to trigger tumorigenesis, and normal hormone-induced proliferation and/or differentiation (promotion) of mammary epithelial cells is essential for tumor formation.[166] Thus, ovariectomized NMU-treated female rats do not develop mammary tumors.[165,166] Although these studies provide unequivocal evidence that *ras* genes can be activated during the early stages of tumor development, *ras* activation can also occur in a cell that is already tumorigenic, and in these systems *ras* may also play a role in tumor progression.[168]

Gene Amplification

Cellular oncogenes have been found in multiple copies in various tumors and transformed cell lines. The amplified oncogene copies can occur in homogeneously staining chromosomal regions or double-minute chromosomes.[169,170] Oncogene amplification has also been observed by hybridization techniques in tumor cells in the absence of microscopic chromosomal changes.[169] The mechanism of gene amplification and structure of the amplified DNA has been characterized in tissue culture after selection for cells with resistance to cytotoxic drugs.[171] Although not fully understood, illegitimate DNA replication occurring more than once during a single cell cycle could account for the increase of multiple segments (amplification units) of DNA from 200 to 2000 kb in size.[172]

All amplified oncogenes express high levels of the corresponding oncogene RNA and appear to be unrearranged, at least at the level of sensitivity of restriction endonuclease mapping, and based on the size of RNA transcripts produced. However, the amplification unit containing the proto-oncogene DNA can be at a site distant from its normal locus as a heterogeneously staining region. The c-*myc* gene was the first proto-oncogene shown to be amplified. In the promyelocytic leukemia cell line HL60, as well as in the primary tumor, 8 to 30 copies of c-*myc* per cell were detected.[173,174] Other oncogenes, including c-*myb*, c-*erb*B (EGFR), HER-2 (also called c-*erb*B2 and corresponds to *neu* in the rat), and c-*myc* family members, have also been shown to be amplified in certain tumors or tumor cell lines (Table 5-6). The presence of multiple copies of oncogenes in tumor cells has been associated with poor prognosis. N-*myc*, which was first identified as an amplified gene in a human neuroblastoma,[175] is present in multiple copies in 40 percent of neuroblastomas, and its amplification correlates with more advanced stages of the disease.[176] Amplification of members of the *myc* gene family (c-*myc*, N-*myc*, L-*myc*) in small cell lung carcinomas also appears to be associated with the more malignant stages of the tumor.[177] The amplified proto-oncogene is frequently tumor-specific; for example, N-*myc* or c-*myc* appear to be associated with the progression of neuroblastomas and small cell lung carcinoma cells, the EGFR (c-*erb*B1) gene has been found to be amplified in glioblastomas and several squamous carcinomas,[178,179] and the related HER-2 gene is often found amplified in adenocarcinomas[180] and in advanced, hormone-independent mammary tumors with a poor prognosis.[181,182] This suggests that increased expression of these proto-oncogenes plays a role in the development and progression of these tumors. In agreement with this, the normal EGFR, HER2 (ERB-2)[183,184] or the *ras* proto-oncogene,[185] when overexpressed in NIH3T3 cells will transform these cells.

Table 5-6 Cellular Oncogenes Amplified in Human Tumors

Tumor	*Oncogene*	*Amplification*	*Ref.*
Small cell lung cancer	c-*myc*	up to 80X	177
	N-*myc*	up to 50X	176
	L-*myc*	up to 20X	323
Neuroblastomas	N-*myc*	up to 250X	170
Glioblastomas	c-*erb*B1(EGFR)	up to 50X	171
Mammary carcinoma	c-*erb*B2(HER2)	up to 30X	181,182

ONCOGENE ACTIVITY ASSAYS

In addition to the previously described NIH3T3 DNA transfection and/or transformation assay for studying oncogene activity, the in vitro rat embryo fibroblast (REF) assay and the in vivo mouse transgenic models have provided novel information regarding oncogene transforming activity in vivo and in vitro.

Cooperating Oncogenes

It has been possible to further subdivide the oncogenes into two groups based on their phenotypes in DNA transfection assays performed in REF cells that have a finite life in culture. It was first demonstrated that the transforming genes of certain DNA tumor viruses [adenovirus (Ad) and polyoma virus (Py)] display different biologic activities in REF. One class of genes (Ad E1A and Py large T-antigen gene) rescues secondary REF from senescence, thus allowing cells to be continuously maintained in culture (immortalization), while the second class (Ad E1B and Py middle T-antigen genes) morphologically alter the rescued cells and render them tumorigenic (transformation).[186–188] It was subsequently discovered that many of the oncogenes could be assigned to either the immortalization group, or the transformation group. Furthermore, members of the immortalization group, whether a gene from DNA tumor viruses (Ad, Py) or a v-*onc* or c-*onc* gene, act synergistically with members of the transformation group to transform REF; for example, foci of transformed cells appear when REFs are transfected with both v-H-*ras* and v-*myc* oncogenes.[188,189] The v-*myc* oncogene rescues cells from senescence and therefore belongs to the immortalization-complementation group, which includes the *myc* gene family, Py large T, Ad E1A, and p53[188–192] (Tables 5-1 and 5-7). In the assay, the v-*ras* gene morphologically transforms immortalized REF and belongs to the transformation-complementation group. This group contains members of the *ras* gene family, Py middle T-antigen gene, and Ad E1B gene (Table 5-7).[45]

NIH3T3 cells have properties similar to those of REF cells immortalized with a member(s) of the first complementation group, and therefore these cells are particularly useful in DNA transfection assays for identifying genes of the second complementation group (e.g., *ras*). In general, the protein products of the members of the first group are found in the nucleus, whereas products of the second group are found in the cytoplasm and, in most cases, are associated with the cytoplasmic side of the plasma membrane. Assignment of c-*onc* and v-*onc* genes to the same complementation groups as genes from DNA tumor viruses suggests that they may transform cells by a similar mechanism. Many of the viral genes that are active in this assay regulate viral gene expression and viral DNA replication, and may have an analogous function in cell transformation, for example, the Ad Ela gene product and SV40 large T antigen both bind cellular DNA and have been shown to induce expression of (transactivate) some cellular genes.[20,190] In addition, they may interact with and modulate the activity of normal genes. An interesting example involves the Py middle T antigen gene product and the c-*src* gene product. Middle T is a membrane-associated phosphoprotein that forms a complex with the c-*src* protein[193] and appears to mediate its transforming properties by altering the kinase activity of the c-*src* protein in a fashion analogous to the activated v-*src* protein.[84,194]

Table 5-7 Oncogene Complementation Groups in Rat Embryo Fibroblast Transformation Assay

Group I, rescue from senescence	*Group II, morphologic transformation*
E1A	E1B
SV40 large T	Polyoma middle T
Polyoma large T	H-*ras*
c-*myc*	K-*ras*
N-*myc*	N-*ras*
p53	

Transgenic Mouse Model

Many important questions about the role of oncogenes in the development of cancer cannot be approached using cells in culture. The use of transgenic mice is providing a powerful experimental approach to these questions. Specific genes (transgenes) are introduced into the germ line of mice by microinjection of recombinant DNA into the male pronucleus of fertilized eggs.[195] Progeny from implanted transgenic embryos are scored for the presence of the transgene by analysis of DNA extracted from the tail of the newborn animal. In this system the action of activated oncogenes can be assessed in a host capable of mounting a physiological response to tumor formation.[195–198]

The introduction of oncogenes under the transcriptional control of constitutive promoter elements or tissue-specific promoter-enhancer elements from heterologous genes allows the effects of expression of an activated oncogene to be assessed either in many tissue types, in a particular tissue, or at a specific developmental stage. In general, when a mouse strain is generated carrying an oncogene-transgene, neoplasia or hyperplasia occurs only in specific tissues and not in all tissues expressing the oncogene. For example, a mouse strain carrying a c-*myc* transgene with an MMTV-LTR promoter develops mammary tumors and occasional B-cell lymphomas. Salivary tumors do not develop even though c-*myc* is expressed at high levels in the salivary gland. Transgenic animals with the v-H-*ras* gene expressed from the same promoter develop salivary gland tumors, mammary tumors, and hyerplasia of the Harderian glands.[199] These results show that tumorigenesis caused by activated oncogene expression can be tissue-specific.

In many cases, oncogene expression precedes tumor formation by many months. Long latencies and variable penetrance may be observed; for example, mice bearing the MMTV LTR-*myc* transgene require 6 to 14 months for tumor development in 50 percent of the animals.[200] Furthermore, a c-*myc* transgene regulated by the lymphoid-specific immunoglobulin H enhancer is probably expressed in all cells of the B lineage, but these cells do not become uniformly transformed.[201] The tumors that do arise are both rare and clonal, inferring that other events are necessary. While some of these changes may involve the activation of additional oncogenes by somatic mutation, they may also involve epigenetic changes.

The synergistic action of the *myc* and *ras* oncogenes was tested in vivo by crossing MMTV LTR-*ras* and MMTV LTR-*myc* transgenic mice.[199] Expression of v-H-*ras* and c-*myc* constructs under the MMTV promoter in the same transgenic animal results in a higher incidence of tumors with a shorter latent period when compared to mouse strains carrying either oncogene alone.[199] The incidence of B-cell malignancies in dual carriers is 30 percent, whereas that of transgenic animals with MMTV v-H-*ras* or MMTV c-*myc* alone is 3 percent. Similarly, the incidence of mammary tumors is increased in these animals. In all cases, tumors arise as clonal outgrowths, and nonmalignant cells expressing both oncogenes predominate.

These systems have not yet provided the explanation for the tissue-specific tumorigenicity of oncogenes. One of the possible explanations for the absence of neoplasia in certain tissues could be that the oncogene transgene is not expressed during a stage of differentiation or development when appropriate substrates or targets for the oncogene may not be present in nonresponding tissues. Hormonally regulated tissue-specific transgene constructs may be used to address questions regarding the mechanism of cooperativity and the distinction between synergistic and sequential models of oncogene action.

MECHANISMS OF ACTION OF ONCOGENES/PROTO-ONCOGENES

Growth factors are, at least in part, responsible for the proliferation and differentiation of cells.[202,203] Thus, qualitative and quantitative modulation of growth factor expression can regulate cell proliferation in a specific tissue. Growth factors must be supplied in vitro as components of culture media, they stimulate DNA synthesis and proliferation of appropriate target cells, and they are essential for the survival of nontransformed cells in culture.[204] Transformation of cells occurs with a concomitant, partial, or complete relaxation of cell growth factor requirement.

The transforming DNA tumor viruses and acute transforming retroviruses can rescue cells from senescence and stimulate cell proliferation, and it is possible to overcome growth factor dependence in certain cell lines by infecting them with specific v-*onc*-containing acute transforming retroviruses.[205] This suggests that the v-*onc* products override normal growth factor-receptor signal transduction pathways either by mimicking the action of ligands or their receptors[206] or through key regulatory intermediates in the cascade that follows mitogenic stimulation.

The molecular mechanisms that produce the functional responses when ligands bind to their individual target cells are unknown, but it is known that growth factor-receptor complexes induce transmembrane signal(s) capable of affecting gene expression at either the transcriptional or translational level.[207] These signals may affect a second messenger system, which is similar to the adenyl cyclase cascade that characterizes certain rapidly acting hormones (Fig. 5-11). The adenyl cyclase system uses a complex family of G (GTP-binding) proteins which connect the occupied receptor to the effector enzyme (adenyl cyclase).[207] Some ligand-mediated mitogenic responses activate the second messenger system of phospholipase C-mediated cleavage of phosphoinositides (Fig. 5-11).[208] In this pathway, diacylglycerol is generated; this activates protein C kinase and mediates the production of phosphorylated inositols.[208] The latter act to mobilize calcium stores from the endoplasmic reticulum, increase the cytoplasmic pH, and stimulate a calcium-dependent protein kinase resulting in the phosphorylation of protein substrates (Fig. 5-11).[207] Protein C kinase phosphorylates numerous substrates. The mechanism by which the phosphorylated substrates mediate the cellular response leading ultimately to DNA replication is unknown. However, it is known that protein C kinase is also the receptor for phorbol ester tumor promoters[207] and phorbol esters promote tumor formation. Perhaps tumor promotion mediated through protein C kinase is analagous to estrogen stimulation of the developing mammary gland in the steroid-dependent mammary carcinogenesis model in NMU-treated female rats.

Many of the oncogenes have been shown to be identical to or related to polypeptide growth factors (v-*sis*, *int2*, KS3/*hst*) or to tyrosine kinase growth factor receptors (v-*erb*B, v-*kit*, v-*fms*, *neu*, *met*, *trk*) or appear to be related to proteins involved in the transfer of the mitogenic stimulus from the cell surface to the nucleus. In analogy to the G protein-adenyl cyclase systems, it has been suggested that the *ras* protein products may serve to connect growth factor receptors with appropriate effector molecules.[47] The *src* family of tyrosine kinase oncogenes (Table 5-1) may act to mimic the tyrosine kinase functions of growth factor receptors,[73] whereas the nuclear oncogene products may directly participate in this pathway by regulating the expression of genes involved in DNA replication. Thus, the relaxation of requirements of transformed cells for growth factors could be mediated by an activated oncogene at each level of the signal transduction pathway.

Growth Factors

The first direct correlation of an oncogene with a growth factor was revealed from a computer-assisted comparison that showed that the amino acid sequence of the v-*sis* oncogene product was highly related to the B chain of PDGF.[206,209,210] PDGF is released from platelets during clotting and is recognized as an important serum mitogen required for mesenchymal cell growth in culture.[211] Connective tissue tumors such as sarcomas and glioblastomas have been shown to express the

Fig. 5-11 Role of diacylglycerol (DG) and inositol lipid hydrolysis in the control of DNA synthesis. Some growth factors acting on specific receptors (R) use a GTP-binding protein (GP) to stimulate a phosphodiesterase (PDE), which cleaves phosphatidylinositol 4,5-biphosphate (Ptd Ins 4,5P_2) to diacylglycerol (DG) and inositol 1,4,5-triphosphate (Ins 1,45P_3). Diacylglycerol has several functions including the stimulation of the same protein C-kinase that can be activated by phorbol esters with the subsequent activation of an Na^+-H^+ exchanger. Ins 1,4,5P_3 acts to mobilize intracellular calcium, which results in stimulation of a calmodulin kinase (CaM). Adapted from Berridge.[207]

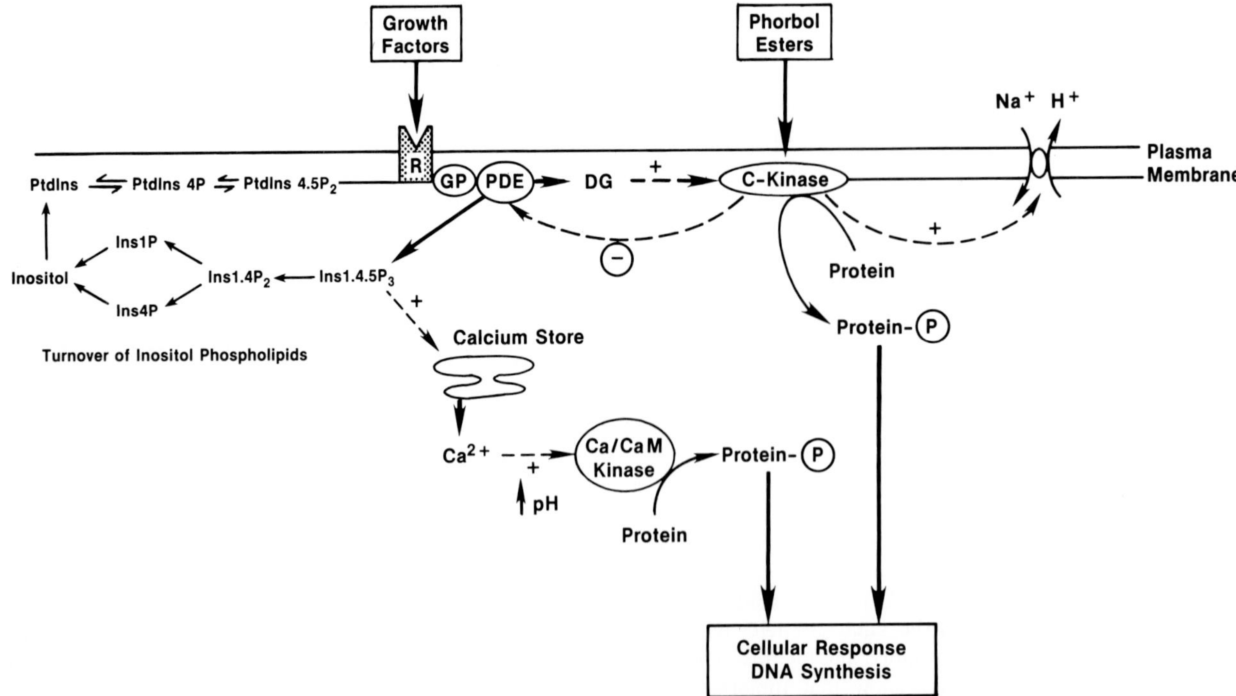

c-*sis* proto-oncogene, whereas their normal tissue counterparts did not.[212] Thus, in an autocrine fashion, the sarcoma and glial tumor cells appear to synthesize the mitogen to which they are responsive (see Fig. 5-6).

In addition to v-*sis*, *int*-2, whose expression is activated by MMTV proviral insertion in mouse mammary carcinomas,[213,214] the *KS3* oncogene identified in a Kaposi's sarcoma[56] and *hst*, a transforming gene identified in a human stomach cancer by DNA transfection[55,215] are members of the basic or acidic fibroblast growth factor (FGF) family.[216] FGFs have angiogenic properties and are members of a family of related peptide mitogens,[217] each possibly with different cell type or receptor specificities. The human *KS3* and *hst* oncogenes are identical in nucleotide sequence and show significant homology with, but are distinct from, the mouse *int*-2 gene. Expression of *int*-2 is detected only in embryos prior to day 7.5 of gestation and is most abundant in cells of the primitive endodermal lineage.[108] Thus, the low level of induction of *int*-2 expression by proviral insertion may contribute to the development of MMTV-induced mammary carcinomas through inappropriate production of a growth factor that may function as a mitogen for these cells.

In addition to the oncogenes that have been shown to be derived from growth factors, two other autocrine systems have been described in tumors. These are the production of transforming growth factors (TGFs) by a number of tumor types and of bombesin in small cell carcinomas of the lung. The term TGF is applied to two distinct growth factors called TGFα and TGFβ; TGFα is a homolog of EGF and binds to the EGF receptor, while TGFβ binds to a unique cellular receptor.[218] TGFα is not detected in most normal adult tissues and appears to be synthesized only for a short period during embryogenesis.[219] Cells that express EGFR are sensitive to TGFα. TGFα and TGFβ are released from virally transformed rodent fibroblasts (TGFα: v-*ras*, v-*abl*, v-*mos*, v-*fos*; TGFβ: v-*ras* and v-*mos* transformants) and from human carcinomas,[220] and it has been possible to show by cell growth in serum-free medium that the TGFs function as autocrines in some virally transformed rodent cells.[221] This has not yet been demonstrated in human tumor systems. However, in small cell carcinoma of the lung where bombesinlike peptides are produced by the tumor cells, cell growth can be inhibited both in vivo and in vitro by antibodies against bombesin.[222] These results demonstrate the dependency of these cells for secretion of the autocrine to maintain cell growth.

Tyrosine Protein Kinases

Transmembrane Protein Tyrosine Kinases. In addition to homology in the tyrosine-specific protein kinase domains of polypeptide growth factor receptors, the receptor-related oncogenes have other structural similarities with these proteins. They are transmembrane proteins that traverse the membrane once and possess an extracellular (ligand-binding) domain at the N terminus and a cytoplasmic tyrosine kinase domain at the C terminus (Fig. 5-12).

Comparison of the complete primary amino acid sequence of the human EGFR[223–225] revealed that the v-*erb* B oncogene product is a truncated form of the EGFR. Recently the v-*fms* oncogene was shown to be the homologue of the macrophage colony-stimulating factor-1 receptor (CSF-1R)[89] (Fig. 5-10). In addition, the v-*ros*,[226] v-*kit*,[96] *met*,[98] *trk*,[52] and *neu*/*erb*B2/HER2[50,51] oncogenes are tyrosine kinases that are derived from proto-oncogenes with structural characteristics of the tyrosine kinase growth factor receptor gene family (Fig. 5-12). In the receptor-related oncogenes so far examined, the structural changes that activate the transforming potential appear

Fig. 5-12 Schematic comparison of structural features of cell surface receptors and tyrosine kinase oncogene products. Regions of high cysteine concentration are shown as hatched boxes, and single cysteine residues are filled circles. The tyrosine kinase domain is represented as cross-hatched boxes and the position of carboxy terminal tyrosine residues is shown (Y). The deletions that activate v-erbB, v-*fms*, and v-src are illustrated. EGF = epidermal growth factor; PDGF = platelet-derived growth factor; CSF-1 = mononuclear phagocyte colony stimulating factor.

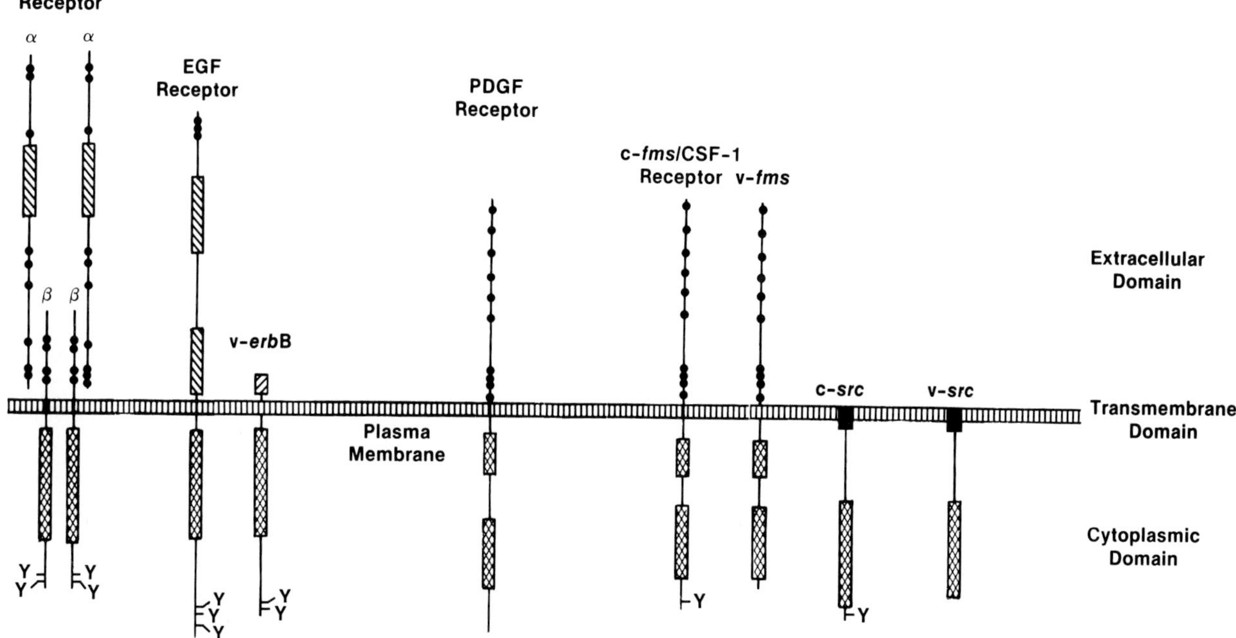

to deregulate the receptor kinase activity. This alteration may chronically stimulate signal transduction pathways and result in altered cell growth (see Figs. 5-11 and 5-12).

Nonintegral Membrane-Associated Protein Tyrosine Kinases. The protein products of v-*src*, v-*fes*, v-*fps*, v-*abl*, v-*fgr*, and v-*yes* are associated with the plasma membrane but are not transmembrane proteins. Many of these proteins have a myristilated N-terminal glycine residue that appears to direct it to the cell membrane.[73] The cytoplasmic tyrosine protein kinase domain is in the C terminus, and all these oncogene proteins are homologous in this region (a stretch of 250 amino acids, Fig. 5-13[73]). This domain is responsible for catalyzing the transfer of the phosphate group of ATP to tyrosine residues during trans- and autophosphorylation. This kinase domain is also homologous to the *raf*, *mil*, and *mos* members, which have phosphorylation specificity for serine and threonine (Fig. 5-13).[227,228] Phosphorylation on tyrosine is a rare event in normal cells and accounts for only 0.05 percent of all protein phosphorylation,[229] but tyrosine phosphorylation may be intimately involved in the complex regulatory system that maintains cellular shape and controls cell growth.[230]

The members of the *src* proto-oncogene subfamily appear to be expressed at high levels in different cell types such that each tyrosine kinase may serve an equivalent function in its specific cell type. For example, the *src* proto-oncogene product is expressed at low levels in most vertebrate cells[231] but is expressed at high levels in non-dividing cells such as platelets and neurons.[232] Similarly, the *Drosophila c-src* homolog is expressed at highest levels in the eye and brain of the adult fruit fly.[233] Thus, c-*src* may be coupled as part of a signal transduction system to a surface receptor or an ion channel specific for neurons. No substrates for phosphorylation by c-*src* have been identified, whereas several cellular cytoskeletal proteins are known to be substrates of v-*src*.[234] Since v-*src* induces fibrosarcomas in chickens and transforms fibroblasts, it is possible that v-*src*-transforming activity may result from the aberrant unregulated tyrosine phosphorylation of cellular proteins specific for these cell lineages.[230] Likewise, the c-*abl* proto-oncogene is expressed in many tissues, but it transforms only cells of the hemopoietic lineage (B cells, macrophages, and myeloid cell lineages).[235] This implies that the activated *abl* oncogene may transform hemopoietic cells through a target or substrate common to these cell lineages.

Protein Kinases in Yeast. An overriding problem in the study of kinase oncogenes is the identification of relevant substrates and the determination of their normal mechanism of action. One approach has been to study homologs of the *src* kinase family in yeast where classic and molecular genetic approaches are possible. Although no tyrosine kinase genes have been identified, many proteins with serine/threonine kinase activity have been described. From the study of cell division cycle mutants (CDC28 in *Saccharomyces cerevisiae* and Cdc2$^+$ in *Schizosaccharomyces pombe*) it has been demonstrated that the products of serine-threonine kinases are required for movement past a specific point in G1 of the cell cycle.[236,237] This point is regulated by at least three protein kinases; the Cdc2$^+$ protein is regulated by a protein kinase, Nce1$^+$,[237] and this kinase is in turn regulated by anotehr protein kinase, Nim1$^+$.[238] Moreover, genes related to CDC28/Cdc2$^+$ have been isolated from mammals[239–241a] and the human Cdc2$^+$ equivalent complements the Cdc2$^+$ mutation in *S. pombe*, suggesting that these genes and their functions have been highly conserved in the evolutionary process.[239] Several oncogenes have been identified which appear to be serine protein kinases [e.g., *mos; raf* (Table 5-1)]. Their function is unknown, but by analogy to the yeast cell-cycle serine protein

Fig. 5-13 Comparison of the cytoplasmic kinase domain of v-*src*, v-*abl*, EGFR, epidermal growth factor, v-*raf*, and v-*mos*. Residues which are identical with v-src in three or more of the proteins are boxed, and gaps (shown by hyphens) were introduced for optimal alignment. Asterisks and a triangle indicate the putative ATP binding domain consensus sequences including Gly-X-Gly-X-X-Gly and a lysine residue (K), where X is any amino acid. Amino acids are represented by a single letter code: A = alanine; R = arginine; N = asparagine; D = aspartic acid; C = cysteine; Q = glutamine; E = glutamic acid; G = glycine; H = histidine; I = isoleucine; L = leucine; K = lysine; M = methionine; F = phenylalanine; P = proline; S = serine; T = threonine; W = tryptophan; Y = tyrosine; and V = valine.

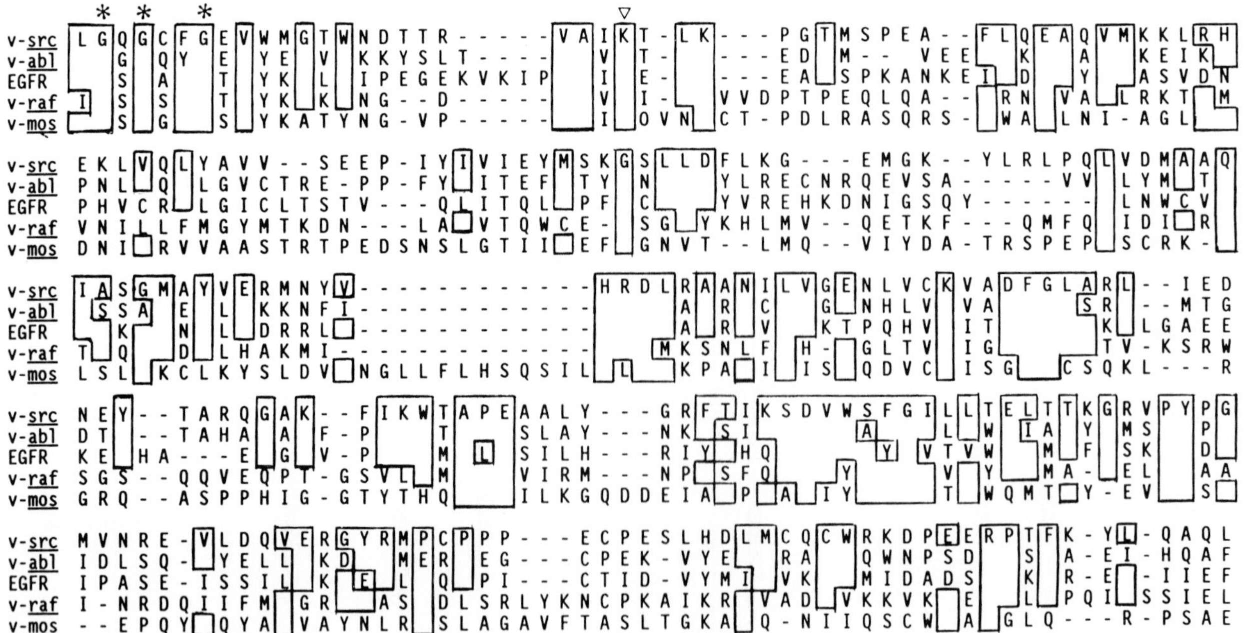

kinases, the *mos* proto-oncogene, which is primarily expressed in male and female germ cells, may be important in meiotic division.[241b]

The *ras* Family of Oncogenes/GTP Binding Proteins

The *ras* gene is also highly conserved[72]; members of this family of genes have been identified in mammals, chickens,[242] fruit flies *(Drosophila melanogaster)*,[72] slime molds,[244] and yeasts.[245,246] Three *ras* gene family members designated c-H-*ras*, c-K-*ras*, and N-*ras* have been characterized in the mammalian genome. The three *ras* proto-oncogenes (c-H-*ras*, c-K-*ras*, and N-*ras*) encode proteins of 21,000 daltons (p21)[247] and have very homologous amino acid sequences. They have been shown to bind guanine nucleotides (GTP and GDP), to possess GTPase activity,[249,250] and to be associated with the cytoplasmic surface of the plasma membrane.[251,252]

***ras* Genes Are Related to G Proteins.** Certain domains in the p21 *ras* protein are homologous to the α subunit of G proteins, in regions involved in guanine nucleotide binding.[253] The G-protein family includes the stimulatory (Gs) and inhibitory (Gi) effectors of adenylate cyclase[254] and transducin, the regulator of retinal rod cyclic GMP phosphodiesterase.[255] This family also includes cytoskeletal proteins, such as tubulin,[256] and cytosolic translational initiation and elongation factors of protein synthesis. These latter proteins bind and hydrolyze GTP but do not transduce regulatory signals. The similarity of p21 *ras* to the hormone and growth factor signal transduction pathway G proteins suggests that it may also be involved in signal transduction.[254] G proteins are functionally regulated or activated by the binding of guanine nucleotides, an event that is triggered by an appropriate signal from a receptor on the cell surface. The activation is transient due to the intrinsic GTPase activity of the molecule. The model proposed for the p21 *ras* proto-oncogene product is that it exists in equilibrium between two conformations: active, with GTP bound; and inactive, with GDP bound (Fig. 5-14). Response to a cell membrane signal results in the exchange of GDP for GTP, converting *ras* from an inactive to an active form[257–259] able to interact with an effector molecule(s)[43] (Fig. 5-12). Mutations resulting in *ras* activation (e.g., amino acid substitutions at positions #12, #13, #59, #61) decrease intrinsic GTPase activity,[79] but they increase transforming potential, probably by altering the kinetics of decay to the inactive GDP-bound form.[260]

In response to ligands, many receptors trigger the breakdown of inositol phospholipid, resulting in rapid intracellular second messenger responses.[207] Certain oncogenes may act in this mitogenic-signal transduction pathway to effect expression of the transformed phenotype. It has been suggested that p21 *ras* may couple certain growth factor receptors to inositol phosphate production via stimulation of phospholipase C[261,262] or phospholipase A_2; however, the exact role of *ras* in this pathway is unknown.

***ras* Genes in Lower Organisms.** The multigenic nature of the *ras* gene family limits functional studies in mammalian cells. For example, it is not known whether each of the three members of the *ras* gene family has a unique biologic function, is expressed in a developmentally regulated manner, or is expressed in specific cell types or tissues. However, identification of *ras* genes in the yeast *S. cerevisiae*[263,264] and in *Dictostellium discoydeum* has made it possible to investigate *ras* function in these organisms by classic and molecular genetics.

Saccharomyces cerevisiae contains two genes (*RAS-1* and *RAS-2*) that are 65 percent homologous to the *ras* p21 protein at their N terminals.[263] Eliminating both *RAS-1* and *RAS-2* in yeast (null mutations) is lethal, but alteration to only one *RAS* gene is not.[265,266] Yeast cells with null mutations in *RAS*-1 and *RAS*-2 are viable if the yeast *RAS* genes are replaced by a human *ras* gene.[266] Moreover, a yeast *RAS*-1 gene mutated at the equivalent codon which activates mammalian *ras* genes, and lacking the yeast-specific C-terminus, will transform NIH3T3 cells.[245,263] Thus, *ras* genes from *S. cerevisiae* and mammals appear to have retained analogous functional properties. Like the mammalian proteins, yeast *RAS* proteins bind guanine nucleotides and have intrinsic GTPase activity.[267,268] Yet yeast *RAS* proteins appear to regulate cyclic AMP levels through adenylate cyclase,[269,270] and both normal and mutant *RAS* proteins activate adenylate cyclase when they bind GTP. Suppressor mutations that rescue *RAS*-defective strains have been shown to map to components of the adenylate cyclase system.[269,270] However, in *D. discoideum*, in *Xenopus* oocytes, or in mammalian cells[244,271] p21 *ras* does not appear to function through adenylate cyclase and is thought to be involved in phosphatidyl inositol metabolism. Clearly, much remains to be learned about these systems.

Oncogenes with Nuclear Products

The products of oncogenes and proto-oncogenes localized to the nucleus are directly implicated in the control of gene expression involved in cellular proliferation and differentiation. The v-*myc*, v-*myb*, v-*fos*, v-*ski*, v-*jun*, and v-*erb*A oncogenes (Table 5-1) and their cellular homologues encode products located in the nucleus, and many appear to possess DNA-binding activity (e.g., v-*myc*,[272] v-*fos*,[273] v-*myb*,[227] p53,[192] v-*jun*,[275] and v-*erb*A[274]). Although none of these products shares sequence homology to the degree shown in the *src* protein kinase or *ras* gene family, several *myc* related genes (c, N, L) have been identified.[176,276] As described previously, many of the nuclear oncogenes can rescue REF cells from senescence, suggesting that in this assay *myc*, Ad E1A, Py large T, and p53 all appear to function in a similar manner.

Cell Cycle Expression of Nuclear Oncogenes. Consistent with the hypothesis that nuclear oncogenes have central roles in events involved in cellular proliferation, the proto-oncogene forms of these genes are normally expressed in a variety of cell types during proliferation and have RNA and protein products with short half-lives. Because of the lability of the RNA and protein products, changes in transcription could lead to relatively rapid fluctuations in the steady state levels of RNA and protein.[277] Studies have shown that c-*fos* and c-*myc* are expressed in replicating cells but that their expression is negligible in serum-starved cells. When quiescent murine fibroblasts are stimulated with serum and enter the G1 phase of growth, a transient increase in the levels of c-*myc*, c-*fos*, c-*myb*, and p53 is observed (Fig. 5-15). The kinetics of induction varies: c-*fos* peaks at 30 min and rapidly declines[277–279]; c-*myc*, peaks at 2 h and declines by 4 h postinduction[281]; and c-*myb*, reaches a peak 4 to 8 h after stimulation and declines slowly,[281] whereas p53 RNA peaks 18 to 24 h poststimulation.[282]

Purified growth factors such as PDGF are efficient at inducing c-*myc*, c-*fos*, c-*myb*, and p53 mRNA levels in quiescent

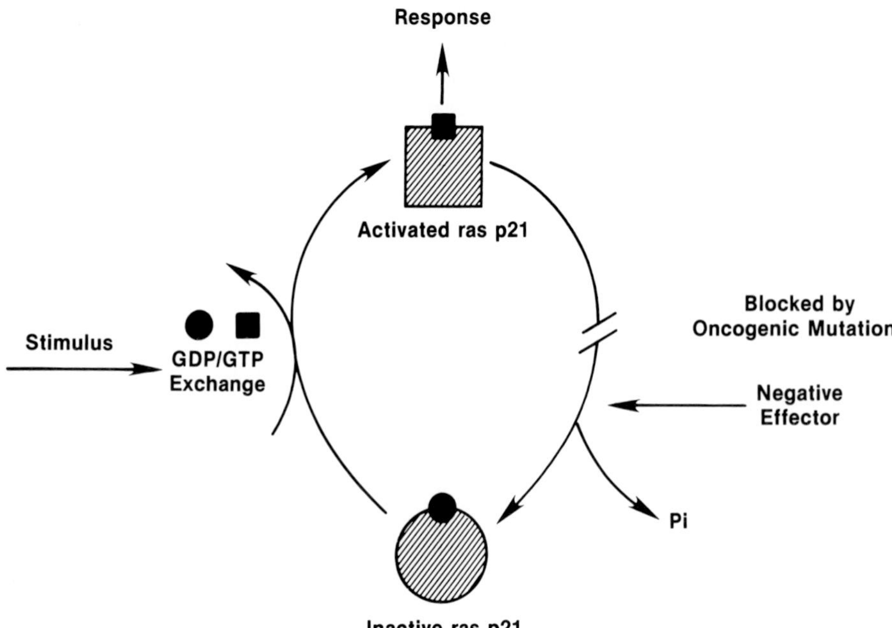

Fig. 5-14 Model for regulation of the *ras* p21 product. The alternating relaxed and activated states of the protein are shown. These are at least in part controlled by the rate of GTP hydrolysis by the intrinsic *ras* GTPase. GTP is diagrammatically represented as the filled small square and GDP as the filled small circle. The putative stimulus that positively regulates and an effector that negatively regulates the activity of p21 *ras* are shown.

NIH3T3 mouse fibroblasts.[279] Quiescent NIH3T3 cells briefly exposed to PDGF become competent for DNA replication, but they progress through G1 and enter S phase only in response to EGF and insulin growth factors[283] (Fig. 5-13). PDGF-induced competence persists after removal of the growth factor and is apparently promoted by the increased expression of a family of competence genes that includes c-*fos* and c-*myc*.[284,285] The peaks in c-*myc* and c-*fos* expression precede the onset of DNA synthesis by many hours, and they are unlikely to be directly involved in DNA replication. In contrast, in cell lines where c-*myb* expression has been observed, this peak appears to correlate with progression of cells through late G1 and early S phase.[281] These findings suggest that induction of the expression of these nuclear oncogenes is required for cells either to traverse specific points in the cell cycle or to transit from a resting state (G0) to a state in which proliferation can proceed (G1). However, the relationship between cell proliferation and nuclear oncogene expression is more complex; for example, transient increases in the expression of both c-*myc* and c-*fos* genes can occur at other points in the cell cycle when purified growth factors are added to synchronized cells.[285]

Further evidence for the role of the c-*myc* and c-*myb* products in cell proliferation is that the expressions of c-*myc* and c-*myb* decrease dramatically during terminal differentiation.[286] For example, the expressions of c-*myc* and c-*myb* are switched off in a promyelocytic cell line (HL60) when it is induced to terminally differentiate.[287,288] c-*myb* is also expressed at high levels in immature T cells and may function during the process of T-cell differentiation,[289] whereas constitutive expression of c-*myc* prevents cell differentiation and promotes cell division.[290] Conversely, induction of c-*fos* is observed during promonocyte differentiation and macrophage proliferation,[291] and expression of c-*fos* is associated in this system with cell differentiation rather than cell proliferation.

The retroviruses that have transduced *myc*, *myb*, and *fos* constitutively express these genes in infected cells at levels higher than their cellular counterparts.[292] Similarly, the expression of the rearranged c-*myc* locus in Burkitt lymphomas and c-*myb* locus in murine myeloid neoplasias is no longer subjected to control, and these genes are expressed constitutively. Thus, the unregulated and/or ectopic expression of these genes may provide a constant stimulation that promotes cell proliferation.

Nuclear Oncogenes as Regulators of Gene Expression. The possibility that nuclear oncogenes regulate gene expression is supported by studies showing that c-*myc*, c-*fos*, v-*jun*, v-*erb*A, and Ad E1A can either directly or indirectly alter the expression of specific cellular genes.[293,294] In addition to promonocyte differentiation, expression of the c-*fos* gene product has been associated with adipocyte differentiation.[295] In this case, the c-*fos* product appears to be a component of a nucleoprotein complex that acts as a negative regulator for expression of a lipid-binding protein (adipocyte P2, that is not expressed in preadipocytes, but is expressed in adipocytes). The c-*fos* pro-

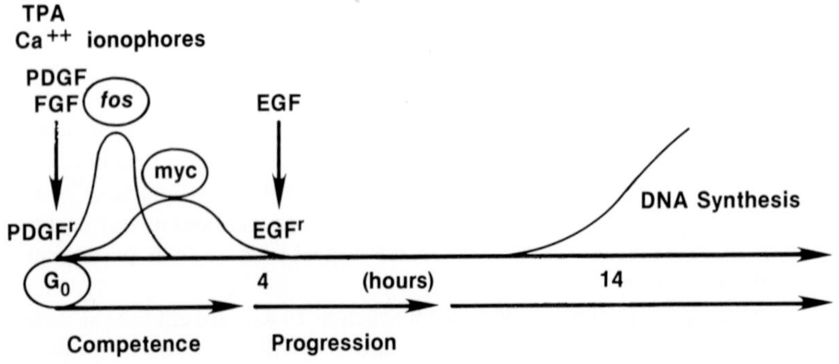

Fig. 5-15 Stimulation of quiescent murine fibroblasts to enter the G1 phase of growth by addition of platelet-derived growth factor (PDGF) or fibroblast growth factor (FGF). A transient increase in the expression of both c-*fos* and c-*myc* occurs following PDGF or FGF stimulation or treatment of cells with phorbol ester (TPA) or a calcium ionophore. Cells rendered competent require epidermal growth factor to progress through the cell cycle.

tein product is directly required for binding of the nucleoprotein complex to a specific DNA sequence element in the adipocyte P2 gene promoter.[295] Thus, the c-*fos* product may participate as a factor that regulates the expression of other genes related to cell growth and differentiation.

Further evidence for the role of nuclear oncogenes as trans-acting factors that regulate gene expression is revealed from studies of v-*jun*.[296] DNA sequence analysis showed that the C terminus of the predicted v-*jun* protein was 45 percent homologous to the C terminus of a transcriptional activator protein (GCN-4) in *S. cerevisiae*.[297] Moreover, *jun* and GCN-4 bind the same DNA sequence element[275] which is the consensus binding sequence for the mammalian transcription factor AP-1 that interacts with phorbol ester-inducible promoter elements. This similarity suggests that the v-*jun* oncogene is related to or is the homologue of the normal AP-1 transcription factor.[298] This suggests that alterations in the level of activity of a normal transcription factor can contribute to tumor development, and it should now be possible to identify genes under the control of c-*jun* that affect cell growth and neoplasia.

Moreover, the nuclear oncogene v-*erb*A first shown to be related to receptors for steroid hormones [with the highest amino acid homology (45 percent) located in the putative DNA-binding region[299]] was identified as a nuclear receptor for thyroid hormones triodothyronine T_3 and thyroxine T_4.[300,301] The thyroid hormone receptor T_3 binding is known to either positively or negatively regulate the expression of a wide variety of genes.[302] Similarly, v-*erb*A has been shown to arrest expression of two genes that may play an important role in red cell differentiation; the anion transporter (band 3), which may serve as a major plasma membrane anchor for the red-cell skeleton,[303] and γ-aminolevulinic acid synthetase, a key enzyme in hemin synthesis. The v-*erb*A gene has no detectable oncogenic potential of its own,[304] but v-*erb*A completely blocks spontaneous differentiation of erythroblasts transformed with v-*erb*B.[304] The v-*erb*A gene product does not bind T_3 or T_4 due internal point mutations and terminal deletion of a region homologous to the steroid hormone ligand binding domain. Thus, the v-*erb*A gene encodes a ligand-independent form of the thyroid hormone receptor that binds to DNA and may constitutively either up- or down-regulate the expression of its target genes and thereby interrupt the regulation of genes essential for erythroblast differentiation.

Since at least some of the nuclear oncogenes have been implicated in trans-activating and/or trans-repressing gene expression, it is possible that alteration of these genes either directly (activated c-*myc*, v-*jun*, v-*erb*A) or indirectly (e.g., induction of their expression by an activated growth factor receptor) may lead to an imbalance in the delicate network of gene expression that regulates cell differentiation and growth control.

SUMMARY: THE ROLE OF ONCOGENES IN TUMOR DEVELOPMENT

It is commonly accepted that cancer is a multistep process and that activation of oncogenes is involved in at least some steps of this pathway. Although the link between oncogene activation and initiation or progression of human cancer is complex, it has been possible to identify several oncogenes in human cancers.

The members of the *ras* gene family (H-*ras*, K-*ras*, and N-*ras*) are the most prevalent, occurring in at least 15 percent of human neoplasias. Evidence from animal model systems suggests that *ras* oncogenes can be involved in both initiation and progression of carcinogenesis. A single dose of NMU, a direct-acting carcinogen with a very short half-life, induces mammary tumors in rats with the c-H-*ras* locus activated in 85 percent of the cases.[166,167] Thus, oncogene activation in this system is thought to be concomitant with the initiation of carcinogenesis. Similarly, one allele of the c-H-*ras* gene is activated in benign papillomas induced by topical application of DMBA followed by treatment with tumor promoters. However, as the tumor progresses to malignancy, the mutant c-H-*ras* allele may become homozygous or amplifed,[305] suggesting that activation of c-H-*ras* is involved in both initiation and progression. Activation of *ras* genes has also been observed during metastasis.[168,306] The *myc* gene family members are also frequently found in human tumors. All Burkitt lymphomas carry c-*myc* oncogenes activated by chromosomal translocations, and amplification of c-*myc* and L-*myc* in small cell lung carcinomas and N-*myc* in neuroblastomas have been implicated in the emergence of highly malignant tumors.[170,177,276]

Both DNA-mediated gene transfer and retroviruses have been used to demonstrate how two different oncogenes can act synergistically to generate a transformed cell. In this respect, there are examples of tumors and tumor cell lines that have alterations in two proto-oncogenes, suggesting that these genes may represent independent steps in tumorigenesis. For example, c-*myc* amplification is accompanied by activation of c-K-*ras* by point mutation in a human lung cancer.[307] Activated c-*ras* genes are also frequently found in Burkitt lymphomas and other hematopoietic tumors that contain rearranged c-*myc* genes.[43] There are also cases of high-grade B-cell malignancies with two chromosomal translocations involving the Bc12 locus [t(14;18)] and the c-*myc* gene [t(8;14)].[308] Rat thymic lymphomas induced by Moloney murine leukemia virus consistently carry DNA rearrangements due to proviral integration in more than one locus Mlvi-1 and Mlvi-2, and the cellular genes *int*-1 and *int*-2, identified as common targets for activation by MMTV, are thought to act cooperatively in the genesis of mouse mammary tumors.[309] However, tumorigenesis initiated by a combination of c-*myc* and c-*ras* in transgenic mice appears to require additional events for the development of a tumor.

The high correlation of the clinical pattern of CML with the Ph1 chromosome and expression of the chimeric *bcr-abl* protein argue for a role of the *bcr-abl* gene in the development of CML. Other cellular oncogenes have been implicated in the development of human neoplasia. The HER-2 gene is amplified in mammary carcinomas with poor prognosis, and the EGFR (c-*erb*B) and c-*myb* genes have been found to be amplified and overexpressed in certain tumors. The expression of the growth factor c-*sis* (B-chain PDGF) is increased in some human sarcoma and glioblastoma cell lines and tumors and may function as an autocrine for these tumors.

Thus, on the basis of circumstantial evidence, alterations to proto-oncogenes have been implicated in the genesis of human and animal tumors. The same rearrangements and mutations involving genes already identified by retroviral transduction have been found repeatedly in human and animal tumors. Clearly, the link between oncogene activation and development of human cancer is complex, but the discovery of oncogenes has provided a new method, particularly in hematologic malignancies, for tumor diagnosis and should ultimately lead to the development of new treatments for neoplastic disease.

Research sponsored by the National Cancer Institute, DHHS, under contract No. NO1-CO-74101 with Bionetics Research, Inc. The contents of this publication do not necessarily reflect the views or policies of the Department of Health and Human Services, nor does mention of trade names, commercial products, or organizations imply endorsement by the U.S. Government.

REFERENCES

1. TEMIN HM: On the origin of genes for neoplasia: G.H.A. Clowes Memorial Lecture. *Cancer Res* 34:2835, 1974.
2. CAIRNS J: Mutation selection and the natural history of cancer. *Nature* 255:197, 1975.
3. CAIRNS J: The origin of human cancers. *Nature* 289:353, 1981.
4. KLEIN G: The role of gene dosage and genetic transpositions in carcinogenesis. *Nature* 294:313, 1981.
5. ROUS P: A sarcoma of the fowl transmissible by an agent separable from the tumor cells. *J Exp Med* 13:397, 1911.
6. GROSS L: *Oncogenic Viruses*. New York, Pergamon, 1970.
7. WEISS R: Experimental biology and assay of RNA tumor viruses, in Weiss R, Bernstein E (eds), *RNA Tumor Viruses*, 2d ed. Cold Spring, NY, Cold Spring Harbor Laboratory, 1984, pp 209–260.
8. STEHLIN D, VARMUS HE, BISHOP JM, VOGT PK: DNA related to the transforming gene(s) of avian sarcoma viruses is present in normal avian DNA. *Nature* 260:170, 1976.
9. BISHOP JM: Enemies within: The genesis of retrovirus oncogenes. *Cell* 23.5, 1982.
10. BLAIR DG, OSKARSSON M, WOOD TG, MCCLEMENTS WL, FISHINGER PJ, VANDE WOUDE G: A molecular model for oncogenesis. *Science* 212:941, 1981.
11. TEMIN HM: Origin of retroviruses from cellular moveable genetic elements. *Cell* 21:599, 1980.
12. BISHOP JM: Cellular oncogenes and retroviruses. *Annu Rev Biochem* 52:301, 1983.
13. TEMIN HM: Structure, variation and synthesis of retrovirus long terminal repeat. *Cell* 27:1, 1981.
14. HAYWARD WS, NEEL BG, ASTRIN SM: Activation of a cellular *onc* gene by promoter insertion in ALV-induced lymphoid leukosis. *Nature* 290:475, 1981.
15. PAYNE GS, BISHOP JM, VARMUS HE: Multiple arrangements of viral DNA and an activated host oncogene in bursal lymphomas. *Nature* 295:209, 1982.
16. TOOZE J: Molecular biology of tumor viruses, in *DNA Tumor Viruses*, 3d ed. Cold Spring Harbor, NY, Cold Spring Harbor Laboratory, 1980.
17. BERK AJ, LEE F, HARRISON T, WILLIAMS J, SHARP PA: A pre-early adenovirus 5 gene produce regulates synthesis of early viral messenger RNAs. *Cell* 17:935, 1979.
18. JONES N, SHENK T: An adenovirus type 5 early gene function regulates expression of other early viral genes. *Proc Natl Acad Sci USA* 76:3665, 1979.
19. REISMAN D, SUGDEN B: Trans-activation of gene expression by the Epstein-Barr viral nuclear antigen (EBNA-1). *Mol Cell Biol* 6:3838, 1986.
20. RIGBY PWJ, LANE DP: Structure and function of simian virus 40 large T-antigen, in Klein G (ed): *Advances in Viral Oncology, Viral Oncology*. New York, Raven, 1983, vol 3, pp 31–57.
21. GREEN MR, TREISMAN R, MANIATIS T: Transcriptional activation of cloned human B-globin genes by viral immediate-early gene products. *Cell* 35:137, 1983.
22. LUPTON S, LEVINE AJ: Mapping genetic elements of Epstein-Barr virus that facilitate extrachromosomal persistence of Epstein-Barr virus derived plasmids in human cells. *Mol Cell Biol* 5:2533, 1985.
23. REISMAN D, YATES AJ, SUGDEN B: A putative origin of replication of plasmids derived from Epstein-Barr virus is composed of two cis-acting components. *Mol Cell Biol* 5:1822, 1985.
24. HILL M, HILLOVA J: Virus recovery in chicken cells tested with Rous sarcoma cell DNA. *Nature* 237:35, 1972.
25. GRAHAM FL, VAN DER EB AJ: A new technique for the assay of infectivity of human adenovirus 5DNA. *Virology* 52:456, 1973.
26. WEINBERG RA: Use of transfection to analyze genetic information and malignant transformation. *Biochim Biophys Acta* 651:25, 1981.
27. COOPER GM, OKENQUIST S, SILVERMAN L: Transforming activity of DNA of chemically transformed and normal cells. *Nature* 284:418, 1980.
28. BLAIR DG, COOPER CS, OSKARSSON MK, EADER LA, VANDE WOUDE GF: New method for detecting cellular transforming genes. *Science* 218:1122, 1982.
29. FASANO O, BIRNBAUM D, EDLUND L, FOGH J, WIGLER M: New human transforming genes detected by a tumorigenicity assay. *Mol Cell Biol* 4:1695, 1984.
30. SCHMID CW, JELINEK WR: The *alu* family of dispersed repetitive sequences. *Science* 216:1065, 1982.
31. SHIH C, WEINBERG RA: Isolation of a transforming sequence from a human bladder carcinoma cell line. *Cell* 29:161, 1982.
32. PULCIANI S, SANTOS E, LAUVER AV, LONG LK, AARONSON SA, BARBACID M: Oncogenes in solid human tumours. *Nature* 300:539, 1982.
33. GOLDFARB M, SHIMIZU K, PERUCHO M, WIGLER M: Isolation and preliminary characterization of a human transforming gene from T24 bladder carcinoma cells. *Nature* 296:404, 1982.
34. HARVEY TT: An unidentified virus which causes the rapid production of tumors in mice. *Nature* 204:1104, 1964.
35. KIRSTEN WH, MEYER LA: Morphological responses to a murine erythroblastosis virus. *J Natl Cancer Inst* 39:311, 1967.
36. DER CJ, KRONTIRIS TG, COOPER GM: Transforming genes of human bladder and lung carcinoma cell lines are homologous to the *ras* genes of Harvey and Kirsten sarcoma viruses. *Proc Natl Acad Sci USA* 79:3637, 1982.
37. PARADA LF, TABIN CJ, SHIH C, WEINBERG RA: Human EJ bladder carcinoma oncogene is homologue of Harvey sarcom avirus *ras* gene. *Nature* 297:474, 1982.
38. SANTOS E, TRONICK SR, AARONSON SA, PULCIANA S, BARBACID M: T24 human bladder carcinoma oncogene is an activated form of the normal human homologue of BALB- and Harvey-MSV transforming genes. *Nature* 298:343, 1982.
39. MCCOY MS, TOOLE JJ, CUNNINGHAM JM, CHANG EH, LOWY DR, WEINBERG RA: Characterization of a human colon/lung carcinoma oncogene. *Nature* 302:79, 1983.
40. PERUCHO M, GOLDFARB M, SHIMIZU K, LAMA C, FOGH J, WIGLER M: Human-tumor-derived cell lines contain common and different transforming genes. *Cell* 27:467, 1981.
41. MURRAY MJ, SHILO B-Z, SHIH C, COWING D, HSU HW, WEINBERG RA: Three different human tumor cell lines contain different oncogenes. *Cell* 25:355, 1981.
42. HALL A, MARSHALL CJ, SPURR NK, WEISS RA: Identification of the transforming gene in two human sarcoma cell lines as a new member of the *ras* gene family located on chromosome 1. *Nature* 303:396, 1983.
43. MURRAY MJ, CUNNINGHAM JM, PARADA LF, DAUTRY F, LEBOWITZ P, WEINBERG RA: The HL-60 transforming sequence: A *ras* oncogene coexisting with altered *myc* genes in hematopoietic tumors. *Cell* 33:749, 1983.
44. SHIMIZU K, BIRNBAUM D, RULEY MA, FASANO O, SUARD Y, EDLUND L, TAPAROWSKY E, GOLDFARB M, WIGLER M: Structure of the Ki-*ras* gene of the human lung carcinoma cell line Calu-1. *Nature* 304:497, 1983.
45. MARSHALL C: Human oncogenes, in Weiss R, Bernstein E (eds), *RNA Tumor Viruses*, 2d ed. Cold Spring, NY, Cold Spring Harbor Laboratory, 1984, pp 487–565.
46. VARMUS HE: The molecular genetics of cellular oncogenes. *Annu Rev Genet* 18:553, 1984.
47. BARBACID M: *ras* Genes. *Annu Rev Biochem* 56:779, 1987.
48. FORRESTER K, ALMOGUERA C, HAN K, GRIZZLE WE, PERUCHO M: Detection of high incidence of K-*ras* oncogenes during human colon tumorigenesis. *Nature* 327:298, 1987.
49. BOS JL, FEARON ER, HAMILTON SR, VERLAAN-DE VRIES M, VAN BOOM JH, VAN DER EB AJ, VOGELSTEIN B: Prevalence of *ras* gene mutations in human colorectal cancers. *Nature* 327:293, 1987.
50. BARGMANN CI, HUNG M-C, WEINBERG RA: Multiple independent activations of the *neu* oncogene by a point mutation altering the transmembrane domain of p185. *Cell* 45:649, 1986.
51. COOPER CS, PARK M, BLAIR DG, TAINSKY MA, HUEBNER K, CROCE CM, VANDE WOUDE GF: Molecular cloning of a new transforming gene from a chemically transformed human cell line. *Nature* 311:29, 1984.
52. MARTIN-ZANCA D, HUGHES SH, BARBACID M: A human oncogene formed by the fusion of truncated tropomyosin and protein tyrosine kinase sequences. *Nature* 319:743, 1986.
53. YAMAMOTO T, IKAWA S, AKIYAMA T, SEMBA K, NOMURA N, MIYAJIMA N, SAITO T, TOYOSHIMA K: Similarity of protein encoded by the human c-*erb*-B-2 gene to epidermal growth factor receptor. *Nature* 319:230, 1986.
54. COUSSENS L, YANG-FENG TL, LIAO Y, CHEN E, GRAY A, MCGRATH J, SEEBURG PH, LIBERMANN TA, SCHLESSINGER J, FRANCKE U, LEVINSON A, ULLRICH A: Tyrosine kinase receptor with extensive homology to EGF receptor shares chromosomal location with *neu* oncogene. *Science* 230:1132, 1985.
55. YOSHIDA T, MIYAGAWA K, ODAGIRI H, SAKAMOTO H, LITTLE PFR, TERADE M, SUGIMURA T: Genomic sequence of *hst*, a transforming gene encoding a protein homologous to fibroblast growth factors and the *int*-2-encoded protein. *Proc Natl Acad Sci USA* 84:7305, 1987.

56. BOVI PD, CURATOLA AM, KERN FG, GRECO A, ITTMAN M, BASILICO C: An oncogene isolated by transfection of Kaposi's sarcoma DNA encodes a growth factor that is a member of the FGF family. *Cell* 50:729, 1987.
57. ROWLEY JD: Human oncogene locations and chromosome aberrations. *Nature* 301:290, 1983.
58. YUNIS JJ, SORENG AL, BOWE AE: Fragile sites are targets of diverse mutagens and carcinogens. *Oncogene* 1:59, 1987.
59. MITELMAN F: *Catalogue of Chromosome Aberrations in Cancer,* 2d ed. New York, AR Liss, 1985.
60. ROWLEY JD, TESTA JR: Chromosome abnormalities in malignant hematologic diseases. *Adv Cancer Res* 36:103, 1982.
61. CROCE CM, NOWELL PC: Molecular basis of human B cell neoplasia. *Blood* 65:1, 1985.
62. HEISTERKAMP N, STEPHENSON JR, GROFFEN J, HANSEN PF, DE KLEIN A, BARTRAM CR, GROSVELD G: Localization of the c-*abl* oncogene adjacent to a translocation break point in chronic myelocytic leukemia. *Nature* 306:239, 1983.
63. TSUJIMOTO Y, JORGE Y, ONORATO-SHOWE L, ERIKSON J, NOWELL PC, CROCE CM: Molecular cloning of the chromosomal breakpoint of B-cell lymphomas and leukemias with the t(11;14) chromosome translocation. 1403, 1984.
64. TSUJIMOTO Y, FINGER LR, YUNIS J, NOWELL PL, CROCE CM: Cloning of the chromosome breakpoint of neoplastic B cells with the t(14;18) chromosome translocation. *Science* 226:1097, 1984.
65. VOGEL F: Genetics of retinoblastoma. *Hum Genet* 52:1, 1979.
66. BENEDICT WF, MURPHREE AL, BANERJEE A, SPINA CA, SPARKES MC, SPARKES RS: Patient with 13 chromosome deletion: Evidence that the retinoblastoma gene is a recessive cancer gene. *Science* 219:973, 1983.
67. CAVENEE WK, DRYJA TP, PHILLIPS RA, BENEDICT WF, GODBOUT R, GALLIE BL, MURPHEE AL, STRONG LC, WHITE RL: Expression of recessive alleles by chromosomal mechanisms in retinoblastoma. *Nature* 305:779, 1983.
68. SPARKES RS: Cytogenetics of retinoblastoma. *Cancer Surv* 3:479, 1984.
69. VAN-HEYNINGEN V, BOYD PA, SEARWRIGHT A, FLETCHER JM, FANTES JA, BUCKTON KE, SPOWART G, PORTEOUS DJ, HIU RE, NEWTON MS, HASTIE ND: Molecular analysis of chromosome 11 deletions in aniridia-Wilms' tumor syndrome. *Proc Natl Acad Sci USA* 82:8592, 1985.
70. FRIEND SH, BERNARDS R, ROGEL S, WEINBERG RA, RAPAPORT JM, ALBERT DM, DRYJA TP: A human DNA segment with properties of the gene that predisposes to retinoblastoma and osteosarcoma. *Nature* 323:643, 1986.
71. LEE W-H, BOOKSTEIN R, HONG F, YOUNG L-H, SHEW J-Y, LEE EYHP: Human susceptibility gene: Cloning, identification and sequence. *Science* 235:1394, 1987.
72. SHILO B-Z, WEINBERG RA: DNA sequences homologous to vertebrate oncogenes are conserved in Drosophila melanogaster. *Proc Natl Acad Sci USA* 78:6789, 1981.
73. HUNTER T, COOPER JA: Epidermal growth factor induces rapid tyrosine phosphorylation of proteins in A431 human tumor cells. *Cell* 24:741, 1981.
74. COFFIN JM, TSICHLIS PN, BARKER CS, VOYNOW S: Variation in avian retrovirus genomes. *Ann NY Acad Sci* 354:410, 1980.
75. KAN NC, FLARDELLIS CS, MARK GE, DUESBERG PH, PAPAS TS: Nucleotide sequence of avian carcinoma virus MH2. Two potential *onc* genes are related to MC29 and the other related to murine sarcoma virus 3611. *Proc Natl Acad Sci USA* 81:3000, 1984.
76. ALITALO K, BISHOP JM, SMITH DH, CHEN GY, COLBY WW, LEVINSON AD: Nucleotide sequence of the v-*myc* oncogene of avian retrovirus MC29. *Proc Natl Acad Sci USA* 80:100, 1983.
77. CURRAN T, MILLER AD, ZOKAS L, VERMA IM: Viral and cellular *fos* proteins: A comparative analysis. *Cell* 36:259, 1984.
78. MEIJLINK F, CURRAN T, MILLER AD, VERMA IM: Removal of a 67-base-pair sequence in the noncoding region of proto-oncogene *fos* converts it to a transforming gene. *Proc Natl Acad Sci USA* 82:4987, 1985.
79. LEVINSON AD: Normal and activated *ras* oncogenes and their encoded products. *Trend Genet* 2:81, 1986.
80. TAKEYA T, HANAFUSA H: Structure and sequence of the cellular gene homologous to the RSV *src* gene and the mechanism for generating the transforming virus. *Cell* 32:881, 1983.
81. KLEMPNAUER K-H, GONDA TJ, BISHOP JM: Nucleotide sequence of the retroviral leukemia gene v-*myb* and its cellular progenitor c-*myb:* The architecture of a transduced oncogene. *Cell* 31:453, 1982.
82. PRYWES R, FOULKES JG, ROSENBERG N, BALTIMORE D: Sequences of the A-MuLV protein needed for fibroblast and lymphoid cell transformation. *Cell* 34:569, 1983.
83. KMIECIK TE, SHALLOWAY D: Activation and suppression of pp60c-src transforming ability by mutation of its primary sites of tyrosine phosphorylation. *Cell* 49:65, 1987.
84. COURTNEIDGE SA: Activation of the pp60c-*src* kinase by middle T antigen binding or by dephosphorylation. *EMBO J* 4:1471, 1985.
85. COOPER JA, GOULD KL, CARTWRIGHT CA, HUNTER T: Tyr527 is phosphorylated in pp60c-*src:* Implications for regulation. *Science* 231:1431, 1986.
86. COOPER JA, KING CS: Dephosphorylation or antibody binding to the carboxy terminus stimulates pp60c-*src*. *Mol Cell Biol* 6:4467, 1986.
87. KAWAKAMI T, PENNINGTON CY, ROBBINS KC: Isolation and oncogenic potential of a novel human *src*-like gene. *Mol Cell Biol* 6:4195, 1986.
88. SUKEGAWA J, SEMBA K, YAMANASHI Y, NISHIZAWA M, MIYAJIMA N, YAMAMOTO T, TOYOSHIMA K: Characterization of cDNA clones for the human c-*yes* gene. *Mol Cell Biol* 7:41, 1987.
89. SHERR CJ, RETTENMIER CW, SACCA R, ROUSSEL MF, LOOK AT, STANLEY ER: The c-*fms* proto-oncogene product is related to the receptor for the mononuclear phagocyte growth factor, CSF-1. *Cell* 41:665, 1985.
90. BROWNING PJ, BUNN HF, CLINE A, SHUMAN M, NIENHUIS A: "Replacement" of COOH-terminal truncation of v-*fms* with c-*fms* sequences markedly reduces transformation potential. *Proc Natl Acad Sci USA* 83:7800, 1986.
91. COUSSENS L, VAN BEVEREN C, SMITH D, CHEN E, MITCHELL RL, ISACKE CM, VERMA IN, ULLRICH A: Structural alteration of viral homologue of receptor proto-oncogene *fms* at carboxyl terminus. *Nature* 320:277, 1986.
92. DOWNWARD J, YARDEN Y, MAYES E, SCRACE G, TOTTY N, STOCKWELL P, ULLRICH A, SCHLESSINGER J, WATERFIELD MD: Close similarity of epidermal growth factor receptor and v-*erb*-B oncogene protein sequences. *Nature* 307:521, 1984.
93. DOWNWARD J, PARKER P, WATERFIELD MD: Autophosphorylation sites on the epidermal growth factor receptor. *Nature* 311:483, 1984.
94. SCHLESSINGER J: Allosteric regulation of the epidermal growth factor receptor kinase. *J Cell Biol* 103:2067, 1986.
95. GOULD KL, WOODGETT JR, COOPER JA, BUSS JE, SHALLOWAY D, HUNTER T: Protein kinase C phosphorylates pp60c-*src* at a novel site. *Cell* 42:849, 1985.
96. YARDEN Y, KUANG WJ, YANG-FENG T, COUSSENS L, MUNEMITSU S, DULL TJ, CHEN E, SCHLESSINGER J, FRANCKE U, ULLRICH A: Human proto-oncogene c-*kit:* A new cell surface receptor tyrosine kinase for an unidentified ligand. *EMBO* 6:3341, 1987.
97. PARK M, DEAN M, COOPER CS, SCHMIDT M, O'BRIEN SJ, BLAIR DG, VANDE WOUDE GF: Mechanism of *met* oncogene activation. *Cell* 45:895, 1986.
98. PARK M, DEAN M, KAUL K, BRAUN MJ, GONDA MA, VANDE WOUDE GF: Sequence of *met* proto-oncogene cDNA has features characteristic of the tyrosine kinase family of growth factor receptors. *Proc Natl Acad Sci USA* 84:6379, 1987.
99. NILSEN TW, MARONEY PA, GOODWIN RG, ROTTMAN FM, CRITTENDEN LB, RAINES MA, KUNG H-J: c-*erb*B activation in ALV-induced erythroblastosis: Novel RNA processing and promoter insertion result in expression of an amino-truncated EGF receptor. *Cell* 41:719, 1985.
100. KLEMPNAUER K-H, RAMSAY G, BISHOP JM: The product of the retroviral transforming gene v-*myb* is a truncated version of the protein encoded by the cellular oncogene c-*myb*. *Cell* 33:345, 1983.
101. NUSSE R, VARMUS HE: Many tumors induced by the mouse mammary tumor virus contain a provirus integrated in the same region of the host genome. *Cell* 31:99, 1982.
102. PETERS G, BROOKES S, SMITH R, DICKSON C: Tumorigenesis by mouse mammary tumor virus: Evidence for a common region for provirus integration in mammary tumors. *Cell* 33:369, 1983.
103. TSICHLIS PN, STRAUSS PG, HU LF: A common region for proviral DNA integration in MoMuLV-induced rat thymic lymphomas. *Nature* 302:445, 1983.
104. CUYPERS HT, SELTEN G, QUINT W, ZIJLSTRA M, MAANDAG ER, BOELENS W, VAN WEZENBEEK P, MELIEF C, BERNS A: Murine leukemia virus-induced T-cell lymphomagenesis: Integration of proviruses in a distinct chromosomal region. *Cell* 37:141, 1984.
105. MARTH JD, PEET R, KREBS EG, PERLMUTTER RM: A lymphocyte-specific protein-tyrosine kinase gene is rearranged and overexpressed in the murine T cell lymphoma LSTRA. *Cell* 43:393, 1985.
106. VORONOVA AF, SEFTON BM: Expression of a new tyrosine protein kinase is stimulated by retrovirus promoter insertion. *Nature* 319:682, 1986.
107. SELTEN G, CUYPERS HT, BOELENS W, ROBANUS-MAANDAG E, VERBEEK J, DOMEN J, VAN BEVEREN C, BERNS A: The primary structure of the putative oncogene *pim*-1 shows extensive homology with protein kinases. *Cell* 46:603, 1986.
108. JAKOBOVITS A, SHACKLEFORD GM, VARMUS HE, MARTIN GR: Two proto-oncogenes implicated in mammary carcinogenesis, *int*-1 and *int*-2, are independently regulated during mouse development. *Proc Natl Acad Sci USA* 83:7806, 1986.
109. WILKINSON DG, BAILES JA, MCMAHON AP: Expression of the proto-oncogene *int*-1 is restricted to specific neural cells in the developing mouse embryo. *Cell* 50:79, 1987.
110. METCALF D, BEGLEY CG, NICOLA NA, JOHNSON GR: Quantitative responsiveness of murine hemopoietic population *in vitro* and *in vivo* to recombinant multi-CSF (IL-3). *Exp Hematol* 15:288, 1987.

111. HAPEL AJ, VANDE WOUDE G, CAMPBELL HD, YOUNG IG, ROBINS T: Generation of an autocrine leukaemia using a retroviral expression vector carrying the interleukin-3 gene. *Lymphokine Res* 5:249, 1986.

112. CHEN SJ, HOLBROOK NJ, MITCHELL KF, VALLONE CA, GREENGARD JS, CRABTREE GR, LIN Y: A viral long terminal repeat in the interleukin 2 gene of a cell line that constitutively produces interleukin 2. *Proc Natl Acad Sci USA* 82:7284, 1985.

113. YMER S, TUCKER QJ, SANDERSON CJ, HAPEL AJ, CAMPBELL HD, YOUNG IG: Constitutive synthesis of interleukin-3 by leukaemia cell line WEH1-3B is due to retroviral insertion near the gene. *Nature* 317:255, 1985.

114. SEIKI M, HATTORI S, HIRAYAMA Y, YOSHIDA M: Human adult T-cell leukemia virus: Complete nucleotide sequence of the provirus genome integrated in leukemia cell DNA. *Proc Natl Acad Sci USA* 80:3618, 1983.

115. POIESZ BJ, RUSCETTI FW, GAZDAR AF, BUNN PA, MINNA JD, GALLO RC: Detection and isolation of type C retrovirus particles from fresh and cultured lymphocytes of a patient with cutaneous T-cell lymphoma. *Proc Natl Acad Sci USA* 77:7415, 1980.

116. HINUMA Y, NAGATA K, HANAOKA M, NAKAI M, MATSUMOTO T, KINOSHITA K-I, SHIRAKAWA S, MIYOSHI I: Adult T-cell leukemia: Antigen in an ATL cell line and detection of antibodies to the antigen in human sera. *Proc Natl Acad Sci USA* 78:6476, 1981.

117. ROBERT-GUROFF M, NAKAO Y, NOTAKE K, ITO Y, SLISKI A, GALLO RC: Natural antibodies to human retrovirus HTLV in a cluster of Japanese patients with adult T cell leukemia. *Science* 215:975, 1982.

118. GALLO RC, KALYANARAMAN VS, SARNGHADHARAN MG, SLISKI A, VONDERHEID EC, MAEDA M, NAKAO Y ET AL: Association of the human type C retrovirus with a subset of adult T-cell cancers. *Cancer Res* 43:3892, 1983.

119. BURNY A: Leukaemogenesis by bovine leukaemia virus, in *Mechanisms of Viral Leukaemogenesis*. London, Churchill Livingston, 1984, vol 1, pp 229–230.

120. SAGATA N, YASUNAGA T, TSUZUKU-KAWAMURA J, OHISHI K, OGAWA Y, IKAWA I: Complete nucleotide sequence of the genome of bovine leukemia virus: Its evolutionary relationship to other retroviruses. *Proc Natl Acad Sci USA* 82:677, 1985.

121. HAZELTINE NA, SODROSKI J, PATARCA R, BRIGGS D, PERKINS D, WONG-STAAL F: Structure of the 3′-terminal region of type II human T lymphotropic virus: Evidence of new coding region. *Science* 225:419, 1984.

122. LEE TH, COLIGAN JE, SODROSKI JG, HASELTINE NA, SALAHUDDIN SZ, WONG-STAAL F, GALLO RC, ESSEX M: Antigens encoded by the 3′-terminal region of human T-cell leukemia virus: Evidence for a functional gene. *Science* 226:57, 1984.

123. SODROSKI J, ROSEN C, GOH WC, HASELTINE W: A transcriptional activator protein encoded by the x-lor region of the human T-cell leukemia virus. *Science* 228:1430, 1985.

124. FELBER BK, PASKALIS H, KLEINMAN-EWING C, WONG-STAAL F, PAVLAKIS G: The pX protein of HTLV-I is a transcriptional activator of its long terminal repeats. *Science* 229:675, 1985.

125. CHEN ISY, SLAMON DJ, ROSENBLATT JD, SHAN NP, QUAN SG, WACHSMAN W: The γ gene is essential for HTLV replication. *Science* 229:54, 1985.

126. NEEL BG, JHANWAR SC, CHAGANTI RSK, HAYWARD WS: Two human c-*onc* genes are located on the long arm of chromosome 8. *Proc Natl Acad Sci USA* 79:7842, 1982.

127. DALLA-FAVERA R, FRANCHINI G, MARTINOTTI S, WONG-STAAL F, GALLO RC, CROCE CM: Chromosomal assignment of the human homologues of feline sarcoma virus and avian myeloblastosis virus *onc* genes. *Proc Natl Acad Sci USA* 79:4714, 1982.

128. KIRSCH IR, MORTON CC, NAKAHARA K, LEDER P: Human immunoglobulin heavy chain genes map to a region of translocations in malignant B lymphocytes. *Science* 216:301, 1982.

129. ERIKSON J, MARTINIS J, CROCE CM: Assignment of the genes for human K immunoglobulin chains to chromosome 22. *Nature* 294:173, 1981.

130. ERIKSON J, NISHIKURA K, AR-RUSHDI A, FINAN J, EMANUEL B, LENOIR G, NOWELL PC, CROCE CM: Translocation of an immunoglobulin J locus to a region 3′ of an unrearranged c-*myc* oncogene enhances c-*myc* transcription. *Proc Natl Acad Sci USA* 80:7581, 1983.

131. MCBRIDE OW, HIETER PA, HOLLIS GF, SWAN D, OTEY MC, LEDER P: Chromosomal location of human kappa and lambda immunoglobulin light chain constant region genes. *J Exp Med* 155:1480, 1982.

132. DE LA CHAPELLE A, LENOIR G, BOUÉ J, BOUÉ A, GALLANO P, HUERRE C, SZAJNERT M-F, JEANPIERRE M, LALOUEL J-M, KAPLAN J-C: Lambda Ig constant region genes are translocated to chromosome 8 in Burkitt's lymphoma with t(8;22). *Nucleic Acids Res* 11:1133, 1983.

133. CROCE CM, NOWELL PC: Molecular basis of human B cell neoplasia. *Blood* 65:1, 1985.

134. STANTON LW, WATT R, MARCU KB: Translocation, breakage and truncated transcripts of c-*myc* oncogene in murine plasmacytomas. *Nature* 303:401, 1983.

135. FEO S, AR-RUSHDI A, HUEBNER K, FINAN J, NOWELL PC, CLARKSON B, CROCE CM: Suppression of the normal mouse c-*myc* oncogene in human lymphoma cells. *Nature* 313:493, 1985.

136. PIECHACZYK M, YANG J-Q, BLANCHARD J-M, JEANTEUR P, MARCU KB: Posttranscriptional mechanisms are responsible for accumulation of truncated c-*myc* RNAs in murine plasma cell tumors. *Cell* 42:589, 1985.

137. RABBITTS PH, WATSON JV, LAMOND A, FORSTER A, STINSON MA, EVAN G, FISCHER W, ATHERTON E, SHEPPARD R, RABBITTS TH: Metabolism of c-*myc* gene products: c-*myc* mRNA and protein expression in the cell cycle. *EMBO J* 4:2009, 1985.

138. REMMERS EF, YANG J-Q, MARCU KB: A negative transcriptional control element located upstream of the murine c-*myc* gene. *EMBO J* 5:899, 1986.

139. CESARMAN E, DALLA-FAVERA R, BENTLEY D, GROUDINE M: Mutations in the first exon are associated with altered transcription of c-*myc* in Burkitt lymphoma. *Science* 238:1272, 1987.

140. LEDER P, BATTEY J, LENOIR G, MOULDING C, MURPHY W, POTTER H, STEWART T, TAUB R: Translocations among antibody genes in human cancer. *Science* 222:765, 1983.

141. TAUB R, MOULDING C, BATTEY J, MURPHY W, VASICEK T, LENOIR GM, LEDER P: Activation and somatic mutation of the translocated c-*myc* gene in Burkitt lymphoma cells. *Cell* 36:339, 1984.

142. CROCE CM, THIERFELDER W, ERIKSON J, NISHIKURA K, FINAN J, LENOIR GM, NOWELL PC: Transcriptional activation of an unrearranged and untranslocated c-*myc* oncogene by translocation of a C K locus in Burkitt lymphoma cells. *Proc Natl Acad Sci USA* 80:6922, 1983.

143. NOWELL PC, HUNGERFORD DA: A minute chromosome in human chronic granulocytic leukemia. *Science* 132:1497, 1960.

144. HEISTERKAMP N, GROFFEN J, STEPHENSON JR, SPURR NK, GOODFELLOW PN, SOLOMON E, CARRITT B, BODMER WF: Chromosomal localization of human cellular homologues of two viral oncogenes. *Nature* 299:747, 1982.

145. DE KLEIN A, VAN KESSEL AG, GROSVELD G, BARTRAM CR, HAGEMEIJER A, BOOTSMA D, SPURR NK, HEISTERKAMP N, GROFFEN J, STEPHENSON JR: A cellular oncogene is translocated to the Philadelphia chromosome in chronic myelocytic leukaemia. *Nature* 300:765, 1982.

146. GROFFEN J, STEPHENSON JR, HEISTERKAMP N, DE KLEIN A, BARTRAM CR, GROSVELD G: Philadelphia chromosomal breakpoints are clustered within a limited region, *bcr*, on chromosome 22. *Cell* 36:93, 1984.

147. CANAANI E, STEINER-SALTZ D, AGHAI E, GALE RP, BERREBI A, JANUSZEWICZ E: Altered transcription of an oncogene in chronic myeloid leukaemia. *Lancet* i:593, 1984.

148. COLLINS SJ, KUBONISHI I, MIYOSHI I, GROUDINE MT: Altered transcription of the c-*abl* oncogene in K-562 and other chronic myelogenous leukemia cells. *Science* 225:72, 1984.

149. KONOPKA, JB, WATANABE SM, WITTE ON: An alteration of the human c-*abl* protein in K562 leukemia cells unmasks associated tyrosine kinase activity. *Cell* 37:1035, 1984.

150. WITTE ON: Functions of the *abl* oncogene. *Cancer Surv* 5(2):183, 1986.

151. SHTIVELMAN E, LIFSHITZ B, GALE RP, CANAANI E: Fused transcript of *abl* and *bcr* genes in chronic myelogenous leukaemia. *Nature* 315:550, 1985.

152. KONOPKA JB, WITTE ON: Detection of c-*abl* tyrosine kinase activity *in vitro* permits direct comparison of normal and altered *abl* gene products. *Mol Cell Biol* 5:3116, 1985.

153. PIERCE JH, DI FIORE PP, AARONSON SA, POTTER M, PUMPHREY J, SCOTT A, IHLE JN: Neoplastic transformation of mast cells by Abelson-MuLV: Abrogation of IL-3 dependence by a nonautocrine mechanism. *Cell* 41:685, 1985.

154. REDDY EP, SMITH MJ, SRINIVASAN A: Nucleotide sequence of Abelson murine leukemia virus genome: Structural similarity of its transforming gene product to other *onc* gene products with tyrosine-specific kinase activity. *Proc Natl Acad Sci USA* 80:3623, 1983.

155. TABIN CJ, BRADLEY SM, BARGMANN CI, WEINBERG RA, PAPAGEORGE AG, SCOLNICK EM, DHAR R, LOWY DR, CHANG EG: Mechanism of action of a human oncogene. *Nature* 300:143, 1982.

156. TAPAROWSKY E, SHIMIZU K, GOLDFARB M, WIGLER M: Structure and activation of the human N-*eas* gene. *Cell* 34:581, 1983.

157. SHIH TY, WEEKS MO: Oncogenes and cancer: p21 *ras* genes. *Cancer Invest* 2:109, 1984.

158. FERAMISCO JR, GROSS M, KAMATA T, ROSENBERG M, SWEET RW: Microinjection of the oncogene form of the human H-*ras* (T-24) protein results in rapid proliferation of quiescent cells. *Cell* 38:109, 1984.

159. STACEY DW, KUNG H-F: Transformation of NIH 3T3 cells by microinjection of Ha-*ras* p21 protein. *Nature* 310:508, 1984.

160. FERAMISCO JR, CLARK R, WONG G, ARNHEIM N, MILLEY R, MCCORMICK F: Transient reversion of *ras* oncogene-induced cell transformation by antibodies specific for amino acid 12 of *ras* protein. *Nature* 314:639, 1985.

161. HSIANG-FU K, SMITH MR, BEKESI E, MANNE V, STACEY DW: Reversal of transformed phenotype by monoclonal antibodies against Ha-*ras* proteins. *Exp Cell Res* 162:363, 1986.

162. EADIE JS, CONRAD M, TOORCHEN D, TOPAL MD: Mechanism of mutagenesis by 06-methylguanine. *Nature* 308:201, 1984.

163. LOECHLER EL, GREEN CL, ESSIGMANN JM: In vivo mutagenesis by 06-methylguanine built into a unique site in a viral genome. *Proc Natl Acad Sci USA* 81:6271, 1984.

164. BALMAIN A, PRAGNELL IB: Mouse skin carcinomas induced in vivo by chemical carcinogens have a transforming Harvey-*ras* oncogene. *Nature* 303:72, 1983.

165. HUGGINS C, BRIZIARELLI G, SUTTON H: Rapid induction of mammary carcinoma in the rat and the influence of hormones on the tumors. *J Exp Med* 109:25, 1959.

166. SUKUMAR S, NOTARIO V, MARTIN-ZANCA D, BARBACID M: Induction of mammary carcinomas in rats by nitroso-methylurea involves malignant activation of H-*ras*-1 locus by single point mutations. *Nature* 306:658, 1983.

167. ZARBL H, SUKUMAR S, ARTHUR AV, MARTIN-ZANCA D, BARBACID M: Direct mutagenesis of Ha-ras-1 oncogenes by N-nitroso-N-methylurea during initiation of mammary carcinogenesis in rats. *Nature* 315:382, 1985.

168. VOUSDEN KH, MARSHALL CJ: Three different activated *ras* genes in mouse tumours; evidence for oncogene activation during progression of a mouse lymphoma. *EMBO J* 3:913, 1984.

169. ALITALO K, SCHWAB M, LIN CC, VARMUS HE, BISHOP JM: Homogeneously staining chromosomal regions contain amplified copies of an abundantly expressed cellular oncogene (c-*myc*) in malignant neuroendocrine cells from a human colon carcinoma. *Proc Natl Acad Sci USA* 80:1707, 1983.

170. SCHWAB M, ALITALO K, KLEMPNAUER K-H, VARMUS HE, BISHOP JM, GILBERT F, BRODEUR G, GOLDSTEIN M, TRENT J: Amplified DNA with limited homology to *myc* cellular oncogene is shared by human neuroblastoma cell lines and a neuroblastoma tumour. *Nature* 305:245, 1983.

171. SCHIMKE RT: Gene amplification in cultured animal cells. *Cell* 37:705, 1984.

172. SHILO Y, SHIPLEY J, BRODEUR GM, BRUNS G, KORF B, DONLON T, SCHRECK RR, SEEGER R, SAKAI K, LATT SA: Differential amplification, assembly, and relocation of multiple DNA sequences in human neuroblastomas and neuroblastoma cell lines. *Proc Natl Acad Sci USA* 82:3761, 1985.

173. COLLINS S, GROUDINE M: Amplification of endogenous *myc*-related DNA sequences in a human myeloid leukaemia cell line. *Nature* 298:679, 1982.

174. DALLA FAVERA R, WONG-STAAL F, GALLO RC: *onc* Gene amplification in promyelocytic leukaemia cell line HL-60 and primary leukaemic cells of the same patient. *Nature* 299:61, 1982.

175. SCHWAB M, VARMUS HE, BISHOP JM, GRZESCHIK KH, NAYLOR SL, SAKAGUCHI AY, BRODEUR G, TRENT J: Chromosome localization in normal cells and neuroblastomas of a gene related to c-*myc*. *Nature* 308:288, 1984.

176. BRODEUR GM, SEEGER RC, SCHWAB M, VARMUS HE, BISHOP JM: Amplification of N-*myc* in untreated human neuroblastomas correlates with advanced disease stage. *Science* 224:1121, 1984.

177. LITTLE CD, NAU MM, CARNEY DN, GAZDAR AF, MINNA JD: Amplification and expression of the c-*myc* oncogene in human lung cancer cell lines. *Nature* 306:194, 1983.

178. LIBERMANN TA, NUSBAUM HR, RAZON N, KRIS R, LAX I, SOREQ H, WHITTLE N, WATERFIELD MD, ULLRICH A, SCHLESSING J: Amplification, enhanced expression and possible rearrangement of EGF receptor gene in primary human brain tumours of glial origin. *Nature* 313:144, 1985.

179. YAMAMOTO T, KAMAT N, KAWANO H, SHIMIZU S, KUROKI T, TOYOSHIMA K, RIKIMARU K, NOMURA N, ISHIZAKI R, PASTAN I, GAMOU S, SHIMIZU N: High incidence of amplification of the epidermal growth factor receptor gene in human squamous carcinoma cell lines. *Cancer Res* 46:414, 1986.

180. YOKOTA J, TERADA M, TOYOSHIMA K, SUGIMURA T, YAMATO T, BATTIFORA H, CLINE MJ: Amplification of the c-*erb*B-2 oncogene in human adenocarcinomas *in vivo*. *Lancet* 1:765, 1986.

181. ZHOU D, BATTIFORA H, YOKOTA J, YAMAMOTO T, CLINE MJ: Association of multiple copies of the C-*erb*B-2 oncogene with spread of breast cancer. *Cancer Res* 47:6123, 1987.

182. KING CR, KRAUS MH, AARONSON SA: Amplification of a novel v-*erb*B-related gene in a human mammary carcinoma. *Science* 229:974, 1985.

183. HUDZIAK RM, SCHLESSINGER J, ULLRICH A: Increased expression of the putative growth factor receptor p185 HER2 causes transformation and tumorigenesis of NIH 3T3 cells. *Proc Natl Acad Sci USA* 84:7159, 1987.

184. DI FIORE PP, PIERCE JH, KRAUS MH, SEGATTO O, KING CR, AARONSON SA: *erb*B-2 is a potent oncogene when overexpressed in NIH/3T3 cells. *Science* 237:178, 1987.

185. CHANG EH, FURTH ME, SCOLNICK EM, LOWY DR: Tumorigenic transformation of mammalian cells induced by a normal human gene homologous to the oncogene of Harvey murine sarcoma virus. *Nature* 297:479, 1982.

186. SHIRO K, SHIMOJO H, SWAADA Y, VEMIZO Y, FUJIMAGA K: Incomplete transformation of rat cells by a small fragment of adenovirus 12 DNA. *Virology* 95:127, 1979.

187. HOUWELING A, VAN DEN ELSEN PJ, VAN DER EB AJ: Partial transformation of primary rat cells by the left-most 4-5 D fragment of adenovirus 5 DNA. *Virology* 105:537, 1980.

188. VAN DEN ELSEN P, DE PATER S, HOUWELING A, VAN DER VEER J, VAN DER EB A: The relationship between region Ela and Elb of human adenoviruses in cell transformation. *Gene* 18:175, 1982.

189. RULEY HE: Adenovirus early region 1A enables viral and cellular transforming primary cells in culture. *Nature* 304:602, 1982.

190. PARADA LF, LAND H, WEINBERG RA, WOLFE D, ROTTER V: Cooperation between gene encoding P53 tumour antigen and *ras* in cellular transformation. *Nature* 312:648, 1984.

191. ELIYAHU D, RAZ A, GRUSS P, GIVOL D, OVEN M: Participation of p53 cellular tumor antigen in transformation of normal embryonic cells. *Nature* 312:647, 1984.

192. YANCOPDOUS GD, NISEN PD, TESFAYE A, KOHL NE, GOLDFARB MP, ATT FW: N-*myc* can cooperate with *ras* to transform normal cells in culture. *Proc Natl Acad Sci USA* 82:5455, 1985.

193. COURTNEIDGE SA, SMITH AE: Polyoma virus transforming protein associates with the product of the c-*src* cellular gene. *Nature* 303:435, 1983.

194. BOLEN JP, THIELE CJ, ISRAEL MA, YONEMOTO W, LIPSICH LA, BRUGGE JS: Enhancement of cellular *src* gene product associated tyrosyl kinase activity following polyoma virus infection and transformation. *Cell* 38:767, 1984.

195. BRINSTER RL, CHEN HV, TRUMBAUER ME, YAGLE MK, PALMITER RD: Factors effecting the efficiency of introducing foreign DNA into mice by microinjecting eggs. *Proc Natl Acad Sci USA* 82:4438, 1985.

196. STEWART TA, PATTENGALE PK, LEDER P: Spontaneous mammary adenocarcinomas in transgenic mice that carry and express MTV/*myc* fusion genes. *Cell* 38:627, 1984.

197. HANAHAN D: Heritable formation of pancreatic B cell tumours in transgenic mice expressing recombinant insulin/simian virus 40 oncogenes. *Nature* 315:115, 1985.

198. MESSING A, CHEN H-Y, PALMITER RD, BRINSTER RL: Peripheral neuropathies, hepatocellular carcinomas and islet cell adenomas in transgenic mice. *Nature* 316:461, 1985.

199. SINN E, MULLER W, PATTENGALE P, TEPLER I, WALLACE R, LEDER P: Coexpression of MMTV/v-Ha-*ras* and MMTV/c-*myc* genes in transgenic mice: Synergistic action of oncogenes *in vivo*. *Cell* 49, 465, 1987.

200. LEDER A, PATTENGALE PK, KUO A, STEWART TA, LEDER P: Consequences of widespread deregulation of the c-*myc* gene in transgenic mice: Multiple neoplasms and normal development. *Cell* 45:485, 1986.

201. ADAMS JM, HARRIS AW, PINKERT CA, COCORAN LM, ALEXANDER WS, CORY S, PALMITER RD, BRINSTER RL: The c-*myc* oncogene driven by immunoglobin enhancers induces lymphoid malignancy in transgenic mice. *Nature* 318:533, 1985.

202. ROBB RJ: Interleukin 2: The molecule and its function. *Immunol Today* 5:203, 1984.

203. TUSHINSKI RJ, OLIVER IT, GUILBERT LJ, TYNAN PW, WARNER JR, STANLEY ER: Survival of mononuclear phagocytes depends on a lineage-specific growth factor that the differentiated cells selectively destroy. *Cell* 28:71, 1982.

204. HAMILTON JA, STANLEY ER, BURGESS AW, SHADDUCK RK: Stimulation of macrophage plasminogen activator activity by colony-stimulating factors. *J Cell Physiol* 103:435, 1980.

205. WEISSMAN BE, AARONSON SA: BALB and Kirsten murine sarcoma viruses alter growth and differentiation of EGF-dependent Balb/c mouse epidermal keratinocyte lines. *Cell* 32:599, 1983.

206. DOOLITTLE RF, HUNKAPILLER MW, HOOD LE, DEVARE SG, ROBBINS KC, AARONSON SA, ANTONIADES HN: Simian sarcoma virus *onc* gene, v-*sis*, is derived from the gene (or genes) encoding a platelet-derived growth factor. *Science* 221:275, 1983.

207. BERRIDGE MJ: Insoditol triphosphate and diacylglycerol: two interacting second messengers. *Annu Rev Biochem* 56:159, 1987.

208. NISHIZUKA Y: Studies and perspectives of protein kinase C. *Science* 233:305, 1986.

209. CHIU I-M, REDDY EP, GIVOL D, ROBBINS KC, TRONICK SR, AARONSON SA: Nucleotide sequence analysis identifies the human c-*sis* proto-oncogene as a structural gene for platelet-derived growth factor. *Cell* 37:123, 1984.

210. WATERFIELD MD, SCRACE GT, WHITTLE N, STROOBANT P, JOHNSSON A, WASTESON A, WESTERMARK B, HELDIN C-H, HUANG JS, DEUEL TF: Platelet-derived growth factor is structurally related to the putative transforming protein p28 *sis* of simian sarcoma virus. *Nature* 304:35, 1983.

211. ROSS R, GLOMSET J, KARIYA B, HARKER L: A platelet-dependent serum factor that stimulates the proliferation of arterial smooth muscle cells in vitro. *Proc Natl Acad Sci USA* 71:1207, 1974.

212. EVA A, ROBBINS KC, ANDERSEN PR, SRINIVASAN A, TRONICK SR, REDDY EP, ELLMORE NW, ET AL: Cellular genes analogous to retroviral *onc* genes are transcribed in human tumour cells. *Nature* 295:299, 1982.

213. DICKSON C, SMITH R, BROOKES S, PETERS G: Tumorigenesis by mouse mammary tumor virus: Proviral activation of a cellular gene in the common integration region *int-2*. *Cell* 37:529, 1984.

214. DICKSON C, PETERS G: Potential oncogene product related to growth factors. *Nature* 326:833, 1987.

215. TAIRA M, YOSHIDA T, MIYAGAWA K, SAKAMOTO H, TERADA M, SUGIMURA T: cDNA sequence of human transforming gene *hst* and identification of the coding sequence required for transforming activity. *Proc Natl Acad Sci USA* 84:2980, 1987.

216. ABRAHAM JA, MERGIA A, WHANG JL, TUMOLO A, FRIEDMAN J, HJERRILD KA, GOSPODAROWICZ D, FIDDES JC: Nucleotide sequence of a bovine clone encoding the angiogenic protein, basic fibroblast growth factor. *Science* 233:545, 1986.

217. ESCH F, BAIRD A, LING N, UENO N, HILL F, DENOROY L, KLEPPER R, GOSPODAROWICZ D, BZHLEN P, GUILLEMIN R: Primary structure of bovine pituitary basic fibroblast growth factor (FGF) and comparison with the amino-terminal sequence of bovine brain acidic FGF. *Proc Natl Acad Sci USA* 82:6507, 1985.

218. ROBERTS AB, SPORN MB: Growth factors and transformation. *Cancer Surv* 5:405, 1986.

219. TWARDZIK DR, TODARO GJ, MARQUARDT H, REYNOLDS FH, STEPHENSON JR: Transformation induced by abelson murine leukemia virus involves production of a polypeptide growth factor. *Science* 216:894, 1982.

220. DELARCO JE, TODARO GJ: Growth factors from murine sarcoma virus-transformed cells. *Proc Natl Acad Sci USA* 75:4001, 1978.

221. KAPLAN PL, OZANNE B: Cellular responsiveness to growth factors correlates with a cell's ability to express the transformed phenotype. *Cell* 33:931, 1983.

222. CUTTITTA F, CARNEY DN, MULSHINE J, MOODY TW, FEDORKO J, FISCHLER A, MINNA JD: Bombesin-like peptides can function as autocrine growth factors in human small cell lung cancer. *Nature* 316:823, 1985.

223. WEBER W, GILL GN, SPIESS J: Production of an epidermal growth factor receptor-related protein. *Science* 224:294, 1984.

224. MERLINO GT, XU Y-H, ISHII S, CLARK AJL, SEMBA K, TOYOSHIMA K, YAMAMOTO T, PASTAN I: Amplification and enhanced expression of the epidermal growth factor receptor gene in A431 human carcinoma cells. *Science* 224:417, 1984.

225. ULLRICH A, COUSSENS L, HAYFLICK JS, DULL TJ, GRAY A, TAM AW, LEE J, YARDEN Y, LIBERMANN TA, SCHLESSINGER J, DOWNWARD J, MAYES ELV, WHITTLE N, WATERFIELD MD, SEEBURG PH: Human epidermal growth factor receptor cDNA sequence and aberrant expression of the amplified gene in A431 epidermoid carcinoma cells. *Nature* 309:418, 1984.

226. EBINA Y, ELLIS L, JARNAGIN K, EDERY M, GRAF L, CLAUSER E, OU J-H, MASIARZ F, KAN YW, GOLDFINE ID, ROTH RA, RUTTER WJ: The human insulin receptor cDNA: The structural basis for hormone-activated transmembrane signalling. *Cell* 40:747, 1985.

227. MOELLING K, PFAFF E, BEUG H, BEIMLING P, BUNTE T, SCHALLER HE, GRAF T: DNA-binding activity is associated with purified *myb* proteins from AMV and E26 viruses and is temperature-sensitive for E26 *ts* mutants. *Cell* 40:983, 1985.

228. MAXWELL SA, ARLINGHAUS RB: Serine kinase activity associated with Moloney murine sarcoma virus-124-encoded $p37^{mos}$. *Virology* 143:321, 1985.

229. SEFTON BM, HUNTER T, BEEMON K, ECKHART W: Evidence that the phosphorylation of tyrosine is essential for cellular transformation by Rous sarcoma virus. *Cell* 20:807, 1980.

230. COOPER JA, BOWEN-POPE DF, RAINES E, ROSS R, HUNTER T: Similar effects of platelet-derived growth factor and epidermal growth factor on the phosphorylation of tyrosine in cellular proteins. *Cell* 31:263, 1982.

231. SPECTOR DH, SMITH K, PADGETT T, MCCOMBE P, ROULLAND-DOUSSOIX D, MOSCOVICI C, VARMUS HE, BISHOP JM: Uninfected avian cells contain RNA related to the transforming gene of avian sarcoma viruses. *Cell* 13:371, 1978.

232. BRUGGE JS, COTTON PC, QUERAL AE, BARRETT JN, NONNER D, KEANE RW: Neurones express high levels of a structurally modified, activated form of pp60c-*src*. *Nature* 316:554, 1985.

233. SIMON MA, DREES B, KORNBERG T, BISHOP JM: The nucleotide sequence and tissue-specific expression of Drosophila c-*src*. *Cell* 42:831, 1985.

234. SEFTON BM, HUNTER T, BALL EH, SINGER SJ: Vinculin: A cytoskeletal substrate of the transforming protein of Rous sarcoma virus. *Cell* 24:165, 1981.

235. WHITLOCK CA, WITTE ON: The complexity of virus-cell interactions in Abelson virus infection of lymphoid and other hematopoietic cells, in FJ Dixson (ed): *Advances in Immunology*. New York, Academic, 1985, vol 37, pp 73–98.

236. REED SI, HADWIGER JA, LORINCZ AT: Protein kinase activity associated with the product of the yeast cell cycle gene CDC28. *Proc Natl Acad Sci USA* 82:4055, 1985.

237. SIMANIS V, NURSE PM: The cell cycle control gene *cdc2*+ of yeast encodes a protein kinase potentially regulated by phosphorylation. *Cell* 45:261, 1986.

238. RUSSELL P, NURSE P: The mitotic inducer *nim1*+ functions in a regulatory network of protein kinase homologs controlling the initiation of mitosis. *Cell* 49:569, 1987.

239. LEE MG, NURSE P: Complementation used to clone a human homologue of the fission yeast cell cycle control gene *cdc2*. *Nature* 327:31, 1987.

240. HANKS SK: Homology probing: Identification of cDNA clones encoding members of the protein-serine kinase family. *Proc Natl Acad Sci USA* 84:388, 1987.

241*a*. DRAETTA G, BRIZUELA L, POTASHKIN J, BEACH D: Identification of p34 and p13, human homologs of the cell cycle regulators of fission yeast encoded by *cdc2*+ and *suc1*+. *Cell* 50:319, 1987.

241*b*. PROPST F, ROSENBERG MP, IYER A, KAUL K, VANDE WOUDE GF: c-*mos* Proto-oncogene RNA transcripts in mouse tissues: Structural features, developmental regulation and localization in specific cell types. *Mol Cell Biol* 7:1629–1637, 1987.

242. WESTAWAY D, PAPKOFF J, MOSCOVICI C, VARMUS HE: Identification of a provirally activated c-Ha-*ras* oncogene in an avian nephroblastoma via a novel procedure: cDNA cloning of a chimaeric viral-host transcript. *EMBO J* 5:301, 1986.

243. SWANSON ME, ELSTE AM, GREENBERG SM, SCHWARTZ JH, ALDRICH TH, FURTH ME: Abundant expression of *ras* proteins in Aplysia neurons. *J Cell Biol* 103:485, 1986.

244. REYMOND CD, GOMER RH, MEHDY MC, FIRTEL RA: Developmental regulation of a Dictyostelium gene encoding a protein homologous to mammalian *ras* protein. *Cell* 39:141, 1984.

245. DEFEO-JONES D, SKOLNICK E, KOLLER R, DHAR R: *ras*-Related gene sequences identified and isolated from *Saccharomyces cerevisiae*. *Nature* 306:707, 1983.

246. POWERS S, KATAOKA T, FASANO O, GOLDFARB M, STRATHERN J, BROACH J, WIGLER M: Genes in S. cerevisiae encoding proteins with domains homologous to the mammalian *ras* proteins. *Cell* 36:607, 1984.

247. SHIH TY, WEEKS MO, YOUNG HA, SCOLNICK EM: Identification of a sarcoma virus-coded phosphoprotein in nonproducer cells transformed by Kirsten or Harvey murine sarcoma virus. *Virology* 96:64, 1979.

248. SHIH TY, PAPAGEORGE AG, STOKES PE, WEEKS MO, SCOLNICK EM: Guanine nucleotide-binding and autophosphorylating activities associated with the p21*src* protein of Harvey murine sarcoma virus. *Nature* 287:686, 1980.

249. GIBBS JB, SIGAL IS, POE M, SCOLNICK EM: Intrinsic GTPase activity distinguishes normal and oncogenic *ras* p21 molecules. *Proc Natl Acad Sci USA* 81:5704, 1984.

250. MCGRATH JP, CAPON DJ, GOEDDEL DV, LEVINSON AD: Comparative biochemical properties of normal and activated human *ras* p21 protein. *Nature* 310:644, 1984.

251. WILLINGHAM MC, PASTAN I, SHIH TY, SCOLNICK EM: Localization of the *src* gene product of the Harvey strain of MSV to plasma membrane of transformed cells by electron microscopic immunocytochemistry. *Cell* 19:1005, 1980.

252. SHIH TY, WEEKS MO: Oncogenes and cancer: The p21 *ras* genes. *Cancer Invest* 2:109, 1984.

253. HURLEY JB, SIMON MI, TEPLOW DB, ROBISHAW JD, GILMAN AG: Homologies between signal transducing G proteins and *ras* gene products. *Science* 226:860, 1984.

254. GILMAN AG: G proteins and dual control of adenylate cyclase. *Cell* 36:577, 1984.

255. STRYER L: Cyclic GMP cascade of vision. *Annu Rev Neurosci* 9:87, 1986.

256. HUGHES SM: Are guanine nucleotide binding proteins a distinct class of regulatory proteins? *FEBS Lett* 164(1):1, 1983.

257. MCCORMICK F, CLARK BFC, LA COUR TFM, KJELDGAARD M, NORSKOV-LAURITSEN L, NYBORG J: A model for the tertiary structure of p21, the product of the *ras* oncogene. *Science* 228:96, 1985.

258. CLANTON DJ, HATTORI S, SHIH TY: Mutations of the *ras* gene product p21 that abolish guanine nucleotide binding. *Proc Natl Acad Sci USA* 83:5076, 1986.

259. WILLUMSEN BM, CHRISTENSEN A, HUBBERT NL, PAPAGEORGE AG, LOWY DR: The p21 *ras* C-terminus is required for transformation and membrane association. *Nature* 310:583, 1984.

260. SEEBURG PH, COLBY WW, CAPON DJ, GOEDDEL DV, LEVINSON AD: Biological properties of human c-Ha-*ras1* genes mutated at codon 12. *Nature* 312:71, 1984.

261. FLEISCHMAN LF, CHAWALA SB, CANTLEY L: *Ras*-transformed cells: Altered levels of phosphatidylinositol-4,5-biphosphate and catabolites. *Science* 231:407, 1986.

262. WAKELAM MJO, DAVIES SA, JOUSLAY MD, MCKAY I, MARSHALL CJ, HALL A: Normal $p21^{N\text{-}ras}$ couples bombesin and other growth factor receptors to inositol phosphate production. *Nature* 232:173, 1986.

263. KATAOKO T, POWERS S, CAMERON S, FASANO O, GOLDFARB M, BROACH J, WIGLER M: Functional homology of mammalian and yeast *ras* genes. *Cell* 40:19, 1985.

264. DEFEO-JONES D, TATCHELL K, ROBINSON LC, SIGAL IS, VASS WC, LOWY DR, SCOLNICK EM: Mammalian and yeast *ras* gene products: Biological function in their heterologous systems. *Science* 228:179, 1985.

265. TATCHELL K, CHALEFF DT, DEFEO-JONES D, SCOLNICK EM: Requirement of either of a pair of *ras*-related genes of Saccharomyces cerevisiae for spore viability. *Nature* 309:523, 1984.

266. KATAOKA T, POWERS S, MCGILL C, FASANO O, STRATHERN J, BROACH J, WIGLER M: Genetic analysis of yeast RAS1 and RAS2 genes. *Cell* 37:437, 1984.

267. TAMANOI F, WALSH M, KATAOKA T, WIGLER M: A product of yeast RAS2 gene is a guanine nucleotide binding protein. *Proc Natl Acad Sci USA* 81:6924, 1984.

268. TEMELES GL, GIBBS JB: Yeast and mammalian *ras* proteins have conserved biochemical properties. *Nature* 313:700, 1985.

269. BROEK D, SAMIY N, FASANO O, FUJIYAMA A, TAMANOI F, NORTHUP J, WIGLER M: Differential activation of yeast adenylate cyclase by wild-type and mutant *ras* proteins. *Cell* 41:763, 1985.

270. TODA T, UNO I, ISHIKAWA T, POWERS S, KATAOKA T, BROEK D, CAMERON S, BROACH J, MATSUMOTO K, WIGLER M: In yeast, *ras* proteins are controlling elements of adenylate cyclase. *Cell* 40:27, 1985.

271. BECKNER SK, HATTORI S, SHIH TY: The *ras* oncogene product p21 is not a regulatory component of adenylate cyclase. *Nature* 317:71, 1985.

272. DONNER P, GREISER-WILKE I, MOELLING K: Nuclear localization and DNA binding of the transforming gene product of avian myelocytomatosis virus. *Nature* 296:262, 1982.

273. SAMBUCETTI L, CURRAN T: The *fos* protein complex is associated with DNA in isolated nuclei and binds to DNA cellulose. *Science* 234:1417, 1986.

274. MCLEOD K, BAXTER J: Chromatin receptors for thyroid hormones. *J Biol Chem* 251:7380, 1976.

275. STRUHL K: The DNA-binding domains of the *jun* oncoprotein and the yeast GCN4 transcriptional activator protein are functionally homologous. *Cell* 50:841, 1987.

276. KOHL NE, KANDA N, SCHRECK RR, BRUNS G, LATT SA, GILBERT F, ALT FW: Transposition and amplification of oncogene-related sequences in human neuroblastomas. *Cell* 35:359, 1983.

277. GREENBERG ME, ZIFF EB: Stimulation of mouse 3T3 cells induces transcription of the c-*fos* oncogene. *Nature* 311:433, 1984.

278. KRUIJER W, COOPER JA, HUNTER T, VERMA IM: Platelet-derived growth factor induces rapid but transient expression of the c-*fos* gene and protein. *Nature* 312:711, 1984.

279. MOLLER R, BRAVO R, BURCKHARDT J, CURRAN T: Induction of c-*fos* gene and protein by growth factors precedes activation of c-*myc*. *Nature* 312:716, 1984.

280. KELLY K, COCHRON BH, STILES CD, LEDER P: Cell-specific regulation of the c-*myc* gene by lymphocyte mitogens and platelet derived growth factor. *Cell* 35:603, 1983.

281. THOMPSON CB, CHALLONER PB, NEIMAN PE, GROUDINE M: Expression of the c-*myb* proto-oncogene during cellular proliferation. *Nature* 319:374, 1986.

282. REICH NC, LEVINE AJ: Growth regulation of a cellular tumour antigen, p53, in nontransformed cells. *Nature* 308:199, 1984.

283. STILES CD, CAPONE GT, SCHER CD, ANTONIADES HN, VAN WYK JJ, PLEDGER WJ: Dual control of cell growth by somatomedins and platelet-derived growth factor. *Proc Natl Acad Sci USA* 76:1279, 1979.

284. LEOF EB, WHARTON W, VAN WYK JJ, PLEDGER WJ: Epidermal growth factor (EGF) and somatomedin C regulate G1 progression in competent BALB/c-3T3 cells. *Exp Cell Res* 141:107, 1982.

285. CURRAN T, MORGAN JI: Superinduction of the c-*fos* by nerve growth factor in the presence of peripherally active benzodiazeprines. *Science* 229:1265, 1985.

286. EISENMAN RN, HANN SR: Biosynthesis of *myc*-encoded proteins and regulation of *myc* gene expression, in Cooper G (ed): *Viral and Cellular Oncogenes*. Boston, MA, Martinus Nishoff, 1988.

287. WESTIN EH, GALLO RC, ARYA SK, EVA A, SOUZA LM, BALUDA MA, AARONSON SA, WONG-STAAL F: Differential expression of the *amv* gene in human hematopoietic cells. *Proc Natl Acad Sci USA* 79:2194, 1982.

288. CAMPISI J, GRAY HE, PARCHEE AB, DEAN M, SOERSHEIM GE: Cell-cycle control of c-*myc* but not c-*ras* expression is lost following chemical transformation. *Cell* 36:241, 1984.

289. TORELLI G, SELLERI L, DONELLI A, FERRARI S, EMILIA G, VENTURELLI D, MORETTI L, TORELLI U: Activation of c-*myb* expression by phytohemagglutinin stimulation in normal human T lymphocytes. *Mol Cell Biol* 5:2874, 1985.

290. PROCHOWNIK EV, KUKOWSKA J: Deregulated expression of c-*myc* by murine erythroleukemia cells prevents differentiation. *Nature* 32:848, 1986.

291. MITCHELL RL, ZOKAS L, SCHREIBER RD, VERMA IM: Rapid induction of the expression of proto-oncogene *fos* during human monocytic differentiation. *Cell* 40:209, 1985.

292. GONDA TJ, SHEINESS DK, BISHOP JM: Transcripts from the cellular homologs of retroviral oncogenes: Distribution among chicken tissues. *Mol Cell Biol* 2:617, 1982.

293. KINGSTON RE, BALDWIN AS, SHARP PA: Transcription control by oncogenes. *Cell* 41:3, 1985.

294. KADDURAH-DAOUK R, GREENE JM, BALDWIN AS JR, KINGSTON RE: Activation and repression of mammalian gene expression by the c-*myc* protein. *Genes Develop* 1:347, 1987.

295. DISTEL RJ, RO H-S, ROSEN BS, GROVES DL, SPIEGELMAN BM: Nucleoprotein complexes that regulate gene expression in adipocyte differentiation: Direct participation of c-*fos*. *Cell* 49:835, 1987.

296. MAKI Y, BOS TJ, DAVIS C, STARBUCK M, VOGT PK: Avian sarcoma virus 17 carries the *jun* oncogene. *Proc Natl Acad Sci USA* 84:2848, 1987.

297. VOGT PK, BOS TJ, DOOLITTLE RF: Homology between the DNA-binding domain fo the GCN4 regulatory protein of yeast and the carboxyl-terminal region of a protein coded for by the oncogene *jun*. *Proc Natl Acad Sci USA* 84:3316, 1987.

298. BOHMANN D, BOS TJ, ADMON A, NISHIMURA T, VOGT PK, TJIAN R: Human proto-oncogene c-*jun* encodes a DNA binding protein with structural and functional properties of transcription factor AP-1. *Science* 238:1386, 1987.

299. WEINBERGER C, HOLLENBERG SM, ROSENFELD MG, EVANS RM: Domain structure of the human glucocorticoid receptor and its relationship to the v-*erb*A oncogene product. *Nature* 318:670, 1985.

300. SAP J, MUNOZ A, DAMM K, GLYSDAEL, J, LEUTZ A, BEUG H, VENNSTROM B: The v-*erb*A protein is a high affinity receptor for thyroid hormone. *Nature* 324:635, 1986.

301. WEINBERGER C, THOMPSON C, ONG E, GRUOLD, EVANS R: The C-v-*erb*A gene encodes a thyroid hormone receptor. *Nature* 324:641, 1986.

302. OPPENHEIMER H, SAMUELS HH (eds): *Molecular Basis of Thyroid Hormone Action*. New York, Academic, 1983.

303. WOODS CM, BOYER B, VOGT PK, LAZORIDES E: Asynchronous expression of the anion transporter and the peripheral components of the membrane skeleton in AZV- and S13-transformed cells. *J Cell Biol* 103:1789, 1986.

304. FRYKBERG L, PALMIERI S, BENG H, CRAF T, HAYMAN MJ, VENNSTRON B: Transforming capacities of avian erythroblastosis virus mutants deleted in the v-*erb*A or *erb*B oncogenes. *Cell* 32:227, 1983.

305. QUINTANILLA M, BROWN K, RAMSDEN M, BALMAIN A: Carcinogen-specific mutation and amplification of Ha-*ras* during mouse skin carcinogenesis. *Nature* 322:78, 1986.

306. ALBINO AP, LE STRANGE R, OLIFF AI, FURTH ME, OLD LJ: Transforming *ras* genes from human melanoma: A manifestation of tumour heterogeneity? *Nature* 308:69, 1984.

307. TAYA Y, HOSOGAI K, HIROHASHI S, SHIMOSATO Y, TSUCHIYA R, TSUCHIDA N, FUSHIMI M, SEKIYA T, NISHIMURA S: A novel combination of K-*ras* and *myc* amplification accompanied by point mutational activation of k-*ras* in a human lung cancer. *EMBO J* 3:2943, 1984.

308. PEGORARO L, PALUMBO A, ERIKSON J, FALDA M, GIOVANAZZO B, EMANUEL BS, ROVERA G, NOWELL PC, CROCE CM: A 14;18 and an 8;14 chromosome translocation in a cell line derived from an acute B-cell leukemia. *Proc Natl Acad Sci USA* 81:7166, 1984.

309. PETERS G, LEE AE, DICKSON C: Concerted activation of two potential proto-oncogenes in carcinomas induced by mouse mammary tumour virus. *Nature* 320:628, 1986.

310. BISTER K, DUESBERG PH: Genetic structure and transforming genes of avian retroviruses, in G. Klein (ed): *Advances in Viral Oncology*. New York, Raven, 1982, vol 1, pp 3–42.

311. NAHARRO G, ROBBINS KC, REDDY EP: Gene product of v-*fgr* onc: Hybrid protein containing a portion of actin and tyrosine-specific protein kinase. *Science* 223:63, 1984.

312. STEPHENSON JR, TODARO GJ: Viral-encoded transforming proteins and transforming growth factors, in G. Klein (ed): *Advances in Viral Oncology*. New York, Raven, 1982, vol 1, pp 107–126.

313. BESMER P, HARDY WD JR, ZUCKERMAN EE: The Hardy-Zuckerman 2-FeSV, a new feline retrovirus with oncogene homology to Abelson-MuLV. *Nature* 303:825, 1983.

314. HAYMAN MJ, RAMSAY GM, SAVIN K: Identification and characterization of the avian erythroblastosis virus *erb*B gene product as a membrane glycoprotein. *Cell* 32:579, 1983.

315. BESMER P, MURPHY JE, GEORGE PC, QIU F, BERGOLD PJ, LEDERMAN L, SNYDER HW, BRODEUR D, ZUCKERMAN EE, HARDY WD: A new acute transforming feline retrovirus and relationship of its oncogene v-*kit* with the protein kinase gene family. *Nature* 320:415, 1986.

316. PAPKOFF J, VERMA IM, HUNTER T: Detection of a transforming gene product in cells transformed by Moloney murine sarcoma virus. *Cell* 29:417, 1982.

317. RAPP UR, GOLDSBOROUGH MD, MARK GE: Structure and biological activity of v-*raf*, a unique oncogene transduced by a retrovirus. *Proc Natl Acad Sci USA* 80:4218, 1983.

318. CURRAN T, TEICH NM: Candidate product of the FBJ murine osteosarcoma virus oncogene: Characterization of 55,000-dalton phosphoprotein. *J Virol* 42:114, 1982.

319. STAVNEZER E, GERHARD DS, BINARI RC: Generation of transforming viruses in cultures of chicken fibroblasts infected with an avian leukosis virus. *J Virol* 39:920, 1981.

320. ROBBINS KC, DEVARE SG, REDDY EP, AARONSON SA: *In vivo* identification of the transforming gene product of simian sarcoma virus. *Science* 218:1131, 1982.

321. STEPHENS RM, RICE NR, HIEBSCH RR: Nucleotide sequence of v-*rel:* The oncogene of reticuloendotheliosis virus. *Proc Natl Acad Sci USA* 80:6229, 1983.

322. NUNN MF, SEEBURG PH, MOSCOVICI C: Tripartite structure of the avian erythroblastosis virus E26 transforming gene. *Nature* 306:391, 1983.

323. NAU MM, BROOKS BJ, BATTEY J, SAUSVILLE E, GAZDAR AF, KIRSCH IR, MCBRIDE OW, BERTNESS V, HOLLIS GF, MINNA JD: L-*myc*, a new *myc*-related gene amplified and expressed in human small lung cancer. *Nature* 318:69, 1985.

324a. NISHIZAWA M, SEMBA K, YOSIDA MC, YAMAMOTO T, SASAKI M, TOYOSHIMA K: Structure, expression and chromosomal location of the human c-*fgr* gene. *Mol Cell Biol* 6:511, 1986.

324b. RABIN M, WATSON M, BARKER PE, RYAN J, BERG WR, RUDDLE FH: N-*ras* transforming gene maps to region p11-p13 on chromosome 1 by *in situ* hybridization. *Cytogenet Cell Genet* 38:70, 1984.

325. ROWLEY JD: Biological implications of consistent chromosome rearrangements in leukemia and lymphoma. *Cancer Res* 44:3159, 1984.

326. BARBACID M: Personal communication.

327. BROWNELL E, KOZAK CA, FOWLE JR, MODI WS, RICE NR, O'BRIEN SJ: Comparative genetic mapping of cellular *rel* sequences in man, mouse, and the domestic cat. *Am J Hum Genet* 39:194, 1986.

328. BONNER T, O'BRIEN SJ, NASH WG, RAPP UR, MORTON CC, LEDER P: The human homologous of *raf (mil)* oncogene are located on human chromosomes 3 and 4. *Science* 223:71, 1984.

329. ROUSSEL MF, SHERR CJ, BARKER PE, RUDDLE FH: Molecular cloning of the c-*fms* locus and its assignment to human chromosome 5. *J Virol* 48:770, 1983.

330. NAGARAJAN L, LOUIS E, TWSUJIMOTO Y, AR-RUSHDI A, HUEBNER K, CROCE CM: Localization of the human *pim* oncogene (PIM) to a region of chromosome 6 involved in translocations in acute leukemias. *Proc Natl Acad Sci USA* 83:2556, 1986.

331. RABIN M, BIRNBAUM D, YOUNG D, BIRCHMEIER C, WIGLER M, RUDDLE, FH: Human *ros*1 and *mas* 1 oncogenes located in regions of chromosome 6 associated with tumor-specific rearrangements. *Oncogene Res* 1:169, 1987.

332. HARPER ME, FRANCHINI G, LOVE J, SIMON ML, GALLO RC, WONG-STAAL F: Chromosomal sublocalization of human c-*myb* and c-*fes* cellular *onc* genes. *Nature* 304:169, 1983.

333. SPURR NK, SOLOMON E, JANSSON M, SHEER DD, GOODFELLOW PN, BODMER W, VENNSTROM B: Chromosomal localisation of the human homologues to the oncogenes v-*erb*A and B. *EMBO J* 3:159, 1984.

334. PARK M, TESTA JR, BLAIR DG, PARSA NZ, VANDE WOUDE GF: Two rearranged *met* alleles in MNNG-HOS cells reveal the orientation of *met* on chromosome 7 to other markers tightly linked to the cystic fibrosis locus. *Proc Natl Acad Sci USA*, in press.

335. CAUBET J-F, MATHIEU-MAHUL D, BERHNEIM A, LARSEN C-J, BERGER R: Human proto-oncogene c-*mos* maps to 8q11. *EMBO J* 4:2245, 1985.

336. DE MARTINVILLE B, GIACALONE J, SHIH C, WEINBERG RA, FRANCKE U: Oncogene from human EJ bladder carcinoma is located on the short arm of chromosome 11. *Science* 219:498, 1983.

337. HORN TM, HUEBNER K, CROCE C, CALLAHAN R: Chromosomal locations of members of a family of novel endogenous human retroviral genomes. *J Virol* 58:955, 1986.

338. DETAISNE C, GEGONNE A, STEHELIN D, BERNHEIM A, BERGER R: Chromosomal localization of the human proto-oncogene c-*ets*. *Nature* 310:581, 1984.

339. MCBRIDE OW, SWAN DC, TRONICK SR, GOL R, KLIMANIS D, MOORE DE, AARONSON SA: Regional chromosomal location of N-*ras*, K-*ras*-1, K-*ras*-2 and *myb* oncogenes in human cells. *Nucleic Acid Res* 11:8221, 1983.

340. VAN'T VEER LJ, VAN KESSEL AG, VAN HEERIKHUIZEN H, VAN OOYEN A, NUSSE R: Molecular cloning and chromosomal assignment of the human homolog of *int*-1, a mouse gene implicated in mammary tumorigenesis. *Mol Cell Biol* 4:2532, 1984.

341. BARKER PE, RABIN M, WATSON M, BREG WR, RUDDLE FH, VERMA IM: Human c-*fos* oncogene mapped within chromosomal region 14q21-q31. *Proc Natl Acad Sci USA* 81:5826, 1984.

342. MCBRIDE OW, MERRY D, GIVOL D: The gene for human p53 cellular tumor antigen is located on chromosome 17 short arm (17p13). *Proc Natl Acad Sci USA* 83(1):130, 1986.

343. SEMBA K, YAMANASHI Y, NISHIKAWA M, SUKEGAWA J, YOSHIDA M, SASAKI M, YAMAMOTO T, TOYOSHIMA K: Location of the c-*yes* gene on the human chromosome and its expression in various tissues. *Science* 227:1038, 1985.

344. SAKAGUCHI AY, NAYLOR SL, SHOWS TB: A sequence homologous to Rous sarcoma virus v-*src* is on human chromosome 20. *Prog Nucleic Acid Res* 29:279, 1983.

345. WATSON DK, ET AL: The avian and mammalian *ets* genes: Molecular characterization, chromosome mapping and implication in human leukemia. *Anticancer Res* 6:631, 1986.

346. DALLA FAVERA R, GALLO RC, GIALLONGO A, CROCE CM: Chromosomal localization of the human homolog (c-*sis*) of the simian sarcoma virus *onc* gene. *Science* 218:686, 1982.

347. NEIL JC, HUGHES D, MCFARLANE R, WILKIE NM: Transduction and rearrangement of the *myc* gene by feline leukaemia virus in naturally occurring T-cell leukaemias. *Nature* 308:814, 1984.

348. SCHEN-ONG GLC, MORSE HC III, POTTER M, MUSHINSKI JF: Two modes of c-*myb* activation in virus-induced mouse myeloid tumors. *Mol Cell Biol* 6:380, 1986.

349. SILVER J, KOZAK C: Common proviral integration region on mouse chromosome in lymphomas and myelogenous leukemias induced by Friend murine leukemia virus. *J Virol* 57:526, 1986.

350. CANAANI E, DREAZEN O, KLAR A, RECHAVI G, RAM D, COHEN JB, GIVOL D: Activation of the c-*mos* oncogene in a mouse plasmacytoma by insertion of an endogenous intracisternal A particle genome. *Proc Natl Acad Sci USA* 80:7118, 1983.

351. VILLENEUVE L, RASSART E, JOLICOEUR P, GRAHAM M, ADAMS JM: Proviral integration site *Mis*-1 in rat thymomas corresponds to the *pvt*-1 translocation breakpoint in murine plasmacytomas. *Mol Cell Biol* 6:1834, 1986.

352. MUCENSKI ML, TAYLOR BA, IHLE JN, HARLEY JW, MORSE HC, JENKINS NA, COPELAND NG: Identification of a common ecotropic viral integration site, *Evi*-1, in the DNA of AKXD murine myeloid tumors. *Mol Cell Biol* 8:301, 1988.

353. BUCHBERG AM, BEDIGIAN HG, TAYLOR BA, BROWNELL E, IHLE JN, NATAGA S, JENKINS N, COPELAND NG: Localization of Evi-2 to Chromosome 11: Linkage to other proto-oncogene and growth factor loci using interspecific backcross mice. *Oncogene Res* 2:149, 1988.

354. ERIKSON J, FINAN J, NOWELL PC, CROCE CM: Translocation of immunoglobulin VH genes in Burkitt lymphoma. *Proc Natl Acad Sci USA* 79:5611, 1982.

355. LENOIR GM, PREUD'HOMME JL, BERNHEIM A, BERGER R: Correlation between immunoglobin light chain expression and variant translocation in Burkitt's lymphoma. *Nature* 298:474, 1982.

356. SANDBERG A, KOHNO S, WAKE N, MINOWADA N: Chromosome and causation of human cancer and leukemia. XLII. *Cancer Genet Cytogenet* 2:145, 1980.

357. HUNTER T: The epidermal growth factor receptor gene and its product. *Nature* 311:414, 1984.

CHAPTER 6

GENETIC MARKERS IN MEDICINE: DNA Sequence Variants in the Human Population Reveal Genetic Basis for Metabolic Variation

RAY WHITE
JEAN MARC LALOUEL

1. *The primary linkage map of the human genome, now more than 90 percent covered by polymorphic DNA markers, provides a way to investigate defective genes when the biochemical defect deriving from the mutation is not known. Genetic linkage between a marker and a defective locus segregating in a family can localize the mutation to a narrow chromosomal region, a first step toward isolating and cloning of the gene; markers that segregate with a disease phenotype also serve to diagnose prenatal and preclinical risk status within affected families.*
2. *DNA markers for the genetic map must be polymorphic; that is, they must exist in two or more alleles within the population. To be fully informative in a family linkage study, they must be present as two different alleles at the marker locus in each parent. A new class of markers, called VNTRs, is defining an increasing number of highly polymorphic loci for the map: a VNTR reflects a variable number of tandem repeats of an oligonucleotide sequence at a locus, and 20 or more alleles of some VNTRs have been found in population samples.*
3. *As the number of markers available for mapping has increased, so have the statistical demands of linkage analysis. Methods and computer programs have been designed to analyze several loci jointly, to order them on the map, and, when a genetic defect is localized within a linkage group, to refine the position of the mutant gene on the chromosome. Tightly linked markers can localize a gene to within a region comprising perhaps 1 to 3 million base pairs, a range amenable to techniques for moving physically closer to the gene and for ultimately isolating it. Cloned genes make it possible to identify defects at the molecular level and to devise therapeutic strategies.*

Linkage studies with genetic markers based on variations in DNA sequence can now map very precisely the mutant genes that cause human disease. The mapping information provides a basis for the creation of diagnostic tools to define the genotypes of individuals and to identify and clone defective genes. The recent cloning of genes responsible for Duchenne muscular dystrophy, chronic granulomatous disease, and retinoblastoma[1–3] provides a paradigm. The linkage strategy, which does not require biochemical knowledge of the gene product, allows us to approach directly the genetics and molecular biology of the thousands of Mendelian conditions that have been characterized in human families.[4]

The cloned gene is a powerful probe into a metabolic pathway. Used as a hybridization probe, it can determine whether messenger RNA is expressed in specific cells of interest, even in tissue slices. This approach, coupled with *in situ* hybridization to the tissue at different times in development, can determine the time of expression and the type of cell expressing the gene. Of equal interest, the cloned DNA segment can be sequenced to provide, after translation, the amino acid sequence of the encoded protein. Given this information, we can construct synthetic peptides and raise antibodies capable of revealing the location of the mature protein in cells and tissues.

A cloned gene also permits accurate diagnosis of the presence of a mutant allele. At its most refined, the DNA sequence of the cloned gene serves as the basis for the determination of the very mutational lesions at specific loci. For example, the mutant allele of the β-globin gene that is responsible for sickle cell anemia can be directly assayed by its effect on an *Mst*II restriction site. Sickle cell anemia represents a particularly straightforward example because it is always caused by a mutation at the same location. This circumstance may not be unique; both α_1-antitrypsin deficiency and cystic fibrosis probably each have a single mutational origin. But where the specific lesions are not known or are diverse, diagnosis can sometimes be accomplished by linkage analysis in a family context: the chromosomal region harboring the mutant gene at the origin of a Mendelian disease can be identified by correlating in affected families the distribution of individual phenotypes with the segregation of genetic markers embedded within the DNA sequence of the region. The closer the two genetic loci, the greater is the likelihood of the chromosome segment they define being transmitted without genetic recombination.

THE HUMAN GENETIC MAP

DNA Markers for the Map

For the linkage strategy to be effective in marking the sites of genetic defects, many markers must be available throughout the genome. A large collection of genetic markers, based on detection of common variants in DNA sequence within human populations, has been developed only recently. Although the DNA sequences of homologous regions of homologous chromosomes are almost identical, normal variation does exist. Many of the variant loci are detectable with a combination of restriction enzymes and recombinant DNA probes. The probe sequence defines the locus, and the enzyme—a bacterial endonuclease that recognizes and cleaves a specific sequence of bases—detects the polymorphism.

One detects common population variants by comparing the DNA from several individuals, using the method of Southern[5] to reveal the pattern of specific DNA fragments. A change in DNA sequence that affects a restriction site for a given enzyme will alter the length of the DNA fragment produced by enzymatic cleavage. Variation in the fragment pattern at a probed locus among the individuals in the test set, therefore, signals the presence of a DNA sequence polymorphism. The inheritance of either the presence or absence of the restriction site can thus be followed, and either form can be detected in the presence of the other. This type of polymorphism creates a codominant genetic marker.

Thousands of loci have now been screened for associated DNA sequence polymorphisms, and hundreds of DNA sequence variants have been identified.[6] The great majority seem to reflect small changes: a substitution of one base for another to create or destroy a restriction site (although insertions or deletions of one or a few bases often cannot be excluded). Some restriction sites seem more likely than others to be polymorphic. *Msp*I and *Taq*I recognition sites show a higher frequency of polymorphism than was first expected, apparently because the cytosine of the CpG dimer found in the recognition sequence for each of the two enzymes is methylated.[7]

Genetic markers with a high information content command a high premium in human genetics. Information content is closely related to heterozygosity, although not quite identical.[8] When an individual is homozygous for a marker, that locus cannot reveal the occurrence of recombination events in the interval it defines with another locus. Heterozygosity is a function of the number and the relative frequencies of different alleles found at the locus in the population. Because the restriction site variants described above are limited to two alleles, their maximum expected heterozygosity is 50 percent. To increase the heterozygosity observed in a population sample at such a locus, we must use a variety of enzymes to identify and score several nearby site polymorphisms. Even then, additional site polymorphisms will not always increase heterozygosity at the locus because severe allelic association, a phenomenon discussed later in this chapter, can occur among polymorphic sites that are so close together.

Fortunately, a second class of DNA sequence polymorphism exists, and it provides the basis for highly informative marker systems. This polymorphism reflects variation in the number of tandem repeats of an oligonucleotide sequence (VNTRs). Such sequences are clustered at a number of loci throughout the human genome. The repeating units found to date range in length from 14 to 70 bp; the number of repeats at each locus varies from a few copies to hundreds of copies. In fact, the first "arbitrary" human DNA polymorphism—a segment with no apparent coding function—to be reported[9] was later determined to be a VNTR locus[10]; the structural basis for the variation at VNTR loci was determined when two alleles of the insulin locus were sequenced.[11] Similarity in a core sequence of 10 to 15 bp has lately been discovered for a large set of VNTR loci.[12] This partial sequence homology provides the basis for protocols that allow us to screen genomic libraries for similar tandem repeat loci; a large proportion of such loci have turned out to be variable within sample populations. This approach has led to the systematic isolation and characterization of a large collection of VNTR loci.[13]

Construction of a Genetic Map

Early on, investigators realized that DNA markers would be more useful if they could be arrayed into linkage groups and assigned to specific chromosomes. Several considerations provide a rationale for such an effort. First, many genetic disease loci have a priori information that would suggest their location on a particular chromosome. For example, rare cytogenetic findings, such as the deletions within chromosome 13 associated with retinoblastoma[14] and the deletion within chromosome 5q that recently pointed the way for the mapping of the gene for familial polyposis coli,[15] suggest important hypotheses and demand markers from the implicated chromosomes for their testing.

Furthermore, if the markers are mapped to chromosomes, an efficient testing strategy can be devised to cover a particular region with minimal unintentional overlap. For example, it makes little sense to test both of the tightly linked markers H-*ras* and insulin in order to determine whether a gene is located in the p15 region of chromosome 11; either one will do. After an initial indication of linkage, the reciprocal becomes true: it is now valuable to know which other marker loci lie in the vicinity in order to confirm and refine the localization.

Lastly, the power to determine whether a gene is located in a particular region is significantly increased if the markers from the region can be analyzed jointly based on their known linkage relationships. Up to twice as much linkage information can be obtained by this approach, as compared to pairwise analysis.[16–18] As sample size always limits the available information in human genetics, this increment can be very important. However, because the number of possible orders of a set of loci increases as a factorial function of the number of loci, joint analysis requires powerful automated computer procedures.[18,19]

The resolving power required of the map depends on the purpose of the investigator. For primary localization of disease genes, a map with markers spaced at 20-centimorgan (cM) intervals is adequate. For gene cloning by physical methods, the map location of the disease gene must be narrowed to a few centimorgans, reflecting one to a few megabases of DNA, under the constraints of currently available technology. At present, a map of markers at this level of resolution needs to be developed in the neighborhood of any newly mapped Mendelian condition. Much greater efficiency will be possible at this stage when a high-resolution genetic map becomes available for the entire human genome.

Linkage Analysis by the Method of Maximum Likelihood

A genetic map consists of a linear order of linked loci, where the distance between adjacent loci reflects the estimated recombination frequencies. The relationship between genetic distance on the map and recombination frequency is not a simple one, however. Genetic distance reflects the frequency of occurrence of crossing-over; what is actually observed is recombination frequency, which results only from the occurrence of an odd number of crossings-over. Moreover, crossings-over may not occur independently from one another. The latter phenomenon, called interference, is usually ignored in genetic mapping as a first-order approximation. Consequently, recombination, r, relates to genetic distance, d, through a simple function introduced in 1919 by Haldane,[20] such that $r = \exp(1 - 2d)/2$ and $d = -\ln(1 - 2r)/2$.

Examination of recombination frequencies separately in the two sexes has introduced a further complication: while overall recombination is usually more frequent in females, the effect of sex appears to be highly variable from one chromosomal region to another. Moreover, while sex difference in recombination can often be summarized in terms of a constant ratio relating female to male genetic distances for a given group of linked markers, significant departures from a constant ratio have been noted in some parts of the human gene map. For example, intervals between certain markers on chromosomes 11,[21] 12,[22] and 16 (unpublished data) exhibit significantly higher recombination rates in males than in females (Fig. 6-1). It follows that sex-specific maps must be derived for each chromosome and that the sex-specific map distances characterizing various regions are likely to evolve continually as more loci are added to the map.

Estimation and Detection of Linkage. Homologous chromosomes pair at meiosis and experience reciprocal exchanges through crossing-over. Recombination between two loci can

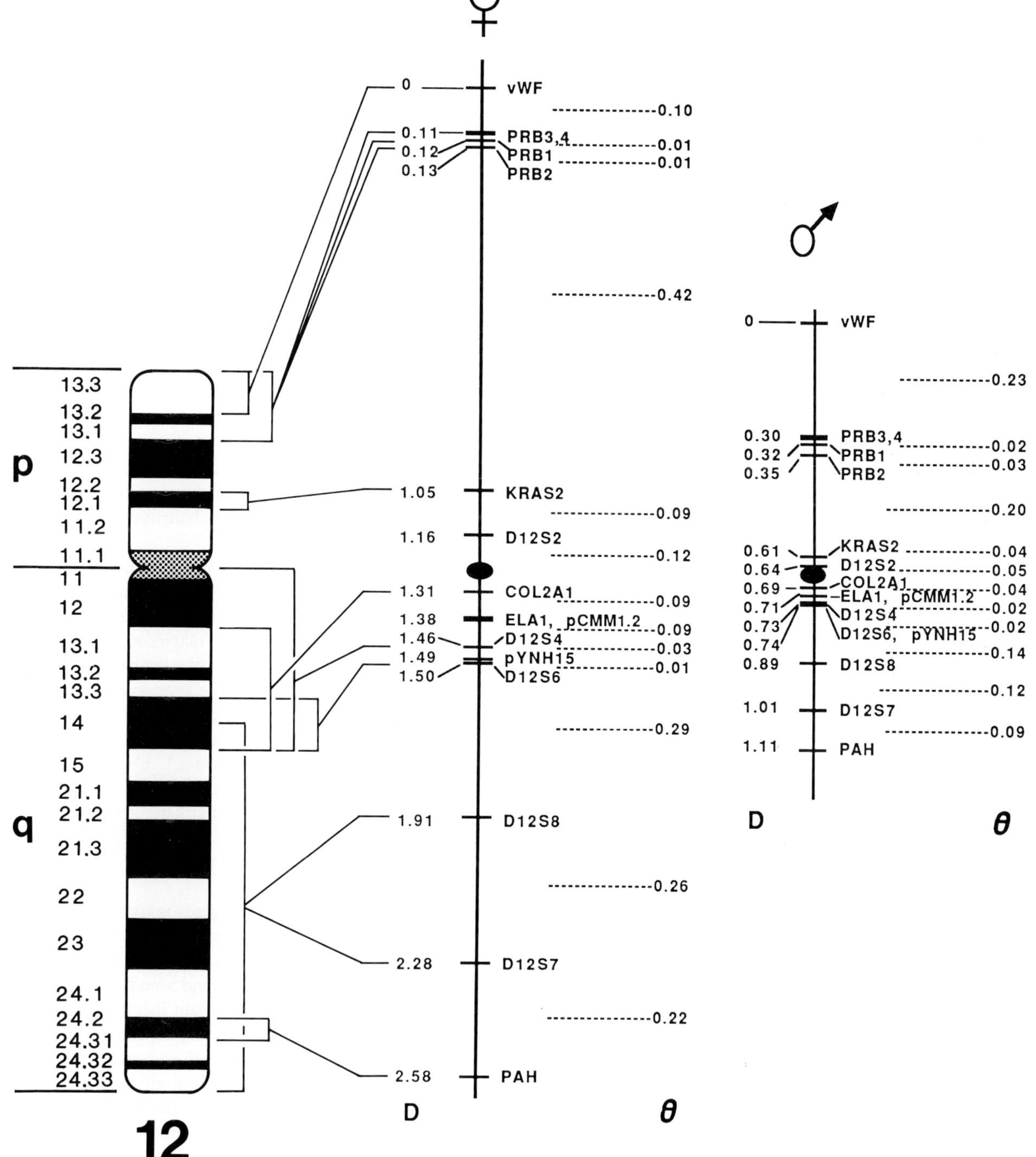

Fig. 6-1 Male and female genetic maps of chromosome 12. Recombination is more frequent in males than in females between the vWF and PRB2 loci, but female recombination rates exceed those in males over the rest of the genetic map of this chromosome. Known physical localizations are indicated by brackets on the karyogram. Genetic distance (D) is measured cumulatively in morgans from the vWF locus; Θ = recombination fraction. *(From O'Connell et al.[22] Used by permission of Academic Press.)*

be detected only when the genes at each locus present distinct allelic states. When the configuration of the alleles on the parental chromsomes, or "phase," is known, a recombination event can be detected directly in the offspring. When the phase is not known, recombination can be inferred only through a probabilistic argument. While a nuclear family may not provide phase information, additional family members may resolve phase.

The frequency of recombination between two loci can be estimated from the distribution of phenotypes or genotypes in families. Linkage is detected when recombination occurs significantly less often than the frequency of 0.5 predicted for independent segregation. Estimation of recombination rates and detection of linkage are performed by the method of maximum likelihood: the probability of the phenotypes observed at two loci is expressed as a function of the frequency of recombination between these loci, and the maximum-likelihood estimate of the recombination frequency is that value which mazimizes this probability. The odds in favor of linkage can be assessed by comparing the maximum-likelihood solution to the probability of the data when recombination is assumed to be 0.5. In linkage studies, a long-standing convention expresses such likelihood ratios on a decimal logarithmic scale; the logarithm of these odds, or LOD score, is considered significant when it exceeds the value 3.[23]

In simple situations, such probabilities can be easily derived by hand, as illustrated in Table 6-1 for a double backcross in a nuclear family. For general pedigree structures, computer programs implement recursive calculations in pedigrees; LIPED[24] was the first program available for this purpose.

Independent families or studies can be combined in one of two ways: the individual data can be combined and analyzed jointly, providing an overall estimate of recombination and a new test of linkage; alternatively, LOD scores computed at conventional predetermined values of recombination can be summed and the linkage evidence reassessed. The latter convention of reporting LOD score tables[23] allows investigators to combine published data by simple addition; they need not have access to the original data.

Modeling Inheritance. Linkage analysis of a clinical phenotype requires the definition of a genetic model that can relate genotype to phenotype. For most Mendelian conditions, this means specifying the dominance relationship between wild-type and mutant alleles and specifying also the probability that an individual be normal or affected given his or her genotype. Incomplete penetrance must often be taken into account, incorporating such effects as sex or age on clinical onset. Models of inheritance are usually obtained by formal segregation analysis or by careful characterization of familial clustering. The discovery of a linked marker corroborates the model; it may even settle controversy over the model, as in the case of idiopathic hemochromatosis.[25]

Table 6-1 Detection of Linkage in a Double Backcross, AaBb × aabb

Phase of first parent	*Prior probability*
Coupling: AB/ab	1/2
Repulsion: Ab/aB	1/2

Conditional probabilities of gametes produced by first parent

Phase	*Gametes: AB*	*Ab*	*aB*	*ab*	*Total*
Coupling	$(1 - r)/2$	$r/2$	$r/2$	$(1 - r)/2$	1
Repulsion	$r/2$	$(1 - r)/2$	$(1 - r)/2$	$r/2$	1

SOURCE: R. White and J.M. Lalouel, in *Advances in Human Genetics*, vol. 16. H. Harris and K. Hirschhorn (eds). New York: Plenum, 1987, p. 164. Reprinted by permission.

Etiologic Heterogeneity. Linked markers can also be used to resolve etiologic heterogeneity. For example, Morton[26] was able to demonstrate that the distribution of recombination events between the Rh-factor locus and the mutation causing elliptocytosis in a set of affected families departed from that expected under the assumption of a single elliptocytosis locus: an Rh-linked form appeared to account for only a subset of the families. Recently, locus heterogeneity in the X-linked form of spastic paraplegia was demonstrated when the two clinically distinct forms of the disorder were shown to be tightly linked to separate marker loci that are distant from each other on the X chromosome.[27] On the other hand, linkage tests have been able to provide support for single-locus etiology in cystic fibrosis,[28] type 1 neurofibromatosis,[29] and familial polyposis coli/Gardner syndrome.[30,31]

Two distinct statistical tests for locus heterogeneity are available, as reviewed by Ott.[32] The first of these[26] applies to instances where the data can be partitioned on the basis of predefined criteria such as family units, ethnic or geographic origin, or clinical symptoms. The second test[33] rests on the hypothesis that, for a given marker, both a linked and an unlinked form of the disease exist and the two are indistinguishable; evidence of etiologic heterogeneity involves the estimation and test of an "admixture" parameter that reflects the relative frequencies of the two forms.[34]

The power to detect etiologic heterogeneity among families by statistical tests increases with sample size and tight linkage. But etiologic heterogeneity can also occur within families, particularly for common traits or disorders. While intrafamily etiologic heterogeneity can be included in statistical modeling, it represents a much greater analytic challenge.

Recurrence Risks. We can use a genetic marker, mapped or not, to assess the probability that a particular family member has inherited a certain allele at a linked locus. Thus genetic risks can be computed by a simple extension of the logic used in linkage analysis: we can express the probability of an individual genotype as a function of the genotype inherited at the marker locus, the phenotypic observations at both loci in family members and the estimated recombination frequency, as illustrated by the example of Fig. 6-2*A*. Computer programs are available to perform such computations in general pedigrees.[24,35] When closely linked markers are available, this analysis provides an efficient diagnostic tool for inherited conditions.

Multiple Markers. Multiple linked markers afford much greater accuracy to linkage analysis and risk assessment than do simple linkages. Consider the case of two markers flanking an autosomal dominant mutation, and assume that the recombination frequency between the mutant locus and each marker is equal to r. If the chromosome carrying the mutation in the affected parent also carries allele 1 of each marker locus (Fig. 6-2*B*), the probability that a child inheriting allele 1 at both loci did not inherit the mutation is of the order r^2, for recombination would have to have occurred in both intervals defined by the three loci. When only one marker is available, however,

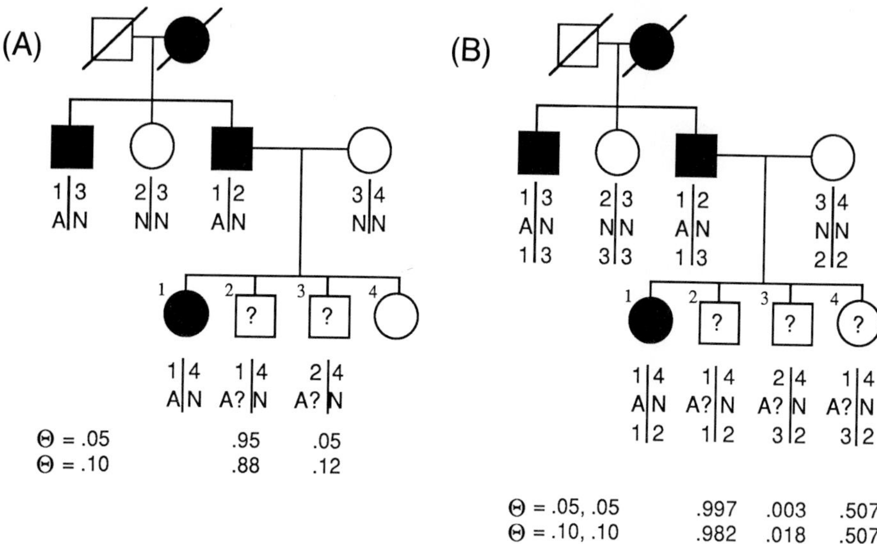

Fig. 6-2 A. Assessment of genetic risk with one linked marker, in a pedigree segregating a rare autosomal dominant condition with full penetrance. For each of two tested offspring of unknown clinical status, the probability of becoming affected has been computed for two recombination frequencies (Θ). N = normal allele, A = mutant allele. B. The probability has been computed for each of three tested offspring when flanking markers are available. The increase in precision of prospective diagnosis is evident for offspring nos. 2 and 3. Note, however, that when the markers are equidistant from the "A" locus, a recombination event between the markers (as has occurred in offspring no. 4) renders genetic testing inconclusive.

the corresponding probability is only of order r. The accuracy of diagnosis is therefore significantly enhanced by flanking markers. In general, because of the limited heterozygosity available at linked loci, several markers may have to be tested before the optimal situation is achieved.

Reference Panel for Genotyping of Marker Loci

While estimates of recombination frequencies between all pairs of loci in a linkage group reflect their linear order, much of the information on gene order is discarded when simultaneous occurrence of crossing over in distinct intervals is ignored.[16,17,36] This means that genotypes at these loci must be characterized on the same reference set of families. Families containing parents, grandparents, and large sibships provide an optimal structure for this purpose.[21]

To provide access by investigators interested in contributing to a linkage map of the human genome to a common set of families of ideal structure, Jean Dausset has established in Paris the Centre d'Etude du Polymorphisme Humain (CEPH). The CEPH distributes DNA samples from 40 families, including 27 Utah families,[21] to collaborators willing to return to the CEPH data base the primary genotypic information from markers that they characterize. The collaborators also have access to the current data base of genotypes that characterizes the families. The CEPH collaboration thus paves the way for combination of mapping data that have been obtained independently in many collaborating laboratories; maps of markers characterized on the reference panel will continue to be updated and published.

Complementary Mapping Strategies

Apart from linkage analysis, information on the relative order of markers and genes on a chromosome can be obtained from each of several independent approaches to locating the position of genes within the genome. For example, the radiolabeled DNA probe that defines a genetic marker used in a linkage study can also be hybridized directly to metaphase chromosomes. The location of specific hybridization is noted in relation to the banding pattern of the chromosome. Although radioactive grains are usually scattered throughout the metaphase spread, a concentration of grains can permit assignment of the probe's locus to a specific chromosome band, if not a subband.

A second approach to localization of a marker segment or a gene to and within a chromosome takes advantage of somatic cell hybrids that contain only one or a few human chromosomes in a rodent background. By hybridizing the probe defining a marker locus to a small panel of such hybrids, one can correlate the marker locus with the presence or absence of a specific chromosome.[37] Higher-resolution physical maps can be obtained when somatic cell hybrids contain human chromosomes with deletions or translocations. With a panel of deletions, for example, the order of marker loci can be determined with good resolution.[38]

Status of the Human Genetic Map

The complete definition of a genetic map should consist of the order of the loci (including the odds in favor of the reported order with respect to other possible orders, to document the degree of confidence that can be associated with each segment of the map) and the sex-specific recombination estimates for each interval. Because reliability of a genetic map is a function of sample size, it should always be kept in mind that any recombination estimate has an associated statistical error.

A typical example of a primary human genetic map, indicating physical localizations obtained by techniques such as those just described, is shown in Fig. 6-3. Evidence for linkage is complete across the map; the odds supporting continuity of the linkage group are better than 1000:1 for each interval. The most critical parameter for a genetic map is the support provided by the data for the order of the loci; the most relevant measure of the support for order is the relative likelihood of the most likely order with respect to the several next most likely orders. As the figure shows, none of the several next most likely orders for markers on chromosome 10 is within 100:1 odds of the most likely; confidence is good that the most likely order is indeed the correct one. Analysis of the sex-specific recombination frequencies did not provide significant support for heterogeneity among various intervals in the ratio of female map distances to male map distances on this

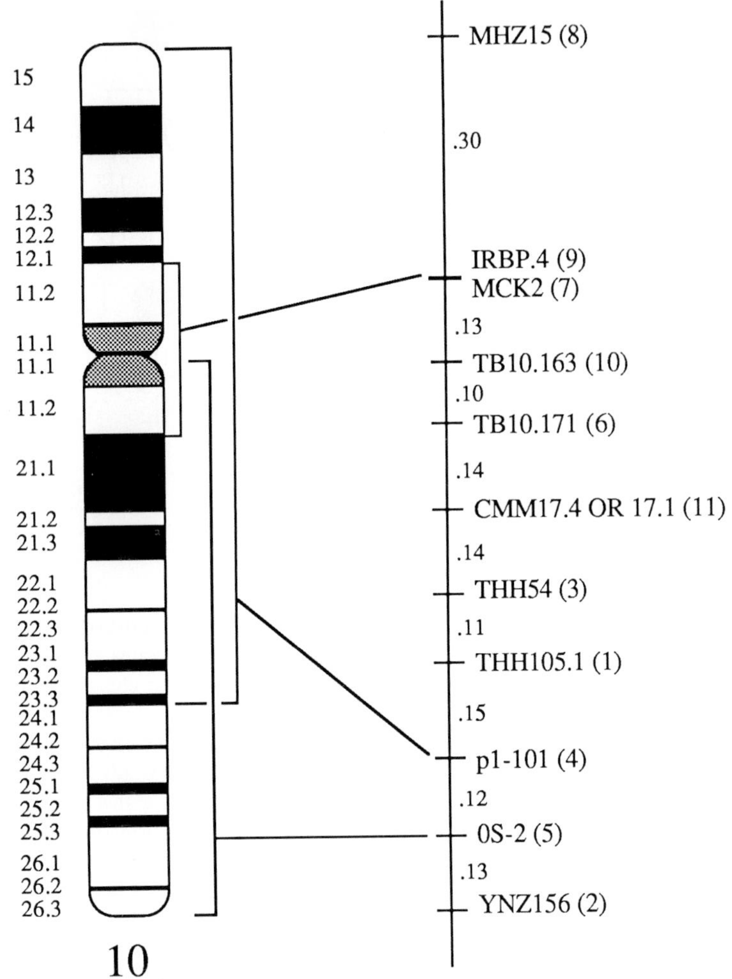

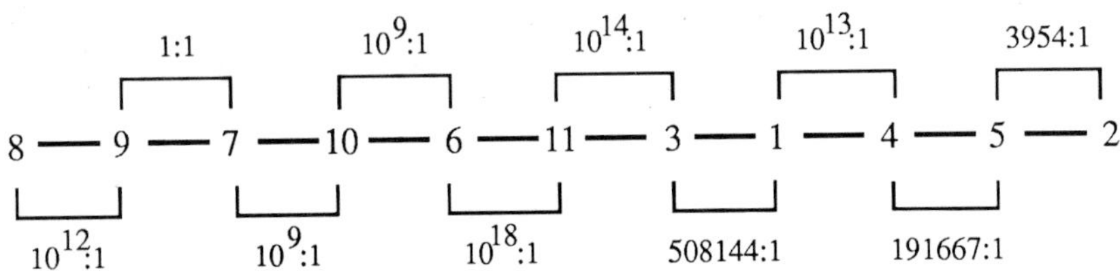

Fig. 6-3 Primary genetic map of chromosome 10 in females, with physical locations indicated for selected markers. Scale is in genetic distance (morgans); recombination fractions for female meioses are indicated between markers. Odds against the permutation of adjacent loci in the map of chromosome 10 are shown at the bottom. *(From Lathrop et al.[39] Used by permission of Academic Press.)*

chromosome; therefore, a constant ratio over the entire chromosome (a single linkage group) was applied in generating the female genetic map shown here.[39]

Given a particular order for the marker loci, we should also have some measure of the quantitative uncertainty in map location for each of the markers, i.e., a measure of expected variation in the estimates of recombination frequency. The statistical difficulties are not trivial, but we can obtain a useful impression of the uncertainty in map location for each marker by calculating the relative likelihood for the location of the marker within its assigned interval between two other markers. The results of these calculations for chromosome 10 are represented in Fig. 6-4 by the horizontal bars above each marker locus. The ends of the bars represent the map location for which the likelihood of location of the marker locus falls tenfold below the maximum.

An important feature of the chromosome 10 map is that the average recombination frequency between each adjacent pair of marker loci is no more than 30 percent. This means the maximum distance between a disease locus on this chromosome and an adjacent marker would be <15 percent; a figure that virtually ensures its "capture" by the detection of linkage. Because we have no markers for the telomeres of human chromosomes, however, it is not possible to determine the linkage distance between the most distal markers and the ends of the chromosome arms.

The construction of primary genetic maps of markers for the remainder of the chromosomes is very close to completion. Genetic maps of chromosomes 7, 12, 13, and X have been published.[22,40,40a,41] Preliminary maps of markers covering each of the human chromosomes were presented at the 1987 Human Gene Mapping Workshop.[6] An interim summary of linkage maps has also been published, combining data from published chromosome maps with new data developed on a subset of the CEPH families.[42]

Physical and genetic mapping data relevant to the now vast

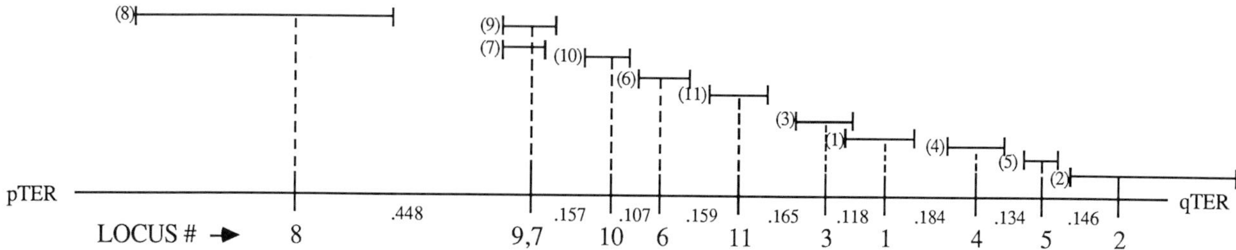

Fig. 6-4 Genetic distance (in morgans) between markers on the female map of chromosome 10, with confidence limits for placement of each locus. Locus numbers are identified in Fig. 6-3. *(From Lathrop et al.*[39] *Used by permission of Academic Press.)*

number of available genetic markers are available to the scientific community through the Human Gene Mapping Library maintained by a group of scientists at Yale University. This computer data base, which can be accessed remotely, is connected with the Catalog of Mendelian Inheritance in Man that is maintained in Baltimore by Victor McKusick and his collaborators at Johns Hopkins University. The collection of marker loci now available should make it possible to map virtually any human genetic disease for which adequate family materials are available. The specific family requirements will vary depending on the nature of the genetic disease, e.g., its penetrance, whether it is recessive or dominant, and whether it is subject to locus heterogeneity. But a kindred segregating a fully penetrant autosomal dominant disease will usually provide sufficient evidence to support linkage of a fully informative genetic marker system.

MAPPING DELETERIOUS MUTATIONS

Prior to 1980, a number of inherited disorders were localized to chromosomes either by physical mapping methods or by linkage analysis with classic protein polymorphisms.[4] Since then, identification of many arbitrary DNA markers has permitted other inherited conditions of unknown etiology to be mapped by genetic linkage. Foremost among them are Duchenne muscular dystrophy on chromosome X,[43] Huntington's disease on 4,[44] cystic fibrosis on 7,[45–47] polycystic kidney disease on 16,[48] type 1 (peripheral) neurofibromatosis on 17,[29,49] type 2 (central) neurofibromatosis on 22,[50] multiple endocrine neoplasia type IIa on 10,[51,52] and familial multiple polyposis on 5.[30,31] Linkage has also been reported for familial Alzheimer's disease on 21[53] and for a form of major depression on 11 in an Amish pedigree.[54] However, as chromosome 11 markers have been found to be unlinked to affective illness in other pedigrees, heterogeneity in the genetic component of mental depression is indicated.

Progress toward the identification of the genes and the elucidation of the pathophysiology of the conditions listed above is at various stages. The gene that is altered in Duchenne muscular dystrophy has been isolated,[1] as described in Chap. 118. On the other hand, the Huntington's disease gene at the tip of the short arm of chromosome 4 has so far resisted efforts to identify a flanking marker. Once cystic fibrosis (CF) was precisely mapped to a short segment of chromosome 7 by genetic linkage, closer DNA sequences were cloned; the new markers exhibit strong linkage disequilibrium with the CF mutation,[55] and this high degree of linkage disequilibrium has provided good support for the hypothesis that all or most cases of cystic fibrosis result from mutation at the same locus. Several research groups are cloning DNA sequences in the vicinity of the CF-linked markers. A by-product of the search for deleterious genes is the characterization of genetic markers that can have immediate relevance for clinical diagnosis.

Application of Genetic Maps of Markers to the Localization of Mutant Genes

With the almost complete coverage of the human genome afforded by the present set of markers, genetic mapping of inherited conditions is likely to progress rapidly. The genetic maps permit two significant improvements in disease-mapping strategy. The first is that the maps allow the definition of a primary set of optimally spaced markers that will effectively scan each chromosome to detect linkage. As each chromosome is now investigated in turn with an efficient marker set, the full power of multilocus linkage analysis can be brought to bear. The "home" of a locus within the genetic map can be determined by the method of location scores,[18] where the placement of the new locus is varied along the current genetic map and maximum-likelihood estimates are made at each position.

Once a genetic locus of unknown molecular character has been assigned an approximate location in the primary map, a more precise localization can be sought with additional markers from within the region. If such markers are already mapped, they can be tested directly and most efficiently by scoring them in the meioses within a sample set of affected families that are known to be recombinant in the region. The precision of this final linkage localization of a disease gene depends heavily on the family resources available and on the quality and number of additional markers from the region.

If the additional markers available from the known maps are not sufficient, new polymorphic markers can be developed from clone libraries of chromosomal subsegments that have been transferred into somatic cell hybrids. The primary identifying markers become key in characterizing the somatic cell hybrids. The further characterization of close markers, whether those markers come from a high-resolution map or are newly cloned from the candidate genomic region, will narrow the localization of the target gene to a region of such reduced complexity that it will become amenable to molecular cloning.

The degree of resolution inherent in linkage analysis should permit localization of a gene to within a few million base pairs, a region likely to contain fewer than a dozen genes that will be expressed within a particular target tissue. Genomic clones from the region can be used to identify candidate cDNA clones. The candidates must, of course, be tested then to determine which is actually the disease gene. The methods for such a determination will likely vary considerably from one biologic system to the next; for the few genes that have so far been cloned following receipt of location information, observations that physically delimit the location of the gene—chromosomal rearrangements, deletions, or translocations—have been especially helpful. In the absence of such hallmarks or of a biologic test for the gene product, sequencing of large numbers of mutant and normal alleles of each of the candidates may be required.

Linkage with Candidate Genes

Knowledge about the pathophysiology of a disease may suggest to us that mutation in a known gene may be responsible for the disorder. Linkage analysis can be an efficient way to test such a hypothesis. Polymorphic restriction sites within or adjacent to the candidate locus can transform the locus into a genetic marker whose alleles can be followed in family studies. Because the polymorphic sites are very close to the mutation responsible for the disease, recombination events are very unlikely; the finding of one or two obligate recombinants in a data set of families segregating the disorder can rigorously eliminate the candidate gene from further consideration.

Such a test was used early on to examine whether Gardner syndrome, a colon polyposis disease, was caused by inherited mutation in either the Kirsten-*ras* or Harvey-*ras* oncogenes[56]; both were known to be involved in the somatic events that lead to colon cancer. When multiple recombinants were found between the disease gene and each of the *ras* loci, it was apparent that no inherited alleles in either gene were causing the syndrome (Fig. 6-5). On the other hand, when the low-density lipoprotein (LDL) receptor was investigated as a candidate for causing the high LDL cholesterol levels observed in a specific family,[57] perfect correspondence was evident between the high cholesterol concentrations in blood and the inheritance of a particular allele at the LDL receptor locus; the linkage findings provided strong support for the etiologic role of defective LDL receptor in that family's anomalous lipid profile (Fig. 6-6).

Allelic Associations

The distribution of alleles at two distinct loci may depart from that expected under the assumption of independence, as a consequence of linkage disequilibrium. Consider the occurrence of a new mutation that creates allele A1 at locus A, on a chromosome carrying allele B1 at locus B. Initially, individuals presenting A1 will also carry allele B1 on that chromosome. With each passing generation, this allelic association, or haplotype (A1-B1), will decay as a function of frequency of recombination events occurring between the two loci. Depending on evolutionary time and recombination frequency, significant linkage disequilibrium may be observed between the loci. Confounding factors, however—recent admixture or population stratification in particular—can lead to allelic associations which do not arise from linkage disequilibrium.

Linkage disequilibrium can be expected for Mendelian conditions of recent origin involving only one or a few initial mutations. When a candidate locus can be postulated, such associations are usually sought by contrasting allelic frequencies in cases and controls. HLA and disease associations constitute a paradigm of this approach (see Chap. 4); in congenital adrenal hyperplasia (Chap. 74) and diabetes mellitus (Chap. 10), associations at the HLA gene complex have clarified etiology. By contrast, allelic associations, sometimes involving extended haplotypes, have been documented for loci causing thalassemias (Chap. 93), or phenylketonuria (Chap. 15). Tight linkage of several markers with cystic fibrosis is corroborated by significant allelic associations.[28,55] Recent studies reporting associations between polymorphisms at the apolipoprotein (apo) AI[58–60] and apo B loci[61] in coronary patients may incriminate these genes in the etiology of coronary heart disease. The latter results should be interpreted cautiously before concluding that mutations at apolipoprotein gene loci are risk factors in atherosclerosis; they may be significant in only a subset of the patients. Moreover, the allelic associations may be attributable to an unrecognized and therefore uncontrolled difference between cases and controls with respect to ethnic origin.

Fig. 6-5 Alleles of the *TaqI* polymorphisms at the *Kras2* and *Hras1* loci in individuals from an informative portion of a kindred segregating a gene for Gardner syndrome (shaded symbols represent affected individuals). The high frequency of recombination events is inconsistent with the occurrence of the Gardner mutation at the locus of either of these two oncogenes. *(Adapted from Barker et al.[56] Used by permission of Academic Press Ltd., London.)*

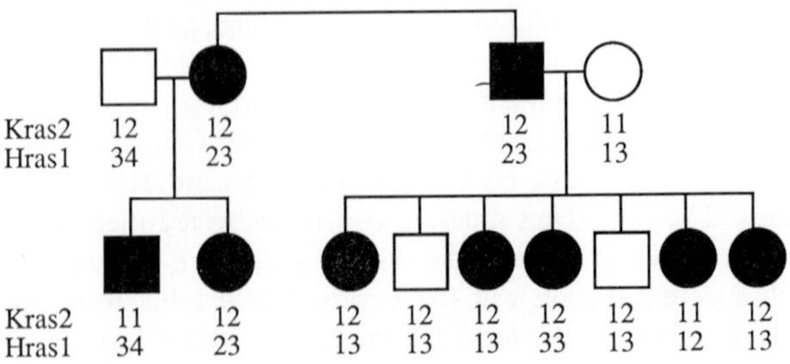

DIAGNOSIS OF GENETIC DISEASE

Genetic maps that mark mutant alleles, combined with DNA probes that reveal the genotypes of individuals, add powerful new diagnostic tools to the physician's arsenal. It is now possible to determine whether individuals at risk of genetic disease actually carry a mutant allele. These diagnoses can be carried out at very early stages, well in advance of symptoms and even prenatally in many cases. Prenatal diagnosis of the presence of a mutant gene that will likely cause a serious genetic disorder can serve as the basis for a decision as to whether to continue a pregnancy; often prospective parents would like very much to undertake or to continue a pregnancy if the risk of delivering a child with a serious genetic disease can be significantly reduced. The diagnostic tests fall into two distinct categories, with quite different properties: those based on direct detection of the mutation and those based on observation of linkage within a family setting.

Cloned Genes: Identification of Specific Mutations

Direct detection of a mutation is straightforward and represents a goal for development of diagnostic tests; diagnosis of the sickle globin allele of the β-globin locus offers a paradigm. The mutation to sickle globin is the result of an adenine-to-thymine transition that leads to a glutamic acid-to-valine amino acid change in the protein. The HbS mutant allele can be detected by digestion with restriction enzymes; the DNA change eliminates an *Mst*II site, thus changing the length of a

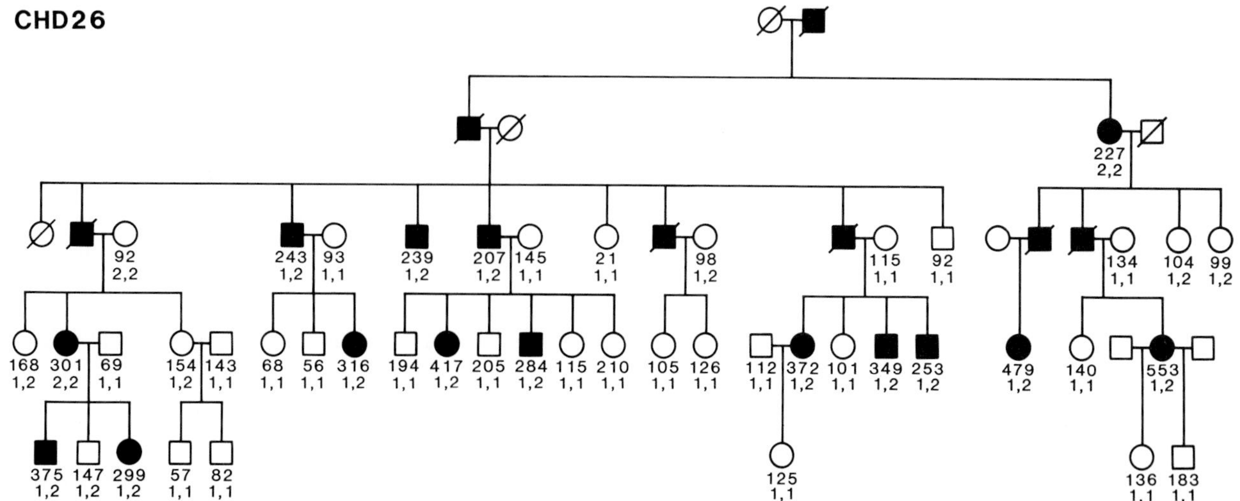

Fig. 6-6 Abbreviated pedigree of a family with dominantly inherited hypercholesterolemia and a high incidence of early myocardial infarction. The first number under each symbol represents the age- and sex-adjusted LDL cholesterol value for that individual; the second set of numbers represents the genotype at the LDL receptor locus. Affected status is designated on the pedigree as shaded symbols; for each individual, affection status was assigned by taking into account his and her relatives' LDL cholesterol levels under the assumption of autosomal dominant inheritance. The distribution of LDL cholesterol levels in this pedigree suggests a bimodality consistent with a significant genetic component. *(From Leppert et al.[57] Used by permission of The American Society of Human Genetics.)*

restriction fragment from ≈1 to ≈1.35 kb. Alternatively, the mutation can be revealed by hybridization of the DNA sample to oligonucleotide probes that are only 17 to 20 bp long. The melting temperature of the double-stranded DNA is highly sensitive to the presence of base-pair mismatches (illustrated in Fig. 6-7); probes that have hybridized with a mismatch can be melted off at a temperature several degrees lower than the temperature required to denature a perfectly paired DNA sequence. Probe oligonucleotides based on the normal and mutant sequences can determine unequivocally the genotype of an individual.[62]

At present, only a few genetic defects can be detected as directly as sickle cell anemia at the molecular level, because the DNA sequences of the mutant and the normal alleles must first be known. α_1-Antitrypsin deficiency is one such disease.[63] In this case, however, the mutation does not affect a restriction site, and oligonucleotide probes are required for detection of sequence mismatches.

The number of disorders for which such tests are available should increase dramatically over the next decade. The rapid changes taking place mean that data banks such as the Yale system will be the best way for clinicians to keep abreast of new developments for diagnosis of any particular genetic disease.

Linked Markers in Affected Families

Often the specific mutation that is segregating within a family will not be recognized, or a large variety of different mutations may exist in the gene, too many to seek individually. More likely, however, the spectrum of mutations will simply not be known. It is possible nevertheless to determine whether certain individuals in a family that is segregating a disease have indeed inherited the mutant allele, by linkage analysis of tightly linked markers in that family. These can be arbitrary markers within a few percent recombination or variants at the disease locus itself, that are detected with the cloned gene as probe (the variants are not necessarily the disease-causing mu-

Fig. 6-7 Detection of a single-base-pair substitution with two oligonucleotide probes, on schematic Southern blots. Probe 1 is an oligonucleotide constructed with an A for C substitution, and under stringent thermal conditions it will detect a single mutation (G→T) in a complementary DNA sequence: the probe will hybridize to the mutant (m) DNA, but base-pair mismatch will prevent hybridization between the A-substituted probe and the normal DNA sequence. Probe 2 is the corresponding normal oligonucleotide sequence, which hybridizes to wild-type DNA; a mutation at a single site (T substituted for G in this example) will result in a mismatch that prevents hybridization between the probe and the mutant DNA. In both cases, carrier status for the mutant (heterozygosity) can be detected also, as a band with half the intensity of the homozygote band. *(From White and Lalouel, in* Advances in Human Genetics, *vol. 16. H. Harris and K. Hirschhorn (eds). New York: Plenum, 1987, p. 132. Used by permission.)*

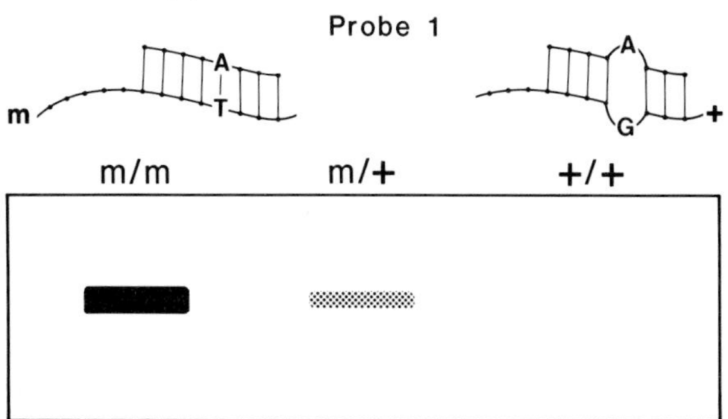

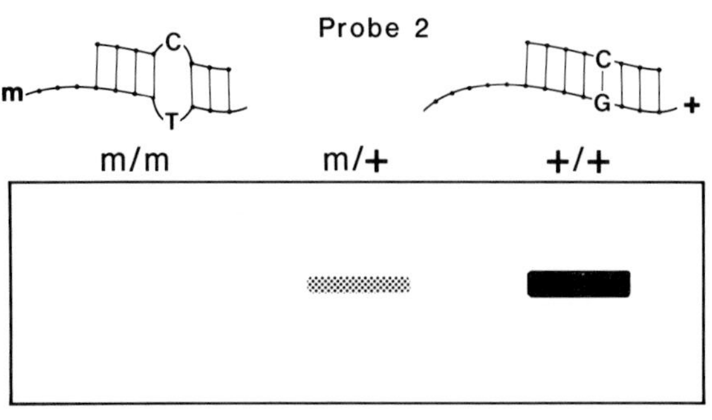

tation). Diagnostic tests of this gene should be available for any disease gene shortly after discovery of its linkage to a DNA marker.

Common Disease and Complex Inheritance

Because many common disorders exhibit familial aggregation, genetic factors are suspected in their etiology. Mental illnesses such as schizophrenia and manic-depression, breast or colon cancers, coronary heart disease and essential hypertension, and diabetes mellitus have been subjected to intense genetic scrutiny and remain a challenge. Because they do not exhibit clear-cut Mendelian ratios, a single-gene interpretation would require the assumption of a very low penetrance. Multiple factors may be at play, whether genetic or environmental, and the latter may themselves account for a significant part of the noted familial aggregation.

Models have been proposed which subsume Mendelian as well as multifactorial transmission.[64–66] Because clinical definition may rest on the measurement of a continuous variable, such as blood pressure or glucose tolerance, classic Mendelian genetics and quantitative, or biometrical, genetics have been reconciled to describe discrete as well as continuous phenotypes.

Nevertheless, the challenge persists for several reasons. Late onset may defy the study of vertical transmission under controlled conditions. Clinical delineation, which lacks specificity, may lead to the confusion of multiple distinct etiologies. The interplay between major genetic susceptibility and a variety of precipitating factors may result in variable clinical presentation. When biologic parameters can be investigated, they may be so removed from the initial metabolic disturbance that the major cause may not be identified. With those caveats in mind, it remains conceivable that progress in understanding the metabolic pathways involved, and the isolation of genes coding for critical products in such pathways, will lead to identification of well defined genetic conditions that account for some complex disorders.

GENETIC STUDY OF METABOLIC VARIANTS

The principle of linkage analysis extends to investigations of human metabolic variants. With an abundance of genetic markers in hand, individuals of similar genotype can be identified within families and characterized with respect to specific metabolic characteristics. Furthermore, if a genetic basis for the variation can be confirmed, a new role for the genetic markers comes into play, as variations in the cloned gene become a window into the complex metabolic pathway.

Genetic Basis of Variation in Human Metabolism

Sometimes we know that a variation in metabolic function observed from one individual to the next can be attributed to the inheritance of variant alleles at specific genetic loci. For example, with a well known disease such as Lesch-Nyhan syndrome, symptoms are attributable to an individual having inherited a mutant and defective gene for hypoxanthine phosphoribosyltransferase (HPRT). In other cases, it can be difficult to determine whether the variation should be attributed to variant genes or whether other factors are primarily responsible. It would be helpful if we could define a population of individuals, all of whom carry the variant gene. If the characteristic were genetically encoded in such a population, we would expect to see a relatively homogeneous representation of the variant phenotype. The problem with human populations is to identify individuals of like genotype. Within families, however, one can sometimes identify individuals of like genotype at specific loci, using linked genetic markers.

GENETIC MAPPING AND THE FUTURE

Family-Based Medicine

One consequence of our increasing knowledge about the medical implications of genetic inheritance must be a greater attention on the part of the physician to a family's history of potentially heritable disorders and predispositions. Knowledge of health risks that are increased for certain individuals as a consequence of genetic inheritance should greatly aid the physician in counseling patients with respect to modification of lifestyle or preventive therapy; specific differential diagnoses may even be possible. A corollary of some interest is whether families should routinely freeze DNA samples for storage as a kind of insurance with respect to future genetic diagnoses.

Ethical Questions

A second apparent consequence of our increasing ability to discern risk factors in specific individuals is that institutions may choose to screen people for those factors. Executives being considered for key positions might be expected to submit to the construction of genetic profiles. Persons applying for insurance will surely have new eligibility requirements thrust upon them unless specific legislation is passed forbidding the use of genetic data as criteria of insurability. These possibilities raise serious questions of individual privacy, that is, the rights of individuals to know but not to reveal their genotype.

On the other hand, what rights might one individual have with respect to knowledge of another's genotype? For example, an individual at risk for Huntington's disease might want to determine whether he or she in fact carries the HD gene; this knowledge might be conditional on whether some other family member might also carry the gene. The other family member, however, not wanting to possess such information, may refuse testing. In another context, the possibility of genetic testing as part of the marriage contract has also emerged; it would not be unreasonable for the prospective partners to each wish to be reassured that the other partner is not bringing to the marriage some hidden genetic liability. The ethical considerations connected with genetic information promise a rich field for study and discussion.

None of these considerations should seriously detract from the ultimate promise of the new genetics. Every prospect is that we can safely take full advantage of the multiplicity of research opportunities offered by the availability of human mutations for analysis. The insights that these mutants offer into various complex metabolic pathways, ranging from risk status for cardiovascular disease to genetic errors causing psychiatric disorders, will provide an ongoing revelation of basic mechanisms in human metabolism.

REFERENCES

1. MONACO A, NEVE R, COLLETTI-FEENER C, BERTELSON C, KURNIT D, KUNKEL L: Isolation of candidate cDNAs for portions of the Duchenne muscular dystrophy gene. *Nature* 323:646, 1986.
2. ROYER-POKORA B, KUNKEL L, MONACO A, GOFF S, NEWBURGER P, BAEHNER R, COLE F, CURNUTTE J, ORKIN S: Cloning the gene for an inherited human disorder—chronic granulomatous disease—on the basis of its chromosomal location. *Nature* 322:32, 1986.
3. FRIEND S, BERNARDS R, ROGELJ S, WEINBERG R, RAPAPORT J, ALBERT D, DRYJA T: A human DNA segment with properties of the gene that predisposes to retinoblastoma and osteosarcoma. *Nature* 323:643, 1986.
4. McKUSICK V: *Mendelian Inheritance in Man: Catalogs of Autosomal Dominant, Autosomal Recessive, and X-linked Phenotypes,* 7th ed. Baltimore, Johns Hopkins University Press, 1986.
5. SOUTHERN E: Detection of specific sequences among DNA fragments separated by gel electrophoresis. *J Mol Biol* 98:503, 1975.
6. Human Gene Mapping 9 Workshop, Paris, September 1987. *Cytogenet Cell Genet (Suppl),* in press.
7. BARKER D, SCHAFER M, WHITE R: Restriction sites containing CpG show a higher frequency of polymorphism in human DNA. *Cell* 36:131, 1984.
8. BOTSTEIN D, WHITE R, SKOLNICK M, DAVIS R: Construction of a genetic linkage map in man using restriction fragment length polymorphisms. *Am J Hum Genet* 32:314, 1980.
9. WYMAN A, WHITE R: A highly polymorphic locus in human DNA. *Proc Natl Acad Sci USA* 77:6754, 1980.
10. WYMAN A, MULHOLLAND J, BOTSTEIN D: Oligonucleotide repeats involved in the highly polymorphic locus D14S1. *Am J Hum Genet* 39*(Suppl)*:A226, 1986.
11. ULLRICH A, DULL T, GRAY A: Genetic variation in the human insulin gene. *Science* 209:612, 1980.
12. JEFFREYS AJ, WILSON V, THEIN SL: Hypervariable "minisatellite" regions in human DNA. *Nature* 314:67, 1985.
13. NAKAMURA Y, LEPPERT M, O'CONNELL P, WOLFF R, HOLM T, CULVER M, MARTIN C, FUJIMOTO E, HOFF M, KUMLIN E, WHITE R: Variable number of tandem repeat (VNTR) markers for human gene mapping. *Science* 235:1616, 1987.
14. SPARKES R, SPARKES M, WILSON M, TOWNER J, BENEDICT W, MURPHREE A, YUNIS J: Regional assignment of genes for human esterase D and retinoblastoma to chromosome band 13q14. *Science* 208:1042, 1980.
15. HERRERA L, KAKATI S, GIBAS L, PIETRZAK E, SANDBERG A: Brief clinical report: Gardner syndrome in a man with an interstitial deletion of 5q. *Am J Med Genet* 25:473, 1986.
16. THOMPSON EA: Information gain in joint linkage analysis. *IMA J Math Appl Med Biol* 1:31, 1984.
17. LATHROP GM, LALOUEL J-M, JULIER C, OTT J: Multilocus linkage analysis in humans: Detection of linkage and estimation of recombination. *Am J Hum Genet* 37:482, 1985.
18. LATHROP GM, LALOUEL J-M, JULIER C, OTT J: Strategies for multilocus linkage analysis in humans. *Proc Natl Acad Sci USA* 81:3443, 1984.
19. LATHROP GM, LALOUEL J-M: Efficient computations in multilocus linkage analysis. *Am J Hum Genet* 42:498, 1988.
20. HALDANE JBS: The combination of linkage values, and the calculation of distance between the loci of linked factors. *J Genet* 8:299, 1919.
21. WHITE R, LEPPERT M, BISHOP T, BARKER D, BERKOWITZ J, BROWN C, CALLAHAN P, HOLM T, JEROMINSKI L: Construction of linkage maps with DNA markers for human chromosomes. *Nature* 313:101, 1985.
22. O'CONNELL P, LATHROP GM, LAW M, LEPPERT M, NAKAMURA Y, HOFF M, KUMLIN E, THOMAS W, ELSNER T, BALLARD L, GOODMAN P, AZEN E, SADLER J, CAI G, LALOUEL J-M, WHITE R: A primary genetic linkage map for human chromosome 12. *Genomics* 1:93, 1987.
23. MORTON NE: Sequential tests for the detection of linkage. *Am J Hum Genet* 7:277, 1955.
24. OTT J: Estimation of the recombination fraction in human pedigrees: Efficient computation of the likelihood for human linkage studies. *Am J Hum Genet* 26:588, 1974.
25. SIMON M, BOUREL M, GENETET B, FAUCHET R: Idiopathic hemochromatosis. Demonstration of recessive transmission and early detection by family HLA typing. *N Engl J Med* 297:1017, 1977.
26. MORTON NE: The detection and estimation of linkage between the genes for elliptocytosis and the Rh blood types. *Am J Hum Genet* 8:80, 1956.
27. KEPPEN L, LEPPERT M, O'CONNELL P, NAKAMURA Y, STAUFFER D, LATHROP M, LALOUEL J-M, WHITE R: Etiological heterogeneity in X-linked spastic paraplegia. *Am J Hum Genet* 41:933, 1987.
28. BEAUDET A, BOWCOCK A, BUCHWALD M, CAVALLI-SFORZA L, FARRALL M, KING M-C, KLINGER K, LALOUEL J-M, LATHROP GM, NAYLOR S, OTT J, TSUI L-C, WAINWRIGHT B, WATKINS P, WHITE R, WILLIAMSON R: Linkage of cystic fibrosis to two tightly linked DNA markers: Joint report from a collaborative study. *Am J Hum Genet* 39:681, 1986.
29. BARKER D, WRIGHT E, NGUYEN K, CANNON I, FAIN P, GOLDGAR D, BISHOP DT, CAREY J, BATY B, KIVLIN J, WILLARD H, WAYE JS, GREIG G, LEINWAND L, NAKAMURA Y, O'CONNELL P, LEPPERT M, LALOUEL J-M, WHITE R, SKOLNICK M: Gene for von Recklinghausen neurofibromatosis is in the pericentromeric region of chromosome 17. *Science* 236:1100, 1987.
30. BODMER W, BAILEY C, BODMER J, BUSSEY H, ELLIS A, GORMAN P, LUCIBELLO F, MURDAY V, RIDER S, SCAMBLER P, SHEER D, SOLOMON E, SPURR N: Localization of the gene for familial adenomatous polyposis on chromosome 5. *Nature* 328:614, 1987.
31. LEPPERT M, DOBBS M, SCAMBLER P, O'CONNELL P, NAKAMURA Y, STAUFFER D, WOODWARD S, BURT R, HUGHES J, GARDNER E, LATHROP M, WASMUTH J, LALOUEL J-M, WHITE R: The gene for familial polyposis coli maps to the long arm of chromosome 5. *Science* 238:1411, 1987.
32. OTT J: *Analysis of Human Genetic Linkage.* Baltimore, Johns Hopkins University Press, 1985.
33. SMITH CAB: Testing for heterogeneity of recombination values in human genetics. *Ann Hum Genet* 27:175, 1963.
34. OTT J: Linkage analysis and family classification under heterogeneity. *Ann Hum Genet* 47:311, 1983.
35. LATHROP GM, LALOUEL J-M: Easy calculations of LOD scores and genetic risks on small computers. *Am J Hum Genet* 36:460, 1984.
36. BISHOP DT: The information content of phase-known matings for ordering genetic loci. *Genet Epidemiol* 2:349, 1985.
37. DEISSEROTH A, NIENHUIS A, TURNER P, VELEZ R, ANDERSON W, RUDDLE F: Localization of the human alpha-globin structural gene to chromosome 16 in somatic cell hybrids by molecular hybridization assay. *Cell* 12:205, 1977.
38. GERHARD D, JONES C, MORSE H, HANDELIN B, WEEKS V, HOUSMAN D: Analysis of human chromosome 11 by somatic cell genetics—Reexamination of derivatives of human hamster cell line J1. *Somatic Cell Mol Genet* 13:293, 1987.
39. LATHROP M, NAKAMURA Y, CARTWRIGHT P, O'CONNELL P, LEPPERT M, JONES C, TATEISHI H, BRAGG T, LALOUEL J-M, WHITE R: A primary genetic map of markers for human chromosome 10. *Genomics* 2: in press.
40. BARKER D, GREEN P, KNOWLTON R, SCHUMM J, LANDER E, OLIPHANT A, WILLARD H, AKOTS G, BROWN V, GRAVIUS T, HELMS C, NELSON C, PARKER C, REDIKER K, RISING M, WATT D, WEIFFENBACH B, DONIS-KELLER H: Genetic linkage map of human chromosome 7 with 63 DNA markers. *Proc Natl Acad Sci USA* 84:8006, 1987.
40a. LEPPERT M, CAVENEE W, CALLAHAN P, HOLM T, O'CONNELL P, THOMPSON K, LATHROP GM, LALOUEL J-M, WHITE R: A primary genetic map of chromosome 13q. *Am J Hum Genet* 39:425, 1986.
41. DRAYNA D, WHITE R: The genetic linkage map of the human X chromosome. *Science* 230:753, 1985.
42. DONIS-KELLER H, GREEN P, HELMS C, CARTINHOUR S, WEIFFENBACH B, STEPHENS K, KEITH T, BOWDEN D, SMITH D, LANDER E, BOTSTEIN D, AKOTS G, REDIKER K, GRAVIUS T, BROWN V, RISING M, PARKER C, POWERS J, WATT D, KAUFFMAN E, BRICKER A, PHIPPS P, MULLER-KAHLE H, FULTON T, NG S, SCHUMM J, BRAMAN J, KNOWLTON R, BARKER D, CROOKS S, LINCOLN S, DALY M, ABRAHAMSON J: A genetic linkage map of the human genome. *Cell* 51:319, 1987.
43. DAVIES K, PEARSON P, HARPER P, MURRAY J, O'BRIEN T, SARFARAZI M, WILLIAMSON R: Linkage analysis of two cloned sequences flanking the Duchenne muscular dystrophy locus on the short arm of the human X chromosome. *Nucleic Acids Res* 11:2302, 1983.
44. GUSELLA J, WEXLER N, CONNEALLY P, NAYLOR S, ANDERSON M, TANZI R, WATKINS P, OTTINA K, WALLACE M, SAKAGUCHI A, YOUNG A, SHOULSON I, BONILLA E, MARTIN J: A polymorphic DNA marker genetically linked to Huntington's disease. *Nature* 306:234, 1983.
45. TSUI L-C, BUCHWALD M, BARKER D, BRAMAN J, KNOWLTON R, SCHUMM J, EIBERG H, MOHR J, KENNEDY D, PLAVSIC N, ZSIGA M, MARKIEWICZ D, AKOTS G, BROWN V, HELMS C, GRAVIUS T, PARKER C, REDIKER K, DONIS-KELLER H: Cystic fibrosis locus defined by a genetically linked polymorphic DNA marker. *Science* 230:1054, 1985.
46. WAINWRIGHT B, SCAMBLER P, SCHMIDTKE J, WATSON E, LAW H, FARRALL M, COOKE H, EIBERG H, WILLIAMSON R: Localization of cystic fibrosis locus to human chromosome 7cen-q22. *Nature* 318:384, 1985.
47. WHITE R, WOODWARD S, LEPPERT M, O'CONNELL P, HOFF M, HERBST J, LALOUEL J-M, DEAN M, VANDE WOUDE G: A closely linked genetic marker for cystic fibrosis. *Nature* 318:382, 1985.
48. REEDERS S, BREUNING M, DAVIES K, NICHOLLS R, JARMAN A, HIGGS D, PEARSON P, WEATHERALL D: A highly polymorphic DNA marker linked to adults polycystic kidney disease on chromosome 16. *Nature* 317:542, 1985.
49. SEIZINGER B, ROULEAU G, OZELIUS L, LANE A, FARYNIARZ A, CHAO M,

HUSON S, KORF B, PARRY D, PERICAK-VANCE M, COLLINS F, HOBBS W, FALCONE B, IANNUZZI J, ROY J, ST. GEORGE-HYSLOP P, TANZI R, BOTHWELL M, UPADHYAYA M, HARPER P, GOLDSTEIN A, HOOVER D, BADER J, SPENCE M, MULVIHILL J, AYLESWORTH A, VANCE J, ROSSENWASSER G, GASKELL P, ROSES A, MARTUZA R, BREAKFIELD X, GUSELLA J: Genetic linkage of von Recklinghausen neurofibromatosis to the nerve growth factor receptor gene. *Cell* 49:589, 1987.

50. ROULEAU G, WERTELECKI W, HAINES J, HOBBS W, TROFATTER J, SEIZINGER B, MARTUZA R, SUPERNEAU D, CONNEALLY M, GUSELLA J: Genetic linkage of bilateral acoustic neurofibromatosis to a DNA marker on chromosome 22. *Nature* 329:246, 1987.

51. MATHEW CGP, CHIN K, EASTON D, THORPE K, CARTER C, LIOU G, FONG S-L, BRIDGES CDB, HAAK H, KRUSEMAN A, SCHIFTER S, HANSEN H, TELENIUS H, TELENIUS-BERG M, PONDER B: A linked genetic marker for multiple endocrine neoplasia type 2a on chromosome 10. *Nature* 328:527, 1987.

52. SIMPSON N, KIDD K, GOODFELLOW P, MCDERMID H, MYERS S, KIDD J, JACKSON C, DUNCAN AMV, FARRER L, BRASCH K, CASTIGLIONE C, GENEL M, GERNER J, GREENBERG C, GUSELLA J, HOLDEN JJA, WHITE B: Assignment of multiple endocrine neoplasia type 2a to chromosome 10 by linkage. *Nature* 328:528, 1987.

53. ST.GEORGE-HYSLOP PH, TANZI RE, POLINSKY RJ, HAINES JL, NEE L, WATKINS P, MYERS RH, FELDMAN RG, POLLEN D, DRACHMAN D, GROWDON J, BRUNI A, FONCIN J-F, SALMON D, FOMMELT P, AMADUCCI L, SORBI S, PIACENTINI S, STEWART GD, HOBBS WJ, CONNEALLY PM, GUSELLA JF: The genetic defect causing familial Alzheimer's disease maps on chromosome 21. *Science* 235:885, 1987.

54. EGELAND JA, GERHARD DS, PAULS DL, SUSSEX JN, KIDD KK, ALLEN CR, HOSTETTER AM, HOUSMAN DE: Bipolar affective disorders linked to DNA markers on chromosome 11. *Nature* 325:783, 1987.

55. ESTIVILL X, FARRALL M, SCAMBLER P, BELL G, HAWLEY K, LENCH N, BATES G, KRUYER H, FREDERICK P, STANIER P, WATSON E, WILLIAMSON R, WAINWRIGHT B: A candidate for the cystic fibrosis locus isolated by selection for methylation-free islands. *Nature* 326:840, 1987.

56. BARKER D, MCCOY M, WEINBERG R, GOLDFARB M, WIGLER M, BURT R, GARDNER E, WHITE R: A test of the role of two oncogenes in inherited predisposition to colon cancer. *Mol Biol Med* 1:199, 1983.

57. LEPPERT M, HASSTEDT S, HOLM T, O'CONNELL P, WU L, ASH O, WILLIAMS R, WHITE R: A DNA probe for the LDL receptor gene is tightly linked to hypercholesterolemia in a pedigree with early coronary disease. *Am J Hum Genet* 39:300, 1986.

58. FERNS G, GALTON D: Haplotypes of the human apoprotein AI-CIII-AIV gene cluster in coronary atherosclerosis. *Hum Genet* 73:245, 1986.

59. ORDOVAS J, SCHAEFER E, SALEM D, WARD R, GLUECK C, VERGANI C, WILSON P, KARATHANASIS S: Apolipoprotein A-I gene polymorphism associated with premature coronary artery disease and familial hypoalphalipoproteinemia. *N Engl J Med* 314:671, 1986.

60. HEGELE R, BRESLOW J: Apolipoprotein genetic variation in the assessment of atherosclerosis susceptibility. *Genet Epidemiol* 4:163, 1987.

61. HEGELE R, HUANG L-S, HERBERT P, BLUM C, BURING J, HENNEKENS C, BRESLOW J: Apolipoprotein B—Gene DNA polymorphism associated with myocardial infarction. *N Engl J Med* 315:1509, 1986.

62. CONNER B, REYES A, MORIN C, ITAKURA K, TEPLITZ R, WALLACE RB: Detection of sickle cell β^{s}-globin allele by hybridization with synthetic oligonucleotides. *Proc Natl Acad Sci USA* 80:278, 1983.

63. KIDD V, WALLACE RB, ITAKURA K, WOO SLC: Alpha$_1$-antitrypsin deficiency detection by direct analysis of the mutation in the gene. *Nature* 304:230, 1983.

64. ELSTON RC, STEWART J: A general model for the genetic analysis of pedigree data. *Hum Hered* 21:523, 1971.

65. MORTON NE, MACLEAN CJ: Analysis of family resemblance. III. Complex segregation of quantitative traits. *Am J Hum Genet* 26:489, 1974.

66. LALOUEL J-M, MORTON NE: Complete segregation analysis with pointers. *Hum Hered* 31:312, 1981.

PART 2

CHROMOSOMES

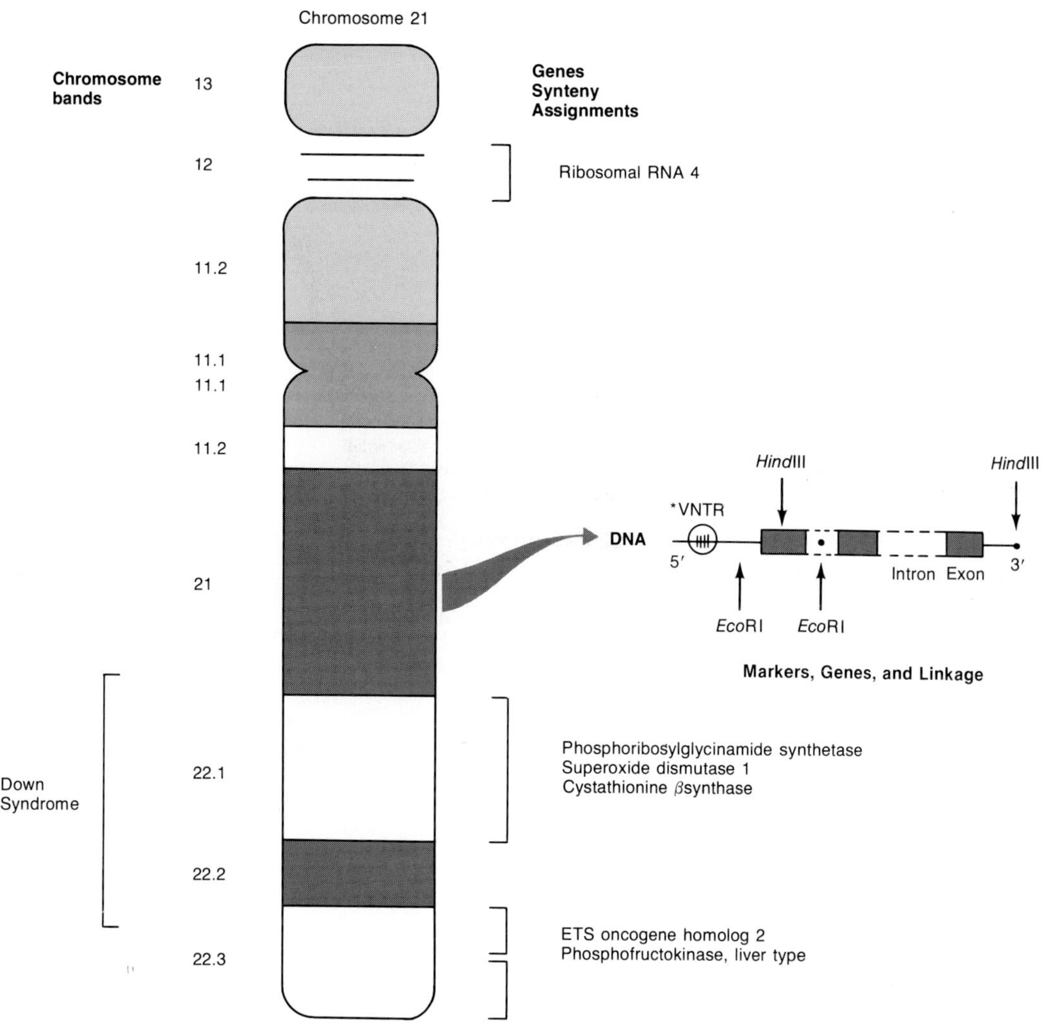

*VNTR = Variable number tandem repeats

CHAPTER 7

DOWN SYNDROME (Trisomy 21)

CHARLES J. EPSTEIN

1. *The salient clinical features of Down syndrome include several minor malformations or dysmorphic features which, while not all invariably present, together constitute the distinctive physical phenotype of the syndrome. Mental retardation and hypotonia are virtually always present, and congenital heart disease (particularly endocardial cushion defects) occurs in about 40 percent of affected individuals. Gastrointestinal anomalies (especially duodenal atresia and Hirschsprung disease) are found in about 5 percent.*
2. *There is a wide range of ultimate intellectual attainment and rate of psychomotor development which may, to some extent, be influenced by both environmental and genetic factors. No pharmacologic therapy has as yet been shown to have a beneficial effect. The specific causes of mental retardation have not been elucidated, although decreased nerve cell densities, changes in phospholipid composition, and alterations in certain electrophysiological properties of the brain and isolated neurons have been demonstrated. The pathologic, metabolic, and neurochemical changes of Alzheimer's disease are present after the third decade in the brains of all individuals with Down syndrome, who also have a progressive loss in cognitive functions. Many develop a frank dementia.*
3. *There is a fifteen- to twentyfold increase in the incidence of leukemia in children with Down syndrome, with acute megakaryoblastic leukemia being particularly frequent among those with nonlymphocytic leukemia. Leukemoid reactions or transient leukemia occurs in infants, as does macrocytosis and increased hematocrit. The activities of several erythrocyte and granulocyte enzymes not coded for by genes on chromosome 21 are increased, and hyperuricemia may be present.*
4. *Males with Down syndrome are infertile, whereas females, while decreased in fertility, are often capable of reproduction. Longitudinal growth is impaired, and there is an increased frequency of thyroid dysfunction in newborns and of thyroid autoantibodies throughout life. A variety of cellular abnormalities are present and include enhanced responses to interferon and β-adrenergic agonists and possibly small increases in sensitivity to radiation, mutagenic and carcinogenic chemicals, and viruses.*
5. *The principal causes of death in Down syndrome are infection, congenital heart disease, and malignancy. Longevity has been steadily increasing in recent years, and estimated life expectancy for individuals without congenital heart disease is 50 to 60 years. The increased susceptibility to infection appears to be the result of abnormalities of the immune system, particularly in the functions of T lymphocytes.*
6. *Down syndrome results in most instances from trisomy 21, the presence of an extra chromosome 21 either free or as part of a Robertsonian fusion chromosome. Occasional occurrences result from triplication of just the distal part of the long arm of chromosome 21 or from the presence of trisomy 21/diploid mosaicism. Depending on the frequency and distribution of trisomic cells, mosaic individuals may range from being normal to having the typical phenotypic features of Down syndrome. There is a very strong effect as a result of maternal age, but not paternal age, on the incidence of trisomy 21. The nondisjunction event leading to the trisomy occurs in the mother about 80 percent of the time, with the error in either mother or father being predominantly in meiosis I. Other than an increased frequency of maternal thyroid autoantibodies, no environmental factor has been found to correlate with the occurrence of nondisjunction.*
7. *The risk for recurrence of nondisjunction is increased in younger mothers (≤30 to 35 years) of children with Down syndrome, and the risk of aneuploid offspring is much higher in mothers than in fathers who are carriers of balanced Robertsonian translocations. Prenatal diagnosis by amniocentesis or chorionic villus sampling is capable of detecting fetuses with Down syndrome, and maternal serum α-fetoprotein screening can identify a proportion of pregnancies in which a fetus with Down syndrome is present.*
8. *Aneuploid phenotypes, while often variable in their expression, are differentiable from one another and are, in terms of overall pattern, specific. Nonspecific effects, while they may occur, are not major determinants of aneuploid phenotypes. Phenotypic variability may result from a combination of genetic, stochastic, and environmental factors. Individual features of aneuploid phenotypes can often be assigned to specific regions of the genome. The existence of a trisomic state results in the production of 50 percent more of the products of genes present on the unbalanced chromosome segment, and these gene dosage effects are in turn responsible for the abnormalities of development and function which constitute the aneuploid phenotype.*
9. *Chromosome 21 is the smallest of the human autosomes. It constitutes about 1.7 percent of the haploid genome and has a genetic length of about 46 cM. Loss of the short arm, which contains ribosomal RNA genes and other highly repeated DNA sequences, does not impair normal function or development. About 15 loci of known function have been mapped to the long arm of chromosome 21, as have over 60 anonymous DNA sequences. Physical and genetic maps are presently being constructed. The physical phenotype of Down syndrome is thought to be produced by imbalance of the region which comprises bands q22.1 to q22.3.*
10. *Gene dosage effects have been demonstrated for several loci on chromosome 21, and work is presently underway to determine whether the increases in gene product activity or concentration have secondary effects on the functions of these gene products. In particular, studies are being carried out to assess the roles of increased superoxide dismutase-1 activity and of increased synthesis of the amyloid β-protein precursors in the pathogenesis of Alzheimer's disease and of an extra copy of the oncogene homolog* ETS2 *in leukemogenesis.*
11. *Several mouse models have been developed to facilitate studies of the mechanisms of the pathogenesis of Down syndrome.*

These include the trisomy 16 mouse, in which much of the mouse genome homologous to the distal part of human chromosome 21 is triplicated, the trisomy 16/diploid mouse chimera, which is analogous to human trisomy 21/diploid mosaics, and transgenic mice producing increased quantities of individual chromosome 21 gene products.

Down syndrome (DS) is the first chromosomal disorder to have been clinically defined,[1] the first (by a week) to be proven actually to be chromosomal in origin—the result of trisomy 21[2-4]—and the most common recognized genetic cause of mental retardation. As such, it has been the prototype of human autosomal aneuploidy and has been the subject of intense clinical, cytogenetic, epidemiologic, and molecular investigation (for recent reviews see Refs. 5 to 12). With the rapid advances in molecular genetics, it is now possible to envision that the genetic structure of human chromosome 21 will be completely defined and that the pathogenetic relationship between the presence of an extra set of chromosome 21 genes and the many features of Down syndrome phenotype will be understood.

Although an aneuploid condition such as DS might not ordinarily be considered to be a metabolic disease, it is, in fact, a collection of many metabolic disorders which stem from the presence of these extra genes and, as a result, of extra amounts of the products of these genes. Since these gene products must exert their effects, in the main, by their biochemical actions, aneuploidy is no less metabolic than are conditions such as thalassemia or porphyria.[8] Trisomy 21, the cause of DS, can therefore be placed on a conceptual continuum which ranges from the complete absence of one or several genes, on the one hand, to a high degree of gene amplification, as occurs in certain malignant states, on the other.[13] What is different in aneuploidy from the more conventional metabolic diseases is the number of loci involved, not necessarily how their functions are perturbed by the change in gene number.

CLINICAL ASPECTS OF DOWN SYNDROME

Dysmorphic Features

The most immediately apparent, if not the most serious, manifestations of Down syndrome are the minor dysmorphic features which collectively constitute its distinctive physical phenotype (Fig. 7-1). A list of these features is presented in Table 7-1. Detailed descriptions of the minor anomalies are contained in references.[5,14] Although any single individual will have many of the characteristic features and be easily recognized as having DS, none of these features is present in all persons with DS. Conversely, it will be very rare for any single individual with DS to have all the features contained in the list. It should also be kept in mind that none of the features in the list is unique either to DS or to chromosome abnormalities in general. Accordingly, the presence of one or a few minor dysmorphic features in an otherwise normal individual does not in itself signify the existence of a chromosomal abnormality.

In addition to the features listed in Table 7-1, there is a series of dermatoglyphic features that are quite characteristic of DS.[15] These used to play a much greater role in clinical diagnosis than they now do, but they represent, nevertheless,

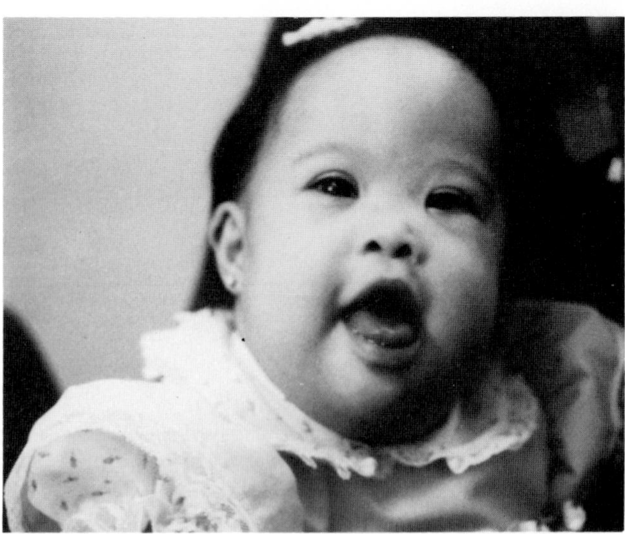

Fig. 7-1 Eight-month-old child with Down syndrome.

distinctive aspects of the phenotype of DS. Particularly characteristic are the arch tibial pattern on the hallucal area of the foot, ulnar loops on the second fingers, and a distal axial palmar triradius.[16] In fact, these features, along with ear length (short), the distance between the first and second toes (wide), the internipple distance (< -1 SD), and the presence of Brushfield spots of the iris and the excessive skinfolds or a fat pad on the neck, can be used to construct an index capable of permitting the diagnosis of 95 percent of patients suspected of having DS with an accuracy of 99.9 percent.[16] In this regard it is of interest that about 75 to 85 percent of infants clinically suspected of having DS actually have trisomy 21.[16]

Mental Retardation and Neurologic Abnormalities

While the dysmorphic features just discussed are of clinical significance, the one condition of overriding clinical importance in DS is, of course, mental retardation. The brain, insofar as it is involved in cognition and other highly integrated mental functions, seems to be the organ most vulnerable to

Table 7-1. Physical Characteristics of Down Syndrome

Feature	*Frequency, %**
Oblique (upslanting) palpebral fissures	82
Loose skin on nape of neck	81
Narrow palate	76
Brachycephaly	75
Hyperflexibility	73
Flat nasal bridge	68
Gap between first and second toes	68
Short, broad hands	64
Short neck	61
Abnormal teeth	61
Epicanthic folds	59
Short fifth finger	58
Open mouth	58
Incurved fifth finger	57
Brushfield spots	56
Furrowed tongue	55
Transverse palmar crease	53
Folded or dysplastic ear	50
Protruding tongue	47

*Means of frequencies in Table 5-1 of Pueschel et al.[14]
SOURCE: Reprinted by permission from Epstein.[8]

the deleterious effects of autosomal aneuploidy, whichever chromosome is involved. Although gross abnormalities often do occur in certain aneuploid states, they do not in themselves provide a complete explanation for the very severe functional abnormalities which are almost invariably present. In addition to its effects on intelligence and control of muscle tone early and throughout life, trisomy 21 is also associated with a process of neuronal degeneration during the adult years. This process, which is pathologically identical with Alzheimer's disease (presenile and/or senile dementia), results in significant pathologic changes in the brain and may further compromise the already impaired mental functioning.

Mental Retardation. Although newborns with DS may, with the exception of the profound hypotonia (see "Muscle Tone" below), appear reasonably normal behaviorally, developmental retardation generally becomes obvious during the first several months of life. On the mean, the attainment of developmental landmarks becomes increasingly more delayed as time goes on. Thus, whereas the average delay may be of the order of 2 months for the very early landmarks (e.g., rolling over, transferring objects), it gradually lengthens and reaches 1 to 2 years for functions that ordinarily appear at about 2 years of age (Fig. 7-2).[17] However, because of the great variability in attainment of landmarks (Fig 7-3),[18] this delay may or may not be obvious for any single child with DS. For institutionalized individuals, progress continues during the first decade of life, following which there is usually a plateau in mental age.[19] Some individuals may continue to progress mentally for another 5 years or so. There is then a second plateau and ultimately a decline (see "Alzheimer's Disease," below).[19]

Many studies of development during the first decade of life have indicated that even with DS children reared at home, there is a progressive, virtually linear decline in developmental quotient (DQ) or IQ starting within the first year[18,20] (Fig. 7-4). The same appears to be true of social quotients (SQ) as well.[20] Once again, the wide range of IQ and SQ should be noted. In contrast to these results are those recently obtained in a prospective study of infants with DS over the first 3 years of life.[2] In this group, mean DQs based on the mental scale of the Bayley Scales of Infant Development remained constant at 55 to 58, although the mean on the motor scale did drop from 67 at 6 months to 53 at 3 years. Cardiac status did not significantly influence mental development, but it did influence motor development.[21] Both mental and motor development appeared to correlate with muscle tone.[21,22]

GENETIC AND ENVIRONMENTAL EFFECTS. In rare instances, children with DS without known mosaicism have attained IQs above 80 and have performed in the low average range.[23] One has even written a book.[24] Although these cases must for the present be considered as atypical, they once again point out the variability of the syndrome and raise the question of what factors do or could influence mental development. One possible factor is, of course, the intrinsic genetic differences among individuals. An approach to looking at this has been to examine the relationship between parental education levels or IQs and the IQs of their children with DS, and evidence both for[25,26] and against[27] the existence of such correlations has been reported. Two recent studies have again affirmed the association. In one group of children reared at home and followed longitudinally, the mean DQ or IQ at a mean age of about 6 years was 74.6 ± 14.9 (SD) for children of mothers with ≥16 years of schooling and 58.8 ± 12 for children of mothers with <12 years of schooling.[28] In another group with a mean age of 5.2 years, the IQs were 70.3 and 28.8, respectively, when the father's schooling was similarly scored.[29]

The results just cited are consistent with a genetic basis for the differences in the IQs of persons with DS, and there is no reason to believe that such genetic influences should not be

Fig. 7-2 Median time of appearance of developmental landmarks in children with Down syndrome (•) as compared with a normal population (|). Data from Share and Veale.[17]

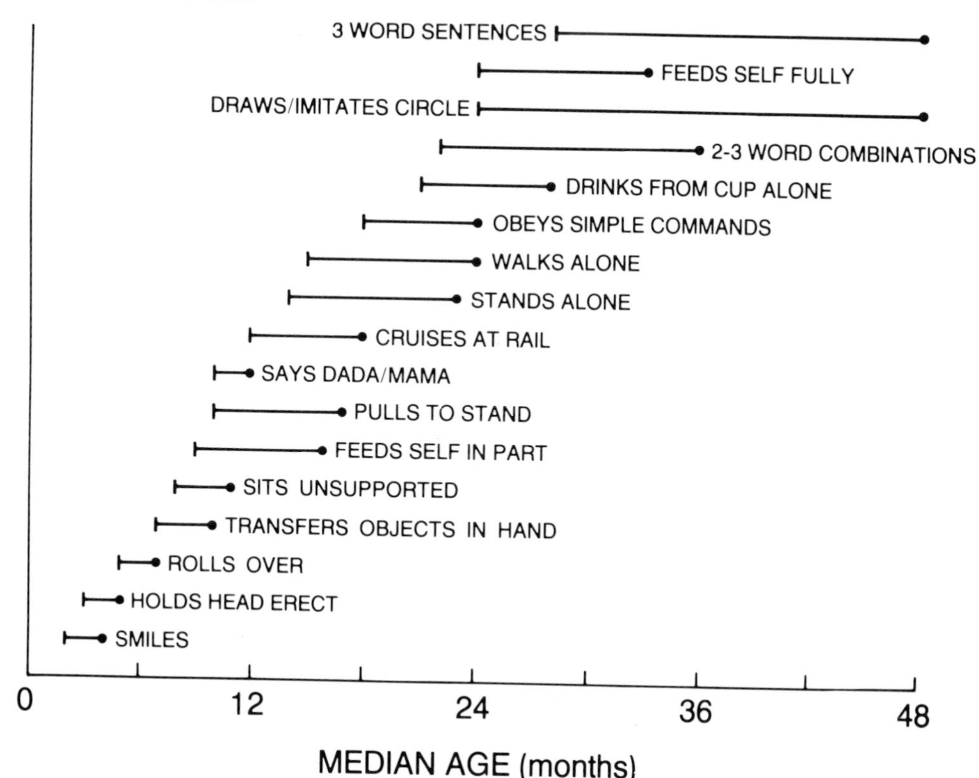

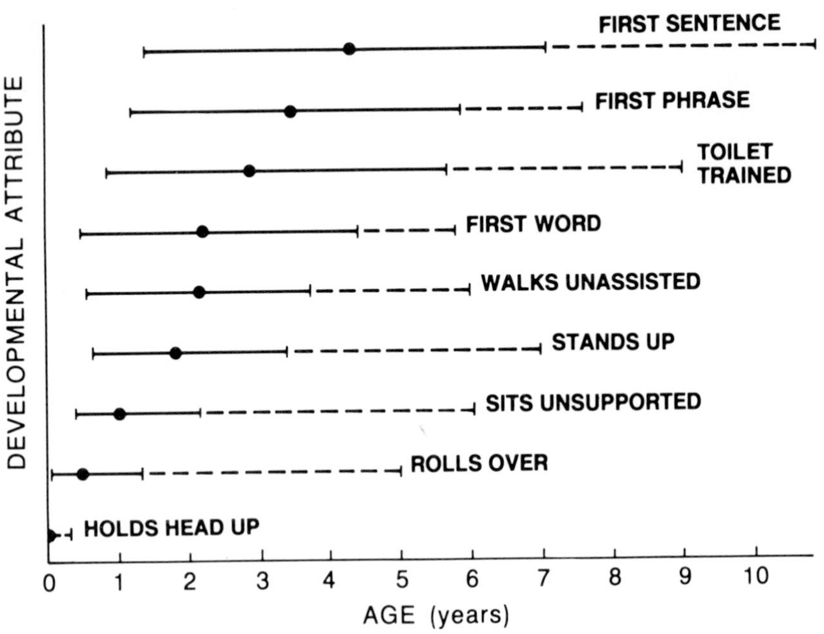

Fig. 7-3 The mean and range of the time of appearance of developmental landmarks in children with Down syndrome. The vertical marks to the left of the dashed lines indicate the upper limits for 95% of the Down syndrome group. For sitting, standing, walking, and speaking the first word, the figures given are for boys. *(Data from Melyn and White.[18])*

operating. However, some authors argue to the contrary,[19] and it is also possible, of course, that social and educational practices relating to the child are influenced by parental IQ and/or education and that these environmental factors also play a role. Evidence for the potential impact of environmental factors on intellectual development stems principally from two sources: studies of the outcomes of home-reared versus institutionalized persons with DS and the results of early intervention programs.

Several investigations carried out 20 to 30 years ago have concluded that children reared at home, if only during the first 2.5 years of life, do better than children institutionalized or in foster care since birth. IQs measured between 2.5 and 7 years of age have been 7 to 15 points greater in the early home-reared group.[30–32] These early conclusions have been seriously questioned on methodological grounds and must be considered as unproven,[19] although a later study again showed a positive benefit with an increase in IQ of ≥17 points at 9 to 10 years of age.[33]

Early intervention with intellectual and motor stimulation starting in infancy has also been described to have a positive effect on development.[27,33,34] Both short-term[35] and long-term[33,34] gains have been claimed, although these conclusions are not always based on carefully controlled investigations and the performance of such controlled studies poses problems of its own.[36] In one study in which a control group was used, early intervention and preschool stimulation resulted in a mean increase in IQ of 6.3 points above control levels at 9 to 10 years of age, but it did not significantly alter the gradual decline in IQ when the subjects were followed longitudinally over a 10-year period.[33] The long-term effects of early intervention programs remain to be proven. While it does appear that evidence exists that early intervention can have a positive effect on early development,[37,38] research in this area is difficult for a variety of reasons[36] and definitive conclusions are difficult to obtain.

COGNITIVE IMPAIRMENT. A considerable literature on the nature of the cognitive impairment in DS has developed and is critically reviewed in detail by Gibson.[19] Unfortunately, much of this literature has been criticized as being characterized by "the relatively poor quality of research design and data management. . . . It has been possible to reach conclusions, on a tentative basis, by assuming that consensus has power and methodological error is randomly distributed. Both arguments are subject to dispute."[19] Personality stereotypes attributed to individuals with DS have also been seriously questioned and probably have little validity.[19,39] Nevertheless, despite these indictments, the present state of affairs seems to be well summarized as follows[40]:

> Although delays appear already in young DS infants in all areas, it seems that, given the appropriate stimulating environment, it is not

Fig. 7-4 The mean and observed range of the intelligence quotient (IQ) of children with Down syndrome as a function of age. *(Data from Morgan.[20])*

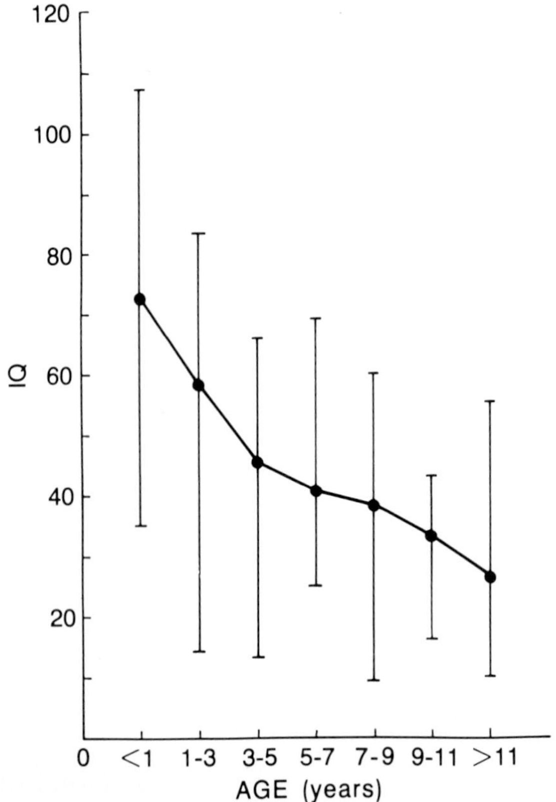

really until the DS child reaches school age that the delays start to cause problems serious enough to require very intensive and specialized training. The major problem seems to be the lack of ability to handle more advanced cognitive strategies and processes. Thus, in whichever area of development one may look at, the inability to comprehend instructions, to plan alternative approaches to the problem, to attend to several variables at one time, or to express oneself clearly to another to be able to receive help, for example, are all deficiencies which are serious enough to be a major hindrance in pursuing a "normal" life.

Newer methods of psychologic approach are being applied to DS and should ultimately provide important information about the specific nature of the intellectual deficits in DS and their neurologic and biochemical bases.

Muscle Tone. Perhaps the single most characteristic feature of DS in newborns and infants is hypotonia, and several investigators regard it as a universal finding.[41,42] In a longitudinal study, the muscle tone of DS newborns was rated as 1.6 ± 0.84 (SD) and 1.5 ± 0.70 for males and females, respectively, increasing to 2.8 ± 0.28 and 2.7 ± 0.33, respectively at 2 years of age (with 0 = extremely, 1 = moderately, and 2 = mildly hypotonic; 3 = normal).[43] During the first year of life, tone was significantly less in infants with moderate to severe congenital heart disease.[43] Tone was also rated as decreased in older children aged 4 to 17 years, with a mean of 2.74 versus a control mean of 3.14.[44] Patellar reflexes, a stretch reflex response considered to be related to the involuntary reflex responses which are the genesis of muscle tone, were also less smooth and less brisk (2.32 cm versus 6.06 cm in controls) in the DS group.[44] Grip strength was also decreased at all ages between 4 and 17 years, and there was a positive and significant correlation between strength and tone ($r = 0.65$, $p < 0.01$).[44]

The basis for the decreased muscle tone is unknown. It has been proposed that it results from a decrease in the concentration of 5-hydroxytryptamine (serotonin) in the peripheral blood,[45,46] and initial studies suggested that tone and development could be improved by administration of 5-hydroxytryptophan.[47] However, these results have not been confirmed by subsequent investigation,[48–50] and 5-hydroxytryptophan was found to induce infantile spasms in 14 percent of infants receiving the drug.[51] Similarly, vitamin B_6 administration, which also elevates blood serotonin, had no beneficial effects on tone or development.[50,52]

It has also been suggested that the hypotonia may reflect a skeletal muscle fiber abnormality, associated with an increased diameter and decreased number of nuclei per unit length.[53] However, there is no further evidence supporting this hypothesis, and for the present it must be assumed that the hypotonia is central in origin.

Attempts at Therapy. In addition to the unsuccessful trials with 5-hydroxytryptophan, numerous other agents have been used in an attempt to improve the development of children with DS.[54] Prominent among these have been the so-called orthomolecular approaches based upon the administration of mixtures of vitamins, minerals, thyroid hormone, and other substances.[55–57] Despite claims for remarkable successes, with IQ reported to increase between 10 and 25 points over a 4- to 8-month period,[56] these results have not been replicated in carefully controlled trials.[58,59] Another approach has been sicca cell therapy in which lyophilized embryonic animal cells are injected at frequent intervals. Again, contrary to the claims of its proponents,[60] this form of therapy has not been shown in controlled trials to have any efficacy.[61–63] There is, in fact, considerable concern that it may be dangerous.

At present there is no specific form of pharmacologic therapy known to have a reproducibly beneficial effect on the signs or symptoms of DS.

Neuropathology. Like so many aspects of DS, there has been considerable disagreement about the frequency and nature of anatomic abnormalities of the brain. However, the present consensus is that in the majority of patients with Down syndrome the results of neuropathologic study are normal,[64,65] and that it is futile to look for a description of the "mongoloid brain."[66] Although the histologic findings have been inconsistent, brain weight is in the low normal range and the size of the cerebellum and brain stem may be reduced to an even greater extent.[67] Among the semispecific findings in DS are nerve cell heterotopias in the white layers of the cerebellum and vermis, which are found in 16 percent of infantile and fetal DS brains.[64] These heterotopias are attributed to a disturbance or retardation of embryonal cell migration. The anterior commissure in adults with Down syndrome is reduced in cross-sectional area.[68]

Detailed neuronal architecture, studied with Golgi-type preparations, has been analyzed in a handful of cases. Because of the limitations in numbers, all reports must be viewed with caution. Several authors have commented on diminutions and/or abnormalities in the morphology of dendritic spines in infants and children with DS.[69–71] These abnormalities of spine morphology and number are probably nonspecific and can probably be interpreted as representing secondary changes in neurons which are metabolically or otherwise affected by the trisomic state. (See Addendum.)

Other evidence for defects in brain histogenesis has also been reported. This includes a poverty of granular cells, possibly the aspinous stellate cells, throughout the cortex and, in individuals ranging in age from newborn to 14 years, of decreased neuronal densities in layers II and IV of the occipital cortex (area 17).[72,73] This decrease averaged 30 percent during the first year and 20 to 25 percent thereafter. In the brain of a single infant studied at 5.5 months, cholinergic cells were decreased ≈50 percent in the substantia innominata and locus ceruleus.[74] Synaptic density in the neocortex has been reported as normal, although pre- and postsynaptic width and length may be reduced.[75] Similarly, the surface area of synaptic contact may be lower than normal in the occipital cortex.[73]

From the above it is obvious that a clear picture of the state of the "wiring" of the brain in DS does not emerge. Although there is accumulating evidence for abnormalities of neuronal differentiation and migration in fetal and infant brains, it is not certain, if the developmental plasticity of the young brain is taken into account, how many of the changes are permanent or functionally significant.

Neurochemistry. It has been reported that all the phospholipids of myelin contain reduced amounts of monounsaturated fatty acids but do not have unequivocally abnormal amounts of polyunsaturated fatty acids (PUFA).[76] However, the opposite seems to be true of synaptosomal phospholipids, with reduced proportions of PUFA and normal amounts of monounsaturated fatty acids being found. Monounsaturated fatty acids are reduced in sphingomyelin. The basis for these abnormalities, which are also found in phenylketonuria, is unknown, and it is not clear whether they result in[76] or result from[77] other developmental and functional abnormalities of the nervous system.

In studies of phosphoglycerides from fetal DS brains, it was again found that while the total proportions of PUFA were normal, the ratio of PUFA in the (n-3) series to PUFA in the (n-6) series was significantly elevated in both serine and ethanolamine phosphoglycerides.[78] Docosahexaenoyl [22:6(n-3)] groups were increased and arachidonyl [20:4(n-6)] groups decreased, and it was speculated that these alterations could result in membrane abnormalities and consequently in functional disturbances.

Neurophysiology. Biochemical analyses, while providing valuable information about the chemical structure of elements of the nervous system in DS, do not directly speak to the question of alterations in function. Unfortunately, there are few data that really bear on this issue, and they principally involve electrophysiological studies of one type or another. There are no specific EEG patterns associated with DS, and the abnormalities that have been observed are not well correlated with specific behavioral or neurologic signs and symptoms.[79] However, it has been suggested that there is an incomplete postnatal development of neuronal interconnections or an immaturity of cerebral development.[80,81] These conclusions were considered to be consistent with the independently described histologic findings of dendritic abnormalities mentioned earlier. Although some of the physiological observations that underlie them are in question,[82] recent supportive evidence has come from work on the spectral analysis of the EEG, which showed that the most important deviation from normal was a reduction in relative α power.[83]

Somewhat closer to the issue of neuronal function in DS are the studies of visual and auditory evoked potentials. Significant differences in patterns are found between DS and other retarded and nonretarded subjects, with the former having significantly larger evoked potential amplitudes in the long-latency-evoked cortical responses, greater latency and smaller amplitude in the very long (P300) cortical component, and shorter latencies and smaller amplitudes for the auditory brainstem-evoked response indicative of a shortened central conduction time.[82,84,85] The meaning of these differences remains to be established, but they do not appear to be attributable to the presence of hearing deficits even though mild to moderate high frequency loss or abnormal impedence are found in as many as 73 percent of adults with DS.[85]

Perhaps the most intriguing functional studies of DS neurons to date are those on fetal and infant dorsal root ganglion neurons cultured in vitro.[75,86] Virtually all calculated electrical parameters of Down syndrome neurons were found to be altered, often by as much as 20 to 40 percent. Although changes were also found in cells from a single culture of trisomy 18 neurons, the pattern was not the same as in trisomy 21, implying some degree of specificity. Work carried out subsequently also found several physiological parameters of cultured trisomy 21 dorsal root ganglia neurons to be altered, and it was postulated that the changes observed were the result of an increase in the fast potassium current in the trisomic neurons.[87] Although there is no evidence to prove it, it has been speculated that similar abnormalities may also occur in central nervous system neurons and could be the neurologic basis of the mental retardation in DS.[86,87] These inferences are, of course, highly speculative.

Neuropharmacology. Considerable interest has focused on peripheral neurotransmitter function in DS. Hypersensitivity to the mydriatic effect of atropine has been repeatedly confirmed.[88–90] There is, however, still debate about its cardioacceleratory effects, and both increased[91] and normal sensitivity[89,92] have been reported. The activity of the enzyme, dopamine-β-hydroxylase, which converts dopamine to norepinephrine, is significantly decreased in the plasma of individuals with DS.[93] Nevertheless, although urinary epinephrine excretion was decreased, urinary norepinephrine excretion was not, and plasma concentrations of both epinephrine and norepinephrine were normal.[94] (See Addendum.)

PLATELET SEROTONIN. A considerable literature has accumulated on abnormalities of tryptophan metabolism and platelet serotonin (5-hydroxytryptamine) in DS, with the latter being of particular interest because of its possible relevance to understanding central nervous system neurotransmitter function. The principal observation has been that the concentration of serotonin is decreased in whole blood to about 65 percent of normal, a decrease attributable to a reduction in the level of platelet serotonin to levels as low as 35 to 40 percent of normal.[95,96] Studies of serotonin uptake by platelets have demonstrated a reduced rate of influx[96] which has been variously attributed to a reduction in Na^+, K^+-ATPase activity with concomitant abnormalities of sodium, potassium, and/or calcium fluxes.[97,98] The possibility that many of the effects are secondary to an overall change in platelet physiology is raised by the findings that DS platelets are reduced in volume[99] and that serotonin content may be correlated with volume,[100] but such an explanation would not apply to the reported 60 to 70 percent decreases in erythrocyte membrane Na^+, K^+- and Mg^{2+}-ATPase activities,[101] nor to the decreased binding of imipramine to DS platelets.[102]

It has been suggested that the platelet, with its uptake and storage of amines, can serve as a model for synaptosomes in the central nervous system.[103,104] However, although direct studies of serotonin concentration and uptake in central nervous system neurons have not been conducted, the cerebrospinal fluid concentration of 5-hydroxyindoleacetic acid, the principal catabolite of serotonin, is not significantly reduced in DS.[105] Therefore, in view of both this finding and the questions raised by the possible reduction in platelet volume, it remains to be shown whether the platelet abnormalities have any relevance for central nervous system function.

RESPONSE TO β-ADRENERGIC AGONISTS. When skin fibroblasts obtained from a variety of sources were treated with 1 μM isoproterenol, the cAMP content of trisomy 21 cells increased to 29 times the initial level in 10 min, in comparison with the 2.5 to 3.2 times increase observed in diploid cells and in cells trisomic for chromosomes other than 21, a differential of ninefold.[106] Epinephrine had a similar although less pronounced effect, and epinephrine-induced platelet aggregation (supposedly an α-adrenergic function in platelets) was produced at a considerably lower concentration with trisomy 21 than with control platelets.[107,108] These alterations in response could not be attributed to increased adenylate cyclase or decreased phosphodiesterase activity or to a gene dosage effect at the receptor level. Although much remains to be done to confirm these observations and to understand their basis, they do bespeak some alteration in the function of a membrane receptor-controlled system which could have important implications for a variety of physiological and possible developmental processes in which catecholamines and cAMP are involved. Unfortunately, related work has not yet been carried out in cells other than fibroblasts, so it is difficult to know how generalizable the results are.

While somewhat confusing, the results of studies on peripheral neurotransmitters and related agents do suggest that abnormalities are present in DS. The basis of these abnormalities has yet to be defined, but is certainly worthy of investigation. Perhaps of even greater importance is to ascertain whether neurotransmitter abnormalities are present in the central nervous system. Although abnormalities of the cholinergic system are present in adult life (see section on Alzheimer's disease), the real question is whether these or any other types of neurotransmitter abnormalities are present in infants and children. If such abnormalities are present and if they contribute to the development of mental retardation, they could provide a rational point for pharmacologic intervention. While the trial with 5-hydroxytryptamine had no beneficial effect on the development of intelligence,[49] this certainly does not rule out the possibility that beneficial agents may ultimately be found.

Alzheimer's Disease. The possibility of a relationship between DS and dementia has been recognized for over 100 years[109] and between DS and Alzheimer's disease (AD) (as defined pathologically) for over 50 years.[110] This relationship is now well established and the evidence for it is summarized in Table 7-2. The consensus of a large number of reports is that the brains of adults with DS possess all the pathologic and neurochemical hallmarks of AD. Furthermore, although cerebral glucose metabolism is actually increased (≈30 percent) in young adults with DS prior to the time they develop AD, there is then a decrease as other manifestations of AD appear.[111] (See Addendum.)

The time of appearance and the frequency of the lesions of AD in DS have been matters of particular concern, since the interest in the relationship between the two conditions has been as much a function of the early and generalized appearance of the lesions as of the nature of the lesions themselves. In an extensive autopsy series, which included 347 cases of DS, 5 out of 312 (1.6 percent) brains from individuals dying under the age of 40 (20 to 38 years) and 35 of 35 (100 percent) from individuals over the age of 40 (42 to 69 years) had the gross pathologic changes of AD.[112] Of the latter, 60 percent were described as severe and comparable to the most advanced cases of AD, and 40 percent were mild to moderate. In a study of 100 brains of institutionalized individuals with DS, senile plaques and tangles were found in all cases over 30 years of age, and brain weights were generally below the mean −2 SD from the second decade on.[113] It is, therefore, generally believed that the neuropathologic changes of AD are almost universal over the age of 35 years.[114]

Table 7-2 Similarities Between Adults with Down Syndrome and Individuals with Alzheimer's Disease

Neuropathology
- Similar qualitative and quantitative appearance and geographic distribution of granulovacuolar changes, senile plaques, neurofibrillary tangles, and neuronal loss[113–115,119–123]

Neurochemistry
- Enzymes: decreased choline acetyltransferase and acetylcholinesterase[124,124a]
- Monoamines: decreased norepinephrine, dopamine, and serotonin (5-HT)[124a,125–127]
- Similar or identical structure(s) of cerebrovascular amyloid β-protein fibrils and of amyloid plaque core proteins[128,129]
- Elevation in concentration of Alz-50 (67k) protein antigen[130]

Cerebral metabolism
- Reduction in cerebral glucose metabolism from premorbid levels[111,131,132]

Neuropsychology
- Dementia in ≥ 25 percent of DS adults; gradual loss of intellectual functions in most or all DS adults[111,115,116,118]

SOURCE: From Epstein.[133]

CLINICAL MANIFESTATIONS. Although the pathology may be virtually invariant in its occurrence, a significant proportion of adults with DS do not appear to have dementia by any criteria. While the best estimate is that only about 25 percent are in fact demented,[115] frequencies as high as 45 percent have been suggested.[116] It has been proposed that although the appearance of dementia is dependent of the presence of pathologic abnormalities, the number of these abnormalities (plaques and tangles) must exceed a threshold value before symptoms and signs appear—a threshold which for some reason is higher in DS than non-DS individuals.[117] Why this should be the case is not obvious. In this regard it should be noted that, irrespective of whether frank dementia occurs, there is a progressive loss of a variety of intellectual functions not attributable simply to mental retardation in many if not all older individuals with DS.[111,116,118] For discussion of the pathogenesis of AD in DS, see "Pathogenesis of Specific Features of Down Syndrome," below. (See Addendum.)

Major Congenital Malformations

Despite the presence of many dysmorphic features in DS, relatively few major malformations are produced by trisomy 21. Those that do occur are quite specific and principally involve two systems—the heart and the gastrointestinal tract.

Congenital Heart Disease. The most frequent major congenital abnormality in DS is congenital heart disease, and 16 to 62 percent of children have been reported as being affected.[134] The most unbiased estimates for living children range from 29 to 39 percent.[135,136] In unselected DS abortuses, 45 percent were found to have forms of congenital heart disease that would not be expected to close after birth,[64] and an overall estimate of 40 percent thus appears to be a reasonable one. A variety of estimates also exist for the frequencies of specific cardiac lesions in affected children: atrioventricular canal, 18 to 54 percent (mean 39 percent); ventricular septal defect, 27 to 43 percent (mean 31 percent); atrial septal defect, 2 to 17 percent (mean 9 percent); tetralogy of Fallot, 1 to 15 percent (mean 6 percent); patient ductus arteriosus, 2 to 24 percent (mean 9 percent).[134] In the fetal cases, 73 percent of those with cardiac anomalies were judged to have an atrioventricular canal.[64] Despite the variety of lesions described, it is believed that most represent variations of a common problem in the formation of the venous inflow tract of the heart, although other lesions, such as aortic arch anomalies can also occur.[64] In a survey of institutionalized adults with DS, unsuspected aortic regurgitation or mitral valve prolapse was detected in 20 percent.[137,137a]

Survival of children with congenital heart disease is better than was formerly believed, and 80 percent survival to 15 years of age of children with atrioventricular canal defects has been reported.[138] Development of pulmonary hypertension is generally considered to occur earlier and more severely in children with DS with congenital heart disease,[139,140] although this conclusion has been disputed.[141] Abnormal development of the lung parenchyma and of the pulmonary vasculature which could contribute to the development of pulmonary hypertension may also be present. Pulmonary hypoplasia characterized by a diminished number (<50 percent of normal) of alveoli in relation to acini and a reduction in total alveolar surface area has been reported to be independent of the presence of heart disease,[142] and a thinning of the medial layer of the small pulmonary arteries has been described.[143]

Gastrointestinal Tract Abnormalities. Although much less common than congenital heart disease, there is nevertheless an increased frequency of specific intestinal anomalies in DS. The most characteristic lesion is duodenal stenosis or atresia, sometimes with annular pancreas, which has been reported with frequencies of 2.6 to 4.8 percent, followed by imperforate anus (0.7 to 2.7 percent) and Hirschsprung disease (0.4 to 2.1 percent). The lower figures are from a total ascertainment community survey in which the overall incidence of gastrointestinal abnormalities was 5.2 percent,[135] while the higher ones are from a hospital-based retrospective review.[144] Conversely, 5.9 percent of infants with Hirschsprung disease had DS,[145] as did 11 to 44 percent of patients with duodenal atresia or stenosis[144,146] and 20 percent with annular pancreas.[147]

Leukemia and Leukemoid Reactions

Incidence. An increased incidence of leukemia has long been recognized in DS. Estimates of the relative risk have ranged from 10 to 18 times normal in children up to 15 years of age,[148,149] and adults over 20 years also have an excessive rate of mortality from leukemia.[150] The distribution of leukemia by type is shown in Table 7-3. Congenital and newborn cases (<1 year of age) are predominantly acute nonlymphoblastic leukemia (ANLL), but from age 3 years on the distribution of types is the same for both DS and non-DS subjects.[151,152] The age of onset of ANLL is younger in DS than in diploid patients, but the ages are the same for ALL.[153] The length of survival of DS individuals after diagnosis of ALL is less than that of diploid individuals. (See Addendum.)

Acute Megakaryoblastic Leukemia. Although major emphasis has been placed on ALL and ANLL, it should be noted that the latter may include other forms of leukemia, such as acute megakaryoblastic leukemia, in addition to acute myelocytic leukemia.[154] It has been suggested that acute megakaryoblastic leukemia may be much more common in DS than previously suspected. Out of 24 cases of leukemia in DS seen over a 10-year period at a single hospital, 4 (17 percent) originally diagnosed as having ALL were believed to have this form of leukemia. It has been estimated that 20 to 40 percent of all cases of acute leukemia and leukemoid reactions or transient leukemia are of this type.[155] Conversely, most cases of acute megakaryoblastic leukemia in young children are thought to occur in individuals with trisomy 21 or trisomy 21/2n mosaicism, and the overall incidence of this form of leukemia may be 200 to 400 times greater in the DS than in the chromosomally normal population.[155] (See Addendum.)

The response of children with DS to therapy differs from that of chromosomally normal patients.[156] For so-called ALL, which could include misdiagnosed and hence inappropriately treated acute megakaryoblastic leukemia,[155] remission induction is reduced (80 percent versus 94 percent) in non-DS cases and mortality is higher (14 percent versus 3 percent), with death resulting principally from infection.[156] The 5-year survival is also decreased (50 percent versus 65 percent), but this is mainly attributable to the initial failure to induce a remission.

Leukemoid Reactions. A high frequency of "transient" acute leukemia or leukemoid reactions has been reported to be present in newborns with DS.[151] In these cases, there is apparently a complete remission, and it is now believed by most investigators that the affected individuals never had true leukemia at all (although a report claiming the opposite has appeared).[157] Rather, they appear to have had what has been termed *ineffective regulation of granulopoiesis masquerading as congenital leukemia.*[158] Unlike true acute leukemia, there are normal numbers of granulocytes and macrophage stem cells (CFU-GM) in the bone marrow.[159–161] However, that the presence of an extra chromosome 21 is of importance in this condition is borne out by the fact that, in several cases of such leukemoid reactions recently described in phenotypically normal trisomy 21/2n mosaics, the abnormally proliferating cell population was always trisomic for chromosome 21.[159,162,163]

The relationship between leukemoid reactions and true leukemia still remains to be defined. While it is, of course, possible that they are unrelated, it is tempting to try to visualize

Table 7-3 Types of Leukemia in Down Syndrome

			*Proportion of types, (%)**		
Sources of cases	*Age*	*Total cases*	*ALL*	*ANLL*	*AUL*
Acute leukemia	<1 mo	5	20.0	80.0	—
group B[151]	1 mo–19 yr	41	69.8	30.2	—
Literature[151]	<1 mo	47	42.1	57.9	—
	1 mo–19 yr	229	69.1	30.9	—
Oxford study of	<1 yr	10	10.0	80.0	10.0
childhood cancer[152]	1–2 yr	25	44.0(82.2)†	52.0(13.7)	4.0(4.1)
	3–14 yr	35	80.0(79.2)	17.1(18.2)	2.9(2.6)

*Abbreviations: ALL = acute lymphoblastic leukemia; ANLL-acute nonlymphoblastic leukemia; AUL = acute undifferentiated or unspecified leukemia.
†Proportions in non-Down syndrome population in parentheses.
SOURCE: Reprinted by permission from Epstein.[8]

some significant relationship between two such infrequent aberrations affecting leukocyte proliferation. Furthermore, the finding of other hematologic abnormalities in trisomic newborns, especially an increased hematocrit, but also including either thrombocytosis or thrombocytopenia,[164,165] is compatible with the notion of a generalized abnormality in stem cell regulation. In fact, it has been suggested, although not shown, that there is an extensive congenital defect of bone marrow function in DS newborns, possibly due to the presence of a marrow-stimulating humoral substance.[166]

A view dissenting from the prevailing one that the leukemoid reactions and true leukemia are distinct entities has very recently been published.[155] This view holds that leukemoid reactions are, in fact, transient but true leukemia which most often is acute megakaryoblastic leukemia. In most cases this leukemia regresses spontaneously, but in about 25 percent it recurs during the first 3 years of life, again as acute megakaryoblastic leukemia.

Immunologic Defects

Antibodies. The immunologic status of individuals with DS has been the subject of intensive investigation for many years, primarily because of clinical observations suggesting that they are more susceptible to a variety of infectious diseases[167] and, as has just been discussed, to the development of leukemia. Infection still constitutes the leading cause of death of trisomic individuals (see "Life Expectancy and Causes of Death," below). In general, the literature (summarized in Refs. 5, 8, 168, and 169) has been characterized by considerable disagreement and contradiction stemming, in large part, from differences in subject selection (age, institutionalized versus noninstitutionalized), choice of control subjects, and the methodologies employed. Nevertheless, a picture of immunologic impairment associated with DS still emerges.

The consensus is that serum IgG is elevated, particularly in older subjects. However, there are reports of normal IgG levels and, in newborns, of decreased concentrations.[170] The situation with regard to IgM and IgA is less clear. Serum concentrations of IgM have been variously reported as decreased, normal, and even increased, and the differences do not appear to be age-related. Similarly, IgA has been reported to be decreased, normal, and increased. A transition from normal levels in children to elevated levels in adults has been claimed[171,172] and may explain some of the discrepancy.

T Lymphocytes. Quantitative studies of T lymphocytes in institutionalized subjects with DS have revealed a reduction, often quite small, in the proportion or absolute number of T lymphocytes,[173,174] although normal proportions or numbers of T and B lymphocytes in DS children have also been seen.[175,176] The proportion of T-helper cells (OKT4$^+$, Leu-3a$^+$) is decreased, resulting in a decreased, perhaps reversed (<1.0) ratio of helper to suppressor (OKT8$^+$, Leu-2a$^+$) cells.[177,178]

Quite discrepant results have been obtained in the assessment of phytohemagglutinin (PHA)-stimulated lymphocyte transformation or proliferation in vitro, and both normal and decreased responses have been reported (summarized in Ref. 8). Of note, however, are the reports demonstrating an age dependence of the proliferative response to PHA in DS lymphocytes but not in normal lymphocytes. Thus, normal responses to PHA were found in cells from trisomic subjects up to 10 years of age and decreased responses in subjects over 10 years.[173,179] Similarly, a strong negative correlation ($r = -0.69$) between proliferative response and age was demonstrated.[180]

RESPONSE TO ANTIGENS. Studies on the in vitro response of DS T lymphocytes to specific antigens have demonstrated normal responses to PPD and to staphylococcal, streptococcal, and Sendai virus antigens.[181,182] By contrast, significantly reduced responses, as measured by proliferation, interleukin 2 production, and in vitro antibody production, to tetanus toxoid and to influenza virus antigens have been found.[178,183] Further dissection of this system has shown that the depressed proliferative response to influenza virus antigen results from a diminished responsiveness of T-helper cells rather than from an increased T-suppressor activity.[183] An intrinsic defect in B-cell antibody production has also been noted, as has a defect in the enhancement of B-cell antibody production by T-helper cells.

The in vitro observations on tetanus toxoid and influenza antigens are compatible with earlier reports of diminished in vivo responses to tetanus toxoid and typhoid vaccine[184] (although normal responses were found by other investigators),[185] influenza vaccine,[186] bacterophage ϕX174,[187] pneumonococcal polysaccharide,[188] and exposure to hepatitis infection.[189] Decreased natural antibody titers have also been found.[190,191]

THYMUS. Further evidence implicating abnormalities of the T-lymphocyte system in the immunologic defects of DS derives from anatomic and possibly functional abnormalities of the thymus. In comparison to age-matched controls, thymuses from infants with Down syndrome from 1 day to 15 months of age have marked lymphoid depletion, with a thin cortex and poor corticomedullary demarkation.[174] The Hassall corpuscles are increased in size and frequently cystic.[174] Furthermore, it has been claimed that the activities of putative thymus-derived serum factors are decreased,[192,193] but the significance of these observations is unclear.

Hematologic Alterations

Red Cells. In addition to the neonatal hematologic abnormalities just cited, several other erythrocyte and leukocyte alterations are found in DS. Macrocytosis is commonly observed, with the mean corpuscular volume increased 11 to 14 percent above control values.[194,195] The enzymes, glutamic oxalacetic transaminase (SGOT), glucose-6-phosphate dehydrogenase (G-6-PD), 6-phosphogluconate dehydrogenase, adenosine deaminase, and catechol-O-methyltransferase, are increased 15 to 60 percent,[196–198] but membrane ATPase activity (total, Mg^{2+}, and Na^+, K^+) is decreased by 60 to 70 percent.[101] The red cell adenine nucleotides have been variously reported as increased, decreased, or unchanged,[197,199,200] and it is not clear why there has been such variability in the results obtained.

Leukocytes. Several enzymes are increased in activity in leukocytes, including alkaline phosphatase, acid phosphatase, galactose-l-phosphate uridyltransferase, and G-6-PD.[196] The increases in acid and alkaline phosphatases and G-6-PD are found in both granulocytes and lymphocytes. A variety of abnormalities in leukocyte function, of unknown physiological significance, have been reported.[201–203]

No satisfactory explanation has provided for the numerous alterations in the activities of enzymes, none of which are coded for by chromosome 21, in DS erythrocytes and leukocytes or for the increased size of the DS erythrocytes. However, these observations do highlight the difficulty in attempting to infer the location of genes for enzymes on the basis of putative dosage effects on their activities in erythrocytes and leukocytes. The same non-gene dosage-related increases in enzyme activity are not observed in cultured fibroblasts or other nucleated cells.[204]

Hyperuricemia

Increases in serum uric acid levels have been reported by several investigators (for a summary, see Ref. 205), with the increases ranging from 16 to 44 percent. A particularly thorough study[206] found a mean increase of 44 percent in trisomic individuals, with significant differences from normal being found in all age groups. Since urinary uric acid excretion was, if anything, increased, it was inferred that the hyperuricemia was the result of purine overproduction. Other suggestions regarding the etiology of the hyperuricemia have been made, including increased degradation of purines resulting from enhanced leukocyte turnover[207] or associated with an increased adenosine deaminase activity.[197,208] The increased enzyme activity could also be an effect of increased synthesis rather than a cause of increased degradation. Furthermore, the issue of overproduction (or increased purine degradation) versus diminished excretion has still not been fully resolved, and the role of increased purine biosynthetic enzyme activity (see "Secondary Effects," below) remains to be determined. At issue with regard to the latter is whether the cellular concentrations of these enzymes control the flux of metabolites through the purine biosynthetic pathway.

Thyroid Dysfunction and Autoimmunity

Both hypothyroidism and hyperthyroidism have been reported in individuals with DS. In newborn infants studied in a statewide newborn screening program, 12 of 1130 (1.1 percent) with DS had congenital hypothyroidism. This was persistent in 8, an incidence 28 times that of the general population.[209] An increase in thyroid antibodies was not detected. In children aged 4 months to 3 years studied retrospectively, 3 of 49 (6.1 percent) had congenital hypothyroidism, 1 had acquired hypothyroidism, and 1 had acquired hyperthyroidism; 13 had mildly elevated TSH but normal thyroxine levels.[210] Only the two patients with acquired disease had thyroid antibodies. In institutionalized adults with DS, hypothyroidism was found in 17 percent, hyperthyroidism in 2.5 percent, and goiter in 18 percent.[211] Although these results would suggest a progressive age-dependent increase in thyroid antibodies and disease in DS, contradictory results were obtained in a study which demonstrated a high frequency of antibodies against thyroglobulin in DS subjects of all ages from 1 to 50 years.[212] However, an age-dependent increase in hepatitis B surface antigen (HBsAg) was observed, and the frequency of HBsAg carriers was higher in individuals with thyroid antibodies (mean = 41.8 percent versus control mean = 19.7 percent) than in those without. The etiology of the thyroid abnormalities is not known, but it has been speculated that they are related in part to the abnormalities of immune function described above. Although it is often stated that persons with DS have a propensity to develop autoimmune disorders, this is not well documented except for thyroid autoantibodies.

Growth and Stature

Newborns with DS are slightly smaller, on the mean, than chromosomally normal infants, with length being reduced by about 0.5 standard deviation of the mean.[213] After correcting for potential confounding influences, the mean reduction of weight, in comparison to the birth weight of sibs, was found to be 0.24 kg, about 7 percent.[214] In a Swedish group, mean length was reduced at birth by 1.5 SD in females and 0.5 SD in males.[215] This reduction in stature persists throughout life, with the difference from normal individuals becoming greater with increasing age. In the Swedish infants, mean height was reduced by 3 SD at age 3 years.[215] Similarly, in a longitudinally studied home-reared Japanese group, mean stature was reduced >1 SD up to 24 months of age and ≥3 SD after 30 months.[216] The lower limbs were disproportionately short, and incremental growth rates for both total stature and lower limb length were significantly decreased at all ages up to 4 years. A similar decrease in growth velocity was also observed in home-reared American children with DS, and mean bone age was reduced and had a greater variance than normal at 24 and 30 months.[213]

In a longitudinal 12-year study of institutionalized children and adolescents with DS, standing and sitting mean heights were both reduced >2 SD in comparison with a normal non-institutionalized control population.[217] Since bone age was retarded in the DS subjects, these differences were less in the prepubertal years. The stability of the growth pattern between 10 and 18 years of age was the same in both the DS and control groups, and final adult heights were considered to be equally predictable from the heights at 10 years of age in both groups. It was concluded, therefore, that the biologic mechanisms that regulate growth in this age range are not appreciably altered in DS.[217]

In addition to shortness of stature, children and adults with DS tend to be overweight.[218,219] In the latter, an increase in the proportion of body fat of the order of 50 percent or more has been noted in both males and females, and it has been suggested that both environmental (poor diet, lack of activity) and genetic factors may be involved.[219] (See Addendum.)

Growth Factors. In an attempt to define a specific mechanism for the reduction in growth, measurements of growth hormone and somatomedins have been carried out. Plasma growth hormone levels do not appear to be reduced in children with DS,[220,221] and serum insulin-like growth factor 1 (IGF-1) is increased during the first 2 years of life.[215] However, rather than undergoing the normal twofold increase in concentration between early childhood and adult life, IGF-1 remains constant throughout life. By contrast, the serum concentration of IGF-2 is normal, as are the levels of insulin and somatomedin receptors in the brains of fetuses with DS.[222,223] Treatment of DS children between 3.5 and 6.5 years of age with growth hormone resulted in increases in the levels of both immunoreactive IGF-1 and IGF-2, the former to the normal range, and 50 to 200 percent increases in growth velocity.[221] The significance of these findings is presently unclear, but they do suggest that the growth impairment in DS may result from specific growth regulatory defects rather than being a general or nonspecific effect of the aneuploid condition.

Reproduction

Sterility in Males. No proven example of reproduction by a male with trisomy 21 has been reported, although males with mosaic trisomy 21 have fathered both normal and trisomic offspring.[224] The principal defect in reproduction appears to be in spermatogenesis, with all degrees of impairment from mild reduction to total arrest having been reported for males with DS between 16 and 52 years of age.[225] In a few cases, the impairment was so mild as to be compatible with fertility, at least as judged histologically.[226] Sperm counts in nine cases have been reported to be greatly reduced in five and zero in four.[227] Penile and testicular size have been described as normal in adolescents,[228] although diminished testicular size approaching that found in Klinefelter syndrome was reported for 17 individuals with a mean age of 30.7 years.[229] In the latter group, significantly elevated levels of FSH (about threefold control) were observed in both young and old individuals and of LH (about 1.5 times increased) only in individuals over 30 years of age.[229] Although a control group was not studied, apparently normal levels of FSH, LH, and testosterone were reported in adolescents reared at home,[228] and normal plasma testosterone levels were found in other studies as well.[230,231] (See Addendum.)

The cause of the spermatogenic arrest in males with DS is unknown. It has been suggested that it results from a direct interference by the extra autosome with meiosis, possibly because the extra chromosome 21 associates with the sex vesicle.[225] A similar impairment of spermatogenesis has been observed in mice heterozygous for Robertsonian fusion translocations, albeit in a balanced state.[232] It is also possible, although untested, that the trisomic state is itself, by a dosage effect, deleterious to spermatogenesis. While failure of spermatogenesis may be a sufficient explanation of fertility in males, other factors probably also play a role. These may include a decrease in libido and a diminished opportunity for sexual intercourse.

Fertility in Females. In contrast to the apparent total sterility of males, reproduction has been documented in females. At least 24 women with DS have had children, including a stillborn pair of twins, of which 10 of 25 had trisomy 21.[224] Although equal numbers of disomic and euploid gametes might be expected, a proportion of less than 0.5 for trisomic offspring at term is consistent with the high fetal mortality of trisomy 21. Histologic examination of the ovaries of females with DS between birth and 14.5 years of age revealed an absence or retardation of follicle growth, with a reduced number of antral follicles,[223] and there was no evidence for ovulation in 4 out of 13 (31 percent) institutionalized women with DS.[234]

Life Expectancy and Causes of Death

Longevity. With the changing patterns of institutionalization and of the utilization and methods of medical and surgical therapy provided to persons with DS, it is difficult to obtain accurate current figures for life expectancy. Comprehensive reviews of earlier studies[235,236] indicate that mean life expectancy has improved dramatically in the last half-century since its estimated value of 9 years in 1929.[237] The major determinant of survival during the first decade of life, and especially the first 4 to 5 years, is the presence or absence of congenital heart disease, and recent figures from a Japanese study[238] are presented in Table 7-4. Long-term survival rates and life expectancy are not calculated with regard to the presence of congenital heart disease, but its impact is in part revealed by comparison of the survival rates of the total DS population with those alive at age 10 and by the increase in total life expectancy during the first 5 years of life (Table 7-4).[239] When compared with the background (whole) population, the life expectancy of an individual with DS at any point in time is 10 to 20 years fewer, with the difference being greater for females than males.[239] Furthermore, the absolute fractional survival rates for institutionalized individuals are 0.10 to 0.15 lower than for persons with DS living outside of institutions.[239] When compared with other mentally retarded persons, whether institutionalized or not, the survival rates of individuals with DS are not significantly different until age 30, but become lower thereafter.[235] (See Addendum.)

Mortality. The major causes of death in DS recorded in earlier studies were respiratory disease including pneumonia (23 to 41 percent), congenital heart disease (30 to 35 percent), other infectious diseases (2 to 15 percent), malignancy (2 to 9 percent), and "senility" and stroke (0 to 9 percent).[235,240–242]

Table 7-4 Survival Rates and Life Expectancy in Down Syndrome

	Japanese study				*Danish study*		
	Rate of survival				*Rate of survival*		
	*Without CHD**		*With CHD*				
Age	*Male*	*Female*	*Male*	*Female*	*Total population*	*Population alive at age 10 years*	*Estimated life expectancy, years*
0							46.5
1	0.98	1.00	0.85	0.89	0.92		49.5
5	0.96	0.97	0.72	0.77	0.84		50.0
10	0.96	0.95	0.70	0.77	0.83		45.9
20					0.80	0.97	37.1
30					0.75	0.92	29.2
40					0.71	0.86	20.8
50					0.64	0.77	12.4
60					0.40	0.49	6.3
70					0.10	0.12	5.1

*CHD = congenital heart disease.
SOURCE: Data from Masaki et al.[238] and Dupont et al.[239]

In an analysis of the causes of death of persons with DS dying in 1976, it was found that age-corrected rates for deaths from pneumonia were increased 5.6 times and constituted 16 percent of the total deaths observed.[240] For congenital anomalies (83 percent of which were congenital heart disease), the increase was 4.7 times with 38 percent of the total; for leukemia and lymphatic neoplasms, 1.7 and 1.30 times, and 3.0 percent and 1.1 percent, respectively. Increased rates for other types of infectious diseases, including kidney infections, influenza, enteritis, and meningitis, were also found. Congenital defects (heart disease) were the leading cause of death up to age 35 years. The increased mortality from pneumonia and congenital anomalies (heart disease) was found over all age groups, while that for leukemia was increased at ages 1 to 4 and 20 to 34 years and for lymphatic neoplasms from 20 to 34 years. Mortality rates for cancers at other sites were greatly diminished (to 0.32 or less than expected), as were the rates for ischemic heart disease (0.57) and cirrhosis of the liver (0.44). (See Addendum.)

Table 7-5 Responsiveness of Cultured Trisomy 21 Cells to Interferon

	*Mean responsiveness of trisomic cells**	
Property	*IFN-α*	*IFN-γ*
Binding to fibroblasts	1.57	—
Induction of intracellular peptides in fibroblasts	1.57	2.52
Induction of (2′-5′) oligoisoadenylate synthetase in fibroblasts	1.69	1.33
Induction of diacylglycerol in fibroblasts	4	—
Protection of fibroblasts against viral challenge	6.5	14.4
Inhibition of proliferation of fibroblasts	6.7	—
Inhibition of maturation of monocytes to macrophages	3.7	—
Inhibition of lectin-induced lymphocyte mitogenesis	4.0	—

*Ratio of binding, synthesis (polypeptides), or activity (2′-5′ synthetase) in trisomic cells versus diploid cells or of amounts of interferon required to produce the same biologic effect (all others) in diploid versus trisomic cells.
SOURCE: Data from Epstein and Epstein,[245] Epstein et al.,[244,246] Weil et al.,[243,247] Yap et al.[248]

Alterations in Cultured Cells

Several aspects of the DS phenotype have been defined in cultured cells which represent an enhanced responsiveness to external stimuli. Although in many instances the differences between trisomic and diploid cells are relatively small, in some cases they are quite marked. One such difference, in the responsiveness of cultured fibroblasts to β-adrenergic agonists, is discussed in "Neuropharmacology," above.

Response to Interferon. Because of the location of the gene for the interferon-α/β receptor (*IFNAR*) on chromosome 21, the responsiveness of DS cells to interferon has been examined in detail. These results, summarized in Table 7-5, indicate that trisomic cells show an enhanced sensitivity to several biologic actions of interferon-α (IFN-α). DS cells are also more responsive to IFN-α when certain intracellular biochemical events are analyzed.

It is tempting to attribute the enhanced functional and biochemical responses to IFN-α to the presence of an increased copy of the IFN-α receptor gene (see below), but it is not clear that this is entirely the case. Although the IFN-γ receptor gene is not believed to be on chromosome 21, enhanced responses of DS cells have been observed for the antiviral[243] and for the polypeptide[244] and (2′-5′) oligoisoadenylate synthetase-inducing[243] effects of IFN-γ (Table 7-5). This appears to be due to the fact that a component of the INF-γ receptor, referred to as a transducer, is coded for by chromosome 21.[244a] DS cells may also be more responsive in general to a variety of external stimuli acting through cell surface receptors.

Cell Proliferation. Several reports have suggested that there is a decreased rate of DNA synthesis or cell doubling in cultured DS fibroblasts[249,250] or prolongation of the G2[251] or G1[252] phase of the cell cycle. Lower growth rates for trisomic lymphoblastoid lines have also been reported.[253] In continuous cell culture, the rate of cell population doubling of matched pairs of fibroblasts decreased linearly with time, with the DS cells always having a slightly lower rate (about 10 to 15 percent).[254] Furthermore, the cumulative number of population cell doublings was reduced by 20 percent (from a mean of 51.5 to 40) in the cultured DS cells.

In contrast to these results, all suggesting some degree of impairment of cell proliferation in vitro, other workers also using matched fibroblasts found that the mean number of cumulative population doublings was not reduced and that doubling times were not significantly increased.[255,256] However, each of these means had a substantial standard deviation. At present, therefore, the data favoring or denying a difference in proliferative rates and cumulative population doublings seem to be about equally persuasive.

Sensitivity to Radiation and Chemicals. Because of the increased susceptibility of children with DS to the development of leukemia, considerable interest has been focused on the sensitivity of trisomic cells to mutagenic and carcinogenic agents, including radiation, chemicals, and viruses. The objective of these studies has been to determine whether there is an intrinsic defect in DS cells which might make them more susceptible to oncogenic transformation.

RADIATION. There have been numerous reports describing an increased radiosensitivity of trisomic lymphocytes as measured by a variety of techniques and at different stages of the cell cycle. When data from several of these reports were summarized,[8] the most striking conclusion was that an effect, when one is present, is relatively small—the increased production of aberrations by trisomic cells being of the order of 1.1 to 2.1 times. In some experiments, when the dose of irradiation or the stage of the cell cycle at which radiation occurred was changed, the effect was no longer detectable.

It was originally speculated that there is an intrinsic increase in cellular radiosensitivity of DS lymphocytes.[257] Recent opinion has turned against this interpretation, and it has been proposed that the apparent hypersensitivity may be the result of a difference in the state of unstimulated lymphocytes[258] or in the rate at which trisomic lymphocytes respond to mitogenic stimulation.[259] However, based on experiments with lymphoblastoid lines, a contrary view has been proposed. When five DS lines were compared with 30 diploid lines, the mean survival 3 days after exposure to 100 rads of x-rays was reduced from about 0.54 in diploid cells to 0.43 in trisomic cells.[260] This decreased survival was attributed to a defective repair rather than to an increased amount of x-ray-induced damage.

MUTAGENIC AND CARCINOGENIC CHEMICALS. Data on the effects of mutagenic and carcinogenic chemicals, generally alkylating agents, on the induction of chromosome aberrations in trisomic cells are more limited than for radiation. As they now stand, little can be inferred from them. In the best analyzed work on lymphocytes,[258] the considerations that apply to radiation seem to hold for the chemical agent bleomycin as well. The available fibroblast results are flawed by the inadequate matching of cells or the limited number of cell strains studied, although the finding of a 3.9 to 4.6 times difference in response to the alkylating agent trenimone between trisomic and diploid cells in the same sample from a trisomy 21/2n mosaic are of interest.[261] For the present, however, the published data are insufficient to support a conclusion that trisomic cells are inherently more sensitive to mutagenic or carcinogenic chemicals.

Effects of Viruses. Another probe of the sensitivity of DS lymphocytes to chromosomal damage has been viral infection, either spontaneous or induced by vaccination. Measles infection has been reported to increase the number of chromosome breaks per cell 4.8 times in individuals with DS, whereas the increase in normal subjects was only 1.2 times.[262] Similarly, the number of chromosome breaks per cell immediately after chicken pox infection increased 2.8 times in DS but only 1.8 times in normal individuals.[263] These data are insufficient to know what significance to attach to them.

CELL TRANSFORMATION. Of greater interest than studies of virus-induced chromosome aberrations have been the investigations of cell transformation induced by transforming viruses. Simian virus 40 (SV40) has been the principal virus studied, and DS cells appear to be more sensitive to transformation than do diploid controls, the increase in sensitivity being of the order of two- to threefold.[264–266] However, the significance of these observations is uncertain. First, as with many similar types of studies, the selection and matching of cells is frequently open to question. When the matching was good, as, for example, when trisomic and diploid cells were cloned from trisomy 21/2n mosaic cell populations, the trisomy 21-diploid difference did not necessarily hold up.[266] Second, the results were sometimes quite dependent on the choice of assay conditions. Thus, induction of SV40 T antigen in nondividing cells, as opposed to the dividing cells used to derive the values cited above, was greater in diploid cells than in trisomic cells by a factor as great as eightfold.[267] Finally, the observations on SV40 transformation, whatever they do mean, do not appear to be unique to DS,[268] and elevated frequencies of T-antigen expression have been found in cells from individuals with a variety of different aneuploid states.[264,268]

The situation with DS and SV40 transformation, as it presently stands, is not dissimilar from that described earlier for cell proliferation and sensitivity to radiation. There seems to be something different between DS and diploid cells, albeit generally small in magnitude. But, the results are not always consistent, their interpretation is unclear, and their significance is uncertain. Despite the great amount of effort devoted to them, the outcome of these investigations must be considered as disappointing.

THE CHROMOSOMAL BASIS AND EPIDEMIOLOGY OF DOWN SYNDROME

Types of Chromosome Abnormalities

Down syndrome is the phenotypic manifestation of trisomy 21. As such, it occurs when an extra copy of chromosome 21 is present in the genome, whether as a free chromosome (Fig. 7-5), part of a Robertsonian (rb) fusion chromosome, or, in rare instances, as part of a reciprocal translocation (Fig. 7-6). All cells of the body are trisomic, except for the 2 to 4 percent of cases in which mosaicism exists. In the latter, two populations of cells, one diploid and one trisomic, are present, with the number and distribution of trisomic cells being sufficient to cause the DS phenotype to manifest itself (see "Mosaicism," below). The proportions of the various cytogenetic forms of trisomic 21 are shown in Table 7-6. As can be seen in these data, the vast majority of cases are 47,+21, with the other categories constituting ≤5 percent each.

The data in Table 7-6 represent means for all cases of DS, independent of maternal age. Since the frequency of 47,+21 is a function of maternal age, whereas the other forms of aneuploidy producing DS do not appear to be, its proportion and that of 47,+21/46 mosaicism rise progressively with maternal age while that of the Robertsonian translocations decreases (Table 7-7). Of the cases associated with Robertsonian translocations between chromosome 21 and one of the D-group chromosomes (i.e., chromosomes 13 to 15), approximately 40 to 45 percent are familial in that they are inherited from a cytogenetically balanced parent of genotype 45,−D,−21,+rb(D;21).[271] For the G-group Robertsonian translocations, only about 4 percent are familial.[271] When considered together with the age dependance of nontranslocation trisomy 21, the likelihood that a child with DS has an unbalanced translocation of familial origin falls from 2.2 percent at maternal age 20

Fig. 7-5 *Metaphase spread of G-banded chromosomes from person with trisomy 21. The three chromosomes 21 are circled. (Courtesy of Dr. Steven A. Schonberg.)*

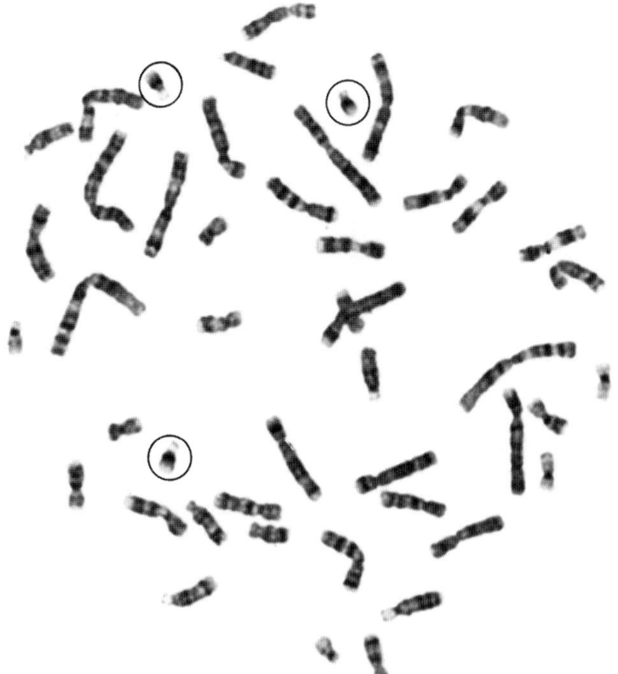

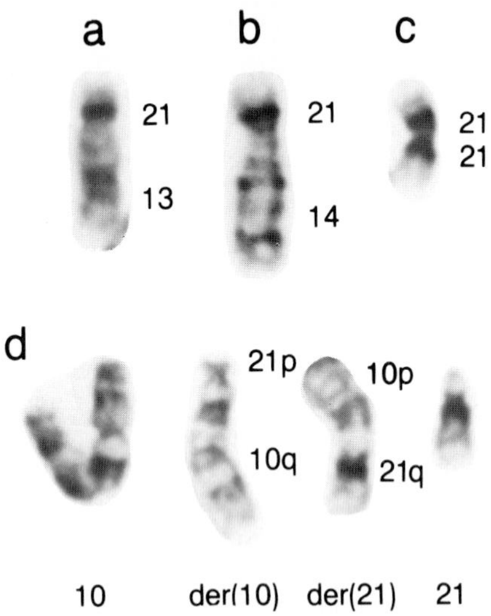

Fig. 7-6 Translocations predisposing to the occurrence of Down syndrome. G-banded chromosomes. A–C: Robertsonian translocations. *A.* rob(13;21); *B.* rob(14;21), the most common translocation predisposing to Down syndrome; *C.* rob(21;21). All children of a balanced carrier of the latter translocation have Down syndrome since the complementary product, monosomy 21, is not viable. *D.* rcp(10;21)(p11;p12). This is a reciprocal translocation in which the end of the short arm of a chromosome 21 is translocated to the short arm of a chromosome 10 near the centromere, and most of the short arm of the chromosome 10 is translocated to the short arm of the chromosome 21 near the centromere. The resulting chromosomes appear to have the short arm (p) of 21 on the long arm (q) of 10 [der (10)] and the short arm of 10 on the long arm of 21 [der (21)] (der = derivative). Down syndrome occurs by 3:1 nondisjunction in which chromosomes der(10), der(21), and 21 all migrate to the same pole at the first meiotic division. Robertsonian translocation rob(21;22) and other reciprocal translocations involving chromosome 21 can also give rise to Down syndrome. *(Courtesy of Dr. Steven A. Schonberg.)*

years to 1.0 percent at age 30, 0.4 percent at age 35, and 0.1 percent at age 40.[272]

The cytogenetic abnormalities just described involve most or all of chromosome 21, whether free or as part of a Robertsonian fusion chromosome (in which case only the long arm, 21q, is present in an extra copy). However, there are, as has been noted, rare cases in which only part of the long arm of the chromosome is triplicated, and such cases have been used to define the region of chromosome 21 responsible for the DS phenotype. This type of analysis is discussed in "Down Syndrome Region," below. Even rarer are the cases of phenotypic DS in which the chromosomes appear to be normal. These cases have been attributed either to undetected mosaicism,[273] which could occur since only peripheral blood lymphocytes and skin fibroblasts are routinely karyotyped, or to undetected duplication of only part of chromosome 21.[270] Evidence for the latter possibility has been very recently obtained from gene dosage studies which demonstrated the presence of extra copies of three chromosome 21 genes in two cases of phenotypic but chromosomally normal DS (see below).[274,275]

Table 7-6 Types of Chromosome Abnormalities in Individuals with Down Syndrome

Cytogenetic abnormality	Proportion, %	
	By direct observation	*Corrected for ascertainment bias*
47,+21	89.3–93.9	93–96
47,+21/46 mosaicism	1.0–3.7	2–4
Robertsonian translocations		2–5
46,−14,+rb(14;21)	1.5–3.4	—
46,−13,+rb(13;21)	0.1–0.6	—
46,−15,+rb(15;21)	0.2–0.6	—
46,−21,+rb(21;21)	1.6–2.1	—
46,−22,+rb(21;22)	0.1–0.3	—
Reciprocal translocations	0.2–0.3	<1

SOURCE: From Thuline and Pueschel[269] and Hook.[270]

Table 7-7 Types of Chromosome Abnormalities in Individuals with Down Syndrome as a Function of Maternal Age

Maternal age, years	Cytogenetic abnormality, %		
	47,+21	*47,+21/46 mosaicism*	*46,rb(−;21)*
15–19	84.9	5.0	10.1
20–24	89.8	1.2	9.0
25–29	91.1	2.1	6.9
30–34	92.7	2.7	4.5
35–39	97.2	1.4	1.5
40–44	97.1	2.0	1.7
≥44	96.6	2.3	1.1

SOURCE: From Hook.[270]

Mosaicism

Trisomy 21 mosaicism (47,+21/46) may result from either meiotic or mitotic nondisjunction. In the former instance, the extra chromosome 21 is lost from a cell soon after fertilization occurs. In the latter, nondisjunction occurs during early embryogenesis to generate both 47,+21 and 45,−21 cell populations, with the monosomic cells presumably being lost during embryonic and fetal life. Based on analysis of maternal ages at time of birth, it has been estimated that about 20 percent of phenotypically recognized mosaics may be of mitotic origin.[276] Mosaicism for the other types of chromosome abnormalities leading to the presence of an extra chromosome 21q can also exist.

Detection of Mosaicism. Trisomy 21 mosaicism is generally recognized in one of three ways: during the cytogenetic investigation of typical cases of DS, during the evaluation of so-called mild or of possible cases of DS or of mildly retarded and/or dysmorphic children without any obvious diagnosis, and in the course of studies on parents who have had more than one child with trisomy 21. In the latter instances, particularly when the proportion of trisomic cells may be quite low, there are serious methodological problems involved in the detection and quantification of a mosaic state—in fact, in defining whether mosaicism is actually present or, conversely, can be considered as being reasonably well excluded.[270] One such problem derives from the fact that the proportions of trisomic cells in peripheral blood lymphocytes are generally lower than in skin fibroblasts cultured from the same individual.[276,277] Furthermore, the detected proportion of mosaicism can change with time.[278–280] Some of the difficulties in detection should be alleviated by cytogenetic analysis based on the use of chromosome-specific probes in situ in interphase cells,[281] a procedure which would permit a large number of cells to be analyzed. For these reasons, estimates of both the frequency of trisomy 21 mosaicism and the proportions of trisomic and diploid cells in mosaic individuals must be considered as only approximate. Nevertheless, it has been estimated that parental mosaicism, as defined by the detection of at least two trisomic cells, is present in about 3 percent of females (i.e., 1.5 percent of parents) having one child with trisomy 21;[282,283] if only one trisomic cell is accepted as evidence of mosaicism, the frequency rises to 4.3 percent of families.[282] The mosaic individuals in these families, while phenotypically normal, may have proportions of trisomic cells as high as 20 to 25 percent in lymphocytes and fibroblasts,[276] although ≤6 percent[283] or even ≤3 percent[282] for lymphocytes is more usual.

Phenotypes of Mosaics. If mosaic cases ascertained from cytogenetic evaluation because of presumed or suspected DS or because of mental retardation are considered, there does not appear to be any correlation between mental development and the proportion of trisomic cells present in either peripheral blood lymphocytes[284,285] or fibroblasts,[285] although such a correlation had been claimed for the latter.[286] No data are available that would permit an assessment of the degree of mosaicism in other tissues of the body, particularly the brain, as is now possible in animal model systems (see "Chimeric and Transgenic Mice," below). Nevertheless, when considered as a group, the mean intelligence and developmental quotients (IQ and DQ) for the mosaic cases do appear to be somewhat higher, perhaps 10 to 20 points, than in matched individuals with nonmosaic trisomy 21.[284] But, because of the wide variability, the existence of mosaicism per se is not of great prognostic value.[284,287] The physical phenotype can be quite variable, ranging from "typical" Down syndrome to only mental retardation and very subtle dysmorphic features. Congenital heart disease appears to occur very infrequently, if at all.[285] Although mosaicism associated with clinical abnormality and parental mosaicism have been discussed as though they were separate entities, they really ought to be considered as different points on a continuum ranging from no clinically detectable abnormalities to the full Down syndrome phenotype. There are undoubtedly many mosaic individuals who are not recognized because there is no reason to carry out the extensive chromosome studies that would be required to detect the existence of chromosomal mosaicism.

Parental Origin of Extra Chromosome 21

The existence of structural heteromorphisms (variations) in the satellites of the short arm of chromosome 21 (Fig. 7-7) and, more recently, of restriction fragment length polymorphisms in cloned DNA sequences has permitted the parental source of the extra chromosome in trisomy 21 to be ascertained. As is shown in Table 7-8, which is based on cytogenetic analysis of liveborns, 80 percent of all cases that could be classified were maternal in origin, and of these ≈80 percent were meiosis I errors. For paternally derived cases, 63 percent were in meiosis I. Similar distributions were also observed in spontaneously aborted fetuses with trisomy 21.[288] Similarly, 74 percent of *de novo* (nonfamilial) Robertsonian translocations (21;21 and 14;21) ascertained in liveborns were maternal in origin.[289] Mean maternal ages were the same in cases of either paternal or maternal origin and of meiosis I and meiosis II errors,[290,291] an unexpected finding in view of the very strong maternal age effect on the incidence of trisomy 21.

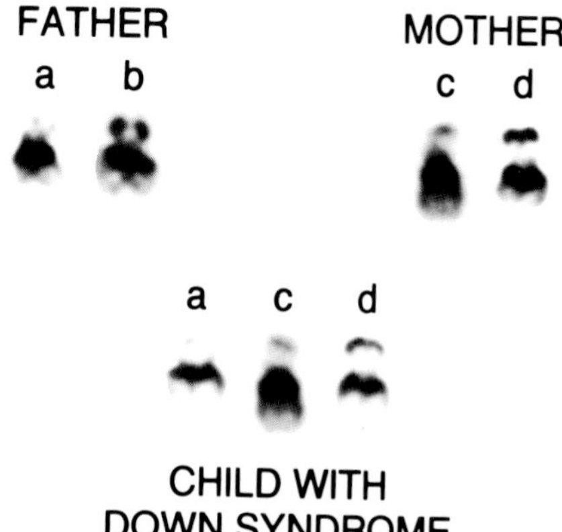

Fig. 7-7 Origin of trisomy 21 by nondisjunction at meiosis I in the mother's oocyte. Note that the affected child has both of the mother's chromosomes 21 (C and D). *(Courtesy of Dr. Steven A. Schonberg.)*

Maternal Age and the Incidence of Down Syndrome

It has long been recognized that the risk of having a child with DS increases with maternal age and that the distribution of maternal age in the population of women having children is the primary determinant of the overall incidence of DS.[292] Over the period from 1960 to 1978, the proportion of women in the United States giving birth who were ≥35 years of age declined from 10.9 to 4.5 percent, and the estimated crude incidence of DS fell from 1.33 to 0.99 per 1000 births.[292] Because of changes over the years in the proportions of cases actually ascertained, it is difficult to determine with certainty whether there have been any changes in age-specific incidence rates. Present evidence suggests that these rates have remained constant.[270,292]

Effect of Maternal Age on Incidence. A variety of estimates of the incidence of DS in the newborn population have been made, and most recent figures are in the vicinity of 1 per 1000.[270] The figures can be broken down to provide maternal age-specific rates, and these rates are shown in Fig. 7-8 and, in abbreviated form, in Table 7-9. Although it has been suggested otherwise, there is no evidence that the rate levels off at the upper extreme of maternal age (>46 years).[293] On the other hand, there is a suggestion that the rate is slightly higher for mothers under 20 years of age.[270] Overall, the rate of DS increases quite gradually in a linear fashion, about 0.04 to 0.05 per 1000 per year until about age 30 to 31 years. There is then an apparently abrupt shift to more of an exponential pattern of increase. It is not clear whether this represents a true change in the mechanism(s) responsible for nondisjunction or

Table 7-8 Type and Parental Origin of Meiotic Error Leading to Trisomy 21 Ascertained Postnatally

Parental origin	Type of error, %			
	Meiosis I	*Meiosis II*	*Unknown*	*Total*
Maternal	56	15	9	80
Paternal	12	7	1	20
Combined	68	22	10	100

SOURCE: From Mikkelsen.[289]

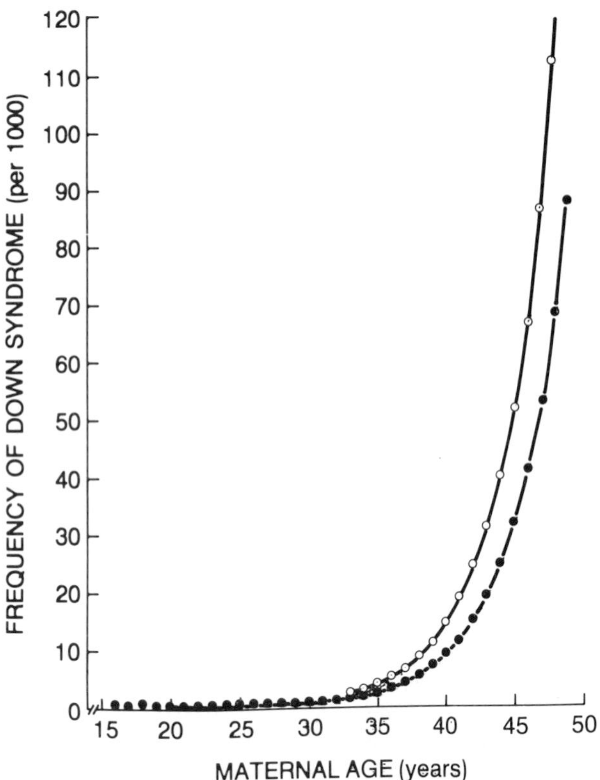

Fig. 7-8 Maternal age dependence of incidence of trisomy 21 at birth (●) and at the time of amniocentesis (○). [*The birth data are from Hook*[270] *(points are means of three reported studies) and the amniocentesis data from Hook, Cross, and Schreinemachers.*][294]

actually derives from two processes, one constant and one exponential, which coexist throughout the childbearing years.[270]

RATES IN FETUSES. The estimates for the incidence of Down syndrome in the newborn population are corrected for underreporting, a quite serious problem in the compilation of accurate statistics. Even so, the rates observed at birth are still only two-thirds of the rates observed in fetuses monitored by midgestational amniocentesis (Table 7-9, Fig. 7-8).[294] These differences are attributable in whole or in part to fetal death leading to spontaneous abortion between the time the amniocentesis is performed and term. In a survey of pregnancies in which 47, +21 was detected at the 16th to 18th week of gestation and therapeutic abortion was not carried out, over 20 percent of the DS fetuses died in utero.[295] How frequently trisomy 21 fetuses die prior to the usual time of amniocentesis is not known. Such information should become available when sufficient cases are detected by chorionic villus sampling to permit maternal age-dependent rates to be calculated. However, among all clinically recognized pregnancies, the frequency of 47, +21 is between 3 and 5 per 1000 for mothers between 20 and 39 years of age, and 22 per 1000 for mothers ≥40 years, if a spontaneous abortion rate of 15 percent is assumed.[296] Many of these trisomic fetuses were aborted prior to the time at which amniocentesis would have been performed,[297] so that the rates just given would be roughly additive with the rates derived from amniocentesis data to give a closer approximation to the true conceptional incidence of trisomy 21. Trisomy 21 abortuses tended to be recognized as fetuses, rather than as tissue fragments, and several had the unusual finding of short arms and legs.[298] Overall it is estimated that ≤≈30 percent of DS fetuses survive to term.[270,299]

Table 7-9 Maternal Age Dependence of Down Syndrome Fetuses and Liveborns

Maternal age, years	*Rate per 1000*	
	Liveborns	*Midtrimester fetuses*
20	0.58	—
25	0.80	—
30	1.04	—
33	1.57	2.5
35	2.59	4.1
37	4.28	6.8
38	5.50	8.8
39	7.07	11.3
40	9.09	14.7
42	15.04	24.2
44	24.89	40.2
46	41.22	66.9

SOURCE: From Hook[270] and Hook et al.[294]

Causes of Maternal Age Effect. Despite decades of investigation, it is fair to say that we do not understand the basis of the very strong effect of maternal age on incidence. This effect is so strong that it has been estimated that the majority of oocytes, or at least of recognizable pregnancies of women ≥40 years of age, may be aneuploid.[296] Several types of hypotheses have been advanced, and, in considering these possibilities, it should be kept in mind that both age-dependent and age-independent factors may be operating simultaneously.[300] (See Addendum.)

AGING OF OVA. Hypotheses in this category hold that cumulative events, either intrinsic or extrinsic (environmental) in origin, lead to a breakdown in meiosis, and, in turn, to nondisjunction. Such events could be either an age-dependent decay in spindle fibers or their components or a failure in nucleolar breakdown, on the one hand, or an accumulation of the effects of radiation, hormonal imbalances, infection, or the like. Few data are available to support the latter possibilities (see "Environmental and Other Factors," below), and the former are still quite inferential and based primarily on work in animals.[301] Although hypotheses of this type would be compatible with the predominantly meiosis I origin of nondisjunction, they would not explain why the maternal age effect is found even when the meiotic error occurs in the father.[291]

DELAYED FERTILIZATION. Because of a declining rate of coitus in older couples, and also a probably low rate in very young mothers, it was postulated that delayed fertilization, with "aging" of the ovum *after* ovulation, could be responsible for the age-dependence of nondisjunction.[302] Experimental evidence from animals would support this notion, but many objections have been raised.[300] In particular, a mechanism involving postovulatory events would have to work at the level of meiosis II, not meiosis I as is most frequent in human aneuploidy (Table 7-8) and would not, again, explain the maternal age dependence of paternally derived aneuploidy. Also, the findings of an increased frequency of DS in the offspring of Orthodox Jewish women who have intercourse close to the time of ovulation[303] would not be consistent with this proposal.

THE PRODUCTION LINE HYPOTHESIS. Based on studies in the mouse, a "production line" hypothesis was proposed which states that oocytes with greater numbers of chiasmata are formed earlier during embryogenesis and are ovulated earlier in adult life than are oocytes with fewer chiasmata.[304] A decrease in chiasmata would result in an increased frequency of univalents during meiosis I and, it is believed, in nondisjunction. At present, the evidence in favor of such a production line or of a relationship between meiosis I univalents and nondisjunction appears to be weak.[300]

RELAXATION OF SELECTION IN UTERO. In contrast to all the foregoing hypotheses, which operate at the level of prezygotic events associated with meiosis, the fourth major hypothesis is that there is a decrease in the rate of abortion of aneuploid embryos and fetuses, rather than in their rate of production. The equivalent maternal age effects in maternally and paternally derived trisomy 21 would be consistent with this notion, but failure to find a maternal age effect for DS resulting from Robertsonian translocations of the rb(D;21) type would not.[305] Selection, if it occurs, is considered likely to be very early in pregnancy, prior to the time of recognizable spontaneous abortions.[291] Nevertheless, it is believed by one investigator that the "indirect evidence . . . must be regarded as making a presumptive (but not definitive) case for selection effects."[291] Others, by contrast, believe "that it is some factor in the adult maternal environment which is the real cause of age-related aneuploidy."[300]

Ir is clear that no consistent explanation can be given for the maternal age effects. In the long run, it is likely that a variety of factors will be shown to interact and to be of importance.[306] Furthermore, these age-related factors may or may not ultimately explain the basic mechanisms leading to aneuploidy, the nature of which are the subject of considerable debate.[307]

Paternal Age Effects on Incidence

In contrast to the very strong effect of maternal age, the age of the father has only a small, if any, effect on incidence.[270] It was originally claimed that an effect of paternal age, independent of maternal age (with which it is of course closely correlated), could be detected if appropriate statistical analysis were used and that men over 55 years of age have a significantly increased risk of having children with Down syndrome.[308] This risk was estimated as 20 to 30 percent (over the maternal age-specific risk),[309] although even higher estimates (up to twofold maternal age-dependent risks) based on cases diagnosed prenatally were calculated.[310] Other studies have not been able to detect such elevated risks in the general DS population,[311–313] or in the population of DS cases in which the nondisjunctional event occurred in the father.[314] Furthermore, direct examination of the chromosomal constitution of sperm from men of different ages did not reveal a paternal age effect in the frequency of aneuploid sperm.[315] At present it is difficult to reconcile all these conflicting calculations and observations, unless one assumes, with Hook and Cross,[311] that there is a weak paternal age effect independent of maternal age in most if not all populations which, because of statistical fluctuation, is significant in only some data sets. On this assumption, it was estimated that a relative increase in risk for each maternal age of about 1 percent per year of paternal age could explain all the reported observations.[311] Thus, whereas a 35-year-old woman with a 35-year-old husband might have a risk of 0.28 percent, the risk would be 0.34 percent if the husband were 55 years old.

Environmental and Other Factors

A large number of environmental and other factors have been considered with regard to their potential roles in the etiology of nondisjunction and causation of trisomy 21. A list of these factors, most of which have given inconsistent (seasonality, infectious disease, sex hormones, radiation) or negative results, is given in Table 7-10. Three items do, however, require specific discussion. The first is the observed increase in the rate of DS in the offspring of West Jerusalem Jewish women of North African or Asian origin, with incidence rates of 2.1 to 2.4 per 1000 live births.[303] No explanation for this more than twofold increase has been provided. The second factor is inbreeding and consanguinity, on which studies have been carried out to obtain evidence for the participation of recessive traits in the etiology of nondisjunction. While the data are quite susceptible to different interpretations, depending on the statistical analysis used,[270,316] the finding of a fourfold increase in trisomy 21 within consanguineous matings, after controlling for maternal age and birth order, would be compatible with a role for genetic factors[317] operating by undefined mechanisms.

The third factor, maternal thyroid autoimmunity, is regarded as the only factor which, aside from advanced maternal age, consistently indicates an increased maternal risk for trisomy 21.[306] The proportion of women with thyroid autoantibodies has been found to be increased twofold among all mothers having children with DS, but the discrepancy is greater (close to fourfold) in mothers ≤32 years of age.[318] The frequency of thyroid disease was also increased in the mothers.[319] Other types of autoantibodies are also reported as being increased.[306] The meaning of these findings is still uncertain.

Table 7-10 Environmental and Other Factors Considered in the Etiology of Down Syndrome

Factor	*Consensus*
Seasonality	No consistent effect
Infectious disease	No consistent effect
Socioeconomic status	No effect
Ethnic and racial differences	No effect except for high incidence in non-Ashkenazi Jews in Israel
Birth order (independent of maternal age)	No significant effect
Consanguinity (parental) and inbreeding	Possibly an increase in incidence: fourfold increase in risk in Kuwait
Exogenous agents	
Sex hormones (contraceptive use)	No consistent effect
Spermicides	No effect
Fluoride in water	No effect
Tobacco	Perhaps a slight decrease in incidence
Caffeine, alcohol, marijuana	Unknown
Radiation	Mixed reports; probably no consistent effect
Thyroid autoantibodies	Positive association in young mothers

SOURCE: From Hook,[270] Crowley et al.,[306] Kline and Stein,[320] Warburton,[321] Janerich and Bracken.[322]

Recurrence Risks

Trisomy 21. Does the birth of one child with trisomy 21 predispose to the birth of another? In analyses based on liveborn data, the recurrence risk was estimated as 1.4 percent for maternal age <30 years in the pregnancy at risk, and 0.5 percent for women ⩾30 years.[270] These risks are quite approximate and are based on relatively few cases. More recent figures, based on amniocentesis data, are presented in Table 7-11. These data indicate that women under 30 to 35 years of age who have a child with trisomy 21 have a significantly increased risk of having another, while the increased risk is little if any over the usual maternal age-dependent incidence if the mother at risk is older.[321] As was noted earlier, the risk to liveborns would be about two-thirds of the figures given in the table, or about 0.8 to 1.1 percent (1 percent in round numbers) for a major chromosome abnormality in each of the maternal age groups. The dichotomy between the increases in risks to the younger and older mothers of index cases would be consistent with the belief that cases occuring in younger mothers result principally from causes which are maternal age-independent.[321] Despite one report to the contrary,[323] second-degree relatives do not appear to be at significantly increased risk.[324,325]

Translocations. Although *de novo* Robertsonian translocations would appear unlikely to recur, a recurrence risk as high as 2.6 percent was calculated for DS resulting from rb(21q;21q) because of the finding of mosaicism or a pericentric inversion in one member each of 4 out of 112 sets of parents.[326]

When a Robertsonian translocation causing DS is inherited, the risks to future offspring depend on parental sex (Table 7-12).[327–329] For translocations inherited from the mother, the risks are in the range of 10 to 15 percent, whereas they are only 1 to 2 percent when the father is the carrier. The reason for this difference is not known. However, for the rare case of balanced parental 45,−21,−21,+rb(21q;21q), the risk of DS from a 46,−21,+rb(21q;21q) chromosome constitution is 100 percent, since the only other possible chromosome arrangement, 45,−21, is not compatible with viability.

Prenatal Diagnosis

Three methods for screening pregnancies for DS are now being employed. The first two, amniocentesis and chorionic villus sampling (CVS), are used for a limited segment of the childbearing population. The third, maternal serum α-fetoprotein (AFP) screening, can be carried out on all pregnant women. The principal indications for amniocentesis and CVS carried out to detect chromosomally abnormal fetuses are the birth of a previous child with trisomy 21 or another chromosome disorder, a carrier state for a Robertsonian or other translocation in one of the parents, advanced maternal age, and a low value of maternal serum AFP (see "Maternal Serum α-Fetoprotein Screening," below). Several other nonchromosomal indications also exist.[330]

Amniocentesis and Chorionic Villus Sampling. In most prenatal diagnosis programs, a maternal age of ≥35 years is used as a rough threshold for determining when amniocentesis or chorionic villus sampling is indicated. However, because of the distribution of ages of women having children, only a minority of children with DS are born to mothers ≥35 years of age. Thus, in the period 1968–1976, only 4.5 percent of total births occurred in this age group, accounting for only 23.1 percent of all infants with DS.[292] Similar figures have been obtained for births about a decade later.[331] In 1983, only 7.2 percent of livebirths occurred in women ≥35 years of age, about half of whom sought amniocentesis[332]; 18.6 percent of births occurred to women from 30 to 34 years of age. Based on these data, it could be estimated from the maternal age dependence of DS that 27 percent of all DS pregnancies could be detected by amniocentesis or CVS if half of pregnant women ≥30 years of age were monitored.[332] This is nearly double the figure detectable by prenatal diagnosis at or after 35 years of age.

Amniocentesis is usually carried out at 14 to 16 weeks of gestation and CVS at 6 to 10 weeks. The choice of procedure is a function of several factors. These include safety (with amniocentesis believed to be somewhat less risky than CVS in terms of fetal mortality), methods available for pregnancy termination, desire of the parents to be tested prior to the time

Table 7-12 Risks for Unbalanced Progeny When One Parent Is the Carrier of a Robertsonian or Reciprocal Translocation

Translocation	*Parent carrying*	*Liveborn, % abnormal*	*At amniocentesis, % abnormal*
rb(Dq;21q)	Mother	10–11	15
	Father	2.4	—
rb(21q;22q)	Mother	14	16
		(1–2)	—
t(21; −)*		—	10

*Ascertained through infants with unbalanced translocations.
SOURCE: From Stene[327] and Hamerton[328] for liveborns, Boué and Gallano[329] for amniocentesis.

Table 7-11 Recurrence Risks at Amniocentesis for Trisomy 21 and for All Trisomies after Birth of Liveborn Child with Trisomy 21

Maternal age at birth of index case (years)	*Maternal age at amniocentesis (years)*			
	<30	*⩾30*	*<35*	*⩾35*
	Trisomy 21 (all trisomies), %		*Trisomy 21 (all aneuploidy), %*	
<30	0.78 (1.18) [8.1×]*	0.68 (1.02) [2.5×]	—	—
⩾30		0.76 (1.19) [1.0×]	—	—
All ages			0.6 (1.3)	1.2 (1.6)

*Increase over expected frequency.
SOURCE: From Warburton[321] (left) and Stene et al.[316] (right).

the pregnancy becomes obvious and/or fetal quickening occurs, and the time that prenatal care is first sought.

The methods of amniocentesis and CVS and for the analysis of the samples obtained have been extensively described.[333–335] The detection of chromosomally abnormal fetuses follows the expected maternal age dependence, and the figures for DS detected at amniocentesis have already been presented in Table 7-9 and Fig. 7-8.

Maternal Serum α-Fetoprotein Screening. As second trimester maternal serum α-fetoprotein (MS-AFP) screening programs for neural tube defects were being implemented during the early 1980s, it was noted that pregnancies with DS were associated with lower than normal levels of MS-AFP.[336,337] These findings were soon extended to amniotic fluid AFP values,[338] and in both instances the median value of AFP concentration was 0.64 to 0.72 that found in normal pregnancies.[337,338] Similar results have also been found for MS-AFP values obtained as early as the eighth week of gestation.[339] The basis for the lower AFP levels in Down syndrome pregnancies is not known, and the finding is not truly unique, since other proteins, such as the enzymes γ-glutamyl transpeptidase and amino peptidase M (leucine aminopeptidase) are also decreased in concentration.[340] It has been suggested that the lower AFP levels during pregnancy may be related in mechanism to somewhat decreased serum albumin (a homologous and closely linked protein) concentrations in children and adults.[341] However, a relative decrease in MS-AFP occurs even in the presence of neural tube abnormalities that greatly increase amniotic fluid AFP,[342] suggesting that serum AFP concentrations may not necessarily be directly related to amniotic fluid concentrations.

In screening programs, a series of gestational age-dependent cutoffs are established so that the risk of DS in the identified pregnancy is approximately 1/365, equal to the risk at age 35 when amniocentesis or chorionic villus sampling is considered indicated. When both maternal age and MS-AFP values are considered, the cutoffs are approximately $\leq$0.4 multiples of the median (MOM) at maternal age 21 years, $\leq$0.6 MOM at age 25 years, 0.7 MOM at age 30 years, and $\leq$0.9 at age 32 years.[343] Women whose values fall at or below these values are offered amniocentesis for the purpose of fetal karyotyping. It has been estimated that a combined program of amniocentesis or chorionic villus sampling in pregnancies of women $\geq$34 years of age and of MS-AFP screening with a $\leq$0.5 MOM cutoff for younger women would detect 48 percent of pregnancies with DS fetuses.[337]

GENERAL PRINCIPLES OF THE EFFECTS OF ANEUPLOIDY

The problem of defining how an extra copy of all or part of chromosome 21 results in the phenotype of DS is a specialized case of the general problem of explaining how chromosome imbalance involving any part of the genome produces abnormalities of function and development. Accordingly, any principles that can be derived from an examination of the effects of a large number of aneuploid states should assist in solving the specific problem of DS. Such an examination has recently been undertaken, and the conclusions are presented in the following sections. For a fuller treatment, the reader is referred to Ref 8.

Differentiability of Phenotypes

Aneuploid phenotypes, while frequently overlapping, are differentiable from one another. Thus, while the same dysmorphic features or congenital malformations may be part of the phenotype of two or more different aneuploid states,[344] the patterns of individual aneuploid states are specific enough to permit them to be distinguished from one another clinically. In fact, using quantitative methods of pattern analysis, it is possible to distinguish very closely related aneuploid states which might, at first glance, appear to be very similar or even identical with one another and to conclude that "although there are few if any physical features which are exclusive to a particular chromosomal defect, the *pattern* of defects is distinct."[345]

Specificity and Variability of Phenotypes

Although there may be a significant degree of variability in the expression of the phenotype of a given type of chromosome imbalance, the phenotype, in terms of overall pattern, is nonetheless a specific one. As has already been discussed with regard to the phenotype of Down syndrome and as is illustrated by the data in Table 7-1, no single phenotypic feature, with the possible exceptions of mental retardation and hypotonia, is present all of the time. The same is even true within families. In fact, if randomly selected series of cases of duplications in sibs reported in the literature are compared with regard to the concordance for the abnormal features which they exhibit, the mean concordance for all sets of sibs is about 75 percent.[8] Even aneuploid identical twins may not be completely concordant.[346] Nevertheless, as has just been discussed, it is still possible to recognize individual aneuploid states on the basis of the overall pattern of defects.

Sources of Variability. Variability in phenotypic expression stems from three sources—genetic, stochastic, and extrinsic—with the last term subsuming all nongenetic influences except for those randomly generated developmental events which are referred to as *stochastic*. Genetic factors can be thought of as being of two kinds—differences in the precise genetic constitution of the chromosomes or chromosome segments that are unbalanced or, conversely, differences in the balanced remainder of the genome. With regard to the latter, a state of chromosome imbalance does not operate in a vacuum but is superimposed on the overall genetic constitution of the person or animal—a genetic constitution that, except in identical twins, necessarily differs from individual to individual. The great differences in development encompassed within the concept of *normal* are such that it would not be surprising that the genetic perturbations associated with aneuploidy would not always act in a uniform matter. What is perhaps even more surprising is that relatively subtle phenotypic manifestations, such as the facies in DS, can be detected so readily even when superimposed on vastly different genetic backgrounds. Direct evidence for the operation of genetic factors in the determination of phenotypes has been obtained from work on experimentally produced mouse aneuploids.[8,347]

STOCHASTIC AND ENVIRONMENTAL FACTORS. Stochastic factors refer to the inherent variability normally present in any developmental process so that, all also being equal, more than one outcome is possible. The operation of such factors in the genesis of endocardial cushion defects in DS has been postulated (see "Congenital Heart Disease," below). Perhaps the best evidence for the existence of such factors is the lack of complete concordance for congenital abnormalities in identical twins.[348] A major implication of the existence of stochastic factors is that relatively weak genetic perturbations, such as might exist in aneuploid states, may not always be sufficient to lead consistently to the appearance of a particular abnormality.

Extrinsic or environmental factors refer to everything else that could affect expression of the aneuploid phenotype. Included would be variations in maternal anatomy and metabolism, as well as specific external agents which might be acting as teratogens. In practice it may be difficult to distinguish extrinsic from stochastic factors, and there is at present no experimental evidence actually demonstrating the existence of extrinsic factors.

Genetic Basis of Phenotypic Features

Individual phenotypic features can often be assigned or mapped to specific regions of the genome.

The features of segmental aneuploidies can often be added together to generate the phenotypes of combined aneuploidies. These two principles are complements of one another. The first states that it is possible to dissect an aneuploid phenotype so as to be able to assign particular features to specific regions of the unbalanced genome. The best examples of this phenotypic mapping which, it must be admitted, is still relatively crude, are derived from duplications and deletions of chromosome 13[8,349,350] and from the several small deletion syndromes. Examples of the latter, discussed in more detail in Chap. 9, include retinoblastoma, aniridia-Wilms tumor, and the Prader-Willi, Miller-Dieker, Langer-Giedion, and DiGeorge syndromes.[8,351]

The second of these two principles holds that it is possible to construct a complex aneuploid phenotype by adding together the individual features attributable to imbalance of particular regions within the entire unbalanced region of the genome. However, statement of these two principles is not intended to negate the fact that the combination of segmental aneuploidies may, through an interaction of the effects produced by each, result either in the expression of new phenotypic features not characteristic of either alone or in the masking of certain features characteristic of one or both. The existence of such interactive effects, especially those involved in the development of new phenotypic features, indicates that particular abnormalities need not—indeed, should not—always be attributed to imbalance of only a single locus. Nevertheless, it is not unlikely that it will often turn out to be the case that only a single locus is involved.

What implications do these principles have for the consideration of mechanisms regarding the pathogenesis of the phenotypes of aneuploid states? Overall, I consider the implications to be the following: It is legitimate to look for and to expect to find specific mechanisms to explain the relationships between particular phenotypic characteristics and the imbalance of individual loci or sets of loci. Contributions to the phenotype are likely to come from all parts of the unbalanced genome and not solely from just one or a very few loci. While some loci may have a greater phenotypic effect or representation than others, it is the cumulative effect of imbalance of many loci that determines the overall phenotype. As complicated as the relationships between genetic loci and phenotypic effects may be, and with whatever element of randomness they may be associated, these relationships should nonetheless exist and be discoverable. The generation of aneuploid phenotypes is not, therefore, a game of chance but is an exercise of the conventional rules of developmental genetics and developmental biology.

Nonspecific Effects of Aneuploidy. In making the statements just presented, I am explicitly rejecting arguments that *the* or even *a* major determinant of aneuploid phenotypes operates by mechanisms which may be considered as nonspecific in nature.[8] These nonspecific mechanisms could include alterations in the cell cycle,[352] general retardation of development,[353,354] disruption of developmental and physiological homeostasis,[355,356] and generalized regulatory disturbances.[357] While such mechanisms could conceivably operate to affect some aspects of the aneuploid phenotype, any major role for them would have the force of obscuring those relationships expressed in the first three principles above, which clearly do exist.

Mechanisms of the Effects of Aneuploidy

The term *mechanisms* is used in the plural, and this is important. My overall sense of the clinical, theoretical, and experimental considerations applicable to an understanding of the effects of aneuploidy is that no single mechanism can explain how aneuploidy produces its deleterious consequences. There is no simple solution to the problem of aneuploidy—only a series of multifaceted individual solutions, each applicable to a particular aneuploid state.

Gene Dosage Effects. The one given in the analysis of mechanisms—call it another principle or rule, if you will—is that *strictly proportional, quantitative gene dosage effects do exist.* Dosage compensation, such as exists for X-linked loci in mammals and for some autosomal loci in *Drosophila*,[358] does not appear to occur for autosomal loci in humans. While it will never be possible to state that this principle is inviolate for all classes of gene products, it certainly seems clear that it holds quite well for at least one particular class, that of enzymes. When gene products of 37 human and 7 mouse loci were examined in a variety of aneuploid states, nearly always in either blood cells or fibroblasts, the mean activities or concentrations in trisomic cells were 1.61 ± 0.25 (SD) and 1.55 ± 0.10 times normal (diploid) levels for the human and mouse products, respectively.[8] For monosomies or deletions the values were 0.52 ± 0.11 and 0.50, respectively. With one exception, all the loci examined were for enzymes and enzymelike serum proteins. Nevertheless, despite the absence of general validation for all types of loci, I have taken the existence of proportional gene dosage effects as the starting premise for a detailed exploration of a variety of potential mechanisms.[8]

Precedents for Mechanisms. For the most part, clinical or experimental precedents for potential mechanisms, if they exist at all, are derived from the study of inherited metabolic diseases and not of aneuploid states per se. It is necessary, therefore, to be quite careful to discriminate between the effects of changes in the concentration of gene products as opposed to the effects of either qualitative alterations or the total absence of the products. Keeping this in mind, it is possible to make arguments that changes in the concentrations of enzymes, structural proteins, transport system components, regulatory molecules, receptors, and cell surface constituents can each produce an effect on the development or functioning of an organism. However, not all types of mechanisms are likely to be of equal importance in all situations.

Unfortunately, from the point of view of trying to understand the pathogenesis of DS, it is, in general, easier to come to grips with monosomies than trisomies, since lack of a product seems, at least in theory, to lead to more severe effects than does an excess in nearly any type of system under consideration. It is, therefore, not difficult to understand why monosomies as a group should do less well than the corresponding trisomies. Nevertheless, it is still necessary to explain the abnormalities associated with the trisomies, and certain systems—in particular, receptors, cell surface recognition and adhesion molecules, growth factors and morphogens, and specific regulatory molecules—are quite attractive as candidates for playing a major role in the pathogenesis of trisomic phenotypes.[8]

The principal precedents for a significant role for regulatory molecules are derived from the studies of somatic cell hybrids, which point to the existence of trans-acting regulatory molecules that can modulate the expression of differentiated functions.[8] Because these effects, which are quite dosage-dependent, are highly specific in nature, it would be expected that regulatory disturbances in aneuploid cells would be highly specific as well. It is not surprising, therefore, that the considerable experimental evidence now available, while not actually disproving the existence of such specific regulatory effects, does argue against the existence of generalized regulatory abnormalities in aneuploid cells, including those with trisomy 21.[8,359–361]

In making judgments about the likely impact of the various mechanisms on the generation of aneuploid phenotypes, I have not distinguished between effects on morphogenesis and effects on function. Such a distinction would, to some extent, be an arbitrary one, since any perturbation of cellular growth and function during the period of morphogenesis could certainly affect tissue differentiation and morphogenesis. Nevertheless, certain types of mechanisms could be of particular importance during morphogenesis—in particular, those involving cellular interactions, growth factors and morphogens, and receptors (insofar as they were concerned with growth factors and morphogens).

THE PATHOGENESIS OF DOWN SYNDROME

The Structure of Chromosome 21

Chromosome 21 is the smallest of the human autosomes, constituting approximately 1.7 percent of the length of the haploid genome. Accordingly, it consists of approximately 51×10^6 base pairs (since the total size of the human haploid genome is estimated at 3×10^9 base pairs), with a genetic length of about 46 cM (assuming a total length of 2700 cM for the human genome[362]). The correspondence between DNA and genetic lengths is reasonable, since it is assumed that 1 cM is roughly equivalent to 10^6 base pairs.

In physical terms, chromosome 21 is an acrocentric chromosome with the centromere very close to one end and with a very small short arm. The short arm (21p) terminates in a satellite region which may vary in size (Fig. 7-7). Proximal to the satellite is the stalk (secondary constriction) which, as the nucleolar organizer region (NOR), contains multiple copies of the ribosomal RNA genes *(RNR4)* and stains characteristically with silver.[363] The degree of silver staining appears to be a representation of the molecular activity of the ribosomal RNA genes that the chromosome contains.[364] The region of 21p adjacent to the centromere contains highly repeated DNA sequences which consist of the satellite (including alphoid) and the "724" families of sequences.[365,366] None of these gene families is unique to chromosome 21.

It is believed that these families of repeated gene sequences may be involved in the juxtaposition or association of the satellite regions (satellite association) of the acrocentric chromosomes during mitotic metaphase and with formation of the nucleolus during interphase.[367,368] Furthermore, it has been suggested that a similar process operating during meiosis might contribute to nondisjunction,[369] and evidence has been presented that the existence of a double nucleolar organizer region (dNOR) on one of the acrocentric chromosomes is found in high frequency (≈30 percent) in the parents of children with Down syndrome.[370] Both claims have been disputed by several investigators.[371–373]

The major part of chromosome 21 is the long arm (21q) which has a characteristic banding pattern consisting of three or four bands at low resolution and as many as 11 dark and light bands resolvable by prometaphase banding[374] (Fig. 7-9). All genes of known function (other than for ribosomal RNA) are located on this arm of chromosome 21, and only this arm is essential for normal development and function. The presence of a Robertsonian fusion (or translocation) chromosome in which the short arms of two acrocentric chromosomes (sometimes both chromosomes 21) are deleted does not cause detectable abnormalities if the genome is otherwise balanced.

Genes and Sequences on Chromosome 21

A summary of the loci of known function or with known products mapped to human chromosome 21 is presented in Table 7-13.[375–380] At the time this chapter was written, the most recent official summary of human chromosome 21 loci was that presented in Human Gene Mapping.[375] I consider two loci in the official list as quite doubtful—a locus for a renal β-amino acid transport system *(AABT)*[376] and one for control of 5-hydroxytryptamine (serotonin) concentration in blood (5-hydroxytryptamine regulator, *HTOR*).[377] The latter situation has already been discussed and does not warrant designation as a specific locus. A third provisional locus, the enzyme phosphoribosylaminoimidazole synthetase *(PAIS)*, is probably part of a multifunctional enzyme, phosphoribosylglycinamide synthetase *(PRGS)*, as is also glycinamide ribonucleotide transformylase *(PGFT)*.[378] This enzyme system is involved in the biosynthesis of purines.

In addition to the loci mentioned above, Human Gene Mapping 9 lists over 100 anonymous DNA segments derived from chromosome 21 (designated D21S1 to D21S112, with some omissions), and more have been described since. While the functions, if any, of the regions from which these segments are derived are unknown, these sequences provide valuable probes for mapping the chromosome and for following the segregation of loci at meiosis.

Attempts have been made to map unidentified polypeptides

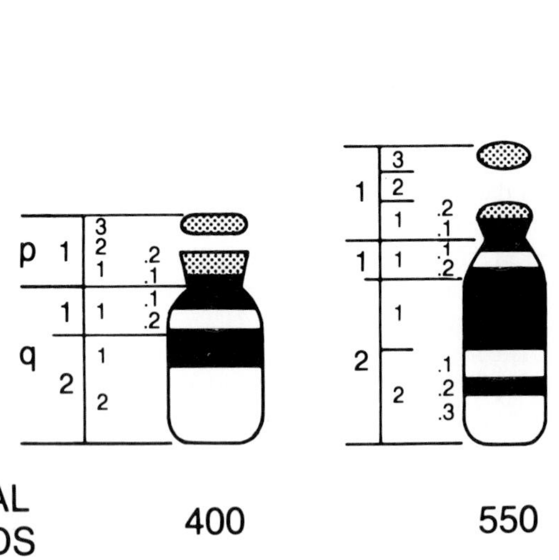
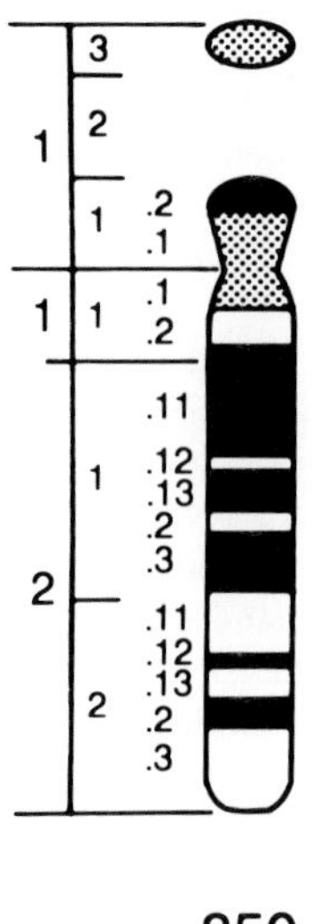

Fig. 7-9 Giemsa banding patterns of chromosome 21 at increasing degrees of resolution. *(Redrawn from Yunis[374] and reprinted by permission of Saunders Co.)*

to human chromosomes by two-dimensional electrophoresis, either by using human × animal cell hybrids segregating human chromosomes or by looking at dosage effects in cells aneuploid for chromosome 21.[360,361,381,381a] Although a very small number of such polypeptides have been tentatively assigned to chromosome 21, the results of these studies are still inconclusive.

Maps of Chromosome 21. Two types of maps of chromosome 21 are now under construction. The first is a *physical* map on which the physical location of individual loci are placed, using the banding pattern of the chromosome as specific landmarks. Construction of a physical map is based on the use of either somatic cell hybrids in which structurally altered human chromosomes 21 are present,[385] DNA dosage studies of individuals with chromosome 21 duplications or deletions,[386,387] or *in situ* hybridization of labeled DNA probes to metaphase chromosomes.[388–390] Using one of more of these techniques, it has been possible to map regionally many of the defined and anonymous loci on chromosome 21,[375,385,391–393] and the results of these efforts are contained in Table 7-13 and Fig. 7-10.

Table 7-13 Known Genes Assigned to Chromosome 21

Symbol	*Name of locus*	*Regional assignment*
RNR4	RNA, ribosomal 4	p12
IFNAR } *IFNBR* }	Interferons α and β, receptor for	q21-qter
APP	Amyloid β precursor protein	q21
AD1	Alzheimer disease 1	q21
SOD1	Superoxide dismutase 1, soluble	q22.1
PRGS	Phosphoribosylglycinamide synthetase*	q22.1
PGFT	Phosphoribosylglycinamide formyltransferase	q11.2-q22.2
BCEI	Estrogen-inducible sequence, expressed in breast cancer	q22.3
CBS	Cystathionine-β-synthase	q22.3
COL6A1	Collagen, type VI, α1	q22.3
COL6A2	Collagen, type VI, α2	q22.3
ETS2	Avian erythroblastosis virus E26 (v-*ets*) oncogene homolog 2	q22.3
CRYA1	Crystallin, α1 polypeptide	q22.3
PFKL	Phosphofructokinase, liver type	q22.3
S100β†	Protein S100 β subunit	q22.3
PAIS	Phosphoribosylaminoimidazole synthetase	
CD18	Antigen CD18 (lymphocyte function-associated antigen 1, β subunit)	
ERG	Avian erythroblastosis virus E26 (v-*ets*) oncogene-related protein	
HSPA3	Heat shock 70 KD protein 3	
IFNGT1	Interferon, γ transducer 1	
S14	Surface antigen	

*May also include functions assigned to *PAIS* and *PGFT* loci.
†Official symbol not designated yet.
SOURCE: From Human Gene Mapping Library,[375] Hards et al.,[378] Tanzi et al.,[380] Van Keuren et al.,[382] Allore et al.,[383] Münke et al.[384]

The second type of chromosome 21 map is a *genetic* map, which shows the linkage relationships between loci and the inferred genetic distances of loci from one another. This type of map is derived from studies of the segregation of polymorphic loci within families.[394-396] Because of intensive efforts now devoted to the mapping of chromosome 21, the genetic map is rapidly evolving at present, and a recent version of the map is presented in Fig. 7-11.

DOWN SYNDROME REGION. Cases in which only part of chromosome 21 is duplicated have been intensively studied to arrive at a phenotypic map which will permit a correlation of particular phenotypic features with specific regions or loci of the chromosome. Unfortunately, nearly all studies reported so far were carried out before molecular markers became available. Furthermore, it must be realized that in these studies the phenotype has been considered mainly on subjective grounds, and quantitative diagnostic approaches such as have recently been advocated[16] (see also Ref. 345) have not been used. The present consensus is that the full DS phenotype appears when band 21q22 is duplicated, and of this, subbands 21q22.1 and probably 21q22.2 are required.[397,398] It is estimated that this region carries 50 to 100 genes.[399] Claims have also been made for the importance of 21q22.3,[400] although the cases on which this was based were described as having "moderate" DS.

Still at issue is the proximal margin of the DS zone, both in terms of its precise chromosomal location and its relationship to superoxide dismutase-1 (*SOD1*). Although all classic cases of Down syndrome were originally thought to have an elevated SOD-1 activity, recent reports have raised questions about this association. Several reports[401–403] indicate that an extra copy of the *SOD1* locus and/or of the immediate region surrounding

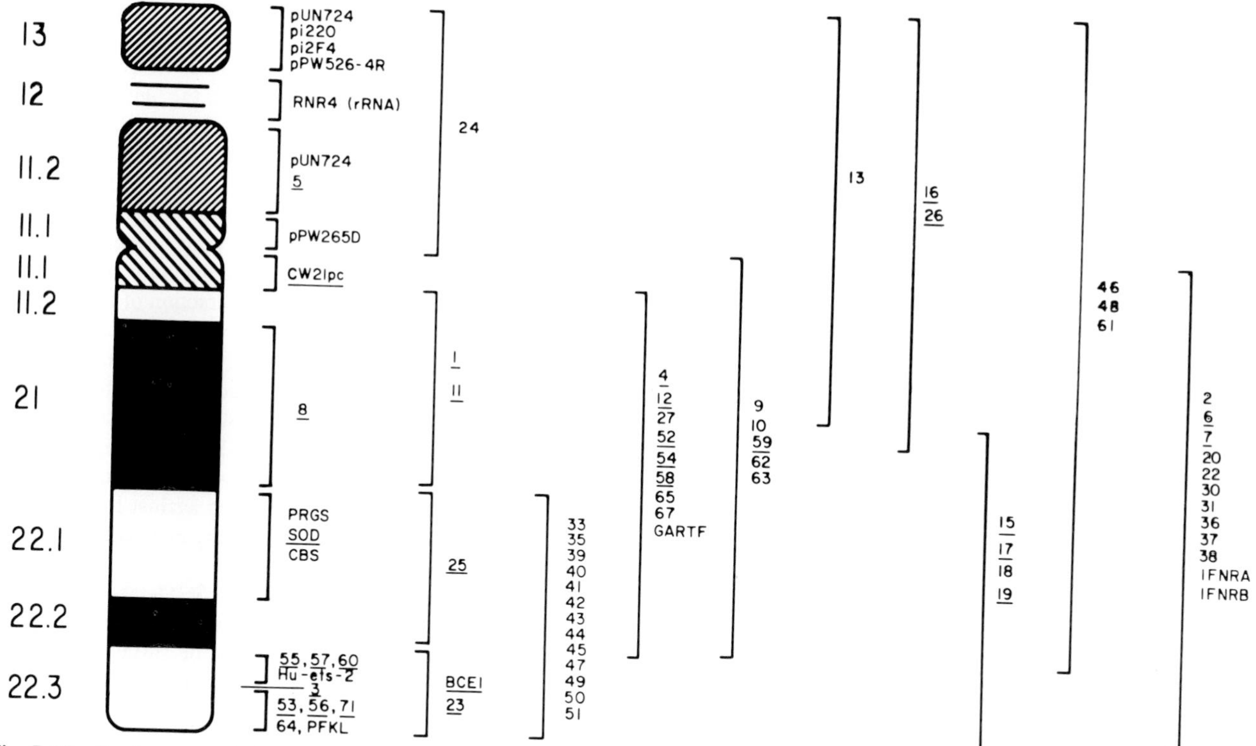

Fig. 7-10 Physical map of chromosome 21. *(Reprinted by permission from Watkins et al.[392])*

it is not sufficient in itself to produce the full phenotype of DS if enough of band q22 and possibly q21 is not also triplicated. Conversely, supposedly clinically typical cases, which may include congenital heart disease in their phenotype, have been reported in which SOD-1 activity has been reported to be normal.[404,405,405a] By contrast, two cases of phenotypic DS without any detectable chromosome abnormalities have been found to have extra copies of *SOD1, ETS2,* and *APP*.[274,274a] It is this approach, using cloned chromosome 21 probes, that will ultimately permit specific regions of the chromosome to be correlated with specific aspects of the Down syndrome phenotype.

Fig. 7-11 Genetic map of chromosome 21. *(Redrawn with modifications from Watkins et al.,[392] Neve,[393] and St. George Hyslop et al.[430])*

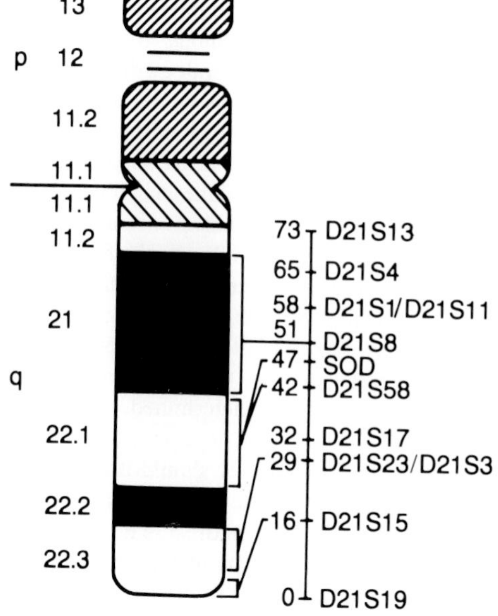

The reason for much of the interest in SOD-1 and its relationship to the phenotype of Down syndrome is, as will become apparent shortly, that much has been written about the possible pathogenetic significance of the increase in SOD-1 activity. In addition, *SOD1* is being used as one of the loci to define a chromosome segment in the mouse which is homologous to human chromosome segment 21q (see "Mouse Trisomy 16," below). Nevertheless, however the matter is eventually resolved (and at present I consider it unresolved), it should be kept in mind that the *SOD1* locus is triplicated in virtually all cases of trisomy 21 and that mental retardation still occurs if the region carrying this gene is present in an extra dose, irrespective of whether the full DS phenotype is present. Therefore, imbalance of the chromosomal region around *SOD1*, and perhaps of *SOD1* itself, does have phenotypic effects worthy of consideration. Furthermore, duplication of the region 21q11→q22 also results in mental retardation, even in the absence of other gross phenotypic abnormalities, indicating that it should also be considered when the pathogenesis of the mental retardation of trisomy 21 is being studied. It should also be kept in mind that none of the cases of "partial trisomy 21" reported to date provide any information about the regions responsible for the development of Alzheimer's disease in individuals with DS.

Effects of Imbalance of Chromosome 21 Loci

Gene Dosage Effects. As was noted above, the immediate consequence of an aneuploid state is a gene dosage effect for each of the loci present on the unbalanced chromosome or chromosome segment. Such gene dosage effects have been reported for six chromosome 21 loci and are summarized in Ta-

Table 7-14 Gene Dosage Effects in Trisomy 21

Locus	*Function*	*Ts/2n**
CBS	Cystathionine β-synthase activity in stimulated lymphocytes	1.61
IFNRA	Interferon-α binding to fibroblasts	1.57
PFKL	Phosphofructokinase activity in red cells and fibroblasts	1.46
PRGS	Phosphoribosylglycinamide synthetase activity in fibroblasts	1.56
SOD1	Superoxide dismutase-1 activity in red cells, fibroblasts, platelets, lymphocytes, brain, and granulocytes	1.52
CD18	Binding of antibody against LFA-1β to EBV-transformed β-lymphoblastoid cell lines	1.21

*Mean ratio of activities in or binding to trisomic (Ts) and diploid (2n) cells.
SOURCE: From Epstein,[8] Taylor et al.,[406] Annerén et al.,[387] Arias et al.[407]

ble 7-14. With the exception of the leukocyte cell adhesion molecule, for which there was a very wide experimental variation in the binding ratios (1.2 to 5.0),[406] the measured increases in activities or concentrations in trisomic cells were very close to the theoretically expected values of 1.5. This result is perhaps somewhat unexpected for phosphofructokinase activity, since the liver isoenzyme is not the only one present in red cells and fibroblasts and, as a result, a variety of heterotetramers, each with its own unique kinetic properties and stability, is therefore formed.[407] Nevertheless, taken in the aggregate, these results confirm the existence of quite precise gene dosage effects in cells aneuploid for chromosome 21. And, although quantitative measurements have not been reported, the concentration of the amyloid β protein precursor mRNA is reported to be higher than normal in the brain of a fetus with trisomy 21.[380]

Secondary Effects. Although the known chromosome 21 loci and their products represent but a small fraction of the genetically active loci present on chromosome 21, it is still of interest to enquire whether imbalance of any of them has detectable phenotypic effects secondary to the gene dosage effects. In the case of the interferon-α/β receptor, it is possible to ascribe direct effects to the ≈1.5 times increase in receptor number and to the 1.4 to 1.8 times enhanced synthesis of several intracellular proteins and (2′,5′) oligoisoadenylate synthetase (see "Response to Interferon," above).[243,247] No measurements of intracellular metabolic flux have been made which would permit any inferences to be drawn about the significance of the increased phosphofructokinase, cystathionine β-synthase, or phosphoribosylglycinamide synthetase (PRGS) activities, although it has been suggested the increased activity of PRGS (and of the other activities, PAIS and PGFT, if they are actually part of the same complex) may result in increased *de novo* purine biosynthesis in trisomic individuals and consequently in hyperuricemia.[399] Studies of the effects of increased leukocyte cell adhesion molecule concentration are in progress.[406]

SUPEROXIDE DISMUTASE. Arguments for a possible effect from increased superoxide dismutase-1 (SOD-1) activity have been more extensive, although any conclusions are still highly inferential. SOD-1 catalyzes the dismutation of superoxide radicals, O_2^-, to H_2O_2 by the reaction

$$O_2^- + O_2^- + 2H^+ \rightarrow H_2O_2 + O_2$$

SOD-1 is generally regarded as a protective enzyme, and numerous examples exist of beneficial effects of exogenously added enzyme (summarized in Refs. 8 and 408). However, because the H_2O_2 generated as a result of SOD-1 action is itself toxic and may, in combination with O_2^-, give rise to the even more dangerous hydroxyl radical (OH·), it has been argued that increased SOD-1 activity may, under certain circumstances, have a negative effect.[409,410] In support of this proposal, it has been claimed that trisomic fibroblasts are more sensitive to the toxic effects of high oxygen tensions than are diploid cells and produce higher concentrations of lipid peroxides.[411] The latter result from the interaction of unsaturated lipids with H_2O_2 and other highly active oxygen radicals. Increased fibroblast lipid peroxidation (≈60 percent) has also been observed in unstimulated trisomic cells.[412] Further support for a deleterious effect of increased SOD-1 comes from studies in which the activity of SOD-1 in cultured cells was increased by transfection with the cloned human SOD-1 gene.[413] While these cells were protected against the lethal effects of paraquat, a superoxide generator, increased lipid peroxidation was noted.

Another putative effect of increased SOD-1 activity is an increase in glutathione peroxidase activity. This could result from a decrease in the concentration of intracellular O_2^-, which may inactivate the peroxidase.[414] Increases (20 to 90 percent) in the activity of this enzyme have been reported in trisomic erythrocytes[410,415] and fibroblasts[409,412] but not in trisomic fetal human or mouse brain.[412,416] It thus remains an open question whether increased SOD-1 activity has any effect on the balance of oxygen metabolites and, if so, whether this altered balance causes deleterious effects. Animal models, described below, are now being used to investigate this problem.

Pathogenesis of Specific Features of Down Syndrome

Congenital Heart Disease. A hypothesis has been developed to explain the high frequency but not invariant occurrence of congenital heart disease in DS, as well as the range of lesions observed.[417] Based on the experimental observation that lung and endocardial cushion fibroblasts derived from fetuses with trisomy 21 are more adhesive in vitro than control fetuses,[418] it is proposed that there is a chromosome 21-determined increase, perhaps of the order of 50 percent, in the concentration of an adhesive molecule on the surface of the endocardial cells which give rise to the endocardial cushions. Using a computer simulation of a stochastic model of endocardial cell migration, division, and adhesion, conditions could be defined which would result in complete fusion under normal circumstances and in failure of fusion in the expected 40 percent of instances when the concentration of the adhesion molecule is increased as in DS. The fact that fusion fails to occur in some but not all cases results from the stochastic nature of the processes of migration and division, processes that cannot be completely specified genetically. Similar mechanisms may be operative in congenital heart disease of other etiologies, as well as in other types of congenital defects, whether chromosomally, monogenically, or multifactorially determined.

Leukemia. The argument that trisomy 21 should itself be regarded as the predisposing factor in the development of leukemia has been developed at great length.[419] The evidence cited includes the data cited above on the incidence of leukemia and on the relationship of leukemoid reactions to the presence of trisomic cells in trisomy 21/2n mosaics, as well as the fact that trisomy 21, alone or with other types of chromosome imbalance, is the most common acquired change in the leukemic cells in ALL (31 percent in children, 7 percent in adults) and one of the most common in ANLL (7 percent in children, 5 percent in adults) occurring in constitutionally diploid individuals. The equating of such acquired aneuploidy with a constitutional abnormality has been strongly objected to, however, as has the idea that constitutional trisomy 21 is directly responsible for acute leukemia in DS.[420] Nevertheless, a relationship clearly exists.

The crux of the matter, of course, is the mechanistic nature of the relationship. Although the situation in DS has been compared to that which exists with the two chromosomal deletions, of 11p and 13q, which predispose individuals to the development, respectively, of Wilms tumor and retinoblastoma (see Chap. 9),[419] there is presently no real evidence to support such an argument. Furthermore, unlike the malignancies associated with deletions, with frequencies of one-third or higher in chromosomally abnormal individuals, the frequency of leukemia in DS, however high the relative risk, is still one or two orders of magnitude lower, suggesting that another type of mechanism might be operative.

The possibility that mechanisms such as increased susceptibility to radiation, chemical, and/or virus-induced chromosomal genetic damage and transformation are involved in the susceptibility to leukemogenesis provided the rationale for the studies in these areas described earlier in this chapter. As has already been noted, the evidence concerning an increased sensitivity of trisomic cells is still far from persuasive. Therefore, claims for a causal relationship between increased susceptibility to chromosomal damage and increased susceptibility to leukemia[264,421,422] must be viewed with caution.

Another possibility is an altered host defense or tumor surveillance system related to abnormalities of lymphocyte function or of the response to interferon. Insofar as the latter is concerned, the result would be a paradoxical one, since it might be expected (although there is no real evidence pro or con) that enhanced sensitivity to interferon should be protective against malignancy rather than increasing susceptibility. With regard to the immune system itself, an analogy has been drawn between the situation in Down syndrome and the association of leukemia with a variety of primary immunodeficiency disorders, and it has been speculated that the leukemoid reactions might be the result of a lack of homeostatic control within the lymphoid system which results, in turn, from a deficiency of suppressor T lymphocytes.[423] Finally, possible roles for increased SOD-1 activity, by mechanisms described earlier,[424] or for increased expression of the *ETS2* oncogene, by mechanisms still to be worked out, have also been suggested.

We are thus left with many possibilities, none proven. In the end, the explanation might derive from some still undefined factor or from a combination of factors, both of the type considered here and yet to be discovered. This factor or factors might operate alone or be superimposed on the potentially enhanced proliferative capacity of trisomic hemopoietic stem cells.

Alzheimer's Disease. Earlier in this chapter numerous anatomic, histologic, biochemical, and functional changes in the nervous systems of young individuals with DS were discussed. It is presumed that some combination of these abnormalities results in the impaired cognitive functioning which we denote as mental retardation. No precise mechanisms have been worked out, and it is still not known to what extent the functional or physiological defects, as opposed to structural abnormalities, actually determine the intellectual outcome.

EXOGENOUS AGENTS. A number of proposals have been put forward to explain the development of Alzheimer's disease in adults with Down syndrome (for summaries see Refs. 8 and 425), and these can be summarized in two principal categories. The first is that the genetic imbalance present in trisomy 21 indirectly causes AD by enhancing the susceptibility of the brain to exogenous agents that cause AD, by causing the nervous system to be intrinsically defective from early in life and therefore predisposed to degenerative changes, or by causing premature aging. With regard to these possibilities, there is no hard evidence that premature aging is a consequence of trisomy 21[8]; in fact, the major point in favor of such an assumption is the existence of AD itself! The nervous system, as has already been described, probably is intrinsically abnormal from early in life, but it is not obvious how the observed deficiencies and defects would predispose to degenerative changes later in life. And, since no exogenous agents have yet been shown to cause AD, the third possibility must remain entirely speculative, although the existence of immune defects does make it worthy of consideration.

DIRECT EFFECTS OF IMBALANCE. The second category of proposals is that the genetic imbalance in trisomy 21 directly causes AD because the increased dosage of one or more chromosome 21 loci results in increased activities or concentrations of one or more gene products which, in turn, produce injury to the brain. In other words, an AD gene is actually present on chromosome 21.[426] One candidate for the responsible gene product has been SOD-1,[410] and the potential deleterious effects of increased SOD-1 activity have already been discussed. On the assumption that AD itself might be the result of a microduplication of chromosome 21,[426] the status of the *SOD1* gene in patients with AD has been examined. The results have been interesting, although not entirely consistent. One group has reported an increase in mean SOD-1 activity of 1.53 times normal in five fibroblast strains from patients with familial Alzheimer's disease,[427] while another has reported duplication, deletion, or no change in *SOD1* and/or *ETS2* in lymphocytes from five patients with sporadic Alzheimer's disease.[428]

AMYLOID β PRECURSOR PROTEIN GENE. Since the amyloid β protein is deposited in the neuritic plaques and cerebral blood vessels of the brains of individuals with AD, whether associated with DS or not, it was guessed that this protein might be determined by chromosome 21[429] and this has, in fact, been found to be the case (see "Genes and Sequences on Chromosome 21," above). Furthermore, a putative gene (AD1) for familial AD has also been localized to chromosome 21, but not in close linkage to *APP*.[430] Dosage studies on the latter in cases of AD indicate that an extra copy is present in the DNA of patients with sporadic AD.[431,432] The possible role(s) of the increased dosage of *APP* and *AD1* in the pathogenesis of *AD* in *DS* is currently under intensive investigation in many laboratories.

One other point relating to AD and DS requires mention, and that is the observation that the frequency of Down syndrome is increased in family members of persons with AD.[433,434] This finding led to the suggestion that there is a "unitary genetic etiology" to both conditions in which a postulated genetic defect of microtubules and microfilaments leads both to the neurofibillary tangles and other degenerative changes of AD and to meiotic abnormalities causing trisomy 21.[434] The validity of this notion remains to be proven.

Animal Models of Down Syndrome

The fact that many of the consequences of aneuploidy in humans arise during the period of morphogenesis places a special stumbling block in the way of their investigation. Research on events occurring during gestation, especially early gestation, is both technically impractical and, at the present time and for the forseeable future, ethically and legally impossible. It is for this reason that interest has turned to the development of models.

In a sense, there are numerous models for studying the effects of aneuploidy.[8] Thus, heterozygosity for an enzyme deficiency is a model for deletion of one enzyme locus; an increased concentration of an adhesive molecule in an in vitro aggregation experiment is a model for a duplication of the relevant gene; and a 2s × 1s somatic cell hybrid can be regarded, depending on the circumstances, as a model for either tetrasomy or monosomy. Models of this type are very helpful, and their usefulness will increase further as we begin to identify more loci that will be of particular interest. However, none of these types of models permits us to deal with more complex developmental or functional issues and to appreciate the consequences of aneuploidy at the level of the whole organism. This is what we hope that specific organismic models of aneuploidy will do for us.

Since ultimate concern is with humans and with human disease, we require models that will duplicate the human condition—in developmental and functional terms—as closely as possible. No model can be an exact one, since no other organism duplicates the human with respect to all of his or her biologic and genetic attributes. Nevertheless, models based on other mammals, which share numerous biologic similarities with humans, seem most appropriate. Even though primates with the genetic and clinical equivalent of trisomy 21 and DS have been observed.[435,436] the mouse has been the animal of choice as a model system. Its greatest attractiveness, beyond ease of manipulation and genetic control, is that the processes of morphogenesis and probably of central nervous system function (in neurobiologic if not psychological terms) are probably quite similar to those of humans. And, despite considerable rearrangement of the mammalian genome, sizable regions still appear to be intact and structurally similar in both humans and mice.[437] On the other hand, it may not always be easy or even possible to obtain postnatally viable animals with the desired region of imbalance for functional studies.[8] And, even if one could, these animals will never be able to duplicate the higher central nervous system functions, such as cognition, which appear to be so vulnerable to the effects of aneuploidy in humans, probably because of the great numbers of loci which are involved. It is difficult enough to define mental retardation in an aneuploid human. It is even more difficult to specify the proper functional homology in an aneuploid mouse.

Mouse Trisomy 16. To create a mouse model for human trisomy 21, genes known to be present on chromosome 21 were mapped onto the mouse genome by somatic cell genetic techniques. Three loci, *SOD1*, *IFNRA*, and *PRGS*, were mapped initially and all were found to be on mouse chromosome 16.[438–440] Two more loci have been mapped subsequently, and both, *ETS2* and *APP*, were also found to be on chromosome 16.[441,442] Except for *IFNRA*, which has not been further localized, all these loci map to the distal one-fifth of mouse chromosome 16, distal to the T28H breakpoint.[442–444] The present status of the comparative maps of human chromosome 21 and mouse chromosome 16 is shown in Fig. 7-12 (see also Refs. 445 and 445a).

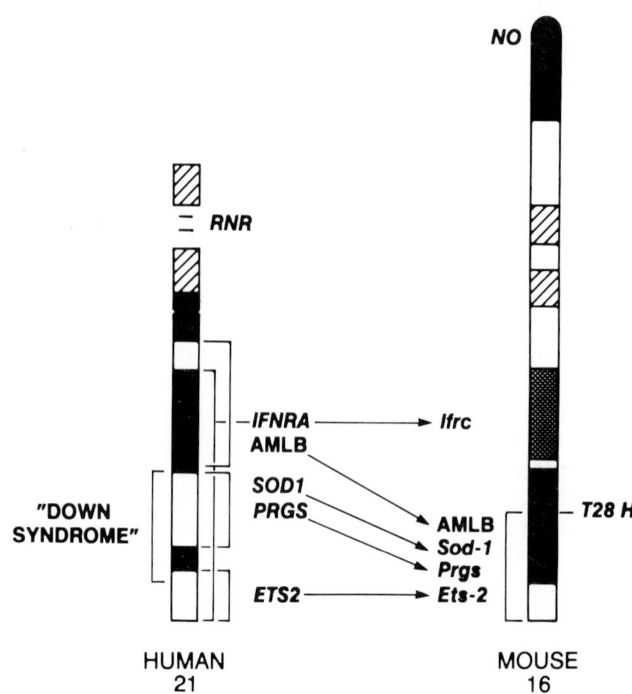

Fig. 7-12 Comparative mapping of human chromosome 21 and mouse chromosome 16 showing significant homology between the distal parts of each chromosome. *(See Addendum for additional references and Table 7-13 for explanation of symbols.)(Redrawn with modifications from Epstein.[8])*

These results indicate that most, if not all of the "Down syndrome region" of human chromosome 21, including perhaps all of q22 and in addition part of band q21, is contained within the distal segment of mouse chromosome 16. However, mouse chromosome 16 is certainly not completely homologous to human 21 since genes present on the former map to other human chromosomes, and not all human chromosome 21 genes map to mouse chromosome 16 (see Addendum).[446,447] Furthermore, the size of mouse chromosome 16 is about 35 percent larger than that of human chromosome 21 in terms of total genetic length in centimorgans. Therefore, trisomy for all of mouse 16 will result in a degree of genetic imbalance more extensive than in human trisomy 21, and more appropriate models would be an animal with duplication of just the distal part of chromosome 16 or transgenic mice into which the relevant human chromosome 21 genes have been inserted (see "Chimeric and Transgenic Mice," below).

PHENOTYPE. Trisomy 16 fetuses are generated by using males doubly heterozygous for two Robertsonian chromosomes which share an arm (chromosome 16) in common.[448] These animals usually begin to die at day 14 of gestation, but many survive to but not beyond term. The salient phenotypic features of these trisomic mice are listed in Table 7-15.[8,449,450] It is, of course, intriguing that an endocardial cushion defect

Table 7-15 The Phenotype of Mouse Trisomy 16 in Comparison with That of Human Trisomy 21

	Mouse trisomy 16 (fetal)	*Human trisomy 21 (postnatal)*
Survival beyond term	None	≤30% of conceptions
Growth in utero (weight)	Decreased 10–25%	Reduced ≈10% at birth
Edema in utero	Transient massive generalized edema	Transient edema of neck
Facies	Flat snout, short neck, open eyelids; retarded craniofacial development	Flat face, short neck, epicanthal folds
Congenital heart disease	Present in 96%, with aortic arch anomalies in >80% and endocardial cushion defect in ≈50%	Present in ≈45% with endocardial cushion defect in ≈32% and aortic lesions in ≈15%
Brain development	Weight reduced ≈65%	Head circumference decreased ≈2% at birth
	Decreased cell proliferation and migration in cortex	Deficiencies of cells in cortical layers
	Retarded development of cerebellar foliation and hippocampal fissure formation	Disproportionately small cerebellum; decreased neuron density in hippocampus
	Reductions in several neuronal neurotransmitter markers	Reduction in cholinergic markers in later life (associated with Alzheimer's disease)
	Structural alterations of cochlear and vestibular portions of the inner ear	Anomalies of the inner ear
Dorsal root ganglion neurons	Altered electrical properties	Altered electrical properties
Immunologic and hematologic	Severe thymic hypoplasia	Thymic hypoplasia at birth; reduced T lymphocyte responses
	Delayed maturation of thymic lymphocytes in vitro	Decreased antibody responses
	Reduction in pre-B and B lymphocytes	? Decreased circulating granulocyte-macrophage stem cells
	Reduced stem cell populations in liver (erythroid, granulocyte-macrophage, multipotential)	Reduced proportion of trisomic lymphocytes in blood of trisomy 21/2n mosaics
	Poor lymphoid and erythroid cell survival in radiation and aggregation chimeras	
Other	Rib, vertebral, and renal anomalies, hydronephrosis, placental hypoplasia	

SOURCE: From Epstein,[8] Epstein et al.,[449] Oster-Granite et al.[450]

is present in about half of the mouse trisomy 16 fetuses and in about 32 percent of DS fetuses and that aortic arch defects, which are so characteristic of mouse trisomy 16, are also found in human trisomy 21. Aside from these quite striking defects, and perhaps the retarded development of the brain (cholinergic deficits have not been shown to be characteristic of DS in early life), the electrophysiological abnormalities of the dorsal root ganglion cells, the transient edema, and the shortened neck and snout, the phenotype of complete mouse trisomy 16 does not, as expected, precisely mimic that of human trisomy 21 (Table 7-15). The immunologic and stem cell defects are certainly more severe than are found in DS. However, even without straining credulity, those similarities which are present are not trivial. Considering the genetic differences, the prenatal and perinatal lethality of mouse trisomy 16, possible differences in the formation of the limbs and face, and the absence of very many striking gross phenotypic features in Down syndrome, it is not obvious in what ways the human and mouse phenotypes could be more similar morphologically.

Chimeric and Transgenic Mice. Because of the pre- and perinatal lethality of trisomy 16, other approaches have been used to develop fully viable models for DS. One has involved the formation of trisomy 16 ↔ 2n aggregation chimeras, animals which are formally analogous to human trisomy 21/2n mosaics. Such chimeras may contain as much as 50 to 70 percent trisomic cells in tissues such as the brain, but the trisomic representation in lymphoid and hematopoietic elements is extremely low.[451,452] Behavioral studies on two chimeras have revealed increased activity during the dark part of the light cycle, with greater distance traveled, increased speed of movement, and excessive grooming activity.[452] Neurochemical abnormalities of unknown significance were also present.[452] Congenital heart disease was not observed,[451,452] but the trisomic contribution to the cells of the endocardial cushion was <5 percent.[452] When inoculated intracerebrally with the scrapie prion, trisomy 16 ↔ 2n chimeras had an accelerated incubation period, a more fulminant course, and an earlier time of death than did 2n ↔ 2n chimeric controls.[133]

Another approach to overcoming the problem of lethality, which at the same time also permits the analysis of the effects of increased dosage of individual human chromosome 21 genes, is the construction of transgenic mice. In these animals, the cloned gene(s) of interest is introduced into the male pronuclei of fertilized mouse eggs and becomes integrated into the somatic and germ line cells of the animal. Several strains of such transgenic mice carrying the gene for human SOD-1 have been made and shown to have from 1.6- to six-fold increased activities of SOD-1 in the brain and other tissues.[453] The effects of this increased activity of SOD-1 are presently under investigation.

THE PERSON WITH DOWN SYNDROME

While this chapter has been written principally from the point of view of the relationship between the genetic imbalance present in trisomy 21 and the phenotype which ensues, it must be kept in mind that Down syndrome may create many problems for the individuals who have it, for their families, and for society in general. Since specific forms of therapy, other than surgery for congenital heart disease and major gastrointestinal anomalies, are not available, the issue of medical management has not been discussed in detail except to indicate some of the forms of therapy that have been found not to be useful. Similarly, only brief mention has been made of the educational and psychological aspects of management. However, much has happened in recent years to improve the well-being of individuals with Down syndrome and their place in society, and more still needs to be done. For recent discussions of these important aspects of Down syndrome, see Refs. 6 and 10.

ADDENDUM

Since this chapter was written, several important and relevant articles have appeared that are briefly summarized here.

Examination of the neurons of the visual cortex of eight children with DS revealed atrophy of the dendritic tree, rather than the normal expansion of dendritic arborization.[454] Studies of monoamine metabolism in young adults with DS were interpreted as indicating an increased turnover of monoamines, but this alteration was not believed to be related to a cognitive decline with age which the investigators think occurs in DS.[455,456] However, not all investigators agree that an intellectual decline is always associated with age in DS, and one group reported that less than one-third of DS individuals over 35 years of age exhibited mental deterioration.[457] Anatomic studies of the brains of middle-aged individuals with DS revealed severe atrophy and degeneration of pigmented dopaminergic nerve cells from the ventral tegmental area, very similar to what is found in the brains of persons with AD.[458] However, detailed morphometric analyses suggest that the pathological changes found in adult DS brains may differ quantitatively in some areas from those found in AD.[459] However, the brains of younger adults with DS already had neuronal deficits not present in control brains.[459]

A general review of leukemia in DS has recently appeared.[460] Analysis of a series of 24 cases of leukemia in DS revealed severe methotrexate toxicity at standard therapeutic doses.[461] This toxicity was postulated to result from increased tetrahydrofolic acid demand, and hence greater sensitivity to an antifolate agent, because of a presumed increased rate of purine synthesis.

Growth charts for children with DS have been developed.[462] A diminished growth rate was most apparent in infancy and in adolescence, and children with congenital heart disease were smaller in stature and weight than those without. A tendency to be overweight was present throughout the growing years. In contrast to other reports, men with DS had significantly elevated serum levels of FSH and LH, but plasma testosterone was normal.[463] Among 14 women with DS, 6 had primary gonadal dysfunction.[463]

A study of individuals with DS born between 1952 and 1981 in British Columbia revealed the survivals of individuals with and without congenital heart disease, respectively, to be 76.3 percent and 90.7 percent to age 1 year, 61.8 percent and 87.2 percent to age 5, 57.1 percent and 84.9 percent to age 10, 53.1 percent and 81.9 percent to age 20, and 49.9 percent and 79.2 percent to age 30.[464] Survival of individuals with DS without congenital heart disease was still significantly lower than was found in a comparison group of mentally retarded persons. Major causes of death were found to be congenital malformations (principally heart disease), infection, and leukemia.[465]

A hypothesis has been advanced that aging of sperm in the male reproductive tract, associated with infrequent coitus, is responsible for the maternal age effect in cases of DS in which the extra chromosome 21 is derived from the father.[466] In addition, it is believed that such aging of sperm explains the excess frequency of DS in unwed teenaged mothers and that it may possibly play a role at all maternal ages. Conversely, consideration of cases of trisomy 21/2n mosaicism was thought to provide further evidence against failure of elimination of trisomic embryos and fetuses as an explanation for the maternal age effect.[467] Analysis of the recombination frequencies of restriction fragment length polymorphisms on the long arm of chromosome 21 demonstrated a reduced rate of recombination. This is believed to be consistent with the hypothesis that reduced chiasma frequency (which would reduce recombination) predisposes to nondisjunction.[468]

Comparative mapping studies in mouse and human reveal that while most human chromosome 21 genes map to mouse chromosome 16, some genes located in region 21q22.3 map to mouse chromosome 10 or 17 (see Fig. 7-12).[383,469,470]

REFERENCES

1. DOWN JLH: Observations on an ethnic classification of idiots. *London Hosp Clin Lects Reps* 3:259, 1866.
2. LEJEUNE J, GAUTHIER M, TURPIN R: Les chromosomes humains en culture de tissus. *CR Acad Sci* 248:602, 1958.
3. JACOBS PA, BAIKIE AG, COURT B, BROWN WM, STRONG JA: The somatic chromosomes in mongolism. *Lancet* 1:710, 1959.
4. LEJEUNE J, GAUTIER M, TURPIN R: Étude des chromosomes somatiques de neuf enfants mongoliens. *CR Acad Sci* 248:1721, 1959.
5. SMITH GF, BERG JM: *Down's Anomaly.* Edinburgh, Churchill-Livingstone, 1976.
6. PUESCHEL SM, RYNDERS JE (eds): *Down Syndrome. Advances in Biomedicine and the Behavioral Sciences.* Cambridge, MA, Ware Press, 1982.
7. SMITH GF (ed): Molecular structure of the number 21 chromosome and Down syndrome. *Ann NY Acad Sci* 450:1985.
8. EPSTEIN CJ: *The Consequences of Chromosome Imbalance. Principles, Mechanisms, and Models.* New York, Cambridge University Press, 1986.
9. BURGIO GR, FRACCARO M, TIEPOLO L, WOLF U (eds): *Trisomy 21. An International Symposium.* Berlin, Springer-Verlag, 1981.
10. PUESCHEL SM, TINGEY C, RYNDERS JE, CROCKER AC, CRUTCHER DM (eds): *New Perspectives on Down Syndrome.* Baltimore, PH Brookes, 1987.
11. EPSTEIN CJ (ed): *The Neurobiology of Down Syndrome.* New York, Raven, 1986.
12. MCCOY EE, EPSTEIN CJ (eds): *Oncology and Immunology of Down Syndrome.* New York, AR Liss, 1987.
13. EPSTEIN CJ: Aneuploidy in mouse and man, in Vogel F, Sperling K (eds): *Human Genetics: Proceedings of the 7th International Congress, Berlin, 1986.* Heidelberg, Springer-Verlag, 1987, p 260.
14. PUESCHEL SM, SASSAMAN EA, SCOLA PS, THULINE HC, STARK AM, HORROBIN M: Biomedical aspects in Down syndrome, in Pueschel SM, Rynders JE (eds): *Down Syndrome. Advances in Biomedicine and the Behavioral Sciences.* Cambridge, MA, Ware Press, 1982, p 169.
15. RODEWALD A, ZANG KD, ZANKL H, ZANKL M: Dermatologic peculiarities in Down's syndrome. Detection of mosaicism and balanced translocation carriers, in Burgio GR, Fraccaro M, Tiepolo L, Wolf U (eds): *Trisomy 21. An International Symposium.* Berlin, Springer-Verlag, 1981, p 41.
16. REX AP, PREUS M: A diagnostic index for Down syndrome. *J Pediatr* 100:903, 1982.
17. SHARE JB, VEALE AM: *Developmental Landmarks for Children with Down's Syndrome.* Duneden, University of Otago Press, 1974.
18. MELYN MA, WHITE DT: Mental and developmental milestones of noninstitutionalized Down's syndrome children. *Pediatrics* 52: 542, 1973.
19. GIBSON D: *Down's Syndrome. The Psychology of Mongolism.* Cambridge, Cambridge University Press, 1978.
20. MORGAN SB: Development and distribution of intellectual and adaptive skills in Down syndrome children: Implications for early intervention. *Ment Retard* 17:247, 1979.
21. SCHNELL RR: Psychomotor development, in Pueschel SM (ed): *The Young Child with Down Syndrome.* New York, Human Sciences Press, 1984, p 207.
22. GATH A, GUMLEY D: Down's syndrome and the family: Follow-up of children first seen in infancy. *Dev Med Child Neurol* 26:500, 1984.
23. KOUSEFF BG: Trisomy 21 with average intelligence?! *Birth Defects.* 14(6C):323, 1978.
24. HUNT N: *The World of Nigel Hunt.* New York, Garrett Publications, 1967.
25. GOLDEN W, PASHAYAN HM: The effect of parental education on the eventual mental development of noninstitutionalized children with Down syndrome. *J Pediatr* 89:603, 1976.
26. FRASER FC, SADOVNICK AD: Correlation of IQ in subjects with Down's syndrome and their parents and sibs. *J Ment Defic Res* 20:179, 1976.
27. BENNETT FC, SELLS CJ, BRAND C: Influences on measured intelligence in Down's syndrome. *Am J Dis Child* 133:700, 1979.
28. SHARAV T, COLLINS R, SCHLOMO L: Effect of maternal education on prognosis of development in children with Down syndrome. *Pediatrics* 76:387, 1985.

29. LIBB JW, MYERS GJ, GRAHAM E, BELL B: Correlates of intelligence and adaptive behavior in Down's syndrome. *J Ment Defic Res* 27:205, 1983.

30. CENTERWALL SA, CENTERWALL WR: A study of children with mongolism reared in the home compared to those reared away from home. *Pediatrics* 25:678, 1960.

31. SHIPE D, SHOTWELL AM: Effect of out-of-home care on mongoloid children: A continuation study. *Am J Ment Defic* 69:649, 1965.

32. STEDMAN DJ, EICHORN DH: A comparison of the growth and development of institutionalized and home-reared mongoloids during infancy and early childhood. *Am J Ment Defic* 69:391, 1964.

33. LUDLOW JR, ALLEN LM: The effect of early intervention and preschool stimulus on the development of the Down's syndrome child. *J Ment Defic Res* 23:29, 1979.

34. SHARAV T, SHLOMO L: Stimulation of infants with Down syndrome: Long term effects. *Ment Retard* 24:81, 1986.

35. SLOPER P, GLENN SM, CUNNINGHAM CC: The effect of intensity of training on sensori-motor development in infants with Down's syndrome. *J Ment Defic Res* 30:149, 1986.

36. BRICKER D: Further notes on early intervention, in Pueschel SM, Tingey C, Rynders JE, Crocker AC, Crutcher DM (eds): *New Perspectives on Down Syndrome*. Baltimore, PH Brookes, 1987, p 171.

37. SPIKER D: Early intervention for young children with Down syndrome: New directions in enhancing parent-child synchrony, in Pueschel SM, Rynders JE (eds): *Down Syndrome. Advances in Biomedicine and the Behavioral Sciences*. Cambridge, MA, Ware Press, 1982, p 331.

38. HANSON MJ: Early intervention for children with Down syndrome, in Pueschel SM, Tingey C, Rynders JE, Crocker AC, Crutcher DM (eds): *New Perspectives on Down Syndrome*. Baltimore, PH Brookes, 1987, p 149.

39. BRIDGES FA, CICCHETTI D: Mothers' ratings of the temperament characteristics of Down syndrome infants. *Dev Psychol* 18:238, 1982.

40. HARTLEY XY: A summary of recent research into the development of children with Down syndrome. *J Ment Defic Res* 30:1, 1986.

41. COWIE VA: *A Study of the Early Development of Mongols*. London, Pergamon Press, 1970.

42. HALL B: *Mongolism in Newborns: A Clinical and Cytogenetic Study*. Lund, Berlingska Boktryckeriet, 1964.

43. YESSAYAN L, PUESCHEL SM: Neurological investigations, in Pueschel SM (ed): *The Young Child with Down Syndrome*. New York, Human Sciences Press, 1984, p 263.

44. MORRIS AF, VAUGHAN SE, VACCARO P: Measurement of neuromuscular tone and strength in Down's syndrome children. *J Ment Defic Res* 26:41, 1982.

45. ROSNER F, ONG BH, PAINE RS, MAHANAND D: Blood-serotonin activity in trisomic and translocation Down syndrome. *Lancet* 1:1191, 1965.

46. TU J-B, ZELLWEGER H: Blood-serotonin deficiency in Down's syndrome. *Lancet* 2:715, 1965.

47. BAZELON M, PAINE RS, COWIE VA, HUNT P, HOUCK JC, MAHANAND D: Reversal of hypotonia in infants with Down's syndrome by administration of 5-hydroxytryptophan. *Lancet* 1:1130, 1967.

48. COLEMAN M, STEINBERG L: A double blind trial of 5-hydroxytryptophan in trisomy 21 patients, in Coleman M (ed): *Serotonin in Down Syndrome*. Amsterdam, North-Holland, 1973, p 43.

49. WEISE P, KOCH R, SHAW KNF, ROSENFELD MJ: The use of 5-HTP in the treatment of Down's syndrome. *Pediatrics* 54:165, 1974.

50. PUESCHEL SM, REED RB, CRONK CE: Evaluation of the effect of 5-hydroxytryptophan and/or pyridoxine administration in young children with Down syndrome, in Pueschel SM (ed): *The Young Child with Down Syndrome*. New York, Human Sciences Press, 1984, p 59.

51. COLEMAN M: Infantile spasms induced by 5-hydroxytryptophan in patients with Down's syndrome. *Neurology* 21:911, 1971.

52. COLEMAN M, SOBEL S, BHAGAVAN HN, COURSIN D, MARQUARDT A, GUAY M, HUNT C: A double blind study of vitamin B6 in Down's syndrome infants. Part 1—Clinical and biochemical results. *J Ment Defic Res* 29:233, 1985.

53. LANDING BH, SHANKLE W: Reduced number of skeletal muscle fiber nuclei in Down syndrome: Speculation on a "shut off" role of chromosome 21 in control of DNA and nuclear replication rates, possibly via determination of cell surface area per nucleus. *Birth Defects* 18(3B):81, 1982.

54. SHARE JB: Review of drug treatment for Down's syndrome persons. *Am J Ment Defic* 80:388, 1976.

55. TURKEL H: Medical amelioration of Down's syndrome incorporating the orthomolecular approach. *J Orthomolecular Psychiatr* 4:102, 1975.

56. HARRELL RF, CAPP RH, DAVIS DR, PEERLESS J, RAVITZ LR: Can nutritional supplements help mentally retarded children? An exploratory study. *Proc Natl Acad Sci USA* 78:574, 1981.

57. TURKEL H, NUSBAUM I: *Medical Treatment of Down Syndrome and Genetic Diseases*, 4th rev ed. Southfield, MI, Ubiotica, 1985.

58. SMITH GF, SPIKER D, PETERSON CP, CICCHETTI D, JUSTICE P: Use of megadoses of vitamins and minerals in Down syndrome. *J Pediatr* 105:228, 1984.

59. BUMBALO TS, MORELEWICZ HV, BERENS DL: Treatment of Down's syndrome with the "U" series of drugs. *JAMA* 187:361, 1964.

60. SCHMID F: Cell therapy: Experimental basis and clinics. *Cytobiologische Rev* 2:65, 1980.

61. BARDON L: Siccacell treatment in mongolism. *Lancet* 2:234, 1964.

62. BLACK D, KATO J, WALKER G: A study of improvement in mentally retarded children accruing from siccacell therapy. *Am J Ment Defic* 70:499, 1966.

63. PRUESS JB, FEWELL RR: Cell therapy and the treatment of Down syndrome: A review of research. *Trisomy 21* 1:3, 1985.

64. REHDER H: Pathology of trisomy 21, in Burgio GR, Fraccaro M, Tiepolo L, Wolf U (eds): *Trisomy 21. An International Symposium*. Berlin, Springer-Verlag, 1981, p 57.

65. GULLOTTA F, REHDER H, GROPP A: Descriptive neuropathology of chromosomal disorders in man. *Hum Genet* 57:337, 1981.

66. WARKANY J: *Congenital Malformations. Notes and Comments*. Chicago, Year Book, 1971.

67. CROME L, COWIE V, SLATER E: A statistical note on cerebellar and brain stem weight in mongolism. *J Ment Defic Res* 10:69, 1966.

68. SYLVESTER PE: The anterior commissure in Down's syndrome. *J Ment Defic Res* 30:19, 1986.

69. MARIN-PADILLA M: Pyramidal cell abnormalities in the motor cortex of a child with Down's syndrome. A Golgi study. *J Comp Neurol* 167:63, 1976.

70. SUETSUGA M, MEHRAEIN P: Spine distribution along the apical dendrites of the pyramidal neurons in Down's syndrome. *Acta Neuropathol* 50:207, 1980.

71. TAKASHIMA S, BECKER LE, ARMSTRONG DL, CHAN F: Abnormal neuronal development in the visual cortex of the human fetus and infant with Down's syndrome: A quantitative and qualitative Golgi study. *Brain Res* 225:1, 1981.

72. WISNIEWSKI KE, LAURE-KAMIONOWSKA M, WISNIEWSKI HM: Morphometric studies on the cortex during postnatal brain development in Down syndrome, submitted for publication.

73. WISNIEWSKI KE, LAURE-KAMIONOWSKA M, CONNELL F, WEN GY: Neuronal density and synaptogenesis in the postnatal stage of brain maturation in Down syndrome, in Epstein CJ (ed): *The Neurobiology of Down Syndrome*. New York, Raven, 1986, p 29.

74. MCGEER EG, NORMAN M, BOYES B, O'KUSKY J, SUZUKI J, MCGEER PL: Acetylcholine and aromatic amine systems in postmortem brain of an infant with Down's syndrome. *Exp Neurol* 87:557, 1985.

75. SCOTT BS, BECKER LE, PETIT TL: Neurobiology of Down's syndrome. *Prog Neurobiol* 21:199, 1983.

76. SHAH SN: Fatty acid composition of lipids of human brain myelin and synaptosomes: Changes in phenylketonuria and Down's syndrome. *Int J Biochem* 10:477, 1979.

77. BANIK NL, DAVISON AN, PALO J, SAVOLAINEN H: Biochemical studies on myelin isolated from the brains of patients with Down's syndrome. *Brain* 98:213, 1975.

78. BROOKSBANK BWL, MARTINEZ M, BALAZS R: Altered composition of polyunsaturated fatty acyl groups in phosphoglycerides of Down's syndrome fetal brain. *J Neurochem* 44:869, 1985.

79. ELLINGSON RJ, EISEN JD, OTTERSBERG G: Clinical electroencephalographic observation on institutionalized mongoloids confirmed by karyotype. *Electroencephalogr Clin Neurophysiol* 34:193, 1973.

80. ELUL R, HANLEY J, SIMMONS JQ III: Non-Gaussian behavior of the EEG in Down's syndrome suggests decreased neuronal connections. *Acta Neurol Scand* 51:21, 1975.

81. TANGYE SR: The EEG and incidence of epilepsy in Down's syndrome. *J Ment Defic Res* 23:17, 1979.

82. GALBRAITH GC: Unique EEG and evoked response patterns in Down syndrome individuals, in Epstein CJ (ed): *The Neurobiology of Down Syndrome*. New York, Raven, 1986, p 109.

83. SCHMID RG, SADOWSKY K, WEINMAN H-M, TIRSCH WS, PÖPPL SJ: Z-transformed EEG power spectra of children with Down syndrome vs a control group. *Neuropediatrics* 16:218, 1985.

84. FOLSOM RC, WIDEN JE, WILSON WR: Auditory brain-stem responses in infants with Down's syndrome. *Arch Otolaryngol* 109:607, 1983.

85. SQUIRES N, OLLO C, JORDAN R: Auditory brain stem responses in the mentally retarded: audiometric correlates. *Ear Hear* 7:83, 1986.

86. SCOTT BS, PETIT TL, BECKER LE, EDWARDS BAV: Abnormal electric membrane properties of Down's syndrome DRG neurons in cell culture. *Dev Brain Res* 2:257, 1982.

87. NIEMINEN K, RAPOPORT SI: Electrical membrane properties of cultured

fetal dorsal root ganglia neurons from normal human and Down's syndrome. *Soc Neurosci Abstr* 12:1360, 1986.

88. BERG JM, BRANDON MWG, KIRMAN BH: Atropine in mongolism. *Lancet* 2:441, 1959.
89. MIR GH, CUMMING GR: Response to atropine in Down's syndrome. *Arch Dis Child* 46:61, 1971.
90. LEJEUNE J, BOURDAIS M, PRIEUR M: Sensibilité pharmacologique de l'iris des enfants trisomiques 21. *Thérapie* 31:447, 1976.
91. HARRIS WS, GOODMAN RM: Hyper-reactivity to atropine in Down's syndrome. *N Engl J Med* 279:407, 1968.
92. WARK HJ, OVERTON JH, MARIAN P: The safety of atropine premedication in children with Down's syndrome. *Anesthesia* 38:871, 1983.
93. WETTERBERG L, GUSTAVSON K-H, BÄCKSTRÖM M, ROSS SB, FRÖDÉN U: Low dopamine-β-hydroxylase activity in Down's syndrome. *Clin Genet* 3:152, 1972.
94. KEELE DK, RICHARDS C, BROWN J, MARSHALL J: Catecholamine metabolism in Down's syndrome. *Am J Ment Defic* 74:125, 1969.
95. LOTT IT, CHASE TN, MURPHY DL: Down's syndrome: Transport, storage and metabolism of serotonin in blood platelets. *Pediatr Res* 6:730, 1972.
96. BAYER SM, MCCOY EE: A comparison of the serotonin and ATP content in platelets from subjects with Down's syndrome. *Biochem Med* 9:225, 1974.
97. MCCOY EE, SNEDDON JM: Decreased calcium content and $^{45}Ca^{2+}$ uptake in Down's syndrome blood platelets. *Pediatr Res* 18:914, 1984.
98. MCCOY EE, ENNS L: Current status of neurotransmitter abnormalities in Down syndrome, in Epstein CJ (ed): *The Neurobiology of Down Syndrome.* New York, Raven, 1986, p 73.
99. MORE R, AMIR N, MEYER S, KOPOLOVIC J, YAROM R: Platelet abnormalities in Down's syndrome. *Clin Genet* 22:128, 1982.
100. SHUTTLEWORTH RD, O'BRIEN JR: Effect of age and operations on platelet serotonin (5HT) and platelet volume. *Thromb Haemost* 46:198, 1981.
101. XUE Q-M, SHEN D-G, DONG W: ATPase activity of erythrocyte membrane in patients with trisomy 21 (Down's syndrome). *Clin Genet* 26:429, 1984.
102. TANG SW, BERG J, BRUNI J, DAVIS A: Decreased platelet [^{3}H] imipramine binding in Down's syndrome. *Soc Neurosci Abstr* 11:137, 1985.
103. PAASONEN MK: Platelet 5-hydroxytryptamine as a model in pharmacology. *Ann Med Exp Biol Fenn* 46:416, 1968.
104. ABRAMS WB, SOLOMON HM: The human platelet as a pharmacologic model for the adrenergic neuron. *Clin Pharmacol Ther* 10:702, 1969.
105. LOTT IT, MURPHY DL, CHASE TN: Down's syndrome. Central monoamine turnover in patients with diminished platelet serotonin. *Neurology* 22:967, 1972.
106. MCSWIGAN JD, HANSON DR, LUBINIECKI A, HESTON LL, SHEPPARD JR: Down syndrome fibroblasts are hyperresponsive to β-adrenergic stimulation. *Proc Natl Acad Sci USA* 78:7670, 1981.
107. SHEPPARD JR, MCSWIGAN JD, WEHNER JM, WHITE JG, SHOWS TB, JAKOBS KH, SCHULTZ G: The adrenergic responsiveness of Down syndrome cells, in Sheppard JR, Anderson VE, Eaton JW (eds): *Membranes and Genetic Disease.* New York, AR Liss, 1982, p 307.
108. REED WD, OSTER-GRANITE ML, PISCHKOFF SA, BARB P, OZAND PT: Beta adrenergic markers in cultured cells of human trisomy 21 and murine trisomy 16. *Pediatr Res* 17:141A, 1983.
109. FRASER J, MITCHELL A: Kalmuc idiocy: Report of a case with autopsy; with notes on sixty-two cases. *J Ment Sci* 22:169, 1876.
110. STRUWE F: Histopathologische Untersuchungen über Entstehung und Wesen der senilen Plaques. *Z Gesamte Neurol Psychiatr* 122:291, 1929.
111. SCHAPIRO MB, HAXBY JV, GRADY CL, RAPOPORT SI: Cerebral glucose utilization, quantitative tomography, and cognitive function in adult Down syndrome, in Epstein CJ (ed): *The Neurobiology of Down Syndrome.* New York, Raven, 1986, p 89.
112. MALAMUD N: Neuropathology of organic brain syndromes associated with aging, in Gartz CM (ed): *Aging and the Brain.* New York, Raven, 1972, p 63.
113. WISNIEWSKI KE, WISNIEWSKI HM, WEN GY: Occurrence of neuropathological changes and dementia of Alzheimer's disease in Down's syndrome. *Ann Neurol* 17:278, 1985.
114. WHALLEY LB, BUCKTON KE: Genetic factors in Alzheimer's disease, in Glen AIM, Whalley LJ (eds): *Alzheimer's Disease. Early Recognition of Potentially Reversible Defects.* Edinburgh, Churchill Livingstone, 1979, p 36.
115. WISNIEWSKI KE, DALTON AJ, CRAPPER MCLACHLAN DR, WEN GY, WISNIEWSKI HM: Alzheimer's disease in Down's syndrome: Clinicopathologic studies. *Neurology* 35:957, 1985.
116. THASE ME, LISS L, SMELTZER D, MALOON J: Clinical evaluation of dementia in Down's syndrome. *J Ment Defic Res* 26:239, 1982.
117. WISNIEWSKI HM, RABE A: Discrepancy between Alzheimer-type neuropathology and dementia in people with Down syndrome. *Ann NY Acad Sci* 477:247, 1986.
118. THASE ME, TIGNER R, SMELTZER DJ, LISS L: Age-related neuropsychological deficits in Down's syndrome. *Biol Psychiatry* 19:571, 1984.
119. ELLIS WG, MCCULLOCH JR, CORLEY CL: Presenile dementia in Down's syndrome. Ultrastructural identity with Alzheimer's disease. *Neurology* 24:101, 1974.
120. BALL MJ, NUTTALL K: Neurofibrillary tangles, granulovacuolar degeneration, and neuron loss in Down syndrome: Quantitative comparison with Alzheimer dementia. *Ann Neurol* 7:462, 1980.
121. BALL MJ, NUTTALL K: Topography of neurofibrillary tangles and granulovacuoles in hippocampi of patients with Down's syndrome: Quantitative comparison with normal aging and Alzheimer's disease. *Neuropathol Appl Neurobiol* 7:13, 1981.
122. MANN DMA, YATES PO, MARCYNIUK B: Alzheimer's presenile dementia, senile dementia of the Alzheimer type and Down's syndrome in middle age form an age related continuum of pathologic changes. *Neuropathol Appl Neurobiol* 10:185, 1984.
123. BALL MJ, SCHAPIRO MB, RAPOPORT SI: Neuropathological relationships between Down syndrome and senile dementia Alzheimer type, in Epstein CJ (ed): *The Neurobiology of Down Syndrome.* New York, Raven, 1986, p 45.
124. YATES CM, SIMPSON J, MALONEY AJF, GORDON A, REID AH: Alzheimer-like cholinergic deficiency in Down syndrome. *Lancet* 2:979, 1980.
124a. GODRIDGE H, REYNOLDS GP, CZUDEK C, CALCUTT NA, BENTON M: Alzheimer-like neurotransmitter deficits in adult Down's syndrome brain tissue. *J Neurol Neurosurg Psychiatr* 50:775, 1987.
125. YATES CM, RITCHIE J, SIMPSON J, MALONEY AJF, GORDON A: Noradrenaline in Alzheimer-type dementia and Down syndrome. *Lancet* 2:39, 1981.
126. NYBERG P, CARLSSON A, WINBLAD B: Brain monoamines in cases with Down's syndrome with and without dementia. *J Neural Transm* 55:289, 1982.
127. REYNOLDS GR, GODRIDGE H: Alzheimer-like brain monoamine deficits in adults with Down's syndrome. *Lancet* 1:1368, 1985.
128. WONG CW, QUARANTA V, GLENNER GG: Neuritic plaques and cerebrovascular amyloid in Alzheimer disease are antigenically related. *Proc Natl Acad Sci USA* 82:8729, 1985.
129. MASTERS CL, SIMS G, WEINMAN NA, MALTHAUP G, MCDONALD BL, BEYREUTHER K: Amyloid plaque core protein in Alzheimer disease and Down syndrome. *Proc Natl Acad Sci USA* 82:4245, 1985.
130. WOLOZIN BL, PRUCHNICKI A, DICKSON DW, DAVIES P: A neuronal antigen in the brains of Alzheimer patients. *Science* 232:648, 1986.
131. DE LEON MJ, FERRIS SH, GEORG AE, REISBERG B, CHRISTMAN DR, KRICHEFF IC, WOLF AP: Computed tomography and positive emission transaxial tomography evaluation of normal aging and Alzheimer's disease. *J Cereb Blood Flow Metab* 3:391, 1983.
132. FOSTER NL, CHASE TN, MANSI L, BROOKS R, FEDIO P, PATRONAS NJ, DICHIRO G: Cortical abnormalities in Alzheimer's disease. *Ann Neurol* 16:649, 1984.
133. EPSTEIN CJ, ANNERÉN KG, FOSTER D, GRONER Y, PRUSINER SB, SMITH SA: Pathogenetic relationships between Down syndrome and Alzheimer's disease: studies with animal models, in Davies P, Finch CE (eds): *Banbury Report 27: Molecular Neuropathology of Aging.* Cold Spring Harbor, New York, Cold Spring Harbor, 1987, p 339.
134. PUESCHEL SM: Cardiology, in Pueschel SM, Rynders JE (eds): *Down Syndrome. Advances in Biomedicine and the Behavioral Sciences.* Cambridge, MA, Ware Press, 1982, p 203.
135. FABIA J, DROLETTE M: Malformations and leukemia in children with Down's syndrome. *Pediatrics* 45:60, 1970.
136. BUCKLEY LP: Cardiac assessments, in Pueschel SM (ed): *A Study of the Young Child with Down Syndrome.* New York, Human Sciences Press, 1983, p 351.
137. GOLDHABER SZ, RUBIN IL, BROWN W, ROBERTSON N, STUBBLEFIELD F, SLOSS LJ: Valvular heart disease (aortic regurgitation and mitral valve prolapse) among institutionalized adults with Down's syndrome. *Am J Cardiol* 57:278, 1986.
137a. GOLDHABER SZ, BROWN WD, ST. JOHN SUTTON MG: High frequency of mitral valve prolapse and aortic regurgitation among asymptomatic adults with Down's syndrome. *JAMA* 258:1793, 1987.
138. BULL C, RIGBY ML, SHINEBOURNE EA: Should management of complete atrioventricular canal defect be influenced by coexistent Down syndrome? *Lancet* 1:1147, 1985.
139. CHI TPL, KROVETZ LJ: The pulmonary vascular bed in children with Down syndrome. *J Pediatr* 86:533, 1975.
140. MORRAY JP, MACGILLIVRAY R, DUKER G: Increased perioperative risk following repair of congenital heart disease in Down's syndrome. *Anesthesiology* 65:221, 1986.
141. WILSON SK, HUTCHINS GM, NEILL CA: Hypertensive pulmonary vascular disease in Down syndrome. *J Pediatr* 95:722, 1979.

142. COONEY TP, THURLBECK WM: Pulmonary hypoplasia in Down's syndrome. *N Engl J Med* 307:1170, 1982.
143. YAMAKI S, HORIUCHI T, SEKINO Y: Quantitative analysis of pulmonary vascular disease in simple cardiac anomalies with the Down syndrome. *Am J Cardiol* 51:1502, 1983.
144. BUCHIN PJ, LEVY JS, SCHULLINGER JN: Down's syndrome and the gastrointestinal tract. *J Clin Gastroenterol* 8:111, 1986.
145. GARVER KL, LAW JC, GARVER B: Hirschsprung disease: a genetic study. *Clin Genet* 28:503, 1985.
146. PURI P, O'DONNELL B: Outlook after surgery for congenital intrinsic duodenal obstruction in Down syndrome. *Lancet* 2:802, 1981.
147. MILUNSKY A, FISHER JH: Annular pancreas in Down's syndrome. *Lancet* 2:575, 1968.
148. MILLER RW: Neoplasia and Down's syndrome. *Ann NY Acad Sci* 171:637, 1970.
149. EVANS DIK, STEWARD JK: Down's syndrome and leukaemia. *Lancet* 2:1322, 1972.
150. SCHOLL T, STEIN Z, HANSEN H: Leukemia and other cancers, anomalies and infections as causes of death in Down's syndrome in the United States during 1976. *Dev Med Child Neurol* 24:817, 1982.
151. ROSNER F, LEE SL: Down's syndrome and acute leukemia: myeloblastic or lymphoblastic? *Am J Med* 53:203, 1972.
152. STILLER CA, KINNIER WILSON LM: Down syndrome and leukaemia. *Lancet* 2:1343, 1981.
153. ROBISON LL, NESBIT ME JR, SATHER HN, LEVEL C, SHAHIDI N, KENNEDY MS, HAMMOND D: Down syndrome and acute leukemia in children: A 10-year retrospective survey from Children's Cancer Study Group. *J Pediatr* 105:235, 1984.
154. LEWIS DS, THOMPSON M, HUDSON E, LIBERMAN MM, SAMSON D: Down's syndrome and acute megakaryoblastic leukemia. Case report and review of the literature. *Acta Haematol* 70:236, 1983.
155. ZIPURSKY A, PEETERS M, POON A: Megakaryoblastic leukemia and Down's syndrome—A review, in McCoy EE, Epstein CJ (eds): *Oncology and Immunology of Down Syndrome*. New York, AR Liss, 1987, p 33.
156. ROBISON LL, NEGLIA JP: Epidemiology of Down syndrome and childhood acute leukemia, in McCoy EE, Epstein CJ (eds): *Oncology and Immunology of Down Syndrome*. New York, AR Liss, 1987, p 19.
157. ROGERS P, DENEGRI JF, THOMAS JW, KALOUSEK D, GILLEN J, BAKER MA: Down's syndrome—leukemia vs pseudoleukemia. *Blood* 52 (*Suppl* 1):273, 1978.
158. ROSS JD, MOLONEY WC, DESFORGES JF: Ineffective regulation of granulopoiesis masquerading as congenital leukemia in a mongoloid child. *J Pediatr* 63:1, 1963.
159. HEATON DC, FITZGERALD PH, FRASER GJ, ABBOTT GD: Transient leukemoid proliferation of the cytogenetically unbalanced +21 cell line of a constitutional mosaic boy. *Blood* 57:883, 1981.
160. BARAK Y, MOGILNER BM, KAROV Y, NIR E, SCHLESINGER M, LEVIN S: Transient acute leukaemia in a newborn with Down's syndrome. Prediction of its reversibility by bone marrow cultures. *Acta Paediatr Scand* 71:699, 1982.
161. ROGERS PC, KALOUSEK DK, DENEGRI JF, THOMAS JW, BAKER MA: Neonate with Down's syndrome and transient congenital leukemia. In vitro studies. *Am J Pediatr Hematol Oncol* 5:59, 1983.
162. BRODEUR GM, DAHL GV, WILLIAMS DL, TIPTON RE, KALWINSKY DK: Transient leukemoid reaction and trisomy 21 mosaicism in a phenotypically normal newborn. *Blood* 55:691, 1980.
163. SEIBEL NL, SOMMER A, MISER J: Transient neonatal leukemoid reactions in mosaic trisomy 21. *J Pediatr* 104:251, 1984.
164. MILLER JC, SCHERRILL JG, HATHAWAY WE: Thrombocythemia in the myeloproliferative disorders of Down's syndrome. *Pediatrics* 40:847, 1967.
165. MILLER M, COSGRIFF JM: Hematological abnormalities in newborn infants with Down syndrome. *Am J Med Genet* 16:173, 1983.
166. WEINBERGER MM, OLEINICK A: Congenital marrow dysfunction in Down's syndrome. *J Pediatr* 77:273, 1970.
167. SIEGEL M: Susceptibility of mongoloids to infection. I. Incidence of pneumonia, influenza A and Shigella dysenteriae (Sonne). *Am J Hyg* 48:53, 1948.
168. RIGAS DA, ELSASSER P, HECHT F: Impaired in vitro response of circulating lymphocytes to phytohemagglutinin in Down's syndrome: dose- and time-response curves and relation to cellular immunity. *Int Arch Allergy Appl Immunol* 39:587, 1970.
169. NURMI T: *Disturbed Immune Functions Associated with Chromosome Abnormalities*. Academic Dissertation. Oulu, University of Oulu, 1982.
170. MILLER ME, MELLMAN WJ, OSKI FA, KOHN G: Immunoglobulins in Down's syndrome. *Lancet* 2:257, 1967.
171. DYGGVE H, CLAUSEN J: The serum immunoglobulin level in Down's syndrome. *Dev Med Child Neurol* 12:193, 1970.
172. ROSNER F, KOZINN PJ, JERVIS GA: Leukocyte function and serum immunoglobulins in Down's syndrome. *NY State J Med* 73:672, 1973.
173. BURGIO GR, UGAZIO AG, NESPOLI L, MARCIONI AE, BOTTELLI AM, PASQUALI F: Derangements of immunoglobulin levels, phytohemagglutinin responsiveness and T and B cell markers in Down's syndrome at different ages. *Eur J Immunol* 5: 600, 1975.
174. LEVIN S, SCHLESINGER M, HANDZEL Z, HAHN T, ALTMAN Y, CZERNOBILSKY B, BOSS J: Thymic deficiency in Down's syndrome. *Pediatrics* 63:80, 1979.
175. EPSTEIN LB, EPSTEIN CJ: T-lymphocyte function and sensitivity to interferon in trisomy 21. *Cell Immunol* 51:303, 1980.
176. WALFORD RL, GOSSETT TC, NAEIM F, TAM CF, VAN LANCKER JL, BARNETT EV, CHIA D, SPARKES RS, FAHEY JL, SPINA C, GATTI RA, MEDICI MA, GROSSMAN H, HIBRAWI H, MOTOLA M: Immunological and biochemical studies of Down's syndrome as a model of accelerated aging, in Segre D, Smith L (eds): *Immunological Aspects of Aging*. New York, Marcel Dekker, 1982, p 479.
177. BURGIO GR, UGAZIO A, NESPOLI L, MACCARIO R: Down syndrome: A model of immunodeficiency. *Birth Defects* 19(3):325, 1983.
178. PHILIP R, BERGER A, MCMANUS NH, WARNER NH, PEACOCK MA, EPSTEIN LB: Abnormalities of the *in vitro* cellular and humoral response to bacterial and viral antigens with concomitant numerical alterations in lymphocyte subsets in Down syndrome (trisomy 21). *J Immunol* 136:1661, 1986.
179. SEGER R, BUCHINGER G, STRÖDER J: On the influence of age on immunity in Down's syndrome. *Eur J Pediatr* 124:77, 1977.
180. KARTTUNEN R, NURMI T, ILONEN J, SURDEL H-M: Cell-mediated immunodeficiency in Down's syndrome: Normal IL-2 production but inverted ratio of T cell subsets. *Clin Exp Immunol* 55:257, 1984.
181. FOWLER I, HOLLINGSWORTH DR: Response to stimulation in vitro of lymphocytes from patients with Down's syndrome. *Proc Soc Exp Biol Med* 144:475, 1973.
182. FUNA K, ANNERÉN G, ALM GV, BJÖRKSTÉN B: Abnormal interferon production and NK cell responses to interferon in children with Down's syndrome. *Clin Exp Immunol* 56:493, 1984.
183. EPSTEIN LB, PHILIP R: Abnormalities of the immune response to influenza antigen in Down syndrome (trisomy 21), in McCoy EE, Epstein CJ (eds): *Oncology and Immunology of Down Syndrome*. New York, AR Liss, 1987, p 163.
184. SIEGEL M: Susceptibility of mongoloids to infection. II. Antibody response to tetanus toxoid and typhoid vaccine. *Am J Hyg* 48:63, 1948.
185. GRIFFITHS AW, SYLVESTER PE: Mongols and non-mongols compared in their response to active tetanus immunisation. *J Ment Defic Res* 11:263, 1967.
186. GORDON MC, SINHA SK, CARLSON SD: Antibody responses to influenza vaccine in patients with Down's syndrome. *Am J Ment Defic* 75:391, 1971.
187. LOPEZ V, OCHS HD, THULINE HC, DAVIS SD, WEDGWOOD RS: Defective antibody response to bacteriophage $\phi \times 174$ in Down syndrome. *J Pediatr* 86:207, 1975.
188. NURMI T, LEINONEN M, HÄIVÄ V-M, TIILIKAINEN A, KOUVALAINEN K: Antibody response to pneumococcal vaccine in patients with trisomy-21 (Down's syndrome). *Clin Exp Immunol* 48:485, 1982.
189. HOLLINGER FB, GOYAL RK, HERSH T, POWELL HC, SCHULMAN RJ, MELNICK JL: Immune response to hepatitis virus type B in Down's syndrome and other mentally retarded patients. *Am J Epidemiol* 95:356, 1972.
190. UGAZIO AG, LANZAVECCHIA A, JAYAKAR S, PLEBANI A, DUSE M, BURGIO GR: Immunodeficiency in Down's syndrome: Titres of "natural" antibodies to E. coli and rabbit erythrocytes at different ages. *Acta Paediatr Scand* 67:705, 1978.
191. FEKETE G, KULCSÁR G, DÁN P, NÁSZ I, SCHULER D, DOBOS M: Immunological and virological investigations in Down's syndrome. *Eur J Pediatr* 138:59, 1982.
192. DUSE M, BRUGO MA, MARTINI A, TASSI C, FERRARIO C, UGAZIO AG: Immunodeficiency in Down's syndrome: Low levels of serum thymic factor in trisomic children. *Thymus* 2:127, 1980.
193. FABRIS N, AMADIO L, LICASTRO F, MOCCHEGIANI E, ZANNOTTI M, FRANCESCHI C: Thymic hormone deficiency in normal ageing and Down's syndrome: Is there a primary failure of the thymus? *Lancet* 1:983, 1984.
194. NAIMAN JL, OSKI FA, MELLMAN WJ: Phosphokinase activity of erythrocytes in mongolism. *Lancet* 1:821, 1965.
195. EASTHAM RD, JANCAR J: Macrocytosis in Down's syndrome and during long-term anticonvulsant therapy. *J Clin Pathol* 23:296, 1970.
196. HSIA DY-Y, JUSTICE P, SMITH GF, DOWBEN RM: Down's syndrome. A critical review of the biochemical and immunological data. *Am J Dis Child* 121:153, 1971.
197. PUUKKA R, PUUKKA M, LEPPILAMPI M, LINNA S-L, KOUVALAINEN K: Erythrocyte adenosine deaminase, purine nucleoside phosphorylase and

phosphoribosyl-transferase activity in patients with Down's syndrome. *Clin Chim Acta* 126:275, 1982.

198. BRAHE C, SERRA A, MORTON NE: Erythrocyte catechol-O-methyltransferase activity: Genetic analysis in nuclear families with one child affected by Down syndrome. *Am J Med Genet* 21:373, 1985.

199. KEDZIORA J, HÜBNER H, KANSKI M, JESKE J, LEYKO W: Efficiency of the glycolytic pathway in erythrocytes of children with Down's syndrome. *Pediatr Res* 6:10, 1972.

200. STOCCHI V, MAGNANI M, CUCCHIARINI L, NOVELLI G, DALLAPICCOLA B: Red blood cell adenine nucleotides. Abnormalities in Down syndrome. *Am J Med Genet* 20:131, 1985.

201. BARKIN RM, WESTON WL, HUMBERT JR, MAIRE F: Phagocytic function in Down syndrome—I. Chemotaxis. *J Ment Defic Res* 24:243, 1980.

202. BARKIN RM, WESTON WL, HUMBERT JR, SUNADA K: Phagocytic function in Down syndrome—II. Bactericidal activity and phagocytosis. *J Ment Defic Res* 24:251, 1980.

203. BARROETA O, NUNGARAY L, LÓPEZ-OSUNA M, ARMENDARES S, SALAMANCA F, KRETSCHMER RR: Defective monocyte chemotaxis in children with Down's syndrome. *Pediatr Res* 17:292, 1983.

204. HSIA DY-Y, NADLER HL, SHIH L-Y: Biochemical changes in chromosomal abnormalities. *Ann NY Acad Sci* 155:716, 1968.

205. PUESCHEL SM: Biomedical aspects in Down syndrome: Biochemistry, in Pueschel SM, Rynders JE (eds): *Down Syndrome. Advances in Biomedicine and the Behavioral Sciences.* Cambridge, MA, Ware Press, 1982, p 249.

206. PANT SS, MOSER HW, KRANE SM: Hyperuricemia in Down's syndrome. *J Clin Endocrinol Metab* 28:472, 1968.

207. MELLMAN WJ, RAAB SD, OSKI FA, TEDESCO TA: Abnormal leukokinetics in 21 trisomy. *Ann NY Acad Sci* 155:1020, 1968.

208. PUUKKA R, PUUKKA M, PERKKILÄ L, KOUVALAINEN K: Levels of some purine metabolizing enzymes in lymphocytes from patients with Down's syndrome. *Biochem Med Metab Biol* 36:45, 1986.

209. FORT P, LIFSHITZ F, BELLISARIO R, DAVIS J, LANES R, PUGLIESE M, RICHMAN R, PORT EM, DAVID R: Abnormalities of thyroid function in infants with Down syndrome. *J Pediatr* 104:545, 1984.

210. CUTLER AT, BENEZRA-OBEITER R, BRINK SJ: Thyroid function in young children with Down syndrome. *Am J Dis Child* 140:479, 1986.

211. SARE Z, RUVALCABA RHA, KELLEY VC: Prevalence of thyroid disorder in Down syndrome. *Clin Genet* 14:154, 1978.

212. UGAZIO AG, JAYAKAR S, MARCIONI AF, DOSE M, MONAFO V, PASQUALI F, BURGIO GR: Immunodeficiency in Down's syndrome: Relationship between presence of human thyroglobulin antibodies and HBsAg carrier status. *Eur J Pediatr* 126:139, 1977.

213. CRONK CE, PUESCHEL S: Anthropometric studies, in Pueschel SM (ed): *A Study of the Young Child with Down Syndrome.* New York, Human Sciences Press, 1983, p 105.

214. PUESCHEL SM, ROTHMAN KJ, OGILBY JD: Birth weight of children with Down's syndrome. *Am J Ment Defic* 80:442, 1976.

215. SARA VR, GUSTAVSON K-H, ANNERÉN G, HALL K, WETTERBERG L: Somatomedins in Down's syndrome. *Biol Psychiatry* 18:803, 1983.

216. IKEDA Y, HIGURASHI M, HIRAYAMA M, ISHIKAWA N, HOSHINA H: A longitudinal study on the growth of stature, lower limb and upper limb length in Japanese children with Down's syndrome. *J Ment Defic Res* 21:139, 1977.

217. RARICK GL, SEEFELDT V: Observations from longitudinal data on growth in stature and sitting height of children with Down's syndrome. *J Ment Defic Res* 18:63, 1974.

218. CHUMLEA WC, CRONK CE: Overweight among children with trisomy 21. *J Ment Defic Res* 25:275, 1981.

219. BRONKS R, PARKER AW: Anthropometric observation of adults with Down syndrome. *Am J Ment Defic* 90:110, 1985.

220. RUVALCABA RHA, THULINE HC, KELLEY VC: Plasma growth hormone in patients with chromosomal anomalies. *Arch Dis Child* 47:307, 1972.

221. ANNERÉN G, SARA VR, HALL K, TUVEMO T: Growth and somatomedin responses to growth hormone in Down's syndrome. *Arch Dis Child* 61:48, 1986.

222. ANNERÉN G, ENBERG G, SARA VR: The presence of normal levels of serum immunoreactive insulin-like growth factor 2 (IGF-2) in patients with Down's syndrome. *Ups J Med Sci* 89:274, 1984.

223. SARA VR, SJÖGREN B, ANNERÉN G, GUSTAVSON K-H, FORSMAN A, HALL K, WAHLSTRÖM J, WETTERBERG L: The presence of normal receptors for somatomedin and insulin in fetuses with Down's syndrome. *Biol Psychiatry* 19:591, 1984.

224. JAGIELLO G: Reproduction in Down syndrome, in de la Cruz FF, Gerald PS (eds): *Trisomy 21 (Down Syndrome). Research Perspectives.* Baltimore, University Park Press, 1981, p 151.

225. JOHANNISSON R, GROPP A, WINKING H, COERDT W, REHDER H, SCHWINGER E: Down's syndrome in the male. Reproductive pathology and meiotic studies. *Hum Genet* 63:132, 1983.

226. SHRÖDER J, LYDECKEN K, DE LA CHAPELLE A: Meiosis and spermatogenesis in G-trisomic males. *Humangenetik* 13:15, 1971.

227. STEARNS PE, DROULARD KE, SAHHAR FH: Studies bearing on fertility of male and female mongoloids. *Am J Ment Defic* 65:37, 1960.

228. PUESCHEL S, ORSON JM, BOYLAN JM, PEZZULLO JC: Adolescent development in males with Down syndrome. *Am J Dis Child* 139:236, 1985.

229. CAMPBELL WA, LOWTHER J, MCKENZIE I, PRICE WH: Serum gonadotrophins in Down's syndrome. *J Med Genet* 19:98, 1982.

230. HORAN RF, BEITINS IZ, BODE HH: LH-RH testing in men with Down's syndrome. *Acta Endocrinol* 88:594, 1978.

231. HASEN J, BOYAR RM, SHAPIRO LR: Gonadal function in trisomy 21. *Hormone Res* 12:345, 1980.

232. GROPP A, WINKING H, REDI C: Consequences of Robertsonian heterozygosity: Segregational impairment of fertility versus male-limited sterility, in Crosignani PG, Rubin BL (eds): *Serono Clinical Colloquia on Reproduction 3. Genetic Control of Gamete Production and Function.* London, Academic Press/Grune & Stratton, 1982, p 115.

233. HØJAGER B, PETERS H, BYSKOV AG, FABER M: Follicular development in ovaries of children with Down syndrome. *Acta Paediatr Scand* 67:637, 1978.

234. TRICOMI V, VALENTI C, HALL JE: Ovulatory patterns in Down's syndrome. A pilot study. *Am J Obstet Gynecol* 89:651, 1964.

235. THASE ME: Longevity and mortality in Down's syndrome. *J Ment Defic Res* 26:177, 1982.

236. FRYERS T: Survival in Down's syndrome. *J Ment Defic Res* 30:101, 1986.

237. PENROSE LS: The incidence of mongolism in the general population. *J Ment Sci* 9:10, 1949.

238. MASAKI M, HIGURASHI M, IIJIMA K, ISHIKAWA N, TANAKA F, FUJII T, KUROKI Y, MATSUI I, IINUMA K, MATSUO N, TAKESHITA K, HASHIMOTO S: Mortality and survival for Down syndrome in Japan. *Am J Hum Genet* 33:629, 1981.

239. DUPONT A, VAETH M, VIDEBECH P: Mortality and life expectancy of Down's syndrome in Denmark. *J Ment Defic Res* 30:111, 1986.

240. SCHOLL T, STEIN Z, HANSEN H: Leukemia and other cancers, anomalies, and infections as causes of death in Down's syndrome in the United States during 1976. *Dev Med Child Neurol* 24:817, 1982.

241. ØSTER J, MIKKELSEN M, NIELSEN A: Mortality and life-table in Down's syndrome. *Acta Paediatr Scand* 64:243, 1975.

242. BALARJAN R, DONNAN SPB, ADELSTEIN AM: Mortality and causes of death in Down's syndrome. *J Epidemiol Community Health* 36:127, 1982.

243. WEIL J, TUCKER G, EPSTEIN LB, EPSTEIN CJ: Interferon induction of (2′-5′)oligoisoadenylate synthetase in diploid and trisomy 21 fibroblasts: Relation to dosage of the interferon receptor gene (IFRC). *Hum Genet* 65:108, 1983.

244. EPSTEIN CJ, WEIL J, EPSTEIN LB: Abnormalities in the interferon response and immune systems in Down syndrome: Studies in human trisomy 21 and mouse trisomy 16, in McCoy EE, Epstein CJ (eds): *Oncology and Immunology of Down Syndrome.* New York, AR Liss, 1987, p 191.

244a. JUNG V, RASHIDBAIGI A, JONES C, TISCHFIELD JA, SHOWS TB, PESTKA S: Human chromosomes 6 and 21 are required for sensitivity to human interferon gamma. *Proc Natl Acad Sci USA* 84:4151, 1987.

245. EPSTEIN CJ, EPSTEIN LB: Genetic control of the response to interferon in man and mouse. *Lymphokines* 8:277, 1983.

246. EPSTEIN LB, WEIL J, LUCAS DO, COX DR, EPSTEIN CJ: The biology and properties of interferon-gamma: An overview, studies of production of T lymphocyte subsets, and analysis of peptide synthesis and antiviral effects in trisomy 21 and diploid human fibroblasts, in DeMaeyer E, Galasso G, Schellekens H (eds): *The Biology of the Interferon System.* Amsterdam, Elsevier/North Holland, 1981, p 247.

247. WEIL J, EPSTEIN CJ, EPSTEIN LB, VAN BLERKOM J, XUONG NH: Computer-assisted analysis demonstrates that polypeptides induced by natural and recombinant interferon-α are the same and that several have related primary structures. *Antiviral Res* 3:303, 1983.

248. YAP WH, TEO TS, TAN YH: An early event in the interferon-induced transmembrane signaling process. *Science* 234:355, 1986.

249. KABACK MM, BERNSTEIN LH: Biologic studies of trisomic cells growing in vitro. *Ann NY Acad Sci* 171, 526, 1970.

250. SEGAL DJ, MCCOY EE: Studies on Down's syndrome in tissue culture. I. Growth rates and protein contents of fibroblast cultures. *J Cell Physiol* 83:85, 1973.

251. PATON GR, SILVER MF, ALLISON AC: Comparison of cell cycle time in normal and trisomic cells. *Humangenetik* 23:173, 1974.

252. CUMMINGS MR, ALL J, BARO D: Altered cell growth in Down syndrome fibroblasts cultured in vitro. *Am J Hum Genet* 33:145A, 1981.

253. OTSUKA F, TARONE RE, SEQUIN LR, ROBBINS JH: Hypersensitivity to ionizing radiation in cultured cells from Down syndrome patients. *J Neurol Sci* 69:103, 1985.

254. SCHNEIDER EL, EPSTEIN CJ: Replication rate and lifespan of cultured fi-

broblasts in Down's syndrome. *Proc Soc Exp Biol Med* 141:1092, 1972.

255. RUBLE MF, BRYANT EM, RABINOVITCH PS, HOEHN H: Growth kinetics and life spans of fibroblast cultures from patients with constitutional aneuploidy: Effects of chromosome constitution. *J Cell Biol* 79:393a, 1978.

256. HOEHN H, SIMPSON M, BRYANT EM, RABINOVITCH PS, SALK D, MARTIN GM: Effects of chromosome constitution on growth and longevity of human skin fibroblast cultures. *Am J Med Genet* 7:141, 1980.

257. SASAKI MS, TONOMURA A: Chromosomal radiosensitivity in Down's syndrome. *Jpn J Hum Genet* 14:81, 1969.

258. MORIMOTO K, KANEKO T, IIJIMA K, KOIZUMI A: Proliferative kinetics and chromosome damage in trisomy 21 lymphocyte cultures exposed to γ-rays and bleomycin. *Cancer Res* 44:1499, 1984.

259. LEONARD JC, MERZ T: The influence of cell cycle kinetics on the radiosensitivity of Down's syndrome lymphocytes. *Mutat Res* 109:111, 1983.

260. TARONE RE, LIAO K, ROBBINS JH: Effects of DNA-damaging agents on Down syndrome cells: Implications for defective DNA-repair mechanisms, in McCoy EE, Epstein CJ (eds): *Oncology and Immunology of Down Syndrome.* New York, AR Liss, 1987, p 93.

261. ALDENHOFF P, WEGNER R-D, SPERLING K: Different sensitivity of diploid and trisomic cells from patients with Down syndrome mosaic after treatment with the trifunctional alkylating agent Trenimon. *Hum Genet* 56:123, 1980.

262. HIGURASHI M, TAMURA T, NAKATAKE T: Cytogenetic observations in cultured lymphocytes from patients with Down's syndrome and measles. *Pediatr Res* 7:582, 1973.

263. HIGURASHI M, TADA A, MIYAHARA S, HIRAYAMA M: Chromosome damage in Down's syndrome induced by chickenpox infection. *Pediatr Res* 10:189, 1976.

264. TODARO GJ, MARTIN GM: Increased susceptibility of Down's syndrome fibroblasts to transformation by SV40. *Proc Soc Exp Biol Med* 124:1232, 1967.

265. AARONSON SA: Susceptibility of human cell strains to transformation by simian virus 40 and simian virus 40 deoxyribonucleic acid. *J Virol* 6:470, 1970.

266. LUBINIECKI AS, BLATTNER WA, MARTIN GR, FIALKOW PJ, DOSIK H, EATHERLY C, FRAUMENI JF JR: SV40 T-antigen expression in cultured fibroblasts from patients with Down syndrome and their parents. *Am J Hum Genet* 31:469, 1979.

267. POTTER CW, POTTER AM, OXFORD JS: Comparison of transformation and T antigen induction in human cell lines. *J Virol* 5:293, 1970.

268. LUBINIECKI AS, BLATTNER WA, FRAUMENI JF JR: Elevated expression of T-antigen in simian papovavirus 40-infected skin fibroblasts from individuals with cytogenetic defects. *Cancer Res* 37:1580, 1977.

269. THULINE HC, PUESCHEL SM: Cytogenetics in Down syndrome, in Pueschel SM, Rynders SM (eds): *Down Syndrome. Advances in Biomedicine and the Behavioral Sciences.* Cambridge, MA, Ware Press, 1982, p 133.

270. HOOK EG: Epidemiology of Down syndrome, in Pueschel SM, Rynders JE (eds): *Down Syndrome. Advances in Biomedicine and the Behavioral Sciences.* Cambridge, MA, Ware Press, 1982, p 11.

271. GIRAUD F, MATTEI JF: Aspects epidemiologues de la trisomy 21. *J Genet Hum* 23 *Suppl.*:1, 1975.

272. ALBRIGHT SG, HOOK EB: Estimates of the likelihood that a Down's syndrome child of unknown genotype is a consequence of familial translocation. *Am J Hum Genet* 30:107A, 1978.

273. PARLOIR C, FRYNS JP, VAN DEN BERGHE H: Down's syndrome in brother and sister without evident trisomy 21. *Hum Genet* 51:227, 1979.

274. DELABAR J-M, GOLDGABER D, LAMOUR Y, NICOLE A, HURET J-L, DE GROUCHY J, BROWN P, GAJDUSEK DC, SINET P-M: β Amyloid gene duplication in Alzheimer's disease and karyotypically normal Down syndrome. *Science* 235:1390, 1987.

274a. DELABAR JM, SINET PM, CHADEFAUX B, NICOLE A, GEGONNE A, STEHELIN D, FRIDLANSKY F, CRÉAU-GOLDBERG N, TURLEAU C, DE GROUCHY J: Submicroscopic duplication of chromosome 21 and trisomy 21 phenotype (Down syndrome). *Hum Genet* 76:225, 1987.

275. HURET J-L, DELABAR JM, MARLHENS F, AURIAS A, NICOLE A, BERTHIER M, TANZER J, SINET PM: Down syndrome with duplication of a region of chromosome 21 containing the CuZn superoxide dismutase gene without detectable karyotypic abnormality. *Hum Genet* 75:251, 1987.

276. RICHARDS BW: Investigation of 142 mosaic mongols and mosaic parents of mongols: Cytogenetic analysis and maternal age at birth. *J Ment Defic Res* 18:199, 1974.

277. FORD CE: Nondisjunction, in Burgio GR, Fraccaro M, Tiepolo L, Wolf U (eds): *Trisomy 21. An International Symposium.* Berlin, Springer-Verlag, 1981, p 103.

278. UCHIDA IA, WHELAND T: A rare case of mosaic Down syndrome 46, XY/46,XY, −21, +i(21q). *Clin Genet* 17:271, 1980.

279. WILSON MG, TOWNER JW, FORSMAN I: Decreasing mosaicism in Down's syndrome. *Clin Genet* 17:335, 1980.

280. TAYSI K, KOHN G, MELLMAN WJ: Mosaic mongolism. II. Cytogenetic studies. *J Pediatr* 76:880, 1970.

281. PINKEL D, TRASK B, VAN DEN ENGH G, FUSCOE J, VAN DEKKEN H, GRAY JW: Genetic analysis by quantitative microscopy and flow cytometry using fluorescence in situ hybridization with chromosome-specific nucleic acid probes. *Am J Hum Genet* 39:A129, 1986.

282. UCHIDA JA, FREEMAN VCP: Trisomy 21 Down syndrome. Parental mosaicism. *Hum Genet* 70:246, 1985.

283. HARRIS DJ, BEGLEITER ML, CHAMBERLIN J, HANKINS L, MAGENIS RE: Parental trisomy 21 mosaicism. *Am J Hum Genet* 34:125, 1982.

284. FISHLER K, KOCH R, DONNELL GN: Comparison of mental development in individuals with mosaic and trisomy 21 Down's syndrome. *Pediatrics* 58:744, 1976.

285. KOHN G, TAYSI K, ATKINS TE, MELLMAN WJ: Mosaic mongolism. I. Clinical correlations. *J Pediatr* 76:874, 1970.

286. ROSENCRANS CJ: The relationship of normal/21-trisomy mosaicism and intellectual development. *Am J Ment Defic* 72:562, 1968.

287. CARLIN ME, LEON S, GILBERT JD: A comparison between a trisomy 21 child (probably mosaic) with normal intelligence and a mosaic Down syndrome population. *Birth Defects* 14(6C):327, 1978.

288. HASSOLD T, CHIU D, YAMANE JA: Parental origin of autosomal trisomies. *Ann Hum Genet* 48:129, 1984.

289. MIKKELSEN M: Parental origin of the extra chromosome in Down's syndrome. *J Ment Defic Res* 26:143, 1982.

290. MATTEI JF, AYME S, MATTEI MG, GIRAUD F: Maternal age and origin of non-disjunction in trisomy 21. *J Med Genet* 17:368, 1980.

291. HOOK EB: Maternal age, paternal age, and human chromosome abnormality: nature, magnitude, etiology, and mechanisms of effects, in Dellarco VL, Voytek PE, Hollaender A (eds): *Aneuploidy. Etiology and Mechanisms.* New York, Plenum, 1985, p 117.

292. ADAMS MM, ERICKSON JD, LAYDE PM, OAKLEY GP: Down's syndrome. Recent trends in the United States. *JAMA* 246:758, 1981.

293. HOOK EB, CROSS PK, REGAL RR: The frequency of 47,+21, 47,+18, and 47,+13 at the uppermost extremes of maternal ages: Results on 56,094 fetuses studied prenatally and comparisons with data on live-births. *Hum Genet* 68:211, 1984.

294. HOOK EB, CROSS PK, SCHREINEMACHERS DM: Chromosomal abnormality rates at amniocentesis and in live-born infants. *JAMA* 249:2034, 1983.

295. HOOK EB: Spontaneous deaths of fetuses with chromosomal abnormalities diagnosed prenatally. *N Engl J Med* 299:1036, 1978.

296. HASSOLD T, CHIU D: Maternal age-specific rates of numerical chromosome abnormalities with special reference to trisomy. *Hum Genet* 70:11, 1985.

297. HASSOLD T, CHEN N, FUNKHOUSER J, JOOSS T, MANUEL B, MATSUURA J, MATSUYAMA A, WILSON C, YAMANE JA, JACOBS PA: A cytogenetic study of 1000 spontaneous abortions. *Ann Hum Genet* 44:151, 1980.

298. BYRNE J, WARBURTON D, KLINE J, BLANC W, STEIN Z: Morphology of early fetal deaths and their chromosomal characteristics. *Teratology* 32:297, 1985.

299. BOUÉ J, DELUCHAT CC, NICOLAS H, BOUÉ A: Prenatal losses of trisomy 21, in Burgio GR, Fracarro M, Tiepolo L, Wolf U (eds): *Trisomy 21. An International Symposium.* Berlin, Springer-Verlag, 1981, p 183.

300. BOND DJ, CHANDLEY AC: *Aneuploidy.* Oxford, Oxford University Press, 1983.

301. CHANDLEY AC: Maternal aging as the important etiological factor in human aneuploidy, in Dellarco VL, Voytek PE, Hollaender A (eds): *Aneuploidy. Etiology and Mechanisms.* New York, Plenum, 1985, p 409.

302. GERMAN J: Mongolism, delayed fertilization and human sexual behavior. *Nature* 217:516, 1968.

303. HOOK EB, HARLAP S: Differences in maternal age-specific rates of Down syndrome between Jews of European origin and of North African or Asian origin. *Teratology* 20:243, 1979.

304. HENDERSON SA, EDWARDS RG: Chiasma frequency and maternal age in mammals. *Nature* 218:22, 1968.

305. HOOK EB: Down syndrome rates and relaxed selection of older maternal ages. *Am J Hum Genet* 35:1307, 1983.

306. CROWLEY PH, HAYDEN TL, GULATI DK: Etiology of Down syndrome, in Pueschel SM, Ryders JE (eds): *Down Syndrome. Advances in Biomedicine and the Behavioral Sciences.* Cambridge, MA, Ware Press, 1982, p 89.

307. DELLARCO VL, VOYTEK PE, HOLLAENDER A (eds): *Aneuploidy. Etiology and Mechanisms.* New York, Plenum, 1985.

308. STENE J, FISCHER G, STENE E, MIKKELSEN M, PETERSEN E: Paternal age effects in Down's syndrome. *Ann Hum Genet* 40:299, 1977.

309. ERICKSON JD, BJERKEDAL T: Down syndrome associated with father's age in Norway. *J Med Genet* 18:22, 1981.

310. STENE J, STENE E, STENGEL-RUTKOWSKI S, MURKEN J-D: Paternal age and Down's syndrome. Data from prenatal diagnosis (DFG). *Hum Genet* 59:119, 1981.

311. HOOK EB, CROSS PK: Paternal age and Down's syndrome genotypes diag-

nosed prenatally: No association in New York State data. *Hum Genet* 62:167, 1982.

312. ROECKER GO, HUETHER CA: An analysis for paternal-age effect in Ohio's Down syndrome births, 1970–1980. *Am J Hum Genet* 35:1297, 1983.

313. ROTH M-P, FEINGOLD J, BAUMGARTEN A, BIGEL P, STOLL C: Reexamination of paternal age effect in Down's syndrome. *Hum Genet* 63:149, 1983.

314. HOOK EB, REGAL RR: A search for a paternal-age effect upon cases of 47,+21 in which the extra chromosome is of paternal origin. *Am J Hum Genet* 36:413, 1984.

315. MARTIN RH, RADEMAKER A: The effect of age on the frequency of sperm chromosome abnormalities in normal men. *Am J Hum Genet* 39:A123, 1986.

316. STENE J, STENE E, MIKKELSEN M: Risk for chromosome abnormality at amniocentesis following a child with a non-inherited chromosome aberration. A European collaborative study in prenatal diagnoses 1981. *Prenat Diagn* 4 *(Spec Iss):* 81, 1984.

317. ALFI OS, CHANG R, AZEN SP: Evidence for genetic control of nondisjunction in man. *Am J Hum Genet* 32:477, 1980.

318. FIALKOW PJ: Thyroid autoimmunity and Down's syndrome. *Ann NY Acad Sci* 171:500, 1970.

319. FIALKOW PJ, THULINE HC, HECHT F, BRYANT J: Familial predisposition to thyroid disease in Down's syndrome: Controlled immunochemical studies. *Am J Hum Genet* 23:67, 1971.

320. KLINE J, STEIN Z: Environmental causes of aneuploidy: Why so elusive? in Dellarco VL, Voytek PE, Hollaender A (eds): *Aneuploidy. Etiology and Mechanisms*. New York, Plenum, 1985, p 149.

321. WARBURTON D: Genetic factors influencing aneuploidy frequency, in Dellarco VL, Voytek PE, Hollaender A (eds): *Aneuploidy. Etiology and Mechanisms*. New York, Plenum, 1985, p 133.

322. JANERICH DT, BRACKEN MB: Epidemiology of trisomy 21: A review and theoretical analysis. *J Chronic Dis* 39:1079, 1986.

323. TAMAREN J, SPUHLER K, SUJANSKY E: Risk of Down syndrome among second- and third-degree relatives of a proband with trisomy 21. *Am J Med Genet* 15:393, 1983.

324. EUNPU DL, MCDONALD DM, ZACKAI EM: Trisomy 21: Rate in second-degree relatives. *Am J Med Genet* 25:361, 1986.

325. ABUELO D, BARSEI-BOWERS G, BUSCH W, PUESCHEL S, PEZZULLO J: Risk for trisomy 21 in offspring of individuals who have relatives with trisomy 21. *Am J Med Genet* 25:365, 1986.

326. STEINBERG C, ZACKAI EH, EUNPU DL, MENNUTI MT, EMANUEL BS: Recurrence rate for de novo 21q21q translocation Down syndrome: A study of 112 families. *Am J Med Genet* 17:523, 1984.

327. STENE J: Statistical inference on segregation ratios for D/G-translocations, when the families are ascertained in different ways. *Ann Hum Genet* 34:93, 1970.

328. HAMERTON J: *Human Cytogenetics*. New York, Academic, 1971, vol I, p 278.

329. BOUÉ A, GALLANO P: A collaborative study of the segregation of inherited chromosome structural rearrangements in 1356 prenatal diagnoses. *Prenat Diagn* 4*(Spec Iss)*:45, 1984.

330. EPSTEIN CJ, COX DR, SCHONBERG SA, HOGGE WA: Recent developments in the prenatal diagnosis of genetic diseases and birth defects. *Ann Rev Genet* 17:49, 1983.

331. HUETHER CA: Projection of Down's syndrome births in the United States 1979–2000 and the potential effects of prenatal diagnosis. *Am J Public Health* 73:1186, 1983.

332. CRANDALL BF, LEBHERZ TB, TARSH K: Maternal age and amniocentesis: Should this be lowered to 30? *Prenat Diagn* 6:237, 1986.

333. GOLBUS MS, LOUGHMAN WD, EPSTEIN CJ, HALBASCH G, STEPHENS JD, HALL BD: Prenatal genetic diagnosis in 3000 amniocenteses. *N Engl J Med* 300:157, 1979.

334. HOGGE WA, SCHONBERG SA, GOLBUS MS: Prenatal diagnosis by chorionic villus sampling: Lessons of the first 600 cases. *Prenat Diagn* 5:393, 1985.

335. SIMONI G, GIMELLI G, CUOCO C, ROMITTI L, TERZOLI G, GUERNERI S, ROSSELLA F, PESCETTO L, PEZZOLO A, PORTA S, BRAMBATI B, PORRO E, FRACCARO M: First trimester fetal karyotyping: One thousand diagnoses. *Hum Genet* 72:203, 1986.

336. MERKATZ IR, NITOWSKY HN, MACRI JN, JOHNSON WE: An association between low maternal serum α-fetoprotein and fetal chromosomal abnormalities. *Am J Obstet Gynecol* 148:886, 1984.

337. CUCKLE HS, WALD NJ, LINDENBAUM RH: Maternal serum alpha-fetoprotein measurement: A screening test for Down syndrome. *Lancet* 1:926, 1984.

338. CUCKLE HS, WALD NJ, LINDENBAUM RH, JONASSON J: Amniotic fluid AFP levels and Down syndrome. *Lancet* 1:290, 1985.

339. BRAMBATI B, SIMONI G, BONACCHI I, PICENI L: Fetal chromosomal aneuploidies and maternal serum alpha-fetoprotein levels in first trimester. *Lancet* 2:165, 1986.

340. MULLER F, REBIFFÉ M, DER SARKISSIAN H, BOUÉ J, BOUÉ A: Diminution de certaines activités enzymatiques dans la liquide amniotique de foetus porteurs d'anomalies chromosomiques. *Ann Genet* 29:27, 1986.

341. VOIGTLÄNDER T, VOGEL F: Low alpha-fetoprotein and serum albumin levels in *Morbus Down* may point to a common regulatory mechanism. *Hum Genet* 71:276, 1985.

342. MACRI JN, BUCHANAN PD, GOLD MP: Low α-fetoprotein and trisomy. *Lancet* 2:405, 1986.

343. HERSHEY DW, CRANDALL BF, PERDUE S: Combining maternal age and serum α-fetoprotein to predict the risk of Down syndrome. *Obstet Gynecol* 68:177, 1986.

344. LEWANDOWSKI RC JR, YUNIS JJ: Phenotypic mapping in man, in Yunis JJ (ed): *New Chromosomal Syndromes*. New York, Academic, 1977, p 369.

345. PREUS M, AYMÉ S: Formal analysis of dysmorphism: objective methods of syndrome definition. *Clin Genet* 23:1, 1983.

346. ELDER FFB, FERGUSON JW, LOCKHART LH: Identical twins with deletion 16q syndrome: evidence that 16q12.2-q13 is the critical band region. *Hum Genet* 67:233, 1984.

347. EPSTEIN CJ: The mouse trisomies: Experimental systems for the study of aneuploidy, in Kalter H (ed): *Issues and Reviews in Teratology*. New York, Plenum, 1985, vol. 3, p 171.

348. VOGEL F, MOTULSKY AG: *Human Genetics. Problems and Approaches*, 2d ed. Berlin, Springer-Verlag, 1986.

349. WENGER SL, STEELE MW: Meiotic consequences of pericentric inversions of chromosome 13. *Am J Med Genet* 9:275, 1981.

350. YUNIS JJ, LEWANDOWSKI RC: High resolution cytogenetics. *Birth Defects*. 19(5):11, 1983.

351. SCHMICKEL RD: Contiguous gene syndromes: A component of recognizable syndromes. *J Pediatr* 109:231, 1986.

352. MITTWOCH U: Mongolism and sex: A common problem of cell proliferation? *J Med Genet* 14:151, 1977.

353. HALL B: Delayed ontogenesis in human trisomy syndromes. *Hereditas* 52:335, 1965.

354. AZIZ MA: Possible "atavistic" structure in human aneuploids. *Am J Phys Anthropol* 54:347, 1981.

355. SHAPIRO BL: Down syndrome—A disruption of homeostasis. *Am J Med Genet* 14:241, 1983.

356. OPITZ JM, GILBERT EF: Pathogenetic analysis of congenital anomalies in humans. *Pathobiology Annual 1982* 12:301, 1982.

357. KRONE W, WOLF U: Chromosomes and protein variation, in Brock DJH, Mayo O (eds): *The Biochemical Genetics of Man*, 2d ed. London, Academic, 1978, p 93.

358. DEVLIN RH, HOLM DG, GRIGLIATTI TA: Autosomal dosage compensation in Drosophila melanogaster strains trisomic for the left arm of chromosome 2. *Proc Natl Acad Sci USA* 79:1200, 1982.

359. WEIL J, EPSTEIN CJ: The effect of trisomy 21 on the patterns of polypeptide synthesis in human fibroblasts. *Am J Hum Genet* 31:478, 1979.

360. VAN KEUREN M, MERRIL CK, GOLDMAN D: Proteins affected by chromosome 21 and ageing in vitro, in Celis JE, Bravo R (eds): *Gene expression in Normal and Transformed Cells*. New York, Plenum, 1983, p 349.

361. KLOSE J, ZEINDL E, SPERLING K: Analysis of protein patterns in two-dimensional gels of cultured human cells with trisomy 21. *Clin Chem* 28:987, 1982.

362. MORTON NE, LINDSTEN J, ISELIUS L, YEE S: Data and theory for a revised chiasma map of man. *Hum Genet* 62:266, 1982.

363. EVANS HJ, BUCKLAND RA, PARDUE ML: Location of the genes coding for 18S and 28S ribosomal RNA in the human genome. *Chromosoma* 48:405, 1974.

364. MILLER DA, TANTRAVAHI R, DEV VG, MILLER OJ: Frequency of satellite associations of human chromosomes is correlated with amount of Ag-staining of the nucleolus organizer region. *Am J Hum Genet* 29:490, 1977.

365. GOSDEN JR, MITCHELL AR, BUCKLAND RA, CLAYTON RP, EVANS HJ: The location of four human satellite DNAs on human chromosomes. *Exp Cell Res* 92:148, 1975.

366. KURNIT DM, NEVE RL, MORTON CC, BRUNS GAP, MA NSF, COX DR, KLINGER HP: Recent evolution of DNA sequence homology in the pericentromeric regions of human acrocentric chromosomes. *Cytogenet Cell Genet* 38:99, 1984.

367. SCHMID M, KRONE W, VOGEL W: On the relationship between the frequency of association and the nucleolar constriction of individual acrocentric chromosomes. *Humangenetik* 23:267, 1974.

368. GRAHAM GJ, BARO DJ, GARCIA MJ, CUMMINGS MR: Molecular organization in the proximal region of human acrocentric chromosomes. *Ann NY Acad Sci* 450:55, 1985.

369. HANSSON A, MIKKELSEN M: The origin of the extra chromosome 21 in Down syndrome. Studies of fluorescent variants and satellite association in 26 informative families. *Cytogenet Cell Genet* 20:194, 1978.

370. JACKSON COOK CK, FLANNERY DB, COREY LA, NANCE WE, BROWN JA: Nucleolar organizer region variants as a risk factor for Down syndrome. *Am J Hum Genet* 37:1049, 1985.

371. TAYSI K: Satellite association: Giemsa banding studies in parents of Down syndrome patients. *Clin Genet* 8:313, 1975.

372. HASSOLD T, PETTAY D: Nucleolar organizing region variants in parents of trisomic spontaneous abortions. *Am J Hum Genet* 39:A116, 1986.

373. SPINNER NB, EUNPU DL, SCHMICKEL RD, ZACKAI E, BUNIN G, EMANUEL BS: The role of cytologic and molecular NOR variants in trisomy 21. *Am J Hum Genet* 39:A133, 1986.

374. YUNIS JJ: Chromosomes and cancer: New nomenclature and future directions. *Hum Pathol* 12:494, 1981.

375. HUMAN GENE MAPPING LIBRARY: Regional localization of genes and DNA segments on human chromosomes. Number 3, Febrary 1988. Howard Hughes Medical Institute, 1988, p 21.

376. CONNOLLY BA, GOODMAN HO, SWANTON CH: Evidence for inheritance of a renal beta-amino acid transport system and its localization to chromosome 21. *Am J Hum Genet* 31:43A, 1979.

377. TERNAUX JR, MATTEI JF, FAUDON M, BARRITT MC, ARDISSONE JP, GIRAUD F: Peripheral and central 5-hydroxytryptamine in trisomy 21. *Life Sci* 25:2017, 1979.

378. HARDS RG, BENKOVIC SJ, VAN KEUREN MK, GRAW SL, DRABKIN HA, PATTERSON D: Assignment of a third purine biosynthesis gene (glycinamide ribonucleotide transformylase) to human chromosome 21. *Am J Hum Genet* 39:179, 1986.

379. GOLDGABER D, LERMAN MI, MCBRIDE OW, SAFFIOTTI U, GAJDUSEK DC: Characterization and chromosomal localization of a cDNA encoding brain amyloid of Alzheimer's disease. *Science* 235:877, 1987.

380. TANZI RE, GUSELLA JF, WATKINS PC, BRUNS GAP, ST GEORGE-HYSLOP P, VAN KEUREN ML, PATTERSON D, PAGAN S, KURNIT DM, NEVE RL: Amyloid β protein gene: cDNA, mRNA distribution, and genetic linkage near the Alzheimer locus. *Science* 235:880, 1987.

381. SCOGGIN CH, PAUL S, MILLER YE, PATTERSON D: Two-dimensional electrophoresis of peptides from human-CHO cell hybrids containing human chromosome 21. *Somatic Cell Genet* 9:687, 1983.

381a. DEVINE-CAGE EA, BROWN WT, JENKINS EC, DUTKOWSKI R, SAMMONS D: Assignment of proteins to human chromosome 21 using two-dimensional gel electrophoresis and somatic cell genetics: An approach to the study of Down syndrome. *J Neurogenet* 4:215, 1987.

382. VAN KEUREN M, DRABKIN H, HART I, HARKER D, PATTERSON D, VORA S: Regional assignment of human liver-type 6-phosphofructokinase to chromosome 21q22.3 by using somatic cell hybrids and a monoclonal anti-L antibody. *Hum Genet* 74:34, 1986.

383. ALLORE R, O'HANLON D, PRICE R, NEILSON K, WILLARD HF, COX DR, MARKS A, DUNN RJ: Gene coding for β subunit of S100 protein is on chromosome 21. Implications for Down syndrome. *Science* 239:1311, 1988.

384. MUNKE M, KRAUS J, WATKINS P, TANZI R, GUSELLA J, MILLINGTON WARD A, WATSON M, FRANCKE U: Homocystinuria gene on human chromosome 21 mapped with cloned cystathionine beta-synthase probe and in situ hybridization of other chromosome 21 probes. *Cytogenet Cell Genet* 40:706, 1985.

385. VAN KEUREN ML, WATKINS PC, DRABKIN HA, JABS EW, GUSELLA JF, PATTERSON D: Regional localization of DNA segments on chromosome 21 using somatic cell hybrids. *Am J Hum Genet* 38:793, 1986.

386. KORENBERG JR, KALOUSEK DK, ANNERÉN KG, HALL JG, EPSTEIN CJ, COX DR: Deletion of chromosome 21 and normal intelligence: Molecular definition of the lesion. *Am J Hum Genet* 39:A119, 1986.

387. ANNERÉN KG, KORENBERG JR, EPSTEIN CJ: Phosphofructokinase activity in fibroblasts aneuploid for chromosome 21. *Hum Genet* 76:63, 1987.

388. DEVINE EA, NOLIN SL, HOUCK GE JR, JENKINS EC, MILLER DL, BROWN WT: Isolation and regional localization by in situ hybridization of a unique gene segment to chromosome 21. *Biochem Biophys Res Commun* 121:380, 1984.

389. DEVINE EA, NOLIN SL, HOUCK GE JR, JENKINS EC, BROWN WT: Chromosomal localization of several families of repetitive sequences by in situ hybridization. *Am J Hum Genet* 37:114, 1985.

390. ROBAKIS NK, WISNIEWSKI HM, JENKINS EC, DEVINE-GAGE EA, HOUCK GE, YAO X-L, RAMAKRISHNA N, WOLFE G, SILVERMAN WP, BROWN WT: Chromosome 21q21 sublocalisation of gene encoding beta-amyloid peptide in cerebral vessels and neuritic (senile) plaques of people with Alzheimer disease and Down syndrome. *Lancet* 1:384, 1987.

391. TANZI RE, HAINES JL, STEWART GD, WATKINS PC, GIBBONS KT, FARYNIARZ AG, WALLACE MR, HALLEWELL R, YOUNT E, WEXLER NS, CONNEALLY PM, GUSELLA JF: Genetic linkage map for the long arm of human chromosome 21. *Proc Natl Acad Sci USA*, in press.

392. WATKINS PC, TANZI RE, CHENG SV, GUSELLA J: Molecular genetics of human chromosome 21. *J Med Genet* 24:257, 1987.

393. NEVE RL: Molecular structure of chromosome 21, in McCoy EE, Epstein CJ (eds): *Oncology and Hematology of Down Syndrome.* New York, AR Liss, 1987, p 3.

394. GUSELLA JF, TANZI RE, WATKINS PC, GIBBONS KT, HOBBS WJ, FARYNIARZ AG, HEALEY ST, ANDERSON MA: Genetic linkage map for chromosome 21. *Ann NY Acad Sci* 450:25, 1985.

395. KITTUR SD, ANTONARAKIS SE, TANZI RE, MEYERS DA, CHAKRAVARTI A, GRONER Y, PHILLIPS JA, WATKINS PC, GUSELLA JF, KAZAZIAN HH JR: A linkage map of three anonymous human DNA fragments and SOD-1 on chromosome 21. *EMBO J* 4:2257, 1985.

396. HOUCK GE JR, GENOVESE MJ, GROSS AC, BROWN WT, DEVINE-GAGE EA: Linkage of chromosome 21-specific probes along the chromosome. *Am J Hum Genet* 39:A158, 1986.

397. SUMMITT RL: Chromosome specific segments that cause the phenotype of Down syndrome, in de la Cruz FF, Gerald PS (eds): *Trisomy 21 (Down Syndrome). Research Perspectives.* Baltimore, University Park Press, 1981, p 225.

398. RETHORÉ M-O: Structural variation of chromosome 21 and symptoms of Down's syndrome, in Burgio GR, Fracarro M, Tiepolo L, Wolf U (eds): *Trisomy 21. An International Symposium.* Berlin, Springer-Verlag, 1981, p 173.

399. PATTERSON D, JONES C, SCOGGIN C, MILLER YE, GRAW S: Somatic cell genetic approaches to Down's syndrome. *Ann NY Acad Sci* 396:69, 1982.

400. HABEDANK M, RODEWALD A: Moderate Down's syndrome in three siblings having partial trisomy 21q22.2→qter and therefore no SOD-1 excess. *Hum Genet* 60:74, 1982.

401. COTTONI-DURAND M: *Contribution à l'étude de la carte factorielle du chromosome 21.* Medical Dissertation. Nancy, 1979.

402. JENKINS EC, DUNCAN CJ, WRIGHT CE, GIORDANO FM, WILBUR L, WISNIEWSKI K, SKLOWER SL, FRENCH JH, JONES C, BROWN WT: Atypical Down syndrome and partial trisomy 21. *Clin Genet* 24:97, 1983.

403. FRAISSE J, PHILIP T, BERTHEAS M-F, LAURAS B: Six cases of partial duplication-deficiency 21 syndrome: 21dup q22delp23 due to maternal pericentric inversion: inv(21)(p12;q22). *Ann Genet* 29:177, 1986.

404. TAYSI K, SPARKES R, O'BRIEN TJ, DENGLER DR: Down's syndrome phenotype and autosomal gene inactivation in a child with presumed (X;21) de novo translocation. *J Med Genet* 19:144, 1982.

405. LÉONARD C, GAUTIER M, SINET PM, SELVA J, HURET JL: Two Down syndrome patients with rec(1)dupq, inv(21)(p11;q2109) from a familial pericentric inversion. *Ann Genet* 29:181, 1986.

405a. MIYAZAKI K, YAMANAKA T, OGASAWARA N: A boy with Down's syndrome having recombinant chromosome 21 but no SOD-1 excess. *Clin Genet* 32:383, 1987.

406. TAYLOR GM, WILLIAMS A, D'SOUZA SW, FERGUSSON WD, DONNAI D, FENNELL J, HARRIS R: The expression of CD18 is increased in trisomy 21 (Down syndrome) lymphoblastoid cells. *Clin Exp Immunol* 71:324, 1988.

407. ARIAS S, PARADISI I, ROLO M: Cystathionine beta-synthase (CBS) location excluded from 21pter→q11, but confirmed to 21q, by gene dosage in trisomy 21. *Cytogenet Cell Genet* 40:570, 1985.

408. HALLIWELL B, GUTTERIDGE JMC: *Free Radicals in Biology and Medicine.* Oxford, Clarendon Press, 1985.

409. SINET P-M, LEJEUNE J, JEROME H: Trisomy 21 (Down syndrome). Glutathione peroxidase, hexose monophosphate shunt and IQ. *Life Sci* 24:29, 1979.

410. SINET PM: Metabolism of oxygen derivatives in Down's syndrome. *Ann NY Acad Sci* 396:83, 1982.

411. MAYES J, MUNEER R, SIFERS M: Superoxide dismutase activity and oxygen toxicity in Down syndrome fibroblasts. *Am J Hum Genet* 36:15S, 1984.

412. ANNERÉN KG, EPSTEIN CJ: Lipid peroxidation and superoxide dismutase-1 and glutathione peroxidase activities in trisomy 16 fetal mice and human trisomy 21 fibroblasts. *Pediatr Res* 21:88, 1987.

413. ELROY-STEIN O, BERNSTEIN Y, GRONER Y: Overproduction of human Cu/Zn-superoxide dismutase in transfected cells: extenuation of paraquat-mediated cytotoxicity and enhancement of lipid peroxidation. *EMBO J* 5:615, 1986.

414. BLUM J, FRIDOVICH I: Inactivation of glutathione peroxidase by superoxide radical. *Arch Biochem Biophys* 240:500, 1985.

415. ANNEREN G, EDQVIST L-E, GEBRE-MEDHIN, GUSTAVSON K-H: Glutathione peroxidase activity in erythrocytes in Down's syndrome. (Abnormal variation in relation to age and sex through childhood and adolescence.) *Trisomy 21* 1:9, 1985.

416. BROOKSBANK BWL, BALAZS R: Superoxide dismutase, glutathione peroxidase and lipoperoxidation in Down's syndrome fetal brain. *Dev Brain Res* 16:37, 1984.

417. KURNIT DM, ALDRIDGE JF, MATSUOKA R, MATTHYSE S: Increased adhesiveness of trisomy 21 cells and atrioventricular canal malformations in Down's syndrome: A stochastic model. *Am J Med Genet* 20:385, 1985.

418. WRIGHT TC, DESTREMPES M, ORKIN R, KURNIT DM: Increased adhesive-

ness of Down syndrome fetal fibroblasts in vitro. *Proc Natl Acad Sci USA* 81:2426, 1984.

419. ROWLEY JD: Down syndrome and acute leukemia: Increased risk may be due to trisomy 21. *Lancet* 2:1020, 1981.

420. HECHT F: Leukaemia and chromosome 21. *Lancet* 1:286, 1982.

421. COUNTRYMAN PJ, HEDDLE JA, CRAWFORD E: The repair of X-ray-induced chromosomal damage in trisomy 21 and normal diploid lymphocytes. *Cancer Res* 37:52, 1977.

422. ATHANASIOU K, BARTSOCAS CS: The implications of S-phase exchanges for the mechanisms of radiosensitivity in trisomy 21. *Am J Med Genet* 12:141, 1982.

423. UGAZIO AG: Down's syndrome. Problems of immunodeficiency, in Burgio GR, Fraccaro M, Tiepolo L, Wolf U (eds): *Trisomy 21. An International Symposium*. Berlin, Springer-Verlag, 1981, p 33.

424. TEYSSIER JR, BEHAR C, BAJOLLE F, POTRON G: Selective involvement of cells carrying extra chromosome 21 in a child with acute nonlymphocytic leukaemia. *Lancet* 1:290, 1984.

425. EPSTEIN CJ: Down's syndrome and Alzheimer's disease: What is the relation? in Glenner GG, Wurtman RI (eds): *Advancing Frontiers in Alzheimer's Disease Research*. Austin, University of Texas Press, 1987, p 155.

426. SCHWEBER M: A possible unitary genetic hypothesis for Alzheimer's disease and Down syndrome. *Ann NY Acad Sci* 450:223, 1985.

427. ZEMLAN FP, THIENHAUS OJ, BOSMANN HB: Increased chromosome 21q22.1 marker in Alzheimer's disease and Down's syndrome. *Soc Neurosci Abstr* 12:1314, 1986.

428. DELABAR JM, LAMOUR Y, GEGONNE A, DAVOUS P, ROUDIER M, NICOLE A, CEBALLUS I, STEHELIN D, SINET PM: Rearrangements of chromosome 21 in Alzheimer's disease. *Ann Genet* 29:226, 1986.

429. GLENNER GG: On causative theories in Alzheimer's disease. *Hum Pathol* 16:435, 1985.

430. TANZI RE, ST GEORGE-HYSLOP PH, HAINES JL, POLINSKY RJ, NEE L, FONCIN J-F, NEVE RL, MCCLATCHEY AJ, CONNEALLY PM, GUSELLA JF: The genetic defect in familial Alzheimer's disease is not tightly linked to the amyloid β-protein gene. *Nature* 329:156, 1987.

431. TANZI RE, BIRD ED, LATT SA, NEVE RL: The amyloid β protein gene is not duplicated in brains from patients with Alzheimer's disease. *Science* 238:666, 1987.

432. PODLISNY MB, LEE G, SELKOE DJ: Gene dosage of the amyloid β precursor protein in Alzheimer's disease. *Science* 238:669, 1987.

433. HESTON LL, MASTRI AR: The genetics of Alzheimer's disease. Association with hematologic malignancy and Down's syndrome. *Arch Gen Psychiatry* 34:976, 1977.

434. HESTON LL, MASTRI AR, ANDERSON VE, WHITE J: Dementia of the Alzheimer type. Clinical genetics, natural history, and associated conditions. *Arch Gen Psychiatry* 38:1085, 1981.

435. MCCLURE HM, BELDEN KH, PIEPER WA, JACOBSON CB: Autosomal trisomy in a chimpanzee: resemblance to Down's syndrome. *Science* 165, 1010, 1969.

436. ANDRLE M, FIEDLER W, RETT A, AMBROS P, SCHWEIZER D: A case of trisomy 22 in Pongo pygmaeus. *Cytogenet Cell Genet* 24:1, 1979.

437. NADEAU JH, TAYLOR BA: Lengths of chromosomal segments conserved since divergence of man and mouse. *Proc Natl Acad Sci USA* 81:814, 1984.

438. FRANCKE U, TAGGART RT: Assignment of the gene for cytoplasmic superoxide dismutase (SOD-1) to a region of the chromosome 16 and of Hprt to a region of the X chromosome in the mouse. *Proc Natl Acad Sci USA* 76:5230, 1979.

439. COX DR, EPSTEIN LB, EPSTEIN CJ: Genes coding for sensitivity to interferon (IfRec) and soluble superoxide dismutase (SOD-1) are linked in mouse and man and map to mouse chromosome 16. *Proc Natl Acad Sci USA* 77:2168, 1980.

440. COX DR, GOLDBLATT D, EPSTEIN CJ: Chromosomal assignment of mouse PRGS: further evidence for homology between mouse chromosome 16 and human chromosome 21. *Am J Hum Genet* 33:145A, 1981.

441. WATSON DK, MCWILLIAMS-SMITH MJ, KOZAK C, REEVES R, GEARHART J, NUNN MF, NASH W, FOWLE JR III, DUESBERG P, PAPAS TS, O'BRIEN SJ: Conserved chromosomal positions of dual domains of the *ets* protooncogene in cats, mice, humans. *Proc Natl Acad Sci USA* 83:1792, 1986.

442. LOVETT M, GOLDGABER D, ASHLEY P, COX DR, GAJDUSEK DC, EPSTEIN CJ: The mouse homolog of the human amyloid β protein (AD-AP) gene is located on the distal end of human chromosome 16: Further extension of the homology between human chromosome 21 and mouse chromosome 16. *Biochem Biophys Res Commun*, 144:1069, 1987.

443. COX DR, EPSTEIN CJ: Comparative gene mapping of human chromosome 21 and mouse chromosome 16. *Ann NY Acad Sci* 450:169, 1985.

444. ASHLEY PL, COX DR: Regional assignment of a putative protooncogene (*Ets-2*) and the somatostatin gene (*Sst*) on mouse chromosome 16. *Cytogenet Cell Genet*, in press.

445. REEVES RH, GEARHART JD, LITTLEFIELD JW: Genetic basis for a mouse model of Down syndrome. *Brain Res Bull* 16:803, 1986.

445a. REEVES RH, ROBAKIS NK, OSTER-GRANITE ML, WISNIEWSKI HM, COYLE JT, GEARHART JD: Genetic linkage in the mouse of genes involved in Down syndrome and Alzheimer's disease in man. *Mol Brain Res* 2:215, 1987.

446. FRANCKE U, DE MARTINVILLE B, D'EUSTACHIO P, RUDDLE FH: Comparative gene mapping: Murine lambda light chains are located in region cen→B5 of mouse chromosome 16 not homologous to human chromosome 21. *Cytogenet Cell Genet* 33:267, 1982.

447. RODERICK TH, LALLEY PA, DAVISSON MT, O'BRIEN SJ, WOMACK JE, CRÉAU-GOLDBERG N, ECHARD G, MOORE KL: Report of the committee on comparative mapping. *Cytogenet Cell Genet* 37:312, 1984.

448. GROPP A, KOLBUS U, GIERS D: Systematic approach to the study of trisomy in the mouse. II. *Cytogenet Cell Genet* 14: 42, 1975.

449. EPSTEIN CJ, COX DR, EPSTEIN LB: Mouse trisomy 16: An animal model of human trisomy 21 (Down syndrome). *Ann NY Acad Sci* 450:157, 1985.

450. OSTER-GRANITE ML, GEARHART JD, REEVES RH: Neurobiological consequences of trisomy 16 in mice, in Epstein CJ (ed): *The Neurobiology of Down Syndrome*. New York, Raven, 1986, p 137.

451. COX DR, SMITH SA, EPSTEIN LB, EPSTEIN CJ: Mouse trisomy 16 as an animal model of human trisomy 21 (Down syndrome): Formation of viable trisomy 16↔diploid mouse chimeras. *Dev Biol* 101:416, 1984.

452. GEARHART JD, SINGER HS, MORAN TH, TIEMEYER M, OSTER-GRANITE ML, COYLE J: Mouse chimeras composed of trisomy 16 and normal (2N) cells: Preliminary studies. *Brain Res Bull* 16:815, 1986.

453. EPSTEIN CJ, AVRAHAM KB, LOVETT M, SMITH S, ELROY-STEIN O, ROTMAN G, BRY C, GRONER Y: Transgenic mice with increased CuZn-superoxide dismutase activity: Animal model of dosage effects in Down syndrome. *Proc Natl Acad Sci USA* 84:8044, 1987.

454. BECKER LE, ARMSTRONG DL, CHAN F: Dendritic atrophy in children with Down's syndrome. *Ann Neurol* 20:520, 1986.

455. SCHAPIRO MB, KAY AD, MAX C, RYKER AK, HAXBY JV, KAUFMAN S, MILSTIEN S, RAPOPORT SI: Cerebrospinal fluid monoamines in Down's syndrome adults at different ages. *J Ment Defic Res* 31:259, 1987.

456. SCHAPIRO MB, CREASEY W, SCHWARTZ M, HAXBY JV, WHITE B, MOORE A, RAPOPORT SI: Quantitative CT analysis of brain morphometry in adult Down's syndrome at different ages. *Neurology* 37:1424, 1987.

457. FENNER ME, HEWITT KE, TORPY DM: Down's syndrome: intellectual and behavioral functioning during adulthood. *J Ment Defic Res* 31:241, 1987.

458. MANN DMA, YATES PO, MARCYNIUK B: Dopaminergic neurotransmitter systems in Alzheimer's disease and in Down syndrome at middle age. *J Neurol Neurosurg Psychiatr* 50:341, 1987.

459. MANN DMA, YATES PO, MARCYNIUK B, RAVINDRA CR: Loss of neurons from cortical and subcortical areas in Down's syndrome patients at middle age. Quantitative comparisons with younger Down's patients and patients with Alzheimer's disease. *J Neurolog Sci* 80:79, 1987.

460. FONG C-T, BRODEUR GM: Down's syndrome and leukemia: epidemiology, genetics, cytogenetics and mechanisms of leukemogenesis. *Cancer Genet Cytogenet* 28:55, 1987.

461. PEETERS M, POON A: Down syndrome and leukemia: unusual clinical aspects and unexpected methotrexate sensitivity. *Eur J Pediatr* 146:416, 1987.

462. CRONK C, CROCKER AC, PUESCHEL SM, SHEA AM, ZACKAI E, PICKENS G, REED RB: Growth charts for children with Down syndrome: 1 month to 18 years of age. *Pediatrics* 81:102, 1988.

463. HSIANG Y-HH, BERKOVITZ GD, BLAND GL, MIGEON CJ, WARREN AC: Gonadal function in patients with Down syndrome. *Am J Med Genet* 27:449, 1987.

464. BAIRD PA, SADOVNICK AD: Life expectancy in Down syndrome. *J Pediatr* 110:849, 1987.

465. BAIRD PA, SADOVNICK AD: Causes of death to age 30 in Down syndrome. *Am J Hum Genet*, in press.

466. MARTIN-DELEON PA, WILLIAMS MB: Sexual behavior and Down syndrome: the biological mechanism. *Am J Med Genet* 27:693, 1987.

467. PETERS GB, FORD JH, NICHOLL JK: Trisomy 21 mosaicism and maternal age effect. *Lancet* 1:1202, 1987.

468. WARREN AC, CHAKRAVARTY A, WONG C, SLAUGENHAUPT SA, HALLORAN SL, WATKINS PC, METAXOTOU C, ANTONARAKIS SE: Evidence for reduced recombination on the nondisjoined chromosomes 21 in Down syndrome. *Science* 237:652, 1987.

469. CHENG SV, NADEAU JH, TANZI RE, WATKINS PC, SACCHI N, NEVE RL, GUSELLA JF: Synteny in man and mouse of DNA markers from the chromosomal region linked to familial Alzheimer's disease and Down syndrome. *Am J Hum Genet* 41:A161, 1987.

470. MÜNKE M, KRAUS JP, OHURA T, FRANCKE U: The gene for cystathionine β-synthase (*CBS*) maps to the subtelomeric region on human chromosome 21q and to proximal mouse chromosome 17. *Am J Hum Genet* 42:550, 1988.

CHAPTER **8**

THE FRAGILE X SYNDROME

ROBERT L. NUSSBAUM
DAVID H. LEDBETTER

1. *The syndrome of X-linked mental retardation with fragile X affects 1 to 2 per 2600 males and 1 to 2 per 4100 females, making it the single most common form of inherited mental retardation. Based on the incidence of disease and estimates of penetrance (see below), the carrier frequency in the population is approximately 1 in 866. The clinical phenotype in males consists of mental retardation to a varying degree, mild dysmorphic features, and enlargement of the testes in adults. Approximately one-third of female heterozygotes may also be mentally impaired. The syndrome is associated with the* fragile X, *a chromosomal fragile site on the distal long arm of the X chromosome. Cytogenetic expression of the fragile X is the only laboratory test available for diagnosing the fragile X syndrome, but the pathophysiological relationship between the cytogenetic abnormality and the clinical disorder is unknown. The syndrome was initially thought to be inherited as an X-linked Mendelian trait but is now known to have a far more complicated inheritance pattern that is unique in human genetics.*
2. *The fragile X is not present in routine metaphase chromosome preparations but must be induced using culture conditions that deprive cells of pyrimidine nucleotide precursors of DNA synthesis. Such conditions may slow DNA replication or damage DNA, thereby evoking cellular repair mechanisms. Fragile sites may be areas of DNA that are especially sensitive to the effects of the induction conditions and fail to condense in mitosis owing to incomplete replication, DNA damage, or ongoing repair.*
3. *The relationship between genetic carrier status, cytogenetic fragile X expression, and clinical disease is complex. Although most hemizygous males are mentally retarded and show the fragile X, 20 percent of males carrying the mutation may be phenotypically and cytogenetically normal* (transmitting males). *Two-thirds of carrier females are mentally normal; of these, only one-third have cytogenetic expression. Among the one-third of carrier females who are mentally retarded, up to 10 percent may have no cytogenetic expression of the fragile X. Differences in levels of cytogenetic expression in different cell types and with different induction protocols constitute technical factors that may further complicate laboratory diagnosis. Prenatal diagnosis by cytogenetic expression studies in amniocytes or chorionic villus cells has been accomplished, but technical difficulties in inducing fragile X expression in these cell types make its reliability uncertain at present.*
4. *The inheritance pattern of the fragile X syndrome is unusual. The male offspring of carrier females all have 50 percent a priori risk of inheriting the mutation, but the penetrance can vary from 18 to 100 percent, depending on the clinical status of the carrier mother and where she is situated within the family pedigree. Similar variability in penetrance occurs in daughters of carrier females in whom the penetrance ranges from 10 to 40 percent. In the daughters of transmitting males, however, who must all inherit the fragile X mutation, the penetrance is close to 0 percent. There is no clear explanation for why the sex and intellectual status of carrier parents have an effect on the risk of clinical disease in their offspring.*
5. *Linkage analysis using polymorphic markers that flank the fragile site provides strong evidence that the genetic locus for the fragile X syndrome and the fragile site are very close, if not identical. To date, genetic markers that appear to be close to the fragile site by physical mapping methods are at substantial recombination distance from the locus but may still be useful for carrier detection and prenatal diagnosis in some families.*
6. *There is no specific treatment for fragile X syndrome, and management depends on medical, physical, and occupational therapy directed toward alleviating the neurologic and behavioral manifestations of the disorder. Extensive family testing and genetic counseling are required in the management of this disorder.*

The syndrome of X-linked mental retardation associated with the Xq27 fragile site (McKusick #30955; Martin-Bell syndrome) is one of the most important, yet poorly understood, disorders in medical genetics. (For reviews, see Refs. 1 to 5.) It is characterized by mental retardation of variable severity associated with an inducible cytogenetic abnormality, a fragile site, on the long arm of the X chromosome. The syndrome at first appeared to be inherited in a typical X-linked manner; however, its inheritance is now known to be far more complex and unusual. Although the biochemical bases for both the clinical phenotype and the cytogenetic abnormality remain unknown, inclusion of this important disease entity in this volume is appropriate for several reasons. First, the syndrome represents the most common heritable form of mental retardation in humans. Second, because the retardation demonstrates a unique inheritance pattern and an unusual inducible cytogenetic phenotype, research into the molecular mechanisms underlying this important disease should provide major insights into many areas of clinical medicine and molecular and cellular biology.

HISTORY

A 25 percent excess of males over females among individuals in institutions for the retarded has been known for almost a century.[6,7] The male excess was attributed to more frequent institutionalization of retarded males due to higher societal expectations for males relative to females.[1] In 1943, Martin and Bell[8] described the first extended kindred with mental retardation segregating in an X-linked manner. However, it was not until the early 1970s that X-linked inheritance of mental retardation was considered a contributing factor to the excess of males in retarded populations.[6,7,9]

Nonstandard abbreviations used in this chapter are: APC = aphidicolin, TS = thymidylate synthase.

A fragile site on the X chromosome was first observed by Lubs in 1969[10] and was described as a *marker X* present in affected males and obligate carrier females of a family with X-linked mental retardation. The marker consisted of a constriction or gap at the distal end of the long arm of the X chromosome. Confirmation of this finding did not come until 1976–1977 when groups in France[11] and Australia[12] independently described additional cases of X-linked mental retardation associated with a similar marker X chromosome. The delay in confirming the initial observation was soon explained by the discovery that cytogenetic detection of the marker X is dependent on the type of medium used for culturing the cells prior to cytogenetic analysis.[13] Because the constriction or gap in the marker X chromosome gave the appearance of being easily breakable, the abnormality came to be known as a *fragile site* and the whole chromosome came to be known as a *fragile X*. In this chapter, the fragile X syndrome is used to refer to the clinical entity, and the cytogenetic marker, the Xq27 fragile site, will be called the fragile X (gene symbol FRAXA).[14]

POPULATION STUDIES

From the initial observation of mental retardation associated with the marker X in 1969 to the present, well over 900 papers have been published on X-linked mental retardation in general and the fragile X syndrome in particular.[15–17] It is now generally established that X-linked forms of mental retardation affect 1 in 145 individuals and constitute a heterogeneous but very important class of heritable mental retardation responsible for approximately 20 percent of all mental retardation.[18] Furthermore, a significant proportion of all X-linked mental retardation, approximately 20 percent, results from a single identifiable disorder, the fragile X syndrome, defined by a characteristic neurologic and somatic phenotype and an inducible fragile site on the X chromosome at Xq27.[18–20] For example, when male children attending schools for the mentally handicapped in Britain, Australia, Sweden, Hawaii, Italy, and South Africa were screened, between 1 and 7 percent of males without a previously identified diagnosis were found to have the fragile X syndrome.[18–24] Workers in Britain and Australia used the prevalence of fragile X syndrome among retarded children to estimate that the overall prevalence of retardation due to the fragile X syndrome is between 1 and 2 per 2600 males and 1 and 2 per 4100 females.[19,20] Therefore, the fragile X syndrome is one of the most common heritable causes of mental retardation worldwide.

CLINICAL PHENOTYPE

Males

Somatic Features. The diagnosis of the fragile X syndrome in a male infant is very difficult in the immediate newborn period. Except for somewhat greater than average birth weight, males with the fragile X syndrome appear normal.[25–27] Somatic features generally appear in childhood and include increased head circumference, coarsening of facial features, hypotonia, and prominence of the ears, forehead, and jaw. A connective tissue disorder may be suspected because of joint hyperextensibility, pectus excavatum, pes planus, mitral valve prolapse, and dilation of the aortic root.[28–32] Enlarged testes (macroorchidism) is uncommon prior to puberty (15 percent) but is present in nearly 90 percent of postpubertal males.[25]

The variability and subtlety of facial appearance seen in the fragile X syndrome is shown in Fig. 8-1. Figure 8-1*A* to *C* shows three unrelated males, ages 11, 40, and 65, affected with the syndrome. A relatively long face, large ears, and prominent jaw are seen, but overall facial morphology is normal. Figure 8-1*D* shows the patient from Fig. 8-1*B* with his three roommates in a residential home for the retarded. All four males have documented fragile X syndrome.

Neurologic Features. Mental retardation is common but varies in severity in males with the fragile X syndrome, even within the same family.[33] Over 90 percent of male patients have IQ scores in the 20 to 60 range, with a mean between 30 and 45.[34] Seizures occur in approximately 10 percent of patients.[34] Certain behavioral abnormalities are frequently present in childhood and may aid in the diagnosis. These include attention deficit disorder or hyperactivity, poor eye contact, and stereotypic hand movements.[27] In verbal patients, rapid speech with stuttering and perseveration is seen frequently.[35] Patients are often pleasant or docile, but violent disruptive behavior occurs in a significant minority of patients and has required institutionalization in a number of cases.[27,36] Males with the fragile X syndrome share some of but not all the behavioral abnormalities seen in infantile autism.[37–39] Conversely, the fragile X chromosome has been found in a substantial fraction of male patients carrying a diagnosis of autism defined by criteria established by the *American Psychiatric Association Diagnostic and Statistical Manual (DSMIII)*.[38,40] Thus, there appears to be some overlap in clinical manifestations of these two puzzling disorders. Many of the behavioral abnormalities wane as patients enter adulthood.

Transmitting Males

Although the majority of males hemizygous for the fragile X mutation show, at least in part, some of the abnormalities described above, a significant minority appear to be clinically normal and do not demonstrate the chromosomal fragile site using standard induction protocols.[41–43] Such clinically normal hemizygous males are termed *transmitting males* because their existence can be inferred only from their position in the pedigree as obligatory carriers of the gene rather than by clinical or cytogenetic findings. Indeed, segregation analysis of the fragile X syndrome in the offspring of obligatory female carriers shows that only 40 percent of male offspring are affected, instead of the 50 percent expected for a fully penetrant, X-linked disorder.[44–45] Since there is no evidence of in utero male lethality or distortion of the sex ratio at birth, these data suggest that transmitting males may constitute as many as 20 percent of all males carrying the mutation.

Clinical Phenotype in Females

Heterozygous carriers of the fragile X syndrome demonstrate an extremely variable phenotype.[1,25,27,34] Two-thirds of female heterozygotes are clinically normal. Of the approximately one-third of carrier females who do show mental impairment, the intellectual deficits range from learning disability with normal

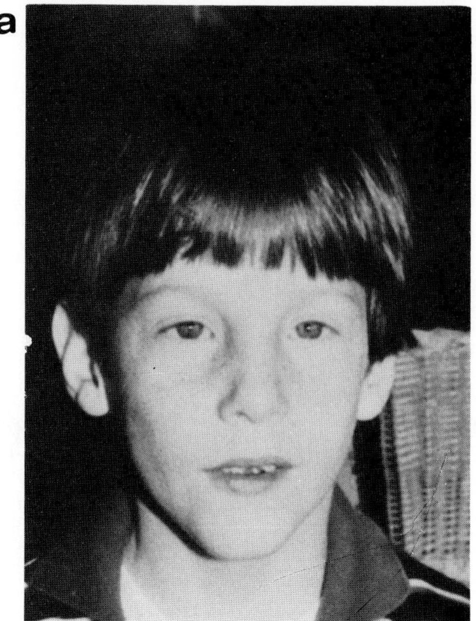

Fig. 8-1 Photographs of institutionalized male patients with the fragile X syndrome. In panels *A* to *C* are shown three males, aged 11, 40, and 63. In panel *D* are shown the individual from panel *B* and his three roommates in a residential home for the mentally retarded. The patients in panel *D* had originally chosen to room with each other because of mutual interests and compatible personalities; during screening a number of years later, all four men were found to have the fragile X syndrome. *(Courtesy of Brenda Finucane, M.S., and the Elwyn Institute.)*

formal IQ testing to severe retardation.[33,46] No characteristic behaviors have been noted in mentally impaired female carriers of the fragile X syndrome. Facial features similar to those seen in affected males may be present in retarded female carriers, and it has been suggested that the degree of somatic expression of the gene defect in females correlates with the severity of mental retardation.[47]

Pathologic Studies in Fragile X Syndrome

Pathologic examination of affected tissues has not revealed a unifying biochemical or physiological process to explain the somatic abnormalities and neurologic dysfunction. Histologic examination of enlarged testes from affected adult males shows edema and a generalized increase in extracellular matrix components and connective tissue, particularly collagen.[48,49] Disturbed spermatid differentiation has also been reported, perhaps due to pressure on seminiferous tubules from edema.[48] Gonadotropin hormone secretion and steroid hormone levels appear normal and do not explain the testicular abnormalities.[50] Abnormal testicular histology is generally absent in prepubertal males,[25] although abnormalities were reported in affected male fetuses.[49,51] Ovarian enlargement with cystic changes has been found in affected female carriers suggesting that female as well as male gonads may be affected.[52] Elastin structure has been reported to be abnormal in histologic studies of skin from affected male patients.[53] Neuropathologic examination of the brain of a 62-year-old male with fragile X syndrome demonstrated some minor nonspecific abnormalities in dendritic spine and synaptic structure in the cortex but was otherwise unrevealing.[54] Thus, the pathogenesis of the abnormalities seen in this disorder remains obscure.

CHROMOSOMAL FRAGILE SITES

Definition and Appearance

A fragile site is a specific point on a chromosome (i.e., chromosome band) which is prone to breakage, usually appearing as a nonstaining gap or constriction involving one or both chromatids of a metaphase chromosome.[55] Less frequently, the site may undergo a complete break, producing an acentric fragment which may be deleted or, by mitotic nondisjunction, duplicated (triradial figure). Most fragile sites do not appear spontaneously under routine cell culture conditions but must be induced by exposing cells to one of several types of appropriate medium conditions or drug treatments during the DNA synthesis phase (S phase) prior to mitosis. All fragile site induction methods produce random chromosome breakage so that, by definition, a fragile site is any "hot spot" for chromosome breakage in which the frequency is significantly elevated above background random breakage.[14]

Examples of the various appearances of a fragile site are shown in Fig. 8-2 for the fragile site on chromosome 10 at band q25. Because this fragile site is interstitially located and distant from the telomere, a rather large acentric fragment is produced by breakage at q25 making this fragile site easy to visualize. The fragile site at q27 on the X chromosome is closer to the telomere of the long arm, making its appearance less obvious (Fig. 8-3).[56] Because of the very small acentric fragment produced, it is difficult to identify cells in which this segment is completely deleted, although this is occasionally reported.[57] Scoring of the presence of the fragile site on X is therefore somewhat subjective and requires an experienced observer.

Fig. 8-2 Fragile site on chromosome 10, band q25, shown in G-banded preparations in which it can appear as *(A and B)* single chromatid breaks, *(C)* isochromatid gaps or breaks, *(D)* deletion of q25-qter, and less frequently as *(E)* triradials, and *(F)* inverted duplications of q25→q11. *(Reprinted with permission from S. Gollin, HG.-O. Bock, C.T. Caskey, D.H. Ledbetter, American Journal of Medicine Genetics 21:643, 1985.)*

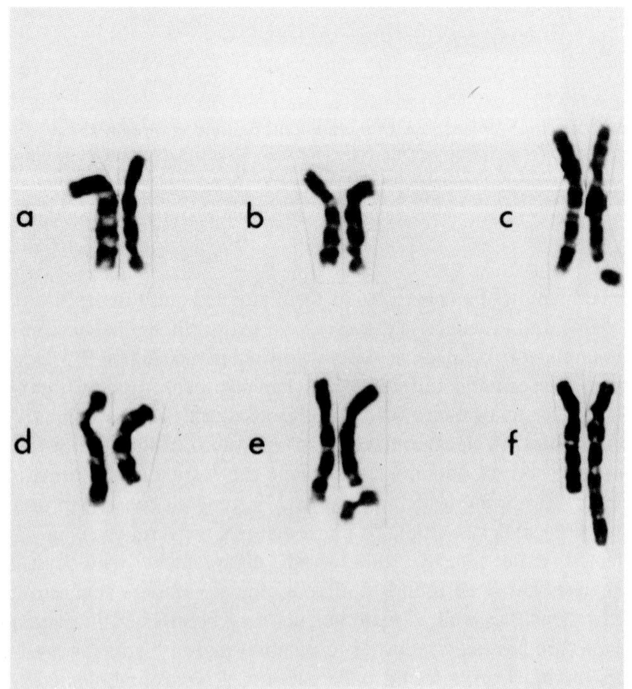

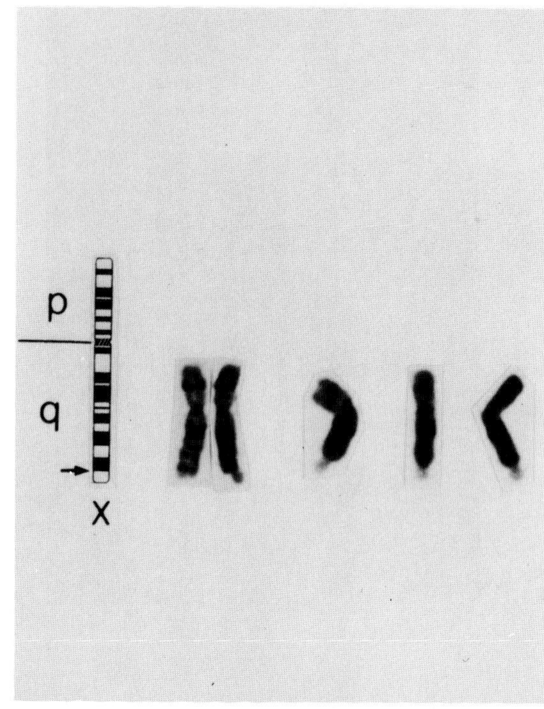

Fig. 8-3 Fragile Xq27 in G-banded metaphase chromosomes. At far left is an idiogrammatic representation of the X chromosome at approximately the 550 band stage of resolution.[56] The arrow indicates the location of the fragile site in the distal portion of the G-positive dark band, q27. The paired chromosomes show a normal X *(left)* and a fragile X *(right)*, which has an apparent break in one chromatid, with displacement of the distal fragment, and a less prominent constriction in the other chromatid. Three individual fragile X chromosomes show the typical appearance of an isochromatid gap or constriction at distal q27 with a very pale staining distal fragment (band q28) *(Reproduced with permission from Nussbaum and Ledbetter.[3])*

Fragile site studies are performed on metaphase chromosomes using light microscopy. Only one report of scanning electron microscopy of a fragile site, Xq27, is available.[58] This study shows that the fragments distal to the fragile site remained attached to the proximal segment of the chromosome by individual 25-nm fibers, a size consistent with previous measurements of single fibers of normal chromatin.

Rare and Common Fragile Sites

Classification. Many fragile sites exist in the human genome and are currently divided into two major categories: rare and common.[14] A rare fragile site is one which is found in a minority of the population (usually less than 1 percent), most often affects only one homolog of the chromosome pair, and is inherited in a Mendelian codominant fashion. To date, 18 such rare fragile sites have been identified on 12 autosomes and the X chromosome (See Fig. 8-4).[14] Most of the rare fragile sites are folate-sensitive, i.e., they are induced by growth

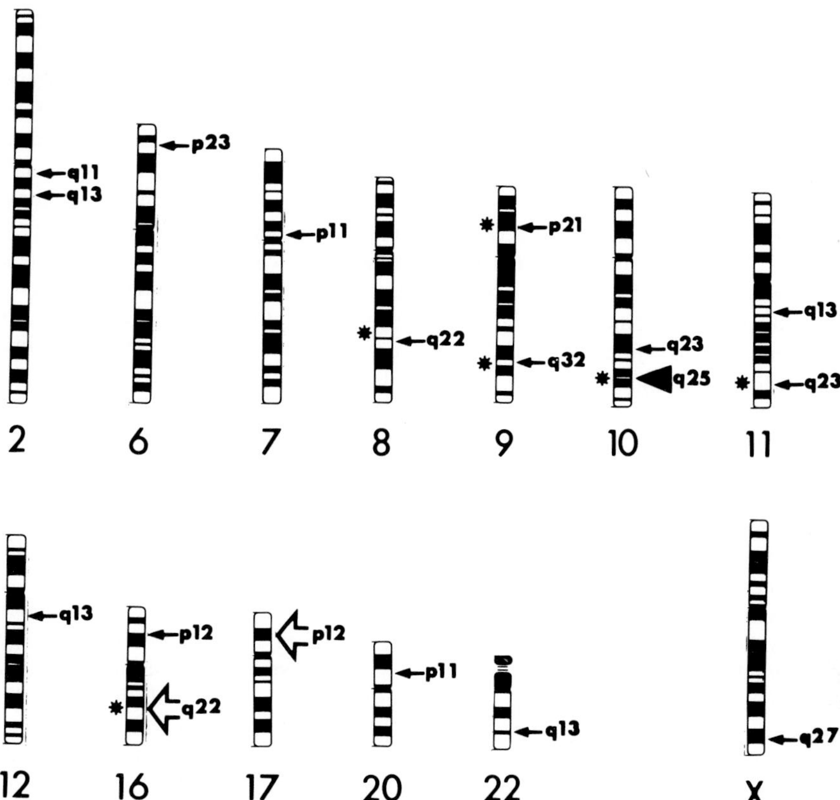

Fig. 8-4 Idiogram of the 18 known rare fragile sites. Small solid arrows with band designations represent the 15 folate-sensitive rare sites, including Xq27. The large solid arrowhead indicates the single BrdU-sensitive site at 10q25. The open arrows indicate the two distamycin-sensitive sites. Asterisks to the left of the chromosome indicate six common fragile site locations which occur in the same chromosome band as rare sites.[14] *(Modified from Sutherland et al.[5] and additional data from Berger et al.,[14] with permission.)*

in one of three cell culture conditions: medium deficient in folic acid and thymidine, medium containing the folate antagonist methotrexate, or medium with fluorodeoxyuridine (FUdR) added as an inhibitor of thymidylate synthase. Three rare fragile sites are not folate-sensitive: two are often expressed spontaneously but are preferentially induced by distamycin A and related compounds, and one is specifically induced by bromodeoxyuridine (BrdU).[14]

Common fragile sites were discovered more recently.[59–61] As the name implies, common fragile sites are present in most or all individuals in the population and are found in both homologs of the chromosome pair. At least 11, and perhaps 50 or more such common sites may be present throughout the human genome.[14] Most of these sites are particularly sensitive to induction by aphidicolin (APC),[60] although a smaller number are induced by 5-azacytidine or BrdU.[62]

The possible relationship between common and rare fragile sites is not well understood. Most common fragile sites are only weakly induced by conditions that induce folate-sensitive sites, and the folate-sensitive rare sites are poorly induced by APC. Although their mechanism of induction therefore seems different, it is an intriguing finding that of 18 rare fragile sites, six occur in the same chromosome band as a common fragile site (Fig. 8-4). This coincidence in location raises the possibility that at least some rare fragile sites may represent mutations or alterations of preexisting common fragile sites.[61,63]

Clinical Significance of Fragile Sites. Of all rare and common fragile sites, only the site at Xq27 has to date been associated with mental retardation or other clinical disease. Since deletions can be observed at fragile sites,[55,57] it is clear that true chromosome breakage occurs at these sites. Recent experiments have shown that chromosome rearrangements at rare or common fragile sites can be induced in cell culture by prolonged growth under fragile site induction conditions.[64–65] These data raise the possibility that fragile sites might predispose to constitutional deletions or translocations. Retrospective studies of breakpoint locations of constitutional rearrangements have suggested that they may be preferentially located in bands with fragile sites.[66–67] Occasional case reports of *de novo* translocations[68] or deletions[69–70] associated with a parental rare fragile site have appeared. Because of the small amount of data available and its circumstantial nature, it is premature to consider rare fragile sites as a risk factor for chromosomal abnormalities. More data are needed to assess the role of rare and common fragile sites in constitutional chromosome rearrangement.

Similar retrospective comparisons of rare and common fragile site locations and recurring translocation breakpoints in leukemias and other cancers have suggested a correlation (reviewed in Ref. 71). In several instances, rare fragile sites have been observed in the normal cells of individuals with a chromosome rearrangement involving the same band in their malignant cells.[71–72] The strongest such association noted to date is between a rare fragile site at 16q22 and the 16q22 breakpoint found in inversions, deletions, or translocations associated with acute myelomonocytic leukemia. However, it was recently shown that the fragile site and cancer breakpoint are not identical on the molecular level, thus decreasing the likelihood of a causal relationship.[73] Similar analysis at a molecular level is required for other fragile sites and cancer breakpoints before any association can be verified or discounted.

Induction of Fragile Site Expression

Because of its great clinical significance, the Xq27 fragile site has been the focus of numerous investigations to determine the optimum conditions for its expression and to define its biochemical mechanism. In this section, we review the key features of induction of the Xq27 fragile site, which appears identical with that of the other folate-sensitive fragile sites, and compare these to the induction properties of aphidicolin induced common fragile sites (see Table 8-1). More detailed discussion of other classes of fragile sites and their induction conditions can be found elsewhere.[14,74]

Folic Acid-Sensitive Sites. Sutherland was the first to demonstrate that fragile site expression in peripheral blood lymphocytes was dependent on the growth medium used.[13] The Xq27 fragile site was induced in Medium 199 but not in other commercially available media tested. Further studies showed that the essential feature of this medium was its relatively low levels of folic acid and thymidine and that the folate antagonist methotrexate also induced Xq27 fragile site expression.[55] Folate-sensitive sites are strongly induced by FUdR, whose metabolite 5-fluorodeoxyuridyl monophosphate (FdUMP) is a potent inhibitor of thymidylate synthase (TS).[75,76] Expression of the Xq27 fragile site is also induced in TS-deficient hybrid cells when deprived of exogenous thymidine.[77] These induction conditions must be present during the late S phase prior to the mitosis in which expression is observed. Either thymidine or folic acid can completely suppress fragile site expression induced by folate deficiency or methotrexate,[55] but only thymidine can reverse the effect of FUdR.[74] Thymidine triphosphate (dTTP) depletion during S phase (directly by inhibition or absence of TS or indirectly through depletion of its cofactor methylene tetrahydrofolate) is therefore an effective but not exclusive method for inducing the Xq27 fragile site.[74–77]

More recently, high concentrations of thymidine (1 to 2 mM) have been shown to induce Xq27 fragile site expression effectively.[78,79] This effect of thymidine is thought to be due to high levels of dTTP which inhibit reduction of cytidine diphosphate (CDP) by ribonucleotide reductase causing a deficiency of deoxycytidine triphosphate (dCTP) for DNA synthesis.[80] This mechanism for Xq27 fragile site induction was supported by the finding that addition of deoxycytidine inhibited induction by high thymidine.[78,79]

A summary of the pathways involved in the induction of expression of the Xq27 fragile site is shown in Fig. 8-5. Supplies of dTTP may be depleted by directly inhibiting TS with FdUMP [reaction (1), Fig. 8-5] or by indirectly inhibiting TS, either by depleting reduced folic acid with methotrexate or by limiting folic acid in the medium [reaction (2), Fig. 8-5]. High thymidine, through its metabolite dTTP, severely reduces the supply of dCTP by allosteric feedback inhibition of the reduction of CDP to dCDP by ribonucleotide reductase [reaction (3), Fig. 8-5]. Thus, all induction conditions appear to have as their final common pathway the depletion of cellular supplies of dTTP or dCTP available for DNA synthesis.

Common Fragile Sites. Common fragile sites are only weakly induced by folic acid deficiency, methotrexate, or FUdR, but are strongly induced by 0.2 μM aphidicolin.[60] APC is a relatively specific inhibitor of DNA polymerase α, which is involved primarily (but not exclusively) in DNA replication. APC inhibits by competition with dCTP for DNA polymerase [reaction (4), Fig. 8-5].[81] This concentration of the APC is only a weak inducer of Xq27 fragile site expression.[60,82] Interestingly, APC seems to decrease Xq27 fragile site expression when used in combination with thymidylate deprivation.[60]

Caffeine Enhancement of Fragile Site Expression. Yunis and Soreng[61] recently demonstrated that caffeine (2 mM) significantly enhances levels of expression of common fragile sites and the Xq27 fragile site when used in conjunction with FUdR induction. Although other investigators have failed to replicate this finding for fragile X in lymphocytes or lymphoblasts,[82–84] caffeine consistently enhances Xq27 fragile site expression in interspecific hybrids.[84] Caffeine, or its analog theophylline, also enhances APC-induced expression of the Xq27 fragile site and common fragile sites in lymphocytes,[82] lymphoblasts, and hybrid cells (S. A. Ledbetter and coworkers, unpublished).

Caffeine has a synergistic effect with many DNA-damaging agents (reviewed in Ref. 85). Its effect is largely indirect: it relieves the mitotic delay usually associated with DNA damage, and thus permits replication and completion of the cell cycle despite existence of regions of DNA damage.[86,87] In a thymidylate synthase-deficient hybrid system, it was shown directly that, following 24 h of thymidine deprivation, there is a 3 to 4-h delay in the appearance of mitotic cells after refeeding with thymidine. Caffeine abolished this delay and increased Xq27 fragile site expression.[84] The results with caffeine suggest that, in both common as well as some folate-

Table 8-1 Methods of Fragile Site Induction and Probable Mechanisms of Action

Method of induction	*Folate-sensitive rare sites (including fragile X)*	*Common sites*	*Probable mechanism*
Folate deficiency	+ +	+	Indirect decrease in thymidylate synthase (TS) activity; decreases dTTP
Methotrexate (10^{-5} M)	+ +	+	Indirect decrease in TS activity; decreases dTTP
FUdR (10^{-8}–10^{-7} M)	+ +	+	Direct TS inhibition; decreases dTTP
High thymidine (1–2 mM)	+ +	?	Indirect decrease in ribonucleotide reductase activity; decreases dCTP
Aphidicolin (0.2 μM)	+	+ +	Inhibits DNA polymerase α
Caffeine (2 mM)	Enhances	Enhances	Relieves mitotic delay; decreases time for replication

SOURCE: Nussbaum and Ledbetter,[3] by permission of Annual Review of Genetics.

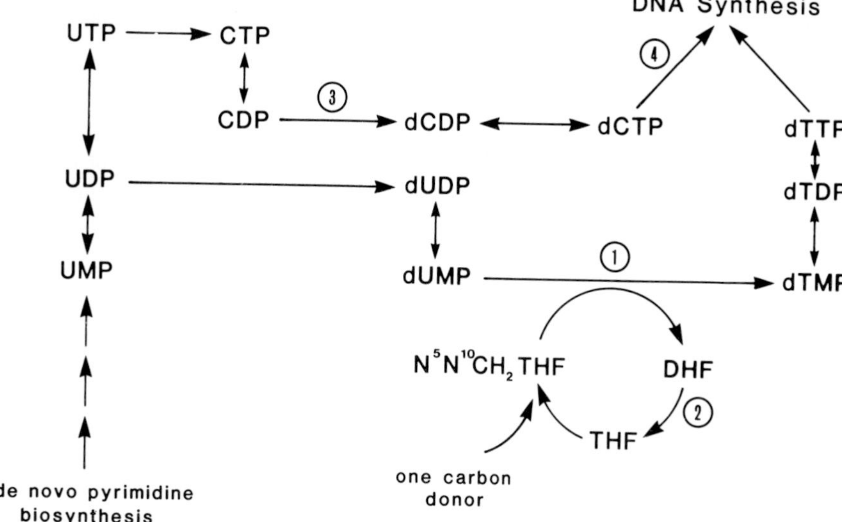

Fig. 8-5 Diagram of important pathways involved in fragile site induction. Enzyme 1 = thymidylate synthase; 2 = dihydrofolate reductase; 3 = ribonucleotide reductase; 4 = DNA polymerase α. UMP, UDP, and UTP = uridine mono-, di-, and triphosphate; CDP and CTP = cytidine di- and triphosphate; dTMP, dTDP, and dTTP = thymidine mono-, di-, and triphosphate; dUMP, dUDP, dCDP, dCCTP = 2′ deoxy derivatives of UMP, UDP, CDP, CTP. DHF, THF: di,tetrahydrofolate.

sensitive rare fragile sites, the cytogenetic appearance may be the result of failure to complete DNA replication or repair prior to entry into mitosis (*vide infra*).

Molecular Basis of Fragile Sites

Mechanisms of Fragile Site Induction. The pathways by which growth of cells under induction conditions leads to expression of the Xq27 rare fragile site, as well as other rare and common fragile sites, are unknown. What is known, however, is that rare fragile sites are inherited as Mendelian codominant traits and therefore must be the result of specific DNA sequence modifications at the fragile sites themselves. The only clues to the nature of this sequence are the culture conditions which produce the cytogenetic expression. However, the different sensitivity of rare and common fragile sites to various induction methods does not necessarily indicate a fundamentally different molecular basis for the two classes of fragile sites.

Deprivation of pyrimidine deoxyribonucleoside triphosphates appears to be necessary for expression of the Xq27 fragile site.[74,78,79] Decreased pyrimidine nucleoside triphosphate levels slow DNA replication.[80] In addition, when either dTTP or dCTP is extremely limiting for DNA synthesis, marked pyrimidine nucleotide pool imbalances may occur, leading to misincorporation of deoxyuridylate for thymidylate or thymidylate for deoxycytidylate.[88–89] Alternatively, misincorporation may lead to a state of continuous but ineffective repair as excision of misincorporated bases proceeds in the face of the severe pool imbalance.[75,90,91] In either case, a region of underreplicated or partially repaired DNA can give the appearance of a decondensed chromatin conformation (gap) when forced to condense at mitosis.[92] Finally, it has been suggested that incorporation of uracil for thymine under conditions of severe dTTP deficit might in and of itself disrupt chromatin conformation by a mechanism independent of DNA replication or repair[93] and lead to the cytogenetic appearance of a fragile site.

There are few data which directly address the relative merits of the possible molecular bases for fragile site expression. Any model for fragile sites should not only delineate the molecular mechanisms involved in fragile site induction but must also explain why these induction conditions have their effect at specific sites in the genome.

RELATIONSHIP BETWEEN PHENOTYPE AND FRAGILE SITE EXPRESSION

Males. It is estimated from segregation analysis that only 80 percent of males who bear the fragile X mutation are clinically affected.[44,45] Of these affected males, all but perhaps 1 percent are positive for fragile X expression (Table 8-2). Even though the fragile X mutation is present in every cell, expression of the Xq27 fragile site is seen in only a fraction of metaphase cells. Even under optimal induction conditions, the fragile site is almost never seen in more than 50 percent of cells, and the typical range of expression is 10 to 50 percent. The frequency of expression for an individual is relatively constant over time if tested in the same laboratory under the same induction conditions.[94,95] Although affected sibs may show significantly different frequencies of fragile X expression, variation between families is greater than that within families[96] indicating some important familial factors in the levels of expression. Most studies have shown no correlation between level of fragile X expression in males and degree of retardation.[44]

An estimated 20 percent of males carrying the fragile X mutation are clinically normal, transmitting males (See Table 8-2).[44] Of those identified by pedigree analysis, most show no fragile X expression.[41–43] However, recent data using somatic cell hybrids demonstrated up to 12 percent fragile X expression in two unrelated transmitting males,[97] a level significantly lower than that seen in affected males, but higher than that of normal controls. These data provide evidence for a partial or premutation in transmitting males.

Females. The relationship between cytogenetic expression and clinical phenotype in females heterozygous for the fragile X mutation is much more complicated. There are four categories of carrier females (Table 8-2): (1) clinically normal, fragile site negative; (2) clinically normal, fragile site positive; (3) intellectually impaired, fragile site positive; (4) intellectually impaired, fragile site negative.

Table 8-2 Relationship of Mental Status and Cytogenetic Expression in Males and Females Bearing the Fragile X Mutation

Cytogenetic expression	Males, %			Females, %		
	Retarded	*Normal*	*Total*	*Retarded*	*Normal*	*Total*
Positive	79%	Rare	79%	27%	26%	53%
Negative	1%	20%*	21%	3%	44%	47%
Total	80%	20%	100%	30%	70%	100%

*The percentage of normal IQ fragile X negative males is a theoretical estimate based on the apparent 20% nonpenetrance of the gene in offspring of obligate carrier females.[44,45] The actual occurrence of normal males proven to carry the mutation by transmission to affected grandsons is much less frequent.
SOURCE: Date from Sherman et al.[44]

Approximately two-thirds of obligate carrier females are intellectually normal. Of these, a majority will show no fragile X expression at all, and those who express the fragile site tend to do so in less than 5 percent of their cells.[44] Thus, carrier detection prior to the birth of an affected child is impossible for about half of all females with this mutation. Of those females who are intellectually impaired, 90 percent are fragile X positive, although the average frequency of expression is somewhat lower than that of affected males. In females, unlike males, the level of fragile X expression does tend to correlate with degree of retardation.[44]

The reasons for the extreme variation in clinical and cytogenetic expression in carrier females remains unclear. One possibility is that some female carriers are the equivalent of transmitting males and, like such males, carry alterations at Xq27 that are neither clinically or cytogenetically apparent. However, the large number of clinically unaffected females who show no cytogenetic expression cannot be accounted for as female counterparts of transmitting males. Another complementary explanation invokes variation in the pattern of X-chromosome inactivation to explain the variation: i.e., clinically affected females may have a higher frequency of active X chromosomes bearing the fragile X mutation.

One particularly interesting case report describes identical twin females heterozygous for the fragile X mutation, one of whom was retarded while the other was intellectually normal.[98] Both showed 7 percent fragile X expression, but in the normal twin the fragile X was the active X chromosome in only 30 percent of her cells while in her mentally retarded sister, it was active in 85 percent of her cells. Unfortunately, attempts to address this relationship in larger numbers of carrier females have yielded contradictory results: four studies conclude intelligence is correlated with inactivation pattern[99–102] and three studies conclude there is no relationship.[103–105] These studies are technically difficult to carry out, as the BrdU labeling methods used to identify the late-replicating, inactive X chromosome also suppress fragile X expression. Although the experimental evidence is therefore inconclusive, it is still an attractive explanation that X-inactivation pattern plays an important role in determining intellectual status.

INHERITANCE OF THE FRAGILE X SYNDROME

Although hundreds of families have been reported in which the fragile X syndrome followed an apparent X-linked inheritance pattern,[15–17] the existence of transmitting males and their tendency to be clustered within particular sibships of an extended kindred was noted in even the earliest reports.[41–43] Formal pedigree analysis of fragile X syndrome families by Sherman and her coworkers has confirmed that this disorder is inherited in an unusual and unique manner.[44–45] The main features of their analysis are summarized in the artificial composite pedigree shown in Fig. 8-6.

The clinical status of the mother passing on the fragile X syndrome mutation seems to affect the penetrance of retardation in offspring. Among the children of mentally normal female carriers, the sons (III-1) and daughters (III-3) have an incidence of retardation of 40 percent and 16 percent, respectively. Thus, penetrance in males is 80 percent and in females is 32 percent when the mutation is inherited from a normal carrier mother. In comparison, when a mother is mentally impaired (III-2), an average of 50 percent of her sons (IV-1) and 28 percent of her daughters (IV-2) are retarded, for an overall penetrance of 100 percent in males and 56 percent in females.

The sex of the normal parent passing on the fragile X syndrome mutation has an even greater effect on the penetrance of retardation in the offspring. For example, the daughters (III-4) of transmitting males (II-4) all inherit the fragile X syndrome mutation and yet are nearly always clinically normal, implying 0 percent penetrance. In contrast, daughters (III-3) of clinically normal female carriers (II-2) are only at 50 percent risk for inheriting the mutation, and yet 16 percent of them on average show mental impairment, for a penetrance of 32 percent.

The risk of mental retardation in the offspring of mentally normal females may be different depending on whether a transmitting male is present in a sibship. Overall, the risk of mental retardation in the sons (III-1) and daughters (III-3) of mentally normal females (II-2) is 40 percent and 16 percent, respectively. However, the sibs of transmitting males (II-4) appear to have a much lower risk of retardation. Only 9 percent of the sons (II-1) and 5 percent of the daughters (II-5) of such mothers (I-1) are retarded.

Detailed family studies, including cytogenetic analysis, have been performed in families containing an apparently sporadic retarded male with fragile X syndrome detected through relatively unbiased population surveys.[45,106] Such studies have routinely uncovered other family members carrying the fragile X mutation, indicating that the vast majority of isolated cases of the disorder are inherited rather than arising *de novo* by new mutation in the proband.[106] One interpretation for this finding is that new mutations at the fragile X syndrome locus may all be occurring in the sibships containing transmitting males and may not be capable themselves of causing clinically significant mental retardation. Development of the clinical disorder may require a second event that occurs during subsequent inheritance of the mutation to make retardation clinically manifest in the descendants.

The unusual inheritance pattern of this disorder has important implications for both human genetics and clinical medicine. The problem of transmitting males makes genetic management and risk assessment far more difficult than in other X-linked disorders. Equally important is that the inheritance pattern is an unusual one and demands unique and profound biologic explanations. Possible models to explain the inheritance pattern have been the subject of discussion elsewhere[3] and are beyond the scope of this chapter.

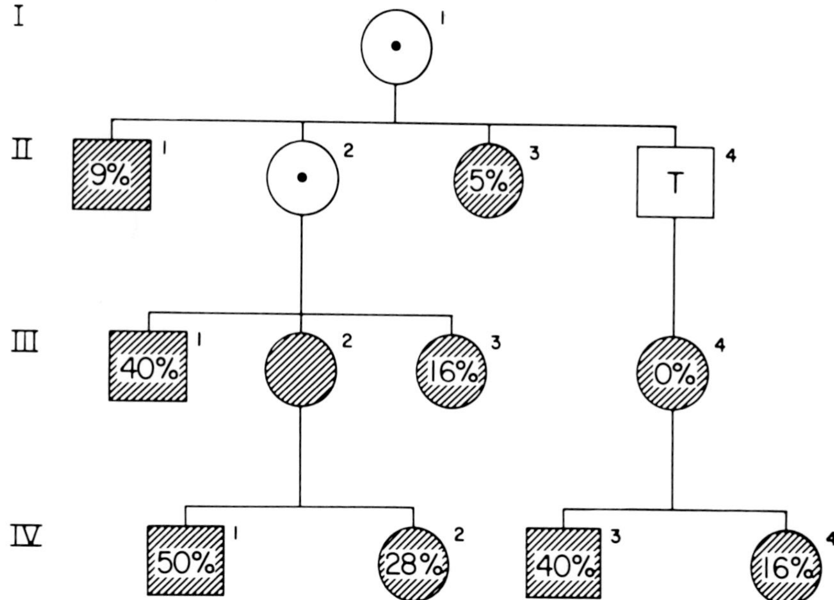

Fig. 8-6 Artificial pedigree of fragile X syndrome family. A female carrier of normal intelligence is symbolized by an outlined circle with a central dot. A transmitting male is symbolized by a square containing a T. The risk for mental retardation for a particular individual is shown as a percent figure superimposed on a shaded background. *(Reproduced by permission from the* Annual Review of Genetics.[3])

DIAGNOSIS

Clinical and Differential Diagnosis

A diagnosis of the fragile X syndrome is often suspected based on clinical phenotype and family history of X-linked mental retardation. Clinicians must be aware of the more than 60 different X-linked disorders in which mental retardation is a prominent feature.[18,52,107] A subset of 18 rare X-linked mental retardation syndromes included in the differential diagnosis of the fragile X syndrome is given in Table 8-3. Within this subset, distinctive features such as microcephaly, spasticity, or hypogenitalism, may help distinguish these disorders from the fragile X syndrome. However, there still remains the problem of X-linked mental retardation without other distinguishing features and without the Xq27 fragile site (McKusick #30953).[108] It is currently not known if this form of X-linked mental retardation represents undetected fragile X syndrome due to technical problems with older protocols for induction of fragile sites, a disorder that is allelic with the fragile X syndrome but without the Xq27 fragile site, or a syndrome resulting from mutations at entirely different genetic loci. Thus, diagnosis of the fragile X syndrome should not be made on phenotypic grounds alone, but must be confirmed with cytogenetic analysis for the Xq27 fragile site.

Laboratory Diagnosis of Fragile X Males

A variety of culture methods can be used to elicit fragile X expression in chromosomes from peripheral blood cultures. The most frequently used condition has been a medium deficient in folic acid and thymidine, such as Medium 199. However, this method is sensitive to dietary folic acid intake,[109–111] to folic acid and thymidine present in fetal calf serum,[112] and to the length of time in culture.[112] Examples of false negative results in Medium 199, which were positive after FUdR induction, are known,[109,113] suggesting that Medium 199 should not be the sole method of screening for the Xq27 fragile site in a clinical laboratory setting. FUdR and high thymidine induction methods seem to have the benefits of greater reliability and should be used in addition to or in place of Medium 199.

Since the range of expression in affected males is large, and a significant number fall in the 5 to 10 percent range,[44] adequate numbers of metaphase cells must be analyzed to avoid false negative results. For example, to rule out 6 percent or greater expression at a 95 percent confidence level requires analysis of 50 cells,[114] a number which seems appropriate and practical for most diagnostic laboratories. Since as many as 1 percent of affected males in families will be fragile X negative,[44] more than one affected male in a family should be tested before excluding the diagnosis of fragile X syndrome.

Caution is warranted in the interpretation of very low levels of fragile X expression (one or two fragile X positive cells out of 50 to 100 metaphases) owing to the frequent observation of low level expression in lymphocytes of normal control individuals (reviewed in Ref. 115). Expression in normal individuals has been reported to occur in as many as 1/200[115] to 1/300[116] metaphase cells. In fact, at least one fragile X cell was seen in all six controls studied by Marlhens et al.[116] Expression in normal controls has been confirmed in somatic cell hybrid studies, in which somewhat higher expression rates (4 to 5 percent) were obtained in two control males.[97] Thus, low expression in the retarded individual necessitates repeated studies with multiple induction conditions to prove significance.

Fragile X expression can also be induced in fibroblast cultures, although these cells do not show expression in folic acid and thymidine deficient media but require the use of FUdR,[75,117] methotrexate,[118,119] or high thymidine.[120] Expression levels in fibroblasts, regardless of technique, tend to be significantly lower than in lymphocytes so that they are not an optimal tissue for diagnostic studies.

Epstein-Barr virus-transformed lymphoblastoid cell lines show no expression in medium deficient in folic acid and thymidine but show expression levels comparable to or higher than that of lymphocytes when treated with FUdR.[121] Lymphoblasts are therefore a very useful cell type for establishing permanent patient cell lines and for in vitro experimentation.

Table 8-3 Differential Diagnosis of X-Linked Mental Retardation

Syndrome (McKusick #)	*Clinical Features*
Fragile X (#30955)	Normal or macrocephaly, macroorchidism, Xq27 fragile site
Renpenning (#30950)	Microcephaly, normal testes
Nonspecific mental retardation (#30953)	Similar to fragile X syndrome, without Xq27 fragile site
Allan-Herndon-Dudley (#30960)	Hypotonia, muscular atrophy, contractures
Juberg-Marsidi (#30959)	Microcephaly, hypogenitalism, small palpebral fissures, epicanthic folds, deafness, postnatal growth failure
Coffin-Lowry (#30360)	Growth deficiency, coarse facies, vertebral defects and scoliosis, tufted terminal phalanges
Mental retardation (MRSD) (#30964), spastic diplegia	Retardation, progressive CNS degeneration
Mental deficiency; epilepsy; spasticity; deafness (MESD)	Microcephaly, seizures, spasticity, normal testes
Golabi-Ito-Hall	Microcephaly, multiple congenital anomalies, brittle hair
Mental retardation; hypotonia; gonadal and skeletal defects (MHGS)	Microcephaly, hypogenitalism, intrauterine hypotonia
Gareis-Mason	Absent extensor pollicis brevis
Schimke	Microcephaly, choreoathetosis, external ophthalmoplegia
Seemanova	Microcephaly, spastic diplegia, absent abdominal reflexes, cerebral atrophy
Fitzsimmons	Spastic diplegia, palmar and plantar hyperkeratosis
Wieacker-Wolff	Severe congenital contractures, progressive distal muscular atrophy
Atkin-Flaitz	Macrocephaly, macroorchidism, short stature, coarse facial features
Waisman-Laxova	Megalencephaly, normal testes, basal ganglia abnormalities
Hockey	Precocious puberty, normal head size
Lujan	Marfanoid habitus

SOURCE: Opitz[18] and Opitz and Sutherland.[107]

Indications for Laboratory Diagnosis

Males. Cytogenetic analysis for the Xq27 fragile site is almost certainly an underutilized diagnostic test in many clinical settings. In view of the high prevalence of the fragile X syndrome and the substantial genetic risk it poses in other family members, the test should be performed in any retarded male in whom another reasonable explanation for retardation has not been found. Absence of family history should not preclude cytogenetic analysis. Other groups that are particularly important to study are males that carry a diagnosis of severe autism rather than mental retardation or learning disability, since a total of 47 of 614 (7.7 percent) autistic males reported in 12 different studies were found to have the fragile X syndrome.[38] As discussed above, however, very low frequency expression in a developmentally delayed or mentally retarded individual must be interpreted with caution, and repeat studies with additional induction conditions may be required for clarification.

Screening for the Xq27 fragile site in all retarded males who lack a clear diagnosis is easily justifiable not only because of the high prevalence of the disorder but also because of the significant risk it poses for other members of the proband's family. For example, in one study of the costs and benefits of screening retarded males for the fragile X syndrome, it was estimated that the cost of identifying an at-risk female carrier through diagnosis of the fragile X syndrome in a retarded male relative was only 3 percent of the cost of institutional care for an affected male born to such a female carrier.[20] Only by identifying such at risk female relatives can appropriate counseling and management be offered.

Some fragile X syndrome families have been reported in which one of the affected males has the clinical phenotype for the fragile X or Martin-Bell syndrome without cytogenetic evidence of the Xq27 fragile site.[107] It has been estimated that 1 percent of affected males in fragile X syndrome families may not express the fragile site,[44] although other members of the family do. Such lack of expression in an individual in a fragile X syndrome family may be the result of technical difficulties involved in inducing the Xq27 fragile site, especially with older methods involving growth in Medium 199 rather than FUdR or high thymidine induction. However, we have personally seen one family in which a male with the fragile X syndrome phenotype repeatedly showed no Xq27 fragile site in his lymphocytes under multiple induction conditions, and yet his mother and two maternal uncles all demonstrated both the clinical and cytogenetic features of the fragile X syndrome. The lack of expression in a small fraction of males from fragile X syndrome families may therefore have a more profound explanation that may help us understand the precise relationship in what is now only an observed correlation between the clinical disease and the cytogenetic abnormality.

Females. Cytogenetic analysis for fragile X syndrome, performed either for carrier detection in an intellectually normal female or for clinical diagnosis in a retarded female, is subject to the same technical considerations described above, with the additional difficulty that the average frequency of expression in females is lower than that in males. Clearly, all appropriate females in families with a documented male with the fragile X syndrome should be studied, particularly but not exclusively if the female shows behavioral abnormalities or mental impairment. However, false negative results in females are common since two-thirds of intellectually normal carriers and 10 percent of intellectually impaired females with fragile X syndrome show either no fragile X expression or frequencies below 5 percent.[44] To minimize such false negative results, laboratories may need to analyze up to 100 metaphase cells to rule out 3 percent or greater fragile X expression at the 95 percent confidence level.

Carrier detection and diagnosis in the fragile X syndrome is further complicated by the potential for false positive fragile X expression studies. False positive results may arise because the generally lower expression rates in female heterozygotes for the fragile X syndrome may be difficult to distinguish from the low frequency expression seen in normal individuals. Such false positive studies are of particular concern in an isolated, mentally retarded, nondysmorphic female because a diagnosis of the fragile X syndrome has such important implications for the rest of the family. Laboratories should establish some minimum criteria for declaring an individual, male or female, fragile X positive.

In summary, high expression levels constitute significant evidence for the fragile X syndrome in females, but low or absent expression are therefore of limited value for either making or rejecting a diagnosis of the fragile X syndrome. The uses and interpretation of cytogenetic analysis for fragile X, particularly in females, remain problematic and require improvements in diagnostic testing methods.

Prenatal Diagnosis

The feasibility of prenatal diagnosis of fragile X using amniocytes was first shown in 1981–1982.[122–123] Since then, a total of approximately 147 potentially at risk pregnancies have been prospectively studied, the majority involving amniocentesis.[52,124] Although 31 affected fragile X positive males and females have been identified and confirmed cytogenetically, significant problems with this approach are apparent.

Like fibroblasts, amniocytes do not show fragile X expression in folic acid and thymidine deficient media, but require induction by FUdR, methotrexate, or high thymidine.[124,125] The frequency of expression in amniocytes is usually lower than in lymphocytes and has varied dramatically from one laboratory to another and among different induction methods on the same sample. Many of the positive prenatal diagnostic predictions have been based on fragile X expression frequencies in the 1 to 4 percent range,[52,124] while a number of authors have noted 1 to 2 percent fragile X expression in normal control cultures.[115,124] Several cases would have yielded false negative results had the specimen been studied in only one laboratory or had only one induction method been utilized. At present, there are at least two incorrect diagnoses: one false negative and one false positive.[52,124]

Sutherland and Baker[120] demonstrated improved fragile X expression in fibroblasts using high thymidine induction and recently reported that this method may also be superior to FUdR or methotrexate in amniocytes.[125] Although fragile X expression has been observed in chorionic villus cells in the successful prenatal diagnosis of a male fetus,[126] experience to date is too limited to determine whether these cells are any better or worse than amniocytes for fragile X detection.

The best cell source for fragile X induction is peripheral blood, and one of the largest prenatal diagnostic series for fragile X has been done on blood samples obtained by fetoscopy. Webb et al.[113] reported 19 pregnancies monitored for fragile X through fetal blood studies. In most instances, amniocentesis was performed first to determine the sex of the fetus, and most of the fetal blood samplings were carried out on known male pregnancies. As expected, expression frequencies in blood were generally much higher than in amniotic fluids on the same pregnancy. Correct prenatal diagnosis was made in all six males predicted to be affected and all five males predicted to be unaffected, confirmed by fragile X expression studies in blood samples obtained either from liveborn males or from abortuses. This study also showed that Medium 199 alone is not an appropriate fragile X test system, as three of seven males positive in FUdR and methotrexate were negative in Medium 199 and would have yielded false negative predictions. This may be due to exogenous folate in prescription prenatal vitamins taken by many pregnant women. Additionally, of 12 fetuses determined to be negative, low frequency expression (<2 percent) was observed in eight. This supports the notion that fragile X expression can be observed at low frequencies in all X chromosomes and increases the concern of declaring a fetus affected in the presence of very low levels of fragile X expression.

The disadvantage of peripheral blood for prenatal diagnosis is the limited availability of fetal blood sampling and the higher risk of pregnancy loss associated with fetoscopy compared to amniocentesis. Although fetal blood sampling by fetoscopy is associated with a 4 to 5 percent risk of spontaneous abortion,[127] newer methods of sampling by direct ultrasound guidance may have a significantly lower rate of loss.[128–129] As this technique becomes more widely available, it will probably be the method of choice for prenatal diagnosis of fragile X.

At present, prenatal cytogenetic diagnosis of fragile X in males is considered an experimental procedure which is available in only a small number of research centers.[52] If fetal blood sampling is available, this provides the most cytogenetically reliable method of prenatal diagnosis. If not, chorionic villus cells or amniocytes can be studied, but caution is warranted in the interpretation of low frequency expression or negative results.

Prenatal diagnosis in a female fetus is beset not only with the same technical difficulties as with male fetuses but also with additional uncertainty due to the imperfect correlation between cytogenetic expression and clinical status. Since 10 percent of retarded females and most intellectually normal carriers show no fragile X expression,[44] a negative result prenatally does not accurately discriminate between affected, normal carrier and noncarrier females. High expression levels are suggestive of an affected female, but a significant percentage of intellectually normal carriers can also have high expression.[44] Thus, the usefulness of prenatal diagnosis for a female fetus remains questionable.

LINKAGE ANALYSIS IN FRAGILE X SYNDROME

Although the finding of the cytogenetic abnormality, a fragile site at Xq27, in the fragile X syndrome suggested that the disease locus resided at Xq27 as well, firmer evidence for localizing the fragile X syndrome to this region was obtained through linkage analysis of the syndrome to genetic markers in this region. The fragile X syndrome locus is linked at 6 percent recombination to the glucose-6-phosphate dehydrogenase locus, located in Xq28,[130] as well as to many restriction fragment length polymorphism (RFLP) markers in this region,[131–132] confirming that the mutations causing the disease locus and the DNA alterations responsible for the cytogenetic marker must be quite closely linked if not identical.

In view of the difficulty of carrier detection in transmitting males and heterozygous females and the uncertainty in prenatal diagnosis by cytogenetic analysis, a major effort has been made to identify markers closely linked to the locus of the fragile X syndrome in order to follow the inheritance of the mutation in families. A number of RFLP loci both proximal and distal to the disease locus have been used to study recombination in this region of the X chromosome.[3,131] Some of the more commonly used markers, and their physical locations with respect to the Xq27 fragile site,[133–136] are shown in Fig. 8-7. Markers proximal to the fragile X syndrome locus, such as Factor 9 and DXS51, are tightly linked to each other.[137,138] Markers distal to the locus, such as Factor 8, DXS52 and glucose-6-phosphate dehydrogenase, are likewise tightly linked to each other. However, the distal markers, as a group, are only

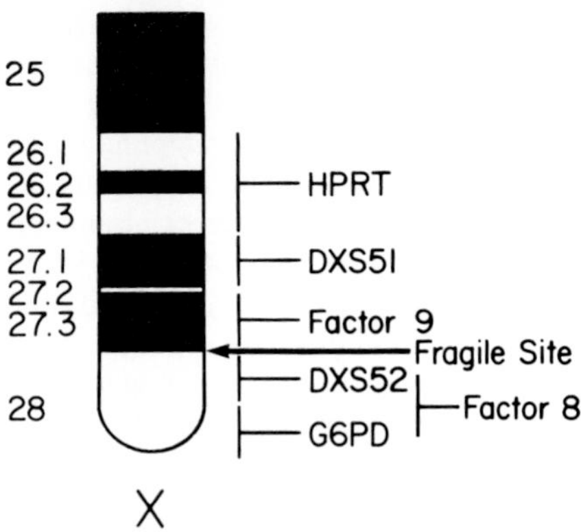

Fig. 8-7 Idiogram of the distal long arm of the X chromosome showing the RFLP markers that have been used in physical mapping and linkage analysis of the Xq27 fragile site and the fragile X syndrome. *(Reproduced by permission of the* Annual Review of Genetics.[3])

loosely linked to the proximal group of markers, and all the markers show 5 to 15 percent recombination with the fragile X syndrome locus.[131] These results, coupled with the observation that the Xq27-28 region has an above average rate of recombination in control families,[139] has led to speculation that there is nonlinearity in recombination frequency in Xq27-28 due to a "hot spot" for recombination at or near the fragile X syndrome locus,[140] and perhaps the increased recombination is itself involved in producing the fragile X syndrome mutation.[141–142] However, much more data will be needed to corroborate or disprove this hypothesis.

Although none of the RFLP markers in Xq27-28 are tightly linked to the fragile X syndrome, RFLP markers such as Factor 9 or DXS52 that show 10 to 15 percent recombination to the disease locus can still be used in clinical applications. As shown in Fig. 8-8, two sisters II-2 and II-4, are heterozygous for RFLPs at both the coagulation Factor 9 locus that is proximal to the fragile X syndrome locus (F9, alleles A and B) and the DXS52 locus distal to it (DXS52, alleles 3, 4, and 8). Individuals III-7 and III-8 inherited both RFLP alleles flanking the fragile X syndrome mutation in their mother II-4 (F9 allele A, DXS52 allele 3), while individuals III-5 and III-6 inherited neither of these RFLP alleles. Individuals III-5 and III-6 therefore would inherit the fragile X syndrome mutation only if two crossovers occurred, one between the fragile X syndrome locus and F9 and one between the disease locus and DXS52. A double crossover is unlikely and would occur only 1 to 2 percent of the time, a frequency approximately equal to the product of the recombination frequencies between the disease locus and each RFLP locus. The carrier state can be excluded therefore in III-5 and III-6 with reasonable confidence. When a single recombination between the flanking markers is seen, however, as for example in individuals III-2 and III-4, prediction of genotype at the fragile X syndrome locus becomes impossible because crossovers proximal or distal to the disease locus cannot be distinguished. It is certain that more DNA markers will be isolated in the near future that are more tightly linked to the fragile X syndrome locus, thus providing more accurate diagnosis by linkage methods.

TREATMENT

No specific treatment for the fragile X syndrome is available.[143] Because folic acid depletion is known to induce the fragile site in cultured cells, folic acid supplementation has been used in a variety of studies for treatment of the intellectual and behavioral deficits in the fragile X syndrome. The preponderance of data suggests that folic acid therapy is of no benefit,[52,144] although there are some reports of improved be

Fig. 8-8 Pedigree and RFLP haplotype information in an extended family with fragile X syndrome. This family demonstrates the use of linked markers to follow the inheritance of the fragile X syndrome. Note the occurrence of an obvious transmitting male (individual II-5). *(Courtesy of Dr. Rhonda Schnur.)*

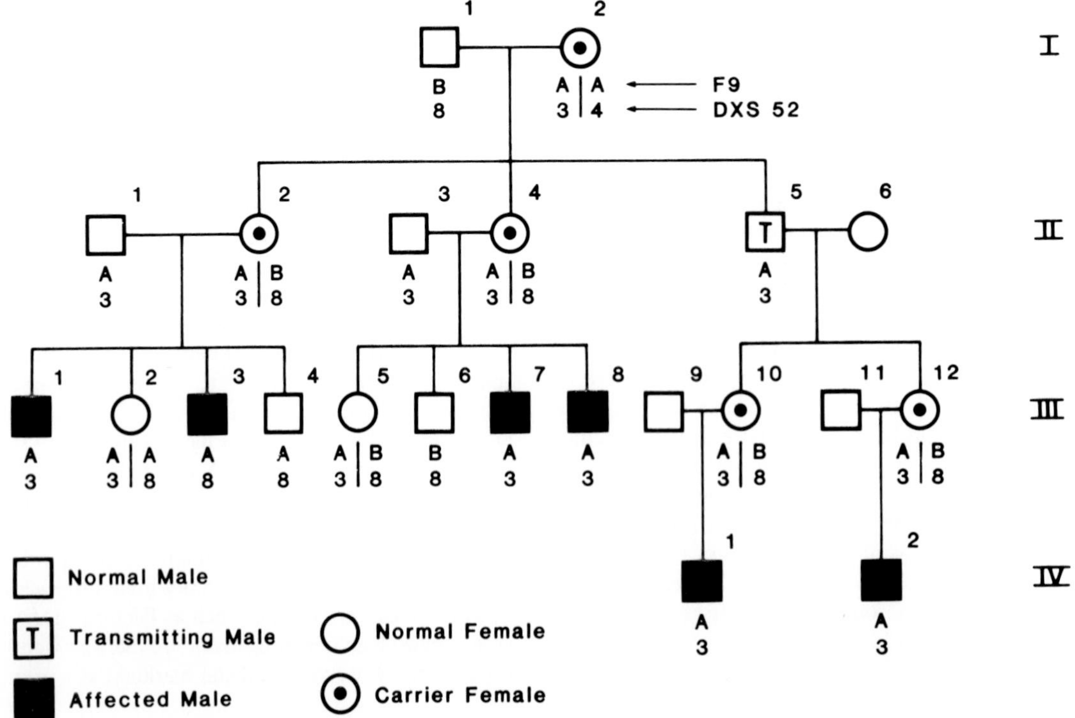

havior in a subset of affected children.[111,145] Until new evidence appears to the contrary, the use of folic acid should be restricted to properly designed, controlled studies. In the absence of rational metabolic therapy for the disease, physicians must use supportive therapy directed toward alleviating neurologic dysfunction.[27] Management of behavior problems with medical therapy may be important in patients showing violent or disruptive behavior. Medical therapy with stimulants has been used with some success in children with hyperactivity to improve attention span and learning performance. Speech and occupational therapy may help patients reach their own intellectual potential.

REFERENCES

1. TURNER G, JACOBS P: Marker (X) linked mental retardation. *Adv Hum Genet* 13:83, 1983.
2. HAGERMAN RJ, MCBOGG PM: *The Fragile X Syndrome: Diagnosis, Biochemistry, and Intervention.* Dillon, CO, Spectra Publishing, 1983.
3. NUSSBAUM RL, LEDBETTER DH: Fragile X syndrome: a unique mutation in man. *Annu Rev Genet* 20:109, 1986.
4. BROWN WT, JENKINS EC, KRAWCZUN MS, WISNIEWSKI K, RUDELLI R, COHEN IL, GISCH G, WOLF-SCHEIN E, MIEZEJESKI C, DOBKIN C: The fragile X syndrome. *Ann NY Acad Sci* 477:129, 1986.
5. SUTHERLAND GR, HECHT F, MULLEY JC, GLOVER TW, HECHT BK: *Fragile Sites on Human Chromosomes.* New York, Oxford University Press, 1985.
6. TURNER G: Historical overview, in Hagerman RJ, McBogg PM (eds): *The Fragile X Syndrome: Diagnosis, Biochemistry and Intervention.* Dillon, CO, Spectra Publishing, 1983.
7. LEHRKE RG: X-linked mental retardation and verbal disability. *Birth Defects* 10c:1, 1974.
8. MARTIN JP, BELL J: A pedigree of mental defect showing sex-linkage. *J Neurol Neurosurg Psychiatry* 6:154, 1943.
9. TURNER G, TURNER B: X-linked mental retardation. *J Med Genet* 11:109, 1974.
10. LUBS HA: A marker X chromosome. *Am J Hum Genet* 21:231, 1969.
11. GIRAUD F, AYME S, MATTEI JF, MATTEI MG: Constitutional chromosomal breakage. *Hum Genet* 34:125, 1976.
12. HARVEY J, JUDGE C, WIENER S: Familial X-linked mental retardation with an X chromosome abnormality. *J Med Genet* 14:46, 1977.
13. SUTHERLAND GR: Fragile sites on human chromosomes: Demonstration of their dependence on the type of tissue culture medium. *Science* 197:265, 1977.
14. BERGER R, BLOOMFIELD CD, SUTHERLAND GR: Report of the committee on chromosome rearrangements in neoplasia and on fragile sites. 8th International Workshop on Human Gene Mapping. *Cytogenet Cell Genet* 40:490, 1985.
15. OPITZ JM, HOLD MC, SPANO LM: Bibliography on X-linked mental retardation and related subjects I. *Am J Med Genet* 17:62, 1984.
16. OPITZ JM, HOLT MC, SPANO LM. Bibliography on X-linked mental retardation and related subjects II. *Am J Med Genet* 21:719, 1985.
17. OPITZ JM, HOLT MC, SPANO LM: Bibliography on X-linked mental retardation and related subjects II. *Am J Med Genet* 23:69, 1986.
18. OPITZ JM: Editorial comment: On the gates of hell and a most unusual gene. *Am J Med Genet* 23:1, 1986.
19. WEBB TP, BUNDEY SE, THAKE AI, TODD J: Population incidence and segregation ratios in the Martin-Bell syndrome. *Am J Med Genet* 23:573, 1986.
20. TURNER G, ROBINSON H, LAING S, PURVIS-SMITH S: Preventive screening for the fragile X syndrome. *N Engl J Med* 315:607, 1986.
21. JACOBS PA, MAYER M, ABRUZZO MA: Studies of the fragile (X) syndrome in populations of mentally retarded individuals in Hawaii. *Am J Med Genet* 23:567, 1986.
22. SANFILIPPO S, RAGUSA RM, MUSUMECI S, NERI G: Fragile X mental retardation: Prevalence in a group of institutionalized patients in Italy and description of a novel EEG pattern. *Am J Med Genet* 23:589, 1986.
23. VENTER PA, HOF JO, COETZEE DJ: The Martin-Bell syndrome in South Africa. *Am J Med Genet* 23:597, 1986.
24. GUSTAVSON K-H, BLOMQUIST H, K:SON HB, HOLMGREN G: Prevalence of the fragile-X syndrome in mentally retarded boys in a Swedish county. *Am J Med Genet* 23:581, 1986.
25. SUTHERLAND GR, HECHT F, MULLEY JC, GLOVER TW, HECHT BK: The fragile X: physical phenotype, in *Fragile Sites on Human Chromosomes.* New York, Oxford University Press, 1985.
26. TURNER G, DANIEL A, FROST M: X-linked mental retardation, macroorchidism, and the Xq27 fragile site. *J Pediatr* 96:837, 1980.
27. CHUDLEY AE, HAGERMAN RJ: Fragile X syndrome. *J Pediatr* 110:821, 1987.
28. HAGERMAN RJ, SMITH ACM, MARINER R: Clinical features of the fragile X syndrome, in Hagerman RJ, McBogg PM (eds): *The Fragile X Syndrome: Diagnosis, Biochemistry, and Intervention.* Dillon, CO, Spectra Publishing, 1983.
29. OPITZ JM, WESTPHAL JM, DANIEL A: Discovery of a connective tissue dysplasia in the Martin-Bell syndrome. *Am J Med Genet* 17:101, 1984.
30. HAGERMAN RJ, VAN HORSEN K, SMITH ACM, MCGAVRAN L: Consideration of connective tissue dysfunction in the fragile X syndrome. *Am J Med Genet* 17:111, 1984.
31. HAGERMAN RJ, SYNHORST DP: Mitral valve prolapse and aortic dilatation in the fragile X syndrome. *Am J Med Genet* 17:123, 1984.
32. LOEHR JP, SYYNHORST DP, WOLFE PR, HAGERMAN RJ. Aortic root dilatation and mitral valve prolapse in the fragile X syndrome. *Am J Med Genet* 23:189, 1986.
33. CHUDLEY AE, KNOLL J, GERRARD JW, SHEPEL L, MCGAHEY E, ANDERSON J: Fragile (X) X-linked mental retardation I: Relationship between age and intelligence and the frequency of expression of fragile (X) (q28). *Am J Med Genet* 14:699, 1983.
34. SUTHERLAND GR, HECHT F, MULLEY JC, GLOVER TW, HECHT BK: The fragile X: Intelligence, behaviour and treatment, in *Fragile Sites on Human Chromosomes.* New York, Oxford University Press, 1985, p 113.
35. HANSON DM, JACKSON AW, HAGERMAN RJ: Speech disturbances (cluttering) in mildly impaired males with the Martin-Bell/fragile X syndrome. *Am J Med Genet* 23:195, 1986.
36. JACOBS P, GLOVER TW, MAYER M, FOX P, GERRARD JW, DUNN HG, HERBST DS: X-linked mental retardation: A study of 7 families. *Am J Med Genet* 7:471, 1980.
37. HAGERMAN RJ, JACKSON AW, LEVITAS A, RIMLAND B, BRADEN M: An analysis of autism in fifty males with the fragile X syndrome. *Am J Med Genet* 23:359, 1986.
38. BROWN WT, JENKINS ED, COHEN IL, FISCH GS, WOLF-SCHEIN EG, GROSS A, WATERHOUSE L, FEIN D, MASON-BROTHERS A, RITVO E, RUTTENBERG BA, BENTLEY W, CASTELLS S: Fragile X and autism: A multicenter survey. *Am J Med Genet* 23:341, 1986.
39. NIELSEN KB: Diagnosis of the fragile X syndrome (Martin-Bell syndrome): Clinical findings in 27 males with the fragile site at Xq28. *J Ment Defic Res* 27:211, 1983.
40. WAHLSTRÖM J, GILLBERG C, GUSTAVSON K-H, HOLMGREN G: Infantile autism and the fragile X. A Swedish multicenter study. *Am J Med Genet* 23:403, 1986.
41. FROSTER-ISKENIUS U, MCGILLIVRAY BC, DILL FJ, HALL JG, HERBST DS: Normal male carriers in the fra(X) form of X-linked mental retardation (Martin-Bell syndrome). *Am J Med Genet* 23:619, 1986.
42. FROSTER-ISKENIUS U, SCHULZE A, SCHWINGER E: Transmission of the marker X syndrome trait by unaffected males: Conclusions from studies of large families. *Hum Genet* 67:419, 1984.
43. HOWARD-PEEBLES PN, FRIEDMAN JM: Unaffected carrier males in families with fragile X syndrome. *Am J Hum Genet* 37:956, 1985.
44. SHERMAN SL, MORTON NE, JACOBS PA, TURNER G: The marker (X) syndrome: A cytogenetic and genetic analysis. *Ann J Hum Genet* 48:21, 1984.
45. SHERMAN SL, JACOBS PA, MORTON NE, FROSTER-ISKENIUS U, HOWARD-PEEBLES PN, NIELSEN KB, PARTINGTON MW, SUTHERLAND GR, TURNER G, WATSON M: Further segregation analysis of the fragile X syndrome with special reference to transmitting males. *Hum Genet* 69:289, 1985.
46. TURNER G, BROOKWELL R, DANIEL A, SELIKOWITZ M, ZILIBOWITZ M: Heterozygous expression of X-linked mental retardation and X chromosome marker fra(X)(q27). *N Engl J Med* 303:662, 1980.
47. FRYNS J-P: The female and the fragile X: A study of 144 obligate carrier females. *Am J Med Genet* 23:157, 1986.
48. JOHANNISSON R, REHDER H, WENDT V, SCHWINGER E: Spermatogenesis in two patients with the fragile X syndrome I. Histology: light and electron microscopy. *Hum Genet* 76:141, 1987.
49. CANTU JM, SCAGLIA H, MEDINA M, GONZALEZ-DIDDI M, MORATO T, MORENO ME, PEREZ-PALACIOS G: Inherited congenital normofunctional testicular hyperplasia and mental deficiency. *Hum Genet* 33:23, 1976.
50. BERKOVITZ GD, WILSON DP, CARPENTER NJ, BROWN TR, MIGEON CJ: Gonadal function in men with the Martin-Bell (fragile-X) syndrome. *Am J Med Genet* 23:227, 1986.
51. JENKINS ED, BROWN WT, BROOKS J, DUNCAN CJ, RUDELLI RD, WISNIEWSKI HM: Experience with prenatal fragile X detection. *Am J Med Genet* 17:215, 1984.
52. TURNER G, OPITZ JM, BROWN WT, DAVIES KE, JACOBS PA, JENKINS EC, MIKKELSEN M, PARTINGTON MW, SUTHERLAND GR: Conference report:

Second International Workshop on the fragile X and X-linked mental retardation. *Am J Med Genet* 23:11, 1986.

53. WALDSTEIN G, MIERAU G, AHMAD R, THIBODEAU SN, HAGERMAN RJ, CALDWELL S: Fragile X syndrome: Skin elastin abnormalities: in Gilbert EF, Opitz JM (eds): Genetic aspects of developmental pathology. *Birth Defects* 23(1):103, 1987.
54. RUDELLI RD, BROWN WT, WISNIEWSKI K, JENKINS EC, LAURE-KAMIONOWSKA M, CONNELL F: Adult fragile X syndrome, clinico-pathological findings. *Acta Neuropathol* 67:289, 1985.
55. SUTHERLAND GR: Heritable fragile sites on human chromosomes. I. Factors affecting expression in lymphocyte culture. *Am J Med Genet* 31:125, 1979.
56. HARNDEN DG, KLINGER HP (eds): *ISCN: An International System for Human Cytogenetic Nomenclature*. Published in collaboration with *Cytogen Cell Genet*. Basel, Karger, 1985.
57. FITCHETT M, SEABRIGHT M: Deleted X chromosomes in patients with the fragile X syndrome. *J Med Genet* 21:373, 1984.
58. HARRISON CJ, JACK EM, ALLEN TD, HARRIS R: The fragile X: A scanning electron microscope study. *J Med Genet* 20:280, 1983.
59. DANIEL A, EKBLOM L, PHILLIPS S: Constitutive fragile sites 1p31, 3p14, 6q26, and 16q23 and their use as controls for false-negative results with the fragile (X). *Am J Med Genet* 18:483, 1984.
60. GLOVER TW, BERGER C, COYLE J, ECHO B: DNA polymerase alpha inhibition by aphidicolin induces gaps and breaks at common fragile sites in human chromosomes. *Hum Genet* 67:136, 1984.
61. YUNIS JJ, SORENG AL: Constitutive fragile sites and cancer. *Science* 226:1199, 1984.
62. SUTHERLAND GR, PARSLOW MI, BAKER E: New classes of common fragile sites induced by 5-azacytidine and BrdU. *Hum Genet* 69:233, 1985.
63. DANIEL A: Clinical implications and classification of the constitutive fragile sites. *Am J Med Genet* 23:419, 1986.
64. YUNIS JJ, SORENG AL, BOWE AE: Fragile sites are targets of diverse mutagens and carcinogens. *Oncogene* 1:59, 1987.
65. WARREN ST, ZHANG F, LICAMELI GR, PETERS JF: The fragile X site in somatic cell hybrids: An approach for molecular cloning of fragile sites. *Science* 237:420, 1987.
66. HECHT F, HECHT BK: Fragile sites and chromosome breakpoints in constitutional rearrangements. I. Amniocentesis. *Clin Genet* 26:169, 1984.
67. HECHT F, HECHT BK: Fragile sites and chromosome breakpoints in constitutional rearrangements. II. Spontaneous abortions, stillbirths and newborns. *Clin Genet* 26:174, 1984.
68. GARCIA-SAGREDO JM, SAN ROMAN C, GOMEZ MEG, LLEDO G: Fragile chromosome 16(q22) causes a balanced translocation at the same point. *Hum Genet* 65:211, 1983.
69. SHABTAI F, HART J, KLAR D, HALBRECHT I: Familial fragile site found at the cancer breakpoint (1)(q32): Inducibility by distamycin A, concomitance with fragile (16)(q22). *Hum Genet* 73:232, 1986.
70. VOULLAIRE LE, WEBB GC, LEVERSHA MA: Chromosome deletion at 11q23 in an abnormal child from a family with inherited fragility at 11q23. *Hum Genet* 76:202, 1987.
71. LEBEAU MM: Chromosomal fragile sites and cancer-specific rearrangements. *Blood* 67:849, 1986.
72. GOLLIN SM, PERROT LJ, GRAY BA, KLETZEL M: Spontaneous expression of fra(11)(q23) in a patient with Ewing's sarcoma and t(11;22)(q23;q11). *Cancer Genet Cytogenet* 20:331, 1986.
73. SIMMERS RN, SUTHERLAND GR, WEST A, RICHARDS RI: Fragile sites at 16q22 are not at the breakpoint of the chromosomal rearrangement in AMMoL. *Science* 236:92, 1987.
74. SUTHERLAND GR, HECHT F, MULLEY JC, GLOVER TW, HECHT BK: Biochemistry of fragile site expression, in *Fragile Sites on Human Chromosomes*. New York, Oxford University Press, 1985, p 80.
75. GLOVER TW: FUdR induction of the X chromosome fragile site: Evidence for the mechanism of folic acid and thymidine inhibition. *Am J Hum Genet* 33:234, 1981.
76. TOMMERUP N, POULSEN H, NIELSEN KB: 5-Fluoro-2′-deoxyuridine induction of the fragile site on Xq28 associated with X-linked mental retardation. *J Med Genet* 18:374, 1981.
77. NUSSBAUM RL, WALMSLEY RM, LESKO JG, AIRHART SD, LEDBETTER DH: Thymidylate synthase-deficient Chinese hamster cells: A selection system for human chromosome 18 and experimental system for the study of thymidylate synthase regulation and fragile X expression. *Am J Hum Genet* 37:1192, 1982.
78. SUTHERLAND GR, BAKER E, FRATINI A: Excess thymidine induces folate sensitive fragile sites. *Am J Med Genet* 22:433, 1985.
79. SUTHERLAND GR, BAKER E: Effects of nucleotides on expression of the folate sensitive fragile sites. *Am J Med Genet* 23:409, 1986.
80. BJURSELL G, REICHARD P: Effects of thymidine on deoxyribonucleoside triphosphate pools and deoxyribonucleic acid synthesis in Chinese hamster ovary cells. *J Biol Chem* 248:3904, 1973.
81. COLLINS ARS, DOWNES CS, JOHNSON RT: Introduction: An integrated view of inhibited repair, in Collins A, Downes CS, Johnson RT, (eds): *DNA Repair and Its Inhibition,* London, Nucleic Acids Symposium Series, 1984, vol 13, pp 1–12.
82. GLOVER TW, COYLE-MORRIS J, MROGAN R: Fragile sites: Overview, occurrence in acute nonlymphocytic leukemia, and effects of caffeine on expression. *Cancer Genet Cytogenet* 19:141, 1986.
83. ABRUZZO MA, PETTAY D, MAYER M, JACOBS PA: The effect of caffeine on fragile X expression. *Hum Genet* 73:20, 1986.
84. LEDBETTER DH, AIRHART SD, NUSSBAUM RL: Caffeine enhances fragile (X) expression in somatic cell hybrids. *Am J Med Genet* 23:445, 1986.
85. ROBERTS JJ: Mechanism of potentiation by caffeine of genotoxic damage induced by physical and chemical agents, in Collins A, Downes CS, Johnson RT (eds): *DNA Repair and Its Inhibition*. London, Nucleic Acids Symposium Series, 1984, vol 13, pp 193–215.
86. LAU CC, PARDEE AB: Mechanism by which caffeine potentiates lethality of nitrogen mustard. *Proc Natl Acad Sci USA* 79:2942, 1982.
87. PAINTER RB, YOUNG BR: Radiosensitivity in ataxiatelangiectasia: A new explanation. *Proc Natl Acad Sci USA* 77:7315, 1980.
88. PHEAR G, NALBANTOGLU J, MEUTH M: Next-nucleotide effects in mutations driven by DNA precursor pool imbalances at the aprt locus in Chinese hamster ovary cells. *Proc Natl Acad Sci USA* 84:4450, 1987.
89. RICHARDS RG, SOWERS LC, LASZLO J, SEDWICK WD: Occurrence and consequences of deoxyuridine in DNA. *Adv Enzyme Regul* 22:157, 1984.
90. GOULIAN M, BLEILE B, TSENG BY: The effect of methotrexate on levels of dUTP in animal cells. *J Biol Chem* 255:10630, 1980.
91. GOULIAN M, BLEILE B, TSENG BY: Methotrexate-induced incorporation of uracil into DNA. *Proc Natl Acad Sci USA* 77:1956, 1980.
92. HITTLEMAN WN: Prematurely condensed chromosomes: A model system for visualizing effects of DNA damage, repair and inhibition at the level of chromosome structure, in Collins A, Downes CS, Johnson RT (eds): *DNA Repair and Its Inhibition*. London, Nucleic Acids Symposium Series, 1984, vol 13, pp 341–347.
93. KRUMDIECK CL, HOWARD PEEBLES PN: On the nature of folic acid sensitive fragile sites on human chromosomes: An hypothesis. *Am J Med Genet* 16:23, 1983.
94. EBERLE G, ZANKL M, ZANKL H: The expression of fragile X chromosomes in members of the same family at different times of examination. *Hum Genet* 61:254, 1982.
95. RHOADS FA, OGLESBY AC, MAYER M, JACOBS PA: Marker X syndrome in an oriental family with probable transmission by a normal male. *Am J Med Genet* 12:205, 1982.
96. SOUDEK D, PARTINGTON MW, LAWSON JS: The fragile X syndrome I: Familial variation in the proportion of lymphocytes with the fragile site in males. *Am J Hum Genet* 17:241, 1984.
97. LEDBETTER DH, LEDBETTER SA, NUSSBAUM RL: Implications of fragile X expression in normal males for the nature of the mutation. *Nature* 324:161, 1986.
98. TUCKERMAN E, WEBB T, BUNDEY SE: Frequency and replication status of the fragile X, fra(X)(q27-28), in a pair of monozygotic twins of markedly differing intelligence. *J Med Genet* 22:85, 1985.
99. UCHIDA IA, JOYCE EM: Activity of the fragile X in heterozygous carriers. *Am J Hum Genet* 34:286, 1982.
100. UCHIDA IA, FREEMAN VCP, JAMRO H, PARTINGTON MW, SOLTAN HC: Additional evidence for fragile X activity in heterozygous carriers. *Am J Hum Genet* 35:861, 1983.
101. PAUL J, FROSTER-ISKENIUS U, MOJE W, SCHWINGER E: Heterozygous female carriers of the marker-X-chromosome: IQ estimation and replication status of fra(X)(q). *Hum Genet* 66:344, 1984.
102. KNOLL JH, CHUDLEY AE, GERRARD JW: Fragile (X) X-linked mental retardation II. Frequency and replication pattern of fragile (X)(q28) in heterozygotes. *Am J Hum Genet* 36:640, 1984.
103. NIELSEN KB, TOMMERUP N, POULSEN H, JACOBSEN P, BECK B, MIKKELSEN M: Carrier detection and X-inactivation studies in the fragile X syndrome. Cytogenetic studies in 63 obligate and potential carriers of the fragile X. *Hum Genet* 64:240, 1983.
104. FRYNS JP, KLECZKOWSKA A, KUBIEN E, PETIT P, VAN DEN BERGHE H: Inactivation pattern of the fragile X in heterozygous carriers. *Hum Genet* 65:401, 1984.
105. CARPENTER NJ, LEICHTMAN LG, SAY B: Fragile X-linked mental retardation. A survey of 65 patients with mental retardation of unknown origin. *Am J Dis Child* 136:392, 1982.
106. JACOBS PA, SHERMAN S, TURNER G, WEBB T: The fragile (X) syndrome: The mutation problem. *Am J Med Genet* 23:611, 1986.
107. OPITZ JM, SUTHERLAND GR: Conference Report: International workshop

on the fragile X and X-linked mental retardation. *Am J Med Genet* 17:5, 1984.

108. MCKUSICK VA: *Mendelian Inheritance in Man,* 7th ed. Baltimore, Johns Hopkins University Press, 1986, p 1417.

109. FROSTER-ISKENIUS U, HALL JG, CURRY CJR: False negative results in patients with fra(X)(q) mental retardation taking oral vitamin supplements (letter to the editor). *N Engl J Med* 316:1093, 1987.

110. BROWN WT, JENKINS EC, FRIEDMAN E, BROOKS J, COHEN IL, DUNCAN C, HILL AL, MALIK MN, MORRIS V, WOLF E, WISNIEWSKI K, FRENCH JH: Folic acid therapy in the fragile X syndrome. *Am J Med Genet* 17:289, 1984.

111. FROSTER-ISKENIUS U, BODEKER K, OEPEN T, MATTHES R, PIPER U, SCHWINGER E: Folic acid treatment in males and females with fragile-(X)-syndrome. *Am J Med Genet* 23:273, 1986.

112. SUTHERLAND GR, HECHT F, MULLEY JC, GLOVER TW, HECHT BK: Tissue culture factors in fragile site expression, in *Fragile Sites on Human Chromosomes*. New York, Oxford University Press, 1985, p 59.

113. WEBB TP, RODECK CH, NICOLAIDES KH, GOSDEN CM: Prenatal diagnosis of the fragile X syndrome using fetal blood and amniotic fluid. *Prenat Diagn* 7:203, 1987.

114. DEARCE MA: Tables for the cytogenetic study of fragile X chromosomes for diagnostic purposes. *Clin Genet* 24:320, 1983.

115. JENKINS ED, BROWN WT, BROOKS J, DUNCAN CJ, SANZ MM, SILVERMAN WP, LELE KP, MASIA A, KATZ E, LUBIN RA, NOLIN SL: Low frequencies of apparently fragile X chromosomes in normal control cultures: A possible explanation. *Exp Cell Biol* 54:40, 1986.

116. MARLHENS F, AL ACHKAR W, AURIAS A, COUTURIER J, DUTRILLAUX AM, GERBAULT-SEREAU M, HOFFSCHIR F, LAMOLIATTE E, LEFRANCOIS D, LOMBARD M, MULERIS M, PRIEUR M, PROD'HOMME M, SABATIER L, VIEGAS-PEQUIGNOT E, VOLOBOUEV V, DUTRILLAUX B: The rate of chromosome breakage is age dependent in lymphocytes of adult controls. *Hum Genet* 73:290, 1986.

117. TOMMERUP N, NIELSEN KB, MIKKELSEN M: Marker X chromosome induction in fibroblasts by FUdR. *Am J Med Genet* 9:263, 1981.

118. FONATSCH C: A simple method to demonstrate the fragile X chromosome in fibroblasts. *Hum Genet* 59:186, 1981.

119. MATTEI MG, MATTEI J-F, VIDAL I, GIRAUD F: Expression in lymphocyte and fibroblast culture of the fragile X chromosome: A new technical approach. *Hum Genet* 59:166, 1981.

120. SUTHERLAND GR, BAKER E: Induction of fragile sites in fibroblasts. *Am J Hum Genet* 38:573, 1986.

121. JACOBS PA, HUNT PA, MAYER M, WANG J-C, BOSS GR, ERBE RW: Expression of the marker (X)(q28) in lymphoblastoid cell lines. *Am J Hum Genet* 34:552, 1982.

122. JENKINS EC, BROWN WT, DUNCAN CJ, BROOKS J, YISHAY MB, GIORDANO FM, NITOWSKY HM: Feasibility of fragile X chromosome prenatal diagnosis demonstrated. *Lancet* 2:1292, 1981.

123. SHAPIRO LR, WILMOT PL, BRENHOLZ P, LEFF A, MARTINO M, HARRIS G, MAHONEY MJ, HOBBINS JC: Prenatal diagnosis of fragile X chromosome. *Lancet* 1:99, 1982.

124. JENKINS EC, BROWN WT, WILSON MG, LIN MS, ALFI OS, WASSMAN ER, BROOKS J, DUNCAN CJ, MASIA A, KRAWCZUN MS: The prenatal detection of the fragile X chromosome: Review of recent experience. *Am J Med Genet* 23:297, 1986.

125. SUTHERLAND GR, BAKER E, PURVIS-SMITH S, HOCKEY A, KRUMINS E, EICHENBAUM SZ: Prenatal diagnosis of the fragile X using thymidine induction. *Prenat Diagn* 7:197, 1987.

126. TOMMERUP N, SONDERGAARD F, TONNESEN T, KRISTENSEN M, ARVEILER B, SCHINZEL A: First trimester prenatal diagnosis of a male fetus with fragile X. *Lancet* 1:870, 1985.

127. International Fetoscopy Group Special Report: The status of fetoscopy and fetal tissue sampling. *Prenat Diagn* 4:79, 1984.

128. DAFFOS F, CAPELLA-PAVLOVSKY M, FORESTIER F: Fetal blood sampling via the umbilical cord using a needle guided by ultrasound: Report of 66 cases. *Prenat Diagn* 3:271, 1983.

129. HOBBINS JC, GRANNUM PA, ROMERO R, REECE EA, MAHONEY MJ: Percutaneous umbilical blood sampling. *Am J Obstet Gynecol* 152:1, 1985.

130. FILIPPI G, RINALDI A, ARCHIDIACONO N, ROCCHI M, BALASZ I, SINASCALCO M: Brief rerport: Linkage between G6PD and fragile X syndrome. *Am J Med Genet* 15:113, 1983.

131. GOODFELLOW PN, DAVIES KE, ROPERS H-H: Report of the committee on the genetic constitution of the X and Y chromosomes. Eighth International Workshop on Human Gene Mapping. *Cytogenet Cell Genet* 40:296, 1985.

132. DAVIES KE: DNA studies of X-linked mental retardation associated with a fragile site at Xq27. *Am J Med Genet* 23:633, 1986.

133. MATTEI MG, BAETEMAN MA, HELIG R, OBERLE I, DAVIES K: Localization by in situ hybridization of the coagulation factor IX gene and of two polymorphic DNA probes with respect to the fragile X site. *Hum Genet* 69:327, 1985.

134. OBERLE I, HEILIG R, MOISAN JP, KLOEPFER C: Fragile-X mental retardation syndrome with two flanking polymorphic DNA markers. *Proc Natl Acad Sci USA* 83:1016, 1986.

135. PURRELLO M, ALHODEFF B, ESPOSITO D, SZABO P, ROCCHI M, SINASCALCO M: The human genes for hemophilia A and hemophilia B flank the X chromosome fragile site at Xq27.3. *EMBO J* 4:725, 1985.

136. PURRELLO M, STEVENSON RE, SAUL RA, MANDEL JL, SINASCALCO M: The common RFLP detected by probe St14 is located between the loci for the fragile-X syndrome and G6PD. *Am J Hum Genet* 37:A171, 1985.

137. DRAYNA D, DAVIES K, HARTLEY D, MANDEL J-L, CAMERINO G: Genetic mapping of the human X chromosome by using restriction fragment length polymorphisms. *Proc Natl Acad Sci USA* 81:2836, 1984.

138. DRAYNA D, WHITE R: The genetic linkage map of the human X chromosome. *Science* 230:753, 1985.

139. HARTLEY DA, DAVIES KE, DRAYNA D, WHITE RL, WILLIAMSON R: A cytological map of the human X chromosome—evidence for nonrandom recombination. *Nucleic Acids Res* 12:5277, 1984.

140. SZABO P, PURRELLO M, ROCCHI M, ARCHIDIACONO N, ALHADEFF B: Cytological mapping of the human glucose-6-phosphate dehydrogenase gene distal to the fragile-X-site suggests a high rate of meiotic recombination across this site. *Proc Natl Acad Sci USA* 81:7855, 1984.

141. NUSSBAUM RL, AIRHART SD, LEDBETTER DH: Recombination and amplification of pyrimidine-rich sequences may be responsible for initiation and progression of the Xq27 fragile site: An hypothesis. *Am J Med Genet* 23:715, 1986.

142. PEMBREY ME, WINTER RM, DAVIES KE: A premutation that generates a defect at crossing over explains the inheritance of fragile X mental retardation. *Am J Med Genet* 21:709, 1985.

143. LEVITAS A, BRADEN M, VAN NORMAN K: Treatment and intervention, in Hagerman RJ, McBogg PM (eds): *The Fragile X Syndrome: Diagnosis, Biochemistry, and Intervention*. Dillon, CO, Spectra Publishing, 1983, p 201.

144. BROWN WT, COHEN IL, FISCH GS, WOLF-SCHEIN EG, JENKINS VA, MALIK MN, JENKINS EC: High dose folic acid treatment of fragile(X) males. *Am J Med Genet* 23:263, 1986.

145. HAGERMAN RJ, JACKSON AW, LEVITAS A, BRADEN M, MCBOGG P, KEMPER M, MCGAVRAN L, BERRY R, MATUS I, HAGERMAN PJ: Oral folic acid versus placebo in the treatment of males with the fragile X syndrome. *Am J Med Genet* 23:241, 1986.

CHAPTER 9

MOLECULAR CYTOGENETICS: Interface of Cytogenetics and Monogenic Disorders

DAVID H. LEDBETTER
WEBSTER K. CAVENEE

1. *High-resolution cytogenetic techniques have allowed the delineation of a number of microdeletion or microduplication syndromes (also referred to as contiguous gene syndromes), including Langer-Giedion, Beckwith-Wiedemann, aniridia-Wilms tumor, retinoblastoma, Prader-Willi, Miller-Dieker, and DiGeorge. Specific features of these disorders may occur singly as Mendelian conditions, and it is presumed that the complex phenotypes of each are caused by deletion or duplication of multiple, unrelated loci physically contiguous on the chromosome. Molecular genetics strategies are being applied to identify DNA segments which map within the critical chromosomal regions with the ultimate goal of cloning the genes involved in each disorder. This "reverse genetics" strategy (cloning a gene of unknown function by its location in the genome) has already been successful in the identification of a candidate gene for retinoblastoma, and progress for other disorders is rapid.*
2. *Other Mendelian conditions, both autosomal and X-linked, are occasionally associated with gross chromosomal translocations or deletions. These rare circumstances may provide the crucial first step for reverse genetics strategies, i.e., identifying the physical localization of a gene. The most obvious of this class are instances in which sporadic females are found with full clinical manifestation of an X-linked disorder. This is frequently due to an X;autosome translocation in which the break point on X disrupts the locus and the resulting nonrandom pattern of Lyonization causes the allele on the normal X to be inactivated. Duchenne muscular dystrophy was first mapped to Xp21 by the recognition of several affected females with translocations involving this break point and this led to the successful cloning of the DMD gene. Other recent successes include the cloning of the gene for chronic granulomatous disease and a candidate gene for the testis determining factor, with rapid progress to be expected for other loci.*

ADVANCES IN CYTOGENETICS RESOLUTION

Chromosome banding techniques, developed in the early 1970s, allow unambiguous identification of each human chromosome and the detection of most structural abnormalities including translocations, deletions, and duplications. Banding techniques are now routine procedures in all clinical cytogenetics laboratories, and a brief overview of the clinical situations which require routine cytogenetic study is given in Chap. 1. The syndromes described here result from extremely subtle cytogenetic changes which frequently are not detectable by routine banding analysis and require instead the application of high resolution cytogenetic methodologies.

The concept and major technique for high resolution chromosome analysis was introduced in 1976 by Yunis.[1] In brief, it involved the synchronization of phytohemagglutinin-stimulated lymphocyte cultures by blocking cells in S phase with the folate antagonist amethopterin (methotrexate) for one cell cycle to accumulate all cells at one point in the cycle. This block is released by removing the amethopterin and adding thymidine to reinitiate DNA synthesis. This cohort of synchronized cells enters the early stages of mitosis approximately 5 to 6 h later, at which time a brief exposure to colcemid (5 to 15 min) results in an enriched population of cells in prophase and prometaphase rather than the middle to late stages of metaphase more characteristic of conventional harvesting techniques.

A comparative illustration of metaphase and prometaphase chromosomes is shown in Fig. 9-1 for human chromosome 17. It has been shown that each band seen at metaphase actually represents multiple subbands in earlier stages which have "fused together" as the chromosome contracts. Whereas a typical metaphase cell contains on the order of 300 to 400 bands per haploid genome, synchronized chromosome preparations make it possible to visualize 500 to 1000 bands per haploid set. Although resolution up to 2000 bands has been achieved in humans,[2] this has not been reproduced by others or utilized in clinical applications. A standardized idiogrammatic representation of human chromosomes at the 400-, 550-, and 850-band stages of resolution has been developed as part of the International System for Human Cytogenetic Nomenclature.[3]

Practically, it is not possible to apply high resolution chromosome analysis to all clinical cytogenetic studies. Besides the extra steps involved in synchronizing the cultures, analysis is significantly more difficult and time-consuming. It is also difficult to construct complete karyotypes from prophase cells in which the highly elongated chromosomes are frequently bent and overlapped with other chromosomes. Therefore the primary application of high resolution analysis has come in circumstances in which a particular chromosomal region is to be studied in greater detail. In fact, despite impressions to the contrary, the new chromosomal deletion syndromes were not initially discovered by high-resolution methods. In most cases, a candidate chromosome was identified through routine metaphase chromosome analysis, with high-resolution analysis subsequently being used to characterize the critical region and define the frequency of deletions for a disorder.

For example, the first deletions associated with retinoblastoma[4,5] and aniridia-Wilms tumor[6] were described before the development of high resolution techniques (the first retinoblastoma deletion was detected even prior to chromosome band-

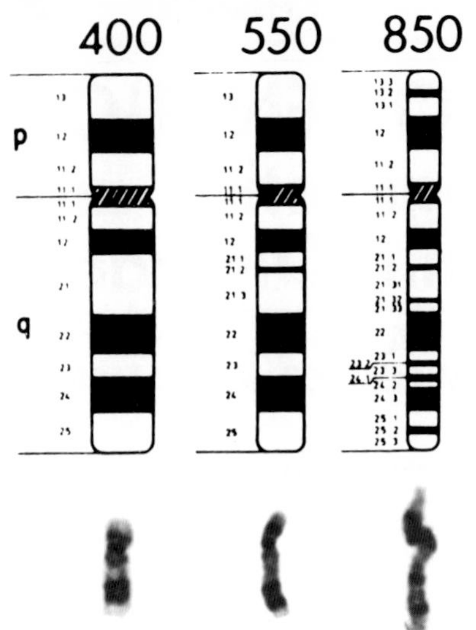

Fig. 9-1 Comparison of routine and high resolution cytogenetic analysis. An idiogram of human chromosome 17 is shown at approximately the 400 (routine), 550, and 850 (high resolution) bands per haploid genome stages of chromosome condensation.[3] Below the idiograms are examples of G-banded chromosome 17s at approximately the same stages of contraction.

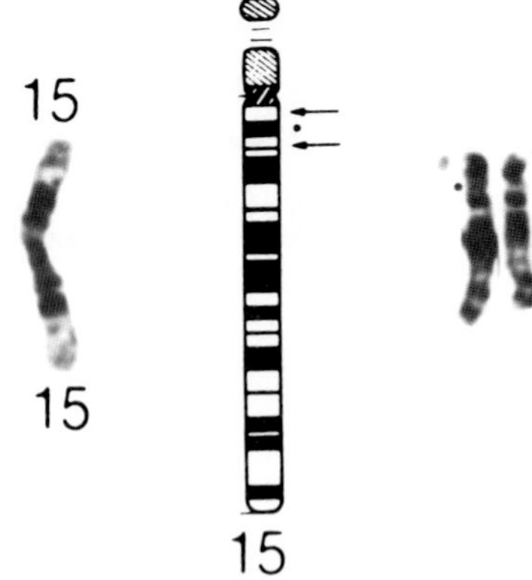

Fig. 9-2 Candidate chromosome for Prader-Willi syndrome (PWS). On the left is a 15;15 Robertsonian translocation from a PWS patient detected by routine cytogenetic analysis, similar to the chromosome findings in the patient of Hawkey and Smithies,[7] which led to the hypothesis that abnormalities of chromosome 15 may play a role in PWS. The center idiogram of chromosome 15 at approximately the 850-band stage of resolution[3] shows the breakpoints (arrows) of the subtle interstitial deletion found by high resolution analysis in most PWS patients. The dot marks band q12, which is usually included in the deletion. To the right is a typical deletion in PWS observed by high resolution analysis in which the q12 band is clearly visible in the normal homologue on the left and is missing from the deleted homologue on the right.

ing). Likewise, candidate chromosomes involved in Prader-Willi syndrome (Fig. 9-2)[7] and DiGeorge syndrome[8] were initially identified due to gross translocations observed using routine methods and that of Miller-Dieker syndrome as a result of a patient with a ring chromosome (Fig. 9-3).[9] After the candidate chromosome regions were identified, high-resolution techniques were crucial in the determination of the specific chromosome band or subband involved in each disorder. Many patients previously thought to have normal karyotypes were subsequently found with deletions too small to be observed using routine cytogenetic techniques.

Comparison of Cytogenetic and Molecular Resolution

How much resolution has been gained in cytogenetics by new methodology? Prior to chromosome banding techniques, most cytogenetic abnormalities described were aneuploid conditions representing gain or loss of entire chromosomes. Since there are approximately 3×10^9 bp of DNA in the human genome, an average chromosome represents about 150×10^6 bp. Trisomy 21 represents aneuploidy for one of the smallest chromosomes, involving about 60×10^6 bp. While several deletion syndromes were described prior to the development of chromosome banding, deletions large enough to be reliably detected by these methods were probably on the order of 10 to 30×10^6 bp. With the development of banding methods in the early 1970s, the human karyotype could be divided into 300 to 400 discrete bands, or about 7 to 10×10^6 bp per band. A much greater number of deletions, duplications, and translocations could be detected at this level of resolution. High resolution techniques, from 500 to 2000 bands per haploid genome, provide a resolution of about 1 to 5×10^6 bp per band. Therefore, the smallest deletion visible in the light microscope is generally considered to be on the order of 2 to 3×10^6 bp.

What are the possibilities for increased cytogenetics resolution? Although improved cell culture and banding techniques might make it possible to achieve 2000 or more bands in the human karyotype, the difficulty of processing and analyzing this information by hand would appear to make it impractical for routine application. It therefore seems unlikely that any significant improvements over current high resolution cytogenetic techniques will soon become available. Rather, it appears that the resolution gap between cytogenetic techniques and molecular analysis is quickly being closed from the molecular side by the advances in pulsed-field gel electrophoresis, field inversion gel electrophoresis, and related methods (see Chap. 2). With these techniques, it is now possible to separate very large DNA fragments in the 10^6-bp range, with success re-

Fig. 9-3 Candidate chromosome for Miller-Dieker syndrome (MDS). On the left is the ring chromosome 17 in an MDS patient, which is easily detectable by routine cytogenetic analysis and which identified chromosome 17 as a candidate chromosome for MDS.[9] In the center is an idiogram of chromosome 17 at approximately the 850-band stage of resolution[3] with an arrow indicating the break point of a small, terminal deletion of 17p13 in an MDS patient. To the right are two pairs of 17s from this MDS patient showing the small, terminal deletion in the homologue on the right of each pair. This subtle deletion would almost certainly be missed by routine cytogenetic methods and requires the application of high resolution techniques.

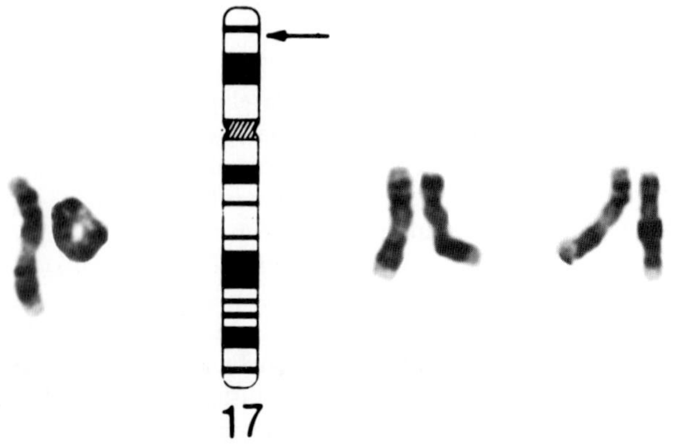

ported for fragments as large as 5 to 10 $\times$ 10^6 bp.[10,11] This level of analysis overlaps with that of high resolution and even routine cytogenetic analysis and should be useful in the identification of deletions at or just below the detection level of the light microscope.

CHROMOSOMAL MICRODELETION/ MICRODUPLICATION SYNDROMES

The syndromes discussed in this chapter are illustrated in Fig. 9-4. They are examples in which high resolution cytogenetic analysis has played a major role in defining precisely the specific chromosomal band which, when deleted or duplicated, gives rise to a specific abnormal phenotype. For most of these syndromes, the cytogenetic abnormality is consistently small and is difficult or impossible to detect by routine methods. Moreover, in each disorder some patients with the full clinical phenotype demonstrate no visible cytogenetic abnormality even after high resolution analysis. This suggests that submicroscopic deletions or duplications exist which require molecular technologies for detection.

Schmickel[12] has proposed the term *contiguous gene syndromes* for this group of microdeletion/microduplication syndromes. The common features shared by these disorders are presented in Table 9-1. They represent a group of recognizable syndromes which were described as clinical entities prior to the knowledge of their chromosomal etiology. The complex mixture of phenotypic abnormalities suggest that at least several genes are involved, and a deletion of unrelated genes which are contiguous on a chromosome provides a reasonable etiologic mechanism. This mechanism has been best documented for a few rare patients with deletions in the short arm of the X chromosome. Patients have been described with variable size overlapping deletions which result in clinical combinations of glycerol kinase deficiency, congenital adrenal hypoplasia, Duchenne muscular dystrophy, chronic granulomatous disease, McCleod phenotype, and ornithine transcarbamylase (OTC) deficiency. Each of these disorders occurs as an X-linked recessive condition, and molecular deletions have been documented of varying size and position to account for the occurrence of several of these conditions in combination (see Chap. 36 and 118). Variability in the size of deletions provides an explanation for the tremendous variability in phenotype seen within these syndromes, as some patients may have deletions which include different numbers of contiguous genes. Mental retardation is usually involved in these disorders and may reflect a general feature of deletion of multiple genes.

This list of contiguous gene syndromes is almost certainly incomplete. As suggested by Schmickel,[12] other sporadic syndromes with complex phenotypes, such as Rubenstein-Taybi

Table 9-1 Features of Microdeletion/Microduplication Syndromes

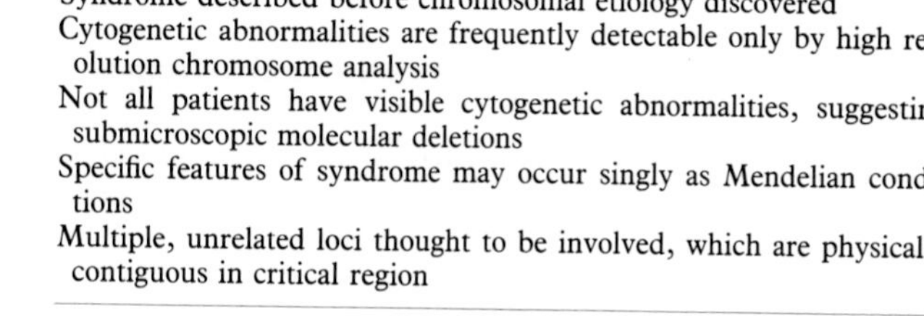

Syndrome described before chromosomal etiology discovered
Cytogenetic abnormalities are frequently detectable only by high resolution chromosome analysis
Not all patients have visible cytogenetic abnormalities, suggesting submicroscopic molecular deletions
Specific features of syndrome may occur singly as Mendelian conditions
Multiple, unrelated loci thought to be involved, which are physically contiguous in critical region

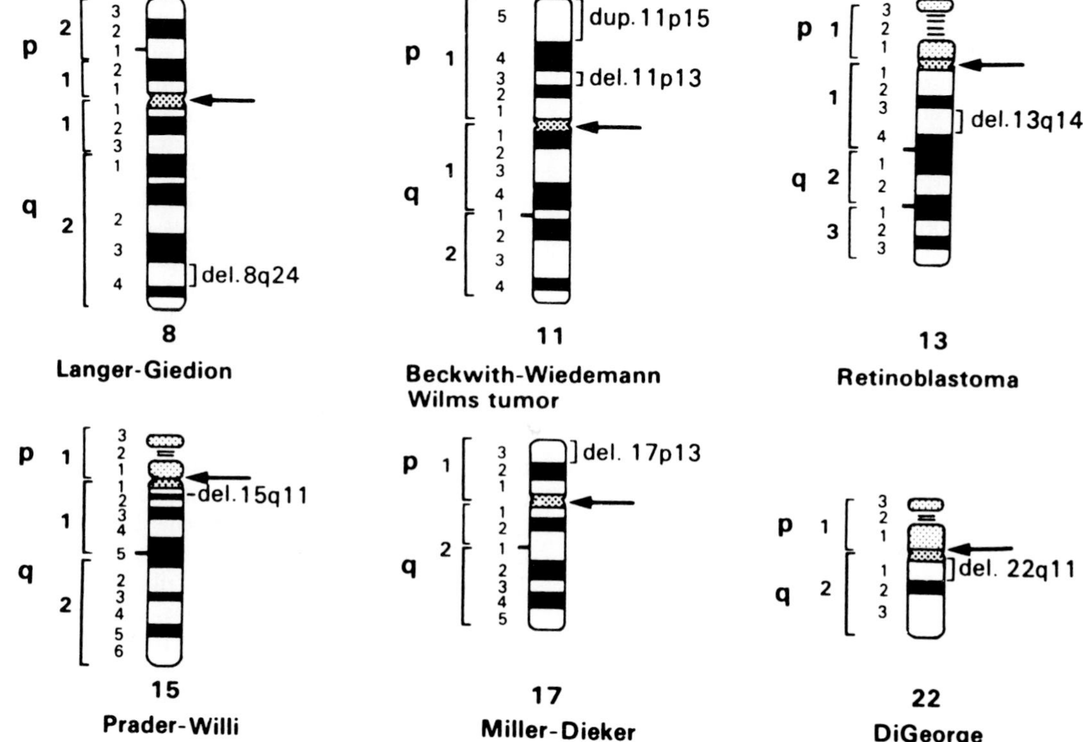

Fig. 9-4 Critical chromosome regions deleted or duplicated in the seven microdeletion/microduplication syndromes ("contiguous gene syndromes") discussed in this chapter. The arrows indicate the centromere position of each chromosome. Chromosome band number is given to the right of brackets which indicate regions which are deleted (del.) or duplicated (dup.). *(From Schmickel.[12] Used by permission of Journal of Pediatrics.)*

and Cornelia de Lange syndromes, may similarly be caused by microdeletion/microduplication mechanisms, but the critical chromosomal region is as yet unidentified.

Reverse Genetics and Contiguous Gene Syndromes

Reverse genetics is a term which has been loosely applied to strategies for isolating and characterizing a gene without prior knowledge of its protein product or function[13] (see Chap. 2). The usual steps involved are first to identify the map position of the gene either by linkage analysis or by the identification of patients with cytogenetic abnormalities (either deletions or translocations) which localize the gene. Strategies are then devised for identifying anonymous DNA segments and cloned genes that map genetically and physically closer and closer to the target gene. Eventually, candidate gene sequences are identified that show no genetic recombination with the locus and whose mutation (or absence) correlates with the disease state.

The greatest successes of the reverse genetics approach have been the cloning of the Duchenne muscular dystrophy (DMD) (see Chap. 118) and chronic granulomatous disease genes. For both, the initial key event was the mapping of DMD to Xp21 by the identification of affected females with balanced X;autosome translocations with a consistent break point in Xp21. Following this preliminary localization, affected DMD males and females were found with barely visible cytogenetic deletions. One of these males had a visible deletion of Xp21 and was affected with DMD, chronic granulomatous disease, retinitis pigmentosa, and McLeod syndrome.[14] Anonymous DNA segments from within this deleted segment were cloned by a subtractive hybridization strategy referred to as PERT (phenol enhanced reassociation technique) cloning.[15] One of six such PERT clones obtained was found to be deleted in about 5 percent of DMD patients and showed very tight linkage to DMD.[16] Chromosome walking in the region and further characterization of patient deletions led to the identification of a huge gene of perhaps 2×10^6 bp responsible for DMD. By somewhat different technical strategies, clones from the PERT library were also used to identify the protein responsible for chronic granulomatous disease.[17]

Similar strategies are currently being employed for most of the microdeletion/microduplication syndromes described in this chapter. Because many of the patients with these disorders do not have visible deletions or duplications, one of the practical goals of this work is to identify specific DNA segments consistently involved in the disorders as additional diagnostic aids. On a more basic level, identification and characterization of the major gene or genes responsible for the complex phenotypic abnormalities for each condition is desired.

Table 9-2 gives a brief summary of the current status of the reverse genetic characterization of each of the contiguous gene syndromes to be considered. We review the status of each of these, starting with retinoblastoma, in which the most has been accomplished in molecular characterization of this chromosomal region and a candidate gene has been identified.

Table 9-2 Reverse Genetic Progress in Microdeletion and Microduplication Syndromes

1. Establish precise chromosomal position of gene(s) involved by high resolution cytogenetic analysis of overlapping deletions: all
2. Identify anonymous DNA segments or cloned genes which map close to critical region (i.e., within visible deletion/duplication cases): retinoblastoma, Wilms tumor, Prader-Willi, Miller-Dieker, DiGeorge
3. Detection of submicroscopic deletions in patients with no cytogenetically visible abnormality: retinoblastoma, Miller-Dieker
4. Identify candidate genes within critical region: retinoblastoma
5. Proof that the gene is functionally related to the disease phenotype: none

Retinoblastoma

Clinical. Retinoblastoma is the most common intraocular malignancy in children with an incidence of about one in 14,000 livebirths.[18] Although the disease may be congenitally apparent, most diagnoses are made between the ages of 1 and 3 years and virtually always before age 7 years. The most common symptoms at presentation are leucocoria, strabismus, poor vision, hyphema, mydriasis, orbital cellulitis, and heterochromia iridis.[19]

Since many of these symptoms are clearly not specific to retinoblastoma and since early surgical or radiotherapeutic intervention is of primary importance in the survival of these patients, it is imperative to confirm these impressions by examination under anesthesia with the indirect opthalmoscope using scleral indentation. Ultrasonography and roentgenography are useful adjuncts to such examinations.

The most frequent form of retinoblastoma is the endophytic type, in which the tumor extends into the vitreous and may, therefore, show exfoliated cells or clumps on adjacent retinal surfaces or in the vitreous. The exophytic form, which underlies the retina, is less common. The major cause of mortality from the disease is extraocular extension along the optic nerve into the intracranial cavity as well as more distant metastases via invasion of the choroid. Since retinoblastoma tumors can be effectively managed with radiotherapy, photocoagulation, cryotherapy, and surgical enucleation, detection of the tumor at early stage is the primary prognostic indicator.[19]

The progenitor cell from which retinoblastoma arises is ill-defined. Histologically, the tumor consists of densely packed cells that are small, generally round, and hyperchromatic with scanty cytoplasm. The cells can be of variable differentiation states ranging from extremely primitive to well differentiated arrays of Flexner-Wintersteiner rosettes. The initiating lesion has been postulated to arise in neuronal, glial, or retinal stem cells.[20–22] More recent studies[23] demonstrating the presence of neuron-specific enolase and glial fibrillary acidic protein in a single retinoblastoma cell line implicate a primitive neuroectodermal cell as the tumor progenitor.

In patients in which retinoblastoma is associated with a visible chromosome deletion (see "Cytogenetics," below), other clinical features may include mental retardation and a characteristic facial appearance. Surprisingly, mental retardation is seen in less than half of these deletion patients, and major anomalies are usually not present.[24] Consistent phenotypic features include a coarse facial appearance, broad nasal bridge, upturned nares, long philtrum, and long, thin upper lip.[24,25] Other features seen in some patients include brachycephaly, large ears with folded lobules, and postauricular pitting.[26] This phenotype has also been described in patients with 13q deletion but without retinoblastoma, indicating that the risk of tumor development is not 100 percent for these patients.

Genetics. Retinoblastoma has served as the prototypic example of a genetic predisposition to cancer.[27] The disease is apparent predominantly in young children and shows no obvious geographic or sex-specific clustering. Although the majority of tumors occur with no precedent family history, the inherited form of the disease has been extensively documented.[28–30] The familial disease is transmitted with few exceptions as a typical Mendelian autosomal dominant trait with virtually full penetrance. It has been estimated from epidemiologic data[31] that about 60 percent of cases are nonhereditary and unilateral, 15 percent are hereditary and unilateral, and 25 percent are hereditary and bilateral.

Although there are examples of apparent nonpenetrance among antecedent or collateral relatives of familial retinoblastoma cases, among descendants of such cases penetrance is virtually complete.[31] There have been few pedigrees reported in which the disease seems to have truly skipped a generation, in other words from grandparent to grandchild via an unaffected parent. Retrospective analyses of families of retinoblastoma probands have yielded several examples of presumed obligate carriers who did not develop the disease. Examination of a number of retinoblastoma pedigrees[19,29–33] showed apparent nonpenetrance in 52 of 128 families, either through multiply affected sibships with both parents unaffected or through other affected relatives (such as cousins and aunts) with unaffected intervening relatives. In contrast, when pooled data from published sources was used to determine the segregation ratio among offspring of familial retinoblastoma patients, it was observed that bilaterally affected parents had 49 percent affected offspring, as expected for a dominantly inherited disease with complete penetrance, whereas unilaterally affected parents had 42 percent affected offspring, indicating some lack of penetrance.[33] These data were relevant to the proposal of a "host resistance model," whereby heritable resistance factors to a predisposing gene are minimal in bilaterally affected individuals, intermediate in unilaterally affected individuals, and maximal in unaffected carriers.[33]

A model has been proposed[27,31] encompassing the observations that familial cases are generally multifocal and bilateral whereas sporadic cases typically present with unilateral unifocal disease of later diagnosis. According to the model, as few as two stochastic mutational events are required for tumor formation, the first of which can be inherited through the germ line (in heritable cases) or can occur somatically in individual retinal cells (in nonheritable cases). The second event occurs somatically in either case and leads to tumor formation in each doubly defective retinal cell. This empirically based hypothesis has been supported through direct experimental scrutiny using molecular genetic approaches.

Cytogenetics. The involvement of genetic alteration in the first step of this pathway of oncogenesis has been supported by cytogenetic analyses which showed that a small proportion of patients carry a microscopically visible deletion of one chromosome 13 homologue in all their constitutional cells. Since the first such report[4] more than 30 deletions have been described occurring in a small percentage of retinoblastoma cases[34–36]; the common region of overlap of such deletions is chromosome 13, band q14.11.[5,37] An example of such a deletion of one constitutional chromosome 13 homologue is illustrated in Fig. 9-5. In the context of the "two-hit" model, such deletions could act as the first hit, and, when they are germinal, they could confer the risk of tumor formation in an autosomal dominant manner. Evidence that the same locus is involved in retinoblastoma cases that lack an apparent chromosomal deletion was provided through the demonstration of tight genetic linkage between the retinbolastoma and esterase D loci,[38] the latter being a moderately polymorphic isozymic enzyme whose encoding locus also maps to 13q14.[39]

Furthermore, cytogenetic analyses have provided important information concerning the occasional occurrence of apparent nonpenetrance in some retinoblastoma families. A large kindred has been reported in which unilateral retinoblastoma was transmitted by a number of unaffected individuals. Each affected individual carried the same constitutional deletion involving 13q14, whereas the unaffected carriers had a balanced insertional translocation involving the same region.[40] This and other related reports of chromosomal translocations, inversions, or deletions in transmitting parents[40–42] provide a clear biologic basis for segregation distortion without invoking nonpenetrance. Additionally, two reports describe individuals carrying a constitutional deletion involving 13q14 but who have no signs of retinoblastoma at age 5[42] or 25 years.[43] The latter individual transmitted her deletion to two daughters, one of whom developed unilateral retinoblastoma.[44] Whether a significant proportion of unaffected carriers can be accounted for by such mechanisms remains to be demonstrated. Another theoretical explanation for isolated multiply affected sibships with unaffected parents is parental mosaicism. Chromosomal mosaicism for deletions involving 13q14 was reported in lymphocytes from 5 of 50 sporadic retinoblastoma patients[45] in one series. In these cases a significant proportion of retinal cells must have carried the deletion; alternatively, if relatively few retinoblasts carried the deletion, then an individual could be at low risk for expressing the disease but at high risk for its transmission. The increasing resolution of cytogenetic technology and the use of DNA probes for loci in the immediate

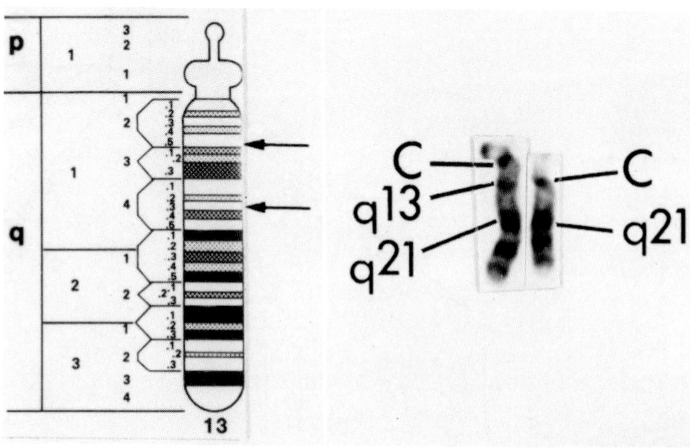

Fig. 9-5 Chromosome 13 deletion in constitutional cells from a patient with retinoblastoma. The idiogram of chromosome 13 to the left indicates the two break points (arrows) of the interstitial deletion. To the right is a G-banded partial karyotype with the normal homologue on the left (centromere, C, bands q13 and q21 indicated) and the deleted homologue on the right (centromere and q21 band indicated). Note that only one chromosome homologue is altered. Hence this aberration may represent the first, and predisposing, event in the child.

vicinity of the *RB1* locus (as described in the next section) may soon permit the detection of more subtle genomic rearrangements than have been detectable previously and allow specific questions concerning penetrance to be addressed.

The presence of 13q14 deletion in patients without mental retardation or major anomalies[24] and in familial cases in which transmission might appear to be autosomal dominant[46] suggests that high-resolution chromosome analysis should be done in all patients with retinoblastoma. When a deletion is found in a proband, parental studies should be considered to rule out deletion, insertional translocation, or mosaicism.

Molecular Genetics. Specific predictions as to the nature of the second tumor-eliciting event in the two-step model of oncogenesis[27,31] have been proposed[47]: (1) The autosomal dominant hereditary form of retinoblastoma, in the absence of a gross chromosomal deletion, involves the same genetic locus as that involved in cases showing large deletions of chromosome 13. Thus, the first step in the pathway towards tumorigenesis in these cases is a submicroscopic mutational event at the *RB1* locus. (2) The same genetic change which has occurred as a germ-line mutation in hereditary retinoblastoma occurs as a somatic genetic alteration of the *RB1* locus in a retinal cell in nonhereditary retinoblastoma. (3) The second step in tumorigenesis in both heritable and nonhereditary retinoblastoma involves somatic alteration of the normal allele at the *RB1* locus in such a way that the mutant allele is unmasked. Thus, the first mutation in this process, although it may be inherited as an autosomal dominant trait at the organismal level, is, in fact, a recessive defect in the individual retinal cell.

The model which arises from these considerations is shown in Fig. 9-6, which outlines specific chromosomal mechanisms which would allow phenotypic expression of a recessive germinal mutation of the *RB1* locus (Fig. 9-6*A*). This aberration is inherited by an individual who thus carries such a mutation in all somatic as well as germ line cells (Fig. 9-6*B*). Any additional event that results in homozygosity or hemizygosity for the mutant allele (that is, mutant at the *RB1* locus on both chromosome 13 homologues) will result in a tumor clone. Several chromosomal mechanisms can be imagined in this process: (1) mitotic nondisjunction with loss of the wild-type chromosome (Fig. 9-6*C*) resulting in hemizygosity at all loci on chromosome 13, (2) mitotic nondisjunction with reduplication of the mutant chromosome (Fig. 9-6*D*) resulting in homozygosity at all loci on the chromosome, (3) mitotic recombination (Fig. 9-6*E*) between the *RB1* locus encoding the mutant allele and the centromere resulting in heterozygosity at loci in the proximal region and homozygosity throughout the rest of the chromosome including the *RB1* locus, (4) several other more regionalized events such as gene conversion (Fig. 9-6*F*), deletion (Fig. 9-6*G*), or mutation (Fig. 9-6*H*). Both nonheritable and hereditary retinoblastoma could arise through the appearance of homozygosity at the *RB1* locus, the difference being two somatic events in the former and one germinal and one somatic event in the latter instance.

The approach which has been taken to examine these hypotheses relies on the variability of DNA sequences among humans, which results in inherited differences in restriction endonuclease recognition sites (See Chap. 6). In this approach, segments of the human genome are isolated in recombinant DNA form, and the loci homologous to these probe segments are tested for their encompassing restriction endonuclease recognition sequences which vary between unrelated individuals.

Fig. 9-6 Chromosomal mechanisms which could reveal recessive mutations. In this example, an affected male who carries a recessive defect at the *RB1* locus on chromosome 13, designated rb, in all his cells mates with a genotypically wild-type, "+," female. One of their children (Fig. 9-6B) inherits the defective chromosome 13 from his father and so is rb/+ at the *RB1* locus in all his cells. A tumor of his retinal cells may develop by eliminating the dominant wild-type allele at the *RB1* locus by the mechanisms required to effect the tumor cell genotype shown schematically in C to H. *(Reprinted by permission from* Nature, *vol. 305, p. 779, copyright 1983, Macmillan Journals, Limited.)*

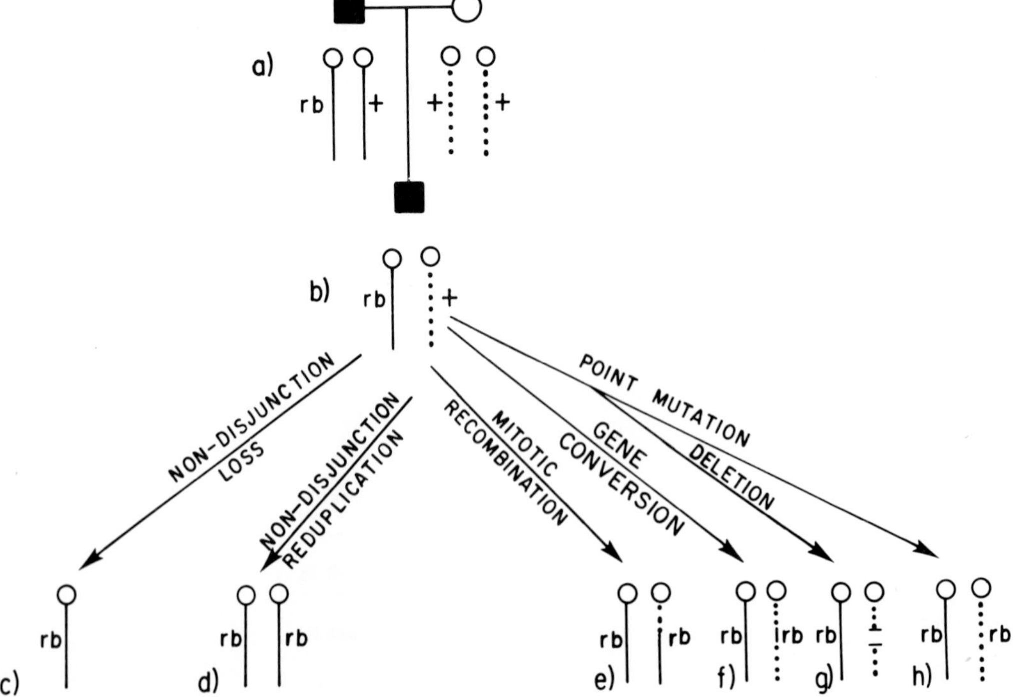

Two types of such variation have been defined. The first, and most abundant, results from simple base-pair changes within the recognition site sequence for a particular restriction endonuclease and yields alleles of longer (when the effect of the mutation is loss of a site) or shorter (when the effect of the mutation is the gain of a site) length.[48] The second type results from the insertion or deletion of varying numbers of blocks of like DNA sequence into or out of the genomic locus.[49] Practically, the net result is the observation of two alleles at the locus encompassing a site change (presence or absence of the site) or numerous alleles at a locus subject to insertion or deletion of larger segments of DNA, respectively. In either case, however, any given individual will reveal only two alleles at the locus, one from the paternally derived chromosome and one from the maternally derived homologue. In all cases examined to date these types of markers have been shown to behave in family studies as would be predicted for simple Mendelian codominant alleles. Recombinant DNA probes for loci mapped along the length of human chromosome 13 have been isolated, characterized,[50,51] and used in multilocus analyses to detect alterations in the somatic genotypes of tumors as compared with the germ-line genotype of the individuals harboring the tumors.[47,52,53] A reasonably large series of retinoblastoma cases has been examined in this manner; examples are illustrated in Fig. 9-7 and 9-8.

NONDISJUNCTION AND DUPLICATION. The mechanism depicted in Fig. 9-6*D*, where together with the nondisjunctional loss of the wild-type chromosome, the mutant chromosome is duplicated would be difficult to detect cytogenetically or by quantitation of esterase D activity. However, by using codominant DNA markers these events were detected as a loss of one allele at each informative locus on the chromosome. The patient described in Fig. 9-7 was found to be heterozygous at the *ESD* locus and showed no visible abnormality of either chromosome 13. An examination of tumor tissue from this individual again showed no abnormalities of chromosome 13, except that in addition to the expected two copies of the chromosome another copy was present as a translocation involving chromosomes 13 and 14. However, the tumor cells exhibited only one of the two isozymic types of the esterase D enzyme, that being the allele from the father. It was proposed[54] that this had resulted from somatic inactivation of the maternally derived allele of the *ESD* locus on one homologue of chromosome 13.

Constitutional and tumor cells derived from this patient were tested with seven recombinant DNA probes. Three of the probes revealed heterozygosity in the germ line tissue: p9A7, which maps in the region 13q22-qter, and pHU26 and pHU10, both of which map in the region 13q12-q22. In each of these cases (Fig. 9-7*A* to *C*) although both codominant alleles were present in the germ line, only one allele at each locus was present in the tumor, and this allele was derived, in each case, from the chromosome 13 inherited from the father. A reasonable interpretation of these results is diagramed in Fig. 9-7*D*. Rather than somatic inactivation of the *ESD* locus on one chromosome 13 homolog, these data are consistent with the complete loss of the entire maternally derived chromosomes accompanied by duplication of the paternally derived chromosome. It is likely that this chromosome carried a *de novo* germinal mutation, since the father showed no evidence of retinoblastoma, but the individual was bilaterally affected. It is also possible that one or two of the chromosomes 13 in the tumor were derived by mitotic exchange between the

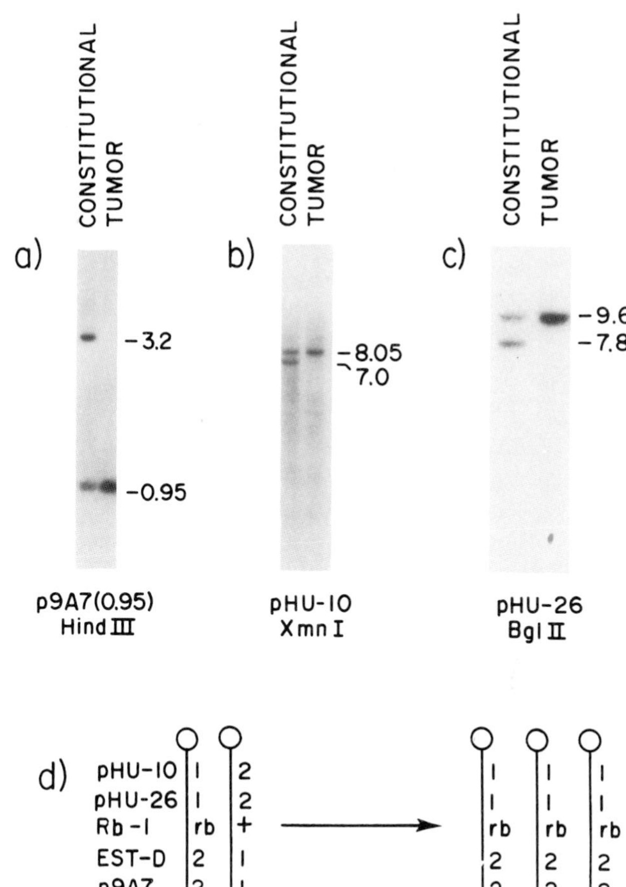

Fig. 9-7 Homozygosity effected by segregation of one chromosome 13 homologue with reduplication of the remaining one. *A.* Results obtained when HindIII-digested DNA was hybridized to p9A7, which contains an insert homologous to a locus on chromosome 13 which maps between band q22 and the terminus of the long arm. *B.* The pattern obtained when XmnI-digested DNA was hybridized to the insert fragment derived from the plasmid pHU10, which is homologous to a locus on chromosome 13 which maps between bands q12 and q22. *C.* The pattern obtained when Bgl II-digested DNA was hybridized to the insert fragment isolated from the plasmid pHU26, which is homologous to a locus on chromosome 13 which maps between bands q12 and q22. *D.* A schematic diagram incorporating these data with previous analyses of the esterase D alleles present and the karyotype of the two samples from patient Rb-409. *(Reprinted by permission from* Nature, *vol. 305, p. 780, copyright 1983, Macmillan Journals, Limited.)*

wild-type and mutant chromosomes (as diagramed in Fig. 9-6*E*) such that an original mutant chromosome and a recombinant chromosome (or two) were maintained. If this had happened, the point of interchange must have been proximal to the region detected by the most proximal marker locus, since all the markers including esterase D (which maps to 13q14) show reduction to homozygosity in the tumor.

MITOTIC RECOMBINATION. Another possible mechanism whereby part of a pair of chromosomes may become homozygous, although not previously observed in humans, is illustrated in Fig. 9-6*E*. A somatic, or mitotic, recombination between the mutant and wild-type chromosome homologues, with subsequent segregation, can result in a cell which maintains heterozygosity at loci proximal to the break point of the recombinational event but which shows homozygosity at loci distal to such a break point. An instance of such a mechanism

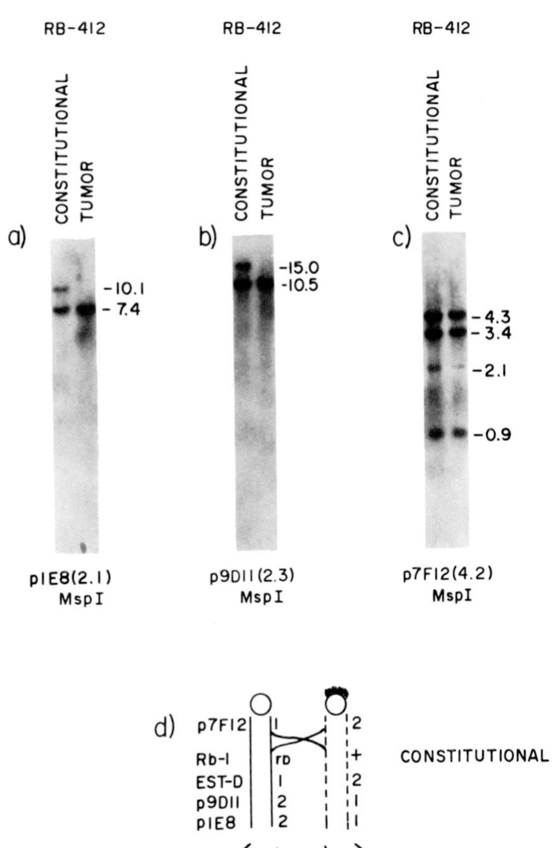

Fig. 9-8 Homozygosity effected by a mitotic recombinational event. A. The pattern obtained when the hybridization probe was pIE8, which is homologous to a locus on chromosome 13 mapping between band q22 and the terminus of the long arm. B. Results obtained when the hybridization probe was p9D11, which is homologous to a locus on chromosome 13 mapping to band q22. C. Results obtained with the hybridization probe was p7F12, which is homologous to a locus on chromosome 13 mapping between bands q12 and q14. D. Schematic diagram showing inferred haplotypes on each chromosome derived from karyology, esterase D determinations and data described here. The cap on the chromosome homologues represented by the dashed lines denotes a fluorescent-staining heterochromatic region. In this figure the point of crossover must lie between the *RB1* and 7F12 loci and is shown occurring between chromatids of the chromosome 13 homologue at the four-strand stage of mitotic chromosome replication. *E* to *H*. Schematic diagram of the four possible combinations of wild-type and recombinant homologues. Possibilities *E* to *G* result in a phenotypically wild-type cell. The allelic data shown in H corresponds to the experimental data and results in homozygosity for the mutant (rb) allele at the *RB1* locus. *(Reprinted by permission from* Nature*, vol. 305, p. 781, copyright 1983, Macmillan Journals, Limited.)*

was presented in patient Rb-412.[47] The germ-line cells from this person had been determined to be heterozygous at the *ESD* locus as well as heterozygous for a quinacrine-staining satellite heteromorphism on the short arm of chromosome 13. An examination of the tumor cells derived from this patient showed the presence of both types of satellite staining but only one isozymic form of esterase D. A reasonable interpretation of these data[53] was that both chromosomes 13 were present in their entirety in the Rb-412 tumor and that a somatic inactivation of one of the isozymic forms of esterase D had occurred during tumor formation. Alternatively, a mitotic recombination event occurring between the centromere and the *ESD* locus, as described above, could also generate chromosomes consistent with these results. Germ-line and tumor genotypes of this patient were examined at chromosome 13 loci defined by seven DNA probes, and the results shown in Fig. 9-8 were obtained. Three of the markers were heterozygous in skin fibroblasts from Rb-412: pIE8 which maps distal to 13q22; p9D11, which maps at 13q22; and p7F12, which maps between the *RB1* locus and the centromere. The tumor tissue from this patient showed a loss of one allele at the *9D11* and *1E8* loci, whereas the *7F12* locus remained heterozygous (Fig. 9-8*C*) An interpretation of these results, taken together with the satellite heteromorphism and esterase D data described above, is illustrated in Fig. 9-8*D* and suggests that a recombination event took place between the mutant and wild-type chromosomes 13 in the cell that gave rise to the tumor. The crossover point was between the *7F12* and the *RB1* loci, and each locus distal to the latter became homozygous. Between *RB1* and the terminus of the short arm, however, two markers maintained both the maternal and paternal haplotypes.

Data similar to those shown in Figs. 9-7 and 9-8 have been obtained in greater than 75 percent of retinoblastoma tumors obtained. They provide experimental support for the proposed recessive model of oncogenesis[27,31,47] whereby predisposing mutations are revealed by elimination of the homologous wild-type locus through chromosomal segregation or recombination rather than simple point mutation. The supposition that it was the chromosome 13 homologue carrying the wild-type *RB1* allele that was lost during the process of tumorigenesis was tested by comparing constitutional and tumor genotypes of patients with familial retinoblastoma. The model described in Fig. 9-6 demands that the chromosome 13 remaining in the tumors of such children be derived from their affected parent. The analysis[54] of one such case, KS2H, is shown in Fig. 9-9. This child was constitutionally heterozygous at the *HU26* locus. His retinoblastoma tumor tissue (Rb-KS2H) showed only the longer allele at this locus. His unaffected parent, KS2C, was constitutionally heterozygous at this locus, while his affected parent, KS2F, was homozygous for the longer allele. The proband must, therefore, have inherited the shorter allele at the locus from his unaffected parent, and it was this chromosome that was lost in the tumor. The chromosome remaining in the tumor was inherited from his diseased parent and must be the one carrying the initial predisposing mutation at *RB1*. In this family, the proband inherited the predisposition to retinoblastoma from his father, KS2F, who had inherited it from his mother, KS2G (Fig. 9-9*B*). He obtained the shorter allele from his unaffected mother and the longer allele from his affected father. It is this latter chromosome that must contain the mutant *RB1* locus, and it was this chromosome that was retained in the child's tumor. Corroborating evidence of this interpretation was obtained by examining genotypic combinations at other loci on chromosome 13 in other members of the family. Assignment of the alleles at each of these loci, in combination with those for *HU26*, and a consideration of the allelic combinations from the grandparents (KS2A, KS2B and KS2G), parents (KS2C and KS2F), child (KS2H), and child's tumor (Rb-KS2H) made it possible to infer chromosomal hap-

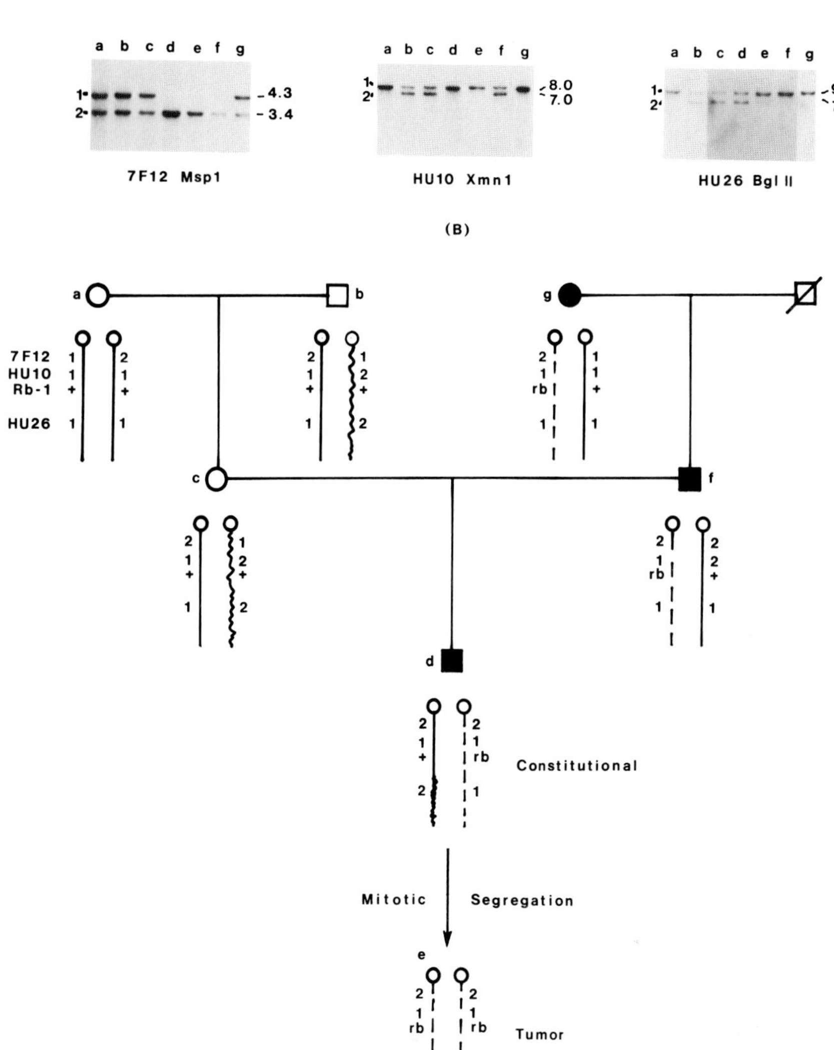

Fig. 9-9 Loss of germ-line heterozygosity in a hereditary retinoblastoma tumor. *A.* DNA was isolated from peripheral blood leukocytes from each of the indicated individuals and from primary tumor biopsy from the proband KS2H. The DNA was digested with the indicated restriction endonucleases, separated by electrophoresis through 0.8 percent agarose gels, transferred to nylon membranes, and hybridized to the indicated probes homologous to loci on human chromosome 13. The family members are designated: (a) KS2A, (b) KS2B, (c) KS2C, (d) KS2H, (e) Rb-KS2H (tumor), (f) KS2F, and (g) KS2G. *B.* Pedigree Rb-KS2 and inferred chromosome 13 haplotypes at the *7F12, HU10, RB1,* and *HU26* loci. Filled symbols = individuals with retinoblastoma; dashed line = nonrecombinant chromosome; straight and wavy lines = recombinant chromosome. *(Reprinted by permission from Cavenee et al. Science 228:501–503, 26 April 1985, copyright 1985, American Association for the Advancement of Science.)*

lotypes (Fig. 9-9*B*). The proband (KS2H) inherited a nonrecombinant chromosome from his paternal grandmother (KS2G) through his father (KS2F) and a recombinant chromosome from his mother (KS2C). It appears that the chromosome retained in the tumor (Rb-KS2H) was inherited from his affected grandmother (KS2G) through his affected father (KS2F). In other cases examined, the prediction that the chromosome 13 derived from the affected parent would be retained in the tumor has also been fulfilled.

It is noteworthy that, although the unmasking of predisposing mutations at the *RB1* locus occurs in mechanistically similar ways in sporadic and heritable retinoblastoma cases, only the latter carry the initial mutation in each of their cells. Patients with heritable disease also seem to be at greatly increased risk for the development of second primary tumors, particularly osteogenic sarcoma.[55] A testable corollary of the model outlined above is that this high propensity is not merely fortuitous but is genetically determined by the predisposing *RB1* mutation. This notion of a pathogenetic causality in the clinical association between these two rare tumor types was tested by determining the constitutional and osteosarcoma genotypes at RFLP loci on chromosome 13. The data indicated that osteosarcomas arising in retinoblastoma patients had become homozygous specifically around the chromosomal region carrying the *RB1* locus.[56] Furthermore, these same chromosomal mechanisms eliciting losses of constitutional heterozygosity were observed in sporadic osteosarcomas suggesting a genetic similarity in pathogenetic causality. These findings are of obvious relevance to the interpretation of human mixed cancer families as they suggest differential expression of a single pleiotropic mutation in the etiology of clinically associated cancer of different histologic types.

A likely explanation for the association between retinoblastoma and osteosarcoma is that both tumors arise subsequent to chromosomal mechanisms which unmask recessive mutations. This may involve either one common locus that is involved in normal regulation of differentiation of both tissues or separate loci that are located closely within chromosome region 13q14. In either case, germ-line deletions of the retinoblastoma locus may also affect the "osteosarcoma locus." Deletions are likely to be an important form of predisposing mutations at the *RB1* locus since a considerable fraction of bilateral retinoblastoma cases carry visible constitutional chromosome deletions[34–36] and submicroscopic deletions have been detected by reduction of esterase D activity.[39]

These epidemiologic, genetic, cytogenetic, and molecular

genetic studies provided data with which to make specific predictions about the nature of the *RB1* locus useful in its molecular isolation. First, any candidate gene should map to the 13q14.1 region of the genome. Second, by analogy with other human diseases such as Duchenne muscular dystrophy,[16] chronic granulomatous disease,[17] and several of the hemoglobinopathies, at least a proportion of mutations at the *RB1* locus should be submicroscopic deletions. Third, a comparison of normal and tumor tissues from heritable cases should show hemizygous aberrancy in the former and homozygous defects in the latter. Last, even in the absence of detectable genomic alteration, alterations in the mRNA transcribed from the locus in tumors should be detected. The underlying assumption of this path of investigation is that the identification and isolation of the genomic DNA or transcribed RNA corresponding to the locus will allow an entry into determining the function of the locus.

In order to provide DNA probes for landmark locations within 13q14, metaphase chromosomes 13 were sorted using a fluorescence-activated cell sorter and portions thereof were used in the derivation of a chromosome-enriched recombinant DNA library.[57] Several unique sequence probes were isolated from this library and their physical location determined by *in situ* hybridization to metaphase chromosomes and by determining hybridization dosage in normal cells from retinoblastoma patients with cytogenetically visible deletions of chromosome 13. One such probe, termed H3-8, was localized to the region 13q14.1, thus fulfilling the first criterion above.[58] When this probe was used to determine the genomic organization of its cognate locus in retinoblastoma tumors, 2 of 37 showed hybridization patterns consistent with homozygous deletion[59] thus fulfilling the second criterion. Additionally, these deletions were shown to arise either germinally or somatically in bilateral or unilateral disease, respectively,[59] thereby fulfilling criterion number 3. The H3-8 probe was used to isolate overlapping larger segments of DNA, and a unique sequence subfragment of one of these was used as a hybridization probe for RNA samples from retinal cells, retinoblastomas and osteosarcomas.[60] A single transcript of 4.7 kb was identified and cloned as a complementary DNA. When this cDNA was used to determine genomic organization and transcription patterns in tumor and normal tissues, two provocative findings arose. First, in some cases deletions that were entirely contained within the locus were observed. Second, an RNA transcript which was not apparent in retinoblastoma or osteosarcoma tumors was detected in retinal cells and several other tissues. These results have been extended by two other groups,[61,62] and transcripts of aberrant size were identified in tumors of normal genomic structure. Furthermore, the protein product encoded by this gene has been identified as a 110-kDa phosphoprotein with DNA binding ability, which varies in amount coordinately with the normality of genomic or transcript structure.[63] As described above, these observations satisfy the physical criteria required to identify the *RB1* locus. As in all cases of "reverse genetics," however, proof of its identity requires biochemical and functional analysis. The nature of this gene and the effect its elimination has on oncogenesis is as yet unclear, but its isolation is another example of the power of this approach to gene identification through physical and genetic mapping.

Prenatal Diagnosis. Advantage has been taken of the increasingly precise molecular elucidation of genomic alterations in retinoblastoma tumors to provide conceptual and methological approaches to the assignment of disease risk likelihood.[64,65] These methods are either indirect and linkage-based[64] or direct[65] in detection of genetic defects.

The first approach uses polymorphic restriction fragment length alleles as linkage markers to deduce genotypes at the *RB1* locus in children of retinoblastoma gene carriers. This method takes advantage of neutral DNA sequence variation in the population, which results in the variable presence of bacterial restriction endonuclease recognition sites at loci on chromosome 13. This approach has three major limitations. First, most of the loci identified by restriction fragment length polymorphism[50,51] are genetically distant from the *RB1* locus,[66] and consequently the reliability of the method is reduced by the occurrence of meiotic recombination. Second, the population frequencies of alleles of these loci are such that only a fraction of families are informative. Third, the method requires an affected parent and a first child to define haplotypic phase. Therefore, analysis has been restricted to nuclear families where informative allelic combinations can be discerned at loci flanking the *RB1* locus.

The family described in Fig. 9-10 illustrates how parental haplotypes of chromosome 13 can be deduced through the analysis of the parents and an affected first child. In this example, the first child (II-1) has inherited the predisposition for retinoblastoma (Fig. 9-10*B*) and the longer alleles at the 7F12 and 9D11 loci (Fig. 9-10*A*) from his affected father. The fetus (II-2) however, inherited the alternative chromosome 13, which carried the shorter alleles at the 7F12 and 9D11 loci. Since the 7F12 and 9D11 loci flank the *RB1* locus at recombination distances of approximately 12 and 30 percent, respectively, the fetus will have inherited the predisposition for retinoblastoma only if two meiotic crossovers had occurred between these two loci. The risk estimate for the development of retinoblastoma by this child arises from the conjoint probability of two such crossing-over events. Since the parental haplotype was inferred from the first child, these risk estimates must also consider crossovers in both children, giving a joint probability of 84 percent that the second child will not develop retinoblastoma. At age 2 years this child showed no signs of the disease, in accord with such a prediction.

To date, we have examined 13 families in which retinoblastoma was an inherited disease[64] (unpublished results). Four families were uninformative for RFLP analysis, thus precluding prediction. One family was identified as carrying a translocation of the region containing the *RB1* locus, such that members who inherited the unbalanced translocation developed disease whereas members who inherited the balanced translocation were unaffected carriers. Finally, seven cases were informative and correctly diagnosed, while one child was predicted as 70 percent likely to develop disease but has remained disease free.

These families illustrate the major limitations of this method at present. First, chromosome 13 haplotypes cannot be determined in the carrier parent unless there is either one affected grandparent or one previously affected child or the first unaffected child has passed the age of developing retinoblastoma, which is 7 years or more. Second, there is a small chance that gene carriers will remain unaffected due to the somewhat less than absolute penetrance of these predisposing mutations. Last, relatively few and incompletely informative markers for chromosome 13 have been isolated to date, and these markers are not tightly linked to the *RB1* locus. Resultant risk esti-

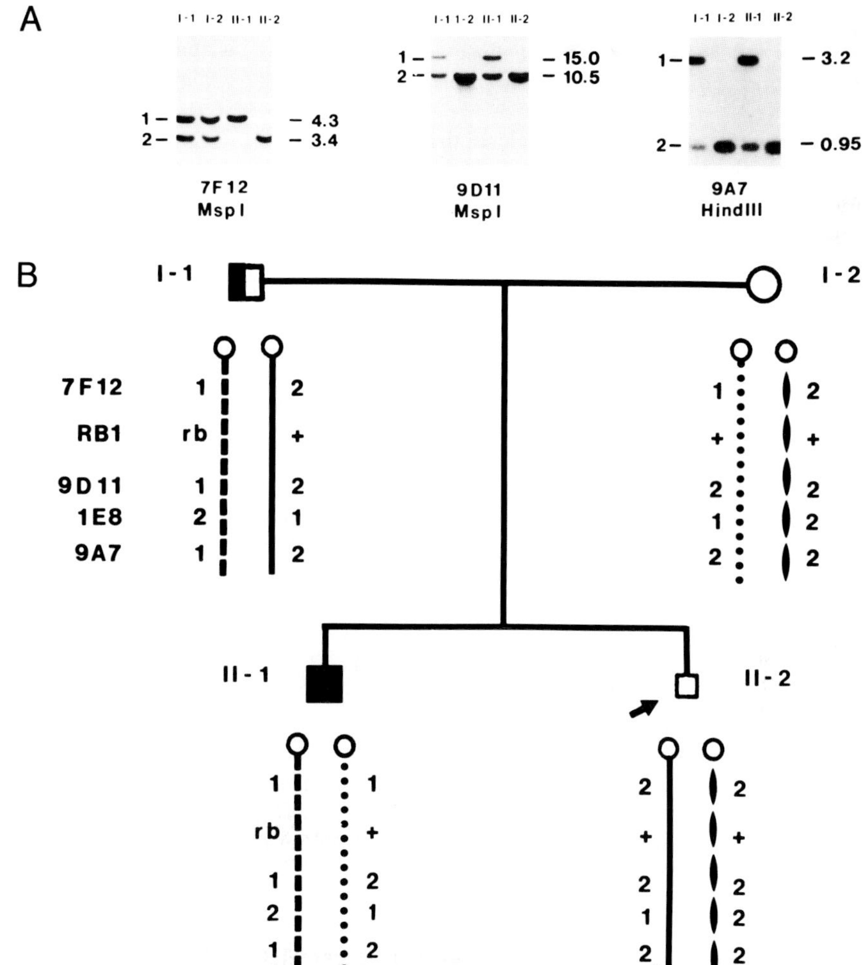

Fig. 9-10 Pedigree of a familial retinoblastoma case that shows no evidence of meiotic recombination. Closed symbols = bilaterally affected family members; half-closed symbols = unilaterally affected members; open symbols = unaffected members. Arrows indicate the family member for whom diagnosis before illness was performed; the indications of the presence or absence of disease are based on subject's status at their most recent ophthalmic examination. Inferred alleles at the retinoblastoma (*RB1*) locus are designated "rb" for a mutant allele and "+" for a wild-type allele. The circles with vertical lines below them that are shown under each family-member symbol represent the member's two constitutional chromosome 13 homologues. The numbers beside each chromosome symbol represent the allelic form of each locus. The vertical order of loci within each family is the same as that shown under the symbol for its I-1 member. The data illustrate the power of information about a first child in discriminating which chromosome a second child has inherited from the affected parent. *(Reprinted by permission of the* New England Journal of Medicine, *vol. 314, pp. 1201–1207, 1986.)*

mates are much less precise than desired and in only very few cases can clinical decisions be based solely on these analyses at present. Most of these limitations can be minimized if several highly informative and closely linked markers were isolated. The first steps to attaining this situation have recently been accomplished. The isolation of a cDNA for the closely linked gene, esterase D, has been reported,[67,68] and this probe detects an RFLP with better allele frequencies than the protein polymorphism at the same locus. Furthermore a set of genomic probes has been isolated from within the region of the proposed retinoblastoma locus and which recognize highly polymorphic sites.[69] These and other markers currently being isolated may provide more reliable premorbid determination of predisposition to retinoblastoma.

Clearly, the most desirable situation in this regard would be the ability to directly determine the gene defect in individual retinoblastoma cases. This is particularly important for counseling families with a single case of bilateral retinoblastoma since, in most instances, linkage-based analysis can be used only if there is more than one affected family member. There is a similar need for direct determination of mutations of the *RB1* locus in cases of sporadic unilateral retinoblastoma; such patients constitute more than 50 percent of all retinoblastoma cases, and about 10 percent of these carry germline mutations. One possible approach that has been used to detect submicroscopic deletions is quantitative DNA hybridization with two different markers, one outside the 13q14 region and one closely linked to the *RB1* locus.[65] Furthermore, it is possible that the recently isolated retinoblastoma gene probe[60–62] can be used to generate a set of markers capable of detecting germline mutations in the *RB1* locus. However, structural heterogeneity of the predisposing mutations in retinoblastoma gene carriers may preclude such approaches, and as for other inherited disorders, we may yet have to rely on linkage-based analyses for genetic counseling purposes.

Wilms Tumor

Clinical. Nephroblastoma is the most common intrabdominal neoplasm of childhood with an incidence of about 1 in 10,000 livebirths.[70] These renal tumors can be congenitally apparent, and 90 percent of diagnoses are made in children under the age of 7 years. The most common symptoms at presentation are abdominal masses, acute abdominal pain, hematuria, fever, anorexia, vomiting, and malaise.[71] Treatment of Wilms tumor has been dramatically effective, and the survival of affected children has increased from 10 percent in 1938 to greater than 90 percent at present.[72] This success has been achieved primarily through the use of combined modality therapy, including surgery and combination chemotherapy and radiotherapy. As with most pediatric tumors, extent of disease at the time of diagnosis is one of the strongest prognostic indicators, and thus early detection is crucial to successful management. Clinical staging of the disease relies on the extent to which the tumor is confined as well histopathologic features and has proven reliable in prediction of disease course.[73]

Wilms tumors are generally considered to arise from embryonic metanephric blastema,[74] a tissue which is no longer present at about 30 weeks of gestation. However, since most tumors are not congenitally apparent, it has been proposed[75] that the tumors actually derive from foci of metanephric precursors which can persist postnatally as hamartomatous lesions.

An increased association of aniridia in patients with Wilms tumor was first demonstrated in 1964.[76] Since that time, a chromosome deletion syndrome comprising Wilms tumor, aniridia, genitourinary tract abnormalities, growth retardation, and variable mental retardation has been well documented.[6,77]

Genetics. Although most Wilms tumors occur as sporadic cases, two classes of observation suggest a genetic component in the etiology of the disease. The first is that several families have been described in which more than one member has developed this rare disease.[78,79] An extensive analysis of 24 such kindreds[80] revealed an inheritance pattern consistent with an autosomal dominant Mendelian trait, albeit with reduced penetrance and variable expressivity. A large number of Wilms tumor cases of unilateral, bilateral, and familial presentation have been analyzed for various parameters[81] in the same manner discussed above for retinoblastoma.[27,31] These analyses suggested a two-step model for carcinogenesis involving two postzygotic events in nonhereditary cases and one germinal and one postzygotic event in heritable cases. Alternative hypotheses have been put forth as well to explain the apparent lack of penetrance and variable expressivity discussed above, which include host resistance, delayed mutation, and multiallelism. In any case, the hallmark features of heritable disease are multifocal tumors, bilateral involvement, and early ascertainment.

The second suggestion of a heritable component in the development of Wilms tumor arises from the congenital malformations with which it is frequently associated. These include genitourinary anomalies such as cryptorchidism, hypospadias, and fusion kidneys[82]; hemiphypertrophy[83]; and aniridia.[76,84] Additionally, Wilms tumor is apparent with a high incidence in children with the Beckwith-Wiedemann Syndrome, which also encompasses hemihypertrophy as one of its features.[85] The causal relationship between these congenital malformations and tumor formation in embryonal kidney is unknown. However, the significant association of nodular renal blastema or nephroblastomatosis with frank Wilms tumor and, in turn, its association with developmental anomalies[75,78,82–84] may have profound implications for understanding the mechanism whereby this tumor develops.

Cytogenetics. As discussed in the preceding section for retinoblastoma, the idea that Wilms tumor has a genetic component in its etiology has been strongly supported by direct examination of the chromosomes from constitutional and tumor cells from affected children. The first suggestion of the chromosomal localization for a locus playing a role in the genesis of nephroblastoma was provided by the identification of a constitutional deletion of chromosome 11, band p13.[6] The careful evaluation of many such cases[86–90] has solidified this proposal. In patients demonstrating the aniridia/Wilms tumor complex (including growth and mental retardation and genitourinary abnormalities), 41 of 43 showed a visible deletion of 11p13 by high resolution cytogenetic analysis.[89,90] Furthermore, a family has been described in which a portion of chromosome 11 including the p13 band was carried as a balanced insertional translocation in unaffected members, whereas all members who inherited a deleted chromosome 11 without coinheritance of the reciprocal chromosome developed Wilms tumor.[91] These latter cases provide strong support for the involvement of the 11p13 region in the disease and also suggest the necessity for removal of the locus rather than positional inactivation in order for neoplastic activity to occur.

The aforementioned identification of specific constitutional deletions of 11p13 in Wilms tumor patients suggests the involvement of a locus contained therein for predisposition of high risk individuals. More direct evidence that such a locus is involved in tumor development has been provided through the ascertainment of similar chromosomal abnormalities in direct preparations of Wilms tumor cells.[92,93] The concordance of constitutional and tumor-specific genomic alteration strongly suggests their etiologic involvement. The notion that persistence of blastemal elements in postnatal kidney may serve as the precursor lesion for Wilms tumor has also gained support by demonstrating a somatic deletion of chromosome 11p in a specimen of nodular renal blastema.[94]

Molecular Genetics. It should be emphasized that, although cytogenetically visible chromosome 11 deletions have been identified in several patients, for the most part these have been in sporadic cases associated with aniridia. Since aniridia can also be apparent without Wilms tumor, the relatively large genomic deletions must encompass several loci. That a specific locus for aniridia exists at 11 p13 is supported by two families with aniridia, but without Wilms tumor, segregating with balanced translocations involving a break in 11p13 in each case.[95,96] Furthermore, deletions have been observed in only a small proportion of cases. By analogy to the retinoblastoma model,[27,28,31,47] it might be anticipated that the attainment of homozygous defectiveness at the "Wilms tumor locus" would involve more subtle chromosomal malsegregation or recombination events.

The identification of patients with various size deletions of chromosome 11 has allowed for regional mapping of DNA probes for loci which lie on this chromosome.[97,98] Genes localized to this region include the enzyme catalase and the β subunit of follicle stimulating hormone (FSHB).[98] Although catalase deficiency has been reported in patients with visible 11p13 deletions, it has not been useful in demonstration of submicroscopic deletions in patients with normal chromosomes.[99] Although it has been speculated that FSHB deficiency in 11p might be related to the genitourinary tract abnormalities in males, this has not been documented. Through comparison of patients with different overlapping deletions, the most likely gene order on 11p has been summarized as: centromere-catalase-Wilms tumor-aniridia-FSHB-telomere.[98,99]

Since many loci in this region of 11p exhibit restriction site variation, a comparison of constitutional and tumor genotypes could be made in the manner described for retinoblastoma.[47,53] A compilation of data from several groups[100–103] indicated that about 65 percent of Wilms tumors had, in fact, attained homozygosity for chromosome 11p in ways which were mechanistically similar to those for chromosome 13 in retinoblastoma.

An example of these analyses is shown in Fig. 9-11. Furthermore, these events took chromosomal forms which included loss, loss and duplication, and somatic recombination[104] as had been shown for retinoblastoma tumors. Whether the chromosomes becoming homozygous in the tumors are, in fact, those carrying the mutant allele has not been shown because of the rarity of Wilms tumor families. Indeed, one report indicated a nonrandom loss of the maternal chromosome 11 in a small series of tumors,[105] suggesting a possible role for gametic origin and perhaps genome imprinting in tumorigenesis. The definition of these mechanisms in tumors as well as the ascertainment of small overlapping sets of chromosomal deletions is now setting the stage for the isolation of an increasingly large set of DNA segments with close proximity to the presumed locus.[98,106] Such probes should serve well in the molecular isolation of the Wilms tumor gene(s) by methodologies which have been useful for other diseases[16,17,60–62] and hold much promise for a molecular understanding of this neoplasm.

Beckwith-Wiedemann Syndrome

Clinical. The combination of macroglossia, exomphalos, and visceromegaly has been designated the Beckwith-Wiedemann syndrome.[107,108] Several other organismal abnormalities have been described as well including fetal adrenocortial cytomegaly, hypoglycemia due to pancreatic islet hyperplasia, transverse linear creases of the ear lobule, hemihypertrophy, and accelerated osteos maturation. Additionally, infants with this syndrome also are at particularly high risk for the development of Wilms tumors, adrenal cortical carcinomas, hepatoblastomas, and rhabdomyosarcomas, cumulatively estimated at between 5 and 20 percent.[109–113] Clinical management of children with this syndrome generally entails surgical repair of the omphalocele and partial resection of the tongue to lessen occlusion of the respiratory tract, pharmacologic management of the hypoglycemia, and frequent examination for the possibility of abdominal tumors.

Genetics. Although most cases of Beckwith-Wiedemann syndrome are sporadic, several instances of apparent autosomal dominant inheritance have been described,[114–116] albeit with reduced penetrance and variable expressivity. Additionally, many of the morphologic manifestations of renal dysplasia, Wilms tumor, and fetal gigantism common to the Beckwith-Wiedemann syndrome also occur in the Perlman syndrome, which may be transmitted as an autosomal recessive trait.[117] Of particular interest to the formal mode of inheritance is the report of a set of monzygotic twins, one of whom was entirely normal while the other had bilateral renal dysplasia, macroglossia, hypoglycemia, and hemihypertrophy.[118] Such a case would argue for a multifactorial cause of the syndrome involving the interaction of predisposing mutations and the fetal environment.

Cytogenetics. Cytogenetic examinations of constitutional cells from children with Beckwith-Wiedemann syndrome (BWS) has sometimes shown structural abnormalities of chromosome

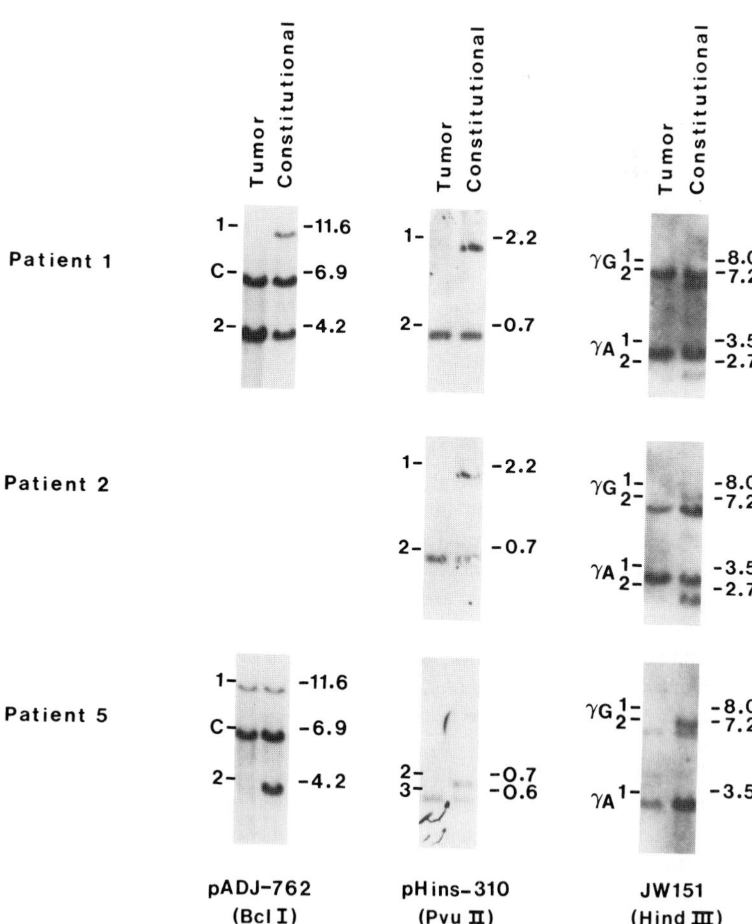

Fig. 9-11 Loss of heterozygosity at loci on human chromosome 11p in three cases of Wilms tumor. DNA from paired tissues was digested to completion with the indicated restriction endonuclease, subjected to agarose gel electrophoresis, transferred to membranes and hybridized to the ^{32}P-labeled nick translated probes pADJ762, pHins-310, or JW151. Each tumor was obtained prior to any therapy. Alleles at each locus are designated 1, 2, or 3, according to decreasing length; C indicates a common, invariant band. Numbers to the right of each autoradiograph indicate the molecular size of the indicated allele in kilobases, derived from standards run with each gel. *(Reprinted by permission from* Nature*, vol. 309, p. 170, copyright 1984, Macmillan Journals, Limited.)*

11. Although this is reminiscent of the alterations seen in Wilms tumor patients as described above, the best described are not only deletions. Rather, they entail one patient with a partial duplication of the chromosome 11p13-p15 region,[119] three patients with duplication of 11p15 region only,[119,120] as well as one patient each with deletion of the 11p11-p13 portion[121] or the 11p11 region.[122] In a high resolution cytogenetic survey of BWS, Pettenati et al.[123] failed to find any abnormality of chromosome 11 in 19 patients, suggesting that visible chromosome 11 abnormalities represent a minority of cases. The significance of these observations is unclear at present, however they do implicate the short arm of chromosome 11 as a likely location for at least one of the genes involved in the Beckwith-Wiedemann syndrome.

Molecular Genetics. Although the molecular analysis of the Beckwith-Wiedemann syndrome is yet at an early stage, several potentially relevant findings have been reported. Perhaps the most robust are analyses of a subset of the tumors associated with the syndrome. As discussed above, a comparison of genotypes obtained in normal and Wilms tumor tissues (but from patients without the syndrome) indicated an attainment of homozygosity for a mutant allele(s) on chromosome 11p.[100–103] Similar analyses of hepatoblastomas such as those shown in Fig. 9-12 and rhabdomyosarcomas such as those in Fig. 9-13 (from children with or without hemihypertrophy) demonstrated that the same chromosomal mechanisms were operative in these latter two tumor types as well.[124] Whether these events encompass alternative manifestations of the mutation eliciting the organismal phenotype, or represent the homozygously defective phenotype whereas the heterozygote appears as the Beckwith-Wiedemann syndrome, or whether the frequency of chromosomal malsegregation is enhanced by the primary Beckwith-Wiedemann abnormality are possibilities which will be addressed through enhanced resolution molecular cytogenetics.

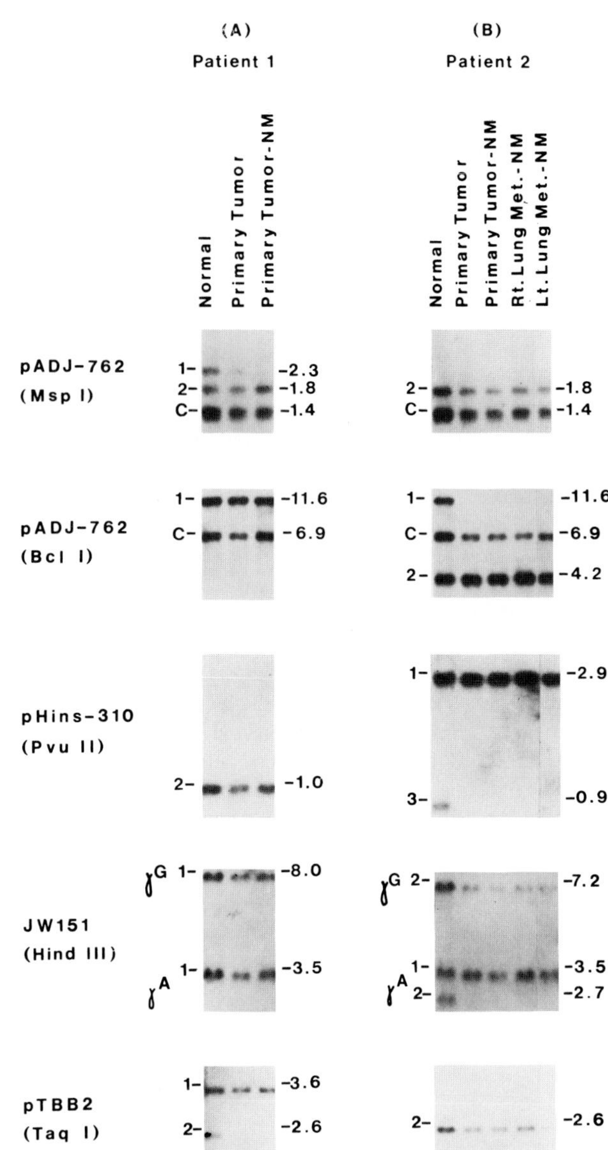

Fig. 9-12 Loss of constitutional heterozygosity at loci on human chromosome 11p in hepatoblastoma: A. Patient 1. B. Patient 2. DNA was isolated from normal tissue (peripheral leukocytes), surgical specimens of primary tumor, or a xenograft of the primary tumor passaged twice in immunodeficient nude mice (NM), as described previously. DNA was also isolated from xenograft tumors derived from right and left lung metastases (passages 3 and 1, respectively) removed from patient 2 following thorocotomy and wedge resection to remove metastatic hepatoblastoma nodules. DNA from each of these tissues was digested to completion with the indicated restriction endonucleases, subjected to agarose gel electrophoresis, and transferred. The membranes were prehybridized and then hybridized to four recombinant DNA probes physically homologous to loci unique to the subregion p15 of the short arm of human chromosome 11, reveal restriction fragment length polymorphisms, and exhibit close genetic linkage. Alleles at each locus are designated 1 or 2 according to decreasing length; C indicates a common, invariant band. Numbers to the right of each autoradiograph indicate the molecular size of the indicated allele in kilobases, derived from the standards run with each gel. *(Reprinted by permission from* Nature, *vol. 316, pp. 330–334, copyright 1985, Macmillan Journals, Limited.)*

Prader-Willi Syndrome

Clinical. The Prader-Willi syndrome (PWS) was first described in 1956.[125] In phase I, it is characterized by severe muscular hypotonia and poor suck at birth, usually requiring gavage feeding. Males usually have undescended testes and females hypoplastic labia. At 2 to 3 years of age patients enter phase 2, characterized by hyperphagia, with an insatiable appetite leading to obesity unless caloric intake is strictly reduced. These patients gain weight on relatively restricted diets and maintain normal weight at about 60 percent of normal caloric intake. A characteristic facial appearance is present including a narrow bitemporal diameter, almond shaped eyes, upslanting palpebral fissures, and strabismus. Other physical features include short stature, small hands and feet, and fair hair and skin color (hypopigmentation) relative to other family members. Excellent reviews of the clinical features and diagnostic criteria for PWS have been published by Holm[126] and Cassidy.[127]

All individuals with PWS have some degree of cognitive dysfunction, with a wide range of formal IQ test scores. In fact, as many as 40 percent may test in the normal or borderline normal IQ range, with the remainder testing in the mildly to moderately retarded range. Academic performance is, however, generally poor relative to IQ, with mathematics a significant weakness, while reading skills are generally good. Significant behavioral abnormalities are present, including stubbornness, temper tantrums, and poor peer interactions. The behavioral and emotional problems frequently require psychiatric intervention. Because of their intellectual limita-

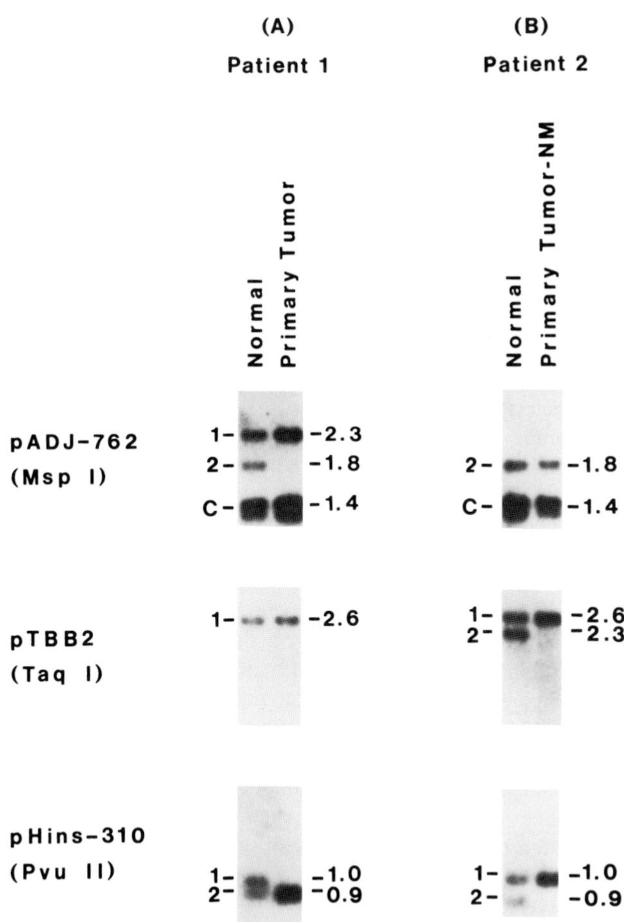

Fig. 9-13 Loss of constitional heterozygosity at loci on human chromosome 11p in rhabdomyosarcoma: *A*. Patient 1. *B*. Patient 2. *A*. Normal tissue DNA was isolated from peripheral leukocytes and tumor DNA isolated directly from the primary tumor specimen obtained at surgery. *B*. Normal tissue DNA was isolated from peripheral leukocytes; tumor DNA was isolated from a first passage xenograft of the primary tumor (NM). Alleles at each locus are designated 1 or 2 according to decreasing length; C indicates a common, invariant band. Numbers to the right of each autoradiograph indicate the molecular size of the indicated allele in kilobases, derived from standards run with each gel. *(Reprinted by permission from* Nature, *vol. 316, pp. 330–334, copyright 1985, Macmillan Journals, Limited.)*

tions, behavioral and emotional abnormalities, and requirement for close supervision of food intake, most PWS adults require supervised living arrangements and sheltered employment.

Prader-Willi syndrome can be diagnosed at birth based on the severe hypotonia, hypogenitalism, and slight facial dysmorphism. Chromosome studies (see "Cytogenetics") may serve to confirm the clinical diagnosis. However, at present, the diagnosis is more typically made well after the onset of phase 2 when hyperphagia and obesity are present. The frequency of PWS is estimated at 50 to 100 cases per million births,[126] making it the most common of the microdeletion syndromes and one of the most common recognizable syndromes seen in genetics clinics.

Genetics. Autosomal recessive and autosomal dominant modes of inheritance had been ascribed to PWS prior to the finding of a chromosome deletion in most patients.[128] In the great majority of cases, the condition is sporadic. Documented familial cases are few, although one family with three affected sibs with normal chromosomes[129] and a second family with multiple affected individuals on the basis of a familial translocation[130] are known. On the basis of only one familial recurrence with normal karyotype, Cassidy[131] estimated the recurrence risk for PWS as less than 1/1000.

Cytogenetics. Hawkey and Smithies[7] first suggested a correlation between rearrangements of chromosome 15 and PWS. This was based on their own patient with a 15;15 Robertsonian translocation (see Fig. 9-2) and a review of the literature showing several other instances of translocations involving chromosome 15. They postulated that loss of the short arm of chromosome 15 was the critical event in PWS and that chromosome abnormalities might be involved in as many as 10 percent of all PWS cases.

These cases of gross translocations of chromosome 15, observed by routine cytogenetic methods, led to the first high resolution investigation of chromosome 15 in PWS patients in 1981. In this study, Ledbetter et al.[132,133] found that greater than 50 percent of all patients had a very small, interstitial deletion of proximal 15q (Fig. 9-2). A recent tabulation of nine high resolution chromosome surveys of PWS patients shows that 63 percent have a visible abnormality of chromosome 15, the great majority being *de novo* interstitial deletions and a smaller number due to *de novo* unbalanced translocations deleting essentially the same segment.[134] It has been hypothesized, but not yet proven, that submicroscopic deletions in proximal 15q may account for at least a portion of the remaining 37 percent of cases.

There are several interesting features of the chromosome 15 abnormalities associated with PWS which make it a challenge to understand at the cytogenetic and molecular levels. First, it is an extremely common cytogenetic abnormality. If PWS occurs at a frequency of approximately 10^{-4}, and a visible deletion is present in over half of all cases, the frequency of this cytogenetic abnormality is approximately 0.5×10^{-4}. The deletion of 5p associated with the cri cu chat syndrome, with a frequency estimated at 20 per million births,[135] is generally considered the most common deletion syndrome in humans but may not be as common as the 15q deletion of PWS. Second, studies using chromosomal polymorphisms have shown that nearly all the *de novo* deletions found in PWS are paternal in origin.[136,137] Third, in a small percentage of PWS patients, duplications, rather than deletions, of this region of chromosome 15 are found. These have occurred as tandem duplication, resulting in three copies of the critical region[138] and as additional marker chromosomes in the form of dicentric inverted duplication chromosomes, producing four copies of the critical region.[139] This is a unique circumstance in human cytogenetics that trisomy and tetrasomy of a chromosomal region produce the same phenotype as monosomy.

This high frequency and variability in cytogenetic findings in PWS is unique, and suggests a high degree of chromosomal instability in this region. Some investigators have even proposed that the chromosomal abnormalities observed are a characteristic feature of PWS rather than its cause.[140] This seems highly unlikely since only one homologue is affected in any individual patient and somatic mosaicism is rarely observed.

Not only are cytogenetic findings variable, but clinical manifestations of 15q deletions are also quite variable. A number of patients with proximal 15q deletions, apparently identical with that seen in PWS at a cytogenetic level, have been reported who exhibit few or none of the classic features of PWS.[141,142] Even more striking are recent reports of a proximal 15q deletion in one patient with Williams syndrome[143] and four patients with Angelman syndrome.[143,144] One can only hypothesize that some submicroscopic difference exists in the size or position of the deletion, which affects a different combination of contiguous genes located on 15q. Molecular characterization of this region should be valuable for understanding several dysmorphology syndromes.

Molecular Genetics. A novel approach to the isolation of cloned DNA sequences specific to proximal 15q has been taken by Latt and coworkers.[145,146] Chromosome 15 is one of the few human chromosomes that does not resolve well as a unique peak by flow cytometry, usually cosegregating with the similar size chromosome 14. This makes it difficult to generate a recombinant DNA library specific for 15 from normal human cells. Lalande et al.[145]overcame this problem by flow sorting an abnormal chromosome 15, an inverted duplication 15 marker chromosome. Since this small chromosome contains only the short arm and proximal long arm region of 15 (Fig. 9-14*A*), sorting and cloning of this chromosome greatly enriches for sequences from the PWS critical region. Using this strategy, Donlon et al.[146] were successful in obtaining a purified fraction of inv dup(15) chromosomes (Fig. 9-14*B*) and constructed *Hind*III libraries in the lambda phage vector Charon 21A. Eight of twleve chromosome 15-specific probes isolated from this library were shown to map to the region 15q11-q13 and were further tested in dosage analysis of PWS patients. Four of the eight probes were shown to be deleted in a patient with the classic cytogenetic deletion of 15q, making them potentially useful in diagnostic studies. However, none of the four was deleted in a PWS patient with a smaller than usual deletion of 15q. Consequently, at present there is no molecular confirmation of submicroscopic deletions in PWS patients, although larger numbers of probes from this region can be tested by the same strategy initiated by these investigators.

Miller-Dieker Syndrome

Clinical. Miller-Dieker Syndrome (MDS) is a multiple malformation syndrome characterized by type I lissencephaly and a characteristic facial appearance.[147–149] Lissencephaly is a severe brain malformation whereby the typical convolutions (gyri and sulci) are absent and the brain surface is smooth (Fig. 9-15*B* and *C*); type I refers to the classic form with a four-layered cortex. The specific sequelae of lissencephaly include bitemporal hollowing, a small jaw, and neurologic abnormalities.[150] In addition to the brain abnormalities, a characteristic facial appearance is present, which includes midface hypoplasia, a broad nasal bridge, a short nose with upturned nares, a long, thin upper lip, and malformed or malpositioned ears (Fig. 9-15*A*). Other physical findings include abnormal palmar creases, cryptorchidism, and sacral dimples. Severe postnatal growth retardation and seizures are also present. Various additional anomalies have been observed in patients with unbalanced translocations, presumably due to tirsomy for other autosomal segments involved in the rearrangements.

Genetics. MDS was initially considered an autosomal recessive disorder based on the occurrence of several families with multiple affected sibs.[149] Subsequently, it was shown that

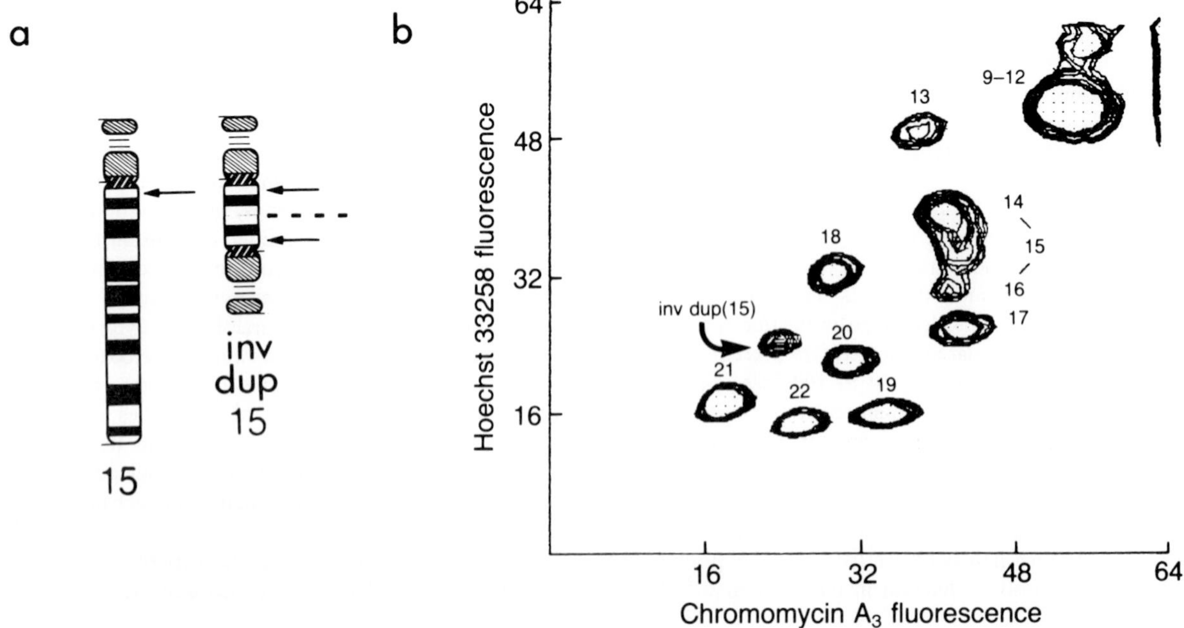

Fig. 9-14 Strategy for cloning DNA sequences specific to Prader-Willi syndrome (PWS) critical region. (a) An idiogram of chromosome 15 is shown to the left with an arrow indicating band q11.2, the critical band deleted in most PWS patients. To the right is an inverted duplication 15, with the dotted line indicating the breakpoint. To either side of the dotted line is an identical copy of the short arm and proximal long arm of chromosome 15 with arrows indicating the presence of two copies of the critical band, q11.2. Therefore, this small chromosome contains two copies of the critical region and little other unique DNA sequences. (b) Flow histogram of this patient's cell line indicating that the normal chromosome 15 overlaps with chromosome 14 and 16 peaks, but the inverted duplication chromosome is distinctly separated from the other small human chromosomes. Sorting of this peak allowed for purification and cloning of a highly enriched library for the PWS critical region.[146] *(b from Donlon et al.,* [146] *with permission)*

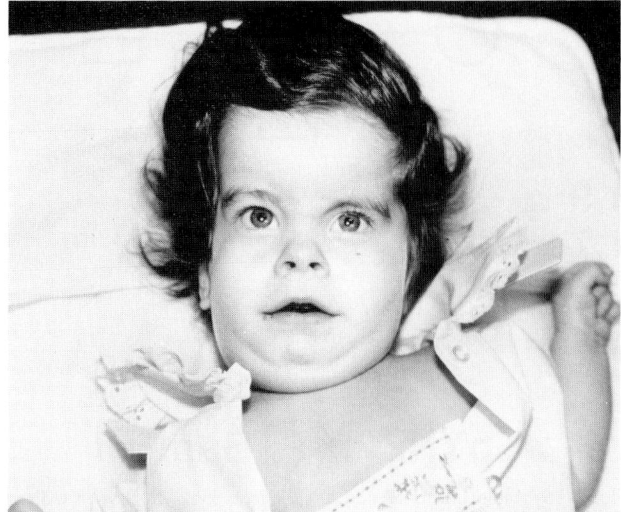

A.

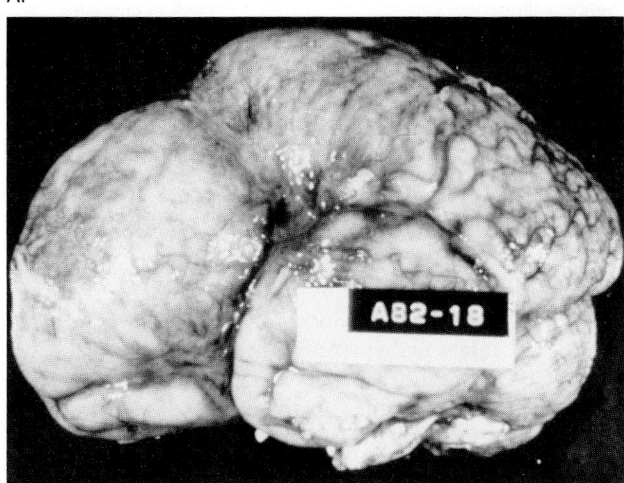

C.

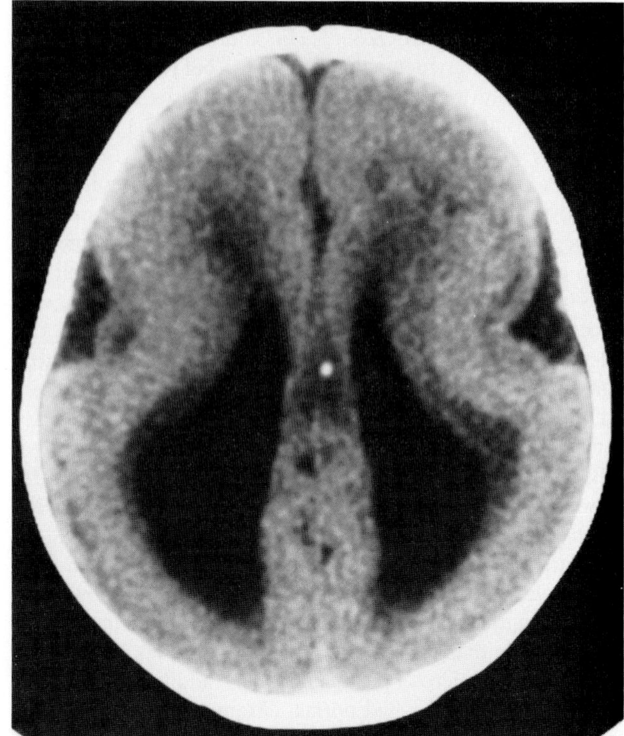

B.

Fig. 9-15 Clinical features of the Miller-Dieker syndrome (MDS). A. MDS patient at 18 months. *(From Dobyns et al.*[9] *Used by permission* of Journal of Pediatrics.) *B.* CT scan in MDS patient showing type I lissencephaly with smooth cerebral surface, figure eight shape, smooth subsurface line separating cortex and white matter, midline calcification, and colpocephaly. *C.* Lateral view of brain from MDS patient showing widespread lissencephaly with a few abortive sulci. *(Courtesy of Dr. J. A. Minielly.)*

most of the known familial cases are due to a parental balanced translocation or pericentric inversion.[151,152] A minority of cases show normal karyotypes and, unless submicroscopic deletions can be documented (see "Molecular Genetics," below), autosomal recessive inheritance cannot be ruled out. Autosomal recessive inheritance seems most likely for the single consanguineous family with the Norman-Roberts lissencephaly syndrome and may be one of the etiologies for isolated lissencephaly sequence.[150]

Cytogenetics. The first observation of a chromosome abnormality in MDS was case 1 of Dobyns et al.[9] The patient was found to have a ring chromosome 17 by routine chromosome analysis (Fig. 9-3), which presumably deleted a very small portion of distal 17p and distal 17q. Subsequently, high-resolution analysis showed very subtle *de novo* deletions (Fig. 9-3) or familial translocations involving distal 17p, band p13, in an additional seven cases and normal karyotypes in three cases[9,151,152] (unpublished data). This high frequency of abnormality is probably biased by selected inclusion of familial cases.

Prior to the discovery of a chromosomal basis for MDS, patients were counseled that it was an autosomal recessive condition with a 25 percent recurrence risk and that no method of prenatal diagnosis was available. Of the cases reported with cytogenetic abnormalities, examples exist of *de novo* terminal deletions, ring chromosomes, and inherited unbalanced products of parental translocations and pericentric inversions.[151,152] For *de novo* abnormalities, families can be reassured that recurrence risk is negligible and prenatal diagnosis is not indicated. The finding of a parental translocation or inversion, however, suggests a significant recurrence risk, but prenatal diagnosis by chorion villus sampling or amniocentesis can be offered and has led to the first successful prenatal diagnosis of MDS by cytogenetic analysis following amniocentesis.[151]

The size of the deletion in these patients has varied from the largest involving most of band p13 (case 5, Ref. 151) to the ring chromosome patient in which the deletion is confined to within subband p13.3.[9] The latter is estimated to represent a molecular size smaller than 2×10^6 bp. There is no apparent difference in clinical manifestation among patients with different size deletions. This suggests that a small number of genes mapping within the smallest visible deletion are responsible for the severe brain defect and other characteristic physical findings of MDS. Phenotype variability among patients is largely due to additional features found in patients with unbalanced translocations producing trisomic segments for other autosomal regions.

Molecular Genetics. A large number of cloned genes and anonymous DNA segments are now known to map to human chromosome 17.[153] Several genes have been localized to the distal short arm of chromosome 17, including myosin heavy chain (MYH2), the tumor antigen p53 (TP53), and RNA polymerase II (RNAPO2A).[154] In addition, several highly polymorphic anonymous clones of the VNTR type (variable number tandem repeat)[155] have been mapped by linkage analysis to distal 17p. These include pYNZ22.1 (D17S5), pYNH37.3 (D17S28), and pMCT35.1 (D17S31) (Y. Nakamura, P. O'Connell, and R. White, personal communication).

Analyses utilizing these cloned genes and anonymous probes has been carried out to determine whether they map to the MDS critical region[154,156] (unpublished data). Somatic cell hybrids were constructed between a TK^- mouse cell line and three MDS patients and clones identified which retained the deleted or translocated chromosome 17 bearing the selectable gene thymidine kinase. The abnormal 17s included the largest MDS deletion as well as the smallest visible cytogenetic deletion, the ring chromosome 17.

By Southern analysis, MYH2, TP53, and RNAPO2A showed positive hybridization to DNA from hybrids containing the abnormal 17s from the three MDS patients; i.e., these genes are not deleted and therefore map outside the MDS critical region. Conversely, pYNZ22.1 and pYNH37.3 showed no hybridization signal to any of the three MDS patient hybrids and therefore map within the critical region. To test for the presence of submicroscopic deletions, one additional MDS patient was studied who had normal chromosomes by high resolution analysis. Using restriction fragment length polymorphism (RFLP) analysis, it was shown that the affected male patient had only one allele for pYNZ22.1 inherited from his mother and no paternal allele (Fig. 9-16). Nonpaternity was excluded at a high probability by standard HLA and red cell markers. To confirm this result, the two 17 homologues of this patient were isolated from each other in somatic cell hybrids and clones containing the maternal and paternal homologues distinguished by RFLP analysis. Both pYNZ22.1 and pYNH37.3 showed positive hybridization to hybrids containing the maternal homologue but negative hybridization to hybrids containing the paternal homolog. By RFLP analysis and dosage analysis, a deletion of both probes was similarly demonstrated for a second, unrelated MDS patient with normal chromosomes. Thus, *de novo,* submicroscopic deletions have been demonstrated in two MDS patients. Both informative probes lie within a critical region for MDS of less than 2×10^6 bp (deletion below the limits of cytogenetic resolution).

The two probes should prove useful as diagnostic tools to supplement high resolution cytogenetic analysis. Since they are both highly polymorphic, it will be possible in many cases to identify deletions by demonstration of failure to inherit an allele from one of the two parents (Fig. 9-16). Alternatively, densitometric analysis of Southern blots can be performed to determine dosage as being either normal or showing a 50 percent reduction in hybridization signal intensity for patients with a deletion. However, it should be emphasized that molecular detection of deletions will not substitute for high resolution cytogenetics, since demonstration of a molecular deletion in a proband does not clarify whether a *de novo* deletion or parental translocation event is the causal mechanism.

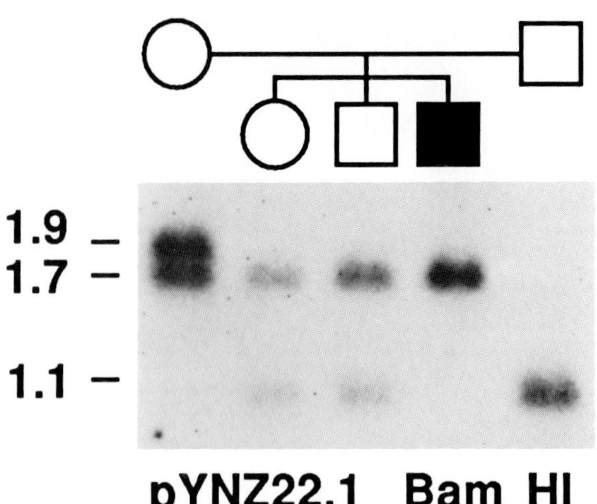

Fig. 9-16 Molecular detection of submicroscopic deletion in Miller-Dieker syndrome (MDS). Pedigree of an affected MDS male (filled square) with normal chromosomes by high resolution analysis. Hybridization to probe pYNZ22.1 showed the mother to be heterozygous for a 1.7- and 1.9-kb allele and the father to be homozygous for a 1.1-kb allele. Both of the two normal children inherited the 1.7-kb band from their mother and the 1.1-kb band from their father. The affected male inherited the 1.7-kb band from his mother but no allele from his father. Thus, a *de novo* paternal deletion which is below the level of high resolution cytogenetic detection is suggested. This result was subsequently confirmed by analysis of somatic cell hybrids of the patient.

DiGeorge Syndrome

Clinical. In 1965, DiGeorge described a patient with hypoparathyroidism and cellular immune deficiency similar to other patients he had seen with absent parathyroids and thymus at autopsy.[157] Since then a number of patients have been reported with absent or hypoplastic thymus and absent or hypoplastic parathyroid, frequently in combination with unusual cardiac malformations (interrupted aortic arch or truncus arteriosis).[158] In fact, congenital heart disease is the most frequent presenting complaint in these patients and has been the major contributor to a high morbidity in the first weeks of life.

Dysmorphic facial features including hypertelorism, cleft lip and palate, bifid uvula, and low-set ears are frequently observed.[158] Other congenital anomalies may include abnormalities of the diaphragm, the eye, and the kidney. Central nervous system abnormalities are also common, and most of the patients who survive infancy are mildly to moderately retarded. The extreme variation in manifestations of this disorder have resulted in controversy as to whether it should be called a syndrome, a sequence, a complex, or a spectrum.[159,160]

Genetics. Most cases of DiGeorge syndrome (DGS) are sporadic, although a number of familial cases are now known. The etiology is likely to be extremely heterogeneous, with chromosomal abnormalities accounting for a significant minority of cases and perhaps most familial cases.

Cytogenetics. A specific association with deletion of the proximal portion of the long arm of chromosome 22 was first proposed in 1981.[8] Two reports of complete monosomy 22 and 12 cases of partial monosomy involving band 22q11 have been published.[161] The majority of the 22q11 monosomy cases are due to unbalanced translocations, several of which involved unbalanced segregation of a parental balanced translocation in multiple affected offspring.

The frequency of chromosome 22 abnormalities in DGS has not been accurately determined. Since most of the reported chromosome abnormalities involve gross translocations detectable by routine cytogenetic analysis, it may be hypothesized that, analogous to Prader-Willi syndrome, high resolution cytogenetic analysis will reveal a much higher frequency of small, interstitial deletions of proximal 22q. However, in the only high resolution survey of DGS patients to date, only three abnormalities (11 percent) of chromosome 22 were found.[161] Two were unbalanced translocations detectable by routine methods, and only one case of a subtle, interstitial deletion detectable only by high resolution methods was found. This represents a frequency much lower than that observed for Prader-Willi syndrome. This could mean that a much smaller deletion is usually involved which cannot be detected even by high resolution analysis. The relatively homogeneous banding pattern characteristic of proximal 22q is such that small deletions in this region would be difficult to demonstrate.

From a review of the literature, it is evident that a number of other chromosomal abnormalities have been associated with DGS, particularly deletions of distal 10p.[161,162] Thus, the etiology of DGS is clearly heterogeneous, but chromosome 22 abnormalities are the single most frequent cause and account for perhaps 10 percent of all cases.

Molecular Genetics. Molecular analysis of DGS patients and their families has recently been reported using an anonymous, polymorphic probe, D22S9, previously isolated and mapped by *in situ* hybridization to 22q11.[163] Fibison and Emanuel[164] studied cell lines from one balanced translocation carrier parent, three unbalanced translocation DGS patients, and several karyotypically normal DGS patients. By *in situ* hybridization, D22S9 was shown to stay on the derivative 22 in the balanced 10;22 translocation carrier; i.e., it maps between the centromere and the break point of the translocation and may be within the critical region for DGS. Southern blot and densitometric analysis of the three unbalanced patient cell lines showed a deletion of D22S9 in all three, further confirming its localization to the DGS critical region and suggesting its usefulness as a diagnostic tool. However, no deletions could be documented in the karyotypically normal DGS patients, so that evidence for a submicroscopic deletion in this region of 22 as a cause of DGS is currently lacking.

Langer-Giedion Syndrome (Trichorhinophalangeal Syndrome Type 2)

Clinical. The association of sparse hair, a characteristic facial appearance including a pear-shaped nose with bulbous tip and tented alae nasi, and cone-shaped phalangeal epiphyses was first described by Giedion in 1966[165] and termed the *trichorhinophalangeal syndrome* (TRP, now referred to as type I). Affected individuals are intellectually normal. In 1969, several groups independently reported patients with features of TRPI, who, in addition, exhibited multiple cartilaginous exostoses and mental retardation, a combination which has become known as the TRPII or the Langer-Giedion syndrome (LGS).[166] Other clinical features of LGS may include microcephaly; large, protruding ears; elongated upper lip; micrognathia; lax skin; and short stature.[166,167] Although mental retardation was originally considered a constant feature, recent reviews have shown that intelligence is extremely variable. Approximately 29 percent of patients show normal or dull normal intelligence, 17 percent are mildly retarded, 40 percent are moderately retarded, and 14 percent are profoundly retarded.[167]

Genetics. TRPI is listed by McKusick[168] under both autosomal recessive and autosomal dominant modes of inheritance, although the latter is unequivocal on the basis of at least five families. Families with multiple cartilaginous exostoses (ME) identical with that seen in LGS have been observed with autosomal dominant transmission.[168] LGS is generally a sporadic condition with the notable exception of a set of twins and one case of an affected father and daughter.[167] It is interesting to note that there is a 3:1 preponderence of affected males to females in the literature.[167]

Cytogenetics. In 1980, Buhler et al.[169] and Pfeiffer[170] reported cases of LGS with *de novo* deletions in the long arm of chromosome 8. Subsequently, at least 18 cases of LGS with deletions of chromosome 8 have been reported.[167,171] After considerable controversy over the exact nature of the deletion and the critical band involved, current consensus places the critical region at subband 8q24.1, with most cases resulting from *de novo* interstitial deletions. In the largest review, only 52 percent of 25 cases had a visible deletion of chromosome 8, the remainder showing apparently normal chromosomes.[167] However, not all these patients had high resolution cytogenetic studies performed, and the frequency of the deletion may therefore be somewhat higher.

A model has developed which suggests that TRPI and ME are individual loci in close proximity to each other on the long arm of chromosome 8, each of which is involved in separate autosomal dominant Mendelian conditions.[168] A location at 8q for TRPI is strongly supported by the finding that two patients with TRPI without exostoses or mental retardation had visible deletions in the same region of 8q as LGS.[172,173] According to this model, LGS represents a deletion of both TRPI and ME, which will usually be detectable by high resolution cytogenetic analysis. The intellectual function in LGS is quite variable and may depend on the exact position and extent of deletion surrounding the TRPI and ME loci. At least one LGS patient has been reported with a visible 8q deletion but normal intelligence.[171]

Molecular Genetics. No linkage studies have yet been reported for TRPI or ME families to confirm their localization to 8q. As far as we are aware, a search for molecular deletions in LGS without microscopically visible chromosome 8 deletions has not been undertaken, although this is feasible given the availability of cloned genes and anonymous DNA segments in that region of 8q.

OTHER CHROMOSOMAL REARRANGEMENTS ASSOCIATED WITH MENDELIAN CONDITIONS

The syndromes discussed to this point are all clinically recognizable entities comprising multiple, unrelated phenotypic features. The cause, at least in a percentage of cases for each disorder, is known to be a deletion of a specific chromosomal region. In the case of retinoblastoma, linkage analysis has demonstrated that the Mendelian form of the disease is located in the same chromosomal region as the microdeletion syndrome. In other cases, a phenotypic feature of the microdeletion syndrome is known to occur as a Mendelian trait (e.g., Wilms tumor, aniridia, TRPI, and ME), but localization of the Mendelian form to the chromosome deletion region has not been proven. Finally, for several of the disorders, no specific Mendelian condition is known, but it is expected that single genes will be discovered in these regions to account for individual phenotypic traits (e.g., lissencephaly in MDS).

Aside from these known cytogenetic syndromes, a number of isolated examples exist in the literature in which Mendelian disorders have been observed in rare patients or families with a visible cytogenetic abnormality. Some of these are balanced translocations, in which it is hypothesized that one of the two break points involved in the translocation has disrupted the gene locus. The supportive evidence is the cosegregation of the translocation and affected status within the family. Other cases involve deletions associated with mental retardation and various phenotypic abnormalities but also include the specific features of a Mendelian disorder.

In several instances, discovery of these rare individuals or families has provided an important clue to the localization of the gene which has subsequently been confirmed by standard linkage analysis. Thus, these rare clinical occurrences have been extremely valuable in the first step of the reverse genetic process of cloning a gene of unknown function, i.e., establishing its position in the genome. In the following sections, we list and briefly review examples of both autosomal and sex chromosome abnormalities associated with Mendelian diseases which have already led or may lead to the localization and eventual cloning of the gene.

Autosomal Translocations and Deletions

A list of 10 different Mendelian conditions that have been associated with an autosomal cytogenetic abnormality is presented in Table 9-3. The majority are disorders usually inherited as autosomal dominant traits in families containing an apparently balanced reciprocal translocation.

One of the most recent examples of the rapid progress from observation of a patient with a gross chromosome abnormality to the confirmation of gene localization is Gardner syndrome (GS), or familial polyposis coli (FPC), localized to chromosome 5. A patient was described with a deletion in the long arm of chromosome 5 who had mental retardation, other congenital abnormalities, and what appeared to be Gardner syndrome.[174] Subsequent analysis with polymorphic loci known to map on 5q revealed that the autosomal dominant GS-FPC locus maps to this region.[175,176] Parallel studies indicate loss of heterozygosity for 5q polymorphic markers in sporadic colorectal adenocarcinomas,[177] apparently supporting the hypothesis that sporadic and inherited forms of the cancer result from mutations at the same locus. However, loss of heterozygosity was observed in only 23 percent of tumors, and other recent data show a higher frequency loss of heterozygosity for 17p markers (>75 percent) in familial and sporadic colon carcinomas.[178]

In the case of von Recklinghausen neurofibromatosis (NF1), linkage was recently established to the pericentromeric and long arm region of chromosome 17 by a random search of polymorphic markers.[179,180] Following publication of this localization, a family with a balanced 1p;17q translocation cosegregating with NF1 was reported.[181] Although a small number of individuals were studied in this family, it is an intriguing hypothesis that the break point at 17q11.2 is within, or very close, to the NF1 gene. This family would therefore serve to refine the physical map position of NF1 and may prove useful in reverse genetics strategies to clone the translocation break point and, thus, the gene.

Renal cell carcinoma (RCC) is rarely familial, but cases of presumed autosomal dominant inheritance have been reported.[168] Additionally, RCC may be associated with the autosomal dominant von Hippel-Lindau disease (McKusick no. 19330). A particularly interesting family with RCC was reported by Cohen et al.[182] In this family, a balanced 3p;8q translocation showed concordant segregation of RCC and the translocation in eight family members. The break points, originally reported as 3p21 and 8q24, have subsequently been revised to 3p14.2 and 8q24.1 by high resolution chromosome analysis.[183]

The chromosome 3 break point appears to coincide with the common fragile site in band p14 and may play a role in the translocation event.[184] Also of interest is the fact that the c-myc oncogene maps to 8q24 and has been shown to move to 3p in the translocation of this family.[185] However, no alterations in the c-myc gene were observed by conventional Southern blot analysis. Recently, Zbar et al.[186] showed loss of heterozygosity for chromosome 3 markers in 11 of 11 informative patients with nonhereditary RCC, supporting the hypothesis that a locus resides in 3p whose recessive mutant allele plays a role in tumor development. Interestingly, small cell carcinoma of the lung (SCLC) has been associated with a specific cytogenetic deletion of 3p[187] and has been shown to have a high frequency of allele loss for 3p polymorphic markers.[188] Thus, by anology to retinoblastoma and osteosarcoma, it seems possible that a single recessive mutation on 3p plays a role in development of histologically distinct tumors. Finally, von Hippel-Lindau disease, which has a high frequency of RCC, was recently mapped to the distal short arm of chromosome 3 by linkage to the RAF1 oncogene.[189] However, crossovers were observed, indicating RAF1 is not the gene itself. Further delineation of the relationship of RCC to von Hippel-Lindau and SCLC can be expected to proceed rapidly.

One of the earliest examples of gene localization by identification of a chromosome rearrangement is that of hereditary spherocytosis, one of the most common forms of dominantly inherited anemia. In 1975, a family was described with a balanced 8p;12p translocation cosegregating with spherocytosis in 11 family members.[190] Although this did not indicate which chromosomal break point was the key event, a second report of a 3p;8p translocation in a mother and son with hereditary spherocytosis strongly suggested a localization of the gene to the proximal short arm of chromosome 8, band p11.[191] More recently, three affected individuals in two families have been reported with mental retardation, multiple congenital anomalies, hereditary spherocytosis, and a small interstitial deletion of 8p11.[192,193] To our knowledge, no linkage studies with chromosome 8 markers has yet been conducted to confirm this probable assignment.

In three other dominant conditions found cosegregating with balanced translocations in single families, no linkage information is yet available to determine which chromosomal break point (if either) represents the location of the gene. These include the Greig polysyndactyly syndrome and t(3p;7p),[194] anterior polar cataracts and t(2p;14q),[195] and the Moebius syndrome and t(1p;13q).[196]

The piebald trait is an autosomal dominant condition consisting of a white forelock and absence of pigmentation in the

Table 9-3 Other Autosomal Translocations/Deletions Associated with Mendelian Disorders

Disease	*Inheritance (McKusick no.)*	*Cytogenetic abnormality*	*Comments*
Gardner syndrome	Dominant (*17520)	del(5)(q13q15 or q15q22)	1 affected individual with severe mental retardation[174]; confirmed by linkage[175,176]
von Recklinghausen neurofibromatosis	Dominant (*16220)	t(1;17)(p34.3;q11)	3 affected individuals,[181] linkage chromosome 17[179,180]
Renal cell carcinoma	Dominant (14470)	t(3;8)(p21;q24)	8 affected individuals[182,183]; loss of heterozygosity 3p[186]
Spherocytosis	Dominant (*18290)	t(8; __)(p11; __)	2 unrelated families, 13 affected individuals[190,191]; 3 additional cases from 2 families with deletion (8) (p11p21)[192,193]
Greig polysyndactyly syndrome	Dominant (*17570)	t(3;7)(p21.2;p13)	6 affected individuals[194]
Anterior polar cataracts	Dominant (*11565)	t(2;14)(p25;q24)	4 affected individuals[195]
Moebius syndrome	Dominant (15790)	t(1;13)(p34;q13)	7 affected individuals[196]
Piebald trait	Dominant (*17280)	del(4q12)	3 unrelated cases with severe mental retardation, overlapping deletions[197]
Tyrosinemia, type II	Recessive (*27660)	del(16)(q22.1q22.3)	*De novo* paternal deletion (visible), inherited maternal deletion (submicroscopic)[198]
Hemoglobin H related mental retardation	Recessive (14175)	del(16p13) (not visible)	4 unrelated cases, *de novo* molecular deletion, inherited α thalassemia mutation[199,200] (Chap. 93)

medial portion of the face, chest, abdomen, and extremities. It is similar to the Waardenburg syndrome (McKusick no. 19350) but without accompanying deafness. Hoo et al.[197] described a patient with severe mental retardation and the piebald trait associated with an interstitial deletion of 4q. Reviewing the literature, they found two other cases of deletion 4q involving band q12 with similar abnormal pigmentation. They proposed that the gene for piebald trait mapped to 4q12, but no linkage support for this is yet available.

Two autosomal recessive Mendelian conditions have been associated with *de novo* deletions detectable by high resolution cytogenetics or by submicroscopic deletions. Tyrosinemia type II was observed in a male patient with severe mental retardation and multiple congenital abnormalities.[198] Molecular analysis showed the patient to have a homozygous deletion for the tyrosine aminotransferase (TAT) gene. Parental studies showed a large molecular deletion (>27 kb) in the mother, including the entire TAT gene inherited by the child, but no abnormality in the father. Several earlier chromosome studies on the child had been reported as normal. Since the TAT gene had recently been mapped to 16q22-q24, chromosome studies were repeated by high resolution techniques with special attention to 16q. A small *de novo* interstitial deletion was observed at 16q22.1-q22.3. Further molecular studies of other genes mapped to 16q showed the haptoglobin locus was also deleted. Thus, the child's homozygous deletion state was due to inheritance of a maternal submicroscopic deletion and a *de novo* paternal microdeletion.

At least four unrelated patients have been described with a mental retardation syndrome which includes hemoglobin H disease[199,200] (see also Chap. 93). Other clinical findings include microcephaly, hypotonia, and undescended testes. In two of the patients molecular investigation demonstrated that a *de novo* deletion including the entire α-globin gene complex was inherited from a normal parent. This *de novo* deletion, combined with an α-thalassemia mutant allele inherited from the other parent, produced a homozygous deletion for the α-globin sequences. In the four cases described, the *de novo* deletion has not been large enough to observe microscopically. Weatherall et al.[199] have suggested that deletions of this region could be a relatively frequent cause of mental retardation, but this would not be detected in patients who do not also inherit the α-thalassemia mutant allele from the other parent and therefore do not display hemoglobin H disease. Screening of mentally retarded individuals of unknown etiology has not been carried out to test this hypothesis.

X Chromosome Translocations Associated with Mendelian Disorders

For most X-linked disorders, males are clinically affected since they possess a single X chromosome (hemizygous) bearing the mutant gene, and females are clinically unaffected carriers with one mutant and one normal copy of the gene (heterozygous). Depending on the disorder, carrier females may show no clinical features or only mild clinical features, presumably because half-normal levels of an enzyme are sufficient for normal function. Females with full clinical expression of X-linked disorders are rare, and several mechanisms have been put forward to explain this event. The most common is "unfortunate Lyonization," in which it is proposed that by chance, the X chromosome with the normal gene is inactivated in most cells of affected tissues.

A second mechanism, balanced X-autosome translocation, has been appreciated only more recently. The classic paradigm is Duchenne muscular dystrophy, in which approximately 20 females with full clinical expression of the disease are known in families with a negative family history (for review, see Chap. 118). All these translocations have in common a break point in the short arm of the X chromosome at band p21. It was known from earlier studies that females with balanced X-autosome translocations have a nonrandom X-inactivation pattern when lymphocytes or fibroblasts are studied with tritiated thymidine- or bromodeoxyuridine-labeling methods. In such cases, the majority of cells show the normal X to be late replicating (i.e., inactive), with the two X-autosome translocation products early replicating (i.e., active). This is explained by the hypothesis that a single inactivation center resides on the proximal long arm of the X chromosome, so that inactivation of the translocated chromosome would include only one of the two derivative chromosomes, and lead to a gross genetic imbalance.

It was therefore reasoned that the break point in Xp21 disrupted the DMD gene in these females and that the normal gene was functionally inactivated in most cells by Lyonization. Localization of the DMD gene to Xp21 was subsequently confirmed by linkage analysis. A more complete discussion of the linkage studies and molecular characterization of this region leading to the cloning of the DMD gene by reverse genetics strategies can be found in Chap. 118.

The mapping of a number of X-linked disorders has followed a similar course with the discovery of affected females with balanced X-autosome translocations and is summarized in Table 9-4 and Fig. 9-17. In the case of Norrie disease (congenital blindness, retinal dysplasia), linkage studies had already established the localization of the gene to Xp11 prior to discovery of the translocation patient.[201–203] The cell line from this patient may still serve to facilitate mapping of clones relative to the disease locus and perhaps in efforts to clone the translocation junction. For Menkes disease (copper transport disease producing growth retardation, neurologic degeneration, and kinky hair), a previous study using X-chromosome C-banding polymorphisms suggested a localization near the centromere.[204] The same authors suggested a map assignment on the proximal long arm (q13) based on the relative position of the homologous mouse mutant, *mottled.*[204] The translocation patient's break point in q13[205] is consistent with this hypothesis.

For Lowe oculocerebrorenal syndrome (congenital cataracts, mental retardation, and defective tubular function) and Hunter syndrome (mucopolysaccharidosis type II, iduronate-2-sulfate sulfatase deficiency), no mapping information was available prior to identification of X-autosome translocation patients.[206,207] In both cases, the break points were confirmed as the site of the gene by linkage analyses.[208,209] These data have placed Lowe syndrome at Xq25 and Hunter syndrome at Xq26-q27.

For two other X-linked disorders, incontinentia pigmenti and Goeminne syndrome, no linkage data exist to confirm the map localization, but more than one patient with an X-autosome translocation with the same X break point makes the localization highly probable. For incontinentia pigmenti, an X-linked disorder with presumed lethality in males, causing a disturbance of skin pigmentation with abnormalities of the eye, teeth, skeleton, and heart, three different X-autosome translocations share a break point in Xp11.[210,211] An additional case of incontinentia pigmenti associated with a small ring X chromosome would appear to confirm a localization near the centromere.[212] For Goeminne syndrome (torticollis, keloids, cryptorchidism, and renal dysplasia), Zuffardi and Fraccaro[213] noted the coincidence of two unrelated previously published cases of X-autosome translocation with break points in Xq28 and features of Goeminne syndrome.

In two presumed X-linked disorders, Aicardi syndrome (agenesis of corpus callosum, ocular and skeletal abnormalities) and Aarskog syndrome (short stature, shawl scrotum, cryptorchidism), a single case of X-autosome translocation has been reported, but other mapping confirmation is not yet available.[214,215]

X Chromosome Deletions Associated with Mendelian Disorders

In addition to the X-autosome translocations discussed above, a number of patients have been described with one or more X-linked Mendelian disorders shown to be associated with molecular deletions, which, in some instances, are just detectable by high resolution chromosome analysis (Table 9-5, Fig. 9-17). The most thoroughly investigated of these involves the region around the Duchenne muscular dystrophy locus in band p21 (see Chaps. 36 and 118). The first patient to be described had a complex phenotype which combined four known X-linked diseases: Duchenne muscular dystrophy, chronic granulomatous disease (CGD), McCleod syndrome, and retinitis pigmentosum.[14] With the knowledge that DMD mapped to Xp21, high-resolution cytogenetic analysis was performed which revealed a very small deletion of Xp21. DNA from this patient was used by Kunkel et al.[15] in the PERT cloning strat-

Table 9-4 X-Autosome Translocations Associated with Mendelian Disorders

Disorder	*McKusick no.*	*Cytogenetic abnormality*	*Comments*
Duchenne/Becker muscular dystrophy	*31020, *31010	t(X; —)(p21.2; —)	>20 cases; confirmed by linkage (Chap. 118)
Norrie disease	*31060	t(X;10)(p11;p14)	Previously mapped by linkage to Xp11[201–203]
Menkes disease	*30940	t(X;2)(q13;q32.2)	Previously linked to centromere; q13 proposed by mouse homology[204,205]
Lowe syndrome	*30900	t(X;3)(q25;q27)	Confirmed by linkage[206,208]
Hunter syndrome	*30990	t(X;5)(q26–27; q31–32)	Confirmed by linkage[207,209]
Incontinentia pigmenti	*30830	t(X; —)(p11; —)	3 cases; no other mapping data[210,211]
Goeminne syndrome	31430	t(X; —)(q28; —)	2 cases; no other mapping data[213]
Aicardi syndrome	30405	t(X;3)(p22;q12)	No other mapping data[214]
Aarskog	30540	t(X;8)(q13;p21.2)	No other mapping data[215]

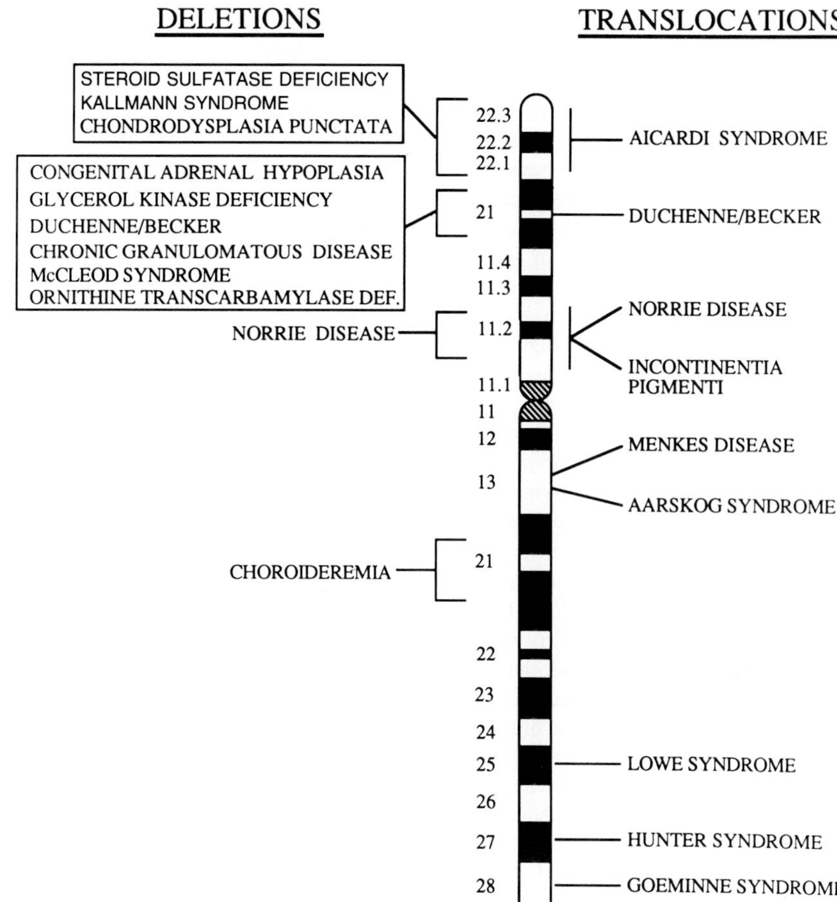

Fig. 9-17 Deletions and translocation of the X chromosome associated with Mendelian diseases. An idiogram of the X chromosome is shown with deletions indicated by brackets to the left of the idiogram and break points of balanced translocations indicated to the right of the chromosome.

egy to identify sequences from the DMD gene. A number of other patients with cytogenetic or molecular deletions of varying size have now been described for the region Xp21 (reviewed in Refs. 99 and 216; see also Chaps. 36 and 118). The phenotypic features have included various combinations of glycerol kinase deficiency, congenital adrenal hypoplasia, Duchenne muscular dystrophy, chronic granulomatous disease, McCleod phenotype, retinitis pigmentosum, and ornithine transcarbamylase deficiency. Many of these patients also have varying degrees of mental retardation. The different combinations of diseases in these patients has allowed the construction of a deletion map of Xp21 with a proposed ordering of the loci discussed above[99,216] (see Chaps. 36 and 118), which has been adopted in Fig. 9-17.

A similar situation has been described for microdeletions of the distal portion of the short arm of the X chromosome involving band p22. The steroid sulfatase (STS) gene has been mapped to Xp22, and its deficiency is the basic defect in X-linked ichthyosis (see Chap. 76). Recently, the STS gene has been cloned, and it has been shown that a very high frequency

Table 9-5 X-Chromosome Deletions Associated with Mendelian Disorders

Disorder	*McKusick no.*	*Cytogenetic abnormality*	*Comments*
Duchenne/Becker muscular dystrophy	*31020/*31010	del Xp21	Multiple patients[99,216] (Chap. 118)
Chronic granulomatous disease	*30640	del Xp21	1 patient[14,99,216]
McCleod syndrome	*31485	del Xp21	1 patient[14,99,216]
OTC deficiency	*31125	del Xp21	1 patient[14,99,216]
Glycerol kinase deficiency	*30703	del Xp21	Multiple patients[99,216] (Chap. 36)
Congenital adrenal hypoplasia	*30020	del Xp21	Multiple patients[99,216] (Chap. 36)
Steroid sulfatase deficiency	*30810	del Xp22	Multiple patients[99] (Chap. 76)
Kallmann syndrome	*30870	del Xp22	Multiple patients[99,217,218] (Chap. 76)
Chondrodysplasia punctata	*30295	del Xp22	2 cases[219] (Chap. 76)
Norrie disease	*31060	del Xp11	2 cases[220,221]
Choroideremia	*30310	del Xq21	4 cases[224–226]

of patients with STS deficiency have a complete deletion of the gene.[217,218] In addition, deletions of STS have been shown in patients with ichthyosis combined with Kallmann syndrome, another X-linked condition characterized by hypogonadism and anosmia. In most of these patients, chromosome studies have been normal, although several males with ichthyosis, or ichthyosis and hypogonadism, have been shown to have X;Y translocations which presumably delete a small portion of distal Xp (Chap. 76). In addition, two unrelated patients with ichthyosis, mental retardation, and X-linked chondrodysplasia punctata have been described with small terminal deletions of Xp detectable by high resolution analysis.[219] The mechanism for these deletions and translocations may involve unequal crossover within the pairing region of the X and Y chromosomes (see Chap. 76). The combined information from these patients has yielded a proposed gene order on Xp of: telomere-steroid sulfatase deficiency–Kallmann syndrome (hypogonadism-anosmia)–chondrodysplasia punctata.[99]

Norrie disease, discussed above in association with an X-autosome translocation, has also been reported in two families as part of a more complex X-linked syndrome which includes severe mental retardation.[220,221] In one of the two families, the syndrome also included microcephaly, hypogonadism, growth disturbances, and an increased susceptibility to infection.[221] Although no visible cytogenetic abnormality was evident with high resolution cytogenetic analysis, molecular studies showed that probe L1.28 (DXS7), previously mapped to Xp11 and shown to be closely linked to Norrie disease, was deleted in affected males in both families.

Choroideremia is an X-linked retinal dystrophy leading to eventual blindness in affected males by the third to fourth decade of life. Localization to Xq13-q21 was first established by tight linkage to several polymorphic markers mapped to that region.[222,223] Several patients have recently been reported in which choroideremia is associated with mental retardation.[224–226] In three of the four families, a cytogenetically visible deletion was observed in band q21, and the DNA marker DXYS1 (previously mapped to Xq13-q21) was missing in affected males. In two of the families, deafness, in addition to choroideremia and mental retardation, was present in affected males.[226] One of the families had a small, visible deletion which was shown by molecular analysis to include DXYS1. In the second family, high resolution cytogenetics failed to establish the presence of a deletion, and molecular studies showed DXYS1 was not deleted in affected males. Hypothesizing that this second family must also have a submicroscopic deletion, Nussbaum et al.[226] performed a PERT cloning experiment to identify sequences from normal X DNA not present in the affected male DNA. Two such sequences were identified, which mapped to Xq21 and were deleted in the affected males of both families, confirming the presence of a submicroscopic deletion. These two clones, and the very small deletion present in this latter family, should be useful in efforts to identify and clone the choroideremia locus.

Microdeletions and Microduplications of the Y Chromosome

In this final section, a brief summary is given of recent data on patients with sex reversal (males with 46,XX karyotype and females with 46,XY karyotype) demonstrating very small deletions or duplications of Y-chromosomal material. It was shown earlier by high resolution cytogenetic analysis that some XX males result from X;Y translocations in which a small segment of the short arm of the Y chromosome is translocated to the distal tip of the short arm of the X chromosome.[227] Conversely, several XY females have been described with small

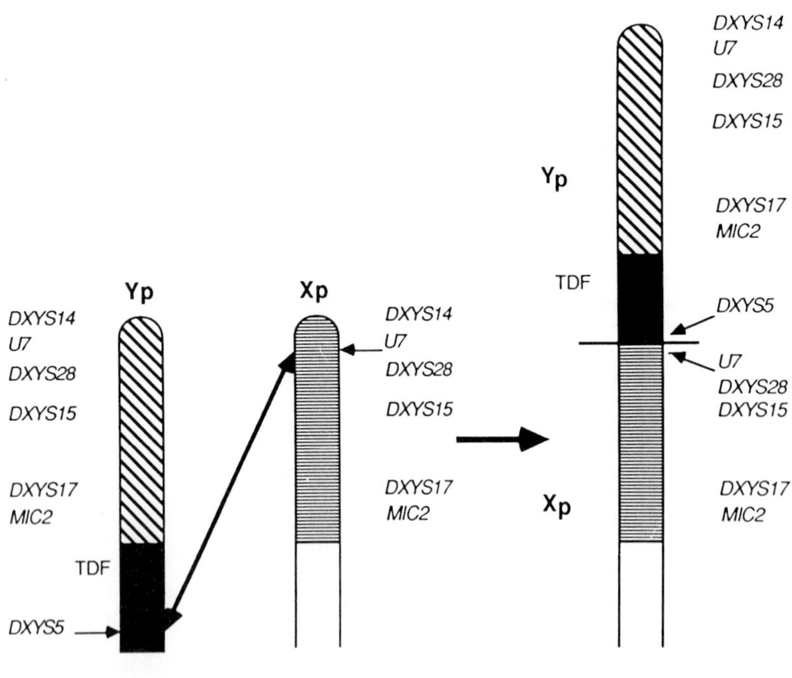

Fig. 9-18 Schematic representation of the abnormal X-Y interchange producing duplication of Y-chromosome sequences, including the testis determining factor (TDF), in an XX male. Blackened regions represent Y-chromosome-specific sequences, white regions represent X-chromosome-specific sequences, and oblique and horizontal hatching represents the pseudoautosomal portions of the Y and X chromosomes, respectively. *(From Rouyer et al.[226] Used by permission of Cell.)*

deletions of the short arm of the Y chromosome visible by high resolution analysis.[228] Recent molecular studies using Y-chromosome-specific probes have revealed that most XX males, including some without visible X;Y translocations, carry Y-chromosome DNA sequences.[229] The mechanism for this unbalanced translocation has been shown to result, in most cases, from unequal crossing over in the X-Y pairing region at the distal short arm of each chromosome (Fig. 9-18).[230–232]

A collection of XX males and XY females has now been used to define the smallest region of overlap for Y sequences necessary and sufficient for male determination,[233] which should contain the presumed testis determining factor (TDF). One XY female is deleted for only 140 kb of the Y chromosome, while one XX male possesses only 350 kb of the Y chromosome. Page et al.[233] recently described the identification of a highly conserved, expressed sequence that maps to this critical region and is therefore a candidate for the TDF. Confirmation of this would represent another significant success for the reverse genetics approach utilizing microdeletion and microduplication patient material.

REFERENCES

1. YUNIS JJ: High resolution of human chromosomes. *Science* 191:1268, 1976.
2. YUNIS JJ: Mid-prophase human chromosomes. The attainment of 2000 bands. *Hum Genet* 56:293, 1981.
3. ISCN (1985): In Harnden DG, Klinger HP (eds): *An International System for Human Cytogenetic Nomenclature.* Published in collaboration with *Cytogenet Cell Genet,* Basel, Karger, 1985.
4. LELE KP, PENROSE LS, STALLARD HB: Chromosome deletion in a case of retinoblastoma. *Ann Hum Genet* 27:171, 1963.
5. FRANCKE U: Retinoblastoma and chromosome 13. *Cytogenet Cell Genet* 16:131, 1976.
6. RICCARDI VM, SUJANSKY E, SMITH AC, FRANCKE U: Chromosomal imbalance in the aniridia-Wilms tumor association: 11p interstitial deletion. *Pediatrics* 61:604, 1978.
7. HAWKEY CJ, SMITHIES A: The Prader-Willi syndrome with a 15/15 translocation: Case report and review of the literature. *J Med Genet* 13:152, 1976.
8. de la CHAPELLE A, HERVA R, KOIVISTO M, AULA P: A deletion in chromosome 22 can cause DiGeorge syndrome. *Hum Genet* 57:253, 1981.
9. DOBYNS WB, STRATTON RF, PARKE JT, GREENBERG F, NUSSBAUM RL, LEDBETTER DH: The Miller-Dieker syndrome: Lissencephaly and monosomy 17p. *J Pediatr* 102:552, 1983.
10. ANAND R: Pulsed field gel electrophoresis: A technique for fractionating large DNA molecules. *Trends Genet* 2:278, 1986.
11. BARLOW DP, LEHRACH H: Genetics by gel electrophoresis: The impact of pulsed field gel electrophoresis on mammalian genetics. *Trends Genet* 3:167, 1987.
12. SCHMICKEL RD: Contiguous gene syndromes: A component of recognizable syndromes. *J Pediatr* 109:231, 1986.
13. ORKIN SH: Reverse genetics and human disease. A Review. *Cell* 47:845, 1986.
14. FRANCKE U, OCHS HD, De MARTINVILLE B, GIACALONE J, LINDGREN V, DISTECHE C, PAGON RA, HOFKER MH, van OMMEN G-JB, PEARSON PO, WEDGEWOOD RJ: Minor Xp21 chromosome deletion in a male associated with expression of Duchenne muscular dystrophy, chronic granulomatous disease, retinitis pigmentosa and McLeod syndrome. *Am J Hum Genet* 37:250, 1985.
15. KUNKEL LM, MONACO AP, MIDDLESWORTH W, OCHS HD, LATT SA: Specific cloning of DNA fragments absent from the DNA of a male patient with an X chromosome deletion. *Proc Natl Acad Sci USA* 82:4778, 1985.
16. MONACO AP, BERTELSON CJ, MIDDLESWORTH W, COLLETTI C-A, ALDRIDGE J, FISCHBECK KH, BARTLETT R, PERICAK-VANCE MA, ROSES AD, KUNKEL LM: Detection of deletions spanning the Duchenne muscular dystrophy locus using a tightly linked DNA segment. *Nature* 316:842, 1985.
17. ROYER-POKORA B, KUNKEL LM, MONACO AP, GOFF SC, NEWBURGER PE, BAEHNER PL, COLE FS, CURNUTTE JT, ORKIN SH: Cloning the gene for an inherited human disorder—chronic granulomatous disease—on the basis of its chromosomal location. *Nature* 322:32, 1986.
18. SORSBY A: Bilateral retinoblastoma. A dominantly inherited affection. *Br Med J* 2:580, 1971.
19. ELLSWORTH RM: The practical management of retinoblastoma. *Trans Am Ophthalmol Soc* 67:461, 1969.
20. POPOFF NA, ELLSWORTH RM: The fine structure of retinoblastoma: in vivo and in vitro observations. *Lab Invest* 25:389, 1971.
21. TAYLOR HR, CARROLL N, JACK I, CROCK GW: A scanning electron microscopic examination of retinoblastoma in tissue culture. *Br J Ophthalmol* 63:551, 1979.
22. LANE JC, KLINTWORTH GK: A study of astrocytes in retinoblastomas using the immunoperoxidase technique and antibodies to glial fibrillary acidic protein. *Am J Ophthalmol* 95:197, 1982.
23. KYRITIS AP, TSOKOS M, TRICHE TJ, CHADER GJ: Retinoblastoma—Origin from a primitive neuroectodermal cell? *Nature* 307:471, 1984.
24. WILSON WG, CAMPOCHIARO PA, CONWAY BP, CARTER BT, SUDDUTH KW, WATSONBA, SPARKES RS: Deletion (13) (q14.1q14.3) in two generations: Variability of ocular manifestations and definition of the phenotype. *Am J Med Genet* 28:675, 1987.
25. MOTEGI T, KAGA M, YANAGAWA Y, KADOWAKI H, WATANABE K, INOUE A, KOMATSU M, MINODA K: A recognizable pattern of the mid-face of retinoblastoma patients with interstitial deletion of 13q. *Hum Genet* 64:160, 1983.
26. MOTEGI T, IKEDA K, WATANABE K, YANAGAWA Y, MINODA K: Deletion of (13) (q13q14.3) with retinoblastoma: Confirmation and extension of a recognizable pattern of clinical features in retinoblastoma patients with 13q deletion. *J Med Genet* 24:696, 1987.
27. HETHCOTE HW, KNUDSON AG JR: Model for the incidence of embryonal cancers: Application to retinoblastoma. *Proc Natl Acad Sci USA* 75:2453, 1978.
28. FALLS HF, NEEL JV: Genetics of retinoblastoma. *Arch Ophthalmol* 151:197, 1951.
29. SCHAPPERT-KIMMIJSER J, HEMMES GD, NIJLAND R: The heredity of retinoblastoma. *Ophthalmologica* 151:197, 1966.
30. VOGEL F: Neue untersuchungen zur genetik des retinoblastoms. *Z menschl Vereb Konstit Lehre* 34:205, 1957.
31. KNUDSON AG JR: Mutation and cancer: Statistical study of retinoblastoma. *Proc Natl Acad Sci USA* 68:820, 1971.
32. MACKLIN MT: A study of retinoblastoma in Ohio. *Am J Hum Genet* 12:1, 1960.
33. MATSUNAGA E: Hereditary retinoblastoma: Delayed mutation or host resistance? *Am J Hum Genet* 30:406, 1978.
34. CHAUM E, ELLSWORTH RM, ABRAMSOM DH, HAIK BG, KITCHIN FD, CHAGANTI RSK: Cytogenetic analysis of retinoblastoma: Evidence for multifocal origin and in vivo gene amplification. *Cytogenet Cell Genet* 38:82, 1984.
35. TURLEAU C, de GROUCHY U, CHAVIN-COLIN F, JUNIEN C, SEGER J, SCHLEINGER P, LEBLANC A, HAYE C: Cytogenetic forms of retinoblastoma: Their incidence in a survey of 66 patients. *Cancer Genet Cytogenet* 16:321, 1985.
36. SQUIRE J, GALLIE BL, PHILLIPS RA: A detailed analysis of chromosomal changes inheritable and non-heritable retinoblastoma. *Hum Genet* 70:291, 1985.
37. WARD P, PACKMAN S, LOUGHMAN W, SPARKES M, SPARKES RS, MCMAHON A, GREGORY T, ABLIN A: Location of the retinoblastoma susceptibility gene(s) and the human esterase D locus. *J Med Genet* 21:92, 1984.
38. SPARKES RS, MURPHREE AL, LINGUA RW, SPARKES MC, FIELD LL, FUNDERBURK SJ, BENEDICT WF: Gene for hereditary retinoblastoma assigned to human chromosome 13 by linkage analysis to esterase D. *Science* 219:971, 1983.
39. SPARKES RS, SPARKES MC, WILSON MG, TOWNER JW, BENEDICT WF, MURPHREE AL, YUNIS JJ: Regional assignment of genes for esterase D and retinoblastoma to chromosome band 13q14. *Science* 208:1042, 1980.
40. STRONG LC, RICCARDI VM, FERRELL RD, SPARKES RS: Familial retinoblastoma and chromosome 13 deletion transmitted via an insertional translocation. *Science* 213:1501, 1981.
41. SPARKES RS, MULLER H, KLISAK I: Retinoblastoma with 13q-chromosomal deletion associated with maternal paracentric inversion of 13q. *Science* 203:1027, 1979.
42. RICCARDI VM, HITTNER HM, FRANCKE U, PIPPIN S, HOLMQUIST GP, KRETZER FL, FERRELL R: Partial triplication and deletion of 13q: Study of a family presenting with bilateral retinoblastoma. *Clin Genet* 15:332, 1979.
43. WARBURTON D, ANYANE-YEBOA K, TATERKA P: Deletion of 13q14 without retinoblastoma: A case of non-penetrance. *Am J Hum Genet* 39:A137, 1986.

44. WILSON WG, CARTER BT, CONWAY BP, ATKIN JF, WATSON BA, SPARKES RS: Variable manifestations of deletion (13)(q14.1-q14.3) in two generations. *Am J Hum Genet* 39:A47, 1986.
45. MOTEGI T: High rate of detection of 13q14 deletion mosaicism among retinoblastoma patients (using more extensive methods). *Hum Genet* 61:95, 1982.
46. FUKUSHIMA Y, KUROKI Y, ITO T, KONDO I, NISHIGAKI I: Familial retinoblastoma (mother and son) with 13q14 deletion. *Hum Genet* 77:104, 1987.
47. CAVENEE WK, DRYJA TP, PHILLIPS RA, BENEDICT WF, GODBOUT R, GALLIE BL, MURPHREE AL, STRONG LC, WHITE RL: Expression of recessive alleles by chromosomal mechanisms in retinoblastoma. *Nature* 305:779, 1983.
48. BARKER D, SCHAEFER M, WHITE RL: Restriction sites containing CpG show a higher frequency of polymorphism in human DNA. *Cell* 36:131, 1984.
49. WYMAN AR, WHITE RL: A highly polymorphic locus in human DNA. *Proc Natl Acad Sci USA* 77:6754, 1980.
50. CAVENEE WK, LEACH RJ, MOHANDAS T, PEARSON P, WHITE RL: Isolation and regional localization of DNA segments revealing polymorphic loci from human chromosome 13. *Am J Hum Genet* 36:10, 1984.
51. DRYJA TP, RAPAPORT JM, WEICHSELBAUM R, BRUNS GAP: Chromosome 13 restriction fragment length polymorphisms. *Hum Genet* 65:320, 1984.
52. DRYJA TP, CAVENEE WK, WHITE RL, RAPAPORT JM, PETERSON R, ALBERTA DM, BRUNS GAP: Homozygosity of chromosome 13 in retinoblastoma. *N Engl J Med* 310:550, 1984.
53. GODBOUT R, DRYJA TP, SQUIRE JA, GALLIE BL, PHILLIPS RA: Somatic inactivation of genes on chromosome 13 is a common event in retinoblastoma. *Nature* 304:451, 1983.
54. CAVENEE WK, HANSEN MF, NORDENSKJOLD M, KOCK E, MAUMENEE I, SQUIRE JA, PHILLIPS RA, GALLIE BL: Genetic origin of mutations predisposing to retinoblastoma. *Science* 228:501, 1985.
55. ABRAMSON DH, ELLSWORTH RM, KITCHIN FD, TUNG G: Second nonocular tumors in retinoblastoma survivors. Are they radiation-induced? *Ophthalmology* 99:1351, 1984.
56. HANSEN MF, KOUFOS A, GALLIE BL, PHILLIPS RA, FODSTAD O, BROGGER A, GEDDE-DAHL T, CAVENEE WK: Osteosarcoma and retinoblastoma: A shared chromosomal mechanism revealing recessive predisposition. *Proc Natl Acad Sci USA* 82:6216, 1985.
57. LALANDE M, DRYJA TP, SCHRECK RR, SHIPLEY J, FLINT A, LATT SA: Isolation of human chromosome 13-specific DNA sequences cloned from flow sorted chromosomes and potentially linked to the retinoblastoma locus. *Cancer Genet Cytogenet* 13:283, 1984.
58. LALANDE M, DONLON T, PETERSEN RA, LIEBERFARB R, MANTER S, LATT SA: Molecular detection and differentiation of deletions in band 13q14 in human retinoblastoma. *Cancer Genet Cytogenet* 23:151, 1986.
59. DRYJA TP, RAPOPORT JM, JOYCE JM, PETERSEN RA: Molecular detection of deletions involving band q14 of chromosome 13 in retinoblastomas. *Proc Natl Acad Sci USA* 83:7391, 1986.
60. FRIEND SH, BERNARDS R, ROGELJ S, WEINBERG RA, RAPOPORT JM, ALBERT DM, DRYJA TP: A human DNA segment with properties of the gene that predisposes to retinoblastoma and osteosarcoma. *Nature* 323:643, 1986.
61. LEE W-H, BOOKSTEIN R, HONG F, YOUNG L-J, SHEW J-Y, LEE E Y-H P: Human retinoblastoma susceptibility gene: Cloning, identification and sequence. *Science* 235:1394, 1987.
62. FUNG Y-K T, MURPHREE AL, T'ANG A, QIAN J, HINRICHS SH, BENEDICT WF: Structural evidence for the authenticity of the human retinoblastoma gene. *Science* 236:1657, 1987.
63. LEE W-H, SHEN J-Y, HONG FD, SERY TW, DONOSO LA, YOUNG L-J, BOOKSTEIN R, LEE EY-HP: The retinoblastoma susceptibility gene encodes a nuclear phosphoprotein associated with DNA binding activity. *Nature* 329:642, 1987.
64. CAVENEE WK, MURHPREE AL, SHULL MS, BENEDICT WF, SPARKES RS, KOCK E, NORDENSKJOLD M: Prediction of familial predisposition to retinoblastoma. *N Engl J Med* 314:1201, 1986.
65. HORSTHEMKE B, BARNERT HJ, GREGER V, PASSARGE E, HÖPPING W: Early diagnosis in hereditary retinoblastoma by detection of molecular deletions at gene locus. *Lancet* Feb 28:p 511, 1987.
66. LEPPERT M, CAVENEE W, CALLAHAN P, HOLM T, O'CONNELL P, THOMPSON K, LATHROP GM, LALOUEL J-M, WHITE R: A primary genetic map of chromosome 13q. *Am J Hum Genet* 39:425, 1986.
67. LEE EY-H P, LEE WH: Molecular cloning of the human esterase D gene, a genetic marker for retinoblastoma. *Proc Natl Acad Sci USA* 83:6337, 1986.
68. SQUIRE J, DRYJA TP, DUNN J, GODDARD A, HOFFMAN T, MUSARELLA M, WILLARD HF, BECKER AJ, GALLIE BL, PHILLIPS RA: Cloning of the esterase D gene: A polymorphic probe closely linked to the retinoblastoma locus on chromosome 13. *Proc Natl Acad Sci USA* 83:6573, 1986.
69. WIGGS J, NORDENSKJOLD M, YANDELL D, RAPAPORT J, GRONDIN V, JANSON M, WERELIUS B, PETERSON R, CRAFT A, RIEDEL K, LIBERFARB R, WALTON D, WILSON W, DRYJA TP: Prediction of risk of hereditary retinoblastoma using DNA polymorphisms within the retinoblastoma gene. *N Engl J Med* 318:151, 1988.
70. YOUNG JL, MILLER RW: Incidence of malignant tumors in U.S. children. *J Pediatr* 86:254, 1975.
71. GREENWOOD MF, HOLLAND P: Clinical and biological manifestations of Wilms tumor, in Pochedly C, Baum ES (eds): *Wilms Tumor: Clinical and Biological Manifestations.* Amsterdam, Elsevier, 1984, pp 9–30.
72. D'ANGIO GJ, BECKWITH JB, BRESLOW NE, et al: Wilms tumor: An update. *Cancer* 45:1791, 1980.
73. BECKWITH JB, PALMER NF: Histopathology and Wilms tumor: Results from the first National Wilms tumor study. *Cancer* 41:1937, 1978.
74. BALSAVER AM, GIBLEY CW, TESSMER CF: Ultrastructural studies in Wilms tumor. *Cancer* 22:417, 1986.
75. BOVE KE, MCADAMS AJ: The nephroblastomatosis complex and its relationship to Wilms tumor: A clinicopathologic treatise. *Perspect Pediatr Pathol* 3:185, 1976.
76. MILLER RW, FRAUMENI JF, MANNING MD: Association of Wilms tumor with anirida, hemihypertrophy and other congenital malformation. *N Engl J Med* 270:922, 1964.
77. RICCARDI VM, HITTNER HM, FRANCKE U, YUNIS JJ, LEDBETTER D, BORGES W: The Aniridia-Wilms tumor association: The critical role of chromosomes band 11p13. *Cancer Genet Cytogenet* 2:131, 1980.
78. MEADOWS AT, LICHENFELD JL, KOOP EC: Wilms tumor in three children of a woman with congenital hemihypertrophy. *N Engl J Med* 291:23, 1974.
79. BROWN WT, PURANIK SR, ALTMAN DH, HARDIN HC: Wilms tumor in three successive generations. *Surgery* 72:756, 1972.
80. MATSUNAGA E: Genetics of Wilms tumor. *Hum Genet* 57:231, 1981.
81. KNUDSON AG, STRONG LC: Mutation and cancer: A model for Wilms tumor of the kidney. *J Natl Cancer Inst* 48:313, 1972.
82. PENDERGRASS TW: Congenital anomalies in children with Wilms tumor, a new survey. *Cancer* 37:403, 1976.
83. FRAUMENI JF, GEISER CF, MANNING MD: Wilms tumor and congenital hemihypertrophy: Report of five new cases and review of literature. *Pediatrics* 40:886, 1967.
84. HAICKEN BN, MILLER DR: Simultaneous occurrence of congenital aniridia, hamartoma and Wilms tumor. *J Pediatr* 78:497, 1971.
85. SOTELO-AVILA C, GONZALEZ-CRUSSI F, FOWLER JA: Complete and incomplete forms of Beckwith-Wiedemann Syndrome. Their oncogenic potential. *J Pediatr* 96:47, 1980.
86. FRANCKE U, HOLMES LB, ATKINS L, RICCARDI VM: Aniridia-Wilms tumor association: Evidence for specific deletion of 11p13. *Cytogenet Cell Genet* 24:185, 1979.
87. RICCARDI VM, HITTNER HM, FRANCKE U, YUNIS JJ, LEDBETTER D, BORGES W: The Aniridia-Wilms tumor association: The critical role of chromosome band 11p13. *Cancer Genet Cytogenet* 2:131, 1980.
88. SLATER R, de KRAKER J: Chromosome 11 and Wilms tumor. *Cancer Genet Cytogenet* 5:237, 1982.
89. NAKAGOME Y, ISE T, SAKURAI M, NAKAJO T, OKAMOTO E, TAKANO T, NAKAHORI Y, TSUCHIDA Y, NAGAHARA N, TAKADA T, OHSAWA Y, SAWAGUCHI S, TOYOSAKA A, KOBAYASHI N, MATSUNAGA E, SAITO S: High resolution studies in patients with aniridia—Wilms tumor association, Wilms tumor or related congenital abnormalities. *Hum Genet* 67:245, 1984.
90. TURLEAU C, de GROUCHY J, TOURNADE M-F, GANADOUX M-F, JUNIEN C: Del 11p/aniridia complex. Report of three patients and review of 37 observations from the literature. *Clin Genet* 26:356, 1984.
91. YUNIS JJ, RAMSAY NKC: Familial occurrence of the aniridia—Wilms tumor syndrome with deletion 11p13-14.1. *J Pediatr* 96:1027, 1980.
92. KONDO K, CHILCOTE RR, MAURER HS, ROWLEY JD: Chromosome abnormalities in tumor cells from patients with sporadic Wilms tumor. *Cancer Res* 44:5376, 1984.
93. SLATER RM: The cytogenetics of Wilms tumor. *Cancer Genet Cytogenet* 19:37, 1986.
94. HEIDEMAN RL, MCGAVRAN L, WALDSTEIN G: Nephroblastomatosis and deletion of 11p. The potential etiologic relationship to subsequent Wilms tumor. *Am J Pediatr Hematol Oncol* 8(3):231, 1986.
95. SIMOLA KOJ, KNUUTILA S, KAITILA I, PIRKOLA A, POHJA P: Familial aniridia and translocation t(4;11) (q22;p13) without Wilms tumor. *Hum Genet* 63:158, 1983.
96. MOORE JW, HYMAN S, ANTONARAKIS SE, MULES EH, THOMAS GH: Familial isolated aniridia associated with a translocation involving chromosomes 11 and 22 [t(ll;22) (p13:q12.2)]. *Hum Genet* 72:297, 1986.
97. MANNENS M, HEYTING C, van KESSEL AG, GOEDDE-SALZ E, FRANTS RR, van OMMEN GJB, PEARSON PL: Regional localization of DNA probes on

the short arm of chromosome 11 using aniridia-Wilms tumor-associated deletions. *Hum Genet* 75:180, 1987.

98. GLASER T, LEWIS WH, BRUNS GAP, WATKINS PC, ROGLER CE, SHOWS TB, POWERS VE, WILLARD HG, GOFUEN JM, SIMOLA KOJ, HOUSMAN DE: The β-subunit of follicle-stimulating hormone is deleted in patients with aniridia and Wilms tumor, allowing a further definition of the *WAGR* locus. *Nature* 321:882, 1986.

99. FRANCKE U: Microdeletions and Mendelian phenotypes, in F. Vogel and K. Sperling (eds), *Human Genetics: Proceedings of the 7th International Congress of Human Genetics, Berlin, 1986*. Berlin, Springer-Verlag, 1987, p 201.

100. KOUFOS A, HANSEN MF, LAMPKIN BC, WORKMAN ML, COPELAND NG, JENKINS NA, CAVENEE WK: Loss of alleles at loci on human chromosome 11 during genesis of Wilms tumor. *Nature* 309:170, 1984.

101. ORKIN SH, GOLDMAN DS, SALLAN SE: Development of homozygosity for chromosome 11p markers in Wilms tumor. *Nature* 309:172, 1984.

102. REEVE AP, HOUSIAUX PJ, GARDINER RJ, CHEWINGS WE, GRINDLEY RM, MILLOW LJ: Loss of a Harvey ras allele in sporadic Wilms tumor. *Nature* 309:174, 1984.

103. FEARON ER, VOGELSTEIN B, FEINBERG AP: Somatic deletion and duplication of genes on chromosome 11 in Wilms tumors. *Nature* 309:176, 1984.

104. DAO DT, SCHROEDER WT, CHAO L-Y, KIKUCHI H, STRONG LC, RICCARDI VM, PATHAK S, NICHOLS WW, LEWIS WH, SAUNDERS GF: Genetic mechanisms of tumor-specific loss of 11pDNA sequences in Wilms tumor. *Am J Hum Genet* 41:202, 1987.

105. SCHROEDER WT, CHAO L-Y, DAO DT, STRONG LC, PATHAK S, RICCARDI VM, LEWIS WH, SAUNDERS GF: Nonrandom loss of maternal chromosome 11 alleles in Wilms tumors. *Am J Hum Genet* 40:413, 1987.

106. PORTEOUS DJ, BICKMORE W, CHRISTIE S, BOYD PA, CRANSTON G, FLETCHER JM, GOSDEN JR, ROUT D, SEAWRIGHT A, SIMOLA KOJ, van HEYNINGEN V, HASTIE ND: HRAS1-selected chromosome transfer generates markers that colocalize anirdidia- and genitourinary-associated translocation breakpoints and the Wilms tumor gene within band 11p13. *Proc Natl Acad Sci USA* 84:5355, 1987.

107. BECKWITH JB, WANG C-I, DONNELL GN, GWINN JL: Hyperplastic fetal visceromegaly with macroglossia, omphalocele, cytomegaly of the adrenal cortex: Postnatal somatic gigantism and other abnormalities: A newly recognized syndrome. *Abstr Am Pediatr Soc Ann Meeting* 1964, p 56.

108. WIEDEMANN HR: Complexe malformatif familial avec hernie ombilicale et macroglossie—Un "syndrome nouveau?" *J Genet Hum* 13:223, 1964.

109. WIEDEMANN HR: Exomphalos-gigantismus-syndrom. Berardinelli-Seip syndrom und Sotos syndrom—Eine vergleichende betrachtung unter ausgewahlten aspekten. *Z Kinderheilk* 115:193, 1973.

110. MULLER S, GADNER H, WEBER B, VOGEL M, RIEHM H: Wilms tumor and adrenocortical carcinoma with hemihypertrophy and hamartomas. *Eur J Pediatr* 127:219, 1978.

111. SOTELO-AVILA C, GONZALEZ-CRUSSI F, FOWLER JW: Complete and incomplete forms of Beckwith-Wiedemann syndrome: Their oncogenic potential. *J Pediatr* 96:47, 1980.

112. GRUNER M, GILHAUME A, MONTAGE J, FAURE C: Nephroblastome et syndrome de Beckwith-Wiedemann. *Ann Radiol* 24(1):39, 1981.

113. TANK ES, KAY R: Neoplasms associated with hemihypertrophy, Beckwith-Wiedemann syndrome and aniridia. *J Urol* 124:266, 1980.

114. TOVAR JA, ARENA J, ZUBIGALLA P: L'héredité du syndrome de Wiedemann-Beckwith. *Chir Pediatr* 20:187, 1979.

115. SOMMER A, COHEN B, CUTLER E: Familial occurrence of Wiedemann-Beckwith syndrome. *Am J Med Genet* 1:59, 1977.

116. BEST LG, HOEKSTRA RE: Wiedemann-Beckwith syndrome: Autosomal-dominant inheritance in a family. *Am J Med Genet* 9:291, 1981.

117. NERI G, MARTINI-NERI ME, KATZ BE, OPITZ JM: The Perlman syndrome: familial renal dysplasia with Wilms tumor, fetal gigantism and multiple congenital anomalies. *Am J Med Genet* 9:195, 1984.

118. BERRY AC, BELTON EM, CHANTLER C: Monzygotic twins discordant for Wiedemann-Beckwith syndrome and the implications for genetic counselling. *J Med Genet* 17:136, 1980.

119. WAZIRI M, PATIL SR, HANSON JW, BARTLEY JA: Abnormality of chromosome 11 in patients with features of Beckwith-Wiedemann syndrome. *J Pediatr* 102:873, 1983.

120. TURLEAU C, de GROUCHY J, CHAVIN-COLIN F, MARTELLI H, VOYER M, CHARLAS R: Trisomy 11p15 and Beckwith-Wiedemann syndrome. A report of two cases. *Hum Genet* 67:219, 1984.

121. SCHMUTZ SM: Deletion of chromosome 11 (p11p13) in a patient with Beckwith-Wiedemann syndrome. *Clin Genet* 30:154, 1986.

122. HAAS OA, ZOUBEK A, GRUMAYER ER, GADNER H: Constitutional interstitial deletion of 11p11 and pericentric inversion of chromosome 9 in a patient with Wiedemann-Beckwith syndrome and hepatoblastoma. *Cancer Genet Cytogenet* 23:95, 1986.

123. PETTENATI MJ, HAINES JL, HIGGINS RR, WAPPNER RS, PALMER CG, WEAVER DD: Wiedemann-Beckwith syndrome: Presentation of clinical and cytogenetic data on 22 new cases and review of the literature. *Hum Genet* 74:143, 1986.

124. KOUFOS A, HANSEN MF, COPELAND NG, JENKINS NA, LAMPKIN BC, CAVENEE WK: Loss of heterozygosity in three embryonal tumors suggests a common pathogenetic mechanism. *Nature* 316:330, 1985.

125. PRADER A, LABHART A, WILLI H: Ein syndrom von adipositas, kleinwuchs, kryptorchismus und oligophrenie nach myatonieartigem zustand in neugeborenalter. *Schweiz Med Wochenschr* 86:1260, 1956.

126. HOLM VA: The diagnosis of Prader-Willi syndrome, in Holm VA, Sulzbacher S, Pipes PL (eds): *Prader-Willi Syndrome*. Baltimore, MD, University Park Press, 1981, p 27.

127. CASSIDY SB: Prader-Willi syndrome. *Curr Probl Pediatr* 14:1, 1984.

128. HANSON JW: A view of the etiology and pathogenesis of Prader-Willi syndrome, in Holm VA, Sulzbacher S, Pipes PL (eds): *Prader-Willi Syndrome*. Baltimore, MD, University Park Press, 1981, p 45.

129. LUBINSKY M, ZELLWEGER H, GREENSWAG L, LARSON G, HANSMANN I, LEDBETTER D: Familial Prader-Willi syndrome with apparently normal chromosomes. *Am J Med Genet* 28:37, 1987.

130. HASEGAWA T, HARA M, ANDO M, OSAWA M, FUKUYAMA Y, TAKAHASI M, YAMADA K: Cytogenetic studies of familial Prader-Willi syndrome. *Hum Genet* 65:325, 1984.

131. CASSIDY SB: Letter to the editor: Recurrence risk in Prader-Willi syndrome. *Am J Med Genet* 28:59, 1987.

132. LEDBETTER DH, RICCARDI VM, AIRHART SD, STROBEL RJ, KEENAN BS, CRAWFORD JD: Deletions of chromosome 15 as a cause of the Prader-Willi syndrome. *N Engl J Med* 304:325, 1981.

133. LEDBETTER DH, MASCARELLO JT, RICCARDI VM, HARPER VD, AIRHART SD, STROBEL RJ: Chromosome 15 abnormalities and the Prader-Willi syndrome: A follow-up report of 40 cases. *Am J Hum Genet* 34:278, 1982.

134. LEDBETTER DH, GREENBERG F, HOLM VA, CASSIDY SB: Conference report: Second Annual Prader-Willi Syndrome Scientific Conference. *Am J Med Genet* 28:779, 1987.

135. NIEBUHR E: The cri du chat syndrome. *Hum Genet* 44:227, 1978.

136. BUTLER MG, MEANEY FJ, PALMER CG: Clinical and cytogenetic survey of 39 individuals with Prader-Labhart-Willi syndrome. *Am J Med Genet* 23:793, 1986.

137. NIIKAWA N, ISHIKIRIYAMA S: Clinical and cytogenetic studies of the Prader-Willi syndrome. Evidence of phenotype-karyotype correlation. *Hum Genet* 69:22, 1985.

138. PETTIGREW AL, GOLLIN SM, GREENBERG F, RICCARDI VM, LEDBETTER DH: Duplication of proximal 15q as a cause of Prader-Willi syndrome. *Am J Med Genet* 28:791, 1987.

139. MATTEI MG, SOUIAH N, MATTEI JF: Chromosome 15 anomalies and the Prader-Willi syndrome: Cytogenetic analysis. *Hum Genet* 66:313, 1984.

140. KOUSSEFF BG: The cytogenetic controversy in the Prader-Labhart-Willi syndrome. *Am J Med Genet* 13:431, 1982.

141. SCHWARTZ S, MAX SR, PANNY SR, COHEN MM: Deletions of proximal 15q and non-classical Prader-Willi syndrome phenotypes. *Am J Med Genet* 20:255, 1985.

142. GREENBERG F, LEDBETTER DH: Deletions of proximal 15q without Prader-Willi syndrome. *Am J Med Genet* 28:813, 1987.

143. KAPLAN LC, WHARTON R, ELIAS E, MANDELL F, DONLON T, LATT S: Clinical heterogeneity associated with deletions in the long arm of chromosomes 15—Report of 3 new cases and their possible genetic significance. *Am J Med Genet* 28:45, 1987.

144. MAGENIS RE, BROWN MG, LACY DA, BUDDEN S, LAFRANCHI S: Is Angelman syndrome an alternate result of del(15)(q11q13)? *Am J Med Genet* 28:829, 1987.

145. LALANDE M, SCHRECK RR, HOFFMAN R, LATT SA: Identification of inverted duplicated #15 chromosomes using bivariate flow cytometric analysis. *Cytometry* 6:1, 1985.

146. DONLON TA, LALANDE M, WYMAN A, BRUNS G, LATT SA: Isolation of molecular probes associated with the chromosome 15 instability in the Prader-Willi syndrome. *Proc Natl Acad Sci USA* 83:4408, 1986.

147. MILLER JQ: Lissencephaly in two siblings. *Neurology (Minneapl)* 13:841, 1963.

148. DIEKER H, EDWARDS RH, ZU RHEIN G, CHOU SM, HARTMAN HA, OPITZ JM: The lissencephaly syndrome. *Birth Defects* 5:53, 1969.

149. JONES KL, GILBERT EF, KAVEGGIA EG, OPITZ JM: The Miller-Dieker syndrome. *Pediatrics* 66:277, 1980.

150. DOBYNS WB, STRATTON RF, GREENBERG F: Syndromes with lissencephaly. I: Miller-Dieker and Norman-Roberts syndromes and isolated lissencephaly. *Am J Med Genet* 18:509, 1984.

151. STRATTON RF, DOBYNS WB, AIRHART SD, LEDBETTER DH: New chromosome syndrome: Miller-Dieker syndrome and monosomy 17p13. *Hum Genet* 67:193, 1984.

152. GREENBERG F, STRATTON RF, LOCKHART LH, ELDER FFB, DOBYNS WB,

LEDBETTER DH: Familial Miller-Dieker syndrome associated with pericentric inversion of chromosome 17. *Am J Med Genet* 23:853, 1986.

153. PEARSON PL, KIDD KK, WILLARD HF: Report of the Committee on Human Gene Mapping by Recombinant DNA Techniques. Human Gene Mapping (1987): Ninth International Workshop on Human Gene Mapping. *Cytogenet Cell Genet* 46:390, 1987.

154. VANTUINEN P, RICH DC, SUMMERS KM, LEDBETTER DH: Regional mapping panel for human chromosome 17: Application to neurofibromatosis Type 1. *Genomics* 1:374, 1987.

155. NAKAMURA Y, LEPPERT M, O'CONNELL P, WOLFF R, HOLM T, CULVER M, MARTIN C, FUJIMOTO E, HOFF M, KUMLIN E, WHITE R: Variable number of tandem repeat (VNTR) markers for human gene mapping. *Science* 235:1616, 1987.

156. VANTUINEN P, DOBYNS WB, LEDBETTER DH: Molecular detection of visible and submicroscopic deletion in Miller-Dieker syndrome. *Am J Hum Genet* 41 *(suppl)*:A144, 1987.

157. DI GEORGE AM: Discussions on a new concept of the cellular base of immunology. *J Pediatr* 69:907, 1965.

158. CONLEY ME, BECKWITH JB, MANCER JFK, TENCKHOFF L: The spectrum of the DiGeorge syndrome. *J Pediatr* 94:883, 1979.

159. CAREY JC: The spectrum of DiGeorge syndrome. *J Pediatr* 96:955, 1980.

160. LAMMER EJ, OPITZ JM: The DiGeorge anomaly as a developmental field defect. *Am J Med Genet (suppl)* 2:113, 1986.

161. GREENBERG F, ELDER FFB, HAFFNER P, NORTHRUP H, LEDBETTER DH: Cytogenetic findings in a prospective series of patients with DiGeorge anomaly. *Am J Hum Genet* (in press).

162. GREENBERG F, VALDES C, ROSENBLATT HM, KIRKLAND JL, LEDBETTER DH: Hypoparathyroidism and T-cell immune defect in a patient with 10p deletion syndrome. *J Pediatr* 109:489, 1986.

163. MCDERMID HE, DUNCAN AMV, BRASCH KR, HOLDEN JJA, MAGENIS E, SHEEHY R, BURN J, KARDON N, NOEL B, SCHINZEL A, TESHIMA I, WHITE BN: Characterization of the supernumerary chromosome in cat eye syndrome. *Science* 232:646, 1986.

164. FIBISON WJ, EMANUEL BS: Molecular mapping in DiGeorge syndrome. *Am J Hum Genet* 41:A119, 1987.

165. GIEDION A: Das Tricho-Rhino-Phalangeale Syndrom. *Helv Paediatr Acta* 21:475, 1966.

166. HALL BD, LANGER LO, GIEDION A, SMITH DW, COHEN MM, BEALS RK, BRANDNER M: Langer-Giedion syndrome. *Birth Defects* 10:147, 1974.

167. LANGER LO, KRASSIKOFF N, LAXOVA R, SCHEER-WILLIAMS M, LUTTER LD, GORLIN RJ, JENNINGS CG, DAY DW: The tricho-rhinophalangeal syndrome with exostoses (or Langer-Giedion syndrome): Four additional patients without mental retardation and review of the literature. *Am J Med Genet* 19:81, 1984.

168. MCKUSICK VA: *Mendelian Inheritance in Man,* 7th ed. Baltimore, MD, Johns Hopkins University Press, 1986.

169. BUHLER EM, BUHLER UK, STADLER GR, JANI L, JURIK LP: Chromosome deletion and multiple cartilaginous exostoses. *Eur J Pediatr* 133:163, 1980.

170. PFEIFFER RA: Langer-Giedion syndrome and additional congenital malformations with interstitial deletion of the long arm of chromosome 8: 46XYdel8(q13-22). *Clin Genet* 18:142, 1980.

171. BOWEN P, BIEDERMAN B, HOO JJ: The critical segment for the Langer-Giedion syndrome: 8q24.11->q24.12. *Ann Genet* 28:224, 1985.

172. FRYNS JP, VAN DEN BERGHE H: 8q24.12 Interstitial deletion in tricho-rhinophalangeal syndrome type I. *Hum Genet* 74:188, 1986.

173. GOLDBLATT J, SMART RD: Tricho-rhino-phalangeal syndrome without exostoses, with an interstitial deletion of 8q23. *Clin Genet* 29:434, 1986.

174. HERRERA L, KAKATI S, GIBAS L, PIETRZAK E, SANDBERG AA: Brief clinical report: Gardner syndrome in a man with an interstitial deletion of 5q. *Am J Med Genet* 25:463, 1986.

175. BODMER WF, BAILEY CJ, BODMER J, BUSSEY HJR, ELLIS A, GORMAN P, LUCIBELLO FC, MURDAY VA, RIDER SH, SCAMBLER P, SHEER D, SOLOMON E, SPURR NK: Localization of the gene for familial adenomatous polyposis on chromosome 5. *Nature* 328:614, 1987.

176. LEPPERT M, DOBBS M, SCAMBLER P, O'CONNELL P, NAKAMURA Y, STAUFFER D, WOODWARD S, BURT R, HUGHES J, GARDNER E, LATHROP M, WASMUTH J, LALOUEL J-M, WHITE R: The gene for familial polyposis coli maps to the long arm of chromosome 5. *Science* 238:1411, 1987.

177. SOLOMON E, VOSS R, HALL V, BODMER WF, JASS JR, JEFFREYS AJ, LUCIBELLO FC, PATEL I, RIDER SH: Chromosome 5 allele loss in human colorectal carcinomas. *Nature* 328:616, 1987.

178. FEARON ER, HAMILTON SR, VOGELSTEIN B: Clonal analysis of human colorectal tumors. *Science* 238:193, 1987.

179. BARKER D, WRIGHT E, NGUYEN K, CANNON L, FAIN P, GOLDGAR D, BISHOP DT, CAREY J, BATY B, KIVLIN J, WILLARD H, WAYE JS, GREIG G, LEINWAND L, NAKAMURA Y, O'CONNELL P, LEPPERT M, LALOUEL J-M, WHITE R, SKOLNICK M: Gene for von Recklinghausen neurofibromatosis is in the pericentromeric region of chromosome 17. *Science* 236:1100, 1987.

180. SEIZINGER BR, ROULEAU GA, OZELIUS LJ, LANE AH, FARYNIARZ AG, CHAO MV, HUSON S, KORF BR, PARRY DM, PERICAK-VANCE MA, COLLINS FS, HOBBS WJ, FALCONE BG, IANNAZZI JA, ROY JC, ST GEORGE-HYSLOP PH, TANZI RE, BOTHWELL MA, UPADHYAYA M, HARPER P, GOLDSTEIN AE, HOOVER DL, BADER JL, SPENCE MA, MULVIHILL JJ, AYLSWORTH AS, VANCE JM, ROSSENWASSER GOD, GASKELL PC, ROSEC AD, MARTUZA RL, BREAKEFIELD XO, GUSELLA JF: Genetic linkage of von Recklinghausen neurofibromatosis to the nerve growth factor receptor gene. *Cell* 49:589, 1987.

181. SCHMIDT MA, MICHELS VV, DEWALD GW: Cases of neurofibromatosis with rearrangements of chromosome 17 involving band 17q11.2. *Am J Med Genet* 28:771, 1987.

182. COHEN AJ, LI FP, BERG S, MARCHETTO DJ, TSAI S, JACOBS SC, BROWN RS: Hereditary renal-cell carcinoma associated with a chromosomal translocation. *N Engl J Med* 301:592, 1979.

183. WANG N, PERKINS KL: Involvement of band 3p14 in t(3;8) hereditary renal carcinoma. *Cancer Genet Cytogenet* 11:479, 1984.

184. GLOVER TW, COYLE-MORRIS JF, LI FP, BROWN RS, BERGER CS, GEMMILL RM, HECHT F: Translocation t(3;8)(p14.2;q24.1) in renal cell carcinoma affects expression of the common fragile site at 3p14 (FRA3B) in lymphocytes. *Cancer Genet Cytogenet* 31:69, 1988.

185. DRABKIN HA, BRADLEY C, HART I, BLESKAN J, LI FP, PATTERSON D: Translocation of c-*myc* in the hereditary renal cell carcinoma associated with a t(3;8)(p14.2;q24.13) chromosomal translocation. *Proc Natl Acad Sci USA* 82:6980, 1985.

186. ZBAR B, BRAUCH H, TALMADGE C, LINEHAN M: Loss of alleles of loci on the short arm of chromosome 3 in renal cell carcinoma. *Nature* 327:721, 1987.

187. WHANG-PENG J, KAO-SHAN CS, LEE EC, BUNN PA, CARNEY DN, GAZDAR AF, MINNA JD: Specific chromosome defect associated with human small cell lung cancer: Deletion 3p(14-23). *Science* 215:181, 1982.

188. NAYLOR SL, JOHNSON BE, MINNA JD, SAKAGUCHI AY: Loss of heterozygosity of chromosome 3p markers in small-cell lung cancer. *Nature* 329:451, 1987.

189. SEIZINGER BR and 31 coauthors: Von Hippel Lindau disease maps to the region of chromosome 3 associated with renal cell carcinoma. *Nature* 332:268, 1988.

190. KIMBERLING WJ, FULBECK T, DIXON L, LUBS HA: Localization of spherocytosis to chromosome 8 or 12 and report of a family with spherocytosis and a reciprocal translocation. *Am J Hum Genet* 27:586, 1975.

191. BASS EB, SMITH SW, STEVENSON RE, ROSSE WF: Further evidence for location of the spherocytosis gene on chromosome 8. *Ann Intern Med* 99:192, 1983.

192. CHILCOTE RR, LE BEAU MM, DAMPIER C, PERGAMENT E, VERLINSKY Y, MOHANDAS N, FRISCHER H, ROWLERY JD: Association of red cell spherocytosis with deletion of the short arm of chromosome 8. *Blood* 69:156, 1987.

193. KITATANI M, CHIYO H, OZAKI M, SHIKE S, MIWA S: Localization of the spherocytosis gene to chromosome segment 8p11.22-8p21.1. *Hum Genet* 78:94, 1988.

194. TOMMERUP N, NIELSON F: A familial reciprocal translocation t(3;7)(p21.1;p13) associated with the Greig polysyndactyly-craniofacial anomalies syndrome. *Am J Med Genet* 16:313, 1983.

195. MOROSS J, VAITHILINGAM SS, STYLES S, GARDNER HA: Autosomal dominant anterior polar cataracts associated with a familial 2;14 translocation. *J Med Genet* 21:52, 1984.

196. ZITER FA, WISER WC, ROBINSON A: Three-generation pedigree of a Mobius syndrome variant with chromosome translocation. *Arch Neurol* 34:437, 1977.

197. HOO JJ, HASLAM RHA, van ORMAN C: Tentative assignment of piebald trait gene to chromosome band 4q12. *Hum Genet* 73:230, 1986.

198. NATT E, WESTPHAL E-M, TOTH-FEJEL SE, MAGENIS RE, BUIST NRM, RETTENMEIER R, SCHERER G: Inherited and de novo deletion of the tyrosine aminotransferase gene locus at 16q22.1→q22.3 in a patient with tyrosinemia type II. *Hum Genet* 77:352, 1987.

199. WEATHERALL DJ, HIGGS DR, BUNCH C, OLD JM, HUNT DM, PRESSLEY L, CLEGG JB, BETHLENFALVAY NC, SJOLIN S, KOLER RD, MAGENIS E, FRANCIS JL, BEBBINGTON D: Hemoglobin H disease and mental retardation: A new syndrome or a remarkable coincidence? *N Engl J Med* 305:607, 1981.

200. BOWCOCK AM, van TONDER S, JENKINS T: The haemoglobin H disease mental retardation syndrome: Molecular studies on the South African case. *Br J Haematol* 56:69, 1984.

201. BLEEKER-WAGEMAKERS LM, FRIEDRICH U, GAL A, WIENKER TF, WAR-

BURG M, ROPERS HH: Close linkage between Norrie disease, a cloned DNA sequence from the proximal short arm, and the centromere on the X chromosome. *Hum Genet* 71:211, 1985.

202. GAL A, STOLZENBERGER C, WIENKER TF, WIEACKER PF, ROPERS HH, FRIEDRICH U, BLEEKER-WAGEMAKERS EM, PEARSON P, WARBURG M: Norrie's disease: Close linkage with genetic markers from the proximal short arm of the X chromosome. *Clin Genet* 27:282, 1985.

203. OHBA N, YAMASHITA T: Primary vitreoretinal dysplasia resembling Norrie's disease in a female: Association with X autosome chromosomal translocation. *Br J Ophthalmol* 70:64, 1986.

204. HORN N, STENE J, MOLLEKAER AM, FRIEDRICH U: Linkage studies in Menkes' disease Xg blood group system and C-banding of the X chromosome. *Ann Hum Genet* 48:161, 1984.

205. KAPUR S, HIGGINS JV, DELP K, ROGERS B: Menkes syndrome in a girl with X-autosome translocation. *Am J Med Genet* 26:503, 1987.

206. HODGSON SV, HECKMATT JZ, HUGHES E, CROLLA JA, DUBOWITZ V, BOBROW M: A balanced de novo X/autosome translocation in a girl with manifestations of Lowe syndrome. *Am J Med Genet* 23:837, 1986.

207. MOSSMAN J, BLUNT S, STEPHENS R, JONES EE, PEMBREY M: Hunter's disease in a girl: Association with X:5 chromosomal translocation disrupting the Hunter gene. *Arch Dis Child* 58:911, 1983.

208. SILVER DN, LEWIS RA, NUSSBAUM RL: Mapping the Lowe oculocerebrorenal syndrome to Xq24-q26 by use of restriction fragment length polymorphisms. *J Clin Invest* 79:282, 1987.

209. UPADHYAYA M, SARFARAZI M, BAMFORTH JS, THOMAS NST, OBERLE I, YOUNG I, HARPER PS: Localisation of the gene for Hunter syndrome on the long arm of X chromosome. *Hum Genet* 74:391, 1986.

210. HODGSON SV, NEVILLE B, JONES RWA, FEAR C, BOBROW M: Two cases of X/autosome translocation in females with incontinentia pigmenti. *Hum Genet* 71:231, 1985.

211. GILGENKRANTZ S, TRIDON P, PINEL-BRIQUEL N, BEUREY J, WEBER M: Translocation (X;9)(p11;q34) in a girl with incontinentia pigmenti (IP): Implications for the regional assignment of the IP locus to Xp11? *Ann Genet* 28:90, 1985.

212. de GROUCHY J, TURLEAU C, DOUSSAU de BAZIGNAN M, MAROTEAUX P, THIBAUD D: Incontinentia pigmenti (IP) and r(X). Tentative mapping of the IP locus to the X juxtacentromeric region. *Ann Genet* 28:86, 1985.

213. ZUFFARDI O, FRACCARO M: Gene mapping and serendipity. The locus for torticollis, keloids, cryptorchidism and renal dysplasia (31430, McKusick) is at Xq28, distal to the G6PD locus. *Hum Genet* 62:281, 1982.

214. ROPERS HH, ZUFFARDI O, BIANCHI E, TIEPOLO L: Agenesis of corpus callosum, ocular, and skeletal anomalies (X-linked dominant Aicardi's syndrome) in a girl with balanced X/3 translocation. *Hum Genet* 61:364, 1982.

215. BAWLE E, TYRKUS M, LIPMAN S, BOZIMOWSKI D: Aarskog syndrome: Full male and female expression associated with an X-autosome translocation. *Am J Med Genet* 17:595, 1984.

216. FRANCKE U, HARPER JF, DARRAS BT, COWAN JM, MCCABE ERB, KOHLSCHUTTER A, SELTZER WK, SAITO F, GOTO J, HARPEY J-P, WISE JE: Congenital adrenal hypoplasia, myopathy, and glycerol kinase deficiency: Molecular genetic evidence for deletions. *Am J Hum Genet* 40:212, 1987.

217. BALLABIO A, SEBASTIO G, CARROZZO R, PARENTI G, PICCIRILLO A, PERSICO MG, ANDRIA G: Deletions of the steroid sulphatase gene in "classical" X-linked ichthyosis and in X-linked ichthyosis associated with Kallmann syndrome. *Hum Genet* 77:338, 1987.

218. YEN PH, ALLEN E, MARSH B, MOHANDAS T, WANG N, TAGGART RT, SHAPIRO LJ: Cloning and expression of steroid sulfatase cDNA and the frequent occurrence of deletions in STS deficiency: Implications for X-Y interchange. *Cell* 49:443, 1987.

219. CURRY CJR, MAGENIS RE, BROWN M, LANMAN JT, TSAI J, O'LAGUE P, GOODFELLOW P, MOHANDAS T, BERGNER EA, SHAPIRO LJ: Inherited chondrodysplasia punctata due to a deletion of the terminal short arm of an X chromosome. *N Engl J Med* 311:1010, 1984.

220. de la CHAPELLE A, SANKILA E-M, LINDLOF M, AULA P, NORIO R: Norrie disease caused by a gene deletion allowing carrier detection and prenatal diagnosis. *Clin Genet* 28:317, 1985.

221. GAL A, WIERINGA B, SMEETS DFCM, BLEEKER-WAGEMAKERS L, ROPERS HH: Submicroscopic interstitial deletion of the X chromosome explains a complex genetic syndrome dominated by Norrie disease. *Cytogenet Cell Genet* 42:219, 1986.

222. NUSSBAUM RL, LEWIS RA, LESKO JG, FERRELL R: Choroideremia is linked to the restriction fragment length polymorphism DXYS1 at Xq13-21. *Am J Hum Genet* 37:473, 1985.

223. LESKO JG, LEWIS RA, NUSSBAUM RL: Multipoint linkage analysis of loci in the proximal long arm of the human X chromosome: Application to mapping the choroideremia locus. *Am J Hum Genet* 40:303, 1987.

224. SCHWARTZ M, ROSENBERG T, NIEBUHR E, LUNDSTEEN C, SARDEMANN H, ANDERSEN O, YANG H-M, LAMM LU: Choroideremia: Further evidence for assignment of the locus to Xq13-Xq21. *Hum Genet* 74:449, 1986.

225. HODGSON SV, ROBERTSON ME, FEAR CN, GOODSHIP J, MALCOLM S, JAY B, BOBROW M, PEMBREY ME: Prenatal diagnosis of X-linked choroideremia with mental retardation, associated with a cytologically detectable X-chromosome deletion. *Hum Genet* 75:286, 1987.

226. NUSSBAUM RL, LESKO JG, LEWIS RA, LEDBETTER SA, LEDBETTER DH: Isolation of anonymous DNA sequences from within a submicroscopic X chromosomal deletion in a patient with choroideremia, deafness, and mental retardation. *Proc Natl Acad Sci USA* 84:6521, 1987.

227. MAGENIS RE, WEBB MJ, MCKEAN RS, TOMAR D, ALLEN LJ, KAMMER H, VANDYKE DL, LOVRIEN E: Translocation (X;Y) (p22.33;p11.2) in XX males: Etiology of male phenotype. *Hum Genet* 62:271, 1982.

228. DISTECHE CM, CASANOVA M, SAAL H, FRIEDMAN C, SYBERT V, GRAHAM J, THULINE H, PAGE DC, FELLOUS M: Small deletions of the short arm of the Y chromosome in 46,XY females. *Proc Natl Acad Sci USA* 83:7841, 1986.

229. GUELLAEN G, CASANOVA M, BISHOP C, GELDWERTH D, ANDRE G, FELLOUS M, WEISSENBACH J: Human XX males with Y single-copy DNA fragments. *Nature* 307:172, 1984.

230. ROUYER F, SIMMLER M-C, PAGE DC, WEISSENBACH J: A sex chromosome rearrangement in a human XX male caused by Alu-Alu recombination. *Cell* 51:417, 1987.

231. PETIT C, de la CHAPELLE A, LEVILLIERS J, CASTILLO S, NOEL B, WEISSENBACH J: An abnormal X-Y interchange accounts for most but not all cases of human XX maleness. *Cell* 49:595, 1987.

232. PAGE DC, BROWN LG, de la CHAPELLE A: Exchange of terminal portions of X- and Y-chromosomal short arms in human XX males. *Nature* 328:437, 1987.

233. PAGE DC, MOSHER R, SIMPSON EM, FISHER EMC, MARDON G, POLLACK J, MCGILLIVRAY B, de la CHAPELLE A, BROWN LG: The sex-determining region of the human Y chromosome encodes a finger protein. *Cell* 51:1091, 1987.

PART 3

CARBOHYDRATES

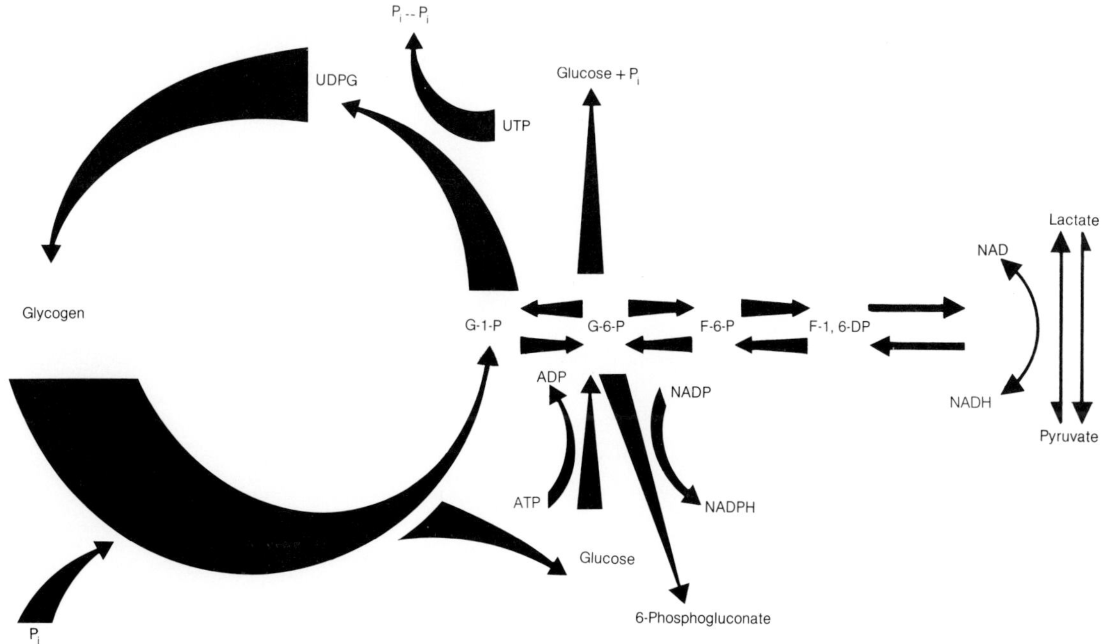

Glycogen metabolism

CHAPTER 10

DIABETES MELLITUS

DANIEL W. FOSTER

1. *Primary diabetes mellitus is a disease characterized by relative or absolute insulin deficiency and relative or absolute glucagon excess. These hormonal derangements produce a set of metabolic abnormalities and a complement of long-term complications involving the eyes, kidneys, nerves, and blood vessels.*
2. *There are two major forms of the primary illness: insulin dependent diabetes mellitus and non-insulin dependent diabetes mellitus. The former is characterized by susceptibility to ketoacidosis in the absence of administered insulin, while the latter is not. Heterogeneity probably exists within both forms. Hyperglycemia occurring in the context of some other disease or genetic abnormality is termed secondary diabetes. The prevalence of diabetes is about 10 per 1000 in the general population, with one-fourth being insulin dependent and the remainder non-insulin dependent. The terms type 1 and type 2, previously considered synonyms for insulin dependent and non-insulin dependent diabetes, respectively, are now reserved for pathogenetic mechanisms. Type 1 diabetes is immune-mediated, while type 2 is not.*
3. *Type 1 diabetes appears to require a permissive genetic background and, in most cases, an environmental factor which may be a virus. The susceptibility gene(s) is probably located on the short arm of the sixth chromosome in the HLA D region. A key feature of pathogenesis is a self → nonself transformation in the β cell of the islets of Langerhans, which activates humoral and cell-mediated autoimmune attack. An early sign of impending immune destruction is the appearance of islet cell antibodies in the blood. The autoimmune process may proceed slowly (years). Thin patients with apparent non-insulin dependent diabetes are often type 1 diabetics in slow evolution.*
4. *Type 2 diabetes seems to be almost completely determined by genetic factors. Autoimmunity is not involved. A secretory defect exists in the β cell, and insulin resistance plays a major role. Obesity accounts for a significant portion of the latter, but an intrinsic lesion may be operative as well. Insulin resistance appears to be primarily due to failure of tyrosine kinase activation following the binding of insulin to the receptor.*
5. *The preeminent metabolic abnormality of diabetes is hyperglycemia caused by consistent overproduction of glucose in the liver (inappropriate gluconeogenesis) coupled with inefficient disposal of glucose in peripheral tissues. Ketogenesis in insulin dependent subjects is due to accelerated mobilization of free fatty acids from the adipose mass and concomitant activation of the fatty acid oxidizing system in the liver. Both hyperglycemia and ketogenesis result from a combination of insulin deficiency and glucagon excess. Insulin deficiency is primarily responsible for the defect in disposal of glucose and increased rates of lipolysis in adipocytes, while glucagon excess manifests itself by altering the hepatic capacity for gluconeogenesis and ketogenesis. The reason that ketogenesis is not activated in non-insulin dependent diabetes is unknown.*
7. *The cause of late degenerative complications in diabetes is not known but an attractive possibility is accumulation of sorbitol in involved tissues consequent to polyol pathway (aldol reductase) activity. In experimental animals retinopathy, neuropathy, and nephropathy can be prevented with inhibitors of aldol reductase. Sorbitol appears to act by inducing deficits of myoinositol which in turn alter phosphoinositide metabolism and Na^+,K^+-ATPase activity. Accelerated atherosclerosis may be caused directly or indirectly by nonenzymatic glycosylation of proteins.*

The term *diabetes mellitus* is not precisely defined. In practice, any condition in which there is an elevation of the plasma glucose under fasting conditions tends to be called diabetes. A number of diseases are associated with persistent hyperglycemia and thus qualify for the diagnosis. This chapter focuses on what might best be called *primary diabetes mellitus*, a human illness characterized by relative or absolute insulin deficiency, relative or absolute glucagon excess, a set of metabolic abnormalities caused by these hormonal derangements, and a complement of long-term complications involving the eyes, kidneys, nerves, and blood vessels.[1]

Diabetes mellitus is an extremely serious disease. Because it is so common, it is now the leading cause of adult blindness and amputations in the United States and a major cause of renal failure, heart attacks, and strokes.[2] Estimates from the Communicable Disease Center indicate that there are 50,000 persons with blindness due to diabetes in the United States with new cases developing at a rate of 5800 per year.[3] Entry rates for amputation (40,000 per year) and end stage renal disease (4000 per year) are also high. Diabetes-associated cardiovascular disease is said to cause 323,000 deaths per year. Although the data on which these figures are based may be somewhat soft, there is no argument that diabetes is a public health problem of enormous proportions.

DIAGNOSIS

The diagnosis of symptomatic diabetes is quite simple since hyperglycemia-induced osmotic diuresis and its associated thirst are easily recognizable. There is also little controversy about diagnosis based on elevated concentrations of glucose in plasma after an overnight fast even if the patient is asymptomatic. The difficulty comes in those subjects considered to be candidates for diabetes but who do not have fasting hyperglycemia. Such persons often are given an oral glucose tolerance test. It is now widely recognized that the standard test over-diagnoses diabetes if the original criteria of Fajans and Conn[4] are utilized.[5] This has resulted in two sets of problems. First, many patients have been given a false diagnosis of serious disease, with resultant high costs in both emotional and economic terms. Second, and more important for the concerns of this chapter, a number of research studies have been rendered suspect because patients were labeled diabetic who probably never had the disease. This is especially true if a glucose tolerance test is done in a patient hospitalized for another illness such as a heart attack. Glucose intolerance under these conditions may be simply the consequence of stress-induced hormonal changes which impair the response to a glucose challenge nonspecifically.[6] In an attempt to deal with these problems, the National Diabetes Data Group has published a new set of standards for the diagnosis of diabetes.[5] The fasting and 2-h postglucose values have been accepted by the World Health Organization.[7] They are as follows:

1. Fasting plasma glucose concentration (venous) $\geq$ 7.8 m*M* (140 mg/dl) on at least two separate occasions.

2. Plasma glucose concentrations (venous) $\geq$ 11.1 m*M* (200 mg/dl) at 2 h and one other intervening point after oral ingestion of 75 g glucose.

Whole blood values are 15 percent less than plasma. Since most early studies used whole blood, corrections are necessary when comparisons are made with investigations where plasma is analyzed.

Although the above criteria diminish the incidence of false positive diagnoses, they are not absolute. It remains possible for a normal person to have a glucose tolerance test in the diagnostic range for diabetes due to stress. Such persons may never develop symptomatic disease.[8] In general, oral glucose tolerance testing should be reserved for research studies.

CLASSIFICATION

An overall classification of diabetes is given in Table 10-1. *Primary* and *secondary* forms are recognized. This classification differs from that recommended by the National Diabetes Data Group[5] and is based on the modification of Unger and Foster.[1]

Previously the terms insulin dependent diabetes mellitus (IDDM) and type 1 diabetes have been considered synonyms as have non-insulin dependent diabetes mellitus (NIDDM) and type 2 diabetes. As constituted here insulin dependent and non-insulin dependent denote physiological states, while the terms type 1 and type 2 refer to pathogenetic mechanisms. *Insulin dependent* means that the patient requires insulin for maintenance of life and will develop ketoacidosis on its withdrawal. *Non-insulin dependent* means that ketoacidosis does not appear even in the absence of exogenous insulin; i.e., subjects with this variant are ketoacidosis-resistant. *Type 1* refers to an immune-mediated destruction of the insulin-producing β cells of the pancreas, while *type 2* signifies that the pathogenetic mechanism is not autoimmune. As is discussed subsequently, it is now recognized that type 1 diabetes mellitus may develop slowly over a number of years and appear at middle age or even late in life. Such patients may have symptomatic hyperglycemia in the absence of risk for ketoacidosis over prolonged periods although the pathogenetic mechanism is autoimmune.[9,10] The clinical clue is that the subjects are not obese, while the vast majority of subjects with type 2 NIDDM are overweight. Patients who are nonobese and develop late onset insulin dependent diabetes express the same HLA susceptibility markers seen in classic early onset IDDM.[11] For this reason the classification shown in Table 10-1 divides NIDDM into type 1 and type 2 categories, the former representing subjects in slow evolution from NIDDM to IDDM due to an autoimmune process. Formal identification of the autoimmune mechanism (not currently a necessity in the clinical situation) requires the demonstration of the expected HLA determinants, islet cell antibodies, and hypoinsulinemia rather than the normal or elevated values of insulin characteristically seen in classic type 2 NIDDM.[12] Tropical pancreatic diabetes, which is sometimes considered a variant of type 2 NIDDM, is actually a secondary form of diabetes due to chronic pancreatitis.[13] It is not seen in the United States or Western Europe.

To summarize, three forms of primary diabetes can be identified: *type 1 insulin dependent diabetes, type 1 non-insulin dependent diabetes,* and *type 2 non-insulin dependent diabetes.* Recognition that some persons with apparent NIDDM actually have type 1 disease in slow evolution has helped explain the observation that some patients have their first episode of ketoacidosis in middle age or later. This seemed a paradox when it was thought that type 1 IDDM, which has a peak age of onset around 14 years, never developed beyond the third decade. Now it is recognized that type 1 disease may become clinically manifest at any age although onset is statistically rare beyond the late twenties.

There are numerous conditions that fit into the category of *secondary* diabetes. Some produce only mild glucose intolerance, while others cause a full-blown diabetic syndrome even to the point of ketoacidosis. *Pancreatic diseases,* the most common of which is chronic pancreatitis in alcoholics, induce hyperglycemia because the β-cell mass is decreased in the generalized destructive process, resulting in hypoinsulinemia. *Hormonal diabetes* may result from primary endocrine disease (acromegaly, Cushing syndrome, pheochromocytoma) or as a consequence of the administration of hormones for therapeutic purposes. Mechanisms include both inhibition of insulin release and induction of insulin resistance. Numerous *drugs* act in similar fashion (a list is available in Ref. 5). An interesting secondary syndrome is glucose intolerance due to *dysfunction of insulin receptors* in the plasma membranes of cells; these are discussed briefly at the end of this chapter. A variety of *genetic syndromes* are associated with clinical diabetes or abnormal glucose tolerance.[14] The best known are the lipodystrophic states, ataxia telangiectasia, and myotonic dystrophy. The category designated *other* is undefined, the only condition listed by the National Diabetes Data Group being severe malnutrition.

Table 10-1 Classification of Diabetes

A. Primary
  1. Insulin dependent diabetes mellitus (IDDM), type 1
  2. Non-insulin dependent diabetes mellitus (NIDDM)
    a. Type 1 (nonobese)
    b. Type 2 (obese)

B. Secondary
  1. Pancreatic disease
  2. Hormonal abnormalities
  3. Drug- or chemical-induced
  4. Insulin receptor abnormalities
  5. Genetic syndromes
  6. Other

PREVALENCE

The prevalence of diabetes mellitus is difficult to determine accurately because of the problems of diagnosis outlined above. Further, rates differ according to the race, age, and sex of the sample under study. For example, Pima Indians of the United States have an overall prevalence for diabetes of 19 percent. This increases to 47 percent in men between the ages 65 and 74 and reaches 69 percent in women between ages 55 and 64.[15] By contrast, hyperglycemia and glucose intolerance are extremely rare in Alaskan Indians and Inuits at any age.[16]

In the United States the National Health Interview Survey estimated the prevalence of all diabetes at 2.4 percent.[17] This was based solely on self-identification without access to medical verification. Utilizing medical records, prevalence is in the 1.4 to 1.6 percent range in the United States.[18] In Sweden a value of 1.5 percent has been cited.[8] In a massive diabetes detection program in Cleveland, 307,208 subjects (essentially all >20 years of age) had glucose concentrations determined in capillary whole blood 2 h after ingestion of 75 g glucose.[19] A value of greater than 7.8 m*M* (140 mg/dl) was obtained in 12,600 (4.1 percent). Of these, 40 percent were 10 m*M* (180 mg/dl) or higher. Since 10 m*M* is close to the 11.1 m*M* 2-h postprandial value considered the diagnostic level for diabetes after glucose tolerance testing by the National Diabetes Data Group and the World Health Organization, the prevalence in this population would appear to be no more than 1.6 percent of the adult population. The percentage of abnormal test results increased with age, a reproducible finding in all studies of glucose tolerance in large populations. Thus there is a remarkable similarity in estimates of prevalence for unclassified diabetes in Western societies utilizing laboratory testing in large populations. These figures are probably still too high, since a 5-year follow-up of the subjects with 2-h posttest glucose values of ⩾ 10 m*M* showed a progression to overt diabetes in only 31 percent in the Cleveland study.[19] These data suggest that the true prevalence of diabetes in the general population may be somewhere around 1 percent, with symptomatic diabetes being even less.

Solid estimates for yearly rates of appearance of diabetes are virtually nonexistent, although a figure of 140 per 100,000 annually has been claimed in Sweden,[8] 112 per 100,000 in Rochester, Minnesota,[20] and 267 per 100,000 by the survey method[3] in the United States. Even the lower figures may be too high since most of the patients in Rochester whose initial diagnosis was based on glucose tolerance testing did not deteriorate to overt diabetes.

Data on yearly rates in children are more reliable since ascertainment is usually based on the development of symptomatic disease or elevated fasting plasma glucose values rather than on glucose tolerance testing. A registry of newly diagnosed diabetics under the age of 16 in Great Britain indicated a yearly appearance rate of 8 per 100,000.[21] A similar study in New Zealand found the annual prevalence to be 10.4 per 100,000 in subjects under 20 years of age.[22] Rates between ages 11 and 19 were double those of ages 1 to 9, the peak occurring in the 10- to 15-year range. The most thorough study in the United States was carried out in Allegheny County, Pennsylvania, between 1965 and 1976.[23] All cases under the age of 20 were identified from hospital records and surveys of pediatric practices in the county. The number of persons at risk was a little over a half-million. Annual rates were (per 100,000): white males, 16; white females, 15; nonwhite males, 10; and nonwhite females, 11. The highest prevalence in all groups was between 10 and 14 years of age. The authors cited 10 population-based surveys of the prevalence of type 1 diabetes. The lowest rate was 3.7 per 100,000 per year in France, while the highest was 19.6 per 100,000 per year in Sweden. Utilizing 13 per 100,000 as an average annual rate of appearance (based on the Pittsburgh study), the prevalence of type 1 diabetes in the United States at age 20 should be approximately 0.26 percent (20 × 0.013 percent). Walker and Cudworth estimated the prevalence in England at age 16 to be 0.22 percent.[24] Comparison of these figures with the total estimate of the prevalence of diabetes in adults (about 1 percent) suggests that about one-fourth of the total cases will represent type 1 disease while three-fourths will be other forms, the bulk of which represent primary type 2 illness. Ratios of type 1 to type 2 diabetes are higher in young populations and much lower in the older age range. Some authors have stated that overall type 2 NIDDM is 10 times more prevalent than type 1 diabetes.[3] Such ratios are obtained by subtracting the relatively hard figures for the latter from the soft figures for total diabetes based on surveys. These high ratios are not valid because the prevalence of total diabetes has been overestimated, as noted above.

PATHOGENESIS OF TYPE 1 DIABETES MELLITUS

A current overview of pathogenesis of type 1 diabetes may be stated as follows (Fig. 10-1). Susceptibility is genetically determined with a primary vulnerability gene located in the D region of the major histocompatibility locus on the short arm of the sixth chromosome which codes for histocompatibility leukocyte antigens (HLA). In most cases the genetic determinant is permissive and not causal so that an environmental triggering event is normally required. As a consequence of the genetic-environmental interaction the insulin-producing β cells of the pancreas undergo a self → nonself transition that renders them recognizable by the immune system which becomes activated for attack. A common (invariant?) accompaniment of the process is infiltration of the islets of Langerhans by activated T lymphocytes, a process designated *insulitis*. Early evidence of the autoimmune process is the appearance in plasma of islet cell antibodies of a variety of types. Signs of cell-mediated immunity are also seen. With time virtually the entire β-cell population is destroyed, symptoms ordinarily not appearing until 10 percent or fewer of the β-cells remain. The destructive process may occur rapidly but usually appears to follow a more indolent course over a several-year period.

Although this formulation has attractive features, it must still be considered tentative at almost every point. The various aspects will be discussed separately in the following sections.

Genetics

The genetics of type 1 diabetes is not well understood. Phenotypic expression (overt disease) does not allow conclusions to be drawn in classic Mendelian terms. The primary susceptibility gene has not been identified although it is essentially certain that at least one gene is located in the HLA-D region. More than 90 percent, probably 95 percent, of patients ex-

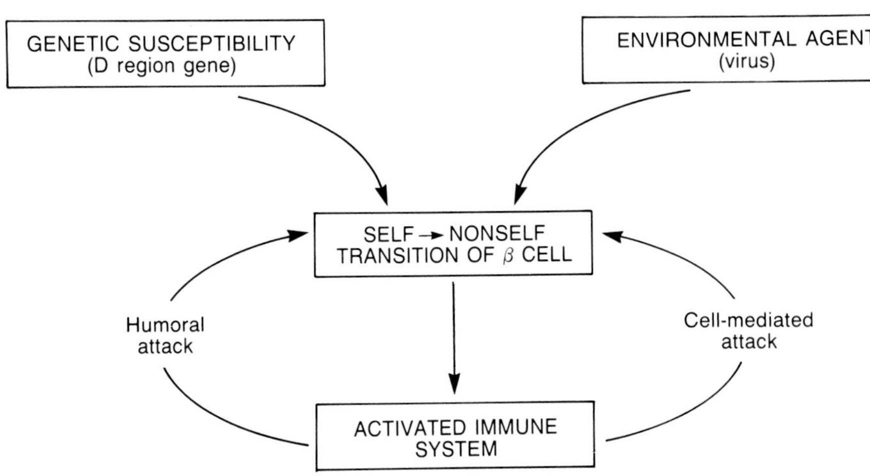

Fig. 10-1 Overview of the pathogenesis of type 1 diabetes mellitus. Genetic susceptibility appears to reside in the HLA-D region of the sixth chromosome. In most cases an environmental agent, possibly viral, is required. The key event is transformation of the β cell from self (immunologically invisible) to nonself (immunologically visible). Activation of the immune system results with destruction of insulin-producing cells by both humoral and cell-mediated attack.

press HLA-DR3 or DR4 with a significant percentage (≈30 percent) bearing the heterozygous DR3/DR4 combination.[25–28] The latter confers increased risk relative to DR3 or DR4 homozygotes or to either gene in combination with an allele other than 3 or 4 (DR3/x or DR4/x, x being non 3 or 4). Expression of DR3 or 4 alone confers increased risk relative to the non 3/4 population. However, type 1 diabetes can exist in the absence of DR3 or DR4, and the converse is also true, namely, DR3 or DR4 may be present in the absence of diabetes. Estimates of gene frequency for HLA-DR3 and DR4 in the normal white population vary from 20 to 40 percent and average 25 percent.

A number of authors have postulated a second susceptibility gene for diabetes located either on the sixth chromosome or elsewhere.[26,27] Candidate sites have been the 5′ upstream region of the insulin gene on chromosome 11,[29] the region coding for the heavy chain of immunoglobulin (G_m allotype) on chromosome 14,[30,31] the gene for the kappa light chain (K_m allotype)[32] and the Kidd marker[33] on chromosome 2. Polymorphisms at the haptoglobin site have also been discussed. By and large these associations have proven weak or nonexistent.[34–39] The assumption will be made here that the major susceptibility gene is located in the HLA complex. Less attractive is the possibility that the inducing gene is simply in linkage disequilibrium with the major histocompatibility region.[40]

Although the genetic picture remains murky, some conclusions can be drawn from studies in families and from molecular insights into the operation of the HLA D region.

Family Studies. The risk for diabetes in identical twins, where one twin has type 1 disease and the other does not, is less than 50 percent.[41] The risk for first-degree relatives of a proband with IDDM is under 10 percent in white families (Table 10-2).[42–44] Estimates for blacks, Hispanics, and Asians are not available although it is known that prevalence of type 1 diabetes is less in these populations.[45,46] Transmission mechanisms in blacks are probably similar to those in whites since it is highly likely that susceptibility to IDDM in blacks is due to infusion of white genes.[47] This is in accord with the observation that HLA distribution in American blacks reflects that found in whites and does not mirror the makeup found in African populations.[48]

Table 10-2 Empirical Risk for Type 1 Diabetes to Age 80

Proband's age at onset, years	Parents (n = 1083)	Siblings (n = 982), % ± SEM	Children (n = 649)
<25	2.2 ± 0.6	6.9 ± 1.3	5.6 ± 2.8
⩾25	4.9 ± 1.4	5.8 ± 1.8	4.3 ± 2.2
Total	2.9 ± 0.6	6.6 ± 1.1	4.9 ± 1.7

SOURCE: Data from Tillil and Köbberling.[44]

The low transmission rates just cited have forced attention on HLA patterns as clues to mechanisms of inheritance. The debate has been lively. As noted above, the presence of either DR3 or DR4 alone increases the risk of diabetes and DR3/DR4 heterozygosity further multiplies it. It is also known that the risk of disease in first degree relatives is haplotype-dependent.[49] If a nondiabetic sib shares both HLA haplotypes with a diabetic sib, the risk of getting diabetes is 20 to 30 percent, roughly equivalent to the risk in identical twins. If one haplotype is shared, the risk falls to about 5 percent, and if neither is shared, the chance of getting diabetes is only 1 percent. The most popular explanation of these findings is a "mixed" model of inheritance in which one allele conferring susceptibility acts recessively while the other behaves in dominant fashion.[50] The putative dominant allele is thought to be associated with the HLA DR4 serotype, while HLA-DR3 is presumed to express the weaker or recessive function.[51] Some authors continue to favor a strict recessive inheritance,[52] but this view is not widely accepted.[50,53]

Some odd things have been noted about the transmission of diabetes in families. There may be a preferential (nonrandom) transfer of the presumed susceptibility alleles from parents to offspring, especially diabetic offspring.[54,55] Parents expressing DR3/x or DR4/x are reported to pass the diabetogenic alleles more than the predicted 50 percent of the time to all offspring and nearly 75 percent of the time to diabetic offspring. Preferential transfer was greater from fathers than from mothers, although this phenomenon has not always been confirmed.[51] Transmission distortion may account for the fact that type 1 diabetes is not decreasing in the population despite lethal complications that shorten life expectancy. A confounding observation is that preferential transfer of DR3/DR4 heterozygosity may apply to the first child of conducive parents with diabetes but not later affected sibs; i.e., an excess of DR3/DR4 was found in the first sib with diabetes, as expected, but not in second diabetic children.[52]

Another puzzling observation is that children of fathers with type 1 diabetes are approximately five times more likely to inherit the disease than children of mothers with diabetes.[56] Explanations are speculative, but two have received emphasis:

excess intrauterine loss of the fetus in diabetic mothers and diminished reparative recombinations between linked loci during gametogenesis in males.

HLA-D region genes may have other effects than on susceptibility to diabetes. Patients with type 1 IDDM and the DR3 serotype appear to have a milder illness with less ketoacidosis than subjects expressing DR4.[28,57] DR3/DR4 heterozygotes have more rapid destruction of β cells and shorter remissions ("honeymoon periods") than non-DR3/DR4 subjects.[58] T-lymphocyte response to antigen is lower with DR3-linked HLA restriction than with DR4.[59]

Molecular Genetics. The critical question at the molecular level is whether the putative diabetes susceptibility gene(s) on the sixth chromosome is in the D region itself or only in linkage disequilibrium with the D region (i.e., segregates nonrandomly with certain D alleles). The concept of linkage is based on the fact that diabetes may occur in the absence of the high risk DR3/DR4 genes[52,60] and on the observation that "extended" haplotypes (e.g., HLA-B15, C4-A3B3, Bf-S, HLA-DR4) often confer greater risk than DR3 or DR4 assayed as single alleles.[40,61–63] These findings would be compatible with a gene location outside the D region. However, for reasons to be discussed, the view that susceptibility gene(s) itself is in the D region is attractive. The data on extended haplotypes may simply indicate that certain structural configurations predispose to induction of diabetogenic mutations or favor transmission of the susceptibility gene(s) to offspring.

The HLA System. Advances in understanding of the HLA system and its function have been rapid such that terminology is not always uniform. A schematic overview of the human major histocompatibility complex is shown in Fig. 10-2. Each site is designated by letter with identifiable alleles given numbers (e.g., HLA-DR3, HLA-B15). A small *w* indicates a provisional antigen not yet considered definitive by the International Histocompatibility Workshop. Gene products of the A, B, and C regions are designated *class I* molecules, while cell surface proteins coded by the D region are called *class II* molecules. Class I molecules are present on all nucleated cells, while class II molecules are normally present only on cells of the immune system: monocyte-macrophages, B lymphocytes, and activated T lymphocytes. Class I but not class II molecules are closely associated with the insulin receptor.[64,65] Class I molecules are thought to have a primary role in defending against viruses. Class II molecules function primarily as restriction agents in activation and regulation of the immune response to foreign or self-antigens. Complement-related gene products (C2, Bf, C4A,B) are sometimes called *class III* molecules.

The D region, which is of primary interest in type 1 diabetes, consists of DP, DQ, and DR sites and a less well understood region tentatively designated DO or DZ.[66] DP and DQ consist of two α and two β genes, although in some reports the second α- and β-chain genes at DP are called SXα and SXβ, while the second set at DQ is called DXα and DXβ. The DR region has a single invariant α gene and three β genes, the second of which is a pseudogene, missing the first domain found in DR βI and DR βIII. How these genes are controlled is not yet known, but it is presumed that only one α and one β gene are active at each site in a given individual.[67]

Assays for the D region antigens vary.[67] DR and DQ are ordinarily analyzed serologically in clinical situations, but both can also be identified by radioimmunoassays, monoclonal antibodies, and T-cell responses. DP is assayed by T-lymphocyte reactivity and by monoclonal antibodies. Tests based on cell typing are designated *MLC* (mixed lymphocyte culture), *HTC* (homozygous typing cell), or *PLT* (primed lymphocyte typing). Serologically defined and T-lymphocyte-determined antigens are not identical. Overlapping determinants are called *supertypic*; e.g., DQw1 is supertypic to DR1, DR2, and DRw6, which in turn are said to be *subtypic* to DQw1. Thus all individuals expressing one of these three DR alleles will likely also express DQw1.

D-Region Subclassification. It is now known that serologic assessment of DR alleles is too broad to accurately determine genetic risk for type 1 IDDM or identify the susceptibility genes. Particular subtypes of a given DR may confer much higher risk than that predicted by serologic assessment.[68–70] A popular approach to subclassification is based on restriction endonucleases to evaluate restriction fragment length polymorphisms (RFLP). The most informative probes for both susceptibility[71–77] and resistance[76,78] to type 1 diabetes derive from DQα and DQβ clones.

An illustration of the explanatory power of subclassification follows. It is known that persons with type 1 diabetes rarely express HLA-DR2, which has been designated a protective or resistance allele. Occasionally, however, diabetes occurs with DR2. When 11 such patients were studied, it was found that nine carried a DQβ allele designated DQR1.[74] Only two healthy controls expressed this allele. The interesting point is that DQR1 is normally associated with HLA-DR1, an allele known to increase the risk of diabetes. Thus one could conclude that recombinations had shifted the genetic makeup from the normal HLA-DR1/DQR1 to HLA-DR2/DQR1,

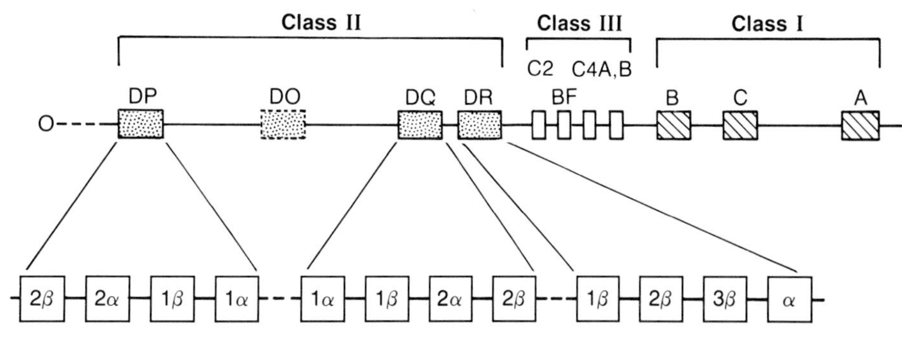

Fig. 10-2 The HLA System. A schematic view of the HLA region on the short arm of the sixth chromosome is shown. Gene products encoded at sites A, B, and C are given the shorthand designation class I, while D region products are designated class II. Complement-related products are sometimes called class III molecules. The DO site is provisional. DP and DQ regions have two α and two β genes. The DR site has a single α and three β genes. *(Modified from CB Carpenter, Harrison's Principles of Internal Medicine, 11th ed. New York: McGraw-Hill, 1987, p. 337.)*

thereby converting HLA-DR2 from "resistant" to "susceptible." The narrowing capacity of subclassification is further illustrated in Table 10-3. Individuals bearing HLA-DR2 and the supertypic DQw1 have differing disease susceptibilities depending on DQ subsets. The presence of Dw2 by MLC and the DQR2.6 RFLP predisposes to multiple sclerosis, while Dw"AZH" by MLC and the DQR1 RFLP indicates vulnerability to type 1 IDDM. Along similar lines both type 1 diabetes and juvenile rheumatoid arthritis are associated with HLA-DR4. However, the two can be clearly distinguished by a DQβ probe: type 1 IDDM, DR4/DQ3.2; juvenile rheumatoid arthritis, DR4/DQ3.1.[75] It is likely that sequencing of D-region genes will further clarify these issues. Distinct nucleotide abnormalities have already been found that correlate with type 1 IDDM,[79] and "hot spots" of gene conversion have been demonstrated. For example, such a spot exists between nucleotides 190 and 210 in the first domain of the β1 locus in individuals expressing HLA-DR1 by serologic typing.[80] Point mutations or the shift of small nucleotide segments from one gene to another could result in the appearance of epitopes in the protein structure of the gene product that might cause immune activation but not be reflected in serologic tests. In this regard it has been noted that absence of aspartic acid at position 57 of DQβ alleles strongly correlates with susceptibility to insulin dependent diabetes in whites.[80a] Homozygosity for aspartate 57 appears to render the subject resistant to diabetes while the presence of one aspartate 57 confers resistance that is not complete. The role of gene conversion has been extensively explored in the murine histocompatibility complex[81] and has also been directly demonstrated in the human D region where the βIII gene of DR6 was shown to be donor to the βI gene of DR3.[80] The system is even more complicated because of the possibility of *transcomplementation*. This refers to the construction of hybrid molecules between chains of opposite haplotypes on the cell surface; i.e., a DQα chain from the maternal haplotype could mix with a DQβ chain from the paternal haplotype to give a functionally distinct DQ molecule. A well known phenomena in mice, transcomplementation has now been demonstrated directly in a human with type 1 IDDM.[82]

How might a particular D-region molecule function to confer risk of diabetes? Almost certainly the answer will prove to be, one way or another, by coupling with other antigens in such a way as to induce autoimmunity.[66] One possibility, to be discussed below, is that D-region antigens appear on the β cell where they are normally not found. In the presentation of protein or peptide antigens (e.g., viruses, bacteria) to the immune system the initial step is uptake or engulfment by monocyte-macrophages with breakdown of the antigen to short peptides. These peptides are then inserted into the plasma membrane where they bind to a class II HLA molecule that is constitutively present and genetically determined. A major function of the class II molecule appears to be positioning of the antigen for recognition by the T-cell receptor on the responding helper-inducer T lymphocyte.[83] The T lymphocyte cannot "dock" on the antigen presenting cell unless the class II molecule is recognizable for binding by the T-cell receptor.[84] Each class II molecule has a single site for peptide binding, but this site can recognize groups of antigens which interact competitively.[85] The way in which binding takes place determines whether the immune system is activated. For example, even a foreign antigen might be recognized as *self* (nonimmunogenic) if bound in a particular configuration.[83,85] It is conceivable that the reverse is also true, namely, that a mutated D-region molecule might bind a self-antigen, constitutively present on the surface of the cell, in such a configuration that it appeared to be *nonself*.

On the basis of these data it seems attractive to conclude that the primary susceptibility genes for type 1 diabetes are altered D-region molecules capable of presenting antigens on the β cell in a configuration that is not immunologically silent. Possible conditions for the appearance of class II molecules on the β cell are discussed below. Modulating factors ("second genes") likely involve the repertoire of T cells capable of recognizing the neoantigen or variations in the effector response of the immune system (e.g., lymphokine production, activation of T cells).

The Environmental Event

The suggested requirement for a nongenetic trigger from the environment for initiation of type 1 diabetes is based primarily on the previously mentioned observation that monozygotic twins are concordant for diabetes less than 50 percent of the time[41] and that siblings who are HLA haplotype identical have concordance rates of only 20 to 30 percent.[26,49] Viruses are usually postulated to be the initiating agent.[26] In principle, chemicals could act in the same manner, although only the rat poison Vacor has been documented to have this effect in humans.[86] The evidence for a viral cause is really quite soft.[87] On one occasion Coxsackie B4 was isolated from the pancreas of a boy dying with recent onset diabetes and ketoacidosis.[88] When the virus was injected into rodents, the animals developed hyperglycemia. A Coxsackie B5 virus isolated from the stool of a 16-month-old child who developed diabetes caused glucose intolerance when transferred to mice.[89] Perhaps the best documented relationship is with rubella virus. Twelve to twenty percent of children with the congenital rubella syndrome develop type 1 diabetes.[90] Affected subjects carry the

Table 10-3 Disease Associations in Subdivisions of HLA-DR2*

Serology		*Cellular (MLC)*	*2 D gel electrophoresis*	*RFLP*	*Disease*
DR2	DQw1	Dw2	DR β2	DQR2.6	Multiple sclerosis, narcolepsy
DR2	DQw1	Dw"AZH"	DR β2	DQR1	Type 1 diabetes

*Widely differing disease associations are found with the same DR serotype. HLA-DR2 is normally considered a protection or resistance allele against type 1 diabetes mellitus. However, a subset of DR2 identified by restriction fragment length polymorphism (RFLP) DQR1 and the Dw"AZH" antigen in mixed lymphocyte culture (MLC) is highly susceptible to type 1 diabetes. The presence of RFLP DQR2.6 coupled with MLC-determined Dw2 identifies susceptibility to entirely different diseases: multiple sclerosis or narcolepsy.

typical HLA predisposing genes and develop islet cell antibodies. Rubella virus also causes diabetes in the golden Syrian hamster.[91]

Indirect evidence for a possible role of viruses continues to accumulate. For example between 1982 and 1984 the incidence of IDDM doubled in Poland, strongly suggesting a major alteration in environmental risk factors.[92] Two-thirds of children with new onset diabetes in Sweden had IgM antibodies against Coxsackie B, while only 12 percent of normal children had evidence of recent infection.[93]

It is usually assumed that diabetogenic viruses act by inducing autoimmunity. However, under certain circumstances they appear to initiate disease directly via inflammatory destruction and not through immune mechanisms.[94] An early lesion in all forms of diabetes is loss of glucose-induced insulin release. This occurs with some viral infections even though permanent diabetes or altered structure of the islets does not result.[95] The fact that viruses can reproduce the characteristic initial lesion of diabetes would be in accord with a pathogenetic role.

There seems to be little doubt that environmental agents alter the probability of developing type 1 diabetes.[49] The critical question is whether an environmental trigger is *necessary* to develop the disease. A final answer cannot be given, but evidence against the necessity of an environmental factor can be summarized as follows. (1) Identical twins may not be identical shortly after birth because of diversity introduced in immunoglobulin molecules and the T-cell receptor.[49,66] This removes the power of the concordance argument from twin studies. (2) The nonobese diabetic (NOD) mouse and the Biobreeding (BB) rat, models of type 1 diabetes, appear to develop diabetes independently from environmental factors.[49] Diet can prevent diabetes in the BB animal but does so by modulating the immune system.[96] (3) The same genetic lesion may produce quantitatively different physiological responses. Thus diabetes-prone BB animals that remain nondiabetic have diminished insulin response to glucose, although the defect is not as marked as in the frankly diabetic BB rats.[97] In other words, the same genotype produced differing phenotypes even when animals were kept in identical environments. Presumably some as yet unknown factor altered the extent of β-cell damage in the susceptible animals that did not progress to overt disease. (4) An interesting experimental model suggests that gene expression in the β cell may be under some sort of timing control with markedly different outcomes depending on the time of expression. When a fusion gene made up of the promoter region of the insulin structural gene and the T antigen of the SV40 virus was prepared and injected into fertilized eggs, it was expressed exclusively in the pancreatic β cells.[98] In some of the transgenic mice, antibodies to T developed, but in others autoimmunity did not develop. Early expression of the T antigen seemed to induce tolerance, while later expression appeared to be associated with autoimmunity.

On the basis of these clues it seems possible, even likely, that some patients develop type 1 diabetes in the absence of an environmental trigger. In most cases the process is probably induced or speeded by an environmental factor which acts in the self → nonself transition.

The Autoimmune Process

There seems to be little doubt that type 1 diabetes is an autoimmune disease.[25–27,99] Islet cell antibodies of a variety of types (cytoplasmic, surface, complement fixing, and immunoprecipitating) are ubiquitous in newly diagnosed diabetic subjects[100] and are likewise present prior to development of symptomatic disease.[101] The fact that the islet cell antibodies cross-react with other endocrine tissues[102] may account for the fact that type 1 diabetes may occur with other endocrine disease as part of the immune endocrinopathy syndrome.[103] Anti-insulin antibodies are common.[104–107] They probably represent simply another marker of the autoimmune process, although some workers continue to think they serve to differentiate a particular subset of the disease.[108] Interpretation is difficult because common viruses have the capacity to induce insulin autoantibodies but only rarely cause the appearance of islet cell antibodies.[109] Persuasive evidence that autoimmunity is cause rather than consequence of β-cell destruction comes from the observation that a variety of immune interventions prevents diabetes in the NOD mouse and the BB rat.[99] Under certain circumstances, human diabetes can be reversed by immunosuppression.[110]

The cause of the autoimmune process leading to type 1 diabetes is unknown, but interest has focused on two areas: (1) an imbalance in immunoregulation due to abnormality in suppressor T-cell function and (2) the appearance of class II HLA molecules on the surface of β cells in the pancreas where they are not normally found.

Is There a Defect in Suppressor T-Cell Function in Type 1 Diabetes (and Other Autoimmune Diseases)? The answer to this question cannot be given with certainty. Direct evidence for a functional defect in immune suppression is essentially nonexistent. Peripheral blood monocytes from normal individuals reportedly inhibit cytotoxic attack against isolated islets by activated T lymphocytes from patients with type 1 diabetes, while similar cells from diabetic subjects do not, but the experiments are unpersuasive.[111]

It is known that lymphopenia is necessary for development of diabetes in the BB rat and that a specific subset of T cells (RT6) is involved.[112] This subset contains both helper and suppressor T cells, but overall the number of apparent suppressor cells was depressed to a greater extent than the fraction bearing surface markers suggestive of helper function. Helper-suppressor T-cell ratios have been extensively examined in human type 1 diabetes. Early reports suggested disproportionate deficiencies of suppressor T cells (which would leave helper cells unbalanced, favoring exuberant immune response), but better studies have failed to confirm such a deficit.[113–115] Modest lymphopenia is generally found, but surprisingly the CD4 (T4) subset of cells (ordinarily considered to be primarily helper) has generally been found to be more depressed than the CD8 (T8) suppressor fraction.[113–116] This may be important, since in lupus erythematosus,[117] multiple sclerosis,[118] and probably rheumatoid arthritis[119] a subset of helper cells that *induces* suppressor clones is deficient, resulting in decreased suppressor activity in mixed lymphocyte culture together with increased IgG production in vitro. In other words, deficiency of an inducer population results in diminished suppressor function, presumably due to absence of a small but important fraction of suppressor T lymphocytes that may not be detected in counts of CD8-bearing cells. It follows that CD4/CD8 ratios, often used as clues to up-regulated or down-regulated immune systems, may be insufficient to understand regulatory dysfunction in a number of autoimmune diseases. Compatible with a primary inducer defect is the observation that infusion of helper T cells prevents diabetes in the diabetes-prone BB rat.[120]

It is concluded that decreased suppressor function may be important in the autoimmunity of type 1 diabetes. An entirely plausible scenario might be: ↓ CD4+ (inducer) subset → ↓ CD8+ suppressor subset → selective activation or hyperresponsiveness of the immune system. The nature of the putative inducer defect and whether it is constitutive or acquired is not known.

Is the Self → Nonself Transition Mediated by the Appearance of Class II HLA Molecules on the Surface of the β Cell? The most popular hypothesis for endocrine autoimmunity follows the suggestion of Bottazzo, Pujol-Borrell, and Hanafusa[121] that initiation of the process is due to an acquired expression of HLA D-region products on endocrine cells. The basic idea is that the appearance of the class II molecule allows presentation of autoantigens (presumably already on the cell surface) in such a way that the immune system would see them as foreign.[122] It is clear that class II molecules are found on the β cells of humans dying with type 1 diabetes.[123,124] They are not expressed on α cells. Some investigators have reported similar findings in the diabetic BB rat.[125] Class II antigens have also been found on human thyroid epithelial cells.[121,126]

The presumption has been that D-region products are induced by lymphokines with primary emphasis placed on γ-interferon.[121] The latter agent has been directly shown to stimulate the appearance of class II molecules on murine islets[127,128] as well as thyroid cells.[129] Human islets appear to require the combined activity of γ-interferon and another lymphokine for induction in vitro.[130] This may account for reports that γ-interferon induced class I but not class II molecules on both human pancreatic cells obtained from brain-dead donors and a rat insulinoma cell line.[131,132] In the BB strain only diabetes-prone animals show the effect; diabetes-resistant BB rats and normal Wistar animals do not induce with γ-interferon.[127] In normal mice interferon may induce expression of class II molecules on both β and non-β cells.[128]

Viral illness is considered the ordinary inducer of γ-interferon release in humans. The overall sequence would thus be: virus → γ interferon production → appearance of class II molecules.[121] However, it is of interest that messenger RNA for the DRα chain is readily demonstrable in normal thyroid tissue.[133] The amounts of message were higher in glands from patients with autoimmune thyroid disease. This finding raises the possibility that "autonomous" (not requiring viral infection or any environmental stimulus) induction of class II molecules might occur in some patients. A potential mechanism might be altered methylation of the structural genes for D-region molecules. For example, DR expression on B lymphocytes is low in lupus erythematosus.[134] Examination of 12 cell lines from normal subjects showed identical methylation patterns at 5 CCGG sites in the HLA DRα locus. By contrast, 28 cell lines from patients with lupus erythematosus showed distinct methylation and hypermethylation patterns. Presumably hypermethylation accounted for decreased transcription rates of the DRα gene. Hypomethylation would be expected to have the reverse effect.

The overall hypothesis is shown in Fig. 10-3.[135] In the nondiabetic state the β cell is devoid of D-region antigens on the cell surface presumably because the genes are inactive (or, if transcribed, trafficked in such a way that the products do not reach the plasma membrane). Initiation of the pathogenetic sequence would commonly involve acquisition of a viral infection affecting the pancreas with local production of γ-interferon and other lymphokines. Interferon would then induce the appearance of class II molecules on the cell surface. If the individual's D region contains a susceptibility gene for diabetes, then the immune system would be activated. If a nonsusceptible or resistance molecule was induced, the immune system would not be activated. As noted earlier, susceptibility genes likely code for class II molecules that present self-antigens in a conformation recognized by the helper T cell as nonself, while resistance genes code for proteins that present surface antigens in a conformation read by the helper T cell as self. The activated immune system then attacks by both hormonal and cell-mediated mechanisms, eventually destroying the β cells and leading to diabetes.

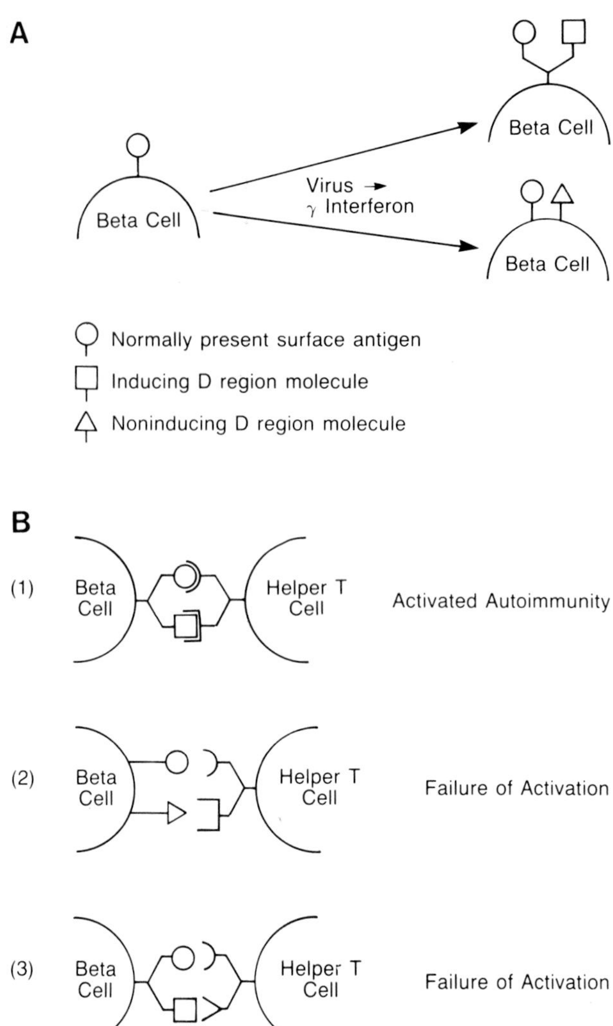

Fig. 10-3 A hypothesis for activation of autoimmunity in type 1 IDDM by induction of class II molecules on the β cell. *A.* Viral infection induces the appearance of class II molecules on β cells from two genetically different individuals. In the top arrow the D-region molecule expressed is diabetogenic (e.g., mutated DQ) and forms a neoantigen with a normally present surface antigen. In the lower arrow the D region molecule induced is nondiabetogenic and does not form a neoantigen. *B.* In line 1 autoimmunity is activated because a helper T-cell clone that recognizes the neoantigen is available. Line 2 indicates failure of activation because a diabetogenic class II molecule was not induced, while in line 3 failure of activation is due to absence of a recognizing helper T-cell clone. *(Based on Ref. 35.)*

Although this scheme envisions induction of class II molecules on the β cells, this is not a requirement. The "shared epitope" theory could equally account for autoimmune destruction. This theory is based on the idea that a virus or other agent could infect tissue other than pancreas, induce an immune response, and produce cytotoxic T lymphocytes and/or antibodies against the virus, which could cross-react with the β cell, provided the latter expressed a surface peptide with homology to the viral antigen (as few as five to eight amino acids).[66] Known examples include streptococcal antigens and the heart in acute rheumatic fever,[136] intestinal bacteria and the acetylcholine receptor in myasthenia gravis,[137] and adenovirus type 12 and A-gliadin in celiac disease.[138] Ordinarily the immune response against viruses involves recognition of antigen in association with class I HLA molecules. Because the susceptibility genes for diabetes appear to be located in the D region, the shared epitope theory seems less attractive than the induction of class II molecules on the β cell as a primary event. However, a shared epitope mechanism with class II major histocompatibility complex restriction has been postulated.[139]

Since autoimmunity is relatively rare and viral and other environmental onslaughts are common, it is clear that some sort of narrowing specificity is involved that prevents everyone from getting autoimmune disease following common infections. Three narrowing factors suggest themselves. (1) As already discussed, part of specificity resides in the likelihood that only a few genetic variants in the D region are able to present self-antigens in a way recognizable as nonself. (2) There may be only a few T lymphocytes bearing a T-cell receptor capable of recognizing this configuration; e.g., one might have the right D region molecule for induction but not a recognizing T lymphocyte.[66,84,139,140] The analogy might be the right key and the wrong lock or vice versa. (3) There may be differences in a variety of effector responses to activated immunity in type 1 diabetes and other diseases. Candidate sites might include cellular responses,[141–143] lymphokine generation,[144,145] and complement activation.[146]

What Is the Target Antigen? The answer to this question is not known, and it may be that there are several important antigens. Initial attention was focused on a 64K protein of unknown function.[25,147] Antibodies against this protein are frequent in newly diagnosed diabetic children and may precede the appearance of islet cell antibodies. They have also been seen in the diabetes-prone BB rat. A second group of candidate antigens are surface gangliosides and glycoproteins.[49] One monoclonal antibody against glycoproteins has been shown to block parathyroid hormone release by raising calcium levels in the parathyroid gland; i.e., the antibody has regulatory capacities in the endocrine system. This is important because abnormal regulation of insulin secretion appears to be the earliest functional lesion in human[148] and rodent[97] diabetes. An attractive possibility is that a primary antigen recognized by islet cell antibodies is the specific glucose transporter of the β cell. In support of such a possibility, islet cell antibodies have been shown to block glucose-induced insulin release.[149] Interleukin 1 can also cause loss of insulin response to glucose.[150,151] It has been speculated that a newly described insulin inhibitory peptide called pancreastatin might also be involved,[152] but there is no firm evidence on this point. Identification of the triggering antigen(s) thus remains a high priority.

Insulitis

In the pancreas of patients with new-onset diabetes there is an infiltration of activated T lymphocytes expressing class II antigens. The cells, which surround and infiltrate islets, are mostly of the cytotoxic type, but natural killer cells are also represented.[153] Such infiltrations are characteristic of other forms of immune endocrinopathy. In the past it was thought that insulitis represented an inflammatory response to virus or other environmental insult and functioned in the initiation of autoimmunity. It seems more likely that insulitis is the cell-mediated component of the autoimmune mechanism, a consequence of activated immunity and not the cause.

Summary

The pathogenesis of type 1 diabetes, based on current clues and subject to revision, can be summarized as follows: (1) The primary genetic susceptibility gene is an altered D region molecule, sometimes DR, sometimes DQ, and probably sometimes DP. Serologic and even RFLP assessments include normal, susceptible, and resistant genes. (2) In most cases the autoimmune process is initiated by the appearance of class II molecules expressing a susceptibility configuration and thus capable of presenting one or more surface antigens as nonself. The induction of class II antigens is often due to an environmental event (viral, chemical) but could be purely genetic. Modulating factors may involve polymorphisms of the T-cell receptor or differences in immune effector response. (3) The destruction of the β cells is immune-mediated and involves both humoral and cellular attack. (4) Explanation for differences in the age of onset (first day of life to the eighth decade) and speed of development (few weeks to a decade) remains unknown. Possibilities include an intrinsic (genetic) biologic clock, repeated viral infections, or a smoldering autocatalytic sequence. For the last case the scenario might run as follows: viral infection induces class II molecules on a few beta cells → attraction of cytotoxic and regulatory T lymphocytes which destroy class II bearing cells while releasing additional lymphokines → induction of class II molecules on an additional few percent of β cells → etc.

PATHOGENESIS OF TYPE 2 DIABETES MELLITUS

Progress in understanding the pathogenesis of type 2 (non-immune-mediated) diabetes has not been as great as is the case in type 1 disease. What can be said with reasonable certainty is that the genetic component is powerful, that β cells are not destroyed (at least initially) but rather are dysfunctional, and that insulin resistance plays a major role. Dissecting the contributions of these factors is difficult because of the likelihood mentioned earlier that some patients with apparent non-insulin dependent diabetes in fact have type 1 diabetes in slow evolution.[1] A second confounding variable is obesity. Because obesity is so common in true type 2 diabetes, its metabolic effects merge with the primary disease, rendering identification of genetically determined susceptibility to diabetes difficult. If one attempts to avoid this by studying nonobese subjects with non-insulin dependent diabetes, one has likely selected a population in which many patients have slowly developing type 1 disease.

Genetics

Non-insulin dependent diabetes is the most common of the hyperglycemic states and occurs throughout the world. Prevalence varies widely, from as low as 1 to 2 percent in Japan, Indonesia, India, and native Alaskans to close to 40 percent in the Pima Indians of the United States.[1,16] The prevalence in whites in the United States is probably a little less than 1 percent. Blacks have approximately the same prevalence as whites, but higher rates are found in Hispanics.[154]

The mode of inheritance is not known for the common form of the disease. Unfortunately there are no genetic markers available to give a clue as to mechanisms as is the case with type 1 disease. The only associations with HLA, of borderline significance, have been the A2 antigen in the Pima Indians[155] and the Xhosas of South Africa.[156] It was early thought that alcohol-induced flushing after pretreatment with chlorpropamide constituted a genetic clue,[157] but this view has fallen by the wayside since negative responders with known insulin dependent disease can be transformed to positive responders by short-term pretreatment with chlorpropamide.[158] The hope that a specific allele in the 5′ flanking region of the insulin gene, a polymorphic site located on the short arm of the eleventh chromosome, might be predictably associated with type 2 diabetes[159] has not proven to be true.[29,35,160]

Despite the absence of specific markers, studies in families indicate that the genetic influence is very strong in non-immune-mediated diabetes. For example, concordance rates in monozygotic twins where diabetes develops in the index case after age 40 is greater than 90 percent.[41] This is in contrast to disease developing in young twins (who presumably have type 1 disease) where concordance rates are considerably less than 50 percent. Similarly, while children or sibs of subjects with immune-mediated diabetes develop the disease less than 10 percent of the time,[42–44] the figures for sibs and children have been estimated to be 38 percent and 33 percent, respectively, in families with non-insulin dependent diabetes.[161] It is not likely that inheritance is due to a simple recessive trait since children of two parents with presumed type 2 diabetes have the disease no more than 30 percent of the time.[162,163]

One form of non-immune-mediated diabetes appears to demonstrate dominant inheritance of the classic Mendelian type. This illness, designated maturity onset diabetes of the young (MODY), or Mason type, diabetes, is characterized by glucose intolerance or mild hyperglycemia with a lower rate of complications than is seen in the common forms of NIDDM.[164] The original description was in white families, but a similar variant has been found in blacks.[165] Afflicted subjects are not obese, do not express the HLA markers characteristic of type 1 disease, and do not have islet cell antibodies.

A Dysfunctional β Cell

Insulin levels in plasma of patients with presumed NIDDM may be high, normal, or low when considered in absolute terms (μU/ml plasma).[166] However, by definition there is always a relative deficiency of insulin when impaired glucose tolerance or frank hyperglycemia is present. This is best demonstrated by comparison of diabetic and nondiabetic subjects at the same glucose levels. If the plasma glucose of the latter is raised to the level of the former, then insulin concentrations in the normal subjects surpass those of the diabetic subjects despite the fact that basal levels in the diabetic subjects may have been higher.[167,168]

The nature of the islet cell defect in type 2 NIDDM is not known. In the early phases of the disease β-cell mass is normal[169] and the capacity to secrete larger than normal amounts of insulin is maintained (although not enough to sustain normoglycemia).[166–168] The key defect appears to be a loss of glucose-induced insulin release, a lesion most easily demonstrated by injecting a bolus of glucose intravenously.[166,168] The capacity to release insulin in response to other inducers such as arginine and sulfonylureas remains intact initially.[167,170] In established hyperglycemia the insulin response to arginine also becomes impaired.[171] With severe hyperglycemia insulin secretory capacity may be virtually absent.[168,172] Whether longstanding type 2 diabetes is associated with a decrease in β-cell mass[168,173] is controversial, but the best evidence indicates not.[169]

The cause of the β-cell defect is not known. There has been considerable discussion as to whether it is primary or secondary to the characteristic insulin resistance of type 2 NIDDM.[173–176] If secondary, the idea would be that insulin resistance leads to hyperglycemia which either damages the β cell directly (glucose toxicity) or "exhausts" it. Glucose toxicity may play a role in pathogenesis,[177,178] as evidenced by temporary improvement of glucose-induced insulin release after aggressive insulin therapy, which substantially lowers the plasma glucose from previously elevated values.[170,179] Glucose toxicity could also play a role in a sequence initiated by a primary islet defect with insulin deficiency; i.e., islet cell dysfunction → hyperglycemia → more islet cell dysfunction, etc.

On balance it seems likely that the sine qua non of type 2 NIDDM is a dysfunctional β cell. This follows from the fact that many massively obese subjects with severe insulin resistance never develop hyperglycemia. Presumably a normal β cell can overcome ordinary forms of insulin resistance, failing only in extreme cases such as the type B insulin resistance syndrome (see below) where antibodies to the insulin receptor block access of the hormone to the effector site. In type 2 NIDDM the dysfunctional β cell, although able initially to increase plasma insulin levels above normal, cannot in the end overcome the insulin resistance imposed by obesity or other factors.

Insulin Resistance

Insulin resistance is said to exist whenever there is a diminished biologic effect for a given concentration of insulin in plasma, which reflects roughly the concentration of the hormone in the interstitial fluid bathing the insulin receptor on plasma membranes of target cells. All aspects of insulin action may be involved, but in diabetes focus has been on glucose production by the liver and glucose disposal in nonhepatic tissues such as muscle and fat.[180,181] Insulin resistance is implied whenever plasma concentrations of the hormone are high relative to the plasma glucose, but best estimates are obtained by use of the insulin clamp technique.[182] In this procedure the insulin concentration is raised to a given level above basal and maintained in the steady state. Glucose is infused at variable rates to maintain plasma levels in the normal basal range. The exogenous infusion rate, added to measured endogenous production by the liver, indicates overall glucose disposal, which is a measure of the response to the infused insulin.

Insulin resistance may be due to several mechanisms operating independently or in concert.[180,183] *Prereceptor* resistance is most often due to the presence of anti-insulin antibodies (IgG) in patients treated with insulin for significant periods of time. The production of an abnormal insulin that will not react with a normal insulin receptor also is considered a prereceptor defect. *Receptor*-mediated resistance may be due to diminished numbers of receptors, receptors with abnormal binding characteristics, or antireceptor antibodies. *Postreceptor* resistance refers to a defect occurring subsequent to formation of the hormone-receptor complex, i.e., a biologic defect that cannot be overcome by saturation of the insulin binding sites on the plasma membrane.

The insulin resistance of type 2 NIDDM is mixed in terms of both mechanism and cause. In some patients a receptor-mediated mechanism plays a role, but in most circumstances a postreceptor defect predominates.[184] The way the insulin-insulin receptor complex exerts the multiple biologic effects of insulin is not known. The β subunit of the receptor is a tyrosine kinase[185] and it is attractive to suppose that activation of this kinase after binding of insulin to the α subunit is an early and perhaps necessary step in the subsequent chain of reactions. Inhibition of tyrosine kinase activity by a blocking monoclonal antibody[186] or mutation of the ATP binding site[187] blocks biologic effects of the hormone. It has been demonstrated that tyrosine kinase is not activated normally following insulin binding in type 2 NIDDM.[188,189] While uncoupling of binding from kinase activity could account for the resistance state, other mechanisms and second messengers could also be involved.[190–193]

Regardless of the connecting link, insulin ultimately stimulates glucose uptake in most tissues of the body. Glucose enters cells on a protein carrier that transports it from plasma to cytoplasm.[194] Some glucose transport units are always present in the plasma membrane, but a cryptic or reserve set of transporters is maintained intracellularly in association with the low density microsome fraction. Insulin probably causes both an activation of *in situ* transporters[195,196] and rapid mobilization of the cryptic units to the cell surface.[197–199] In experimental animals both obesity and uncontrolled diabetes are accompanied by diminished numbers of cryptic glucose transporters in adipose tissue.[200,201] It is conceivable, therefore, that the defect in insulin-mediated glucose transport is at least partially accounted for by the decrement in recruitable transport units. Hyperglycemia may contribute to the process by blocking transfer of remaining transporter units from storage sites to cell surface.[202]

Insulin resistance can be demonstrated in liver as well as nonhepatic tissues, but the latter is thought to predominate.[203,204] Hepatic glucose overproduction is more easily reversible with insulin than is the impairment in glucose disposal.[180,203] Lowering hyperglycemia by intensive insulin therapy, sulfonylureas, or diet can improve glucose utilization, indicating at least partial reversal of even the more resistant peripheral defect.[205–207] There are conflicting reports regarding antilipolytic effects of insulin in non-insulin dependent diabetes; some workers report resistance and others sensitivity.[208,209] The α cell in pancreatic islets is partially resistant to insulin since abnormal glucagon release to protein signals cannot be reversed.[210,211]

It is probable that insulin resistance in type 2 diabetes has two sources, one intrinsic to diabetes[176,212] and the other consequent to obesity, which induces resistance in the absence of hyperglycemia.[213] The relative contribution of each is uncertain and may vary from patient to patient. There can be little doubt, however, that obesity is a major contributor in many if not most patients with type 2 NIDDM. This follows from the observation that dietary restriction with modest weight loss can significantly ameliorate the defect and return plasma glucose to near normal levels.[207]

Summary

The genetic abnormality leading to nonautoimmune diabetes, though powerful, is not known. The phenotypic expression is characterized by a dysfunctional β cell that cannot release insulin adequately in response to a glucose signal and by insulin resistance that leads to uncontrolled hepatic glucose production and a defect in glucose disposal in muscle and adipose tissue. The insulin-resistant state may exist without obesity, but in most cases obesity is the dominant cause. The explanation of insulin resistance at the molecular level is only partially understood. The number of insulin receptors is usually decreased and affinity for insulin impaired, but postreceptor resistance appears to be more important. Impaired activation of tyrosine kinase following formation of the insulin-insulin receptor complex (an uncoupling defect) could be involved. A direct or indirect effect of kinase failure, presumably acting through regulatory phosphorylations, might be impaired synthesis or abnormal cycling of the glucose transport units normally held in reserve for recruitment by insulin when increased glucose utilization is required. Alternatively, the defect could operate in the plasma membrane to prevent insulin-induced activation of *in situ* receptors or later events such as the internalization and degradation of insulin.[214] The role of other factors potentially involved in the regulation of glucose transport, such as phosphorylation by the protein kinase C system,[215,216] remains to be worked out. Regardless of mechanism, insulin resistance either causes or worsens hyperglycemia which may function as a biochemical coup de grace, completing the pathogenetic process by toxic effects on both the β cells and insulin responsive tissues throughout the body.[217]

It is not possible to confidently assign primacy to the dysfunctional β cell or insulin resistance. Possible scenarios are shown in Fig. 10-4.

METABOLIC ASPECTS

Of the multiple metabolic disturbances that characterize uncontrolled diabetes, two are of preeminent importance from the standpoint of producing acute symptoms: *disturbed glucose metabolism,* which results in hyperglycemia, obligatory osmotic diuresis, thirst, and weight loss, and *accelerated ketone body production* (in type 1 disease), which results in ketoacidosis. Other abnormalities (e.g., hypertriglyceridemia, defects in the renin-angiotensin axis with hyperkalemia, altered leukocyte function) are of lesser immediate importance, although they contribute to the composite clinical picture of primary diabetes in both insulin dependent and non-insulin dependent subjects.[1] The metabolic changes of diabetes are hormonally induced. In this section, these hormonal alterations and their effects on glucose metabolism and ketogenesis are briefly reviewed.

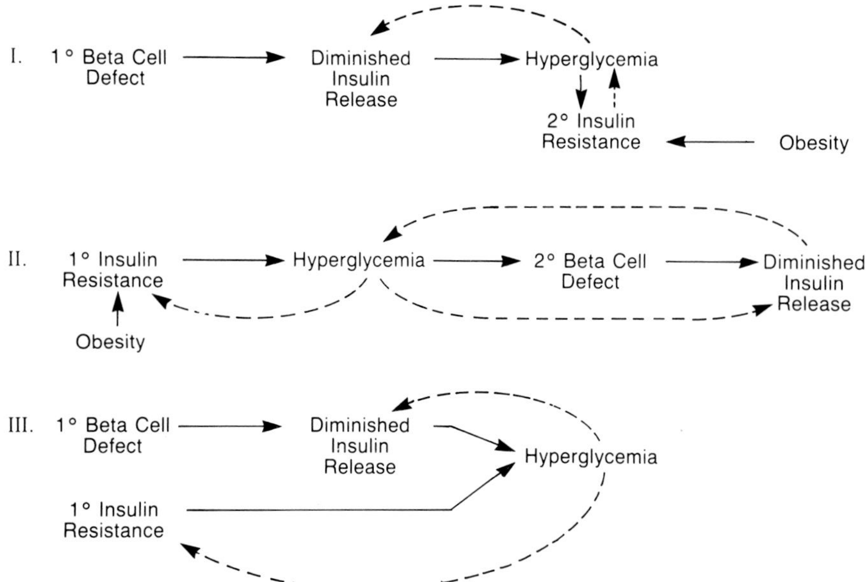

Fig. 10-4 Hypothetical mechanisms for the pathogenesis of type 2 NIDDM. Scheme I postulates a primary β-cell defect, while scheme II envisions insulin resistance as primary. In scheme III the β-cell defect and insulin resistance operate in parallel. Dotted lines indicate possible direct toxic effects of hyperglycemia.

Hormonal Changes

Six hormones are important in regulating fuel metabolism in humans: insulin, glucagon, epinephrine, norepinephrine, cortisol, and growth hormone. In broad terms, insulin can be considered the primary anabolic hormone (linked with synthesis and storage of body fuels), while the other five subserve catabolic function (the breakdown and oxidation of stored fuels for the provision of energy in the absence of food intake). Since their biologic effects are, in general, opposite to those of insulin, they have been called *counterregulatory*. Basal plasma concentrations of cortisol, epinephrine, and growth hormone tend to be normal in diabetic subjects[218–220]; when plasma is sampled repeatedly throughout a 24-h period, integrated values for epinephrine, norepinephrine, and growth hormone (but not cortisol) are slightly elevated in young insulin-dependent patients.[221] During physical or emotional stress, or in response to hypoglycemia, concentrations of the counterregulatory hormones in plasma rise, sometimes to very high levels.[222] Under these circumstances, they contribute to the development of both hyperglycemia and ketosis.

The two primary hormones involved in diabetes are insulin and glucagon. In untreated diabetic subjects (regardless of type) there is relative or absolute hypoinsulinemia and relative or absolute hyperglucagonemia so that the ratio of glucagon to insulin is increased even under basal conditions.[223,224] The deficiency and excess, respectively, of the β- and α-cell hormones become exaggerated during stress. While the role of glucagon was once controversial,[225] it now seems overwhelmingly likely that the metabolic changes of uncontrolled diabetes are not due solely to insulin deficiency and that glucagon plays a critical role in initiating and controlling the hyperglycemic and ketogenic processes.[223,224] Hyperglucagonemia is probably a secondary consequence of insulin deficiency since glucagon concentrations can be restored to normal by aggressive insulin therapy in type 1 IDDM[226,227] and toward normal in type 2 NIDDM.[210,211]

Insulin is considered to act directly in nonhepatic target cells to accelerate transport of glucose, amino acids, and other ions through the plasma membrane,[228] to inhibit the hormone-sensitive lipase of adipose tissues such that free fatty acid mobilization is impaired,[229] and to stimulate the synthesis of protein, fat, and glycogen.[230] The role of insulin in the liver is complicated; while there is no doubt that it can reverse the increased hepatic production of glucose and ketones that occur in fasting and uncontrolled diabetes, increasing evidence suggests that its major effect is to antagonize glucagon-induced activation of these processes.[231,232] In other words, the effects of insulin on hepatocytes not activated by glucagon (or catecholamines) are small.

As noted above, the mechanism(s) by which insulin exerts its biologic effects are not known. Intense interest has focused on activation of tyrosine kinase in the insulin receptor as the initial step, and the best evidence is that this is required for biologic effects.[186,187] Insulin also has the capacity to induce or alter a variety of other signaling molecules such as cyclic AMP, calcium, diacylglycerol, and glycolipid-derived molecules containing inositol and glucosamine.[190–193,233] The result of changes in cyclic AMP concentrations are reasonably well understood, but the nature of interactions with the other messengers remains to be dissected.

Glucagon, like insulin, acts in many tissues, but its primary site of action is the liver. When insulin-glucagon molar ratios are high (anabolic state), the liver stores glucose as glycogen, synthesizes long chain fatty acids from excess glucose, esterifies fatty acids to triglycerides, and transports fat to nonhepatic tissues in very low density lipoprotein carriers.[234] In the anabolic state fatty acid oxidation is inhibited and ketone production is nil. When the insulin-glucagon molar ratio is low (catabolic state) the liver becomes an organ of glucose production via glycogen breakdown and gluconeogenesis. Fat synthesis ceases and fatty acid oxidation-ketogenesis is activated. All actions of glucagon are mediated by cyclic AMP-mediated phosphorylation of key enzymes with alteration of their functional activity, either up or down.[1,235] Thus, phosphorylation of glycogen synthase blocks its activity and stops glycogen synthesis, while phosphorylation of phosphorylase *b* activates glycogenolysis. A key event in glucagon-mediated changes in hepatic metabolism is phosphorylation of the bifunctional enzyme 6-phosphofructo-2-kinase/fructose-2,6-bisphosphatase which causes a fall in concentration of fructose-2,6-bisphosphate (F-2,6-P_2), the major regulator of traffic over the glycolytic and gluconeogenic pathways.[236] When F-2,6-P_2 levels fall, glycolysis is interrupted at the phosphofructokinase step while gluconeogenesis is activated at the fructose-1,6-bisphosphatase reaction. The interruption of glycolytic flux eventuates in a fall of malonyl-CoA concentrations which then activates fatty acid oxidation and the overproduction of acetoacetic and β-hydroxybutyric acids as described below.[234] Insulin has the capacity to reverse the catabolic sequence in the liver by inhibiting glucagon release from the pancreas and by counteracting its action in the hepatocyte.[224,231]

Altered Glucose Metabolism

The hyperglycemia of diabetes is the consequence of both increased hepatic production and diminished peripheral utilizatin of glucose as noted earlier. In the first few hours of a fast in humans, the bulk of hepatic glucose production comes from glycogen breakdown.[237] As glycogen stores are depleted, endogenous glucose production is maintained by gluconeogenesis in both the liver and the kidney. Quantitatively the liver is significantly more important.[238] The same sequence operates following the withdrawal of insulin in diabetic subjects.[239] Although hepatic overproduction of glucose accounts for fasting hyperglycemia and initiates the osmotic diuresis of uncontrolled diabetes, diminished utilization of glucose plays an increasingly important role as the period of insulin withdrawal becomes more prolonged.[239] This progressive decrease in glucose utilization causes plasma concentrations to remain high in spite of the fact that hepatic production rates are maximal several hours after insulin withdrawal and subsequently decline (although remaining elevated). The reason for the diminished rate of glucose production with time is not known, but glycogen depletion may be involved; that is, after glycogen stores have been dissipated, the residual rate of glucose production reflects gluconeogenesis, a process which presumably has a lower maximal rate than glycogenolysis.

While terms such as insulin deficiency or insulin withdrawal are frequently used to indicate the cause of decompensation in diabetes, glucagon is crucial to the initiation of hepatic overproduction of glucose and ketones. This was shown most explicitly by a classic experiment in which somatostatin was infused in type 1 diabetic subjects taken off insulin. Under these circumstances, the appearance of hyperglycemia and ketoacidosis was markedly delayed compared to control experiments in which saline was infused.[240] Somatostatin has the capacity to block both insulin and glucagon release from the pancreas, but in insulinopenic patients its only significant effect is to lower plasma glucagon levels. Along the same lines, only glucagon, of all the counterregulatory hormones, increases in parallel with rising glucose and ketone concentrations during the developmental stage of diabetic ketoacidosis.[239] Many other experiments are in accord with the conclusion that glucagon has powerful hyperglycemic and ketogenic effects.[234,241] As decompensation progresses, all the other counterregulatory hormones rise so that at the time of admission epinephrine, norepinephrine, cortisol, growth hormone, renin, and aldosterone are found elevated many fold.[242]

The interrelationships between glucagon and insulin are shown schematically in Fig. 10-5. The two hormones form an integrated metabolic unit for the control of plasma glucose concentration and ketone body production.[224] In the liver (and possibly other tissues), the two hormones exert opposing effects. Large changes in concentrations are not required to produce major metabolic responses. Thus, a decrease in insulin occurring against the background of a normal glucagon concentration may result in the same change in liver metabolism that would be seen with a major absolute increase of glucagon coupled with a normal or even modestly elevated insulin concentration. This has led to the concept, previously alluded to, that the molar ratio of insulin to glucagon is more important than the absolute level of either.[223,224] The α- and β-cell hormones also interact within the islets of Langerhans; insulin inhibits the release of glucagon, while glucagon stimulates secretion of insulin.[224] The complex interrelationships between glucagon and insulin existing both within the islets and in target tissues have rendered interpretation of in vivo studies extremely difficult. This is because perturbation of hormones and substrates induces multiple changes in other hormones and substrates such that primary and secondary changes are difficult to dissect.[243] Nonetheless, it appears safe to state that the hyperglycemia of both type 1 and type 2 diabetes mellitus (and probably all forms of endogenous hyperglycemia) is due to relative or absolute deficiency of insulin coupled with relative or absolute excess of glucagon.[224]

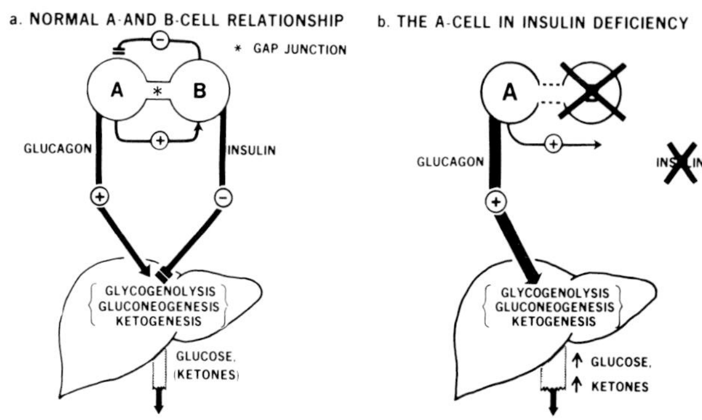

Fig. 10-5 Insulin-glucagon relationships in normal persons and diabetic subjects. As indicated in panel A, within the islets insulin inhibits glucagon release, while glucagon stimulates insulin secretion. In target tissues such as the liver, the two hormones are biologic antagonists. In diabetes (panel B), destruction or dysfunction of the β cell removes the inhibitory influence of insulin on glucagon release in the islets and allows unrestrained activity of the α-cell hormone in target tissues. *(From Unger and Orci,[224] by permission of the New England Journal of Medicine.)*

Ketogenesis

The same hormonal changes that cause glycogen breakdown and increased gluconeogenesis in uncontrolled diabetes also induce hepatic ketogenesis in insulin dependent subjects.[234,241] The substrate for acetoacetate and β-hydroxybutyrate production in the liver is long chain fatty acids mobilized in response to hypoinsulinemia with or without a concomitant rise in lipolytic counterregulatory hormones. Fatty acids taken up by the liver in the normal fed state or in well controlled diabetic subjects are reesterified to form triglycerides and are largely transported back into the plasma as very low density lipoproteins.[244] This is because the system of enzymes that oxidize fatty acids is inactive when the insulin-glucagon molar ratio is high. Following a fast of several hours or in uncontrolled diabetes, a shift in this ratio favoring glucagon activates the oxidative sequence for fatty acids in the liver and preferentially shunts incoming free fatty acids into ketone body production.

The rate-limiting step for fatty acid oxidation is transport of substrate across the inner mitochondrial membrane (Fig. 10-6). Long chain fatty acyl-CoA molecules cannot traverse

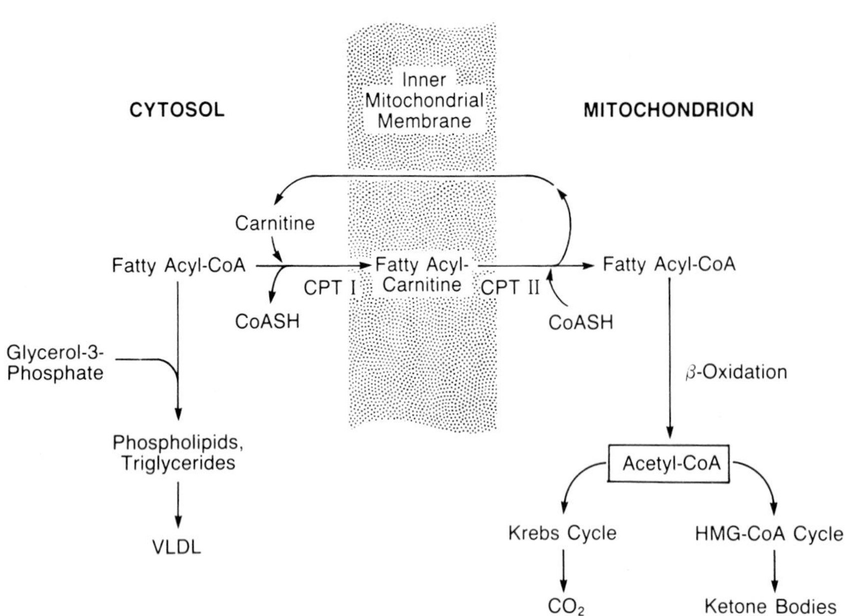

Fig. 10-6 The fatty acid oxidizing system. Long-chain fatty acids of dietary or endogenous origin are taken up by the liver and are esterified to coenzyme A. In the normal fed state carnitine palmitoyltransferase I (CPT I) is inhibited and the activated fatty acids are reesterified to triglycerides for transport to peripheral tissues as very low density lipoprotein (VLDL). In fasting or uncontrolled diabetes CPT I is disinhibited allowing formation of fatty acylcarnitine which, unlike CoA esters, can traverse the mitochondrial inner membrane. Inside the mitochondrion the carnitine:CoA transesterification is reversed by CPT II, and the fatty acyl-CoA molecule is oxidized primarily to ketone bodies. Rates of terminal oxidation to CO_2 and HOH are low in liver relative to ketogenesis. Nonhepatic fatty acid oxidizing tissues do not synthesize ketones in significant amounts but otherwise utilize an identical system of fatty acid oxidation. Significant amounts of CPT I are now known to be located on the inner aspect of the outer mitochondrial membrane.[302] CPT I and CPT II are separate enzymes.[303,304]

the barrier membrane, but fatty acids bound to carnitine are freely permeable.[234,241] Transesterification of the acyl-CoA to its carrier molecule is accomplished through the action of carnitine palmitoyltransferase I, with reversal of the process inside the mitochondrion under the influence of carnitine palmitoyltransferase II. Since the β-oxidative sequence for fatty acids is a high capacity system, and presumably is fully active at all times, entry of fatty acids into the mitochondrion is followed by the obligatory production of ketone bodies because only a minor fraction of the acetyl-CoA formed from fatty acids enters the tricarboxylic acid cycle.[245]

Carnitine palmitoyltransferase I is a regulated enzyme which is powerfully inhibited in the presence of a high insulin-glucagon molar ratio.[246] This inhibition is exerted by malonyl-CoA, the primary substrate for fatty acid synthesis.[247] When glucagon levels rise, flux from glucose-6-phosphate to malonyl-CoA is inhibited at the phosphofructokinase step by a fall in fructose-2,6-P_2 levels as described above and illustrated in Fig. 10-7. In addition, acetyl-CoA carboxylase, the enzyme that synthesizes malonyl-CoA from acetyl-CoA, is directly inhibited by glucagon-induced phosphorylation and by the high levels of fatty acyl-CoA that result from increased transport of free fatty acids from adipose tissue to liver.[234] The result is a rapid drop in malonyl-CoA concentrations with activation of carnitine palmitoyltransferase I. Consequent to this activation long chain fatty acyl-CoA molecules are rapidly and efficiently taken into the mitochondrion for oxidation to acetoacetic and β-hydroxybutyric acids. The process is further facilitated by a rise in the hepatic concentration of carnitine, which tends to drive the process by mass action.[248] Once the hepatic ketone-

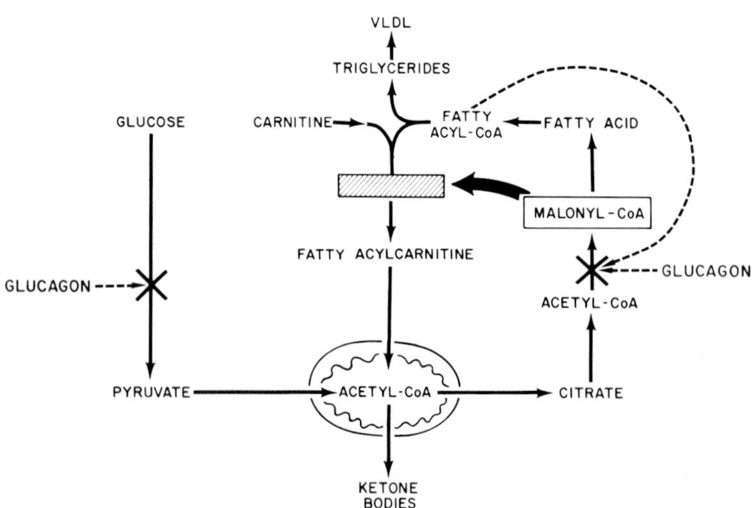

Fig. 10-7 Interrelationships of glucose oxidation, fatty acid oxidation, fatty acid synthesis, and ketogenesis in the liver. When the [insulin]:[glucagon] ratio is high, malonyl CoA levels are elevated, blocking fatty acid oxidation and ketogenesis through inhibition of carnitine palmitoyltransferase I. Fatty acid synthesis is brisk. Glucagon excess blocks malonyl CoA formation, thereby activating carnitine palmitoyltransferase I and the fatty acid oxidative-ketogenic sequence with cessation of fatty acid synthesis. High levels of fatty acyl CoA contribute to the fall of malonyl CoA concentration in uncontrolled diabetes by blocking acetyl CoA carboxylase. *(From McGarry and Foster,[241] by permission of* The Annual Review of Biochemistry, *Annual Reviews, Inc.)*

synthesizing machinery is activated, the rate of ketogenesis is determined by the concentration of fatty acids present in the liver according to first-order kinetics. Hepatic uptake of fatty acids is the passive consequence of plasma concentrations. Since free fatty acid levels in plasma are high in uncontrolled diabetes, major ketone production is assured.[249] Hepatic overproduction of ketones is the primary cause of ketoacidosis, although the capacity to oxidize acetoacetate and β-hydroxybutyrate in peripheral tissues appears to become saturated at high plasma concentrations.[239] Following administration of insulin, all metabolic abnormalities are reversed.

Metabolic Crises

The diabetic patient is vulnerable to three major types of crises: ketoacidosis; hyperosmolar, nonketotic coma; and hypoglycemia. All three of these may lead to serious consequences. *Diabetic ketoacidosis* is the end result of decompensated control in insulin dependent diabetic subjects. Its characteristics are extracellular volume depletion, dehydration, and severe metabolic acidosis.[249] The fluid abnormalities are due to the development of hyperglycemia which causes a major osmotic diuresis. Glucose enters the renal tubule by glomerular filtration and is reabsorbed proximally. The tubular maximum for reabsorption is about 225 mg/min, which means that with a glomerular filtration rate of 120 ml/min, glycosuria will appear at a plasma glucose concentration of 180 to 190 mg/dl. If glomerular filtration rates fall because of intrinsic renal disease or volume depletion, higher plasma concentrations are requred to induce glycosuria. During osmotic diuresis, obligate loss of free water together with electrolytes accounts for both volume depletion and dehydration.[250] The fluid deficit in diabetic ketoacidosis is usually limited (3 to 5 liters) because nausea and vomiting or Kussmaul breathing signal serious illness and bring the patient to the hospital; only occasionally are fluid losses equivalent to those characteristically seen in hyperosmolar coma. The metabolic acidosis is accounted for almost exclusively by the ketone bodies, although modest elevations of lactate contribute to the anion gap.[249]

Hyperosmolar coma occurs in type 2 diabetic subjects who are resistant to ketosis. The clinical picture of extreme hyperglycemia, profound volume depletion (on average 10 to 12 liters), altered central nervous system function (stupor, coma, convulsions), hyperviscosity with diffuse intravascular coagulation and hemorrhage, and ultimate vascular collapse is due to prolonged and unrestrained osmotic diuresis.[251] A frequent complication is septicemia or pneumonia due to gram-negative organisms.[252,253] The reason for the absence of ketoacidosis in non-insulin dependent diabetic subjects, even when stress is extreme, is unknown. Limited mobilization of free fatty acids and an antiketogenic effect of dehydration have been evoked, but both appear untenable as sole explanations since some patients with the syndrome have extremely high levels of fatty acids in plasma and since full blown ketoacidosis can occur in type 1 patients in the face of severe hyperosmolarity.[251] It is possible that portal vein insulin levels in these patients are sufficiently high to prevent activation of fatty acid oxidation in the liver. Such an explanation is not very convincing, however, since with severe stress residual insulin release should be blocked by catecholamines, with a concomitant rise in glucagon providing the necessary change in the [insulin]:[glucagon] ratio required for activation of ketogenesis. A more reasonable explanation might be a genetically determined resistance of the fatty acid oxidation-ketogenic sequence to activation by glucagon. The site of resistance could be at carnitine palmitoyltransferase I or beyond. While such an abnormality has not been demonstrated in humans, partial hepatic resistance to glucagon has been observed in the ob/ob mouse and the Zucker obese rat, genetically obese animals with certain biochemical characteristics reminiscent of human type 2 diabetes.[254,255] It seems highly likely that hepatic malonyl-CoA levels do not fall in poorly controlled type 2 NIDDM, but it has so far not been possible to measure the intermediate in the metabolic crises of human diabetes. It is known that the malonyl-CoA system is functional in humans.[256]

Hypoglycemia in the diabetic subject is almost always due to imbalance between injected insulin and food intake; i.e., the patient, having taken insulin, delays a meal or eats too little. It is a particular problem when meticulous ("tight") control is attempted. If the plasma glucose is kept within near normal limits by scrupulous control, there is little margin of safety. An additional problem is that patients with longstanding diabetes may lose their capacity to mount a counterregulatory response to hypoglycemia.[257] Because neither glucagon nor catecholamines rise in response to hypoglycemia, affected patients are metabolically defenseless, a situation that is compounded by the fact that the warning signals of impending hypoglycemia, which are epinephrine-induced, are not available. Interestingly, meticulous control itself may blunt counterregulatory response in patients whose intrinsic defenses are intact.[258]

Hypoglycemia due to sulfonylurea therapy in patients with type 2 NIDDM is rare but tends to be severe and long-lasting when it occurs.[259]

Rebound hyperglycemia following an episode of recognized or unrecognized hypoglycemia, the *Somogyi phenomenon*, has been thought to contribute to instability of diabetic control, but probably is of limited significance in most patients.[260]

LATE COMPLICATIONS

The four major complications of long-term diabetes are retinopathy, nephropathy, neuropathy, and atherosclerosis, and it is these complications that are the primary cause of death and disability from the disease.[3] Their exact prevalence is unknown, although it seems clear that they increase with the duration of disease. In two older series describing patients who had diabetes for more than 40 years, retinopathy was found in up to 75 percent, while estimates of nephropathy and neuropathy ranged from 8 to 48 percent.[261,262] These patients may not reflect the general diabetic population, most of whom do not live so long with their disease. In one cohort of 372 insulin dependent subjects followed prospectively by the same team of physicians from the time of diagnosis, nephropathy (clinically diagnosed by the presence of proteinuria) was present in 4 percent after 16 years and 14 percent after 26 years.[263] Equivalent figures for retinopathy were 27 and 85 percent. The 16-year percentage may be low since retinal angiography was not available in the early phases of the study. Whatever the exact incidence, it is clear that the problem of late complications is huge. Diabetes is a major cause of new blindness in the United States[3] and represents a significant portion of all persons with renal failure. Disability from neuropathy, hard to quantitate, is also great.

It is suspected, but not yet proven, that the degenerative complications of diabetes are directly related to hyperglycemia and the degree of diabetic control (e.g., Refs. 264 to 267). Strong support for the view that altered metabolism leads to complications comes from observations with kidney transplants. When kidneys from normal individuals are transplanted into diabetic subjects they rapidly develop the lesions of diabetic nephropathy.[268] By contrast, a kidney grafted into a patient "cured" of diabetes by a pancreatic transplant appeared to sustain normality, suggesting that hyperglycemia or some metabolic defect accompanying hyperglycemia causes the Kimmelstiel-Wilson lesion.[269]

Accumulating evidence indicates that a common mechanism may cause retinal, renal, and neurologic disease in diabetes.[270,271] The suspect biochemical sequence, usually called the *polyol pathway,* has as its critical feature the production of sorbitol from glucose under the influence of the enzyme aldol reductase (D-aldose:NAD^+ 1 oxidoreductase, EC 1.1.1.121). The enzyme, which has a high K_m for glucose and thus is relatively inactive during normoglycemia, is present in retina, lens, Schwann cells, aorta, and kidney, all tissues frequently damaged in diabetes.[272] Sorbitol appears to function as a tissue toxin. It induces a fall in tissue myoinositol levels, lowers the activity of protein kinase C (through decreased mobilization of calcium and diminished formation of diacylglycerol), and inhibits the activity of the plasma membrane Na^+,K^+-ATPase.[270,271] Confirmation that sugar alcohols are toxic comes from the observation that galactose feeding in animals produces retinal changes similar to those seen in diabetes.[273] Galactitol, the galactose-derived sugar alcohol equivalent to sorbitol, is elevated in the blood, but glucose, free fatty acids, branched chain amino acids, and insulin are all normal, suggesting that these factors do not cause the retinopathy.[274] Aldose reductase inhibitors have been shown to prevent or reverse retinal changes, neuropathy, and the hyperperfusion of the kidney that characterizes early nephropathy in diabetic animals.[270,271,273,275] They also prevent galactose-induced retinopathy.[273] Trials in humans have been less conclusive,[270] although the leaky blood-retinal barrier of early retinopathy appeared to be stabilized by an aldol reductase inhibitor.[276] It thus seems possible that these major degenerative complications of diabetes are polyol-mediated. Some investigators believe that hemodynamic changes are the primary cause of complications, particularly in renal disease where hyperperfusion and enlargement of the kidneys is a reproducible early lesion.[277–279] Increased hydrostatic pressure, the consequence of decreased arteriolar resistance, presumably allows leakage of potentially damaging proteins and other macromolecules (such as immune complexes) in renal parenchyma. Mesangial and basement membrane dysfunction follow. That renal hyperperfusion occurs is beyond doubt, but if the hemodynamic changes are preventable by inhibiting the polyol pathway[271] these changes would have to be considered secondary.

It is not thought that the polyol pathway is primarily involved in large vessel atherosclerosis leading to heart attacks, strokes, and ischemia of the legs and internal organs although Na^+,K^+-ATPase of arteries is impaired in diabetes.[271] It is more likely that nonenzymatic glycosylation of proteins is central to the atherosclerotic process, with modulating influences being smoking, an atherogenic diet, and hypertension. Enzymatic glycosylation is a normal posttranslational event that greatly expands the structural and functional repertoire of proteins. Such glycosylation increases the available amino acids from 20 to over 140.[280] Nonenzymatic glycosylation, on the other hand, has no physiological purpose. When proteins are exposed to high concentrations of glucose, the hexose forms a Schiff base with lysine and valine residues, which subsequently are slowly converted to the stable ketoamine form.[281] The prototypic reaction is the formation of hemoglobin A_1C, which is used clinically to assess the degree of diabetic control over 2- to 3-month periods.[282] Important proteins known to exhibit altered function when glycosylated include albumin, collagen, fibrin, the glycoprotein recognition system of hepatic endothelial cells, and low and high density lipoproteins.[1,283,284] Increased glycosylation is found in coronary arteries, aorta, and glomerular basement membranes in diabetes,[285] and increased crosslinking by glycosylation products may predispose to vascular disease.[286] The glycosylated arterial wall may trap lipoproteins more efficiently.[287] Glycosylated LDL does not bind to the LDL receptor and thus would be preferentially available to the arterial matrix.[288] Similarly, the turnover of glycosylated HDL is increased,[289] a factor that may contribute to the lower levels of this lipoprotein in some diabetic subjects.

Despite the evidence that hyperglycemia causes biochemical changes that become more marked the higher the ambient glucose concentration and the observation that both the sorbitol pathway and nonenzymatic glycosylation of proteins induce dysfunctional changes in tissues, it has not been possible to show that meticulous control of diabetes prevents the degenerative changes of the disease.[290]

The one area where normalization of the blood sugar clearly is beneficial is in the pregnant diabetic subject. Complications in the perinatal period such as toxemia and hydramnios in the mother and intrauterine death, macrosomia, pulmonary dysfunction, and hypoglycemia in the fetus can be largely prevented by meticulous control.[290a] Developmental abnormalities that occur in the first few days of fetal life (such as cardiac and neural tube defects) probably require meticulous control *prior* to conception.

RARE FORMS OF DIABETES

Diabetic syndromes other than the two common primary types discussed in the bulk of this chapter are rare.[14] Two are of considerable importance because they provide insights into the genetics, biochemistry, and physiology of insulin synthesis and action. The first is diabetes due to an *abnormal insulin.*[291–293] Patients with this disorder exhibit modest fasting hyperglycemia and hyperinsulinemia, suggesting insulin resistance, but respond normally to exogenous insulin. When purified, the first of the abnormal insulins was found to have a diminished capacity to bind to insulin receptors on IM-9 lymphocytes and isolated adipocytes, and its biologic activity was 15 percent of normal. Subsequent studies showed that the defect was due to substitution of a leucine for phenylalanine at position 25 of the β chain consequent to G (guanylate) for C (cytidylate) substitution at position 385.[294] This mutant was dubbed insulin Chicago. Two other mutant insulins have been described, insulin Los Angeles ($Phe^{B24} \rightarrow Ser^{B24}$) and insulin Wakayama ($Val^{A3} \rightarrow Leu^{A3}$). The biologic effects of these changes on binding of hormone to receptor are under study.[295] It is likely that additional patients currently classified as having mild non-insulin dependent diabetes have mutant insulin syndromes. A mutation at the junction of the β chain to the connecting peptide results in familial hyperproinsulinemia, but this abnormality does not cause clinical diabetes.[296]

Diabetes may also be due to *impairment of insulin receptor function*. Two major syndromes have been recognized. The first, designated type A, is found in women with androgen excess and menstrual abnormalities (usually polycystic ovary syndrome).[297] Although the number of insulin receptors may be decreased, a dysfunctional receptor with impaired phosphorylation capacity may be more important.[298] The second syndrome, designated type B, is due to insulin receptor antibodies[297] although in younger women androgen excess is also present.[299] Occuring in patients with an underlying immunologic disease (lupuslike) and acanthosis nigricans, the defect may be mild or severe. The antibodies may function either as agonists or antagonists.[297,300] In the former mode they cause hypoglycemia, in the latter hyperglycemia with or without ketosis.[301] Insulin receptor dysfunction may also be seen in leprechaunism, an insulin-resistant state found in children with elfin facies, hirsutism, generalized skin thickening, and diminished body fat. The receptor in one patient had the peculiar property of binding insulin with higher than normal affinity in the face of diminished biologic response (a postreceptor defect).[305–307] Other patients have shown diminished insulin binding, suggesting heterogeneous defects at the receptor level.

REFERENCES

1. UNGER RH, FOSTER DW: Diabetes mellitus, in Wilson JD, Foster DW (eds): *Williams Textbook of Endocrinology,* 7th ed. Philadelphia, Saunders, 1985, p 1018.
2. NATIONAL DIABETES ADVISORY BOARD: *Progress and Promise in Diabetes Research.* US Department of Health and Human Services, Public Health Service, National Institutes of Health, NIH Publication 84-661, 1984.
3. MAZZE RS, SINNOCK P, DEEB L, BRIMBERRY JL: An epidemiological model for diabetes mellitus in the United States: Five major complications. *Diabetes Res Clin Pract* 1:185, 1985.
4. FAJANS SS, CONN JW: The early recognition of diabetes mellitus. *Ann NY Acad Sci* 82:208, 1959.
5. NATIONAL DIABETES DATA GROUP: Classification and diagnosis of diabetes mellitus and other categories of glucose intolerance. *Diabetes* 28:1039, 1979.
6. HAMBURG S, HENDLER R, SHERWIN RS: Influence of small increments of epinephrine on glucose tolerance in normal humans. *Ann Intern Med* 93:566, 1980.
7. WORLD HEALTH ORGANIZATION: *Diabetes Mellitus.* Geneva, World Health Organization Technical Report Series 727, 1985.
8. SARTOR G, SCHERSTEN B, CARLSTRÖM S, MELANDER A, NORDEN Å, PERSSON G: Ten-year follow-up of subjects with impaired glucose tolerance. Prevention of diabetes by tolbutamide and diet regulation. *Diabetes* 29:41, 1980.
9. GORSUCH AN, LISTER J, DEAN BM, SPENCER KM, MCNALLY JM, BOTTAZZO GF, CUDWORTH AG: Evidence for a long prediabetic period in type I (insulin-dependent) diabetes mellitus. *Lancet* 2:1363, 1981.
10. SRIKANTA S, GANDA OP, EISENBARTH GS, SOELDNER JS: Islet-cell antibodies and beta-cell function in monozygotic triplets and twins initially discordant for type I diabetes mellitus. *N Engl J Med* 308:322, 1983.
11. PITTMAN WB, ACTON RT, BARGER BO, BELL DS, GO RCP, MURPHY CC, ROSEMAN JM: HLA-A, -B, and -DR associations in type I diabetes mellitus with onset after age forty. *Diabetes* 31:122, 1982.
12. GROOP L, GROOP P-H, KOSKIMIES S: Relationship between B-cell function and HLA antigens in patients with type 2 (non-insulin-dependent) diabetes. *Diabetologia* 29:757, 1986.
13. MOHAN V, MOHAN R, SUSHEELA L, SNEHALATHA C, BHARANI G, MAHAJAN VK, RAMACHANDRAN A, VISWANATHAN M, KOHNER EM: Tropical pancreatic diabetes in South India: Heterogeneity in clinical and biochemical profile. *Diabetologia* 28:229, 1985.
14. ROTTER JI, RIMOIN DL: The genetics of diabetes. *Hosp Pract* 22:79, 1987.
15. BENNETT PH, RUSHFORTH NB, MILLER M, LECOMPTE PM: Epidemiologic studies of diabetes in the Pima Indians. *Recent Prog Horm Res* 32:333, 1976.
16. ZIMMET P: Type 2 (non-insulin-dependent) diabetes—An epidemiological overview. *Diabetologia* 22:399, 1982.
17. HERMAN WH, SINNOCK P, BRENNER E, BRIMBERRY JL, LANGFORD D, NAKASHIMA A, SEPE SJ, TEUTSCH SM, MAZZE RS: An epidemiologic model for diabetes mellitus: Incidence, prevalence, and mortality. *Diabetes Care* 7:367, 1984.
18. BENDER AP, SPRAFKA JM, JAGGER HG, MUCKALA KH, MARTIN CP, EDWARDS TR: Incidence, prevalence, and mortality of diabetes mellitus in Wadena, Marshall, and Grand Rapids, Minnesota: The three-city study. *Diabetes Care* 9:343, 1986.
19. GENUTH SM, HOUSER HB, CARTER JR JR, MERKATZ I, PRICE JW, SCHUMACHER OP, WIELAND RG: Community screening for diabetes by blood glucose measurement. Results of a five year experience. *Diabetes* 25:1110, 1976.
20. MELTON LJ III, PALUMBO PJ, CHU C-P: Incidence of diabetes mellitus by clinical type. *Diabetes Care* 6:75, 1983.
21. BLOOM A, HAYES TM, GAMBLE DR: Registry of newly diagnosed diabetic children. *Br Med J* 3:580, 1975.
22. CROSSLEY JR, UPSDELL M: The incidence of juvenile diabetes mellitus in New Zealand. *Diabetologia* 18:29, 1980.
23. LAPORTE RE, FISHBEIN HA, DRASH AL, KULLER LH, SCHNEIDER BB, ORCHARD TJ, WAGENER DK: The Pittsburgh insulin dependent diabetes mellitus (IDDM) registry. The incidence of insulin dependent diabetes mellitus in Allegheny County, Pennsylvania (1965–1976). *Diabetes* 30:279, 1981.
24. WALKER A, CUDWORTH AG: Type 1 (insulin-dependent) diabetic multiplex families. Mode of genetic transmission. *Diabetes* 29:1036, 1980.
25. LERNMARK A: Molecular biology of type 1 (insulin-dependent) diabetes mellitus. *Diabetologia* 28:195, 1985.
26. EISENBARTH GS: Type 1 diabetes mellitus. A chronic autoimmune disease. *N Engl J Med* 314:1360, 1986.
27. BOTTAZZO GF: Death of a beta cell: Homicide or suicide? *Diabetic Med* 3:119, 1986.
28. EBERHARDT MS, WAGENER DK, ORCHARD TJ, LAPORTE RE, CAVENDER DE, RABIN BS, ATCHISON RW, KULLER LH, DRASH AL, BECKER DJ: HLA heterogeneity of insulin-dependent diabetes mellitus at diagnosis. The Pittsburgh IDDM study. *Diabetes* 34:1247, 1985.
29. BELL GI, HORITA S, KARAM JH: A polymorphic locus near the human insulin gene is associated with insulin-dependent diabetes mellitus. *Diabetes* 33:176, 1984.
30. SCHERNTHANER G, MAYR WR: Immunoglobulin allotype markers and HLA-DR genes in type 1 diabetes mellitus. *Metabolism* 33:833, 1984.
31. FIELD LL, ANDERSON CE, NIESWANGER K, HODGE SE, SPENCE MA, ROTTER JI: The interactions of HLA and immunoglobulin (Gm) antigens in insulin-dependent diabetes mellitus. *Diabetologia* 27:504, 1984.
32. ADAMS DD, ADAMS YJ, KNIGHT JG, MCCALL J, WHITE P, HORROCKS R, LOGHEM E: A solution to the genetic and environmental puzzles of insulin-dependent diabetes mellitus. *Lancet* 1:420, 1984.
33. HODGE SE, ANDERSON OE, NEISWANGER K, FIELD LL, SPENCE MA, SPARKES RS, SPARKES MC, CRIST M, TERASAKI PI, RIMOIN DL, ROTTER JI: Close genetic linkage between diabetes mellitus and Kidd blood group. *Lancet* 2:893, 1981.
34. TAKEDA J, SEINO Y, FUKUMOTO H, KOH G, OTSUKA A, IKEDA M, KUNO S, YAWATA M, MORIDERA K, MORITA T, TSUDA K, IMURA H: The polymorphism linked to the human insulin gene: Its lack of association with either IDDM or NIDDM in Japanese. *Acta Endocrinol* 113:268, 1986.
35. FERNS GAA, HITMAN GA, TREMBATH R, WILLIAMS L, TARN A, GALE EA, GALTON DJ: DNA polymorphic haplotypes on the short arm of chromosome 11 and the inheritance of type I diabetes mellitus. *J Med Genet* 23:210, 1986.
36. BERTRAMS J, BAUR MP: No interaction between HLA and immunoglobulin IgG heavy chain allotypes in early onset type 1 diabetes. *J Immunogenet* 12:81, 1985.
37. DIZIER MH, DESCHAMPS I, HORS J, BLANC M, RIVAT L, CLERGET-DARPOUX F: Interactive effect of HLA and Gm tested in a study of 135 juvenile insulin-dependent diabetic families. *Tissue Antigens* 27:269, 1986.
38. TAIT BD, PROPERT DN, HARRISON L, MANDEL T, MARTIN FIR: Interaction between HLA antigens and immunoglobulin (Gm) allotypes in susceptibility to type I diabetes. *Tissue Antigens* 27:249, 1986.
39. RICH SS, WEITKAMP LR, GUTTORMSEN S, BARBOSA J: Gm, Km, and HLA in insulin-dependent type 1 diabetes mellitus. A log-linear analysis of association. *Diabetes* 35:927, 1986.
40. RAUM D, AWDEH Z, YUNIS EJ, ALPER CA, GABBAY KH: Extended major histocompatibility complex haplotypes in type 1 diabetes mellitus. *J Clin Invest* 74:449, 1984.

41. BARNETT AH, EFF C, LESLIE RDG, PYKE DA: Diabetes in identical twins. A study of 200 pairs. *Diabetologia* 20:87, 1981.

42. CHERN MM, ANDERSON VE, BARBOSA J: Empirical risk for insulin-dependent diabetes (IDD) in sibs. Further definition of genetic heterogeneity. *Diabetes* 31:1115, 1982.

43. ORCHARD TJ, ROSENBLOOM AL: The development of insulin-dependent diabetes mellitus among relatives. *Diabetes Care* 8 (*Suppl* 1):45, 1985.

44. TILLIL H, KÖBBERLING J: Age-corrected empirical genetic risk estimates for first-degree relatives of IDDM patients. *Diabetes* 36:93, 1987.

45. LORENZI M, CAGLIERO E, SCHMIDT NJ: Racial differences in incidence of juvenile-onset type 1 diabetes: Epidemiologic studies in southern California. *Diabetologia* 28:734, 1985.

46. LAPORTE RE, TAJIMA N, DORMAN JS, CRUICKSHANKS KJ, EBERHARDT MS, RABIN BS, ATCHISON RW, WAGENER DK, BECKER DJ, ORCHARD TJ, SONGER TJ, SLEMENDA CW, KULLER LH, DRASH AL: Differences between blacks and whites in the epidemiology of insulin-dependent diabetes mellitus in Allegheny County, Pennsylvania. *Am J Epidemiol* 123:592, 1986.

47. REITNAUER PJ, GO RCP, ACTON RT, MURPHY CC, BUDOWLE B, BARGER BO, ROSEMAN JM: Evidence for genetic admixture as a determinant in the occurrence of insulin-dependent diabetes mellitus in U.S. blacks. *Diabetes* 31:532, 1982.

48. MacDONALD MJ, FAMUYIWA OO, NWABUEBO IA, BELLA AF, JUNAID TA, MARRARI M, DUQUESNOY RJ: HLA-DR associations in black type 1 diabetics in Nigeria. Further support for models of inheritance. *Diabetes* 35:583, 1986.

49. EISENBARTH GS: Genes, generator of diversity, glycoconjugates, and autoimmune β-cell insufficiency in type 1 diabetes. *Diabetes* 36:355, 1987.

50. LOUIS EJ, THOMSON G: Three-allele synergistic mixed model for insulin-dependent diabetes mellitus. *Diabetes* 35:958, 1986.

51. MACDONALD MJ, GOTTSCHALL J, HUNTER JB, WINTER KL: HLA-DR4 in insulin-dependent diabetic parents and their diabetic offspring: A clue to dominant inheritance. *Proc Natl Acad Sci USA* 83:7049, 1986.

52. RUBINSTEIN P, WALKER M, GINSBERG-FELLNER F: Excess of DR3/4 in type 1 diabetes. What does it portend? *Diabetes* 35:985, 1986.

53. ROTTER JI, ANDERSON CE, RUBIN R, CONGLETON JE, TERASAKI PI, RIMOIN DL: HLA genotypic study of insulin-dependent diabetes. The excess of DR3/DR4 heterozygotes allows rejection of the recessive hypothesis. *Diabetes* 32:169, 1983.

54. KAY PH, WILTON AN, DAWKINS RL: Preferential paternal transmission of the diabetogenic supratype marked by HLA B18 BfF1 DR3. *J Immunogenet* 12:327, 1985.

55. VADHEIM CM, ROTTER JI, MACLAREN NK, RILEY WJ, ANDERSON CE: Preferential transmission of diabetic alleles within the HLA gene complex. *N Engl J Med* 315:1314, 1986.

56. WARRAM JH, KROLEWSKI AS, GOTTLIEB MS, KAHN CR: Differences in risk of insulin-dependent diabetes in offspring of diabetic mothers and diabetic fathers. *N Engl J Med* 311:149, 1984.

57. LUDVIGSSON J, SAMUELSSON U, BEAUFORTS C, DESCHAMPS I, DORCHY H, DRASH A, FRANCOIS R, HERZ G, NEW M, SCHOBER E: HLA-DR3 is associated with a more slowly progressive form of type 1 (insulin-dependent) diabetes. *Diabetologia* 29:207, 1986.

58. KNIP M, ILONEN J, MUSTONEN A, AKERBLOM HK: Evidence of an accelerated B-cell destruction in HLA-Dw3/Dw4 heterozygous children with type 1 (insulin-dependent) diabetes. *Diabetologia* 29:347, 1986.

59. BRUSERUD O, THORSBY E: HLA control of the proliferative T lymphocyte response to antigenic determinants on mumps virus. Studies of healthy individuals and patients with type 1 diabetes. *Scand J Immunol* 22:509, 1985.

60. EISENBARTH GS, SRIKANTA S, FLEISCHNICK E, GANDA OP, JACKSON RA, BRINK SJ, SOELDNER JS, YUNIS EJ, ALPER C: Progressive autoimmune beta cell insufficiency: Occurrence in the absence of high-risk HLA alleles DR3, DR4. *Diabetes Care* 8:477, 1985.

61. SHEEHY MJ, ROWE JR, FULLER TC, YUNIS EJ, GABBAY KH: A minor subset of HLA-DR3 haplotypes is preferentially increased in type 1 (insulin-dependent diabetes). *Diabetologia* 28:891, 1985.

62. PARTANEN J, KOSKIMIES S, ILONEN J, KNIP M: HLA antigens and complotypes in insulin-dependent diabetes mellitus. *Tissue Antigens* 27:291, 1986.

63. HÄGGLÖF B, HOLMGREN G, HOLMLUND G, LINDBLOM B, OLAISEN B, TEISBERG P: Studies of HLA, factor B (Bf), complement C2 and C4 haplotypes in type 1 diabetic and control families from northern Sweden. *Hum Hered* 36:201, 1986.

64. PHILLIPS ML, MOULE ML, DELOVITCH TL, YIP CC: Class I histocompatibility antigens and insulin receptors: Evidence for interactions. *Proc Natl Acad Sci USA* 83:3474, 1986.

65. DUE C, SIMONSEN M, OLSSON L: The major histocompatibility complex class I heavy chain as a structural subunit of the human cell membrane insulin receptor: Implications for the range of biological functions of histocompatibility antigens. *Proc Natl Acad Sci USA* 83:6007, 1986.

66. STROMINGER JL: Biology of the human histocompatibility leukocyte antigen (HLA) system and a hypothesis regarding the generation of autoimmune diseases. *J Clin Invest* 77:1411, 1986.

67. BACH FH: The HLA class II genes and products: The HLA-D region. *Immunol Today* 6:89, 1985.

68. SHEEHY MJ, ROWE JR, MACDONALD MJ: A particular subset of HLA-DR4 accounts for all or most of the DR4 association in type 1 diabetes. *Diabetes* 34:942, 1985.

69. STETLER D, GRUMET FC, ERLICH HA: Polymorphic restriction endonuclease sites linked to the HLA-DRα gene: Localization and use as genetic markers of insulin-dependent diabetes. *Proc Natl Acad Sci USA* 82:8100, 1985.

70. TOSI R, VELA M, ADORNO D, LONGO A, PAPOLA F, MACCARONE D, CENTIS D, TANIGAKI N, RAPONI MP, CANDELA A, CAMPEA L, ORSINI M, FERRARA GB: Radioimmunoassay typing gives a more precise definition of the HLA association of type 1 (insulin-dependent) diabetes. *Diabetologia* 29:430, 1986.

71. BÖHME J, CARLSSON B, WALLIN J, MÖLLER E, PERSSON B, PETERSON PA, RASK L: Only one DQ-β restriction fragment pattern of each DR specificity is associated with insulin-dependent diabetes. *J Immunol* 137:941, 1986.

72. HITMAN GA, NIVEN MJ, FESTENSTEIN H, CASSELL PG, AWAD J, WALKER-SMITH J, LEONARD JN, FRY L, CICLITIRA P, KUMAR P, SACHS JA: HLA class II alpha chain gene polymorphisms in patients with insulin-dependent diabetes mellitus, dermatitis herpetiformis, and celiac disease. *J Clin Invest* 79:609, 1987.

73. HITMAN GA, SACHS J, CASSELL P, AWAD J, BOTTAZZO GF, TARN AC, SCHWARTZ G, MONSON JP, FESTENSTEIN H: A DR3-related DXα gene polymorphism strongly associates with insulin-dependent diabetes mellitus. *Immunogenetics* 23:47, 1986.

74. COHEN N, BRAUTBAR C, FONT MP, DAUSSET J, COHEN D: HLA-DR2-associated Dw subtypes correlate with RFLP clusters: Most DR2 IDDM patients belong to one of these clusters. *Immunogenetics* 23:84, 1986.

75. NEPOM BS, PALMER J, KIM SJ, HANSEN JA, HOLBECK SL, NEPOM GT: Specific genomic markers for the HLA-DQ subregion discriminate between $DR4^+$ insulin-dependent diabetes mellitus and $DR4^+$ seropositive juvenile rheumatoid arthritis. *J Exp Med* 164:345, 1986.

76. SCHREUDER GMT, TILANUS MGJ, BONTROP RE, BRUINING GJ, GIPHART MJ, VAN ROOD JJ, DE VRIES RRP: HLA-DQ polymorphism associated with resistance to type 1 diabetes detected with monoclonal antibodies, isoelectric point differences, and restriction fragment length polymorphism. *J Exp Med* 164:938, 1986.

77. SEGALL M, NOREEN H, SCHLUENDER L, SWENSON M, BARBOSA J, BACH FH: $DR2^+$ haplotypes in insulin-dependent diabetes: Analysis of DNA restriction fragment length polymorphisms. *Hum Immunol* 17:61, 1986.

78. MICHELSEN B, LERNMARK A: Molecular cloning of a polymorphic DNA endonuclease fragment associates insulin-dependent diabetes mellitus with HLA-DQ. *J Clin Invest* 79:1144, 1987.

79. OWERBACH D, RICH C, TANEJA K: Characterization of three HLA-DR beta genes isolated from an HLA-DR 3/4 insulin-dependent diabetic patient. *Immunogenetics* 24:41, 1986.

80. GORSKI J, MACH B: Polymorphism of human Ia antigens: Gene conversion between two DR β loci results in a new HLA-D/DR specificity. *Nature* 322:67, 1986.

80a. TODD JA, BELL JI, McDEVITT HO: HLA-DQβ gene contributes to susceptibility and resistance to insulin-dependent diabetes mellitus. *Nature* 329:599, 1987.

81. MENGLE-GAW L, MCDEVITT HO: Genetics and expression of mouse Ia antigens. *Annu Rev Immunol* 3:367, 1985.

82. NEPOM BS, SCHWARZ D, PALMER JP, NEPOM GT: Transcomplementation of HLA genes in IDDM. HLA-Dq α- and β-chains produce hybrid molecules in DR3/4 heterozygotes. *Diabetes* 36:114, 1987.

83. GUILLET JG, LAI MZ, BRINER TJ, BUUS S, SETTE A, GREY HM, SMITH JA, GEFTER ML: Immunological self, nonself discrimination. *Science* 235:865, 1987.

84. ACUTO O, REINHERZ EL: The human T-cell receptor. Structure and function. *N Engl J Med* 312:1100, 1985.

85. BUUS S, SETTE A, COLON SM, MILES C, GREY HM: The relation between major histocompatibility complex (MHC) restriction and the capacity of Ia to bind immunogenic peptides. *Science* 235:1353, 1987.

86. KARAM JH, LEWITT PA, YOUNG CW, NOWLAIN RE, FRANKEL BJ, FUJIYA H, FREEDMAN ZR, GRODSKY GM: Insulinopenic diabetes after rodenticide (Vacor) ingestion. A unique model of acquired diabetes in man. *Diabetes* 29:971, 1980.

87. YOON JW, RAY UR: Perspectives on the role of viruses in insulin-dependent diabetes. *Diabetes Care* 8 (*Suppl* 1):39, 1985.

88. YOON JW, AUSTIN M, ONODERA T, NOTKINS AL: Virus-induced diabetes

mellitus. Isolation of a virus from the pancreas of a child with diabetic ketoacidosis. *N Engl J Med* 300:1173, 1979.

89. CHAMPSAUR H, DUSSAIX E, SAMOLYK F, FABRE M, BACH C, ASSAN R: Diabetes and Coxsackie virus B5 infection. *Lancet* 1:251, 1980.

90. RUBINSTEIN P, WALKER ME, FEDUN B, WITT ME, COOPER LZ, GINSBERG-FELLNER F: The HLA system in congenital rubella patients with and without diabetes. *Diabetes* 31:1088, 1982.

91. RAYFIELD EJ, KELLY KJ, YOON JW: Rubella virus-induced diabetes in the hamster. *Diabetes* 35:1278, 1986.

92. REWERS M, LAPORTE RE, WALCZAK M, DMOCHOWSKI K, BOGACZYNSKA E: Apparent epidemic of insulin-dependent diabetes mellitus in midwestern Poland. *Diabetes* 36:106, 1987.

93. FRISK G, FOHLMAN J, KOBBAH M, EWALD U, TUVEMO T, DIDERHOLM H, FRIMAN G: High frequency of Coxsackie-B-virus-specific IgM in children developing type 1 diabetes during a period of high diabetes morbidity. *J Med Virol* 17:219, 1985.

94. YOON JW, MCCLINTOCK PR, BACHURSKI CJ, LONGSTRETH JD, NOTKINS AL: Virus-induced diabetes mellitus. No evidence for immune mechanisms in the destruction of β-cells by the D-variant of encephalomyocarditis virus. *Diabetes* 34:922, 1985.

95. RAYFIELD EJ, KELLY KJ: Virus-induced alterations in cyclic adenosine monophosphate generation in hamster islets of Langerhans. *J Clin Invest* 77:958, 1986.

96. SCOTT FW, MONGEAU R, KARDISH M, HATINA G, TRICK KD, WOJCINSKI Z: Diet can prevent diabetes in the BB rat. *Diabetes* 34:1059, 1985.

97. TOMINAGA M, KOMIYA I, JOHNSON JH, INMAN L, ALAM T, MOLTZ J, CRIDER B, STEFAN Y, BAETENS D, MCCORCKLE K, ORCI L, UNGER RH: Loss of insulin response to glucose but not arginine during the development of autoimmune diabetes in BB/W rats: Relationships to islet volume and glucose transport rate. *Proc Natl Acad Sci USA* 83:9749, 1986.

98. ADAMS TE, ALPERT S, HANAHAN D: Non-tolerance and autoantibodies to a transgenic self antigen expressed in pancreatic β cells. *Nature* 325:223, 1987.

99. ROSSINI AA, MORDES JP, LIKE AA: Immunology of insulin-dependent diabetes mellitus. *Annu Rev Immunol* 3:289, 1985.

100. LERNMARK A, BAEKKESKOV S: Islet cell antibodies—theoretical and practical implications. *Diabetologia* 21:431, 1981.

101. SRIKANTA S, RICKER AT, MCCULLOCH DK, SOELDNER JS, EISENBARTH GS, PALMER JP: Autoimmunity to insulin, beta cell dysfunction, and development of insulin-dependent diabetes mellitus. *Diabetes* 35:139, 1986.

102. GARZELLI C, TAUB FE, JENKINS MC, DRELL DW, GINISBERG-FELLNER F, NOTKINS AL: Human monoclonal autoantibodies that react with both pancreatic islets and thyroid. *J Clin Invest* 77:1627, 1986.

103. NEUFELD M, MACLAREN NK, BLIZZARD RM: Two types of autoimmune Addison's disease associated with different polyglandular autoimmune (PGA) syndromes. *Medicine* 60:355, 1981.

104. ARSLANIAN SA, BECKER DJ, RABIN B, ATCHISON R, EBERHARDT M, CAVENDER D, DORMAN J, DRASH AL: Correlates of insulin antibodies in newly diagnosed children with insulin-dependent diabetes before insulin therapy. *Diabetes* 34:926, 1985.

105. MCEVOY RC, WITT ME, GINSBERG-FELLNER F, RUBINSTEIN P: Anti-insulin antibodies in children with type 1 diabetes mellitus. Genetic regulation of production and presence at diagnosis before insulin replacement. *Diabetes* 35:634, 1986.

106. DEAN BM, BECKER F, MCNALLY JM, TARN AC, SCHWARTZ G, GALE EAM, BOTTAZZO GF: Insulin autoantibodies in the pre-diabetic period: correlation with islet cell antibodies and development of diabetes. *Diabetologia* 29:339, 1986.

107. SRIKANTA S, RICKER AT, MCCULLOCH DK, SOELDNER JS, EISENBARTH GS, PALMER JP: Autoimmunity to insulin, beta cell dysfunction, and development of insulin-dependent diabetes mellitus. *Diabetes* 35:139, 1986.

108. KARJALAINEN J, KNIP M, MUSTONEN A, ILONEN J, AKERBLOM HK: Relation between insulin antibody and complement-fixing islet cell antibody at clinical diagnosis of IDDM. *Diabetes* 35:620, 1986.

109. BODANSKY JH, DEAN BM, BOTTAZZO GF, GRANT PJ, MCNALLY J, HAMBLING MH, WALES JK: Islet-cell antibodies and insulin autoantibodies in association with common viral infections. *Lancet* 2:1351, 1986.

110. STILLER CR, DUPRÉ J, GENT M, JENNER MR, KEOWN PA, LAUPACIS A, MARTELL R, RODGER NW, GRAFFENRIED BV, WOLFE BMJ: Effects of cyclosporine immunosuppression in insulin-dependent diabetes mellitus of recent onset. *Science* 223:1362, 1984.

111. LOHMANN D, KRUG J, LAMPETER EF, BIERWOLF B, VERLOHREN HJ: Cell-mediated immune reactions against B cells and defect of suppressor cell activity in type 1 (insulin-dependent) diabetes mellitus. *Diabetologia* 29:421, 1986.

112. GREINER DL, HANDLER ES, NAKANO K, MORDES JP, ROSSINI AA: Absence of the RT-6 T cell subset in diabetes-prone BB/W rats. *J Immunol* 136:148, 1986.

113. QUINIOU-DEBRIE MC, DEBRAY-SACHS M, DARDENNE M, CZERNICHOW P, ASSAN R, BACH JF: Anti-islet cellular and humoral immunity, T-cell subsets, and thymic function in type 1 diabetes. *Diabetes* 34:373, 1985.

114. HITCHCOCK CL, RILEY WJ, ALAMO A, PYKA R, MACLAREN NK: Lymphocyte subsets and activation in prediabetes. *Diabetes* 35:1416, 1986.

115. PONTESILLI O, CHASE HP, CAROTENUTO P, HERBERGER MJ, HAYWARD AR: T-lymphocyte subpopulations in insulin-dependent (type I) diabetes mellitus. *Clin Exp Immunol* 63:68, 1986.

116. CROSTI F, SECCHI A, FERRERO E, FALQUI L, INVERARDI L, PONTIROLI AE, CIBODDO GF, PAVONI D, PROTTI P, RUGARLI C, POZZA G: Impairment of lymphocyte-suppressive system in recent-onset insulin-dependent diabetes mellitus. Correlation with metabolic control. *Diabetes* 35:1053, 1986.

117. MORIMOTO C, STEINBERG AD, LETVIN NL, HAGAN M, TAKEUCHI T, DALEY J, LEVINE H, SCHLOSSMAN SF: A defect of immunoregulatory T cell subsets in systemic lupus erythematosus patients demonstrated with anti-2H4 antibody. *J Clin Invest* 79:762, 1987.

118. MORIMOTO C, HAFLER DA, WEINER HL, LETVIN NL, HAGAN M, DALEY J, SCHLOSSMAN SF: Selective loss of the suppressor-inducer T-cell subset in progressive multiple sclerosis. Analysis with anti-2H4 monoclonal antibody. *N Engl J Med* 316:67, 1987.

119. TOSATO G, STEINBERG AD, BLAESE RM: Defective EBV-specific suppressor T-cell function in rheumatoid arthritis. *N Engl J Med* 305:1238, 1981.

120. MORDES JP, GALLINA DL, HANDLER ES, GREINER DL, NAKAMURA N, PELLETIER A, ROSSINI AA: Transfusions enriched for W3/25$^+$ helper/inducer T lymphocytes prevent spontaneous diabetes in the BB/W rat. *Diabetologia* 30:22, 1987.

121. BOTTAZZO GF, PUJOL-BORRELL R, HANAFUSA T: Role of aberrant HLA-DR expression and antigen presentation in induction of endocrine autoimmunity. *Lancet* 2:1115, 1983.

122. UNANUE ER, ALLEN PM: The basis for the immunoregulatory role of macrophages and other accessory cells. *Science* 236:551, 1987.

123. BOTTAZZO GF, DEAN BM, MCNALLY JM, MACKAY EH, SWIFT PGF, GAMBLE DR: In situ characterization of autoimmune phenomena and expression of HLA molecules in the pancreas in diabetic insulitis. *N Engl J Med* 313:353, 1985.

124. FOULIS AK, FARQUHARSON MA: Aberrant expression of HLA-DR antigens by insulin-containing β-cells in recent-onset type 1 diabetes mellitus. *Diabetes* 35:1215, 1986.

125. DEAN BM, WALKER R, BONE AJ, BAIRD JD, COOKE A: Pre-diabetes in the spontaneously diabetic BB/E rat: lymphocyte subpopulations in the pancreatic infiltrate and expression of rat MHC class II molecules in endocrine cells. *Diabetologia* 28:464, 1985.

126. WEETMAN AP, VOLKMAN DJ, BURMAN KD, GERRARD TL, FAUCI AS: The *in vitro* regulation of human thyrocyte HLA-DR antigen expression. *J Clin Endocrinol Metab* 61:817, 1985.

127. WALKER R, COOKE A, BONE AJ, DEAN BM, VAN DER MEIDE P, BAIRD JD: Induction of class II MHC antigens *in vitro* on pancreatic B cells isolated from BB/E rats. *Diabetologia* 29:749, 1986.

128. WRIGHT JR JR, LACY PE, UNANUE ER, MUSZYNSKI C, HAUPTFELD V: Interferon-mediated induction of Ia antigen expression on isolated murine whole islets and dispersed islet cells. *Diabetes* 35:1174, 1986.

129. IWATANI Y, GERSTEIN HC, IITAKA M, ROW VV, VOLPE R: Thyrocyte HLA-DR expression and interferon-γ production in autoimmune thyroid disease. *J Clin Endocrinol Metab* 63:695, 1986.

130. PUJOL-BORRELL R, TODD I, DOSHI M, BOTTAZZO GF, SUTTON R, GRAY D, ADOLF GR, FELDMANN M: HLA class II induction in human islet cells by interferon-γ plus tumour necrosis factor or lymphotoxin. *Nature* 326:304, 1987.

131. CAMPBELL IL, BIZILJ K, COLMAN PG, TUCH BE, HARRISON LC: Interferon-γ induces the expression of HLA-A,B,C but not HLA-DR on human pancreatic β-cells. *J Clin Endocrinol Metab* 62:1101, 1986.

132. CAMPBELL IL, HARRISON LC, COLMAN PG, PAPAIOANNOU J, ASHCROFT RG: Expression of class I MHC proteins on RIN-m5F cells is increased by interferon-γ and lymphokine-conditioned medium. *Diabetes* 35:1225, 1986.

133. PICCININI LA, SCHACHTER BS, DAVIES TF: HLA-DR α chain expression in human thyroid cells. *Endocrinology* 118:2611, 1986.

134. SANO H, COMPTON LJ, SHIOMI N, STEINBERG AD, JACKSON RA, SASAKI T: Low expression of human histocompatibility leukocyte antigen-DR is associated with hypermethylation of human histocompatibility leukocyte antigen-DRα gene regions in B cells from patients with systemic lupus erythematosus. *J Clin Invest* 76:1314, 1985.

135. BOTTAZZO GF, PUJOL-BORRELL R, GALE E: Etiology of diabetes: The role of autoimmune mechanisms, in Alberti KGMM, Krall LP (eds): *The Diabetes Annual 1*. Amsterdam, Elsevier, 1985, p 16.

136. VAN DE RIJN I, ZABRISKIE JB, MCCARTHY M: Group A streptococcal antigens cross-reactive with myocardium. Purification of heart-reactive anti-

body and isolation and characterization of the streptococcal antigen. *J Exp Med* 146:579, 1977.

137. STEFANSSON K, DIEPERINK ME, RICHMAN DP, GOMEZ CM, MARTON LS: Sharing of antigenic determinants between the nicotinic acetylcholine receptor and proteins in *Escherichia coli, Proteus vulgaris* and *Klebsiella pneumoniae*. Possible role in the pathogenesis of myasthenia gravis. *N Engl J Med* 312:221, 1985.

138. KAGNOFF MF, AUSTIN RK, HUBERT JJ, BERNARDIN JE, KASARDA DD: Possible role for a human adenovirus in the pathogenesis of celiac disease. *J Exp Med* 160:1544, 1984.

139. RUPP F, BRECHER J, GIEDLIN MA, MOSMANN T, ZINKERNAGEL RM, HENGARTNER H, JOHO RH: T-cell antigen receptors with identical variable regions but different diversity and joining region gene segments have distinct specificities but cross-reactive idiotypes. *Proc Natl Acad Sci USA* 84:219, 1987.

140. HOOVER ML, MARKS J, CHIPMAN J, PALMER E, STASTNY P, CAPRA JD: Restriction fragment length polymorphism of the gene encoding the α chain of the human T cell receptor. *J Exp Med* 162:1087, 1985.

141. JACKSON RA, MORRIS MA, HAYNES BF, EISENBARTH GS: Increased circulating Ia-antigen-bearing T cells in type 1 diabetes mellitus. *N Engl J Med* 306:785, 1982.

142. NEGISHI K, WALDECK N, CHANDY G, BUCKINGHAM B, KERSHNAR A, FISHER L, GUPTA S, CHARLES MA: Natural killer cell and islet killer cell activities in type 1 (insulin-dependent) diabetes. *Diabetologia* 29:352, 1986.

143. WODA BA, BIRON CA: Natural killer cell number and function in the spontaneously diabetic BB/W rat. *J Immunol* 137:1860, 1986.

144. ZIER KS, LEO MM, SPIELMAN RS, BAKER L: Decreased synthesis of interleukin-2 (IL-2) in insulin-dependent diabetes mellitus. *Diabetes* 33:552, 1984.

145. KAYE WA, ADRI MNS, SOELDNER JS, RABINOWE SL, KALDANY A, KAHN CR, BISTRIAN B, SRIKANTA S, GANDA OP, EISENBARTH GS: Acquired defect in interleukin-2 production in patients with type 1 diabetes mellitus. *N Engl J Med* 315:920, 1986.

146. SUNDSMO JS, PAPIN RA, WOOD L, HIRANI S, WALDECK N, BUCKINGHAM B, KERSHNAR A, ASCHER M, CHARLES MA: Complement activation in type 1 human diabetes. *Clin Immunol Immunopathol* 35:211, 1985.

147. GERLING I, BAEKKESKOV S, LERNMARK A: Islet cell and 64K autoantibodies are associated with plasma IgG in newly diagnosed insulin-dependent diabetic children. *J Immunol* 137:3782, 1986.

148. SRIKANTA S, GANDA OP, GLEASON RE, JACKSON RA, SOELDNER JS, EISENBARTH GS: Pre-type 1 diabetes. Linear loss of beta cell response to intravenous glucose. *Diabetes* 33:717, 1984.

149. KANATSUNA T, LERNMARK A, RUBENSTEIN AH, STEINER DF: Block in insulin release from column-perifused pancreatic β-cells induced by islet cell surface antibodies and complement. *Diabetes* 30:231, 1981.

150. MANDRUP-POULSEN T, BENDTZEN K, NERUP J, DINARELLO CA, SVENSON M, NIELSEN JH: Affinity-purified human interleukin 1 is cytotoxic to isolated islets of Langerhans. *Diabetologia* 29:63, 1986.

151. ZAWALICH WS, DIAZ VA: Interleukin 1 inhibits insulin secretion from isolated perifused rat islets. *Diabetes* 35:1119, 1986.

152. TATEMOTO K, EFENDIC S, MUTT V, MAKK G, FEISTNER GJ, BARCHAS JD: Pancreastatin, a novel pancreatic peptide that inhibits insulin secretion. *Nature* 324:476, 1986.

153. BOTTAZZO GF: β-Cell damage in diabetic insulitis: Are we approaching a solution? *Diabetologia* 26:241, 1984.

154. GARDNER LI JR, STERN MP, HAFFNER SM, GASKILL SP, HAZUDA HP, RELETHFORD JH, EIFLER CW: Prevalence of diabetes in Mexican Americans. Relationship to percent of gene pool derived from native American sources. *Diabetes* 33:86, 1984.

155. KNOWLER WC, SAVAGE PJ, NAGULESPARAN M, HOWARD BV, PETTITT DJ, LISSE JR, ARONOFF SL, BENNETT PH: Obesity, insulin resistance and diabetes mellitus in the Pima Indians, in Köbberling J, Tattersall J (eds): *The Genetics of Diabetes Mellitus. Proceedings of the Serono Symposia*. London, Academic, 1982, vol 47, p 243.

156. BRIGGS BR, JACKSON WPU, DUTOIT ED, BOTHA MC: The histocompatibility (HLA) antigen distribution in diabetes in southern African blacks (Xhosa). *Diabetes* 29:68, 1980.

157. LESLIE RDG, PYKE DA: Chlorpropamide-alcohol flushing: A dominantly inherited trait associated with diabetes. *Br Med J* 2:1519, 1978.

158. FUI SNT, KEEN H, JARRETT J, GOSSAIN V, MARSDEN P: Test for chlorpropamide-alcohol flush becomes positive after prolonged chlorpropamide treatment in insulin-dependent and non-insulin-dependent diabetics. *N Engl J Med* 309:93, 1983.

159. ROTWEIN P, CHYN R, CHIRGWIN J, CORDELL B, GOODMAN HM, PERMUTT MA: Polymorphism in the 5′-flanking region of the human insulin gene and its possible relation to type 2 diabetes. *Science* 213:1117, 1981.

160. KNOWLER WC, PETTITT DJ, VASQUEZ B, ROTWEIN PS, ANDREONE TL, PERMUTT MA: Polymorphism in the 5′ flanking region of the human insulin gene. Relationships with noninsulin-dependent diabetes mellitus, glucose and insulin concentrations, and diabetes treatment in the Pima Indians. *J Clin Invest* 74:2129, 1984.

161. KÖBBERLING J, TILLIL H: Empirical risk figures for first degree relatives of non-insulin dependent diabetics, in Köbberling J, Tattersall R (eds): *The Genetics of Diabetes Mellitus. Proceedings of the Serono Symposia*. London, Academic, 1982, vol 47, p 201.

162. TATTERSALL RB, FAJANS SS: Prevalence of diabetes and glucose intolerance in 199 offspring of thirty-seven conjugal diabetic parents. *Diabetes* 24:452, 1975.

163. GANDA OP, SOELDNER SS: Genetic, acquired, and related factors in the etiology of diabetes mellitus. *Arch Intern Med* 137:461, 1977.

164. TATTERSALL RB: Mild familial diabetes with dominant inheritance. *Q J Med* 43:339, 1974.

165. WINTER WE, MACLAREN NK, RILEY WJ, CLARKE DW, KAPPY MS, SPILLAR RP: Maturity-onset diabetes of youth in Black Americans. *N Engl J Med* 316:285, 1987.

166. EFENDIC S, LUFT R, WAJNGOT A: Aspects of the pathogenesis of type 2 diabetes. *Endocr Rev* 5:395, 1984.

167. HALTER JB, GRAF RJ, PORTE D JR: Potentiation of insulin secretory responses by plasma glucose levels in man: Evidence that hyperglycemia in diabetes compensates for impaired glucose potentiation. *J Clin Endocrinol Metab* 48:946, 1979.

168. PFEIFER MA, HALTER JB, PORTE D JR: Insulin secretion in diabetes mellitus. *Am J Med* 70:579, 1981.

169. RAHIER J, GOEBBELS RM, HENQUIN JC: Cellular composition of the human diabetic pancreas. *Diabetologia* 24:366, 1983.

170. VAGUE P, MOULIN J-P: The defective glucose sensitivity of the B cell in non insulin dependent diabetes. Improvement after twenty hours of normoglycaemia. *Metabolism* 31:139, 1982.

171. WARD WK, BOLGIANO DC, MCKNIGHT B, HALTER JB, PORTE D JR: Diminished B cell secretory capacity in patients with noninsulin-dependent diabetes mellitus. *J Clin Invest* 74:1318, 1984.

172. OSEI K, FALKO JM, O'DORISIO TM, ADAM DR, CATALAND S: Significance of spontaneous ketonuria and serum C-peptide levels in obese type II diabetic patients. *Diabetes Care* 7:442, 1984.

173. WEIR GC: Non-insulin-dependent diabetes mellitus: Interplay between B-cell inadequacy and insulin resistance. *Am J Med* 73:461, 1982.

174. TURNER RC, HOLMAN RR, MATTHEWS D, HOCKADAY TDR, PETO J: Insulin deficiency and insulin resistance interaction in diabetes: Estimation of their relative contribution by feedback analysis from basal plasma insulin and glucose concentrations. *Metabolism* 28:1086, 1979.

175. BOGARDUS C, LILLIOJA S, HOWARD BV, REAVEN G, MOTT D: Relationships between insulin secretion, insulin action, and fasting plasma glucose concentration in nondiabetic and noninsulin-dependent diabetic subjects. *J Clin Invest* 74:1238, 1984.

176. SWISLOCKI ALM, DONNER CC, FRAZE E, CHEN Y-DI, REAVEN GM: Can insulin resistance exist as a primary defect in noninsulin-dependent diabetes mellitus? *J Clin Endocrinol Metab* 64:778, 1987.

177. BONNER-WEIR S, TRENT DF, WEIR GC: Partial pancreatectomy in the rat and subsequent defect in glucose-induced insulin release. *J Clin Invest* 71:1544, 1983.

178. UNGER RH, GRUNDY S: Hyperglycaemia as an inducer as well as a consequence of impaired islet cell function and insulin resistance: Implications for the management of diabetes. *Diabetologia* 28:119, 1985.

179. ANDREWS WJ, VASQUEZ B, NAGULESPARAN M, KLIMES I, FOLEY J, UNGER R, REAVEN GM: Insulin therapy in obese, non-insulin-dependent diabetes induces improvements in insulin action and secretion that are maintained for two weeks after insulin withdrawal. *Diabetes* 33:634, 1984.

180. OLEFSKY JM, KOLTERMAN OG: Mechanisms of insulin resistance in obesity and noninsulin dependent (type II) diabetes. *Am J Med* 70:151, 1981.

181. DEFRONZO RA, SIMONSON D, FERRANNINI E: Hepatic and peripheral insulin resistance: A common feature of type 2 (non-insulin-dependent) and type 1 (insulin-dependent) diabetes mellitus. *Diabetologia* 23:313, 1982.

182. DEFRONZO RA, TOBIN JD, ANDRES R: Glucose clamp technique: A method for quantifying insulin secretion and resistance. *Am J Physiol* 237:E214, 1979.

183. KAHN CR: Role of insulin receptors in insulin-resistant states. *Metabolism* 29:455, 1980.

184. OLEFSKY JM: Insulin resistance and insulin action. An in vitro and in vivo perspective. *Diabetes* 30:148, 1981.

185. KAHN CR: The insulin receptor and insulin: The lock and key to diabetes. *Clin Res* 31:326, 1983.

186. MORGAN DO, ROTH RA: Acute insulin action requires insulin receptor kinase activity: Introduction of an inhibitory monoclonal antibody into mammalian cells blocks the rapid effects of insulin. *Proc Natl Acad Sci USA* 84:41, 1987.

187. CHOU CK, DULL TJ, RUSSELL DS, GHERZI R, LEBWOHL D, ULLRICH A, ROSEN OM: Human insulin receptors mutated at the ATP-binding site lack protein tyrosine kinase activity and fail to mediate postreceptor effects of insulin. *J Biol Chem* 262:1842, 1987.

188. SINHA MK, PORIES WJ, FLICKINGER EG, MEELHEIM D, CARO JF: Insulin-receptor kinase activity of adipose tissue from morbidly obese humans with and without NIDDM. *Diabetes* 36:620, 1987.

189. COMI RJ, GRUNBERGER G, GORDEN P: Relationship of insulin binding and insulin-stimulated tyrosine kinase activity is altered in type II diabetes. *J Clin Invest* 79:453, 1987.

190. SALTIEL AR, CUATRECASAS P: Insulin stimulates the generation from hepatic plasma membranes of modulators derived from an inositol glycolipid. *Proc Natl Acad Sci USA* 83:5793, 1986.

191. BOLLAG GE, ROTH RA, BEAUDOIN J, MOCHLY-ROSEN D, KOSHLAND DE JR: Protein kinase C directly phosphorylates the insulin receptor *in vitro* and reduces its protein-tyrosine kinase activity. *Proc Natl Acad Sci USA* 83:5822, 1986.

192. SALTIEL AR, FOX JA, SHERLINE P, CUATRECASAS P: Insulin-stimulated hydrolysis of a novel glycolipid generates modulators of cAMP phosphodiesterase. *Science* 233:967, 1986.

193. FARESE RV, KONDA TS, DAVIS JS, STANDAERT ML, POLLET RJ, COOPER DR: Insulin rapidly increases diacylglycerol by activating de novo phosphatidic acid synthesis. *Science* 236:586, 1987.

194. SIMPSON IA, CUSHMAN SW: Hormonal regulation of mammalian glucose transport. *Ann Rev Biochem* 55:1059, 1986.

195. BALY DL, HORUK R: Dissociation of insulin-stimulated glucose transport from the translocation of glucose carriers in rat adipose cells. *J Biol Chem* 262:21, 1987.

196. KURODA M, HONNOR RC, CUSHMAN SW, LONDOS C, SIMPSON IA: Regulation of insulin-stimulated glucose transport in the isolated rat adipocyte. cAMP-independent effects of lipolytic and antilipolytic agents. *J Biol Chem* 262:245, 1987.

197. KAHN BB, HORTON ES, CUSHMAN SW: Mechanism for enhanced glucose transport response to insulin in adipose cells from chronically hyperinsulinemic rats. Increased translocation of glucose transporters from an enlarged intracellular pool. *J Clin Invest* 79:853, 1987.

198. TOYODA N, FLANAGAN JE, KONO T: Reassessment of insulin effects on the Vmax and Km values of hexose transport in isolated rat epididymal adipocytes. *J Biol Chem* 262:2737, 1987.

199. MATTHAEI S, GARVEY WT, HORUK R, HUECKSTAEDT TP, OLEFSKY JM: Human adipocyte glucose transport system. Biochemical and functional heterogeneity of hexose carriers. *J Clin Invest* 79:703, 1987.

200. KARNIELI E, HISSIN PJ, SIMPSON IA, SALANS LB, CUSHMAN SW: A possible mechanism of insulin resistance in the rat adipose cell in streptozotocin-induced diabetes mellitus: Depletion of intracellular glucose transport systems. *J Clin Invest* 68:811, 1981.

201. HISSIN PJ, FOLEY JE, WARDZALA LJ, KARNIELI E, SIMPSON IA, SALANS LB, CUSHMAN SW: Mechanism of insulin-resistant glucose transport activity in the enlarged adipose cell of the aged, obese rat. Relative depletion of intracellular glucose transport systems. *J Clin Invest* 70:780, 1982.

202. GARVEY WT, OLEFSKY JM, MATTHAEI S, MARSHALL S: Glucose and insulin co-regulate the glucose transport system in primary cultured adipocytes. A new mechanism of insulin resistance. *J Biol Chem* 262:189, 1987.

203. DEFRONZO RA, GUNNARSSON R, BJÖRKMAN O, OLSSON M, WAHREN J: Effects of insulin on peripheral and splanchnic glucose metabolism in non-insulin-dependent (type II) diabetes mellitus. *J Clin Invest* 76:149, 1985.

204. CARO JF, ITTOOP O, PORIES WJ, MEELHEIM D, FLICKINGER EG, THOMAS F, JENQUIN M, SILVERMAN JF, KHAZANIE PG, SINHA MK: Studies on the mechanism of insulin resistance in the liver from humans with noninsulin-dependent diabetes. Insulin action and binding in isolated hepatocytes, insulin receptor structure, and kinase activity. *J Clin Invest* 78:249, 1986.

205. KOLTERMAN OG, GRAY RS, SHAPIRO G, SCARLETT JA, GRIFFIN J, OLEFSKY JM: The acute and chronic effects of sulfonylurea therapy in type II diabetic subjects. *Diabetes* 33:346, 1984.

206. GARVEY WT, OLEFSKY JM, GRIFFIN J, HAMMAN RF, KOLTERMAN OG: The effect of insulin treatment on insulin secretion and insulin action in type II diabetes mellitus. *Diabetes* 34:222, 1985.

207. HENRY RR, WALLACE P, OLEFSKY JM: Effects of weight loss on mechanisms of hyperglycemia in obese non-insulin-dependent diabetes mellitus. *Diabetes* 35:990, 1986.

208. HOWARD BV, SAVAGE PJ, NAGULESPARAN M, BENNION LJ, UNGER RH, BENNETT PH: Evidence for marked sensitivity to the antilipolytic action of insulin in obese maturity-onset diabetics. *Metabolism* 28:744, 1979.

209. FRAZE E, DONNER CC, SWISLOCKI ALM, CHIOU Y-AM, CHEN Y-DI, REAVEN GM: Ambient plasma free fatty acid concentrations in noninsulin-dependent diabetes mellitus: Evidence for insulin resistance. *J Clin Endocrinol Metab* 61:807, 1985.

210. RASKIN P, AYDIN I, UNGER RH: Effect of insulin on the exaggerated glucagon response to arginine stimulation in diabetes mellitus. *Diabetes* 25:227, 1976.

211. RASKIN P, AYDIN I, YAMAMOTO T, UNGER RH: Abnormal alpha cell function in human diabetes. The response to oral protein. *Am J Med* 64:988, 1978.

212. HOLLENBECK CB, CHEN Y-DI, REAVEN GM: A comparison of the relative effects of obesity and non-insulin-dependent diabetes mellitus on in vivo insulin-stimulated glucose utilization. *Diabetes* 33:622, 1984.

213. KOLTERMAN OG, INSEL J, SAEKOW M, OLEFSKY JM: Mechanisms of insulin resistance in human obesity. Evidence for receptor and postreceptor defects. *J Clin Invest* 65:1272, 1980.

214. JOCHEN AL, BERHANU P, OLEFSKY JM: Insulin internalization and degradation in adipocytes from normal and type II diabetic subjects. *J Clin Endocrinol Metab* 62:268, 1986.

215. WITTERS LA, VATER CA, LIENHARD GE: Phosphorylation of the glucose transporter *in vitro* and *in vivo* by protein kinase C. *Nature* 315:777, 1985.

216. MARTZ A, MOOKERJEE BK, JUNG CY: Insulin and phorbol esters affect the maximum velocity rather than the half-saturation constant of 3-0-methylglucose transport in rat adipocytes. *J Biol Chem* 261:13606, 1986.

217. IMAMURA T, KOFFLER M, HELDERMAN H, PRINCE D, THIRLEBY R, INMAN L, UNGER RH: Severe diabetes induced in subtotally depancreatized dogs by sustained hyperglycemia. *J Clin Invest*, in press.

218. SPERLING MA, BACON G, KENNY FM, DRASH AL: Cortisol secretion in acidotic and nonacidotic diabetes mellitus. *Am J Dis Child* 124:690, 1972.

219. CRYER PE, SILVERBERG AB, SANTIAGO JV, SHAH SD: Plasma catecholamines in diabetes. The syndromes of hypoadrenergic and hyperadrenergic postural hypotension. *Am J Med* 64:407, 1978.

220. SANTIAGO JV, CLARKE WL, SHAH SD, CRYER PE: Epinephrine, norepinephrine, glucagon and growth hormone release in association with physiological decrements in the plasma glucose concentration in normal and diabetic man. *J Clin Endocrinol Metab* 51:877, 1980.

221. ZADIK Z, KAYNE R, KAPPY M, PLOTNICK LP, KOWARSKI AA: Increased integrated concentration of norepinephrine, epinephrine, aldosterone and growth hormone in patients with uncontrolled juvenile diabetes mellitus. *Diabetes* 29:655, 1980.

222. CRYER PE: Glucose counter-regulation in man. *Diabetes* 30:261, 1981.

223. UNGER RH: The milieu interieur and the islets of Langerhans. *Diabetologia* 20:1, 1981.

224. UNGER RH, ORCI L: Glucagon and the A cell. Physiology and pathophysiology. *N Engl J Med* 304:1518, 1575, 1981.

225. UNGER RH: Role of glucagon in the pathogenesis of diabetes: The status of the controversy. *Metabolism* 27:1691, 1978.

226. RASKIN P, PIETRI A, UNGER RH: Changes in glucagon levels after four to five weeks of glucoregulation by portable insulin infusion pumps. *Diabetes* 28:1033, 1079.

227. KAWAMORI R, SCHICHIRI M, KIKUCHI M, YAMASAKI Y, ABE H: Perfect normalization of excessive glucagon responses to intravenous arginine in human diabetes mellitus with the artificial beta-cell. *Diabetes* 29:762, 1980.

228. CZECH MP: Insulin action and the regulation of hexose transport. *Diabetes* 29:399, 1980.

229. KHOO JC, STEINBERG D, THOMPSON B, MAYER SE: Hormonal regulation of adipocyte enzymes. The effects of epinephrine and insulin on the control of lipase, phosphorylase kinase, phosphorylase and glycogen synthase. *J Biol Chem* 248:3823, 1973.

230. JEFFERSON LS: Role of insulin in the regulation of protein synthesis. *Diabetes* 29:487, 1980.

231. BOYD ME, ALBRIGHT EB, FOSTER DW, MCGARRY JD: *In vitro* reversal of the fasting state of liver metabolism in the rat. Reevaluation of the roles of insulin and glucose. *JClin Invest* 68:142, 1981.

232. GABBAY RA, LARDY HA: Site of insulin inhibition of cAMP-stimulated glycogenolysis. cAMP-dependent protein kinase is affected independent of cAMP changes. *J Biol Chem* 259:6052, 1984.

233. FAIN JN: Insulin secretion and action. *Metabolism* 33:672, 1984.

234. FOSTER DW: From glycogen to ketones—and back. *Diabetes* 33:1188, 1984.

235. RODBELL M: The actions of glucagon at its receptor: Regulation of adenylate cyclase, in Lefèbvre PJ (ed): *Glucagon I*. Berlin, Springer-Verlag, 1983, p 263.

236. HERS H-G, VAN SCHAFTINGEN E: Fructose-2,6-bisphosphate two years after its discovery. *Biochem J* 206:1, 1982.

237. RUDERMAN NB, AOKI TT, CAHILL GF JR: Gluconeogenesis and its disorders in man, in Hanson RW, Mehlman MA (eds): *Gluconeogenesis: Its Regulation in Mammalian Species*. New York, Wiley, 1976, p 515.

238. OWEN OE, PATEL MS, BLOCK BSB, KREULEN TH, REICHLE FA, MAZZOLI MA: Gluconeogenesis in normal, cirrhotic, and diabetic humans, in Han-

son RW, Mehlman MA (eds): *Gluconeogenesis: Its Regulation in Mammalian Species*. New York, Wiley, 1976, p 533.

239. MILES JM, RIZZA RA, HAYMOND MW, GERICH JE: Effects of acute insulin deficiency on glucose and ketone body turnover in man. Evidence for the primacy of overproduction of glucose and ketone bodies in the genesis of diabetic ketoacidosis. *Diabetes* 29:926, 1980.
240. GERICH JE, LORENZI M, BIER DM, SCHNEIDER V, TSALIKIAN E, KARAM JH, FORSHAM PH: Prevention of human diabetic ketoacidosis by somatostatin. Evidence for an essential role of glucagon. *N Engl J Med* 292:985, 1975.
241. MCGARRY JD, FOSTER DW: Regulation of hepatic fatty acid oxidation and ketone body production. *Annu Rev Biochem* 49:395, 1980.
242. WALDHÄUSL W, KLEINBERGER G, KORN A, DUDCZAK R, BRATUSCH-MARRAIN P, NOWOTNY P: Severe hyperglycemia: Effects of rehydration on endocrine derangements and blood glucose concentration. *Diabetes* 28:577, 1979.
243. CHERRINGTON AD, WILLIAMS PE, LILJENQUIST JE, LACY WW: The control of glycogenolysis and gluconeogenesis *in vivo* by insulin and glucagon, in Pierluissi J (ed): *Endocrine Pancreas and Diabetes*. Amsterdam, Excerpta Medica, 1979, p 172.
244. GOLDSTEIN JL, KITA T, BROWN MS: Defective lipoprotein receptors and atherosclerosis. Lessons from an animal counterpart of familial hypercholesterolemia. *N Engl J Med* 309:288, 1983.
245. MCGARRY JD, FOSTER DW: The regulation of ketogenesis from octanoic acid. The role of the tricarboxylic acid cycle and fatty acid synthesis. *J Biol Chem* 246:1149, 1971.
246. MCGARRY JD, LEATHERMAN GF, FOSTER DW: Carnitine palmitoyl-transferase I. The site of inhibition of hepatic fatty acid oxidation by malonyl-CoA. *J Biol Chem* 253:4128, 1978.
247. MCGARRY JD, TAKABAYASHI Y, FOSTER DW: The role of malonyl-CoA in the coordination of fatty acid synthesis and oxidation in isolated rat hepatocytes. *J Biol Chem* 253:8294, 1978.
248. MCGARRY JD, ROBLES-VALDES C, FOSTER DW: Role of carnitine in hepatic ketogenesis. *Proc Natl Acad Sci USA* 72:4385, 1975.
249. FOSTER DW, MCGARRY JD: The metabolic derangements and treatment of diabetic ketoacidosis. *N Engl J Med* 309:159, 1983.
250. FEIG PU, MCCURDY DK: The hypertonic state. *N Engl J Med* 297:1444, 1977.
251. FOSTER DW: Insulin deficiency and hyperosmolar coma. *Adv Intern Med* 19:159, 1974.
252. ARIEFF AI, CARROLL HJ: Nonketotic hyperosmolar coma with hyperglycemia: Clinical features, pathophysiology, renal function, acid-base balance, plasma-cerebrospinal fluid equilibria and the effects of therapy in 37 cases. *Medicine* 51:73, 1972.
253. CARROLL P, MATZ R: Uncontrolled diabetes mellitus in adults: experience in treating diabetic ketoacidosis and hyperosmolar nonketotic coma with low-dose insulin and a uniform treatment regimen. *Diabetes Care* 6:579, 1983.
254. MA GY, GOVE CD, HEMS DA: Effects of glucagon and insulin on fatty acid synthesis and glycogen degradation in the perfused liver of normal and genetically obese (ob/ob) mice. *Biochem J* 174:761, 1978.
255. McCUNE SA, DURANT PJ, JENKINS PA, HARRIS RA: Comparative studies on fatty acid synthesis, glycogen metabolism, and gluconeogenesis by hepatocytes isolated from lean and obese Zucker rats. *Metabolism* 30:1170, 1981.
256. MCGARRY JD, MILLS SE, LONG CS, FOSTER DW: Observations on the affinity for carnitine, and malonyl-CoA sensitivity of carnitine palmitoyltransferase I in animal and human tissues. Demonstration of the presence of malonyl-CoA in non-hepatic tissues of the rat. *Biochem J* 214:21, 1983.
257. CRYER PE, GERICH JE: Glucose counterregulation, hypoglycemia, and intensive insulin therapy in diabetes mellitus. *N Engl J Med* 313:232, 1985.
258. AMIEL SA, TAMBORLANE WV, SIMONSON DC, SHERWIN RS: Defective glucose counterregulation after strict glycemic control of insulin-dependent diabetes mellitus. *N Engl J Med* 316:1376, 1987.
259. JORDAN RM, KAMMER H, RIDDLE MR: Sulfonylurea-induced factitious hypoglycemia. A growing problem. *Arch Intern Med* 137:390, 1977.
260. HAVLIN CE, CRYER PE: Nocturnal hypoglycemia does not commonly result in major morning hyperglycemia in patients with diabetes mellitus. *Diabetes Care* 10:141, 1987.
261. PAZ-GUEVARA AT, HSU T-H, WHITE P: Juvenile diabetes mellitus after forty years. *Diabetes* 24:559, 1975.
262. OAKLEY WG, PYKE DA, TATTERSALL RB, WATKINS PJ: Long-term diabetes. A clinical study of 92 patients after 40 years. *Q J Med* 169:145, 1974.
263. LESTRADET H, PAPOZ L, HELLOUIN DE MENIBUS C, LEVAVASSEUR F, BESSE J, BILLAUD L, BATTISTELLI F, TRIC P, LESTRADET F: Long-term study of mortality and vascular complications in juvenile-onset (type 1) diabetes. *Diabetes* 30:175, 1981.
264. KNUIMAN MW, WELBORN TA, McCANN VJ, STANTON KG, CONSTABLE IJ: Prevalence of diabetic complications in relation to risk factors. *Diabetes* 35:1332, 1986.
265. KROLEWSKI AS, WARRAM JH, RAND LI, CHRISTLIEB AR, BUSICK EJ, KAHN CR: Risk of proliferative diabetic retinopathy in juvenile-onset type I diabetes: A 40-yr follow-up study. *Diabetes Care* 9:443, 1986.
266. GROOP LC, TEIR H, KOSKIMIES S, GROOP P-H, MATIKAINEN E, VERKKALA E, SCHEININ T, KONTIAINEN S, TEPPO A-M, TOLPPANEN E-M, TALLGREN LG: Risk factors and markers associated with proliferative retinopathy in patients with insulin-dependent diabetes. *Diabetes* 35:1397, 1986.
267. KAMENETZKY SA, BENNETT PH, DIPPE SE, MILLER M, LECOMPTE PM: A clinical and histologic study of diabetic nephropathy in the Pima Indians. *Diabetes* 23:61, 1974.
268. MAUER SM, MILLER K, GOETZ FC, BARBOSA J, SIMMONS RL, NAJARIAN JS, MICHAEL AF: Immunopathy of renal extracellular membranes in kidneys transplanted into patients with diabetes mellitus. *Diabetes* 25:709, 1976.
269. GLIEDMAN ML, TELLIS VA, SOBERMAN R, RIFKIN H, VEITH FJ: Long-term effects of pancreatic transplant function in patients with advanced juvenile-onset diabetes. *Diabetes Care* 1:1, 1978.
270. GREENE DA, LATTIMER SA, SIMA AAF: Sorbitol, phosphoinositides, and sodium-potassium-ATPase in the pathogenesis of diabetic complications. *N Engl J Med* 316:599, 1987.
271. WINEGRAD AI: Does a common mechanism induce the diverse complications of diabetes? *Diabetes* 36:396, 1987.
272. GABBAY KH: Hyperglycemia, polyol metabolism, and the complications of diabetes mellitus. *Annu Rev Med* 26:521, 1975.
273. ROBISON WG JR, KADOR PF, KINOSHITA JH: Retinal capillaries: basement membrane thickening by galactosemia prevented with aldose reductase inhibitor. *Science* 221:1177, 1983.
274. ENGERMAN RL, KERN TS: Experimental galactosemia produces diabetic-like retinopathy. *Diabetes* 33:97, 1984.
275. ROBISON WG JR, KADOR PF, AKAGI Y, KINOSHITA JH, GONZALEZ R, DVORNIK D: Prevention of basement membrane thickening in retinal capillaries by a novel inhibitor of aldose reductase, tolrestat. *Diabetes* 35:295, 1986.
276. CUNHA-VAZ JG, MOTA CC, LEITE EC, ABREU JR, RUAS MA: Effect of sorbinil on blood-retinal barrier in early diabetic retinopathy. *Diabetes* 35:574, 1986.
277. PARVING H-H, VIBERTI GC, KEEN H, CHRISTIANSEN JS, LASSEN NA: Hemodynamic factors in the genesis of diabetic microangiopathy. *Metabolism* 32:943, 1983.
278. CHRISTIANSEN JS, GAMMELGAARD J, FRANDSEN M, PARVING H-H: Increased kidney size, glomerular filtration rate and renal plasma flow in short-term insulin-dependent diabetics. *Diabetologia* 20:451, 1981.
279. ZATZ R, MEYER TW, RENNKE HG, BRENNER BM: Predominance of hemodynamic rather than metabolic factors in the pathogenesis of diabetic glomerulopathy. *Proc Natl Acad Sci USA* 82:5963, 1985.
280. UY R, WOLD EF: Posttranslational covalent modification of proteins. Only 20 amino acids are used in protein synthesis, yet some 140 "amino acids" are found in various proteins. *Science* 198:890, 1977.
281. HIGGINS PJ, BUNN HF: Kinetic analysis of the nonenzymatic glycosylation of hemoglobin. *J Biol Chem* 256:5204, 1981.
282. BUNN HF: Evaluation of glycosylated hemoglobin in diabetic patients. *Diabetes* 30:613, 1981.
283. BROWNLEE M, VLASSARA H, CERAMI A: Nonenzymatic glycosylation and the pathogenesis of diabetic complications. *Ann Intern Med* 101:527, 1984.
284. KENNEDY L, BAYNES JW: Non-enzymatic glycosylation and the chronic complications of diabetes: An overview. *Diabetologia* 26:93, 1984.
285. VOGT BW, SCHLEICHER ED, WIELAND OH: Σ-Amino-lysine-bound glucose in human tissues obtained at autopsy. Increase in diabetes mellitus. *Diabetes* 31:1123, 1982.
286. MONNIER VM, VISHWANATH V, FRANK KE, ELMETS CA, DAUCHOT P, KOHN RR: Relation between complications of type 1 diabetes mellitus and collagen-linked fluorescence. *N Engl J Med* 314:403, 1986.
287. BROWNLEE M, VLASSARA H, CERAMI A: Nonenzymatic glycosylation products on collagen covalently trap low-density lipoprotein. *Diabetes* 34:938, 1985.
288. WITZTUM JL, MAHONEY EM, BRANKS MJ, FISHER M, ELAM R, STEINBERG D: Nonenzymatic glucosylation of low-density lipoprotein alters its biologic activity. *Diabetes* 31:283, 1982.
289. WITZTUM JL, FISHER M, PIETRO T, STEINBRECHER UP, ELAM RL: Nonenzymatic glucosylation of high-density lipoprotein accelerates its catabolism in guinea pigs. *Diabetes* 31:1029, 1982.

290. RASKIN P, ROSENSTOCK J: Blood glucose control and diabetic complications. *Ann Intern Med* 105:254, 1986.

290a. FREINKEL N, DOOLEY SL, METZGER BE: Care of the pregnant woman with insulin-dependent diabetes mellitus. *N Engl J Med* 313:99, 1985.

291. STEINER DF: The biosynthesis of insulin: Genetic, evolutionary, and pathophysiologic aspects. *Harvey Lect* 78:191, 1984.

292. TAGER H, GIVEN B, BALDWIN D, MAKO M, MARKESE J, RUBENSTEIN A, OLEFSKY J, KOBAYASHI M, KILTERMAN O, POUCHER R: A structurally abnormal insulin causing human diabetes. *Nature* 281:122, 1979.

293. GIVEN BD, MAKO ME, TAGER HS, BALDWIN D, MARKESE J, RUBENSTEIN AH, OLEFSKY J, KOBAYASHI M, KOLTERMAN O, POUCHER R: Diabetes due to secretion of an abnormal insulin. *N Engl J Med* 302:129, 1980.

294. KWOK SCM, STEINER DF, RUBENSTEIN AH, TAGER HS: Identification of a point mutation in the human insulin gene giving rise to a structurally abnormal insulin (insulin Chicago). *Diabetes* 32:872, 1983.

295. NAKAGAWA SH, TAGER HS: Role of the phenylalanine B25 side chain in directing insulin interaction with its receptor. Steric and conformational effects. *J Biol Chem* 261:7332, 1986.

296. ROBBINS DC, BLIX PM, RUBENSTEIN AH, KANAZAWA Y, KOSAKA R, TAGER HS: A human proinsulin variant at arginine 65. *Nature* 291:679, 1981.

297. FLIER JS, KAHN CR, ROTH J: Receptors, antireceptor antibodies and mechanisms of insulin resistance. *N Engl J Med* 300:413, 1979.

298. GRIGORESCU F, FLIER JS, KAHN CR: Characterization of binding and phosphorylation defects of erythrocyte insulin receptors in the type A syndrome of insulin resistance. *Diabetes* 35:127, 1986.

299. TAYLOR SI, DONS RF, HERNANDEZ E, ROTH J, GORDEN P: Insulin resistance associated with androgen excess in women with autoantibodies to the insulin receptor. *Ann Intern Med* 97:851, 1982.

300. MANDARINO L, TSALIKIAN E, BARTOLD S, MARSH H, CARNEY A, BUERKLIN E, TUTWILER G, HAYMOND M, HANDWERGER B, RIZZA R: Mechanism of hyperglycemia and response to treatment with an inhibitor of fatty acid oxidation in a patient with insulin resistance due to antiinsulin receptor antibodies. *J Clin Endocrinol Metab* 59:658, 1984.

301. MUGGEO M, FLIER JS, ABRAMS RA, HARRISON LC, DEISSERROTH AB, KAHN CR: Treatment by plasma exchange of a patient with autoantibodies to the insulin receptor. *N Engl J Med* 300:477, 1979.

302. MURTHY MSR, PANDE SV: Malonyl-CoA binding site and the overt carnitine palmitoyltransferase activity reside on the opposite sides of the outer mitochondrial membrane. *Proc Natl Acad Sci USA* 84:378, 1987.

303. DECLERCQ PE, FALCK JR, KUWAJIMA M, TYMINSKI H, FOSTER DW, MCGARRY JD: Characterization of the mitochondrial carnitine palmitoyltransferase enzyme system. I. Use of inhibitors. *J Biol Chem* 262:9812, 1987.

304. WOELTJE KF, KUWAJIMA M, FOSTER DW, MCGARRY JD: Characterization of the mitochondrial carnitine palmitoyltransferase enzyme system. II. Use of detergents and antibodies. *J Biol Chem* 262:9822, 1987.

305. KOBAYASHI M, OLEFSKY JM, ELDERS J, MAKO ME, GIVEN BD, SCHEDWIE HK, FISER RH, HINTZ RL, HORNER JA, RUBENSTEIN AH: Insulin resistance due to a defect distal to the insulin receptor: Demonstration in a patient with leprechaunism. *Proc Natl Acad Sci USA* 75:3469, 1978.

306. TAYLOR SI, HEDO JA, UNDERHILL LH, KASUGA M, ELDERS MJ, ROTH J: Extreme insulin resistance in association with abnormally high binding affinity of insulin receptors from a patient with Leprechaunism: Evidence for a defect intrinsic to the receptor. *J Clin Endocrinol Metab* 55:1108, 1982.

307. BALLARD FJ, READ LC, GUNN JM: Protein synthesis and breakdown rates associated with the insulin resistance of fibroblasts from patients with Leprechaunism. *J Clin Endocrinol Metab* 61:1146, 1985.

CHAPTER **11**

DISORDERS OF FRUCTOSE METABOLISM

RICHARD GITZELMANN
BEAT STEINMANN
GEORGES VAN DEN BERGHE

1. *Fructose is an important source of dietary carbohydrates. In Western societies, the daily intake of adults is presently approximately 100 g. The liver, kidney, and small intestine are the main sites of fructose metabolism, but adipose tissue participates. Fructose, given intravenously in high doses, is clearly toxic and causes hyperuricemia, hyperlactatemia, and ultrastructural alterations in liver and intestinal cells.*
2. *Essential fructosuria is a benign, asymptomatic metabolic anomaly caused by the absence of fructokinase. Alimentary hyperfructosemia and fructosuria are the principal signs. In spite of the interruption of the specific fructose pathway, up to nine-tenths of the administered fructose is retained by fructokinase-deficient subjects.*
3. *Hereditary fructose intolerance is characterized by severe hypoglycemia and vomiting shortly after the intake of fructose. Prolonged fructose ingestion in infants leads to poor feeding, vomiting, hepatomegaly, jaundice, hemorrhage, a proximal renal tubular syndrome, and finally, hepatic failure and death. Patients develop a strong distaste for sweet food. A chronic course is, therefore, observed only in the preschool-age child. Fructose-1-phosphate aldolase of liver, kidney cortex, and small intestine is deficient. Hypoglycemia after fructose ingestion is caused by fructose-1-phosphate inhibiting glycogenolysis at the phosphorylase level and gluconeogenesis at the mutant aldolase level. Patients remain healthy on a fructose- and sucrose-free diet.*
4. *Hereditary fructose-1,6-bisphosphatase deficiency is characterized by episodic spells of hyperventilation, apnea, hypoglycemia, ketosis, and lactic acidosis, with a precipitous and often lethal course in the newborn infant. Later episodes are often triggered by fasting and febrile infections. Due to the enzyme defect, gluconeogenesis is severely impaired. Gluconeogenic precursors such as amino acids, lactate, and ketones accumulate as soon as liver glycogen stores are depleted. Patients do not vomit after fructose intake and do not develop aversion to sweets. Their tolerance to fasting grows with age. Patients past early childhood seem to develop normally.*
5. *All three defects are inherited as autosomal recessive traits.*
6. *D-Glyceric aciduria, erythrocyte aldolase deficiency, and fructose malabsorption are briefly mentioned.*

Three inherited abnormalities of fructose metabolism are known. Two of these are caused by a defect of one of the enzymes of the specialized fructose pathway: *essential fructosuria* and *hereditary fructose intolerance,* the former a harmless and the latter a potentially lethal condition. Although not a defect of the specialized fructose pathway, the more recently described hepatic *fructose-1,6-bisphosphatase deficiency* is usually classified as an error of fructose metabolism. The defect of this enzyme of the gluconeogenic pathway becomes clinically manifest through hypoglycemia and lactic acidosis on fasting and may also be life-threatening. The description of the clinical symptoms and biochemical anomalies in the three inborn errors of metabolism will be preceded by an outline of the metabolism of fructose. The potential toxic effects of fructose loads on normal organisms will also be discussed since their comprehension is essential for the understanding of the pathophysiology of hereditary fructose intolerance and of fructose-1,6-bisphosphatase deficiency.

D-Glyceric aciduria, erythrocyte aldolase deficiency, and *fructose malabsorption* are briefly mentioned.

METABOLISM OF FRUCTOSE

Chemical Properties and Determination of Fructose

Fructose (β-D-fructose) is a 6-carbon ketose with levorotatory optical activity in solution, hence its older name levulose. Although it contains no aldehyde group, fructose has a reducing power of approximately 98 percent of that of glucose, which is due to its tautomeric isomerization from the keto into the enol form in basic solution. The presence of fructose, like that of galactose, should thus be suspected in urine samples giving a positive test for reducing sugars and a negative reaction with glucose oxidase. Both hexoses are not attacked by the latter enzyme. No completely specific method is available for the determination of fructose in the presence of other sugars since even fructokinase can utilize other ketohexoses. Most colorimetric methods are derived from the Seliwanoff reaction which is based on the conversion of fructose to hydroxymethylfurfural and condensation with resorcinol in hot acid to form a red product. As modified by Roe et al. in 1949[1] or by Higashi and Peters in 1950,[2] the technique is satisfactory for the quantitative determination of fructose in blood and urine in clinical situations. To further ascertain that a reducing substance which gives a positive Seliwanoff reaction is fructose, chromatography can be used. Easy thin-layer chromatographic methods,[3] as well as more elaborated gas[4] and liquid[5] chromatography techniques, have been described. A D-fructose dehydrogenase has been used for measurements of seminal fructose.[6]

Sources and Uses of Fructose

Fructose is a widely distributed natural compound. As the free monosaccharide, it is found in honey and in numerous vegetables and fruits, where it can account for up to 40 percent of the dry weight. As the disaccharide sucrose, which consists of one molecule of fructose attached to a molecule of glucose by an oside-oside link between their anomeric carbons, C1 of glucose and C2 of fructose, it is found in many more nutrients and constitutes an important source of dietary carbohydrate. Lists of the fructose content of various foodstuffs are available.[7,8] Fructose is also a constituent of the trisaccharide raffinose and of the tetrasaccharide stachyose, e.g., in soy beans; since small-intestinal mucosa has neither β-fructosidase nor α-galactosidase,[9] these sugars play no role in human nutrition. Inulin is a polymer of fructose found in vegetables such as chicory and sweet potatoes. It is hydrolyzed to fructose in acid at high temperatures, but in the intestine only insignificant quantities of fructose are split off and absorbed. It should be mentioned that fructose constitutes the main sugar of seminal fluid. Its synthesis in the accessory glands of the male reproductive tract is testosterone-dependent and involves the reduction of glucose by aldose reductase to sorbitol and the oxidation of the latter by sorbitol dehydrogenase to fructose.[10] The presence of the latter enzyme in numerous tissues explains why the polyol sorbitol constitutes another source of fructose. Although less abundant than fructose, sorbitol is also widely distributed in fruits and vegetables.

Fructose, as sucrose or the free monosaccharide, is extensively used in human nutrition as a sweetening additive to foods, medications, and even infant formulas. In Western societies, its intake has steadily increased since the beginning of this century and is presently approximately 100 g/day per adult[11] or more.[12] A trend toward further increases in the consumption of free fructose is also recorded.[13] This may be explained by its sweetening power, which, for the same caloric intake, is 1.5 to 1.7 times that of sucrose, and by the development of technologies for its industrial production. Oral fructose has also been investigated as a means to avoid hypoglycemia[14] and muscle glycogen depletion[15] during athletic exercise. The increase in the consumption of fructose has provoked concern in view of observations in animals and humans indicating that the ketohexose may elevate plasma triglycerides, a primary risk factor for atherosclerosis. The issue has been discussed in several symposia[16–18] and reviews.[19, 20]

Two medical uses for fructose have been advocated. The observation by Minkowski in 1893[21] that the utilization of fructose does not require insulin resulted in the still widespread belief that fructose as well as sorbitol are adequate sweetening agents for patients with diabetes mellitus, an issue outside the scope of this chapter. In fact, intravenous and oral fructose do produce an insulin response when blood glucose is elevated.[22] The development of intravenous nutrition in the early fifties has led to the utilization of various compounds, among them fructose and sorbitol, as a source of energy in this therapy. Solutions of equimolar amounts of fructose and glucose, prepared by the hydrolysis of sucrose and known as *invert sugar,* as well as solutions of pure fructose, sometimes still named *levulose,* are available. The use of sorbitol is fostered by its chemical stability. As will be discussed in a later section, the infusion of fructose and sorbitol carries important risks to normal individuals and becomes life-threatening in hereditary fructose intolerance and fructose-1,6-bisphosphatase deficiency. Their use as glucose substitutes in parenteral nutrition should therefore be strongly discouraged.

Utilization of Fructose by the Body as a Whole

Several studies of the utilization of fructose at the whole body level in humans and experimental animals have shown that the ketohexose is utilized mainly by liver, kidney, and small intestine (reviewed in Ref. 23). Only data obtained in humans are summarized here.

Taken by mouth, fructose is absorbed by the small intestine at a rate roughly one-half that of the other monosaccharides glucose and galactose.[24,25] In human small intestine, fructose is not converted to glucose, and a large proportion of it is absorbed unchanged.[24,26] Following the instillation of approximately 0.7 g/kg fructose into the jejunal lumen, its concentration in the portal system may reach about 2.5 m*M* within 5 to 15 min.[24] Once fructose reaches the bloodstream, it is utilized rapidly. Administered in a peripheral vein at the dose of 0.5 g/kg body weight over 30 min, fructose disappears from the circulation twice as fast as glucose, its half-life being about 18 min,[27] compared with 43 min for glucose.[28] Studies of the utilization of fructose during prolonged perfusion in subjects with hepatic vein catheterization show that approximately one-half of the fructose load is taken up by the splanchnic bed, the liver accounting for more than 75 percent and the small intestine for approximately 10 percent of this uptake.[29,30] Catheterization of the renal vein shows that about 20 percent of an intravenous fructose load is taken up by the kidney.[31] That liver, kidney, and small intestine constitute the main sites of fructose utilization is explained by the presence in these tissues of the specialized pathway of fructose metabolism described below. That this metabolism is highly efficient is evidenced by the observations that, following the oral ingestion of 1 g/kg fructose, its concentration in peripheral veins does not increase above 0.3 to 0.35 m*M*[32] and that, although there is virtually no renal threshold for fructose, only a small percentage of the administered dose is recovered in the urine.[27,29,33,34]

Transport of Fructose

The study of the membrane transport of fructose is complicated by the fact that it may be rapidly utilized after its penetration into the cells, particularly in tissues possessing the specialized enzymes of fructose metabolism. Investigation of the intestinal transport of fructose is further confounded by species differences. Most studies nevertheless support the existence of a specific system which is distinct from that of glucose and operates more slowly.[35–38] Its energy dependence and its affinity for fructose have not been clearly established. A carrier-mediated diffusion process as well as an active transport mechanism have been proposed, and the reported fructose concentrations required for half-maximal influx vary from 0.9[35] to above 100 m*M*.[38] Incomplete fructose absorption is briefly reviewed below.

Fructose does not enter the hepatocyte freely, as evidenced by the steep gradient between its extra- and intracellular concentrations.[39,40] Computations from the kinetics of fructose uptake and metabolism in the perfused rat liver[39] are in accordance with a carrier-mediated transport with a K_m of 67 m*M* and a V_{max} equal to 30 μmol/min per gram of tissue. Experiments performed, to avoid interference of fructose metabolism, over less than 1 min with isolated rat hepatocytes have given an even higher K_m value of around 200 m*M*.[41] Competition studies indicate that fructose is transported into the liver cell, at least in part, by the same system as glucose and galactose.[41,42]

In adipose tissue, fructose is transported by at least two different carriers. A specific fructose transporter requires a concentration of about 25 m*M* for half-maximal saturation and is insensitive to glucose and to insulin. Fructose can also enter the adipocyte by the glucose transporter, which has a five- to tenfold lower K_m for it than the specific carrier and an approximately 50 percent lower V_{max}, which is roughly doubled by insulin. A participation of the latter carrier in the transport of fructose into adipocytes under physiological conditions is, however, unlikely owing to the competition exerted by glucose.[43–45]

Enzymes of Fructose Metabolism

The predominance of liver, kidney, and small intestine in the metabolism of fructose is explained by the existence in these tissues of a specialized pathway composed of three enzymes, fructokinase, aldolase type B, and triokinase, which convert fructose into intermediates of the glycolytic-gluconeogenic pathway (Fig. 11-1). A detailed account of the experiments that led to the elucidation of the fructose pathway can be found in a monograph by Hers.[46] The enzymes of the specialized fructose pathway have been investigated chiefly in rat liver.

Fructokinase (EC 2.7.1.3). Fructokinase catalyzes the phosphorylation of fructose to fructose-1-phosphate.[47–49] The enzyme is not specific for fructose since it also utilizes L-sorbose, D-tagatose, D-xylulose, L-galactoheptulose,[48,50–52] 5-keto-D-fructose,[53,54] and certain 2,5-anhydroalditols, such as 2,5-anhydro-D-mannitol.[54a] It is therefore considered a ketohexokinase. The phosphoryl donors are ATP, to a minor extent 2′-dATP and 3′-dATP,[50] and, as recently demonstrated, GTP.[55] The K_m for fructose is about 0.5 mM.[48,50,52,56] Affinity constants for Mg^{2+}-ATP, obtained by different authors, vary between 0.2 and 2 mM.[50,52,56,56a] The V_{max} in crude extracts of rat and human liver reaches 2 to 3 μmol/min per gram of tissue at 22 to 25°C[40,50,57,58] or about 10 μmol/min per gram at 37°C. Fructokinase requires high concentrations of KCl[59] and is strongly inhibited by ADP, one of the products of the re-

Fig. 11-1 The pathway of fructose metabolism in the liver and its defects. DHA = dihydroxyacetone; GAH = glyceraldehyde; F = fructose; G = glucose; GA = glycerate; (1) fructokinase, (2) fructaldolase, (3) triokinase, (4) glycerol-3-P dehydrogenase, (5) alcohol dehydrogenases and aldose reductase, (6) sorbitol dehydrogenase, (7) triose phosphate isomerase, (8) glycerol kinase, (9) hexokinase and glucokinase, (10) glucose-6-phosphatase, (11) fructose-1,6-bisphosphatase, (12) phosphofructokinase, (13) phosphohexose isomerase, (14) phosphoglucomutase, (15) glycogen phosphorylase, (16) galactokinase, (17) aldehyde dehydrogenase, (18) glycerate kinase, (19) aldose reductase.

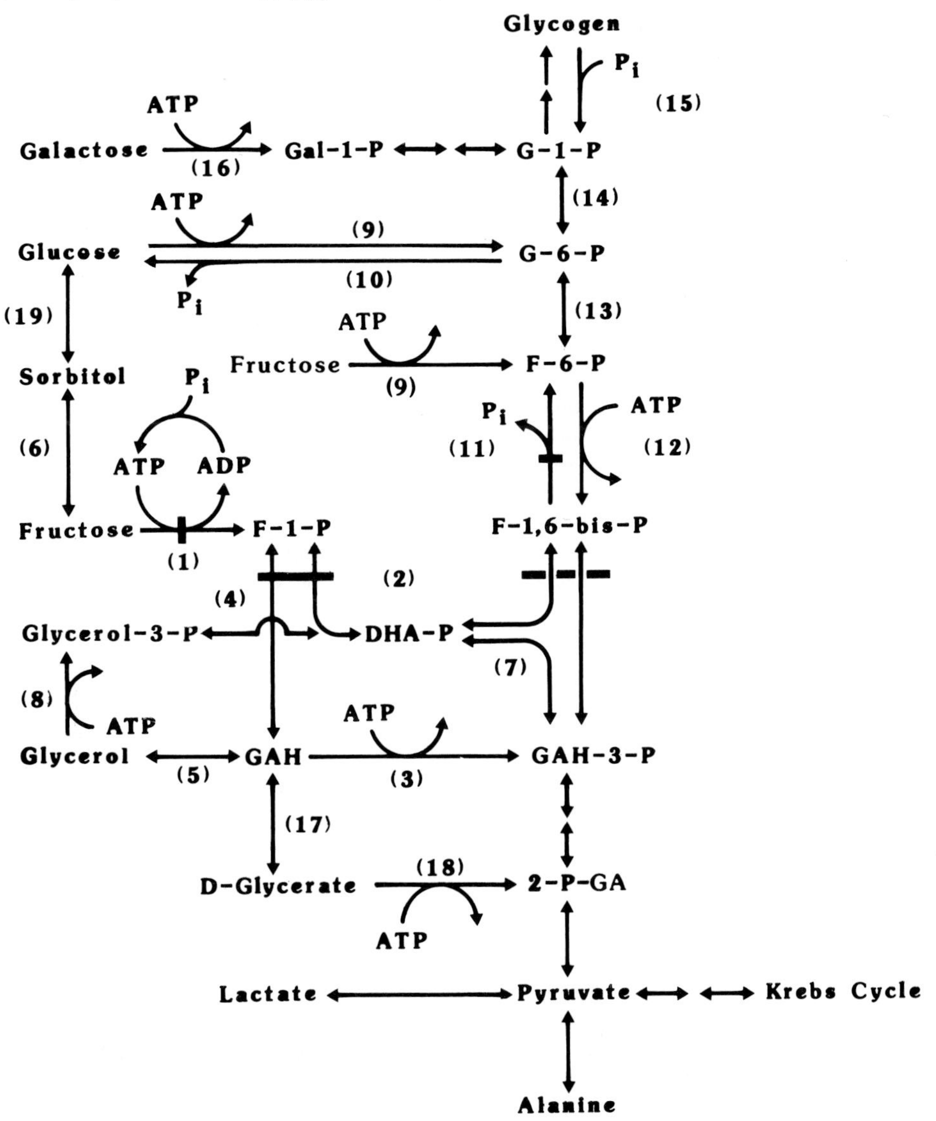

action.[56] Rat liver fructokinase is presumably a monomer with a molecular weight of 28,000 daltons,[52] but the beef liver enzyme was reported to be a dimer with a molecular weight of 56,000.[54]

Fructaldolase (Fructose-1,6-Bisphosphate Aldolase, Aldolase, EC 4.1.2.13). Three aldolase isozymes are known and, recently, at least three different aldolase genes have been identified. They are related and probably derive from a single ancestral gene (reviewed in Ref. 60). Aldolase of liver, kidney, and small intestine, or aldolase B, reversibly splits fructose-1-phosphate into D-glyceraldehyde and dihydroxyacetone phosphate. Similarly to its isozymes found in muscle (aldolase A) and in brain (aldolase C), aldolase B also catalyses the splitting of the glycolytic-gluconeogenic intermediate fructose-1,6-bisphosphate into D-glyceraldehyde-3-phosphate and dihydroxyacetone phosphate, and the condensation of the latter triosephosphates. The three aldolases can be distinguished by their catalytic and immunologic properties as well as by their tissue and cellular distribution. Liver aldolase B has approximately the same V_{max} with fructose-1-phosphate and with fructose-1,6-bisphosphate,[61,62] reaching 2 to 3 μmol/min per gram of tissue at 25°C in rat[40] and in human liver.[57,62] In contrast, aldolase A and C have a 50- and 10-fold lower maximal activity with fructose-1-phosphate than with fructose-1,6-bisphosphate.[63] The K_m of human liver aldolase B is around 1 mM for fructose-1-phosphate and 4 to 12 μM for fructose-1,6-bisphosphate.[61,64] The aldolases have a molecular weight of about 160,000 and are composed of four subunits which are immunologically distinct in the isozymes A, B, and C.[65,66] Evidence has been presented that liver aldolase could form a complex with fructose-1,6-bisphosphatase.[67,68]

Interestingly, early fetal human liver, kidney, and small intestine contain mainly aldolase A[69,70] and also adolase C[71]; their subsequent replacement by aldolase B with different kinetic characteristics suggests adaptation to specific metabolic needs. Hepatoma formation, on the other hand, is associated with the repression of aldolase B and the reappearance of the A and C isoenzymes.[71,72] In the kidney, aldolase B is found mainly in the proximal tubules, whereas aldolase A is predominant in the distal tubules and glomeruli.[73–76] In small-intestinal epithelium, aldolase B predominates in the absorptive villus cells and aldolase A in the rapidly dividing crypt cells.[77] Human erythrocytes[78,79] and cultured fibroblasts[80,81] contain aldolase A.

During fasting, the activity of rabbit liver aldolase decreases to less than one-half the fed value.[82] The finding that this decrease was not accompanied by a decrease in total immunoreactive protein has led to the identification of several lysosomal proteinases that catalyse inactivation of the enzyme by limited proteolysis.[83,84] Although liver aldolase is susceptible to proteolytic degradation during its purification,[85] results obtained under conditions that avoid disruption of lysosomes during the isolation procedure[84] suggest that the modifications induced by fasting occur in vivo.

In recent years, the molecular biology of aldolases has been extensively investigated, mainly because of the opportunity it offers to study the regulatory mechanisms of tissue specific gene expression in eukaryotic cells.[86] The increase in liver aldolase B recorded during fetal development has been shown to be linked to an increase of isozyme-specific mRNA in humans[87] and in rats.[88] Cloning and characterization of cDNA for aldolase B has been achieved in rats[89–91] and humans.[92,93] The complete structure and genomic organization of both rat and human aldolase B genes has been published.[94–95a] The human aldolase B gene is present in a single copy and its chromosomal location is 9q13 → q32.[96,97] It is 14,500 base pairs long, contains nine exons encoding for 364 amino acids.[93,95,95a,98] At least four aldolase B mRNA species exist in human liver.[98]

Aldolase A and C genes have been mapped to chromosomes 16 and 17, respectively.[98b,98c]

Triokinase (EC 2.7.1.28). This enzyme converts D-glyceraldehyde into D-glyceraldehyde-3-phosphate, allowing thereby the nonphosphorylated product of the cleavage of fructose-1-phosphate to reach the glycolytic-gluconeogenic pathway.[61] Triokinase utilizes preferentially ATP as phosphoryl donor, but ITP can be utilized at 14 percent and GTP at 10 percent of the rate of utilization of the adenine nucleotide.[98d] The V_{max} of the enzyme is around 2 μmol/min per gram at 37°C in rat[57,99] and human[57] liver, while the K_m values are 0.01 mM for D-glyceraldehyde[100] and 0.8 mM for Mg^{2+}-ATP.[98a]

Fructose-1,6-Bisphosphatase (EC 3.1.3.11). Fructose-1,6-bisphosphatase, also called hexose bisphosphatase, catalyzes the splitting of fructose-1,6-bisphosphate to fructose-6-phosphate and P_i. The reaction is irreversible, but the opposite conversion can be accomplished by the equally irreversible phosphofructokinase reaction, which forms fructose-1,6-bisphosphate from fructose-6-phosphate, using ATP as the phosphoryl donor (Fig. 11-1). Owing to their irreversibility, both reactions play an essential role in directing the metabolic flux through the Embden-Meyerhof pathway toward either glycolysis or gluconeogenesis. This is achieved by opposite changes in the activity of both enzymes not necessarily involving complete inhibition of either. Indeed, simultaneous operation of phosphofructokinase and hexose bisphosphatase, resulting in a so-called futile cycle, proceeds to a significant extent in the liver of fed rats, although little or not in starved ones.[101] The V_{max} of fructose-1,6-bisphosphatase reaches approximately 6.5 and 4.1 μmol/min per gram of tissue at 25°C in rat and human liver, respectively.[57] The enzyme possesses complex regulatory properties.[102,103,103a] It is Mg^{2+} dependent and, in the absence of effectors, displays Michaelian kinetics for fructose-1,6-bisphosphate, with a K_m in the micromolar range. Hexose bisphosphatase is inhibited by physiological concentrations of fructose-6-phosphate and P_i, the products of the reaction, and, in an allosteric fashion, by AMP and fructose-2,6-bisphosphate. The latter regulatory molecule, discovered in 1980 (reviewed in Refs. 104 and 105), together with AMP at physiological concentrations, changes the substrate-saturation curve from hyperbolic to sigmoidal.[106] This results in a very low activity of the enzyme at physiological fructose-1,6-bisphosphate concentrations. Because fructose-2,6-bisphosphate is also a potent stimulator of phosphofructokinase,[107] an elevation of the regulator concentration will orient the metabolic flux toward glycolysis and a decrease will promote gluconeogenesis. The main stimulator of the synthesis of fructose-2,6-bisphosphate in the liver is glucose, whereas its principal inhibitor is glucagon. Glucose promotes glycolysis and glucagon and fasting gluconeogenesis; this is explained by the elevation and decrease of fructose-2,6-bisphosphate (approximately 4 nmol/g tissue in the basal fed state), which they induce.

Liver fructose-1,6-bisphosphatase is a tetramer with a molecular weight of around 140,000.[108] The enzyme is susceptible to limited proteolysis by two lysosomal proteases,[109,110] rendering the enzyme more active at alkaline pH and more sensitive to stimulation by histidine, the latter effect being probably related to the chelation of inhibitory Zn^{2+} ions.[111] The long-term increase in activity of fructose-1,6-bisphosphatase in gluconeogenic conditions such as prolonged starvation, diabetes, or corticoid treatment, has been attributed to this mechanism, since histidine increases in these situations. The mode of regulation of fructose-1,6-bisphosphatase by zinc seems complex.[112] Intestinal fructose-1,6-bisphosphatase of some animal species has been shown to differ from the liver enzyme in its AMP inhibition characteristics.[113]

Alternate Pathways of Fructose Metabolism

Phosphorylation of Fructose to Fructose-6-Phosphate. The marked affinity for fructose and the high activity of fructokinase explain the preferential utilization of the ketose and its phosphorylation to fructose-1-phosphate by the tissues possessing the enzyme. Nevertheless, these and other tissues can, in theory, metabolize fructose also to fructose-6-phosphate using hexokinase and even glucokinase (hexokinase D).[114] However, in the presence of physiological concentrations of glucose, this conversion will be severely restricted since the affinity of the hexokinases for fructose is several orders of magnitude lower than that for glucose.[114–116] The capacity of several tissues to metabolize fructose has been investigated in detail by Froesch and Ginsberg.[43,117] Human erythrocytes and leukocytes, incubated in the absence of glucose, metabolize fructose nearly as fast as glucose; in the presence of a physiological concentration of glucose (approximately 5 m*M*), the utilization of 5 m*M* fructose is about 90 percent inhibited. Both muscle and adipose tissue may nevertheless participate to some extent in the metabolism of fructose. In the rat diaphragm, the utilization of 5 m*M* fructose is only 50 percent inhibited by the addition of glucose at physiological concentrations. This is attributed to the low concentration of free glucose inside muscle cells. Under this condition, the utilization of 5 m*M* fructose reaches, nevertheless, only 20 percent of that of a similar concentration of glucose. The utilization of fructose by adipose tissue may be more important. At a concentration of 10 m*M*, fructose is utilized at two-thirds of the rate of glucose by rat epididymal fat. When both sugars are added together, rates are nearly additive. This can be explained by the virtual absence of free glucose in the adipocyte because it is bound to its carrier.

Conversion of D-Glyceraldehyde to Triose Phosphate. Two alternate pathways (Fig. 11-1) to the formation of glyceraldehyde-3-phosphate by triokinase have been proposed: (1) reduction to glycerol by NADH and alcohol dehydrogenase or by NADPH and aldose reductase, followed by phosphorylation to glycerol-3-phosphate and subsequent oxidation to dihydroxyacetone phosphate; and (2) oxidation to D-glycerate and conversion to 2-phosphoglycerate. As was discussed by Hers,[46] studies of the randomization of the fructose carbons indicate that D-glyceraldehyde is utilized by triokinase in vivo. This was confirmed by a kinetic study of the glyceraldehyde-metabolizing enzymes[100] and by experiments with [4-^{3}H,6-^{14}C] fructose.[118] Nevertheless, as is discussed below, the description of patients with D-glyceric aciduria suggests that the first step of the second alternate pathway mentioned above may be operating in some inborn errors of metabolism.

End Products of Fructose Metabolism

Controversies surround the use of fructose for parenteral nutrition and as a sweetener in normal and diabetic subjects. It is further suspected to exert a hypertriglyceridemic effect. Therefore, several studies have been devoted to the determination of the end products of its metabolism. In isolated rat liver perfused with fructose, about 50 to 75 percent is recovered as glucose and 20 to 25 percent as lactate plus pyruvate.[39,40,119] Similar results were obtained in studies of the metabolism of fructose, perfused intravenously at the rate of 0.3 g/kg per hour, by the human liver and kidney, involving sampling in the hepatic and renal veins.[31] However, with higher doses of fructose, up to 60 percent are taken up by the human liver and converted to lactic acid, whereas the release of glucose from the splanchnic area is not modified or even reduced.[120,121] Glycogen constitutes quantitatively the third most important product of fructose metabolism, accounting for 8 percent of its utilization by the perfused rat liver.[119] Studies with radioactive fructose have also shown its conversion to triglycerides,[122–125] estimated to represent 1 to 3 percent of its overall metabolism.[126] Additional data concerning the further metabolism of fructose can be found elsewhere.[19,20,23,127]

TOXICITY OF FRUCTOSE

After the discovery of hereditary fructose intolerance, fructose toxicity was first thought to be limited to individuals with the aldolase B defect. In the late 1960s, deleterious effects of high doses of intravenous fructose were also recognized clinically in healthy persons. Hyperuricemia[128] and lactic acidosis[129] were the prominent findings. These observations have led to the recommendation of great caution in the use of fructose in parenteral nutrition.[130–133] Deleterious effects can be traced to the very rapid metabolism after parenteral administration by tissues possessing the specialized enzymes fructokinase, aldolase B, and triokinase, and to the resulting accumulation of fructose-1-phosphate. The high V_{max} of fructokinase (about 10 μmol/min per gram of tissue at 37° C) is a major determinant of this rapid metabolism. In the liver for instance, the maximal rate of phosphorylation of fructose is more than 10 times higher than the glucose-phosphorylating capacity of glucokinase.[134] The V_{max} of fructokinase is, however, not the only determinant of the fructose uptake rate. Since the affinity constant of the hepatic transport system for fructose is more than an order of magnitude higher than the K_m of fructokinase (approximately 0.5 m*M*), its entrance rate into the cells and hence the rate of its phosphorylation is critically dependent on the blood fructose concentration. As already seen, it can reach about 2.5 m*M* in the portal vein after an oral load.[24] Severalfold higher concentrations may, however, be obtained by intravenous infusion. At rates of 0.5, 1.0, and 1.5 g of fructose per kilogram per hour, fructosemia reaches 2.3, 4.8, and 7 m*M* in humans.[27] The mode of administration of fructose thus plays a determining role in the rate of its uptake by the liver.

The first consequence of the rapid metabolism of fructose is the accumulation of fructose-1-phosphate, initially recognized in the liver. Within minutes after a fructose load, the concentration of the fructose ester, normally undetectable, may reach 10 μmol/g.[40,56a,135–140] The accumulation of fructose-1-phosphate demonstrates that its formation is much faster than its further metabolism. The limiting step has been a subject of controversy. Although IMP inhibits liver aldolase,[40] its accumulation cannot explain the initial build-up of fructose-1-phosphate because the latter precedes it.[140] The utilization of fructose-1-phosphate thus seems limited by triokinase and by the glycolytic and gluconeogenic pathways originating from the triose phosphates. Indeed, the V_{max} of triokinase reaches only 1.5 μmol/min per gram of liver at 37°C,[99] and the maximal flux through each of the latter pathways does not exceed 2 μmol of C6 units per minute per gram liver at 37°C[119] so that the additive rate of both is less than half the activity of fructokinase. The accumulation of fructose-1-phosphate provokes important changes in the concentration of several other metabolites, which explain the toxic effects of fructose.

The Hyperuricemic Effect of Fructose

In 1967, Perheentupa and Raivio[128] reported that the intravenous administration of 0.5 g fructose per kilogram of body weight provoked hyperuricemia and hyperuricosuria not only in patients with hereditary fructose intolerance but also in normal children. This observation has been repeatedly confirmed[141,142] in patients as well as in healthy adult volunteers, especially at infusion rates above 1.0 to 1.5 g/kg per hour.[143] Although other authors have not observed the effect with lower infusion rates,[144–146] a rise of serum uric acid has been found after the infusion of as little as 0.16 g/kg fructose per hour in critically ill subjects.[147] A single intravenous test dose of 200 mg/kg fructose provokes a rise of serum uric acid in healthy children and adults (Figs. 11-7 and 11-8). The urinary excretion of uric acid, expressed as the creatinine ratio, is a more sensitive indicator of the effect of fructose than is hyperuricemia.[148,149] Increased urinary excretion of precursors of uric acid, namely, inosine, hypoxanthine, and xanthine, and their rise in plasma have also been reported in humans and in animals.[141,150,151]

Investigations in animals by Mäenpää et al.[152] and later in humans[138,153] demonstrated that the hyperuricemic effect of fructose results from the degradation of adenine nucleotides. Indeed, within 2 min after a parenteral fructose load to rats, the concentration of hepatic ATP falls to 40 percent of its normal value without an equivalent increase of ADP and AMP.[152] There is also a marked decrease in the concentration of P_i preceding that of ATP. The decrease of ATP is explained by its utilization in the fructokinase reaction. The P_i depletion results from its participation in the rephosphorylation of ADP in mitochondria (Fig. 11-2). In recent years, the accumulation of fructose-1-phosphate and the depletion of ATP and P_i have also been documented by ^{31}P nuclear magnetic resonance spectroscopy. Studies have been performed in intact perfused rat liver[154] and in human liver in vivo[155,155a] (Fig. 11-3). It is worth mentioning that in the latter study the hepatic concentration of ATP decreased by 60 percent and that of P_i by 80 percent with the infusion of as little as 250 mg/kg fructose, a dose which did not raise plasma uric acid above the limits established for healthy controls.[62]

The concentrations of several other nucleotides: uridine triphosphate, UDP-glucose[156,157] and guanosine triphosphate (GTP)[140] are also diminished following fructose infusion. The decrease of GTP may be due to its utilization in both the fructokinase[55] and the triokinase reactions.[98a] Depletion of high energy phosphates has also been observed in other fructose-metabolizing tissues, namely, kidney[157,158] and small intestine[159] following the administration of fructose. Studies with single rat nephrons have shown that in accordance with the localization of fructokinase and aldolase B, the effects of fructose are confined to the proximal tubule.[75] The contribution of the kidney and small intestine to the hyperuricemic effects of fructose is difficult to assess since in humans, xanthine oxidase is found only in liver and small intestinal mucosa.[160]

The catabolism of the adenine nucleotides ATP, ADP, and AMP (maintained in equilibrium by adenylate kinase) can theoretically begin either by deamination of AMP, catalyzed by AMP deaminase, followed by dephosphorylation of IMP to inosine by the cytoplasmic 5′-nucleotidase, or by dephosphorylation of AMP by the same enzyme, followed by deamination of adenosine to inosine by adenosine deaminase (Fig. 11-4). From inosine, the successive action of nucleoside phosphorylase and xanthine oxidase leads to the formation of uric acid, the end product of purine nucleotide catabolism in humans and higher apes. The catabolism of the adenine nucleotides has to be kept to a minimum for two reasons: (1) adenine nucleotides play a major role in the energy metabolism of the cell; and (2) the low solubility of uric acid, coupled with its limited renal excretion, poses the danger of precipitation of crystals, with the damaging consequences found in gout. Studies of the catabolism of the adenine nucleotides in isolated rat hepatocytes have shown that in this tissue the initial catabolism of AMP proceeds exclusively by way of AMP deaminase under physiological conditions.[161,162] More recently it has been found that dephosphorylation of AMP by the cytoplasmic 5′-nucleotidase takes place but does not contribute to the production of uric acid, because the resulting adenosine is continuously recycled by adenosine kinase.[163] AMP deaminase is the limiting step in the catabolism of the hepatic adenine nucleotides and therefore controls their breakdown. The enzyme has complex allosteric properties and is strongly influenced by var-

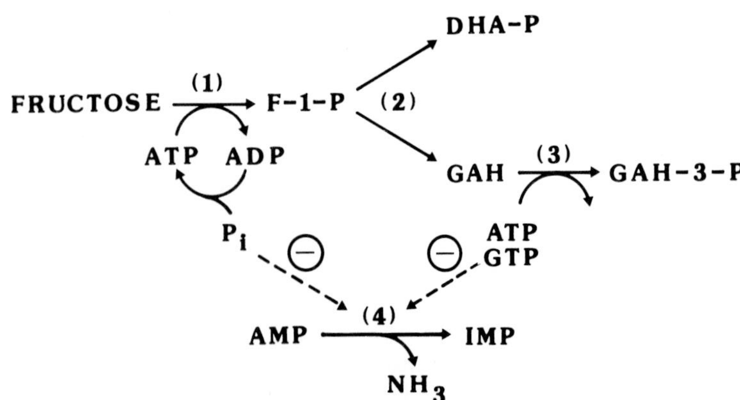

Fig. 11-2 The mechanism of fructose-induced hyperuricemia. (1) fructokinase, (2) aldolase, (3) triokinase, (4) AMP deaminase, ⊖ denotes inhibition. Further explanations are given in the text.

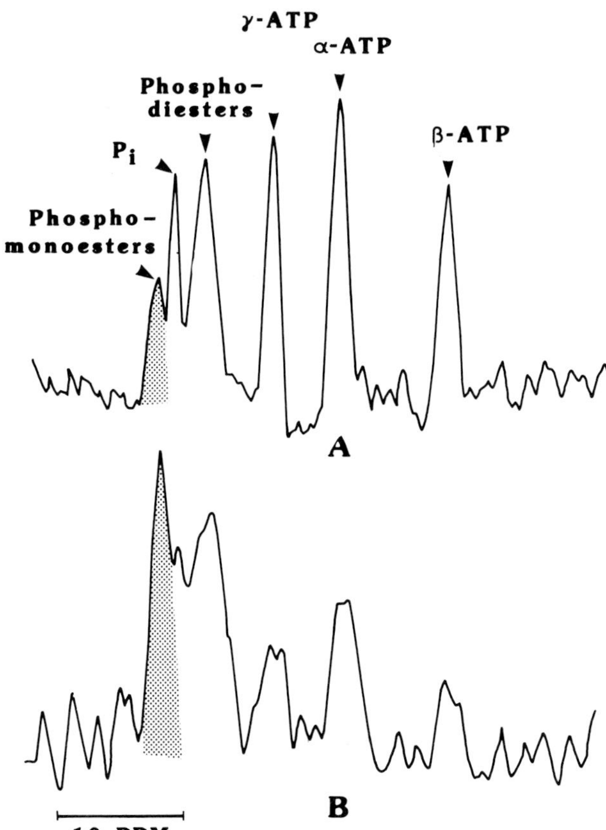

Fig. 11-3 Effect of intravenous fructose on liver metabolites of a healthy adult assessed by ^{31}P magnetic resonance spectroscopy. *(A)* before (1024 scans), and *(B)* 5 to 10 min after bolus injection of 250 mg/kg fructose (512 scans; data obtained at a 2 s^{-1} pulse repetition rate). Phosphomonoesters comprise: glycerol-3-phosphate, sugar phosphates, phosphocholine, phosphoethanolamine, inosine, and adenosine monophosphates. *(Adapted from: Oberhaensli et al.,[155] by permission.)*

ious metabolites: ATP is a potent activator, whereas P_i and GTP are inhibitory. At physiological concentrations of substrate and effectors, the enzyme is 95 percent inhibited.[140]

The mechanism of the fructose-induced degradation of the adenine nucleotide pool has been investigated mainly in liver. Studies with isolated hepatocytes have shown that similarly to physiological catabolism it proceeds by way of AMP deaminase.[161] It is explained by a release of the physiological inhibition of AMP deaminase[140] caused by the decrease in the concentrations of P_i and GTP during fructose metabolism (Fig. 11-2). The accumulation of IMP following fructose administration, first recorded by Woods et al.,[40] is a reflection of the increased flux through AMP deaminase.

The fructose-induced hyperuricemia is thus not a harmless phenomenon. Rather, it indicates degradation of ATP, i.e., the main "energy currency" of the cell. ATP degradation is reflected by a decrease in tissue, and increase in plasma Mg^{2+},[164] owing to the loss of this potent Mg^{2+} chelator. In the fructose-metabolizing tissues, depletion of ATP results in a series of disturbances. They include inhibition of protein[138,152,165] and RNA[138,166] synthesis, disaggregation of ribosomes,[164] interference with the formation of cyclic AMP,[139] and detoxication of ammonia.[167] Marked ultrastructural lesions such as loss of ribosomes in rat hepatocytes[167a,168] and smooth endoplasmic reticulum proliferation in mouse jejunal absorptive cells[169] have been described.

Theoretically, the degradation of adenine nucleotides may be prevented by the administration of phosphate. Data obtained in animals indicate that, although the infusion of phosphate largely prevents the fructose-induced degradation of adenine nucleotides in the kidney cortex, it is much less effective in the liver, probably because of its limited entry into this tissue.[158]

The fructose-induced catabolism of the purine nucleotides is followed by a compensatory increase in their *de novo* synthesis.[170] This involves several mechanisms: (1) conversion of PRPP amidotransferase, the limiting enzyme of the *de novo* pathway from its large, inactive, into its small, active form[171]; (2) elevation of the concentration of PRPP,[171,172] which also increases the recovery of hypoxanthine by the salvage pathway.[172]

The Increase in Blood Lactate Provoked by Fructose

Whereas the intravenous infusion of glucose on the average does not elevate the concentration of blood lactate more than twofold, two- to fivefold increases have been reported after the infusion of fructose in healthy volunteers and in patients.[145,149,173,174] Wide individual variations and the observed bimodal distribution have led to the suggestion of genetic differences in the metabolism of fructose.[175] The faster formation of lactate from fructose than from glucose can be explained by several factors: (1) the higher activity of fructokinase compared with the capacity of hexokinase plus glucokinase to phosphorylate glucose; (2) the fact that fructolysis bypasses phosphofructokinase, the first regulatory enzyme along the

Fig. 11-4 Pathways of adenine nucleotide catabolism in the liver. (1) Adenylate kinase, (2) AMP deaminase, (3) cytoplasmic 5'-nucleotidase, (4) adenosine deaminase, (5) adenosine kinase, (6) nucleoside phosphorylase, (7) xanthine oxidase.

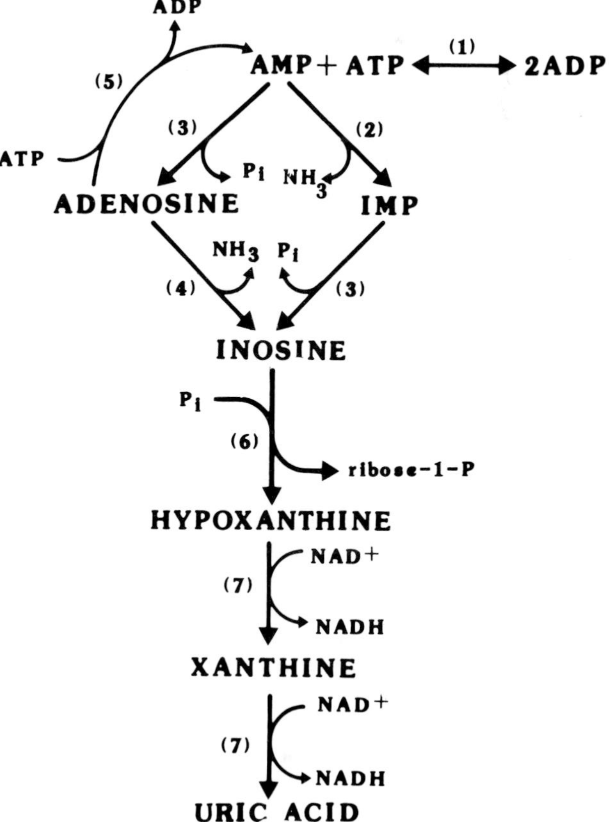

glycolytic pathway; (3) a stimulation of pyruvate kinase, the second regulatory step of glycolysis, by fructose-1-phosphate[176] and by fructose-1,6-bisphophate.[177] Additional data concerning the effect of fructose on the glycolytic-gluconeogenic pathway can be found elsewhere.[23]

The fructose-induced increase in lactic acid may provoke metabolic acidosis in adults[129,178] and children.[179,180] Metabolic acidosis has also been reported in the fetus of mothers receiving intravenous fructose during labor.[181] It may become life-threatening in liver failure, as exemplified by the case reports provided by Craig and Crane[178] and by Woods and Alberti.[131] Fructose is therefore a potentially dangerous substitute for glucose in parenteral nutrition. Inborn errors of fructose, lactate, and ammonia metabolism, glycogenosis type I, and acquired conditions in which the hepatic utilization of peripherally produced lactate is impaired such as anoxia, liver disease, and diabetes mellitus are absolute contraindications.

ESSENTIAL FRUCTOSURIA—HEPATIC FRUCTOKINASE DEFICIENCY (MIM 22980)

Historical Note and Definition[182]

This rare and benign error of metabolism was first described in 1876 independently by Czapek[183] and by Zimmer[184] in a man who also suffered from diabetes mellitus. In 1961 Laron[185] counted 50 published cases, and in 1969 Steinitz and Mizrahy counted fewer than 80.[186] Since the disorder is asymptomatic and harmless, many cases may remain undetected and the detected ones unpublished. The original name of the disorder, *essential fructosuria*, became obsolete in 1961–1962 when the fructokinase defect was discovered, but it is still in use. A nonalimentary fructosuria of obscure etiology has been observed in one child.[187]

Laboratory Findings, Biochemical Defects, Functional Studies

Affected persons are usually discovered on routine urinalysis by the presence of a reducing substance. They are healthy and have otherwise normal liver function. Fructosuria depends on the time and amount of fructose and sucrose intake, and thus it is inconstant. After an overnight fast, fructose is measurable only in small quantities, if at all, in the blood of the affected persons, just as in normal persons. The misdiagnosis of diabetes mellitus[188,189] or renal diabetes[189] is avoided only when the nonglucose nature of the sugar is recognized. This can be done by means of thin-layer or paper chromatography.

The disorder is caused by the inherited deficiency of fructokinase (EC 2.7.1.3) normally present in the liver, intestine, and kidney cortex.[57,75,190,191] The deficiency was demonstrated in the liver of an adult by Schapira et al.[192] using the assay designed by Hers and Joassin.[193] Assays of intestinal or kidney cortex fructokinase have to our knowledge not been done in persons with essential fructosuria. The metabolic block appears to be as follows:

$$\text{Fructose} \xrightarrow[\quad /\!/ \quad]{\text{fructokinase}} \text{Fructose-1-phosphate}$$

After an oral or intravenous load, e.g., with 1 g/kg body weight, blood fructose rises rapidly far beyond the level of 10 to 30 mg per 100 ml seen in controls, falls slowly, and does not disappear for 6 h or longer.[146,185] Between 10 and 20 percent of the administered dose is excreted in urine,[185,194] compared with 1 to 2 percent[185] or less[146] in normal subjects. Blood glucose, lactate, pyruvate, and urate change little, in contrast to the rise of these metabolites in normal persons; phosphorus, magnesium, standard bicarbonate, free fatty acids, and insulin remain constant[146,194–196] (Fig. 11-5). The rise of the respiratory quotient after fructose ingestion in fasting patients with essential fructosuria is less than in normal subjects.[188,195] These findings indicate a slower than normal utilization of fructose. An 11½-year-old girl weighing 40 kg, on a 1-h-long continuous fructose infusion (1 g/kg body weight) retained from 40 to 60 mg of the sugar per minute.[185] The nine-tenths of a dose of fructose, which is retained by fructosuric subjects after a bolus, is most probably metabolized via fructose-6-phosphate in adipose tissue[43,117] and skeletal muscle. As in normal subjects, D-sorbitol is converted to fructose, which becomes measurable in blood (Fig. 11-5)[146,197]; urinary loss as fructose is only about one-half that seen after a fructose load.[146,197] Almost 80 percent of a 5-g sorbose load was lost in urine by a fructosuric woman.[188]

Genetics

The most careful study of the mode of inheritance of essential fructosuria is that of Lasker.[198] After reviewing the literature

Fig. 11-5 Oral fructose and sorbitol tolerance tests in two sibs with essential fructosuria. Fructose: ■ = R. K. ♂, 16 years; ● = A. K. ♀, 19 years; •--• = controls (*N* = 5). Sorbitol: □ = R. K. In the probands, phosphorus, magnesium, standard bicarbonate, free fatty acids, and insulin remained unchanged. *(From Steinmann et al.[146])*

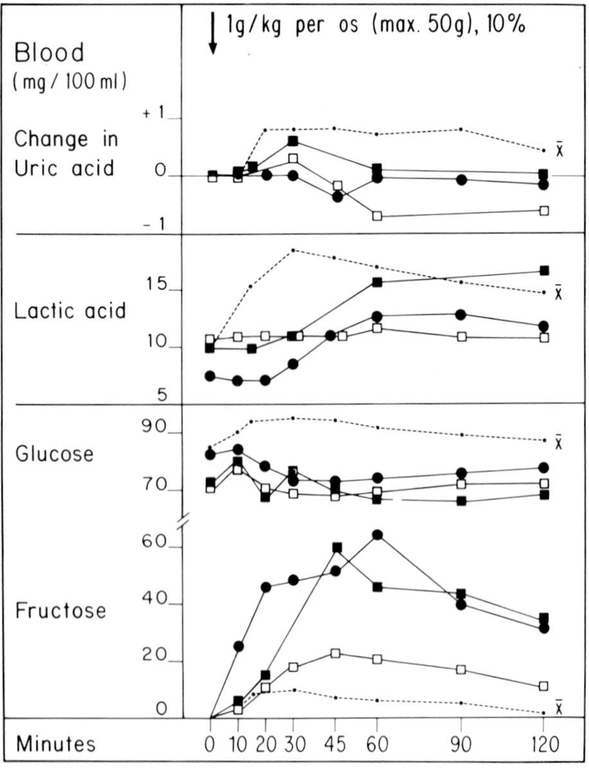

and her own cases, she concluded that the anomaly was inherited as an autosomal recessive trait and occurred perhaps once in 130,000 individuals. She gave good reasons why this was only an approximate figure and stated that the disorder may be even rarer. On the other hand, given its benign character, it may escape discovery during a lifetime. Marble[199] reported only four cases among 29,000 cases of mellituria seen at the Joslin Clinic. Heterozygotes appear to excrete no more fructose after an oral load than normal subjects.[200] Fructokinase has not been assayed in heterozygotes. Essential fructosuria has been reported from many parts of the world.[198] By 1961, the proportion of Jews in the known and proven cases of this disorder was 18 out of 50 cases.[185]

HEREDITARY FRUCTOSE INTOLERANCE (HFI) (MIM 22960)

Historical Note and Definition

In 1956 Chambers and Pratt[201] described a "idiosyncrasy to fructose" in a 24-year-old "spinster" who complained, apart from minor phobic symptoms, of vomiting after taking fruit or sugar. She could take glucose without ill effects, although she did not enjoy the taste. Symptoms had appeared on weaning at age 10 months. The authors recognized that the condition differed from fructosuria, speculated that symptoms were presumably caused by a toxic intermediate, and proposed that the condition be considered as a cause of difficulty in weaning. Froesch et al.[202] reported the typical syndrome of hereditary fructose intolerance in 1957 in two sibs and two relatives and suspected a deficiency of aldolase as its cause. The defect was characterized by Hers and Joassin in 1961, on two liver biopsy specimens, as a loss of the ability of the enzyme to split fructose-1-phosphate.[193] By 1971, 100 cases had been recorded in the literature[203] from Europe and the United States, and since then, additional reports have been numerous. The disorder, once considered a rare inborn error of metabolism, is sufficiently common for certain centers to have collected the records of dozens of patients.[62,204,205]

Only in 1970 was hereditary fructose-1,6-bisphosphatase deficiency recognized as a separate disorder[206] causing somewhat less intolerance to fructose. After a reinvestigation in 1972, familial galactose and fructose intolerance, originally described in 1961, must now be questioned as a disease entity.[207]

Clinical and Laboratory Findings

Infants and adult patients with hereditary fructose intolerance are perfectly healthy and asymptomatic as long as they do not ingest any food containing fructose or sucrose. Thus during breast feeding, no metabolic derangement occurs. At weaning, with the intake of fruits and vegetables, the first symptoms appear. The younger the child[208] and the higher the dietary fructose load, the more severe the reaction. The newborn infant who is not breast-fed but receives a cow's milk formula with fructose or sucrose substituting for lactose is in danger of death.

In the infant and small child,[204,205] leading symptoms are poor feeding, vomiting, and failure to thrive (Table 11-1). All other symptoms occur less frequently but are more specific and indicative of gastrointestinal discomfort, hypoglycemia, shock, and liver disease. As the clinical presentation is multifaceted in the small infant, the diagnosis is easily missed. If the intake of the noxious sugar persists, hypoglycemic episodes recur and liver and kidney failure progress, eventually leading to death. In one series,[204] clinical findings in the order of decreasing frequency were hepatomegaly, pallor, hemorrhages such as melena, hematemesis and suffusions, trembling and jerks, shock, jaundice, edema, tachypnea, ascites, oliguria or anuria as signs of severe shock, splenomegaly, fever, and rickets. Laboratory findings are those of liver failure, of proximal renal tubular dysfunction, and of certain derangements of intermediary metabolism (Table 11-2).

The child survives and symptoms regress when the formula is changed to a nonnoxious one or replaced by intravenous infusions with glucose as the carbohydrate. If the patient escapes diagnosis at this point, the disease takes a protracted, uphill-downhill course. By experience, certain mothers learn quickly how to select harmless formulas and foods for their affected child. The protracted course is also typical for the patient whose first exposure to fructose occurs at regular

Table 11-1 Symptoms and Signs in Hereditary Fructose Intolerance*

Acute exposure	*Chronic exposure*
Sweating	Poor feeding, vomiting
Trembling	Failure to thrive
Dizziness	Incessant crying, irritability
Nausea	Drowsiness, apathy
Vomiting	Jaundice
Apathy, lethargy, coma	Abdominal distention
Convulsions	Hepatomegaly
	Hemorrhages
	Diarrhea
	Tremor, jerking
	Edema, ascites
	Poor growth

*Sequelae: Protracted fibrosis, cirrhosis, steatosis of the liver; aversion to sweets and peculiar feeding habits; lack of dental caries.

Table 11-2 Laboratory Findings in Acute and Chronically Exposed Patients with Hereditary Fructose Intolerance

Urine	*Blood*
Fructose ↑	Phosphorus ↓
Glucose ↑	Glucose ↓
Phosphorus ↑	Urate ↑
Urate ↑	Magnesium ↑
Bicarbonate ↑	Potassium ↓
Lactate ↑	Fructose ↑
Aminoacids ↑	Lactate ↑
Potassium ↑	pH ↓
Protein ↑	Bicarbonate ↓
	Proteins ↓
	Coagulation factors ↓
	Hepatic enzymes ↑
	Bilirubin ↑
	Methionine, tyrosine etc. ↑
	Anemia
	Thrombocytopenia
	Acanthocytes, fragmentocytes

weaning. Here, the prominent features are abdominal distention, hepatomegaly, and poor growth. Acute episodes become rarer as the child develops a distinct aversion to discomfort-causing sweetened foods and drinks. Aversion to sweet food is neither general nor indiscriminate[201] but selective and directed at particular sweetened foods or drinks. Thus it is not innate but acquired by learning. For instance, a fructose-intolerant medical student not knowing her diagnosis disliked all desserts with the exception of glucose candies. Children usually adopt peculiar feeding habits which protect them but are not always understood by surrounding persons, who sometimes resort to forcing sweet foods.[209–211] Diagnosis during preschool and school age is usually made during examination for suspected storage disorder, for delayed growth, or sometimes for anomalous behavior[209] (Fig. 11-6) and only after carefully taking the nutritional history. Other patients, following a self-imposed low fructose diet, go on undiagnosed into adulthood and may be discovered by chance. Approximately half of all adults with hereditary fructose intolerance are completely free of caries,[208,210,212–214] a fact indicating that dietary sucrose is the chief caries-promoting agent.[215] It also leads dentists to suspect hereditary fructose intolerance.[211] Some adult patients are diagnosed during a family investigation after the discovery of an affected young relative,[211,212,216] sometimes their own child.[217,218] Yet other undiagnosed fructose-intolerant children and adults are less fortunate and receive infusions of fructose, sorbitol, or invert sugar, sometimes for unrelated health reasons,[219,220] e.g., after routine surgery. Consequently, some die from acute poisoning.[221–226]

It must be stressed that in the two casuistic reviews[204,205] comprising 75 children, hypoglycemia was documented only in a minority. It correlated poorly with jerking and trembling in the infant. Hypoglycemia, while considered a major and dangerous metabolic manifestation of hereditary fructose intolerance, is short-lived, lasting only a limited time after each ingestion of fructose. It thus easily escapes detection.

Fig. 11-6 A 12-year-old girl with hereditary fructose intolerance "eating" an apple. She had been referred for anomalous behavior at age 8 years.

Histologic examination of the liver performed by diagnostic biopsy shows diffuse steatosis of liver cells, necrosis of a few scattered hepatocytes, periportal and intralobular fibrosis, and, in more advanced stages of the disease, cirrhosis.[205,227,228] At autopsy, findings include hepatic dystrophy and necrosis.[228–230] In the kidney, histologic changes are remarkably discrete. They include some granulation and perhaps vacuolization of epithelial cells lining the proximal tubules, which may be slightly dilated.[229,230] In the small intestine, gross inspection and microscopic examination may reveal submucosal or serosal hemorrhages. Intracranial[205,208] and intraocular hemorrhages[204] have been reported.

Ultrastructural studies done by Spycher[231] on three liver biopsy specimens revealed that hepatocytes and sometimes Kupffer cells contained polymorphous cytoplasmic inclusions of different size, in part membrane-bound and probably lysosomal. Inclusions contained amorphous, electron-dense masses and numerous concentric membranous arrays varying greatly in size and often surrounded by an electron-lucent halo. Similar findings had been reported earlier.[232]

Molecular Defect

The enzyme defect (Fig. 11-1) is that of aldolase B (fructose-1,6-bisphosphate aldolase, EC 4.1.2.13) of the liver, kidney cortex, and small intestine. Aldolase A and C,[65,66,73] prevalent in other organs such as skeletal muscle and brain, are not affected. The activity of the liver enzyme is reduced to 15 percent of normal or less with fructose-1-phosphate and to a distinctly lesser degree with fructose-1,6-bisphosphate. A representative sample of measurements on liver biopsy specimens is shown in Table 11-3. It confirms the findings of an earlier series[233] and shows that in the patients, the ratio of activities measured with fructose-1,6-bisphosphate as substrate to fructose-1-phosphate as substrate is increased, a fact of diagnostic value originally pointed out by Hers and Joassin[193] and Schapira et al.[192] Fructose-1-phosphate aldolase activity was undetectable in 5 of 35 biopsy specimens in one series[62] but was never absent in the 34 biopsy specimens of another series.[233] The activities of liver fructokinase[192,193,234] and fructose-1,6-bisphosphatase (Table 11-3) are normal. A similar reduction of fructaldolase activities is found in biopsied jejunal mucosa and in kidney cortex at operation and at autopsy (Table 11-4).[225]

The significance of residual fructaldolase activities in liver, kidney, and intestine of patients with hereditary fructose intolerance is still controversial. Mature human liver contains all three forms of fructaldolase, but B predominates with 98 percent of the protein.[73] Aldolase A, with less than 2 to 3 percent of protein,[73,233] contributes 15 percent of the total activity[233] owing to its higher specific activity. Residual liver fructose-1,6-bisphosphate aldolase has been attributed variably to a persisting fetal enzyme, shortly to be recognized as aldolase A,[193,234,235] and to aldolase C.[233] Both are unaffected by the mutation and have a higher fructose-1,6-bisphosphate aldolase/fructose-1-phosphate aldolase activity ratio (13 and 7) than normal aldolase B (0.9).[236] Conceivably, the partially inactive

Table 11-3 Fructaldolase and Fructose-1,6-Bisphosphatase (FDPase) Measured in Liver Biopsy Specimens of Children with Hereditary Fructose Intolerance (HFI) and Controls (IU per Gram Wet Weight)

		Fructaldolase			
		FDP	*F-1-P*	*FDP/F-1-P*	*FDPase*
HFI	$\bar{x}$ (or median)	0.46	0.11	(3.9)	3.82
	SD	0.16	0.09		1.66
	Range	0.13–0.82	0.00–0.36	1.7–∞	1.71–7.20
	N	35	35		24
Controls*	$\bar{x}$	2.61	2.40	1.1	3.78
	SD	0.46	0.49	0.1	0.74
	Range	2.07–3.79	1.82–3.40	1.0–1.2	2.73–4.98
	N	10	10	10	7

*Nine adult organ donors and one child with a histologically normal liver. SOURCE: Data from Steinmann and Gitzelmann.[146]

mutant aldolase B itself has an increased activity ratio. In the majority of biopsy specimens studied, a cross-reacting material was present,[62,233,237–239] and an abnormally high K_m for fructose-1,6-bisphosphate[64] and fructose-1-phosphate,[233] and decreased heat stability[62] of mutant human aldolase have been reported. Furthermore, a certain restoration of fructose-1-phosphate aldolase activity in extracts of biopsied liver was achieved in vitro by reducing agents,[233] and in a minority of tissue specimens, antibodies to aldolase B activated the residual enzyme.[62,239] At any rate, the residual aldolase activity never appears to become rate-limiting in glycolysis or gluconeogenesis except after fructose loading. Normal functioning of gluconeogenesis is amply documented by the prompt rise of blood glucose after oral dihydroxyacetone[146,240–242] and by the patients' normal tolerance to fasting.

In four patients, Cross et al. have recently discovered a single base substitution (G → C) in exon 5 resulting in an amino acid substitution (Ala → Pro) at position 149 of the aldolase B,[242a] entailing a major conformational disturbance.[242b]

Functional Studies

In individuals with hereditary fructose intolerance, both the ingestion and the injection of *fructose* cause chemical changes, symptoms, and signs, some of which are also seen in normal persons, albeit to a far lesser degree. After a rapid intravenous load, patients and healthy persons[243] experience dull epigastric pain, which is unexplained; it usually starts 2 to 3 min after the bolus and tapers off after 10 min. Only the patients report

Table 11-4 Activity Ratios of Fructose-1,6-Bisphosphate to Fructose-1-Phosphate Aldolase, Measured in Tissues of Patients with Hereditary Fructose Intolerance and Controls, at Biopsy or Autopsy, and in Purified Human Aldolases A, B, and C

	Controls			*Hereditary fructose intolerance*			
	Mean	*Range*	*N*	*Mean (or median)*	*Range*	*N*	*Ref.*
Liver	1.0	0.9–1.1	5	6.2; 6.2		2	193
	1.1	1.0–1.2	10	(3.9)	1.8–∞	33	62
				1.7; 11*		2	62
		1.0–1.2		6.6	2.9–11.0	34	233
	1.4*	1.1–1.8*	6	9.0*		1	225
	1.7		11				57
Intestine	1.9	1.0–2.5	28	(26.7)	3.1–∞	8	350
				1.8		1	208
		3.5–4.0	4				190
	1.7	1.1–2.3	7	32.6; 3.5		2	351
				9.1*		1	352
Kidney cortex	2.8*		5				191
	1.3		1				353
	3.2	2.6–4	6	∞		1	354
	1.7; 2.5*		2	18*		1	62
	2.7*						74
Kidney medulla	6*		4				191
	23		1				353
	5.8; 9.6*		2				62
	3.4*						74
Aldolase A	13						236
Aldolase B	0.9						236
Aldolase C	7						236

*Values refer to measurements at autopsy.

a nagging hunger feeling toward and during the second hour.[62] An oral fructose load causes occasional diarrhea in control persons but no other ill effects. In contrast, patients become limp and nauseated and vomit, sometimes with blood, are covered with cold sweat, and develop signs of shock and hypoglycemia. The ill effects are dose dependent [201,202] and may last for several hours. Proteinuria, generalized aminoaciduria, a rise of serum transaminases, and jaundice may appear and last for several days.[227,244,245]

The chemical signs provoked by fructose in the patient consist of a rapid fall, first of serum phosphate and then of blood glucose, and a rise of urate and magnesium. Blood alanine, lactate, glycerol, and nonesterified fatty acids rise.[211,212,246] Insulin remains constant or falls,[208,212,213,247,248] while growth hormone rises,[212,248] probably in response to hypoglycemia. Effects are clearly dose dependent.[242] The degree of fructose intolerance may diminish with age,[202] but considerable differences in the individual patient have also been recorded.[209] Because of the ill effects of oral loads and the unreliability of results, fructose tolerance tests should not be done orally. Figures 11-7 and 11-8 illustrate the course of intravenous tolerance tests in normal and fructose-intolerant children and adults.[62] The small dose of 200 mg/kg is recommended. Fructose-intolerant children and adults extract fructose from the blood normally[62] except when the administered dose is excessive.[249] In intolerant children, chemical responses are generally

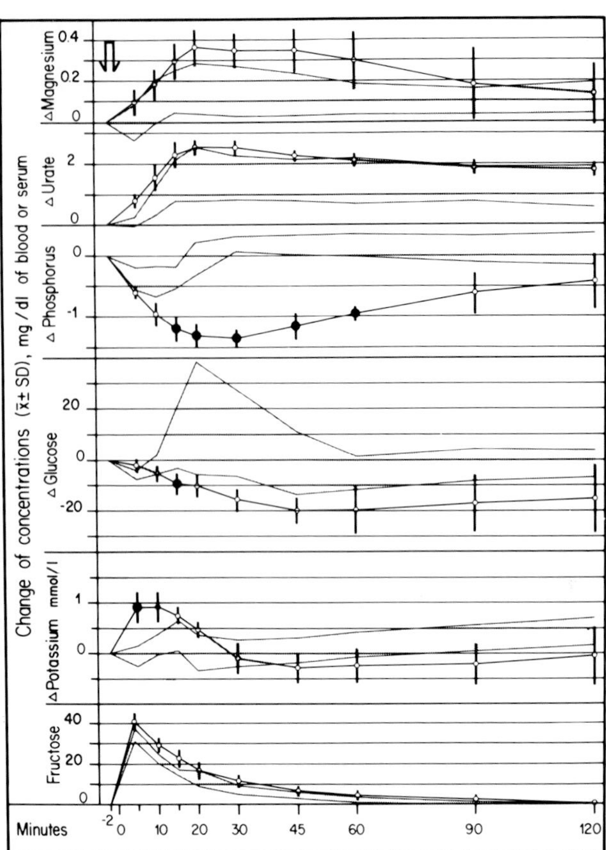

Fig. 11-8 Intravenous fructose tolerance tests (200 mg/kg; 20 percent solution) in six adults with hereditary fructose intolerance and six controls. For symbols, see Fig. 11-7. *(From Steinmann and Gitzelmann.[62])*

Fig. 11-7 Intravenous fructose tolerance tests (200 mg/kg; 20 percent solution) in 10 children with hereditary fructose intolerance and 16 control children. The shaded areas represent means ± 1 SD of the controls; bars represent the means + 1 SD in the patients. Symbols: ● = mean, no overlap between the two groups, • = mean, the extreme values of both groups coincided; ○ = mean, overlap occurred between the two groups. *(From Steinmann and Gitzelmann.[62])*

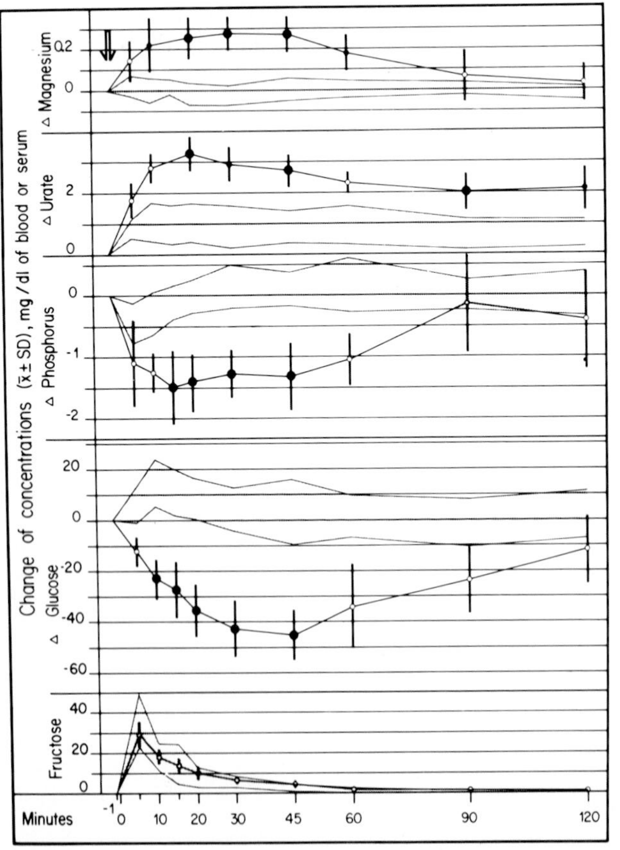

more prompt and pronounced than in adult patients. After an equal per weight fructose dose (i.e., a higher per unit surface area dose), hypoglycemia in the adults is milder and somewhat delayed, and thus is not an independent diagnostic criterion. One girl, repeatedly tested, was found to convert to the adult type of blood response between ages 12 and 18½ years.[62] Adults experience a short-lived hyperkalemia[62] followed by a decline in serum potassium,[62,213] and this was also seen in one child.[62] Urinary excretion of lactate, alanine, urate, and magnesium increases after the intravenous load,[62,146] changes also seen after an oral load.[245] That intravenous fructose tests are not at all harmless even when fructose is given in a small dose must be concluded from the observation of a test-induced proximal renal tubular syndrome in adult patients.[62,250] Acute fructose hepatotoxicity for the fructose-intolerant subject is evident from the investigations by Odièvre.[251] Four-hour infusions of fructose in children caused clotting factors II, V, VII and X to drop after 2 to 4 h; they reverted to normal levels only after 24 to 48 h. Interesting morphologic observations in the liver and small intestine of an adult patient 2 h after an oral load with 50 g fructose were made by Phillips et al.[252] By light microscopy, there were no changes, but electron microscopy revealed striking fine structural alterations reminiscent of those seen in fructose-loaded laboratory animals[253] (see "Toxicity of Fructose," above). They included concentric and irregularly disposed membranous arrays in and marked rarefaction of the hyaloplasm of hepatocytes. Concentric arrays of smooth endoplasmic reticulum were visible in the supranuclear region of enterocytes.

The intravenous loading with *sorbitol* causes the same chemical changes in the patient, but only insignificant fructosemia[62] or none at all.[213] This documents the fact that intravenous sorbitol is rapidly converted to fructose in the liver and that fructosemia is not a prerequisite for hypoglycemia and the other observed changes. It is noteworthy that the test does not appear to cause epigastric discomfort.[213]

The disappearance of L-*sorbose* from the blood of normal subjects is somewhat slower than that of fructose. This would be expected from the fact that liver fructokinase phosphorylates fructose faster than sorbose and in preference to this ketose.[51] The half-life of sorbose, calculated from data of Froesch et al.,[213] lies between 24 and 29 min. In two normal subjects about 30 percent of the administered L-sorbose was excreted in urine, compared to 1 to 2 percent with fructose.[213] In patients with hereditary fructose intolerance, the sorbose level rose higher and fell more slowly, with a half-life of approximately 64 min, and accordingly these patients excreted over 80 percent of the administered sorbose in the urine within 24 h. The ability to assimilate sorbose obviously was greatly impaired, but patients had no symptoms and neither blood glucose nor inorganic phosphorus changed.[213,217,247] Furthermore, prior administration of sorbose did not alter or delay the response of patients with hereditary fructose intolerance to subsequent administration of fructose.[213] One might speculate that because of the small affinity of fructokinase for sorbose, only a small amount of sorbose-1-phosphate accumulates in the liver cells, too little to cause the metabolic effects attributed to fructose-1-phosphate accumulation (see "Pathophysiology," below).

Sucrose tolerance tests are not routinely done when hereditary fructose intolerance is suspected. One 10-month-old boy suspected of having intestinal sucrose-isomaltase deficiency was given an oral sucrose load (50 g/m^2). He developed hypoglycemia, whereupon the correct diagnosis was made.[254] A fructose-intolerant woman volunteered for an oral *raffinose* loading test (42 g) when it was not clear whether this fructose-containing trisaccharide of vegetable origin could be hydrolyzed in the human small intestine.[255] She experienced no hypoglycemia, although with an equivalent dose of oral fructose (12 g) she did.[9] In contrast to sucrose, raffinose is not hydrolyzed in the intestine and thus is safe for consumption by fructose-intolerant persons.

The *fructose-induced hypoglycemia* seen in the patients is not due to hyperinsulinism[208,212,213,247,249] and is not corrected by exogenous glucagon[139,212,213,242,246,256] or dibutyryl cyclic AMP.[139] On the other hand, when administration of oral or intravenous fructose is accompanied[241] or followed[212,242] by oral or intravenous galactose, the fructose-induced hypoglycemia is prevented or corrected. Neither dihydroxyacetone[241,242] nor inorganic phosphate[203,242,247,256] has a corrective effect. These facts demonstrate that during a limited period of time after the fructose load, hepatic glucose formation by way of glycogenolysis and gluconeogenesis is impaired.

Pathophysiology

As can be expected from the study of normal metabolism of fructose, its intake will result in the accumulation of fructose-1-phosphate in liver, kidney, and small intestine. Owing to the inability of the defective aldolase B to split the fructose ester, fructose-1-phosphate will accumulate not only after fructose loads but also after the ingestion of physiological amounts of the ketohexose. The pathophysiological effects, e.g., hyperuricemia and lactic acidosis, will thus constitute a marked exaggeration of the deleterious effects observed in normal individuals (see "Toxicity of Fructose," above). In addition, conversion of fructose to blood glucose will be hampered. Direct proof that the changes in intracellular metabolites observed after fructose loads in animals also occur in patients with hereditary fructose intolerance is, of course, scarce for ethical reasons. The accumulation of fructose-1-phosphate has been verified.[258,259] A depletion of intracellular P_i can be inferred from the long lasting fall of serum inorganic phosphate in the patients after fructose. For instance, it was calculated that the conversion of 6.6 mmol (= 1.2 g) fructose to fructose-1-phosphate by an infant patient weighing 8.8 kg required more P_i than the amount present in the entire extracellular fluid.[213] The increase of serum magnesium and uric acid after fructose in the patients[208,260] most probably reflects the loss of ATP from the fructose-metabolizing tissues. Indeed, ATP is a strong Mg^{2+} chelator, and a drop in its concentration is likely to result in the release of cellular Mg^{2+}. Undoubtedly, several of the toxic effects of fructose in the patients are caused by the depletion of ATP. The loss of hepatic ATP, by its effect on protein synthesis, may explain the hyperaminoacidemia, the decrease in blood clotting factors, and the other signs of liver failure. The complex renal tubular dysfunction resembling the Fanconi syndrome[261] may be caused by the degradation of ATP in the kidney. A modulation of the renal dysfunction by the level of parathyroid hormone has been reported.[250] The metabolic acidosis is due to both lactic acidosis and proximal renal tubular acidosis, the former being far more important.[245]

The profound *fructose-induced hypoglycemia* is seen only in patients with hereditary fructose intolerance or fructose-1,6-bisphosphatase deficiency, although the rapid intravenous infusion of fructose may exceptionally induce a slight lowering of blood glucose in normal newborn infants[262] and in healthy adults.[263] Its mechanism is not immediately apparent and has been the subject of extensive investigations. It is not due to increased glucose utilization by the peripheral tissues but is caused by a block of glucose release from the liver.[249]

Decreased gluconeogenesis is apparent from the fact that the fructose-induced hypoglycemia cannot be corrected by dihydroxyacetone, which enters the glycolytic-gluconeogenic pathway at the triokinase step. The hindrance of dihydroxyacetone conversion to glucose may be due to several mechanisms. Inhibition by fructose-1-phosphate of two gluconeogenic enzymes, glucose-6-phosphate isomerase[264] and liver aldolase[265] has been reported. When residual aldolase was assayed in the direction of condensation of the triose phosphates to fructose-1,6-bisphosphate, inhibition was observed in patient liver homogenate but not in control liver.[265] The inhibition of glucose-6-phosphate isomerase by fructose-1-phosphate may account for the occasional occurrence of a transient decrease in blood glucose upon rapid infusion of the ketose in normal subjects.[262,263] Depletion of ATP may also explain decreased gluconeogenesis. Indeed, studies of perfused rat liver have shown that this rate depends on the concentration of ATP up to the physiological level, a half-maximal effect being observed at 0.6 m*M* ATP.[266] Even complete inhibition of gluconeogenesis cannot, by itself explain the rapid, fructose-induced fall in blood glucose characteristic of hereditary fructose intolerance. Several hours of fasting are required for patients with fructose-1,6-bisphosphatase deficiency to become hypoglycemic.

A *block of glycogenolysis* during fructose-induced hypoglycemia is evidenced by the inability of glucagon to correct the blood glucose. The increase of liver glycogen measured in a biopsy by Cain and Ryman[267] is in keeping with this observation. Inhibition of phosphoglucomutase by fructose-1-phosphate in vitro was suggested by Sidbury.[268] However, fructose-induced hypoglycemia can be corrected by galactose,[212] and thus conversion of glucose-1-phosphate to glucose-6-phosphate and free glucose is not impaired in vivo. Therefore, breakdown of liver glycogen must be blocked at the level of phosphorylase.

The effects of fructose on the different steps of glycogenolysis have been investigated in detail[139,269] (for reviews see Refs. 127 and 270). The glucagon-induced accumulation of cyclic AMP is markedly reduced by prior administration of fructose. This effect was observed in the urine of patients after a diagnostic dose of intravenous fructose and in the livers of rats receiving fructose loads, where it correlated with the decrease of ATP, the substrate of adenylate cyclase. Slowed formation of cyclic AMP did not explain the suppression of the hormonal effect, since fructose-induced hypoglycemia was not corrected by the injection of dibutyryl cyclic AMP. Furthermore, the amount of cyclic AMP formed in the livers of experimental animals was still sufficient to bring about the conversion of phosphorylase b to the active form a. Competitive inhibition of phosphorylase a from animal liver by fructose-1-phosphate was demonstrated.[139,271–274] It is enhanced by lowering the concentration of P_i. The inhibition seemed insufficiently pronounced at the concentration of fructose-1-phosphate and P_i prevailing in the livers of experimental animals after fructose administration to account for the complete abolition of the phosphorolytic degradation of glycogen. Total inhibition of phosphorylase a could nevertheless be evidenced in animals in vivo.[270,274] Van den Berghe,[270] after loading rats with tagatose, concluded that part of the total P_i measured may be bound and consequently unavailable for phosphorylase a, resulting in the enhancement of the inhibitory effect of fructose-1-phosphate. The absence of a corrective effect of phosphate infusions may be related to the limited entry of P_i into the liver.[158]

In spite of the loss of the ability of the liver, kidney, and small intestine to metabolize fructose beyond fructose-1-phosphate, only 10 to 20 percent of the administered ketohexose is excreted in the patient's urine. This led to an investigation of their metabolism of fructose. As expected, red and white blood cells metabolized fructose normally, by way of hexokinase, in the absence of glucose; in liver tissue, oxidation of [U-^{14}C]fructose to $^{14}CO_2$ and incorporation of the label into glycogen was only 1 to 6 percent of normal.[213] Studies in vivo by Landau et al.[275] indicate that this limited metabolism occurs by phosphorylation of fructose to fructose-6-phosphate. The amount of fructose utilized by the liver of these patients is too small to explain why as much as 90 percent of the administered fructose is assimilated. It has therefore been suggested that adipose tissue is the main site of fructose utilization in patients with hereditary fructose intolerance as well as in those with essential fructosuria.[43,117]

Diagnosis, Treatment, Course

The diagnosis of hereditary fructose intolerance can be suspected from a detailed nutritional history and the clinical picture.[204,227] A high degree of clinical awareness is often needed for prompt diagnosis, as the spectrum of symptoms and signs is wide and nonspecific.[204,205,219,251,276] Small infants are referred for vomiting of unknown etiology, possible pyloric stenosis or gastroesophageal reflux, or toxic disorders, while older infants and small children are referred for hepatomegaly.[204,205,277] Usually, hepatitis, intrauterine infection, septicemia, hemolytic-uremic syndrome, tumor of the liver or storage disorder, galactosemia, tyrosinosis, and Wilson's disease are considered. Suspicion is fostered by the presence of reducing substances in the urine (glucose or fructose, or both) or by hyperaminoaciduria and high blood methionine and tyrosine, discovered by selective screening. It is important to know that fructosuria may have disappeared at the time of urinalysis.

As soon as fructose intolerance is suspected, all sucrose, fructose, and sorbitol must be eliminated at once from the diet and from medications. The beneficial effect of withdrawal, usually seen within days, is the first positive element of diagnosis. It must be confirmed, preferably after several weeks of fructose abstinence, by an intravenous fructose tolerance test (200 mg/kg) (Figs. 11-7 and 11-8) and, in case of doubt, by the assay[278] of fructaldolase in a biopsy of liver or, perhaps, small intestine (Tables 11-3 and 11-4). Liver is the preferred organ for biopsy.[9] Fructaldolase activities in the serum of patients are only slightly diminished and hence of no diagnostic value.[279] Enzymatic diagnosis from blood cells is not possible,[278a] and the same must be said of cultured skin fibroblasts and placenta, since they appear to express predominantly aldolase A.[80,81,280,281]

Treatment consists of the elimination from the diet of all sources of sucrose and fructose.[7,8,282,283] Supportive measures such as infusion of fresh frozen plasma or exchange transfusion may alleviate the clotting disorder and restore complement deficiency.[284] Recovery of renal and hepatic functions takes days. Small infants recover more slowly than older ones and may yet die of hepatic and renal failure several days after the withdrawal of fructose. Once recovery is made, the further course is uneventful, intellectual development is unimpaired, and catch-up growth proceeds.[227,285,286]

Children with HFI during their first year of life start protecting themselves by a self-imposed exclusion diet which, though sufficiently stringent to spare them intolerance symptoms is liberal enough to cause hepatomegaly and stunted growth. Therefore, after diagnosis, the child's aversion cannot be relied upon and a diet must be prescribed. Two treated preschool boys after partial relaxation of their diet to 250 mg/kg fructose per day had sustained increases in serum and urinary uric acid and magnesium, yet no symptoms of intolerance.[286]

Small children usually have hepatomegaly for months or years in spite of adequate treatment.[205] The reason for this is unclear, but it may be connected with a particularly high degree of intolerance during childhood[213] and also with hidden sources[214] of dietary fructose and sucrose. It is interesting that a group of adult patients on the average consumed 2.5 g sucrose daily, i.e., 5 percent of what was consumed by controls.[214] Dietary indiscretion in an adult was elegantly detected by ^{31}P magnetic resonance spectroscopy.[155a] A rapid disappearance of intralobular hepatic fibrosis and a decrease of periportal fibrosis were observed in serial liver biopsy specimens, but fatty vacuolization of liver cells persisted or increased, and its distribution changed from diffuse to periportal.[205,282]

The oldest known patient was born in 1886 and was properly recognized toward the end of the last century as intolerant to sugar, although never reported. She had lived sugar-free and died at age 83 of an unrelated cause. The diagnosis was verified biochemically on postmortem liver examination.[287]

Patients (or their parents) should state their intolerance to fructose on any hospital admission. Infusion solutions containing fructose, sorbitol, or invert sugar, unfortunately still in wide use, e.g., after routine surgery, constitute an immediate threat to the life of patients.[288] Such accidents, fatal and nonfatal, have been published,[204,219–226] and a number of unpublished[289–291] iatrogenic deaths are known.

Genetics

The majority of cases have been reported from Europe and North America. One child was Indian.[292] The true incidence is not known but has been estimated at approximately 1:20,000 for Switzerland.[293] In recent years, evidence has grown that considerable numbers of children and adult patients must live undiagnosed in the general population. This can be concluded from the following facts: reports of iatrogenic accidents and deaths following infusions of fructose, invert sugar, and sorbitol in hospitals, published and unpublished; the surfacing of undiagnosed patients among older sibs and other relatives of young probands during extended family investigations[211,212,227,244]; the self-diagnosis of medical students during a lecture on hereditary fructose intolerance[9]; and the frequent occurrence of parent-child[211,216–218,289,293–296] or grandparent-grandchild[297] cases. Hereditary fructose intolerance occurs in all parts of the world. Sex distribution among the affected is even. Affected monozygotic twins have been observed.[216,250] The overwhelming majority of parents are unaffected. Consanguinity of parents is not uncommon. One pair of affected parents produced four children, all affected.[222] The mode of inheritance is thus autosomal recessive. An apparently dominant case may be the child of an affected homozygous parent and a healthy heterozygote (pseudodominance).[298] All parents examined so far have had normal liver fructaldolase activity,[299] a fact incompatible with dominant inheritance.

Heterozygotes for hereditary fructose intolerance cannot be identified by conventional means. Oral or intravenous fructose tolerance tests have been done in six sets of parents,[208,212,299] and in another parent and his healthy grandchild, who was the daughter of a patient.[211] The results were normal, without exception. In one set of parents given a continuous fructose infusion, fructose blood clearance was diminished when compared to that of controls.[300] This could not be confirmed in 11 parents.[146,203,249] In seven, significant differences were not found even though blood glucose, standard bicarbonate, phosphorus, lactate, urate and urinary urate/creatinine, and magnesium/creatinine ratios were determined.[146] Heterozygote detection through estimation of immunoreactive aldolase in intestinal biopsy may become possible,[238] yet ^{31}P magnetic resonance spectroscopy after a fructose bolus revealing an increment of sugar phosphates, and a fall of inorganic phosphates in the liver, may soon become the method of choice for this purpose.[155a]

Given the variation of liver enzyme activities between patients, Levin et al.[208] speculated that there may be more than one genotype involved. Koster et al. suspected the same from different K_m values for fructose-1-phosphate between patients.[64] Stronger evidence for genetic heterogeneity stems from studies by Steinmann, Gitzelmann, et al.[62,239] and Schapira,[301] who found that antibodies to normal aldolase B stimulated fructose-1-phosphate cleavage in liver homogenates of some patients but not others. Wide variations of heat stability of the residual fructose-1,6-bisphosphate aldolase were disovered.[62] Genetic heterogeneity was further demonstrated at the protein level by Cox et al.,[242b] and at the DNA level by Grégori et al.[302] Restriction fragments of aldolase B were studied in 11 patients; one proved to be a compound heterozygote.[302] In another study of four patients, three were homozygous for a single base substitution and the fourth was heterozygous, i.e., a compound heterozygote.[242a]

FRUCTOSE-1,6-BISPHOSPHATASE DEFICIENCY (MIM 22970)

Historical Note

Fructose-1,6-bisphosphatase deficiency was first described in 1970 by Baker and Winegrad.[206] Two further reports appeared within a year[240,303] and were followed by a number of observations.[304–317] We are now aware of 85 patients, all children, whose cases are published and unpublished.[318] A variant form of fructose-1,6-bisphosphatase deficiency in a woman and her daughter[319] and combined fructose-1,6-bisphosphatase and glucose-6-phosphatase deficiency in another female[320] has been observed.

Clinical and Laboratory Findings

Fructose-1,6-bisphosphatase deficiency is a severe disorder of gluconeogenesis causing life-threatening episodes in newborn infants and small children. Approximately one-half of the afflicted children had their first symptoms between their first and fourth day of life and the remainder in equal numbers before and after their sixth month. The latest manifestation, with one exception, was at age 4 years.[315] In the newborn, hyperventilation is the commonest symptom, usually caused by profound acidosis. Irritability, somnolence or coma, apneic spells, dyspnea and tachycardia, muscular hypotonia, and a moderate hepatomegaly may be observed. Hypoglycemia may be an isolated chemical sign[312] but is usually detected when sought, together with ketonuria. The first attacks in the newborn period are promptly overcome by the administration of glucose and sodium bicarbonate. Weeks or many months of apparent well-being can pass between the first and further attacks.

Later episodes are usually triggered by febrile infections. Refusal to feed and vomiting, which often accompany febrile infections in children, precipitate the onset. The evolution is usually dramatic: hyperventilation, trembling, lethargy, coma, and convulsions follow in short succession within a few hours and reflect profound acidosis, ketosis, and hypoglycemia. Apnea and cardiac arrest have been observed.[240] Flushing[240] and hematemesis[307,308] have occurred exceptionally. Lactate, ketones, alanine, and uric acid[313,314] are elevated in the blood and appear in the urine.[240,308] Also detected in urine were glycerol during fasting[321] and glycerol-3-phosphate during episodes of hypoglycemia.[322,323] Blood glucose is low, but attacks of ketoacidosis without hypoglycemia have been observed.[313,314] Hepatomegaly and muscle weakness are often present. Failure to thrive is the exception.[314] In one child, the clinical and biochemical presentation and course were suggestive of tyrosinosis,[303,304] with liver dysfunction, hyperaminoaciduria, wasting, sepsis, and death. In contrast to hereditary fructose intolerance, disturbances of liver function are the exception,[310] and renal tubular function and blood coagulation are undisturbed. EEG tracings may be abnormal during attacks but later return to normal. A slow wave pattern has been described.[313] Two sibs had a peculiar low amplitude pattern with slowed background activity and intermittent, spindle-shaped, fast-activity bursts.[240] The third sib had multifocal spikes and sharp waves on low background activity.

Most affected children experience a number of acute attacks before the diagnosis is made. Once the diagnosis is established and treatment begins, the course is favorable. The patients do not develop an aversion to sweet foods; in fact, they may even enjoy eating fruits and sweets.[206] Hepatomegaly regresses slowly or more rapidly, but lapses occur[307,313,317] and may be related to the intake of fructose and sucrose. Somatic, psychomotor, and intellectual development seems unimpaired.

The clinical features of the unusual mother-child cases of Taunton et al.[319] differed from the common ones. The mother presented at age 20 years with emotional lability, dizziness, fatigability, and symptomatic hypoglycemia and the child at age 13 months with unresponsiveness and confusion.

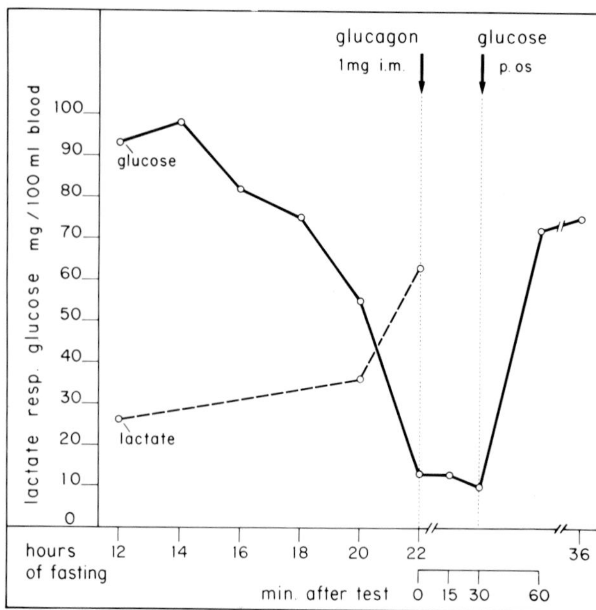

Fig. 11-9 Prolonged fasting in a 17-month-old boy (T. M.) with fructose-1,6-bisphosphatase deficiency. (From Baerlocher et al.[240])

Biochemical Defect, Functional Studies, Pathogenesis

Deficiency of fructose-1,6-bisphosphatase (hexose bisphosphatase, fructose-1,6-bisphosphatase, EC 3.1.3.11) can be demonstrated in the liver and also in the jejunum,[306] kidney,[303,308] and probably the leukocytes.[324] In two-thirds of the children, liver fructose-1,6-bisphosphatase activity was either absent or reduced to a trace and in the others was reduced to one-fifth or less. Anomalous kinetic behavior of the residual enzyme has been reported.[325] Inactivity of fructose-1,6-bisphosphatase in the liver and active enzyme in skeletal muscle was demonstrated in one patient[305]; in another, the enzyme activity was absent in the liver, kidney, and leukocytes but was present in skeletal muscle extract.[308] These findings, together with further biochemical evidence, demonstrate that muscle contains a distinct enzyme not involved in this disorder.

Liver glycogen was normal in four liver biopsy specimens but was increased in two others.[240,308] Liver glucose-6-phosphatase was measured and was normally active in 10 children. The combined deficiency of fructose-1,6-bisphosphatase and glucose-6-phosphatase observed in an adult[320] is thus exceptional. Other enzymes examined in the liver included aldolase, pyruvate kinase, phosphoenolpyruvate carboxykinase, phosphorylase, phosphoglucomutase, phosphofructokinase, amylo-1,6-glucosidase, and acid maltase. They were normal.

Fructose-1,6-bisphosphatase is a key enzyme of gluconeogenesis. Its inactivity prevents the endogenous formation of glucose from the precursors lactate, glycerol, and gluconeogenic amino acids such as alanine. It is not surprising that more than half of the afflicted infants become symptomatic within the first week of life when they are dependent on gluconeogenesis.[326] On subsequent days, higher milk volume and more frequent feedings seem to postpone further manifestations until insufficient food intake together with higher energy expenditure during infectious fever induces further episodes.

Dependence of fructose-1,6-bisphosphatase-deficient children on exogenous glucose can easily be demonstrated. During *fasting*, maintenance of blood glucose depends on glycogenolysis, and the duration of normoglycemia depends, therefore, on the amount of available liver glycogen. Blood glucose may drop within a few hours[308] or only after 14 h or more.[206,240,316] Simultaneously, lactate and pyruvate rise[206,240,308,316] and their ratio increases. Blood ketones and alanine also rise. When hypoglycemia is reached, the blood glucose level is irresponsive to injected glucagon. This indicates that liver glycogen stores have been depleted (Fig. 11-9). In the fed state, patients have a normal hyperglycemic response to glucagon. Feeding a diet excessively high in protein or fat equally provokes hypoglycemia, acidosis, and ketonemia.[305] High lactate/pyruvate and glycerol-3-phosphate/dihydroxyacetone phosphate ratios, demonstrated in biopsied liver, indicate the accumulation of glyceraldehyde-3-phosphate and insufficient oxidation of NADH.[305]

Fructose-1,6-bisphosphatase-deficient patients have reduced tolerance to *fructose* and *sorbitol*, but generally it is higher than in patients with hereditary fructose intolerance. For instance, one infant tolerated 5 g/kg sucrose per day in his formula.[146] Fructose-1,6-bisphosphatase-deficient patients do not develop gastrointestinal symptoms after an oral load.[206,240] As in hereditary fructose intolerance, blood glucose and phosphorus drop after the load, while lactate, urate, magnesium, and alanine rise (Fig. 11-10). Fructose-induced hypoglycemia is not related to insulin release[206,240,305,307,311] and cannot be corrected by injecting glucagon[206,307,312,313] or epinephrine.[308] The response to fructose is similar when given intravenously or orally and is clearly dose-dependent.[240,312,313] Although, in fructose-1,6-bisphosphatase-deficient children, fructose-induced changes of blood metabolites seem somewhat less drastic than they are in children with hereditary fructose intolerance, fructose tolerance tests are not without risk. The 20-month-old patient studied by Corbeel et al.[313] became comatose after the injection of 500 mg/kg fructose. Repeated therapeutic sorbitol infusions in a 2-year-old patient were deleterious[327,328] (Fig. 11-11).

Oral administration of *glycerol*[206,240,305,306,309,311,312,314,316,317] provokes a response quite similar to that seen after fructose administration. Hypoglycemia is paralleled by a drop in phosphorus and bicarbonate; lactate rises. In contrast, children with intact gluconeogenesis respond with an increase of blood glucose but not of lactic acid.[305] Hypoglycemia is again unrelated to insulin release[206,305] and is refractory to glucagon.[206]

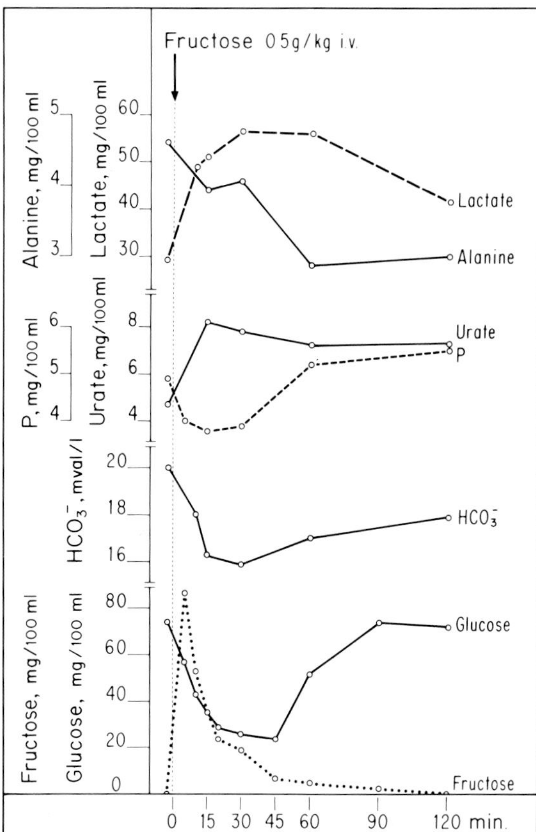

Fig. 11-10 Intravenous fructose tolerance test in a 21-month-old boy (T. M.) with fructose-1,6-bisphosphatase deficiency[240], with the high dose of 500 mg/kg. The lower dose of 200 mg/kg is preferable.[62] *(From Steinmann and Gitzelmann.[349])*

Alanine, given intravenously or orally, can cause a similar though milder hypoglycemic response[305,311–313] or none at all.[306,307,311,317] The responses to alanine infusion after 6 and 12 h of fasting were divergent in Pagliara's patient.[305] After a 6-h fast, alanine caused a rise of glucose and after a 12-h fast a

Fig. 11-11 Final course of a 2-year-old girl, M. M., older sib of T. M.,[240] with undiagnosed fructose-1,6-bisphosphatase deficiency after repeated sorbitol infusions for assumed cerebral edema. After each sorbitol dose, severe acidosis followed and was corrected with sodium bicarbonate and buffer (THAM). *(From Gitzelmann et al.[327] and Baerlocher et al.[328])*

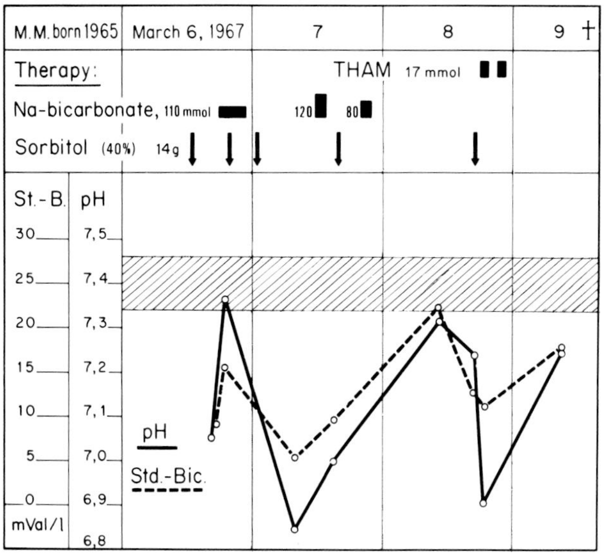

late fall. The handling of a *dihydroxyacetone* load (1 g/kg orally) was tested in only one patient on two occasions.[146,240] On both occasions, he vomited 25 min after the ingestion. During the first half-hour blood glucose fell in the patient but rose in adult controls and in a child with hereditary fructose intolerance.[146] In all, blood lactate rose and phosphorus and bicarbonate fell. The adult controls had a delayed hypoglycemic response due to hyperinsulinism.[146]

Fructose-1,6-bisphosphatase-deficient children have normal *galactose* tolerance. Injection or ingestion is followed by normoglycemia or mild hyperglycemia, indicating normal assimilation of this sugar.

Hypoglycemia occurs after prolonged fasting when glycogen stores are depleted and the liver switches from glycogen breakdown to glucose production from gluconeogenic precursors. Precursors cannot be converted to glucose, and lactate accumulates and causes metabolic acidosis. Blood levels of precursors such as pyruvate, ketones, glycerol, and alanine also rise. The newborn patient is particularly prone to hypoglycemia and acidosis as food intake is limited and only little glycogen available in the liver. The patient's tolerance to fasting depends on the size of the glycogen stores and is shortened in situations of increased catabolism and energy expenditure, e.g., in febrile infections. Tolerance to fasting, although limited (Fig. 11-9), is not nil (Fig. 11-12). It seems to improve somewhat with age. A correlation with residual fructose-1,6-bisphosphatase activity in the liver should exist but has not been documented.

Reactive hypoglycemia after fructose, sorbitol, glycerol, dihydroxyacetone, and alanine is somewhat more complex (Fig. 11-1). As in hereditary fructose intolerance, phosphate esters may accumulate intracellularly and inhibit glycogen

Fig. 11-12 Patient T. M.,[240] fructose-1,6-bisphosphatase deficient, aged 4 years and obese because of overnutrition. Five months later, he had lost 6 kg by dieting (800 to 900 kcal/m^2 per day; carbohydrates 66 percent, proteins 22 percent, fat 12 percent). At ages 14 and 16½ years, he dieted again and, after hard exercise, he ate insufficiently. The following mornings he suffered from life-threatening hypoglycemic attacks.

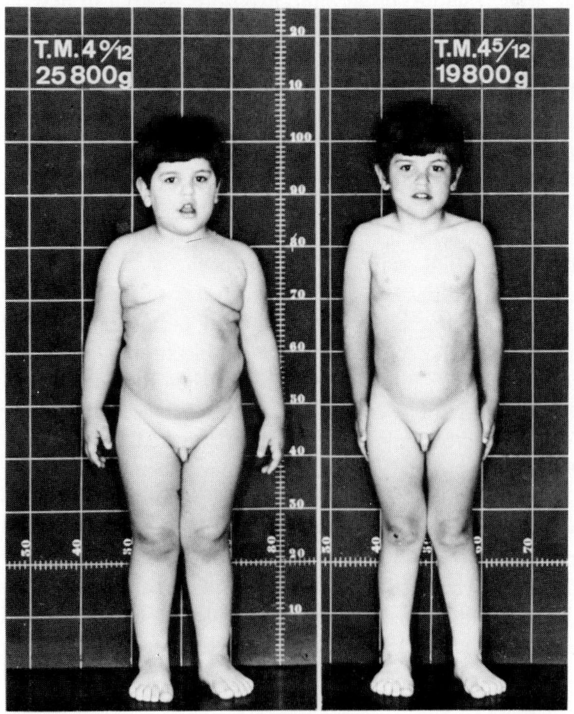

phosphorylase. This presumption is supported by the glucagon refractoriness of hypoglycemia. The appearance of glycerol-3-phosphate in urine[322] is surprising as organophosphates are not usually excreted; it has been confirmed[323] in the case of Dremsek et al.[321] during fasting but not in Baerlocher's patient[240] after recovery.

Liver phosphorylase is inhibited in various ways by fructose-1-phosphate, fructose-1,6-bisphosphate, and glycerol-3-phosphate.[139,271,272,274] Inhibition is more pronounced as intracellular inorganic phosphate drops. Hyperuricemia and hypermagnesemia reflect adenine nucleotide breakdown (see pathophysiology of "Hereditary Fructose Intolerance," above).

The cause of hepatomegaly and of fatty infiltration of the liver is uncertain. Fat deposition is likely to result from a constant flooding with amino acids and glycerol that can either be released as lactate or converted to fat and stored.

Diagnosis, Treatment, Prognosis

Fructose-1,6-bisphosphatase deficiency must be suspected in full-term newborns of normal birth weight suffering from hyperventilation, convulsions, and coma accompanied by hypoglycemia, ketosis, and acidosis, especially when signs of neonatal infection, cerebral hemorrhage, and left heart failure are absent. The disorder must also be suspected in small children suffering from episodic hypoglycemia triggered by febrile infection or starvation. Other causes of lactic acidosis, such as the deficiencies of glucose-6-phosphatase, pyruvate carboxylase, pyruvate dehydrogenase, and phosphoenolpyruvate carboxykinase,[328a] may be difficult to exclude. Fasting tests (Fig. 11-9) and tolerance tests with fructose (Fig. 11-10), sorbitol, glycerol, alanine, or dihydroxyacetone[146,328] must be postponed until remission and should be carried out with adequate monitoring. A fructose load should not be given by mouth unless hereditary fructose intolerance is definitely excluded. The use of a moderate dose, e.g., 200 mg/kg intravenously is recommended,[62] since higher doses may be dangerous.[313] Aversion to sweets and signs of a proximal renal tubular syndrome after fructose (or sorbitol) exposure, as seen in hereditary fructose intolerance, are absent in fructose-1,6-bisphosphatase deficiency.

The diagnosis is established by demonstrating an enzyme deficiency in a liver biopsy specimen.[278] Although the defect has also been demonstrated in leukocytes by some investigators,[309,313,317,324,329] others,[330] including ourselves, have attempted this in vain in peripheral leukocytes and in Epstein-Barr virus-transformed lymphoblasts.[323] After criticism,[330] the originally reported activities of leukocytes[308,324] were corrected.[331] Difficulties seem to have been due to the extremely low activity in white blood cells. Culturing peripheral lymphocytes increased the specific fructose-1,6-bisphosphatase activity considerably[332]; this may become of diagnostic use.[333] Successful diagnosis of two Lebanese children by enzyme assay on freshly isolated leukocytes has been reported.[334] Fructose-1,6-bisphosphatase deficiency has also been documented in jejunal biopsy material[306] and in the kidney at autopsy.[303,308] Results of enzyme assays on tissues obtained at autopsy must be interpreted with caution, since the enzyme inactivates rapidly owing to autolysis.[62,323] Fructose-1,6-bisphosphatase is unmeasurable in cultured skin fibroblasts and in amniotic fluid cells.[323,324] Fructose-1,6-bisphosphatase in biopsied chorionic villi has not been measured. Prenatal diagnosis is thus impossible.

Light microscopy of biopsied and autopsied liver usually reveals fatty infiltration but neither fibrosis nor disturbed architecture, as is common in hereditary fructose intolerance. Electron-microscopic findings[240,307,315] have not been revealing.

Treatment of acute attacks consists of correction of hypoglycemia and acidosis by intravenous infusion and is usually rapidly successful. Later, avoidance of fasting prevents further episodes. Fructose and sucrose should be limited in the diet but probably need not be eliminated. The degree of intolerance to fructose may vary considerably between patients and even in the individual.[307] Acute episodes may be precipitated by fructose or sucrose ingestion. For instance, one newborn gained weight on a sucrose-containing formula during his first and further weeks of life,[240] and another infant had her second and repeated attacks at age 7 months when weaned to baby food.[305] An 8-year-old boy, in remission for 2 years, suffered a relapse which led to diagnosis upon being prescribed a fructose-containing syrup for asthenia.[315] The liver size usually diminishes, but lapses occur.[307,310,313,315,317] Substitution of part of the dietary fat with carbohydrates and reduction of protein to the basic requirement have been recommended.[305] Treatment with folic acid was advocated[306] and repeatedly tried in typical cases[309,315] as well as in the "new mild variant,"[319] but its benefit remains to be proven.[316]

As a rule, the firstborn child with the disease dies or suffers more than the following children, who profit from the experience gained by parents and physicians with the first. Once the diagnosis is established, the course seems benign, and growth and development are normal. Lapses during febrile infections are controlled easily by glucose, either alone or in combination with sodium bicarbonate. Baker and Winegrad[206] have the clinical impression that tolerance to fasting increases with age, and our experience supports this impression. It may be assumed that undiagnosed fructose-1,6-bisphosphatase-deficient adults exist in the general population. These persons, like those with undiagnosed hereditary fructose intolerance, may be endangered by the indiscriminate use of fructose, invert sugar, or sorbitol in infusion solutions.

Genetics

Seventeen years after its first description, the incidence of fructose-1,6-bisphosphatase deficiency is still unknown. We know of 85 patients and affected sibs, 34 boys and 51 girls, whose cases are unpublished[318] or published. Two-thirds of all were diagnosed by enzyme assay in biopsied liver. (The unusual cases of Taunton et al.[319] and Service et al.[320] are not counted here.) Most affected sibs were older than the probands and had died under circumstances similar to those which led to the hospital admission of the probands. Most families lived in Europe and the United States, two in Japan[317,333] and two in Lebanon.[334] One patient was a black North American[306] and one an Indian child living in England.[310]

Parental consanguinity was reported.[240,303,304,312,334] The parents are healthy. One couple had normal responses to intravenous fructose and glycerol.[305] All three parents tested had intermediate fructose-1,6-bisphosphatase activity in the liver,[307,327] but results of activity measurements in leukocytes were less than conclusive.[308,317,324] A radiochemical procedure, though apparently superior to the commonly used spectrophotometric method still does not allow the identification of all carriers.[334] The use of cultured lymphocytes may improve discrimination of heterozygotes from normal individuals.[333] The mode of inheritance is autosomal recessive.

D-GLYCERIC ACIDURIA

This metabolic disorder has been described in only four unrelated children, three of European[335–338] and one of Afghan parents.[339] Symptoms appeared soon after birth. In one child, tachypnea, tachycardia, and refusal to feed led to the discovery of persistent metabolic acidosis necessitating permanent treatment with sodium bicarbonate.[339] Motor delay and a moderate degree of mental retardation was noted during the next 16 months. In the other three children, hypotonia, myoclonic jerks, seizures, severe developmental delay, and hyperglycinuria suggested the diagnosis of nonketotic hyperglycinemia. All patients excreted D-glyceric acid, a compound not usually found in urine. One set of parents excreted only traces of D-glycerate.[338] Two children also had D-glyceric acidemia. Of three tested children, two responded to *oral fructose loads* with increased D-glyceric acid excretion in urine, one by a rise of both urinary and plasma D-glycerate concentrations. In the last child, oral dihydroxyacetone caused the same effect.[338] This girl responded to the restriction of dietary fructose and sucrose by the reduction of seizures and a lowering of D-glycerate excretion.

Low leukocyte D-glyceric acid dehydrogenase and only 10 percent of glycine cleavage activity in liver at autopsy was reported in one,[337] low red cell glyceraldehyde-3-phosphate dehydrogenase and normal erythrocyte triokinase in the other patient.[338] Although a defect of hepatic triokinase appears a reasonable suggestion,[338] the primary metabolic defect remains to be established. In fact, this group of patients may be heterogeneous.

ERYTHROCYTE ALDOLASE DEFICIENCY WITH NONSPHEROCYTIC HEMOLYTIC ANEMIA (ALDOLASE A DEFICIENCY) (MIM 20335)

This defect was first observed[340,341] in a boy born to first cousins, small-for-date with dysmorphic facial features, a short neck, and lax skin. At 6 weeks nonspherocytic hemolytic anemia was noted. Urine amino acids, blood glucose, and karyotype were normal. At 4 months, a liver biopsy revealed mild elevation of glycogen content (7.2 g %) and an increase of fibrous tissue judged compatible with congenital hepatic fibrosis. The boy required blood transfusions until his second year of life. When last seen at age 7 years, moderate hepatomegaly persisted. He was microcephalic, his growth was stunted, and his intellectual development delayed. Biochemical findings included a rise of blood glucose after a fructose load, indicating normal function of hepatic aldolase B, and a marked deficiency of red cell and fibroblast aldolase. The child's parents had normal red cell aldolase activity.

Erythrocytes and fibroblasts in culture normally express aldolase A.[79,81] Since both cell types were aldolase-deficient, Beutler's assumption[340] that this child suffered from a deficiency of type A aldolase, perhaps on the basis of a regulatory mutation, seems justified. Aldolase A is the isoenzyme of fetal tissues occurring in brain, liver, and kidney. Postnatally, it is the predominant isoenzyme in muscle, presumably the red cell and—together with aldolase C—in brain.[60] There can be little doubt that the impairment of glycolysis due to aldolase A deficiency was the cause of hemolysis, although it remains unclear why the latter did not persist beyond the second year. As to the remainder of the phenotype, it is tempting to speculate that aldolase A deficiency caused prenatal liver damage and that it compromised brain development from fetal to postnatal life. Dysmorphism and slowing of intrauterine and postnatal growth could equally be viewed as consequences of impaired glycolysis in growing tissues. Nevertheless, since this child's parents were first cousins, the patient could have been homozygous for a number of recessive traits unrelated to aldolase activity.

Two brothers with spherocytosis and a syndrome remarkably similar to that seen in Beutler's patient were observed recently.[341a] As aldolase levels were reduced only by the amount predicted for the degree of hemolysis, aldolase deficiency was not judged responsible for the syndrome in the two brothers.

Only once was red cell aldolase deficiency reported again,[342] though it was of a different type. Two related boys, Japanese islanders aged 14 months and 13 years, had mild nonspherocytic hemolytic anemia since infancy aggravated by infections. In contrast to Beutler's patients, they were orthomorphic and normally developed. Red cell aldolase activity was grossly reduced in the boys and intermediate in both sets of parents and in some other family members. Red cell fructose-1,6-bisphosphate was elevated in the two patients, and hexose monophosphate shunt activity reduced, presumably due to the inhibition of glucose-6-phosphate dehydrogenase by fructose-1,6-bisphosphate. Red cell aldolase was heat labile and had reduced affinity for fructose-1,6-bisphosphate. A structural mutation of aldolase A was assumed.

In one patient, a single nucleotide substitution was demonstrated.[343]

FRUCTOSE MALABSORPTION

Recently, it has been recognized that one out of three healthy adults[344,345] and two out of three children[346] incompletely absorb fructose when administered orally at a dose of 0.7 to 2 g/kg. This finding may account for the abdominal symptoms such as bloating, rumbling, pain, flatulence, and watery diarrhea experienced by some persons after the ingestion of fructose,[22] fruit,[347] and other fructose-containing foods. Symptoms usually disappear after the elimination of fructose from the diet. In only one patient, sucrose intolerance was also documented. This 12-year-old girl had normal small intestinal sucrase activity and was intolerant of as little as 1 g of oral fructose.[348] The basic defect in these persons remains to be established.

REFERENCES

1. ROE JH, EPSTEIN JH, GOLDSTEIN NP: A photometric method for the determination of inulin in plasma and urine. *J Biol Chem* 178:839, 1949.
2. HIGASHI A, PETERS L: Rapid colorimetric method for determination of inulin in plasma and urine. *J Lab Clin Med* 35:475, 1950.
3. KRAFFCZYK F, HELGER R, BREMER HJ: Thin-layer chromatographic screening tests for carbohydrate anomalies in plasma, urine and faeces. *Clin Chim Acta* 42:303, 1972.
4. CLAMP JR, BHATTI T, CHAMBERS RE: The determination of carbohydrate

in biological materials by gas-liquid chromatography. *Methods Biochem Anal* 19:229, 1971.

5. PALMER JK, BRANDES WB: Determination of sucrose, glucose and fructose by liquid chromatography. *J Agr Food Chem* 22:709, 1974.
6. NAKASHIMA K, TAKEI H, ADACHI O, SHINAGAWA E, AMEYAMA M: Determination of seminal fructose using D-fructose dehydrogenase. *Clin Chim Acta* 151:307, 1985.
7. HARDINGE MG, SWARNER JB, CROOKS H: Carbohydrates in foods. *J Am Diet Assoc* 46:197, 1965.
8. SOMOGYI JC, TRAUTNER K: Der Glukose-, Fruktose- und Saccharosegehalt verschiedener Gemüsearten. *Schweiz Med Wochenschr* 104:177, 1974.
9. GITZELMANN R: Unpublished.
10. HERS HG: L'aldolase-réductase. Le méchanisme de la formation du fructose séminal et du fructose foetal. *Biochim Biophys Acta* 37:120, 127, 1960.
11. ANDERSON TA: Recent trends in carbohydrate consumption. *Annu Rev Nutr* 2:113, 1982.
12. YUDKIN J: Sugar and health. *Lancet* 1:918, 1987.
13. US DEPARTMENT OF AGRICULTURE: Sugar and sweetener—Outlook and situation. *Sugar Sweetener Rep.* 6:40, 1981.
14. KOIVISTO VA, KARONEN SL, NIKKILÄ EA: Carbohydrate ingestion before exercise: Comparison of glucose, fructose and sweet placebo. *J Appl Physiol* 51:783, 1981.
15. LEVINE L, EVANS WJ, CADARETTE BS, FISHER EC, BULLEN BA: Fructose and glucose ingestion and muscle glycogen use during submaximal exercise. *J Appl Physiol* 55:1767, 1983.
16. NIKKILÄ EA, HUTTUNEN JK (ed): Clinical and metabolic aspects of fructose. *Acta Med Scand Suppl* 542, 1972.
17. SIPPLE HL, MCNUTT KW: *Sugars in Nutrition*. New York, Academic, 1974.
18. GUGGENHEIM B: *Health and Sugar Substitutes*. Basel, Karger, 1979.
19. MAYES PA, LAKER ME: Effects of acute and long-term fructose administration on liver lipid metabolism, in Paoletti R (ed), *Progress in Biochemical Pharmacology: Metabolic Effects of Dietary Carbohydrates*, Macdonald I, Vrána A (volume eds): Karger, Basel, 1986, vol. 21, pp 33–58.
20. VRÁNA A, KAZDOVÁ L: Effects of dietary sucrose or fructose on carbohydrate and lipid metabolism. Animal studies, in Paoletti R (ed), Macdonald I, Vrána A, (volume eds): *Progress in Biochemical Pharmacology: Metabolic Effects of Dietary Carbohydrates*. Karger, Basel, 1986, vol 21, pp 59–73.
21. MINKOWSKI O: Untersuchungen über den Diabetes mellitus nach Exstirpation des Pankreas. *Arch Exp Pathol Pharmakol* 31:85, 1893.
22. REISER S, PWELL AS, YANG C-Y, CANARY JJ: An insulinogenic effect of oral fructose in humans during postprandial hyperglycemia. *Am J Clin Nutr* 45:580, 1987.
23. VAN DEN BERGHE G: Fructose: Metabolism and short-term effects on carbohydrate and purine metabolic pathways, in Paoletti R (ed), Macdonald I, Vrána A, (volume eds): *Progress in Biochemical Pharmacology: Metabolic Effects of Dietary Carbohydrates*. Karger, Basel, 1986, vol 21, pp 1–32.
24. HOLDSWORTH CD, DAWSON AM: Absorption of fructose in man. *Proc Soc Exp Biol Med* 118:142, 1965.
25. MEHNERT H, DIETZE G, HASLBECK M: Zucker und Zuckeraustauschstoffe in der Diätetik von Störungen des Kohlenhydratstoffwechsels. *Nutr Metab* 18 *(Suppl* 1):171, 1975.
26. COOK GC: Absorption and metabolism of D(-)fructose in man. *Am J Clin Nutr* 24:1302, 1971.
27. SMITH LH, ETTINGER RH, SELIGSON D: A comparison of the metabolism of fructose and glucose in hepatic disease and diabetes mellitus. *J Clin Invest* 32:273, 1953.
28. CONARD V: Mesure de l'assimilation du glucose: Bases théoriques et application cliniques. *Acta Gastroenterol Belg* 18:655, 1955.
29. MENDELOFF AI, WEICHSELBAUM TE: Role of the human liver in the assimilation of intravenously administered fructose. *Metabolism* 2:450, 1953.
30. WOLFE BM, AHUJA SP, MARLISS EB: Effects of intravenously administered fructose and glucose on splanchnic amino acid and carbohydrate metabolism in hypertriglyceridemic men. *J Clin Invest* 56:970, 1975.
31. BJÖRKMAN O, FELIG P: Role of the kidney in the metabolism of fructose in 60-hour fasted humans. *Diabetes* 31:516, 1982.
32. MACDONALD I, TURNER LJ: Serum-fructose levels after sucrose or its constituent monosaccharides. *Lancet* 1:841, 1968.
33. LANE HC, DODD K: Use of glucose, invert sugar and fructose for parenteral feeding of children. *Pediatrics* 20:668, 1957.
34. MILLER M, DRUCKER WR, OWENS JE, CRAIG JW, WOODWARD H JR: Metabolism of intravenous fructose and glucose in normal and diabetic subjects. *J Clin Invest* 31:115, 1952.
35. GRACEY M, BURKE V, OSHIN A: Active intestinal transport of D-fructose. *Biochim Biophys Acta* 266:397, 1972.
36. HONEGGER P, SEMENZA G: Multiplicity of carriers for free glucalogues in hamster small intestine. *Biochim Biophys Acta* 318:390, 1973.
37. MACRAE AR, NEUDOERFFER TS: Support for the existence of an active transport mechanism of fructose in the rat. *Biochim Biophys Acta* 288:137, 1972.
38. SIGRIST-NELSON K, HOPFER U: A distinct D-fructose transport system in isolated brush border membrane. *Biochim Biophys Acta* 367:247, 1974.
39. SESTOFT L, FLERON P: Determination of the kinetic constants of fructose transport and phosphorylation in the perfused rat liver. *Biochim Biophys Acta* 345:27, 1974.
40. WOODS HF, EGGLESTON LV, KREBS HA: The cause of hepatic accumulation of fructose 1-phosphate on fructose loading. *Biochem J* 119:501, 1970.
41. CRAIK JD, ELLIOTT KRF: Transport of D-fructose and D-galactose into isolated rat hepatocytes. *Biochem J* 192:373, 1980.
42. HOOPER RH, SHORT AH: The hepatocellular uptake of glucose, galactose and fructose in conscious sheep. *J Physiol* 264:523, 1977.
43. FROESCH ER, GINSBERG JL: Fructose metabolism of adipose tissue. I. Comparison of fructose and glucose metabolism in epididymal adipose tissue of normal rats. *J Biol Chem* 237:3317, 1962.
44. HALPERIN ML, CHEEMA-DHADLI S: Comparison of glucose and fructose transport into adipocytes of the rat. *Biochem J* 202:717, 1982.
45. SCHOENLE E, ZAPF J, FROESCH ER: Transport and metabolism of fructose in fat cells of normal and hypophysectomized rats. *Am J Physiol* 237:E325, 1979.
46. HERS HG: *Le Métabolisme du Fructose*. Editions Arscia, Brussels, 1957.
47. CORI GT, OCHOA S, SLEIN MW, CORI CF: The metabolism of fructose in liver. Isolation of fructose-1-phosphate and inorganic pyrophosphate. *Biochim Biophys Acta* 7:304, 1951.
48. HERS HG: La fructokinase du foie. *Biochim Biophys Acta* 8:416, 1952.
49. LEUTHARDT F, TESTA E: Die Phosphorylierung der Fructose in der Leber II. Mitteilung. *Helv Chim Acta* 34:931, 1951.
50. ADELMAN RC, BALLARD FJ, WEINHOUSE S: Purification and properties of rat liver fructokinase. *J Biol Chem* 242:3360, 1967.
51. KUYPER CMA: Studies on fructokinase. 1. Substrate specificity. *Proc K Ned Akad Wet* 62:137, 1959.
52. SANCHEZ JJ, GONZALEZ NS, PONTIS HG: Fructokinase from rat liver. I. Purification and properties. *Biochim Biophys Acta* 227:67, 1971.
53. ENGLARD S, BERKOWER I, AVIGAD G: 5-keto-D-fructose. VII. Phosphorylation by liver fructokinase and the monophosphate ester as an inhibitor of liver aldolase. *Biochim Biophys Acta* 279:229, 1972.
54. RAUSHEL FM, CLELAND WW: Bovine liver fructokinase: Purification and kinetic properties. *Biochemistry* 16:2169, 1977.

54a. RAUSHEL FM, CLELAND WW: The substrate and anomeric specificity of fructokinase. *J Biol Chem* 248:8174, 1973.

55. PHILLIPS MI, DAVIES DR: The mechanism of guanosine triphosphate depletion in the liver after a fructose load. The role of fructokinase. *Biochem J* 228:667, 1985.
56. PARKS RE, BEN-GERSHOM E, LARDY HA: Liver fructokinase. *J Biol Chem* 227:231, 1957.

56a. SESTOFT L: Regulation of fructose metabolism in the perfused rat liver. Interrelation with inorganic phosphate, glucose, ketone body and ethanol metabolism. *Biochim Biophys Acta* 343:1, 1974.

57. HEINZ F, LAMPRECHT W, KIRSCH J: Enzymes of fructose metabolism in human liver. *J Clin Invest* 47:1826, 1968.
58. THIEDEN HID, GRUNNET N, DAMGAARD SE, SESTOFT L: Effect of fructose and glyceraldehyde on ethanol metabolism in human liver and in rat liver. *Eur J Biochem* 30:250, 1972.
59. SANCHEZ JJ, GONZALEZ NS, PONTIS HG: Fructokinase from rat liver. II. The role of K^+ on the enzyme activity. *Biochim Biophys Acta* 227:79, 1971.
60. SALVATORE F, IZZO P, PAOLELLA G: Aldolase gene and protein families: Structure, expression and pathophysiology, in Blasi F (ed) Quagliariello E, Palmieri F (series eds): *Human Genes and Diseases: Horizons in Biochemistry and Biophysics*. Wiley, New York, 1986, vol 8, pp 611–665.
61. HERS HG, KUSAKA T: Le métabolisme du fructose-1-phosphate dans le foie. *Biochim Biophys Acta* 11:427, 1953.
62. STEINMANN B, GITZELMANN R: The diagnosis of hereditary fructose intolerance. *Helv Paediatr Acta* 36:297, 1981.
63. PENHOET E, RAJKUMAR T, RUTTER WJ: Multiple forms of fructose diphosphate aldolase in mammalian tissues. *Proc Natl Acad Sci USA* 56:1275, 1966.
64. KOSTER JF, SLEE RG, FERNANDES J: On the biochemical basis of hereditary fructose intolerance. *Biochem Biophys Res Commun* 64:289, 1975.
65. PENHOET EE, KOCHMAN M, RUTTER WJ: Isolation of fructose diphosphate aldolases A, B and C. *Biochemistry* 8:4391, 1969.
66. PENHOET EE, KOCHMAN M, RUTTER WJ: Molecular and catalytic properties of aldolase C. *Biochemistry* 8:4396, 1969.
67. MACGREGOR JS, SINGH VN, DAVOUST S, MELLONI E, PONTREMOLI S, HORECKER BL: Evidence for formation of a rabbit liver aldolase-rabbit liver

fructose-1,6-bisphosphatase complex. *Proc Natl Acad Sci USA* 77:3889, 1980.

68. HORECKER BL, MACGREGOR JS, SINGH VN, MELLONI E, PONTREMOLI S: Aldolase and fructose bisphosphatase: Key enzymes in the control of gluconeogenesis and glycolysis. *Curr Top Cell Regul* 18:181, 1981.

69. LEBHERZ HG, RUTTER WJ: Distribution of fructose diphosphate aldolase variants in biological systems. *Biochemistry* 8:109, 1969.

70. REHBEIN-THÖNER M, PFLEIDERER G: The changes in aldolase isoenzyme pattern during development of the human kidney and small instestine—demonstrated in organ extracts and tissue sections. *Hoppe-Seyler's Z Physiol Chem* 358:169, 1977.

71. SCHAPIRA F, HATZFELD A, WEBER A: Resurgence of some fetal isozymes in hepatoma, in Markert CL (ed): *Isoenzymes*. New York, Academic, 1975, vol. 3, pp 987–1003.

72. MUKAI T, JOH K, ARAI Y, YATSUKI H, HORI K: Tissue-specific expression of rat aldolase A mRNAs. *J Biol Chem* 261:3347, 1986.

73. PFLEIDERER G, DIKOW AL, FALKENBERG F: Verteilungsmuster der Aldolase A, B und C in menschlichen Organ- und Gewebsextrakten sowie in normalen und pathologischen Seren. *Hoppe-Seyler's Z Physiol Chem* 355:233, 1974.

74. PFLEIDERER G, THÖNER M, WACHSMUTH ED: Histological examination of the aldolase monomer composition of cells from human kidney and hypernephroid carcinoma. *Beitr Pathol Bd* 156:266, 1975.

75. BURCH HB, CHOI S, DENCE CN, ALVEY TR, COLE BR, LOWRY OH: Metabolic effects of large fructose loads in different parts of the rat nephron. *J Biol Chem* 255:8239, 1980.

76. HIBI N, ARII S, IIZUMI T, NEMOTO T, CHU TM: Human monoclonal antibody recognizing liver-type aldolase B. *Biochem J* 240:847, 1986.

77. WACHSMUTH ED: Differentiation of epithelial cells in human jejunum: Localization and quantification of aminopeptidase, alkaline phosphatase and aldolase isozymes in tissue sections. *Histochemistry* 48:101, 1976.

78. STRAPAZON E, STECK TL: Interaction of the aldolase and the membrane of human erythrocytes. *Biochemistry* 16:2966, 1977.

79. YELTMAN DR, HARRIS BG: Purification and characterization of aldolase from human erythrocytes. *Biochim Biophys Acta* 484:188, 1977.

80. BURTON BK, CHACKO CM, NADLER HL: Aldolase in cultivated human fibroblasts. *Proc Soc Exp Biol Med* 146:605, 1974.

81. IZZO P, COSTANZO P, LUPO A, RIPPA E, BORGHESE AM, PAOLELLA G, SALVATORE F: A new human species of aldolase A mRNA from fibroblasts. *Eur J Biochem* 164:9, 1987.

82. PONTREMOLI S, MELLONI E, SALAMINO F, SPARATORE B, MICHETTI M, HORECKER BL: Changes in activity of fructose-1,6-bisphosphate aldolase in livers of fasted rabbits and accumulation of crossreacting immune material. *Proc Natl Acad Sci USA* 76:6323, 1979.

83. PONTREMOLI S, MELLONI E, MICHETTI M, SALAMINO F, SPARATORE B, HORECKER BL: Limited proteolysis of liver aldolase and fructose 1,6-bisphosphatase by lysosomal proteinases: Effect on complex formation. *Proc Natl Acad Sci USA* 79:2451, 1982.

84. PONTREMOLI S, MELLONI E, MICHETTI M, SALAMINO F, SPARATORE B, HORECKER BL: Characterization of the inactive form of fructose 1,6-bisphosphate aldolase isolated from livers of fasted rabbits. *Proc Natl Acad Sci USA* 79:5194, 1982.

85. CHAPPEL A, HOOGENRAAD NJ, HOLMES RS: Purification and properties of the native form of rabbit liver aldolase. Evidence for proteolytic modification after tissue extraction. *Biochem J* 175:377, 1978.

86. MUNNICH A, BESMOND C, DARQUY S, REACH G, VAULONT S, DREYFUS J-C, KAHN A: Dietary and hormonal regulation of aldolase B gene expression. *J Clin Invest* 75:1045, 1985.

87. GRÉGORI C, BESMOND C, KAHN A, DREYFUS JC: Characterization of messenger RNA for aldolase B in adult and fetal human liver. *Biochem Biophys Res Commun* 104:369, 1982.

88. NUMAZAKI M, TSUTSUMI K, TSUTSUMI R, ISHIKAWA K: Expression of aldolase isozyme mRNAs in fetal rat liver. *Eur J Biochem* 142:165, 1984.

89. TSUTSUMI K, MUKAI T, HIDAKA S, MIYAHARA H, TSUTSUMI R, TANAKA T, HORI K, ISHIKAWA K: Rat aldolase isozyme gene. Cloning and characterization of cDNA for aldolase B messenger RNA. *J Biol Chem* 258:6537, 1983.

90. TSUTSUMI K, MUKAI T, TSUTSUMI R, MORI M, DAIMON M, TANAKA T, YATSUKI H, HORI K, ISHIKAWA K: Nucleotide sequence of rat liver aldolase B messenger RNA. *J Biol Chem* 259:14572, 1984.

91. SIMON MP, BESMOND C, COTTREAU D, WEBER A, CHAUMET-RIFFAUD P, DREYFUS JC, SALA TRÉPAT J, MARIE J, KAHN A: Molecular cloning of cDNA for rat L-type pyruvate kinase and aldolase B. *J Biol Chem* 258:14576, 1983.

92. BESMOND C, DREYFUS JC, GREGORI C, FRAIN M, ZAKIN MM, SALA TRÉPAT J, KAHN A: Nucleotide sequence of a cDNA clone for human aldolase B. *Biochem Biophys Res Commun* 117:601, 1983.

93. ROTTMANN WH, TOLAN DR, PENHOET EE: Complete amino acid sequence for human aldolase B derived from cDNA and genomic clones. *Proc Natl Acad Sci USA* 81:2738, 1984.

94. TSUTSUMI K, MUKAI T, TSUTSUMI R, HIDAKA S, ARAI Y, HORI K, ISHIKAWA K: Structure and genomic organization of the rat aldolase B gene. *J Mol Biol* 181:153, 1985.

95. TOLAN DR, PENHOET EE: Characterization of the human aldolase B gene. *Mol Biol Med* 3:245, 1986.

95a. MUKAI T, YATSUKI H, ARAI Y, JOH K, MATSUHASHI S, HORI K: Human aldolase B gene: Characterization of the genomic aldolase B gene and analysis of sequences required for multiple polyadenylations. *J Biochem* 102:1043, 1987.

96. HENRY I, GALLANO P, BESMOND C, WEIL D, MATTEI MG, TURLEAU C, BOUÉ J, KAHN A, JUNIEN C: The structural gene for aldolase B (ALDB) maps to 9q13→32. *Ann Hum Genet* 49:173, 1985.

97. LEBO RV, TOLAN DR, BRUCE BD, CHEUNG MC, KAN YW: Spot-blot analysis of sorted chomosomes assigns a fructose intolerance disease locus to chromosome 9. *Cytometry* 6:478, 1985.

98. SAKAKIBARA M, MUKAI T, YATSUKI H, HORI K: Human aldolase isozyme gene: The structure of multispecies aldolase B mRNAs. *Nucleic Acids Res* 13:5055, 1985.

98a. PAOLELLA G, SANTAMARIA R, BUONO P, SALVATORE F: Mapping of a restriction fragment length polymorphism within the human aldolase B gene. *Hum Genet* 77:115, 1987.

98b. SERERO S, MAIRE P, VAN CONG N, COHEN-HAGUENAUER O, GROSS MS, JÉGOU-FOUBERT C, DE TAND MF, KAHN A, FREZAL J: Localization of the active gene of aldolase on chromosome 16, and two aldolase A pseudogenes on chromosomes 3 and 10. *Hum Genet* 78:167, 1988.

98c. TOLAN DR, NICLAS J, BRUCE BD, LEBO RV: Evolutionary implications of the human aldolase-A, -B, -C, and -pseudogene chromosome locations. *Amer J Hum Genet* 41:907, 1987.

99. HERS HG: Triokinase, in Colowick SP, Kaplan NO (eds): *Methods in Enzymology*. Academic, New York, 1962, vol 5, pp 362–364.

100. SILLERO MAG, SILLERO A, SOLS A: Enzymes involved in fructose metabolism in liver and the glyceraldehyde metabolic crossroads. *Eur J Biochem* 10:345, 1969.

101. HUE L: The role of futile cycles in the regulation of carbohydrate metabolism in the liver. *Adv Enzymol* 52:247, 1981.

102. BENKOVIC SJ, DEMAINE MM: Mechanism of action of fructose 1,6-bisphosphatase. *Adv Enzymol* 53:45, 1982.

103. TEJWANI GA: Regulation of fructose-bisphosphatase activity. *Adv Enzymol* 54:121, 1982.

103a. DZUGAJ A, KOCHMAN L: Purification of human liver fructose-1,6-bisphosphatase. *Biochim Biophys Acta* 614:407, 1980.

104. HERS HG, VAN SCHAFTINGEN E: Fructose 2,6-bisphosphate 2 years after its discovery. *Biochem J* 206:1, 1982.

105. VAN SCHAFTINGEN E: Fructose 2,6-bisphosphate. *Adv Enzymol* 59:315, 1987.

106. VAN SCHAFTINGEN E, HERS HG: Inhibition of fructose-1,6-bisphosphatase by fructose 2,6-bisphosphate. *Proc Natl Acad Sci USA* 78:2861, 1981.

107. VAN SCHAFTINGEN E, JETT MF, HUE L, HERS HG: Control of liver 6-phosphofructokinase by fructose 2,6-bisphosphate and other effectors. *Proc Natl Acad Sci USA* 78:3483, 1981.

108. TRANIELLO S, MELLONI E, PONTREMOLI S, SIA CL, HORECKER BL: Rabbit liver fructose 1,6-diphosphatase. Properties of the native enzyme and their modification by subtilisin. *Arch Biochem Biophys* 149:222, 1972.

109. HORECKER BL, MELLONI E, PONTREMOLI S: Fructose 1,6-bisphosphatase: Properties of the neutral enzyme and its modification by proteolytic enzymes. *Adv Enzymol* 42:193, 1975.

110. PONTREMOLI S, DEFLORA A, SALAMINO F, MELLONI E, HORECKER BL: Hormonal effects on structure and catalytic properties of fructose 1,6-bisphosphatase. *Proc Natl Acad Sci USA* 72:2969, 1975.

111. TEJWANI GA, PEDROSA FO, PONTREMOLI S, HORECKER BL: Dual role of Zn^{2+} as inhibitor and activator of fructose 1,6-bisphosphatase of rat liver. *Proc Natl Acad Sci USA* 73:2692, 1976.

112. COWEN LA, BELL DE, HOADLEY JE, COUSINS RJ: Influence of dietary zinc deficiency and parenteral zinc on rat liver fructose 1,6-bisphosphatase activity. *Biochem Biophys Res Commun* 134:944, 1986.

113. MIZUNUMA H, TASHIMA Y: Evidence for the intestinal type of fructose 1,6-bisphosphatase in mouse, rat, and golden hamster. *Arch Biochem Biophys* 217:512, 1982.

114. CARDENAS ML, RABAJILLE E, NIEMEYER H: Fructose is a good substrate for rat liver "glucokinase" (hexokinase D). *Biochem J* 222:363, 1984.

115. KATZEN HM, SCHIMKE RT: Multiple forms of hexokinase in the rat: Tissue distribution, age dependency and properties. *Proc Natl Acad Sci USA* 54:1218, 1965.

116. SOLS A, CRANE RK: Substrate specificity of brain hexokinase. *J Biol Chem* 210:581, 1954.

117. FROESCH ER: Fructose metabolism in adipose tissue from normal and di-

abetic rats, in Renold AE, Cahill GF Jr (eds): *Handbook of Physiology: Adipose Tissue*. Washington, DC, American Physiology Society, 1965, vol 52, pp 281–293.

118. HUE L, HERS HG: The conversion of [4-^{3}H]fructose and of [4-^{3}H]glucose to liver glycogen in the mouse. An investigation of the glyceraldehyde crossroads. *Eur J Biochem* 29:268, 1972.

119. EXTON JH, PARK CR: Control of gluconeogenesis in liver. 1. General features of gluconeogenesis in the perfused livers of rats. *J Biol Chem* 242:2622, 1967.

120. BERGSTRÖM J, HULTMAN E: Synthesis of muscle glycogen in man after glucose and fructose infusion. *Acta Med Scand* 182:93, 1967.

121. TYGSTRUP N, WINKLER K, LUNDQUIST F: The mechanism of the fructose effect on the ethanol metabolism of the human liver. *J Clin Invest* 44:817, 1965.

122. BAR-ON H, STEIN Y: Effect of glucose and fructose administration on lipid metabolism in the rat. *J Nutr* 94:95, 1968.

123. PEREIRA JN, JANGAARD NO: Different rates of glucose and fructose metabolism in rat liver tissue in vitro. *Metabolism* 20:392, 1971.

124. ZAKIM D, PARDINI RS, HERMAN RH, SAUBERLICH HE: Mechanism for the differential effects of high carbohydrate diets on lipogenesis in rat liver. *Biochim Biophys Acta* 114:242, 1967.

125. ZAKIM D, HERMAN RH, GORDON WC: The conversion of glucose and fructose to fatty acids in the human liver. *Biochem Med* 2:427, 1969.

126. NIKKILÄ EA: Control of plasma and liver triglyceride kinetics by carbohydrate metabolism and insulin. *Adv Lipid Res* 7:63, 1969.

127. VAN DEN BERGHE G: Metabolic effects of fructose in the liver. *Curr Top Cell Regul* 13:97, 1978.

128. PERHEENTUPA J, RAIVIO K: Fructose-induced hyperuricaemia. *Lancet* 2:528, 1967.

129. BERGSTRÖM J, HULTMAN E, ROCH-NORLUND AE: Lactic acid accumulation in connection with fructose infusion. *Acta Med Scand* 184:359, 1968.

130. HERS HG: Misuses for fructose. *Nature* 227:241, 1979.

131. WOODS HF, ALBERTI KGMM: Dangers of intravenous fructose. *Lancet* 2:1354, 1972.

132. SESTOFT L: Fructose-en advarsel. *Ugeskr Laeger* 134:571, 1972.

133. VAN DEN BERGHE G, HERS HG: Dangers of intravenous fructose and sorbitol. *Acta Paediatr Belg* 31:115, 1978.

134. BONTEMPS F, HUE L, HERS HG: Phosphorylation of glucose in isolated rat hepatocytes. Sigmoidal kinetics explained by the activity of glucokinase alone. *Biochem J* 174:603, 1978.

135. KJERULF-JENSEN K: The phosphate esters formed in the liver tissue of rats and rabbits during assimilation of hexoses and glycerol. *Acta Physiol Scand* 4:249, 1942.

136. GÜNTHER MA, SILLERO A, SOLS A: Fructokinase assay with a specific spectrophotometric method using 1-phosphofructokinase. *Enzymol Biol Clin* 8:341, 1967.

137. HEINZ F, JUNGHÄNEL J: Metabolitmuster in Rattenleber nach Fructoseapplikation. *Hoppe-Seyler's Z Physiol Chem* 350:859, 1969.

138. BODE JC, ZELDER O, RUMPELT HJ, WITTKAMP U: Depletion of liver adenosine phosphates and metabolic effects of intravenous infusion of fructose or sorbitol in man and in the rat. *Eur J Clin Invest* 3:436, 1973.

139. VAN DEN BERGHE G, HUE L, HERS HG: Effect of the administration of fructose on the glycogenolytic action of glucagon. An investigation of the pathogeny of hereditary fructose intolerance. *Biochem J* 134:637, 1973.

140. VAN DEN BERGHE G, BRONFMAN M, VANNESTE R, HERS HG: The mechanism of adenosine triphosphate depletion in the liver after a load of fructose. A kinetic study of liver adenylate deaminase. *Biochem J* 162:601, 1977.

141. FOX IH, KELLEY WN: Studies on the mechanism of fructose-induced hyperuricemia in man. *Metabolism* 21:713, 1972.

142. NARINS RG, WEISBERG JS, MYERS AR: Effects of carbohydrates on uric acid metabolism. *Metabolism* 23:455, 1974.

143. HEUCKENKAMP PU, ZÖLLNER N: Fructose-induced hyperuricaemia. *Lancet* 1:808, 1971.

144. CURRERI PW, PRUITT BA: Absence of fructose-induced hyperuricaemia in men. *Lancet* 1:839, 1970.

145. HESSOV I: Effects of fructose and glucose infusions on blood acid-base equilibrium in the postoperative period. *Acta Chir Scand* 140:347, 1974.

146. STEINMANN B, BAERLOCHER K, GITZELMANN R: Hereditäre Störungen des Fruktosestoffwechsels: Belastungsproben mit Fruktose, Sorbitol und Dihydroxyaceton. *Nutr Metab* 18 *Suppl* 1:115, 1975.

147. PEASTON MJT: Dangers of intravenous fructose. *Lancet* 1:266, 1973.

148. KOGUT MD, ROE TF, NG WON, DONNELL GN: Fructose-induced hyperuricemia: Observations in normal children and in patients with hereditary fructose intolerance and galactosemia. *Pediatr Res* 9:774, 1975.

149. SAHEBJAMI DH, SCALETTAR R: Effects of fructose infusion on lactate and uric acid metabolism. *Lancet* 1:366, 1971.

150. EDWARDS NL, GELFAND EW, BIGGAR D, FOX IH: Partial deficiency of purine nucleoside phosphorylase: Studies of purine and pyrimidine metabolism. *J Lab Clin Med* 91:736, 1978.

151. KURTZ TW, KABRA PM, BOOTH BE, AL-BANDER HA, PORTALE AA, SERENA BG, TSAI HC, MORRIS RC: Liquid-chromatographic measurements of inosine, hypoxanthine and xanthine in studies of fructose-induced degradation of adenine nucleotides in humans and rats. *Clin Chem* 32:782, 1986.

152. MÄENPÄÄ PH, RAIVIO KO, KEKOMÄKI MP: Liver adenine nucleotides: Fructose-induced depletion and its effect on protein synthesis. *Science* 161:1253, 1968.

153. HULTMAN E, NILSSON LH, SAHLIN K: Adenine nucleotide content of human liver. Normal values and fructose-induced depletion. *Scand J Clin Lab Invest* 35:245, 1975.

154. ILES RA, GRIFFITHS JR, STEVENS AN, GADIAN DG, PORTEOUS R: Effect of fructose on the energy metabolism and acid-base status of the perfused starved-rat liver. *Biochem J* 192:191, 1980.

155. OBERHAENSLI RD, GALLOWAY GJ, TAYLOR DJ, BORE PJ, RADDA GK: Assessment of human liver metabolism by phosphorus-31 magnetic resonance spectroscopy. *Br J Radiol* 59:695, 1986.

155a. OBERHAENSLI RD, RAJAGOPALAN B, TAYLOR DJ, RADDA GK: Study of hereditary fructose intolerance by use of ^{31}P magnetic resonance spectroscopy. *Lancet* 2:931, 1987.

156. BURCH HB, MAX P, CHYU K, LOWRY OH: Metabolic intermediates in liver of rats given large amounts of fructose or dihydroxyacetone. *Biochem Biophys Res Comm* 34:619, 1969.

157. BURCH HB, LOWRY OH, MEINHARDT L, MAX P, CHYU K: Effect of fructose, dihydroxyacetone, glycerol, and glucose on metabolites and related compounds in liver and kidney. *J Biol Chem* 245:2092, 1970.

158. MORRIS RC, NIGON K, REED EB: Evidence that the severity of depletion of inorganic phosphate determines the severity of the disturbance of adenine nucleotide metabolism in the liver and renal cortex of the fructose-loaded rat. *J Clin Invest* 61:209, 1978.

159. LAMERS JMJ, HÜLSMANN WC: The effect of fructose on the stores of energy-rich phosphate in rat jejunum in vivo. *Biochim Biophys Acta* 313:1, 1973.

160. WATTS RWE, WATTS JEM, SEEGMILLER JE: Xanthine oxidase activity in human tissues and its inhibition by allopurinol (4-hydroxypyrazolo (3, 4-d) pyrimidine). *J Lab Clin Med* 66:688, 1965.

161. VAN DEN BERGHE G, BONTEMPS F, HERS HG: Purine catabolism in isolated rat hepatocytes. Influence of coformycin. *Biochem J* 188:913, 1980.

162. VAN DEN BERGHE G: Regulation of purine catabolism, in Hue L, Van de Werve G (eds): *Short-Term Regulation of Liver Metabolism*. Amsterdam, Elsevier/North-Holland, 1981, pp 361–376.

163. BONTEMPS F, VAN DEN BERGHE G, HERS HG: Evidence for a substrate cycle between AMP and adenosine in isolated hepatocytes. *Proc Natl Acad Sci USA* 80:2829, 1983.

164. MÄENPÄÄ PH: Fructose-induced alterations in liver polysome profiles and Mg^{2+} levels. *FEBS Lett* 24:37, 1972.

165. MÄENPÄÄ PH: Fructose and liver protein synthesis. *Acta Med Scand* Suppl 542:115, 1972.

166. LINDQVIST L, NYYSSÖNEN K, MÄENPÄÄ PH: Quantitative changes in aminoacylation of transfer RNA and in free amino acids during fructose-induced depletion of adenine nucleotides in rat liver. *Biochim Biophys Acta* 763:107, 1983.

167. VAN DEN BERGHE G, VINCENT MF: Effect of fructose on the metabolization of ammonia. Presented at the Annual Meeting of the European Society for Paediatric Research, Turku (Finland), June 25–29, 1978.

167a. PHILLIPS MJ, HETENYI G, ADACHI F: Ultrastructural hepatocellular alterations induced by in vivo fructose infusions. *Lab Invest* 22:370, 1970.

168. YU DT, BURCH HB, PHILLIPS MJ: Pathogenesis of fructose hepatotoxicity. *Lab Invest* 30:85, 1974.

169. HUGON JS, MAESTRACCI D, MÉNARD D: Smooth endoplasmic reticulum proliferation in mouse enterocytes induced by fructose feeding. *Histochemie* 29:189, 1972.

170. RAIVIO KO, BECKER MA, MEYER LJ, GREEN ML, NUKI G, SEEGMILLER JE: Stimulation of human purine synthesis de novo by fructose infusion. *Metabolism* 24:861, 1975.

171. ITAKURA M, SABINA RL, HEALD PW, HOLMES EW: Basis for the control of purine biosynthesis by purine ribonucleotides. *J Clin Invest* 67:994, 1981.

172. VINCENT MF, VAN DEN BERGHE G, HERS HG: Effect of fructose on the concentration of phosphoribosylpyrophosphate in isolated hepatocytes. *Adv Exp Med Biol* 195b:615, 1986.

173. ASHARE R, MOORE R, ELLISON EH: Utilization of glucose, fructose and invert sugar. Comparison in diseases of the liver and pancreas. *Arch Surg* 70:428, 1955.

174. KAYE R, WILLIAMS ML, BARBERO G: Comparative study of glucose and fructose metabolism in infants with reference to utilization and to the accumulation of glycolytic intermediates. *J Clin Invest* 37:752, 1958.

175. COOK GC, JACOBSON J: Individual variation in fructose metabolism in man. *Br J Nutr* 26:187, 1971.
176. EGGLESTON LV, WOODS HF: Activation of liver pyruvate kinase by fructose-1-phosphate. *FEBS Lett* 6:43, 1970.
177. MAPUNGWANA SW, DAVIES DR: The effect of fructose on pyruvate kinase activity in isolated hepatocytes. Inhibition by allantoin and alanine. *Biochem J* 208:171, 1982.
178. CRAIG GM, CRANE CW: Lactic acidosis complicating liver failure after intravenous fructose. *Br Med J* 4:211, 1971.
179. ANDERSSON G, BROHULT J, STERNER G: Increasing metabolic acidosis following fructose infusion in two children. *Acta Paediatr Scand* 58:301, 1969.
180. ODIÈVRE M, POIRIER C, LEVILLAIN P, MODIGLIANI E, STRAUCH G: Étude des réponses glucosémiques, lactacidémiques et insulinémiques après administration intraveineuse rapide de doses variables de fructose chez l'enfant normal. *Arch Fr Pediatr* 27:1057, 1970.
181. PEARSON JF, SHUTTLEWORTH R: The metabolic effects of a hypertonic fructose infusion on the mother and fetus during labor. *Am J Obstet Gynecol* 111:259, 1971.
182. KRANE SM: Fructosuria, in Stanbury JB, Wyngaarden JB, Fredrickson DS (eds): *The Metabolic Basis of Inherited Disease*, 1st ed. New York, McGraw-Hill, 1960, pp 144–155.
183. CZAPEK F: Eine seltene Form von Diabetes mellitus. *Prager Med Wochenschr* 1:245, 265, 1876.
184. ZIMMER K: I. Levulose im Harn eines Diabetikers. *Dtsch Med Wochenschr* 1:329, 1876.
185. LARON Z: Essential benign fructosuria. *Arch Dis Child* 36:273, 1961.
186. STEINITZ H, MIZRAHY O: Essential fructosuria and hereditary fructose intolerance. *N Engl J Med* 280:222, 1969.
187. KHACHADURIAN AK: Nonalimentary fructosuria. *Pediatrics* 32:455, 1963.
188. HEERES PA, VOS H: Fructosuria. *Arch Intern Med* 44:47, 1929.
189. LENZNER AR: Fructosuria: Report of a case. *Ann Intern Med* 45:702, 1956.
190. HEINZ F, SCHLEGEL F, KRAUSE PH: Enzymes of fructose metabolism in human small intestine mucosa. *Enzyme* 19:93, 1975.
191. HEINZ F, SCHLEGEL F, KRAUSE PH: Enzymes of fructose metabolism in human kidney. *Enzyme* 19:85, 1975.
192. SCHAPIRA F, SCHAPIRA G, DREYFUS J-C: La lésion enzymatique de la fructosurie bénigne. *Enzymol Biol Clin* 1:170, 1961–1962.
193. HERS HG, JOASSIN G: Anomalie de l'aldolase hépatique dans l'intolérance au fructose. *Enzymol Biol Clin* 1:4, 1961.
194. SACHS B, STERNFELD L, KRAUS G: Essential fructosuria. Its pathophysiology. *Am J Dis Child* 63:252, 1942.
195. RYNBERGEN HJ, CHAMBERS WH, BLATHERWICK NR: Respiratory metabolism in fructosuria. *J Nutr* 21:553, 1941.
196. BAYLON H, SCHAPIRA F, WEGMANN R, DREYFUS J-C, MOULIAS R, POYART C, COUMEL P: Note préliminaire sur l'étude clinique, biologique, histochimique et enzymatique de la fructosurie familiale essentielle. *Rev Fr Etud Clin Biol* 7:531, 1962.
197. SILVER S, REINER M: Essential fructosuria. Report of three cases with metabolic studies. *Arch Intern Med* 54:412, 1934.
198. LASKER M: Essential fructosuria. *Hum Biol* 13:51, 1941.
199. MARBLE A: The diagnosis of the less common meliturias. Including pentosuria and fructosuria. *Med Clin North Am* 31:313, 1947.
200. LEONIDAS JC: Essential fructosuria. *NY State J Med* 65:2257, 1965.
201. CHAMBERS RA, PRATT RTC: Idiosyncrasy to fructose. *Lancet* 2:340, 1956.
202. FROESCH ER, PRADER A, LABHART A, STUBER HW, WOLF HP: Die hereditäre Fructoseintoleranz, eine bisher nicht bekannte kongenitale Stoffwechselstörung. *Schweiz Med Wochenschr* 87:1168, 1957.
203. PERHEENTUPA J, RAIVIO KO, NIKKILÄ EA: Hereditary fructose intolerance. *Acta Med Scand (suppl)* 542:65, 1972.
204. BAERLOCHER K, GITZELMANN R, STEINMANN B, GITZELMANN-CUMARASAMY N: Hereditary fructose intolerance in early childhood: A major diagnostic challenge. Survey of 20 symptomatic cases. *Helv Paediatr Acta* 33:465, 1978.
205. ODIÈVRE M, GENTIL C, GAUTIER M, ALAGILLE D: Hereditary fructose intolerance in childhood. *Am J Dis Child* 132:605, 1978.
206. BAKER L, WINEGRAD AI: Fasting hypoglycaemia and metabolic acidosis associated with deficiency of hepatic fructose-1,6-diphosphatase activity. *Lancet* 2:13, 1970.
207. TURNER RC, SPATHIS GS, NABARRO JDN, DORMANDY TL: Familial fructose and galactose intolerance. *Lancet* 2:872, 1972.
208. LEVIN B, SNODGRASS GJAI, OBERHOLZER VG, BURGESS EA, DOBBS RH: Fructosaemia. Observations on seven cases. *Am J Med* 45:826, 1968.
209. SWALES JD, SMITH ADM: Adult fructose intolerance. *Q J Med* 35:455, 1966.
210. MARTHALER TM, FROESCH ER: Hereditary fructose intolerance. Dental status of eight patients. *Br Dent J* 123:597, 1967.
211. KÖHLIN P, MELIN K: Hereditary fructose intolerance in four Swedish families. *Acta Paediatr Scand* 57:24, 1968.
212. CORNBLATH M, ROSENTHAL IM, REISNER SH, WYBREGT SH, CRANE RK: Hereditary fructose intolerance. *N Engl J Med* 269:1271, 1963.
213. FROESCH ER, WOLF HP, BAITSCH H, PRADER A, LABHART A: Hereditary fructose intolerance. An inborn defect of hepatic fructose-1-phosphate splitting aldolase. *Am J Med* 34:151, 1963.
214. NEWBRUN E, HOOVER C, METTRAUX G, GRAF H: Comparison of dietary habits and dental health of subjects with hereditary fructose intolerance and control subjects. *J Am Dent Assoc* 101:619, 1980.
215. HOWARTH D: Sugar intake and dental caries. *Lancet* 1:827, 1983.
216. RAMPA M, FROESCH ER: Eleven cases of hereditary fructose intolerance in one Swiss family with a pair of monozygotic and dizygotic twins. *Helv Paediatr Acta* 36:317, 1981.
217. WOLF H, ZSCHOCKE D, WEDEMEYER FW, HÜBNER W: Angeborene hereditäre Fructose-Intoleranz. *Klin Wochenschr* 37:693, 1959.
218. BARRY RGG, ST COLUM SR, MAGNER JW: Hereditary fructose intolerance in parent and child. *J Ir Med Assoc* 61:308, 1968.
219. LAMEIRE N, MUSSCHE M, BAELE G, KINT J, RINGOIR S: Hereditary fructose intolerance: A difficult diagnosis in the adult. *Am J Med* 65:416, 1978.
220. DE VROEDE M, MOZIN M-J, CADRANEL S, LOEB H, HEIMANN R: Découverte d'une fructosémie à l'occasion d'une insuffisance hépatique aigue chez un enfant de 16 mois. *Pédiatrie* 35:353, 1980.
221. HEINE W, SCHILL H, TESSMANN D, KUPATZ H: Letale Leberdystrophie bei drei Geschwistern mit hereditärer Fruktoseintoleranz nach Dauertropfinfusionen mit sorbitolhaltigen Infusionslösungen: *Dtsch Gesundheitswes* 24:2325, 1969.
222. SCHULTE M-J, LENZ W: Fatal sorbitol infusion in patient with fructose sorbitol intolerance. *Lancet* 2:188, 1977.
223. HACKL JM, BALOGH D, KUNZ F, DWORZAK E, PUSCHENDORF B, DECRISTOFORO A, MAIER F: Postoperative Fruktoseinfusion bei wahrscheinlich hereditärer Fruktoseintoleranz. *Wien Klin Wochenschr* 90:237, 1978.
224. GIRGENSOHN H: Die hereditäre Fructoseintoleranz beim Erwachsenen. *Verh Dtsch Ges Pathol* 66:637, 1982.
225. MÜLLER-WIEFEL DE, STEINMANN B, HOLM-HADULLA M, WILLE L, SCHÄRER K, GITZELMANN R: Infusionsbedingtes Nieren- und Leberversagen bei undiagnostizierter hereditärer Fructose-Intoleranz. *Dtsch med Wochenschr* 108:985, 1983.
226. WAGNER K, WOLF AS: Todesfall nach Fructose- und Sorbitinfusionen. *Anaesthesist* 33:573, 1984.
227. BLACK JA, SIMPSON K: Fructose intolerance. *Br Med J* 4:138, 1967.
228. ROSCHLAU G: Fruktose-Intoleranz, in *Leberbiopsie im Kindesalter*. Jena, Fischer Verlag, 1978, pp 80–83.
229. DUBOIS R, LOEB H, MALAISSE-LAGAE F, TOPPET M: Étude clinique et anatomo-pathologique de deux cas d'intolérance congénitale au fructose. *Pédiatrie* 20:5, 1965.
230. BRINER J, SCHNEIDER J: Personal communication.
231. SPYCHER MA: Unpublished data.
232. ROSSNER JA, FEIST D: Hereditäre Fructoseintoleranz. *Verh Dtsch Ges Pathol* 55:376, 1971.
233. SCHAPIRA F, HATZFELD A, GRÉGORI C: Studies on liver aldolases in hereditary fructose intolerance. *Enzyme* 18:73, 1974.
234. SHAPIRA F, DREYFUS J-C: L'aldolase hépatique dans l'intolérance au fructose. *Rev Fr Etud Clin Biol* 12:486, 1967.
235. SCHAPIRA F, NORDMANN Y, GRÉGORI C: Hereditary alterations of fructose metabolizing enzymes. *Acta Med Scand Suppl* 542:77, 1972.
236. DIKOW AL, JECKEL D, PFLEIDERER G: Isolierung und Charakterisierung von Aldolase A, B und C aus menschlichen Organen. *Hoppe-Seyler's Z Physiol Chem* 352:1151, 1971.
237. GRÉGORI C, SCHAPIRA F, KAHN A, DELPECH M, DREYFUS J-C: Molecular studies of liver aldolase B in hereditary fructose intolerance using blotting and immunological techniques. *Ann Hum Genet* 46:281, 1982.
238. COX TM, O'DONNELL MW, CAMILLERI M, BURGHES AH: Isolation and characterization of a mutant liver aldolase in adult hereditary fructose intolerance. *J Clin Invest* 72:201, 1983.
239. GITZELMANN R, STEINMANN B, BALLY C, LEBHERZ HG: Antibody activation of mutant human fructosediphosphate aldolase B in liver extracts of patients with hereditary fructose intolerance. *Biochem Biophys Res Commun* 59:1270, 1974.
240. BAERLOCHER K, GITZELMANN R, NÜSSLI R, DUMERMUTH G: Infantile lactic acidosis due to hereditary fructose 1,6-diphosphatase deficiency. *Helv Paediatr Acta* 26:489, 1971.
241. GENTIL C, COLIN J, VALETTE AM, ALAGILLE D, LELONG M: Étude du métabolisme glucidique au cours de l'intolérance héréditaire au fructose. Essai d'interprétation de l'hypoglucosémie. *Rev Fr Etud Clin Biol* 9:596, 1964.
242. ROSSIER A, MILHAUD G, COLIN J, JOB J-C, BRAULT A, BEAUVAIS P, LEM-

ERLE J: Intolérance congénitale au fructose. Deux cas familiaux avec étude biochimique in vitro. *Arch Fr Pediatr* 23:533, 1966.

242a. CROSS NCP, TOLAN DR, COX TM: Catalytic deficiency of human aldolase B in hereditary fructose intolerance caused by a common missense mutation. *Cell* 53:881, 1988.

242b. COX TM, O'DONNELL MW, CAMILLERI M: Allelic heterogeneity in adult hereditary fructose intolerance. *Mol Biol Med* 1:393, 1983.

243. SAXON L, PAPPER S: Abdominal pain occurring during the rapid administration of fructose solutions. *N Engl J Med* 256:132, 1957.

244. FROESCH ER, PRADER A, WOLF HP, LABHART A: Die hereditäre Fructoseintoleranz. *Helv Paediatr Acta* 14:99, 1959.

245. RICHARDSON RMA, LITTLE JA, PATTEN RL, GOLDSTEIN MB, HALPERIN ML: Pathogenesis of acidosis in hereditary fructose intolerance. *Metabolism* 28:1133, 1979.

246. PERHEENTUPA J, PITKÄNEN E, NIKKILÄ EA, SOMMERSALO O, HAKOSALO J: Hereditary fructose intolerance. A clinical study of four cases. *Ann Paediatr Fenn* 8:221, 1962.

247. NIVELON J-L, MATHIEU M, KISSIN C, COLLOMBEL C, COTTE J, BÉTHENOD M: Intolérance au fructose. Observation et méchanisme physiopathologique de l'hypoglucosémie. *Ann Pediatr (Paris)* 43:817, 1967.

248. MODIGLIANI E, STRAUCH G, ODIÈVRE M: Hormonal response to intra-venous fructose in normal and fructosaemic children: A study of insulin and growth hormone secretion. *Rev Eur Etud Clin Biol* 15:882, 1970.

249. DUBOIS R, LOEB H, OOMS HA, GILLET P, BARTMAN J, CHAMPENOIS A: Étude d'un cas d'hypoglycémie fonctionelle par intolérance au fructose. *Helv Paediatr Acta* 16:90, 1961.

250. MORRIS RC, MCSHERRY E, SEBASTIAN A: Modulation of experimental renal dysfunction of hereditary fructose intolerance by circulating parathyroid hormone. *Proc Natl Acad Sci USA* 68:132, 1971.

251. ODIÈVRE M: Les difficultés du diagnostic de l'intolérance héréditaire au fructose chez le nourrisson. *Arch Fr Pediatr* 26:5, 1969.

252. PHILLIPS MJ, LITTLE JA, PTAK TW: Subcellular pathology of hereditary fructose intolerance. *Am J Med* 44:910, 1968.

253. PHILLIPS MJ, YU DT, BURCH HB: Animal model of human disease: Hereditary fructose intolerance. *Am J Pathol* 75:591, 1974.

254. PRADER A: Unpublished.

255. GITZELMANN R, AURICCHIO S: The handling of soya alpha-galactosides by a normal and a galatosemic child. *Pediatrics* 36:231, 1965.

256. DESBUQUOIS B, LARDINOIS R, GENTIL C, ODIÈVRE M: Effets d'une surcharge en phosphate de sodium sur l'hypoglucosémie dans onze observations d'intolérance héréditaire au fructose. *Arch Fr Pediatr* 26:21, 1969.

258. PITKÄNEN E, PERHEENTUPA J: Eine biochemische Untersuchung über zwei Fälle von Fructoseintoleranz. *Ann Paediatr Fenn* 8:236, 1962.

259. HUE L: Unpublished data.

260. LEVIN B, OBERHOLZER VG, SNODGRASS GJAI, STIMMER L, WILMERS MJ: Fructosaemia. An inborn error of fructose metabolism. *Arch Dis Child* 38:220, 1963.

261. MORRIS RC JR: An experimental renal acidification defect in patients with hereditary fructose intolerance. II. Its distinction from classic renal tubular acidosis; its resemblance to the renal acidification defect associated with the Fanconi syndrome of children with cystinosis. *J Clin Invest* 47:1648, 1968.

262. SCHWARTZ R, GAMSU H, MULLIGAN PB, REISNER SH, WYBREGT SH, CORNBLATH M: Transient intolerance to exogenous fructose in the newborn. *J Clin Invest* 43:333, 1964.

263. RENOLD AE, WINEGRAD AI, FROESCH ER, THORN GW: Studies on the site of action of the arylsulfonylureas in man. *Metabolism* 5:757, 1956.

264. ZALITIS J, OLIVER IT: Inhibition of glucose phosphate isomerase by metabolic intermediates of fructose. *Biochem J* 102:753, 1967.

265. BALLY C, LEUTHARDT F: Unpublished data.

266. WILKENING J, NOWACK J, DECKER K: The dependence of glucose formation from lactate on the adenosine triphosphate content in the isolated perfused rat liver. *Biochim Biophys Acta* 392:299, 1975.

267. CAIN ARR, RYMAN BE: High liver glycogen in hereditary fructose intolerance. *Gut* 12:929, 1971.

268. SIDBURY JB: Zur Biochemie der hereditären Fructoseintoleranz. *Helv Paediatr Acta* 14:317, 1959.

269. RAMBAUD P, JOANNARD A, BOST M, MARCHAL A, RACHAIL M, ROGET J: Trouble de la glycogénolyse dans l'intolérance héréditaire au fructose. Étude de deux observations chez l'enfant. *Arch Fr Pediatr* 30:1051, 1973.

270. VAN DEN BERGHE G: Biochemical aspects of hereditary fructose intolerance, in Hommes FA, van den Berg CJ (eds): *Normal and Pathological Development of Energy Metabolism*. London, Academic, 1975, pp 211–228.

271. MADDAIAH VT, MADSEN NB: Kinetics of purified liver phosphorylase. *J Biol Chem* 241:3873, 1966.

272. KAUFMANN U, FROESCH ER: Inhibition of phosphorylase-a by fructose-1-phosphate, α-glycerophosphate and fructose-1,6-diphosphate: Explanation for fructose-induced hypoglycaemia in hereditary fructose intolerance and fructose-1,6-diphosphatase deficiency. *Eur J Clin Invest* 3:407, 1973.

273. THURSTON JH, JONES EM: Decrease and inhibition of liver phosphorylase (LP) after fructose: An experimental model for the study of hereditary fructose intolerance (HFI). *Pediatr Res* 5:392, 1971.

274. THURSTON JH, JONES EM, HAUHART RE: Decrease and inhibition of liver glycogen phosphorylase after fructose. An experimental model for the study of hereditary fructose intolerance. *Diabetes* 23:597, 1974.

275. LANDAU BR, MARSHALL JS, CRAIG JW, HOSTETLER KY, GENUTH SM: Quantitation of the pathways of fructose metabolism in normal and fructose-intolerant subjects. *J Lab Clin Med* 78:608, 1971.

276. MERCIER J-C, BOURRILLON A, BEAUFILS F, ODIÈVRE M: Intolérance héréditaire au fructose à révélation précoce. *Arch Fr Pediatr* 33:945, 1976.

277. PERHEENTUPA J, PITKÄNEN E: Symptomless hereditary fructose intolerance. *Lancet* 1:1358, 1962.

278. GITZELMANN R: Enzymes of fructose and galactose metabolism; galactose-1-phosphate, in Curtius H CH, Roth M (eds): *Clinical Biochemistry: Principles and Methods*. Berlin, New York, de Gruyter, 1974, pp 1236–1251.

278a. GITZELMANN R, STEINMANN B, TUCHSCHMID P: Patients with hereditary fructose intolerance have normal erythrocyte aldolase activity. In preparation.

279. HUE L, VAN HOOF F, HERS H-G: Serum aldolase in Tay-Sachs disease and in fructose intolerance. *Am J Med* 51:785, 1971.

280. GLIKSMAN R, GHOSH NK, COX RP: Comparison of aldolase isozymes in placenta, HeLa cells, and human fibroblast cultures. *Enzyme* 22:416, 1977.

281. SHIN YS, RIMBÖCK H, ENDRES W: Fructose-1-phosphate aldolase activity in human fetal and adult tissues as well as leukocytes and cultured fibroblasts in hereditary fructose intolerance. *J Inherited Metab Dis* 5 (Suppl 1) :45, 1982.

282. ODIÈVRE M, GAUTIER M, RIEU D: Intolérance héréditaire au fructose du nourrisson. Évolution des lésions histologiques hépatiques sous traitment diététique prolongé. (Étude de huit observations). *Arch Fr Pediatr* 26:433, 1969.

283. CORNBLATH M, SCHWARTZ R: Disorders of carbohydrate metabolism in infancy, 2d ed. *Major Problems in Clinical Pediatrics* (series). Philadelphia, Saunders, 1976, vol 3.

284. WYKE RJ, RAJKOVIC IA, EDDLESTON ALWF, WILLIAMS R: Defective opsonization and complement deficiency in serum from patients with fulminant hepatic failure. *Gut* 21:643, 1980.

285. NÜSSLI R: Das Wachstum von Patienten mit hereditärer Fruktoseintoleranz oder hereditärer Saccharose-Isomaltose-Malabsorption. *Helv Paediatr Acta* 26:637, 1971.

286. MOCK DM, PERMAN JA, THALER MM, MORRIS RC: Chronic fructose intoxication after infancy in children with hereditary fructose intolerance: A cause of growth retardation. *N Engl J Med* 309:764, 1983.

287. BRAUMAN J, KENTOS P, FRISQUE P, GEPTS W, VERBANCK M: Intolérance héréditaire au fructose chez une femme de 83 ans. *Acta Clin Belg* 26:65, 1971.

288. GITZELMANN R, STEINMANN B, MÜLLER-WIEFEL DE, HOLM-HADULLA M, WILLE L, SCHÄRER K: Infusionslösungen. *Dtsch Med Wochenschr* 108:1656, 1983.

289. BLOM W, FERNANDES J: Unpublished data.

290. FROESCH ER: Unpublished data.

291. TROST C: Personal communication.

292. SITADEVI C, RAMAIAH Y, ASKARI Z: Fructose intolerance associated with congenital cataract. *Indian J Pediatr* 35:496, 1968.

293. GITZELMANN R, BAERLOCHER K: Vorteile und Nachteile der Fructose in der Nahrung. *Paediatr Fortbildungskurse Prax* 37:40, 1973.

294. LINDÉN AL, NISELL J: Hereditär fruktosintolerans. *Sven Laekartidn* 61:3185, 1964.

295. KURZ R, HÄCHL G, HOHENWALLNER W, BERGER H: Hereditäre Fruktoseintoleranz mit vermutlich dominantem Erbang. *Arch Kinderheilkd* 183:233, 1971.

295a. LEVINE R, HUDDLESTUN B: The comparative action of insulin on the disposal of intravenous fructose and glucose. *Fed Proc* 6:151, 1947.

296. VON RUECKER A, ENDRES W, SHIN YS, BUTENANDT I, STEINMANN B, GITZELMANN R: A case of fatal hereditary fructose intolerance. Misleading information on formula composition. *Helv Paediatr Acta* 36:599, 1981.

297. LEUPOLD D: Unpublished data.

298. COX TM, CAMILLERI M, O'DONNELL MW, CHADWICK VS: Pseudodominant transmission of fructose intolerance in an adult and three offspring. *N Engl J Med* 307:537, 1982.

299. RAIVIO K, PERHEENTUPA J, NIKKILÄ EA: Aldolase activities in the liver in parents of patients with hereditary fructose intolerance. *Clin Chim Acta* 17:275, 1967.

300. BEYREISS K, WILLGERODT H, THEILE H: Untersuchungen bei heterozygoten Merkmalsträgern für Fructoseintoleranz. *Klin Wochenschr* 46:465, 1968.

301. SCHAPIRA F: Kinetic and immunological abnormalities of aldolase B in hereditary fructose intolerance. *Biochem Soc Trans* 3:232, 1975.

302. GRÉGORI C, BESMOND C, ODIÈVRE M, KAHN A, DREYFUS JC: DNA analysis in patients with hereditary fructose intolerance. *Ann Hum Genet* 48:291, 1984.

303. HÜLSMANN WC, FERNANDES J: A child with lactacidemia and fructose diphosphatase deficiency in the liver. *Pediatr Res* 5:633, 1971.

304. BAKKER HD, DE BREE PK, KETTING D, VAN SPRANG FJ, WADMAN SK: Fructose-1,6-diphosphatase deficiency: Another enzyme defect which can present itself with the clinical features of "tyrosinosis." *Clin Chim Acta* 55:41, 1974.

305. PAGLIARA AS, KARL IE, KEATING JP, BROWN BI, KIPNIS DM: Hepatic fructose-1,6-diphosphatase deficiency. A cause of lactic acidosis and hypoglycemia in infancy. *J Clin Invest* 51:2115, 1972.

306. GREENE HL, STIFEL FB, HERMAN RH: "Ketotic hypoglycemia" due to hepatic fructose-1,6-diphosphatase deficiency. *Am J Dis Child* 124:415, 1972.

307. SAUDUBRAY J-M, DREYFUS J-C, CEPANEC C, LE LO'CH H, TRUNG PH, MOZZICONACCI P: Acidose lactique, hypoglycémie et hépatomégalie par déficit héréditaire en fructose-1,6-diphosphatase hépatique. *Arch Fr Pediatr* 30:609, 1973.

308. MELANCON SB, KHACHADURIAN AK, NADLER HL, BROWN BI: Metabolic and biochemical studies in fructose 1,6-diphosphatase deficiency. *J Pediatr* 82:650, 1973.

309. DE ROSAS FJ, WAPNIR RA, LIFSHITZ F, SILVERBERG M, OLSON M: Folic acid enhanced gluconeogenesis in glycerol-induced hypoglycemia and fructose-1,6-diphosphatase deficiency. Presented at the 56th Annual Meeting of the Endocrine Society, Atlanta, 1974.

310. EAGLE RB, MACNAB AJ, RYMAN BE, STRANG LB: Liver biopsy data on a child with fructose 1,6-diphosphatase deficiency that closely resembled many aspects of glucose 6-phosphatase deficiency (von Gierke's type I glycogen-storage disease). *Biochem Soc Trans* 2:1118, 1974.

311. ODIÈVRE M, BRIVET M, MOATTI N, DREYFUS J-C, BEAUFILS F, LEJEUNE C, FEFFER J: Déficit en fructose-1,6-diphosphatase chez deux soeurs. *Arch Fr Pediatr* 32:113, 1975.

312. RETBI J-M, GABILAN J-C, MARSAC C: Acidose lactique et hypoglycémie à début néonatal par déficit congénital en fructose-1,6-diphosphatase hépatique. *Arch Fr Pediatr* 32:367, 1975.

313. CORBEEL L, EGGERMONT E, EECKELS R, JAEKEN J, CASTEELS-VAN DAELE M, DEVLIEGER H, DELMOTTE B: Recurrent attacks of ketotic acidosis associated with fructose-1,6-diphosphatase deficiency. *Acta Paediatr Belg* 29:29, 1976. CORBEEL LM, EGGERMONT E, BETTENS W, CASTEELS-VAN DAELE M, TIMMERMANS J: Fructose intolerance with normal liver aldolase. *Helv Paediatr Acta* 25:626, 1970. NOTE: The FDPase activity, reported to be low in the Note-Added-in-Proof, was later reinvestigated by more refined techniques and found deficient (De Barsy T, personal communication).

314. HOPWOOD NJ, HOLZMAN I, DRASH AL: Fructose-1,6-diphosphatase deficiency. *Am J Dis Child* 131:418, 1977.

315. DE PRÀ M, LAUDANNA E: La malattia di Baker-Winegard. *Minerva Pediatr* 30:1973, 1978.

316. RALLISON ML, MEIKLE AW, ZIGRANG WD: Hypoglycemia and lactic acidosis associated with fructose-1,6-diphosphatase deficiency. *J Pediatr* 94:933, 1979.

317. KINUGASA A, KUSUNOKI T, IWASHIMA A: Deficiency of glucose-6-phosphate dehydrogenase found in a case of hepatic fructose-1,6-diphosphatase deficiency. *Pediatr Res* 13:1361, 1979.

318. BORRONE C, Genoa; BROWN BI, St. Louis; DE BARSY T, Bruxelles; ENDRES W, München; GITZELMANN R, Zürich; HUG G, Cincinnati; LEMONNIER A, Kremlin-Bicêtre; LEONARD JV, London; MARSAC C, Paris; MAIRE I and MATHIEU M, Lyon; SAUDUBRAY JM, Paris; SCHAUB J, Kiel; SMIT PA, Groningen: Personal communication.

319. TAUNTON OD, GREENE HL, STIFEL FB, HOFELDT FD, LUFKIN EG, HAGLER L, HERMAN Y, HERMAN RH: Fructose-1,6-diphosphatase deficiency, hypoglycemia, and response to folate therapy in a mother and her daughter. *Biochem Med* 19:260, 1978.

320. SERVICE FJ, VENEZIALE CM, NELSON RA, ELLEFSON RD, GO VLW: Combined deficiency of glucose-6-phosphatase and fructose-1,6-diphosphatase. Studies of glucagon secretion and fuel utilization. *Am J Med* 64:696, 1978.

321. DREMSEK PA, SACHER M, STÖGMANN W, GITZELMANN R, BACHMANN C: Fructose-1,6-diphosphatase deficiency: Glycerol excretion during fasting test. *Eur J Pediat* 144:203, 1985.

322. KRYWAWYCH S, KATZ G, LAWSON AM, WYATT S, BRENTON DP: Glycerol-3-phosphate excretion in fructose-1,6-diphosphatase deficiency. *J Inherited Metab Dis* 9:388, 1986.

323. GITZELMANN R, CURTIUS H-C, WIRTH R, STEINMANN B: Unpublished.

324. MELANCON SB, NADLER HL: Detection of fructose-1,6-diphosphatase deficiency with use of white blood cells. *N Engl J Med* 286:731, 1972.

325. HOMMES FA, CAMPBELL R, STEINHART C, ROESEL RA, BOWYER F: Biochemical observations on a case of hepatic fructose-1,6-diphosphatase deficiency. *J Inherited Metab Dis* 8:169, 1985.

326. PAGLIARA AS, KARL IE, HAMMOND M., KIPNIS DM: Hypoglycemia in infancy and childhood, Parts I and II. *J Pediatr* 82:365,558, 1973.

327. GITZELMANN R, BAERLOCHER K, PRADER A: Hereditäre Störungen im Fructose- und Galaktosestoffwechsel. *Monatsschrift Kinderheilkd* 121:174, 1973.

328. BAERLOCHER K, GITZELMANN R, STEINMANN B: Clinical and genetic studies of disorders in fructose metabolism, in Burman D, Holton JB, Pennock CA (eds): *Inherited Disorders of Carbohydrate Metabolism*, Lancaster, MTP Press, 1980, pp 163–190.

328a. ROBINSON BH, TAYLOR J, SHERWOOD WG: The genetic heterogeneity of lactic acidosis: Occurrence of recognizable inborn errors of metabolism in a pediatric population with lactic acidosis. *Pediatr Res* 14:956, 1980.

329. SCHRIJVER J, HOMMES FA: Activity of fructose-1,6-diphosphatase in human leukocytes. *N Engl J Med* 292:1298, 1975.

330. CAHILL J, KIRTLEY ME: FDPase activity in human leukocytes. *N Engl J Med* 292:212, 1975.

331. MELANCON SB, NADLER HL: FDPase activity in human leukocytes. *N Engl J Med* 292:212, 1975.

332. FONG W-F, HYNIE I, LEE H, MCKENDRY JBR: Increase of fructose-1,6-diphosphatase activity in cultured human peripheral lymphocytes and its suppression by phytohemagglutinin. *Biochem Biophys Res Commun* 88:222, 1979.

333. ITO M, KURODA Y, KOBASHI H, WATANABE T, TAKEDA E, TOSHIMA K, MIYAO M: Detection of heterozygotes for fructose 1,6-diphosphatase deficiency by measuring fructose 1,6-diphosphatase activity in their cultured peripheral lymphocytes. *Clin Chim Acta* 141:27, 1984.

334. ALEXANDER D, ASSAF M, KHUDR A, HADDAD I, BARAKAT A: Fructose-1,6-diphosphatase deficiency: Diagnosis using leukocytes and detection of heterozygotes with radiochemical and spectrophotometric methods. *J Inherited Metab Dis* 8:147, 1985.

335. BRANDT NJ, RASMUSSEN K, BRANDT S, KØLVRAA S, SCHØNHEYDER F: D-glyceric-acidaemia and non-ketotic hyperglycinaemia. *Acta Paediatr Scand* 65:17, 1976.

336. GRANDGEORGE D, FAVIER A, BOST M, FRAPPAT P, BOUJET C, GARREL S, STOEBNER P: L'acidémie D-glycérique. *Arch Fr Pediatr* 37:577, 1980.

337. KØLVRAA S, GREGERSEN N, CHRISTENSEN E: In vivo studies on the metabolic derangement in a patient with D-glyceric acidaemia and hyperglycinaemia. *J Inherited Metab Dis* 7:49, 1984.

338. DURAN M, BEEMER FA, BRUINVIS L, KETTING D, WADMAN SK: D-glyceric acidemia: An inborn error associated with fructose metabolism. *Pediatr Res* 21:502, 1987.

339. WADMAN SK, DURAN M, KETTING D, BRUINVIS L, DE BREE PK, KAMERLING JP, GERWIG GJ, VLIEGENTHART JFG, PRZYREMBEL H, BECKER K, BREMER HJ: D-glyceric acidemia in a patient with chronic metabolic acidosis. *Clin Chim Acta* 71:477, 1976.

340. BEUTLER E, SCOTT S, BISHOP A, MARGOLIS N, MATSUMOTO F, KUHL W: Red cell aldolase deficiency and hemolytic anemia: A new syndrome. *Trans Assoc Am Physicians* 86:154, 1973.

341. LOWRY RB, HANSON JW: "Aldolase A" deficiency with syndrome of growth and developmental retardation, midfacial hypoplasia, hepatomegaly and consanguineous parents. *Birth Defects* XIII 3B:223, 1977.

341a. HURST JA, BARAITSER M, WINTER RM: A syndrome of mental retardation, short stature, hemolytic anemia, delayed puberty, and abnormal facial appearance. Similarities to a report of aldolase A deficiency. *Amer J Med Genet* 28:965, 1987.

342. MIWA S, FUJII H, TANI K, TAKAHASHI K, TAKEGAWA S, FUJINAMI N, SAKURAI M, KUBO M, TANIMOTO Y, KATO T, MATSUMOTO N: Two cases of red cell aldolase deficiency associated with hereditary hemolytic anemia in a Japanese family. *Am J Hematol* 11:425, 1981.

343. KISHI H, MUKAI T, HIRONO A, FUJII H, MIWA S, HORI K: Human aldolase A deficiency associated with a hemolytic anemia: Thermolabile aldolase due to a single base mutation. *Proc Natl Acad Sci USA* 84:8623, 1987.

344. RAVICH WJ, BAYLESS TM, THOMAS M: Fructose: Incomplete intestinal absorption in humans. *Gastroenterology* 84:26, 1983.

345. STEINMANN B: Personal experience.

346. KNEEPKENS CMF, VONK RJ, FERNANDES J: Incomplete intestinal absorption of fructose. *Arch Dis Child* 59:735, 1984.

347. ANDERSSON DEH, NYGREN A: Four cases of long-standing diarrhoe and colic pains cured by fructose-free diet—A pathogenetic discussion. *Acta Med Scand* 203:87, 1978.

348. BARNES G, MCKELLAR W, LAWRANCE S: Detection of fructose malabsorp-

tion by breath hydrogen test in a child with diarrhea. *J Pediatr* 103:575, 1983.

349. STEINMANN B, GITZELMANN R: Fruktose und Sorbitol in Infusionsflüssigkeiten sind nicht immer harmlos, in Ritzel G, Brubacher G (eds): *Monosaccharides and Polyalcohols in Nutrition, Therapy and Dietetics. Int J Vitam Nutr Res Suppl* 15:289, 1976.

350. STREB H, POSSELT HG, WOLTER K, BENDER SW: Aldolase activities of the small intestinal mucosa in malabsorption states and hereditary fructose intolerance. *Eur J Pediatr* 37:5, 1981.

351. NISELL J, LINDÉN L: Fructose-1-phosphate aldolase and fructose-1,6-diphosphate aldolase activity in the mucosa of the intestine in hereditary fructose intolerance. *Scand J Gastroenterol* 3:80, 1968.

352. MÉTAIS P, JUIF J, SACREZ R: Étude biochimique d'un cas d'intolérance héréditaire au fructose. *Ann Biol Clin* 20:801, 1962.

353. KRANHOLD JF, LOH D, MORRIS RC: Renal fructose-metabolizing enzymes: Significance in hereditary fructose intolerance. *Science* 165:402, 1969.

354. MORRIS RC, UEKI I, LOH D, EANES RZ, MCLIN P: Absence of renal fructose-1-phosphate aldolase activity in hereditary fructose intolerance. *Nature* 214:920, 1967.

CHAPTER **12**

GLYCOGEN STORAGE DISEASES

HENRI-GÉRY HERS
FRANÇOIS VAN HOOF
THIERRY de BARSY

1. *Glycogen is present in all animal cells, and is particularly abundant in liver and muscle. It is degraded both by phosphorolysis and by hydrolysis, and deficiencies of all enzymes specifically involved in this degradation have been observed in humans. The liver can store large amounts of glycogen, the role of which is to be converted to blood glucose for the benefit of other tissues. The deficiency of an enzyme involved in this conversion causes a considerable hepatomegaly associated with hypoglycemia, hypoinsulinism, and retardation of growth. By contrast, the role of muscle glycogen is to be used locally as a glycolytic fuel. The deficiency of an enzyme involved in the conversion of muscle glycogen to lactic acid is responsible for cramps and contractures during strenuous exercise. Over 10 forms of glycogen storage diseases are presently known. With the exception of one form of liver phosphorylase kinase deficiency, the inheritance of all these diseases is autosomal recessive.*
2. *Type 1 glycogenosis is defined as the deficiency of glucose-6-phosphatase, an enzyme which is normally present in liver, kidney, and intestine. It is the most severe form of the hepatomegalic type of glycogen storage disease, and it is complicated by hyperlacticacidemia and hyperuricemia. In a subgroup of the disease, called glycogenosis type 1b, glucose-6-phosphatase is normally active in frozen liver samples but is inactive in the fresh tissues and also in vivo because of the lack of the translocase responsible for the transfer of glucose-6-phosphate into the endoplasmic reticulum. In this subgroup, there is also a striking neutropenia complicated by recurrent infections.*
3. *Type II glycogenosis is the deficiency in lysosomal acid α-glucosidase and is the prototype of an inborn lysosomal disease. The excess glycogen is stored in vacuoles derived from lysosomes in nearly all types of cells. In most cases, there is striking cardiomegaly and profound muscular hypotonia, which cause death by cardiorespiratory failure during the first year of life. Some patients do not show significant cardiac involvement and survive into adulthood.*
4. *Type III glycogenosis, also called limit dextrinosis, is the deficiency of amylo-1,6-glucosidase. A polysaccharide with short outer branches accumulates in all tissues including erythrocytes and leukocytes. Hepatomegaly is predominant in young patients who, except for a lesser fasting hyperlacticacidemia and of hyperuricemia, are difficult to distinguish from those with type I disease. Several biochemical subtypes have been delineated on the basis of tissue variability. The muscular and cardiac symptomatology, though minimal during childhood, may become predominant in adults.*
5. *Type IV glycogenosis, also known as amylopectinosis, is the deficiency of branching enzyme. A polysaccharide with long outer chains is present in moderate amounts in many tissues, particularly the liver. The dominant symptomatology results from progressive cirrhosis of the liver with hepatosplenomegaly and ascites. The disease is very rare, and death usually occurs before 3 years of age.*
6. *Type V glycogenosis, also known as McArdle disease, is the deficiency of muscle phosphorylase. The liver is normal, and there is no hypoglycemia. Cramps and contractures during exercise, sometimes complicated by myoglobinuria, usually appear during the second or third decade of life. Typically, there is no increase in venous lactate during ischemic exercise.*
7. *Type VI glycogenosis includes several enzymic deficiencies, which are responsible for a low activity of liver phosphorylase. The defect may involve phosphorylase itself or one of the four different subunits of phosphorylase kinase. One form of phosphorylase kinase deficiency is restricted to the liver, leukocytes, and erythrocytes and does not affect the muscle. Only males are affected, and the transmission is typically X-linked. In another form of the disease, phosphorylase kinase is deficient in both liver and muscle as well as in blood cells, and the inheritance is autosomal recessive. The symptomatology of type VI glycogenosis is similar to but milder than that of type III, the liver being mostly affected during childhood and the muscle being affected in young adults, at least in the autosomal type of phosphorylase kinase deficiency.*
8. *Type VII is the deficiency of muscle phosphofructokinase-1; it is the rarest form of glycogenosis. The liver enzyme is normal but the erythrocyte's phosphofructokinase activity is reduced by about 50 percent. The symptomatology of this disorder is similar to but more severe than that of McArdle disease, and also includes a mild hemolytic anemia.*

   A symptomatology similar to that of McArdle disease has also been observed in a few patients deficient in other muscle glycolytic enzymes.

Glycogen is present in moderate amount in all animal cells, where it is used as an easily available glycolytic fuel. It is present in larger concentration in the liver after a meal and is stored there as a reserve of glucose to be used during fasting by the whole body. Glycogen synthesis and degradation are tightly regulated by homeostatic and hormonal mechanisms which ensure an optimal utilization of the polysaccharide.

Glycogen storage diseases include at least 10 different genetic entities. Each results from a deficiency affecting one of the enzymes or transporters involved in glycogen metabolism. All are characterized by storage of glycogen in abnormal quantity or with an abnormal structure. They may affect specifically the liver or the muscle or be generalized to all tissues. Excessive glycogen storage of nutritional or endocrine origin is not included in the group. Glycogen storage diseases have been an invaluable source of information for biochemists and physiologists. In turn, precise knowledge of the underlying fundamental mechanisms of these disorders has allowed a rational approach to the pathophysiology and therapy of these disorders.

GLYCOGEN AND GLYCOGEN METABOLISM

Structure and Function

Glycogen is a polymer of glucose present in most animal cells, but is particularly abundant in liver and muscle. The treelike structure (see Fig. 12-1) of the polymer accommodates 20,000 to 30,000 glucose units in a single globular and very soluble molecule. This structure has been established by enzymatic and chemical analysis.[1,2] Extensive methylation followed by acid hydrolysis revealed that one out of every 15 glucose units has free (methylated) hydroxyls in positions 2, 3, 4, and 6 and is, therefore, a nonreducing end; a similar proportion of glucose residues has methylated hydroxyls in positions 2 and 3 only, indicating that positions 4 and 6 are linked to adjacent units by a 1,4 or a 1,6 (branching points) glucosidic linkage. The remaining glucose monomers (more than 80 percent of the total) are methylated in 2, 3, and 6 positions, indicating that they are constituted of linear amyloselike structures. Figure 12-1 also suggests that each glycogen molecule should bear one reducing group. However, there is now a general belief that the so-called reducing end of the molecule is bound to a protein,[3] possibly by a glucosyl-tyrosine linkage.[4] Enzymatic analysis revealed an average length of four residues for the internal chains (between two branching points) and of nine residues for the external ones, which constitute about 60 percent of the molecular mass. There are two major advantages of the structure of glycogen: (1) The storage of glucose is in a form that exerts a negligible osmotic pressure. (2) As much as 7 to 10 percent of the residues are terminal and directly exposed to the action of degradative or biosynthetic enzymes.

Glycogen is characterized by the covalent linkage of its glucose units. Its molecular weight ranges between 2 and 5 million[2,5] for the treelike structure, schematized in Fig. 12-1. This structure, which can be seen with the electron microscope as a spherule of approximately 30 nm in diameter, is called the β particle.[6] The β particle cannot increase greatly in size as a sphere without reducing its relative surface area and the accessibility of its nonreducing ends to enzymes. In the liver, where the concentration of glycogen may be much higher than in other tissues,[7] many (30 on average) β particles appear to be associated together in the form of a rosette called the α particle[6] with a diameter of 110 to 150 nm (see Fig. 12-10). The molecular weight of the α particles may reach 10^9. The kind of linkage by which the β particles are held together to form a α particle is unknown.

The role of glycogen is different in liver and muscle. Liver glycogen is stored, not for the benefit of the liver itself, which consumes mostly fatty acids, but to provide glucose to the blood for the benefit of other tissues, particularly the brain during short periods of fast. The paramount importance of this function justifies the complex regulatory control mechanism of glycogen metabolism and of gluconeogenesis in the liver. The role of liver glycogen also explains that its concentration varies from very low values (below 0.1 percent) during fasting to approximately 5 percent under normal conditions of nutrition and reaches 14 percent in the livers of fasted-refed rats.[7] The mechanism that allows such an enormous accumulation of glycogen under the latter condition is unknown. By contrast, the muscle maintains a glycogen concentration close to 1 percent as a reserve of glycolytic fuel to be used locally when oxygen or glucose declines. It should also be noted that glycogen is very hydrated, as it retains 2.4-fold its own weight of water and salt in the liver.[7,8] The energetic value of 1.2 kcal/g of hydrated polysaccharide is therefore far below that of fat. In fact, the glycogen store of the liver is relatively small, being exhausted after less than a day of fasting. The high degree of hydration also explains the remarkable hepatomegaly characteristic of glycogenoses in which the liver is affected.

As illustrated in Fig. 12-2, glycogen is formed from and (up to 93 percent) degraded to hexose phosphates. Hexose phosphates for glycogen synthesis originate by phosphorylation of glucose or from gluconeogenesis. The latter mechanism predominates during fasting, because of the low blood sugar level and a decreased activity of glucokinase. This old observation has recently been called the *glucose paradox*.[9] Since the glucose units in the glycogen molecule are held together by both α-1,4 and α-1,6 glucosidic linkages, different cytosolic enzymes are involved in both degradation (respectively phosphorylase and amylo-1,6-glucosidase) and biosynthesis (glycogen synthase and branching enzyme) of each type of linkage. By contrast, acid α-glucosidase alone allows the hydrolysis of both types of linkage and the complete degradation of glycogen in the lysosome.

Fig. 12-1 Model of a segment of a glycogen molecule ○ = glucose residue in α-1,4-linkage; ● = residue in α-1,6-linkage. The broken line indicates the limit of degradation by phosphorylase. *(Modified from Ref. 2.)* The insert represents the degradation of the limit dextrin (LD) by amylo-1,6-glucosidase. ⊘-⊘-⊘ is the oligoglycan transferred from the side chain to the main chain of the polysaccharide during the first reaction catalyzed by the bifunctional enzyme.

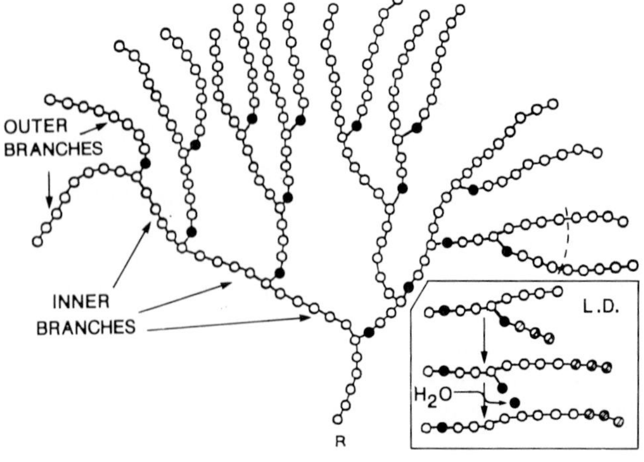

Glycogen Phosphorylase and Its Converter Enzymes

The *a* and *b* Forms of Glycogen Phosphorylase. Glycogen phosphorylase catalyzes the transfer of a glucose unit present at the nonreducing end of the polysaccharide onto inorganic phosphate.[10–13] The equilibrium is reached when the ratio glucose-1-phosphate/P_i is close to 3 at neutral pH. The reaction is easily reversible in vitro, but not in vivo, as the concentration of inorganic phosphate is usually 100-fold that of glucose-1-phosphate in cells. The reaction proceeds from the nonreducing ends until about four glucose residues remain on each

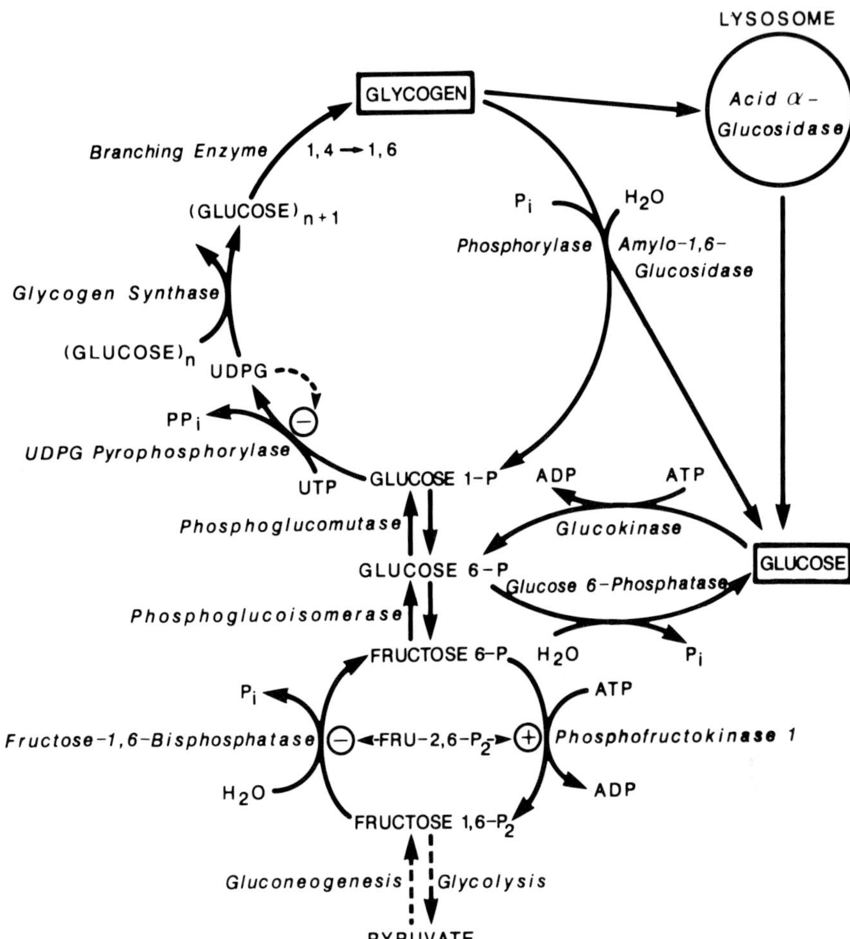

Fig. 12-2 Glycogen and related metabolism in the liver.

external chain.[14] The resulting polysaccharide, called a phosphorylase limit dextrin, is the substrate of amylo-1,6-glucosidase and can be further degraded by phosphorolysis only after the removal of the branching point by the latter enzyme.

Glycogen phosphorylase is the prototype of interconvertible enzymes, the activity of which is modified by phosphorylation and dephosphorylation (see Fig. 12-3). Phosphorylase *a* is the form which is active under the ionic conditions prevailing in the cell; it bears a phosphate group on the hydroxyl group of the serine residue in position 14. Phosphorylase *b* is the inactive dephosphoenzyme, which may be activated by nonphysiological concentrations of AMP. The determination of the two forms of phosphorylase is therefore usually based on the measurement of the activity in the presence and absence of AMP; it should be noted, however, that liver phosphorylase *b* is not completely inactive in the absence of AMP under the usual assay conditions unless caffeine is present.[15]

Muscle and liver phosphorylases are immunologically different[16] and are therefore under different genetic control. The muscle enzyme has been the most extensively investigated, and many of its basic properties are similar to those of phosphorylase from liver and other animal tissues. These enzymes are dimers or tetramers of a subunit with a molecular weight close to 100,000 to which one essential pyridoxal phosphate is bound as a Schiff base to a lysine residue close to the active site.

Phosphorylase *b* Kinase. Phosphorylase *b* kinase[17,18] allows the conversion of phosphorylase *b* into phosphorylase *a* by the transfer of the terminal phosphate of ATP to a serine group in position 14. The same enzyme also phosphorylates glycogen synthase.[19] Phosphorylase *b* kinase itself exists as a phosphorylated active and a nonphosphorylated less active form. The latter is only active in the presence of calcium ($K_a = 10^{-6}\ M$), a property which is of primary importance for the initiation of glycogenolysis in muscle during contraction and also in the liver subjected to calcium-mediated hormonal stimuli. The phosphorylation of phosphorylase *b* kinase is catalyzed by cyclic-AMP-dependent protein kinase. Protein kinase activates the enzyme fifteen- to twentyfold at saturating calcium concentrations and decreases the K_a for calcium fifteenfold.[18]

Phosphorylase kinase is a large protein of molecular weight 1,300,000 with the structure $(\alpha\beta\gamma\delta)_4$. The α and β subunits are the components phosphorylated by cyclic-AMP-dependent protein kinase, and the γ-peptide appears to be the catalytic subunit. The δ subunit is identical with the calcium binding protein calmodulin.[20]

Phosphorylase Phosphatase. The dephosphorylation and resulting inactivation of phosphorylase by phosphorylase phosphatase was established by Wosilait and Sutherland in 1956.[21] Despite a considerable amount of work devoted to that subject,[22–24] the precise identity and specificity of the various protein phosphatases involved in glycogen and other areas of intermediary metabolism remain controversial. This is because, besides spontaneously active protein phosphatases present in freshly prepared homogenates, tissues like liver[25] and muscle[26] contain about a tenfold excess of latent enzyme(s), which are easily activated either by proteolysis, by dilution, or by treatment with ethanol or mercaptoethanol.

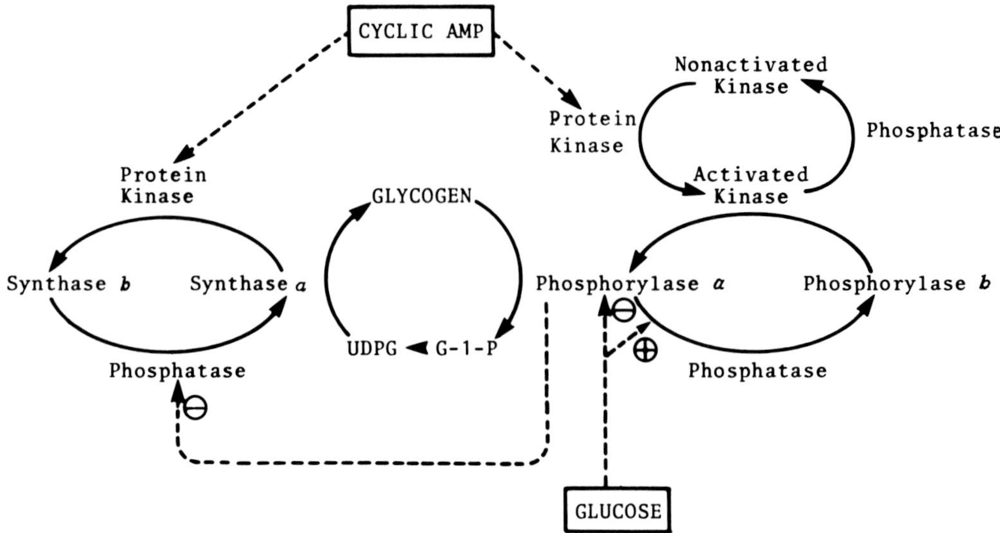

Fig. 12-3 The control of glycogen metabolism in the liver. *(Modified from Ref. 75.)*

The activity of the native phosphorylase phosphatase present in crude liver preparations is increased severalfold in the presence of glucose or caffeine. These effects are counteracted by AMP.[27] The action of these effectors is explained by their association with the substrate of the reaction, phosphorylase *a*.[28] These compounds effect a change in the spatial configuration of phosphorylase *a* as revealed by x-ray diffraction analysis.[12,13] The effect of glucose is to expose the serine phosphate group to the action of the phosphatase.

Glycogen Synthase and Its Converter Enzymes

The *a* and *b* Forms of Glycogen Synthase. In 1957, Leloir and Cardini[29] discovered an enzyme (reviewed in Refs. 30 and 31) that catalyzes the synthesis of glycogen from uridine diphosphate-glucose (UDPG) according to the reaction:

$$(\text{Glucose})_n + \text{UDPG} \rightleftharpoons (\text{glucose})_{n+1} + \text{UDP}$$

The name *glycogen synthetase* was first used to designate that enzyme. More recently it was named *glycogen synthase* following the new rules of enzyme nomenclature, because the reaction does not involve the transfer of the terminal phosphate of a triphosphate nucleotide.[32] Leloir and his coworkers also discovered that glucose-6-phosphate is a potent activator of the enzyme. It was on the basis of differential sensitivity to that activator that Larner and his coworkers[33,34] recognized the existence of two forms of the enzyme, that they called I (glucose-6-phosphate-independent) and D (glucose-6-phosphate-dependent). The two forms are interconvertible by phosphorylation and dephosphorylation. Later, it was recognized that the activity of both forms can be affected by glucose-6-phosphate, but that this effect is minimal under the ionic conditions prevailing inside cells, the I form being then fully active and the D form fully inactive, whatever the concentration of glucose-6-phosphate. The terms *a* (active) and *b* (less active) are therefore preferred to I and D.[35,36] The greater activity of the *a* form is related to its higher affinity for UDPG in the case of the liver enzyme, and to a higher V_{max}, when measured at physiological glucose-6-phosphate concentration, in the case of the muscle enzyme. All forms have a great affinity for glycogen (K_m close to 50 μg/ml) and remain associated with it during differential centrifugation of crude tissue extracts. They consist of two or four subunits of molecular weight close to 85,000.

Synthase Kinase. Several protein kinases can phosphorylate glycogen synthase (reviewed in Refs. 18 and 31). The predominant one is cyclic-AMP-dependent protein kinase. The calcium-dependent enzymes include phosphorylase kinase and protein kinase C. Several cyclic-AMP- and calcium-independent kinases also act on glycogen synthase. The inactivation of glycogen synthase by protein kinases in a liver extract is inhibited by glucose-6-phosphate[37] at physiological concentration.[38]

Synthase Phosphatase. There is good evidence that synthase phosphatase is an enzyme different from phosphorylase phosphatase.[25,39] The main regulatory property of the muscle enzyme is inhibition by glycogen,[40] whereas the liver enzyme is inhibited by phosphorylase *a*.[41,42] Inhibition by calcium may also play a role,[43] at least when enough glycogen is present. The liver enzyme is composed of two components: a G component, which binds tightly to glycogen particles, and a cytosolic S component.[44] The cooperation of the two components is required to allow synthase activation. The G component is responsible for the inhibitory effects of both phosphorylase *a*[45] and calcium.[46]

Enzymes Acting at the Branching Point

Amylo-1,6-Glucosidase. Amylo-1,6-glucosidase is a bifunctional enzyme,[47] which converts the phosphorylase limit dextrin into a glycogen with external chains of normal length and liberates free glucose by hydrolysis of the α-1,6 glucosidic linkage (reviewed in Ref. 48). The first step of this conversion is the α-1,4 ⇌ α-1,4 transfer of an oligoglucan of three to four glucose units from the side chain to the main chain of the phosphorylase limit dextrin, thereby exposing the α-1,6-linked glucose unit of the branching point. The second step is the hydrolysis of the latter linkage and the formation of glucose. The slight reversibility of this reaction[49] allows a simple assay of the enzyme in crude tissue preparations by the incorporation of [^{14}C]glucose into glycogen.[50] The combined action of phosphorylase and of amylo-1,6-glucosidase causes the complete degradation of glycogen into glucose-1-phosphate for 93 percent, and glucose for 7 percent.

Branching Enzyme. Branching of glycogen is effected by the transfer of a segment of at least six α-1,4-linked glucosyl units from the outer chains of glycogen into a 1,6 position.[51] Rabbit liver branching enzyme is a monomeric protein of molecular weight close to 70,000; it is thirtyfold more abundant in liver than in muscle.[52]

UDPG Pyrophosphorylase

As shown in Fig. 12-2, this enzyme allows the formation of UDPG and inorganic pyrophosphate from UTP and glucose-1-phosphate.[53] Although the reaction is easily reversible, the formation of UDPG is favored by the enzymatic hydrolysis of pyrophosphate. A most interesting property of the enzyme is inhibition by UDPG, a reaction product, competitively with UTP.[54,55] The rate of reaction is therefore essentially controlled by the removal of its product, UDPG, itself dependent on the activity of glycogen synthase. This property eliminates the hypothesis[56,57] that the rate of glycogen synthesis is controlled by a "push" given to the pathway by an increase in the concentration of glucose phosphate.

Phosphoglucomutase

This enzyme allows the reversible conversion of glucose-1-phosphate to glucose-6-phosphate. The thermodynamic equilibrium is in favor of glucose-6-phosphate (20:1). Glucose-1,6-bisphosphate is a cofactor and participates in the reaction as a phosphate donor.[58] Phosphoglucomutase is the only enzyme common to glycogen synthesis and degradation.

The Glucose/Glucose-6-Phosphate Interconversion

Hexokinases and Glucokinase. Most cells possess one or several low (10^{-7} to 10^{-6} *M*) K_m hexokinases, that form glucose-6-phosphate and ADP from glucose and ATP and also act similarly, but with a lower affinity, on mannose and fructose. These enzymes are inhibited by glucose-6-phosphate[59] (K_i = 0.5 m*M*), an effect which is of great importance in the control of glucose utilization in muscle.[60] The hepatocyte differs from other cells by the low affinity of its hexokinase for its sugar substrates and inhibitor. This liver enzyme is called glucokinase, because glucose is the only sugar that is phosphorylated under physiological conditions (reviewed in Refs. 61 and 62). An important point is that the K_m of glucokinase for glucose (10 m*M*) is in the normal range of glycemia and that, therefore, the rate of glucose phosphorylation in the liver will be affected by the level of glycemia, although not by the level of glucose-6-phosphate (K_i = 60 m*M*).

Glucokinase is a monomeric protein of molecular weight close to 50,000, which is one-half that of most other hexokinases. However, the saturation curve for glucose is slightly sigmoidal (Hill coefficient = 1.6), and a mechanism has been proposed to explain the cooperativity of a monomeric enzyme.[62] The phosphorylation of glucose in isolated hepatocytes, as measured by the release of [^{3}H]H_2O in the presence of [2-^{3}H]glucose, is entirely accounted for by the activity of glucokinase.[63] Cooperativity for glucose, which was also observed in the cellular system, renders the reaction most sensitive to a small change in glucose concentration in the physiological range of 5 to 10 m*M*. No other short-term regulation of liver glucokinase is known; this control is therefore essentially by substrate concentration. Long-term control occurs at the level of protein synthesis, since the concentration of glucokinase in rat liver (3 units per gram) is decreased by about 50 percent with prolonged fasting or in diabetes.[64]

Glucose-6-Phosphatase. This enzyme catalyzes the hydrolysis of glucose-6-phosphate into glucose and P_i (reviewed in Ref. 65). With the exception of the small amount of glucose liberated by amylo-1,6-glucosidase and acid α-glucosidase, it is entirely responsible for the formation of endogenous glucose originating from gluconeogenesis and from glycogenolysis. Glucose-6-phosphatase is present in liver and kidney and also, in some species, including humans, in the intestinal mucosa. The enzyme can be destroyed by an incubation of the tissue extract for a few minutes at pH 5 and 37°C without loss of the contaminating acid phosphatase activity.[50] This finding is of practical value in correcting for nonspecific phosphatase activity when assaying liver tissue from patients.

Glucose-6-phosphatase is bound to the luminal face of the endoplasmic reticulum and therefore recovered in the microsomal fraction in the course of differential centrifugation.[66] The significance of this specific intracellular location is unknown, except that it could play a role in the segregation of calcium ions by the reticulum.[67,68] Arion et al.[69,70] (see Fig. 12-4) have proposed that three components of the endoplasmic reticulum participate in the process of glucose-6-phosphate hydrolysis: (1) a glucose-6-phosphate specific transporter, called T_1, that mediates penetration of its substrate into the microsomal cisternae and is rate-limiting for the hydrolysis of glucose-6-phosphate by intact microsomes; (2) a phosphohydrolase localized on the luminal side of the reticulum network, acting on glucose-6-phosphate, mannose-6-phosphate, and pyrophosphate, and also able to act as a phosphotransferase; and (3) a second translocase, called T_2, controlling the permeability of microsomes to P_i, PP_i, and carbamyl phosphate. Whereas the three components would be required for the hydrolysis of glucose-6-phosphate by intact microsomes, only the second is necessary after disruption of the membrane by various means. T_2, but not T_1, is required for the hydrolysis of pyrophosphate, but only disrupted microsomes can hydrolyze mannose-6-phosphate.

Fig. 12-4 Schematization of the glucose-6-phosphatase system. T_2 also allows the translocation of carbamyl phosphate and possibly other anions. Mannose-6-phosphate is not translocated by either T_1 or T_2. *(Modified from Ref. 70.)*

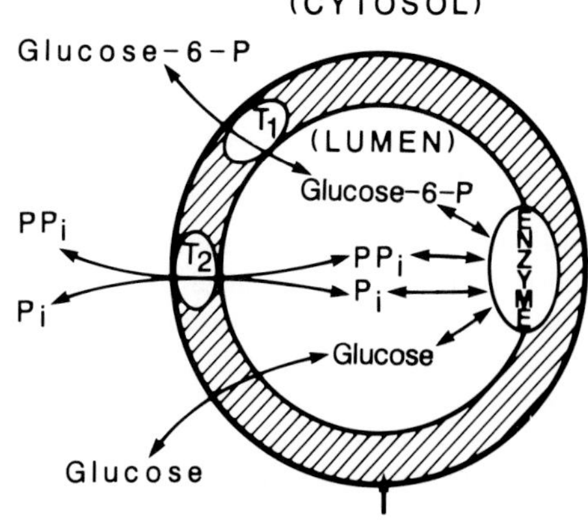

The liver of normally fed rats contains about 10 units of glucose-6-phosphatase per gram. This amount is doubled by an overnight fast. The K_m of the undisrupted enzyme for glucose-6-phosphate is around 2 mM, i.e., about tenfold greater than the usual concentration of glucose-6-phosphate in the liver. The hydrolysis of glucose-6-phosphate is therefore clearly a first-order reaction, essentially controlled by substrate concentration.[71] P_i is a weak inhibitor, acting competitively with glucose-6-phosphate. This inhibition would not exceed a few percent under normal in vivo conditions.

The Control of Glucose Uptake and Output by the Liver. As there is apparently no on/off mechanism of control of glucokinase and of glucose-6-phosphatase, these two enzymes are always simultaneously in operation in the adult liver. Because its net balance is the hydrolysis of ATP into ADP and P_i, this conversion is called a futile cycle. With the use of doubly labeled glucose, this cycle has been shown to operate in isolated hepatocytes, in intact rats,[72,73] and in children, but not in patients deficient in glucose-6-phosphatase.[73,74] In such a recycling system, glucose uptake and output are determined by the difference between the activities of glucokinase and of glucose-6-phosphatase. It has been calculated that, at a level of glycemia equal to 5.7 mM, the two activities would be equal to 0.9 μmol of substrate converted per minute per gram of liver and balance each other, so that there is no net flux of metabolite through the system. Since the two enzymic activities are controlled by the concentration of their substrates, a net uptake occurs when the concentration of glucose is increased and/or when that of glucose-6-phosphate is decreased, as occurs when glycogen synthesis is intense and exerts a pull on the concentration of the intermediary metabolites UDPG and glucose-6-phosphate. Conversely, the large increase in glucose-6-phosphate concentration that occurs when glycogenolysis is stimulated greatly increases glucose output. The advantage of the system is that it allows very large changes of flux, controlled only by substrate concentration.[71,75]

6-Phosphofructokinases

The name phosphofructokinase is currently used to designate the enzyme of glycolysis that phosphorylates fructose-6-phosphate into fructose-1,6-bisphosphate at the expense of ATP. Another phosphofructokinase which forms fructose-2,6-bisphosphate by a similar reaction has recently been discovered (reviewed in Ref. 76). It has been called phosphofructokinase-2, the classic phosphofructokinase becoming then phosphofructokinase-1. This nomenclature indicates both the carbon of fructose-6-phosphate, which is phosphorylated, and the order of discovery of the two enzymes.

Phosphofructokinase-1. Phosphofructokinase-1 is the prototype of a multimodulated enzyme. Its control can be summarized by saying that one of its substrates, ATP, acts as a negative allosteric effector, which induces marked cooperativity for the second substrate, fructose-6-phosphate. The latter acts as a positive effector, which relieves the inhibition by ATP. Numerous other substances have an allosteric effect similar to and usually synergistic with those of ATP or fructose-6-phosphate. Citrate and H^+ are negative effectors. The most important positive effectors are AMP and the newly discovered[77] fructose-2,6-bisphosphate.

Numerous isoenzymes of phosphofructokinase-1 have been isolated from various types of cells (reviewed in Ref. 78). Their catalytic and physicochemical properties are usually similar.

Phosphofructokinase-2/Fructose-2,6-Bisphosphatase. This bifunctional protein has two active sites: one allowing the formation of fructose-2,6-bisphosphate from fructose-6-phosphate and ATP, the other causing its hydrolysis to fructose-6-phosphate and P_i. Since fructose-2,6-bisphosphate is required for the activity of phosphofructokinase-1, a deficiency of phosphofructokinase-2 (as yet not reported) would have consequences similar to those observed in phosphofructokinase-1 deficiency.

Liver, but not muscle, phosphofructokinase-2/fructose-2,6-bisphosphatase is an interconvertible enzyme. It is a substrate of cyclic-AMP-dependent protein kinase and its phosphorylation causes the inactivation of phosphofructokinase-2 and the activation of fructose-2,6-bisphosphatase, resulting in the disappearance of fructose-2,6-bisphosphate from the liver.[76]

Regulation of Glycogen Metabolism in the Liver

The Control by Glucose. By 1940, Soskin[79] had already pointed out that the concentration of glucose in the blood is the primary stimulus that elicits glucose uptake or output by the liver, and he compared this homeostatic control of the level of glycemia to a thermostat-furnace arrangement. He defined the hepatic threshold to glucose as the glucose concentration at which the liver is converted from an organ of glucose output into an organ of glucose uptake. This threshold corresponds to the level of glycemia that the animal usually maintains and may vary according to the endocrine conditions. In the normally fed animal, glycogen synthesis and degradation represent the bulk of glucose uptake and output by the liver. Their control by glucose (reviewed in Refs. 75 and 80, see Fig. 12-3) can now be explained by the binding of the hexose to phosphorylase *a*, the glucose receptor of the liver, which is then somewhat less active and, more importantly, is now a much better substrate for phosphorylase phosphatase. The effect of a high glucose concentration is, therefore, to cause the conversion of phosphorylase *a* into phosphorylase *b* and to arrest glycogenolysis. Furthermore, since phosphorylase *a* is a potent inhibitor of synthase phosphatase, its disappearance allows now the latter enzyme to activate glycogen synthase and, in doing so, to initiate glycogen synthesis. It is indeed quite remarkable that the activation of glycogen synthase by glucose in vivo as well as in isolated hepatocytes or in a cell-free system is preceded by a lag period. This lag corresponds precisely to the time required for the nearly complete inactivation of phosphorylase. Activation of synthase will start only when approximately 90 percent of phosphorylase is in the *b* form (see Fig. 12-5).

A rise in glucose concentration in the liver is also expected to increase the activity of glucokinase and, secondarily, the concentration of glucose-6-phosphate. Contrary to the latter expectation, the concentrations of glucose-6-phosphate and UDPG are not increased but decreased, at least in normally fed animals, allowing glucose uptake by decreasing the activity of glucose-6-phosphatase versus that of glucokinase (see "The Pull Mechanism," below).

The Control by Glucose-6-Phosphate. In the liver of fasted rats, the concentration of phosphorylase *a* is rather low and

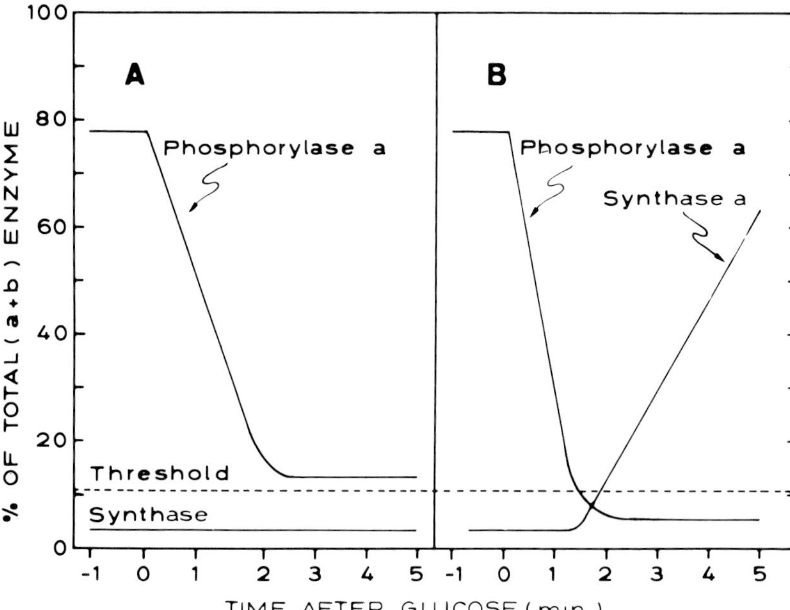

Fig. 12-5 Sequential inactivation of glycogen phosphorylase and activation of glycogen synthase in the liver of fed rats. This schematic representation illustrates that glycogen synthase starts to be activated only if and when the concentration of phosphorylase *a* is lowered below a threshold value (dotted line), approximately equal to 10 percent of total (*a* + *b*) phosphorylase. This sequence has been observed in cell free extracts, in isolated hepatocytes, and in vivo. The B type of response is produced by higher concentrations of glucose. (*Modified from Ref. 75.*)

glycogen synthase is partially active. It has been repeatedly observed that, in hepatocytes isolated from these livers, glycogen synthase could be further activated by adding to the incubation medium various gluconeogenic precursors[81,82] or amino acids,[83,84] but without decreasing the already low activity of phosphorylase. It has been proposed[38,85] that these effects could be mediated by an increase in the concentration of glucose-6-phosphate, which is low during fasting because of the lack of glycogen, and particularly in isolated liver preparations, because of the lack of gluconeogenic precursors. As explained above, one effect of glucose-6-phosphate is to increase the concentration of synthase *a* by inhibiting synthase kinase.

The Control by Hormones. Glucagon is the principal hormone that controls glycogen metabolism in the liver. Its action is easily explained by its ability to activate the membranous adenylate cyclase and to increase the concentration of cyclic AMP in the liver (see upper part of Fig. 12-3). The most reproducible effect of insulin on glycogen metabolism in the liver is to counteract the action of low concentrations of glucagon.[86] A similar inhibitory effect of insulin seems also to exist at the level of the phenylephrine-stimulated intracellular calcium release.[87]

Vasopressin, angiotensin, and α-adrenergic agonists are known to induce glycogenolysis in the liver by a cyclic-AMP-independent mechanism.[88] These agents appear to generate two intracellular messengers, calcium and diacylglycerol. The initial event (reviewed in Ref. 89) would be the breakdown of phosphatidylinositol bisphosphate into inositol trisphosphate, which causes the release of free calcium from intracellular stores, and diacylglycerol, which activates protein kinase C.[90] The stimulation of phosphorylase *b* kinase by calcium explains the activation of phosphorylase and, hence, the increased glycogenolysis. The same hormones also cause a substantial inactivation of glycogen synthase (see Ref. 46), an effect which appears to be mediated[91] by the inhibition of synthase phosphatase by phosphorylase *a*[41] and by calcium.[43,46] Phosphorylation of glycogen synthase by protein kinase C[92,93] may also be involved.

As well documented by Long et al.,[94] glucocorticoids induce, within 2 to 3 h, a large deposition of glycogen in the liver of both fasted or fed animals. This rapid rate of glycogen synthesis is explained by a proportional activation of glycogen synthase and is accompanied by a decrease in the concentration of UDPG and of glucose-6-phosphate.[95,96] The activation of glycogen synthase occurs even at low glucose concentration and without previous inactivation of phosphorylase; it is prevented by the administration of actinomycin D and has been explained by the formation of a protein endowed with the ability to prevent the inhibition of synthase phosphatase by phosphorylase *a*.[97]

The Pull Mechanism. As explained in the preceding paragraphs, an increased rate of glycogen synthesis in the liver is always secondary to an activation of glycogen synthase, associated with a decrease in the concentration of UDPG and, often, of glucose-6-phosphate. The activation of glycogen synthase is caused by three mechanisms: (1) the previous inactivation of phosphorylase (glucose effect), (2) the formation of a protein that prevents the inhibition of synthase phosphatase by phosphorylase *a* (glucocorticoid effect), and (3) an inhibition of synthase kinase (glucose-6-phosphate effect). The secondary decrease in the concentration of UDPG,[95,96,98–100] an inhibitor of UDPG pyrophosphorylase,[54,55] allows that enzyme to automatically keep up with the increased rate of synthesis; the secondary decrease in the concentration of glucose-6-phosphate[96,98,100–102] causes a proportional decrease of the activity of glucose-6-phosphatase and allows glucose uptake by the liver. This so-called pull mechanism is currently opposed to the push hypothesis,[56,57] in which an increase in the concentration of the precursor metabolites, glucose and hexose phosphates, would sequentially increase the activity of UDPG pyrophosphorylase, the concentration of UDPG, and the rate of synthase reaction. The push hypothesis is supported by the increased concentration of glucose-6-phosphate observed in isolated liver preparations obtained from fasted rats and incubated under various experimental conditions[56,81–84] but which, strikingly, is accompanied by an activation of glycogen synthase. The push hypothesis is incompatible with the fact that UDPG pyrophosphorylase is inhibited by UDPG and with the correlation that exists between the rate of glycogen synthesis and the concentration of synthase *a* in the liver.[98,103,104] It is also contradicted by the observed changes in the concentration of UDPG of glucose-6-phosphate under many conditions.

Regulation of Glycogen Metabolism in the Muscle

In the muscle, insulin favors glycogen synthesis by its well-known ability to promote glucose transport through the membrane.[105] It also causes a moderate activation of glycogen synthase even in the absence of glucose.[33] This effect may be mediated by a still ill-defined messenger.[106] Cyclic AMP concentration is not affected by glucagon, for which muscle has no receptor, but its concentration is increased by adrenaline and other catecholamines. Control by glucose does not exist, since the concentration of this sugar in muscle is negligible. The two most important local regulators appear to be calcium, which stimulates the dephosphorylated form of phosphorylase *b* kinase, and glycogen itself which, by inhibiting synthase phosphatase, prevents an excessive synthesis of the polysaccharide.[40]

The Hydrolytic Degradation of Glycogen

The discovery that generalized glycogenosis, also called Pompe disease, is caused by a deficiency of a lysosomal acid α-glucosidase,[107] and is accompanied by a striking accumulation of glycogen inside lysosomes[108] (see Fig. 12-10), also revealed that, in nearly all normal animal cells, some glycogen is continuously degraded hydrolytically in the lysosomes. Acid α-glucosidase was described by Lejeune et al.,[109] who also demonstrated its lysosomal localization. It also catalyzes transglucosylation from maltose onto glycogen. The highly purified rat liver,[110] rabbit muscle,[111] and human placenta[112] enzymes act on both maltose and isomaltose and completely degrade glycogen into glucose.[110] The K_m value is on the order of 30 mg/ml for glycogen, 5 m*M* for maltose, and 30 m*M* for isomaltose. Since the enzyme is an exoglucosidase, freely diffusible glucose is the only reaction product and glycogen degradation can be completed without increase of the intralysosomal osmotic pressure.

The role of acid α-glucosidase is to degrade glycogen that has penetrated into the lysosomal system. As there is no glycogen in the extracellular fluid, where it would be destroyed by α-amylase, no glycogen penetrates into the lysosomes through the process of heterophagy. On the contrary, glycogen is frequently seen in autophagic vacuoles. The role of the hydrolytic mechanism is therefore quite different from that of phosphorolysis. It is not meant to provide glucose to the cell but to degrade the glycogen which, together with other cellular components, has been engulfed in autophagic vacuoles and needs to be digested. This appears to be a continuous process.

INHERITED ABNORMALITIES OF GLYCOGEN METABOLISM

Deficiencies of all enzymes and transporters specifically involved in glycogen degradation have been recognized in humans and, for some of them, in animals. In the case of phosphorylase, the protein is different in liver and muscle, and deficiencies of both enzymes are known. Furthermore, when several polypeptides constitute one enzyme, each subunit can be specifically affected, and this explains the existence of both an X-linked and an autosomal form of phosphorylase *b* kinase deficiency. Finally, the situation is further complicated by the existence of allelic mutations and of genetic compounds. In 1954, G. T. Cori[2] initiated a numerical classification of these disorders, which was later extended by others and is still widely used, at least up to number VII. For the convenience of the reader, we will follow that numerical order in the description of the various forms of glycogen storage disease

The multiplicity of defects affecting the same metabolic pathway not only indicates that glycogen is not essential for life but also illustrates that different diseases, each of them defined on the basis of the primary genetic defect, can share a similar clinical expression and, therefore, require a specific enzymic determination for their identification. Liver and muscle are, by far, the two tissues in which glycogen metabolism is the most intense and are therefore expected to be the most seriously affected by a metabolic defect.

When the liver is affected, as in glycogen storage disease types I, III, and VI, the symptomatology is essentially related to the inability of that tissue to convert glycogen to glucose, leading to hepatomegaly and hypoglycemia. Hepatomegaly is associated with a large increase in the size of hepatocytes, which acquire the appearance of plant cells; hypoglycemia is expressed as sweating or convulsions and is responsible for hypoinsulinism, hyperglucagonemia, hyperlipidemia, and retardation of growth (reviewed in Refs. 50 and 113 to 119). Although patients are expected not to respond to the hyperglycemic action of glucagon, the response is, for various reasons, normal or only partially reduced in many cases. The main clinical and laboratory features observed in patients with glycogenosis types I, III, and VI and their evolution after childhood are shown in Tables 12-1 and 12-2.

When the muscle is affected, as typically occurs in types V and VII, but also in type III and in a subgroup of type VI,

Table 12-1 Main Clinical and Laboratory Features in 62 Patients with Hepatomegalic Glycogenosis

	Type Ia	*Type Ib*	*Type III*	*Type VI*
Number of patients	17	7	15	23
Age of clinical onset				
<1 month	4	3		1
1 mo–1 yr	9	4	13	16
1–2 yr	3			4
2–4 yr	1		2	2
Hypoglycemia				
Clinical signs	10	5	7	2
Seizures	3	5	6	
Doll's face	12	4	7	10
Epistaxis	8	1	1	
Enlarged liver	17	7	15	23
Enlarged kidneys	8/8			
Xanthoma	2		1	
Adenomas	6	1	4	
Muscular weakness			9	
Low fasting glycemia	13	7	7	1
High fasting lacticacidemia	15	6	3	
Hypertriglyceridemia	17	7	13	10
Hypercholesterolemia	15	6	15	16
Hyperuricemia	9	2	2	
Abnormal liver tests	14/14	5	13	18
Elevated creatine kinase			10	
Osteoporosis	12	2	4	4
Death	1	1		

SOURCE: Courtesy of Professor M. Odièvre, Hôpital A. Béclère, Clamart, France.

Table 12-2 Main Clinical and Laboratory Features in 74 Patients over 12 Years Old with Hepatomegalic Glycogenosis

	Type I	*Type III*	*Type VI*
Number of patients	22	32	20
Mean age at time of inquiry (year)	22	19	19
Mean deviation from standard percentile of height			
Before end of puberty	−3.85	−1.8	−1.3
After puberty	−1.6	−0.1	+0.1
End of puberty (year)	18	18	16
Normal scholarship and social outcome in life	13/18	11/21	15/18
Enlarged liver	22/22	24/28	3/20
Normal liver functional tests	11/16	17/32	9/9
Adenomata	11/20	3/7	0
Hypoglycemia (clinical signs)	1/22	1/32	
Hyperlacticacidemia	11/15		
Hyperuricemia	14/20	0	0
Hypercholesterolemia	16/21	4/27	2/13
Hypertriglyceridemia	17/20	6/20	0/8
Skeletal muscle involvement		10/28	

SOURCE: Courtesy of Professor P. Guibaud, Hôpital Debrousse, Lyons, France.

the symptoms are related to the inability of the tissue to provide rapidly a glycolytic fuel for contraction; this symptomatology is usually mild, becoming apparent only in the young adult and during strenuous exercise (reviewed in Refs. 50 and 113 to 123). Similar symptoms can be observed in other rare defects of muscle glycolysis which, however, do not cause an excessive deposition of glycogen in the tissue.[121]

In two other forms of glycogen storage disease, type II and type IV, there is no impairment of the phosphorolytic degradation of glycogen, and the clinical manifestation is related to the overloading of the cells by glycogen either in an unusual subcellular location (type II) or with an abnormal structure (type IV).

Table 12-3 shows the mean glycogen concentration in liver and muscle in the various forms of glycogenosis. Table 12-4 gives an estimation of the frequency of each type of glycogenosis. The overall frequency of glycogenoses has been calculated from European data to be around one new patient for every 20,000 to 25,000 births. Useful laboratory techniques can be found in Refs. 50, 124, and 125.

Type I Glycogenosis (Glucose-6-Phosphatase Deficiency)

History. In 1929, von Gierke[126] reported the detailed autopsies of a 7-year-old girl and a 5-year-old boy in whom the most remarkable findings were a threefold increase in liver size and a twofold hypertrophy of the kidneys. Both tissues were overloaded with glycogen. The muscle was not examined, and blood lactate and urate values were not given, but the record of frequent nose bleeding suggests that these two initial cases were actually of type I. In 1952, the Coris[127] reported the near complete deficiency of glucose-6-phosphatase in the livers of two similar patients, contrasting with a normal or subnormal activity of the same enzyme in four other patients. The biochemical heterogeneity of the hepatomegalic glycogenoses was therefore apparent, and glucose-6-phosphatase deficiency was classified as type I glycogenosis by G. T. Cori[2] in 1954.

Starting from 1959 (reviewed in Ref. 128), it became apparent that, contrary to expectation, a normal activity of glucose-6-phosphatase could be measured in frozen samples of livers from some of the patients presenting the pathognomonic symptomatology of glucose-6-phosphatase deficiency, including the inability to form glucose from galactose and to decrease the $^3H/^{14}C$ ratio of specifically labeled glucose (see below). This paradox was solved in 1978, when Narisawa et al.[29] recognized that a defect in the glucose-6-phosphate transport system was responsible for this "Ib type" of glycogenosis.

General Description. Physical examination reveals a short stature and a protuberant abdomen, with lumbar lordosis related to a very large increase in liver size (Fig. 12-6). The spleen is not enlarged. A typical doll-like appearance results from a tendency to adiposity, particularly of the cheeks, breast, buttocks, and back of the arms and thighs. Xanthoma may be observed over the elbows, knees, buttocks, and hips.

Fasting blood glucose concentration may be extremely low, but it usually is in the range of 2 to 3 m*M*. Hypoglycemic convulsions and/or severe acidosis are the main causes of death, but profound hypoglycemia may occur without clinical symptoms. This is currently explained by the high (5 to 10 m*M*) concentration of blood lactate, which is a substitute for glucose as an energy source for the brain.[130] Strikingly, the concentration of ketone bodies is not elevated.[131,132] A value of 7.34 for fasting plasma pH has been reported by Zuppinger and Rossi,[133] who stressed that the patients tolerate severe chronic metabolic acidosis because of respiratory compensation and that the slightest respiratory derangement could lead to a very dangerous pH imbalance. Serum lipids are greatly increased, and this is mainly due to hypertriglyceridemia (up to 10 percent by volume[113]), which gives the serum a milky appearance. Cholesterol and phospholipids are only moderately increased. Hyperuricemia is a frequent finding, even during childhood, and increases with age, leading to clinical gout. The glucagonemia is about twice the normal value but can be normalized by an oral glucose load. Urine contains a large excess of lactate and 2-oxoglutarate,[134,135] and frequently of C-6 to C-10 dicarboxylic acids.[136] In older patients, protein-

Table 12-3 Tissue Glycogen Content in Glycogenosis*

Type of disease	*Liver glycogen conc. (% of wet weight)*	*Muscle glycogen conc. (% of wet weight)*
Type Ia	9.8 ± 2.4 (17)	0.73 ± 0.45 (10)
Ib	9.4 ± 2.7 (8)	
	9.0 ± 2.3 (17) [119]	
Type II		
Infantile	9.6 ± 2.7 (17)	10.1 ± 3.0 (21)
		8.4 ± 1.9 (21) [119]
Adult form	3.1 ± 1.9 (4)	2.7 ± 2.0 (4)
		1.2 ± 0.5 (14) [119]
Type IIIA	13.6 ± 2.6 (32)	5.6 ± 2.9 (34)
		5.3 ± 1.3 (16) [119]
IIIB	14.1 ± 2.2 (5)	1.2 ± 0.6 (5)
		0.9 ± 0.3 (5) [119]
Type IV	4.6 ± 0.5 (4)	—
Type V	—	3.3 ± 2.4 (5)
Type VI		
Without muscle involvement	11.3 ± 3.7 (24)	0.96 ± 0.35 (18)
With muscle involvement		3.0 ± 2.2 (8)
Controls	3.3 ± 1.7 (56)	0.94 ± 0.55 (76)
		1.02 ± 0.32 (36) [119]

*Mean ± SEM (number of patients).
SOURCE: Data from the authors' laboratory and from Ref. 119.

Table 12-4 Distribution of 1118 Patients among the Various Types of Glycogenosis

	(1)*	(2)*	(3)*	% of total
Type I	124	125	27	24.7%
(of which Ib)	(15)	(9)		
Type II	93	71	11	15.6%
Type III	124	108	15	22.1%
Type IV	5	22	2	2.6%
Type V	15	11		2.3%
Type VI	205	109	51	32.7%
Type VII	0	0		0%
Total	566	446	106	100%

*(1) Data from the authors' laboratory: 95 percent of these patients are Europeans, 17 percent are from Belgium. (2) Data from Ref. 119. (3) Information kindly provided by Dr. J. Fernandes, Department of Pediatrics, University Hospital, Groningen, The Netherlands. In an other series of 109 cases of hepatomegalic glycogenosis published by C. Baussan-Valette, Hôpital Bicêtre, Paris, in her thesis on hepatic glycogenoses (1986) 39 patients were of type I (9 of which were type Ib), 27 of type III, and 43 of type VI.

uria, indicative of a progressive renal dysfunction, has recently been reported as a frequent complication of the disease.[137] Osteoporosis is a common finding.

Severe nosebleeds and prolongation of the bleeding time in the absence of thrombocytopenia or coagulation factor deficiency have been documented in a large number of patients.[138] This has been attributed to a reduction of platelet adhesiveness,[139] secondary to hypoglycemia.[140]

The use of ultrasonography and liver scan have revealed a high incidence of adenomatous nodules developing mainly during the second decade.[141] These benign tumors are similar to those resulting from contraceptive steroids and can be associated with massive bleeding. A few of them apparently undergo malignant degeneration, with elevation of serum α-fetoprotein, leading to hepatoma or liver carcinoma.[142–144] It has been suggested[142] that adenomas are related to the hepatoproliferative action of glucagon,[145] since they tend to regress after adequate dietary treatment.[142]

Type Ib and Other Variants. In addition to the symptomatology described above, type Ib patients exhibit a predisposition for infection (recurrent otitis, pneumonia, multiple abscesses pyoderma, urinary tract infection, etc.), which is related to neutropenia. Although total white blood cell counts are normal, the neutrophil count may be as low as one-tenth of the lowest normal value. Various degrees of impairment of the neutrophil function have been observed.[146–154] One patient developed myelogenous leukemia.[155]

The heterogeneity of the Ib group is indicated by the fact that the in vivo functional deficiency of glucose-6-phosphatase could be demonstrated by the $^3H/^{14}C$ test in some patients,[156,157] although not in others.[149,158] In a few patients in the second group, there was also an extremely rapid, still unexplained, turnover of blood glucose.[159] The disease of these patients is called *pseudo type I glycogenosis.*[73]

The Biochemical Defect. In type Ia, glucose-6-phosphatase is completely or nearly completely inactive, if the assay is corrected for the activity of nonspecific phosphatases.[50] In type Ib, glucose-6-phosphatase is active after freezing and thawing of the liver sample or in the presence of detergent (deoxycholate), but totally or partially inactive in a fresh liver preparation. This situation indicates a deficiency of the glucose-6-phosphate translocase, T_1, but could theoretically also result from a deficiency of T_2, the translocase common to P_i, PP_i, and carbamyl phosphate (see Fig. 12-3). One can indeed assume that, in the absence of T_2, P_i would accumulate and competitively inhibit the enzyme. Since T_2 is required for the pyrophosphatase activity of intact microsomes, and since this activity was present in a case of glycogenosis Ib, Lange et al.[160] concluded that deficiency of T_1 was present. A deficiency in the glucose-6-phosphate transport system in the microsomes of one patient has also been demonstrated by Igarashi et al.[161] In another patient suspected of type I glycogenosis, Nordlie et al.[162] observed a 75 percent latency of glucose-6-phosphatase activity, but 100 percent latency of pyrophosphatase in fresh microsomes. They concluded that T_2 was deficient and called the corresponding disease type Ic glycogenosis. However, the expected progressive inhibition of glucose-6-phosphate hydrolysis by P_i accumulating in microsomes was not observed. Furthermore, the patient was diabetic, and since diabetes is known to affect the glucose-6-phosphatase system,[65,69] the genetic origin of the Ic abnormality remains to be established. Another alleged Ic patient was also clinically atypical.[163]

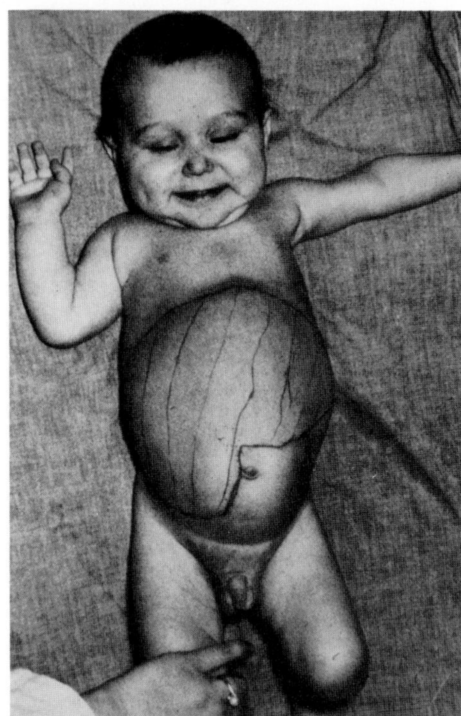

Fig. 12-6 A 9-month-old patient with type 1 glycogenosis. The liver contour has been outlined with a marking pencil (*Courtesy of Professor M. Odièvre, Hôpital A. Béclère, Clamart, France.*)

Functional Tests. Glucagon or epinephrine causes little or no hyperglycemia, but, typically, a marked increase in blood lactate occurs. The intravenous administration of galactose (1 g/kg) causes an increase in blood glucose concentration in a normal subject but not in a patient deficient in glucose-6-phosphatase.[164] This valuable test can also be performed with oral galactose (1.75 g/kg), and a flat curve is pathognomonic of the disease. The blood lactate always increases during the test. A glucose tolerance test detects hypoinsulinism and is also characterized by a decrease in blood lactate.[165]

A more complex functional test of the in vivo activity of glucose-6-phosphatase is based on the faster turnover rate of

[2-^{3}H] glucose than of [^{14}C] glucose. This difference is due to the fact that, during futile recycling between glucose and glucose-6-phosphate, tritium is lost from [2-^{3}H] glucose-6-phosphate during its reversible conversion to fructose-6-phosphate by hexose-6-phosphate isomerase, allowing [^{14}C] glucose but not [2-^{3}H] glucose to return to the blood under the action of glucose-6-phosphatase. In types Ia and Ib the ^{3}H/^{14}C ratio remains constant rather than decreases normally (see Fig. 12-7).

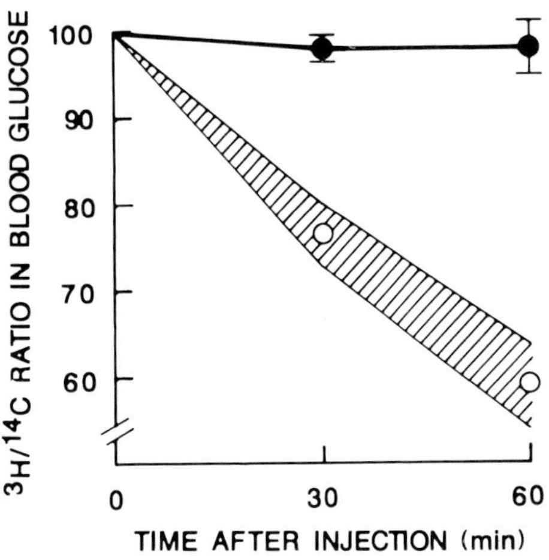

Fig. 12-7 Tritium/radiocarbon ratio ± SEM (shaded area) in blood glucose after injection of [2 − ^{3}H]glucose and [^{14}C]glucose ○ = controls (n = 12); ● = type I (nine cases of Ia and eight cases of Ib). *(Source: Prof. L. Hue, Laboratoire de Chimie Physiologique, Université Catholique de Louvain, Brussels, Belgium.)*

The Mechanism of Hyperlacticacidemia. In glucose-6-phosphatase deficiency, blood lactate reaches five- to tenfold the normal value (1 m*M*), in part because lactic acid, formed by extrahepatic tissues, mainly erythrocytes and muscle, cannot be converted to glucose by the liver, as it would be normally. Part of the lactate is eliminated by urinary excretion when the lacticacidemia exceeds the renal threshold which is 5 to 6 m*M*. Another important factor is that the liver, which normally consumes lactic acid and converts it to glucose, is now an abundant producer. This is because all the precursors normally converted to glucose in the liver are now converted to lactic acid. These include glycogen, galactose, fructose, glycerol, gluconeogenic amino acids, and glucose itself, since the futile cycle between glucose and glucose-6-phosphate (1 μmol/min per gram liver) is interrupted. Glycogen is degraded during fasting, but only 7 percent of its mass is converted to glucose by action of amylo-1,6-glucosidase on the α-1,6-linked glucose units. The rest of glycogen is converted to lactic acid.

The administration of glucose to these patients causes an important decrease, although not a normalization of the hyperlacticacidemia.[165] This can be explained since glucose arrests glycogenolysis and initiates glycogen synthesis.[75] One can calculate that the conversion of 1 m*M* lactate (0.5 mmol/kg body weight, assuming a lactate space of 50 percent) gives rise to only 0.04 percent glycogen in the liver (assuming that the liver represents 12 percent of the body weight in these patients[126]).

Following the initial observation of Lowe and Mosovich,[166] it has been repeatedly observed[133,167] that patients with type I glycogenosis are extremely resistant to the inebriating action of ethanol, which they metabolize at a rate two to five times faster than a normal subject. It is not clear if this fast rate is related to the increased liver size or to a faster reoxidation of NADH. Remarkably, ethanol infusion causes a considerable decrease in blood lactate and an even greater decrease in pyruvate, indicating an increase in the NADH/NAD$^+$ ratio. These data suggest an arrest of glycolysis or a stimulation of gluconeogenesis and of glycogen formation by an action at the level of triose-phosphate dehydrogenase. More difficult to understand is the absence of interference of ethanol in the metabolism of galactose in these patients, as well as their apparently normal hyperglycemic response to glucagon after ethanol administration.[166]

The Mechanism of Lipid Abnormalities. In glucose-6-phosphatase deficiency, the liver is in the fed state, while the peripheral tissues are paradoxically fasted.[168] The disease is indeed characterized by a block in the formation of glucose from both glycogenolysis and gluconeogenesis. As stated above, liver carbohydrates have, therefore, no other path than to be converted to lactic acid. This highly glycolytic condition is expected to increase fatty acid synthesis at the first step, acetyl CoA carboxylase, and raise the concentration of glycerol-3-phosphate. The malonyl CoA produced by acetyl CoA carboxylase inhibits carnitine palmitoyl transferase,[169] preventing the transfer of fatty acids into the mitochondria and thus preventing their β oxidation and further conversion to ketone bodies. Glycerol-3-phosphate is a precursor and a limiting factor[170] for the esterification of fatty acids. Therefore, the situation greatly favors the formation of triglycerides and of VLDL. If apolipoprotein becomes limiting, the excess triglyceride remains in the liver.

The fasting state of the periphery is due to the low concentration of glucose and to the associated low insulin/glucagon ratio. This results in an abundant release of free fatty acids and glycerol from the adipose tissue and a high level of these compounds in the blood.[171,172] A large fraction of these free fatty acids is taken up by the liver and esterified to form triglycerides, which will be either exported as VLDL or stored in lipid vacuoles. The excess VLDL formation explains the elevated plasma levels of triglycerides, phospholipids, and cholesterol, which are characteristic of the disease. Inhibition of β oxidation concurrent with an increased fatty acid flux also results in increased ω oxidation of fatty acids, producing elevated levels of dicarboxylic acids.[136]

The Mechanism of Hyperuricemia. Hyperuricemia is partly explained by competitive inhibition of renal tubular secretion of urate by lactate.[173–175] A second factor is an increase in purine synthesis, as indicated by a rise in labeled glycine incorporation into urinary uric acid.[176–177] This excessive production of uric acid is presumably secondary to an increased rate of purine catabolism, analogous to that known to operate after a fructose load and in which a decrease in P_i concentration plays a major role (see Chap. 11). P_i is a potent inhibitor of liver AMP deaminase, which catalyzes the rate limiting step in the conversion of adenine nucleotides to uric acid and which is normally 95 percent inhibited. Patients with glucose-6-phosphatase deficiency have a lower blood P_i level and an increased sensitivity to the hyperuricemic effect of fructose.[178]

The concentration of P_i is expected to be low in the liver of these patients because of the absence of its formation by glucose-6-phosphatase (normally about 1 μmol/min per gram of liver under basal conditions). It would be further decreased when glycogenolysis is in operation, as in the presence of glucagon, because of its storage as phosphate esters. Under this condition there is a paradoxical stimulation of glycolysis, despite the inactivation of pyruvate kinase by cyclic-AMP-dependent protein kinase. In fact, an accumulation of phosphate esters (hexose-6-phosphates, fructose-1,6-bisphosphate, and triose phosphates) and depletion of ATP were observed by Greene et al.[179] in the liver of patients after administration of glucagon. By contrast, the concentration of glucose-6-phosphate was in the normal range in liver biopsies taken under nonglycogenolytic conditions,[50,179] as expected when glycogen synthesis is in operation.[75]

The Endogenous Formation of Glucose. Several studies[180–184] performed on both adult and young patients clearly indicate that, contrary to expectation, some glucose can be formed from endogenous sources during fasting in type I glycogenosis. The rate of 4 mg/min per kilogram body weight[184] would correspond to a hepatic production of 0.2 μmol/min per gram liver, i.e., about one-fifth of the normal value under basal conditions. Three mechanisms might account for this endogenous production of glucose: (1) Amylo-1,6-glucosidase could liberate as glucose several times more than the theoretical 7 percent of the glycogen degraded by phosphorolysis (the rest appearing as lactate) if, because of the high concentration of glucose-6-phosphate, futile recycling occurs between glycogen and glucose-1-phosphate. (2) Acid α-glucosidase liberates as glucose all the glycogen degraded by autophagy; since the half-life of liver constituents has been estimated to be 50 h,[185] one calculates, assuming a glycogen concentration of 10 percent, that as much as 0.1 μmol glucose/min per gram of liver could be formed by this mechanism, particularly if one takes into account that glucagon stimulates autophagy.[186] (3) In some patients, the defect of glucose-6-phosphatase is not complete, and the residual activity is expected to be increased by fasting. It must be kept in mind that, if some glucose-6-phosphatase is present, its activity would also be greatly favored by the high concentration of its substrate observed after glucagon administration.[179] In favor of the first and second hypotheses and against the third is the fact that, in two studies,[183,184] the patients were unable to form any glucose from galactose or fructose.

Diagnosis. Glycogen storage disease type I is suggested by hypoglycemia in association with hyperlacticacidemia (above 3 m*M* under fasting conditions), which decreases after glucose administration and is increased after glucagon. These, in combination with hyperuricemia and an absence of hyperglycemia after a galactose load, in a patient with hepatic-type glycogen storage disease, gives a high probability of type I. Neutropenia and recurrent infections, when superimposed on this symptomatology, are highly suggestive of type Ib. Light or electron microscopy of the liver does not allow differentiation of the various forms of hepatomegalic glycogenosis, except for the fact that lipid overloading is usually highest in type I. The large amount of lipid present in the livers of these patients explains their relatively lower glycogen content (see Table 12-3).

The complete biochemical diagnosis of the disease requires the measurement of glucose-6-phosphate hydrolysis in a fresh liver biopsy in the presence and the absence of detergent. With a normal liver, the activity of the enzyme on glucose-6-phosphate is about the same with and without detergent. In type Ib, a latency of 90 to 95 percent is released by the addition of detergent. As described in Ref. 119, the assay can also be performed on frozen biopsies, but the latency will be less complete. Under these conditions, the extent of disruption of microsomes due to freezing and thawing can be estimated by the activity measured with 20 m*M* mannose-6-phosphate, which is not transported by the translocase. It is important to remember that all biochemical analyses are fallible and that their results should be considered with great caution when they markedly disagree with the clinical data, as was the case for two patients with a so-called partial type Ia glycogen storage disease.[163]

Treatment. The prognosis of type I glycogenosis has been dramatically improved since the introduction by Greene et al. in 1976[187] of nocturnal nasogastric infusion of a high glucose formula in addition to the usual frequent meals during daytime. By constantly maintaining a nearly normal level of blood glucose, this treatment causes a remarkable decrease, although not a normalization, of blood lactate, urate, and triglyceride and also of the bleeding time values. Another striking change is an accelerated rate of growth, which may reach 1 cm/month during the first year of treatment. The demonstrable decrease in hepatic size was attributable primarily to a decrease in triglyceride content rather than in glycogen content. The glucagonemia is markedly decreased, and insulinemia is increased.[188–190] Regression of adenoma was reported in one[142] but not in all[191] cases. The treatment is not without danger, since the patients are more sensitive to hypoglycemia probably because of the decreased lacticacidemia. Hypoglycemia can result from accidental interruption of feeding and lead to a fatal outcome.[192]

A second major improvement in the treatment, introduced by Chen et al.[193] in 1984, was the use of uncooked starch (a 50 percent suspension in tap water) in the regimen. Because of its slow degradation by α-amylase, this nutrient, at the dose of 2 g/kg body weight, allows for maintenance of a normal blood glucose level for as long as 6 h.[194,195] This regimen appears to be as effective as continuous nocturnal nasogastric feeding and is often preferred to it. Not all parents are able to cope with the technical and emotional stress of the infusion pump and tube feeding. Accidental interruption of the pump is indeed not exceptional. On the other hand, uncooked starch can induce diarrhea. Precise recommendations are available for the use of nocturnal nasogastric feeding and of uncooked starch in patients with hepatomegalic glycogenosis of various ages and severity.[196,197] Avoidance of lactose and sucrose is also recommended because of the rapid conversion of galactose and fructose into lactate and because of the phosphate trapping effect of fructose. Hyperuricemia is successfully treated with allopurinol.

Portacaval diversion, which is expected to decrease both the overfeeding of the liver and the fasting condition of the periphery, has given good results in the treatment of the hepatomegalic types of glycogenosis,[198,199] but failure has also been reported;[199a] it has no obvious advantage over the two methods described above. Hepatic transplantation has given excellent results in one case.[200] It should only be performed after failure of other therapy to prevent the most serious complications, such as bleeding adenomas or malignant degeneration. Malignant degeneration of adenomas would be revealed by an elevation of serum α-fetoprotein. Renal transplantation did not correct fasting hypoglycemia,[201] indicating a minor role for renal gluconeogenesis in glucose homeostasis.

The treatment of type Ib glycogenosis is essentially the same as described above, but no improvement of the neutropenia and recurrent infections are to be expected.[154] A dramatic and persistent increase in granulocyte count has been observed after portacaval diversion in one case[149] but not in another.[202] The responsive patient reported[149] was atypical since a normal release of glucose by the liver was observed by the $^3H/^{14}C$ method.

Type II Glycogenosis (Acid α-Glucosidase Deficiency)

History. In 1932, Pompe[203] described the case of a 7-month-old girl who died suddenly with idiopathic hypertrophy of the heart after a short illness. Histochemical investigation revealed a large excess of glycogen in nearly all tissues. A similar observation was almost simultaneously reported by Putschar.[204] The disease was known as Pompe disease or generalized glycogenosis and was classified by G. T. Cori[2] as type II glycogenosis. The striking cardiomegaly, which was considered characteristic by many authors, is not always present. The same disease had, therefore, been described as two different entities; one of them, known as glycogen disease of the heart, has been reviewed by Di Sant'Agnese et al.[205] whereas the other simulates Werdnig-Hoffmann disease, but with a high muscle glycogen content.[206] The common etiology was suspected by several authors and has been proven by the demonstration of an identical enzymic defect in tissues. Indeed, one of the five patients in which Hers[107] initially demonstrated the deficiency of acid α-glucosidase belonged to the second group. Subsequently patients with a relatively mild myopathy who survived to age 60 were found to lack acid α-glucosidase. Despite the great variation in the clinical manifestations, type II glycogenosis is defined as the situation in which acid α-glucosidase is deficient (reviewed in Refs. 113 to 123, 207, and 208).

Clinical Manifestations. Although nearly all types of cells are affected, functional impairment is mostly seen in heart, skeletal muscle, and nervous system. In the infantile form (Pompe disease), the symptoms usually become manifest during the first months of life, with poor motor activity, respiratory difficulties and cardiac failure. In many cases, the main symptom

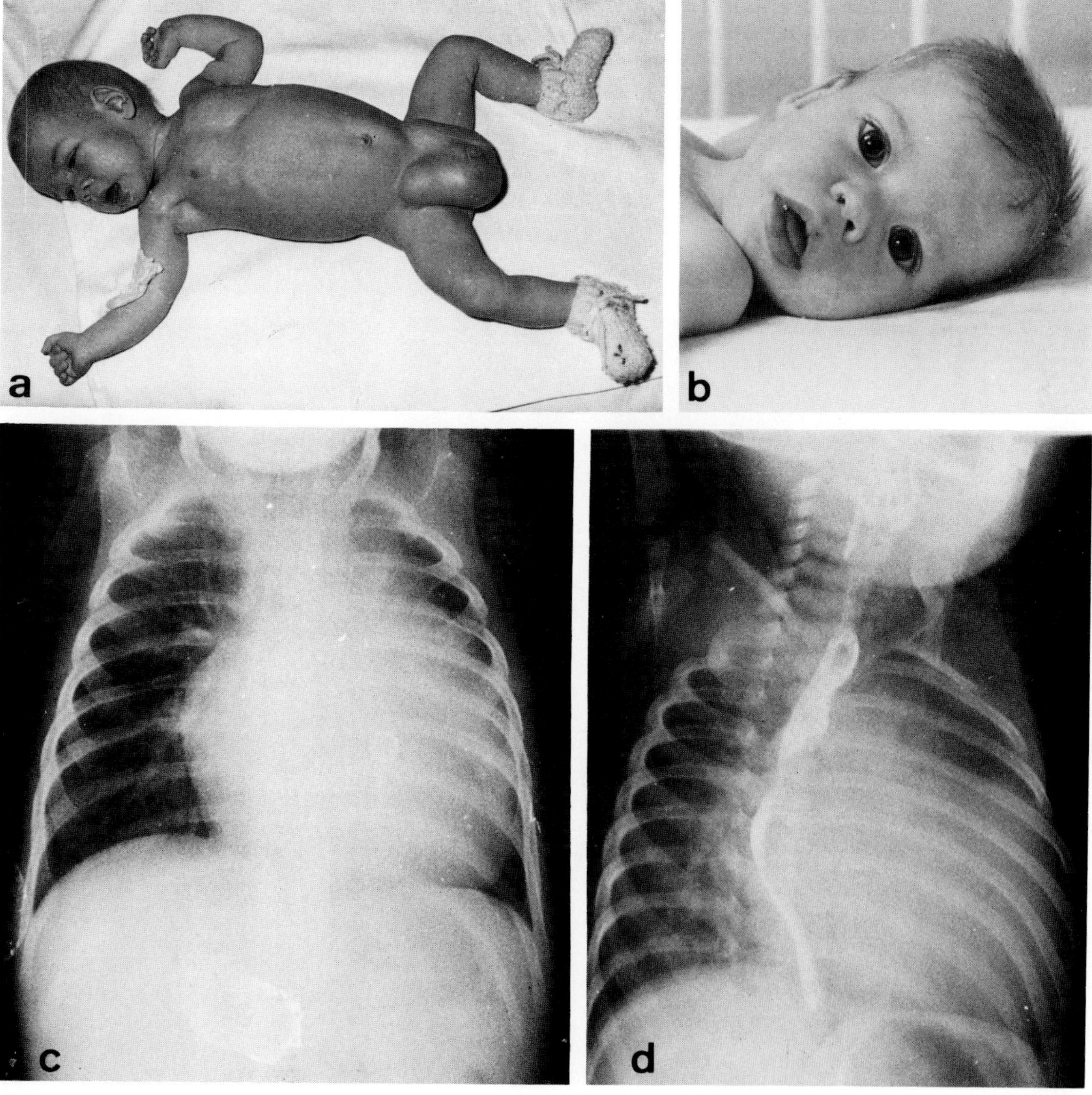

Fig. 12-8 A 4-month-old patient with severe hypotonia and protrusion of the tongue *A, B.* In this case, there were bilateral inguinoscrotal hernias. X-ray of the chest illustrates the large cardiac silhouette *C, D.*

is a progressive and general muscular weakness, patients being unable to hold their head or to sit; they lie in a flaccid position (Fig. 12-8). In general, the muscles are firm and hypertrophic; macroglossia is frequent; sucking and swallowing difficulties and an abnormal cry have often been reported. X-ray examination of the chest shows a large cardiac silhouette and, sometimes, complete opacity of the hemithorax caused by a secondary atelectasia of the lung. Electrocardiographic alterations include a marked left axis deviation, short P-R interval, large amplitude of the QRS, and inversion of the T wave. Electromyography reveals a myopathic pattern, with normal motor and sensory conduction velocities.

There is a sharp contrast between the gross motor dysfunction and the normal mental development. The liver becomes progressively enlarged, but its function is undisturbed. There is neither hypoglycemia nor ketosis, and the mobilization of glycogen by glucagon or epinephrine is normal. Most patients with cardiomegaly die from cardiac failure during the first year of life. When their hearts are not enlarged, patients can survive much longer, depending on the degree of muscular and neurologic dysfunction.

In the late infantile and juvenile cases, difficulty in walking is usually the first symptom of the disease. Physical examination reveals signs of progressive muscular dystrophy; visceromegaly is variable. Evolution can take many years until patients die from cardiorespiratory decompensation. Adult patients may have no complaint until the second or third decade; the condition develops progressively as a girdle myopathy (Fig. 12-9) beginning at the lower limbs and evolving slowly without hepatomegaly or cardiac signs except sometimes in the terminal phase. Electromyography is very useful in these cases, since it reveals a myopathic pattern usually with pseudomyotonic discharges, in the absence of clinical myotonia. Table 12-5 summarizes the main clinical features observed in 129 cases.

Clinical variation within a single sibship is limited, but the concurrence of the infantile (or juvenile) and the adult form in the same family, although not in the same sibship, has been reported.[209–211] This would be compatible with various compound heterozygous states.

Morbid Anatomy. When the heart is enlarged, its form is globular and its weight may reach 3 to 10 times the normal value. There is a striking enlargement of the ventricular walls without anatomic defect. Periodic acid-Schiff reaction reveals a large excess of glycogen in nearly all tissues.[208] Basophilic and metachromatic substances are often observed in skeletal muscle, brain, and heart.[208,212,213]

The ultrastructural examination of all tissues reveals the overloading of lysosomes which is typical of inborn lysosomal diseases. Baudhuin et al.[108] were the first to report the dual localization of glycogen, in both the hepatocytes and Kupffer cells. Whereas part of the polysaccharide was freely dispersed in the cytoplasm, as in normal liver, another part was segregated in vacuoles surrounded by a single membrane (see Fig. 12-10). In the hepatocytes, the shape of these vacuoles was very variable, and their diameter could exceed that of the nucleus. Glycogen was also present in a few smaller vacuoles together with myelinic figures. No normal dense bodies were seen. The intravacuolar glycogen was mostly of the α-particulate type. Glycogen-filled vacuoles were also present in Kupffer cells, but in these cells glycogen was segregated, as expected, in the form of β particles. The postmortem

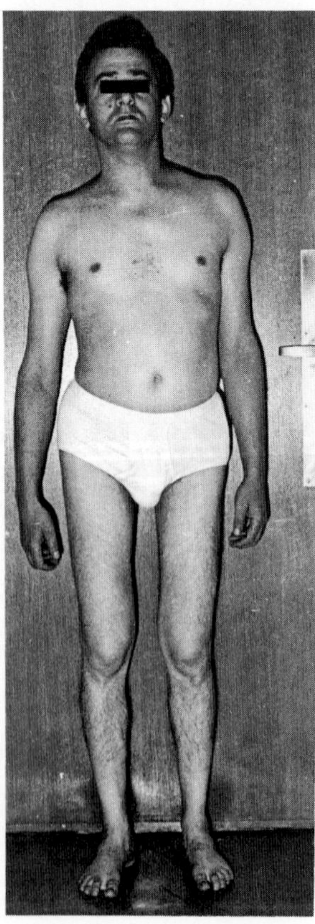
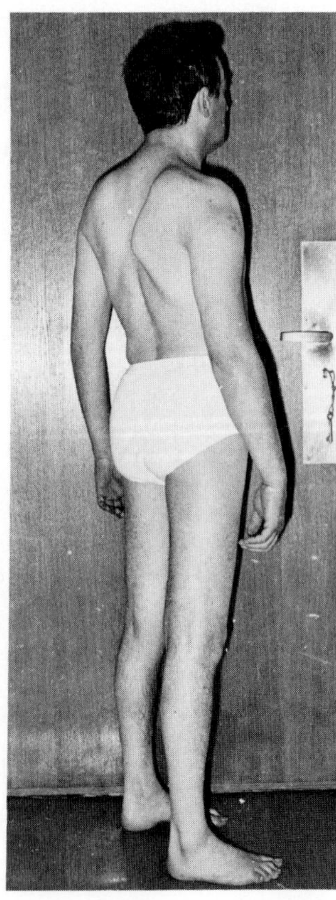
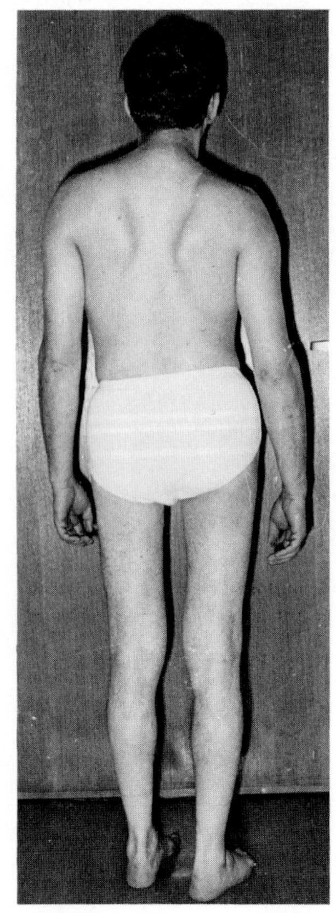

Fig. 12-9 A 42-year-old patient with type II glycogenosis. Muscular wasting is more pronounced in the lower limbs, and there is winging of the scapulae. Note also scoliosis and lordosis. (*From Ref. 208.*)

Table 12-5 Clinical Features in 129 Patients with Type II Glycogenosis

Type	*No. of cases*	*Age of onset, years*			*Age at death, years*			*Muscular weakness*	*Cardio-megaly*	*Hepato-megaly*	*Macro-glossia*	*Involvement of respiratory muscles*
		<2	*2–15*	*>15*	*<2*	*2–15*	*>15*					
Infantile	78*	77	1	0	71	1	0	75	74	64	48	75
Juvenile	24†	14	10	0	0	7	2	24	1	7	2	9
Adult	27	0	0	27	0	0	5	27	0	1	1	11

*36 males and 42 females.
†16 males and 8 females.
SOURCE: This series includes 73 cases from Ref. 120 and 56 cases from the authors' laboratory.

examination of the liver of the same patient revealed that free cytoplasmic glycogen had disappeared, whereas glycogen present inside vacuoles was unaltered, illustrating the different metabolic fate of the two pools of polysaccharide. Later, the same ultrastructure was also observed in kidney, lymphocytes, epithelial and perithelial cells of blood vessels, skin, cultured fibroblasts, and nervous system, mainly in the glial cells and in the neurons of the brain stem. In the skeletal and heart muscles, a large part of the glycogen seems to be extravacuolar, but in all cases, glycogen-filled vacuoles were observed.[208,212]

In the juvenile and adult cases, glycogen-filled vacuoles were regularly observed in the muscle and also occasionally in liver.[214] A large variation in glycogen content and morphologic abnormalities were observed from muscle to muscle even in the same patient.[215–218] Brain and heart are unaffected.[218]

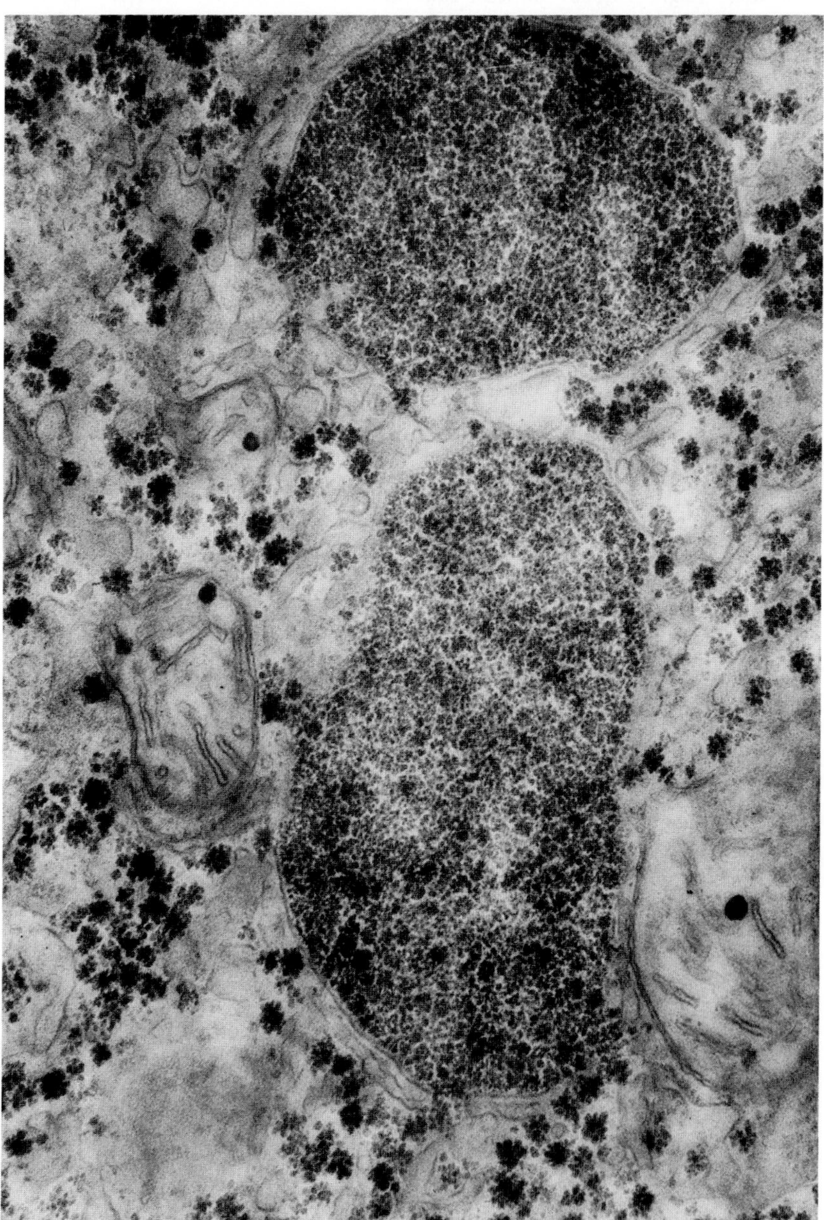

Fig. 12-10 Electron micrograph of a portion of a hepatic parenchymatous cell from a liver biopsy of a patient with type II glycogenosis. Two vacuoles filled with glycogen are shown. A membrane can be followed around most of the periphery of the vacuoles. (Magnification ×87,000.) (*From Ref. 108.*)

The Enzymic Defect. In the infantile cases, the capacity of acid α-glucosidase to hydrolyze maltose and to catalyze transglucosylation from maltose onto glycogen is close to zero in liver and muscle.[107] Juvenile and adult cases often show some residual acid α-glucosidase activity, but there are exceptions to this rule. Furthermore, cases have been reported in which the transferase activity was much more affected than the hydrolytic one.[159,215,217] de Barsy et al.[219] have also described the case of an 8-year-old boy in whom the two activities of the enzyme were normal in muscle but severely reduced in leukocytes and in cultured fibroblasts. Other cases with intralysosomal glycogen strorage, but normal activity of acid α-glucosidase in the muscle, were subsequently reported.[220–222]

The genetic heterogeneity of the defect has been intensively investigated by Tager and his coworkers[223–226] in cultured fibroblasts from patients. They observed that, like other lysosomal enzymes, acid α-glucosidase is synthesized as a precursor form (molecular weight = 105,000) in the endoplasmic reticulum and then modified by addition of a mannose-6-phosphate recognition signal which allows its transport to the lysosomes, where it is partially degraded into a mature form of molecular weight 76,000. At least four different mutations were found to affect the formation or maturation of acid α-glucosidase, but a clear correlation with the clinical expression of the disease could not be established.

Recently, the cDNA for human acid α-glucosidase has been isolated and was found to hybridize with a 3.4-kb mRNA, a value which is consistent with the size of the precursor protein. This cDNA was used for the analysis of the corresponding mRNA of three patients. In one cell line originating from an infantile case, the 3.4-kb mRNA was present, but it was undetectable in another. In one adult-onset cell line, an mRNA of reduced size and amount was found.[227]

Pathophysiology. Acid α-glucosidase deficiency was the first inborn lysosomal disease to be clearly defined and has been a model for delineating the pathogenesis of other storage diseases.[228,229] It has been assumed that the deficiency of the lysosomal glucosidase causes the intravacuolar deposition of glycogen and also, possibly, of other molecules with an α-glucosidic moiety which would require the same enzyme for their degradation. The "nonglycogen polysaccharide" reported to accumulate in the muscles of patients with glycogenosis type II[230] could be such a molecule, the presence of which was predicted by the lysosomal theory. The presence of a normal amount of cytosolic glycogen in the liver and its normal availability for phosphorolytic degradation explain that the patients never become hypoglycemic and respond normally to hyperglycemic hormonal stimulation. The excess glycogen is expected to be, at least initially, in the vacuolar system. This was observed in the liver and also in most types of cells. However, in muscle, most of the polysaccharide appears to be extravacuolar. As discussed in Refs. 208 and 212, this may reflect the fact that the glycogen is so densely packed in the skeletal muscle of these patients that surrounding membranes are difficult to see. Another possibility is that the intense mechanical pressure exerted on the large vacuoles during muscular contraction provokes the rupture of the lysosomal membrane, perhaps allowing lysosomal contents to be released into the cytosol.[231,232]

Diagnosis. The diagnosis rests on the determination of acid α-glucosidase activity, mostly in muscle or liver. Leukocytes can also be used.[233] However, one must be aware of potential tissue heterogeneity,[219] and a correction needs to be introduced for the interference of a nonlysosomal isoenzyme. This can be done by using glycogen as substrate in the presence of antibodies directed against the lysosomal enzyme[234,235] or by removing the interfering activity by isoelectric precipitation at pH 5[236] or by high speed centrifugation.[237] Cultured amniotic cells[238] and chorionic villi[239] have been used for prenatal diagnosis. The electron-microscopic demonstration of glycogen-filled lysosomes is by itself highly suggestive of type II glycogenosis and has proved useful for prenatal diagnosis when applied to uncultured fetal cells.[240] However, prenatal diagnosis should rest on enzyme assay.

In the infantile form, the concentration of glycogen is approximately 10 percent in liver and muscle. In the adult cases, this concentration is only slightly elevated or even in the normal range (see Table 12-3). Highly variable concentrations are found in the juvenile form.

Genetics. All data indicate an autosomal recessive mode of transmission. Detection of heterozygotes has tentatively been proposed, by using leukocytes,[234,241] muscle,[242] or other material[243] as a source of enzyme. This is true for many diseases and is of very little interest in type II. The acid α-glucosidase locus has been localized on chromosome 17.[244,245]

Treatment. As pointed out by de Duve,[246] the fact that substances taken into cells by endocytosis are likey to end up within lysosomes opens up, in lysosomal diseases, many possibilities for therapeutic interaction, including replacement therapy. It was therefore logical to expect that the uptake of the purified enzyme by the affected cells would allow a normalization of their enzymic equipment. In order to prevent a rapid destruction by cathepsins in lysosomes and to avoid immunologic complications, this purified enzyme should be of lysosomal and human origin. Human placenta and urine are potential sources of such enzymes, and this therapeutic approach has been successfully applied to fibroblast cultures from the skin of an infantile patient.[247] However, in patients in whom the enzymic protein has never been formed, even the human enzymes might be recognized as foreign and rejected by antibodies. A major limitation of this therapeutic approach is that some tissues, such as muscle and nervous tissue, display only a weak if any endocytic activity. Furthermore, brain is protected by the blood-brain barrier.

A first unsuccessful attempt was made by Baudhuin et al.[108] with a commercial extract of *Aspergillus niger* containing enzymes with α-amylase, α-amyloglucosidase, and maltase activities. Subsequently, other similar attempts,[248] including one with purified human placental enzyme,[249] gave negative results regarding muscle and brain pathology.

Animal Models. A deficiency of acid α-glucosidase with vacuolar deposition of glycogen has been observed in cattle.[250] A herd of these cattle was established, in which recessive autosomal transmission was clearly apparent. Of seven affected animals, two have shown cardiomegaly and died of heart failure at ages 3 and 5 months. The five other animals remained clinically normal until 9 months of age when they failed to maintain weight gain and showed muscular weakness.[251] A deficiency of acid α-glucosidase has also been observed in a Lapland dog[252] with a high level of glycogen in muscles, whereas a vacuolar glycogen deposition, suggestive of the same disorder, was reported in a flock of sheep,[253] in one cat,[254] and in Japanese quail.[255]

Type III Glycogenosis (Amylo-1,6-Glucosidase Deficiency)

History. In 1952, Illingworth and Cori[256] recognized the abnormal structure of the glycogen present in excess in both the liver and muscles of a patient who had been investigated clinically by Forbes.[257] Because this glycogen had very short outer chains, as in a phosphorylase limit dextrin, they suspected a deficiency in amylo-1,6-glucosidase, and this was actually demonstrated in 1956.[258] The disease is also called limit dextrinosis or Forbes disease.

General Description. The deficiency of amylo-1,6-glucosidase is generalized to all types of cell, and its clinical manifestations include the hepatic and the muscular symptomatology reported above, but with varying severity from patient to patient and at different ages (see Tables 12-1 and 12-2). During infancy and childhood, the disease is difficult to distinguish from type I, and there is usually no complaint of muscular disease. The heart may be clinically affected and cardiac failure with sudden death has been reported, even in infancy.[259,260] Hepatomegaly tends to disappear after puberty, and some patients reexamined in adult life were clinically normal.

Muscular symptoms appear mostly in adult life and only in some patients. They consist of a slowly progressive weakness with wasting. Among 23 adult cases with muscular manifestation reviewed,[121,123] there was a large preponderance of males over females (16/6). Seven of these patients already had manifestations of the disease during childhood, and 13 still had hepatomegaly. The response to epinephrine or glucagon was abnormal in all cases tested; 14/17 of the patients had an abnormal ECG, 15/17 had an abnormal EMG. In one adult patient with unsteady gait, an abnormal accumulation of glycogen was observed in peripheral nerve axons.[261]

Genetic Heterogeneity. In 1968, Van Hoof and Hers[262] measured the activity of amylo-1,6-glucosidase by four methods in the livers and muscles of 45 patients with type III glycogenosis. They found that, in 34 patients, the enzyme was inactive in both tissues, whatever the method used for its detection; this group was classified as IIIA. In the other patients, an important residual activity of amylo-1,6-glucosidase could be detected either in the muscle (IIIB) or in the liver, or only by some of the methods used. In all cases, the stored polysaccharide had the structure of a phosphorylase limit dextrin.

Functional Tests and Diagnosis. As already discussed, type III can be distinguished from type I by a normal or even exaggerated hyperglycemic response to galactose and usually also by a lower level of blood lactate and urate. It can be distinguished from type VI by the absence of hyperglycemic response to glucagon under fasting conditions and by the presence of a hyperglycemic response 2 h after a meal. There is no rise in blood lactate during this test.

In most patients, the biochemical analysis can be done on erythrocytes, which contain a large excess of glycogen and show deficiency of amylo-1,6-glucosidase.[263] In case of doubt, the enzymic analysis should be repeated on a muscle or liver biopsy, in which the abnormal structure of glycogen is also pathognomonic of the disease. The presence of an excess of glycogen in the muscle, as well as of an excess of plasma creatine kinase at rest (see Table 12-1), is strongly against a diagnosis of type I or type VI. The defect in muscle glycogenolysis can also be demonstrated, like in type V, by the forearm ischemic exercise test, which causes either absence or reduction of the rise in blood lactate.

Genetics. The transmission is clearly autosomal recessive. Prenatal diagnosis is possible.[119,264] The frequency of type III is elevated (1/5400 births) in non-Ashkenazi Jewish communities of North African extraction.[265]

Treatment. The treatment is similar to but usually less stringent than that of type I, most patients tolerating longer fasting periods.

Animal Model. Type III glycogenosis has been observed in a 15-month-old dog with muscular weakness.[266]

Type IV Glycogenosis (Branching Enzyme Deficiency)

History and General Description. In 1952, Andersen[267] described the case of an infant who was suspected of glycogen storage disease because of a very large liver and poor hyperglycemic response to epinephrine; however, the level of blood glucose rose after an intravenous administration of galactose, therefore excluding a deficiency of glucose-6-phosphatase. The spleen was also enlarged, but not the kidneys. Subsequently, the patient developed ascites and died at 17 months of age with cirrhosis. At autopsy, Andersen encountered difficulty in extracting glycogen from the liver and was struck by its poor solubility and by its abundance in the reticuloendothelial system. Considering that this glycogen was abnormal, she sent it for further analysis to G.T. Cori, who recognized its amylopectinlike structure and suspected a deficiency of the branching enzyme.[2,256] This deficiency was actually demonstrated by Brown and Brown in 1966.[268] The disease is also called amylopectinosis or Andersen disease.

Type IV glycogen storage disease is very rare (see Table 12-4). Patients usually appear normal at birth and for some months thereafter. There is then an insidious onset with nonspecific gastrointestinal symptoms and progressive hepatosplenomegaly, leading to cirrhosis with portal hypertension, prominence of the superficial veins over the abdomen, ascites and esophageal varices. There is only one report of an abnormally low level of blood glucose.[268a] However, the response to glucagon or epinephrine has been found to be normal, subnormal, or flat.[269–273] Neuromuscular abnormalities include poor development, hypotonia, muscular atrophy, and decreased or absent tendon reflexes.[273] Death usually occurs before the third year of life, but two patients survived 8 years.[119,273a] Exceptionally, cardiopathy and exercise intolerance predominated over the liver symptoms.[273a] The report of an adult case of amylopectinosis[274] was poorly documented.

The Glycogen Abnormality. The concentration of glycogen in the liver does not exceed 5 percent. Liver and heart cells contain cytoplasmic periodic acid-Schiff positive deposits, which are stained purple-brown, or blue with iodine[269,271] and are partially resistent to amylase digestion. Ultrastructural studies show cytoplasmic deposits consisting of three components: glycogen particles, fibrils, and finely granular material (see Fig. 12-11). Hepatocytes also contain normal α-particulate glycogen.[271,273] Abnormal glycogen is detected histochem-

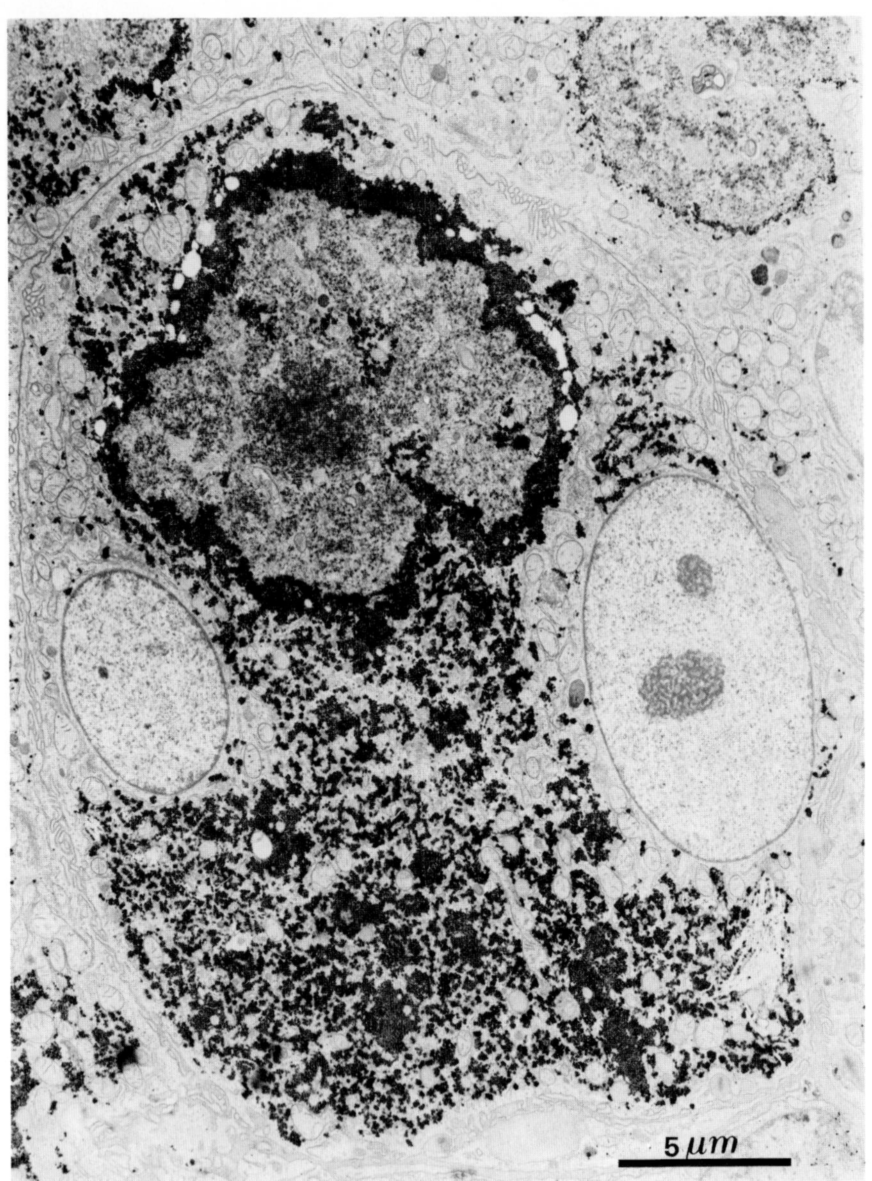

Fig. 12-11 Electron micrograph of a liver biopsy from a patient with type IV glycogenosis. A binucleated hepatocyte contains a large targetlike inclusion, rich in filamentous material, and also normal α-glycogen particles dispersed in the rest of the cytoplasm.

ically, ultrastructurally, or chemically, but in very variable amounts, not only in the liver but also in numerous other tissues, including skeletal muscle, heart, spleen, rectal mucosa, and nervous tissue.[269,273,275,276] Levin et al.[270] reported that only about 50 percent of the liver glycogen could be extracted by cold trichloroacetic acid, and this fraction was readily soluble in water and gave a brown-red color with iodine. Furthermore, degradation of this glycogen by β-amylase was in the normal range. Glycogen extracted with hot KOH was much less soluble and formed a blue complex with iodine. Chain length analysis revealed its similarity with amylopectin (3.5 percent branch points, as compared with 6.7 in normal glycogen). However, more refined analysis of the type IV polysaccharide has revealed important differences with amylopectine.[277,278] Ultrastructural, histochemical, and chemical similarities among the deposits in type IV glycogenosis, those in basophilic degeneration of the myocardium, Lafora bodies and visceral deposits in myoclonus epilepsy, and corpora amylacea suggest a common structure and possibly common etiologic factors.[279]

Pathogenesis. At first view, the deficiency of branching enzyme does not offer a satisfactory explanation for a situation in which normal α-particulate glycogen is associated with an amylopectinlike polysaccharide, which is itself a highly branched structure. It is known, however, that the reaction catalyzed by amylo-1,6-glucosidase is slightly reversible,[49] and Huijing et al.[280] could demonstrate the formation of glycogen from glucose-1-phosphate by an association of that enzyme with phosphorylase. It seems, therefore, that the several types of glycogen present in the tissues of patients with amylopectinosis could be formed by the combined action of glycogen synthase and either amylo-1,6-glucosidase[280] or a residual branching enzyme activity.[281] The poor solubility of the abnormal glycogen appears to be the origin of the cellular injuries, including deposition of an amylopectinlike material in lysosomes, mostly of the reticuloendothelial system. The presence of normal glycogen explains the absence of hypoglycemia.

Genetics. All data, including affected sibs[267] and consanguinity of the parents,[272] point to an autosomal recessive transmission of the disease.

Diagnosis. The diagnosis rests essentially on the abnormal glycogen structure and on the determination of the branching enzyme deficiency in muscle, leukocytes, cultured fibroblasts, or amniotic cells.[268,272,282] Prenatal diagnosis is feasible.[119]

Treatment. Liver transplantation[268a,283] deserves serious consideration, since it is expected to relieve the major symptomatology, although one has to keep in mind that many tissues other than the liver are affected.

Type V Glycogenosis (Muscle Phosphorylase Deficiency)

History and General Description. In 1951, McArdle[284] described the case of a 30-year-old man who suffered from muscular pain, weakness, and stiffness following slight exercise. In contrast to normal, blood lactate fell during exercise. The epinephrine-induced rise in blood lactate was less marked than normal. Exercise of a muscle which had been rendered ischemic resulted in the development of swelling due to contracture (defined as a reversible shortening of the muscle fiber, unassociated with electrical activity). From these observations, McArdle concluded that his patient was unable to convert muscle glycogen into lactate. The deficiency of muscle phosphorylase was clearly established in 1958 by several groups of investigators[285–287] in very similar cases.

As reviewed earlier[113–123,288] the disease is usually diagnosed in the second or third decade, though many patients remember fatigability during childhood and adolescence. Typically, cramps occur after exercise. Moderate exercise, such as walking on level ground, can be performed by most patients at their own pace, even for long periods. More vigorous activities can also be accomplished if they are intermittent. Many patients experience a characteristic "second wind" phenomenon; if they can sustain the exercise after symptoms appear, the pain disappears after a few minutes even though exercising is prolonged. Grand mal seizures following strenuous exercise have been reported. The concentration of serum creatine kinase at rest is usually elevated and may reach many times the normal value after exercise. The increases in blood ammonia, inosine, and hypoxanthine, which are normally observed after anoxic exercise, are exaggerated,[289,290] indicating an excessive degradation of the adenine nucleotide pool. By contrast, ^{31}P NMR measurements of ATP concentration in the muscle showed only a slight reduction under similar conditions.[291–293] Electromyography may reveal a myogenic pattern. Table 12-6 summarizes the main clinical and laboratory findings and their frequency.

As indicated in the table, about half of the patients have experienced occasional benign myoglobinuria. There are also a few reports of renal failure,[294,295] one of them persisting for 18 days, following intense myoglobinuria and a 2000-fold increase in serum creatine kinase. These patients were men who had performed vigorous exercise during which they were aware that they were exceeding their usual tolerance.

The absence of symptomatology during infancy and often childhood is unexplained. Remarkably, two unrelated patients had no complaint until the age of 74,[296,297] an observation which shows that some adults deficient in muscle phosphorylase can escape clinical detection. Failure of detection in females could explain the male preponderance of about 2/1 (Table 12-6) since males probably are required to exercise their muscles more intensively than females. The same comment applies to the muscular manifestations in types III, VI, and VII.

Table 12-6 Main Clinical Laboratory Features in 74 Patients with Type V Glycogenosis

	Incidence	%
Age of onset : <20 years	68/74	92
>20 years	6/74	8
Exercise intolerance	71/74	96
Myoglobinuria	38/74	51
Renal failure	5/74	7
Seizures	4/74	5
Permanent muscular weakness	16/71	22
Positive family history	39/74	53
Creatine kinase elevated at rest	31/33	94
Abnormal EMG at rest	10/25	40

SOURCE: This series includes 51 males and 23 females. Sixty-two cases are from Ref. 120 and 12 cases from the authors' laboratory.

The Enzymic Defect and the Mode of Transmission. A complete deficiency of skeletal muscle phosphorylase has been demonstrated in may cases, either by direct biochemical methods or by a histochemical procedure. The familial distribution of affected individuals clearly points to an autosomal recessive mode of transmission. Phosphorylase activity can, however, be detected histochemically in regenerating fibers, which are particularly abundant in biopsies after an episode of myoglobinuria, and can also be observed in muscle cells in culture.[298,299] When measured biochemically, this activity would represent about 0.1 percent of the normal value. It is not due to normal muscle phosphorylase but to both the fetal and liver forms of enzyme.[300,301] Phosphorylase of the smooth muscles is normally active.[302–303]

The genetic heterogeneity of the disease became apparent when it was reported that, in the muscle of some patients, a variable amount (from 1 to more than 100 percent of the normal) of inactive protein could be measured by immunologic methods[294,304,305] or by electrophoresis in sodium dodecylsulfate.[306] Furthermore, it has been reported that when a muscle extract of this type was dialyzed and then incubated with ATP-Mg, cyclic AMP, and either cyclic-AMP-dependent protein kinase or phosphorylase kinase (two enzymes expected to be already present in the extract), phosphorylase was phosphorylated and became active.[307] This surprising observation of an in vitro repair of the enzymic defect cannot be explained on the basis of our present biochemical knowledge. Molecular heterogeneity has also been demonstrated at the level of mRNA, which was absent in some cases but present in decreased amounts in others.[308,309]

There are also in the literature two reports of an apparently dominant transmission of the disease.[310,311] In one of these two families,[311] a defect of phosphorylase was demonstrated histochemically in a mother and her son. The completeness of the defect could be explained in both patients if they are homozygotes for the autosomal recessive trait, in which case the "pseudodominant" inheritance could be explained by assuming that the father was a heterozygote.

The gene for muscle phosphorylase has been cloned and mapped to chromosome 11q13-11qter.[311a]

Diagnosis. The absence of venous lactate response to ischemic work is characteristic of all diseases in which there is an impairment in the conversion of glycogen or glucose to lactate in the muscle. This includes the deficiencies in muscle phosphorylase, phosphorylase *b* kinase, amylo-1,6-glucosidase, glucosephosphate isomerase, phosphofructokinase-1, or other glycolytic enzymes. As initially described by McArdle,[284] a sphygmomanometer cuff placed about the upper arm is inflated above the systolic pressure, and the subject squeezes the sphygmomanometer bulb once every second for 1 min. Affected patients are usually unable to perform the work for more than 40 to 50 s. The cuff is released after 1 min. The evolution of venous lactate concentration is schematized in Fig. 12-12. If there is no rise in blood lactate, it is essential to measure the activity of muscle phosphorylase, phosphofructokinase-1, or possibly other enzymes to distinguish between the various disorders listed above. The determination of ammonia in these blood samples would reveal a normal or exaggerated rise,[312] whereas a flat curve would be observed in patients with AMP deaminase deficiency.[313]

Morphologic alterations of the muscle include excess of glycogen in subsarcolemmal and intermyofibrillar spaces and disorganization of the myofibrillar structure at the level of the I band.[314,315] The enzymic defect can be demonstrated by biochemical or histochemical[316] techniques.

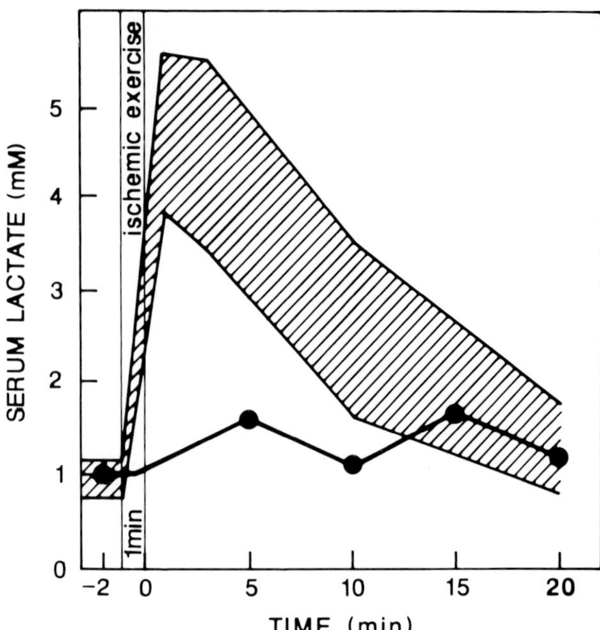

Fig. 12-12 Effect of ischemic work of the forearm muscles on the blood lactate in normal subjects (shaded area) and in a patient (●) with McArdle syndrome (muscle phosphorylase deficiency).

Pathophysiology. Resting or minimally active muscle derives most of its energy from the oxidation of fatty acids. During intense muscular contraction, the oxygen supply becomes insufficient for the aerobic oxidative mechanism. A further limitation arises from the relatively slow rate of entry of lipds and carbohydrate nutrients into the muscle fiber. Then glucose units are promptly released from glycogen by phosphorolysis and fed into the glycolytic pathway. Normally the transition from aerobic to predominantly anaerobic (from rest to active) metabolism is detectable only by the formation of lactate, which rapidly diffuses into the blood.[317] The ATP content of the muscle does not decrease markedly (maximally from about 5 to 3.5 μmol/g[318–320]), but changes in energy-rich phosphate occur with phosphocreatine decreasing from about 17 to 4 μmol/g, with an equivalent rise in P_i. The degradation of the adenine nucleotide pool after strenuous exercise is reflected in a rise in the concentration of blood ammonia, produced by the deamination of AMP to IMP, and also of hypoxanthine and even of uric acid.[318]

Muscle fatigue is defined as the inability to maintain a given power output. Its mechanism is poorly understood. In sustained exercise, muscle glycogen consumption is progressive, and exhaustion occurs when the polysaccharide store is depleted. In various individuals, the time taken to the point of fatigue is directly proportional to the initial level of glycogen in the muscle.[319] Contracture, cramp, and the second wind phenomenon may also be observed in normal exercising subjects.[317] Alteration of the muscle membrane is reflected by the appearance of several typical muscle enzymes and of myoglobin in the plasma. Because of its low molecular weight, myoglobin is rapidly excreted in the urine. In McArdle patients, all these normal manifestations of muscular fatigue occur under much milder exercising conditions because of the inability to utilize glycogen. The only surprise is the relative mildness of the disease. Because a clear decrease in ATP has not been demonstrated in the muscle of patients after exercise,[291–293] Lewis and Haller[321] recently hypothesized that the premature fatigue of McArdle patients could be due to an inhibition of the myofibrillar Ca^{2+} and Na^+-K^+-ATPase reactions by the excess of P_i and ADP.

The beneficial effects of glucose and of glucagon (acting as a hyperglycemic agent) are probably mediated by the secondary hyperinsulinemia, which allows the penetration of the sugar into the muscle. They are also favored by the remarkably low intracellular concentration of glucose-6-phosphate[322] a potent inhibitor of muscle hexokinase.[65] The increased concentration of plasma free fatty acids and the low respiratory quotient registered during the second wind indicates that this phenomenon results from the mobilization of free fatty acids, presumably secondary to catecholamine stimulation of adipocyte lipase.[323] The high blood flow through the muscles after ischemic exercise[284] may also be of importance.

Treatment. Oral administration of glucose and injection of glucagon provide transient improvement of some patients but should not be recommended on a long-term basis. Ubiquinone[322] and a protein-rich diet[324] have been reported to cause a prolonged improvement, each in a single patient. In general, there is no need for a specific therapy, other than avoidance of excessively strenuous exercise.

Rare Clinical Variants. DiMauro and Hartlage[325] described the case of a 12-week-old girl with muscle phosphorylase deficiency and marked muscular weakness who died of progressive hypoxia and acidosis. The sister of this patient was also affected and died at the age of 4 months. An electrophoretic investigation of the phosphorylase isoenzymes present in her heart revealed the absence of the slow muscle isoenzyme and of the intermediary hybrid normally formed by the skeletal and cardiac isoenzymes. The fast cardiac isoenzyme was present and normally active.[326] It is likely that a similar situation exists in other patients with myophosphorylase deficiency and explains why they do not have clinical heart disease. Two other infantile patients of myophosphorylase deficiency were reported.[327,328]

Type VI Glycogenosis (Liver Phosphorylase or Phosphorylase *b* Kinase Deficiency)

History and General Description. Three patients, one boy and two girls, with the hepatomegalic type of glycogen storage disease, normal activities of glucose-6-phosphatase and amylo-1,6-glucosidase, but a greatly diminished activity of phosphorylase in their livers, were described by Hers in 1959.[329] This residual phosphorylase could not be reactivated upon incubation of the liver extract with ATP and cyclic AMP. Considering the complexity of the phosphorylase system, no conclusion was drawn at that time on the precise nature of the primary defect responsible for the disease. The glycogen content was normal in the muscle of these patients. This form of glycogen-storage disease has been classified as type VI or Hers disease by Stetten and Stetten.[330]

In 1966, Hug et al.[331] described another girl with a low activity of liver phosphorylase that could not be reactivated on incubation with ATP and Mg^{2+}, unless exogenous phosphorylase *b* kinase was added. Although no direct measurement of phosphorylase *b* kinase had been performed, they concluded that the cause of the disorder was the deficiency of that enzyme.

Huijing[332] and Huijing and Fernandes[333] described a series of patients with an X-linked hepatomegalic glycogenosis in whom a deficiency of phosphorylase *b* kinase could be demonstrated in leukocytes and erythrocytes. Other reports of X-linked phosphorylase *b* kinase deficiency have indicated an almost complete defect of that enzyme in the liver and a normal activity in the muscle.[334,335]

As summarized by Lederer et al.[336] type VI includes at least three different genetic defects: (1) the X-linked phosphorylase *b* kinase deficiency, in which the muscle enzyme is unaffected[333]; (2) the autosomal phosphorylase *b* kinase deficiency, which affects both liver and muscle[337,338]; (3) the deficiency of liver phosphorylase, which may be complete[339,340] or partial.[336] Although Huijing[341] initially suggested that the X-linked disorder be classified as type VIa, different numbers have been used by different authors, and it is best to refer to this disorder as X-linked phosphorylase *b* kinase deficiency and omit a numerical designation. Similarly, autosomal recessive phosphorylase *b* kinase deficiency should be so designated without numerical assignment. The clinical manifestations of all three disorders are essentially those of a mild form of hepatomegalic glycogenosis, without hyperlacticacidemia and hyperuricemia. Strikingly, most of these patients respond normally to the hyperglycemic action of glucagon. The evolution is usually benign. Puberty is not retarded, and scholarship as well as social outcome are normal (see Table 12-2). These patients can, however, develop liver adenomas and malignant tumors (three deaths in our series of 205 patients) or liver cirrhosis with esophageal varices (two cases in our series). Clinical muscle involvement in patients with the autosomal recessive form of phosphorylase kinase deficiency has rarely been reported. It was mild in a 4-year-old patient[339] but of the McArdle type in a 35-year-old man.[342]

It is also of interest to mention that phosphorylase *b* kinase activity was undetectable in the heart of a patient who died at the age of 5 months from heart failure. The heart contained 6 percent glycogen and the enzyme was normally active in liver and muscle.[343]

Diagnosis. Although the symptomatology is milder than in type I and type III, only the biochemical analysis allows a clear diagnosis. Phosphorylase *b* kinase can be measured not only in a liver biopsy but also in leukocytes[332] or erythrocytes.[336] Its normal activity permits the diagnosis of liver phosphorylase deficiency when the activity of liver phosphorylase is low.

Treatment. Most patients do not require a specific treatment.

Animal Models. Autosomal liver phosphorylase *b* kinase deficiency has been described in rats.[344,345] Muscle phosphorylase *b* kinase deficiency is known to occur in mice as an X-linked transmissible disorder.[346] The four subunits of the enzyme are absent, suggesting that the deficiency of a control gene located on the X chromosome may cause instability of the complex, although other explanations are possible.[347]

Type VII Glycogenosis (Deficiency of Muscle Phosphofructokinase)

History and Clinical Description. In 1965, Tarui et al.[348] described three sibs, a 13-year-old female and 23- and 27-year-old males, complaining of easy fatigability and presenting symptoms similar to but more severe than those of McArdle disease. Muscle glycogen was increased (up to 4 percent), and the concentration of glucose-6-phosphate was about 30 times normal. Phosphorylase was normally active, but phosphofructokinase activity was almost undetectable. Erythrocyte phosphofructokinase was also decreased by about 50 percent. Subsequently, similar cases were reported (reviewed in Refs. 120 to 123), confirming the similarity of symptomatology with McArdle disease, including myoglobinuria following strenuous exercise. Table 12-7 summarizes clinical and laboratory findings in 26 patients. The disease is also known as Tarui disease. It is apparent from Table 12-4 that it is very rare in Europe.

In two adult cases[349] and one late-onset case,[350] an abnormal periodic acid-Schiff positive material, similar to that present in the tissues of patients with type IV glycogenosis, was seen in a few percent of the muscle fibers. It has been hypothesized that, because of the very high concentration of glucose-6-phosphate, a well-known activator of glycogen synthase, a greater than normal ratio of glycogen synthase-branching enzyme activity could result in the synthesis of an abnormal glycogen.

Pathophysiology. Two important factors which differentiate type VII and type V are as follows: (1) The muscle in type VII is unable to utilize glucose and does not benefit from glucose or glucagon administration. (2) The erythrocytes in type VII are affected, causing a hemolytic tendency and increased reticulocyte counts as well as an elevated serum bilirubin. The

Table 12-7 Main Clinical and Laboratory Features in 26 Patients with Glycogenosis Type VII

	Incidence	%
Exercise intolerance	20/20	100
Pigmenturia	8/20	40
Recurrent jaundice	6/14	43
Permanent weakness	9/25	36
Onset in childhood	21/22	95
Positive family history	7/20	35
Increased serum creatine kinase at rest	14/16	88
Abnormal EMG at rest	7/13	54
Increased reticulocyte count	15/15	100
Increased serum bilirubin	15/18	83
Gout	4/13	31
Hyperuricemia	9/14	64

SOURCE: Courtesy of Dr. S. Tarui, Osaka University, Medical School, Japan. This series includes 18 males and 8 females.

50 percent decrease in activity of the erythrocyte phosphofructokinase is due to the fact that this enzyme is a tetrameric hybrid of which two subunits are of the muscle type.[351,352] Since erythrocytes have no other source of energy than glycolysis, and phosphofructokinase catalyzes a limiting step, this partial defect is responsible for the shorter life span of these cells.

For these reasons, phosphofructokinase deficiency is the most severe specifically muscular glycogenosis. In these patients, muscle exercise is accompanied by hyperuricemia.[320] Actually, ammonia, inosine, hypoxanthine, and uric acid all increase as a result of accelerated degradation of purine nucleotides. A similar myogenic hyperuricemia can be observed, to a minor degree, in types III and V[320] and probably also in other defects of muscle glycolysis (see below).

Diagnosis. The diagnosis rests on the biochemical[348] or histochemical[353] determination of the enzymic defect. The absence of the M isoenzyme of phosphofructokinase in various cells, including leukocytes and fibroblasts, can also be demonstrated by immunoprecipitation.[354]

Animal Models. The deficiency of the M isoenzyme of phosphofructokinase has been observed in the dog.[355]

Other Enzyme Deficiencies Related to Glycogen Metabolism

Glycogen Synthase Deficiency. This disorder was first described by Lewis et al.[356] in 1963, and a second case has been extensively documented by Aynsley-Green et al.[357] in 1977. The patients suffered from fasting hypoglycemia and hyperketonemia. Hyperglycemia and hyperlacticacidemia occurred after meals; at that time glucagon decreased lactate and increased glucose. Glucagon had no effect under fasting conditions. Glycogen synthase was completely inactive in the liver but present in muscle, erythrocytes,[358] and cultured skin fibroblasts.[359] Surprisingly, the liver contained glycogen (about 0.5 percent 4 to 6 h after a meal).

Except for the presence of glycogen in the liver, which is not understood, the absence of glycogen synthase explains that glucose is preferentially converted to lactate, which in turn is reconverted to glucose when gluconeogenesis is stimulated by glucagon.

The patients were thought to be homozygotes for the abnormal gene that is transmitted as an autosomal recessive character. Consistent with this mode of transmission is the fact that both patients had affected sibs and normal parents.

Deficiency of Phosphoglucoisomerase. An 8-year-old girl with this known hemolytic disorder also had muscular fatigue and liver enlargement. Excess glycogen was demonstrated in liver and erythrocytes. Contrary to fructose, oral glucose or galactose failed to increase the lacticacidemia.[360]

Defects of Muscle Glycolysis Not Causing Excessive Glycogen Deposition. A few patients with a deficiency of muscle phosphoglycerate kinase,[361] phosphoglycerate mutase,[362–364] or lactate dehydrogenase[365] presented symptoms analogous to those of McArdle disease but with no or minimal[364] excess of glycogen in their muscles.

REFERENCES

1. MANNERS DJ: The molecular structure of glycogen. *Adv Carbohyd Chem* 12:261, 1957.
2. CORI GT: Glycogen structure and enzyme deficiencies in glycogen storage disease. *Harvey Lect* 48:145, 1954.
3. WHELAN WJ: The initiation of glycogen synthesis. *Bioessays* 5:136, 1986.
4. RODRIGEZ IR, WHELAN WJ: A novel glycosyl-amino acid linkage: Rabbit muscle glycogen is covalently linked to a protein via tyrosine. *Biochem Biophys Res Commun* 132:829, 1985.
5. REVEL JP: Electron microscopy of glycogen. *J Histochem Cytochem* 12:104, 1964.
6. DROCHMANS P: Morphologie du glycogène. *J Ultrastruct Res* 6:141, 1962.
7. FENN WO: The deposition of potassium and phosphate with glycogen in rat livers. *J Biol Chem* 128:297, 1939.
8. PUCKETT HL, WILEY FH: The relation of glycogen to water storage in the liver. *J Biol Chem* 96:367, 1932.
9. KATZ J, KUWAJIMA M, FOSTER DW, McGARRY JD: The glucose paradox: New perspectives on hepatic carbohydrate metabolism. *Trends Biochem Sci* 113:136, 1986.
10. FISCHER EH, HEILMEYER LMG Jr, HASCHKE RH: Phosphorylase and the control of glycogen degradation. *Curr Top Cell Regul* 4:211, 1971.
11. GRAVES DJ, WANG JH: α-Glucan phosphorylases—Chemical and physical basis of catalysis and regulation. *The Enzymes* (2d ed.) 7:435, 1972.
12. FLETTERICK RJ, MADSEN NB: X-rays reveal phorphorylase architecture. *Trends Biochem Sci* 2:145, 1977.
13. FLETTERICK RJ, MADSEN NB: The structures and related functions of phosphorylase *a*. *Annu Rev Biochem* 49:31, 1980.
14. WALKER GJ, WHELAN WJ: The mechanism of carbohydrase action. 8. Structures of the muscle-phosphorylase limit dextrins of glycogen and amylopectin. *Biochem J* 76:264, 1960.
15. STALMANS W, HERS HG: The stimulation of liver phosphorylase *b* by AMP, fluoride and sulfate. *Eur J Biochem* 54:341, 1975.
16. HENION WF, SUTHERLAND EW: Immunological differences of phorphorylases. *J Biol Chem* 224:477, 1957.
17. WALSH DA, KREBS EG: Protein kinases. *The Enzymes* (2d ed) 8:555, 1973.
18. COHEN P: The role of protein phosphorylation in neural and hormonal control of cellular activity. *Nature* 296:613, 1982.
19. DEPAOLI-ROACH AA, ROACH PJ, LARNER J: Rabbit skeletal muscle phosphorylase kinase. Comparison of glycogen synthase and phosphorylase as substrates. *J Biol Chem* 254:4212, 1979.
20. COHEN P, BURCHELL A, FOULKES G, COHEN PTW, VANAMAN TC, NAIRN AC: Identification of the Ca^{++}dependent modulator protein as the fourth subunit of rabbit skeletal muscle phosphorylase kinase. *FEBS Lett* 92:287, 1978.
21. WOSILAIT WD, SUTHERLAND EW: The relationship of epinephrine and glucagon to liver phosphorylase; enzymatic inactivation of liver phosphorylase. *J Biol Chem* 218:469, 1956.
22. INGEBRITSEN TS, COHEN P: Protein phosphatases: Properties and role in cellular regulation. *Science* 221:331, 1983.
23. MERLEVEDE W, VANDENHEEDE JR, GORIS J, YANG SD: Regulation of ATP-Mg-dependent protein phosphatase. *Curr Top Cell Regul* 23:177, 1984.
24. MERLEVEDE W, DI SALVO J (eds): *Advances in Protein Phosphatases*. Leuven University Press, vols. 1–4, 1985–1987.
25. LALOUX M, STALMANS W, HERS HG: Native and latent forms of liver phosphorylase phosphatase. The non-identity of native phosphorylase phosphatase and synthase phosphatase. *Eur J Biochem* 92:15, 1978.
26. LALOUX M, HERS HG: Native and latent forms of skeletal muscle phosphorylase phosphatase. *FEBS Lett* 105:239, 1979.
27. STALMANS W, DE WULF H, LEDERER B, HERS HG: The effect of glucose and of a treatment by glucocorticoids on the inactivation in vitro of liver glycogen phosphorylase. *Eur J Biochem* 15:9, 1970.
28. STALMANS W, LALOUX M, HERS HG: The interaction of liver phosphorylase a with glucose and AMP. *Eur J Biochem* 49:415, 1974.
29. LELOIR LF, CARDINI CE: Biosynthesis of glycogen from uridine diphosphate glucose. *J Am Chem Soc* 79:6340, 1957.
30. STALMANS W, HERS HG: Glycogen synthesis from UDPG. *The Enzymes* (2d ed) 9:309, 1973.
31. ROACH PJ: Glycogen synthase and glycogen synthase kinases. *Curr Top Cell Regul* 20:45, 1981.
32. Nomenclature committee of IUB NC-IUB and IUPAC-IUB joint commission on biochemical nomenclature JCBN: Newsletter 1984. *Eur J Biochem* 138:5, 1984.
33. VILLAR-PALLASI C, LARNER J: Insulin-mediated effect on the activity of UDPG-glycogen transglucosylase of muscle. *Biochim Biophys Acta* 39:171, 1960.

34. FRIEDMAN DL, LARNER J: Studies on UDPG-α-glucan transglucosylase. III. Interconversion of 2 forms of UDPG-α-glucan transglucosylase by a phosphorylation-dephosphorylation reaction sequence. *Biochemistry* 2:669, 1963.

35. MERSMANN HJ, SEGAL HL: An on-off mechanism for liver glycogen synthetase activity. *Proc Natl Acad Sci USA* 58:1688, 1967.

36. DE WULF H, STALMANS W, HERS HG: The influence of inorganic phosphate, adenosine triphosphate and glucose 6-phosphate on the activity of liver glycogen synthetase. *Eur J Biochem* 6:545, 1968.

37. DE WULF H, HERS HG: The interconversion of liver glycogen synthetase a and b in vitro. *Eur J Biochem* 6:552, 1968.

38. PASSAMONTI S, VAN SCHAFTINGEN E: Personal communication.

39. TAN AWH, NUTTALL FQ: Evidence for the non-identity of proteins having synthase phosphatase, phosphorylase phosphatase and histone phosphatase activity in rat liver. *Biochim Biophys Acta* 522:139, 1978.

40. VILLAR-PALASI C: Oligo- and polysaccharide inhibition of muscle transferase D phosphatase. *Ann NY Acad Sci* 166:719, 1969.

41. STALMANS W, DE WULF H, HERS HG: The control of liver glycogen synthetase phosphatase by phosphorylase. *Eur J Biochem* 18:582, 1971.

42. ALEMANY S, COHEN P: Phosphorylase a is an allosteric inhibitor of the glycogen and the microsomal forms of rat hepatic protein phosphatase-1. *FEBS Lett* 198:194, 1986.

43. van de WERVE G: Inhibition of liver glycogen synthase phosphatase by calcium: New evidence for an interaction between synthase activation and phosphorylase *a*. *Biochem Biophys Res Commun* 102:1323, 1981.

44. DOPERE F, VANSTAPEL F, STALMANS W: Glycogen-synthase phosphatase activity in rat liver. *Eur J Biochem* 104:137, 1980.

45. MVUMBI L, DOPERE F, STALMANS W: The inhibitory effect of phosphorylase *a* on the activation of glycogen synthase depends on the type of synthase phosphatase. *Biochem J* 212:407, 1983.

46. MVUMBI L, BOLLEN M, STALMANS W: Calcium ions and glycogen act synergistically as inhibitors of hepatic glycogen-synthase phosphatase. *Biochem J* 232:697, 1985.

47. TAYLOR C, COX AJ, KERNOHAN JC, COHEN P: Debranching enzyme from rabbit skeletal muscle. *Eur J Biochem* 51:105, 1975.

48. SMITH EE, TAYLOR PM, WHELAN WJ: Enzymic process in glycogen metabolism, in Dickens F, Randle PJ, Whelan WJ (eds): *Carbohydrate Metabolism and Its Disorders*. New York, Academic, 1968, vol 1, pp 89–138.

49. LARNER J, SCHLISELFELD LH: Studies on amylo-1,6-glucosidase. *Biochim Biophys Acta* 20:53, 1956.

50. HERS HG: Glycogen storage disease. *Adv Metab Disorders* 1:1, 1964.

51. VERHUE W, HERS HG: A study of the reaction catalysed by the liver branching enzyme. *Biochem J* 99:222, 1966.

52. ZIMMERMAN CP, GOLD AM: Isolation and characterization of glycogen branching enzyme from rabbit liver. *Biochemistry* 22:3387, 1983.

53. TRUCCO RE: Enzymatic synthesis of uridine diphosphate glucose. *Arch Biochem Biophys* 34:482, 1951.

54. TSUBOI KK, FUKUNAGA K, PETRICCIANI JC: Purification and specific kinetic properties of erythrocyte uridine diphosphate glucose pyrophosphorylase. *J Biol Chem* 244:1008, 1969.

55. ROACH PJ, WARREN KR, ATKINSON DE: Uridine diphosphate glucose synthase from calf liver: Determinants of enzyme activity in vitro. *Biochemistry* 14:5445, 1975.

56. NORDLIE RC, SUKALSKI A, ALVARES FL: Responses of glucose 6-phosphate levels to varied glucose loads in the isolated perfused rat liver. *J Biol Chem* 255:1834, 1980.

57. YOUN JH, YOUN MS, BERGMAN RN: Synergism of glucose and fructose in net glycogen synthesis in perfused rat livers. *J Biol Chem* 261:15960, 1986.

58. LELOIR LF, TRUCCO RE, CARDINI CE, PALADINI AC, CAPUTTO R: The coenzyme of phosphoglucomutase. *Arch Biochem* 19:339, 1948.

59. CRANE RK, SOLS A: The non-competitive inhibition of brain hexokinase by glucose-6-phosphate and related compounds. *J Biol Chem* 210:597, 1954.

60. KREBS HA: The Pasteur effect and the relations between respiration and fermentation. *Essays in Biochemistry* 8:1, 1972.

61. WEINHOUSE S: Regulation of glucokinase in liver. *Curr Top Cell Regul* 11:1, 1976.

62. POLLARD-KNIGHT D, CORNISH-BOWDEN A: Mechanism of liver glucokinase. *Mol Cell Biochem* 44:71, 1982.

63. BONTEMPS F, HUE L, HERS HG: Phosphorylation of glucose in isolated rat hepatocytes. Sigmoidal kinetics explained by the activity of glucokinase alone. *Biochem J* 174:603, 1978.

64. NIEMEYER H, URETA T, CLARK-TURRI L: Adaptive character of liver glucokinase. *Mol Cell Biochem* 6:109, 1975.

65. NORDLIE RC: Metabolic regulation by multifunctional glucose-6-phosphatase. *Curr Top Cell Regul* 8:33, 1974.

66. HERS HG, BERTHET J, BERTHET L, DE DUVE C: Le système hexose-phosphatasique. III. Localisation intracellulaire des ferments par centrifugation fractionnée. *Bull Soc Chim Biol* 33:21, 1951.

67. BENEDETTI A, FULCERI R: On a possible role for glucose-6-phosphatase in the regulation of liver cell cytosolic concentration. *Trends Biochem Sci* 11:284, 1986.

68. HERS HG: Comment on the paper by A Benedetti et al. *Trends Biochem Sci* 11:285, 1986.

69. ARION WJ, WALLIN BK, LANGE AJ, BALLAS LM: On the involvement of a glucose 6-phosphate transport system in the function of microsomal glucose-6-phosphatase. *Mol Cell Biochem* 6:75, 1975.

70. ARION WJ, LANGE AJ, WALLS HE, BALLAS LM: Evidence for the participation of independent translocases for phosphate and glucose-6-phosphate in the microsomal glucose-6-phosphatase system. *J Biol Chem* 255:10396, 1980.

71. HUE L, HERS HG: Utile and futile cycles in the liver. *Biochem Biophys Res Commun* 58:540, 1974.

72. KATZ J, ROGNSTAD R: Futile cycles in the metabolism of glucose. *Curr Top Cell Regul* 10, 237, 1976.

73. HUE L: The role of futile cycles in the regulation of carbohydrate metabolism in the liver. *Adv Enzymol* 52:247, 1981.

74. VAN HOOF F, HUE L, DE BARSY T, JACQUEMIN P, DEVOS P, HERS HG: Glycogen storage diseases. *Biochimie* 54:745, 1972.

75. HERS HG: The control of glycogen metabolism in the liver. *Ann Rev Biochem* 45:167, 1976.

76. VAN SCHAFTINGEN, E: Fructose 2,6-bisphosphate. *Adv Enzymol* 59:315, 1986.

77. VAN SCHAFTINGEN E, HUE L, HERS HG: Fructose 2,6-bisphosphate, the probable structure of the glucose- and glucagon-sensitive stimulator of phosphofructokinase. *Biochem J* 192:897, 1980.

78. UYEDA K: Phosphofructokinase. *Adv Enzymol* 48:193, 1979.

79. SOSKIN S: The liver and carbohydrate metabolism. *Endocrinology* 26:297, 1940.

80. STALMANS W: The role of the liver in the homeostasis of blood glucose. *Curr Top Cell Regul* 11:51, 1976.

81. HEMS DA, WHITTON PD, TAYLOR EA: Glycogen synthesis in the perfused liver of the starved rat. *Biochem J* 129:529, 1972.

82. CIUDAD CJ, MASSAGUE J, GUINOVART JJ: The inactivation of glycogen phosphorylase is not a prerequisite for the activation of liver glycogen synthase. *FEBS Lett* 99:321, 1979.

83. KATZ J, GOLDEN S, WALS PA: Stimulation of hepatic glycogen synthesis by amino acids. *Proc Natl Acad Sci USA* 73:3433, 1976.

84. CHEN KS, LARDY HA: Multiple requirements for glycogen synthesis by hepatocytes isolated from fasted rats. *J Biol Chem* 260:14683, 1985.

85. CIUDAD CJ, CARABAZA A, GUINOVART JJ: Glucose 6-phosphate plays a central role in the activation of glycogen synthase by glucose in hepatocytes. *Biochem Biophys Res Commun* 141:1195, 1986.

86. EXTON JH, LEWIS SB, HO RJ: The role of cyclic AMP in the interaction of glucagon and insulin in the control of liver metabolism. *Ann NY Acad Sci* 185:85, 1971.

87. THOMAS AP, MATIN-REQUERO A, WILLIAMSON JR: Interactions between insulin and α1-adrenergic agents in the regulation of glycogen metabolism in isolated hepatocytes. *J Biol Chem* 260:5963, 1985.

88. KEPPENS S, VANDENHEEDE JR, DE WULF H: On the role of calcium as second messenger in liver for the hormonally induced activation of glycogen phosphorylase. *Biochim Biophys Acta* 496:448, 1977.

89. BERRIDGE MJ: Inositol trisphosphate and diacylglycerol as second messengers. *Biochem J* 220:345, 1984.

90. NISHIZUKA Y: The role of protein kinase C in cell surface signal transduction and tumour promotion. *Nature* 308:693, 1984.

91. STRICKLAND WG, IMAZU M, CHRISMAN TD, EXTON JH: Regulation of rat liver glycogen synthase. Roles of CA^{++}, phosphorylase kinase and phosphorylase *a*. *J Biol Chem* 258:5490, 1983.

92. ROACH PJ, GOLDMAN M: Modification of glycogen synthase activity in isolated rat hepatocytes by tumor-promoting phorbol esters: Evidence for differential regulation of glycogen synthase and phosphorylase. *Proc Natl Acad Sci USA* 80:7170, 1983.

93. BLACKMORE PF, STRICKLAND WG, BOCCKINO SB, EXTON JH: Mechanism of hepatic glycogen synthase inactivation induced by Ca^{++}-mobilizing hormones. *Biochem J* 237:235, 1986.

94. LONG CNH, KATZIN B, FRY EG: The adrenal cortex and carbohydrate metabolism. *Endocrinology* 26:309, 1940.

95. HORNBROOK KR, BURCH HB, LOWRY OH: The effects of adrenalectomy

and hydrocortisone on rat liver metabolites and glycogen synthase activity. *Mol Pharmacol* 2:106, 1966.

96. DE WULF H, HERS HG: The stimulation of glycogen synthesis and of glycogen synthetase in the liver by glucocorticoids. *Eur J Biochem* 2:57, 1967.

97. LALOUX M, STALMANS W, HERS HG: On the mechanism by which glucocorticoids cause the activation of glycogen synthase in mouse and rat livers. *Eur J Biochem* 136:175, 1983.

98. DE WULF H, HERS HG: The stimulation of glycogen synthesis and of glycogen synthetase in the liver by the administration of glucose. *Eur J Biochem* 2:50, 1967.

99. NIEWOEHNER CB, GILBOE DP, NUTALL FQ: Metabolic effects of oral glucose in the liver of fasted rats. *Am J Physiol* 246:E89, 1984.

100. NEWGARD C, FOSTER DW, McGARRY JD: Evidence for suppression of hepatic glucose-6-phosphatase with carbohydrate feeding. *Diabetes* 33:192, 1984.

101. CLAUS TH, NYFELER F, MUENKEL HA, BURNS MG, PILKIS SJ: Changes in fructose-2,6-bisphosphate levels after glucose loading of starved rats. *Biochem Biophys Res Commun* 122:529, 1984.

102. HUE L, SOBRINO F, BOSCA L: Difference in glucose sensitivity of liver glycolysis and glycogen synthesis. Relationship between lactate production and fructose 2,6-bisphosphate concentration. *Biochem J* 224:779, 1984.

103. HUE L, BONTEMPS F, HERS HG: The effect of glucose and of potassium ions on the interconversion of the two forms of glycogen phosphorylase and of glycogen synthetase in isolated rat liver preparations. *Biochem J* 152:105, 1975.

104. BOLLEN M, GEVERS G, STALMANS W: The activity of glycogen synthase phosphatase limits hepatic glycogen deposition in the adrenalectomized starved rat. *Biochem J* 214:539, 1983.

105. LEVINE R, GOLDSTEIN M, KLEIN S: The action of insulin on the distribution of galactose in eviscerated nephrectomized dogs. *J Biol Chem* 179:985, 1949.

106. LARNER J: Insulin mediator. Fact or fancy. *J Cyclic Nucleotide Res* 8:289, 1982.

107. HERS HG: α-glucosidase deficiency in generalized glycogen storage disease (Pompe's disease). *Biochem J* 86:11, 1963.

108. BAUDHUIN P, HERS HG, LOEB H: An electron microscopic and biochemical study of type II glycogenosis. *Lab Invest* 13:1139, 1964.

109. LEJEUNE N, THINES-SEMPOUX D, HERS HG: Tissue fractionation studies. 16: Intracellular distribution and properties of α-glucosidases in rat liver. *Biochem J* 86:16, 1963.

110. JEFFREY PL, BROWN DH, ILLINGWORTH BROWN B: Studies of lysosomal α-glucosidase. II Kinetics of action of the rat liver enzyme. *Biochemistry* 9:1416, 1970.

111. PALMER TN: The maltase, glucoamylase and transglucosylase activities of acid α-glucosidase from rabbit muscle. *Biochem J* 124:713, 1971.

112. de BARSY T, JACQUEMIN P, DEVOS P, HERS HG: Rodent and human acid α-glucosidase. Purification, properties and inhibition by antibodies. Investigation in Type II glycogenosis. *Eur J Biochem* 31:156, 1972.

113. FIELD RA: Glycogen deposition diseases, in Stanbury JB, Wyngaarden JB, Fredrickson DS (eds): *The Metabolic Basis of Inherited Disease,* 2d ed. New York, McGraw-Hill, 1966, pp 141–177.

114. CORNBLATH M, SCHWARTZ R: Disorders of carbohydrate metabolism in infancy, in Schaffer AJ (ed): *Major Problems in Clinical Pediatrics*. Philadelphia and London, Saunders, 1966, vol III.

115. MOSES SW, GUTMAN A: Inborn errors of glycogen metabolism. *Adv Pediatr* 19:95, 1972.

116. HUIJING F: Glycogen metabolism and glycogen-storage diseases *Physiol Rev* 55:609, 1975.

117. ODIEVRE: Glycogénoses. *Encycl Med Chir Pediatr* 4059L10:1, 1979.

118. HOWELL RR, WILLIAMS JC: The glycogen storage diseases, in Stanbury JB, Wyngaarden JB, Fredrickson DS, Goldstein JL, Brown MS (eds): *The Metabolic Basis of Inherited Disease,* 5th ed. New York, McGraw-Hill, 1983, pp 141–166.

119. BROWN BI: Diagnosis of glycogen storage disease, in Wapnir RA (ed): *Congenital Metabolic Diseases*. Basel, Switzerland, Dekker, 1985, pp 227–250.

120. DiMAURO S: Metabolic myopathies, in Vinken PJ, Bruyn GW, Ringel SP (eds): *Handbook of Clinical Neurology*. Amsterdam, North Holland, 1978, pp 175–234.

121. DiMAURO S, BRESOLIN N, HAYS AP: Disorders of glycogen metabolism of muscle. *CRC Crit Rev Clin Neurobiol* 1:83, 1984.

122. PELLISSIER JF, de BARSY T, TOGA M: Glycogénoses musculaires. *Encycl Med Chir Neurol* 17180A10:1–18, 1984.

123. CORNELIO F, DiDONATO S: Myopathies due to enzyme deficiencies. *J Neurol* 232:329, 1985.

124. STEINITZ K: Laboratory diagnosis of glycogen diseases, in Sobotka H, Stewart CP (eds): *Advances in Clinical Chemistry*. 1967, vol 9, pp 227–354.

125. TURNBULL DM, SHERRATT HSA: Metabolic studies using isolated skeletal-muscle. Investigation of metabolic myopathies, in Alberti KGMM, Home PD, Taylor R (eds): *Techniques for Metabolic Investigation in Man*. Sussex UK, Baillères, Tindall & WB Saunders Co, 1987, pp 967–997.

126. VON GIERKE E: Hepato-nephro-megalia glykogenia (Glykogenspeicherkrankheit der Leber und Nieren). *Beitr Pathol Anat* 82:497, 1929.

127. CORI GT, CORI CF: Glucose-6-phosphatase of the liver in glycogen storage disease. *J Biol Chem* 199:661, 1952.

128. SCHAUB J, HEYNE K: Glycogen storage disease type Ib. *Eur J Pediatr* 140:283, 1983.

129. NARISAWA K, IGARASHI Y, OTOMO H, TADA K: A new variant of glycogen storage disease type I probably due to a defect in the glucose-6-phosphate transport system. *Biochem Biophys Res Commun* 83:1360, 1978.

130. FERNANDES J, BERGER R, SMIT GPA: Lactate as a cerebral metabolic fuel for glucose-6-phosphatase deficient children. *Pediatr Res* 18:335, 1984.

131. FERNANDES J, PIKAAR NA: Ketosis in hepatic glycogenosis. *Arch Dis Child* 47:41, 1972.

132. BINKIEWICZ A, SENIOR B: Decreased ketogenesis in von Gierke's disease (type I glycogenosis). *J Pediatr* 83:973, 1973.

133. ZUPPINGER K, ROSSI E: Metabolic studies in liver glycogen disease with special reference to lactate metabolism. *Helv Med Acta* 35:406, 1969.

134. KODAMA H, OKADA S, INUI K, YUTAKA T, YABUUCHI H: Studies on α-ketoglutaric aciduria in type I glycogenosis. *Tohoku J Exp Med* 131:347, 1980.

135. FERNANDES J, BERGER R: Urinary excretion of lactate, 2-oxoglutarate, citrate, and glycerol in patients with glycogenosis type I. *Pediatr Res* 21:279, 1987.

136. DOSMAN J, CRAWHALL JC, KLASSEN GA, MAMER OA, NEUMANN P: Urinary excretion of C6-C10 dicarboxylic acids in glycogen storage disease types I and III. *Clin Chim Acta* 51:93, 1974.

137. CHEN Y-T, COLEMAN RA, SCHEINMAN JI, KOLBECK PC, SIDBURY JB: Renal disease in Type I glycogen storage disease. *N Engl J Med* 318:7, 1988.

138. LELONG M, ALAGILLE D, GENTIL C, GABILAN JC: Glycogenose hépatique par déficit en glucose-6-phosphatase associée à une thrombopathie. *Rev Fr Etud Clin Biol* 5:672–683, 1960.

139. GILCHRIST GS, FINE RN, DONNELL GN: The hemostatic defect in glycogen storage disease, type I. *Acta Pediatr Scand* 57:205, 1968.

140. HUTTON RA, MACNAB AJ, RIVERS PA: Defect of platelet function associated with chronic hypoglycemia. *Arch Dis Child* 51:49, 1976.

141. HOWELL RR, STEVENSON RE, BEN-MENACHEN Y, PHYLIKI RL, BERRY DH: Hepatic adenomata with type I glycogen storage disease. *JAMA* 236:1481, 1976.

142. PARKER P, BURR I, SLONIM A, GHISHAN FK, GREENE H: Regression of hepatic adenomas in type Ia glycogen storage disease with dietary therapy. *Gastroenterology* 81:534, 1981.

143. COIRE CI, QIZILBASH AH, CASTELLI MF: Hepatic adenomata in Type Ia Glycogen Storage Disease. *Arch Pathol Lab Med* 111:166, 1987.

144. BANNASCH P, HACKER HJ, KLIMEK F, MAYER D: Hepatocellular glycogenosis and related pattern of enzymatic changes during hepatocarcinogenesis. *Adv Enzyme Regul* 22:97, 1984.

145. LEFFERT HL, KOCH KS, MORAN T, RUBALCAVA B: Hormonal control of rat liver regeneration. *Gastroenterology* 76:1470, 1979.

146. BEAUDET AL, ANDERSON DC, MICHELS VV, ARION WJ, LANGE AJ: Neutropenia and impaired neutrophil migration in type IB glycogen storage disease. *J Pediatr* 97:906, 1980.

147. ANDERSON DC, MACE ML, BRINKLEY BR, MARTIN RR, SMITH CW: Recurrent infection in glycogenosis Ib: Abnormal neutrophil motility related to impaired redistribution of adhesion sites. *J Infect Dis* 143:447, 1981.

148. BARTRAM CR, PRZYREMBEL H, WENDEL U, BREMER HJ, SCHAUB J, HAAS JR: Glycogenosis type Ib complicated by severe granulocytopenia resembling inherited neutropenia. *Eur J Pediatr* 137:81, 1981.

149. CORBEEL L, BOOGAERTS M, VAN DEN BERGHE G, EVERAERTS MC, MARCHAL G, EECKELS R: Haematological findings in type Ib glycogen storage disease before and after portacaval shunt. *Eur J Pediatr* 140:273, 1983.

150. GAHR M, HEYNE K: Impaired metabolic function of polymorphonuclear leukocytes in glycogen storage disease Ib. *Eur J Pediatr* 140:329, 1983.

151. DI ROCCO M, BORRONE C, DALLEGRI F, FRUMENTO G, PATRONE F: Neutropenia and impaired neutrophil function in glycogenosis type Ib. *J Inherited Metab Dis* 7:151, 1984.

152. SEGER R, STEINMANN B, TIEFENAUER L, MATSUNAGA T, GITZELMANN R: Short communication. Glycogenosis Ib: Neutrophil microbicidal defects due to impaired hexose monophosphate shunt. *Pediatr Res* 18:297, 1984.

153. AMBRUSO DR, MCCABE ER, ANDERSON D, BEAUDET A, BALLAS LM, BRANDT IK, BROWN B, COLEMAN R, DUNGER DB, FALLETTA JM, FRIEDMAN HS, HAYMEND MW, KEATING JP, KINNEY TR, LEONARD JV, MAHONEY DH, MATALON R, ROE TF, SIMMONS P, SLONIM AE: Infectious and

bleeding complications in patients with glycogenosis Ib. *Am J Dis Child* 139:691, 1985.

154. NARISAWA K, ISHIZAWA S, OKUMURA H, TADA K, KUZUYA T: Neutrophil metabolic dysfunction in genetically heterogeneous patients wtih glycogen storage disease type Ib. *J Inherited Metab Dis* 9:297, 1986.

155. SIMMONS PS, SMITHSON WA, GRONERT GA, HAYMOND MW: Acute myelogenous leukemia and malignant hyperthermia in a patient with type Ib glycogen storage disease. *J Pediatr* 105:428, 1984.

156. SANN L, MATHIEU M, BOURGEOIS J, BIENVENU J, BETHENOD M: In vitro evidence for defective activity of glucose-6-phosphatase in type Ib glycogenosis. *J Pediatr* 96:691, 1980.

157. BAUSSAN C, MOATTI N, BRIVET M, LEMONNIER A: Type Ib glycogen storage disease: An in vivo and in vitro study of two cases. *J Inherited Metab Dis* 7(S2):147, 1984.

158. GARIBALDI LR: Pathogenesis of glycogen storage disease IB. *J Pediatr* 98:669, 1981.

159. HERS HG, de BARSY T, LEDERER B, HUE L, VAN HOOF F: Glycogen storage diseases. *Biochem Soc Trans* 2:1051, 1974.

160. LANGE AJ, ARION WJ, BEAUDET AL: Type Ib glycogen storage disease is caused by a defect in the glucose-6-phosphate translocase of the microsomal glucose-6-phosphatase system. *J Biol Chem* 255:8381, 1980.

161. IGARASHI, KATO S, NARISAWA K, TADA K, AMANO Y, MORI T, TAKEUCHI S: A direct evidence for defect in glucose-6-phosphate transport system in hepatic microsomal membrane of glycogen storage disease type IB. *Biochem Biophys Res Commun* 119: 593, 1984.

162. NORDLIE RC, SUKALSKI KA, MUNOZ JM, BALDWIN JJ: Type Ic, a novel glycogenosis. Underlying mechanisms. *J Biol Chem* 258:9739, 1983.

163. BURCHELL A, JUNG RT, LANG CC, BENNET W, SHEPHERD AN: Diagnosis of type Ia and type Ic glycogen storage diseases in adults. *Lancet* I:1059, 1987.

164. SCHWARTZ R, ASHMORE J, RENOLD AE: Galactose tolerance in glycogen storage disease. *Pediatrics* 19:585, 1957.

165. FERNANDES J, HUIJING F, VAN de KAMER JH: A screening method for liver glycogen diseases. *Arch Dis Child* 44:311, 1969.

166. LOWE CU, MOSOVICH LL: The paradoxical effect of alcohol on carbohydrate metabolism in four patients with liver glycogen disease. *Pediatrics* 35:1005, 1965.

167. SADEGHI-NEJAD A, HOCHMAN H, SENIOR B: Studies in type I glycogenosis: The paradoxical effect of ethanol on lactate. *J Pediatr* 86:37, 1975.

168. WILLIAMS JC: Nutritional goals in glycogen storage disease. *N Engl J Med* 314:709, 1981.

169. MCGARRY JD, FOSTER DW: Regulation of hepatic fatty acid oxidation and ketone body production. *Ann Rev Biochem* 49:395, 1980.

170. TZUR R, TAL E, SHAPIRO B: α-Glycerophosphate as a regulatory factor in fatty acid esterification. *Biochim Biophys Acta* 84:18, 1964.

171. OCKERMAN PA: Glucose, glycerol and free fatty acids in glycogen storage disease type I: Blood levels in the fasting and non-fasting state. Effect of glucose and adrenalin administration. *Clin Chim Acta* 12:370, 1965.

172. OCKERMAN PA: In vitro studies of adipose tissue metabolism of glucose, glycerol and free fatty acids in glycogen storage disease type I. *Clin Chim Acta* 12:383, 1965.

173. HOWELL R, ASHTON R, WYNGAARDEN JB: Lipid carbohydrate and purine abnormalities in Von Gierke's disease. *J Clin Invest* 39:997, 1960.

174. JEANDET J, LESTRADET H: L'hyperlactacidémie, cause probable de l'hyperuricémie dans la glycogénose hépatique. *Rev Fr Etud Clin Biol* 6:71, 1961.

175. ALEPA FP, HOWELL RR, KLINENBERG JR, SEEGMILLER JE: Relationships between glycogen storage disease and tophaceous gout. *Am J Med* 42:58, 1967.

176. JAKOVCIC S, SORESEN LB: Studies of uric acid metabolism in glycogen storage disease associated with gouty arthritis. *Arthritis Rheum* 10:129, 1967.

177. KELLEY WN, ROSENBLOOM FM, SEEGMILLER JE, HOWELL RR: Excessive production of uric acid in type I glycogen storage disease. *J Pediatr* 72:488, 1968.

178. ROE TF, KOGUT MD: The pathogenesis of hyperuricemia in glycogen storage disease type I. *Pediatr Res* 11:664, 1977.

179. GREENE HL, WILSON FA, HEFFERAN P, TERRY AB, MORAN JR, SLONIM AE, CLAUS TH, BURR IM: ATP depletion, a possible role in the pathogenesis of hyperuricemia in glycogen storage disease type I. *J Clin Invest* 62:321, 1978.

180. HAVEL RJ, BALASSE EO, WILLIAMS HE, KANE JB, SEGEL N: Splanchnic metabolism in von Gierke's disease (glycogenosis type I). *Trans Assoc Am Physicians* 82:305, 1969.

181. SADEGHI-NEJAD A, PRESENTE E, BINKIEWICZ A, SENIOR B: Studies in Type I glycogenosis of the liver. The genesis and disposition of lactate. *J Pediatr* 85:49, 1974.

182. KALHAN SC, GILFILLAN C, TSERNG K-Y, SAVIN SM: Glucose production in type I glycogen storage disease. *J Pediatr* 101:159, 1982.

183. POWELL RC, WENTWORTH SM, BRANDT IK: Endogenous glucose production in type I glycogen storage disease. *Metabolism* 30:443, 1981.

184. TSALIKIAN E, SIMMONS P, GERICH JE, HOWARD C, HAYMOND MW: Glucose production and utilization in children with glycogen storage disease type I. *Am J Physiol* 247:E513, 1984.

185. HENELL F, GLAUMANN H: Effect of leupeptin on the autophagic vacuolar system of rat hepatocytes. Correlation between ultrastructure and degradation of membrane cytosolic proteins. *Lab Invest* 51:46, 1984.

186. DETER RL, de DUVE C: Influence of glucagon, an inducer of cellular autophagy, on some physical properties of rat liver lysosomes. *J Cell Biol* 33:437, 1967.

187. GREENE HL, SLONIM AE, O'NEIL JA, BURR IM: Continuous nocturnal intragastric feeding for management of type I glycogen-storage disease. *N Engl J Med* 294:423, 1976.

188. EHRLICH RM, ROBINSON BH, FREEDMAN MH, HOWARD NJ: Nocturnal intragastric infusion of glucose in management of defective gluconeogenesis with hypoglycemia. *Am J Dis Child* 132:241, 1978.

189. FERNANDES J, JANSEN H, JANSEN TC: Nocturnal gastric drip feeding in glucose-6-phosphatase deficient children. *Pediatr Res* 13:225, 1979.

190. GREENE HL, SLONIM AE, BURR IM, MORAN JR: Type I glycogen storage disease: Five years of management with nocturnal intragastric feeding. *J Pediatr* 96:590, 1980.

191. MICHELS VV, BEAUDET AL, POTTS VE, MONTANDON CM: Glycogen storage disease: Long-term follow-up of nocturnal intragastric feeding. *Clin Genet* 21:136, 1982.

192. LEONARD JV, DUNGER DB: Hypoglycaemia complicating feeding regimens for glycogen-storage disease. *Lancet* II:1203, 1978.

193. CHEN YT, CORNBLATH M, SIDBURY JB: Cornstarch therapy in type I glycogen storage disease. *N Engl J Med* 310:171, 1984.

194. SMIT GPA, BERGER R, POTASNICK R, MOSES SW, FERNANDES J: The dietary treatment of children with type I glycogen storage disease with slow release carbohydrate. *Pediatr Res* 18:879, 1984.

195. SIDBURY JB, CHEN YT, ROE CR: The role of raw starches in the treatment of type I glycogenosis. *Arch Intern Med* 146:370, 1986.

196. SCHWENK WF, HAYMOND MW: Optimal rate of enteral glucose administration in children with glycogen storage disease type I. *N Engl J Med* 314:682, 1986.

197. FERNANDES J, LEONARD JV, MOSES SW, ODIEVRE M, DI ROCCO M, SCHAUB J, SMIT GPA, ULLRICH K: Glycogen storage disease; recommendations for treatment. *Eur J Pediatr*, in press, 1988.

198. BOLEY SJ: Surgical therapy of glycogen storage disease. *Pediatrics* 46:929, 1970.

199. STARZL TE, PUTNAM CW, PORTER KA, HALGRIMSON CG, CORMAN J, BROWN BI, GOTLIN RW, RODGERSON DO, GREENE HL: Portal diversion for the treatment of glycogen storage disease in humans. *Ann Surg* 178:525, 1973.

199a. BOROWTIZ SM, GREENE HL, GAY JC, NEBLETT WW: Comparison of dietary therapy and portacaval shunt in the management of a patient with type IB glycogen storage disease. *J Ped Gastroenterol Nutr* 6:635, 1987.

200. MALATACK JJ, FINEGOLD DN, IWATSUKI S, SHAW BW, GARTNER JC, ZITELLI BJ, ROE T, STARZL TE: Liver transplantation in type I glycogen storage disease. *Lancet* 1:1073, 1983.

201. EMMETT M, NARINS RG: Renal transplantation in type I glycogenosis. Failure to improve glucose metabolism. *J Am Med Assoc* 239:1642, 1978.

202. McCABE ERB, GITHENS JH, ROBINSON WA, NICHOLSON JF: Correction of neutropenia by portacaval shunt in type IB glycogen storage disease. Replies. *J Pediatr* 100:168, 1982.

203. POMPE JC: Over idiopatische hypertrophie van het hart. *Ned T Geneesk* 76:304, 1932.

204. PUTSCHAR M: Über angeborene Glykogenspeicher-Krankheit des Herzens. "Thesaurismosis glycogenica" (v. Gierke). *Beitr Pathol Anat Allg Pathol* 90:222, 1932.

205. DI SANT AGNESE P, ANDERSEN DH, MASON HH: Glycogen storage disease of the heart. *Pediatrics* 6:607, 1950.

206. GUNTHER R: Beitrag zur Kenntnis der Glykogen-Speicherkrankheit. *Virchows Arch (A)* 304:87, 1939.

207. ENGEL AG, GOMEZ MR, SEYBOLD ME, LAMBERT EH: The spectrum and diagnosis of acid maltase deficiency. *Neurology* 23:95, 1973.

208. HERS HG, de BARSY T: Type II glycogenosis: Acid maltase deficiency, in Hers HG, Van Hoof I (eds): *Lysosomes and Storage Diseases*. New York, Academic, 1973, pp 197–216.

209. KOSTER JF, BUSCH HFM, SLEE RG, VAN WEERDEN TW: Glycogenosis type II: The infantile- and late-onset acid maltase deficiency observed in one family. *Clin Chim Acta* 87:451, 1978.

210. LOONEN MCB, BUSCH HFM, KOSTER JF, MARTIN JJ, NIERMEIJER MF, SCHRAM AW, BROUWER-KELDER B, MEKES W, SLEE RG, TAGER JM: A fam-

ily with different clinical forms of acid maltase deficiency (glycogenosis type II): Biochemical and genetic studies. *Neurology* 31:1209, 1981.

211. DANON MJ, DiMAURO S, SHANSKE S, ARCHER FL, MIRANDA AF: Juvenile-onset acid maltase deficiency with unusual familial features. *Neurology* 36:818, 1986.

212. MARTIN JJ, de BARSY T, VAN HOOF F, PALLADINI G: Pompe's disease: An inborn lysosomal disorder with storage of glycogen. *Acta Neuropathol* 23:229, 1973.

213. GRIFFIN JL: Infantile acid maltase deficiency. III. Ultrastructure of metachromatic material and glycogen in muscle fibers. *Virchows Arch (B)* 45:51, 1984.

214. COURTECUISSE V, ROYER P, HABIB R, MONNIER C, DEMOS J: Glycogénose musculaire par deficit d'α-1-4-glucosidase simulant une dystrophie musculaire progressive. *Arch Fr Pediatr* 22:1153, 1965.

215. HERS HG, VAN HOOF F: Glycogen storage disease. Type II and type VI glycogenosis, in Dickens F, Randle PJ, Whelan W (eds): *Carbohydrate Metabolism and Its Disorders*. New York, Academic, 1968, vol II, pp 151–160.

216. ENGEL AG: Acid maltase deficiency in adults: Studies in four cases of a syndrome which may mimic muscular dystrophy or other myopathies. *Brain* 93:599, 1970.

217. MARTIN JJ, de BARSY T, DE SCHRIJVER F, LEROY JG, PALLADINI G: Acid maltase deficiency (Type II glycogenosis). Morphological and biochemical study of a childhood phenotype. *J Neurol Sci* 30:155, 1976.

218. MARTIN JJ, de BARSY T, DEN TANDT WR: Acid maltase deficiency in non-identical adult twins. *J Neurol* 213:105, 1976.

219. de BARSY T, FERRIERE G, FERNANDEZ-ALVAREZ E: Uncommon case of type II glycogenosis. *Acta Neuropathol* 47:245, 1979.

220. DANON MJ, OH SJ, DiMAURO S, MANALIGOD JR, EASTWOOD A, NAIDU S, SCHLISEFELD LH: Lysosomal glycogen storage disease with normal acid maltase. *Neurology* 31:51, 1983.

221. BYRNE E, DENNETT X, CROTTY B, TROUNCE I, SANDS JM, HAWKINS R, HAMMOND J, ANDERSON S, HAAN EA, POLLARD A: Dominantly inherited cardioskeletal myopathy with lysosomal glycogen storage and normal acid maltase levels. *Brain* 109:523, 1986.

222. RIGGS JE, SCHOCHET SS, GUTMANN L, SHANSKE S, NEAL WA, DiMAURO S: Lysosomal glycogen storage disease without acid maltase deficiency. *Neurology* 33:873, 1983.

223. OUDE ELFERINK RPJ, BROUWER-KELDER EM, SURYA I, STRIJLAND A, KROOS M, REUSER AJJ, TAGER JM: Isolation and characterization of a precursor form of lysosomal α-glucosidase from human urine. *Eur J Biochem* 139:489, 1984.

224. OUDE ELFERINK RPJ, VAN DOORN-VAN WAKEREN J, HENDRIKS T, STRIJLAND A, TAGER JM: Transport and processing of endocytosed lysosomal α-glucosidase in cultured human skin fibroblasts. *Eur J Biochem* 158:339, 1986.

225. REUSER AJJ, KROOS M, OUDE ELFERINK RPJ, TAGER JM: Defects in synthesis, phosphorylation, and maturation of acid α-glucosidase in glycogenosis type II. *J Biol Chem* 260:8336, 1985.

226. REUSER AJJ, KROOS M, WILLEMSEN R, SWALLOW D, TAGER JM, GALJAARD H: Clinical diversity in glycogenosis type-II-biosynthesis and in situ localization of acid α-glucosidase in mutant fibroblasts. *J Clin Invest* 79:1689, 1987.

227. MARTINIUK FM, MEHLER M, PELLICER A, TZALL S, LA BADIE G, HOBART C, ELLENBOGEN A, HIRSCHHORN R: Isolation of a cDNA for human acid α-glucosidase and detection of genetic heterogeneity for mRNA in three α-glucosidase deficient patients. *Proc Natl Acad Sci USA* 83:9641, 1986.

228. HERS HG: Inborn lysosomal diseases. *Gastroenterology* 48:625, 1965.

229. HERS HG: The concept of inborn lysosomal disease, in Hers HG, Van Hoof F (eds): *Lysosomes and Storage Diseases*. New York, Academic, 1973, pp 625–633.

230. WOLFE HJ, COHEN RB: Nonglycogen polysaccharide storage in glycogenosis type 2. *Arch Pathol* 86:579, 1968.

231. GRIFFIN JL: Infantile acid maltase deficiency. I. Muscle fiber destruction after lysosomal rupture. *Virchows Arch (B)* 45:23, 1984.

232. GRIFFIN JL: Infantile acid maltase deficiency. II. Muscle fiber hypertrophy and the ultrastructure of end-stage fibers. *Virchows Arch (B)* 45:37, 1984.

233. HUIJING F, VAN CREVELD S, LOSEKOOT G: Diagnosis of generalized glycogen storage disease (Pompe's disease). *J Pediatr* 63:984, 1963.

234. KOSTER JF, SLEE RG, HULSMANN WC: The use of leucocytes as an aid in the diagnosis of glycogen storage disease type II (Pompe's disease). *Clin Chim Acta* 51:319, 1974.

235. de BARSY T, HERS HG: Biochemical and ultrastructural study of leucocytes in type II glycogenosis. *Arch Intern Physiol Biochim* 83:954, 1975.

236. BROADHEAD DM, BUTTERWORTH J: Pompe's disease: Diagnosis in kidney and leucocytes using 4-methylumbelliferyl α-D-glucopyranoside. *Clin Genet* 13:504, 1978.

237. DREYFUS JC, POENARU L: Alpha glucosidases in white blood cells with reference to the detection of acid α-1,4-glucosidase deficiency. *Biochem Biophys Res Commun* 85:615, 1978.

238. NITOWSKI HM, GRUNFELD A: Lysosomal α-glucosidase in type II glycogenosis: Activity in leukocytes and cell cultures in relation to genotype. *J Lab Clin Med* 69:472, 1967.

239. BESANCON AM, CASTELNAU L, NICOLESCO H, DUMEZ Y, POENARU L: Prenatal diagnosis of glycogenosis type II (Pompe's disease) using chorionic villi biopsy. *Clin Genet* 27:479, 1985.

240. HUG G: Prenatal diagnosis of type II glycogenosis. *Lancet* I:1002, 1970.

241. HIRSCHHORN K, NADLER HL, WAITHE WI, BROWN BI, HIRSCHHORN R: Pompe's disease: Detection of heterozygotes by lymphocyte stimulation. *Science* 166:1632, 1969.

242. ENGEL AG, GOMEZ MR: Acid maltase levels in muscle in heterozygous acid maltase deficiency and in non-weak and neuromuscular disease controls. *J Neurol Neurosurg Psychiatry* 33:801, 1970.

243. LOONEN MCB, SCHRAM AW, KOSTER JF, NIERMEIJER MF, BUSCH HFM, MARTIN JJ, BROUWER-KELDER B, MEKES W, SLEE RG, TAGER JM: Identification of heterozygotes for glycogenosis 2 (acid maltase deficiency). *Clin Genet* 19:55, 1981.

244. D'ANCONA GG, WURM J, CROCE CM: Genetics of type II glycogenosis: Assignment of the human gene for acid α-glucosidase to chromosome 17. *Proc Natl Acad Sci USA* 76:4526, 1979.

245. MARTINIUK F, ELLENBOGEN A, HIRSCHHORN K, HIRSCHHORN R: Further regional localization of the genes for human acid alpha glucosidase (GAA), peptidase D (PEPD), and α-mannosidase B (MANB) by somatic cell hybridization. *Hum Genet* 69:109, 1985.

246. de DUVE C: From cytases to lysosomes. *Fed Proc* 23:1045, 1964.

247. de BARSY T, LEROY J: in de DUVE C, de BARSY T, POOLE B, TROUET A, TULKENS P, VAN HOOF F: Commentary. Lysosomotropic agents. *Biochem Pharmacol* 23:2495, 1974.

248. HUG G, SCHUBERT WK: Lysosomes in type II glycogenosis. Changes during administration of extract from Aspergillus niger. *J Cell Biol* 35:C1, 1967.

249. de BARSY T, VAN HOOF F: Enzyme replacement therapy with purified human acid α-glucosidase in type II glycogenosis, in Tager JM, Hooghwinkel GJM, Daems WT (eds): *Enzyme Therapy in Lysosomal Storage Diseases*. Amsterdam, North Holland, 1974, p 277.

250. RICHARDS RB, EDWARDS JR, COOK RD, WHITE RR: Bovine generalized glycogenosis. *Neuropathol Appl Neurobiol* 3:45, 1977.

251. HOWELL JM, DORLING PR, COOK RD, ROBINSON WF, BRADLEY S, GAWTHORNE JM: Infantile and late onset form of generalized glycogenosis type II in cattle. *J Pathol* 134:267, 1981.

252. WALVOORT HC, SLEE RG, KOSTER JF: Canine glycogen storage disease type II. A biochemical study of an acid α-glucosidase-deficient Lapland dog. *Biochim Biophys Acta* 715:63, 1982.

253. MANKTELOW BW, HARTLEY WJ: Generalized glycogen storage disease in sheep. *J Comp Pathol* 85:139, 1975.

254. SANDSTROM B, WESTMAN J, OCKERMAN PA: Glycogenosis of the central nervous system in the cat. *Acta Neuropathol (Berlin)* 14:194, 1969.

255. NUNOYA T, TAJIMA M, MIZUTANI M: A new mutant of Japanese quail (Coturnix coturnix japonica) characterized by generalized glycogenosis. *Lab Anim* 17:138, 1983.

256. ILLINGWORTH B, CORI GT: Structure of glycogens and amylopectins. III. Normal and abnormal human glycogen. *J Biol Chem* 199:653, 1952.

257. FORBES GB: Glycogen storage disease. Report of a case with abnormal glycogen structure in liver and skeletal muscle. *J Pediatr* 42:645, 1953.

258. ILLINGWORTH B, CORI GT, CORI CF: Amylo-1,6-glucosidase in muscle-tissue in generalized glycogen storage disease. *J Biol Chem* 218:123, 1956.

259. MILLER CG, ALLEYNE GA, BROOKS SEH: Case report. Gross cardiac involvement in glycogen storage disease type III. *Br Heart J* 34:862, 1972.

260. ROSSIGNOL A-M, MEYER M, ROSSIGNOL B, PALCOUX M-P, RAYNAUD, E-J, BOST M: La myocardiopathie de la glycogénose type III. *Arch Fr Pediatr* 36:303, 1979.

261. UGAWA Y, INOUE K, TAKEMURA T, IWAMASA T: Accumulation of glycogen in sural nerve axons in adult-onset type III glycogenosis. *Ann Neurol* 19:294, 1986.

262. VAN HOOF F, HERS HG: The subgroups of type III glycogenosis. *Eur J Biochem* 2:265, 1967.

263. VAN HOOF F: Amylo-1,6-glucosidase activity and glycogen content of the erythrocytes of normal subjects, patients with glycogen storage disease and heterozygotes. *Eur J Biochem* 2:271, 1967.

264. JUSTICE P, RYAN C, HSIA DY: Amylo-1,6-glucosidase in human fibroblasts: Studies in type III glycogen storage disease. *Biochem Biophys Res Commun* 39:301, 1970.

265. LEVIN S, MOSES SW, CHAYOTH R, JAGODA N, STEINITZ K: Glycogen storage disease in Israël. A clinical, biochemical and genetic study. *Isr J Med Sci* 3:397, 1967.

266. CEH L, HAUGE JG, SVENKERUD R, STRANDE A: Glycogenosis type III in the dog. *Acta Vet Scand* 17:210, 1976.

267. ANDERSEN DH: Familial cirrhosis of the liver with storage of abnormal glycogen. *Lab Invest* 5:11, 1956.

268. BROWN BI, BROWN DH: Lack of an α-1,4-glucan: α-1,4-glucan 6-glycosyl transferase in a case of type IV glycogenosis. *Proc Natl Acad Sci USA* 56:725, 1966.

268a. GREENE HL, GHISHAN FK, BROWN B, MCCLENATHAN DT, FREESE D: Hypoglycemia in type IV glycogenosis: Hepatic improvement in two patients with nutritional management. *J Pediatr* 112:55, 1988.

269. HOLLEMAN LWJ, van der HAAR JA, de VAAN GAM: Type IV glycogenosis. *Lab Invest* 15:357, 1966.

270. LEVIN B, BURGESS EA, MORTIMER PE: Glycogen storage disease type IV: Amylopectinosis. *Arch Dis Child* 43:548, 1968.

271. REED GB, DIXON JFP, NEUSTEIN HB, DONNELL GN, LANDING BH: Type IV glycogenosis. Patient with absence of a branching enzyme α-1,4-glucan:α-1,4-glucan 6-glycosyl transferase. *Lab Invest* 19:546, 1968.

272. FERNANDES J, HUIJING F: Branching enzyme deficiency glycogensosis: Studies in therapy. *Arch Dis Child* 43:347, 1968.

273. McMASTER KR, POWERS JM, HENNIGAR GR, WOHLTMANN HJ, FARR GH: Nervous system involvement in type IV glycogenosis. *Arch Pathol Lab Med* 103:105, 1979.

273a. SERVIDEI S, RIEPE RE, LANGSTON C, TANI LY, BRICKER JT, CRISP-LINDGREN N, TRAVERS H, ARMSTRONG D, DiMAURO S: Severe cardiopathy in branching enzyme deficiency. *J Ped* 111:51, 1987.

274. FERGUSON IT, MAHON M, CUMMINGS WJ: An adult case of Andersen's disease—Type IV glycogenosis. A clinical, histochemical, ultrastructural and biochemical study. *J Neurol Sci* 60:337, 1983.

275. ISHIHARA T, UCHINO F, ADACHI H, TAKAHASHI M, WATANABE S, TSUNETOSHI S, FUJI T, IKEKE Y: Type IV glycogenosis—A study of two cases. *Acta Pathol Jpn* 25:613, 1975.

276. CANTIN M, BROCHU P, TURGEON-KNAACK C, BERDNIKOFF G, SIMARD P, MORIN C: Rectal biopsy in type IV glycogenosis. *Arch Pathol Lab Med* 100:422, 1976.

277. MERCIER C, WHELAN WJ: The fine structure of glycogen from type IV glycogen-storage disease. *Eur J Biochem* 16:579, 1970.

278. MERCIER C, WHELAN WJ: Further characterization of glycogen from type IV glycogen storage disease. *Eur J Biochem* 40:221, 1973.

279. SCHOCHET SS, McCORMICK WF, KOVARSKY J: Light and electron microscopy of skeletal muscle in type IV glycogenosis. *Acta Neuropathol* 19:137, 1971.

280. HUIJING F, LEE EYC, CARTER JH, WHELAN WJ: Branching action of amylo-1,6-glucosidase/oligo-1,4-1,6-glucantransferase. *FEBS Lett* 7:251, 1970.

281. BROWN DH, BROWN BI: Studies of the residual glycogen branching enzyme activity present in human skin fibroblasts from patients with type IV glycogen storage disease. *Biochem Biophys Res Commun* 111:636, 1983.

282. HOWELL RR, KABACK MM, BROWN BI: Type IV glycogen storage diseases: Branching enzyme deficiency in skin fibroblasts and possible heterozygote detection. *J Pediatr* 78:638, 1971.

283. STARZL TE, KOEP LJ, SCHROTER GPJ, HALGRIMSON CG, PORTER KA, WEIL R: Liver transplantation for pediatric patients. *Pediatrics* 63:825, 1979.

284. McARDLE B: Myopathy due to a defect in muscle glycogen breakdown. *Clin Sci* 10:13, 1951.

285. MOMMAERTS WFHM, ILLINGWORTH B, PEARSON CM, CUILLORY RJ, SERAYDARIAN K: A functional disorder of muscle associated with the absence of phosphorylase. *Proc Natl Acad Sci USA* 45:791, 1959.

286. LARNER J, VILLAR-PALASI C: Enzymes in a glycogen storage myopathy. *Proc Natl Acad Sci USA* 45:1234–1235, 1959.

287. SCHMID R, MAHLER R: Chronic progressive myopathy with myoglobinuria: Demonstration of a glycogenolytic defect in the muscle. *J Clin Invest* 38:2044, 1959.

288. FATTAH SM, RUBULIS A, FALOON WW: McArdle's disease. Metabolic studies in a patient and review of the syndrome. *Am J Med* 48:693, 1970.

289. MINEO I, KONO N, SHIMIZU T, HARA N, YAMADA Y, SUMI S, NONAKA K, TARUI S: Excess purine degradation in exercising muscles of patients with glycogen storage disease types V and VII. *J Clin Invest* 76:556, 1985.

290. BROOKE MH, PATTERSON VH, KAISER KK: Hypoxanthine and McArdle disease: A clue to metabolic stress in the working forearm. *Muscle Nerve* 6:204, 1983.

291. ROSS BD, RADDA GK, GADIAN DG, ROCKER G, ESIRI M, FALCONER-SMITH J: Examination of a case of suspected McArdle's syndrome by ^{31}P nuclear magnetic resonance. *N Engl J Med* 304:1338, 1981.

292. LEWIS SF, HALLER RG, COOK FD, NUNNALLY RL: Muscle fatigue in McArdle's disease studied by ^{31}P-NMR: Effect of glucose infusion. *J Appl Physiol* 59:1991, 1985.

293. DUBOC D, JEHENSON P, TRAN DINH S, MARSAC C, SYROTA A, FARDEAU M: Phosphorus NMR spectroscopy study of muscular enzyme deficiencies involving glycogenolysis and glycolysis. *Neurology* 37:663, 1987.

294. GRUNFELD JP, GANEVAL D, CHANARD J, FARDEAU M, DREYFUS JC: Acute renal failure in McArdle's disease. *N Engl J Med* 286:1237, 1972.

295. BANK WJ, DiMAURO S, ROWLAND LP: Renal failure in McArdle's disease. *N Engl J Med* 287:1102, 1972.

296. HEWLETT RH, GARDNER-THORPE C: McArdle's disease—What limit to the age of onset? *S Afr Med J* 53:60, 1978.

297. POURMAND R, SANDERS DB, CORWIN HM: Late-onset McArdle's disease with unusual electromyographic findings. *Arch Neurol* 40:374, 1983.

298. ROELOFS RI, ENGEL WK, CHAUVIN PB: Histochemical phosphorylase activity in regenerating muscle fibers from myophosphorylase-deficient patients. *Science* 177:795, 1972.

299. MITSUMOTO H: McArdle disease: Phosphorylase activity in regenerating muscle fibers. *Neurology* 29:258, 1979.

300. SATO K, IMAI F, HATAYAMA I, ROELOFS RI: Characterization of glycogen phosphorylase isoenzymes present in cultured skeletal muscle from patients with McArdle's disease. *Biochem Biophys Res Commun* 78:663, 1977.

301. DiMAURO S, ARNOLD S, MIRANDA A, ROWLAND LP: McArdle's disease: The mystery of reappearing phosphorylase activity in muscle culture—A fetal isoenzyme. *Ann Neurol* 3:60, 1978.

302. ENGEL WK, EYERMAN EL, WILLIAMS HE: Late-onset type of skeletal-muscle phosphorylase deficiency. *N Engl J Med* 268:135, 1963.

303. HUG G, SCHUBERT WK, CHUCK G: McArdle's syndrome: Demonstration of normal smooth muscle phosphorylase. *Clin Res* 15:321, 1967.

304. KOSTER JF, SLEE RG, JENNEKENS FGI, WINTZER AR, VAN BERKEL TJC: McArdle's disease: A study on the molecular basis of two different etiologies of myophosphorylase deficiency. *Clin Chim Acta* 94:229, 1979.

305. DAEGELEN-PROUX D, KAHN A, MARIE J, DREYFUS JC: Research on molecular mechanisms of McArdle's disease (muscle glycogen phosphorylase deficiency). *Ann Hum Genet* 45:113, 1981.

306. FEIT H, BROOKE MH: Myophosphorylase deficiency: Two different molecular etiologies. *Neurology* 26:963, 1976.

307. CERRI GC, WILLNER JH: Phosphorylation of McArdle phosphorylase induces activity. *Proc Natl Acad Sci USA* 78:2688, 1981.

308. DAEGELEN D, MUNNICH A, LEVIN MJ, GIRAULT A, GOASGUEN J, KAHN A, DREYFUS JC: Absence of functional messenger RNA for glycogen phosphorylase in the muscle of two patients with McArdle's disease. *Ann Hum Genet* 47:107, 1983.

309. GAUTRON S, DAEGELEN D, MENNECIER F, DUBOCQ D, KAHN A, DREYFUS JC: Molecular mechanisms of McArdle's disease. RNA and DNA analysis. *J Clin Invest* 79:275, 1987.

310. SCHIMRIGK K, MERTENS HG, RICKER C, FUHR J, EYER P, PETTE D: McArdle-syndrom (Myopathie bei fehlender Muskelphosphorylase) *Klin Wochenschr* 45:1, 1967.

311. CHUI LA, MUNSAT TL: Dominant inheritance of McArdle syndrome. *Arch Neurol* 33:636, 1976.

311a. LEBO RV, GORIN F, FLETTERICK RJ, KAO F-T, CHEUNG M-C, BRUCE BD, KAN YW: High resolution chromosome sorting and DNA spot-blot analysis assign McArdle's syndrome to chromosome II. *Science* 225:57, 1984.

312. KONO N, MINEO I, SHIMIZU T, HARA N, YAMADA Y, NONAKA K, TARUI S: Increased plasma uric acid after exercise in muscle phosphofructokinase deficiency. *Neurology* 36:106, 1986.

313. FISHBEIN WN, ARMBRUSTMACHER VW, GRIFFIN JL: Myoadenylate deaminase deficiency: A new disease of muscle. *Science* 200:545, 1978.

314. BROWNELL B, HUGHES T, GOLDBY FS, WOODS HF: McArdle's myopathy. A report of a case with observations on the muscle ultrastructure. *J Neurol Sci* 9:515, 1969.

315. SCHOTLAND DL, SPIRO D, ROWLAND LP, CARMEL P: Ultrastructural studies of muscle in McArdle's disease. *J Neuropathol Exp Neurol* 24:629, 1985.

316. TAKEUCHI T, KURIAKI H: Histochemical detection of phosphorylase in animal tissues. *J Histochem Cytochem* 3:153, 1956.

317. PEARSON CM, RIMER DG, MOMMAERTS WFHM: A metabolic myopathy due to absence of muscle phosphorylase. *Am J Med* 30:502, 1961.

318. SUTTON JR, TOEWS CJ, WARD GR, FOX RH: Purine metabolism during strenuous muscular exercise in man. *Metabolism* 29:254, 1980.

319. NEWSHOLME EA, LEECH AR: *Biochemistry for the Medical Sciences*. Chichester, Wiley, 1983.

320. MINEO I, KONI N, HARA N, SHIMIZU T, YAMADA Y, KAWACHI M, KIYOKAWA H, WANG YL, TARUI S: Myogenic hyperuricemia. *N Engl J Med* 317:25, 1987.

321. LEWIS SF, HALLER RG: The pathophysiology of McArdle's disease: Clues to regulation in exercise and fatigue. *J Appl Physiol* 61:391, 1986.

322. KONO N, MINEO I, SUMI S, SHIMIZU T, KANG J, NONAKA K, TARUI S: Metabolic basis of improved exercise tolerance: Muscle phosphorylase deficiency after glycogen administration. *Neurology* 34:1471, 1984.

323. PORTE D JR, CRAWFORD DW, JENNINGS DB, ABER C, McILROY MB: Cardio-

vascular and metabolic responses to exercise in a patient with McArdle's syndrome. *N Engl J Med* 275:406, 1966.

324. SLONIM AE, GOANS PJ: Myopathy in McArdle's syndrome. Improvement with a high-protein diet. *N Engl J Med* 312:355, 1985.

325. DiMAURO S, HARTLAGE PL: Fatal infantile form of muscle phosphorylase deficiency. *Neurology* 28:1124, 1978.

326. MIRANDA AF, NETTE EG, HARTLAGE PL, DiMAURO S: Phosphorylase isoenzymes in normal and myophosphorylase-deficient human heart. *Neurology* 29:1538, 1979.

327. de LA MARZA M, PATTEN BM, WILLIAMS JC, CHAMBERS JP: Myophosphorylase deficiency: A new cause of infantile hypotonia simulating infantile muscular atrophy. *Neurology* 30:402, 1980.

328. CORNELIO F, BRESOLIN N, DiMAURO S, MORA M, BALESTRINI MR: Congenital myopathy due to phosphorylase deficiency. *Neurology* 33:1383, 1983.

329. HERS HG: Étude enzymatique sur fragments hépatiques. Applications à la classification des glycogénoses. *Rev Int Hepat* 9:35, 1959.

330. STETTEN DW JR, STETTEN MR: Glycogen metabolism. *Physiol Rev* 40:505, 1960.

331. HUG G, SCHUBERT WK, CHUCK G: Phosphorylase kinase of the liver: Deficiency in a girl with increased hepatic glycogen. *Science* 153:1534, 1966.

332. HUIJING F: Phosphorylase kinase in leukocytes of normal subjects and of patients with storage disease. *Biochim Biophys Acta* 148:601, 1967.

333. HUIJING F, FERNANDES J: X-chromosomal inheritance of liver glycogenosis with phosphorylase kinase deficiency. *Am J Hum Genet* 21:275, 1969.

334. MORISHITA Y, NISHIYAMA K, YAMAMURA H, KODAMA S, NEGISHI H, MATUSO M, MATSUO T, NISHIZUKA Y: Glycogen phosphorylase kinase deficiency: A survey of enzymes in phosphorylase activating system. *Biochem Biophys Res Commun* 54:833, 1973.

335. SCHIMKE RN, ZAKHEIM RM, CORDER RC, HUG G: Glycogen storage disease type IX: Benign glycogenosis of liver and hepatic phosphorylase kinase deficiency. *J Pediatr* 83:1031, 1973.

336. LEDERER B, VAN HOOF F, VAN DEN BERGHE G, HERS HG: Glycogen phosphorylase and its converter enzymes in haemolysates of normal human subjects and of patients with type VI glycogen storage disease. A study of phosphorylase kinase deficiency. *Biochem J* 147:23, 1975.

337. LEDERER B, van de WERVE G, de BARSY T, HERS HG: The autosomal form of phosphorylase kinase deficiency in man: Reduced activity of the muscle enzyme. *Biochem Biophys Res Commun* 92:169, 1980.

338. BASHAN N, IANCU TC, LERNER A, FRASER D, POTASHNIK R, MOSES SW: Glycogenosis due to liver and muscle phosphorylase kinase deficiency. *Pediatr Res* 15:299, 1981.

339. FERNANDES J, KOSTER JF, GROSE WFA, SORGEDRAGER N: Hepatic phosphorylase deficiency. Its differentiation from other hepatic glycogenoses. *Arch Dis Child* 49:186, 1974.

340. LEDERER B, STALMANS W: Human liver glycogen phosphorylase. Kinetic properties and assay in biopsy specimens. *Biochem J* 159:689, 1976.

341. HUIJING F: Glycogen-storage disease Type VIa: Low phosphorylase kinase activity caused by a low enzyme-substrate affinity. *Biochim Biophys Acta* 206:199, 1970.

342. ABARBANEL JM, BASHAN N, POTASHNIK R, OSIMANI A, MOSES SW, HERISHANU Y: Adult muscle phosphorylase "*b*" kinase deficiency. *Neurology* 36:560, 1986.

343. EISHI Y, TAKEMURA T, SONE R, YAMAMURA H, NARISAWA K, ICHINOHASAMA R, TANAKA M, HATAKEYAMA S: Glycogen storage disease confined to the heart with deficient activity of cardiac phosphorylase kinase: A new type of glycogen storage disease. *Hum Pathol* 16:193, 1985.

344. MALTHUS R, CLARK DG, WATTS C, SNEYD GT: Glycogen-storage disease in rats, a genetically determined deficiency of liver phosphorylase kinase. *Biochem J* 188:99, 1980.

345. CLARK DG, NEVILLE SD, BRINKMAN M, NELSON PV, ILLMAN RJ, GUTHBERLET A, HAYNES DG: Age-related augmentation of phosphorylase *b* kinase in hepatic tissue from the glycogen-storage-disease (gsd/gsd) rat. *Biochem J* 238:811, 1986.

346. LYON JB JR, PORTER J: The relation of phosphorylase to glycogenolysis in skeletal muscle and heart of mice. *J Biol Chem* 238:1, 1963.

347. COHEN PTW, BURCHELL A, COHEN P: The molecular basis of skeletal muscle phosphorylase kinase deficiency. *Eur J Biochem* 66:347, 1976.

348. TARUI S, OKUNO G, IKURA Y, TANAKA T, SUDA M, NISHIKAWA M: Phosphofructokinase deficiency in skeletal muscle: A new type of glycogenosis. *Biochem Biophys Res Commun* 19:517, 1965.

349. AGAMANOLIS DP, ASKARI AD, DiMAURO S, HAYS A, KUMAR K, LIPTON M, RAYNOR A: Muscle phosphofructokinase deficiency: Two cases with unusual polysaccharide accumulation and immunologically active protein. *Muscle Nerve* 3:456, 1980.

350. HAYS AP, HALLETT M, DELFS J, MORRIS J, SOTREL A, SHEVCHUK MM, DiMAURO S: Muscle phosphofructokinase deficiency: Abnormal polysaccharide in a case of late-onset myopathy. *Neurology* 31:1077, 1981.

351. TARUI S, KONO N, NASU T, NISHIKAWA M: Enzymatic basis for the coexistence of myopathy and hemolytic disease in inherited muscle phosphofructokinase deficiency. *Biochem Biophys Res Commun* 34:77, 1969.

352. LAYZER RB, ROWLAND LP, BANK WJ: Physical and kinetic properties of human phosphofructokinase from skeletal muscle and erythrocytes. *J Biol Chem* 244:3823, 1969.

353. BONILLA E, SCHOTLAND DL: Histochemical diagnosis of muscle phosphofructokinase deficiency. *Arch Neurol* 22:8, 1970.

354. KAHN A, WEIL D, COTTREAU D, J-C DREYFUS: Muscle phosphofructokinase deficiency in man: Expression of the defect in blood cells and cultured fibroblasts. *Ann Hum Genet* 45:5, 1981.

355. VORA S, GIGER U, TURCHEN S, HARVEY JW: Characterization of the enzymatic lesion in inherited phosphofructokinase deficiency in the dog: An animal analogue of human glycogen storage disease type VII. *Proc Natl Acad Sci USA* 82:8109, 1985.

356. LEWIS GM, SPENCER-PEET J, STEWART KM: Infantile hypoglycemia due to inherited deficiency of glycogen synthetase in liver. *Arch Dis Child* 38:40, 1963.

357. AYNSLEY-GREEN A, WILLIAMSON DH, GITZELMANN R: Hepatic glycogen synthetase deficiency. *Arch Dis Child* 52:573, 1977.

358. SPENCER-PEET J: Erythrocyte synthetase in glycogen storage deficiency resulting from the absence of this enzyme from liver. *Clin Chim Acta* 10:481, 1964.

359. GITZELMANN R, STEINMANN B, AYNSLEY-GREEN A: Hepatic glycogen synthetase deficiency not exprressed in cultured skin fibroblasts. *Clin Chim Acta* 130:111, 1983.

360. VAN BIERVLIET J PGM, STAAL GEJ: Excessive hepatic glycogen storage in glucosephosphate isomerase deficiency. *Acta Paediatr Scand* 66:311, 1977.

361. DiMAURO S, DALAKAS M, MIRANDA AF: Phosphoglycerate kinase deficiency: A new cause of recurrent myoglobinuria. *Trans ANA* 106:202, 1981.

362. DiMAURO S, MIRANDA AF, KHAN S, GITLIN K, FRIEDMAN R: Human muscle phosphoglycerate mutase deficiency: Newly discovered metabolic myopathy. *Science* 212:1277, 1981.

363. DiMAURO S, MIRANDA AF, OLARTE M, FRIEDMAN R, HAYS AP: Muscle phosphoglycerate mutase deficiency. *Neurology* 32:584, 1982.

364. BRESOLIN N, RO Y-I, REYES M, MIRANDA AF, DIMAURO S: Muscle phosphoglycerate mutase (PGAM) deficiency: A second case. *Neurology* 33:1049, 1983.

365. KANNO T, SUDO K, TAKEUCHI I, KANDA S, HONDA N, NISHIMURA Y, OYAMA K: Hereditary deficiency of lactate dehydrogenase M-subunit. *Clin Chim Acta* 108:267, 1980.

CHAPTER **13**

DISORDERS OF GALACTOSE METABOLISM

STANTON SEGAL

1. *Three inherited disorders of galactose metabolism resulting in galactosemia have been delineated. They are transmitted by autosomal recessive inheritance.*
2. *The genetic disturbance is expressed as a cellular deficiency of either galactokinase, galactose-1-phosphate uridyl transferase or uridine diphosphate galactose-4-epimerase, the enzymes catalyzing the reactions in the unique pathway by which galactose is converted to glucose.*
3. *The clinical manifestations are toxicity syndromes resulting from exposure of the patients to galactose. Toxicity in galactokinase deficiency is milder and is mainly manifested by cataracts. In transferase and generalized epimerase deficiency, galactose ingestion is characterized by inanition, failure to thrive, vomiting, liver disease, cataracts, and mental retardation.*
4. *The diagnosis is suggested by the detection of galactose and galactose-1-phosphate in blood or galactose in urine and is established by demonstration of the enzyme deficiency in peripheral blood cells. Adequate procedures are available for screening large populations for transferase deficiency.*
5. *In these disorders, there is an alternative metabolic route of galactose metabolism through reduction to galactitol and oxidation to galactonate. Galactitol is not further metabolized but is excreted by the kidney. Transferase deficiency is associated with the accumulation of galactose-1-phosphate in the tissues in addition to galactitol and galactonate accumulation. In epimerase deficiency cellular uridine diphosphate galactose is also elevated.*
6. *Most patients with galactose-1-phosphate uridyl transferase deficiency can oxidize only a small fraction of galactose to carbon dioxide. This ability does not increase with age, and it seems unlikely that alternative metabolic pathways involving sugar nucleotides develop to circumvent the block in galactose conversion to glucose. There is, however, a group of galactosemic patients, all of whom are black, who in spite of the absence of transferase in the red cells can oxidize limited amounts of galactose. These patients have about 10 percent of normal transferase activity in the liver and intestine. Several other clinical variants of transferase deficiency with altered electrophoretic mobility of the enzyme have been described.*
7. *In transferase-deficient red cells a protein immunologically identical to the active enzyme has been found. Chemical characterization of the protein reveals no gross differences from the normal enzyme. This suggests a structural mutation involving an amino acid near the active site.*
8. *The cause of the entire toxicity syndrome in transferase deficiency is uncertain. On present evidence, it is reasonable to conclude that the cataract formation in both disorders of galactose metabolism is secondary to galactitol formation in the lens.*
9. *Two forms of uridine diphosphate-4-epimerase deficiency have been described. One is benign, involves only red and white blood cells without deranged metabolism in other tissues, and is detected by screening procedures which assay red cell galactose-1-phosphate. The other presents with a constellation of findings resembling transferase deficiency and responds to a restriction of dietary galactose. In this condition some dietary galactose is necessary since the exogenous sugar is required for the formation of the uridine diphosphate galactose essential in various metabolic processes.*

The name *galactosemia* has been given to a toxicity syndrome associated with the administration of galactose to patients with an inherited disorder of galactose utilization.[1–5] The constellation of nutritional failure, liver disease, cataracts, and mental retardation results from a deficiency of galactose-1-phosphate uridyl transferase[6] but can also be observed in the rare patient with uridine diphosphate-4-epimerase deficiency.[7,8] Another inherited syndrome of elevated plasma galactose concentration associated with galactosuria and juvenile cataracts has been described as resulting from galactokinase deficiency.[9] Since there are multiple etiologies for *galactosemia* the term has become inadequate. Also the name *galactose diabetes* for galactokinase deficiency[10] seems inappropriate. The three known syndromes are designated *transferase deficiency galactosemia, galactokinase deficiency galactosemia,* and *epimerase deficiency galactosemia* and are discussed as such in this chapter.

THE BIOCHEMISTRY AND PHYSIOLOGY OF GALACTOSE UTILIZATION

The Uridine Nucleotide Pathway

The main dietary source of galactose is the disaccharide lactose, the principal carbohydrate of mammalian milk. Hydrolysis of lactose by the galactosidase, lactase, of the intestinal microvillae results in release of the monosaccharides, glucose and galactose. These two sugars differ only by the configuration of the hydroxyl group about the fourth carbon (Fig. 13-1). The main pathway of galactose metabolism in humans is the conversion of galactose to glucose, without disruption of the carbon skeleton, by the epimerization of the hydroxyl group of carbon 4. This requires several enzymatic steps, as elucidated by Leloir and associates[11–13] and Kalckar and coworkers,[14] and is shown in Fig. 13-2.

Galactokinase. This enzyme has been described in yeast,[11,15,16] bacteria,[17,18] and mammalian tissues.[12] Galactose reacts with ATP to form galactose-1-phosphate and ADP; Mg^{2+} is required. The equilibrium is far in the direction of sugar phosphorylation, but the reaction is reversible.[19] The *Escherichia coli* enzyme has been purified, the amino acid composition found, and the molecular weight determined to be

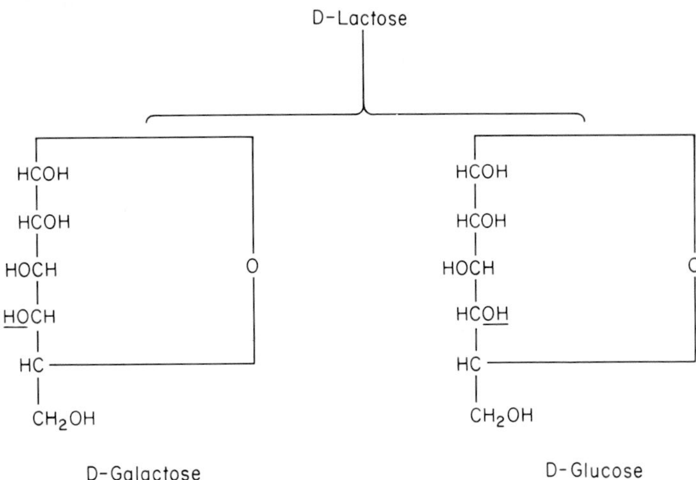

Fig. 13-1 Structure of galactose and glucose, the monosaccharides in lactose. Note the difference in the spatial relation of the hydroxyl group on the fourth carbon.

40,000.[18] The reaction of the bacterial enzyme is of the random bimolecular type.[20] Protection by thiols is a property common to the bacterial and liver enzyme. The yeast enzyme has also been purified and has properties similar to those of the *E. coli* enzyme, with a monomeric structure and a molecular weight of 58,000.[21] A DNA fragment containing the galactokinase gene has been maintained and shown to be expressed in a mutant of *E. coli* with deletion of its own gene.[22]

The mammalian enzyme has been studied in detail in tissue homogenates or purified preparations in rat[23,24] and pig liver,[25] human red cells,[26,27] human leukocytes, and cultured human fibroblasts,[28,29] human placenta,[30] and various human fetal tissues in which it is detected after the seventh week of gestation.[31] Liver enzyme reacts with galactosamine and 2-deoxygalactose, but the yeast enzyme is more specific for galactose. In the rat, activity of the liver enzyme is inhibited by high levels of both substrate and product, regulatory phenomena which would tend to decrease formation of galactose-1-phosphate, a possible toxic metabolite. The specific activity of rat liver enzyme increases after birth to a maximum at about 5 days of age, followed by a progressive fall (Fig. 13-3).[23,24] This decrease in specific activity is compensated for by increased organ size, so that the total activity in liver increases to a maximum at about 20 days of age.[32] In the human fetus, the liver-specific enzyme activity increases progressively from the seventh week until term without change in the enzyme K_m.[31,32]

The developmental changes in liver activity do not appear to be regulated by dietary galactose. Normal human fibroblasts in tissue culture show enhanced galactokinase when grown in the presence of galactose.[34] Galactokinase activity is higher in red blood cells from human infants than in cells from adults.[26] Fractionation of adult red cells reveals the highest activity to be in reticulocytes with decay in activity as red cells age.[35] The red cell enzyme has been purified over 3000-fold and found to have a dimeric structure, the monomers having a molecular weight of 25,000 to 27,000.[36] Isoelectric focusing of galactokinase of lens and other tissues reveals a single isoenzyme whose isoelectric point is the same in tissues of the same species but different from species to species.[37] The red cell enzyme resembles that of other mammalian tissue galactokinases in its substrate affinities but differs from that of *E. coli*. The red cell enzyme, like that of liver, undergoes substrate and product inhibition.[27] This type of regulation would tend to decrease the formation of galactose-1-phosphate. Higher galactokinase activity in newborn erythrocytes than in adults may be related to differences in substrate affinity.[27] Tedesco et al.[38] have presented evidence for racial polymorphism within the black population, noting three levels of red cell galactokinase activity. The assignment of the gene for galactokinase has been made to human chromosome 17, and its regional localization on the chromosome has been assigned to band q21-22.[39] The red cell enzymes of various mammals have been compared,[40] and a gene locus controlling galactokinase activity in mouse blood has been described.[41] In the mouse the interstrain difference in blood galactokinase was not reflected, however, by parallel differences in activity of the liver enzymes.[42]

Galactokinase synthesis has been carried out in vitro, employing bacteriophage DNA coding for the enzyme and a cell-free extract prepared from a Gal deletion strain of *E. coli*.[43] Cyclic adenosine monophosphate is required for the process in vitro.[44] Cyclic adenosine monophosphate stimulates *E. coli* galactokinase activity[45] as well as that of the protozoan Tetrahymena.[46] Although there has been doubt that cyclic nucleotide plays a role in the expression in vivo of the galactose operon in *E. coli*,[47] recent work has shown the importance of cyclic AMP and its receptor protein in regulation of the galactose operon.[48]

1. Galactose + ATP $\xrightleftharpoons{A}$ galactose-1-phosphate + ADP
2. Galactose-1-phosphate + UDP-glucose $\xrightleftharpoons{B}$ UDP-galactose + glucose-1-phosphate
3. UDP-galactose $\xrightleftharpoons{C}$ UDP-glucose
4. UDP-Glucose + PP $\xrightleftharpoons{D}$ UTP + glucose-1-phosphate

A = Galactokinase
B = Galactose-1-phosphate uridyltransferase
C = UDP-Galactose-4-epimerase
D = UDP-Glucose pyrophosphorylase

Fig. 13-2 Reactions of galactose metabolism responsible for the galactose-glucose interconversion in the uridine nucleotide pathway.

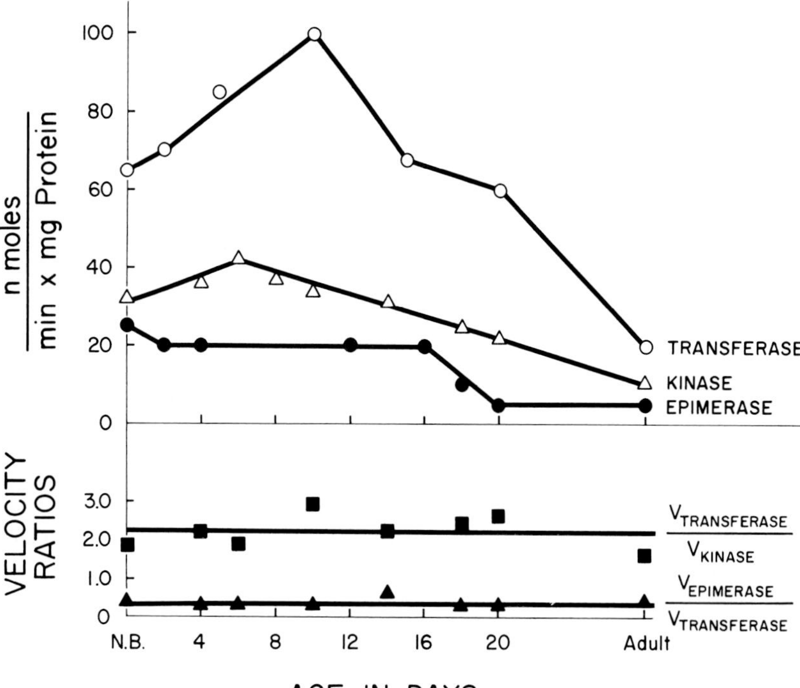

Fig. 13-3 The specific activity of galactokinase, galactose-1-phosphate uridyl transferase, and UDP-galactose-4-epimerase in rat liver as a function of age. *(From Cuatrecasas and Segal,[23] Bertoli and Segal,[50] and Cohn and Segal.[101])*

Galactose-1-phosphate Uridyl Transferase. This enzyme catalyzes the second step in the galactose-glucose interconversion in which the product of the galactokinase reaction, galactose-1-phosphate, reacts with uridine diphosphate glucose (UDP-glucose) to give UDP-galactose and glucose-1-phosphate.[14] The enzyme is present in bacteria[49] and most mammalian tissues.[50] Bacterial transferase has been purified to homogeneity and consists of two structural subunits of molecular weight 40,000.[51] The enzymatic mechanism of the bacterial enzyme is of the ping-pong type.[52] The stereochemical course[53] and N-terminal and C-terminal amino acid sequences of the *E. coli* enzyme have been determined.[54] The nucleophile to which the uridylyl group is bonded in the bacterial enzyme intermediate has been found to be imidazole N of a histidine residue[55] and the stereochemical course of the reaction has been described.[56] Highly purified yeast enzyme is similar to that of *E. coli* with a molecular weight of 86,100 and with two identical subunits.[57]

Calf[58,59] and human liver[60–62] enzymes have been partially purified. Isoelectric focusing indicates a microheterogeneity of human liver transferase, with several bands of activity on acrylamide gel.[63] Transferase is present in human fetal tissues, the liver enzyme-specific activity being highest at 28 weeks gestation with unchanging K_m values throughout gestation.[31] The properties of rat liver enzyme have also been examined.[50] Liver transferase has a K_m for UDP-glucose of 0.1 to 0.2 mM, a value within the physiological range of liver UDP-glucose concentration.[64] Thus, the rate of the reaction may be regulated by substrate concentration and limited by UDP-glucose substrate inhibition of the transferase observed at higher levels. Glucose-1-phosphate is a potent inhibitor of the enzyme.[50] Uridine nucleotides such as uridine di- and triphosphate are extremely powerful competitive inhibitors of substrate UDP-glucose.[65] Substantial data indicate that the enzyme is influenced by the general state of carbohydrate metabolic processes. During perfusion with galactose of suckling but not adult liver, transferase-specific activity is initially increased but falls to low levels after 90 min.[66] This phenomenon is also observed when glucose is perfused.

Dietary and hormonal influences on the liver enzyme have not been reported. Transferase has been examined extensively in both human[67] and rat intestine,[68] including developmental characteristics in the rat.[68] Feeding a high-galactose diet increases transferase activity in rat intestinal mucosa.[69] Properties of the enzyme in human diploid fibroblasts in culture and amniotic fluid cells have been delineated.[70–73] Hammersen, Mandell, and Levy have shown that the fibroblast enzyme consists of four activity bands on starch-gel electrophoresis.[74]

The most extensive studies have been made of purified human red cell enzyme.[61,75–77] The kinetic characteristics of the pure enzyme are similar to those in crude preparations. Although Tedesco[61] postulated a trimeric structure with a 90,000 molecular weight, Dale and Popjak[76] and Williams[77] found that the enzyme consists of two identical subunits with a molecular weight of 88,000. Wu et al.[78] and Markus et al.[79] proposed a ping-pong mechanism in the enzymatic activity which proceeds through two half-reactions with a uridylyl-enzyme intermediate. Williams et al.,[80] based on inhibition studies, concluded that the enzyme contains both cysteinyl and histidyl residues within its active center.

Uridine Diphosphate Galactose-4-epimerase. This enzyme is responsible for the inversion of the hydroxyl group at the fourth carbon of the hexose chain to form glucose from galactose. It is bifunctional, catalyzing the interconversion of UDP-glucose with UDP-galactose and UDP-*N*-acetylglucosamine with UDP-*N*-acetylgalactosamine[81,81a] and has a much broader biologic significance than merely the catabolism of galactose. It is also important for the conversion of UDP-glucose to UDP-galactose in those situations where only glucose is available to the organism and galactose is required as a constituent of complex polysaccharides. In fact, in cultured Chinese hamster ovary cells epimerase deficiency is one cause of deficient expression of the low density lipoprotein receptor on the cell surface.[81a] When the cells are grown in medium containing glucose as the sole sugar source, this mutation results in deficient production of UDP-galactose and UDP-*N*-acetylgalactosamine, the donor substrates for transfer of galactose and *N*-acetylgalactosamine to the low density lipoprotein receptor. Inadequate glycosylation results in instability of the receptor and the receptor minus phenotype. The enzyme has been highly purified from bacteria[82–84] and yeast[85,86] in which a polymeric structure of the enzyme has been found. In these organisms 1 mol of NAD is bound per mole of enzyme, which in the presence of uridine nucleotides and galactose exhibits fluorescence and conformational changes.[87,88] The role of UMP (uridine monophosphate) and sugars as activators has been studied by Kang et al.[89] and by Ketley and Schellenberg.[90] Circular dichroism spectra of the E. coli enzyme indicate that the conversion of the bound NAD to NADH is accompanied by an increase in α-helix structure[91] and alteration in binding characteristics.[92] The mechanism of the inversion has generated considerable interest. Kalckar[93] has reviewed the data, which indicate that neither hydrogen from water nor NAD is exchanged with hydroxyl hydrogen at carbon 4. Oxygen 18 from isotopic water is not involved. A novel mechanism for oxidation and reduction at carbon 4 involving the hydrogen of the uracil ring of UDP-glucose has been proposed.[94] Maitra and Ankel[95] and Adair and Gabriel[96] have evidence that a 4-ulose is involved in an oxidoreductase mechanism.

For liver enzyme activity, exogenous NAD is required, and NADH is a potent inhibitor of the enzyme.[97] At equilibrium the ratio of UDP-galactose to UDP-glucose is 1:3. Epimerase from calf liver has been purified 3000-fold and found to be a dimer of molecular weight 70,000.[98] NAD binds to the enzyme and induces a conformation resulting in enzyme activity. It has been calculated that in a normal catalytic cycle NAD dissociates once in every 9000 catalytic events. Metabolic control of galactose metabolism by regulation of liver epimerase activity is likely. Any process disturbing the NAD/NADH ratio, such as ethanol metabolism which generates NADH, will impair galactose utilization.[99] Since greater NADH inhibition occurs at physiological pH than at the alkaline pH optimum of the enzyme, intracellular pH may be an important factor in the rate of the reaction. In this regard, intact cells with a high glycolytic rate show little epimerase activity, whereas broken cell preparations have considerable enzyme function.[100] Cellular levels of UDP-glucose, as well as other uridine nucleotides, may also exert rate-regulating effects.[101,102] Animal age appears important, since the liver of newborn rats has a higher activity, which remains elevated during the period of milk ingestion[103] (Fig. 13-3). The data of Fig. 13-3 suggest that epimerase may be the rate limiting enzyme in rat liver. Epimerase activity of intestinal mucosa is low during the suckling period and increases with age.[103] The intestinal enzyme activity can be enhanced by feeding diets high in glucose or galactose content.[69] The enzyme in human fibroblasts has been characterized, and activity was found not to be related to galactose concentration of the incubation medium.[104] The enzyme in human red cells has a higher activity in newborns than in adults, and hemolysate activity of newborns does not require exogenous NAD, as does that of adults.[105] Considerable NAD remains in hemolysates because NAD nucleosidase is deficient in the newborn. Starch-gel electrophoresis reveals two distinct activity bands for epimerase on hemolysates from newborn, but only one band of different mobility in the adult. NAD added to the gel caused the enzyme of the adult cells to have a two-banded pattern.[105] The gene for epimerase has been assigned to human chromosome 1.[106,107]

Uridine Diphosphate Glucose Pyrophosphorylase. The activity of this enzyme not only enables the carbon chain of galactose originally phosphorylated (Fig. 13-2) to enter the pathway of glucose metabolism as glucose-1-phosphate but also is responsible for the important function of the synthesis of UDP-glucose from UTP and glucose. Originally found in yeast,[108,109] it is abundant in mammalian liver, from which it has been crystallized.[110] A polymeric subunit structure has been determined.[111] The crystalline enzyme from human liver reacts to some extent with other sugar nucleotides besides UDP-glucose, including UDP-galactose. Bovine mammary gland enzyme is inhibited by galactose-1-phosphate.[112] Certain *E. coli* strains with defective galactose metabolism have been shown to have an absence of this enzyme.[113,114] The molecular weight of the mammalian enzyme is approximately 400,000, with eight identical subunits.[115]

Alternative Pathways of Galactose Metabolism

Reduction to Galactitol. The presence of galactitol in the tissues of animals fed galactose[116–118] and in the tissues[119,120] and urine of patients with both transferase[121] and galactokinase deficiency galactosemia[122] demonstrates the importance of the reduction of galactose in mammalian metabolism (Fig. 13-4). Reduction of sugars to the polyol, first described by Hers in the seminal vesicle and placenta of sheep,[123] may be catalyzed by two enzymes found in most animal tissues.[124] One is aldose reductase or polyol: NADP-oxidoreductase, which reacts with a variety of aldehydes, glyceraldehyde being the principal substrate.[125,126] The K_m values for galactose of highly purified enzymes from lens[125] and brain[127] are 12 and 20 mM, respectively. The other enzyme, L-hexonate dehydrogenase[128] or L-gulonate:NADP-oxidoreductase, is an enzyme whose preferred substrates are uronic acids and their lactones, but which acts on galactose with much less affinity than aldose reductase. The K_m of purified brain enzyme for galactose is 159 mM.[127] The very high K_m values indicate that only when tissue levels of galactose are much elevated would reduction be important, being catalyzed primarily by aldose reductase. Under normal circumstances galactose would be phosphorylated by way of galactokinase.

The tissue distribution of both reductive enzymes has been demonstrated by starch-gel electrophoresis.[124] Lens is the only tissue with aldose reductase activity exclusively. In peripheral nerve, aldose reductase has been localized to the Schwann cells[129] and in kidney primarily in the renal papillae.[130] Aldose

Fig. 13-4 The conversion of galactose to galactitol by aldose reductase.

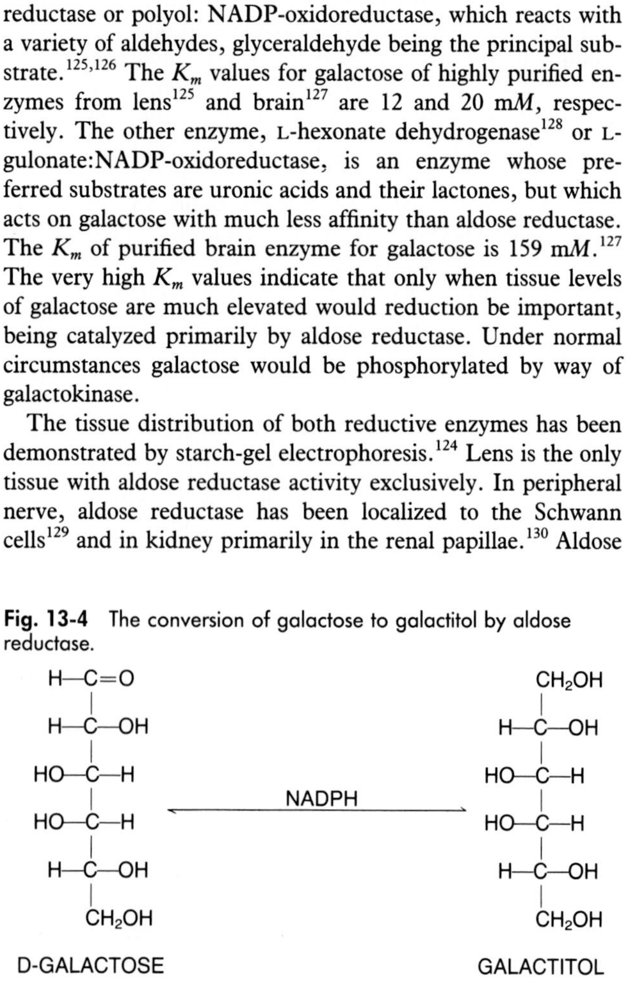

D-GALACTOSE		GALACTITOL
H—C=O		CH₂OH
H—C—OH		H—C—OH
HO—C—H	NADPH (⇄)	HO—C—H
HO—C—H		HO—C—H
H—C—OH		H—C—OH
CH₂OH		CH₂OH

reductase activity of lens and other tissues is stimulated by sulfate ions[125] and ATP.[131] It is inhibited by various keto and fatty acids[101] and ADP.[131] Increased enzyme activity has been observed in rat brain after birth.[132]

Oxidation of Galactose to Galactonate. Patients with transferase-deficient galactosemia excrete galactonate in urine after galactose is administered,[133] and rats fed a high galactose diet not only excrete galactonate in urine but accumulate galactonic acid in several tissues, including liver, intestine, heart, and kidney.[134] Galactonolactone, the cyclized form of galactonate, accumulates in liver and other tissues of guinea pigs fed a high galactose diet. The accumulation is accentuated in lens and plasma when aldose reductase and galactitol formation is inhibited.[135] Galactonate accumulates in suckling rat liver perfused with high concentrations of galactose.[136] The difference in the rate of radioactive CO_2 formation from oxidation of (1-^{14}C)galactose and (2-^{14}C)galactose by transferase-deficient patients led Segal and Cuatrecasas to postulate that a direct oxidative pathway may play a role in galactose disposition when the normal pathway is blocked.[137]

A pathway of galactose metabolism in rat liver has been described in which galactose reacts with NAD to form galactonic acid.[138] The latter compound is then oxidized to form β-keto-galactonic acid, which undergoes decarboxylation to D-xylulose, a sugar capable of further metabolism.[138] The initial enzyme was characterized in the soluble cell fraction as a galactose dehydrogenase with a K_m of 26 mM.[139,140] Strivastava and Beutler[141] failed to demonstrate the oxidation of galactose to galactonate but showed the formation of galactose-6-phosphate and its subsequent oxidation to 6-phosphogalactonic acid. Rancour et al.[134] demonstrated that rat liver microsomes produce galactonic acid when incubated with 30 mM galactose. Oxygen was not required, and formation of hydrogen peroxide was observed. A liver sample obtained at autopsy from a transferase-deficient galactosemic patient contained galactonate, suggesting that a similar system might be responsible for galactonate production when galactose metabolism by the uridine nucleotide pathway is blocked.[134]

Uridine Diphosphate Galactose Pyrophosphorylase. This enzyme, first detected in yeast[14] and subsequently identified in mammalian liver,[142,143] catalyzes the reaction of galactose-1-phosphate with uridine triphosphate to form UDP-galactose and pyrophosphate. Function of this enzyme could circumvent the block in galactose metabolism due to transferase deficiency, and indeed, preliminary data indicated that this could be the case.[142] However, the activity of this enzyme in human liver is low and does not increase with age.[144,145] There is now considerable doubt that catalysis is due to an enzyme with a unique affinity for galactose-1-phosphate. It is probable that the enzyme performing this function is UDP-glucose pyrophosphorylase.[110] The enzyme has been found to be present in human fibroblasts in tissue culture.[146]

Physiological Aspects of Galactose Metabolism

Human beings are capable of metabolizing large quantities of galactose given orally or intravenously, as demonstrated by the rapid elimination of galactose from blood[147] and the oxidation of radioactive galactose to $^{14}CO_2$.[148] A rise in the level of plasma glucose is found after galactose loading, because of the conversion of galactose to glucose through the uridine nucleotide pathway. When tracer amounts of radioactive galactose are given intravenously to normal subjects, 50 percent of the radioactivity may be found in the body glucose pools within 30 min. Curves of $^{14}CO_2$ excretion in expired air closely resemble those seen after the administration of radioactive glucose itself.[148] Plasma galactose is so rapidly removed by the liver that the rate of galactose clearance is a measure of hepatic blood flow.[149] The mechanism appears to be saturated at plasma levels of 50 mg/dl. Tygstrup[150] and Keiding[151] estimate that the capacity of hepatic elimination corresponds to the limits of the ability of galactokinase to phosphorylate the sugar. Galactose clearance can be utilized in clinical situations to measure hepatic blood flow[152,153] but may not be reliable in the cat.[154] This subject has recently been reviewed by Schirmer et al.[155] Urinary elimination is not a significant factor in the disposition of galactose loads.[156] Studies of the resorption of galactose by the human kidney reveal a low and incomplete threshold at plasma levels of 10 to 20 mg/dl.

Galactose tolerance tests have been used to estimate impaired liver function[157,158] and have shown that clearance of intravenously administered galactose is slow and the oxidation of isotopic galactose impaired in the presence of liver damage.[159,160] Ethanol administration slows galactose elimination from blood in both humans[147,148,161] and rats,[162] the effect presumably being due to tissue elevation of NADH and inhibition of UDP-galactose-4-epimerase.[99]

Sex may be a factor in galactose disposition. Female rats placed on an elevated galactose diet achieve higher serum galactose and galactitol concentrations than do male counterparts.[163]

Age may have some influence on galactose metabolism. Maximal utilization of galactose by rat liver in vitro occurs in tissue from the newborn and young.[164] This corresponds to the elevated enzyme levels shown in Fig. 15-3. Haworth and Ford[165] and Mulligan and Schwartz[166] have demonstrated that human neonates have a higher elevation of blood glucose after galactose administration than adults. The elimination of intravenous galactose in the neonate has been reported by some to be slower than in the adult,[166,167] while others report no difference.[168] Vink and Kroes reported the elimination rate to be faster in young children than in adults.[169]

The importance of galactose in metabolism of the young animal has been emphasized in recent studies involving perfusion of the immature liver. Sparks et al.[170] have reported that galactose infused into the isolated near-term monkey fetal liver regulates glycogen metabolism by enhancing the activity of glycogen synthetase and inhibiting phosphorylase, a phenomenon also seen in the adult.[176] In a series of studies of galactose infusion into liver of suckling 15-day-old rats, greater glucose output in the young compared to the adult was observed.[172] Almost quantitative conversion of galactose to glucose and a suppression of glucose formation from endogenous precursors occur in perfused suckling rat liver.[173] In addition, there is a lability of galactose metabolizing enzymes, especially galactokinase and galactose-1-phosphate uridyl transferase, which is not observed during perfusion of adult rat liver.[66]

Galactose Enzymes and Mutations in Microorganisms

Studies of metabolism and genetic regulation in microorganisms have contributed greatly to modern concepts of gene function and enzyme synthesis. The work done with galactose mutants in bacteria, especially *E. coli*, deserves some mention in a consideration of disorders of galactose metabolism in human beings. Although the direct application of *E. coli* genetics cannot be made to humans, the knowledge gives a greater conceptual framework for viewing the human mutations.

Normally the ability of *E. coli* to metabolize galactose is inducible, i.e., incubation in solutions containing galactose is followed by the appearance of high levels of the enzymes of the uridine nucleotide pathway, galactokinase, galactose-1-phosphate uridyl transferase, and UDP-Gal-4-epimerase.[174–176] Numerous mutants have been described that are unable to metabolize galactose, the so-called Gal^- mutants.[177] Analysis of these mutants has shown an absence of one or more of the enzymes of the pathway. In addition, Gal^- mutants have been described with defective UDP-glucose pyrophosphorylase.[113,114] Constitutive mutants have been described in which the enzymes are expressed even when the organisms are grown in media lacking galactose.[178] Genetic mapping of the galactose genes on the *E. coli* chromosome has been done. The sequence of the genes is kinase, transferase, epimerase, and operator (K-T-E-O).[179–181] The UDP-glucose pyrophosphorylase maps in a different position on the *E. coli* chromosome. The K-T-E-O genes function as an operon, with a regulator gene that is not linked to the Gal region being present elsewhere on the chromosome.[178] Some constitutive mutations are located at the regulator gene site, but one is a mutation in the terminal region of the epimerase gene. This is a so-called operator constitutive mutation which no longer recognizes the ability of the product of the regulator gene to repress initiation of enzyme synthesis.[178] Recent studies indicate that two overlapping promotors control the expression of the gal operon in *E. coli* and that cyclic AMP and its receptor protein regulate promotor activity. In addition, DNA mapping and sequencing of the operator of the *E. coli* operon have been reported.[48] The works of Wilson and Hogness characterizing the protein structure of *E. coli* galactokinase[18] and UDP-galactose-4-epimerase[83] suggest that the genes are made up of 1100 base pairs. The molecular expression and regulation of galactose pathway enzymes in yeast have also been reported.[182–185]

The effects of galactose on mutants with various enzyme deficiencies have been studied.[186,187] The presence of galactose does not impair the growth of galactokinase-deficient organisms but does impede the growth of transferase-deficient organisms. Galactose-1-phosphate accumulates in the latter bacteria, and this inhibits glycerolkinase formation.[188] Epimerase-deficient[189,190] and UDP-glucose pyrophosphorylase-deficient[113,114] organisms have marked alterations in the composition of polysaccharides in their cell walls.

Perhaps the most fascinating aspect of *E. coli* galactose operon genetics is that the lysogenic bacteriophage λ may incorporate the whole or a part of the galactose region of the *E. coli* chromosome into its own gene complement.[191] These phage particles have been termed λ dg. The λ dg phage is able to transduce the genes of the galactose operon into *E. coli* Gal^- mutants.[192] That is, the λ dg may bring into a cell genetic material that will function to produce the galactose enzymes which the mutant was unable to produce because of the genetic makeup of its own galactose operon. Such phenomena may ultimately have application to human genetic engineering for the correction of inherited metabolic defects. In theory at least, it seems possible that nonpathogenic viruses may be found which when grown in normal human fibroblasts will incorporate specific genetic material and which could be used to infect body cells with reparative genes. Indeed, Merril et al.[193] have reported that transferase-deficient human fibroblasts transfected with viral DNA viral transferase activity.

TRANSFERASE DEFICIENCY GALACTOSEMIA

Clinical Aspects

The first detailed description of this syndrome by Mason and Turner in 1935[1] was followed over the ensuing 25 years by numerous case descriptions that clearly established the clinical entity. The first reports of large groups of patients followed over a period of time appeared in 1961, when Hsia and Walker[194] discussed the variable clinical manifestations in 45 patients and Donnell et al.[195] described the growth of 24 affected children. The findings in 55 patients have been reported by Nadler and associates,[196] and in 39 patients by Donnell et al.[197] In 1970 Komrower and Lee reported a long-term follow-up of the 60 known cases of the disease in Great Britain.[198] Fishler et al.[199] updated the 27-year experience of the Los Angeles group in 1980.

The most common initial clinical symptom is failure to thrive. This occurs in almost all cases (Fig. 13-5). Vomiting or diarrhea was found in 52 out of 55 patients, usually starting within a few days of milk ingestion.[196] Signs of deranged liver function, either jaundice or hepatomegaly, are present almost as frequently after the first week of life. The jaundice of intrinsic liver disease may be accentuated by the severe hemolysis which may occur in some patients. Indeed, the peripheral blood picture may resemble that of erythroblastosis. Ascites may develop and is usually found in those infants who succumb. Cataracts have been observed within a few days of birth. These may be found only on slit-lamp examination by the ophthalmologist and are missed with an ophthalmoscope, since they consist of punctate lesions in the fetal lens nucleus. Retarded mental development may be apparent after the first several months of life. There appears to be a high frequency of neonatal death due to *E. coli* sepsis, with a fulminant course.[200] This may be due to inhibition of leukocyte bactericidal activity.[201]

Signs of increased intracranial pressure and cerebral edema have been observed as a presenting feature.[202] Occasionally, patients found to be homozygous for the disorder in the course of genetic studies have been asymptomatic while ingesting milk. These patients, in many instances, are black, and may be capable of metabolizing some galactose.[203] There may be other patients who do not present a failure-to-thrive syndrome and are seen months after birth with motor retardation, hepatomegaly, and cataracts. The physician may be confronted with a child several years old with mental retardation and cataracts who proves to have this disorder. These children frequently have a history of partial treatment with milk substitutes and reduced milk intake instituted because of vomiting on milk formulas.

The chemical findings, besides those of deranged liver function, include elevated blood galactose, galactosuria, hyperchloremic acidosis, albuminuria, and aminoaciduria.[2,3] On rare occasions, there may be a depression of blood glucose concentration. Hyperchloremic acidosis may be secondary to the gastrointestinal disturbance and poor food intake but can be a result of renal tubular dysfunction and a defect in urine acidification mechanisms.[2] The albuminuria[3] and the general-

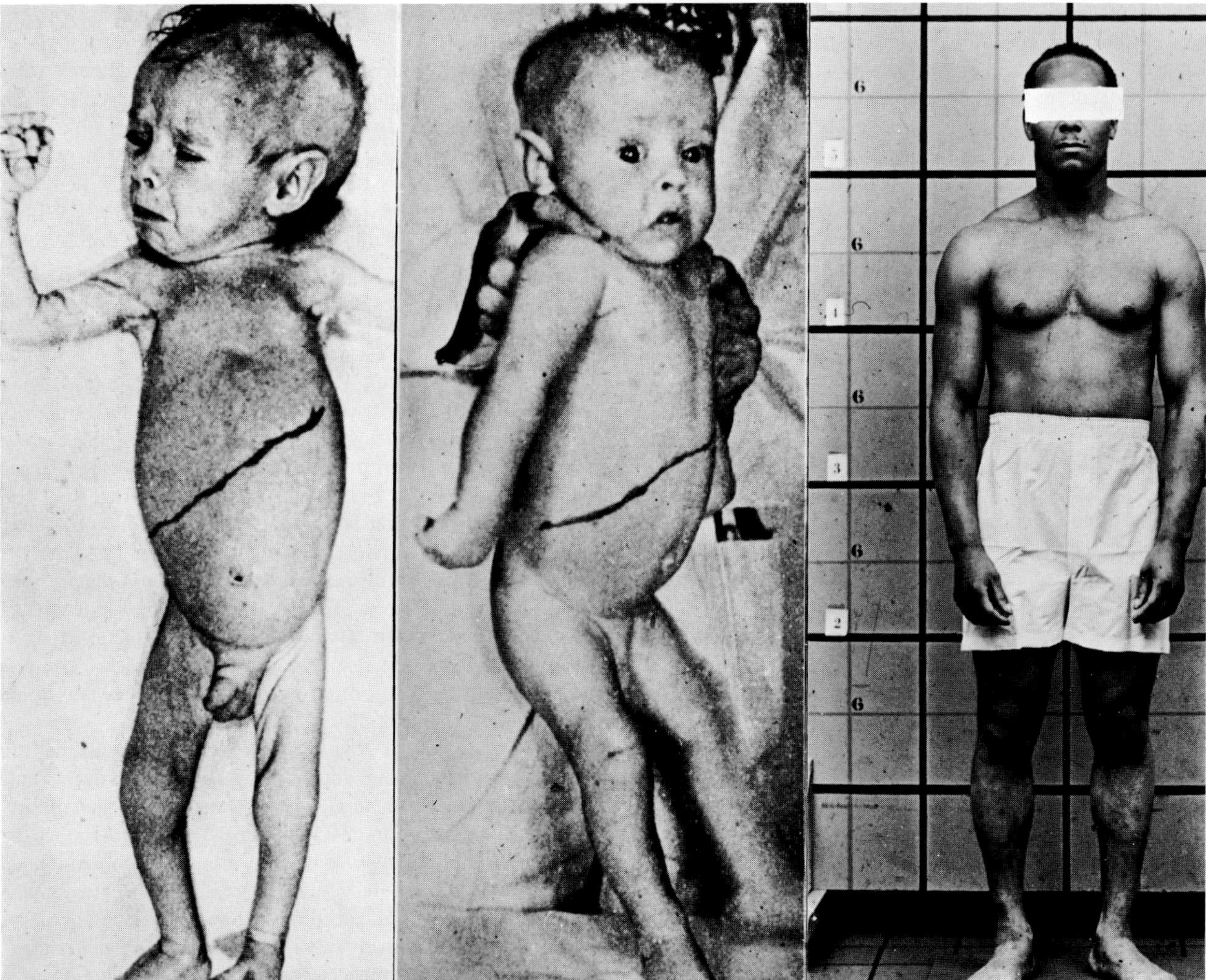

Fig. 13-5 Patients with galactose-1-phosphate uridyl transferase deficiency. The left picture shows a child age 3½ months with inanition and hepatomegaly. In the middle is the same child after galactose restriction for 3 months. On the right is a 30-year-old man diagnosed in infancy by Mason and Turner.[1]

ized renal aminoaciduria[204,205] are manifestations of a renal toxicity syndrome. The galactosuria may be intermittent because of poor food intake or may disappear within 3 or 4 days with the use of intravenous glucose feeding. The finding of a urinary reducing substance which does not react in a glucose oxidase test is the alerting sign for considering a diagnosis of galactosemia. Yet these latter findings do not establish the diagnosis, since lactosuria also occurs in intestinal lactase deficiency, and severely impaired liver function due to viral or other causes may be accompanied by diminished galactose metabolism and galactosuria and be confused with galactosemia. The liver of affected patients has a characteristic acinar formation, so that liver biopsy on occasion has been helpful in establishing the diagnosis.[206]

Management of Patients and Subsequent Course

At present the management of patients with galactosemia rests on the elimination of galactose from the diet. Failure to eliminate this sugar will usually result in progressive liver failure and death. Complete elimination of the sugar is the desired goal, but this may be difficult to accomplish. The preparations employed in infancy are Nutramigen, a casein hydrolysate, and soybean milks. Nutramigen may contain small amounts of lactose since it is prepared from milk, but this appears not to affect the therapeutic efficacy of the preparation. The use of soybean milk has been questioned because of the presence of sugars containing galactose such as raffinose and stachyose. However, Gitzelmann and Auricchio have shown that these galactose oligosaccharides are not hydrolyzed to their component sugars by human intestinal mucosa.[207] Furthermore, Donnell et al. have employed a soybean preparation in the treatment of several patients and have concluded there was no absorption of galactose.[197]

As the children grow it is important to be aware of sources of galactose in foods other than milk. A list of permitted foods has been published.[208] The success of the procedure depends on parent education. There is no good evidence that at a prescribed age the diet can be relaxed. In childhood the ingestion of milk will result in gastrointestinal symptoms. It has frequently been observed that after puberty milk ingestion is tolerated without symptoms. Such findings have been interpreted as indication of the development of a metabolic capability. On the contrary, there are data to suggest that the patients with transferase-deficient galactosemia do not develop the ability to metabolize galactose as they increase in age.[203] In older patients, there may be psychological problems associated with the adherence to stringent galactose restriction, and permission to include cakes, bread, and similar food should be considered. Milk restriction should be maintained.

Schwarz[209] and Donnell and associates[197,210] have advocated assays of erythrocyte galactose-1-phosphate for monitoring adherence to the diet. The normal range of galactose-1-phosphate in erythrocytes in 0 to 45 μg per gram of hemoglobin[211] with levels observed in well treated galactosemics being about 100 μg per gram.[210,211] Newly diagnosed patients have markedly elevated values which decline to those of well treated patients after several weeks of dietary therapy. Galactose-1-phosphate can be used to measure the occurrence of dietary lapses. The basis for erythroycte galactose-1-phosphate of well treated galactosemics being higher than normals has been attributed to endogenous production of the metabolite.[212]

There is no evidence that dietary galactose restriction is harmful. Since the UDP-galactose-4-epimerase reaction is reversible and UDP-glucose cna be converted to UDP-galactose, the body is able to provide adequately for the galactose component for brain cerebrosides and complex polysaccharides. Human intestinal lactase does not appear to be diminished in patients with galactosemia who have not ingested lactose for many years.[213]

Recently attention has focused on the restriction of dietary galactose during the pregnancies of women who have had children with galactosemia. This has stemmed from observations that the galactosemic syndrome is present at birth[194] from experimental evidence that the pups of pregnant rats fed high galactose diets are born with cataracts, and from other findings of galactose toxicity.[214,215] Donnell et al. have carried out this restriction in 11 pregnancies resulting in transferase-deficient infants.[197] One had cataracts at birth, but the other 10 were normal.

In those children with the manifestations of the toxicity syndrome, the galactose-free diet will cause a striking regression of all the symptoms and signs. Nausea and vomiting cease and weight gain ensues. Liver abnormalities clear; galactosuria, proteinuria, and aminoaciduria disappear. Cataracts will regress, and those visible with the ophthalmoscope may revert to small lesions seen only on slit-lamp examination. If the initial cataracts are not extensive, galactosemic patients who are well treated do not have impairment of sight because of cataracts. Subsequent growth and physical development appear to be within the normal range according to the findings in the large American groups.[196,197,199] The British experience[198] seems to be different, with most patients being below the 50th percentile in height and many below the 10th percentile. The explanation for this may be that the British collection of patients included many who were on poorly controlled diets and who were not cared for by the capable physicians who performed the survey. The experience of observers in this country has been that poor dietary control is associated with poor growth.

Mental retardation is the most significant outcome of clinical toxicity. The extent of retardation in transferase deficiency galactosemia differs from that of phenylketonuria in that extremely low IQ values are not generally seen even in those patients whose dietary therapy is started late in the first year. Of 41 patients followed by Donnell and associates,[197] 29 had an IQ greater than 85 and 7 had an IQ within the 70 to 84 range. Only 3 were severely retarded. In this group, those whose mothers were on a galactose-free diet and who were treated from birth had normal IQ values. One patient first treated at 14 months of age also had a normal IQ. Nadler and coworkers,[186] reviewing 44 patients, found 8 with IQs below 70 and 10 with IQs between 71 and 89. Those in the normal range as a group had lower IQs than their sibs. The correlation with time of institution of therapy and IQ was not clear in this series. In the British experience the average IQ of 32 patients on a good diet was 84, and of 22 patients on a moderately or poorly galactose-restricted diet was 77. Komrower and Lee[198] seem pessimistic about the outcome of dietary therapy. The eventual level of intelligence may be influenced by varying degrees of intrauterine damage due to fetal exposure to galactose. The best results are those of Donnell's group in whom intrauterine exposure to galactose was prevented by restricting lactose intake during pregnancy.[197]

The assessment of long-term development published in 1972[216] has recently been updated by Donnell's group. Table 13-1 summarizes the intelligence, visual-perceptual ability, and electroencephalogram findings in 60 patients grouped by age. Children identified at birth to 1 month of age maintained the highest level of intellectual progress. Of 30 patients who met this criterion, 15 had abnormal visual-perceptual status and 8 of 29 tested had abnormal electroencephalograms.[199] Komrower[217] has summarized the long-term follow-up of a group of galactosemic patients in England where intellectual outcome has not been optimal despite dietary treatment.

The actual measurement of IQ does not reveal the entire mental picture of these patients. Many with normal IQs are one or more grades behind in school and have specific learning disability involving spatial relationships and mathematics. Behavorial problems are frequent because of short attention span. Psychological problems seem to be prevalent, with inadequate drive, shyness, and withdrawal.[196,198] Speech and language deficits have been documented in children treated from an early age.[218] These children may perform much better with close teacher supervision.

Neurologic sequelae have been described in some older patients with galactosemia.[219–221] The findings have included cerebellar ataxia, tremor, choreoathetosis, and encepalopathy.

Table 13-1 Distribution of Intelligence, Visual-Perceptual Ability, and EEG Findings in Galactosemic Patients*

Group	Number	Age range, years	DQ/IQ range	Mean DQ/IQ	Standard deviation	Visual-perceptual status		EEG status	
						Normal	Abnormal	Normal	Abnormal
I	13	0–5	70–125	102	12.8	4	—	4	1
II	25	6–16	50–117	91	17.5	7	18	12	12
III	22	17–29	72–119	94	18.2	14	8	17	5
Total sample				95	16				

*$N = 60$.

SOURCE: From Fishler, Koch, Donnell, and Wenz.[199]

Neuropathologic findings, however, in the two instances reported[219,220] could be related to the severe neonatal jaundice and kernicterus. Jan and Wilson[221] and Lo et al.[222] reported adequately treated patients who later in childhood developed tremors and ataxia. The triad of mental retardation, tremor, and cerebellar dysfunction has been proposed as a neurologic syndrome occurring in a subgroup of patients with transferase deficiency galactosemia.

A high incidence of ovarian failure with hypergonadotrophic hypogonadism has been documented in transferase-deficient galactosemic females who have had adequate dietary therapy.[223–227] In the study of 26 affected females by Kaufman et al.[235] all but two had ovarian dysfunction which may be found to occur in patients as young as 1 year if gonadotropin release is measured in stimulation tests. Patients with normal ovarian function have been observed to develop abnormalities over a 4-year follow-up. Amenorrhea may be primary or secondary and can occur even after pregnancy. Ultrasonography of the pelvis shows diminished or absent ovarian tissue. Levy et al.[228] found the ovary of a 5-day-old infant who died of sepsis to have abundant oocytes and normal folliculogenesis, which together with clinical data suggest ovarian abnormalities are a result of continued galactose toxicity. Robinson et al.[226] found far fewer but normal follicles in an ovarian biopsy of a 16-year-old patient. Despite the occurrence of ovarian failure in most affected females, successful pregnancies have occurred.[229–231] In a series of women with premature ovarian failure, none were found who were heterozygous for uridyltransferase.[232] Male gonads appear to escape this manifestation of galactose toxicity.

Detection of the Enzymatic Deficiency

The observation of Schwarz and associates[233] that galactose-1-phosphate levels were elevated in the red cells of patients with galactosemia was an important clue to the nature of the enzymatic defect. These observations suggested that the enzyme defect was in the subsequent metabolism of galactose-1-phosphate. Analysis of the enzymes catalyzing galactose conversion to glucose by Isselbacher et al.[6] subsequently demonstrated that these red blood cells specifically lacked the enzyme galactose-1-phosphate uridyl transferase. The deficiency of this enzyme has been demonstrated also in the white blood cells,[234] skin fibroblasts,[235] intestinal mucosa,[67] and liver[60,236] of these patients. Preliminary data suggested that the red cells of these patients contain a protein capable of neutralizing antibody to liver transferase.[237]

Although an abnormally high amount of red cell galactose-1-phosphate has been used as a diagnostic criterion, the direct assay of red cell transferase activity provides the definitive diagnosis. The development of the red cell uridine diphosphate glucose consumption test by Anderson et al.[238] provided the means of making the diagnosis and has been used extensively over the last decade. This procedure is based on the assay of UDP-glucose before and after incubation with galactose-1-phosphate and red cell hemolysate by measurement of the NAD formed in the conversion of UDP-glucose to UDP-glucuronic acid by UDP-glucose dehydrogenase. The kinetics of the reaction have subsequently been improved by increasing the substrate levels[239] and stabilizing the enzyme with sulfhydryl compounds.[240] With this procedure a complete absence of red cell transferase in homozygous patients is found, and intermediate levels appear to characterize heterozygous carriers.[241] Several studies utilizing the UDP-glucose consumption test have been summarized by Hsia.[242] Normal red cell values are 6 μmol UDP-glucose consumed per hour per milliliter of RBC, or 25 μmol UDP-glucose consumed per hour per gram of hemoglobin.

Other approaches to the assay of Gal-1-P-uridyl transferase have involved the use of radioactive galactose[243] and galactose-1-phosphate as substrates, with an assay of the UDP-[^{14}C]galactose formed.[234,236,244,245] This procedure has proved valuable for the study of reaction kinetics.[50] The oxidation of [^{14}C]galactose to $^{14}CO_2$ has also been used to assess a defect of galactose metabolism in various tissues.[246,247] Employing this procedure, Ng and associates have shown that the red cells of three patients with absent transferase by the UDP-glucose consumption test had detectable $^{14}CO_2$ liberation and formation of small amounts of labeled UDP-galactose.[248] This type of test does not specifically determine a deficiency of transferase and may give abnormal results in galactokinase deficiency or any other deficient step in the series of reactions by which galactose is converted to CO_2.

Numerous methods for detection of the reaction product of the transferase reaction, glucose-1-phosphate, have been devised. These depend on conversion to glucose-6-phosphate and an assay of the NADPH formed when glucose-6-P dehydrogenase is added. This reaction has been coupled to the reduction of methylene blue,[249] but NADPH may also be determined fluorometrically.[250] In galactosemic cells there is no dye decolorization, whereas in normal red cells the dye decolorizes in a fixed time interval (Fig. 13-6). This has been shown to be an effective screening method,[249,251] as has the spot test devised by Beutler and Baluda in which the NADPH formed a

Fig. 13-6 Reduction of methylene blue by venous blood samples as a detection method for transferase deficiency. Methylene blue is converted to its leuko form by the formation of NADPH resulting from the transferase assay procedure. The color change is detected visually. (*From Beutler, Baluda, and Donnell.*[249])

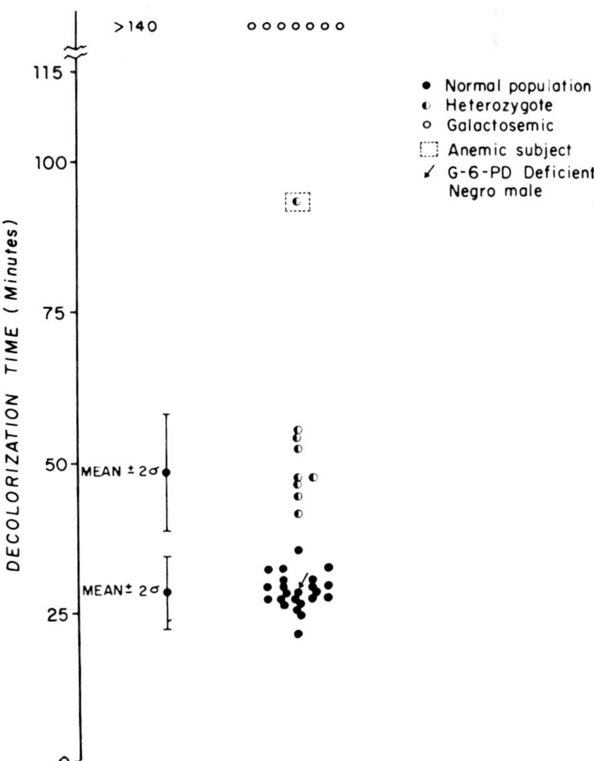

bright fluorescence under uv light in normal samples but was absent in cells from transferase-deficient galactosemic patients.[252,253]

The presumptive diagnosis of galactosemia may be made by the identification of galactose in the urine and blood of affected individuals. The finding of a reducing substance in urine which does not react with glucose oxidase reagents, such as Clinistix, is consistent with the presence of galactose, but lactose, fructose, and pentose may give similar results. The identification of the sugar may be made by paper chromatography[254] or gas-liquid chromatography.[255,256] The intermittent nature of the galactosuria may make its detection difficult, and the sugar may not be detected in extremely dilute urine. Perhaps a greater hazard is the fact that many hospital laboratories routinely test urine only for glucose, with commercial glucose oxidase preparations which will not detect galactose. The unwary physician may believe the urine to be sugar-free. The same possibility holds for missing high blood galactose levels in hospital laboratories where a blood glucose test is performed by glucose oxidase methods. Relatively specific methods for determining galactose in blood and urine with the use of galactose oxidase[160,257–259] and galactose dehydrogenase[260] have been introduced. Dahlqvist has devised a paper impregnated with galactose oxidase which is very sensitive and when dipped in urine will permit detection of abnormal amounts of galactose.[260,261] This appears to be useful in routine screening for galactosuria. It should be pointed out that many normal infants,[260,262] especially premature infants[260,263] in the postnatal period have a physiological melituria. Normal newborns have up to 60 mg galactose per deciliter urine in the first 5 days of life, while this level may be detected well into the second week of life in premature infants.[260] Some children with a high consumption of milk may have galactosuria.[264] The demonstration of galactosemia and galactosuria by the performance of a galactose tolerance test is not desirable as a diagnostic procedure.

Because of widespread screening of newborns for galactosemia, many patients have been identified, allowing for early institution of dietary therapy. Guthrie et al.[265] have summarized a broad experience with the three most commonly used procedures, the *E. coli* metabolite inhibition assay, the *E. coli*-bacterophage lysis assay,[266] and the Beutler and Baluda fluorescence assay.[252,253] The two former detect other forms of galactosemia, while the Beutler-Baluda test detects only transferase deficiency. The *E. coli*-phage test may be the most efficient in case detection, but the Beutler-Baluda test can be performed most rapidly. The latter may give false positives especially during hot summer months when transferase activity of samples may be inactivated by exposure to high ambient temperatures in transit to the reference laboratory. Newer rapid methods have been devised to detect galactose and galactose-1-phosphate in red cells with galactose dehydrogenase.[267,268] Bowring and Brown describe a complete protocol for detection of all abnormalities of galactose metabolism.[269]

Nadler et al.,[196] Fensom et al.,[270] Holton and Raymont,[271] and Shin et al.[272] have reported the use of amniocentesis and uridyltransferase assay of amniotic cells for the intrauterine detection of the homozygous fetus. Jakobs et al.[273] have analyzed amniotic fluid galactitol by mass spectrometry to provide a rapid method of prenatal diagnosis of galactosemia. Another method which obviates the need for growth of amniotic cells for prenatal detection is the measurement of uridyltransferase in chorionic villus biopsy.[274]

Galactose Metabolism in Patients with Transferase Deficiency

Early attempts to measure the ability of galactosemic patients to metabolize galactose depended on determination of the fraction of ingested galactose excreted in the urine. This ranged from 15 to 60 percent in 24 h; the remainder presumably was stored in the body or metabolized.[3,275] A more accurate quantitative assessment has been devised in which the conversion of intravenously administered [^{14}C]galactose to $^{14}CO_2$ is measured for a period of 5 h.[137,203,276] Of a group of 14 patients so studied, 9 converted the sugar slowly to $^{14}CO_2$, excreting 0 to 8 percent of the administered ^{14}C; and 5 oxidized the sugar at near-normal rates (Fig. 13-7). The ability to metabolize galactose to CO_2 was not related to sex, age, or puberty (Table 13-2). Those patients in the first group were reevaluated at intervals over a period of several years and did not develop greater ability to carry out the conversion. All these patients were Caucasian. The five subjects who oxidized significant amounts of galactose in spite of an absence of red cell transferase were all black. One of these was the patient reported by Mason and Turner in 1935[1] in the first careful delineation of the galactosemic syndrome associated with transferase defi-

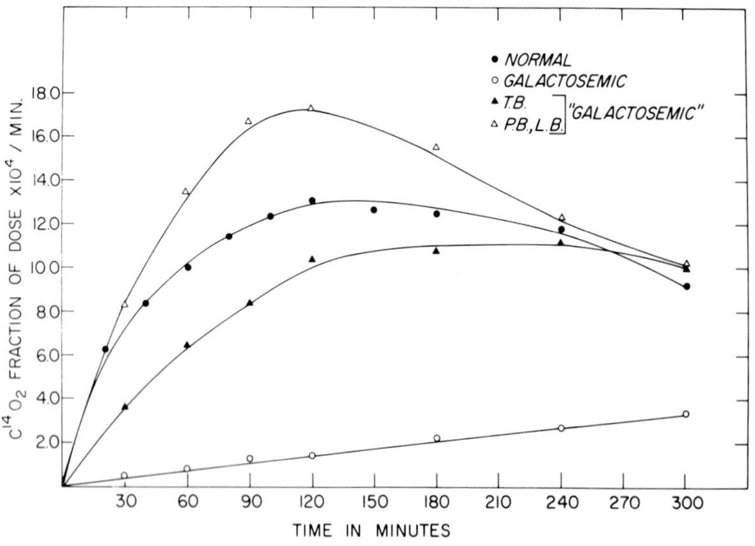

Fig. 13-7 The excretion of $^{14}CO_2$ in expired air by normal subjects and patients with transferase deficiency after intravenous administration of 1-g quantities of sugar containing (1-^{14}C)galactose. *(From Segal, Blair, and Roth.[203])*

Table 13-2 The Oxidation of Intravenous [1-^{14}C]Galactose by Normal Subjects and Patients with Transferase Deficiency Galactosemia

Subject	*Age, yr*	*Sex*	*Race**	*Amount,* g*	*Administered ^{14}C in expired $^{14}CO_2$ in 5 h, % injected†*
Patients					
W.Wa	3	M	N	TR	21
	8			1.0	27
J.O.	6	M	C	TR	1
M.Wa	7	M	N	1.0	28
B.A.	7	M	C	1.0	8
L.F.	7	F	C	TR	8
E.W.	9	M	C	TR	0
P.R.	9	F	C	TR	3
	11			1.0	7
	15			1.0	7
P.Br.	10	F	N	TR	45
				1.0	42
L.J.	11	M	C	TR	1
	15			TR	5
	19			1.0	11
L.Br.	11	M	N	TR	36
				1.0	35
H.T.	14	M	C	TR	5
	17			1.0	5
J.S.	16	M	C	1.0	2
J.D.	16	M	C	TR	3
				1.0	5
T.B.	30	M	N	TR	19
				1.0	26
				2.0	28
				10.0	19
Normal individuals‡					
3	18–21	M	C	TR	30–35
2	25–35	M	C	1.0	31–33
1	18	M	C	10.0	29
3	18–21	M	C	20.0	25–27

*TR = tracer, 1 to 5 mg; N = Negro; C = Caucasian.
†Patients received 1 to 3 μCi of ^{14}C sugar; normal individuals, 5 μCi.
‡Total number of normal subjects studied.
SOURCE: From Segal, Blair, and Roth[203]; Segal and Cuatrecasas[137]; Baker et al.[276]; and some unpublished data of the author.

ciency (Fig. 13-5). One of these black subjects was asymptomatic while ingesting galactose; his condition was detected only by family screening.[276] A similar black patient has been described by Hsia.[242] The ability of one subject to metabolize 10 g given intravenously was limited, but he could ingest 40 g galactose per day for 5 days without developing elevated blood galactose levels.[277] This patient converted galactose to blood glucose,[203] demonstrated ethanol inhibition of galactose metabolism,[203] and oxidized [1-^{14}C]galactose and [2-^{14}C]galactose in a normal pattern.[137] These observations are consistent with the function of the sugar nucleotide pathway. Liver biopsy specimens from two black patients oxidized [1-^{14}C]galactose to $^{14}CO_2$.[276,278] Assay for the transferase activity of intestinal mucosa[67] and liver tissue[60] from black subjects has disclosed levels of about 10 percent of normal (Table 13-3). Caucasian patients have no enzyme detectable in these tissues. The findings strongly indicate that the capacity of some black patients with galactosemia to metabolize limited amounts of galactose is based on residual transferase activity in visceral tissue. While the ability to metabolize galactose is correlated with race, a genetic basis is not truly established. The fact that sibs are involved favors a genetic origin. Why these same individuals may have a galactose toxicity syndrome in the neonatal period is not known; perhaps this phenomenon is due to the large amount of galactose ingested relative to the limited enzyme capacity.

Why any galactose oxidation is seen in Caucasian patients when no transferase is detectable in tissues is also unanswered. Measurements of $^{14}CO_2$ for up to 9 h after the administration of labeled sugar have shown a progressive increase in the amount oxidized.[137] In these patients, we find a different pattern and yield of $^{14}CO_2$ when C-1 and C-2 labeled sugar is given. This is consistent with the direct oxidation of galactose to galactonate and the subsequent decarboxylation of C-1.[138] Indeed, these patients excrete galactonate in urine after galactose is administered.[115] There is no indication that UDP-galactose pyrophosphorylase, which could circumvent the block at the transferase step, is active in these patients. Abraham and Howell[144] have demonstrated that this enzyme activity, which is very low, does not increase with age as postulated by Isselbacher,[142] and Segal et al.[60] have shown insignificant activity in biopsy specimens of the liver of patients with galactosemia.

Several attempts have been made to stimulate galactose oxidation in Caucasian patients. Progesterone[279] and menthol[280] administration have enhanced the oxidation of tracer amounts of [^{14}C]galactose, but the effect was not observed when larger amounts of the sugar were given.[281] Corticosteroids in high dosage cause no acceleration impaired galactose metabolism.[281] Administration of orotic acid has been reported to be therapeutic when given to children showing galactose toxicity,[282] but under experimental conditions the oral administration of orotic acid seemed to have no influence on [^{14}C]galactose oxidation.[283]

An alternate metabolic route which clearly is functioning is that in which galactose is reduced by the enzyme aldose reductase to form the sugar alcohol, galactitol.[125,126] Galactitol has been isolated from the tissues and urine of patients,[119–121] and radioactive galactose given to a patient was converted to galactitol.[284] The sugar alcohol is not metabolized further or converted to carbon dioxide. After the administration of [^{14}C]galactitol to normal subjects, all of the label is excreted in the urine, with none appearing as $^{14}CO_2$.[285] Galactitol excretion in the urine continues for several days after galactosuria disappears. This seems to be the main route of elimination. Tissue accumulation of galactitol may be important in galactose toxicity.

In 1962 Inouye et al. demonstrated the presence of galactose-6-phosphate in galactosemic erythrocytes.[286] Presumably this ester could be formed from galactose-1-phosphate by the action of phosphoglucomutase. The galactose-6-phosphate can be oxidized further to 6-phosphogalactonate by hexose-6-phosphate dehydrogenase, an enzyme found in red cells[286] and liver.[287,288] The significance of this pathway is unknown.

Galactose-1-phosphate can be generated in erythrocytes of transferase-deficient patients by pyrophosphorolysis of UDP-galactose, which is formed by the epimerization of UDP-glucose.[189,190] Thus, galactose-1-phosphate accumulation in red cells is not necessarily due to phosphorylation of galactose by galactokinase.

Galactose utilization has been examined in cultured human fibroblasts from transferase-deficient[291–293] and galactokinase-deficient patients.[293] When incubated with radioactive galactose, transferase-deficient cells produce $^{14}CO_2$ but at a very slow rate. Since little labeled carbon dioxide is obtained from galactokinase-deficient cells, it appears that the metabolic pathway involved utilizes galactose-1-phosphate. The clinical significance of these observations is open to question, since the

Table 13-3 Activity of Human Liver and Intestinal Galactose-1-phosphate Uridyl Transferase

Subject	Age, yr	Race	Sex	*Transferase activity, nmol/mg protein·min* Liver	Intestine
Controls					
B	41	C	F	11.8	
S	37	C	F	17.2	
C	2	C	F	16.1	
K	9	C	M	14.7	
U	4 (mo)	C	F	15.0	
S	23	C	M		15.2
D	21	C	M		12.2
H	22	C	F		8.9
M	22	C	F		12.3
L	22	C	M		15.8
Galactosemia*					
L.W.	7 (mo)	N	F		1.0
W.Wa	9	N	M	1.3	0.5
M.Wa	8	N	M	1.8	1.6
C.Wi	5	C	F	Nondetectable	Nondetectable
F.R.	2	C	M	Nondetectable	Nondetectable

*Nondetactable red blood cell transferase.
SOURCE: From Segal, Rogers, and Holtzapple[60]; Rogers, Holtzapple, Mellman, and Segal.[67]

substrate concentrations used are so minute as to have no physiological significance. Transferase-deficient cells accumulate galactose-1-phosphate whether they are grown with galactose or glucose.[292] Pulse-chase studies with radioactive galactose indicate that galactose is taken up and phosphorylated, with the resulting galactose-1-phosphate then dephosphorylated to free galactose. Galactose then leaves the cell in a futile cycle of phosphorylation and dephosphorylation. Radioactive galactose incorporation in cell-surface glycoproteins of lymphocytes from transferase-deficient patients is only 7 percent of normal.[294] Despite this fact, there is no evidence for a deficiency of cell-surface galactose groups with good response to galactose-binding mitogens and sensitivity to galactose-binding toxic lectin.

Variants of Transferase Deficiency Galactosemia

In addition to the black variant described above, other variants have been defined on the basis of activity and migration of the protein in starch gel electrophoresis (Table 13-4). In 1965 Beutler and associates,[295,296] employing more sensitive methods, described another mutation at the transferase locus, termed the *Duarte* variant, which results in diminished red cell transferase activity but no clinical disorder. While screening a large number of blood samples for transferase activity, these workers found a number of specimens in which the enzyme level was 50 percent of normal. This was suggestive of heterozygosity for galactosemia, but pedigree studies revealed that the red cells of parents of these propositi have about 75 percent of normal enzyme levels. This was inconsistent with the genetics of the standard form of transferase deficiency galactosemia[297] (Fig. 13-8). Subsequent investigation of the enzyme of this variant showed that it is indistinguishable from normal with regard to the pH optimum, thermal stability, and Michaelis constant,[75] but that it migrates faster on starch-gel electrophoresis.[298] Ng et al.[299] have demonstrated two distinct enzyme bands for the Duarte red cell enzyme, which migrate faster on gel electrophoresis than the single normal enzyme band. The enzyme activity of a sample from a parent of a subject homozygous for the Duarte variant reveals three bands, the normal and two bands for the variant enzyme. Gel isoelectric focusing has emerged as a useful technique for distinguishing variant forms of red cell transferase.[145,272,300]

All the data are consistent with the Duarte gene being allelic with the normal and galactosemic gene. Indeed, Beutler et al.,[297] Mellman and associates,[301] and Gitzelmann and coworkers[302] have described individuals with lower levels of red cell transferase than the 50 percent of normal of either the galactosemic heterozygote or the Duarte homozygote. These subjects with 25 percent of normal enzyme activity are genetic compounds with one Duarte allele and one galactosemia allele (Fig. 13-8). Levy et al.[303] reported that the genetic compound for the Duarte variant and classic galactosemic alleles is the most common biochemical phenotype detected by screening newborn infants for uridyl transferase deficiency. In none of the 10 subjects studied by Levy et al.[303] were clinical abnormalities observed, although small amounts of galactose were present in two subjects after milk ingestion. On the other hand, Kelly,[304] who also observed 10 such genetic compound individuals, believes that this condition is not entirely benign early in life. One subject exhibited clear-cut signs of galactose toxicity for a brief period after birth, and three others had high blood galactose levels after several days of milk feeding. Galactose intolerance is quite prevalent in this condition with increase in blood galactose and galactose-1-phosphate being

Table 13-4 Characteristics of Galactose-1-phosphate Uridyl Transferase Variants

Variant	*Erythrocyte transferase activity, % of normal*	*Starch-gel electrophoretic mobility (compared with normal)*	*Other characteristics*
Homozygotes			
Classic	0	Nondetected	
Duarte	50	Faster	
"Negro"	0	Nondetected	10% activity in liver and intestine
Münster	30	Nondetected	Inhibition by glucose-1-P
Heterozygotes			
Indiana	0–45	Slower	Unstable enzyme
Rennes	7	Slower	
Los Angeles	140	Faster	
Chicago	27	Faster	

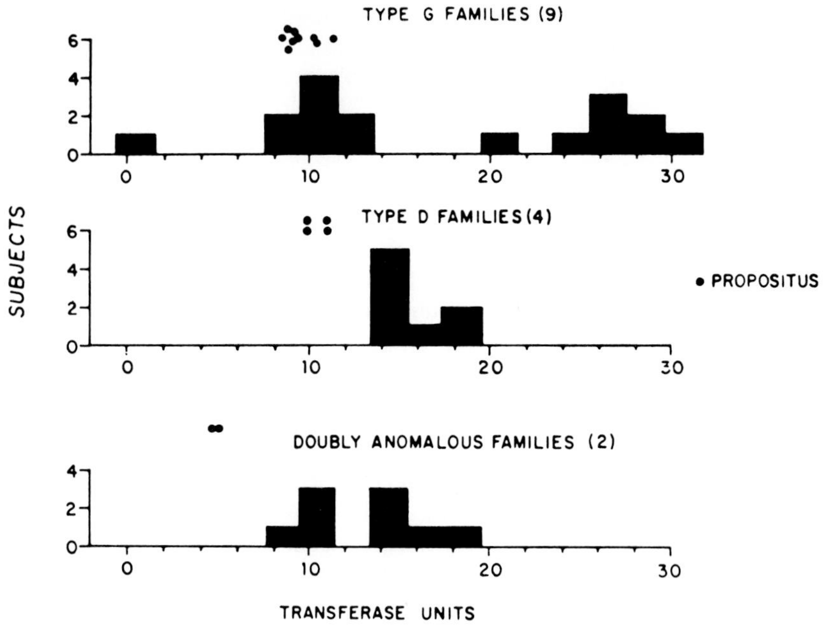

Fig. 13-8 Distribution of galactose-1-phosphate uridyl transferase activity (solid columns) in the red blood cells of parents and offspring of propositi found to have reduced transferase activity in a population screening. The activity of each propositus is indicated by the position of the solid dots relative to the horizontal axis. Type G families are segregating the classic transferase-deficient allele, type D families the Duarte variant allele, and in the doubly anomalous families, the propositi are genetic compounds for the classic transferase-deficient and Duarte alleles.

observed in 27 patients in whom oral galactose tolerance tests were performed.[305]

Adults with this phenotype appear healthy. In those infants with high blood galactose-1-phosphate levels, treatment with a low galactose diet seems prudent for the first few months of life. Ng et al. indicate that galactose intolerance in these Duarte classic galactosemic compound individuals does not last much beyond the first year of life.[306]

Schapira and Kaplan[307] have reported two Congolese sibs living in France, ages 2 and 16 months, with the usual features of transferase deficiency galactosemia in the first few weeks of life. Red cell transferase was about 7 percent of normal, and starch-gel electrophoresis of the red cell enzyme revealed a fluorescence band which moved more slowly (i.e., had less anodic mobility) than the normal enzyme and on isoelectric focusing was more basic with an isoelectric point between pH 6.0 and 6.2 instead of the normal 5.8.[308] The name *Rennes* was given to this variant. Hammersen, Houghton, and Levy,[309] during the course of screening newborns for transferase deficiency, detected a Caucasian baby with about 10 percent of normal transferase activity in both erythrocytes and skin fibroblasts. The enzyme mobility during starch-gel electrophoresis was slower than normal and corresponded to that of the Rennes variant. The child was apparently healthy during the first 3 weeks of life while on milk in spite of moderate galactosemia. Blood galactose levels after an oral galactose tolerance test rose to levels above 50 mg/dl, but the sugar was cleared from the blood by 3 h, contrary to what happens in subjects with classic uridyl transferase deficiency. The child's parents had enzyme activity in red cells and fibroblasts between 35 and 60 percent of normal, but no abnormal transferase was found on electrophoresis of hemolysates of either parent. Fibroblast enzyme from the mother, however, showed an electrophoretic pattern suggesting that she is a carrier for the slowly moving Rennes variant. The best explanation is that the child was a genetic compound for a classic transferase deficiency galactosemic allele and a Rennes variant allele.

A variant designated *Indiana* has been described[310] in an 18-month-old Caucasian girl who, when challenged with milk, had galactosemia, galactosuria, and galactose-1-phosphate elevation in her red cells. She had been on a galactose-free diet from birth because a sib had died at age 6 weeks with symptoms consistent with those of transferase deficiency galactosemia. Her erythrocyte transferase activity, which was approximately 35 percent of normal, was highly unstable, with rapid loss of activity in heparin or in isotonic phosphate buffer. No activity of transferase was detected on electrophoresis of a hemolysate from this child's blood, probably because of instability of the mutant enzyme. Erythrocyte transferase activities in the mother and maternal grandmother were 75 percent of normal and showed instability on storage and a decreased mobility on electrophoresis. Pedigree analysis suggested that the father was a carrier for the classic transferase deficiency galactosemia allele, while the mother carried the Indiana variant allele, which would make the patient a genetic compound.

Ng, Bergren, and Donnell[311] have detected six families with a variant enzyme termed *Los Angeles*, and Ibarra et al.[312] have reported an additional family. Homozygotes and heterozygotes have erythrocyte transferase activity higher than normal but with an electrophoretic pattern similar to that observed with the Duarte variant enzyme. There is no associated abnormality of galactose metabolism. In the pedigree analyses, subjects were found who appeared to be genetic compounds for Los Angeles and Duarte variant alleles as well as for Los Angeles and classic transferase deficiency galactosemia alleles. Of 418 presumed-normal Caucasian adults, 4.5 percent were found to be Los Angeles variant carriers. Immunochemical studies of the Duarte and Los Angeles variant enzyme indicate that rabbit antibody to the human placental enzyme immunoprecipitates all three forms.[313] Several other variants have been described. One, termed *Chicago*, was described in an apparent genetic compound in which there is about 27 percent normal red cell activity and a faster electrophoretic pattern.[314] Of particular interest is what appears to be a homozygous deficiency in a patient from Munster, West Germany.[315] Within the first 2 weeks of life, the patient developed vomiting, jaundice, failure to thrive, and hepatosplenomegaly, which reversed on a galactose-free diet. Analysis of red cell transferase indicated 30 percent of normal activity in a standard assay.[316] The enzyme became inactivated within 30 min of incubation. This was attributed to inhibition by the product, glucose-1-phosphate, an inhibition also produced by addition of other sugar phosphates. The enzyme exhibited a lowered affinity for galactose-1-phosphate, non-Michaelis-Menten kinetics with UDP-glucose, and was not detected on Collogel electrophoretograms.

Genetics and the Genetic Defects

Numerous investigations of red and white cell transferase of family members have indicated that the disease is transmitted as an autosomal recessive trait.[317–321] Obligate heterozygotes for classic transferase deficiency galactosemia have about 50% of normal activity.[241,243,244,317–321] The detection of the genotype in cultured fibroblasts and leukocytes is more accurate if the transferase/galactokinase ratio is determined.[322] Estimates of the prevalence of transferase deficiency galactosemia based on the detection of heterozygotes in Wales,[323] Denmark,[324] and the United States[297,302,325,326] range from 1:18,000 to 1:180,000. The prevalence at birth has been 1:70,000 in the British Isles.[318] In a large-scale screening program in New York State involving 141,000 infants, a prevalence of 1:35,000 has been detected,[327] while the frequency in Massachusetts is 1:190,000.[327] The overall figure summarized by Levy[329] in tests of 6 million newborns is 1 in 62,000. Population studies have indicated that from 0.9 to 1.25 percent are heterozygous for the classic galactesemia allele and that from 8 to 13 percent carry the Duarte allele.[297,301] Segregation analysis of 693 Italian families combining transferase activity and electrophoresis indicate the frequencies of the Duarte and Los Angeles alleles to be 3.7 and 4.0 percent, respectively.[330]

Early, indirect studies suggested that the galactose-1-phosphate uridyl transferase gene was on chromosome 21.[331–337] Subsequent studies utilizing linkage with chromosome 9 heteromorphisms and dosage determinations in partial chromosome 9 deletions have localized the transferase locus to 9p13.[338–340] Chromosome-mediated gene transfer experiments and other somatic cell methods mapped galactokinase to 17q21-22[39] and the epimerase to 1pter-p32.

Significant studies have been made concerning the genetic defect at the protein level. Tedesco and collaborators,[341,342] by double immunodiffusion techniques, have shown that rabbit antibody to purified human red cell galactose-1-phosphate uridyl transferase reacts with protein from patients with no red cell enzyme activity, thus establishing that there is an immunologic cross-reacting material identical with the normal enzyme but devoid of catalytic activity. Banrogues et al. found immunologically active enzyme with a molecular subunit of 46,000 daltons similar to normal. The amount of immunologically reactive protein ranged from 20 to 100 percent.[308] Red cell extracts from Duarte-variant individuals give precipitin bands of complete identity against rabbit antibody to the human enzyme.[61] Duarte-variant erythrocyte transferase required twice as much antibody for complete precipitation of enzyme activity as the normal enzyme. These data suggest that the Duarte molecule is similar to normal transferase but with less efficient catalytic activity. Dale and Popjak[76] isolated the inactive protein from transferase-deficient red cells in a pure state by affinity chromatography and have shown that peptide maps made after tryptic hydrolysis are identical to similarly prepared normal enzyme. All the data indicate that the inactive transferase results from a structural gene mutation resulting in the replacement of an amino acid, possibly near the catalytic site. Wu et al.[78] and Markus et al.[79] present evidence that red cell transferase may utilize a ping-pong mechanism and that isotropic exchange reactions carried out by the normal enzyme do not occur with enzyme of transferase-deficient cells; they postulate that the mutant enzyme either has a defective uridine diphosphate hexose binding site or is unable to cleave or release hexose-1-phosphate from an enzyme-nucleotide sugar complex. Nadler, Chacko, and Rachmeler,[72] employing cell fusion technique, have found that hybrid cells formed from human diploid fibroblasts from different patients with transferase deficiency galactosemia demonstrate enzyme activity. The enzyme of these hybrid cells was similar to the normal in regard to K_m, pH, and electrophoretic mobility, but differed in V_{max}, specific activity, and thermal lability. They postulated interallelic complementation in the hybrid cells. Other interpretations are possible, especially with the demonstration that the enzyme consists of a dimeric structure.[76,77]

Molecular Genetics of Galactose-1-phosphate Uridyl Transferase

Reichardt and Berg recently have reported cloning a cDNA for galactose-1-phosphate uridyl transferase from a human fibroblast cDNA library.[342a] Utilizing degenerate oligonucleotide pools corresponding to regions of conserved amino acid sequence in a comparison of the transferases from *Saccharomyces cerevisiae* and *E. coli*, they isolated a 1.4-kb cDNA which has a 72-bp 5′ untranslated region, a 1140-bp open reading frame, and 97 base pairs of 3′ nontranslated sequence extending to the poly (A) addition site. The open reading frame encodes a 43 kDa protein in good agreement with the 44 kDa estimate for monomers of the red cell enzyme. To confirm that the cDNA encodes the transferase, Reichardt and Berg showed that transfections with a recombinant expression vector containing the putative transferase cDNA resulted in a forty- to sixtyfold increase in transferase activity in recipient monkey kidney cells (COS cells) and also conferred transferase activity to a fibroblast cell line from a galactosemic individual. The cDNA hybridizes to a single-1.4 kb mRNA on Northern blots of lymphoid cell or fibroblast mRNA and to a single fragment in Southern blots of human genomic DNA digested with several different restriction endonucleases. Preliminary Southern blot analysis revealed no alterations in the genomic DNA of 10 transferase-deficient galactosemic individuals.[342a]

Pathogenesis of Galactose Toxicity

Since the patient with transferase deficiency exhibits a toxicity syndrome on ingestion of galactose, it has been assumed that the patient never exposed to the sugar should have no abnormalities. Long-term follow-up seems to indicate that this is not the case.[199] Galactose-1-phosphate can be elevated in red cells of patients not exposed to the sugar[289,290] and can be formed from uridine diphosphogalactose by pyrophosphorylytic cleavage. This led Gitzelmann and Hansen[343] to postulate that galactosemics may have a continuous self-intoxication and that there may be biosynthesis of galactose from glucose even in well-treated infants. The fact that galactose-1-phosphate is the metabolite which accumulates behind the metabolic block has suggested that high levels of this substance cause derangements of cellular metabolism.[344] With the discovery that galactitol, the product of an alternate route, also accumulates in tissues, the emphasis has shifted to the toxic effects of this polyol. The biochemical cause for the toxicity in any organ may differ and be dependent on the peculiar metabolic patterns and structure of the organ. Investigation of the underlying disruption of cellular processes has depended mainly on changes induced in animals, especially young rats[214,215,345,346] and chicks,[347–350] which are fed diets abnormally high in galactose. In making use of these animal models, we must not lose sight of the fact that the enzymes of the uridine nucleotide pathway are present but in limiting quantity. Since the kinetics of the multienzyme galactose pathway and the rate limiting step have not been clearly delineated, the situation is not entirely analogous to a complete metabolic block at the transferase step. For example, UDP-glucose appears to be depleted and UDP-galactose increased in tissues of these galactose-fed animals, a situation which may not obtain in the human disease.[351,352]

The Lens. Investigations to elucidate the cause of the cataract provide a panoramic view of research in this field. The feeding of a 40 to 50 percent galactose diet to weanling rats uniformly induces cataracts within 2 to 3 weeks.[279,345,353] The amount of galactose in the diet and the age of the rat are critical, cataracts being induced most readily in the fetal rats whose mother is fed a high galactose diet[214] and with greater difficulty in older rats. The female rat is at greater risk to develop galactose-induced cataracts.[354,355] Prolactin accelerates cataract formation in the female fed galactose.[354] Diets containing less than 30 percent galactose may induce cataracts only in some weanling rats and only after prolonged feeding.[279] A high fat diet,[356] progesterone administration,[279] and hypophysectomy[357] decrease the incidence of cataract induced by galactose. Galactose-1-phosphate is increased in the lens of the rat fed galactose,[358] as well as in the lens of patients with galactosemia.[359] Early observations by Lerman[360] attempted to explain the cataract as a result of the inhibition by galactose-1-phosphate of glucose-6-phosphate dehydrogenase with a consequent decrease in glucose metabolism, but this has not been confirmed. Cataracts induced by feeding galactose to rats are reversible when galactose is removed from the diet. The reverse process has been well studied.[361–363]

The demonstration by van Heyningen[116] that galactitol accumulates in the lens of galactose fed rats was followed by the work of Kinoshita and his associates, who demonstrated the presence of aldose reductase in the lens[125] and also demonstrated that the cataracts were closely associated with the imbibition of water by the lens as galactitol accumulated.[364,365] Galactitol is formed within the lens and becomes osmotically active because it diffuses from the lens with difficulty. Experiments with the lens in vitro have shown that balancing the osmolality of the incubation media to the osmotic properties of galactitol prevents cataract formation. In experiments with an inhibitor of aldose reductase, 3,3-tetramethyleneglutaric acid, Kinoshita et al. found that prevention of polyol accumulation blocked the water accumulation and resulted in a transparent lens after 3 day's incubation in galactose[366] (Fig. 13-9).

Sorbinil, a potent aldose reductase inhibitor, also prevents cataract formation and has become an important investigative tool.[367] The process of cataract formation and the role of aldose reductase in the etiology of both diabetic and galactosemic cataracts has been reviewed by Kador et al.[368] Magnesium, which stimulates aldose reductase, accelerates cataract formation in galactose fed rats.[369]

Many biochemical alterations occur concurrently in the lens undergoing galactose-induced cataract formation. These include alteration in protein synthesis,[370,371] lens fiber cell messenger RNA production,[372] amino acid transport,[373–375] ion fluxes,[376,377,378] sodium content,[379] Na,K-ATPase activity,[378] prostaglandin biosynthesis,[380] carbohydrate enzymes,[381] glutathione reductase,[382] and abnormal phase separation of lens fiber cytoplasm.[383] An early change after the increased fluid uptake is a marked decrease in lens glutathione.[365] ATP changes occur late in the process and do not appear to be involved with the fundamental changes.[384] Glycolysis and respiration of the lens are reduced about 30 percent after 2 days of galactose feeding and remain at this level until cataracts occur.[381] It seems conclusive that the initiator of the cataractous process in rats is galactitol, not galactose-1-phosphate, the latter accumulating only late in the process. Substantiating evidence is found in patients with galactokinase deficiency who have cataracts in the absence of galactose-1-phosphate formation.[9]

Concomitant with increases in galactitol accumulation is a

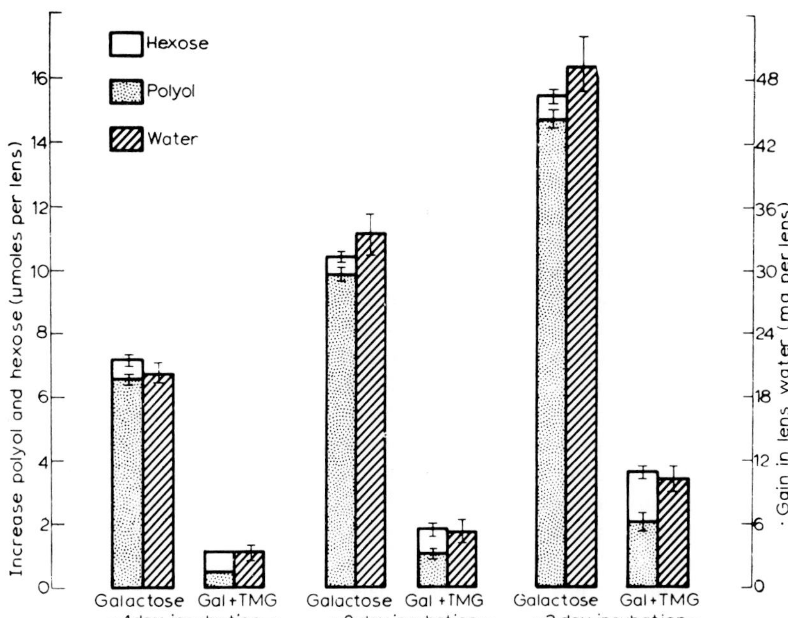

Fig. 13-9 Prevention of galactitol (polyol) formation and water accumulation by 3,3-tetramethylone glutaric acid (TMG), an aldose reductase inhibitor, in rabbit lens incubated with galactose. In 30 mM galactose solution, the lens which has been incubated for 3 days with 10 mM TMG remains clear. *(From Kinoshita, Dvornik, Kraml, and Gabbay.[366])*

decrease in lens inositol content,[355,375,378,385,386] but the role of inositol depletion is not clear. Lenses incubated in vitro in medium containing high galactose concentrations have impaired inositol uptake, which is corrected by the presence of sorbinil or rendering the medium hypertonic to prevent lens swelling.[378] Galactonolactone is found in lenses of galactose fed guinea pigs, but its level is only a tenth that of galactitol[387] and its significance undelineated. The formation of cataracts in galactose fed rats can be prevented by nutrient supplements.[388] This suggests the nutrient imbalance may be a prime etiologic factor in the toxicity of galactose, especially in the lens.

Whether exposure to galactose and impaired galactose metabolism is related to human presenile or senile cataracts has been a vexing question.[389] Rinaldi et al.[390] found a very high percentage of adults with idiopathic presenile and senile cataracts had persistent intestinal lactase activity and galactose absorption in an adult population generally deficient in lactase activity and concluded adults able to absorb galactose from a lactose containing diet are susceptible to cataract formation. Simonelli et al.[391] found that 21 percent of Neapolitan patients with presenile or senile cataracts have abnormally low red cell transferase activity, but no correlation with stage of development and clinical form of cataract could be made. The observation that the lens of rats exposed to galactose is more susceptible to laser induced injury supports the hypothesis that galactose is a risk factor for presenile or senile cataracts.[392] On the other hand, Brivet et al. found no cataracts in mothers or children heterozygous for transferase deficiency[393] and Muhlemann et al. found no galactose intolerance in patients with atopic cataracts.[394]

Liver. If the cause of cataracts seems clear, the reason for toxicity in the liver remains obscure. The severe liver damage seen in transferase deficiency is not observed in rats fed a high-galactose diet. Although the liver of children with galactosemia has elevated levels of galactose-1-phosphate[209] and galactitol,[120] the livers of rats fed galactose accumulate galactose-1-phosphate but not galactitol.[117] Chicks fed galactose accumulate large amounts of galactitol without severe liver damage.[118] Patients with galactokinase deficiency who ingest large quantities of galactose and who form galactitol have no liver damage.[9] It may be that an as yet unknown metabolite is responsible for the liver damage. Of importance may be the recent demonstration of galactonate in the liver of galactose-fed rats and a galactosemic patient.[134,135] Galactosamine is known to induce liver damage in animals,[395–398] and 2-deoxy-D-galactose injection in rats is associated with inorganic phosphate and ATP depletion, which is associated with liver abnormalities.[399,400] This may serve as a model for the study of liver cell injury in galactosemia.

Though microscopic liver damage is not seen in animals given galactose, biochemical abnormalities have been observed. In rats there is a decrease in liver glycogen[401] and diminished hexose phosphorylation,[401] and in chicks an abnormal glycogen-containing galactose.[402] No decrease in ATP levels occurs. The hypoglycemia sometimes seen clinically and induced by feeding galactose to patients may be related to deranged hepatic metabolism, since galactose does not stimulate the release of insulin from the pancreas.[403,404] Sidbury postulated galactose-1-phosphate inhibition of phosphoglucomutase as an explanation,[344] but this can be shown only in vitro in the absence of cofactor glucose-1-6-diphosphate. Patients given galactose have impaired hepatic glucose output[405] and do not respond normally to glucagon administration.[406] In a biopsy specimen from a single patient, the formation of glycogen from glucose was impaired.[407] Canine pups fed galactose have diminished glucose production and utilization rates.[408]

Kidney. Galactose-1-phosphate[209] and galactitol[120] have been detected in the kidney of patients with galactosemia. Galactitol accumulates in the kidney of rats fed galactose, large quantities being found in the renal papillae.[130] The aminoaciduria of transferase deficiency has not been seen in patients with galactokinase deficiency, who excrete large amounts of galactitol.[9] Aminoaciduria has been induced in rats fed a high galactose diet[409] and in normal human subjects to whom galactose was given intravenously.[410] Galactose toxic rats have increased albumin and *N*-acetylglucosaminidase excretion.[411]

The incubation of slices of kidney cortex with galactose produces impairment of amino acid accumulation by tubule cells.[412] The inhibition, which is noncompetitive in nature, has been observed also in the intestinal mucosa of rats,[413] a tissue which accumulates galactose-1-phosphate during galactose feeding.[414]

Brain and Nerve. One manifestation of galactose toxicity which may not be reversible is mental retardation. In patients with transferase deficiency, galactitol is found in the brain,[119] and in rats fed galactose, galactitol accumulates to a greater extent in the brain than in any other tissue except the lens.[117] Enzymes of galactitol formation are active in nerve tissue.[127] The weanling or adult rat develops no apparent brain abnormality when fed galactose, but the fetuses of pregnant rats fed galactose have decreased brain development[415] and decreased amounts of brain DNA, especially in the cerebrum.[416] Wells and Wells have shown an impaired conversion of glucose to inositol in brain slices from newborn rats exposed to galactose in utero.[417] No impairment of glucose conversion to inositol or alteration in inositol concentration was observed in isolated synaptosomes from similarly exposed animals,[418] which may suggest that nonneuronal cellular elements may be responsible for the findings in brain slices. Some of the effects on brain development may reflect the smaller body weight and placentas which occur in this mode.[214] Decreased nerve conduction has been reported in toxic rats.[419,420] The peripheral neuropathy associated with high galactose diets in rats is characterized by endoneurial edema, increased tissue pressure, and diminished nerve blood flow with demylinization of nerve fibers.[420a] The edema and increased endoneurial sodium can be reversed by administration of an aldose reductase inhibitor.[420b] There is also abnormal nerve regeneration in galactose neuropathy.[420c] In edematous nerves there is an accumulation of glycogen in Schwann cells.[420a] Galactose is known to impair the uptake of inositol by cultured rat Schwann cells.[421]

The chick given galactose in water develops ataxia and convulsions, followed by death.[86,118,347,348,422–424] The findings are more severe in females and in certain strains and are associated with galactose-1-phosphate,[423] galactose-6-phosphate,[425] and galactitol accumulation in brain.[118] They are reversible if the galactose is removed. This suggests that the changes seen pathologically in these brains[426] may be secondary.

Wells and his colleagues[424,427–433] have performed an elegant series of biochemical studies of the effect of galactose feeding on chick brain metabolism. The changes resulting from galactose administration were a diminution of ATP and energy charge, diminution of brain glucose and glycolytic intermediates, redistribution of hexokinase, enhanced fragility of neural lysosomes, and a decrease in fast axoplasmic transport. Slight decrease in brain amino acid pools occurred, but polyribosomal profiles and protein synthesis were unaltered. The administration of glucose to the neurotoxic chick resulted in temporary cessation of symptoms,[429] with brain ATP and glucose concentration returning to normal. Malone, Wells, and Segal[434] reported that the chick neurotoxicity syndrome correlated with hyperosmolar dehydration resulting from galactose feeding and also showed decreased entry of glucose into brain.[435] They did not find a significant depletion of ATP. The decrease in ATP and energy charge observed by Granett et al.,[428] although less than 10 percent, was statistically significant. The chick galactose toxicity syndrome may result from several factors, such as plasma hyperosmolarity and change in energy metabolism resulting from galactose phosphorylation or interference with transport of glucose into brain. Whether the chick neurotoxicity syndrome is related to the mental retardation observed in humans is open to question. Its acuteness and reversibility lead one to think it may not be. The rat does not respond to galactose administration with acute brain toxicity, although a decrease in brain glucose[132] and amino acids has been observed.[436] The finding of pseudotumor cerebri as a toxicity manifestation of both human transferase[202,437] and galactokinase[438] deficiency indicates changes relative to osmolality of brain tissue and biologic fluids. Detailed studies of inositol and phosphatidylinositol metabolism in synaptosomes from galactose-fed rats have indicated that there is an impaired response to acetylcholine in increasing the incorporation of inositol into phosphatidylinositol.[418] Incorporation of inorganic phosphate as a response to acetylcholine was not impaired. This suggests that the effect of galactose feeding is at a biochemical site distal to the acetylcholine receptor.[439] Woolley has suggested that serotonin depletion in the brain is a basic cause of mental retardation in various toxic states.[440] Woolley and Gommi explain the retardation of galactosemia on the basis of decreased serotonin receptors.[441] No abnormality has been observed on direct measurement of serotonin uptake by synaptosomes from galactose intoxicated rats,[442] which raises some doubt about the Woolley and Gommi hypothesis.

Gonads. Ovarian atrophy appears to be an important manifestation of galactose toxicity with clinical and biochemical evidence of ovarian dysfunction being present in nearly all affected females.[224–227] The basis of the toxicity has not yet been defined. Chen et al.[443] reported that female offspring of pregnant rats fed a high galactose diet throughout gestation had a significantly decreased number of primary ovarian follicles while the male gonad was undisturbed[444] and postulated that the ovarian failure resulted from developmental galactose toxicity. The observation of Levy et al.[228] that the ovary of a 5-day-old child with galactosemia had normal follicles suggests that the ovaries are damaged postnatally. This fits with the clinical observations in older females where normal ovarian function has converted to abnormal on long-term follow-up. A diminished number of normal appearing follicles was found in the atrophic ovary of a 16-year-old.[226] This occurrence, despite adequate dietary restriction and minimal elevation of erythrocyte galactose-1-phosphate, suggests intrinsic ovarian biochemical toxicity. The disturbance of ovarian follicle numbers in female offspring of rats fed a high galactose diet during pregnancy may be difficult to interpret since a large element of malnutrition complicates the experimental observations.[443] Chang et al.[445] report that adult male rats fed a 50% galactose diet exhibit prostatic atrophy and a marked decrease in plasma testosterone indicative of hypogonadism. A high galactose diet produces a decrease in the normal ovulatory response in adult female mice and a failure of an increase in ovulatory response to gonadotropin.[445a]

Microvessels. Galactose ingestion for short periods causes increased permeation of albumin of the aorta, vessels of the eye, sciatic nerve, and new granulation tissue, which is obviated by aldose reductose inhibition.[445,446] Long-term galactose feeding of rats produces cerebral cortical vessel basement membrane thickening,[447] which is also prevented by aldose reductase inhibition.[448–450] Long-term ingestion by dogs causes retinal microaneurysms and a picture typical of diabetic retinopathy.[451] Segal and Hwang[452] found no effect of galactose fed to rats or added in vitro on the uptake of amino acids or sugar by isolated rat brain capillaries, but Gjedde[453] observed high blood galactose impaired glucose movement through the blood-brain barrier of rats. Collagen solubility of new granulation tissue formed during galactose feeding is markedly increased.[445] Galactitol is formed in microvessels[454,455] and appears to be implicated in microvessel galactose toxicity.

Cell Toxicity. Galactose toxicity has been demonstrated in tissue culture.[456] The growth of fibroblast cultures from patients with transferase deficiency is inhibited by galactose. Electron microscopy of transferase-deficient cells incubated with galactose reveals striking dilatation of the endoplasmic reticulum and cytoplasmic degeneration and cell death within 72 h. Fibroblasts from transferase-deficient cells have impaired incorporation of radioactive sulfate when exposed to galactose.[457] Red cells with the defect have impaired oxygen uptake when incubated with galactose.[233] A decrease in ATP described under these conditions[458] has not been confirmed.[459] The fact that mutants of *E. coli* deficient in transferase have an impaired growth in galactose media, while galactokinase mutants do not, implies that galactose-1-phosphate is related to the toxicity in bacteria.[186–187]

GALACTOKINASE DEFICIENCY GALACTOSEMIA

Clinical Aspects

This disorder was first described in 1965.[9,10] Since the first reports, there have been several others.[460–469] The wealth of knowledge garnered about the transferase deficiency disorder over the past three decades has not yet been duplicated in galactokinase deficiency.

The first patient recognized to have galactokinase deficiency was a male 44 years old at the time of biochemical diagnosis by Gitzelmann.[9,10] Galactosuria after milk ingestion was detected when he was treated for cataracts in 1932 at the age of 9. Investigations at that time led Fanconi to call the patient's condition *galactose diabetes*.[470] His sisters had been seen in 1909 at ages 5½ and 7½ by ophthalmologists because of cataracts, but melituria had not been recognized. The impression by physicians was that both girls were mentally retarded. Dietary restrictions were never imposed, and the patients developed recurrent cataracts, poor vision, and blindness. Both females married and had several children. When studied, the 44-year-old male was ingesting 3 qt of milk a day without obvious effects. He was blind and complained of weakness and pain in his extremities which was attributed to neurofibromatosis. No IQ tests were performed on any of these patients, but the impression was that though they were illiterate, their intelligence as adults was normal. There was never any evidence of jaundice or liver disease, and no aminoaciduria or proteinuria was detected.[9]

The newborn with this disorder reported by Thalhammer et al.[462] was an apparently normal female who on a routine screen of capillary heel blood at 7 days of life was found to have 100 mg galactose per deciliter of blood. Routine examination at the time revealed no hepatosplenomegaly or gastrointestinal disturbance. When the infant was 17 days old and still on milk feedings, the liver and spleen were felt just below the costal margin. Ophthalmologic examination revealed circumscript opacities along the posterior lens suture, but they were not thought to be abnormal. Jaundice was not present. Total serum bilirubin was 2.0 mg/dl (direct, 1.2 mg/dl). Serum enzyme tests of liver function were normal. The infant was placed on a galactose-free diet on day 20 and at age 4½ months was found to be thriving and without other abnormalities.

The 9-year-old child reported by Monteleone et al.[460] had cataracts and red cells deficient in galactokinase, but no evidence of liver or renal disease or mental retardation. The two 4-month-old twins of Ollambiwanni et al.[461] were admitted to a hospital for hernia repair and were discovered incidentally to have high blood galactose levels and high urinary galactitol but no liver disease or aminoaciduria. Ophthalmologic examination revealed bilateral perinuclear zonular cataracts in both infants. Pickering and Howell[468] have described a patient in whom development was normal (except for cataracts) until age 17, when there was the onset of uncontrollable generalized seizures and severe debilitation. The relationship, however, of the neurologic involvement to the enzyme deficiency is unclear, especially since the patient had been on an essentially galactose-free diet from an early age. Two sibs have been described with galactokinase deficiency who are quite retarded mentally.[471] Gitzelmann, in Zurich, has diagnosed 21 patients, including 10 who were of gypsy, Bulgarian, or Yugoslavian background.[472]

Diagnosis

The absence of inanition, gastrointestinal dysfunction, and jaundice in the newborn period and the appearance of cataracts in the older patients on unrestricted diets differentiate this disorder from transferase deficiency galactosemia. In the absence of severe manifestations, it is apparent that the diagnosis in early infancy will depend on the routine screening of blood and urine for galactose. Since cataracts may be the first and only abnormality, this disorder should be suspected in any child with cataracts. Galactokinase deficiency should also be considered in patients with pseudotumor cerebri.[438]

The presence of a reducing substance in the urine may be identified as galactose by the methods described above for transferase deficiency. Thalhammer and coworkers[462] indicate that high blood galactose levels are best detected after milk feedings and that the level may be low in morning fasting specimens. The diagnosis can be made by the finding of normal amounts of galactose-1-phosphate uridyl transferase and an absence of galactokinase in the red blood cells.[9] Like transferase-deficient red cells, those with no galactokinase will be unable to oxidize galactose ^{14}C to $^{14}CO_2$.[9] The urine of all young patients with cataracts should be examined for sugar with methods other than those using glucose oxidase; there should also be an assay of the red cells for the defect. In the kindred reported by Monteleone et al.,[460] cataracts developed later in life in heterozygous relatives. This led Beutler et al.[473] to suggest that heterozygotes may be at risk for cataracts. In a subsequent survey of galactokinase activity of blood of 210 patients who developed cataracts before the age of 40, Beutler et al.[474] found two patients with absence of galactokinase. These patients developed cataracts in the first year of life. There was a statistically significant lowering of enzyme activity among 92 other patients whose cataracts developed during the first year of life. Skalka and Prchal[475] have also found a significant reduction of red cell galactokinase in 47 percent of patients age 50 or under who had bilateral cataracts. In the Italian population Magnani et al.[476] found no decrease in red cell galactokinase in 70 patients with cataracts including 15 subjects under the age of 1 year and no cataracts in heterozygotes. Stambolian et al.,[477] who detected an increase prevalence of cataracts in heterozygotes, points out that the occurrence of cataracts may be dependent on the amount of galactose in the diet of carriers for the abnormal gene. Therapy for the disorder should be aimed at galactose restriction, as in transferase deficiency.

Galactose Metabolism in Galactokinase Deficiency

Gitzelmann studied the 44-year-old male with this disorder by milk loading and found that large quantities of ingested galactose were excreted as galactitol.[9] After ingesting 360 g of galactose over a period of 5 days without ill effects, he excreted 192 g as galactose and 48 g as galactitol. On most test procedures the urinary galactitol-to-galactose ratio was about 1:4.

The author, in collaboration with Dr. Gitzelmann and Dr. H. J. Wells, has studied the metabolism of galactose in the same male patient by injection of radioactive galactose and determination of $^{14}CO_2$ expired over a 5-h period.[478] After injection of [1-^{14}C]galactose, only 5 percent of the label appeared in expired air, an amount similar to that seen in Caucasian transferase-deficient patients (Table 13-2). Essentially no label was excreted as CO_2 after the injection of [^{14}C]galactitol or galactonate. Thelow yield of $^{14}CO_2$ from galactose indicated that galactokinase deficiency exists in tissues other than the peripheral blood cells, the only type of cells directly assayed. This finding indicates that lack of severe galactose-induced toxicity is not due to a situation similar to that seen in black subjects with transferase deficiency, where the subjects lack the enzyme in the blood cells but have residual enzyme activity in the liver (Table 13-3) and can metabolize the sugar (Table 13-2 and Fig. 13-7). The lack of galactitol oxidation and almost total excretion of the labeled galactitol in urine are consistent with galactitol being an end product in galactose metabolism.

Genetics and Screening

Gitzelmann's erythrocyte assay for galactokinase among the kindred of the three adult patients revealed several members with values intermediate between those of the patients and a group of 100 normal subjects.[9] Mayes and Guthrie[479] have screened the red blood cells of 642 persons for galactokinase and have found the cells in six of them to have half the normal activity. Their data are consistent with an autosomal recessive inheritance. The estimate of heterozygotes is 1:107 and for homozygous births is about 1:40,000. The newborn described by Thalhammer and colleagues[462] with complete deficiency was the first detected with galactosemia after the analysis of 35,770 blood samples for galactose. It is interesting that the first four patients described were members of unrelated gypsy families. Tedesco et al.[38,326] have observed a racial polymorphism for erythrocyte galactokinase, with activity being about 30 percent lower in pregnant black females than in white females. Their genetic analysis[326] suggests that there is a variant gene in the black population. Magnani et al.[35] describe a variant red cell enzyme with reduced catalytic activity, altered K_m for Mg-ATP, and increased instability in very young erythrocytes. Mellman et al.[480] have reported that some individuals heterozygous for galactokinase deficiency may have an abnormal galactose tolerance test. The results of screening 6 million infants world-wide reported by Levy[329] indicate the detection of only six infants with galactokinase deficiency, in contrast to 97 with transferase deficiency. Pickering and Howell[468] have assessed galactokinase activity in human fibroblasts from a homozygous patient and obligate heterozygotes. Fibroblasts from the patient had no detectable activity, while heterozygote cells had about half the normal activity. Thymidine-kinase activity is diminished in fibroblasts of galactokinase-deficient patients.[481]

Toxicity Factors

The basis of the galactose toxicity syndromes has been discussed above under "Transferase Deficiency Galactosemia." The topic is considered again here because of the contribution to the understanding of galactose-induced toxicity by the discovery of galactokinase deficiency. It seems clear that cataracts are the reduction of galatose to galactitol through an alternative metabolic route. The absence of liver and kidney damage in galactokinase deficiency and the presence of damage to these organs in transferase deficiency make it likely that toxicity in the latter condition is in some way associated with galatose-1-phosphate formation. Not enough information is at hand to dissociate conclusively the mental retardation from galactokinase deficiency, although the evidence suggests that retardation is not a feature. If this is true, then brain damage in transferase deficiency would be the result of galactose phosphorylation and of the failure of galactose-1-phosphate to be further metabolized.

Animal Models. Galactose toxicity has been studied in the galactose fed rat and chick, as indicated earlier. In both these instances, the enzymes of galactose metabolism are normal, but their capacity is exceeded by the large amounts of ingested sugar. These models, therefore, are not entirely comparable to patients with single enzyme deficiencies. Stephens et al.[482,483] have detected what may be a suitable animal model. They reported the occurrence of cataract formation and diarrhea in orphan kangaroos fed cow's milk during rearing. The red cells of the gray kangaroo were found to contain only about 10 percent of the galactokinase and uridyl transferase activity of human red cells. Red kangaroo erythrocytes contain 10 percent of human cell galactokinase activity and 50 percent of the human cell transferase activity. A subsequent study was made of galactose handling by the kangaroo.[484] Galactose tolerance of young kangaroos was greatly impaired but improved markedly at the stage at which definitive structure of the ruminant type of stomach in adults is formed. Cataract formation was seen only in pouch-young animals. Erythrocyte enzymes have been analyzed in a variety of marsupial species. Many show both galactokinase and transferase deficiency. The koala and wombat have primarily a transferase deficiency and may be suitable models for transferase deficiency galactosemia. Kangaroo milk contains little lactose, so that the enzymatic deficiencies are of no physiological concerns except when the animals are given lactose-containing milk.

UDP-GALACTOSE-4-EPIMERASE DEFICIENCY

Gitzelmann[485] has reported a newborn child who was found by a bacterial screening procedure for blood galactose to have elevated galactose levels but who had normal uridyl transferase and galactokinase levels. Red cell UDP-galactose-4-epimerase was absent. Subsequent investigation revealed that the level of galactose was not elevated in the blood but that the level of red cell galactose-1-phosphate was elevated. (The bacterial assay was capable of detecting the phosphorylated compound.) A 2-year follow-up report of the patient by Gitzelmann and Steinmann[486] revealed normal growth and development, with normal ability to metabolize ingested galactose. The only metabolic consequence of galactose ingestion was the elevation of galactose-1-phosphate in red cells, without any resulting red cell abnormality.

Epimerase activity was absent in both erythrocytes and leukocytes but was normal in cultured skin fibroblasts and in a liver biopsy specimen from the patient. Thirty-nine members of the family were examined for red cell enzyme activity. The related parents both have levels of epimerase activity below the range of normal, and the pedigree analysis was consistent with a recessive inheritance of the trait. Gitzelmann et al.[487] have now reported eight cases of UDP-galactose-4-epimerase deficiency in three families. All persons were healthy and had normal galactose tolerance, the only abnormality being a rise in red cell galactose-1-phosphate. The enzyme deficiency was restricted to circulating blood cells. Screening programs have been established in Japan,[488,489] where the incidence was 1 in 23,000.

Mitchell et al.[490] have reported that phytohemagglutinin stimulation of leukocytes from these patients results in the appearance of epimerase activity. The enzyme activity is also present in lymphocytes maintained in long-term culture. Properties of the enzyme in such cultures are similar to those of the normal enzyme except for heat stability at 40°C. The mutant enzyme appears to be unstable and to require higher NAD concentration for maximum activity.[487]

A severe form of galactosemia has been reported in a female child of a consanguinous marriage in a Pakistani family with red cell UDP-galactose-4-epimerase deficiency.[7,8] The presentation at age 10 days resembled classic transferase deficiency with jaundice, vomiting, weight loss, hypotonia, hepatomegaly, generalized amino aciduria, and galactosuria. The symptoms responded to a galactose-free diet. Red cell transferase activity was normal. At 19 months of age both motor and intellectual development was delayed. The red cell epimerase activity of parents was diminished consistent with a recessive form of inheritance. Metabolic studies[8] revealed that with a galactose intake of 1 and 2 g/day red cell galactose-1-phosphate was normal but became elevated when 4 g was given. Uridine diphosphate galactose levels were elevated at even the lower galactose intake. At age 7 years the patient was physically well but had severe sensory neural deafness, little expressive speech with an IQ for the deaf of 85, and no cataracts.[491] A second patient has been described who was detected at 2 weeks of age because of abnormal aminoaciduria, who at 3 years is retarded with nerve deafness.[492] Like the first case, red cell UDP-galactose is constantly elevated but galactose-1-phosphate increases with excessive dietary galactose. In contrast to the benign form of epimerase deficiency, which is limited to erythrocytes and leukocytes, the severe form represents a systemic loss of enzyme activity in liver and other tissues. As predicted by the bifunctional activity of the epimerase, fibroblasts from one of these patients also have been shown to be deficient in UDP-*N*-acetylgalactosamine-4-epimerase activity.[493]

The treatment of this disorder requires a different strategy from that of transferase deficiency. Since epimerase forms UDP-galactose from UDP-glucose, a complete absence of galactose from the diet and lack of formation of UDP-galactose via transferase would have serious consequence. There would be an inability to form complex carbohydrates and galactolipids, which require UDP-galactose for synthesis. Therapy has relied on providing small amounts of dietary galactose, which do not provoke overt toxicity and presumably supply an amount of galactose adequate for galacto-protein and galacto-lipid synthesis. A prenatal diagnostic procedure can be performed for this disorder.[8]

Despite the expectation of a galactose requirement, fibroblasts from one of these patients, grown in a galactose-free medium, expressed normal amounts of the low density lipoprotein receptors, a protein whose stability and function depend on the posttranslational addition of galactose and *N*-acetylgalactosamine.[493] Additional study of the possible pleiotropic consequences of this inborn error will be of great interest.

REFERENCES

1. MASON HH, TURNER ME: Chronic galactosemia. *Am J Dis Child* 50:359, 1935.
2. KOMROWER GM, SCHWARZ V, HOLZEL A, GOLDBERG L: A clinical and biochemical study of galactosemia. *Arch Dis Child* 31:254, 1956.
3. HOLZEL A, KOMROWER GM, SCHWARZ V: Galactosemia. *Am J Med* 22:703, 1957.
4. ISSELBACHER, KJ: Galactose metabolism and galactosemia. *Am J Med* 26:715, 1959.
5. HOLZEL A: Galactosemia. *Br Med Bull* 17:213, 1961.
6. ISSELBACHER KJ, ANDERSON EP, KURAHASHI K, KALCKAR HM: Congenital galactosemia, a single enzymatic block in galactose metabolism. *Science* 123:635, 1956.
7. HOLTON JB, GILLETT MG, MacFAUL R, YOUNG R: Galactosaemia: A new severe variant due to uridine diphosphate galactose-4-epimerase deficiency. *Arch Dis Child* 56:883, 1981.
8. HENDERSON MJ, HOLTON JB, MacFAUL R: Further observations in a case of uridine diphosphate galactose-4-epimerase deficiency with a severe clinical presentation. *J Inherited Metab Dis* 6:17, 1983.
9. GITZELMANN R: Hereditary galactokinase deficiency, a newly recognized cause of juvenile cataracts. *Pediatr Res* 1:14, 1967.
10. GITZELMANN R: Deficiency of erythrocyte galactokinase in a patient with galactose diabetes. *Lancet* 2:670, 1965.
11. CAPUTIO R, LELOIR LF, TRUCCO RE: Lactase and lactose fermentation in *S. fragilis*. *Enzymologia* 12:350, 1948.
12. CARDINI CE, LELOIR LF: Enzymatic phosphorylation of galactosamine and galactose. *Arch Biochem Biophys* 45:55, 1953.
13. LELOIR LF: Enzymatic transformation of uridine diphosphate glucose into galactose derivative. *Arch Biochem Biophys* 33:186, 1951.
14. KALCKAR HM, BRAGANCA B, MUNCH-PETERSEN A: Uridyl transferase and the formation of uridine diphosphate galactose. *Nature* 172:1038, 1953.
15. WILKINSON JF: The pathway of the adaptive fermentation of galactose by yeast. *Biochem J* 44:460, 1949.
16. HEINRICH MR: The purification and properties of yeast galactokinase. *J Biol Chem* 239:50, 1964.
17. SHERMAN JR, ADLER J: Galactokinase from *E. coli*. *J Biol Chem* 238:874, 1963.
18. WILSON D, HOGNESS D: The enzymes of the galactose operon in *E. coli*. III. The size and composition of galactokinase. *J Biol Chem* 244:2137, 1969.
19. ATKINSON M, BARTON R, MORTON R: Equilibrium constant of phosphoryl transfer from adenosine triphosphate to galactose in the presence of galactokinase. *Biochem J* 78:813, 1961.
20. GULBINSKY J, CLELAND W: Kinetic studies of *Escherichia coli* galactokinase. *Biochemistry* 7:566, 1968.
21. SCHELL MA, WILSON DB: Purification and properties of galactokinase from *Saccharomyces cerevisiae*. *J Biol Chem* 252:1161, 1977.
22. CITRON BA, FEISS M, DONELSON JE: Expression of the yeast galactokinase gene in *Escherichia coli*. *Gene* 6:251, 1979.
23. CUATRECASAS P, SEGAL S: Mammalian galactokinase. *J Biol Chem* 240:2382, 1965.
24. WALKER DG, KHAN HH: Some properties of galactokinase in developing rat liver. *Biochem J* 108:169, 1968.
25. BALLARD FJ: Purification and properties of galactokinase from pig liver. *Biochem J* 98:347, 1966.
26. NG WG, DONNELL GN, BERGREN WR: Galactokinase activity in human erythrocytes of individuals at different ages. *J Lab Clin Med* 66:115, 1965.
27. MATHAI C, BEUTLER E: Biochemical characteristics of galactokinase from adult and fetal human red cells. *Enzymologia* 33:14, 1967.
28. TEDESCO TA, MELLMAN WJ: Galactose-1-phosphate uridyltransferase and galactokinase activity in cultured human diploid fibroblasts and peripheral blood leukocytes. 1. Analysis of transferase genotypes by the ratio of the activities of the two enzymes. *J Clin Invest* 48:2390, 1969.
29. CHACKO CM, MCCRONE L, NADLER HL: A study of galactokinase and glucose 4-epimerase from normal and galactosemic skin fibroblasts. *Biochim Biophys Acta* 284:552, 1972.
30. SRIVASTAVA SK, BLUME KG, VAN LOON C, BEUTLER E: Purification and kinetic properties of galactokinase from human placenta. *Arch Biochem Biophys* 150:191, 1972.
31. SHIN-BUEHRING YS, BEIER T, TAN A, OSANG M, SCHAUB J: The activity of galactose-1-phosphate uridyltransferase and galactokinase in human fetal organs. *Pediatr Res* 11:1003, 1977.
32. COHN R, SEGAL S: Galactose metabolism and its regulation. *Metabolism* 22:627, 1973.
33. SHIN-BUEHRING YS, STUEMPFIGL, POUGET E, RAHM D, SCHAUB J: Characterization of galactose-1-phosphate uridyl-transferase and galactokinase in human organs from the fetus and adult. *Clin Chim Acta* 112:257, 1981.
34. ZACCHELLO P, BENSON PF, BROWN S, CROLL P, GIANNELLI F: Induction of galactokinase in fibroblasts from heterozygous and homozygous subjects. *Nature* 239:95, 1972.
35. MAGNANI M, CUCCHIARINI L, DACHA M, FORNAINI G: A new variant of galactokinase. *Hum Hered* 32:329, 1982.
36. BLUME KG, BEUTLER E: Purification and properties of galactokinase from human red blood cells. *J Biol Chem* 246:6507, 1971.
37. STAMBOLIAN D, SCARPINO-MEYERS V, HARRIS H: Isoelectric-focusing of galactokinase in lens and other tissues. *Exp Eye Res* 38:231, 1984.
38. TEDESCO IA, BONOW R, MILLER K, MELLMAN WJ: Galactokinase: Evidence for a new racial polymorphism. *Science* 178:176, 1972.
39. ELSEVIER SM, KUCHERLAPATI RS, NICHOLS EA, CREAGAN RP, BILES RE, RUDDLE FH, WILLECKE K, MCDOUGALL JK: Assignment of the gene for galactokinase to human chromosome 17 and its regional localisation to band q21-22. *Nature* 251:633, 1974.
40. MAGNANI M, CUCCHIARINI L, STOCCHI V, BOSSU M, DACHA M, FORNAINI G: Comparative studies of galactokinase activity on mammal's red blood cells. *Comp Biochem Physiol* 64B:267, 1979.
41. MISHKIN JD, TAYLOR BA, MELLMAN WJ: Glk: A locus controlling galactokinase activity in the mouse. *Biochem Gene* 14:635, 1976.
42. ROGERS S, KIRSCH S, SEGAL S: Enzymes of galactose metabolism in erythrocytes and liver of inbred strains of mice. *Life Sci* 24:2159, 1979.
43. PARKS JS, GOTTESMAN M, PERLMAN RL, PASTAN I: Regulation of galactokinase synthesis by cyclic adenosine 3′,5′-monophosphate in cell-free extracts. *J Biol Chem* 246:2419, 1971.
44. NISSLEY SP, ANDERSON WB, GOTTESMAN ME, PERLMAN RL, PASTAN I: *In vitro* transcription of the gal operon requires cyclic adenosine monophosphate and cyclic adenosine monophosphate receptor protein. *J Biol Chem* 246:4671, 1971.
45. TAO M, SCHWEIGER M: Stimulation of galactokinase synthesis in *Esche-*

richia coli by adenosine 3′,5′ cyclic monophosphate. *J Bacteriol* 102:38, 1970.

46. ROBERTS CT JR, MORSE DE: Genetic regulation of galactokinase in *Tetrahymena* by cyclic AMP, glucose, and epinephrine. *Proc Natl Acad Sci USA* 75:1810, 1978.

47. ROTHMAN-DENES LB, HESSE JE, EPSTEIN W: Role of cyclic adenosine 3′,5′-monophosphate in the *in vitro* expression of the galactose operon of *Escherichia coli*. *J Bacteriol* 114:1040, 1973.

48. DILAURO R, TANIGUCHI T, MUSSO R, DE CROMBRUGGHE B: Unusual location and function of the operator in the *Escherichia coli* galactose operon. *Nature* 279:494, 1979.

49. KURAHASHI K, SUGIMURA A: Purification and properties of galactose-1-phosphate uridyl transferase from *E. coli*. *J Biol Chem* 235:940, 1960.

50. BERTOLI D, SEGAL S: Developmental aspects and some characteristics of mammalian galactose-1-phosphate uridyl transferase. *J Biol Chem* 241:4023, 1966.

51. SAITO S, OZUTSUMI M, KURASHASHI K: Galactose-1-phosphate uridyl transferase of *E. coli*. *J Biochem* 242:2362, 1967.

52. WONG LJ, FREY PA: Galactose-1-phosphate uridyl transferase: Rate studies confirming a uridyl-enzyme intermediate on the catalytic pathway. *Biochemistry* 13:3889, 1974.

53. REX SHEU KF, RICHARD JP, FREY PA: Stereochemical courses of nucleotidyltransferase and phosphotransferase action. Uridine diphosphate glucose pyrophosphorylase, galactose-1-phosphate uridylyltransferase, adenylate kinase, and nucleoside diphosphate kinase. *Biochemistry* 18:5548, 1979.

54. RAYCHOWDHURY R, SCHLESINGER DH, WILSON DB: *E. coli* galactose-1-phosphate uridyl transferase: N-terminal and C-terminal sequences. *Mol Cell Biochem* 23:167, 1979.

55. YANG S-LL, FREY PA: Nucleophile in the active site of *Escherichia coli* galactose-1-phosphate uridylyltransferase: Degradation of the uridylenzyme intermediate to N^3-phosphohistidine. *Biochemistry* 18:2980, 1979.

56. ARABSHAHI RS, BRODY A, SMALLWOOD A, TSAI TC, FREY A: Galactose-1-phosphate uridylytransferase. Purification of the enzyme and sterochemical course of each step of the double-displacement mechanisms. *Biochemistry* 25:5583, 1986.

57. SEGAWA T, FUKASAWA T: The enzymes of the galactose cluster in *Saccharomyces cerevisiae*. *J Biol Chem* 254:10707, 1979.

58. KURAHASHI K, ANDERSON E: Galactose-1-phosphate uridyl transferase, its purification and application. *Biochim Biophys Acta* 29:498, 1958.

59. MAYER JS, HANSON RG: Galactose-1-phosphate uridyl transferase, in Wood WA (ed): *Methods of Enzymology*. New York, Academic, 1966, vol 9, p 708.

60. SEGAL S, ROGERS S, HOLTZAPPLE PG: Liver galactose-1-phosphate uridyl transferase: Activity in normal and galactosemic subjects. *J Clin Invest* 50:500, 1971.

61. TEDESCO TA: Human galactose-1-phosphate uridyl transferase. *J Biol Chem* 247:6631, 1972.

62. BANROQUES J, GREGORI C, DREYFUS JC: Purification of human liver uridylyl transferase and comparison with the erythrocyte enzyme. *Biochim Extrait du Tome* 65:7, 1983.

63. SCHAPIRA F, GREGORI C, BANROQUEST J: Microheterogeneity of human galactose-1-phosphate uridyl transferase. Isoelectrofocusing results. *Biochem Biophys Res Commun* 80:291, 1978.

64. KEPPLER D, FROHLICH J, REUTER W, WIELAND O, DECKER K: Changes in uridine nucleotides during liver perfusion with D-galactosamine. *FEBS Lett* 4:278, 1969.

65. SEGAL S, ROGERS S: Nucleotide inhibition of mammalian liver galactose-1-phosphate uridyl transferase. *Biochem Biophys Acta* 250:351, 1971.

66. ROGERS S, SEGAL S: Changing activities of galactose metabolizing enzymes during perfusion of suckling rat liver. *Am J Physiol* 240:E333, 1981.

67. ROGERS S, HOLTZAPPLE PG, MELLMAN WJ, SEGAL S: Characteristics of galactose-1-phosphate uridyl transferase in intestinal mucosa of normal and galactosemic humans. *Metabolism* 19:701, 1970.

68. KOO C, ROGERS S, SEGAL S: Developmental aspects of galactose-1-phosphate uridyltransferase in rat intestine. *Biol Neonate* 27:153, 1975.

69. STIFEL FB, HERMAN RH, ROSENWEIG NS: Dietary regulation of galactose metabolizing enzymes: Adaptive changes in rat jejunum. *Science* 162:692, 1968.

70. TEDESCO TA, MELLMAN WJ: The UDP glucose consumption assay for gal-1-P uridyl transferase, in Hsia DYY (ed): *Galactosemia*. Springfield, IL, Charles C Thomas, 1969, p 66.

71. TEDESCO TA, MELLMAN WJ: Galactose-1-phosphate uridyl transferase and galactokinase activity in cultured human diploid fibroblasts and peripheral blood leukocytes. *J Clin Invest* 48:2390, 1969.

72. NADLER HI, CHACKO CM, RACHMELER M: Interallelic complementation in hybrid cells derived from human diploid strains deficient in galactose-1-phosphate uridyl transferase activity. *Proc Natl Acad Sci USA* 67:976, 1970.

73. SHIN-BUEHRING Y, LEITNER H, HENSELEIT H, WIRTZ A, HAAS B, SCHAUB J: Characteristics of galactokinase and galactose-1-phosphate uridyltransferase in cultivated fibroblasts and amniotic fluid cells. *Hum Genet* 48:31, 1979.

74. HAMMERSEN G, MANDELL R, LEVY HL: Galactose-1-phosphate uridyl transferase in fibroblasts: Isozymes in normal and variant states. *Ann Hum Genet* 39:147, 1975.

75. BEUTLER E, BALUDA M: Biochemical properties of human red cell galactose-1-phosphate uridyl transferase (UDP glucose: α-D Galactose-1-phosphate uridyl transferase) from normal and mutant subjects. *J Lab Clin Med* 67:947, 1966.

76. DALE GL, POPJAK G: Purification of normal and inactive galactosemic galactose-1-phosphate uridylyl transferase from human red cells. *J Biol Chem* 251:1057, 1976.

77. WILLIAMS VP: Purification and some properties of galactose 1-phosphate uridylyltransferase from human red cells. *Arch Biochem Biophys* 191:182, 1978.

78. WU JW, TEDESCO TA, KALLEN RG, MELLMAN WJ: Human galactose-1-phosphate uridylyltransferase. *J Biol Chem* 249:7038, 1974.

79. MARKUS HB, WU LJW, BOCHES FS, TEDESCO TA, MELLMAN WJ, KALLEN RG: Human erythrocyte galactose-1-phosphate uridylyltransferase. *J Biol Chem* 252:5363, 1977.

80. WILLIAMS VP, FRIED C, POPJAK G: Human red cell galactose 1-phosphate uridylyltransferase: Effects of site-specific reagents on catalytic activity. *Arch Biochem Biophys* 206:353, 1981.

81. SALO W, NORDIN J, PETERSON D, BEVILL R, KIRKWOOD S: The specificity of UDP-glucose 4-epimerase from the yeast *Saccharomyces fragilis*. *Biochim Biophys Acta* 151:484, 1968.

81a. KINGSLEY DM, KOZARSKY KF, HOBBIE L, KRIEGER M: Reversible defects in O-linked glycosylation and LDL receptor expression in a UDP-Gal/UDP-GalNAc 4-epimerase deficient mutant. *Cell* 44:749, 1986.

82. WILSON D, HOGNESS D: The enzymes of the galactose operon in *E. coli*. I. Purification and characterization of uridine diphosphogalactose-4-epimerase. *J Biol Chem* 239:2469, 1964.

83. WILSON D, HOGNESS D: The enzymes of the galactose operon in *E. coli*. II. The subunits of uridine diphosphoglucose-4-epimerase. *J Biol Chem* 244:2132, 1969.

84. DEELEY R, BLACKBURN P, FERDINAND W: The first enzyme of the gal operon in inducible and operator-constitutive strains of *Escherichia coli*. A comparison of the properties and amino-terminal sequences of UDP galactose 4-epimerase. *Eur J Biochem* 60:371, 1975.

85. DARROW R, RODSTROM R: Subunit association and catalytic activity of uridine diphosphate galactose-4-epimerase from yeast. *Proc Natl Acad Sci USA* 55:205, 1966.

86. DARROW R, RODSTROM R: Uridine diphosphate galactose 4-epimerase from yeast. *J Biol Chem* 245:2036, 1970.

87. BERTLAND A, BUGGE B, KALCKAR H: Fluorescence enhancement of uridine diphosphogalactose 4-epimerase induced by specific sugars. *Arch Biochem Biophys* 116:280, 1966.

88. BERTLAND A, KALCKAR H: Reversible changes of ordered polypeptide structures in oxidized and reduced epimerase. *Proc Natl Acad Sci USA* 61:629, 1968.

89. KANG UG, NOLAN D, FREY PA: Uridine diphosphate galactose 4-epimerase. *J Biol Chem* 250:7099, 1975.

90. KETLEY JN, SCHELLENBERG KA: Substrate stereochemical requirements in the reductive inactivation of uridine diphosphate galactose 4-epimerase by sugar and 5′-uridine monophosphate. *Biochemistry* 12:315, 1973.

91. WONG SS, CASSIM JY, FREY PA: *Escherichia coli* uridine diphosphate galactose 4-epimerase: Circular dichroism of the protein and protein bound dihydronicotinamide adenine dinucleotide. *Biochemistry* 17:516, 1978.

92. WONG SS, FREY PA: Uridine diphosphate galactose 4-epimerase: Nucleotide and 8-anilinolnaphthalenesulfonate binding properties of the substrate binding site. *Biochemistry* 17:3551, 1978.

93. KALCKAR HM: Uridine diphosphogalactose metabolism, enzymology and biology. *Adv Enzymol* 20:111, 1958.

94. DE ROBICHON-SZULMAJSTER H: Sur un noveau méchisme d'oxydoréduction, appliqué à la réaction d'epimérisation: uridinediphosphogalactose uridine diphosphoglucose. *J Mol Biol* 3:253, 1961.

95. MAITRA US, ANKEL H: Uridine diphosphate-4-keto-glucose, an intermediate in the uridine diphosphate-galactose-4-epimerase reaction. *Proc Natl Acad Sci USA* 68:2660, 1971.

96. ADAIR WL JR, GABRIEL O: 4-Uloses as intermediates in enzyme-nicotinamide adenine dinucleotide-mediated oxidoreductase mechanisms. I. Uridine diphosphate-galactose-4-epimerase. *J Biol Chem* 248:4653, 1973.

97. MAXWELL E: The enzymatic interconversion of uridine diphosphogalactose and uridine diphosphoglucose. *J Biol Chem* 229:139, 1957.

98. LANGER R, GLASER L: Interaction of nucleotides with liver uridine diphosphate-glucose-4′-epimerase. *J Biol Chem* 249:1126, 1974.

99. ISSELBACHER KJ, KRANE SM: Studies on the mechanism of the inhibition of galactose oxidation by ethanol. *J Biol Chem* 236:2394, 1961.

100. ROBINSON E, KALCKAR H, TROEDSON H: Metabolic inhibitions of mammalian uridine diphosphate galactose-4-epimerase in cell cultures and tumor cells. *J Biol Chem* 241:2737, 1966.

101. COHN R, SEGAL S: Regulation of mammalian liver uridine diphosphogalactose-4-epimerase by pyrimidine nucleotides. *Biochim Biophys Acta* 222:533, 1970.

102. GEREN CR, GEREN LM, EBNER KE: Inhibition and inactivation of bovine mammary and liver UDP-galactose-4-epimerases. *J Biol Chem* 252:2089, 1977.

103. COHN R, SEGAL S: Some characteristics and developmental aspects of rat uridine diphosphogalactose-4-epimerase, *Biochim Biophys Acta* 171:333, 1969.

104. CHACKO CM, MCCRONE L, NADLER HL: A study of galactokinase and glucose epimerase from normal and galactosemic skin fibroblasts. *Biochim Biophys Acta* 284:552, 1972.

105. BERGEN WR, NG WG, DONNELL GN: Uridine diphosphate galactose-4-epimerase in human and other mammalian hemolysates. *Biochim Biophys Acta* 315:464, 1973.

106. LIN MS, OIZUMI J, NG WG, ALFI OS, DONNELL GN: Assignment of the gene for uridine diphosphate galactose-4-epimerase to human chromosome 1 by human-mouse somatic cell hybridization. *Somatic Cell Genet* 5:363, 1979.

107. BENN PA, SHOWS TB, D'NCONA GG, CROCE CM, ORKWISZEWSKI KG, MELLMAN WJ: Assignment of a gene for uridine diphosphate galactose-4-epimerase to human chromsome 1 by somatic cell hybridization, with evidence for a regional assignment to 1pter→1p21. *Cytogenet Cell Genet* 24:138, 1979.

108. MUNICH-PETERSEN A, KALCKAR H, CUTOLO E, SMITH E: Uridyl transferases and the formation of uridine triphosphate. *Nature* 172:1036, 1953.

109. MUNICH-PETERSEN A: Investigations of the properties and mechanism of the uridine diphosphate glucose pyrophosphorylase reaction. *Acta Chem Scand* 9:1523, 1955.

110. KNOP J, HANSEN R: Uridine diphosphate glucose pyrophosphorylase. IV. Crystallization and properties of the enzyme from human liver. *J Biol Chem* 245:2499, 1970.

111. LEVINE S, GILLETT TA, HOGEMAN E, HANSEN RG: Uridine diphosphate glucose pyrophosphorylase. II. Polymeric and subunit structure. *J Biol Chem* 244:5729, 1969.

112. STEELMAN VS, EBNER KE: The enzymes of lactose biosynthesis. 1. Purification and properties of UDPG pyrophosphorylase from bovine mammary tissue. *Biochim Biophys Acta* 128:92, 1966.

113. SUNDARARAJAN TA, RAPIN AM, KALCKAR HM: Biochemical observations on *E. coli* mutants defective in uridine diphosphoglucose. *Proc Natl Acad Sci USA* 48:2187, 1962.

114. FUKASAWA T, JOKURA K, KURAHASHI H: Mutations in *E. coli* that affect uridine diphosphate glucose pyrophosphorylase activity and galactose fermentation. *Biochim Biophys Acta* 74:608, 1963.

115. TURNQUIST RL, GILLETT TD, HANSEN RG: Uridine diphosphate glucose pyrophosphorylase. *J Biol Chem* 249:7695, 1974.

116. VAN HEYNINGEN R: Formation of polyols by the lens of the rat with "sugar" cataracts. *Nature* 184:194, 1959.

117. QUAN-MA R, WELLS W: The distribution of galactitol in tissues of rats fed galactose. *Biochem Biophys Res Commun* 20:486, 1965.

119. WELLS W, PITTMAN T, WELLS H, EGAN T: The isolation and identification of galactitol from the brains of galactosemia patients. *J Biol Chem* 240:1002, 1965.

120. QUAN-MA R, WELLS H, WELLS W, SHERMAN F, EGAN T: Galactitol in the tissues of a galactrosemic child. *Am J Dis Child* 112:477, 1966.

121. WELLS W, PITTMAN T, EGAN T: The isolation and identification of galactitol from the urine of paitents with galactosemia. *J Biol Chem* 239:3192, 1964.

122. GITZELMANN R, CURTIUS HC, MULLER M: Galactitol excretion in the urine of a galactokinase deficient man. *Biochim Biophys Res Commun* 22:437, 1966.

123. HERS HG: L'Aldose-reductase. *Biochim Biophys Acta* 37:120, 1960.

124. CLEMENTS R, WEAVER J, WINEGRAD A: The distribution of polyol: NADP oxidoreductase in mammalian tissues. *Biochem Biophys Res Commun* 37:347, 1969.

125. HAYMAN S, KINOSHITA JH: Isolation and properties of lens aldose reductase. *J Biol Chem* 240:877, 1965.

126. HAYMAN S, LOU M, MEROLA L, KINOSHITA JH: Aldose reductase activity in the lens and other tissues. *Biochim Biophys Acta* 128:474, 1966.

127. MOONSAMMY G, STEWART M: Purification and properties of brain aldose reductase and L-hexonate dehydrogenase. *J Neurochem* 14:1187, 1967.

128. MANO Y, SUZUKI K, YAMADA K, SCHIMAZONO N: Enzymic studies on TPN L-hexonate dehydrogenase from rat liver. *J Biochem (Tokyo)* 49:618, 1961.

129. GABBAY K, O'SULLIVAN J: The sorbitol pathway: Enzyme localization and content in normal and diabetic nerve and cord. *Diabetes* 17:239, 1968.

130. GABBAY K, O'SULLIVAN J: The sorbitol pathway: in diabetes and galactosemia: Enzyme and substrate localization and changes in kidney. *Diabetes* 17:300, 1968.

131. CLEMENTS R, WINEGRAD A: Modulation of mammalian polyol: NADP oxidoreductase activity by ADP and ATP. *Biochem Biophys Res Common* 36:1006, 1969.

132. WELLS WW: Galactitol metabolism, in Hsia DYY (ed): *Galactosemia.* Springfield, IL, Charles C Thomas, 1969, p 227.

133. BERGREN W, NG W, DONNELL G: Galactonic acid in galactosemia. *Science* 176:683, 1972.

134. RANCOUR NJ, HAWKINS ED, WELLS WW: Galactose oxidation in liver. *Arch Biochem Biophys* 193:232, 1979.

135. WADA E: r-Galactonolactone in experimental galactosemic animals. *Arch. Biochem. & Biophys.* 251:215, 1986.

136. ROGERS S, LICHTENSTEIN G, GENTILE D, SEGAL S: Accumulation of galactonate in liver of suckling rats perfused with galactose. *Biochem Biophys Res Commun* 118:304, 1984.

137. SEGAL S, CUATRECASAS P: The oxidation of C^{14} galactose by patients with congenital galactosemia. *Am J Med* 44:340, 1968.

138. CUATRECASAS P, SEGAL S: Galactose conversion to D-xylulose: An alternate route of galactose metabolism. *Science* 153:549, 1966.

139. CUATRECASAS P, SEGAL S: Mammalian galactose dehydrogenase. I. Identification and purification in rat liver. *J Biol Chem* 241:5904, 1966.

140. CUATRECASAS P, SEGAL S: Mammalian galactose dehydrogenase. II. Properties, substrate specificity and developmental changes. *J Biol Chem* 241:5910, 1966.

141. SRIVASTAVA SK, BEUTLER E: Auxiliary pathways of galactose metabolism. *J Biol Chem* 244:6377, 1969.

142. ISSELBACHER KJ: Evidence for an accessory pathway of galactose metabolism in mammalian liver. *Science* 126:652, 1957.

143. ISSELBACHER K: A mammalian uridinediphosphate galactose pyrophosphorylase. *J Biol Chem* 232:429, 1958.

144. ABRAHAM H, HOWELL R: Human hepatic uridine diphosphate galactose pyrophosphorylase. *J Biol Chem* 244:545, 1969.

145. SHIN YS, NIEDERMEIER, HP, ENDRES W, SCHAUB J, WEIDINGER S: Agarose gel isoelectrofocusing of UDP-galactose pyrophosphorylase and galactose-1-phosphate uridyltransferase. Developmental aspect of UDP-galactose pyrophosphorylase. *Clin Chim Acta* 166:27, 1987.

146. CHACKO CM, MCCRONE ML, NADLER HL: Uridine diphosphoglucose pyrophosphorylase and uridine diphosphogalactose phosphorylase in human skin fibroblasts from normal and galactosemic individuals. *Biochim Biophys Acta* 268:113, 1972.

147. STENSTAM T: Peroral and intravenous galactose tCTOSE ests: Comparative study of their significance in different conditions. *Acta Med Scand (suppl)*:177, 1946.

148. SEGAL S, BLAIR A: Some observations on the metabolism of D-galactose in normal man. *J Clin Invest* 40:2016, 1961.

149. TYGSTRUP N, WINKLER K: Galactose blood clearance as a measure of hepatic blood flow. *Clin Sci* 17:1, 1958.

150. TYGSTRUP N: Determination of the hepatic elimination capacity (Lm) of galactose by single injection. *Scand J Clin Lab Invest (suppl)* 18:92, 118, 1966.

151. KEIDING S: Galactose elimination capacity in the rat. *Scand J Clin Lab Invest* 31:319, 1973.

152. HENDERSON JM, HANNA SS: Effective liver blood flow: Determination by galactose clearance. *Can J Surg* 26:129, 1983.

153. RYPINS EB, SANKARY H, WYNN MJ: Bedside micro-method for measuring effective hepatic blood flow, with use of first-order galactose clearance pharmacokinetics. *Clin Chem* 31:1557, 1985.

154. BURCZYNSKI FJ, GREENWAY CV: Hepatic blood flow: Accuracy of estimation from galactose clearances in cats. *Can J Physiol Pharmacol* 64:1310, 1986.

155. SCHIRMER WJ, TOWNSEND MC, SCHIRMER JW, HAMPTON WW, FRY DE: Galactose clearance as an estimate of effective hepatic blood flow: Validation and limitations. *J Sur Res* 41:543, 1986.

156. TYGSTRUP N: The urinary excretion of galactose and its significance in clinical intravenous galactose tolerance tests. *Acta Physiol Scand* 51:263, 1961

157. COLCHER H, PATEK AJ, KENDALL FE: Galactose disappearance from the blood stream: Calculation of a galactose removal constant and its application as a test of liver function. *J Clin Invest* 25:768, 1946.

158. HENDERSON JM, KUTNER MH, BAIN RP: First-order clearance of plasma galactose: The effect of liver disease. *Gastroenterology* 83:1090, 1982.
159. TENGSTRÖM B: An intravenous galactose tolerance test with an enzymatic determination of galactose: A comparison with other diagnostic aids in hepatobiliary diseases. *Scand J Clin Invest* 18:132, 1966.
160. SHREEVE WW, SHOOP JD, OTT DG, MCINTEER BB: Test for alcoholic cirrhosis by conversion of [^{14}C] or [^{13}C]galactose to expired CO_2. *Gastroenterology* 71:98, 1976.
161. TYGSTRUP N, LUNDQUIST F: The effect of ethanol on galactose elimination in man. *J Lab Clin Med* 59:102, 1962.
162. SALASPURO MP, SALASPURO AE: The effect of ethanol on galactose elimination in rats with normal and choline-deficient fatty livers. *Scand J Clin Lab Invest* 22:49, 1968.
163. ADRIAN J, KECHRID RM, POIFAIT A: Galactose metabolism in male and female rats I. Blood and urinary differences. *Int J Vitam Nutr Res* 56:303, 1986.
164. SEGAL S, ROTH H, BERTOLI D: Galactose metabolism by rat liver tissue: Influence of age. *Science* 142:1311, 1963.
165. HAWORTH JC, FORD JD: Variation of the oral galactose tolerance test with age. *J Pediatr* 63:276, 1963.
166. MULLIGAN PB, SCHWARTZ R: Hepatic carbohydrate metabolism in the genesis of neonatal hypoglycemia. *Pediatrics* 30:125, 1962.
167. HJELM M, SJÖLIN S: Changes in the elimination rate from blood of intravenously injected galactose during the neonatal period. *Scand J Clin Invest* (Suppl) 18:92, 126, 1966.
168. THEODORE GM, FORD JD, HAWORTH JC: The intravenous galactose tolerance test in infancy. *Arch Dis Child* 39:505, 1964.
169. VINK CDL, KROES AA: Liver function and age. *Clin Chim Acta* 4:674, 1959.
170. SPARKS JW, LYNCH A, CHEZ RA, GLINSMANN W: Glycogen regulation in isolated perfused near term monkey liver. *Pediatr Res* 10:51, 156.
171. SPARKS JW, LYNCH A, GLINSMANN WH: Regulation of rat liver glycogen synthesis and activities of glycogen cycle enzymes by glucose and galactose. *Metabolism* 25:47, 1976.
172. BERMAN W, ROGERS S, BAUTISTA J, SEGAL S: Galactose and glucose metabolism in the isolated perfused 15-day old and adult rat liver. *Metabolism* 27:1721, 1978.
173. BERMAN W, ROGERS S, BAUTISTA J, SEGAL S: Galactose metabolism in isolated perfused suckling rat liver. *Am J Physiol* 236(6):E633, 1979.
174. JORDAN E, YARMOLINSKY MB, KALCKAR HM: Control of inducibility of enzymes of the galactose sequence in *Escherichia coli*. *Proc Natl Acad Sci USA* 48:32, 1962.
175. BUTTIN G: Mécanismes regulateurs dans la biosynthèse des enzymes du metabolisme du galactose chez. *E. coli* K-12: I. La biosynthèse induite de la galactokinase et l'induction simultance de la séquence enzymatique. *J Mol Biol* 7:183, 1963.
176. WU HCP, KALCKAR HM: Endogenous induction of the gal operon in *E coli* K-12. *Proc Natl Acad Sci USA* 55:622, 1966.
177. KALCKAR HM, KURAHASHI K, JORDAN E: Hereditary defects in galactose metabolism in *E coli* mutants. 1. Determination of enzyme activities. *Proc Natl Acad Sci USA* 45:1776, 1959.
178. BUTTIN G: Mécanismes regulateurs dans la biosynthèse des enzymes du metabolisme du galactose chez. *E coli* K-12. II. Le déterminisme génetique de la régulation. *J Mol Biol* 7:183, 1963.
179. MORSE ML: Preliminary genetic map of seventeen galactose mutations in *E coli* K-12. *Proc Natl Acad Sci USA* 48:1314, 1962.
180. BUTTIN G: Sur la structure de l'opéron galactose chez *E coli* K-12. *CR Acad Sci (Paris)* 255:1233, 1962.
181. ADLER J, KAISER AD: Mapping of the galactose genes of *Escherichia coli* by transduction with phage PI. *Virology* 19:117, 1963.
182. HOPPER JE, BROACH JR, ROWE LB: Regulation of the galactose pathway in *Saccharomyces cerevisiae:* Induction of uridyl transferase mRNA and dependency on *GAL4* gene function. *Proc Natl Acad Sci USA* 75:2878, 1978.
183. BROACH JR: Galactose regulation in *Saccharomyces cerevisiae*. The enzymes encoded by the *GAL7, 10, 1* cluster are co-ordinately controlled and separately translated. *J Mol Biol* 131:41, 1979.
184. MATSUMOTO K, TOH-E A, OSHIMA Y: Genetic control of galactokinase synthesis in *Saccharomyces cerevisiae:* Evidence for constitutive expression of the positive regulatory gene *gal4*. *J Bacteriol* 134:446, 1978.
185. HOPPER JE, ROWE LB: Molecular expression and regulation of the galactose pathway genes in *Saccharomyces cerevisise*. *J Biol Chem* 253:7566, 1978.
186. KURAHASHI K, WAHBA AJ: Interference with growth of certain *E. coli* mutants by galactose. *Biochim Biophys Acta* 30:298, 1958.
187. YARMOULINSKY MB, WIESMEYER H, KALCKAR HM, JORDAN E: Hereditary defects in *E. coli* mutants. II. Galactose induced sensitivity. *Proc Natl Acad Sci USA* 45:1786, 1959.
188. SUNDARARAJAN TA: Interference with glycerokinase induction in mutants of *E. coli* accumulating Gal-1-P. *Proc Natl Acad Sci USA* 50:463, 1963.
189. FUKASAWA T, NIKAIDO H: Galactose sensitive mutants of *Salmonella*. I. Metabolism of galactose. *Biochim Biophys Acta* 48:460, 1961.
190. FUKASAWA T, NIKAIDO H: Galactose sensitive mutants of *Salmonella*. II. Bacteriolysis induced by galactose. *Biochim Biophys Acta* 48:470, 1961.
191. MORSE ML, LEDERBERG EM, LEDERBERG J: Transduction in *E. coli* K-12. *Genetics* 41:142, 1956.
192. ADLER J, TEMPLETON B: The amount of galactose genetic material in Δ dg bacteriophage with difference densities. *J Mol Biol* 7:710, 1963.
193. MERRIL CR, GEIER MR, PETRICCIANI JC: Bacterial virus gene expression in human cells. *Nature* 233:398, 1971.
194. HSIA DYY, WALKER FA: Variability in the clinical manifestations of galactosemia. *J Pediatr* 59:872, 1961.
195. DONNELL GN, COLLADO M, KOCH R: Growth and development of children with galactosemia. *J Pediatr* 58:836, 1961.
196. NADLER HL, INOUYE T, HSIA DYY: Clinical galactosemia: A study of fifty-five cases, in Hsia DYY (ed): *Galactosemia*. Springfield, IL, Charles C Thomas, 1969, p 127.
197. DONNELL GN, KOCH R, BERGREN WR: Observations on results of management of galactosemic patients, in Hsia DYY (ed): *Galactosemia*. Springfield, IL, Charles C Thomas, 1969, p 247.
198. KOMROWER GM, LEE DH: Long term follow-up of galactosemia. *Arch Dis Child* 45:367, 1970.
199. FISHLER K, KOCH R, DONNELL GN, WENZ E: Developmental aspects of galactosemia from infancy to childhood. *Clin Pediatr* 19:38, 1980.
200. LEVY HL, SEPE SJ, SHIH VE, VAWTER GF, KLEIN JO: Sepsis due to *Escherichia coli* in neonates with galactosemia. *N Engl J Med* 297:823, 1977.
201. LITCHFIELD WJ, WELLS WW: Effects of galactose on free radical reactions of polymorphonuclear leukocytes. *Arch Biochem Biophys* 188:26, 1978.
202. BELMAN AL, MOSHE SL, ZIMMERMAN RD: Computered tomographic demonstration of cerebral edema in a child with galactosemia. *Pediatrics* 78:606, 1986.
203. SEGAL S, BLAIR A, ROTH H: The metabolism of galactose by patients with congenital galactosemia. *Am J Med* 38:62, 1965.
204. HOLZEL A, KOMROWER GM, WILSON VK: Aminoaciduria in galactosemia. *Br Med J* 1:194, 1952.
205. CUSWORTH DC, DENT CE, FLYNN FV: The aminoaciduria in galactosemia. *Arch Dis Child* 30:150, 1955.
206. SMETANA HF, OLEN F: Hereditary galactose disease. *Am J Clin Pathol* 38:3, 1962.
207. GITZELMANN R, AURICCHIO S: The handling of soya alpha galactosides by a normal and a galactosemic child. *Pediatrics* 36:231, 1965.
208. KOCH R, ACOSTA P, DONNELL GN, LIEBERMAN E: Nutritional therapy of galactosemia. *Clin Pediatr (Phila)* 4:571, 1965.
209. SCHWARZ V: The value of galactose phosphate determinations in the treatment of galactosemia. *Arch Dis Child* 35:428, 1960.
210. DONNELL GN, BERGREN WR, PERRY G, KOCH R: Galactose-1-phosphate in galactosemia. *Pediatrics* 31:802, 1963.
211. PESCE MA, BODOURIAN SH: Clinical significance of plasma galactose and erythrocyte galactose-1-phosphate measurements in transferase-deficient galactosemia and in individuals with below-normal transferase activity. *Clin Chem* 28:301, 1982.
212. GIZELMANN R, STEINMANN B: Galactosemia: How does long-term treatment change the outcome? *Enzyme* 32:37, 1984.
213. KOGUT MD, DONNELL GN, SHARO KNF: Studies of lactose absorption in patients with galactosemia. *J Pediatr* 71:75, 1967.
214. SEGAL S, BERNSTEIN H: Observations on cataract formation in the newborn offspring of rats fed a high-galactose diet. *J Pediatr* 62:363, 1963.
215. SPATZ M, SEGAL S: Transplacental galactose toxicity in rats. *J Pediatr* 67:438, 1965.
216. FISHLER K, DONNELL GN, BERGREN WR, KOCH R: Intellectual and personality development in children with galactosemia. *Pediatrics* 50:412, 1972.
217. KOMROWER GM: Galactosaemia—thirty years on the experience of a generation. *J Inherited Metab Dis* 5:96, 1982.
218. WAISBREN SE, NORMAN TR, SCHNELL RR, LEVY HL: Speech and language deficits in early treated children with galactosemia. *J Pediatr* 102:75, 1983.
219. HABERLAND C, PEROU M, BRUNNGRABER EG ET AL: The neuropathology of galactosemia: A histopathological and biochemical study. *J Neuropathol Exp Neurol* 30:431, 1971.
220. CROME L: A case of galactosemia with the pathological and neuropathological findings. *Arch Dis Child* 37:415, 1962.
221. JAN JE, WILSON RA: Unusual late neurological sequelae in galactosemia. *Dev Med Child Neurol* 15:72, 1973.
222. LO W, PACKMAN S, NASH S, SCHMIDT K, IRELAND S, DIAMOND I, NG W, DONNELL G: Curious neurologic sequelae in galactosemia. *Pediatrics* 73:309, 1984.

223. KAUFMAN FR, KOGUT MD, DONNELL GN, GOEBELSMANN U, MARCH C, KOCH R: Hypergonadotropic hypogonadism in female patients with galactosemia. *N Engl J Med* 304:994, 1981.

224. STEINMANN B, GITZELMANN R, ZACHMANN M: Hypogonadism and galactosaemia. *N Engl J Med* 305:464, 1981.

225. KAUFMAN FR, DONNELL GN, ROE TF, KOGUT MD: Gonadal function in patients with galactosaemia. *J Inherited Metab Dis* 9:140, 1986.

226. ROBINSON ACR, DOCKERAY CJ, CULLEN MJ: Hypergonadotrophic hypogonadism in classical galactosemia: Evidence for defective ogenesis. *Br J Obstet Gynaecol* 91:199, 1984.

227. FRASER IS, RUSSELL P, GRECO S, ROBERTSON D: Resistant ovary syndrome and premature ovarian failure in young women with galactosemia. *Clin Reprod Fertil* 4:133, 1986.

228. LEVY HL, DRISCOLL SG, PORENSKY RS, WENDER DF: Ovarian failure in galactosemia. *N Engl J Med* 310:50, 1984.

229. ROE TF, HALLAT JG, DONNELL GN, NG WG: Childbearing by a galactosemic woman. *J Pediatr* 78:1026, 1971.

230. TEDESCO TA, MORROW G, MELLMAN WJ: Normal pregnancy and childbirth in a galactosemic woman. *J Pediatr* 81:1159, 1972.

231. SARDHARWALLA IB, KOMROWER GM, SCHWARZ V: Pregnancy in classical galactosaemia, in Bauman D, Holton JB, Pennock CA (eds): *Inherited Disorders of Carbohydrate Metabolism.* MTP papers Ltd., Lancaster, England 1980, p 125.

232. FRASER IS, SHEARMAN RP, WILCKEN B, BROWN A, DAVIS K: Failure to identify heterozygotes for galactosaemia in women with premature ovarian failure. *Lancet* II:566, 1987.

233. SCHWARZ V, GOLDBERG L, KOMROWER GM, HOLZEL A: Some disturbances of erythrocyte metabolism in galactosemia. *Biochem J* 62:34, 1956.

234. INOUYE T, NADLER HL, HSIA DYY: Galactose-1-phosphate uridyl transferase in red and white blood cells. *Clin Chim Acta* 19:169, 1968.

235. KROOTH R, WINBERG AN: Studies on cell lines developed from the tissues of patients with galactosemia. *J Exp Med* 113:1155, 1961.

236. ANDERSON EP, KALCKAR HM, ISSELBACHER KJ: Defect in the uptake of galactose-1-phosphate into liver nucleotides in congenital galactosemia. *Science* 125:113, 1957.

237. MAYES JS: Thesis for the Ph.D. degree, Michigan State University 1965. Quoted by Hansen RG: Some chemical aspects of galactosemia, in Hsia DYY (ed): *Galactosemia.* Springfield, IL, Charles C Thomas, 1969, p 55.

238. ANDERSON EP, KALCKAR HM, KURAHASHI K, ISSELBACHER KJ: A specific enzymatic assay for the diagnosis of congenital galactosemia. *J Lab Clin Med* 50:569, 1957.

239. BEUTLER E, BALUDA MC: Improved method for measuring galactose-1-phosphate uridyl transferase activity of erythrocytes. *Clin Chim Acta* 13:369, 1966.

240. MELLMAN WJ, TEDESCO TA: An improved assay of erythrocyte and leukocyte galactose-1-phosphate uridyl transferase: Stabilization of the enzyme by a thiol protective reagent. *J Lab Clin Med* 66:980, 1965.

241. DONNELL GN, BERGREN WR, BRETTHAUER MS, HANSEN RG: The enzymatic expression of heterozygosity in families of children with galactosemia. *Pediatrics* 25:572, 1960.

242. HSIA DYY: Clinical variants of galactosemia. *Metabolism* 16:419, 1967.

243. ROBINSON A: The assay of galactokinase and galactose-1-phosphate uridyl transferase activity in human erythrocytes. *J Exp Med* 118:359, 1963.

244. NG WG, BERGREN WR, DONNELL GN: Galactose-1-phosphate uridyl transferase assay by use of radioactive galactose-1-phosphate. *Clin Chim Acta* 10:337, 1964.

245. NG WG, BERGREN WR, DONNELL GN: An improved procedure for the assay of hemolysate galactose-1-phosphate uridyl transferase activity by the use of ^{14}C labeled galactose-1-phosphate. *Clin Chim Acta* 15:489, 1967.

246. WEINBERG AN: Detection of congenital galactosemia and the carrier state using galactose C^{14} and blood cells. *Metabolism* 10:728, 1961.

247. EGGERMONT E, HERS HG: Une nouvelle méthode de détection de la galactosémie congénitale. *Clin Chim Acta* 7:437, 1962.

248. NG WG, BERGREN WR, DONNELL GN: Galactose-1-phosphate uridyltransferase activity in galactosaemia. *Nature* 203:845, 1964.

249. BEUTLER E, BALUDA M, DONNELL GN: A new method for the detection of galactosemia and its carrier state. *J Lab Clin Med* 64:694,-1964.

250. COPENHAVER JH, BAUSCH LC, FITZGIBBONS JF: A fluorometric procedure for estimation of galactose-1-phosphate uridyl transferase activity in red blood cells. *Anal Biochem* 30:327, 1969.

251. GATTI R, MANFIELD P, HSIA DYY: Screening for galactosemia in the newborn. *J Pediatr* 69:1126, 1936.

252. BEUTLER E, BALUDA MC: A simple spot screening test for galactosemia. *J Lab Clin Med* 68:137, 1966.

253. NELSON K, HSIA DYY: Screening for galactosemia and glucose-6-phosphate dehydrogenase deficiency in newborn infants. *J Pediatr* 71:582, 1967.

254. HAWORTH JC, BARCHUK NH: A simple chromatographic screening test for the detection of galactosemia in newborn infants. *Pediatrics* 39:608, 1967.

255. WELLS WW, CHIN T, WEBER B: Quantitative analysis of serum and urine sugars by gas chromatography. *Clin Chim Acta* 10:352, 1964.

256. COPENHAVER JH: Quantitative analysis of plasma galactose and glucose by gas-liquid chromatography. *Anal Biochem* 17:76, 1966.

257. DE VERDIER CH, HJELM M: A galactose oxidase method for the determination of galactose in blood plasma. *Clin Chim Acta* 7:742, 1962.

258. ROTH H, SEGAL S, BERTOLI D: The quantitative determination of galactose—an enzymatic method using galactose oxidase with application to blood and other biological fluids. *Anal Biochem* 10:32, 1965.

259. TENGSTROM B: Enzymatic determination of glucose and galactose in urine. *Scand J Lab Invest* 18 *(suppl)*:92, 104, 1966.

260. DAHLQVIST A, SVENNINGSEN NW: Galactose in the urine of newborn infants. *J Pediatr* 75:454, 1969.

261. DAHLQVIST A: Test paper for galactose in urine. *Scand J Clin Lab Invest* 22:87, 1968.

262. BICKEL H: Mellituria, a paper chromatographic study. *J Pediatr* 59:641, 1961.

263. HAWORTH JC, MacDONALD MS: Reducing sugars in urine and blood of premature babies. *Arch Dis Child* 32:417, 1952.

264. HALL WK, CRAVEY CE, CHEN PT, OOSTENDORFF ME, HOLLOWELL JG JR, THEVAOS TG: An evaluation of galactosuria. *J Pediatr* 77:625, 1970.

265. GUTHRIE R, BLOOM S, MURPHEY W, SUSI A: A comparison of three newborn screening tests for galactosemia, in Naruse H, Irie M (eds): *Neonatal Screening. Proceedings of the Second International Conference on Neonatal Thyroid Screening.* Tokyo, Amsterdam-Oxford-Princeton, 1982, p 243.

266. PAIGEN K, PACHOLEC F, LEVY HL: A new method of screening for inherited disorders of galactose metabolism. *J Lab Clin Med* 99:895, 1982.

267. MISUMA H, WADA H, KAWAKAMI M, NINOMIYA H, SHOHMORI T: Galactose and galactose-1-phosphate spot test for galactosemia screening. *Clin Chim Acta* 111:27, 1981.

268. HILL G, O'REILLY D, ROBERTSON EA: A simple screening test for galactosaemia based on accumulation of galactose and galactose-1-phosphate, in Naruse H, Irie M (eds): *Neonatal Screening. Proceedings of the International Symposium of Neonatal Screening for Inborn Errors of Metabolism.* Excerpta Medica, Amsterdam/Osford/Princeton, 1983, p 252.

269. BOWRING FG, BROWN ARD: Development of a protocol for newborn screening for disorders of the galactose metabolic pathway. *J Inherited Metab Dis* 9:99, 1986.

270. FENSOM AH, BENSON PF, BLUNT S: Prenatal diagnosis of galactosemia. *Br Med J* 4:386, 1974.

271. HOLTON JB, RAYMONT CM: Prenatal diagnosis of classical galactosaemia, in Burman D, Holton JB, Pennock CA (eds): *Inherited Disorders of Carbohydrate Metabolism.* Lancaster, England, MTP Press, Falcon House, 1980, p 141.

272. SHIN YS, RIETH WE, SCHAUB J: Prenatal diagnosis of galactosemia and properties of galactose-1-phosphate uridyltransferase in erythrocytes of galactosemic variants as well as in human fetal and adult organs. *Clin Chim Acta* 128:271, 1983.

273. JAKOBS C, WARNER TG, SWEETMAN L, NYHAN WL: Stable isotope dilution analysis of galactitol in amniotic fluid: An accurate approach to the prenatal diagnosis of galactosemia. *Pediatr Res* 18:714, 1984.

274. ROLLAND MO, MANDON G, FARRIAUX JP, DORCHE C: Galactose-1-phosphate uridyl transferase activity in chorionic villi: A first trimester prenatal diagnosis of galactosaemia. *J Inherited Metab Dis* 9:284, 1986.

275. BRUCK E, RAPOPORT S: Galactosemia in an infant with cataracts: Clinical observations and carbohydrate studies. *Am J Dis Child* 70:267, 1945.

276. BAKER L, MELLMAN WJ, TEDESCO TA, SEGAL S: Galactosemia: Symptomatic and asymptomatic homozygotes in one Negro sibship. *J Pediatr* 68:551, 1966.

277. SEGAL S: The Negro variant of congenital galactosemia, in Hsia DYY (ed): *Galactosemia.* Springfield, IL, Charles C Thomas, 1969, p 176.

278. TOPPER YJ, LASTER L, SEGAL S: Galactose metabolism: Phenotype differences among tissues of a patient with congenital galactosemia. *Nature* 196:1106, 1962.

279. PESCH LA, SEGAL S, TOPPER Y: Progesterone effects on galactose metabolism in prepubertal patients with congenital galactosemia and in rats maintained on high galactose diets. *J Clin Invest* 39:178, 1960.

280. ELDER TD, SEGAL S, MAXWELL ES, TOPPER Y: Some steroid hormone like effects of menthol. *Science* 132:255, 1960.

281. SEGAL S: Isotopic studies of galactose oxidation in galactosemia, in Hsia DYY (ed): *Galactosemia.* Springfield, IL, Charles C Thomas, 1969, p 42.

282. TADA K, KUDO Z, OHNO T, AKABONE J, CHICA R: Congenital galactosemia and orotic acid therapy with promising results. Preliminary report. *Tohoku J Exp Med* 77:340, 1962.

283. SEGAL S, ROTH H, BLAIR A: Observations of orotic acid on galactose metabolism in congenital galactosemia. *J Pediatr* 68:135, 1966.

284. EGAN TJ, WELLS WW: Alternate metabolic pathway in galactosemia. *Am J Dis Child* 111:400, 1966.

285. WEINSTEIN AN, SEGAL S: The metabolic fate of 1.^{14}C galactitol in mammalian tissue. *Biochim Biophys Acta* 156:9, 1965.

286. INOUYE T, TANNENBAUM M, HSIA DYY: Identification of galactose-6-phosphate in galactosemic erythrocytes. *Nature* 193:67, 1962.

287. INOUYE T, SCHNEIDER JA, HSIA DYY: Enzymatic oxidation of galactose-6-phosphate. *Nature* 204:1304, 1964.

288. OHNO S, PAYNE HW, MORRISON M, BEUTLER E: Hexose-6-phosphate dehydrogenase found in human liver. *Science* 153:1015, 1966.

289. GITZELMANN R: Formation of galactose-1-phosphate from uridine diphosphate galactose in erythrocytes from patients with galactosemia. *Pediatr Res* 3:279, 1969.

290. GITZELMANN R, HANSEN RG: Galactose biogenesis and disposal in galactosemics. *Biochim Biophys Acta* 372:374, 1974.

291. PETRICCIANI JC, BINDER MK, MERRIL CR, GREIER MR: Galactose utilization in galactosemia. *Science* 175:1368, 1972.

292. MAYES JS, MILLER LR: The metabolism of galactose by galactosemic fibroblasts *in vitro*. *Biochim Biophys Acta* 313:9, 1973.

293. FRIEDMAN TB, YARKIN RJ, MERRIL CR: Galactose and glucose metabolism in galactokinase deficient, galactose-1-*p*-uridyl transferase deficient and normal human fibroblasts. *J Cell Physiol* 85:569, 1974.

294. BROWN E, HUGHES RC, WATTS RWE: Biochemical expression of the galactosemic defect in lymphocytes and the effects on glycoprotein synthesis. *Metabolism* 26:1047, 1977.

295. BEUTLER E, BALUDA MC, STURGEON P, DAY RW: A new genetic abnormality resulting in galactose-1-phosphate uridyl transferase deficiency. *Lancet* 1:353, 1965.

296. BEUTLER E: The Duarte variant in galactosemia, in Hsia DYY (ed): *Galactosemia*. Springfield, IL, Charles C Thomas, 1969, p 163.

297. BEUTLER E, BALUDA MC, STURGEON P, DAY RW: The genetics of galactose-1-phosphate uridyl transferase deficiency. *J Lab Clin Med* 68:646, 1966.

298. MATHAI CK, BEUTLER E: Electrophoretic variation of galactose-1-phosphate uridyl transferase. *Science* 154:1179, 1966.

299. NG WG, BERGREN WR, FIELD M, DONNELL GN: An improved electrophoretic procedure for galactose-1-phosphate uridyl transferase: Demonstration of multiple activity bands with the Duarte variant. *Biochem Biophys Res Commun* 37:354, 1969.

300. VACCARO A, MUSCILLO M, MANDARA I, SALVIOLI R: Improved isoelectric focusing of normal and variant forms of erythrocyte galactose-1-phosphate uridyl transferase. *Electrophoresis* 3:58, 1982.

301. MELLMAN WJ, TEDESCO TA, FEIGL P: Estimation of the gene frequency of the Duarte variant of galactose-1-phosphate uridyl transferase. *Ann Hum Genet* 32:1, 1968.

302. GITZELMANN R, POLEY JR, PRADER A: Partial galactose-1-phosphate uridyltransferase deficiency due to a variant enzyme. *Helv Paediatr Acta* 22:252, 1967.

303. LEVY HL, SEPE SJ, WALTON DS, SHIH VE, HAMMERSEN G, HOUGHTON S, BEUTLER E: Galactose-1-phosphate uridyl transferase deficiency due to Duarte/galactosemia combined variation: Clinical and biochemical studies. *J Pediatr* 93:390, 1978.

304. KELLY S: Significance of the Duarte/classical galactosemia genetic compound. *J Pediatr* 92:937, 1979.

305. SCHWARTZ HP, ZUPPINGER KA, ZIMMERMAN A, DAUWALDER H, SCHERZ R, BIER DM: Galactose intolerance in individuals with double heterozygosity for duarte variant and galactosemia. *J Pediatr* 100:704, 1982.

306. NG WG, LEE JS, DONNELL GN: Transferase-deficiency galactosemia and the Duarte variant. *JAMA* 257:187, 1987.

307. SCHAPIRA F, KAPLAN JC: Electrophoretic abnormality of galactose-1-phosphate uridyl transferase in galactosemia. *Biochem Biophys Res Commun* 35:451, 1969.

308. BANROQUES J, SCHAPIRA F, GREGORI C, DREYFUS JC: Molecular studies on galactose 1 phosphate uridylyl transferase from normal and mutant subjects. An immunological approach. *Ann Hum Genet* 47:177, 1983.

309. HAMMERSEN G, HOUGHTON S, LEVY HL: Rennes like variant of galactosemia: Clinical and biochemical studies. *J Pediatr* 87:50, 1975.

310. CHACKO CM, CHRISTIAN JC, NADLER HL: Unstable galactose-1-phosphate uridyl transferase: A new variant galactosemia. *J Pediatr* 78:454, 1971.

311. NG WG, BERGREN WR, DONNELL GN: A new variant of galactose-1-phosphate uridyltransferase in man: The Los Angeles variant. *Ann Hum Genet* 37:1, 1973.

312. IBARRA B, VACA G, SANCHEZ-CORONA J, HERNANDEZ A, RAIMEREZ ML, CNTU JM: Los Angeles variant of galactose-1-phosphate uridyltransferase (EC 2.7.7.12) in a Mexican family. *Hum Genet* 48:121, 1979.

313. ANDERSON MW, WILLIAMS VP, SPARKES MC: Transferase-deficiency galactosemia: Immunochemical studies of the Duarte and Los Angeles variants. *Hum Genet* 65:287, 1984.

314. CHACKO CM, WAPPNER RS, BRANDT IK, NADLER HL: The Chicago variant of clinical galactosemia. *Humangenetick* 37:261, 1977.

315. MATZ D, ENZENAUER J, MENNE F: Über einen Fall von Atypischer Galaktosamie. *Humangenetik* 27:309, 1975.

316. LANG A, GROEBE H, HELLKUHL B, VON FIGURA K: A new variant of galactosemia: Galactose-1-phosphate uridyltransferase sensitive to product inhibition by glucose 1-phosphate. *Pediatr Res* 14:729, 1980.

317. KIRKMAN HN, BYNUM E: Enzymatic evidence of a galactosemic trait in parents and galactosemic children. *Ann Hum Genet* 23:117, 1959.

318. SCHWARZ V, WELLS AR, HOLZEL A, KOMROWER GM: A study of the genetics of galactosemia. *Ann Hum Genet* 25:179, 1961.

319. HUGH-JONES K, NEWCOMB AL, HSIA DYY: The genetic mechanism of galactosemia. *Arch Dis Child* 35:521, 1960.

320. WALKER FA, HSIA DYY, SLATIS HM, STEINBERG AG: Galactosemia: A study of 27 kindreds in North America. *Ann Hum Genet* 25:287, 1962.

321. GITZELMANN R, HODORN R: Zur biochemischen Genetik der Galaltosämie. *Helv Paediatr Acta* 16:1, 1961.

322. MELLMAN WJ, TEDESCO TA: Galactose-1-phosphate uridyl transferase and galactokinase activity in cultured human diploid fibroblasts and peripheral blood leukocytes. *J Clin Invest* 48:2391, 1969.

323. MCGUINESS R, SAUNDERS RA: Erythrocyte galactose-1-phosphate uridyl transferase and glucose-6-phosphate dehydrogenase activity in the population of Rhonda Foch. *Clin Chim Acta* 16:221, 1967.

324. BRANDT NJ: Frequency of heterozygotes for heriditary galactosemia in a normal population. *Acta Genet (Basel)* 17:289, 1967.

325. HANSEN RG, BRETTHAUER RK, MAYES J, NORDIN JH: Estimation of frequency of occurrence of galactosemia in the population. *Proc Soc Exp Biol Med* 115:560, 1964.

326. TEDESCO TA, MILLER KL, RAWNSLEY BE, MENNUTI MT, SPIELMAN RS, MELLMAN WJ: Human erythrocyte galactokinase and galactose-1-phosphate uridyltransferase: A population survey. *Am J Hum Genet* 27:737, 1975.

327. KELLY S, KATZ S, BURNS J, BOYLAN J: Screening for galactosemia in New York State. *Public Health Rep* 85:575, 1970.

328. SHIH VE, LEVY HL, KAROLKEWICZ V, HOUGHTON S, EFRON ML, ISSELBACHER KJ, BEUTLER F, MACCREADY RA: Galactosemia screening of newborns in Massachusetts. *N Engl J Med* 2 4:753, 1971.

329. LEVY HL: Screening for galactosaemia, in Burman D, Holton JB, Pennock CA (eds): *Inherited Disorders of Carbohydrate Metabolism*. Lancaster, England, MTP Press Ltd, Falcon House, 1980, p 133.

330. VACCARO AM, MANDARA I, MUSCILLO M, CIAFFONI F, DE PELLEGRIN S, BENINCASA A, NOVELLETTO A, TERRENATO L: Polymorphism of erythrocyte galactose-1-phosphate uridyl-transferase in Italy: Segregation analysis in 693 families. *Hum Hered* 34:197, 1984.

331. BRANDT NJ, FORLAND A, MIKKELSEN M, NIELSEN M, NIELSEN A, TOLSTRUP N: Galactosaemia locus and the Down's syndrome chromsome. *Lancet* 2:700, 1963.

332. HSIA DYY, INOUYE T, WONG P, SOUTH A: Studies on galactose oxidation in Down's syndrome. *N Engl J Med* 270:1085, 1964.

333. ROSNER F, ONG BH, PAINEY RS, MAHANAND D: Biochemical differentiation of trisomic Down's syndrome (mongolism) from that due to translocation. *N Engl J Med* 273:1356, 1965.

334. WANG MYFW, DESFORGES JF: The Philadelphia chromosome and galactose-1-phosphate uridyl transferase. *Blood* 29:790, 1967.

335. KRONE W, WOLF U, GOEDDE HW, BAITSCH H: Untersuchungen über der aktivität der galaktokinase im blut von normal personen und von patienten mit G_{DO}-trisomie. *Hum Genet* 1:279, 1965.

336. MELLMAN WJ, OSKI FA, TEDESCO TA, HARRIS H: Leucocyte enzymes in Down's syndrome. *Lancet* 2:674, 1964.

337. DAHLQVIST A, HALL B, KÄLLÉN B: Blood galactose-1-phosphate uridyl transferase activity in dysplastic patients with and without chromosomal aberrations. *Hum Hered* 19:628, 1969.

338. MOHANDAS T, SPARKES RS, SPARKES MC, SHULKIN JD: Assignment of the human gene for galactose-1-phosphate uridyltransferase to chromosome 9: Studies with Chinese hamster-human somatic cell hybrids. *Proc Natl Acad Sci USA* 74:5628, 1977.

339. MOHANDAS T, SPARKES RS, SPARKES MC, SHULKIN JD, TOOMEY KE, FUNDERBURK SJ: Regional localization of human gene loci on chromosome 9: Studies of somatic cell hybrids containing human translocations. *Am J Hum Genet* 31:586, 1979.

340. SPARKES RS, SPARKES MC, FUNDERBURK SJ, MOEDJONO S: Expression of GALT in 9p chromosome alterations: Assignment of GALT locus to 9cen → 9p22. *Ann Hum Genet* 43:343, 1980.

341. TEDESCO TA, MELLMAN WJ: Galactosemia: Evidence of a structural gene mutation. *Science* 172:727, 1971.

342. TEDESCO TA, WU JW, BOCHES FS, MELLMAN WJ: The genetic defect in galactosemia. *N Engl J Med* 292:737, 1975.

342a. REICHARDT KV, BERG P: Cloning and characterization of a cDNA encoding human galactose-1-phosphate uridyl transferase. *Mol Biol Med*, in press.

343. GITZELMANN R, HANSEN RG: Galactose metabolism, hereditary defects and their clinical significance, in Burman D, Holton JB, Pennock CA (eds): *Inherited Disorders of Carbohydrate Metabolism*. Lancaster, England, MTP Press Ltd, Falcon House, 1980.

344. SIDBURY JB JR: The role of galactose-1-phosphate in the pathogenesis of galactosemia, in Gardner LE (ed): *Molecular Genetics and Human Disease*. Springfield, IL, Charles C Thomas, 1960, p 61.

345. MITCHELL HS: Cataract in rats fed on galactose. *Proc Soc Exp Biol Med* 32:971, 1935.

346. CRAIG J, MADDOCK C: Observations on nature of galactose toxicity in rats. *AMA Arch Pathol* 55:118, 1953.

347. DAM H: Galactose-poisoning in chicks. *Proc Soc Exp Biol Med* 55:57, 1944.

348. RUTTER WJ, KRICHEVSKY P, SCOTT HM, HANSEN RG: The metabolism of lactose and galactose in the chick. *Poult Sci* 32:706, 1953.

349. PERRY J, MOORE A, THOMAS D, HIRD F: Galactose intolerance: Observations on an experimental animal. *Acta Paediatr* 45:228, 1956.

350. NORDIN JH, WILKIN DR, BRETTHAUER RK, HANSEN RG, SCOTT HM: A consideration of galactose toxicity in male and female chicks. *Poult Sci* 39:802, 1960.

351. HANSEN RG, FREELAND RA, SCOTT HM: Lactose metabolism. V. The uridine nucleotides in galactose toxicity. *J Biol Chem* 219:391, 1956.

352. KLETHI J, MANDEL P: Uridine diphosphate hexoses of lens from rats on a galactose rich diet. *Biochem Biophys Acta* 57:379, 1962.

353. PATTERSON JW: Cataractogenic sugars. *Arch Biochem* 58:24, 1955.

354. GONA O, FU S-CJ: Effect of prolactin on galactose-induced cataractogenesis in the rat. *Proc Soc Exp Biol Med* 171:288, 1982.

355. KECHRID RM, ADRIAN J, POIFFAIT: Galactose metabolism in male and female rats II. Eye-ball differences. *Int J Vitam Nutr Res* 56:269, 1983.

356. PATTERSON JW, PATTERSON ME, KENSEY VE, REDDY DVN: Lens assay on diabetic and galactosemic rats receiving diets that modify cataract development. *Invest Ophthalmol* 4:98, 1965.

357. COTLIER E: Hypophysectomy effect on lens epithelium mitosis and galactose cataract development in rats. *Arch Ophthalmol* 67:476, 1962.

358. SCHWARZ V, GOLDBERG L: Galactose-1-phosphate in galactose cataract. *Biochim Biophys Acta* 18:310, 1955.

359. GITZELMANN R, CURTIUS HC, SCHNELLER I: Galactitol and galactose-1-phosphate in the lens of a galactosemic infant. *Exp Eye Res* 6:1, 1967.

360. LERMAN S: Pathogenic factors in experimental cataract. Part I. *Arch Ophthalmol* 63:128, 1960.

361. UNAKAR NJ, GENYEA C, REDDAN JR, REDDY VN: Ultrastructural changes during the developmental and reversal of galactose cataracts. *Exp Eye Res* 26:123, 1978.

362. UNAKAR NJ, SMART T, REDDAN JR, DEVLIN I: Regression of cataracts in the offspring of galactose fed rats. *Ophthal Res* 11:52, 1979.

363. BEYER-MEARS A, FARNSWORTH PN: Regional analyses of the opaque galactose cataract and the reversal process. *Metab Pediatr Ophthalmol* 4:9, 1980.

364. KINOSHITA JH, MEROLA LO: Hydration of the lens during the development of galactose cataract. *Invest Ophthalmol* 3:577, 1964.

365. SIPPEL TO: Changes in the water, protein and glutathione contents of the lens in the course of galactose cataract development in rats. *Invest Ophthalmol* 5:568, 1966.

366. KINOSHITA JH, DVORNIK D, KRAML M, GABBAY KH: The effect of aldose reductase inhibition on the galactose exposed rabbit lens. *Biochem Biophys Acta* 158:472, 1968.

367. HU TS, DATILES M, KINOSHITA JH: Reversal of galctose cataract with sorbinil in rats. *Invest Ophthalmol Vis Sci* 24:640, 1983.

368. KADOR PF, AKAGI Y, KINOSHITA JH: The effect of aldose reductase and its inhibition on sugar cataract formation. *Metabolism* 35:15, 1986.

369. RIBAYA-MERCADA JD, GERSHOFF SN: Effects of magnesium on galactose-induced cataract formation and lens aldose reductase activity in rats. *Nutr Res* 6:699, 1986.

370. DISCHE Z, ZELMENIS G, YOULOUS J: Studies on protein and protein synthesis—during the development of galactose cataract. *Am J Ophthalmol* 44:332, 1957.

371. KADOR PF, ZIGLER JS, KINOSHITA JH: Alterations of lens protein synthesis in galactosemic rats. *Invest Ophthalmol Vis Sci* 18:696, 1979.

372. HSU, M-Y, JASKOLL TF, UNAKAR NJ, BEKHOR I: Survival of fiber cells and fiber-cell messenger RNA in lens of rats maintained on a 50% galactose diet for 45 days. *Exp Eye Res* 44:577, 1987.

373. KINOSHITA JH, MEROLA LO, HAYMAN S: Osmotic effects on the amino acid concentration mechanisms in the rabbit lens. *J Biol Chem* 240:310, 1965.

374. REDDY D: Amino acid transport in the lens in relation to sugar cataracts. *Invest Ophthalmol* 4:700, 1965.

375. KINOSHITA JH, BARBER GW, MEROLA LO, TUNG B: Changes in levels of free amino acids and myo-inositol in the galactose-exposed lens. *Invest Ophthalmol* 8:625, 1969.

376. COTLIER E, BECKER B: Rubidium 86 accumulation and dulcitol distributions in lens of galactose-fed rats. *Exp Eye Res* 4:340, 1965.

377. KINOSHITA JH, MEROLA LO, TUNG B: Changes in cation permeability in the galactose-exposed rabbit lens. *Exp Eye Res* 7:80, 1968.

378. KAWABA T, CHENG H-M, KINOSHITA JH: The accumulation of myoinositol and rubidium ions in galactose-exposed rat lens. *Invest Ophthalmol Vis Sci* 27:1522, 1986.

379. BURNS MS, FILE DM: Quantitative microlocalization of diffusible ions innormal and galactose cataractous rat lens by secondary ion mass spectrometry. *J Microscopy* 144:157, 1986.

380. KEETING PH, DONG D-S, LYSZ TW, FU S-C J: Rat lens prostaglandin biosynthesis during galactose-induced cataractogenesis. *Exp Eye Res* 43:1103, 1986.

381. SIPPEL TO: Enzyme of carbohydrate metabolism in developing galactose cataracts of rats: *Invest Ophthalmol* 6:59, 1967.

382. KORC I: Biochemical studies on cataracts in galactose fed rats. *Arch Biochem* 94:196, 1961.

383. ISHIMOTO C, GOALWIN PW, SUN S-T, NISHIO I, TANAKA T: Cytoplasmic phase separation in formation of galactosemic cataract in lenses of young rats. *Proc Natl Acad Sci USA* 76:4414, 1979.

384. SIPPEL T.O: Energy metabolism in the lens during development of galactose cataract in rats. *Invest Ophthalmol* 5:576, 1966.

385. BROCKHUYSE R: Changes in myo-inositol permeability in the lens due to cataractous condition. *Biochim Biophys Acta* 163:269, 1968.

386. STEWART M, KURIEN M, SHERMAN W, COTLIER E: Inositol changes in nerve and lens of galactose fed rats. *J Neurochem* 15:941, 1968.

387. WADA E, TSUMITA T: Finding of a galactose-oxidation-product in lens of galactose-fed guinea pig. *Biochem Biophys Res Commun* 125:643, 1984.

388. BEFFLEY JD, WILLIAMS RJ: The nutritional teamwork approach: Prevention and regression of cataracts in rats. *Proc Natl Acad Sci USA* 71:4164, 1974.

389. SIMOONS FJ: A geographic approach to senile cataracts. Possible links with milk consumption, lactase activity, and galactose metabolism. *Dig Dis Sci* 27:257, 1982.

390. RINALDI E, ALBINI L, COSTAGLIOLA C, DE ROSA G, AURICCHIO G: High frequency of lactose absorbers among adults with idiopathic senile and presenile cataract in a population with a high prevalence of primary adult lactose malabsorption. *Lancet* 355, 1984.

391. SIMONELLI F, DE ROSA G, AURICCHIO RL: Possible role of galactose-1-P-uridyl transferase activity deficiency in red blood cells in the development of the presenile and senile cataract. *Ophthalmic Res* 18:309, 1986.

392. GONA O, WHITE JH: Response of the lens of the galactose-fed rat to YAG laser-induced injury. *Exp Eye Res* 42:117, 1986.

393. BRIVET M, ABADIE V, SONI T, CHERON G, DUFIER JL: Inexplicable infantile cataracts and partial maternal galactose disorder. *Arch Dis Child* 61:445, 1986.

394. MUHLEMANN MF, MOUNT JN, CREAM JJ: Galactose tolerance in patients with atopic cataracts. *Br J Derm* 117:37, 1987.

395. KEPPLER D, RUDIQIER J, REUTTER W, LESCH R, DECKER K: Orotate prevents galactosamine hepatitis. *Hoppe-Seylers Z Physiol Chem* 35:102, 1970.

396. KEPPLER D, DECKER K: Studies on the mechanism of galactosamine hepatitis. *Eur J Biochem* 10:219, 1969.

397. SCHIESSEL C, FORSTHOVE C, KEPPLER D: ^{45}Calcium uptake during the transition from reversible to irreversible liver injury induced by D-galactosamine *in vivo*. *Hepatology* 4:855, 1984.

398. MORIYAMA T, AOYAMA H, OHNISHI S, IMAWARI M: Protective effects of fibronectin in galactosamine-induced liver failure in rats. *Hepatology* 6:1334, 1986.

399. STARLING JJ, KEPPLER DOR: Metabolism of 2-deoxy-d-galactose in liver induces phosphate and uridylate trapping. *Eur J Biochem* 80:373, 1977.

400. LATTKE H, KOCH HK, LESCH R, KEPPLER DOR: Consequences of recurrent phosphate trapping induced by repeated injections of 2-deoxy-DO galactose. *Virchows Arch B* 30:297, 1979.

401. LANDAU B, HASTINGS A, ZOTTA S: Studies on carbohydrate metabolism in rat liver slices. *J Biol Chem* 233:1257, 1958.

402. NORDIN J, HANSEN RG: Isolation and characterization of galactose from hydrolysates of glycogen. *J Biol Chem* 238:489, 1963.

403. GRODSKY CM, BATES AA, BENNETT II, VOELLA C, MCWILLIAMS NB, SMITH DF: Effects of carbohydrates on secretion of insulin from isolated rat pancreas. *Am J Physiol* 205:638, 1963.

404. GITZELMANN R, ILLIC R: Inability of galactose to metabolize insulin in galactokinase deficient individuals. *Diabetologia* 5:143, 1969.

405. DUBOIS R, LOEB H, OOMS HA: Étude de métabolisme glucidique dans la galactosémie et la fructosémic. *Rev Fr Etud Clin Biol* 7:509, 1962.

406. GENTH C, VALLETTE AM, LEMONNIER A, COLIN J, ODIENRE M, LELUC R, THUONG TRILU C, ALAGILLE D: Étude de métabolisme glucidique an ecours de la galactosémie congénitale. *Arch Fr Pediatr* 23:509, 1966.

407. TADA K: Glycogenesis and glycolysis in the liver from congenital galactosemia. Tohoku *Exp Med* 82:168, 1964.
408. KLIEGMAN R, MIETTNEN E, ADAM KS, ADAM P: The effect of enteric galactose on neonatal canine carbohydrate metabolism. *Metabolism* 30:1109, 1981.
409. ROSENBERG I, WEINBERG A, SEGAL S: The effect of high galactose diets on urinary excretion of amino acids in the rat. *Biochim Biophys Acta* 48:500, 1961.
410. FOX M, THIER S, ROSENBERG L, SEGAL S: Impaired renal tubular function induced by sugar infusion in man. *J Clin Endocrinol* 24:1318, 1964.
411. LORENTZ WB, SHIHABI ZK, WEIDNER N: Galactosemic nephropathy in the rat. *Clin Physiol Biochem* 5:261, 1987.
412. THIER S, FOX M, ROSENBERG L, SEGAL S: Hexose inhibition of amino acid uptake in the rat-kidney-cortex slice. *Biochim Biophys Acta* 93:106, 1964.
413. SAUNDERS S, ISSELBACHER KJ: Inhibition of intestinal amino acid transport by hexoses. *Biochim Biophys Acta* 102:397, 1965.
414. DIEDRICH D, ANDERSON L: Galactose 1-phosphate in the intestinal tissue of the rat during galactose absorption. *Biochim Biophys Acta* 43:490, 1960.
415. HAWORTH JC, FORD JD, YOUNOSZAL MK: Effect of galactose toxicity on growth of the rat fetus and brain. *Pediatr Res* 3:441, 1969.
416. HAWORTH JC, FORD JD, HO HK: The effect of galactose toxicity on growth of the developing rat brain. *Brain Res* 21:385, 1970.
417. WELLS HJ, WELLS WW: Galactose toxicity and myoinositol metabolism in developing rat brain. *Biochemistry* 6:1168, 1967.
418. WARFIELD A, SEGAL S: Myoinositol and phosphatidylinositol metabolism in synaptosomes from galactose-fed rats. *Proc Natl Acad Sci USA* 75:4568, 1978.
419. GABBAY KH, SNIDER JJ: Galactosemic neuropathy: A model for diabetic neuropathy. *Diabetes* 19:357, 1970.
420. MYERS RR, COSTELLO ML, POWELL HC: Increased endoneurial fluid pressures in galactose neuropathy. *Muscle Nerve* 299, 1979.
420a. MYERS RR, POWELL HC: Galactose neuropathy: Impact of chronic endoneurial edema on nerve blood flow. *Annals of Neurol* 16:587, 1984.
420b. MIZISIN AP, POWELL HC, MYERS RR: Edema and increased endoneurial sodium in galactose neuropathy. *J of the Neurological Sciences* 74:35, 1986.
420c. POWELL HC, PATH MRC, LONGO FM, LE BEAU BS, MYERS RR: Abnormal nerve regeneration in galactose neuropathy. *J of Neuropath and Exp Neurol* 45:151, 1986.
421. SEGAN S, HWANG SM, STERN J, PLEASURE D: Inositol uptake by cultured isolated rat schwann cells. *Biochem Biophys Res Commun* 120:486, 1984.
422. KOZAK LP, WELLS WW: Effect of galactose on energy and phospholipid metabolism in the chick brain. *Arch Biochem Biophys* 135:371, 1969.
423. MAYES JS, MILLER IR, MYERS FK: The relationship of galactose-1-phosphate accumulation and uridyltransferase activity to the differential galactose toxicity in male and female chicks. *Biochem Biophys Res Commun* 39:661, 1970.
424. WELLS HJ, GORDON M, SEGAL S: Galactose toxicity in the chick: Oxidation of radioactive galactose. *Biochim Biophys Acta* 222:327, 1970.
425. MUSICK WDL, WELLS WW: Studies on galactose metabolism on heart and brain: The identification of D-galactose 6-phosphate in brains of galactose-intoxicated chicks and rat hearts perfused with galactose. *Arch Biochem Biophys* 165:217, 1974.
426. RIGDON RH, COUCH JR, CREGES CR, FERGUSON TM: Galactose intoxication pathologic study in the chick. *Experientia* 19:349, 1963.
427. KOZAK LP, WELLS WW: Studies on the metabolic determinants of D-galactose-induced neurotoxicity in the chick. *J Neurochem* 18:2217, 1971.
428. GRANETT SE, KOZAK LP, MCINTYRE JP, WELLS WW: Studies on cerebral energy metabolism during the course of galactose neurotoxicity in chicks. *J Neurochem* 19:1659, 1972.
429. KNULL HR, WELLS WW: Recovery from galactose-induced neurotoxicity in the chick by the administration of glucose. *J Neurochem* 20:415, 1973.
430. BLOSSER JC, WELLS WW: Enhanced fragility of neural lysosomes from chicks suffering from galactose toxcity. *J Neurochem* 19:1539, 1972.
431. BLOSSER JC, WELLS WW: Studies on amino acid levels and protein metabolism in the brains of galactose-intoxicated chicks. *J Neurochem* 19:69, 1972.
432. KNULL HR, TAYLOR WF, WELLS WW: Effects of energy metabolism on in vivo distribution of hexokinase in brain. *J Biol Chem* 248:5414, 1973.
433. KNULL HR, LOBERI PF, WELLS WW: Galactose neurotoxicity in chicks. Effects on fast axoplasmic transport. *Brain Res* 79:524, 1974.
434. MALONE J, WELLS H, SEGAL S: Decreased uptake of glucose by brain of the galactose toxic chick. *Brain Res* 43:700, 1972.
435. MALONE J, WELLS HJ, SEGAL S: Galactose toxicity in the chick: Hyperosmolality. *Science* 174:952, 1971.
436. CARVER NJ: Disturbances by galactose of the free amino acids of fetal rat brain. *Biochim Biophys Acta* 130:514, 1966.
437. HUTTENLOCHER PR, HILLMAN RE, HSIA YE: Pseudotumor cerebri in galactosemia. *J Pediatr* 76:902, 1970.
438. LITMAN N, KANTER A, FINBERG L: Galactokinase deficiency presenting as pseudotumor cerebri. *J Pediatr* 86:410, 1975.
439. BERRY G, YANDRASITZ J, SEGAL S: Experimental galactose toxicity: Effects on synaptosomal phosphatidyl-inositol metabolism. *J Neurochem* 37:888, 1981.
440. WOOLLEY DW: *Biochemical Basis of Psychosis or the Serotonin Hypothesis about Mental Diseases*. New York, Wiley, 1962.
441. WOOLLEY DW, GOMMI BW: Serotonin receptors. IV. Specific deficiency of receptors in galactose toxicity and its possible relationship to the idiocy of galactosemia. *Proc Natl Acad Sci USA* 52:14, 1964.
442. YANDRASITZ JR, HWANG SM, COHN R, SEGAL S: On the involvement of serotonin in galactose brain toxicity. *J Neurochem* 33:1289, 1979.
443. CHEN YT, MATTISON DR, FEIGENBAUM L, FUKUI H, SCHULMAN JD: Reduction in oocyte number following prenatal exposure to a diet high in galactose. *Science* 214:1145, 1981.
444. CHEN YT, MATTISON DR, BERCU BB, SCHULMAN JD: Resistance of the male gonad to a high galactose diet. *Pediatr Res* 18:345, 1984.
445. CHANG K, TOMILINSON M, JEFFREY JR, TILTON RG, SHERMAN WR, ACKERMANN KL, BERGER RA, CICERO TJ, KILO C, WILLIAMSON JR: Galactose ingestion increases vascular permeability and collagen solubility in normal male rats. *J Clin Invest* 367, 1987.
445a. SCHWARTZ WJ, MATTISON DR: Galactose inhibition of ovulation in mice. *Fertility and Sterility* 49:522, 1988.
446. LIGHTMAN S, RECHTHAND E, TERUBAYASHI H, PALESTINE A, RAPOPORT S, KADOR P: Permeability changes in blood-retinal barrier of galactosemic rats are prevented by aldose reductase inhibitors. *Diabetes* 36:1271, 1987.
447. FRANK RN, DUTTA S, FRANK SE: Cerebral cortical capillary basement membrane thickening in galactosaemic rats. *Diabetologia* 30:739, 1987.
448. FRANK RN, KEIRN RJ, KENNEDY A, FRANK KW: Galactose-induced retinal capillary basement membrane thickening: Prevention by sorbinil. *Invest Ophthalmol Vis Sci* 24:1519, 1983.
449. ROBISON WG JR, KADOR PJ, KINOSHITA JH: Retinal capillaries: Basement membrane thickening by galactosemia prevented with aldose reductase inhibitor. *Science* 221:1177, 1983.
450. ROBISON WB JR, KADOR PF, AKAGI Y, KINOSHITA JH, GONZALEZ R, DVORNIK K: Prevention of basement membrane thickening by galactosemia prevented with aldose reductase inhibitor. *Science* 221:1177, 1983.
451. ENGERMAN RL, KERN TS: Experimental galactosemia produces diabetic-like retinopathy. *Diabetes* 33:97, 1984.
452. SEGAL S, HWANG SM: On the ability of galactose to influence hexose and amino acid uptake by isolated rat brain capillaries. *J Neurochem* 40:1373, 1983.
453. GJEDDE A: Blood-brain transfer of galactose in experimental galactosemia, with special reference to the competitive interaction between galactose and glucose. *J Neurochem* 43:1654, 1984.
454. KENNEDY AR, FRANK N, VARMA SD: Aldose reductase activity in retinal and cerebral microvessels and cultured vascular cells. *Invest Ophthalmol Vis Sci* 24:1250, 1983.
455. KERN TS, ENGERMAN RL: Hexitol production by canine retinal microvessels. *Invest Ophthalmol Vis Sci* 26:382, 1985.
456. MILLER LR, GORDON GB, BENCH KG: Cytologic alterations in hereditary metabolic disorders. I. The effects of galactose on galactosemia fibroblasts *in vitro*. *Lab Invest* 19:428, 1968.
457. TEDESCO TA, MILLER KL: Galactosemia: Alterations in sulfate metabolism secondary to galactose-1-phosphate uridyltransferase deficiency. *Science* 205:1395, 1979.
458. PENNINGTON JS, PRANNERD TAJ: Studies of erythrocyte phosphate enter metabolism in galactosemia. *Clin Sci* 17:385, 1958.
459. ZIPURSKY A, ROWLAND M, FORD, JD, HAWORTH JC, ISRAELS LG: Erythrocyte metabolism in galactosemia. *Pediatrics* 35:126, 1965.
460. MONTELEONE JA, BRUTLER F, MONTELLEONE PL, URZ CI, CASEY FC: Cataracts galactosemia in hypergalactosemia due to galactokinase deficiency. *Am J Med* 50:403, 1971.
461. OLAMBIWONNI NO, MCVIE R NC, WC, FRASIER SD, DONNELL GN: Galactokinase deficiency in twins: Clinical and biochemical studies. *Pediatrics* 53:314, 1974.
462. THALHAMMER O, GITZELMANN R, PANTILFESCRO M: Hypergalactosemia and galactosuria due to galactokinase deficiency in a newborn. *Pediatrics* 42:441, 1968.
463. DAHLQVIST A, GAMSTORP I, MADSEN H: A patient with hereditary galactokinase deficiency. *Acta Paediatr Scand* 59:669, 1970.
464. LINNEWEH F, SCRAUMLOFFEI F, VETRELLA M: Galaktokinase-defelt bei einem Neugeborenen. *Klin Wochenschbr* 48:31, 1970.
465. VIGNFRON C, MARCHAL C, DEIFTS C: Deficit partiel et transitoire en galactokinase erythrocytaire chez un nouveau ne: étude biochimique. *Arch Fr Pediatr* 27:523, 1970.

466. COOK JGH, DON NA, MANN, TP: Hereditary galactokinase deficiency. *Arch Dis Child* 46:465, 1971.

467. LEVY NS, KRILLE AF, BEUTLER F: Galactokinase deficiency and cataracts. *Am J Ophthalmol* 74:41, 1972.

468. PICKERING WR, HOWELL RR: Galactokinase deficiency: Clinical and biochemical findings in a new kindred. *J Pediatr* 81:50, 1972.

469. KALOUD H, SITZMANN FC, AYER R, PALINUF F: Klinische and biochemische Befunde bei emen Kleinkind mit hereditarem Galakto-kimasdefekt. *Klin Padiatr* 185:18, 1973.

470. FANCONI G: Hochgradiage galaktose-Intoleranz galacktose-Diabetes bei einem Kinde Unit Neurofibromatosim Recklinghansen. *Jahrb Kinderheilkd* 138:1, 1933.

471. SEGAL S, RUTMAN JY, FRIMPTER GW: Galactokinase deficiency and mental retardation. *J Pediatr* 95:750, 1979.

472. GITZELMANN R: Hereditary galactokinase deficiency. *Citation Classics in Current Contents* 30:14, 1987.

473. BEUTLER E, KRILL A, COMINGS D, TRINIDAD F: Galactokinase deficiency: An important cause of familial cataracts in children and young adults. *J Lab Clin Med* 76:1006, 1970.

474. BEUTLER E, MAISUMOTO F, KUM W, KRILL A, LEVY N, SPARKES R, DEGNIS M: Galactokinase deficiency as a cause of cataracts. *N Engl J Med* 288:1203, 1973.

475. SKALKA HW, PRCHAL JT: Presenile cataract formation and decreased activity of galactosemic enzymes. *Arch Ophthalmol* 98:269, 1980.

476. MAGNANI M, CUCCIARINI L, STOCCHI V, DACHA M: Red blood cell galactokinase activity and presenile cataracts. *Enzyme* 29:58, 1983.

477. STAMBOLIAN D, SCARPINO-MYERS V, EAGLE RC JR, HODES B, HARRIS H: Cataracts in patients heterozygous for galactokinase deficiency. *Invest Ophthal Vis Sci* 27:329, 1986.

478. GITZELMANN R, WELLS HJ, SEGAL S: Galactose metabolism in a patient with hereditary galactokinase deficiency. *Eur J Clin Invest* 4:79, 1974.

479. MAYES JS, GUTHRIE R: Detection of heterozygotes for galactokinase deficiency a human population. *Biochem Genet* 2:219, 1968.

480. MELLMAN WJ, RAWNSLEY BE, NICHOLS CW, NEEDLEMAN B, MENNUTI MT, MALONE J, TEDESCO TA: Galactose tolerance studies of individuals with reduced galactose pathway activity. *Am J Hum Genet* 27:748, 1975.

481. SCHOEN RC, COX SH, WAGNER RP: Thymidine-kinase activity of cultured cells from individuals with inherited galactokinase deficiency. *Am J Hum Genet* 36:822, 1984.

482. STEPHENS T, IRVINE S, MUTTON P, GUPTA JD, HARLEY JD: Deficiency of two enzymes of galactose metabolism in kangaroos. *Nature* 248:524, 1974.

483. STEPHENS T, IRVINE S, MUTTON P, GUPTA JD, HARLEY JD: The case of the cataractous kangaroo. *Med J Aust* 2:910, 1974.

484. STEPHENS T, CROLLINE C, MUTTON P, GUPTA JD, HARTLEY JD: Galactose metabolism in relation to cataract formation in marsupials. *Aust J Exp Biol Med Sci* 53:233, 1973.

485. GITZELMANN R: Deficiency of uridine diphosphate galactose 4-epimerase in blood cells of an apparently healthy infant. *Helv Paediatr Acta* 27:125, 1972.

486. GITZELMANN R, STEINMANN B: Uridine diphosphate galactose 4-epimerase deficiency. H. Clinical follow-up. *Helv Paedtr Acta* 28:49, 1973.

487. GITZELMANN R, STEINMANN B, MITCHELL B, HAIGIS E: Uridine diphosphate galactose 4′-epimerase deficiency. *Helv Paediatr Acta* 31:441, 1976.

488. FUJIMURA Y, KAWAMURA M, NARUSE H: A new mass screening method of detecting UDP-galactose-4-epimerase deficiency. *Tohoku J Exp Med* 131:15, 1980.

489. MISUMI H, WADA H, KAWAKAKAMI M, NINOMIYA H, SUEISHI T, ICHIBA Y, SHOHMORI T: Detection of UPD-galactose-4-epimerase deficiency in a galactosemia screening program. *Clin Chim Acta* 116:101, 1981.

490. MITCHELL B, HAIGIS F, STEINMAN B, GITZELMANN R: Reversal of UDP galactose-4-epimerase deficiency of human leukocytes in culture. *Proc Natl Acad Sci USA* 72:5026, 1975.

491. MacFAUL: Personal communication.

492. SARDHARWALLA IB, WIAITH JE, BRIDGE C, FOWLER B, ROBERTS SA: A patient with severe type epimerase deficiency galactosemia. *Inherited Met Dis*. In press.

493. KINGSLEY DM, KRIEGER M, HOLTON JB: Structure and function of low-density-lipoprotein receptors in epimerase-deficient galactosemia. *N Engl J Med* 314:1257, 1986.

CHAPTER 14

PENTOSURIA*

HOWARD H. HIATT

1. *Essential pentosuria is an inborn error of metabolism in which 1.0 to 4 g of the pentose* L*-xylulose is excreted in the urine each day. It is a benign disturbance which occurs principally in Jews and which behaves genetically as an autosomal recessive characteristic.*
2. *This disorder bears no relationship to diabetes mellitus and is easily distinguished from several other varieties of pentosuria in which milligram quantities of a number of pentoses other than* L*-xylulose appear in the urine.*
3. *Essential pentosuria is the result of a defect in the glucuronic acid oxidation pathway. In this route of carbohydrate metabolism the carboxyl carbon atom of* D*-glucuronic acid is removed in a series of reactions, giving rise to the pentose* L*-xylulose. The latter may then be converted to its stereoisomer,* D*-xylulose, which, in turn, may be phosphorylated.* D*-Xylulose-5-phosphate may participate in reactions of the pentose phosphate pathway which lead to its conversion to hexose phosphate. (Glucuronic acid → gulonic acid →* L*-xylulose → xylitol →* D*-xylulose → pentose phosphate pathway → hexose phosphate.) The glucuronic acid oxidation pathway serves no essential function in humans.*
4. *The block results from reduced activity of the NADP-linked xylitol dehydrogenase, the enzyme that catalyzes the conversion of* L*-xylulose to xylitol.*
5. *The heterozygote can be recognized by demonstrating either an intermediate level of erythrocyte activity of xylitol dehydrogenase or increased urinary or serum* L*-xylulose, or both, in a glucuronolactone loading test.*

The first six decades which followed the original description by Salkowski and Jastrowitz in 1892 of an individual with essential pentosuria[1] produced much information concerning the clinical aspects of this condition but virtually none that cast light on the nature of the biochemical lesion. Clinical and laboratory studies in the ensuing 18 years, however, led to identification of the metabolic defect. As a result, and perhaps even more significantly, important information was uncovered concerning the operation in normal individuals of a previously unknown pathway of carbohydrate metabolism. Such an elucidation of a normal mechanism by studies of an accident of nature led Garrod[2] 43 years ago to stress "the lesions of rare maladies," and prompted Harvey[3] 300 years earlier to note that "nature is nowhere accustomed more openly to display her secret mysteries than in cases where she shows traces of her workings apart from the beaten path."

A consideration of essential pentosuria requires its separation from other conditions in which a five-carbon sugar is excreted in the urine. *Essential pentosuria,* or chronic essential pentosuria, is the only member of the group in which a genetic defect accounts for the melituria. It may be further defined as an innocuous condition, presumably present from birth, in which a relatively constant amount of the pentose L-xylulose appears in the urine. It has no apparent relation to diabetes mellitus and has been described almost exclusively in Jews. It is the result of an impairment in the metabolism of glucuronic acid (Fig. 14-1) and may easily be distinguished from several other situations in which much smaller quantities of certain pentoses other than L-xylulose are found in the urine (Table 14-1). The structure of some of the urinary pentoses follows:

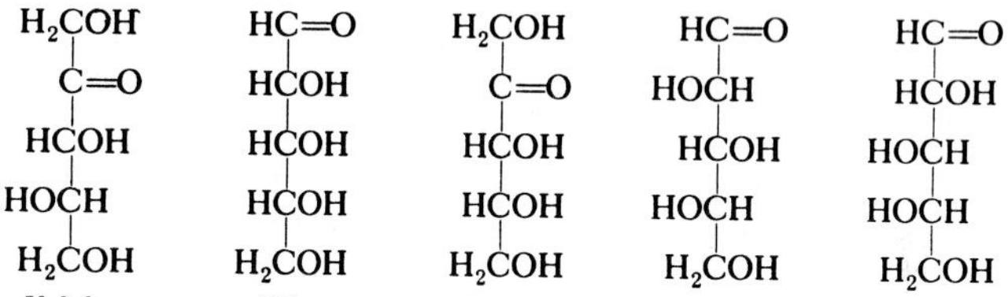

H_2COH	HC=O	H_2COH	HC=O	HC=O
C=O	HCOH	C=O	HOCH	HCOH
HCOH	HCOH	HCOH	HCOH	HOCH
HOCH	HCOH	HCOH	HOCH	HOCH
H_2COH	H_2COH	H_2COH	H_2COH	H_2COH
L-Xylulose	D-Ribose	D-Ribulose	L-Xylose	L-Arabinose

Alimentary pentosuria is the term applied to the excretion of small amounts of arabinose or xylose† following the ingestion of unusually large quantities of such fruits as plums, cherries, and grapes and fruit juices.[4–6] Small amounts of D-ribose are often present in urine from healthy persons, and slightly larger quantities may be found in the urine of some patients with muscular dystrophy,[7] presumably as a result of the excessive breakdown of ribose-containing nucleotide in degenerating muscle. Finally, traces of L-xylulose[8,9] and of D-ribulose[9] may be found in the urine of normal individuals. It is essential pentosuria with which this chapter is primarily concerned.

HISTORICAL SURVEY

In 1887 Kiliani[10] demonstrated that arabinose, the sugar of gum arabic, was a member of a hitherto undescribed class of sugars containing, in contrast to the hexoses, only five carbon atoms. Shortly thereafter, the wood sugar xylose was identified as another member of this group. The biologic significance of this class of sugars was strengthened by the report by Salkowski and Jastrowitz of a human being in whose urine a pentose was consistently excreted.[1] This sugar was not fermented by yeast, was optically inactive, and yielded an osazone with a melting point of 159°C. The latter observation led these authors to suggest that the sugar was a pentose. Several similar case reports appeared in the German literature during the next decade, and in 1906 Janeway,[11] in a paper entitled "Essential Pentosuria in Two Brothers," recorded the first instances in an American publication. Although Janeway acknowledged that in many of the previous reports in the literature neurasthenic symptoms were prominent, he stressed that no harmful

*This chapter is reprinted from the fourth edition with an addendum by the editors.

†Although L-arabinose and L-xylose are said to be the alimentary pentoses,[4,5] the evidence for this chemical identification is not convincing.

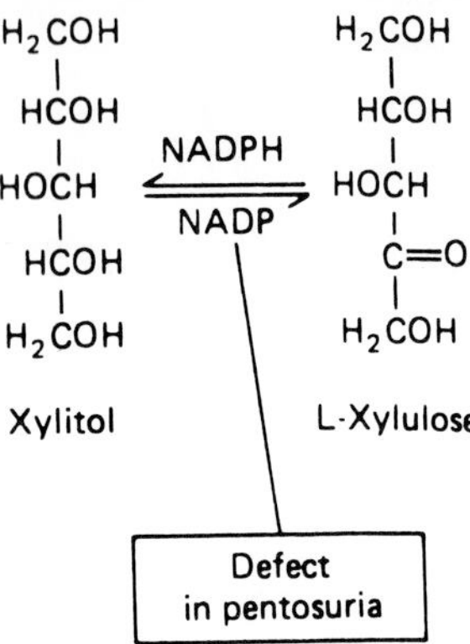

Fig. 14-1 The metabolic defect in pentosuria caused by deficiency in NADP-linked xylitol dehydrogenase.

effects of the disorder were known. He emphasized that the most important responsibility of the physician was to explain carefully to the patient the difference between the patient's ailment and diabetes mellitus and to effect "the removal of any dietetic restrictions he may have been subjected to." Although more than a half century has elapsed since Janeway's report, his advice still points out an essential function of any physician confronted by a person with pentosuria. Two years after Janeway's paper, in his classic Croonian lectures of 1908, Garrod[12] reviewed 30 recorded cases of essential pentosuria, and he assigned this abnormality along with cystinuria, alcaptonuria, and albinism to a category which he labeled as "inborn errors of metabolism." He stressed the differences between essential pentosuria and the alimentary variety. Garrod noted the incidence of essential pentosuria in Jews, and the tendency for the condition to occur in several members of the same family. A prevalent early impression that pentosuria frequently accompanies diabetes mellitus[13] has not been borne out.

Much of the present knowledge concerning the clinical aspects of pentosuria, its genetic transmission, and the nature of the urinary sugar is derived from the careful observations of Enklewitz and Lasker.[14–20] More than half their 70 subjects with pentosuria were followed for periods in excess of 16 years. Fifty years following the first description of pentosuria, Derivaux[21] was able to collect 163 case reports from the literature, and in a 1958 review of the subject this figure exceeded 200.[22]

For many years controversy existed concerning the nature of the sugar in pentosuric urine. The first chemical identification was that of Neuberg,[23] who in 1900 reported that the sugar present in the urine of one person with pentosuria was racemic arabinose. Five additional individuals with arabinosuria were subsequently described by Cammidge and Howard,[24] and single similar patients were presented by a number of authors, including Aron,[25] Luzzatto,[26] and Schüler.[27] Zerner and Waltuch[28] in 1913 presented convincing evidence that the urinary pentose was optically active and that it was not arabinose. The following year Levene and LaForge showed that the urinary sugar of a person with pentosuria was L-xylulose.[*,29] Their identification was based on the following observations:

1. An osazone of the urinary sugar had a melting point of 160 to 163°C; when it was mixed with an osazone of D-xylose, the melting point was increased by 40°.

2. The initial optical rotation of the osazone was lower than the equilibrium rotation; this is characteristic of xylosazone but not of arabinosazone.

3. The foregoing observations indicated that the urinary pentosazone was a xylosazone. On the basis of the optical rotation of the urinary sugar ($\alpha_D^{20} = +33.1°$), the character of its *p*-bromphenylhydrazone, and its behavior in oxidation experiments, Levene and LaForge concluded that the urinary pentose could only have been L-xylulose.

In the same year Zerner and Waltuch[30] isolated the sugar from the urine of two patients with pentosuria and also concluded that it was L-xylulose. A similar conclusion concerning the pentose in their patients' disease was reached by Hiller,[31] Greenwald,[32] and Lasker and Enklewitz.[15] Some of the early reports of arabinosuria were subsequently corrected. For example, a patient of Solis Cohen was first described in 1909 as having arabinosuria.[33] At that time the author assumed from previously reported cases that arabinose was the urinary sugar excreted in pentosuria. However, his patient was followed for almost three decades, and in a follow-up report which appeared in 1936,[34] the same author indicated that he had identified the patient's urinary sugar as L-xylulose and that his earlier impression had been in error. Similarly, a patient reported as having arabinosuria in 1913[25] was reexamined 40 years later; paper chromatography of his urine revealed the major sugar component to be L-xylulose; no evidence of arabinose was found.[35]

The question of arabinosuria was considered at length in 1950 by Lasker,[19] who indicated that she had identified L-xylulose in the urine of 72 individuals with pentosuria but had never seen a patient with arabinosuria. She further stated that no case of arabinosuria had been reported since 1928 and that since in early reports the arabinose was always identified by

*The early reports of "D-xyloketose" excretion were published prior to the adoption of the current practice of classifying sugars according to their structural relation to D- and L-glyceraldehyde. Throughout this chapter the present convention is followed, regardless of the terminology applied in the original reports.

Table 14-1 Types of Pentosuria

Type	*Urine pentose*	*Amount excreted, g/24 h*	*Cause*	*Origin of pentose*
Essential	L-Xylulose	1.0–4.0	Metabolic error	D-Glucuronic acid
Alimentary	L-Arabinose, L-Xylose	Less than 0.100	Excessive fruit intake	Dietary fruit
"Ribosuria"	D-Ribose	Up to 0.030	Muscular dystrophy	Muscle coenzymes (?)
Normal	L-Xylulose	Up to 0.060		
	D-Ribose	Up to 0.015		
	D-Ribulose	Traces		

the same method, this impression may have been in error. Studies with paper chromatographic techniques have provided further corroboration that L-xylulose is the only sugar excreted in substantial amounts in pentosuria. In addition to L-xylulose a small quantity of L-arabitol has been isolated from the urine of one pentosuric patient;[36] other reports that pentosuric patients excrete more than one pentose[35,37] are considered below.

The constancy of the amount of urine pentose excreted by individuals with pentosuria has long been recognized. Enklewitz and Lasker[16] found that the excretion in five adults varied from 1.1 to 3.7 g per 24 h, but that the daily variation in any given subject never exceeded 0.9 g. The excretion is independent of dietary variations: Early reports by Janeway[11] and Klercker[13] that the amount of urinary pentose can be altered by changes in dietary nucleic acid or protein have not been substantiated. Margolis noted a marked increase in pentose excretion in pentosuric subjects following aminopyrine ingestion.[38] When Enklewitz and Lasker observed a similar stimulation not only following the intake of certain other drugs, including borneol, antipyrine, and menthol, but also after the administration of glucuronic acid,[16] they ascribed the effect of the drugs to their glucuronogenic action. The metabolic interrelations of glucuronic acid and L-xylulose, however, remained obscure, and there was no experimental evidence for Everett's postulate that an abnormal enzyme system existed in pentosuric patients which decarboxylated glucuronic acid to L-xylulose.[39] The identification of L-xylulose as an intermediate in the metabolism of glucuronic acid,[40,41] the elucidation of the reactions involved in the further metabolism of L-xylulose,[42,43] and the demonstration of xylitol metabolism by erythrocytes[44,45] were followed by the localization of the biochemical defect.[46] Much of the present concept stems from the careful studies of Touster and his associates.[40–43] Further contributions have come from the laboratories of Ashwell,[47–51] Burns,[52] Ul Hassan and Lehninger,[53] the author,[54–57] Wang and van Eys,[46] and others. Not only have these studies permitted insight into the biochemical aberration in pentosuria, but they have also provided important information concerning the operation of the glucuronic acid oxidation pathway in normal individuals.

PENTOSE METABOLISM IN HUMAN BEINGS

Several five-carbon sugars are known to be present in human beings. Some, such as ribose and deoxyribose, are present as part of more complex substances, including the nucleic acids and certain coenzymes. Others, including D-xylulose, D-ribulose, and L-xylulose, are intermediates in metabolic pathways and normally are not detectable in body fluids or are present only in trace quantity. Finally, there are those which are not known to be synthesized by humans but which occasionally may be ingested and thereafter are excreted in the urine. These include arabinose and xylose.

Many pathways of carbohydrate metabolism involve pentoses as key intermediates (for a summary see Ref. 58). A consideration of these pathways is essential to understanding the several varieties of pentosuria that have been described, including essential pentosuria.

The Pentose Phosphate Pathway

Ribose, the sugar moiety found in all ribonucleic acids and several coenzymes, may be synthesized from glucose by either the oxidative or the nonoxidative reactions of the pentose phosphate pathway (Fig. 14-2).[59] In the oxidative reactions glucose-6-phosphate is converted successively to 6-phosphogluconolactone, 6-phosphogluconic acid, and, following oxidative removal of its first carbon atom, ribulose-5-phosphate. The latter may be isomerized to ribose-5-phosphate. In this series of reactions, for every molecule of pentose phosphate synthesized from hexose phosphate, two molecules of nicotinamide adenine dinucleotide phosphate (NADP) are reduced to NADPH. Much information has accumulated indicating that the conversion of the coenzyme from its oxidized to its reduced form is as important a function of these reactions as pentose production.[58] This conclusion is based on the evidence for the NADPH requirement of a variety of reductive synthetic reactions and on observations which suggest that the oxidative reactions of the pentose phosphate pathway are the principal means available to the cell for NADP reduction.

Ribose may also be produced nonoxidatively from hexose phosphate via the transketolase and transaldolase reactions. In these reactions the first two carbon atoms of one molecule of fructose-6-phosphate may be cleaved and condensed with a molecule of triose phosphate, under the influence of the enzyme transketolase. This results in the formation of one molecule of xylulose-5-phosphate and one of erythrose-4-phosphate. The latter, together with another molecule of fructose-6-phosphate, may then participate in the transaldolase reaction, resulting in the production of a molecule of sedoheptulose-7-phosphate and one of triose phosphate. In another reaction catalyzed by transketolase these products may undergo conversion to xylulose-5-phosphate and ribose-5-phosphate. The xylulose-5-phosphate may be epimerized to ribulose-5-phosphate, which, as already noted, can be isomerized to ribose-5-phosphate. Thus, in this series of reactions there is no net loss of carbon, and two molecules of hexose phosphate and one of triose phosphate may be converted to three molecules of pentose phosphate. Available data indicate that in animals[60,61] and in human beings[62] ribose is normally synthesized from hexose by way of both the oxidative and the nonoxidative reactions of the pentose phosphate pathway. The fact that thiamine pyrophosphate is a cofactor for the enzyme transketolase[63] accounts for the block in ribose synthesis by way of the nonoxidative sequence of reactions in the thiamine-deficient animal.[64]

In contrast to the oxidative reactions, which afford only a mechanism for pentose production from hexose, the transketolase-transaldolase sequence is reversible and provides a means for the interconversion of hexose and pentose.[65] Evidence has been presented demonstrating that the nonoxidative reactions mediate the conversion of ribose to hexose in human beings.[66] It has also been shown that ribose may participate directly in riboside[64] and nucleic acid[67] synthesis. Thus, mechanisms exist for the disposition of any ribose released in nucleic acid or coenzyme breakdown.

Small quantities [up to 2.8 μmol/(24 h · kg body weight)] of ribose have been reported in normal human urine.[7] This presumably represents either newly synthesized ribose or pentose released from nucleic acids or coenzymes which escapes further metabolism. It has been asserted that ribose excretion

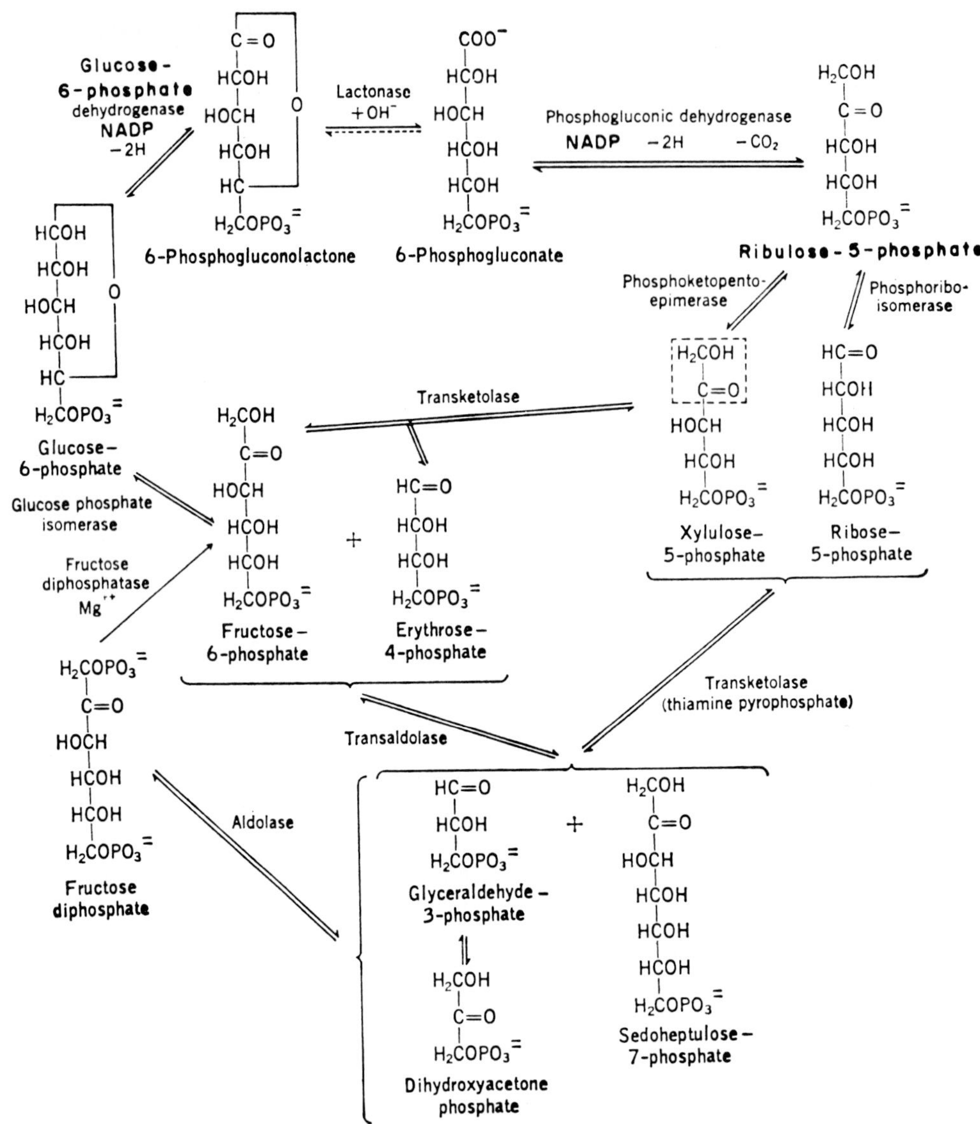

Fig. 14-2 The phosphogluconate-oxidative pathway. *(By permission of B. L. Horecker and H. H. Hiatt.[58])*

is slightly but significantly increased in patients with myopathies, presumably because of the increased breakdown of ribose-containing compounds in diseased muscle,[7] but this observation has not met universal acceptance.[68] A metabolite of histamine, imidazoleacetic acid, is excreted by the rat[69,70] and by human beings[62] in part as the riboside. Ribulose, a trace constituent of normal urine,[9] is presumably excreted following hydrolysis of the phosphate ester, which is an intermediate in the pentose phosphate pathway.

Deoxyribose, the sugar component of deoxyribonucleic acid, is apparently synthesized by way of direct reduction of the ribose molecule at the nucleoside diphosphate level.[71]

The Glucuronic Acid Oxidation Pathway

The pentoses L-xylulose and D-xylulose and the pentitol xylitol are intermediates in the glucuronic acid oxidation pathway (Fig. 14-3). The carbon skeleton of D-glucuronic acid is known to originate in glucose,[72,73] and uridine nucleotides are involved as intermediates.[74,75] As has been noted, the studies of Touster,[40–43] Ashwell,[47–51] Burns,[52] and Lehninger,[53] and their associates have provided much information concerning the further metabolism of D-glucuronic acid. A reductive reaction involving NADPH as a cofactor results in the conversion of D-glucuronic acid to L-gulonic acid. L-Gulonolactone has been shown to be an intermediate in the synthesis of ascorbic acid in most animal species, but in primates and in the guinea pig this transformation cannot take place. L-Gulonic acid, however, may in all animal species examined be oxidized to β-keto-L-gulonic acid,[50] which, in turn, is enzymatically decarboxylated to L-xylulose.[49,51] In the latter reaction the atom corresponding to the sixth carbon atom of the parent glucose molecule is oxidized to CO_2. Carbon atom 1 of L-xylulose is derived from the fifth carbon atom of glucose. Touster has prepared two enzymes from guinea pig liver, one of which catalyzes the reduction of L-xylulose to the sugar alcohol xylitol and the other of which promotes the oxidation of xylitol to D-xylulose.[42,43] These reactions require NADPH and nicotinamide adenine dinucleotide (NAD), respectively. It is noteworthy that in contrast to other schemes of intermediary car-

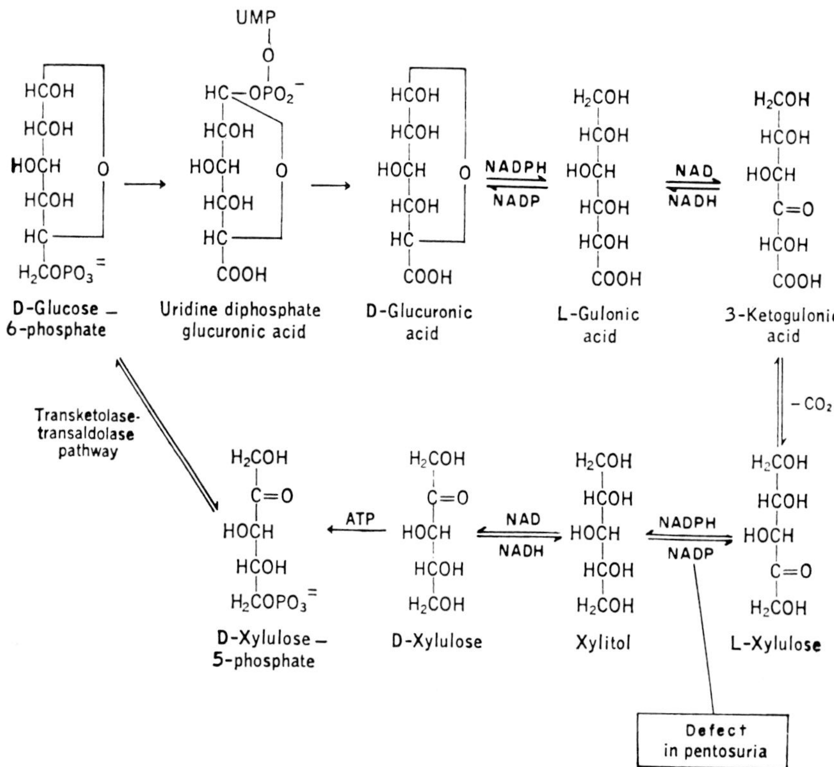

Fig. 14-3 The glucuronic acid oxidation pathway.

bohydrate metabolism in which only phosphate esters participate, these reactions involve the free sugars. Hickman and Ashwell[48] have described a kinase for D-xylulose in mammalian liver. D-Xylulose-5-phosphate will be recognized as an intermediate in the pentose phosphate pathway and may, of course, be converted to ribose-5-phosphate and to hexose phosphate. A kinase for L-xylulose has been purified from bacteria,[76] but there is no evidence for this enzyme in mammalian tissues. Evidence has been presented[77] suggesting that the pathway is operative in rat adipose tissue and that activity is increased in tissue from starved or diabetic animals and in human diabetic patients.[78]

The elucidation of the reactions involved in glucuronic acid metabolism provides insight not only into the origin of the L-xylulose found in trace amounts in normal urine, but also into the site of the defect in individuals with chronic essential pentosuria. Further, it explains the hitherto poorly understood increase in L-xylulose excretion by pentosuric subjects given glucuronic acid.

The glucuronic acid oxidation pathway does not play an indispensable role in human metabolism, for individuals with pentosuria, in whom the pathway is blocked, suffer no ill effects from the abnormality. It does appear to be responsible for *myo*-inositol catabolism.[79] Although the reactions of the glucuronic acid oxidation pathway together with those of the pentose phosphate pathway provide a potential mechanism for ribose biosynthesis from hexose (i.e., hexose phosphate → glucuronic acid → xylulose → xylulose phosphate → ribose phosphate), animal studies indicate that little ribose is normally produced by way of this sequence of reactions.[54] In most mammalian species the early reactions of the pathway are required for the production of L-gulonic acid, a precursor of ascorbic acid.[80] In primates and the guinea pig, however, ascorbic acid cannot be synthesized.* Thus, in humans the pathway serves to return a portion of glucuronic acid carbon to the mainstream of carbohydrate metabolism.

Effects of Drugs. The basis for the effect of drugs and hormones on the glucuronic acid oxidation pathway remains a fascinating but poorly understood area. Margolis' early observation that aminopyrine stimulates the excretion of L-xylulose by individuals with pentosuria[38] was followed by reports indicating that this drug and others, such as chloretone and barbital, stimulate free glucuronic acid[82] and ascorbic acid[83] excretion in animals. The drug effect is apparently not related to any known detoxification mechanism, since barbital is excreted unchanged. Studies of Burns and his associates indicate that the drugs enhance the production of glucuronic acid, as well as ascorbic acid (and presumably L-xylulose in pentosuria), from glucose[84] and from galactose.[85] Increased levels of uridine diphosphate glucose dehydrogenase have been found in livers of animals treated with some of,[86,87] but not all,[87] the drugs known to stimulate ascorbic acid production. Hormonal involvement in this process is indicated by the observation of Burns and his associates that the administration of chloretone or barbital to hypophysectomized rats is not followed by an increase in ascorbic acid excretion.[82] It has also been observed that thyroid hormone stimulates pentose excretion in the rat,[88] and that the increase in pentose excretion which results from exposure to low temperatures is prevented by the administration of thyroid-blocking agents.[89] An increase in L-xylulose excretion by normal human beings given triiodothyronine has been reported.[90]

*A report of the urinary excretion of radioactive ascorbic acid following administration of radioactive glucuronolactone[81] requires confirmation and amplification.

THE BIOCHEMICAL ABNORMALITY IN ESSENTIAL PENTOSURIA

Nature of the Urinary Sugar

As has been pointed out, there is now conclusive evidence that the urinary sugar excreted by pentosuric persons is L-xylulose (L-xyloketose, L-threopentulose). In the light of present knowledge one must conclude that the early purported demonstrations of urinary arabinose either were in error because of deficiencies in the experimental methods employed or else were concerned with patients who do not fit into this category. L-Xylulose is excreted in fairly constant amounts, ranging between 1.0 and 4.0 g per 24 h. The excretion is increased following the intake of glucuronic acid and of certain drugs, but it is unaffected by diet and is not altered by insulin administration.

Much smaller quantities of other sugars in addition to L-xylulose have been reported in pentosuric urine. Touster and Harwell[36] found arabitol and suggested that this sugar alcohol may be derived from L-xylulose reduction. Wolfson, Cohn, and Devaney[37] observed a second unidentified component following chromatography of pentosuric urine, and Barnes and Bloomberg[35] found small amounts of several substances in addition to large quantities of L-xylulose following chromatography of deionized urine from several pentosuric subjects.

Since one substance which appeared in all the urines examined by Barnes and Bloomberg had a chromatographic mobility similar to that of xylose, some of the author's unpublished observations seem pertinent. Following the procedure of Barnes and Bloomberg, the author, too, found a xyloselike component in the urine of two pentosuric subjects. This material was eluted from paper chromatograms and was found by Ashwell[91] to behave like L-xylose in several enzymatic reactions. However, this substance was not present in pentosuric urine subjected to paper chromatography *without* prior exposure to ion-exchange resins. In addition, normal urine to which only L-xylulose was added and which was then deionized and chromatographed on paper also exhibited the xylose spot. Accordingly, the author has concluded that the appearance of L-xylose in chromatograms of pentosuric urine is an artifact attributable to the preparative procedure.

Site of the Defect

Although Enklewitz and Lasker[16] demonstrated more than 20 years earlier that glucuronic acid administration greatly enhanced the excretion of L-xylulose, it was not until the elucidation of the glucuronic acid oxidation pathway that a plausible hypothesis could be advanced concerning the biochemical abnormality in pentosuria. Even before the recent work that established the site of the metabolic lesion,[46] evidence was available to support the following propositions:

1. Glucuronic acid is a direct precursor of the urinary pentose.
2. Glucuronic acid is incompletely metabolized in pentosuric individuals.
3. Although the pentosuric person can convert glucuronic acid to L-xylulose, a block exists in the further metabolism of the pentose.

Touster and his associates[40] confirmed the observation of Enklewitz and Lasker that the ingestion of glucuronolactone is followed by an increased excretion oif L-xylulose by pentosuric persons, and they postulated that the conversion of glucuronolactone to xylulose is direct. They substantiated this hypothesis by two studies of a pentosuric subject.[41] First, they demonstrated that the administration of glucuronolactone labeled with ^{13}C in its sixth carbon atom (the carboxyl carbon) was followed by the excretion of nonisotopic L-xylulose. Second, they showed that the ingestion of [l-^{13}C]glucuronolactone was followed by the urinary excretion of heavily labeled pentose, the isotope of which was predominantly in the fifth carbon atom. These data indicate that the carboxyl carbon of glucuronic acid is lost in the conversion to L-xylulose but that the rest of the molecule is preserved intact. Touster also demonstrated that some normal human beings and guinea pigs excrete traces of L-xylulose and that this excretion is slightly augmented following glucuronolactone ingestion. These observations strengthened the concept that L-xylulose is a metabolic intermediate in normal subjects.

The following study from Hiatt's laboratory supported the hypothesis that a defect in glucuronic acid metabolism exists in pentosuria. Let us postulate that a pentosuric person can remove carbon atom 6 of glucuronolactone with unimpaired efficiency but is incapable of metabolizing the remainder of the carbon chain. Then, following the administration of glucuronolactone uniformly labeled with ^{14}C, there should be six times as much $^{14}CO_2$ in the expired air of a normal person as in that of the pentosuric person. These expectations were fulfilled in an experiment (Fig. 14-4) in which 5 μCi of glucuronolactone uniformly labeled with ^{14}C was given intravenously to a 16-year-old male with essential pentosuria and to 22-year-old female with no abnormality of carbohydrate metabolism. Samples of expired air were collected at intervals for 6 h thereafter and were analyzed for CO_2 and for radioactivity. In this period 16 percent of the administered ^{14}C appeared in the expired air of the normal subject and 2.6 percent in that of the pentosuric subject, almost exactly the sixfold difference that was predicted. In the first 12 h, 57 percent of the administered radioactivity appeared in the urine of the normal individual and 76 percent in that of the pentosuric person. Thus, the total ^{14}C

Fig. 14-4 $^{14}CO_2$ excretion in the expired air following the intravenous administration of glucuronolactone uniformly labeled with ^{14}C to a normal subject and to a pentosuric individual.

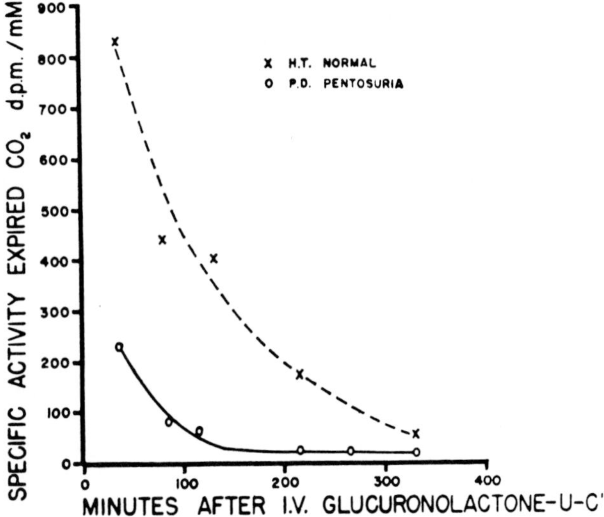

excretion in urine and expired air of the normal and pentosuric subjects during the intervals measured was in excess of 73 and 79 percent, respectively.

Further Isotope Experiments

The foregoing study strongly supports the view that glucuronic acid metabolism is impaired in pentosuria. Some information concerning the site of the defect was deduced from the results of a published experiment,[55] which will be briefly summarized. Using a "ribose-trapping" technique suggested by the observations of Tabor and Hayaishi[69] and of Karjala[70] that imidazoleacetic acid is excreted in the urine in part as a riboside, Hiatt demonstrated ribose synthesis from hexose in humans by way of the oxidative and nonoxidative reactions of the pentose phosphate pathway.[62] If the glucuronic acid oxidation pathway were operative in normal individuals, it would afford a mechanism for the conversion of glucuronolactone carbon to ribose in this way: glucuronolactone → L-xylulose → D-xylulose → D-xylulose-5-phosphate → D-ribose-5-phosphate. (For an outline of the reactions involved, see Fig. 14-3.) Thus, the administration of imidazoleacetic acid and of glucuronolactone uniformly labeled with ^{14}C should be followed by the excretion of imidazoleacetic acid riboside containing [^{14}C]ribose. On the other hand, if this pathway were blocked in pentosuria at a site beyond L-xylulose, then a pentosuric subject might be expected to excrete radioactive L-xylulose but nonisotopic riboside ribose. (Since there is no reason to postulate an impairment in the pentose phosphate pathway in pentosuria, the synthesis and excretion of the riboside ribose should proceed normally.) The results of such an experiment are described in Table 14-2. The significant ^{14}C incorporation in the urinary riboside ribose of the normal subject is consistent with the conversion of glucuronolactone to ribose by way of the reactions of the glucuronic acid oxidation and the pentose phosphate pathways (Fig. 14-3). The pentosuric subject excreted ribose in an amount comparable to that

Table 14-2 Urinary L-Xylulose and Ribose in Normal and Pentosuric Subjects Given Imidazoleacetic Acid (ImAA) and D-Glucuronolactone Uniformly Labeled with ^{14}C

Test	*Normal person*	*Pentosuric subject*
D-Glucuronolactone administered,		
counts/min	1.57×10^7	7.85×10^6
μmol	370	185
ImAA hydrochloride administered,		
μmol	2000	1000
Urinary L-xylulose (0–10 h), μmol	0.5	3950
Relative molar activity, counts/(min · μmol)		85
Total ^{14}C content, counts/min	300*	3.36×10^5
Percent administered ^{14}C	0.002*	4.3
Ribose from urinary ImAA riboside		
(0–10 h), μmol	275	208
Percent administered ImAA	14	21
Relative molar activity, counts/(min · μmol)	33	
Total ^{14}C content, counts/(min · μmol)	9100	190*
Percent administered ^{14}C	0.058	0.002*

*Significance doubtful because of small quantity of radioactivity.

excreted by the normal individual, but the virtual absence of radioactivity indicated that it was derived from sources other than glucuronolactone. The large quantity of isotope in the urinary L-xylulose is in agreement with Touster's demonstration that glucuronic acid is a direct precursor of the pentose. This experiment not only provides information concerning the impairment in pentosuria, but also helps to establish the concept that the glucuronic acid oxidation pathway is operative in normal individuals.

Knox pointed out that impaired L-xylulose reabsorption by the renal tubule could be the defect present in pentosuria.[22] An experiment which was cited in support of this possibility is that of Enklewitz and Lasker,[14] who gave 5 g L-xylulose by mouth to a pentosuric subject and found only 0.5 g "additional" L-xylulose in the urine. This suggested metabolism of the pentose. However, in the absence of information concerning the efficiency of L-xylulose absorption from the human gastrointestinal tract, the Enklewitz and Lasker experiment cannot be thus interpreted. Indeed, there are published studies which indicate that although parenteral administration of L-xylulose to animals is followed by extensive metabolism,[40,92,93] the pentose orally administered is not glycogenic in rats.[94] Moreover, even if considerable absorption takes place, the possibility exists that the absorbed pentose might inhibit endogenous L-xylulose production by way of a feedback mechanism.

Following the publication of Knox's review, three studies appeared which convincingly excluded the renal abnormality hypothesis. Bozian and Touster[95] found in the plasma of a pentosuric subject, but not of two normal individuals, a sugar which was identified as xylulose by paper chromatographic techniques. (Flynn[96] had previously demonstrated xylulose in pentosuric plasma by chromatography.) After glucuronolactone administration, the serum xylulose level in a pentosuric subject of Bozian and Touster reached 11 mg/dl. Simultaneous with the Bozian and Touster study, Freedberg, Feingold, and Hiatt[57] used the specific enzymatic assay of Hickman and Ashwell[97] to measure L-xylulose levels in the serum and urine of several non-Jewish controls, three pentosuric persons, and four close relatives of pentosuric persons (Table 14-3). This work was later extended,[56] and one additional relative is included in Table 14-3. From the latter work, several points merit emphasis. Fasting serum L-xylulose levels in all three pentosuric persons were in excess of 1 mg/dl, while in the serums of all but one of the other individuals no L-xylulose was detectable in the fasting state. In all but two subjects D-glucuronolactone led to a rise in serum L-xylulose levels, with a peak generally reached within 1 h of feeding. The rise in serum pentose level was accompanied by a marked increase in urinary pentose in the pentosuric persons and by the appearance of urinary pentose in all other subjects tested. The serum levels of four heterozygotes (D and H in Table 14-3 are the parents of A; E is the mother of B; G's mother has pentosuria) and of a fifth individual, F, with three pentosuric sibs, were considerably greater than those of the control individuals reported here and of the large number described elsewhere.[56] On the basis of his serum level and his family history, F is considered to be heterozygous. The urine levels of the two heterozygous subjects tested were considerably greater than those of the control subjects. Assuming normal glomerular filtration rates for these subjects, one can calculate that virtually all L-xylulose entering the renal glomeruli appears in the urine of normal, as well as of heterozygous and pentosuric, subjects.

Table 14-3 Serum and Urine L-Xylulose Levels Before and After Oral Administration of D-Glucuronolactone

		Serum L-xylulose			Urine L-xylulose		
Subject	*Amount of glucurono-lactone, g*	*Fasting, mg/dl*	*Maximal, mg/dl*	*Time after glucurono-lactone, min*	*Fasting, mg/h*	*Maximal, mg/h*	*Time after glucurono-lactone, h*
Pentosuric subjects:							
A	5	1.2	7.2	60		320	1–2
B	10	1.3	9.9	60	106	549	1–2
C	10	1.7	14.7	30	88	450	1–2
Relatives of pentosuric subjects:							
D	25	*	1.26	60	*		
E	25	*	3.9	30	*		
F	25	0.18	0.71	30	*	81	0–1
G	25	*	1.41	30	0.1	63	0–1
H	25	*	0.77	30			
Control subjects:							
I	25	*	*		*	9	0–1
J	25	*	*		*	22	0–1
K	25	*	0.22	90	*	16	0–1
L	25	*	0.29	90	0.6	13	0–1
M	25	*	0.15	60	0.3	18	1–2

*Less than 0.1 mg/dl.

Thus, a "defect" in renal tubular reabsorption of L-xylulose appears to exist in *all* subjects, but it is clearly not the metabolic error which distinguishes the pentosuric from the normal person.

Unequivocal proof that a block in the glucuronic acid oxidation pathway is the metabolic lesion in pentosuria was provided by Wang and van Eys in 1970.[46] These workers found in the erythrocytes of three subjects homozygous for pentosuria a marked decrease in activity of the NADP-linked xylitol dehydrogenase, the enzyme involved in the conversion of L-xylulose to xylitol. Two activities, one "normal" and one "abnormal," were found in the erythrocytes of a heterozygous subject. In contrast, activity of the NAD-linked xylitol dehydrogenase, which catalyzes the interconversion of xylitol and D-xylulose, was normal in both homozygous and heterozygous subjects.

CLINICAL CONSIDERATIONS

Manifestations

Pentosuria can be classified with those inborn errors of metabolism in which no disturbance of function has been demonstrated to result from the genetic abnormality. Indeed, the most frequent difficulty encountered by pentosuric subjects is consequent to a mistaken diagnosis of diabetes mellitus and the institution thereafter of dietary and insulin "therapy." A number of reports in the literature indicate that only after an episode of insulin-induced hypoglycemia has the correct diagnosis been made. No abnormality of glucose metabolism is demonstrable, except in those rare instances in which pentosuria and diabetes mellitus coincide. Several authors have commented on the frequency and severity of psychological disturbances encountered in subjects with pentosuria, but a causal relationship between such disturbances and the error in carbohydrate metabolism has not been established, and the suggestion is often made that at least some neurotic complaints may be related to the conflicting medical opinions to which many patients have been subjected. Lasker has followed 40 pentosuric individuals for periods in excess of 16 years and has found no decrease in life expectancy as compared with normal individuals.[20] Some typical clinical considerations may best be presented by citing a report of a case of pentosuria first diagnosed in 1958.

Patient A: P. D., a 16-year-old high school sophomore, was first seen in the Outpatient Department of the Beth Israel Hospital in February 1958. One year previously a physician had found a reducing substance in the patient's urine and had placed him on a low carbohydrate diet. Despite his faithful adherence to this regimen, the urine continued consistently to show a 1+ reaction in the Benedict test. For this reason his physician suggested instituting insulin therapy, and the patient's father brought him to the Beth Israel Hospital to seek additional opinion. The patient had never noted polydipsia, polyuria, or polyphagia, and during the 6 months prior to admission he had gained 8 lb. The father could not recall a single negative urine sugar test during this period, but at no time did he find more than a 1+ reduction. There was a family history of diabetes mellitus in a paternal great-uncle but not of other known disturbances of carbohydrate metabolism. The patient was an only child of Austrian-born Jewish parents, who were not consanguine and whose forebears had come from Poland. His past medical history was not contributory except in two important respects. Ten years and six years previously the patient had been seen in the Pediatric Clinic of the Beth Israel Hospital for upper respiratory infections. Urinalyses carried out on both occasions were recorded as having shown a 1+ positive Benedict test. In addition, he had frequently been seen by psychiatrists during the previous decade because of problems of behavior. During the year prior to admission his emotional disturbances were apparently magnified by his concern over his condition and also by his resentment at the dietary restrictions to which he had been subjected.

Physical examination revealed a well-developed, well-nourished young male who appeared in good health. Vital signs were normal, and no significant abnormalities were found on examination. Laboratory studies revealed a normal hemogram, a 2-h postprandial blood sugar of 95 mg/dl, and a urinalysis that was normal except for a 1+ positive test for a reducing substance. The urine, however, did not give a positive reaction with Testape (an enzyme-impregnated paper which reacts specifically with glucose). The urine sugar was shown to be L-xylulose by preparation of the osazone and by paper chromatography in *n*-butanol-ethanol-water (50:10:40) with authentic L-xylulose as a standard, followed by staining with the orcinol-trichloroacetic acid reagent.[98] A glucose tolerance test (50 g glucose by mouth) showed a fasting blood sugar level of 80 mg/dl and blood glucose levels at 30, 60, 120, 180, and 240 min of 120, 110, 95, 80, and 60 mg/dl, respectively. The patient's 24-h urinary excretion of L-xylulose was found to be 2 g, and this rose to 4 g during the 24 h following the ingestion of 5 g of D-glucuronolactone. Studies of L-xylulose levels in the patient (A in Table 14-3), his mother (D), and his father (H) before and after glucuronolactone administration strengthen the assumption that the parents are heterozygous for the aberration apparent in the son. The patient and his parents were reassured concerning the benign nature of this disturbance in carbohydrate metabolism and specifically concerning the absence of any relationship of his condition to diabetes mellitus. He was returned to an unrestricted diet and, according to his parents, within a month many of the behavioral disturbances which had been present during the previous year were greatly diminished.

Diagnostic Measures

A diagnosis of pentosuria should be suspected in any person, and particularly in a Jewish person, who has none of the symptoms of diabetes mellitus but in whose urine a small quantity of a reducing substance is consistently found. This possiblity is strengthened in those instances in which the urine does not give a positive test with any of the enzymatic methods specific for glucose. The measures which have proved most useful in establishing the diagnosis of pentosuria may be summarized as follows:

1. *Reduction of Benedict's reagent at low temperature.*[15] L-Xylulose is a strong reducing substance and in contrast to glucose and most other urinary sugars will reduce Benedict's reagent at 55°C in 10 min or at room temperature in 3 h. (Fructose will also reduce Benedict's reagent at low temperature.)
2. *Paper chromatography.* On paper chromatography L-xylulose can be readily distinguished from other sugars. For example, with a mixture of *n*-butanol, ethanol, and water (50:10:40) as the solvent, L-xylulose has a characteristic mobility (R_F = 0.26) which exceeds those of other commonly observed urinary sugars[98] and gives a red color on staining with the orcinol-trichloroacetic acid reagent.[99] Chromatography is the most convenient means of establishing an unequivocal diagnosis.
3. *Cysteine-carbazole test.*[100]
4. *Behavior of osazone.*[29] The phenylosazone of L-xylulose has a melting point of about 160°C. When it is mixed with the osazone of D-xylose, the crystalline appearance is radically altered, and the melting point rises approximately 40°.
5. *Demonstration of the enzymatic defect in erythrocytes.*[46] This can be carried out only in a laboratory in which special facilities are available.

GENETICS

Estimates of the incidence of pentosuria vary. The most widely accepted figure, 1 in 40,000 to 50,000, is derived from examinations of applicants for life insurance in the United States.[94,101] All these cases were found in Jews; thus, the occurrence in American Jews is considered to be about 1:2000 to 2500. Mizrahi and Ser reported an incidence of pentosuria of 1:5000 in Israeli Jews; their 18 cases, 8 males and 10 females, were all born in Eastern European countries.[102] The vast majority of pentosuric persons are Jews at present resident in widely dispersed areas, but the antecedents of a substantial number have been traced to Eastern Europe.[103] Two sisters of Lebanese descent with xylulosuria have been found in South Africa,[35] and further study of four generations of the same family revealed an additional 8 cases in 127 members.[104] In this study individuals were reported to show pentosuria weeks to years after negative urine examinations. Twelve cases of pentosuria were found in sixty members of three other well-studied Lebanese families—these in Lebanon.[105] Among them was an infant with xylulosuria from at least the second week of life. The earlier reports that pentosuria occurs predominantly in males[12] are not substantiated by studies of the families of pentosuric persons, in which the incidence seems evenly divided between the sexes.

Garrod first proposed that a homozygous state was required for the expression of pentosuria,[12] and this thesis has been amply supported by the very careful family studies of Lasker.[18,103] The latter[103] has found 31 of 122 sibs (excluding propositi) to have pentosuria when both parents were negative. When one parent had the disturbance, however, 17 of 31 sibs were afflicted. The incidence of consanguinity in 79 marriages which produced pentosuric offspring was 12.6 percent.

The sensitivity of the enzymatic assay for L-xylulose, which permits measurement of serum levels far below those found in individuals with pentosuria, has made possible the demonstration of a partial lesion in parents and children of pentosuric individuals.[57] This provides unequivocal confirmation of the theories of Garrod and Lasker concerning a homozygous genotype in pentosuria. Relatives of pentosuric individuals with one normal and one abnormal gene apparently have sufficient competent enzyme to deal with the products of normal metabolism. However, when the glucuronic acid oxidation pathway is stressed, as occurs during the "loading test" with glucuronolactone, the pentosuria heterozygote is not able to metabolize the extra L-xylulose produced as efficiently as in the normal individual. The data in Table 14-3 demonstrate that following glucuronolactone administration, both parents of one person with pentosuria, the mother of a second, and the child of a third all had serum levels of L-xylulose significantly higher than those of control subjects, but far below those of pentosuric patients. Thus, it is apparent that while the presence of two abnormal genes is required to produce the clinical picture of essential pentosuria, the consequences of one abnormal gene are recognizable not only by enzyme studies[46] but also under the special conditions which prevail following glucuronolactone administration.

This work was supported in part by funds from the American Cancer Society, Inc., and the Public Health Service. The author is most grateful to Dr. Margaret W. Lasker and Dr. J. H. Renwick for their very helpful suggestions.

EDITORS' ADDENDUM

The proper nomenclature for the deficient enzyme in pentosuria is L-xylulose reductase (EC 1.1.1.10).[106] The enzyme deficiency described by Wang and van Eys[46] (termed NADP-linked xylitol dehydrogenase by them) has been confirmed by numerous investigators. Although pentosuria had been described primarily in Ashkenazi Jews and among the Lebanese, a Japanese case of pentosuria with L-xylulose reductase deficiency was identified.[107] In agreement with the original report of Wang and van Eys,[46] these investigators reported an increased K_m for NADP in the pentosuric subject.[107] Pentosuria was reported in three cousins in a highly inbred family from Andhra Pradesh, India.[108]

In 1985, Lane reported the separation of a major and a minor isozyme for L-xylulose reductase in human erythrocytes.[109] The major isozyme had a cathodal position and was absent from patients with pentosuria. The minor or anodal band was present in pentosuric and normal subjects. The separation of the two isozymes was confirmed using CM-cellulose chromatography. Lane[109] did not confirm the increased K_m for NADP reported by Wang and van Eys.[46] The difference in results may be related to the fact that Wang and van Eys measured the production of NADPH when xylitol is converted to L-xylulose, while Lane measured the production of $NADP^+$ when L-xylulose is converted to xylitol, the latter being the predominant direction in vivo. The more recent studies found a similar K_m for NADP from normal and pentosuric subjects. Significant increases in K_m were found for xylitol and L-xylulose in pentosuric subjects, but the data indicated that the differences were due to the selective preservation of the minor isozyme in these individuals. Cellular fractionation studies indicated that the major isoenzyme is present in mitochondria and cytosol, whereas the minor isoenzyme occurs only in the cytosol.[110]

Using the newer assay method, Lane and Jenkins[110] restudied a Lebanese family previously reported to show dominant inheritance of pentosuria.[104] The reanalysis convincingly documented the presence of a single pentosuric individual. Other family members previously reported to be affected were heterozygotes. These investigators also surveyed a population of Ashkenazi Jewish students and found L-xylulose reductase activity in erythrocytes to be more than two standard deviations below the mean in 7 of 237 individuals. Six of these seven individuals underwent a loading test with D-glucuronolactone, and five showed a major increase in serum L-xylulose, although one did not. These results suggested a heterozygote frequency of 0.0127 in this Ashkenazim population.

REFERENCES

1. SALKOWSKI E, JASTROWITZ M: Ueber eine bisher nicht beobachtete Zuckerart im Harn. *Zentralbl Med Wiss* 30:337, 1892.
2. GARROD AE: The lessons of rare maladies. *Lancet* 1:1055, 1928.
3. *The Works of William Harvey, M.D.*, translated by Robert Willis, Sydenham, London, 1847, p 616. (Cited in ref. 2.)
4. PETERS JP, VAN SLYKE DD: *Quantitative Clinical Chemistry. Interpretations*, Williams & Wilkins, Baltimore, 1946, vol I.
5. HAWK PB, OSER BL, SUMMERSON WH: *Practical Physiological Chemistry*, McGraw-Hill, New York, 1954, pp 844–845.
6. JOHNSTONE RW: Pentosuria: Chronic and alimentary. *Edinburgh Med J* 20:138, 1906.
7. TOWER DB, PETERS EL, POGORELSKIN MA: Nature and significance of pentosuria in neuromuscular disease. *Neurology* (6(37):125, 1956.
8. TOUSTER O, HUTCHESON RM, REYNOLDS VH: The formation of L-xylulose in mammals and its utilization by liver preparations. *J Am Chem Soc* 76:5005, 1954.
9. FUTTERMAN S, ROE JH: The identification of ribulose and L-xylulose in human and rat urine. *J Biol Chem* 215:257, 1955.
10. KILIANI H: Ueber die Zusammensetzung und Constitution der Arabinose carbonsüre bezw. der Arabinose. *Ber Dtsch Chem Ges* 20:339, 1887.
11. JANEWAY TC: Essential pentosuria in two brothers. *Am J Med Sci* 132:423, 1906.
12. GARROD AE: Inborn errors of metabolism. *Lancet* 2:217, 1908.
13. KLERCKER KO: Studien über die Pentosurie. *Nord Med Ark* 38:1, 1905.
14. ENKLEWITZ M, LASKER M: Studies in pentosuria: A report of 12 cases. *Am J Med Sci* 186:539, 1933.
15. LASKER M, ENKLEWITZ M: A simple method for the detection and estimation of L-xyloketose in urine. *J Biol Chem* 101:289, 1933.
16. ENKLEWITZ M, LASKER M: The origin of L-xyloketose (urine pentose). *J Biol Chem* 110:443, 1935.
17. ENKLEWITZ M, LASKER M: Pentosuria in twins. *JAMA* 105:958, 1935.
18. LASKER M, ENKLEWITZ M, LASKER GW: The inheritance of L-xyloketosuria (essential pentosuria). *Hum Biol* 8:243, 1936.
19. LASKER M: The question of arabinosuria. *Am J Clin Pathol* 20:485, 1950.
20. LASKER M: Mortality of persons with xyloketosuria. *Hum Biol* 27:294, 1955.
21. DERIVAUX RC: Essential pentosuria (xyloketosuria). *South Med J* 36:587, 1943.
22. KNOX WE: Sir Archibald Garrod's inborn errors of metabolism. IV. Pentosuria *Am J Hum Genet* 10:385, 1958.
23. NEUBERG C: Ueber die Harnpentose ein optisch inactives natürlich vorkomnendes Kohlehydrat. *Ber Dtsch Chem Ges* 33:2243, 1900.
24. CAMMIDGE PJ, HOWARD HAH: Seven cases of essential pentosuria. *Br Med J* 2:777, 1920.
25. ARON H: Einfall von Pentosuria im frühen Kindesalter. *Monatsschr Kinderheilk* 1:177, 1913.
26. LUZZATTO R: Récherches dans un cas de pentosurie chronique. *Arch Ital Biol* 51:469, 1909.
27. SCHÜLER L: Ueber inaktive und rechtsdrehende Arabinose ausscheidung im Harn. *Berlin Klin Wochenschr* 47:1322, 1910.
28. ZERNER E, WALTUCH R: Ein Beitrag zur Kenntnis der Pentosurie vom chemischen Standpunkt. *Monatsschr Chem* 34:1639, 1913.
29. LEVENE PA, LAFORGE FB: Note on a case of pentosuria. *J Biol Chem* 18:319, 1914.
30. ZERNER E, WALTUCH R: Zur Frage des Pentosuriezuckers. *Biochem Z* 58:410, 1913.
31. HILLER A: The identification of the pentose in a case of pentosuria. *J Biol Chem* 30:129, 1917.
32. GREENWALD I: The nature of the sugar in four cases of pentosuria. *J Biol Chem* 88:1, 1930.
33. SOLIS COHEN S: Essential pentosuria. *Am J Med Sci* 139:349, 1910.
34. SOLIS COHEN S, GERSHENFELD L: Supplemental report of a case of essential pentosuria of twenty-eight years' standing. *Am J Med Sci* 192:610, 1936.
35. BARNES HD, BLOOMBERG BM: Paper chromatography of the urinary sugar in essential pentosuria. *S Afr J Med Sci* 18:93, 1953.
36. TOUSTER O, HARWELL S: The isolation of L-arabitol from pentosuric urine. *J Biol Chem* 230:1031, 1958.
37. WOLFSON WG, COHN C, DEVANEY WA: An improved apparatus and procedure for ascending chromatography on large size filter paper sheets. *Science* 109:541, 1949.
38. MARGOLIS JI: Chronic pentosuria and migraine. *Am J Med Sci* 177:348, 1929.
39. EVERETT MR: *Medical Biochemistry*. Hoeber-Harper, New York, 1942, p 312.
40. TOUSTER O, HUTCHESON RM, RICE L: The influence of D-glucuronolactone on the excretion of L-xylulose by humans and guinea pigs. *J Biol Chem* 215:677, 1955.
41. TOUSTER O, MAYBERRY RH, MCCORMICK DB: The conversion of 1-^{13}C-D-glucuronolactone to 5-^{13}C-L-xylulose in a pentosuric human. *Biochim Biophys Acta* 24:196, 1957.
42. TOUSTER O, REYNOLDS VH, HUTCHESON RM: The reduction of L-xylulose to xylitol by guinea pig liver mitochondria. *J Biol Chem* 221:697, 1956.
43. HOLLMAN S, TOUSTER O: The L-xylulose-xylitol enzyme and other polyol dehydrogenases of guinea pig liver mitochondria. *J Biol Chem* 225:87, 1957.
44. BÄSSLER KH, REIMOLD WV: Lactatbildung aus Zuckern und Zuckeralkoholen in Erythrocyten. *Klin Wochenschr* 43:169, 1965.
45. ASAKURA T, ADACHI K, MINAKAMI S, YOSHIKAWA H: Nonglycolytic sugar metabolism in human erythrocytes. I. Xylitol metabolism. *J Biochem* 62:184, 1967.
46. WANG YM, VAN EYS J: The enzymatic defect in essential pentosuria. *N Engl J Med* 282:892, 1970.
47. ASHWELL G: Enzymatic degradation of D-galacturonic and D-glucuronic acid. *Fed Proc* 16:146, 1957.
48. HICKMAN J, ASHWELL G: Purification and properties of D-xylulokinase in liver. *J Biol Chem* 232:737, 1958.
49. ASHWELL G, KANFER J, BURNS JJ: Studies of the mechanism of L-xylulose formation by kidney enzymes. *J Biol Chem* 234:472, 1959.
50. SMILEY JD, ASHWELL G: Purification and properties of β-L-hydroxy acid hydrogenase. II. Isolation of β-keto-L-gulonic acid, an intermediate in L-xylulose biosynthesis. *J Biol Chem* 236:357, 1961.
51. WINKELMAN J, ASHWELL G: Enzymic formation of L-xylulose from β-keto-L-gulonic acid. *Biochim Biophys Acta* 52:170, 1961.

52. BURNS JJ, KANFER J: Formation of L-xylulose from L-gulonolactone in rat kidney. *J Am Chem Soc* 79:3604, 1957.
53. UL HASSAN M, LEHNINGER AL: Enzymatic formation of ascorbic acid in rat liver extracts. *J Biol Chem* 223:123, 1956.
54. HIATT HH, LAREAU J: Studies of ribose metabolism. VII. An assessment of ribose biosynthesis from hexose by way of the C-6 oxidation pathway. *J Biol Chem* 233:1023, 1958.
55. HIATT HH: Studies of ribose metabolism. IV. The metabolism of D-glucuronolactone in normal and pentosuric subjects. *Biochim Biophys Acta* 28:645, 1958.
56. KUMAHARA Y, FEINGOLD DS, FREEDBERG IM, HIATT HH: Studies of pentose metabolism in normal subjects and in patients with pentosuria and pentosuria trait. *J Clin Endocrinol Metab* 21:887, 1961.
57. FREEDBERG IM, FEINGOLD DS, HIATT HH: Serum and urine L-xylulose in pentosuric and normal subjects and in individuals with pentosuria trait. *Biochem Biophys Res Commun* 1:328, 1959.
58. HORECKER BL, HIATT HH: Pathways of carbohydrate metabolism in normal and neoplastic cells. *N Engl J Med* 258:177, 255, 1958.
59. HORECKER BL, MEHLER AH: Carbohydrate metabolism. *Annu Rev Biochem* 24:207, 1955.
60. MARKS PA, FEIGELSON P: Biosynthesis of nucleic acid ribose and of glycogen glucose in the rat. *J Biol Chem* 226:1001, 1957.
61. HIATT HH: Studies of ribose metabolism. II. A method for the study of ribose synthesis *in vivo*. *J Biol Chem* 229:725, 1957.
62. HIATT HH: Studies of ribose metabolism. VI. Pathways of ribose synthesis in man. *J Clin Invest* 37:1461, 1958.
63. HORECKER BL, SMYRNIOTIS PZ: The coenzyme function of thiamine pyrophosphate in pentose phosphate metabolism. *J Am Chem Soc* 75:1009, 1953.
64. HIATT HH: Studies of ribose metabolism. V. Factors influencing *in vivo* ribose synthesis in the rat. *J Clin Invest* 37:1453, 1958.
65. HORECKER BL, GIBBS M, KLENOW H, SMYRNIOTIS PZ: The mechanism of pentose phosphate conversion to hexose monophosphate. I. With a liver enzyme preparation. *J Biol Chem* 207:393, 1954.
66. HIATT HH: Studies of ribose metabolism. III. The pathway of ribose carbon conversion to glucose in man. *J Clin Invest* 37:651, 1958.
67. HIATT HH: Studies of ribose metabolism. I. The pathway of nucleic acid ribose synthesis in a human carcinoma cell in tissue culture. *J Clin Invest* 36:1408, 1957.
68. PERKOFF GT, TYLER FH: Studies in disorders of muscle. XI. The problem of pentosuria in progressive muscular dystrophy. *Metabolism* 5:563, 1956.
69. TABOR H, HAYAISHI O: The excretion of imidazoleacetic acid riboside following the administration of imidazoleacetic acid or histamine to rats. *J Am Chem Soc* 77:505, 1955.
70. KARJALA SA: The partial characterization of a histamine metabolite from rat and mouse urine. *J Am Chem Soc* 77:504, 1955.
71. REICHARD P: Enzymatic synthesis of deoxyribonucleotides. I. Formation of deoxycytidine diphosphate from cytidine diphosphate with enzymes from *Escherichia coli*. *J Biol Chem* 237:3513, 1962.
72. MOSBACH EH, KING CG: Tracer studies of glucuronic acid biosynthesis. *J Biol Chem* 185:491, 1950.
73. EISENBERG F JR, GURIN S: The biosynthesis of glucuronic acid from 1-C^{14}-glucose. *J Biol Chem* 195:317, 1952.
74. GINSBURG V, WEISSBACH A, MAXWELL ES: Formation of glucuronic acid from uridinediphosphate glucuronic acid. *Biochim Biophys Acta* 28:649, 1958.
75. POGELL BM, LELOIR LF: Nucleotide activation of liver microsomal glucuronidation. *J Biol Chem* 236:293, 1961.
76. ANDERSON RL, WOOD WA: Purification and properties of L-xylulokinase. *J Biol Chem* 237:1029, 1962.
77. WINEGRAD AI, SHAW WN: Glucuronic acid pathway acitvity in adipose tissue. *Am J Physiol* 206:165, 1964.
78. WINEGRAD AI, BURDEN CL: Hyperactivity of the glucuronic acid pathway in diabetes mellitus. *Trans Assoc Am Physicians* 78:158, 1965.
79. HANKES LV, POLITZER WM, TOUSTER O, ANDERSON L: Myoinositol catabolism in human pentosurics: The predominant role of the glucuronate-xylulose-pentose phosphate pathway. *Ann NY Acad Sci* 165:564, 1969.
80. ISHERWOOD FA, CHEN YT, MAPSON LW: Synthesis of L-ascorbic acid in plants and animals. *Biochem J* 56:1, 1954.
81. BAKER EM, SAUBERLICH HE, WOLFSKILL SJ, WALLACE WT, DEAN EE: Tracer studies of vitamin C utilization in men: Metabolism of D-glucuronolactone-6-C^{14}, D-glucuronic-6-C^{14} acid, and L-ascorbic-1-C^{14} acid. *Proc Soc Exp Biol Med* 109:737, 1962.
82. BURNS JJ, EVANS C, TROUSOF N, KAPLAN J: Stimulatory effect of drugs on excretion of L-ascorbid acid and non-conjugated D-glucuronic acid. *Fed Proc* 16:286, 1957.
83. LONGENECKER HF, FRICKE HH, KING CG: The effect of organic compounds upon vitamin C synthesis in the rat. *J Biol Chem* 135:497, 1940.
84. BURNS JJ, EVANS C, TROUSOF N: Stimulatory effect of barbital on urinary excretion of L-ascorbic acid and non-conjugated D-glucuronic acid. *J Biol Chem* 227:785, 1957.
85. EVANS C, CONNEY AH, TROUSOF N, BURNS JJ: Metabolism of D-galactose to D-glucuronic acid, L-gulonic acid, and L-ascorbic acid in normal and barbital-treated rats. *Biochim Biophys Acta* 41:9, 1960.
86. CONNEY AH, BRAY GA, EVANS C, BURNS JJ: Metabolic interactions between L-ascorbic acid and drugs. *Ann NY Acad Sci* 92:115, 1961.
87. HOLLMANN S, TOUSTER O: Alterations in tissue levels of uridine diphosphate glucose dehydrogenase, uridine diphosphate glucuronic acid pyrophosphatase, and glucuronyl transferase induced by substances influencing the production of ascorbic acid. *Biochim Biophys Acta* 62:338, 1962.
88. ROE JH, COOVER MO: Role of the thyroid gland in urinary pentose excretion in the rat. *Proc Soc Exp Biol Med* 75:818, 1950.
89. COOVER MO, FEINBERG LJ, ROE JH: Effect of cold, adrenocorticotropic, and thyroid hormones on urinary excretion of pentose in the rat. *Proc Soc Exp Biol Med* 74:146, 1950.
90. BAKER EM, PLOUGH IC, BIERMAN EL: Alternate pathways of glucose metabolism in man: Factors influencing the excretion of ketopentose. *Clin Res Proc* 6:406, 1958.
91. ASHWELL G: Personal communication.
92. GREENWALD I: The possible significance of L-xyloketose (urine pentose) in normal metabolism. *J Biol Chem* 91:731, 1931.
93. LARSON HW, CHAMBERS WH, BLATHERWICK NR, EWING ME, SAWYER SD: The metabolism of D- and L-xylulose in the depancreatized dog. *J Biol Chem* 129:701, 1939.
94. LARSON HW, BLATHERWICK NR, BRADSHAW PJ, EWING ME, SAWYER SD: The metabolism of L-xylulose. *J Biol Chem* 138:353, 1941.
95. BOZIAN RC, TOUSTER O: Essential pentosuria: Renal or enzymic disorder. *Nature* 184:463, 1959.
96. FLYNN FV: Essential pentosuria. *Br Med J* 1:391, 1955.
97. HICKMAN J, ASHWELL G: A sensitive and stereospecific enzymatic assay for xylulose. *J Biol Chem* 234:758, 1957.
98. LEDERER E, LEDERER M: *Chromatography*. Elsevier, Amsterdam, 1955.
99. HOUGH L, JONES JKN, WADMAN WH: Quantitative analysis of mixtures of sugars by the method of partition chromatography. Part V. Improved methods for the separation and detection of the sugars and their methylated derivatives on the paper chromatogram. *J Chem Soc* 1702, 1950.
100. DISCHE Z, BORENFREUND E: A new spectrophotometric method for the detection and determination of keto sugars and trioses. *J Biol Chem* 192:583, 1951.
101. WRIGHT WT: Incidence of pentosuria. *N Engl J Med* 265:1154, 1961.
102. MIZRAHI O, SER I: Essential pentosuria, in Goldschmidt E (ed): *Genetics of Migrant and Isolate Populations*. Baltimore, Williams & Wilkins, 1963, p 300.
103. LASKER M: Personal communication.
104. POLITZER WM, FLEISCHMANN H: L-Xylulosuria in a Lebanese family. *Am J Hum Genet* 14:256, 1962.
105. KHACHADURIAN AK: Essential pentosuria. *Am J Hum Genet* 14:249, 1962.
106. WEBB EC: *Enzyme Nomenclature*. New York, Academic, 1984.
107. SOYAMA K, FURUKAWA N: A Japanese case of pentosuria. *J Inherited Metab Dis* 8:37, 1985.
108. REDDI OS, REDDY SV, REDDY KR: Familial incidence of L-xylulosuria. *Hum Genet* 39:143, 1977.
109. LANE AB: On the nature of L-xylulose reductase deficiency in essential pentosuria. *Biochem Genet* 23:61, 1985.
110. LANE AB, JENKINS T: Human L-xylulose reductase variation: Family and population studies. *Ann Hum Genet* 49:227, 1985.

PART 4

AMINO ACIDS

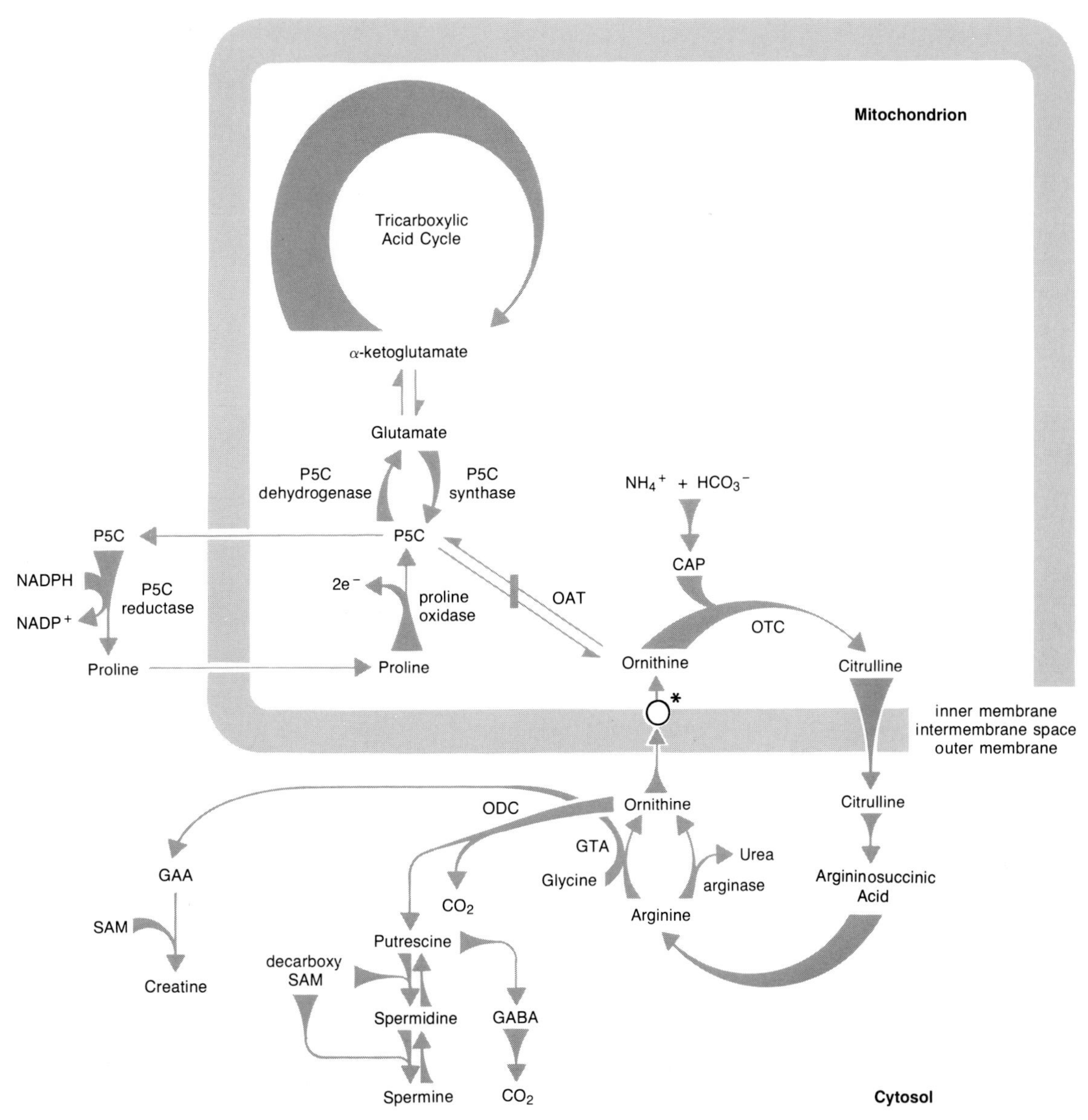

CHAPTER 15

THE HYPERPHENYLALANINEMIAS

CHARLES R. SCRIVER
SEYMOUR KAUFMAN
SAVIO L. C. WOO

1. *The hyperphenylalaninemias are disorders of phenylalanine hydroxylation. The minimum requirements for the reaction are phenylalanine hydroxylase (PAH), oxygen, phenylalanine, and tetrahydrobiopterin (BH_4) cofactor. For the pterin cofactor to function catalytically, dihydropteridine reductase (DHPR) and reduced pyridine nucleotide are required. BH_4 is an obligatory component, and there is a pathway for its synthesis; it has successive steps catalyzed by guanosine triphosphate cyclohydrolase (GTP-CH), 6-pyruvoyltetrahydropterin synthase (6-PTS, formerly called phosphate eliminating enzyme), sepiapterin reductase, and, probably, tetrahydropterin 2'-keto reductase.*

2. *Hyperphenylalaninemia, defined as a plasma phenylalanine value above 0.12 mM (2 mg/dl), is a heterogeneous phenotype caused by mutations at the loci encoding components of the hydroxylation reaction. The known forms are either PAH-deficient (PKU and non-PKU hyperphenylalaninemia) and caused by alleles at the PAH locus at chromosome 12q22-q24.1 or BH_4-deficient and caused by alleles at three other loci: DHPR (chromosome 4p15.3), GTP-CH (unmapped), and 6-PTS (unmapped).*

3. *The associated diseases are autosomal recessive, but two conditions are, in general, necessary for clinical manifestations, namely, mutation and exposure to phenylalanine (an essential amino acid). PKU has plasma phenylalanine values above ≈ 1.2 mM; non-PKU hyperphenylalaninemia has lower values. PKU is a disease with impaired cognitive development; non-PKU hyperphenylalaninemia is benign. Different clinical manifestations in the two phenotypes suggest that the amount of phenylalanine overburden influences pathogenesis. BH_4-deficient forms of hyperphenylalaninemia have an additional pathogenetic mechanism: deficiency of BH_4 impairs two other hydroxylases (tyrosine and tryptophan) and synthesis of the corresponding neurotransmitter precursors (DOPA and 5-hydroxytryptophan).*

4. *DNA analysis has identified six mutations, so far, in the PAH gene (90 kb, 13 exons); all cause the PKU phenotype. They are a splicing mutation in intron 12; mis-sense mutations in exons 7, 9, and 12; a deletion in the region of exons 1 and 2; and a deletion spanning exon 3. A PKU allele in American Blacks is either linked to or causes a new MspI site near exon 9. Different populations tend to carry different PKU alleles. Linkage disequilibrium exists between particular RFLP haplotypes and PAH alleles in Northern European populations. Certain RFLPs by themselves and in combination are highly informative and are used for prenatal diagnosis of PKU. Analysis of DHPR alleles is less advanced, but informative RFLPs have been identified.*

5. *Unusual gene dosage effects are seen with mutations at the PAH, DHPR, or 6-PTS loci. The wild-type enzymes are all homopolymers. Heterozygotes for CRM-positive, PAH, DHPR, and 6-PTS alleles, in general, have activities significantly less than half normal, indicating deviant gene dosage effects in the heteropolymeric forms. The long-term medical histories of such heterozygotes have not been well studied. Some 6-PTS deficient heterozygotes with deviant gene dosage have an abnormal metabolic phenotype.*

6. *Effective treatment of PKU keeps phenylalanine values well below 1.2 mM. The bulwark of treatment is still the low phenylalanine diet. Outcome of treatment by conventional means is clearly better than the consequences of no treatment, but there are neuropsychological deficits even in treated patients. Premature termination of treatment, in general, increases the deficits. "Malignant" forms of hyperphenylalaninemia require additional treatment, notably BH_4 replacement or supplementation with DOPA and 5-hydroxytryptophan and, for DHPR deficiency, supplements of folinic acid or another form of tetrahydrofolate.*

7. *The overall incidence of hyperphenylalaninemia is ≈100 per million livebirths. There is great geographic and ethnic variation in the incidence of PKU (5 to 190 cases per million births). Non-PKU hyperphenylalaninemia (15 to 75 cases per million births) is less prevalent than PKU in most populations. The BH_4-deficient forms are panethnic and pangeographic. Their overall incidence is ≈1 to 2 per million births (1 to 2 percent of hyperphenylalaninemia cases). Newborn screening for hyperphenylalaninemia is the best method for early diagnosis. Classification of phenotype and case finding for BH_4-deficient probands among the hyperphenylalaninemia cases requires measurements of phenylalanine, pterins (neopterin and biopterin, and BH_4), and neurotransmitter derivatives in plasma, urine, and CSF. Enzyme activities (except PAH) can be mea-*

Nonstandard abbreviations used in this chapter are: BH_4 = tetrahydrobiopterin [(6*R*)-L-*erythro*-5,6,7,8-tetrahydrobiopterin)]; CRM = cross-reacting material (antigen); DHPR = dihydropteridine reductase; DHFR = dihydrofolate reductase; $DMPH_4$ = 6,7-dimethyltetrahydropterin; GTP-CH = Guanosine triphosphate cyclohydrolase; $6MPH_4$ = 6-methyltetrahydropterin; PAH = phenylalanine hydroxylase (phenylalanine 4-monooxygenase); PAL = phenylalanine ammonia lyase; PKU = phenylketonuria; 6-PTS = 6-pyruvolyltetrahydropterin synthase; qBH_2 = quinonoid form of dihydrobiopterin; RFLP = restriction fragment length polymorphism.

Enzyme Classification (EC) numbers: PAH, 1.14.16.1; DHPR, 1.6.99.7, also called GDPR, 1.6.5.1; DHFR, 1.5.1.3; 6-PTS, no EC number assigned; GTP-CH, 3.5.4.16.

McKusick Numbers: PAH deficiency: PKU, 26160; non-PKU hyperphenylalaninemia, 26158; DHPR deficiency, 26163; GTP-CH, 23391; "dihydrobiopterin synthetase" or "biopterin deficiency" (6-PTS deficiency), 26164, 26169.

sured in a variety of somatic cells. DNA analysis is increasingly useful, particularly in the PAH deficiencies.

8. *Prenatal diagnosis by various combinations of DNA analysis, enzyme assay, and measurement of pterins in amniotic fluid is feasible in all forms of hyperphenylalaninemia.*
9. *Maternal phenylketonuria is an embryopathy/fetopathy that compromises growth and causes congenital malformations, microcephaly, and mental retardation. It is a consequence of intrauterine phenylalanine excess which occurs in the gravid female with persistent hyperphenylalaninemia. The observed average fetal/maternal plasma phenylalanine ratio is 1.48 (range, 1.13 to 2.91). Registers are recommended for tracking females with hyperphenylalaninemia for purposes of reproductive counseling. Treatment to prevent maternal PKU must begin before conception and be continued throughout the pregnancy.*

Hyperphenylalaninemia is the subject of this chapter. It is a generic phenotype distinguished by a persistently elevated phenylalanine concentration above the normal distribution of plasma values. This disturbance in metabolic homeostasis can have clinical consequences depending on its pathogenesis and its degree. The clinical manifestation of principal concern is impaired development of the central nervous system; it can occur in the individual with hyperphenylalaninemia and in the offspring of an affected female.

The genetic causes of hyperphenylalaninemia are the focus of this chapter. They include mutations at the locus encoding the subunit of *L-phenylalanine hydroxylase* (PAH); at loci for at least two enzymes in the pathway for synthesis of *tetrahydrobiopterin* (BH_4), the cofactor for the hydroxylation reaction; and at the locus for *dihydropteridine reductase* (DHPR), the enzyme which regenerates BH_4 from the oxidized product of the hydroxylation reaction. Mutations at the PAH locus affect apoenzyme integrity and are responsible for the disease we call *phenylketonuria* (PKU); it is a homozygous mutant phenotype with mental retardation, but the associated genotypes may be homozygous or compound. There are other mutant alleles at the PAH locus which cause a lesser degree of hyperphenylalaninemia; the associated risk of mental retardation in probands is small, but it is elevated, owing to the intrauterine effect, in the offspring of affected females. The PAH-deficient metabolic phenotypes have been endowed with a variety of names in the older medical literature, but here we call them simply *PKU* and *non-PKU variants at the PAH locus*.

The other forms of hyperphenylalaninemia that are not PAH-deficient, are called here *BH_4-deficient* and *DHPR-deficient hyperphenylalaninemias;* a more precise nomenclature may emerge when their genetic causes are better known. They attract special attention since BH_4 homeostasis serves two additional hydroxylation reactions involving L-tryptophan and L-tyrosine. The hydroxylation products of these substrates, 5-hydroxytryptophan and L-dopa, are precursors of serotonin and catecholamines, respectively. As neurotransmitter substances they influence brain development and function. Accordingly, diagnosis of these variants is relevant for prognosis and treatment of patients with hyperphenylalaninemia.

The Mendelian forms of hyperphenylalaninemia are considered "genetic" disorders. In fact they are multifactorial diseases since environmental and genetic components are each necessary for occurrence of the metabolic phenotype and the associated disease. L-Phenylalanine is an essential nutrient amino acid in humans. Accordingly, when a mutant allele affecting phenylalanine hydroxylation is expressed, it interacts with a universal human environment. This fact is used in treatment. By creating a particular environment—in this case with a low phenylalanine diet—expression of the mutant allele is neutralized, the metabolic phenotype is abrogated, and disease manifestations are prevented if the treatment is instituted successfully and early in the expressed phenotype.

TRANSITION

Previous editions of this text presented different views of PKU and the hyperphenylalaninemias. In the early editions[1–3] the emphasis was on PKU itself; later[4,5] it was on the growing diversity of phenotypes and the associated enzymes. In this edition, we emphasize the hydroxylation reaction, genes encoding it, their mutant forms, and the associated phenotypes, along with new knowledge about the efficacy of treatment for symptomatic forms of hyperphenylalaninemia and of maternal hyperphenylalaninemia. Citation of the scientific literature is selective.*

We begin with information about the normal phenotype and homeostasis, the hydroxylation reaction, and the principal genes. Information about the variant states is presented next in reverse order: mutations, polypeptides, metabolic phenotypes pathogenesis, clinical features, and treatment. We end with three general topics: screening and diagnosis; genetics and significance of heterozygosity; and maternal hyperphenylalaninemia. We have built a story. The reader can choose to read all of it or only parts of it.

The trends in PKU-related research are apparent in some representative reviews and overviews. A typical overview of PKU in 1955[6] could be followed up within the decade by reports of remarkable progress in the prevention of PKU disease,[7,8] while at the same time real deficits in the knowledge base were becoming evident.[9] Several reviews in 1980[10–14] saw PKU as an epitome of human biochemical genetics, a disease seemingly overcome by the application of knowledge, even though the generic hyperphenylalaninemias were becoming a challenge in diagnosis and treatment. While deficits in our ability to treat the hyperphenylalaninemias[15,16] and to deal with maternal hyperphenylalaninemia[17] command more attention now, our knowledge of pterin metabolism and of BH_4 synthesis in particular improves,[18,19] as does our knowledge of the phenylalanine hydroxylation reaction[20] and the gene that encodes phenylalanine hydroxylase.[21,22] The change in emphasis came as the 50th anniversary of Fölling's discovery of PKU[23] was being celebrated.[24–26]† It is noteworthy that one of the celebrants was also coauthor of a review about the molecular genetics of PKU,[27] fulfilling in his own work the aphorism: "Life must be lived forward but it can only be understood backward" (Kierkegaard). That point of view is again appreciated in Penrose's inaugural lecture as Galton Professor[28] and Ledley's modern reflections on it.[29] Penrose saw PKU as a prototype of preventive medicine where it was possible to capitalize on chemical individuality; Ledley ad-

*A MEDLINE search for the period January 1, 1985, to August 15, 1987, identified 171 articles with PKU as the main concept, and 705 articles under the *Index Medicus* heading: phenylalanine, phenylalanine hydroxylase, phenylalanine ammonia lyase.

†Reference 26 is a reminiscence by Professor Fölling's daughter, about her father, his career, and the circumstances of his discovery of "imbecilitas phenylpyrouvica," as Fölling called it.[23] The event was clearly the result of an opportunity, an observation, and Fölling's ability to convert observation into concept.

dresses the ultimate form of chemical individuality—genotype in PKU—and sees possibilities for somatic gene therapy. We do not know what Fölling thought about genes: he apparently knew of Garrod's work, perceived he had discovered a new inborn error of metabolism, and, in collaboration with Lous Mohr, the geneticist, demonstrated that inheritance of the disease was autosomal recessive.[26]

PHENYLALANINE HOMEOSTASIS

Claude Bernard recognized that constancy of the internal milieu was a necessary condition of life;[30] Walter B. Cannon called it *homeostasis.*[31] Hyperphenylalaninemia is a metrical phenotype recognizable by a phenylalanine value greater than the normal value. The normal value represents a steady state, and the deviant value is a new steady-state, which may or may not have consequences for health.

The steady state is a dynamic one in which the concentrations of components in the system remain fixed in the face of a constant flux through the system.[32] Any persistent change in these fluxes will eventually change the steady-state value. Regulatory mechanisms control steady-state values so that they experience only minor, transitory changes within certain limits under usual circumstances.[33] Dispersion of values around the central tendency (the mean value) represents both intraindividual and interindividual variation. The normal value for plasma phenylalanine *within* an individual shows infradiem oscillation[34] which is not greater than about 50 percent of the nadir value implying that the plasma phenylalanine value is regulated. The mechanisms of regulation are not as well understood as they are for glucose or phosphate, for example, but some are known as we show for the phenylalanine hydroxylation reaction. The differences in values *between* individuals are also modest, indicating that normal persons have similar homeostatic mechanisms derived presumably through inheritance. The evidence for heritability in plasma amino acid values, including phenylalanine values, is conventional; the values are more similar within monozygotic twin pairs than they are between nontwin subjects.[35] Accordingly, it is no surprise that individuals have "private" plasma amino acid phenotypes, with distributions of values that are smaller than the "public" distribution of values in a population of unrelated individuals.[34] This point will bear on our view of patients with PKU or the other hyperphenylalaninemias since their mutations are always expressed on the background of all their other genes that determine phenylalanine homeostasis; it will be relevant to treatment.

Normal Plasma Values

The normal plasma phenylalanine value is not significantly different in young and adult-age subjects.[34,36] The normal adult value under physiological conditions is 58 ± 15 μmol/liter; (mean and SD); the corresponding values in children (mean age 8 years) and adolescents (mean age 16 years) are 62 ± 18 and 60 ± 13, respectively. Sex of the individual affects the value only in adolescents (male values are higher).[36] Values in newborn and older infants are similar to those of the older subjects and the uppermost normal value in the newborn is taken as 120 μmol per liter.[35]

Determinants of the Steady-State

The plasma phenylalanine value is an extracellular value; it may be different from values in other fluid compartments, but at the steady-state the compartments are in equilibrium (which is far from chemical equilibrium, of course). The flux of phenylalanine through the plasma compartment has both input and runout components. Input of phenylalanine has two major sources: exogenous from dietary phenylalanine and endogenous from bound (polypeptide) and free pools. Runout involves incorporation into bound pools, oxidation to tyrosine, and conversion to minor metabolites. We discuss these separately.

Input. Phenylalanine is an essential amino acid in humans. A dietary source of the amino acid (*l*-enantiomorph) is necessary to maintain phenylalanine homeostasis, and the requirement for exogenous phenylalanine must be met.[37,38] The nutritional requirement for L-phenylalanine is difficult to estimate in the normal subject because catabolic runout perturbs the estimate of the anabolic requirement. Accordingly, the blocked catabolic state in PKU is useful to estimate the actual requirement. Empirical estimates in treated PKU patients indicate that requirement is on the order of 200 to 500 mg/day in the infant and young child and not more than 1.5 times greater than these values in older children (see "Treatment," below). The conventional method of estimation, made in normal children and adults receiving tyrosine in the diet, yields values similar or somewhat higher (Table 15-1). The requirement for phenylalanine is greater in the absence of tyrosine in subjects with intact phenylalanine hydroxylation.[37,38] The observed range of daily requirement for phenylalanine in PKU and normal subjects probably reflects interindividual differences in the genetic determinants of homeostasis as well as allelic differences at the PAH locus in the PKU subjects. The estimate for adult requirement (Table 15-1) is probably lower than the true requirement for technical reasons,[37] and values in adults, obtained by ^{13}C-labeled amino acid kinetic analysis, resemble those for young children when expressed per unit of total protein requirement. This revisionist view may be relevant to the treatment of hyperphenylalaninemia in the affected pregnant woman.

Input from the turnover of endogenous peptide-bound pools also contributes to the plasma phenylalanine value. When nutrition is inadequate, protein catabolism occurs and phenylalanine is released; as a consequence, plasma phenylalanine values will rise in the PKU patient in negative nitrogen balance. Failure to recognize this phenomenon can confound treatment of PKU patients (see below).

Runout. Input of phenylalanine will expand the plasma phenylalanine pool unless there is compensating runout. Incor-

Table 15-1 Estimates of Phenylalanine Requirement in Humans[37,38]

	mg/day	*mg/(kg · day)*	*mg/g protein*
Infant		25–90[38]	
Preschool child	200–500*[38]	69	63
Older child	200–500*	22	22
Young adult		14	19

NOTE: Estimates are from normal subjects with normal PAH activity and tyrosine present in the diet.
*Estimates are from PKU subjects with near total deficiency of PAH activity.

poration, oxidation, and metabolic conversion provide runout on a background of interorgan amino acid flow and cellular uptake. The relative contributions of these components to phenylalanine homeostasis are of theoretical and practical interest.

In an important theoretical study Kacser and Burns[39] reasoned that each component in a network of steady-state determinants has a value (called the *sensitivity coefficient*) proportional to its importance in setting the summation property (value = 1) of the steady state maintained by the network. The quantitative values of the components in phenylalanine runout have been measured in two different studies. Kaufman[40] estimated the relative kinetic values (micromoles per gram of tissue per minute) for incorporation into protein, hydroxylation, and transamination of L-phenylalanine in the rat at various extracellular concentrations of the amino acid (Fig. 15-1). At physiological concentrations, incorporation and hydroxylation account for about a quarter and three quarters of runout, respectively; conversion to phenylpyruvic acid is significant only at elevated plasma concentrations of phenylalanine. Salter et al.[41] estimated the sensitivity coefficient of PAH under basal conditions in rats perfused with radiolabeled phenylalanine. They estimated that half the runout occurred by the hydroxylation reaction; transport-mediated uptake, which precedes the incorporation and conversion reactions, accounted for the remainder. Both estimates[40,41] imply that phenylalanine hydroxylation is an important determinant of the steady-state value for plasma phenylalanine in the mammal. It follows that impaired hydroxylation will raise the steady-state value if input of phenylalanine is not reduced. On the other hand, since the sensitivity coefficient of the hydroxylation component is considerably less than 1.0, it follows, according to Kacser and Burns,[39] that hyperphenylalaninemia must be a recessive phenotype, which indeed it is, and that heterozygotes will not have significant hyperphenylalaninemia, which they do not (see "Heterozygosity," below). These quantitative considerations invite reflection on the other components of the homeostatic network before we describe PAH itself and the hydroxylation reaction it serves.

INTERORGAN PHENYLALANINE FLOW AND UPTAKE. PAH in humans is present and active only in liver cells (the hepatocytes). On the other hand, phenylalanine is incorporated into protein in all organs and tissues, and metabolic conversions of phenylalanine occur in many tissues other than liver. Accordingly, there are interorgan fluxes of this amino acid in total body nutrition,[42] and phenylalanine transport across cellular plasma membranes must occur before phenylalanine can enter its intracellular pathways. L-Phenylalanine uptake by mammalian cells is mediated by carriers which are Na^+-gradient-coupled in the brush border membranes of renal[43,44] and intestinal epithelia[45] and Na^+-independent in other plasma membranes (cited in Refs. 42, 46, and 47). The nephron, which contains both high-affinity and low-affinity phenylalanine carriers,[43] achieves near-total absorption of the amino acid from filtrate under physiological conditions. The systems have a capacity that does not saturate even at high filtered loads,[35,48] which means they continue to function in the homeostatic network contributing to the hyperphenylalaninemia of the phenylketonuric subject.

Phenylalanine enters parenchymal cells on a Na^+-independent, weakly concentrative carrier shared with branched-chain and aromatic amino acids[49–51] and it leaves cells on a system shared with many additional neutral-charge amino acids.[46,47] Because of the interactions between amino acids on the phenylalanine carrier, there is much interest in the role that perturbed phenylalanine transport may play in pathogenesis of the brain phenotype in PKU.

THE "SECOND" PHENYLALANINE CONVERSION PATHWAY. Conversion to tyrosine is the first and major metabolic pathway. Conversion of phenylalanine to nontyrosine derivatives is the "second" pathway (Fig. 15-2), the details of which were reviewed in previous editions of this text.[1–3] Alternative runouts such as these are mentioned here to complete the discussion, to name the derivatives, and to set the scene for considerations of pathogenesis later. The initial reaction in the second pathway is transamination of L-phenylalanine to form phenylpyruvate. This and subsequent metabolic transformations in the transamination pathway are restricted to the alanine side chain

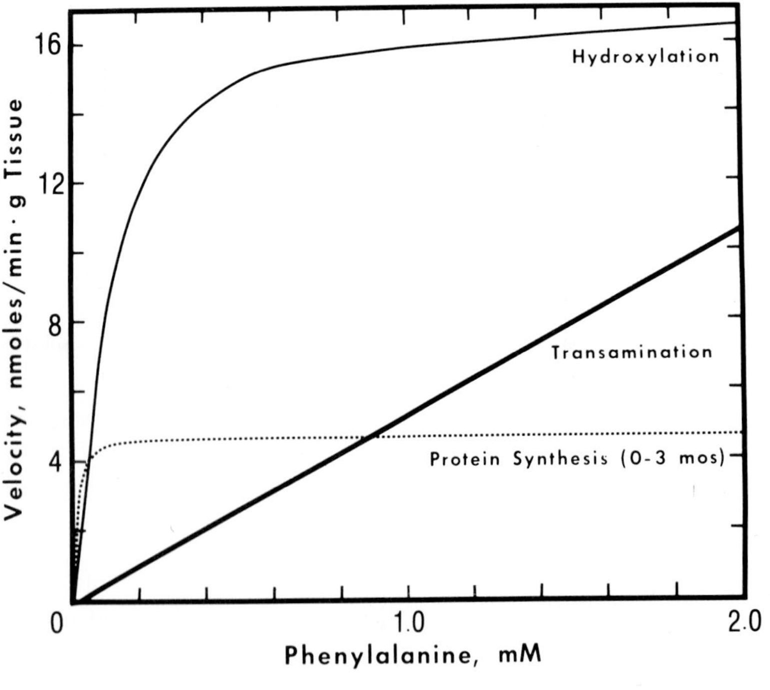

Fig. 15-1 Phenylalanine outflow from the extracellular pool as a function of its concentration. The hydroxylation-initiated outflow is controlled by PAH. Transamination is catalyzed by phenylalanine-alanine amino transferase. Incorporation into protein is a conventional process. Rates were calculated by Kaufman.[40] *(From Scriver and Clow.[12] Used by permission.)*

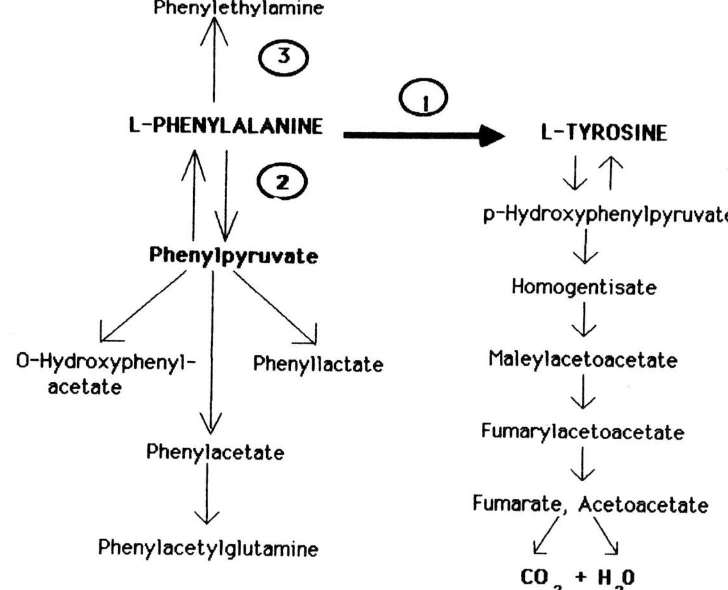

Fig. 15-2 The metabolic pathways (excluding incorporation into protein) and their relative importance for outflow of L-phenlalanine outflow in the normal steady state: 1 = the hydroxylation reaction mediated by PAH (major); 2 = the transamination reaction (minor); 3 = the decarboxylation reaction (minor).

of the molecule. Urine levels of products in this pathway account for only a small fraction of the phenylalanine that is metabolized daily by normal individuals.[52] This finding confirms that the transamination pathway is normally a minor one, and it is explained by the fact that the transaminase, relative to the hydroxylase, has a high K_m for phenylalanine;[40] only when the minor catabolic pathway is blocked or overloaded, so that phenylalanine concentration increases, does the transamination pathway become important (Fig. 15-1).

The opinion[5] that decarboxylation of phenylalanine to phenylethylamine (Fig. 15-2) is a major route of metabolism when phenylalanine concentration is elevated in vivo does not appear to be valid for humans. When PKU patients are given an inhibitor of monoamine oxidase to block further metabolism of phenylethylamine, amine excretion remains trivial compared with that of the transamination products.[52]

THE PHENYLALANINE HYDROXYLATING SYSTEM

The most important single determinant of phenylalanine homeostasis in humans is the hydroxylation reaction. To understand the mutant phenotypes associated with hyperphenylalaninemia, the normal components of the hydroxylation should be familiar. It is a complex reaction and through its fine tuning the flux of phenylalanine is controlled to confer the steady state.

General Characteristics

The phenylalanine hydroxylation reaction is an obligatory and rate limiting step in the catabolic pathway that leads to the complete oxidation of phenylalanine to CO_2 and water.[53] The ketogenic (e.g., acetoacetate) and gluconeogenic (e.g., fumarate) intermediates in the pathway (Fig. 15-2) contribute to the organism's pool of two carbon metabolites and glucose. In view of the brain's partial dependence on a peripheral supply of glucose, the ability of phenylalanine to provide gluconeogenic substrates perhaps plays a role in normal brain development and function. Hydroxylation of phenylalanine plays another important role in mammalian metabolism; it provides the organism with an endogenous supply of the nonessential amino acid, tyrosine. When hydroxylation is deficient, tyrosine becomes an "essential" amino acid. The formal name for PAH enzyme is L-phenylalanine-4-monooxygenase (EC 1.14.16.1).

Tissue Distribution of Hydroxylating Activity

It was thought, at one time, that PAH is not present in the nonhepatic tissues.[54] However, subsequent studies demonstrated appreciable activity in crude mouse kidney and pancreas[55] and in rat and guinea pig kidney.[56] The putative presence of hydroxylase activity in pancreas has not been confirmed.[57] Rat kidney PAH is in an unusual state of activation relative to the rat liver enzyme, and the kidney enzyme might account for as much as 50 percent of the total phenylalanine hydroxylase activity in the rat.[58] The status of the kidney hydroxylase in humans is unclear; some workers have reported hydroxylase activity in kidney,[59,59a] or PAH monomers[59b] whereas others have not in either human or nonhuman primate kidney.[60] In support of the latter finding, rat hydroxylase cDNA hybridizes with rat kidney RNA but not with baboon kidney RNA.[61]

PAH is not present in brain[62] contrary to an earlier claim.[63] Brain does contain another enzyme, tyrosine hydroxylase, which catalyzes the conversion of phenylalanine to tyrosine at a rate comparable to its ability to hydroxylate tyrosine.[64] Perhaps tyrosine hydroxylase, acting on phenylalanine, provides the developing brain with a significant fraction of the tyrosine it needs for protein synthesis[65]; whether it might in PKU is not known.

The Hydroxylating System

The hepatic phenylalanine hydroxylating system contains three essential components, PAH, dihydropteridine reductase, and the unconjugated pterin tetrahydrobiopterin (2-amino-4-hydroxy-6-[L-*erythro*-1′,2′-dihydroxypropyl] tetrahydropteridine).[66,67] The structure of BH_4 is shown in Fig. 15-3. Like all other naturally occurring compounds of this type, BH_4 is a 2-amino-4-hydroxypteridine (trivial name, *pterin*); it is classi-

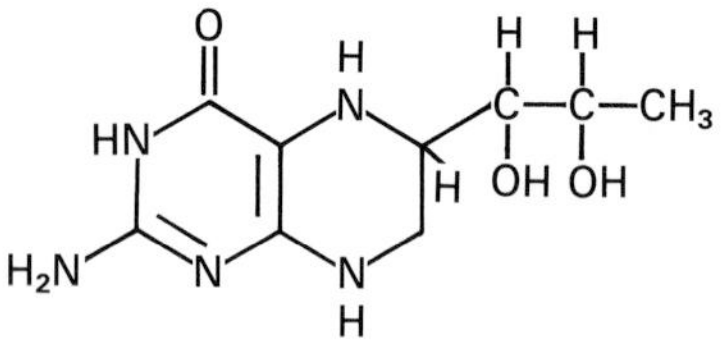

Fig. 15-3 Structure of tetrahydrobiopterin (BH_4) [2-amino-4-hydroxy-6-(L-*erythro* 1′,2′-dihydroxypropyl)-tetrahydropteridine], the natural coenzyme (cofactor) for PAH (see Refs. 66 and 67).

fied as an unconjugated pterin to distinguish it from its relatives, the folates. The latter compounds are called *conjugated pterins* because their pterin rings are conjugated with a *para*-aminobenzoyl-glutamate(s) substituent at position 6 of the pteridine ring. Unlike the folates, BH_4 is not a vitamin for mammals, since it can be synthesized by them. Several synthetic tetrahydropterins with simple alkyl substituents at position 6, such as 6-methyltetrahydropterin ($6MPH_4$) and 6,7-dimethyltetrahydropterin ($DMPH_4$), are even more active than BH_4 on the phenylalanine hydroxylating system.[68]

The reactions catalyzed by PAH hydroxylase and DHPR in the presence of the pterin appear in Fig. 15-4. PAH catalyzes a coupled reaction in which phenylalanine is oxidized to tyrosine and the tetrahydropterin is oxidized to the corresponding quinonoid-dihydropterin (qBH_2). The oxygen in the para position of the benzene ring of the tyrosine product is derived from molecular oxygen rather than from water[69]; accordingly, the hydroxylase is an oxygenase. During the hydroxylation reaction, the second atom of oxygen in the oxygen molecule is normally reduced to the level of water.

The minimum requirements for phenylalanine hydroxylation are the hydroxylase, oxygen, phenylalanine, and BH_4, but under these conditions BH_4 can function only stoichiometrically; i.e., the amount of tyrosine formed cannot exceed the amount of BH_4 present. For the pterin coenzyme to function catalytically, there must be another component of the system: DHPR (along with a reduced pyridine nucleotide). Although the reductase is active with both NADH and NADPH, NADH is the better substrate in vitro.[70–72] It is not known whether NADH or NADPH, or both, function with the reductase in vivo. In addition to the NADH-dependent DHPR-catalyzed regeneration of BH_4 from the qBH_2 derivative, reduction of the latter compound to BH_4 can also proceed nonenzymatically in the presence of millimolar concentrations of reducing agents such as mercaptans and ascorbate.[73] Attempts to demonstrate ascorbate-mediated regeneration of BH_4 in humans have not been successful.

The pterin coenzyme cycles between the tetrahydro and the qBH_2 derivative during the hydroxylation reaction (Fig. 15-4). Actually, the primary pterin product formed in the hydroxylase-catalyzed reaction is the corresponding pterin-4-α-carbinolamine.[73,74] A protein, isolated in pure form from liver, named *phenylalanine hydroxylase stimulator protein*,[75,76] catalyzes conversion of the carbinolamine to the corresponding qBH_2.[73,74,77] Since the reaction catalyzed by the protein also occurs quite rapidly nonenzymatically,[73,74] it is not clear whether normal rates of phenylalanine hydroxylation in vivo are dependent on the activity of the stimulator protein. It seems likely that even its total absence would not cause severe loss of hydroxylating activity but might cause mild hyperphenylalaninemia.

Another enzyme may play a role in phenylalanine hydroxylation in vivo: it is dihydrofolate reductase (DHFR) (EC 1.6.99.7). This enzyme has a well-established role in one-carbon metabolism catalyzing the reduction of 7,8-dihydrofolate.

$$\text{NADPH} + \text{H}^+ + \text{7,8-dihydrofolate} \rightarrow \text{NADP}^+ + \text{tetrahydrolfolate} \quad (15\text{-}1)$$

The enzyme can also catalyze the analogous reaction with 7,8-dihydrobiopterin.[78]

$$\text{NADPH} + \text{H}^+ + \text{7,8-dihydrobiopterin} \rightarrow \text{NADP}^+ + \text{tetrahydrobiopterin} \quad (15\text{-}2)$$

The second reaction assumes importance for phenylalanine hydroxylation when the rate of the DHPR-catalyzed reduction of qBH_2 lags behind the rate of the PAH-catalyzed formation of the quinonoid derivative (Fig. 15-4). Under such conditions, the extremely unstable qBH_2 will undergo a rearrangement to the corresponding 7,8-dihydrobiopterin;[78] the latter is not a substrate for DHPR. Therefore, when DHPR limits the rate of phenylalanine hydroxylation, DHFR could salvage some of the biopterin diverted to the 7,8-dihydro derivative

Fig. 15-4 The phenylalanine hydroxylating reaction catalyzed by hepatic PAH uses BH_4 stoichiometrically and regenerates cofacter from the oxidized product quinonoid dihydrobiopterin (qBH_2) by a coupled reaction catalyzed by dihydropteridine reductase (DHPR).

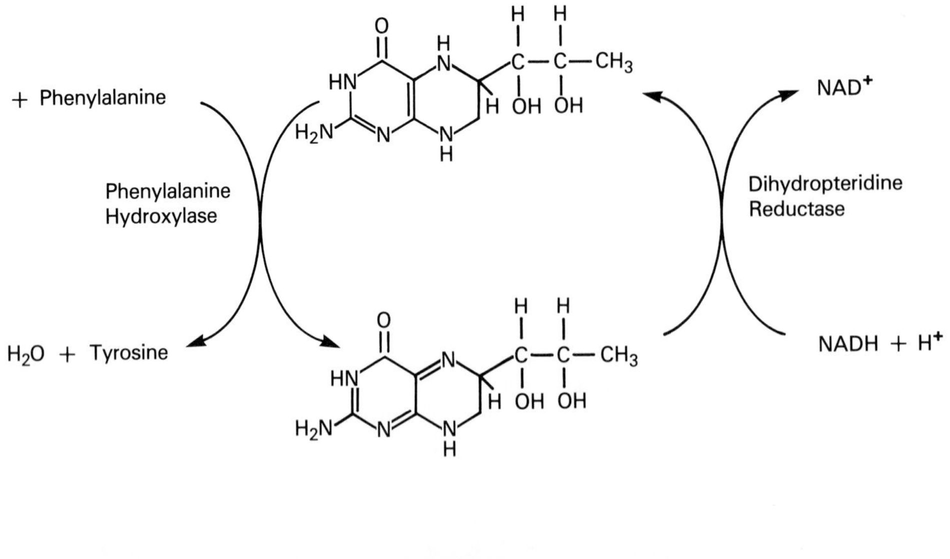

and could thereby potentially support some phenylalanine hydroxylation. However, since the near-total absence of DHPR leads to hyperphenylalaninemia (see below), it is evident that neither DHFR, nor any other enzyme, is as effective as DHPR at sustaining normal rates of phenylalanine hydroxylation.

The reactions involving phenylalanine depicted in Fig. 15-4 were the first to establish a metabolic role for an unconjugated pterin and to reveal the coenzyme role of BH_4. It was shown subsequently that BH_4 and DHPR play precisely the same roles in the hydroxylating systems for tyrosine and tryptophan.[79–81] Accordingly, these two components are essential for the biosynthesis of the neurotransmitters dopamine, norepinephrine, and serotonin. A fuller realization of the *in situ* role of BH_4 and DHPR in these other hydroxylating systems became clear with the discovery of variant forms of phenylketonuria caused by defects in BH_4 regeneration or biosynthesis (see section on diseases below).

Physical Properties of PAH

Many of the properties of PAH were first determined with enzyme purified from rat liver extracts.[82] The properties of the human liver enzyme are similar to those of the rat enzyme, with exceptions which are mentioned below.

Rat Enzyme. Essentially pure rat liver PAH appeared initially to be a mixture of two different polymeric forms.[82] Based on a determination of their Stokes radii and sedimentation constants, molecular weights of 210,000 and 110,000 were calculated for the major and minor species, respectively. Since the molecular weight of the subunit(s) is about 49,000 to 51,000,[82] the two forms are putative tetramers and dimers, respectively. A more detailed study of the oligomeric composition of the pure rat liver enzyme isolated by high performance gel permeation chromatography showed that the mixture consists of 75 to 80% tetramer and 20 to 25% dimer at 25°C.[83] When assayed with the synthetic pterin cofactor, $6MPH_4$, both species have identical specific activities; when assayed with BH_4,[83] the specific activity of the tetramer was five times that of the dimer. The ability to determine distinctive catalytic properties of the two species and their ready separation during gel permeation chromatography indicate that the dimer and tetramer are not in rapid equilibrium even under assay conditions.

Existence of the rat enzyme as a mixture of tetramers and dimers[83] was disputed[5] with the implication that native PAH consists of a single dimeric species M_r = 110,000. Most of the conflict on this point is concerned with the issue of whether *any* dimeric species can be detected. The finding that the enzyme exists as a mixture of dimers and tetramers has now been confirmed,[84,85] while some state it exists solely as tetramers[86,87] and others[88] detect only dimers. There is also an unconfirmed report that, whereas the enzyme exists solely as a M_r = 110,000 species, omission of dithiothreitol and an early filtration step, presumably to remove lipids, results in partial conversion of the M_r = 110,000 species to a M_r = 250,000 species.[89] These inconsistencies can be explained by the observation that prolonged frozen storage of purified enzyme increases the proportion of dimers in the mixture (Kaufman and Iwaki, unpublished results). Moreover, incubation of the enzyme with phenylalanine increases conversion of dimers to tetramers.[88] We propose, until it is proven otherwise, that rat liver PAH exists in solution predominantly, if not exclusively, as tetramers.

Whether rat liver PAH is composed of more than one type of subunit is another contentious issue. Electrophoresis of rat PAH on polyacrylamide gels, in the presence of sodium dodecyl sulfate (SDS), yields two electrophoretically distinguishable subunits with M_r values of 49,000 and 50,000.[82] Two closely spaced protein bands were also seen on gel electrophoresis in the absence of SDS[86] and in its presence.[90] On the other hand, only a single band was observed by some investigators when the hydroxylase was subjected to electrophoresis under denaturing conditions.[85,87] Again, there are explanations for these divergent findings; in one case, it is genetic. The Sprague-Dawley rat has one or the other or both forms of the PAH subunit, and the three phenotypes segregate in Mendelian fashion.[91] Accordingly, the polymorphic forms of rat enzyme are considered products of two allelic genes,[91] a hypothesis supported by the finding of threonine at residue 371 in one form and isoleucine in the other.[92]

In the second case the explanation is posttranscriptional modification of subunits. Phosphorylation converts one form of the two electrophoretically distinguishable bands to the other.[93] In the Sprague-Dawley rat used for these experiments, analysis of the primary structure indicated that hepatic PAH is otherwise composed of identical subunits.[94]

Rat liver phenylalanine hydroxylase contains one atom of iron per subunit.[95] The iron is essential for catalytic activity,[87,96] although its role has not been elucidated. The claim that the enzyme contains one atom of copper and a bound molecule of FAD[89] has not been confirmed.

Human Enzyme. The physical properties of human PAH are broadly similar to those of the rat liver enzyme, but there are significant differences. According to one review,[5] human and rat liver phenylalanine hydroxylase both have a native molecular weight of 110,000. If, as reported[97–99] (see also Ref. 134), the subunit size of the human hydroxylase is similar to the rat liver enzyme, a value of M_r = 110,000 for native human enzyme suggests that it is a dimer, but this conclusion is not in accord with most published data. With the sole exception of an early study[100] reporting a value of 108,000, the M_r values for the human enzyme are higher, for example, 275,000,[101] 150,000,[99] and 165,000.[97] Choo et al.[101] reported that the adult enzyme has a single subunit, M_r = 49,000 and 52,000, and the M_r of native fetal enzyme is 160,000.[99] Only a single type of subunit, M_r = 54,000, was detected for the human fetal enzyme in earlier work.[102] Together, these findings provoke two hypotheses:[97,99] first, adult human liver phenylalanine hydroxylase exists as a trimer composed of subunits of identical size; second, the structures of the human and rat liver enzymes are not identical. Evidence that rat and human PAH activities may not be regulated in the same way (see below) is compatible with these hypotheses.

Regulation of Phenylalanine Hydroxylase

The majority of studies on regulation have been done on rat liver PAH. Human PAH has some significant differences in its regulated properties, and these are stated in the appropriate section below.

Since PAH catalyzes the rate limiting step in the major pathway by which phenylalanine is catabolized to CO_2 and water, it is a likely site for regulation of phenylalanine homeostasis.[53] The enzyme can play this role because its catalytic activity is exquisitely sensitive to changes in concentrations of its substrate, phenylalanine. This sensitivity assures that exposure of tissues to high levels of phenylalanine will be kept to a minimum, while it also assures that the hydroxylase-catalyzed conversion of phenylalanine to tyrosine will not lead to depletion of phenylalanine to the point where normal protein synthesis is compromised.

This delicate balance is accomplished by a synergistic interaction between two types of regulating mechanisms; activation by phenylalanine and activation-deactivation by phosphorylation-dephosphorylation. Together, they accommodate short-term regulation of PAH activity. These mechanisms permit a more responsive coupling between hydroxylase activity and tissue levels of phenylalanine than could be achieved by an enzyme having simple Michaelis-Menten kinetics. The Michaelis-Menten relationship describes a rectangular hyperbolic response in the initial velocity to variation in substrate concentration; it shows that activity of the enzyme is geared to availability of substrate. While it may constitute an adequate regulatory mechanism at substrate concentrations at or below K_m values, it is a relatively insensitive coupling device at higher substrate concentrations.

Regulation by Substrate and Cofactor. The first evidence for short-term regulation of rat liver PAH was the twenty- to thirtyfold increase in the BH_4-dependent activity upon brief exposure to a phospholipid such as lysolecithin.[103,104] By contrast, activity of the enzyme in the presence of $DMPH_4$, a synthetic pterin cofactor, was only slightly increased by lysolecithin treatment.[103] The sigmoid relationship between initial velocity and phenylalanine concentration in the presence of BH_4 changed to hyperbolic with lysolecithin.[103,104] Diverse treatments of PAH such as limited proteolysis[104] and alkylation of a single sulfhydryl group[105] also markedly increased the BH_4-dependent hydroxylase activity. These findings indicated that PAH in the presence of BH_4 is predominantly in a low-activity form, expressing only 3 to 5 percent of its potential activity.

Although there is no evidence to indicate that any of the above modes of activation are of physiological significance, they delineate some of the characteristics of the activated hydroxylase. Activation by substrate is probably involved in acute physiological regulation of PAH. It was a process independently discovered by Nielson,[71] who used $6MPH_4$ to assay the enzyme, and by Kaufman,[75] who used BH_4, the natural cofactor. The activation process was later reported in detail by Tourian,[88] Ayling et al.,[106] Shiman et al.,[107] and others (see Ref. 108).

The results of these studies can be accommodated by a single model that depicts PAH in equilibrium between a low activity conformation, E, and an active conformation, E′.[108]

$$\text{Phe} \longrightarrow \underset{\text{E}}{\overset{\text{E}'}{\uparrow\downarrow}} \longleftarrow \text{BH}_4 \qquad (15\text{-}3)$$

According to this formulation, the E′ conformation of the PAH can be stabilized by the binding of phenylalanine to a regulatory site, whereas the E conformation can be stabilized by the binding of BH_4 in the absence of, or prior to, phenylalanine binding. In contrast to the natural coenzyme BH_4, synthetic analogues such as $DMPH_4$ are not effective in pushing the equilibrium in the direction of E; hence, more of the enzyme would exist as E′.

The model assumes that there is a second site distinct from the catalytic site that binds phenylalanine which, when occupied, leads to activation. Phenylalanine increases the binding of PAH to a hydrophobic matrix,[86] and it changes the fluorescence of the enzyme.[109] These observations support the model since they imply that phenylalanine changes the conformation of the enzyme. The notion that activation by phenylalanine might involve binding of phenylalanine to a second site with a regulatory role was first postulated by Tourian.[88] The amount of phenylalanine bound by rat liver PAH hydroxylase is 1.5 mol phenylalanine bound per mole PAH subunit[105]; this finding provides direct experimental support for the existence of a second phenylalanine binding site. It was reported recently that the regulatory or activator sites for phenylalanine are absent in the dimeric species of the rat enzyme; they are formed or become functional only when two dimers interact to form tetramers,[83] a process favored by preincubation of the enzyme with phenylalanine.[83,88]

Regulation by Phosphorylation/Dephosphorylation of Subunits. Activity of the hydroxylase is increased several-fold by phosphorylation, a reaction catalyzed by cAMP-dependent protein kinase.[110,111] Activation by phosphorylation is fully expressed when the enzyme is assayed in the presence of BH_4; it is not when in the presence of $DMPH_4$ or $6MPH_4$.[111] Activation is accompanied by the incorporation of about 0.70 mol inorganic phosphate per M_r = 50,000 subunit.[111] Because less than stoichiometric amounts of phosphate are incorporated into the pure hydroxylase in vitro, it seems likely that PAH isolated from rat liver is already partially phosphorylated; and indeed, five different preparations of the native hepatic enzyme isolated by the Kaufman and Fisher procedure[82] had an average phosphate content per mole of M_r = 50,000 subunit of 0.31 mol (range, 0.23 to 0.42).[111]

The amino acid sequence at the ^{32}P phosphorylation site of rat liver phenylalanine hydroxylase was reported by Wretborn et al.[112] as Ser-Arg-Lys-[^{32}P]SerP-Asx-Phe-Gly-Glx-Glx. The amount of this peptide was at least twice that calculated from the radioactivity of the sample, implying that it contained a substantial amount of endogenous phosphate.[112] The finding provides independent evidence for the conclusion that hepatic PAH in untreated rats is a mixture of phosphorylated and nonphosphorylated forms.

It also provides an explanation for the earlier observation of Barranger and coworkers[113] who found three "isozymes" of rat PAH [designated by the authors as *pi*, *kappa*, and *upsilon* (P, K, U)] when crude liver extracts were chromatographed on cellulose-calcium phosphate-gel columns. Chemical analyses of their major forms (the so-called kappa and upsilon PAH isozymes), showed that they contained different amounts of protein-bound phosphate, with the predominant form corresponding to the monophosphorylated tetramer (M_r = 200,000); the second most prevalent form corresponded to the diphosphorylated tetramer.[93] The catalytic properties of the two forms PAH were fully consistent with their states of phosphorylation; relative PAH activity (in the presence of BH_4) was higher for the diphosphorylated tetrameric form than for the monophosphorylated species.[93] These results indicate that the major, if not the sole, structural determinant for elution time of different forms of PAH, on the calcium phosphate column, is the amount of protein-bound phosphate in PAH. If we believe this variation in phosphate content is a posttranslational event, there is no good reason to believe that so-called PAH isozymes[113] are genetically determined. Indeed, the isozyme (genetic) hypothesis is not supported by the amino acid composition data; the different elution products have similar amino acid compositions.[87]

A phosphatase has been purified from rat liver extracts which catalyzes dephosphorylation of PAH.[114,115] Its properties include relative lack of sensitivity to protein phosphatase inhibitors 1 and 2, activity in the absence of added cations, and ability to catalyze the dephosphorylation of a variety of phosphorylated proteins, including glycogen synthase and phosphorylase *a*.[116] Accordingly, this phenylalanine hydroxylase phosphatase would be classified, in the system devised by Ingebritsen and Cohen,[117] as a type 2A phosphatase, a conclusion compatible with findings in a study that utilized an antibody to protein phosphatase 2A.[118,119]

Activation of rat liver hydroxylase by phosphorylation has physiological significance. Treatment of rats with glucagon, a hormone known to activate hepatic adenyl cyclase and thereby increase hepatic levels of cAMP, causes fourfold activation of rat hepatic PAH.[120] The effect is rapid, activation being detectable within 30 min, and transient with hydroxylase activity returning to basal levels within 2 h. The glucagon effect can be elicited by a repeat injection, implying that decay of the activated state is due to dephosphorylation of PAH and not due to proteolytic degradation of the hydroxylase. The effect of glucagon is detectable when the hydroxylase is assayed in the presence of BH_4 but not in the presence of synthetic cofactor analogs such as $DMPH_4$. When glucagon is administered intraperitoneally, the dose required to produce half-maximal effects is 270 μg/kg.[120] When it is administered intravenously, the half-maximal response is observed at 15 μg/kg.[116] Glucagon-mediated activation of the hydroxylase involves increased phosphorylation of the enzyme.[120] Activation of PAH by glucagon has also been demonstrated in rat hepatocytes in vitro.[121,122] The hormone increases PAH phosphorylation.[122,123]

Because glucagon and insulin have broadly opposing metabolic effects in vivo, it was expected that a relative lack of insulin, as in diabetes, might have the same effect on PAH as excess glucagon; i.e., it might lead to activation of the hydroxylase. Phenylalanine hydroxylation activity, measured as a flux rate of radiolabeled substrate in hepatocytes from rats that had been made diabetic with streptozotocin, is about twofold greater than in hepatocytes from control rats.[124] The addition of glucagon to hepatocytes from diabetic rats stimulated this elevated activity another 50 percent.[122]

These results were confirmed in studies of PAH activity in liver extracts from rats 3 days after the onset of diabetes. There was a twofold increase in BH_4-dependent PAH activity and a smaller (32 percent) increase in the $DMPH_4$-dependent activity.[125] Although the state of phosphorylation of the enzyme was not measured in these experiments, indirect evidence indicates that it is more highly phosphorylated in diabetic livers. The finding that diabetes increases not only the BH_4-dependent PAH activity but also the $DMPH_4$ (and $6MPH_4$)-dependent activities[116,125] suggests that the increased hepatic phenylalanine hydroxylase activity seen in the diabetic rat may be due not only to an increased degree of phosphorylation but perhaps also to an increased amount of hydroxylase protein.

Effect of Ligands on PAH. Phenylalanine and BH_4 have opposite effects on the rate of phosphorylation and activation of purified rat liver PAH. Physiological concentrations of the naturally occurring 6-*R* diastereoisomer of BH_4 (6 to 8 μ*M*) inhibit phosphorylation and activation by 80 percent, whereas 200 μ*M* L-phenylalanine stimulates both processes to a modest extent; phenylalanine can overcome completely the inhibition caused by BH_4.[108,126] Inhibition of phosphorylation is quite specific for the 6-*R* diastereoisomer of BH_4; relatively large concentrations of $6MPH_4$ and $DMPH_4$ do not inhibit.[108,126,127] The phosphorylated PAH requires less phenylalanine to be activated than the nonphosphorylated form;[127,128] 29 and 51 μ*M* phenylalanine were required to obtain half-maximal activation of the phosphorylated and nonphosphorylated forms, respectively. These findings are consistent with the notion that the enzyme exists as an equilibrium mixture of high (E′) and low (E) activity conformations (equation 15-3). Inhibition of phosphorylation in the presence of BH_4 and stimulation in the presence of phenylalanine implies that the active form of PAH (E′) is a better substrate for phosphorylation than is the low activity form (E).

It seems likely that the opposing effects of BH_4 and phenylalanine on both direct activation of the enzyme and kinase-mediated activation are a dominant feature of the physiological regulation of hepatic phenylalanine hydroxylase. In the case of the kinase reaction, the effect of BH_4 could be to limit the extent of phosphorylation, and thus activation, when the levels of hepatic phenylalanine are very low and high hydroxylase activity is not required. This would be true under basal conditions. Higher concentrations of phenylalanine would then be able to overcome the inhibitory effect of BH_4, allowing an increase in the extent of phosphorylation and activation of the hydroxylase when the organism needs higher hydroxylase activity to catabolize excess phenylalanine. This inhibitory effect of BH_4 would then serve to protect against depletion of the organism's pool of phenylalanine below essential levels.

Activation of PAH by phosphorylation and phenylalanine are probably synergistic modes of regulation. Phosphorylation (and activation) by cAMP-dependent protein kinase is stimulated by phenylalanine,[126,127] whereas phosphorylation sensitizes the enzyme to activation by phenylalanine.[122,127,129] A useful adaptive consequence of these interlocking control mechanisms is enhanced responsiveness of hydroxylase activity to altered levels of phenylalanine.

This regulatory process in the rat would be triggered by the ingestion of a protein-containing meal.[116] Pancreatic glucagon secretion is stimulated by protein feeding.[130] Blood glucagon increases in association with the postprandial rise in blood amino acids, and amino acids are potent stimulators of pancreatic glucagon release.[131,132] Since glucagon activates hepatic adenylate cyclase with an increase in hepatic cAMP levels, activation of cAMP-dependent protein kinase and phosphorylation-mediated activation of PAH will follow protein feeding. A consequence of this regulatory response to a postprandial rise of blood phenylalanine is an accelerated catabolism of the amino acid to maintain homeostasis.

Since phenylalanine is also a glycogenic amino acid,[133,35] activation of phenylalanine hydroxylase may also be geared to the needs of the organism for increased gluconeogenesis.[116] This limb of the regulatory process would be coupled to the blood glucose level. A fall in blood glucose would increase glucagon release and suppress insulin release, resulting in phosphorylation-mediated activation of PAH with a resultant gluconeogenic effect.

Is Human Liver PAH Regulated by Phosphorylation Dephosphorylation? PAH from fresh human liver is apparently not activated by the action of cAMP-dependent protein kinase,[95] in contrast to the case of rat liver enzyme. In the presence of [^{32}P]ATP and the kinase, there was no incorporation of ^{32}P into the human enzyme. On the other hand, Smith et al.[134] found incorporation of 0.25 mol of $^{32}P_i$ into human phenylalanine hydroxylase from [^{32}P]ATP in the presence of bovine heart kinase. If hydroxylase was first treated with alkaline phosphatase, the amount of $^{32}P_i$ incorporated into the enzyme increased to 0.67 mol per mole of PAH subunit. This finding suggests that the preparation of the human liver enzyme was more highly phosphorylated than that of the rat liver enzyme. They did confirm[134] an earlier observation[95] that BH_4-dependent hydroxylase activity is not stimulated by phosphorylation. The failure to detect phosphorylation-mediated activation of the human enzyme[134] is best explained[116] by assuming the preparation of human enzyme was already highly phosphorylated. Inability to activate human liver PAH is probably not an artifact due to a change in the enzyme's properties on purification. Crude human liver PAH is not activated by exposure to cAMP-dependent protein kinase,[116] and the same is true of crude guinea pig and monkey liver PAH.[116] By comparison rat liver enzyme appears to be unusually responsive to activation by phosphorylation.

Long-Term Regulation of Hepatic Phenylalanine Hydroxylase. The possibility that phenylalanine hydroxylase activity in rat liver is under hormonal control, in particular, under control of steroid hormones, has been intensively investigated during the last 25 years. Some of the discrepant findings in this area, may be attributable to the use of assays for PAH activity in which all of the ancillary components of the hydroxylating system were not added in excess. Other explanations are given in due course.

Stimulatory effects of glucocorticoids on PAH in vivo, on the order of 50 to 25 percent increased activity, were reported by some[135–137] and not by other investigators.[57,138] There was a twofold increase of the naturally low enzyme activity when the hormone was administered to rat sucklings.[57,138] At the other extreme, Koller et al.[139] reported that cortisol administration to adult rats *decreased* hepatic PAH activity to 13 percent of control values, a unique result that most likely was caused by the use of an inadequate assay for the hydroxylase. The way the results are expressed affects interpretation;[140] the apparent response is greater per whole-liver weight than per gram wet liver or per milligram protein. Some of the discrepancies between reports can be thus explained. There is general agreement that the modest steroid-induced increase in hepatic PAH activity involves new protein synthesis since the response is blocked by inhibitors of protein synthesis.[138,140]

Kidney PAH, even in 8-day-old rats, is unaffected by cortisol treatment,[57] another indication that kidney and liver enzymes are in different states in the rat. Adrenalectomy modestly decreases PAH activity, and glucocorticoids restore it to the level found in steroid-treated controls.[137,140] The *in situ* PAH activity in hepatocytes isolated from adrenalectomized rats with and without glucocorticoid supplementation responds in a similar fashion. (Adrenalectomy decreases activity and dexamethasone increases the depressed levels.[141]) In contrast to these effects on *in situ* hydroxylase activity, neither adrenalectomy nor steroid treatment affects enzyme activity in extracts prepared from hepatocytes, implying that steroid treatment influences phenylalanine metabolism by "altering factors other than the hydroxylase protein concentration."[141] Although this possibility exists, PAH activity in these extracts[141] was measured following preincubation with phenyloalanine. This procedure activates the enzyme thereby making it difficult to detect a 26 to 60 percent change in its activity.

Studies of PAH regulation in cultured hepatoma cells (H_4-II-EC3 cells) compliment those in the whole animal. Glucocorticoids, such as hydrocortisone and dexamethasone, stimulate PAH activity to levels seen in adult rat liver.[142] Cell density, serum, N^6-$O^{2'}$-dibutyryl cAMP, and insulin each increase enzyme activity.[142–147]

Control of PAH Synthesis in Tissue Culture by Serum and Insulin. Although some of the properties and effects of the serum factor(s) which stimulate PAH in cultured hepatocytes have been determined, the active substance(s) have not yet been identified. The serum factor is nondialyzable, and it can be precipitated with 50 percent saturated ammonium sulfate,[145,147] implying it is a protein. It is moderately heat stable and not destroyed by heating at 65° for 15 min[145] but 90 percent inactivated when heated at 75°C for 20 min.[147] Serum-mediated stimulation of PAH in cultured hepatocytes is additive to the effects of insulin[145,147] and hydrocortisone,[145] indicating that serum stimulation cannot be explained solely by the presence of these two hormones.

The stimulatory effects of serum and dexamethasone, but not that of insulin, were observed in R-Y121B cells, a subline of H_4-II-E hepatoma cells adapted to grow in serum-free medium.[148] In fact, insulin partially inhibited induction of PAH by serum or dexamethasone during a 24-h incubation.[148] This is concordant with the effect of diabetes in vivo, which increases the activity of hepatic PAH, an effect partially reversed by treatment with insulin.

Studies of PAH in cultured cells have further elucidated the phenomenon of its multiple forms. Adult rat liver contains different forms of PAH, not isozymes,[113] but different states of phosphorylated PAH.[120,149] The forms differ in their isoelectric points.[150] The form corresponding to half-phosphorylated tetramers (containing 0.05 mol P_i/mole of hydroxylase subunit), designated form III,[93,149] has an isoelectric point of 5.20; that of the quarter-phosphorylated tetramers (0.25 mol P_i per mole of subunit; form II) is 5.30, and for the nonphosphorylated species (form I) it is 5.60. Form II is the most and form I the least prevalent. In contrast to normal rat liver cells, H_4 hepatoma cells contain a single form of the hydroxylase,[151,152] which is similar in its behavior to the half-phosphorylated tetramers. By immunochemical criteria, the single species of PAH in hepatoma cells is distinct from the three forms present in normal adult rat liver and the single form in rat kidney.[150,151] Treatment of hepatoma cells with hydrocortisone selectively "induces" the expression of the two forms that are present in adult liver but missing in hepatoma cells;[152] i.e., the pattern after hydrocortisone treatment of cultured cells was similar to that in rat liver. The old notion that hydrocortisone induced the expression of different hydroxylase isozymes is not relevant since the so-called isozymes[113] differ only in their states of phosphorylation.[93] The new findings indicate that the hydrocortisone effect is a complex one involving some kind of posttranslational modification of the enzyme, in addition to its effect on the amount of the enzyme in the cell.

Fetal Development of Phenylalanine Hydroxylase. Reports that fetal and newborn mammals had impoverished hydroxylase activity[153,154] which did not develop to mature levels until after birth were later shown to be wrong.[155,156] Human hepatic hydroxylase activity is detectable as early as the eighth week of fetal life, it reaches adult levels by the midtrimester, and it manifests deficient activity in the PKU phenotype expressed in fetal liver[156–159]; see also Ref. 577a. The naturally occurring pterin cofactor, presumably BH_4, and "DHPR activity" are present in late first-trimester human fetal liver.[158] With regard to DHPR, the actual observation showed a small decrease in PAH activity when NADH was omitted from the hydroxylase assay. Since reduced pyridine nucleotides can reduce quinonoid dihydropterins nonenzymatically,[160] DHPR was perhaps not present, as reported[158] in the fetal extracts. Catalytic properties of the human fetal liver PAH appear to be the same as those of the adult enzyme.[156,159]

Dihydropteridine Reductase

Dihydropteridine reductase is an essential enzyme in the hydroxylating systems for phenylalanine, tyrosine, and tryptophan (see "Homologies in Aromatic Amino Acid Hydroxylases and Genes," below). In contrast to PAH, DHPR is widely distributed in animal tissues.[70,161] Whereas its occurrence in brain and adrenal medulla[70] is not surprising in view of its role in the tyrosine hydroxylation system in these tissues, and in the trytophan hydroxylation system in brain, why DHPR should be found in tissues such as heart and lung which have little or no aromatic amino acid hydroxylating activity is obscure. Its wide distribution, together with BH_4, hints at undiscovered roles for both BH_4 and DHPR. In addition to its role in regenerating BH_4, it has been proposed that DHPR plays an ancillary role (together with dihydrofolate reductase) in brain to keep folate in the tetrahydro form.[162] Prompted by the discovery of a variant form of hyperphenylalaninemia caused by the lack of DHPR (see section on disease below), activity of this enzyme has also been detected in cultured fibroblasts,[163] aminocytes,[164] lymphocytes,[165] leukocytes,[166] erythrocytes,[167] and platelets.[168,169]

The enzyme has been purified to homogeneity from sheep liver[70,170] and extensively purified from rat and bovine liver, bovine adrenal medulla and brain, and sheep brain.[70,170] The human enzyme has been purified from liver[171] and platelets.[168,169] The molecular weights of the native enzyme and its subunits are 45,000 to 52,000 and 22,400 to 26,000, respectively. The human liver enzyme[171] has a molecular weight of 100,000, a value that suggests it is a tetramer. This value must be confirmed since the molecular weight of the enzyme and its subunits from human platelets are 45,000 and 25,000 to 28,000, respectively,[169] and the corresponding values of 52,000 and 27,000 for the human placental enzyme[172] are within the range found for the enzyme from all other mammalian species and tissues. In animals, where the enzyme has been characterized from several different tissues, there is no evidence for tissue-specific isozymes, and molecular weights are similar in bovine liver adrenals and brain. On the other hand, multiple forms of the enzyme have been detected in bovine liver,[173] bovine kidney,[174] and human platelets.[169] The apparent multiple forms of the enzyme in bovine kidney and liver probably represent free enzyme and enzyme complexed with NADH rather than two different isozymes. The significance of multiple forms of DHPR in human platelets is less clear since one form has a K_m for NADH that is two times higher and a V_{max} that is one-half as great as the values for the other.[169] The significance of finding three bands of DHPR activity on polyacrylamide gel electrophoresis in a single human liver extract is also not clear.[172]

Table 15-2 summarizes the K_m values for NADH and pterin cofactors for human DHPR from various tissues. The K_m for BH_4 is markedly lower than the K_m value for the commonly employed synthetic analogue $DMPH_4$. Although the comparisons between K_m values of BH_4 and $DMPH_4$ are not ideal, because they involve determinations from different laboratories, it is reassuring that Craine et al.[70] found that sheep liver DHPR also has a much lower K_m for BH_4 (1.0 μM) than for $DMPH_4$ (15.2 μM), both determined in the presence of NADH. The V_{max} with $DMPH_4$ is three times greater than it is with BH_4.[70]

Biosynthesis of BH_4

The cofactor (enzyme) function of BH_4 in the hydroxylation reaction with aromatic amino acids is related to its ability to reduce molecular oxygen; BH_4 provides electrons and in turn is oxidized to qBH_2.[67,175] The consumption of BH_4 is stoichiometric with the formation of product from substrate. Whereas the DHPR-catalyzed reaction regenerates BH_4 from qBH_2 moment by moment, so that cofactor functions catalytically, the steady state of BH_4 is ultimately dependent on biosynthesis from precursors. This complex area of biochemistry is shared by a vast array of life forms;[18] we confine the discussion here to details relevant to humans. The pathway of BH_4 biosynthesis, which begins with guanosine triphosphate (GTP), and as it is presently understood,[18,176–178] is shown in Fig. 15-5.

GTP Cyclohydrolase. GTP is the major precursor of atoms in the pterin nucleus.[179] The initial step in the pathway is conversion of GTP to D-*erythro*-7,8-dihydroneopterin triphosphate, a reaction catalyzed by the enzyme GTP-cyclohydrolase.[180] There are two GTP-cyclohydrolases in living systems;[176] GTP-cyclohydroylase I (EC 3.5.4.16) is the enzyme of interest here. GTP-cyclohydroase II is Mg^{2+}-dependent, and its product is a pyrimidine, possibly an intermediate in the biosynthesis of riboflavin in microorganisms. GTP-cyclohydrolase I has been purified by affinity chromatography 300-fold from human liver.[181] The enzyme is heat-stable at physiological temperatures and has a K_m value of 31 μmol/liter for GTP. This nucleotide is the only one accepted by the enzyme. Deficiency of GTP-cyclohydrolase I impairs BH_4 synthesis and causes a form of hyperphenylalaninemia (see section on diseases below).

Table 15-2 K_m **Values (**μM**) for Human Dihydropteridine Reductase**

Tissue	*NADH*	BH_4	$DMPH_4$	*Source (reference no.)*
Liver	8.0	1.1	—	70
Liver*	—	—	45	165
Liver	—	—	3.3	168
Fibroblasts*	—	—	38	165
Platelets	12	—	16	168
Platelets				
A	20	—	46	169
B	9.0	—	49	169

*Determined at 37°C. All other values were determined at 25°C.

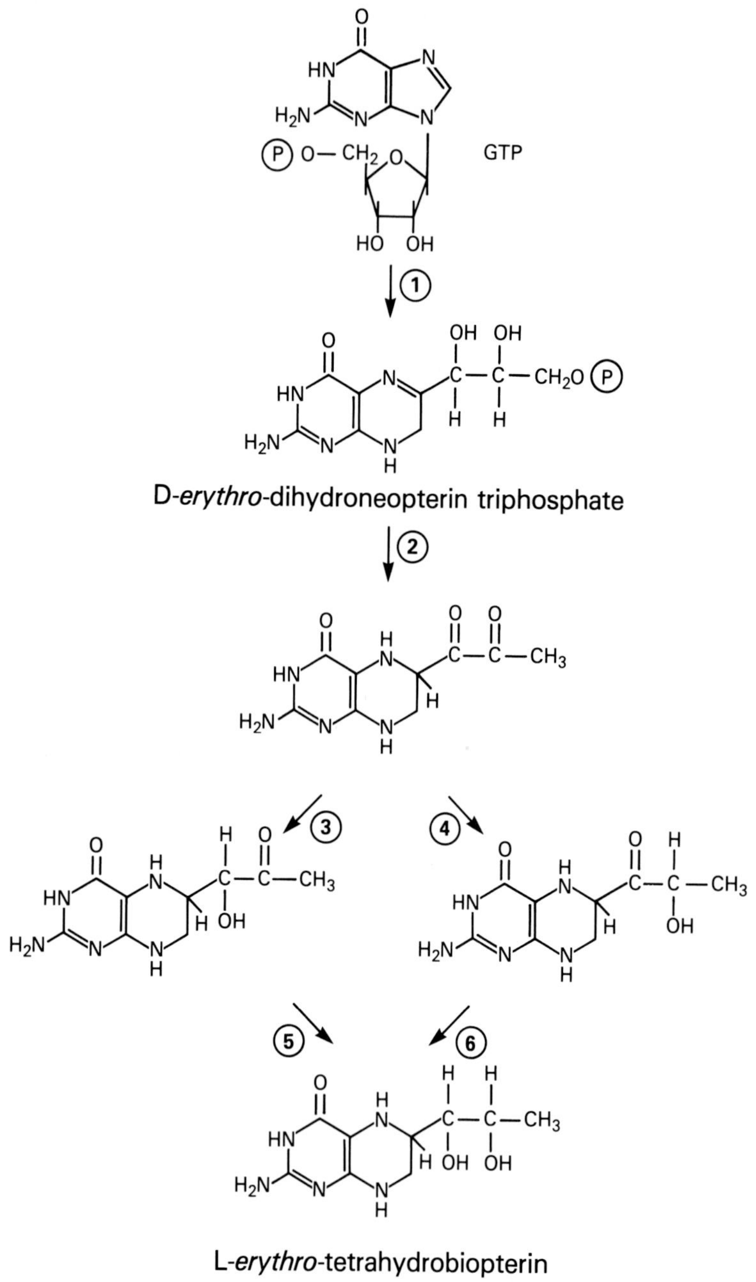

GTP

D-*erythro*-dihydroneopterin triphosphate

L-*erythro*-tetrahydrobiopterin

Fig. 15-5 The pathway for synthesis of BH_4 (L-*erythro*-tetrahydrobiopterin) from guanosine triphosphate (GTP). Reaction 1 is catalyzed by GTP cyclohydrolase I; reaction 2 by 6-pyruvoyltetrahydropterin synthase (6-PTS), or phosphate eliminating enzyme (PPE), old name; reactions 3 and 5 are catalyzed by sepiapterin reductase; reaction 4, forming the 6-lactoyltetrahydropterin derivative, is catalyzed by the 2′-keto reductase.

The Subsequent Pathway. Until recently, it was believed that BH_4 synthesis proceeded through a series of dihydropterin intermediates, meaning that all of the pterin intermediates beyond dihydroneopterin triphosphate were presumed to be at the dihydro level of oxidation. This idea faded in the face of strong evidence[182–184] against the involvement of the dihydropterins, sepiapterin or dihydrobiopterin, as significant intermediates in the *de novo* synthesis of BH_4 from GTP in extracts of bovine adrenal medulla. Subsequent studies with a variety of tissue preparations came to the same conclusion.[185,186] Even though sepiapterin is not an important intermediate, there is evidence that sepiapterin reductase is nonetheless involved in the *de novo* biosynthesis of BH_4.[184]

The part of the BH_4 biosynthesis pathway where there is still some uncertainty involves the steps from the intermediate 6-pyruvoyltetrahydropterin (a diketopterin) which is the product of reaction (2) catalyzed by the enzyme 6-pyruvoyltetrahydropterin synthase (Fig.15-5). The scheme depicts two routes to BH_4: one involving the formation of the 1′-hydroxy-2′-keto tetrahydropterin (sequence 2→3→5), the other involving the formation of 1′-keto-2′-hydroxytetrahydropterin (6-lactoyltetrahydropterin) (sequence 2→4→6). Existence of the latter route, involving the formation of 6-lactoyltetrahydropterin as an intermediate, was surmised when it was shown that another enzyme, distinct from sepiapterin reductase, is present in brain and that it catalyzes the NADPH-dependent reduction of 6-pyruvoyltetrahydropterin to 6-lactoyltetrahydropterin.[187] Some investigators have concluded that the sequence going through the latter intermediate is on a salvage pathway,[188] whereas others have presented evidence that, in brain tissue at least, this pterin is the major intermediate in the conversion of the diketotetrahydropterin (6-pyruvoyltetrahydropterin) to BH_4.[178] Curtius et al.[177] have also presented evidence in favor of the alternate route involving 6-lactoyltetrahydropterin as an intermediate. The most recent evidence,[188a] indicates that the limb catalyzed by sepiapterin reductase is on the principal biosynthetic pathway to BH_4.

6-Pyruvoyltetrahydropterin Synthase (6-PTS) (Formerly, Phosphate Eliminating Enzyme). The role of the phosphate eliminating enzyme, now called 6-pyruvoyltetrahydropterin synthase (6-PTS), in the synthesis of BH_4 from dihydroneopterin triphosphate has been studied. It is the rate limiting step in the pathway. The enzyme is heat-stable with an apparent molecular weight of 63,000.[189,190] Purified human liver 6-PTS,[191,192] (molecular weight ≈ 83,000), is a homotetramer with four identical subunits, a feature which has significance for gene dosage in heterozygous phenotypes (see "6-Pyruvoyltetrahydropterin Deficiency," below). The presence of carbohydrates in the native enzyme probably explains some of the observed discrepancies in molecular weight. In the presence of Mg^{2+}, 7,8-dihydroneopterin triphosphate is the substrate (K_m, 10 μmol/liter); the product of the reaction is the presumed intermediate 6-pyruvoyltetrahydropterin, which is converted to BH_4 in the presence of NADPH and sepiapterin reductase.[191,192] Accordingly, this pathway obviates the direct involvement of dihydrofolate reductase in the synthesis of BH_4 from dihydroneopterin triphosphate.[193] Deficiency of the 6-PTS enzyme causes a form of hyperphenylalaninemia; the enzyme can be assayed in erythrocytes, and diagnosis of deficiency states does not require more invasive procedures.

BH_4 Biosynthesis and the Immune Response. There is an interesting correlation between the cellular response to infections and pterin metabolism.[194–197] Human cellular immune responses are associated with increased neopterin excretion in vivo. T lymphocytes, but not macrophages, produce BH_4,[194–196] presumably because only the former cells do not have an intact pathway for biosynthesis of BH_4. Activation of the immune response in vitro, with human γ-interferon and mitogens, for example,[194–196] increases the GTP pool and GTP cyclohydrolase I activity in T lymphocytes and macrophages; it increases the intracellular pool of dihydroneopterin triphosphate and leads to extracellular excretion of neopterin derivatives. The physiological role of this response is unknown; it is manifest in urine pterin excretion patterns in patients with acquired immune deficiency syndrome (AIDS).[197,197a] They resemble, incidentally, the pterin pattern in urine of newborn infants (see below and Fig. 15-15).

GENES ENCODING THE PHENYLALANINE HYDROXYLATION REACTION COMPONENTS

In this section we give information about two of the genes encoding polypeptide components of the phenylalanine hydroxylation reaction: phenylalanine hydroxylase and dihydropteridine reductase. At the time of writing, the genes for other components, such as those involved in regulation of PAH activity and in BH_4 synthesis, had not been cloned, mapped to chromosomes, or characterized. Nor, for example, is there information about the mechanism controlling tissue-specific expression of the PAH gene.

The PAH Gene

Molecular Cloning and Primary Structure of the Human PAH Gene. The initial success in cloning a rat liver PAH cDNA was reported by Robson et al.[61] Authenticity of the rat phenylalanine hydroxylase cDNA clones was established by comparing the amino acid sequence deduced from the nucleotide sequences of the clones with the amino acid sequence obtained from the purified enzyme.[198] The rat PAH cDNA clone was then utilized as a hybridization probe to screen a human liver cDNA library. A positive clone, designated phPAH247, contained 2448 bp of human DNA and an open reading frame starting with the initiation codon ATG at position 223 and ending with the termination codon TAA at position 1579; it encoded a protein of 451 amino acid residues.[199] The deduced amino acid sequence constitutes a protein of 51,672 daltons and an amino acid composition very similar to that reported for the human enzyme.[98,107,200] Comparison of human and rat cDNA sequences showed there is extensive sequence similarity between the corresponding PAH enzymes.[198,199,201] Within the carboxyl half of the encoded protein, similarity is 89 percent at the nucleotide level and 96 percent at the amino acid level; similarity is less at the amino terminal end. Full-length PAH cDNA clones have been isolated from rat[201] and mouse liver (S.L.C. Woo, unpublished results); the overall amino acid sequence similarity between the human enzyme and the two rodent enzymes is 92 percent. The full-length rat cDNA probe[201] was used to study the two mRNA species in rat liver derived from alternate polyadenylation signals. The PAH enzyme has a high degree of homology with rat tyrosine hydroxylase at the carboxyterminal end[201] and with rabbit tryptophan hydroxylase (see Ref. 216 and section below on homologies).

Human PAH Is a Homopolymer Encoded by a Single Genetic Locus. In an earlier section, we described the evidence that rat and human PAH enzymes have different multimeric structures. The rat enzyme is apparently a tetramer, the human enzyme is probably a trimer,[95,97] but the subunit size is similar in the two species.[95–97] The finding of two forms of PAH subunit in the rat[91,92,201] could be explained by alleles at a single genetic locus or by two independent genetic loci for PAH in mammals. The first hypothesis is favored,[92,201] but a more direct analysis of the PAH gene has resolved the issue: one locus is sufficient for PAH activity as shown by the following experiments.

The full-length human PAH cDNA was engineered behind the human metallothionein gene promoter and the recombinant was introduced into cultured NIH 3T3 cells, which normally do not express PAH activity.[202,202a] The DNA-transformed mouse fibroblasts expressed human PAH mRNA of the proper size as analyzed by Northern blot hybridization and immunoreactive protein of the proper molecular weight as determined by Western blot analysis. PAH activity was detected in BH_4-supplemented extracts of the transformed NIH 3T3 cells and it was sufficient to offset tyrosine auxotrophy in these cells. Accordingly, a single human cDNA is sufficient to confer functional enzymatic activity in a mammalian cell not normally engaged in the expression of PAH gene.

The full-length human PAH cDNA was also introduced into a bacterial expression vector and transduced into *Escherichia coli*.[203] The transformed bacteria expressed immunoreactive PAH and pterin-dependent conversion of phenylalanine to tyrosine. The optimal reaction conditions, kinetic constants, and sensitivity to substrate inhibition of the recombinant PAH were identical with those of the native enzyme from human liver.

These findings demonstrate unequivocally that the assembled functioning human enzyme is homopolymeric and that human PAH is encoded by a single gene. Corresponding studies with a rat PAH cDNA (see ref. 432) lead to similar conclusions about the rat enzyme.

The PKU Locus in Humans Is on Chromosome 12q22-q24.1. The PKU locus in humans was first studied, with inconclusive results,[204–206] by analysis of linkage with other polymorphic human protein markers in PKU families. The locus was originally assigned to chromosome 1 from evidence of moderate linkage with the phosphoglucomutase locus PGM-1[204] and the amylase loci AMY-1 and AMY-2.[205] Improved methods for classification of heterozygotes for purposes of linkage analysis in PKU families refuted this assignment.[206]

Chromosomal assignments of human genetic loci can be made when cloned genes are used as probes and molecular hybridization of probe to genomic DNA is measured in human/rodent cell hybrids that contain different assortments of human chromosomes. When the phPAH247 clone was used to analyze a clonal panel of human/mouse hybrid cells, segregation of the PAH gene was concordant with human chromosome 12.[207] This assignment was corroborated by analyzing an independent human/hamster hybrid cell panel. The chromosomal locus of the human PAH gene was further refined to band region q22-q24.1 by *in situ* hybridization using the ph PAH247 probe and metaphase chromosome preparations from a human lymphoblastoid cell line of normal karytoype.[208] Since PKU is the result of mutational events in the human PAH gene (see below), the PKU locus in man is identical to that of the PAH locus. The structures of the PAH gene and its exons, introns, and restriction sites for haplotype construction are given in the section on the PKU gene (see below).

Comparison of chromosomal linkage groups in humans and mice is a topic of current interest. Awareness of the linkage group containing PAH on human chromosome 12[208a] was helpful in mapping the mouse gene (Pah) to mouse chromosome 10 region C2-D1.[208b]

The DHPR Gene

Cloning and Expression of Human cDNA for DHPR. A monospecific antibody raised to purified DHPR was used to screen a human liver cDNA library constructed in the expression vector γgt-11 and identify a cDNA clone capable of hybrid-selecting the proper mRNA from human liver.[209] Additional clones were obtained by rescreening the library with the positive clone. Two independent isolates containing long DNA inserts were selected for sequence analysis. These two clones, designated hDHPR-1 and hDHPR-13, have an identical open reading frame of 732 bp and encode a protein of 244 amino acid residues.[209] The predicted molecular weight (25,774 daltons) is similar to the observed values for human liver[171,210] and platelet DHPR.[169] The authenticity of the human DHPR cDNA clone was further verified by obtaining a partial sequence of purified sheep DHPR to compare with the sequence predicted from the human cDNA clone.[209] Only 8 of 112 overlapping residues at the carboxyl terminus of the enzyme from the two species were different and even then most were highly conservative substitutions. Insertion of the full-length cDNA clone into a COS cell expression vector lead to expression of authentic DHPR activity in extracts of cells transformed with the recombinant.[209] These findings are in complete agreement with a hDHPR cDNA clone isolated independently by Dahl et al.[211] Characterization of rat liver cDNA clones with a reading frame of 720 bp encoding 240 amino acids revealed that rat and human DHPR proteins are very similar, in fact differing in only 10 amino acids, all conservative substitutions.[211a]

The predicted amino acid sequence of human DHPR has no apparent sequence similarity with any other protein of known sequence. This result was somewhat surprising since two other enzymes, dihydrofolate reductase and methylene tetrahydrofolate reductase, have analogous activities. All three enzymes act on substituted pterin substrates and utilize a pyridine nucleotide cofactor.[70,170,212] Furthermore, while the folate enzymes can both catalyze the reduction of qBH_2 to BH_4,[213] DHFR acts primarily to maintain folate in the tetrahydro form.[162] The only similarities in the corresponding sequences of DHPR and DHFR are in regions known to contain the binding sites for methotrexate and the pyridine nucleotide cofactors. These results suggest that the analogous activities of DHFR and DHPR represent vestigial homologies at loci that have diverged in evolution to the point that sequence similarity can no longer be demonstrated by statistical means.

The DHPR Locus in Humans Is on Chromosome 4p15.1-p16.1. The chromosomal locus encoding DHPR was assigned to human chromosome 4 in human/mouse somatic cell hybrid lines.[172] The assignment was confirmed by *in situ* hybridization with cDNA clones.[214,215] The human DHPR gene was then localized to band region p15.1-p16.1 on chromosome 4 in one study[214] and to band p15.3 in another.[215] Linkage analysis places the DHPR locus near D4S10, an anonymous DNA marker tightly linked to the Huntington locus;[214] the linkage of DHPR to D4S10 is not tight, excluding DHPR as a candidate gene in Huntington disease.

Homologies in Aromatic Amino Acid Hydroxylases and Genes

The BH_4-requiring aromatic amino acid hydroxylases catalyze mixed function oxidation reactions that consume BH_4, molecular oxygen, and the corresponding aromatic amino acid (Fig. 15-6). They have corresponding EC numbers: PAH, EC 1.14.16.1; tyrosine hydroxylase (TYH), EC 1.14.16.2; and tryptophan hydroxylase (TPH), EC 1.14.16.4. Each enzyme is rate limiting in its pathway. Antibody raised to PAH cross reacts with TYH and TPH (cited in Ref. 216). Cloned and sequenced cDNAs have been obtained for PAH, TYH,[217] and TPH.[216] There are striking homologies between the genes and the corresponding proteins.[94,201,216,218] The genes probably evolved by duplication and divergence, beginning about 750 million years ago, from original sequence encoding TYH, TPH, and PAH, then evolving from each other after 600 million years, rat and human PAH diverging about 75 million years ago.[216] On the other hand, there are important differences in the hydroxylases. Despite alternative mRNA splicing, there is only one hepatic PAH species to our knowledge (see

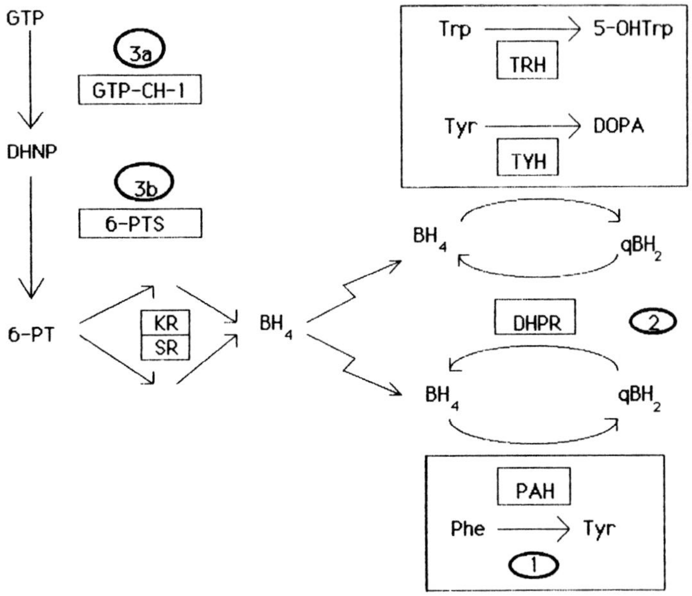

Fig. 15-6 Interrelations between PAH, DHPR, and the BH_4 biosynthesis pathway serving aromatic amino acid hydroxylation reactions. Mutations at the relevant chromosomal loci impair the hydroxylation reaction(s) with effects on (1), PAH activity only; (2) DHPR activity, impairing all three hydroxylations; (3a) GTP-CH-1 activity; and (3b) 6-PTS activity both impairing function of the three hydroxylases. Abbreviations: GTP = guanosine triphosphate; GTP-CH-1 = GTP-cyclohydrolase 1; DHNP = dihydroneopterin triphosphate; 6-PTS = 6-pyruvoyltetrahydropterin synthase; 6-PT = 6-pyruvoyltetrahydropterin; KR = 2′-ketotetrahydropterin reductase; SR = sepiapterin reductase; BH_4 = tetrahydrobiopterin; qBH_2 = quinonoid dihydrobiopterin; PAH = phenylalanine hydroxylase; DHPR = dihydropterin reductase; TYH = tyrosine hydroxylase; TRH = tryptophan hydroxylase.

GTP → (3a) GTP-CH-1 → DHNP → (3b) 6-PTS → 6-PT → KR / SR → BH_4

Trp → 5-OHTrp (TRH); Tyr → DOPA (TYH); BH_4 ⇄ qBH_2; DHPR (2); BH_4 ⇄ qBH_2; Phe → Tyr (PAH) (1)

Ref. 201), whereas with TYH, for example, there are at least three different mRNAs with specific phenotypic expression in different parts of the human brain.[218a]

Two domains are apparent in each of the aromatic amino acid hydroxylases;[201,216,219] the one at the carboxy-terminal end, beginning at or near amino acid 100 is more highly conserved than the other at the amino-terminal end of the polypeptides. The former apparently contains the determinants for hydroxylation activity including BH_4 interaction with the polypeptide; the latter contains the determinants for phosphorylation, regulation and substrate specificity.[220] These findings bear on our understanding of pathogenesis in the variant forms of hyperphenylalaninemia where various modes of impaired BH_4 homeostasis impinge on tyrosine and tryptophan hydroxylations and contribute to brain dysfunction.

MENDELIAN DISORDERS OF PHENYLALANINE HOMEOSTASIS

This section has two orientations. First, *hyper*phenylalaninemia is the metabolic phenotype of concern; no inherited form of isolated persistent hypophenylalaninemia is known.* Second, all that is hyperphenylalaninemia is not PKU; there are variants of PAH deficiency and forms arising from disorders of DHPR integrity and BH_4 biosynthesis (Fig. 15-6).

Disorders of PAH Integrity (PKU and Non-PKU Hyperphenylalaninemia)

Two forms of hyperphenylalaninemia are discussed here. One is *phenylketonuria*, the name given by Penrose and Quastel[222] to the disease discovered by Fölling.[23] The other is *non-PKU hyperphenylalaninemia*, a variant in which the degree of phenylalanine dyshomeostasis is less than is the case in PKU, and excessive formation of phenylpyruvic acid is either minimal or absent. Both forms are associated with a primary deficiency of PAH activity, PKU having the more severe deficiency.

*When and if the latter phenotype is reported, we predict it will reflect a disorder in a key phenylalanine transport system, perhaps as yet uncharacterized, in epithelial cells of intestine or kidney or both. Hartnup disorder (see Chap. 101) is a Mendelian impairment of neutral amino acid transport (involving phenylalanine) in intestine and/or kidney. The plasma phenylalanine concentration is not significantly lowered in Hartnup probands[221] presumably because auxillary transport systems sustain homeostasis, except under specific adverse conditions.

Mutation in the PAH Gene. PKU mutations map to the PAH gene. The normal gene spans about 90 kb of genomic DNA and contains 13 exons with introns ranging in size from 1 to 23 kb[223] (Fig. 15-7). Exons at the 3′ end of the gene are compactly clustered; those at the 5′ end are separated by large introns.[223] The transcribed mature mRNA is about 2.4 kb. Several polymorphic restriction sites have been mapped within the locus,[219,223–225] and there are two human PAH cDNA probes, phPAH247[199] and hPH7.[226]

IS CLASSIC PKU A DELETION OF THE ENTIRE PAH GENE? The first attempt to answer this question[224] used genomic DNA from two PKU probands and two normal individuals. Identical hybridization signals were obtained with the phPAH 247 cDNA probe on DNA preparations from the four subjects, indicating that the PAH gene is present and its overall organization is unchanged in these probands. Comparison of densitometer tracings of the gel lanes containing normal and PKU DNA showed further that the hybridization signals generated by the mutant samples were not manifestations of compound heterozygotes with deletions in nonoverlapping regions of the PAH gene in the two alleles present in each proband. Accordingly, classic PKU in these patients was not caused by deletion of the entire PAH gene.[224] Several hundred PKU chromosomes have now been analyzed; deletion mutations account for only a tiny fraction of the total PKU alleles analyzed in Caucasians (S. L. C. Woo, unpublished data). The Yemenite-Jewish[227] and Scottish[227a] PKU deletion mutations are exceptions. The PAH genes of 13 PKU probands in the Yemenite-Jewish enclave[227] have been analyzed. All 26 PKU alleles contain a partial deletion spanning exon 3 in the PAH gene. This deletion accounts for all PKU homozygotes (and heterozygotes) in the Yemenite population. A single mutational event in an in-

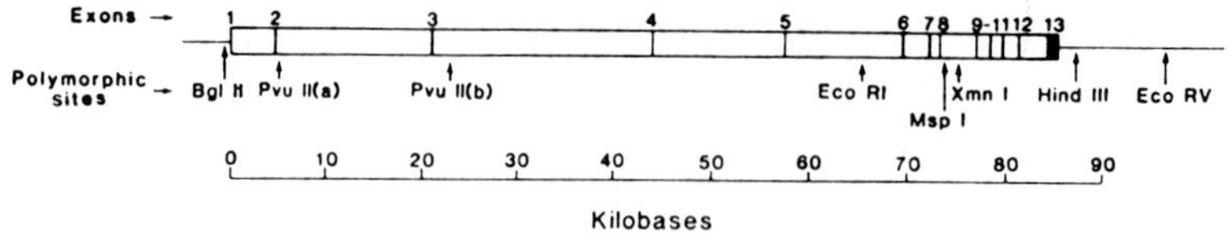

Exons — 1 2 3 4 5 6 7 8 9-11 12 13

Polymorphic Sites — Bgl II Pvu II(a) Pvu II(b) Eco RI Xmn I Msp I Hind III Eco RV

0 10 20 30 40 50 60 70 80 90

Kilobases

Haplo-types	Bgl II	Pvu IIa	Pvu IIb	Eco RI	Msp I	Xmn I	Hind III	Eco RV	Frequency in Normal	Frequency in PKU
1	−	+	−	−	+	−	−	−	23	12
2	−	+	−	−	+	−	+	+	3	13
3	−	+	−	+	−	+	−	−	2	25
4	−	+	−	+	−	+	+	+	21	9
5	+	−	+	+	+	−	−	+	7	0
6	+	−	+	+	+	−	−	−	0	2
7	+	−	−	+	−	+	−	−	7	1
8	−	+	−	+	+	−	−	+	1	0
9	+	+	−	+	+	−	−	+	0	1
10	−	+	−	+	+	−	−	−	1	0
11	+	−	−	+	+	−	−	+	1	1
12	−	+	−	−	+	−	=	+	0	2
								Totals	66	66

Fig. 15-7 *Top.* Structure of the gene and location of informative polymorphic restriction sites at the PAH locus. *Bottom.* Haplotypes for eight polymorphic sites and (in box) frequencies on chromosomes bearing normal or PKU alleles in Northern European (white) populations. Symbols + and − represent short and long (kilobase) restriction fragments, respectively; = symbol is for the 4.4-kb HindIII fragment (see Table 15-3).

terbreeding group was apparently spread by "founder effect" to the contemporary population. The Scottish deletion[227a] is not yet fully characterized but it apparently affects exons 1 and 2 (S. L. C. Woo, unpublished data).

RESTRICTION LENGTH POLYMORPHISMS (RFLPS) IN THE HUMAN PAH LOCUS. Molecular analysis of "the PKU gene" began by identifying RFLPs in the PAH gene,[223–226] which were then used as markers for segregation analysis of PKU kindreds. To estimate the frequencies of specific polymorphism, genomic DNA samples were isolated from unrelated Caucasian individuals, digested with a battery of restriction enzymes, and analyzed by Southern hybridization with the phPAH247 cDNA. Nine cleavage sites are polymorphic in the human PAH locus; the corresponding restriction enzymes are: *Bgl*II, *Pvu*II (two sites), *Eco*RI, *Msp*I, *Xmn*I, *Hind*III, *Eco*RV, and *Sph*I[224,225] (Fig. 15-7). The *Hind*III site is particularly informative in some populations,[226] whereas the *Sph*I site is of less use generally. Restriction fragment length polymorphism (RFLP) frequencies[225] at the human PAH locus in Caucasians (Table 15-3) are such that the observed heterozygosity is about 90 percent. Segregation analysis indicates that the combination of *Pvu*II, *Xmn*I, and *Eco*RV is nearly as informative for diagnosis of PKU genotypes as all eight sites together (excluding *Sph*I) and will be informative in about 87 percent of cases.[228,228a] A crude relationship between standardized linkage disequilibrium and physical map distances of the polymorphic sites indicates there is no obvious hot-spot for recombination in the human PAH gene.[228] Thus, RFLPs can be used with considerable confidence to perform prenatal diagnosis.[228a]

RFLP HAPLOTYPES AT THE PAH LOCUS AND THEIR ASSOCIATION WITH PKU. Haplotypes of individual RFLP alleles constitute a powerful molecular genetic tool to analyze genetic deficiencies in humans. (Haplotypes are composite profiles of individual RFLPs at the corresponding locus on a chromosome.) In theory, 1152 haplotypes can exist with the eight polymorphic restriction sites mentioned above. RFLP haplotype analysis of the normal chromosomes and chromosomes bearing PKU mutations demonstrated only 12 haplotypes in Danish families (Fig. 15-7) implying that there may be a high degree of linkage disequilibrium between the polymorphic sites in this population.[228–228a] The haplotype patterns vary between populations (e.g., between French and Danes[228c]), the associations

Table 15-3 Polymorphic Restriction Sites at the Human PAH Locus Used to Construct Haplotypes and Calculate Frequencies of Fragments Identified with Full-Length pH PAH247 cDNA Clone as Probe*

Restriciton sites	*Fragment size, kb*	*Frequency**
*Bgl*II	3.6	0.59
	1.7	0.41
*Pvu*IIa	19.0	0.44
	6.0	0.56
*Pvu*IIb	11.5	0.69
	9.1	0.31
*Xmn*I	9.4	0.67
	6.5	0.33
*Eco*RI	17.0	0.59
	11.0	0.41
*Msp*I	23.0	0.38
	19.0	0.62
*Eco*RV	30.0	0.47
	25.0	0.53
*Hind*III	(4.4)†	—
	4.2	0.61
	4.0	0.39

*Frequencies for the Danish population were estimated from 18 unrelated normal individuals.

†The *Hind*III polymorphism has three alleles: the 4.4-kb allele is uncommon in some populations[225] and prevalent in others;[226] in the latter, it is highly informative for PKU diagnosis.

SOURCE: Adapted from Lidsky et al.[225]

between haplotypes and PKU alleles also vary, and the number of observed RFLP haplotypes exceeded 40 as this book went to press, but the phenomenon of linkage disequilibrium between RFLP haplotypes and the PAH alleles affecting enzyme activity is ubiquitous. The relative frequencies of the various haplotypes are significantly different on the PKU and normal chromosomes, but there is no unique haplotype characterizing the PKU chromosome.[228] No significant association (linkage disequilibrium) exists between any single polymorphic site and PKU; either the PKU mutation is very ancient and it has reached linkage equilibrium or PKU is the result of multiple mutations on several haplotypes.[228] The latter is the actual case. About 90 percent of PKU alleles in northern European populations appear to be restricted to four RFLP haplotypes[21,228] (Fig. 15-7), but as analysis continues, other alleles on other haplotypes are being discovered.

DNA haplotypes at the PAH locus tend to correlate with the associated hyperphenylalaninemia phenotypes in specific populations[229,230] (but not necessarily between different populations). Danish probands who are homozygous for haplotypes 2 and 3, or genetic compounds thereof, have PKU, by which we mean they have plasma phenylalanine values greater than 1 m*M* when receiving a normal diet and they have no or only trivial PAH activity *in vivo et situ*. On the other hand, probands with homozygous phenotypes associated with combinations of haplotypes 1 and 4 usually have the non-PKU form of hyperphenylalaninemia (at least in the Danish population), and their plasma phenylalanine is below 1m*M* under usual dietary conditions. Families in which PKU and non-PKU hyperphenylalaninemia occur in the same sibship reveal that PKU and mild hyperphenylalaninemia are phenotypic expressions of multiple PAH alleles in various combinations.[231] In this chapter, we accept the evidence that certain pairs of alleles are associated with the PKU phenotype while others confer a less severe hyperphenylalaninemic phenotype.

THE MOLECULAR BASIS OF PKU. Molecular analysis of the PKU phenotype was hampered for decades because the human PAH gene is apparently expressed only in liver.[60] An alternative is now available since PAH genes can be isolated from leukocytes of patients, amplified by the polymerase chain reaction,[231a] and analyzed by molecular methods.

The structural organization of the normal PAH gene (Fig. 15-7) was established by analysis of overlapping PAH cosmid clones, spanning more than 125 kb of the genetic locus.[223] Mutant genes were then cloned from homozygous PKU probands and sequenced. The first mutant PAH gene to be analyzed was associated with DNA haplotype 3, the one most frequently associated with a PKU allele in the Danish population (approximately 38 percent of the PKU alleles;[228] see Fig. 15-7). Sequence analysis of the mutant clones[232] demonstrated a single base substitution in the gene with a G-to-A transition at the canonical 5′ donor splice site of intron 12 and expression of a truncated protein product lacking the C-terminus region (Fig. 15-8). This mutation causes the PKU phenotype. Normal and mutant mini-PAH genes were constructed.[233] The mini-gene containing intron 12 in the normal DNA sequence was placed behind a strong eukaryotic promoter, and the engineered gene was transferred into cultured mammalian cells. Transformants containing the normal intron 12 segment produced authentic human PAH mRNA and adequate enzyme activity, indicating that the intron was properly processed in the cell. The counterpart PKU gene containing the mutant intron 12 donor splice site produced PAH mRNA in adequate amounts but "no" expressed enzymatic activity in the transformed cells; more than 1 percent of normal PAH activity could have been detected with the assay.[233] Cells transformed with the normal gene accumulated immunoreactive protein in the cytoplasm, while those transformed with the mutant gene did not (CRM negative phenotype), suggesting that the mutant allele produces an unstable protein. This experiment proved that the G-to-A transition at the donor splice site of intron 12 in the PAH gene inactivates PAH and causes PKU. It constituted the first characterization of a mutant PAH gene.

A PKU allele associated with haplotype 2 has been analyzed by cosmid cloning and sequencing;[234] it is a missense mutation. The mutant gene, obtained from a homozygous proband, contained a C-to-T transition in exon 12, encoding an arginine-to-tryptophan substitution at residue 408 of the PAH monomer (Fig. 15-9*A*). Site-directed mutagenesis with specific oligonucleotides performed in the normal PAH cDNA to create the mutant allele yielded a PKU phenotype in vitro.[234] When normal and mutant constructs were introduced into cultured monkey kidney cells, only the former produced immunoreactive protein and active enzyme in the cytoplasm; both alleles produced similar levels of mRNA. These findings confirm that the amino acid substitution (Arg to Trp) at residue 408 in the PAH monomer inactivates PAH and causes PKU. This PKU allele constitutes about 20 percent of PKU genes in Northerm Europeans.[228,234]

A third and much rarer mutation in the PAH gene has recently been characterized in a PKU patient living in Ger-

Fig. 15-8 An RNA splicing mutation in the human PAH gene associated with the mutant haplotype 3 allele and expressed as the PKU phenotype in homozygotes.[232] *A*. A schematic representation of the GT-to-AT substitution that causes skipping of the preceding exon during RNA splicing. *B*. The truncated protein expressed from the mutant PAH allele.

A

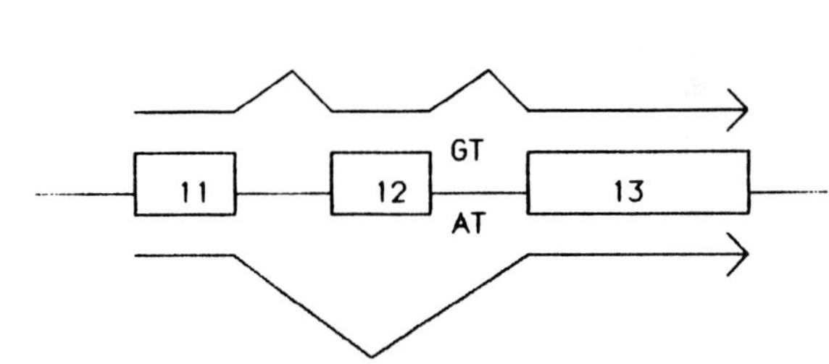

B

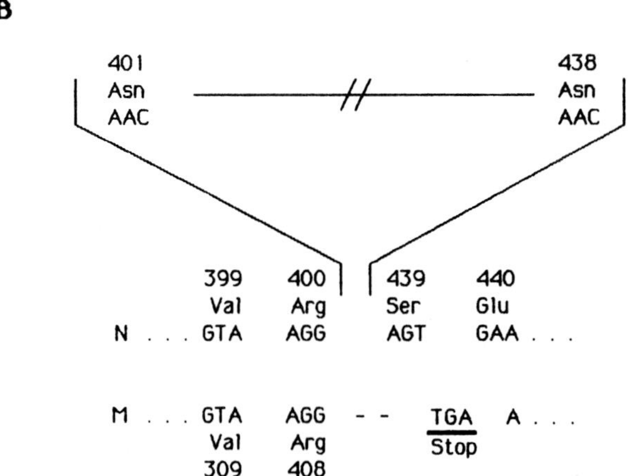

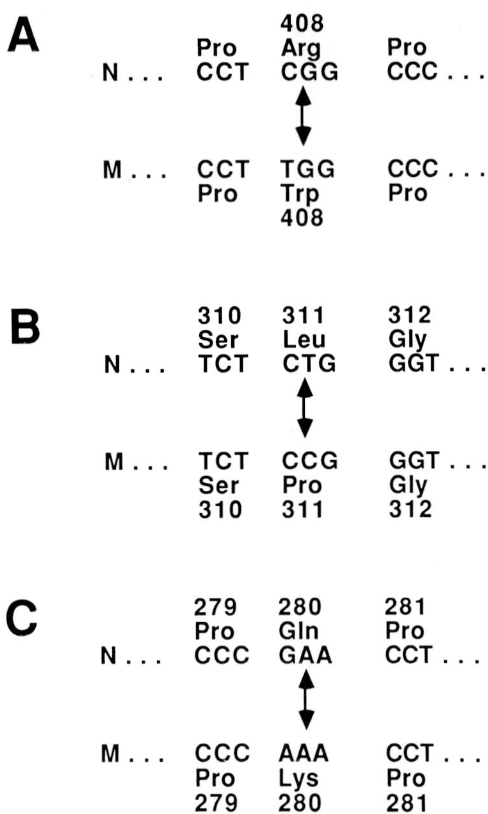

Fig. 15-9 Missense mutations in the human PAH gene that cause PKU. A. An *Arg*[408]-to-*Trp*[408] substitution associated with haplotype 2.[234] B. A *Leu*[311]-to-*Pro*[311] substitution associated with a rare PKU allele in German and Greek probands.[235] C. A *Glu*[280]-to-Lys[280] substitution associated with a new haplotype in North African (Algerian) probands[236a]; this allele causes non-PKU hyperphenylalaninemia.

many;[235] it is another missense mutation. An additional *Msp*I restriction site was found in association with one of the PKU alleles in this patient. Cloning and sequence analysis of the new restriction site revealed a T-to-C transition in exon 9, the single base substitution creating the new *Msp*I site while converting a leucine codon to a proline codon encoding residue number 311 in the PAH monomer (Fig. 15-9*B*). This mutation has now been found in another German family (see Ref. 236b). Site-directed mutagenesis and expression analysis showed that this particular missense mutation caused a CRM-negative PAH phenotype.[235] The "German" missense allele has been found in a Greek PKU patient on haplotype 7; it was on haplotype 1 in the German patient (K. Hofman and D. Valle, personal communication, 1987).

Molecular analysis of two unrelated American black PKU patients of West African descent demonstrated another new *Msp*I restriction site not in exon 9 and on a new haplotype (type D).[236] This allele is not the "German" allele (K. Hofman and D. Valle, personal communication, 1987). The background haplotype may be a recombinant or a change in a restriction site. It is not yet clear whether the new *Msp*I site is caused by a PKU mutation or is only associated with it in the American black families.

Yet another missense mutation is known; it occurs in exon 7.[236a] A transition from G to A in the codon for amino acid residue 280 encodes the substitution of *Lys* for *Glu* and inactivates PAH. The allele confers non-PKU hyperphenylalaninemia. A survey of 47 Algerian PKU patients with the corresponding oligonucleotide probe identified 10 with this mutation, which is in linkage disequilibrium with a novel RFLP haplotype not found in northern Europeans.

The deletion allele in Yemenite Jews[227] is the sixth allele characterized at the molecular level so far.

ASSOCIATIONS BETWEEN RFLP HAPLOTYPES AND SPECIFIC MUTATIONS IN THE PAH GENE. Splicing[232] and *Arg* to *Trp* missense[234] mutations are associated with RFLP haplotypes 3 and 2, respectively. This was shown by using the corresponding synthetic oligonucleotides probes to hybridize with genomic DNA prepared from Northern European PKU individuals bearing mutant PAH alleles on various haplotypes.[232,234,236c] DNA haplotype 3 chromosomes carried the splicing mutation,[232] and none of the nonhaplotype 3 chromosomes carried it. DNA haplotype 2 chromosomes in the same population carried the same missense mutation (Arg→Trp) and none of the nonhaplotype 2 chromosomes carried it.[234] The consistent associations between DNA haplotypes 3 and 2 and the splicing and missense mutations, respectively, provide strong evidence for linkage disequilibrium in the PAH gene and spread in populations from historical centers of diffusion. However, it should be said again: RFLP haplotype-PAH allele associations are not necessarily consistent between different populations.

PKU GENOTYPES ARE HETEROGENOUS AND OFTEN COMPOUND. There is plenty of evidence that PKU is a heterogeneous phenotype. First there are both CRM-positive and -negative phenotypes at the enzyme level[99,237,238,239b]; second, some patients have no detectable PAH mRNA in liver, while others have ample amounts[240]; third, there are at least six PKU alleles at the PAH locus.[227,232,234,235,236,236a,236b]

Because there is linkage disequilibrium between specific mutations and RFLP haplotypes in the PAH gene in certain populations,[228,232,234] genotypes of PKU patients can be deduced with considerable confidence in these populations. PKU probands in Northern Europeans or their descendents homozygous for DNA haplotypes 2 or 3 should have the same mutant allele at the PAH locus on both homologous chromosomes, while those who are compound for DNA haplotypes 2 and 3 should be compounded heterozygotes for mutant PKU alleles. Furthermore, because the intron 12 splicing mutation and the exon 12 missense mutation are not represented on other DNA haplotypes associating with the PKU phenotype, probands who are heterozygous for haplotypes 2 and 3 or any of the other PKU-associated haplotypes could also be classified as compound heterozygotes. By this reasoning, it is estimated that about three quarters of PKU patients in the Northern European population are genetic compounds in various combinations. Accordingly, there are many molecular causes of hyperphenylalaninemia, and this allelic heterogeneity will account for some of the variability in metabolic and clinical phenotypes. Segregation of several different alleles in the same family can cause significant differences in the associated metabolic phenotype.[231]

Enzyme Phenotypes. Rather little is known about the mutant PAH enzyme phenotype because a liver biopsy is required to characterize PAH. The experience up to 1985 is summarized elsewhere.[19,40,241] Jervis[242] and others[237,243–246] performed the classic measurements showing that the conversion of phenylalanine to tyrosine and hepatic phenylalanine hydroxylating activity were severely deficient in PKU. These observations showed for the first time, that hepatic PAH stimulatory protein cofactor, and DHPR activities were normal in PKU.[237,246]

Measurements of PAH in PKU liver, done in the early studies with appropriately constituted assays and antibodies, demonstrated, for example,[247,247a] a CRM-positive phenotype with negligible PAH activity, an unchanged K_m value for phenylalanine, and changes in several other properties of the mutant enzyme. However, because of the genetic heterogeneity in PKU, there is no reason to believe that the enzyme phenotype in one proband will necessarily be found in another, particularly when the probands come from different regions or populations. Therefore the published reports of hepatic PAH activity in PKU should be taken as particular and not universal descriptions.

This point of view is well illustrated in the study by Bartholomé et al.[248] PAH activity was measured in needle biopsy liver samples taken from a large group of patients with various degrees of hyperphenylalaninemia. There was considerable variation in residual PAH activity: below 1 percent normal in cases classified as PKU and up to 35 percent normal in non-PKU forms of hyperphenylalaninemia (Fig. 15-10). Further studies[239] found one PKU proband with a variant electrophoretic PAH phenotype in a group of 10 who were CRM-positive. The electrophoretic mutant had a less positive charge. The finding, based on DNA analysis, that the majority of hyperphenylalaninemic probands are genetic compounds had already been surmised from measurements of hepatic PAH activity in vitro and metabolite levels in vivo.[248a]

Values for PAH activity in vitro have been compared with tolerance for phenylalanine in vivo.[248,249] Despite the limitations of the in vitro studies (for example, the PAH activities in PKU livers were related only to activity in control samples and neither set of data was normalized to a control enzyme), patients with less than 1 percent normal PAH activity by and large have a PKU metabolic phenotype in vivo; patients with more than 5 percent normal activity have a non-PKU form of hyperphenylalaninemia. Other studies[249–251] on these lines have corroborated these general conclusions.

It was noticed[248,249] there is no close correlation between phenylalanine tolerance and residual PAH activity below 5 percent normal in the mutant phenotypes. A flaw in normalizing the data is one explanation; another is physiology. Components other than PAH affect phenylalanine outflow, and they assume greater importance in the PAH-deficient subject. Since the sensitivity coefficients (the term is used as defined in Ref. 39) of these components are encoded by other genes which, assuming normal polymorphism, will differ between individuals, it follows that we should not anticipate tight correlation of metabolic phenotype and residual PAH activity in severely deficient patients. On the other hand, the metabolic phenotype did correlate inversely and quite well with PAH activity when the latter was above 5 percent normal.[248,251] This finding indicates rather nicely that PAH activity is indeed the major determinant of phenylalanine homeostasis, even at much reduced levels of enzyme activity.

The evidence for heterogeneity in the enzyme phenotype took a novel turn when Bartholomé et al.[248] found one patient with persistent in vivo hyperphenylalaninemia and normal PAH activity in vitro. The latter finding was an artifact of great importance. The assay procedure, which provides cofactor in vitro for the hydroxylation reaction, had masked the actual abnormality, which was a disorder of tetrahydrobiopterin homeostasis in this patient. When PAH activity was measured *in vivo et situ* with another procedure, it was shown that the patient had less than 5 percent normal phenylalanine hydroxylating activity. This was one of the first demonstrations that PAH integrity and phenylalanine hydroxylating activity are not synonymous.

Kaufman et al. measured PAH activity in liver biopsy material from probands and parents in three families with non-PKU hyperphenylalaninemia.[252] PAH activity in the probands was about 5 percent normal. The predicted value for PAH activity in the obligate heterozygote would be about half-normal. The observed value was about 13 percent normal (mean of the six heterozygous samples), indicating a deviant gene dosage effect. The values in PKU heterozygotes also show a deviant gene dosage effect (range 14 to 44 percent[239]; 29 percent, $n = 9$, range 18 to 39 percent[239a]; and 33 and 41 percent, $n = 2$).[239b] Negative cooperativity between subunits in the heteropolymeric heterozygous phenotype is an explanation for the finding.[252] The quantitative difference in gene dosage in PKU and non-PKU hyperphenylalaninemia may be of interest.

PAH activity can be measured *in vivo et situ* with tracer amounts of deuterated phenylalanine.[53,251,253–258] Intravenous infusion or ingestion of labeled substrate is followed by mea-

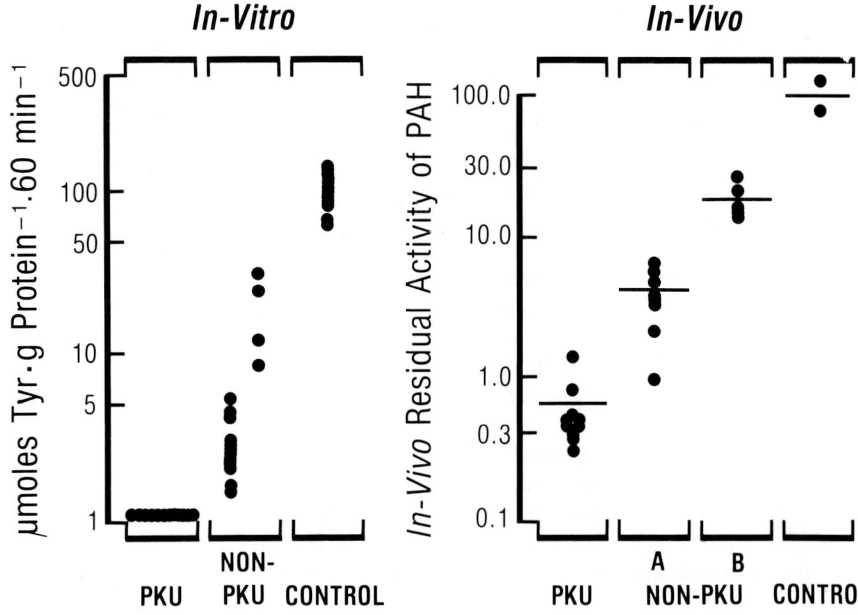

Fig. 15-10 Phenylalanine hydroxylase (PAH) activity in vitro in hepatic needle biopsy material *(left)* and *in vivo et situ (right)*. The in vitro assay[248] was done at pH 6.9 in phosphate buffer containing 2 mM dithiothreitol, 0.1 mM labeled phenylalanine, 1 mM lysolecithin, and 25 μM BH_4; formation of labeled tyrosine in 60 min was measured. The in vivo assay[251] was performed with an infusion of heptadeuterated-L-phenylalanine, and the rate of labeled tyrosine measured at steady state. [*Redrawn composite of figure 3 from Bartholomé et al.*[248] *(left) and figure 1 from Trefz et al.*[251] *(right). Used by permission.*]

surement of labeled water[53] or tyrosine; in the latter case the simultaneous rate of tyrosine disposal must be measured to estimate PAH activity correctly. The method is sufficiently sensitive to measure PAH adaptation and regulation in humans in vivo,[255] and estimates correlate well with the corresponding in vitro measurements of enzyme activity in patients with primary disorders of PAH integrity[251] (Fig. 15-10). Accordingly, it should be possible to estimate systematically the in vivo PAH activity associated with the different mutations affecting the PAH locus and the other mutations affecting phenylalanine hydroxylation.

Neither the hepatic PAH assay or the isotopic in vivo measurement of hydroxylating activity are easy procedures and Crawfurd et al.[259] examined the possibility that human PAH might be expressed in nonhepatic tissues. With an appropriate assay dependent on added pterin cofactor, they confirmed the absence of PAH activity in cultured skin fibroblasts and amniotic fluid cells, short-term lymphocyte cultures, long-term lymphoblastoid cultures, hair roots, and placental extracts. Others have claimed that human platelets have phenylalanine hydroxylating activity which is impaired in PKU. Since this bizarre finding did not appear to be dependent on added pterin cofactor (indeed, the activity was inhibited by cofactor), it is better to say the hydroxylating activity in platelets, whatever it is, is not PAH.

Metabolic Phenotypes and Pathogenesis of Brain Disease. "DNA makes RNA makes protein" is received dogma, but when the PKU gene is expressed as the corresponding polypeptide only in hepatocytes and PKU affects brain to cause mental retardation, it follows that a metabolic phenotype associated with PAH deficiency must link brain and hepatic phenotypes. Moreover, since PKU is largely accompanied by severe mental retardation and non-PKU hyperphenylalaninemia is not, there must be significant differences in the corresponding metabolic phenotypes to explain heterogeneity in clinical phenotype. This remains the most elusive area for the interpretation of PKU.

The proper study of PKU is the human patient, but there are severe limits to such an investigation. To study pathogenesis in depth we need a Mendelian homologue of PKU and its PAH variants in an animal, and there is none. [The most promising animal model is a deficiency of GTP-cyclohydrolase-I activity (see below).] The alternative is an animal "model" achieved by phenylalanine loading, usually in conjunction with an inhibitor of PAH, but this approach also has its limits.[19] The case for transgenic mouse experiments with cloned DNA segments encoding PKU or non-PKU hyperphenylalaninemia genes is compelling even though different metabolic relationships and schedules of brain development in humans will have some bearing on pathogenesis of the brain disease.

It has been said: there are no abnormal metabolites in PKU, only normal metabolites in abnormal amount(s).[3] Their array and concentrations in blood and urine and their role in the pathogenesis of PKU have been of enduring interest. (See Refs. 3, 9a, 12, 13, 15a, 19, 40, 261, 261a for additional information.)

Here we develop an argument as follows. There is a threshold level of phenylalanine in extracellular fluids below which there is no apparent harm to brain (the non-PKU hyperphenylalaninemia phenotype). Above that level, persistent postnatal hyperphenylalaninemia (or fetal hyperphenylalaninemia) causes *irreversible* brain damage; it does so by competitive interaction with brain amino acid transport systems, perturbation of metabolite distributions, and inhibition of neurotransmitter synthesis and many other biochemical processes. Impaired myelin synthesis and neuronal development are the consequences. If the threshold value is exceeded only in later life, as for example when treatment is terminated after satisfactory brain development has occurred in the early treated PKU subject, *reversible* chemical changes appear initially, notably affected neurotransmitter synthesis.[262,263] If they are prolonged (for months and years), deterioration in neuropsychological function may take place in some individuals. Since these deficits are not then reversible (see below), it follows that the effects of prolonged severe hyperphenylalaninemia in later life are ultimately hazardous.

IS THERE A THRESHOLD VALUE OF PLASMA PHENYLALANINE IN PKU? The empirical evidence in patients indicates that plasma phenylalanine values above 1 m*M* are harmful to the development and function of the brain. Recent studies[262] established a threshold value at about 1.3 m*M* in 10 treated PKU subjects, 6 to 24 years old; the corresponding value for the infant with a developing brain has not been established. High plasma phenylalanine values in the older subject are associated with measurable impairment of higher integrative brain functions[262] and electroencephalographic abnormalities.[263] Urine dopamine excretion[262] and plasma L-dopa values[263] both correlate inversely with plasma phenylalanine values and positively with abnormalities of brain function in hyperphenylalaninemia. (Of course, there may be no correlation between plasma and brain dopa levels.) The normal circadian rhythm for plasma phenylalanine[34] is altered in PKU,[10,264] and this may further influence pathogenesis.

ARE METABOLITES, OTHER THAN PHENYLALANINE, OF INTEREST? Many metabolites derived from phenylalanine accumulate in body fluids in the hyperphenylalaninemias: they are phenylpyruvate, phenyllactate, phenylacetate and its conjugate phenylacetylglutamine, dihydroxyphenylacetate, and phenylethylamine, among others. None has a known dominant role in pathogenesis. The interindividual plasma values for phenylalanine do not correlate with urine concentrations of its derivatives,[262,265] and there is no direct correlation between the excess of phenylalanine derivatives per se and severity of the brain phenotype in PKU.[3] New measurements of phenylethylamine by mass fragmentography[266] indicate that previously published values in normal subjects were too high, perhaps by three orders of magnitude; values in hyperphenylalanimic subjects have not yet been reported.

Some derivatives of phenylalanine are products of intestinal bacterial metabolism in PKU patients. The excess of amino acid in plasma establishes equilibrium with amino acid in the intestinal lumen,[267] and the latter excess is substrate for bacterial metabolism; phenylpropionic acid[268] and phenylacetate[269] are products thereof.

Mass fragmentography detected an unusual tetrahydroisoquinoline, 3′,4′-deoxynorlaudanosinecarboxylic acid, in urine of PKU children.[270] It is derived from dopamine and phenylpyruvate, it accumulates in brain in an animal pharmacologic model, and it inhibits dopamine β-hydroxylase.

HOW MIGHT DEVIANT PHENYLALANINE METABOLISM CAUSE THE PKU BRAIN PHENOTYPE? Pathogenesis can be considered from three viewpoints: (1) a putative deficiency of tyrosine; (2) the effect of phenylalanine on transport mechanisms and distribution of metabolites; (3) secondary effects on neurochemical reactions. No single process seems to explain the brain phenotype in PKU, which is surely multifactorial. The relative importance of one process over another probably varies between one patient (or family) and another because the phenotype has many determinants.

1. *Tyrosine deficiency?* Complete PAH deficiency makes tyrosine an essential amino acid for the affected subject. PKU homozygotes are the obligate offspring of maternal heterozygotes. A line of reasoning, called the *justification hypothesis*,[271] notes that this circumstance constitutes double jeopardy. Formation of tyrosine from phenylalanine is virtually absent in the fetus and partially compromised in the mother during the period of prenatal brain development. Tyrosine deficiency in the fetus is a potential hazard of this joint circumstance. It follows that if tyrosine deficiency were a cause of brain damage, tyrosine supplementation should prevent it. Is there evidence in PKU to support the justification hypothesis? The answer is, no. First, postnatal tyrosine supplementation without reduction of phenylalanine intake does not prevent severe mental retardation in PKU.[272] Second, postnatal phenylalanine restriction by itself should not be beneficial; yet it is, and it largely prevents brain damage in PKU (see "Treatment," below). Third, there is no consistent or significant reduction of plasma tyrosine in the untreated PKU patient,[273] and, when there is, it occurs in association with a deficiency of other plasma amino acids[3] for which there is an explanation[46,47] (see next section). Fourth, there is no significant deficiency of blood tyrosine in cord-blood samples obtained from newborns with PKU or non-PKU hyperphenylalaninemia, whereas blood phenylalanine levels are already significantly raised in the same samples.[274]

These findings pertain only to extracellular tyrosine, but the corresponding intracellular values are probably higher than normal since the mechanism by which tyrosine is depleted from plasma leads to intracellular accumulation.[46,47] Measurements in blood lymphocytes show that the intracellular tyrosine concentration is indeed elevated above normal in PKU homozygotes and heterozygotes[275] (see below for the apparent mechanism). The finding was confirmed[276] and extended to subjects with non-PKU hyperphenylalaninemia. Measurements of intracellular tyrosine in PKU have been made only in parenchymal cells so far; brain cells have not been studied.

2. *Effect on transport processes and metabolic distributions.* Phenylalanine crosses plasma membranes as it moves in and out of cells and organs.[42] The corresponding fluxes are mediated by the system L carrier in plasma membranes of parenchymal cells. The carrier permits weak net intracellular accumulation of phenylalanine against its electrochemical gradient. The intracellular concentration of phenylalanine is abnormally elevated in PKU and non-PKU hyperphenylalaninemia.[275–277]

Many neutral amino acids have low plasma concentrations in the PKU phenotype.[3] Christensen[46,47] has explained this phenomenon. Several neutral amino acids interact with transport systems other than system L to achieve steeply concentrative uptake into parenchymal cells; phenylalanine does not interfere with this process. However these same amino acids can leave the cell on system L, and high intracellular levels of phenylalanine block this process. Accordingly, amino acids are sequestered in parenchymal tissues in untreated PKU. In brain, where the corresponding transport relationships are different, an excess of phenylalanine impedes the influx of amino acids. The net effect of this disruption of amino acid traffic in PKU is to deprive brain of its amino acid supply and to sequester amino acids elsewhere.[47]

Phenylalanine transport at the human blood-brain barrier has been studied with the isolated brain capillary preparation.[278] A high affinity system ($K_m \approx 20\ \mu M$) operates on the blood side of brain capillary endothelium, and a very high affinity system ($K_m \approx 0.25\ \mu M$) operates at the brain surface of the capillary. This arrangement keeps the interstitial brain amino acid concentration low and stable in the face of the normal diurnal fluctuation in the plasma level.[34,279] It also operates to deliver phenylalanine at its normal plasma concentration more efficiently to brain cells than to parenchymal cells where system L has lower affinity. In vitro kinetic values are similar in human and rat brain capillary preparations,[278] and studies in rat indicate that K_m values for phenylalanine uptake from circulating blood in vivo[280] and from the lumen side in the capillary preparation *in vitro*[279] are similar. Competition between the large neutral amino acids and phenylalanine occurs on this brain transport system in humans[278] and rats.[280] Accordingly, elevated concentrations of phenylalanine will impair brain uptake of the branched-chain amino acids tyrosine and tryptophan.

Competition between amino acids for uptake occurs at other membranes in the brain. Synaptosomal plasma membrane vesicles exhibit competitive inhibition of tyrosine[281] and tryptophan transports[282] in the presence of phenylalanine concentrations likely to occur in PKU brain. It has been estimated that sequestration of tyrosine in parenchymal tissues and inhibition of its brain and syntaptosomal uptake causes twofold reduction in tyrosine availability for neurotransmitter synthesis in the PKU brain.[283]

Although cerebrospinal fluid (CSF) metabolite levels do not necessarily reflect events in synaptosomal, interstitial, and intracellular spaces, CSF tyrosine is twofold higher than normal in PKU patients; CSF phenylalanine values are also elevated.[284] The CSF/plasma phenylalanine ratio is not significantly altered in PKU, but the corresponding tyrosine ratio is much increased. This finding suggests that phenylalanine competes with tyrosine for a carrier that serves transit from CSF back into blood. This putative interaction between aromatic amino acids apparently involves 5-hydroxytryptophan as well.[285]

Some propose[40,286–289] that the interactions between amino acids during transport in brain can be used to advantage in treatment. Diet supplements of branched chain amino acids sufficient to double their plasma values reduce the phenylalanine level in plasma and CSF in PKU patients,[286] with an associated improvement in psychological test performance.[287] Corresponding studies in the rat showed that lysine infusions reduce the harmful effects of hyperphenylalaninemia on brain development in suckling animals,[288] apparently by preventing depletion of brain tryptophan and serotonin.[289] The mechanism of the lysine effect is not clear.

The human renal system for reabsorption of phenylalanine from filtrate (see figure 3-5 of Ref. 35) and the brain system for uptake from blood[278] cannot be compared. Interactions between aromatic amino acids occur at different concentrations on renal and brain systems, and we should not extrapolate from renal clearance data and surmise about events in brain as is done sometimes.[262] Yet renal handling of metabolites has some bearing on the metabolic phenotype in hyperphenylalaninemia. For example, while plasma phenylpyruvate increases linearly as plasma phenylalanine rises above 0.5 mM,[290] urine phenylpyruvate excretion reaches its maximum value when plasma phenylalanine is at 1 mM. The finding implies the kidney has a finite capacity to excrete the keto acid. Accordingly, tissue and plasma levels of keto acid change in parallel with phenylalanine in the PKU phenotype.[290]

A minor metabolite of phenylalanine, N-acetylphenylalanine, behaves as an organic anion. It is excreted in the urine by the probenecid-inhibited transtubular secretory system for organic anions.[291] Drugs that compete for organic anion binding sites on albumin, or that block renal secretion of organic anions will enhance retention of *N*-acetylphenylalanine. Whether this molecule plays any role in the pathogenesis of disease in PKU is not known.

3. *Effects on neurochemistry and metabolism.* Metabolic abnormalities occur in the brain exposed to high levels of phenylalanine and its derivatives.[261,261a] Abnormalities are found also in noncerebral tissues as part of the global metabolic phenotype in PKU,[292] but they are not of primary interest here.

Phenylalanine is a troublemaker in PKU, and its bulky apolar side chain makes it a candidate for perturbing water structure with an anestheticlike effect in brain. However, L-phenylalanine, at concentrations found in PKU, does not perturb water structure in vitro[292a] and presumably does not in the PKU patient. Other than a study like this one, there are few that can be done without recourse to analysis of brain itself. That can be done only in the living or once living organism, and there are many limitations in this approach.

Studies in animals are a major source of published data on the metabolic and chemical changes in brain associated with hyperphenylalaninemia.[293,294] Phenylalanine loads are used to produce hyperphenylalaninemia, but because this also produces an overburden of tyrosine in the animal with intact PAH activity, it is necessary to inhibit the enzyme to have isolated hyperphenylalaninemia. Unfortunately, the agents much used for this purpose, *p*-chlorophenylalanine and α-methylphenylalanine, have their own secondary effects, notably inhibition of other aromatic amino acid hydroxylations[19]; hence, these particular models are not homologues of human PAH deficiency.

When the objective is to study the effects of a minor phenylalanine metabolite on brain, it is usually measured after exposure of the animal to only one metabolite at a time at concentrations and in relation to other metabolites uncharacteristic of the circumstance in PKU patients.

Disturbances of neurotransmitter synthesis and action have been a dominant focus of interest in the PKU phenotype,[262,263,295] echoed also in the design of animal studies.[296,297] If reappearance of neurotransmitter dishomeostasis follows cessation of dietary treatment in PKU patients (see below and Refs. 262 and 263), the cost to brain function of this disturbance must be known, and it is appropriate to measure it in an animal model.[298]

The enormous variety of metabolic effects in brain brought about by phenylalanine and its metabolites[261,261a] includes unusual ones, for example: biphasic effects on Na^+,K^+-ATPase activity in synaptosomes[299]; impaired phosphoadenosine phosphosulfate (PAPS) synthesis in brain by inhibition of ATP:sulfate adenyltransferase (ATP-sulfurylase)[300]; and disturbed ontogeny of brain carboxylic ester hydrolases.[301] Whether these abnormalities occur in the PKU brain phenotype in humans is, of course, unknown.

Abnormal myelination is found in brain of the untreated older PKU patients, and its pathogenesis is a continuing focus of experimental work in the animal model.[300,302–307] Perturbed brain protein synthesis is another effect observed in the animal model. It is the result of polysome disaggregation and a reduced rate of polypeptide chain elongation.[308] This effect is prevented when the large neutral amino acids (branched-chain forms, tryptophan and tryosine), are given to the hyperphenylalaninemic animal.[309] Polysome disaggregation also occurs in heart and brain of fetal rats exposed to maternal hyperphenylalaninemia[310] (a finding that bears on the fetopathy associated with human maternal hyperphenylalaninemia). Exaggerated protein degradation is not a factor in the experimental PKU brain phenotype.[311]

Brain histology and cellular development are impaired in human PKU and the corresponding animal models. The number and spread of dendritic basilar processes of large pyramidal cells are reduced in the hyperphenylalaninemic rat pup.[312] Animals treated with phenylacetate (this metabolite does not conjugate with glutamine in rats, as it does in humans[9a]) have increased numbers of apical dendritic spines in hippocampal pyramidal cells[313] because the normal maturational loss of spines in this region is retarded by the abnormal metabolic environment.[314] Prenatal exposure of rat pups to phenylacetate produces lesion in layer 5 cortical pyramidal cells; and dendritic spines are larger and thinner than normal and reduced in number.[315] The effect of phenylacetate on developing brain encompasses sialoglycoproteins[316] and gangliosides,[317] and cell adhesion molecules may be affected by the disturbance of sialoglycoprotein metabolism.[317] High levels of phenylalanine and its metabolites, both in culture[318] and in vivo,[319,320] cause decreased proliferation and increased loss of neurones in the rodent. DNA content is decreased in the affected brain cells,[320] and its synthesis is impaired.[321] The net effect is impaired brain growth in the animal model. In like manner, long exposure to the unmitigated metabolic phenotype affects brain development in PKU patients. There are abnormalities in myelination, width of the cortical plate, cell packing and density, dendritic arborization, and number of synaptic spines.[322]

In the pathogenesis of PKU, phenylalanine itself is probably the chief villain. The metabolites of phenylalanine, so attractive in animal models, are not found in the human disease at sufficiently high concentrations to disturb metabolic and chemical relationships in brain as described in the animal models. Whatever the mechanism, the consequences of PKU are impairments of brain development and function.

Clinical Phenotypes. Clinical manifestations occur in PKU, but their absence is a distinguishing feature of non-PKU hyperphenylalaninemia. The clinical phenotype of PKU is largely a matter of historical interest now, because the disease is prevented by early diagnosis and treatment in all but a tiny minority of PKU patients. Nonetheless a steady trickle of clinical papers on a potpourri of topics shows that bedside investigation of PKU is not exhausted.

New dermatoglyphic patterns are not abnormal in treated PKU patients.[323] It would be of interest to know whether they are abnormal in offspring of mothers with hyperphenylalaninemia. Irons and Levy[324] described the dermatologic manifestations of typical PKU (eczema, pigment dilution, and sclerodermalike lesions) in their review of metabolic syndromes affecting skin. Sclerodermalike changes[325,326] attract notice because the secondary abnormalities of tryptophan metabolism in PKU resemble those reported in earlier studies of scleroderma (cited in Ref. 325). There are no unique dental manifestations of PKU.[327] Eye abnormalities in the untreated patient are not exceptional,[328] and none is considered an effect of the mutant gene except those associated with hypopigmentation.[3,9a] Impaired postnatal physical growth affecting head circumference and height occur in untreated PKU.[329] Phenylalanine deficiency induced by zealous treatment of PKU also impairs growth. This hazard is avoided by appropriate supervision.[330] Untreated male PKU patients have reduced semen volume and sperm count, both inversely related to the plasma phenylalanine level.[331] Occasional probands with confirmed PKU and normal intelligence, despite lack of treatment, continue to be reported.[332] About two percent of PKU cases have this phenotype.[3] Among various explanations (see, e.g., Ref. 9a) are exceptional environmental factors and genetic background. These are EEG findings of putative diagnostic interest[333] that apparently correlate with metabolic phenotype.[263,333] Behavioral disorders accompany hyperphenylalaninemia when it is induced in treated PKU patients[334]; they seem to be the psychiatric counterparts of the neuropsychological[262] and neurophysiological[263] abnormalities observed in this circumstance.

Concurrence of PKU or non-PKU hyperphenylalaninemia[325] with other Mendelian disorders (for example, cystinuria,[335] Fahr disease,[336] Duchenne muscular dystrophy,[337] neonatal myotonic dystrophy,[338] galactosemia,[339] hypo-β-lipoproteinemia,[340] and pyruvate kinase deficiency[341]) continues to attract notice. Earlier reports of PKU coexistent with neurofibromatosis, hypophosphatasia, familial hypercalcemia, cystathioninuria, hyperammonemia, and leukodystrophy (Schilder type) were cited in a recent article.[336] Coincidence is the likely explanation for these cases. Those in which the second disease is caused by mutation at an autosomal locus not yet mapped might be investigated for a chromosomal microdeletion on the remote chance that proximity of loci on chromosome 12q explains the joint Mendelian phenotype.

Treatment (by Preventing Hyperphenylalaninemia). PKU is an example that confounds typologic thinkers. Is it a "genetic" disease (an inborn error of metabolism) or a "nutritional" disease (harm is caused by dietary phenylalanine)? The answer is, of course, both. Nature and nurture are each necessary causes of the disease,[342] and the prevailing treatment practice capitalizes accordingly. PKU was the first "genetic" disease to be treated effectively by "nutritional" means.

Mental retardation is not present at the bith of the PKU patient, by any measure known so far. The metabolic phenotype, itself barely apparent at birth,[274] appears progressively in the days thereafter, and harm to brain development follows later still. Measures taken early in the course of brain development to reduce the overburden of phenylalanine in PKU patients (and in the fetus of a mother with hyperphenylalaninemia) prevent the clinical consequences of severe persistent hyperphenylalaninemia. The decline of new PKU admissions to institutions for the mentally retarded in the years following the systematic use of early treatment attests to this.[343]

In this section, we review the evidence that early-onset treatment largely prevents the irreversible brain disorder in PKU. Inasmuch as there is a considerable body of evidence that neuropsychological and cognitive functions at the end of treatment are not quite normal on average in PKU patients, there are apparent imperfections in the treatment of PKU as it is currently practiced. Next, there is the issue of treatment termination. It has been the custom to stop treatment when brain growth is completed. A growing body of evidence indicates that this practice amounts to *premature termination* of treatment. When the PKU metabolic phenotype reappears, in many but not all patients there is a subsequent deterioration of cognitive and neuropsychological performance. In its early stages this may be a reversible phenomenon; it seems to be irreversible if it is prolonged. These retrospective findings are major causes for concern, and since they are associated with use of low-phenylalanine diets which have known imperfections, there is much interest in alternative modes of treatment.

LOW PHENYLALANINE DIETS. That phenylalanine levels in PKU should be brought to normal or near-normal was enunciated as a cardinal component of treatment long ago[344] and soon put into practice. The corresponding reports[345–347] are among the classics in PKU lore, nutrition, and medical genetics. The findings were sufficiently encouraging to launch further projects, studies, and programs, and several ways to normalize phenylalanine levels in PKU have subsequently been identified. Tyrosine supplementation by itself is not an effective treatment for PKU.[272]

One cannot curtail protein intake sufficiently by itself to prevent hyperphenylalaninemia in PKU without causing deficiencies of other essential amino acids. PKU patients are consumers with special needs,[348] and they need *selective restriction* of phenylalanine intake. The tolerance for dietary phenylalanine to maintain plasma phenylalanine levels at nontoxic levels in young PKU patients is on the order of 250 to 550 mg/day.[9a,349] A semisynthetic diet low in phenylalanine and adequate in other nutrients meets the requirements for treatment. Several commercial products, either modified protein hydrolysates or mixtures of free amino acids, provide the essential amino acids in suitable proportions for treatment of PKU patients.[38,349a] Other nutrients are supplied either in the product itself or from natural foods.

Most of the products used for treatment of PKU and other inborn errors of metabolism have nutrient compositions greatly deviant from human milk[350]—the nutritional environment to which humans are adapted in early life. Some low-phenylalanine products have been redesigned to resemble human milk in all other aspects.[351]

Nutrient intakes must be sufficient to meet anabolic requirements and maintain essential conversion reactions. PKU and normal subjects have similar nitrogen requirements,[352–354] and the PKU phenotype has been used effectively to evaluate the requirements proposed by the (U.S.) Food and Nutrition Board and the joint FAO/WHO Ad Hoc Expert Committee.[355] The phenylalanine requirement in the PKU patient is finely tuned to nitrogen retention and turnover and the intake of proteins that supports growth.[355] The tolerance for phenylalanine is of course much narrower between its lower and upper limits in PKU patients than in subjects with greater PAH activity.[9a] Transient *hyper*phenylalaninemia is a hazard of over-restricting phenylalanine or protein intake in PKU patients. This apparent paradox is the result of impaired runout of phenylalanine to anabolic nitrogen pools when protein synthesis is blocked by nutrient deficiency. The intake of phenylalanine and protein must be adjusted with particular care in the preterm infant with PKU.[356]

Intakes and bioavailability of trace nutrients may be inadequate according to some representative reports.[16a,357–362] Zinc in plasma and hair roots[357,358] and plasma selenium values[359,360] are low in treated PKU patients partly because of low bioavailability of these micronutrients.[357] The low selenium values are associated with low erythrocyte glutathione peroxidase activity; correction of the former increases the latter.[360a] No overt clinical consequences of the nutrient deficiencies have been identified so far. Plasma chromium and manganese val ues are not abnormal in treated PKU patients,[361] but serum ferritin values are low[362] and hair copper and calcium levels are elevated.[358] The observed deviations have their chief origins in the composition of the diet, in the way it is prescribed,[360] and in bioavailability of nutrients. Treated PKU patients have plasma cholesterol values slightly below normal.[363]

MODIFIED DIETARY TREATMENT. The low phenylalanine products for treatment of PKU subjects have unpleasant organoleptic properties which affect compliance with their use.[248] Three approaches are adopted to assist treatment. First, a more relaxed treatment protocol has been used to compensate and permit more natural foods in the diet. This approach allows a modest degree of hyperphenylalaninemia (still well below 1 m*M*) and avoids the undesirable effects of overtreatment.[364] The modified but not normalized metabolic phenotype, in practice, mimics non-PKU hyperphenylalaninemia, which is a benign phenotype.[365] Second, taste and character of the conventional treatment products are improved[350,351] and novel products[366,367] with adequate organoleptic and nutrient properties developed. A third method is still experimental. It presumes that the effect of conventional low-phenylalanine diet products can be enhanced by supplementing amino acids whose entry into brain cells is likely to be impaired by phenylalanine.[40,368,369] This approach might allow increased phenylalanine intake if the effects of phenylalanine are offset by the adjuncts. Phenylalanine levels were reduced by this procedure in brain in an animal model[370] and in the CSF of PKU patients.[268] Neuropsychological performance also improved in the patients.[287] Supplementation with tryptophan or tyrosine or both amino acids increases CSF levels of neurotransmitter derivatives and has some beneficial effects on reaction times, vigilance, and behavior in PKU patients.[371,371a] Accordingly, adjunct therapy may relax the treatment protocol and improve its effects. It might also be useful in the retarded PKU patient with irreversible brain damage who will not comply with conventional treatment.[372] Lastly, it might benefit normal IQ PKU patients who terminate treatment.

The practical issues in dietary treatment of PKU (and maternal PKU) are clearly many. They have been examined in helpful fashion by nutritionists and dieticians.[372a]

ENZYME THERAPY. The phenylalanine hydroxylating reaction has many components, and all are necessary for normal function. Although only a fraction of normal activity is required to prevent hyperphenylalaninemia, replacement and maintenance of PAH activity in vivo is a formidable challenge. A protected, nonimmunogenic, stabilized enzyme is the first requirement. The PAH apoenzyme is difficult to stabilize in the purified state. Entrapment of purified rat liver PAH in polyacrylamide by photocatalytic polymerization does not protect it[373]; nor is there improved PAH stability when it is reacted with a variety of diazonium, monofunctional or bifunctional reagents, or by covalent coupling to polyamino and dextran supports.[374]

Another form of enzyme therapy substitutes bacterial phenylalanine ammonia lysase (PAL) for PAH. PAL converts phenylalanine to ammonia and *trans*-cinnamic acid, a nontoxic metabolite. PAL, immobilized in a hollow fiber extracorporeal enzyme reactor, causes rapid depletion of phenylalanine in circulating blood in the phenylalanine-infused dog[375,376] and monkey.[376] Treatment of an adult PKU patient with an extracorporeal PAL reactor achieved modest (30 percent) reduction of blood phenylalanime during 5.5 h of reactor treatment over a 2-week period.[377] However, dependence on an extracorporeal reactor is likely to be an imposition no less serious than the diet it would replace. Although erythrocyte-entrapped PAL lowers plasma phenylalanine in mice,[378] there would be a significant invasive component in this form of treatment in human patients. The most promising approach, so far, puts PAL in the intestinal lumen.[379,380] PAH inside semipermeable microcapsules is not immunogenic, is protected from proteolysis, has one-fifth the activity of the free enzyme, and at appropriate dosage reduces plasma phenylalanine by 75 percent in a rat model of hyperphenylalaninemia.[379,380] Moreover, intestinal PAL activity decreases brain phenylalanine levels in hyperphenylalaninemic rats and corrects the secondary deficiency of tryptophan and tyrosine in brain (T. M. S. Chang and L. Bourget, personal communication, 1987). PAL entrapped in silk fibroin can also be used to deliver enzyme to the intestinal lumen.[381]

PAL given by mouth in enteric coated gelatin capsules has a beneficial effect on blood phenylalanine in the PKU patient.[382,383] *Trans*-cinnamic acid, the product of the reaction, is excreted primarily as hippuric acid.[382] No overt side effects accompanied one brief clinical trial of PAL "treatment."

The very high cost of PAL may explain why there are so few reports of its use in human patients. Because PAL therapy would be an attractive option for the management of maternal hyperphenylalaninemia, there is a compelling reason to study further its ability to restore normal or near-normal phenylalanine homeostasis in hyperphenylalaninemic subjects.

Outcome of Early Treatment. The efficacy of early treatment in PKU was well shown in a study of 28 sib pairs[385] in which the index case had presented with mental retardation and the sib with PKU was ascertained prospectively (early treatment) or retrospectively (missed case with no or late treatment). The difference in intellectual outcome between early treated (IQ values all above 80) and late or nontreated cases (mean IQ 45, range 30 to 81) indicated a highly beneficial treatment effect. A less rigorously designed study with paired sibs (table 15-6 of Ref. 9a) showed a similar effect of early treatment [IQ scores 93 and 53 for early and late treated sibs, respectively (n = 10 pairs)]. Another study[386] compared 36 treated PKU cases with their unaffected siblings; the mean IQ values were 94 and 99, respectively ($p < 0.02$). The North American Collaborative Study[387] then undertook to evaluate systematically the outcome of treatment; it measured IQ values at 4 years of age in 111 PKU children whose treatment began between 3 and 92 days after birth.[388] The mean score (Stanford Binet Intelligence Scale) for the whole group was 93: cases treated from the first month had a higher mean score (IQ 95) than those first treated between 31 and 65 days of age (IQ 85). The Collaborative Study next evaluated 132 PKU children at 6 years of age[389] and demonstrated a mean IQ value of 98. Regression analysis showed that IQ scores at 6 years were related to maternal intelligence, age at onset of treatment, and average lifetime plasma phenylalanine values achieved by treatment. Continuing evaluation[390] with a larger panel of psychological tests, observation up to 8 years of age in the PKU group, and comparisons with matched, non-PKU siblings showed again the benefits of early treatment (WISC Full Scale IQ score, 100; n = 55). However, the PKU sibs had an IQ deficit relative to their normal sibs (IQ, 107; p = 0.001). Furthermore, PKU patients who had terminated treatment at an earlier age scored lower than those who had continued it longer.

Physical growth of treated PKU patients is of interest.[391,392] Height growth in treated PKU patients fulfills genetic potential, but there is a tendency for excessive weight gain; pubertal maturation is normal.[392a]

Mental, not physical, development is the problem in treated PKU patients. While there are no serious doubts that early treatment benefits cognitive development in PKU,[393–396] there is ample evidence that the outcome is not quite normal. Treated patients with near-normal IQ values have performance deficits in conceptual and visuospatial and language skills,[15a,397,398,398a,398b] which proably account for the earlier measured deficiencies in reading and arithmetic skills,[390] and a wide range of perceptual motor dysfunctions, learning disabilities, emotional and behavioral disturbances are found in "normal-IQ" treated PKU patients.[390,393,397–400a,401] Despite these handicaps treated, adult-age PKU patients function reasonably well in society.[402]

What is the cause of these deficits? There is probably no single explanation. The treatment is difficult, and its circumstances are unusual relative to those of other family members. Certainly, quality of treatment is one determinant[398] and age at loss of dietary control another.[397] The factor likely to be common to these two determinants is a high blood phenylalanine value. There is a growing body of evidence[262,263,402a] that performance on neuropsychological tests and blood phenylalanine are inversely correlated.

When to Terminate Treatment. The merits of a controlled trial notwithstanding,[403] no such study of early treatment was ever done. On the other hand, the tantalizing evidence that an inadvertant or purposeful closure of treatment might exact a cost on intellectual performance was an open invitation to do a controlled trial of continued versus terminated treatment in PKU, and it was indeed done.[404] It showed a four-point deficit in the IQ score (not significant) in a group (n = 14) of 6-year-olds in whom treatment had been stopped at 4 years of age. "No harmful effects of diet termination were noted," the authors concluded, "but a longer period of observation in a larger number of subjects is needed."[404] Subsequent experience has proved them right in the caveat and wrong in the observation (Table 15-4).

When treatment is stopped in PKU, the consequence is what one afficianado has called "late-onset phenylalanine intoxication."[405] If untreated PKU causes irreversible brain damage, avoidable only by early treatment, there is likely to be a corresponding form of harm to brain in later life when the treated patient reexperiences hyperphenylalaninemia. Since the effects of the late and early insults are likely to be different, the tests to measure them should be different.[405] Retrospective[397,406–408a,409,410] and prospective[408b] studies of treatment termination in PKU indicate now that the effect on brain function is not as great as the effect on no treatment at all (Fig. 15-11), but it is enough to cause alarm. It is still unclear whether the "premature termination" effect is universal or whether only certain patients are susceptible to it.

Evidence that cognitive function deteriorated following termination of treatment in PKU patients was published quite early in the history of PKU treatment.[406–408] The patients all had classic PKU, they had been treated from early life, and they were under experienced supervision at centers in London, Warsaw, and Heidelberg; the intervals between the last measured IQ on treatment and the measurements obtained after diet termination were from 2 to 6 years. Treatment was stopped at two centers (London and Warsaw) and relaxed at the third (Heidelberg). A significant drop, probably progressive[407] in IQ scores (change, −5 to −30 points) was observed in the treatment-terminated patients[407,408]; there was little change in the treatment-relaxed group.[408] Because other groups did not find significant deficits in posttermination IQ scores,[408a,408b] the issue seemed to require clarification. After reviewing 19 studies of treatment, it was decided "methodological difficulties and the varying results reported" left the case for so-called late-onset phenylalanine toxicity unresolved.[409] However, since then many studies[15a,410–413] using various measurements have shown that treatment termination is followed by performance deficits in many but not all PKU patients. We might say that the gain in social freedom that goes with treatment termination is offset by its probability of hazard on average and by its costs, if the hazard is encountered, of a decline in IQ scores,[398,407,408,410] deviant EEG patterns,[410,411] decreased neurotransmitter synthesis,[412] impaired vigilance as measured by reaction time variability,[412] and deficits in social quotients as measured by Vineland Social Quotients.[413] Ten of twenty-six PKU patients developed behavioral and neurologic problems after termination of treatment, whereas only 4 of 51 developed symptoms when a relaxed form of treatment was maintained.[15a] There is, so far, no unambiguous predictor of outcome for the individual patients, although the plasma phenylalanine value off diet has a negative correlation with performance and catecholamine metabolites a positive correlation.[15a,262] No satisfactory controlled trial has yet been successfully completed, in which multiple secular measurements were made of phenylalanine and other large neutral amino acids, metabolites of phenylalanine and neuro-

Table 15-4 Effect of Treatment Termination on IQ Scores of PKU Patients

Source (Ref. no.)	n	*ΔIQ score (mean)*	*Significance*	*Age tested (mean), yr*	*Months off diet (mean)*	*Study design*
404	14	−3.8	NS	6	24	Longitudinal
406	17	−6.3		8	41	Longitudinal
407	6	−7.8		3.6	12	Longitudinal
407	6	−14.2		6.6	48	Longitudinal
408	16	−8.3	$<$0.001	11	34	Longitudinal
408	7	−9.1	$<$0.05	13	44	Longitudinal
408a	30	−0.8	NS	6	24	Longitudinal
408b	55	−5	$<$0.01	6	24	Controlled trial
408c	115	+1*	NS	8	24	Controlled trial
410	14	−14	$<$0.005	11	6	Longitudinal

*The diet termination group showed significant deterioration on school achievement data (WRAT scores) relative to the treatment continuation group.

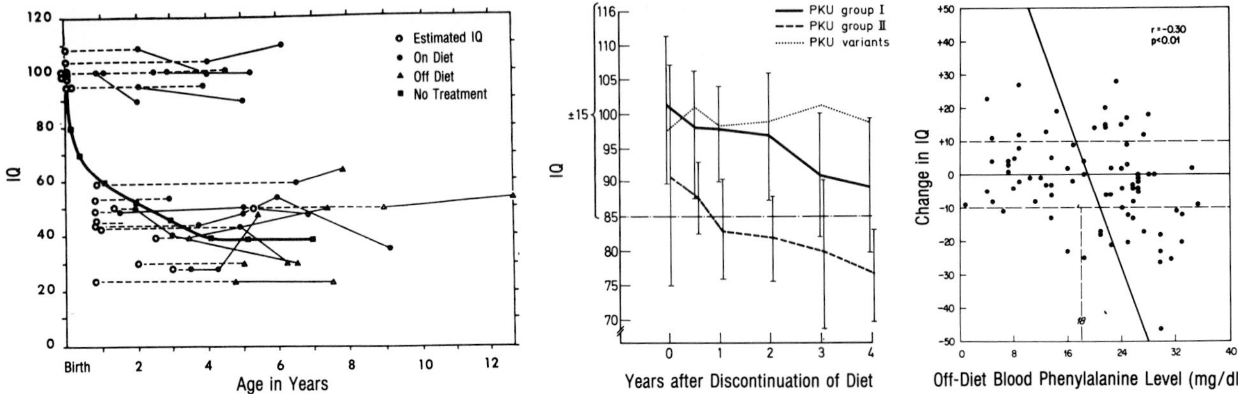

Fig. 15-11 *Left.* The benefits of early treatment and the costs of delayed treatment to PKU patients expressed as IQ (or DQ) scores related to patient age. The heavy line (●—●) represents mean IQ scores in groups of patients diagnosed at mean ages as indicated (○---). *(From figure 15-7 of Scriver and Rosenberg.[35] Used by permission.) Middle.* The effect of terminated treatment on IQ score in early treated PKU patients related to time off diet: PKU group I (——), classic PKU cases (n = 22), treated 4⁸⁄₁₂ years (average); PKU group II (--), younger classical PKU cases (n = 10) treated 2⁴⁄₁₂ years (average); PKU variants (....), apparent non-PKU hyperphenylalanemia cases (n = 5), treated nonetheless for 3⁸⁄₁₂ years average IQ. *Right.* Change in IQ scores related to off-diet blood phenylalanine value in early treatment PKU and non-PKU hyperphenylalaninemia patients. Risk of IQ decline was 36 percent when blood phenylalanine value exceeded 1.1 m*M*. *(From Waisbren et al.[398] Used by permission.)* The three panels together indicate that severe hyperphenylalaninemia in early life impairs cognitive development irreversibly in PKU patients and impairs neuropsychological function (in general but not uniformly and perhaps reversibly) when it reappears in later life in PKU patients taken off diet.

transmitter related metabolites in body fluids, and their correlation with measurements of neuropsychological function examined. Until the factors that cause impaired cognitive function in certain PKU subjects who go off treatment are ferreted out, we should assume that excess phenylalanine is a troublemaker in both later and early life and to act accordingly. There was no standard policy in the United States in 1978 for termination of PKU treatment,[414] but 4 years later when the rumor was circulating that premature termination might not be harmless, two-thirds of 90 PKU clinics were recommending indefinite continuation of dietary treatment.[415] A year after that, PKU patients who had gone off treatment were trying to resume treatment in substantial numbers.[416]

Why do patients forsake treatment when common sense and evidence indicate that it is beneficial to continue it? Again there is no single answer to this question, as there was none to the one about the cause of posttermination deterioration. Several factors undoubtedly contribute: the social character of the treatment (a restriction); the properties of low-phenylalanine diets (poor organoleptic quality); nutritional considerations (how to keep phenylalanine intake low and other nutrients at adequate levels as the patient grows); and just plain lack of knowledge. These issues and others that we have not mentioned or do not know about confound attempts to continue or reinstate dietary treatment in older children and adolescents. Success rates are poor.[417] Deterioration in cognitive function follows diet termination in this group as well, and it is hard to reverse once it has occurred.[417–420] Reinstallment of metabolic control is achieved only with enormous effort,[419] and the gains in neuropsychological function are disappointing.[420]

RÉSUMÉ. The circumstances of optimal treatment for PKU are few and simple in theory but difficult in practice: (1) Early onset (within 1 month of birth); (2) continuation throughout childhood and adolescence, perhaps for life (and certainly through pregnancy for the benefit of the offspring); (3) restriction of phenylalanine intake to amounts (250 to 500 mg/day) sufficient to hold plasma phenylalanine values well below 1 m*M* and above 0.25 m*M*. (The tolerance for phenylalanine varies between patients, and excessive restriction impairs growth and development.) The roles of better treatment products, nutrient supplements (large neutral amino acids and micronutrients in particular), and enzyme (PAL) substitution have yet to be evaluated. Support, particularly in its paramedical component, is as important as any other component of treatment.

Outcome in Untreated Non-PKU Hyperphenylalaninemia. Adult women with plasma phenylalanine values below 1 m*M*, ascertained by cord blood screening at delivery, have no demonstrable intellectual defects.[421] Infants with non-PKU hyperphenylalaninemia, ascertained by newborn screening, develop normally without treatment[391,403] and with it.[407] This experiment of nature tells us that the goal of treatment for disorders of PAH integrity is to convert the metabolic phenotype of PKU to that of non-PKU hyperphenylalaninemia.

Aspartame. *N*-aspartylphenylalanine methyl ester (trivial name, aspartame) is an artificial sweeteneer which upon hydrolysis in the intestinal lumen releases free L-phenylalanine and L-aspartic acid. Aspartame is widely available following bans on other artificial sweeteners and notwithstanding a dispute over approval for its use in the North American market.[422] Therefore, it is prudent that patients with PKU and all other forms of hyperphenylalaninemia be made aware of aspartame and that there be appropriate labeling to identify products containing it; for example, a quart of Koolaid contains 280 mg phenylalanine.[423] Ignorance about aspartame in the world of persons with any form of hyperphenylalaninemia, including the maternal form, makes them liable to a potential hazard.[423,424]

The effect of aspartame ingestion on plasma phenylalanine has been studied. The plasma response, up to 6 h after aspartame ingestion (34 mg/kg by single oral dose) is slightly greater in male than female adults, but in both it is trivial.[425] Although female PKU heterozygotes have a greater increase in plasma phenylalanine (mean peak value 151 ± 47 μM versus preload value 59 ± 15 μM) than nonheterozygotes, their postaspartame values are not in a harmful range.[425] The plasma phenylalanine response was further reinvestigated[426] in PKU and non-PKU hyperphenylalaninemia patients (children on unrestricted diets), PKU heterozygotes (adults, sex unspecified), and young adults (controls). The aspartame load in this study was 10 mg/kg (single dose), in keeping with likely exposures in everyday life. Plasma phenylalanine did not increase further in the patients (the value was already high); it did rise (+20 percent) in the heterozygotes, but the 1 h peak value (82 + 17 μM) was within the range of normal variation.[34] A third study[427] found that single-dose aspartame loading in normal lactating women with a high dose level (50 mg/kg) had only a trivial effect on phenylalanine in breast milk.

Gene Therapy. The idea that expression of mutant resident genes can be modified by incoming normal genes grips the imagination and commands the efforts of many geneticists.[29,428] The problems associated with conventional treatment lend encouragement to this line of thinking about PKU. Gene insertion in PKU research has another side to it; a heritable animal model of hyperphenylalaninemia could perhaps be made for the study of pathogenesis. Germline therapy is a remote possibility; somatic cell gene therapy is more promising. The prerequisites for the latter in PKU are those for any genetic disease: availability of the cloned gene or cDNA, an efficient means of gene transfer, and acquisition of the incoming gene in the resident genome with transmission of its encoded phenotype to daughter cells. The gene does not need to be expressed in brain cells to benefit the PKU phenotype.

The human cDNA clone (phPAH 247), when transferred into cultured mouse NIH 3T3 fibroblasts, expresses mRNA, immunoreactive protein, and PAH activity.[429] These findings meet the first requirement; other procedures are needed for the second and third. Human cDNA has been packaged in a "defective" retroviral vector[430] and used to infect both NIH 3T3 cells and a mouse hepatoma cell line. Both cell lines are totally deficient in resident PAH activity; after transfection they expressed the encoded mRNA, the protein, and pterin-dependent PAH activity[431]; Fig. 15-12 shows the effect of transfection on the hepatoma line. Mouse LTK$^-$ cells are PAH-deficient; they have been transformed with a rat PAH cDNA.[432] There has been some initial success with transfection of dividing primary cultures of rodent hepatocytes with a recombinant gene,[433,434] but studies with the PAH gene itself have not yet been reported.

There are numerous ways that an animal model of heritable PKU might be developed. Recent successes at creating mutants in the mouse by homologous recombination, using mutagenized embryonic stem cells inserted into developing blastocytes, to create a model of Lesch-Nyhan syndrome (see Chap. 38), indicate one approach. Mutant PAH genes corresponding to human alleles could be used in such a system where pathogenesis of the brain phenotype is accessible to investigation.

Disorders of Tetrahydrobiopterin Homeostasis

Phenylalanine hydroxylation is pterin-dependent, and impaired tetrahydrobiopterin (BH_4) homeostasis impairs hydroxylation not only of phenylalanine but also of tyrosine and tryp-

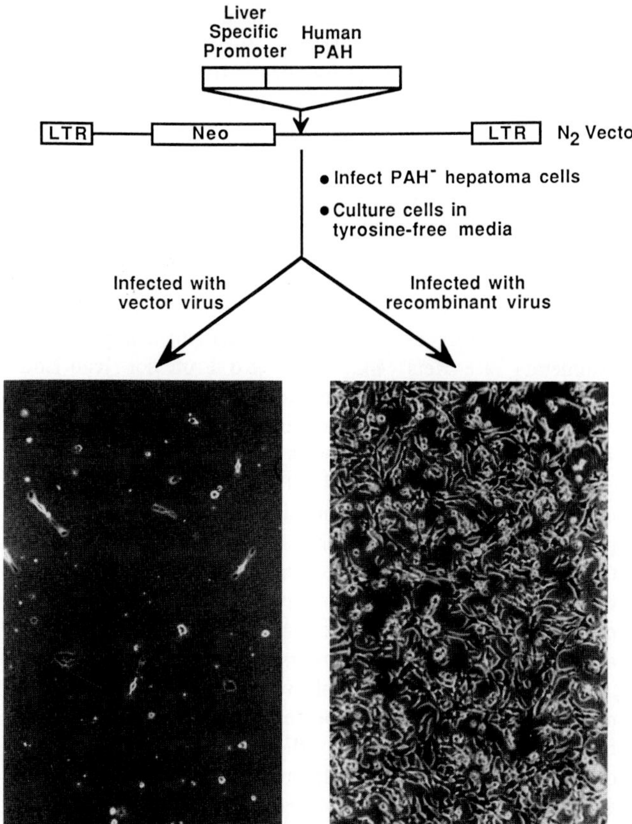

Fig. 15-12 Correction of a genetic defect in cultured hepatoma cells by retroviral-mediated gene transfer. The cells lack resident PAH activity and cannot grow in a tryosine-free medium *(left panel)*. After infection, with a recombinant retrovirus containing the human PAH cDNA,[431] they acquired the ability to grow in the selective medium *(right panel)*. Thus incoming recombinant DNA encoding human PAH activity corrected the resident deficiency in the hepatoma cell. *(Unpublished data, F. D. Ledley, H. M. Grenett, M. McGinnis-Shelnutt, and S. L. C. Woo.)*

tophan (Fig. 15-6). It was postulated a priori[67,435] that hyperphenylalaninemia need not be a primary disorder of PAH integrity. The hypothesis became fact when an atypical PKU patient was discovered[436] with persistent hyperphenylalaninemia, normal PAH activity in vitro,[248,436] and normal hepatic activities of DHPR and cofactor.[437] Later (this patient is mentioned in four different articles[248,436–438]) *Crithidia* factor activity was found deficient in blood, urine, and liver,[438] indicating a deficiency of BH_4. In retrospect, the normal hepatic cofactor activity associated with the assay of PAH in vitro[437] is perhaps explained by an abundance of neopterin* in the patient's tissues. The clinical course of this patient became a source of great concern when he developed a progressive neu-

*The terms *neopterin* and *biopterin* appear repeatedly here and in the source literature. Neopterin is a degradation product of dihydroneopterin triphosphate (the substrate of 6-pyruvoyltetrahydropterin synthase, Figs. 15-5 and 15-6); neopterin is derived from the latter via dihydroneopterin; the alternate pathway is shown in Refs. 443 and 482. Biopterin [6-(2,3-dihydroxypropylpterin)] is a completely conjugated (oxidized) degradation product of tetrahydrobiopterin (BH_4). Neopterin and biopterin are each only one of the degradation products of their precursors, but, being the major ones, they give the generic names to their classes of by-products. The precursors (dihydroneopterin triphosphate and BH_4) are on the main pathway for *de novo* synthesis of BH_4 (Figs. 15-5 and 15-6); their by-products, neopterin and biopterin, respectively, bear a corresponding relationship to each other. Accordingly, blocks in BH_4 synthesis either decrease neopterin and biopterin together (GTP-CH deficiency) or raise neopterin and deplete biopterin (6-PTS deficiency).

rologic disorder despite adequate treatment for PKU.[436,437]

Progressive neurologic disease in treated hyperphenylalaninemia patients worried others also.[439] In a group of English patients, it was attributed to impaired BH_4 homeostasis,[439] an abnormality that was actually identified in liver, brain, and skin fibroblasts of a patient.[163,440] Among early descriptions of the progressive neurologic phenotype (sometimes called *malignant hyperphenylalaninemia*[438]) there was a French article describing one patient with evidence of DHPR deficiency and a second with intact DHPR activity and decreased pterin levels in plasma and urine.[441] As awareness increased, cases were found and by July 1987, a register of malignant hyperphenylalaninemia (see Refs. 442, 442a) (c/o Professor Jean-Louis Dhondt, Faculté Libre de Médecine, 59046 Lille, France) contained 40 patients with biopterin synthetase deficiency, 14 with partial, or peripheral, forms of this deficiency, four with GTP-CH deficiency, 34 with DHPR deficiency, and eight with unclassified disorders. Their incidence is 1 to 2 percent of hyperphenylalaninemia cases (or ≈1 per million livebirths) and their occurrence is worldwide. Their existence is confounding to counsellors of patients with apparent PKU or non-PKU hyperphenylalaninemia for these reasons: first, plasma phenylalanine in these aggressive disorders sometimes mimics the level in benign non-PKU hyperphenylalaninemia (i.e., below 1 m*M*), and they might then be considered of no medical concern; and second, treatment of them with a low phenylalanine diet alone is not sufficient. Although the vast uncertainty they generate in PKU prevention programs far exceeds their incidence, it is essential that the uncertainty be dispelled. Otherwise it must affect counseling of all cases of hyperphenylalaninemia. This has been accomplished by the accumulation of knowledge about them[11–16,20,24,443] and the application of new diagnostic methods in PKU screening programs. We describe here the disorders of DHPR activity and of BH_4 biosynthesis; the programmatic diagnostic methods are described later.

Dihydropteridine Reductase (DHPR) Deficiency. Deficiency of DHPR activity was the first disorder of BH_4 homeostasis to be documented.[163,440] The original proband was a 14-month-old male infant who developed seizures and other signs of neurologic deterioration despite excellent dietary control of blood phenylalanine concentrations from the third week of life. The hepatic levels of phenylalanine hydroxylase and BH_4 were adequate, but there was no DHPR activity under conditions where 1 percent normal activity could have been detected.[163] Antibody studies failed to detect any cross-reacting DHPR protein in extracts from this patient's liver.[163] Some DHPR-deficient patients resemble this first case, whereas others have a CRM-positive form of DHPR deficiency.[19,443a]

Deficiency of DHPR has a profound effect on metabolism. It is likely to affect the oxidative cleavage of glyceryl ethers,[444] and if the enzyme also serves to keep folate in the active tetrahydro form,[162] then folate deficiency could be a further consequence of DHPR deficiency.[445] Patients lacking DHPR are deficient in the neurotransmitters whose synthesis depends on the normal activity of DHPR-dependent tyrosine and tryptophan hydroxylases.[79–81] They have low levels of urinary and CSF 3-methoxy-4-hydroxyphenylglycol (MHPG) and vanillyl mandelic acid (VMA), both being metabolites of norepinephrine; of homovanillic acid (HVA), a metabolite of dopamine; and of 5-hydroxyindoleacetic acid (5-HIAA), a metabolite of serotonin.[443,446–448] The levels of HVA and 5-HIAA in CSF approached 15 percent normal and that of MHPG 40 percent normal in one study.[447] CSF levels apparently reflect brain tissue levels.[446] The greater turnover of dopamine relative to norepinephrine in mammalian brain[449] probably explains the greater deficiency of dopamine metabolites in DHPR deficiency; high turnover probably accounts for the severe deficiency of 5-HIAA as well. In keeping with the turnover hypothesis, it was found that probenicid, a drug that inhibits egress of those metabolites from CSF, provoked less than the anticipated accumulation of HVA and 5-HIAA in CSF in a patient with DHPR deficiency.[446]

Whereas there is indeed an impairment of neurotransmitter synthesis in PKU which is secondary to metabolite competition and correctable by lowering the phenylalanine level,[262,263,450] the corresponding impairment in DHPR deficiency reflects a different mechanism, one in which the catalysts involved in neurotransmitter synthesis are fundamentally impaired. Accordingly, their dysfunction cannot be corrected by low-phenylalanine diet therapy[447] and this has implications both for treatment, just as the finding of a progressive brain phenotype in BH_4-deficient phenotypes has implications for unraveling its pathogenesis in the hyperphenylalaninemias in general.

Published cases classified as DHPR deficiency have had near-complete deficiency of DHPR activity. Some authors suggest that partial deficiency of DHPR activity may also be associated with impaired neurotransmitter homeostasis and progressive mental retardation, with or without hyperphenylalaninemia.[451,452] This possibility has not yet been examined carefully.

TREATMENT. DHPR-deficient patients require combined therapy. The goal, first defined in a note[452a] pertaining to a patient[436] who probably does *not* have DHPR deficiency, is to control hyperphenylalaninemia by dietary restriction of phenylalanine, and to restore neurotransmitter homeostasis by oral administration of L-dopa (≈12 mg/kg per day), 5-hydroxytryptophan (≈10 mg/kg per day), and other agents. Carbidopa, an inhibitor of peripheral aromatic amino acid decarboxylase, reduces the therapeutic dose of L-dopa in DHPR deficiency.[437] In general, the effectiveness of combined treatment varies inversely with the age at which it is initiated.[437,442,446,451,453–455] Some have speculated that there may even be a prenatal effect of severe DHPR deficiency.[445] BH_4 therapy alone is not feasible in severe DHPR deficiency because it cannot be given in sufficient amounts to maintain an adequate pool of BH_4 in the absence of the endogenous reducing system sustained by DHPR.

Folate levels were low in serum and brain of the first reported patient,[162,163] and this finding was subsequently reported by others.[456–458] Assuming that DHPR plays a rolein tetrahydrofolate homeostasis,[162] some form of folate therapy is a reasonable adjuvant in DHPR deficiency.[15a,16,20,445,446,458,459,459a] Folinic acid is a preferred form for treatment,[16,445] and it has been given to several patients[445,446,458,459] with apparent benefit. The combination of folinic acid (≈12.5 mg/day), neurotransmitter precursor supplements (L-dopa and 5 hydroxytryptophan), and phenylalanine restriction begun 2 months after birth prevented neurologic damage in one patient with DHPR deficiency.[445] The mechanism by which folinic acid offsets the effect of DHPR deficiency is uncertain, but it probably involves formation of 5-CH_3-tetrahydrofolate in peripheral tissues with subsequent uptake by brain and the penetration of brain by folinic acid and synthesis of 5-CH_3-tetrahydrofolate there.[16,445]

DIAGNOSIS. DHPR deficiency can be surmized from measurements of related metabolites in urine, blood, and CSF; it can be confirmed only by specific assay of enzyme activity.[459a,459b] DHPR activity can be measured in cultured skin fibroblasts,[163] blood leukocytes,[165,166] lysed erythrocytes,[167] and dried filter-paper samples of whole blood.[460] The assay procedure requires care.[19,163]

Metabolite assays are popular for diagnosis of suspected DHPR deficiency, but they have pitfalls and they must be used with caution to avoid false-negative diagnosis.[16] The problem is biologic rather than analytic. The urine pattern is the most widely used diagnostic procedure, and comparison of reduced and oxidized pterins is likely to be the best approach; there are reliable analytic methods (HPLC) for pterins.[461–462] The majority of urine pterins occur in their reduced forms, mainly BH_4, in PKU and normal subjects. We expect to find little or none in this form in subjects with severe DHPR deficiency,[461] and most of the urine pterin is found in oxidized forms. The urine pterin content is more often expressed as the neopterin/biopterin ratio or as percent biopterin,[448] and both values are expected to be low in DHPR deficiency. In the actual case they are not greatly deviant from the lower normal range; and the diagnosis is missed in about a third of the cases,[16,443,448] particularly in very young patients.

Another indirect diagnostic test, namely, a falling plasma phenylalanine value after oral or intravenous BH_4 (2 to 10 mg/kg),[456,459b,462a] can also miss the diagnosis of DHPR deficiency.[16] The explanation is as follows. In the DHPR-deficient patient, BH_4 functions stoichiometrically, not catalytically, in the hydroxylation reaction. If the dose of BH_4 is insufficient to maintain repeated cycles of hydroxylation, the PAH reaction cannot continue; it will be insufficient as long as DHPR activity is not adequate to regenerate the pool. Accordingly, severe or complete DHPR deficiency could be missed by a BH_4 loading test and the persistence of hyperphenylalaninemia interpreted as PAH deficiency. Partial DHPR deficiency and the various forms of impaired BH_4 synthesis have a better chance of being recognized by the test, in theory, but the practice could be risky nonetheless.

PRENATAL AND MOLECULAR DIAGNOSIS. DHPR activity is present in amniocytes[164,463] (Table 15-5), and prenatal diagnosis has been performed by enzyme assay.[463] DNA analysis can also serve prenatal diagnosis of DHPR deficiency in informative families.[465] One *Msp I* and two *Ava II* RFLPs are in linkage with the DHPR locus (chromosome 4, region p15.3), and the near full-length human DHPR cDNA clone[211] hybridizes with these RFLPs. There is no evidence, so far, of tight association between DHPR deficiency alleles and RFLP haplotypes.

Table 15-5 Dihydropteridin Reductase (DHPR) Activity; Gene Dosage Effects in Mutants

Reference	*Tissue*	*Subject*	*DHPR activity mean ± SD (range)*	*% normal*
164	Fibroblasts	Controls (n = 22)	21.5 ± 1.6* (15.0–35.3)	
463	Fibroblasts	Controls (n = 16)	49.8 ± 8.8* (35.4–60.5)	
164	Amniocytes	Controls (n = 6)	13.7 ± 1.9* (8.3–20.9)	
463	Amniocytes	Controls (n = 5)	48.4 ± 6.6 (41.0–55.3)	
165	Lymphocyte-platelet preparation	Controls (n = 12)	29.5 ± 4.8* (21.4–39.1)	
166	Leukocytes	Controls (n = 28)	25 ± 5.2† (16.8–35.4)	
166	Fibroblasts	Controls (n = 16)	31.7 ± 13.4* (15.0–58.3)	
164	Fibroblasts	**Mother R‡**	**2.4**	**11**
		Father R	9.6	45
		Mother M	11.6	54
		Father M	11.9	55
165,456	Fibroblasts	**Mother P**	**12.8**	**26**
	Lymphocyte/platelet	"	**6.4**	**22**
	Fibroblasts	Father P	20.5	41
	Lymphocyte/platelet	"	10.3	35
456	Fibroblasts	Mother Z	19.1	39
		Father Z	22.3	45
166	Leukocytes	Mother S	12.1	48
		Father S	11.4	46
451	Fibroblasts	Mother L	13.6	63§
		Father L	11.2	52§
164,166, 451,456	Fibroblasts, leukocytes	Probands		
		[R,M(164)]	0	0
		[P,Z(456)]	0	0
		[S1,S2,(166)]	0	0
		[L(451)]	2.7	12§,¶

*Enzyme units are nanomoles of NADH oxidized per minute per milligram of protein.

Enzyme units are nmoles cytochrome C reduced per minute per miligram of protein. Values for correspond to about 56 percent of †.

†**Bold type** indicates subjects with deviant gene dosage.†

§Controls values taken from Milstien et al.[164]

¶Further studies[464] showed proband L had no DHPR activity in liver or lymphocytes.

GENETIC HETEROGENEITY, GENE DOSAGE, AND INHERITANCE. DHPR activity in obligatate heterozygotes is expected to be about half-normal, assuming a normal gene dosage effect. Most heterozygotes have normal gene dosage for DHPR activity in fibroblasts and peripheral blood cells, but some have expressed an excessive gene dosage effect[164,165,443a] (Table 15-5). DHPR is dimeric,[464] and heterozygotes with a CRM-positive mutant allele make heterodimeric enzyme which, in some cases, seems unstable. Diversity in heterozygous phenotypes indicates genetic heterogeneity in DHPR deficiency complimenting the corresponding evidence in the homozygous phenotype.[465–467] Affected probands (homozygotes or compounds)[465] are either CRM-positive or negative (see table 12.10 in Ref. 19 and Ref. 443a). DHPR deficiency is autosomal recessive on the basis of locus assignment, usual gene dosage, and inheritance.

Disorders of BH_4 Synthesis. Not all patients initially reported with so-called malignant hyperphenylalaninemia[438] had DHPR deficiency. Bartholomé's troublesome patient[248,436–438] was one of them, and there were others[440,441,468–470] (see also Refs. 438 and 442). In time, many patients were identified who had intact PAH and DHPR activities and impaired BH_4 synthesis. Deficient BH_4 synthesis has two recognized forms, guanosine triphosphate cyclohydrolase (GTP-CH) deficiency and 6-pyruvoyltetrahydropterin synthase (6-PTS) deficiency; of the two. The latter is about five times more prevalent. No disorders of sepiapterin or 2′-keto reductase activity have been reported yet.

Guanosine Triphosphate-Cyclohydrolase Deficiency. Four patients (R. Matalon, unpublished observation, 1987; Refs. 471–473) with GTP-CH deficiency (putative or verified) are listed in Dhondt's register. The more severely affected cases[471,472] had progressive neurologic disease with truncal hypotonia, limb hypertonia, convulsions, and intermittent hyperthermia without infection; helper T lymphocytes were depressed in one patient.[472] Early treatment with biopterin may forestall progession of the disease,[473] but a good outcome is not assured.[472]

The metabolic phenotype in GTP-CH deficiency has the identifying features expected of a block at the beginning of the BH_4 synthesis pathway (see Figs. 15-5 and 15-6). Neopterin and biopterin levels are both low, and the neopterin/biopterin ratio is normal in urine, plasma, and CSF; the high levels of phenylalanine and low levels of neurotransmitter derivatives in body fluids move toward the normal range with BH_4 replacement.[471–473]

GTP-CH activity in liver[471,472] and phytohemagglutinin-stimulated blood lymphocytes[471,472] is severely deficient (below 4 percent normal) in symptomatic patients. (Normal skin fibroblasts appear not to have the enzyme.) Two obligate heterozygotes had 30 and 46 percent normal activity in stimulated lymphocytes.[474] Gene dosage, occurrence of the disease in both sexes, and consanguinity in one family[471] indicate the condition is autosomal recessive.

AN ANIMAL MODEL. Ethylnitrosourea mutagenesis of spermatogonial stem cells produced autosomal recessive GTP-CH deficiency in mice.[475–477] The murine mutation is called *hph-1*, and it maps close to *Np-1* on mouse chromosome 14.[475] Mutant homozygotes have hyperphenylalaninemia, and pterin treatment normalizes plasma phenylalanine.[476] Hepatic PAH activity is normal, but GTP-CH activity is severely deficient and the tissue pterin level is low.[477] Homozygous mutant mice do not have a neurologic phenotype for reasons not yet understood.[477]

6-Pyruvoyltetrahydropterin Synthase (6-PTS) Deficiency. The earliest reported patients[248,436–438,440,441,468–470] with evidence of a specific defect in BH_4 synthesis have subsequently been reclassified as 6-PTS-deficient (confirmed or probable).

Impaired synthesis of BH_4 was first demonstrated indirectly.[478] Cofactor activity in liver of an affected patient[470,478] was 10 percent normal, serum and urine contained low levels of biopterinlike compounds, and a phenylalanine load, which raises serum biopterin levels in normal persons, failed to have this effect in the patient. Furthermore, PAH activity measured *in situ et in vivo* by a tritium release assay was only 2.3 percent normal. Levels of neurotransmitter derivative in urine were low. The patient had severely delayed motor and cognitive development despite a history of adequate therapy with the low phenylalanine diet. While he was being investigated, another patient with a similar history and findings[479] was infused with BH_4 (2.5 mg/kg); plasma phenylalanine, which was elevated before the infusion, promptly fell and stayed normal for 2 days; a similar response followed oral BH_4.[479]

The functional deficiency of BH_4 in these patients could be the result of impaired synthesis or increased degradation of the pterin. Evidence in favor of a block in synthesis soon accumulated, although it would be some time before the enzyme deficiency itself could be documented. Urine neopterin and biopterin values were abnormal[462,480] with high neopterin levels and low biopterin; 3′-hydroxysepiapterin, a derivative of neopterin, was also present in elevated amounts.[481] An appropriate metabolic response (decline of plasma phenylalanine) when L-sepiapterin (1 mg/kg) was given by mouth[480] implied the block was at an early step in the pathway (Figs. 15-5 and 15-6). Urine of affected patients contained no detectable biopterin.[482] The relationship between urine biopterin and the pterin ratio was considered useful in diagnosis[483] (Fig. 15-13).

The associated clinical disorder mimics the one described for GTP-CH deficiency. There is a characteristic truncal hypotonia, limb hypertonia with pronated hand postures, difficulty in swallowing, somnolence, irritability, episodic hyperthermia, seizures, and delayed cognitive development. There can be circadian fluctuation in symptoms.[483a]

Evidence of a block in BH_4 synthesis invited attempts to treat these patients with BH_4 replacement alone (so-called monotherapy) or with adjuvant treatment (phenylalanine restriction and neurotransmitter precursor supplementation).[483–487] Treatment was successful in some and not in other patients,[488] early treated patients responding, in general, better than late treated. The possibility that harm had occurred in utero (see, e.g., the published discussion following Ref. 443) is one explanation for a poor postnatal response, but another is impaired ability of the exogenous pterin to penetrate brain. The latter idea arose in studies of rats[489,490] and humans[456] given BH_4, where it was shown that peripherally administered pterin did not enter brain and CSF. Accordingly, low-dose monotherapy (2.5 to 10 mg/kg per day) that might be adequate for hepatic PAH activity could be inadequate for brain tyrosine and tryptophan hydroxylases and would not then correct the well-documented deficiency of brain neurotransmitter synthesis.[491] The alternatives in this case are threefold: (1) to use combined therapy (pterin plus phenylalanine restriction, with oral dopa, 5 hydroxytryptophan, and carbidopa),[437,441,478,482,491] hoping to restore not only

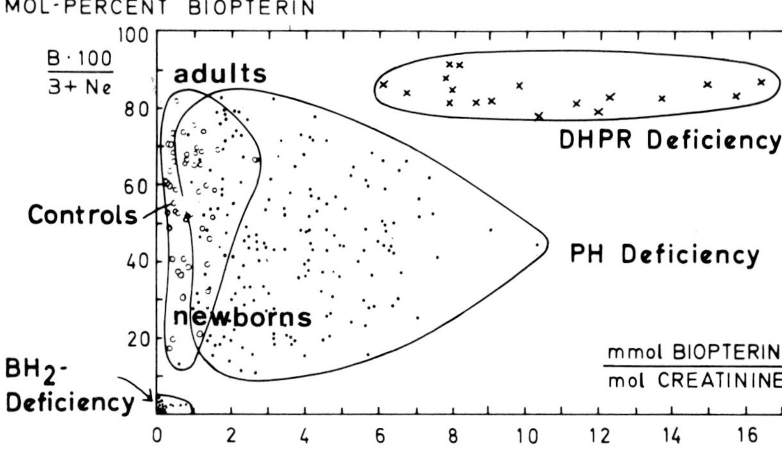

Fig. 15-13 Classification of different forms of hyperphenylalaninemia by urine pterin relationships (a metabolic phenotype). Abscissa, biopterin (B) concentration in urine; ordinate, percent biopterin/biopterin + neopterin (N). Measurements were made on 12-h urine samples collected when patients had elevated plasma phenylalanine levels. *(From Niederwieser et al.*[483] *Used by permission.)*

the quantity but the rhythm of neurotransmitter homeostasis in brain; (2) to use a synthetic pterin analogue with cofactor activity and a specific side-chain configuration[492] which would more readiy penetrate brain and not be unduly hepatotoxic[491,493]; (3) to give an effective pterin by mouth at much higher doses (20 to 40 mg/kg per day),[494] thereby demonstrably increasing brain/CSF biopterin levels in the affected patient.[495]

Whereas the theory is apparently good, the achievement in practice is unpredictable and often unsatisfactory, even with an early onset of postnatal treatment. A satisfactory clinical response correlated with the change in biogenic amine metabolites in CSF during pterin therapy in some patients[491,495a] but not in others.[496] It would seem prudent now to use combined therapy as early as possible after birth since a good outcome can occur under such circumstances.[497] There is speculation[16,491] that nonresponsiveness reflects deficient development of neuronal tyrosine and tryptophan hydroxylases when BH_4 is absent during critical periods of brain development.

THE ENZYME DEFICIENCY. The metabolic phenotype of affected cases indicates which enzyme is deficient. It is not sepiapterin reductase; in all likelihood it is the step catalyzed by the phosphate eliminating enzyme (PEE), as it was once known, now called 6-pyruvoyltetrahydropterin synthase (6-PTS). Measurement of PEE in liver biopsy samples from five patients with typical clinical and metabolic phenotypes of dihydrobiopterin synthase deficiency demonstrated severely deficient activity of PEE.[498] Sepiaterin reductase activity was normal, and mixing experiments ruled out an endogenous inhibitor of PEE.

The liver enzyme characterized as PEE[189] on further study[191,192] had activity corresponding to the reaction catalyzed by 6-PTS.[192] Erythrocytes were then found to have 6-PTS activity,[499] thus simplifying the investigation of patients. It was soon confirmed that dihydrobiopterin synthetase deficiency[480] and so-called sepiapterin synthesising enzyme-1 deficiency[500] were both apparently 6-PTS deficiency. The typical patient had very low 6-PTS activity (below four percent normal) in erythrocytes.[499]

It had been noted earlier that some BH_4 deficient patients had a mild form of putative dihydrobiopterin synthetase deficiency.[442,443,501,502] They had essentially normal values of neurotransmitter derivatives and pterins in CSF (normal brain phenotype), yet they had low values in blood and urine and manifested persistent hyperphenylalaninemia (mutant peripheral and hepatic phenotype). This variant, called *peripheral BH_4 deficiency,* presumably has a benign prognosis when treated by low phenylalanine diet. The affected patients had a partial deficiency of erythrocyte 6-PTS activity with values between 5 and 23 percent normal.[503,504]

Terms such as *partial, peripheral,* and *transitory*[505–508] relating to patients with BH_4 deficiency may describe their clinical and metabolic phenotypes, but the corresponding erythrocyte 6-PTS activities are actually not very predictive of the corresponding clinical phenotype or its prognosis. Typical patients have 0 to 20 percent normal 6-PTS activities,[503] and patients with the peripheral variant can have activity as low as 5 percent normal.[504] These findings imply genetic heterogeneity in 6-PTS deficiency. The observed phenotypes are the homozygous, compound, and heterozygous expressions of mutant alleles.[503,504] That the heterozygous phenotype can be clinically symptomatic in the newborn[503,504] and be expressed as a metabolic phenotype in adults[501,502] is a matter of further concern for interpretation, counseling, and treatment of this autosomal recessive disease.

A tentative explanation of exaggerated expression of the 6-PTS deficiency allele(s) in erythrocytes of heterozygotes is deviant gene dosage.[504] Erythrocyte 6-PTS activity in seven of eight heterozygotes was 19 to 23 percent normal instead of half-normal (Fig. 15-14). An associated deficiency of biopterin synthesis found in about half of the heterozygotes (Fig. 15-14) implies the deviant gene dosage is not limited to erythrocytes but is expressed in parenchymal cells where biopterin synthesis occurs. The abnormal gene dosage effect may arise in an unstable heteropolymeric 6-PTS enzyme in the heterozygote; the normal enzyme is a tetramer of identical subunits.[192]

DIAGNOSTIC CRITERIA. The BH_4 loading test (2.5 to 10 mg/kg) in 6-PTS deficiency gives a prompt fall in plasma phenylalanine levels.[448] Because DHPR is intact, BH_4 functions catalytically and small amounts of cofactor support hydroxylation of very large amounts of phenylalanine.

Pterin patterns are characteristic in 6-PTS deficiency. Neopterin values are high, biopterin low, and the N/B ratio high. The values are abnormal in urine and CSF in typical 6-PTS deficiency and normal in CSF in the peripheral form of 6-PTS deficiency.[502–504] Age-matched controls are important for interpretation of values in very young subjects[16] (see "Screening" and "Diagnosis," below).

Deficient 6-PTS activity and normal sepiapterin reductase in erythrocytes, confirms the diagnosis. Peripheral and typical forms of 6-PTS deficiency are not readily distinguished by erythrocyte assay alone.

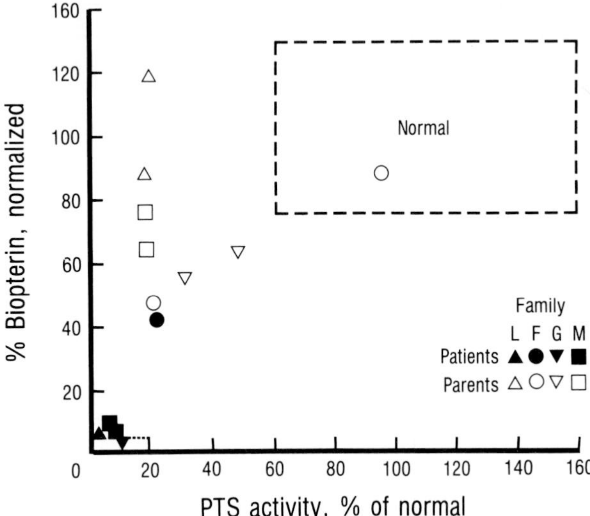

Fig. 15-14 Erythrocyte 6-PTS activity shows deviant gene dosage effect (abscissa) in patients (open symbols) of patients (closed symbols) with 6-PTS deficiency; most heterozygotes, including one proband, have less than half-normal erythrocyte 6-PTS activity. Deficiency of 6-PTS is associated with low biopterin content in urine (ordinate) in many heterozygotes and all probands. Boxed area represents range of normal values. Initials refer to families reported in Scriver et al.[504] *(Adapted from figure I of Scriver et al.[504] Used by permission.)*

Prenatal diagnosis is possible by measurement of pterin levels and ratio in amniotic fluid. The procedure has been used to identify affected[503] and normal fetuses (Kaufman, Milstien, Packman, and Golbus, unpublished observation, 1987). Normal values (n = 10) in amniotic fluid (midtrimester, 15 to 20 weeks) are 29 to 62 nmol/liter for neopterin and 12 to 29 nmol/liter for biopterin; the mean N/B ratio of 3.3.[503] The ratio in another study was 2.5 (n = 10, 16 to 18 weeks gestation) (Kaufman et al., unpublished observation, 1987). The option of prenatal diagnosis is likely to be taken seriously by consultands and counselors faced with a condition in which there is much uncertainty about prognosis (see, e.g., Refs. 483a and 508), treatment (particularly in the peripheral form of 6-PTS deficiency), and prenatal damage (see discussion in Ref. 443). The effect of deviant gene dosage on pterin levels unfortunately undermines confidence that measurements of pterins in amniotic fluid are predictive of fetal status and prognosis.[504]

Other Forms of Hyperphenylalninemia/ Phenylketonuria

A patient with confirmed severe deficiency of hepatic PAH activity had a normal urine pattern of phenylalanine derivatives, no phenylpyruvic aciduria, plasma phenylalanine values above 1 m*M*, and tolerance for dietary phenylalanine (≈350 mg/day) in the PKU range.[509] By definition, this patient had "nonphenylketonuric phenylketonuria (PAH deficiency)." Similar cases, in which PAH activity was not measured, were classified as apparent phenylalanine aminotransferase deficiency.[510,511] However (see "Mendelian Disorders of Phenylalanine Homeostasis," above), transaminase deficiency cannot cause hyperphenylalaninemia when PAH activity is intact (see Fig. 15-1 for kinetic explanation). These patients[510,511] probably had PAH deficiency *and* defective transaminase activity. Transient deficiency of transamination or delayed induction of transaminase activity without phenylketonuria[9a] was a well-known cause of missed cases when case finding or monitoring was done by the ferric chloride test on urine. The aforementioned cases[510,511] are unusual in that their putative transamination deficiency was persistent.

The converse relationship (persistent phenylketonuria *without* hyperphenylalaninemia) has been observed in two sisters.[512] The condition is benign and its mechanism obscure. A mutant transaminase with increased affinity for phenylalanine is one explanation.

Transient hyperphenylalaninemia/phenylketonuria is reported from time to time.[9a,506,507,513] A regulatory defect affecting PAH activity is one explanation; a transient disorder of biopterin metabolism another. Transient hyperphenylalaninemia is yet another reason for careful and continuous monitoring of treated patients to avoid phenylalanine deficiency when tolerance increases.[9a]

A puzzling case[514] had apparent PAH deficiency, intact DHPR activity, and no evidence of a biopterin defect; the clinical course was "malignant" at birth and death occurred at 46 days, on combined therapy. The authors proposed two disorders, PKU and a neurodegenerative disease. Since the report contains no details about the enzyme assays and no quantitative data for hepatic PAH and DHPR activities, the possibility that this patient lacked DHPR cannot be ruled out.

SCREENING AND DIAGNOSIS

On the order of 10 million newborn infants worldwide are screened annually for hyperphenylalaninemia. As a public health practice, medical screening permits presumptive identification of a disease by the application of a test in a population.[515] The goal is to reduce the effect of the disease on individuals and the population. Screening for PKU began as a public health procedure to prevent a form of mental retardation, and awareness of its genetic cause was initially unimportant.[516] But newborn screening for PKU is indeed a form of genetic screening, and it has two rationales in that context.[516] First, it permits the diseases (PKU, the "malignant" forms of hyperphenylalaninemia, and maternal PKU) to be detected at their incipient stages so that harm can be deflected by appropriate treatment; second, it serves research, for example, enumeration of gene frequencies in populations and delineation of genetic heterogeneity. Population screening for hyperphenylalaninemia, after a quarter century of practice, is unquestionably one of the great ventures in public health, and it has become a prototype for applied human genetics.

Screening

The screening test for hyperphenylalaninemia is simple. A capillary blood sample (liquid or dried on filter paper) is analyzed for its phenylalanine content by a microbiologic inhibition assay, chromatography, or fluorometry.[9a] The first method (the Guthrie test) is the one most widely used, and refinements of it continue, for example, in better selection of inhibitor-sensitive clones of *Bacillus subtilis* ATCC 6051 and ATCC 6633,[517] and in the preparation of filter paper samples to destroy contaminating antimicrobial substances.[518] Phenylalanine in dried blood spots on filter paper disks is stable for years under reasonable conditions of storage,[519,520] and such samples can be used for retrospective studies.[274,519] The Guthrie test is semiquantitative with a cutoff (threshold) value for blood phenylalanine below which it is unreliable. The fluorometric method is more quantitative and can measure phenylalanine in amounts "down to zero"; it also has a lower coefficient of variation than the Guthrie test.[520]

Blood phenylalanine is rising in the affected infant during the first week of life,[3,7,8,9a] and the screening test for hyperphenylalaninemia is done then. A follow-up test to capture infants with false negative initial tests was recommended at one time, but this procedure is inefficient[521]; cases missed on the first test are few and due largely to noncompliance with the program.[521] Legislation that mandates testing does not improve compliance,[516,522] whereas structure of the health care system has a big influence on participation in and efficiency of the screening program.[516,523–525]

Pitfalls. Social and economic factors threatened to erode the integrity of PKU screening programs in America and elsewhere, beginning in the 1980s.[526,527] Early discharge of infant and mother from hospital or birthing unit after the delivery was one of them. This practice, according to statistical estimates,[527,528] lowers sensitivity (increases the false negative rate) of PKU screening on days 1, 2, and 3 after birth; the corresponding rates of missed cases (maximum estimates) are 16.1, 2.2, and 0.3 percent, respectively. A recommendation was made[527] to retest, within 2 weeks, all infants whose first test occurred on the first day of life. The proposal generated surprisingly little reaction considering its importance; some of it was contrary,[529] some supportive.[530] Compliance with the recommendation suggests that PKU screening is just part of life in a modern society, and people adapt to changes recommended for their benefit.

Since rescreening increases costs,[529] alternatives had to be considered,[531] some social, others technical; the latter include: (1) lowering the threshold value in the Guthrie test[528,531] while accepting a tolerable increase in the rate of false positive tests (decreased specificity); (2) changing to the "no-theshold," fluorometric assay for phenylalanine, which has near perfect sensitivity in screening programs, so far.[524,532] The former has been the favored adjustment.

False negative tests, being of such concern (and incidentally a source of lawsuits), have been investigated as to their prevalence and cause. Only one case of PKU is missed for every 70 detected in America[533] and the United Kingdom.[534] The cause can be errors of compliance and procedure,[533–535] and it most certainly is also biologic,[9a,527,528,531,533,534,536–538] being related to circumstances in which the postnatal rise of phenylalanine is too modest for discrimination from the age-dependent distribution of blood phenylalanine values in normal infants. The slow rise of blood phenylalanine is more prevalent in female infants[526] and particularly in those with non-PKU hyperphenylalaninemia, the apparent result being a deficiency of female cases in the latter disorder.[528a]

Screening for PKU by the ferric chloride test (for urine phenylpyruvate) has been abandoned because of its low sensitivity.[534] Screening for PKU and allied disorders is done best by methods that measure blood phenylalanine; the more quantitative the assay and the better the statistical control, the greater the sensitivity of the test.[531,532] Participants (parents in this case) will tolerate false positive tests[539] as a necessary cost for achieving better sensitivity in screening and, of course, a higher likelihood that an unpleasant disease will be prevented. The cost effectiveness to society in PKU screening is considered reasonable.[540,541]

Diagnosis

Newborn screening at first disclosed only two classes of hyperphenylalaninemia: PKU and a benign non-PKU form,[542,543] the former being more prevalent in most populations. Monitoring of PKU patients subsequently revealed that a small proportion of them had a disease that was not typical PKU; these patients had BH_4-deficient forms of hyperphenylalaninemia. Although PKU screening programs were well established, uncertainty now gripped them. Additional diagnostic methods for purposes of classification, prognosis, counseling, and treatment of the newly recognizable variant forms—so-called malignant hyperphenylalaninemia—were sorely needed.[11–16] The tests had to be applicable to the young infant; clinicians could not wait for clarifying loading tests and the like, which could be carried out only when the infant was several months old.[544,545] The rationales and the pitfalls of these tests are discussed here. Tests for diagnosis of probands and for classification of heterozygotes are described separately.

Probands.

METABOLITE TESTS.

1. *Phenylalanine.* The upper normal value for blood phenylalanine in the newborn is about 0.15 m*M*[35]; it is about 0.12 m*M* in older infants, children, and adults in the semifasting state.[34–36] A value of about 1.2 m*M* separates PKU cases, which have higher values, from the non-PKU form of PAH deficiency; BH_4-deficient forms of hyperphenylalaninemia have no distinctive range of values.

   Filter paper disks and glass capillary tubes are suitable vehicles for blood samples when screening or monitoring.[9a] Phenylalanine is measured reliably by several methods[546–549] in addition to conventional column chromatography.[9a] Measurement of urine phenylalanine is not recommended for newborn screening.
2. *Phenylalanine Metabolites.* Urine phenylpyruvate is unreliable for newborn screening[534] or monitoring of treatment (see figure 15-12 of Ref. 9a). Formation of the keto acid is dependent on transaminase activity and the plasma phenylalanine concentration; the relationship between substrate concentration in plasma and presence of keto acid in urine is an ogive in PKU patients[550]; some patients excrete keto acid at about 0.5 m*M*, half do so at 1 m*M*, and virtually all do at 2 m*M* after 24 h of hyperphenylalaninemia. Capillary gas chromatography measures phenylalanine metabolites effectively,[551] as do many older methods (see Refs. 1 to 3).
3. *Phenylalanine Loading Tests.* The rate of phenylalanine clearance from plasma and the peak value or "area under the curve" after a standardized load (by mouth or vein), were once widely used to classify hyperphenylalaninemia phenotypes. However, they cannot be used when most needed (in the newborn), and they are not as reliable[544] as when other procedures are combined with assays of enzyme activities. Nonetheless, refinements of loading tests are still being described.[552,553] The *in vivo et situ* isotopic infusion assay and in vitro assays of PAH activity correspond well, and both correlate inversely and satisfactorily with the peak blood phenylalanine value in the newborn period and the value after phenylalanine loading tests in later life.[553a]

4. *Plasma Phenylalanine Response to BH_4 Loading.* BH_4-deficient forms of hyperphenylalaninemia will, in theory, show a fall in plasma phenylalanine after a dose (oral or intravenous) of BH_4 (2.5 to 20 mg/kg). The test is not reliable in DHPR deficiency (see Refs. 16, 443, 448, and 554), where BH_4 is only a stoichiometric and *not* a catalytic component of the phenylalanine hydroxylating reaction. Rates of intestinal absorption and dosage determine responsiveness in disorders of BH_4 synthesis. For these reasons, the test is recommended only with caution.
5. *Pterin Metabolites.* There are many methods to measure pterins in tissues and body fluids. Each measures something specific, and what is measured differs with the method. The assays are highly specialized; where they are done and by whom are best learned from the current primary literature. In general, pterin levels and patterns are similar in CSF, plasma, and urine, the exception being peripheral 6-PTS deficiency, where the CSF levels and pattern are not abnormal. Samples must be handled to protect reduced pterins from spontaneous oxidation; ascorbate (10 mg/ml of urine, for example) is used for this purpose. (The often used terms *neopterin* and *biopterin* are explained in the footnote on page 521.)
   a. *Cofactor activity:* This test measures the pterin activity in tissue or fluid that sustains phenylalanine hydroxylation in the presence of excess PAH and DHPR, under various conditions in vitro.[163,461] Values are high in PKU because hyperphenylalaninemia stimulates BH_4 synthesis (see next paragraph); and low in DHPR and biopterin synthesis deficiency where BH_4 levels are low. By adjusting conditions of the assay,[163] percentage BH_4 in total cofactor activity can be estimated. It is about 50 percent in normal tissues and greatly decreased in DHPR deficiency[163]; the trivial amount found in BH_4 synthesis deficiency is nearly all BH_4.[478]
   b. *Crithidia growth factor assay:* Biopterin can be measured by protozoologic bioassay using the haemoflagellate *Crithidia fasciculata*[555]; the active factors in human fluids and tissues are 7,8-dihydrobiopterin and BH_4, among others.[556] The assay can be applied to dried blood spots on filter paper disks.[557] Normal biopterin levels in the presence of normal phenylalanine are 1 to 3.5 μg/liter,[556] and they are increased in hyperphenylalaninemic subjects with intact BH_4 synthesis.[558] Low blood *Crithidia* factor values and a blunted response to hyperphenylalaninemia indicate an impairment of BH_4 synthesis.[468,557,558]
   c. *Pterin patterns:* The assay for hydroxylation cofactor activity[163,461] can indirectly identify the fraction present as BH_4, but this approach has been superceded. Oxidation of samples containing BH_4 in either alkaline or acidic iodine solutions converts the BH_4 to pterin and biopterin, respectively. 7,8-Dihydro derivatives of biopterin and neopterin are oxidized to biopterin and neopterin under both conditions. Several investigators[461,461a,483a,559–561] have used this approach, measuring the oxidized pterins[461a] by liquid chromatography[461–462,559a–562] or gas chromatography-mass spectrometry[563,564] to identify their specific forms.

      There are typical chromatographic elution profiles of pterins in the different diseases (see Refs. 443 and 471). The relationships between biopterin and neopterin in these disorders[483,560] are shown in Fig. 15-13. The neopterin/biopterin ratio in urine is age-dependent because neopterin synthesis in the first part of the pathway (see Figs. 15-5 and 15-6) is high relative to biopterin synthesis in the lower part in newborns.[565–567] The pterin pattern is also influenced by the phenylalanine level.[461a,565,566] The age- and phenylalanine-dependent relationships are shown in Fig. 15-15.

      In general, the patterns in normal and hyperphenylalaninemic phenotypes are as follows (principal finding italicized):

      Normal subjects have half or more of biopterin in the tetrahydro form; the normal neopterin (N) to biopterin (B) ratio (N/B ratio) is about 1; the urine ratio is elevated (up to eightfold) in the first month of life.

      PKU patients have *elevated values for total pterin, N, and B;* N/B ratio and percent BH_4 are normal.

      DHPR-deficient patients have elevated N, B, and total values, usually low but sometimes normal N/B ratio, and *greatly reduced or absent BH_4* levels.

      Typical 6-PTS deficient patients have greatly *increased neopterin and N/B ratio values;* patients with peripheral 6-PTS deficiency have a similar and urine pterin pattern, but *the CSF pterin pattern is normal.*

      GTP-CH deficient patients have *low total, N, and B values;* the N/B ratio is normal.

      All patients with neonatal hyperphenylalaninemia should be systematically investigated by urine pterin analysis.[526,567,568] Dried urine samples on filter paper can be used for this purpose.[569]
6. *Neurotransmitter derivatives.* Metabolites of dopa, catecholamines, and serotonin reflect synthesis of the precursors. Levels in plasma, urine, and CSF are modestly depressed in PKU and very low in DHPR deficiency or impaired BH_4 synthesis; the CSF values are normal in peripheral 6-PTS deficiency.

ENZYME ASSAYS.

1. *PAH.* Assay in vitro requires liver biopsy. The assay mixture must have catalytic amounts of cofactor.[237,247,248] In vivo assay of PAH activity is feasible when labeled substrate is administered and the formation of labeled products measured; for example, water (D_2O) or tyrosine in plasma, metabolites in urine, or CO_2 in expired air.[53,250,251,253–258,570–573] The tritium release assay[53] does not require measurement of the tyrosine disappearance rate to estimate the rate of tyrosine formation. The decay problem can be handled if labeled $[^2H]$phenylalanine and $[^{13}C]$tyrosine are simultaneously infused and measurements are made at isotopic steady state.[255] In vivo and in vitro measurements of PAH activity in the same individual correlate well (*r*, 0.95) in PKU and non-PKU forms of PAH deficiency.[251,553a,570]

2. *DHPR.* Standard assays measure DHPR activity in liver biopsy samples,[163] cultured skin fibroblasts,[193,164] amniocytes,[164,463] erythrocytes,[167,460] leukocytes,[165,166] platelets,[165] and dried blood spots on filter paper.[460]

3. *GTP-CH.* Enzyme activity has been measured in liver

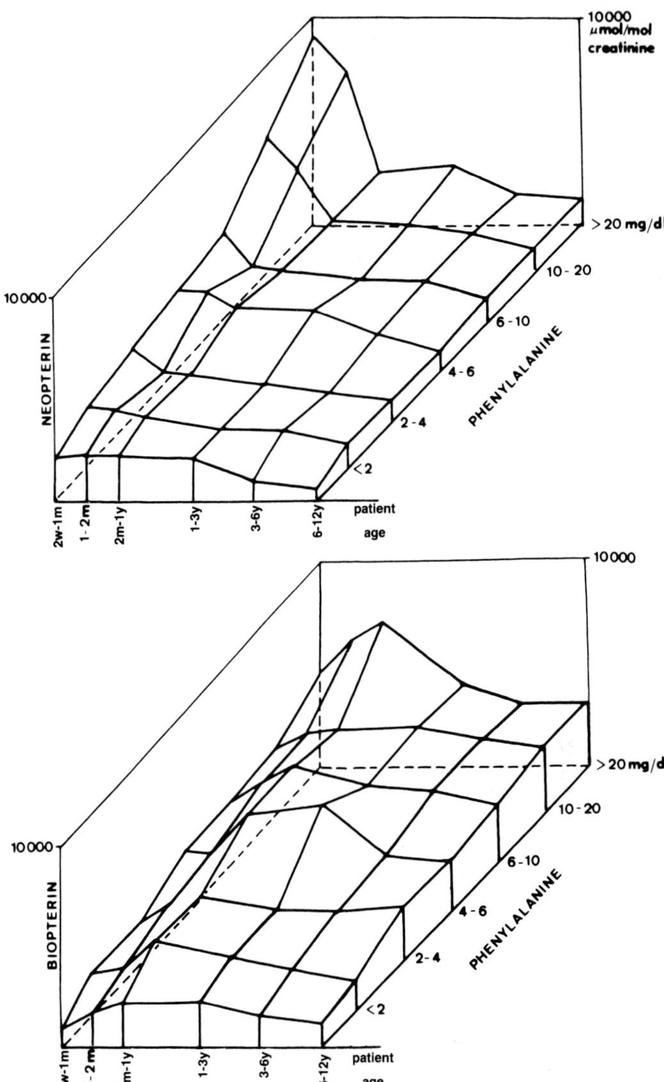

Fig. 15-15 Neopterin and biopterin levels in urine of infants related to age and plasma phenylalanine concentration. Neopterin to biopterin (N/B) ratio is high immediately after birth, falling thereafter. Neopterin and biopterin values increase syncronously in response to hyperphenylalaninemia. Values pertain to normal individuals and patients with PAH deficiency. *(From Dhondt et al.*[566] *Used by permission.)*

biopsy samples[471,473b] and phytohemagglutinin-stimulated mononuclear leukocytes[474]; GTP-CH activity is low in unstimulated cells even in normal subjects[474] and should not be mistaken for the inherited deficiency. Fibroblasts have no apparent GTP-CH activity.

4. *6-PTS.* (This is also called phosphate eliminating enzyme.) Low activity is demonstrable in liver[498] and erythrocytes[499,503,504] of patients with typical and peripheral forms of 6-PTS deficiency. Erythrocyte activity is not a clear index of the two forms.

DNA ANALYSIS. Oligonucleotide probes are anticipated soon for the characterized PKU mutations. RFLP haplotypes associate with particular PKU mutations, but they are not themselves diagnostic.[230] RFLP haplotypes at the PAH and DHPR loci can be used for prenatal diagnosis. GTP-CH and 6-PTS genes have not been cloned, mapped, or characterized. The polymerase chain reaction (see Refs. 231a, 592, and 593) will facilitate DNA analysis especially if it can be applied to dried blood spots.

PRENATAL DIAGNOSIS. The indications for prenatal diagnosis are not trivial in the hyperphenylalaninemias. Treatment is still experimental in some forms and not wholly successful in others. Accordingly, prognosis for probands is uncertain, and consultands must be counseled accordingly. There is growing evidence that parents at risk for having children with PKU desire and seek prenatal diagnosis.[573a,573b] In countries such as China, for example, where PKU is as prevalent as it is in North America, the number of cases huge, and the resources for treatment still very limited, reliable prenatal diagnosis is an option the family can take to have an unaffected child in a society that does not otherwise encourage the birth of sibs.[573c] Families at risk for recurrence of severe PAH, DHPR, and 6-PTS deficiencies can have prenatal diagnosis by analysis of DNA, enzyme activity, or metabolite levels, respectively.

1. *PAH Deficiency (PKU).* Prenatal diagnosis for PAH deficiency requires DNA analysis. Linkage disequilibrium exists between various RFLPs and the PAH locus, and certain PAH alleles associate with specific RFLP haplotypes.[224,230,574,575] There is evidence that prenatal diagnosis is desired by some families,[576] and the use of linked markers makes fetal diagnosis possible in the majority of such families. [228b,577,577a] The two-allele[225] and three-allele *Hind* III (226) polymorphisms can detect affected fetuses,[228b,577] and the *Eco* RI polymorphism can detect heterozygosity in a fetus.[228b] An affected family member is required to decide phase (Fig. 15-16), and the RFLPs must be informative. In a Central European population the three-allele *Hind* III polymorphism by itself is highly informative.[226] In the Danish population the RFLP polymor-

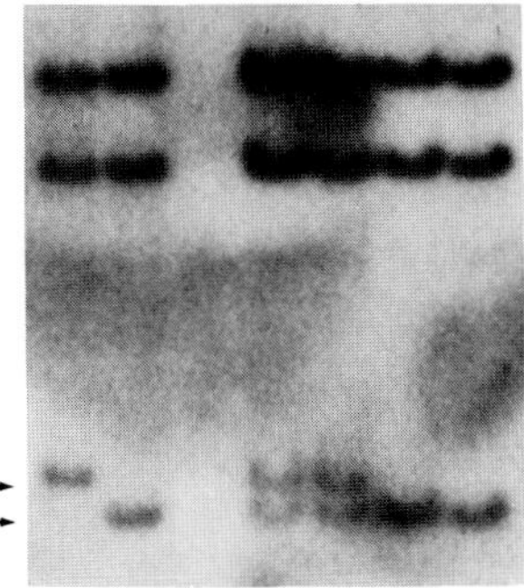

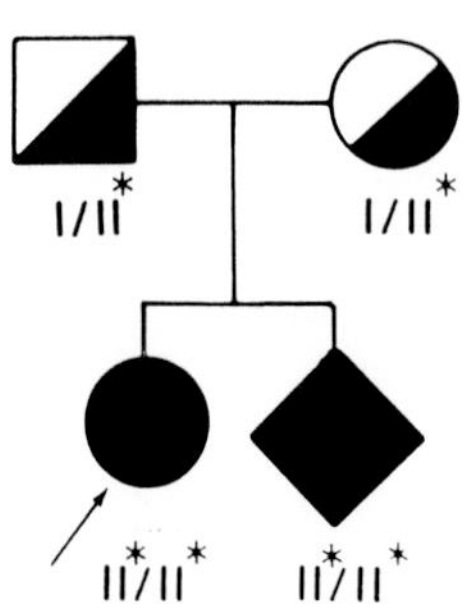

Fig. 15-16 Fetal diagnosis for PKU by DNA analysis of two-allele (4.0, 4.2 kb) *Hind* III RFLP on amniocyte genomic DNA in a Danish family. The affected proband (arrow) gives phase for the linked marker (4-kb Hind III fragment) and the PKU allele (marker and allele are cis). The fetus at risk (diamond symbol) is apparently homozygous for the PKU phenotype (homozygous 4 kb *Hind* III haplotype). The diagnosis was confirmed by the postnatal metabolic phenotype, and the infant was treated for PKU. *(Adapted from Lidsky et al. 1985.[228b] Used by permission.)*

phism information content (PIC), for purposes of prenatal diagnosis, is 85 percent with the three best of eight restriction sites (*Pvu* II, *Xmn* I, *Eco* RV).[228a]

Prenatal diagnosis, performed successfully by DNA analysis, has led to measurements of hepatic PAH activity in an affected 19-week-old fetus[577a]; neither PAH activity nor immunoreactive protein was detected, but PAH mRNA was present.

2. *DHPR Deficiency*. Amniocytes have DHPR activity (Table 15-5). Midtrimester prenatal diagnosis has been performed by DHPR assay[463] and by DNA RFLP linkage analysis at the DHPR locus.[465] The latter method requires an informative family and an affected proband to ascertain the phase of marker and allele.

3. *6-PTS Deficiency*. There are no DNA methods yet for prenatal diagnosis of this condition. Enzyme activity is accessible in fetal erythrocytes obtained by fetoscopy.[578] Pterin levels in midtrimester amniotic fluid can indicate an affected fetus,[499,578] but the pterin phenotype may not distinguish between homozygous and heterozygous phenotypes.[504]

4. *GTP-CH Deficiency*. Amniocytes do not express enzyme activity, and DNA analysis of the corresponding gene is not yet feasible. Pterin analysis in amniotic fluid is feasible, in theory, and has apparently been performed for the purpose of fetal diagnosis (cited in Ref. 579).

Heterozygotes. Reliable classification of heterozygotes is important in linkage analysis (see Ref. 206), for estimates of gene frequency (see Ref. 592 below), and in reproductive counseling. Heterozygosity for DHPR (Table 15-5), GTP-CH,[474] and 6-PTS[504] deficiencies can be determined reliably by the appropriate enzyme assays. The case for PAH deficiency is more difficult.

In vitro measurements of hepatic PAH activity are impractical for diagnosis of heterozygosity. The in vivo isotope loading test (oral route) appears to be a useful alternative[580]; its classification error is only 2 percent, equaling or improving on other methods. The isotopic method is done with small loads, and the measurements are made under quasi-steady-state conditions. These circumstances maximize the sensitivity coefficient of PAH activity in vivo; large loads of unlabeled phenylalanine lose this advantage, yet they have been widely used since first described over 30 years ago.[581] The results obtained by high dose loads, followed by measurement of plasma clearance rate, are influenced by route of administration (oral or intravenous load), pregnancy, contraceptive medication, sex, age, and body weight[582]; genetic heterogeneity further complicates matters.[583,584]

Because loading studies of any sort are cumbersome, simpler methods have appeal, especially ones that can accommodate diurnal variation in plasma phenylalanine and tyrosine values.[34] Semifasting, noon-time plasma values for phenylalanine and tyrosine[585,586] are convenient and informative, and by appropriate manipulations they reveal genetic heterogeneity at the PAH locus.[585] When combined with prior probability of heterozygosity in a quadratic discriminant function,[587,588] they can distinguish heterozygosity in a manner somewhat superior[589] to corresponding linear discriminant functions.[590] The relative merits of quadratic and linear discriminant functions continue to be a popular topic in PKU research.[591]

Analysis of DNA identifies PKU heterozygotes in the appropriate circumstance. Splicing[232] and missense[234] mutations already account for about half of the PKU alleles in the Danish population; unraveling the other prevalent mutations associated with haplotypes 1 and 4 will accommodate 90 percent of PKU alleles in Danes. With the appropriate oligonucleotide probes and application of DNA[231a] it should be possible to convert analysis of PAH-deficient hyperphenylalaninemia into the corresponding codominant genetic systems and to detect heterozygotes without recourse to family studies, knowledge of affected probands, or phenotype analysis. Of course, the relative importance of any specific probe will probably vary among regional and ethnic populations because of genetic drift and founder effects. That is why the population genetics of PKU is becoming so relevant—and at the same time so interesting.

The polymerase chain reaction[231a,592,593] will facilitate population studies by DNA analysis, and the method is apparently applicable to dried blood spots.

GENETICS OF THE HYPERPHENYLALANINEMIAS

All known inherited forms of hyperphenylalaninemia are autosomal. Affected patients are homozygotes or compounds, although there is tentative evidence for symptomatic heterozygosity in peripheral 6-PTS deficiency.[504]

Hyperphenylalaninemia is a classic example of heterogeneity in a metabolic phenotype. The principal explanation here is genetic heterogeneity due to mutations at different loci [PAH, chromosome 12q24.1[208]; DHPR, 4p15.3[216]; GTP-CH (unmapped); and 6-PTS (unmapped)] and multiple alleles at each locus. Details are given above under the appropriate disease headings.

PAH alleles are distributed throughout human populations usually but not invariably at high frequencies (Table 15-6); non-PAH forms of hyperphenylalaninemia are panethnic and pangeographic, but their alleles occur at very low frequencies (Table 15-6). The incidences of PKU, non-PKU PAH-deficiency, and BH_4-deficient hyperphenylalaninemia probands are on the order of 100, 50, and 1 per million livebirths, respectively. The incidence of PKU places it among the most prevalent of Mendelian diseases in humans. Incidence is usually ascertained from newborn screening, but when compliance is poor or absent, incidence of PKU can still be estimated from rates of consanguineous marriages, for example.[594a,594b]

By tradition, PKU is a "Caucasian disease" presumably of Celtic origin according to one theory.[595,596] This opinion is under revision; it may be true for northern Europe, but it is not an inclusive explanation. For example, newborn screening in Chinese populations shows that the incidence of PKU in Chinese[597] is similar to that in Europeans (see Table 15-6) implying, incidentally, that maternal PKU (see below) will require equally systematic approaches to prevent its effects on the fetus in both populations.[598] Meanwhile, reports of probands in populations otherwise not known for their PKU burden[599–602] indicate awareness of and interest in the problem in those regions. The fact that the inbreeding coefficient is often higher there[600] in families of affected cases than in non-affected families is a classic observation in genetics[603] but in a new setting.

Population Genetics of PKU

Why is PKU so prevalent in some regions and populations? One does not expect the frequency of the PKU gene to be ≈ 0.01 when it has so great a disadaptive effect in the homozygous phenotype, unless the mutation rate at the PAH locus is high, there is a large founder effect, or the heterozygote has a compensating advantage.

There is no evidence yet that the mutation rate is greatly elevated at the PAH locus. Is there a founder effect? The answer is both yes and no. The ubiquitous PKU mutation among Yemenite Jews[227] has the earmark of founder effect. Celtic migration is one explanation[595,596] for a founder effect in European PKU with its west to east gradient across Northern Europe,[542] and various studies[604,605] are showing how founders brought PKU genes into other geographic regions; it is an intersting way to do history. For example, DNA analysis shows that three different RFLP haplotypes bearing mutant PAH alleles entered the French-Canadian population in the mid-seventeenth century, and spread from a few founders. The associated alleles have a combined frequency of 0.007 in their descendants today.[605] And genealogies of probands detected by newborn screening show that recent local migration, east to west, explains the frequency of PKU in a region of Germany today.[604] These are specific local explanations. What about the larger picture? The growing evidence of multiple PAH alleles in most PKU-bearing populations makes unlikely the following mechanisms[606]: (1) a single founder effect on modern populations; (2) random genetic drift since it would have had to affect several PKU alleles concordantly; (3) hitchhiking of PKU alleles through selection on a nearby locus (although the proximity of interferon γ at the chromosome 12q24.1 region does provoke speculation about the possibility

Table 15-6 Incidences of Hyperphenylalaninemia Variants by Phenotype, Region, and Ethnic Group*

Variant	*Geographic region of ethnic group*	*Incidence (per 10^6 births)*	*Source*†
PKU	Yememite Jews	190	542
	Scotland	190	542
	Eire	190	542
	Czechoslovakia	150	542
	Poland	130	542
	Hungary	90	594
	France	75	542
	Scandinavia		
	Denmark	85	542
	Norway	70	594b
	Sweden	25	542,594a
	Finland	5	542
	England (London region)	70	542
	Italy	60	594a
	China	50	597
	Canada	45	538a
	Japan	5	542
	Ashkenazi Jews	5	542
Non-PKU hyperphenylalaninemia	All regions except Finland	15-75	542,597
BH_4-deficient hyperphenylalaninemia	Panethnic and panregional	1-2	438,442,443

*Newborn screening for hyperphenylalaninemia and case finding for BH_4-deficient variants are the principal sources of incidence data. Incidence has also been estimated from rates of consanguineous marriages in Norway[594b] and Italy.[594a]

†Woolf LI and Lentner C: *Geigy Scientific Tables*, 8th ed. Basel, 1986, vol. 4, p. 231, was used as an additional source for these data and to corroborate the remainder.

of a hitchhiking effect on PAH haplotypes). That leaves compensating advantage in heterozygotes as the best explanation for the high frequency of the PKU "gene" in many modern populations.[606]

The conventional view sees PKU heterozygosity either as a neutral phenotype or perhaps as one with a disadaptive effect. The latter idea was first advanced by Lionel Penrose[607] and reexamined a half-century later.[608] If there is a disadaptive effect of PKU heterozygosity, it is small[608]; moreover, it could not be a mechanism to raise allele frequency. Selective advantage is the mechanism for that. Selection must act on a property (phenotype) of the organism; the object selected is the sequence of nucleotides in DNA conferring the property.[609] Hyperphenylalaninemia is a phenotype; might it be the property under selection? It must be a property of heterozygotes in this case, and indeed there is a slight but significant elevation of plasma phenylalanine in heterozygotes.[3,585,587]

Environment (the selective experience) affects gene frequency either through viability selection or by altering reproductive fitness. PKU mutations may improve viability of the offspring or fertility of the female carrier. There is evidence both for[596,610] and against[611,612] compensation through improved fertility and/or viability. The conflicting evidence originates perhaps because the families in these studies were ascertained through PKU probands although correction was made for this bias in the major study.[598,613] Ascertainment through heterozygote screening would avoid bias, and classification of the offspring (heterozygous or not) would allow one to discern between maternal and fetal effects of heterozygosity. All this is interesting, but it might be of no avail. Any study of selection in contemporary heterozygotes might find nothing if the putative selective agent had been encountered only by ancestral populations and was no longer present. Selection of the magnitude postulated in PKU requires an agent affecting great numbers of people; such agents are likely to be infectious or nutrient. That the agent might be ochratoxin A, a mycotoxin in contaminated grains and lentils, is useful speculation[614] because its effect could, with sufficient ingenuity, be measured by experiment (e.g., in transgenic heterozygous mice).

Gene Dosage

The average level of enzyme activity in heterozygotes in most Mendelian phenotypes is about half-normal; occasionally it is significantly less or more than half.[615] The exception constitutes the phenomenon of deviant gene dosage, and it occurs in the hyperphenylalaninemias. Although most heterozygotes with these phenotypes have the expected dosage effect, many do not. The latter presumably express CRM-positive mutations that are different from those conferring conventional gene dosage; the odd ones are expressed frequently in PKU,[239,239a] in non-PKU PAH deficiency,[252] in 6-PTS deficiency (Fig. 15-14), and occasionally in DHPR deficiency (Table 15-5).

Does a mechanism for deviant gene dosage common to all these phenotypes suggest itself? The answer is yes in all three cases. All three native enzymes are both multimeric and homopolymeric; PAH is believed to be a homotrimer,[97,99] DHPR a homodimer,[464] and 6-PTS a hometetramer.[191,192] Heterozygotes bearing CRM-positive mutant alleles can form heteropolymeric enzyme molecules. If interaction between normal (wild type) and mutant subunits abolishes activity of the native enzyme, residual activity in the heterozygous phenotype will be proportional to the number of enzyme molecules containing only normal subunits; this amount is 1/4, 1/8, and 1/16 normal for dimeric, trimeric and tetrameric enzymes, respectively [derived from $(a+b)^2$, $(a+b)^3$ and $(a+b)^4$]. The estimates assume equal rates of synthesis and random association of the wild type *a* and mutant *b* subunit. Departure from these simplifying assumptions is the simplest explanation for discrepancy between observed and predicted enzyme activity. The proposed mechanism has been called *negative allelic complementation*[252]; it resembles the phenomenon designated *dominant negative mutation*,[616] and it may explain some examples of *metabolic interference*.[616a]

Is there a consequence of deviant gene dosage? Conclusions, up to now, about gene dosage have been based on in vitro measurements; the corresponding dosage effect in vivo is generally not known. Nonetheless, it is apparent that endogenous phenylalanine hydroxylation under the conditions of daily life cannot be seriously compromised even in heterozygotes with deviant gene dosage since they do not have more obvious hyperphenylalaninemia than do heterozygotes with normal gene dosage. On the other hand, urine pterin metabolites are affected in most of the 6-PTS-deficient heterozygotes with exaggerated gene dosage,[504] and occasionally there is a clinical consequence even in the heterozygote.[503,504] We do not know whether there is a late-onset effect on brain function in heterozygotes with deviant gene dosage; but the possibility deserves investigation.

MATERNAL HYPERPHENYLALANINEMIA

Maternal hyperphenylalaninemia is a variant metabolic phenotype of significance in the preconceptual/intrapartum state. Its consequences are usually referred to as maternal phenylketonuria by which is meant a damaged product of conception (with microcephaly, mental retardation, impaired growth, and malformations). The fetal disease and postnatal PKU probably have similar pathogenesis. A pregnant female with PKU is at greater risk to harm her fetus than one with non-PKU hyperphenylalaninemia; the reason is likely to be the difference in maternal plasma phenylalanine in the two phenotypes.

Maternal PKU was described first by Charles Dent[617] and then by Mabry and colleagues.[618] Once the problem was out in the open, there was concern[619] that if nothing could be done about it, there would be a rebound in the incidence of mental retardation related to expression of the PKU gene in the female beneficiaries of newborn PKU screening. The issue has commanded increasing attention ever since,[17,543,620–623] and it is now the major problem for directors of PKU disease prevention programs.

The Maternal PKU Phenotype

The consequences of the fetus of maternal hyperphenylalaninemia are now well known.[620] When the intrapartum maternal plasma phenylalanine level exceeds ≈ 1.1 m*M* (PKU phenotype), the incidence of fetal pathology is high: mental retardation in 92 percent of offspring; microcephaly, 72 percent; intrauterine growth delay, 40 percent; congenital heart malformation, 12 percent. Incidence of these abnormalities is lower when maternal plasma phenylalanine is lower.[620] The IQ score of the offspring correlates inversely with the maternal phenylalanine value at term.[624] Evidence for an apparent maternal threshold value (≈1.1 m*M*),[624] below which there is low risk of harm to intelligence in the offspring does not fit findings in an earlier study[620] in which there seemed to be risk associated with maternal phenylalanine values much lower than the so-called threshold value. Objections have been put to the threshold concept because there appears to be danger in its application. Counselors of maternal hyperphenylalaninemia need to be more prudent than brave, and it is clearly wiser to be noncategorical about threshold values at the moment. Risk to whom is the contentious issue.

Pathogenesis

Maternal plasma phenylalanine values are not the same as fetal values (when measured in cord blood at term); fetal values are higher. The average fetal/maternal plasma or blood phenylalanine ratio is 1.48 (mean of 12 studies cited in Ref. 623); the range is 1.13 to 2.91. Assuming accurate and representative measurements, this evidence implies important interindividual variation in the fetal/maternal ratio and in fetal phenylalanine level. For example, at 0.5 m*M* maternal plasma phenylalanine, putatively a "safe" level, the pregnancy with the highest maternal/fetal ratio (2.91), generates ≈1.5 m*M* fetal phenylalanine (an "unsafe" level); while that with the lowest ratio (1.13) generates a corresponding fetal value of ≈0.55 m*M* (a "safe" value). Since there is no way to anticipate the maternal/fetal ratio, it seems best to consider every woman with hyperphenylalanemia to be at risk for harm to her fetus.

What is the mechanism of harm? It is probably the same in the fetal stage as it is in postnatal PKU. Phenylalanine is probably the initiator of harm. Some experimental models of maternal phenylketonuria[625,626] indicate this is so, but they are pharmacologic models, not true phenocopies of the human situation. Nonetheless, one such model[310] produced polysome disaggregation in brain and heart of fetal rats; fetal brain and heart are principal targets of human maternal PKU. A single study of brain in a 4 month-old infant affected by the maternal PKU syndrome, revealed neuronal loss, immature cortical pyramidal cell bodies and dendritic spines.[626a] Clearly, tyrosine deficiency is not a cause of maternal PKU, in the rat at least, since there are high fetal levels of tyrosine as well as phenylalanine in a model which systematically produces fetal microcephaly[627]; loading pregnant rats with tyrosine alone does not have this effect on the fetus. Genotype in the human fetus, whether heterozygous or homozygous for PKU, is not a significant determinant of the phenotype since it does not influence the fetal blood phenylalanine value.[268] These observations together imply that the principal determinant of maternal PKU is the maternal phenylalanine value, the transplacental gradient of phenylalanine, or the metabolites of phenylalanine that accumulate in the fetus; they imply further that treatment to prevent maternal hyperphenylalaninemia could prevent maternal PKU.

Prevention

Maternal hyperphenylalaninemia is seen as a loophole in PKU screening.[629,630] For instance, the incidence of non-PKU hyperphenylalaninemia (PAH-deficient) in the pregnant female population is similar to that in newborns ($\approx 0.5 \times 10^{-4}$).[17] The condition is benign in one form (for the mother) and harmful in the other (for the fetus of the affected mother).[17,624] Maternal blood phenylalanine level is the silent threat to the next generation. The hazard is not in breast milk should the mother breast feed the infant, because the extra burden of phenylalanine in the milk is slight.[631] The threat, as we now know it, is in utero; at birth, the harm has already been done. What can be done to avoid this hazard?

Awareness of maternal hyperphenylalaninemia needs to be improved among health professionals likely to encounter the problem.[632,633] Registers of probands identified by newborn screening can keep track of them for later counseling,[633,635] the goal of which is to ensure that women at risk conceive and carry their offspring at near-normal maternal plasma phenylalanine values. Since maternal PKU is both an embryopathy and a fetopathy,[636] its effects can be avoided only by avoidance of transplacental phenylalanine toxicity at the outset of pregnancy. The evidence accumulates[620,623,637–641,642] that meticulous treatment, beginning before conception and continuing to term, prevents maternal phenylketonuria; delay in the onset of treatment, and backsliding once it has begun, incurs a high risk to the fetus. Prospective studies[622,641] are evaluating these findings.

The evidence that maternal PKU can be averted is reassuring. Otherwise, we might suppose that the knowledge described in this chapter and its apparent benefits for society were obtained in a Faustian bargain.

Lynne Prevost, Huguette Rizziéro, Kathleen Carter, Kelly Porter, and Debbie Martin prepared the typescript of this chapter. We thank our many colleagues who will recognize the results of their own work and discussions with us. We were supported by the Medical Research Council of Canada, the National Institutes of Health, and the Howard Hughes Medical Institute, among others.

REFERENCES

1. KNOX WE: Phenylketonuria, in Stanbury JB, Wyngaarden JB, Fredrickson DS (eds): *The Metabolic Basis of Inherited Disease*. McGraw-Hill, New York, 1960, p 321.
2. KNOX WE: Phenylketonuria, in Stanbury JB, Wyngaarden JB, Frederickson DS (eds): *The Metabolic Basis of Inherited Disease*, 2d ed. McGraw-Hill, New York, 1966, p 258.
3. KNOX WE: Phenylketonuria, in Stanbury JB, Wyngaarden JB, Fredrickson DS (eds): *The Metabolic Basis of Inherited Disease*, 3d ed. McGraw-Hill, New York, 1972, p 266.
4. TOURIAN AY, SIDBURY JB: Phenylketonuria, in Stanbury JB, Wyngaarden JB, Fredrickson DS (eds): *The Metabolic Basis of Inherited Disease*, 4th ed. McGraw-Hill, New York, 1978, p 241.
5. TOURIAN A, SIDBURY JB: Phenylketonuria and hyperphenylalaninemia, in Stanbury JB, Wyngaarden JB, Fredrickson DS (eds): *The Metabolic Basis of Inherited Disease*, 5th ed. McGraw-Hill, New York, 1983, p 270.
6. LANG-BONN K: II. Die Phenylpyruvische oligophrenie. *Ergeb Inn Med Kinderheilkd* 6:87, 1955.
7. HSIA DY-Y: Phenylketonuria: A study of human biochemical genetics. *Pediatrics* 38:173, 1966.
8. HSIA DY-Y: Phenylketonuria 1967. *Dev Med Child Neurol* 9:531, 1967.
9. KLEINMAN DS: Phenylketonuria. A review of some deficits in our information. *Pediatrics* 33:123, 1964.
9a. SCRIVER CR, ROSENBERG LE: *Amino Acid Metabolism and Its Disorders*. Philadelphia, Saunders, 1973, p 290.
10. GUTTLER F: Hyperphenylalaninemia: Diagnosis and classification of the various types of phenylalanine hydroxylase deficiency in childhood. *Acta Paed Scand* 280:*Suppl* 1, 1980.
11. SCRIVER CR, CLOW CL: Phenylketonuria and other phenylalanine hydroxylation mutants in man. *Annu Rev Genetics* 14:179, 1980.
12. SCRIVER CR, CLOW CL: Phenylketonuria: Epitome of human biochemical genetics. *N Engl J Med* 303:1336, 1980.

13. SCRIVER CR, CLOW CL: Phenylketonuria: Epitome of human biochemical genetics. *N Engl J Med* 303:1394, 1980.
14. BICKEL H: Phenylketonuria: Past, Present, Future. *J Inherited Metab Dis* 3:123, 1980.
15. BICKEL H: Differential diagnosis and treatment of hyperphenylalaninemia. *Prog Clin Biol Res* 177:93, 1985.
15a. SMITH I: The Hyperphenylalaninemias, in Lloyd JK, Scriver CR (eds): *Genetic and Metabolic Disease in Pediatrics.* London, Butterworths, 1985, p 166.
16. KAUFMAN S: Unsolved problems in diagnosis and therapy of hyperphenylalaninemia caused by defects in tetrahydropterin metabolism. *J Pediatr* 109:572, 1986.
17. LEVY HL: Maternal PKU. *Prog Clin Biol Res* 177:109, 1985.
18. NICHOL CA, SMITH GK, DUCH DS: Biosynthesis and metabolism of tetrahydrobiopterin and molybdopterin. *Ann Rev Biochem* 54:729, 1985.
19. COTTON RGH: Inborn errors of pterin metabolism, in Blakley RL (ed): *Folates and Pterins. Nutritional, Parmacological and Physiological Aspects.* New York, Wiley, 1987, vol 3, p 359.
20. KAUFMAN S: Phenylketonuria and its variants. *Adv Hum Genet* 13:217, 1983.
21. WOO SL, GUTTLER F, LEDLEY FD, LIDSKY AS, KWOK SC, DILELLA AG, ROBSON KJ: The human phenylalanine hydroxylase gene. *Prog Clin Biol Res* 177:123, 1985.
22. WOO SL, DILELLA AG, MARVIT J, LEDLEY FD: Molecular basis of phenylketonuria and potential somatic gene therapy. *Cold Spring Harbor Symp Quant Biol* 1:395, 1986.
23. FÖLLING A: Über Ausscheidung von Phenylbrenztraubensaüre in den Harn als Stoffwechselanomalie in Verbindung mit Imbezillität. *Z Physiol Chem* 227:169, 1934.
24. GUTTLER F: Phenylketonuria: 50 years since Fölling's discovery and still expanding our clinical and biochemical knowledge. *Acta Paediatr Scand* 73:705, 1984.
25. NYHAN WL: Asbjörn Fölling and phenylketonuria. *Trends Biochem Sci* 9:71, 1984.
26. ELGJO RF: Asbjörn Fölling. His life and work. *Prog Clin Biol Res* 117:79, 1985.
27. GUTTLER F, WOO SLC: Molecular genetics of PKU. *J Inherited Metab Dis* 9:*Suppl* 1, 58, 1986.
28. PENROSE LS: Phenylketonuria. A problem in eugenics. *Lancet* 1:949, 1946.
29. LEDLEY FD: Somatic gene therapy of human disease: A problem of eugenics? *Trends Genet* 3:112, 1987.
30. BERNARD C: *Les Phénomènes de la Vie.* Paris, Libraire J-B Baillière et Fils, 1878, vol 1, p 879.
31. CANNON WB: Organization for physiological homeostasis. *Physiol Rev* 9:399, 1929.
32. COHN RM, PALMIERI MJ, MCNAMARA PD: Non equilibrium thermodynamics, non covalent forces, and water, in Herman RH, Cohn RM, McNamara PD (eds): *Principles of Metabolic Control in Mammalian Systems.* New York, Plenum, 1980, p 63.
33. MURPHY EA, PYERITZ RE: Homeostasis VII. A conspectus. *Am J Med Genet* 24:735, 1986.
34. SCRIVER CR, GREGORY DM, SOVETTS, D, TISSENBAUM G: Normal plasma free amino acid values in adults: The influence of some common physiological variables. *Metabolism* 34:868, 1985.
35. SCRIVER CR, ROSENBERG LE: *Amino Acid Metabolism and Its Disorders.* Philadelphia, Saunders, 1973, p 39.
36. GREGORY DM, SOVETTS D, CLOW CL, SCRIVER CR: Plasma free amino acid values in normal children and adolescents. *Metabolism* 35:967, 1986.
37. YOUNG VR, PELLETT PL: Protein intake and requirements with reference to diet and health. *Am J Clin Nutr* 45:1323, 1987.
38. AMERICAN ACADEMY OF PEDIATRICS. Committee on Nutrition. Special diets for infants with inborn errors of amino acid metabolism. *Pediatrics* 57:783, 1976.
39. KACSER H, BURNS JA: The molecular basis of dominance. *Genetics* 97:639, 1981.
40. KAUFMAN S: Phenylketonuria: Biochemical mechanisms. *Adv Neurochem* 2:1, 1976.
41. SALTER M, KNOWLES RG, POGSON CI: Quantification of the importance of individual steps in the control of aromatic amino acid metabolism. *Biochem J* 234:635, 1986.
42. CHRISTENSEN HN: Interorgan amino acid nutrition. *Physiol Rev* 62:1193, 1982.
43. KRAGH-HANSEN U, RIGAARD-PETERSEN H, JACOBSEN C, SHEIKH MI: Renal transport of neutral amino acids. Tubular localization of Na^+-dependent phenylalanine and glucose-transport systems. *Biochem* 220:15, 1984.
44. SAMARZIJA I, FROMTER E: Electrophysiological analysis of rat renal sugar and amino acid transport III. Neutral amino acids. *Pflugers Arch* 393:199, 1982.
45. BERTELOOT A, KHAN AH, RAMASWAMY K: K^+ and Na^+-gradient-dependent transport of L-phenylalanine by mouse intestinal brush border membrane vesicles. *Biochim Biophys Acta* 691:321, 1982.
46. CHRISTENSEN HN: Where do the depleted plasma amino acids go in phenylketonuria? *Biochem J* 236:929, 1986.
47. CHRISTENSEN HN: Hypothesis: Where the depleted plasma amino acids go in phenylketonuria, and why. *Perspect Biol Med* 30:186, 1987.
48. OWENS CWI: Effects of phenylalanine analogues on renal tubular reabsorption of amino acids in the rat. *Clin Sci Mol Med* 53:355, 1977.
49. PARDRIDGE WM: Phenylalanine transport at the human blood-brain barrier, in Kaufman S (ed): *Amino Acids in Health and Disease: New Perspectives.* New York, AR Liss, 1987, p 43.
50. SMITH QR: Kinetic analysis of neutral amino acid transport across the blood-brain barrier, in Kaufman S (ed): *Amino Acids in Health and Disease: New Perspectives.* New York, AR Liss, 1987, p 65.
51. SERSHEN H, DEBLER EA, LAJTHA A: Alterations of cerebral amino acid transport processes, in Kaufman S (ed): *Amino Acids in Health and Disease: New Perspectives.* New York, AR Liss, 1987, p 87.
52. RAMPINI S, VOLLMAN JA, BOSSHARD HR, MULLER M, CURTIUS HC: Aromatic acids in urine of healthy infants, persistent hyperphenylalaninemia, and phenylketonuria, before and after phenylalanine load. *Pediatr Res* 8:704, 1974.
53. MILSTIEN S, KAUFMAN S: Studies on the phenylalanine hydroxylase system *in vivo.* An *in vivo* assay based on the liberation of deuterium or tritium into the body water from ring-labelled L-phenylalanine. *J Biol Chem* 250:4782, 1975.
54. UDENFRIEND S, COOPER JR: The enzymatic conversion of phenylalanine to tyrosine. *J Biol Chem* 194:503, 1952.
55. TOURIAN A, GODDARD J, PUCK TT: Phenylalanine hydroxylase activity in mammalian cells. *J Cell Physiol* 73:159, 1969.
56. BERRY HK, CRIPPS R, NICHOLLS K, MCCANDLESS D, HARPER C: Development of phenylalanine hydroxylase activity in guinea pig liver. *Biochim Biophys Acta* 261:315, 1972.
57. MCGEE MM, GREENGARD O, KNOX WG: The quantitative determination of phenylalanine hydroxylase in rat tissues. Its developmental formation in liver. *Biochem J* 127:669, 1972.
58. RAO DN, KAUFMAN S: Purification and state of activation of rat liver phenylalanine hydroxylase. *J Biol Chem* 261:8866, 1986.
59. AYLING JE, HELFAND GD, PIRSON WD: Phenylalanine hydroxylase from human kidney. *Enzyme* 20:6, 1975.
59a. AYLING JE, PIRSON WD, AL-JANABI JM, HELFAND GD: Kidney phenylalanine hydroxylase from man and rat: Comparison with the liver enzyme. *Biochemistry* 13:78, 1974.
60. MURTHY LI, BERRY HK: Phenylalanine hydroxylase activity in liver from humans and subhuman primates: Its probable absence in kidney. *Biochem Med* 12:392, 1975.
61. ROBSON KJ, CHANDRA T, MacGILLIVRAY RT, WOO SLC: Polysome immunoprecipitation of phenylalanine hydroxylase mRNA from rat liver and cloning of its cDNA. *Proc Natl Acad Sci USA* 79:4701, 1982.
62. ABITA JP, DORCHE C, KAUFMAN S: Further studies on the nature of phenylalanine hydroxylation in brain. *Pediatr Res* 8:714, 1974.
63. WAPNIR RA, HAWKINS RL, STEVENSON JH: Ontogenesis of phylalanine and tryptophan hydroxylation in rat brain and liver. *Biol Neonate* 118:85, 1971.
64. KATZ I, LLOYD T, KAUFMAN S: Studies on phenylalanine and tyrosine hydroxylation by rat brain tyrosine hydroxylase. *Biochim Biophys Acta* 445:567, 1976.
65. KAUFMAN S: Aromatic amino acid hydroxylases, in Krebs E (ed): *The Enzymes. Phosphorylation Control,* 3d ed. New York, Academic, vol XVIII, part B, 1987.
66. KAUFMAN S: The structure of phenylalanine hydroxylation cofactor. *Proc Natl Acad Sci USA* 50:1085, 1963.
67. KAUFMAN S: The phenylalanine hydroxylating system from mammalian liver. *Adv Enzymol* 35:245, 1971.
68. KAUFMAN S, LEVENBERG B: Further studies on the phenylalanine hydroxylation cofactor. *J Biol Chem* 234:2683, 1959.
69. KAUFMAN S, BRIDGERS WF, ISENBERG G, FRIEDMAN S: The source of oxygen in the phenylalanine hydroxylase and the dopamine-β-hydroxylase catalyzed reaction. *Biochem Biophys Res Acta* 9:497, 1962.
70. CRAINE JE, HALL ES, KAUFMAN S: The isolation and characterization of dihydropteridine reductase from sheep liver. *J Biol Chem* 247:6082, 1972.
71. NEILSEN KH: Rat liver phenylalanine hydroxylase: A method for the measurement of activity, with particular reference to the distinctive features of the enzyme and the pteridine cofactor. *Eur J Biochem* 7:360, 1969.
72. SCRIMGEOUR KG, CHEEMA S: Quinoid dihydropterin reductase. *Ann NY Acad Sci* 186:115, 1971.

73. KAUFMAN S: Studies on the mechanism of phenylalanine hydroxylase: Detection of an intermediate, in Pfleiderer W (ed): *Chemistry and Biology of Pteridines*. Walter de Gruyter, New York, 1975, p 291.
74. KAUFMAN S: On the nature of an intermediate that is formed during the enzymatic conversion of phenylalanine to tyrosine, in Mower KT, Hayaishi O (eds): *Iron and Copper Proteins. Advances in Experimental Medicine and Biology*. 1976, vol 74, p 9.
75. KAUFMAN S: A protein that stimulates rat liver phenylalanine hydroxylase. *J Biol Chem* 245:4751, 1970.
76. HUANG CY, MAX EE, KAUFMAN S: Purification and characterization of phenylalanine hydroxylase-stimulating protein from rat liver. *J Biol Chem* 248:2435, 1973.
77. LAZARUS RA, BENKOVIC SJ, KAUFMAN S: Phenylalanine hydroxylase stimulator protein is a 4α-carbinolamine dehydratase. *J Biol Chem* 258:10960, 1983.
78. KAUFMAN S: Metabolism of phenylalanine hydroxylation cofactor. *J Biol Chem* 242:3934, 1967.
79. BRENNEMAN AR, KAUFMAN S: The role of tetrahydropteridine in the enzymatic conversion of tyrosine to 3,4-dihydroxyphenylalanine. *Biochem Biophys Res Commun* 17:177, 1964.
80. SHIMAN R, AKINO M, KAUFMAN S: Solubilization and partial purification of tyrosine hydroxylase from bovine adrenal medulla. *J Biol Chem* 246:1330, 1971.
81. FRIEDMAN PA, KAPPELMAN AH, KAUFMAN S: Partial purification and characterization of tryptophan hydroxylase from rabbit hindbrain. *J Biol Chem* 247:4165, 1972.
82. KAUFMAN S, FISHER DB: Purification and some physical properties of phenylalanine hydroxylase from rat liver. *J Biol Chem* 245:4745, 1970.
83. PARNIAK MA, KAUFMAN S: Catalytically active oligomeric species of phenylalanine hydroxylase. *Biochemistry* 24:3379, 1985.
84. DOSKELAND AL, JONES T, SKOTLAND T, FLATMARK TN: Phenylalanine 4-monoxygenase from bovine and rat liver. Some physical and chemical properties. *Neurochem Res* 7:407, 1982.
85. WEBBER S, HARZER G, WHITELEY JM: Isolation of rat liver phenylalanine hydroxylase using a novel pteridine matrix. *Anal Biochem* 106:63, 1980.
86. SHIMAN R, GRAY DW, PATER A: A simple purification of phenylalanine hydroxylase by substrate-induced hydrophobic chromatography. *J Biol Chem* 254:11300, 1979.
87. NAKATA H, FUJISAWA H: Purification and characterization of phenylalanine 4-monoxygenase from rat liver. *Biochim Biophys Acta* 614:313, 1980.
88. TOURIAN A: Activation of phenylalanine hydroxylase by phenylalanine. *Biochim Biophys Acta* 242:345, 1971.
89. GILLAM SS, WOO SLC, WOOLF LI: The isolation and properties of phenylalanine hydroxylase from rat liver. *Biochem J* 139:731, 1974.
90. CHOO KH, COTTON RGH, DANKS DM, JENNINGS IG: Genetics of mammalian phenylalanine hydroxylase system. *Biochem J* 181:285, 1979.
91. MERCER JFB, GRIMES A, JENNINGS I, COTTONG RGH: Identification of two molecular-mass forms of phenylalanine hydroxylase that segregate independently in rats. Specific association of each form with certain rat strains. *Biochem J* 219:891, 1984.
92. MERCER JFB, MCADAM W, CHAMBERS GW, WALKER ID: The W and L allelic forms of phenylalanine hydroxylase in the rat differ by a threonine to isoleucine substitution. *Biochem J* 236:679, 1986.
93. DONLON J, KAUFMAN S: Relationship between the multiple forms of rat hepatic phenylalanine hydroxylase and degree of phosphorylation. *J Biol Chem* 255:2146, 1980.
94. IWAKI M, PARNIAK MA, KAUFMAN S: Studies on the primary structure of rat liver phenylalanine hydroxylase. *Biochem Biophys Res Commun* 126:922, 1985.
95. FISHER DB, KIRKWOOD R, KAUFMAN S: Rat liver phenylalanine hydroxylase, an iron enzyme. *J Biol Chem* 247:5161, 1972.
96. GOTTSCHALL DW, DIETRICH RF, BENKOVIC SJ, SHIMAN R: Phenylalanine hydroxylase. Correlation of the iron content with activity and the preparation and reconstitution of the apoenzyme. *J Biol Chem* 257:845, 1982.
97. ABITA J-P, BLANDIN-SAVOJA F, REY F: Phenylalanine hydroxylase. Evidence that the enzyme from human liver might not be a phosphoprotein. *Biochem Int* 7:727, 1983.
98. ABITA J-P, BLANDIN-SAVOJA F, REY F: Phenylalanine 4 mono-oxygenase from human liver, in Kaufman S (ed): *Methods in Enzymology*. New York, Academic, 1987, vol 142, p 27–35.
99. YAMASHITA M, MINATO S, ARAI M, KISHIDA Y, NAGATSU T, UMEZAWA H: Purification of phenylalanine hydroxylase from human adult and foetal livers with a monoclonal antibody. *Biochem Biophys Res Commun* 133:202, 1985.
100. WOO SLC, GILLAM SS, WOOLF LI: The isolation and properties of phenylalanine hydroxylase from human liver. *Biochem J* 139:741, 1974.
101. CHOO KH, COTTON RG, DANKS DM, JENNINGS IG: Genetics of the mammalian phenylalanine hydroxylase system. Studies of human liver phenylalanine hydroxylase subunit structure and of mutations in phenylketonuria. *Biochem J* 181:285, 1979.
102. WOOLF LI: The isolation, properties, and assay of phenylalanine hydroxylase from human and rat liver. *Biochem Med* 16:284, 1976.
103. FISHER DB, KAUFMAN S: The stimulation of rat liver phenylalanine hydroxylase by phospholipids. *J Biol Chem* 247:2250, 1972.
104. FISHER DB, KAUFMAN S: The stimulation of rat liver phenylalanine hydroxylase by lysolecithin and alpha-chymotrypsin. *J Biol Chem* 248:4345, 1973.
105. PARNIAK MA, KAUFMAN S: Rat liver phenylalanine hydroxylase: Activation by sulfhydryl modification. *J Biol Chem* 256:6876, 1981.
106. AYLING JE, HELFAND GD: Effect of pteridine cofactor structure on regulation of phenylalanine hydroxylase activity, in Pfleiderer W (ed): *Chemistry and Biology of Pteridines*. New York, Walter de Gruyter, 1975, p 304.
107. SHIMAN R, GRAY DW: Substrate activation of phenylalanine hydroxylase. A kinetic characterization. *J Biol Chem* 255:4793, 1980.
108. PHILLIPS RS, KAUFMAN S: Ligand effects on the phosphorylation states of hepatic phenylalanine hydroxylase. *J Biol Chem* 259:2474, 1984.
109. PHILLIPS RS, PARNIAK MA, KAUFMAN S: Spectroscopic investigation of ligand interaction of hepatic phenylalanine hydroxylase: Evidence for a conformational change. *Biochemistry* 23:3836, 1984.
110. MILSTIEN S, ABITA J-P, CHANG N, KAUFMAN S: Hepatic phenylalanine 4-monooxygenase is a phosphoprotein. *Proc Natl Acad Sci USA* 73:1591, 1976.
111. ABITA J-P, MILSTIEN S, CHANG N, KAUFMAN S: *In vitro* activation of rat liver phenylalanine hydroxylase by phosphorylation. *J Biol Chem* 251:5310, 1976.
112. WRETBORN M, HUMBLE E, RAGNARSSON U, ENGSTROM L: Amino acid sequence at the phosphorylation site of rat liver phenylalanine hydroxylase and phosphorylation of a corresponding peptide. *Biochem Biophys Res Commun* 93:403, 1980.
113. BARRANGER JA, GEIGER PJ, NUZINO A, BESSMAN SP: Isozymes of phenylalanine hydoxylase. *Science* 175:903, 1972.
114. JEDLICKI E, KAUFMAN S, MILSTIEN S: Partial purification and characterization of rat liver phenylalanine hydroxylase phosphatase. *J Biol Chem* 252:7711, 1977.
115. KAUFMAN S, HASEGAWA H, WELGUS H, PARNIAK M: Regulation of hepatic phenylalanine hydroxylase activity by phosphorylation and dephosphorylation, in *Cold Spring Harbor Conferences on Cell Proliferation. Protein Phosphorylation*. Cold Spring Harbor Laboratory, 1981, vol 8, p 1391.
116. KAUFMAN S: Regulation of the activity of hepatic phenylalanine hydroxylase. *Adv Enz Regul* 25:37, 1986.
117. INGEBRITSEN TA, COHEN P: Protein phosphatases: Properties and role in cellular regulation. *Science* 221:331, 1983.
118. ALEMANY S, TUNG HYL, SHENOLKAR S, PILKIS SJ, COHEN P: The protein phosphatases involved in cellular regulation. Antibody to protein phosphatase-2A as a probe of phosphatase structure and function. *Eur J Biochem* 145:51, 1984.
119. PELECH S, COHEN P, FISHER MJ, POGSON CI, EL-MAGHRABI MR, PILKIS SJ: The protein phosphatases involved in cellular regulation. Glycolysis, gluconeogenesis and aromatic amino acid breakdown in rat liver. *Eur J Biochem* 145:39, 1984.
120. DONLON J, KAUFMAN S: Glucagon stimulation of rat hepatic phenylalanine hydroxylase through phosphorylation *in vivo*. *J Biol Chem* 253:6657, 1978.
121. ABITA J-P, CHAMRAS H, ROSSELIN G, REY F: Hormonal control of phenylalanine hydroxylase activity in isolated rat hepatocytes. *Biochem Biophys Res Commun* 92:912, 1980.
122. CARR FPA, POGSON CI: Phenylalanine metabolism in isolated liver cells: Effects of glucagon and diabetes. *Biochem J* 198:655, 1981.
123. GARRISON JC, WAGNER JD: Glucagon and the Ca^{2+}-linked hormones angiotensin II, norepinephrine, and vasopressin stimulate the phosphorylation of distinct substrates in intact hepatocytes. *J Biol Chem* 257:13135, 1982.
124. SANTANA MA, FISHER MJ, BATE AJ, POGSON CI: The effect of experimental diabetes on phenylalanine metabolism in isolated liver cells. *Biochem J* 227:169, 1985.
125. DONLON J, BEIRNE D: Modulations of rat hepatic phenylalanine hydroxylase due to diabetes or high protein diet. *Biochem Biophys Res Commun* 108:746, 1982.
126. KAUFMAN S: Regulatory properties of phenylalanine, tyrosine and tryptophan hydroxylase. *Biochem Soc Trans* 13:433, 1985.
127. DOSKELAND AP, DOSKELAND SO, OGREID D, FLATMARK T: The effect of ligands of phenylalanine 4-monooxygenase on the cAMP-dependent phosphorylation of the enzyme. *J Biol Chem* 257:11242, 1984.
128. SHIMAN R, MORTIMORE GE, SCHWORER CM, GRAY DW: Regulation of phenylalanine hydroxylase activity by phenylalanine *in vivo, in vitro* and in perfused rat liver. *J Biol Chem* 257:11213, 1982.

129. SHIMAN R: Relationship between the substrate activation site and catalytic site of phenylalanine hydroxylase. *J Biol Chem* 225:10029, 1980.

130. MÜLLER WA, FALOONA GR, AQUILAR-PARADA F, UNGER RH: Abnormal alpha-cell function in diabetes. *N Engl J Med* 283:109, 1970.

131. ROCHA DM, FALOONA GR, UNGER RH: Glucagon-stimulating activity of 20 amino acids in dogs. *J Clin Invest* 51:2346, 1972.

132. GUTTLER F, KUHL C, PEDERSEN L, PABY P: Effects of oral phenylalanine load on plasma glucagon, insulin, amino acid and glucose concentrations in man. *Scand J Clin Lab Invest* 38:255, 1978.

133. LEHNINGER A: *Biochemistry*, 2d ed. New York, Worth, 1975, p 629.

134. SMITH SC, KEMP BE, MCADAM WJ, MERCER JEB, COTTON RG: Two apparent molecular weight forms of human and monkey phenylalanine hydroxylase are due to phosphorylation. *J Biol Chem* 259:11284, 1984.

135. FREEDLAND RA: Factors affecting the activity *in vitro* of the tryptophan- and phenylalanine-hydroxylating systems. *Biochim Biophys Acta* 73:71, 1963.

136. CHARI-BITRON A: Hydroxylation of phenylalanine and tryptophan by liver enzyme of adrenalectomized rats. *Biochem Biophys Res Commun* 12:310, 1963.

137. HAGGERTY DF, CHIAPPELLI F, KERN R, SCULLY S, LYNCH M: Regulation by glucocorticoids of rat-liver phenylalanine hydroxylase *in vivo*. *Biochem Biophys Res Commun* 115:965, 1983.

138. GREENGARD O, DELVALLE JA: The regulation of phenylalanine hydroxylase in rat tissues *in vivo*. Substrate and cortisol-induced elevations in phenylalanine hydroxylase activity. *Biochem J* 154:619, 1976.

139. KOLLER C, KLINGER R, ANDERSON G: Adaptation of hepatic phenylalanine hydroxylase in the rat. *Enzyme* 17:155, 1974.

140. NAMBOODIRI MAA, RAMASARMA T: Increase in hepatic phenylalanine hydroxylase on cortisol treatment. *Indian J Biochem Biophys* 15:178, 1978.

141. STANLEY JC, FISHER MJ, POGSON CI: The metabolism of L-phenylalanine and L-tyrosine by liver cells isolated from adrenalectomized rats and from streptozotocin-diabetic rats. *Biochem J* 228:249, 1985.

142. HAGGERTY D, YOUNG PL, POPJAK G, CARNES WH: Phenylalanine hydroxylase in cultured hepatocytes. I. Hormonal control of enzyme levels. *J Biol Chem* 248:223, 1973.

143. HAGGERTY DF, YOUNG PL, BUESE JV: The effect of population density of phenylalanine hydroxylase activity in rat hepatoma cells in culture. *Dev Biol* 40:16, 1974.

144. HAGGERTY DR, YOUNG PL, BUESE JV, POPJAK G: Effect of serum on phenylalanine hydroxylase levels in cultured hepatoma cells. *J Biol Chem* 250:8428, 1975.

145. MCCLURE D, MILLER M, SHIMAN R: Correlation of phenylalanine hydroxylase activity with cell density in cultured hepatoma cells. *Exp Cell Res* 90:31, 1975.

146. MCCLURE D, MILLER MR, SHIMAN R: Cell density dependent regulation of phenylalanine hydroxylase activity in hepatoma cells. Evidence for both an active and inactive enzyme form. *Exp Cell Res* 98:223, 1976.

147. TOURIAN A: Control of phenylalanine hydroxylase synthesis in tissue culture by serum and insulin. *Cell Physiol* 87:15, 1976.

148. SORIMACHI K, NIWA A, YASUMURA Y: Hormonal regulation of tyrosine aminotransferase and phenylalanine hydroxylase in rat hepatoma cells continuously cultured in a serum-free medium. Effect of serum, dexamethasone and insulin. *Cell Struct Function* 6:61, 1981.

149. DONLON J, KAUFMAN S: Modification of the multiple forms of rat hepatic phenylalanine hydroxylase by *in vitro* phosphorylation. *Biochem Biophys Res Commun* 78:1011, 1977.

150. TOURIAN A, TREIMAN L, ABE K: Three immunologically distinct isozymes of phenylalanine hydroxylase. *Biochemistry* 14:4055, 1975.

151. TOURIAN A: The unique identity of rat hepatoma phenylalanine hydroxylase. *Biochem Biophys Res Commun* 68:51, 1976.

152. MILLER MR, SHIMAN R: Hydrocortisone induction of phenylalanine hydroxylase isozymes in cultured hepatoma cells. *Biochem Biophys Res Commun* 68:740, 1976.

153. REEM GH, KRETCHMER N: Development of phenylalanine hydroxylase in liver of the rat. *Proc Soc Exp Biol Med* 96:458, 1957.

154. KENNEY FT, KRETCHMER N: Hepatic metabolism of phenylalanine during development. *J Clin Invest* 38:2189, 1959.

155. BRENNEMAN AR, KAUFMAN S: Characteristics of the phenylalanine-hydroxylating system in newborn rats. *J Biol Chem* 240:3617, 1965.

156. FRIEDMAN PA, KAUFMAN S: A study of the development of phenylalanine hydroxylase in fetuses of several mammalian species. *Arch Biochem Biophys* 146:321, 1971.

157. RYAN WL, ORR W: Phenylalanine conversion to tyrosine by the human fetal liver. *Arch Biochem Biophys* 113:684, 1986.

158. JAKUBOVIC A: Phenylalanine-hydroxylating system in the human fetus at different development ages. *Biochim Biophys Acta* 237:469, 1971.

159. RÄIHÄ NCR: Phenylalanine hydroxylase in human liver during development. *Pediatr Res* 7:1, 1973.

160. KAUFMAN S: Studies on the mechanism of the enzymatic conversion of phenylalanine to tyrosine. *J Biol Chem* 234:2677, 1959.

161. MITOMA C: Studies on partially purified phenylalanine hydroxylase. *Arch Biochem Biophys* 60:476, 1956.

162. POLLOCK RJ, KAUFMAN S: Dihydropteridine reductase may function in tetrahydrofolate metabolism. *J Neurochem* 31:115, 1978.

163. KAUFMAN S, HOLTZMAN NA, MILSTIEN S, BUTLER IJ, KRUMHOLZ A: Phenylketonuria due to a deficiency of dihydropteridine reductase. *N Engl J Med* 293:785, 1975.

164. MILSTIEN S, HOLTZMAN NA, O'FLYNN ME, THOMAS GH, BUTLER IJ, KAUFMAN S: Hyperphenylalaninemia due to dihydropteridine reductase deficiency. *J Pediatr* 89:763, 1976.

165. FIRGAIRA FA, COTTON RGH, DANKS DM: Dihydropteridine reductase deficiency diagnosis by assays on peripheral blood-cells. *Lancet* 2:1260, 1979.

166. NARISAWA K, ARAI N, ISHIZAWA S, OGASAWARA Y, ONUMA A, IINUMA K, TADA K: Dihydropteridine reductase deficiency: Diagnosis by leukocyte enzyme assay. *Clin Chim Acta* 105:335, 1980.

167. NARISAWA K, ARAI N, HAYAKAWA H, TADA K: Diagnosis of dihydropteridine reductase deficiency by erythrocyte assay. *Pediatrics* 68:591, 1981.

168. ABELSON HT, GORKA C, BEARDSLEY GP: Identification of dihydropteridine reductase in human platelets. *Blood* 53:116, 1979.

169. SHEN R-S, ABELL DW: Purification of dihydropteridine reductase from human platelets. *J Neurosci Res* 6:193, 1981.

170. CHEEMA S, SOLDIN SJ, KNAPP A, HOLMANN KT, SCRIMGEOUR KG: Properties of purified quinonoid dihydropterin reductase. *Can J Biochem* 51:1229, 1973.

171. COTTON RGH, JENNINGS IG: Affinity chromatography of phenylalanine hydroxylase. *Eur J Biochem* 85:357, 1978.

172. KUHL P, OLEK K, WARDENBACH P, GRZESCHIK K-H: Assignment of a gene human quinoid-dihydropterine reductase (QDPR, EC 1.6.5.1) to chromosome 4. *Hum Genet* 53:47, 1979.

173. HASEGAWA H: Dihydropterine reductase from bovine liver. Purification, crystallization, and isolation of a binary complex with NADH. *J Biochem* 81:169, 1977.

174. CHAUVIN MM, KORRI KK, TIRPAK A, SIMPSON RC, SCRIMGEOUR KG: Purification of dihydropterin reductase using immobilized Cibacron Blue. *Can J Biochem* 57:178, 1979.

175. REMBOLD S, GYUER WL: Biochemistry of the pteridines. *Angew Chem* 11:1061, 1972.

176. BLAU N, NIEDERWIESER A: GTP-cyclohydrolases: A review. *J Clin Chem Clin Biochem* 23:169, 1985.

177. CURTIUS H-Ch, TAKIKAWA S, NIEDERWIESER A, GHISLA S: Tetrahydrobiopterin biosynthesis in man, in Cooper BA, Whitehead VM (eds): *Chemistry and Biology of Pteridines*. New York, Walter de Gruyter, 1986, p 142.

178. MILSTIEN S, KAUFMAN S: The biosynthesis of tetrahydrobiopterin in rat brain, in Cooper BA, Whitehead VM (eds): *Chemistry and Biology of Pteridines*. New York, Walter de Gruyter, 1986, p 169.

179. ETO I, FUKUSHIMA K, SHIOTA T: Enzymatic synthesis of biopterin from D-*erythro*-dihydroneopterin triphosphate by extracts of kidneys from Syrian golden hamsters. *J Biol Chem* 251:6505, 1976.

180. BURG AW, BROWN GM: The biosynthesis of folic cid. VIII. Purification and properties of the enzyme that catalyzes the production of formate from carbon atom 8 of guanosine triphosphate. *J Biol Chem* 243:2349, 1968.

181. BLAU N, NIEDERWIESER A: The application of 8-aminoguanosine triphosphate, a new inhibitor of GTP cyclohydrolase I, to the purification of the enzyme from human liver. *Biochim Biophys Acta* 880:26, 1986.

182. NICHOL CA, LEE CL, EDELSTEIN MP, CHAO JY, DUCH DS: Biosynthesis of tetrahydrobiopterin by *de novo* and salvage pathways in adrenal medulla extracts, mammalian cell cultures, and rat brain *in vitro*. *Proc Natl Acad Sci USA* 80:1546, 1983.

183. SMITH GK, NICHOL CA: Tetrahydrobiopterin is synthesized by separate pathways from dihydroneopterin triphosphate and from sepiapterin in adrenal medulla preparations. *Arch Biochem Biophys* 227:272, 1983.

184. MILSTIEN S, KAUFMAN S: Tetrahydro-sepiapterin is an intermediate in tetrahydrobiopterin biosynthesis. *Biochem Biophys Res Commun* 115:888, 1983.

185. HEINTEL D, GHISLA S, CURTIUS H-C, NIEDERWIESER A, LEVINE RA: Biosynthesis of tetrahydrobiopterin: Possible involvement of tetrahydropterin intermediates. *Neurochem Int* 6:141, 1984.

186. SWITCHENKO AC, PRIMUS JP, BROWN GM: Intermediates in the enzymic synthesis of terahydrobiopterin in *Drosophila melanogaster*. *Biochem Biophys Res Commun* 120:754, 1984.

187. MILSTIEN S, KAUFMAN S: Biosynthesis of tetrahydropterin: Conversion of dihydroneopterin triphosphate to tetrahydropterin intermediates. *Biochem Biophys Res Commun* 128:1099, 1985.

188. ABOU-DONIA MM, WILSON SP, ZIMMERMAN TP, NICHOL CA, VIVEROS OH: Regulation of guanosine triphosphate cyclohydrolase and tetrahydrobiop-

terin levels and the role of the cofactor in tyrosine hydroxylation in primary cultures of adrenomedullary chromaffin cells. *J Neurochem* 46:1190, 1986.

188a. SMITH GK: On the role of sepiapterin reductase in the biosynthesis of tetrahydrobiopterin. *Arch Biochem Biophys* 255:254, 1987.

189. HEINTEL D, LEIMBACHER W, REDWEIK U, ZAGALAK B, CURTIUS H-Ch: Purification and properties of the phosphate eliminating enzyme involved in the biosynthesis of BH_4 in man. *Biochem Biophys Res Commun* 127:213, 1985.

190. CURTIUS H-Ch, GHISLA DS, LEIMBACHER TKW, NIEDERWIESER A: Biosynthesis of tetrahydrobiopterin in man. *J Inherited Metab Dis* 8:28, 1985.

191. TAKIKAWA S, CURTIUS H-Ch, REDWEIK U, GHISLA S: Purification of 6-pyruvoyl-tetrahydropterin synthase from human liver. *Biochem Biophys Res Commun* 134:646, 1986.

192. TAKIKAWA S-I, CURTIUS H-C, REDWEIK U, LEIMBACHER W, GHISLA S: Biosynthesis of tetrahydrobiopterin. Purification and characterization of 6-pyruvoyl-tetrahydropterin synthase from human liver. *Eur J Biochem* 161:295, 1986.

193. CURTIUS H-Ch, HEINTEL D, GHISLA S, HUSTER T, LEIMBACHER W, NIEDERWIESER A: Tetrahydropterin biosynthesis. Studies with specificity labelled [^{2}H]NAD[P]H and [^{2}H]$_2$O and of the enzymes involved. *Eur J Biochem* 148:413, 1985.

194. SCHOEDON G, TROPPMAIR J, ADOLF G, HUBER C, NIEDERWEISER A: Interferon-γ enhances biosynthesis of pterins in peripheral blood mononuclear cells by induction of GTP-cyclohydrolase I activity. *J Interferon Res* 6:697, 1986.

195. TROPPMAIR J, LANG A, HUBER CH: Intracellular changes in pterin releasing peripheral blood mononuclear cells after stimulation with interferon-gamma, in Wachter H, Curtius H-Ch (eds): *Biochemical Clinical Aspects of Pteridines*. New York, Walter de Gruyter, 1985, vol 4, p 369.

196. SCHOEDON G, NIEDERWIESER A, TROPPMAIR J, HUBER C: Metabolism of pterins in human peripheral blood mononuclear cells, in Wachter H, Curtius H-Ch (eds): *Biochemical Clinical Aspects of Pteridines*. New York, Walter de Gruyter, 1985, vol 4, p 369.

197. ABITA J-P, COST H, MILSTEIN S, KAUFMAN S, SAIMOT G: Urinary neopterin and biopterin levels in patients with AIDS-related complex. *Lancet* 2:51, 1985.

197a. NIEDERWIESER A, JOLLER P, SEGER R, BLAU N, PRADER A, BETTEX JD, LUTHY R, HIRSCHEL B, SCHAEDELIN J, VETTER U: Neopterin in AIDS, other immunodeficiencies, and bacterial and viral infections. *Klin Wochenschr* 64:333, 1986.

198. ROBSON KJH, BEATTIE W, JAMES RJ, COTTON RGH, MORGAN FJ, WOO SLC: Sequence comparison of rat liver phenylalanine hydroxylase and its cDNA clones. *Biochemistry* 23:5671, 1984.

199. KWOK SCM, LEDLEY FD, DILELLA AG, ROBSON KJH, WOO SLC: Nucleotide sequence of a full-length complementary DNA clone and amino acid sequence of human phenylalanine hydroxylase. *Biochemistry* 24:556, 1985.

200. FRIEDMAN PA, KAUFMAN S: Some characteristics of partially purified human liver phenylalanine hydroxylase. *Biochim Biophys Acta* 293:56, 1973.

201. DAHL H-H, MERCER JFB: Isolation and sequence of a cDNA clone which contains the complete coding region of rat phenylalanine hydroxylase. Structural homology with tyrosine hydroxylase, glucocorticoid regulation, and use of alternate polyadenylation sites. *J Biol Chem* 261:4148, 1986.

202. LEDLEY FD, GRENETT HE, DILELLA AG, KWOK SCM, WOO SLC: Gene transfer and gene expression of human phenylalanine hydroxylase. *Science* 228:77, 1985.

202a. LEDLEY FD, HAHN T, WOO SL: Selection for phenylalanine hydroxylase activity in cells transformed with recombinant retroviruses. *Somatic Cell Mol Genet* 13:145, 1987.

203. LEDLEY FD, GRENETT HE, WOO SLC: Biochemical characterization of recombinant human phenylalanine hydroxylase produced in Escherichia coli. *J Biol Chem* 262:2228, 1987.

203a. CHOO KH, FILBY RG, JENNINGS IG, PETERSON G, FOWLER K: Vectors for expression and amplification of cDNA in mammalian cells: Expression of rat phenylalanine hydroxylase. *DNA* 5:529, 1986.

204. BERG K, SAUGSTAD LF: A linkage study of phenylketonuria. *Clin Genet* 6:147, 1974.

205. KAMARYT J, MRSKOS A, PODHRADSKA O, KOLCOVA V, CABALSKA B, DUCZYNSKA N, BORZYMOWSKA J: PKU locus: Genetic linkage with human amylase (Amy) loci and assignment to linkage group I. *Hum Genet* 43:205, 1978.

206. PAUL TD, BRANDT IK, ELSAS LJ, JACKSON CE, NANCE CS, NANCE WE: Linkage analysis being heterozygote detection in phenylketonuria. *Clin Genet* 16:217, 1979.

207. LIDSKY AS, ROBSON K, CHANDRA T, BARKER P, RUDDLE F, WOO SLC: The PKU locus in man is on chromosome 12. *Am J Hum Genet* 36:527, 1984.

208. LIDSKY AS, LAW ML, MORSE HG, KAO FT, RABIN M, RUDDLE FH, WOO SLC: Regional mapping of the human phenylalanine hydroxylase gene and the phenylketonuria locus on chromosome 12. *Proc Natl Acad Sci USA* 82:6221, 1985.

208a. O'CONNELL P, LATHROP GM, LAW M, LEPPORT M, NAKAMURA Y, HOFF M, KUMLIN E, THOMAS W, ELSNER T, BALLARD L, GOODMAN P, AZEN E, SADLER JE, CAI GY, LALOUEL J-M, WHITE R: A primary genetic linkage map for human chromosome 12. *Genomics* 1:93, 1987.

208b. LEDLEY FD, LEDBETTER SA, LEDBETTER DH, WOO SLC: Localization of mouse phenylalanine hydroxylase locus (Pah) on chromosome 10. *Cytogenet and Cell Genet*, 47:125, 1988.

209. LOCKYER J, COOK RG, MILSTIEN S, KAUFMAN S, WOO SLC, LEDLEY FD: Structure and expression of human dihydropteridine reductase. *Proc Natl Acad Sci USA* 84:3329, 1987.

210. FIRGAIRA FA, CHOO KH, COTTON RGH, DANKS DM: Molecular and immunological comparison of human dihydropteridine reductase in liver, cultured fibroblasts and continuous lymphoid cells. *Biochem J* 197:45, 1981.

211. DAHL HH-M, HUTCHISON W, MCADAM W, WAKE S, MORGAN FJ, COTTON RGH: Human dihydropteridine reductase: Characterization of a cDNA clone and its use in analysis of patients with dihydropteridine reductase deficiency. *Nucleic Acids Res* 15:1921, 1987.

211a. SHAHBAZ M, HOCH JA, TRACH KA, HURAL JA, WEBBER S, WHITELEY JM: Structural studies and isolation of cDNA clones providing the complete sequence of rat liver dihydropteridine reductase. *J Biol Chem* 262:16412, 1987.

212. NIELSEN KH, SIMONSEN V, LIND KE: Dihydropteridine reductase: A method for the measurement of activity, and investigations of the specificity for NADH and NADPH. *Eur J Biochem* 9:497, 1969.

213. MATTHEWS RG, KAUFMAN S: Characterization of the dihydropterin reductase activity of pig liver methylenetetrahydrofolate reductase. *J Biol Chem* 255:6014, 1980.

214. MACDONALD ME, ANDERSON MA, LOCKYER JL, MILSTIEN S, HOBBS WJ, FARYRIARZ AG, KAUFMAN S, LEDLEY FD, WOO SLC, GUSELLA JF: Physical and genetic localization of quinonoid dihydropteridine reductase gene (QDPR) on short arm of chromosome 4. *Somatic Cell Mol Genet* 13:569, 1987.

215. BROWN RM, DAHL H-HM: Localization of the human dihydropteridine reductase gene to band p15.3 of chromosome 4 by *in situ* hybridization. *Genomics* 1:67, 1987.

216. GRENETT HE, LEDLEY FD, REED LL, WOO SLC: Full-length cDNA for rabbit tryptophan hydroxylase: Functional domains and evolution of aromatic amino acid hydroxylases. *Proc Natl Acad Sci USA* 84:5530, 1987.

217. GRIMA B, LAMOUREUX A, BLANOT F, BIQUET NF, MALLET J: Complete coding sequence of rat tyrosine hydroxylase mRNA. *Proc Natl Acad Sci USA* 82:617, 1985.

218. LEDLEY FD, DILELLA AG, KWOK SCM, WOO SLC: Homology between phenylalanine and tyrosine hydroxylases reveals common structural and functional determinants. *Biochemisty* 24:3389, 1985.

218a. GRIMA B, LAMOUREUX A, BONI C, JULIEN J-F, JAVOY-AGID F, MALLET J: A single human gene encoding multiple tyrosine hydroxylases with different predicted functional characteristics. *Nature* 326:707, 1987.

219. LEDLEY FD, DILELLA AG, WOO SLC: Molecular biology of phenylalanine hydroxylase and phenylketonuria. *Trends Genet* 1:309, 1985.

220. IWAKI M, PHILLIPS RS, KAUFMAN S: Proteolytic modification of the amino-terminal and carboxy-terminal regions of rat hepatic phenylalanine hydroxylase. *J Biol Chem* 261:2051, 1986.

221. SCRIVER CR, MAHON B, LEVY HL, CLOW CL, READE TM, KRONICK J, LEMIEUX B, LABERGE C: The Hartnup phenotype: Mendelian transport disorder, multifactorial disease. *Am J Hum Genet* 40:401, 1987.

222. PENROSE L, QUASTEL JH: Metabolic studies in phenylketonuria. *Biochem J* 31:266, 1937.

223. DILELLA AG, KWOK SCM, LEDLEY FD, MARVIT J, WOO SLC: Molecular structure and polymorphic map of the human phenylalanine hydroxylase gene. *Biochemisty* 25:743, 1986.

224. WOO SLC, LIDSKY A, GUTTLER F, CHANDRA T, ROBSON K: Cloned human phenylalanine hydroxylase gene allows prenatal diagnosis and carrier detection of classical phenylketonuria. *Nature* 306:151, 1983.

225. LIDSKY AS, LEDLEY FD, DILELLA AG, KWOK SCM, DAIGER SP, ROBSON KJH, WOO SLC: Extensive restriction site polymorphism at the human phenylalanine hydroxylase locus and application in prenatal diagnosis of phenylketonuria. *Am J Hum Genet* 37:619, 1985.

226. SPEER A, DAHL H-H, RIESS O, COBET G, HANKE R, COTTON RGH, COUTELLE C: Typing of families with classical phenylketonuria using three alleles of the *Hind* III linked restriction fragment polymorphism, detectable with a phenylalanine hydroxylase cDNA probe. Family typing for PKU for linked Hind III RFLP. *Clin Genet* 29:491, 1986.

227. AVIGAD S, COHEN BE, WOO SLC, SHILOH Y: A specific deletion within the phenylalanine hydroxylase gene is common to most Yemenite Jewish phenylketonuria patients. *Am J Hum Genet* 41:A205, 1987.

227a. SULLIVAN SE, LIDSKY AS, BRAYTON K, DILELLA AG, KING M, CONNOR M,

COCKBURN F, WOO SLC: Phenylalanine hydroxylase deletion mutant from a patient with classical PKU. *Amer J Hum Genet* 37:A177, 1985.

228. CHAKRABORTY R, LIDSKY AS, DAIGER SP, GUTTLER F, SULLIVAN S, DILELLA AG, WOO SLC: Polymorphic DNA haplotypes at the human phenylalanine hydroxylase locus and their relationship with phenylketonuria. *Hum Genet* 76:40, 1987.

228a. DAIGER SP, LIDSKY AS, CHAKRABORTY R, ROCH R, GUTTLER F, WOO SLC: Effective use of polymorphic DNA haplotypes at the phenylalanine hydroxylase locus in prenatal diagnosis of phenyketonuria. *Lancet* 1:229, 1986.

228b. LIDSKY AS, GUTTLER F, WOO SLC: Prenatal diagnosis of classical phenylketonuria by DNA analysis. *Lancet* 1:549, 1985.

228c. REY F, MUNNICH A, LYONNET S, REY J: Classification et heterogénéité des hyperphenylalaninemémies liées à un deficit en phenylalanine hydroxylase. *Arch Fr Pediatr* 44:639, 1987.

229. DILELLA AG, WOO SLC: Molecular basis of phenylketonuria and its clinical applications. *Mol Biol Med* 4:183, 1987.

230. GUTTLER F, LEDLEY FD, LIDSKY AS, DILELLA AG, SULLIVAN SE, WOO SLC: Correlation between polymorphic DNA haplotypes at phenylalanine hydroxylase locus and clinical phenotypes of phenylketonuria. *J Pediatr* 110:68, 1987.

231. LEDLEY FD, LEVY HL, WOO SLC: Molecular analysis of the inheritance of phenylketonuria and mild hyperphenylalaninemia in families with both disorders. *N Engl J Med* 314:1276, 1986.

231a. DILELLA AG, HUANG W-M, WOO SL: Screening for phenylketonuria mutations by DNA amplification with the polymerase chain reaction. *Lancet* 1:497, 1988.

232. DILELLA AG, MARVIT J, LIDSKY AS, GUTTLER F, WOO SLC: Tight linkage between a splicing mutation and a specific DNA haplotype in phenylketonuria. *Nature* 322:799, 1986.

233. MARVIT J, DILELLA AG, BRAYTON K, LEDLEY FD, ROBSON KJH, WOO SLC: GT to AT transition at a splice donor site causes skipping of the preceding exon in phenylketonuria. *Nucleic Acids Res* 15:5613, 1987.

234. DILELLA AG, MARVIT J, BRAYTON K, WOO SLC: An amino acid substitution involved in phenylketonuria is in linkage disequilibrium with DNA haplotype 2. *Nature* 327:333, 1987.

235. LICHTER-KONECKI U, KONECKI DS, DILELLA AG, BRAYTON K, MARVIT J, TREFZ FK, WOO SLC: Phenylalanine hydroxylase deficiency caused by a single base substitution in an exon of the human phenylalanine hydroxylase gene. *Biochemistry* 27:2881, 1988.

236. HOFMAN K, VALLE D, KAZAZIAN H, SYNDERMAN S: Haplotype analysis of the phenylalanine hydroxylase (PH) gene in US blacks with phenylketonuria (PKU). *Am J Hum Genet* 41:A256, 1987.

236a. LYONNET S, CAILLAUD C, REY F, BERTHELON M, FREZAL J, REY J, MUNNICH A: Guthrie cards and needle biopsy of the liver for detection of point mutations in phenylketonuria. (submitted)

236b. RIESS O, MICHEL A, SPEER A, MEISKE W, COBET G, COUTELLE C: Linkage disequilibrium between RFLP haplotype 2 and the affected PAH allele in PKU families from the Berlin area of the German Democratic Republic. *Hum Genet* 78:343, 1988.

236c. LICHTER-KONECKI U, SCHLOTTER M, KONECKI DS, LABEIT S, WOO SLC, TREFZ K: Linkage disequilibrium between mutation and RFLP haplotype at the phenylalanine hydroxylase locus in the German population. *Hum Genet* 78:347, 1988.

236d. AULEHLA-SCHOLZ C, VORGERD M, SAUTTER E, LEUPOLD D, MAHLMANN R, ULLRICH K, OLEK K, HORST J: Phenylketonuria: distribution of DNA diagnostic patterns in German families. *Hum Genet* 78:353, 1988.

237. CHOO KH, COTTON RG, DANKS DM, JENNINGS IG: Genetics of the mammalian phenylalanine hydroxylase system. Studies of human liver phenylalanine hydroxylase subunit structure and of mutations in phenylketonuria. *Biochem J* 181:285, 1979.

238. CHOO KH, COTTON RGH, JENNINGS IG, DANKS DM: Observations indicating the nature of the mutation in phenylketonuria. *J Inherited Metab Dis* 2:79, 1980.

239. GRIMM U, KNAPP A, SCHLENZKA K, HESSE R: Phenylalaninhydroxylase-Aktivität beiketerozygoten Analgeträgen für das Phenylketerurie-Gen. *Acta Biol Med Ger* 36:1179, 1977.

239a. BARTHOLOMÉ K: Genetics and biochemistry of the phenylketonuria—Present state. *Hum Genet* 51:241, 1979.

239b. BARTHOLOMÉ K, DRESEL A: Studies on the molecular defect in phenylketonuria and hyperphenylalaninaemia using antibodies against phenylalanine hydroxylase. *J Inherited Metab Dis* 5:7, 1982.

240. DILELLA AG, LEDLEY FD, REY F, MUNNICH A, WOO SLC: Detection of phenylalanine hydroxylase messenger RNA in liver biopsy samples from patients with phenylketonuria. *Lancet* 1:160, 1985.

241. COTTON RGH: The primary molecular defects in phenlketonuria and its variants. *Int J Biochem* 8:333, 1977.

242. JERVIS GA: Phenylpyruvic oligophrenia: Deficiency of phenylalanine oxidizing system. *Proc Soc Exp Biol Med* 82:514, 1953.

243. UDENFRIEND S, BESSMAN S: The hydroxylation of phenylalanine and antipyrene in phenylpyruvic oligophrenia. *J Biol Chem* 203:961, 1953.

244. WALLACE HW, MOLDAVE K, MEISTER A: Studies on conversion of phenylalanine to tyrosine in phenylpyruvic oligophrenia. *Proc Soc Exp Biol Med* 94:532, 1957.

245. MITOMA C, AULD RM, UDENFRIEND S: On the nature of enzymatic defect in phenylpyruvic oligophrenia. *Proc Soc Exp Biol Med* 94:634, 1957.

246. KAUFMAN S: Phenylalanine hydroxylation cofactor in phenylketonuria. *Science* 128:1506, 1958.

247. FRIEDMAN PA, FISHER DB, KANG ES, KAUFMAN S: Detection of hepatic phenylalanine 4-hydroxylase in classical phenylketonuria. *Proc Natl Acad Sci USA* 70:552, 1973.

247a. FRIEDMAN PA, KAUFMAN S, KANG-SONG E: Nature of the molecular defect in phenylketonuria and hyperphenylalaninaemia. *Nature* 240:157, 1972.

248. BARTHOLOMÉ K, LUTZ P, BICKEL H: Determination of phenylalanine hydroxylase activity in patients with phenylketonuria and hyperphenylalaninemia. *Pediatr Res* 9:899, 1975.

248a. BARTHOLOMÉ K, OLEK K, TREFZ F: Compound heterozygotes in hyperphenylalaninaemia. *Hum Genet* 65:405, 1984.

249. DHONDT JL, FARRIAUX JP: Hepatic phenylalanine hydroxylase activity in hyperphenylalaninaemia. *J Inherited Metab Dis* 4:59, 1981.

250. TREFZ FK, ERLENMAIER T, HUNNEMAN DH, VARTHOLOMÉ K, LUTZ P: Sensitive *in vivo* assay ofthe phenylalanine hydroxylating system with a small intravenous dose of haptadeutero-L-phenylalanine using high pressure liquid chromatography and capillary gas chromatography/mass fragmentography. *Clin Chim Acta* 99:211, 1979.

251. TREFZ FK, BARTHOLOMÉ K, BICKEL H, LUTZ P, SCHMIDT H, SEYBERTH HW: *In vivo* residual activity of the phenylalanine hydroxylating system in phenylketonuria and variants. *J Inherited Metab Dis* 4:101, 1981.

252. KAUFMAN S, MAX EE, KANG ES: Phenylalanine hydroxylase activity in liver biopsies from hyperphenylalaninemia heterozygotes: Deviation from proportionality with gene dosage. *Pediatr Res* 9:632, 1975.

253. CURTIUS HC, VÖLLMIN JA, BAERLOCHER K: The use of deuterated phenylalanine for the elucidation of the phenylalanine-tyrosine metabolism. *Clin Chim Acta* 37:277, 1972.

254. TREFZ FK, BYRD DJ, BLASKOVICS ME, KOCKEN W, LUTZ P: Determination of deutrium labelled phenylalanine and tyrosine in human plasma with high pressure liquid chromatography and mass spectrometry. *Clin Chim Acta* 73:431, 1976.

255. CLARKE JTR, BIER DM: The conversion of phenylalanine to tyrosine in man. Direct measurement by continuous intravenous tracer infusions of L-(ring-$^{2}H_5$) phenylalanine and L-(1-^{13}C) tyrosine in the postabsorptive state. *Metabolism* 31:999, 1982.

256. MATALON R, MATTHEWS DE, MICHALS K, BIER D: The use of deuterated phenylalanine for the *in vivo* assay of phenylalanine hydroxylase activity in children. *J Inherited Metab Dis* 5:17, 1982.

257. LEHMANN WD, THEOBALD N, FISCHER R, HEINRICH HC: Stereospecificity of phenylalanine plasma kinetics and hydroxylation in man following oral application of a stable isotope-labelled pseudo-racemic mixture of L- and D-phenylalanine. *Clin Chim Acta* 128:181, 1983.

258. LEHMANN WD, HEINRICH HC: Oral versus intravenous L-phenylalanine loading compared by simultaneous application of L-($^{2}H_5$) and L-(^{15}N) phenylalanine. *Clin Chim Acta* 147:261, 1985.

259. CRAWFURD MD, GIBBS DA, SHEPPARD DM: Studies on human phenylalanine mono-oxygenase. I. Restricted expression. *J Inherited Metab Dis* 4:191, 1981.

260. UEBELHACK R, FRANKE L, KUTTER D, THOMA J, SEIDEL K: Platelet phenylalanine hydroxylating activity in phenylketonurics and normal controls. *Biochem Med* 34:376, 1985.

261. PATEL MS, ARINZE IJ: Phenylketonuria: Metabolic alterations induced by phenylalanine and phenylpyruvate. *Am J Clin Nutr* 28:183, 1975.

261a. BLAU K: Phenylalanine hydroxylase deficiency; biochemical, physiological and clinical aspects of phenylketonuria and related hyperphenylalaninemias, in Youdin MBH (ed): *Aromatic Amino Acid Hydroxylases and Mental Disease*. New York, Wiley, 1979, p 77.

262. KRAUSE W, HALMINSKI M, MCDONALD L, DEMBURE P, SALVO R, FRIEDES SR, ELSAS L: Biochemical and neuropsychological effects of elevated plasma phenylalanine in patients with treated phenylketonuria. *J Clin Invest* 75:40, 1985.

263. KRAUSE W, EPSTEIN C, AVERBROOK A, DEMBURE P, ELSAS L: Phenylalanine alters the mean power frequency of electroencephalograms and plasma L-DOPA in treated patients with phenylketonuria. *Pediatr Res* 20:1112, 1986.

264. FARQUHAR DL, STEVEN F, WESTWOOD A: Preliminary report on inverse diurnal variation of phenylalanine: Implications of maternal phenylketonuria. *Hum Nutr Appl Nutr* 39:224, 1985.

265. MICHALS K, MATALON R: Phenylalanine metabolites, attention span and hyperactivity. *Am J Clin Nutr* 42:361, 1985.

266. SZYMANSKI HV, NAYLOR EW, KAROUM F: Plasma phenylethylamine and phenylalanine in chronic schizophrenic patients. *Biol Psychol* 22:194, 1987.

267. CHRISTENSEN N, FELDMAN H, HASTINGS A: Concentrative and reversible character of intestinal amino acid transport. *Am J Physiol* 205:255, 1963.

268. POLLITT RJ: Phenlproprionic acid in the urine of patients with PKU and normals. *Clin Chim Acta* 55:317, 1974.

269. HRYHORCZUK LM, NOVAK EA, GERSHON S: Gut flora and urinary pheny lacetic acid. *Science* 226:996, 1984.

270. LASALA JM, COSCIA CJ: Accumulation of a tetrahydroisoquinoline in phenylketonuria. *Science* 203:283, 1979.

271. BESSMAN SP, WILLIAMSON ML, KOCH R: Diet, genetics and mental retardation interaction between phenylketonuria heterozygous mother and fetus to produce nonspecific diminution of IQ: Evidence in support of the justification hypothesis. *Proc Natl Acad Sci USA* 75:1562, 1978.

272. BATSHAW ML, VALLE D, BESSMAN SP: Unsuccessful treatment of phenylketonuria with tyrosine. *J Pediatr* 99:159, 1981.

273. KOEPP P, HELD KR: Serum-tyrosine in patients with hyperphenylalaninaemia. *Lancet* 2:92, 1977.

274. SCRIVER CR, COLE DEC, HOUGHTON SA, LEVY HL, GRENIER A, LABERGE C: Cord-blood tyrosine levels in the full-term phenylketonuria fetus and the "justification hypothesis." *Proc Natl Acad Sci USA* 77:6175, 1980.

275. THALHAMMER O, POLLAK A, LUBEC G, KONIGSHOFER H: Intracellular concentrations of phenylalanine, tyrosine and alpha-aminobytyric acid in 13 homozygotes and 19 heterozygotes for PKU compared with 26 normals. *Hum Genet* 54:213, 1980.

276. THALHAMMER O, LUBEC G, KONIGSHOFER H, SCHEIBENREITER S, CORADELLO H: Intracellular phenylalanine and tyrosine concentration in homozygotes and heterozygotes for phenylketonruia (PKU) and hyperphenylalaninemia compared with normals. *Hum Genet* 60:320, 1982.

277. ANDREWS TM, MCKERAN RO, WATTS RWE, MCPHERSON K, LAX R: Relationship between the granulocyte content and the degree of disability in phenylketonuria. *Q J Med* XLII:805, 1973.

278. CHOI TB, PARDRIDGE WM: Phenylalanine transport at the human blood-brain barrier. *J Biol Chem* 261:6536, 1986.

279. MAHER TJ, GLAESER BS, WURTMAN RJ: Diurnal variations in plasma concentrations of basic and neutral amino acids and in reduced concentrations of aspartate and glutamate: Effects of dietary protein intake. *Am J Clin Nutr* 39:722, 1984.

280. MOMMA S, AOYAGI M, RAPOPORT SI, SMITH QR: Phenylalanine transport across the blood-brain barrier as studied with the in situ brain perfusion technique. *J Neurochem* 48:1291, 1987.

281. ARAGON MC, GIMENEZ C, VALDIVIESO F: Inhibition by L-phenylalanine of tyrosine transport by synaptosomal plasma membrane vesicles: Implications in the pathogenesis of phenylketonuria. *J Neurochem* 39:1185, 1982.

282. HERRERO E, ARAGON MC, GIMENEZ C, VALDIVIESO F: Inhibition by L-phenylalanine of tryptophan transport of synaptosomal plasma membrane vesicles: Implications in the pathogenesis of phenylketonuria. *J Inherited Metab Dis* 6:32, 1983.

283. PETERSON NA, SHAH SN, RAGHUPATHY E, RHOADS DE: Presynaptic tyrosine availability in the phenylketonuric brain: A hypothetical evaluation. *Brain Res* 272:189, 1983.

284. RATZMANN GW, GRIMM U, JAHRIG K, KNAPP A: On the brain barrier system function and changes of cerebrospinal fluid concentrations of phenylalanine and tyrosine in human phenylketonuria. *Biomed Biochem Acta* 43:197, 1984.

285. PIEL N, LANE JD, HUTHER G, NEUHOFF V: Impaired permeability of the blood-cerebrospinal fluid barrier in hyperphenylalaninaemia. *Neuropediatrics* 13:88, 1982.

286. BERRY HK, BOFINGER MK, HUNT MM, PHILLIPS PJ, GUILFOILE MB: Reduction of cerebrospinal fluid phenylalanine, after oral administration of valine, isoleucine, and leucine. *Pediatr Res* 16:751, 1982.

287. JORDAN MK, BRUNNER RL, HUNT MM, BERRY HK: Preliminary support for the oral administration of valine, isoleucine and leucine for phenylketonuria. *Dev Med Child Neurol* 27:33, 1985.

288. HEUTHER G, KAUS R, NEUHOFF V: Amino acid depletion of the blood and brain tissue of hyperphenylalaninemic rats is abolished by the administration of additional lysine: A contribution to the understanding of the metabolic defects in phenylketonuria. *Biochem Med* 33:334, 1985.

289. HEUTHER G: The depletion of tryptophan and serotonin in the brain of developing hyperphenylalaninemic rats is abolished by the additional administration of lysine. *Neurochem Res*11:1663, 1986.

290. LANGENBECK U, BEHBEHANI A, LUTHE H: Renal transport of aromatic acids in patients with phenylketonuria. *J Inherited Metab Dis* 4:69, 1981.

291. OKAJIMA K, INOUE M, MORINO Y: Studies on the mechanism for renal elimination of N-acethylphenylalanine: Its pathophysiologic significance in phenylketonuria. *J Lab Clin Med* 105:132, 1985.

292. BARASHNEV YI, KORNEICHUK VV, KLEMBOVSKY AI, KLYUSHINA LA: Role of the liver in the pathogenesis of cerebral disorders of phenylketonuria. *J Inherited Metab Dis* 5:204, 1982.

292a. NEAL JL, SCRIVER CR: Abnormally high concentrations of hydrophobic-side-chain amino acids do not affect cell function by modifying water structure in phenylketonuria and branched-chain aminoaciduria. *FRCS* 2:1700, 1974.

293. LANE JD, NEUHOFF V: Phenylketonuria: Clinical and experimental considerations revealed by the use of animal models. *Naturwissenschaften* 67:227, 1980.

294. VORHEES CV, BUTCHER RE, BERRY HK: Progress in experimental phenylketonuria: A critical review. *Neurosci Biobehav Rev* 5:177, 1981.

295. GUTTLER F, LOU H: Dietary problems of phenylketonuria: Effect on CNS transmitters and their possible role in behaviour and neuropsychological function. *J Inherited Metab Dis* 9:169, 1986.

296. BRASS CA, GREENGARD O: Modulation of cerebral catecholamine concentrations during hyperphenylalaninaemia. *Biochem J* 208:765, 1982.

297. GREENGARD O, WOLFE J: Cerebral serotinin regulation by phenylalanine analogues during hyperphenylalaninemia. *Biochem Pharmacol* 36:965, 1987.

298. TAYLOR EH, HOMMES FA, STEWART DE: Effect of experimental hyperphenylalaninemia on biogenic amine synthesis at later stages of brain development. *Biochem Med* 29:307, 1983.

299. DWIVEDY AK, SHAH SN: Effects of phenylalanine and its deaminated metabolites on Na^+, K^+-ATPase activity in synaptosomes from rat brain. *Neurochem Res* 7:717, 1982.

300. MATSUO K, HOMMES F: Regional distribution of the phenylalanine-sensitive ATP-sulphurylase in brain. *J Inherited Metab Dis* 10:62, 1987.

301. HUETHER G, NEUHOFF V: Individual carboxylic ester hydrolases of the developing cerebellum. Influence of experimental hyperphenylalaninaemia. *Cell Mol Biol* 28:313, 1982.

302. SHAH SN: Minireview: Fatty acid composition of lipids of human brain myelin and synaptosomes: Changes in phenylketonuria and Down's syndrome. *Int J Biochem* 10:477, 1979.

303. JOHNSON RC, SHAH SM: Effects of alpha-methylphenylalanine plus phenylalanine treatment during development of myelin in rat brain. *Neurochem Res* 5:709, 1980.

304. DWIVEDY AK, SHAH SN: Effect of hyperphenylalaninemia on polyphosphoinositides content of rat brain. *Experientia* 38:1458, 1982.

305. HEUTHER G, KAUS R, NEUHOFF V: Brain development in experimental hyperphenylalaninaemia: Myelination. *Neuropediatrics* 13:177, 1982.

306. TAYLOR EH, HOMMES FA: Effect of experimental hyperphenylalaninemia on myelin metabolism at later stages of brain development. *Int J Neurosci* 20:217, 1983.

307. BABA H, SATO S, INUZUKA T, MIYATAKE T: Developmental changes of myelin-associated glycoprotein in rat brain: Study on experimental hyperphenylalaninemia. *Neurochem Res* 12:459, 1987.

308. BINEK PA, JOHNSON TC, KELLY CJ: Effect of alpha-methylphenylalanine and phenylalanine on brain polyribosomes and protein synthesis. *J Neurochem* 36:1476, 1981.

309. BINEK-SINGER P, JOHNSON TC: The effects of chronic hyperphenylalaninaemia on mouse brain protein synthesis can be prevented by other amino acids. *Biochem J* 206:407, 1982.

310. OKANO Y, CHOW IZ, ISSHIKI G, INOUE A, OURA T: Effects of phenylalanine loading on protein synthesis in the fetal heart and brain of rat: An experimental approach to maternal phenylketonuria. *J Inherited Metab Dis* 9:15,1986.

311. SCHÖOTER J, SCHOTT KJ, PURTILL MA, NEUFHOFF V: Lysosomal protein degradation in experimental hyerphenylalaninemia. *J Inherited Metab Dis* 9:273, 1986.

312. CORDERO ME, TREJO M, COLOMBO M, ARENDA V: Histological maturation of the neocortex in phenylketonuric rats. *Early Hum Dev* 8:157, 1983.

313. LACEY DJ: Hippocampal dendritic abnormalities in a rat model of phenylketonuria. *Ann Neurol* 16:577, 1984.

314. LACEY DJ: Normalization of dendritic spine numbers of rat hippocampus after termination of phenylacetate injections (PKU model). *Brain Res* 329:354, 1985.

315. LACEY DJ: Cortical dendritic spine loss in rat pups whose mothers were prenatally injected with phenylacetate (maternal PKU model). *Brain Res* 392:283, 1986.

316. LOO YH, POTEMPSKA A, WISNIEWSKI HM: A biochemical explanation of phenylacetate neurotoxicity in experimental phenylketonuria. *J Neurochem* 45:1596, 1985.

317. LOO YH, HYDE HR, LIN FH, WISNIEWSKI HM: Cerebral biochemical abnormalities in experimental maternal phenylketonuria: Gangliosides and sialoglycoproteins. *Life Sci* 37:2099, 1985.

318. SWAIMAN KF, WU SR: Phenylalanine and phenylacetate adversely affect developing mammalian brain neurons. *Neurology* 34:1246, 1984.

319. HUETHER G, NEUHOFF V: Use of alpha-methylphenylalanine for studies of brain development in experimental phenylketonuria. *J Inherited Metab Dis* 4:67, 1981.

320. HUETHER G, NEUHOFF V, KAUS R: Brain development in experimental hyperphenylalaninaemia: Disturbed proliferation and reduced cell numbers in the cerebellum. *Neuropediatrics* 14:12, 1983.

321. JOHNSON RC, SHAH SN: Effect of hyperphenylalaninemia induced during suckling on brain DNA metabolism in rat pups. *Neurochem Res* 9:517, 1984.

322. BAUMAN ML, KEMPER TL: Morphologic and histoanatomic observations of the brain in untreated human phenylketonuria. *Acta Neuropathol* 58:55, 1982.

323. STEFFENS C: No difference in dermatoglyphics of fingers and palms between phenylketonuria patients and controls. *Hum Genet* 69:195, 1985.

324. IRONS M, LEVY HL: Metabolic syndromes with dermatologic manifestations. *Clin Rev Allergy* 4:101, 1986.

325. LASSER AE, SCHULTZ BC, BEAFF D, BIELINSKI S, KIRSCHENBAUM MB: Phenylketonuria and scleroderma. *Arch Dermatol* 114:1215, 1978.

326. BROWN EH, BERRY HK, OLSEN J, LEVINSON J: Phenylketonuria and scleroderma. *J Inherited Metab Dis* 9:405, 1986.

327. WALKER JD, CRALL JJ, MCDONNELL JE; Phenylketonuria and dentistry: Review of the literature. *ASDC J Dent Child* 49:280, 1982.

328. ZWANN J: Eye findings in patients with phenylketonuria. *Arch Ophthalmol* 101:1236, 1983.

329. HOLM VA, KNOX WE: Physical growth in phenylketonuria: I. A retrospective study. *Pediatrics* 63:694, 1979.

330. CLOW CL, READE TM, SCRIVER CR: Management of hereditary metabolic disease: The role of allied health personnel. *N Engl J Med* 284:1292, 1971.

331. FISCH RO, TSAI MY, CLARK BA, OKAGAKI T: Semen studies on phenylketonurics. *Biochemistry* 26:427, 1981.

332. PRIMROSE DA: Phenylketonuria with normal intelligence. *J Ment Defic Res* 27:239, 1983.

333. DE GIORGIS GF, ANTONOZZI I, DEL CASTELLO PG, ROSANO M, LIOZZO A: EEG is a possible prognostic tool in phenylketonuria. *Electroenceph Clin Neurophysiol* 55:60, 1983.

334. REALMUTO GM, GARFINKEL BD, TUCKMAN M, TSAI MY, CHANG PN, FISCH RO, SHAPIRO S: Psychiatric diagnosis and behavioural characteristics of phenylketonuric children. *J Nerv Ment Dis* 174:536, 1986.

335. MINAMI R, OLEK K, WARDENBACH P: Phenylketonuria in a patient with cystinuria. *Humangenetik* 28:319, 1975.

336. PARKER CE, LANDING BH: Coincidence of Fahr disease and PKU. *J Pediatr* 91:273, 1977.

337. ROTH KS, COHN RM, BERMAN P, SEGAL S: Phenylketonuria and Duchenne muscular dystrophy: A case report. *J Pediatr* 88:689, 1976.

338. CROSLEY CS, SCHNEIDER AJ: Phenylketonuria and neonatal myotonic dystrophy. *Clin Pediatr* 21:56, 1982.

339. FISCH RO, GOOSENS KA, TSAI MY, SEELIG S, SCHWICHTENBERG K: The occurrence of phenylketonuria and galactosemia within the same family. *Clin Pediatr* 24:456, 1985.

340. LEITTITIS JK, STAHL M, TACKMANN W, WICK H, WILDBERG A: Homozygous hypobetalipoproteinaemia and phenylketonuria. *Eur J Pediatr* 144:174, 1985.

341. MONTEAGUDO FS, KLIBEL MA: Combined phenylketonuria and pyruvate kinase deficiency. A case report. *S Afr Med J* 69:761, 1986.

342. SCRIVER CR: Treatment of inborn errors of metabolism. The nature:nurture argument specified, in Crawfurd MD, Gibbs DA, Watts RW (eds): *Advances in the Treatment of Inborn Errors of Metabolism.* New York, Wiley, 1982, p 289.

343. MACCREADY RA: Admissions of phenylketonuric patients to residential institutions before and after screening programs of the newborn infant. *J Pediatrics* 85:383, 1974.

344. WOOLF LI, VULLIAMY DG: Phenylketonuria with a study of the effect upon it of glutamic acid. *Arch Dis Child* 26:487, 1951.

345. WOOLF LI, GRIFFITHS R, MONCRIEFF A: Treatment of phenylketonuria with a diet low in phenylalanine. *Br Med J* 1:57, 1955.

346. BICKEL H, GERRARD J, HICKMANS EM: Influence of phenylalanine intake on the chemistry and behaviours of a phenylketonuric child. *Acta Paediatr* 43:64, 1954.

347. ARMSTRONG MD, TYLER FH: Studies on Phenylketonuria. I. Restriction phenylalanine intake in phenylketonuria. *J Clin Invest* 34:565, 1955.

348. SCRIVER CR: Mutants: Consumers with special needs. *Nutr Rev* 29:155, 1971.

349. ACOSTA PB, TRAHMS C, WELLMAN NS, WILLIAMSON M: Phenylalanine intakes of 1- to 6-year-old children with phenylketonuria undergoing therapy. *Am J Clin Nutr* 38:694, 1983.

350. NAYMAN R, THOMSON E, SCRIVER CR, CLOW CL: Observations on the composition of milk-substitute products for treatment of inborn errors of amino acid metabolism. Comparisons with human milk. *Am J Clin Nutr* 32:1279, 1979.

351. LINK RM, WACHTEL U: Clinical experiences with an amino acid preparation in children with phenylketonuria. *Rev Med Liege* 39:429, 1984.

352. ACOSTA PB, WENZ E, WILLIAMSON M: Nutrient intake of treated infants with phenylketonuria. *Am J Clin Nutr* 30:198, 1977.

353. KINDT E, HALVORSEN S: The need of essential amino acids in children. An evaluation on the intake of phenylalanine, tyrosine, leucine, isoleucine, and valine in children with phenylketonuria, tyrosine amino transferase defect and maple syrup urine disease. *Am J Clin Nutr* 33:279, 1980.

354. KINDT E, MOTZFELDT K, HALVORSEN S, LIE SO: Protein requirements in infants and children: A longitudinal study of children treated for phenylketonuria. *Am J Clin Nutr* 37:778, 1983.

355. KINDT E, MOTZFELDT K, HALVORSEN S, LIE SO: Is phenylalanine requirement in infants and children related to protein intake? *Br J Nutr* 51:435, 1984.

356. SHORTLAND D, SMITH I, FRANCIS DEM, ERSSER R, WOLFF OH: Amino acid and protein requirements in a preterm infant with classic phenylketonuria. *Arch Dis Child* 60:263, 1985.

357. ACOSTA PB, FERNHOFF PM, WARSHAW HS, ELSAS LJ, HAMBIDGE KM, ERNEST A, MCCABE ER: Zinc status and growth of children undergoing treatment for phenylketonuria. *J Inherited Metab Dis* 5:107, 1982.

358. TAYLOR CJ, MOORE G, DAVIDSON DC: The effect of treatment on zinc, copper and calcium status in children with phenylketonuria. *J Inherited Metab Dis* 7:160, 1984.

359. LOMBECK I, EBERT KH, KASPEREK K, FEINENDEGEN LE, BREMER HJ: Selenium intake of infants and young children, healthy children and dietetically treated patients with phenylketonuria. *Eur J Pediatr* 143:99, 1984.

360. ROTTOLI A, LISTA G, ZECCHINI G, BUTTE C, LONGHI R: Plasma selenium levels in treated phenylketonuric patients. *J Inherited Metab Dis* 8:127, 1985.

360a. ZACHARA BA, WASOWICZ W, GROMADZINSKA J, SKLODOWSKA M, CABALSKA B: Red blood cell glutathione peroxidase activity as function of selenium supplementation in dietary treated children with phenylketonuria. *Biomed Biochem Acta* 46:S209, 1987.

361. ROTTOLI A, RIVA E, LISTA G, GORGATTI L, ORTISI MT, LONGHI R, GIOVANNINI M: Plasma chromium and manganese levels in treated PKU patients. *J Inherited Metab Dis* 9:215, 1986.

362. SCAGLIONI S, ZUCCOTTI G, VEDOVELLO M, ROTTOLI A, PACCANELLI S, LONGHI R, RIVA E, GIOVANNINI M: Study of serum ferritin in 58 children with classic phenylketonuria and persistent hyperphenylalaninaemia. *J Inherited Metab Dis* 8:160, 1985.

363. GALLUZZO CR, ORTISI MT, CASTELLI L, AGOSTONI C, LONGHI R: Plasma lipid concentrations in 42 treated phenylketonuric children. *J Inherited Metab Dis* 8:129,1985.

364. HANLEY WB, LINSAO L, DAVIDSON W, MOES CAF: Malnutrition with early treatment of phenylketonuria. *Pediatr Res* 4:318, 1970.

365. LEVY HL, SHIH VE, KAROLKEWICZ V, FRENCH WA, CASS V, KENNEDY JL JR, MACCREADY RA: Persistent mild hyperphenylalaninemia in the untreated state. A prospective study. *N Engl J Med* 285:424, 1971.

366. YAMASHITA M, ARAI S, FUJIMAKI M: A low-phenylalanine, high-tyrosine plastein as an acceptable dietetic food. Method of preparation by use of enzymatic protein hydrolysis and resynthesis. *J Food Sci* 41:1029, 1976.

367. NAKHOST Z, HSIEH DS, SHIH V, RHA CK: Synthesis of low-phenylalanine polypeptides. *Int J Pediatr Protein Res* 20:267, 1982.

368. PRATT OE: A new approach to the treatment of phenylketonuria. *J Ment Defic Res* 24:203, 1980.

369. PRATT OE: The needs of the brain for amino acids and how they are transported across the blood-brain barrier, in Belton NR, Toothill C (eds): *Transport and Inherited Disease.* Boston, MTP Press, 1981, p 87.

370. ANDERSON AE, AVINS L: Lowering brain phenylalanine levels by giving other large neutral amino acids. *Arch Neurol* 33:684, 1976.

371. LOU H: Large doses of tryptophan and tyrosine as potential therapeutic alternative to dietary phenylalanine restriction in phenylketonuria. *Lancet* 2:151, 1985.

371a. LOU HC, LYKKELUND C, GERDES AM, UDESEN H, BRUHN P: Increased vigilance and dopamine synthesis by large doses of tyrosine or phenylalanine restriction in phenylketonuria. *Acta Paediatr Scand* 76:560, 1987.

372. BRUNNER RL, BROWN EH, BERRY HK: Phenylketonuria revisited: Treatment of adults with behavioural manifestations. *J Inherited Metab Dis* 10:171, 1987.

372a. CASSELL JA: Inborn errors of metabolism. *Top Clin Nutr* 2:1, 1987.

373. WEISS B, HUI M, LAJTHA A: Entrapment of phenylalanine hydroxylase in a polyacrylamide matrix. *Biochem Med* 18:330, 1977.

374. WEISS B, HUI M, THAYER C, LAJTHA A: VI. Efforts at stabilization of rat

liver phenylalanine hydroxylase. *Res Commun Chem Pathol Pharmacol* 26:597, 1979.

375. AMBRUS CM, AMBRUS JL, HORVATH C, PEDERSEN H, SHARMA S, KANT C, MIRAND E, GUTHRIE E, PAUL T: Phenylalanine depletion for the management of phenylketonuria: Use of enzyme reactors with immobilized enzymes. *Science* 201:837, 1978.

376. AMBRUS CM, SHARMA SD, HORVATH C, KALGHATGI K, ANTHONE S, AMBRUS JL, COOLEY C, MIRAND EA: *In vivo* safety of hollow fiber enzyme-reactors with immobilized phenylalanine ammonia-lyase in a large animal model for phenylketonuria. *J Pharmacol Exp Ther* 224:598, 1983.

377. AMBRUS CM, ANTHONE S, HORVATH C, KALGHATGI K, LELE AS, EAPEN G, AMBRUS JL, RYAN AJ, LI P: Extracorporeal enzyme reactors for depletion of phenylalanine in phenylketonuria. *Ann Intern Med* 106:531, 1987.

378. SPRANDEL U: Erythrocytes as carrier for therapeutic enzymes—An approach towards enzyme therapy of inborn errors of metabolism. *Bibl Haematol* 51:7, 1985.

379. BOURGET L, CHANG TM: Phenylalanine ammonia-lyase immobilized in semipermeable microcapsules for enzyme replacement in phenylketonuria. *FEBS Lett* 180:5, 1985.

380. BOURGET L, CHANG TMS: Phenylalanine ammonia-lyase immobilized in microcapsules for the depletion of phenylalanine in plasma in phenylketonuric rat model. *Biochim Biophys Acta* 883:432, 1986.

381. INOUE S, MATSUNAGA Y, IWANE H, SOTOMURA M, NOSE T: Entrapment of phenylalanine ammonia-lyase in silk fibroin for protection from proteolytic attack. *Biochem Biophys Res Commun* 26:165, 1986.

382. HOSKINS JA, JACK G, WADE HE, PEIRIS RJD, WRIGHT EC, STARR DJT, STERN J: Enzymatic control of phenylalanine intake in phenylketonuria. *Lancet* 1:392, 1980.

383. HOSKINS JA, HOLLIDAY SB, GREENWAY AM: The metabolism of cinnamic acid by healthy and phenylketonuria adults: A kinetic study. *Biomed Mass Spectrom* 11:296, 1984.

384. LARUE C, MUNNICH A, CHARPENTIER C, SAUDUBRAY JM, FRÉZAL, RÉMY MH, RIVAT C: An extracorporeal hollow fibre reactor for phenylketonuria using immobilized phenylalanine ammonia lyase. *Dev Pharmacol Ther* 9:73, 1986.

385. SMITH I, WOLFF OH: Natural history of phenylketonuria and influence of early treatment. *Lancet* 2:540, 1974.

386. DOBSON JC, KUSHIDA E, WILLIAMSON M, FRIEDMAN G: Intellectual performance of 36 phenylketonuria patients and their nonaffected siblings. *Pediatrics* 58:53, 1976.

387. WILLIAMSON M, DOBSON C, KOCH R: Collaborative study of children treated for phenylketonuria: Study design. *Pediatrics* 60:815, 1977.

388. DOBSON JC, WILLIAMSON ML, AZEN C, KOCH R: Intellectual assessment of 111 four-year-old children with phenylketonuria. *Pediatrics* 60:822, 1977.

389. WILLIAMSON ML, KOCH R, AZEN C, CHANG C: Correlates of intelligence test results in treated phenylketonuric children. *Pediatrics* 68:161, 1981.

390. KOCH R, AZEN C, FRIEDMAN EG, WILLIAMSON ML: Paired comparisons between early treated PKU children and their matched sibling controls on intelligence and school achievement test results at eight years of age. *J Inherited Metab Dis* 7:86, 1984.

391. HOLM VA, KRONMAL RA, WILLIAMSON M, ROCHE AF: Physical growth in phenylketonuria: II. Growth of treated children in the PKU collaborative study from birth to 4 years of age. *Pediatrics* 63:700, 1979.

392. WHITE JE, KRONMAL RA, ACOSTA PB: Excess weight among children with phenylketonuria. *J Am Coll Nutr* 1:293, 1982.

392a. SCAGLIONI S, VIRDIS R, ZUCOTTI G, VEDOVELLO M, MARCIANESI M, LONGHI R, RIVA F, GIOVANNINI M, GIOVANNELLI G: Pubertal maturation and classical phenylketonuria. *J Inherited Metab Dis* 9:285, 1986.

393. BERRY HD, O'GRADY DJ, PERLMUTTER LJ, BOFINFER MK: Intellectual development and academic achievement of children treated early for phenylketonuria. *Dev Med Child Neurol* 21:311, 1979.

394. GRUBEL-KAISER S, SCHMID-RÜTER E: Phenylketonuria: Schulerfolq bei Fruherfassung Katamnese bei 50 phenylketonurischen Kindern mit Diätbeginn im ersten und zweiten Lebensmonat. *Monatsschr Kinderheilkd* 126:379, 1978.

395. FARRIAUX JP, DESOMBRE-DENYS D, CHARLES-BASSI MA, DHONDT JL: Le traitement de la phénylcétonurie. Remarques á propos d'une analyse de vingt et un cas. *Ann Pediatr* 27:291, 1980.

396. WRONA RM: A clinical epidemiologic study of hyperphenylketonuria. *Am J Public Health* 69:673, 1979.

397. HOLTZMAN NA, KRONMAL RA, van DOORNINCK W, AZEN C, KOCH R: Effect of age at loss of dietary control on intellectual performance and behavior of children with phenyketonuria. *N Engl J Med* 314:593, 1986.

398. PENNINGTON BF, van DOORNINCK WJ, MCCABE ILL, MCCABE ER: Neuropsychological deficits in early treated phenylketonuric children. *Am J Ment Defic* 89:467, 1985.

398a. RAPOPORT D, SAUDUBRAY JM, OGIER H, HATT A, BERGES J, DEPONDT E, CHARPENTIER C, FREZAL J: Psychological prospects and scholastic performance of 33 children with early diagnosis of hyperphenylalaninemia. *Arch Fr Pediatr* 40:273, 1983.

398b. MELNICK CR, MICHALS KK, MATALON R: Linguistic development of children with phenylketonuria and normal intelligence. *J Pediatr* 98:269, 1981.

399. WAISBREN SE, MAHON BE, SCHNELL RR, LEVY HL: Predictors of intelligence quotient and intelligence quotient change in persons treated for phenylketonuria early in life. *Pediatrics* 79:351, 1987.

400. FAUST D, LIBON D, PUESCHEL S: Neuropsychological functioning in treated phenylketonuria. *Int J Psychiatr Med* 16:169, 1986–87.

400a. SMITH HC, BEASLEY MG, WOLFF OH, ADES AE: Behavior disturbance in 8-year-old children with early treated phenylketonuria. *J Pediatr* 112:403, 1988.

401. NETLEY C, HANLEY WB, RUDIER HL: Phenylketonuria and its variants. Observations on intellectual functioning. *Can Med Assoc J* 131:1984.

402. KOCK R, YUSIN M, FISHLER K: Successful adjustment to society by adults with phenylketonuria. *J Inherited Metab Dis* 8:209, 1985.

402a. BRUNNER RL, JORDAN MK, BERRY HK: Early-treated phenylketonuria: Neuropsychological consequences. *J Pediatr* 102:831, 1983.

403. HOLTZMAN NA: Anatomy of a trial. *Pediatrics* 60:932, 1977.

404. HOLTZMAN NA, WELCHER DW, MELLITS ED: Termination of restricted diet in children with phenylketonuria: A randomized controlled study. *N Engl J Med* 293:1121, 1975.

405. WOOLF, LI: Late onset phenylalanine intoxication. *J Inherited Metab Dis* 2:19, 1979.

406. SMITH I, LOBASCHER M, STEVENSON J, WOOLF OH: Effect of stopping the low phenylalanine diet on the intellectual progress of children with phenylketonuria. *Ann Clin Biochem* 14:134, 1977.

407. CABALSKA B, DUCZYNSKA N, BORZYMOWSKA J, ZORSKA K, KOSLACZ-FOLGA A, BOZKOWA K: Termination of dietary treatment in phenylketonuria. *Eur J Pediatr* 126:253, 1977.

408. SMITH I, LOBASCHER ME, STEVENSON JE, WOLFF OH, SCHMIDT H, GRUBEL-KAISER S, BICKEL H: Effect of stopping low-phenylalanine diet on intellectual progress of children with phenylketonuria. *Br Med J* 2:723, 1978.

408a. KOFF E, KAMMERER B, BOYLE P, PEUSCHEL SM: Intelligence and phenylketonuria: Effects of diet termination. *J Pediatr* 94:534, 1979.

408b. WILLIAMSON M, KOCK R, BERLOW L: Diet discontinuation in phenylketonuria. *Pediatrics* 63:823, 1979.

408c. KOCH R, AXEN CG, FRIEDMAN EG, WILLIAMSON ML: Preliminary report on the effects of diet discontinuation in PKU. *J Pediatr* 100:870, 1982.

409. WAISBREN SE, SCHNELL RR, LEVY HL: Diet termination in children with phenylketonuria: A review of psychological assessment used to determine outcome. *J Inherited Metab Dis* 3:149, 1980.

410. SEASHORE MR, FRIEDMAN E, NOVELLY RA, BAPAT V: Loss of intellectual function in children with phenylketonuria after relaxation of dietary phenylalanine restriction. *Pediatrcs* 75:226, 1985.

411. BEHBEHARI AW: Termination of strict diet therapy in phenylketonuria. A study on EEG sleep patterns and computer spectral analysis. *Neuropediatrics* 16:92, 1985.

412. LOU HC, GÜTTLER F, LYKKELUND C, BRUHN P, NIEDERWIESSER A: Decreased vigilance and neurotransmitter synthesis after discontinuation of dietary treatment of phenylketonuria in adolescents. *Eur J Pediatr* 144:17, 1985.

413. MATTHEWS WS, BARABAS G, CUSACK E, FERRARI M: Social quotients of children with phenylketonuria before and after discontinuation of dietary treatment. *Am J Ment Defic* 91:92, 1986.

414. SCHUETT VE, GURDA RF, BROWN ES: Diet discontinuation policies and practices of PKU clinics in the United States. *Am J Public Health* 70:498, 1980.

415. SCHUETT VE, BROWN ES: Diet policies of PKU clinics in the United States. *Am J Public Health* 74:501, 1984.

416. SCHUETT VE, BROWN ES, MICHALS K: Reinstitution of diet therapy in PKU patients from twenty-two US clinics. *Am J Public Health* 75:39, 1985.

417. HUNT MM, BERRY HK, WHITE PP: Phenylketonuria, adolescence and diet. *J Am Diet Assoc* 85:1328, 1985.

418. MICHALS K, DOMINIK M, SCHUETT V, BROWN E, MATALON R: Return to diet therapy in patients with phenylketonuria. *J Pediatr* 106:933, 1985.

419. HOGAN SE, GATES RD, MacDONALD GW, CLARKE JTR: Experience with adolescents with phenylketonuria returned to phenylalanine-restricted diets. *J Am Diet Assoc* 86:1203, 1986.

420. CLARKE JTR, GATES RD, HOGAN SE, BARRETT M, MacDONALD GW: Neuropsychological studies on adolescents with phenylketonuria returned to phenylalanine-restricted diets. *Am J Ment Retardation* 92:255, 1987.

421. WAISBREN SE, SCHNELL R, LEVY HL: Intelligence and personality characteristics in adults with untreated atypical phenylketonuria and mild hyperphenylalaninemia. *J Pediatr* 105:955, 1984.

422. SMITH RJ: Aspartame approved despite risks. *Science* 213:986, 1981.

423. WENZ E: Aspartame and PKU. *J Am Diet Assoc* 84:101, 1984.

424. GUTTLER F, LOU H: Aspartame may imperil dietary control of phenylketonuria. *Lancet* 1:525, 1985.

425. STEGINK LK, KOCH R, BLASKOVICS ME, FILER LJ JR, BAKER GL, MCDONNEL JE: plasma phenylalanine levels in phenylketonuric heterozygous and normal adults administered aspartame at 34 mg/kg body weight. *Toxicology* 20:81, 1981.

426. CABELLERO B, MAHON BE, ROHR FJ, LEVY HL, WURTMAN RJ: Plasma amino acid levels after single-dose aspartame consumption in phenylketonuria, mild hyperphenylalaninemia and heterozygous state for phenylketonuria. *J Pediatr* 109:668, 1986.

427. STEGINK LD, FILER LJ JR, BALLER GL: Plasma, erythrocyte and human milk levels of free amino acids in lactating women administered aspartame or lactose. *J Nutr* 109:2173, 1979.

428. LEDLEY FD: Somatic gene therapy for human disease: Background and prospects. Part II. *J Pediatr* 110:167, 1987.

429. LEDLEY FD, GRENETT HE, DILELLA AG, KWOK SCM, WOO SLC: Gene transfer and expression of human phenylalanine hydroxylase. *Science* 228:77, 1985.

430. MANN R, MULLIGAN RC, BALTIMORE D: Construction of a retrovirus packaging mutant and its use to produce helper-free defective retrovirus. *Cell* 33:153, 1983.

431. LEDLEY FD, GRENETT HE, MCGINNIS-SHELNUTT M, WOO SLC: Retroviral-mediated gene transfer of human phenylalanine hydroxylase into NIH 3T3 and hepatoma cells. *Proc Natl Acad Sci USA* 83:409, 1986.

432. CHOO KH, FILBY RG, JENNINGS IG, PETERSON G, FOWLER K: Vectors for expression and amplification of cDNA in mammalian cells: Expression of rat phenylalanine hydroxylase. *DNA* 5:529, 1986.

433. WOLFF JA, YEE J-K, SKELLY HF, MOORES JC, RESPESS JG, FRIEDMANN T, LEFFERT H: Expression of retrovirally transduced genes in primary cultures of adult rat hepatocytes. *Proc Natl Acad Sci USA*84:3344, 1987.

434. LEDLEY FD, DARLINGTON GJ, HAHN T, WOO SLC: Retroviral gene transfer into primary hepatocytes: Implications for genetic therapy of liver-specific functions. *Proc Natl Acad Sci USA*84:5335, 1987.

435. TAYLOR D, HOCHSTEIN P: Potential variants of phenylketonuria. *Lancet* 1:1378,1975.

436. BARTHOLOMÉ K: A new molecular defect in PKU. *Lancet* 2:1580, 1974.

437. BARTHOLOMÉ K, BYRD J, KAUFMAN S, MILSTIEN S: Atypical phenylketonuria with normal phenylalanine hydroxylase and dihydropteridine reductase activity *in vitro*. *Pediatrics* 59:757, 1977.

438. DANKS DM, BARTHOLOME K, CLAYTON BE, CURTIUS H, GRÖBE H, KAUFMAN S, LEEMING R, PFLEIDERER W, REMBOLD D, REY F: Malignant hyperphenylalaninaemia—Current status. *J Inherited Metab Dis* 1:49, 1978.

439. SMITH I, CLAYTON BE, WOLFF OH: New variant of phenylketonuria with progressive neurological illness unresponsive to phenylalanine restriction. *Lancet* 1:1108, 1975.

440. KAUFMAN S, MILSTIEN S, BARTHOLOMÉ K: New form of phenylketonuria. *Lancet* 2:708,1975.

441. REY F, HARPEY J-P, LEEMING RJ, BLAIR J-A, AICARDI J, REY J: Les hyperphenylalaninémies avec activité normale de la phenylalanine-hydroxylase. *Arch Fr Pediatr* 34:cix, 1977.

442. DHONDT JL: Tetrahydrobiopterin deficiencies: Preliminary analysis from an international survey. *J Pediatr* 104:501, 1984.

442a. DHONDT JL: Les déficits en tetrahydrobioptérine. Enseignements de l'analyze de 90 patients colligés dans le régistre international. *Arch Fr Pediatr* 44:655, 1987.

443. NIEDERWIESER A, CURTIUS H-CH: Tetrahydrobiopterin deficiencies in hyperphenylalaninemia, in Bickel H, Wachtel U (eds): *Inherited Diseases of Amino Acid Metabolism. Recent Progress in Understanding, Recognition and Management.* New York, Georg Thieme Verlag, 1985, p 104.

443a. PONZONE A, GUARDAMAGNA O, FERRARIS S, BRACCO G, NIEDERWIESER A, COTTON RGH: Two mutations of dihydropteridine reductase deficiency. *Arch Dis Child* 63:154, 198.

444. TIETZ A, LINDBERG M, KENNEDY EP: A new pterindine-requiring enzyme system for the oxidation of glyceryl ethers. *J Biol Chem* 239:4081, 1964.

445. IRONS M, LEVY HL, O'FLYNN E, STACK CV, LANGLAIS PJ, BUTLER IJ, MILSTIEN S, KAUFMAN S: Folinic acid therapy in treatment of dihydropteridine reductase deficiency. *J Pediatr* 110:61, 1987.

446. BUTLER IJ, KRUMHOLZ A, HOLTZMAN A, KOSLOW SH, KAUFMAN S, MILSTIEN S: Dihidropteridine reductase deficiency variant of phenyketonuria: A disorder of neurotransmitters. *Arch Neurol* 32:350, 1975.

447. BUTLER IJ, KOSLOW SH, KRUMHOLZ A, HOLTZMAN NA, KAUFMAN S: A disorder of biogenic amines in dihydropteridine reductase deficiency. *Ann Neurol* 3:224, 1978.

448. NIEDERWIESER A, PONZONE A, CURTIUS H-CH: Differential diagnosis of tetrahydrobiopterin deficiency. *J Inherited Metab Dis* 8(*suppl* 1):34, 1985.

449. COSTA E, CARENZI A, GUIDOTTI A, REVUELTA A: Narcotic analgesics and the regulation of neuronal catecholamine stores, in Usidin E, Snyder SH (eds): *Frontiers in Catecholamine Research.* New York, Pergamon, 1973, p 1003.

450. MCKEAN CM: The effects of high phenylalanine concentration of serotinin and catecholamine metabolism in the human brain. *Brain Res* 47:469, 1972.

451. GRÖBE H, BARTHOLOMÉ K, MILSTIEN S, KAUFMAN S: Hyperphenylalaninaemia due to dihdryopteridine reductase deficiency. *Eur J Pediatr* 129:93, 1978.

452. SAHOTA A, LEMMING RJ, BLAIR JA, ARMSTRONG RA, GREEN A, COHEN BE: Partial dihydropteridine reductase deficiency and mental retardation. *J Inherited Metab Dis* 9 (*suppl* 2):247, 1986.

452a. BARTHOLOMÉ K, BYRD DJ: Tetrahydrobiopterin treatment of variant form of phenylketonuria. *Lancet* 2:1042, 1975.

453. BREWSTER TG, MOSKOWITZ MA, KAUFMAN S, BRESLOW JL, MILSTIEN S, ABROMS IF: Dihdropteridine reductase deficiency associated with severe neurologic disease and mild hyperphenylalaninemia. *Pediatrics* 63:94, 1979.

454. LONGHI R, RIVA E, VALSASINA R, PACCANELLI S, GIOVANNINI M: Phenylketonuria due to dihydropteridine reductase deficiency: Presentation of two cases. *J Inherited Metab Dis* 8(*suppl* 2):97, 1985.

455. CERONE R, SCALISI S, COTELLESSA M, SCHIAFFINO MC, CARUSO U, ROMANO C: Dihydropteridine reductase deficiency. Clinical, biochemical and therapeutic aspects. *J Inherited Metab Dis* 9 (*suppl* 2):244, 1986.

456. DANKS DM, SCHLESINGER R, FIRGAIRA F, COTTON RGH, WATSON BM, REMBOLD H, HENNINGS G: Malignant hyperphenylalaninemia—Clinical features, biochemical findings, and experience with administration of biopterins. *Pediatr Res* 13:1150, 1979.

457. TADA K, NARISAWA K, ARAI N, OGASAWARA Y, ISHIZAWA S: A sibling case of hyperphenylalaninemia due to a deficiency of dihydropteridine reductase: Biochemical and pathological findings. *Tohoku J Exp Med* 132:123, 1980.

458. HARPEY JP: Les défauts de synthèse des biopterines: Les déficits complets (réductase et synthétase). *Arch Fr Pédiatr* 40:231, 1983.

459. SMITH I, LEEMING R: Clinical role of pteridine therapy in tetrahydrobiopterin deficiency. *J Inherited Metab Dis* 8 (*suppl* 1):39, 1985.

459a. KAUFMAN S: Hyperphenylalaninemia caused by defects in biopterin metabolism. *J Inherited Metab Dis* 8 (*suppl* 1):20, 1985.

459b. DANKS DM, COTTON RG: Early diagnosis of hyperphenylalaninemia due to tetrahydrobiopterin deficiency (malignant hyperphenylalaninemia). *J Pediatr* 96:854, 1980.

460. ARAI N, NARISAWA K, HAYAKAWA H, TADA K: Hyperphenylalaninemia due to dihydropteridine reductase deficiency: Diagnosis by enzyme assay on dried blood spots. *Pediatrics* 98:426, 1982.

461. MILSTIEN S, KAUFMAN S, SUMMER GK: Hyperphenlalaninemia due to dihydropteridine reductase deficiency: Diagnosis by measurement of oxidized and reduced pterins in urine. *Pediatrics* 65:806, 1980.

461a. NIXON JC, LEE CL, MILSTIEN S, KAUFMAN S, BARTHOLOMÉ K: Neopterin and biopterin levels in patients with atypical forms of phenylketonuria. *J Neurochem* 35:898, 1980.

462. NIEDERWIESER A, STAUDENMANN W, WETZEL E: High-performance liquid chromatography with column switching for the analysis of biogenic amine metabolites and pterins. *J Chromatogr* 290:237, 1984.

462a. DANKS DM, COTTON RGH, SCHLESINGER P: Diagnosis of malignant hyperphenylalaninaemia. *Arch Dis Child* 54:329, 1979.

463. FIRGAIRA FA, COTTON RGH, DANKS DM, FOWLER K, LIPSON A, YU JS: Prenatal determination of dihydropteridine reductase in a normal fetus at risk for malignant hyperphenylalaninemia. *Prenat Diagn* 3:7, 1983.

464. KUHL P, OLEK K, WARDENBACH P: Dihydropteridine reductase variation in man and the characid fish "cheirodon axelrodi"; evidence for a dimeric enzyme structure. *Hum Genet* 55:99, 1980.

465. DAHL H-HM, WAKE S, COTTON RGH, DANKS DM: The use of restriction fragment length polymorphisms in prenatal diagnosis of dihydropteridine reductase deficiency. *J Med Genet* 25:25, 1988.

466. FIRGAIRA FA, CHOO KM, COTTON RGM, DANKS DM: Heterogeneity of the molecular defect in human dihydropteridine reductase deficiency. *Biochem J* 198:677, 1981.

467. COTTON RGH, JENNINGS IG, BRACCO G, PENZONE A, GUARDAMAGNA O: Tetrahydrobiopterin non-responsiveness in dihydropteridine reductase deficiency is associated with the presence of mutant protein. *J Inherited Metab Dis* 9:239,1986.

468. LEMMING RJ, BLAIR JA, REY F: Biopterin derivatives in atypical phenylketonuria. *Lancet* 1:99, 1976.

469. REY F, BLANDIN-SAVOJA F, REY J: Atypical phenylketonuria with normal dihydropteridine reductase activity. *N Engl J Med* 295:1138, 1976.

470. MILSTIEN S, ORLOFF S, SPIELBERG S, BERLOW S, SCHULMAN J, KAUFMAN S: Hyperphenylalaninemia due to phenylalanine hydroxylase cofactor deficiency. *Pediatr Res* 11:460, 1977.

471. NIEDERWIESER A, BLAU N, WANG M, JOLLER P, ATARES M, CARDESA-GARCIA J: GTP cyclohydrolase I deficiency, a new enzyme defect causing hyperphenylalaninemia with neopterin, biopterin, dopamine, and serotonin deficiencies and muscular hypotonic. *Eur J Pediatr* 141:208, 1984.

472. DHONDT JL, FARRIAUX JP, BOUDHA A, LARGILLIERE C, RINGEL J, ROGER MM, LEMMING RJ: Neonatal hyperphenylalaninemia presumably caused by guanosine triphosphate-cyclohydrolase deficiency. *J Pediatr* 106:954, 1985.

473. NAYLOR EW, ENNIS D, DAVIDSON AGF, WONG LTK, APPLEGARTH DA, NEIDERWIESER A: Guanosine triphosphate cyclohydrolase I deficiency: Early diagnosis by routine urine pteridine screening. *Pediatrics* 79:374, 1987.

474. BLAU N, JOLLER P, ATARES M, CARDESA-GARCIA J, NIEDERWIESER A: Increase of GTP cyclohydrolase I activity in mononuclear blood cells by stimulation: Detection of heterozygotes of GTP cyclohydrolase I deficiency. *Clin Chim Acta* 148:47,1985.

475. BODE VC, MCDONALD JD, GUENET J-L, SIMON D: *hyp-1:* A mouse mutant with hereditary hyperphenylalaninemia induced by ethylnitrosourea mutagenesis. *Genetics,* 118:299, 1988.

476. MCDONALD JD, BODE VC: Hyperphenylalaninemia in the *hph-1* mouse mutant. *Pediatr Res,* 23:63, 1988.

477. MCDONALD JD, COTTON RGH, JENNINGS I, LEDLEY FD, WOO SLC, BODE VC: Biochemical defect of the *hph-1* mouse mutant is a deficiency of GTP-cyclohydrolase activity. *J Neurochem* 50:655, 1988.

478. KAUFMAN S, BERLOW S, SUMMER GK, MILSTIEN S, SCHULMAN JD, ORLOFF S, SPIELBERG S, PUESCHEL S: Hyperphenylalaninemia due to a deficiency of biopterin. *N Engl J Med* 299:673, 1978.

479. SCHAUB J, DÄUMLING S, CURTIUS H-CH, NIEDERWIESER A, BARTHOLOMÉ K, VISCONTINI M, SCHIRCKS B, BIERI JH: Tetrahydrobiopterin therapy of atypical phenylketonuria due to defective dihydrobiopterin biosynthesis. *Arch Dis Child* 53:674, 1978.

480. NIEDERWIESER A, CURTIUS H-CH, BETTONI O, BIERI J, SCHIRCKS B, VISCONTINI M, SCHAUB J: Atypical phenylketonuria caused by 7,8-dihydrobiopterin synthetase deficiency. *Lancet* 1:131, 1979.

481. NIEDERWEISER A, MATASOVIC A, CURTIUS H-CH, ENDRES W, SCHAUB J: 3′-hydroxysepiapterin in patients with dihydrobiopterin deficiency. *FEBS Lett* 118:299, 1980.

482. CURTIUS H-CH, NIEDERWIESER A, VISCONTINI M, OTTEN A, SCHAUB J, SCHEIBENREITER S, SCHMIDT H: Atypical phenylketonuria due to tetrahydrobiopterin deficiency. Diagnosis and treatment with tetrahydrobiopterin, dihydrobiopterin and sepiapterin. *Clin Chim Acta* 93:251, 1979.

483. NIEDERWIESER A, CURTIUS H-CH, WANG M, LEUPOLD D: Atypical phenylketonuria with defective biopterin metabolism. Monotherapy with tetrahydrobiopterin or sepiapterin, screening and study of biosynthesis in man. *Eur J Pediatr* 138:110, 1982.

483a. TANAKA K, YONEDA M, NAKAJIMA T, MIYATAKE T, OWADA M: Dihydrobiopterin synthesis defect: An adult with diurnal fluctuation of symptoms. *Neurology* 37:519, 1987.

484. NIEDERWIESER A, CURTIUS H-CH, VISCONTINI M, SCHAUB J, SCHMIDT H: Phenylketonuria variants. *Lancet* 1:550, 1979.

485. ENDRES W, NIEDERWIESER A, CURTIUS H-CH, WANG M, OHRT B, SCHAUB J: Atypical phenylketonuria due to biopterin deficiency. *Helv Pediatr Acta* 37:489, 1982.

486. DHONDT J-L, LEROUX B, FARRIAUX JP, LARGILLIERE C, LEMMING RJ: Dihydrobiopterin synthesis defect. *Eur J Pediatr* 141:92, 1983.

487. BECK B, BRANDT NJ, CHRISTENSEN E, NIEDERWIESER A, PEDERSEN PS: Diagnostic and therapeutic aspects of dihydrobiopterin deficiency. *Acta Paediatr Scand* 72:449, 1983.

488. LEVINE RA, HEINTEL D, LEIMBACHER W, NIEDERWIESER A, CURTIUS H-C, GHISLA S: Recent advances in tetrahydrobiopterin biosynthesis and the treatment of human disease, in *Biochemical and Clinical Aspects of Pteridines.* New York, Walter de Gruyter, 1983, vol 2, p 325.

489. KETTLER R, BARTHOLINI G, PLETSCHER A: *In vivo* enhancement of tyrosine hydroxylation in rat striatum by tetrahydrobiopterin. *Nature* 249:476, 1974.

490. REMBOLD H: Metabolism and metabolic roles of 6-polyhydroxyalkylpterins. *J Inherited Metab Dis* 1:61, 1978.

491. MCINNES RR, KAUFMAN S, WARSCH JJ, VAN LOON GR, MILSTIEN S, KAPATOS G, SOLDIN S, WALSH P, MacGREGOR D, HANLEY WB: Biopterin synthesis defect. Treatment with L-dopa and 5-hydroxytryptophan compared with therapy with a tetrahydropterin. *J Clin Invest* 73:458, 1984.

492. LEVINE RA, ZOEPHEL GP, NIEDERWIESER A, CURTIUS H-CH: Tetrahydrobiopterin analogues and their ability to enter the rat striatum after peripheral administration, in *Biochemical and Clinical Aspects of Pteridines.* 1985, vol 4, p 269.

493. MUENZER J, MILSTIEN S, SIDBURY J, BERLOW S, KAUFMAN S: Treatment of hyperphenylalaninemia secondary to a deficiency of biopterin with reduced pterins. *Pediatr Res* 18:297a, 1984.

494. KAPATOS G, KAUFMAN S: Peripherally administered reduced pterins do enter the brain. *Science* 212:955, 1981.

495. KAUFMAN S, KAPATOS G, MCINNES RR, SCHULMAN JD, RIZZO WB: Use of tetrahydropterins in the treatment of hyperphenylalaninemia due to defective synthesis of tetrahydrobiopterin: Evidence that peripherally administered tetrahydropterins enter the brain. *Pediatrics* 70:376, 1982.

495a. KAUFMAN S, KAPATOS G, RIZZO WB, SCHULMAN JD, TAMARKIN L, VON LOON GR: Tetrahydropterin therapy for hyperphenylalaninemia caused by defective synthesis of tetrahydrobiopterin. *Ann Neurol* 14:308,1983.

496. COHEN BE, SZEINBERG A, QUINT J, NORMAND M, BLONDER J, PELED I: Malignant phenylketonuria due to defective synthesis of dihydrobiopterin. *Isr J Med Sci* 21:520, 1985.

497. SYNDERMAN SE, SANSARICQ C, PULMONES MT: Successful longterm therapy of biopterin deficiency. *J Inherited Metab Dis* 10:260, 1987.

498. NIEDERWIESER A, LEIMBACHER W, CURTIUS C-CH, PONZONE A, REY F, LEUPOLD D: Atypical phenylketonuria with "dihydrobiopterin synthetase" deficiency: Absence of phosphate-eliminating enzyme activity demonstrated in liver. *Eur J Pediatr* 144:13, 1985.

499. NEIDERWIESER A, SHINTAKU H, HASLER TH, CURTIUS H-CH, LEHMANN H, GUARDAMAGNA O, SCHMIDT H: Prenatal diagnosis of "dihydrobiopterin synthesis" deficiency, a variant form of phenylketonuria. *Eur J Pediatr* 145:176, 1986.

500. YOSHIOKA S, MASADA M, YOSHIDA T, MIZOKAMI T, AKINO M, MATSUO N: Atypical phenylketonuria due to bipopterin deficiency diagnosis by assay of an enzyme involved in the synthesis of sepiapterin from dihydroneopterin triphosphate. *Zool Sci* 1:74, 1984.

501. HREIDARSSON S, ALLE D, HOLTZMAN N, COYLE J, SINGER H, KAPATOS G, KAUFMAN S: A peripheral defect in biopterin synthesis: A new mutant? *Pediatr Res* 16:192A, 1982.

502. HOGANSEN G, BERLOW S, KAUFMAN S, MILSTIEN S, SCHUETT V, MATALON R, NAYLOR E, SEIFERT W: Bipterin synthesis defects: Problems in diagnosis. *Pediatrics* 74:1004, 1984.

503. NIEDERWIESER A, SHINTAKU H, LEIMBACHER W, CURTIUS H-CH, HYANEK J, ZEMAN J, ENDRES W: Peripheral tetrahydrobiopterin deficiency with hyperphenylalaniemia due to incomplete 6-pyruvoyl tetrahydropterin synthase deficiency or heterozygosity. *Eur J Pediatr* 146:228, 1987.

504. SCRIVER CR, CLOW CL, KAPLAN P, NIEDERWIESER A: Hyperphenylalaninemia due to deficiency of 6-pyruvoyl tetrahydropterin synthase. Unusual gene dosage effect in heterozygotes. *Hum Genet* 77:168, 1987.

505. HSIAO K-J, CHIN P-C, CHEN W-H, CHAO S-L: Atypical phenylketonuria with mild mental retardation caused by tetrahydrobiopterin deficiency in a Chinese Family. *J Inherited Metab Dis* 9 (*suppl* 2):240, 1986.

506. REY F, LEMMING RJ, CURTIUS H-CH, NIEDERWIESER A, VISCONTINI M, REY J: "Transitory" phenylketonuria. A permanent deficit. *Arch Fr Pediatr* 36 (*suppl* 9):xlviii,1979.

507. REY F, LEMMING RJ, BLAIR JA, REY J: Biopterin defect in a normal-appearing child affected by a transient phenylketonuria. *Arch Dis Child* 55:637, 1980.

508. GUTTLER F, LOU H, LYKKELUND C, NIEDERWIESER A: Combined tetrahydrobiopterin-phenylalanine loading test in the detection of partially defective biopterin synthesis. *Eur J Pediatr* 142:126, 1984.

509. YUDKOFF M, SEGAL S: Absent phenylalanine hydroxylase activity without phenylketonuria. *Eur J Pediatr* 134:85, 1980.

510. AUERBACH VH, DIGEORGE AM, CARPENTER GG: Phenylalaninemia. A study of the diversity of disorders which produce elevation of blood concentration of phenylalanine, in Nyhan W (ed): *Amino Acid Metabolism and Genetic Variation.* New York, McGraw-Hill, 1967, p 11.

511. BLAU K, LEVITT GA, HARVEY DR: Hyperphenylalaninemia with defective transamination. *Clin Chim Acta* 132:43, 1983.

512. WADMAN SK, KETTING D, DE BREE PK, VAN DER HEIDEN C, GRIMBERG MT, KRUIJSWIJK H: Permanent chemical phenylketonuria and a normal phenylalanine tolerance in two sisters with a normal mental development. *Clin Chim Acta* 65:197, 1975.

513. ALM J, BODEGÅRD G, LARSSON A, NYBERG G, ZETTERSTRÖM R: Children with inborn errors of phenylalanine metabolism: Prognosis and phenylalanine tolerance. *Acta Paediatr Scand* 75:619, 1986.

514. WESTWOOD A, BARR DG: Phenylketonuria with a progressive neurological disorder not responsive to tetrahydrobiopterin. *Acta Paediatr Scand* 71:859, 1982.

515. WILSON JMG, JUNGNER G: Principles and practice of screening for disease. Public Health Papers 34. Geneva, World Health Organization, 1968.

516. NATIONAL ACADEMY OF SCIENCES (National Research Council): Genetic Screening. Programs, Principles and Research. Washington, DC, 1975.

517. JINKS DC, GUTHRIE R, NAYLOR EW: Simplified procedure for producing cillus subtilis spores for the Guthrie phenylketonuria and other microbiological screening tests. *J Clin Microbiol* 21:826, 1985.

518. CLEMENS P, VOLTMER C, PLETTNER C: Effect of antimicrobial agents on Guthrie test and its reversal by autoclaving. *Lancet* 2:778, 1985.

519. LEVY HL, SIMMONS JR, MACREADY RA: Stability of amino acids and galactose in the newborn screening filter paper blood specimen. *J Pediatr* 107:757, 1985.

520. SPIERTO FW, HEARN TL, GARDNER FH, HANNON WH: Phenylalanine analyses of blood-spot control materials: Preparation of samples and evaluation of interlaboratory performance. *Clin Chem* 31:235, 1985.

521. SEPE SJ, LEVY HL, MOUNT FW: An evaluation of routine follow-up blood screening of infants for phenylketonuria. *N Engl J Med* 300:606, 1979.

522. ANAS GJ: Mandatory PKU screening: The other side of the looking glass. *Am J Public Health* 72:1401, 1982.

523. STARFIELD B, HOLTZMAN NA: A comparison of effectiveness of screening for PKU in the United States, United Kingdom and Ireland. *N Engl J Med* 293:118, 1975.

524. SCRIVER CR, LABERGE C, CLOW CL, FRASER FC: Genetics and medicine: An evolving relationship. *Science* 200:946, 1978.

525. AMERICAN ACADEMY OF PEDIATRICS. COMMITTEE ON GENETICS: Screening for congenital metabolic disorders in the newborn infant: Congenital deficiency of thyroid hormone and hyperphenylalaninemia. *Pediatrics* 60:389, 1977.

526. SCRIVER CR: Screening for medical intervention: The PKU experience in human genetics. *Prog Clin Biol Res* 103B:437, 1982.

527. AMERICAN ACADEMY OF PEDIATRICS. COMMITTEE ON GENETICS: New issues in newborn screening for phenylketonuria and congenital hypothyroidism. *Pediatrics* 69:104, 1982.

528. MCCABE ERB, MCCABE L, MOSHER GA, ALLEN RJ, BERMAN JL: Newborn screening for phenylketonuria: Predictive validity as a function of age. *Pediatrics* 72:390,1983.

529. SCHOEN EJ, CUNNINGHAM GC, KOCH R: More on newborn screening for phenylketonuria: Recommendations of the Committee on Genetics. *Pediatrics* 72:139, 1983.

530. LEVY HL, MITCHELL ML, RIDLEY SE: Newborn screening. *Pediatrics* 73:417, 1984.

531. SCRIVER CR: More on newborn screening for phenylketonuria: In reply. *Pediatrics* 72:141, 1983.

532. KARKMAN HN, CARROLL CL, MOORE EG, MATHESON MS: Fifteen-year experience with screening for phenylketonuria with an automated fluorometric method. *Am J Hum Genet* 34:743, 1982.

533. HOLTZMAN C, SLAZYK WE, CORDERO JF, HANNON WH: Descriptive epidemiology of missed cases of phenylketonuria and congenital hypothyroidism. *Pediatrics* 78:553, 1986.

534. MEDICAL RESEARCH COUNCIL; STEERING COMMITTEE FOR MRC/DHSS PHENYLKETONURIA REGISTER: Routine neonatal screening for phenylketonuria in the United Kingdom 1964–78. *Br Med J* 1:1680, 1981.

535. MCCABE ERB, MCCABE L: Screening for PKU in sick or premature neonates. *J Pediatr* 103:502, 1983.

536. BINDER J, JOHNSON CF, SABOE B, DRUGE-WISPE S: Delayed elevation of serum phenylalanine level in a breast-fed child. *Pediatrics* 63:334, 1979.

537. MORRIS AF, HOLTON JB, BURMAN D, COLLEY JR: Phenylalanine and tyrosine levels in newborn screening blood samples. *Arch Dis Child* 58:271, 1983.

538. WALKER V, CLAYTON BE, ERSSER RS, FRANCIS DE, LILLY P, SEAKINS JW, SMITH I, WHITEMAN PD: Hyperphenylalaninemia of various types among three-quarters of a million neonates tested in a screening programme. *Arch Dis Child* 56:759, 1981.

538a. LABERGE C, FERREIRA P, GRENIER A, LAFRAMBOISE R, MORISETTE J: Hyperphenylalaninémies—Expérience canadienne et québecoise. *Arch Fr Pediatr* 44:643, 1987.

539. SORENSEN JR, LEVY HL, MANGIONE TW, SEPE SJ: Parental response to repeat testing of infants with "false-positive" results in a newborn screening program. *Pediatrics* 73:183, 1984.

540. BUSH JW, CHEN MM, PATRICK DL: Health status index in cost effectiveness: Analysis of PKU program, in Berg RL (ed): *Health Status Indexes Hospital Research and Educational Trust.* London, 1973, p 172.

541. DAGENAIS DL, COURVILLE L, DAGENAIS MG: A cost-benefit analysis of the Quebec Network of Genetic Medicine. *Soc Sci Med* 20:601, 1985.

542. THALHAMMER O et al: A collaborative study. Frequency of inborn errors of metabolism especially in PKU, in some representative newborn screening centres around the world. *Humangenetik* 30:273, 1975.

543. SCRIVER CR et al: Population screening: Report of a Workshop, in Marois M (ed): *Prevention of Physical and Mental Congenital Defects. Epidemiology, Early Detection and Therapy and Environmental Factors.* New York, AR Liss, 1983, part B, p 89.

544. DHONDT JL, LARGILLIERE C, FARRIAUX JP: Essai de classification des hyperphénylalaninemias. A propos de 62 malades. *Arch Fr Pediatr* 40:243, 1983.

545. LUTZ P, SCHMIDT H, FREY G, BICKEL H: Standardized loading test with protein for the differentiation of phenylketonuria from hyperphenylalaninemia. *J Inherited Metab Dis* 5:29, 1982.

546. GUTHRIE R, SUSI A: A simple phenylalanine method for detecting phenylketonuria in large populations of newborn infants. *Pediatrics* 32:338, 1963.

547. MCAMAN MW, ROBINS E: Fluorometric method for the determination of phenylalanine in serum. *J Lab Clin Med* 59:885, 1962.

548. ROESEL RA, BLANKENSHIP PR, HOMMES FA: HPLC assay of phenylalanine and tyrosine in blood spots on filter paper. *Clin Chim Acta* 15:91, 1986.

549. SHEN RS, RICHARDSON CJ, ROUSE BM, ABELL CW: An enzymatic assay of plasma phenylalanine and tyrosine for the detection and management of phenylketonuria. *Biochem Med* 26:211, 1981.

550. KNOX WE: Retrospective study of phenylketonuria: Relation of phenylpyruvate excretion of plasma phenylalanine. *Phenylketonuria Newsletter* 2, February 1970.

551. TUCHMAN M, FISCH RO, RAMNARAINE ML, KRIVIT W: Acidic metabolites of phenylalanine in plasma of phenylketonurics. *Biochem Med* 34:203, 1985.

552. HSIEH MC, BERRY HK, GOFINGER MK, PHILLIPS PJ, GUILFOILE MB, HUNT MM: Comparative diagnostic value of phenylalanine challenge and phenylalanine hydroxylase activity in phenylketonuria. *Clin Genet* 23:415, 1983.

553. BLITZER MG, BAILEY-WILSON JE, SHAPIRA E: Discrimination of phenylketonurics from persistent hyperphenylalaninemia patients using a simple phenylalanine loading test. *Clin Chim Acta* 153:137, 1985.

553a. TREFZ FK, SCHMIDT H, BARTHOLOMÉ K, MAHLE M, MATTHIS P, PECHT G: Differential diagnosis and significance of various hyperphenylalaninemias, in Bichel H, Wachtel U (eds): *Inherited Diseases of Amino Acid Metabolism.* New York, Georg Thieme Verlag, 1985, pp 86-100.

554. ENDRES W, IBEL H, KIERAT L, BLAU N, CURTIUS H-CH: Tetrahydrobiopterin and "non-responsive" dihydropteridine reductase deficiency. *Lancet* 2:223, 1987.

555. LEMMING RJ, PHEASANT AE, BLAIR JA: The role of tetrahydrobiopterin in neurological disease: A review. *J Ment Defic Res* 25:231, 1981.

556. LEMMING RJ, BLAIR JA, MELIKIAN V, O'GORMAN DJ: Biopterin derivatives in human body fluids and tissues. *J Clin Pathol* 29:444, 1976.

557. LEMMINGRJ, BARFORD PA, BLAIR JA, SMITH I: Blood spots on Guthrie cards can be used for inherited tetrahydrobiopterin deficiency screening in hyperphenylalaninemic infants. *Arch Dis Child* 59:58, 1984.

558. LEMMING RJ, BLAIR JA, GREEN A, RAINE DN: Biopterin derivatives in normal and phenylketonuric patients after oral loads of L-phenylalanine, L-tyrosine, and L-tryptophan. *Arch Dis Child* 51:771, 1976.

559. FUKUSHIMA T, NIXON JC: Oxidation and conversion of reduced forms of bipterin, in Kisliuk RL, Brown GM (eds): *Chemistry and Biology of Pteridines.* New York, Elsevier, 1979, p 31.

559a. FUKUSHIMA T, NIXON JC: Analysis of reduced forms of biopterin in biological tissues and fluids. *Anal Biochem* 102:176, 1980.

560. DHONDT J-L, LARGILLIÈRE C, ARDOUIN P, FARRIAUX J-P, DAUTREVAUX M: Diagnosis of variants of hyperphenylalaninemia by determination of pterins in urine. *Clin Clin Acta* 110:205, 1981.

561. MAISUBARA Y, HEININGER JA, LIN YY: Improved diagnosis of classical vs atypical phenylketonuria by liquid chromatography. *Clin Chem* 30:278, 1984.

562. HAYAKAWA H, NARISAWA K, ARAI N, TADA K, MATSUO N, TANAKA T, NARITOMI K: Differential diagnosis of variant forms of hyperphenylalaninemia by urinary pterins. *J Inherited Metab Dis* 6:123, 1983.

563. KUSTER T, NIEDERWEISER A: Gas chromatography-mass spectrometry of trimethylsilyl pteridines. *J Chromatogr* 278:245, 1983.

564. KUSTER T, MATASOVIC A, NIEDERWIESER A: Appication of gas chromatography-mass spectrometry to the study of biopterin metabolism in man. *J Chromatogr* 290:303, 1984.

565. DHONDT JL, ARDOUIN P, SHAYTE JM, FARRIAUX JP: Developmental aspects of pteridine metabolism and relationships with phenylalanine metabolism. *Clin Chim Acta* 116:143, 1981.

566. DHONDT JL, FARRIAUX JP, HAYTE JM: Bilan de 5 années de dépistage des hyperphénylalaninémies par déficit en cofacteur. *Arch Fr Pediatr* 43:785, 1986.

567. MATALON R, MIXHALS K, LEE CL, NIXON JC: Screening for biopterin defects in newborns with phenylketonuria and other hyperphenylalaninemias. *Ann Clin Lab Sci* 12:411, 1982.

568. MOHYUDDIN F, RUPAR CA, EVERS MC: Screening for biopterin defects among hyperphenylalaninemic patients: Report of a Canadian program after 3 years, in Cooper BA, Whitehead VM (eds): *Chemistry and Biology of Pteridines.* New York, Walter de Gruyter, 1986, p 243.

569. NARISAWA K, AYAKAWA H, ARAI N, MATSUO N, TANAKA T, NARITOMI K, TADA K: Diagnosis of variant forms of hyperphenylalaninemia using filter paper spots of urine. *J Pediatr* 103:577, 1983.

570. TREFZ FK, BARTHOLOMÉ K, BICKEL H, LUTZ P, SCHMIDT H: *In vivo* determination of phenylalanine hydroxylase activity using heptadeutero-phe-

nylalanine and comparison to the *in vitro* assay values. *Monogr Hum Genet* 9:108, 1978.

571. FELL V, HOSKINS JA, POLLITT RJ: The labelling of urinary acids after oral doses of deuterated L-phenylalanine and L-tyrosine in normal subjects. Quantitative studies with implications for the deuterated phenylalanine load test in PKU. *Clin Chim Acta* 83:259, 1978.

572. LEHMANN WD, THEOBALD N, HEINRICH HC: Assay for plasma free phenylalanine and tyrosine by high-pressure liquid chromatography and field desorption mass spectrometry and its application to an *in vivo* study of the phenylalanine hydroxylating system in man. *Biomed Mass Spectrom* 8:598, 1981.

573. LEHMANN WD, FISHER R, HEINRICH HC, CLEMENS P, GRÜTTNER R: Metabolic conversion of L-[$U^{14}C$] phenylalanine to respiratory $^{14}CO_2$ in healthy subjects, phenylketonuria heterozygotes and classic phenylketonurics. *Clin Chim Acta* 157:253, 1986.

573a. BARWELL BE, POLLITT RJ: Attitude des parents vis-à-vis due diagnostic prénatal de la phenylcétonurie. *Arch Fr Pediatr* 44:665, 1987.

573b. RIESS O, MICHEL A, SPEER A, COBET G, COUTELLE C: Introduction of genomic diagnosis of classical phenylketonuria to the health care system of the German Democratic Republic. *Clin Genet* 32:209, 1987.

573c. LO WHY: Medical Genetics in China. *J Med Genet* 25:253, 1988.

574. WOO SLC: Prenatal diagnosis and carrier detection of classic phenylketonuria by gene analysis. *Pediatrics* 74:412, 1984.

575. WOO SLC, LIDSKY A, CHANDRA T, GUTTLER F, ROBSON K: Prenatal diagnosis of classical phenylketonuria by gene mapping. *JAMA* 251:1998, 1984.

576. SCRIVER CR, CLOW CL: Avoiding phenylketonuria: Why parents seek prenatal diagnosis. *J Pediatr*, 113:495, 1988.

577. SPEER A, BOLLMAN R, MICHEL A, NEUMANN R, BOMMER CH, HANKE R, RIESS O, COBET G, COUTELLE CH: Prenatal diagnosis of classical phenylketonuria by linked restriction fragment length polymophism analysis. *Prenat Diagn* 6:447, 1986.

577a. LEDLEY FD, KOCH R, JEW K, BEAUDET A, O'BRIAN WE, WOO SLC: Phenylalanine hydoxylase expression and activity in the liver of a fetus with phenylketonuria. *J Pediatr*, 113:463, 1988.

578. NIEDERWIESER A, SHINTAKU H, HASLER TH, CURTIUS H-CH: Prenatal diagnosis of tetrahydrobiopterin deficiency, in Cooper BA, Whitehead VM (eds): *Chemistry and Biology of Pteridines*. New York, Walter de Gruyter, 1986, p 399.

579. BLAU N, NIEDERWIESER A, CURTIUS H-CH, LEIMBACHER W, KIERAT L, MATASOVIC A, STAUDENMANN W: Prenatal diagnosis of tetrahydrobiopterin deficiency, in Curtius H-CH, Blau N (eds): *Unconjugated Pterins and Related Biogenic Amines*. Berlin, Walter de Gruyter, 1987, p 238.

580. LEHMANN WD, THEOBALD N, HEINRICH HC, CLEMENS P, GRUTTNER R: Detection of heterozygous carriers for phenylketonuria by a L-($^2H_5$)phenylalanine stable isotope loading test. *Clin Chim Acta* 138:59, 1984.

581. HSIA DY-Y, DRISCOLL KW, TROLL W, KNOX WE: Detection of phenylalanine tolerance tests of heterozygous carriers of phenylketonuria. *Nature* 178:1239, 1956.

582. BLITZER MG, BAILEY-WILSON JE, SHAPIRA E: Discrimination of heterozygotes for henylketonuria, persistent hyperphenylalaninemia and controls by phenylalanine loading. *Clin Chim Acta* 161:347, 1986.

583. WOOLF LI, CRANSTON WI, GOODWIN BL: Genetics of phenyketonuria. *Nature* 213:882, 1967.

584. WOOLF LI, GOODWIN BL, CRANSTON WI, WADE DN, WOOLF F, HUDSON FP, MCBEAN MS: A third allele at the phenylalanine-hydroxylase locus in mild phenylketonuria (hyperphenylalaninemia). *Lancet* 1:114, 1968.

585. ROSENBLATT D, SCRIVER CR: Heterogeneity in genetic control of phenylalanine metabolism in man. *Nature* 218:677, 1968.

586. HILTON MA, SHARPE HN, HICKS LG, ANDREWS BF: A simple method for detection of heterozygous carriers of the gene for classic phenylketonuria. *J Pediatr* 109:601, 1986.

587. GOLD RJM, MAAG UR, NEAL JL, SCRIVER CR: The use of biochemical data in screening for mutant alleles and in genetic counselling. *Ann Hum Genet* 37:315, 1974.

588. WESTWOOD A, RAINE DN: Heterozygote detection in phenylketonuria. *J Med Genet* 12:327, 1975.

589. FREEHAUF CL, LEZOTTE D, GOODMAN SI, MCCABE ERB: Carrier screening for phenylketonuria: Comparison of two discriminant analysis procedures. *Am J Hum Genet* 36:1180, 1984.

590. PAUL TD, BRANDT IK, ELSAS LJ, JACKSON CE, MAMUNE P, NANCE CS, NANCE WE: Phenylketonuria heterozygote detection in families with affected children. *Am J Hum Genet* 30:293, 1978.

591. WENGER SL, VIEIRA PW, BRECK JM, STEELE MW: Relative reliability of three different discriminant analysis methods for detecting PKU gene carriers. *Clin Genet* 30:38, 1986.

592. SAIKI RK, SCHARF S, FALOONA F, MULLIS KB, HORN GT, ERLICH HA, ARNHEIM N: Enzymatic amplification of β-globin genomic sequences and restriction site analysis for diagnosis of sickle cell anemia. *Science* 230:1350, 1985.

593. ORKIN SH: Genetic diagnosis of DNA analysis. *N Engl J Med* 317:1023, 1987.

594. SZABO L, SOMOGYI C, MÁTÉ M: Experience based on 800,000 newborn screening tests in the Budapest phenylketonuria center. *Acta Paediatr Hung* 26:113, 1985.

594a. ROMEO G, MENOZZI P, FERLINI A, POSPER L, CERONE R, SCALISI S, ROMANO C, ANTONOZZI I, RIVA E, PICENI SERENI L, ZAMMARCHI E, LENZI G, SARTORIO R, ANDRIA G, BIONI M, FOIS A, BURRONI M, BURLINA AB, CARNAVALE F: Incidence of classic PKU in Italy estimated from consanguineous marriages and from neonatal screening. *Clin Genet* 24:339, 1983.

594b. SAUGSTAD LF: Frequency of phenylketonuria in Norway. *Clin Genet* 7:40, 1975.

595. SAUGSTAD LF: Anthropological significance of phenylketonuria. *Clin Genet* 7:52, 1975.

596. WOOLF LI, MCBEA MS, WOOLF FM, CAHALANE SF: Phenylketonuria as a balanced polymorphism: The nature of the heterozygote advantage. *Ann Hum Genet Lond* 38:461, 1975.

597. LIU SR, ZUO QH: Newborn screening for phenylketonuria in eleven districts. *Clin Med J* 99:113, 1986.

598. HSIAO KJ, CHEN CH, CHIU PC, HUANG SC, WUU KD: A Chinese family with phenylketonuria and maternal phenylketonuria detected by family screening. *Eur J Pediatr* 145:409, 1986.

599. FARHUD DD, KABIRI M: Incidence of phenylketonuria (PKU) in Iran. *Indian J Pediatr* 49:685, 1982.

600. TEEBI AS, AL-AWADI SA, FARAZ TI, NAQUIB KK, EL-KHALIFA MY: Phenylketonuria in Kuwait and Arab countries. *Eur J Pediatr* 146:59, 1987.

601. GAIND BN, MAHESHWARI MC, KISHAN J, CHADDHA BB: A family with phenylketonuria. *Indian J Pediatr* 49:631, 1982.

602. LAZUARDI S, ISMAEL S, HENDARTO SK, SETIADI E, PARWATI AS, GUANDISETJADININGRAT AS: Phenylketonuria: A case report. *Paediatr Indones* 26:205, 1986.

603. GARROD AE: About alkaptonuria. *Lancet* 2:1484, 1901.

604. FLATZ G, OELBE M, HERRMANN H: Ethnic distribution of phenylketonuria in the north German population. *Hum Genet* 65:396, 1984.

605. JOHN S, ROZEN R, LAFRAMBOISE R, LABERGE C, SCRIVER CR: Phenylalanine hydroxylase gene (PAH) hyperphenylalaninemia alleles and associated RFLP haplotypes in French Canadians. *Genome* 30 (Suppl 1):32, 1988.

606. KIDD KK: Phenylketonuria. Population genetics of a disease. *Nature* 327:282, 1987.

607. PENROSE LS: Inheritance of phenylpyruvic amentia (phenylketonuria). *Lancet* 2:192, 1935.

608. VOGEL F: Phenotypic deviations in heterozygotes of phenylketonuria (PKU). *Prog Clin Biol Res* 177:337, 1985.

609. SOBER E: *The Nature of Selection. Evolutionary Theory in Philosophical Focus*. Cambridge, MA, MIT Press, 1984, p 278.

610. SAUGSTAD LF: Heterozygote advantage for the phenylketonuria allele. *J Med Genet* 14:20, 1977.

611. SAUGSTAD LF: Increased "reproductive casualty" in heterozygotes for phenylketonuria. *Clin Genet* 4:105, 1973.

612. PAUL TD, GRECO J JR, BRANDT IK, JACKSON CE, NANCE WE: Is there a heterozygote advantage in the birthweight and number of children born to PKU heterozygotes? *Am J Hum Genet* 31:140A, 1979.

613. TEN KATE LP: On estimating the actual rate of foetal loss in families with an autosomal recessive disorder and Woolf's data on PKU. *Ann Hum Genet* 41:463, 1978.

614. WOOLF LI: The heterozygote advantage of phenylketonuria. *Am J Hum Genet* 38:773, 1986.

615. HARRIS H: *The Principles of Human Biochemical Genetics*, 3d ed rev. New York, Elsevier, 1980, p 246.

616. HERSKOWITZ I: Functional inactivation of genes by dominant negative mutations. *Nature* 329:219, 1987.

616a. JOHNSON WG: Metabolic interference and the + − heterozygote. A hypothetical form of simple inheritance which is neither dominant nor recessive. *Am J Hum Genet* 32:374, 1980.

617. DENT CE: Relation of biochemical abnormality to development of mental defect in phenylketonuria. Discussion of paper by Armstrong MD in, Etiological factors in mental retardation. *Report of 23rd Ross Ped Res Conf*. Ross Labs, Columbus Ohio, 1957, p 32.

618. MABRY CC, DENNISTON JC, NELSON TL, CHOON DS: Maternal phenylketonuria: A cause of mental retardation in children without the metabolic defect. *N Engl J Med* 269:1404, 1963.

619. SCRIVER CR: Treatment in medical genetics, in Crow JF, Neel JV (eds): *Proc 3rd Int Cong Hum Genet*. Baltimore, The Johns Hopkins Press, 1967, p 45.

620. LENKE RR, LEVY HL: Maternal phenylketonuria and hyperphenylalanemia. An international survey of untreated and treated pregnancies. *N Engl J Med* 303:1202, 1980.

621. LEVY HL: Effect of mutation on maternal-fetal metabolic homeostasis: Maternal aminoacidopathies, in Lloyd JK, Scriver CR (eds): *Genetic and Metabolic Disease in Pediatrics*. London, Butterworths, 1985, p 250.

622. KOCH R, FRIEDMAN EG, WENZ E, JEW K, CROWLEY C, DONNELL G: Maternal phenylketonuria. *J Inherited Metab Dis* 9 (*suppl* 2):159,1980.

623. HANLEY WB, CLARKE JTR, SCHOONKEYT W: Maternal phenylketonuria (PKU)—A review. *Clin Biochem* 20:149, 1987.

624. LEVY HL, WAISBREN SE: Effects of untreated maternal phenylketonuria and hyperphenylalaninemia on the fetus. *N Engl J Med* 309:1269, 1983.

625. BRASS CA, ISAACS CE, McHESNEY R, GREENGARD O: The effects of hyperphenylalaninemia on fetal development: A new animal model of maternal phenylketonuria. *Pediatr Res* 16:388, 1982.

626. LOO YH, POTEMPSKA A, WANG P, FERSKI R, WISNIEWSKI HM: Experimental maternal phenylketonuria: An examination of two animal modes. *Dev Neurosci* 6:227, 1983.

626a. LACEY DJ, TERPLAN K: Abnormal cerebral cortical neurons on a child with maternal PKU syndrome. *J Child Neurol* 2:201, 1987.

627. LEWIS SA, LYON IC, ELLIOTT RB: Outcome of pregnancy in the rat with mild hyperphenylalaninemia and hypertyrosinemia: Implications for the management of "human maternal PKU." *J Ineherited Metab Dis* 8:113, 1985.

628. LEVY HL, LENKE RR, KOCH R: Lack of fetal effect on blood phenylalanine concentration in maternal phenylketonuria. *J Pediatr* 104:245, 1984.

629. APPLETON RE, BAUMER JH, HOLTON JB: A loophole in the phenylketonuria screening programme. *Lancet* 2:752, 1984.

630. DeKLERK JB, WADMAN SK, DIJKHUIS HJ, MEULEMAN EE: Maternal PKU syndrome in an exceptional family with unexpected PKU. *J Inherited Metab Dis* 10:162, 1987.

631. BRADBURN NC, WAPPNER RS, LEMONS JA, MEYER BA, ROBERTS RS: Lactation and phenylketonuria. *Am J Perinatol* 2:138, 1985.

632. AMERICAN ACADEMY OF PEDIATRICS. COMMITTEE ON GENETICS: Maternal phenylketonuria. *Pediatrics* 76:313, 1985.

633. GHAVAMI M, LEVY HL, ERBE RW: Prevention of fetal damage through dietary control of maternal hyperphenylalaninemia. *Clin Obstet Gynecol* 29:580, 1986.

634. SMITH I, WOLFF OH: MRC/DHSS Phenylketonuria Register. Newsletter no 5, London, 1978, p 5.

635. CARTIER L, CLOW CL, LIPPMAN-HAND A, MORISSETTE J, SCRIVER CR: Prevention of mental retardation in offspring of hyperphenylalaninemic mothers. *Am J Public Health* 72:1386, 1982.

636. RISCH RO, BURKE B, BASS J, FERRARA TB, MASTRI A: Maternal phenylketonuria—Chronology of the detrimental effects on embryogenesis and fetal development: Pathological report, survey, clinical application. *Pediatr Pathol* 5:449, 1986.

637. MURPHY D, SAUL I, KIRBY M: Maternal phenylketonuria and phenylalanine restricted diet. Studies of 7 pregnancies and of offspring produced. *Ir J Med Sci* 154:66, 1985.

638. BUSH RT, DUKES PC: Women with phenylketonuria: Successful management of pregnancy and implications. *N Z Med J* 98:181, 1985.

639. SOETERS RP, SENGERS RC, VAN DONGEN PW, TRIJBELS JM, ESKES TK: Maternal phenylketonuria: Comparison of two treated full-term pregnancies. *Eur J Pediatr* 145:221, 1986.

640. FARQUHAR DL, SIMPSON GK, STEVEN F, MUNRO JF, FARQUHAR JW: Preconceptual dietary management for maternal phenylketonuria. *Acta Paediatr Scand* 76:279, 1987.

641. ROHR FJ, DOHERTY LB, WAISBREN SE, BAILEY IV, AMPOLA MG, BENACERRAF B, LEVY HL: New England maternal PKU project. Prospective study of untreated and treated pregnancies and their outcomes. *J Pediatr* 110:391, 1987.

642. DROGARI E, SMITH I, BEASELY M, LLOYD JK: Timing of strict diet in relation to fetal damage in maternal phenylketonuria. An International Collaborative Study by the MRC/DHSS Phenylketonuria Register. *Lancet* 2:927, 1987.

CHAPTER **16**

TYROSINEMIA AND RELATED DISORDERS

LOWELL A. GOLDSMITH
CLAUDE LABERGE

1. *Tyrosinemia II (Richner-Hanhart syndrome) is an inherited disease associated with a deficiency of hepatic tyrosine aminotransferase (TAT), the rate limiting enzyme of tyrosine catabolism.*
2. *Tyrosinemia, tyrosinuria, and increases in urinary phenolic acids,* N*-acetyltyrosine, and tyramine persist for life. The metabolism of other amino acids and of renal and hepatic functions is otherwise normal.*
3. *Corneal erosions and plaques, palm and sole erosions, and hyperkeratoses usually occur during the first months of life and do not respond to conventional therapy. Mental retardation sometimes occurs.*
4. *The disease has autosomal recessive inheritance; the carrier state has not been detected biochemically.*
5. *Therapy with a low-tyrosine, low-phenylalanine diet is curative.*
6. *The syndrome occurs as an autosomal recessive trait in ranch mink and is reproduced by feeding rats a low-protein, high tyrosine diet.*
7. *4-Hydroxyphenylpyruvate acid oxidase deficiency may have an associated syndrome of tyrosinemia and central nervous system symptoms but no eye or skin manifestations.*
8. *Asymptomatic tyrosinemia associated with increased excretion of tyrosine and its metabolites is found (usually by amino acid screening programs) in 0.2 to 10 percent of neonates. It is more common in premature and less common in breast-fed infants.*
9. *The long-term sequelae of this tyrosinemia are moot but may include mild mental retardation.*
10. *Dietary restriction of protein rapidly decreases plasma tyrosine to normal. The efficacy of ascorbic acid supplementation is questionable.*
11. *The enzymatic nature of the defect is unknown since there are no direct measurements of the hepatic enzymes from these relatively healthy infants.*
12. *Tyrosinemia I is an inherited defect of fumarylacetoacetate (FAA) hydrolyase. Succinylacetoacetone and succinylacetone accumulate and inhibit renal tubular function, hepatic enzymes of tyrosine catabolism, and porphobilinogen synthetase (δ-aminolevulinic acid dehydratase).*
13. *The acute form of the disease, due to severe enzyme deficiency, is associated with liver failure, a cabbagelike odor, and often death by the age of 1 year. In the chronic form of the disease, renal tubular dysfunction, vitamin D-resistant rickets, and acute intermittent porphyrialike symptoms may be present. Hepatoma is a late complication.*
14. *Anemia, abnormal liver function, increased plasma α-fetoprotein, moderate increases in plasma tyrosine and its metabolites, and increased plasma methionine are present. The urine contains succinylacetone and succinylacetoacetone. Generalized aminoaciduria, phosphaturia, glycosuria, and uricosuria occur.*
15. *FAA hydrolyase activity is decreased in this disease. Fructose-1-phosphate aldolase deficiency and galactose-1-phosphate uridyl transferase deficiency produce similar renal and hepatic abnormalities.*
16. *The disease has autosomal recessive inheritance. It has a worldwide distribution and a high prevalence in Quebec (especially in the Chicoutini-Lac St. Jean region), Northern France, and Scandinavia.*
17. *Prenatal diagnosis is feasible by enzymatic analysis on cultured cells or by direct or indirect detection of succinylacetone.*
18. *Treatment with a low tyrosine, low phenylalanine diet is palliative. Liver transplantation has been done with benefit.*

Tyrosinemia, tyrosinuria, and phenolaciduria accompany several inborn errors of metabolism. Over the past 50 years, many investigators have attempted to identify and establish the enzymatic basis of the individual diseases having this chemical phenotype. This chapter presents the current state of knowledge of these disorders and of normal tyrosine metabolism.

The metabolic basis of tyrosinemia II (Richner-Hanhart syndrome) is discussed first since it is best established. This disease is marked by an accumulation of tyrosine and its metabolites following classic Garrodian principles, and it is caused by a genetic deficiency in hepatic tyrosine aminotransferase. Tyrosinemia I (tyrosinosis) has a more complicated pathophysiology since metabolic products accumulate which inhibit many transport functions and enzymatic activities, including those related to tyrosine metabolism. The consequences of decreased tyrosine catabolism in the neonatal period are also discussed.

Information on several patients with abnormal tyrosine metabolism, of an as yet undiscovered cause, including a patient studied by Medes over 50 years ago, completes the chapter.

TYROSINEMIA II (RICHNER-HANHART SYNDROME)

Clinical Aspects

Richner and Hanhart recognized a distinctive oculocutaneous syndrome.[1,2] Its association with tyrosinemia was suggested 35 years after the original clinical description.[3] A new study of

Nonstandard abbreviations used in this chapter are: FAA = fumarylacetoacetate; FAH = fumarylacetoacetate hydrolyase; PHPAA = *p*-hydroxyphenylacetic acid; PHPLA = *p*-hydroxyphenyllactic acid; PHPPA = *p*-hydroxyphenylpyruvic acid; TAT = tyrosine amino transferase.

some of their original patients confirmed the association. In the previous edition of this text a large number of patients are described in tabular form[4–27]; newer cases are reported in this edition when they contribute to our understanding of the disorder. This chapter does not constitute a definitive listing of all cases. Cases of the syndrome before its biochemical basis was recognized have been reviewed.[28] Recent tabulations have been published,[29] including one emphasizing the dermatologic findings.[30]

Cases have been described from several countries. Both parents of several of the probands have been Italian or of Italian ancestry; an Italian registry for the disease has been established.[29] The probands of Italian background have been reported from Italy,[14,20,21] Australia,[18] Canada,[8] Lausanne, Switzerland,[22] and the United States.[3] Probands of non-Italian ancestry have been reported from Switzerland,[27] Spain,[27] southwestern France,[24] Norway,[15] the United States,[4,12,17,23,26] a Turkish family living in Germany,[31] United Arab Emirates,[32] and Japan.[33]

Eye Lesions. These usually begin during the first few months of life. One patient whose palmar lesions started at age seven months had eye lesions beginning at age 17.[34] Symptoms may be limited to lacrimation, photophobia, and redness (Fig. 16-1). Signs may include mild corneal herpetiform erosions, dendritic ulcers, and, rarely, corneal and conjunctival plaques.[13] Neovascularization may be prominent. The ulcers stain poorly, if at all, with fluorescein, and bacterial and viral studies are negative. Lesions have occurred in a corneal transplant.[24] Long-term effects include corneal scarring,[4] nystagmus,[8,28] exodeviation, and glaucoma. There are families with skin lesions and no eye lesions.[35]

Skin Lesions. These begin with or after the eye lesions (Fig. 16-2). In some cases, no skin lesions are reported. The lesions are painful, nonpruritic, and sometimes associated with hyperhidrosis; they are limited to the palms and soles, especially the tips of the digits and the thenar and hypothenar eminences. They may be linear or subungual. They begin as blisters or erosions which crust and become hyperkeratotic. Autografted thigh skin to the sole remains lesion-free, although surrounding skin is hyperkeratotic.[36] One patient was symptom-free in the morning, worse during the day, and developed erythema and pain during a tyrosine tolerance test.[18] Hyperkeratosis of the tongue is reported.[24] Hyperpigmentation is not present.

Neurologic Features. In the classic cases of Richner-Hanhart syndrome, mental retardation is an inconstant feature.[14] In those with biochemically proved tyrosinemia II, retardation to a mild to moderate degree has been reported, but this may reflect an ascertainment bias. Self-mutilating behavior has occurred,[4] as have disturbances of fine coordination.[22] Language defects have been more prominent than mathematical defects (unpublished observations).

Involvement of other organs has been limited to one child with multiple congenital anomalies, including cleft lip and palate, microcephaly, inguinal hernias, talipes equinovarus, and one kidney.[4] One patient had radiographic findings in the femura.[8,37]

Clinical Differential Diagnosis. The multiple forms of keratosis involving the palms or soles (generically keratosis palmaris and plantaris) and the multiple forms of epidermolysis bullosa which present as erosions must be considered. The skin lesions per se could resemble eczema or psoriasis. Several distinct forms of autosomal dominant keratosis may be associated with significant corneal lesions. One form is described, and others are well reviewed.[38]

Histopathology

Skin biopsy is not diagnostic. It may show hyperkeratosis, acanthosis, and parakeratosis. Electron microscopy showed 2- to 3-μm lipidlike granules with 10-nm filaments and myelin-like figures intermixed with the granules[3,39] in two cases and keratinocytes with increased tonofibrils but no tyrosine crystals in four other cases[33,39] and edematous mitochondria.[39] Very tightly packed microtubular and tonofibrillar masses were noted,[40] as were dense polyhedral cytoplasmic inclusions.[39] A conjunctival plaque showed increased bundles of keratofibrils and Alcian blue-positive inclusions.[13] Endothelial cells contained similar inclusions and whorled membranous structures. Fine, needlelike crystals were seen in the fibroblasts.

Fig. 16-1 Corneal changes in tyrosinemia II. Patient is VI-1 in Fig. 16-6. *A.* Corneal opacity and neovascularization in eye before therapy. *B.* Eye after 6 weeks of therapy with a low tyrosine, low phenylalanine diet. [*From Goldsmith LA, in Fitzpatrick T.B. et al. (eds):* Dermatology in General Medicine. *New York, McGraw-Hill, 1987, 3d ed, p. 1634. Used by permission.*]

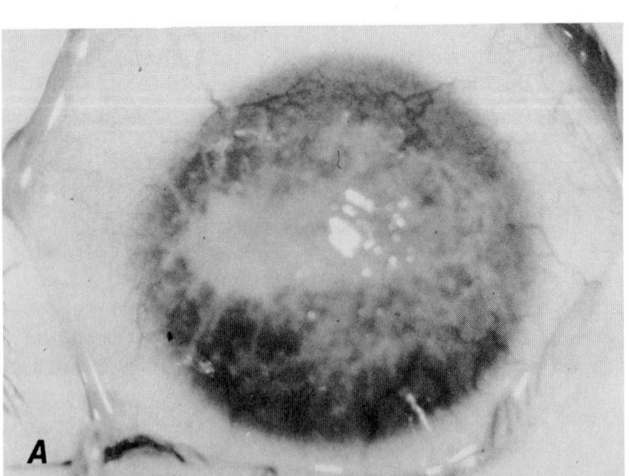

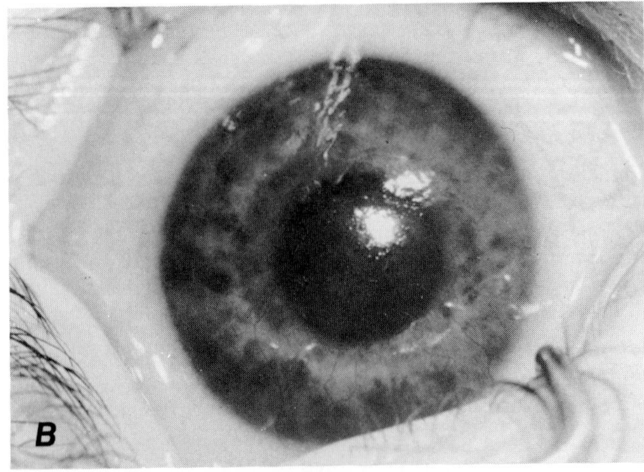

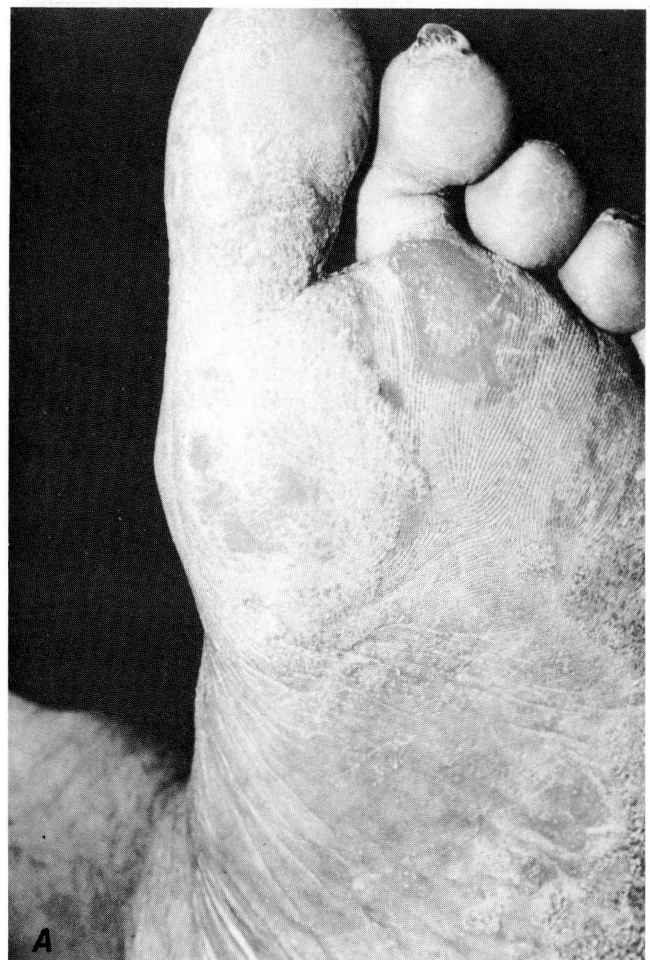

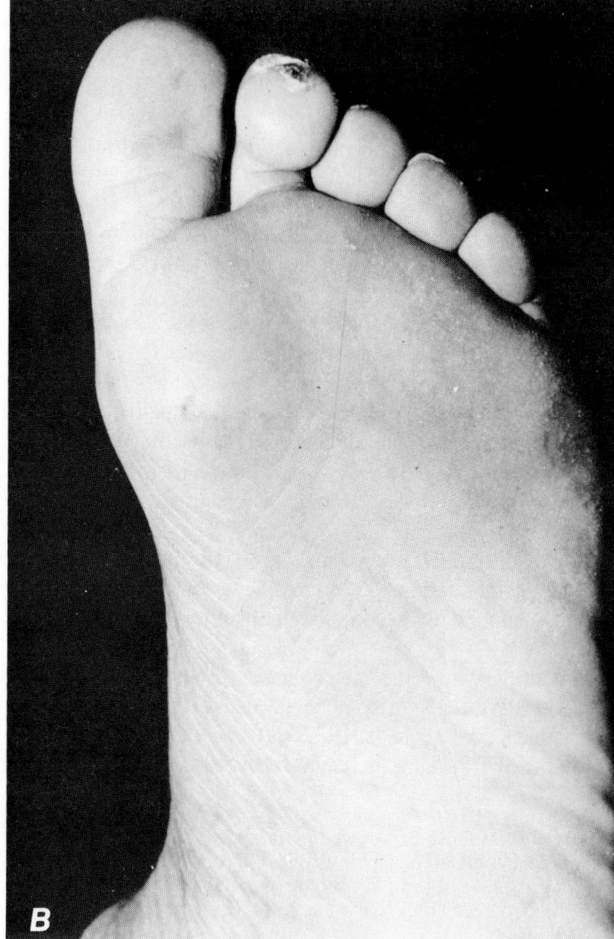

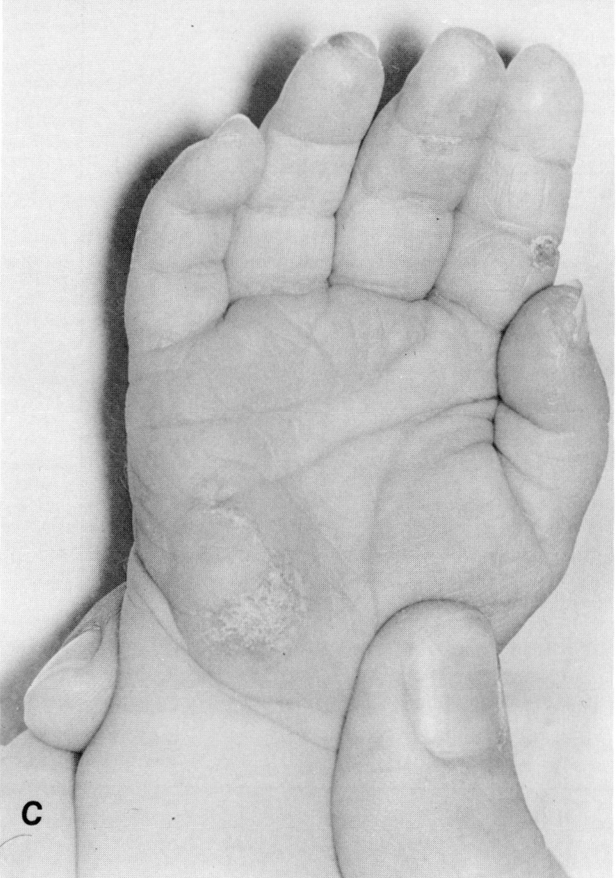

Fig. 16-2 Skin abnormalities in tyrosinemia II. Patient is IV-4 in Fig. 16-6. *A.* Soles of 55-year-old male with tyrosinemia II before therapy. *B.* Soles after 2 months of a low tyrosine, low phenylalanine diet. C. Hyperkeratotic and erosive lesions in 13-month-old girl with tyrosinemia II. [*From Goldsmith L.A., in Fitzpatrick T.B. et al. (eds):* Dermatology in General Medicine. *New York, McGraw-Hill, 1987, 3d ed, p. 1634. Used by permission.*]

Biochemical Features

Tyrosinemia and Tyrosinuria. Tyrosinemia is a diagnostic feature of the syndrome (normal < 0.18 mM). A higher tyrosine level is seen in younger patients (Table 13-1, previous edition of this text). The plasma tyrosine levels (millimolar) (mean + SD) for patients aged up to 7 years are 2.39 ± 0.60 ($n = 8$) and for ages 8 to 55, 1.27 ± 0.29 ($n = 12$). The means differ at the $p < 0.001$ level of significance. Many of the older patients have had skin and eye lesions with blood tyrosine levels at which younger patients have been completely asymptomatic. These findings suggest that tyrosine levels decrease with age in this disease and that local tissue factors which influence disease may have age-associated changes. Skin abnormalities have been most apparent in older patients.[27,28] The tyrosinemia responds rapidly to a low tyrosine diet[41] (Fig. 16-3).

Tyrosine is the only amino acid increased in the urine of these patients. Tyrosine clearance is essentially normal, with renal tubular absorption of over 99 percent of filtered tyrosine.[3,42] Routine liver and renal studies are normal. In three patients, cerebral spinal fluid tyrosine levels ranged from 0.19 to 0.44 mM, with blood tyrosine values of 1.38 to 2.82 mM.[8,22,25]

The urinary tyrosine metabolites, *p*-hydroxyphenylpyruric acid (PHPPA), *p*-hydroxyphenyllactic acid (PHPLA), *p*-hydroxyphenylacetic acid (PHPAA), *N*-acetyltyrosine, and *p*-tyramine (Fig. 16-4) are increased from 88 to 170 times normal levels.[3,7,8,10,12,19,22,24,25] In one patient,[8] PHPPA was not increased with normal protein intake. *N*-acetyltyrosine is elevated up to 160 times normal levels,[7] and *p*-tyramine is elevated up to 88 times normal levels.[7,10] The responses of these metabolites to various tyrosine levels in tyrosinemic patients have been studied extensively. The ratio of PHPPA to PHPLA has varied from 0.16 to 1.14 in different patients.[7,19,22,25] During a tyrosine load test, the ratio of PHPPA to PHPLA fell progressively from 1.14 to 0.13.[22] *N*-acetyltyrosine excretion is increased with tyrosinemia of any cause. In one patient,[7] 75 percent of unoxidized tyrosine was excreted as *n*-acetyltyrosine. *p*-Tyramine metabolism was not influenced by sterilization of the intestine in two patients.[7,10,11]

Metabolic studies with deuterated tyrosine in one patient showed a normal pattern of labeled metabolites when the blood tyrosine was five times normal.[10] In one patient, plasma phenylalanine which was elevated fivefold became normal with treatment.[25] The plasma PHPAA concentration is not measurable in normal patients but was ~20 μM in one patient.[7]

Pattern of Urinary Metabolites in Tyrosinemia. Multiple metabolic pathways[42,43] are available for tyrosine (Fig. 16-4 and 16-5). Details of plasma concentrations, and clearance of tyrosine are published.[43] This obfuscates attempts to predict enzyme deficiencies on the basis of urinary metabolites. PHPPA can be formed by deamination of tyrosine in the kidney and directly excreted.[43] Even in the absence of TAT, tyrosine can be oxidized to PHPPA in tissues (e.g., liver, kidney, heart, muscle, and brain) which contain significant amounts of mitochondrial TAT (aspartate aminotransferase) (Fig. 16-5).[6,44,45] Since three of these tissues (heart, muscle, and brain) lack *p*-hydroxyphenylpyruvate oxidase (hydroxy-

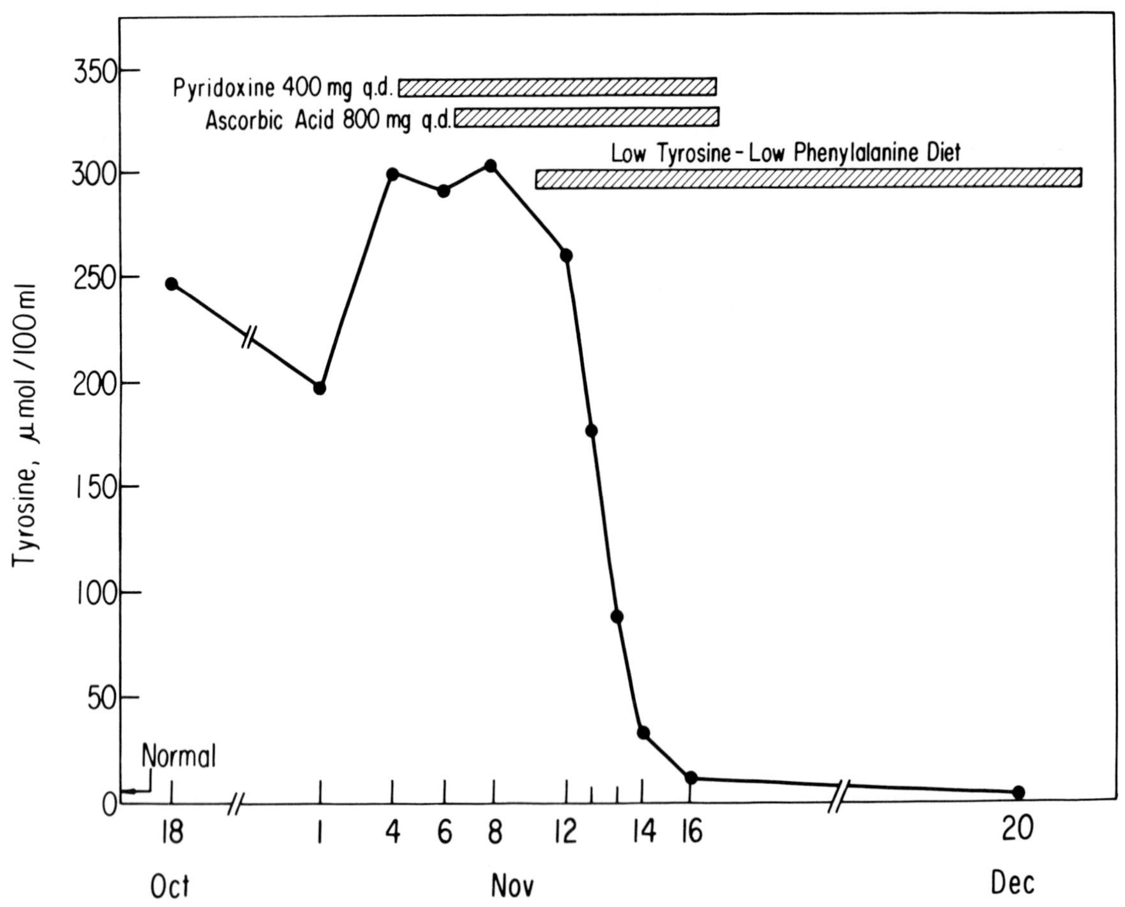

Fig. 16-3 Response of elevated plasma to tyrosine, low phenylalanine diet in patient in Fig. 16-1. [*From Goldsmith L.A., in Fitzpatrick T.B. et al. (eds): Dermatology in General Medicine. New York, McGraw-Hill, 1987, 3d ed, p. 1634. Used by permission.*]

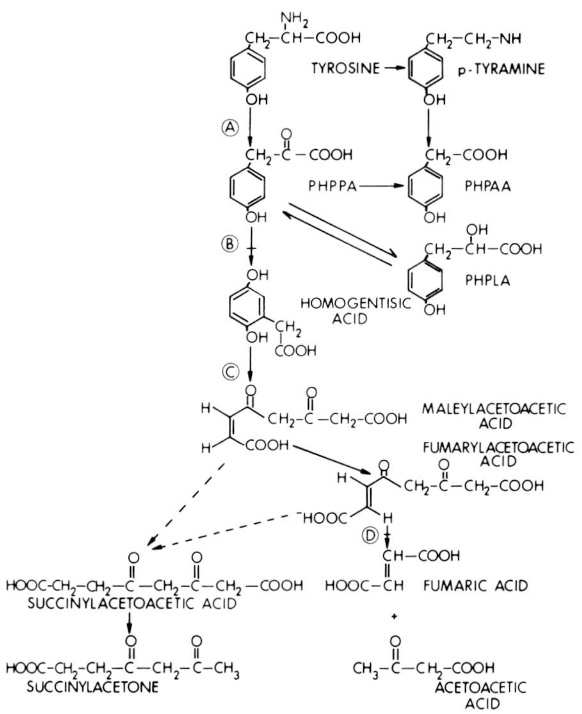

Fig. 16-4 Major pathway for tyrosine catabolism. Major tyrosine metabolites include p-tyramine, PHPPA (p-hydroxyphenylpyruvic acid), PHPAA (p-hydroxyphenylacetic acid), PHPLA (p-hydroxyphenyllactic acid), and homogentisic acid. Enzymes include tyrosine aminotransferase (A), p-hydroxyphenylpyruvate oxidase hydrolyase (B), homogentistic acid oxidase (C), and fumarylacetoacetate (FAA) hydrolyase (D).

lase), PHPPA cannot be metabolized further and may appear in the circulation and be filtered directly by the kidney. PHPPA can be reduced in the liver to PHPLA by lactic dehydrogenase or aromatic keto acid reductase[43] and then excreted. Since the renal clearance of PHPPA is two to three times higher than the creatinine clearance, tubular secretion accounts for some of the urinary metabolites.[42]

Hepatic Enzymes in Tyrosinemia II. Tyrosine aminotransferase (EC 2.6.1.5) activity has been assayed in the supernatant of liver homogenates in five patients with tyrosinemia II.[5,19,25,26,33] Activity was absent in two patients[5,25] and reduced in two others.[19,33,26] In a personally studied patient,[26] the value was reported at one-half control values (the units of activity for that patient and controls were in nmoles of PHHPA formed not micromoles as in the text). Other transaminases may have been responsible for the activity in the oldest patient studied,[26] and technical criticisms of one of the studies have been made.[46,47]

Mitochondrial aspartate aminotransferase was normal in one patient[5] and slightly increased in two patients[25,26]; the increase in its activity may represent a compensatory response to high plasma tyrosine levels.

Liver *p*-hydroxyphenylpyruvate hydroxylase was normal in two patients.[5,33]

Fig. 16-5 Proposed pathways of tyrosine metabolism in normal individuals and those with tyrosinemia II. The normal pathway is in boldface arrows and the metabolism in tyrosinemia II in broken lines. [From Goldsmith L.A., in Fitzpatrick T.B. et al. (eds): *Dermatology in General Medicine*. New York, McGraw-Hill, 1987, 3d ed, p. 1634. Used by permission.]

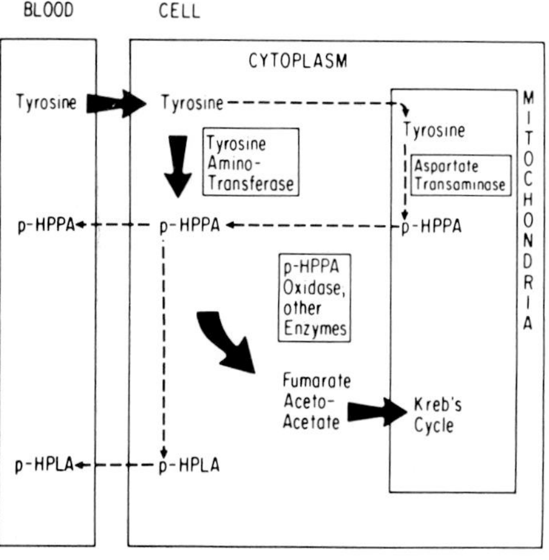

Genetics of Tyrosinemia II

Consanguinity occurred in five families.[3,10,17,20,23,26] The sexes are equally affected. All data are consistent with autosomal recessive inheritance as is information from the classic cases of the syndrome.[28] The pedigree from a large North Carolina kindred[23] shows consanguinity (Fig. 16-6). The detailed genetic mapping studies (vide infra) confirm the recessive basis of the syndrome.

Treatment

A low-tyrosine, low-phenylalanine diet[4] (e.g., Mead Johnson 3200 AB) has been used successfully in several patients,[3,4,8,15,17,26,27,48] with rapid resolution of the clinical symptoms and signs (Figs. 16-2 and 16-3). A low phenylalanine diet per se did not improve eye lesions.[49] A low protein diet may ameriolate symptoms. Pyridoxine,[3,4,10,15,48] vitamin C,[3,7,10,17,34] danazol,[26] and cortisone[4] have not been successful. The diet should be optimized for good growth and development, but there are no guidelines on how strict dietary control must be to prevent mental retardation and whether there is a critical age at which strict is necessary. Strict dietary control has not been necessary to prevent skin and eye lesions.[16,26,31]

Oral retinoids can improve skin lesions without changing the tyrosine levels, probably through an anti-inflammatory effect.[50]

Animal Model for Tyrosinemia II

The phenotypic features of tyrosinemia II can be reproduced by feeding rats a low protein diet with excess L-tyrosine.[51] Corneal erosions and edema begin within a few days, and all animals are eventually affected. Alopecia, cheilitis, erythema and swelling of the toes, brown urine, and arthritis of the tibiotarsal joints also occur. Younger rats and males are more seriously affected.[51] The disease is prevented or alleviated by increasing dietary protein,[52] L-threonine,[53] or methionine[54] or by thiouracil,[51] glucagon,[52] or phenobarbital administration.[55] Glucocorticoids and pregnenolone-16-α-carbonitrile prevent the syndrome; ethylestrenol, spironolactone, and progesterone decrease its frequency.[55] Thyroxine aggravates the syndrome.[51] Most of the agents work by increasing the levels of hepatic TAT, although glucagon may act by directly decreasing plasma amino acid levels, since it does not induce TAT.[52]

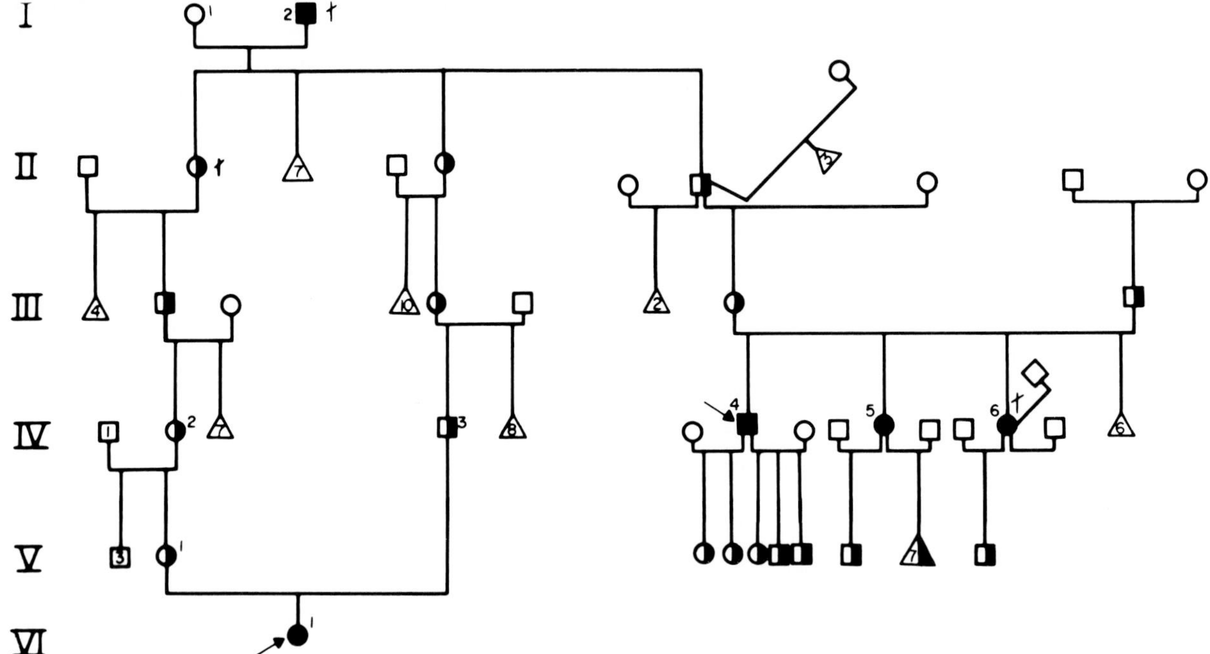

Fig. 16-6 Abbreviated pedigree of eastern North Carolina kindred with tyrosinemia II. IV-2 and IV-6 are said to have had the syndrome; heterozygotes are presumed, as biochemical definition of heterozygotes has not yet been possible.

Rats fed PHPPA did not develop the syndrome.[56] Although their blood tyrosine was increased (back reaction of TAT), it was as high as that achieved by tyrosine feeding. This study suggests that tyrosine and not its products is responsible for the clinical syndrome. Desoxypyridoxine, when administered with a vitamin B_6-deficient diet, produced tyrosinemia (up to 2.9 mM in lactating females).[57]

Mechanism for Tissue Damage. The evolution of the eye lesions in tyrosinemic rats has been investigated.[58–60] Long, slender (0.5 to 1.1 μm) birefringent crystals with prismatic shapes are limited to damaged areas in the corneal epithelium. Similar shapes are seen in electron micrographs. The crystals pass through the cell and nuclear membranes. Levels of tyrosine in the aqueous humor parallel and are slightly less than serum tyrosine levels.[58] Edema occurs within 24 h, and polymorphonuclear leukocytes infiltrate the stroma and cause opacities. By 7 days, new blood vessels invade the corneal epithelium.[59] Cyclophosphamide decreased leukocytes and prevents corneal lesions.[61]

The supernatant from cultured corneal epithelia of tyrosinemic animals contained three heat-labile chemotactic factors with approximate molecular weights of 11,000, 1,100, and 380.[62]

Skin lesions follow a similar course, are limited to volar surfaces, and are associated with dense polymorphonuclear infiltrates.[63]

Intracellular crystallization is proposed as the mechanism for tissue damage.[60,63,64] Tyrosine levels in plasma exceed saturation, and the levels of amino acids in the epidermis may exceed those in plasma.[65] Since tyrosine crystals destabilize lysosomes[66] and lyse erythrocyte membranes,[67] release of cellular proteolytic enzymes may be the initial step in the inflammatory cascade. This pathogenic mechanism is consistent with the clearing of skin and eye lesions while tyrosine levels are still many times normal, since it implies that a critical threshold for tyrosine must be exceeded for the appearance of clinical disease.

Tyrosinemia II in the Mink. Ranch mink (*Mustela vison* Schreb.) have an inherited disease with many of the features of human tyrosinemia II.[68–72] The disease has autosomal recessive inheritance, and affected kits after weaning have exudative eye and volar skin lesions. Blood tyrosine levels are 35 to 40 times normal. Hepatic TAT activity is markedly reduced biochemically and immunologically.[70]

Detailed breeding and biochemical studies in a large mink kindred in Denmark are interpreted as showing three varieties of clinical disease with early onset of symptoms (at 6 weeks), intermediate (symptoms at 3 months), and late (symptoms at 6 months). There is evidence for two different alleles, and one completely devoid of activity and one producing a TAT with a low affinity for pyridoxal phosphate.[71]

A dog has been described with clinical and biochemical tyrosinemia II.[73]

Patients with Unclassified Abnormalities of Tyrosine Metabolism. There are several patients with increased levels of plasma tyrosine as their unifying feature whose exact place among the genetic disorders of tyrosine metabolism is unclear. Some of these patients have been grouped as a possible 4-hydroxyphenylpyruvic acid oxidase deficiency syndrome *(vide infra)*.

A 5-month-old Turkish child developed undulating nystagmus which lasted for 1½ years and then slowly cleared.[74] At age 2 years he developed torticollis when concentrating on near objects. Moderate psychomotor retardation present during the first year of life was said to improve by age 5 years when the child had reached the maturity of a 4-year-old. Slight corneal clouding but no skin lesions are described. The boy had a tyrosine level of 0.79 mM, other amino acids were normal, and phenolaciduria was present. His sister had generally retarded psychomotor retardation. Tyrosine aminotransferase levels in this patient were less than 10 percent of normal; an even lower level was present in his sister's biopsy. This case may represent typical tyrosinemia II before skin lesions or it may be more related to the deficiencies of 4-hydroxyphenylpyruvate oxidase, which are described below. That enzyme was not measured in this case.

A 3½-year-old retarded girl had joint swelling, no reported eye or skin symptoms, increased urinary tyrosine levels, and tyrosine crystals in her bone marrow. Familial generalized aminoaciduria also was present.[75] The tyrosine crystals in the marrow may have reflected only the high blood levels. Marrow aspiration on patients with documented tyrosinemia II has not been reported.

Over 50 years ago, Medes studied a 49-year-old male with myasthenia gravis who had high levels of urinary PHPPA, which increased with a high protein or a high tyrosine diet. With a high tyrosine diet, dopa was excreted in the urine. Despite extensive study then and speculation later,[76] this patient cannot be identified with any of the currently described disorders of tyrosine metabolism. No similar patient has been described.

An 18-year-old severely retarded girl with microcephaly, mental retardation, and growth retardation had plasma tyrosine levels of 0.38 to 0.61 m*M* and increased urinary levels of tyrosine and its metabolites PHPPA, PHPLA, and PHPAA.[77] No acute eye or skin symptoms were present, but cataracts began at age 17. Although several authors believed this patient had tyrosinemia II, the clinical picture is atypical for that disorder, and her plasma tyrosine would be the lowest of any of the patients with the bona fide syndrome. She remains a patient difficult to classify.

A female with growth retardation and intractable seizures had tenfold elevations in plasma methionine and fivefold elevations in plasma tyrosine.[78] Urinary *p*-hydroxyphenyllactic acid and *p*-hydroxyphenylacetic acid were elevated, but urinary succinylacetone was not detected. 4-Hydroxyphenylpyruvic acid oxidase activity could not be measured. Multimodular cirrhosis was found at necropsy. This case remains difficult to classify.

Hypertyrosinemia and Liver Disease. Serum tyrosine is increased over twofold in advanced fatty degeneration and in cirrhosis.[79] Controls and those with moderate fatty change had similar TAT levels, but those with cirrhosis or advanced fatty change had TAT activity 47 percent of normal. The mechanism for this decreased activity is unknown.

Normal Tyrosine Metabolism: Tyrosine Aminotransferase

Enzymology. Hepatic TAT is the rate limiting enzyme in tryosine metabolism. It is found predominantly in liver and is absent in skin[80]; its presence in fibroblasts is moot. The normal physiological role of TAT is to transaminate tyrosine to yield PHPAA. TAT requires pyridoxal phosphate as a coenzyme and is fastidious in requiring α-ketoglutarate as a cosubstrate; it is specifically inhibited with an antibody that does not react with other transaminases.[81] The earlier literature often did not distinguish between true TAT and TAT-like activity, especially of the mitochondrial and cytoplasmic forms of aspartate aminotransferase, and should be interpreted with caution. Although true TAT has been reported in kidney and heart,[6] recent studies inhibiting proteolysis of TAT, using hydroxyl apatite chromatography and the ability of aspartate aminotransferase to transaminate monoidotyrosine, show no TAT in brain, heart, or kidney.[82] The rat hepatic enzyme is synthesized as a 53,000-dalton monomer (form I) that is enzymatically active, but the enzyme is present as a dimer.[83,84] A lysosomal thiol protease (convertase) generated a 49,000-dalton subunit (form III) with normal enzyme activity.[83–88] The enzyme cleaves a single 4500-dalton peptide from the C-terminal portion of form I.[89] Rat and mouse have multiple forms of TAT, while guinea pig, rabbit, cow, and sheep liver have only a single form of the enzyme.[90] TAT from human liver was purified to homogeneity and had three fractions on isoelectric focusing.[91] The enzyme has been purified from dogs.[76] TAT is a phosphoprotein, but the significance of that phosphorylation is unknown.[92]

The transaminase is inhibited by sulfhydryl reagents such as iodoacetate and *p*-chloromercuriphenylsulfonate but not by metal binding agents such as α, α′-dipyridyl, diethyldithiocarbamate, and δ-hydroxyquinoline.[76] Cystine inhibits TAT in an oxygen-independent reaction.[93,94]

Control of Synthesis. The rat hepatic enzyme has a half-life of 2 h in vivo and in HTC (an established line of rat hepatoma tissue culture) cells in vitro.[84] In vivo, enzyme activity is induced by cyclic AMP,[95,96] glucagon, corticosteroids,[97,98] a high tyrosine diet,[52] or nicotinamide[76] in a process that requires the synthesis of new mRNA for TAT.[96–98]

Insulin increases TAT transcription[99] and also increases TAT levels twofold in HTC cells by decreasing the rate of TAt degradation.[100] There is no time lag before insulin increases TAT,[100] although there is a lag period for most other inducers. Insulin produces a completed sensitization to TAT induction at a postbinding step.[101] Cyclic nucleotides and phosphodiesterase inhibitors (e.g., theophylline, papaverine) increase the rate of degradation of TAT up to two and one-half times that of general cellular protein.[102] Increasing endogenous cGMP or added exogeneous 8-bromo-cGMP reduces TAT degradation in cultured rat hepatocytes.[103] The purine nucleoside methylthioinosine, in noncytotoxic concentrations, increases TAT degradation by an unknown mechanism without altering its synthesis.[104] Genetic variants of HTC lacking TAT activity but responding to corticosteroids have been described.[105]

The increased TAT activity seen after hydrocortisone or dibutyryl cyclic AMP administration is due to a specific increase in the level of functional mRNA for the enzyme.[95–98] Increased transcription is the mechanism of the mRNA increase due to cAMP.[106] Dibutyryl cyclic AMP also appears to increase the rate of TAT-specific peptide chain elongation.[107] Messenger RNA for TAT has an estimated half-life of 1.2 h.[98] Inhibitors of protein synthesis (cycloheximide, puromycin, emetine) increase TAT-mRNA levels.[108–110] Actinomycin D causes superinduction by decreasing the activity of a TAT-degrading enzyme.[111] Diacylglycerol enhanced TAT induction[112] and polyamines can inhibit induction.[113] The increase in mRNA for TAT in the presence of inhibitors of protein synthesis suggests that the synthesis of other new proteins is not a necessary step in the inductive process. Thus TAT enzyme synthesis is regulated in a complex fashion involving transcriptional, posttranscriptional, and translational controls.

In rats TAT activity is very low in fetal life but is inducible by tyrosine, dexamethasone, and cyclic AMP.[114,115] β_2-Adrenergic agents increase TAT in fetal rat and human liver.[116]

Molecular Biology. The genes for rat[117,118] and mouse[119] TAT have been characterized. Rat TAT mRNA is 2.4 kb long, codes for a 50,634-molecular weight protein, and is formed from a gene which is 11 kb long with 11 introns.[117] The mouse gene also has 11 introns and an extensive sequence identity with the rat gene. A noncoding 5′ sequence similar to a sequence in trytophan oxygenase (also a corticosteroid-inducible enzyme) and a glucocorticoid receptor in mouse mammary tumor virus may be the site for the interaction with the corticosteroid receptor.[117] A DNAase-hypersensitive site 2 kb upstream of the promoter appears with glucocorticoid induction.[120]

Gene Mapping and Transacting Controlling Genes. The structural gene for human tyrosine aminotransferase has been mapped to chromosome 16, the 16q22-q24 region.[121,122] Detailed genetic studies of a patient from Oregon with tyrosinemia[123] have shown her to have a continguous gene deletion syndrome (see Chap. 9) involving at least 11 of the 12 TAT exons which are maternally inherited and a small *de novo* deletion in q22.1::q22.3. Since other patients with TAT deficiency have not had the multiple congenital anomalies found in this patient, it is possible those abnormalities may be related to the other genes which may be deleted in this patient.

The mouse gene maps to chromosome 8 distal to the serum esterase locus.[119,124] A transacting control function required for tyrosine aminotransferase function maps to mouse chromosome 7 near the albino locus.[125] Another transacting controlling factor mapping to mouse chromosome 11, tissue-specific extinguisher-1 (Tse-1), inhibits tyrosine aminotransferase mRNA.[126]

CLINICAL AND BIOCHEMICAL PHENOTYPES OF 4-HYDROXYPHENYLPYRUVATE ACID OXIDASE DEFICIENCY STATE

Clinical Aspects

The biochemical phenotype defining this syndrome includes increased levels of tyrosine, phenolicaciduria, decreased liver PHPPA oxidase levels, and normal hepatic tyrosine aminotransferase activity. Central nervous dysfunction of several forms characterizes the patients, although no definite neurologic syndrome is present.

At 17 months an Egyptian girl living in Italy developed acute ataxia and drowsiness. On examination, she demonstrated confusion, motor incoordination, hypotonia, and no reflexes and did react to pain.[127] She responded to electrolytes and glucose although she was not hypoglycemic. During a tyrosine loading test she became drowsy and was mildly ataxic. At age 3½ years she was doing well, and her height was at the 25th percentile. Her tyrosine level was between 49.6 and 80.5 μmol/dl, other amino acids were normal, and PHPLA, PHPAA, and PHPPA were all elevated. A liver biopsy showed an undetectable level of PHPPA oxidase, a normal level of tyrosine amino acid transferase, and a twofold increase in the level of mitochondrial aminotransferase.

A 21-day-old Japanese child, whose parents were siblings, developed seizures resembling infantile spasms associated with spikes and polyspikes on the left parietal or cortical lobe. Mild brain atrophy was found with brain CAT scan. He died 3 months after accidental asphyxia. Tyrosine was 0.64 m*M*, and elevated levels of PHPPA, PHPLA, and PHPAA were found in the urine.[128] Liver PHPPA oxidase was 5 percent of control values, and the enzyme had a K_m for PHPP four times control levels. Tyrosine aminotransferase and fumarylacetoacetase were normal. The patient's mother had increased levels of blood tyrosine and increased excretion of phenolicacids.

A 3½-year-old native Canadian Indian girl without known consanguinity developed seizures at 8 months and had motor, language, and social delay by age 6 months. No skin or eye lesions were present. At 11 months, her plasma tyrosine concentration was 0.90 m*M*; other plasma amino acids were normal.[129] Urinary tyrosine was three and one-half to seven times normal, and plasma PHPLA was ≈5 μ*M* (normally undetectable). Urinary PHPPA, PHPLA, and PHPAA were increased. A soluble TAT activity was decreased in fibroblasts. The TAT in fibroblasts had a K_m for pyridoxal phosphate 100-fold higher than normal and a normal K_m for tyrosine. Patients with tyrosinemia II usually have higher plasma tyrosine levels in childhood.

A short (less than third percentile), retarded (IQ = 46) adult with no eye or skin lesions had a plasma tyrosine of 21.6 mg/dl, an elevated plasma PHPPA of 0.37 mg/dl, and increased urinary levels of PHPPA, PHPLA, PHPAA, and *N*-acetyltyrosine.[130] Other amino acids were not increased. Dihydroxyphenylalanine (dopa) and dopamine were increased in urine. The patient had a tremor accentuated during L-dopa administration.[18] Tyrosine crystals were seen in a marrow aspirate. When studied in parallel with a patient with tyrosinemia II, the latter had no urinary dopa or dopamine and had low levels of phenolic labeling after tolerance tests with deuterated tyrosine.[19] Tyrosine aminotransferase activity in liver biopsy tissue was decreased 30 percent compared to a control. PHPPA oxidase was absent or markedly reduced. These results were thought consistent with a primary defect in PHPPA oxidase.

Enzymology of PHPPA Oxidase

PHPPA oxidase (hydroxylating) (EC 1.14.2.2) catalyzes the oxidation of PHPPA to homogentistic acid. This enzyme is present in the liver and kidney of various mammalian species, including hogs, rabbits, rats, dogs, and humans.[76] It is not present in muscle, heart, or brain.[45] Purified PHPPA oxidase has been prepared from beef, pig, dog, chicken, rat, and human liver.[76] Human fetal liver (fetus, <340 g) has normal adult levels of the enzyme.[131] Properties of the enzyme have been summarized.[76] Since the conversions of phenylpyruvate to *o*-hydroxyphenylpyruvate and of PHPPA to homogentisic acid remain constant during purification, it is assumed that the same enzyme performs both oxidations.[76]

The conversion of PHPPA to homogentisic acid requires two atoms of oxygen and the liberation of one molecule of carbon dioxide. The reaction mechanism is complex and involves hydroxylation of the aromatic ring, migration of the side chain, and oxidation and decarboxylation of the side chain from pyruvate to acetate.[76]

PHPPA oxidase in vitro requires nonstoichiometric amounts of ascorbic acid or one of the group of compounds that can replace the vitamin, such as the reduced form of 2,6-dichlorophenolindophenol. These agents appear to prevent a gradual inhibition of the enzyme by its substrate.[76] In vitro, the substrate PHPPA generates peroxide in the presence of oxygen, and the hydrogen peroxide inhibits the enzyme. Catalase and horseradish peroxidase protect the enzyme. It is undecided whether inhibition of the enzyme occurs in vivo.[45]

The enzyme can be inhibited by relatively low concentrations of diethyldithiocarbamate and 1,10-phenanthroline and by sulfhydryl-binding agents, such as *p*-chloromercuribenzoic acid.[76]

The amount of tyrosine which follows other metabolic pathways has been debated. Most investigators agree that only 0.3 to 1.0 percent of dietary tyrosine is decarboxylated to tyramine.[132]

The tyrosine metabolites, Hawkinsin [(2-cysteine-*S*-yl-1,4-dihydroxy-cyclohex-5-enxyl) acetic acid], and *cis*- and *trans*-4-hydroxycyclohexylacetic acid, have been described in a family with transient tyrosinemia in which the infant had prolonged acidosis[133–135] (Fig. 16-7). It has been postulated[135] that these metabolites are derived from an intermediate in the 4-hydroxyphenylpyruvate hydroxylase reaction.

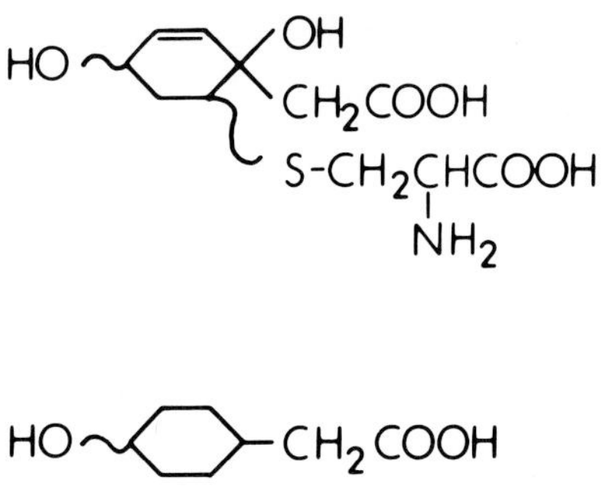

HAWKINSIN

1,4-HYDROXYCYCLOHEXYLACETIC ACID

Fig. 16-7 Two tyrosine metabolites. Hawkinsin and its product, 1.4-dihydroxycyclohexylacetic acid, have been found in a family with a presumptive abnormality in *p*-hydroxyphenylpyruvate oxidase.

Tyrosine Tolerance Tests. Tyrosine tolerance tests are complicated by the insolubility of tyrosine and must be critically evaluated. Phenylalanine tolerance tests have been proposed, overcoming the problems with solubility. Tolerance tests with deuterated L-[$^2H_2$] tyrosine and L-[$^2H_2$] phenylalanine indicate that plasma and liver tyrosine are not in equilibrium.[136] Analysis of the labeling pattern further suggested that synthesis of labeled tyrosine from labeled phenylalanine in liver is unlikely and that labeling occurs in several distinct anatomic compartments, consistent with the hypotheses used to explain the pattern of urinary metabolites in tyrosinemia II. In the postabsorptive rat 22 percent of the plasma tyrosine could be attributed to phenylalanine oxidation, a percentage similar to the 16 percent reported in humans.[137–138]

NEONATAL TYROSINEMIA

Clinical Aspects

Neonatal tyrosinemia and increased excretion of tyrosine and its metabolites are not uncommon. Males and premature infants are more frequently affected.[16,139] The prevalence of this diagnosis varies in different populations from 0.2 to 10 percent, according to feeding practices. In Belgium, with over 30,000 newborns screened annually, there was a decrease in neonatal tyrosinemia from 0.7 to 0.2 percent in infants over 2500 g and from 3.6 to 0.4 percent in infants under 2500 between 1972 and 1977.[16] Similar decreases occurred in Scandinavia. This was correlated with more breast-feeding and more feeding of low protein ("humanized") cow's milk.[16] In the Canadian Inuits, who breast-feed their children, the incidence of tyrosine levels over 0.4 m*M* was 14.8 and 6.2 percent in two separate studies performed in 1970-1972, and 1973-1974, respectively.[140] Although initially associated with low ascorbate levels, other factors probably are involved since ascorbate supplementation did not significantly affect the incidence.[141] Tyrosinemia among Inuits can not be dissociated from a low T4 level which suggests that the tyrosinemia may represent an adaptive phenotype associated with temperature homeostasis.[142]

Children with neonatal tyrosinemia may be somewhat lethargic and have difficulty swallowing, impaired motor activity, prolonged jaundice, and increased levels of galactose, phenylalanine, histidine, and cholesterol.[16] Follow-up of nine such infants showed four with mild metabolic acidosis after the tyrosinemia had cleared.[143] More severe metabolic acidosis, which resolved at age 1 year, was found in a family with unusual tyrosine metabolites.[133–35,144] Mild retardation and decreased psycholinguistic abilities have been associated with neonatal tyrosinemia.[145] Not all studies agree (reviewed in Ref. 145). Identifying tyrosinemia as a critical variable among the other features of "physiological immaturity" will be difficult.

Biochemistry

Blood tyrosine, blood phenylalanine, urine tyrosine, PHPAA, PHPLA, PHPPA, *N*-acetyltyrosine, and *p*-tyramine are all increased.[146]

Etiology

It is usually assumed that this disorder is due to a relative deficiency of *p*-hydroxyphenylpyruvate oxidase.[43] High protein diets with resulting high tyrosine and phenylalanine levels stress this enzyme. It is assumed that ascorbate protects the enzyme from substrate inhibition, although there is no evidence that this occurs in vivo.[45] The response of some patients to ascorbate and the increase of tyrosine metabolites in scorbutic animals and people is consistent with this hypothesis, as are studies in vitro with PHPPA oxidase.[45] With no study of that enzyme and tyrosine aminotransferase in patients in neonatal tyrosinemia, this hypothesis is unproven. Since tyrosine aminotransferase is the rate limiting enzyme of tyrosine metabolism and since the mechanism proposed by Fellman et al.[44] can explain the increased levels of tyrosine metabolites, the basic defect in neonatal tyrosinemia is still to be determined.

Therapy

Most cases are controlled by reducing protein to 2 to 3 g/kg per day or by breast-feeding. The value of ascorbic acid supplementation at 100 mg four times a day has been questioned,[146] but since some patients respond dramatically to vitamin C therapy, there may be two kinds of neonatal tyrosinemia. Establishing whether there is more than one form would be important, since patients with neurologic sequelae may represent a distinct subset.

TYROSINEMIA I (FUMARYLACETOACETATE HYDROLYASE DEFICIENCY)

Synonyms

Most cases of tyrosinemia I are due to deficiency of fumarylacetoacetate hydrolyase (EC 3.7.1.2). The rational name for the disease will have to compete with the historical precedent of several other names including tyrosinosis, hereditary tyrosinemia, tyrosinemia I, and congenital tyrosinosis. Computerized searches should include English and American spellings of tyrosinemia for complete ascertainment. The name is more than a nosological concern since the screening and prenatal diagnosis for this disorder is based on the fumarylacetoacetate hydrolyase deficiency. This disorder, although not a primary disorder of tyrosine metabolism, is accompanied by the elevated levels of tyrosine and its metabolites. Over 100 instances fo the syndrome are reported,[76] and the syndrome has been reviewed.[147,148]

Clinical Aspects

Acute and chronic form of the disease occur within the same family. In the acute form, during the first few weeks to months of life there is failure to thrive, vomiting, diarrhea, and a cabbagelike odor. Hepatomegaly, fever, edema, melena, and epistaxis are frequent. If untreated, death from liver failure ensues in 6 to 8 months.[76,147,148]

The chronic form of the disease has similar but milder features characterized by chronic liver disease, renal tubular dysfunction (deToni-Fanconi syndrome; see Chap. 104), and hypophosphatemia with rickets, which dominate the clinical features by age 1 year. Death occurs usually during the first decade. Hypertrophic obstructive cardiomyopathy may be associated with the syndrome.[149] Abdominal crises and polyneuropathy are related to acute, intermittent, porphyrialike chemical abnormalities.[150] Hypertension may appear.

Hepatoma is a late complication in 37 percent of patients.[144] In five patients who were eventually transplanted regenerating hepatic nodules could not be distinguished from heptocellular carcinoma with ultrasound, nuclear scans, or CT.[145]

Laboratory Findings

Normocytic anemia and leukocytosis are always present, and the platelet count may be increased.[43,76] Serum bilirubin and hepatic enzymes are increased, cholesterol is decreased, and prothrombin time is prolonged; α-fetoprotein is increased.[153] α-Fetoprotein is increased in cord blood before there is an increase in plasma tyrosine.[154]

Plasma tyrosine and methionine are increased, especially in the acute form, and other amino acids may be increased as well.[30,76,147] Urinary excretion of tyrosine and its metabolites, including PHPPA and PHPLA, are increased.[43,76] Hematuria may be present. Glycosuria, phosphaturia, and a generalized aminoaciduria,[43,76] as well as an increase in glyceraldehyde, are also present.[155] The urine,[156,157] as well as serum,[157] contains succinylacetone. Urinary δ-aminolevulinic acid and catecholamines are increased.[150]

The amino acids excreted in excessive amounts, in decreasing order, are tyrosine (64 to 150 times normal), proline (10 to 125 times normal), threonine (10 to 37 times normal), alanine (9 to 30 times normal), glycine (8 to 20 times normal), phenylalanine (8 to 16 times normal), α-aminobutyric acid (7 to 30 times normal), isoleucine (5 to 24 times normal,) serine (5 to 8 times normal), leucine and aspartic acid (3 to 10 times normal), and methionine (2 to 14 times normal).[76,147]

The reduced glutathione level in erythrocytes is decreased, as is the plasma cysteine level.[158]

The liver shows chronic active hepatitis,[76] with fatty infiltration and tubular or pseudoacinar structures, lobular regeneration, and frequently hepatoma.[151,152] There is cellular swelling in the kidneys and astrogliosis in the white matter of the brain.[159] The pancreatic islets are hyperplastic, and there is hypoglycemia unresponsive to glucagon in many patients.

Diagnosis

Tyrosinemia type I should be considered in the differential diagnosis of liver failure in childhood. If a high tyrosine level is detected in infancy and childhood, tyrosinemia I, neonatal tyrosinemia, and tyrosinemia II must be considered, along with fructose-1,6-diphosphatase deficiency, fructose-1-phosphate aldolase deficiency, galactose-1-phosphate uridyl transferase deficiency, giant cell hepatitis, neonatal hemochromatosis, and neonatal infections. Urinary tests for succinylacetone and tissue analysis for fumarylacetoacetate hydrolase establish the diagnosis (see prenatal diagnosis for details).

Treatment

A low tyrosine, low phenylalanine (and often low methionine) diet has been the mainstay of therapy on the assumption that tyrosine, methionine, and their metabolites play significant roles in the toxicity.[160] Tyrosine and its immediate metabolites seem unlikely candidates for such roles considering the experience with tyrosinemia II. Cysteine supplementation has helped at least one patient.[150] Although the serum tyrosine may be normalized by a restricted diet, the increase in methionine may persist and in one case was associated with intrahepatic cholestasis.[161]

A phenylalanine-tyrosine deficiency syndrome associated with growth failure, anorexia, lethargy, hypotonia, and an increase in plasma nonaromatic amino acids should be avoided if the low tyrosine, low phenylalanine diet is used.[162]

Liver homotransplantation has been accomplished in an effort to prevent hepatoma and is effective treatment for the metabolic abnormalities.[163] Two patients after transplantation had persistent excretion of elevated levels of succinylacetone, which increased during tyrosine loading.[164,165] The possibility that the succinylacetone originated in the renal tubular cells of this patient and others was suggested.[164–166] Renal failure may be a complication of this disease even after hepatic transplantation.[164]

Since erythrocytes contain FAH, a trial of blood exchange transfusions was made in three patients[167] without dramatic results.

Identification of succinylacetone and related products, as well as the low plasma cysteine and low erythrocyte glutathione levels in patients have led to treatment with cysteine supplementation or penicillamine.[158,168] It was thought that SH-containing compounds would form adducts with MAA and FAA and inhibit these potentially toxic compounds.[156] The long-term effect of therapy remains to be determined.

Patient follow-up should include monitoring of clinical criteria and the maintaining of adequate protein intake to maintain growth. Repeated measurement of blood tyrosine, methionine, α-fetoprotein, and blood and urinary succinylacetone equivalents is indicated.

Etiology and Pathogenesis

Enzymatic Defect. A deficiency of FAH is the cause of the disease.[141,153,156,169] Maleylacetoacetate hydrolyase may be decreased as well.[153] It is proposed that the degree of residual FAH activity determines whether the disease will be acute or chronic in any affected patient.[153,169] Patients with the acute form have no immunologically cross-reactive protein in liver kidney, lymphocytes, or fibroblasts by immunoblotting using a polyclonal rabbit antiserum against beef liver FAH.[170] Those with chronic disease have variable amounts of enzyme protein[171] (Fig. 16-8).

Reports of acute and chronic forms are based on clinical phenotype only. The forms have not been documented by quantitative enzyme studies either in Quebec or in Scandinavian patients. Epistatic explanations are the only ones available until such cases are documented through enzyme or genomic studies. The primary deficiency of FAH, with or without

Fig. 16-8 Immunoblot of liver proteins from HT-1 patients born in Northeastern Quebec. Proteins were separated on SDS-polyacrylamide gels and reacted with antirat fumarylaceoacetate hydrolase antibody. The liver homogenates of five patients with acute tyrosinemia (T) show no immunoreactive protein (lanes 1 to 7), while two with chronic tyrosinemia (CT) patients (lanes 8, 9) show ± 20 percent residual enzyme compared with three controls. The plate has been slightly overexposed. *(Courtesy of Dr. R.M. Tanguay.)*

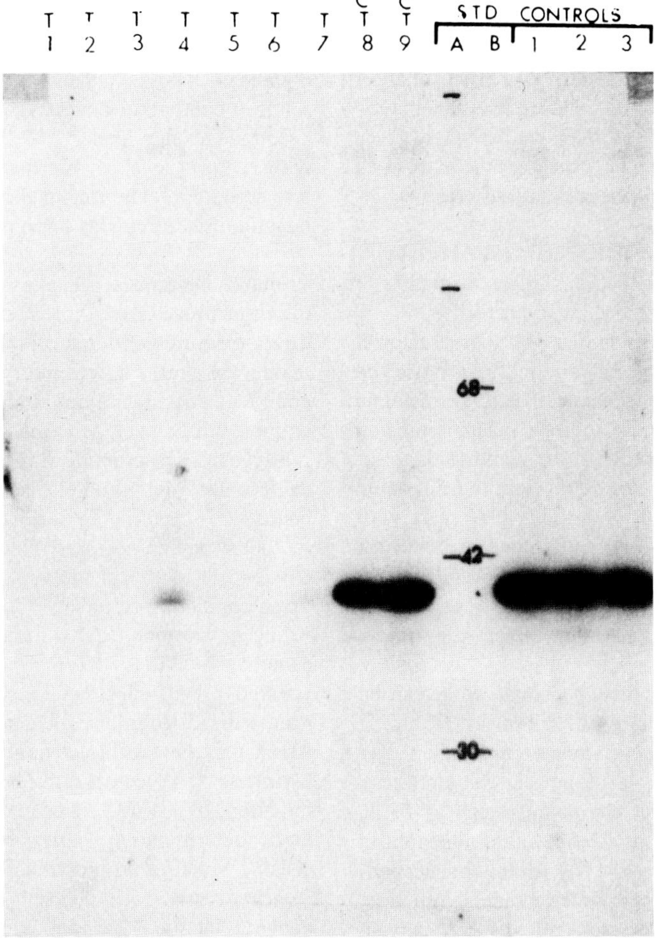

some residual activity, creates perhaps an endogenous toxicity. Genetic regulation of detoxification is the determinant of acute or chronic outcome according to this speculation. Homogentisate loading and measurement of δ-aminolevulinate dehydratase inhibition do indeed suggest the existence of independent loci controlling a polymorphic response, but the work is as yet incomplete on this aspect of the problem.

Human liver has an FAH with a monomer molecular weight of 43,000. The liver enzyme consists of two subunits. It is estimated that this enzyme is 0.2 percent of liver protein and 0.14 percent of liver mRNA in the rat.[172] Rat messenger RNA for this enzyme has been isolated from polysomes using a rat anti-FAH which cross-reacts with human FAH.[172]

FAH can be measured by a spectrophotometric technique in most human tissues including liver kidney, fibroblasts, lymphocytes, and cultured amniotic cells.[173–175] Liver-specific activity is four times that of kidney. Normal chorionic villi have significant enzyme activity,[170] which increases to the levels normally found in kidney after culture.[170] Erythrocytes contain FAH which is one-half normal in carriers and about 10 percent of normal in patients.[176] In some normal subjects loading tests with homogentisic acid, to stress FAA hydrolyase, lead to accumulation of succinylacetone equivalents detected by a decrease in red cell δ-aminolevulinic acid dehydratase levels.[177] The degree of decrease is not greater in heterozygotes than it is in a group of controls.

Toxic Substrate Accumulation and Consequences

The tyrosinemia may result from the endogenous decrease in 4-hydroxyphenylpyruvic acid oxidase, which is found on direct assay of liver biopsies,[166,177] or lead to decreased function of this enzyme in vivo, which can be deduced from load studies with deuterated L-tyrosine.[178] Direct incubation of liver homogenates with succinylacetone or fumarylacetoacetate does not inhibit this enzyme.[179] Tyrosine aminotransferase is decreased in liver biopsies.[153,166,180]

It has been hypothesized that deficiency of FAH activity leads to accumulation of FFA and MAA and the formation of succinylacetone and succinylacetoacetate, respectively.

Succinylacetone is structurally similar to maleic acid, a known inhibitor of renal tubular function, and may cause the renal tubular defects. Succinylacetone, a structural analogue of δ-aminolevulinic acid, markedly inhibits porphobilinogen synthetase (δ-amino acid dehydratase)[156,181,182] and leads to increased levels of δ-aminolevulinic acid and symptoms of acute intermittent porphyria. Reduced glutathione may react with MAA and FAA, leading to decreased glutathione levels, which may interfere with glutathione-dependent detoxification mechanisms.[177] Succinylacetone inhibits renal transport of glucose[183] and amino acids,[183] which may explain the tubulopathy.

Amino acid and albumin adducts of succinylacetone can be found in a patient's urine by their absorption at 315nm.[184] Succinylacetone and the lysine-succinylacetone adduct had similar abilities to inhibit δ-aminolevulinic acid dehydratase.

In addition to succinylacetone, compounds such as FAA, MAA, fumarylacetone, and fumarylacetone glutathione inhibit δ-aminolevulinic acid dehydratase.[170,177] Although succinylacetone does not inhibit *S*-adenosylmethionine synthetase, the other compounds listed above do, and this may explain the high methionine levels in the acute phase of the disease.

Mechanism of Hepatic Malignancy. The levels of liver glutathione, arylhydrocarbon hydroxylase, and 7-ethoxycoumarin deethylase were decreased in one patient and suggested that the carcinogenesis in this disease might be due to decreased hepatic detoxification of carcinogens.[157] In hepatocyte culture, succinylacetone increased δ-levulinic acid synthetase and decreased P_{450} induction.[185] It is hypothesized that fumarylacetone and maleylacetoacetate may be natural alkylating agents and be responsible for malignancy in the disease.[173]

Genetics

This disorder has autosomal recessive inheritance, both sexes are equally affected, and there is a high prevalence of the trait in the French-Canadian population of Quebec where consanguineous mating is historically frequent.[186] The overall prevalence in Quebec is 80 per million births. In the Lac-St. Jean region of Quebec the heterozygote prevalence is 1:14, and one in 685 are born with the disease.[186] A founder effect is documented for the high gene frequency in this region.[187a] Screening studies have established a prevalence of the disease of 1:120,000 in Sweden and 1:100,000 in Norway.[16]

Carrier State. Heterozygotes have half-normal levels of FAH in fibroblasts and lymphocytes.[173]

Pseudodeficiency. The lymphocytes of some control individuals have levels of FAH in the range of heterozygotes and even of patients with the disease, but a tyrosine load in such a person does not cause succinylacetone excretion. Family studies show an autosomal dominant trait which could act as a pseudodeficiency gene.[187] This could be clinically relevant in counseling a compound heterozygote for FAH deficiency and the pseudodeficiency gene.[174,187] Pseudodeficiency is associated with reduced levels of in vivo δ-aminolevulinic acid dehydratase activity.[188] The role of decreased levels of that enzyme in hepatic disease remains to be determined.

Prenatal Diagnosis. Diagnosis is achieved by at least three different procedures: direct determination of enzyme activity, direct measurement of succinylacetone by combined gas chromatography/mass spectrometry (GC/MS) techniques, and the ability of succinylacetone and related products to inhibit δ-aminolevulinic acid dehydratase. All these methods are currently used on aminotic fluid, amniotic cells, and chorionic vellus cells. The pseudodeficiency trait must be taken into account,[157,188] and in an individual patient a combination of methods may be necessary since each assay measures a different feature of the phenotype. The different techniques have given conflicting results.[189,190]

Succinylacetone (SA) is measured in the amniotic fluid and urine by GC/MS.[191] Normal values are less than 6 nmol/liter affected pregnancies, SA exceeds 100 nmol/liter. There is a standardized technique for determining *all* of the compounds which may be capable of inhibiting δ-aminolevulinic acid dehydratase.[192] A comparative study of succinylacetone determination by GC/MS, enzymatic inhibition and FAH enzymatic determination[174] has been done on cultured amniotic cells.[175] Six affected individuals were detected by FAH assay. In three cases with deficient FAH, amniotic fluid SA was above 1000 nmol/liter and in two cases about 80 nmol/liter (normal < 30 nmol/liter) One case had conflicting results based on GC/MS determinations. The authors concluded that since SA levels may be close to the normal range in some affected pregnancies, FAH determination is desirable, especially since it can be performed on chorionic villus material at 10 weeks of gestation.

ADDENDUM

An infant with the clinical manifestations of hereditary tyrosinemia type 1 [fumarylacetoacetate hydrolase (FAH) deficiency] had typical chemical findings with one significant exception: There was no excess of succinylacetone in urine. FAH activity in liver biopsy material was normal. On the other hand, there was complete deficiency of maleylacetoacetate isomerase activity in liver (postmortem?) and near complete deficiency of this activity in cultured skin fibroblasts. Parents of the proband had "low MAA isomerase activity suggesting an autosomal recessive inheritance" for the disorder. The authors of this report[193] propose to call this disease tyrosinemia type 1b; type 1a would be the form with FAH deficiency.

REFERENCES

1. RICHNER H: Hornhautaffektion bei Kerotoma palmare et plantare hereditarium. *Klin Monatsol Augenheilkd* 100:580, 1938.
2. HANHART E: Neue Sonderformen von keratosis palmo-plantaris, u.a. eine regelmassig dominante mit systematisierten lipomen, ferner 2 einfachrezessive mit Schwachsinn und z.T. mit Hornhautveranderungen des Auges (Ektodermalsyndrom). *Dermatologica* 94:286,1947.
3. GOLDSMITH LA, KANG E, BIENFANG DC, JIMBOW K, GERALD P, BADEN HP: Tyrosinemia with plantar and palmar keratosis and keratitis. *J Pediatr* 83:798, 1973.
4. BURNS RP: The tyrosine aminotransferase deficiency: An unusual cause of corneal ulcers. *Am J Opthalmol* 73:400, 1972.
5. BURNS RP, GIPSON IK, MURRAY MJ: Keratopathy in tyrosinemia. *Birth Defects* XII:169, 1976.
6. FELLMAN JH, VANBELLINGHEN PJ, JONES RT, KOLER RD: Soluble and mitochondrial forms of tyrosine aminotransferase. Relationship to human tyrosinemia. *Biochemistry* 8:615, 1969.
7. KENNAWAY NG, BUIST NRM: Metabolic studies in a patient with hepatic cytosol tyrosine aminotransferase deficiency. *Pediatr Res* 5:287, 1971.
8. HILL A, ZALESKI WA: Tyrosinosis: Biochemical studies of an unusual case. *Clin Biochem* 4:263, 1971.
9. ZALESKI WA, HILL A, KUSHNIRUK W: Skin lesions in tyrosinosis: Response to dietary treatment. *Br J Dermatol* 88:335, 1973.
10. HOAK GN, HILL A, ZALESKI W: Urinary p-tyramine in hereditary tyrosinemia: I. Levels as compared to normal individuals, effect of diet, and relationship to urinary tyrosine. *Clin Biochem* 10:24, 1977.
11. HOAK GN, HILL A, ZALESKI WL: Urinary p-tyramine in hereditary tyrosinemia: II. Origin of urinary p-tyramine. *Clin Biochem* 10:26, 1977.
12. HOLSTON JL JR, LEVY HL, TOMLIN GA, ATKINS RJ, PATTON TH, HOSTY TS: Tyrosinosis: A patient without liver or renal disease. *Pediatrics* 48:393, 1971.
13. BIENFANG DC, KUWABARA T, PUESCHEL SM: The Richner-Hanhart syndrome. Report of a case with associated tyrosinemia. *Arch Ophthalmol* 94:1133, 1976.
14. ZAMMARCHI E, LaCAUZA C, CALZOLARI C: Un caso di ipertirosinemia con tirosiluria. *Minerva Pediatr* 26:203, 1974.
15. SANDBERG HO: Bilateral keratopathy and tyrosinosis. *Acta Ophthalmol* 53:760, 1975.
16. HALVORSEN S: Screening for disorders of tyrosine metabolism, in Bickel H, Guthrie R, Hammersen G (eds): *Neonatal Screening for Inborn Errors of Metabolism.* New York, Springer-Verlag, 1980, p 45.
17. GOLDSMITH LA, REED J: Tyrosine-induced eye and skin lesions. *JAMA* 236:382, 1976.
18. BILLSON FA, DANKS, DM: Corneal and skin changes in tyrosinaemia. *Aust J Ophthalmol* 3:112, 1975.
19. FAULL KF, GAN I, HALPERN B, HAMMOND J, IM S, COTTON RGH, DANKS DM: Metabolic studies in two patients with nonhepatic tyrosinemia using deuterated tyrosine loads. *Pediatr Res* 11:631, 1977.
20. GARIBALDI LR, SILIATO F, DeMARTINI I, SCARSI MR, ROMANO C: Oculocutaneous tyrosinosis. Report of two cases in the same family. *Helv Paediatr Acta* 32:173, 1977.
21. BARDELLI AM, BORGOGNI P, FARNETANI MA, FOIS A, FREZZOTTI R, MATTEI R, MOLINELLI M, SARGENTINI I: Familial tyrosinaemia with eye and skin lesions. *Ophthalmologica* 175:5, 1977.
22. PELET B, ANTENERI, FAGGIONI R, SPAHR A, GAUTIER E: Tyrosinemia without liver or renal damage with plantar and palmar keratosis and keratitis (hypertyrosinemia). *Helv Paediatr Acta* 34:177, 1979.
23. GOLDSMITH LA: Tyrosinemia II. A large North Carolina kindred. *Arch Intern Med* 145:1697, 1985.
24. LARREGUE M, De GIACOMONI PH, BRESSIEU JM, ODIEVRE ML: Syndrome de Richner-Hanhart ou tyrosinose oculo-cutanee. *Ann Dermatol Venereol* 106:53, 1979.
25. LEMONNIER F, CHARPENTIER C, ODIEVRE M, LARREGU M, LEMONNIER A: Tyrosine aminotransferase isoenzyme deficiency. *J Pediatr* 94:931, 1979.
26. GOLDSMITH LA, THROPE JM, ROE CR: Hepatic enzymes of tyrosine metabolism in tyrosinemia II. *J Invest Dermatol* 73:530, 1979.
27. HUNZIKER N: Richner-Hanhart syndrome and tyrosinemia type II. *Dermatologica* 160:180, 1980.
28. FRANCESCHETTI AT, SCHNYDER UW, FELGENHAUER WR: Die cornea beim Richner-Hanhart syndrom. *Bericht über die 71, Zusammenkunft der Deutschen Ophthalm Gesellschaft in Heidelberg,* 1979, p 109.
29. FOIS A, BORGOGNI P, CIONI M, MOLINELLI M, FREZZOTTI R, et al: Presentation of the data of the Italian registry of oculocutaneous tyrosinaemia. *J Inherited Metab Dis* 9:262, 1986.
30. GOLDSMITH LA: Tyrosinemia II: Lessons in molecular pathophysiology. *Pediatr Dermatol* 1:25, 1983.
31. JAEGER W, GALLASCH G, SCHNYDER UW, LUTZ P, SCHMIDT H: Tyrosinemia and bilateral pseudokeratitis dendritica (Richner-Hanhart syndrome). *Metab Pediatr Ophthalmol* 3:111, 1979.
32. LESTRINGANT GG: Tyrosinemia type II with incomplete Richner-Hanhart's syndrome. Personal communication.
33. MACHINO H, MIKI Y, KAWATSU T, KIDA K, MATSUDA H: Successful dietary control of tyrosinemia II. *J Am Acad Dermatol* 9:533, 1983.
34. COLDITZ PB, YU JS, BILLSON FA, ROGERS M, MOLLOY HF, O'HALLORAN M, WILCKEN B: Tyrosinaemia II. *Med J Aust* 141:244, 1984.
35. REHAK A, SELIM MM, YADAV G: Richner-Hanhart syndrome (tyrosinaemia-II) (report of four cases without ocular involvement). *Br J Dermatol* 104:469, 1981.
36. CROVATO F, DESIRELLO G, GATTI R, BABBINI N, REBORA A: Richner-Hanhart syndrome spares a plantar autograft. *Arch Dermatol* 121:539, 1985.
37. ZALESKI WA, HOUSTON CS, HILL A: Unusual radiological changes in tyrosinosis. *Lancet* 2:46, 1972.
38. ZMEGAC ZJ, SARAJLIC MV: A rare form of an inheritable palmar and plantar keratosis. *Dermatologica* 130:40, 1964.
39. LARREGUE M, de GIACOMONI PH, ODIEVRE M, BABIN PH, LORETTE G: Tyrosinose oculo-cutanee (syndrome de Richner-Hanhart). *Ann Anat Pathol* 25:185, 1980.
40. BOHNERT A, ANTON-LAMPRECHT I: Richner-Hanhart's syndrome: Ultrastructural abnormalities of epidermal keratinization indicating a causal relationship to high intracellular tyrosine levels. *J Invest Dermatol* 79:68, 1982.
41. HILL A, NORDIN PM, ZALESKI WA: Dietary treatment of tyrosinosis. *J Am Diet Assoc* 56:308, 1970.
42. BUIST NRM, KINNAWAY NG, FELLMAN JH: Disorders of tyrosine metabolism, in Nyhan WR (ed): *Heritable Disorders of Amino Acid Metabolism: Patterns of Clinical and Genetic Variaton.* New York, Wiley, 1974, p 160.
43. SCRIVER CR, ROSENBERG LE: Tyrosine, in Scriver CR, Rosenberg LE (eds): *Amino Acid Metabolism and Its Disorders.* Philadelphia, Saunders, 1973, p 338.
44. FELLMAN JH, BUIST NRM, KENNAWAY NG, SWANSON RE: The source of aromatic ketoacids in tyrosinaemia and phenylketonuria. *Clin Chim Acta* 39:243, 1972.
45. FELLMAN JH, FUJITA TS, ROTH ES: Assay, properties and tissue distribution of p-hydroxyphenylpyruvate hydroxylase. *Biochim Biophys Acta* 284:90, 1972.
46. BUIST NRM, FELLMAN JH, KENNAWAY N: Letter to the editor: Metabolic studies in tyrosinemia. *Pediatr Res* 12:56, 1978.
47. DANKS DM: Letter to the editor: Reply to Dr. Buist. *Pediatr Res* 12:57, 1978.
48. NEY D, BAY C, SCHNEIDER JA, KELTS D, NYHAN WWL: Dietary management of oculocutaneous tyrosinemia in an 11-year old child. *Am J Dis Child* 137:995, 1983.
49. CHARLTON KH, BINDER PS, WOZNIAK L, DIGBY DJ: Pseudodendritic keratitis and systemic tyrosinemia. *Ophthalmology* 88:355, 1981.
50. HUNZIKER N, BRUN R, JEANNERET JP: Richner-Hanhart syndrome (RHS)—Tyrosinemia type II and oral aromatic retinoid (Ro 10-9359).

Report of two cases, in Orfanos CE, Braun-Falco O, Farber EM, Grupper CH, Polano MK, Schuppli R (eds): *Retinoids. Advances in Basic Research and Therapy*. New York, Springer-Verlag, 1982, p 453.

51. SCHEIZER W: Studies on the effect of l-tyrosine on the white rat. *J Physiol* 106:167, 1947.

52. IP CCY, HARPER AE: Effects of dietary protein content and glucagon administration on tyrosine metabolism and tyrosine toxicity in the rat. *J Nutr* 103:1594, 1973.

53. ALAM SQ, BECKER RV, STUCKI WP, ROGERS QR: Effect of threonine on the toxicity of excess tyrosine and cataract formation in the rat. *J Nutr* 89:91, 1966.

54. YAMAMOTO Y, TOYOSHIMA R, MURAMATSU K: Effect of additional protein or methionine and threonine on tyrosine catabolism in rats fed diets high in tyrosine. *Agric Biol Chem* 43:2585, 1979.

55. SELYE H: Steroids influencing the toxicity of L-tyrosine. *J Nutr* 101:515, 1971.

56. BOCTOR AM, HARPER AE: Tyrosine toxicity in the rat: Effect of high intake of p-hydroxyphenylpyruvic acid and of force-feeding high tyrosine diet. *J Nutr* 95:535, 1968.

57. EASTON EJ, SIMPSON I, MARTIN JK, CAMPBELL DJ: Tyrosinemia induced by a pyridoxine antagonist, desoxypyridoxine. *Clin Chem* 18:161, 1972.

58. RICH LF, BEARD ME, BURNS RP: Excess dietary tyrosine and corneal lesions. *Exp Eye Res* 17:87, 1973.

59. BEARD ME, BURNS RP, RICH LF, SQUIRES E: Histopathology of keratopathy in the tyrosine-fed rat. *Invest Ophthalmol* 13:1037, 1974.

60. GIPSON IK, BURNS RP, WOLFE-LANDE JD: Crystals in corneal epithelial lesions of tyrosine fed rats. *Invest Ophthalmol* 14:937, 1975.

61. RIPPLE RE, LOHR KM, TWINING SS, HYNDIUK RA, CAYAG JG: Role of leukocytes in ocular inflammation of tyrosinemia II. *Invest Ophthalmol Vis Sci* 27:926, 1986.

62. LOHR KM, HYNDIUK RA, HATCHELL DL, KURTH CE: Corneal organ cultures in tyrosinemia release chemotactic factors. *J Clin Lab Med* 105:573, 1985.

63. GOLDSMITH LA: Molecular biology and molecular pathology of a newly described molecular disease–tyrosinemia II (the Richner-Hanhart syndrome). *Exp Cell Biol* 46:96, 1978.

64. GOLDSMITH LA: Tyrosine-induced skin disease. *Br J Dermatol* 98:119, 1978.

65. TABACHNICK J, LABADIE JH: Studies on the biochemistry of epidermis. IV. The free amino acids, ammonia, urea, and pyrrolidone carboxylic acid content of conventional and germ-free albino guinea-pig epidermis. *J Invest Dermatol* 54:24, 1970.

66. GOLDSMITH LA: Hemolysis and lysosomal activation by solid state tyrosine. *Biochem Biophys Res Commun* 64:558, 1975.

67. GOLDSMITH LA: Haemolysis induced by tyrosine crystals. Modifiers and inhibitors. *Biochem J* 158:17, 1976.

68. SCHWARTZ TM, SCHACKELFORD RM: Pseudodistemper is apparently new ailment of mink. *US Fur Rancher* 52:6, 1973.

69. CHRISTENSEN K, FISCHER P, KNUDSEN KEB, LARSEN S, SORENSEN H, VENGE O: A syndrome of hereditary tyrosinemia in mink (*Mustela vison* Schreb). *Can J Comp Med* 43:333, 1979.

70. GOLDSMITH LA, THORPE JM, MARSH RF: Tyrosine aminotransferase deficiency in mink *Mustela vison:* A model for human tyrosinemia II. *Biochem Genet* 19:687, 1981.

71. CHRISTENSEN K, HENRIKSEN P, SORENSEN H: New forms of hereditary tyrosinemia type II in mink: Hepatic tyrosine aminotransferase defect. *Hereditas* 104:215, 1986.

72. GOLDSMITH LA, LESIEWICZ J: Tyrosinemia in the Mink, in Maibach H, Lowe N (eds): *Models in Dermatology,* Basel, Karger, 1985, vol 1, p 77.

73. KUNKLE GA, JEZYK PF, WEST CS, GOLDSCHMIDT MH, O'KEEFE CO: Tyrosinemia in a dog. *Am Anim Hosp Assoc* 20:615, 1984.

74. ANDERSSON S, NEMETH A, OHISALO J, STRANDVIK B: Persistent tyrosinemia associated with low activity of tyrosine aminotransferase. *Pediatr Res* 18:675, 1984.

75. JAISWAL RB, BHAI I, NATH N, NATH MC: Tyrosinosis-Part 1: Clinical, radiological and biochemical aspects. *Indian Pediatr* 6:1, 1969.

76. LA DU BN, GJESSING LR: Tyrosinosis and tyrosinemia, in Stanbury JB, Wyngaarden JB, Fredrickson DS (eds): *Metabolic Basis of Inherited Disease,* 4th ed. New York, McGraw-Hill, 1978, p 256.

77. WADMAN SK, VAN SPRANG FJ, MAAS JW, KETTING D: An exceptional case of tyrosinosis. *J Ment Defic Res* 12:269, 1968.

78. SESHIA SS, PERRY TL, DAKSHINAMURTI K, SNODGRASS PJ: Tyrosinemia and intractable seizures. *Epilepsia* 25:457, 1984.

79. ANDERSSON SM, SALASPURO M, OHISALO JJ: Metabolic basis of hypertyrosinemia in liver disease. *Gastroenterology* 82:554, 1982.

80. THORPE JM, GOLDSMITH LA: Tyrosine aminotransferase activity in skin. *J Invest Dermatol* 75:371, 1980.

81. SPENCER CJ, GELEHRTER TD: Pseudoisozymes of hepatic tyrosine aminotransferase. *J Biol Chem* 249:577, 1974.

82. HARGROVE JL, MACKIN RB: Organ specificity of glucocorticoid-sensitive tyrosine aminotransferase. Separation from aspartate aminotransferase isoenzymes. *J Biol Chem* 259:386, 1984.

83. LEE K-L, ROBERSON LE, KENNEY FT: Properties of tyrosine aminotransferase from rat liver. *Anal Biochem* 95:188, 1979.

84. HARGROVE JL, DIESTERHAFT M, NOGUCHI T, CRANNER DK: Identification of native tyrosine aminotransferase and an explanation for the multiple forms. *J Biol Chem* 255:71, 1980.

85. RUBENSTEIN PA, IVARIE RD: Isolation of two different molecular weight polypeptides copurifying with rat liver tyrosine aminotransferase. *Arch Biochem Biophys* 194:299, 1979.

86. SMITH GJ, PEARCE PH, OLIVER IT: A lysosomal factor that interconverts multiple forms of rat liver tyrosine aminotransferase. *Life Sci* 19:1763, 1976.

87. BOCTOR A, GROSSMAN A: Tyrosine aminotransferase converting factor, kinetic properties, cellular localization, and tissue distribution. *Biochem Biophys Acta* 543:137, 1978.

88. GOHDA E, PITOT HC: Purification and characterization of a factor catalyzing the conversion of the multiple forms of tyrosine aminotransferase from rat liver. *J Biol Chem* 255:7371, 1980.

89. HARGROVE JL, GOHDA E, PITOT HC, GRANNER DK: Cathepsin T (Convertase) generates the multiple forms of tyrosine aminotransferase by limited proteolysis. *Biochemistry* 21:283, 1982.

90. DICOLA D, FEDERICI G: Absence of tyrosine aminotransferase multiple forms in several mammalian animals. *Comp Biochem Physiol* 76:87, 1983.

91. ANDERSSON SM, PISPA JP: Purification and properties of human liver tyrosine aminotransferase. Clinica Chimica Acta 125:117, 1982.

92. LEE K-L, NICKOL JM: Phosphorylation of tyrosine aminotransferase in vivo. *J Biol Chem* 249:6024, 1974.

93. FEDERICI G, DICOLA D, SACCHETTA P, DI ILIO C, DEL BOCCIO G, POLIDORO G: Reversible inactivation of tyrosine aminotransferase from guinea pig liver by thiol and disulfide compounds. *Biochem Biophys Res Commun* 81:650, 1978.

94. BUCKLEY WT, MILLIGAN LP: Participation of cysteine and cystine in inactivation of tyrosine aminotransferase in rat liver homogenates. *Biochem J* 176:449, 1978.

95. ERNEST MJ, FEIGELSON P: Increase in hepatic tyrosine aminotransferase mRNA during enzyme induction by N6O2[1] diibutyryl cyclic AMP. *J Biol Chem* 253:319, 1978.

96. NOGUCHI T, DIESTERHAFT M, GRANNER D: Dibutyryl cyclic AMP increases the amount of functional messenger RNA coding for tyrosine aminotransferase in rat liver. *J Biol Chem* 253:1332, 1978.

97. OLSON PS, THOMPSON EB, GRANNER DK: Regulation of hepatoma tissue culture cell tyrosine aminotransferase messenger ribonucleic acid by dexamethasone. *Biochemistry* 19:1705, 1980.

98. NICKOL JM, LEE K-L, KENNEY FT: Changes in hepatic levels of tyrosine aminotransferase messenger RNA during induction by hydrocortisone. *J Biol Chem* 253:4009, 1978.

99. LEE KL, ISHAM KR, JOHNSON A, KENNEY FL: Insulin enhances transcription of the tyrosine aminotransferase gene in rat liver. *Arch Biochem Biophys* 248:597, 1986.

100. SPENCER CJ, HEATON JH, GELEHRTER TD, RICHARDSON KI, GARWIN JL: Insulin selectively slows the degradation of rat tyrosine aminotransferase. *J Biol Chem* 253:7677, 1978.

101. HEATON JH, KRETT NL, GELEHRTER TD: Regulation of insulin and insulin-like growth factor (IGF) responsiveness by IGF in rat hepatoma cells. *Endocrinology* 118:2555, 1986.

102. STELLWAGEN RH, SAILOR RD, KOHLI KK: Acceleration of the degradation of tyrosine aminotransferase in rat hepatoma (HTC) cells by inhibitors of cyclic nuleotide phophodiesterase. *Biochem Biophys Res Commun* 78:1162, 1977.

103. STRINDEN ST, STELLWAGEN RH: Possible involvement of cGMP in the control of tyrosine aminotransferase degradation in rat hepatocytes. *J Cell Physiol* 117:69, 1983.

104. KOONTZ JW, WICKS WD: Stimulation of tyrosine aminotransferase degradation by methylthioinosine. *J Biol Chem* 259:929, 1984.

105. THOMPSON EB, GRANNER KD, GELEHRTER TD, HAGER GL: Unlinked control of multiple glucocorticoid-sensitive processes in spontaneous HTC cell variants, in Sato GH, Ross R (eds): *Hormones and Cell Culture.* Cold Spring Harbor, New York, Cold Spring Harbor Laboratory, 1979, p 339.

106. HASHIMOTO S, SCHMID W, SCHUTZ G: Transcriptional activation of the rat liver tyrosine aminotransferase gene by cAMP. *Proc Natl Acad Sci USA* 81:6637, 1984.

107. ROPER MD, WICKS WD: Evidence of acceleration of the rate of elongation of tyrosine aminotransferase nascent chains by dibutyryl cyclic AMP. *Proc Natl Acad Sci USA* 75:140, 1978.

108. ERNEST MJ, DELAP L, FEIGELSON P: Induction of hepatic tyrosine aminotransferase mRNA by protein synthesis inhibitors. *J Biol Chem* 253:2895, 1978.

109. HOFER E, SEKERIS CE: Cycloheximide causes increased accumulation of translatable mRNA for tyrosine aminotransferase and tryptophan oxygenase in livers of cortisol-treated rats. *Eur J Biochem* 86:547, 1978.

110. LIU AY-C: Role of cyclic AMP-dependent protein kinase in the induction of tyrosine aminotransferase. *J Biol Chem* 255:4421, 1980.

111. KROGER H, DONNER I, VOSS H, PLOTZE G: Superinduction of tyrosine aminotransferase in RLC-cells. *Biomedicine* 31:89, 1979.

112. KIDO H, FUKUSEN N, ISHIDOH K, KATUNUMA N: Diacylglycerol amplifies the induction in vivo of tyrosine aminotransferase and ornithine decarboxylase by glucocorticoid. *Biochem Biophys Res Commun* 138:275, 1986.

113. AUBERGER P, SAMSON M, LeCAM A: Inhibition of hormonal induction of tyrosine aminotransferase by polyamines in freshly isolated rat hepatocytes. *Biochem J* 214:679, 1983.

114. COUFALIK AH, MONDER C: Regulation of the tyrosine oxidizing system in fetal rat liver. *Arch Biochem Biophys* 199:67, 1980.

115. ANDERSSON SM: beta-Adrenergic induction of tyrosine aminotransferase in foetal rat liver. *Biochem J* 186:609, 1980.

116. ANDERSSON SM: beta-adrenergic induction of tyrosine aminotransferase organ culture of fetal rat and fetal human liver. *Endocrinology* 112:466, 1983.

117. SHINOMIYA T, SCHERER G, SCHMID W, ZENTGRAF H, SCHUTZ G: Isolation and characterization of the rat tyrosine aminotransferase gene. *Proc Natl Acad Sci USA* 81:1346, 1984.

118. GRANGE T, GUENET C, DIETRICH JB, CHASSEROT S, FROMONT M, BEFORT N, JAMI J, BECK G, PICTET R: Complete complementary DNA of rat tyrosine aminotransferase messenger RNA. Deduction of the primary structure of the enzyme. *J Mol Biol* 184:347, 1985.

119. MULLER G, SCHERER G, ZENTGRAF H, RUPPERT S, HERRMANN B, LEHRACH H, SCHUTZ, G: Isolation, characterization and chromosomal mapping of the mouse tyrosine aminotransferase gene. *J Mol Biol* 184:367, 1985.

120. BECKER P, RENKAWITZ R, SCHUTZ G: Tissue-specific DNaseI hypersensitive sites in the 5′-flanking sequences of the trytophan oxygenase and the tyrosine aminotransferase genes. *EMBO J* 3:2015, 1984.

121. NATT E, KAO PT, RETTENMEIER R, SCHERER G: Assignment of the human tyrosine aminotransferase gene to chromosome 16. *Hum Genet* 72:225, 1986.

122. BARTON DE, YANG-FENG TL, FRANCKE U: The human tyrosine aminotransferase gene mapped to the long arm of chromosome 16 (region 16q22–q24) by somatic cell hybrid analysis and in situ hybridization. *Hum Genet* 72:221, 1986.

123. NATT E, MAGENIS RE, BUIST NRM, SCHERER G: Inherited and de novo deletion of the tyrosine aminotransferase gene locus at 16q 22.1 to q 22.3 in a patient with tyrosinemia II. *Hum Genet* 77:352, 1987.

124. PETERSON TC, KILLARY AM, POURNIER RB: Chromosomal assignment and trans regulation of the tyrosine aminotransferase structural gene in hepatoma hybrid cells. *Mol Cell Biol* 5:2491, 1985.

125. SCHMID W, MULLER G, SCHUTZ G, GLUECKSOHN-WAELSCH S: Deletions near the albino locus on chromosome 7 of the mouse affect the level of tyrosine aminotransferase mRNH. *Proc Natl Acad Sci USA* 82:2866, 1985.

126. KILLARY AM, FOURNIER RE: A genetic analysis of extinction: Trans-dominant loci regulate expression of liver-specific traits in hepatoma hybrid cells. *Cell* 38:523, 1984.

127. GIARDINI O, CANTANI A, KENNAWAY NG, D'EUFEMIA P: Chronic tyrosinemia associated with 4-hydroxyphenylpyruvate dioxygenase deficiency with acute intermittent ataxia and without visceral and bone involvement. *Pediatr Res* 17:25, 1983.

128. ENDO F, KITANO A, UEHARA I, NAGATA N, MATSUDA I, SHINKA T, KUHARA T, MATSUMOTO I: Four-hydroxyphenylpyruvic acid oxidase deficiency with normal fumarylacetoacetase: A new variant form of hereditary hypertyrosinemia. *Pediatr Res* 17:92, 1983.

129. DEGROOT GW, DAKSHINAMURTI K, ALLAN L, HAWORTH JC: Defect in soluble tyrosine aminotransferase in skin fibroblasts of a patient with tyrosinemia. *Pediatr Res* 14:896, 1980.

130. LOUIS WJ, PITT DD, DAVIES H: Biochemical studies in a patient with "Tyrosinosis." *Aust NZ J Med* 4:281, 1974.

131. OHISALO JJ, LASKOWSKI-KLITA T, ANDERSSON SM: Development of tyrosine aminotransferase and p-hydroxyphenylpyruvate dioxygenase activities in fetal and neonatal human liver. *J Clin Invest* 70:198, 1982.

132. FELLMAN JH, ROTH ES, FUJITA TS: Decarboxylation to tyramine is not a major route of tyrosine metabolism in mammals. *Arch Biochem Biophys* 174:562, 1976.

133. NIEDERWIESER A, MATASOVIC A, TIPPETT P, DANKS DM: A new sulfur amino acid, named Hawkinsin, identified in a baby with transient tyrosinemia and her mother. *Clin Chim Acta* 76:345, 1977.

134. NIEDERWIESER A, MATASOVIC A, NEUHEISER F, WETZEL E: New tyrosine metabolites in humans: Hawkinsin and cis- and trans-4-hydroxycyclohexylacetic acids. Unusual adsorption of deuterated and non-deuterated Hawkinsin during gas chromatography. *J Chromatogr* 146:207, 1978.

135. NIEDERWIESER A, WADMAN SK, DANKS DM: Excretion of cis- and trans-4-hydroxycyclohexylacetic acid in addition to Hawkinsin in a family with a postulated defect of 4-hydroxyphenylpyruvate dioxygenase. *Clin Chim Acta* 90:195, 1978.

136. FELL V, HOSKINS JA, POLLITT RJ: The labelling of urinary acids after oral doses of deuterated L-phenylalanine and L-tyrosine in normal subjects. Quantitative studies with implications for the deuterated phenylalanine load test in phenylketonuria. *Clin Chim Acta* 83:259, 1978.

137. MOLDAWER LL, KAWAMURA I, BISTRIAN, BLACKBURN GL: The contribution of phenylalanine to tyrosine metabolism *in vivo*. *Biochem J* 210:811, 1983.

138. CLARKE JTR, BIER DM: The conversion of phenylalanine to tyrosine in man. Direct measurement by continuous intravenous taracer infusion of L-(ring-$^{2}H_5$) phenylalanine and L-(1-^{13}C) tyrosine in the postabsorptive state. *Metabolism* 31:999, 1982.

139. WONG PWK, LAMBERT AM, KOMROWER GM: Tyrosinaemia and tyrosyluria in infancy. *Dev Med Child Neurol* 9:551, 1967.

140. CLOW CL, LABERGE C, SCRIVER CR: Neonatal hypertyrosinemia and evidence for deficiency of ascorbic acid in arctic and subarctic peoples. *CMA J* 113:624, 1975.

141. SCRIVER CR, PERRY JRT, LASLEY L, CLOW CL, COULTER D, LABERGE C: Neonatal tyrosinemia (NT) in the Eskimo. Result of protein polymorphism. *Pediatr Res* 11:411, 1977.

142. SCRIVER CR, MORISSETTE J, PERRY TJR, LASLEY L, CLOW CL, COULTER D, LABERGE C: La tyrosinemie neonatale chez les Inuit. *Med Sci* 1:271, 1985.

143. FERNBACH SA, SUMMONS RF, PEREIRA WE, DUFFIELD AM: Metabolic studies of transient tyrosinemia in premature infants. *Pediatr Res* 9:172, 1975.

144. DANKS DM, TIPPETT P, ROGERS J: A new form of prolonged transient tyrosinemia presenting with severe metabolic acidosis. *Acta Paediatr Scand* 64:209, 1975.

145. MAMUNESP, PRINCE PE, THORNTON NH, HUNT PA, HITCOCK ES: Intellectual deficits after transient tyrosinemia in the term neonate. *Pediatrics* 57:675, 1976.

146. BAKKER HD, WADMAN SK, VAN SPRANG FJ, VAN DER HEIDEN C, KETTING D, DeBREE PK: Tyrosinemia and tyrosyluria in healthy prematures: Time courses not vitamin C-dependent. *Clin Chim Acta* 61:73, 1975.

147. PARTINGTON M, SCRIVER CR, SASS-KORTSAK A (eds): Conference on hereditary tyrosinemia. *Can Med Assoc J* 97:1045, 1967.

148. KVITTINGEN EA: Hereditary tyrosinemia type I—An overview. *Scand J Clin Lab Invest* 46:27, 1986.

149. EDWARDS MA, GREEN A, COLLI A, RYLANCE G: Tyrosinaemia type I and hypertrophic obstructive cardiomyopathy. *Lancet i*:1437, 1987.

150. STRIFE CF, ZUROWESTE EL, MEETT EA, FINELLI VN, PETERING HG, BERRY HK: Tyrosinemia with acute intermittent porphyria: Aminolevulinic acid dehydratase deficiency related to elevated urinary aminolevulinic acid levels. *J Pediatr* 90:400, 1977.

151. WEINBERG AG, MIZE CE, WORTHEN HG: The occurrence of hepatoma in the chronic form of hereditary tyrosinemia. *J Pediatr* 88:434, 1976.

152. DAY DL, LETOURNEAU JG, ALLAN BT, SHARP HL, ASCHER N, DEHNER LP, THOMPSON WM. Hepatic regenerating nodules in hereditary tyrosinemia. *AJR* 149:391, 1987.

153. LABERGE C, GRENIER A, VALET JP, LESCAULT A: AFP in new born screening for tyrosinemias: The Quebec experience 1983. in Mizejewski GJ, Porter IH (eds): *Alpha-Fetoprotein and Congenital Disorders.* Orlando, Fl, Academic Press, 1985, p 123.

154. HOSTETTER MK, LEVY HL, WINTER HS, KNIGHT GJ, HADDOW JE: Evidence for liver disease preceding amino acid abnormalities in hereditary tyrosinemia. *N Engl J Med* 308:1265, 1983.

155. TOMER KB, ROTHMAN R, YUDKOFF M, SEGAL S: Unusual pattern of metabolites in the urine of a child with tyrosinemia: Glyceraldehyde. *Clin Chim Acta* 81:109, 1977.

156. LINDBLAD B, LINDSTEDT S, STEEN G: On the enzymic defects in hereditary tyrosinemia. *Proc Natl Acad Sci USA* 74:4641, 1977.

157. STONER E, STARKMAN H, WELLNER D, WELLNER VP, SASSA S, RIFKIND AB, GRENIER A, STEINHERZ PG, MEISTER A, NEW MI, LEVINE LS: Biochemical studies of a patient with hereditary hepatorenal tyrosinemia: Evidence of glutathione deficiency. *Pediatr Res* 18:1332, 1984.

158. SOIRDAHL S, LIE SO, JELLUM E, STOKKE O: Increased need for L-cysteine in hereditary tyrosinemia. *Pediatr Res* 13:74, 1979.

159. CARSON NAJ, BIGGART JD, BITTLES AH, DONOVAN D: Hereditary tyrosinaemia. Clinical, enzymatic and pathological study of an infant with the acute form of the disease. *Arch Dis Child* 51:106, 1976.

160. MICHAELS K, MATALON R, WONG PWK: Importance of methionine restriction. Dietary treatment of tyrosinemia type I. *J Am Diet Assoc* 73:508, 1978.

161. AMEEN VZ, POWELL GK, RASSIN DK: Cholestasis and hypermethioninemia during dietary management of hereditary tyrosinemia type I. *J Pediatr* 108:949, 1986.

162. COHN RM, YUDKOFF M, YOST B, SEGAL S: Phenylalanine-tyrosine deficiency syndrome as a complication of the management of hereditary tyrosinemia. *Am J Clin Nutr* 30:209, 1977.

163. FISCH RO, MCCABE ERB, DOEDEN D, KOEP LJ, KOHLHOFF JG, SIVERMAN A, STARZL TE: Homotransplantation of the liver in a patient with hepatoma and hereditary tyrosinemia. *J Pediatr* 93:592, 1978.

164. KIVITTINGEN EA, JELLUM E, STOKKE O, FLATMARK A, BEGAN A, SODAL G, HALVORSEN S, SCHRUMPF E, GJONE E: Liver transplantation in a 23-year-old tyrosinaemia patient: Effects on the renal tubular dysfunction. *J Inherited Metab Dis* 9:216, 1986.

165. TUCHMAN M, FREESE DK, SHARP HL, WHITLEY CB, RAMNARAINE ML, ULSTRON RA, NAJARIAN JS, ASCHER N: Persistent succinylacetone excretion after liver transplantation in a patient with hereditary tyrosinaemia type I. *J Inherited Metab Dis* 8:21, 1985.

166. TUCHMAN M, FREES DK, SHARP HL, RAMNARAINE MLR, ASCHER N, BLOOMER JR: Contribution of extraheptatic tissues to biochemical abnormalities in hereditary tyrosinemia type I: Study of three patients after liver transplantation. *J Pediatr* 110:399, 1987.

167. LINDBLAD B, FRIDEN J, GRETER J, HOLME E, LINDSTEDT S, SIOSTEEN C: Treatment of hereditary tyrosinaemia (fumarylacetoacetase deficiency) by enzyme substitution. *J Inherited Metab Dis* 9:257, 1986.

168. FALLSTROM SP, LINDBLAD B, LINDSTEDT S, STEEN G: Hereditary tyrosinemia-fumarylacetoacetase deficiency. *Pediatr Res* 13:78a, 1979.

169. MELANCON SB, GAGNE R, GRENIER A, LESCAULT A, DALLAIRE L, LABERGE C, POTIER M: Deficiency of fumarylacetoacetase in the acute form of hereditary tyrosinemia with reference to prenatal diagnosis, in Fisher MM, Roy CC (eds): *Pediatric Liver Disease*. New York, Plenum, 1983, p 223.

170. BERGER R, van FAASEN H, TAANMAN JW, DEVRIES H, AGSTERIBBE E: Type I tyrosinemia: Lack of immunogically detectable fumarylacetoacetase enzyme protein in tissues and cell extracts. *Pediatr Res* 22:394, 1987.

171. TANGUAY RT, LABERGE C, LESCAULT A, VALET JP, DUBAND JL, QUENNEVILLE Y: Molecular basis of hereditary tyrosinemias: Proof of the primary defect by Western blot, in Amhad F et al (eds): *Advances in Gene Technology: Human Genetic Disorders*. ICSU Short Reports 1984, vol 1, p 256.

172. NICOLE LM, VALET JP, LABERGE C, TANGUAY RM: Purification of mRNA coding for the enzyme deficient in hereditary tyrosinemia, fumarylacetoacetate hydrolase. *Biochem Cell Biol* 64:489, 1986.

173. KVITTINGEN EA, HALVORSEN S, JELLUM E: Deficient fumarylacetoacetate fumarylhydrolase activity in lymphocytes and fibroblasts from patients with hereditary tyrosinemia. *Pediatr Res* 14:541, 1983.

174. KVITTINGEN EA, STEINMANN B, GITZELMANN R, LEONARD JV, ANDRIA G, BORRESEN AL, MOSSMAN J, MICARA G, LINDBLAD B: Prenatal diagnosis of hereditary tyrosinemia by determination of fumarylacetoacetase in cultured amniotic fluid cells. *Pediatr Res* 19:334, 1985.

175. KVITTINGEN EA, BRODTKORB E: The pre- and post-natal diagnosis of tyrosinemia type I and the detection of the carrier state by assay of fumarylacetoacetase. *Scand J Clin Lab Invest* 46:35, 1986.

176. HOLME E, LINDBLAD B, LINDSTEDT S: Possibilities for treatment for early prenatal diagnosis of hereditary tyrosinaemia. *Lancet* i:527, 1985.

177. LABERGE C, LESCAULT A, TANGUAY RM: Hereditary tyrosinemias (type I): A new vista on tyrosine toxicity and cancer, in Poirier LA, Newbarne PM, Pariza MW (eds): *Essential Nutrients in Carcinogenesis*. New York, Plenum, 1986, p 209.

178. WADMAN SK, DURAN M, KETTING D, BRUINVIS L, van SPRANG FJ, BERGER R, SMIT GPA, STEINMANN B, LEONARD JV, DIVRY P, FARRIAUX JP, CARTIGNY B: Urinary excretion of deuterated metabolites in patients with tyrosinemia type I after oral loading with deuterated L-tyrosine. *Clin Chim Acta* 130:231, 1983.

179. BERGER R, van FAASSEN H, SMITH GPA: Biochemical studies on the enzymatic deficiencies in hereditary tyrosinemia. *Clin Chim Acta* 134:129, 1983.

180. FURUKAWA N, HAYANO T, SATO N, INOUE F, MACHIDA Y, KINUGASA A, IMASHUKU S, KUSUNOKI T, TAKAMATISU. The enzyme defects in hereditary tyrosinaemia type I. *J Inherited Metab Dis* 7:137, 1984.

181. EBERT PS, HESS RA, FRYKHOLM BC, TSCHUDY DP: Succinylacetone, a potent inhibitor of heme biosynthesis: Effect of cell growth, heme content and δ-aminolevulinic acid dehydratase activity of malignant murine erythroleukemia cells. *Biochem Biophys Res Commun* 88:1382, 1979.

182. SASSA S, KAPPAS A: Hereditary tyrosinemia and the heme biosynthetic pathway. Profound inhibition of δ-aminolevulinic acid dehydratase activity by succinylacetone. *J Clin Invest* 71:625, 1983.

183. ROTH KS, SPENCER PD, HIGGINS ES, SPENCER RF: Effects of succinylacetone on methyl α-D-glucoside uptake by the rat renal tubule. *Biochim Biophys Acta* 820:140, 1985.

184. MANABE S, SASSA S, KAPPAS A: Hereditary tyrosinemia. Formation of succinylacetone-amino acid adducts. *J Exp Med* 162:1060, 1985.

185. GIGER U, MEYER UA: Effect of succinylacetone on heme and cytochrome P450 synthesis in hepatocyte culture. *FEBS Lett* 153:335, 1983.

186. BERGERON P, LABERGE C, GRENIER A: Hereditary tyrosinemia in the province of Quebec: Prevalence at birth and geographic distribution. *Clin Genet* 5:157, 1974.

187. KVITTINGEN EA, BORRESEN AL, STOKKE O, van der HAGEN CB, LIE SO: Deficiency of fumarylacetoacetase without hereditary tyrosinemia. *Clin Genet* 27:550, 1985.

187a. LABERGE C: Hereditary tyrosinemia in a French Canadian isolate. *Am J Hum Genet* 21:31, 1969.

188. KVITTINGEN EA, LEONARD JV, PETTIT BR, KING GS: Concentrations of succinylacetone after homogentisate and tyrosine loading in healthy individuals with low fumarylacetoacetase activity. *Clin Chim Acta* 152:271, 1985.

189. GRENIER A, LESCAULT A, LABERGE C, GAGNE R, MAMER O: Detection of succinylacetone and the use of its measurement in mass screening for hereditary tyrosinemia. *Clin Chim Acta* 123:93, 1982.

190. GAGNE R: Liver disease in hereditary tyrosinemia. *N Engl J Med* 309:1063, 1983.

191. PETTIT BR, MacKENZIE F, KING GS: The antenatal diagnosis and aid to the management of hereditary tyrosinaemia by use of a specific and sensitive GC-MS assay for succinylacetone. *J Inherited Metab Dis* 7:135, 1984.

192. GRENIER A, LESCAULT A: Succinylacetone, in Bergmeyer J, Grabi M (eds): *Methods of Enzymatic Analysis*. Weinheim, Verlagsgesellschaft, 1985, p 73.

193. BERGER R, MICHALS K, GALBRAETH J, MATALON R: Tyrosinemia type 1b caused by maleylacetoacetate isomerase deficiency: A new enzyme defect. *Pediatr Res* 23:328A, 1988.

CHAPTER 17

DISORDERS OF HISTIDINE METABOLISM

HARVEY L. LEVY

1. *Histidinemia is an autosomal recessive disorder that is benign in most affected individuals. It seems possible that the imposition of unusual circumstances, such as perinatal hypoxia, may allow histidinemia to impact unfavorably and produce the central nervous system disease noted in a few histidinemic patients. The enzyme defect is in histidase, an enzyme normally expressed only in skin and liver. The defect is determined by demonstrating reduced histidase activity in skin, or more simply, little or no urocanic acid in skin. The biochemical consequences of the metabolic block include increased concentrations of histidine in blood and urine and metabolites of histidine transamination in urine. Treatment with a histidine-restricted diet will normalize the biochemical phenotype but is not indicated for this probably harmless disorder. The incidence from newborn screening is 1:10,000, making histidinemia one of the most frequent of the inborn errors.*
2. *Atypical histidinemia is a biochemically milder form of the disorder and may account for a substantial minority of those with histidinemia. The reported individuals have been clinically normal. They have higher residual skin histidase activities and lower elevations of histidine and histidine metabolites than those with the classic disorder. Histidinemia may be a biochemically heterogeneous disorder, perhaps due to several allelic mutations.*
3. *Maternal histidinemia is probably benign to the fetus. At least 53 offspring from 21 histidinemic mothers have been reported. The offspring generally have been normal.*
4. *Histidinuria without histidinemia has been described in four children. Three were mentally retarded and two had myoclonic seizures, but an association between the histidinuria and central nervous system manifestations has not been established. All had substantially reduced renal tubular reabsorption for histidine with normal reabsorption of other amino acids, indicating that there is an histidine-specific transport system that is defective in this disorder. Two sibs also had evidence of an intestinal defect in histidine transport. The disorder seems to be transmitted as an autosomal recessive trait.*
5. *Urocanic aciduria has been found in at least six children. The four discovered by specific testing have been mentally retarded, but two identified by newborn urine screening have been mentally normal, suggesting that the mental retardation may not be related to the metabolic disorder. Four of the six children have had growth retardation. The enzyme defect is in urocanase, proven by liver biopsy in three patients. Urocanic acid is greatly increased in urine, while histidine and histidine metabolites have been normal or only mildly increased. Autosomal recessive inheritance seems to be the most likely pattern of transmission.*

Interest in histidine metabolism and its disorders was sparked by the discovery of histidinemia in 1961. Ghadimi and his coworkers[1] found increased concentrations of histidine in blood and urine from two sisters and concluded that this represented an inborn error of histidine metabolism. One of these sisters had a speech defect, which led to the suspicion that histidinemia could cause clinical abnormalities. Subsequently, other investigators encountered children with histidinemia by testing patients who had learning disabilities or other medical problems. The study of histidine metabolism in these children and in normal individuals who served as controls has elucidated the biochemical derangements in this metabolic disorder and clearly defined the normal pathways of histidine degradation in the human. La Du[2] reviewed this information in the early editions of this text.

In the decade since the chapter on histidinemia was last included in this text, new information about this disorder and about mammalian histidine metabolism has emerged. In addition, at least one other disorder of histidine metabolism, urocanic aciduria, has been discovered; and what may be a defect in histidine transport has been reported. This information has substantially enlarged our view of the role that derangements of histidine metabolism and transport play in human adaptation.[3]

METABOLISM OF HISTIDINE

Requirement for Histidine

Histidine is required for growth in salmon,[4] chick,[5] pig,[6] mouse,[7] and rat.[8–10] Its essentiality for humans is less clear. Early studies indicated that adult humans maintain positive nitrogen balance on histidine-free diets.[11] More recent studies, however, show that when the histidine restricted diet contains a lower total nitrogen content, adults develop negative nitrogen balance, lower histidine levels in plasma, urine, and muscle, and decreased serum albumin.[12–14] It is possible that under certain conditions and for a limited time, the histidine requirement for humans can be met by endogenous histidine released from hemoglobin, which is rich in histidine,[15] or from histidine-rich glycoprotein.[16] In support of this possibility is the observation that when dietary histidine is restricted, the hemoglobin level decreases while nitrogen balance is maintained.[12–14,17] Another possible endogenous source of histidine is the peptide carnosine (β-alanyl-L-histidine) (see Chap. 26). Muscle carnosine decreases markedly, although body weight is maintained for the short term, in chicks[18] and rats[19] receiving a histidine-free diet; the mouse lacking muscle carnosine rapidly loses weight when administered a diet devoid of histidine.[7] Furthermore, carnosine can replace histidine on an equimolar basis in the diet of the rat.[20] The adult human may also synthesize histidine at a low rate.[21,22]

Histidine is almost certainly an essential amino acid for the

Nonstandard abbreviation used in this chapter is: FIGLU = formimino glutaric acid.

human infant. Snyderman et al.[23] found that withdrawal of histidine from the diet of young infants resulted in a lower rate of weight gain and a fall in nitrogen retention. In addition, a rash resembling early infantile eczema developed when dietary histidine was omitted.[23-25] They estimated the dietary requirement of histidine for the young infant to be somewhat less than 35 mg/kg per day. Perhaps the most convincing evidence that histidine is essential for not only the infant but also the young child comes from the dietary treatment of histidinemia. The general experience in these patients is that the blood histidine level is lowered in direct response to restriction of dietary histidine.[26-29]

The effect of low dietary histidine on older children and adults over long periods remains uncertain. It is clear that if histidine biosynthesis occurs, it is sufficient only for basic physiological needs and is insufficient to support growth or to meet the requirements produced by physiological stress.[30,31] Thus irrespective of biosynthesis, histidine would be an essential amino acid for the growing child and, over a period of time, for the adult as well.

Histidine Degradation

In contrast to the uncertainty about histidine synthesis, the pathways of histidine utilization in mammalian tissue are quite well understood. They are summarized in Fig. 17-1. The major pathway is through urocanic acid to glutamic acid; four enzymes catalyze this sequence of reactions.

Histidase. The first reaction in this pathway is nonoxidative deamination of histidine to urocanic acid catalyzed by histidine ammonia-lyase (EC 4.3.1.3), more commonly referred to as histidase. Histidase has attracted attention because it is the enzyme defect in histidinemia. The reaction seems to involve the formation of an aminoenzyme and subsequent release of the amino group as ammonia.[32] Histidase is a cytoplasmic enzyme with an unusual tissue distribution; it is expressed with high activity in the liver of all animal species and in the skin of most mammals,[33] but not in other tissues.[34] Studies of the purified rat liver enzyme indicate that it is probably a trimer with a M_r of 220,000 and identical subunits each weighing 70,000 to 75,000.[35-39] The K_m for L-histidine is between 0.45 and 2.0 mM at pH 8.8 to 9.2, the optimal pH for the reaction[35-37]; but at physiologic pH (7.2), the K_m for L-histidine is greater than 2.0 mM.[37] It is activated by thiols such as glutathione and mercaptoethanol, which by reduction convert the inactive polymer to the active monomeric form,[36] suggesting that mammalian histidase, like the bacterial enzyme,[40-42] may contain a cysteine residue at the active site. It is inhibited by compounds such as sodium borohydride and nitromethane, indicating that there is an electrophilic center at the active site, perhaps a derivative of dehydroalanine.[43] A divalent ion such as zinc, manganese, magnesium, or cadmium is essential for catalytic activity[35,36]; it has been suggested that the divalent ion binds to the activating thiol and that the two, along with the substrate, form a complex at the active site.[44] The purified enzyme from monkey liver is very similar to the rat liver enzyme.[45]

Epidermal histidase has been of particular interest, since skin is a readily accessible tissue with which to study the enzyme defect in histidinemia. While skin histidase activity is present in most mammals, it is absent in amphibian, avian, and reptilian species, suggesting significance as an evolution-

Fig. 17-1 Pathways of histidine catabolism. The major pathway is through urocanic acid, yielding glutamic acid and a formimino group that is transferred to tetrahydrofolic acid. The enzymes that mediate the steps in this pathway include (A) histidase, the defective enzyme in histidinemia; (B) urocanase, which is deficient in urocanic aciduria; imidazolonepropionate amidohydrolase; and formiminotransferase, the enzyme defective in glutamate formiminotransferase deficiency. The most prominent of the minor pathways is the transamination of histidine to imidazolepyruvic acid, catalyzed by histidine-pyruvate transaminase. In histidinemia this serves as a significant means for the degradation of histidine and results in the formation of imidazolepyruvic acid, imidazolelactic acid, imidazoleacetic acid and other related metabolites.

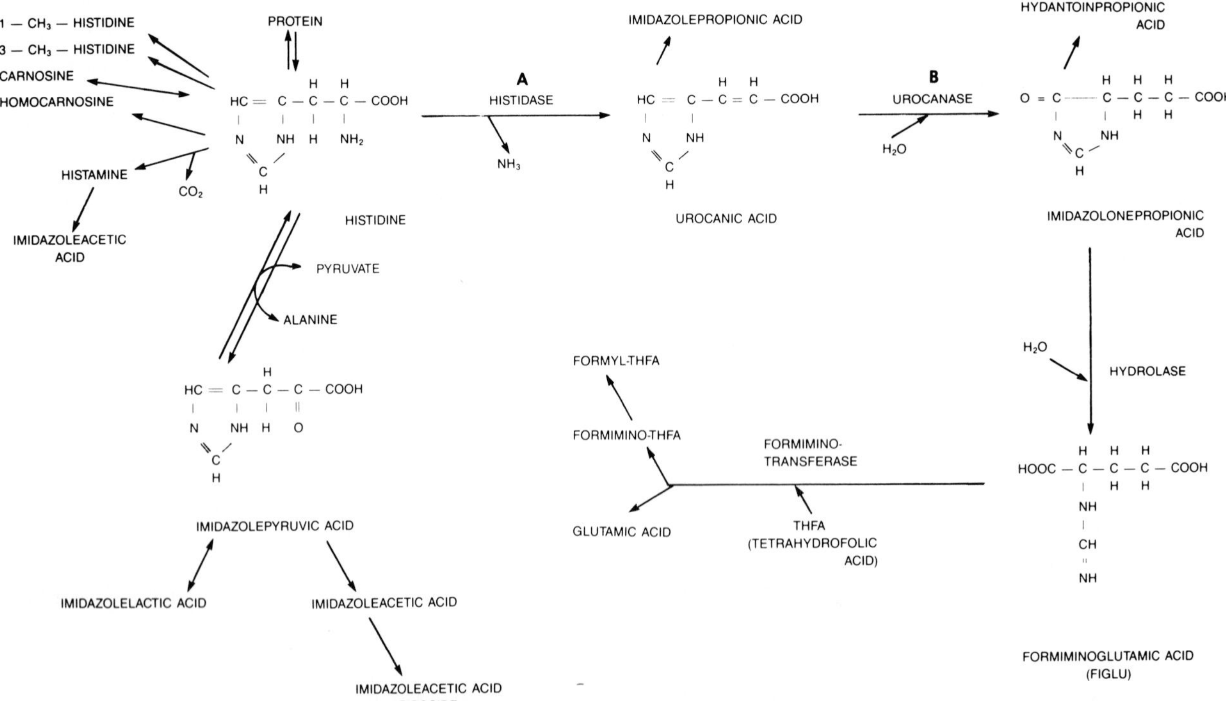

ary change.[46] The activity is found almost exclusively in cells of the stratum corneum, and the enzyme is probably active in vivo only in this layer.[47] Histidase activity is also detectable in epithelial cells grown in human skin culture, not not in fibroblastlike cells from these cultures.[48] The epidermal enzyme is very similar to the hepatic enzyme. In the guinea pig, both have a M_r of 220,000 and are composed of identical subunits each of 70,000.[39] Whether the enzyme is identical in the two tissues, however, is unclear. Bhargava and Feigelson[34] found kinetic and immunologic identity between epithelial and hepatic histidase in the rat. In the studies of Baden and Gavioli,[49] however, rat liver and skin histidase differed in their K_m's for histidine, electrophoretic migration, and thermal stability; and in the guinea pig there are subtle kinetic and immunologic differences between the two tissue forms.[39] In histidinemia the histidase defect is expressed in both skin and liver in the human[50] and the mutant mouse.[51] Thus it is likely that epithelial and hepatic histidase are encoded from a single locus and that any differences in histidase between the two tissues are due to posttranslational modification.

Histidase in the rat has a very interesting polyphasic developmental pattern. Liver activity is absent until after birth, then rises progressively with accelerated increases at weaning and puberty.[34] On the other hand, skin histidase activity is detectable in the near-term fetus and rises to maximum activity during the first postnatal week, thereafter declining.[34] These developmental changes in catalytic activity seem to result from altered amounts of enzyme protein.[38,52] Likewise, the absence of histidase activity in other tissues is apparently due to lack of enzyme protein, not to inhibition of activity.[38] Histidase development in the human follows a different developmental pattern; it is present in fetal liver and skin as early as 15 weeks gestation.[53] The differences in ontogeny of human and rat liver histidase are similar to the differences between human and murine liver phenylalanine hydroxylase.[53a]

Multihormonal regulation seems to account for the developmental changes in rat liver histidase. Most striking is the induction of histidase biosynthesis by estrogen, accounting for the steep rise in both catalytic activity and immunoreactive protein in the postpubertal female and the two- to threefold greater activity in the adult female than in the adult male.[54,55] Cortisol and glucagon also induce histidase in rat liver,[56] while thyroxine[57] and pituitary hormones such as growth hormone and ACTH[55] act as histidase suppressors. An intact pituitary gland is critical for normal hormonal regulation; hypophysectomy increases histidase synthesis in the male, but not in the female,[58,59] and paradoxically prevents the estrogen response in the female.[58] The factor(s) responsible for regulation by the pituitary has not been identified.

Histidase is also influenced by the level of dietary protein, with rat liver activity rising in proportion to dietary protein[60–63] but epidermal histidase activity decreasing with increasing protein intake.[60] The increase in liver histidase activity is functionally significant as evidenced by increased histidine catabolism in vivo.[62–64] Interestingly, dietary histidine, in contrast to dietary protein, has no effect on histidase activity.[63–65]

Regulation of histidase has not been studied in skin or in the human. Thus whether the regulatory features of hepatic histidase apply to the skin enzyme in the rat or to the human enzyme in either tissue is unknown. Indirect information from histidine loading studies, however, indicates that regulation of the human enzyme might be different from that in the rat. For instance, clearance of histidine from the blood is faster in infants than in older children and slowest in the adult,[66] quite different from what would be expected if liver histidase activity in the human increases progressively after birth, as it does in the rat. Furthermore, mothers of histidinemic children consistently have slower clearance of histidine from blood after loading than do fathers.[67–71] Despite the presumed reduction in total liver histidase activity in these obligate carrier parents, the mothers should have no less, and perhaps more, residual activity than the fathers, if adult humans have a sex specific difference in liver histidase similar to the rat. Instead, the slower clearance of histidine by the mothers suggests that in the human liver histidase activity might even be lower in the adult female than in the male.

The human gene that encodes histidase has not yet been cloned, but a partial cDNA of the rat liver gene was recently isolated.[71a] The human gene has not been mapped. In the mouse a locus assigned to chromosome 10 seems to determine the amount of liver histidase protein synthesized in different inbred strains.[72,73] Whether this is a structural locus for histidase or a regulatory locus is not known.

Urocanase. This enzyme (EC 4.2.1.49) catalyzes the nonoxidative conversion of urocanic acid to imidazolonepropionic acid by the addition of water across the conjugated double bond system of urocanic acid. Urocanase is deficient in the liver of patients with urocanic aciduria.[74,75] The bacterial enzyme requires NAD,[76,77] but this is not a requirement for the mammalian reaction.[78] The mammalian enzyme has been partially purified from beef liver[78] and purified from cat liver.[79] The latter enzyme has an estimated M_r of 127,000. The pH optimum for activity is 6.8 to 7.6, considerably lower than that for histidase. The K_m for urocanic acid is 1.5 μM in beef liver [78] and 7.1 μM in cat liver,[79] indicating that urocanase has a much stronger affinity for urocanic acid that does histidase for histidine. The apparent K_m's of mouse and human liver urocanase for urocanic acid are 3.2 and 2.2 μM, respectively.[80] The cat liver enzyme is competitively inhibited by imidazolepropionic acid,[79] as is the bacterial enzyme.[81]

Urocanase activity seems to be limited to liver. Unlike with histidase, there is no detectable activity in epithelium, which accounts for the large amount of urocanic acid normally present in skin.[82] The regulation of liver urocanase in the rat has features in common with that of histidase. Urocanase activity increases with dietary protein, although not as dramatically as does histidase.[60] Thyroxine suppresses urocanase activity as it does histidase, but again not to the same extent.[57] On the other hand, urocanase activity is lowered by folate deficiency in the rat, while histidase activity is unchanged.[83] The developmental pattern of urocanase and the effect of hormones other than thyroxine on its activity have not been studied. Urocanase activity does not vary as markedly as does histidase in different strains of inbred mice.[84]

At the time of this writing, the gene for urocanase has not been cloned, and its chromosome locus is unknown.

Imidazolonepropionic Acid Hydrolase. Imidazolonepropionic acid is converted to formiminoglutamic acid (FIGLU), an important intermediate which links histidine catabolism to folate metabolism. FIGLU is a donor of formyl groups to tetrahydrofolic acid and is a marker for folic acid deficiency (see Chap. 81). The reaction involves cleavage of the imidazolone ring of imidazolonepropionate with the addition of water; it is catalyzed by imidazolonepropionate amidohydrolase (EC 3.5.2.7), an enzyme which has been identified in bacteria and mammalian liver.[85] The purified rat liver enzyme has a pH optimum 7.4 to 7.8 and a K_m of 7.0 μ*M* for imidazolonepropionic acid.[86] The gene encoding this enzyme had not been cloned or mapped at the time of this writing. The enzyme has not been studied in humans.

Formiminotransferase. This enzyme [*N*-formimino-L-glutamate: THF 5-formiminotransferase (EC 2.1.2.5)] catalyzes the formation of formiminotetrahydrofolic acid from FIGLU and tetrahydrofolic acid. Glutamic acid is liberated. Folic acid deficiency results in a strikingly increased excretion of FIGLU in response to loading with L-histidine, presumably due to the reduction in available tetrahydrofolic acid.[87] Formiminotransferase deficiency has been identified in several patients.[88] These patients and the enzyme defect are described in Chap. 81.

HISTIDINEMIA

The primary disorder of histidine metabolism is histidinemia, characterized by markedly reduced histidase activity. The block in conversion of histidine to urocanic acid (Fig. 17-1) results in an increased concentration of histidine in blood and urine and the abnormal presence of histidine metabolites in the urine.

Clinical Phenotype

Information about the 60 cases of histidinemia reported through 1970 was in a previous edition of this text.[2] About one-third were mentally retarded, and about one-half had speech difficulties. Most of those with speech impairment were retarded or had low normal intelligence,[89,90] suggesting that histidinemia might not cause a specific disorder of speech as had earlier been proposed on the basis of studying histidinemic children who had speech defects without mental retardation.[91,92] Other clinical findings in one or more of these reported cases included cerebellar ataxia, hydrocephalus, emotional disturbances, short stature, delayed bone age, seizure disorder, recurrent infections, precocious puberty, congenital hypoplastic anemia, idiopathic thrombocytopenia purpura, and multiple congenital anomalies.[2] La Du concluded that "the wide variation in the clinical features in patients with histidinemia makes any claim about the consequences of the metabolic disease open to question. . . ."[2]

Until 1970 most of the cases of histidinemia were identified among children and adults who were studied because of a clinical abnormality. Thus a high frequency of clinical features would be expected. The occasional case that came to light by other means, such as urine screening after renal transplantation,[68] tended to reveal no abnormal features that could be related to histidinemia. In 1974 the published results of histidinemia identification by routine neonatal urine screening in Massachusetts provided data supporting the view that histidinemia might not cause disease.[93] The 20 prospectively studied children who had been identified in this manner and their six histidinemic sibs, all untreated, were clinically normal. In particular, their speech was normal, and their mean IQ (±SD) was 107 ± 12, as compared with 108 ± 11 for their nonhistidinemic sibs. From this experience we concluded that most likely histidinemia is a benign disorder. A similar conclusion was reached by the groups in Los Angeles[94] and Japan,[95] also

Table 17-1 Correlation between Histidinemia and Central Nervous System Phenotype in Sibs of Probands

	CNS phenotype			
	Sibs with histidinemia		*Sibs without histidinemia*	
Proband phenotype	*With*	*Without*	*With*	*Without*
With CNS phenotype	11	8	5	21
Without CNS phenotype	2	5	0	11
Totals	13	13	5	32

SOURCE: Rosenmann, Scriver, Clow, and Levy.[97]

from studying histidinemic children identified by newborn screening.

These studies have not settled the question of whether histidinemia is benign. The Montreal group surveyed the published experience in histidinemic sibs identified by family screening and found, as shown in Table 17-1, that 50 percent had abnormal or impaired central nervous system development, as compared to a 13.5 percent frequency of similar impairment among the nonhistidinemic sibs[96,97] On the other hand, an update of the prospective experience in Massachusetts again indicated a normal clinical course among the histidinemic children identified by newborn screening; there were no differences from their nonhistidinemic sibs in growth and development, speech acquisition, and IQ scores (Table 17-2).[98] There were no biochemical differences between the histidinemic sibs surveyed by the Montreal group and the cases in the Massachusetts study.[97] Hence the clinical differences could not be explained on the basis of metabolic variance.

In reconciling these seemingly discrepant findings, we postulated that histidinemia is not a "disease" in humans but that it may have a disadaptive impact on the central nervous system under certain unusual circumstances, such as perinatal hypoxia.[3] It also is possible that histidinemia, despite a consistent biochemical phenotype, may include more than one disorder, including a more frequent typical form that is benign and a less frequent disadaptive form.[3]

Table 17-2 Psychological Assessment Scores (Mean ± SD) of Histidinemic Children and Their Age-Matched Sibling Controls

WISC-R	*Histidinemia* (*n* = 10)	*Sib controls* (*n* = 10)
Age (years)	11.2 ± 3.3	11.8 ± 3.5
Full scale IQ	102.8 ± 16.7	102.2 ± 13.4
Verbal IQ	98.9 ± 18.2	96.8 ± 13.4
Information	8.6 ± 2.5	8.6 ± 2.2
Vocabulary	9.7 ± 3.9	9.2 ± 3.0
Digit span	11.5 ± 3.3	9.8 ± 3.2
Arithmetic	9.7 ± 2.2	8.4 ± 1.7
Comprehension	11.7 ± 4.2	11.9 ± 3.1
Similarities	9.6 ± 4.7	9.6 ± 3.3
Performance IQ	106.2 ± 14.8	107.6 ± 12.5
Picture completion	10.2 ± 3.1	11.1 ± 1.9
Picture arrangment	10.8 ± 2.4	10.5 ± 2.9
Block design	10.7 ± 3.2	11.7 ± 3.1
Object assembly	11.1 ± 4.6	12.8 ± 3.8
Coding	10.9 ± 3.3	9.5 ± 2.6
Mazes	10.8 ± 2.4	12.6 ± 2.5

SOURCE: Coulombe, Kammerer, Levy, Hirsch, and Scriver.[98]

Biochemical Features

The biochemical abnormalities are a consequence of a defect in histidase producing an inability to metabolize histidine to urocanic acid (Fig. 17-1). Histidine accumulates as do the products of histidine transamination, such as imidazolepyruvic acid, imidazolelactic acid, imidazoleacetic acid, and imidazoleacetic acid riboside. The products of histidine degradation beyond the histidase reaction, including intermediates such as urocanic acid and FIGLU, are reduced.

Blood. The characteristic finding in histidinemia is a specifically increased concentration of blood histidine varying from 290 to 1420 μM (normal 70 to 120 μM).[2,93] These are equivalent to values of 4.5 to 22.0 mg/dl (normal 1.1 to 1.9 mg/dl). The level tends to be highest at age 1 year and slightly lower in older children and adults.[93,98] Nevertheless, the variation in the observed blood histidine concentrations among patients reflects dietary protein (histidine) intake and the degree of metabolic block much more than age. Kuroda and coworkers[99] have shown that in histidinemic infants and children, the serum histidine concentration rises with increasing dietary histidine (Fig. 17-2) but that, at either a high level of intake or in the fasting state, the serum concentration is greater in those with less residual skin histidase activity (Figs. 17-2 and 17-3).

Oral loading with L-histidine, usually 100 mg/kg, produces a marked accentuation of the blood histidine level at 1 h with much less clearing than in normal individuals even at 4 h after the load (Fig. 17-4).

Blood amino acid concentrations other than that of histidine have been normal. The single exception is alanine, which has been elevated in several affected individuals.[50,68,71,100] We found hyperalaninemia in only 1 of 26 histidinemic children.[93] The origin of the hyperalaninemia, if it is related to histidinemia in an occasional case, has not been explained. Intravenous loading of normal individuals with L-histidine raises the

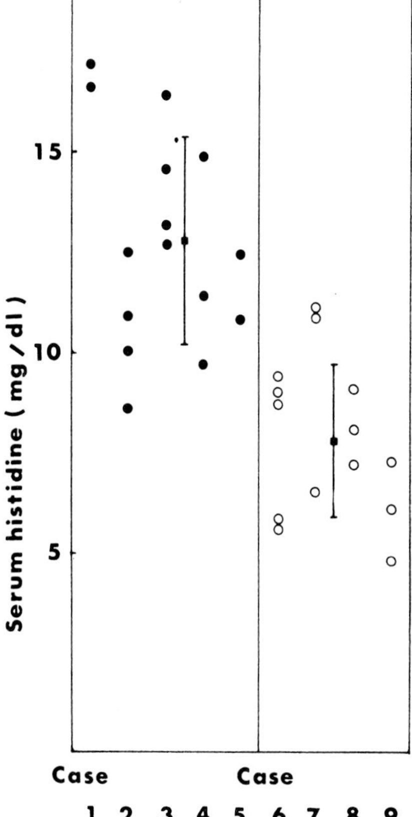

Fig. 17-3 The relationship between residual skin histidase activity and the fasting serum histidine concentration in histidinemia. Closed and open circles show values for patients in groups 1 and 2, respectively (see legend for Fig. 17-2). Closed squares with extensions indicate mean ± SD of the serum histidine level for each group. *(From Kuroda, Ogawa, Ito, Watanabe, Takeda, Toshima, and Miyao.[99] Used by permission of the Journal of Pediatrics.)*

Fig. 17-2 The effect of histidine intake and the amount of residual histidase activity on the serum histidine level in histidinemia. Closed circles indicate patients with less than 10 percent (group 1) and open circles patients with about 20 percent (group 2) of normal skin histidase activity. Closed and open squares with extensions indicate mean ±SD values for serum histidine for groups 1 and 2, respectively, at comparable levels of dietary histidine. *(From Kuroda, Ogawa, Ito, Watanabe, Takeda, Toshima, and Miyao.[99] Used by permission of the Journal of Pediatrics.)*

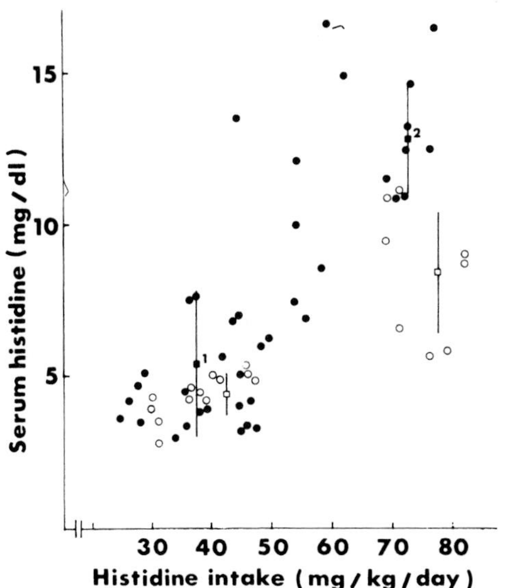

Fig. 17-4 The plasma histidine response to an L-histidine load in normal adults (black area of graph), a patient (proband) with histidinemia (open circles), her mother (open triangles), and her father (open squares). The plasma histidine level in the patient rises much higher and remains higher up to 4 h after the load than the controls of either parent. The parents are intermediate between the patient and the control adults. Note that the mother as a decidedly slower clearance of histidine than the father. *(From Rosenblatt, Mohyuddin, and Scriver.[68] Used by permission of Pediatrics.)*

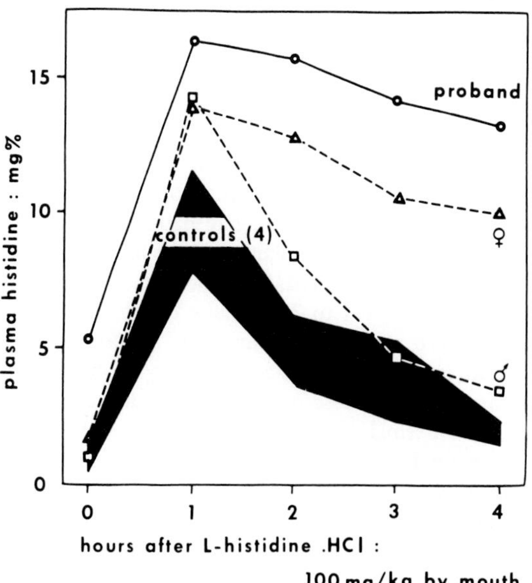

blood alanine concentration,[101] suggesting that histidine may lead to the synthesis of alanine, perhaps via transamination with pyruvate (Fig. 17-1). In histidinemic individuals with hyperalaninemia, however, the blood alanine level is not further accentuated by histidine loading,[102] although it may be normalized along with the blood histidine level when dietary histidine is restricted.[50]

Urocanic acid, the product of the histidase reaction, is not detectable in blood from histidinemic patients, whereas it is normally present in blood.[103,104] Other metabolites of histidine that appear in large quantities in histidinemic urine have not been detected in blood,[105] presumably because there is little or no capacity for their renal reabsorption.

Serum zinc levels are normal in histidinemic children,[106] in contrast to the reductions induced by loading nonhistidinemic adults with histidine.[107] This was unexpected in histidinemia, since histidine releases albumin-bound zinc by forming a histidine-zinc ligand[108] and since urinary zinc is increased in histidinemia.[106] Serotonin in platelets or platelet-rich plasma has been normal in most patients,[102,109] although reduced in the patients of Auerbach et al.[110] and Corner et al.[27]

Urine. Among the most striking biochemical findings in histidinemia are the marked excretion of histidine and the products of histidine transamination (Fig. 17-1). Indeed, it is the presence of imidazolepyruvic acid in the urine that led to the discovery of histidinemia. Ghadimi and his colleagues,[1] investigating the cause of speech retardation in a 3-year-old girl, found that her urine had a positive green reaction to the addition of ferric chloride reagent, much like that in phenylketonuria. They thought she had phenylketonuria, but further study disclosed that her urine contained a large excess of histidine rather than phenylalanine. Auerbach et al.[110] later identified imidazolepyruvic acid, the immediate transamination product of histidine, as the substance that produces the positive ferric chloride reaction in histidinemia. They also identified the increased excretion of other imidazole metabolites related to histidine transamination, including imidazolelactic and imidazoleacetic acids, in their patient.

The amount of histidine and imidazole metabolies excreted is directly related to the protein intake and the blood histidine concentration. Histidine excretion has been about 2 to 6 mmol/day, representing a six- to tenfold increase over normal values.[2] In relation to urinary creatinine, histidine excretion has been 3 to 27 mmol/g creatinine, the normal value being <2 mmol/g creatinine.[93,105] Imidazolepyruvic acid is not normally detectable in urine; in histidinemia the excretion has varied from trace amounts to a maximum of about 2 mmol/g creatinine.[2,105] Imidazolepyruvic acid is a relatively unstable compound, however, and the actual values could be higher than those recorded.[111] The quantities of other imidazole metabolites in urine from histidinemic patients, as measured by Wadman et al.[105] using column chromatography, were as follows: imidazolelactic acid, 0.4 to 5.0 mmol/g creatinine; imidazoleacetic acid, 0.1 to 2.2 mmol/g creatinine; *N*-acetylhistidine, 0.1–0.6 mmol/g creatinine. The values for imidazolelactic and imidazoleacetic acids are five- to fiftyfold greater than normal, while those for *N*-acetylhistidine are two- to fivefold above normal.[105] Histamine and its metabolites, including N^{t}-methylhistamine and imidazoleacetic acid conjugates, also are increased in the histidinemic urine.[112]

Imamura et al.[113] recently identified N^{t}-ribosylhistidine in urine from normal and histidinemic children. The latter excreted sevenfold greater than normal amounts. Rats fed histidine supplements increased their excretion of N^{t}-ribosylhistidine thirtyfold. Additional studies indicated that the ribosylation of histidine is mediated by a system different from imidazoleacetic acid phosphoribosyltransferase, which catalyzes the formation of ribosylimidazolylacetic acid.[114]

Neonates with histidinemia often lack the large quantities of histidine transamination products observed in urine from older infants and children with histidinemia.[115] Even after histidine loading, histidinemic neonates excrete much smaller quantities of imidazolepyruvic, imidazolelactic, and imidazoleacetic acids than do older children, despite excreting a comparable percentage of ingested histidine. We have explained this on the basis of delayed postnatal maturation of histidine transaminase. In some histidinemic infants maturation of the histidine transamination system may not occur until several months of age.

Cerebrospinal Fluid. Histidine has been increased in the cerebrospinal fluid in histidinemia when quantitative analysis has been employed. Wadman et al.[111] found a tenfold increase in one patient, with values of 142 and 129 μM compared with the normal value of 13 μM. Shaw et al.[116] found a cerebrospinal fluid histidine level of 48 μM in their patient, approximately a threefold elevation.

Enzyme Defect

In their initial report of the first two histidinemic patients, Ghadimi et al.[1] suggested that the metabolic defect was probably in an early enzymatic step in histidine metabolism, either histidase or urocanase. Auerbach and his colleagues[110] could not detect in their patient intermediary metabolites such as urocanic acid and FIGLU, which are synthesized distal to the metabolic reaction catalyzed by histidase (Fig. 17-1), even after loading with histidine; but intravenous loading with urocanic acid produced large amounts of FIGLU. They concluded that the metabolic block is at the level of histidase.

La Du et al.[117] verified this conclusion by identifying a deficiency of histidase activity as the enzyme defect in histidinemia. They found that skin samples (stratum corneum) from two histidinemic sibs lacked histidase activity, while activity was readily demonstrable in similar tissue from normal children and adults. Subsequently, Auerbach et al.[50] demonstrated absence of histidase activity in liver from two other patients with histidinemia while urocanase activity was normal or even somewhat greater than normal. Accordingly, it is clear that in histidinemia histidase is specifically defective in the two tissues that normally express this enzyme.

Deficient activity of skin histidase has been demonstrated in many other cases of histidinemia.[2,66,68,99,109,118–120] With a sensitive radiochemical method,[121] Japanese investigators have been able to detect very low but measurable amounts of residual skin histidase activity in most of the affected infants identified by routine newborn screening in Japan. In these studies Matsuda et al.[119] found that skin histidase activity among 20 histidinemic children was 0.48 ± 0.54 μmol/h per gram tissue compared to the normal 8.6 ± 4.3 μmol/h per gram tissue, Kuroda et al.[99] found a range of 0.24 to 2.73 μmol/h per gram tissue among nine children with a normal range of 9.7 to 15.3 μmol/h per gram tissue, and Ito et al.[118] found <0.1 to 0.2 μmol/h per gram tissue among six of seven children compared with their relatively low control range of 1.4 to 1.5 μmol/h per gram tissue. Using an equally sensitive assay, Shin et al.[120]

obtained values of 1.46 ± 0.80 nmol/h per milligram protein (normal 52.3 ± 16.5 nmol/h per milligram protein) for skin histidase activity among 24 histidinemic children from Germany and Austria. Thus skin histidase activity is almost always less than 20 percent of normal in histidinemia and is usually less than 10 percent of normal. There does appear to be a negative correlation between the plasma histidine level and the skin histidase activity[99] (Fig. 17-3) and a positive correlation between skin histidase activity and FIGLU excretion,[119] indicating correspondence between residual histidase activity determined in vitro and histidase function in vivo.

The molecular characteristics and the precise impairment of histidase in histidinemia have not been determined. There are suggestions that at least in some patients the synthesized histidase is defective. Kuroda and coworkers[122] demonstrated an altered sensitivity of skin histidase to denaturation in two patients, and Shin et al.[120] found unspecified altered kinetic properties in skin histidase among the patients they studied.

The histidase defect can be indirectly determined by a simple chromatographic analysis of urocanic acid in skin.[68,123] Most histidinemic individuals will have no detectable urocanic acid by this method, whereas urocanic acid is prominent in normal skin. Very small amounts of urocanic acid, not visible by chromatography, can be measured in skin from histidinemic children.[66,118,124] The amount is far below that present in normal skin.[66,124] Determining the ratio of urocanic acid to histidine in skin also provides an unmistakable differentiation between histidinemic children and normal children.[118,125]

The absence of urocanic acid also can be determined by analyzing sweat from histidinemic patients.[2] This corresponds to the absence of urocanic acid in skin,[68] since urocanic acid in sweat is not a product of sweat glands but diffuses from epithelial skin cells.[123,126] Urocanic acid once was considered to protect the skin from ultraviolet irradiation, but patients with histidinemia do not have unusual sensitivity to sunlight, despite the absence of urocanic acid.[2] The function of urocanic acid in skin is not clear.

Four patients with persistently increased blood histidine levels and other biochemical features of histidinemia have had normal skin histidase activity and normal amounts of urocanic acid in sweat or skin.[118,127] None has had liver histidase measured, so whether they might have a defect in the liver enzyme, without a corresponding skin enzyme defect, is unknown. Three of these patients, all sibs, had unusually low elevations of histidine and a less pronounced response to histidine loading than usually observed in histidinemia.[127]

Measurement of both skin and liver histidase activity in the same histidinemic patient has not been reported. However, Schön[128] has measured or estimated skin histidase activity and estimated liver histidase activity in 14 infants with histidinemia. Six had no detectable activity in either tissue; one had trace activity in both tissues; one had trace activity in skin but no liver activity; and six had trace activity in liver and no activity in skin. These observations indicate that there is close correspondence between the skin and liver enzyme defects but that at least a slight difference may be present in a number of affected individuals.

Diagnosis

The diagnosis of histidinemia is based on finding an elevation of histidine in the blood and increased excretion of histidine in the urine. The urinary metabolite, imidazolepyruvic acid, can usually be detected by the ferric chloride test or by dipping the Phenistix reagent strip* into the urine; most of the earlier reported cases came to attention in this way.[2] The green color obtained is very similar to that observed with urine from a subject with phenylketonuria. In histidinemia the color usually develops more slowly and remains longer than in phenylketonuria, but this difference is not sufficiently specific to use as a differential diagnostic test. The ferric chloride reaction in histidinemia also may be dark gray or black, in contrast to the greener reaction of phenylketonuria. The histidinemic urine is sometimes only weakly positive or negative on ferric chloride testing, reflecting either the instability of imidazolepyruvic acid, the relation of its excretion to protein intake,[2] immaturity of histidine transaminase,[115] or a combination of these factors. Other metabolites, such as imidazolelactic and imidazoleacetic acid, are usually identified in urine from histidinemic children and adults but are often absent in neonates and young infants with histidinemia.[115] These metabolites can be identified by paper or thin-layer chromatography using diazotized sulfanilic acid (Pauly reagent) for location[115] or by automated column chromatography.[105]

Increased excretion of histidine and even imidazole metabolites occurs in conditions other than histidinemia, and a diagnosis cannot be made on these urinary findings alone. Pregnancy is well known to produce histidinuria and imidazoleuria.[2,129] Hyperthyroidism also may result in an increased excretion of imidazole metabolites following histidine loading.[130] Hyperhistidinuria without an increased level of blood histidine, presumably due to a defect in the renal transport of histidine, has been reported.[131–133]

Histidinemia is now most frequently identified by routine newborn screening. Urine screening by paper chromatography[134] or thin-layer chromatography[135] has detected many affected infants; blood screening also has been effective.[136–139]

The diagnosis is confirmed by demonstrating the absence or marked reduction of histidase activity in skin or the absence of urocanic acid in skin or sweat. A deficiency of liver histidase activity also will confirm the diagnosis but liver biopsy is an unnecessary risk for the diagnosis of this predominantly benign disorder.

Prenatal diagnosis of histidinemia has not been reported. Histidase activity is not detectable in normal uncultured amniotic cells obtained before 39 weeks gestation[53] and is present only in the relatively few epitheliallike cells that represent early growth in normal amniotic cell culture.[140] The irregular appearance of these latter cells in culture militates against using lack of histidase activity as a reliable indication of histidinemia in the fetus.

Treatment

Restricting dietary histidine will normalize the blood histidine level and eliminate the urinary imidazole metabolites in infants and children with histidinemia.[26–29] This has been accomplished with a dietary regimen consisting of a specific protein hydrolysate or amino acid mixture containing little or no histidine in combination with low protein foods. Three histidine-free amino acid formulas are currently available for this pur-

*Phenistix reagent strips, Ames Company, Elkhart, IN 46514.

pose.* This diet is analogous to the phenylalanine restricted diet for the treatment of phenylketonuria. The biochemical abnormalities are brought under control within 2 weeks of dietary initiation in histidinemia.[141] During the first year of life, biochemical control is achieved with a histidine intake of 20 to 30 mg/kg per day. Thereafter, dietary histidine must be restricted to 10 to 20 mg/kg per day for control.[26,28] Normal growth has been observed with these intakes.[28,29] A lower histidine intake, with reduction of the blood histidine level below the normal range, has produced an erythematous rash that has cleared with the provision of more dietary histidine.[29] The rash is similar to that which Snyderman et al.[23,24] encountered in normal infants receiving a histidine-free diet.

Treatment, accompanied by even excellent biochemical control, generally has not produced clinical improvement in the abnormalities noted in histidinemic children. Mental retardation and other severe neurologic signs have continued unabated.[26,141] Infantile spasms with hypsarhythmia did not change in one infant.[142] In an exceptional infant, however, myoclonic seizures eased 10 days after the diet began.[29] An older child also showed improvement in coordination, tremulousness, hyperactivity, and school performance.[28] Whether the usually negative results with diet indicate no relationship between the biochemical and clinical abnormalities or are due to already irreversible damage is unknown.

Most infants identified by routine newborn screening have not received treatment and have remained clinically normal.[98] The New York group has treated several; the children also have shown normal growth and development.[28] Current evidence indicates that about 99 percent of histidinemic patients do not require treatment and that only 1 percent might benefit.[3] In this circumstance, histidinemia would not meet the criteria for routine early dietary therapy, although treatment might be considered in any histidinemic infant who also has clinical abnormalities.

Genetics

Histidinemia is transmitted as an autosomal recessive trait. Males and females are equally affected[98]; sibs often have histidinemia, while parents rarely do,[2] and the frequency of occurrence among sibs in informative families is approximately 0.25.[96,143]

Heterozygotes for histidinemia are usually identifiable by metabolic or enzymatic testing. Histidine loading has revealed higher peak levels and slower clearance of blood histidine than in normal individuals (Fig. 17-4). Studies from Japan, however, represent a notable exception; they have shown no clearly defined distinction in histidine tolerance between parents of histidinemic children and controls.[118] The histidine intolerance, when demonstrable, has consistently been more evident in mothers than in fathers.[67–71] The reason for this parental difference is not known, but it is not related to a difference in skin histidase activity.[121] Urinary FIGLU excretion after histidine loading is usually about one-half of that in controls.[70,119,144]

Skin histidase activity in obligate heterozygotes also has been about one-half of mean control activity. This has been a consistent finding, whether determined by direct assay[66,118–120,145,146] or by the indirect methods of skin urocanic acid content[66,124] or the ratio of urocanic acid to histidine.[118,125] All methods of heterozygote detection have had overlap at the lower control levels, limiting reliability for heterozygote detection in the general population.

An autosomal dominant pattern of inheritance has been suggested in one family since affected members appeared in successive generations.[147] We also have had this experience, but occurrence in successive generations can happen in any autosomal recessive disorder and does not disprove recessive inheritance.[148]

Histidinemia has been found in every geographic area and ethnic group in which it has been sought. This includes the United States,[134,138] Canada,[135] Australia,[103] Europe,[137,149,150] Zimbabwe,[69] South Africa,[151] Japan,[139] China,[152] and among blacks.[153]

Prevalence and Screening

Before routine newborn screening, histidinemia was considered to be a very rare inborn error. For almost a decade after its discovery, only a few cases had been identified.[2] Newborn screening dramatically altered this view. Histidinemia has been among the most frequent of the metabolic disorders identified in those programs that included screening for histidinemia.[154] The difference can be explained by lack of clinical symptoms. These are necessary for identifying cases in populations screened for medical diagnosis but irrelevant for newborn screening detection.

The frequency of histidinemia has ranged from 1:7,800 in Quebec[155] to 1:90,000 in New York.[138] The composite frequency derived from screening over 10 million newborns is about 1:10,000 (Table 17-3). In Japan histidinemia has been by far the most frequent of the inborn errors screened in neonates. The incidence of 1:8,400 (Table 17-3) may be com-

*Histinaid, Milner Scientific and Medical Research C., Ltd., Liverpool, UK (Dietary Specialties, Rochester, NY 14601); HIST-1 and HIST-2, Milupa Corp., Darien, CT 06820.

Table 17-3 Frequency of Histidinemia in Newborn Screening Programs

Program	*Specimen screened*	*Number screened*	*Number identified*	*Frequency*	*Reference*
Quebec	Urine	1,106,094	142	1:7,800	155
Japan	Blood	6,311,754	754	1:8,400	139
England	Blood	110,000	10	1:11,000	149
Austria	Blood	827,139	54	1:15,000	150
Massachusetts	Urine	750,000	45	1:17,000	156
Australia	Urine	1,000,000	52	1:19,000	157
Sweden	Blood	73,700	2	1:57,000	137
Totals		10,178,687	1,059	1:9,600	

pared with Japanese incidences of 1:109,000 for phenylketonuria and 1:790,000 for galactosemia.[139]

Newborn screening for histidinemia has been conducted with urine or blood. Urine screening employs a sample collected in filter paper and consists of paper chromatography directly from the specimen[134] or thin-layer chromatography of an eluate from the specimen.[155] Blood screening employs the specimen collected for routine newborn screening and is performed by either the Guthrie bacterial inhibition assay for histidine[158] or the Scriver method of paper chromatography.[159] Based on rates of detection, these methods seem equally effective in identifying infants with histidinemia (Table 17-3). Several programs have discontinued screening for histidinemia, convinced that the disorder has little or no medical impact.[3,137,157]

The original suggestion that histidinemia might produce speech difficulties has led to selective screening of children with speech disorders. This has failed to identify new cases in Poland among 657 screened children[160] or in Czechoslovakia among 200 children considered to be stutterers and "clutterers."[161] The study from Poland did detect several children with low skin histidase activity considered to possibly represent the heterozygous state, but further studies of these children and their families have not been reported.

Atypical Histidinemia

There is heterogeneity in histidinemia, as there is in other inborn errors of metabolism. Anakura et al.[162] reported two sibs with histidinemia, one of whom had relatively mild biochemical abnormalities and a partial defect in skin histidase. He was clinically normal. We have followed two sibs with similar findings.[93]

Studies of infants identified by newborn screening in Japan indicate that there are two groups with respect to residual skin histidase activity.[163] One group, the larger, is characterized by activities of 0.5 μmol/h per gram tissue or less (normal 9.5 ± 4.1 μmol/h per gram tissue); and the other group, by activities of 1.8 to 2.7 μmol/h per gram tissue. Lower fasting blood histidine levels (Fig. 17-3) and higher tolerances to dietary histidine (Fig. 17-4) correspond to the higher residual histidase activity in the second or atypical group.[99] Skin histidase from two sibs in the atypical group manifested heat instability; this was not present in other patients in this group or in any from the first group.[122,162]

It is likely that atypical histidinemia represents a different mutant allele from that which produces classic histidinemia; there may be several allelic mutations that result in histidinemia. The occurrence of both forms of histidinemia in sibships[162,163] indicates that genetic compounds of two different mutant alleles might account for some cases of atypical histidinemia. If so, histidinemia would be analogous to phenylketonuria and mild hyperphenylalaninemia, which also may occur together in sibships seemingly due to different combinations of two mutant alleles.[164]

MATERNAL HISTIDINEMIA

Recognition that maternal phenylketonuria causes fetal damage (see Chap. 15) has led to an interest in whether other maternal inborn errors similarly affect the fetus.[165] Maternal histidinemia has been uppermost in this interest, since it is one of the most frequently identified metabolic disorders.

At least 53 offspring from 21 histidinemic mothers have been reported.[95,147,166–170] These offspring have generally been normal and have not had the microcephaly, congenital anomalies, and mental retardation seen in maternal phenylketonuria offspring. The children in one family had lower IQ scores than their parents,[167] but we found no difference in IQ between histidinemic mothers and their children, both groups scoring in the normal range.[170]

Animal Models for Histidinemia and Maternal Histidinemia

Several groups have attempted to duplicate human histidinemia by feeding histidine to animals. This produces a marked hyperlipidemia, affecting all serum lipids in monkeys[171] but mainly cholesterol in rabbits and rats.[172] The hypercholesterolemia seems to result from increased incorporation of acetate into unesterified cholesterol and cholesterol esters.[173] Reduced growth and hepatomegaly with glycogen accumulation also are seen in histidine-supplemented rats.[172,174] However, neither hepatomegaly nor hyperlipidemia is present in humans with histidinemia.

Nitromethane reacts with an electrophilic center at the active site of histidase and inactivates the enzyme.[43] Rats injected with nitromethane develop increased plasma and urine histidine levels comparable to those observed in patients with histidinemia and have markedly reduced liver histidase activity.[175] Their liver size is unchanged, but when large amounts of nitromethane are administered, growth is suppressed, and neurologic disturbances characterized by ataxia and convulsions are observed.[176]

Kacser and his coworkers[177,178] have identified a mutant mouse (his/his) with the biochemical phenotype of human histidinemia. Blood, urine, and tissue histidine levels are twelve- to twentyfold increased, imidazole metabolites are excreted in large quantities, and histidase activity in both liver and skin is markedly reduced. Offspring from selective matings segregate as expected for an autosomal recessive trait.

Histidase was compared in the mutant and normal mouse.[51] Liver histidase was barely detectable in both at birth. In the normal mouse liver, histidase activity rose postnatally in the expected pattern of development, while virtually no activity appeared in the mutant mouse liver. Skin histidase activity in the mutant mouse was much lower at birth than in the normal mouse. Studies of partially purified liver histidase disclosed evidence for two components in normal liver, one with much higher activity than the other. On the basis of different patterns of heat stability and enzyme kinetics, it was concluded that the mutant mouse histidase consisted only of the very low activity component, having mutationally lost the major component.

The most striking characteristics of this mutant mouse are the clinical changes which result not from the mutant genotype but from prenatal exposure to the maternal biochemical phenotype. Offspring of his/his mothers usually manifest a balance defect characterized by circling behavior and/or head tilting, regardless of whether the offspring has the his/his or the his/+ genotype.[179,180] Offspring of heterozygous (his/+) mothers are normal, regardless of the offspring genotype. The offspring abnormality also could be produced by feeding a histidine supplemented diet to heterozygous (his/+) mothers and inducing increased plasma histidine levels during the second week (middle third) of pregnancy. Histidine loading during the first or third weeks of pregnancy did not have this effect. Conversely, the offspring abnormality could be prevented or substantially lessened by treating homozygous (his/his) mothers during the second week of pregnancy with a histidine restricted diet and sharply reducing the plasma histidine concentration. The observed behavior of the offspring is related to changes in the inner ear; abnormalities found include absence of the otoliths; enlarged or distorted cochlea, enlarged ampullae, shortened crus commune, and thin or misshapen semicircular canals.[179]

Although the offspring abnormality is clearly related to the maternal phenotype, it is not completely independent of the offspring genotype. Heterozygous (his/+) offspring of histidinemic mothers were less severely affected than homozygous (his/his) offspring.[177] Normal (+/+) offspring produced by egg transfer into histidinemic mothers had no visible evidence of a balance defect but did show subclinical damage to the inner ear.[179] Hence the offspring genotype at the his locus seemed to modify the severity of the maternal effect. This was emphasized by the observation that during a period of 5 years, the frequency of abnormal offspring dramatically decreased in Edinburgh, where the studies were conducted, despite no changes in the maternal phenotype, while the frequency remained high in Cambridge, where the mutant strain was maintained.[180] Intercrossing of the two stocks led to the conclusion that the Edinburgh stock had probably become heterogenous for less susceptible loci because of relaxation of selection for high incidence while the Cambridge stock had continued to be bred for high frequency.

The precise relationship between the mutant mouse and human histidinemia is unclear. There appears to be an extraordinary degree of biochemical homology between the two, although further evidence of homology will require molecular characterization of the enzyme and gene defects. There also appears to be a degree of clinical concordance, in that both the homozygous mutant mouse from a nonhistidinemic mother and the histidinemic human are usually normal. The difference seems to be in maternal histidinemia, with inner ear defects in mouse offspring but no obvious abnormalities in the human offspring. Perhaps genetic loci that may render the mouse susceptible to the effects of maternal histidinemia do not exist in the human or only rarely exist. If the latter is true, inner ear abnormalities may occasionally appear in human offspring of maternal histidinemia.

HISTIDINURIA

Increased urinary histidine with a normal blood histidine concentration has been reported in four children from three families.[131–133] Although histidase activity was not determined in any of these patients, evidence against histidinemia, in addition to the normal blood levels, included no histidine metabolites in urine[131,133] and normal cerebrospinal fluid histidine concentration.[131]

Renal tubular reabsorption for histidine calculated for three of the children was 40.1 to 68.7 percent of the filtered amino acid (normal > 90 percent); tubular reabsorption of other amino acids was normal. Two sibs had lower levels of blood histidine and a slower rise in response to histidine loading than controls, suggesting an intestinal defect in histidine transport as well as a renal defect.[133]

Three of the patients, including two sibs, were mentally retarded[131,133] and two, one of whom was mentally retarded, had myoclonic seizures.[131,132] Since all were tested because of the clinical abnormalities, a relationship between histidinuria and mental retardation or myoclonic seizures has not been established. Autosomal dominant inheritance was suggested in the first reported family because the mother also had increased urinary histidine,[132] but the pattern of occurrence in at least one other well studied family is consistent with an autosomal recessive trait.[133]

Histidine is known to be transported by the system that carries neutral amino acids across renal tubular cells and probably intestinal mucosa as well.[181] This system is defective in the Hartnup disorder (see Chap. 101).[182] These cases of histidinuria are of particular interest, since they indicate the probability that histidine also is transported by a system specific to it and that this system is present in both the kidney and intestine.

UROCANIC ACIDURIA

Four children with urocanic aciduria have been described.[74,75,183] All were mentally retarded, and at least three also had growth retardation.[74,75]

Biochemical studies were consistent with a defect in urocanase (Fig. 17-1). Urocanic acid was greatly increased in urine, estimated at ten-to fiftyfold greater than normal.[74,75] Histidine loading exaggerated the urocanic acid excretion and in two patients also led to the production of imidazolepropionic acid, a by-product of urocanic acid.[74,183] On the other hand, metabolites such as imidazolonepropionic acid and FIGLU, which are distal to the metabolic step catalyzed by urocanase, were not present in urine after loading with histidine or urocanic acid. Urocanase deficiency in liver was proven by enzyme assay in three patients,[74,75] while histidase activity was normal in skin from one patient[74] and increased in liver from a second child.[75]

Interestingly, all the patients had evidence of abnormal histidine accumulation after histidine loading. In one the serum histidine response was exaggerated,[74] and in three others there was increased histidine and metabolites of histidine transamination in the urine.[75,183] It is possible that this is a result of the huge urocanic acid elevation; histidase is an irreversible reaction, but urocanic acid is a competitive inhibitor of histidase in bacteria[184] and might similarly inhibit the mammalian enzyme in vivo, although histidase was not inhibited in vitro in these patients.[74,75]

Despite mental retardation in all four reported cases of urocanic aciduria, this might not be related to the metabolic disorder. All the patients were ascertained as a result of investigation to determine the cause of their mental retardation. Through routine newborn urine screening, we have identified two children with urocanic aciduria. Both have maintained normal development without dietary or other therapy. One has short stature, but several other members of her family who do not have urocanic aciduria also are short. Thus whether urocanic aciduria causes clinical disease or is benign is not known. Autosomal recessive transmission seems the most likely pattern of inheritance.

REFERENCES

1. GHADIMI H, PARTINGTON MW, HUNTER A: A familial disturbance of histidine metabolism *N Engl J Med* 265:221, 1961.
2. LA DU BN: Histidinemia, in Stanbury JB, Wyngaarden JB, Fredrickson DS (eds): *The Metabolic Basis of Inherited Disease,* 4th ed. New York, McGraw-Hill, 1978, p 317.
3. SCRIVER CR, LEVY HL: Histidinaemia. Part I: Reconciling retrospective and prospective findings. *J Inherited Metab Dis* 6:51, 1983.
4. HALVER JE, SHANKS WE: Nutrition of salmonoid fishes: VIII. Indispensable amino acids for sockeye salmon. *J Nutr* 72:340, 1960.
5. ALMQUIST HJ: Evaluation of amino acid requirements by observations on the chick. *J Nutr* 34:543, 1947.
6. RECHCIGL M JR, LOOSLI JK, HORVATH DJ, WILLIAMS HH: Histidine requirement of baby pigs. *J Nutr* 60:619, 1956.
7. PARKER CJ JR, RIESS GT, SARDESAI VM: Essentiality of histidine in adult mice. *J Nutr* 115:824, 1985.
8. FRAZIER LE, WISSLER RW, STEFFEE CH, WOOLRIDGE RL, CANNON PR: Studies in amino acid utilization. I. The dietary utilization of mixtures of purified amino acids on protein-depleted adult albino rats. *J Nutr* 33:65, 1947.
9. WISSLER RW, STEFFEE CH, FRAZIER LE, WOOLRIDGE RL, BENDITT EP: Studies in amino acid utilization. III. The role of the indispensable amino acids in maintenance of the adult albino rat. *J Nutr* 36:245, 1948.
10. BENDITT EP, WOOLRIDGE RL, STEFFEE CH, FRAZIER LE: Studies in amino acid utilization. IV. The minimum requirements of the indispensable amino acids for maintenance of the adult well-nourished male albino rat. *J Nutr* 40:335, 1950.
11. ROSE WC, HAINES WJ, WARNER DT, JOHNSON JE: The amino acid requirements of man. II. The role of threonine and histidine. *J Biol Chem* 188:49, 1951.
12. KOPPLE JD, SWENDSEID ME: Evidence that histidine is an essential amino acid in normal and chronically uremic man. *J Clin Invest* 55:881, 1975.
13. KOPPLE JD, FIGUEROA WG, SWENDSEID ME: Histidine, an essential amino acid in adult humans, in Kluthe R, Katz NR (eds): *Histidine. Metabolism. Clinical Aspects. Therapeutic Use.* Stuttgart, Georg Thieme, 1978, p 8.
14. CHO ES, ANDERSON HL, WIXOM RL, HANSON KC, KRAUSE GF: Long-term effects of low histidine intake on men. *J Nutr* 114:369, 1984.
15. SEBRELL WH Jr, MCDANIEL EG: Amino acids in the production of blood constituents in rats. *J Nutr* 47:477, 1952.
16. LEUNG LLK, HARPEL PC, NACHMAN RL, RABELLINO EM: Histidine-rich glycoprotein is present in human platelets and is released following thrombin stimulation. *Blood* 62:1016, 1983.
17. NASSET ES, GATEWOOD VH: Nitrogen balance and hemoglobin of adult rats fed amino acid diets low in L- and D-histidine. *J Nutr* 53:163, 1954.
18. OUSTERHOUT LE: Survival time and biochemical changes in chicks fed diets lacking different essential amino acids. *J Nutr* 70:226, 1960.
19. CLEMENS RA, KOPPLE JD, SWENDSEID ME: Metabolic effects on histidine-deficient diets fed to growing rats by gastric tube. *J Nutr* 114:2138, 1984.
20. TAMAKI N, FUNATSUKA A, FUJIMOTO S, HAMA T: The utilization of carnosine in rats fed on a histidine-free diet and its effect on the levels of tissue histidine and carnosine. *J Nutr Sci Vitaminol* 30:541, 1984.
21. SHENG Y-B, BADGER, TM, ASPLUND JM, WIXON RL: Incorporation of $^{15}NH_4Cl$ into histidine in adult man. *J Nutr* 107:621, 1977.
22. WIXOM FL, ANDERSON HL: Histidine-limited synthesis in normal, adult man, in Kluthe R, Katz NR (eds): *Histidine. Metabolism. Clinical Aspects. Therapeutic Use.* Stuttgart, Georg Thieme, 1978, p 19.
23. SNYDERMAN SE, BOYER A, ROITMAN E, HOLT LE JR, PROSE PH: The histidine requirement of the infant. *Pediatrics* 31:786, 1963.
24. SNYDERMAN S: An eczematoid dermatitis in histidine deficiency. *J Pediatr* 66:212, 1965.
25. SNYDERMAN SE: The histidine requirements of infants, in Kluthe R, Katz NR (eds): *Histidine. Metabolism. Clinical Aspects. Therapeutic Use.* Stuttgart, Georg Thieme, 1978, p 2.
26. VAN SPRANG FJ, WADMAN SK: Treatment of a patient with histidinemia. *Acta Paediatr Scand* 54:493, 1967.
27. CORNER BD, HOLTON JB, NORMAN RM, WILLIAMS PM: A case of histidinemia controlled with a low histidine diet. *Pediatrics* 41:1074, 1968.
28. SNYDERMAN SE, SANSARICQ C, NORTON PM, MANKA M: The nutritional therapy of histidinemia. *J Pediatr* 95:712, 1979.
29. DYME IZ, HORWITZ SJ, BACCHUS B, KERR DS: Histidinemia. A case with resolution of myoclonic seizures after treatment with a low-histidine diet. *Am J Dis Child* 137:256, 1983.
30. STIFEL FB, HERMAN RH: Is histidine an essential amino acid in man? *Am J Clin Nutr* 25:182, 1972.
31. ALBANESE AA: Editorial: histidine—essential or not. *Nutr Rep Intern* 6:115, 1972.
32. MEISTER A: *Biochemistry of the Amino Acids,* 2d ed. New York, Academic, 1965.
33. DHANAM M, RADHAKRISHNAN AN: Comparative studies on histidase: Distribution in tissues, properties of liver histidase and its development in rat. *Indian J Exp Biol* 14:103, 1976.
34. BHARGAVA MM, FEIGELSON M: Studies on the mechanisms of histidase development in rat skin and liver. I. Basis for tissue specific developmental changes in catalytic activity. *Dev Biol* 48:212, 1976.
35. CORNELL NW, VILLEE CA: Purification and properties of rat liver histidase. *Biochim Biophys Acta* 167:172, 1968.
36. OKAMURA H, NISHIDA T, NAKAGAWA H: L-histidine ammonia-lyase in rat liver. I. Purification and general characteristics. *J Biochem* 75:139, 1974.
37. BRAND LM, HARPER AE: Histidine ammonia-lyase from rat liver. Purification, properties and inhibition by substrate analogues. *Biochemistry* 15:1814, 1976.
38. HRYB DJ, FEIGELSON M: Histidase mRNA. Nature of translational products, tissue specificity and differential development in male and female rat liver. *J Biol Chem* 258:11377, 1983.
39. ALLEN RL, HOPEWELL R, PROTTEY C: A comparative study of hepatic and epidermal histidase in the guinea-pig (Cavia porcellus). *Comp Biochem Physiol* 84B:523, 1986.
40. HASSALL H, SOUTAR AK: Amino acid sequence of a peptide containing the active cysteine residue of histidine ammonia-lyase. *Biochem J* 137:559, 1974.
41. KLEE CB, GLADNER JA: Isolation of a cysteine-peptide at the active site of histidine ammonia-lyase. *J Biol Chem* 247:8051, 1972.
42. KLEE GB: Stereospecific irreversible inhibition of histidine ammonia-lyase by L-cysteine. *Biochemistry* 13:4501, 1974.
43. GIVOT IL, ABELES RH: Mammalian histidine ammonia-lyase. In vivo inactivation and presence of an electrophilic center at the active site. *J Biol Chem* 245:3271, 1970.
44. CORNELL NW, LIEN LL: Roles of zinc and glutathione in histidase activity. *Physiol Chem Phys* 2:523, 1970.
45. DHANAM M, RADHAKRISHNAN AN: Purification and properties of histidine ammonia-lyase from monkey liver. *Indian J Biochem Biophys* 11:1, 1974.
46. BADEN HP, SVIOKLA S, MADERSON PFA: A comparative study of histidase activity in amphibian, avian, reptilian and mammalian epidermis. *Comp Biochem Physiol* 30:889, 1969.
47. SCOTT IR: Factors controlling the expressed activity of histidine ammonia-lyase in the epidermis and the resulting accumulation of urocanic acid. *Biochem J* 194:829, 1981.
48. BARNHISEL ML, PRIEST RE, PRIEST JH: Histidase function in human epithelial cells. *J Cell Physiol* 76:7, 1970.
49. BADEN HP, GAVIOLI L: Histidase activity in rat liver and epidermis. *J Invest Dermatol* 63:479, 1974.
50. AUERBACH VH, DIGEORGE AM, CARPENTER GG: Histidinemia, in Nyhan WL (ed): *Amino Acid Metabolism and Genetic Variation.* New York, McGraw-Hill, 1967, p 145.
51. WRIGHT AF, BULFIELD G, ARFIN SM, KACSER H: Comparison of the properties of histidine ammonia-lyase in normal and histidinemic mutant mice. *Biochem Genet* 20:245, 1982.
52. BHARGAVA MM, FEIGELSON M: Studies on the mechanisms of histidase development in rat skin and liver. II. Alterations in enzyme levels and synthetic rates during development. *Dev Biol* 48:226, 1976.
53. OTA DM: The use of histidase for the study of amniotic cell origin and histidinemia. *Am J Obstet Gynecol* 117:567, 1973.
53a. APPELMAN Z, GOLBUS MS: The ontogeny of human and mouse phenylalanine hydroxylase gene expression. *Am J Hum Genet* 41:A148, 1987.
54. FEIGELSON M: Estrogenic regulation of hepatic histidase during postnatal development and adulthood. *J Biol Chem* 243:5088, 1968.
55. FEIGELSON M: Multihormonal regulation of hepatic histidase during postnatal development. *Enzyme* 15:169, 1973.
56. LAMARTINIERE CA, FEIGELSON M: Effects of estrogen, glucocorticoid, glucagon, and adenosine 3′:5′-monophosphate on catalytic activity, amount, and rate of de novo synthesis of hepatic histidase. *J Biol Chem* 252:3234, 1977.
57. NEUFELD E, HARELL A, CHAYEN R: The effect of L-thyroxine on histidine metabolism. *Biochim Biophys Acta* 237:465, 1971.
58. ARMSTRONG EG, FEIGELSON M: Effects of hypophysectomy and triiodothyronine on de novo biosynthesis, catalytic activity, and estrogen induction of rat liver histidase. *J Biol Chem* 255:7199, 1980.
59. LAMARTINIERE CA: Endocrine regulation of sex differences in hepatic histidase activity. *Biochem J* 231:785, 1985.
60. SAHIB MK, MURTI CRK: Induction of histidine-degrading enzymes in protein-starved rats and regulation of histidine metabolism. *J Biol Chem* 244:4730, 1969.

61. SCHIRMER MD, HARPER AE: Adaptive responses of mammalian histidine-degrading enzymes. *J Biol Chem* 245:1204, 1970.

62. MORRIS ML, LEE S-C, HARPER AE: Influence of differential induction of histidine catabolic enzymes on histidine degradation in vivo. *J Biol Chem* 247:5793, 1972.

63. KANG-LEE YAE, HARPER AE: Effect of histidine intake and hepatic histidase activity on the metabolism of histidine in vivo. *J Nutr* 107:1427, 1977.

64. KANG-LEE YAE, HARPER AE: Effect of induction of histidase on histidine metabolism in vivo. *J Nutr* 109:291, 1979.

65. KOLENBRANDER HM, BERG CP: Role of urocanic acid in the metabolism of L-histidine. *Arch Biochem Biophys* 119:110, 1967.

66. NEVILLE BGR, BENTOVIM A, CLAYTON BE, SHEPHERD J: Histidinaemia. Study of relation between clinical and biological findings in 7 subjects. *Arch Dis Child* 47:190, 1972.

67. HOLTON JB, LEWIS FJW, MOORE GR: Biochemical investigation of histidinaemia. *J Clin Pathol* 17:671, 1964.

68. ROSENBLATT D, MOHYUDDIN F, SCRIVER CR: Histidinemia discovered by urine screening after renal transplantation. *Pediatrics* 46:47, 1970.

69. KIBEL MA, LEVY HL: A further case of histidinaemia: Clinical and biochemical aspects. *S Afr Med J* 44:242, 1970.

70. LA DU BN, HOWELL RR, JACOBY GA, SEEGMILLER JE, SOBER EK, ZANNONI VG, CANBY JP, ZIEGLER LK: Clinical and biochemical studies on two cases of histidinemia. *Pediatrics* 32:216, 1963.

71. GHADIMI H, PARTINGTON MW, HUNTER A: Inborn error of histidine metabolism. *Pediatrics* 29:714, 1962.

71a. TAYLOR RG, SEXSMITH E, LAMBERT M, MAHURAN DJ, KACSER H, MCINNES RR: Murine histidinemia as a model for gene therapy: Cloning of cDNA for histidase. *Am J Hum Genet* 41:A241, 1987.

72. HANFORD WC, ARFIN SM: Genetic differences in the rate of histidase synthesis in inbred mice. *J Biol Chem* 252:6695, 1977.

73. ARFIN SM, HANFORD WC, TAYLOR BA: Assignment of histidase-regulating locus to chromosome 10 of the mouse. *Biochem Genet* 17:529, 1979.

74. YOSHIDA T, TADA K, HONDA Y, ARAKAWA T: Urocanic aciduria: A defect in the urocanase activity in the liver of a mentally retarded. *Tohoku J Exp Med* 104:305, 1971.

75. KALAFATIC Z, LIPOVAC K, JEZERINAC Z, JURETIC D, DUMIC M, ZURGA B, RES L: A liver urocanase deficiency. *Metabolism* 29:1013, 1980.

76. EGAN RM, MATHERLY LH, PHILLIPS AT: Mechanism of urocanase as studied by deuterium isotope effects and labeling patterns. *Biochemistry* 20:132, 1981.

77. MATHERLY LH, DEBROSSE CW, PHILLIPS AT: A covalent nicotinamide adenine dinucleotide intermediate in the urocanase reaction. *Biochemistry* 21:2789, 1982.

78. FEINBERG RH, GREENBERG DM: Studies on the enzymic decomposition of urocanic acid. *J Biol Chem* 234:2670, 1959.

79. SWAINE D: The effect of substrate analogues on the activity of cat liver urocanase. *Biochim Biophys Acta* 178:609, 1969.

80. COLTORTI M, DI SIMONE A, BUDILLON G: Histidine and urocanase activities of liver and plasma. Correlations between tissue enzyme levels and plasmatic increases during human and mouse viral hepatitis. *Clin Chim Acta* 13:568, 1966.

81. HASSALL H, RABIE F: The bacterial metabolism of imidazolepropionate. *Biochim Biophys Acta* 115:521, 1966.

82. ZANNONI VG, LA DU BN: Determination of histidine α-deaminase in human stratum corneum and its absence in histidinemia. *Biochem J* 88:160, 1963.

83. BALDRIDGE RC: The metabolism of histidine. II. Effects of folic acid deficiency. *J Biol Chem* 231:207, 1958.

84. HANFORD WC, NEP RL, ARFIN SM: Genetic variation in histidine ammonia-lyase activity in the mouse. *Biochem Biophys Res Commun* 61:1434, 1974.

85. RAO DR, GREENBERG DM: Studies on the enzymic decomposition of urocanic acid. IV. Purification and properties of 4(5)-imidazolone-5(4)-propionic acid hydrolase. *J Biol Chem* 236:1758, 1961.

86. SNYDER SH, SILVA OL, KIES MW: The mammalian metabolism of L-histidine. IV. Purification and properties of imidazolone propionic acid hydrolase. *J Biol Chem* 236:2996, 1961.

87. LUHBY AI, COOPERMAN JM, TELLER DN: Histidine metabolic loading test to distinguish folic acid deficiency from vit. B_{12} in megaloblastic anemias. *Proc Soc Exp Biol Med* 101:350, 1959.

88. ERBE RW: Inborn errors of folate metabolism, in Blakley RL (ed): *Folates and Pterins: Nutritional, Pharmacological and Physiological Aspects.* New York, Wiley, 1986, vol 3, p 413.

89. LOTT IT, WHEELDEN JA, LEVY HL: Speech and histidinemia: Methodology and evaluation of four cases. *Dev Med Child Neurol* 12:596, 1970.

90. GORDON N: Delayed speech and histidinaemia. *Dev Med Child Neurol* 12:104, 1970.

91. WITKOP CJ JR, HENRY FV: Sjögren-Larsson syndrome and histidinemia: Hereditary biochemical diseases with defects of speech and oral functions. *J Speech Hear* 28:109, 1963.

92. GHADIMI H, PARTINGTON MW: Salient features of histidinemia. *Am J Dis Child* 113:83, 1967.

93. LEVY HL, SHIH VE, MADIGAN PM: Routine newborn screening for histidinemia. Clinical and biochemical results. *N Engl J Med* 291:1214, 1974.

94. ALFI OS, SHAW KNF, FISHLER K, WENZ E: Histidinemia: Follow-up of 13 patients. *Am J Hum Genet* 30:20A, 1978.

95. TADA K, TATEDA H, ARASHIMA S, SAKAI K, KITAGAWA T, AOKI K, SUWA S, KAWAMURA M, OURA T, TAKESADA M, KURODA Y, YAMASHITA F, MATSUDA I, NARUSE H: Intellectual development in patients with untreated histidinemia. *J Pediatr* 101:562, 1982.

96. POPKIN JS, SCRIVER CR, CLOW CL, GROVE J: Is hereditary histidinaemia harmful? *Lancet* 1:721, 1974.

97. ROSENMANN A, SCRIVER CR, CLOW CL, LEVY HL: Histidinaemia. Part II: Impact; a retrospective study. *J Interited Metab Dis* 6:54, 1983.

98. COULOMBE JT, KAMMERER BL, LEVY HL, HIRSCH BZ, SCRIVER CR: Histidinaemia. Part III: Impact; a prospective study. *J Inherited Metab Dis* 6:58, 1983.

99. KURODA Y, OGAWA T, ITO M, WATANABE T, TAKEDA E, TOSHIMA K, MIYAO M: Relationship between skin histidase activity and blood histidine response to histidine intake in patients with histidinemia. *J Pediatr* 97:269, 1980.

100. CARTON D, DHONDT F, DE SCHRIJVER F, SAMYN W, KINT J, DELBEKE MJ, HOOFT C: Histidinemia. *Helv Paediatr Acta* 25:127, 1970.

101. HAMBLIN TJ, HOLTON JB: The effect of an intravenous histidine load on the plasma level of other amino acids. *Clin Chim Acta* 42:37, 1972.

102. GHADIMI H, ZISCHKA R: Histidinemia, in Nyhan WL (ed): *Amino Acid Metabolism and Genetic Variation.* New York, McGraw-Hill, 1967, p 133.

103. WILCKEN B, BROWN DA: Histidinaemia—Evaluation of an improved method for confirmation and the implications of the diagnosis. *Aust Paediatr J* 11:126, 1975.

104. MATSUDA I, NAGATA N, ENDO F: Blood histidine levels during course of histidinaemia. *Lancet* 1:162, 1982.

105. WADMAN SK, DE BREE PK, VAN DER HEIDEN C, VAN SPRANG FJ: Automatic column chromatographic analysis of urinary and serum imidazoles in patients with histidinaemia and normals. *Clin Chim Acta* 31:215, 1971.

106. KITANO A, HIGASHI A, NAGATA N, MATSUDA I, HASE Y, OURA T: Zinc status of untreated histidinemic children. *J Pediatr Gastroenterol Nutr* 4:752, 1985.

107. HENKIN RI, PATTEN BM, RE PK, BRONZERT DA: A syndrome of acute zinc loss. *Arch Neurol* 32:745, 1975.

108. GIROUX EL, HENKIN RI: Competition for zinc among serum albumin and amino acids. *Biochim Biophys Acta* 273:64, 1972.

109. BROWN ES, WAISMAN HA, GEISON RL, GERRITSEN TH: Sibship with histidinemia and an unrelated encephalopathy. *Helv Paediatr Acta* 32:401, 1977.

110. AUERBACH VH, DIGEORGE AM, BALDRIDGE RC, TOURTELLOTTE CD, BRIGHAM MP: Histidinemia. A deficiency in histidase resulting in the urinary excretion of histidine and of imidazolepyruvic acid. *J Pediatr* 60:487, 1962.

111. WADMAN SK, VAN SPRANG FJ, VAN STEKELENBURG GJ, DE BREE PK: Three new cases of histidinemia. Clinical and biochemical data. *Acta Paediatr Scand* 56:485, 1967.

112. IMAMURA I, WATANABE T, HASE Y, SAKAMOTO Y, FUKUDA Y, YAMAMOTO H, TSURUHARA T, WADA H: Histamine metabolism in patients with histidinemia: Determination of urinary levels of histamine, N^{tau}-methylhistamine, imidazole acetic acid, and its conjugate(s). *J Biochem* 96:1925, 1984.

113. IMAMURA I, WATANABE T, SAKAMOTO Y, WAKAMIYA T, SHIBA T, HASE Y, TSURUHARA T, WADA H: N^{t}-ribosylhistidine, a novel histidine derivative in urine of histidinemic patients. *J Biol Chem* 260:10526, 1985.

114. IMAMURA I, WATANABE T, WADA H: Formation of N^{tau}-ribosylhistidine, a novel histadine derivative found in the urine in histidinemia, from histidine and $NAD(P)^+$ catalyzed by an $NAD(P)^+$ glycohydrolase system. *Biochem Biophys Res Commun* 130:501, 1985.

115. LEVY HL, MADIGAN PM, PENEVA P: Evidence for delayed histidine transamination in neonates with histidinemia. *Pediatrics* 47:128, 1971.

116. SHAW KNF, BODER E, GUTENSTEIN M, JACOBS EE: Histidinemia. *J Pediatr* 63:720, 1963.

117. LA DU BN, HOWELL RR, JACOBY GA, SEEGMILLER JE, ZANNONI VG: The enzymatic defect in histidinemia. *Biochem Biophys Res Commun* 7:398, 1962.

118. ITO F, AOKI K, ETO Y: Histidinemia. Biochemical parameters for diagnosis. *Am J Dis Child* 135:227, 1981.

119. MATSUDA I, MATSUO K, ENDO F, UEHARA I, NAGATA N, JINNO Y, CHIKA-

ZAWA S, MIYAKITA T, MIURA H: Skin histidase activity and urine formiminoglutamic acid (FIGLU) in patients with histidinemia found by screening newborn infants. *Clin Chim Acta* 119:319, 1982.

120. SHIN YS, WEGELE G, MALLY E, ENDRES W, SCHEIBENREITER S: A simple method for histidase assay and an alteration in the affinity of skin histidase for histidine in histidinaemia. *J Inherited Metab Dis* 6:113, 1983.

121. KURODA Y, ITO M, OGAWA T, TAKEDA E, TOSHIMA K, MIYAO M: A new sensitive method for assay of histidase in human skin and detection of heterozygotes for histidinemia. *Clin Chim Acta* 96:139, 1979.

122. KURODA Y, WATANABE T, ITO M, TOSHIMA K, MIYAO M: Altered kinetic properties of skin histidase in two patients with histidinaemia. *J Inherited Metab Dis* 5:73, 1982.

123. LEVY HL, BADEN HP, SHIH VE: A simple indirect method of detecting the enzyme defect in histidinemia. *J Pediatr* 75:1056, 1969.

124. YOKOYA S, TOKUHIRO E, SUWA S, MAESAKA H: Measurement of the skin urocanic acid content in normal and histidinemic infants. *Eur J Pediatr* 140:330, 1983.

125. ITO F, OTA H, AOKI K, ETO Y: Urocanic acid contents in histidinaemic infant and developing rat epidermis. *J Inherited Metab Dis* 4:55, 1981.

126. BRUSILOW SW, IKAI K: Urocanic acid in sweat: An artifact of elution from the epidermis. *Science* 160:1257, 1968.

127. WOODY NC, SNYDER CH, HARRIS JA: Histidinemia. *Am J Dis Child* 110:606, 1965.

128. SCHÖN R, THALHAMMER O: Personal communication, 1976.

129. AYALON D, CHAYEN R, HARELL A, NEUFELD E, TOAFF R: Excretion of imidazole derivatives following a histidine load in pregnancy. *Isr J Med Sci* 7:1203, 1971.

130. HARELL A, NEUFELD E, KISCH E: The excretion of imidazoles following histidine loading in cases of thyrotoxicosis. *Clin Chim Acta* 35:245, 1971.

131. KAMOUN PP, PARVY P, CATHELINEAU L, MEYER B: Renal histidinuria. *J Inherited Metab Dis* 4:217, 1981.

132. HOLMGREN G, HAMBRAEUS L, DE CHATEAU P: Histidinemia and "normohistidinemic histidinuria." Report of three cases and the effect of different protein intakes on urinary excretion of histidine. *Acta Paediatr Scand* 63:220, 1974.

133. SABATER J, FERRÉ C, PULIOL M, MAYA A: Histidinuria: A renal and intestinal histidine transport deficiency found in two mentally retarded children. *Clin Genet* 9:117, 1976.

134. LEVY HL, MADIGAN PM, SHIH VE: Massachusetts metabolic disorders screening program. I. Technics and results of urine screening. *Pediatrics* 49:825, 1972.

135. DALLAIRE L, MELANCON SB, POTTER M, VANASSE M: Histidinemia: A clinical and genetic evaluation of patients ascertained through a newborn screening program. *Clin Genet* 10:354, 1976.

136. SCHÖN R: Neugeborenen—massenscreening auf histidinämie: Erhöte effizienz durch selektive dünnschichtchromatographie. *Wien Klin Wochenschr* 89:353, 1977.

137. ALM J, HOLMGREN G, LARSSON A, SCHIMPFESSEL L: Histidinaemia in Sweden. Report on a neonatal screening programme. *Clin Genet* 20:229, 1981.

138. AMADOR PS, CARTER TP: Historical review of newborn screening in New York state: Twenty years experience, in Carter TP, Willey AM (eds): *Genetic Disease. Screening and Management.* New York, AR Liss, 1986, p 343.

139. TADA K, TATEDA H, ARASHIMA S, SAKAI K, KITAGAWA T, AOKI K, SUWA S, KAWAMURA M, OURA T, TAKESDA M, KURODA Y, YAMASHITA F, MATSUDA I, NARUSE H: Follow-up study of a nation-wide neonatal metabolic screening program in Japan. *Eur J Pediatr* 142:204, 1984.

140. MELANCON SB, LEE SY, NADLER HL: Histidase activity in cultivated human amniotic fluid cells. *Science* 173:627, 1971.

141. GATFIELD PD, KNIGHTS RM, DEVEREUX M, POZSONYI JP: Histidinemia: Report of four new cases in one family and the effect of low-histidine diets. *Can Med Assoc J* 101:465, 1969.

142. DUFFNER PK, COHEN ME: Infantile spasms associated with histidinemia. *Neurology* 25:195, 1975.

143. ROSTENBERG I, GUÍZAR-VÁZQUEZ J, ARMENDARES S: Analisis genetico en familias con histidinemia. *Rev Invest Clin* 27:217, 1975.

144. MACHIDA Y, OHTA T, KINUGASA A, KUSUNOKI T: Histidinemia: A neurologic study and a diagnosis of heterozygotes. *Teratology* 22:28A, 1980.

145. HOLTON JB: Skin L-histidine ammonia-lyase activity in the family of a child with histidinaemia. *Clin Chim Acta* 11:193, 1965.

146. KIHARA H, BOGGS DE, LASSILA EL, WRIGHT SW: Histidinemia: Studies on histidase activity in stratum corneum. *Biochem Med* 2:243, 1968.

147. BRUCKMAN C, BERRY HK, DASENBROCK RJ: Histidinemia in two successive generations. *Am J Dis Child* 119:221, 1970.

148. LENKE RR, LEVY HL: Maternal phenylketonuria and hyperphenylalaninemia. An international survey of the outcome of untreated and treated pregnancies. *N Engl J Med* 303:1202, 1980.

149. NEVILLE BGR, LILLY PM: Histidinaemia: Its significance in neonatal screening. *Arch Dis Child* 48:325, 1973.

150. THALHAMMER O, SCHEIBENREITER S, KNOLL E, WEHLE E, SCHÖN R: Zwölf jahre österreichische Programm zur früherfassung angeborener Stoffwechselanomalien—Ergebnisse unter besonderer Berücksichtigung von Phenylketonurie, Hyperphenylalaninämie und Histidinämie. *Klin Padiatr* 192:589, 1980.

151. REINECKE CJ, MIENIE LJ: Some inborn errors of metabolism at a local institute for mentally retarded patients. *J Inherited Metab Dis* 4:119, 1981.

152. ZHOU AQ, YUAN FL, ZHANG WM, LUO HY, LIU TC, HC BZ: Case of histidinemia. *Chung Kuo I Hsueh Ko Hsueh Yuan Hsueh Pao* 5:246, 1983.

153. KAPPELMAN M, THOMAS GH, HOWELL R: Histidinemia in a Negro child. *Am J Dis Child* 122:212, 1971.

154. LEVY HL: Genetic screening. *Avd Hum Genet* 4:1, 1973.

155. LEMIEUX B, AURAY-BLAIS C, GIGUÈRE R, SHAPCOTT D, SCRIVER CR: Newborn urine screening experience with over one million infants in the Quebec network of genetic medicine. *J Inherited Metab Dis* 11:45, 1988.

156. LEVY HL, LAWLER MG: Unpublished data, 1987.

157. WILCKEN B, SMITH A, BROWN DA: Urine screening for aminoacidopathies: Is it beneficial? *J Pediatr* 97:492, 1980.

158. GUTHRIE R: Screening for "inborn errors of metabolism" in the newborn infant—A multiple test program. *Birth Defects* 4:92, 1968.

159. SCRIVER CR, DAVIES E, CULLEN AM: Application of a simple micromethod to the screening of plasma for a variety of aminoacidopathies. *Lancet* 2:230, 1964.

160. PIENIAZEK D, STECKO E, KUBALSKA J, KRASSOWSKA A, ZYCHOWICZ K: Metabolism of histidine in children with speech abnormalities. *Acta Med Pol* 26:27, 1985.

161. RAISOVÁ V, HYÁNEK J: Speech disorders associated with histidinemia and other hereditary disorders of amino acid metabolism. *Folia Phoniatr* 38:43, 1986.

162. ANAKURA M, MATSUDA I, ARASHIMA S, FUKUSHIMA N, OKA Y: Histidinemia. Classical and atypical form in siblings. *Am J Dis Child* 129:858, 1975.

163. KURODA Y, WATANABE T, ITO M, TAKEDA E, TOSHIMA K, MIYAO M: Genetic heterogeneity of histidinemia detected by screening newborn infants in Japan. *Jpn J Hum Genet* 30:287, 1985.

164. LEDLEY FD, LEVY HL, WOO SLC: Molecular analysis of the inheritance of phenylketonuria and mild hyperphenylalaninemia in families with both disorders. *N Engl J Med* 314:1276, 1986.

165. LEVY HL: Effect of mutation on maternal-fetal metabolic homeostasis: Maternal aminoacidopathies, in Lloyd JK, Scriver CR (eds): *Genetic and Metabolic Disease in Pediatrics* London, Butterworths, 1985, p 250.

166. NEVILLE BGR, HARRIS RF, STERN DJ, STERN J: Maternal histidinaemia. *Arch Dis Child* 46:119, 1971.

167. LYON ICT, GARDNER RJM, VEALE AMO: Maternal histidinaemia. *Arch Dis Child* 49:581, 1974.

168. ARMSTRONG MD: Maternal histidinaemia. *Arch Dis Child* 50:830, 1975.

169. MATSUDA I, NAGATA N, ENDO F: A family with histidinemic parents. *J Pediatr* 103:169, 1983.

170. LEVY HL, BENJAMIN R: Maternal histidinemia: Study of families identified by routine cord blood screening. *Pediatr Res* 19:250A, 1985.

171. KERR GR, WOLF RC, WAISMAN HA: A disorder of lipid metabolism associated with experimental hyperhistidinemia in macaca mulatta, in *Some Recent Developments in Comparative Medicine* (Symposium of the Zoological Society of London). New York, Academic, 1966, p 371.

172. SOLOMON JK, GEISON RL: Effect of excess dietary L-Histidine on plasma cholesterol levels in weanling rats. *J Nutr* 108:936, 1978.

173. SOLOMON JK, GEISON RL: L-Histidine-induced hypercholesterolemia: Characteristics of cholesterol biosynthesis in rat livers. *Proc Soc Exp Biol Med* 159:44, 1978.

174. AOYAMA Y, OHMURA E, YOSHIDA A, ASHIDA K: Liver composition of rats fed a histidine-excess diet. *Nutr Reps Intern* 31:863, 1985.

175. LEE S-C, WANG M-L: Histidinemia produced in the rat by treatment with nitromethane. *Nutr Metab* 18:79, 1975.

176. DOUAY O, KAMOUN PP: Serotonin in experimental histidinemia. *Neurochem Res* 5:897, 1980.

177. KACSER H, BULFIELD G, WALLACE ME: Histidinaemic mutant in the mouse. *Nature* 244:77, 1973.

178. BULFIELD G, KACSER H: Histidinaemia in mouse and man. *Arch Dis Child* 49:545, 1974.

179. KACSER H, MYA KM, DUNCKER M, WRIGHT AF, BULFIELD G, MCLAREN A, LYON MF: Maternal histidine metabolism and its effect on fetal development in the mouse. *Nature* 265:262, 1977.

180. KACSER H, MYA KM, BULFIELD G: Endogenous teratogenesis in maternal

histidinaemia, in Hommes FA (ed): *Models for the Study of Inborn Errors of Metabolism* Amsterdam, Elsevier/North Holland, 1979, p 43.

181. SCRIVER CR, HECHTMAN P: Human genetics of membrane transport with emphasis on amino acids. *Adv Hum Genet* 1:211, 1970.

182. SCRIVER CR, MAHON B, LEVY HL, CLOW CL, READE TM, KRONICK J, LEMIEUX B, LABERGE C: The Hartnup phenotype: Mendelian transport disorder, mulifactorial disease. *Am J Hum Genet* 40:401, 1987.

183. VAN GENNIP AH, RAJNHERC J, DE BREE PK, WADMAN SK: "Urocanase deficiency" in a 7-year-old boy with psychomotor retardation. *Soc Study IEM*, Lyon, France, Sept 6–9, 1983, p 119.

184. HUG DH, ROTH D, HUNTER J: Regulation of histidine catabolism by succinate in Pseudomonas putida. *J Bacteriol* 96:396, 1968.

CHAPTER **18**

DISORDERS OF PROLINE AND HYDROXYPROLINE METABOLISM

JAMES M. PHANG
CHARLES R. SCRIVER

1. Δ^1-Pyrroline-5-carboxylate (P-5-C) is both the immediate precursor and the degradative product of proline. P-5-C reductase (EC 1.5.1.2) catalyzes the conversion of P-5-C to proline as the committed step in biosynthesis, and proline oxidase (no EC number assigned) catalyzes the degradation of proline to P-5-C. Other sources of P-5-C are ornithine and glutamate in reactions catalyzed by ornithine aminotransferase (EC 2.6.1.13) and P-5-C synthase, respectively. The P-5-C "outflow" is primarily to glutamate in a reaction catalyzed by P-5-C dehydrogenase (EC 1.5.1.12). Although ornithine aminotransferase theoretically can convert P-5-C back to ornithine, the significance of the flux back to ornithine is questionable.

Disorders in this metabolic system are in the degradative limb, which result in hyperprolinemia. Two distinct conditions are known, each due to a mutation in a different genetic locus; both are apparently autosomal recessive. Type I hyperprolinemia is due to a deficiency of proline oxidase, and type II hyperprolinemia is due to a deficiency of P-5-C dehydrogenase. Proline levels are only three- to fivefold elevated in the former, whereas they are ten- to fifteenfold elevated in the latter. The distinguishing biochemical findings in type II hyperprolinemia are high plasma P-5-C levels and urinary excretion of P-5-C.

2. 4-Hydroxy-L-proline is not synthesized as the free imino acid. Instead, it is produced by hydroxylation of the third position proline in the prevalent tripeptide Gly-Pro-Pro in the procollagen polypeptide chain. Free hydroxyproline is derived from endogenous collagen turnover and from breakdown of dietary collagen. Degradation of hydroxyproline resembles that of proline. Δ^1-Pyrroline-3-hydroxy-5-carboxylate, the oxidation product of hydroxyproline, is dehydrogenated to 4-erythro-hydroxy-L-glutamate. Transamination with oxalacetate results in 4-hydroxy-2-ketoglutarate, which is then cleaved to glyoxylate and pyruvate in an aldolase reaction. The enzymes catalyzing these reactions are distinct from those for the degradation of proline with one exception. The dehydrogenation of P-5-C and hydroxy-P-5-C is catalyzed by the same enzyme.

Hyperhydroxyprolinemia is an autosomal recessive trait resulting from a deficiency of hydroxyproline oxidase (no EC number assigned). The condition does not affect the metabolism of collagen itself. The metabolism of proline is also normal.

3. Prolidase (EC 3.4.13.9) is an exopeptidase that cleaves imidopeptides (X-Pro, X-Hypro structures in which the tertiary nitrogen of the peptide bond is not susceptible to other peptidases). The enzyme plays a critical role in the recovery of imino acids from endogenous collagen turnover as well as from exogenous dietary proteins.

Prolidase deficiency is an autosomal recessive trait with a characteristic clinical syndrome that includes chronic dermatitis, mental retardation, and recurrent infections. The inability to cleave X-Pro and X-Hypro dipeptides results in their being excreted in excessive amounts in the urine.

Proline and hydroxyproline are nonessential amino acids. Because they have only one hydrogen atom attached to the nitrogen atom that is inserted in a pyrrolidine ring (Fig. 18-1), they are usually designated by the trivial name imino acid. L-Proline is a major metabolic substrate in extracellular fluids rivaled only by glutamine and alanine in the amino acid pool. Hydroxyproline is not prominent in its free form and is found primarily as an oligopeptide in body fluids. The principal form of hydroxyproline in humans is 4-hydroxy-L-proline, and its major source is collagen; 3-hydroxy-L-proline is present in much smaller amounts in body fluids. Important pathways provide for the biosynthesis and degradation of free proline through the formation of related intermediates (Fig. 18-1). Analogous pathways of less quantitative significance also exist, in part, for free hydroxyproline metabolism. Proline and 4-hydroxyproline share the second step of their respective oxidative pathways. Hydroxyproline is derived from the hydroxylation of peptide-linked proline in the nascent collagen polypeptide chain; evidence for synthesis of free hydroxyproline from any other source is not convincing.

Several Mendelian disorders of imino acid metabolism exist, and they have helped to elucidate the corresponding metabolic relationships in humans. Although the specific enzyme deficiencies result in a number of metabolic abnormalities, causation of a disease syndrome has not been proven. The *hyperprolinemias* comprise two separate disorders of proline oxidation: *type I* (McKusick 23950) involves proline oxidase; *type II* (McKusick 23951) involves Δ^1-pyrroline-5-carboxylic acid dehydrogenase. *Hyperhydroxyprolinemia* (McKusick 23700) is a disorder of free hydroxyproline catabolism, involving the step catalyzed by hydroxyproline oxidase. Hydroxyproline metabolism is compromised in type II hyperprolinemia, but only its pyrroline metabolites accumulate in this disorder.

Prolidase (peptidase D, PEPD, EC 3.4.13.9) is an exopeptidase. Prolidase deficiency (McKusick 26413) is the autosomal recessive phenotype for several rare activity-modifying alleles at a locus on chromosome 19qcen-13.2. Common structure modifying alleles at the same locus cause codominantly inherited benign electrophoretic polymorphism of PEPD (McKusick 17010). Prolidase cleaves imidodipeptides (X-pro, X-hypro structures). Prolidase deficiency is associated with massive imidodipeptiduria (metabolic phenotype). Twenty-eight cases are known. Six cases are asymptomatic, five of whom were diagnosed prospectively by newborn urine screening; one prospectively diagnosed patient developed skin lesions at 10 years of age. The remainder, all diagnosed retrospectively, have clinical signs: mild to severe

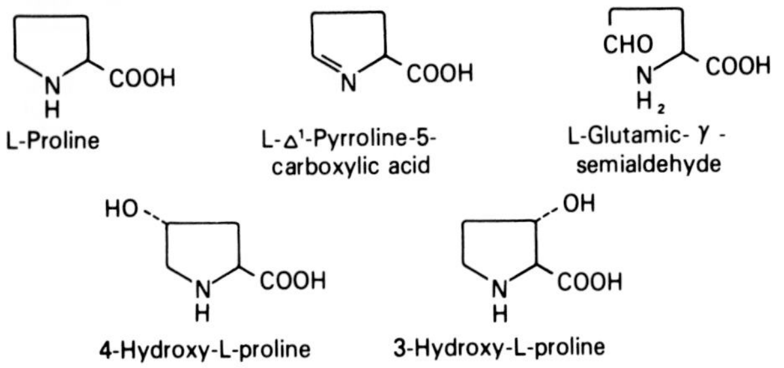

L-Proline

L-Δ^1-Pyrroline-5-carboxylic acid

L-Glutamic-γ-semialdehyde

4-Hydroxy-L-proline

3-Hydroxy-L-proline

Fig. 18-1 Schematic structures for proline, intermediates in the proline metabolic pathways, and the two forms of hydroxyproline present in mammalian tissues.

skin lesions in all; impaired development in two-thirds; other manifestations including frequent infections in two-thirds. Age at onset of symptoms is variable (birth to 22 years). Mutant enzyme phenotypes include K_m, V_{max}, and CRM$^-$ variants. Prolidase can be measured in hemolysates and homogenates of fibroblasts and amniocytes. The treatment record is not impressive.

METABOLISM OF THE IMINO ACIDS

For certain amino acids, the preservation of the ability for their synthesis makes them nutritionally nonessential. But having an endogenous source of these nonessential amino acids provides little advantage to the animal species, since nonessential amino acids are no less abundant in dietary protein than essential amino acids. However, the synthetic process per se, by providing a metabolic advantage, may have been selectively preserved.

For many nonessential amino acids, such as alanine, serine, aspartate, and glutamate, the importance of their respective synthetic processes has been recognized.[1] However, for proline, also a nonessential amino acid, the metabolic function derived from its biosynthesis and interconversions has not been generally appreciated. Recent findings suggest that the synthesis and degradation of proline, like that for other nonessential amino acids, has a special function in regulating cellular metabolism.[2]

In lower organisms, proline has a number of functions apparently unrelated to its serving as a substrate for protein synthesis. For example, proline can serve as a defense against osmotic challenge,[3,4] as a redox shuttle,[5] and as a mediator of parasite-induced pathophysiology in the host.[6] Proline added to the medium appears necessary for certain cultured cells to respond to mitogenic signals.[7] Although the mechanisms mediating these seemingly unrelated phenomena are not well understood, these effects of proline emphasize functions other than as substrate for protein synthesis.

Pyrroline-5-carboxylate (P-5-C), the intermediate common to both synthetic and degradative pathways for proline, together with proline itself constitute a redox couple.[2,8] They participate in a metabolic interlock linked to the NADPH/NADP$^+$ redox couple and the pentose phosphate shunt[2,9–12] (see below). How this metabolic interlock relates to the effects of proline listed above remains unclear. Nevertheless, the synthesis and degradation of proline must be considered with this metabolic feature as an end point.

PROLINE METABOLISM

The aforementioned special metabolic functions of proline may be due to its unique structure (Fig. 18-1). The absence of a primary amino group excludes the imino acids from those pyridoxal-5′-phosphate coenzyme-catalyzed decarboxylation and transamination reactions that are otherwise of general importance for amino acid metabolism.[13] Instead, proline is metabolized by reactions catalyzed by its own special enzymes that can be regulated by mechanisms independent of those for other amino acids (Fig. 18-2).

Proline Synthesis

Ornithine and glutamate are the precursors for proline with P-5-C or glutamic-γ-semialdehyde (the uncyclized tautomer with which P-5-C is in spontaneous equilibrium) as the common intermediate.[14–16] Ornithine aminotransferase is localized to the mitochondrial matrix[16] and found in all tissues tested,[17] with the notable exception of erythrocytes.[10] The enzyme catalyzes the conversion of ornithine to P-5-C with an α-ketoacid, such as α-ketoglutarate, as the amino acceptor. P-5-C synthase is the trivial name for the enzyme(s) mediating the production of P-5-C from glutamate.[18–20] In animals, enzyme activity is found only in extracts from intestinal mucosa cells[20] and is localized to mitochondria.[20] However, cultured cells of diverse origins have measurable activity. On the basis of measured activities and tissue localization, ornithine appears to be the predominant source for proline, but proline synthesis from either precursor appears to be adequate to maintain optimal growth in tissue culture.[21]

P-5-C reductase, which catalyzes the conversion of P-5-C to proline with either NADH or NADPH as cofactor,[22–24] is found in all tissues.[17] The enzyme has been purified from rat retina[25] and from human erythrocytes.[26] Interestingly, the turnover number of P-5-C reductase is very high, being several logs higher than for most metabolic enzymes, and the abundance of enzyme protein is very low.[26] Because the V_{max} is higher with NADH than with NADPH, NADH has been considered the cofactor nucleotide.[22,23] However, the K_m for NADPH is considerably lower, and the K_m for P-5-C is lower with NADPH.[24,25] Based on these kinetic characteristics and the physiological concentrations for reduced pyridine nucleotides and P-5-C, the calculated activity in situ is primarily dependent on NADPH. Studies using purified human P-5-C reductase incubated with P-5-C labeled with ^{14}C and NADPH labeled with tritium in the exchangeable position have provided direct evidence that NADPH is the preferred cofactor.[26] Furthermore, detailed studies suggest that the enzyme may be functionally associated with certain subcellular particles.[27] The significance of this association remains unknown. Nevertheless, the classification of P-5-C reductase as a typical cytosolic enzyme is probably oversimplistic.

Proline Degradation

The first step in proline degradation is catalyzed by proline oxidase. The enzyme is found primarily in liver, kidney, and brain and is tightly bound to mitochondrial inner mem-

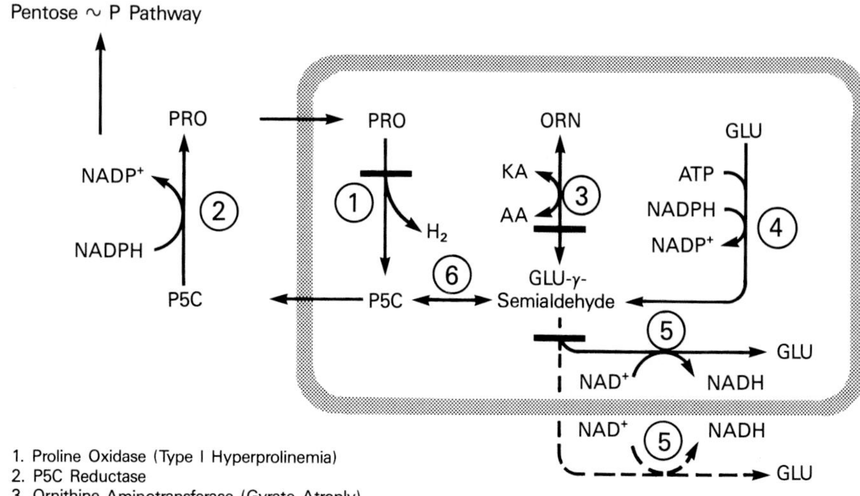

Fig. 18-2 Summary of the pathways of proline synthesis and degradation in mammalian tissues. The complete system is present only in certain tissues (see text). The shaded area represents mitochondria. Reaction (5) catalyzed by P-5-C dehydrogenase occurs mainly in mitochondria but may also occur in the cytosol (dashed line).

branes.[28–30] The electrons donated by proline enter the mitochondrial electron transport chain probably through an intervening flavoprotein.[31] The enzyme can be solubilized by treatment with detergents but has not been purified.[32] P-5-C can then be converted to glutamate by a $NAD(P)^+$-dependent dehydrogenase.[33,34] P-5-C dehydrogenase is widely distributed and localized to the mitochondrial matrix, but a cytosolic component has been suggested.[35]

Regulation of the Pathway and the Metabolic Interlock

One end point of the regulation appears to be meeting the demands of protein synthesis for proline.[36–38] An increase in the enzymes of proline synthesis correlates with an increase in the demand for proline. Furthermore, both P-5-C synthase[19] and P-5-C reductase[39] are inhibited by proline as an example of negative feedback control. The induction of proline oxidase by glucocorticosteroids[40,41] suggests that the diversion of proline carbons into the TCA cycle either as fuel or for anaplerosis may be another metabolic end point. However, several regulatory mechanisms are difficult to interpret with the production or utilization of proline per se as the only end point.[32,42,43] The early studies of P-5-C reductase from red cells,[24] corroborated by recent studies with the purified enzyme,[25,26] show that NADPH is the preferred cofactor. In contrast to the NADH-mediated activity, the NADPH-mediated activity is insensitive to inhibition by proline.[24,26] Furthermore, $NADP^+$ is a potent inhibitor of both NADH and NADPH activities.[24,26] These findings led us to propose that the regulation of the NADPH/$NADP^+$ redox couple may be an important function of proline metabolism.

Unlike NADH/NAD^+, the NADPH/$NADP^+$ redox couple does not play a significant role in energy transfer. Its role appears to be that of a defense mechanism against deleterious redox perturbations[44] or as a regulator of metabolic pathways.[45] Since P-5-C reductase appears to be intimately associated with the NADPH/$NADP^+$ redox couple, we examined the effects of P-5-C on metabolic pathways regulated by this redox couple. In human red cells,[10] as well as a variety of cultured cells,[9] P-5-C markedly stimulates the flux through the oxidative arm of the pentose phosphate shunt (Fig. 18-3). In fact, in red cells the flux through the pentose phosphate shunt is stoichiometrically coupled to the conversion of P-5-C to proline.[46] By stimulating the flux through the shunt, P-5-C increases the production of phosphoribosyl pyrophosphate and purine nucleotides.[47–50] In quiescent fibroblasts, this effect on phosphoribosyl pyrophosphate is synergistic to the effect of growth factors, but the mechanism of the synergism cannot be accounted for only by the P-5-C effect on the pentose shunt.[2]

Because of the cellular localization and tissue distribution of the enzymes that catalyze the interconversions of P-5-C and proline, i.e., proline oxidase is localized in mitochondria of liver, kidney, and brain, whereas P-5-C reductase is cytosolic and present in all tissues, a proline-P-5-C cycle can be demonstrated that transfers reducing-oxidizing potential between cellular compartments[11,51–53] and, indeed, between cells of different types.[8,54] Thus, P-5-C and proline can function as a shuttle mechanism as well as an intercellular communicator (Fig 18-2).

A special uptake mechanism for P-5-C may facilitate these special effector functions. Uptake of P-5-C occurs through a saturable, energy-dependent mechanism unshared by other amino acids.[55] Studies suggest that it has high capacity, is independent of sodium ion, and is a group translocation linked to the oxidation of pyridine nucleotides.

The physiological relevance of these in vitro findings is supported by the identification of P-5-C in human plasma[56] (Fig. 18-4) and the finding of diurnal fluctuations in plasma P-5-C levels.[57] From a low of 0.2 μM in the early morning, the levels rise with several peaks and reach a high of about 2.0 μM in the late evening. Temporally, the peaks are associated with meals and are abolished by fasting.[57] No other amino acid shows such diurnal variations. Although these fluctuations in plasma P-5-C may form the basis for intercellular communication, the mediation of redox transfers in the intact animal has yet to be shown.

The superimposition of hormone regulation on these effects of P-5-C is of special interest. On the cellular level, the P-5-C stimulation of phosphoribosyl pyrophosphate synthesis is markedly augmented by growth factors, such as platelet-de-

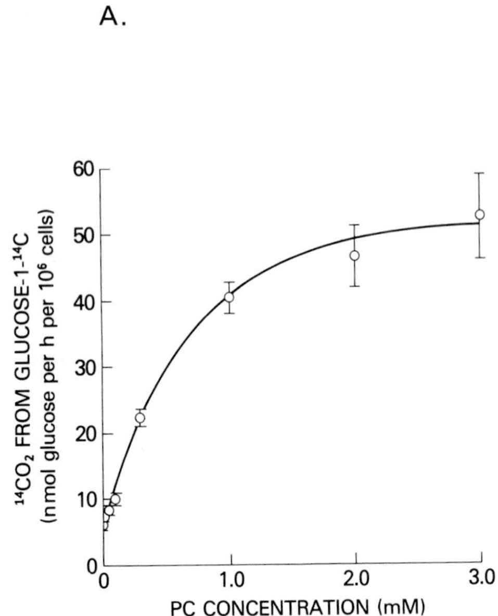

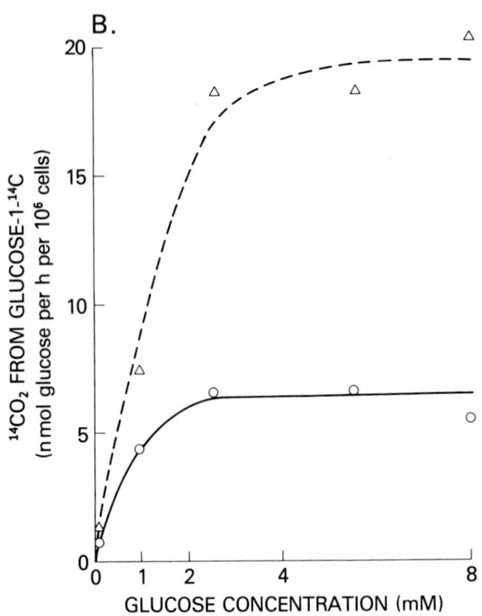

Fig. 18-3 Stimulation of the pentose phosphate pathway by P-5-C in cultured normal human fibroblasts. *A.* The production of $^{14}CO_2$ from [1-^{14}C]glucose as a measure of pentose phosphate pathway activity increases with increasing P-5-C. *B.* Pentose phosphate pathway activity in control incubations (○—○) and in the presence of 0.3 mM L-pyrroline-5-carboxylate (Δ----Δ). *(Used by permission from Ref. 9.)*

rived growth factor.[2,58,59] Indeed, P-5-C may serve as a nutrition-sensitive signal to modulate cellular responses to hormones. Whether the circulating levels of P-5-C are themselves hormonally modulated remains to be seen.

4-HYDROXYPROLINE METABOLISM

Biosynthesis

The principal route of 4-hydroxy-L-proline biosynthesis in mammals is posttranslational hydroxylation of proline on nascent chains of procollagen.[60] Prolyl hydroxylase catalyzes the reaction, and ferrous iron, α-ketoglutarate, and O_2 are required. Collagen biosynthesis and proline hydroxylation are discussed in detail in Chap. 115.

Fig. 18-4 Distribution of plasma P-5-C levels in normal males (○) and females (●). The bar indicates the mean and the shaded area the standard deviation. *(Taken from Ref. 56.)*

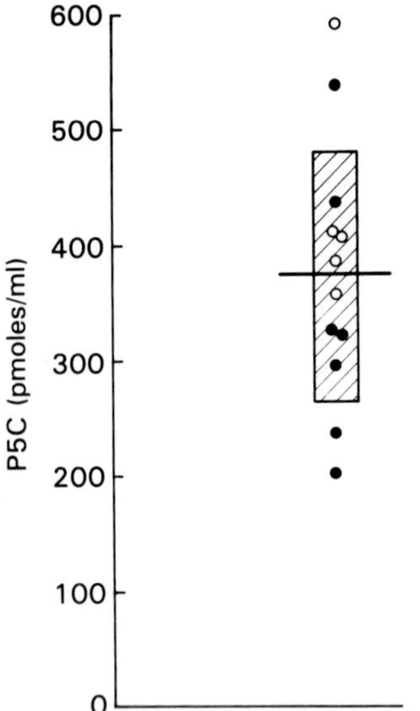

Free hydroxyproline is not utilized in protein synthesis as no mammalian transfer RNA for hydroxyproline has been identified. Thus, hydroxyproline found in other proteins, elastin,[61] the C1q component of complement,[62] acetylcholinesterase,[63] and several other partially characterized proteins,[64] is presumed to occur posttranslationally. Free hydroxyproline arises exclusively from the breakdown of hydroxyproline-containing proteins from either dietary or endogenous sources.

Degradation

The initial steps in the degradation of free hydroxy-L-proline parallel those for proline (Fig. 18-5). Hydroxyproline is oxidized to Δ^1-pyrroline-3-hydroxy-5-carboxylic acid by an enzymatic mechanism similar to that mediating proline oxidation.[65] The pyrroline product is then converted to 4-erythrohydroxy-L-glutamate by an NAD-dependent dehydrogenase,[65] and hydroxyglutamate is subsequently transaminated with oxalacetate-forming 3-hydroxy-2-oxoglutarate.[66] Here, the parallelism with proline ends; hydroxyoxoglutarate is cleaved to glyoxylate and pyruvate. Despite the similarities in the reactions for the degradation of the two imino acids, the analogous reactions are catalyzed by distinct enzymes with one exception—a single enzyme catalyzes the NAD-dependent dehydrogenation of both P-5-C and pyrroline-3-hydroxy-5-carboxylate.[67]

3-HYDROXYPROLINE METABOLISM

Unlike 4-hydroxyproline, 3-hydroxyproline occurs at extremely low frequencies in interstitial collagen. However, in basement membrane collagen, 3-hydroxyproline is relatively abundant (25 residues per 1000 residues). The ratio of 3-hy-

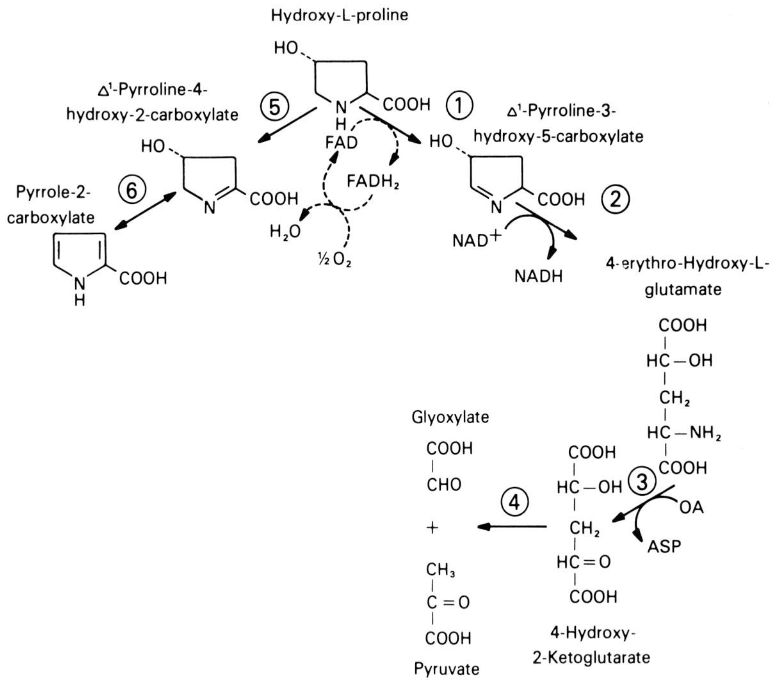

Fig. 18-5 The pathways for the degradation of 4-hydroxy-L-proline in mammalian tissues. Major pathway: Although reaction (1) is analogous to that for proline oxidation, it is catalyzed by an enzyme distinct from that for proline.[18] Reaction (2), however, is catalyzed by a dehydrogenase common to the hydroxyproline and proline pathways.[91] The enzymes and their enzyme classification are (1) hydroxy-L-proline oxidase (EC number not assigned); (2) Δ'-pyrroline-3-hydroxy-5-carboxylate dehydrogenase (EC 2.6.1.12); (3) glutamic-oxalacetate aminotransferase probably (EC 2.6.1.1); and (4) 4-hydroxy-2-oxoglutaric acid lyase (EC 4.1.3.16). Minor pathway: Reaction (5) is catalyzed by L-amino acid oxidase, and reaction (6) is spontaneous. Pyrrole-2-carboxylic acid is found in the urine of patients with a defective major pathway (type II hyperprolinemia).

droxyproline to 4-hydroxyproline has been used to estimate the ratio of basement membrane collagen to total collagen in tissues.[68] Formation of 3-hydroxyproline is posttranslational, analogous to the formation of 4-hydroxyproline, and requires similar cofactors but is catalyzed by a different prolyl hydroxylase.[69] Because of its infrequent occurrence, knowledge of 3-hydroxyproline metabolism is still limited. Nevertheless, the urinary excretion of 3-hydroxyproline has been useful as an indication of basement membrane turnover.[70–72]

Interaction with Proline Metabolism

The inability to demonstrate the condensation of glyoxylate and pyruvate to form 3-hydroxy-2-oxoglutarate in animals makes the *de novo* synthesis of free hydroxyproline unlikely. But the formation of hydroxyproline by reduction of the intermediate, pyrroline-3-hydroxy-5-carboxylate, occurs in vitro.[65] A common reductase for P-5-C and pyrroline-3-hydroxy-5-carboxylate has not been proven, but nevertheless, each will inhibit the reaction reducing the other to its respective imino acid.[65] A common enzyme catalyzing the dehydrogenation reaction for both pyrroline carboxylates has been described.[67] The reactions using P-5-C as substrate exhibit higher affinity than those for the hydroxylated analogue, suggesting that P-5-C is the preferred substrate. However, the intermediates of hydroxyproline degradation could affect the metabolic flux of the proline intermediates. Whether this regulation plays a physiological role in proline synthesis and degradation remains unknown.

DISTRIBUTION OF IMINO ACIDS IN BODY FLUIDS

Free Proline

The normal concentration of proline in human plasma is between 100 and 450 μ*M*.[73] The mean value is lower during growth in children relative to the mean value of mature subjects.[74] Beyond the period of early infancy, virtually no proline is seen in normal urine.[73] Neonatal iminoglycinuria is a normal phenomenon; postnatal prolinuria is due to immaturity of the tubular transport systems for proline reclamation (see Chap. 102, "Familial Renal Iminoglycinuria"). The concentration of proline in cerebrospinal fluid is low (4.2 μ*M*).[73] Proline is present in human amniotic fluid at an unchanging low concentration throughout pregnancy.

Free Hydroxyproline

Less than 25 percent of hydroxyproline in plasma is in the free form; the remainder is in peptide linkage.[75,76] The age-dependent pattern of hydroxyproline excretion in urine parallels that of proline (see Chap. 102). Hydroxyproline is a negligible constituent of other body fluids.

Urinary Imino Acids in the Bound Form

A large literature describes urinary excretion of peptide-bound hydroxyproline and proline.[13,77–82] The ratio of total proline to total hydroxyproline in urine (*total* means the sum of free and bound fractions) rises from an average of about 1.2 in childhood to about 2.4 in adults.[78] Excretion of peptide-bound hydroxyproline increases during rapid somatic growth (infancy and adolescence) (Table 18-1), reflecting the greater rate of endogenous collagen turnover during growth.[77] Excretion of free hydroxyproline is not increased in late infancy and adolescence because renal reabsorption of imino acids is efficient beyond early infancy. A wide variety of proline-containing oligopeptides is found in normal urine.[78] The predominant hydroxyproline-containing peptides, prolylhydroxyproline and glycylprolylhydroxyproline, account for 60 to 75 percent of bound hydroxyproline in urine[77]; bound hydroxyproline is 96 percent of total hydroxyproline excretion beyond early infancy.[79]

Table 18-1 Urinary Excretion of Imino Acid-Containing Peptides

Hydroxyproline excretion†		*Imino acid peptide excretion ratio‡*	
	Total hydroxyproline, (mg/24 h·m²)‡*		*Total proline/total hydroxyproline*
Age, yr	*± 2 SD from mean*	*Age, yr*	*Mean*
<1	40–191	1–4	1.28
1–2	40–121	4–8	1.21
2–10	34–93	8–12	1.31
11–14	40–113	12–16	1.39
18–21	13–28	16–20	1.58
22–65	9–23	20–40	2.13
65	7–20	40–60	2.55

*Total hydroxyproline (bound + free), after the first 3 months of life, is 95 percent peptide bound. Data are uncorrected for surface area (Ref. 77). From subjects on gelatin-free diets.
†From Refs. 80 to 82.
‡From Ref. 78.

MEMBRANE TRANSPORT OF IMINO ACIDS

Interpretation of the metabolic phenotype in disorders of imino acid metabolism requires some knowledge of renal reabsorption of these substances (see Chap. 102).

Free Imino Acids

L-Proline and hydroxy-L-proline are taken up by tissues on stereospecific, substrate-specific, energy-coupled membrane transport systems[83] and are well documented for kidney and fetal bone.[84,85] The findings in kidney delineate the nature of epithelial transport of imino acids; those in fetal bone serve for a tissue important in collagen synthesis.

Characterized in cultured cells, the uptake of proline occurs primarily through system A, the system that can be regulated by both transinhibition and repression mechanisms.[83] Furthermore, this system is sensitive to a variety of hormones. Interestingly, system A is defined using the nonmetabolizable analogue, *N*-methyl-α-aminoisobutyric acid, an imino acid. The naturally occurring imino acid, proline, may be the most specific substrate for this transport system.

Proline interacts competitively with hydroxyproline and glycine on a shared carrier in the brush-border membrane of proximal nephron,[86] which serves for uptake preferentially at concentrations in excess of 100 μ*M*. In kidney, and probably in bone as well, a second system is used preferentially by imino acids at concentrations of solute below 100 μ*M*.[86] The presence of these carriers in the nephron explains the complex hyperaminoaciduria in patients with hyperiminoacidemias.

Proline[87] and hydroxyproline[88] both have maximum rates of renal tubular absorption (Tm) in humans; Tm_{Pro} is between 180 and 300 μmol/min per 1.73 m^2, and Tm_{Hypro} is between 60 and 135 μmol/min per 1.73 m^2. The venous plasma threshold concentration at which prolinuria occurs is about 800 μ*M* proline; for hydroxyprolinuria, it is about 400 μ*M* hydroxyproline. The normal plasma concentration of the two imino acids is well below threshold levels; accordingly, urine is free of imino acids in healthy adults. A "combined" hyperaminoaciduria occurs when the concentration of the specific imino acid exceeds the threshold level. When either imino acid proceeds to saturate the renal transport system, competition occurs for reabsorption and displacement of the other imino acid and of glycine. The corresponding interactions have been observed in fetal bone.[84,85] Collagen synthesis in fetal bone was thought to be inhibited when the extracellular concentration of hydroxyproline was sufficiently elevated (>200 μ*M*) to inhibit the transport of L-proline [at a quasiphysiological concentration (≈140 μ*M*) in the medium]. There appears to be no clinical counterpart to these in vitro findings in patients with hyperhydroxyprolinemia.

Peptide-Linked Imino Acids

Imino acids in oligopeptides are transported by systems independent of those used by the free imino acids. Rubino et al.[89] and Ganapathy et al.[90] described a saturable, Na^+-independent mechanism for glycylproline transport in kidney and intestine brush-border membrane. This dipeptide does not interact directly with the free imino acid transport systems. Whereas dipeptide membrane transport systems operate efficiently under the conditions of intestinal absorption, their contribution to net reabsorption of imino acid-containing peptides from filtrate is poor in the kidney, perhaps because there is a realtive dearth of peptide hydrolysis activity in kidney epithelium. Proline-containing dipeptides are cleared into urine at high rates in humans,[87] and the same is true of the hydroxyproline-containing oligopeptides.[91] The discrepancy between efficient reabsorption of free imino acids and inefficient transport of the corresponding peptides apparently explains the large peptide fraction in human urine (95 percent of the total imino acid excretion).

THE HYPERPROLINEMIAS

Clinical Phenotypes

The Mendelian hyperprolinemia phenotype exists in two forms: *type I* associated with deficient proline dehydrogenase (oxidase) activity and *type II* with deficient Δ^1-pyrroline-5-carboxylic acid dehydrogenase activity. Information about probands in 12 type I families of 7 type II families was tabulated in the previous edition of this text and has archival value. There is no categorical evidence that either disorder of metabolism was a cause of the associated clinical manifestations in these reported probands, but we remain cautious about this position in the type II phenotype.

Type I Hyperprolinemia (Proline Oxidase Deficiency)

The metabolic phenotype was discovered in a proband with Alport-like nephropathy.[92,93] There should have been no misunderstanding about the association of hyperprolinemia with the renal disease in this pedigree; the former segregated as an autosomal recessive phenotype, whereas the renal phenotype

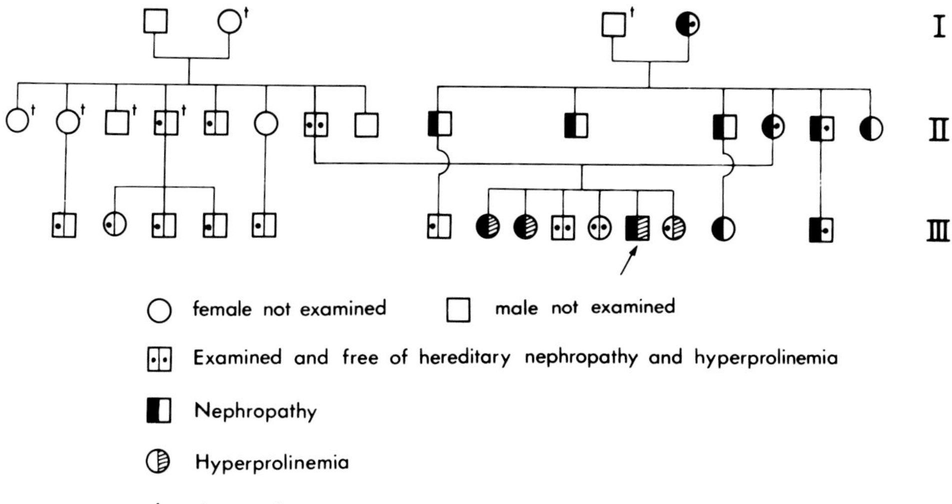

Fig. 18-6 Abbreviated pedigree of proband A with type I hyperprolinemia, showing dominant inheritance of familial nephropathy and apparent autosomal recessive inheritance of the hyperprolinemia. Clinical and genetic evidence suggest there is no cause and effect relationship between the hyperprolinemia and the nephropathy. *(Redrawn from Ref. 93, by permission.)*

was clearly an autosomal dominant (Fig. 18-6). Since individuals could have one phenotype without the other, there was no reason to presume that hyperprolinemia "caused" the nephropathy or vice versa.

In 11 reported families[92,94–98] with presumed type I hyperprolinemia, the metabolic phenotype came to attention retrospectively during investigation of a clinical disorder in the probands. The clinical disorders that attracted attention were not shared by all probands and included several forms of renal disease (e.g., summary by Mollica and Pavone[99]), different forms of ocular disease, mental retardation, and other neurologic manifestations.

Retrospective ascertainment of type I hyperprolinemia introduces a bias associating clinical manifestations with the metabolic disorder. Prospective studies of probands ascertained through newborn screening[94,96] indicated that the metabolic disorder is not necessarily associated with clinical manifestations. Contact with directors of various newborn urine screening programs (H. Levy, B. Wilcken, B. Lemieux, personal communications, 1986) corroborates this point of view. "Collateral" ascertainment of hyperprolinemic siblings in retrospectively ascertained families[93,95,97,100–102] and again in prospectively identified families[94] shows that the metabolic disorder can be free of any associated clinical manifestation. On these grounds, we assume that type I hyperprolinemia is a benign disorder until proven otherwise.

Type II Hyperprolinemia

Four probands were ascertained retrospectively[103–106]; another three were discovered incidentally.[107–109] Asymptomatic hyperprolinemic siblings were identified in two pedigrees.[104,109] Neurologic manifestations (seizures, mental retardation) predominated in the symptomatic patients. Ascertainment bias is the simplest explanation for an apparent association between metabolic phenotype and clinical disease. Although type II hyperprolinemia may be a benign metabolic disorder, it may also predispose affected subjects to the occasionally associated neurologic manifestations.

METABOLIC AND POLYPEPTIDE PHENOTYPES

Type I Hyperprolinemia

The plasma proline value is usually less than 2000 μM (normal value, 100 to 450 μM) in type I subjects. Pedigree data indicate that hyperprolinemia occurs in type I heterozygotes (Fig. 18-7). Hyperprolinemia in homozygotes with the type I phenotype, on average, is less than in the type II phenotype.

The proline concentration is elevated in cerebrospinal fluid,[110] but the plasma/cerebrospinal fluid proline ratio is not abnormal, implying that the source of proline accumulation in cerebrospinal fluid is not from brain.[73]

Urine proline is elevated; hence probands can be detected by urine screening of newborn infants. The mechanism of hyperprolinuria in human patients is predominantly prerenal with saturation of the reabsorption mechanism (see below).

Subjects with type I hyperprolinemia do not have an excess of Δ^1-pyrroline-5-carboxylic acid in urine or plasma. This finding indicates that the cause of proline accumulation is either overproduction (no evidence) or decreased catabolism due to deficient proline dehydrogenase (oxidase) activity. This enzyme is not present in skin fibroblasts or leukocytes. A single report[110] describes the catabolic defect in liver of a proband. Efron[110] assayed proline oxidation in liver homogenates; she did not assay proline oxidase specifically. She obtained liver from a proband at autopsy approximately 1 h postmortem. The tissue was homogenized,[65] incubated with L-proline and 4-hydroxy-L-proline, and assayed for production of Δ^1-pyrroline-5-carboxylic acid and Δ^1-pyrroline-3-hydroxy-5-carboxylic acid. The pyrroline compounds were measured by the *o*-aminobenzaldehyde reaction.[15] Aliquots of homogenates were also incubated with L-[^{14}C] proline and DL-hydroxyproline, and the formation of labeled glutamic and γ-hydroxyglutamic acid was measured. The results were compared with 23 control human liver samples obtained by biopsy or at autopsy. Conversion of proline to glutamate in the patient with type I hyper-

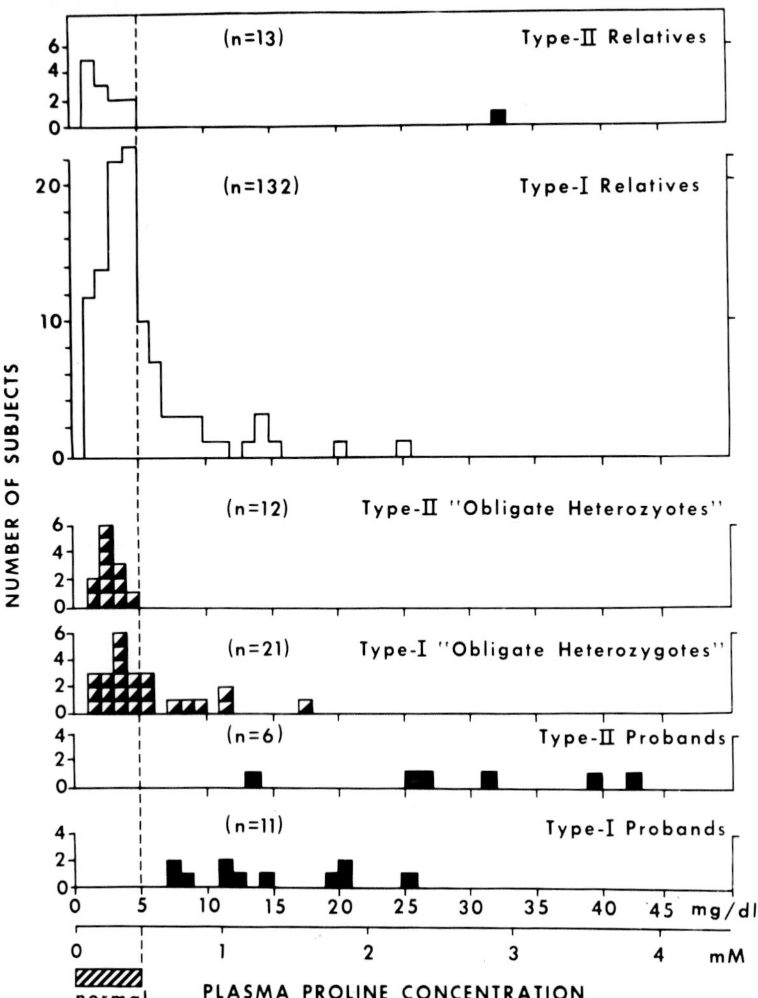

Fig. 18-7 Distribution diagram of plasma proline concentration in type I and type II hyperprolinemia probands, their parents ("obligate heterozygotes," assuming autosomal recessive inheritance), and relatives of probands. *(Data compiled from all reports cited in Table 18-2 of Ref. 112a. Thirty-seven additional subjects in the type I pedigree K,[95] whose plasma proline concentrations all fell in the normal range, are not included on the graph.)*

prolinemia was less than 10 percent of normal. There was such variation in the measurement of proline oxidation in the controls that it was not possible to document the presumed heterozygous phenotype in liver biopsy material obtained from the father of the proband.

Oxidation of hydroxyproline was "normal" in the proband's liver sample. This finding implies that oxidation of the two imino acids proceeds by different pathways in humans. Human brain has "oxidase" activity for proline but not for hydroxyproline.[110,111]

Type II Hyperprolinemia

The plasma proline value usually exceeds 2000 μM (normal value, 100 to 450 μM) in type II homozygotes. Heterozygotes do not have hyperprolinemia (Fig. 18-7). Proline values in cerebrospinal fluid and urine are correspondingly greater in type II homozygotes than in type I subjects.

Type II homozygotes excrete an *o*-aminobenzaldehyde-reacting substance into urine identified as Δ^1-pyrroline-5-carboxylic acid.[107,108,112–114] The concentrations are 10 to 40 times normal in plasma and urine.[56] The presence of this compound differentiates type II from type I hyperprolinemia.

Type II homozygotes excrete a second *o*-aminobenzaldehyde-reacting substance that is Δ^1-pyrroline-3-hydroxy-5-carboxylic acid.[107,115,116] This compound is a derivative of 4-hydroxy-L-proline. A loading test with 4-hydroxy-L-proline (100 mg/kg) markedly increases urinary Δ^1-pyrroline-3-hydroxy-5-carboxylate and is associated with attenuated clearance of hydroxyproline from plasma in type II probands.[107,116] These findings imply that the mutant polypeptide in type II hyperprolinemia is shared by the second step of the proline and hydroxyproline oxidative pathways.[67]

The mutant catalytic phenotype can be measured in vitro in skin fibroblasts and blood leukocytes in type II hyperprolinemia.[67,117,118] Δ^1-Pyrroline-5-carboxylate (P-5-C) dehydrogenase activity is absent in type II homozygotes and about one-half normal in the obligate heterozygote. Activities of P-5-C reductase and ornithine-aminotransferase are normal. Catalytic activity measured in vitro with Δ^1-pyrroline-3-hydroxy-5-carboxylate as substrate is deficient in the type II hyperprolinemia phenotype.[67] This finding confirms that the second step is common to the pathways of proline and hydroxyproline oxidation. However, plasma hydroxyproline is not increased in type II hyperprolinemia.

Mechanism of Hyperprolinemia in Type I and Type II Phenotypes

Two findings require explanation. First, the plasma proline value is higher, on average, in type II homozygotes than in type I homozygotes. Second, about one-third of type I heterozygotes have hyperprolinemia, whereas type II heterozygotes have normal plasma proline values. These quantitative features of the metabolic phenotype are apparent in Fig. 18-7. Their explanation, more truly a hypothesis, appears in Fig. 18-2.

The major metabolite, mole for mole, accumulating in type II hyperprolinemia is proline, not P-5-C, the substrate of the deficient enzyme (P-5-C dehydrogenase).[108,119] Ornithine, which feeds into the P-5-C "bridge" between urea and tricarboxylic cycles, apparently expands the free proline pool in type II hyperprolinemia.[119,120] Synthesis of glutamic-γ-semialdehyde from glutamate via P-5-C synthase could have a similar effect. Expansion of the P-5-C pool exists in type II hyperprolinemia[56] because outflow by P-5-C dehydrogenase is impaired while its synthesis from proline is unimpaired. Accordingly, substrate is plentiful (P-5-C) for the reductase whose product is proline. The total activity of P-5-C reductase in liver is greater than the corresponding activity of proline oxidase; moreover, the K_m values of these enzymes favor proline synthesis over proline degradation.[22,117] It follows that proline accumulation will be greater when proline dehydrogenase is deficient (type II hyperprolinemia) and the P-5-C pool is increased than when the block is at the level of proline oxidase (type I hyperprolinemia) and the P-5-C pool is not expanded.

We use Fig. 18-7 to explain hyperprolinemia in the type I heterozygote. This finding is a rare example of a metabolic phenotype occurring in the heterozygote for an autosomal recessive disorder. In this sense, type I hyperprolinemia is "dominantly expressed." Kacser and Burns[121] offer a molecular explanation for dominance. They note that metabolic homeostasis, meaning maintenance of the normal concentration of a metabolite, is usually the product of many enzymes acting in concert. The relative contribution (the sensitivity coefficient) of a catalyst to control the flux of substrate through the homeostatic pool, on the average, is inversely proportional to the number of catalysts contributing to the homeostatic value. Accordingly, half-normal activity (in the heterozygote) of one component in a large network of catalysts will perturb the metabolite value only minimally. On the other hand, half-normal activity of a catalyst with a large sensitivity coefficient perturbs the metabolite value more. Inspection of the "pathway" involved in type I hyperprolinemia (Fig. 18-2) shows it to be a "one-enzyme" pathway, whereas the pathway affected in type II hyperprolinemia is a "network" comprising many enzymes. It follows that half-normal activity of proline oxidase in the type I phenotype (an assumption, since no data on this point are available) will have a large effect on proline flux through its oxidative pathway, whereas the corresponding state in the type II phenotype affects an enzyme with a lower sensitivity coefficient at a different point in a network and will not significantly perturb proline homeostasis in the heterozygote.

Hyperaminoaciduria in the Hyperprolinemias

Whereas only proline is raised in plasma in type I and II phenotypes, three amino acids (proline, hydroxyproline, and glycine) are increased in urine. When plasma proline exceeds 800 μM in probands, the associated "iminoglycinuria" is directly proportional to the plasma proline concentration.[87,92] This finding reflects the "combined" mechanism of hyperaminoaciduria occurring in the hyperprolinemias. **Prolinuria** occurs when its tubular transport mechanism saturates at high substrate (proline) concentration in filtrate[87]; this saturation occurs at plasma concentrations in excess of about 800 μM. Glycine and hydroxyproline share a carrier with proline; when the latter is present at high concentration, transport of the other substrates is inhibited competitively and **iminoglycinuria** occurs. Hyperprolinemia was the first disorder in which the phenomenon of **combined hyperaminoaciduria** was recognized. The finding led to identification of a renal transport system with preference for imino acids and glycine (see Chap. 102).

Clinical Manifestations of the Interlock

One would expect that the metabolic interlock as defined in vitro would result in metabolic abnormalities in patients with inherited disorders of proline or P-5-C metabolism, especially in type II hyperprolinemia in which both proline and P-5-C are markedly elevated in plasma. However, the causation of clinical manifestations (i.e., seizures and mental retardation) by these metabolic abnormalities have not been proved. The occurrence of the biochemical phenotype free of clinical manifestations militates against direct causation. Recently, the identification of a subject with type II hyperprolinemia and the prospective screening of his relatives belonging to a subpopulation of Irish itinerants led to some interesting insights (M. Finn, personal communication). Three additional hyperprolinemic subjects were found in this population, and, though they are currently asymptomatic, they shared a common historical finding of frequent seizures during infancy. The identification of proline as a neuromodulator may be relevant here, as is the occurrence of learning deficits in hyperprolinemic PRO/Re mice.[121a] Thus, in spite of the conclusion that the biochemical disorder does not directly cause the clinical manifestations, the metabolic abnormalities may contribute to a multifactorial pathogenesis, resulting in some of the clinical manifestations.

In subjects with type II hyperprolinemia and a deficiency of P-5-C dehydrogenase, high concentrations of circulating P-5-C[56] have been added to the list of metabolic abnormalities that include hyperprolinemia and iminoglycinuria. The levels of P-5-C are fifteen- to twentyfold elevated over those of normal subjects. Glutamate levels are normal, and ornithine levels have been moderately elevated in certain subjects. Based on the high concentrations of proline and P-5-C found in these subjects and the cycling of proline and P-5-C established in vitro,[2] one would expect that the flux within this cycle is greatly increased. The increase in the flux through the proline-P-5-C cycle would augment the transfer of reducing potential from cytosol into mitochondria in tissues with a complete cycle. In peripheral tissues lacking proline oxidase in which the cycle is incomplete, oxidizing potential would be taken up as P-5-C and reducing potential as proline would be exported and transferred to the liver.

What are the indirect metabolic abnormalities that occur in subjects with the biochemical phenotype of type II hyperprolinemia? Unfortunately, systematic studies in a large population of subjects have been impossible. Nevertheless, we have done extensive studies in a single subject, and, within the context of the now established proline-mediated metabolic interlock and the proline-P-5-C cycle, these findings can be related to the primary defect.

Strikingly, peripheral oxygen utilization was frequently reduced in this subject (G. A. Fleming, A. N. Granger, J. M. Phang, unpublished observations). Bright red venous blood was noted on several occasions, and the documentation of high venous P_{O_2} in the face of normal arterial P_{O_2} followed. From over 30 samplings, 18 venous samples had a P_{O_2} value greater than 70 mmHg and 8 were over 90 mmHg. No evidence of anatomic or functional shunting, abnormal hemoglobin, or decreased total oxygen consumption was seen. In the face of markedly decreased peripheral O_2 consumption, pyruvate/lactate ratios were normal or even increased. Quite possibly, these findings indicate that increased levels of proline and P-5-C facilitated the transfer of oxidizing potential to peripheral tissues in the form of P-5-C and reducing potential back to the liver as proline. Thus, the redox perturbation generated by the cycle would decrease the utilization of O_2 for oxidizing NADH generated by glycolysis.

Another area of abnormality that has been identified is the concentration of amino acid neurotransmittors in the cerebrospinal fluid (CSF). γ-Aminobutyric acid,[122] glutamate,[123] and proline,[124,125] which are all known to have neuromodulator properties, were elevated in the patient with type II hyperprolinemia. Whether this abnormality in CSF amino acids or the aforementioned perturbation of redox contributes to the neurologic manifestations in certain subjects with this disorder remains an intriguing but unanswered question.

THE PRO/Re MOUSE: AN ANIMAL MODEL OF TYPE I HYPERPROLINEMIA

There are few nonhuman vertebrate models of human inborn errors of amino acid metabolism[126,127]; the PRO/Re mouse with hyperprolinemia and hyperprolinuria is one.[128,129] These mice have a learning deficit.[121a] Hepatic renal and brain proline dehydrogenase (oxidase) activity is 10 percent normal in homozygous PRO/Re mice.[129,130] Loss of proline oxidase activity represents expression of an autosomal allele at the locus designated *pro-1* for control of component 1 activity in the proline dehydrogenase complex of inner mitochondrial membrane,[130] and residual activity in PRO/Re tissue represents intact component 2 of proline dehydrogenase. Component 2 activity might be a hydroxyproline oxidase with some activity for proline substrate.[64] F_1 hybrid PRO/Re mice have intermediate hepatic enzyme activity and normal or elevated endogenous proline concentration in blood.[128–131]

The defect in proline oxidation in PRO/Re is located at the step corresponding to type I hyperprolinemia in humans; urinary excretion of Δ^1-pyrroline-5-carboxylic acid is normal in PRO/Re mice. PRO/Re and human hyperprolinemia type I phenotypes appear to be homologous in their effects on proline metabolism. No abnormalities of renal morphology are apparent,[131] and there is no apparent defect in learning or memory in PRO/Re mice.[132]

Three features of proline metabolism in the PRO/Re mutant are relevant to an understanding of the human counterpart. First, steady-state proline oxidation in kidney cortex slices is substantial in PRO/Re mice, probably due to component 2 proline dehydrogenase activity (e.g., Table 17-3, 4th edition of this text[133]); less than 4 percent residual enzyme activity sustains about 20 percent normal flux of proline through the oxidation pathway at physiological concentrations of substrate (about 100 μ*M* proline in extracellular fluid). The principal site of proline oxidation in kidney coincides with its major site of reabsorption. Second, the higher the proline concentration, the greater the oxidative flux[134]; accordingly, renal proline oxidation is supported in the mutant phenotype. Third, urinary excretion of proline in vivo is far in excess of that expected from the level of proline in plasma, and intracellular proline in PRO/Re kidney cortex is elevated about fourfold.[133] Whereas uptake of proline in vitro is not altered in PRO/Re kidney cortex slices, reclamation of proline from urine in vivo is impaired.[133] The block in proline metabolism is presumed to impair net proline reabsorption through its effect on the intracellular pool of proline, which, in its expanded state, enhances backflux at the luminal membrane, because proline leaking into the moving column of urine cannot be reclaimed and appears in bladder urine. From the PRO/Re mouse, we learn that intracellular "run out" (metabolism) of substrate is a component of net reabsorption by proximal tubule cells.[133,134] (This concept is discussed in further detail in Chap. 102.)

GENETICS OF THE HYPERPROLINEMIAS

Different enzymes are affected in type I and II hyperprolinemia; therefore, different loci in the two phenotypes are involved. The loci have not been mapped to particular chromosomes. Inheritance patterns indicate the loci are autosomal. Gyrate atrophy (one form is caused by an allele on chromosome 10; see Chap. 19) and aniridia (one form is associated with an allele on chromosome 11; see Chap. 9) occurred, respectively, in two different families with type I hyperprolinemia.[98,135] In neither family did the hyperprolinemia and ocular phenotypes segregate together. Accordingly, the likelihood of an inherited chromosomal microdeletion involving adjacent genes for the ocular and metabolic phenotypes is remote in these families. Moreover, the hypothesis, which involves two different chromosomes, could stand only if mutant alleles at the putative loci affected different polypeptides in the proline oxidase complex.[64]

It is not yet known whether type I subjects with the more extreme plasma proline values are homozygotes or compound heterozygotes. No opportunity to perform molecular genetic analyses of genotypes in this disorder to examine these alternatives has been available. Some probands were presumably homozygous because their parents were consanguinous.[95,101,136] The issue of genetic heterogeneity is relevant because type I heterozygotes may or may not have the hyperprolinemia phenotype (Fig. 18-6). One explanation for phenotypic heterogeneity is genetic heterogeneity. The other (in the case of type I hyperprolinemia) is the molecular theory of dominance[121] mentioned above ("Mechanism of Hyperprolinemia in Type I and Type II Phenotypes"). Phenotypic heterogeneity among type I heterozygotes is explained in this model by differences in background genotype among them and against which the type I allele plays. With regard to the available data (Fig. 18-7), the mean plasma proline value in **obligate** heterozygotes is higher than the normal mean value: 9 of 21 type I obligate heterozygotes have frank hyperprolinemia. Among 132 relatives of unspecified genotype, 35 have hyperprolinemia. Because the latter group excludes many euprolinemic relatives in one large pedigree,[95] the segregation ratio is not meaningful other than to show that the frequency of hyperprolinemia in relatives of type I probands is higher than expected for an autosomal recessive phenotype.

Probands with the type II hyperprolinemia metabolic phenotype are never heterozygous on the basis of present evidence and are either homozygotes or genetic compounds. The explanation for the recessive metabolic phenotype in type II heterozygotes is conventional.[121]

Diagnosis

Type I hyperprolinemia (homozygous, compound, or heterozygous genotypes) is recognized by persistent elevation of the plasma proline value above normal (450 μ*M*). High urine proline is not a sufficiently specific finding to permit the diagnosis.

The associated occurrence of iminoglycinuria is dependent on the plasma proline value and is not an obligatory feature of the phenotype. Urine P-5-C is not increased in type I subjects. Standard chemical assays and partition and ion exchange elution chromatographic methods serve for the measurement of proline (see previous editions of this text).

Type II hyperprolinemia is distinguished by coexistent hyperprolinemia and elevated excretion of P-5-C in urine. This compound may be identified by the yellow color it produces when reacted with *o*-aminobenzaldehyde (0.5 percent weight by volume) and trichloroacetic acid (5 percent volume by volume) in alcohol.[15,33,110] P-5-C can be measured in plasma by a specific method.[56] Discrimination between P-5-C and Δ^1-pyrroline-3-hydroxy-5-carboxylic acid (both are excreted in the type II phenotype) can be achieved by column chromatography.[107]

Therapy

Treatment is not indicated on the understanding that the hyperprolinemias, as we currently know them, are probably not diseases. In a particularly useful observation, Whelan and Connors[137] reported the outcome of two pregnancies in a woman with untreated type I hyperprolinemia; neither offspring was harmed by maternal hyperprolinemia (plasma proline 1300 to 2100 μ*M*).

Proline, a nonessential acid, is readily synthesized from precursors. Moreover, most dietary proteins contain proline (lactalbumin is an exception[138]). Accordingly, control of endogenous proline concentration by dietary methods is improbable. Those who attempted dietary therapy in probands with type I or II hyperprolinemia achieved a modest control of the plasma proline value, caused no apparent harm to the subject, and made no impact on the associated clinical disease.[119,139–142] The fact that dietary therapy reduces proline accumulation somewhat suggests that endogenous proline synthesis is not sufficient to meet metabolic needs, particularly in the young infant, and implies that dietary proline might be a "limiting" amino acid during rapid growth.[119,140]

(HYPER)HYDROXYPROLINEMIA

Clinical Phenotype

Hydroxyprolinemia is characterized by a plasma hydroxyproline value at least tenfold normal (normal value < 10 μ*M*). Hyperhydroxyprolinemia is the correct term since hydroxyproline is a normal constituent of plasma. There is no evidence that the metabolic phenotype is a cause of clinical manifestations. A bias of ascertainment exists in all published reports of probands because they had a disease, were investigated, and the identification of hyperhydroxyprolinemia was retrospective. There are no follow-up reports of prospectively identified probands from newborn screening.

Six probands have been reported.[143–148] The associated clinical disease is heterogeneous in this group. Healthy siblings with hyperhydroxyprolinemia were discovered in one of the pedigrees.[144,149]

Biochemical Phenotype

In Blood. The concentration of 4-hydroxyproline in plasma is abnormally high (range, 140 to 500 μ*M;* normal, <10 μ*M*). Concentrations of the other plasma amino acids are normal. The erythrocyte hydroxyproline pool is increased above normal.[147]

In Cerebrospinal Fluid. The hydroxyproline value is not elevated.

In Urine. Free hydroxyproline excretion is greatly increased (285 to 550 mg per 24 h), as reported in two studies.[141,149] Only trace amounts are found in the urine of normal subjects older than 6 months. Renal reabsorption of free hydroxyproline saturates normally in the hyperhydroxyprolinemia phenotype.[147] Whereas excretion of peptide-bound hydroxyproline (about 25 to 40 mg per 24 h)[111,149,150] and the profile of peptides are normal,[150] the bound hydroxyproline fraction in relation to total hydroxyproline is diminished; the fraction is >0.95 in normal subjects; it was <0.15 in hyperhydroxyprolinemia probands.[111,149]

If the block in free hydroxyproline oxidation is assumed to be complete, the urine data imply that about 90 percent of hydroxyproline released during collagen turnover is degraded by the free hydroxyproline pathway in the normal state, representing the turnover of 2 g or more of collagen daily.[77]

Metabolic Studies

Loading studies with 4-hydroxy-L-proline (100 to 200 mg/kg by mouth) showed that plasma hydroxyproline increased more in subjects with hyperhydroxyprolinemia than in controls and remained at elevated levels longer.[111,147,149] Up to one-half of the hydroxyproline load was excreted into urine within 24 h. Excretion of *o*-aminobenzaldehyde-reacting material (Δ^1-pyrroline-3-hydroxy-5-carboxylic acid is the relevant metabolite) did not increase after loading probands; normal subjects show an increase under these conditions (Fig. 18-8).

The rise in plasma proline after a load of L-proline (100 mg/kg by mouth) is normal in hyperhydroxyprolinemia subjects.[111] Pyrrole-2-carboxylic acid is excreted after the ingestion of allohydroxy-D-proline.[111] These findings indicate that proline oxidation and D-amino acid oxidase activity (allohydroxyproline-preferring) are both normal in the hyperhydroxyprolinemia phenotype. Pyrrole-2-carboxylate is excreted in increased amounts in hyperhydroxyprolinemia.[151] This metabolite is formed from the labile intermediate Δ^1-pyrroline-4-hydroxy-2-carboxylate (see Fig. 18-5 of the 5th edition of this text), the associated metabolic pathway perhaps disposing of

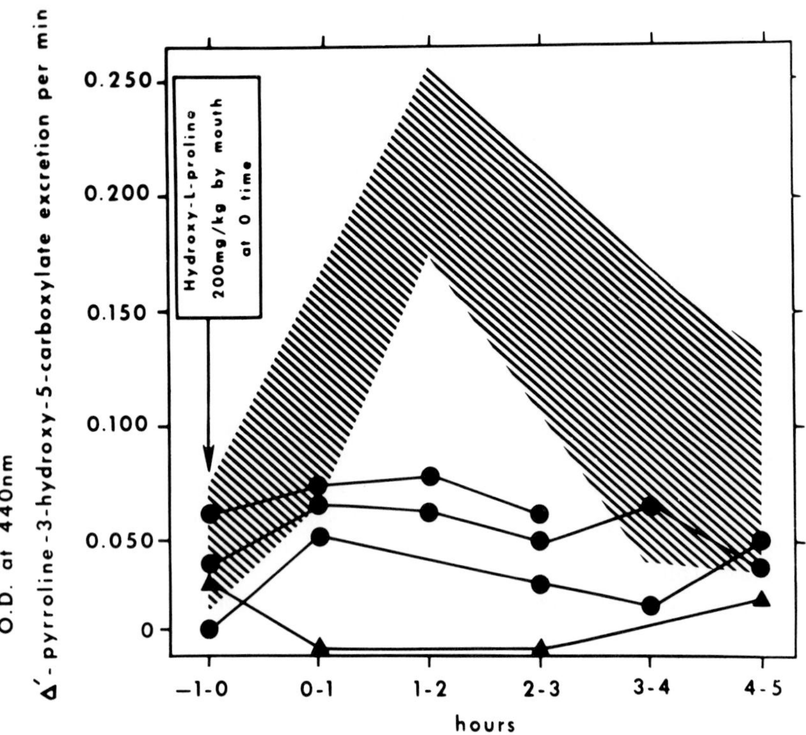

Fig. 18-8 Excretion of Δ^1-pyrroline-3-hydroxy-5-carboxylate in urine by normal subjects (shaded area, n = 13) and by proband A (○—○)[111] studies three times and proband B (Δ—Δ)[149] before and after receiving a hydroxyproline load (200 mg/kg body weight orally). The results are presented as optical density readings for 1 min aliquots of urine from timed (1- to 2-h) collections. The urine sample was adjusted to a final volume of 2.0 ml (by dilution or evaporation); 2.0 ml of o-aminobenzaldehyde reagent was added,[111] and the OD at 440 nm measured to estimate Δ^1-pyrroline-3-hydroxy-5-carboxylate.

any hydroxyproline accumulating in type II hyperprolinemia.[116] Metabolism of 3-hydroxyproline is not abnormal.[70]

The hyperhydroxyprolinemia phenotype provides an opportunity to examine biosynthesis of this imino acid in humans. Intravenous infusion of [1-^{14}C]glyoxylate in a proband caused small amounts of labeled hydroxyproline, 4-hydroxyglutamate, and 4-hydroxy-2-oxoglutarate (accounting in all for 0.2 percent of the administered radioactivity) to be excreted in the next 24 h.[150] Whether this finding indicates endogenous synthesis of hydroxyproline from glyoxalate, according to the findings of Goldstone and Adams,[152] cannot be said. Minimal transfer of label to hydroxyproline after an intravenous pulse of [^{14}C]glyoxylate, as observed in the clinical study, could have occurred by an indirect route, such as cycling of label through proline and collagen pools with subsequent release of hydroxyproline. Labeling of the peptide hydroxyproline pool in urine was not measured in the mutant phenotype. Adams[13] interprets the clinical study as evidence ***against*** significant biosynthesis of free hydroxyproline through reversal of the degradative pathway in humans.

Probable Nature of the Enzyme Defect in Hydroxyprolinemia

Direct measurements of enzymes or metabolic fluxes in vitro have not been performed in the hyperhydroxyprolinemia phenotype. Absence of Δ^1-pyrroline-3-hydroxy-5-carboxylate in urine[111,149] and evidence for decreased formation of this substance and other metabolites in the main degradative pathway for hydroxyproline in proband[111,147] imply that conversion of 4-hydroxy-L-proline to Δ^1-pyrroline-3-hydroxy-5-carboxylic acid is impaired. Proline oxidation is normal in the hyperhydroxyprolinemia phenotype,[141] which is taken as an indication that "proline oxidase" and "hydroxyproline oxidase" are separate catalytic activities.

Iminoaciduria in Hyperhydroxyprolinemia

Urinary excretion and endogenous renal clearance of free hydroxyproline are both increased in the phenotype, as expected if the filtered load of substrate is elevated sufficiently to permit saturation of the tubular transport mechanism.[88] Renal clearance rates for proline and glycine are not elevated in probands even though hydroxyproline, proline, and glycine share a renal transport system, and clearance rates of hydroxyproline and glycine are likely to be raised in the hyperprolinemia phenotype. The steady-state plasma hydroxyproline concentration must exceed 400 μM for inhibition to occur[88]; plasma hydroxyproline is usually below the threshold value in the mutant phenotype.

The occurrence of hydroxyprolinuria in hydroxyproline oxidase deficiency may depend, to some extent, on impaired metabolic "runout" of hydroxyproline in renal epithelium (see discussion of concept in "The PRO/Re mouse: An Animal Model of Type I Hyperprolinemia," above). Hydroxyproline is oxidized in mammalian kidney,[28,34] and the free hydroxyproline content of normal mammalian kidney cortex is negligible (C. R. Scriver, unpublished observation). A block in renal oxidation of hydroxyproline, with an increase of intracellular hydroxyproline in tubular epithelium, would inhibit net reabsorption by enhancing backflux at the luminal membrane.

Genetics

Consanguinity of parents in some pedigrees and appearance of the trait in both sexes and among siblings of probands indicate that the phenotype is autosomal recessive.

The Heterozygous Phenotype. Parents of probands have normal plasma hydroxyproline values,[111,147,149] but clearance of hydroxyproline from plasma after a loading test is delayed in the heterozygote.[147] The heterozygous child of a homozygote[149] excreted an excess of free hydroxyproline (16.5 to 18 percent of total excretion; normal, <5.2 percent[81]). Since hydroxyproline oxidation is physiologically attenuated in infancy[153] and this heterozygote was 2 years old, the "defect" in hydroxyproline oxidation in this subject might have been an adjunct of ontogeny and heterozygosity. Adult obligate heterozygotes have normal hydroxyproline excretion patterns.[149]

Diagnosis

Measurement of hydroxyproline in body fluids is possible with a variety of chemical and chromatographic methods (see previous editions of this text for details). Quantitative analysis is most reliable by elution chromatography on an ion exchange column.

The presence of hydroxyprolinuria does not constitute a diagnosis of hydroxyprolinemia. Hydroxyprolinuria is a normal finding for at least 3 months after birth,[73] and it is found also in hyperprolinemia and hereditary renal iminoglycinuria. Modest hyperhydroxyprolinemia (up to 100 μM) occurs as a physiological event in young infants,[153,154] and the plasma value may be even higher in infants alimented with formulas containing gelatin.[155] The excretion patterns of intermediates in the oxidation pathway of free hydroxyproline have not been described for the immature subject; a study of this type would identify the effect of ontogeny on hydroxyproline oxidation.

Therapy

There is no evidence that hyperhydroxyprolinemia is a disease. Therefore, there is no indication for therapy. A diet free of hydroxyproline did not lower plasma and urine hydroxyproline values in a treated proband.[141] Since collagen breakdown is the principal endogenous source of free hydroxyproline, it is unlikely that extracellular hydroxyproline can be lowered either by dietary limitations[111,141] or manipulation of its renal excretion.[145]

PROLIDASE DEFICIENCY WITH HYPERIMIDODIPEPTIDURIA

Prolidase or peptidase D (PEP D), an exopeptidase, cleaves imidodipeptides. Prolidase deficiency (McKusick 26413) is an autosomal recessive phenotype caused by several rare alleles at a locus on chromosome 19qcen-13.2. PEP D (prolidase) polymorphism (McKusick 17010) reflects common alleles at the same locus. The metabolic phenotype in prolidase deficiency is massive imidodipeptiduria (imidodipeptides have X-pro or X-hypro structures). Prolidase deficiency was not associated with a clinical phenotype in about one quarter of known cases at the time they were reported; all symptomatic patients had skin lesions and two-thirds had impaired cognitive development. Twenty-eight cases are known. We describe the enzyme, its putative role in metabolism, and the clinical, metabolic, and polypeptide phenotypes in prolidase deficiency. The rare alleles impair activity; the polymorphic alleles cause benign structural variants of prolidase.

Prolidase and Its Substrate

Imino acid-containing dipeptides are split by two enzymes with different biochemical properties. Prolinase, an exopeptidase (*imino*dipeptidase, EC 3.4.13.8) splits the peptide bond when the imino acid is N-terminal.[156] We are not concerned here with this enzyme, and there is no known example of prolinase deficiency in humans. Prolidase (*imido*dipeptidase, EC 3.4.13.9) is another exopeptidase. It splits the peptide bond when the imino acid is C terminal.[156] It is the enzyme of interest here.

Prolidase cleaves imidodipeptides after they have been transported into the cell. In epithelial cells of small intestine and proximal nephron, an imidodipeptide-preferring carrier mediates transport of substrate at the brush-border membrane.[89,90] Prolidase serves net uptake of imidodipeptides because it contributes to metabolic runout of the transported substrate. The process also serves nutrition because a significant fraction of dietary protein nitrogen is available as oligopeptides,[157] among which will be imidodipeptides in gelatin-containing diets.

Prolidase was first identified in pig intestinal mucosa[158] and was later purified from horse erythrocytes[156] and pig kidney[159] for studies of its properties. Prolidase has a wide distribution in mammalian tissues,[160] and activity is prominent even in brain[161]; deficient activity in that tissue may account for the "brain phenotype" in human prolidase deficiency (see below). Erythrocytes were a useful source for initial studies of the human enzyme.[162] The erythrocyte activity is quite similar among mammalian species and stable in frozen lysates.[162]

Prolidase is a cytosolic glycoprotein containing about 0.5 percent carbohydrate by weight.[163,164] It has been purified to apparent homogeneity from several nonhuman tissues,[165–168] human erythrocytes[169] (A. Richter et al., personal communication, 1987), and cultured human skin fibroblasts.[170] The native enzyme from various tissues has a relative molecular weight (M_r) of 108,000 to 116,000[168–171] and appears to exist as a dimer of polypeptide M_r 56,000 to 58,000.[168–171] Whether the different M_r values of native enzyme and subunit in different tissues are artifacts or the result of variations in posttranslation glycosylation of the polypeptide is not known. Amino acid composition data indicate prolidase is rich in glutamate and aspartate residues.[163,165,168] The primary sequence is not yet known.

Prolidase has a specific requirement for Mn^{2+}.[159] Ion is bound by a sulfhydryl residue, and reducing agents enhance prolidase activity in vitro.[159] Mn^{2+} apparently participates in a ligand between the active site and the exposed carboxyl group of the N-terminal residue of the dipeptide.[161,172] Native enzyme requires prolonged incubation at 37°C in the presence of Mn^{2+} (0.008 to 20 mM) for maximum activity in vitro and is stable thereafter (Fig. 18-9). The molecular change in prolidase associated with in vitro activation has not been identified, but it does not appear to involve conversion of a zymogen (A. Boright, personal communication, 1987). The significance of in vitro activation is not understood; in vivo activity in erythrocytes, for example, is expressed at 37°C in the presence of about 1 nM Mn^{2+} (viz., Ref. 216). The pH optimum of native enzyme is 7.6 to 7.8[171]; the isoelectric point is pH 4.4 to 4.5[171] in keeping with the preponderance of acidic amino acids in its structure. Erythrocyte prolidase has absolute preference for the trans isomer of dipeptide over the cis isomer.[172,173] In gen-

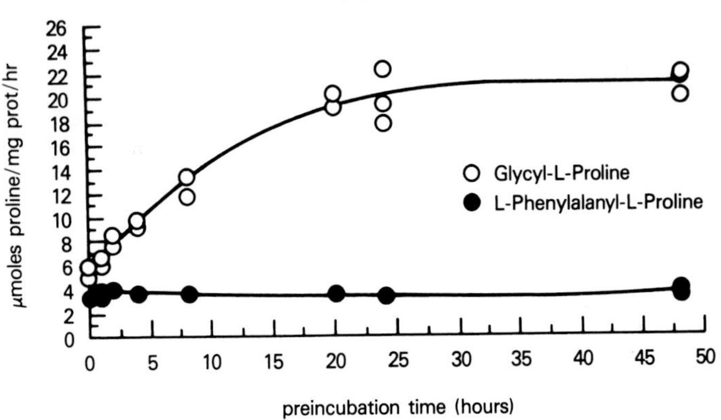

Fig. 18-9 Evidence for (1) activation of enzyme in vitro by preincubation for various periods (abscissa) and (2) substrate preference of prolidase. Activation of enzyme in sonicates of confluent fibroblast cultures required incubation at 37°C, pH 7.8, in the presence of 1 mM Mn^{2+} and 50 mM substrate. Activation times were varied (30 min to 48 h); assay incubation time was constant (1 h). Enzyme has greater cleavage activity against glycylproline *(A. Boright and C. R. Scriver, unpublished data.)*

eral, the smaller the N-terminal residue, the greater the specific cleavage activity[169] (see Fig. 18-9).

Sources of substrates for prolidase are both exogenous (dietary) and endogenous (collagen). The endogenous imidodipeptides are released in the final stages of collagen degradation. Since the source of substrate is extracellular and prolidase is mainly an intracellular enzyme, it follows that transport precedes hydrolysis of imidodipeptides. Transport is truly the rate limiting step for metabolism of extracellular glycylproline in the erythrocyte.[169,174] The transporter in brush-border membrane of intestinal and renal epithelium has a strong preference for imidodipeptides and is saturable, and the uptake process is concentrative, electrogenic, and energized by an inward-oriented proton gradient (peptide-H^+ cotransport).[175–177] Glycylproline transport in human erythrocytes is saturable,[174] but its other properties are poorly understood.

Prolidase Deficiency

Twenty-eight individuals with proven (or suspected[178,179]) prolidase deficiency have either been reported in the past 20 years or are known to us through personal communications (D. Danks, 1983; I. N. Targoff, 1986). Because there are multiple reports on particular probands or sibs, the corresponding references are bracketed (for the individual reports) to assist anyone wishing further to collate intra- and interindividual observations.[178,180;179;181,182;183,184;184,185;186;187–192;193–196;197–199;200–202;203,169;204,190–192;205,206;207;208;209;210]

Five asymptomatic cases (three probands and two sibs)[209,210] were ascertained prospectively by newborn urine screening. They are all still young and may yet develop symptoms. Two other asymptomatic persons, each a sib of a retrospectively diagnosed proband in two unrelated families, were 6[196] and 26[197] years of age when reported. The asymptomatic group is one-quarter of the total sample. Affected sibs[196,197,203,207,209] and cousins[203] of probands and consanguinity in parents[188;193;197,199;203;205] indicate that prolidase deficiency is inherited as an autosomal recessive phenotype.

Clinical Phenotype. Clinical manifestations of prolidase deficiency are pleomorphic and variable in age at onset (Fig. 18-10). Seven subjects[196,197,209,210] were asymptomatic at the time they were reported. One, at age 15 years, had developed skin lesions[196] (J. Arata, personal communication, 1987). Perhaps every person with prolidase deficiency will eventually manifest disease if life span is sufficient. At present, we have no explanation for the clinical heterogeneity. Accordingly, prognosis is uncertain and counseling of probands difficult, particularly for those identified by newborn screening.

We show a composite of the clinical phenotype in 19 symptomatic patients with known age at onset of manifestations (Fig. 18-10). The median age at diagnosis was about 7 years. Onset of first manifestation varied from birth to 22 years, which is either an artifact of reporting or representative of true phenotypic (and genetic) heterogeneity. All symptomatic cases had skin lesions, either in mild form on the face, palms, and soles (diffuse telangiectasia purpuric rash, ecchymosis, crusting erythematous dermatitis) or severe progressive ulceration, particularly on the lower legs. One proband required bilateral foot amputations (I. N. Targoff, personal communication, 1986), and at least one patient is known to have died.[199]

Impaired motor or cognitive development was the second most important manifestation; about two-thirds of symptomatic patients had this finding. About two-thirds of symptomatic cases had an increased frequency of infections classified in Fig. 18-10 as an impairment of the "immune system." A craniofacial phenotype was described in some severely affected cases comprising prominent skull sutures, ptosis, and ocular proptosis. Abnormalities of posture and gait were described in some patients. One report[178] described the conditions as "lathyritic."

Histologic findings have been reported. Widened cords of Billroth, swollen sinusoidal lining cells, and thickened arterial walls in the spleen were found in one severely affected patient.[178] The skin ulcers were biopsied in another patient.[182] The medium size vessels contained amyloid deposits in the walls with occasional occlusion of the lumen and apparent impairment of dermal microcirculation. Pathogenesis of these lesions and their role in clinical manifestations is unclear, but it seems likely that prolidase deficiency predisposes patients to skin that is susceptible to trauma and recalcitrant ulcers.

Metabolic Phenotype. Hyperimidodipeptiduria occurs in prolidase deficiency. Various amino acids occupy the N-terminal position of the dipeptide.[179,180,183,187,193,197,201,206] The major dipeptide is glycylproline,[180,187,193,201,206] comprising one-fifth or more of excreted dipeptides. The proline/hydroxyproline peptide excretion ratio is several times higher than normal[184] (see Table 18-1 for normal values). The excretion of peptide-bound hydroxyproline is also increased,[184,196,187] and gelatin feeding abnormally augments hydroxyproline peptide excretion in prolidase deficiency; 39 to 47 percent of the load

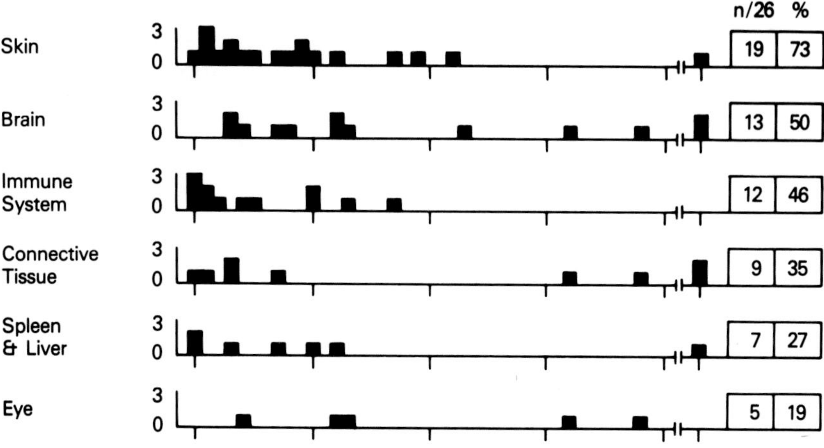

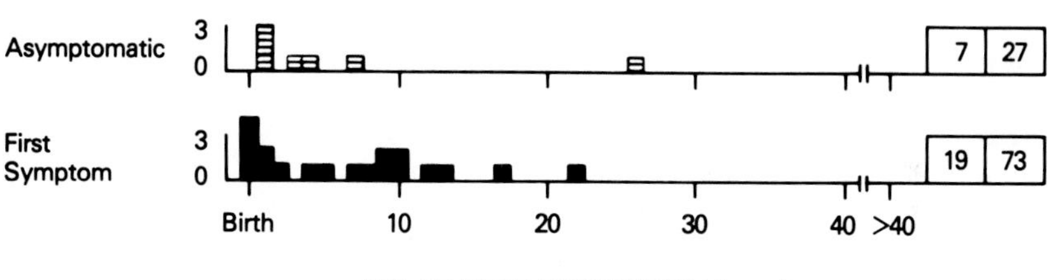

Fig. 18-10 The clinical phenotype in prolidase deficiency. It is pleomorphic and variable in age at onset. Age at diagnosis shown for asymptomatic cases; one of these, diagnosed at age 7 years, has subsequently developed skin lesions. Data shown for only 19 symptomatic cases; age-related data not available for two additional cases *(A. Boright and C. R. Scriver, from Ref. 170.)*

was excreted in one proband, compared with 6 percent in the control subjects,[184] implying that imidodipeptides are absorbed but not adequately hydrolyzed by intestinal mucosa in prolidase deficiency.

High urinary excretion of imidodipeptides has several mechanisms. First, their plasma levels and the corresponding filtered loads are apparently increased.[178,206] Second, renal reabsorption is impaired.[178] The latter has three possible components: (1) there is saturation of a renal transport system with rather low capacity[177]; (2) deficiency of intracellular prolidase impairs net reabsorption; and (3) there is evidence for "negative" reabsorption (secretion) since renal clearance of glycylproline exceeds the glomerular filtration rate.[178] Secretion was absent in a patient with hyperglycylprolinuria not attributed to prolidase deficiency.[87] Dipeptide secretion in prolidase deficiency can be explained if there is raised cellular concentration of substrate supported by uptake at the basolateral membrane with efflux at brush-border membrane.

Hyperimidodipeptiduria in prolidase-deficient subjects has been used to estimate collagen turnover rates in humans.[179,184,186] Rates were 1, 4.5, and 6 g/day in three unrelated probands aged 3, 48, and 7 years, respectively. When compared with 2 g/day in subjects without prolidase deficiency,[13,77,150] the rate in prolidase deficiency appears to be increased. Measurement of collagen catabolism in cultured skin fibroblasts indicated the rate was increased in one patient[202] but not in another.[189] If collagen turnover is increased in prolidase deficiency, dipeptide accumulation is the net result of overproduction and decreased hydrolysis.

Enzyme Phenotype. Prolidase activity is usually measured in erythrocytes for convenience, but cultured skin fibroblasts were used to study the mutant prolidase in several patients.[170,190,192,194,202,204,206] Published data are difficult to interpret and compare because different activation protocols and substrates were used by investigators. Symptomatic probands, in general, have very low cellular prolidase activity (below 7 percent normal when the latter refers to the author's protocol). Prolidase deficiency is expressed in cord blood.[209] Whereas the normal distribution of prolidase activity in filter-paper-dried blood spots has been reported,[211] corresponding values for erythrocyte hemolyates and fibroblast homogenates are not available. Cell density modifies fibroblast prolidase activity,[212] and specific activity increases several times as skin fibroblasts (and amniocytes presumably) achieve confluence. A reported effect of ascorbate on fibroblast prolidase activity[202] is an indirect effect of ascorbate on cell growth and density.[213] Age in culture (cumulative population doublings) does not influence fibroblast prolidase activity.[214]

The fibroblast prolidase phenotype is heterogeneous, which implies a coresponding genetic heterogeneity. Catalytic rate is reduced with or without reduced affinity for substrate (Fig. 18-11). Substrate specificity of the mutant enzyme is also apparently altered.[191] One group[192] claimed that two prolidase peaks elute from DEAE-cellulose columns. Fibroblasts from two probands were deficient in peak I, and peak II had reduced affinity for substrate. Corroboration of this finding has not been reported. Studies with antibodies (polyclonal and monoclonal) to purified human prolidase indicate that probands are either positive[170] or negative[215] for cross-reacting material. All mutant fibroblast cell strains studied so far show increased heat lability of prolidase.[170,192] Severity of clinical manifestations is loosely and inversely correlated with fibroblast prolidase activity.[170] Complementation analysis with fibroblast strains from six probands was negative for all fusion pairs.[170]

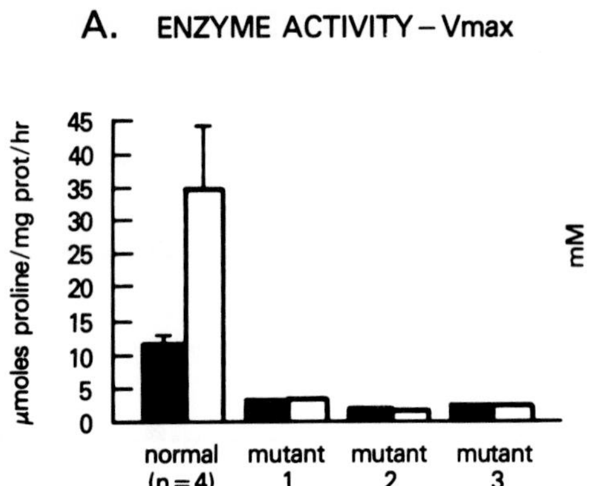

Fig. 18-11 Evidence for heterogeneity of polypeptide phenotype in prolidase deficiency. Sonicates of confluent skin fibroblast; culture from probands were used to assay prolidase. *A.* Three mutants have decreased V_{max} values; *B.* two also have significantly increased K_m values. Interindividual variation in cleavage of two different substrates is also apparent. (*A. Boright and C. R. Scriver, unpublished data.*)

Pathogenesis of Disease in Prolidase Deficiency

There is no simple explanation for the clinical manifestations associated with prolidase deficiency. Mn^{2+} content is increased two- to threefold in prolidase-deficient erythrocytes,[208] but it is not known whether this finding pertains to other cells or has clinical relevance. Complement C1q has collagenlike amino acid sequences, but there was no overt abnormality of serum C1q concentration in a symptomatic proband.[207] Collagen in dermis[198] and culture skin fibroblasts[202] had an elevated type III/type I collagen ratio. Collagen proline hydroxylation and collagen secretion by skin fibroblasts were normal.[189] Total collagen was normal in amount, the intracellular proline pool was decreased, and collagen catabolism was increased in a fibroblast study.[202] These findings imply that collagen metabolism is, in some manner, altered in prolidase deficiency. Defective metabolism of proline-containing peptides in brain may contribute to the pathogenesis of the "brain phenotype" in prolidase deficiency, and, conversely, the Mendelian phenotype may be informative about the role of prolidase in brain.[216]

Genetics

The Locus. Prolidase, called PEPD on human genome maps, was assigned initially to chromosome 19[217] and confirmed.[218] In mouse, the locus is on chromosome 7.[219] Studies of regional localization and linkage relationships on human chromosome 19[220–222] suggest the physical and genetic map of the PEPD region is: [LDL receptor-20cM-[complement component 3 (C3)]-6cM-[PEPD, myotonic dystrophy (DM)]-9cM-[Secretor]-10cM-[apolipoproteins APOE, APOC1, APOC2]. PEPD was mapped initially to region 19p13-cen.[222] The PEPD locus was reassigned to the proximal long arm (19qcen-13.2) by two groups (J. D. Brook et al.; M. B. Davis et al.) reporting (Abstracts 532 and 112, respectively) at Human Genome Mapping Workshop—9 (Paris, September 6–11, 1987). The DM (myotonic dystrophy) locus is also in region 19qcen-13.2 (HGM9, unpublished data). The relative order of loci (APOC2, TGFB, PVR, DM, PEPD) and linked markers (D19S7, D19S8, D19S9, MSK19, CYP1) is moot. It is a possibility that the proximity of PEPD to DM[223] and the occurrence of polymorphic restriction sites in the linkage group[224] may have clinical relevance in counseling for myotonic dystrophy (see Chap. 118). Physical distances between genes in the PEPD linkage group are different on male and female chromosomes,[222,225] with higher recombination frequencies in female then male meioses in the relevant region.[225]

Polymorphism. The human PEPD locus is polymorphic (McKusick 17010) and expressed as inherited electrophoretic variants of PEPD.[226] The codominantly expressed polymorphic alleles affect PEPD structure without any obvious effect on enzyme activity. Heterozygotes (with combinations of the common and variant alleles) show three activity bands or gels. Three PEPD phenotypes were observed in a sample of 1000 unrelated persons living in London, England.[226] The most prevalent homozygous phenotype is designated PEPD1; the polymorphic heterozygous phenotypes are PEPD2-1 and PEPD3-1. PEPD2-1 is found in Europeans (incidence, 0.022), East Indians (0.017), and West Indian blacks (0.048). PEPD3-1 was found only in Asian Indians (0.004) and blacks (0.041). The homozygous PEPD2 phenotype is rare; homozygous PEPD3 and heterozygous PEPD1-3 phenotypes were not observed in the original study.[226] The phenotypes are compatible with dimeric multimers of PEPD. If the PEPD1 polypeptide phenotype is designated D^1D^1, the polypeptide products would combine in PEPD2-1 heterozygotes to yield three isozymes, D^1D^1, D^1D^2, and D^2D^2, assuming combination of subunits is random and rates of synthesis and degradation are similar for the different subunits. If the three isozymes have similar cleavage activities, the bands on the gel should be in the ratio of 1:2:1 for D^1D^1, D^1D^2, and D^2D^2 isozymes, respectively; the observed ratio was approximately as predicted. The explanation for three activity bands for the PEPD3-1 phenotype is analogous.

Codominantly inherited electrophoretic polymorphism of prolidase also occurs in mouse[227] and king snake.[228]

Rare Alleles. Prolidase deficiency (McKusick 26413) is the homozygous or genetic compound expression of one or more mutant alleles. Unlike the polymorphic alleles, they have a major effect on PEPD activity. Studies of fibroblast enzyme show at least three classes of alleles associated with severe prolidase deficiency.[170,215] CRM positive alleles reduce either the V_{max} value or the affinity of enzyme for substrate; a third type affects polypeptide synthesis (CRM negative phenotype). Complementation analysis indicates no complementation between CRM and alleles, implying they are at one locus.[170]

Heterozygotes have the expected gene dosage effect, and prolidase activity is about one-half normal in erythrocytes[182,183,193,200,203,207,209] and confluent fibroblast cultures.[170,204] This finding implies that negative cooperativity does not occur between subunits in the rare allele heteropolymer.

The incidence of prolidase deficiency, estimated by prospective ascertainment in newborn screening programs,[209,210] is one to two probands per 1 million births. The corresponding allele frequencies are less than 0.001, assuming heterogeneity of rare alleles.

Diagnosis

The hyperimidodipeptiduria of prolidase deficiency can be measured by conventional partition and elution chromatography and by direct chemical ionization mass spectrometry.[187] The finding is present in the newborn.[209,210] Persons with heavy imidodipeptiduria do not necessarily have prolidase deficiency.[87] Heterozygotes appear not to have increased imidodipeptiduria.[170,197]

Hemolysates and homogenates of leukocytes, fibroblasts, and amniocytes are sources of prolidase for clinical studies. Activity should not be measured in intact cells because substrate transport is rate limiting.[169] Methods that measure simultaneous disappearance of substrate and appearance of product[174,229] have been described. A reliable assay, based on the Chinard reaction to measure formation of free proline,[230] has been used extensively for clinical investigations. Hemoglobin interferes with the assay of Josefsson and Lindberg,[231] and it cannot be used on erythrocytes.

Prolidase activity is severely deficient in affected persons. The normal value, according to a particular protocol, has been reported for dried blood spots on filter paper (233 ± 43 nmol/h per 3-mm disk). Prolidase activity in dried blood spots decreases on prolonged storage.[209] Interlaboratory referent normal values for erythrocytes and fibroblasts cannot be compared when different assays are used. Interproband quantitative values for deficiency phenotype can be compared only by expressing them as a percentage of the intralaboratory normal referent values. There is a concern about the biologic significance of values obtained by in vitro assays. Optimal conditions for assay[230] involve prior "activation" of prolidase at bizarre concentrations of Mn^{2+}, and the assay uses substrate concentrations that are supraphysiological. Partial prolidase "deficiency" at levels expressed by heterozygotes for rare alleles has been reported in the erythrocytes of uremic patients.[232]

Treatment and Counseling

Although some prolidase-deficient subjects do not have clinical disease, the majority of retrospectively ascertained cases had manifestations. The question of treatment must therefore be considered. Dietary supplements of L-proline, $MgCl_2$, and ascorbate were used in one patient[204]; an associated improvement in skin lesions could not be attributed solely to this treatment. Treatment for 1 month with oral ascorbate and Mn^{2+} and an inhibitor of collagenase improved skin ulcers and decreased imidodipeptide excretion one-half in another patient.[200,201] Transfusion with normal erythrocytes, as a form of enzyme replacement, raised blood prolidase activity to the heterozygous range for 6 weeks[169] but had no effect on urine peptide excretion and no effect on skin in two patients.[198,203] Skin grafts have been disappointing.[203] Daily applications of topical ointment containing L-proline and glycine significantly improved leg ulcers in one patient.[195] The potential benefits of treatment for the other putative manifestations of prolidase deficiency have not been investigated. Further studies with the prolidase inhibitor captopril in a rat model[233] would be of interest to investigate pathogenesis and treatment.

The counselor of a prospectively ascertained proband faces a dilemma; age at onset and severity of clinical disease cannot be predicted or explained. Risk for occurrence in siblings can be given, and prenatal diagnosis is theoretically possible.[204]

We thank Andrew Boright, graduate student, Department of Biology, McGill University, for sharing with us his knowledge of the prolidase enzyme and preliminary findings in prolidase-deficient patients.

REFERENCES

1. CAHILL GF JR, AOKI TT, SMITH RJ: Amino acid cycles in man, in Estabrook R (ed): *Current Topics in Cellular Regulation.* New York, Academic, 1981, vol 18, pp 389–400.
2. PHANG JM: The regulatory functions of proline and pyrroline-5-carboxylic acid, in Horecker BL, Stadtman ER (eds): *Current Topics in Cellular Regulation.* New York, Academic, 1985, vol 25, pp 92–132.
3. BROWN LM, HELLEBUST JA: Sorbitol and proline as intracellular osmotic solutes in the green alga *Stichococcus bacillaris. Can J Bot* 56:676, 1978.
4. CSONKA LN: Proline over-production results in enhanced osmotolerance in salmonella typhimurium. *Mol Gen Genet* 182:82, 1981.
5. BALBONI E: A proline shuttle in insect flight muscle. *Biochem Biophys Res Commun* 85:1090, 1978.
6. ISSEROFF H, SAWMA JT, KEINO D: Fascioliasis: Role of proline in bile duct hyperplasia. *Science* 198:1157, 1977.
7. SMITH GH: Functional differentiation of virgin mouse mammary epithelium in explant culture is dependent upon extracellular proline. *J Cell Physiol* 131:190, 1987.
8. PHANG JM, YEH GC, HAGEDORN CH: The intercellular proline cycle. *Life Sci* 28:53, 1981.
9. PHANG JM, DOWNING SJ, YEH GC, SMITH RJ, WILLIAMS JA: Stimulation of the hexose-monophosphate pentose pathway by Δ^1-pyrroline-5-carboxylic acid in human fibroblasts. *Biochem Biophys Res Commun* 87:363, 1980.
10. YEH GC, PHANG JM: The function of pyrroline-5-carboxylate reductase in human erythrocytes. *Biochem Biophys Res Commun* 94:450, 1980.
11. PHANG JM, DOWNING SJ, YEH GC: Linkage of the HMP pathway to ATP generation by the proline cycle. *Biochem Biophys Res Commun* 93:462, 1980.
12. PHANG JM, DOWNING SJ, YEH GC, SMITH RJ, WILLIAMS JA: Stimulation of the hexose-monophosphate pentose pathway by Δ^1-pyrroline-5-carboxylate in cultured cells. *J Cell Physiol* 110:255, 1982.
13. ADAMS E: Metabolism of proline and hydroxyproline. *Int Rev Connect Tissue Res* 5:1, 1970.
14. VOGEL HJ, DAVIS BD: Glutamic acid γ-semialdehyde and Δ^1-pyrroline-5-carboxylic acid, intermediates in the biosynthesis of proline. *J Am Chem Soc* 74:109, 1952.
15. STRECKER HJ: The interconversion of glutamic acid and proline 1. The formation of Δ^1-pyrroline-5-carboxylic acid from glutamic acid in *Escherichia coli. J Biol Chem* 225:825, 1957.
16. PERAINO C, PITOT HC: Ornithine-δ-transaminase in the rat. I. Assay and some general properties. *Biochim Biophys Acta* 73:222, 1963.
17. HERZFELD A, MEZL VA, KNOX WE: Enzymes metabolizing Δ^1-pyrroline-5-carboxylate in rat tissues. *Biochem J* 166:95, 1977.
18. ROSS G, DUNN D, JONES ME: Ornithine synthesis from glutamate in rat intestinal mucosa homogenates: Evidence for the reduction of glutamate to γ-glutamyl semialdehyde. *Biochem Biophys Res Commun* 85:140, 1978.
19. SMITH RJ, DOWNING SJ, PHANG JM, LODATO RF, AOKI TT: Pyrroline-5-carboxylate synthase activity in mammalian cells. *Proc Natl Acad Sci USA* 77:5221, 1980.
20. WAKABAYASHI Y, HENSLEE JG, JONES ME: Pyrroline-5-carboxylate synthesis from glutamate by rat intestinal mucosa. *J Biol Chem* 258:3873, 1983.
21. SMITH RJ, PHANG JM: The importance of ornithine as a precursor for proline in mammalian cells. *J Cell Physiol* 98:475, 1979.
22. PEISACH J, STRECKER HJ: The interconversion of glutamic acid and pro-

line: V. The reduction of Δ^1-pyrroline-5-carboxylic acid to proline. *J Biol Chem* 237:2255, 1962.

23. SMITH ME, GREENBERG DM: Preparation and properties of partially purified glutamic semialdehyde reductase. *J Biol Chem* 226:317, 1957.
24. YEH GC, HARRIS SC, PHANG JM: Pyrroline-5-carboxylate reductase in human erythrocytes: A comparison of differential regulation. *J Clin Invest* 67:1042, 1981.
25. SHIONO T, KADOR PF, KINOSHITA JJ: Purification and characterization of rat lens pyrroline-5-carboxylate reductase. *Biochim Biophys Acta* 881:72, 1986.
26. MERRILL MJ, YEH GC, PHANG JM: Human erythrocyte pyrroline-5-carboxylate reductase: preferential utilization of NADPH as cofactor. (In Preparation)
27. DOWNING SJ, YEH GC, PHANG JM: Association of P5C reductase with subcellular organelles in cultured cells. (In Preparation)
28. TAGGART JV, KRAKAUR RB: Studies on the cyclophorase system: V. The oxidation of proline and hydroxyproline. *J Biol Chem* 177:641, 1949.
29. JOHNSON AB, STRECKER HJ: The interconversion of glutamic acid and proline. IV. The oxidation of proline by rat liver mitochondria. *J Biol Chem* 237:1876, 1962.
30. KRAMAR R, FITSCHA P: Studies on the dehydrogenation of proline and hydroxyproline in animal tissues. *Enzymologia* 39:101, 1970.
31. MEYER J: Proline transport in rat liver mitochondria. *Arch Biochem Biophys* 178:387, 1977.
32. KOWALOFF EM, PHANG JM, GRANGER AS, DOWNING SJ: Regulation of proline oxidase activity by lactate. *Proc Natl Acad Sci USA* 74:5368, 1977.
33. STRECKER HJ: The interconversion of glutamic acid and proline: III. Δ^1-pyrroline-5-carboxylic acid dehydrogenase. *J Biol Chem 235:3218, 1960.*
34. ADAMS E, GOLDSTONE A: Hydroxyproline metabolism. IV. Enzymatic synthesis of γ-hydroxyglutamate from Δ^1-pyrroline-3-hydroxy-5-carboxylate. *J Biol Chem* 235:3504, 1960.
35. BRUNNER G, NEUPERT W: Localization of proline oxidase and Δ^1-pyrroline-5-carboxylic acid dehydrogenase in rat liver. *FEBS Lett* 3:283, 1969.
36. MEZL VA, KNOX WE: Metabolism of arginine in lactating rat mammary gland. *Biochem J* 166:105, 1977.
37. YIP MCM, KNOX WE: Function of arginase in lactating mammary gland. *Biochem J* 127:893, 1972.
38. SMITH RJ, PHANG JM: Proline metabolism in cartilage: The importance of proline biosynthesis. *Metabolism* 27:685, 1978.
39. VALLE D, DOWNING SJ, HARRIS SC, PHANG JM: Proline biosynthesis: Multiple defects in Chinese hamster ovary cells. *Biochem Biophys Res Commun* 53:1130, 1973.
40. KOWALOFF EM, GRANGER AS, PHANG JM: Glucocorticoid control of hepatic proline oxidase. *Metabolism* 26:893, 1977.
41. KOWALOFF EM, PHANG JM, GRANGER AS, DOWNING SJ: Glucocorticoid induction of proline oxidase in LLC-RK1 cells. *J Cell Physiol* 97:153, 1978.
42. PHANG JM, DOWNING SJ, SMITH RJ, YEH GC: The inhibition of proline oxidase by long-chain fatty acyl-Coenzyme As. *Fed Proc* 37:1480, 1978.
43. KADOWAKI H, PATTON GM, KNOX WE: Proline oxidase inhibition by free fatty acids of rat pancreas. *Biochem Biophys Acta* 614:294, 1980.
44. KOSOWER NS, KOSOWER EM: The glutathione status of cells. *Int Rev Cytol* 54:109, 1978.
45. EGGLESTON LV, KREBS HA: Regulation of the pentose phosphate cycle. *Biochem J* 138:425, 1974.
46. YEH GC, ROTH EF JR, PHANG JM, HARRIS SC, NAGEL RL, RINALDI A: The effect of pyrroline-5-carboxylic acid on nucleotide metabolism in erythrocytes from normal and glucose-6-phosphate dehydrogenase deficient subjects. *J Biol Chem* 259:5454, 1984.
47. YEH GC, PHANG JM: Activation of purine nucleotide formation by pyrroline-5-carboxylate in human erythrocytes. *J Biol Chem* (In press), 1988.
48. YEH GC, PHANG JM: The stimulation of purine nucleotide production by pyrroline-5-carboxylate in human erythrocytes. *Biochem Biophys Res Commun* 103:118, 1981.
49. YEH GC, PHANG JM: Pyrroline-5-carboxylate stimulates the conversion of purine antimetabolites to their nucleotide forms by a redox dependent mechanism. *J Biol Chem* 258:9774, 1983.
50. SMITH ML, BUCHANAN JM: Nucleotide and pentose synthesis after serum stimulation of resting 3T6 fibroblasts. *J Cell Physiol* 101:293, 1979.
51. HAGEDORN CH, PHANG JM: Transfer of reducing equivalents into mitochondria by the interconversions of proline and Δ^1-pyrroline-5-carboxylate. *Arch Biochem Biophys* 225:95, 1983.
52. HAGEDORN CH, PHANG JM: Catalytic transfer of hydride ions from NADPH to oxygen by the interconversions of proline and Δ^1-pyrroline-5-carboxylate. *Arch Biochem Biophys* 248:166, 1986.
53. HAGEDORN CH: Demonstration of a NADPH-linked Δ^1-pyrroline-5-carboxylate-proline shuttle in a cell-free rat liver system. *Biochim Biophys Acta* 884:11, 1986.
54. HAGEDORN CH, YEH GC, PHANG JM: Transfer of 1-pyrroline-5-carboxylate as oxidizing potential from hepatocytes to erythrocytes. *Biochem J* 202:31, 1982.
55. MIXSON AJ, GRANGER AN, PHANG JM: The uptake of pyrroline-5-carboxylate: Group translocation mediating redox transfers. *Fed Proc* 46(6):2166, 1987.
56. FLEMING GA, HAGEDORN CH, GRANGER AS, PHANG JM: Pyrroline-5-carboxylate in human plasma. *Metabolism* 33:739, 1984.
57. FLEMING GA, ROGERS QR, GRANGER AN, FORD DB, PROSSER M, PHANG JM: Peak plasma pyrroline-5-carboxylate levels reach 6-12 X basal in humans. *Clin Res* 35:(3)578A, 1987.
58. PHANG JM, DOWNING SJ: Synergistic stimulation of phosphoribosyl pyrophosphate by pyrroline-5-carboxylate and growth factors. *Clin Res* 33:(2)573A, 1985.
59. DOWNING SJ, PHANG JM: Mechanism of interaction between pyrroline-5-carboxylate and platelet-derived growth factor on phosphoribosyl pyrophosphate synthesis. (In Preparation)
60. PROCKOP DJ, BERG RA, KIVIRIKKO KI, VITTO J: Intracellular steps in the biosynthesis of collagen, in Ramchandran GN, Reddi AH (eds): *Biochemistry of Collagen*. New York, Plenum, 1976.
61. BENTLEY JP, HANSON AN: The hydroxyproline of elastin. *Biochim Biophys Acta* 175:339, 1969.
62. PORTER RR, REID KBM: The biochemistry of complement. *Nature* 275:699, 1978.
63. ANGLISTER L, ROGOZINSKI S, SILMAN L: Detection of hydroxyproline in preparations of acetylcholinesterase from the electric organ of the electric eel. *FEBS Lett* 69:129, 1976.
64. ADAMS E, FRANK L: Metabolism of proline and the hydroxyprolines. *Annu Rev Biochem* 49:1005, 1980.
65. ADAMS E, GOLDSTONE A: Hydroxyproline metabolism: Enzymatic preparation and properties of Δ^1-pyrroline-3-hydroxy-5-carboxylate. *J Biol Chem* 235:3492, 1960.
66. ROSSO RG, ADAMS E: Metabolism of gamma-hydroxyglutamic acid. *J Biol Chem* 237:3476, 1962.
67. VALLE D, GOODMAN SI, HARRIS SC, PHANG JM: Genetic evidence for a common enzyme catalyzing the second step in the degradation of proline and hydroxyproline. *J Clin Invest* 64:1365, 1979.
68. MAN M, ADAMS E: Basement membrane and interstitial collagen content of whole animals and tissues. *Biochem Biophys Res Commun* 66:9, 1975.
69. TRYGGVASON K, MAJAMAA K, KIVIRRIKO KI: Prolyl-3-hydroxylase and 4-hydroxylase activities in certain rat and chick embryo tissues and age-related changes in their activities in the rat. *Biochem J* 178:127, 1979.
70. ADAMS E, RAMASWAMY S, LAMON M: 3-Hydroxy-proline content of normal urine. *J Clin Invest* 61:1482, 1978.
71. BISKER A, PAILLER V, RANDOUX A, BOREL JP: A new sensitive method for the quantitative evaluation of the hydroxyproline isomers. *Anal Biochem* 122:52, 1982.
72. CHANARD J, SZYMANOWICZ A, BRUNOIS JP, TOUPANCE O, MELIN JP, BIREMBAUT P, RANDOUX A, BOREL PJ: Increased renal excretion of 3-hydroxyproline in patients with active glomerular nephropathies and with polycystic renal disease. *Clin Nephrol* 17:64, 1982.
73. SCRIVER CR, ROSENBERG LE: *Amino Acid Metabolism and Its Disorders.* Philadelphia, Saunders, 1973.
74. GREGORY DM, SOVETTS D, CLOW CL, SCRIVER CR: Plasma free amino acid values in normal children and adolescents. *Metabolism* 35:967, 1986.
75. KIBRICK AC, KITAGAWA G, MASKALERIS ML, GAINES R JR, MILHORAT AT: Hydroxyproline in human blood: Forms in which it is present. *Proc Soc Exp Biol Med* 119:622, 1965.
76. OYE I: The amount of free hydroxyproline in human blood serum. *Scand J Clin Lab Invest* 14:259, 1962.
77. KIVIRIKKO KI: Urinary excretion of hydroxyproline in health and disease. *Int Rev Connect Tissue Res* 5:93, 1970.
78. NUSGENS B, LAPIERE CHM: The relationship between proline and hydroxyproline urinary excretion in humans as an index of collagen metabolism. *Clin Chim Acta* 48:203, 1973.
79. MEILMAN E, URIVETZKY MM, RAPOPORT CM: Urinary hydroxyproline peptides. *J Clin Invest* 42:40, 1963.
80. KIVIRIKKO KI, LAITINEN O: Clinical significance of urinary hydroxyproline determinations in children. *Ann Paediatr Fenn* 11:148, 1965.
81. LAITINEN O, NIKKILA EA, KIVIRIKKO KI: Hydroxyproline in the serum and urine. Normal values and clinical significance. *Acta Med Scand* 179:275, 1966.
82. UITTO J, LAITINEN O, LAMBERG BA, KIVIRIKKO KI: Further evaluation of the significance of urinary hydroxyproline determinations in the diagnosis of thyroid disorder. *Clin Chim Acta* 22:583, 1968.
83. CHRISTENSEN HN: On the strategy of kinetic discrimination of amino acid transport systems. *J Membr Biol* 84:97, 1985.

84. FINERMAN GAM, ROSENBERG LE: Amino acid transport in bone: Evidence for separate transport systems for neutral amino and imino acids. *J Biol Chem* 241:1487, 1966.

85. FINERMAN GAM, DOWNING S, ROSENBERG LE: Amino acid transport in bone. II. Regulation of collagen synthesis by perturbation of proline transport. *Biochim Biophys Acta* 135:1008, 1967.

86. SAMARZIJA I, FROMTER E: Electrophysiological analysis of rat renal sugar and amino acid transport. III. Neutral amino acids. *Pflugers Arch* 393:119, 1982.

87. SCRIVER CR, EFRON ML, SCHAFER IA: Renal tubular transport of proline, hydroxyproline and glycine in health and in familial hyperprolinemia. *J Clin Invest* 43:374, 1964.

88. SCRIVER CR, GOLDMAN H: Renal tubular transport of proline, hydroxyproline and glycine. II. Hydroxy-L-proline as substrate and as inhibitor in vivo. *J Clin Invest* 45:1357, 1966.

89. RUBINO A, FIELD M, SCHWACHMAN H: Intestinal transport of amino acid residues of dipeptides. I. Influx of the glycine residue of glycyl-L-proline across mucosal border. *J Biol Chem* 246:3542, 1971.

90. GANAPATHY V, MENDICINO JF, LEIBACH FH: Transport of glycyl-L-proline into intestinal and renal brush border vesicles from rabbit. *J Biol Chem* 256:118, 1981.

91. BENOIT FL, WATTEN RH: Renal tubular transport of hydroxyproline peptides: Evidence for reabsorption and secretion. *Metabolism* 17:20, 1968.

92. SCRIVER CR, SCHAFER IA, EFRON ML: New renal tubular amino acid transport system and a new hereditary disorder of amino acid metabolism. *Nature* 192:672, 1961.

93. SCHAFER IA, SCRIVER CR, EFRON ML: Familial hyperprolinemia, cerebral dysfunction and renal anomalies occurring in a family with hereditary nephritis and deafness. *N Engl J Med* 267:51, 1962.

94. FONTAINE G, FARNIAUX JP, DAUTREVAUX M: L-Hyperprolinemie de type I. Étude d'une observation familiale. *Helv Paediatr Acta* 25:165, 1970.

95. WOODY NC, SNYDER CH, HARRIS JA: Hyperprolinemia: Clinical and biochemical family study. *Pediatrics* 44:554, 1969.

96. MOLLICA F, PAVONE L, ANTENER I: Pure familial hyperprolinemia: Isolated inborn error of amino acid metabolism without other anomalies in a Sicilian family. *Pediatrics* 48:225, 1971.

97. POTTER JL, WAICKMAN FJ: Hyperprolinemia. I. A study of a large family. *J Pediatrics* 83:635, 1973.

98. FUSCO G, CARLOMAGNO S, ROMANO A, RINALDI E, CEDROLA G, CIANCIARUSO L, CURTO A, ROSOLIA S, AURICCHIO G: Type-I hyperprolinemia in a family suffering from aniridia and severe dystrophia of ocular tissues. *Ophthalmologica* 173:1, 1976

99. MOLLICA F, PAVONE L: Hyperprolinemia: A disease which does not need treatment. *Acta Paediatr Scand* 65:206, 1976.

100. KOPELMAN H, ASATOOR AM, MILINE MD: Hyperprolinaemia and hereditary nephritis. *Lancet* 2:1075, 1964.

101. PERRY TL, HARDWICK DF, DOWRY RB, HANSEN S: Hyperprolinemia in two successive generations of a North American Indian family. *Ann Hum Genet* 31:401, 1968.

102. HAINAUT H, HARIGA J, WILLEMS C, HEUSDEN A, CHAPELLE P: Hyperprolinemie essentielle familiale. *Presse Med* 79:945, 1971.

103. BERLOW S, EFRON ME: A new cause of hyperprolinemia associated with the excretion of Δ^1-pyrroline-5-carboxylic acid. *Proc Soc Pediatr Res*, 34th Annual Meeting, Seattle, 1964, p 43.

104. SIMILA S, VISAKORPI JK: Hyperprolinemia without renal disease. *Acta Paediatr Scand (Suppl)* 177:122, 1967.

105. EMERY FA, GOLDIE L, STERN J: Hyperprolinaemia Type II. *J Ment Defic Res* 12:187, 1968.

106. JEUNE M, COLLOMBEL C, MICHEL M, DAVID M, GUIBAULT P, GUERRIER G, ALBERT J: Hyperleucinisoleucinemie par defaut partiel de transamination associe a une hyperolinemie de Type II. Observation familiale d'une double aminoacidopathie. *Sem Hop (Ann Pediatr)* 17:85, 1970.

107. GOODMAN SI, MACE JW, MILES BS, TENG CC, BROWN SB: Defective hydroxyproline metabolism in type II hyperprolinemia. *Biochem Med* 10:329, 1974.

108. APPLEGARTH DA, INGRAM P, HINGSTON J, HARDWICK DF: Hyperprolinemia type II. *Clin Biochem* 7:14, 1974.

109. PAVONE L, MOLLICA F, LEVY HL: Asymptomatic type-II hyperprolinemia associated with hyperglycinaemia in three sibs. *Arch Dius Child* 50:637, 1975.

110. EFRON ML: Familial hyperprolinemia. Report of a second case, associated with congenital renal malformations, hereditary hematuria and mild mental retardation, with demonstration of an enzyme defect. *N Engl J Med* 272:1243, 1965.

111. EFRON ML, BIXBY EM, PRYLES CV: Hydroxyprolinemia. II. A rare metabolic disease due to a deficiency of the enzyme "hydroxyproline oxidase." *N Engl J Med* 272:1299, 1965.

112. EFRON ML: Disorders of proline and hydroxyproline metabolism, in Stanbury JB, Wyngaarden JB, Frederickson DS (eds): *The Metabolic Basis of Inherited Disease,* 2d ed. New York, McGraw-Hill, 1966, p 376.

112a. SCRIVER CR, SMITH RJ, PHANG JM: Disorders of proline and hydroxyproline metabolism, in Stanbury JB, Wyngaarden JB, Frederickson DS (eds): *The Metabolic Basis of Inherited Disease,* 5th ed. New York, McGraw-Hill, 1983, p 360.

113. SELKOE DJ: Familial hyperprolinemia and mental retardation. A second metabolic type. *Neurology* 19:494, 1969.

114. SIMILA S: Hyperprolinemia type II. *Ann Clin Res* 2:143, 1970.

115. DOOLEY KC, APPLEGARTH DA: Hyperprolinemia type II: Evidence of the excretion of 3-hydroxy delta 1-pyrroline-5-carboxylic acid. *Clin Biochem* 12:62, 1979.

116. SIMILA S: Hydroxyproline metabolism in type II hyperprolinemia. *Ann Clin Biochem* 16:177, 1979.

117. VALLE DL, PHANG JM, GOODMAN SI: Type II hyperprolinemia: Absence of Δ^1-pyrroline-5-carboxylic acid dehydrogenase activity. *Science* 185:1053, 1974.

118. VALLE D, GOODMAN SI, APPLEGARTH DA, SHIH VE, PHANG JM: Type II hyperprolinemia. Δ^1-pyrroline-5-carboxylic acid dehydrogenase deficiency in cultured skin fibroblasts and circulating lymphocytes. *J Clin Invest* 58:598, 1976.

119. SIMILA S: Dietary treatment in hyperprolinemia type II. *Acta Paediatr Scand* 63:249, 1974.

120. SIMILA S: The catabolism of ornithine after intravenous loading in normal subjects and two patients with hyperprolinemia type II. *Clin Chim Acta* 28:457, 1970.

121. KACSER H, BURNS JA: The molecular basis of dominance. *Genetics* 97:639, 1981.

121a. DAVIS JL, PICO RM, FLOOD JF: Differences in learning between hyperprolinemic mice and their congenic controls. *Behav Neural Biol* 48:128, 1987.

122. FELIX D, KUNZLE H: in Costa E, Giacobini E, Paoletti R (eds): *Advances in Biochemical Psychopharmacology,* New York, Raven, vol 15, pp 165–173, 1976.

123. VAN HERREVELD A, FIFKOVA E: Effects of amino acids on the isolated chicken retina, and on its response to glutamate stimulation. *J Neurochem* 20:947, 1973.

124. RHOADS DE, PETERSON NA, RAGHUPATHY E: Selective inhibition of synaptosomal proline uptake by leucine and methionine enkephalins. *J Biol Chem* 258:12233, 1983.

125. RHOADS DE, SAMKARAM H, PETERSON NA, RAGHUPATHY E: Interaction of enkephalins and des-tyrosyl-enkaphalins with synaptosomal plasma membrane vesicles: Enkephalin binding and inhibition of proline transport. *Biochemistry* 25:1580, 1986.

126. LUSH IE: The biochemical genetics of vertebrates except man, in Neuberger A, Tatum EL (eds): *Frontiers of Biology,* Amsterdam, North-Holland, 1967, vol 3.

127. BULFIELD G: Inherited metabolic disease in laboratory animals: A review. *J Inherited Metab Dis* 3:133, 1980.

128. BLAKE RL, RUSSELL ES: Hyperprolinemia and prolinuria in a new inbred strain of mice, PRO/Re. *Science* 176:809, 1972.

129. BLAKE, RL: Animal model for hyperprolinemia: Deficiency of mouse proline oxidase activity. *Biochem J* 129:987, 1972.

130. BLAKE RL, HALL JG, RUSSELL ES: Mitochondrial proline dehydrogenase deficiency in hyperprolinemic PRO/Re mice: Genetic and enzymatic analyses. *Biochem Genet* 14:739, 1976.

131. KANWAR YS, KRAKOWER CA, MANALIGOD JR, JUSTIC P, WONG PW: Biochemical, morphological and hybrid studies in hyperprolinemic mice. *Biomedicine* 22:209, 1975.

132. BAXTER CF, BALDWIN RA, DAVIS JL, FLOOD JF: High proline levels in the brains of mice as related to specific learning deficits. *Pharmacol Biochem Behav* 22:1053, 1985.

133. SCRIVER CR, MCINNES RR, MOHYUDDIN F: Role of epithelial architecture and intracellular metabolism in proline uptake and transtubular reclamation in PRO/Re mouse kidney. *Proc Natl Acad Sci USA* 72:1431, 1975.

134. SIMELL O, SCRIVER CR, MOHYUDDIN F: Structural relationships between metabolism and transport of proline in the nephron. *Pediatr Res* 10:444, 1976.

135. DOUGLAS EP: Hyperprolinemia and gyrate atrophy of the choroid and retina in members of the same family. *Br J Ophthalmol* 69:588, 1985.

136. GOYER RA, REYNODS J, BURKE J, BURKHOLDER P: Hereditary renal disease with neurosensory hearing loss, prolinuria and ichthyosis. *Am J Med Sci* 256:166, 1968.

137. WHELAN DT, CONNORS WC: Maternal hyperprolinemia. *Lancet* 1:981, 1980.

138. BLOCKS RJ, BOLLING D: *The Amino Acid Composition of Proteins and Foods*. Springfield, IL, Charles C Thomas, Publisher, 1951.

139. PIESOWICZ AT: Hyperprolinaemia. *Arch Dis Child* 43:748, 1968.

140. HARRIES JT, PIESOWICZ AT, SEAKINS JWT, FRANCIS DEM, WOLFF OH: Low proline diet in type-I hyperprolinemia. *Arch Dis Child* 46:72, 1971.

141. EFRON ML: Treatment of hydroxyprolinemia and hyperprolinemia. *Am J Dis Child* 113:166, 1967.

142. GOYER RA, MITCHELL BJ, LEONARD DL: Dietary reduction of hyperprolinemia. *J Lab Clin Med* 73:819, 1969.

143. EFRON ML, BIXBY EM, PALATTAO LG, PRYLES CV: Hydroxyprolinemia associated with mental deficiency. *N Engl J Med* 267:1193, 1962.

144. PELKONNEN R, LAHDEVIRTA J, VISAKORPI JK, KIVIRRIKO KI: Hydroxyprolinemia: A case without mental deficiency. *Scand J Clin Lab Invest* 23(*suppl* 108): 21, 1969.

145. RAINE DN: Defects in renal tubular reabsorption, in Benson PF (ed): *Defects in Cellular Organelles and Membranes in Relation to Mental Retardation*. London, Churchill, Livingston, Institute for Research into Mental Retardation Study Group No. 2, 43, 1971.

146. RAMA RAO BS, SUBHASH MN, MARAYANAN HS: Hydroxyprolinemia: A case report. *Indian Pediatr* 11:829, 1974.

147. ROESEL RA, BLANKENSHIP PR, LYNCH WR, CORYELL ME, THEVAOS TS, HALL WK: Hydroxyproline metabolism in two sisters with hydroxyprolinemia. *Hum Hered* 29:364, 1979.

148. ROBINSON MJ, MENZIES IS, SLOAN I: Hydroxyprolinemia with normal development. *Arch Dis Child* 55:484, 1980.

149. PELKONEN R, KIVIRIKKO KI: Hydroxyprolinemia. *N Engl J Med* 283:451, 1970.

150. EFRON ML, BIXBY EM, HOCKADAY TDR, SMITH LH JR, MESHORER E: Hydroxyprolinemia. III. The origin of free hydroxyproline in hydroxyprolinemia. Collagen turnover. Evidence for a biosynthetic pathway in man. *Biochim Biophys Acta* 165:238, 1968.

151. HEACOCK AM, ADAMS E: Formation and excretion of pyrrole-2-carboxylate in man. *J Clin Invest* 54:810, 1974.

152. GOLDSTONE A, ADAMS E: Further metabolic reactions of γ-hydroxyglutamate: Amidation of γ-hydroxyglutamine possible reduction to hydroxyproline. *Biochem Biophys Res Commun* 16:71, 1964.

153. MORROW G III, KIVIRIKKO KI, PROCKOP DJ: Catabolism and excretion of free hydroxyproline in infancy. *J Clin Endocrinol* 27:1365, 1967.

154. MORROW G III, KIVIRIKKO KI, PROCKOP DJ: Hydroxyprolinemia and increased excretion of free hydroxyproline in early infancy. *J Clin Endocrinol* 26:1012, 1966.

155. HUMAN PE, SHAPIRO LJ: Dietary hydroxyprolinemia. *J Pediatr* 104:595, 1984.,

156. ADAMS E, SMITH EL: Peptidases of erythrocytes. II. Isolation and properties of prolidase. *J Biol Chem* 198:67, 1952.

157. ADIBI SA, MERCER DW: Protein digestion in human intestine as reflected in luminal, mucosal and plasma amino acid concentration after meals. *J Clin Invest* 52:1586, 1973.

158. BERGMANN M, FRUTON JS: On proteolytic enzymes. XII. Regarding the specificity of aminopeptidase and carboxypeptidase. A new type of enzyme in the intestinal tract. *J Biol Chem* 117:189, 1937.

159. DAVIS NC, SMITH EL: Purification and some properties of prolidase and swine kidney. *J Biol Chem* 224:261, 1956.

160. SMITH EL: The peptidases of skeletal, heart, and uterine muscle. *J Biol Chem* 173:553, 1948.

161. HUI KS, LAJTHA A: Prolidase activity in brain: Comparison with other organs. *J Neurochem* 30:321, 1978.

162. ADAMS E, MCFADDEN M, SMITH EL: Peptidases of erythrocytes. I. Distribution in man and other species. *J Biol Chem* 198: 663, 1952.

163. SJORSTROM H, NOREN O: Structural properties of pig intestinal proline dipeptidase. *Biochim Biophys Acta* 359:177, 1974.

164. NOREN O, DABELSTEEN E, SJOSTROM H, JOSEFSSON L: Histological localization of two dipeptidases in the pig small intestine and liver, using immunofluroescence. *Gastroenterology* 72:87, 1977.

165. MANAO G, NASSI P, CAPPUGI G, CAMICI G, RAMPONI G: Swine kidney prolidase: Assay, isolation procedure, and molecular properties. *Physiol Chem Phys* 4:75, 1972.

166. SJOSTROM H, NOREN O, JOSEFSSON L: Purification and specificity of pig intestinal prolidase. *Biochim Biophys Acta* 327:457, 1973.

167. BAKSI K, RADHAKRISHNAN AN: Purification and properties of prolidase (imidodipeptidase) from monkey small intestine. *Indian J Biochem Biophys* 11:7, 1974.

168. YOSHIMOTO T, MATSUBARA F, KAWANO E, TSURO D: Prolidase from bovine intestine: Purification and characterization. *J Biochem* 94:1889, 1983.

169. ENDO F, MATSUDA I, OGATA A, TANAKA S: Human erythrocyte prolidase and prolidase deficiency. *Pediatr Res* 16:227, 1982.

170. BORIGHT AP, CHOY F, LANCASTER GA, SCRIVER CR: Prolidase (Pep D) deficiency: Polypeptide heterogeneity underlies the variable clinical phenotype. *Am J Hum Genet* 41(3):A4, 1987.

171. MYARA I, CHARPENTIER C, LEMONNIER A: Minireview. Prolidase and prolidase deficiency. *Life Sci* 34:1985, 1984.

172. KING GF, MIDDLEHURST CR, KUCHEL PW: Direct NMR evidence that prolidase is specific for the trans isomer of imidodipeptide substrates. *Biochemistry* 25:1054, 1986.

173. LIN L-N, BRANDTS JF: Evidence suggesting that some proteolytic enzymes may cleave only the trans form of the peptide bond. *Biochemistry* 18:43, 1979.

174. KING GF, KUCHEL PW: A proton n.m.r. study of imidodipeptide transport and hydrolysis in the human erythrocyte. *Biochem J* 220:553, 1984.

175. GANAPATHY V, LEIBACH FH: Role of pH gradient and membrane potential in dipeptide transport in intestinal and renal brush-border membrane vesicles from the rabbit. *J Biol Chem* 258:14189, 1983.

176. GANAPATHY V, BURCKHARDT G, LEIBACH FH: Characteristics of glycylsarcosine transport in renal intestinal brush-border membrane vesicles. *J Biol Chem* 259:8954, 1984.

177. GANAPATHY V, LEIBACH FH: Carrier-mediated reabsorption of small peptides in renal proximal tubule. *Am J Physiol* 251:F945, 1986.

178. GOODMAN SI, SOLOMONS CC, MUSCHENHEIM F, MACINTYRE CA, MILES B, O'BRIEN D: A syndrome resembling lathyrism associated with iminodipeptiduria. *Am J Med* 45:152, 1968.

179. JOHNSTONE RAW, POVALL TJ, BATY JD, POUSSET J-L, CHARPENTIER C, LEMONNIER A: Determination of dipeptides in urine. *Clin Chim Acta* 52:137, 1974.

180. BUIST NRM, STRANDHOLM JJ, BELLINGER JF, KENNAWAY NG: Further studies on patient with iminodipeptiduria: A probable case of prolidase deficiency. *Metabolism* 21:1113, 1972.

181. LAPIERE CH. M, NUSGENS B: Plaies cutanées torpides et trouble du metabolisme du collagene. *Arch Belg Dermatol Syphiligraph* XXV:353, 1969.

182. PIERARD GE, CORNIL F, LAPIERE CH.M: Pathogenesis of ulcerations in deficiency of prolidase. *Am J Dermatopathol* 6:491, 1984.

183. POWELL GF, RASCO MA, MANISCALCO RM: A prolidase deficiency in man with iminodipeptiduria. *Metabolism* 23:505, 1974.

184. POWELL GH, MANISCALCO RM: Bound hydroxyproline excretion following gelatin loading in prolidase deficiency. *Metabolism* 25:503, 1976.

185. POWELL GF, KUROSKY A, MANISCALCO RM: Prolidase deficiency: Report of a second case with quantitation of the excessively excreted amino acids. *J Pediatr* 91:242, 1977.

186. JACKSON SH, DENNIS AW, GREENBERG M: Iminodipeptiduria: A genetic defect in recycling collagen; a method for determining prolidase in erythrocytes. *Can Med Assoc J* 113:759, 1975.

187. FAULL KF, SCHIER GM, SCHLESINGER P, HALPERN B: The mass spectrometric identification of dipeptides in the urine of a patient suffering from chronic skin ulceration and oedema. *Clin Chim Acta* 70:313, 1976.

188. SHEFFIELD LJ, SCHLESINGER P, FAULL K, HALPERN BJ, SCHIER GM, COTTON RGH, HAMMOND J, DANKS DM: Iminopeptiduria, skin ulcerations, and edema in a boy with prolidase deficiency. *J Pediatr* 91:578, 1977.

189. ROYCE PM, DANKS DM: Normal hydroxylation of proline in collagen synthesized by skin fibroblasts from a patient with prolidase deficiency. *J Inherited Metab Dis* 5:111, 1982.

190. PRIESTMAN DA, BUTTERWORTH J: Prolidase deficiency: Characteristics of human skin fibroblast prolidase using colorimetric and fluorimetric assays. *Clin Chim Acta* 142:263, 1984.

191. BUTTERWORTH J, PRIESTMAN D: Substrate specificity of manganese-activated prolidase in control and prolidase-deficient cultured skin fibroblasts. *J Inherited Metab Dis* 7:32, 1984.

192. BUTTERWORTH J, PRIESTMAN DA: Presence in human cells and tissues of two prolidases and their alteration in prolidase deficiency. *J Inherited Metab Dis* 8:193, 1985.

193. KODAMA H, UMEMURA S, SHIMOMURA M, MIZUHARA S, ARATA J, YAMAMOTO Y, YASUTAKE A, IZUMIYA N: Studies on a patient with iminopeptiduria I. Identification of urinary iminopeptides. *Physiol Chem Phys* 8:463, 1976.

194. ARATA J, UMEMURA S, YAMAMOTO Y, HAGIYAMA M, NOHARA N: Prolidase deficiency. Its dermatological manifestations and some additional biochemical studies. *Arch Dermatol* 115:62, 1979.

195. ARATA J, HATAKENAKA K, OONO T: Effect of topical application of glycine and proline on recalcitrant leg ulcers of prolidase deficiency. *Arch Dermatol* 122:626, 1986.

196. UMEMURA S: Studies on a patient with iminodipeptiduria. II. Lack of prolidase activity in blood cells. *Physiol Chem Phys* 10:279, 1978.

197. ISEMURA M, HANYU T, GEJYO F, NAKAZAWA R, IGARASHI R, MATSUO S, IKEDA K, SATO Y: Prolidase deficiency with imidodipeptiduria. A familial case with and without clinical symptoms. *Clin Chim Acta* 93:401, 1979.

198. ISEMURA M, HANYU T, ONO T, IGARASHI R, SATO Y, GEJYO F, NAKAZAWA R, MIYAKAWA T, TAKAGI T, KUBOKI Y, SASAKI S: Studies on prolidase de-

ficiency with a possible defect in collagen metabolism. *Tohoku J Exp Med* 134:21, 1981.

199. SEKIYA M, OHNISHI Y, KIMURA K: An autopsy case of prolidase deficiency. *Virchows Arch (A)* 406:125, 1985.

200. CHARPENTIER C, DAGBOVIE K, LEMONNIER A, LARREQUE M, JOHNSTONE RAW: Prolidase deficiency with iminodipeptiduria: Biochemical investigations and first results of attempted therapy. *J Inherited Metab Dis* 4:77, 1981.

201. LARREGUE M, CHARPENTIER C, LAIDET B, LAMBERT M, BRESSIEUX J-M, PRIGENT F, CANUEL C, TANZER J: Deficit en prolidase et en manganese. A propos d'une observation: diagnostic et traitement. *Ann Dermatol Venereol* 109:667, 1982.

202. MYARA I, CHARPENTIER C, WOLFROM C, GAUTIER M, LEMONNIER A: In vitro responses to ascorbate and manganese in fibroblasts from a patient with prolidase deficiency and iminodipeptiduria: Cell growth, prolidase activity and collagen metabolism. *J Inherited Metab Dis* 6:27, 1983.

203. OGATA K, TANAKA S, TOMODA T, MURAYAMA E, ENDO F, KIKUCHI I: Autosomal recessive prolidase deficiency. Three patients with recalcitrant leg ulcers. *Arch Dermatol* 117:689, 1981.

204. PEDERSEN PS, CHRISTENSEN E, BRANDT NJ: Case Report. Prolidase deficiency. *Acta Paediatr Scand* 72:785, 1983.

205. DER KALOUSTIAN VM, FREIJ BJ, KURBAN AK: Prolidase deficiency: An inborn error of metabolism with major dermatological manifestations. *Dermatologica* 164:293, 1982.

206. FREIJ BJ, LEVY HL, DUDIN G, MUTASIM D, DEEB M, DER KALOUSTIAN VM: Clinical and biochemical characteristics of prolidase deficiency in siblings. *Am J Med Genet* 19:561, 1984.

207. GRAY RGF, GREEN A, WARD AM, ANDERSON I, PECK DS: Biochemical and immunological studies on a family with prolidase deficiency. *J Inherited Metab Dis* 6(suppl 2):143, 1983.

208. LOMBECK I, WENDEL U, VERSIECK J, VAN BALLENBERGHE L, BREMER HJ, DURAN R, WADMAN S: Increased manganese content and reduced arginase activity in erythrocytes of a patient with prolidase deficiency (iminodipeptiduria). *Eur J Pediatr* 114:571, 1986.

209. NAUGHTEN ER, PROCTOR SP, LEVY HL, COULOMBE JT, AMPOLA MG: Congenital expression of prolidase defect in prolidase deficiency. *Pediatr Res* 18:259, 1984.

210. LEMIEUX B, AURAY-BLAIS C, GIGUERE R, SHAPCOTT D: Prolidase deficiency: Detection of cases by a newborn urinary screening programme. *J Inherited Metab Dis* 7(suppl 2):145, 1984.

211. ENDO F, MATSUDA I: Screening method for prolidase deficiency. *Hum Genet* 56:349, 1981.

212. MYARA I, CHARPENTIER C, GAUTHER M, LEMONNIER A: Cell density affects prolidase and prolinase activity and intracellular amino acid levels in cultured human cells. *Clin Chim Acta* 150:1, 1985.

213. MYARA I, WOLFROM C, CHARPENTIER C, GAUTIER M, LEMONNIER A: Relationship between cell density and prolidase activity in human skin fibroblasts: effects of ascorbate and fructose. *Biochimie* 66:445, 1984.

214. SAMBUY Y, BITTLES AH: The effects of in vitro ageing on the exopeptidases of human diploid fibroblasts. *Mech Ageing Dev* 26:13, 1984.

215. ENDO F, MOTOHARA K, INDO Y, MATSUDA I: Immunochemical studies of human prolidase with monoclonal and polyclonal antibodies: Absence of the subunit of prolidase in erythrocytes from a patient of prolidase deficiency. *Pediatr Rev* 22:627, 1987.

216. HUI K-S, LAJTHA A: Prolidase activity in rat brain; developmental, regional and subcellular distribution. *Brain Res* 153:79, 1978.

217. MCALPINE PJ, MOHANDAS T, RAY M, WANG H, HAMERTON JL: Assignment of the *peptidase D* gene locus *(PEPD)* to chromosome 19 in man. *Cytogenet Cell Genet* 16:204, 1976.

218. BROWN S, LALLEY PA, MINNA JD: Assignment of the gene for peptidase S *(PEPS)* to chromosome 4 in man and confirmation of peptidase D *(PEPD)* assignment to chromosome 19. *Cytogenet Cell Genet* 22:167, 1978.

219. LALLEY PA, FRANCKE U, MINNA JD: Comparative gene mapping in man and mouse: assignment of the genes for lactate dehydrogenase-A, peptidase-D, and isocitrate dehydrogenase-2 to mouse chromosome 7. *Cytogenet Cell Genet* 22:577, 1978.

220. EIBERG H, MOHR J, NIELSEN S, SIMONSEN N: Genetics and linkage relationships of the C3 polymorphism: Discovery of C3-Se linkage and assignment of LES-C3-DM-Se-PEPD-Lu synteny to chromosome 19. *Clin Genet* 24:159, 1983.

221. BROOK JD, SHAW DJ, MEREDITY L, BURNS GAP, HARPER PS: Localization of genetic markers and orientation of the linkage group on chromosome 19. *Hum Genet* 68:282, 1984.

222. LUSIS AJ, HEINZMANN C, SPARKES RS, SCOTT J, KNOTT TJ, GELLER R, SPARKES MC, MOHANDAS T: Regional mapping of human chromosome 19: Organization of genes for plasma lipid transport (APOC1, -C2, and -E and LDLR) and the genes C3, PEPD, and GP1. *Proc Natl Acad Sci USA* 83:3929, 1986.

223. O'BRIEN T, BALL S, SARFARAZI M, HARPER PS, ROBSON EB: Genetic linkage between the loci for myotonic dystrophy and peptidase D. *Ann Hum Genet* 47:117, 1983.

224. SHAW DJ, MEREDITH AL, SARFARAZI M, HARLEY HG, HUSON SM, BROOK JD, BUFTON L, LITT M, MOHANDAS T, HARPER PS: Regional localizations and linkage relationships of seven RFLPs and myotonic dystrophy on chromosome 19. *Hum Genet* 74:262, 1986.

225. SHAW DJ, MEREDITH AL, BROOK JD, SARFARAZI M, HARLEY HG, HUSON SM, BELL GI, HARPER PS: Linkage relationships of the insulin gene with the complement component 3, LDL receptor, apolipoprotein C2 and myotonic dystrophy loci on chromosome 19. *Hum Genet* 74:267, 1986.

226. LEWIS WHP, HARRIS H: Peptidase (D) (prolinase) variants in man. *Ann Hum Genet* 32:317, 1969.

227. SKOW LC: Genetic variation for prolidase (PEP-4) in the mouse maps near the gene for glucosephosphate isomerase (GPI-1) on chromosome 7. *Biochem Genet* 19:695, 1981.

228. DESSAUER HC, ZWEIFEL RG: Inheritance of transferrin, phosphoglucomutase, 6-phosphogluconate dehydrogenase, and prolidase in a breeding colony of kingsnakes. *J Hered* 72:453, 1981.

229. MIKASA H, ARATA J, KODAMA H: Measurement of prolidase activity in erythrocytes using isotachophoresis. *J Chromatogr* 310:410, 1984.

230. MYARA I, CHARPENTIER C, LEMONNEIR A: Optimal conditions for prolidase assay by proline colorimetric determination: Application to iminodipeptiduria. *Clin Chim Acta* 125:193, 1982.

231. JOSEFSSON L, LINDBERG T: Intestinal dipeptidases. I. Spectrophotometric determination and characterization of dipeptidase activity in pig intestinal mucosa. *Biochim Biophys Acta* 105:149, 1965.

232. GEJYO F, KISHORE BK, ARAKAWA M: Prolidase and prolinase activities in the erythrocytes of patients with chronic uremia. *Nephron* 35:58, 1983.

233. GANAPATHY V, PASHLEY SJ, ROESEL A, PASHLEY DH, LEIBACH FH: Inhibition of rat and human prolidases by captopril. *Biochem Pharmacol* 34:1287, 1985.

CHAPTER **19**

THE HYPERORNITHINEMIAS

DAVID VALLE
OLLI SIMELL

1. *Ornithine is a nonprotein amino acid that is the substrate or product of five enzymatic reactions and is the ligand of a transmitochondrial transport protein. Two of these enzymes, ornithine-δ-aminotransferase and ornithine decarboxylase, catalyze reactions that consume ornithine. The former catalyzes the major catabolic reaction for ornithine. The source of ornithine is arginine in dietary protein, although under certain circumstances,* de novo *synthesis of ornithine apparently occurs by a reversal of the normal flux in the ornithine-δ-aminotransferase reaction.*
2. *There are two distinct genetic disorders which result in hyperornithinemia: gyrate atrophy of the choroid and retina and the hyperornithinemia-hyperammonemia-homocitrullinuria (HHH) syndrome.*
3. *Gyrate atrophy of the choroid and retina is a progressive chorioretinal degeneration which is inherited as an autosomal recessive trait. It is caused by a deficiency of ornithine-δ-aminotransferase. We know of over 100 biochemically documented cases, about half of which are Finnish. There is myopia, night blindness, and loss of peripheral vision starting late in the first decade, proceeding to tunnel vision and eventual blindness by the third and fourth decades. Posterior subcapsular cataracts are present in nearly all patients by the end of the second decade. The ocular fundus exhibits sharply demarcated circular areas of complete chorioretinal degeneration which start in the midperiphery and gradually extend to the posterior pole. Tubular aggregates are present in the type II fibers of skeletal muscle. Plasma ornithine values range from 400 to 1400* μM, *and 0.5 to 10 mmol of ornithine is excreted daily. Plasma glutamate, glutamine, lysine, creatine, and creatinine concentrations are modestly reduced. Ornithine-δ-aminotransferase activity in the cells and tissues of patients is from 0 to 6 percent that in controls, and obligate heterozygotes have intermediate values. Six patients have had in vitro and in vivo responses to pharmacologic doses of pyridoxal phosphate or pyridoxine. Additional therapeutic approaches have included an arginine-restricted diet which in some patients has lowered plasma ornithine to normal values; administration of pharmacologic doses of* L*-lysine or α-aminoisobutyric acid to increase renal losses; and administration of proline or creatine. The outcome of patients treated in these ways has been variable, and no form of therapy is unequivocally effective in preventing chorioretinal degeneration. Creatine administration has resulted in improvement of the histologic abnormalities in muscle.*
4. *Human, rat, and yeast ornithine-δ-aminotransferase cDNAs have been cloned and sequenced. The human ornithine-δ-aminotransferase gene has been mapped to 10q26 and its structure determined. A cluster of apparently nonfunctional ornithine-δ-aminotransferase–related sequences map to Xp11–Xp21. About 85 percent of gyrate atrophy patients express approximately normal amounts of normally sized ornithine-δ-aminotransferase mRNA in their cultured fibroblasts. At this writing, five well-documented missense mutations causing gyrate atrophy have been delineated.*
5. *The HHH syndrome is an autosomal recessive inherited disorder that has been described in over 30 patients. The clinical symptoms are related to the hyperammonemia and resemble those of the urea cycle disorders. No visual problems or ocular fundus changes are present. Plasma ornithine concentrations range from 209 to 1020* μM *on a self-restricted protein diet and in general are slightly lower than in gyrate atrophy. The pathophysiology of the disease may involve diminished ornithine transport into the mitochondria with ornithine accumulation in the cytoplasm and reduced intramitochondrial ornithine causing impaired ureagenesis and orotic aciduria. An ornithine translocator has been partially purified from beef liver and reconstituted in liposomes. Direct studies of its function and integrity in HHH syndrome tissues have not been performed. Ornithine-δ-aminotransferase is normal. Homocitrulline is thought to originate from transcarbamylation of lysine. Its excretion is increased by lysine supplementation. The patients tolerate 1.2 to 1.5 g/kg protein daily without hyperammonemia. Further elevation of plasma ornithine by ornithine supplementation has reduced ammonia levels in some but not all patients. The long-term efficacy of ornithine supplementation in this disorder is unknown.*

Ornithine is a nonprotein amino acid that plays an important role in the metabolism of urea, creatine, and polyamines. The pathways of ornithine metabolism are closely linked with those of proline (see Chap. 18). Together they allow the exchange of molecules between the urea (see Chap. 20) and tricarboxylic acid cycles. The major source of ornithine is arginine in dietary protein. The fates of the ornithine carbon atoms include incorporation into protein as arginine, proline, glutamate, or any of the α-ketoglutarate–derived nonessential amino acids; conversion to the polyamines and γ-aminobutyric acid; and oxidation in the tricarboxylic acid cycle.

There are two inherited disorders which result in hyperornithinemia: gyrate atrophy of the choroid and retina, with symptoms limited mainly to the eye; and the hyperornithinemia-hyperammonemia-homocitrullinuria (HHH) syndrome, with symptoms resulting from ammonia accumulation and protein aversion. The former condition is due to a deficiency of the mitochondrial matrix enzyme ornithine-δ-aminotransferase (Fig. 19-1), while the basic defect in the latter is thought to be caused by an impairment in the carrier-mediated entry of ornithine into mitochondria.

Nonstandard abbreviation used in this chapter is: HHH = hyperornithinemia-hyperammonemia-homocitrullinuria.

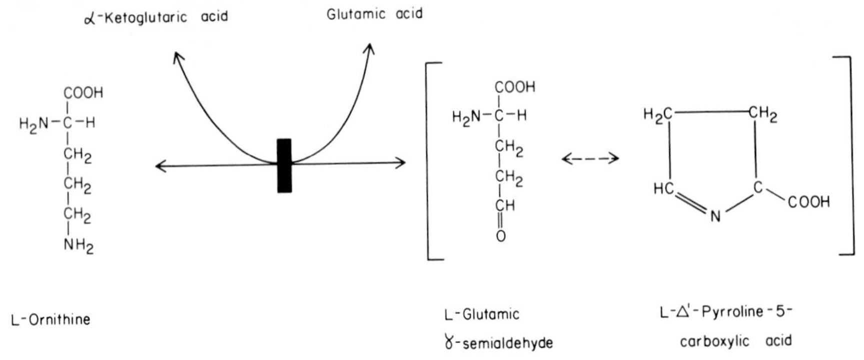

α-Ketoglutaric acid — Glutamic acid

L-Ornithine — L-Glutamic γ-semialdehyde ⇠⇢ L-Δ[1]-Pyrroline-5-carboxylic acid

Fig. 19-1 Deficiency of ornithine-δ-aminotransferase: the primary enzymatic defect in gyrate atrophy of the choroid and retina.

ORNITHINE METABOLISM

Ornithine is either a substrate or a product of five enzymes and a mitochondrial transport protein (Fig. 19-2). The chemical characteristics of these proteins are listed in Table 19-1. Ornithine metabolism can be considered in four sections: the urea cycle; polyamine biosynthesis; creatine synthesis; and the ornithine-δ-aminotransferase reaction. Depending on the physiological circumstances, the last reaction functions as a component in arginine degradation, proline biosynthesis, or *de novo* ornithine synthesis.

The Urea Cycle

In most instances, ornithine serves as a catalyst in the urea cycle, providing the molecular foundation upon which urea is assembled from nitrogen atoms contributed by ammonium and aspartate and a carbon atom from bicarbonate. Each molecule of ornithine converted to citrulline in the mitochondrial matrix is eventually reformed from arginine in the cytoplasm. Stoichiometric or noncatalytic utilization of ornithine in the urea cycle occurs in two special circumstances: (1) when the urea cycle is interrupted by inherited enzyme deficiencies which lead to the accumulation of citrulline, arginosuccinate,

Fig. 19-2 Ornithine metabolic pathways. The outer and inner mitochondrial membranes are indicated. Not all of the enzymes shown are expressed in all tissues. For example, ornithine transcarbamoylase is expressed mainly in liver and, to a much lesser extent, in the epithelial cells of the small intestine and renal cortex. Glycine transamidinase is expressed mainly in renal cortex, pancreas, and liver. See text for details. The subcellular localization of glycine transamidinase is not well known; in rat kidney it appears to be located on the outer (cytoplasmic) aspect of the inner mitochondrial membrane.[353] The black vertical rectangle signifies the site of the metabolic block in gyrate atrophy. The asterisk indicates the probable site of the metabolic block in the HHH syndrome. AdoMet = *S*-adenosylmethionine; CAP = carbamoyl phosphate; GABA = γ-aminobutyric acid; GTA = glycine transamidinase; MTA = methylthioadenosine; OAT = ornithine-δ-aminotransferase; ODC = ornithine decarboxylase; OTC = ornithine transcarbamoylase; P5C = Δ^1-pyrroline-5-carboxylate.

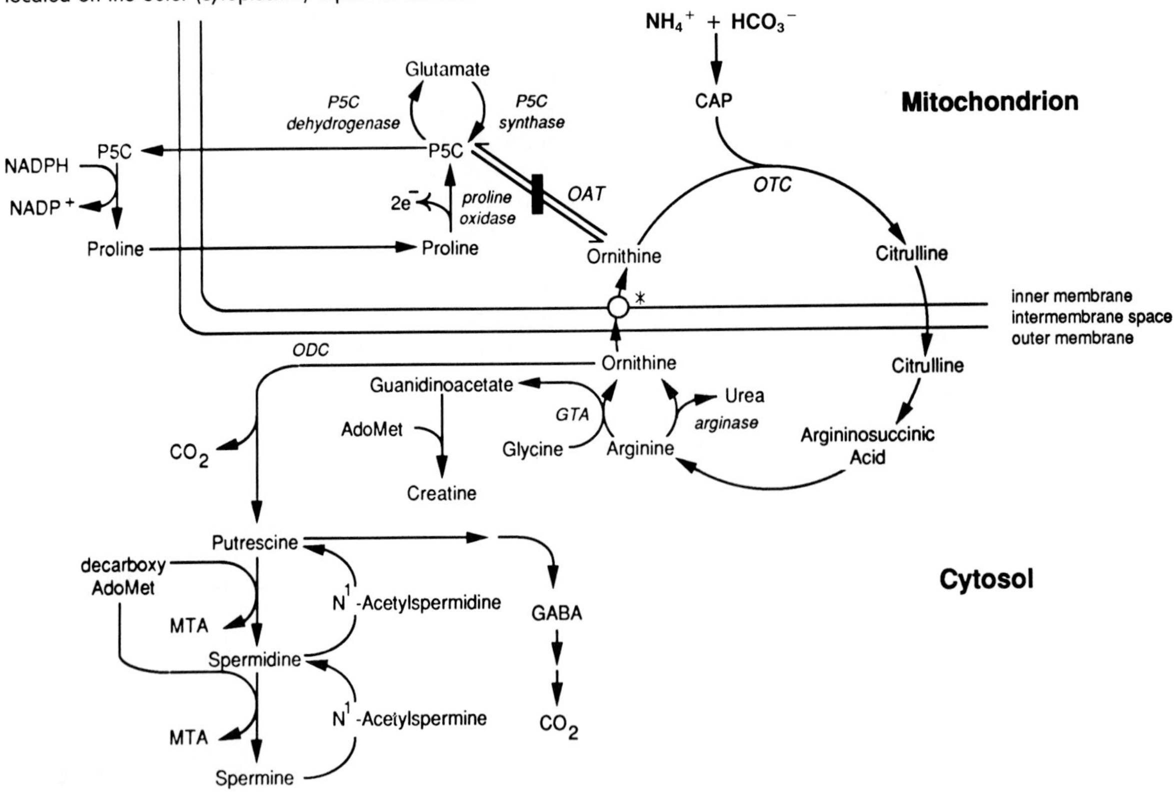

Table 19-1 Enzymes of Ornithine Metabolism*

Enzyme	*Subcellular compartment*	*Subunit molecular mass, kDa*	*Structure*	*Cofactor*	*Kinetic parameters*	*Organ distribution*	*Ref.*
Ornithine aminotransferase (EC2.6.1.13)	Mitochondrial matrix	49→45†	Homohexamer or homotetramer	Pyridoxal phosphate	$K_{m_{orn}}$ = 1.8 mM $K_{m_{\alpha KG}}$ = 2.7 mM $K_{m_{PLP}}$ = 0.7 μM	General	10, 76, 87
Ornithine transcarbamoylase (EC2.1.3.3)	Mitochondrial matrix	40→36†	Homotrimer	—	$K_{m_{orn}}$ = 0.47 mM $K_{m_{CAP}}$ = 0.7 mM	Primarily liver; low activity in gut, brain, kidney	1, 8
Ornithine decarboxylase (EC4.1.1.17)	Cytoplasm	51	Monomer	Pyridoxal phosphate	$K_{m_{orn}}$ = 0.1 mM	General; high in rapidly dividing tissues	34, 54
Arginase (EC3.5.3.1)	Cytoplasm	30	Homotetramer	Mn^{2+}	$K_{m_{arg}}$ = 10 mM	Liver, gut and erythrocytes; a second gene product expressed in kidney	9, 18
Glycine transamidinase (EC2.1.4.1)	‡	45	Homodimer	—	$K_{m_{arg}}$ = 2.5 mM $K_{m_{gly}}$ = 2.5 mM	Pancreas, kidney, liver	67

*Human sources for all. Abbreviations: αKG = α-ketoglutarate; arg = arginine; CAP = carbamoyl phosphate; gly = glycine; orn = ornithine; PLP = pyridoxal phosphate.

†Cleavage of mitochondrial signal sequence.

‡Subcellular location in human tissues not known; in rat kidney, reported to be on the cytoplasmic side of the inner mitochondrial membrane.[353]

or arginine and result in the urinary loss of ornithine carbon skeletons in the form of the accumulated intermediate; and (2) when dietary arginine is less than that required for protein accretion. In this instance, ornithine and the reactions of the urea cycle are utilized for arginine synthesis.

Citrulline Synthesis. Citrulline is formed in the mitochondrial matrix of hepatocytes and, to a much lesser extent, the epithelium of the small intestine and kidney by the transfer of the carbamoyl moiety of carbamoyl phosphate to the δ-amino nitrogen of ornithine. The reaction is catalyzed by ornithine transcarbamoylase and is markedly influenced by pH with maximal rates between pH 8 and 9. This pH dependence suggests that zwitterionic ornithine, with an unionized δ-amino group (approximately 10 percent of the total isoelectric form at physiological pH) is the actual substrate for ornithine transcarbamoylase.[1,2] Although substrate specificity is high at pH 8, some homocitrulline is formed by transcarbamoylation of L-lysine at pH 9.[3]

Ornithine transcarbamoylase activity, like that of the other urea cycle enzymes and ornithine-δ-aminotransferase, is directly related to the quantity of dietary protein.[4,5] The mechanism(s) for this coordinate regulation is uncertain but is mainly pretranslational and may involve glucagon and cyclic adenosine monophosphate (cAMP).[6] The human and rat ornithine transcarbamoylase genes have been cloned and their promoter sequences reported.[7,8] Interestingly, a common 13-base pair sequence has been recognized in the 5′ flanking region of ornithine transcarbamoylase, ornithine-δ-aminotransferase, and other urea cycle enzyme genes.[9,10] This sequence is a candidate for a cis-acting regulatory element important for the coordinated regulation of these genes and is discussed in more detail below (see "Molecular Biology of Ornithine-δ-Aminotransferase").

The substrate regulation of the ornithine transcarbamoylase reaction is complex and plays an important role in the moment to moment synthesis of citrulline and urea. Within the mitochondrial matrix of hepatocytes, ornithine concentrations are set by ornithine entry and the activity of ornithine transcarbamoylase and ornithine-δ-aminotransferase. Some have suggested that the availability of carbamoyl phosphate limits the transcarbamoylase reaction under most physiological circumstances and that ornithine, by an uncertain mechanism, may stimulate carbamoyl phosphate production.[11,12] Alternatively, Raijman has proposed that, in most instances, matrix ornithine is low in relationship to carbamoyl phosphate and limits citrulline formation.[13] In a recent in vitro study utilizing isolated rat liver mitochondria, she showed that ornithine exerts a regulatory effect on citrulline synthesis in the physiological range of cytoplasmic ornithine concentrations and that there appears to be channeling of transported ornithine directly to ornithine transcarbamoylase so that matrix ornithine concentration remains low at cytoplasmic ornithine concentrations less than 0.5 mM.[14] These conflicting views may indicate that either substrate can regulate citrulline synthesis depending on the physiological state.

An X-linked deficiency of ornithine transcarbamoylase has been described in humans (see Chap. 20) and in the sparse fur mouse.[15,16] In both species, affected males exhibit protein intolerance with lethargy, vomiting, hyperammonemia, coma, and orotic aciduria. Because ornithine catabolism by ornithine-δ-aminotransferase is intact, ornithine accumulation is not a feature of ornithine transcarbamoylase deficiency.

Arginase. Biochemical, electrophoretic, immunologic, and genetic evidence suggests that there are at least two active arginase genes.[17–21] Cytosolic arginase of hepatic cells in ureotelic animals functions in the urea cycle and is remarkable for its activity (highest of all urea cycle enzymes)[22] and low substrate affinity (Table 19-1). Ornithine and lysine are weak inhibitors.[17,23] The cDNA sequence and gene structure are known.[9,24,25] A second form of arginase ("renal arginase"), also weakly inhibitable by ornithine, has been found in kidney, small intestine, pancreas, and mammary gland.[17,19,21,26] In most tissues, this arginase probably functions as the initial enzyme in a sequence of reactions that converts arginine to proline.[26,27]

Arginase deficiency has been described in several children

with mental retardation, neuromuscular abnormalities, and hyperargininemia (see Chap. 20). Arginase activity is deficient in the erythrocytes and liver of these patients. Normal renal arginase activity was found in the kidneys of one of these patients.[28] Plasma ornithine concentrations are normal or only minimally reduced probably because renal arginase and glycine transamidinase provide alternatives for the conversion of arginine to ornithine.

Subcellular Compartmentation and Transport of Ornithine. Three of the urea cycle enzymes, argininosuccinate synthase, lyase, and arginase, are cytosolic, while ornithine transcarbamoylase and carbamoyl phosphate synthase are found in the mitochondrial matrix (Fig. 19-2). Thus, a complete turn of the urea cycle requires the transport of ornithine into and citrulline out of the mitochondria. The mitochondrial boundary is composed of inner and outer membranes with an intervening intermembrane space. The outer membrane is readily permeant to amino acids, while the inner is a true permeability barrier.[29] Ornithine transport into liver mitochondria is mediated by a specific inner membrane carrier, which does not recognize L-arginine or L-lysine.[30–32] There is disagreement on the energy requirements for this process. Gamble and Lehninger found that mitochondria accumulated cationic L-ornithine if respiratory energy (e.g., provided by succinate or glutamate) and a permeant proton-yielding anion (HPO_4^{-2}, $H_2PO_4^-$, acetate, or bicarbonate) were available.[31] Nonrespiring mitochondria were impermeable to either cationic ornithine (the dominant form of ornithine at physiological pH) or the electroneutral analogue, *N*-acetylornithine. In contrast, McGivan and coworkers found that the distribution of ornithine across the mitochondrial membrane was correlated with the transmitochondrial pH gradient, and that the intramitochondrial concentration of ornithine barely exceeded that in the medium when the catabolism of matrix ornithine by ornithine-δ-aminotransferase was blocked by amino-oxyacetate.[30] These results suggested that cationic ornithine is transported electroneutrally in exchange for H^+, without dependency on respiratory energy. McGivan also suggested that an ornithine-citrulline antiporter is present in liver mitochondria coupling the transmitochondrial fluxes of these substrates.[32] Hommes and colleagues reconstituted ornithine transport into liposomes with extracts of bovine liver mitochondria and found evidence for a specific ornithine translocator which exchanged cationic ornithine for a hydrogen ion[33] as predicted by Gamble and Lehninger. These studies and the recent report of Raijman and colleagues[14] indicate that an ornithine-citrulline antiport is not the primary mode of ornithine transport into liver mitochondria.

Putrescine Biosynthesis

The physiological roles of putrescine and other polyamines are poorly understood but as polycations they readily associate with nucleic acids and phospholipids. Recent studies have shown their concentration to be highly regulated and that cellular proliferation and differentiation require polyamine biosynthesis.[34,35] Putrescine (diaminobutane) is synthesized from ornithine in an irreversible reaction catalyzed by the pyridoxal phosphate–dependent enzyme ornithine decarboxylase. Condensation of putrescine with propylamino moieties provided by decarboxy-*S*-adenosylmethionine forms the polyamines spermidine [$H_2N\text{-}(CH_2)_4NH(CH_2)_3NH_2$] and spermine [$H_2N(CH_2)_3NH(CH_2)_4NH(CH_2)_3NH_2$].[34] Approximately 0.5 mmol of spermidine is synthesized daily in normal adult humans.[36,37] The activities of ornithine decarboxylase and *S*-adenosylmethionine decarboxylase are thought to be the major regulatory factors in polyamine synthesis rather than the availability of substrate.[34,38,39] Ornithine decarboxylase activity is low in nondividing and high in rapidly proliferating cells (e.g., embryologic tissues, malignant tumors, and the stem cells of bone marrow and intestinal mucosa). A rapid and substantial (>tenfold) increase in ornithine decarboxylase activity is one of the earliest events following the stimulation of resting cells to proliferate and results in increased cellular levels of putrescine.[40,41] This increment in ornithine decarboxylase is due to increased synthesis which, in large part, reflects a corresponding increase in ornithine decarboxylase mRNA.[42] Degradation of ornithine decarboxylase is rapid and nearly constant with a half-life of 10 to 20 min.[34,43] A putrescine-induced 22-kDa protein called *antizyme* binds specifically to ornithine decarboxylase and may play a role in this rapid degradation.[34,44,45]

A variety of specific inhibitors of ornithine decarboxylase have been used to investigate the regulation of polyamine biosynthesis, including the enzyme-activated, irreversible inhibitor DL-α-difluoromethylornithine.[46–49] This ornithine analogue does not inhibit ornithine-δ-aminotransferase. Pharmacologic inhibition of ornithine decarboxylase results in reduced tissue polyamine levels and interferes with cell proliferation[47,50,51] and growth.[52]

Murine[42,53] and human[54] ornithine decarboxylase cDNAs have been cloned and sequenced and the structure of the murine ornithine decarboxylase gene determined.[55,56]

Putrescine is also a potential precursor of γ-aminobutyric acid. The major source for this neurotransmitter is glutamic acid, which is decarboxylated by glutamic acid decarboxylase.[57] However, two reaction sequences which convert putrescine to γ-aminobutyrate have been described. One involves direct deamination by diamine oxidase (histaminase), while the other utilizes *N*-acetylated intermediates.[57,58] Nirenberg and coworkers[59] found that a significant fraction of chick retina γ-aminobutyrate was derived from ornithine in early embryonic chicks, while glutamate became the major precursor by the time of hatching. In adult rat brain, ornithine may be converted to γ-aminobutyrate in nerve terminals.[60] The degradation of γ-aminobutyrate involves transamination by γ-aminobutyrate transaminase to form succinate semialdehyde, which is further oxidized to succinate and eventually to CO_2. Thus, the conversion of putrescine to γ-aminobutyrate provides a potential pathway for the oxidation of ornithine to CO_2 independent from ornithine-δ-aminotransferase.

Creatine Synthesis

The first reaction in creatine synthesis, transfer of the amidino group of arginine to glycine to form guanidinoacetate and ornithine, is catalyzed by glycine transamidinase (Fig. 19-2) (Table 19-1).[61] Guanidinoacetate is *N*-methylated by *S*-adenosylmethionine:guanidinoacetate *N*-methyltransferase to form creatine. The transamidinase reaction is readily reversible in vitro, but low tissue levels of guanidinoacetate probably prevent significant reverse reaction in vivo.[61,62] In rats, dietary creatine supplementation for 2 weeks reduces transamidinase activity and protein to about one-third pretreatment levels.[62,63]

Immunoprecipitation of the products of in vitro translation reactions programmed with mRNA from these supplemented animals suggests that this decrease is due to reduced translational efficiency or reduced levels of transamidinase mRNA.[63] Ornithine is a potent competitive inhibitor of the transamidinase.[64–66]

Human and rat kidney transamidinases have been purified to homogeneity and characterized biochemically.[67] In human beings and other mammals, both glycine transamidinase and the methyltransferase are present in high activity in renal cortex and pancreas.[61] Immunofluorescence studies in rat show prominent staining in the basilar portions of the proximal tubule cells, hepatocytes, and the pancreatic islet α (glucagon-producing) cells.[68] Available data suggest that creatine is synthesized in these central organs, transported to muscle and nerve, and there phosphorylated to form the high-energy phosphagen, creatine phosphate. The interesting possibility that other tissues, including brain, may be capable of creatine synthesis has been suggested and requires further study.[69,70]

Most of the total-body creatine–creatine phosphate pool is located in muscle and amounts to approximately 120 g (915 mmol) in a 70-kg man. Both creatine and creatine phosphate undergo a first-order, nonenzymatic cyclization to creatinine at fractional rates of 0.011 per day and 0.026 per day, respectively.[61] Thus, in order to maintain the creatine–creatine phosphate pool, an amount of creatine equal to the amount of creatinine formed daily (approximately 2 g in an adult male) must be provided either from dietary sources or by endogenous synthesis. The relative contributions from these two sources are difficult to estimate, but studies of individuals on creatine-free diets indicate that endogenous synthesis can meet the entire requirement.[61] The relative magnitude of the synthetic pathway is indicated by the fact that creatine synthesis is quantitatively the major consumer of *S*-adenosylmethionine–donated methyl groups in the body.[36]

The Ornithine-δ-Aminotransferase Pathway

Ornithine-δ-aminotransferase is a pyridoxal phosphate–requiring Ω-transaminase which catalyzes the reversible conversion of ornithine and α-ketoglutarate to Δ^1-pyrroline-5-carboxylate and glutamate (Fig. 19-1). Glutamate semialdehyde is the initial product formed by removal of the δ-amino group of ornithine; however, it cyclizes spontaneously to form Δ^1-pyrroline-5-carboxylate. Kinetic studies suggest that the cyclization is rapid and reversible.[71–73] Thus, in the subsequent discussions we consider Δ^1-pyrroline-5-carboxylate as the reaction product with the tacit recognition that it is in equilibrium with glutamate semialdehyde.

Chemistry of Ornithine-δ-Aminotransferase. Ornithine-δ-aminotransferase was first described in animal tissues by Quastel and Witty[74] and Meister.[75] Ornithine-δ-aminotransferase has been purified to homogeneity from human liver,[76] rat liver,[71,77–81] and rat kidney.[82–84] The human enzyme is a homopolymer with a subunit molecular mass (M_r) of 45 kDa. There is one molecule of cofactor pyridoxal phosphate per subunit.[83,85,86] The results of several studies of both the human[76] and rat[82,84] enzyme indicated that the holoenzyme was a tetramer. Reinvestigation of the quaternary structure, however, provides strong evidence that the mature enzyme is a 256-kDa homohexamer.[87] This conclusion is based on equilibrium sedimentation measurements, cross-linking experiments, and preliminary crystallographic analysis of rat liver enzyme. The native enzyme has a sedimentation coefficient ($s^o_{20,w}$) of 10 S, and a frictional coefficient which is consistent with a nearly spherical structure. The difficulty in determining a subunit number for the mature protein may be explained by the effects of NaCl on the aggregational state of ornithine-δ-aminotransferase.[87] The results favoring a hexameric structure were obtained in the presence of NaCl whereas in the absence of NaCl (as was the case in the earlier studies), results favoring a tetrameric structure were obtained. The influence of NaCl on the aggregational state of the enzyme indicates that electrostatic interactions play an important role in the assembly and stability of ornithine-δ-aminotransferase subunits.

The kinetic properties of human and rat ornithine-δ-aminotransferase are similar, and the values for the former are provided in Table 19-1. Although this reaction is reversible,[88] the equilibrium constant favors the formation of Δ^1-pyrroline-5-carboxylate.[71] The complete reaction involves two half reactions:[85]

$$\text{Ornithine} + \text{pyridoxal-ornithine-}\delta\text{-aminotransferase} \rightarrow \Delta^1\text{-pyrroline-5-carboxylate} + \text{pyridoxamine-ornithine-}\delta\text{-aminotransferase} \quad (19\text{-}1)$$

$$\text{Pyridoxamine-ornithine-}\delta\text{-aminotransferase} + \alpha\text{-ketoglutarate} \rightarrow \text{glutamate} + \text{pyridoxal-ornithine-}\delta\text{-aminotransferase} \quad (19\text{-}2)$$

The pH optimum of the overall reaction measured in the forward direction (pH 8.0 for the human enzyme) is a compromise between the more alkaline optimum of reaction 1 (approximately pH 9) and the more acidic optimum of reaction 2 (approximately pH 7). The optimum for the reverse reaction is pH 6.5.[72] The pyridoxamine enzyme is unstable and can spontaneously release its amino group allowing the formation of Δ^1-pyrroline-5-carboxylate to exceed that of glutamate under certain conditions.[85] High concentrations of pyridoxal phosphate inhibit catalytic activity and increase the amount of bound cofactor to approximately 4 molecules per protomer.[85] The enzyme has high specificity for ornithine.[76] Lysine, the one-carbon-longer homologue, has no effect on the reaction. Glyoxylate and pyruvate are poor substitutes for α-ketoglutarate. High concentrations of ornithine (>25 m*M*) and particularly α-ketoglutarate (>3 m*M*) are inhibitory.[71] Other low molecular weight compounds which at a concentration of 25 m*M* inhibit activity of the rat enzyme by at least 40 percent in the presence of saturating ornithine concentrations include L-valine, α-ketoisovalerate, α-ketoisocaproate, γ-aminobutyrate, and norvaline.[71,72] Additional inhibiting compounds include nonspecific inhibitors of all B_6-dependent enzymes, e.g., canaline, cycloserine, hydroxylamine, and thiosemicarbazide.[78,89]

Jung and Seiler[90] and others[91] pointed out the similarity of ornithine-δ-aminotransferase and γ-aminobutyrate transaminase-catalyzed reactions. Both involve Ω-transamination of structurally related substrates. Thus, two supposedly specific, enzyme-activated, irreversible inhibitors ("suicide substrates") of γ-aminobutyrate transaminase, 4-aminohex-5-ynoic acid and 5-amino-1,3-cyclohexadienyl-carboxylic acid (gabaculine), also irreversibly inhibit ornithine-δ-aminotransferase both in vitro and in vivo in mice. A third, 4-aminohex-5-enoic acid, has no effect on ornithine-δ-aminotransferase. In the development and use of inhibitors of either enzyme, careful consideration should be given, therefore, to possible interactions with the other.

Ornithine-δ-Aminotransferase Assays. Three general methods of assaying ornithine-δ-aminotransferase activity have been utilized.[71,92,93] The most widely used method depends on the quantitative formation of a dihydroquinozolinium derivative when Δ^1-pyrroline-5-carboxylate is reacted with *o*-aminobenzaldehyde. This derivative is measured spectrophotometrically with an extinction coefficient variously reported as 2.71[71] and 2.59[73] at 441 nm. One caution in interpreting results obtained with this assay is that *o*-aminobenzaldehyde reacts with several Δ^1-pyrroline compounds, including Δ^1-pyrroline-2-carboxylate, the cyclized form of the α-keto acid of ornithine.[75,94,95] Thus, under certain conditions, some of the apparent product measured by this assay may be other than Δ^1-pyrroline-5-carboxylate. A modification of this method utilizing high performance liquid chromatography has increased sensitivity and possibly also specificity.[96]

A second method of measuring ornithine-δ-aminotransferase activity involves the use of radiolabeled ornithine and separation of this precursor from the product Δ^1-pyrroline-5-carboxylate by ion-exchange chromatography.[92] This method can be adapted to either low or high substrate concentrations and has the additional advantages of greater sensitivity and specificity than the standard spectrophotometric assay. The sensitivity of the assay is increased by purifying commercially available, radiolabeled ornithine by ion-exchange chromatography. This removes contaminants (e.g., γ-aminobutyrate) which may be inhibitory to ornithine-δ-aminotransferase activity.

The third method of ornithine-δ-aminotransferase assay utilizes [1-^{14}C]α-ketoglutarate as the labeled substrate; glutamate decarboxylase to decarboxylate the product, [1-^{14}C]glutamate; and $^{14}CO_2$ trapping to quantitate product formation.[93] This method has high sensitivity but requires dialysis of the tissue extracts prior to assay to eliminate endogenous amino acids that would utilize α-ketoglutarate as an amino acceptor in transaminations not catalyzed by ornithine-δ-aminotransferase.

Molecular Biology of Ornithine-δ-Aminotransferase. Ornithine-δ-aminotransferase cDNAs have been isolated from cDNA libraries prepared from human liver,[10,97] human retinoblastoma cell (Y79),[98] rat liver,[10,99,100] and *Saccharomyces cerevisiae*.[101,102] The human cDNA has a 1317-bp open reading frame and a 635-bp 3′ nontranslated region with a single AAUAAA poly(A) addition signal (Fig. 19-3). None of the reported cDNAs are full-length but, by inference from the structural gene, the lengths of the 5′ nontranslated sequences of the predominant transcripts in liver are 81 and 80 depending on which transcriptional initiation site is utilized (see below). The sequence of the three reported human cDNAs (two from liver and one from retinoblastoma cells) are identical except for minor differences at the extreme 5′ and 3′ ends, some of which may be cloning artifacts.

The human and rat cDNA have 84.3 percent nucleotide identity in their coding regions, both predicting a 439-amino acid protein with 90.4 percent of the residues identical between the two species. The predicted M_r of the human ornithine-δ-aminotransferase precursor is 48,534 Da. Mueckler and Pitot noted weak homology of residues 286 to 362 with the pyridoxal phosphate–binding region of the only transaminase whose tertiary structure has been determined, aspartate aminotransferase, and on this basis predicted lysine-292 to be the cofactor-binding residue for ornithine-δ-aminotransferase.[100] Subsequent direct analysis of chymotryptic and tryptic fragments of the rat enzyme by Simmaco et al.[86] confirmed this prediction. This same group also determined that cleavage of the mitochondrial signal peptide occurs between alanine-25 and threonine-26, releasing a mature ornithine-δ-aminotransferase monomer of 414 amino acids with an M_r of 45,852 Da (Fig. 19-4).

In *S. cerevisiae*[103] and other fungi[104] ornithine-δ-aminotransferase is cytoplasmic, and accordingly, the cDNA encodes a protein which lacks a mitochondrial signal peptide. The 406 C-terminal residues of human ornithine-δ-aminotransferase are 54.4 percent identical with the yeast sequence. The identities are not evenly distributed throughout the proteins but are clustered in regions or patches of complete identity of up to

Fig. 19-3 The ornithine-δ-aminotransferase structural gene and major mRNA transcript. The structural gene, with 11 exons, is shown above with the exons indicated as the black rectangles. The mRNA is shown below with the translated portion of the message designated by the shaded rectangle. The position of the first nucleotide in each exon, relative to the first nucleotide of the initiation codon, is indicated at the bottom. As depicted by the dashed lines, the second exon is spliced out of all mature transcripts so far examined. It is present in ornithine-δ-aminotransferase–processed pseudogene sequences on the X chromosome. See text for details. Note different scale for gene and mRNA.

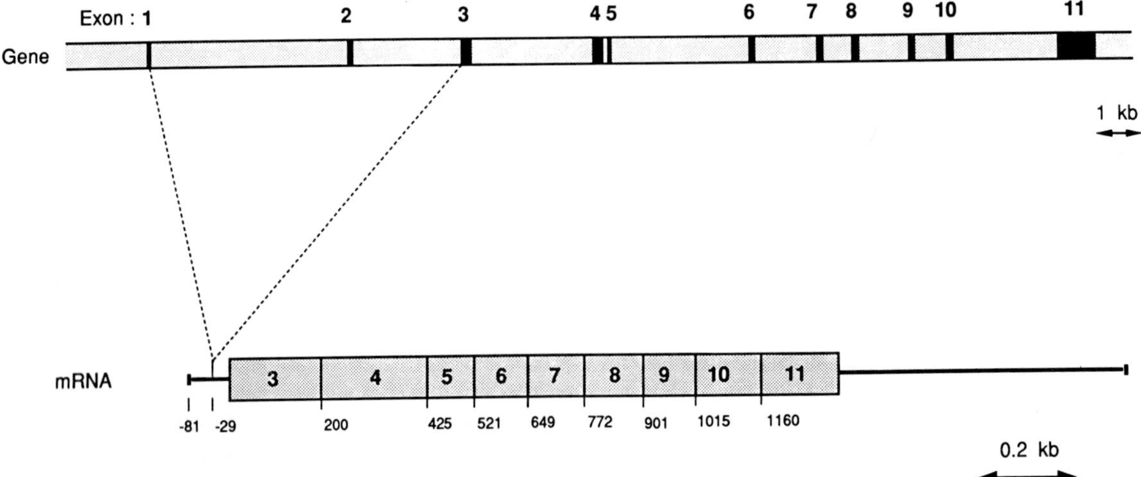

13 residues in length which presumably correspond to important structural or functional regions of the protein (Fig. 19-4). The longest patch contains the pyridoxal phosphate–binding residue, lysine-292.

The ornithine-δ-aminotransferase structural gene contains 11 exons which vary in length from 52 nucleotides (exon 1) to 793 nucleotides (exon 11) and are distributed over 21 kb of genomic DNA[10] (Fig. 19-3). Seven restriction fragment length polymorphisms linked to the gene have been described,[10,105] but the exact positions of these sites relative to the gene structure is known for only one.[10] The translational start site is in exon 3. The cofactor binding lysine-292 and the surrounding highly conserved 13 residues are in exon 8. Primer extension studies indicate two transcriptional start sites separated by a single nucleotide and resulting in exon 1 lengths of either 52 or 51 bp.[10] Exon 2 is not expressed in the predominant mature mRNA transcript found in liver and was identified by homology with corresponding sequences contained in two X-linked, ornithine-δ-aminotransferase–processed pseudogenes.[10,106] It is flanked by acceptable splice sites but is not present in any of the ornithine-δ-aminotransferase cDNAs so far examined. The extent and functional consequences of its expression remain to be determined. A similar example of alternative splicing of an exon in the 5′ untranslated region with predominant expression of a transcript lacking the exon has been observed for argininosuccinate synthase.[107]

The region of the ornithine-δ-aminotransferase gene 5′ to the predicted transcriptional start sites contains elements characteristic of promotors of housekeeping genes and genes whose expression is tissue-specific.[10,108] There is a TATA box–like sequence, TTTAA, at position −29 with respect to the 5′-most transcriptional initiation site and two CCAAT box–like sequences, one at −73 and a second, inverted sequence, ATTGG, at −98. The region is GC-rich (68.6 percent) with three consensus transcription factor Sp1 core sequence binding sites.[109] In addition to these standard promoter features, other sequences in this region are noteworthy. In particular, there is a region starting at −94 (5′ GTATCCTGCCCT 3′) with 10 of 12 nucleotides identical (underlined) to a consensus sequence (5′ GCANCCTGCCCT 3′) recently recognized by Ohtake et al.[9] in the three urea cycle enzymes whose 5′ regions have been characterized. Secondly, there is a 22-bp element with incomplete dyad symmetry extending from −20 to +2. Incomplete dyad symmetry is a common feature of many DNA sites which bind regulatory proteins.[110] This element also has some homology with the estrogen-responsive element of the *Xenopus* vitellogenin A2 gene.[111] Because of the close relation of the estrogen- and glucocorticoid-responsive elements,[112] it is possible that this dyad element may play a role in either the estrogen induction of ornithine-δ-aminotransferase in kidney or the glucocorticoid repression of glucagon-mediated ornithine-δ-aminotransferase induction in liver (see "Regulation of Ornithine-δ-Aminotransferase Activity," below). Additional functional studies will be necessary to determine the significance of these possible cis-acting regulatory sequences.

Chromosomal Localization of Ornithine-δ-Aminotransferase and Related Sequences. Southern blots of human genomic DNA probed with the ornithine-δ-aminotransferase cDNA show a complex pattern (Fig. 19-5). Several studies including analyses of genomic DNA from rodent-human hybrid cell panels and *in situ* hybridization of human chromosome spreads have shown that these hybridizing fragments are located in two sites: one, corresponding to the active structural gene, at 10q26; and a second, apparently nonfunc-

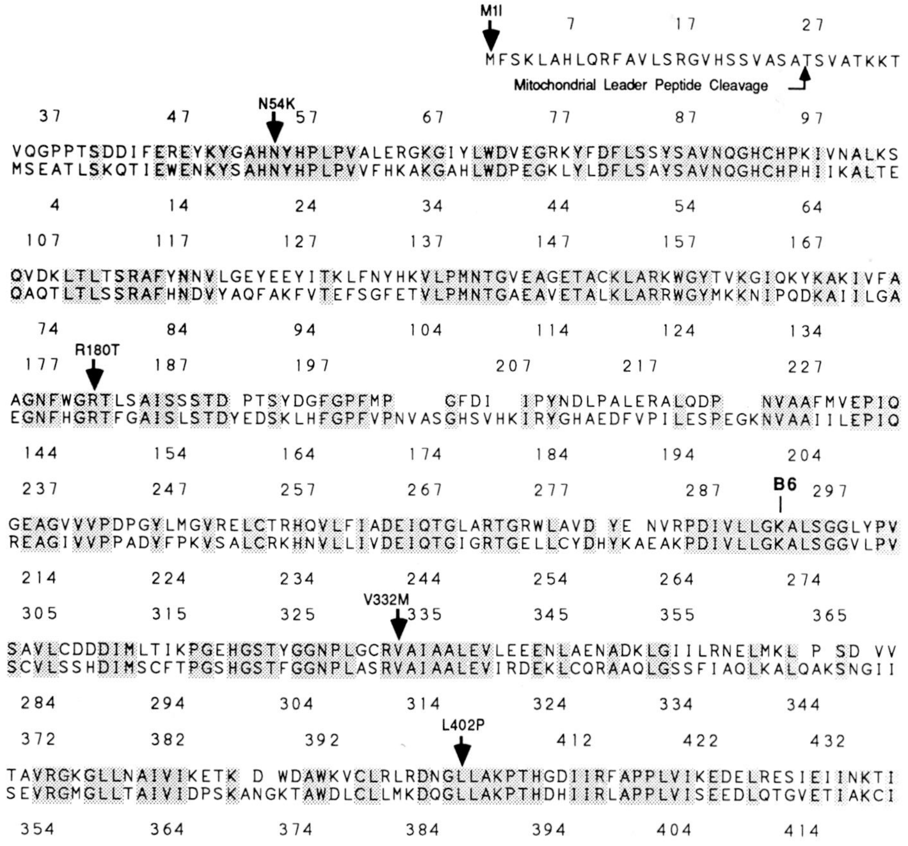

```
                                        M1I
                                         ↓      7         17        27
                                         MFSKLAHLQRFAVLSRGVHSSVASATSVATKKT
                                          Mitochondrial Leader Peptide Cleavage ↑
                      N54K
 37        47          ↓57        67        77        87        97
VQGPPTSDDIFEREYKYGAHNYHPLPVALERGKGIYLWDVEGRKYFDFLSSYSAVNQGHCHPKIVNALKS
MSEATLSKQTIEWENKYSAHNYHPLPVVFHKAKGAHLWDPEGKLYLDFLSAYSAVNQGHCHPHIIKALTE
 4         14        24        34        44        54        64

107       117       127       137       147       157       167
QVDKLTLTSRAFYNNVLGEYEEYITKLFNYHKVLPMNTGVEAGETACKLARKWGYTVKGIQKYKAKIVFA
QAQTLTLSSRAFHNDVYAQFAKFVTEFSGFETVLPMNTGAEAVETALKLARRWGYMKKNIPQDKAIILGA
 74        84        94        104       114       124       134
     R180T
177   ↓    187        197              207       217         227
AGNFWGRTLSAISSSTD PTSYDGFGPFMP     GFDI  IPYNDLPALERALQDP   NVAAFMVEPIQ
EGNFHGRTFGAISLSTDYEDSKLHFGPFVPNVASGHSVHKIRYGHAEDFVPILESPEGKNVAAIILEPIQ
144       154       164       174       184       194       204

237       247       257       267       277        287   B6  297
                                                         |
GEAGVVVPDPGYLMGVRELCTRHQVLFIADEIQTGLARTGRWLAVD YE NVRPDIVLLGKALSGGLYPV
REAGIVVPPADYFPKVSALCRKHNVLLIVDEIQTGIGRTGELLCYDHYKAEAKPDIVLLGKALSGGVLPV
214       224       234       244       254       264       274
                          V332M
305       315       325     ↓335       345       355         365
SAVLCDDDIMLTIKPGEHGSTYGGNPLGCRVAIAALEVLEEENLAENADKLGIILRNELMKL P SD VV
SCVLSSHDIMSCFTPGSHGSTFGGNPLASRVAIAALEVIRDEKLCQRAAQLGSSFIAQLKALQAKSNGII
284       294       304       314       324       334       344
                                  L402P
372       382         392          ↓      412       422       432
TAVRGKGLLNAIVIKETK D WDAWKVCLRLRDNGLLAKPTHGDIIRFAPPLVIKEDELRESIEIINKTI
SEVRGMGLLTAIVIDPSKANGKTAWDLCLLMKDQGLLAKPTHDHIIRLAPPLVISEEDLQTGVETIAKCI
354       364       374       384       394       404       414
```

Fig. 19-4 Comparison of human and *Saccharomyces cerevisiae* ornithine-δ-aminotransferase amino acid sequence. The C-terminal 406 residues of the human monomer (the top sequence) are aligned with the yeast monomer. Gaps were introduced in the human sequence to maximize homology. The identities are shaded. Note that they are clustered in patches which are likely to correspond to structurally or functionally important domains of the protein. The yeast enzyme is cytoplasmic and, accordingly, has no counterpart to the mitochondrial leader peptide of the human monomer. The positions of five well-documented missense mutations causing gyrate atrophy are shown above the arrows (see "Molecular Defects"). B6 denotes the position of the pyridoxal phosphate–binding residue, lysine-292. The single letter amino acid abbreviations are: A = alanine; C = cysteine; D = aspartic acid; E = glutamic acid; F = phenylalanine; G = glycine; H = histidine; I = isoleucine; K = lysine; L = leucine; M = methionine; N = asparagine; P = proline; Q = glutamine; R = arginine; S = serine; T = threonine; V = valine; W = tryptophan; Y = tyrosine.

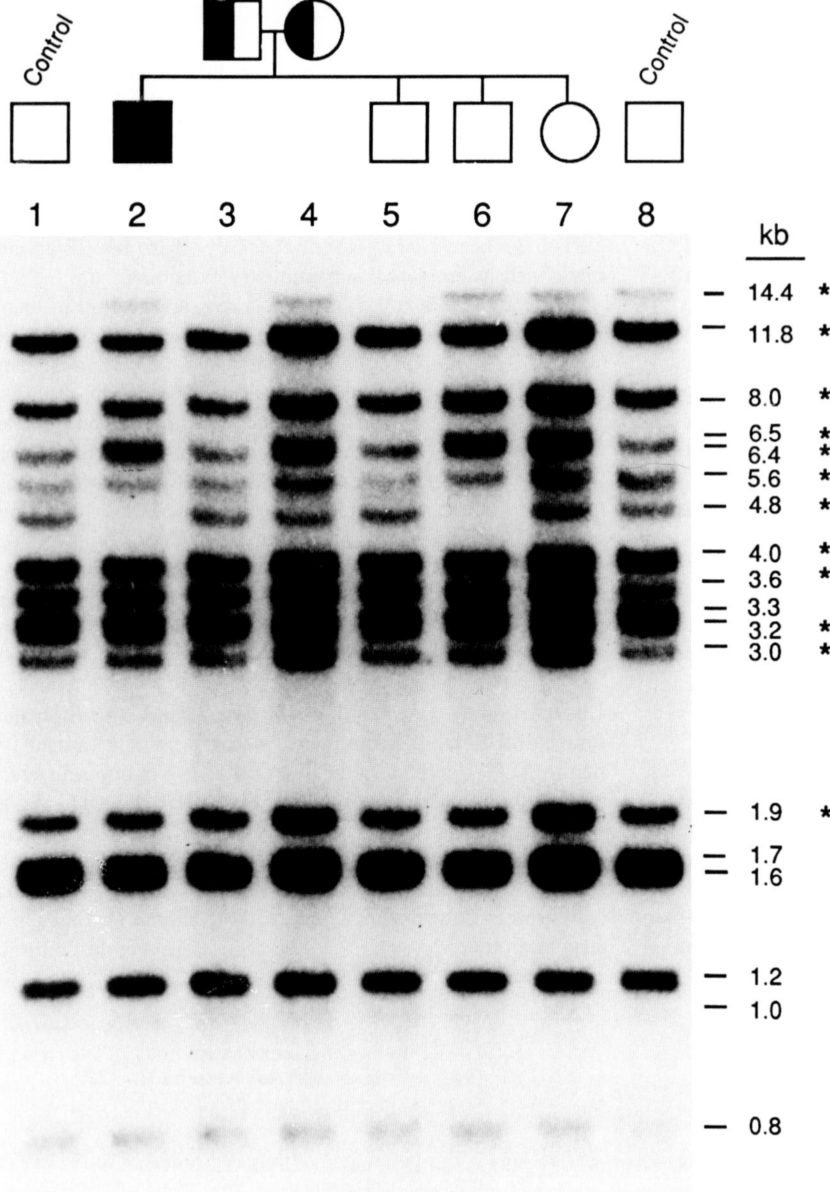

Fig. 19-5 The complicated genomic Southern blot pattern of ornithine-δ-aminotransferase. Genomic DNA from a patient with gyrate atrophy (lane 2), his family members, and controls was digested with the restriction endonuclease *Pst* 1. The blot was hybridized to a near full-length ornithine-δ-aminotransferase cDNA containing 15 bp of exon 1 and all of exons 3–11 and washed at high stringency. The sizes of the hybridizing fragments are indicated on the right. The X-linked ornithine-δ-aminotransferase–hybridizing fragments are indicated by an asterisk following their size. Note that these fragments are more intense in the females. The remaining fragments are from the functional ornithine-δ-aminotransferase gene on chromosome 10. The family is segreting an X-linked, 4.8 kb/6.5 kb *Pst* 1 polymorphism which is unrelated to gyrate atrophy.

tional, set of ornithine-δ-aminotransferase–related sequences at Xp11.1.[113–115] The number of X-linked hybridizing fragments depends on the restriction enzyme but usually is two to three times the number of autosomal fragments. Preliminary characterization of some of the X-linked sequences shows features of processed pseudogenes.[106,116] Why several copies of these sequences should be present in one region of the genome distant from the structural gene is an interesting and, as yet, unanswered question.

Tissue Distribution and Activity. Rat kidney, liver, and small intestine have high ornithine-δ-aminotransferase activity.[77,117–119] The kidneys of animals exposed to estrogen (either normal females or gonadectomized males treated with estrogen) have the highest activity.[117] Lower levels of ornithine-δ-aminotransferase are present in pancreas, submaxillary gland, heart, brain, spleen, adrenal, lung, mammary gland, cartilage, and skeletal muscle.[117–121] The relative activities in several regions of the brain have been reported.[122]

The activity of ornithine-δ-aminotransferase has been measured in the ocular tissues of a variety of species including human beings. Ratzlaff and Baich compared ornithine-δ-aminotransferase activity in retinal pigment epithelium, neural retina, and liver of several vertebrates and found that in mammals and birds, the activity in pigment epithelium was three- to tenfold higher than that in neural retina or liver, while in amphibians and fish it was similar in all three tissues.[123,124] Several other studies have shown high levels of ornithine-δ-aminotransferase activity in pigment epithelium, neural retina, ciliary body, and iris in a variety of mammals.[125–129] Recently two immunohistochemical studies of rat ocular tissues have confirmed the presence of ornithine-δ-aminotransferase in the epithelia of ciliary body, iris, and lens and showed prominent immunoreactivity in pigment epithelium and Müller cells of the retina but none in the photoreceptor cells.[130,131]

Regulation of Ornithine-δ-Aminotransferase Activity. In addition to the regulation by small molecules described above, ornithine-δ-aminotransferase activity varies greatly with changes in developmental, nutritional, and hormonal status. In rat liver and kidney, ornithine-δ-aminotransferase activity is barely detectable prenatally or during the first 2 postnatal weeks, but by 30 days of age it increases approximately fifteenfold to adult levels.[117,132] In the small intestine, ornithine-δ-aminotransferase activity is two to five times higher in the first 3 weeks of life than in adult intestine or liver.[118]

After the first few weeks of life, liver ornithine-δ-aminotransferase activity in rats is markedly influenced by dietary protein intake as is the case for all the enzymes directly involved in the urea cycle.[4,6,22] An increase in dietary protein from 20 to 70 percent by weight results in increased ornithine-δ-aminotransferase–specific activity within 1 day and by 4 days a peak activity sixfold higher than baseline levels. Concomitant high glucose intake prevents this induction.[82,133] Reduction of dietary protein to 5 percent causes a twofold reduction in ornithine-δ-aminotransferase activity. Renal and small intestinal ornithine-δ-aminotransferase activities are not influenced by perturbations in dietary protein intake.[82] The increase in hepatic ornithine-δ-aminotransferase associated with increased dietary protein may be mediated, at least in part, by glucagon, which in turn may work through a cyclic AMP–dependent mechanism. Ornithine-δ-aminotransferase activity in liver increases in response to glucagon;[134,135] and glucagon or dibutyryl cyclic AMP increase ornithine-δ-aminotransferase activity in primary hepatocyte cultures.[136,137]

Administration of estrogen to gonadectomized rats increases renal ornithine-δ-aminotransferase activity tenfold.[135,138–140] Thyroid hormone is necessary for, and augments, the renal estrogen response.[135] Hepatic ornithine-δ-aminotransferase is insensitive to either estrogen or thyroid hormone. In contrast to the discordance in the response of renal and hepatic ornithine-δ-aminotransferase to these various dietary and hormonal perturbations, activity in both tissues is moderately to severely reduced in rats following subcutaneous implantation of hepatic or mammary tumors.[141]

The perturbations of ornithine-δ-aminotransferase activity by nutritional and hormonal factors are due to quantitative changes in the amount of enzyme resulting from increased synthesis rather than decreased degradation.[88,135–137,142,143] Induction in liver results from a two- to fivefold increase in ornithine-δ-aminotransferase mRNA and a twentyfold increase in the translational efficiency of the ornithine-δ-aminotransferase message.[144] The induction of renal ornithine-δ-aminotransferase by estrogen is completely accounted for by an increase in ornithine-δ-aminotransferase mRNA.[143] The response is rapid, beginning with the first hour following estrogen administration and reaching maximal mRNA levels by 20 h.[143] Thyroid hormone also increases renal ornithine-δ-aminotransferase mRNA levels but with slower time course.[143]

The turnover of both hepatic and renal ornithine-δ-aminotransferase has been measured and is faster in liver than in kidney, with a half-life of 0.9 to 1.9 days in liver as compared to 4.0 days in kidney.[145–148]

Metabolic Roles of the Ornithine-δ-Aminotransferase Pathway. The bridging position of the ornithine-δ-aminotransferase reaction as a link between the urea cycle on the one hand and proline metabolism and the tricarboxylic acid cycle on the other results in its involvement in several different metabolic processes.[88]

ORNITHINE AND ARGININE CATABOLISM. The relationships which predict ariginine and ornithine catabolism are shown in the following scheme:

```
                         urine, stool, and skin losses
                            ↗              ↑
Dietary protein → arginine → ornithine → Δ¹pyrroline-5-carboxylate
                     ↙                ↘
               protein             putrescine
               accretion                                  (19-3)
```

Thus in molar units, the amount of arginine catabolized daily to Δ^1-pyrroline-5-carboxylate (Arg_C) equals the amount of arginine in the diet (Arg_D) minus the sum of the arginine requirement for protein accretion (Arg_{Prot}), the ornithine requirement for putrescine synthesis (Orn_{Put}), and the obligatory losses in urine, stool, etc. of both arginine (Arg_L) and ornithine (Orn_L). That is,

$$Arg_C = Arg_D - (Arg_{Prot} + Orn_{Put} + Arg_L + Orn_L) \quad (19\text{-}4)$$

In healthy adults in nitrogen balance, there is no net increase in body protein, and the amount of arginine required for protein accretion approaches zero. In contrast, growing children or adults recovering from an episode of negative nitrogen balance may utilize significant arginine for Arg_{Prot}. Orn_{Put} has not been measured directly but is estimated to be small (less than 0.5 mmol/day in an adult).[36] Normally, Orn_L and Arg_L are negligible but are significant in patients with overflow ornithinuria. These considerations indicate that in a healthy adult, Arg_C by way of the ornithine-δ-aminotransferase pathway is nearly equal to Arg_D. If dietary protein equals 1.5 g protein per kilogram of body weight per day, and if the arginine content of protein approximately equals 5 percent, then the daily ornithine-δ-aminotransferase flux equals ~0.4 mmol/kg or 28 mmol in a 70-kg man.

PROLINE SYNTHESIS. Δ^1-Pyrroline-5-carboxylate, the immediate precursor of proline, can be synthesized either from glutamate in a reaction catalyzed by Δ^1-pyrroline-5-carboxylate synthase or from ornithine in a reaction catalyzed by ornithine-δ-aminotransferase (Fig. 19-2). The regulation of the relative contributions is of interest. Lodato and coworkers[149] have shown that physiological concentrations of ornithine inhibit Δ^1-pyrroline-5-carboxylate synthase. Therefore, high ornithine concentrations should favor the ornithine-δ-aminotransferase–mediated pathway of proline synthesis. In certain cells and tissues this pathway seems to be the preferred or only pathway of proline synthesis. In hormonally stimulated rat mammary gland, arginase, ornithine-δ-aminotransferase, and Δ^1-pyrroline-5-carboxylate reductase activities increase coordinately in response to hormonal stimulation, and arginine (via ornithine) is a major biosynthetic precursor for the proline utilized in milk protein synthesis.[27,120] The proline auxotrophy of Chinese hamster ovary cells is due to a deficiency of both Δ^1-pyrroline-5-carboxylate synthase and ornithine-δ-aminotransferase.[150] Prototrophic revertants with either ornithine-δ-aminotransferase or Δ^1-pyrroline-5-carboxylate synthase activity grow normally. Finally, the work of Ertel and Isseroff suggests that the ornithine-δ-aminotransferase pathway is the major contributor to the tremendous proline biosynthetic capacity of the liver fluke, *Fasciola hepatica*.[151] To summarize, in some cells and tissues the ornithine-δ-aminotransferase–mediated pathway can be shown to play the major role in proline synthesis, although the relative contribution in most tissues with both proline biosynthetic pathways intact and normal substrate concentrations is still not known.

ORNITHINE AND ARGININE SYNTHESIS. As indicated above, the flow of substrates in the ornithine-δ-aminotransferase pathway in most tissues and physiological states is toward Δ^1-pyrroline-5-carboxylate ("forward" ornithine-δ-aminotransferase flux). The reaction is reversible, however, providing the only known pathway of *de novo* ornithine synthesis in mammalian cells.[88] An alternative pathway of ornithine synthesis involving *N*-acetylated intermediates is present in microorganisms but has not been found in mammalian tissues.[95,152] Synthesis of ornithine from glutamate or proline has been shown to occur in mammalian tissues, particularly intestinal mucosa[72,75,95,153,154] and in intact cultured cells.[155] This *de novo* synthesis of ornithine provides a mechanism for replenishment of the urea cycle of catalytic intermediates and, if the urea cycle is intact, for the synthesis of arginine. Thus, when dietary arginine is insufficient for net protein synthesis, "reverse" ornithine-δ-aminotransferase flux assumes major importance. This capability probably explains the nonessentiality of arginine in human infants[156] and adults[157] and the fact that some patients with argininosuccinic acid lyase deficiency excrete more argininosuccinate than can be accounted for by arginine intake.[158,159]

The factors which favor reverse ornithine-δ-aminotransferase flux are poorly understood. Variation in tissue expression of ornithine-metabolizing enzymes certainly plays a role, as do tissue and subcellular differences in the concentrations of the reactants.[88] Matsuzawa showed that the reverse reaction has a much lower pH optimum than the forward reaction and that it may be limited by a very low affinity for glutamate.[72] In some animals (e.g., rat, cat) arginine is essential, and failure to provide it results in growth failure, orotic aciduria, and hyperammonemia.[160,161] These animals have ornithine-δ-aminotransferase activity, although the levels are low in cat liver.[162] Thus, the presence of ornithine-δ-aminotransferase is a necessary but not sufficient requisite for arginine synthesis.

DIFFERENTIAL DIAGNOSIS OF HYPERORNITHINEMIA

In normal individuals fasting morning plasma ornithine concentrations range from 40 to 120 μM with a mean of 60 to 80 μM. Two distinct entities are associated with significant increases in plasma ornithine concentration: gyrate atrophy of the choroid and retina, and the HHH syndrome. In patients with gyrate atrophy visual symptoms are apparent by late childhood and ornithine concentrations in plasma range from 400 to 1300 μM. Plasma ammonium is not elevated. In HHH syndrome the plasma ornithine ranges from 200 to 1100 μM and often is lower than in gyrate atrophy. Plasma ammonium concentrations are increased, particularly after ingestion of a protein load. Urinary excretion of ornithine and its δ-lactam is increased in both types of hyperornithinemia, while homocitrulline, an amino acid usually not present in urine, is found only in the hyperammonemic type. The age of onset of hyperornithinemia in both these disorders is not known. Patients with either disorder studied at 1 year of age have typical hyperornithinemia, but one patient with HHH had a normal ornithine value in a neonatal screening sample.[163] Thus, a normal ornithine value in the neonatal period may not exclude the hyperornithinemia.

Moderate hyperornithinemia (about three times normal) was also present in two siblings reported by Bickel et al.[164] At ages 7 and 3 years this sister and brother had mental retardation, renal tubular dysfunction, abnormal liver function tests, and a 60 to 80 percent reduction in hepatic ornithine-δ-aminotransferase activity possibly because of an unexplained liver disease. At ages 15 and 9 they were severely retarded. The girl was deaf and had petit mal epilepsy. Both had normal ocular exams, normal plasma ornithine, normal liver function tests, generalized aminoaciduria, polyuria, isosthenuria, elevation of serum creatinine level, and hypertension. The etiology of this syndrome remains unknown.[165]

Nongenetic causes of modestly increased plasma ornithine concentrations include isoniazid therapy[166] and spurious elevations due to prolonged (15 min or more) standing of the blood sample at room temperature due to conversion of arginine to ornithine by erythrocyte arginase.

In most urinary amino acid screening systems a similar pattern is observed in the hyperornithinemias, cystinurias, lysinuric protein intolerance, other hyperdibasicaminoacidurias, hyperlysinemias, and possibly in argininemia. The δ-lactam of ornithine, causing a faint brownish spot with ninhydrin, helps differentiate hyperornithinemias from the others, although plasma amino acids have to be measured quantitatively to confirm that diagnosis.

A microfluorometric ornithine assay utilizing two coupling enzymes (ornithine-δ-aminotransferase and Δ^1-pyrroline-5-carboxylate reductase) has been described.[166a] It can be used to measure the ornithine in a 3-mm blood-soaked filter paper and potentially is suitable for mass population screening for hyperornithinemia. Additional study of its sensitivity and reliability would be necessary before it could be utilized.

GYRATE ATROPHY OF THE CHOROID AND RETINA

Historical Note

The first description of a patient with gyrate atrophy of the choroid and retina, as defined by the characteristic appearance of the ocular fundus and a typical history of visual deterioration, was probably that of Jacobsohn in 1888.[167] His report of a case of "atypical retinitis pigmentosa" includes a striking, hand-drawn view of the fundus showing the characteristic lesions of gyrate atrophy. Cutler in 1895[168] and Fuchs in 1896[169] were the first ophthalmologists to recognize this condition as a distinct entity. Fuchs bestowed the disorder with its euphonious appellation. Usher reviewed 26 cases in 1935, emphasizing the genetic aspects.[170] Several additional clinical reviews have been published.[171–175] Hyperornithinemia and ornithinuria were not recognized as the biochemical counterparts of this disorder until the report of Simell and Takki in 1973, 85 years after the initial ophthalmologic description.[176] Ironically, an earlier spark of insight into the nature of this disorder, the observation in 1960 of an abnormally large lysine-ornithine spot in the urine of a patient with gyrate atrophy, did not succeed in lighting the fires of scientific investigation.[171,177]

Clinical Picture

There are over 100 biochemically confirmed cases of gyrate atrophy reported or known to us.[174,175,178–202] The major clinical problem in these patients is a slowly progressive loss of vision leading to blindness, usually by the fourth decade of life.[174,178–181] Myopia and decreased night vision are early symptoms, usually noted before the end of the first decade.[203] Reduced peripheral vision with constriction of the visual fields is obvious in the second decade. Virtually all patients develop posterior subcapsular cataracts late in the second decade or early in the third.[204] The combination of the cataracts and constricted visual fields may result in severe impairment during the third decade. By the fourth to fifth decades, most patients are blind. Variability in the severity of the clinical phenotype is well documented, with a few patients retaining good visual function into their sixth or seventh decade while others experience more rapid deterioration, with nearly complete loss of vision by age 20.

The changes in the ocular fundus parallel the development of the visual symptoms (Fig. 19-6). The ophthalmologic features of the childhood cases have been reviewed recently.[203] Younger patients often come to the attention of the ophthalmologist in late childhood or around the time of puberty for evaluation of myopia or decreased night vision. At this age sharply demarcated, circular areas of chorioretinal degeneration are present in the midperiphery of the ocular fundus. There may be increased pigmentation around the margins of these lesions. When observed over time, the lesions can be seen to start as punctate yellowish "dots" which gradually enlarge to the more typically circular areas of one to two disk diameters in size.[181] Interestingly, in a few young patients, a diffuse depigmentation of the pigment epithelium in the mid- to far periphery occurs before the development of the classic circular lesions (Fig. 19-6*A*).[203] At around the time of puberty, the retinal degeneration seems to proceed at a more rapid pace.[180,181] The lesions enlarge, coalesce, and extend toward the posterior pole of the fundus (Fig. 19-6*B*). The margins of the lesions remain discrete and are often densely pigmented. The few choroidal vessels transversing the atrophic areas are markedly narrowed. In some patients additional foci of atrophy develop in the peripapillary area (Fig. 19-6*C*). By the third decade much of the fundus is involved. Increased pigmentation is common in the macular area, while the optic disc remains pink and does not become atrophic. There are filamentous vitreous opacities. The cornea and iris remain normal in appearance. In older patients there is complete chorioretinal degeneration, with a few thin strands of pigmented material traversing the fundus (Fig. 19-6*D*). Early in the clinical course, the appearance of the fundus is pathognomonic for gyrate atrophy. In the final stages the appearance is less specific and may easily be confused with the end stage of several other forms of chorioretinal degeneration, especially the X-linked disorder choroideremia.[205]

The standard tests of visual function become abnormal at an irregular rate, with periods of rapid progression interspersed with periods of relatively stable function.[174,178–181] Visual acuity decreases gradually over several decades in some patients and abruptly over a few years in others.[180] Visual fields are progressively and concentrically reduced. Those patients with peripapillary atrophy may have ring scotoma in addition to peripheral constriction. The electroretinogram, which may be normal at a time when there are a few peripheral atrophic patches, eventually diminishes in amplitude and usually is totally extinguished well before the atrophy becomes complete. The electro-oculogram, a test of rod function, is also severely diminished. Dark adaptometry is abnormal, with both an increase in the final threshold and a prolongation of

A.

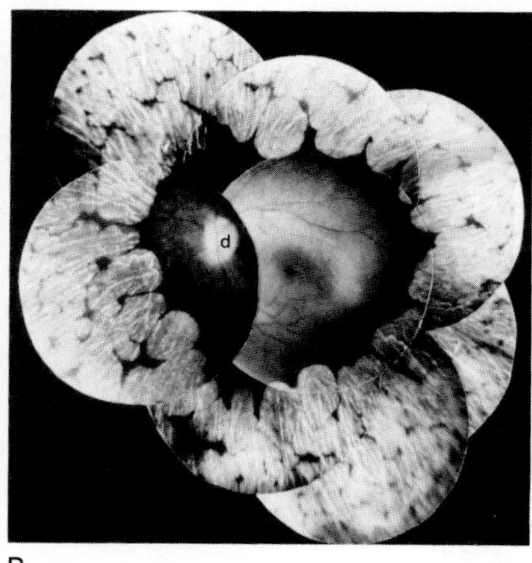

B.

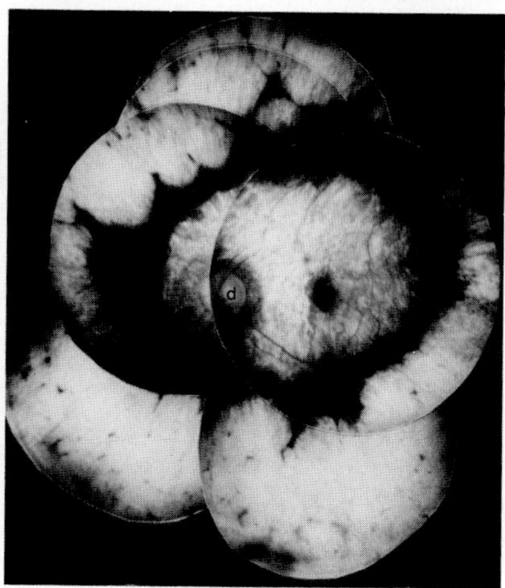

C.

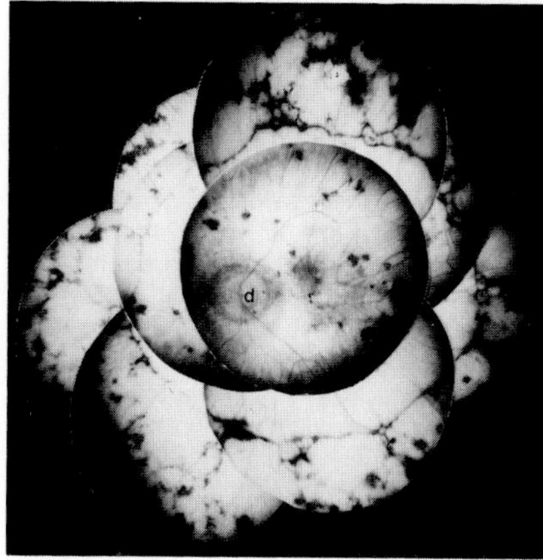

D.

Fig. 19-6 Photographic montages of the ocular fundus of patients with gyrate atrophy of various ages. In these black and white photographs, the normally reddish-brown retina appears middle-dark gray, while the atrophic areas are light gray–white. The area covered by the montage and, thus the magnification of these reproductions, is different in each patient and can be judged roughly by the diameter of the optic disc. The optic disc, with its accompanying retinal vessels, is indicated in each montage with a *d*. *(All montages provided by Dr. Muriel Kaiser-Kupfer, National Eye Institute, Bethesda, MD.)*

A. The right eye of a 6-year-old girl. There are isolated lesions in the mid- and far periphery and circumferential diffuse thinning of the pigment in the midperiphery.[203]

B. The left eye of a 14-year-old girl. The atrophic lesions are more prominent than in *A* and have coalesced. The posterior pole remains normal in appearance.

C. The left eye of a 34-year-old female with much more extensive atrophy than in *B*. The circumferential zone of coalesced atrophic lesions now involves most of the retina. In addition, there is a central area of atrophy surrounding the optic disc, leaving only a thin circular remnant of normal-appearing retina.

D. The left eye of a 62-year-old male with complete chorioretinal atrophy, with only scattered clumps of pigment remaining.

the time required to reach the threshold. In some patients fluorescein angiography has demonstrated a narrow concentric ring around the completely atrophic areas in which an abnormally granular retinal pigment epithelium overlies a normal-appearing choroid.[178,206] This observation plus the description of a diffuse depigmentation of the pigment epithelium in a few very young patients[203] suggests that the initial insult in gyrate atrophy may involve the pigment epithelium.

Aside from visual impairment, patients with gyrate atrophy are for the most part asymptomatic. A few (<10 percent) have mild proximal muscle weakness. Histologic and ultrastructural abnormalities in mitochondria and skeletal muscle fibers have been described in many patients. Mitochondria in liver and iris have shown nonspecific morphologic abnormalities, with serpiginous elongation, branching, and segmentation.[183,207] The functional significance of these abnormalities is not known. Nearly all patients studied have had histologic abnormalities of the type 2 (fast twitch) fibers in skeletal muscle[182,183,187,208,209] (Fig. 19-7). These fibers are reduced in diameter and contain accumulations of abnormally staining material demonstrable by hematoxylin-eosin, Gomori ATPase, or NAD^+-tetrazolium reductase techniques. The accumulations vary in size from small subsarcolemmal deposits to large collections occupying nearly the entire cross-sectional area of the fiber. By electron microscopy, this abnormal material is formed by aggregates of parallel-oriented tubules formed by one or, more typically, two concentric membranes with diameters of 50 to 70 nm for the outer and 25 nm for the inner ("tubular aggregates"; see Refs. 210–212). The type 1 fibers are normal on examination by both light and electron micros-

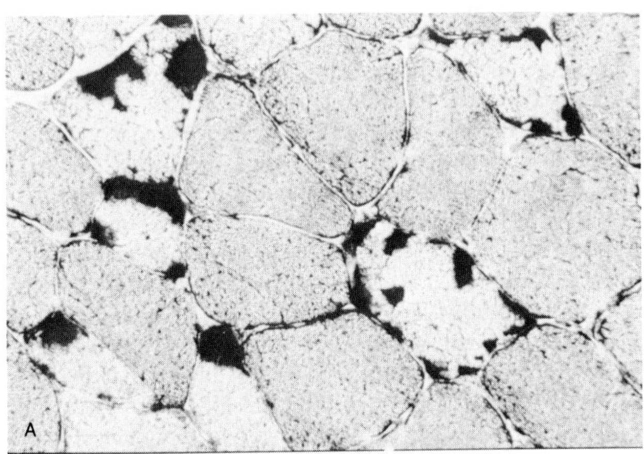

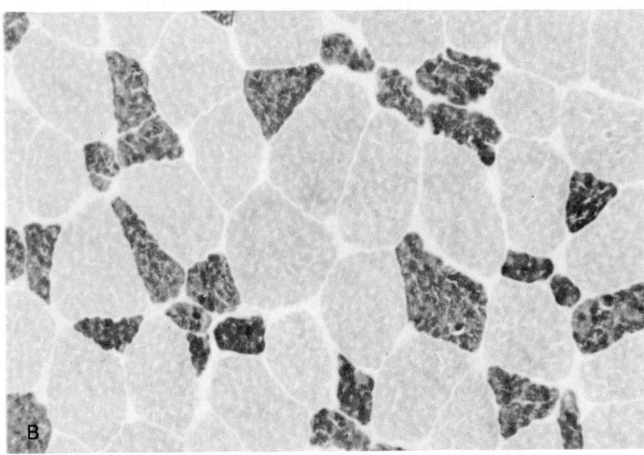

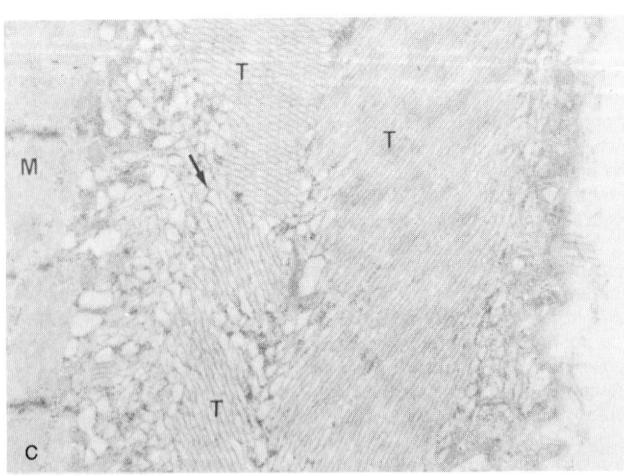

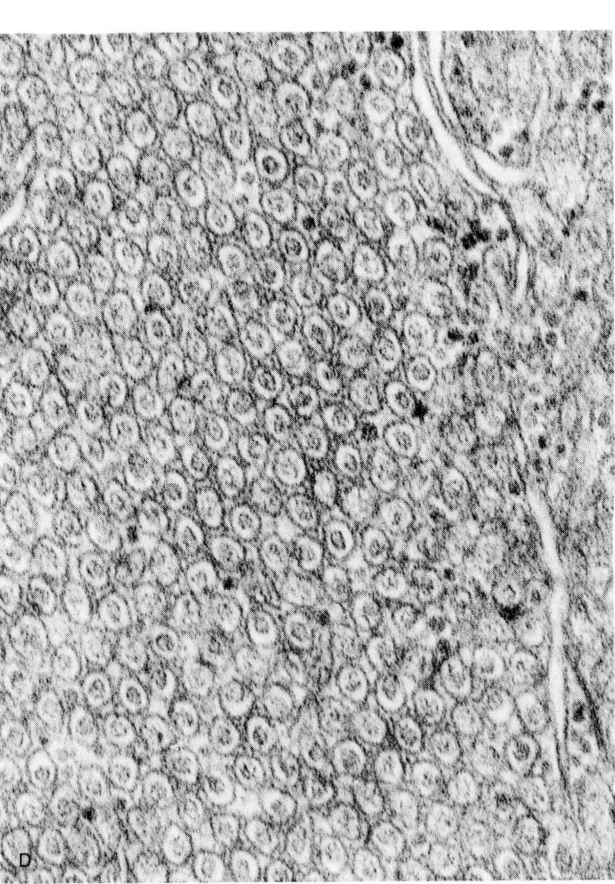

Fig. 19-7 Histologic and ultrastructural abnormalities in the skeletal muscle of patients with gyrate atrophy.

A. NADH-tetrazolium reductase stain demonstrates abnormal, irregular dark areas in the type 2 fibers, which at higher power can be shown to be tubular aggregates. ×340.

B. ATPase stain with preincubation at pH 9.1 stains the type 2 fibers dark and demonstrates several that are atrophic with ragged borders due to lack of enzyme activity in the tubular aggregates. ×136.

C. Ultrastructure of the tubular aggregates in the type 2 fibers showing bundles of parallel tubules (tubular aggregates). The zone between the myofibrils (M) and the regularly aligned tubules (T) consists of haphazardly oriented tubulovesicular structures. The ends of some tubules appear dilated in drumstick fashion. ×20,000.

D. Cross-section of the tubules, most of which contain an inner tubule. ×58,000. *(From Sipila et al.*[208] *Reprinted by permission of the authors and* Neurology.)

Table 19-2 Concentrations of Selected Amino Acids in Body Fluids of Patients with Gyrate Atrophy of the Choroid and Retina

	Plasma, μM		*Cerebrospinal fluid, μM*		*Aqueous humor, μM*	
Amino acid	*Patients,*★ *n*	*Controls,*† *n*	*Patients,*★ *n*	*Controls,*★ *n*	*Patients,*★ *n*	*Controls,*★ *n*
Ornithine	916 (51) 400–1339	75 ± 5 (22)	274 (5) 217–314	8 (5) 6–11	898 (7) 763–987	63 (4) 38–84
Lysine	84 (51) 40–160	207 ± 9 (22)	17 (5) 12–20	26 16–44 (3)	82 (7) 73–92	145 (4) 128–158
Glutamate	20 (11) 5–43	35 ± 7 (22)	—	—	—	—
Glutamine	475 (11) 322–731	669 ± 21 (22)	—	—	—	—

★Mean over range.
† Mean ± SE.
SOURCES: Data from Takki,[178] McCulloch et al.,[183] Yatziv et al.,[194] Stoppoloni et al.,[196] Kennaway et al.,[209] Valle et al.,[214] Valle et al.,[215] Berson et al.[354]

copy. Their number relative to the type 2 fibers increases with age in patients with gyrate atrophy, while in normal subjects the ratio remains constant with age.

Tubular aggregates are not specific for gyrate atrophy. Identical histologic abnormalities have been observed in patients with the various forms of periodic paralysis, hyperthyroidism, porphyria cutanea tarda, myasthenia gravis, myotonic dystrophy, postviral infections, and alcoholism. They have also been observed in low numbers in the muscle of apparently normal male children and adults with nonspecific muscle complaints.[210–213] Aside from patients with gyrate atrophy, they are only rarely observed in females.

In addition to these histologic abnormalities, many patients with gyrate atrophy have abnormal electromyograms with short-duration, low amplitude action potentials of the myopathic type.[208] Despite this, serum creatine phosphokinase activity and usually muscle strength are normal.[182,187,208]

Additional abnormalities include mild to moderate diffuse slowing on electroencephalography in one-third or less of the patients.[178,182,187] Seizures do not occur with increased frequency, and the majority of patients are of normal intelligence.[182,187] Abnormalities of scalp and body hair have been reported.[174,187,203]

Biochemical Abnormalities

The discovery by Simell and Takki of ten- to twentyfold elevations of ornithine in plasma, cerebrospinal fluid, and aqueous humor and of overflow ornithinuria was the first clue to the nature of the primary defect in gyrate atrophy[176,179] (Table 19-2). Modest decreases in the plasma concentrations of other amino acids, including lysine, glutamic acid, and glutamine have been described.[174,175,179,183,194,209,214,215] Plasma lysine levels in patients ingesting a normal diet average about 40 percent of the normal mean and are often below normal range. Cerebrospinal fluid levels of lysine are in low normal range.[179,214]

Urinary excretion of ornithine in adult patients on a regular diet ranges from 0.5 to 10 mmol/day[194,196,214,215] (Table 19-3). The excretion of arginine and lysine is also slightly increased.[196,214] An unusual compound first identified as ornithine-methyl ester[216] and subsequently shown to be 3-amino-piperid-2-one, the cyclic δ-lactam of ornithine which forms spontaneously from ornithine methyl ester[201,217] (Fig. 19-8), is found in the urine of patients with gyrate atrophy and other conditions associated with hyperornithinemia.

The fact that the plasma concentration of this component has been reported as low[219] or unmeasurable[214] suggests that it may originate in the kidney. Small amounts of glutamylornithine also have been identified in the urine of these individuals.[218]

The Enzyme Deficiency

The discovery of hyperornithinemia in gyrate atrophy directed attention to the enzymes of ornithine metabolism, particularly those catalyzing reactions that consume ornithine (Fig. 19-2). Deficiency of ornithine-δ-aminotransferase has been documented in cultured skin fibroblasts,[199,200,209,220–224] in phytohemagglutinin-stimulated lymphocytes,[224,225] in primary skeletal muscle cultures,[226] in hair roots,[226a] and in liver biopsy material.[227] Ornithine-δ-aminotransferase activity measurements have been reported in fibroblasts of at least 15 gyrate atrophy patients in the literature plus >40 in our own laboratory. The ornithine-δ-aminotransferase activity in about two-thirds of the patient cell lines is undetectable (<1 percent of

Table 19-3 Urinary Excretion of Basic Amino Acids in Gyrate Atrophy Patients

		Excretion, μmol/day			
	n	*Ornithine*	*Arginine*	*Lysine*	*δ-Lactam of ornithine*
Patients★	9	3130 (490–7500)	180 (50–3800)	1300 (400–2300)	1090 (520–3100)
Controls†	14	18 ± 23	10 ± 6	155 ± 114	—

★Mean (range).
†Mean ± SD.
SOURCE: Data for patients from Valle et al.,[355] data for controls from Holmgren.[356]

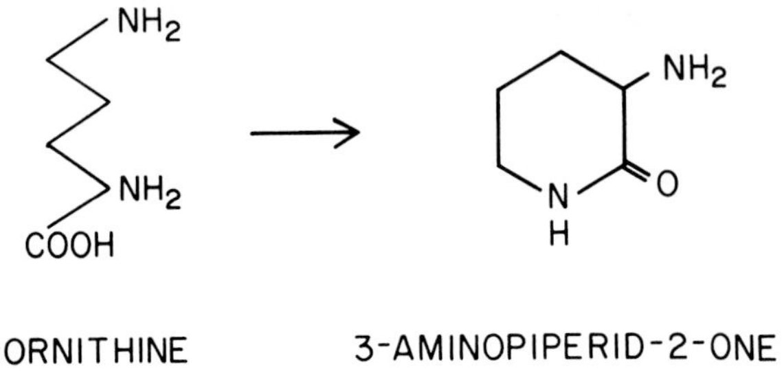

L-ORNITHINE → 3-AMINOPIPERID-2-ONE

Fig. 19-8 3-Aminopiperid-2-one, the δ-lactam of L-ornithine. The mechanism of its formation from ornithine is not known.

normal) while in the remainder, there is residual activity up to as high as 5.7 percent of normal (Table 19-4). In our experience, the presence or absence of residual activity breeds true within a family, a result consistent with the notion that differences in residual activity reflect heterogeneity of mutant ornithine-δ-aminotransferase alleles. Low level ornithine-δ-aminotransferase activity was detected in liver obtained by percutaneous biopsy from two Finnish patients.[227] The residual activity had a greatly reduced affinity for ornithine (K_m approximately 200 mM versus the normal 1.8 mM). Immunologic assays of ornithine-δ-aminotransferase protein in fibroblasts from a small number of patients provide evidence for heterogeneity with the amount of mutant protein varying from normal to nondetectable.[223,228] No evidence has been found for ornithine-δ-aminotransferase inhibitors when gyrate atrophy and control cells or tissue extracts have been mixed.[222,225,227] Ornithine decarboxylase, the other enzyme which catalyzes an ornithine-consuming reaction, was normal in one patient.[225]

Fibroblast ornithine-δ-aminotransferase activity in six patients from five families increased when the concentration of pyridoxal phosphate was increased to high levels in the assay mixture.[209,222,224,229] At usual assay concentrations of cofactor pyridoxal phosphate (16 to 40 μM) the ornithine-δ-aminotransferase activity in these six cell lines ranged from undetectable to 6.5 percent of normal and increased to as much as one-third that of controls when the pyridoxal phosphate concentrations were between 1 and 4 mM. Cultured fibroblasts with appreciable ornithine-δ-aminotransferase activity synthesize radiolabeled proline and glutamate from precursor radiolabeled ornithine (Fig. 19-2). In a convincing study utilizing this "intact cell" assay, Kennaway and her colleagues showed that ornithine-δ-aminotransferase activity in cultured fibroblasts from her four pyridoxine-responsive patients had a higher production of proline and glutamate than did nonresponsive patients, indicating that significant residual enzyme activity is present in the pyridoxine-responsive patients.[229,230] Preliminary kinetic studies of four of these pyridoxine-responsive mutants showed that the K_m for pyridoxal phosphate was increased from a normal value of 0.7 μM to 80 to 130 μM.[76,228] Five of the six patients with an in vitro response had partial reductions in plasma ornithine (averaging about 50 percent) when given pharmacologic doses (500 to 1000 mg/day) of pyridoxine (vitamin B_6, the dietary precursor of pyridoxal phosphate).[209,222,224,230] Three also responded to relatively low doses (15 to 18 mg/day).[191,209,230] One patient described by Kennaway et al.[209] had an in vitro response without an in vivo response, while Valle et al.[215] described a patient with an in vivo response without an in vitro response. In summary, a few gyrate atrophy patients (<5 percent) clearly show evidence (in vivo and/or in vitro) of partial responsiveness to pharmacologic levels of vitamin B_6.

Ornithine-δ-aminotransferase activity also has been assayed in cultured skin fibroblasts from at least 14 obligate heterozygotes (Table 19-4).[200,209,222,224,231] The activity has ranged from 32 to 61 percent of the normal mean. A similar result was obtained in phytohemagglutinin-stimulated lymphocytes.[224,225] This approximately 50 percent reduction in activity in the cells of obligate heterozygotes provides strong genetic evidence for a primary defect in ornithine-δ-aminotransferase as the cause of gyrate atrophy.

Molecular Defects

Heterogeneity in the mutations causing gyrate atrophy was predicted by several early observations: the disorder, although very rare, occurs in individuals of many ethnic origins; interfamilial variability in severity of the clinical phenotype is much greater than intrafamilial variability; and there is interfamilial variability in residual enzyme activity and pyridoxine responsiveness. Complementation studies, testing for recovery of ornithine-δ-aminotransferase activity in heterokaryons produced by fusing fibroblasts from two patients, consistently have shown lack of complementation.[229,231,232] This result suggests that all gyrate atrophy mutations tested are within the same gene.

The recent cloning and sequencing of human ornithine-δ-aminotransferase cDNAs[10,97,98] and the elucidation of the gene structure[10] provided the necessary molecular framework for direct investigation of the mutations responsible for gyrate atrophy (Fig. 19-3). Several additional features of ornithine-δ-aminotransferase have helped these investigations. First, ornithine-δ-aminotransferase is expressed in cultured fibroblasts, providing an accessible source of ornithine-δ-aminotransferase mRNA. Secondly, there is an excellent biologic system for the expression of human ornithine-δ-aminotransferase cDNAs to determine the functional consequences of any variants identified. Chinese hamster ovary cells (CHO-K1), a vigorously growing cell line, are proline auxotrophs, lacking both endogenous Δ^1-pyrroline-5-carboxylate synthase and ornithine-δ-aminotransferase.[150] Ornithine-δ-aminotransferase cDNAs in expression vectors can be transfected into CHO-K1 cells and their protein products examined either in transient transfection assays or by selecting for proline prototrophy.[233,234] Finally, as mentioned above (see "Molecular Biology of Ornithine-δ-Aminotransferase"), the sequence for an ornithine-δ-aminotransferase cDNA from *S. cerevisiae* has recently been reported.[101] The yeast enzyme has regions of high homology

Table 19-4 Ornithine-δ-Aminotransferase Activity in Cultured Skin Fibroblasts of Gyrate Atrophy Patients and Heterozygotes*

Group	(n)	Enzyme activity,† nmol/(h·mg)	Percent of control
Controls	(22)	108.6 ± 19	100
Patients			
No activity	(13)	None detectable	0
Residual activity	(6)	1.8 (0.4–3.9)	2
Obligate heterozygotes	(7)	54.3 (37.8–79.4)	50

*Ornithine-δ-aminotransferase activity was assayed radioisotopically with both substrates present at 0.7 mM and 16 μM pyridoxal phosphate.[92] The division of patient cell lines into groups with no detectable activity and residual activity was unaffected by increasing the substrate concentrations to 15 mM ornithine and 2.5 mM α-ketoglutarate ± 0.6 mM pyridoxal phosphate. The ethnic origin of the patients included Finnish, English, Welsh, Scottish, Portuguese, Spanish, Japanese, and Indian.

†Expressed as mean ± SD or mean (range).

with human ornithine-δ-aminotransferase (Fig. 19-4).[10] The patches of amino acid identity in the proteins from these two distantly related organisms are likely to be important for ornithine-δ-aminotransferase function and are locations where missense mutations can be expected to occur.[10]

Analysis of ornithine-δ-aminotransferase genes in gyrate atrophy patients by Southern blots has proved difficult because of the large number of X-linked ornithine-δ-aminotransferase–hybridizing fragments (Fig. 19-5) and not very rewarding because this technique is not sufficiently sensitive to detect subtle alterations of one or a few base pairs unless the alteration involves a restriction site. A report of one family segregating an ornithine-δ-aminotransferase allele with a partial deletion has appeared,[235] while Southern blots of genomic DNA in probands from 23 pedigrees examined by Mitchell et al.,[236] 4 by Ramesh et al.,[97] and 20 by Inana et al.[237] were normal. These results are in agreement with those for many other genes in which gross size alterations are found in <10 percent of mutant alleles.[238] At the mRNA level, Mitchell et al. have found that 85 percent of patients in 35 pedigrees express normal quantities of normal-sized ornithine aminotransferase mRNA, while the remainder expressed little or none of this mRNA.[236,239] Others also have found a high fraction of mRNA-positive mutants alleles.[97]

Using a combination of RNase A protection assays of patient fibroblast RNA[240,241] and polymerase chain reaction amplification of the appropriate exons,[242,243] Mitchell et al. showed that gyrate atrophy patients in two unrelated Lebanese Maronite families had a G → A transition in the third position of the first codon.[236] This changes the codon from methionine to isoleucine, blocking translation initiation. The mutation creates a new restriction endonuclease site for the enzyme *Ssp*I (AAT$\underline{\text{G}}$TT → AAT$\underline{\text{A}}$TT) providing a means to screen other patients for the same mutation. Southern blots of *Ssp*I-digested genomic DNA from 17 pedigrees of 12 ethnic origins failed to show this Lebanese mutation, providing the first molecular proof of heterogeneity in the mutations causing gyrate atrophy.[236]

Mitchell and colleagues have described two additional missense mutations in Finnish gyrate atrophy patients.[233] Both were shown by expression in CHO-K1 cells to completely inactivate ornithine aminotransferase. One is a G → C transversion at position 539 which results in conversion of arginine-180 to threonine; the second was a T → C transition at position 1205 resulting in conversion of leucine-402 to proline. Utilizing the single letter code for amino acids, these mutations were designated R180T and L402P, respectively. This result is surprising because it demonstrates that at least two mutant ornithine aminotransferase alleles are segregating in the Finnish population, which is relatively small (approximately 4.8 million total) and isolated.[244–246] Both mutations alter restriction sites and can be detected reliably on Southern blots of genomic DNA hybridized with probes specific for the corresponding exon (exon 6 for R180T, exon 11 for L402P). About one-fourth of the known Finnish gyrate atrophy pedigrees have been screened in this manner, with L402P accounting for 85 percent of the mutant alleles and R180T for the remainder. Aside from one American patient homozygous for R180T, no other gyrate atrophy pedigrees had these mutations.[233]

Two additional ornithine-δ-aminotransferase missense mutations have been detected by Ramesh and her colleagues by sequencing ornithine aminotransferase cDNA clones prepared from patient fibroblast RNA.[234] The functional consequences of both were confirmed by expressing the mutant cDNAs in CHO-K1 cells. One was a C → A transversion at position 162 in the cDNA, changing asparagine-54 to lysine (N54K). The second was of particular interest because the patient was one of the few gyrate atrophy patients with a pyridoxine-responsive phenotype. Ornithine aminotransferase activity in extracts of his fibroblasts increased from a level that was barely detectable to 30 percent of control when assay pyridoxal phosphate was increased from 40 to 400 μM. Sequence analysis of a cDNA from this individual showed a G → A transition at position 994 in the cDNA, changing valine-332 to methionine (V332M). When this cDNA was expressed by transient transfection of CHO-K1 cells, the ornithine aminotransferase activity of the expressed protein increased twentyfold from barely detectable to 8 percent of control when assay pyridoxal phosphate was increased from 20 to 200 μM. Valine-332 is 40 residues downstream from lysine-292, the pyridoxal phosphate–binding residue.[86] The investigators hypothesized that the tertiary structure of ornithine-δ-aminotransferase is such that valine-332 participates in the cofactor-binding pocket and that substitution with the larger, sulfur-containing residue in some way alters binding.

A similar situation has been described for another pyridoxal phosphate–requiring enzyme, *Escherichia coli* aspartate aminotransferase, whose structure is known.[247] The pyridoxal phosphate–binding residue is lysine-258. A mutation converting tyrosine-70, a residue known to contribute to the cofactor-binding site, to phenylalanine results in enhanced dissociation of cofactor from the enzyme. When assayed in the presence of excess pyridoxal phosphate, the mutant enzyme completes the first half-reaction of the transamination, converting the cofactor to pyridoxamine phosphate, which is then released from the enzyme. The net result is that pyridoxal phosphate becomes a substrate rather than a cofactor. If this same mechanism is involved in the pyridoxine-responsive ornithine-δ-aminotransferase mutation (V332M), ornithine and pyridoxal phosphate would be substrates and Δ^1-pyrroline-5-carboxylate and pyridoxamine phosphate would be products and the reaction would proceed in the absence of α-ketoglutarate (see "Chemistry of Ornithine-δ-Aminotransferase").

In summary, although the elucidation of ornithine-δ-aminotransferase mutations has just begun, at least six mutations have been well documented. Another two have been mentioned in abstract form.[239,248] All are listed in Table 19-5. As can be seen in Fig. 19-4, all the missense mutations alter residues conserved over the 1.5 billion years of evolutionary time separating humans and yeast. The variety of defects already detected predicts marked heterogeneity in the mutations causing gyrate atrophy. The next challenge will be to determine the structural and functional consequences of these mutations and to use them to better understand the cell biology of ornithine-δ-aminotransferase and the variability among patients with gyrate atrophy. In turn, this information should lead to the development of better therapy.

Pathophysiology

Biochemical Abnormalities. Deficiency of ornithine-δ-aminotransferase explains most of the biochemical abnormalities observed in patients with gyrate atrophy. Hyperornithinemia is a direct result of the block in the ornithine-δ-aminotransferase reaction. An adult with gyrate atrophy ingesting 1.5 g/

Table 19-5 Summary of Ornithine-δ-Aminotransferase Mutations Causing Gyrate Atrophy*

Ethnic origin of proband(s)	*Number of pedigrees*	*cDNA nucleotide position*	*Mutation*	*Consequence*	*Reference*
1. Lebanese-Maronite	2	+3	G → A	Blocks initiation (M1I)	236
2. Not provided	1	+994	G → A	Missense (V332M)	234
3. Not provided	1	+162	C → A	Missense (N54K)	234
4. Finnish	14	+1205	T → C	Missense (L402P)	233
5. Finnish	2	+539	G → C	Missense (R180T)	233
American	1				
6. Iraqi-Jewish	1	+159	del C	Frameshift	239
7. Portuguese	1	+550	del GCT	Deletes Ala-184 (A184Δ)	239
8. Not provided	1	Not provided	Partial deletion		235

*Compiled in August 1988.

kg/day has an arginine intake of approximately 28 mmol/day. Little if any of this arginine is utilized for protein accretion. Arginine is converted to ornithine by arginase and to a lesser extent by glycine transamidinase (Fig. 19-2). A fraction of the ornithine is utilized for the synthesis of putrescine and polyamines (an estimated 0.5 mmol/day), and the remainder accumulates. Ornithine excretion increases concomitantly, particularly at plasma concentrations of more than 600 μM.[215] The high renal filtered load of ornithine also results in increased renal clearances of lysine, arginine, and cystine.[248]

The total urinary excretion of arginine-derived carbon skeletons (arginine, ornithine, the δ-lactam of ornithine, citrulline, and argininosuccinic acid) by patients with gyrate atrophy is much less than the estimated arginine intake (Table 19-3). Therefore, as much as 75 percent of the ingested arginine cannot be accounted for in these patients.[248] Possible explanations for this include residual ornithine-δ-aminotransferase activity,[227] gastrointestinal losses, greater flux to putrescine than estimated, or some unanticipated pathway for the catabolism of arginine, ornithine, or any of the urea cycle intermediates. Transamination of arginine or ornithine would provide such an alternative degradation pathway, but there is no evidence that this occurs in humans.[75,249] The extent of the conversion of ornithine to putrescine by ornithine decarboxylase may have been underestimated by data from studies measuring polyamine excretion[36,37] since putrescine may also be converted to CO_2 via γ-aminobutyrate and succinate (Fig. 19-2). The enzymes necessary for this reaction sequence are present in mammalian tissues.[58,60] Ornithine decarboxylase is so highly regulated by factors related to the growth of cells[34] that it probably limits significant catabolism by this pathway.

The extent of ornithine accumulation in patients with this disorder has not been determined since the compartments in which ornithine has been measured (plasma, cerebrospinal fluid, and aqueous humor) represent only a small fraction (~ 10 percent) of the total-body ornithine pool.[250] The major portion of the free pool of most amino acids is located in the intracellular fluid of skeletal muscle and liver. In normal humans the intracellular ornithine concentration in muscle is fivefold that in plasma.[251] Lower values have been reported for rat muscle.[252,253] If the former ratio is maintained in gyrate atrophy, the total-body pool of ornithine in an adult could be as high as 100 to 150 mmol. A comparison of the intracellular versus plasma fractions of the total-body ornithine pool emphasizes the fact that a minor change in ornithine distribution can lead to a major change in plasma concentration without a change in total-body ornithine. A temporary shift of ornithine from plasma to intracellular fluid may explain the transient, acute reduction of plasma ornithine in gyrate atrophy patients following a glucose load.[182,209,214]

Hyperornithinemia and ornithine accumulation may also account for some of the abnormal concentrations of other plasma metabolites. The hypolysinemia may result from the increased renal clearance of lysine or an effect of ornithine on the catabolism or distribution of lysine.[214] The explanation for the reduced levels of glutamate and glutamine is not known, although it has been suggested that this is due to an alteration in the balance between urea precursors (glutamate, glutamine, ammonia) and urea production due to the increased concentration of ornithine.[214] Thus, the availability of urea precursors, rather than ornithine, may limit urea production in these patients.

Mechanism of the Chorioretinal Degeneration. How a deficiency of ornithine-δ-aminotransferase and subsequent ornithine accumulation lead to the chorioretinal degeneration and cataract formation is not known. Any hypothesis must explain the slowly progressive nature of this disorder, the minimal involvement of other organ systems, and the lack of ocular involvement in patients with the HHH syndrome. Possibilities include a toxic effect of the accumulated precursor (ornithine) or of one of its metabolites, or a deficiency of the reaction product (Δ^1-pyrroline-5-carboxylate) or one of its metabolites. The fact that ornithine-δ-aminotransferase activity is present in retinal neurons and glia (particularly Müller cells)[130,131] and in pigment epithelium[123–125, 128] suggests that the enzyme function may be important in these tissues but does not discriminate between the two general mechanisms (Fig. 19-9).

An additional problem in determining the mechanism of the chorioretinal degeneration is that there are no descriptions of the ocular pathology in humans with gyrate atrophy. Indeed, it is not known for certain which of the many specialized types of cells found in the choroid and retina are the first to be affected. Most attention has centered on the pigment epithelial cells which form the outermost cell layer of the retina[254,255,259] (Fig. 19-9). The inner aspect of these cells surrounds the outer segments of the photoreceptor cells and performs a number of functions necessary for the well-being of the receptor cells. The choroidal aspect of the pigment epithelial cells rests on Bruch's membrane, a complex structure that is composed of basement membrane components produced by both the pigment epithelium and cells in the choriocapillaris. The blood supply to the outermost third of the retina, including the pigment epithelium, is provided by a layer of specialized, dilated capillaries, the *choriocapillaris*, located just beneath Bruch's membrane. The apical lateral surfaces of the pigment epithe-

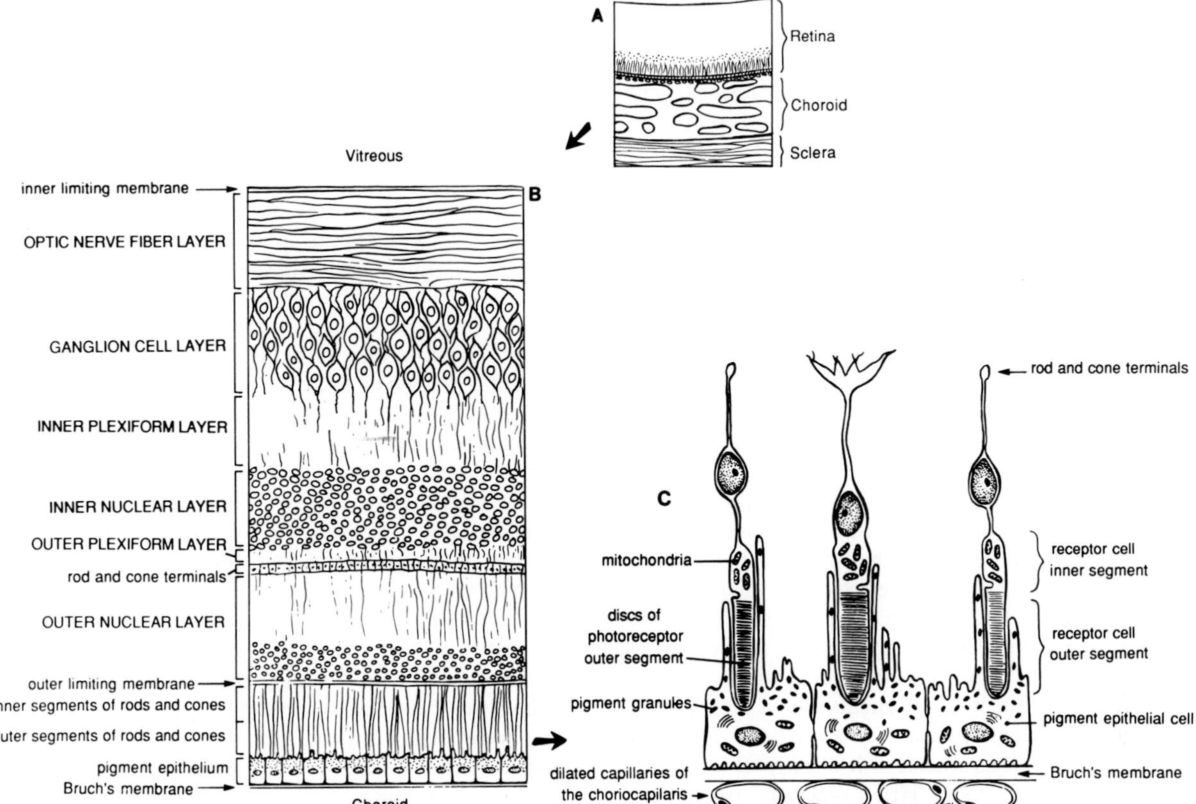

Fig. 19-9 Diagrammatic representation of human ocular tissues. The orientation of each diagram is the same with the inner (vitreal) surface upward and the outer (scleral) surface downward. *A.* Low power view of a cross-section of the posterior aspect of the eye showing the relationship of the three major layers, retina, choroid and sclera. *B.* Higher power view of the retina showing the retinal layers. *C.* Detail of the anatomic relationship of the pigment epithelium and the photoreceptor cells. Three receptor cells are shown; the one in the middle with a broad synaptic terminal is a cone. In vivo, each pigment epithelium cell interacts with the outer segments of several receptor cells.

lial cells are joined to one another by tight junctions which form a zonula occludens blocking intercellular passage of metabolites and corresponding to the blood-retinal barrier on the outer surface of the retina.[257] Thus, metabolites such as glucose and amino acids pass through Bruch's membrane and then are transported intracellularly through the pigment epithelium to the photoreceptor cells. Because of their interdependence, damage to any of these cellular components of the retina may secondarily destroy the others. Pathologic studies in a cat with gyrate atrophy and advanced retinal degeneration showed extensive involvement of the pigment epithelium, neuroretina, and choriocapillaris.[258] The observation in humans by Takki and others of areas of pigment epithelial cell damage over an intact choriocapillaris suggests that the pigment layer is the site of the initial insult in gyrate atrophy.[178,206] In support of this, Kaiser-Kupfer et al. described diffuse circumferential depigmentation of the pigment epithelium starting abruptly in the midperiphery and extending to the peripheral retina of a young patient.[203] Finally, Kuwabara and colleagues have shown that intravitreal injection of ornithine results in degeneration of the pigment epithelial cells in both rats and monkeys.[259]

Two hypotheses for the pathophysiology of gyrate atrophy have been presented (Fig. 19-10). Sipila and coworkers[66,208] have proposed that deficiency of creatine and creatine phosphate may account for both the histologic abnormalities in muscle and the chorioretinal degeneration. They suggest that

Fig. 19-10 Schematic diagram of two different, nonexclusive hypotheses for the pathophysiology of gyrate atrophy of the choroid and retina. In one, high ornithine concentrations inhibit glycine transamidinase, resulting in reduced synthesis of guanidinoacetate and creatine. In the other, the combination of the inherited deficiency of ornithine-δ-aminotransferase and the inhibitory effect of ornithine on Δ^1-pyrroline-5-carboxylate synthase results in decreased formation of Δ^1-pyrroline-5-carboxylate and proline.

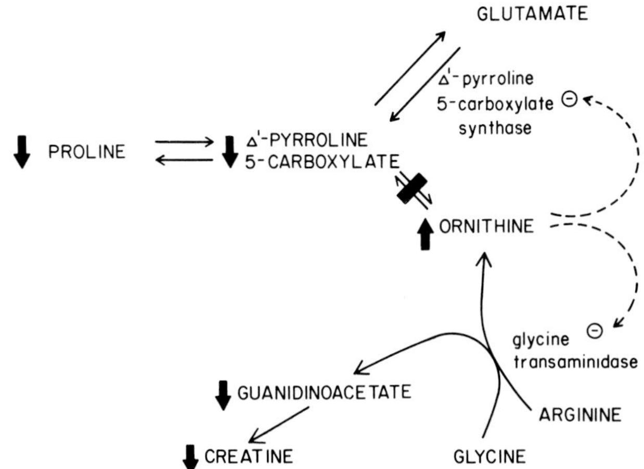

the high ornithine concentrations inhibit glycine transamidinase, thereby reducing creatine synthesis and causing a reduction in total-body creatine and creatine phosphate. Evidence supporting this hypothesis includes the well-documented sensitivity of glycine transamidinase to ornithine in vitro[64–66] and the observations that fasting plasma guanidinoacetate, creatine, and creatinine; daily guanidinoacetate and creatinine excretion; and the excretion of guanidinoacetate and creatine following an arginine load are all reduced in patients with gyrate atrophy as compared to normals[260,261] (Fig. 19-11). These observations indicate that glycine transamidinase is inhibited in vivo as well as in vitro and that there is a reduction of the total-body creatine–creatine phosphate pool in gyrate atrophy patients. The extent of this reduction is not known. Creatinine excretion, although statistically reduced, overlaps with the normal range,[260] and direct measurements of tissue creatine–creatine phosphate concentrations have not been performed. This hypothesis would be consistent with the lack of ophthalmologic abnormalities in the HHH syndrome if the subcellular location of the transamidinase is within the mitochondria and if the defect in HHH syndrome is defective mitochondrial uptake of ornithine (Fig. 19-2).[262] The observations of histologic improvement in the muscles of gyrate atrophy patients given exogenous creatine[263,264] and of modest improvement and/or stabilization of visual function in patients whose plasma ornithine has been reduced by means of an arginine-restricted diet[174,186,214,265,266] are in agreement with this hypothesis. Creatine excretion was low in two HHH syndrome patients on their regular diet (1.2 to 1.5 g/kg/day); however, it rose to normal levels despite pronounced hyperornithinemia, when supplements of arginine or ornithine (2 mmol/kg/day) were added to the diet, suggesting that significant transamidinase activity was present.[262]

Although relatively little is known about the role of creatine and creatine phosphate in retinal function, a recent study of chicken retina strongly suggests that they play an important physiological function in the energy transduction of vision. Wallimann et al. found high concentrations of creatine kinase

Fig. 19-11 Guanidinoacetate (GAA) excretion after intravenous infusion of 1.1 mmol per kilogram body weight of arginine in (■) male and (●) female patients with gyrate atrophy and (□) male and (○) female controls. *(From Sipila et al.[260] Reprinted by permission of the authors and* The Journal of Clinical Investigation.)

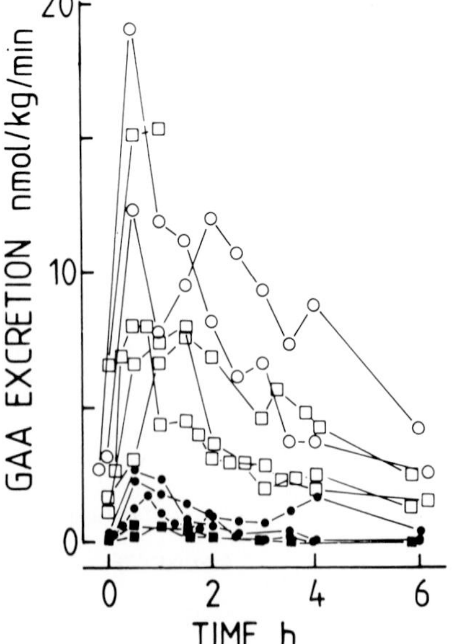

and creatine phosphate in rod and cone photoreceptor cells.[267] Two creatine kinase isoforms were identified and localized by immunofluorescence: the brain isoform was predominant and stained intensely over the inner segment of both rod and cone photoreceptors; the mitochondrial isoform was also present and was localized to the ellipsoid portion of the inner segments known to be rich in mitochondria. Creatine, creatine phosphate, and guanidinoacetate also are present in mammalian brain[61,69,268,269] but appear to cross the blood-brain barrier slowly.[270,271] Thus, local synthesis of creatine may be important in brain and retina. Low glycine transamidinase activity has been found in human brain[272] but was not detected in retina.[128] Creatine phosphate also has been implicated as an important energy source for phagocytosis by peritoneal macrophages.[273] This is intriguing in view of the highly phagocytic nature of the retinal pigment epithelium, although there is no direct evidence of phagocytic abnormalities in gyrate atrophy patients. Pharmacologic agents which deplete tissues of creatine phosphate[62,270,271] and the possible reduction of creatine synthesis in other human and animal disorders[274] provide an as yet unexploited possibility for additional study of the role of creatine depletion in the pathophysiology of gyrate atrophy.

A second hypothesis for the pathophysiology of gyrate atrophy involves the deficient synthesis of Δ^1-pyrroline-5-carboxylate owing to the genetic deficiency of ornithine-δ-aminotransferase and to inhibitory effects of ornithine on Δ^1-pyrroline-5-carboxylate synthase, the enzyme which catalyzes the formation of Δ^1-pyrroline-5-carboxylate from glutamate (Fig. 19-10). The observations which support this model include the recent findings that Δ^1-pyrroline-5-carboxylate synthase is inhibited in vitro by near-physiological concentrations of L-ornithine[149] and that ornithine is toxic to cells lacking ornithine-δ-aminotransferase (gyrate atrophy fibroblasts or Chinese hamster ovary cells at concentrations which are tolerated by control cells).[275–277] This toxic effect of ornithine is prevented by amino acids that inhibit Δ^1-pyrroline-5-carboxylate dehydrogenase, a Δ^1-pyrroline-5-carboxylate–consuming enzyme, and partially prevented by the addition of exogenous Δ^1-pyrroline-5-carboxylate.[277,278] The hypothesis, therefore, predicts that the genetic defect in gyrate atrophy prevents the synthesis of Δ^1-pyrroline-5-carboxylate from ornithine and causes accumulation of an inhibitor (ornithine) of the alternative pathway of Δ^1-pyrroline-5-carboxylate synthesis. The reduced availability of Δ^1-pyrroline-5-carboxylate may be detrimental because of decreased proline synthesis or because of disruption of the regulatory roles that Δ^1-pyrroline-5-carboxylate and its metabolic interconversions have been shown to exert on the intracellular redox level and hexose monophosphate shunt activity.[279–283] Depending on the mechanism, cells with access to extracellular fluid proline or with the ability to synthesize Δ^1-pyrroline-5-carboxylate from proline by the proline oxidase reaction would be predicted to be unscathed in gyrate atrophy. Thus, most cells and tissues would be spared. Retinal pigment epithelium and neural retinal tissue lack proline oxidase,[284] however, and although the availability of proline in the extracellular fluid of retina is not known, it may be low, judging from the fact that proline crosses the blood-brain barrier poorly[285] and is virtually absent from the cerebrospinal fluid.[250]

Phang and his colleagues have recently developed a sensitive, quantitative assay of Δ^1-pyrroline-5-carboxylate in biologic fluids and have shown a normal human plasma value of 100 to 400 n*M*.[286] Preliminary studies show plasma Δ^1-pyrroline-5-carboxylate levels to be normal in gyrate atrophy patients[287] as might be expected since the plasma compartment is exposed to tissues with proline oxidase. What is critical and as yet unknown are the Δ^1-pyrroline-5-carboxylate and proline levels in the ocular tissues of patients with gyrate atrophy. Two recent observations support the notion of an important role for Δ^1-pyrroline-5-carboxylate in ocular metabolism: high Δ^1-pyrroline-5-carboxylate concentrations (3.3 μM or about twentyfold those in plasma) were found in the aqueous tumor of rabbits;[129] and Δ^1-pyrroline-5-carboxylate was shown to be a potent stimulus of lens hexose monophosphate shunt activity.[129,288]

The deficient Δ^1-pyrroline-5-carboxylate synthesis hypothesis would explain the lack of ocular abnormalities in the HHH syndrome on the basis of normal Δ^1-pyrroline-5-carboxylate production from ornithine by intact ornithine-δ-aminotransferase. The possible beneficial effects of reduction of ornithine accumulation[174,186,265,266] would be explained relieving the ornithine inhibition of Δ^1-pyrroline-5-carboxylate synthase. As with the first hypothesis, more information on retinal amino acid and energy metabolism in normals and in patients with gyrate atrophy is necessary.

Additional abnormalities of possible pathologic significance in gyrate atrophy include the modest reductions in the plasma concentrations of glutamate, glutamine, and lysine.[178,214] Of these, only lysine is reduced below the normal range. The hypolysinemia seems unlikely to be related to the chorioretinal degeneration since it probably does not indicate a true lysine deficiency[214] and because other conditions with hypolysinemia (e.g., lysinuric protein intolerance) are not associated with ocular problems.[289] Abnormalities of polyamines or their metabolites could also play a pathologic role in gyrate atrophy. The fragmentary data available suggest that serum spermine, spermidine, and putrescine concentrations are in the normal range.[209]

Treatment

The slow progression of the degenerative changes in gyrate atrophy and the difficulty in measuring small changes in ocular function objectively make evaluation of any therapy difficult.[189] Biochemical parameters (e.g., plasma amino acid concentrations) can be accurately measured, but until the pathophysiology is understood there is no assurance that correction of biochemical abnormalities in plasma will actually be beneficial. Four general approaches to the therapy of gyrate atrophy have been attempted: stimulation of residual ornithine-δ-aminotransferase activity with pharmacologic doses of pyridoxine; correction of ornithine accumulation by reducing the intake of its precursor arginine and/or increasing renal ornithine losses; administration of creatine; and administration of proline.

Pyridoxine-Responsive Gyrate Atrophy. A response to pyridoxine (vitamin B_6), the precursor of the cofactor pyridoxal phosphate, should be an effective therapy regardless of the pathophysiological mechanisms since the end result is a reduction in the accumulated precursor (ornithine) and an increased production of the reaction product (Δ^1-pyrroline-5-carboxylate). Administration of pharmacologic doses of pyridoxine hydrochloride (500 to 1000 mg/day) has been associated with a significant reduction in plasma ornithine in six patients from five sibships.[188–191] The actual reduction has averaged about 50 percent, although interpretation of this result is somewhat obscured by the apparent lack of close regulation of arginine intake during these trials. Where reported, plasma lysine returned to normal coincident with the decrease in plasma ornithine. Weleber and associates found that 15 to 20 mg/day of pyridoxine hydrochloride was just as effective as the higher dosage in some of their patients.[191] This is relevant in view of the association of peripheral neuropathy with chronic ingestion of large amounts of pyridoxine.[290,291] Fibroblast ornithine-δ-aminotransferase activity in these patients responded in vitro to the addition of high concentrations of pyridoxal phosphate to the assay mixture.[209,222] In the patients followed by Weleber et al., despite initial promising results,[191] there has been mild progression of chorioretinal degeneration.[292] Similarly, two Japanese pyridoxine-responsive patients, aged 8 and 17, had some progression of their chorioretinal degeneration over 2 years while receiving 120 and 600 mg of pyridoxine, respectively.[293] Thus, the results of pyridoxine therapy in this small group of patients are disappointing. The possibility that at least the rate of progression has been slowed by this therapy remains to be determined.

Reduction of Ornithine by Nutritional Methods and/or Augmentation of Renal Losses. A second approach to the therapy of gyrate atrophy has involved correction of the ornithine accumulation by restriction of dietary intake of arginine and/or by augmentation of ornithine excretion. Reduction of ornithine should be beneficial if the pathophysiology of gyrate atrophy involves a direct toxic effect of ornithine or reduced synthesis of Δ^1-pyrroline-5-carboxylate, since high levels of ornithine may inhibit the alternate pathway of Δ^1-pyrroline-5-carboxylate synthesis (via Δ^1-pyrroline-5-carboxylate synthase, see "Pathophysiology"). An arginine-restricted diet has been constructed by reducing protein intake to approximately 0.2 g/kg/day and supplying the necessary amounts of essential amino acids, calories, minerals, and vitamins.[174,189,214,215,266] On this regimen, plasma ornithine values have decreased two- to sixfold as ornithine is lost in the urine and consumed for putrescine synthesis, and several patients have maintained normal to near-normal ornithine values for extended periods of time.[174,215] The secondary abnormalities in plasma lysine, glutamate, glutamine, and ammonia have improved coincident with reduction in plasma ornithine. Care must be taken to avoid excessive restriction of arginine, which can lead to hypoargininemia, hypoornithinemia, and acute hyperammonemia, particularly if nitrogen intake is high.[215,266] Kaiser-Kupfer and Valle have instituted an arginine-restricted diet in 19 patients with ages ranging from 2 to 47 years, all of whom had failed to show significant reduction in ornithine values after a 1- to 2-month trial of pharmacologic doses of pyridoxine.[174,186,265,266] A variety of problems with communication and compliance reduced the sample to 12 patients. The degree of biochemical control was graded as good (plasma ornithine < 200 μM), fair (200 to 400 μM), and poor (>400 μM). Only six patients have been consistently in the good range. Two women, both aged 34 at the time of institution of the diet, have had good biochemical control for 10 and 8 years. Both had modest early improvement and subsequent stabilization in subjective and objective tests of visual functions.[174,186,265] The remaining four patients with good control are much younger and have been on diet for a much shorter time. No deterioration has been observed, but longer evaluation is necessary because of the slow progression of disease. Other patients with good biochemical control have had some evidence of modest improvement or stabilization.[266] However, the disease has clearly progressed in older patients on diet, with control in the fair range.[174,294] Of most concern is the recent report of three Finnish patients, on diet for 3 to 5 years, starting at ages 7 to 9 years.[295] Despite good biochemical control there was evidence by fundus photography of enlargement of the atrophic areas, particularly in one. Thus, to date, the results with this highly restrictive diet have been mixed. More experience, particularly with younger patients, with this experimental therapy is necessary before final conclusions can be reached. It is clear that only highly motivated patients with good nutritional and medical management can maintain the diet.

Augmentation of the renal losses of ornithine by administration of compounds known to interfere with dibasic amino acid transport has been attempted alone or in combination with diet therapy. Lysine[194,214,274,296] and the nonmetabolizable amino acid α-aminoisobutyric acid[214,215] have been utilized for this purpose. Both have been shown to increase ornithine excretion, especially when plasma ornithine concentrations are high. As plasma ornithine concentrations decrease (particularly below 300 μ*M*), these compounds become much less effective.[214,215] No studies of the long-term efficacy of this approach have been reported.

Creatine Administration. A third form of therapy for gyrate atrophy derives from the hypothesis that creatine deficiency plays a pathophysiological role in this disorder. Sipila and coworkers have administered 1.5 g creatine daily to seven gyrate atrophy patients for 1 year.[263] In all there was improvement in the histologic abnormalities in muscle; however, four of the seven had some progression in their ophthalmologic abnormalities documented by fundus photography. A 5-year follow-up of 13 patients treated with creatine also showed continued progress of the chorioretinal degeneration and persistent correction of the histologic abnormalities in skeletal muscle.[264] These results indicate that creatine depletion does play a role in the muscle abnormalities. The progression of the ocular abnormalities despite administration of creatine suggests either that the pathophysiology of the chorioretinal degeneration is on a different basis or that at the dose used an inadequate amount of creatine reached the sensitive cells in the eye.

Proline Therapy. A final experimental therapy tried for gyrate atrophy is the administration of proline on the rationale that deficient formation of this nonessential amino acid is the major cause of the chorioretinal degeneration.[293,297] Since plasma proline concentrations are normal in gyrate atrophy, Hayaska et al. propose that deficient local synthesis of proline in retinal tissues is critical and cannot be compensated by normal levels of circulating proline. The reasons why a local deficiency of both Δ^1-pyrroline-5-carboxylate and proline may occur in retina are discussed above in "Pathophysiology." In further support of this hypothesis, the investigators cite a patient with increased excretion of proline and the other amino acids, normal ornithine levels, and a chorioretinal degeneration resembling atypical gyrate atrophy.[298] Plasma proline was normal. How the excessive renal losses could result in chorioretinal degeneration despite normal plasma proline levels was not addressed. Chorioretinal degeneration is not a feature of iminoglycinuria (see Chap. 102). Nevertheless, these investigators have treated four patients, aged 5 to 32, with oral proline supplements in doses ranging from 65 to 488 mg/kg/day. Plasma proline varied from unchanged to threefold increased. In the youngest patient there was "minimal" increase in the atrophic area and "slight" deterioration of the electroretinogram over 5 years. In an 8-year-old patient there was clear progression of the chorioretinal degeneration over 3 years while in two older patients, aged 23 and 32, there was no progression over 3 years. Thus, the outcome of these patients is mixed. Furthermore, since the hypothesis for a pathologic local proline deficiency in the retina is contingent on a lack of entry of proline into the retina from the blood, it is not clear how supplemental proline can be expected to be of therapeutic benefit.

Genetics

The inheritance of gyrate atrophy is autosomal recessive. Males and females are equally affected, consanguinity is common in the reported pedigrees,[170,174,175,299] and obligate heterozygotes have partially reduced ornithine-δ-aminotransferase activity (Table 19-4).

Gyrate atrophy is rare with approximately 130 biochemically confirmed cases known to us. The nationality of the patients has included Finnish, Spanish, Italian, Dutch, English, Welsh, Portuguese, Japanese, Turkish, Mexican, Nicaraguan, German, and Greek.[174] One American black family with multiple affected sibs has been described briefly.[174,300] The incidence is apparently highest in Finland, with approximately 70 documented cases in a population of 4.8 million. Assuming 50 percent ascertainment, an estimated frequency of the disorder in Finland would be about 1 in 50,000 individuals, and the estimated heterozygote frequency would be 1 in 110 individuals. In the United States, the disorder is much rarer. A comprehensive survey of all university-affiliated ophthalmology departments in Japan yielded 15 patients.[175]

HYPERORNITHINEMIA-HYPERAMMONEMIA-HOMOCITRULLINURIA (HHH) SYNDROME

Shih and coworkers[163] described the first patient with the fascinating combination of increased plasma ornithine concentration, postprandial hyperammonemia, and homocitrullinuria in 1969. We currently know of over 30 patients from a variety of ethnic backgrounds.[163,201,262,301–323] Autosomal recessive inheritance is suggested by the fact that several patients are from consanguineous matings and multiple cases have occurred in siblings. Increased plasma ornithine concentration differentiates the syndrome from the other urea cycle disorders, and postprandial hyperammonemia and homocitrullinuria distinguishes it from another defined disease with hyperornithinemia, i.e, gyrate atrophy of the choroid and retina.

The Clinical Phenotype

The symptoms occur during the newborn period[262,301,302,304,314] or may be delayed until late adulthood.[303,309] Pregnancy is uncomplicated, birth size normal, and the neonatal course uneventful if the children are breast-fed. Most patients have typical histories of intermittent hyperammonemia. Many refuse to eat and have vomiting, lethargy, and even episodes of coma when fed high-protein formula or other high-protein foods.

After infancy, most patients spontaneously select a low-protein diet avoiding milk and meat.

Some patients survive to adulthood rather symptom-free, but usually periods of lethargy, vomiting, ataxia or choreoathetosis, or delayed development bring the patient to medical attention during infancy or childhood. Growth is inadequate and developmental milestones are delayed. Muscle hypotonia may occur; spasticity is common later. Seizures are not uncommon: they may begin in infancy[262,303,305,306] and resemble infantile spasms,[163] but often appear later.[302–305,315] The mental outcome has varied from low normal intelligence to severe retardation. The ocular fundi are normal except during episodes of acute hyperammonemia, when papilledema has been reported.[303] The size of the liver and spleen is normal or slightly enlarged. An increased bleeding tendency has been an associated feature in three patients[262,303,304] and the leading clinical sign in one.[304]

Light microscopy of liver biopsy samples has been normal, but ultrastructurally liver mitochondria were elongated and had bizarre shapes and a peculiar periodicity below the level of the inner limiting membrane.[303,312,324–327] The longest mitochondria contained "crystalloid" structures, probably representing elongated systems of cristae or tubules. Occasional liver samples have had normal ultrastructure.[309] The mitochondria of cultured fibroblasts contained triangular structures resembling changes seen in the liver.[328] Loosely laminated structures resembling myelin figures have also been reported in increased numbers in the cytoplasm of the fibroblasts. Abnormal mitochondria also have been found in muscle and leukocytes.[303]

One patient, maintained on 1 g/kg/day protein restriction during her whole pregnancy, has given birth to a normal child.[303]

The Biochemical Phenotype

Plasma ornithine concentrations on an unlimited diet have ranged from 209 to 1020 μM. The values overlap with those in patients with gyrate atrophy but are usually slightly lower. Restriction of protein intake diminishes hyperornithinemia, and with extreme restrictions, the values may reach the normal range.[163,262,306] Plasma arginine is normal, lysine moderately decreased, and glutamine and alanine often increased. Interestingly, protein restriction has in some instances led to a further elevation in plasma glutamine.[31,163] Fasting plasma ammonium is usually within the normal range even though the mean value is slightly higher in patients than in controls. Ammonia values increase after protein ingestion, and high-protein diets result in chronic hyperammonemia. Oral loading tests with 0.1 or 0.2 g/kg ornithine cause greater than normal increases in plasma ornithine, and the return to initial concentrations is slow. The responses of plasma citrulline and ornithine to citrulline loads, plasma lysine to lysine loads, and plasma and urinary homocitrulline to lysine and homocitrulline loads are indistinguishable from normal.[163,303,305,306,309,314,326]

Ornithinuria is highly variable (Table 19-6). Interestingly, identical plasma ornithine concentrations in patients with either the HHH syndrome or gyrate atrophy lead to higher ornithine excretions in the latter,[176,218] implying that kidney ornithine-δ-aminotransferase has a role in ornithine reabsorption. The level of urine homocitrulline also greatly exceeds normal. Its excretion correlates weakly with lysine ingestion, and its renal tubular reabsorption is normal and unaffected by citrulline loads.[163,302,311,326] Altogether, the regulation of homocitrulline excretion remains unclear. Urine of the patients also contains excessive amounts of the δ-lactam of ornithine, 3-amino-piperid-2-one, first believed to be ornithine methyl ester,[201,216,217,308,326] and of γ-glutamylornithine, another uncommon derivative of ornithine[218] (Table 19-6). Both substances also are found in the urine of patients with gyrate atrophy. Their origin and physiological significance are unknown. Several other γ-glutamyl amino acids have been characterized in human urine.[218] Other unidentified peptides are also present in the urine of the patients with either form of hyperornithinemia because hydrolysis of the urine significantly increases the amount of free ornithine detected (free ornithine increases from 41 to 59 percent of total ornithine in patients with the HHH syndrome, and from 76 to 83 percent in patients with gyrate atrophy).

Excretion of creatine was subnormal in two HHH syndrome patients[262] (Table 19-6). Low creatine excretion is also a feature of gyrate atrophy, supporting the hypothesis that the ac-

Table 19-6 Urinary Excretion of Free Ornithine, Homocitrulline, Orotic Acid, 3-Amino-Piperide-2-One, Polyamines, Creatine, and Creatinine by Patients with the HHH Syndrome[a]

	Patient			*Control*		
	Mean	*Range*	*Number of subjects*	*Number of subjects*	*Mean*	*Range*
Free ornithine[b]	656	2–8160	16	32	10	0–120
Homocitrulline	565	20–2380	21	29	20	Trace–90
Orotic acid	410	52–1520	17	21	22	<10–130
3-Amino-peperide-1-one	294	95–459	3	6	ND[c]	
γ-Glutamylornithine	34	13–67	8	8	Trace	
Polyamines, total	132[d]		1	1		21 ± 7[e]
Creatine	16	11–21	2	1		41–104
Creatinine	113	97–130	2	1		88–132

[a]The data are compiled from all cases referred to in the text.[163,262,301–323] If possible, values are for samples taken while the patients were on an unlimited diet. The units are μmol/g creatinine for all except creatine and creatinine, which are in μmol/kg body wt/day.
[b]In eight patients studied for excretion of free and total hydrolyzable ornithine, free ornithine comprised 47% (41–59%) of total ornithine.[218]
[c]ND = not detectable.
[d]This value is from urine collected while the patient was on an unrestricted diet.
[e]Mean ± SD of four controls on an unrestricted diet.

cumulated ornithine inhibits glycine transamidinase, the first enzyme in the creatine biosynthetic pathway (Fig. 19-2). Orotic acid excretion, believed to reflect carbamoyl phosphate accumulation, is elevated (Table 19-6), suggesting that there is underutilization of intramitochondrial carbamoyl phosphate.[262,303,305,308,310,314,315] Urinary orotate levels are often increased even though blood ammonia values are normal.[308] Thus, orotic acid excretion is probably a more sensitive indicator of impaired ureagenesis than plasma ammonium concentrations.

Urinary excretion of polyamines (total; putrescine, cadaverine, spermidine, and spermine) was increased in the one patient studied[312] (Table 19-6). The excretion rates decreased markedly when protein content of the diet was decreased, and even further when supplementary ornithine was added to the low protein diet.

The possibility of an enzymatic deficiency as the cause of this syndrome has been investigated, but no consistent or convincing defects have been demonstrated. The activity of carbamoyl phosphate synthase I (mitochondrial; *N*-acetylglutamate–dependent) is normal in the liver,[309,310,312,315] although an early report suggested it was moderately reduced in both liver and fibroblasts.[303] Other urea cycle enzymes measured in leukocytes and liver have been normal.[303,309,310,312,315] The content of *N*-acetylglutamate, an activator of carbamoyl phosphate synthase I, was normal in the mitochondrial pellet of liver homogenates.[310,315] The activity of ornithine-δ-aminotransferase, the major ornithine-catabolizing enzyme, is normal in liver and other tissues of the patients.[303,306,310,312,315] Ornithine decarboxylase in cultured fibroblasts was 20 to 30 percent of the normal mean in one patient,[329] but urinary excretion of polyamines was increased in another study[312] (Table 19-6). The ATP production by the respiring mitochondria was adequate.[310] The importance of an unknown, prominent heavy protein band in SDS–polyacrylamide gel electrophoresis of the liver of a Japanese patient is unclear.[312] No enzyme measurements in the heterozygotes have been reported.

Screening systems based on detection of increased plasma ornithine concentration will detect patients with the HHH syndrome and those with gyrate atrophy of the choroid and retina[166a] (see "Differential Diagnosis of Hyperornithinemia"). However, there is no practical experience of the use of these screening methods. A possible problem is that plasma ornithine values in the HHH syndrome may be within the normal range during the newborn period, as suggested by the fact that stored blood spots from a patient with the HHH syndrome taken at 5 days and 4 weeks of age and studied several years later failed to detect any abnormality.[163] However, hyperornithinemia, hyperammonemia, and homocitrullinuria were clearly demonstrable in another patient at the age of 19 days.[314]

Pathophysiology of the HHH Syndrome

Ammonia accumulation can be reduced or prevented in vitro in isolated hepatocytes and in vivo in animals and patients with other types of urea cycle disorders by increasing the availability of the urea cycle intermediates arginine, ornithine, or citrulline.[330–335] Accordingly, the hyperornithinemia in gyrate atrophy of the choroid and retina is associated with hypoammonemia.[214] The paradoxical combination of hyperornithinemia and hyperammonemia in the HHH syndrome has led to extensive studies of the mechanisms involved. Even though the exact pathophysiological sequence of events still remains unresolved, the findings favor the original notion of Fell and coworkers that the basic defect is in the transport of ornithine across the inner mitochondrial membrane into the mitochondrial matrix.[302] The entry of ornithine into liver mitochondria is mediated by one or possibly two carriers, one of which may be dependent on respiratory energy[30–32,336–342] (see "Subcellular Compartmentation and Transport of Ornithine"). Recent studies suggest that external ornithine is channeled from its mitochondrial transporter to ornithine carbamoyltransferase, implying some organization within the mitochondrial matrix.[14] Hommes and coworkers were able to extract the ornithine-transporting system from beef liver mitochondria and reconstitute it in liposomes.[33] The uptake of ornithine by the reconstituted vesicles followed Michaelis-Menten kinetics, and was dependent on the intraliposomal pH, the time of sonication of the reconstituted liposomes, and the phospholipid-to-detergent ratio. Unfortunately this technique, though promising, has not been applied for further characterization of the translocase, nor has it been used to study HHH syndrome samples.

If the entry of ornithine into mitochondria in the HHH cells is indeed diminished, the transport defect would decrease citrulline synthesis and impair ammonia detoxication. Furthermore, since ornithine-δ-aminotransferase, the major ornithine-catabolizing enzyme, is also within the mitochondria, diminished entry of ornithine would lead to ornithine accumulation in the cytosolic and extracellular fluids. This hypothesis predicts that increasing the cytosolic ornithine might drive trans-mitochondrial ornithine transport and improve the patients' urea cycle function. With this rationale in mind, Fell and coworkers[302] supplemented their patient with 6 g ornithine daily. This doubled the plasma ornithine concentration and clearly reduced the plasma ammonium concentration. Other studies have supported the idea that ornithine and arginine supplementation will reduce plasma ammonium and improve protein tolerance.[262,305,308,309,312,315] However, in some other patients ornithine or arginine supplementation has had little effect,[163,314] and high arginine supplements have even been deleterious.[305] In one patient the hyperammonemia induced by alanine infusion remained unaltered even when the test was preceded by daily supplementation of 6 g ornithine for 1 week and intravenous infusion of ornithine for 2 h prior to and during the alanine load.[304] These differences in responses to ornithine supplementation suggest heterogeneity in the basic defect(s) causing this biochemical phenotype.

Several attempts have been made to directly characterize ornithine transport by the mitochondria in the patients. Hommes and coworkers[305,306,343] have made the fibroblast cell membrane permeable to amino acids by digitonin without damaging the mitochondria and then measured accumulation of ornithine into the particulate fraction of such cells; this fraction is mainly composed of mitochondria. Their findings support the view that ornithine influx to the mitochondria is decreased in the cells of HHH syndrome. In another study of a single patient, a defect in ornithine uptake has been directly demonstrated using isolated liver mitochondria.[315] Shih et al.[313] and others[308–310,313–315,326,344,345] have shown that the net capacity of the cultured HHH fibroblasts or stimulated lymphocytes to metabolize ornithine is decreased. The cells transfer the label from 1-[^{14}C]-, 5-[^{14}C]-, or U-[^{14}C]ornithine into tissue proteins, proline, glutamate, aspartate, and CO_2 much less efficiently than do control cells, but the conversion of the labeled substrate from glutamate to proline occurs normally. In liver, citrulline synthesis by HHH syndrome mitochondria is significantly decreased.[310] Interestingly, Oyanagi and others have suggested that in some patients with hyperlysinemia (Chap. 21), an identical mitochondrial transport defect specific for lysine exists.[346] Several features in yet another transport disorder, lysinuric protein intolerance (Chap. 100), support the possibility that altered mitochondrial transport of ornithine may play an important part in the pathophysiology of this disease as well.[347]

Additional indirect evidence in favor of a mitochondrial transport defect for ornithine comes from complementation assays of Shih et al.,[313,348] who have shown that heterokaryons formed from HHH syndrome and gyrate atrophy (ornithine-δ-aminotransferase–negative) cells are able to metabolize ornithine normally.

The origin of homocitrulline in these patients is uncertain. Excessive amounts of homocitrulline are also excreted by some patients with hyperlysinemia and saccharopinuria.[349–351] The hypothesis of Fell et al.[302] for the pathophysiology of this syndrome predicts that lysine uptake into mitochondria is normal and that the increased lysine-ornithine ratio in the mitochondrial matrix leads to ornithine transcarbamoylase–catalyzed conversion of lysine to homocitrulline. Carter and coworkers have studied transcarbamoylation of lysine more closely in digitonin-treated rat liver mitochondria.[352] Their results suggest that two separate carbamoylases exist, one for ornithine and another for lysine, and that the lysine transcarbamoylase is localized outside the inner mitochondrial membrane. In one HHH syndrome patient lysine supplementation was followed by a significant rise in homocitrulline excretion.[302] However, the plasma ammonium concentration increased simultaneously, suggesting that this pathway cannot be used for removal of excessive carbamoyl phosphate and ammonia in these patients. In a few other patients, acute lysine loads and prolonged lysine supplementation have failed to show clear correlation between the ingested lysine and excreted homocitrulline, leaving several questions in the metabolism of this amino acid unanswered.[308,311,326]

Treatment

Protein restriction to less than 1.2 g/kg/day prevents postprandial hyperammonemia and results in decreased concentrations of ornithine in plasma. If decreased transport of ornithine into the mitochondria is the primary abnormality in this syndrome and the defect is kinetic by nature, the patients may benefit from ornithine supplementation, i.e., from additional elevation of ornithine concentrations. In one patient, the addition of 6 g ornithine or 7.5 g arginine daily to the diet decreased plasma ammonium to normal or near-normal values, while fasting plasma ornithine rose to as high as 1.5 m*M*.[302] No immediate adverse effects of this pronounced hyperornithinemia were noted. Despite this and the lack of retinal involvement in HHH syndrome, it would seem prudent to follow any patient with ornithine values in this range with periodic ophthalmologic examinations and electroretinograms. In a carefully conducted study by Gordon, Gatfield, and Haust[326] ornithine supplement given with a protein load significantly reduced hyperammonemia. Prolonged ornithine supplementation (0.5 to 1.0 mmol/kg/day, i.e., 66 to 132 mg/kg/day divided in three doses) improved patients' protein tolerance and accelerated growth. Arginine and citrulline are probably effective as well. Interestingly, alanine-induced hyperammonemia could not be prevented in another patient by ornithine supplement (see "Pathophysiology of the HHH Syndrome");[304] the minimal or even harmful effects of ornithine or arginine supplementation in some other patients[305,314] also suggests that the disease may indeed be heterogeneous. Interestingly, orotic acid excretion has been increased in several patients even when plasma ammonium levels were normal, implying that orotic aciduria is a better indicator of the impairment of ureagenesis in these patients.

Genetics

The large Canadian pedigree of Gatfield et al.[303] with six affected subjects from both sexes, the additional reports of more than one affected member in the same sibship, and consanguinity in many families strongly suggest autosomal recessive inheritance of the syndrome. So far, few attempts have been made to characterize the heterozygotes biochemically. In all cases studied, plasma and urine amino acid concentrations and responses of the heterozygotes to ornithine loads have been normal.[163,301,306,308]

The association of the HHH syndrome with deficiency of coagulation factors VII and X in three patients from two different ethnic backgrounds[262,303,304] has led Vici and coauthors[262] to suggest that the HHH syndrome gene(s) might be on chromosome 13. Because the basic defect(s) in the syndrome are still poorly defined and no studies have been aimed at characterization of the abnormality at the DNA level, this suggestion remains hypothetical.

Studies contributing to the information in this chapter were supported in part by National Eye Institute Grant EY02948. David Valle is an investigator with the Howard Hughes Medical Institute.

REFERENCES

1. SNODGRASS PJ: The effects of pH on the kinetics of human liver ornithine-carbamyl phosphate transferase. *Biochemistry* 7:3047, 1968.
2. MARSHALL M, COHEN PP: Ornithine transcarbamylase from *Streptococcus faecalis* and bovine liver. *J Biol Chem* 247:1654, 1972.
3. MARSHALL M: Ornithine transcarbamylase from bovine liver, in Grisolia S, Baguena R, Mayor F (eds): *The Urea Cycle*. New York, Wiley, 1976, p 169.
4. SCHIMKE RT: Adaptive characteristics of urea cycle enzymes in the rat. *J Biol Chem* 237:459, 1962.
5. NUZUM CT, SNODGRASS PJ: Urea cycle enzyme adaptation to dietary protein in primates. *Science* 172:1042, 1971.
6. MORRIS SM Jr, MONCMAN CL, RAND KD, DIZIKES GJ, CEDERBAUM SD, O'BRIEN WE: Regulation of mRNA levels for five urea cycle enzymes in rat liver by diet, cyclic AMP, and glucocorticoids. *Arch Biochem Biophys* 256:343, 1987.
7. HATA A, TSUZUKI T, SHIMADA K, TAKIGUCHI M, MORI M, MATSUDA I: Isolation and characterization of the human ornithine transcarbamylase gene: Structure of the 5′-end region. *J Biochem* 100:717, 1986.
8. TAKIGUCHI M, MURAKAMI T, MIURA S, MORI M: Structure of the rat ornithine carbamoyltransferase gene, a large, X chromosome linked gene with an atypical promoter. *Proc Natl Acad Sci USA* 84:6136, 1987.
9. OHTAKE A, TAKIGUCHI M, SHIGETO Y, AMAYA Y, KAWAMOTO S, MORI M: Structural organization of the gene for rat liver-type arginase. *J Biol Chem* 263:2245, 1988.
10. MITCHELL GA, LOONEY JE, BRODY LC, STEEL G, SUCHANEK M, ENGELHARDT J, WILLARD HF, VALLE D: Human ornithine-δ-aminotransferase: cDNA cloning and analysis of the structural gene. *J Biol Chem* 263:14288, 1988.
11. STEWART PM, WALSER M: Short term regulation of ureagenesis. *J Biol Chem* 255:5270, 1980.
12. MEIJER AJ: Regulation of carbamoyl-phosphate synthase (ammonia) in liver in relation to urea cycle activity. *Trends Biochem Sci* 4:83, 1979.
13. RAIJMAN L: Enzyme and reactant concentrations and the regulation of

urea synthesis, in Grisolia S, Baguena R, Mayor F (eds): *The Urea Cycle.* New York, Wiley, 1976, p 243.

14. COHEN MS, CHEUNG C-W, RAIJMAN L: Channeling of extramitochondrial ornithine to matrix ornithine transcarbamylase. *J Biol Chem* 262:203, 1987.

15. De MARS R, Le VAN SL, TREND BL, RUSSELL LB: Abnormal ornithine carbamoyl transferase in mice having the sparse-fur mutation. *Proc Natl Acad Sci USA* 73:1693, 1976.

16. VERES G, GIBBS RA, SCHERER SE, CASKEY CT: The molecular basis of the sparse fur mouse mutation. *Science* 237:415, 1987.

17. REDDI PK, KNOX WE, HERZFELD A: Types of arginase in rat tissues. *Enzyme* 20:305, 1975.

18. SOBERON G, PALACIOS R: Arginase, in Grisolia S, Baguena R, Mayor F (eds): *The Urea Cycle.* New York, Wiley, 1976, p 221.

19. HERZFELD A, RAPER SM: The heterogeneity of arginases in rat tissues. *Biochem J* 153:469, 1976.

20. CARVAJAL N, CEDERBAUM SD: Kinetics of inhibition of rat liver and kidney arginases by proline and branched chain amino acids. *Biochim Biophys Acta* 870:181, 1986.

21. GRODY WW, DIZIKES GJ, CEDERBAUM SC: Human arginase isozymes. Isozymes. *Curr Top Biol Med Res* 13:181, 1987.

22. AEBI H: Coordinated changes in enzymes of the ornithine cycle and response to dietary conditions, in Grisolia S, Baguena R, Mayor F (eds): *The Urea Cycle.* New York, Wiley, 1976, p 275.

23. BEDINO ST: Allosteric regulation of beef liver arginase activity by L-ornithine. *Ital J Biochem* 26:264, 1977.

24. HARAGUCHI Y, TAKIGUCHI M, AMAYA Y, KAWAMOTO S, MATSUDA I, MORI M: Molecular cloning and nucleotide sequence of cDNA for human liver arginase. *Proc Natl Acad Sci USA* 84:412, 1987.

25. SPARKES RS, DIZIKES GJ, KLISAK I, GRODY WW, MOHANDAS T, HEINZMANN C, ZOLLMAN S, LUSIS AJ, CEDERBAUM SD: The gene for human liver arginase (ARG1) is assigned to chromosome band 6q23. *Am J Hum Genet* 39:186, 1987.

26. KAYSEN GA, STRECKER HJ: Purification and properties of arginase of rat kidney. *Biochem J* 133:779, 1973.

27. GLASS RD, KNOX WE: Arginase isoenzymes of rat mammary gland, liver and other tissues. *J Biol Chem* 248:5785, 1973.

28. SPECTOR EB, RICE SCH, CEDARBAUM SD: Evidence for two genes encoding human arginase. *Pediatr Res* 15:569, 1981.

29. KLINGENBERG M: Metabolic transport in mitochondria: An example for intracellular membrane function. *Essays Biochem* 6:119, 1970.

30. MCGIVAN JD, BRADFORD NM, BEAVIS AD: Factors influencing the activity of ornithine aminotransferase in isolated rat liver mitochondria. *Biochem J* 162:147, 1977.

31. GAMBLE JG, LEHNINGER AL: Transport of ornithine and citrulline across the mitochondrial membrane. *J Biol Chem* 248:610, 1973.

32. BRADFORD NM, MCGIVAN JD: Evidence for the existence of an ornithine/citrulline antiporter in rat liver mitochondria. *FEBS Lett* 113:294, 1980.

33. HOMMES FA, ELLER AG, EVANS BA, CARTER AL: Reconstitution of ornithine transport in liposomes with Lubrol extracts of mitochondria. *FEBS Lett* 170:131, 1984.

34. PEGG AE: Recent advances in the biochemistry of polyamines in eukaryotes. *Biochem J* 234:249, 1986.

35. LUK GD, CASERO RA Jr: Polyamines in normal and cancer cells. *Adv Enzyme Regul* 26:91, 1987.

36. MUDD SH, POOLE JR: Labile methyl balances for normal humans on various dietary regimens. *Metabolism* 24:721, 1975.

37. MUDD SH, EBERT MH, SCRIVER CR: Labile methyl group balances in the human: The role of sarcosine. *Metabolism* 29:707, 1980.

38. PEGG AE, WILLIAMS-ASHMAN HG: Biosynthesis of putrescine in the prostate gland of the rat. *Biochem J* 108:533, 1968.

39. PEGG AE, LOCKWOOD DH, WILLIAMS-ASHMAN HG: Concentrations of putrescine and polyamines and their enzymic synthesis during androgen-induced prostatic growth. *Biochem J* 117:17, 1970.

40. CAMPBELL RA, MORRIS DR, BARTOS D, DAVES GD, BARTOS F: *Advances in Polyamine Research*, vol 2. New York, Raven, 1978.

41. NISSLEY SP, PASSAMANI J, SHORT P: Stimulation of DNA synthesis, cell multiplication and ornithine decarboxylase in 3T3 cells by multiplication stimulating activity (MSA). *J Cell Physiol* 89:393, 1976.

42. KAHANA C, NATHANS D: Isolation of cloned cDNA encoding mammalian ornithine decarboxylase. *Proc Natl Acad Sci USA* 81:3645, 1984.

43. RAINA A, JANNE J: Physiology of the natural polyamines putrescine, spermidine and spermine. *Med Biol* 53:121, 1975.

44. FONG WF, HELLER JS, CANELLAKIS ES: The appearance of an ornithine decarboxylase inhibitory protein upon the addition of putrescine to cell cultures. *Biochim Biophys Acta* 428:456, 1976.

45. HELLER JS, FONG WF, CANELLAKIS ES: Induction of a protein inhibitor to ornithine decarboxylase by the end products of its reaction. *Proc Natl Acad Sci USA* 73:1858, 1976.

46. METCALF BW, BEY P, DANZIN C, JUNG MJ, CASARA P, VERERT JP: Catalytic irreversible inhibition of mammalian ornithine decarboxylase (EC4.1.1.17) by substrate and product analogues. *J Am Chem Soc* 100:2551, 1978.

47. MAMONT PS, DUCHESNE MC, JODER-OHLENBUSCH AM, GROVE J: Effects of ornithine decarboxylase inhibitors on cultured cells, in Seiler N, Jung MJ, Koch-Weser J (eds): *Enzyme-Activated Irreversible Inhibitors.* New York, Elsevier, 1978, p 43.

48. O'LEARY MH, HERREID RM: Mechanism of inactivation of ornithine decarboxylase by α-methylornithine. *Biochemistry* 17:1010, 1978.

49. SEILER N: Polyamines. *J Chromatogr* 379:157, 1986.

50. FOZARD JR, PART ML, PRAKASH NJ, GROVE J, SCHECHTER PJ, SJOERDSMA A, KOCH-WESTER J: L-Ornithine decarboxylase: An essential role in early mammalian embryogenesis. *Science* 208:505, 1980.

51. PORTER CW, SUFRIN JR: Interference with polyamine biosynthesis and/or function by analogs of polyamines or methionine as a potential anticancer chemotherapeutic strategy. *Anticancer Res* 6:525, 1986.

52. BARTOLOME J, HUGUENARD J, SLOTKIN TA: Role of ornithine decarboxylase in cardiac growth and hypertrophy. *Science* 210:793, 1980.

53. KAHANA C, NATHANS D: Nucleotide sequence of murine ornithine decarboxylase. *Proc Natl Acad Sci USA* 82:1673, 1985.

54. HICKOK NJ, SEPPANEN PJ, GUNSALUS GL, JANNE OA: Complete amino acid sequence of human ornithine decarboxylase deduced from complementary DNA. *DNA* 6:179, 1987.

55. BRABANT M, MCCONLOGUE L, van DAALEN WETTERS T, COFFINO P: Mouse ornithine decarboxylase gene: Cloning, structure and expression. *Proc Natl Acad Sci USA* 85:2200, 1988.

56. KATZ A, KAHANA C: Isolation and characterization of the mouse ornithine decarboxylase gene. *J Biol Chem* 263:7604, 1988.

57. BAXTER CF: Some recent advances in studies of GABA metabolism and compartmentation in GABA, in Roberts E, Chase TN, Tower DB (eds): *Nervous System Function.* New York, Raven, 1976, p 61.

58. SEILER N, AL-THERIB MJ: Putrescine catabolism in mammalian brain. *Biochem J* 144:29, 1974.

59. De MELLO FG, BACHRACH U, NIRENBERG M: Ornithine and glutamic acid decarboxylase activities in the developing chick retina. *J Neurochem* 27:847, 1978.

60. MURRIN LC: Ornithine as a precursor for γ-aminobutyric acid in mammalian brain. *J Neurochem* 34:1779, 1980.

61. WALKER JB: Creatine: Biosynthesis, regulation and function. *Adv Enzymol* 50:177, 1979.

62. ROBERTS JJ, WALKER JB: Higher homolog and N-ethyl analog of creatine as synthetic phosphagen precursors in brain, heart, and muscle, repressors of liver amidinotransferase and substrates for creatine catabolic enzymes. *J Biol Chem* 260:13502, 1985.

63. MCGUIRE DM, GROSS MD, van PILSUM JF, TOWLE HC: Repression of rat kidney L-arginine:glycine amidinotranferase synthesis by creatine at a pretranslational level. *J Biol Chem* 259:12034, 1984.

64. RATNER S, ROCHOVANSKY O: Biosynthesis of guanidinoacetic acid. I. Purification and properties of transamidinase. *Arch Biochem Biophys* 63:277, 1956.

65. RATNER S, ROCHOVANSKY O: Biosynthesis of guanidinoacetic acid. II. Mechanism of amidine group transfer. *Arch Biochem Biophys* 63:296, 1956.

66. SIPILA I: Inhibition of arginine-glycine amidinotransferase by ornithine. *Biochim Biophys Acta* 613:79, 1980.

67. GROSS MD, EGGEN MA, SIMON AM, van PILSUM JF: The purification and characterization of human kidney L-arginine:glycine amidinotransferase. *Arch Biochem Biophys* 251:747, 1986.

68. MCGUIRE DM, GROSS MD, ELDE RP, van PILSUM JF: Localization of L-arginine-glycine amidinotransferase protein in rat tissues by immunofluorescence microscopy. *J Histochem Cytochem* 34:429, 1986.

69. DEFALCO AJ, DAVIES RK: The synthesis of creatine by the brain of the intact rat. *J Neurochem* 7:308, 1961.

70. PARDRIDGE WM, DUDUCGIAN-VARTAVARIAN L, CASANELLO-ERTL D, JONES MR, KOPPLE JD: Amino acid and creatine metabolism in adult rat skeletal muscle cells in tissue culture. *Fed Proc* 39:1179, 1980.

71. STRECKER HJ: Purification and properties of rat liver ornithine-δ-aminotransferase. *J Biol Chem* 240:1225, 1965.

72. MATSUZAWA T: Characteristics of the inhibition of ornithine-δ-aminotransferase by branched-chain amino acids. *J Biochem* 75:601, 1974.

73. MEZL VA, KNOX WE: Properties and analysis of a stable derivative of pyrroline-5-carboxylase acid for use in metabolic studies. *Anal Biochem* 74:430, 1976.

74. QUASTEL JH, WITTY R: Ornithine transaminase. *Nature* 167:556, 1951.

75. MEISTER A: Enzymatic transamination reactions involving arginine and ornithine. *J Biol Chem* 206:587, 1954.
76. OHURA T, KOMINAMI E, TADA K, KATUNUMA N: Crystallization and properties of human liver ornithine aminotransferase. *J Biochem* 92:1785, 1982.
77. PERAINO C, PITOT HC: Ornithine-δ-aminotransferase in the rat. I. Assay and some general properties. *Biochim Biophys Acta* 73:222, 1963.
78. KATUNUMA N, MATSUDA Y, TOMINO I: Studies on ornithine-ketoacid transaminase. I. Purification and properties. *J Biochem* 56:499, 1964.
79. MATSUZAWA T, KATSUNUMA T, KATUNUMA N: Crystallization of ornithine transaminase and its properties. *Biochem Biophys Res Commun* 32:161, 1968.
80. PERAINO C, BUNVILLE LG, TAHMISIAN TN: Chemical, physical and morphological properties of ornithine aminotransferase from rat liver. *J Biol Chem* 244:2241, 1969.
81. SANADA Y, SHIOTANI T, OKUNO E, KATUNUMA N: Coenzyme-dependent conformational properties of rat liver ornithine aminotransferase. *Eur J Biochem* 69:507, 1976.
82. SANADA Y, SUEMORI I, KATUNUMA N: Properties of ornithine aminotransferase from rat liver, kidney and small intestine. *Biochim Biophys Acta* 220:42, 1970.
83. KALITA CC, KERMAN JD, STRECKER HJ: Preparation and properties of ornithine-oxo-acid aminotransferase of rat kidney. *Biochim Biophys Acta* 429:780, 1976.
84. YIP MCM, COLLINS RK: Purification and properties of rat kidney and liver ornithine aminotransferase. *Enzyme* 12:187, 1971.
85. PERAINO C: Functional properties of ornithine-ketoacid aminotransferase from rat liver. *Biochim Biophys Acta* 289:117, 1972.
86. SIMMACO M, JOHN RA, BARRA D, BOSSA F: The primary structure of ornithine aminotransferase: Identification of active-site sequence and site of post-translational proteolysis. *FEBS Lett* 199:39, 1986.
87. MARKOVIC-HOUSLEY Z, KANIA M, LUSTIG A, VINCENT MG, JANSONIUS JN, JOHN RA: Quaternary structure of ornithine aminotransferase in solution and preliminary crystallographic data. *Eur J Biochem* 162:345, 1987.
88. JONES EM: Conversion of glutamate to ornithine and proline: Pyrroline-5-carboxylate, a possible modulator of arginine requirements. *J Nutr* 115:509, 1985.
89. KITO K, SANADA Y, KATUNUMA N: Mode of inhibition of ornithine aminotransferase by L-canaline. *J Biochem* 83:201, 1978.
90. JUNG MJ, SEILER N: Enzyme activated irreversible inhibitors of L-ornithine:2-oxoacid aminotransferase. *J Biol Chem* 253:7431, 1978.
91. JOHN RA, JONES ED, FOWLER LJ: Enzyme-induced inactivation of transaminases by acetylenic and vinyl analogues of 4-aminobutyrate. *Biochem J* 177:721, 1979.
92. PHANG JM, DOWNING SJ, VALLE D: A radioisotopic assay for ornithine-δ-aminotransferase. *Anal Biochem* 55:272, 1973.
93. WONG PT-H, MCGEER EG, MCGEER PL: A sensitive radiometric assay for ornithine aminotransferase: Regional and subcellular distributions in rat brain. *J Neurochem* 36:501, 1981.
94. VALLE D, GOODMAN SI, HARRIS SC, PHANG JM: Genetic evidence for a common enzyme catalyzing the second step in the degradation of proline and hydroxyproline. *J Clin Invest* 64:1365, 1970.
95. ADAMS E, FRANK L: Metabolism of proline and the hydroxyprolines. *Annu Rev Biochem* 49:1005, 1980.
96. O'DONNELL JJ, SANDMAN RP, MARTIN SR: Assay of ornithine aminotransferase by high-performance liquid chromatography. *Anal Biochem* 90:41, 1978.
97. RAMESH V, SHAFFER MM, ALLAIRE JM, SHIH VE, GUSELLA JF: Investigation of gyrate atrophy using a cDNA clone for human ornithine aminotransferase. *DNA* 5:493, 1986.
98. INANA G, TOTSUKA S, REDMOND M, DOUGHERTY T, NAGLE J, SHIONO T, OHURA T, KOMINAMI E, KATUNUMA N: Molecular cloning of human aminotransferase mRNA. *Proc Natl Acad Sci USA* 83:1203, 1986.
99. HIMENO M, MUECKLER MM, GONZALEZ FJ, PITOT HC: Cloning of DNA complementary to ornithine aminotransferase mRNA. *J Biol Chem* 257:4669, 1982.
100. MUECKLER MM, PITOT HC: Sequence of the precursor to rat ornithine aminotransferase deduced from a cDNA clone. *J Biol Chem* 260:12993, 1985.
101. DEGOLS G: Functional analysis of the regulatory region adjacent to the carg B gene of Saccharomyces cerevisiae: Nucleotide sequence, gene fusion experiments and cis-dominant regulatory mutation analysis. *Eur J Biochem* 169:193, 1987.
102. DEGOLS G, JAUNIAUS J-C, WIAME J-M: Molecular characterization of transposable-element associated mutations that lead to constitutive L-ornithine aminotransferase expression in Saccharomyces cerevisiae. *Eur J Biochem* 165:289, 1987.
103. JAUNIAUS J-C, URRESTARAZU LA, WIAME J-M: Arginine metabolism in Saccharomyces cerevisiae: Subcellular localization of the enzymes. *J Bacteriol* 133:1096, 1978.
104. DAVIS RH, WEISS RL: Novel mechanisms controlling arginine metabolism in Neurospora. *Trends Biochem Sci* 13:101, 1988.
105. RAMESH V, BENOIT LA, CRAWFORD P, HARVEY PT, SHOWS TB, SHIH VE, GUSELLA JF: The ornithine aminotransferase (OAT) locus: Analysis of RFLPs in gyrate atrophy. *Am J Hum Genet* 42:365, 1988.
106. LOONEY J, MITCHELL G, BRODY L, SUCHANEK M, STEEL G, WILLARD H, VALLE D: Ornithine aminotransferase (OAT) hybridizing regions on the X chromosome: Integration of at least one processed gene on X and subsequent genomic duplication has generated multiple OAT-hybridizing fragments. *Am J Hum Genet* 41:A226, 1987.
107. FREYTAG SO, BEAUDET AL, BOCK HGO, O'BRIEN WE: Molecular splicing of the human argininosuccinate synthetase gene: Occurrence of alternative mRNA splicing. *Mol Cell Biol* 4:1978, 1984.
108. DYNAN WS: Promoters for housekeeping genes. *Trends Genet* 2:196, 1986.
109. KADONAGA JT, JONES KA, TJIAN R: Promoter-specific activation of RNA polymerase II transcription by Sp1. *Trends Biochem Sci* 11:10, 1986.
110. PABO CO, SAUER RT: Protein-DNA recognition. *Annu Rev Biochem* 53:293, 1984.
111. KLEIN-HITPASS L, SCHORPP M, WAGNER U, RYFFEL GU: An estrogen-responsive element derived from the 5′ flanking region of the Xenopus vitellogenin A2 gene functions in transfected human cells. *Cell* 46:1053, 1986.
112. KLOCK G, STRAHLE U, SCHUTZ G: Oestrogen and glucocorticoid responsive elements are closely related but distinct. *Nature* 329:734, 1987.
113. MITCHELL GA, VALLE D, WILLARD H, STEEL G, SUCHANEK M, BRODY L: Human ornithine-δ-aminotransferase (OAT): Cross-hybridizing fragments mapped to chromosome 10 and Xp11.1-21.1. *Am J Hum Genet* 39:163A, 1986.
114. RAMESH V, EDDY R, BRUNS GA, SHIH VE, SHOWS TB, GUSELLA JF: Localization of the ornithine aminotransferase gene and related sequences on two human chromosomes. *Hum Genet* 76:121, 1987.
115. BARRETT DJ, BATEMAN JB, SPARKES RS, MOHANDAS T, KLISAK I, INANA G: Chromosomal localization of human ornithine aminotransferase gene sequences to 10q26 and Xp11.2. *Invest Ophthalmol Vis Sci* 28:1037, 1987.
116. MITCHELL GA, VALLE D, SUCHANEK M, STEEL G, BRODY L, LOONEY J, WILLARD H: Ornithine aminotransferase (OAT): Evidence for a dispersed gene family with member(s) localized to Xp11.1-Xp21.1. *Pediatr Res* 21:292A, 1987.
117. HERZFELD A, KNOX WE: The properties, developmental formation and estrogen induction of ornithine aminotransferase in rat tissues. *J Biol Chem* 243:3227, 1968.
118. HERZFELD A, RAPER S: Enzymes of ornithine metabolism in adult and developing rat intestine. *Biochim Biophys Acta* 428:600, 1976.
119. HERZFELD A, RAPER S: Amino acid metabolizing enzymes in rat submaxillary gland, normal or neoplastic, and in pancreas. *Enzyme* 21:471, 1976.
120. MEZL VA, KNOX WE: Metabolism of arginine in lactating rat mammary gland. *Biochem J* 166:105, 1977.
121. SMITH RJ, PHANG JM: Proline metabolism in cartilage: The importance of proline biosynthesis. *Metabolism* 27:685, 1978.
122. MATSUZAWA T, OBARA Y: Amino acid synthesis from ornithine: Enzymes and quantitative comparison in brain slices and detached retinas from rats and chicks. *Brain Res* 413:314, 1987.
123. BAICH A, RATZLAFF K: Ornithine aminotransferase in chick embryo tissues. *Invest Ophthalmol Vis Sci* 19:411, 1980.
124. RATZLAFF K, BAICH A: Comparison of ornithine activities in the pigment epithelium and retina of vertebrates. *Comp Biochem Physiol* 88B:35, 1987.
125. HAYASAKA S, SHIONO T, TAKAKU Y, MIZUNO K: Ornithine ketoacid aminotransferase in the bovine eye. *Invest Ophthalmol* 19:1457, 1980.
126. HAYASAKA S, MATSUZAWA T, SHIONO T, MIZUNO K, ISHIGURO I: Enzymes metabolizing ornithine-proline pathway in the bovine eye. *Exp Eye Res* 34:635, 1982.
127. VALLE D, KAISER-KUPFER MI: Gyrate atrophy of the choroid and retina, in Daentl DL (ed): *Clinical, Structural, and Biochemical Advances in Hereditary Eye Disorders*. New York, AR Liss, 1982, p 123.
128. RAO GN, COTLIER E: Ornithine delta-aminotransferase activity in retina and other tissues. *Neurochem Res* 9:555, 1984.
129. FLEMING GA, STEEL G, VALLE D, GRANGER AS, PHANG GM: The aqueous humor of rabbit contains high concentrations of pyrroline-5-carboxylase. *Metabolism* 35:933, 1986.
130. KASAHARA M, MATSUZAWA T, KOKUBO M, GUSHIKEN Y, TASHIRO K, KOIDE T, WATANABE H, KATUNUMA N: Immunohistochemical localization of ornithine aminotransferase in normal rat tissues by Fab-′ horseradish peroxidase conjugates. *J Histochem Cytochem* 34:1385, 1986.
131. TAKAHASHI O, ISHIGURO S-I, MITO T, HAYASAKA S, SHIONO T, MIZUNO K, OHURA T, TADA K: Immunocytochemical localization of ornithine amino-

transferase in rat ocular tissues. *Invest Ophthalmol Vis Sci* 28:1617, 1987.

132. RAIHA NCR, KEKOMAKI MP: Studies on the development of ornithine-ketoacid aminotransferase activity in rat liver. *Biochem J* 108:521, 1968.

133. PERAINO C, PITOT HC: Studies on the induction and repression of enzymes in rat liver. *J Biol Chem* 239:4308, 1964.

134. LYONS RT, PITOT HC: The regulation of ornithine aminotransferase synthesis by glucagon in the rat. *Arch Biochem Biophys* 174:262, 1976.

135. LYONS RT, PITOT HC: Hormonal regulation of ornithine aminotransferase biosynthesis in rat liver and kidney. *Arch Biochem Biophys* 180:472, 1977.

136. MERRILL MJ, PITOT HC: Regulation of ornithine aminotransferase by cyclic AMP and glucose in primary cultures of adult rat hepatocytes. *Arch Biochem Biophys* 237:373, 1985.

137. MERRILL MJ, MUECKLER MM, PITOT HC: Levels of ornithine aminotransferase messenger RNA under conditions of cyclic AMP induction in cultured hepatocytes. *J Biol Chem* 260:11248, 1985.

138. IKEDA M, OKADA M: Effect of pyridoxine deficiency on ornithine aminotransferase in rat kidney and liver. *J Nutr Sci Vitaminol* 31:553, 1985.

139. IKEDA M, OKADA M: Regulation of ornithine aminotransferase in rat kidney by estradiol and pyridoxine. *J Nutr Sci Vitaminol* 32:23, 1986.

140. WU C: Estrogen induction of ornithine aminotransferase in rat kidney slices. *Biochem Biophys Res Commun* 82:782, 1978.

141. MATTHAEI KI, WILLIAMS JF: Ornithine aminotransferase turnover in host tissues of tumor-bearing rats. *J Natl Cancer Inst* 79:805, 1987.

142. MUECKLER MM, PITOT HC: Regulation of ornithine aminotransferase mRNA levels in rat kidney by estrogen and thyroid hormone. *J Biol Chem* 258:1781, 1983.

143. MUECKLER MM, MORAN S, PITOT HC: Transcriptional control of ornithine aminotransferase synthesis in rat kidney by estrogen and thyroid hormone. *J Biol Chem* 259:2302, 1984.

144. MUECKLER MM, MERRILL MJ, PITOT HC: Translational and pretranslational control of ornithine aminotransferase synthesis in rat liver. *J Biol Chem* 258:6109, 1983.

145. IP MM, CHEE PY, SWICK RW: Turnover of hepatic mitochondrial ornithine aminotransferase and cytochrome oxidase using ^{14}C-carbonate as tracer. *Biochim Biophys Acta* 354:29, 1974.

146. CHEE PY, SWICK RW: Effect of dietary protein and tryptophan on the turnover of rat liver ornithine aminotransferase. *J Biol Chem* 251:1029, 1976.

147. KOBAYASHI K, KITO K, KATUNUMA N: Effects of estrogen on the turnover rates of ornithine aminotransferase in rat liver and kidney. *J Biochem* 79:787, 1976.

148. AUGUSTINE SL, SWICK RW: Turnover of total proteins and ornithine aminotransferase during liver regeneration in rats. *Am J Physiol* 238:46, 1980.

149. LODATO RF, SMITH RJ, VALLE D, PHANG MJ, AOKI TT: Regulation of proline biosynthesis: The inhibition of pyrroline-5-carboxylase synthase activity by ornithine. *Metabolism* 30:908, 1981.

150. VALLE D, DOWNING SJ, HARRIS SC, PHANG JM: Proline biosynthesis: Multiple defects in Chinese hamster ovary cells. *Biochem Biophys Res Commun* 53:1130, 1973.

151. ERTEL J, ISSEROFF H: Proline in fascioliasis. I. Comparative activities of ornithine-δ-aminotransferase and proline oxidase in *Fasciola* and in mammalian livers. *J Parasitol* 60:574, 1974.

152. SMITH AD, BENZIMAN M, STRECKER HJ: The formation of ornithine from proline in animal tissues. *Biochem J* 104:557, 1967.

153. ROSS G, DUNN D, JONES ME: Ornithine synthesis from glutamate in rat intestinal mucosa homogenates: Evidence for the reduction of glutamate to γ-glutamyl semialdehyde. *Biochem Biophys Res Commun* 85:140, 1978.

154. WINDMUELLER HG, SPAETH AE: Intestinal metabolism of glutamine and glutamate from the lumen as compared to glutamine from blood. *Arch Biochem Biophys* 171:662, 1975.

155. VALLE D, PHANG JM, DOWNING SJ: Unpublished observations.

156. SNYDERMAN SE, BOYER A, HOLT LE: The arginine requirement of the infant. *Am J Dis Child* 97:78, 1959.

157. CAREY GP, KIME Z, ROGERS QR, MORRIS JG, HARGROVE D, BUFFINGTON CA, BRUSILOW SW: An arginine-deficient diet in humans does not evoke hyper- or orotic acidemia. *J Nutr* 117:1734, 1987.

158. MOSER HW, EFRON ML, BROWN H, DIAMOND R, NEUMAN CG: Argininosuccinic aciduria. Report of two new cases and demonstration of intermittent elevation of blood ammonia. *Am J Med* 42:9, 1967.

159. BRUSILOW SW, BATSHAW ML: Personal communication.

160. MORRIS JG, ROGERS QR: Ammonia intoxication in the near-adult cat as a result of a dietary deficiency of arginine. *Science* 199:431, 1978.

161. MORRIS JG, ROGERS QR: Arginine: An essential amino acid for the cat. *J Nutr* 108:1944, 1978.

162. STEWART PM, WALSER M, BATSHAW M, VALLE D: Effects of arginine-free meals on ureagenesis in cats. *Am J Physiol* 241:310, 1981.

163. SHIH V, EFRON ML, MOSER HW: Hyperornithinemia, hyperammonemia, and homocitrullinuria. A new disorder of amino acid metabolism associated with myoclonic seizures and mental retardation. *Am J Dis Child* 117:83, 1969.

164. BICKEL H, FEIST D, MULLER H, QUADBECK G: Ornithinamie, eine weiter aminosaurenstoff-Wechselsturung mit hirnschadigung. *Dtsch Med Wochenschr* 47:2247, 1968.

165. GRUBNER R: Personal communications.

166. PERRY TL, HANSEN S: Biochemical effects in man and rat of three drugs which can increase brain GABA content. *J Neurochem* 30:679, 1978.

166a. FUJIMURA Y, MATSUZAWA T, KAWAMURA M, TADA K, MIZUNO K: Mass screening of urea cycle diseases: A new mass screening method of hyperornithinemia by using two coupling enzymes. *Tohoku J Exp Med* 141:257, 1983.

167. JACOBSOHN E: Ein fall von Retinitis pigmentosa atypica. *Klin Monatsbl Augenheilkd* 26:202, 1888.

168. CUTLER CW: Drei ungewohnliche Falle von Retinochorioideal degeneration. *Arch Augenheilkd* 30:117, 1895.

169. FUCHS E: Ueber zwei der retinitis pigmentosa verwandte Krankheiten (retinitis punctata albescens und atrophia gyrata chorioideae et retinae). *Arch Augenheilkd* 32:111, 1896.

170. USHER CH: The Bowman Lecture—On a few hereditary eye affections. *Trans Ophthalmol Soc UK* 55:164, 1935.

171. KURSTJENS JH: Choroideremia and gyrate atrophy of the choroid and retina. Brief historical review. *Documenta Ophthalmol* 19:1, 1965.

172. FRANCOIS J: Heredity of the choroidal dystrophies. *Adv Ophthalmol* 35:1, 1978.

173. TAKKI K: *Gyrate atrophy of the choroid and retina associated with hyperornithinemia*. Thesis, University of Helsinki, Helsinki, 1975.

174. KAISER-KUPFER MI, VALLE D: Clinical, biochemical and therapeutic aspects of gyrate atrophy, in Osbourne N, Chader J (eds): *Progress in Retinal Research*. Oxford, Pergamon, 1986, p 179.

175. HAYASAKA S, SHIONO T, MIZUNO K, SASAYAMA C, AKIYA S, TANAKA Y, HAYAKAWA M, MIYAKE Y, OHBA N: Gyrate atrophy of the choroid and retina: 15 Japanese patients. *Br J Ophthalmol* 70:612, 1986.

176. SIMELL O, TAKKI K: Raised plasma ornithine and gyrate atrophy of the choroid and retina. *Lancet* 1:1031, 1973.

177. FRANCOIS J, BARBIER F, DE ROUCK A: Les Conducteurs de gene de l'atrophia gyrata chorioideae et retinae de Fuchs (anomalie d'Alder). *Acta Med Genet Med Gemell* 9:74, 1960.

178. TAKKI K: Gyrate atrophy of the choroid and retina associated with hyperornithinemia. *Br J Ophthalmol* 58:3, 1974.

179. TAKKI K, SIMELL O: Gyrate atrophy of the choroid and retina with hyperornithinemia. *Birth Defects* 12:373, 1976.

180. TAKKI K, MILTON RC: The natural history of gyrate atrophy of the choroid and retina. *Ophthalmology* 88:292, 1981.

181. FRANCOIS J: Gyrate atrophy of the choroid and retina. *Ophthalmologica (Basel)* 178:311, 1979.

182. MCCULLOCH C, MARLISS EB: Gyrate atrophy of the choroid and retina with hyperornithinemia. *Am J Ophthalmol* 80:1047, 1975.

183. McCULLOCH JC, ARSHINOFF SA, MARLISS EB, PARKER JA: Hyperornithinemia and gyrate atrophy of the choroid and retina. *Ophthalmology* 85:918, 1978.

184. KAISER-KUPFER MI, VALLE D, DEL VALLE LA: A specific enzyme defect in gyrate atrophy. *Am J Ophthalmol* 85:200, 1978.

185. KAISER-KUPFER MI, VALLE D, BRON AJ: Clinical and biochemical heterogeneity in gyrate atrophy. *Am J Ophthalmol* 89:219, 1980.

186. KAISER-KUPFER MI, DE MONASTERIO F, VALLE D, WALSER M, BRUSILOW SW: Visual results of a long-term trial of a low-arginine diet in gyrate atrophy of the choroid and retina. *Ophthalmology* 88:307, 1981.

187. KAISER-KUPFER MI, KUWABARA T, ASKANAS V, BRODY L, TAKKI K, DVORETZKY I, ENGEL WK: Systemic manifestations of gyrate atrophy of the choroid and retina. *Ophthalmology* 88:302, 1981.

188. BERSON EL, SCHMIDT SY, SHIH VE: Ocular and biochemical abnormalities in gyrate atrophy of the choroid and retina. *Ophthalmology* 85:1018, 1978.

189. BERSON EL, SHIH VE, SULLIVAN PL: Ocular findings in patients with gyrate atrophy on pyridoxine and low-protein, low-arginine diets. *Ophthalmology* 88:311, 1981.

190. WELEBER RG, KENNAWAY NG, BUIST NR: Vitamin B_6 in management of gyrate atrophy of choroid and retina. *Lancet* 2:1213, 1978.

191. WELEBER RG, KENNAWAY NG: Clinical trial of vitamin B_6 for gyrate atrophy of the choroid and retina. *Ophthalmology* 88:316, 1981.

192. JAEGER W, KETTLER JV, LUTZ P, HILSDORF C: Differential diagnosis of gyrate atrophy of the choroid and retina (gyrate atrophy of the choroid and retina with and without hyperornithinemia). *Metab Pediatr Ophthalmol* 3:189, 1979.

193. HODES DT, MUSHIN AS, LAURANCE BM, OBERHOLZER VG, BRIDDON A: Hyperornithinemia with gyrate atrophy of the choroid and retina in two siblings. *J R Soc Med* 73:588, 1980.

194. YATZIV S, STATTER M, MERIN S: Metabolic studies in two families with

hyperornithinemia and gyrate atrophy of choroid and retina. *J Lab Clin Med* 93:749, 1979.

195. IANNETTI F: Hyperornithinemia in the gyrate atrophy of the retina and choroid. *Ann Ottal Clin Ocul* 12:555, 1976.

196. STOPPOLONI G, PRISCO F, SANTINELLI R, TOLONE C: Hyperornithinemia and gyrate atrophy of choroid and retina. *Helv Paediatr Acta* 33:429, 1978.

197. RINALDI E, STOPPOLONI GP, SAVASTANO S, RUSSO S, COTTICELLI L: Gyrate atrophy of choroid associated with hyperornithaenemia: Report of the first case in Italy. *J Pediatr Ophthalmol Strabismus* 16:133, 1979.

198. AKIYA S, OHSAWA M, OGATA T: Gyrate atrophy of the choroid and retina. Long-term observation of two brothers of gyrate atrophy of the choroid and retina with hyperornithinaemia. *Acta Soc Ophthalmol Jpn* 81:310, 1978.

199. TRIJBELS JMF, SENGERS RCA, BAKKEREN JAJM, De KORT AFM, DUTMAN AF: L-Ornithine-ketoacid-transferase deficiency in cultured fibroblasts of a patient with hyperornithinemia and gyrate atrophy of the choroid and retina. *Clin Chim Acta* 79:371, 1977.

200. O'DONNELL JJ, SANDMAN RP, MARTIN SR: Gyrate atrophy of the retina: Inborn error of L-ornithine:2-oxoacid aminotransferase. *Science* 200:200, 1978.

201. OBERHOLZER VG, BRIDDON A: 3-Amino-2-piperidone in the urine of patients with hyperornithinemia. *Clin Chim Acta* 87:411, 1978.

202. DOUGLAS EP: Hyperprolinaemia and gyrate atrophy of the choroid and retina in members of the same family. *Br J Ophthalmol* 69:588, 1985.

203. KAISER-KUPFER MI, LUDWIG IH, De MONASTERIO FM, VALLE D, KRIEGER I: Gyrate atrophy of the choroid and retina: Early findings. *Ophthalmology* 92:394, 1985.

204. KAISER-KUPFER MI, KUWABARA T, UGA S, TAKKI K, VALLE D: Cataracts in gyrate atrophy: Clinical and morphologic studies. *Invest Ophthalmol Vis Sci* 24:432, 1983.

205. KRILL AE: Clinical characteristics, in *Krill's Hereditary Retinal and Choroidal Diseases*, 7th ed. New York, Harper & Row, 1977, p 1012.

206. VANNAS-SULONEN K: Progression of gyrate atrophy of the choroid and retina: A long-term follow-up by fluorescein angiography. *Acta Ophthalmol* 65:101, 1987.

207. VANNAS-SULONEN K, VANNAS A, O'DONNELL JJ, SIPILA I, WOOD I: Pathology of iridectomy specimens in gyrate atrophy of the retina and choroid. *Acta Ophthalmol* 61:9, 1983.

208. SIPILA I, SIMELL O, RAPOLA J, SAINIO K, TUUTERI L: Gyrate atrophy of the choroid and retina with hyperornithinemia: Tubular aggregates and type 2 fiber atrophy in muscle. *Neurology* 29:996, 1979.

209. KENNAWAY NG, WELEBER RG, BUIST NRM: Gyrate atrophy of the choroid and retina with hyperornithinemia: Biochemical and histologic studies and response to vitamin B_6. *Am J Hum Genet* 32:529, 1980.

210. ENGEL WK, BISHOP DW, CUNNINGHAM GG: Tubular aggregates in type II muscle fibers: Ultrastructural and histochemical correlation. *J Ultrastruct Res* 31:507, 1970.

211. ROSENBERG NL, NEVILLE HE, RINGEL SP: Tubular aggregates: Their association with neuromuscular diseases, including the syndrome of myalgias/cramps. *Arch Neurol* 42:973, 1985.

212. NIAKAN E, HARATI Y, DANON MJ: Tubular aggregates: Their association with myalgia. *J Neurol Neurosurg Psychiatry* 48:882, 1985.

213. MARON BJ, FERRANS VJ: Aggregates of tubules in human cardiac muscle cells. *J Mol Cell Cardiol* 6:249, 1974.

214. VALLE DL, WALSER M, BRUSILOW SW, KAISER-KUPFER MI: Gyrate atrophy of the choroid and retina: Amino acid metabolism and correction of hyperornithinemia with an arginine deficient diet. *J Clin Invest* 65:371, 1980.

215. VALLE D, WALSER M, BRUSILOW S, KAISER-KUPFER M, TAKKI K: Gyrate atrophy of the choroid and retina: Biochemical considerations and experience with an arginine-restricted diet. *Ophthalmology* 88:325, 1981.

216. GORDON BA, GATFIELD PD, TALLER E: Ornithine methyl ester. An unusual metabolite encountered in the urine of patients with a urea cycle disorder characterized by hyperammonemia, hyperornithinemia, and homocitrullinuria. *Clin Biochem* 10:78, 1977.

217. FELL V, POLLITT RJ: 3-Aminopiperid-2-one, an unusual metabolite in the urine of a patient with hyperammonaemia, hyperornithinaemia and homocitrullinuria. *Clin Chim Acta* 87:405, 1978.

218. ROESEL RA, CORYELL ME, BLANKENSHIP PR, HOMMES FA: γ-Glutamylornithine excretion in patients with hyperornithinemia. *Clin Chim Acta* 140:133, 1984.

219. OBERHOLZER VG: Personal communication.

220. KENNAWAY NG, WELEBER RG, BUIST NRM: Gyrate atrophy of the choroid and retina: Deficient activity of ornithine-ketoacid aminotransferase in cultured skin fibroblasts. *N Engl J Med* 297:1180, 1977.

221. O'DONNELL JJ, SANDMAN RP, MARTIN SR: Deficient L-ornithine:2-oxoacid aminotransferase activity in cultured fibroblasts from a patient with gyrate atrophy of the retina. *Biochem Biophys Res Commun* 79:396, 1977.

222. SHIH VE, BERSON EL, MANDELL R, SCHMIDT SY: Ornithine ketoacid transaminase deficiency in gyrate atrophy of the choroid and retina. *Am J Hum Genet* 30:174, 1978.

223. OHURA T, KOMINAMI E, TADA K, KATUNUMA N: Gyrate atrophy of the choroid and retina: Decreased ornithine aminotransferase concentration in cultured skin fibroblasts from patients. *Clin Chim Acta* 136:29, 1984.

224. HAYASAKA S, SAITO T, NAKAJIMA H, TAKAKU Y, SHIONO T, MIZUNO K, OHMURA K, TADA K: Gyrate atrophy with hyperornithinaemia: Different types of responsiveness to vitamin B_6. *Br J Ophthalmol* 65:478, 1981.

225. VALLE D, KAISER-KUPFER MI, DEL VALLE LA: Gyrate atrophy of the choroid and retina: Deficiency of ornithine aminotransferase in transformed lymphocytes. *Proc Natl Acad Sci USA* 74:5159, 1977.

226. ASKANAS V, VALLE D, KAISER-KUPFER MI, TAKKI K, ENGEL WK, BLUMENKOPF B: Cultured muscle fibers of gyrate atrophy patients: Tubules, ornithine toxicity and 1-ornithine-2-oxoacid aminotransferase deficiency. *Neurology* 30:368, 1980.

226a. JANSSES AJM, PLAKKE T, TRIJBELS FJM, SENGERS RCA, MONNENS LAH: L-Ornithine ketoacid-transaminase assay in hair roots of homozygotes and heterozygotes for gyrate atrophy. *Clin Chim Acta* 113:213, 1981.

227. SIPILA I, O'DONNELL JJ, SIMELL O: Gyrate atrophy of the choroid and retina with hyperornithinemia: Characterization of mutant liver-L-ornithine:2-oxoacid aminotransferase kinetics. *J Clin Invest* 67:1805, 1981.

228. KENNAWAY NG, STANKOVA L, WIRTZ MK, WELEBER RG: Gyrate atrophy of the choroid and retina (GA): Characterization of heterogeneity and mechanism of response to vitamin B_6. *Am J Hum Genet* 41:A9, 1987.

229. WIRTZ MK, KENNAWAY NG, WELEBER RG: Heterogeneity and complementation analysis of fibroblasts from vitamin B_6 responsive and non-responsive patients with gyrate atrophy of the choroid and retina. *J Inherited Metab Dis* 8:71, 1985.

230. WELEBER RG, WIRTZ MK, KENNAWAY NG: Gyrate atrophy of the choroid and retina: Clinical and biochemical heterogeneity and response to vitamin B_6. *Birth Defects* 18(6):219, 1982.

231. VALLE D, BOISON AP, KAISER-KUPFER MI: Complementation analysis of gyrate atrophy of the choroid and retina. *Pediatr Res* 13:427, 1979.

232. SHIH VE, MANDELL R, JACOBY LB, BERSON EL: Genetic-complementation analysis in fibroblasts from gyrate and atrophy and the syndrome of hyperornithinemia, hyperammonemia and homocitrullinuria. *Pediatr Res* 15:569, 1981.

233. MITCHELL GA, BRODY LC, SIPILA I, LOONEY JE, WONG C, ENGELHARDT JF, PATEL AS, STEEL G, OBIE C, KAISER-KUPFER MI, VALLE D: At least two mutant alleles of ornithine-δ-aminotransferase cause gyrate atrophy of the choroid and retina in Finns. *Proc Natl Acad Sci USA*, in press.

234. RAMESH V, MCCLATCHEY AI, RAMESH N, BENOIT LA, BERSON EL, SHIH VE, GUSELLA JF: Molecular basis of ornithine aminotransferase deficiency in B_6-responsive and nonresponsive forms of gyrate atrophy. *Proc Natl Acad Sci USA* 85:3777, 1988.

235. INANA G, HOTTA Y, ZINTZ C, TAKKI K, WELEBER RG, KENNAWAY NG, NAKAYASU K, NAKAJIMA A, SHIONO T: Expression defect of ornithine aminotransferase gene in gyrate atrophy. *Invest Ophthalmol Vis Sci* 29:1001, 1988.

236. MITCHELL GM, BRODY LC, LOONEY J, STEEL G, SUCHANEK M, DOWLING C, DER KALOUSTIAN V, KAISER-KUPFER MI, VALLE D: An initiator codon mutation in ornithine-δ-aminotransferase causing gyrate atrophy. *J Clin Invest* 81:630, 1988.

237. INANA G, TOTSUKA S, ZINTZ C, HOTTA Y, SHIONO T, OHURA T, KOMINAMI E, KATUNUMA N: Molecular genetics of gyrate atrophy, in Hollyfield JG, Anderson RE, LaVail MM, Mizuno K (eds): *Degenerative Retinal Disorders: Clinical and Laboratory Investigations*. New York, AR Liss, 1987, p 163.

238. VALLE D, MITCHELL GA: Inborn errors of metabolism in the molecular age, in Childs B, Holtzman AN, Kazazian HH, Valle D (eds): *Genetics in Medicine, New Series, Progress in Medical Genetics*. New York, Elsevier, 1988, p 100.

239. MITCHELL G, LOONEY J, BRODY L, STEEL G, SUCHANEK M, ENGELHARDT J, PATEL A, KAISER-KUPFER MI, SIPILA I, VALLE D: Molecular basis of mutations causing gyrate atrophy. *Pediatr Res* 22:332A, 1988.

240. MYERS RM, LARIN Z, MANIATIS T: Detection of single base substitutions by ribonuclease cleavage at mismatches in RNA:DNA duplexes. *Science* 230:1242, 1985.

241. GIBBS RA, CASKEY CT: Identification and localization of mutations at the Lesch-Nyhan locus by ribonuclease A cleavage. *Science* 236:303, 1987.

242. SAIKI RK, SCHARF S, FALOONA F, MULLIS KB, HORN GT, ERLICH HA, ARNHEIM N: Enzymatic amplification of beta-globin genomic sequences and restriction site analysis for diagnosis of sickle cell anemia. *Science* 230:1350, 1985.

243. MULLIS KB, FALOONA FA: Specific synthesis of DNA in vitro via a polymerase catalyzed chain reaction. *Methods Enzymol* 155:335, 1987.

244. NORIO R, NEVANLINNA HR, PERHEENTUPA J: Hereditary diseases in Finland. Rare flora in rare soil. *Ann Clin Res* 5:109, 1973.

245. NEVANLINNA HR: Rare hereditary diseases and markers in Finland: An introduction, in Eriksson AW, Forsius HR, Nevanlinna HR, Workman PL, Norio RK (eds): *Population Structure and Genetic Disorders.* London, Academic, 1980, p 569.

246. NORIO R: Diseases of Finland and Scandinavia, in Rothchild H, Chapman CF (eds): *Biocultural Aspects of Disease.* London, Academic, 1981, p 359.

247. TONEY MD, KIRSCH JF: Tyrosine 70 increases the coenzyme affinity of aspartate aminotransferase. A site-directed mutagenesis study. *J Biol Chem* 262:12403, 1987.

248. INANA G, HOTTA Y, INOUYE L, ZINTZ C, SHIONO T: Single point mutation and amino acid change in ornithine aminotransferase from a gyrate atrophy patient. *Invest Ophthalmol Vis Sci* 29:14, 1988.

249. STETTEN MR: Mechanism of the conversion of ornithine into proline and glutamic acid in vivo. *J Biol Chem* 189:499, 1951.

250. SCRIVER CR, ROSENBERG LE: *Amino Acid Metabolism and Its Disorders.* Philadelphia, Saunders, 1973, p 39.

251. BERGSTROM J, FURST P, NOREE LO, VINNARS E: Intracellular free amino acid concentration in human muscle tissue. *J Appl Physiol* 36:693, 1974.

252. GOPALAKRISHNA R, NAGARAJAN B: A modified method for estimation of ornithine in biological samples. *Anal Biochem* 101:472, 1980.

253. MATSUZAWA T, ITO M, ISHIGURO I: Enzymatic assays of L-ornithine and L-Δ^1-pyrroline-5-carboxylate in tissues and ornithine-load test in human subjects. *Anal Biochem* 106:1, 1980.

254. COHEN AI: The retina and optic nerve, in Moses RA (ed): *Adler's Physiology of the Eye.* St Louis, CV Mosby Co, 1975, p 367.

255. ZINN KM, MARMOR MF: *The Retinal Pigment Epithelium.* Cambridge, MA, Harvard University Press, 1979.

256. DOWLING JE: *The Retina: An Approachable Part of the Brain.* Cambridge, MA, Harvard University Press, 1987.

257. RODIECK RW: *The Vertebrate Retina,* San Francisco, WH Freeman, 1973, p 345.

258. VALLE DL, BOISON AP, JEZYK JP, AGUIRRE G: Gyrate atrophy of the choroid and retina in a cat. *Invest Ophthalmol Vis Sci* 20:251, 1981.

259. KUWABARA T, ISHIKAWA Y, KAISER-KUPFER MI: Experimental model of gyrate atrophy in animals. *Ophthalmology* 88:331, 1981.

260. SIPILA I, SIMELL O, ARJOMAA P: Gyrate atrophy of the choroid and retina with hyperornithinemia. Deficient formation of guanidinoacetic acid from arginine. *J Clin Invest* 66:684, 1980.

261. SIPILA I, VALLE D, BRUSILOW SW, KAISER-KUPFER MI: Defective creatine metabolism in gyrate atrophy of the choroid and retina. *Pediatr Res* 17:226A, 1984.

262. DIONISI VICI C, BACHMANN C, GAMBARARA M, COLOMBO JP, SABETTA G: Hyperornithinemia-hyperammonemia-homocitrullinuria syndrome: Low creatine excretion and effect of citrulline, arginine, or ornithine supplement. *Pediatr Res* 22:364, 1987.

263. SIPILA I, RAPOLA J, SIMELL O, VANNAS A: Supplementary creatine as a treatment for gyrate atrophy of the choroid and retina. *N Engl J Med* 304:867, 1981.

264. VANNAS-SULONEN K, SIPILA I, VANNAS A, SIMELL O, RAPOLA J: Gyrate atrophy of the choroid and retina: A five year follow-up of creatine supplementation. *Ophthalmology* 92:1719, 1985.

265. KAISER-KUPFER MI, De MONASTERIO FM, VALLE D, WALSER M, BRUSILOW S: Gyrate atrophy of the choroid and retina: Improved visual function following reduction of plasma ornithine by diet. *Science* 210:1128, 1980.

266. MCINNES RR, ARSHINOFF SA, BELL L, MARLISS EB, MCCULLOUCH JC: Hyperornithinaemia and gyrate atrophy of the retina: Improvement of vision during treatment with a low-arginine diet. *Lancet* 1:513, 1981.

267. WALLIMANN T, WEGMANN G, MOSER H, HUBER R, EPPENBERGER HM: High content of creatine kinase in chicken retina: Compartmentalized localization of creatine kinase isoenzymes in photoreceptor cells. *Proc Natl Acad Sci USA* 83:3816, 1986.

268. MORI A, KATAYAMA Y, HIGASHIDATE S, KIMURA S: Fluorometrical analysis of guanidino compounds in mouse brain. *J Neurochem* 32:643, 1979.

269. MATSUMOTO M, KOBAYASHI K, MORI A: Distribution of guanidino compounds in bovine brain. *J Neurochem* 32:645, 1979.

270. WOZNICKI DT, WALKER JB: Formation of a supplemental long time-constant reservoir of high energy phosphate by brain in vivo and in vitro and its reversible depletion by potassium depolarization. *J Neurochem* 33:75, 1979.

271. WOZNICKI DT, WALKER JB: Utilization of cyclocreatine phosphate and analogue of creatine phosphate by mouse brain during ischemia and its sparing action on brain energy reserves. *J Neurochem* 34:1247, 1980.

272. METHFESSEL J: Zur organ- und subzellularverteilung der transamidinase bei mensch und ratte. *Acta Biol Med Ger* 35:309, 1976.

273. LOIKE JD, KOZLER VF, SILVERSTEIN SC: Increased ATP and creatine phosphate turnover in phagocytosing mouse peritoneal macrophages. *J Biol Chem* 254:9558, 1979.

274. HARVEY JC: Reduced renal arginine-glycine transamidinase activity in myotonic goats and in patients with myotonic muscular dystrophy. *Johns Hopkins Med J* 125:270, 1969.

275. VALLE D, BOISON AP, KAISER-KUPFER MI: Increased sensitivity of gyrate atrophy fibroblasts to ornithine toxicity. *Pediatr Res* 13:426, 1979.

276. VALLE D, ASKANAS V, KAISER-KUPFER MI, TAKKI K, ENGEL K: Increased sensitivity of gyrate atrophy fibroblasts and cultured muscle cells to ornithine toxicity. *Pediatr Res* 14:528, 1980.

277. BAICH A: Effect of methionine on the accumulation of ornithine by Chinese hamster cells in culture. *Biochim Biophys Acta* 756:238, 1983.

278. VALLE D, BOISON AP, PHANG JM, SMITH RJ, KAISER-KUPFER MI: Unpublished observations.

279. PHANG JM, DOWNING SJ, YEH GC, SMITH RJ, WILLIAMS JA: Stimulation of the hexose-monophosphate pentose pathway by Δ^1-pyrroline-5-carboxylic acid in human fibroblasts. *Biochem Biophys Res Commun* 87:363, 1979.

280. YEH GC, HARRIS SC, PHANG JM: Pyrroline-5-carboxylate reductase in human erythrocytes. *J Clin Invest* 67:1042, 1981.

281. YEH GC, PHANG JM: Pyrroline-5-carboxylate stimulates the conversion of purine antimetabolites to their nucleotide forms by a redox-dependent mechanism. *J Biol Chem* 258:9774, 1983.

282. HAGEDORN CH, PHANG JM: Transfer of reducing equivalents into mitochondria by the interconversions of proline and Δ^1-pyrroline-5-carboxylate. *Arch Biochem Biophys* 225:95, 1983.

283. HAGEDORN CH, PHANG JM: Catalytic transfer of hydride ions from NADPH to oxygen by the interconversions of proline and delta 1-pyrroline-5-carboxylate. *Arch Biochem Biophys* 248:166, 1986.

284. MATSUZAWA T, ISHIGURO I: Hyperornithinemia with gyrate atrophy and enzymes involved in ornithine metabolism of the eye. *Biochem Int* 1:179, 1980.

285. OLDENDORF WH: Brain uptake of radiolabeled amino acids, amines and hexoses after arterial injection. *Am J Physiol* 221:1629, 1971.

286. FLEMING GA, HAGEDORN CH, GRANGER AS, PHANG JM: Pyrroline-5-carboxylate in human plasma. *Metabolism* 33:739, 1984.

287. FLEMING GA, PHANG JM, VALLE D: Unpublished observations.

288. SHIONO T, KADOR PF, KINOSHITA JH: Stimulation of the hexose monophosphate pathway by pyrroline-5-carboxylate reductase in the lens. *Exp Eye Res* 41:767, 1985.

289. RAJANTIE J, SIMELL O, PERHEENTUPA J: Lysinuric protein intolerance. Basolateral transport defect in renal tubuli. *J Clin Invest* 67:1078, 1981.

290. SCHAUMBURG H, KAPLAN J, WINDEBANK A, VICK N, RASMUS S, PLEASURE D, BROWN MJ: Sensory neuropathy from pyridoxine abuse. A new megavitamin syndrome. *N Engl J Med* 309:445, 1983.

291. DALTON K, DALTON MJ: Characteristics of pyridoxine overdose neuropathy syndrome. *Acta Neurol Scand* 76:8, 1987.

292. WELEBER R: Personal communications, 1988.

293. HAYASAKA S, SAITO T, NAKAJIMA H, TAKAHASHI O, MIZUNO K, TADA K: Clinical trials of vitamin B_6 and proline supplementation for gyrate atrophy of the choroid and retina. *Br J Ophthalmol* 69:283, 1985.

294. BERSON EL, HANSON AH, ROSNER B, SHIH VE: A two year trial of low protein, low arginine diets or vitamin B_6 for patients with gyrate atrophy. *Birth Defects* 18(6):209, 1982.

295. VANNAS-SULONEN K, SIMELL O, SIPILA I: Gyrate atrophy of the choroid and retina: The ocular disease progresses in juvenile patients despite normal or near normal plasma ornithine concentration. *Ophthalmology* 94:1428, 1987.

296. GIORDANO D, DE SANTO NG, PLUVIO M, SANTINELLI R, STOPPOLONI G: Lysine in treatment of hyperornithinemia. *Nephron* 22:97, 1978.

297. SAITO T, OMURA K, HAYASAKA S: Hyperornithinemia with gyrate atrophy of the choroid and retina. A disturbance in de novo formation of proline. *Tohoku J Exp Med* 135:395, 1981.

298. SAITO T, HAYASAKA S, YABATA K, OMURA K, MIZUNO K, TADA K: Atypical gyrate atrophy of the choroid and retina and iminoglycinuria. *Tohoku J Exp Med* 135:331, 1981.

299. TAKKI K, SIMELL O: Genetic aspects in gyrate atrophy of the choroid and retina with hyperornithinemia. *Br J Ophthalmol* 58:907, 1974.

300. PAI GS, van RENS GH, MAYFIELD RK, CHAMBERS JK, GENCO PV, VALLE D: Lipoatrophic diabetes and gyrate atrophy of the retina and choroid in a black sibship. *Am J Hum Genet* 40:A14, 1987.

301. WRIGHT T, POLLITT R: Psychomotor retardation, epileptic and stuporous attacks, irritability and ataxia associated with ammonia intoxication, high blood ornithine levels and increased homocitrulline in the urine. *Proc R Soc Med* 66:221, 1973.

302. FELL V, POLLITT RJ, SAMPSON GA, WRIGHT T: Ornithinemia, hyperammonemia, and homocitrullinuria. A disease associated with mental retar-

dation and possibly caused by defective mitochondrial transport. *Am J Dis Child* 127:752, 1974.

303. GATFIELD PD, TALLER E, WOLFE DM, HAUST DM: Hyperornithinemia, hyperammonemia, and homocitrullinuria associated with decreased carbamyl phosphate synthetase I activity. *Pediatr Res* 9:488, 1975.

304. SIMELL O, MACKENZIE S, CLOW CL, SCRIVER CR: Ornithine loading did not prevent induced hyperammonemia in a patient with HHH syndrome. *Pediatr Res* 19:1283, 1985.

305. HOMMES FA, ROESEL RA, METOKI K, HARTLAGE PL, DYKEN PR: Studies on a case of HHH-syndrome (Hyperammonemia, hyperornithinemia, homocitrullinuria). *Neuropediatrics* 17:48, 1986.

306. HOMMES FA, HO CK, ROESEL RA, CORYELL ME: Decreased transport of ornithine across the inner mitochondrial membrane as a cause of hyperornithinaemia. *J Inherited Metab Dis* 5:41, 1982.

307. RENNERT OM, GARNICA AD, CHAN WY: Hyperornithinemia and hyperammonemia: A rare disorder of ammonia metabolism, in Preisign R, Bircher J, Baumgartner G (eds): *The Liver: Quantitative Aspects of Structure and Function.* Aulendorf, Editio Cantor, 1976, p 298.

308. RODES M, RIBES A, PINEDA M, ALVAREZ L, FABREGAS I, FERNANDES ALVAREZ E, COUDE FX, GRIMBER G: A new family affected by the syndrome of hyperornithinaemia, hyperammonaemia and homocitrullinuria. *J Inherited Metab Dis* 10:73, 1987.

309. OYANAGI K, TSUCHIYAMA A, ITAKURA Y, SOGAWA H, WAGATSUMA K, NAKAO T: The mechanism of hyperammonaemia and hyperornithinaemia in the syndrome of hyperornithinaemia, hyperammonaemia with homocitrullinuria. *J Inherited Metab Dis* 6:133, 1983.

310. INOUE I, KOURA M, SAHEKI T, KAYANUMA K, UONO M, NAKAJIMA M, TAKESHITA K, KOIKE R, YUASA T, MIYATAKE T, SAKODA K: Abnormality of citrulline synthesis in liver mitochondria from patients with hyperornithinaemia, hyperammonaemia and homocitrullinuria. *J Inherited Metab Dis* 10:277, 1987.

311. GJESSING LR, LUNDE HA, UNDRUM T, BROCH H, ALME A, LIE SO: A new patient with hyperornithinaemia, hyperammonaemia and homocitrullinuria treated early with low protein diet. *J Inherited Metab Dis* 9:186, 1986.

312. SHIMIZU H, ETO Y, MAEKAWA K, SASAKI H, TANAKA T, SUZUKI T: Biochemical and morphological studies in hyperornithinemia associated with hyperammonemia and homocitrullinuria. *Jikeikai Med J* 34:227, 1987.

313. SHIH VE, MANDELL R, HERZFELD A: Defective ornithine metabolism in cultured skin fibroblasts from patients with the syndrome of hyperornithinemia, hyperammonemia and homocitrullinuria. *Clin Chim Acta* 118:149, 1982.

314. OGIER H, POLL-THE BT, RABIER D, BONTE JB, CHARPENTIER C, SHIH VE, SAUDUBRAY JM: Neonatal onset form of HHH syndrome: Three years clinical course and therapeutic attempts. Personal communication, 1988.

315. KOIKE R, FUJIMORI K, YUASA T, MIYATAKE T, INOUE I, SAHEKI T: Hyperornithinemia, hyperammonemia, and homocitrullinuria: Case report and biochemical study. *Neurology* 37:1813, 1987.

316. KOIKE R, FUJIMORI K, YUASA T, MIYATAKE T: Hyperornithinemia, hyperammonemia and homocitrullinuria syndrome in a family. *Rinsho Shinkeigaku* 27:465, 1987.

317. KIRSCH SE, MCINNES RR: Control of hyperammonemia in the 3H syndrome by ornithine administration. *Pediatr Res* 20:267, 1986.

318. ZAMBONI G, MARRADI P, PRADERIO R, DALL'AGNOLA A: Hyperornithinemia with hyperammonemia and homocitrullinuria in two brothers. *Acta Med Auxol* 14:121, 1982.

319. ENDO T, SAITO A, SAKAMOTO S, YACHI A: A case with hyperornithinemia, hyperammonemia, and homocitrullinuria. *Jpn J Med* 21:253, 1982.

320. SABETTA G, LOMBARDI M, CASTRO M, SCAPATICCI A, GIAMPAOLO R, D'IPPOLITI M, LUCIDI V: Iperammoniemia, iperornitinemia, omocitrullinuria: Descrizione di un caso. *Agg Pediatr* 31:479, 1980.

321. OTTEN A, BUERGER U, BACHMANN C, HILLIG U, WOLF H: Late diagnosis of and therapeutical approach to the HHH syndrome, in *Abstracts of the Third International Symposium on Inborn Error of Metabolism in Humans. March 7–9, Munich.* Basel, Karger, 1984, p 102.

322. HAASS C, PEDICINO R, SABETTA G, PANERO A, COLARIZZI P: Hyperornithinemia, hyperammonemia and homocitrullinuria (HHH syndrome) with neonatal onset and favourable evolution. *Ital J Pediatr* 12:143, 1986.

323. HALVORSEN S: Personal communication, 1988.

324. HAUST DM, GORDON BA: Letter to the editor: Ultra-structural changes in the mitochondria in disorders of ornithine metabolism. *Pediatr Res* 14:1411, 1980.

325. HAUST DM, GATFIELD PD, GORDON BA: Ultrastructure of hepatic mitochondria in a child with hyperornithinemia, hyperammonemia, and homocitrullinuria. *Hum Pathol* 12:212, 1981.

326. GORDON BA, GATFIELD DP, HAUST DM: The hyperornithinemia, hyperammonemia, homocitrullinuria syndrome: An ornithine transport defect remediable with ornithine supplements. *Clin Invest Med* 10:329, 1987.

327. WINTER MS, PEREZ-ATAYADE AR, LEVY ML, SHIH VE: Unique hepatic ultrastructural changes in a patient with hyperornithinemia, hyperammonemia and homocitrullinuria. *Pediatr Res* 14:583, 1980.

328. METOKI K, HOMMES FA, DYKEN P, KELLOES C, TREFZ J: Ultra-structural changes in fibroblast mitochondria of a patient with HHH-syndrome. *J Inherited Metab Dis* 7:147, 1984.

329. SHIH VE, MANDELL R: Metabolic defect in hyperornithinemia. *Lancet* 2:1522, 1974.

330. BRIGGS S, FREEDLAND RA: Effect of ornithine and lactate on urea synthesis in isolated hepatocytes. *Biochem J* 160:205, 1976.

331. GREENSTEIN JP, WINITZ M, GULLINO P, BIRNBAUM SM, OTEY MC: Studies on the metabolism of amino acids and related compounds in vivo. III. Prevention of ammonia toxicity by arginine and related compounds. *Arch Biochem Biophys* 64:342, 1956.

332. NATHANS D, FAHEY JL, SHIP AG: Sites of origin and removal of blood ammonia formed during glycine infusion: Effect of L-arginine. *J Lab Clin Med* 51:124, 1958.

333. BRUSILOW SW, BATSHAW ML: Arginine therapy of argininosuccinase deficiency. *Lancet* 1:124, 1979.

334. SIMELL O, PERHEENTUPA J, RAPOLA J, VISAKORPI JK, ESKELIN LE: Lysinuric protein intolerance. *Am J Med* 59:229, 1975.

335. RAJANTIE J, SIMELL O, RAPOLA J, PERHEENTUPA J: Lysinuric protein intolerance: A two-year trial of dietary supplementation therapy with citrulline and lysine. *J Pediatr* 97:927, 1980.

336. ARONSON DL, DIWAN JJ: Uptake of ornithine by rat liver mitochondria. *Biochemistry* 20:7064, 1981.

337. SHIH VE: Regulation of ornithine metabolism. *Enzyme* 26:254, 1981.

338. METOKI K, HOMMES FA: A possible rate limiting factor in urea synthesis by isolated hepatocytes: The transport of ornithine into hepatocytes and mitochondria. *Int J Biochem* 16:1155, 1984.

339. METOKI K, HOMMES FA: The uptake of ornithine and lysine by isolated hepatocytes and fibroblasts. *Int J Biochem* 16:833, 1984.

340. HOMMES FA, KITCHINGS L, ELLER AG: The uptake of ornithine and lysine by rat liver mitochondria. *Biochem Med* 30:313, 1983.

341. RAIJMAN L: Citrulline synthesis in rat tissues and liver content of carbamoyl phosphate and ornithine. *Biochem J* 138:225, 1974.

342. BRYLA J, HARRIS EJ: Accumulation of ornithine and citrulline in rat liver mitochondria in relation to citrulline formation. *FEBS Lett* 72:331, 1976.

343. METOKI K, HOMMES FA: The pH of mitochondria of fibroblasts from a hyperornithinaemia, hyperammonaemia, homocitrullin uria-syndrome patient. *J Inherited Metab Dis* 7:9, 1984.

344. GRAY RGF, HILL SE, POLLITT RJ: Studies on the pathway from ornithine to proline in cultured skin fibroblasts with reference to the defect in hyperornithinaemia with hyperammonaemia and homocitrullinuria. *J Inherited Metab Dis* 6:143, 1983.

345. GRAY RGF, HILL SE, POLLITT RJ: Reduced ornithine catabolism in cultured fibroblasts and phytohaemagglutinin-stimulated lymphocytes from a patient with hyperornithinaemia, hyperammonaemia and homocitrullinuria. *Clin Chim Acta* 118:141, 1982.

346. OYANAGI K, AOYAMA T, TSUCHIYAMA A, NAKAO T, UETSUJI N, WAGATSUMA K, TSUGAWA S: A new type of hyperlysinaemia due to a transport defect of lysine into mitochondria. *J Inherited Metab Dis* 9:313, 1986.

347. RAJANTIE J, SIMELL O, PERHEENTUPA J: "Basolateral" and mitochondrial membrane transport defect in the hepatocytes in lysinuric protein intolerance. *Acta Paediatr Scand* 72:65, 1983.

348. SHIH VE, MANDELL R: Defective ornithine metabolism in the syndrome of hyperornithinaemia, hyperammonaemia and homocitrullinuria. *J Inherited Metab Dis* 4:95, 1981.

349. CARSON NA, SCALLY BG, NEILL DW, CARRE IJ: Saccharopinuria: A new inborn error of lysine metabolism. *Nature* 218:679, 1968.

350. SIMELL O, VISAKORPI JK, DONNER M: Saccharopinuria. *Arch Dis Child* 47:52, 1972.

351. SIMELL O, SIPILÄ I, RAJANTIE J: Hyperlysinemia with hyperammonemia and homocitrullinuria. *Pediatr Res* 14:174, 1980.

352. CARTER AL, ELLER AG, RUFO S, METOKI K, HOMMES FA: Further evidence for a separate enzymic entity for the synthesis of homocitrulline, distinct from the regular ornithine transcarbamylase. *Enzyme* 32:26, 1984.

353. MACI E, BALDONI G, GRAZI E: On the biosynthesis of creatine, intramitochondrial localization of transamidinase from rat kidney. *FEBS Lett* 55:91, 1975.

354. BERSON EL, SCHMIDT SY, RABIN AR: Plasma amino acids in hereditary retina disease: Ornithine, lysine, and taurine. *Br J Ophthalmol* 60:142, 1976.

355. VALLE D, WALSER M, BRUSILOW S, KAISER-KUPFER MI: Unpublished observations.

356. HOLMGREN G: Effect of low, normal and high dietary protein intake on urinary amino acid excretion and plasma aminogram in children. *Nutr Metab* 16:223, 1974.

CHAPTER **20**

UREA CYCLE ENZYMES

SAUL W. BRUSILOW
ARTHUR L. HORWICH

1. *The urea cycle, which consists of a series of five biochemical reactions, has two roles. In order to prevent the accumulation of toxic nitrogenous compounds, the urea cycle incorporates nitrogen not used for net biosynthetic purposes into urea, which serves as the waste nitrogen product in mammals. The urea cycle also contains several of the biochemical reactions required for the* de novo *synthesis of arginine.*
2. *Five well documented diseases (each with considerable genetic and phenotypic variability) have been described, each representing a defect in the biosynthesis of one of the normally expressed enzymes of the urea cycle. Four of these five diseases, deficiencies of carbamyl phosphate synthetase (CPSD), ornithine transcarbamylase (OTCD), argininosuccinic acid synthetase (ASD), and argininosuccinase (ALD), are characterized by signs and symptoms induced by the accumulation of precursors of urea, principally ammonium and glutamine. The most dramatic clinical presentation of these four diseases occurs in full-term infants with no obstetric risk factors who appear normal for 24 to 48 h and then develop progressive lethargy, hypothermia, and apnea all related to very high plasma ammonium levels. The encephalopathy is characterized by brain edema and swollen astrocytes, the cause of which is unclear although the cell swelling has been attributed to intraglial accumulation of glutamine resulting in osmotic shifts of water into the cell. These four diseases also may present later in infancy, childhood, and adulthood with episodic mental status changes (lethargy, behavioral abnormalities) usually accompanied by vomiting in childhood.*

   A fifth disease, arginase deficiency, is characterized by a clinical picture consisting of progressive spastic tetraplegia and mental retardation; symptomatic hyperammonemia occurs neither as severely or as commonly as in the other four diseases.

   Apart from ornithine transcarbamylase deficiency, which is inherited as an X-linked disorder, the other four diseases are inherited as autosomal recessive traits.

   For fetuses at risk, antenatal diagnosis is available by a number of methods, particular to each disease, including enzyme analysis of fibroblasts cultured from aminocytes, in utero liver biopsy, and DNA analysis.
3. *Molecular genetic analysis of the urea cycle enzymes has addressed their structure and expression and has permitted diagnosis and, in some cases, direct analysis of mutations affecting them. Using the cloned cDNAs as probes, expression in liver of RNAs for all the enzymes has been observed to be increased several-fold by starvation. RNA coding for carbamyl phosphate synthetase (CPS) is detected almost exclusively in the liver and translates a precursor protein representing the product of fusion of two ancestral prokaryotic subunits, joined with an NH_2-terminal mitochondrial targeting sequence. A restriction fragment length polymorphism (RFLP) in the human CPS locus is useful in prenatal diagnosis of deficiency. Like CPS I, ornithine transcarbamylase (OTC) is also expressed principally in the liver, and its subunit is translated as a precursor, comprising an NH_2-terminal mitochondrial targeting sequence that functions via midportion structure and net positive charge, joined with a mature portion that resembles prokaryotic transcarbamylases. Gene deletions have been observed in approximately 10 percent of affected males. In several additional pedigrees point mutations have been observed in a Taq I recognition sequence. Prenatal diagnosis can be offered to most females established as heterozygous carriers by pedigree analysis, protein loading, or allopurinol testing, using several RFLPs identified within the locus. Argininosuccinate synthetase (AS) is programmed from a single locus, but a large number of homologous processed pseudogenes are localized throughout the genome. Expression of AS mRNA has been studied in cultured cells, where the level of mRNA is greatly increased in response to canavanine treatment and repressed by the presence of arginine. The AS coding sequence has been successfully transferred into cultured cells using recombinant retroviruses, providing a potential therapeutic approach to AS deficiency. The cloned cDNA has also been employed in S1 nuclease analysis of mutant mRNAs to reveal heterogeneity in the location of mutation. Such analysis may also assist prenatal diagnostic study. Human argininosuccinate lyase (AL) closely resembles the enzyme from yeast and exhibits striking similarity to Δ crystallin of the lens. Immunoblotting of extracts from mutant cell lines reveals heterogeneity of human mutation at this locus. Arginase in human liver is a cytosolic enzyme whose coding sequence does not hybridize with sequences encoding the nonhepatic, mitochondrial form of the enzyme. The cDNA for the human liver enzyme has been used to identify an RFLP that should be useful in prenatal diagnosis.*
4. *Treatment requires restriction of dietary protein intake and activation of other pathways of waste nitrogen synthesis and excretion. For patients deficient in carbamyl phosphate synthetase, ornithine transcarbamylase, and argininosuccinic acid synthetase, treatment with sodium benzoate and sodium phenylacetate activates the synthesis of hippurate and phenylacetylglutamine, which serve as waste nitrogen products. In patients deficient in argininosuccinic acid synthetase and argininosuccinase, supplementation of the diet with arginine promotes the synthesis of citrulline in the former and argininosuccinate in the latter, both of which serve as waste nitrogen products.*

The urea cycle serves two purposes: (1) it contains, in part, the biochemical reactions required for the *de novo* biosynthesis and degradation of arginine, and (2) it incorporates nitrogen atoms not retained for net biosynthetic purposes into urea,

Nonstandard abbreviations used in this chapter are: AL = argininosuccinase; AS = argininosuccinic acid synthetase; Can^+ = canavanine resistant; cDNA = complementary DNA; CP = carbamyl phosphate; CPS = carbamylphosphate synthetase I; LTR = long terminal repeat; mRNA = messenger RNA; NAG = *N*-acetylglutamate; OTC = ornithine transcarbamylase; RFLP = restriction fragment length polymorphism, Spf = sparse fur; Spf/ash = sparse fur/abnormal skin and hair. When these abbreviations are followed by a D, a deficiency of that enzyme is implied.

which serves as a waste nitrogen product. Campbell's[1] review of the comparative biochemistry of nitrogen metabolism describes other waste nitrogen products (ammonium and purines) found in other animals.

It has also been proposed[2] that the urea cycle plays an important role in the disposal of bicarbonate and hence in pH homeostasis. A number of arguments against this view have been offered.[3] Perhaps the strongest case against this function of the urea cycle can be found in patients with complete, or nearly so, defects in one of the enzymes of the urea cycle; apart from respiratory alkalosis related to the stimulatory effect of ammonium on respiration, these patients have little evidence of a disorder of pH homeostasis.

A defect in the ureagenic pathway has two consequences; arginine becomes an essential amino acid[4] (except in arginase deficiency where the enzyme defect results in a failure of degradation of arginine) and nitrogen atoms accumulate in a variety of molecules, the pattern of which varies according to the specific enzymatic defect although plasma levels ammonium and glutamine are commonly increased in patients not under metabolic control.

WASTE NITROGEN DISPOSAL

Ureagenesis[5-10] is described in Fig. 20-1 and Table 20-1, which represent summaries of the biochemical pathway; waste nitrogen disposal is far more complex requiring interorgan, intrahepatic, and cellular compartmentation relationships in the conversion to urea of nitrogen not used for net biosynthetic purposes. Although it has been known for decades that ammonium and aspartate are the sources of nitrogen for ureagenesis, the pathways from amino acid nitrogen to ammonium and aspartate have been less clear.

Intrahepatic Sources of Nitrogen for Ureagenesis (Fig. 20-2)

It was proposed on theoretical grounds[12] that intramitochondrial ammonium for the CPS reaction was derived from the oxidative deamination of glutamate by glutamate dehydrogenase. Although this interpretation is commonly accepted, attempts to verify this hypothesis in respiring mitochrondria have repeatedly shown that the vast portion of glutamate is not deaminated but rather transaminated,[13,14] suggesting that glutamate is a poor precursor for citrulline biosynthesis. The virtual absence of experimental evidence supporting the hypothesis that oxidative deamination of glutamate via glutamate dehydrogenase is a source of ammonium for the biosynthesis of citrulline and urea has led some to conclude that "Studies of glutamate dehydrogenase in liver have failed to yield any clear consensus of the role of this enzyme,"[15] or "It is still not possible to define the role of this enzyme in animal tissues."[16] McGivan and Chappel[17] proposed that the purine nucleotide cycle in liver might be the source of ammonium for ureagenesis, a hypothesis that Krebs et al.[18] showed to be untenable. Häussinger[19] has offered a novel hypothesis—a glutamine cycle. He suggested that portal vein ammonium is converted to both urea and glutamine in a 2:1 ratio; glutamine is synthesized, released to the circulation, and returned to the liver to

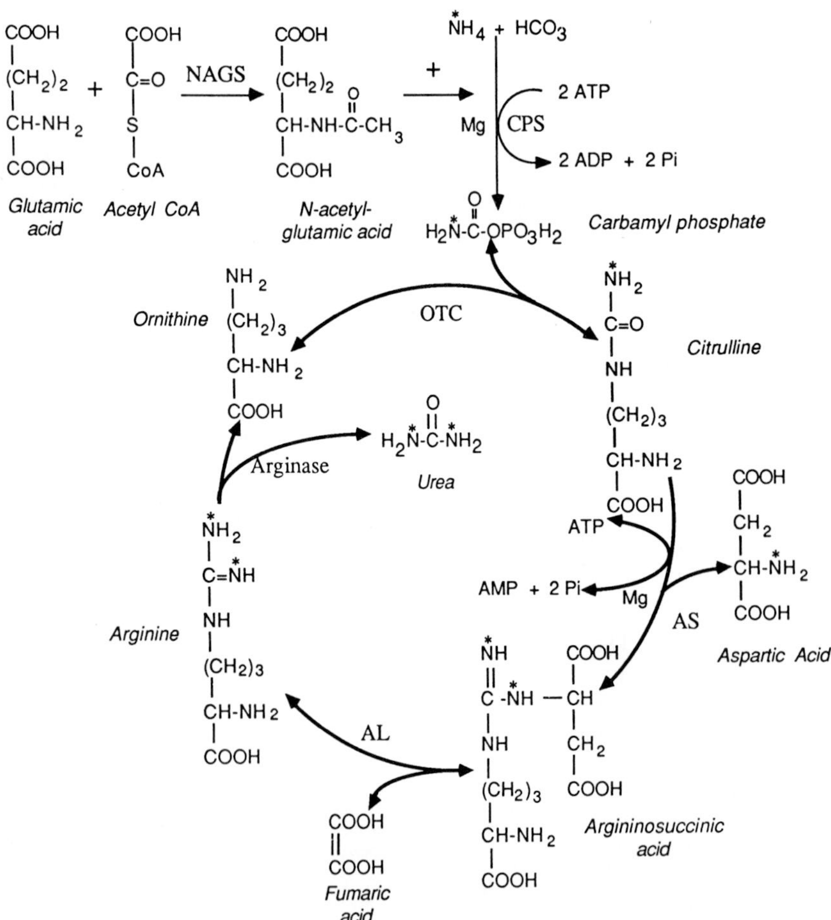

Fig. 20-1 The substrates, products, and cofactors required for ureagenesis. The asterisks denote waste nitrogen atoms. AS = argininosuccinc acid synthetase; AL = argininosuccinase; CPS = carbamyl phosphate synthetase; NAGS = N-acetylglutamate synthetase; OTC = ornithine transcarbamylase.

Table 20-1 The Enzymes of the Urea Cycle*

Enzyme	*Compartment*	*Activity*	M_r	*pH opt*	K_m, *mM*	*Equilibrium constant*	*Tissue distribution*
N-acetyl glutamate synthetase EC 2.3.11	Mitochondrial matrix	0.30–1.49	200,000	8.5	Glu, 3.0 Ac CoA 0.7 Arg, 0.01	Irreversible	Liver, intestine, kidney (trace) spleen
Carbamyl Phosphate Synthetase Ec 6.3.4.16	Mitochondrial matrix	279	310,000 dimer	6.8–7.6	NH_4, 0.8 HCO_3, 6.7 Mg ATP, 1.1 NAG, 0.1	Irreversible	Liver, intestine, kidney (trace)
Ornithine Transcarbamylase EC 2.1.3.3	Mitochondrial matrix	6600	108,000 trimer	7.7	CP, 0.16 Orn, 0.40	$\frac{(\text{Cit})\,(\text{P})}{(\text{Orn})\,(\text{CP})} = 10^5$	Liver, intestine, kidney (trace)
Argininosuccinic acid synthetase EC 6.3.4.5	Cytosol	90	185,000 tetramer	8.7	Asp, .03 Cit, .03	$\frac{(\text{ASA})\,(\text{AMP})\,(\text{Mg PP})\,(2\text{H})}{(\text{Cit})\,(\text{Asp})\,(\text{Mg ATP})} = 0.89$†	Liver, kidney fibroblasts, brain (trace)
Argininosuccinase EC 4.3.2.1	Cytosol	220	173,200 tetramer	7.5	Asp, 0.017 Cit, 0.016 ATP, 0.041	$\frac{(\text{Arg})\,(\text{fumarate})}{\text{ASA}} = 11.4 \times 10^{-3}$	Liver, kidney, brain, fibroblasts
Arginase EC 3.5.3.1	Cytosol	86,600	107,000 tetramer	9.5	Arg, 10.5	Irreversible	Liver, erythrocytes, kidney, lens, brain (trace)

*Enzyme Activity is expressed as micromoles per hour per gram wet weight. Apart from the equilibrium constants, the values described are those of human liver.
†The monomers may have substantial catalytic activity.[10]
SOURCE: Table assembled from Ratner,[5] Snodgrass,[6] Meijer and Hensgens,[7] Jackson et al.,[8] Beaudet et al.,[9] Lusty,[10] and Bachmann et al.[156]
†At pH = 7.0

Table 20-2 Concentration of Urea Cycle Intermediates in Rat Liver

	μmol per g wet weight
Carbamyl phosphate	0.001
Ornithine	0.2–0.6
Citrulline	0.03–0.1
Aspartate	0.3–3.5
Argininosuccinate	0.034
Arginine	0.02–0.1

SOURCE: Data taken from Meijer and Hensgens,[7] except for carbamyl phosphate, which was taken from Cooper et al.[23]

be deamidated. He described the urea cycle as a high capacity-low affinity ammonium detoxification system, whereas glutamine synthetase behaves as a low capacity, high affinity system.

Jungermann[20] reviewed the role of "metabolic zonation" in the liver as it pertains nitrogen homeostasis. It is proposed that periportal hepatocytes predominantly contain enzymes that catalyze transamination reactions and ureagenesis, whereas perivenous hepatocytes predominantly contain enzymes that catalyze the amidation or deamination of glutamate to glutamine or ammonium and α-ketoglutarate, respectively.

Recently Cooper et al.[21] suggested that in vivo no more than 20 percent (and possibly much less) the α-amino moiety of liver glutamate is deaminated, but rather it is predominantly transaminated to aspartate and incorporated into urea. These studies were done in a series of three experiments where ^{13}N-labeled glutamate, alanine, and glutamine (amide) were each injected into the portal vein, following which the liver was freeze clamped at intervals of 5 to 60 s and the distribution of the label described. Aspartate and urea were promptly labeled after [^{13}N]alanine and [^{13}N]glutamate were injected but not after [^{13}N]glutamine (amide). Ammonium and citrulline were not labeled, suggesting that little glutamate was deaminated. The absence of incorporation of glutamine nitrogen into the urea cycle in these in vivo experiments does not support the glutamine channeling hypothesis of Meijer.[22] The rapidity of nitrogen exchange among the linked transaminases in these and other studies[23] was striking: within 10 s of the injection of the labeled amino acids or ammonium. In previous studies[23] these authors showed that intraportal vein injection of [^{13}N]ammonium resulted in labeling of citrulline.

From these studies it may be concluded that, although glutamate may be deaminated, it is not a major source of ammonium for the CPS reaction. As described below, extrahepatic glutamine metabolism provides the single most important source of ammonium for the CPS reaction. However, within the liver there are a number of other amino acids that are deaminated and may provide ammonium for ureagenesis, e.g., histidine, tryptophan, threonine, and lysine.

Extrahepatic Sources of Nitrogen for Ureagenesis (Fig. 20-2)

The Intestines. In a series of studies of the metabolism of the autoperfused rat intestine, Windmueller[24,25] showed not only that glutamine carbon atoms were an important respiratory fuel but also that glutamine nitrogen was converted to the urea precursors ammonium, citrulline, and alanine, all of which were released into the portal circulation. While alanine and ammonium are taken up by the liver, citrulline apparently is not but rather is transported to the kidney where it is converted to arginine.[26]

Kidney. Rat kidney uptake of citrulline is approximately equivalent to its rate of intestinal release.[26] This observation is compatible with the report that anephric animals incorporate

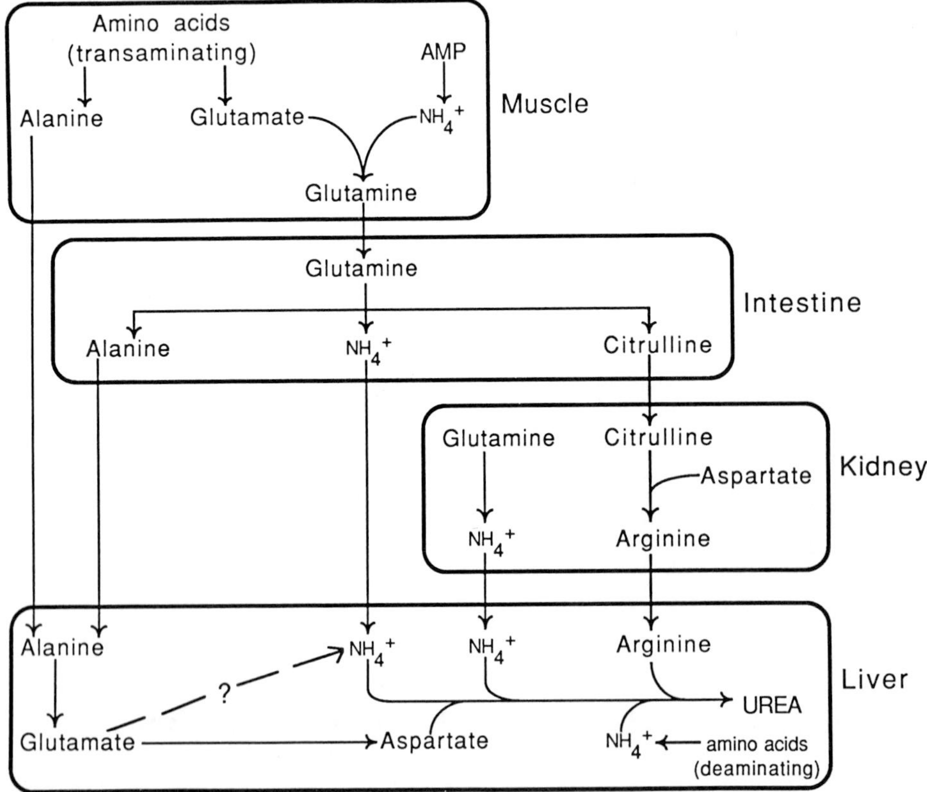

Fig. 20-2 The pathways of waste nitrogen synthesis from amino acids. Muscle by virtue of its production of alanine and glutamine is the major source of nitrogen destined for incorporation into urea. The role of the intestines, kidney, and liver are outlined as desribed in the text. AMP = adenosine monophosphate.

little citrulline into liver.[27] While it is likely that similar relationships exist in humans, some caution may be warranted because of the different response of humans to an arginine-free diet as compared with that of any other species.[28]

That the kidney may be an extrahepatic source of ammonium is suggested by the long known observation that the ammonium concentration of the renal vein exceeds that of the renal artery, a consequence of renal glutaminase activity. Thus, the kidney may supply ammonium directly for the CPS reaction and, as described above, provide another waste nitrogen atom by catalyzing the synthesis of arginine from citrulline and aspartate via renal AS.

Muscle. Because glutamine is constantly being extracted from the circulation by the intestine, a potent source of glutamine must be found elsewhere. The most likely source of glutamine is muscle; several studies have shown a net release of glutamine from muscle in vivo[29,30] and in vitro.[31] The biosynthetic pathway for muscle glutamine synthesis is not entirely clear although glutamine synthetase does play a role.[29] The source of ammonia for amidation is also unclear; purine nucleotide deamination is a possibility.[32,33]

Alanine production by muscle, via transamination of pyruvate, represents another important nitrogen precursor for ureagenesis.

Figure 20-2 presents an integrated view of the interorgan relationships required for synthesis of urea. Muscle appears to be the starting point of waste nitrogen disposal via transamination of amino acid nitrogen to alanine and glutamate and thence amidation of glutamate to produce glutamine.

THE BIOCHEMISTRY OF THE UREA CYCLE

The enzymes, substrates, and cofactors required for ureagenesis are described in Fig. 20-1 and Tables 20-1 and 20-2. CPS, a mitochondrial matrix enzyme, catalyzes the biosynthesis of carbamyl phosphate from ammonium and bicarbonate; N-acetylglutamate (NAG, synthesized from glutamate and acetyl CoA) is an allosteric cofactor for this enzyme and may be an important regulator of ureagenesis (see below). Although CPS is conventionally considered to be active in its dimeric form, Lusty[10] has shown in studies of the purified enzyme that the enzyme activity is mainly in the monomeric form. OTC, also a mitochondrial matrix enzyme, catalyzes the biosynthesis of citrulline from ornithine and carbamyl phosphate (see Chap. 19 for a discussion of the mitochondrial import of ornithine). Citrulline is exported to the cytosol where it condenses with aspartate via AS to form argininosuccinate, which is cleaved to arginine and fumarate by AL. Arginine is subsequently hydrolyzed by arginase to urea and ornithine, the latter again to be transcarbamylated to citrulline.

Studies of urea cycle enzyme activities in the human fetus reveal activity by 10 weeks of gestation; at approximately 20 weeks gestation enzyme activity is similar to that found at birth, which is approximately 50 percent of adult values.[34]

Although the mutant enzymes are mainly characterized by a reduction of their activity under all conditions, a number of other biochemical characteristics have been reported, principally for OTC. K_m mutants for both substrates have been found, as well as sensitivity to other factors such as pH, temperature, and substrates.[35–42]

Also relevant to inborn errors of ureagenesis is the understanding that the α and ω nitrogen atoms of ornithine do not normally serve as waste nitrogen products; only ammonium nitrogen and aspartate nitrogen (Fig. 20-1) constitute waste nitrogen atoms which are incorporated into urea, argininosuccinate, and arginine.

Regulation of Ureagenesis

Enzyme Induction and Repression. Schimke[43] showed that the rat liver content of all urea cycle enzymes increased threefold in a coordinated manner as dietary protein was increased. This tripling in enzyme concentration occurred 4 days after an increase in dietary protein. Similar findings have been reported in primates.[44] More recent studies in rats suggest that the liver urea cycle enzyme activity induction is complete in 30 h.[45] Analysis of CPS and OTC proteins by an immunoblotting technique revealed a similar response to dietary protein.[46] Intestinal OTC, however, does not appear to respond to a dietary protein increase.[47]

In an attempt to evaluate the role of the enzyme content on regulation of ureagenesis Das and Waterlow[45] compared nitrogen excretion in two groups of rats on isonitrogenous diets; one diet contained casein and the other glycine as the sole nitrogen source. Urinary urea nitrogen excretion was higher in the latter group, but urea cycle enzyme activity was lower suggesting the capacity of urea cycle enzymes as determined by in vitro analysis may not be a reliable guide to ureagenic capacity. In support of this are the findings of Rafoth and Onstad[48] who found that urea production in men after a test meal of 2 g protein per kilogram was the same following a 3-day period of a low (1 g/kg per day) or high (3 g/kg per day) protein intake.

Regulatory Cofactors and Substrates. Ornithine has long been thought to be a regulator of ureagenesis. Cohen et al.[49] observed that in the absence of ornithine, carbamyl phosphate synthesis is progressively impaired in isolated mitochondria, presumably as a result of the inhibitory effect of accumulated carbamyl phosphate on CPS. Alternatively it has been suggested that ornithine entry into the mitochondrion is rate limiting for citrulline biosynthesis.[50] In vivo evidence supporting a role for ornithine in ureagenesis was suggested by Valle et al.[51] who described hypoammonemia in patients with gyrate atrophy of the retina who were severely hyperornithinemic on a normal protein intake. When protein intake was reduced, plasma ornithine levels decreased toward normal; despite the decreased nitrogen intake, plasma ammonium levels increased.

Cohen et al.[52] recently demonstrated that mitochondria preloaded with ornithine and subsequently incubated with radiolabeled ornithine produced citrulline of the same specific activity as the external ornithine, while matrix ornithine was unlabeled. This convincing evidence of channeling has a number of interesting implications for ornithine metabolism, the anatomy of matrix enzyme, and the substrate pool.

A novel regulatory role of ornithine on carbamyl phosphate degradation suggests that the absence of intramitochondrial ornithine leads to the degradation of carbamyl phosphate by an as yet incompletely defined enzyme.[53]

NAG, a product of glutamate and acetyl CoA via NAG synthetase, an intramitochondrial matrix enzyme (Fig. 20-1), has received much attention as a regulator of ureagenesis. The vast literature on this subject cannot be covered here (for reviews see Refs. 7, 54, and 55).

Almost 40 years ago it was known that a glutamate derivative later shown to be NAG was required to promote the biosynthesis of citrulline. Shortly thereafter, it was identified as an allosteric activator for CPS, its arginine activated synthetase identified and its degradation pathway described.

That NAG has an important physiological role was suggested by the finding that its mitochondrial level increased as dietary protein was increased; on low and high protein diets liver NAG content varied from 10 to 20 nmol/g to 100 to 150 nmol/g net weight, respectively.[56] Because the activity of NAG synthetase was unaffected, it was later suggested that increased levels of NAG are a function of the substrate- (glutamate-) stimulated flux.[57] Ammonium has also been shown to cause an increase in NAG content in isolated hepatocytes.[58] Once synthesized NAG is exported to the cystosol where it is deacylated via acylaminoacid acylases.[59]

In a series of experiments Meijer and his colleagues[60–62] have presented evidence emphasizing the role of NAG in regulating ureagenesis via its effect on CPS. These authors suggest that in isolated hepatocytes the control of ureagenesis at constant concentrations of ammonia is entirely a function of NAG-regulated CPS activity. Lund and Wiggins,[63,64] however, have suggested that NAG may not be a regulator of CPS, based on the finding that (1) when NAG is measured directly by deacylation (as compared to usual method of coupled enzyme reactions), its level is much higher than previously reported, and (2) the K_a of NAG is lower than previously reported.

An additional factor in the possible role of NAG as a regulator of ureagenesis is the effect of arginine on NAG synthetase. In vitro, arginine is an allosteric activator of this enzyme.[65] The relevance of this finding to the in vivo situation has been questioned by Cheung and Raijman.[67] Furthermore, it was[73] found that the hyperammonemia induced by arginine deprivation in patients with OTCD and ALD was associated with orotic aciduria, suggesting continued carbamyl phosphate synthesis. Furthermore, animal studies[57] revealed an increase of liver *N*-acetyl glutamate levels and CPS activity after intraperitoneal injection of an amino acid mixture regardless of the presence or absence of arginine in the mixture.

Another view of regulation of ureagenesis by Cohen et al.[66] holds that free ammonia, NH_3 (not ammonium, NH_4^+), is an important determinant of carbamyl phosphate synthesis. They suggest that because ammonia is the substrate for the CPS reaction and because the intramitochondrial ammonia level is approximately 7μM, well below the apparent K_m for carbamyl phosphate synthetase (determined by them to be 13 μM), changes in mitochondrial ammonia levels would have rapid and important quantitative effects on ureagenesis and thereby be the principal short-term regulator of ammonium levels and urea synthesis.

Hormonal Effects. Cohen[68] has concluded that the effects of many hormones (corticosteroids, glucagon, growth hormone, cyclic AMP) on the levels or activity of urea cycle enzymes are secondary effects of gluconeogenesis, ATP production, or other metabolic processes. Thyroxine, on the other hand, is known to induce urea cycle enzymes in amphibian metamorphosis. More recently glucagon has been shown to result in increased NAG levels and increased citrulline synthesis in isolated mitochondria.[69]

MOLECULAR ANALYSIS OF UREA CYCLE ENZYMES

Carbamyl Phosphate Synthetase

Molecular analysis of mammalian CPS has enabled prediction of the structure of this large hepatic mitochondrial enzyme and revealed it to be the product of fusion of two ancestral functional domains that catalyse glutamine amide transfer and synthesis of carbamylphosphate. The molecular analysis of the enzyme has in fact been facilitated by the large subunit size, 160,000 daltons. While in liver this protein constitutes as much as 15 to 30 percent of mitochondrial protein and 4 percent of total protein, this is a feature of stability of mitochondrial enzymes, rather than a high rate of synthesis, and the mRNA is of moderately low abundance. However, because the mRNA encoding the subunit is necessarily large, enrichment for it was accomplished in a straightforward manner using sucrose gradient fractionation of poly A^+ mRNA from rat liver.[70] A cDNA clone synthesized from the enriched mRNA was identified by hybrid-selected translation, and this clone was used in turn to identify additional rat and human cDNA clones. Northern analysis using these cDNAs identified a 5-kb mRNA in liver. Developmental analysis of CPS mRNA in rat liver revealed its first appearance late in gestation at day 17, a rise to 30 to 40 percent of adult levels over the following 3 to 4 days, then a decline at the time of birth followed by a slow rise over a 3-week period to adult levels.

Treatment of rats with dibutyryl cAMP or dexamethasone led to a twofold increase of CPS RNA in liver, and starvation for 5 days led to a 37-fold increase in RNA.[71] When levels of CPS RNA were examined in rat hepatoma cells, the line 5123D was found to contain levels of twofold higher than normal adult liver, whereas the line 3294A was devoid of CPS RNA.[72] The cloned human cDNA was also used to map the single-copy gene to the short arm of chromosome 2 using somatic cell hybrids.[70]

Sequence analysis of the cloned rat CPS cDNA indicates that the corresonding mRNA contains a 5′ untranslated sequence of 139 bases, an open reading frame of 4500 nucleotides, and a 3′ untranslated sequence of 905 nucleotides, followed by a poly A tract.[73] Most remarkable is the coding sequence for the CPS I subunit precursor.[73] At its NH_2 terminus, the precursor contains 38 residues constituting a cleavable leader peptide that directs the precursor to mitochondria. When this coding sequence plus 55 codons from the mature portion of CPS were joined with the distal two-thirds of the coding sequence for the mature subunit of ornithine transcarbamylase, the in vitro synthesized hybrid protein was directed to isolated mitochondria.[74] Like other mitochondrial signal peptides analyzed to date, the CPS leader is highly basic in overall amino acid composition, containing four arginine residues, four lysine residues, and only a single aspartate residue.

The mature portion of the rat CPS precursor is strikingly homologous along its length to the CPS enzyme from both *Escherichia coli* and yeast, with 42 and 45 percent identical amino acids, respectively.[73] The latter enzymes comprise two different subunits encoded by separate genes (Fig. 20-3). The small subunit catalyzes transfer of the amide nitrogen from glutamine to a catalytic center for carbamyl phosphate synthesis located on the large subunit. The large subunit comprises two homologous halves, the apparent product of a gene duplication. By itself this subunit can catalyze synthesis of carba-

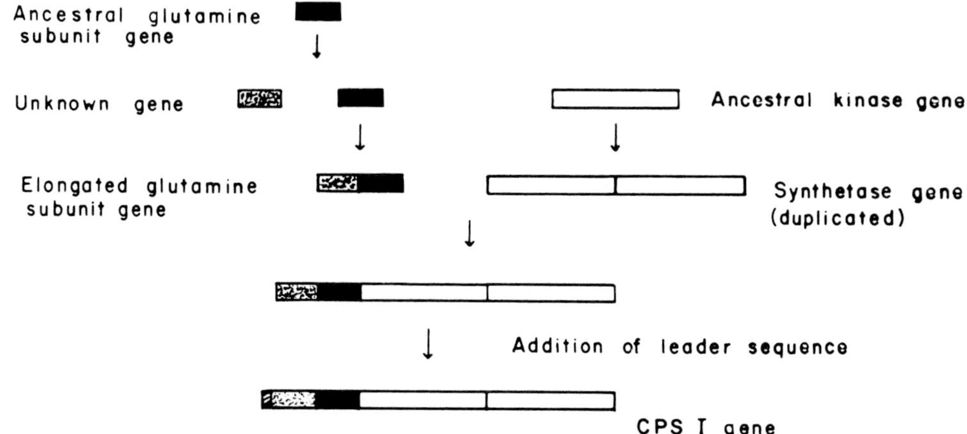

Fig. 20-3 Proposed evolution of carbamyl phosphate synthetase. An ancestral amide transfer gene fused with a leader peptide coding sequence and a synthetase gene to produce the mammalian CPS gene. *(From Nynoya et al.[76] Used by permission.)*

myl phosphate from ammonia, bicarbonate, and ATP.[75] The mammalian enzyme represents a precise gene fusion of the glutamine amide transfer domain corresponding to the small subunit at the NH_2 terminus with the synthetase domain, corresponding to the large subunit at the COOH terminus.[73,76] The glutamine hydrolytic site in *E. coli* and yeast contains a reactive cysteine residue,[77] but in the mammalian enzyme, which fails to catalyze glutamine hydrolysis, the cysteine is absent. While the hydrolytic site is lost, two ATP-binding sites present in the *E. coli* and yeast enzymes are retained in the mammalian enzyme and highly conserved in sequence.

The 3′ portion of the gene encoding rat CPS has been isolated, and the analysis suggests that this is a large gene; 13 exons encoding the COOH terminal, one-third of the protein spanned 29 kb of genomic DNA.[73] More recently, the 5′ flanking portion of the gene has been analyzed and found to contain canonical elements upstream from the site of transcriptional initiation, including a TATA sequence at −30 bases and a CAAT sequence at −88 bases. Enhancer elements have also been defined using analysis of CAT fusion constructs.[78]

Ornithine Transcarbamylase

Molecular genetic analysis of human ornithine transcarbamylase has involved characterization of a large X-linked gene that encodes a subunit precursor that is posttranslationally imported by mitochondria. The human OTC gene has been mapped, using somatic cell hybrids and *in situ* hybridization, to band p21.1 of the X chromosome[79] approximately 12 cM proximal to the Duchenne muscular dystrophy locus.[80] As predicted by this location, it is subject to X-chromosome inactivation in females, which has been elegantly demonstrated by the presence of patches of activity observed on *in situ* enzyme assay in the liver of a female heterozygous for OTC deficiency.[105] In liver, the OTC mRNA constitutes approximately 0.05 to 0.1 percent of poly A^+ mRNA, and cloning of this moderate abundance mRNA was facilitated by the preparation of immunoaffinity-enriched OTC mRNA from rat liver by Kraus and Rosenberg.[81] This enabled preparation of rat OTC cDNA clones[82] and in turn the isolation, by homology, of cDNA clones encoding the human OTC precursor.[83] Subsequent analysis of genomic clones identified using cloned cDNA indicates that the human OTC gene spans a region of greater than 85 kb and contains eight exons.[84,85]

Both human and mouse genomic clones containing the 5′-most sequences found in cloned cDNA have been studied.[85–87] In both cases, DNA sequence information has been obtained extending greater than 600 bp upstream from the translational initiation codon. In the case of the mouse gene, several transcriptional start sites have been identified using procedures of S1 nuclease mapping and primer extension analysis, with a major initiation site identified 136 bases upstream from the translational initiation codon. At a position 25 bases further upstream, a sequence TAACAA is found, and at a position 153 bases upstream, the sequence ATAAATA was identified. Whether these TATA-like sequences function as transcriptional regulatory elements remains to be determined. Some functional elements are apparently present in the 5′ flanking region of the mouse OTC gene because when an 800-bp segment of the 5′ flanking region was joined with the chloramphenicol acetyltransferase (CAT) gene and introduced into the human hepatoma line Hep G2, which expresses OTC enzyme activity at a low level, CAT activity was readily detected. No activity was observed when the promoterless plasmid pSVOCAT was transferred or when the same construct placing the 5′ flanking region in the reverse orientation was transferred.[86]

The 5′ flanking region of the human OTC gene has also been sequenced, and it bears striking homology to the mouse sequence.[87] Homology is observed at a level of approximately 80 percent extending from the translational initiation codon to a position 500 bases upstream, and homology of approximately 40 percent extends farther upstream through the additional 150 bases of sequence that has been analyzed. A multiplicity of transcriptional start sites has been observed for the human OTC message using the two procedures of S1 nuclease mapping and primer extension, with the most common sites at positions 95, 120, 150, 161, and 166 bases upstream from the translational initiation codon. Thus transcription of the human OTC gene appears to initiate not at a particular site but within a region of about 70 bases. Upstream from this region the human sequence contains the sequence CATA, centered at a position 198 bases upstream from the translational initiation codon. Given the diffuseness of transcriptional initiation, this sequence seems unlikely to function in the usual manner of a TATA box in directing efficient transcriptional initiation at a precise site 30 bases downstream. Upstream, the sequence CAAT is identified at −251 from the translational start codon, and additional TATA and CAAT sequences have been identified farther upstream. Situated at position −498 is the sequence GTGGAAAG, identical with the SV40 enhancer core sequence, followed 20 bases downstream by an almost perfect inverted repeat GAAAAGTG. To establish whether any of these sequences play a role in the regulation of OTC transcription, functional assays will be required.

The messenger RNAs encoded by human,[83] rat, [88] and mouse OTC[89] genes are approximately 1600 nucleotides in length, including approximately 150 bases of 5′ untranslated sequence, 1062 bases of sequence encoding the subunit precursor, and, as defined for rat OTC, 360 bases of 3′ untranslated sequence. The coding portion of the OTC subunit precursor includes a leader portion containing 32 codons and a mature portion comprising 322 codons. The latter region is much more highly conserved, with 93 percent homology between rat and human, while the former exhibits only 72 percent homology between these two species, indicating perhaps less evolutionary constraint upon it, permitting divergence.[88] Interestingly, the first exon of both human and mouse OTC genes contains the first 26 codons of the leader portion,[85,86] which as detailed below, provides sufficient information to direct mitochondrial localization of the OTC precursor. Thus, this exon could conceivably have arisen independently in evolution to direct mitochondrial localization.

The OTC leader peptide has been extensively studied as a model for elucidating the role of leader peptides in directing localization of nuclear-encoded mammalian mitochondrial matrix proteins. The precursors are translated in the cytosol on free polyribosomes and enter the mitochondria posttranslationally. Coincident with uptake, the leader peptides are cleaved by cation-dependent mitochondrial proteases to produce mature mitochondrial proteins.[90] The OTC precursor in particular is synthesized in the cytosol of hepatocytes as a 40,000-dalton precursor. It is then specifically recognized by the organelles, perhaps by outer membrane receptor molecules. Cytosolic factors may be required for this step.[91,92] The precursor is then translocated through both outer and inner mitochondrial membranes, apparently at points of contact between these membranes, in a step requiring an intact electrochemical gradient across the inner membrane.[93,94] Support for this mechanism of translocation comes from studies of two mitochondrial proteins of *Neurospora*[95] and from recent topological studies of an intermediate-size form that is observed during mitochondrial entry of the rat OTC precursor.[96] During membrane translocation, the OTC leader peptide is proteolytically cleaved by a cation-dependent protease in the matrix space,[97,98] and subsequently mature OTC subunits assemble in the matrix compartment into an enzymatically active trimer.[99] The OTC leader peptide alone has been shown to contain sufficient information to direct mitochondrial localization. When this peptide was joined with either of two proteins normally localized to the cystosol, the fusion protein was directed into mitochondria.[100,101] The features of the OTC leader peptide responsible for both mitochondrial localization and proteolytic processing have been addressed by synthesizing mutant OTC precursors from cloned cDNA in an in vitro system and then examining their uptake and cleavage by isolated rat liver mitochondria. The midportion of the human leader peptide from residues 8 to 22 is not only necessary but sufficient to direct mitochondrial localization and proteolytic processing of the OTC precursor.[102] In contrast, neither terminus of the leader is required[102] and the NH_2- terminal half of the leader peptide is not sufficient to direct mitochondrial localization. Not only was the penultimate COOH terminus dispensable,[102] but both import and proteolytic processing occurred even when the normal site of leader peptide cleavage was deleted.[103]

In addition to the midportion, basic residues in the OTC leader peptide play a critical functional role. Like other leaders examined to date, the OTC leader contains an abundance of these residues and is devoid of acidic residues. In particular, there are four arginines present in the human OTC leader peptide, and identically positioned arginines plus additional lysine residues are present in the rat and mouse leaders. There is a hierarchy of function to the arginines, with arginine 23, positioned in the leader midportion, being the most critical to both import and proteolytic processing. This residue appears to participate in a functional secondary structure, possibly an α helix.[102] The other basic residues in the OTC leader also function as a collective to produce a net positive charge to the peptide. Alteration of one or more of these basic residues to neutral or introduction of an acidic residue impairs mitochondrial localization.[103] Electrostatic interaction involving these residues may mediate traversal of a positively charged leader peptide through an inner membrane that is relatively charge-negative at its matrix aspect.[95]

Single amino acid substitutions at a host of additional positions in the human OTC leader peptide were without effect except in the cases of arginine 24 and leucine 26 where such substituted precursors were imported by mitochondria but proteolytically processed at unusual positions producing intermediate-size species.[103] Such species could constitute abnormal cleavage products or could be obligatory intermediates involved in a two-step cleavage pathway. Multiply substituted rat OTC precursors have also been examined. One precursor containing multiple single substitutions of glycine for leucine, at positions 5, 8, and 9, could not be imported. Nevertheless, this precursor could be cleaved when incubated with a mitochondrial matrix fraction, distinguishing as independent of each other in this case the signals governing mitochondrial localization and proteolytic processing.[104]

Synthetic peptides have also been employed to analyze leader function. A peptide containing residues 1 to 27 blocked uptake by isolated mitochondria of in vitro synthesized OTC precursor and of two other matrix-bound precursors. In contrast, a peptide containing residues 16 to 27 failed to block uptake.[105] The 1-27 peptide was shown to exhibit α-helical structural properties, particularly in the presence of cardiolipin, an anionic phospholipid that is unique to mitochondrial membranes. Evidence was also obtained from additional physical studies that the synthetic peptide is amphiphilic in character, with a hydrophilic character in one aspect and a hydrophobic character in the opposite.[106]

From the cloned cDNA the sequence of the mature portion of the OTC subunit has also been predicted, and this reveals two regions that are highly conserved with prokaryotic transcarbamylases, one including residues 53 to 62, which could potentially be involved with binding of the substrate carbamyl phosphate, and a second including residues 268 to 273, which could potentially be involved with the binding of ornithine.[84]

The cloned rat cDNA has been used to measure levels of OTC mRNA during development by dot blot analysis. RNA was first detected on day 14 of rat development at a level of 40 percent of adult levels and rose to a peak at day 20, dropped at the time of birth, then rose to adult levels during the second week after birth.[107] When adult rats were starved for 5 days the level of RNA increased sixfold. No change in RNA levels was observed following treatment with dibutyryl cAMP or dexamethasone.

The OTC cDNA has been expressed in several systems. Expression of the rat OTC precursor has been obtained in *E. coli* using a tac promoter, but a substantial portion of the synthesized precursor was apparently cleaved to a smaller form by a protease present in *E. coli.* The precursor was also synthesized in vitro using a coupled transcription-translation system derived from *E. coli,* and when this product was incubated with rat liver mitochondria, it was imported and proteolytically processed.[108] Expression of the human OTC precursor has also recently been programmed in *Saccharomyces cerevisiae* from a 2-μm plasmid in which the cDNA sequence was joined with a galactose operon promotor.[109] Expression of human OTC precursor in intact yeast cells was induced with galactose, and approximately 50 percent of the anti-OTC precipitable products were observed to be converted to the size of the mature subunit. The mature form was localized to the mitochondria in the matrix space. Furthermore, when human OTC was similarly expressed in an *S. cerevisiae* strain deficient in endogenous cytosolic yeast OTC, enzymatic activity in the transformed strain was detected in the mitochondrial matrix. Thus, mitochondrial import of the human OTC precursor is possible in *S. cerevisiae,* presumably by a mechanism evolutionarily related to that present in mammalian mitochondria. An important consequence of these studies is that the yeast system is amenable to classic genetic analysis and may provide a means to determine the genes involved in the uptake of mitochondrial proteins.

The OTC coding region has also been joined with the SV40 early region promoter, and this module was joined in turn with a module expressing a methotrexate-resistant dihydrofolate reductase. The sequences were introduced into cultured HeLa cells, which normally do not exhibit OTC enzymatic activity.[110] Following selection in increasing concentrations of methotrexate, cell lines were isolated that contained OTC enzyme activity at a level similar to that of normal human liver. Immunofluorescence studies revealed that the enzyme present in these cells was correctly localized to the mitochondria. The human OTC cDNA has also been inserted between the mouse metallothionein I promoter and the rat growth hormone gene and introduced into fertilized mouse eggs, following which transgenic mice were identified that unexpectedly exhibited expression of OTC mRNA and enzymatic activity exclusively in the testes of male mice.[111] Expression in these organs was observed in germ cells in the pachytene phase of meiosis.

In a similar experiment, a rat OTC cDNA construct programming expression from an SV40 early region promoter and SV40 downstream regulatory elements was injected into fertilized eggs derived from mating homozygous OTC deficient spf/ash female mice carrying the spf/ash (sparse fur/abnormal hair) mutation with normal C57/BL6 males.[112] One of 21 transgenic offspring, a male, had a normal coat in contrast to the coat abnormalities characteristic of spf/ash hemizygotes suggesting correction of the OTC deficiency in this transgenic animal. This animal's urine did not contain excessive amounts of orotic acid indicating correction of the metabolic disorder, and when sacrificed, a normal level of hepatic OTC enzyme activity was observed, demonstrating correction of OTC deficiency by germ line gene transfer.

A further series of transgenic mice has been produced using a DNA segment joining 800 bp of 5′ flanking sequence from the mouse OTC gene with the bacterial chloramphenicol acetyltransferase coding sequence.[113] Out of four transgenic strains examined, three failed to express CAT activity while one strain expressed low levels of CAT activity in the liver. Whether additional OTC sequences are required to gain consistent expression within the liver remains to be determined.

Argininosuccinic Acid Synthetase

Molecular studies of human AS have revealed interesting regulation of transcription and striking dispersion of AS pseudogenes. Isolation of AS cDNA clones was facilitated by a human cultured cell line which, when growth in media supplemented with the toxic arginine analog, canavanine, produces high levels of AS mRNA.[114] These cDNA clones subsequently were used to isolate and characterize AS genomic sequences and to perform molecular analysis of the mutations causing AS deficiency.

The active AS gene has been localized using somatic cell hybrids to the q34 region of chromosome 9.[115] The gene is 63 kb in size, and is divided into 14 exons, encoding an mRNA of approximately 1600 bases.[116]

Sequence analysis of the nearly full-length cloned AS cDNA reveals an open reading frame of 1236 nucleotides that encodes a protein of approximately 46,400 daltons.[117] The 5′ untranslated sequence of the AS message comprises 102 bases, and at a position 27 bases upstream from the translational start codon there are three in frame tandem arginine codons. These were originally postulated to influence the half-life of the AS message, possibly by interacting with arginyl tRNA. This hypothetical interaction could explain arginine-mediated repression of AS expression, but more recent studies have demonstrated that this repression also occurs in minigenes lacking these sequences.[118] Levels of AS RNA in adult rat liver increase 24-fold following starvation for 5 days and fivefold in response to treatment with either dibutyryl cAMP or dexamethasone.[73]

The 5′ flanking region of the gene has recently been analyzed and found to contain several putative regulatory sequences.[116,119,120] In addition to a TATAA sequence at position −30 there are three GGCGGGG hepatonucleotides similar to the consensus SP1 binding sequence, at positions −116 to −110 and −97 to −91 on the noncoding strand and −71 to −77 on the coding strand. Deletion of sequences to the 5′-most hepatonucleotide had no effect on expression of AS from a minigene plasmid construction introduced into RPMI 2650 cells. However, partial deletion of the hepatonucleotide reduced expression twelvefold, and complete deletion reduced expression fiftyfold.[121] At positions −137 to −129 there is the sequence TGTGAACGC, which resembles an element found in the promoter regions of yeast genes that are derepressed during general amino acid starvation. Deletion of this region from a minigene construct produced a loss of arginine regulation.[121] Farther upstream, at −470, is an octameric sequence, AGAAGTGA, which is also found in the 5′ flanking region of the genes encoding factor VIII and albumin.

These various upstream sequences may contribute to the observed pattern of AS expression. The GC-rich elements, usually found in housekeeping genes, appear to play a role in the low-level expression of AS observed in nonhepatic tissues. The TATAA sequence and octameric element are features of genes expressed in a tissue-specific manner, and these may contribute to the approximately hundredfold higher level of expression of AS observed in the liver as compared with other tissues.

Within the AS gene, the first two exons encode 5′ untranslated sequence, and the translational initiation codon is situated in exon 3. Alternative splicing of these exons occurs in transcripts from human and baboon cells. In human cells exon 1 and 3 are joined, deleting the second exon from most of the AS mRNA. In contrast, the second exon is retained in most of the AS mRNA found in baboon cells.[116]

In addition to the transcriptionally active AS locus, a remarkable number of pseudogenes with homology to cloned human AS cDNA have been detected, mapping to 14 different loci[115,122,123] including two loci on chromosome 9 at positions distant from the active gene, at p13→q11 and q11→q22, two loci on the X chromosome, and one locus on the Y chromosome. Genomic DNA clones of seven of these pseudogenes have been analyzed; all are approximately 2 kb in size and devoid of introns.[124] Three have been sequenced, and they have small insertions or deletions and multiple termination codons in all reading frames. Two have adenine-rich regions at their 3′ termini and are flanked by nearly perfect direct repeats. These features are typical of processed pseudogenes, which probably arise from reverse transcription of a messenger RNA followed by integration of the copied sequences into genomic DNA. Freytag et al. have proposed that the multiplicity of the dispersed processed AS sequences could have, at least in part, arisen from the replication of an intermediate molecule prior to integration.[124]

Regulation of transcription of the argininosuccinate synthetase gene has been examined in cultured human lymphoblastoid cell lines (RPMI 2650). Consistent with previous observations concerning arginine-mediated repression of AS enzyme activity, when wild-type RPMI 2650 cells were grown in the presence of citrulline instead of arginine, a sevenfold increase of AS mRNA was observed. In variants of either the RPMI 2650 cells[125] or of cultured human lymphoid lines[126] selected for resistance to the arginine analog canavanine (Can^r cells), both AS mRNA and AS enzyme are at a level nearly 200-fold greater than wild-type cells grown in arginine. This level of expression corresponds to that observed in normal liver.

The basis of canavanine resistance remains unresolved. Resistance clearly correlates with an increased level of both the AS mRNA and enzyme, and these features, once selected for, are apparently stable, being maintained in the absence of the analogue. At the DNA level, neither alteration in AS gene copy number, as would occur with gene amplification, nor rearrangement of the active gene has been observed.[114] AS pre-mRNA levels are increased in Can^r cells; the mechanism governing the increased RNA level appears to be a trans-acting one. This was most convincingly demonstrated by S1 analysis of RNA from canavanine-resistant human lymphoblasts isolated from an individual heterozygous for a mutation in the AS gene. Increased levels of both the normal and mutant trascript were observed.[127] The trans effect appears to be positively acting, as suggested by a cell fusion experiment in which RPMI 2650 cells were fused with Can^r cells. The level of AS message in the hybrids was equal to that of the Can^r parent.[121] Thus, the increased level of mature AS mRNA could result from increased gene transcription, increased stability of nuclear RNA, or altered nuclear RNA processing. Concerning the last possibility, it seemed conceivable that alternate RNA processing could increase the percentage of AS mRNA containing exon 2 sequences and that this species might be more stable than mRNA lacking this exon; however, examination of Can^r cells revealed predominant elevation in the level of mRNA lacking exon 2 sequences.[116]

Attempts have been made to define the sequences responsible for canavanine resistance using gene transfer into RPMI 2650 cells and canavanine-resistant variants.[118,126] However, when minigene constructs joining the AS 5′ flanking region with a reporter sequence, the chloramphenicol acetyl-transferase gene, were transferred into both parental cells and variant cells, the level of CAT activity detected in the two recipient cell types was similar. The analyzed constructs included as much as 3 kb of 5′ flanking sequence and the first four exons of the gene. While the minigenes failed to express CAT at higher levels in Can^r cells, repression of CAT activity by addition of arginine to the growth medium was observed.[118,126] This effect could be observed when a minigene construct was employed that contained as little as 150 bp of AS 5′ flanking sequence.[118] While arginine-mediated repression has been suggested to be a regulatory effect distinct from canavanine resistance, it is of note that the level of AS mRNA in canavanine-resistant cells is not subject to such repression. Concerning canavanine resistance, it remains possible that additional sequences from the AS gene will be required to observe an elevated level of expression of a transferred minigene construct. If stabilization of mRNA is the mechanism responsible for canavanine resistance, perhaps sequences downstream from those tested to date could be critical. On the other hand, 5′ flanking sequences further upstream may be involved. Definition of the sequences and factors that are responsible for canavanine resistance and exploration of their relationship to the normal pattern of expression of the AS gene will be of major interest.

Expression of a transferred AS gene has been accomplished by a variety of means using AS-recipient Chinese hamster cell lines, which lack AS enzymatic activity and are unable to grow in medium in which citrulline has been substituted for arginine. When metaphase chromosomes derived from a lymphoid line that overproduces AS were transferred into AS-deficient Chinese hamster cells, stable transformants were isolated that could grow in citrulline-containing medium.[128] In most cases these transformants expressed human AS, although several apparently activated expression of the hamster enzyme. In a second type of transfer experiment, genomic DNA derived from Can^r human cells was used for calcium phosphate-mediated transfection of the Chinese hamster line.[129] Transformants were isolated that could grow in citrulline-containing medium. Blot analyses with cloned human AS sequences as a probe confirmed transfer of approximately 80 kb of hybridizable sequence and identified a normal human AS mRNA transcript in five cases out of six. In the sixth case, a transcript corresponding in size to the larger AS mRNA observed in rodent cells was detected, presumed to be the product of activation of the hamster AS gene. More recently, gene transfer has been carried out using recombinant ecotropic retroviruses containing the cloned human AS cDNA sequence.[130] These viruses have been used to infect XC cell lines devoid of AS activity, permitting growth of transformants in citrulline-containing medium. Blot analysis of the transformants revealed presence of the recombinant proviral genome. This genome also contained the bacterial Neo gene, which encodes neomycin phosphotransferase, an enzyme which confers resistance to the neomycin analogue G418. Assay of AS activity in the virus transformants revealed a level approximately 10 percent that of normal human liver. In addition to programming expression of AS using ecotropic retroviruses, an amphotropic retrovirus with a simplified structure, placing the AS cDNA between two LTRs, has now been used as well to infect both XC cells and immortalized human citrullinemic fibroblasts.[131] AS activity was readily detected in these cells by means of incorporation of added [^{14}C]citrulline into total cell protein.

Such virus-mediated transfer of AS could have potential utility for correcting deficiency of enzyme activity in citrullinemia. Introduction of a functional cDNA into either hepatic or nonhepatic cell types might exert a therapeutic effect. In the case of nonhepatic cells, because the substrate citrulline can cross plasma membranes, it is conceivable that its entry into extrahepatic cells containing transferred AS could result in its efficient metabolism. Product argininosuccinate could be further metabolized in these same cells, or because this intermediate is also able to cross membranes, it could be subsequently metabolized in the liver.

Argininosuccinase

Recently, cDNA clones encoding both human[132] and rat[133] AL have been isolated using antibody screening of λ gt11 libraries followed by confirmation of identity using hybrid-selected translation. The human cDNA contained an open reading frame encoding a protein of 463 amino acids, with a predicted size of approximately 52,000 daltons. The predicted protein has the same number of residues as the previously analyzed yeast enzyme and shares 56 percent of its amino acids with that enzyme. It has recently been demonstrated that human AL has 58 and 62 percent similarity with the lens proteins δ 1 and δ 2 crystallin.[134] The mRNA species observed in Northern analysis of rat liver mRNA using the human cDNA as probe was approximately 2 kb in size. Rat AL mRNA increased twelvefold following starvation for 5 days and twofold following treatment with dibutyryl cAMP but did not change following dexamethasone treatment.[72] Southern analysis of somatic cell hybrids confirmed the previous localization of the human AL gene to chromosome 7, although the 5′ portion of the human cDNA hybridized with sequences on chromosome 22.[132] Whether this latter genomic sequence represents a truncated pseudogene remains to be addressed.

The rat cDNA clones contained approximately 1.7 kb of cloned sequence and have been used to correlate the levels of hybridizable mRNA present in a variety of rat hepatoma cell lines with both the amount of immunoblotted AL protein and the amount of AL enzyme activity.[133] The levels of enzymatic activity and mRNA varied over a sixtyfold range, extending from a value lower than that present in cultured human fibroblasts to a value comparable to rat liver. Thus, expression of AL in the various hepatoma lines appears to be governed at the level of transcription, nuclear processing, stability, or transport to the cytoplasm of AL mRNA.

Arginase

Recently, cDNA clones encoding rat liver arginase have been synthesized from mRNA enriched for the arginase species by polysome immunopurification.[135] The clones were verified as encoding arginase by hybrid-selected translation, and when the cloned cDNA was used to probe hepatic poly A^+ RNA, a species of about 1700 bases was identified. Because 900 bases are sufficient to encode the enzyme, the mRNA is predicted to contain approximately 800 bases of untranslated sequence. When mRNA from other tissues was similarly examined, small amounts were detected in kidney and brain at levels consistent with the amount of enzyme activity detected in those locations. In contrast to hepatic arginase which is cytosolic, renal arginase is found in the mitochondrial matrix. The level of hepatic mRNA in adult rats increased 24-fold following 5 days of starvation; sevenfold following treatment with dibutyryl cAMP; and twofold following dexamethasone.[71] When mRNA from H4 hepatoma cells was examined, as predicted from the presence of hepatic arginase enzyme activity in this cell line, a substantial level of arginase mRNA was detected. Hydrocortisone treatment of these cells increased the level of detectable enzyme activity, and the level of hybridizable mRNA was increased correspondingly. Southern blot analysis of rat and mouse genomic DNA carried out with the rat liver cDNA probe revealed a simple pattern suggesting the presence of a single gene whose size is not greater than 15 kb.

Human liver arginase cDNA clones have also been isolated,[136] the longest of which contains 1550 bp and which includes an ATG codon and long open reading frame. When this clone was used to probe human genomic DNA, a hybridization pattern suggesting a single gene was observed. Using somatic cell hybrids, this locus was mapped to band q23 of chromosome 6.[137] When the human liver cDNA was used to probe RNA from the cell line HEK, derived from human embryonic kidney, which contains high levels of the mitochondrial arginase, no hybridization was observed, consistent with the notion that hepatic cytosolic arginase and renal mitochondrial arginase are encoded by two separate genes with substantially different structure.[138]

INBORN ERRORS OF UREA SYNTHESIS

The clinical presentation of patients with CPSD, OTCD, ASD, and ALD are virtually identical. The clinical manifestations may appear in the neonatal period and be fatal, or they may appear any time thereafter with varying degress of severity. The similarity of clinical presentation is related to hyperammonemia, which is common to all these diseases. Their variability is principally a function of the different mutations (and hence enzyme activity) responsible for them. The variability may also be related to the metabolic consequences of the various enzyme deficiencies; e.g., ALD of a degree similar to OTCD may not be as severe a disease because the accumulated argininosuccinate may serve as a waste nitrogen product. An exception to this general rule exists in the female who carries an OTC mutant allele on one chromosome; variability in expression in this case is related also to the proportion of hepatocytes in which the normal (or mutant) allele is active (Lyonization). The other diseases, CPSD, ASD, and ALD, are inherited as autosomal recessive characteristics. These diseases can be distinguished from one another only by appropriate laboratory studies, although a pedigree with evidence of X-linked transmission suggests a diagnosis of OTCD. ALD has two distinguishing features: severe hepatomegaly in the early onset form and a hair abnormality (trichorexis nodosa) in the late onset form. Similar hair abnormalities have also been described in ASD.

Because of the dramatic clinical presentation of these diseases in the neonatal period and the long-term consequences of neonatal hyperammonemia, it is convenient to divide CPSD, OTCD, ASD, and ALD into two clinical groups, one group presenting in the neonatal period and a second group presenting any time thereafter. It should be recognized, however, that this is an arbitrary division of a continuous spectrum of phenotypic expression.

The Neonatal Group

The clinical course of the neonatal group of these diseases is monotonous in its regularity. The infant, almost always the product of a full-term normal pregnancy, labor, and delivery, appears to be normal for at least 24 h. Sometime between 24 and 72 h (occasionally several days later) the infant becomes lethargic and requires stimulation for feeding. Within hours, additional signs and symptoms may develop, including vomiting, increasing lethargy, hypothermia, and hyperventilation, the last often misinterpreted as pulmonary disease notwithstanding a normal chest x-ray and respiratory alkalosis.[139] A workup for sepsis is unrevealing, as would be expected for a full-term infant with no risk factors. Other routine laboratory data are uninformative except for the serum urea nitrogen which may be as low as 1 mg/dl. Without intervention the infant becomes comatose requiring mechanical ventilation. A diagnosis of intracranial hemorrhage may be entertained if a bulging fontanel and increasing head size are noted; however, a CT scan of the head will reveal cerebral edema. If the plasma ammonium level is not measured, the infant's death will be ascribed to sepsis, intracranial hemorrhage or some other disease commonly associated with prematurity, even though the patient is a full-term infant. Regrettably, the family history is often neglected. A history of consanguinity, neonatal sibling deaths, or neonatal male deaths upon pedigree analysis is frequently omitted, only to be discovered after a diagnosis is made.

The finding of an increased plasma ammonium level will direct diagnostic efforts toward an inborn error of metabolism. The differential diagnosis of hyperammonemia in a neonate is limited to urea cycle enzyme deficiencies, an increasing number of organic acidemias, and transient hyperammonemia of the newborn, a poorly understood disease characterized by symptomatic pulmonary disease within the first 24 h of life and severe hyperammonemia.[139,140] Figure 20-4 demonstrates that by combining the clinical characteristics with plasma amino acid values and urinary orotate excretion, transient hyperammonemia of the newborn, the organic acidemias (as a group), and the individual urea cycle enzyme defects can be distinguished from one another.

Diagnosis

Plasma amino acid analysis measured by automated quantitative column chromatography (thin-layer or paper chromatography are unreliable for this purpose) provides sufficient information to make a confident diagnosis of a deficiency of AS or AL.[142] The former is characterized by plasma citrulline levels (normal levels, 10 to 20 μM) between 1000 and 5000 μM; the latter is characterized by the presence of high concentrations of argininosuccinate and its anhydrides, neither of which is normally found in plasma. (An important technical point

Fig. 20-4 Diagnostic flow chart for neonatal hyperammonemia. Symptomatic hyperammonia prior to age 24 h occurs in two groups, THAN (transient hyperammonemia of newborn) and inborn errors of metabolism in which a part of the pathophysiology resides in product deficiency. PDH = pyruvate dehydrogenase deficiency; GA II = glutaric acidemia type II. Most other inborn errors of metabolism, e.g., urea cycle defects, PAA (propionic acidemia), and MMA (methylmalonic acidemia), develop symptoms after age 24 h, presumably as a consequence of a toxic substrate accumulation. All organic acidemias require analysis of urine by gas chromatography and mass spectroscopy for accurate diagnosis. Acidosis and ketosis occasionally may be absent in hyperammonemic neonates with PAA.[141]

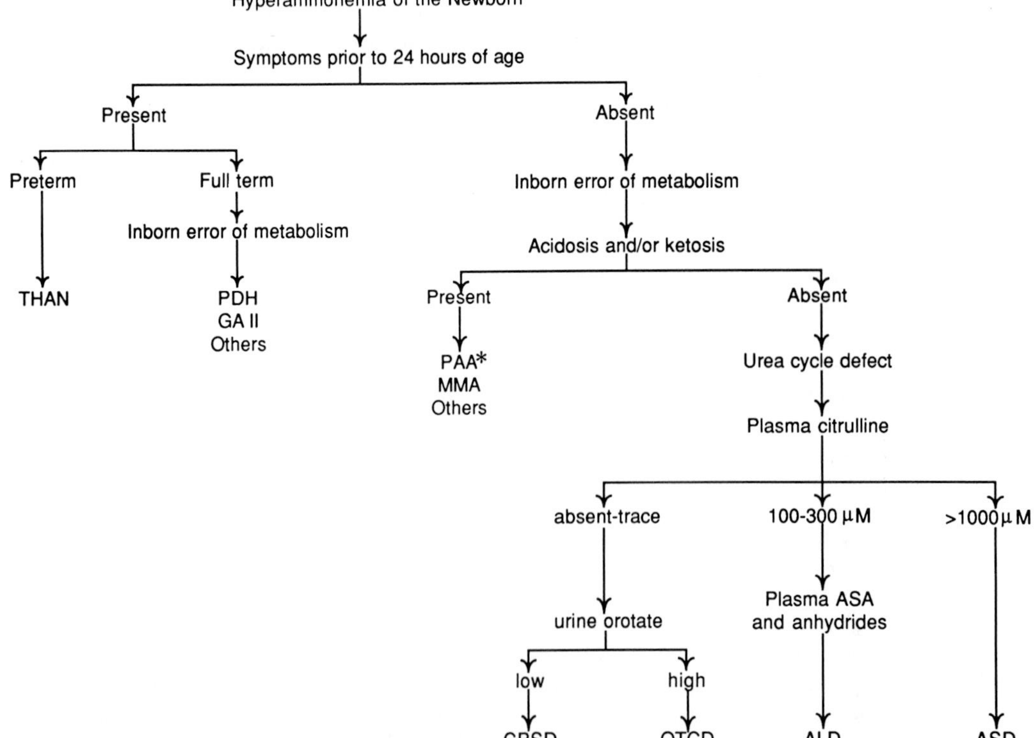

should be noted in analyzing amino acid chromatograms in infants in hyperammonemic coma. Unless the retention time of argininosuccinate is known, it may not be recognized because it may co-chromatograph with normally occurring amino acids.) Plasma citrulline levels are always moderately increased in argininosuccinase deficiency: 100 to 300 μM.

Because citrulline is a product of CPS and OTC, it is undetectable or nearly so in plasma after 24 h of life in hyperammonemic neonates suffering a deficiency in one of those enzymes. CPS and OTC can usually be distinguished by the level of urinary orotate; high levels occur in OTCD as a consequence of diversion of accumulated mitochondrial carbamyl phosphate to the cytosolic pyrimidine synthetic pathway. Other pyrimidines, including uracil, uridine, and pseudouridine, have been found in the urine of patients with OTCD.[143,144] Although the presence of the pyrimidine degradation products has been attributed to pyrimidine overproduction, a failure of rephosphorylation in the pyrimidine salvage pathway may also play a role. (The role of pyrimidine metabolism in OTCD is covered in the section on heterozygote detection in "OTC Deficiency.") The recently introduced allopurinol test may prove to be useful in establishing a diagnosis of OTCD in certain OTCD neonates in whom hyperammonemia and orotic aciduria are prevented by prospective therapy.[145]

Other plasma amino acid levels are frequently abnormal in all four diseases; glutamine and alanine are increased representing nonspecific nitrogen accumulation, and arginine and ornithine are decreased representing failure of *de novo* arginine biosynthesis.

The diagnosis of CPSD is made by exclusion. Because such a diagnosis implies lifetime commitment to an artificial diet and burdensome medication, it may be appropriate to measure CPS activity in liver obtained by percutaneous biopsy. No complications have been encountered with needle biopsy of liver in these infants after metabolic control is established.[146]

An attempt to make a diagnosis of symptomatic urea cycle defects by discontinuing therapy or protein loading is strongly discouraged; the risks of hyperammonemic coma outweigh those of liver biopsy. Measurement of CPS and OTC activity on intestinal samples obtained by biopsy may be useful although experience is limited.[146–148]

Although patients with propionic and methylmalonic acidemia have clinical presentations similar to those with urea cycle defects, there are usually three features that distinguish them: acidosis with ketosis, high plasma glycine levels, and abnormal urinary metabolites that can be detected by gas chromatography and mass spectroscopy.[149]

Neonatal hyperammonemia associated with pyruvate carboxylase deficiency glutaric acidemia type II also has been described.[150–152]

There are number of other inborn errors that are associated with severe hyperammonemia (e.g., medium chain acyl CoA dehydrogenase deficiency, 3-hydroxy,3-methyl glutaryl CoA lyase deficiency, lysinuric protein intolerance), but patients with these disorders rarely present in the neonatal period although a recent report suggests that short chain acyl CoA dehydrogenase deficiency can cause neonatal hyperammonemia.[153] Neonatal hyperammonemia resulting from severe in utero hepatic necrosis[154] superficially resembles the hyperammonemia of urea cycle defects but has a number of distinguishing traits: hypoglycemia, prolonged prothrombin time, and marked generalized hyperaminoacidemia.

N-Acetylglutamate Synthetase Deficiency. A single case of this entity has been reported.[155,156] A male neonate (who had two siblings of unstated sex die in the neonatal period) was closely monitored and found to have asymptomatic hyperammonemic on the third day of life. Pertinent laboratory studies revealed absent *N*-acetylglutamate synthetase activity, normal CPS activity, and approximately 5 percent of normal OTC activity (the last considered to be a consequence of inhibition by the administered benzoate). Plasma citrulline levels were not reported, but the plasma arginine and ornithine level curiously were at the upper limits of normal. Urinary orotate excretion was within normal limits. Treatment with carbamylglutamate as a substitute for the presumed absent *N*-acetylglutamate controlled the hyperammonemia. The effect of carbamylglutamate on urea production was not measured.

The Late Onset Group

Among the four diseases, CPSD, OTCD, ASD, and ALD, there are no phenotypic differences apart from the hair abnormality in ALD and perhaps ASD as well (hepatomegaly does not appear to be as constant a finding in late onset ALD as in the neonatal form) and rarely orotic acid crystalluria in OTCD.[157] The variability in age of onset, severity, and degree of residual enzyme activity is similar among the four enzyme deficiencies; there are cases that present from the first year of life to adulthood.[158–168] The large number of girls in this group is a consequence of symptomatic OTCD in females in whom the mutant allele is expressed in the large majority of hepatocytes. Phenotypic expression of the late onset group of urea cycle enzyme defects is best exemplified in this group of OTCD females.[145,168] The most characteristic in this group is the episodic nature of clinical symptoms.

In infants these episodes are often associated with weaning from breast milk or changing from low protein milk formula to cow's milk; in older children and adults the symptoms may be related to high protein meals. In all patients infection may precipitate symptoms, although not infrequently an episode may occur with no obvious cause. The milder episodes will often abate with cessation of protein intake and/or intravenous infusion of glucose. Many of these patients self-select a low protein diet.

The major symptoms of these episodes of hyperammonemia include vomiting, an abnormal mental status as manifested by lethargy, somnolence often progressing to coma, irritability, agitation, combativeness, disorientation, and ataxia. Seizures, delayed physical growth, and developmental delay are common although there are reports of normal development.[160] Apart from hyperammonemia, routine laboratory studies often reveal a respiratory alkalosis. Diagnostic delay and error are common; median delay of diagnosis was 16 months. Symptoms have been attributed to colic, gastroenteritis, cyclical vomiting, hyperactivity, encephalitis, Reye syndrome, epilepsy, anicteric hepatitis, drug toxicity, glioma, and child abuse.[168]

That patients with asymptomatic defect of ureagenesis spontaneously limit their protein intake may be adduced from preliminary data,[161] which showed that OTC carriers excreted 30 percent less urinary nitrogen than their control female relatives.

It has been suggested that migraine is a feature of symptomatic OTCD females[169]; however, a recent review[168] did not find headaches to be frequent in such patients or their mothers. The role of hyperammonemia in migraine was also evaluated; no significant difference in plasma ammonium levels was found in migrainous patients (within 2 h of an attack) and normal controls.[170–171]

Measurement of plasma amino acid levels by quantitative amino acid chromatography is definitive in making a diagnosis of the late onset group of ASD or ALD; citrulline levels are usually above 1000 μM in ASD and between 100 and 300 μM in ALD with very high concentrations of argininosuccinate and its anhydrides in the latter. However, there is a group of 12 Japanese adults reported to have "citrullinemia" with plasma citrulline levels between 40 and 870 μM and liver AS activity varying from 2 to 50 percent of normal.[172,173] At least one of these patients had very high plasma levels of argininosuccinate.[173] The biochemical and molecular nature of some of these unusual cases remains to be resolved.

Whereas the late onset form of ASD and ALD can be detected by finding increased levels of plasma citrulline or argininosuccinate, the diagnosis of CPSD or OTCD is complicated by the absence of any reliable plasma amino acid abnormality and a differential diagnosis that includes a large number of diseases presenting with hyperammonemia. These include Reye syndrome, lysinuric protein intolerance, and an increasing number of organic acidemias including glutaric acidemia, deficiencies chain acyl CoA dehydrogenase, 3-hydroxy-3-methylglutaryl CoA lyase, as well as late onset propionic, methylmalonic, and isovaleric acidemia.

The hyperammonemia of CPSD, OTCD, Reye syndrome, lysinuric protein intolerance, and organic acidemias may be distinguished from one another by measuring the following (Table 20-3): plasma pH, bicarbonate and amino acids, and urine organic acids by gas chromatography, mass spectroscopy, and urine orotate. All but the organic acidemias present with a respiratory alkalosis secondary to hyperammonemia induced by hyperventilation unless hemodynamic instability occurs.

The marked increase in plasma lysine levels associated with increased serum levels of liver transaminases and the absence of orotic aciduria serve to distinguish Reye syndrome from CPSD and OTCD. A definitive diagnosis of lysinuric protein intolerance requires evidence of hyperexcretion of lysine, ornithine, and arginine in urine. An additional characteristic of lysinuric protein intolerance is an increased serum ferritin level.[174] CPSD and OTCD may be distinguished from one another by evidence of X-linked inheritance and orotic aciduria in the latter.

Diagnosis of the late onset OTCD hemizygote or symptomatic heterozygote when they are not hyperammonemic or orotic aciduric may be aided by the recently introduced allopurinol test.[175] Protein loading as a provocative test in these vulnerable patients is contraindicated.

As with the neonatal onset group, CPSD is a diagnosis of exclusion; demonstration of enzyme activity in liver obtained via percutaneous biopsy is necessary for definitive diagnosis. OTC activity measured in liver obtained by percutaneous biopsy in hemizygous males is reliable but it may not accurately describe in vivo OTC activity in symptomatic OTCD heterozygotes because tissue obtained by biopsy may not be representative of the relative proportion of hepatocytes bearing the mutant and normal alleles.[176]

Pathophysiology

Hyperammonemia. Unlike patients with decompensated liver disease where ammonium is only one of several putative toxins,[177] ammonium appears to be the only cause of the acute encephalopathy seen in urea cycle defects (apart from arginase deficiency). Therefore, hyperammonemic coma as a clinical entity may be different from hepatic coma.

Voorhies et al.[178] have produced an experimental model of hyperammonemic coma over a 24-h period in awake primates. All the clinical signs and symptoms found in hyperammonemic patients were reproduced in those experiments. Plasma levels of ammonia were varied over a fivefold range during which the animals developed the progressive behavioral, physiological, biochemical, electroencephalographic, and neuropathologic changes found in hyperammonemic patients.

At low levels of ammonium the animals exhibited decreased spontaneous activity, disinterest in surroundings, lethargy, and vomiting. These symptoms were associated with slight increases in intracranial pressure and evidence of hyperventilation and a respiratory alkalosis. As the plasma ammonium level increased, all these signs and symptoms worsened: somnolence progressing to coma, seizures, absence of corneal reflexes, apnea, progressive increase in intracranial pressure, worsening of the respiratory alkalosis. Electroencephalographic changes included slow wave appearance correlating with the clinical and biochemical status. Several animals with high ammonium levels exhibited burst suppression and long periods of isoelectricity.

Gross neuropathologic changes included brain swelling, flattening of cortical gyri, and herniation of cerebellar tonsils. Light and electron microscopy revealed astrocyte swelling

Table 20-3 Laboratory Values Useful in Differentiating Diseases Presenting with Hyperammonemia after the Neonatal Period*

Laboratory study	*CPSD*	*OTCD*	*Reye's*	*LPI*†	*Organic acidemias*
Plasma acid-base status	Respiratory alkalosis	Respiratory alkalosis	Respiratory alkalosis	Respiratory alkalosis	Metabolic acidosis
Plasma glucose	Normal	Normal	Normal/low	Normal	Low
Urine orotate	Normal	High	Normal	High	Normal
Plasma glycine	Normal	Normal	Normal	Normal	High
Plasma lysine	Normal	Normal	Increased	Low-normal	
Urine lysine	Normal	Normal	Normal	High	Normal
Urine organic acids	Nonspecific	Nonspecific	Nonspecific	Nonspecific	Specific abnormalities

*ASD and ALD are easily identified by their characteristic plasma amino acid abnormalities (see text). Urine organic acids are identified by gas chromatography and mass spectroscopy.

†Lysinuric protein intolerance is also characterized by increased plasma alanine and ferritin levels.

with pleomorphic mitochondria. No pathologic changes were noted in neurons, axons, dendrites, and synapses.

It is apparent from this study that brain swelling often leading to increased intracranial pressure is a primary physiological response to hyperammonemia and that neurologic symptoms occur in the absence of neuronal pathology. It may be inferred from these data that the brain swelling is a consequence of swelling of the astrocyte, the only brain cell found to be affected. Because of the intimate relationship of the astrocyte processes with cerebral capillaries and venules, it is not surprising to learn that alterations of cerebral blood flow are commonly found in experimental hyperammonemia.[179–181]

Awareness that physiological changes in the absence of neuronal pathology occur very early in the course of hyperammonemia has important implications in interpreting many of the biochemical theories proposed to account for hyperammonemic encephalopathy.[182] These include abnormalities of cerebral energy metabolism, glycolysis, tricarboxylic acid cycle, amino acid metabolism, mitochondrial redox state, high energy phosphates, and intracellular pH. Additional biochemical abnormalities have been proposed[177]: perturbations of fatty acid metabolism, accumulation of mercaptans, and neurotransmitterlike substances (γ-aminobutyrate, octopamine, serotonin, histamine, catecholamines). Brusilow and Traystman[183] proposed that these metabolic abnormalities may all be secondary to the physiological perturbations described earlier: alterations in intracranial pressure and blood flow secondary to astrocyte swelling. They have further hypothesized that astrocyte swelling is a function of the intracellular osmotic effect of glutamine, whose concentration in whole brain increases by 10 mmol/kg during experimental hyperammonemia.[184] Thus glutamine may represent an endogenous osmole which, if confined to astrocytes (which constitute about 30 percent of brain volume), would increase their osmolality to approximately 30 mosmol/liter, thereby resulting in a shift of water into astrocytes. The importance of glutamine is supported by the strong relationship between hyperammonemia, neurologic dysfunction, and cerebrospinal glutamine concentration observed in hepatic encephalopathy.[185] During hyperammonemic coma, cerebrospinal glutamine concentrations in patients with OTCD[186] and ALD[187] are extraordinarily high, 6300 and 8660 μM, respectively (normal limits, 614 ± 241). That ammonium is rapidly incorporated into brain glutamine and that the astrocyte is the site of this incorporation have been well documented.[188,189] The importance of plasma glutamine accumulation as a premonitory sign of impending hyperammonemic coma has also been described (Fig. 20-5).[190]

Arginine Requirement. The essentiality of dietary arginine for those patients with the neonatal form of the disease was demonstrated by Brusilow,[4] who found that removal of arginine from the diet of affected patients (CPSD, OTCD, ASD, or ALD) promptly resulted in nitrogen accumulation as ammonium or glutamine or both, and orotic aciduria in OTCD and ALD. Citrulline but not ornithine could substitute for arginine. For less severely affected patients, a chronic arginine deficiency syndrome characterized by dermatologic features has been reported.[191–193] These patients, all of whom were under 3 months old, developed an erythematous scaling, occasional weeping, cutaneous eruption that was associated either with an interruption of arginine intake or a low protein diet and a disproportionately low plasma arginine level. In these cases plasma arginine levels varied from nondetectable to 30 μM. There was dramatic improvement in the skin lesion with

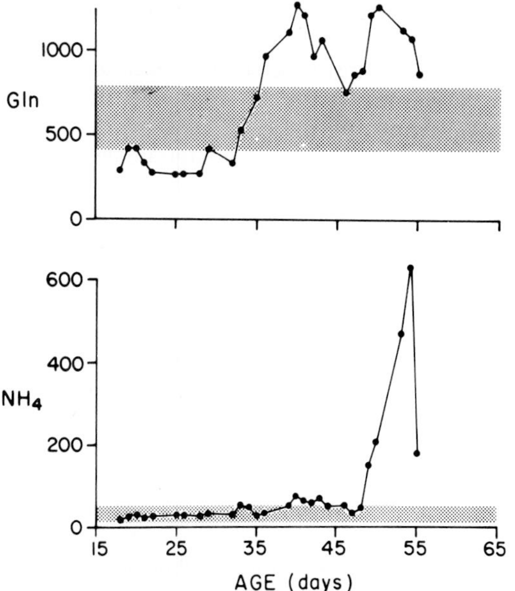

Fig. 20-5 Plasma glutamine (Gln, μM) and ammonium (NH_4, μM) levels in an infant male with OTC deficiency demonstrating the accumulation of glutamine prior to the onset of severe hyperammonemia. *(From Batshaw, Walser, Brusilow.[190] Used by permission of Pediatric Research.)*

dietary arginine supplementation. The eruption resembles the flaky paint dermatosis[193] found in kwashiorkor, suggesting that in part the very low plasma arginine levels found in kwashiorkor[194] may be responsible for this clinical manifestation.

Except for patients with urea cycle defects (apart from arginase deficiency) arginine is a nonessential amino acid in humans, unlike other animals (carnivores and rodents) who, when challenged with an arginine-free diet, develop one or more of the following: hyperammonemia, orotic aciduria, reduced growth rate.[195–197] Infants grow normally on arginine-free diets,[198–199] adults maintain nitrogen balance[200] and do not develop hyperammonemia or orotic aciduria.[27]

Substrate Accumulation. Because patients with ASD have plasma concentrations of citrulline as high as 5000 μM (normal limits, 15 to 30), citrulline itself is a candidate neurotoxin. A similar argument can be made for argininosuccinate and its anhydrides in patients with ALD. Evaluation of the potential toxicity of these two compounds until recently has been difficult because of the confounding effect of persistent low grade hyperammonemia and repeated episodes of inadequately treated hyperammonemic coma. The use of benzoate, phenylacetate, and arginine in ASD and arginine in ALD has permitted the long-term developmental evaluation with the complications of hyperammonemia minimized.[145]

In the case of ASD it appears that the high citrulline levels have little or no toxic effect. Two patients, now ages 12 and 24 months, in whom neonatal hyperammonemia was prevented by prospective therapy have IQ scores of 101 and 88, respectively.

The picture is less clear for ALD. The one patient in whom neonatal hyperammonemia was averted is now 4 years old and is mentally retarded (IQ = 57), even though he has had only one brief mild episode of hyperammonemia. However evidence that argininosuccinate may not be toxic is suggested by the absence of neurodevelopmental deterioration in an 8-year-old girl rescued from neonatal hyperammonemic coma. At 3 and 8 years of age her Stanford Binet scores were 51 and 40, respectively.[145] However, additional studies of prospectively treated ALD and other urea cycle enzyme deficiency patients are necessary to evaluate the role of factors other than hyperammonemia on development.

The role of arginine accumulation in arginase deficiency is discussed separately in that section.

Pathology of Urea Cycle Defects

The Brain. Analysis of the morbid anatomy of the brain of patients with urea cycle defects is hampered not only by genetic and clinical heterogeneity within each of these diseases but also by artifacts induced by the variable agonal periods. Interpretation of the relative effects of acute and chronic metabolic alterations also is difficult, particularly when superimposed on children of varying ages and varying nutritional states. Furthermore, the pathologic features of the brain in urea cycle defects are described in scattered reports of varying thoroughness.[187,201–214]

By and large it appears that there are few differences in the neuropathology of deficiencies of CPS, OTC, AS, or AL when onset, severity, and age of death are considered. Acute hyperammonemia of the newborn resulting in death in the first week of life is associated with brain swelling and Alzheimer type II astrocytes in the cortex and brain stem with few other changes. Occasionally neuronal abnormalities are seen. More rarely cystic necrosis may be noted at the junction of the cortical white and gray matter; however, neuronal changes in this group of patients are either absent or mild.

At the other end of the spectrum are long-term survivors of urea cycle defects, untreated patients with presumed partial defects of CPSD, OTCD, ASD, and ALD. The brains of these children frequently show complete neuronal disappearance with cortical disintegration and generalized gliosis. Other parts of the brain are frequently involved, but there may be sparing of some segments in the presence of severe destruction elsewhere. For example, one 13-month-old OTCD female had gross cerebral atrophy, but the cerebellum was better preserved.[214] In a 4-year-old male dying of ALD, the cerebral cortex appeared to be spared, whereas there was gross neuronal loss in the thalamus.[212] Myelin defects were specifically described in two patients with ALD[212]; whether this is characteristic ALD is unclear.

Filloux et al.[215] suggested that neuropathologic changes in OTCD are acquired in utero based on a finding of multiple cortical infarcts in an OTCD male who died of hyperammonic coma at age 17 days. Convincing evidence that the brain lesion occurred antenatally rather than postnatally during his fatal hyperammonemic episode was lacking.

Computed axial tomography of the brain is useful in describing the extent of brain destruction.[216,217]

The Liver. There are varying degress of portal fibrosis in ALD survivors and girls with OTCD.[218,219] Although a single case of severe liver fibrosis in ALD was reported,[220] a review of liver biopsy specimens in five cases revealed considerable variability, with very mild portal fibrosis being the most common finding.[219] One child with ALD, who was rescued from neonatal hyperammonemic coma, has now been followed for 8 years; light microscopy of a liver biopsy sample is within normal limits.[145]

Electron-microscopic examination of liver occasionally reveals abnormalities which include pleomorphic mitochondria with swollen cristae and dense matrices as well as pathologic changes in the smooth and rough endoplasmic reticulum.[163,221–223] It appears that these ultrastructural changes in CPSD, OTCD, and ALD may not be found unless hyperammonemia is present, except perhaps in ALD where these abnormalities were noted while the patient was under good metabolic control. Similar electron-microscopic findings have been described in mice in whom hyperammonemia was induced by injection.[224]

Liver function, particularly synthetic function, is normal, although increased transaminase levels are not uncommon during and not limited to episodes of hyperammonemia.[219]

Measurement of Plasma Ammonium Levels

Ammonia is a weak organic base having a pk_a of approximately 9.3. Thus, at physiological pH values as much as 99 percent of ammonia is in the ionized form, ammonium, which is the recommended terminology.[225]

There are three satisfactory methods for measuring plasma ammonium levels; ion exchange followed by colorimetric analysis,[226–228] an ammonium-specific electrode,[229–230] and an enzymatic method using the reductive amination of α-ketoglutarate with spectrophotometric or fluorometric analysis or NADH.[231,232]

When these methods are compared, the average plasma ammonium level in infants[233] and adults[229] is approximately 30 μ*M* with a normal range of 15 to 40 μ*M;* these normal values have been approved and adopted by the International Union of Pure and Applied Chemistry and the International Federation of Clinical Chemistry.[225] In the United States two popular automated ammonium methods are used. The Dupont aca analyzer[234] uses an enzymatic spectrophotometric assay and is reported to provide values similar to those described above. The Kodak Ektachem system,[235] a microdiffusion method employing thin films, has normal values somewhat higher, 18 to 54 μ*M*. These assays require venous blood to provide a sufficient volume for the sampling reservoir.

Available micromodifications of these methods permit analysis on plasma obtained from capillary blood.[228,236–239]

A portable "ammonia checker," which relies on a microdiffusion reflectrometric method, may be useful in home management.[240–243] It has a number of advantages, principally ease of operation and a requirement of 20 μl of whole blood. It has a number of disadvantages as a laboratory analytical instrument but nonetheless may prove useful in the home management of patients with urea cycle defects. Preliminary experience suggests that early detection of impending coma may be possible. Falsely low values appear to be infrequent.

The alkaline diffusion technique of Seligson and Hirahara[244] is useful but yields values substantially higher than the more specific methods described above.

Molecular Pathology of Urea Cycle Enzymes

CPS Deficiency. When cloned cDNA was used to examine genomic DNA from seven CPS I-deficient patients, no gross alteration was detected.[245] Graf[246] examined the liver of one CPSD infant who died in the newborn period and detected neither immunoreactive CPS protein nor mRNA that could translate the CPS subunit.

OTC Deficiency. The isolation of cloned human OTC sequences has permitted molecular analysis of OTC deficiency. Rozen and colleagues have carried out Southern blot analysis of genomic DNA from affected males, using cloned cDNA as a probe, and identified gene deletion in four cases out of a total of approximately 50 examined.[247–248] Three of these deletions involved only a portion of the gene, whereas a fourth involved complete deletion of the OTC gene but not two anonymous flanking X-chromosomal loci, L128 and 754. Of these four deletions, two were shown to be inherited from a heterozygous female, while one had arisen de novo. The origin of the complete deletion could not be ascertained. Old et al.[249] have studied a kindred with a deletion in the Xp21 region so large as to be cytogenetically detectable, where both OTC and its neighboring loci were shown to be deleted by Southern blot analysis and where OTC deficiency, glycerol kinase deficiency, and congenital adrenal hypoplasia were all observed. The mother of the proband in this pedigree was shown to be heterozygous for this deletion and underwent prenatal diagnosis using blot hybridization of DNA prepared from amniocytes. Presence of hybridizing OTC sequences in the male fetus indicated it to be unaffected. An additional cytogenetic deletion affecting the OTC gene has been observed by Francke,[250] who identified a mildly retarded woman who had a history of dietary protein intolerance and who exhibited an interstitial deletion of Xp21. When she was given a dietary protein challenge, an elevation in urinary orotic acid was observed, consistent with the presence of partial OTC deficiency.

The majority of OTC-deficient males do not exhibit detectable deletions, and are most likely to harbor either single base substitutions or small deletions in the gene. Where such changes affect a restriction cleavage site, they can be readily detected. Three such OTC-deficient pedigrees have been identified, in which loss of a Taq I restriction site marks the site of OTC mutation.[251,252] In these pedigrees, a new hybridizing Taq I fragment was observed both in the proband and his mother. Several additional female family members displayed this fragment. Several of the women displaying the new Taq I fragment presented a history of dietary protein intolerance in each case correlating the Taq site alteration with presumed heterozygous carrier status. In one of the pedigrees, prenatal DNA diagnosis using Taq I restriction cleavage correctly indicated a male fetus to be unaffected.[251] Recent sequence analysis of the mutant gene in these three pedigrees reveals in one case a C→T transition in codon 109 of the mature subunit sequence, changing an arginine to a stop codon and in two cases a G→A transition changing the arginine codon to a glutamine codon.[253]

While to date RNA from OTC-deficient human liver has not been directly analyzed, Saheki et al.[254] examined RNA from the liver of an affected newborn who exhibited neither detectable enzyme activity nor immunoreactive protein. Interestingly, in this case, translation of hepatic mRNA in rabbit reticulocyte lysate produced an OTC precursor that could be taken up by rat liver and rat kidney mitochondria and processed to a mature-size form. This suggested that in vivo a labile protein was produced that either failed to reach the mitochondria or was rapidly turned over within the organelles. The latter might be particularly likely if the OTC subunits failed to assemble into active enzyme. Kodama et al.[255] similarly examined RNA from the livers of two clinically symptomatic female heterozygotes following death from hyperammonemia. In both cases, the level of translatable OTC mRNA was much lower than controls, and in one case following translation a truncated 30,000-dalton OTC precursor was observed in addition to the normal-size precursor. This smaller species could not be imported by isolated rat liver mitochondria.

An intriguing analysis at the protein level has been carried out with liver tissue from an affected 8-month-old male who exhibited 10 percent residual OTC enzyme activity, a low K_m for carbamyl phosphate, and nearly normal amounts of an immunoreactive subunit with a molecular size approximately 2000 daltons smaller than normal.[256] The molecular nature of this mutation could involve deletion, either inframe within the gene or at the 3′ end, or it could involve point mutation that either alters the site of processing of the leader peptide or produces a nonsense mutation that truncates the precursor at its COOH terminus.

In addition to the human mutations, two strains of inbred laboratory mice with X-linked inherited OTC deficiency have been identified and studied using molecular genetic analyses. One, called sparse fur (spf), exhibits decreased activity at pH 8, equal to 25 percent of normal, while at pH 9, activity is 150 percent of the activity of normal enzyme measured at this pH. A normal-size mature enzyme was detected in the liver of affected males, and it was present in an amount greater than normal.[257,258] Additionally, the specific activity of the enzyme at pH 9 was greater than that at pH 8. When total RNA from the livers of affected spf males was translated in vitro, a normal-size OTC precursor was detected, but the amount was approximately 60 percent of normal, suggesting that the increased amount of enzyme protein observed in spf livers is due to a decreased rate of turnover.[259] Recent study of spf OTC has been carried out using RNAse treatment of hybrids between antisense wild-type mouse OTC mRNA and spf mRNA.[260] This revealed a mismatch at approximately codon 80 in the mature portion. A polymerase chain reaction strategy was then used to directly amplify cDNA from the 5′ portion of the mRNA, and the cDNA was cloned and sequenced. A cytosine-to-adenine transversion was detected, changing the histidine at position 85 in the mature portion to asparagine.[260] The nature of this mutation was confirmed by expression of the sequence in COS cells, using sr40 regulatory elements, to produce an OTC enzyme with the previously observed abnormal features.

A second mouse OTC mutant exhibits both sparse fur and abnormal skin and hair and is called spf^{ash}.[261] Affected males exhibit a level of both enzymatic activity and cross-reacting material approximately 10 percent of normal, and the enzyme itself exhibits normal kinetic parameters. As determined both by in vitro translation of mRNA from affected livers[259,262] and by Northern analysis of the mRNA,[89] the level of OTC mRNA in affected livers is approximately 10 percent of normal. Most interestingly, the mRNA from affected livers, in addition to being present at reduced levels, directs the synthesis of two distinct OTC precursor species, one of the same molecular size as the wild-type precursor and one approximately 1000 daltons larger.[262] Upon incubation of the translation products with mitochondria, at least two new immunoprecipitable species were identified, one of the normal size of the mature subunit and a second form approximately 1000 daltons larger in apparent size. Only the mature-size form could assemble into active enzyme, as judged from binding to a substrate affinity column containing δ-*N*-phosphonoacetylornithine. It has been presumed that aberrant splicing of a portion of the OTC mRNA synthesized in spf^{ash} livers produces the larger precursor by virtue of translation of additional sequences presumably derived from an intron. This has been shown to be the case, as recent studies employing S1 nuclease treatment of hybrids between spf^{ash} liver mRNA and cloned wild-type mouse cDNA detect the insertion of additional sequences in a portion of spf^{ash} mRNA at codon 97 in the mature portion coding sequence, the position of a normal intron-exon boundary. As expected two types of cloned cDNA were isolated from spf^{ash} mRNA. One could encode a normal sized precursor but it contained a point mutation changing arginine 97 (CGT) to histidine (CAT). This mutation is predicted to alter the base at -1 in the exon portion of a splice donor site. As predicted the other cDNA species contains insertion of 16 residues beyond the histidine, corresponding to failure to use the normal splice donor sequence but utilization instead of a new splice donor site further downstream.[90]

Argininosuccinate Synthetase Deficiency. With cloned AS sequences it has been possible to carry out a molecular analysis of both DNA and RNA derived from cultured skin fibroblasts of citrullinemia patients. No abnormalities were observed on Southern blot analysis of genomic DNA derived from 11 citrullinemia cell lines.[263] Furthermore, hybridizable mRNA of a size similar to that from control cell lines was detected in all the cell lines. Six of the cell lines were further analyzed by S1 analysis, involving hybridization of RNA with the cloned end-labeled AS cDNA, followed by treatment of the hybrids with S1 nuclease.[264] Five out of the six lines exhibited a lack of complete protection of the cDNA, indicating structural defects in the mRNA from one or both copies of the AS gene. As shown in Fig. 20-6, the pattern of protected fragments indicated that at least three out of the five patients were double heterozygotes at the AS locus (genetic compounds). The detected defects mapped to a variety of positions along the mRNA and are likely to represent RNA splicing abnormalities caused by base substitution, although deletion or rearrangement within coding sequences could also produce such defects. In a number of cases, fully protected cDNA was observed, either as the exclusive product of S1 treatment or in addition to smaller fragments. This protected cDNA is presumed to result from mutant alleles that express either small defects in AS mRNA, such as single-base substitutions that would not be detectable by S1 analysis or defects in the extreme 5′ region of the mRNA that were not encompassed by the cloned cDNA. The former type of defect may, in at least some cases, be more amenable to detection using the procedure of RNAse digestion of hybrids formed between mRNA from a mutant cell line and complementary RNA produced in vitro as a transcript from cloned cDNA.[265] Neither S1 nuclease nor RNAse analysis can detect an additional type of molecular lesion that presumably occurs in some cases, where there is failure of production of AS RNA. This type of defect in heterozygous RNA negative form would be indistinguishable from the homozygous form of an RNA-positive allele. Only in a homozygous form, where no protected fragments are observed, could it become apparent.

Fig. 20-6 Schematic illustration of structure of AS mRNA in control and citrullinemia cells. Dashed lines indicate S1-sensitive regions of RNA-cDNA hybrid and are likely to reflect either splicing abnormalities or deletion. Scale is in kilobases. *(From Su et al.[264] Used by permission.)*

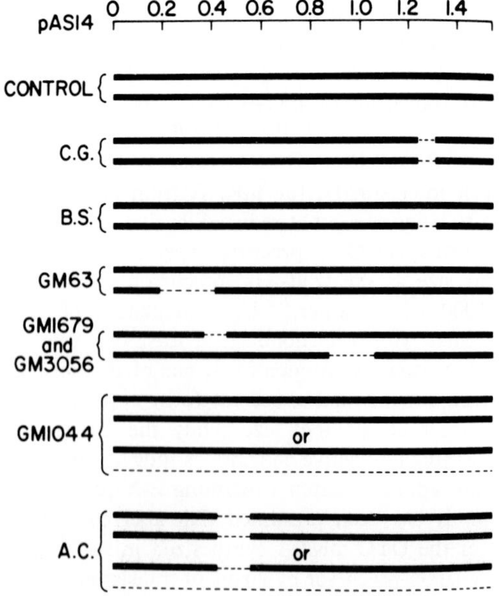

Argininosuccinase Deficiency. McInnes et al.[266] have carried out a complementation analysis of AL deficiency, fusing fibroblasts from 28 patients in pairwise combinations and examining the AL activity in the heterokaryons. All the mutants mapped to a single major complementation group, but extensive interallelic complementation was observed, separating the mutants into 12 subgroups. This suggests the presence of at least 12 allelic mutations and indicates extensive genetic heterogeneity of AL deficiency. Simard et al.[267] examined this heterogeneity at the protein level by fractionation of extracts of affected fibroblasts on SDS-PAGE followed by immunoblotting with AL antiserum. They found that the quantity of cross-reacting material (CRM) does not correlate with the amount of residual enzyme activity, consistent with the heterogeneity previously observed on complementation analysis. Lack of correlation of CRM with enzyme activity is also consistent with the notion that mutation usually affects the structural gene as opposed to a regulatory gene, because mutation of the latter would result in proportionate changes of these measurements. An additional observation from immunoblot analysis was that cross-reacting material was often detected in lower molecular weight bands. This further indicates that the mutations affect the AL structural gene, resulting in these cases in degradation of an unstable monomer.

Additional conclusions could also be made from the immunoblot analysis.[267] First, the presence of CRM in all the AL mutants is consistent with the high frequency of interallelic complementation. Complementation may result from stabilization of defective monomers in the hybrid tetramers formed between complementary alleles. Second, mutations from four mildly affected patients all exhibited significant levels of the 51,000-dalton AL monomer, and, as a correlating feature, cell strains from these patients exhibited substantial catalytic activity. Correspondingly, strains with the 51,000-dalton subunit in very low abundance complemented much less frequently.

Treatment of Urea Cycle Defects (Table 20-4)

The goal of therapy of urea cycle defects is to provide a diet sufficient in protein, arginine, and energy to promote growth and development while preventing the metabolic perturbations associated with hyperammonemia and hyperglutaminemia. Thus, successful therapy can be judged by anthropometric and nutritional assessment and maintenance of normal plasma ammonium and glutamine levels. Measurement of plasma glutamine level may be the best single guide to effective therapy

Table 20-4 Recommended Management of Inborn Errors of Ureagenesis

	G/kg/day
Carbamyl phosphate synthetase or ornithine transcarbamylase deficiency	
Diet*	
Essential amino acids	0.5–0.7
Protein	0.5–0.7
Caloric supplementation with Mead Johnson #80056	
Medication	
Sodium (or calcium) benzoate	0–0.25‡
Sodium phenylacetate†	0.30–0.55‡
Citrulline	0.17
Argininosuccinic acid synthetase deficiency	
Diet	
Protein	1.25–1.5
Caloric supplementation with Mead Johnson #80056	
Medication	
Sodium (or calcium) benzoate	0–0.25‡
Sodium phenylacetate	0.30–0.55‡
Arginine (free base)	0.40–0.70
Argininosuccinase deficiency	
Diet	
Protein	1.25–1.75 g/day
Caloric supplementation with Mead Johnson #80056	
Medication	
Arginine (free base)	0.40–0.70

*Patients with partial deficiencies, including females heterozygous for OTCD receive a diet containing the age-determined minimal daily protein requirement. Essential amino acids are not prescribed.

†Sodium phenylbutyrate (which is rapidly oxidized to phenylacetate in vivo[284]) may be preferable to phenylacetate because of the unpleasant odor of the latter. As a consequence of its higher molecular weight, the dose of sodium phenylbutyrate is 17 percent greater than that of sodium phenylacetate.

‡Because phenylacetate and phenylbutyrate on a molar basis are twice as effective as benzoate, it is recommended that phenylacetate be administered at a dose of 0.55 g/kg per day. If this is not well tolerated, it may be reduced somewhat and a proportionate amount of benzoate substituted. In any case, no less than 0.55 g/kg per day of drugs should be given.

because it appears to be a harbinger of hyperammonemia. It has been demonstrated in two OTCD infants who died during an episode of hyperammonemic coma that plasma glutamine increased from levels of 500 to greater than 1000 μ*M* 1 week before the plasma ammonium level increased to encephalopathic levels (Fig. 20-5).[191]

The importance and role of glutamine accumulation can be estimated from the dog studies of Smith and Wilmore.[268] They plotted the ratio of muscle glutamine concentrations to the extracellular glutamine concentration over a range of plasma glutamine levels from 300 to 1100 μ*M* (Fig. 20-7). At a plasma glutamine level of 300 μ*M*, the ratio was approximately 43 (similar to the ratio found in humans, 34.5[269]; at a plasma glutamine level of 1100, the ratio was approximately 23 indicating that the intracellular glutamine concentration increased from 12.9 to 25.3 μ*M*. When these values are expressed as nitrogen accumulation, it can be calculated that glutamine nitrogen in the extracellular fluid volume increased by approximately 0.32 mmol/kg body weight, whereas glutamine nitrogen in the intracellular fluid volume increased by 10 mmol/kg

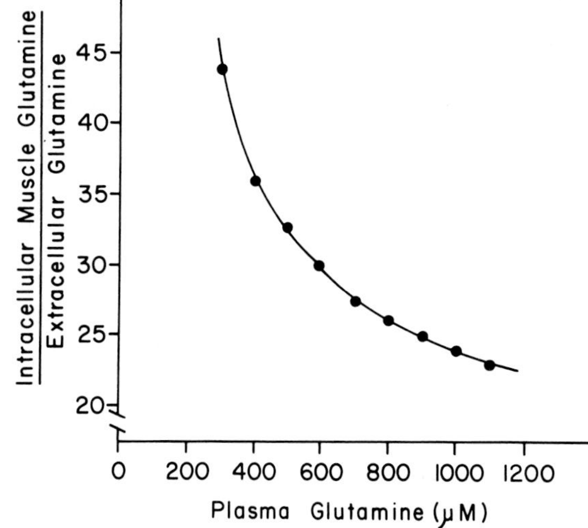

Fig. 20-7 The ratio of intracellular to extracellular glutamine concentration is plotted against increasing plasma glutamine concentrations to demonstrate that, even at high plasma glutamine levels, intracellular glutamine levels are more than twentyfold higher, thus representing a major source of nitrogen retention in hyperammonemic and hyperglutaminemic patients. *(Courtesy of R. J. Smith and D. W. Wilmore.)*

body weight, the total representing a nitrogen accumulation of 294 mg/kg nitrogen; an amount found in a diet of 1.8 g of protein per kilogram.

Based on these observations it appears that glutamine represents a storage form of nitrogen which can offer substantial short-term "buffering" of ammonium. When this mechanism is saturated as evidenced by high plasma glutamine levels, plasma ammonium levels may rapidly increase to encephalopathic levels. Thus, the maintenance of plasma glutamine levels at normal or near normal levels, if possible, may be an important goal of therapy.

Another sensitive measure of metabolic control is urinary orotate excretion in OTCD. Persistent orotic aciduria suggests abnormal nitrogen homeostasis.

There are three components of nitrogen metabolism to consider in designing therapy: nitrogen intake, nitrogen retention in protein (which will vary with growth rate), and nitrogen excretion.

Until recently the only rationale for therapy included the manipulation of dietary nitrogen to reduce the requirement for waste nitrogen synthesis via the urea cycle. This was attempted by providing low protein diets, essential amino acid diets,[270] or a combination of essential amino acids and several of their nitrogen-free analogues.[271] For patients with severe enzyme deficiencies these approaches failed; all such patients died, although there is one long-term surviving OTCD hemizygote treated with keto acids who also received benzoate for hyperammonemic episodes.[272]

The explanation for the failure of dietary therapy probably resides in the mechanism for maintenance of nitrogen balance and nitrogen retention.[273,274] When nitrogen intake falls below a threshold level, the positive balance between protein degradation (which normally is approximately 6.6 g/kg per day in infants) and protein synthesis (which normally is approximately 7.0 g/kg per day) will become negative; protein degradation will exceed protein synthesis, and growth failure will ensue. Because the amount of nitrogen intake required for growth exceeds nitrogen retention, there must be a mechanism to excrete the nitrogen not retained. To the extent that there is residual ureagenic capacity, there will be a residual degree of dietary nitrogen tolerance. In the absence or near absence of residual ureagenesis, some other pathway of waste nitrogen excretion will be necessary to prevent nitrogen accumulation.

It should be noted that during the first 6 to 12 months of life dietary nitrogen tolerance in patients with defective ureagenesis will be substantially greater than in the later years because 18 to 30 percent of dietary nitrogen will be retained then as compared to 5 to 6 percent later in infancy.[274a]

Treatment of Argininosuccinase Deficiency (Neonatal Form)

Because argininosuccinic acid contains the two nitrogen atoms destined for urea synthesis and because its renal clearance is the same as the glomerular filtration rate, Brusilow et al.[275,276] proposed that argininosuccinate might serve as a waste nitrogen product in patients with argininosuccinase deficiency (Fig. 20-8). To promote argininosuccinate biosynthesis in these patients it is necessary to provide large amounts of exogenous arginine because the major pathway for ornithine biosynthesis is impaired, e.g., from arginine via argininosuccinase (Fig. 20-8). Second, although ornithine may be synthesized *de novo* via ornithine aminotransferase, the equilibrium of this reaction greatly favors ornithine degradation; it appears that the reverse reaction cannot supply sufficient ornithine to permit adequate argininosuccinic acid synthesis.

The estimated arginine dose in these patients is approximately 3 mmol/kg per day (Table 20-4). If, after hydrolysis to ornithine, stoichiometric amounts of argininosuccinic acid were synthesized from this arginine intake, 112 mg/kg of waste nitrogen would be available for excretion, equivalent to the nitrogen content found in 0.7 g/kg per day of dietary protein. With this new pathway of waste nitrogen synthesis, patients with argininosuccinase deficiency can tolerate between 1.5 and 2.0 g of dietary protein per kilogram per day, the larger and smaller amounts recommended for infants and older children, respectively.

When the partition of urinary nitrogen was measured in two ALD-deficient patients[145] treated as described above, 40 and 42 percent of urinary nitrogen was derived from argininosuccinate. In these calculations it is assumed that only two of four argininosuccinate nitrogen atoms were waste nitrogen, the remaining two having been derived from the arginine supplement. For the same reason urea nitrogen (all, or nearly all, of which is derived from hydrolysis of dietary arginine) is excluded from calculation of urinary waste nitrogen.

Fig. 20-8 The pathway of waste nitrogen synthesis in patients with ALD when treated as described in Table 20-4. Supplementary dietary arginine supports the continued synthesis of argininosuccinate and hence its excretion as a waste nitrogen product. Asterisks denote the number of waste nitrogen atoms contained in various substrates and products.

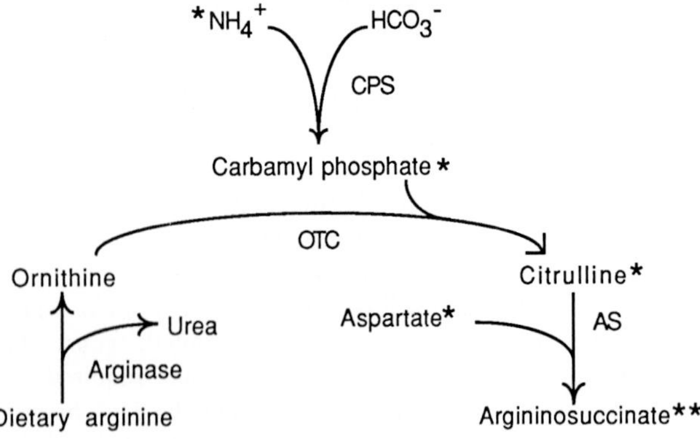

There are two potential side effects of arginine therapy; hyperargininemia and persistently high levels of argininosuccinate. At the present time, their significance is unclear.

Episodes of hyperammonemia are uncommon in ALD and almost promptly resolve when treated with intravenous arginine, as is described below.

Treatment of Carbamyl Phosphate Synthetase and Ornithine Transcarbamylase Deficiency (Neonatal Forms)

Unlike the treatment of ASD or ALD where nitrogen-rich intermediates can be exploited as waste nitrogen products, therapy of CPSD and OTCD must rely upon activation of latent biochemical pathways whose products can serve as substitutes for urea. That such potentially useful pathways exist was shown long ago[277,278] when the administration of benzoate or phenylacetic acid resulted in decreased urea nitrogen excretion, the decrease accounted for by the respective appearance of hippurate nitrogen and phenylacetylglutamine nitrogen in the urine. Brusilow et al.[279] suggested that these pathways may be useful in patients with defective ureagenesis.

Figure 20-9 shows the pathways whereby nitrogen can be diverted from urea synthesis to amino acid acylation and acetylation products after administration of benzoate or phenylacetate, respectively.[279]

Benzoate or phenylacetate are esterified to their CoA esters via medium chain fatty acyl CoA ligase. A glycine specific enzyme, benzoyl CoA:glycine acyltransferase (EC 2.3.1.13) catalyzes the formation of the peptide bond required for hippurate biosynthesis. Another enzyme, specific for glutamine, phenylacetyl CoA:glutamine acetyltransferase (EC 2.3.1.68) catalyzes the formation of the peptide bond required for phenylacetylglutamine biosynthesis. These enzymes are located in the mitochondrial matrix of liver and kidney.[280-282] The enzyme activity in the kidney appears to be greater than that in the liver, suggesting that when corrected for weight both organs have approximately equal conjugating ability.

Virtually all mammals, including primates, convert benzoate to hippurate. However, there is considerable species specificity in the metabolism of phenylacetate.[283] Humans and Old World monkeys synthesize the glutamine conjugate, but not glycine conjugate, with phenylacetate. Only the baboon and chimpanzee are similar to humans in that they conjugate virtually all administered phenylacetate with glutamine. New World monkeys conjugate phenylacetate with both glutamine and glycine. Carnivores and rodents conjugate only with glycine.

The odd and even chain congeners of benzoate and phenylacetate are β oxidized in vivo to benzoate and phenylacetate, respectively.[284]

As glycine is incorporated into hippurate, it is resynthesized from serine, which in turn is the product of two transamination reactions with alanine or glutamate as the nitrogen donor. As glutamine is incorporated into phenylacetylglutamine, it is resynthesized via amidation of glutamate via glutamine synthetase. The net result of benzoate and phenylacetate administration is a flux of nitrogen from the usual urea precursors,

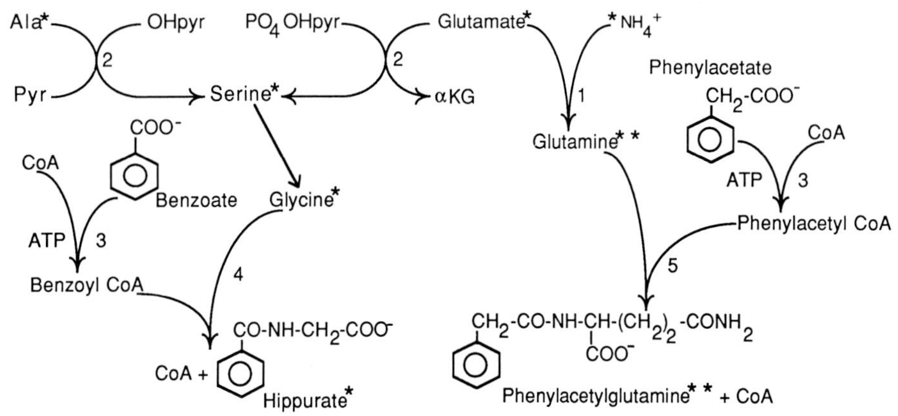

Fig. 20-9 The pathways of waste nitrogen synthesis in patients with CPSD and OTCD when treated as described in Table 20-4. The asterisks denote nitrogen atoms destined for waste nitrogen excretion in hippurate and phenylacetylglutamine. The enzymatic reactions are numbered: 1 = glutamine synthetase; 2 = transamination; 3 = mediumchain fatty acyl CoA ligase; 4 = benzoyl CoA:glycine acyltransferase; 5 = phenylacetyl CoA:glutamine acetyltransferase. αKG = α-ketoglutarate; Ala = alanine; OH pyr = hydroxypyruvate; PO_4OHpyr = phosphohydroxypyruvate; Pyr = pyruvate.

ammonium, alanine, and glutamate, to glycine or glutamine, following which they are respectively conjugated to yield hippurate and phenylacetylglutamine. Presumably the ammonium which ordinarily serves as a substrate for ureagenesis in the mitochondria matrix of the hepatocyte is diverted to glutamate synthesis via glutamate dehydrogenase and then to glutamine via glutamine synthetase. (It is also possible that glycine may be synthesized from ammonium and 5′,10-methyltrahydrofolate via the glycine cleavage complex.) The absence of intestinal CPS or OTC, and hence failure of intestinal citrulline biosynthesis in CPSD and OTCD, suggests that the portal blood ammonium level is probably higher than normal in these diseases, thereby emphasizing the importance of ammonium incorporation into glutamine and glycine and possibly glutamate with subsequent diversion to hippurate and phenylacetylglutamine. When the partition of urinary nitrogen was measured in two CPSD and three OTCD patients,[145] hippurate and phenylacetylglutamine nitrogen contributed an average of 22 and 38 percent of urinary waste nitrogen, respectively.

Quantitative Aspects of Waste Nitrogen Synthesis as Hippurate or Phenylacetylglutamine. As shown in Fig. 20-9, glycine and glutamine, respectively, contain one and two nitrogen atoms. Assuming that both benzoate and phenylacetate are completed converted to their amino acid conjugates, the phenylacetylglutamine pathway would be approximately twice as effective on an equimolar dosage basis in disposing of waste nitrogen as compared with the hippurate pathway. This relationship has important clinical considerations. For example, the usual dose of 1.74 mmol/kg per day of sodium benzoate (250 mg/kg per day) results in the synthesis of 24 mg/kg per day of waste nitrogen as hippurate, an amount of nitrogen contained in only 0.15 g of dietary protein per kilogram per day—not a very effective mechanism for disposal of dietary nitrogen. If an equimolar amount of phenylacetate is added, the amount of waste nitrogen synthetic capacity is tripled, accounting for the dietary nitrogen contained in 0.45 g of protein per kilogram. If only sodium phenylacetate is administered at a dose of 3.5 mmol/kg per day (550 mg/kg per day), waste nitrogen synthetic capacity would be sufficient to dispose of the nitrogen contained in 0.6 g of protein per kilogram per day.

Thus the standard therapeutic protocol described in Table 20-4 may be modified by substituting phenylacetate for benzoate, providing it can be demonstrated that the increased dose of phenylacetate does not exceed the capacity for phenylacetylglutamine biosynthesis by the liver and kidney. Preliminary data[145] suggest that the higher dose of phenylacetate may be tolerated with no accumulation of phenylacetate in plasma. It is hoped that this change may affect the high mortality of these diseases (Fig. 20-10).

Dietary Aspects of Treatment of CPSD and OTCD. Notwithstanding the establishment of new pathways of waste nitrogen synthesis and excretion, some manipulation of dietary nitrogen intake is necessary to reduce the requirement for waste nitrogen synthesis. The current recommended dietary protocol includes 0.7 g/kg per day of food protein and 0.7 g/kg per day of an essential amino acid mixture. The essential amino acids offer two advantages. They ensure a high quality nitrogen intake and they contain only 11 to 12 percent nitrogen as compared with whole protein, of which 16 percent is nitrogen. The diet is supplemented with citrulline, which serves as a source of arginine but contributes one less nitrogen atom to the free amino pool than does arginine. As growth rate slows and protein accretion declines as a percentage of body weight, nitrogen tolerance of CPSD and OTCD patients may decrease. It may then be advisable to reduce nitrogen intake to levels compatible with growth.

Fig. 20-10 Actuarial survival curves for: 27 ASD patients, 26 survivors; 16 CPSD patients, 12 survivors; 16 OTCD patients, 9 survivors. The survival of ASD patients is significantly different from CPS ($p < 0.05$) and OTCD ($p < 0.001$). The apparent increased survival of CPSD patients as compared to those with OTCD does not reach statistical significance.

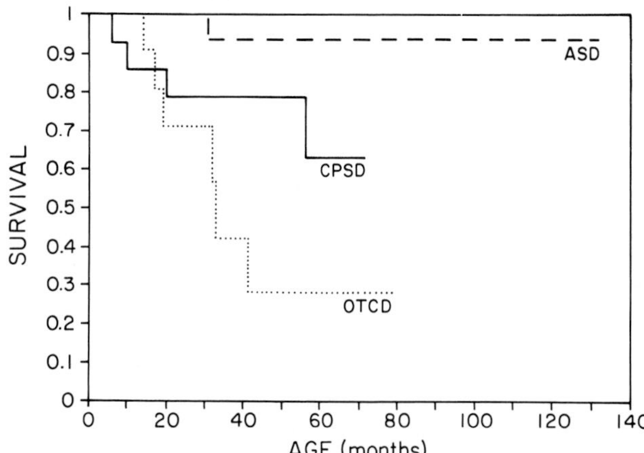

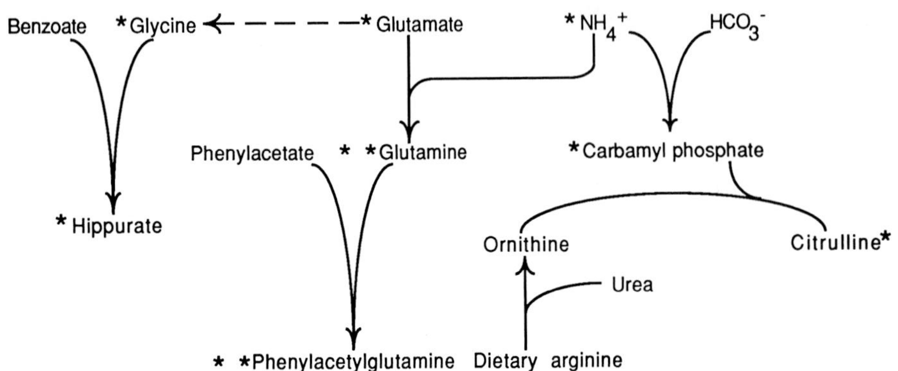

Fig. 20-11 The pathways of waste nitrogen synthesis in patients with ASD when treated as described in Table 20-4. Supplementary dietary arginine supports the continued synthesis of citrulline and hence its excretion as a waste nitrogen product. Benzoate and phenylacetate function as described in Fig. 20-9. The interrupted line denotes a series of reactions described in Fig. 20-9. The asterisks denote nitrogen atoms destined for waste nitrogen excretion in citrulline, hippurate, and phenylacetylglutamine.

Treatment of Argininosuccinic Acid Synthetase Deficiency (Neonatal Form)

The therapy of ASD exploits citrulline as a waste nitrogen product by a mechanism similar to that used in ALD. The diet is supplemented with arginine to stimulate citrulline synthesis and excretion. As a waste nitrogen product, citrulline has two disadvantages as compared with argininosuccinate: it has only one waste nitrogen atom (derived from carbamyl phosphate), and its renal clearance at high plasma citrulline levels is 20 percent of the glomerular filtration rate. However, it appears that when benzoate and/or phenylacetate is added to supplementary dietary arginine, sufficient waste nitrogen capacity is achieved to permit a natural diet with protein intake limited to 1.5 to 2.0 g/kg per day, the higher and lower amounts offered to infants under 1 year of age and older children, respectively. Figure 20-11 describes the pathways of waste nitrogen synthesis and excretion in ASD. Examination of the partition of urinary nitrogen in three ASD patients[145] revealed that citrulline, hippurate, and phenylacetylglutamine nitrogen contributed, respectively, 12, 17, and 22 percent of waste nitrogen. Only one of the citrulline nitrogen atoms was considered to be waste nitrogen in these calculations.

Liver Transplantation. Although allogeneic orthotopic liver transplants have been done in patients with inborn errors of metabolism,[285–287] the indications for transplantation in such patients have been the consequences of liver failure. Because the survival data of liver transplantation may be better than those of OTCD (and perhaps CPSD), liver transplantation may be a useful form of therapy. One patient with OTCD has recently been transplanted[288] with good results after 1 year. A more desirable form of therapy would be hepatocyte[289] or partial liver transplantation; in such cases part of a parental liver could conceivably be used, and complete rejection may then not be fatal.

Treatment of Neonatal Hyperammonemic Coma

Apart from the hyperammonemia of argininosuccinase deficiency which will respond to intravenous arginine therapy, all neonatal patients with severe neonatal hyperammonemic coma (plasma levels greater than 10 times normal) should be hemodialyzed. This procedure results in a reduction of plasma ammonium levels within a matter of hours,[145,290–293] as compared with peritoneal dialysis, which may require 24 h or more before significant changes are noted in plasma ammonium levels.[294,295] The clearance ammonium and amino acids by hemodialysis are approximately 10 times greater than by peritoneal dialysis.[290,295a,295b] Because exchange transfusion is useful in removing toxins principally confined to the vascular space, it has little role in the removal of ammonium and amino acid accumulations, which are distributed through total body water. It is likely that dialytic procedures exert their principal effect by removing the major nitrogen accumulation product, glutamine.[295b] Stoichiometric considerations and experience[145] suggest that benzoate and phenylacetate by themselves will not be effective in controlling the accumulated nitrogen in severe neonatal hyperammonemia. It may be useful, however, to supply arginine in the doses described in Table 20-4. Prompt and repeated hemodialysis appears to be the most effective method of reducing the plasma ammonium level seen in comatose neonates. As plasma ammonium approaches levels three to four times the upper limits of normal, benzoate and phenylacetate may be effective as described, as shown in Table 20-4.

Treatment of Late Onset Urea Cycle Defects, including Symptomatic OTCD Females

Because virtually all symptomatic patients with defective ureagenesis have evidence of brain damage,[169,295,296] some form of therapy should be instituted to attempt to prevent additional episodes of hyperammonemia and, thereby, prevent further brain damage. There is evidence that ostensibly normal women heterozygous for a mutant OTC allele have mild cerebral dysfunction.[297] The goals of patients with partial defects are similar to those described earlier for the more severe forms of the disease: normal growth; maintenance of normal plasma levels of ammonium, glutamine, and arginine; and absence of orotic aciduria in OTCD heterozygotes.

Current therapeutic recommendations for this group of patients are similar to those described in Table 20-4 with less stringent dietary requirements. It is recommended that patients with the late onset form of CPSD and OTCD be treated similarly to those with the neonatal form with dietary nitrogen derived from a low natural protein diet. The late onset ASD and ALD are treated much as the neonatal form is with perhaps a greater protein allowance. Symptomatic OTCD heterozygotes can tolerate a natural low protein diet restricted to the minimum daily requirement for age.

While in mild cases it may be possible to maintain metabolic control using dietary means alone, the use of benzoate and/or phenylacetate confers special advantages to patients with residual ureagenic activity. Preliminary data[145] indicate that when benzoate and/or phenylacetate is administered to such children receiving a fixed nitrogen intake, urinary urea nitrogen excretion decreases, suggesting that net urea synthesis decreases. When protein intake is then increased, urinary urea nitrogen promptly increases. This sequence of urea excretion suggests that, by diverting nitrogen to amino acid acylation products, urea cycle enzyme activity is suppressed and thereby represents a latent homeostatic reserve ureagenic capacity, which can be called upon if needed.

This finding of increased ureagenesis capacity during benzoate administration in a patient with partial urea cycle defect suggests that benzoate does not impair ureagenesis as implied by animal experiments.[298] Benzoate did not appear to impair argininosuccinate synthesis and excretion when administered in high dosage to a patient deficient in argininosuccinase.[296]

Treatment of Intercurrent Hyperammonemia

The daily treatment program described earlier relies on two factors: limitation of dietary nitrogen to minimize the requirement for waste nitrogen synthesis and medication, which activates new pathways of waste nitrogen synthesis. Increased requirement for waste nitrogen synthesis may occur as a result of noncompliance or intercurrent illness, or accidental or surgical trauma because net proteolysis may increase to a degree greater than can be metabolized by the drugs. If there is interruption of oral medication, rapid hyperammonemia may develop, although hyperammonemia may occur in the absence of any discernible cause.[299] In the presence of symptoms suggestive of hyperammonemia, (vomiting, lethargy, combativeness, confusion, ataxia) a plasma ammonium level should be measured; if it is three times the upper limits of normal, the protocol described in Table 20-5 should be followed.[299] Delays in therapy or partial therapy may prove to be disastrous because further nitrogen accumulation may exceed the capacity of these drugs to synthesize waste nitrogen. Should it appear that medical therapy is unsuccessful, hemodialysis remains the only other satisfactory mechanism for controlling hyperammonemia.

Table 20-5 Protocol for management of intercurrent hyperammonemia. All dietary or intravenous nitrogen intake should be discontinued. After plasma ammonium levels approach normal levels, dietary nitrogen can be gradually offered, following which oral medication can be substituted for intravenous medication.

Carbamyl phosphate or ornithine transcarbamylase deficiency	
Priming infusion, mg/kg over 90 min in 35 ml/kg	
10% glucose	
Sodium benzoate	250
Sodium phenylacetate	250
10% arginine HCl	210 (2 ml/kg)
Sustaining infusion I; mg per kg for no more than *12 hours**	
Sodium benzoate	250 followed by sustaining infusion II *immediately* after plasma NH_4^+ decreases
Sodium phenylacetate	250 followed by sustaining infusion II *immediately* after plasma NH_4^+ decreases
10% Arginine HCl	105 (1 ml per kg)
Sustaining infusion II *(mg per kg per 24 hours)*	
Sodium benzoate	250
Sodium phenylacetate	250
10% Arginine HCl	210 (2 ml per kg)
Hemodialysis if plasma ammonium level does not decrease within 12 to 24 h	
Argininosuccinic acid synthetase deficiency	
Priming infusion, mg/kg over 90 min in 35 ml/kg	
10% glucose	
Sodium benzoate	250
Sodium phenylacetate	250
10% arginine HCl	660 (6 ml/kg)
Sustaining infusion, mg/kg per 24 h	
Sodium benzoate	250
Sodium phenylacetate	250
10% arginine HCl	660 (6 ml/kg)
Hemodialysis if plasma ammonium level does not decrease within 12 to 24 h	
Argininosuccinase deficiency	
Priming infusion, mg/kg over 90 min in 35 ml/kg	
10% glucose	
10% arginine HCl	660 (6 ml/kg)
Sustaining infusion, mg/kg per 24 h	
10% arginine HCl	660 (6 ml/kg)
Hemodialysis if unresponsive to above therapy	

*For patients with partial defects, including females heterozygous for OTCD, sustaining infusion II may be omitted in favor of sustaining infusion I.

Prevention of Neonatal Hyperammonemia in Infants at Risk

For neonates in whom an antenatal diagnosis of a urea cycle was made or who are at risk because of a previously affected sibling, a diagnostic and therapeutic protocol which is effective in establishing and early diagnosis and preventing symptomatic neonatal hyperammonemia has been developed.[296,300] The diagnostic protocol relies on the differential diagnostic value of plasma citrulline or argininosuccinate at 60 h of age, as described earlier. The therapeutic protocol begins within hours of birth and is similar to that described in Table 20-4 with two modifications: dietary protein is excluded for the first 24 h, and arginine is substituted for citrulline. Of 13 affected infants (CPSD 5, OTCD 5, ASD 2, ALD 1) treated in this way, 12 escaped symptomatic neonatal hyperammonemia; one OTCD hemizygote developed hyperammonemia and died.

Results of Therapy

Survival. Fig. 20-11 compares the survival of patients with CPSD (n = 16), OTCD (n = 16), ASD (n = 27) who were either rescued from neonatal hyperammonemic coma or treated prospectively because of a previously affected sibling who died in neonatal hyperammonemic coma.[145]

Only 1 of 27 patients with ASD died, representing a survival rate of 94 percent which is statistically better than survival of CPSD patients ($p < 0.01$) and CPSD patients ($p < 0.05$). Twelve of the sixteen CPSD patients died (63 percent survival) and 9 of the 16 OTCD patients died (28 percent survival), an apparent but not statistically significant difference. If these crude data are corrected for deaths from hyperammonemia alone, survival or CPSD patients, two of whom died from other causes, is better (73 percent, $p < 0.05$) than survival or OTCD patients.

Not shown in Fig. 20-11 are the results of the survival of ALD patients of whom there are 27; one profoundly brain damaged child died after arginine was discontinued by parental request.

Intellectual Development. All patients who were rescued from neonatal hyperammonemic coma are brain damaged. The amount of damage is a function of the degree and duration of hyperammonemia. Severe mental retardation (mean IQ, 53 ± 6) with a very high incidence of cerebral palsy[218,296] often of a severe degree, was the most common outcome.

Intellectual development in a group of seven other patients (CPSD 3, OTCD 2, ASD 2) in whom neonatal hyperammonemic coma was prevented by therapy immediately after birth fared considerably better with a mean IQ score of 93 (range, 67 to 133); at the time of testing, their ages ranged from 13 to 49 months with a mean age of 29 months.[300] Furthermore, survival of this group was significantly better than that of the group rescued from neonatal hyperammonemia coma.[145]

Intercurrent Hyperammonemia

Episodes of hyperammonemia were very common in patients with CPSD and OTCD but uncommon in patients with ASD or ALD. It was the cause of death in all but three patients. Preliminary data[145] suggest that these episodes usually do result in further intellectural deterioration unless the episode is associated with prolonged severe hyperammonemia.

Three patients developed visual impairment following a hyperammonemic episode. In all three pupillary reflexes were normal at the time, suggesting the visual impairment was at the level of the visual cortex. One patient recovered his sight completely, two others remain with significant visual impairment. A 32-year-old man with partial OTCD was reported to have developed visual difficulties associated with his episodes of hyperammonemia.[300a] The mechanism of "cortical blindness" following hyperammonemia is unclear, but we postulate that the increased intracranial pressure associated with hyperammonemia may compress the posterior cerebral arteries against the tentorial rim and thereby impair, to varying degrees, circulation to the visual cortex. Lyle[300b] has described reversible cortical visual impairment caused by such a mechanism.

Results of Treatment of OTCD Heterozygotes. Evaluation of 22 such patients is in process at this writing. Although incomplete, the data suggest that with therapy all features of the disease are improved: nutrition, growth, behavior, biochemical anormalities, and frequency of symptomatic hyperammonemia episodes.[145] There appears to be no further deterioration of intellectual development.

No side effects of benzoate or phenylacetate have been noted in the doses used; there have been over 200 patient-years of experience with both drugs. Severe accidental poisoning has occurred twice at doses 4 and 10 times greater than recommended. Clinical signs and symptoms include fever, obtundation, hyperventilation, severe metabolic acidosis, and cardiovascular collapse.[145]

Summary of Therapy. It is apparent that although therapy prolongs life in patients with CPSD and OTCD, mortality and morbidity are high in this group, which consists chiefly of severely brain damaged children. Furthermore, the medical burden of an artificial diet, large doses of medicine, and constant threat of hyperammonemia imposes a huge medical burden on these families.

Whether prospectively treated patients in whom modifications of therapy have been made (substitution of phenylacetate for benzoate and possibly liver transplantation) will improve survival remains to be tested.

It is equally apparent that treatment is highly effective in ASD patients in whom survival is excellent and in whom intellectual development is normal if neonatal coma is prevented. Although survival of ALD patients is equally good, a question remains as to the effectiveness of prospective therapy in preventing brain damage.

If initial clinical impressions are correct, patients with partial deficiencies, especially OTCD heterozygotes, may profit most from therapy especially if diagnosed early before permanent brain damage occurs.

Antenatal Diagnosis

All five inborn errors of ureagenesis can be diagnosed antenatally. The techniques for doing so vary widely and include measurement of an abnormal metabolite in amniotic fluid, analysis of DNA from chorionic villi or amniocytes, and enzyme analysis on in utero liver biopsy samples.

Carbamyl Phosphate Synthetase Deficiency. At the CPS I locus a frequent restriction fragment length polymorphism was detected using the restriction enzyme Bgl I. Three different types of restriction pattern could be observed following digestion with this enzyme, designated A, BC, and CD. In five of six CPS-deficient families examined, at least one parent was heterozygous for a pattern. In two of these families, both parents were heterozygous, and in all four parents the A pattern was associated with a CPS-deficient allele. In the three families with a single heterozygous parent, once again the A pattern was associated frequently with the CPS-deficient allele. Overall, the A pattern frequency is 0.83 in affected individuals as opposed to 0.20 in controls. Thus, linkage disequilibrium exists between the CPS I deficient allele(s) and the Bgl I restriction fragment length polymorphisms (RFLPs).[245]

The Bgl I polymorphism has obvious utility in prenatal diagnosis of CPS deficiency. Where the linkage phases of both parents' alleles are known, the genotype of the fetus can be determined. Where the linkage phase of only one parent's alleles is known, there is a 50 percent chance for each pregnancy that the disorder can be excluded. Where the affected allele has been transmitted by the informative parent, the chances of an affected pregnancy become 50 percent, and in this setting an additional diagnostic tool for consideration is fetal liver biopsy. Overall, using the Bgl I RFLP, the CPS-deficient phenotype can be predicted in about 50 percent of the families at risk.

Ornithine Transcarbamylase Deficiency. For most families affected with OTC deficiency, where neither deletion nor alteration of a restriction site is detected, linkage analysis using RFLPs must be employed for both carrier assessment and prenatal diagnosis. To date, four RFLPs have been detected at the OTC[247,248] locus. Two are produced with the enzyme Msp I, and 69% of females are heterozygous for one or both of these. A third polymorphism is produced with Bam HI, for which 30% of women are heterozygous. Finally, 11 percent of women are heterozygous for a fourth polymorphism with the enzyme Taq I, a polymorphism that is distinct from the Taq I-site alteration associated with OTC deficiency. Taking into account all four RFLPs at the OTC locus, approximately 80 percent of females are heterozygous for one or more of them. It should be emphasized that RFLPs do not themselves identify mutation at the OTC locus and that, as hypothesized by Haldane, as many as one-third of males with a fatal X-linked disorder like OTC deficiency may have a spontaneous mutation.[301] Subsequent pregnancies in these pedigrees are at virtually no risk of recurrence. Thus, the determination of the carrier status of the mother of an affected proband is critical both to assessment of future risks and to utility of RFLPs in diagnosis. Only where women have been established as carriers of OTC deficiency, either by pedigree analysis or by a positive protein loading or allopurinol test, can the RFLPs, where heterozygous, be employed for prenatal diagnosis. The reliability of fetal diagnosis by linkage with RFLPs for these women could be influenced by recombination within the OTC locus between the marker and the mutation, but to date there has been no such recombination. However, given the large size of the OTC gene, such an event could occur, with a frequency empirically less than 1 percent.

Use of RFLP analysis for prenatal diagnosis of OTC deficiency has recently been reported in four pregnancies of heterozygous carriers.[302] Two pregnancies of one woman were studied by chorionic villus sampling and identified in both cases by karyotype analysis to be male fetuses. One was predicted by analysis of an Msp polymorphism to be affected, and the pregnancy was terminated. A second was predicted to be unaffected, and a normal male was delivered at term. A third at-risk pregnancy in another pedigree was studied using amniocentesis, and the fetus was predicted to be affected using the Bam HI polymorphism. Following termination of the pregnancy, analysis of fetal liver confirmed severe deficiency of OTC activity, while the level of activity of another liver-specific enzyme, carbamyl phosphate synthetase I, was normal. A fourth pregnancy carrying a male was examined using the Msp I polymorphism and predicted to be unaffected.[303] Four additional pregnancies carrying males at risk for OTC deficiency have since been monitored using DNA diagnosis, and all were predicted to be affected.[84] Three of these were confirmed to be deficient by enzyme assay performed on fetal liver.

It should be pointed out that RFLP studies carried out for prenatal diagnosis can also indicate whether a female fetus is heterozygous for OTC deficiency as in the pedigree studied by Pembrey et al.[303] This is particularly important because as many as 18 percent of carrier females exhibit clinically symptomatic OTC deficiency and both appropriate counseling and careful analysis of dietary protein tolerance in the postnatal period are warranted.[304] RFLP studies can also indicate whether asymptomatic female members in newly identified pedigrees are gene carriers. For example, the pedigree shown in Fig. 20-12A[248] displays Msp haplotype information that permitted the conclusion that the maternal aunt, individual II-2, cannot be a carrier for OTC deficiency as she did not inherit the affected X chromosome. Using protein loading tests and RFLP data it has also been possible to identify the source of spontaneous OTC mutation in a number of pedigrees. In the pedigree shown in Fig. 20-12B,[248] the Msp haplotype B is linked to the OTC mutation, and since the mother of the proband II-2 received an A allele from her mother, the mutation must have arisen spontaneously in the unaffected grandfather's B haloptype-bearing X chromosome, presumably in the sperm cell. This pattern of mutational origin has been observed in five additional pedigrees and has also been observed with other X-linked diseases, suggesting that sperm may offer a more vulnerable target for the origination of X-linked mutation.

Where a woman is established to be an OTC heterozygous carrier but no informative RFLP is available, the only current means of prenatal diagnosis involves fetal sex determination and, where a pregnancy carrying a male is involved, subsequent biopsy of the fetal liver,[305] feasible at 18 weeks gestation for direct assay of OTC enzyme activity. This procedure, however, carries a much higher risk of fetal loss than amniocentesis or chorionic villus sampling, perhaps as great as 5 to 10 percent.

Argininosuccinate Synthetase Deficiency. Although there are no currently available molecular techniques useful for antenatal diagnosis of ASD, it would be reasonable to expect they will be available. In their absence measurement of AS activity on fibroblasts or chorionic villus samples is necessary.[19,306] Beaudet et al.[9] have emphasized that a major hazard of antenatal diagnosis of AS analysis is the very low level of activity in heterozygous fetuses leading to confusion with the homozygous state. In order to overcome this problem, a sen-

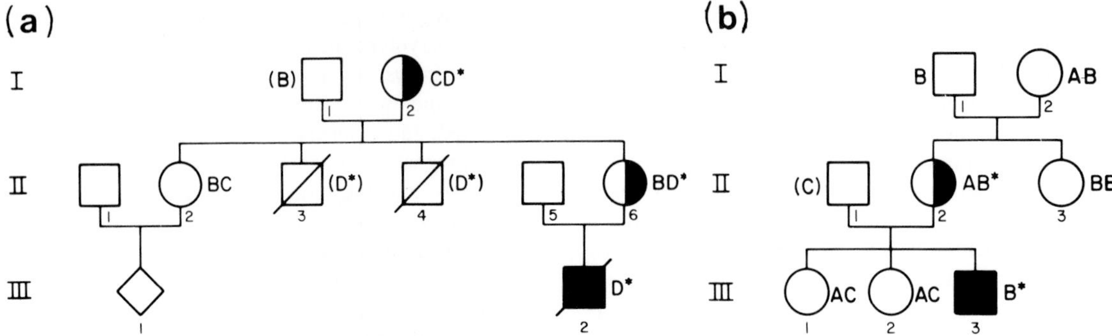

Fig. 20-12 Application of RFLPs for carrier asssessment in two pedigrees at risk for OTC deficiency. Msp haplotypes are designated by letters next to pedigree symbols. Parentheses indicate that the haplotype was inferred from other haplotypes in the pedigree. Asterisks refer to the haplotype of the X chromosome that presumably carries the OTC mutation. *(From Rozen et al.[247] Used by permission.)*

sitive radiometric technique which distinguishes homozygotes from heterozygotes was employed. However, Beaudet et al.[9] suggest that the most reliable technique for detecting homozygous ASD relies on the incorporation of the radioactive label of [^{14}C] citrulline into acid-precipitable protein by intact fibroblasts cultured from amniocytes.

Measurement of citrulline levels in amniotic fluid may also be helpful in diagnosis,[9] although experience with this method is limited.

Argininosuccinase Deficiency. There are two reliable biochemical techniques available for antenatal diagnosis of ASD: measurement of enzyme activity in cultured amniocytes[307] and measurement of argininosuccinic acid levels in amniotic fluid.[307,308] There is currently no molecular approach available for identifying a homozygous ALD fetus.

Arginase Deficiency. A Pvu II restriction fragment length polymorphism has been identified at the human arginase locus and should be of use in carrying out prenatal DNA diagnosis of hyperargininemia.[309] This technique would carry significantly less risk of pregnancy loss than the current method of fetal blood sampling employed for assay of enzymatic activity in erythrocytes (Table 20-1).

Neonatal Screening

Screening newborn infants for urea cycle defects is indicated if three purposes can be fulfilled.[310] Screening should identify neonates sufficiently early in the course of the disease such that prompt therapy will prevent permanent neurologic damage. Screening should be sensitive enough to detect the milder forms of the disease. Screening should also provide useful genetic information.

For infants with the newborn form of urea cycle defects, it is unlikely that screening will be useful for therapeutic purposes.[311,312] Given the delay in the availability of results and the rapidity of onset of signs and symptoms of the disease, it is likely that the permanent brain damage secondary to hyperammonemia could not be confidently prevented. Whether the sensitivity of screening methods can detect these diseases in the asymptomatic neonates remains to be determined, although it is likely in ASD and ALD where the huge accumulation of citrulline and argininosuccinate in plasma and urine offer diagnostic possibilities which are not available in CPSD or OTCD.

The Massachusetts screening program[313] has been successful in identifying late onset ALD in a screening program using paper chromatography of urine obtained at 3 to 4 weeks of age. This study evaluated over 600,000 specimens and found eight cases suggesting a frequency of 1 per 70,000, probably an underestimate because of the loss of an unknown number of ALD patients who died earlier.

The Quebec urine screening program found a similar incidence of ALD by this method, 1.3 per 100,000 samples tested.[314] They were also able to measure urinary citrulline and found an incidence of ASD of 0.4 per 100,000 samples tested.

The Guthrie blood test utilizing appropriate *Bacillus subtilis* auxotrophs has been proposed for screening for ASD, ALD, and arginase deficiency.[315–318] The usefulness of these tests in the neonatal period appears promising for some purposes, but whether they will overcome the reservations cited earlier for detection of the neonatal forms of these diseases remains to be seen.

The Quebec screening program[314] has attempted to identify urea cycle defects by analysis of urinary orotate at 2 to 3 weeks of age. While no cases were identified in this way, this method has the obvious disadvantage of not detecting the severe neonatal forms of the disease.

While neonatal screening may ultimately be shown to have a role in acute metabolic diseases, at the moment there is no substitute for a physician who is keenly aware that all full-term neonates with nonspecific symptoms are candidates for symptomatic inborn errors of metabolism.

Heterozygote Detection in OTC Deficiency

For genetic counseling and antenatal diagnostic purposes, detection of asymptomatic carrier status of the mutant OTC allele is essential. When obligate carrier status can be determined by the presence of multiple cases in a pedigree, the carrier status of other females in the pedigree can often be established by molecular techniques if DNA from an affected patient is available. In the absence of such a pedigree and DNA, a clinical biochemical test currently is the only reliable technique of detecting carriers. The reliability of establishing carrier status of an OTC mutant allele by a history of X-linked inheritance of protein intolerance as suggested by Nussbaum et al.[251] remains to be determined. All biochemical tests for carriers of a mutant OTC allele rely on abnormal ureagenesis in a population of OTCD hepatocytes in the liver of putative

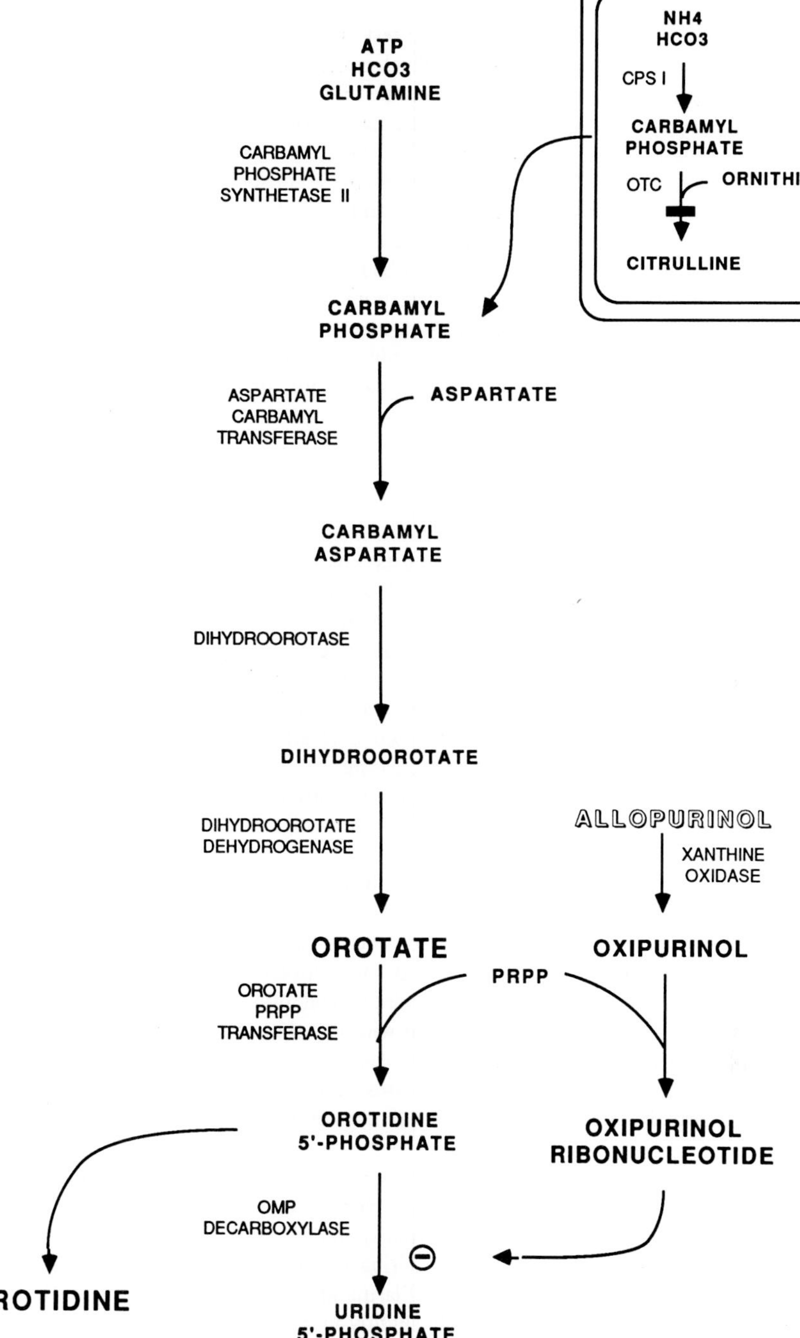

Fig. 20-13 The relationships among intramitochondrial and cytosolic carbamyl phosphate, pyrimidine biosynthesis, and allopurinol metabolism in ornithine transcarbamylase-deficient hepatocytes. When intramitochondrial carbamyl phosphate accumulates in large amounts (as occurs in untreated OTCD hemizygotes or OTCD heterozygotes provoked with a nitrogen challenge), it diffuses into the cytoplasm-stimulating pyrimidine biosynthesis. As a consequence phosphoriboxylpyrophosphate (PRPP) may be depleted, thereby limiting flux through the orotate PRPP transferase reaction resulting in orotate accumulation. However, in asymptomatic OTCD heterozygotes with no ostensible biochemical or clinical abnormalities, pyrmidine biosynthesis will also be increased in the OTCD hepatocytes. Therefore, when orotidine monophosphate decarboxylase (OMP) is inhibited by oxipurinol ribonucleotide (the in vivo reaction produce of allopurinol), orotidine monophosphate accumulates, which leads to orotidine accumulation and orotidinuria, the degree of which serves to distinguish OTCD heterozygotes from normal women.[175]

carriers. The overall hepatic OTC activity is a function of the relative proportion of hepatocytes in which mutant and normal alleles are active.

The hepatocytes bearing the active mutant allele are vulnerable to increased pyrimidine biosynthesis as a consequence of accumulation of carbamyl phosphate, a substrate required for both urea and pyrimidine biosynthesis (Fig. 20-13). The OTC-deficient hepatocytes accumulate mitochondrial carbamyl phosphate, which diffuses into the cytosol,[319,320] where it serves to stimulate pyrimidine biosynthesis. The degree to which carbamyl phosphate accumulates in these cells is a function of its production (presumably related to protein intake) and residual OTC activity, if any. The degree to which increased pyrimidine biosynthesis is detectable in patients is a function of the number of OTCD hepatocytes and sensitivity of methods of detection of pyrimidine overproduction.

The urinary excretion of large amounts of the pyrimidine intermediate, orotic acid, observed in patients with OTCD, is a function not only of increased pyrimidine production but also a consequence of some rate limitation of the orotate phosphoribosyl transferase (OPRT) reaction. It appears that increased flux through the OPRT reaction either because of pyrimidine overproduction or orotate administration leads to depletion of phosphoribosylpyrophosphate, which may limit the OPRT reaction and, thereby, lead to orotate accumulation.[321-323]

The OTC-deficient hepatocytes of putative carriers have until recently been exploited by a nitrogen challenge usually in the form of a high protein meal followed by urinary orotate measurements.[145,324-327] Of known obligate carriers studied this way, 24 were identified by orotic aciduria; two women had negative tests,[145,327] suggesting that such a test is very useful notwithstanding an approximate 10 percent false-negative rate.

The disadvantages of the protein tolerance test have led to the development of the allopurinol test,[175] which relies on two factors: clinically inapparent increased pyrimidine biosynthesis in OTCD hepatocytes and inhibition of orotidine monophosphate decarboxylase by oxopurinol monophosphate, the in vivo reaction product of allopurinol (Fig. 20-13). As a consequence, orotidine monophosphate accumulates and is dephosphorylated with the appearance of orotidine in urine. Of 22 OTCD obligate heterozygotes now tested, 28 had urinary orotidine excretions greater than 4 standard deviations above the upper limits of normal; there were 3 false-negative tests. These preliminary studies suggest the allopurinol test is as reliable as the protein tolerance test but is safer and more convenient.

Arginase Deficiency

Clinical Manifestations. The clinical manifestations of arginase deficiency are strikingly different from those of CPSD, OTCD, ASD, and ALD.[328-336] The major symptoms of arginase deficiency, all of which are progressive, include spastic tetraplegia with the lower limbs affected much more severely than the upper limbs, seizures, psychomotor retardation, hyperactivity, growth failure and in one reported case athetosis.[330] Symptomatic hyperammonemia progressing to coma may occur, but plasma ammonium levels when measured are three to four times normal values, with levels rarely as high as six times normal.

Although there is phenotypic variability with some cases presumably asymptomatic at 4 years of age, close inspection of reported cases suggest clinical manifestations occur early in the first year of life; they include irritability, unconsolable crying, anorexia, vomiting and delayed developmental milestones. A recent report[335] describes a proband with less than 2 percent hepatic arginase activity but with a plasma arginine level of 170 μM, far below other reported cases. The infant was extremely protein-intolerant and died at 49 days of age.

Laboratory Abnormalities. The most prominent laboratory findings include mild hyperammonemia, hyperargininemia as high as 1500 μM, diaminoaciduria (argininuria, lysinuria, cystinuria, ornithinuria), and orotic aciduria. Urinary citrulline and glutamine excretion are also increased. Plasma glutamine levels, if not within normal limits, are only slightly increased.

The increased concentration of many amino acids in cerebrospinal fluid is striking. The very high arginine concentrations are understandable; however no ready hypothesis serves to explain the high cerebrospinal fluid concentration of ornithine, aspartate, threonine glycine, and methionine. As has been noted[336] no pattern characteristic of shared transport systems is apparent.

In addition to orotic aciduria noted above, other pyrimidines—uracil and uridine—are excreted in the urine in greater amounts than normal.[337] The mechanism of pyrimidinuria is unclear. It has been suggested that intramitochondrial ornithine deficiency may be a consequence of the reduced hydrolysis of arginine. As a result, the flux through the OTC reaction may be limited by the relative unavailability of ornithine. The biochemical consequences would then be similar to that found in OTCD: accumulation and diffusion of intramitochondrial carbamyl phosphate into the cytosol and stimulation of pyrimidine biosynthesis. Curiously ornithine administration has no effect on orotic aciduria in arginase deficiency.[338] Another explanation for mitochondrial carbamyl phosphate overproduction and hence pyrimidine overproduction assumes that high intramitochondrial arginine levels inappropriately activate *N*-acetylglutamate synthetase, thereby overstimulating CPS activity.[339] There is little direct evidence to support either of these explanations.

Although large amounts of monosubstituted guanidino compounds are found in the urine of arginase-deficient patients[340-342] most of these are not a result of amidino group donation by arginine, but rather are derivatives of arginine itself; α-keto guanidinovaleric acid (the α-keto analogue of arginine), *N*-acetylarginine, and argininic acid. Of the urinary monosubstituted guanidino groups that are a result of amidino group donation by arginine, guanidinoacetic acid (the normal reaction product of arginine and glycine via glycine transamidinase) is excreted in the largest amount followed by guanidinobutyric acid.

Pathophysiology and Treatment. Unfortunately little is known or has been postulated about the mechanism responsible for the phenotype of arginase deficiency. Presumably the mechanism is some way related to the known laboratory abnormalities described above: episodic mild hyperammonemia, hyperargininemia, and perhaps high plasma and tissue levels of monosubstituted guanidino compounds. Impaired neurotransmitter metabolism has been described in arginase deficiency.[343] Regardless of which one or combination of these factors is culpable, it appears that the restriction of dietary protein and thereby dietary nitrogen may be beneficial. Reduced nitrogen intake will inevitably lead to reduce flux through the attenuated urea cycle and hence reduce arginine biosynthesis. Artificial diets devoid of arginine have been used in an attempt to reduce plasma arginine levels.[338,344,345] These studies are flawed in that nitrogen intake was not constant during the arginine-replete and arginine-deficient study periods. In one of these studies[344] biochemical improvement was noted when 0.9 g/kg per day of an essential amino acid arginine-free diet was substituted for a diet containing 0.9 g/kg per day of protein without recognizing that the artificial diet not only contained no arginine but also contained approximately 30 percent less nitrogen; the essential amino acid mixtures used contained 11 percent nitrogen, whereas natural protein contains 16 percent nitrogen. A similar flaw is noted in a study where the nitrogen-free analogues of several essential amino acids supplemented an essential amino acid arginine-free diet.[338] In formulating dietary treatment of arginase deficiency, it is important to remember that virtually all dietary nitrogen is available for *de novo* synthesis of arginine. This amount is considerably greater than the small amount of arginine residues in dietary protein.

Only preliminary data are available to support the use of benzoate and phenylacetate in arginase deficiency. On theoretical grounds, any diversion of nitrogen from ureagenesis (and hence argininogenesis) should lower plasma arginine levels as well as improve waste nitrogen synthetic capacity. Sodium benzoate at a dose of 375 mg/kg per day led to a reduction of plasma arginine level from 500 to 300 μM in a patient on a very low protein diet (0.5 g/kg per day).[346] On theoretical grounds, the substitution of sodium phenylacetate at a dose of 500 to 550 mg/kg per day should have the salutory effects of diverting twice as much nitrogen from argininogenesis and thereby both permit a more adequate diet and maintain a more normal plasma arginine level. Whether control of plasma arginine has a beneficial clinical effect has yet to be determined.

An interesting approach to therapy employed arginase-loaded erythrocytes which led to in vitro arginine hydrolysis[347]; in vivo studies have yet to be reported.

Supported by grants from the National Institutes of Health (HD 11134, RR52, GM 34433), the Kettering Family Foundation, the M. A. and T. A. O'Malley Foundation, the March of Dimes Birth Defects Foundation, and the John A. Hartford Foundation. We acknowledge the helpful comments of Wayne Fenton and the secretarial assistance of Connie Woznick. We thank Nancy Rent for preparing the manuscript for publication.

REFERENCES

1. CAMPBELL JW: *Comparative Biochemistry of Nitrogen Metabolism.* New York, Academic, 1970.
2. BEAN ES, ATKINSON DE: Regulation of the rate of urea synthesis in liver by extracellular pH. *J Biol Chem* 259:1552, 1984.
3. WALSER M: Roles of urea production, ammonium excretion, and amino acid oxidation in acid-base balance. *Am J Physiol* 250:F181, 1986.
4. BRUSILOW SW: Arginine, an indispensable amino acid for patients with inborn errors of urea synthesis. *J Clin Invest* 72:2144, 1984.
5. RATNER S: Enzymes of arginine and urea synthesis, in Meister A (ed): *Advances in Enzymology.* New York, Wiley, 1973, vol 39, p 1.
6. SNODGRASS PJ: Biochemical aspects of urea cycle disorders. *Pediatrics* 68:273, 1981.
7. MEIJER AJ, HENSGENS HESJ: Ureogenesis, in Sies H (ed): *Metabolic Compartmentation.* New York, Academic, 1982, p 259.
8. JACKSON MJ, BEAUDET AL, O'BRIEN WE: Mammalian urea cycle enzymes. *Annu Rev Genet* 20:431, 1986.
9. BEAUDET AL, O'BRIEN WE, BOCK HGO, FREYTAG SO, SU TS: The human argininosuccinate synthetase locus and citrullinemia, in Harris H, Hirschhorn K (eds): *Advances in Human Genetics.* New York Plenum, 1986, p 161.
10. LUSTY CJ: Catalytically active monomer and dimer forms of rat liver carbamoyl-phosphate synthetase. *Biochemistry* 20:3665, 1981.
11. JERNIGAN HM: Urea formation in rat, bovine and human lens. *Exp Eye Res* 37:551, 1983.
12. BRAUNSTEIN AE: Les voies principales de l'assimilation et dissimilation de l'azote chez les animaux. *Adv Enzymol* 19:335, 1957.
13. DE HANN EJ, TAGER JM, SLATER EC: Factors affecting the pathway of glutamate oxidation in rat-liver mitochondria. *Biochim Biophys Acta* 131:1, 1967.
14. CHARLES R, TAGER JM, SLATER EC: Citrulline synthesis in rat-liver mitochondria. *Biochim Biophys Acta* 131:29, 1967.
15. FRIEDEN C: The regulation of glutamate dehydrogenase, in Grisolia S, Baguena R, Mayor F (eds): *The Urea Cycle.* New York, Wiley, 1976, p 59.
16. MCCARTHY AD, TIPTON KF: Glutamate dehydrogenase, in Hertz L, Kvamme E, McGeer E, Schousbee A (eds): *Glutamate and GABA in the Central Nervous System.* New York, AR Liss, 1983, p 19.
17. MCGIVAN JD, CHAPPEL JB: On the metabolic function of glutamate dehydrogenase in rat liver. *FEBS Lett* 52:1, 1975.
18. KREBS HA, HEMS R, LUND P, HALLIDAY D, READ WWC: Sources of ammonia for mammalian ureas synthesis. *Biochem J* 176:733, 1978.
19. HÄUSSINGER D: Regulation of hepatic ammonia metabolism: The intercellular glutamine cycle. *Adv Enzyme Regul* 25:159, 1986.
20. JUNGERMAN K: Functional heterogeneity of periportal and perivenous hepatocytes. *Enzyme* 35:161, 1986.
21. COOPER JL, NIEVES E, ROSENSPIRE KC, DE RICCO SF, GEBHARD AS, BRUSITOW SW: Short term metabolic fate of L- (13 N) alanine, L-(13 N) glutamate, and L- (amide 13N) glutamine in normal rat liver. *J Biol Chem,* in press.
22. MEIJER AJ: Channeling of ammonia from glutaminase to carbamoylphosphate synthetase in liver mitochondria. *FEBS Lett* 3040:249, 1985.
23. COOPER JL, NIEVES E, COLEMAN AE, FILC-DE RECCO S, GELBARD AS: Short-term fate of [13N] ammonia in rat liver in vivo. *J Biol Chem* 262:1073, 1987.
24. WINDMUELLER HG: Glutamine utilization by the small intestine, in Meister A (ed): *Advances in Enzymology.* New York, Wiley, 1982, p 201.
25. WINDMUELLER HG, SPAETH AE: Respiratory fuels and nitrogen metabolism in vivo in small intestine of fed rats. *J Biol Chem* 255:107, 1980.
26. FEATHERSTON WR, ROGERS QR, FREEDLAND RA: Relative importance of kidney and liver in synthesis of arginine by the rat. *Am J Physiol* 224:127, 1973.
27. WINDMUELLER HG, SPAETH AE: Source and fate of circulating citrulline. *Am J Physiol* 241:E473, 1981.
28. CAREY GP, KIME Z, ROGERS QR, MORRIS JG, HARGROVE D, BUFFINGTON CA, BRUSILOW SW: An arginine deficient diet in humans does not evoke hyperammonemia or orotic aciduria. *J Nutr* 117:1734, 1987.
29. MARLISS EB, AOKI TT, POZEFSKY T, MOST AS, CAHILL GF JR: Muscle and splanchnic glutamine and glutamate metabolism in postabsorptive and starved man. *J Clin Invest* 50:814, 1971.
30. RUDERMAN NB, BERGER M: The formation of glutamine and alanine in skeletal muscle. *J Biol Chem* 249:5500, 1974.
31. GARBER AJ, KARL IE, KIPNIS DM: Alanine and glutamine release from skeletal muscle. *J Biol Chem* 251:826, 1976.
32. LOWENSTEIN JM: Ammonia production in muscle and other tissues: The purine nucleotide cycle. *Physiol Rev* 52:382, 1972.
33. BRADY TG, O'DONOVAN CI: A study of the tissue distribution of adenosine deaminase in six mammal species. *Comp Biochem Physiol* 14:101, 1965.
34. RÄIHÄ NCR, SUIHKONEN J: Development of urea-synthesizing enzymes in human liver. *Acta Paediatr Scand* 57:121, 1968.
35. TEDESCO TA, MELLMAN WJ: Argininosuccinate synthetase activity and citrulline metabolism in cells cultured from a citrullinemic subject. *Proc Natl Acad Sci USA* 57:829, 1967.
36. MATSUDA I, ARASHIMA S, NAMBU H, TAKEKOSHI Y, ANAKURA M: Hyperammonemia due to a mutant enzyme of ornithine transcarbamylase. *Pediatrics* 48:595, 1971.
37. SAUDUBRAY JM, CATHELINEAU L, LAUGIER JM, CHARPENTIER C, LEJUNE JA, MOZZICONACCI P: Hereditary ornithine transcarbamylase deficiency. *Acta Paediatr Scand* 64:464, 1975.
38. HEIDEN CVD, DESPLANQUE J, BAKKER HD: Some kinetic properties of liver ornithine carbamoyl transferase (OCT) in a patient with OCT deficiency. *Clin Chim Acta* 80:519, 1977.
39. QURESHI IA, LETARTE J, OUELLET R: Study of enzyme defect in a case of ornithine transcarbamylase deficiency. *Diabete Metab* 4:239, 1978.
40. BRIAND P, FRANCOIS B, RABIER D, CATHELINEAU L: Ornithine transcarbamylase deficiencies in human males; kinetic and immunochemical classification. *Biochim Biophys Acta* 704:100, 1982.
41. FRANCOIS B, BRIAND P, CATHELINEAU L: Immunochemical assay in 16 boys with ornithine transcarbamylase deficiency. *Adv* Exp Med Biol 153:53, 1982.
42. MATSUDA I, NAGATA N, OHYANAGI K, TSUCHIYAMA A, YAMAMOTO H, HASE Y, KODAMA H, KAI Y: Biochemical heterogeneity of ornithine carbamoyl transferase (OCT) in patients with OCT deficiency. Jpn J Hum Genet 29:327, 1984.
43. SCHIMKE RT: Adaptive characteristics of urea cycle enzymes in the rat. *J Biol Chem* 237:459, 1962.
44. NUZUM CT, SNODGRASS PJ: Urea cycle enzyme adaptation to dietary protein in primates. *Science* 172:1042, 1971.
45. DAS TK, WATERLOW JC: The rate of adaptation of urea cycle enzymes, aminotransferases and glutamic dehydrogenase to changes in dietary protein intake. *Br J Nutr* 32:353, 1974.
46. MCINTYRE P, DEMARTINIS ML, HOOGENRAD N: Changes in carbamyl phosphate synthetase during development and in response to diet. Application of the electrophoretic transfer technique. *Biochem Int* 6:365, 1983.
47. HURWITZ R, KRETCHMER N: Development of arginine-synthesizing enzymes in mouse intestine. *Am J Physiol* 251:G103, 1986.
48. RAFOTH RJ, ONSTAD GR: Urea synthesis after oral protein ingestion in man. *J Clin Invest* 56:1170, 1975.
49. COHEN NS, CHEUNG CW, RAIJMAN L: The effects of ornithine on mitochondrial carbamyl phosphate synthesis. *J Biol Chem* 255:10248, 1980.
50. METOKI K, HOMMES FA: A possible limiting factor in urea synthesis by isolated hepatocytes: The transport of ornithine into hepatocytes and mitochondria. *Int J Biochem* 16:1155, 1984.
51. VALLE D, WALSER M, BRUSILOW SW, KAISER-KUPFER M: Amino acid metabolism and correction of hyperornithinemia with an arginine-deficient diet. *J Clin Invest* 65:371, 1980.
52. COHEN NS, CHEUNG CW, RAIJMAN L: Channeling of extra-mitochondrial ornitine to matrix ornithine transcarbamylase. *J Biol Chem* 262:203, 1987.
53. BANKO G, ZOLLNER H: Does ornithine stimulate carbamoylphosphate synthetase? *Int J Biochem* 17:503, 1985.
54. WALSER M: Urea cycle disorders and other hyperammonemia syndromes, in Stanbury JB, Wyngaarden JB, Fredrickson DS, Goldstein JL, Brown ML (eds): *The Metabolic Basis of Inherited Disease,* 5th ed. New York, McGraw-Hill, 1983, p 402.
55. MEIJER AJ: Regulation of carbamoylphosphate synthase (ammonia) in

liver in relation to urea cycle activity, in Ochs RS, Hanson RW, Hall Z (eds): *Metabolic Regulation*. New York, Elsevier, 1985, p 171.

56. SHIGESDA K, TATIBANA M: Role of acetylglutamate in ureotelism. *J Biol Chem* 246:5588, 1971.

57. STEWART PM, WALSER M: Short term regulation of ureagenesis. *J Biol Chem* 255:5270, 1980.

58. ZOLLNER H: Regulation of urea synthesis. The effect of ammonia on the N-acetylglutamate content of isolated rat liver cells. *Acta Biochim Biophys* 676:170, 1981.

59. MEIJER AJ, VAN WOERKOM GM, WANDERS RJA, LOF C: Transport of N-acetylglutamate in rat-liver mitochondria. *Eur J Biochem* 124:325, 1982.

60. MEIJER AJ, COR LOF, RAMOS IC, VERHOEVEN AJ: Control of ureagensis. *Eur J Biochem* 148:189, 1985.

61. WANDERS RJA, VAN ROERMUND CWT, MEIJER AJ: Analysis of the control of citrulline synthesis in isolated rat-liver mitochondria. *Eur J Biochem* 142:247, 1984.

62. MEIJER AJ, VERHOEVEN AJ: N-acetylglutamate and urea synthesis. *Biochem J* 223:559, 1984.

63. LUND P, WIGGINS D: Is N-acetylglutamate a short-term regulator of urea synthesis? *Biochem J* 218:991, 1984.

64. LUND P, WIGGINS D: Inhibition of carbamoyl-phosphate synthese (ammonia) by Tris and Hepes. *Biochem J* 243:273, 1987.

65. SHIGESADA K, AOYAGI K, TATIBANA M: Role of acetylglutamate in ureotelism. *Eur J Biochem* 85:385, 1978.

66. COHEN NS, KYAN FS, KYAN SS, CHEUNG C, RAIJMAN L: The apparent Km of ammonia for carbamoyl phosphate synthetase (ammonia) in situ. *Biochem J* 229:205, 1985.

67. CHEUNG CW, RAIJMAN L: Arginine, mitochondrial arginase, and the control of carbamyl phosphate synthesis. *Arch Biochem Biophys* 209:643, 1981.

68. COHEN PP: Regulation of the ornithine-urea cycle enzymes, in Waterlow JC, Stephen JML (eds): *Nitrogen Metabolism in Man, Applied Science*, 1981, p 215.

69. VERHOVEN AJ, MEIJER AJ: The effect of hormones on mitochondrial functions in liver in relation to nitrogen metabolism, in Quagliariello E, Slater EC, Kroon AM (eds): *Achievements and Perspectives of Mitochondrial Research, Bioenergetics*. Amsterdam, Elsevier, 1985, vol 1, p 509.

70. ADCOCK MW, O'BRIEN WE: Molecular cloning of cDNA for rat and human carbamyl phosphate synthetase I. *J Biol Chem* 259:13471, 1984.

71. MORRIS SM, MONCMAN CL, RAND KD, DIZIKES GJ, CEDERBAUM SD, O'BRIEN WE: Regulation of in mRNA levels of five urea cycle enzymes in rat liver by diet, cyclic AMP and glucocorticoids. *Arch Biochem Biophys* 256:343, 1987.

72. RYALL J, RACHUBINSKI RA, NGUYEN M, ROZEN R, BROGLIE KE, SHORE GC: Regulation and expression of carbamyl phosphate synthetase I mRNA in developing rat liver and Morris hepatoma 5123D. *J Biol Chem* 259:9172, 1984.

73. NYUNOYA H, BROGLIE KE, WIDGREN EE, LUSTY CJ: Characterization and derivation of the gene coding for mitochondrial carbamyl phosphate synthetase I of rat. *J Biol Chem* 260:9346, 1985.

74. NYUNOYA H, ARGAN C, LUSTY CJ, SHORE GC: Import and processing of hybrid proteins by mammalian mitochondria *in vivo*. *J Biol Chem* 261:800, 1986.

75. RUBINO SD, NYUNOYA H, LUSTY CJ: In vivo synthesis of carbamyl phosphate from NH_3 by the large subunit of Escherichia coli carbamyl phosphate synthetase. *J Biol Chem* 262:4382, 1987.

76. NYUNOYA H, BROGLIE KE, LUSTY CJ: The gene coding for carbamoyl-phosphate synthetase I was formed by fusion of an ancestral glutaminase gene and a synthetase gene. *Proc Natl Acad Sci USA* 82:2244, 1985.

77. RUBINO SD, NYUNOYA H, LUSTY CJ: Catalytic domains of carbamyl phosphate synthetase. Glutamine-hydrolyzing site of *Escherichia coli* carbamyl phosphate synthetase. *J Biol Chem* 261:11320, 1986.

78. SHORE G: Personal communication.

79. LINDGREN V, DE MARTINVILLE B, HORWICH AL, ROSENBERG LE, FRANCKE U: Human ornithine transcarbamylase locus mapped to band Xp21.1, near the Duchenne muscular dystrophy locus. *Science* 226:698, 1984.

80. OTC is 12 cM from DMD. Gene Mapping Workshop, 1986.

81. KRAUS JP, ROSENBERG LE: Purification of low-abundance messenger RNAs from rat liver by polysome immunoabsorption. *Proc Natl Acad Sci USA* 79:4051, 1982.

82. HORWICH AL, KRAUS JP, WILLIAMS K, KALOUSEK F, KONIGSBERG W, ROSENBERG LE: Molecular cloning of the cDNA coding for rat ornithine transcarbamylase. *Proc Natl Acad Sci USA* 80:4258, 1983.

83. HORWICH AL, FENTON WA, WILLIAMS KR, KALOUSEK F, KRAUS JP, DOOLITTLE RF, KONIGSBERG W, ROSENBERG LE: Structure and expression of a complementary DNA for the nuclear coded precursor of human mitochondrial ornithine transcarbamylase. *Science* 224:1068, 1984.

84. FENTON W: Personal communication.

85. HATA A, TSUZUKI T, SHIMADA K, TAKIGUCHI M, MORI M, MASUDA I: Isolation and characterization of the human ornithine transcarbamylase gene: Structure of the 5′ end region. *J Biochem* 100:717, 1986.

86. VERES G, CRAIGEN WJ, CASKEY CT: The 5′ flanking region of the ornithine transcarbamylase gene contains DNA sequences regulating tissue-specific expression. *J Biol Chem* 261:7588, 1986.

87. WEST A: Personal communication.

88. KRAUS JP, HODGES PE, WILLIAMSON CL, HORWICH AL, KALOUSEK F, WILLIAMS KR, ROSENBERG LE: A cDNA clone for the precursor of rat mitochondrial ornithine transcarbamylase: Comparison of rat and human leader sequences and conservation of catalytic sites. *Nucleic Acid Res* 13:943, 1985.

89. HODGES P: Unpublished observations.

90. DOUGLAS MG, MCCAMMON MT, VASSAROTTI A: Targeting proteins into mitochondria. *Microbiol Rev* 50:166, 1986.

91. ARGAN C, LUSTY CJ, SHORE GC: Membrane and cytosolic components affect transport of the precursor for ornithine carbamyl-transferase into mitochondria. *J Biol Chem* 258:6667, 1983.

92. ARGAN C, SHORE GC: The precursor to ornithine carbamyl transferase is transported to mitochondria as a 5S complex containing an import factor. *Biochem Biophys Res Commun* 131:289, 1985.

93. MORI M, MIURA S, MORITA T, TAKIGUCHI M, TATIBANA M: Ornithine transcarbamylase in liver mitochondria. *Mol Cell Biochem* 49:97, 1982.

94. KOLANSKY D, CONBOY JG, FENTON WA, ROSENBERG LE: Energy-dependent transloction of the precursor of ornithine transcarbamylase by isolated rat liver mitochondria. *J Biol Chem* 257:8567, 1982.

95. SCHLEYER M, NEUPERT W: Transport of proteins into mitochondria: Translocation intermediates spanning contact sites between outer and inner membranes. *Cell* 43:339, 1985.

96. SZTUL E: Personal communication.

97. MORI M, MIURA S, TATIBANA M, COHEN PP: Characterization of a protease apparently involved in processing of pre-ornithine transcarbamylase of rat liver. *Proc Natl Acad Sci USA* 77:7044, 1980.

98. CONBOY JG, FENTON WA, ROSENBERG LE: Processing of preornithine transcarbamylase requires a zinc-dependent protease localized to the mitochondrial matrix. *Biochem Biophys Res Commun* 105:1, 1982.

99. KALOUSEK F, ORSULAK MD, ROSENBERG LE: Newly processed ornithine transcarbamylase subunits are assembled to trimers in rat liver mitochondria. *J Biol Chem* 259:5392, 1984.

100. HORWICH AL, KALOUSEK F, MELLMAN I, ROSENBERG LE: A leader peptide is sufficient to direct mitochondrial import of a chimeric protein. *EMBO J* 4:1129, 1985.

101. NYUNOYA H, ARGAN C, LUSTY CJ, SHORE GC: Import and processing of hybrid proteins by mammalian mitochondria *in vitro*. *J Biol Chem* 268:800, 1986.

102. HORWICH AL, KALOUSEK F, FENTON WA, POLLOCK RA, ROSENBERG LE: Targeting of pre-ornithine transcarbamylase to mitochondria: Definition of critical regions and residues in the leader peptide. *Cell* 44:451, 1986.

103. KALOUSEK F, FENTON WA, FURTAK K, POLLOCK RA, ROSENBERG LE: The ornithine transcarbamylase leader peptide directs mitochondrial import through both its midportion structure and net positive charge. *J Cell Biol*, in press.

104. KRAUS J, KALOUSEK F, NOVOTNY J, SWAROOP M, ROSENBERG LE: The role of the most amino terminal sequence of the leader peptide on targeting ornithine transcarbamylase (OTC) to mitochondria. *Am J Hum Genet* 39:A206, 1986.

105. GILLESPIE LL, ARGAN C, TANEJA AT, HODGES RS, FREEMAN KB, SHORE GC: A synthetic signal peptide blocks import of precursor proteins destined for the mitochondrial inner membrane or matrix. *J Biol Chem* 260:16045, 1985.

106. EPAND RM, HUI SW, ARGAN C, GILLESPIE LL, SHORE GC: Structural analysis and amphiphilic properties of a chemically synthesized mitochondrial signal peptide. *J Biol Chem* 261:10017, 1986.

107. MCINTYRE P, GRAF L, MERCER JFB, WAKE SA, HUDSON P, HOOGENRAAD N: The primary structure of the import mitochondrial protein, ornithine transcarbamylase from rat liver: mRNA levels during ontogeny. *DNA* 4:147, 1985.

108. SHEFFIELD WP, NGUYEN M, SHORE GC: Expression in *Escherichia coli* of functional precursor to the rat liver mitochondrial enzyme, ornithine carbamyl transferase. Precursor import and processing *in vitro*. *Biochem Biophys Res Commun* 134:21, 1986.

109. CHENG MY, POLLOCK RA, HENDRICK JP, HORWICH AL: The cytoplasmically-synthesized subunit precursor of human mitochondrial ornithine transcarbamylase can be imported and proteolytically processed to an enzymatically active form by mitochondria of *S. cerevisiae*. *Proc Natl Acad Sci USA* 84:4063, 1987.

110. HORWICH AL, FENTON WA, FIRGAIRA FA, FOX JE, KOLANSKY D, MELLMAN IS, ROSENBERG LE: Expression of amplified DNA sequences of ornithine

transcarbamylase in HeLa cells: Arginine residues may be required for mitochondrial import of enzyme precursor. *J Cell Biol* 100:1515, 1985.

111. KELLEY K: Personal communication.

112. BRIAND P: Personal communication.

113. VERES G, personal communication.

114. SU TS, BOCK HGO, O'BRIEN WE, BEAUDET AL: Cloning of cDNA for argininosuccinate synthetase mRNA and study of enzyme overproduction in a human cell line. *J Biol Chem* 256:11826, 1981.

115. SU TS, NUSSBAUM RL, AIRHART S, LEDBETTER DH, MOHANDAS T, O'BRIEN WE, BEAUDET AL: Human chromosomal assignments for 14 argininosuccinate synthetase pseudogenes: Cloned DNAs as reagents for cytogenetic analysis. *Am J Hum Genet* 36:954, 1984.

116. FREYTAG SO, BEAUDET AL, BOCK HGO, O'BRIEN WE: Molecular structure of the human argininosuccinate synthetase gene: Occurrence of alternative mRNA splicing. *Mol Cell Biol* 4:1978, 1984.

117. BOCK HGO, SU TS, O'BRIEN WE, BEAUDET AL: Sequence for human argininosuccinate synthetase cDNA. *Nucleic Acids Res* 11:6505, 1983.

118. BOYCE FM, ANDERSON MG, RUSK CD, FREYTAG SO: Human argininosuccinate synthetase minigenes are subject to arginine-mediated repression but not to *trans* induction. *Mol Cell Biol* 6:1244, 1986.

119. JINNO Y, NOMIYAMA H, MATUO S, SHIMADA K, MATSUDA I: Structure of the 5′ end region of the human argininosuccinate synthetase gene. *J Inherit Dis* 8:157, 1985.

120. JINNO Y, MATUO S, NOMIYAMA H, SHIMADA K, MATSUDA I: Novel structure of the 5′ end region of the human argininosuccinate synthetase gene. *J Biochem* 98:1395, 1985.

121. FREYTAG SO: Personal communication.

122. BEAUDET AL, SU TS, O'BRIEN WE: Dispersion of argininosuccinate synthetase-like human genes to multiple autosomes and the X chromosome. *Cell* 30:287, 1982.

123. DAIGER SP, WILDIN RS, SU TS: Sequences on the human Y chromosome homologous to the autosomal gene for argininosuccinate synthetase. *Nature* 289:682, 1983.

124. FREYTAG SO, BOCK HGO, BEAUDET AL, O'BRIEN WE: Molecular structures of human argininosuccinate synthetase pseudogenes. Evolutionary and mechanistic implications. *J Biol Chem* 259:3160, 1984.

125. SU TS, BEAUDET AL, O'BRIEN WE: Increased translatable messenger ribonucleic acid for argininosuccinate synthetase in canavanine-resistant human cells. *Biochemistry* 20:2956, 1981.

126. AMOS JA, FLEMING BC, GUSELLA JF, JACOBY LB: Relative argininosuccinate synthetase mRNA levels and gene copy number in canavanine-resistant lymphoblasts. *Biochim Biophys Acta* 782:247, 1984.

127. JACKSON MJ, O'BRIEN WE, BEAUDET AL: Arginine-mediated regulation of an argininosuccinate synthetase minigene in normal and canavanine-resistant human cells. *Mol Cell Biol* 6:2257, 1986.

128. HUDSON LD, ERBE RW, JACOBY LB: Expression of human argininosuccinate synthetase gene in hamster transferents. *Proc Natl Acad Sci USA* 77:4234, 1980.

129. SU TS, O'BRIEN WE, BEAUDET AL: Genomic DNA-mediated gene transfer for argininosuccinate synthetase. *Somatic Cell Mol Genet* 10:601, 1984.

130. WOOD PA, PARTRIDGE CA, O'BRIEN WE, BEAUDET AL: Expression of human argininosuccinate synthetase after retrovirual-mediated gene transfer. *Somatic Cell Mol Genet* 12:493, 1986.

131. WOOD PA, HERMAN GE, CHAO CYJ, O'BRIEN WE, BEAUDET AL: Retrovirus mediated gene transfer of argininosuccinate synthetase into cultured rodent cells and human citrullinemic fibroblasts. *Cold Spring Harbor Symp Quant Biol* 51:1027, part II, 1986.

132. O'BRIEN WE, MCINNES R, KALUMCUK K, ADCOCK M: Cloning and sequence analysis of cDNA for human argininosuccinate lyase. *Proc Natl Acad Sci USA* 83:7211, 1986.

133. LAMBERT MA, SIMARD LR, RAY PN, MCINNES RR: Molecular cloning of cDNA for rat argininosuccinate lyase and its expression in rat hepatoma cell lines. *Mol Cell Biol* 6:1722, 1986.

134. WISTOW G, PIATIGORSKY J: Recruitment of enzymes as lens structural proteins. *Science* 236:1554, 1987.

135. DIZIKES GJ, SPECTOR EB, CEDERBAUM SD: Cloning of rat liver arginase cDNA and the elucidation of the regulation of arginase gene expression in H4 rat hepatoma cells. *Somatic Cell Mol Genet* 12:375, 1986.

136. DIZIKES GJ, GRODY WW, KERN RM, CEDERBAUM SD: Isolation of human arginase cDNA and absence of homology between the two arginase genes. *Biochem Biophys Res Commun*, in press.

137. SPARKES RS, DIZIKES GJ, KLISAK I, GRODY WW, MOHANDAS T, HEINZMANN, ZOLLMAN S, LUSIS AJ, CEDERBAUM SD: The gene for human liver arginase (ARG1) is assigned to chromosome band 6q23. *Am J Hum Genet* 39:186, 1986.

138. GRODY WW, DIZIKES GJ, CEDERBAUM DS: Human arginase isozymes, in *Isozymes: Current Topics in Biological and Medical Research*. New York, AR Liss, in press.

139. HUDAK ML, JONES MD, BRUSILOW SW: Differentiation of transient hyperammonemia of the newborn and urea cycle enzyme defects by clinical presentation. *J Pediatr* 107:712, 1985.

140. BALLARD RA, VINOCUR B, REYNOLDS JW, WENNBERG RP, MERRITT A, SWEETMAN L, NYHAN WL: Transient hyperammonemia of the preterm infant. *N Engl J Med* 299:920, 1978.

141. TUCHMAN M: Personal communication.

142. BATSHAW ML, THOMAS GH, BRUSILOW SW: New approaches to the diagnosis and treatment of inborn errors of urea synthesis. *Pediatrics* 68:290, 1981.

143. WEBSTER DR, SIMMONDS HA, BARRY DMJ, BECROFT DMO: Pyrimidine and purine metabolites in ornithine carbamoyl transferase deficiency. *J Inherited Metab Dis* 4:27, 1981.

144. VAN GENNIP AH, VAN BREE-BLOM EJ, GRIFT J, DE BREE PK, WADMAN SK: Urinary purines and pyrimidines in patients with hyperammonemia of various origins. *Clin Chim Acta* 104:227, 1980.

145. BRUSILOW S: Unpublished observations.

146. HOOGENRAAD NJ, MITCHELL JD, DON NA, SUTHERLAND TM, MCLEAY AC: Detection of carbamyl phosphate synthetase 1 deficiency using duodenal biopsy samples. *Arch Dis Child* 55:292, 1980.

147. MATSUSHIMA A, ORII T: The activity of carbamoyl-phosphate synthetase I and ornithine and ornithine transcarbamylase (OCT) in the intestine and screening for OCT deficiency in the rectal mucosa. *J Inherited Metab Dis* 4:83, 1978.

148. NAGATA N, ENDO F, MATSUDA I: Ornithine carbamoyltransferase (OCT) in jejujal mucosa, as a reference of the liver OCT. *Clin Chim Acta* 134:155, 1983.

149. ROSENBERG L: Disorders of propionate and methylmalonate metabolism, in Scriver C, Beaudet A, Sly W, Valle D (eds): *The Metabolic Basis of Inherited Disease*, 6th ed. New York, McGraw-Hill, 1988, chap 29.

150. MCCORMICK K, VISCARDI RM, ROBINSON B, HEININGER J: Partial pyruvate decarboxylase deficiency with profound lactic acidosis and hyperammonemia: Responses to dichloracetate and benzoate. *Am J Med Genet* 22:291, 1985.

151. MATSUO M, OOKITA K, TAKEMINE H, KOIKE K, KOIKE M: Fatal case of pyruvate dehydrogenase deficiency. *Acta Paediatr Scand* 74:140, 1985.

152. GOODMAN S, FIERMAN W: Glutaric acidemia type II, in Scriver C, Beaudet A, Sly W, Valle D (eds): *The Metabolic Basis of Inherited Disease*, 6th ed. New York, McGraw-Hill, 1988, chap 34.

153. AMENDT BA, GREENE C, SWEETMAN L, CLOHERTY J, SHIH V, MOON A, TEEL L, RHEAD WJ: Short-chain acyl-coenzyme A dehydrogenase deficiency. *J Clin Invest* 79:1303, 1987.

154. GLASGOW AM, KAPUR S, MILLER M, BRUDNO S: Neonatal hyperammonemia resulting from severe in utero hepatic necrosis. *J Pediatr* 108:136, 1986.

155. BACHMANN C, COLOMBO JP, JAGGI K: N-acetylglutamate synthetase (NAGS) deficiency: Diagnosis, clinical observations and treatment. *Adv Exp Med Biol* 153:39, 1981.

156. BACHMANN C, KRÄHENBIIHL S, COLOMBO JP, SCHUBEGER G, JAGGI KH, TONY O: N-acetylglutamate synthetase deficiency: A disorder of ammonia detoxification. *N Engl J Med* 304:543, 1981.

157. MACLEOD P, MACKENZIE S, SCRIVER CR: Partial ornithine carbamyl transferase deficiency: An inborn error of the urea cycle presenting as orotic aciduria in a male infant. *Can Med Assoc J* 107:405, 1972.

158. CALL G, SEAY AR, SHERRY R, QURESHI IA: Clinical features of carbamyl phosphate synthetase-I deficiency in an adult. *Ann Neurol* 16:92, 1984.

159. GRANOT E, LOTAN C, LIJOVETZKY G, MATOTH I, SHVIL Y, YATZIV S: Partial carbamyl phosphate synthetase deficiency, simulating Reye's syndrome, in a 9-year-old-girl. *Isr J Med Sci* 22:463, 1986.

160. YUDKOFF M, YANG W, SNODGRASS PJ, SEGAL S: Ornithine transcarbamylase deficiency in a boy with normal development. *J Pediatr* 96:441, 1980.

161. BRUSILOW SW: Inborn errors of urea synthesis, in Lloyd JK, Scriver CR (eds): *Genetic and Metabolic Disease in Pediatrics*. London, Butterworths, 1985, p 140.

162. OIZUMI J, NG WG, KOCH R, SHAW KNF, SWEETMAN L, VELAZQUEZ A, DONNELL GN: Partial ornithine transcarbamylase deficiency associated with recurrent hyperammonemia, lethargy and depressed sensorium. *Clin Genet* 25:538, 1984.

163. TALLAN HH, SHAFFNER F, TAFFET SL, SCHNEIDMAN K, GAULL GE: Ornithine carbamoyltransferase deficiency in an adult male: Significance of hepatic ultrastructure in clinical diagnosis. *Pediatrics* 71:224, 1983.

164. DIMAGNO EP, LOWE JE, SNODGRASS PJ, JONES JD: Ornithine transcarbamylase deficiency—A cause of bizarre behavior in a man. *N Engl J Med* 315:744, 1986.

165. MCMURRAY WC, RATHBUN JC, MOHYUDDIN F, KOEGLER SJ: Citrullinuria. *Pediatrics* 32:347, 1963.

166. DANKS DM, TIPPETT P, ZENTNER G: Severe neonatal citrullinaemia. *Arch Dis Child* 49:579, 1974.

167. MOSER HW, EFRON ML, BROWN H, DIAMOND R, NEUMANN CG: Argininosuccinic aciduria. *Am J Med* 42:9, 1967.
168. ROWE PC, NEWMAN SL, BRUSILOW SW: Natural history of symptomatic partial ornithine transcarbamylase deficiency. *N Engl J Med* 314:541, 1986.
169. RUSSELL A: The implications of hyperammonemia in rare and common disorders, including migraine. *Mt Sinai J Med* 40:609, 1972.
170. DE BRUIJN JG, BRUYN GW, KLAWANS HL JR: Further observations on the possible relationship between migraine and serum ammonia levels. *Clin Neurol Neurosurg* 79:151, 1976.
171. BRUYN GW, DOUMA GJ, GATHIER JC: Migraine and hyperammonaemia, in Dalessio DJ, Dalssard-Nielsen T, Diamond S (eds): *Proceedings of the International Headache Symposium.* Basel, Sandoz, 1971, p 41.
172. MATSUDO Y, TSUJI A, KATUNUMA N: Qualitative abnormality of liver argininosuccinase synthetase in a patient with citrullinemia. *Adv Exp Med Biol* 153:77, 1982.
173. YAJIMA Y, HIRASAWA T, SAHEKI T: Treatment of adult-type citrullinemia with administration of citrate. *Tohoku J Exp Med* 134:321, 1981.
174. SIPILÄ I: Personal communication.
175. BRUSILOW S, VALLE D: Allopurinol induced orotidinuria: A test of heterozygosity for ornithine transcarbamylase deficiency. *Pediatr Res* 21:289A, 1987.
176. RICCIUTI FC, GELEHRTER TD, ROSENBERG LE: X-chromosome inactivation in human liver: Confirmation of X-linkage of ornithine transcarbamylase. *Am J Hum Genet* 28:332, 1976.
177. FRASER CL, ARIEFF A: Hepatic encephalopathy. *N Engl J Med* 313:865, 1985.
178. VOORHIES TM, EHRLICH ME, DUFFY TE, PETITO CK, PLUM F: Acute hyperammonemia in the young primate: Physiologic and neuropathologic correlates. *Pediatr Res* 17:971, 1983.
179. GJEDDE A, LOCKWOOD AH, DUFFY TE, PLUM F: Cerebral blood flow and metabolism in chronically hyperammonemic rats: Effect of an acute ammonia challenge. *Ann Neurol* 3:325, 1978.
180. BARZILAY Z, BRITTEN AG, KOEHLER RC, DEAN MJ, TRAYSTMAN R: Interaction of CO_2 and ammonia on cerebral blood flow and O_2 consumption in dogs. *Am J Physiol* 248:H507, 1985.
181. CHODOBSKI A, SZMYDYNGER-CHODOBSKA J, URBANSKA A, SZCZEPANSKA-SADOWSKA E: Intracranial pressure, cerebral blood flow, and cerebrospinal fluid formation during hyperammonemia in cat. *J Neurosurg* 65:86, 1986.
182. HINDFELT B: Ammonia intoxication and brain energy metabolism, in Kleinberger G, Deutsch G (eds): *New Aspects of Clinical Nutrition.* Basel, Karger, 1983, p 474.
183. BRUSILOW SW, TRAYSTMAN R: Hepatic encephalopathy. *N Engl J Med* 314:768, 1986.
184. BACHMANN C, COLOMBO JP: Increased tryptophan uptake into the brain in hyperammonemia. *Life Sci* 33:2417, 1983.
185. HOURANI BT, HAMLIN EM, REYNOLDS B: Cerebrospinal fluid glutamine as a measure of hepatic encephalopathy. *Arch Intern Med* 127:1033.
186. LEVIN B, ABRAHAM VG, OBERHOLZER VG, BURGENS EA: Hyperammonemia: A deficiency of liver ornithine transcarbamylase, occurrence in mother and child. *Arch Dis Child* 44:152, 1969.
187. VAN DER ZEE SPM, TRIJBELS JMF, MONNENS LAH, HOMMES FA, SCHRETLEN EDAM: Citrullinaemia with rapidly fetal neonatal course. *Arch Dis Child* 46:847, 1971.
188. COOPER AJL, VERGARA F, DUFFY TE: Cerebral glutamine synthetase, in Hertz E, Krammer E, McGeer EG, Schousbee A (eds): *Glutamine, glutamate, and GABA in the Central Nervous System.* New York, AR Liss, 1983, p 77.
189. DUFFY TE, PLUM F, COOPER AJL: Cerebral ammonia metabolism in vivo, in Hertz E, Krammer E, McGeer EG, Schousbee A (eds): *Glutamine, Glutamate, and GABA in the Central Nervous System,* New York, AR Liss, 1983, p 371.
190. BATSHAW ML, WALSER M, BRUSILOW SW: Plasma α-ketoglutarate in urea cycle enzymopathies and its role as a harbinger of hyperammonemic coma. *Pediatr Res* 14:1316, 1980.
191. THOENE J, BATSHAW M, SPECTOR E, KULOVICH S, BRUSILOW S, WALSER M, NYHAN W: Neonaal citrullinemia: Treatment with keto-analogues of essential amino acids. *J Pediatr* 90:218, 1977.
192. KLINE JJ, HUG G, SCHUBERT WK, BERRY H: Arginine deficiency syndrome. *Am J Dis Child* 135:437, 1981.
193. GOLDBLUM OM, BRUSILOW SW, MALDONADO YA, FARMER ER: Neonatal citrullinemia associated with cutaneous manifestations and arginine deficiency. *J Am Acad Dermatol* 14:321, 1986.
194. HOLT LE, SYNDERMAN SE, NORTON PM: The plasma aminogram in kwashiorkor. *Lancet* 2:1343, 1963.
195. VISEK WJ: Arginine needs, physiologic state and usual diets. A reevaluation. *J Nutr* 116:36, 1986.
196. MORRIS JG: Nutritional and metabolic responses to arginine deficiency in carnivores. *J Nutr* 115:524, 1985.
197. VISEK WJ: Arginine and disease states. *J Nutr* 115:532, 1985.
198. SNYDERMAN SE, BOYER A, HOLT EL: The arginine requirement of the infant. *Am J Dis Child* 97:192, 1959.
199. NAKAGAWA I, TAKAHASHI T, SUZUKI T, KOBAYASHI K: Amino acid requirements of children: Minimal needs of tryptophan, arginine and histidine based on nitrogen balance methods. *J Nutr* 80:305,1963.
200. ROSE WC, HAINES WJ, WARNER DT: The amino acid requirements of man. V The role of lysine, arginine and tryptophan. *J Biol Chem* 206:421, 1954.
201. KRAUER-MAYER B, KELLER M, HOTTINGER A: Ober den frauenmilchinduzierten icterus prolongatus des neugeborenen. *Helv Paediatr Acta* 23:68, 1968.
202. HOPKINS IJ, CONNELLY JF, DAWSON AG, HIRD FJR, MADDISON TG: Hyperammonaemia due to ornithine transcarbamylase deficiency. *Arch Dis Child* 44:143, 1969.
203. LEVIN B, ABRAHAM JM, OBERHOLZER VG, BURGESS EA: Hyperammonaemia: A deficiency of liver ornithine transcarbamylase. *Arch Dis Child* 44:152, 1969.
204. BRUTON CJ, CORSELLIS JAN, RUSSELL A: Hereditary hyperammonemia. *Brain* 93:423, 1970.
205. VIDAILHET, LEVIN B, DAUTREVAUX M, PAYSANT P, GELOT S, BADONNEL Y, PIERSON M, NEIMANN N: Citrullinemie. *Arch Fr Pediatr* 28:521, 1971.
206. MARTIN JJ, SCHLOTE W: Central nervous system lesions in disorders of amino-acid metabolism. *J Neurol Sci* 15:49, 1972.
207. EBELS EJ: Neuropathological observations in a patient with carbamylphosphate synthetase deficiency and in two sibs. *Arch Dis Child* 47:47, 1972.
208. WICK H, BACHMANN C, BAUMGARTNER R, BRECHBUHLER T, COLOMBO JP, WIESMANN U, MIHATSCH MJ, OHNACKER H: Variants of citrullinaemia. *Arch Dis Child* 48:636, 1973.
209. LEIBOWITZ J, THOENE J, SPECTOR E, NYHAN W: Citrullinemia. *Arch Pathol Anat Histol* 377:249, 1978.
210. MARTIN JJ, FARRIAUX JP, DE JONGHE P: Neuropathology of citrullinaemia. *Arch Neuropathol (Berl)* 56:303, 1982.
211. KORNFELD M, WOODFIN BM, PAPILE L, DAVIS LE, BERNARD LR: Neuropathology of ornithine carbamyl transferase deficiency. *Acta Neuropathol* 65:261, 1985.
212. LEWIS PD, MILLER AL: Argininosuccinic aciduria. *Brain* 93:413, 1970.
213. SOLITARE CB, SHIH VE, NELLIGAN DJ, DOLAN TF JR: Argininosuccinic aciduria: Clinical, biochemical, anatomical and neuropathologic observations. *J Ment Defic Res* 13:153, 1969.
214. HARDING BN, LEONARD JV, ERDOHAZI M: Ornithine carbamoyl transferase deficiency: A neuropathological study. *Eur J Pediatr* 141:215, 1984.
215. FILLOUX F, TOWNSEND JJ, LEONARD C: Ornithine transcarbamylase deficiency: Neuropathologic changes acquired in utero. *J Pediatr* 108:942, 1986.
216. KENDALL BE, KINGSLEY DPE, LEONARD JV, LINGAM S, OBERHOLZER VG: Neurological features and computed tomography of the brain in children with ornithine carbamoyl transferase deficiency. *J Neurol Neurosurg Psychiatry* 46:28, 1983.
217. MSALL M, BATSHAW ML, SUSS R, BRUSILOW SW, MELLITS ED: Neurologic outcome in children with inborn errors in urea synthesis. *N Engl J Med* 310:1500, 1984.
218. LABRECQUE DR, LATHAM PS, BIELY CA, HSIA YE, KLATSKIN G: Heritable urea cycle enzyme deficiency—Liver disease in 16 patients. *J Pediatr* 94:580, 1979.
219. FLICK JA, LATHAM PS, PERMAN J, BRUSILOW SW: Hepatic involvement in argininosuccinase deficiency. *Pediatr Res* 20:239A, 1986.
220. ZIMMERMAN A, BACHMANN C, BAUMGARTNER R: Severe liver fibrosis in argininosuccinic aciduria. *Arch Pathol Lab Med* 110:136, 1986.
221. SHAPIRO JM, SCHAFFNER F, TALLAN HH, GAULL GE: Mitochondrial abnormalities of liver in primary ornithine transcarbamylase deficiency. *Pediatr Res* 14:735, 1980.
222. ZIMMERMAN A, BACHMANN C, COLOMBO JP: Ultrastructural pathology in congenital defects of the urea cycle; ornithine transcarbamylase and carbamylphosphate synthetase deficiency. *Virchows Arch (A)* 393:321, 1981.
223. LATHAM PS, LABRECQUE DR, MCREYNOLDS JW, KLATSKIN G: Liver ultrastructure in mitochondrial urea cycle enzyme deficiencies and comparison with Reye's syndrome. *Hepatology* 4:404, 1984.
224. O'CONNOR JE, RENAU-PIQUERAS J, GISOLIA S: Effects of urease-induced hyperammonemia in mouse liver. *Virchows Arch (B)* 46:187, 1984.
225. DYBKAER R: List of quantities in clinical chemistry. *J Clin Chem Clin Biochem* 17:822, 1979.
226. FENTON JCB: The estimation of plasma ammonia by ion exchange. *Clin Chim Acta* 7:163, 1962.
227. TRAVENOL LABORATORIES PUBLICATIONS: D-60132-5214, Blood Ammonia Test, 1968.

228. BRUSILOW SW, BATSHAW ML, WABER L: Neonatal hyperammonemic coma. *Adv Pediatr* 29:69, 1982.

229. PROELSS HF, WRIGHT BW: Rapid determination of ammonia in a perchloric acid supernate from blood, by use of an ammonia-specific electrode. *Clin Chem* 19:1162, 1973.

230. ATTILI AF, AITOZO D, CAPOCACCIA L: Rapid determination of plasma ammonia using an ion specific electrode. *Biochem Med* 14:109, 1975.

231. MONDZAC A, EHRLICH GE, SEEGMILLER JE: An enzymatic determination of ammonia in biological fluids. *J Lab Clin Med* 66:526, 1965.

232. SPOONER RJ, TOSELAND PA, GLODBERG DM: The fluorimetric determination of ammonia in protein-free filtrates of human blood plasma. *Clin Chim Acta* 65:47, 1975.

233. BATSHAW ML, BRUSILOW SW: Asymptomatic hyperammonemia in low birthweight infants. *Pediatr Res* 12:221, 1978.

234. IJPMA ST, BLIJENBERG BG, LEIJNSE B: Evaluation of the Du Pont aca ammonia procedure. *Clin Chem* 24:489, 1978.

235. SUNDBERG MW, BECKER RW, ESDERS TW, FIGUERAS J, GOODHUE CT: An enzymic creatinine assay and a direct ammonia assay in coated thin films. *Clin Chem* 29:645, 1983.

236. OBERHOLZER VG, SCHWARZ KB, SMITH CH, DIETZLER DN, HANNA TL: Microscale modification of a cation-exchange column procedure for plasma ammonia. *Clin Chem* 22:1976, 1976.

237. SAMPSON EJ, DEMERS LM: A comparative study of micro-ammonia determinations in plasma using two different methods. *Clin Biochem* 9:192, 1976.

238. WU J, ASH KO, MAO E: Modified micro-scale enzymatic method for plasma ammonia in newborn and pediatric patients; comparison with a modified cation-exchange procedure. *Clin Chem* 24:2172, 1978.

239. COOKE RJ, JENSEN RL: Micromethod for determining plasma ammonia nitrogen with use of ion-selective electrode. *Clin Chem* 29:867, 1983.

240. HUIZENGA JR, GIPS CH: Determination of blood ammonia using the ammonia checker. *Ann Clin Biochem* 20:187, 1983.

241. RATNAIKE RN, BUTTERY JE, HOFFMANN S: Blood ammonia measurement using a simple reflectometer. *J Clin Chem Clin Biochem* 22:105, 1984.

242. MURAWAKI Y, TANIMOTO K, HIRAYAMA, IKUTA Y, WATABE N: A simple and rapid microdiffusion method for blood ammonia using a reflectance meter and a reagent plate and its clinical evaluation for liver disease. *Clin Chim Acta* 144:195, 1984.

243. ANDERSON D, PENNOCK CA, HENDERSON MJ, HOLTON JB: The ammonia checker. *Ann Clin Biochem* 21:69, 1984.

244. SELIGSON D, HIRAHARA K: The measurement of ammonia in whole blood erythrocytes, and plasma. *J Lab Clin Med* 49:962, 1957.

245. FEARON ER, MALLONEE RL, PHILLIPS JA III, O'BRIEN WE, BRUSILOW SW, ADCOCK MW, KIRBY LT: Genetic analysis of carbamyl phosphate synthetase I deficiency. *Hum Genet* 70:207, 1986.

246. GRAF L, MCINTYRE P, HOOGENRAAD N, BROWN G, HANN EA: A carbamylphosphate synthetase deficiency with no detectable immunoreactive enzyme and no translatable mRNA. *J Inherited Metab Dis* 7:104, 1984.

247. ROZEN R, FOX J, FENTON WA, HORWICH AL, ROSENBERG LE: Gene deletion and restriction fragment length polymorphism at the human ornithine transcarbamylase locus. *Nature* 313:815, 1985.

248. ROZEN R, FOX JE, HACK AM, FENTON WA, HORWICH AL, ROSENBERG LE: DNA analysis for ornithine transcarbamylase deficiency. *J Inherited Metab Dis* 9:49, 1986.

249. OLD JM, PURVIS-SMITH S, WILCKEN B, PEARSON P, WILLIAMSON R, BRIAND PL, HOWARD NJ, HAMMOND J, CATHELINEAU L, DAVIES KE: Prenatal exclusion of ornithine transcarbamylase deficiency by direct gene analysis. *Lancet* 1:73, 1985.

250. FRANCKE U: Random X inactivation resulting in mosaic nullisomy of region Xp21.3 associated with heterozygosity for ornithine transcarbamylase deficiency and for chronic granulomatous disease. *Cytogenet Cell Genet* 38:298, 1984.

251. NUSSBAUM RL, BOGGS BA, BEAUDET AL, DOYLE S, POTTER JL, O'BRIEN WE: New mutation and prenatal diagnosis in ornithine transcarbamylase deficiency. *Am J Hum Genet* 38:149, 1986.

252. MADDALENA A, NUSSBAUM RL: A high frequency site for mutation in the human ornithine transcarbamylase gene. *Clin Genet* A285, 1986.

253. NUSSBAUM RL: Personal communication.

254. SAHEKI T, IMAMURA Y, INOUE I, MIURA S, MORI M, OHTAKE A, TATIBANA M, KATSUMATA N, OHNO T: Molecular basis of ornithine transcarbamylase deficiency lacking enzyme protein. *J Inherited Metab Dis* 7:2, 1984.

255. KODAMA H, OHTAKE A, MORI M, IKABE I, TATIBANA M, KAMOSHITA S: Ornithine transcarbamylase deficiency: A case with a truncated enzyme precursor and a case with undetectable mRNA activity. *J Inherited Metab Dis* 9:175, 1986.

256. HOOGENRAAD N, DE MARTINIS ML, DANKS DM: Immunological evidence for an ornithine transcarbamylase lesion resulting in the formation of enzyme with smaller protein subunits. *J Inherited Met Dis* 6:149, 1983.

257. DE MARS R, LE VAN SL, TREND BL, RUSSELL LB: Abnormal ornithine carbamoyltransferase in mice having the sparse-fur mutation. *Proc Natl Acad Sci USA* 73:1693, 1976.

258. BRIAND P, CATHELINEAU L, KAMOUN P, GIGOT D, PENNINCKX M: Increase of ornithine transcarbamylase protein in sparse-fur mice with ornithine transcarbamylase deficiency. *FEBS Lett* 130:65, 1981.

259. BRIAND P, MIURA S, MORI M, CATHELINEAU L, KAMOUN P, TATIBANA M: Cell-free synthesis and transport of precursors of mutant ornithine carbamoyltransferases into mitochondria. *Biochim Biophys Acta* 760:389, 1983.

260. VERES G, GIBBS RA, SCHERER SE, CASKEY CT: The molecular basis of the sparse fur mouse mutation. *Science* 237:415, 1987.

261. QURESHI IA, LETARTE J, OUELLET R: Spontaneous animal models of ornithine transcarbamylase deficiency; studies on serum and urinary nitrogenous metabolites. *Adv Exp Med Biol* 153:173, 1982.

262. ROSENBERG LE, KALOUSEK F, ORSULAK MD: Biogenesis of ornithine transcarbamylase in spf^{ash} mutant mice: Two cytoplasmic precursors, one mitochondrial enzyme. *Science* 222:426, 1983.

263. SU TS, BOCK HGO, BEAUDET AL, O'BRIEN WE: Molecular analysis of argininosuccinate synthetase deficiency in human fibroblasts. *J Clin Invest* 70:1334, 1982.

264. SU TS, BOCK HGO, BEAUDET AL, O'BRIEN WE: Abnormal mRNA for argininosuccinate synthetase in citrullinemia. *Nature* 301:533, 1983.

265. MEYERS RM, LARIN Z, MANIATIS T: Detection of single base substitutions by ribonuclease cleavage at mismatches in RNA: DNA duplexes. *Science* 230:1242, 1986.

266. MCINNES RR, SHIH V, CHILTON S: Interallelic complementation in an inborn error of metabolism: Genetic heterogeneity in argininosuccinate lyase deficiency. *Proc Natl Acad Sci USA* 81:4480, 1984.

267. SIMARD L, O'BRIEN WE, MCINNES RR: Argininosuccinate lyase deficiency: Evidence for heterogeneous structural gene mutations for immunoblotting. *Am J Hum Genet* 39:38, 1986.

268. SMITH RJ, WILMORE DW: Personal communication.

269. BERGSTÖM J, FURST P, NORÉE LO, VINNARS E: Intracellular free amino acid concentration in human muscle tissue. *J Appl Physiol* 36:693, 1964.

270. SYNDERMAN SE, SANSARICQ C, PHANSALKAR SV, SCHACHT RG, NORTON PM: The therapy of hyperammonemia due to ornithine transcarbamylase deficiency in a male neonate. *Pediatrics* 56:65, 1975.

271. BRUSILOW S, BATSHAW M, WALSER M: Use of keto acids in inborn errors of urea synthesis, in Winick M (ed): *Nutritional Management of Genetic Disorders*. Wiley, 1979, p 65.

272. MICHELS VV, POTTS E, WALSER M, BEAUDET AL: Ornithine transcarbamylase deficiency: long term survival. *Clin Genet* 22:211, 1982.

273. YOUNG VR, STEFFEE WP, PENCHARZ ZB, WINTERER JC, SCRIMSHAW NS: Total human body protein synthesis in relation to protein requirements at various ages. *Nature* 253:192, 1975.

274. BIER DM, YOUNG VR: Assessment of whole-body protein-nitrogen kinetics in the human infant, in Foman SJ, Heird WC (eds): *Energy and Protein Needs During Infancy*. New York, Academic, 1986, p 107.

274a. FOMAN SJ: *Infant Nutrition*, 2nd ed. W.B. Saunders, Philadelphia, 1974, p. 71.

275. BRUSILOW SW, VALLE DL, BATSHAW ML: New pathways of nitrogen excretion in inborn errors or urea synthesis. *Lancet* 2:452, 1979.

276. BRUSILOW SW, BATSHAW ML: Arginine therapy of argininosuccinase deficiency. *Lancet* 1:134, 1979.

277. LEWIS HB: Studies in the synthesis of hippuric acid after benzoate ingestion in man. *J Biol Chem* 18:225, 1914.

278. SHIPLE GJ, SHERWIN CP: Synthesis of amino acids in animal organisms. I. Synthesis of glycocoll and glutamine in the human organism. *J Am Chem Soc* 44:618, 1922.

279. BRUSILOW S, TINKER J, BATSHAW ML: Amino acid acylation: A mechanism of nitrogen excretion in inborn errors of urea synthesis. *Science* 207:659, 1980.

280. WEBSTER LT, SIDDIQUI UA, LUCAS SV, STRONG JM, MIEYAL JJ: Identification of separate Acyl-CoA:glycine and Acyl-CoA:L-glutamine N-acyltransferase activities in mitochondrial fractions from liver of rhesus monkey and man. *J Biol Chem* 251:3352, 1976.

281. KILLENBERG PG, WEBSTER LT: Conjugation by peptide bond formation, in Jakoby WB (ed): *Enzymatic Basis of Detoxication*. Academic, 1980, vol II, p 141.

282. MOLDAVE K, MEISTER A: Synthesis of phenylacetylglutamine by human tissue. *J Biol Chem* 229:463, 1957.

283. JAMES OM, SMITH RL, WILLIAMS RT, REIDENBERG M: The conjugation of phenylacetic acid in man, sub-human primates and some nonprimate species. *Proc R Soc Lond* 182:25, 1972.

284. RAPER HS, WAYNE EJ: XXVII. A quantitative study of the oxidation of phenyl-fatty acids in the animal organism. *Biochem J* 22:188, 1928.

285. MALATACK JJ, IWATSUKI S, GARTNER JC, ROE T, FINEGOLD DN, SHAW BW,

ZITELLI BJ, STARZL TE: Liver transplantation for type I glycogen storage disease. *Lancet* 1:1073, 1983.

286. LEWIS HJ, BONTEMPO FA, SPERO JA, RAGNI MV, STARZL TE: Liver transplantation in a hemophiliac. *N Engl J Med* 312:1189, 1985.

287. TUCHMAN M, FREESE DK, SHARP HL, RAMNARAINE M, ASCHER N, BLOOMER JR: Contribution of extrahepatic tissues to biochemical abnormalities in hereditary tyrosinemia type I: Study of three patients after liver transplantation. *J Pediatr* 110:401, 1987.

288. FLYE W: Personal communication.

289. DEMETRIOU AA, WHITING JF, FELDMAN D, LEVENSON SM, CHOWDHURY NR, MOSCIONI AD, KRAM M, CHOWDHURY JR: Replacement of liver function in rats by transplantation of microcarrier-attached hepatocytes. *Science* 233:1190, 1986.

290. WIEGAND C, THOMPSON T, BOCK GH, MATHIS RK, KJELLSTRAND CM, MAUER SM: The management of life-threatening hyperammonemia: A comparison of several therapeutic modalities. *J Pediatr* 96:142, 1980.

291. DONN SM, SWATZ RD, THOENE JG: Comparison of exchange transfusion, peritoneal dialysis and hemodialysis for the treatment of hyperammonemia in an anuric newborn infant. *J Pediatr* 95:67, 1979.

292. KILEY JE, PENDER JC, WELCH HF, WELCH CS: Ammonia intoxication treated by hemodialysis. *N Engl J Med* 259:1156, 1958.

293. WATSON AJ, KARP JE, WALKER WG, CHAMBER T, RISCH VR, BRUSILOW SW: Transient idiopathic hyperammonaemia in adults. *Lancet* 2:1271, 1985.

294. HERRIN JT, MCCREDIE DA: Peritoneal dialysis in the reduction of blood ammonia levels in a case of hyperammonaemia. *Arch Dis Child* 44:149, 1969.

295. BASHAW ML, BRUSILOW SW: Treatment of hyperammonemic coma caused by inborn errors or urea synthesis. *J Pediatr* 97:893, 1980.

295a. SIEGEL NJ, BROWN RS: Peritoneal clearance of ammonia and creatinine in a neonate. *J Pediatr* 82:1044, 1973.

295b. RUTLEDGE SL, HAYMOND M, KAN JS, MCLEAN RH, VALLE D, BRUSILOW S: Hemodialysis for neonatal maple syrup urine disease encephalopathy. *Pediatr Res*, 23:333A, 1988.

296. BATSHAW ML, BRUSILOW S, WABER L, BLOM W, BRUBAKK AM, BURTON BK, CANN HM, KERR D, MAMUNES P, MATALON R, MYERBERG D, SCHAFER IA: Treatment of inborn errors of urea synthesis. *N Engl J Med* 306:1387, 1982.

297. BATSHAW ML, ROAN Y, JUNG AL, ROSENBERG LA, BRUSILOW SW: Cerebral dysfunction in asymptomatic carriers of ornithine transcarbamylase deficiency. *N Engl J Med* 302:482, 1980.

298. MASWOSWE SM, CYR DM, GRIFFITH AD, TREMBLEY GC: The effect of sodium benzoate on ammonia toxicity in rats. *Biochem Biophys Res Comm* 138:369, 1986.

299. BRUSILOW SW, DANNEY M, WABER LJ, BATSHAW M, BURTON B, LEVITSKY L, ROTH K, MCKEETHREN C, WARD J: Treatment of episodic hyperammonemia in children with inborn errors of urea synthesis. *N Engl J Med* 310:1630, 1984.

300. BARTHOLOMEW D, REICHEL R, BRUSILOW S: Prospective diagnosis and treatment of urea cycle disorders. *Pediatr Res* 21:288A, 1987.

300a. SNEBOLD NG, RUZZO JF III, LESSELL S, PRUETT RC: Transient visual loss in ornithine transcarbamylase deficiency. *Am J Ophthalmol* 104:407, 1987.

300b. LYLE DJ: Eye symptoms produced by tentorial herniation from increased intracranial pressure. *XVII Concilium Ophthalmolgicium* 3:1845, 1954.

301. HALDANE JBS: Rate of spontaneous mutation of the human gene. *J Genet* 31:317, 1935.

302. FOX JE, HACK AM, FENTON WA, GOLBUS MS, WINTER S, KALOUSEK F, ROZEN R, BRUSILOW SW, ROSENBERG LE: Prenatal diagnosis of ornithine transcarbamylase deficiency with use of DNA polymorphisms. *N Engl J Med* 315:1205, 1986.

303. PEMBREY ME, OLD JM, LEONARD JV, RODECK CH, WARREN R, DAVIES KE: Prenatal diagnosis of ornithine carbamoyl transferase deficiency using a gene specific probe. *J Med Genet* 22:462, 1985.

304. BATSHAW ML, MSALL M, BEAUDET AL, TROJAK J: Risk of serious illness in heterozygotes for ornithine transcarbamylase deficiency. *J Pediatr* 108:236, 1986.

305. HOLZGREVE W, GOLBUS MS: Prenatal diagnosis of ornithine transcarbamylase deficiency using fetal liver biopsy. *Am J Hum Genet* 36:320, 1984.

306. FLEISHER L, MITCHELL D, KOPPITCH F, MARRONA F, EVANS M, GOODMAN S, NADLER H: Chorionic villous samples (CVS) for the prenatal diagnosis of amino acidopathies. *Am J Hum Genet* 36:188S, 1984.

307. FLEISHER LD, RASSEN DK, DESNICK RJ, SALWEN HR, ROGERS P, BEAN M, GUALL GE: Argininosuccinic aciduria: Prenatal studies in a family at risk. *Am J Hum Genet* 31:439, 1979.

308. GOODMAN SI, MACE JW, TURNER B, GARRETT WJ: Antenatal diagnosis of argininosuccinic aciduria. *Clin Genet* 4:236, 1973.

309. CEDERBAUM SD: Personal communication.

310. National Academy of Science. National Research Council. Genetic Screening: Programs Principles and Research. Washington, DC 1975.

311. BRUSILOW SW, VALLE DL, BATSHAW ML, WABER LJ: Screening for lethal genetic disease. *Pediatrics* 70:647, 1982.

312. BRUSILOW SW, VALLE DL: Symptomatic inborn errors of metabolism in the neonate, in Nelson NM (ed): *Current Therapy in Neonatal-Perinatal Medicine*. Amsterdam, Elsevier, 1985, p 207.

313. LEVY HL, COULOMBE JT, SHIH VE: Newborn urine screening, in Bickel H, Gunthrie R, Hammersen G (eds): *Neonatal Screening for Inborn Errors of Metabolism*. New York, Springer-Verlag, 1980, p 89.

314. LEMIEUX B, AURAY-BLAIS CH, GIGUERE R: Comparison between amino acids and orotic acid analysis in the detection of urea cycle disorders in the Quebec urinary screening program. *Adv Exp Biol Med* 153:321, 1982.

315. NAYLOR EW, ORFANOS AP, GUTHRIE R: A simple screening test for arginase deficiency (hyperargininemia). *J Lab Clin Med* 89:876, 1977.

316. NAYLOR EW: Newborn screening for urea cycle disorders. *Peidatrics* 68:453, 1981.

317. TALBOT HW, SUMLIN AB, NAYLOR EF, GUTHRIE R: A neonatal screening test for argininosuccinic acid lyase deficiency and other urea cycle disorders. *Pediatrics* 70:526, 1982.

318. NAYLOR EW: Newborn screening for urea cycle disorders. *Adv Exp Biol Med* 153:9, 1982.

319. NATALE PJ, TREMBLAY GC: On the availability of intramitochondrial carbamoylphosphate for the extramitochondrial biosynthesis of pyrimidines. *Biochem Biophys Res Commun* 37:512, 1969.

320. TREMBLAY GC, CRANDALL DE, KNOTT CE, ALFANT M: Orotic acid biosynthesis in rat liver: Studies on the source of carbamoylphosphate. *Arch Biochem Biophys* 178:164, 1977.

321. RAJALAKSHMI S, HANDSCHUMACHER RE: Control of purine biosynthesis de novo by orotic acid in vivo and vitro. *Biochim Biophys Acta* 155:317, 1968.

322. KELLEY WN, GREENE ML, FOX IH, ROSENBLOOM FM, LEVY RI, SEEGMILLER JE: Effects of orotic acid on purine and lipoprotein metabolism in man. *Metabolism* 19:1025, 1970.

323. SKAPER SD, O'BRIEN WE, SCHAFER IA: The influence of ammonia on purine and pyrimidine nucleotide biosynthesis in rat liver and brain in vitro. *Biochem J* 172:457, 1978.

324. HOKANSON JR, O'BRIEN WE, IDEMOTO J, SCHAFER IA: Carrier detection in ornithine transcarbamylase deficiency. *J Pediatr* 93:75, 1978.

325. NG WG, OIZUMI J, KOCH R, SHAW KNF, MCLAREN J, DONNEL GN, CARTER M: Carrier detection of urea cycle disorders. *Pediatrics* 68:448, 1981.

326. HANN EA, DANKS DM, GRIMES A: Carrier detection in ornithine transcarbamylase deficiency. *J Inherited Metab Dis* 5:37, 1982.

327. BECROFT DMO, BARRY DMJ, WEBSTER DR, SIMMONDS HA: Faiure of protein loading tests to identify heterozygosity for ornithine carbamoyltransferase deficiency. *J Inherited Metab Dis* 7:157, 1984.

328. TERHEGGEN HG, SCHWENK A, LOWENTHAL A, VAN SANDH M, COLOMBO JP: Argininaemia with arginase deficiency. *Lancet* 2:748, 1969.

329. TERHEGGEN HG, LAVINHA F, COLOMBO JP, VAN SANDE M, LOWENTHAL A: Familial hyperargininemia. *J Hum Genet* 20:69, 1972.

330. TERHEGGEN HG, LOWENTHAL A, LAVINHA F, COLOMBO JP: Familial hyperargininaemia. *Arch Dis Child* 50:57, 1975.

331. CEDERBAUM SD, SHAW KNF, VALENTE M: Hyperargininemia. *J Pediatr* 90:569, 1977.

332. QURESHI IA, LETARTE J, OUELLET R, LELIEVRE M, LABERGE C: Ammonia metabolism in a family affected by hyperargininemia. *Diabete Metab* 7:5, 1981.

333. TERHEGGEN HG, LOWENTHAL A, COLOMBO JP: Clinical and biochemical findings in argininemia. *Adv Exp Biol Med* 153:111, 1982.

334. BERNAR J, HANSON RA, KERN R, PHOENIX B, SHAW KNF, CEDERBAUM SD: Arginase deficiency in a 12 year old boy with mild impairment of intellectual function. *J Pediatr* 108:432, 1986.

335. JORDA A, RUBIO V, PORTOLES M, VILAS J, GARCIA-PINO J. A new case of arginase deficiency in a Spanish male. *J Inherited Metab Dis* 9:393, 1986.

336. CEDERBAUM SD, SHAW KNF, SPECTOR EB, VERITY MA, SNODGRASS PJ, SUGARMAN GI: Hyperargininemia with arginase deficiency. *Pediatr Res* 13:827, 1979.

337. NAYLOR EW, CEDERBAUM SD: Urinary pyrimidine excretion in arginase deficiency. *J Inherited Dis* 4:207, 1981.

338. CEDERBAUM SD, MOEDJONO SJ, SHAW KNF, CARTER M, NAYLOR E, WALZER M: Treatment of hyperargininaemia due to arginase deficiency with a chemically defined diet. *J Inherited Dis* 5:95, 1982.

339. BACHMANN C, COLOMBO JP: Diagnostic value of orotic acid excretion in heritable disorders of the urea cycle and in hyperammonemia due to organic acidurias. *Eur J Pediatr* 134:109, 1980.

340. WIECHERT P, MORTELMANS J, LAVINHA F, CLARA R, TERHEGGEN HG, LOWENTHAL A: Excretion of guanidino-derivatives in urine of hyperargininemic patients. *J Hum Genet* 24:61, 1976.

341. MARESCAU B, PINTENS J, LOWENTHAL A, TERHEGGEN HG: Excretion of α-keto-δ-guanidinovaleric acid and its cyclic form in patients with hyperargininemia. *Clin Chim Acta* 98:35, 1979.

342. MARESCAU B, LOWENTHAL A: Isolation and identification of some guanidino compounds in the urine of patients with hyperargininaemia by liquid chromatography, thin-layer chromatography and gas chromatography mass spectrometry. *J Chromatogr* 224:185, 1981.

343. HYLAND K, SMITH I, CLAYTON PT, LEONARD JV: Impaired neurotransmitter amine metabolic deficiency. *J Neurol Neurosurg Psychiatry* 48:1189, 1985.

344. SNYDERMAN SE, SANSARICQ C, CHEN WJ, NORTON PM, PHANSALKAR SV: Argininemia. *J Pediatr* 90:563, 1977.

345. SNYDERMAN SE, SANSARICQ C, NORTON PM, GOLDSTEIN F: Brief clinical and laboratory observations. *J Pediatr* 95:61, 1979.

346. QURESHI IA, LETARTE J, OUELLET R, BATSHAW ML, BRUSILOW SW: Treatment of hyperargininemia with sodium benzoate and arginine restricted diet. *J Pediatr* 104:473, 1984.

347. ADRIANENSSENS K, KARCHER D, LOWENTHAL A, TERHEGGEN HG: Use of enzyme loaded erythrocytes in in-vitro correction of arginase deficiency erythrocytes in familial hyperargininemia. *Clin Chem* 22:323, 1976.

CHAPTER 21

ERRORS OF LYSINE METABOLISM

JOSEPH DANCIS
RODY P. COX

1. *Familial hyperlysinemia is an autosomal recessive disease caused by a defect in the bifunctional protein α-aminoadipic semialdehyde synthase. The two associated enzyme activities, lysine-ketoglutarate reductase and saccharopine dehydrogenase, normally initiate the degradation of lysine by removal of the ε-amino group. In familial hyperlysinemia, both activities are reduced to 10 percent of normal or less, causing hyperlysinemia and lysinuria, often accompanied by a relatively mild saccharopinuria. The condition appears to be benign. A variant, saccharopinuria, has been described in which 30 percent of lysine-ketoglutarate activity was retained and the saccharopine dehydrogenase activity was not detectable. Saccharopinuria was prominent, exceeding the associated lysinuria. Experience with the variant is too limited to know if this metabolic abnormality causes disease.*
2. *Removal of the α-amino group of lysine constitutes a minor degradative pathway for lysine with pipecolic acid as a product. Hyperpipecolatemia is regularly observed in familial hyperlysinemia as an "overflow" phenomenon. It is also a common concomitant of Zellweger syndrome, presumably because of a degradative defect. It appears to cause no symptoms in these diseases. No convincing case has yet been reported in which hyperpipecolatemia represents a primary metabolic defect.*

This chapter is devoted to inherited metabolic diseases of the first enzymatic steps in lysine degradation. Familial hyperlysinemia and saccharopinuria are the most prominent and most clearly elucidated abnormalities. Hyperpipecolatemia has recently received considerable attention and will also be briefly discussed. Sporadic reports of hyperlysinemia of uncertain etiology and lysinuria in the absence of hyperlysinemia will not be considered. The latter generally results from transport defects, often as part of a dibasic aminoacid transport defect, and is discussed in Chap. 100.

METABOLISM OF LYSINE

Lysine is an essential 6-carbon dibasic amino acid.[1] In common with other amino acids, an excess beyond that needed for protein synthesis is degraded through the Krebs cycle after removal of amino groups, yielding energy. Early workers in intermediary metabolism noted that the keto acid of lysine could not replace the amino acid in the diet and correctly concluded that lysine did not participate in classic transamination. The initial steps in the degradation of lysine remained uncertain, however, until relatively recently.

Saccharopine Pathway

It is now recognized that the major pathway for the degradation of lysine involves the transfer of the ε-amino group to α-ketoglutarate through the stable intermediate, saccharopine.[2–4] The end result of transamination is thereby achieved, although by a different mechanism. Two enzymatic steps are involved, which are carried out by a bifunctional enzyme, aminoadipic semialdehyde synthase (Fig. 21-1).[5] The two activities contained in the synthase are lysine-ketoglutarate reductase and saccharopine dehydrogenase. In the first step, saccharopine is formed as a ligand between lysine and α-ketoglutarate. In the second step, saccharopine is cleaved to α-aminoadipic acid semialdehyde and glutamic acid completing the transfer of the ε-amino group. The aldehyde is oxidized to α-aminoadipic acid. Subsequent steps in this degradative pathway involve transamination of α-aminoadipic acid to α-ketoadipic acid and successive decarboxylations to form first glutaryl CoA and then crotonyl CoA which, in turn, is oxidized to acetyl CoA. The metabolism distal to α-aminoadipic acid and genetic defects thereof (α-ketoadipic acidemia and glutaric acidemia, type I) are discussed in Chap. 30.

Pipecolic Acid Pathway

The pipecolic acid pathway was long believed to be the major degradative pathway for lysine.[6,7] It is now recognized that its capacity is inadequate for the large amounts of L-lysine that must be degraded with normal dietary intake. It functions as an overflow pathway for L-lysine and as the major pathway for D-lysine.

The initial step in this degradative pathway is removal of the α-amino group by oxidative deamination. The keto acid cyclizes and is reduced to pipecolic acid. L-pipecolic acid is the product of both L- and D-lysine. Pipecolic acid is oxidized to α-aminoadipic semialdehyde, joining the saccharopine pathway.

Bifunctional α-Aminoadipic Semialdehyde Synthase

Investigation of patients with familial hyperlysinemia revealed that the two sequential degradative activities, lysine-ketoglutarate reductase and saccharopine dehydrogenase, were consistently defective.[4,8] It was postulated that both enzyme activities might reside in one protein. This hypothesis was challenged by the report that two separate enzymes had been isolated from rat liver.[9] More recent studies on bovine and baboon liver, however, have provided convincing evidence of a single bifunctional protein.[5] The relative activities of lysine-ketoglutarate reductase and saccharopine dehydrogenase remained constant throughout extensive purification to apparent homogeneity. Activity staining of a native gel demonstrated that both activities (reductase and dehydrogenase) migrate the same distance toward the anode, providing further evidence that the purified synthase is a single protein. Electrophoresis

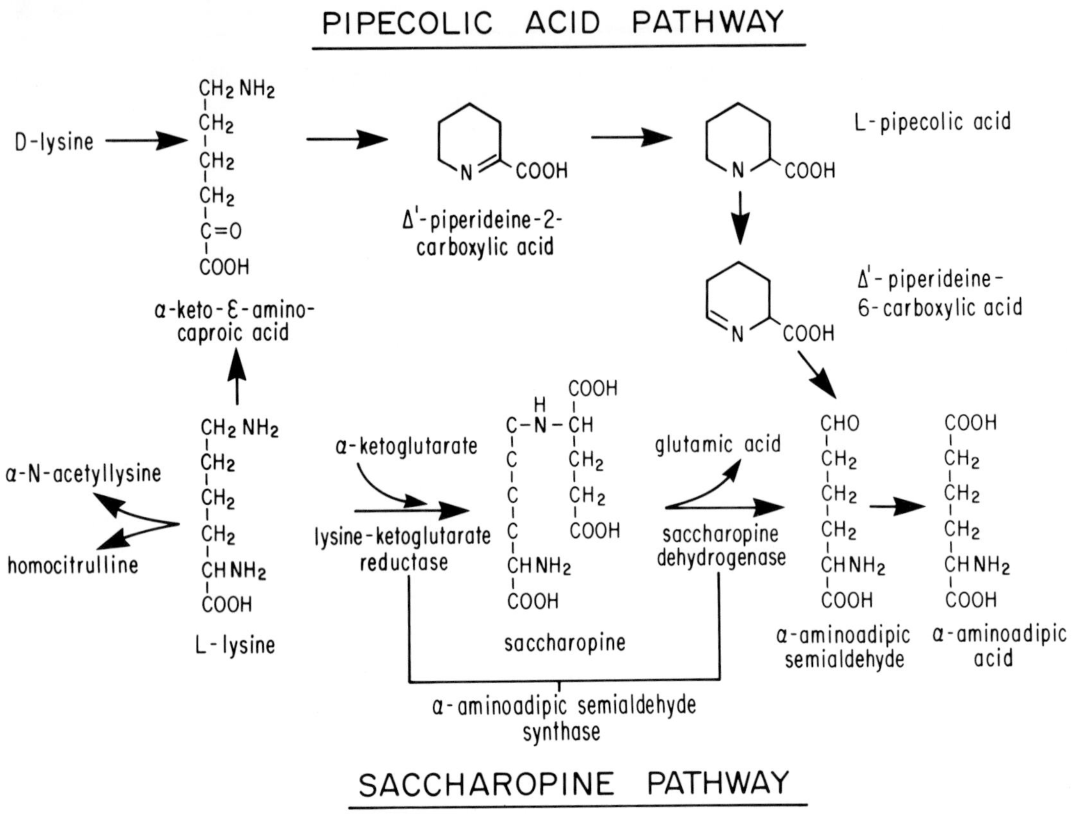

Fig. 21-1 Metabolism of lysine.

on SDS-polyacrylamide gel yielded a single protein band with a molecular weight of 115,000. The synthase has a molecular weight of 468,000 and appears to exist as a tetramer of a 115,000 polypeptide. The domains for lysine ketoglutarate reductase and saccharopine dehydrogenase can be separated by DEAE-Biogel column chromatography following limited digestion with elastase without loss of activity.[10] The isolated reductase and dehydrogenase domains appear to exist in multiple aggregates consisting of peptide fragments of 62,700 and 49,200 daltons, respectively. The results indicate that the reductase and dehydrogenase domains of the aminoadipic semialdehyde synthase are separately folded and functionally independent.

Covalent linkage of functionally related enzymes is not uncommon in eucaryotic organisms, presumably providing an evolutionary advantage. In bacteria and fungi, lysine-ketoglutarate reductase and saccharopine dehydrogenase are represented by two separate proteins with molecular weights of 49,000 and 73,000, respectively.[11,12] One possible advantage of linkage of enzymes is the more efficient utilization of substrate as a result of "channeling." Bound intermediates are subjected to sequential enzymatic reactions while being protected from dilution and competing reactions. Covalent linkage also maintains the component enzymes in equimolar amounts adding to the efficiency of the system.

A striking parallel exists between hereditary orotic aciduria (Chap. 43)[13] and familial hyperlysinemia. Orotic aciduria type 1 exhibits a combined deficiency of orotate phosphoribosyl transferase and orotidine-5′-phosphate decarboxylase, the last two sequential steps in the *de novo* synthesis of uridine. In orotic aciduria type II the second activity, the decarboxylase, is primarily deficient. A bifunctional enzyme UMP synthase (M_r-51,500) has both activities.[14,15]

Multifunctional proteins have also been described for fatty acid synthetase[16,17] and the carbamyl phosphate synthetase-aspartate carbamyltransferase-dehydrogenase (CAD) complex.[18] The molecular mechanism for fusion of lysine-ketoglutarate reductase and saccharopine dehydrogenase, whether at the gene loci or more distal, remains to be elucidated.

FAMILIAL HYPERLYSINEMIA

Biochemical Defect

Lysine-ketoglutarate reductase and saccharopine dehydrogenase are distributed widely in human tissues.[19,20] The skin fibroblast grown in tissue culture proved a convenient approach to the study of the biochemical defect. Both enzyme activities were grossly deficient in patients with familial hyperlysinemia.[4,8] Retrograde splitting of saccharopine to yield lysine was also greatly reduced. It is uncertain as to whether this reaction is catalyzed by a distinct enzyme, saccharopine oxidoreductase, or whether it reflects the reversibility of the lysine-ketoglutarate reductase activity. Liver obtained at autopsy from a hyperlysinemic patient had the same enzyme deficiencies.[4]

The magnitude of the defect in lysine metabolism was estimated in the living subject by administering [^{14}C]lysine and collecting exhaled $^{14}CO_2$.[21] Under conditions of normal dietary intake, the amount of labeled carbon dioxide collected from two hyperlysinemic patients was about 10 percent of that in two control subjects (Fig 21-2). Furthermore the controls had a reserve capacity to handle excesses of lysine. Following the administration of an acute load of lysine, the amount of lysine

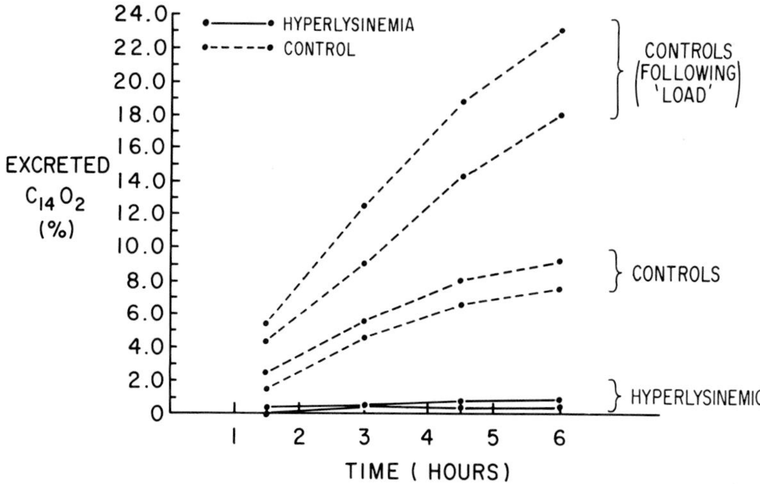

Fig. 21-2 Cumulative excretion of $^{14}CO_2$ following administration of [U-^{14}C]lysine. [^{14}C]Lysine was injected into two control and two hyperlysinemic subjects, and the $^{14}CO_2$ expired was measured. The control subjects were also loaded with 150 mg/kg of the lysine base prior to the injection of [^{14}C]lysine and the measurements repeated. The cumulative excretion of radioactive CO_2 is presented as a percentage of administered radioactivity. *(From Woody, Hutzler, Dancis,[21] by permission of* American Journal of Diseases of Children.)

degraded to CO_2 increased twofold without increasing the fraction excreted into the urine.

An unusual patient with familial hyperlysinemia, presenting with cystinuria, was detected by careful examination of urine.[22] Cystine overlies saccharopine in the usual chromatographic systems. By oxidizing cystine to cysteic acid, it was revealed that the patient had a saccharopinuria as well as a cystinuria. Excesses of saccharopine were unexpected because saccharopine is distal to the defect in lysine-ketoglutarate activity. To confirm this observation, the tentatively identified saccharopine was isolated from the urine and heated to 110°C for 5 h. A new compound appeared with the chromatographic characteristics of pyrosaccharopine. Of an additional six subjects with the double enzyme defect characteristic of familial hyperlysinemia, four had a detectable saccharopinuria. A reasonable explanation of this unexpected finding is that residual lysine-ketoglutarate reductase activity permitted the synthesis of small amounts of saccharopine and a more complete defect in saccharopine dehydrogenase activity prevented its metabolic disposal.

Clinical Presentation

The initial observation is generally an impressive lysinuria detected during biochemical studies of a patient with presumed metabolic disease, often with neurologic symptoms. Measurement of serum amino acids shows the lysine to be considerably elevated, regularly exceeding 680 μM (10 mg/dl) in the classic cases and often reaching twice that concentration. Screening of other family members may reveal asymptomatic individuals with the same biochemical findings. Both sexes are affected, and consanguinity of parents has been reported, indicating autosomal recessive inheritance. Confirmation of the diagnosis is by enzymatic studies on the skin fibroblast.

Diagnosis

Normal skin fibroblasts effectively degrade lysine to carbon dioxide. It was therefore possible to reproduce the studies originally performed in vivo by incubating skin fibroblasts with [^{14}C]lysine.[8] Using skin fibroblasts from seven subjects with enzymatically confirmed diagnoses of familial hyperlysinemia, 5 to 10 percent of the normal amount of radioactive CO_2 was liberated (Table 21-1).

In the presence of significant hyperlysinemia in the patient, a reduction in the degradation of lysine to CO_2 can be assumed to involve a defect in either or both of the first two enzymatic steps in the saccharopine pathway. Hyperlysinemia has not been reported in defects below α-aminoadipic acid or as the result of defects in the pipecolic acid pathway.

Specific diagnoses require assays for lysine-ketoglutarate reductase and saccharopine dehydrogenase activities. These tests are not available in most laboratories, and the latter requires a substrate that is not commercially available. Fortunately there should be few instances in which these specific assays are clinically necessary.

Evolution of $^{14}CO_2$[8]. Skin fibroblasts are grown to confluence. Cells from about 38 cm^2 of growing surface are transferred to a flat-bottomed vial, the medium removed following centrifuging, and replaced with Krebs-Ringer phosphate buffer 0.225

Table 21-1 Metabolism of Skin Fibroblasts*

Hyperlysinemia, patients	*Lysine-ketoglutarate reductase†*	*Saccharopine dehydrogenase‡*	*CO_2 evolution§ (lysine-2-^{14}C)*
1	0	0	—
2	0	0	0.08
3	27	0	0.17
4	0	0	0.03
5	4	0	0.27
6	26	9	0.12
7	35	5	0.06
Mean	13	2	0.12
Range	0–35	0–9	0.03–0.27
Controls			
Number	8	6	12
Mean	357	95.3	2.75
Range	240–402	63–164	0.92–6.0

*Lysine-ketoglutarate reductase and saccharopine dehydrogenase activities were assayed in homogenates and mitochondrial preparations, respectively, as described in the text. The formation of CO_2 was measured following the incubation of intact fibroblasts with [2-^{14}C]lysine.

†Activity, pmol/min per milligram cell protein.

‡Activity, pmo/min per milligram mitochondrial protein.

§$^{14}CO_2$ evolved/min per milligram protein.

SOURCE: Adapted from Dancis, Hutzler, Cox,[8] by permission of The University of Chicago Press.

ml. To this is added 0.025 ml of DL-[^{14}C]lysine labeled in the 2 position, 20 μCi/ml in 0.08 *M* NaCl. The cells are incubated for 4 h at 35°C under oxygen with gentle agitation. CO_2 is collected in a center well containing 0.1 ml 1 *N* NaOH. The well contents are transferred to a scintillant to determine radioactivity.

Prior to incubation, the radioactive substrate is freed of volatile impurities by bubbling with N_2 at pH 3.

Lysine-Ketoglutarate Reductase[3,4]. Fibroblasts are disrupted by repetitive freeze-thawing. Approximately 4 million cells are incubated with L-[U-^{14}C]lysine, 0.5 uc, 1.0 μmol, $MgCl_2$ 0.05 μmol, potassium α-ketoglutarate, 2 μmol, potassium phosphate, pH 7.1, 10 μmol, NADPH, 1.5 μmol, water to final volume of 1 ml. Incubation is for 60 min, with shaking, at 30°C under a stream of N_2. Incubation is terminated by adding 5 μmol saccharopine in 0.05 ml water and placing tubes in boiling water for 5 min. The reaction mixture is centrifuged and the supernatant subjected to high voltage electrophoresis. The saccharopine area is eluted, and saccharopine is isolated by ion-exchange chromatography. Radioactivity is measured, and the synthesis of saccharopine is calculated.

Saccharopine Dehydrogenase[3,4]. The reaction mixture contains 0.1 ml sonicated mitochondria from skin fibroblasts, 0.5 μmol NAD^+ in 0.02 ml Tricine-NaOH buffer, pH 8.9, saccharopine [U-^{14}C]glutaryl, 0.1 μCi, 0.1 μmol in water to 0.25 ml. Incubation is with agitation for 60 min at 25°C. The reaction is stopped by adding 0.1 ml 10 m*M* glutamate solution and 0.05 ml 1 *N* HCl. Radioactive glutamic acid is measured by reacting with glutamic decarboxylase. The substrate, radioactive saccharopine, is synthesized as previously described.

Prognosis

Several of the patients with familial hyperlysinemia were detected as a result of diagnostic studies for neurologic damage and mental retardation. The relation of the metabolic defect to the clinical manifestations was therefore uncertain. To avoid this bias, a study was conducted of patients identified during routine newborn screening or because of family surveys of affected individuals.[23] Ten subjects were located who met these criteria and in whom the diagnosis of familial hyperlysinemia had been confirmed by enzymatic assays of skin fibroblasts. In none was any damage observed that was attributable to the hyperlysinemia.

One case was particularly impressive in confirming the absence of toxicity of extremely high concentrations of lysine. A normal infant was born to a woman with familial hyperlysinemia. Lysine is rapidly transferred across the placenta, establishing levels in the fetal blood that are slightly higher than in the mother. It can be safely assumed, therefore, that the fetus was exposed to severe hyperlysinemia during the susceptible periods of development without ill effect.

Similar information is not available for the variant, saccharopinuria.

Treatment

The above observations make it clear that hyperlysinemia of considerable magnitude can be tolerated without ill effect. They do not establish that hyperlysinemia is always benign. The question of dietary control must therefore be addressed.

Lysine is present in high concentration in most natural foods. A simple low-lysine diet cannot be devised. By reducing protein intake from the high levels that are customary in American diets, it is possible to lower the serum lysine concentration from approximately 1400 μ*M* (18 to 20 mg/dl) to about 680 to 900 μ*M*. Further reductions toward normal can be accomplished only by substituting a mixture of purified amino acids restricted in lysine for dietary protein.

The weight of the evidence at present is against subjecting the family to the financial and psychological burdens of strict dietary control. Some parents and physicians have chosen to limit protein intake; most have avoided any restrictions.

Saccharopinuria

In 1968, a retarded 22-year-old woman was reported with saccharopinuria and a less severe lysinemia. It appeared reasonable at that time to attribute the metabolic defect to the second degradative step in lysine, saccharopine dehydrogenase, with familial hyperlysinemia resulting from a deficiency in the first step, lysine-ketoglutarate reductase. The subsequent recognition that both enzyme activities were defective in familial hyperlysinemia, and that saccharopinuria was also observed, made the distinction between the two entities less certain. It should be emphasized, however, that the magnitude of the saccharopinuria is considerably less in familial hyperlysinemia and that it is overshadowed by the lysinuria, whereas the reverse was true in the patient with saccharopinuria. The lysine/saccharopine ratios in urine have ranged from 56 to 185 in familial hyperlysinemia,[22] whereas it was 0.33 in the reported case of saccharopinuria. Enzyme studies done on the patient's fibroblasts at a later date revealed that the lysine-ketoglutarate reductase activity was reduced to one-third the normal level and no saccharopine dehydrogenase activity was detected.[24] Given the many significant similarities between familial hyperlysinemia and saccharopinuria, it would appear more useful to consider the latter a variant rather than a discrete entity. A second case of saccharopinuria has been reported in which the enzymatic defects have not been as clearly defined.[25]

The diagnosis of saccharopinuria was made in each instance in the course of investigations of neurologic deficits. The relation of the metabolic anomaly to the symptoms is therefore uncertain.

At the molecular level, the relation between familial hyperlysinemia and saccharopinuria might be explained on the basis of polarity of a bifunctional enzyme. Defects near the origin of the protein are likely to affect both enzyme activities, whereas those nearer the termination may preferentially affect saccharopine dehydrogenase.

HYPERPIPECOLATEMIA

Pipecolic acid is not detected in normal plasma with routine ion-exchange chromatography. By modifying the ninhydrin reaction to intensify the color and making additional relatively minor alterations in technique, circulating pipecolic acid can be consistently detected in normal subjects.[26] The plasma concentration is 12 ± 5.6 μ*M* at birth. It decreases during the first few months to 2.1 ± 1.6 μ*M* and is maintained at that level into adulthood. The consistency with which pipecolic acid is formed in the absence of lysine excesses, and the preservation of the pathway in a variety of animal species[27] suggests that it may have a physiological function. It has been suggested that the pipecolic acid pathway is prominent in brain and that pipecolic acid may be a neurotransmitter.[28]

In *familial hyperlysinemia,* the plasma pipecolic acid concentration is elevated many times. In seven patients, the mean concentration was 31.9 ± 10.7 μ*M*, compared with the normal of 2.1 μ*M*. In the same patients, the lysine concentration was 1009 ± 240 μ*M*. It is evident that the capacity to synthesize pipecolic acid is very limited and that degradation is even more limited. It is also clear that concentrations of this magnitude are tolerated without ill effect.[25]

Interest in hyperpipecolatemia has revived recently because of *Zellweger syndrome* (see Chap. 57). Increased plasma concentrations of pipecolic acid are regularly found in the absence of hyperlysinemia excluding "overflow" as the mechanism and suggesting a defect in degradation.[29,30] Excesses of L-pipecolic acid appear in the urine consistent with an interruption in the normal catabolic pathway.[31] The association of hyperpipecolatemia and absence of peroxisomes in Zellweger syndrome[32] led to the presumption that the enzyme responsible for pipecolic acid oxidation resides in the peroxisome. Confirmation has come from a study of subcellular fractions of monkey liver and kidney and of human liver.[33] The rodent (rat,[34] guinea pig[35]) appears to differ in that pipecolic acid oxidation is not catalyzed by the peroxisomal fraction. This interesting indication of species differences merits further investigation.

A limited number of observations suggest that the plasma concentration of pipecolic acid is within normal limits at birth in Zellweger syndrome and increases with age to distinctly abnormal concentrations as has been observed in other aminoacidopathies (Table 21-2). The full spectrum of the major manifestations of Zellweger syndrome was observed before pathologic concentrations were reached, making it questionable that the hyperpipecolatemia contributes significantly to the disease.[36]

Recognition of a case with a specific defect in pipecolic acid metabolism would clarify the issue. Previously reported cases of hyperpipecolatemia with associated neuropathy and hepatomegaly probably were unrecognized examples of Zellweger syndrome.

Table 21-2 Pipecolatemia in Zellweger Syndrome*

Patient	*Age*	*Plasma pipecolic acid, μM*
B. Su	4 days	7.8
M. Ja	10 days	7.7
B. Fl	2 mo	17.0
	4 mo	60.0
S. Ha	2 mo	24.0
	4 mo	245.0
A. Cu	3½ wk	15.0
	4½ wk	19.0
	5½ wk	36.0
	6½ wk	50.0
	2 mo	38.0
	2½ mo	51.0

*The plasma pipecolic acid concentration in the normal newborn infant is 12 ± 5.6 μ*M* and 2.1 ± 1.6 μ*M* in children and adults. The normal range has not been defined for the first months of life. In Zellweger syndrome, Pipecolic acid concentrations increase to abnormal levels after birth.

SOURCE: From Lam, Hutzler, Dancis,[31] by permission of The University of Chicago Press.

REFERENCES

1. LEHNINGER AL: Biosynthesis of amino acids and nucleotides, in *Principles of Biochemistry*. New York, Worth Publishers, 1982, p 615.
2. HIGASHINO K, FUJIAKA M, TAKAKAZU A, YAMAMURA Y: Metabolism of lysine in rat liver. *Biochem Biophys Res Commun* 29:95, 1967.
3. DANCIS J, HUTZLER J, COX RP, WOODY NC: Familial hyperslysinemia with lysine-ketoglutarate reductase insufficiency. *J Clin Invest* 48:1447, 1969.
4. DANCIS J, HUTZLER J, WOODY NC, COX RP: Multiple enzyme defects in familial hyperlysinemia. *Pediatr Res* 10:686, 1976.
5. MARKOVITZ PJ, CHUANG DT, COX RP: Familial hyperlysinemias: Purification and characterization of the bifunctional aminoadipic semialdehyde synthase with lysine-ketoglutarate reductase and saccharopine dehydrogenase activities. *J Biol Chem* 259:11643, 1984.
6. ROTHSTEIN M, MILLER LL: The conversion of lysine to pipecolic acid in the rat. *J Biol Chem* 211:851, 1954.
7. KIM S, BENOITON L, PAIK WJ: ϵ-Alkyl-lysinase; purification and properties of the enzyme. *J Biol Chem* 239:3790, 1964.
8. DANCIS J, HUTZLER J, COX RP: Familial hyperlysinemia: Enzyme studies, diagnostic methods, comments on terminology. *Am J Hum Genet* 31:290, 1979.
9. NODA C, ICHIHARA A: Purification and properties of L-lysine-α-ketoglutarate reductase from rat liver mitochondria. *Biochim Biophys Acta* 525:307, 1978.
10. MARKOVITZ PJ, CHUANG DT: The bifunctional bovine aminoadipic semialdehyde synthase in lysine degradation: Separation of reductase and dehydrogenase domain by limited proteolysis. *J Biol Chem* 262: 9353, 1987.
11. SAUNDERS PP, BROQUIST HP: Saccharopine, an intermediate of the aminoadipic acid pathway of lysine biosynthesis. *J Biol Chem* 241:3435, 1966.
12. JONES EE, BROQUIST HP: Saccharopine, an intermediate of the aminoadipic acid pathway of lysine biosynthesis: III Aminoadipic semialdehyde-glutamate reductase. *J Biol Chem* 241:3430, 1966.
13. KELLEY WN: Hereditary orotic aciduria, in Stanbury JB, Wyngaarden JB, Fredrickson DS, Goldstein JL, Brown MS (eds):*The Metabolic Basis of Inherited Diseases*, 5th ed. New York, McGraw-Hill, 1983, p 1202.
14. BROWN GK, O'SULLIVAN WJ: Subunit structure of the orotate phosphoribosyltransferase-orotidylate decarboxylase complex from human erthyrocytes. *Biochemistry* 16:3235, 1977.
15. MCCLARD RW, BLACK MJ, LIVINGSTONE LR, JONES ME: Isolation and initial characterization of the single polypeptide that synthesizes uridine 5′-monophosphate from orotate in Ehrlich ascites carcinoma. Purification by tandem affinity chromatography of uridine 5′-monophosphate synthase. *Biochemistry* 19:4699, 1980.
16. WAKIL SJ, STOOPS JK, JOSHI VC: Fatty acid synthesis and its regulation. *Annu Rev Biochem* 52:537, 1983.
17. SCHWEIZER E,, KNIEP B, CASTORP H, HOLZNER U: Pantethine-free mutants of the yeast fatty-acid synthase complex. *Eur J Biochem* 39:353, 1973.
18. COLEMAN PF, SUTTLE DP, STARK GR: Purification from hamster cells of the multifunctional protein that initiates *de novo* synthesis of pyrimidine nucleotides. *J Biol Chem* 252:6379, 1977.
19. HUTZLER J, DANCIS J: Lysine-ketoglutarate reductase in human tissues. *Biochim Biophys Acta* 377:42, 1975.
20. HUTZLER J, DANCIS J: Conversion of lysine to saccharopine by human tissues. *Biochim Biophys Acta* 158:62, 1968.
21. WOODY NC, HUTZLER J, DANCIS J: Further studies of hyperlysinemia. *Am J Dis Child* 112:577, 1966.
22. CEDERBAUM SD, SHAW KNF, DANCIS J, HUTZLER J, BLASKOVICS JC: Hyperlysinemia with saccharopinuria due to combined lysine-ketoglutarate reductase and saccharopine dehydrogenase deficiencies presenting as cystinuria. *J Pediatr* 95:234, 1979.
23. DANCIS J, HUTZLER J, AMPOLA JG, SHIH VE, van GELDEREN HH, KIRBY LT, WOODY NC: The prognosis of hyperlysinemia: An interim report. *Am J Hum Genet* 35:438, 1983.

24. FELLOWS FCI, CARSON NAJ: Enzyme studies in a patient with saccharopinuria: A defect of lysine metabolism. *Pediatr Res* 8:42, 1974.
25. SIMELL O, JOHANSSON T, AULA P: Enzyme defect in saccharopinuria. *J Pediatr* 82:54, 1973.
26. HUTZLER J, DANCIS J: The determination of pipecolic acid: Method and results of hospital survey. *Clin Chim Acta* 128:75, 1983.
27. DANCIS J, HUTZLER J: Comparative rates of metabolism of pipecolic acid metabolism in several animal species. *Comp Biochem Physiol* 73B:1011, 1982.
28. NUMURA Y, SCHMIDT-GLENEWINKEL T, GIACOBINI E: Uptake of piperidine and pipecolic acid by synaptosomes from mouse brain. *Neurochem Res* 5:1163, 1980.
29. DANKS DM, TIPPET P, ADAMS C, CAMPBELL P: Cerebro-hepato-renal syndrome of Zellweger. *J Pediatr* 86:382, 1975.
30. TRIJBELS JMF, MONNENS LAH, BAKKEREN JAJM, VAN RAAY-SELTEN AHJ, CORSTIAENSEN JMB: Biochemical studies in the cerebro-hepato-renal syndrome of Zellweger: A disturbance in the metabolism of pipecolic acid. *J Inherited Metab Dis* 2:39, 1979.
31. LAM S, HUTZLER J, DANCIS J: L-pipecolaturia in Zellweger syndrome. *Biochim Biophys Acta* 882:254, 1986.
32. GOLDFISCHER S, MOORE CL, JOHNSTON AB, SPIRO AJ, VALSAMIS MP, WISMEWSKI HK, RITCH RH, NORTON WJ, RAPIN I, GARTNER LM: Peroxisomal and mitochondrial defects in the cerebro-hepato-renal syndrome. *Science* 182:62, 1983.
33. MIHALIK SJ, RHEAD WJ: L-pipecolic acid is oxidized to α-aminoadipic acid in the peroxisome of man and monkey. *Pediatr Res* 21:292A, 1987.
34. ZAAR K, ANGERMULLER S, VOLKI A, FAHIMI HD: Renal and hepatic peroxisomes oxidize pipecolic acid. Implications for Zellweger's cerebro-hepato-renal syndrome (CHRS). *J Cell Biol* 101:67a, 1985.
35. DANCIS J, HUTZLER J: Unpublished observations.
36. DANCIS J, HUTZLER J: The significance of hyperpipecolatemia in Zellweger syndrome. *Am J Hum Genet* 38:707, 1986.

CHAPTER 22

DISORDERS OF BRANCHED CHAIN AMINO ACID AND KETO ACID METABOLISM

DEAN J. DANNER
LOUIS J. ELSAS II

1. *Maple syrup urine disease (MSUD) results from several different inherited defects in the mitochondrial multienzyme complex, branched chain α-keto acid dehydrogenase (BCKD). This impairment produces increased concentrations of the branched chain amino and α-keto acids in body cells and fluids. Disease incidence varies with the population studied from 1/290,000 in a New England newborn screening experience to 1/760 from a selective screening in an inbred Mennonite group. The pattern of inheritance for the classic type is autosomal recessive with partial impairment of BCKD expressed in fibroblasts from obligate heterozygotes. Age of onset depends on the severity of impaired BCKD and on the neonatal intake of protein. If not treated with diets restricted in the branched chain amino acids, mental and physical retardation result. Neonatal screening, diagnosis, and treatment before 2 weeks of age has improved the general clinical outlook. The genetic defect has not been defined at a molecular level for most patients with MSUD. In a few patients, the antigenic absence of the transacylase (E2) protein or the β-subunit of the decarboxylase (E1β) are reported. Since cDNA clones for the genes encoding the proteins of the BCKD complex are being isolated, the genetic basis for these disorders should follow.*
2. *Branched chain amino acids, especially leucine, are implicated in the regulation of several diverse cellular and tissue functions. Leucine stimulates pancreatic cell insulin release, regulates muscle cell protein turnover, and controls its own degradation. These amino acids also promote healing in postoperative patients.*
3. *Transport of the branched chain amino acids across plasma membranes is regulated by system L transport components. No defects in this transport system are reported for humans.*
4. *Conversion of the branched chain amino acids to their keto acids occurs via one or more cytosolic aminotransferases. This reaction, which is freely reversible, is rate limiting only in liver. Only two reported human cases with defects in this reaction are known. One case specifically affected the transamination of valine, while the other specifically affected transamination of isoleucine/leucine.*
5. *Branched chain α-keto acid dehydrogenase, a constitutive multienzyme complex of mitochondria, is encoded by nuclear genes. Knowledge is beginning to appear for synthesis, uptake, and assembly of the component proteins as a mitochondrial complex. Branched chain α-keto acid dehydrogenase is regulated by its own kinase and phosphatase, which control expression of activity in tissues in response to diet and hormones. Thiamine pyrophosphate is a soluble cofactor for this reaction. In saturating amounts, it inhibits the kinase and stabilizes the enzyme complex, particularly the E1α subunit, against proteolytic degradation, thus maintaining the complex in a prolonged active state.*

INTRODUCTION AND HISTORICAL PERSPECTIVE

Leucine, isoleucine, and valine, the three branched chain amino acids (BCAA), are essential components of the human diet, since enzymes for *de novo* synthesis of the BCAAs are not present in human cells.[1] Following uptake by the cell, BCAAs are either incorporated into proteins or catabolized for energy. Attention was directed to this catabolic pathway when a mentally retarded patient with elevated concentrations of the three BCAAs in blood and urine was described.[2] The urine had a characteristic maple syrup odor which previously was noted in a sibship where four of six infants died of otherwise unknown cause.[3] In patients with this disorder, now known as maple syrup urine disease (MSUD), accumulation of the BCAAs results from impaired oxidative decarboxylation of the branched chain α-keto acids (BCKA).[4,5] Assays of BCAA decarboxylation by cells from family members in the original sibship described by Menkes et al.[3] confirmed that these children had a block in this metabolic pathway.[6] To prevent accumulation of the BCKAs, which results in mental and physical retardation, MSUD patients were placed on protein-restricted diets.[7] Dietary restriction of branched chain amino acids remains the primary approach to therapy, which, when combined with neonatal detection through newborn screening, prevents irreversible neurologic damage. Some patients were able to tolerate greater intake of the BCAAs by using pharmacologic doses of thiamine.[8] Study of the abnormal metabolism of the BCAAs in these patients aided our understanding of the general metabolism of these neutral, aliphatic amino acids.

MSUD is a heterogeneous disorder affecting the function of the branched chain α-keto acid dehydrogenase (BCKD) complex. It is difficult to show direct correlation of severity of the phenotype with quantitation of BCKD activity. The pheno-

Nonstandard abbreviations used in this chapter are: BCAA = branched chain amino acids; BCKA = branched chain α-keto acids; BCKD = branched chain α-keto acid dehydrogenase; CoA = coenzyme A; KGDH = α-ketoglutarate dehydrogenase; KIC = α-ketoisocaproate; KIV = α-ketoisovalerate; KMV = α-keto-β-methylvalerate; MSUD = maple syrup urine disease; PDH = pyruvate dehydrogenase; and TPP = thiamine pyrophosphate.

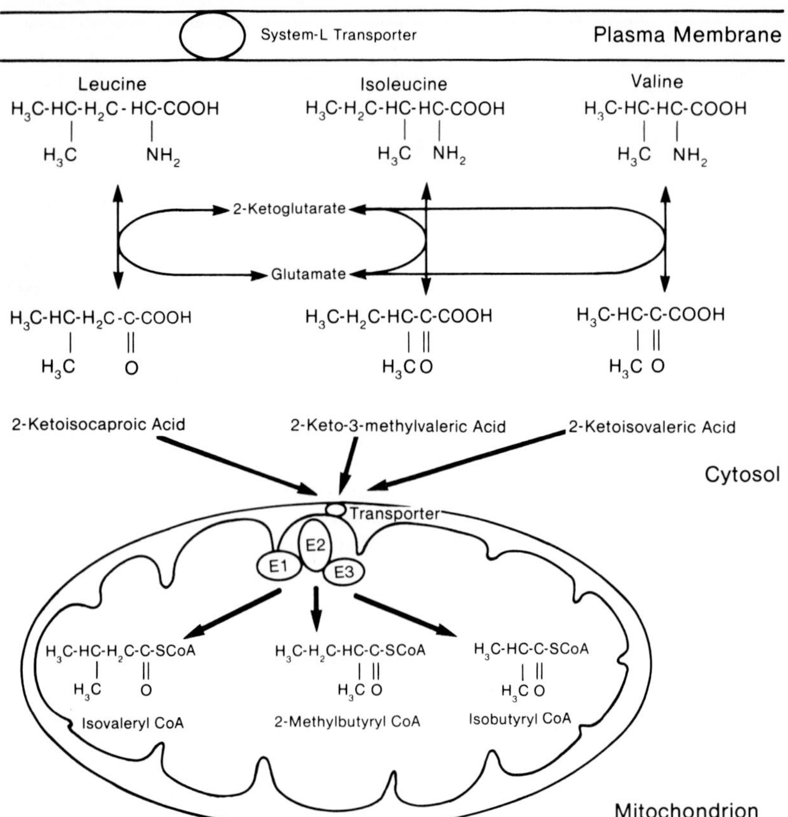

Fig. 22-1 Reactions and subcellular distribution of steps in conversion of the branched chain amino acids to their branched chain acyl CoA esters. The BCKD complex in mitochondria is represented by E1, E2, E3.

type is influenced by the age at which the disease is identified, the degree of enzyme impairment, and the time at which dietary therapy is begun. Newborn identification is now possible through population-based screening for elevation in blood leucine. Although MSUD is the most thoroughly studied disorder in the early steps of BCAA catabolism, only recently have cDNA probes for the genes encoding the BCKD proteins been isolated.[9,9a] It is anticipated that analysis at the gene level will provide a more accurate assessment of the defect.

Figure 22-1 depicts the catabolism of the BCAAs. All three amino acids share a common pathway to the formation of coenzyme A thiol esters. From this point, the thiol esters take independent paths to either acetoacetate from leucine, acetyl CoA from valine, or a mixture of these two products from isoleucine.

BCAAs enter the cell predominantly by the system L transporter.[10] Once inside the cell, BCAAs are either used for protein synthesis, which is dependent on available tRNA, or converted to their respective α-keto acid by a cytosolic aminotransferase.[11,12] BCKAs then enter mitochondria via a specific transporter,[13] where they become oxidatively decarboxylated by the multienzyme complex, BCKD, committing them to complete oxidation.[14]

NORMAL BIOCHEMISTRY AND PHYSIOLOGY

Overview

Leucine has long been implicated in the regulation of its own metabolism and that of other amino acids and metabolites.[15–18] This amino acid and its α-keto acid analogue play important roles in regulation of protein turnover in muscle tissue[19–21] and in the stimulation of pancreatic release of insulin, somatostatin, glycogen, and Zn^{2+}.[22–24] They are used in postoperative patients and in patients with liver disorders to aid in the healing process.[25–28]

Regulation of leucine metabolism in various tissues has received considerable attention during the past 15 years. Investigators have used a variety of approaches, including studies of isolated enzymes, cultured cells, perfused tissues, whole animals, and intact humans.[26–37] A variety of conditions are used to perturb the systems employed, including diet, starvation, metabolites, hormones, and drugs.[38–47]

Using the rat model, it was shown that ingested BCAAs rapidly passed through the liver to peripheral tissue for their initial metabolism. Several laboratories demonstrated a predominant role of skeletal muscle in leucine catabolism.[19,48] Skeletal muscle is considered the major site of leucine transamination to its α-keto acid. Based on comparative measurements of enzyme activity, it was shown that the BCAA aminotransferase exceeds BCKD activity for all tissue except liver.[49,50] Similar data were reported for humans confirming that BCKD activity is minimal in muscle and maximal in liver.[36,51] Thus, the catabolic flow for branched chain amino acids is thought to involve deamination by muscle but oxidation of BCKAs by liver. Support for this idea comes from measurements of newly formed BCKAs in muscle and of the movement of the BCKAs to liver.[52–54] Blood BCKA concentrations in adult humans after an overnight fast are: 30 to 40 μM for α-ketoisocaproate (KIC), 20 to 25 μM for α-keto-β-methylvalerate (KMV), and near 20 μM for α-ketoisovalerate (KIV). The kidney can also oxidize the BCKAs, but based on relative size, liver appears to be the principal organ for oxidation. Amino groups generated in muscle accumulate as newly formed glutamate. However, since the urea cycle enzymes are not present in muscle, alanine rises along with glutamate. Thus leucine metabolism is highly complex and involves all the tissues of the body. This topic remains an active area of investigation and is adequately reviewed.[15–18,55–58]

Transport of BCAA and BCKA

BCAAs cross the intestinal lumen either as free amino acids or contained in small peptides. The two transport systems develop at the same time and mature at similar rates, but are regulated independently.[59] The transport systems may be species specific. In addition, an Na^+-dependent and Na^+-independent transport system for leucine has been reported for intestinal villi.[60] Leucine transport across the basal membrane of intestinal villi uses mechanisms which differ from that of luminal surfaces of the villus. Transport at the basal membrane may be analogous to transport across plasma membrane.

Plasma membrane transport of leucine is mediated mainly by the Na^+-independent system L pathway[61] originally described by Oxender and Christensen[62] in Erhlich ascites cells. Seventeen years later a similar system was shown in cultured human skin fibroblasts.[10] Amino acid transport in this tissue is independent of age in culture but is sensitive to nutrients in the media.[63] Similarly, system L transport is the primary transport pathway for leucine in Chang liver cells (possibly of Hela cell origin), another tissue of human origin,[64] and in tissues of the nervous system.[65]

Demonstration that BCKAs are present in normal blood suggests the presence of transport systems for BCKAs. Such a system has been described for human lymphoblasts.[66] The transport mechanism for BCKAs requires Na^+ and has a high affinity (K_m = 125 μ*M*); the three BCKAs competitively inhibit one another. In rat models, both brain and intestinal villi have specific transport systems for the BCKAs.[67,68]

It appears, therefore, that cells can use either BCAA or BCKA for their growth and energy requirements and that independent transport systems exist for uptake. Based on apparent K_m and V_{max} values for the transport of either BCAA or BCKA compared with the substrate kinetics for branched chain aminotransferase and BCKD, uptake is not limiting for their subsequent catabolism.

BCAA Aminotransferase

Once inside the cell, BCAAs follow either an anabolic or catabolic path. The anabolic pathway involves utilization of BCAA for protein synthesis and is regulated by the availability of tRNAs for the BCAAs. This pathway is more prominent during active growth of the organism. Catabolism begins with conversion of the BCAA to its keto acid through transfer of the α-amino group to a keto acceptor, most often α-ketoglutarate.[69] This process does not commit the amino acid to catabolism, since the reaction is reversible. A single cytosolic amino transferase can convert all three BCAAs to their respective ketoacid (Fig. 22-1). In the mid-1960s, a series of reports from two laboratories described three proteins with the ability to transfer the amino group from the BCAAs to a keto acid acceptor.[11,12,29,70–72] In rat, BCAA aminotransferase activity is most active in heart, kidney, and skeletal muscle with low activity in the liver. Two isozymic forms are reported, a cytosolic form designated I and a mitochondrial form designated II. A third isozyme, designated III, is found in other tissues like brain, ovary, and placenta without a clear description of the subcellular distribution. When the soluble isozyme I is purified from hog heart, the ratio of activity among the three BCAAs remains constant, and the principal acceptor is α-ketoglutarate. For rodents, type II isozyme is present only in liver mitochondria and is specific for leucine. Human tissue has only isozymes I and III.[73] Both isozymes are widely distributed among the different human tissues. The human enzymes are partially inhibited by antisera prepared against the specific rat isozyme, but no extensive characterization of the human amino transferase is reported. Likewise, subcellular distribution of the aminotransferase activity in human tissue is not reported. Both human isozymes act on all three BCAAs and use α-ketoglutarate as the principal acceptor.

Evidence for two BCAA aminotransferases in humans also was shown by somatic cell genetics. Naylor and Shows fused a branched chain aminotransferase-deficient Chinese hamster ovary cell with human cells and found evidence for two apparent branched chain aminotransferase genes.[74] Hybrid cells were selected for their ability to grow on media supplemented only with BCKAs. Growth was correlated with the presence of either human chromosome 12 or 19. Direct measurement of aminotransferase activity was not made. More recently this cell hybridization was used to localize the branched chain aminotransferase gene on chromosome 12 to the short arm.[75] Again selection and characterization included only growth on BCKA supplemented media, and aminotransferase activity was not measured. Since specific assignment of branched chain aminotransferase isozymes to the different chromosomes cannot be made without functional studies in these hybrid cells, both locations are shown on the current human chromosome map without isozyme notation.[76]

A valine-specific aminotransferase may also function in the cytosol,[77,78] and while the rat may have a mitochondrial aminotransferase for leucine,[71,79] transport of the amino acid into mitochondria is minimal.[80] This mitochondrial aminotransferase activity has not been confirmed for human tissue.

Newly formed BCKAs also have several possible fates. They can be reaminated to the amino acid, transported out of the cell as the keto acid, or transported into the mitochondria where they are committed to complete oxidation by the action of the BCKD complex. Recently it was shown that a specific transporter carries the three BCKAs into the mitochondria.[13] Inside the mitochondria the BCKAs are oxidatively decarboxylated by the BCKD complex generating three products: CO_2, NADH, and the corresponding acyl CoA ester.[30,31] (see Figs. 22-1 and 22-2).

Branched Chain α-Keto Acid Dehydrogenase

Overview. The committed step in catabolism of BCKAs is oxidative decarboxylation by the mitochondrial multienzyme complex BCKD. This complex is associated with the inner mitochondrial membrane. Thus, keto acid substrates must be transported across both mitochondrial membranes by a specific translocator protein for catabolism.[13] In rodent mitochondria, BCKA can undergo reamination since rodents have isozyme II aminotransferase.[71,81] The principal fate for BCKAs inside mitochondria is oxidation since transport of BCAAs across the mitochondrial membrane is minimal.[80]

The number of laboratories studying the BCKD complex increased dramatically during the mid-1970s. Interest in

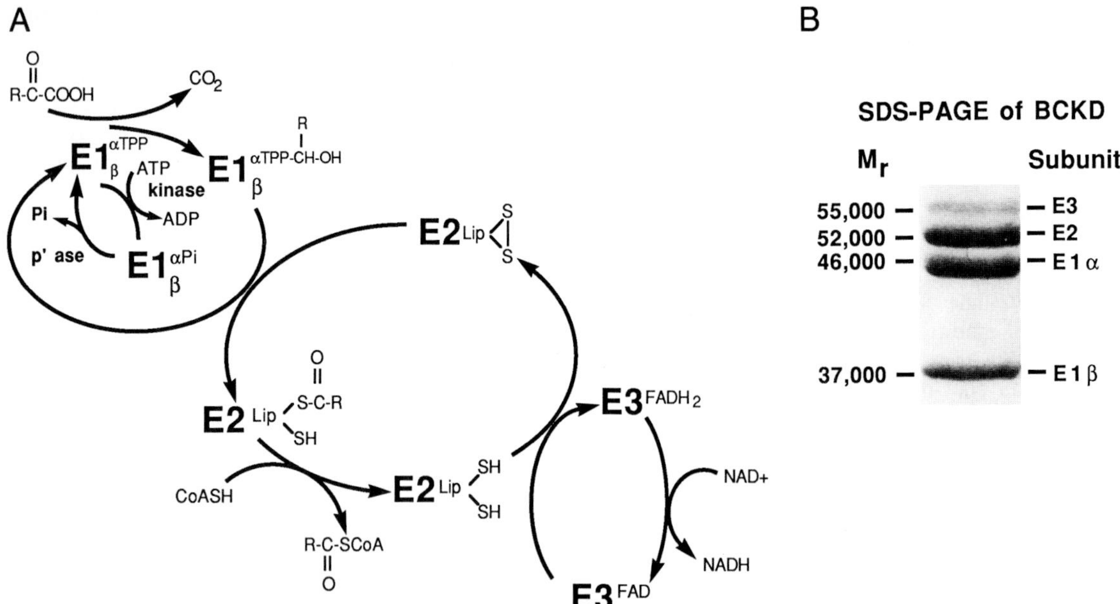

Fig. 22-2 Enzymes and reactions of the branched chain keto acid dehydrogenase complex. *A.* Reaction mechanism. E1αβ = decarboxylase; the kinase and phosphatase (p'ase) act on the E1α subunit to add or remove phosphate. Incorporation of P_i inactivates the complex. E2 = transacylase containing covalent bound lipoate. Acyl groups are transferred to CoASH leaving E2 lipoate in the reduced state. E3 = lipoamide dehydrogenase, a flavoprotein which reoxidizes E2 lipoate. Electrons from E3-FADH are transferred to NAD^+. *B.* The BDKD complex was purified from bovine liver, reduced with β-mercaptoethanol, and analyzed in a 10 to 15 percent gradient polyacrylamide gel containing sodium lauryl sulfate (SDS-PAGE). M_r values are estimated from simultaneously run molecular weight standards.

BCKD was generated from the human inborn errors associated with a decreased function of BCKD complex, from the realization that BCKD is regulated through a kinase/phosphatase relationship, and from the increased awareness of the role of leucine in regulating protein metabolism.[82–84] General reactions are schematically shown in Fig. 22-2. The decarboxylase or E1 component uses thiamine pyrophosphate (TPP) as cofactor to catalyze the decarboxylation of the BCKAs. The branched chain acyl group is then transferred to E2 (acyltransferase), which uses a covalently bound lipoate to transfer the acyl group to coenzyme A (CoA). E3 (lipoamide dehydrogenase) reoxidizes reduced E2-lipoate using the flavin, FAD, to accept H^+, which in turn reduces NAD^+. Branched chain acyl CoA, CO_2, and NADH are produced with a 1:1:1 stoichiometry.[31] The E1 component is the substrate for the kinase. Phosphate incorporation into E1 inactivates the complex.

Isolation of BCKD. A major advance in studies on BCKD came from two independent reports describing the isolation and purification of BCKD.[30,31] Purification of BCKD allowed for direct analysis of the complex under defined conditions. Both reports confirmed that a single complex decarboxylated all three BCKAs, laying to rest the earlier biochemical controversy that separate enzymes existed for the decarboxylation of the individual BCKAs.[85,86] The purified complexes, one from bovine kidney and the other from bovine liver, were not inactivated in the presence of ATP, allowing the debate of regulation by phosphorylation to continue. In 1980, two reports appeared, one from England[87] and the other from the United States[88] providing the first conclusive data that BCKD could be phosphorylated by an ATP-dependent kinase. Incorporation of P_i led to a loss of catalytic activity. Several articles appeared in rapid succession confirming this find.[89–92] By 1983, studies on the regulation of BCKD by phosphorylation provided enough data to merit a minisymposium.[93] Investigators then began studies describing the regulation of the kinase and phosphatase, which in turn regulate BCKD activity.[94,95]

Clarification of the physical and catalytic properties of BCKD continued. BCKD is associated with the inner mitochondrial membrane. Although an earlier report implied the complex was located on the outer side of the inner membrane,[82] current data support a location on the matrix side. The complex consists of four major proteins (Fig. 22-2). Lipoamide dehydrogenase (E3), a flavoprotein with an M_r of 55,000, reoxidizes the reduced lipoate found in E_2. This same protein also functions with the pyruvate dehydrogenase (PDH) and α-ketoglutarate dehydrogenase (KGDH) complexes.[96] Acyltransferase (E2), the core protein whose M_r is 52,000, contains a covalently bound lipoate and catalyzes the transfer of the decarboxylated branched chain acyl moiety to CoA. The decarboxylase (E1) comprises two subunits, α and β, with respective M_r's of 46,000 and 37,000, and it functions to remove CO_2 from the BCKA and transfer the acyl moiety to E2 (see Fig. 22-2).

BCKD is a constitutive component of mitochondria in all mammalian tissues. Originally Dancis et al.[97] suggested that muscle tissue did not have BCKD activity. Four years later Wohlhueter and Harper[42] found that muscle had a low level of BCKD activity. They also showed that activity in liver and kidney BCKD could be increased by including BCAAs in the diet. Clear demonstration that muscle could oxidize leucine to CO_2 came in 1972,[38] and 2 years later it was shown that BCKD activity in muscle could change with intake of dietary protein.[56] Demonstration that BCKD activity could be controlled by phosphorylation-dephosphorylation helped to explain some of the early results with muscle. Wagenmakers et al.[98] convincingly showed that only 6 to 20 percent of muscle BCKD was in the active, dephosphorylated form in rats on a normal diet. These authors further showed in the rat that 98 percent of the liver BCKD was in the active state, while 47 percent of kidney BCKD and 60 percent of brain BCKD were active. A later study by Harris et al.[99] confirmed that rat liver BCKD was >90 percent in the active state under normal dietary conditions. These percentages differ slightly from values reported by Patston et al.[100] which reverse the percentages for kidney (71 percent active) and liver (55 percent active) but find similar values for the muscle (<20 percent active). An extensive study with several tissues and species, plus data with isolated adipocytes, show that phosphorylation regulates BCKD in all tissues.[41,101,102] A compilation of data for liver and muscle BCKD activation state under influences of diet and hormonal state has been published.[103]

Kinase-Phosphatase. The BCKD complex interacts with two other proteins, a kinase and a phosphatase, which regulate activity of BCKD (Fig. 22-2). Although conditions used to isolate BCKD are critical in preserving the kinase activity, the kinase can be found associated with BCKD in preparations from all tissues.[92,104,105] Despite the copurification of kinase activity with the BCKD complex, no individual protein with this kinase activity has been isolated. Two experiments attempted to determine the location of the kinase within the complex with conflicting results. One used photoactivated [α-^{32}P] 8-azido-ATP to cross-link the nucleotide to its catalytic binding site. After cross-linking, autoradiographic analysis showed a single band of radioactive material which migrated on SDS-PAGE to an M_r of 46,000, coincident with the E1α protein.[106] This implied that kinase activity was contained in the E1α component or in a separate protein with migration properties similar to the E1α protein. In the other report, the kinase activity associated with the E2 protein.[107] After separation of the complex into its component parts by molecular sieve chromatography in the presence of high salt, separated E1 would not autophosphorylate, but the mix of E2 plus E1 led to $^{32}P_i$ incorporation into E1α. If the kinase activity is contained in a separate protein, the discrepancy could be explained. When the complex is separated with high salt treatment, the kinase protein associates with the E2 core protein, but under reducing conditions of SDS-PAGE, the kinase migrates with an M_r similar to that of the E1α protein. Resolution of these possible interpretations requires isolation of the kinase protein, which remains problematic.

A variety of compounds inhibit the kinase activity, including all three substrates. KIC inhibits BCKD kinase at the lowest concentration, but all three BCKAs increase BCKD activity through this kinase inhibition.[94] Reaction products of BCKD, isobutyryl CoA and isovaleryl CoA, at 0.1 m*M* inhibited kinase activity by 30 percent. Cofactors used by BCKD were also tested: CoA and NAD were without effect, but TPP, which is a cofactor with E1, inhibited kinase activity.[94,110] Another strong inhibitor of kinase is clofibric acid, the antihyperlipidemic drug.[108] Earlier studies showed that this drug directly inhibited BCKD function.[32,109] If kinase were inhibited, then one should see activation of BCKD, and long-term treatment with clofibrate did result in activation of BCKD under physiological conditions.[33] These differences for the action of clofibrate concerning the effect on BCKD probably reflect the activity state of the purified enzyme and dual effects of the inhibitor.

Kinase activity incorporates two molecules of phosphate per E1α subunit,[101,111-115] and the amino acid sequence at the phosphorylation site is similar to but not identical with the phosphorylation site in the α subunit of PDH. In both sites of both complexes, serine is the phosphorylated amino acid. The sequence for the E1α phosphorylation site is shown below in the single letter amino acid code.

-I-G-H-H-S(P)-T-S-D-D-S-S-A-Y-R-S(P)-V-D-E-V-N-Y-W-D-K-
Site 1 Site 2

Site 1 phosphorylation controls activity of BCKD. Site 2 phosphorylation is specifically blocked by α-chloroisocaproate, but incorporation of P_i into site 1 is allowed. Complex activity is inhibited under these conditions.[101] Since the rate of site 1 phosphorylation is decreased in the presence of α-chloroisocaproate, it is postulated that site 2 incorporation of P_i may influence site 1 phosphorylation. Phosphorylation sites are identical regardless of the tissue source or mammalian species.[101] Some tissue differences are reported regarding site 1 versus site 2 incorporation, but the significance is yet to be determined.

Phosphatase activity proved more elusive. Preparations of isolated BCKD complex never contain the phosphate-removal activity. In 1984, Damuni et al.[95] reported the first isolation and purification of a protein with an M_r of 460,000, which removed covalently bound P_i from the BCKD complex. Specificity favored the BCKD complex, especially when compared with the phosphorylated PDH complex. BCKD-phosphatase was active without divalent cations, being fully active in the presence of EDTA and EGTA, and was not inhibited by the cytosolic phosphatase inhibitors 1 and 2. These properties clearly distinguish the BCKD-phosphatase from other cellular phosphatases. BCKD-phosphatase activity was inhibited by tri- and diphosphate nucleotides but not by monophosphate nucleotides. The acyl CoA products of the BCKD reaction inhibited the phosphatase, while the BCAA and BCKAs had no effect on activity. In addition, a heat-stable protein inhibitor with an M_r of 36,000 was reported to specifically block the BCKD-phosphatase activity.[116] Both the phosphatase and the specific inhibitor were isolated from mitochondria, but location within the organelle was not determined. Recently the catalytic subunit of the BCKD-phosphatase was shown to be a single polypeptide chain with an M_r of 33,000.[117] All the properties associated with the phosphatase of M_r 460,000 applied to this smaller polypeptide. The heat-stable inhibitor protein acted on phosphatase of both sizes, and this inhibition was reversed by Mg^{2+} and spermine.[116,118] The presence of this heat-stable inhibitor might explain why isolation of the BCKD-phosphatase has proved difficult. A recent review compares the mitochondrial kinases and phosphatases.[119]

Major Subunits. As seen in Fig. 22-2, four major subunits copurify with the BCKD complex,[105] although most methods of isolation result in the loss of the largest subunit.[92,104] Lipoamide dehydrogenase (E3) is the largest component and contains covalent FAD. This subunit is common to the BCKD, PDH, and KGDH complexes.[96] Since this flavoprotein is not unique to BCKD, the protein will not be described in detail, but its impaired function will be discussed under subtypes of MSUD.

The acyltransferase protein E2 forms the core protein of the complex based on data for the similar PDH and KGDH complexes.[96] This protein contains a covalent lipoate residue[120] in a single domain.[121,121a,121b] The subcellular site and time of addition of lipoate to E2 is not known. Lipoate addition may play a role in the mitochondrial trapping of this protein (see "Molecular Genetics" below). In the native conformation, E2 is sensitive to trypsin, which cleaves the protein initially into two domains. The lipoate-containing domain retains catalytic activity if assessed with the artificial reaction where [1-^{14}C]isovaleryl CoA or [1-^{14}C]isobutyryl CoA is used as substrate and the transfer of the radioactive acyl group to endogenous dihydrolipoate is quantified. This catalytic fragment has lost its ability to bind the E1 and E3 subunits.[121,122] E2 is strongly antigenic,[123] and antibodies to this protein were used to isolate a cDNA clone for this subunit.[9,121a,121b,124,151]

Complex activity begins with the decarboxylation of the BCKA catalyzed by the E1 subunit, which comprises two proteins, α with an M_r of ≈46,000, and β with an M_r of ≈37,000. The α protein binds TPP creating the keto acid binding site for the release of CO_2.[125] When the E1α subunit is saturated with TPP, a conformational change occurs, rendering the subunit resistant to proteolytic degradation.[125,126] Another role for TPP appears to be inhibition of the kinase activity. With kinase inhibited, the phosphatase can dephosphorylate E1α, restoring catalytic activity to the complex.[110] Recently it was shown that the presence of phosphate on E1α causes the protein to migrate in SDS-PAGE with a slightly greater M_r near 49,000.[127] Thus active versus inactive states of BCKD can be assessed by E1α mobility in SDS-PAGE, by ^{32}P incorporation, or by direct activity measurements. The E1α cDNA was recently cloned and sequenced from a rat liver expression library. Deduced structural and functional aspects of this subunit will be forthcoming.[9a]

E1β, the smallest subunit of the complex at ≈37,000 daltons, has no defined function, although it is commonly thought that it functions in the transfer of the acyl group to E2-lipoate.

Association of Subunits. Assembly of the components of the BCKD complex into a functional unit occurs as with the PDH and KGDH complexes.[96] E2 forms a core upon which the E1 and E3 subunits attach. Reconstitution of BCKD subunits into an active complex from dissociated purified rat liver BCKD confirmed the assembly process.[128] E3 shows a loose association with E2, while E1 forms a more stable association with E2. The specific ratio for E1:E2:E3 is unknown. Difficulty in determining this ratio is based in part on the loose association of the subunits. Cook et al.[107] found that mixing subunits from PDH and BCKD suggested a high specificity for the originator complex. Association of $E1_{BCKD}$ with $E2_{BCKD}$ gave an active unit which decarboxylated the BCKA substrates but not pyruvate. If $E1_{PDH}$ was mixed with $E2_{BCKD}$, there was minimal activity with any substrate. Reverse mixing of $E1_{BCKD}$ with $E2_{PDH}$ also showed only minimal activity with the keto acid substrates. E3 was already known to be common to the two complexes. However, Yeaman et al.[129] showed that free E1 subunits could be found in liver and kidney supernatant fractions and in fact was the activator protein reported earlier by Fatania et al.[130] Unphosphorylated E1 subunits show a sixfold higher affinity for E2 than does phosphorylated E1.[107] These free E1 subunits may explain the source of the soluble KIC oxygenase reported by Sabourin and Bieber,[131] since both stay in the soluble fraction. The 46,000 protein could be free E1α subunits. Data for substrate specificity supports this idea. The KIC oxygenase prefers KIC over the other two BCKAs but also uses α-keto-γ-methiolbutyrate as a substrate. Recently two laboratories showed that BCKD also uses both this keto acid, which is derived from methionine, and the keto acid from threonine as substrates, suggesting that BCKD may function in the catabolism of both these amino acids.[132,133] However, α-keto-γ-methiolbutyrate is not present in patients with impaired BCKD activity.

Two reports appeared in 1983, recounting the induction of BCKD during differentiation of 3T3-L1 fibroblasts to adipocytes.[47,134] Both groups showed a sixteenfold increase in complex activity. One study reported activity of the specific subunits. E1 activity increased seventeen- to twentyfold; E2, sixfold; and E3, fourfold. The same increase for E3 was reported when induction of the PDH complex was followed. These data may provide a clue for the ratios of the protein components within the complex, suggesting that various subunits are not synthesized in equal numbers. In humans, two studies reported activation of BCKD activity. The first showed that 100 mg/day of an oral thiamine supplement to a normal diet resulted in a twofold increase in human liver BCKD activity.[135] The second study showed that growth of cultured human diploid fibroblasts in media with high concentrations of BCAAs resulted in a twofold increase in BCKD activity.[136] Only activity was measured, so the increase in activity may reflect dephosphorylation of existing complex, since both inducers are known to inhibit BCKD-kinase.[110] However, liver BCKD is usually 98 percent in the active state.[98,99] Therefore, the increase in activity reported for liver might be due to mechanisms other than dephosphorylation. Only studies of transcription and translation for the genes directing the synthesis of BCKD proteins will resolve these questions.

Molecular Genetics

Cloning and Chromosome Locations. Gene products as isolated proteins are known only for the branched chain aminotransferase and BCKD complex. Molecules responsible for transport of the amino or ketoacids have not been isolated. Two genetic systems are known for mammalian cells, nuclear and mitochondrial. Based on current available data, all components of BCAA metabolism are nuclear coded. The system L transporter function associates with the presence of human chromosome 20 in Chinese hamster ovary X human fibroblast hybrid cells.[137] Branched chain aminotransferase activity associates with the presence of either human chromosome 12 or 19.[74] Inheritance patterns in families with MSUD show only autosomal recessive transmission[138,139] (Fig. 22-3). No information is available on the location of the gene encoding the mitochondrial translocator, but all mitochondrial open reading frames have assigned products,[140–142] thus implying nuclear coding for this function. Although all proteins of the BCKD complex, except for the kinase, are isolated and partially characterized, the isolation of cDNAs is reported for only two of the proteins associated with the BCKD complex. These are the cDNA for the acyltransferase[9,121a,121b] and for E1α.[9a]

Protein Targeting. Knowledge of the steps involved in cell sorting of proteins has possible implications for the basis of inherited disorders of nuclear coded proteins, which function in various cellular compartments (See Chap. 3). Signal or target sequences within the proteins direct them to their site of function.[143,144] The transporter proteins for BCAA in the plasma membranes would likely be glycoproteins inserted by mechanisms involving the functional Golgi. A single report

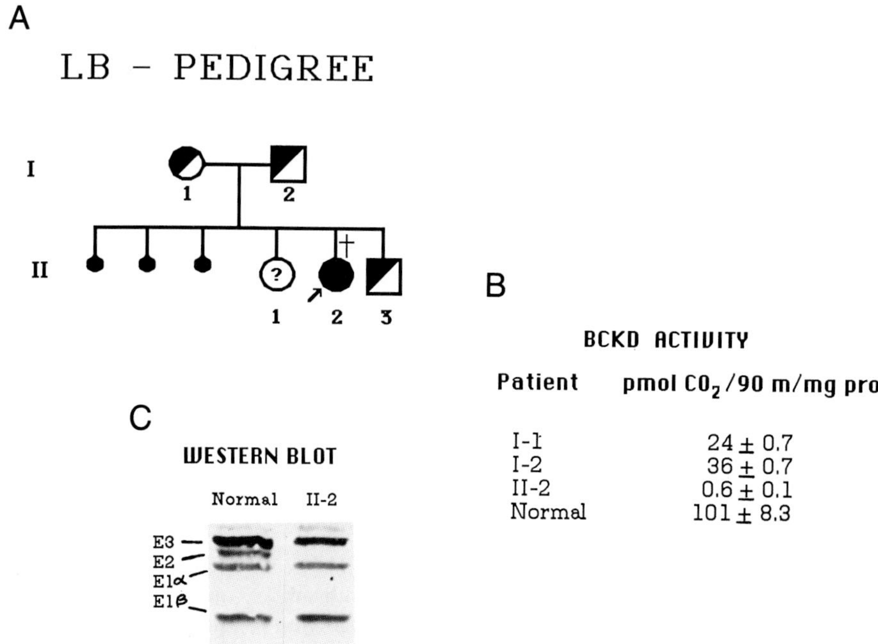

Fig. 22-3 Analysis of BCKD in LB family. *A.* Pedigree. *B.* Western blot of mitochondrial proteins from fibroblasts with normal BCKD activity and from the proband. *C.* BCKD activity was determined using cultured skin fibroblasts and $[1-{}^{14}C]$leucine (0.6 μM) as substrate.

describes efforts to clone the gene directing the synthesis of the system L transporter from human cells.[145]

The principle aminotransferase protein for the BCAAs in humans is present in the cytosol. Although chromosome locations are reported for two leucine aminotransferases in humans, neither have been cloned.

Subsequent catabolic reactions for the BCKAs occur in the mitochondria. The transporter protein for BCKA uptake by mitochondria and the proteins of the BCKD complex are coded in the nucleus and synthesized in the cytosol since products for all the open reading frames on mitochondrial DNA are accounted for with respiratory and ribosomal proteins.[140–142]

Current knowledge of the uptake of mitochondrial proteins from the cytosol is rapidly growing. Depending on the final location of the protein, the targeting sequence is found in different portions of the proteins. Outer membrane components have internal sequences which trap the proteins in this membrane. Proteins destined for the inner membranous space, the inner membrane, or the matrix most often have N-terminal leaders which serve to direct the proteins through the membranes.[146–148] Specific proteases then remove the leader peptide. Often the leader itself is sufficient to direct the protein into mitochondria since chimeric proteins containing leader sequence fused to cytosolic proteins have been constructed, and the chimeric product is directed to the mitochondria, often being proteolytically processed. The number or nature of membrane receptors for this uptake is not yet known, although it is thought that receptors are located in the outer membrane. Proteases for the processing of imported proteins have been partially characterized.[149,150]

Potential Mechanisms for Inherited Defects. Since BCKD comprises four catalytic proteins plus the two regulatory proteins, all coded in the nucleus and then imported into the mitochondria, many theoretical possibilities exist for the genetic mutations which cause BCKD deficiency and MSUD. The obvious mutations would involve changes in the catalytic binding sites which would result from single base mutations altering only the ability to decarboxylate the BCKAs or bind cofactors. The spectrum of BCKD activity in the MSUD population speaks to the variety of underlying mutations. Recently defined mutations, which lead to absence of one of the subunits of BCKD in the mitochondria as seen by antibody detection in a Western blot analysis, suggest another mechanism for MSUD. Examples of missing E2 have been seen in three patients[151–153] (Fig. 22-3). A report of three patients lacking the E1β has appeared.[153] The reason these proteins are missing from the mitochondria could be the absence of the gene, abortive transcription, unstable mRNA, unstable protein, abortive targeting sequence, altered processing site, or defective receptor for uptake. As probes for the genes of the BCKD complex become available, these alternative mechanisms producing absent mitochondrial subunits can be investigated. At present, partial cDNA clones for only two subunits are available, E2[9,121a,121b] and E1α (Ref. 9a and Danner, unpublished).

Other possible mechanisms could involve inherited defects in the kinase or phosphatase which regulate BCKD. If phosphatase was absent or altered, activation of BCKD would not occur or might occur slowly. These patients might present with a late onset phenotype, since they would be able to catabolize BCKAs with newly synthesized BCKD in the unphosphorylated state, but could not rapidly activate phosphorylated BCKD in response to a protein load. A phenotype for a kinase defect would be more difficult to predict. Still other mechanisms which cause MSUD could involve the transporter molecule for uptake of the BCKAs by mitochondria.

DISORDERS OF UPTAKE AND AMINOTRANSFERASE

Although it is conceivable that mutations occur for the transporter systems of the BCAAs in plasma membranes, the need for these amino acids in the human diet suggest this would be a lethal condition. Mutations of this type have not been described in the human population.

Aminotransferases

A single female patient from Japan was reported with isolated hypervalinemia, which was suggested as the cause for clinical abnormalities.[77,78] She presented at birth with an abnormal sucking reflex, frequent vomiting, repeated episodes of fever, and a general failure to thrive. She was hypotonic and hyperkinetic. A low valine diet begun at 9 months of age improved her condition, but supplementation with pyridoxal phosphate had no further effect. Assay of peripheral leukocytes from this patient for the ability to transfer amino groups from the BCAAs showed a defect only for valine conversion.[154] This was consistent with blood and urine findings, which showed only increased concentrations of valine. Leucine and isoleucine were present in plasma at near normal concentrations.

Hyperleucine-Isoleucinemia

A single report for one French family remains the only description of this abnormality.[155] A brother and sister with similar clinical features presented at 2 to 3 months of age with seizures, failure to thrive, and mental retardation. In addition, the girl had retinal degeneration and sensorineuronal hearing loss. Blood analysis showed elevated concentrations of leucine, isoleucine, and proline with normal levels of valine. Urinary BCAA concentrations were normal.

Aminotransferase activity in leukocytes of these two patients showed decreased transfer with leucine and isoleucine but normal activity with valine. Treatment with diets low in leucine and isoleucine did not improve the clinical phenotype, and the boy died in his third year.

Taken with the data from the Japanese patient, the case reports suggest that separate aminotransferases for valine and leucine-isoleucine are present in human cells. Alternatively, one would need to envision a mutation which differentially affected the catalytic activity of the enzyme toward one substrate but not another. However, confirmation of this suggestion with laboratory data remains to be presented. These findings remain unique, and the second interpretation is more consistent with current knowledge of BCAA aminotransferase enzymes in mammals.[11,12,29,70–75] The only aminotransferases characterized in human tissues convert all three BCAAs.[73]

MAPLE SYRUP URINE DISEASE OR BRANCHED CHAIN KETOACIDURIA

Historical Perspectives of Maple Syrup Urine Disease

More than 30 years have passed since Menkes first described four sibs with progressive neurologic disorders and sugary-smelling urine.[3] Using the dinitrophenylhydrazine reaction, BCKAs were identified in urine,[156] and a metabolic block was defined in oxidative decarboxylation of these BCKAs when peripheral leukocytes and cultured skin fibroblasts from affected patients were tested for this reaction.[4,5,157] This impaired reaction resulted in increased concentrations of BCAAs and BCKAs in plasma, urine, and cerebrospinal fluid. Untreated patients showed abnormal brain histopathology.[3,158–162] Dietary restriction of the BCAAs became the treatment of choice to reduce blood concentrations of BCAA and BCKAs into the normal range.[163,164] Clinical manifestations of MSUD were thus ameliorated and the usual sequelae lessened if treatment began in early infancy.[165,166] The pathogenesis of MSUD was therefore associated with excess accumulation of BCKAs and BCAA with consequent "toxic" effects on neurologic functions. Armed with potential dietary therapy, clinicians in the 1970s focused on preventive approaches, including newborn screening, neonatal treatment, genetic counseling, and prenatal monitoring.[166–170] Complementing the clinical endeavors, BCKD was isolated and purified,[30,31] which led to a definition of cofactor interaction with the complex and to the clinical use of pharmacologic doses of thiamine as an adjunct to dietary therapy.[171–181] The use of antibodies made against purified BCKD[123,124,151] began to clarify the heterogeneous phenotypes associated with impaired function of the multienzyme complex[151] (Fig. 22-3, Table 22-1). Both immunoblotting techniques and immunoprecipitation of labeled proteins are now used to identify subunits missing from the mitochondrial multienzyme complex. Restriction fragment length polymorphisms are sought to differentiate normal and mutant genes, using cDNA probes for the BCKD subunits.[9,9a,124] At present no specific mutations are characterized in the BCKD proteins, nor are chromosomal locations established for these genes. However, considerable information is available, regarding heterogeneity of clinical phenotypes, incidence from screening programs, diagnosis using enzyme activity and immunoblotting, pathology, and outcome of treatment.

Clinical Phenotypes

Historically, MSUD classification was based on clinical presentation and outcome. However, impairment of BCKD and increases in BCAA/BCKD in patients' blood and urine did not always correlate with severity of presentation or outcome (Tables 22-1 and 22-2). Several genetic, environmental, and historical factors contribute to this clinical confusion. First, different mutations in the same gene may lead to different degrees of impaired BCKD function. Second, mutations in entirely different genes may result in decreased metabolism of BCKA and BCAA (see "Molecular Genetics," above). The complexity of phenotypic expression is increased when we consider environmental effects on these biochemical values. Many variables affect onset and outcome. Among these are the amount and time in development at which dietary BCAAs are introduced, the age at which BCAA-restricted diet is initiated, the number and severity of intercurrent environmental insults (such as infections, anoxia, and hypoglycemia), and the proficiency of continued dietary control. Besides proficiency of dietary control, recent advances in neonatal intensive care may be the historical means by which outcome is better for patients with neonatal presentations during the last five as compared with the previous 15 years (Table 22-2). Despite a continuum of genetic and environmental variation, clinicians continue to rely on disease typing. Therefore, for pragmatic and historical interest this traditional approach is outlined in Table 22-1.

Seven forms are differentiated by current clinical and biochemical approaches. Several other "new" forms have been described which are based on absent BCKD function with mild presentations, unusually high valine concentrations, or different BCKD activities in the same family. Immunologic approaches have enabled classification of three different mutants based on structural analysis of the multienzyme complex (Table 22-1).

Table 22-1 Clinical Classification of Maple Syrup Urine Disease*

	Clinical features			*Biochemical features*		
Phenotypic classification	*Age of onset*	*Symptoms*	*Prognosis*	*Plasma Leu, μM*	*Leucine decarboxylation by intact cells, percent of control*	*Specific features*
Classic	Neonatal to early childhood	Poor feeding, apnea, ketoacidosis, seizures, hypoglycemia	Death to mild central nervous system impairment	1000–5000	0–2	BCKD proteins present
Intermediate	Infant to adult	Ataxia, failure to thrive, usually no acidosis, progressive	Severe psychomotor delay to normal	400–2000	2–20	BCKD proteins present
Intermittent	Childhood to adult	Intermittent ataxia and ketoacidosis during infection or protein ingestion, normal intervals	Death to normal	50–4000	2–40	BCKD proteins present
Thiamine responsive	Infant to adult	Generally milder than classic onset	Recurrent ataxic attacks to psychomotor delay	50–5000	2–40	Increased specific activity of BCKD after one month of 10–200 mg/kg per day thiamine orally
E1β deficiency	Neonatal	Severe classic	Death	4000	0–1	In Mennonite population, cell GM 1654
E2 deficiency	Neonatal	Apnea, coma, ketoacidosis	Death in infancy	4000	<1	Absent E2 by immunoblot, specific for BCKD deficiency
E3 deficiency	Neonatal	Hypotonia with progressive impairment of CNS	Death in early childhood	400–600	0–10	Absent E3 by immunoprecipitation. Combined deficiency of PDH, KGDH, and BCKD

*PDH = pyruvate dehydrogenase; KGDH = α-ketoglutarate dehydrogenase.

Classic MSUD. A spectrum of presenting signs exists with this classification from sudden apnea, coma, and death during the neonatal period to poor feeding, lethargy, and recurrent ketoacidosis during infancy. Typically, since the mother metabolizes excessive BCAA/BCKAs during gestation, the newborn is normal until about 4 to 7 days of age. The first presenting sign is poor feeding with bottle refusal and sleepiness. Unfortunately, vomiting is not common, and apnea and central nervous sytem depression leading to coma may quickly follow and persist until BCKA concentrations are decreased. Sweet-smelling urine is not always present during this neonatal period, but the fragrant smell may be present in earwax by 2 months of age. This is probably due to the lipophilic nature of whichever organic acids cause the smell, the concentrative effect of cerumen, and the ear canal's inaccessibility to washing. A sniff of the tip of the otoscope cover after an ear examination may provide an inexpensive clinical diagnosis.

If an untreated patient survives the first weeks of life, EEG abnormalities, severe psychomotor retardation, generalized dystonic posturing, and other evidences of structural brain dysfunction are the rule. Bilateral ptosis, ophthalmoplegia, and facial diplegia were observed in several patients.[182–185] Moderate to severe hypoglycemia and hypoalaninemia also occur.[168,186,187]

Intermittent and Intermediate Types. Many patients with variable onset and outcome of disease expression are reported.[176,178,188–205] Typically the postnatal course is uneventful. Clinical signs are seen between 2 months and 40 years of age, triggered by otitis, upper respiratory tract infection, im-

Table 22-2 Change in Outcome for Patients Diagnosed and Treated for Maple Syrup Urine Disease

					Outcome			
		Age at detection and treatment			*Living*		*IQ/DQ†*	
Number of patients	*Range of birthdates*	*<1 mo*	*>1 mo*	*Enzyme activity,* %*	*Yes*	*No*	*>90*	*<90*
10	1965–1980	3	7	5.1 ± 5.4 (0–16)	6	4	2	4
10	1981–1986	10	0	6.2 ± 5.4 (2–17)	10	0	7	3

*Enzyme activity in percent of control [1-^{14}C]leucine decarboxylating activity by fresh peripheral monocytes
†IQ = Intelligence quotient using Stanford Binet for children above age 2 years; DQ = Developmental quotient using Bayley scales for children from age 2 to 24 months.

munization, operation, or sudden increase in dietary protein. Patients become irritable, ataxic, and progressively lethargic. With supportive care the patient recovers, only to experience repeated similar episodes until diagnosed and treated. The maple syrup odor may be noted during these episodes, concomitant with an elevation of BCAAs and BCKAs in blood and urine. During remission and diet therapy, BCAA and BCKA concentrations in body fluids are near normal. Despite a mild and intermittent course, the long-term outcome is occasionally fatal.[176,177]

The subclass "intermediate MSUD" was described in 1970.[201] A 19-month-old female infant had the odor of maple syrup during evaluation for mental retardation. Her postnatal course was unremarkable except for a substantial delay in developmental milestones. Seizures, ataxia, excessive vomiting, and episodic drowsiness were not noted. The patient had tolerated several immunizations and mild febrile illnesses without becoming acutely ill. She consumed large quantities of milk, eggs, and meat during infancy without overt symptoms. There were no focal neurologic abnormalities, although mild generalized hypotonia was present. Unlike typical patients with the intermittent type of MSUD, BCAA and BCKA levels in blood and urine were consistently elevated. Moderate anemia, hyperuricemia, and mild systemic acidosis were also present. Restriction of dietary protein to 1.5 g/kg per day reduced to normal the concentrations of BCAAs and BCKAs in the blood and urine. Several additional cases in this intermediate category are reported.[2,173,176,177,197,202,203] Although they are considered clinically distinct, these different clinical types will require enzymatic, immunologic, and molecular genetic confirmation and classification.

Thiamine-Responsive MSUD

The first thiamine-responsive patient with MSUD was described in 1971.[171,180] This 11-month-old, adopted, white, Canadian female had delayed neurologic development. Plasma leucine concentrations normalized dramatically when she received both 10 mg/day thiamine and a simultaneous protein-restricted diet. She continued taking 10 to 20 mg/day thiamine and a protein-restricted diet at 2 g/kg per day for 15 years with five episodes of metabolic decompensation, two of which included seizures and coma. These episodes were triggered by infections and other intercurrent illnesses. At age 15, she had a normal social life, a normal physical exam, and mildly restricted mental achievement (IQ = 85) and cognitive function (WISC-R = 81). Biochemical assessment of 0.1 m*M* leucine decarboxylation by her peripheral blood leukocytes was 40 percent of control before thiamine, but no follow-up enzyme activities are available. She probably has an intermittent form of MSUD. Since residual BCKD was present, thiamine response is an expected sequela.[8]

From this case history, other published case reports (Table 22-3), and a recent comprehensive review of the literature,[181] several clinical points are apparent regarding thiamine-responsive MSUD. First, all responsive patients have had residual enzyme activity. In general, clinical presentations tend to be less severe than for thiamine nonresponders. However, several classic clinical presentations of MSUD responded to pharmacologic doses of thiamine. Three weeks was required as a minimum time before response was seen. This time lag from initiation of pharmacologic thiamine to observed effect may be related to the time required for stabilization and activation of the normal and mutant BCKD[136] (Fig. 22-4, Table 22-3). Second, all responders required continued restriction of dietary BCAAs. There is no evidence that pharmacologic doses of thiamine alone will return normal function to mutant BCKD.[180] Therefore extra thiamine should be considered an adjunct to dietary treatment, not an alternative or curative approach. Finally, because both normal and abnormal BCKD may show increased activity after prolonged administration of large doses of oral thiamine and there are no serious side effects with these megadoses, a therapeutic trial of 5 to 20 mg/kg per day up to 500 mg/day is suggested in all patients with MSUD.

The biochemical mechanisms for thiamine response have been studied in vivo and in vitro using BCKD assays.[8,126,136,168,173,174,179] Assessment of skin fibroblasts cultured from the Canadian patient resulted in two different kinetic

Table 22-3 A Comparison of Biochemical Data in Patients with Thiamine-Responsive and Thiamine-Nonresponsive MSUD

	Diet		Leucine decarboxylation by peripheral leukocytes, percent of normal		Urinary α-ketoisocaproic acid (mg/24 h/g creatinine)	
Patient (age studied)	*Leu, mg/kg/day*	*Protein, g/kg/day*	*Pre-thiamine*	*During thiamine**	*Pre-thiamine*	*During thiamine*
Responsive						
MC (10 yr)	38	1.25	3	18	215	40
KC (7 yr)	35	1.25	5	14	212	78
JP (17 mo)	95	1.72	5	8	80	33
TMc (2 4/12 yr)	30	1.28	5	11	211	16
VH (9 2/12 yr)†	70	0.97	11	16	40	31
Nonresponsive						
LB (7 days)	0	0.8	0.6	—	312	Died at 13 days
CM (3 1/12 yr)	21	1.24	0.8	0.8	34	35

*Oral thiamine was given for at least 3 weeks in the following amounts: MC and KC (10 mg/kg per day); JP (16 mg/kg per day); TMc (19 mg/kg per day); VH (8mg/kg per day); LB (100 mg/kg per day IV); CM (16 mg/kg per day).
†VH had received 6 mg/kg per day of oral thiamine for 2 years prior to this study. His thiamine was discontinued for 2 months before the study. All other patients recieved only the recommended daily allowance for thiamine.
SOURCE: Compiled from references 8, 151, 168, 174, 175, and 179.

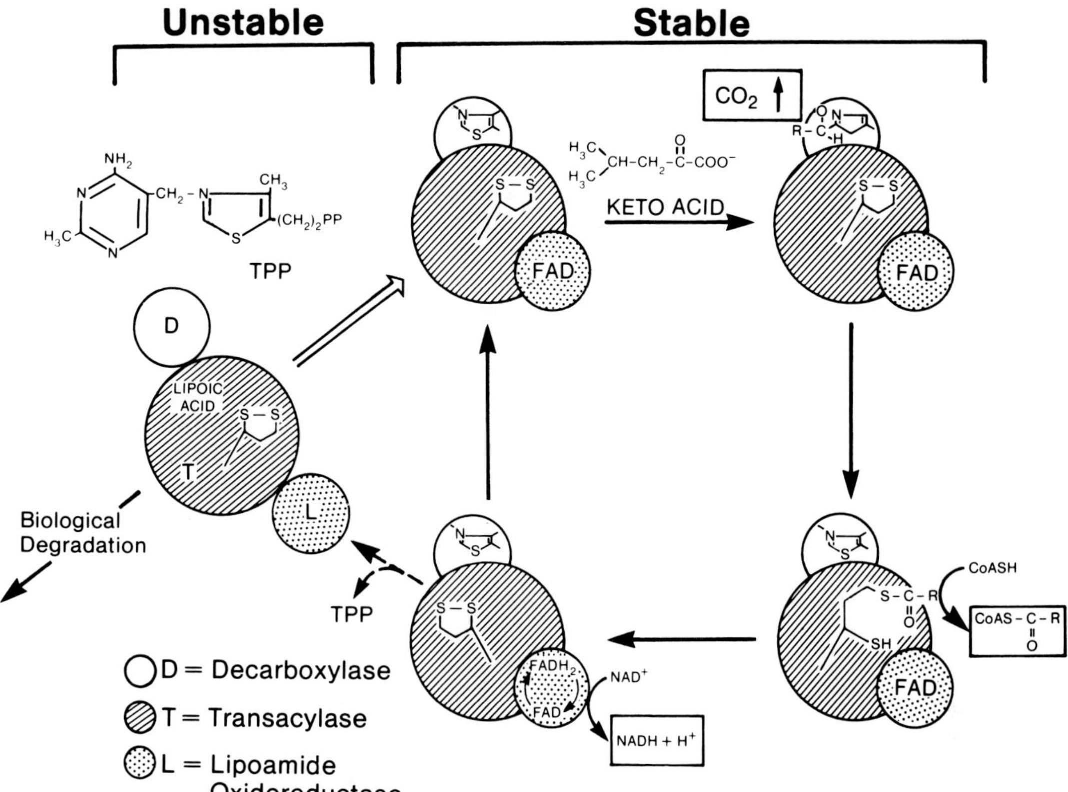

Fig. 22-4 Proposed mechanism for thiamine pyrophosphate (TPP) stabilization of BCKD complex.

interpretations of the effects of added TPP when two different laboratories used two different biochemical methods.[175,204] When thiamine-depleted cells were disrupted by freeze-thaw treatment and KIV used as substrate, BCKD in this broken cell suspension from the patient had a decreased affinity for TPP. A normal apparent K_m value was 1.6 μM, and the value for this patient was 25 μM.[204] In earlier studies, the same cell line was analyzed with KIC as substrate and mitochondrial inner membrane as BCKD source. Mitochondria from the patient cells had a normal K_m value for TPP of 1.6 μM for TPP, but the apparent V_{max} value was decreased. Furthermore, the rate and degree of thiamine response by the Canadian patient and two Georgia patients (MC and KC, Table 22-3) correlated with the degree of decreased capacity for TPP binding to their mutant BCKD. Several points favor the "V_{max}" rather than "K_m" theory for the mechanism of TPP action. First, the broken-cell assay is less satisfactory for determining TPP binding kinetics. Biphasic activity between 0 and 0.5, and 0.5 and 5mM substrates are present in broken cells with reduced BCKD, suggesting that an alternative reaction occurs at supranormal substrate concentrations. Broken cells may reaminate KIV to valine, or other dehydrogenases such as PDH may use KIV at the higher substrate concentrations. Cells from one MSUD patient (GM-612) analyzed by this broken cell technique had considerable activity at high KIV concentration, and the activity was enhanced by added TPP. Other investigators found no E_2 protein for this same cell line by immunoblot.[152] Patients with MSUD whose BCKD has no immunoreactive E2 are not thiamine-responsive[139,151] (Table 22-3). Thus this broken cell assay is complex and unsatisfactory for defining cofactor binding kinetics. The absence of a clinical cure in the Canadian child also speaks against a primary mutation affecting the K_m value for TPP binding alone.

Several biochemical and clinical observations support a hypothesis for the stabilizing effect of TPP on mutant BCKD complex, which is schematized in Fig. 22-4. First, clinical observations were that >150 mg thiamine per day for at least a 3-week period superimposed on a BCAA-restricted diet were required for this response. Second, since residual BCKD activity was present in these patients, it was reasoned that saturation of BCKD with TPP resulted in a decreased turnover of the complex. A similar effect would be expected for normal BCKD. This hypothesis was tested by administering 100 mg/day of oral thiamine to 18 adult patients with normal livers who were undergoing laparotomy and diagnostic liver biopsy for tumor classification.[136] BCKD activity in isolated liver mitochondria was quantified after 5 to 15 or 18 to 28 days of thiamine loading. A twofold increase in BCKD activity was seen only in the group treated for more than 18 days.

Direct in vitro evidence for the stabilizing effect of saturating amounts of TPP was documented in preserving BCKD activity at 37°C[173,175,206] by protecting against heat inactivation by producing conformational changes of purified enzyme complex and by prolonging the time for proteolytic inactivation.[127] Most recently, saturating amounts of TPP were found to retard chymotrypsin digestion of E1α.[126] By increasing thiamine ingestion, intracellular TPP is increased, thus saturating all E1α subunits. Under these conditions, BCKD undergoes a conformational change, making it resistant to degradation and prolonging its biologic half-life.[8,206] The presence of excess TPP also inhibits BCKD kinase activity, maintaining BCKD in the active state[94,110] (see Figs. 22-2 and 22-4).

Immunologic Classification. Polyclonal antibodies specific for BCKD proteins have been used to define mutations resulting in MSUD with immunologically altered proteins. As shown in Table 22-1 and Fig. 22-3B, two different antigen negative mutations are now defined: E1β deficiency and E2 deficiency.[124,151,153] Both of these disorders present as classic MSUD.[151,153,168,181] Antibodies specific for E3 have defined patients with antigenically present but catalytically inactive E3; these patients present with combined lactic and branched chain ketoaciduria.[207–212]

One diploid cell strain (GM 1654) and the transformed lymphoblastoid line from the same patient (GM 1655) have absent E1β and diminished E1α by immunoblot techniques. This Mennonite child presented with classic MSUD and died at 8 months of age. Decarboxylation activity was in the classic range when measured in intact cultured cells. When broken cells were used as the BCKD source, activity near 40 percent of control was found. High concentrations of substrate were used suggesting probable decarboxylation by alternative routes.[153]

Three patients are reported who immunologically lack E2 but antigenically retain E1α, E1β, and E3. These recent findings were postulated more than 15 years ago from studies of BCKD activity in cells from one patient who died within 2 weeks of birth and was nonresponsive to intravenous thiamine and protein restriction.[139] Based on enzyme assays to measure the activity of E1 and E2 independently, a defect in E2 was postulated.[168] Immunologic studies revealed the physical absence of E2[124,151] (Figure 22-3). As shown in Fig. 22-3*A*, MSUD in this family was inherited as an autosomal recessive trait. The mutant allele resulted in reduced activity for BCAA decarboxylation by intact cells. At low substrate concentration, heterozygous cell lines had between 24 and 35 percent of control activity. Parents were clinically normal. The molecular basis for this mutation remains to be solved (see "Molecular Genetics," above).

As stated, E3 is common to BCKD, PDH, and KGDH.[96] Three patients are reported who presented with combined ketoacidosis with increased lactic acid, pyruvic acid, α-ketoglutaric acid, and all three BCKAs in their urine.[207–212] Lactic acidosis with ataxia and progressive extrapyramidal tract disease were associated clinical signs for all patients. Enzyme activity in cultured skin fibroblasts from the patients was 25 percent of control PDH, 40 percent of control KGDH, and 0 to 10 percent of control BCKD. Zero to 60 percent of total lipoamide dehydrogenase was present.[208] Fibroblasts from patients and controls were cultured with [^{35}S]methionine to label cell proteins. Antiserum for E3 was used to immunoprecipitate cell extracts, and E3 was antigenically present in both mutant and control cells. Since there are both cytosolic and mitochondrial forms of E3, it is not clear whether this subunit was absent or structurally altered in mitochondria from these patients. Either fine peptide mapping of normal and mutant E3 immunoprecipitated from isolated mitochondria or molecular analysis of the mutation using E3 cDNA probes may shed light on this enigma.

Genetics and Screening

Autosomal Recessive Inheritance. The severe classic phenotype is inherited with an autosomal recessive pattern (Fig. 22-3*A*). Heterozygotes can be distinguished biochemically using either cofactor-reconstituted broken cells and substrate concentrations below the K_m or intact fibroblasts cultured from parent's skin.[139] In the heterozygote, $^{14}CO_2$ produced from either [1-^{14}C]BCKA or [1-^{14}C]BCAA is approximately 50 percent of control cells.[168]

Considerable heterogeneity exists for mutations which affect BCKD, and different genetic mechanisms are likely. Using BCKA or BCAA oxidation to assess BCKD activity in parental cells, several obligate heterozygote parents showed normal activity, while their mate had 50 percent activity.[196,197,206] In one family mild and severe forms of MSUD were present in siblings who had about 9 and 1.9 percent leucine decarboxylating activity in fibroblasts. Their father had 6.7 percent and mother 66 percent of control.[196,197] No MSUD pedigrees exhibit mitochondrial transmission (maternal inheritance), and there are no BCKD genes in the mitochondrial genome. Questions about the mechanisms by which these nuclear-coded proteins are assembled in mitochondria may be answered by further studies of affected families whose proband has an immunologically absent subunit. Experiments to define the molecular structure of genes controlling the synthesis of BCKD proteins are in progress. Included are studies to define leader sequences required for normal proteins to be recognized, transported, processed, and assembled in mitochondrial membranes.

Screening. The early signs of classic MSUD are not specific, and affected infants may reach a life-threatening state before clinical suspicions are aroused. Leucine concentrations in an affected infant's blood will rise to abnormal concentrations during the first 4 h to 4 days of life, regardless of protein intake.[213] Therefore, nonselective newborn screening is both clinically important and feasible before hospital discharge of the newborn.[214–216] Nonselective, or population-based, newborn screening is accomplished using dried blood on filter paper. Screening programs require immediate retrieval, diagnosis, and management of positive screenees.[169] Leucine concentrations are quantified on the principle that *Bacillus subtilis* spores grow on agar medium containing the leucine analogue and competitive inhibitor, β-2-thienyl-DL-alanine only if blood leucine concentrations are above 2 mg/dl (153 μ*M*). The diameter of bacterial colony growth around a standardized paper punch containing 0.1 ml of dried blood is roughly proportional to the blood concentration of leucine. Any value above 4 mg/dl (305 μ*M*) requires emergency referral to an experienced center for diagnosis and management. Any value above 2 mg/dl requires clinical evaluation of neurologic status and immediate, more quantitative biochemical diagnosis.[214] Selective screening may be done by the clinician at the bedside using a freshly prepared solution of 2 *N* HCl saturated with 2,4-dinitrophenylhydrazine. If α-keto acids are present, an equal mixture of dinitrophenylhydrazine reagent and urine will produce a cloudy solution containing bright yellow crystals of the keto acid-dinitrophenylhydrazone derivatives. This reaction takes about 2 min at room temperature.[156] Confirming diagnosis can be made by thin-layer chromatography of these crystals. A more precise and diagnostic procedure is analysis of the urine for organic acids by gas chromatography and mass spectroscopy (Fig. 22-5). Urine is prepared by converting ketoacids present to trimethylsilyl esters for chromatography.[217–220] Mass spectra for peaks C, D, and E are below (Fig. 22-5). Fragments of mass 275, 260, 232, 186, and 158 are characteristic of the trimethylsilyl derivative of KIV (peak C). The larger keto acids KMV and KIC differ from KIV by a larger fragment of mass 289 and a fragment of mass 246. KMV and KIC differ at fragments of mass 216, 143, 129, and 110 (compare spectrum for peaks D and E). This type of analysis will distinguish the ketoaciduria of catabolism or star-

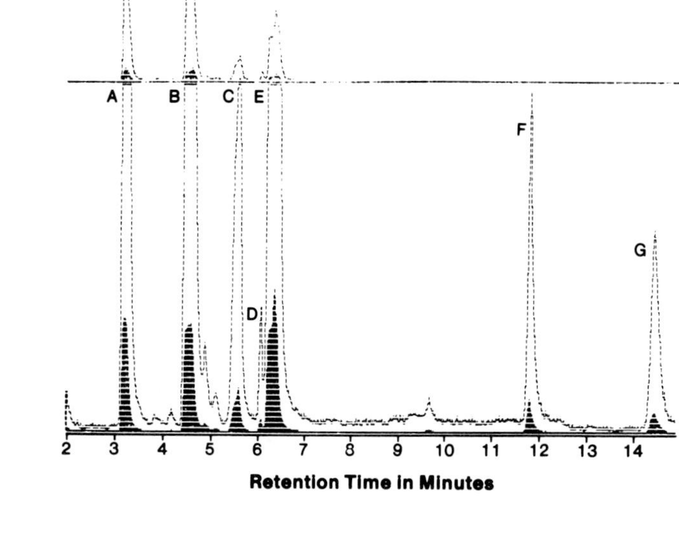

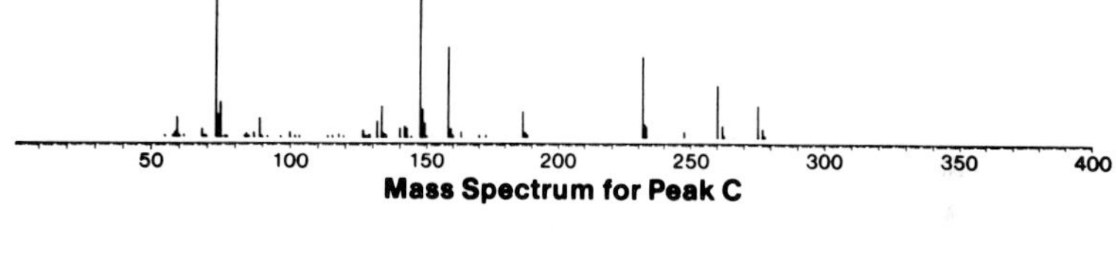

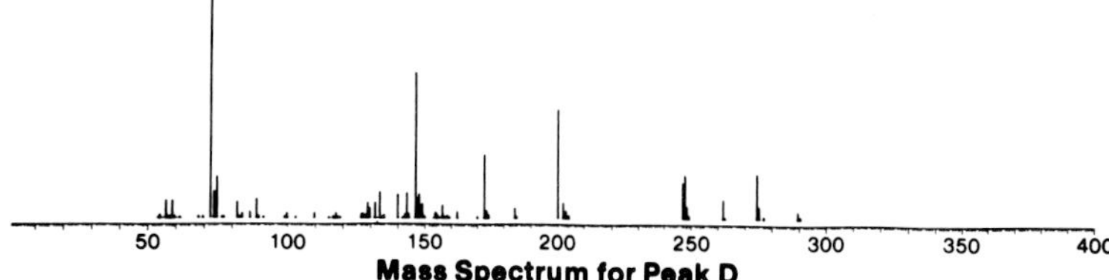

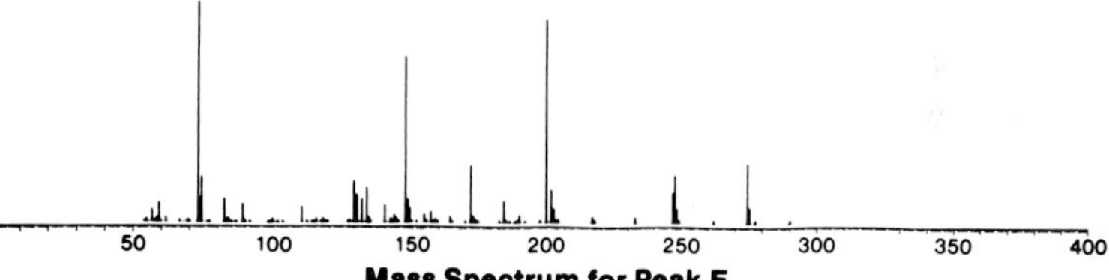

Fig. 22-5 Spectrum of the organic acids present in the urine of MSUD patient. For details of the individual peaks see text.

vation from excessive protein intake in patients with MSUD. When patients with MSUD are calorically overrestricted, organic acid products of β-lipolysis will also be present including β-hydroxybutyric acid, acetoacetic acid, and acetone. Extensive lists of retention times for organic acids are available, and mass spectroscopy continues as an important diagnostic adjunct to assure correct interpretation.[221,222] Mass spectroscopy also enables identification of unknown peaks and provides help for clinically relevant questions, such as the presence or absence of 4-methylthio-2-oxo-butyric acid in patients with MSUD. Although we have not found this compound in the urine of patients with MSUD, BCKD can decarboxylate this transaminated product of methionine.[133,134]

The diagnosis of MSUD is also made by finding elevated plasma concentrations of BCAAs. The presence of L-alloisoleucine is pathognomonic of a clinically significant block in isoleucine catabolism.[7,223] There is no L-alloisoleucine in normal human tissues, because the rate of keto-enol tautomerization of L-isoleucine, and KMV is insignificant at physiological concentrations.[224–226] These four BCAAs are separated by ion-exchange chromatography and quantified by the purple color produced through ninhydrin interaction with their α-amino group. With current instrumentation, diagnosis should be available from an experienced lab within 4 h of receiving 1.0 ml fresh heparinized whole blood. If blood leucine is above 400 μM, or if BCKAs are present in the urine, immediate dietary therapy is suggested consisting of restriction of BCAAs, high caloric intake (150 kcal/kg per day), and normal total protein intake (2.5 g/kg/per day). Orogastric perfusion and hyperalimentation are often necessary to accomplish these emergency nutritional goals.[217]

The ability of intact cells to decarboxylate 1-^{14}C-labeled BCAAs continues to be the preferred diagnostic method. Fresh peripheral monocytes may be used, but controls are necessary to establish cell viability during isolation and sample preparation. Frozen or mailed samples of blood are unsatisfactory due to instability and low activity of BCKD in these specimens. The advantages of assaying fresh peripheral blood cells are the rapidity of results and the ability to evaluate response to excess thiamine. Culture time from skin biopsy to sufficient quantity of fibroblasts for assay is at least 3 weeks. Advantages of using cultured fibroblasts are their test-retest reliability and their stability for mailing, freezing, and reutilization. Fibroblasts can also be used to discern heterozygotes for classic mutations in BCKD (Fig. 22-3*C*). Less test-retest variability has been obtained using labeled BCAAs and intact fibroblasts than labeled BCKAs and broken cell preparations. The latter are unstable and give a high background. Micromethods which use as few as 50,000 cultured fibroblasts or 50 μl of blood have been described.[227–229] Using these approaches, one effective statewide screening program has a mean age at first test of 5 ± 2 days, diagnosis by 10 ± 3 days, and onset of therapy by 10 ± 5 days.[215]

BCKD assays with broken cells also have been used and are preferred by some laboratories.[151,168,205] Cultured cells are freeze-thawed and [1-^{14}C]BCKAs used as substrate. These systems require supplementation with aqueous soluble cofactors and are useful for defining genotype and cofactor requirements in diagnosed cases. Broken cell assays were used for genotyping and prenatal monitoring in the early 1970s.[167,168] In these assays, low substrate concentrations are necessary to avoid alternative pathways of utilization. Lymphoblastoid cells are not of particular diagnostic use but are useful for complementation analysis and to provide sufficient DNA and RNA for molecular studies of mutant BCKD.[199,230]

Several fetuses have been genotyped prenatally using cultured monolayers of amniotic fluid cells to measure the ability to decarboxylate BCAA or BCKA.[168,229,231,232] Amniotic fluid concentrations of BCAAs and BCKAs of an affected fetus between the 16th and 20th weeks of gestation were not different from controls, excluding prental diagnosis by direct BCAA and BCKA quantitation in amniotic fluid.[233]

Recently prenatal diagnosis was made in the first trimester.[234] Chorionic villus biopsies obtained transvaginally in the ninth to tenth week of gestation were dissected into fragments. Careful, equal distribution of villi among at least triplicate microwells provided adequate tissue to assess $^{14}CO_2$ generation from [1-^{14}C]leucine. An affected fetus produced 21 to 92 pmol $^{14}CO_2$ per milligram villus protein per hour as compared with 750 to 1295 pmol $^{14}CO_2$ per milligram villus protein per hour in control tissue.[234] Confirmation can be made by assay of cultured chorionic villus cells. The advantage of early trimester diagnosis is that parents can elect to terminate a pregnancy by aspiration curettage before the 13th week. The ethical aspects of termination of pregnancy for a potentially treatable disease are issues for further debate but are decisions made by at-risk parents and professionals during prenatal counseling sessions.

Incidence

Incidence figures for clinically significant impairment of BCKD in the newborn population remain unknown.[170,235–237] This is due in part to variation in sensitivity of screening methods, ethnic composition of the population being screened, and the heterogeneity of BCKD expression. MSUD is reported in whites,[2,3] blacks,[170] Jews,[239] Indians,[202,240] Japanese,[177,230,238] and Chinese.[241] As seen in Table 22-4, the incidence of MSUD ranges from 1/760 in an inbred, Mennonite population[242–245] to a low of 1/290,000 in a mobile, urban, New England, predominantly white population.[236] These figures do not reflect the severity of impaired BCKD detected in the screened population. In the Georgia population, there was virtually 100 percent compliance with 275,463 black and 480,700 white newborns screened over an 8-year period. Since this screening program tested all infants before hospital discharge with repeat screening at 2 weeks of age, less severe forms of MSUD were detected. A total of nine cases of MSUD were detected and treated. Two were black and had severe disease, while seven were white. Three of these white newborns had residual BCKD activity and responded to pharmacologic thiamine administration. Thus the incidence of classic MSUD detected before discharge from the hospital was 1/137,732 in black and 1/120,175 in white newborns. The incidence of clinically significant disease in whites, which included less severe forms of BCKD impairment, was much higher, 7/480,700 or 1/68,671. The latter figure is probably a more accurate estimate for health planning in screening, retrieval, diagnosis, and management of significantly impaired BCKD in the white population.

Pathology

Mechanisms for toxic effects of increased BCAAs and BCKAs on brain remain problematic. Variables include the unknown complexity of brain development, duration and concentrations reached for the putative toxins, and the stage of brain development at which the insult occurs. Secondary effects of hypoxia, acidosis, and hypoglycemia which may attend classic MSUD crisis in the neonatal period add further confusion. Two major pathologic consequences should be separated: reversible and irreversible neurotoxicity. The latter occurs during early brain development, interrupts normal development, and irreversibly affects myelin composition and oligodendroglial migration.[246–255]

Clinical correlation to reversible toxicity is the reversible apnea, stupor, and frank coma expressed by the neonate and the ataxia, seizures, and stupor which may occur later in the life during periods of uncontrolled BCAA and BCKA acidemia. Theories for the acute reversible mechanisms fall into two general categories: that neurotransmitters are displaced[246,247]; and that energy sources for the brain are suddenly removed.[248–250] Leucine and KIC are usually above 1.0 m*M* in plasma during these acute attacks. Leucine transport across the blood-brain barrier has a K_m value near 0.1 m*M*, and it is assumed that equal or greater concentrations occur intracellularly in brain cells than in the blood. KIC, KIV, and their hydroxyderivatives compete with L-glutamate for decarboxylation by rat brain homogenates and may reduce γ-aminobutyric acid production.[247] Excess dietary leucine reduces brain serotonin in rats.[246] When rat brain slices are incubated with KIV and KIC at 10 μ*M* medium concentrations, there is a 10 to 15 percent reduction in respiration.[248] In human and rat brain or mitochondria from these cells, KIC inhibits PDH and KGDH with K_i values in the millimolar range.[250] In most of these studies the precursor BCAA did not inhibit these enzymes. Thus high concentrations of BCKAs, particularly KIC, inhibited two important enzymes for brain mitochondrial energy production. The apparent K_i values (1.4 to 4.5 m*M*) are within the range of BCKA concentrations in the blood of untreated newborns dying during the acute toxic phase of MSUD.

There is only one natural animal model other than humans for the chronic, permanent neuropathology of MSUD.[255] Poll Hereford calves with MSUD who died during the newborn period had ultrastructural intramyelinic vacuoles. These findings were consistent with observations in human brains from

Table 22-4 Incidence of MSUD

Study (ref.)	Total screenees	Incidence		
		Black	White	Total
Mennonites (243,244)	Unstated	0	1/760	1/760
Georgia (215,245)	756,163	1/137,732	1/68,671	1/84,018
Europe (235)	1,500,000	ND*	1/120,000	1/120,000
Collaborative (U.S.) (237,242)	2,800,000	ND	1/216,000	1/216,000
Massachusetts (238)	873,000	ND	1/290,000	1/290,000

*ND = Not determined.

deceased patients with untreated MSUD[158–162] who had abnormal myelin with decreased lipids, proteolipids, and cerebrosides.[254] These observations led to the hypothesis that a single insult (increased BCAA or BCKA) during a critical time in the developing nervous system can initiate an irreversible change in myelin structure and thus produce a chronic toxic effect.[251,252] Several observations support this hypothesis. Metabolites of MSUD altered neural cells in culture.[251,252] When BCAAs were injected into pregnant rats, the fetal brain amino acid pool was altered owing to transport competition across the rat blood-brain barrier. By increasing intracerebral pools of leucine, displacement of critical amino acids for essential enzymic reactions produced changes in myelin structure.[256] One such process, the condensation of palmitoyl CoA with serine in the production of sphingosine, is critical in myelin formation. Serine pools could be lowered by excess BCAAs. A stable, light membrane fraction of myelin is known, which is synthesized only in the neonatal rat. This core myelin is spread through the brain and, unlike later-forming myelin, does not show biologic turnover. Thus, a critical stable myelin could be altered in infancy by elevated BCAAs or BCKAs and produce permanent neurologic damage.[251,252] A recently developed experimental model is the 14-day-old rat pup, which is injected intracranially with leucine, KIC, and [^{3}H]lysine as a marker of myelin proteins.[253] Significant loss of myelin proteins and increases in their degradation products were found in the treated animals.[253] It was postulated that these MSUD metabolites interfered with processing of H proteins in the rough endoplasmic reticulum and Golgi. H proteins are essential core proteins in myelin, are located in the open-loop region of myelin, and are more susceptible to cytoplasmic enzymes. Thus permanent damage to critical myelin proteins by an episode of branched chain amino and ketoacidosis might produce permanent brain damage. Whether decreased biosynthesis or increased degradation of myelin occurs is unknown. The severity of these changes clearly depends on the degree and duration of BCAA and BCKA exposure to the brain and on the time of central nervous system development at which the insult occurs.

Treatment and Outcome

Treatment is aimed at keeping the concentration of toxic metabolites below pathologic concentrations while maintaining normal growth and development. The primary approach to therapy is diet, while supplements like thiamine are used as an adjunct. Diets should be tailored to meet the specific needs of the patient based on the degree of enzyme impairment, the patient's age, nutritional requirements, and clinical state.[7,217,257–259]

Dietary treatment of the acutely ill neonate with classic MSUD remains difficult and should include use of newborn intensive care units. Pioneering work in diet management of MSUD began in 1961 by Dent and Westall who treated an older child with a BCAA-restricted diet and noted biochemical but not clinical improvement.[163,164] A subsequent sib of this original patient was anticipated and treated from day 6 of life and was described as normal at age 13 months.[164] The dietary approach is based on Snyderman's original determination that BCAAs are essential for infant growth; overrestriction must be avoided, and dietary reduction of BCAA must begin early in life.[7,165,166] By 1964, seven patients had been successfully treated with dietary therapy.[7] Disappointment was voiced over outome in older patients treated with these pioneering formulas.[260,261] Over the past several years, however, advances for treating MSUD have been made.[217] Most important were newborn diagnosis and recognition of the urgency to immediately initiate treatment, availability of neonatal intensive care for effective life support, and commercially available formulas containing all or most essential newborn nutrients except leucine, isoleucine, and valine (Tables 22-5 and 22-6). Feeding of BCAA-free protein and energy should begin as soon as the diagnosis is made in the newborn. The objective is to produce anabolism in the infant and thereby prevent catabolism and accumulation of neurotoxic BCAA and BCKAs. If the newborn will not suckle, orogastric administration of adequate formula is suggested. If orogastric feeding cannot be given, a central line for hyperalimentation with dextrose, lipid, and minimum (1 g/kg per day) protein should be initiated. Since BCAA-free hyperalimentation proteins are not available, smaller volumes of orogastric feeding using BCAA-free formula may be supplemented to provide total BCAA-free protein requirements (2.5 g/kg per day) and other essential nutrients.

Although peritoneal dialysis with nitrogen-free dialysate or exchange transfusion has been advocated and employed successfully, this is seldom necessary if hypercaloric intake can be carried out by mouth or gastrostomy and hyperalimentation.[262–264]

Four new formulas with no BCAAs are now commercially available to use as a source of nitrogen (Table 22-6). MSUD Diet Powder (Mead Johnson) contains fat, carbohydrate, minerals, and vitamins and is intended to be a complete formula except for the BCAAs. However, the nitrogen/calorie ratio of MSUD Diet Powder is very low. This leads to inadequate nitrogen intake, especially when energy intake is low. L-Carnitine (8 mg per 100 g) and taurine (36 mg per 100 g) have been added to MSUD Diet Powder, but chromium, molybdenum, and selenium are not included. MSUD 1[R] and MSUD 2[R] (Milupa) contain, in addition to L-amino acids a small amount of carbohydrate, minerals, and vitamins. Fat, chromium, and selenium are not added. Whether these micronutrients will improve dietary therapy requires further testing. A typical

Table 22-5 Approximate Daily Requirements for Infants and Children with Classic MSUD*

Nutrient	Unit	Age: <6 mo	6 to 12 mo	1 to 4 yr	4 to 7 yr	7 to 11 yr	11 to 15 yr	15 to 19 yr
Fluid	ml/kg	120–150	100	95	90	75	50	50
Energy	kcal/kg	150–170	80–135	—	—	—	—	—
	kcal/day (range)	—	—	1300 (900–1800)	1700 (1300–2300)	2400 (1650–3300)	2200–2700 (1500–3700)	2100–2800 (1200–3900)
Protein	g/kg	1.5–2.5	2.2	—	—	—	—	—
	g/day	—	—	25	30	35	45–50	45–55
Carbohydrate (4 kcal/g)	% of kcal	Approximately 35% of kcal			Approximately 50% of kcal			
Fat (9 kcal/g)	% of kcal	Approximately 50% of kcal			Approximately 35% of kcal			
Isoleucine†	mg/kg/day	30–90	30–80	20–80	20–80	20–30	20–30	20–30
Leucine†	mg/kg/day	40–100	35–60	30–60	30–65	30–60	30–50	15–40
Valine†	mg/kg/day	35–95	30–60	30–60	30–50	25–30	20–30	20–30

*All known other essential amino acids, essential fatty acids, minerals, and vitamins must be provided in adequate amounts.
†Adjustments in these ranges must be made by assessment of plasma aminograms, physical examination, growth, and development.

prescription for an acutely ill 10-day-old (3.5 kg) infant with classic MSUD for the first 72 h of neonatal intensive care hospitalization was: protein, 1.5 g/kg per day; kilocalories, kcal (150 kcal/kg/d); and BCAA-free formula. This is composed of 65 g MSUD Diet Powder and 45 g of protein-free diet powder (Mead Johnson's Product 80056) and made up to a volume of 540 ml which has an osmolality of 390 mosmol. This formula was given by orogastric feeding at 22.5 ml/h. There was a steady weight gain to 4.0 kg, and by age 13 days the formula was changed to accommodate a new daily prescription: isoleucine, 25 mg/kg; leucine, 40 mg/kg; valine, 28 mg/kg; protein, 2g/kg; energy, 125 kcal/kg. This was accomplished with 16 g MSUD-1, 23 ml evaporated milk, 1.3 tablespoons of vegetable oil, and 54.2 g protein-free diet powder (Mead Johnson Product 80056) made up to 600 ml and given by bottle and intermittent gavage at 75 ml every 3 h. This patient was comatose and apneic from age 8 to 12 days, while plasma leucine fell from 4000 to 1000 μM. By age 13 days, he was extubated and by age 14 days, he was feeding from a bottle. He made progressive gains and was discharged at age 5 weeks. He has 2 percent BCKD activity in peripheral lymphocytes and is at present developmentally normal at 1 year of age. He represents the reasonably good prognosis available to these patients over the past 7 years (Table 22-2).

Chronic therapy for MSUD is also by diet.[217,265–267] The objective of chronic nutritional support in the child with MSUD is to maintain plasma concentrations of BCAAs that will allow maximal growth and development of intellect by supplying adequate energy, protein, and other essential nutrients (Table 22-5). Plasma concentrations of BCAAs (3 to 4 h postprandial) should be maintained between the following ranges: isoleucine, 40 to 90 μM; leucine, 80 to 200 μM; valine, 200 to 425 μM.[217]

The objectives of nutritional support are met through use of a combination of medical foods listed in Table 22-6 and natural foods. Since the BCAAs are essential, they cannot be deleted from the diet without producing growth failure and death. In planning nutritional support of the infant or child with MSUD, a formal prescription should be written that includes recommended amounts of BCAAs, protein, energy, and fluid for the day. Suggested ranges are outlined in Table 22-5. Frequent adjustments in the dietary prescription are necessary based on appetite, growth, development, and laboratory analyses of plasma BCAAs and BCKAs. Since leucine residues are more prominent than isoleucine and valine in most natural proteins, supplemental isoleucine and valine as free amino acids may be necessary in the newborn period. Since competition between the free BCAAs at the intestinal cell can cause imbalances in ratios of plasma amino acids, careful monitoring of plasma BCAA is suggested if the free amino acids are provided.[268]

Requirements of BCAAs vary considerably depending on age, growth rate, and extent of the enzyme deficit (Table 22-5). Younger infants normally have greater requirements per unit of body weight than older infants. A rapid decline occurs in requirements for BCAAs between 4 and 6 months of age. Careful monitoring of plasma concentrations and intake of BCAA is required to prevent excess intake when growth rate declines.

Recommended protein intake for infants with MSUD (Table 22-5) after the initial acute period is slightly greater than that for normal infants because the primary protein source consists of individual L-amino acids. After infancy, when the diet contains a variety of food proteins, the recommended daily allowance for protein may be adequate.

Except during illness, protein restriction to 1.5 g/kg per day may be adequate therapy for those patients with 15 percent or more of enzyme activity. However, if any signs of protein malnutrition occur or if growth is slowed, a BCAA-free diet should be supplemented. More thorough descriptions of the nutritional approaches in MSUD are available.[217]

The outcome of newborn screening, retrieval, diagnosis, and management has improved over the last seven years[179,216,217,265–267] (Table 22-2). This impression comes from personal experience with 20 patients, where the first 10 patients had a 40 percent mortality and four of the six survivors have psychomotor impairment. Since 1981, however, there has been 100 percent survival and no major mental retardation in 10 patients (Table 22-2). Several factors produced these improvements. First and foremost was clinical experience gained at a tertiary care center where hospitalization on intensive care units, immediately available laboratory analysis, and anticipated nutritional management became better coordinated and understood. The importance of centralized care and collective clinical experience cannot be overemphasized. Second was improved public health awareness of the need and competence to carry out rapid retrieval, diagnosis, and treatment of the newborn. Third was improved understanding of nutritional requirements during the acute crises of the newborn and the availability of better commercial formulas (Table 22-6).

Table 22-6 Composition and Commerical Sources of Chemically Defined Medical Foods for Branched Chain Amino Acid Restricted Diets

	Branched chain amino acid free products				
Nutrient	*Analog X* Ile, Leu, Val*	*Maxamaid* MSUD*	*MSUD diet† powder*	*MSUD‡ 1*	*MSUD‡ 2*
Energy, kcal	475.00	360.00	466.00	286.00	307.00
Protein equivalent, g	13.50	25.00	8.20	40.90	54.30
Alanine, g	0.79	1.40	0.44	2.40	3.10
Arginine, g	1.40	3.00	0.49	2.00	2.70
Aspartic acid, g	1.31	2.53	1.14	5.70	7.60
Carmitine, g	0.006	0.00	0.008	0.00	0.00
Cystine, g	0.52	0.97	0.25	1.40	1.80
Glutamic acid, g	1.95	3.27	2.10	12.00	16.00
Glutamine, g	0.16	0.30	0.00	0.00	0.00
Glycine, g	1.25	2.40	0.60	1.40	1.80
Histidine, g	0.80	1.74	0.25	1.40	1.80
Isoleucine, g	0.00	0.00	0.00	0.00	0.00
Leucine, g	0.00	0.00	0.00	0.00	0.00
Lysine, g	1.44	3.03	0.51	4.00	5.40
Methionine, g	0.32	0.65	0.25	1.40	1.80
Phenylalanine, g	0.94	1.75	0.55	2.40	3.20
Proline, g	1.50	2.80	0.89	5.40	7.10
Serine, g	0.92	1.70	0.60	3.00	4.00
Taurine, g	0.03	0.00	0.028	0.00	0.00
Threonine, g	1.04	1.94	0.55	2.70	3.60
Tryptophan, g	0.42	0.77	0.20	1.00	1.40
Tyrosine, g	0.94	1.75	0.65	2.90	3.90
Valine, g	0.00	0.00	0.00	0.00	0.00
Carbohydrate, g	57.00	62.00	63.30	30.50	22.50
Fat, g	23.20	0.00	20.00	0.00	0.00
Calcium, mg	300	810	491	2400	1312
Chloride, meq	8.00	12.90	10.50	47.10	28.20
Chromium μg	15.00	0.00	0.00	0.00	0.00
Copper, mg	0.40	2.00	0.40	6.70	2.00
Iodine, μg	47.00	134.00	33.00	234.00	120.00
Iron, mg	5.50	12.00	9.00	34.00	15.00
Magnesium, mg	34.00	200.00	52.00	521.00	156.00
Manganese, mg	0.39	1.60	0.70	2.40	0.70
Molybdenum, μg	25.00	0.06	0.00	107.00	32.00
Phosphorus, mg	226	810	268	1860	1014
Potassium, meq	10.20	21.50	8.60	59.80	34.10
Selenium, μg	15.00	0.00	0.00	0.00	0.00
Sodium, meq	5.30	25.20	9.70	46.40	27.80
Zinc, mg	3.90	13.00	3.00	26.00	7.80
Vitamin A, μg	533	300	357	841	468
D, μg	7.50	12.00	7.40	25.00	33.00
E, mg	4.90	5.90	7.00	34.00	18.00
K,μg	45.00	0.00	74.00	167.00	167.00
Ascorbic acid, mg	41.00	135.00	39.00	234.00	80.00
Biotin, mg	0.03	0.012	0.04	0.10	0.30
B_6, mg	0.34	1.00	0.30	2.20	1.50
B_{12}, μg	1.00	4.00	1.50	7.90	3.00
Choline, mg	65.00	110.00	63.00	434.00	261.00
Folate, μg	38.00	150.00	74.00	340.00	400.00
Inositol, mg	100.00	56.00	22.00	500.00	300.00
Niacin, mg	4.50	12.00	5.90	54.00	24.00
Panthothenic acid, mg	1.70	3.70	2.20	25.00	11.00
Riboflavin, mg	0.60	1.20	0.45	4.00	2.00
Thiamine, mg	0.40	1.08	0.37	2.70	1.40

*Scientific Hospital Supply Ltd., PO Box 117, Gaithersburg, MD 20877, (301)840-0408.
†Mead Johnson, Nutritional Division.
‡Milupa Company, 397 Boston Post Road, Darien, CT 06820, (203)655-6004.

Fourth, analytical methods and laboratory services improved such that branched chain organic acids and amino acids could be monitored at least daily. Finally newborn intensive care specialists became more aware and facile in managing these acutely ill infants, thereby preventing irreversible damage from secondary insults such as hypoxia, shock, arrhythmias, sepsis, and hypoglycemia, which attend the newborn with severe BCAA and ketoacidemia of classic MSUD.

REFERENCES

1. DEVLIN TM: *Textbook of Biochemistry with Clinical Correlations*, 2d ed. New York, Wiley, 1986, p 438.
2. WESTALL RG, DANCIS J, MILLER S: Maple syrup urine disease. *Am J Dis Child* 94:571, 1957.
3. MENKES JH, HURST PL, CRAIG JM: A new syndrome: Progressive familial infantile cerebral dysfunction associated with an unusual urinary substance. *Pediatrics* 14:462, 1954.

4. DANCIS J, HUTZLER J, LEVITZ M: Metabolism of the white blood cells in maple syrup urine disease. *Biochim Biophys Acta* 43:342, 1960.

5. DANCIS J, HUTZLER J, COX RP: Enzyme defect in skin fibroblasts in intermittent branched chain ketonuria and in maple syrup urine disease. *Biochem Med* 2:407, 1969.

6. SHIH VE, MANDELL R, SCHOLL ML: Historical observation in maple syrup urine disease. *J Pediatr* 85:868, 1974.

7. SYNDERMAN SE, NORTON PM, ROITMAN E, HOLT LE: Maple syrup urine disease, with particular reference to dietotherapy. *Pediatrics* 34:454, 1964.

8. ELSAS LJ, DANNER DJ: The role of thiamin in maple syrup urine disease. *Ann NY Acad Sci* 378:404, 1982.

9. LITWER S, DANNER DJ: Identification of a cDNA clone in λgt11 for the transacylase component of branched chain ketoacid dehydrogenase. *Biochem Biophys Res Commun* 131:961, 1985.

9a. ZHANG B, KUNTZ MJ, GOODWIN GW, HARRIS RA, CRABB DW: Molecular cloning of a cDNA for the E1α subunit of rat liver branched chain α-ketoacid dehydrogenase. *J Biol Chem* 262:15220, 1987.

10. GAZZOLA GC, DALL'ASTA V, GUIDOTTI GG: The transport of neutral amino acids in cultured human fibroblasts. *J Biol Chem* 255:929, 1980.

11. ICHIHARA A, KOYAMA E: Transaminase of branched chain amino acids. *J Biochem (Tokyo)* 59:160, 1966.

12. TAYLOR RT, JENKINS WT: Leucine aminotransferase II. Purification and characterization. *J Biol Chem* 241:4396, 1966.

13. HUTSON SM, RANNELS SL: Characterization of a mitochondrial transport system for branched chain α-keto acids. *J Biol Chem* 260:14189, 1985.

14. DANNER DJ, ELSAS LJ: Subcellular distribution and cofactor function of human branched chain σ-ketoacid dehydrogenase in normal and mutant cultured skin fibroblasts. *Biochem Med* 13:7, 1975.

15. CHANG TW, GOLDBERG AL: The origin of alanine produced in skeletal muscle. *J Biol Chem* 253:3677, 1978.

16. CHANG TW, GOLDBERG AL: Leucine inhibits oxidation of glucose and pyruvate in skeletal muscles during fasting. *J Biol Chem* 253:3696, 1978.

17. HARPER AE, BENJAMIN E: Relationship between intake and rate of oxidation of leucine and α-ketoisocaproate in vivo in the rat. *J Nutr* 114:431, 1984.

18. HARPER AE, MILLER RH, BLOCK KP: Branched-chain amino acid metabolism. *Annu Rev Nutr* 4:409, 1984.

19. BUSE MG, REID SS: Leucine: A possible regulator of protein turnover in muscle. *J Clin Invest* 56:1250, 1975.

20. CHUA B, SIEHL DL, MORGAN HE: Effect of leucine and metabolites of branched chain amino acids on protein turnover in heart. *J Biol Chem* 254:8358, 1979.

21. PRYOR JC, BUSE MG: Tunicamycin prevents stimulation of protein synthesis by branched chain amino acids in isolated rat muscles. *Biochem Biophys Res Commun* 125:149, 1984.

22. LECLERCQ-MEYER V, MARCHAND J, WOUSSEN-COLLE MC, GIROIX MH, MALAISSE WJ: Multiple effects of leucine on glucagon, insulin and somatostatin secretion from the perfused rat pancreas. *Endocrinology* 116:1168, 1985.

23. GRODSKY GM, SCHMID-FORMBY F: Kinetic and quantitative relationships between insulin release and ^{65}Zn efflux from perifused islets. *Endocrinology* 117:704, 1985.

24. VARA E, TAMARIT-RODRIGUEZ J: Effects of L-leucine on palmitate metabolism and insulin release by isolated islets of fed and starved rats. *Endocrinology* 119:404, 1986.

25. CHAWLA RK, RUDMAN D: Utilization of α-keto and α-hydroxy analogues of emergency valine by the growing rat. *J Clin Invest* 54:271, 1974.

26. NISSEN S, HAYMOND MW: Effects of fasting on flux and interconversion of leucine and α-ketoisocaproate in vivo. *Am J Physiol* 241:E72, 1981.

27. KANG CW, WALSER M: Nutritional efficiency of α-ketoisocaproate relative to leucine assessed isotopically. *Am J Physiol* 249:E355, 1985.

28. MUNOZ S, WALSER M: Utilization of α-ketoisocaproate for synthesis of hepatic export proteins and peripheral proteins in normal and cirrhotic subjects. *Gastroenterology* 90:1834, 1986.

29. AKI K, OGAWA K, ICHIHARA A: Transaminases of branched chain amino acids IV. Purification and properties of two enzymes from rat liver. *Biochim Biophys Acta* 159:276, 1968.

30. PETTIT FH, YEAMAN SJ, REED LJ: Purification and characterization of branched chain α-keto acid dehydrogenase complex of bovine kidney. *Proc Natl Acad Sci USA* 75:4881, 1978.

31. DANNER DJ, LEMMON SK, BESHARSE JC, ELSAS LJ: Purification and characterization of branched chain α-ketoacid dehydrogenase from bovine liver mitochondria. *J Biol Chem* 254:5522, 1979.

32. PARDRIDGE WM, CASANELLO-ERTL D, DUDUCGIAN-VARTAVARIAN L: Branched chain amino acid oxidation in cultured rat skeletal muscle cells. *J Clin Invest* 66:88, 1980.

33. PAUL HS, ADIBI SA: Leucine oxidation and protein turnover in clofibrate-induced muscle protein degradation in rats. *J Clin Invest* 65:1285, 1980.

34. CRABB DW, HARRIS RA: Studies on the regulation of leucine catabolism in the liver. *J Biol Chem* 253:1481, 1978.

35. SANS RM, JOLLY WW, HARRIS RA: Studies on the regulation of leucine catabolism. *Arch Biochem Biophys* 200:336, 1980.

36. VEERKAMP JH, VAN HINSBERG VW, CORDEWENER JH: Degradation of branched-chain amino acids and 2-oxo acids in human and rat muscle. *Biochem Med* 24:118, 1980.

37. SCHAUDER P, SCHRODER K, MATTHAEI D, HENNING HV, LANGENBECK U: Influence of insulin on blood levels of branched chain keto and amino acids in man. *Metabolism* 32:323, 1983.

38. BUSE MG, BIGGERS JF, FRIDERICI KH, BUSE JF: Oxidation of branched chain amino acids by isolated hearts and diaphragms of the rat. *J Biol Chem* 247:8085, 1972.

39. ADIBI SA: Metabolism of branched-chain amino acids in altered nutrition. *Metabolism* 25:1287, 1976.

40. WAYMACK PP, DEBUYSERE MS, OLSON MS: Studies on the activation and inactivation of the branched chain α-keto acid dehydrogenase in the perfused rat heart. *J Biol Chem* 255:9773, 1980.

41. FRICK GP, GOODMAN HM: Insulin regulation of branched chain α-keto acid dehydrogenase in adipose tissue. *J Biol Chem* 255:6186, 1980.

42. WOHLHUETER RM, HARPER AE: Coinduction of rat liver branched chain α-keto acid dehydrogenase activities. *J Biol Chem* 245:2391, 1970.

43. FRICK GP, TAI L-R, BLINDER L, GOODMAN HM: L-Leucine activates branched chain α-keto acid dehydrogenase in rat adipose tissue. *J Biol Chem* 256:2618, 1981.

44. MAY ME, AFTRING RP, BUSE MG: Mechanism of the stimulation of branched chain oxoacid oxidation in liver by carnitine. *J Biol Chem* 255:8394, 1980.

45. SPYDEVOLD O, HOKLAND B: Oxidation of branched-chain amino acids in skeletal muscle and liver of rat effects of octanoate and energy state. *Biochim Biophys Acta* 676:279, 1981.

46. BUFFINGTON CK, DEBUYSERE MS, OLSON MS: Studies on the regulation of the branched chain α-keto acid dehydrogenase in the perfused rat heart. *J Biol Chem* 254:10453, 1979.

47. FRERMAN FE, SABRAN JL, TAYLOR JL, GROSSBERG SE: Leucine catabolism during the differentiation of 3T3-L1 cells. *J Biol Chem* 258:7087, 1983.

48. ODESSEY R, GOLDBERG AL: Oxidation of leucine by rat skeletal muscle. *Am J Physiol* 223:1376, 1972.

49. SHINNICK FL, HARPER AE: Branched chain amino acid oxidation by isolated rat tissue preparations. *Biochim Biophys Acta* 437:477, 1976.

50. DOHM GL, BROWN WE, BARAKAT HA: Leucine oxidation in rat muscle, heart and liver homogenates. *Biochem Med* 15:306, 1976.

51. WAGENMAKERS AJ, VEERKAMP JH: Degradation of branched chain amino acids and their derived 2-oxo acids and fatty acids in human and rat heart and skeletal muscle. *Biochem Med* 28:16, 1982.

52. LIVSEY G, LUND P: Enzymatic determination of branched chain amino acids and 2-oxoacids in rat tissues. *Biochem J* 188:705, 1980.

53. HUTSON SM, HARPER AE: Blood and tissue branched chain amino and α-ketoacid concentration; Effect of diet, starvation and disease. *Am J Clin Nutr* 34:173, 1981.

54. SCHAUDER P, SCHRODER K, MATTHAEI D, HENNING HV, LANGENBECK U: Influence of insulin on blood levels of branched chain keto and amino acids in man. *Metabolism* 32:323, 1983.

55. PAUL HS, ADIBI SA: Regulation of branched chain amino acid catabolism in Adibi SA, Fekl W, Langenbeck U, Schauder P (eds): *Branched Chain Amino and Keto Acids in Health and Disease.* Basel, Krager, 1984, p 182.

56. SKETCHER RD, FERN EB, JAMES WP: The adaptation in muscle oxidation of leucine to dietary protein and energy intake. *Br J Nutr* 31:333, 1974.

57. WALSER M, WILLIAMSON JR: *Metabolism and Clinical Implications of Branched Chain Amino and Ketoacids.* New York, Elsevier, 1981.

58. PALMER TN, CALDECOURT MA, SNELL K, SUGDEN MC: Alanine and nitrogen relationship in branched chain amino and 2-oxo acid metabolism. *Biosci Rep* 5:1015, 1985.

59. CHEESEMAN CI: Expression of amino acid and peptide transport systems in rat small intestine. *Am J Physiol* 251:G636, 1986.

60. KARASOV W, SOLBERG D, CARTER S, HUGHES M, PHAN D, ZOLLMAN F, DIAMOND J: Uptake pathways for amino acids in mouse intestine. *Am J Physiol* 251:G501, 1986.

61. CHRISTENSEN HM: *Biological Transport,* 2d ed. Reading, MA, Benjamin, 1975, p 178.

62. OXENDER DL, CHRISTENSEN HN: Distinct mediating systems for the transport of neutral amino acids by Ehrlich cell. *J Biol Chem* 238:3686, 1963.

63. BIRCKBICHLER PJ, WHITTLE WL, DELL'ORCO RT: Amino acid uptake in growing and arrested human diploid cell populations. *Proc Soc Exp Biol Med* 149:530, 1975.

64. MITSUMOTO Y, MOHRI T: Leucine transport in relation to the activities of

Na^+-H^+ antiporter and Na^+/K^+ pump stimulated by serum and a tumor promoter. *Biochim Biophys Acta* 861:187, 1986.

65. TAN CH, LEONG MK, NG FH, THIYAGARAJAH P: Sodium independent synaptosomal uptake of leucine. *Biochem Int* 14:161, 1987.

66. TARPEY MM, WILLIS RC, SEEGMILLER JE: Uptake of α-ketoisocaproic acid in lymphoblast line WI-L2. *Biochem Biophys Res Commun* 76:1267, 1977.

67. SHAMBAUGH GE, KOEHLER RA: Fetal fuels VI. Metabolism of α-ketoisocaproic acid in fetal rat brain. *Metabolism* 32:421, 1983.

68. WEBER FL, DEAK SB, LAINE RA: Absorption of keto-analogues of branched chain amino acids from rat small intestine. *Gastroenterology* 76:62, 1979.

69. SCISLOWSKI PWD, ZOLNIEROWICZ S, SWIERCZYNSKI J, ELEWSKI L: Leucine catabolism in human term placenta. *Biochem Med* 30:141, 1983.

70. ICHIHARA A, TAKAHASHI H, AKI K, SHIRAI A: Transaminase of branched chain amino acids II. Physiological change in enzyme activity in rat liver and kidney. *Biochem Biophys Res Commun* 26:674, 1967.

71. AKI K, OGAWA K, SHIRAI A, ICHIHARA A: Transaminase of branched chain amino acids III. Purification and properties of the mitochondrial enzyme from hog heart and comparison with the supernatant enzyme. *J Biochem* 62:610, 1967.

72. TAYLOR RT, JENKINS WT: Leucine amino transferase I. Colorimetric assays. *J Biol Chem* 241:4391, 1966.

73. GOTO M, SHINNO H, ICHIHARA A: Isozyme patterns of branched chain amino acid transaminase in human tissues and tumors. *Gann* 68:663, 1977.

74. NAYLOR SL, SHOWS TB: Branched chain aminotransferase deficiency in Chinese hamster cells complemented by two independent genes on human chromosomes 12 and 19. *Somatic Cell Genet* 6:641, 1980.

75. JONES C, MOORE EE: Localization of a gene which complements branched chain amino acid transaminase deficiency to the short arm of human chromosome 12. *Hum Genet* 66:206, 1984.

76. DE LA CHAPELLE A: Human gene mapping 8. *Cytogenet Cell Genet* 40:1, 1985.

77. WADA Y, TADA K, MINAGAWA A, YOSHIDA T, MORIKAWA T, OKAMURA T: Idiopathic hypervalinemia. *Tohoku J Exp Med* 81:46, 1963.

78. TADA K, WADA Y, ARAKAWA T: Hypervalinemia. *Am J Dis Child* 113:64, 1967.

79. LENZEN S, SCHMIDT W, PANTEN U: Transamination of neutral amino acids and 2-keto acids in pancreatic B-cell mitochondria. *J Biol Chem* 260:12629, 1985.

80. LANOUE KF, SCHOOLWERTH AC: Metabolite transport in mitochondria. *Annu Rev Biochem* 48:871, 1979.

81. HUTSON SM: Influence of mitochondrial transamination on branched chain amino acid oxidation in mitochondria isolated from rat heart. *Fed Proc* 46:753, 1987.

82. JOHNSON WA, CONNELLY JL: Cellular localization and characterization of bovine liver branched chain-keto acid dehydrogenase. *Biochemistry* 11:1967, 1972.

83. PARKER PJ, RANDLE PJ: Inactivation of rat heart branched chain 2-oxoacid dehydrogenase complex by adenosine triphosphate. *FEBS Lett* 95:153, 1978.

84. GUBLER CJ, MALQUIST RL: Effects of conditions favoring enzyme phosphorylation and dephosphorylation on the activity of the σ-keto acid dehydrogenases with particular reference to the branched chain α-keto acid dehydrogenase activities. *Biochem Biophys Res Commun* 86:855, 1979.

85. CONNELLY JL, DANNER DJ, BOWDEN JA: Branched chain a-keto acid metabolism I. Isolation, purification and partial characterization of bovine liver α-ketoisocaproic, α-keto-β-methylvaleric acid dehydrogenase. *J Biol Chem* 243:1198, 1968.

86. GOEDDE HW, HÜFNER M, MÖHLENBECK F, BLUME KG: Biochemical studies on branched chain oxoacid oxidases. *Biochim Biophys Acta* 132:524, 1967.

87. PARKER PJ, RANDLE PJ: Active and inactive forms of branched chain 2-oxoacid dehydrogenase complex in rat heart and skeletal muscle. *FEBS Lett* 112:186, 1980.

88. ODESSEY R: Direct evidence for the inactivation of branched chain oxoacid dehydrogenase by enzyme phosphorylation. *FEBS Lett* 121:306, 1980.

89. LAU KS, FATANIA HR, RANDLE PJ: Inactivation of rat liver and kidney branched chain 2-oxoacid dehydrogenase complex by adenosine triphosphate. *FEBS Lett* 126:66, 1981.

90. HUGHES WA, HALSTRAP AP: The regulation of branched chain 2-oxo acid dehydrogenase of liver, kidney and heart by phosphorylation. *Biochem J* 196:459, 1981.

91. FATANIA HR, LAU KS, RANDLE PJ: Inactivation of purified ox kidney branched chain 2-oxoacid dehydrogenase complex by phosphorylation. *FEBS Lett* 132:285, 1981.

92. PAXTON R, HARRIS RA: Isolation of rabbit liver branched chain α-ketoacid dehydrogenase and regulation by phosphorylation. *J Biol Chem* 257:14433, 1982.

93. HARRIS RA, PAXTON R: Regulation of branched chain α-ketoacid dehydrogenase complex by phosphorylation-dephosphorylation. *Fed Proc* 44:33, 1985.

94. PAXTON R, HARRIS RA: Regulation of branched chain α-ketoacid dehydrogenase kinase. *Arch Biochem Biophys* 231:48, 1984.

95. DAMUNI Z, MERRYFIELD ML, HUMPHREYS JS, REED LJ: Purification and properties of branched chain α-ketoacid dehydrogenase phosphatase from bovine kidney. *Proc Natl Acad Sci USA* 81:4335, 1984.

96. YEAMAN SJ: The mammalian 2-oxoacid dehydrogenases: A complex family. *TIBS* 11:293, 1986.

97. DANCIS J, HUTZLER J, LEVITZ M: Tissue distribution of branched chain ketoacid decarboxylase. *Biochim Biophys Acta* 52:60, 1966.

98. WAGENMAKERS AJM, SCHEPENS JTG, VELDHUIZEN JAM, VEERKAMP JH: The activity state of the branched chain 2-oxoacid dehydrogenase complex in rat tissues. *Biochem J* 220:273, 1984.

99. HARRIS RA, POWELL SM, PAXTON R, GILLIM SE, NAGAE H: Physiological covalent regulation of rat liver branched chain α-ketoacid dehydrogenase. *Arch Biochem Biophys* 243:542, 1985.

100. PATSTON PA, ESPINAL J, RANDLE PJ: Effects of diet and alloxan diabetes on the activity of branched chain 2-oxo acid dehydrogenase complex and of activator protein in rat tissue. *Biochem J* 222:711, 1984.

101. PAXTON R, KUNTZ M, HARRIS RA: Phosphorylation sites and inactivation of branched chain α-ketoacid dehydrogenase isolated from rat heart, bovine kidney, and rabbit liver, kidney, heart, brain and skeletal muscle. *Arch Biochem Biophys* 244:187, 1986.

102. JONES SMA, YEAMAN SJ: Phosphorylation of branched chain 2-oxoacid dehydrogenase complex in isolated adipocytes: Effect of 2-oxoacids. *Biochem J* 236:209, 1986.

103. BLOCK KP, AFTRING RP, BUSE MG, HARPER AE: Estimation of branched-chain α-ketoacid dehydrogenase activation in mammalian tissues. *Methods Enzymol* 166:1988 (In press).

104. LAWSON R, COOK KG, YEAMAN SJ: Rapid purification of bovine kidney branched chain 2-oxoacid dehydrogenase complex containing endogenous kinase activity. *FEBS Lett* 157:54, 1983.

105. DANNER DJ, HEFFELFINGER SC: Isolation of branched chain α-ketoacid dehydrogenase as fully active complex from bovine liver. *Methods Enzymol* 166:1988 (In press).

106. HEFFELFINGER SC, DANNER DJ: Highly purified bovine liver branched chain α-ketoacid dehydrogenase can be inhibited by endogenous kinase. *Fed Proc* 44:38, 1985.

107. COOK KG, BRADFORD AP, YEAMAN SJ: Resolution and reconstitution of bovine kidney branched chain 2-oxoacid dehydrogenase complex. *Biochem J* 225:731, 1985.

108. PAXTON R, HARRIS RA: Clofibric acid, phenylpyruvate, and dichloroacetate inhibition of branched-chain α-ketoacid dehydrogenase kinase in vitro and in perfused rat heart. *Arch Biochem Biophys* 231:58, 1984.

109. DANNER DJ, SEWELL ET, ELSAS LJ: Clofibric acid and phenylpyruvic acid as biochemical probes for studying soluble bovine liver branched chain ketoacid dehydrogenase. *J Biol Chem* 257:659, 1982.

110. LAU KS, FATANIA HR, RANDLE PJ: Regulation of branched chain 2-oxoacid dehydrogenase kinase reaction. *FEBS Lett* 144:57, 1982.

111. COOK KG, LAWSON R, YEAMAN SJ: Multi-site phosphorylation of bovine kidney branched-chain 2-oxoacid dehydrogenase complex. *FEBS Lett* 157:59, 1983.

112. COOK KG, LAWSON R, YEAMAN SJ: Multi-site phosphorylation of branched-chain 2-oxoacid dehydrogenase complex within mitochondria isolated from rat liver, kidney and heart. *FEBS Lett* 164:85, 1983.

113. COOK KG, LAWSON R, YEAMAN SJ, AITKEN A: Amino acid sequence at the major phosphorylation site on bovine kidney branched chain 2-oxoacid dehydrogenase complex. *FEBS Lett* 164:47, 1983.

114. COOK KG, BRADFORD AP, YEAMAN SJ, AITKEN A, FEARNLEY IM, WALKER JE: Regulation of bovine kidney branched chain 2-oxoacid dehydrogenase complex by reversible phosphorylation. *Eur J Biochem* 145:587, 1984.

115. LAU KS, PHILLIPS CE, RANDLE PJ: Multi-site phosphorylation in ox-kidney branched chain 2-oxoacid dehydrogenase complex. *FEBS Lett* 160:149, 1983.

116. DAMUNI Z, TUNG HYL, REED LJ: Specificity of the heat stable protein inhibitor of branched chain α-ketoacid dehydrogenase phosphatase. *Biochem Biophys Res Commun* 133:878, 1985.

117. DAMUNI Z, REED LJ: Purification and properties of the catalytic subunit of the branched-chain α-ketoacid dehydrogenase phosphatase from bovine kidney mitochondria. *J Biol Chem* 262:5129, 1987.

118. DAMUNI Z, HUMPHREYS JS, REED LJ: A potent heat-stable protein inhibitor of [branched-chain α-ketoacid dehydrogenase]-phosphatase from bovine kidney mitochondria. *Proc Natl Acad Sci USA* 83:285, 1986.

119. BRADFORD AP, YEAMAN SJ: Mitochondrial protein kinases and phospha-

tases, in Merlevede WJ, DiSalvo J (eds): *Advances in Protein Phosphatases III*. Belgium, Luvene University Press, 1986, p 73.

120. HEFFELFINGER SC, SEWELL ET, DANNER DJ: Identification of specific subunits of highly purified bovine liver branched chain ketoacid dehydrogenase. *Biochemistry* 22:5519, 1983.

121. HU C-Wc, GRIFFIN TA, LAU KS, COX RP, CHUANG DT: Subunit structure of the dihydrolipoyl transacylase component of branched chain α-ketoacid dehydrogenase complex from bovine liver: Mapping of the lipoyl-bearing domain by limited proteolysis. *J Biol Chem* 261:343, 1986.

121a. HUMMEL KB, LITWER S, BRADFORD AP, AITKEN A, DANNER DJ, YEAMAN SJ: Nucleotide sequence of a cDNA for branched chain acyltransferase with analysis of the deduced protein structure. *J Biol Chem* 263:6165, 1988.

121b. LAU KS, GRIFFIN TA, HU C-WC, CHUANG DT: Conservation of primary structure in the lipoyl-bearing and dihydrolipoyl dehydrogenase binding domains of mammalian branched-chain α-keto acid dehydrogenase complex: Molecular cloning of human and bovine transacylase (E2) cDNAs. *Biochemistry* 27:1972, 1988.

122. CHUANG DT, HU C-WC, KU LS, MARKOVITZ PJ, COX RP: Subunit structure of the dihydrolipoyl transacylase component of branched chain α-ketoacid dehydrogenase complex from bovine liver: Characterization of the inner transacylase core. *J Biol Chem* 260:13779, 1985.

123. HEFFELFINGER SC, SEWELL ET, DANNER DJ: Antibodies to bovine liver branched chain 2-oxoacid dehydrogenase crossreact with this enzyme complex from other tissues and species. *Biochem J* 213:339, 1983.

124. DANNER DJ, ELSAS LJ, LITWER S: Antibodies against branched chain α-ketoacid dehydrogenase proteins for use in defining human mutations and gene isolation. *Methods Enzymol* 166:1988 (In press).

125. HEFFELFINGER SC, SEWELL ET, ELSAS LJ, DANNER DJ: Direct physical evidence for stabilization of branched-chain α-ketoacid dehydrogenase by thiamin pyrophosphate. *Am J Hum Genet* 36:802, 1984.

126. DANNER DJ, LEMMON SK, ELSAS LJ: Stabilization of mammalian liver branched chain α-ketoacid dehydrogenase by thiamin pyrophosphate. *Arch Biochem Biophys* 202:23, 1980.

127. KUNTZ MJ, PAXTON R, SHIMOMURA Y, GOODWIN GW, HARRIS RA: Phosphorylation affects the mobility of the E1α-subunits of branched chain 2-oxoacid dehydrogenase on SDS/polyacryl-amide gel electrophoresis. *Biochem Soc Trans* 14:1077, 1986.

128. ONO K, HAKOZAKI M, KIMURA A, KOCHI H: Purification, resolution, and reconstitution of rat liver branched-chain α-ketoacid dehydrogenase complex. *J Biochem (Tokyo)* 101:19, 1987.

129. YEAMAN SJ, COOK KG, BOYD RW, LAWSON R: Evidence that the mitochondrial activator of phosphorylated branched chain 2-oxoacid dehydrogenase complex is the dissociated E1 component of the complex. *FEBS Lett* 172:38, 1984.

130. FATANIA HR, LAU KS, RANDLE PJ: Activation of phosphorylated branched chain 2-oxoacid dehydrogenase complex. *FEBS Lett* 147:35, 1982.

131. SABOURIN PJ, BIEBER LL: Purification and characterization of an α-keto-isocaproate oxygenase of rat liver. *J Biol Chem* 257:7460, 1982.

132. PAXTON R, SCISLOWSKI PWD, DAVIS EJ, HARRIS RA: Role of branched chain 2-oxoacid dehydrogenase and pyruvate dehydrogenase in 2-oxobutyrate metabolism. *Biochem J* 234:295, 1986.

133. JONES SMA, YEAMAN SJ: Oxidative decarboxylation of 4 methylthio-2-oxobutyrate by branched chain 2-oxoacid dehydrogenase complex. *Biochem J* 237:621, 1986.

134. CHUANG DT, HU C-WC, PATEL MS: Induction of the branched chain 2-oxoacid dehydrogenase complex in 3T3-L1 adipocytes during differentiation. *Biochem J* 214:177, 1983.

135. DANNER DJ, DAVIDSON ED, ELSAS LJ: Thiamine increases the specific activity of human liver branched chain α-ketoacid dehydrogenase. *Nature* 254:529, 1975.

136. DANNER DJ, PRIEST JH: Branched chain ketoacid dehydrogenase activity and growth of normal and mutant human fibroblasts: The effect of branched chain amino acid concentration in culture medium. *Biochem Genet* 21:895, 1983.

137. LOBATON CD, MORENO A, OXENDER DL: Characterization of a Chinese hamster-human hybrid cell line with increased system L amino acid transport activity. *Mol Cell Biol* 4:475, 1984.

138. ELSAS LJ, PASK BA, WHEELER FB, PERL DP, TRUSLER S: Classical maple syrup urine disease: Cofactor resistance. *Metabolism* 21:929, 1972.

139. LANGENBECK U, RUDIGER HW, SCHULZE-SCHENCKING M, KELLER W, BRACKERTZ D, GOEDDE HW: Evaluation of a heterozygote test for maple syrup urine disease in leucocytes and cultured fibroblasts. *Humangenetik* 11:304, 1971.

140. WALLACE DC: Maternal genes: Mitochondrial diseases. *Birth Defects* 23:137, 1987.

141. CHOMYN A, MARIOTTINI P, CLEETER MW, RAGAN CI, MATSUNO-YAGI A, HATEFI Y, DOOLITTLE RF, ATTARDI G: Six unidentified reading frames of human mitochondrial DNA encode components of the respiratory-chain NADH dehydrogenase. *Nature* 314:592, 1985.

142. CHOMYN A, CLEETER MW, RAGAN CI, RILEY M, DOOLITTLE RF, ATTARDI G: URF6, last unidentified reading frame of human mtDNA, codes for an NADH dehydrogenase subunit. *Science* 234:614, 1986.

143. WALTER P, GILMORE R, BLOBEL G: Protein translocation across the endoplasmic reticulum. *Cell* 38:5, 1984.

144. WICKNER WT, LODISH HF: Multiple mechanisms of protein insertion into and across membranes. *Science* 230:400, 1985.

145. EL-GEWELY MR, OXENDER DL: Gene transfer and cloning of the amino-acid transport system L from human cells. *Ann NY Acad Sci* 456:417, 1985.

146. COLMAN A, ROBINSON C: Protein import into organelles: Hierarchical targeting signals. *Cell* 46:321, 1986.

147. DOUGLAS MG, MCCAMMON MT, VASSAROTTI A: Targeting proteins into mitochondria. *Microbiol Rev* 50:166, 1986.

148. TZAGOLOFF A, MYERS AM: Genetics of mitochondrial biogenesis. *Annu Rev Biochem* 55:249, 1986.

149. MIURA S, AMAYA Y, MORI M: A metalloprotease involved in the processing of mitochondrial precursor proteins. *Biochem Biophys Res Commun* 134:1151, 1986.

150. DUQUE-MAGALHÃES MC, RÉGNIER P: Discrimination of distinct proteinases at the four structural levels of rat liver mitochondria. *Biochem J* 233:283, 1986.

151. DANNER DJ, ARMSTRONG N, HEFFELFINGER SC, SEWELL ET, PRIEST JH, ELSAS LJ: Absence of branched chain acyl-transferase as a cause of maple syrup urine disease. *J Clin Invest* 75:858, 1985.

152. EISENSTEIN R, HOGANSON G, MILLER R, HARPER A: Characterization of branch chain keto acid dehydrogenase deficiency in maple syrup urine disease. *Am J Hum Genet* 37:A8, 1985.

153. INDO Y, KITANO A, ENDO F, AKABOSHI I, MATSUDA I: Altered kinetic properties of branched-chain α-keto acid dehydrogenase complex due to mutation of the β-subunit of the branched chain α-keto acid decarboxylase (E1) component in lymphoblastoid cell derived from patients with maple syrup urine disease. *J Clin Invest* 80:63, 1987.

154. DANCIS J, HUTZLER J, TADA K, WADA Y, MORIKAWA T, ARAKAWA T: Hypervalinemia: A defect in valine transmination. *Pediatrics* 39:813, 1967.

155. JEUNE M, COLLOMBEL C, MICHEL M, DAVID M, GUIBAUD P, GUERRIER G, ALBERT J: Hyperleucinisoleucinémie par défaut partiel de transamination associée a une hyperprolinémie de type 2. Observation familiale d'une double aminoacidopathie. *Ann Pediatr* 17:85, 1970.

156. MENKES JH: Maple syrup urine disease: Isolation and identification of organic acids in the urine. *Pediatrics* 23:348, 1959.

157. DANCIS J, JANSEN V, HUTZLER J, LEVITZ M: The metabolism of leucine in tissue culture of skin fibroblasts of maple syrup urine disease. *Biochim Biophys Acta* 77:532, 1963.

158. SILBERMAN J, DANCIS J, FEIGIN IH: Neuropathological observations in maple syrup urine disease: Branched chain ketoaciduria. *Arch Neurol* 5:351, 1961.

159. MENKES JH, PHILIPPORT M, FIOL RE: Cerebral lipids in maple syrup disease. *J Pediatr* 66:584, 1965.

160. PRENSKY AL, MOSER HW: Brain lipids, proteolipids, and free amino acids in maple syrup urine disease. *J Neurochem* 13:863, 1966.

161. MENKES JH, SOLCHER H: Maple syrup urine disease: Effects of dietary therapy on cerebral lipids. *Arch Neurol* 16:486, 1967.

162. PRENSKY AL, CARR S, MOSER HW: Development of myelin in inherited disorders of amino acid metabolism. *Arch Neurol* 19:552, 1968.

163. DENT CE, WESTALL RG: Studies in maple syrup urine disease. *Arch Dis Child* 36:259, 1961.

164. WESTALL RG: Dietary treatment of a child with maple syrup urine disease (branched chain keto-aciduria). *Arch Dis Child* 38:485, 1963.

165. CLOW CL, READE TM, SCRIVER CR: Outcome of early and long-term management of classical maple syrup urine disease. *Pediatrics* 68:856, 1981.

166. ACOSTA PB, ELSAS LJ II: Dietary treatment of branched chain ketoaciduria (MSUD), in *Dietary Management of Inherited Metabolic Disease: Phenylketonuria, Galactosemia, Tyrosinemia, Homocystinuria, Maple Syrup Urine Disease*. Atlanta, ACELMU Publishers, 1976.

167. ELSAS LJ: Perinatal diagnosis of the inborn errors of metabolism. *J Med Assoc Ga* 60:308, 1971.

168. ELSAS LJ, PRIEST JH, WHEELER FB, DANNER DJ, PASK BA: Maple syrup urine disease: Coenzyme function and prenatal monitoring. *Metabolism* 23:569, 1974.

169. FERNHOFF PM, FITZMAURICE N, MILNER J, MCEWEN CT, DEMBURE PP, BROWN AL, WRIGHT L, ACOSTA PB, ELSAS LJ: Coordinated system for comprehensive newborn metabolic screening. *South Med J* 75:529, 1982.

170. ELSAS LJ, BROWN A, FERNHOFF P: Newborn screening for metabolic disorders in the State of Georgia, in Naruse H, Irie M (eds): *Neonatal Screening: Proceedings of the International Symposium on Neonatal Screening*

for Inborn Errors of Metabolism. Amsterdam, Excerpta Medica, 1983, p 117.

171. SCRIVER CR, MACKENZIE S, CLOW CL, DELUIN E: Thiamine responsive maple syrup urine disease. *Lancet* 1:310, 1971.

172. FISCHER MH, GERRITSEN T: Biochemical studies on a variant of branched chain ketoaciduria in a 19-year-old female. *Pediatrics* 48:795, 1971.

173. VAN DER HORST JL, WADMAN SK: A variant form of branched-chain keto aciduria. *Acta Paediatr Scand* 60:594, 1971.

174. ELSAS LJ, DANNER DJ: Effects of thiamine on normal and mutant human branched chain alpha-ketoacid dehydrogenase, in Gubler C, Fujiwara M, Dreyfus PM (eds): *Thiamine*. Wiley, New York, 1976.

175. DANNER DJ, WHEELER FB, LEMMON SK, ELSAS LJ: In vivo and in vitro response of human branched chain α-ketoacid dehydrogenase to thiamine and thiamine pyrophosphate. *Pediatr Res* 12:235, 1978.

176. DURAN M, TIELENS AGM, WADMAN SK, STIGTER JC, KLEIJER WJ: Effects of thiamine in a patient with a variant form of branched chain ketoaciduria. *Acta Paediatr Scand* 67:367, 1978.

177. KODAMA S, SEKI A, HANABUSA M, MORISTA Y, SAKURAI T, MATSUO T: Mild variant of maple syrup urine disease. *Eur J Pediatr* 124:31, 1976.

178. PUESCHEL SM, BRESNAN MJ, SHIH VE, LEVY HL: Thiamine-responsive intermittent branched chain ketoaciduria. *J Pediatr* 94:628, 1979.

179. FERNHOFF PM, LUBITZ DJ, DANNER DP, DEMBURE P, SCHWARTZ HP, HILLMAN R, BIER D, ELSAS LJ: Thiamin response in branched chain alpha-ketoacidemia (maple syrup urine disease). *Pediatr Res* 19:1011, 1985.

180. SCRIVER CR, CLOW CL, GEORGE H: So-called thiamin-responsive maple syrup urine disease: 15-year follow-up of the original patient. *J Pediatr* 107:763, 1985.

181. DURAN M, WADMAN SK: Thiamine-responsive inborn errors of metabolism. *J Inherited Metab Dis* 8:70, 1985.

182. ZEE DS, FREEMAN JM, HOLTZMAN NA: Ophthalmoplegia in maple syrup urine disease. *J Pediatr* 84:113, 1974.

183. MACDONALD JT, SHER PK: Ophthalmoplegia as a sign of metabolic disease in the newborn. *Neurology* 27:970, 1977.

184. CHHABRIA S, TOMASI LG, WONG PW: Ophthalmoplegia and bulbar palsy in variant form of maple syrup urine disease. *Ann Neurol* 6:71, 1979.

185. HAYMOND MW, KARL IE, FEIGIN RD, DEVIVO D, PAGLIARA AS: Hypoglycemia and maple syrup urine disease: Defective gluconeogenesis. *Pediatr Res* 7:500, 1973.

186. HAYMOND MW, BEN-GALIM E, STROBEL KE: Glucose and alanine metabolism in children with maple syrup urine disease. *J Clin Invest* 62:398, 1978.

187. LONSDALE D, MERCER RD, FAULKNER WR: Maple syrup urine disease: Report of two cases. *Am J Dis Child* 106:258, 1963.

188. KIIL R, ROKKONES T: Late manifesting variant of branched-chain ketoaciduria (maple syrup urine disease). *Acta Paediatr Scand* 53:356, 1964.

189. MORRIS MD, FISHER DA, FISER R: Late-onset branched-chain ketoaciduria (maple syrup urine disease). *Lancet* 86:149, 1966.

190. STEEN-JOHNSEN J, VELLAN EJ, GJESSING LR: Maple syrup urine disease variant: Amino acid patterns and problems of treatment during acute attacks. *Acta Paediatr Scand* 59:71, 1970.

191. IRWIN WC, MARTEL SB, GOLUBOFF N: Intermittent branched-chain ketonuria (variant of maple syrup urine disease). *Clin Biochem* 4:52, 1971.

192. HAMBRAEUS L, WESTPHAL O, HAGBERG B: Ketotic hypoglycemia associated with transient branched-chain amino acidemia. *Acta Paediatr Scand* 61:81, 1972.

193. GHODSI A, AJUNDANI TS, GHARAVI M, HATEFI GV: Intermittent maple syrup urine disease: A case report. *S Afr Med J* 51:758, 1977.

194. ZALESKI LA, DANCIS J, COX RP, HUTZER J, ZALESKI WA, HILL A: Variant maple syrup urine disease in mother and daughter. *Can Med Assoc J* 109:299, 1973.

195. GONZALEZ-RIOS MC, CHUANG DT, COX RP, SCHMIDT K, KNOPF K, PACKMAN S: A distinct variant of intermediate maple syrup urine disease. *Clin Genet* 27:153, 1985.

196. SAUDUBRAY JM, AMÉDÉE-MANESME O, MUNNICH A, OGIER H, DEPONDT E, CHARPENTIER C, COUDÉ FX, REY F, FRÉZAL J: Hétérogénéité de la leucinose. Corrélations entre l aspect clinique, la tolérance protéique et le déficit enzymatique. *Arch Fr Pediatr* 39:735, 1982.

197. FRÉZAL J, AMÉDÉE-MANESME O, MITCHELL G, HEUERTZ S, REY F, REY J, SAUDUBRAY JM: Maple syrup urine disease: Two different forms within a single family. *Hum Genet* 71:89, 1985.

198. LANGENBECK U: Pathobiochemical and pathophysiologic analysis of the MSUD phenotype, in Adibi SA, Fekl W, Langenbeck U, Schauder P (eds): *Branched Chain Amino and Ketoacids in Health and Disease*. Basel, Karger, 1985, p 315.

199. JINNO Y, AKABOSHI I, MATSUDA I: Complementation analysis in lymphoid cells from five patients with different forms of maple syrup urine disease. *Hum Genet* 68:54, 1984.

200. VALMAN HB, PATRICK AD, SEAKINS JWT, PLATT JW, GOMPERTZ D: Family with intermittent maple syrup urine disease. *Arch Dis Child* 48:225, 1973.

201. SCHULMAN JD, LUSTBERG TJ, KENNEDY JL, MUSELES M, SEEGMILLER JE: A new variant of maple syrup urine disease (branched chain ketoaciduria). *Am J Med* 49:118, 1970.

202. KALYANARAMAN K, CHAMUKUTTAN S, ARJUNDAS G, GAJANAN N, RAMAMURTHI B: Maple syrup urine disease (branched-chain ketoaciduria) variant type manifesting as hyperkinetic behaviour and mental retardation. Report of two cases. *J Neurol Sci* 15:209, 1972.

203. MORRIS MD, LEWIS BD, DOOLAN PD, HARPER HA: Clinical and biochemical observations on an apparently non-fatal variant of branched-chain ketoaciduria (maple syrup urine disease). *Pediatrics* 28:918, 1961.

204. CHUANG DT, KU LS, COX RP: Thiamin-responsive maple syrup urine disease: Decreased affinity of the mutant branched-chain α-ketoacid dehydrogenase for α-ketoisovalerate and thiamin pyrophosphate. *Proc Natl Acad Sci USA* 79:3300, 1982.

205. CHUANG DT, KU LS, KERR DS, COX RP: Detection of heterozygotes in maple-syrup-urine disease: Measurements of branched chain ketoacid dehydrogenase and its components in cell cultures. *Am J Hum Genet* 34:416, 1982.

206. ELSAS L, DANNER D, LUBITZ D, FERNHOFF P, DEMBURE P: Metabolic consequence in inherited defects in branched chain α-ketoacid dehydrogenase: Mechanism of thiamine action, in Walser M, Williamson JR (eds): *Metabolism and Clinical Implications of Branched Chain Amino and Ketoacids*. New York, Elsevier/North-Holland, 1981, p 369.

207. MATUDA S, KITANO A, SAKAGUCHI Y, YOSHINO M, SAHEKI T. Pyruvate dehydrogenase subcomplex with lipoamide dehydrogenase deficiency in a patient with lactic acidosis and branched chain ketoaciduria. *Clin Chim Acta* 140:59, 1984.

208. OTULAKOWSKI G, NYHAN W, SWEETMAN L, ROBINSON BH: Immuno-extraction of lipoamide dehydrogenase from cultured skin fibroblasts in patients with combined α-ketoacid dehydrogenase deficiency. *Clin Chim Acta* 152:27, 1985.

209. ROBINSON BH, TAYLOR J, SHERWOOD WG: Deficiency of dihydrolipoyl dehydrogenase (a component of the pyruvate and α-ketoglutarate dehydrogenase complex): A cause of congenital chronic lactic acidosis in infancy. *Pediatr Res* 11:1198, 1977.

210. TAYLOR J, ROBINSON BH, SHERWOOD G: A defect in branched chain amino acid metabolism in a patient with congenital lactic acidosis due to dihydrolipoyl dehydrogenase deficiency. *Pediatr Res* 12:60, 1978.

211. ROBINSON BH, TAYLOR J, SHERWOOD WG: The genetic heterogeneity of lactic acidosis: Occurrence of recognizable inborn errors of metabolism in a pediatric population with lactic acidosis. *Pediatr Res* 14:956, 1980.

212. ROBINSON BH, TAYLOR J, KAHLER SG, KIRKMAN HN: Lactic acidemia, neurologic deterioration and carbohydrate dependence in a girl with dihydrolipoyl dehydrogenase deficiency. *Eur J Pediatr* 136:35, 1981.

213. DIGEORGE AM, REZVANI I, GARIBALDI LR, SCHWARTZ M: Prospective study of maple-syrup-urine disease for the first four days of life. *N Engl J Med* 307:1492, 1982.

214. ELSAS LJ: Newborn screening, in Rudolph AM (ed): *Pediatrics*, 17th ed. New York, Appleton-Century-Crofts, 1982.

215. FERNHOFF P, BROWN A, BLAKE E, ELSAS LJ: Newborn metabolic screening in Georgia: Five year experience, in *National Newborn Screening Symposium*. Florida Department of Health and Rehabilitative Services. Jacksonville FL, 1984, p 11.

216. ELSAS L, FERNHOFF P, DEMBURE P, DANNER D: Thiamine responsive maple syrup urine disease, in Naruse H, Irie M (eds): *Neonatal Screening: Proceedings of the International Symposium on Neonatal Screening for Inborn Errors of Metabolism*. Amsterdam, Excerpta Medica, 1983.

217. ELSAS LJ, ACOSTA PB: Nutritional management of inherited metabolic disorders, in Shils ME, Young V. (eds): *Modern Nutrition in Health and Disease*, 7th ed. Philadelphia, Lea and Febiger, 1987, chap 66.

218. TANAKA K, WEST-DULL A, HINE DG, LYNN TB, LOWE T: Gas-chromatographic method of analysis for urinary organic acids. II. Description of the procedure and its application to diagnosis of patients with organic acidurias. *Clin Chem* 26:1847, 1980.

219. LANGENBECK U, HOINOWSKI A, MANTEL K, MOEHRING HU: Quantitative gas chromatography and single-ion detection of aliphatic α-ketoacids from urine as their O-trimethyl-silylquinoxalinol derivatives. *J Chromatogr* 143:39, 1977.

220. LANGENBECK U, MOHRING HU, DIECKMANN KP: Gas chromatography of α-keto acids as their O-trimethyl silylquinoxalinol derivatives. *J Chromatogr* 115:65, 1975.

221. TANAKA K, HINE DG, WEST-DULL A, LYNN TB: Gas-chromatographic method of analysis for urinary organic acids I: Retention indices of 155 metabolically important compounds. *Clin Chem* 26:1839, 1980.

222. MARKEY SP, URBAN WG, LEVINE SP in collaboration with Committee VI, American Society for Mass Spectrometry: Mass spectra of compounds of

biological interest. National Technical Information Service, US Department of Commerce, Springfield, VA.

223. NORTON PM, ROITMAN E, SYNDERMAN SE, HOLT LE JR: A new finding in maple syrup urine disease. *Lancet* 1:26, 1962.

224. HALPERN B, POLLOCK GE: The configuration of the alloisoleucine present in maple syrup urine disease plasma. *Biochem Med* 4:352, 1970.

225. WEINBERG RB, WALSER M: Racemization and amination of the keto-analog of isoleucine in the intact dog. *Biochem Med* 17:164, 1977.

226. MATTHEWS DE, BEN-GALIM E, HAYMOND MW, BIER DM: Alloisoleucine formation in maple syrup urine disease: Isotopic evidence for the mechanism. *Pediatr Res* 14:854, 1980.

227. WENDEL U, WÖHLER W, GOEDDE HW, LANGENBECK U, PASSARGE E, RÜDIGER HW: Rapid diagnosis of maple syrup urine disease (branched chain ketoaciduria) by micro-enzyme assay in leucocytes and fibroblasts. *Clin Chim Acta* 45:433, 1973.

228. FENSOM AH, BENSON PF, BAKER JE: A rapid method for assay of branched-chain keto acid decarboxylation in cultured cells and its application to prenatal diagnosis of maple syrup urine disease. *Clin Chim Acta* 87:169, 1978.

229. WENDEL U, RUDIGER HW, PASSARGE E, MIKKELSEN M: Maple syrup urine disease: Rapid prenatal diagnosis by enzyme assay. *Humangenetik* 19:127, 1973.

230. JINNO Y, AKABOSHI I, KATSUKI T, MATSUDA I: Study on established lymphoid cells in maple syrup urine disease. Correlation with clinical heterogeneity. *Hum Genet* 65:358, 1984.

231. COX R, HUTZLER J, DANCIS J: Antenatal diagnosis of maple syrup urine disease. *Lancet* 2:212, 1978.

232. WENDEL U, CLAUSSEN U: Antenatal diagnosis of maple syrup urine disease. *Lancet* 1:161, 1979.

233. WENDEL U, CLAUSSEN U, LANGENBECK U: Pattern of branched chain α-keto acids in amniotic fluid. *Clin Chim Acta* 102:267, 1980.

234. KLEIJER WJ, HORSMAN D, MANCINI GM, FOIS AJ, BOUE J: First trimester diagnosis of maple syrup urine disease on intact chorionic villi. *N Engl J Med* 333:1608, 1985.

235. Collective results of mass screening for inborn metabolic errors in eight European countries. *Acta Paediatr Scand* 62:413, 1973.

236. LEVY HL: Genetic screening. *Adv Hum Genet* 4:389, 1973.

237. NAYLOR EW, GUTHRIE R: Newborn screening for maple syrup urine disease (branched chain ketoaciduria). *Pediatrics* 61:262, 1978.

238. TADA K, WADA Y, OKAMURA T: A case of maple sugar urine disease. *Tohoku J Exp Med* 79:142, 1963.

239. CHEMKE J, LEVIN S: Maple syrup urine disease. Two cases in Israel. *Isr J Med Sci* 11:809, 1975.

240. RAO GP, RAMANAMURTHY PS, GHAFOORUNNIS A, RAFEEQ MR, PATHAK R: Maple syrup urine disease: Report of a case. *Indian Pediatr* 11:585, 1974.

241. KAM-PUI F, KIT-WUN C, YING-PUI C: Maple syrup urine disease in Chinese. *Chin Med J* 99:119, 1985.

242. NAYLOR EW: Newborn screening for maple syrup urine disease (branched chain ketoaciduria), in Bickel H, Guthrie R, Hammersen G (eds): *Neonatal Screening for Inborn Errors of Metabolism.* Berlin, Springer-Verlag, 1980, p 19.

243. AUERBACH VH, DIGEORGE A: Maple syrup urine disease, in Hommes FA, Van den Berg CJ (eds): *Inborn Errors of Metabolism.* London, Academic, 1973, p 337.

244. MARSHALL L, DIGEORGE A: Maple syrup urine disease in the old order Mennonites. *Am J Hum Genet* 33:139A, 1981.

245. BROWN A, FERNHOFF P, ELSAS LJ: Annual Report of Georgia's Newborn Screening Program for Inherited Metabolic Disease 1978–1986. Department of Human Resources, State of Georgia, 1987.

246. YUWILER A, GELLER: Serotonin depletion by dietary leucine. *Nature* 208:83, 1965.

247. TASHIAN RE: Inhibition of brain-glutamic decarboxylase by phenylalanine, valine, and leucine derivatives: A suggestion concerning the etiology of the neurological defect in phenylketonuria and branched-chain ketonuria. *Metabolism* 10:393, 1961.

248. HOWELL RK, LEE M: Influence of α-keto acids on the respiration of brain in vitro. *Proc Soc Exp Biol Med* 113:660, 1963.

249. HALESTRAP AP, BRAND MD, DENTON RM: Inhibition of mitochondrial pyruvate transport by phenylpyruvate and alpha-ketoisoocaproate. *Biochim Biophys Acta* 367:102, 1974.

250. LAND JM, MOWBRAY J, CLARK JB: Control of pyruvate and beta-hydroxybutyrate utilization in rat brain mitochondria and its relevance to phenylketonuria and maple syrup urine disease. *J Neurochem* 26:823, 1976.

251. SILBERBERG DH: Maple syrup urine disease metabolites studied in cerebellum cultures. *J Neurochem* 16:1141, 1969.

252. LIAO CL, HERMAN MM, BENSCH KG: Prolongation of G_1 and S phase in C-6 glioma cells treated with maple syrup urine disease metabolites: Morphologic and cell cycle studies. *Lab Invest* 38:122, 1978.

253. TRIBBLE D, SHAPIRA R: Myelin proteins: Degradation in rat brain initiated by metabolites causative of maple syrup urine disease. *Biochem Biophys Res Commun* 114:440, 1983.

254. TAKETOMI T, KKUNISHITA T, HARA A, MIZUSHIMA S: Abnormal protein and lipid compositions of the cerebral myelin of a patient with maple syrup urine disease. *Jpn J Exp Med* 53:109, 1983.

255. HARPER PAW, HEALY PJ, DENNIS JA: Ultrastructural findings in maple syrup urine disease poll hereford calves. *Acta Neuropathol (Berl)* 71:316, 1986.

256. PARDRIDGE WM: Blood-brain transport of nutrients. *Fed Proc* 45:2047, 1986.

257. BELL L, CHAO E, MILNE J: Dietary management of maple-syrup-urine disease: Extension of equivalency systems. *J Am Diet Assoc* 74:357, 1979.

258. KINDT E, HALVORSEN S: The need of essential amino acids in children: An evaluation based on the intake of phenylalanine tyrosine, leucine, isoleucine and valine in children with phenylketonuria, tyrosine amino transferase defect, and maple syrup urine disease. *Am J Clin Nutr* 33:279, 1980.

259. American Academy of Pediatrics: Special diets for infants with inborn errors of amino acid metabolism. *Pediatrics* 57:783, 1976.

260. LEVY HL, TRUMAN JT, GANZ RN, LITTLEFIELD JW: Folic acid deficiency secondary to a diet for maple syrup urine disease. *J Pediatr* 77:294, 1970.

261. FOREMAN JW, YIDKOFF M, BERRY G, SEGAL S: Acidosis associated with dietotherapy of maple syrup urine disease. *J Pediatr* 96:62, 1980.

262. GAULL GE: Pathogenesis of maple syrup urine disease: Observation during dietary management and treatment of coma by peritoneal dialysis. *Biochem Med* 3:130, 1969.

263. WENDEL U, BECKER K, PRZYREMBEL H, BULLA M, MANEGOLD C, MENCHHOINOWSKI A, LANGENBECK U: Peritoneal dialysis in maple syrup urine disease: Studies on branched-chain amino and ketoacids. *Eur J Pediatr* 134:57, 1980.

264. HAMMERSEN G, WILLIE L, SCHMIDT H, LUTZ P, BICKEL H: Maple syrup urine disease: Treatment of the acutely ill newborn. *Eur J Pediatr* 129:157, 1978.

265. LIE IE, HAUGSTAD S, HOLM H: Tailoring of the diet for the individual in maple syrup urine disease: Long-term home dietary treatment of an adult patient with MSUD by monitoring of daily intake with a personal computer. A case report. *Hum Nutr Appl Nutr* 39A:130, 1985.

266. NAUGHTEN ER, SAUL IP, ROCHE G, MULLINS C: Early diagnosis and dietetic management in newborn with MSUD. Birth to six weeks. *J Inherited Metab Dis* 8:131, 1985.

267. WENDEL U: Acute and long-term treatment of children with maple syrup urine disease, in Adibi SA, Fekl W, Langenbeck U, Schauder P (eds): *Branched Chain Amino and Keto Acids in Health and Disease.* Basel, Krager, 1984, p 335.

268. CSAKY TZ: *Intestinal Absorption and Malabsorption.* New York, Raven, 1975.

CHAPTER 23

DISORDERS OF TRANSSULFURATION

S. HARVEY MUDD
HARVEY L. LEVY
FLEMMING SKOVBY

1. *Six patients have been described with deficiency of hepatic methionine adenosyltransferase. Most were ascertained during routine screening of newborns for hypermethioninemia. All were clinically well at ages ranging up to 31 years. Each possessed some residual activity of hepatic methionine adenosyltransferase. Methionine adenosyltransferase activities in tissues other than liver were normal, suggesting isoenzymes under separate genetic control. The residual activity of methionine adenosyltransferase in liver, the normal activities in nonhepatic tissues, and the high tissue concentrations of methionine together provide for synthesis of virtually as much* S*-adenosylmethionine by these individuals as is formed by normal persons ingesting a normal diet.*
2. *Cystathionine β-synthase deficiency is the most frequently encountered cause of homocystinuria. In addition to homocyst(e)ine, methionine and a variety of other metabolites of homocysteine accumulate in the body or are excreted in the urine of patients with this deficiency. More than 600 cases of proved or presumptive cystathionine β-synthase deficiency have been studied. Dislocation of the optic lens, osteoporosis, thinning and lengthening of the long bones, mental retardation, and thromboembolism affecting large and small arteries and veins are the most common clinical features. Affected patients vary widely in the extent to which they manifest these abnormalities.*
3. *Cystathionine β-synthase deficiency is inherited as an autosomal recessive trait, but available evidence suggests considerable genetic heterogeneity in known patients. Some patients have small residual activities of cystathionine β-synthase; others have no such activities detected by even the most sensitive methods. The presence of residual activity of cystathionine β-synthase may well be a necessary, but not sufficient, condition for clinical responsiveness of patients to pyridoxine administration. Individuals clinically responsive to pyridoxine generally have milder, or more slowly developing, manifestations than do those not responsive to pyridoxine.*
4. *Individuals with cystathionine β-synthase deficiency have been detected by routine screening of newborns for hypermethioninemia with an overall frequency of 1 in 335,000 livebirths. Striking regional differences are present. Very likely, a significant portion of cystathionine β-synthase-deficient individuals, especially those responsive to pyridoxine, are being missed by such screening programs.*
5. *Management of cystathionine β-synthase-deficient patients emphasizes amelioration of the characteristic biochemical abnormalities by use of low methionine, cystine-supplemented diets for patients not responsive to pyridoxine administration and by pyridoxine treatment, perhaps accompanied by less stringent methionine dietary restriction, for pyridoxine-responsive patients. Treatment with betaine is currently being evaluated, especially for patients not responsive to pyridoxine and in whom dietary management is unsatisfactory. Statistically validated beneficial effects have been demonstrated for methionine restriction initiated in the newborn period in preventing mental retardation and, perhaps, in reducing the incidence of seizures. Pyridoxine treatment has been shown to significantly reduce the rate of initial thromboembolic events.*
6. *γ-Cystathionase deficiency leads to persistent excretion of large amounts of cystathionine in the urine, as well as to accumulation of cystathionine in body tissues and fluids.* N*-Acetylcystathionine and a variety of additional cystathionine metabolites are excreted as well. The clinical status of proved or presumptive γ-cystathionase-deficient patients suggests there are no clinical abnormalities characteristically associated with this enzyme deficiency. The deficiency is inherited as an autosomal recessive trait. Considerable genetic heterogeneity is likely to exist among known patients. One manifestation of genetic heterogeneity is responsiveness to pyridoxine of the cystathioninuria associated with γ-cystathionase deficiency.*

The transsulfuration pathway converts the sulfur atom of methionine into the sulfur atom of cysteine. This pathway is the chief route of disposal of methionine and explains why cysteine is not an essential amino acid in normal human beings. Intimately related are two additional metabolic sequences: the transmethylation reactions, whereby the methyl group of methionine is ultimately transferred to form any of a host of methylated compounds, and the re-formation of methionine by methylation of homocysteine. Structural formulas of the relevant compounds are shown in Fig. 23-1.

METABOLISM OF METHIONINE, HOMOCYSTEINE, AND CYSTATHIONINE

The pertinent reactions of the transsulfuration pathway and related areas of metabolism are summarized in Fig. 23-2. At least nine specific genetic disorders have been recognized which affect one of the reactions shown. In this chapter primary coverage is given to three disorders involving reactions (1), (4), and (5), which are steps in the transsulfuration pathway.

S-Adenosylmethionine Formation

The gateway to all these interconversions is reaction (1), the formation of *S*-adenosylmethionine, catalyzed by methionine adenosyltransferase (ATP:L-methionine *S*-adenosyltransferase; EC 2.5.1.6). In this unusual rection, the adenosyl moiety of ATP is transferred to methionine, forming a sulfonium bond between the 5′-carbon atom of the ribose and the sulfur atom of the amino acid. The tripolyphosphate which results from transfer of the adenosyl portion of ATP remains bound to the enzyme which, by virtue of a second catalytic activity, cleaves the tripolyphosphate to inorganic phosphate and pyro-

$CH_3\text{-}S\text{-}CH_2CH_2CH(NH_2)COOH$

Methionine

$HOOCCH(NH_2)CH_2\text{-}S\text{-}CH_2CH_2CH(NH_2)COOH$

Cystathionine

$H\text{-}S\text{-}CH_2CH_2CH(NH_2)COOH$

Homocysteine

$HOOCCH(NH_2)CH_2CH_2\text{-}S\text{-}S\text{-}CH_2CH_2CH(NH_2)COOH$

Homocystine

$H\text{-}S\text{-}CH_2CH(NH_2)COOH$

Cysteine

$HOOCCH(NH_2)CH_2\text{-}S\text{-}S\text{-}CH_2CH(NH_2)COOH$

Cystine

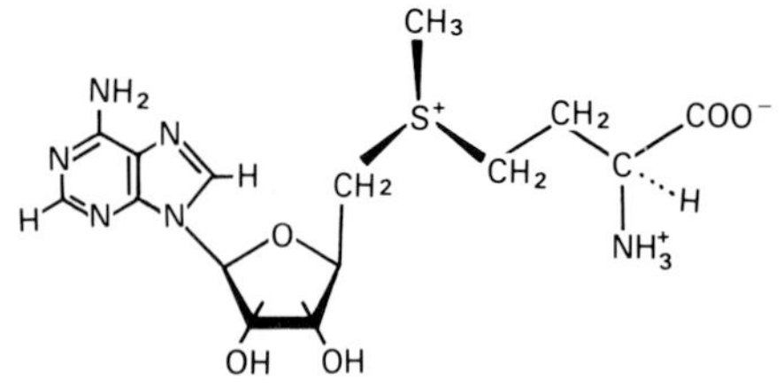

S-Adenosylmethionine

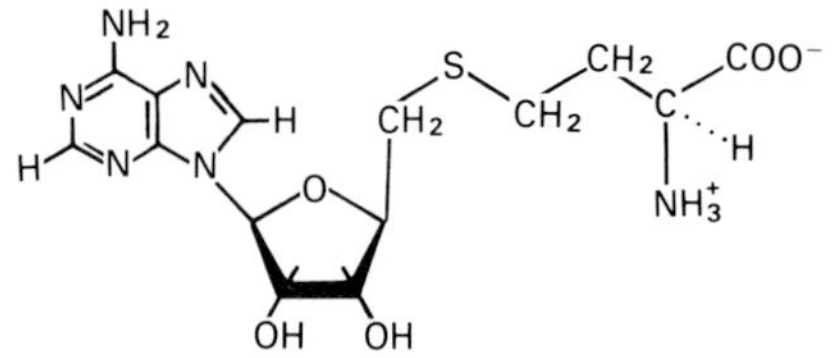

S-Adenosylhomocysteine

$(CH_3)_3N^+CH_2CH_2OH$

Choline

$(CH_3)_3N^+CH_2COOH$

Betaine

Fig. 23-1 Structural formulas of compounds of interest. The naturally occurring amino acids illustrated each have the absolute L configuration at the α carbon atom. In naturally occurring *S*-adenosylmethionine the dominant absolute configuration at the asymmetric sulfonium pole is *S*, i.e., viewed from where the sulfur atom obscures the lone electron pair the adenosyl, the 3-amino-3-carboxypropyl, and the methyl groups are arranged in counter-clockwise order.[1] *S*-Adenosylmethionine and *S*-adenosylhomocysteine are shown in the favored anti conformation at the N(9)—C(1′) bond, i.e., with the ribose pointed away from, rather than toward, the purine ring.[2–4]

phosphate. This tripolyphosphatase activity is specifically and markedly stimulated by *S*-adenosylmethionine.[6,7,7a] Removal of tripolyphosphate assists in making the synthesis of *S*-adenosylmethionine essentially irreversible under physiological conditions.[6] Mammalian methionine adenosyltransferase has been partially purified from pig,[8] rabbit,[9] and rat[10–12] liver; from rat kidney[13] and lens[13a]; from human erythrocytes[14]; and to apparent homogeneity from human lymphocytes[15] and bovine brain.[15a] Activity requires both divalent[13,15–17] and monovalent[13,17] cations. The animal enzyme has a rather strict substrate specificity for ATP,[18] and a somewhat broader specificity for methionine.[8,19–21a]

Mammalian livers contain as many as three chromatographically separable forms of methionine adenosyltransfer-

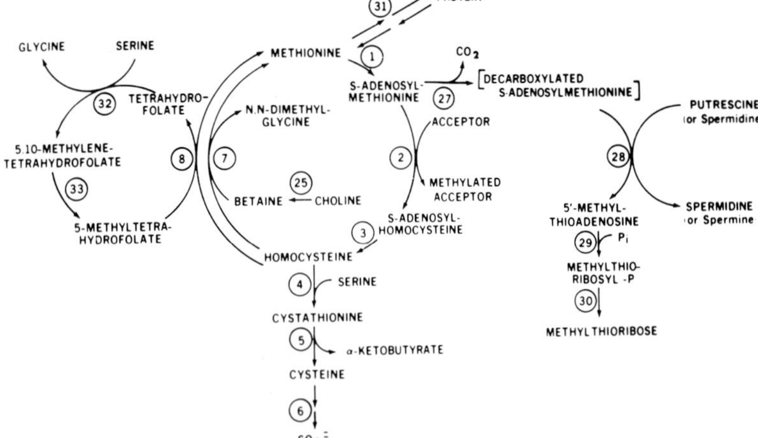

Fig. 23-2 The metabolism of methionine, homocysteine, and cystathionine. *(From Mudd and Poole,[5] by permission.)*

ase.[12,13,22–25] These isoenzymes have widely differing K_m's for methionine.[13,24] Eighty percent of the maximal capacity to synthesize S-adenosylmethionine is provided in rat liver by a high K_m form,[12] which, at nonsaturating substrate concentrations, can be stimulated markedly by dimethylsulfoxide.[13,23,25] This form has been purified to homogeneity from rat liver. It is a dimer composed of two identical subunits, each weighing 48,500 daltons (molecular weight of 110,000). A second liver isozyme is a tetramer composed of four of the same subunits (molecular weight of 210,000). It has a lower K_m for methionine.[7a,12,27,27a,27b] The third isozyme in liver is a small amount of the low K_m isozyme (molecular weight of approximately 120,000) which is widespread in other tissues.[12]

Adenosyltransferase activities in mammalian tissues other than liver are not stimulated by dimethylsulfoxide,[13,25,26] and may differ immunologically from the liver isoenzyme(s).[27] Human erythrocytes, cultured fibroblasts, and cultured lymphocytes each contain tissue-specific mixtures of at least two adenosyltransferase isoenzymes separable by chromatography from each other and from human liver adenosyltransferase.[28] The relationships of these various forms to one another remain to be clarified.

Methyl Transfer Reactions

Because of its sulfonium bonds, S-adenosylmethionine may be regarded as a "high-energy" compound.[29] Each substituent of the sulfonium atom of this compound is energetically capable of participating in one or more transfer reactions. Many methyl transfers originate from S-adenosylmethionine. In addition, this compound, after decarboxylation, is the source of the 3-carbon moieties of the polyamines, spermidine, and spermine.[30] Evidence has been presented indicating that (rat) liver cytosol and mitochondria contain kinetically distinguishable pools of S-adenosylmethionine.[30a] Details of the biochemical mechanisms involved in methyl group transfer have been reviewed elsewhere.[31] The transmethylation reactions likely to occur in normal humans have been compiled, and an assessment has been made of the relative quantitative demands of each on the available supply of S-adenosylmethionine.[5,32] All these reactions produce a common sulfur-containing product, S-adenosylhomocysteine. Measurements carried out with precautions to avoid artifactual changes which occur within seconds of the death of the animal indicate that in normal adult rat liver S-adenosylhomocysteine is present at 13 nmol/g, whereas S-adenosylmethionine is present at 60 to 90 nmol/g.[33,34] Many S-adenosylmethionine-dependent methyltransferases are strongly inhibited by S-adenosylhomocysteine,[35] and it has been calculated that when S-adenosylhomocysteine is present at a ratio of 1:4 with respect to S-adenosylmethionine, a variety of methyltransferases will decrease their activities by 10 to 60 percent.[35]

S-Adenosylhomocysteine Hydrolysis

S-Adenosylhomocysteine is further metabolized by a hydrolase (EC 3.3.1.1.) which cleaves the thioether to homocysteine and adenosine.[36] The mammalian enzyme is a tetramer with a molecular weight of approximately 190,000, composed of four subunits, each weighing 47,000.[37–39] Its cDNA has recently been cloned and sequenced and the corresponding amino acid sequence derived.[40] Each subunit of the enzyme contains 1 mol of tightly bound NAD^+.[37,41] During the catalytic cycle the NAD^+ is reduced to NADH, with concomitant oxidation of the 3′-hydroxyl of S-adenosylhomocysteine to a keto group. After homocysteine is eliminated, the enzyme-bound NADH reduces the keto group back to a hydroxyl before release of adenosine.[41,41a] S-Adenosylhomocysteine hydrolase activity is widely distributed in mammalian tissues.[42–44] Although the equilibrium of the reaction favors S-adenosylhomocysteine accumulation, the reaction may be driven in the hydrolytic direction by removal of one or both of its products.[36] In vivo, homocysteine and adenosine are both normally rapidly removed, so that the hydrolase presumably functions chiefly in the cleavage direction, generating adenosine and homocysteine.

As yet, no inherited disease due to a genetically determined deficiency in the hydrolysis of S-adenosylhomocysteine has been recognized. However, this enzyme is subject to irreversible inactivation by 2′-deoxyadenosine,[45–48] a compound known to accumulate in some patients with adenosine deaminase deficiency (see citations in Ref. 45). Erythrocyte S-adenosylhomocysteine hydrolase activity is markedly deficient in patients with adenosine deaminase deficiency,[49,50] presumably as a result of such inactivation, and in patients with purine nucleoside phosphorylase deficiency[50,51] due to a similar inactivation by inosine. The possible pathophysiological consequences of such inactivation of S-adenosylhomocysteine hydrolase have been discussed elsewhere[51,52] (and Chap. 40).

Homocysteine Methylation

Homocysteine lies at an important metabolic branch point. It may be either converted to cystathionine through the transsulfuration pathway [Fig. 23-2, reaction (4)] or methylated to form methionine [reactions (7) and (8)], thus completing the sulfur conservation cycle. At least two alternative mechanisms exist in humans for homocysteine methylation. In one, the methyl group originates in betaine. Betaine-dependent methylation of homocysteine is catalyzed by the enzyme betaine-homocysteine methyltransferase (EC 2.1.1.5). The reaction is essentially irreversible.[53] In rat and horse liver, two separable enzymes possess this catalytic activity.[54]

The second mechanism for homocysteine methylation utilizes 5-methyltetrahydrofolic acid as methyl donor. The reaction is catalyzed by a cobalamin (vitamin B_{12})-containing enzyme, 5-methyltetrahydrofolate-homocysteine methyltransferase (methionine synthase; EC 2.1.1.13).[55] This enzyme has been purified to homogeneity from human placenta.[55a] Its gene is on human chromosome 1.[55b] Again, the reaction favors methionine formation, with an equilibrium constant of 1.4×10^5 in this direction.[56] This complex methyl transfer reaction involves the intermediate formation of an enzyme-bound methylcobalamin.[55] Several patients have been described who are unable to carry out the 5-methyltetrahydrofolate-dependent methylation of homocysteine because of a primary inability to form or accumulate methylcobalamin.[57,58] Certain other patients are unable to form the cosubstrate, 5-methyltetrahydrofolate, because of lack of activity of 5,10-methylenetetrahydrofolate reductase [EC 1.1.99.15; reaction (33), Fig. 23-2].[57] Patients in both these groups excrete excess homocysteine in their urine (i.e., are homocystinuric) and suffer from other abnormalities of sulfur amino acid metabolism.[57] They are discussed in Chaps. 81 and 82, which deal with disorders in the metabolism of folic acid and vitamin B_{12}, respectively.

Cystathionine Synthesis

In the metabolism of homocysteine, the major alternative to methylation is condensation with serine to form the thioether cystathionine. The reaction is catalyzed by cystathionine β-synthase [L-serine hydro-lyase (adding homocysteine); EC 4.2.1.22]. The locus for human cystathionine β-synthase recently has been mapped to chromosome 21 by study of Chinese hamster-human cell hybrids[59] and demonstration of a gene dosage effect in assays of cystathionine β-synthase from fibroblasts cultured from patients with Down syndrome.[60] Analyses of cells monosomic or trisomic for parts of the long arm of chromosome 21 suggested an assignment between 21q22.1 and 21q21,[60,61] an assignment initially corroborated by DNA hybridization studies using a cDNA probe for cystathionine β-synthase.[62] Additional recent work by the same group has assigned the gene in question more precisely to the subtelomeric region of band 21q22.3 of chromosome 21.[62a]

The primary translational product of the cystathionine β-synthase gene in cultured human fibroblasts is a polypeptide with molecular weight 63,000.[63] In contrast, both the two identical polypeptides which constitute the enzyme purified from human liver each have a molecular weight of 48,000.[64,65] The primary translational product in rat liver is also a 63,000-dalton polypeptide, and this tissue contains in addition a smaller, immunologically related polypeptide with molecular weight 48,000.[65,66] It has been suggested that postranslational processing in liver is responsible for the decrease in size from 63,000 to 48,000 daltons.[66] This processing may account for the higher specific activity of cystathionine β-synthase found in extracts of liver tissue as compared with cultured fibroblasts, but the in vivo role of the decrease in size of the subunit remains to be clarified.

Cystathionine β-synthase has been purified from several vertebrate livers[65] (see also Ref. 64). The purified enzyme contains firmly bound pyridoxal phosphate, on which it depends for activity.[64,67,68] The displacement of the OH group of serine by homocysteine proceeds with retention of configuration.[69] Mammalian cystathionine β-synthase, including the human form, can catalyze an alternative reaction, cysteine sulfhydration, in which sulfide, rather than homocysteine, is combined with serine[64,70,71]:

$$H_2S + \text{serine} \rightarrow \text{cysteine} + H_2O$$

Although the condensation of homocysteine and serine catalyzed by cystathionine β-synthase can be reversed if homocysteine is rapidly removed,[68] the equilibrium of the reaction is very much toward cystathionine formation under physiological conditions. Formation of this thioether therefore serves to remove sulfur from the homocysteine-methionine cycle.[72]

Deficiency of cystathionine β-synthase activity is the most frequently encountered genetic disorder of transsulfuration and is described in a subsequent section ("Cystathionine β-Synthase Deficiency").

Cystathionine Cleavage

The transsulfuration sequence is completed by cleavage of cystathionine to cysteine and α-ketobutyrate [reaction (5)], catalyzed by the enzyme γ-cystathionase [L-cystathionine cysteine-lyase (deaminating]; EC 4.4.1.1). The gene for human γ-cystathionase has been provisionally mapped to chromosome 16 by use of somatic cell hybrids.[73] Molecular weights reported for γ-cystathionase from rat liver have been 170,000 to 210,000[74] and 160,000[75,76]; from mouse liver, 160,000[77]; and from human cultured lymphoid cells, 190,000.[78] The rat liver enzyme is thought to consist of eight like subunits[75]; the mouse liver enzyme, of four like subunits.[77] The crystalline enzyme contains pyridoxal phosphate,[79] on which it depends for activity.[80] Dissociation constants of 1.4×10^{-6} and 4.6×10^{-6} have been reported for the γ-cystathionase-pyridoxal phosphate complex, based, respectively, on fluorimetric titration[81] and measurement of catalytic activity.[82] γ-Cystathionase may be irreversibly inhibited by propargylglycine,[83] β,β,β-trifluoroalanine,[84,85] β-trifluoromethylalanine, and β-trifluorovinylalanine.[86] β,β,β-Trifluoroalanine inhibits γ-cystathionase by combining with an ϵ-amino group of a lysine residue which is part of an active site heptapeptide, Cys-Ser-Ala-Thr-Lys-Tyr-Met.[87] Mammalian γ-cystathionase has several catalytic activities in addition to cystathionine cleavage, including the ability to catalyze cysteine desulfhydration: cysteine + $H_2O \rightarrow$ pyruvate + NH_3 + H_2S.[88] (Other activities are summarized in Ref. 89). Mammalian γ-cystathionase will catalyze the formation of cystathionine if incubated with cysteine in the presence of either homoserine[90–92] or homocysteine.[93] The role of such reverse reactions at physiological concentrations of homoserine or homocysteine is questionable,[93] and reversal in the presence of α-ketobutyrate, the physiological product, has not been reported. Thus, it appears that γ-cystathionase normally functions almost entirely in the direction of cystathionine cleavage to produce, rather than to consume, cysteine. Individuals with genetically determined defects of γ-cystathionase activity are discussed below (under "γ-Cystathionase Deficiency").

Quantitative Relationships among Transmethylation, Transsulfuration, and Homocysteine Methylation

Some information about the quantitative relationships among methyl transfer reactions, transsulfuration, and homocysteine methylation has been provided by studies of normal young adults maintained in metabolic steady states on varying defined intakes of methionine and choline. These studies showed that utilization of methyl groups is normally accounted for chiefly by creatine-creatinine formation. This reaction consumes more *S*-adenosylmethionine than all other transmethylations together. Male subjects utilize more methyl groups for methyl transfer reactions than they consume in a normal diet in the form of methionine. The difference in methyls is made up from two sources: (1) by conversion of an amount of choline equivalent to that ingested in the diet to betaine, a compound capable of transferring one of its performed methyl groups to homocysteine to form methionine, and (2) by de novo formation of methyl groups through the tetrahydrofolate-dependent pathway. The latter methyls are also used to methylate homocysteine. To the extent that homocysteine is methylated, the portion of this compound diverted at any given moment to cystathionine is decreased. In male subjects on normal diets, at least 47 percent of the available homocysteine is methylated. Nevertheless, in the steady-state metabolic condition, the intake of methionine sulfur is balanced by metabolism of an equivalent amount of homocysteine sulfur through the transsulfuration pathway. These observations indicate that during its passage through the body, the average homocysteinyl moiety cycles more than once between methionine and homocysteine. For males on normal diets, the calculated mean of such cycles is at least 1.9; for females, at least 1.5.[5] Extension of such studies to a subject unable to remove sarcosine metabolically because of a genetic defect in her sarcosine-oxidizing system permitted a slight upward revision of the minimal estimate for the number of times the average homocysteinyl moiety cycles in the human female to 2.0. The results also suggest that, when the dietary intake of labile methyl moieties exceeds the amount required for creatine formation and for other ongoing methyl transfer reactions, the excess is disposed of by methylation of glycine, forming sarcosine, which, in the normal human, is then converted to a 1-carbon fragment at the formaldehyde oxidation level, with regeneration of the glycine.[32]

Tissue- and Age-Dependent Variations in Enzyme Patterns

The patterns just described apply only to the total body metabolism of the young adult. The distributions and the specific activities of the pertinent enzymes are such that the bulk of this metabolism must occur in the liver. It is likely that gross departures from the specified patterns occur locally in other tissues. The relevant evidence has been reviewed in detail elsewhere.[94] In brief, available results suggest that almost all human tissues have some capacity to convert methionine to homocysteine but that the apportionment of homocysteine to the transsulfuration or remethylation pathways may vary markedly from tissue to tissue.[57] The fetus probably directs a relatively larger proportion of available homocysteine through the 5-methyltetrahydrofolate-dependent methylation pathway than in the direction of cystathionine synthesis, with concomitant increases in methylneogenesis and conservation of the homocysteine moity. Because fetal tissues and placenta lack γ-cystathionase activity, it has been suggested that cyst(e)ine may be an essential amino acid at this stage of life.[95]

Methionine Transamination

Evidence indicating the existence of a metabolic pathway which provides an alternative to transsulfuration for methionine degradation has been published by Benevenga and associates.[96–99a] Rat liver can catalyze an *S*-adenosylmethionine-independent series of reactions in which methionine is initially transaminated, forming 4-methylthio-2-oxobutyrate. Glutamine transaminase may play a major role in catalyzing this reaction,[100,101] but other transaminases may participate also.[102,103] 4-Methylthio-2-oxobutyrate may in turn be oxidatively decarboxylated to CO_2 and 3-methylthiopropionate.[98] This reaction is catalyzed by branched chain keto acid dehydrogenase[101,104] but not by pyruvate or α-ketoglutarate dehydrogenases.[104] 3-Methylthiopropionate may be further degraded to CO_2, sulfate, methanethiol, and H_2S.[99]

Evidence that transamination of methionine may play a role in humans is provided by the observations that increased amounts of 4-methylthio-2-oxobutyrate have been found in the urine of patients with severe hypermethioninemia due to either hepatic methionine adenosyltransferase deficiency[105,106] or cystathionine β-synthase deficiency.[107] The somewhat more stable hydroxy analogue, 4-methylthio-2-hydroxybutyrate, which may be formed by the action of lactate dehydrogenase upon the keto compound, was present in a sample of urine from a patient with hypermethioninemia and tyrosinemia. This sample had been stored long enough for 4-methylthio-2-oxobutyrate itself to have decomposed.[108] Normal subjects, following ingestion of 7 to 20 mmol of D-, but not L-methionine, excrete increased amounts of 4-methylthio-2-oxobutyrate[109] and 3-methylthiopropionate[110] in the urine, and dimethylsulfide becomes elevated in their breath.[111] The contribution of this transamination pathway to methionine degradation under more physiological conditions remains to be clarified. When precautions were taken to ensure good recovery of 4-methylthio-2-oxobutyrate, normal subjects excreted a mean of approximately 55 μmol of this compound daily, accompanied by 10 μmol of 4-methylthio-2-hydroxybutyrate.[108] When the transsulfuration pathway is blocked, the transamination pathway does not catabolize methionine at a rate sufficient to prevent biochemical abnormalities, as shown by the facts that methionine adenosyltransferase-deficient patients accumulate greatly elevated concentrations of methionine (see "Hepatic Methionine Adenosyltransferase Deficiency," below) and that cystathionine β-synthase-deficient patients can convert methionine sulfur to sulfate at rates only far below the normal maximum capacity.[107] Patients with maple syrup urine disease who lack branched-chain keto acid dehydrogenase activity are said to have no abnormality of methionine metabolism.[101] Specifically, these patients are not hypermethioninemic[112,113] nor do they excrete excessive 4-methylthio-2-oxobutyrate,[113] adding weight to the evidence that there is only "a minor role for the transamination pathway in man."[101]

HYPERMETHIONINEMIA, HOMOCYSTINURIA, CYSTATHIONINURIA: DIFFERENTIAL DIAGNOSES

The terms hypermethioninemia, homocystinuria (or -emia), and cystathioninuria (or -emia) designate biochemical abnormalities, not specific disease entities. Each of these abnormalities may be the result of more than one specific and distinct genetic lesion. For example, seven different genetic abnormalities are now known to lead to the excretion of excessive urinary homocystine (i.e., homocystinuria). The demonstration of one or more biochemical abnormalities in a given patient is often the starting point for a specific diagnosis of the underlying genetic lesion. In this section we present brief differential diagnoses of hypermethioninemia, homocystinuria, and cystathioninuria, including both genetic and nongenetic causes. This discussion is summarized in Table 23-1.

Hypermethioninemia

Aside from protein synthesis, the major pathway for methionine metabolism is initiated by conversion of methionine to *S*-adenosylmethionine (Fig. 23-2). Impairment of this conversion leads to abnormal methionine accumulation and hypermethioninemia, as borne out by studies of patients with methionine adenosyltransferase deficiency (to be discussed below under "Hepatic Methionine Adenosyltransferase Deficiency"). A different type of hypermethioninemia accompanies most cases of cystathionine β-synthase deficiency. Presumably, the homocysteine accumulation, which is the primary result of this enzymatic lesion, leads secondarily to enhanced rates of remethylation by way of reactions (7) and (8). Hypermethioninemia

Table 23-1 Hypermethioninemia, Homocystinuria, Cystathioninura: Differential Diagnoses

I. Hypermethioninemia (-uria)
  A. Methionine adenosyltransferase deficiency
  B. Cystathionine β-synthase deficiency
  C. Severe generalized liver disease
  D. In association with hereditary tyrosinemia
  E. Transient hypermethioninemia of infants
  F. 6-Azauridine triacetate administration
  G. D-Methioninuria due to DL-methionine ingestion
  H. Persistent, with normal methionine adenosyltransferase
    1. With elevated serum folate, with or without myopathy
    2. Without elevated serum folate

II. Homocystinuria (-emia)
  A. Cystathionine β-synthase deficiency
  B. Impaired activity of 5-methyltetrahydrofolate-homocysteine methyltransferase
    1. Failure to convert cobalamin to methyl- or adenosylcobalamin (*cblC* and *cblD*)
    2. Failure to accumulate methylcobalamin (*cblE* and *cblG*)
    3. 5,10-Methylenetetrahydrofolate reductase deficiency
    4. Defective absorption of vitamin B_{12}
    5. Nutritional vitamin B_{12} deficiency
    6. Folate deficiency
  C. 6-Azauridine triacetate administration
  D. Isonicotinic acid hydrazide administration
  E. Artifactual, due to bacterial metabolism of urinary cystathionine

III. Cystathioninuria
  A. Transient cystathioninuria of (usually premature) infants
  B. γ-Cystathionase deficiency
  C. Impaired activity of 5-methyltetrahydrofolate-homocysteine methyltransferase
    1. Failure to form or accumulate methylcobalamin
    2. 5,10-Methylenetetrahydrofolate reductase deficiency
    3. Nutritional vitamin B_{12} deficiency
  D. Vitamin B_6 deficiency
  E. Thyrotoxicosis
  F. Liver disease
  G. Neuroblastoma, ganglioblastoma, hepatoblastoma
  H. Defective renal transport

in patients with cystathionine β-synthase deficiency is due to overproduction of this amino acid, rather than to underutilization. The homocystinuria which accompanies this particular hypermethioninemia serves to distinguish it from most of the other hypermethioninemias discussed here.

Plasma concentrations of methionine, as well as other amino acids, may be elevated in patients with generalized liver disease. The methionine elevation tends to be more striking and more specific in patients with advanced disease, especially those in hepatic coma. In the latter situation, there is also often a disproportionate rise in plasma tyrosine concentration.[114,115] A possibly similar but poorly understood form of hypermethioninemia often accompanies hereditary tyrosinemia. The hypermethioninemia has been attributed by some of the generalized hepatic cirrhosis, which is a part of this disorder,[116,117] and by others to a primary defect in methionine metabolism[118] (see Chap. 16). Recent evidence indicates that in cirrhosis there is a specific decrease in the activity of the 210,000-dalton liver isozyme.[118a,118b] In tyrosinemia, a specific decrease of the high K_m isoenzyme has been reported.[24]

A transient hypermethioninemia has been observed in many infants given diets rich in protein—usually 7 g/kg per day or more.[119–123] These observations may possibly be explained by "immaturity" of methionine adenosyltransferase and cystathionine β-synthase. The mean specific activities of these enzymes in livers of several premature infants were 31 and 19 percent of the mean adult hepatic specific activities.[124] Nevertheless, the hypermethioninemia in question has not been strikingly associated with prematurity and, indeed, has usually developed after several weeks of extrauterine life.[120,122,123] Information on the activities of the pertinent enzymes is not available for this period, but this time sequence suggests that the correct explanation of this form of hypermethioninemia may be complex.

6-Azauridine triacetate treatment brings about significant rises in methionine serum concentrations,[125] accompanied by abnormal homocystine excretion,[126] a pattern suggestive of decreased cystathionine β-synthase activity. The biochemical abnormalities can, at least in rabbits, be prevented by the simultaneous administration of pyridoxine, thereby providing evidence for the suggestion that 6-azauridine triacetate or one of its metabolites acts through interference with pyridoxal phosphate coenzymes.[127]

Urinary excretion of D-methionine has been observed in infants fed diets supplemented with DL-methionine. Inefficient metabolism and ineffective renal tubular reabsorption of the D enantiomorph are presumed to explain the abnormal methionine excretion.[128]

Four patients have been described with persistent hypermethioninemia, apparently normal activities of methionine adenosyltransferase in liver[129,130] (and, where tested, in muscle and erythrocytes[129]), and striking elevations of serum total folate (87 to 1000 μg/L; normal less than 30). Homocystinuria was absent. The first such patient reported, a 7½-year-old Serbo-Croatian girl, was mentally retarded and had proximal myopathy and nonspecific liver changes.[129] Three additional patients were subsequently discovered in Japan as a result of screening programs of the newborn. Each had moderate fatty degeneration of the liver which appeared to improve after several months on a low-methionine diet.[130]

Another patient with persistent hypermethioninemia and apparently normal methionine adenosyltransferase activity differed from the above group by having normal total serum folate. At age 3 years, and without specific treatment, she was free of myopathy and had normal liver histology.[131] The abnormality (or abnormalities) underlying these persistent hypermethioninemias has not been defined, and it remains uncertain how many genetic lesions are involved. Whether the elevations in total folate indicate a crucial difference between these patients will remain unclear until the pathophysiological relationship between the elevations in folate and methionine are established. Patients with hypermethioninemia due to hepatic methionine adenosyltransferase deficiency have, with a single exception,[129] not had abnormal elevations of serum folate.[129,132] Further investigation of folate metabolism in patients with hypermethioninemia of unknown origin might prove rewarding.

Homocystinuria

Decreased rates of metabolism of homocysteine through either the transsulfuration [reaction (4)] or the 5-methyltetrahydrofolate-dependent homocysteine conservation [reaction (8)] pathway lead to accumulation of homocysteine with resultant homocyst(e)inemia and homocystinuria. These two types of homocystinuria may be distinguished by several chemical criteria: Serum methionine concentrations are usually elevated in cystathionine β-synthase deficiency but low or normal when 5-methyltetrahydrofolate-dependent homocysteine methylation is decreased. Excretion of urinary sulfate after a methionine load proceeds at an abnormally low rate in the former condition, but not in the latter.

Several genetic lesions are known to lead to decreases in 5-methyltetrahydrofolate-dependent homocysteine methylation sufficiently severe to cause homocystinuria: (1) Inability to convert cobalamin to either of its biologically active metabolites, adenosylcobalamin or methylcobalamin. These patients have combined homocystinuria and methylmalonic aciduria. The disorder has been divided into two classes, *cblC* and *cblD*, on the basis of complementation studies in cultured fibroblasts (Chap. 82). (2) *CblE* disorder, characterized by an abnormality which affects the formation of methylcobalamin, but not adenosylcobalamin, leading to homocystinuria without methylmalonic aciduria. The original proband with this disorder had homocystinuria and megaloblastic anemia responsive to vitamin B_{12} therapy. 5-Methyltetrahydrofolate-homocysteine methyltransferase activity in cell extracts was decreased only when the assay was performed under suboptimal reducing conditions, leading to the suggestion of a defect in a reducing system required for methionine biosynthesis.[133] Several patients have subsequently been reported with similar clinical findings, decreased accumulation of methylcobalamin, and homocystinuria, but in whose cell extracts 5-methyltetrahydrofolate-homocysteine methyltransferase activity was decreased even under optimal reducing conditions.[134–134b] Complementation for methionine biosynthesis was demonstrated in fused mixed cultures of cells from the two types of patients. The two complementation classes were named *cblE* and *cblG*, respectively.[134a] An additional patient with findings similar to those of the *cblG* group has been described by Hallam et al., although complementation studies were not reported.[134c] Most methylcobalamin in liver cells occurs bound to 5-methyltetrahydrofolate-homocysteine methyltransferase.[134d,134e] Therefore, it seems possible that certain defects of this apoenzyme might produce secondary inability to form or accumulate methylcobalamin, and that such defects will be found among the *cblG* group. (See Chap. 82 for further discussion of these disorders.) Zittoun and coworkers described a 14-year-old boy with megaloblastic anemia unresponsive to cyanocobalamin. 5-Methyltetrahydrofolate-homocysteine methyltransferase activity was not detected in bone marrow and was profoundly depressed in lymphocytes and liver. Studies of methylcobalamin or complementation tests were not reported. It was concluded that this patient had deficiency of 5-methyltetrahydrofolate-homocysteine methyltransferase. Surprisingly, the patient was not homocystinuric.[134f] A *cblE* (or *cblG*) abnormality may explain the homocystinuria found in a patient with orotic aciduria and formiminotransferase/cyclodeaminase deficiency[135] (Chap. 81). (3) 5,10-Methylenetetrahydrofolate reductase deficiency with homocystinuria and hypomethioninemia (Chap. 81). (4) Immerslund syndrome (familial proteinuria and pernicious anemia due to defective absorption of vitamin B_{12} in the presence of intrinsic factor).[57,136]

Homocystinuria, accompanied by cystathioninuria and methylmalonic aciduria, was observed in a 6-month-old infant with severe megaloblastic anemia and coma. These manifestations were secondary to nutritional vitamin B_{12} deficiency brought about because the child was exclusively breast-fed by a strictly vegetarian mother.[137] Recently, abnormal homocyst(e)inemia (total serum homocyst(e)ine up to 476 μ*M*) has been reported in 77 of 78 adults with clinically confirmed cobalamin deficiency.[137a] In another series, in this instance of subjectively healthy vitamin B_{12}-deficient subjects, total plasma homocyst(e)ine was abnormally elevated in 8 of 20 (range up to 70 μ*M*), with the mean value twice that of controls.[137b] Likewise, homocyst(e)inemia was found in 16 of 19 folate-deficient subjects studied in one laboratory,[495] and 18 of 19 folate-deficient subjects (total serum homocyst(e)ine up to 185 μ*M*) in a second laboratory.[137a]

The homocystinuria due to 6-azauridine triacetate administration was mentioned above (under "Hypermethioninemia"). One of six subjects given 300 mg isonicotinic acid hydrazide daily for 1 month developed homocystinuria (approximately 50 μmol per 24 h). This was attributed to interference with pyridoxine metabolism, an interpretation supported by the fact that all six patients developed symptoms of peripheral neuritis and increased cystathionine excretions which, after methionine loads, attained statistical significance.[137c]

Finally, an artifactual form of homocystinuria has been shown to be due to bacterial conversion of cystathionine to homocyst(e)ine. This occurred in contaminated urine specimens from an infant with massive cystathioninuria.[72,138] Whether similar phenomena account for the homocystinuria occasionally reported in additional patients with cystathioninuria[139–143] remains to be clarified. Demonstration of homocyst(e)inemia is a useful means of proving that homocystinuria is not artifactual.

Cystathioninuria

In an extensive study, Endres and Seibold failed to detect cystathionine in the urine of only 17 percent of clinically normal individuals, aged 3 days to 56 years.[144] The amounts ranged up to 146 μmol/g creatinine. Expressed on the basis of body surface area, mean cystathionine excretion did not change with age, but expressed on the basis of urinary creatinine, cystathionine excretion was lower in adults (23 to 56 years of age; median, 7 μmol/g creatinine) than in children (3 days to 14 years; median, 28 μmol/g).

Cystathionine is an almost constant constituent of the urine of premature infants.[145,146] Such premature infants excrete more cystathionine than term infants of similar postgestational ages.[144] Premature infants fed protein-[145] or methionine-enriched[144,146] diets excreted increased amounts of cystathionine, and low-birth-weight infants fed increased protein intakes had mild elevations of cystathionine in plasma and urine.[119] Transient cystathioninuria (amount unspecified) was detected in 13 of 35,809 apparently normal infants screened in Australia at age 6 weeks. By the time these 13 children were age 5 months, cystathionine was not detected in the urine of 11 and was present only in trace amounts in the other two.[142] These findings may be explained by the observations that γ-cystathionase is absent in fetal liver tissue but appears in the liver of newborns.[95] Apparently the capacity to cleave cystathionine is marginal in premature infants, but it matures in almost all children within a few weeks of birth.

Persistent cystathioninuria of genetic origin may be due either to underutilization or to overproduction of cystathionine. Underutilization accounts for the persistent, often massive cystathioninuria encountered in patients with genetically determined impairment of γ-cystathionase activity. Overproduction occurs when a normal amount of cystathionine β-synthase is provided with abnormally elevated concentrations of its substrate, homocysteine. This situation occurs, for example, when 5-methyltetrahydrofolate-homocysteine methyltransferase activity is impaired by lack of methylcobalamin or by lack of 5-methyltetrahydrofolate. The lack of competition for homocysteine by the methyltransferase apparently permits cystathionine β-synthase to utilize this compound to synthesize cystathionine at a rate such that a minor degree of cystathioninuria may occur. Abnormal cystathionine excretion has been noted in some,[137,147,148] but not all,[149,150] patients with such defects and, when present, has been less than the cystathionine excretion of patients with γ-cystathionase deficiency. This difference, and the accompanying homocystinuria, provide means of distinguishing patients with decreased homocysteine methylation from those with γ-cystathionase deficiency.

An unusual type of moderate familial cystathioninuria was suggested by Frimpter to be due to a renal defect affecting the transport of this amino acid. The patient in question excreted virtually all the cystathionine filtered at the glomerulus,[166] whereas normal subjects reabsorb a maximum of approximately 1 μmol/min per 1.73 m^2 body surface area.[167]

A number of nongenetic conditions lead to excessive cystathionine excretion. Vitamin B_6 deficiency produces cystathioninuria in animals[151] and humans.[152,153] The cystathioninuria of premature infants is decreased by large oral doses of vitamin B_6.[146] Both cystathionine β-synthase and γ-cystathionase activities are pyridoxal phosphate-dependent, but studies of vitamin B_6-deficient rats have shown that the γ-cystathionase holoenzyme contents of the liver, kidney, and pancreas of such animals are much more decreased than are the cystathionine β-synthase holoenzyme contents.[154,155] In vitamin B_6-deficient humans, cystathionine synthesis usually continues at a rate such that homocystine may be absent from the urine, or present only in trace amounts, whereas cystathionine excretion may become quite marked.[153] An exceptional patient who became both homocystinuric and cystathioninuric when isonicotinic acid hydrazide interfered with his pyridoxine metabolism has been mentioned above (under "Homocystinuria").[137a] Vitamin B_6-deficient rats[156,157] and pigs[158] do become markedly homocyst(e)inemic.

Abnormal cystathionine excretion has also been reported in thyrotoxic patients.[159] Animal studies have shown that thyroxine administration reduces hepatic γ-cystathionase activity[160] but not the activity of cystathionine β-synthase.[160,161] The cystathioninuria occurring in many instances of severe generalized liver damage[162–165] may also be due to an impaired capacity to cleave cystathionine.

Many functional neural tumors contain relatively high concentrations of cystathionine,[168] and patients with these tumors are cystathioninuric.[169–171] Since nervous tissue contains relatively more cystathionine β-synthase than γ-cystathionase activity,[172,173] this form of cystathioninuria may represent a local imbalance between production and utilization. Similar imbalances could account for the cystathioninuria reported in some cases of hepatoblastoma.[163,174–176]

The majority of these nongenetic causes of cystathioninuria lead to excretion of abnormal amounts of this amino acid in the absence of striking abnormalities of the other sulfur amino acids. Confusion with γ-cystathionase deficiency might therefore be possible, and these nongenetic conditions should be carefully excluded by the usual diagnostic criteria before it is concluded that any particular case of cystathioninuria is due to genetically determined γ-cystathionase deficiency.

HEPATIC METHIONINE ADENOSYLTRANSFERASE DEFICIENCY

Since 1974, six persons (three males and three females) have been reported with specific and persistent hypermethioninemia associated with deficient methionine adenosyltransferase activity in the liver.[132,177–180] Hypermethioninemia was discovered in five during the perinatal period as a result of routine screening procedures, originally introduced as a means of detecting the hypermethioninemia associated with cystathionine β-synthase deficiency. One patient was ascertained at age 31 years during investigation of his complaint of an unusual odor to his breath. At ascertainment, plasma methionine concentrations were 250 to 1270 μ*M* (upper limit of normal approximately 30 μ*M*). Hypermethioninemia of approximately 400 μ*M* has generally persisted when the patients were placed on diets with methionine intakes reduced as low as 55 mg/kg per day. Activity of methionine adenosyltransferase in extracts of liver was between 8 and 18 percent of mean control values when assayed at high (1 to 20 m*M*) methionine concentrations.[178,179] At lower methionine concentrations, in the two patients studied, the rate of *S*-adenosylmethionine formation was approximately 30 percent of mean control values.[178,180] In contrast to control liver extracts, dimethylsulfoxide did not stimulate the rate of product formation by extracts from a patient's liver.[180] These findings are all consistent with the possibility that these patients have a deficient activity chiefly of the high K_m form of hepatic methionine adenosyltransferase, with a relatively unaffected low K_m form still present. In agreement with this possibility, methionine adenosyltransferase activities in erythrocytes, cultured skin fibroblasts, and long-term lymphoid lines were no different from control values in the five patients studied,[106,179] and the activities in fibroblasts and lymphoid cells had the same chromatographic properties as control activities.[28] Thus, the form, or forms, of methionine adenosyltransferase present in nonhepatic tissues are most likely under genetic control separate from that of the high K_m hepatic form

Hepatic activities of *S*-adenosylhomocysteine hydrolase, γ-cystathionase, betaine-homocysteine methyltransferase, and 5-methyltetrahydrofolate-homocysteine methyltransferase have been normal in patients with hepatic methionine adenosyltransferase deficiency.[178–180] Hepatic cystathionine β-synthase has been moderately low in two,[177,179] and questionably low in another,[180] of the four patients in whom this enzyme was assayed. The concentration of *S*-adenosylmethionine in a liver biopsy from one patient was comparable to the mean for postmortem human liver samples,[179] and in another it was somewhat lower than the range reported for fresh human livers.[180] *S*-Adenosylmethionine concentrations, measured in whole blood of two patients at times when they were hypermethioninemic, were at least as high as control values.[179] These findings are in accord with expectations that a complete lack of *S*-adenosylmethionine might be lethal and that, given elevated methionine concentrations, residual adenosyltransferases in liver and peripheral tissues might combine to provide a near-normal supply of *S*-adenosylmethionine.[89,177] Consistent with these expectations, measurements of the excretion of creatinine, creatine, and other methylated compounds by the 31-year-old patient while in a metabolic steady-state on a normal diet indicated that he was synthesizing *S*-adenosylmethionine at a rate comparable to that of normal young adults on normal diets.[106]

In addition to abnormal elevations of methionine, the plasma and urine of these patients contain abnormally high concentrations of methionine sulfoxide[179] (demonstrated in one case to be solely the L-methionine-d-sulfoxide enantiomer[106]). 4-Methylthio-2-oxobutyrate is found in abnormally high amounts in the urine.[105,106] Neither homocystine nor tyrosine is abnormally elevated. The breath odor in the 31-year-old patient was shown to be due to the presence of unusually high amounts of dimethylsulfide.[106]

Steady-state balance studies of the 31-year-old patient demonstrated that he methylates substantial amounts of homocysteine by the N^5-methyltetrahydrofolate-dependent reaction. Thus he conserves homocysteine in the presence of a greatly elevated body load of methionine, a circumstance in which a normal person would degrade homocysteine almost entirely via cystathionine rather than conserve it by methylation to methionine. Two allosteric regulatory effects of *S*-adenosylmethionine, previously demonstrated in vitro, may be important in this regard: First, *S*-adenosylmethionine inhibits methylenetetrahydrofolate reductase, thereby limiting the supply of newly formed methyl moieties available for homocysteine methylation.[180a] Second, *S*-adenosylmethionine stimulates the activity of cystathionine β-synthase.[180b] In the methionine adenosyltransferase-deficient patient the hepatic *S*-adenosylmethionine concentration was slightly below normal. It was suggested that it is the failure of this crucial regulatory compound to become elevated in the face of the elevated methionine which is responsible for the abnormal homocysteine conservation observed in this patient.[106]

Clinically, these patients with proven partial defects of hepatic methionine adenosyltransferase activity have been virtually normal. The 31-year-old patient is currently well physically and mentally. His only complaint is the breath odor. His muscle mass is normal, and he participates in long-distance running.[106] The remaining patients, at last published reports, were each well at ages under 6 years.[177,179] Recent information on three of these[181,182] indicates that on unrestricted diets they are clinically and developmentally normal at ages 7⁹⁄₁₂, 11¹⁰⁄₁₂, and 13 years. Although nonspecific ultrastructural abnormalities in the endoplasmic reticulum and outer mitochondrial membranes of liver have been reported,[179] the liver of the 31-year-old patient was essentially normal histologically,[180] and the other patients are currently free of hepatomegaly or other manifestations of liver disease.[181,182]

The inheritance pattern of hepatic methionine adenosyltransferase deficiency remains obscure. Of the two parents for whom liver adenosyltransferase assays were performed, one father had a value of 55 percent of the mean control value, whereas one mother had normal activity.[179] Another father and one mother had moderately impaired plasma methionine tolerance curves following oral loads of methionine.[179] The presence of isoenzymes under different genetic control and the possibility that hepatic adenosyltransferase activities may be higher in human females than in males (as is the case in rats, see Ref. 183) could confound the interpretation of any of these results.

CYSTATHIONINE β-SYNTHASE DEFICIENCY

The disease entity which is now recognized as cystathionine β-synthase deficiency was first reported in 1962.[184,185] Within 2 to 3 years thereafter, further cases had been discovered, the chief clinical manifestations outlined,[186–189] and the enzyme defect identified.[190]

The Genetic Defect and Genetic Heterogeneity

To date, deficient activity of cystathionine β-synthase has been reported in extracts of liver from at least 40 homocystinuric patients and in extracts of fibroblasts cultured from skin of close to 200 homocystinuric patients.[191] Cystathionine β-synthase activity was also found to be abnormally low in brain,[173] in phytohemagglutinin-stimulated lymphocytes,[192,193] and in long-term cultures of lymphocytes[194] from such patients. Deficient activity of the enzyme has been found also in cultured amniotic fluid cells[195] and chorionic villi.[196]

Numerous studies have investigated the properties of residual cystathionine β-synthases (or immunologically related molecules) in individual patients with deficiencies of this enzyme. Differences have been found both between the mutant enzymes and normal cystathionine β-synthase and between the mutant enzymes in different affected individuals: (1) Among affected individuals, the amounts of residual cystathionine β-synthase activity in cultured fibroblasts differ significantly, ranging from none detected up to 10 percent or more of mean control activity.[197–201] In one large series of patients, Uhlendorf et al.[197] noted there was less variation in residual activities between members of single sibships than between members of different sibships. (2) The stimulation of cystathionine β-synthase activities in crude extracts by addition of pyridoxal phosphate in vitro often differs between patients and control subjects and differs widely among affected patients.[197,198,202] (3) Affinities of residual cystathionine β-synthases for pyridoxal phosphate, measured with partially purified enzymes,[203] crude enzymes from which cofactor had been removed chemically,[198] or enzymes depleted of cofactor by prior growth of cells in pyridoxine-free medium,[204] have usually been lower than control affinity and have differed markedly among affected patients. (4) Less extensive measurements have shown that the affinities of residual cystathionine β-synthase for serine may be slightly lower than normal,[203] that affinities for homocysteine may be lower than normal,[203] and that the effect of homocysteine concentration on residual synthase activities may be qualitatively different from the effect on control enzyme.[199] (5) During heat inactivation, residual cystathionine β-synthase activities may be more labile than control activity,[198,203,205,206] less labile than control activity,[205] or display other differences.[207] (6) In immunologic studies of cultured mutant fibroblasts, cross-reacting material was detected in 17 of 20 cell lines examined with an antiserum raised against cystathionine β-synthase purified from human liver.[208] There was no correlation between the amount of catalytic activity and the amount of cross-reacting antigen. (7) In a study of pulse-labeled intact mutant fibroblasts, 15 of 17 cell lines synthesized enzyme subunits indistinguishable in size from control subunits.[209] One mutant line had no detected cystathionine β-synthase subunit, and no functional mRNA measurable by in vitro translation assays using mRNA prepared from cultured fibroblasts. The latter technique was used also to define the genetic defect in a patient in whose fibroblasts cystathionine β-synthase subunits were barely detected. Messenger RNA from these mutant fibroblasts directed the in vitro synthesis of two polypeptides: a subunit of normal size (63,000 daltons) and a smaller abnormal polypeptide with an apparent molecular weight of

56,000.[63] Similar subunits were observed also in one of the parents of this patient.[209] Taken together, these results strongly suggest that there is much genetic heterogeneity among the lesions which produce cystathionine β-synthase deficiency in different sibships. The available results virtually prove, also, that in at least some individuals the lesion resides in the structural gene for this enzyme, rather than in a regulatory gene. With the isolation of a cDNA clone for cystathionine β-synthase,[62] more detailed analyses of the genetic defects in various cystathionine β-synthase-deficient individuals should soon be forthcoming.

Mode of Inheritance

Cystathionine β-synthase deficiency is inherited as an autosomal recessive trait, as shown both by pedigree studies[210,211] and by studies of enzymes in parents of affected children.[89] Obligate heterozygous individuals have 22 to 47 percent of mean control cystathionine β-synthase activity in extracts of liver,[212–214] 21 to 45 percent in extracts of cultured fibroblasts,[197,201,215,216] and means of 17 percent in phytohemagglutinin-stimulated lymphocytes[193] and 34 percent in long-term cultured lymphocytes.[194] Thus, in each tissue obligate heterozygotes have less than 50 percent of the mean control specific activity of the affected enzyme. It has been suggested that this decrease below 50 percent activity may be due to negative interaction between mutant and normal subunits combined in "hybrid" molecules of cystathionine β-synthase.[89]

Metabolic Sequelae

Among the most characteristic biochemical features of cystathionine β-synthase deficiency is the presence of abnormal accumulations of both homocyst(e)ine and methionine in plasma. Normally, fasting human plasma contains less than 30 μ*M* methionine. Untreated cystathionine β-synthase-deficient patients have been reported with fasting plasma concentrations of methionine up to 2000 μ*M*.[217–219]

The situation for homocyst(e)ine is more complicated because (1) homocysteinyl moieties occur in vivo in plasma in different chemical forms and (2) once a plasma sample has been removed from the body, a variety of changes may occur in the chemical forms in which homocysteinyl moieties will be found. Sensitive and highly specific determinations have established that 75 to 80 percent of the total homocysteinyl moieties present in normal human plasma occur in vivo bound to protein by disulfide bonds.[220] Concentrations of protein-bound homocyst(e)ine were 6.51 ± 0.32 (SEM) and 7.29 ± 0.65 μ*M* for men and women, respectively, with non-protein-bound homocyst(e)inyl moieties at 2.27 and 1.95 μ*M*.[220] Very similar values for protein-bound and non-protein-bound homocyst(e)ine have recently been obtained by a method based on reduction or liberation of thiol compounds from plasma proteins with tri-*n*-butylphosphine, derivatization with a thiol-specific fluorogenic reagent, and separation using high-performance liquid chromatography.[220a] After deproteinization of normal plasma, and routine processing of the sample, the non-protein-bound homocysteinyl moieties are found almost entirely in the form of the mixed disulfide of cysteine and homocysteine.[221] Men were reported to have a value (3.3 ± 0.8 μ*M*) significantly higher than premenopausal women of similar age (2.4 ± 0.7).[222] Studies of patients with abnormally elevated plasma concentrations of total homocysteinyl moieties have been carried out in which precautions were taken to avoid artifactual oxidation to disulfides by trapping the non-protein-bound sulfhydryl form, homocysteine, as the *S*-carboxymethyl derivative. The results showed that in vivo approximately two-thirds of the homocysteinyl moieties in question were present in the —SH form, and only one-third in the —S—S— form.[217,219] In deproteinized plasma samples processed in the usual manner, the —SH form oxidizes almost entirely to the —S—S— form.[219] Therefore, it is reasonable to assume that the homocysteinyl moieties found in the mixed disulfide of cysteine and homocysteine in processed normal human plasma derive, in part at least, from homocysteine which, in vivo, was present as the free sulfhydryl.[222] Indeed, a recent paper reports that free reduced homocysteine is present in normal human plasma at between 0.1 and 0.35 μ*M*, i.e., about one-tenth the concentration of total non-protein-bound homocyst(e)ine.[220a] When plasma is stored without deproteinization, homocysteinyl moieties originally not bound to protein become so bound.[220,223,224] Advantage can be taken of this phenomenon to provide an assay of total plasma homocyst(e)ine by release of the homocysteinyl moieties in samples of stored plasma or serum by treatment with 2-mercaptoethanol[225] or dithiothreitol.[225a,225b]

Untreated cystathionine β-synthase-deficient patients have been found to have fasting plasma concentrations of non-protein-bound homocystine up to 200 μ*M*.[217–219] Cysteine-homocysteine mixed disulfide is also present.[226–228] As indicated above, in vivo approximately two-thirds of these non-protein-bound homocysteinyl moieties were probably in the form of homocysteine.[217,219] The final relative concentrations of homocystine and mixed disulfide in processed samples therefore depend to a great extent on the original relative concentrations of homocysteine and cysteine. When homocysteine predominates, homocystine will outweigh the mixed disulfide in the oxidized products. When cysteine predominates, most homocysteine will end in the mixed disulfide. Another mixed disulfide occurring abnormally in plasma of cystathionine β-synthase-deficient patients is homocysteine-cysteinylglycine. This replaces the normally occurring cystinylglycine, presumably as a result of oxidation of a mixture originally containing homocysteine and cysteinylglycine.[229]

More recent studies have shown that cystathionine β-synthase-deficient patients have an increase in protein-bound homocyst(e)ine as well as non-protein-bound homocyst(e)ine, and that indeed protein-bound homocyst(e)ine may be the more sensitive indicator of an elevation of total plasma homocysteinyl moieties. Thus, several cystathionine β-synthase-deficient patients under various treatments had no detectable, or only moderate, increases in non-protein-bound homocystine (up to 15 μ*M*) at times when protein-bound homocyst(e)ine ranged up to 40 μ*M*.[223,228,230] With more severe non-protein-bound homocystinemia (45 to 137 μ*M*), protein-bound homocyst(e)ine was usually close to 60 μ*M*,[223,228,230,231] although higher values have been recorded.[228,231] These results are especially striking when account is taken of the fact that the protein-bound homocyst(e)ine may have been underestimated in these studies because strong acids were used initially to precipitate the plasma proteins. Such methods give lower values for protein-bound homocyst(e)ine than does a method involving dissolution of homocysteine from native proteins.[220,232] It is of interest, also, that homocysteine appears to compete very favorably with cysteine for protein binding sites.[228,233] A recently appearing detailed study of the interrelations between plasma free and protein-bound homocysteine and cysteine in homocystinuria confirms and extends many of the above conclusions.[233a]

Abnormal accumulations of methionine and homocystine may occur in other body fluids, such as cerebrospinal fluid[234–236] and aqueous humor.[237]

Renal tubular reabsorption of methionine is very efficient, and even at moderate elevations of plasma methionine the urinary excretion of this amino acid may be within normal limits.[187,218,236] Homocystine is reabsorbed less well,[187,218] and, in patients with severe untreated cystathionine β-synthase deficiency, more than 1 mmol of this disulfide may be excreted each day.[217,218]

The metabolically active form of homocystine is the sulfhydryl homocysteine. The presence in tissues of relatively large concentrations of reduced glutathione,[238] as well as an enzyme which catalyzes a disulfide interchange between glutathione and homocyst(e)ine,[239] ensures that intracellularly homocysteine will predominate over homocystine. Few analyses of tissue amino acids have been reported for cystathionine β-synthase-deficient patients. The results of these studies have been summarized in detail elsewhere.[94] In general, methionine concentrations were reported to be abnormally elevated in liver, brain, and erythrocytes, but not in cultured skin fibroblasts.[94,240] Homocystine was usually not detected. Recent studies of rat tissues demonstrate that in vivo almost half the total homocysteinyl moieties in most tissues are bound to protein. Since these homocysteinyl moieties are liberated by dithioerythritol, binding is thought to be due to disulfide bonds.[232] After death of the animal, or removal of tissue, free homocysteinyl moieties quickly become protein-bound.[241] Postmortem rises occur rapidly in *S*-adenosyl-homocysteine concentrations.[33,242] In view of these artifactual changes, the earlier studies of tissue amino acids in cystathionine β-synthase-deficient patients should probably be regarded as nondefinitive.

The abnormal methionine elevations in cystathionine β-synthase deficiency are presumably due to enhanced rates of homocysteine methylation brought about by increased concentrations of the latter compound. Factors affecting the rate of homocysteine methylation affect the balance between the accumulation of methionine and homocyst(e)ine. For example, there is evidence suggesting that some cystathionine β-synthase-deficient patients in the newborn period may accumulate relatively more methionine and less homocystine than do most adult patients.[243] Perhaps such observations will be explained by a carryover of the relatively high activities of 5-methyltetrahydrofolate-homocysteine methyltransferase found in the fetus[124] into the first weeks or months of extrauterine life.[244] Conversely, some untreated older cystathionine β-synthase-deficient patients (as many as 6 percent)[191] have been homocystinemic and homocystinuric, but they did not have plasma methionine concentrations above the normal range.[245–248] Enhanced methionine/homocystine ratios may be brought about in some patients by administration of betaine[249–251] or its metabolic precursor choline,[219] thus providing more substrate for betaine-homocysteine methyltransferase. Treatment with folic acid leads to similar shifts in the methionine/homocystine balance, probably by increasing the rate of 5-methyltetrahydrofolate-dependent homocysteine methylation.[248,252,253]

A number of derivatives of homocysteine and methionine are also present in abnormally elevated amounts in plasma or urine of cystathionine β-synthase-deficient patients. These compounds have been described in detail elsewhere.[89]

Compounds metabolically distal to the block at cystathionine β-synthase would be expected to form at abnormally slow rates in patients with deficiency of this enzyme. Evidence compatible with this expectation has emerged from studies of cystathionine, cyst(e)ine, and sulfate. Again, these studies have been summarized in detail elsewhere.[94]

An important conclusion which emerges from the above data, taken together,[89] is that, although cystathionine β-synthase-deficient patients are unable to convert methionine sulfur to sulfate at a maximal rate even close to normal, they can probably dispose of almost all the methionine in a normal diet by conversion to sulfate and that compounds metabolically proximal to the block at cystathionine β-synthase account for only a minor portion of excretory sulfur. Thus, for untreated patients on relatively normal diets (8 to 12 mmol/day methionine) homocystine, homocysteine-cysteine mixed disulfide, *S*-adenosyl-homocysteine, 5-amino-4-imidazole carboxamide-5′-*S*-homocysteinylribonucleoside, methionine, methionine sulfoxide, and homolanthionine together may account (very approximately) for 2 to 3 mg-atom of daily urinary sulfur. Other compounds are known to be present in the urine in abnormal amounts, but these account for relatively very minor amounts of sulfur. In patients with small, but detectable, residual activities of cystathionine β-synthase, at least 2.5 to 4.0 mmol of methionine sulfur is converted to cysteine daily, and this pathway would explain formation of an almost equivalent amount of sulfate. For patients without residual activities of cystathionine β-synthase, less, if any, cysteine is formed, and some conversion of methionine sulfur to sulfate probably occurs by alternative metabolic routes.[89]

Finally, several additional metabolic sequelae of cystathionine β-synthase deficiency have been reported in recent years: Plasma ornithine concentrations are elevated two- to threefold above normal, without accompanying overflow ornithinuria.[254] Plasma copper is increased about 1.4-fold, with corresponding increases in ceruloplasmin concentrations.[255] Neither of these effects is understood mechanistically. While on folate therapy, cystathionine β-synthase-deficient patients have mildly lower than normal plasma serine concentrations. It was proposed that under these conditions folate-dependent methylation of homocysteine is proceeding faster than normal, leading to depletion of serine, the ultimate source of the 1-carbon unit required for this reaction.[256]

The Pyridoxine Effect and Its Mechanism

In 1967 Barber and Spaeth reported for the first time that three cystathionine β-synthase-deficient patients responded to very high doses (250 to 500 mg daily) of pyridoxine with decreases of plasma methionine levels to normal and virtual elimination of homocystine from plasma and urine.[257] This observation has since been extended to many additional patients by many authors. During the response to pyridoxine, there are decreases in a number of additional compounds formed proximal to the metabolic block at cystathionine β-synthase and increases in compounds distal to the block.[89] Some cystathionine β-synthase-deficient patients are not responsive to pyridoxine; they show little or no change in plasma or urine sulfur amino acids when given comparably large doses of this vitamin. In a 1982–1983 international survey, among patients classified as to responsiveness to pyridoxine, virtually equal proportions of patients were judged to be responsive and nonresponsive.[191] There is ample evidence that the pyridoxine-induced response of those cystathionine β-synthase-deficient patients who do respond is not due to correction of a preexisting vitamin B_6 deficiency or to alleviation of a defect in vitamin B_6 metabolism which renders these patients unable to form pyridoxal-5′-phosphate, the form of vitamin B_6 active as a cofactor for cystathionine β-synthase.[89] Some untreated cystathionine β-synthase-deficient patients have abnormally low serum folate concentrations,[252,253] and this tendency may be exacerbated by treatment with pyridoxine.[258,259] The biochemical response to pyridoxine may not be manifest in folate-depleted patients until after folate replenishment.[253,259] Thus, folate depletion may explain the apparent failure of some patients to respond to pyridoxine treatment, and studies of the effect of pyridoxine are interpretable only in the presence of adequate folate.

When different patients are compared, it is apparent that pyridoxine-responsive patients are not uniform. Some patients in response continue to have slight elevations of homocystine in plasma or urine,[258,260,261] although others do not.[261–263] On the basis of the clinical responses of their patients to pyridoxine, Brenton and Cusworth defined three classes of pyridoxine responsiveness, including a group intermediate between those who display little or no response and those with very clear responses.[261] Approximately 13 percent of patients may show such intermediate responses.[191] Even those patients who respond most favorably are clearly not restored to biochemical normality. Such patients in response have markedly abnormal rises in concentrations of plasma and urinary homocystine after methionine loads,[260,262,264] and restoration of plasma methionine to basal concentrations is delayed.[262] Their maximal capacities for transsulfuration in vivo continue to be far below the maximal capacities of normal subjects, as measured by sulfate excretion following oral methionine loads.[260]

Pyridoxine responsiveness is constant within sibships. Among 104 sibships (total of 223 sibs) with more than one cystathionine β-synthase-deficient member classified as to responsiveness to pyridoxine, there was almost complete concordance within sibships of responsiveness or nonresponsiveness. In no case was a patient judged fully responsive when a sib was judged fully nonresponsive.[191] This concordance indicates not only that the capacity to respond to pyridoxine is genetically determined but also that the genetic determinant governing responsiveness is closely linked with, or identical to, that determining cystathionine β-synthase deficiency itself. If the two genetic factors were unlinked and segregated separately, variation of responsiveness between cystathionine β-synthase-deficient members of the same sibship might be expected. The simplest interpretation is that the same mutation which makes an individual cystathionine β-synthase-deficient also determines whether he or she will be pyridoxine-responsive. A single alteration of apoenzyme structure might well determine both properties.

Studies of cystathionine β-synthase activities support the hypothesis that responsiveness or nonresponsiveness may be determined by the specific properties of the mutant enzyme molecule. There is a strong correlation between the presence of detected residual activity of cystathionine β-synthase and clinical responsiveness to pyridoxine and between absence of detected residual activity and nonresponsiveness. Residual activities have been detected in liver extracts from each of seven pyridoxine-responsive patients but not in extracts from any of three pyridoxine nonresponders.[89] More extensive data with cultured fibroblasts[197,198,200,201,265] show (1) that the presence or absence of detected residual cystathionine β-synthase activity is constant within sibships and (2) that among sibships responsive to pyridoxine, 31 had residual activities of cystathionine β-synthase in cultured fibroblasts; in only eight was such activity not detected. In contrast, among sibships not responsive to pyridoxine, only six had detected residual activity of cystathionine β-synthase, whereas 20 had no detected activity.

Quantitatively, the residual activities of cystathionine β-synthase in extracts of fibroblasts cultured from pyridoxine-responsive patients have varied from about 0.1 to 10 percent of mean control values.[197,198,201] When potentially pyridoxine-responsive patients were receiving normal pyridoxine intakes, their liver extracts, assayed in the presence of ample pyridoxal phosphate, have had residual activities of 1 to 2 percent of mean control values,[260] 3.7 to 9.4 percent,[214] or in one case, 31 percent.[266] When the same patients were receiving large dietary intakes of pyridoxine, the cystathionine β-synthase-specific activities in their liver extracts were enhanced 1.5- to 3.0-fold[260] or 1.3- to 4.5-fold.[214]

Taken together, these results suggest that, in most patients, pyridoxine responsiveness is based on the presence of a small residual activity of mutant cystathionine β-synthase, the steady-state amount of which is enhanced somewhat when the patient is taking large doses of pyridoxine. Although the enhanced activity does not attain control levels, it does become sufficient to metabolize the homocysteine arising from a normal methionine intake without an accumulation severe enough to produce homocyst(e)inemia or homocystinuria. A number of quantitative considerations which support this formulation have been reviewed in more detail elsewhere.[89,267,268] This formulation leaves unexplained the mechanism of response in those responsive patients for whom cystathionine β-synthase activity has not been detected in cultured fibroblasts. If these negative findings for fibroblasts accurately reflect the situation in the livers of such patients, presumably some other basis will have to be found for their pyridoxine responsiveness.

The molecular properties of mutant cystathionine β-synthases crucial in conferring pyridoxine responsiveness remain obscure. The mere presence of some residual cystathionine β-synthase activity is not sufficient, as proven by the finding of clinically nonresponsive patients with readily detected residual activities. With enzymes from responsive patients, restoration of near-normal activity by high concentrations of pyridoxal phosphate in vitro, such as would take place if the mutations affected only the K_m for this cofactor, has usually not occurred.[89,197,198,205] Some of the largest observed enhancements of activity by addition of pyridoxal phosphate in vitro have occurred with enzymes from clinically nonresponsive patients.[197,198] Indeed, Lipson and coworkers[204] have suggested that for a patient to be pyridoxine-responsive, not only must some residual cystathionine β-synthase activity be present but also the affinity of this mutant enzyme for cofactor must not be too severely impaired. Further studies of mutant enzymes resolved from cofactor by growth of fibroblasts in pyridoxine-free medium[204] and of the factors determining the rates of turnover of mutant forms of cystathionine β-synthase in liver and other tissues[268] may be expected to throw additional light on this question.

Clinical Manifestations

Homocystinuria due to cystathionine β-synthase deficiency is accompanied by an abundance and variety of clinical abnormalities. These usually develop after birth.

Table 23-2 Clinical Abnormalities in Cystathionine β-Synthase Deficiency

	References
I. Eye	
A. Frequent	
1. Ectopia lentis	191, 269–271
2. Myopia	210, 270, 272
B. Less frequent	
1. Glaucoma	273–275
2. Optic atrophy	272, 276, 277
3. Retinal degeneration	234, 272
4. Retinal detachment	275, 278
5. Cataracts	234, 272
6. Corneal abnormalities	279
II. Skeletal system	
A. Frequent	
1. Osteoporosis	191, 280–283
2. Biconcave ("codfish") vertebrae	283–286
3. Scoliosis	280, 283–285
4. Increased length of long bones	280–283, 287, 288
5. Irregular, widened metaphyses	281, 283, 285, 289
6. Metaphyseal spicules	281, 282, 284
7. Abnormal size and shape of epiphyses	283, 289
8. Growth arrest lines	283, 284
9. Pes cavus	285, 290
10. High-arched palate	285
B. Less frequent	
1. Arachnodactyly	280–282, 285
2. Enlarged carpal bones	280, 281, 284, 287
3. Abnormal bone age	280, 281, 284, 287
4. Pectus carinatum or excavatum	281, 284, 285
5. Genu valgum	285, 290
6. Kyphosis	280, 283
7. Short fourth metacarpal	291
III. Central nervous system	
A. Frequent	
1. Mental retardation	188, 191, 292
2. Psychiatric disturbances	187, 278, 292–296
B. Less frequent	
1. Seizures	187, 191, 295, 297
2. Abnormal EEG	210, 245, 296, 298–300
3. Extrapyramidal signs	294, 301–303
IV. Vascular system	
A. Frequent	
1. Vascular occlusions	191, 210, 278, 304–306
2. Malar flush	211, 307
3. Livedo reticularis	234, 307
V. Other involvement	
A. Fair, brittle hair	211, 257, 308
B. Thin skin	300, 308, 309
C. Fatty changes in liver	210, 214, 310
D. Inguinal hernia	210, 311
E. Myopathy	312
F. Endocrine abnormalities	313, 314
G. Reduced clotting factors	315, 316, 316a

Four organ systems show major involvement: the eye and the skeletal, central nervous, and vascular systems. Other organs, including the liver, hair, and skin, may also have changes. The abnormalities in question are listed in Table 23-2; most of them are described below. A more detailed description can be found through the references provided in Table 23-2 and in the previous edition of this text.[94] The present information is derived from a review of at least 350 reported cases[94] and was updated and extended in 1982–1983 by an international survey which examined the natural history of cystathionine β-synthase deficiency in more than 600 patients.[191] This survey showed that the risk of developing a manifestation of the disease increases with age and that pyridoxine-responsive patients usually are more mildly affected than pyridoxine-nonresponsive patients. It should be noted that our present picture of the clinical features of cystathionine β-synthase deficiency may be influenced by ascertainment bias, a possibility which has been discussed in detail elsewhere.[191]

Eye.

ECTOPIA LENTIS. Probably the most consistent finding in cystathionine β-synthase deficiency is ectopia lentis (dislocation of the ocular lens). In contrast to patients with Marfan syndrome, the dislocation is usually downward, although it may occur in any direction.[269] Dislocation has been noted only rarely before 2 years of age, but it was observed as early as 4 weeks of age in one patient.[317] Time-to-event graphs for untreated patients showed a lag of approximately 2 years after birth before an appreciable frequency of dislocation was noted (Fig. 23-3). After this age pyridoxine-nonresponsive patients had a higher rate of dislocation than did pyridoxine-responsive patients; 50 percent of nonresponders or responders had ectopia lentis at age 6 to 10 years, respectively. Since the graphs in Fig. 23-3 represent the ages at detection of ectopia lentis, they represent the upper limits for the actual ages of occurrence. By 38 years of age, only 3 percent of all patients had both lenses still in place. These data, therefore, appear to confirm the impression that the great majority of untreated patients eventually develop dislocated lenses. However, ascertainment bias may contribute to overrepresentation of patients with dislocated lenses among those recognized to have cystathionine β-synthase deficiency.[191] Therefore, a normal ophthalmologic examination at any age should not be a reason for rejecting a diagnosis of cystathionine β-synthase deficiency.

OTHER OCULAR FEATURES. Several abnormalities occur secondary to the loosening and subsequent subluxation of the lens. A marked myopia is always associated with ectopia lentis, beginning when the lens loosens and worsening when the subluxation occurs. Iridodonesis (quivering of the iris) is present when the lens has dislocated, because the iris no longer lies on a stationary lens. Acute pupillary block glaucoma may result from anterior dislocation of the lens. Additional complications are listed in Table 23-2.

Skeletal System.

OSTEOPOROSIS. Among the most obvious changes in patients with cystathionine β-synthase deficiency are those of the skeleton. The most consistent of these is osteoporosis. The spine is the most common site for osteoporosis, followed by the long bones. Time-to-event graphs for radiologic evidence of spinal osteoporosis in untreated patients indicate that osteoporosis had been detected in at least 50 percent by the end of the second decade of life (Fig. 23-4). As with ectopia lentis, spinal osteoporosis generally appears earlier in pyridoxine-nonresponsive patients than in those responsive to pyridoxine. Again these graphs represent maximum ages by which spinal osteoporosis is present in given proportions of patients. Perhaps as a result of spinal osteoporosis, scoliosis occurs in many affected individuals, although scoliosis has been reported in

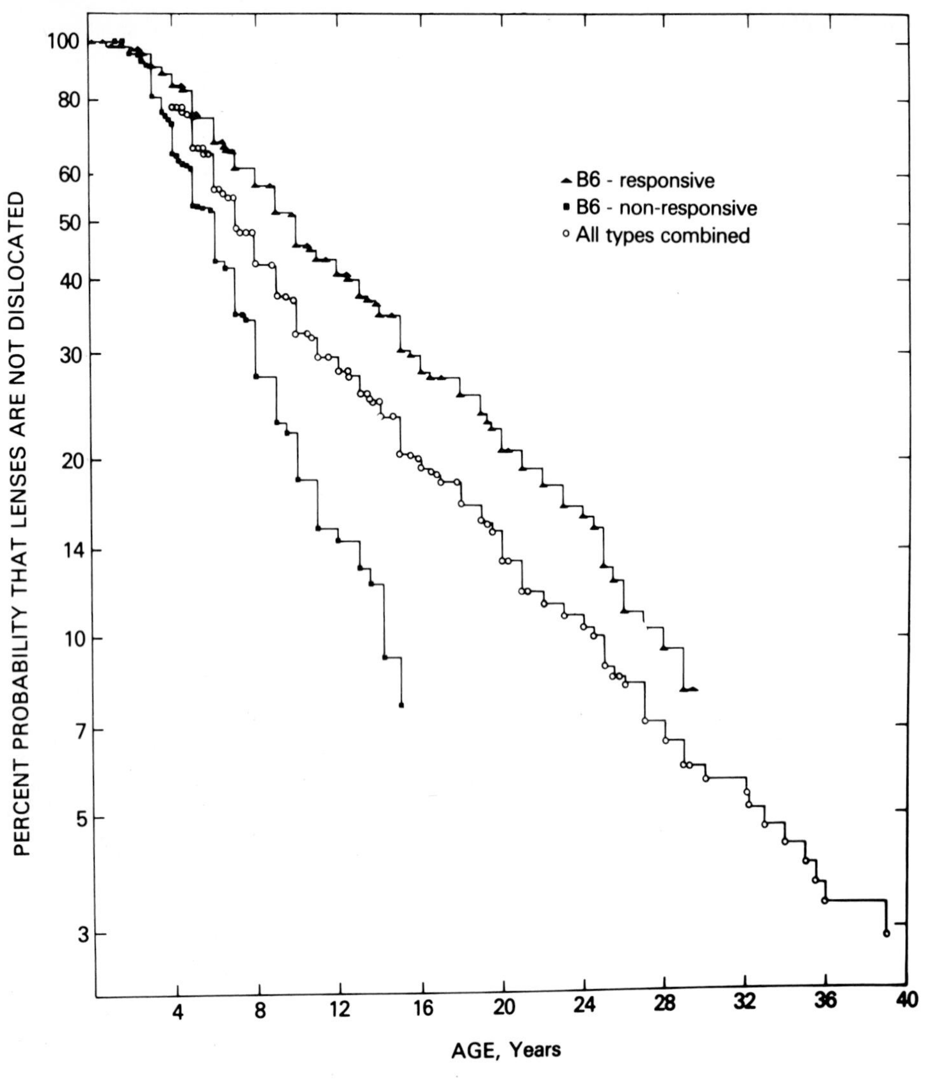

Fig. 23-3 Time-to-event graphs for lens dislocation in untreated patients. Patients were removed from the at-risk groups upon commencement of any therapy. *(From Mudd et al.,* [191] *by permission.)*

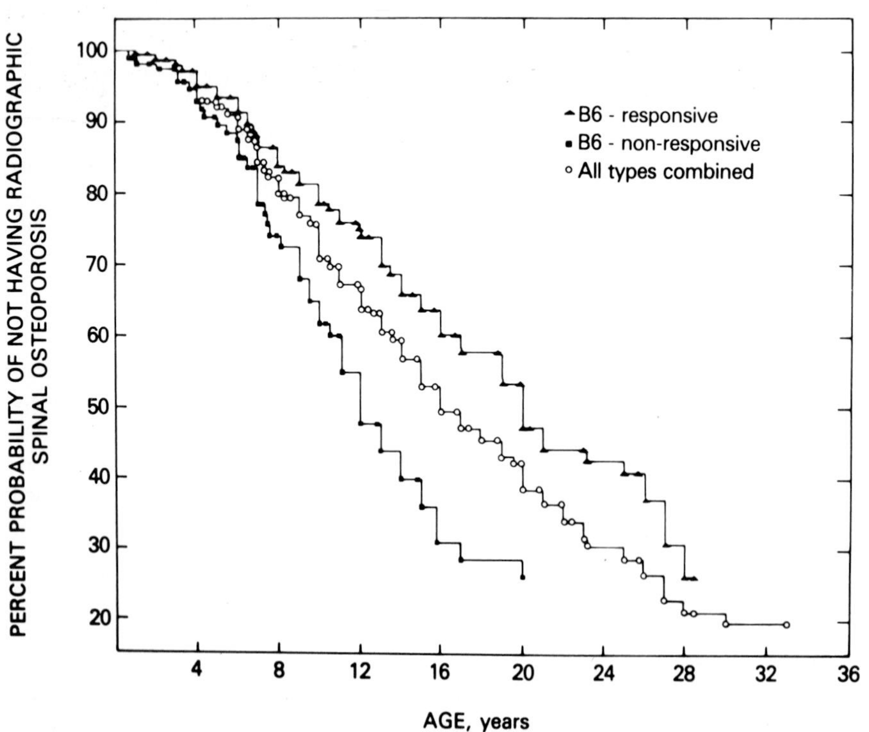

Fig. 23-4 Time-to-event graphs for radiologic spinal osteoporosis in untreated patients. *(From Mudd et al.,* [191] *by permission.)*

the absence of osteoporosis.[284] Osteoporosis of the spine may lead to vertebral collapse.[278,285]

OTHER SKELETAL MANIFESTATIONS. A large number of abnormalities of configuration and maturation of the skeleton also occur in cystathionine β-synthase-deficient patients (Table 23-2). Among the most frequent is thinning and lengthening of the long bones (dolichostenomelia), an abnormality which produces individuals who are tall and thin by the time they reach later childhood. Other frequent abnormalities are pectus carinatum, pes cavus, and genu valgum. Common radiologic findings include biconcave vertebrae and epimetaphyseal widening. One or more of these abnormalities often lead to evaluation by orthopedic surgeons.

Central Nervous System.

MENTAL RETARDATION. The most frequent abnormality of the central nervous system is mental retardation. Often this is the first recognized sign of cystathionine β-synthase deficiency, presenting as developmental delay during the first and second year of life. Walking may not only be delayed, but some patients have been described as having a waddling or "Charlie Chaplin-like" gait.[318] The intellectual capability of patients not treated from the newborn period varies widely. For patients covered in the 1982–1983 international survey, IQ scores ranged from 10 to 138 (Fig. 23-5) with the median of the cumulative frequency curve at approximately 64.[191] The distribution for pyridoxine-responsive patients was shifted toward higher IQs (median 78), as compared with that for pyridoxine-nonresponsive patients (median 56). There is significant clustering of IQ scores within sibships.[292] Longitudinal studies of four pyridoxine-responsive patients receiving pyridoxine and six pyridoxine-nonresponsive patients (of whom two were on dietary therapy[318a]) disclosed no significant changes in IQs over periods of up to 7.5 years.[292, 318a,319]

Fig. 23-5 Distribution of IQs among patients not detected by newborn screening. *(From Mudd et al.,* [191] *by permission.)*

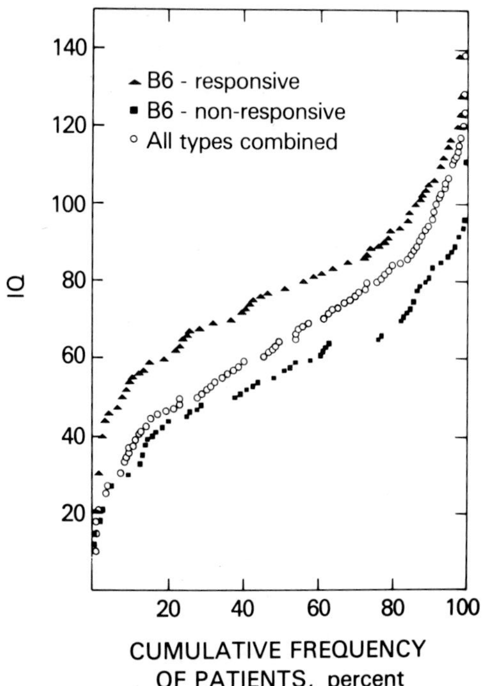

NEUROLOGIC ABNORMALITIES. About 21 percent of patients with cystathionine β-synthase deficiency not treated from early infancy have had seizures, most often of grand mal type.[191] Abnormal electroencephalograms have been reported in patients with and without seizures. Specific neurologic findings have generally not been striking. Hemiparesis or focal neurologic signs suggest the presence of a cerebrovascular occlusion. Dystonia has been observed in a few patients, and other extrapyramidal disturbances have also been noted (Table 23-2). In at least some of these individuals, a cerebrovascular origin of their neurologic symptoms seemed unlikely.

PSYCHIATRIC ABNORMALITIES. Mental illness has been reported to be frequent among individuals with cystathionine β-synthase deficiency. A recent investigation of 63 such patients found clinically significant psychiatric disorders in 51 percent.[292] Four diagnostic categories predominated: episodic depression (10 percent), chronic disorders of behavior (17 percent), chronic obsessive-compulsive disorder (5 percent), and personality disorders (19 percent). Disorders of behavior and obsessive-compulsive disorder prevailed in patients with IQ below 79, whereas personality disorders were unrelated to IQ. There was insufficient evidence to establish a diagnosis of schizophrenia in any individual. Although anecdotal reports have suggested this condition might be common among cystathionine β-synthase-deficient patients, it may, in fact, be uncommon.

Vascular System.

THROMBOEMBOLISM. A major cause of morbidity and the most frequent cause of death in cystathionine β-synthase deficiency is thromboembolism. Vascular occlusion can occur in any vessel at any age. In the 1982–1983 international survey, 158 patients were reported to have had a total of 253 thromboembolic events, whereas 471 patients had had no events.[191] Among the 253 events, 130 (51 percent) involved peripheral veins (32 of which resulted in pulmonary embolism), 81 (32 percent) were cerebrovascular accidents, 28 (11 percent) affected peripheral arteries, 10 (4 percent) produced myocardial infarctions, and 4 (2 percent) fell into none of these categories. Serious complications of thromboembolism have included optic atrophy secondary to occlusion to the optic artery,[276] hemiparesis, seizures or focal neurologic signs due to cerebral thrombosis,[297,320] cor pulmonale secondary to pulmonary artery occlusion,[321] and severe hypertension due to renal infarcts.[321] The occurrence of clinically apparent thromboembolism depends on age and pyridoxine responsiveness (Fig. 23-6). For untreated pyridoxine-responsive patients there was an initial period extending to about age 12 during which there was little risk for thromboembolism. Subsequently, the risk increased so that by the age of 20 years the cumulative risk for a thromboembolic event was about 25 percent. In contrast, untreated pyridoxine-nonresponsive patients had little or no lag and a cumulative risk for a thromboembolic event of 25 percent by age 15 years. For each group during their young adult years the chance that an untreated individual previously free of thromboembolic events would have such an event during the subsequent year was 1:25.

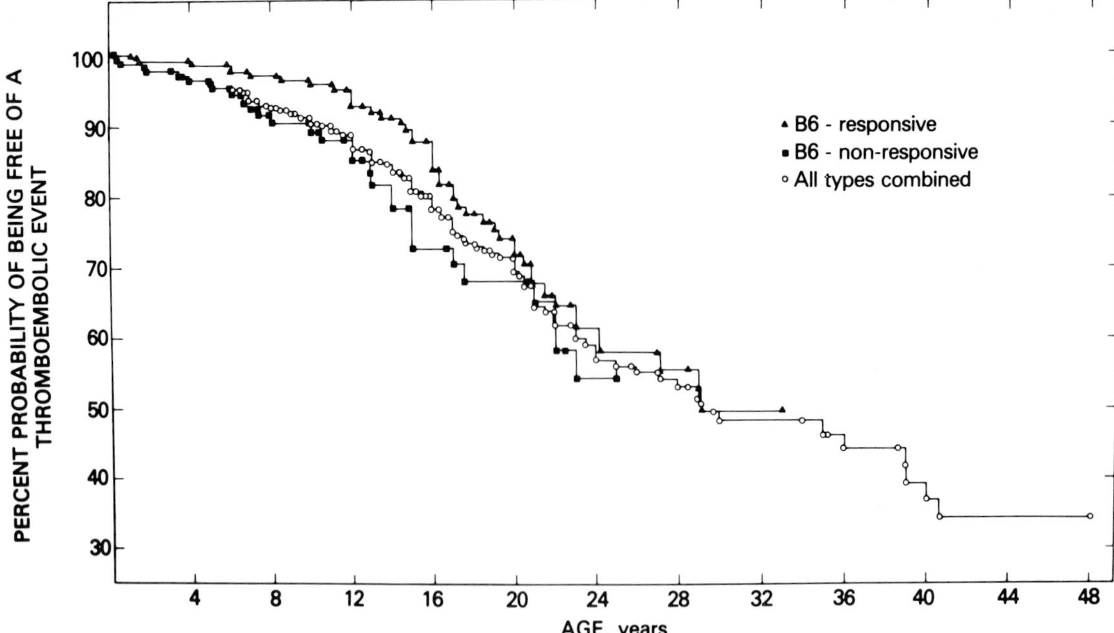

Fig. 23-6 Time-to-event graphs for first clinically detected thromboembolic event in untreated patients. *(From Mudd et al.,*[191] *by permission.)*

RISK OF POSTOPERATIVE THROMBOEMBOLISM. Early reports of patients with cystathionine β-synthase deficiency suggested a high risk of thromboembolism during or immediately following surgery.[210,252,318] The 1982–1983 international survey disclosed only 14 postoperative thromboembolic events among 241 major surgical procedures.[191] Four of these events were fatal. Among 345 eye operations, only 11 postoperative thromboembolic events occurred, two of which were fatal. There was no appreciable difference between pyridoxine-responsive and -nonresponsive patients. These data indicate that, given proper attention,[322] it is possible for the great majority of operations to be conducted without vascular complications in patients with cystathionine β-synthase deficiency.

Other Involvement. The hair has often been reported as fine and brittle and the skin as thin. Hepatomegaly may be present due to fatty change of the liver. The frequency of inguinal hernia seems to be increased. Electromyographic evidence of myopathy has been reported. Hyperinsulinism with abnormal glucose tolerance and increased levels of growth hormone have also been noted.

Reproductive Fitness. The available data on the reproductive performance of women with cystathionine β-synthase deficiency are summarized in Table 23-3. Most conceptions have occurred in pyridoxine-responsive women, and the living offspring have had few abnormalities. The data in this table for fetal loss in pyridoxine-responsive women are strongly influenced by the results from three patients who among them had had 22 spontaneous abortions or stillbirths without a clear relationship to the presence or absence of pyridoxine treatment.[191] Removal of the data from these women would leave 58 pregnancies that ended other than by elective abortion. Fetal losses in these were 5/33 (15 percent) in the absence of pyridoxine treatment, and 5/25 (20 percent) during pyridoxine administration. Therefore, whether there is increased fetal loss due to maternal cystathionine β-synthase deficiency untreated during pregnancy is as yet undetermined. All but one of the 38 recognized conceptions involving cystathionine β-synthase-deficient men resulted in apparently normal offspring.[191,323]

Evidence of greatly increased maternal risk for patients with cystathionine β-synthase deficiency is not strong. Most pregnancies mentioned in the literature have apparently proceeded without mishap for the mother. However, reports have described a 20-year-old who presented with multiple arterial occlusions after pregnancy,[323] a woman who developed postpartum thrombophlebitis,[459] and a 28-year-old who died of superior sagittal sinus thrombosis two to three weeks after a cesarian section.[546]

Mortality. Of the 629 patients covered in the 1982–1983 international survey, 64 were deceased.[191] For five, the cause of death was unknown or unrelated to cystathionine β-synthase deficiency. Of the remaining 59 deaths, thromboembolism was known to be the chief causative factor in 42 patients and a probable, but less clearly established, contributing factor in at least five others. Seven grossly mentally retarded patients died from various infectious diseases, and in five patients the causes of death were of uncertain relationship to their enzyme deficiency. The time-to-event graphs in Fig. 23-7 show that the mortality by age 20 years was less than 5 percent among those responsive to pyridoxine and approximately 20 percent among those not responsive. The overall outlook for cystathionine β-synthase-deficient patients would seem, therefore, to be more favorable than previously thought.[210]

Pathology

Underlying many of the clinical features characteristic of cystathionine β-synthase deficiency are equally characteristic pathologic findings.

Ocular. The most common findings noted on pathologic examination (and also visible clinically) are fraying and disruption of the zonular fibers. The ocular lens, normally held in place by these fibers, becomes subluxated when they break. The zonular fibers often recoil to the surface of the ciliary

Table 23-3 Outcomes of Pregnancies in Cystathionine β-Synthase-Deficient Women

	Therapy during pregnancy				
	Pyridoxine-responsive		*Pyridoxine-nonresponsive*	*Intermediate response*	*Response unknown*
	None	*Pyridoxine*	*Folate, aspirin, and dipyridamole*	*None*	*None*
Full-term, normal child	26	20	2	5	11[a]
Child with abnormality	2[b]	1[c]	—	—	—
Premature birth	—	1[d]	—	1[e]	2[f]
Stillborn	5	2	—	—	2[g]
Spontaneous abortion	19	4	—	3	1
Ectopic pregnancy	1	1	1	—	—
Totals	53	29	3	9	16

[a]Includes one patient who was not specified as either treated or not treated.
[b]One child with coloboma of iris, otherwise normal at age 4; one child with fused sagittal suture and mental retardation.
[c]One child with trisomy 21.[544]
[d]Normal child delivered at 33 weeks.
[e]Died of hyaline membrane disease.
[f]Intrauterine growth retardation prompted cesarian sections at 31 weeks gestation (baby survived) and at 29 weeks (baby died at one week of necrotizing enterocolitis secondary to umbilical artery thrombosis presumably initiated by an umbilical artery catheter).[546]
[g]One child stillborn at 28 weeks.[546] One hydrocephalic child, stillborn as a result of a decompression procedure done to permit delivery.[210]
SOURCE: Combined data from Refs. 191, 323, 542, 543, and 546.

body, there lying matted and fused with the thickened basement membrane of the nonpigmented ciliary epithelium,[324] then assuming the appearance of a thickened PAS-positive amorphous layer that becomes more obvious with age.[325] Zonular remnants have also been observed on the lens, where they acquire the electron-microscopic appearance of masses of short, disorganized filaments similar to that of the fibers attached to the ciliary body.[326]

Other histopathologic changes in the eye include peripheral retinal degeneration, which is common, as is atrophy of the nonpigmented ciliary epithelium.[325] Pigmentation of the retinal periphery and a whitish membrane covering the ciliary processes have also been described.[327] Occlusion of the greater arterial circle of the iris has been reported.[325] The posterior sclera may be thin and the choroid atrophic.[324]

Skeletal. The gross changes in the spine are consistent with the radiographic findings. Thus, the vertebral bodies reveal rarefaction of spongy bone within the intact bony margin and the codfish configuration.[281] Within the long bones there is an enlarged zone of vacuolated cartilage in the epimetaphyseal areas.[281] Histopathologic studies suggest that there is a defect of bone formation preferentially involving endochondral epimetaphyseal ossification.[281]

Central Nervous System. Within the central nervous system lesions in the brain are the most striking. Infarcts, secondary to cerebrovascular occlusions, are common.[296,297,300,320,328,329] These infarcts may contain cystic changes. Chou and Waisman[329a] described a single patient with extensive spongy degeneration and demyelination in the white matter of the cerebrum, cerebellum, basal ganglia, brain stem, and cervical spinal cord. These changes have not been noted in other studies, and Dunn et al.[300] specifically reported the absence of these changes in one of their patients. Gaull et al.[330] reported neuronal loss in the cerebral cortex and hippocampus. The lipid composition of the brain has been analyzed in one patient and was normal.[331]

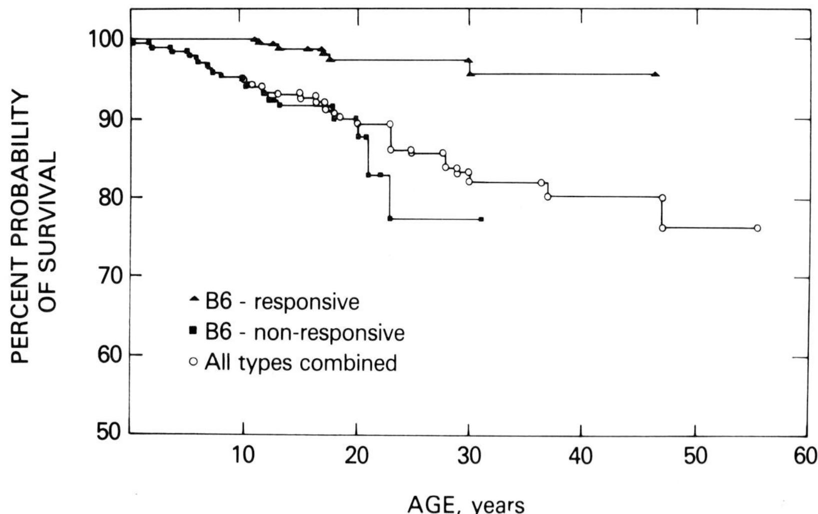

Fig. 23-7 Time-to-event graphs for deaths. Patients were not removed from the at-risk groups upon initiation of therapy. *(From Mudd et al.,[191] by permission.)*

Vascular. The striking vascular lesions associated with cystathionine β-synthase deficiency have attracted much attention at postmortem examination. Thrombi and emboli have been reported in almost every major artery or vein and in many smaller vessels. Involvement of major cerebral vessels has resulted in infarcts in the cerebrum, cerebellum, midbrain, and thalamus.[296,297,300,320,328–330] Thrombi in the dural sinuses have also been reported.[320,329] Other vascular involvement has resulted in coronary occlusions,[278,298] pulmonary infarcts,[191,332] renal infarcts,[297,300] and thrombophlebitis with pulmonary emboli.[191,278]

Arterial walls have been the sites of the most unusual changes. Marked fibrous thickening of the intima is found even in children and young adults.[297,329,333] Intimal fibrosis of the aorta was so extensive in one patient that a mild degree of coarctation was produced.[334] The thickening may be symmetric, with resulting severe luminal narrowing, or patchy with formation of pads.[329] Within the media the muscle fibers are frayed and split, with increased interstitial collagen.[278,329] The elastic fibers in the media of large arteries may be frayed and fragmented,[278,330,333] and there may be changes in the internal elastic lamella.[298,329,333] Advanced atherosclerotic degenerative changes were found in a large abdominal aortic aneurysm from a 36-year-old man.[335] Virtually any large- or medium-sized artery may be affected.[329,333]

Changes in the walls of veins have been noted only by Gibson et al.,[329] who reported fibrous endophlebitis in a renal vein of one patient. Gaull[334] found no lesions in veins.

Other Organs. Fatty change of the liver has been found in virtually all patients studied postmortem or by liver biopsy.[210] Based on their light- and electron-microscopic studies,[214,310] Gaull and his group reported that fat accumulation was largely in the centrolobular hepatocytes. Mitochondria were abnormally shaped, with fingerlike projections and tapered ends, and the smooth endoplasmic reticulum was hypertrophic. Endocardial fibroelastosis of the left atrium has also been reported.[278,329] Structural abnormalities of collagen and elastic fibers of skin have been described.[308]

Pathophysiology

Perhaps no aspect of cystathionine β-synthase deficiency has remained so obscure as the intermediate steps by which the enzyme deficiency leads to the specific clinical manifestations associated with it. Evidence relevant to the pathophysiology of cystathionine β-synthase deficiency available up to 1981 has been reviewed in detail.[89,94] In this chapter, therefore, summary statements only will be presented, with elaboration of more recent experimental work bearing on these matters.

Methionine and Homocysteine Toxicity. It has been known for many years that an excessive intake of either methionine[336] or homocystine retards growth of the rat.[337] Many accompanying metabolic and morphologic changes have been noted.[89] However, cystathionine β-synthase-deficient patients do not develop the specific anatomic changes manifested by rats fed excessive methionine or homocystine, nor, conversely, has mention been made in these experimental animals of dislocated optic lenses, bony changes, or the thromboembolic tendency characteristic of cystathionine β-synthase deficiency. Thus these animal studies appear to offer little hope of clarifying the sequence of metabolic events responsible for these particular clinical phenomena.[89]

Homocyst(e)inemia, Thrombosis, and Atherosclerosis. Thromboembolism is a major clinical feature of cystathionine β-synthase deficiency (see "Clinical Manifestations," above). This complication is related to changes in vascular walls, and perhaps, to enhanced clotting (see "Pathology," above). As initially observed by McCully[338] and subsequently confirmed by others,[339,340] children dying of diseases of homocysteine methylation that produce homocystinemia, but not hypermethioninemia, have often had vascular pathology similar in many important respects to the abnormalities of arteries and perivascular connective tissue found in patients with cystathionine β-synthase deficiency. These findings suggest that homocyst(e)ine, or its derivatives other than methionine, may be the principal contributor(s) to the vascular damage of cystathionine β-synthase deficiency.[94,341–343,343a]

Many investigations have been conducted to define the cause of the abnormal clotting and atherosclerotic tendencies of cystathionine β-synthase-deficient patients, but no coherent, generally accepted view has emerged. At present, evidence exists suggesting that abnormalities either of platelets, vascular endothelium, or soluble factors involved in blood coagulation may contribute. These are reviewed in turn below.

PLATELETS. Using techniques which measure the adherence of platelets to a small glass surface during relatively long times of exposure,[94] McDonald et al.[344] and subsequently other workers[258,263,321,345,346] reported increased adhesiveness of the platelets from at least 26 homocystinemic patients. The platelets from four patients were found normal by such techniques.[258,347] Homocystine[263,344,346] or methionine[346] added to normal blood at concentrations such as might be found in cystathionine β-synthase-deficient patients was reported to bring about increased adhesiveness of platelets. Administration of pyridoxine to pyridoxine-responsive patients has often (but not always) led to restoration of platelet adhesiveness to, or toward, normal.[258,263,321] On the other hand, when platelet adhesiveness has been measured by a technique involving exposure of the platelets to large glass surfaces for relatively brief times,[94] the platelets from at least 17 patients have been reported to be normal[278,347–352]; platelets from only four patients were abnormally adhesive by this method.[348,353] Whether these contrasting results are due to differing methodologies, or to other factors, has not been clarified.[94]

Recently, homocystine (1 m*M*) or D,L-homocysteine (1 m*M*), added in vitro, has been shown to alter arachidonic acid metabolism of normal platelets so that two cyclogenase products, 12-hydroxy-5,8,10-heptadecatrienoic acid and the proaggregatory thromboxane A_2 (measured as its stable end-product thromboxane B_2), increased significantly from control levels. Methionine, cysteine, or cystine did not have similar effects. Changes in arachidonic acid metabolism, if present in vivo at the homocyst(e)ine concentrations found in patients, may contribute to the thrombotic diathesis.[354]

Other abnormalities of platelets, such as those affecting their interactions with ADP[355] or ADP-induced aggregation,[356] have been found in occasional patients but have been absent in larger numbers of additional patients.[89] Reported morphologic abnormalities detected by electron microscopy of platelets from cystathionine β-synthase-deficient patients[357,358] have not been confirmed.[359]

ENDOTHELIAL CELLULAR EFFECTS. Harker and colleagues suggested that toxic effects on endothelial cells in vivo may contribute in an important manner to the vascular abnormalities of cystathionine β-synthase-deficient patients. These workers reported decreased platelet survival times of 4.3 ± 0.6 days in four patients, compared to times of 9.5 ± 0.6 days in normal subjects. Treatment of pyridoxine-responsive patients with pyridoxine, or of any of the patients with dipyridamole, restored platelet survival times virtually to normal.[351] Based on these results, and on the observations that long-term infusion of baboons with homocysteine thiolactone resulted in patchy desquamation of vascular endothelium and decreased platelet survival times,[351,360] they suggested that arterial thrombus formation in homocystinuric patients results from sustained, homocyst(e)ine-induced, endothelial injury with secondary increased platelet consumption and atherogenesis.[351] Subsequent studies have failed to confirm the decreased platelet survival times in such patients, and the cause of the experimentally produced endothelial lesions has been questioned (see below). Normal platelet survival times in six cystathionine β-synthase-deficient patients were found by workers in another laboratory.[359] Since two of these patients had been studied also by Harker et al,[351] it is unlikely the differing results were due to patient selection. Moreover, in studies of 12 other patients by Hill-Zobel et al. no statistical differences were found in mean platelet survival times between normal subjects and pyridoxine-responsive or -nonresponsive patients.[361] A possible explanation of these discordant results lies in the mathematical methods used. In platelet survival studies, the actual data points are usually fitted to a kinetic model to permit calculation of survival times. Hill-Zobel et al. could use any one of several such models without effect upon their conclusions.[361] On the other hand, the particular modeling methods chosen by Harker and coworkers[351] are a possible difficulty affecting the substance of the conclusions at which these workers arrived.[362]

Several studies of cytotoxic effects of homocysteine and its derivatives on endothelial cells grown in tissue culture have been performed. Early reports indicated that homocysteine induces endothelial cell injury in vitro.[363,364] Recently, Starkebaum and Harlan[364a] found that micromolar amounts of copper catalyze an oxygen-dependent oxidation of homocysteine. Copper in ceruloplasmin, or normal human serum [which contains 15 μM copper, primarily as ceruloplasmin (see citations in Ref. 364a)], led to much the same homocysteine oxidation, during the course of which hydrogen peroxide was produced. Cultured bovine aortic endothelial cells were lysed in a time- and dose-dependent manner in the presence of homocysteine (up to 500 μM), but only if copper was also added (maximal effect at 2 μM). Copper in the form of ceruloplasmin was equally effective as copper sulfate. Homocystine plus copper was without effect. Human umbilical vein endothelial cells were also lysed by homocysteine plus copper. Homocysteine plus copper-induced lysis was prevented by catalase, providing evidence that hydrogen peroxide is the active toxic compound.[364a] In retrospect, the earlier findings of Wall et al., of homocysteine-induced radiochromium release from human endothelial cells which was prevented by catalase, may be explained by the same mechanism. These assays were carried out in 100 percent pooled human serum.[363] In possible contrast to these results, Rodgers and Kane[365] reported that concentrations of homocysteine even up to 10 mM caused no changes in morphology of adult bovine aortic endothelial cells, and only 2 percent more ^{51}chromium release than that of control cells during a 16 h incubation. It may be, however, that there was inadequate copper present during these incubations, since the medium contained only 10 percent calf serum.[365,365a] As noted earlier (see "Metabolic Sequelae" above), patients with cystathionine β-synthase deficiency have 1.4-fold increases in plasma copper concentrations.[255] Taken together, these findings strongly suggest the possibility that formation of hydrogen peroxide may play a role in endothelial cell damage in patients with concentrations of homocysteine such as may occur in some with untreated cystathionine β-synthase deficiency.

An additional homocysteine-induced effect has been suggested possibly to be mediated by hydrogen peroxide. Either DL-homocysteine or hydrogen peroxide stimulated (at low concentrations) or inhibited (at high concentrations) synthesis of prostacyclin by arterial tissue. The inhibition by hydrogen peroxide was overcome by catalase.[365b] In earlier experiments, Graeber et al. had not noted such effects of homocysteine.[354] Experimental differences were suggested as a possible explanation of these discordant results.[365b]

Under their conditions, Rodgers and Kane found homocysteine thiolactone to be much more cytotoxic to endothelial cells than homocysteine. The thiolactone, 10 mM, caused gross morphologic changes, and 42 percent lysis during a 16 h incubation.[365] Since in earlier experiments homocysteine had been added as the thiolactone[351] or in a chemical form which was not unequivocally specified,[364] the effects of the thiolactone must be considered. Dudman and Wilcken demonstrated that homocysteine thiolactone is rapidly hydrolyzed at neutral pH by carboxylesterase activity, with the production of acid, that this compound acylates proteins, and that in concentrated solutions it may form the less soluble homocystine diketopiperazine.[366] One or more of these effects, which will not occur with homocyst(e)ine itself, could account for the cytotoxic potential of the lactone.

Another complication is emphasized by a finding of DeGroot et al.[367] When endothelial cells from an obligate heterozygote for deficiency of cystathionine β-synthase were cultured in the presence of methionine or homocystine (each 10 mM), the viability and function of these cells were affected more markedly than were those of cells from a normal subject. It was suggested that partial deficiency of cystathionine β-synthase activity in the former cells predisposed them to accumulate homocyst(e)ine and thus to methionine- or homocyst(e)ine-mediated injury.

Results with intact experimental animals have been equally equivocal. In early studies homocysteine thiolactone, administered to either rabbits[368,369] or baboons,[351,360] produced atherosclerotic changes. Again, interpretation of these results is subject to uncertainty because of the possible nonphysiological reactions caused by thiolactone, but not by homocyst(e)ine.[366,370] Furthermore, the results with rabbits were not reproduced by workers in another laboratory,[371] and production of homocystinuria and hypermethioninemia by infusion of pigs with homocysteine thiolactone for up to 60 days did not produce any changes in vascular morphology.[370]

On the other hand, intravenous injections of rats with homocystine led to increased numbers of circulating endothelial cells in the blood, accompanied by other signs of endothelial damage and by decreases in circulating platelets,[372] and Harker and his colleagues have now repeated their studies of baboons using DL-homocysteine rather than the thiolactone.[373]

After a 3-month chronic infusion of eight baboons, they reported a loss of 7.7 percent of the aortic endothelium (controls, 0 percent), an increase in microscopic intimal lesions, and a significant decrease in platelet survival (2.8 ± 0.6 days; normal, 5.4 ± 0.3). These effects were reduced by therapy with sulfinpyrazone, an inhibitor of platelet function.[373]

A different approach has involved the use of vitamin B_6 deficiency to decrease cystathionine β-synthase activity. Vitamin B_6 deficiency decreased hepatic cystathionine β-synthase activity of experimental rats by 59 percent,[157] and severe homocyst(e)inemia developed.[156] Two pigs, maintained on vitamin B_6-deficient diets, had progressive increases in plasma homocyst(e)ine and protein-bound homocyst(e)ine to concentrations within the ranges observed in cystathionine β-synthase-deficient patients. After 12 weeks, no gross vascular lesions were noted, but there were occasional microscopic foci of intimal degeneration and mural thickening in renal arterioles of both animals and an area of focal medial necrosis in the abdominal aorta of one.[158] In earlier experiments, chronic vitamin B_6 deficiency had been shown to induce arteriosclerotic lesions in monkeys[373a–373c] and dogs[373d] in some, but not all,[373e,374] studies. Unfortunately, the relevance of these studies to possible effects of homocyst(e)ine is uncertain because plasma homocyst(e)ine concentrations were not investigated.

A different effect on endothelial cells has been suggested recently by detailed studies which showed that homocysteine at noncytotoxic concentrations (0.5 to 10 m*M*) increased the factor V activity found in cultured bovine and human endothelial cells by induction of an activator of this factor. Homocystine, methionine, cystine, and cysteine were less effective.[365] Factor V is found in both plasma and platelets. In its activated form, Va, it interacts with factor Xa to accelerate conversion of prothrombin to thrombin.[375,376] Although the role of the factor V intrinsic to endothelial cells remains to be defined in detail,[377,378] Rodgers and Kane suggest that the homocysteine-induced activation of this form of factor V may account, in part, for the increased incidence of thrombosis in patients with homocystinuria.[365]

SOLUBLE FACTORS. Low antithrombin activity (51 to 54 percent of mean control) was found in seven homocystinuric patients.[379] An additional patient studied in Japan had 67 percent of normal,[380] and three patients in Italy had antithrombin III activities of 67 to 74 percent (normal range, 81 to 128 percent), without concomitant decreases in antithrombin III protein.[316] Decreased antithrombin activity has not been clearly associated with homocyst(e)inemia, since antithrombin activity has both remained low in the face of a dietary-induced decrease in plasma and urine homocystine,[380] and returned to normal during pyridoxine administration, which did not decrease homocystinemia.[316] Since studies of many families with inherited deficiencies of antithrombin III have shown that decreases in this factor to 40 to 50 percent of normal are associated with severe tendencies to thrombosis,[381,382] the moderate decreases reported in at least some cystathionine β-synthase-deficient patients could be clinically significant.

A single early report described a clotting abnormality due to activation of the Hageman factor (factor XII) by homocystine.[383] This finding has not been reported in other patients.[94] Homocystine-related decreases in proconvertin (factor VII) to approximately 20 to 45 percent of normal have been reported in eight cystathionine β-synthase-deficient patients.[315,316,316a] Activation of factor VII by tissue thromboplastin is thought to initiate the extrinsic coagulation pathway.[315] Although deficiency of this factor is not contradictory to the occurrence of thromboembolism,[315,316] no mechanism has been suggested whereby such a deficiency might contribute in a positive way to a clotting diathesis.

In summary, despite many studies, no single mechanism has been definitively shown to lead to the thrombotic diathesis present in the several diseases which are associated with homocyst(e)inemia. At present, various lines of evidence suggest abnormalities of platelets, endothelial cells, and soluble factors. None of these abnormalities can be regarded as unequivocally established; nor are they mutually exclusive. It is certainly possible that several abnormalities make some contribution. One report, based on studies of cells from a single heterozygote, suggests that cystathionine β-synthase-deficient cells may be more vulnerable than normal cells to the toxic effects of homocyst(e)ine.[367] If this is borne out by future studies, a deeper understanding may be attained when such mutant cells become available and many of the studies reviewed here have been repeated on them.

The Collagen Structural Abnormality. Considerable experimental support exists for the possibility that homocysteine interferes with the normal cross-linking of collagen. Most collagen molecules are composed of three polypeptide chains which are bound together by inter- and (possibly) intramolecular cross-links. An essential step in cross-linking is the formation of aldehydic groups by the oxidation of the terminal amino groups of several of the lysyl or hydroxylysyl residues in collagen monomers. These aldehydes form cross-links both by Schiff-base formation with amino groups of lysine or hydroxylysine on other chains and by aldol condensation between two aldehydes. These bifunctional cross-links undergo further, as yet poorly characterized, reactions, which produce polyfunctional, nonreducible cross-links of unknown structure.[384–389] Changes in solubility of collagens from some, but not all, cystathionine β-synthase-deficient patients examined have suggested abnormalities of collagen cross-linkage.[94,390–392] Several mechanisms have been proposed to account for this apparent abnormality,[89] including inhibition of lysyl oxidase which occurs at high homocysteine concentrations[392,393] or delays in the synthesis of more complex polyfunctional cross-links.[394–396] In both these actions homocysteine was much more effective than homocystine or methionine, suggesting that the sulfhydryl compound may be the major cause of the collagen abnormality of cystathionine β-synthase deficiency, as it may also be of the thrombotic abnormality.[94]

Which of the particular clinical abnormalities in cystathionine β-synthase-deficient patients will ultimately be found to be secondary effects of the collagen (and probably elastin) structural abnormalities is also a matter of conjecture. Rats given β-aminopropionitrile, an irreversible inhibitor of lysyl oxidase,[389] develop the soft tissue abnormalities of skin, bony abnormalities, kyphoscoliosis, hernias, and dissection of the aorta together known as osteolathyrism.[397,398] Animals fed low doses of D-penicillamine, a sulfhydryl compound with structural similarities to homocysteine, develop the skeletal abnormalities of osteolathyrism.[394] These model systems suggest that the thin skin, the restricted mobility of joints, and perhaps the scoliosis, deformities of long bones, and hernias of homocystinuric patients may eventually be ascribed to connective tissue abnormalities. Although collagen plays a role in promoting the platelet aggregation which is a step in the normal hemostatic sequence initiated by endothelial injury, available evidence indicates that the structural alterations which may be present in the collagen of cystathionine β-synthase-deficient patients are not likely to explain the thrombotic tendency of these patients.[94,399]

Dislocation of the Optic Lenses. A number of authors have considered dislocation of the optic lens as a manifestation of an underlying structural defect in the collagen of cystathionine β-synthase-deficient patients. Direct evidence for this supposition is lacking, and indeed chemical analyses suggest that the degenerative changes in the zonular fibers which are the probable cause of ectopia lentis are not likely to be due to abnormalities of collagen.[94,189,400–402] An alternative possibility, namely, that the degeneration of the zonular fibers might be due to disruption of disulfide bonds,[403] has been discussed more fully elsewhere,[89] as has the pathogenesis of other ocular abnormalities in cystathionine β-synthase-deficient patients.[272]

Does Homocyst(e)ine Replace Cyst(e)ine in Metabolic Reactions? Several investigations, previously reviewed in detail,[89] have produced no evidence to support the hypothetical possibility that homocysteine might cause damage by acting as a structural analogue of cysteine and participating in metabolic reactions for which cysteine is normally the sole substrate, either in protein synthesis or in the reactions leading from cysteine to taurine. Homocysteine can replace cysteine as a substrate for γ-glutamylcysteine synthetase, leading to formation of γ-glutamylhomocysteine,[404,405] which may be split by γ-glutamyl cyclotransferase to pyroglutamate and homocysteine.[405] A single cystathionine β-synthase-deficient patient with homocystinemia of 242 μ*M* was found to have abnormal elevations of pyroglutamic acid in plasma (1.6 m*M*) and urine (4.1 to 9.7 mol/mol creatinine). Neither this patient when his homocystinemia was reduced to 137 μ*M*, nor 10 other homocystinuric patients with more moderate increases in plasma homocystine of 11 to 137 μ*M*, had elevations of pyroglutamic acid. A possible explanation of these observations is that, in the presence of an extreme increase in homocystine, γ-glutamylhomocysteine is formed, then hydrolyzed by γ-glutamyl cyclotransferase to give rise to excessive pyroglutamic acid.[405]

Neurologic Abnormalities and Mental Retardation. Several investigators have considered the possibility that one or another chemical abnormality of the central nervous system might contribute to the neurologic difficulties and mental retardation found in some cystathionine β-synthase-deficient subjects: (1) *Cystathionine.* This immediate product of the cystathionine β-synthase reaction is present in unusually high concentrations in normal human brain as compared with the concentrations either in brains of other species or in other human tissues.[406] It may be located specifically within neurons.[407] Investigations of a possible neurotransmitter role for cystathionine have yielded inconclusive results (reviewed elsewhere; see Ref. 408). Cystathionine β-synthase activity was not detected in brain tissue of the two cystathionine β-synthase-deficient patients examined postmortem, although this enzyme activity is present in control human brain.[173] The three autopsy brain specimens examined from cystathionine β-synthase-deficient patients were grossly deficient in cystathionine.[311,409] The latter results cannot be extrapolated to all cystathionine β-synthase-deficient patients since those with some residual activity of this enzyme may well accumulate significant amounts of cystathionine in brain tissue and since alternative routes exist for cystathionine formation, not dependent upon cystathionine β-synthase and operative under unusual dietary conditions.[89] A reasonably convincing indication that cystathionine is not needed for physiological brain function would be provided by the discovery of individuals lacking any residual cystathionine β-synthase activity, yet of normal intelligence. Several well documented descriptions of pyridoxine-nonresponsive patients with normal IQ values[191,261,410–413] are strong evidence in this regard, and together make it unlikely that gross mental deficiency or neurologic malfunction necessarily results from a virtual absence of cystathionine from the brain. (2) *Homocyst(e)ine and methionine.* Very high intraperitoneal doses of DL-homocysteine induce tonic-clonic seizures of the grand mal type in rats[414–416] and mice.[417] Homocysteine thiolactone, applied locally, produced excitation of neurons[418] and, injected intraperitoneally, induced generalized convulsive status epilepticus in rats with actively epileptogenic cobalt lesions in motor cortex.[418a] Methionine does not, by itself, induce convulsions, but enhances the homocysteine-induced seizures.[419] Vitamin B_6 also enhances homocysteine-induced convulsions,[420] and some evidence has been reported which may support the possibility that a synergistic effect of pyridoxal phosphate and homocysteine in blocking the postsynaptic γ-aminobutyric acid receptor might explain the seizure activity.[421] Homocysteine administered to rodent neocortical tissues trapped adenosine (arising as a result of electrical stimulation) as *S*-adenosylhomocysteine. Since "adenosine is predominantly depressant in cerebral actions," possibly "the convulsive conditions and mental changes associated with administered homocysteine and with homocystinuria are due to cerebral adenosine concentrations being diminished."[422] Lower doses of homocysteine, which did not produce seizures, led to rises in brain ammonia concentrations.[416] Intraperitoneal injections of homocystine, or homocystine and methionine, produced decreases in the concentrations in brain of several amino acids and of dopa, dopamine, and noradrenaline. These effects could be due to decreased amino acid transport into brain,[423] but their implications for the central nervous system dysfunction in cystathionine β-synthase-deficient patients remain to be clarified. (3) *S-Adenosylhomocysteine and S-adenosylmethionine.* An untreated cystathionine β-synthase-deficient patient with hypermethioninemia and homocyst(e)inemia may be expected to have increases in tissue concentrations of both *S*-adenosylmethionine and *S*-adenosylhomocysteine, the former due to increased flux through methionine adenosyltransferase and the latter to condensation of homocysteine with adenosine. *S*-Adenosylmethionine, applied iontophoretically to rat sensorimotor cerebral cortex, increased the rate of spontaneous firing of neurons.[424] Intraperitoneal administration of *S*-adenosylhomocysteine to experimental animals has sleep-inductive and anticonvulsant effects,[425–427] but since it has been proposed that this effect is mediated through formation of adenosine,[428] the relevance of this effect to homocyst(e)inemic patients is questionable. The balance between *S*-adenosylmethionine and *S*-adenosylhomocysteine may affect the rate of a variety of transmethylation reactions in which the former compound is a substrate and the latter an inhibitor.[35,429] Increases in brain *S*-adenosylhomocysteine of mice by administration of adenosine and homocysteine,[430] or homocysteine thiolactone,[431] have been shown to decrease both the rates of methylation of proteins and phosphatidylethanolamine derivatives[432] and the activities of catechol *O*-methyltransferase and histamine *N*-methyltransferase in undialyzed tissue extracts.[431] The functional results of any such effects which may occur in homocyst(e)inemic patients remain unknown. Inactivation of *S*-adenosylhomocysteine hydrolase, the enzyme which acts to remove *S*-adenosylhomocysteine, has been observed in children with adenosine deaminase deficiency, in red blood cells of patients treated with 2′-deoxycoformycin, and in subjects treated with adenine arabinoside.[52] Observation of such individuals may provide some insight into at least the acute effects of *S*-adenosylhomocysteine accumulation on central nervous system function.

In summary, although a variety of chemical mechanisms have been proposed to play some role in the central nervous system dysfunction of cystathionine β-synthase-deficient patients, at the moment none of these can be regarded as definitively established. Further, while the available evidence may suggest reasons for increased excitability and convulsions, specific explanations of the mental retardation are virtually lacking.

An alternative view of the cause of central nervous system dysfunction in cystathionine β-synthase deficiency is that repeated cerebral vascular thromboses produce many infarctions of the brain that are too small individually to come to clinical attention but together sufficient to produce the abnormalities in question.[410] If this hypothesis were true, an increased frequency of focal neurologic signs would be expected among patients with mental retardation. Cerebrovascular occlusions in infancy and early childhood do result in mental retardation,[300] but most patients with mental retardation have no focal neurologic signs.

Diagnosis

The presence of one or more of the typical clinical signs may lead to a suspicion of cystathionine β-synthase deficiency, but definitive diagnosis is based on the presence of certain characteristic biochemical abnormalities. These abnormalities were mentioned earlier in this chapter and are included in Table 23-1.

The most consistent biochemical finding is homocystinuria. No patient in the untreated state and beyond the period of early infancy has yet been described who did not have this abnormality. The presence of homocystine is most easily suspected when the urinary cyanide-nitroprusside reaction is positive.[433,*] Since this test detects most disulfides, it may be positive in other disulfidurias (e.g., cystinuria, β-mercaptolactate-cysteinuria). Consequently, homocystine must be specifically identified. Spaeth and Barber have described a modified nitroprusside colorimetric reagent which does not react with cystine at concentrations as high as 4.2 m*M* and therefore drastically reduces the number of false positives when screening for homocystinuria.[434] Paper or thin-layer chromatography, using either the cyanide-nitroprusside sequence[435] or a modification of the iodoplatinate solution,[436] high-voltage paper electrophoresis,[211] two-way sequential paper chromatography,[437] and, finally, quantitation of amino acids in urine by a sensitive and accurate system of column chromatography,[435] may each be useful in assessing a possible case of homocystinuria.[89] In cystathionine β-synthase-deficient individuals the last procedure may reveal the presence of abnormal amounts of other sulfur-containing compounds, including the mixed disulfide of cysteine and homocysteine, homolanthionine, *S*-adenosylhomocysteine, and 5-amino-4-imidazole-carboxamide-5′-*S*-homocysteinylribonucleoside.[94]

False negative results can be encountered in testing for homocystinuria by the cyanide-nitroprusside test and by paper or thin-layer chromatography. Some individuals with the pyridoxine-responsive form of cystathionine β-synthase deficiency may show marked responses to relatively low intakes of pyridoxine. For example, three patients studied at the National Institutes of Health while maintained on supplemental folate, 2 mg twice weekly, decreased their homocystine excretions almost as much with daily doses of 5 to 10 mg pyridoxine hydrochloride as with doses of up to 300 mg daily. In one of these patients, even 2 mg pyridoxine daily decreased homocystine excretion by 95 percent.[438] Thus an affected individual with this type of responsiveness who ingests as little as one vitamin tablet daily might have negative reactions to screening tests for homocystinuria. (Most general vitamin preparations contain 2 to 5 mg pyridoxine hydrochloride in each tablet or capsule.) In light of the possibility of false negative screening results, all individuals with a clinical problem that strongly suggests the diagnosis of cystathionine β-synthase deficiency (e.g., ectopia lentis), but whose results on screening for homocystinuria are negative, should be questioned about dietary intake with particular attention to supplemental vitamin ingestion. Any source of supplementary pyridoxine should be discontinued, and the patient should be retested in 2 to 4 weeks. In addition, at least one of these urine specimens should be analyzed by column chromatography so that the presence of a small amount of homocystine will not be overlooked.

The presence of homocystinuria is not sufficient to establish unequivocally the diagnosis of cystathionine β-synthase deficiency. Not only is homocystinuria noted in other disorders, for example 5,10-methylenetetrahydrofolate reductase deficiency (see Table 23-1), but it may also be seen as an artifact of bacterial contamination of urine in cystathioninuria.[72,138] Consequently, amino acids in the plasma or serum should be measured in all suspected individuals. In cystathionine β-synthase deficiency this measurement should reveal homocyst(e)ine, usually accompanied by a markedly reduced concentration or even absence of cystine. Furthermore, an increased concentration of methionine is found in most patients (Table 23-1). Hypermethioninemia is an important finding since in the metabolic defects in homocysteine methylation which are alternative causes of homocystinuria the blood methionine concentration is low or normal (see Chaps. 81 and 82). The semiquantitative Guthrie bacterial assay for methionine, often used in screening newborns for hypermethioninemia,[439] offers a relatively simple means of assaying for this abnormality in patients with homocystinuria. A "normal" blood methionine concentration by this method usually indicates a concentration of approximately 100 μ*M*, or less. Since this lower limit of sensitivity is still about three times the normal blood methionine concentration, it is important to measure the blood amino acids of all homocystinuric patients by a more quantitative method when the bacterial assay appears normal. When the bacterial assay indicates an increased blood methionine concentration, cystathionine β-synthase deficiency is the likely diagnosis when homocystinuria is also present.

Direct enzyme assay confirms the diagnosis of cystathionine β-synthase deficiency. This activity can be assayed in liver biopsy specimens,[212] cultured skin fibroblasts,[440] phytohemag-

* This test is performed by adding 1 ml of a 5 percent aqueous solution of sodium cyanide to 1 ml urine, mixing well, and allowing the mixture to remain at room temperature for 5 min. Three to five drops of a 5 percent aqueous solution of sodium nitroferricyanide (nitroprusside) are then added, and the mixture is observed for an immediate color change. In the presence of homocystinuria the color reaction is usually deep red to magenta, although a dilute urine specimen, or one containing less than the usual amount of homocystine, may yield only a deep pink or slightly red color reaction.

glutinin-stimulated lymphocytes,[192] or long-term established lines of such cells.[194] Cystathionine β-synthase activities in extracts of cultured fibroblasts below the ranges for control subjects and heterozygotes have invariably been correlated with other indications of cystathionine β-synthase deficiency.[197,198,202,215,216] An occasional homocystinuric patient, however, may have a specific activity of cystathionine β-synthase in fibroblast extracts that is within the control range and yet may have no other apparent cause for homocystinuria.[94] Such homocystinuria could be due to low hepatic activity of cystathionine β-synthase, and conclusions based solely on fibroblast assays might lead to erroneous conclusions regarding the cause of homocystinuria in such patients.

Management

Medical management of cystathionine β-synthase deficiency has two major aims: (1) control or elimination of biochemical abnormalities with the goal of preventing clinical disease, halting the progression of existing clinical defects, or ameliorating clinical manifestations that may be reversible; and (2) supportive treatment of complications.

Experience with other metabolic diseases, as well as present understanding of the pathophysiology of cystathionine β-synthase deficiency, make it reasonable to assume that one or more of the biochemical abnormalities characteristic of this disease is responsible for its clinical complications and that optimal treatment should aim to minimize these biochemical abnormalities. Whenever possible, therapy to achieve biochemical control should begin before clinical complications occur, since many of these complications are irreversible. Even before clinical effects are recognizable, tissue damage may have occurred. Thus, maximal benefit from therapy may be possible only when the disorder is detected in the newborn period, either as a result of known disease in the family or through a routine neonatal screening program. Since management will usually differ according to the type of patient, it may be helpful to consider separately the management of three categories: (1) pyridoxine-responsive individuals detected after the newborn period, (2) patients diagnosed as newborns, (3) patients not responsive to pyridoxine and detected after the newborn period.

Pyridoxine-Responsive Patients Detected after the Newborn Period. The administration of relatively large amounts of pyridoxine, usually orally in the form of pyridoxine hydrochloride, has been effective in reducing or eliminating the biochemical abnormalities in many patients with cystathionine β-synthase deficiency.[257] The probable dependence of this response on residual cystathionine β-synthase activity, and the fact that about an equal proportion of patients will display little or no response, has already been discussed (see "The Pyridoxine Effect and its Mechanism," above). The doses of pyridoxine administered have varied considerably. Barber and Spaeth[257] utilized doses of 250 to 500 mg/day; Gaull et al.,[441] 800 to 1200 mg/day. Some patients who have a biochemical response at one level of pyridoxine supplementation will have a greater response with a larger amount of pyridoxine.[259] In general, for older children a dose of at least 150 mg pyridoxine per day has been used,[259] although an occasional patient has responded to doses as low as 25 mg/day,[442] or even less, as exemplified by the three patients studied at the National Institutes of Health and discussed in "Diagnosis," above. According to Perry,[410] a patient should not be considered unresponsive to pyridoxine until a dose of 500 to 1000 mg/day has been given for several weeks.

The effectiveness of pyridoxine in preventing initial clinically detected thromboembolic events has recently been validated statistically.[191] Data were collected for 135 late-detected pyridoxine-responsive patients treated with pyridoxine at various ages and for various periods of time. Comparison of these treatment intervals with the time-to-event curve for untreated patients (Fig. 23-6) allowed the calculation that, were pyridoxine treatment without effect, 20 thromboembolic events would have been expected among these patients. In fact, only four occurred, a highly significant decrease ($p < 0.001$). For prevention of thromboembolism alone, therefore, pyridoxine treatment is strongly indicated for pyridoxine-responsive patients diagnosed at any age. A similar analysis suggested that pyridoxine treatment may reduce the frequency of lens dislocation.[191] Finally, improvement in behavior and in IQ has been reported in several late-treated pyridoxine-responsive patients.[443]

Folic acid depletion has been noted in a number of cystathionine β-synthase-deficient patients.[252,253] In two of these depleted patients, therapy with folate alone produced reductions in the excretion of homocystine and increases in the excretion of methionine.[252] In other patients, therapy with folate in combination with vitamin B_{12} and pyridoxine resulted in a lower concentration of homocystine, with little or no increase in the methionine concentration.[253] As already noted, folate repletion may be necessary to permit a pyridoxine response.

Whether pyridoxine therapy alone can be considered adequate treatment for patients who are pyridoxine-responsive, or should be combined with a methionine-restricted diet, cystine supplementation, or other measures, is not settled by existing data. A priori considerations support methionine restriction for patients incompletely responsive to pyridoxine, since this may further correct the biochemical abnormalities. Even patients with maximum pyridoxine responsiveness have reduced tolerance to methionine as measured by methionine loading tests.[260–262] Such patients may in theory experience abnormal episodic increases in methionine or homocyst(e)ine concentrations following protein ingestion. Some methionine restriction or the use of small, frequent feedings might be prudent.[260] Very recently, Wilcken et al.[251] demonstrated that betaine treatment will blunt the plasma total homocyst(e)ine response to methionine loading in pyridoxine-responsive patients, and suggested that betaine should be added to the treatment regimen of pyridoxine and folic acid in pyridoxine-responsive patients so that homocysteine accumulation will be normal throughout the day during normal dietary intake (see also "Patients Not Responsive to Pyridoxine and Detected after the Newborn Period," below).

Toxicity in the form of a sensory neuropathy with ataxia has been reported in otherwise normal adults ingesting large amounts of pyridoxine.[444,445] These reports, as well as others summarized in a recent review of the safety of pyridoxine,[446] suggest that doses lower than 500 mg/day appear to be safe. Most reported cases of sensory neuropathy occurred at doses of 2000 mg/day or more. Abnormalities improved dramatically following withdrawal of pyridoxine, but minor neurologic abnormalities persisted, particularly in vibratory sensation.[444,445] Toxicity from pyridoxine has not been reported in individuals with cystathionine β-synthase deficiency. However, treatment with 1000 mg/day pyridoxal phosphate produced liver dysfunction in a child with pyridoxine-nonresponsive cystathionine β-synthase deficiency.[447] The signs of hepatotoxicity disappeared upon withdrawal of the pyridoxal phosphate and did not appear during therapy with pyridoxine hydrochloride, even at doses as high 1800 mg/day.

Patients Detected as Newborns. The great majority of such patients have, to date, been treated by dietary means. The diets used are specifically low in methionine in order to reduce the accumulation of methionine, homocysteine, and their metabolites, and they are supplemented with L-cystine to provide at least some cyst(e)ine. The latter is an essential amino acid for some, but not all, patients with cystathionine β-synthase deficiency.[448]

The different types of methionine-restricted diets that have been used were mentioned in the previous edition of this text.[94] Currently, proprietary formulas based on a synthetic mixture free of methionine are virtually in exclusive use. At least four such formulas are available.[449,*] The methionine requirement is met during infancy by addition of small amounts of milk; later, by the addition of low protein foods in carefully controlled quantities.[450] The desired amount of dietary methionine is judged by maintenance of blood methionine levels within or near the normal range (20 to 40 μM) and by the absence, or near absence, of homocystine in blood and urine.[450] It is often impossible, however, to eliminate urinary homocystine while maintaining a methionine intake sufficient to sustain normal growth. Moreover, elevations of plasma protein-bound homocyst(e)ine may be present even when free homocystine is undetectable.[223] The proprietary formulas are supplemented with L-cystine.[449] The amount required to maintain detectable levels of blood cystine in affected individuals is 150 to 200 mg/kg body weight per day, but even with these large doses it is usually impossible to achieve normal levels of cyst(e)ine in the blood.[410]

Methionine restriction, started in early infancy, has been shown to be effective in preventing or delaying a number of serious problems. Because most patients discovered by screening of newborns have been pyridoxine-nonresponsive (see "Prevalence and Screening," below), the data for this type of individual are the most convincing. Among 16 pyridoxine-nonresponsive children ascertained by newborn screening and treated with diet from early ages, the mean IQ was 94 ± 4, approximately 35 points above the mean IQ of pyridoxine-nonresponsive patients who were untreated or late-treated.[191] Among an additional 23 early-treated pyridoxine-nonresponsive children for whom only qualitative estimates of mental capabilities were available, 19 (82 percent) were estimated to have average or above average intelligence; only 4 (17 percent) were retarded. Early dietary treatment seems also to delay or prevent dislocation of the lens in some patients.[191] Dietary therapy may also prevent seizures.[191] Early-treated patients are still too young as a group for evaluation of the effects of diet on thromboembolism and osteoporosis.[191]

Most of the relatively few pyridoxine-responsive individuals detected by screening of newborns have been treated by methionine restriction, sometimes accompanied by pyridoxine. The limited data available indicate that most such subjects so treated will attain normal, or near normal, intelligence.[191]

*Methionaid, Scientific Hospital Supplies, Ltd. Liverpool, England, HOM-1 and HOM-2, Milupa AG, Friedrichsdorf, Federal Republic of Germany; M-AM, Maizena Diat GmbH Hamburg, Werk Heilbronn, Federal Republic of Germany.

Patients Not Responsive to Pyridoxine and Detected after the Newborn Period. This category of patients offers the most difficult therapeutic challenge. Methionine restriction through dietary control has often been attempted. However, general experience has been that acceptance of the restrictive and unpalatable diet by an older child or adult may be difficult to achieve.[451–453] When accepted, methionine restriction in older patients has often ameliorated biochemical abnormalities.[227,290,410,443,451,454–457] When very strict management of such patients has been carried out, the results, although not published in detail, appear promising in terms of prevention of thromboembolic events.[290] Anecdotal evidence suggestive of developmental improvement or improvement in school performance has been reported.[443] However, perhaps because of difficulties in compliance, in the 1982–1983 international survey no statistically significant evidence of the effectiveness of methionine restriction in prevention of initial thromboembolic events was forthcoming.

Recently there has been an upsurge of interest in the use of the methyl donor betaine as a treatment especially promising in late-detected pyridoxine-nonresponsive patients.[249,250,315,457a,457b] This compound,[455] or its metabolic precursor, choline,[454] was early shown to lower homocyst(e)ine, with concomitant rises in methionine concentrations, in patients with cystathionine β-synthase deficiency. The mechanism of this effect is presumed to be an increase in the rate of homocysteine methylation through betaine-homocysteine methyltransferase as more substrate for this reaction is made available (Fig. 23-2). This redistribution of metabolites may be desirable on the assumption that methionine and its derivatives make lesser contributions to the pathophysiology of cystathionine β-synthase deficiency than do homocysteine and its metabolites. As discussed in "Pathophysiology," above, this assumption appears reasonable in light of available knowledge. There is the further possibility that, given such redistribution, methionine degradation through the transamination pathway (in which the defective step at cystathionine β-synthase is bypassed) may permit enhanced removal of metabolites which would otherwise accumulate proximal to this block.[249]

Smolin and coworkers[249] treated two pyridoxine-nonresponsive patients with 6 to 9 g/day of betaine. The plasma homocystine concentrations decreased in both. The plasma methionine levels rose somewhat, but not as dramatically as had occurred in earlier studies.[454,455] During more than 2 years of betaine therapy, the patients showed clinical improvement with alleviation of hypertension in one, reduced frequency of seizures in the other, and substantially improved behavior in both. Subsequently, Wilcken et al.[250] treated 10 cystathionine β-synthase-deficient patients with 6 g/day betaine. Eight were pyridoxine-nonresponsive; two were partially responsive to pyridoxine. The plasma total homocyst(e)ine level decreased substantially in all patients, becoming normal in one. The plasma methionine concentration increased in five patients, decreased in two, and remained essentially unchanged in three. The plasma total cysteine level consistently rose. Five of the patients had improved behavior (in one to a dramatic extent); two patients had darkening of their hair, and three patients with bronchial asthma had marked reductions in the number of asthmatic attacks.

It seems that betaine therapy may be useful in the treatment of pyridoxine-nonresponsive patients who will not accept the methionine-restricted diet or as an adjunct to such a diet. It should be noted, however, that the long-term clinical results of such treatment are not yet known, and judgment as to the efficacy should be reserved, especially for those patients in whom very great elevations of plasma methionine are brought about.

Finally, it is noted that some physicians are now routinely giving pyridoxine to even apparently "nonresponsive" patients.[251]

Additional Measures

Replenishment of cystathionine either directly, or by the frequent administration of very large doses of both homoserine and cysteine, has been considered (and was discussed in the previous edition of this text[94]) but, to our knowledge, has not been attempted in patients. Certain other maneuvers which, a priori, might be useful were also discussed in the previous edition of this text.[94] Examples include arginine infusion or the use of α-aminobutyric acid to increase the urinary excretion of homocystine. Since homocystine seems to share a low K_m transport system with cystine and the dibasic amino acids in the rat renal cortical tubule, increased urinary excretion of homocystine might be achieved also by administration of dibasic amino acids other than arginine.[479]

Medical therapy that does not reverse the basic biochemical abnormalities but that might reduce or eliminate the thrombotic tendency has been used in some patients. The decreased platelet survivals reported in cystathionine β-synthase-deficient patients by Harker et al. were found by the same workers to be corrected by dipyridamole, an inhibitor of platelet function, or by a combination of dipyridamole and aspirin.[351] Experience with these therapies in attempting to prevent further thrombotic episodes in patients who had experienced thromboembolism was reviewed in the previous edition.[94] The results have been mixed, one group reporting success,[351] another lack of success.[458,459] Data obtained in the 1982–1983 international survey were insufficient to permit evaluation of the long-term benefits of dipyridamole, or aspirin, or both, in preventing thrombotic complications.[191] Harker et al.[373] reported that in baboons with homocysteine-induced endothelial injury sulfinpyrazone, also an inhibitor of platelet function, markedly reduced aortic endothelial loss and arterial myointimal damage and normalized platelet survival. Treatment with sulfinpyrazone has not yet been reported in patients with cystathionine β-synthase deficiency. Finally, some authors have suggested the possible wisdom of avoiding factors associated with an increased risk of thromboembolism, for example oral contraceptives,[333,410,460] perhaps even pregnancy.[410]

Complications

The supportive treatment of clinical complications in cystathionine β-synthase-deficient patients is essentially the same as the treatment of these complications when due to other causes. Pathologic fractures resulting from osteoporosis are treated by conventional orthopedic procedures. The effects of thrombi and emboli are treated by appropriate medical measures. An exception to conventional treatment is the avoidance of surgery whenever possible. In cystathionine β-synthase deficiency the danger of thromboembolism has been said to be increased postoperatively,[461] presumably as a result of the propensity for clotting to increase under such conditions, superimposed on the predisposition for thrombosis in this disorder.[333] A few patients have died from thromboembolism following ocular surgery.[234,272,318,324] Furthermore, ocular complications of such surgery, including marked and prolonged vitreous hemorrhage, vitreous loss, and retinal detachment, have been reported in cystathionine β-synthase-deficient patients.[273,276,461] Should surgery be necessary, the risk of thromboembolism may be lessened by increasing hydration with intravenous uids preoperatively and postoperatively.[462,463] Pyridoxine should also be given intravenously during and immediately following surgery to patients responsive to pyridoxine, and may even be helpful in nonresponsive patients. Data from the 1982–1983 international survey showed that, when suitable precautions are taken,[322,462–467] the great majority of surgical procedures performed on cystathionine β-synthase-deficient patients do not lead to thromboembolic complications. Among all patients surveyed, 586 major surgical or ophthalmologic operative procedures were followed by 25 thromboembolic events, six of which were fatal.[191]

Acute glaucoma due to pupillary block by the dislocated lens can usually be treated medically.[273,275] Initially, the pupil should be fully dilated with any suitable mydriatic and the lens repositioned from the anterior chamber by pressure on the cornea. Should this fail, a peripheral iridectomy may be performed. Following any of these procedures, miosis should be maintained constantly so as to prevent the lens from again dislocating anteriorly.[273]

Prevalence and Screening

Based on the data available in 1981 from routine screening of newborns, we estimated the frequency of cystathionine β-synthase-deficiency in the general population to be 1:200,000.[94] The results of selective screening among the mentally retarded, the mentally ill, and those with atraumatic dislocation of the optic lens were also presented at that time.[94] The difficulties in interpreting these data were emphasized. Notably, the results of screening of newborns are quite likely to give rise to an underestimate of the actual frequency because screening is carried out for hypermethioninemia, and this abnormality may not be present during the first few days of life when the blood specimen is customarily collected.[94,468]

Table 23-4 presents updated rates of detection of cystathionine β-synthase-deficiency in countries that have screened over 200,000 newborns. From these data it appears that the general rate of detection is 1:335,000, somewhat less than our previous estimate of 1:200,000. Possibly, however, this apparent decrease is to some extent artifactual. Current practices of infant feeding have led progressively to lower protein intakes,[476] and the newborn blood specimen is now often collected earlier in the neonatal period than was formerly the case.[477] Both factors might result in a greater number of infants with cystathionine β-synthase-deficiency being missed now than before. From Table 23-4 and our discussion in the previous edition, it is also apparent that the reported rates of detection of cystathionine β-synthase-deficiency vary widely. Some screening programs have identified no cases[94,469,478]; others have reported relatively high frequencies. To some degree this variation may reflect differences between programs in the extent of mild hypermethioninemia required to trigger further testing. However there seem, also, to be valid regional differences. For example, the incidences in Ireland and England (Manchester) are high, and that in Japan low, compared to

Table 23-4 Frequencies of Cystathionine β-Synthase-Deficiency Identified by Screening of Newborns in Countries That Have Screened More Than 200,000 Infants

Country	*No. screened*	*No. cases detected*	*Estimated frequency*	*Reference*
Japan	6,311,754	6	1:1,052,000	468
United States	4,055,302	10	1:406,000	469
West Germany	3,162,346	17	1:186,000	469
England	961,850	10	1:96,000	470
New Zealand	957,834	2	1:480,000	471
Scotland	824,198	1	1:824,000	472
Switzerland	791,970	0	—	469
Austria	745,475	1	1:745,000	469
Belgium	723,050	0	—	469
Ireland	573,206	10	1:57,000	473
Poland	433,555	0	—	469
Northern Ireland	411,662	4	1:103,000	475, 545
Sweden	316,821	0	—	474
Totals	20,269,023	61	1:332,000	

most other regions (Table 23-4). As a second example, in the New England Regional Newborn Screening Program we have identified three affected infants among 150,000 screened from Maine (1:50,000). A fourth affected infant born in Maine was missed, coming later to attention because of ectopia lentis.[480] By contrast, in Massachusetts only two infants with cystathionine β-synthase-deficiency have been detected by screening approximately 1,600,000 neonates (1:800,000).

Among those patients with cystathionine β-synthase-deficiency who have been identified by newborn screening, the great majority have been pyridoxine-nonresponsive. In Manchester, England, all 10 infants,[470] and in New England all eight patients identified on the basis of early hypermethioninemia have been pyridoxine-nonresponsive.[480] The sole pyridoxine-responsive infant to have come to attention in New England through routine screening had a normal blood methionine concentration in the specimen obtained during the newborn period but an increased concentration in a second blood specimen obtained at 4 weeks of age. At the time, this was a routine procedure in the screening program.[243] More extensive evidence that infants with pyridoxine-responsive cystathionine β-synthase-deficiency are being preferentially missed by newborn screening comes from the 1982–1983 international survey.[191] Among 55 patients who had been both discovered by screening of newborns and classified with respect to pyridoxine responsiveness, only seven (12.7 percent) were pyridoxine-responsive, while 43 (78.2 percent) were nonresponsive and five (9.1 percent) were intermediate in response. These relative frequencies are quite different from those of the patients in the total survey population. Among the 529 classified as to pyridoxine response, 231 (43.7 percent) were judged to be responsive, 231 (43.7 percent) nonresponsive, and 67 (12.7 percent) intermediate in response. Thus, in the total survey population pyridoxine-responsive and pyridoxine-nonresponsive patients were equally represented, whereas among the subgroup identified by screening of newborns there was a 6:1 preponderance of pyridoxine-nonresponsive patients.

Screening urine of neonates for homocystine seems to be even less reliable than screening blood for hypermethioninemia as a means of identifying cystathionine β-synthase deficiency. In Australia only one case was discovered among 700,000 infants tested by screening of urines; another case is known to have been missed.[411] No cases were discovered by this means in Massachusetts.[481] Homocystine may be absent from the urine of neonates with cystathionine β-synthase deficiency,[482] or present in such low concentrations as to go undetected by the usual screening methods.[243] A method for enzymic determination of homocysteine in urine specimens dried on filter paper disks has recently been described.[482a]

Heterozygotes

Identification. Techniques are now available which permit tentative identification of individuals heterozygous for cystathioinine β-synthase deficiency. Four of these methods involve enzyme assays of tissue extracts:

1. *Liver.* Of the eight obligate heterozygotes for whom specific activities of hepatic cystathionine β-synthase have been determined, seven had values below the control range,[212–214] whereas one barely overlapped the low end of the control range.[214]

2. *Phytohemagglutinin-stimulated lymphocytes.* Goldstein et al. measured cystathionine β-synthase activities in extracts of phytohemagglutinin-stimulated lymphocytes grown from 17 obligate heterozygotes. The specific activities for 14 were below the control range, whereas three overlapped this range.[193]

3. *Cultured fibroblasts.* Results of assays of cystathionine β-synthase activities in extracts of fibroblasts cultured from obligate heterozygotes have been published from at least five laboratories involving study of 44 individuals.[197,201,215,216,230,483] As with the other tissues, in each series of fibroblast assays, the mean specific activity of cystathionine β-synthase for obligate heterozygotes was less than 50 percent of the mean control specific activity. Cumulatively, for the series in which control ranges were specified, the values for 15 of 40 obligate heterozygotes overlapped the control range.

4. *Long-term cultured lymphocytes.* Fleisher et al. reported a range of 3.21 ± 0.37 nmol cystathionine per milligram protein per hour for cystathionine β-synthase activity extracted from long-term cultured lymphocytes from three obligate heterozygotes. In this relatively small series there was no overlap with normal activities (mean 9.49 ± 0.98).[194]

In sum, at the moment, enzyme assays have identified some, perhaps most, heterozygotes, but in all extensive studies some heterozygotes have failed to be differentiated with certainty from normal individuals.

Alternative approaches to the identification of heterozygous individuals take advantage of the presence of abnormal concentrations of sulfur-containing metabolites in such individuals under certain experimental conditions. A number of early studies of methionine or homocystine, or both, in urine or in plasma, and of urinary sulfate excretion of obligate heterozygotes after oral L-methionine loads failed to develop criteria which could conclusively distinguish these subjects from normal persons with sufficient reliability to be of practical use (see Ref. 94). More recently, evidence has been produced that normal premenopausal women differ from men (according to some groups[222,484] but not others[485]) and from postmenopausal women[484] in their plasma concentration of cysteine-homocysteine mixed disulfide and in their handling of a methionine load.[484] Taking account of these differences, Boers et al.[483] were able to discriminate 18 of 20 obligate heterozygotes from normal on the basis of peak plasma levels of total non-protein-bound homocyst(e)ine after standard oral methionine loads.

Whether measurements of protein-bound homocyst(e)ine in heterozygotes will be useful in discriminating such individuals from normals is currently under study. In an early report, Kang et al. found that the total fasting protein-bound homocyst(e)ine concentrations for each of the two obligate heterozygotes studied exceeded the control range.[223] Subsequently, four obligate heterozygotes were studied in the same laboratory, using an improved method in which the homocysteine released from protein is rapidly stabilized by conversion to the *S*-carboxymethyl derivative.[231] Two of these heterozygotes showed normal values (less than the control mean + 2 SD), either in the fasting state or after an oral load of methionine (100 mg/kg), although in the latter situation protein-bound homocyst(e)ine had increased three- to fourfold in both normal subjects and the heterozygotes.[486] Using modifications of the method for determination of protein-bound homocyst(e)ine, Smolin and Benevenga found no difference in the ranges for five obligate heterozygotes and 15 controls,[156] whereas Sartorio et al.[230] reported a mean concentration of fasting protein-bound homocyst(e)ine for nine obligate heterozygotes of 9.2 $\mu M \pm 3.4$ (SD) (range, 5.0 to 14.6) but, for 15 control subjects, a mean of 4.3 ± 1.5 (range, 2.1 to 6.7). The difference between the means was significant ($p < 0.001$). Again, however, the values for three of the heterozygotes overlapped the upper end of the control range.[230] Recently, Wiley et al. reported that the mean fasting protein-bound homocyst(e)ine for 14 heterozygotes was significantly higher than that for 17 control subjects ($p < 0.0001$), although there was said to be "some overlap of values between the 2 groups."[233a] In a single study of *total* plasma homocyst(e)ine, the mean for 14 heterozygotes was 13.8 μM, compared to a mean of 11.5 for 21 control subjects. Two of the heterozygotes had values greater than the mean + 2 SD for controls.[137b]

For individual heterozygotes there has been no significant correlation between measurements of cystathionine β-synthase activity in cultured fibroblasts and either the postmethionine peak levels of total non-protein-bound homocyst(e)ine[483] or (based on less extensive data) the fasting protein-bound homocyst(e)ine concentrations.[230] By taking into account the first two of these parameters, Boers et al.[483] were able to discriminate each of the 20 obligate heterozygotes in their study from normals.

Possible Risk for Heterozygotes and/or from Mild Homocyst(e)inemia. In 1976, Wilcken and Wilcken[487] investigated methionine tolerance in male subjects under age 50 years who had angiographic evidence of ischemic heart disease but were free of known risk factors for such disease. Seven of twenty-five patients, but only 1 of 22 control subjects, had peak postmethionine plasma concentrations of homocysteine-cysteine mixed disulfide that were elevated to the same degree as had been reported at that time for obligate heterozygotes for cystathionine β-synthase deficiency.[488] In a later study from the same laboratory,[489] 20 additional patients were investigated; they were selected according to criteria similar to those used initially,[487] except that obese subjects were excluded. No individuals with homocysteine-cysteine values suggestive of heterozygosity for cystathionine β-synthase deficiency were identified, and it was noted that the apparent abnormalities in the earlier study occurred in overweight subjects who, because dosage was determined on the basis of body weight, received larger doses of methionine. Nevertheless, in the ensuing years several investigations have been carried out aimed at evaluating the possibilities that heterozygotes for cystathionine β-synthase deficiency may have an increased risk of early thromboembolic disease, and that mild homocyst(e)inemia may be a risk factor in such disease.

With respect to the risk for heterozygotes, a questionnaire study of parents and grandparents in 203 families with cystathionine β-synthase deficient children revealed no statistically significant increases in the incidence of heart attacks or strokes in these relatives compared with incidence in similar relatives of children with either new-mutation achondroplastic dwarfism or impaired phenylalanine tolerance (i.e., phenylketonuria or mild hyperphenylalaninemia). The data were sufficient to virtually exclude an increase in the cardiovascular risk for heterozygotes for cystathionine β-synthase deficiency of as much as fivefold and to make improbable a relative risk of as much as threefold. Less than 5 percent of such heterozygotes were likely to have a thromboembolic episode by age 50.[490] Likewise, Boers et al.[491] studied 25 patients with premature occlusive coronary artery disease and found none with postmethionine accumulation of total non-protein-bound homocyst(e)ine indicative of heterozygosity. On the other hand, in the same study were included 25 patients under age 50 years with peripheral and 25 with cerebral arterial disease. Seven patients in each of the latter two groups were identified as heterozygotes for cystathionine β-synthase deficiency by the combined criteria of peak postmethionine non-protein-bound plasma homocyst(e)ine and cystathionine β-synthase activity in cultured fibroblasts. Based on a detection rate of cystathionine β-synthase deficiency of 1:335,000 during routine screening of newborns (see "Prevalence and Screening," above), the frequency of heterozygosity for this condition in the general population should be 1:290, or 0.3 percent. Because some persons with cystathionine β-synthase deficiency are probably escaping detection in such programs, the true incidence may well be greater, as high as 1:45,000, as estimated by McKusick,[333] corresponding to a frequency of heterozygosity of 1:100, or 1 percent. Even compared to the latter, the almost 30 percent incidence among the patients with premature occlusive arterial disease studied by Boers et al. is high. It was suggested therefore that such heterozygosity predisposes to this sort of disease.[491] There is no necessary contradiction, however, between the results of the questionnaire study of obligate heterozygotes[490] and the findings of Boers et al.[491] Neither study suggested an increased risk for ischemic heart disease. For all types of occlusive vascular disease, the heterozygote study suggests that less than 1 in 20 of such heterozygotes will have a thromboembolic episode by age 50.[490] Thus, if each heterozygote identified by Boers et al. had been drawn from a population of 2000 to 5800 or greater (i.e., $20 \times 100 = 2000$ to $20 \times 290 = 5800$, or greater), the two sets of results would be compatible.

The possibility that mild homocyst(e)inemia may be a risk factor for thromboembolic disease has now been supported by the results of several studies. Brattström et al. found that, among 19 patients with arteriosclerotic cerebrovascular disease who were 34 to 59 years of age and 17 healthy controls, mean plasma concentrations of homocysteine-cysteine mixed disulfide were significantly elevated ($p < 0.05$) both before and after methionine loading in the patients as compared with that of the controls.[492] Murphy-Chutorian and coworkers reported that 16 (16 percent) of 99 men, age 31 to 65 years, with coronary artery disease had methionine intolerance (judged by postload plasma non-protein-bound homocystine level), as compared with 1 (2 percent) of 39 men without coronary artery disease ($p < 0.04$).[493] Kang et al. measured plasma total homocyst(e)ine in 241 patients with coronary artery disease (173 males and 68 females) and 202 control subjects with angiographically normal coronary arteries (93 males and 109 females). For both males and females the mean total homocyst(e)ine concentrations were significantly ($p < 0.005$) higher for patients than for controls (5.41 ± 1.62 versus 4.37 ± 1.09 μM in men, 5.66 ± 1.93 versus 4.16 ± 1.62 in women).[225] Recently, Israelsson et al.[493a] studied a group of 21 men who had suffered their first myocardial infarction before age 55 years, selected in addition because of a low risk profile for conventional risk factors, together with a relatively high number of relatives with a history of myocardial infarction or stroke. Of these, five had total plasma homocyst(e)ine concentrations higher than the range for 36 controls (matched for age, sex, and risk factors, but with family histories as minimally positive as possible). Post methionine load, three of these five reached values for total plasma homocyst(e)ine beyond the mean + 2 SD for the controls.

The relationship between these studies and those of risk in heterozygotes for cystathionine β-synthase deficiency needs to be more clearly defined. For the moment, it is not established either that (1) any increased risk for heterozygotes is due to homocyst(e)inemia or (2) when homocyst(e)inemia does seem to be a risk factor, this is due in most instances to heterozygosity for cystathionine β-synthase deficiency. With regard to point 1, it has been argued that, since elevations in plasma homocyst(e)ine concentrations have been demonstrated in heterozygotes for cystathionine β-synthase deficiency only after they have received methionine loads of 100 mg/kg (i.e., about four times the dietary intake on a normal Western diet), they are unlikely to have an increased risk of atherogenesis.[489] [This contention might be rephrased now to state that any increased risk in such heterozygotes may not be due to homocyst(e)inemia.] If the recent demonstration of increases in fasting protein-bound homocyst(e)ine in (at least some) heterozygotes[230] is confirmed by more extensive experience, this objection would lose much of its force. The possibility might also be considered that, although heterozygotes do not display abnormalities in the fasting state, they may do so transiently during a normal daily cycle due to the methionine "loads" associated with regular meals. With regard to point 2, in the study of Brattström et al. the patient group included several individuals with abnormally elevated fasting plasma concentrations of homocysteine-cysteine mixed disulfide.[492] Since heterozygotes for cystathionine β-synthase deficiency do not generally have such fasting elevations,[483,489] it was considered that the abnormal methionine tolerances in these patients must be due to some other cause.[492] In the study of Murphy-Chutorian et al,[493] the postmethionine increases in homocystine (and in homocysteine-cysteine) in the patients were at least as high as those noted in obligate heterozygotes for cystathionine β-synthase deficiency, but assays of this enzyme which might have helped define the genetic status of these individuals were not reported. In the study of Kang et al.,[225] the frequency distributions of plasma total homocyst(e)ine values were similar for patients and controls. The increased means for patients were not due to the presence of a few individuals with striking elevations, such as might be suggestive of monofactorial genetically based differences. Swift and Schultz[494] studied nine men at low risk for coronary artery disease and five at high risk, as defined by differences in mean systolic blood pressure, total cholesterol, and total cholesterol/HDL cholesterol ratio. The high-risk group had a significantly higher mean non-protein-bound plasma homocyst(e)ine level (5.6 ± 0.7 μM compared with 3.5 ± 1.2; $p \leq 0.05$). Negative correlations were found between dietary vitamin B_6 intake and plasma protein-bound homocyst(e)ine, and between plasma vitamin B_{12} and plasma homocyst(e)ine. In the study by Israelsson et al., total plasma homocyst(e)ine was negatively correlated with both erythrocyte folate and serum vitamin B_{12}.[493a] Folic acid, administered to normal men and women without folate deficiency, almost invariably and significantly reduces the plasma homocysteine-cysteine[485] and the total plasma homocyst(e)ine[225b] levels, both in the fasting state and after a methionine load. Eighty-four percent of subjects with subnormal serum folate and 56 percent of those with low normal serum folate had elevations of plasma total homocyst(e)ine more than two standard deviations above the mean control value.[495] Thus it is certainly possible that some, perhaps most, of the homocyst(e)inemia in the general population can be modified by dietary or other environmental factors. Clearly, more studies are needed to better define the role of mild homocyst(e)inemia as a risk factor in atherosclerosis, the types and prevalence of the genetic lesions which underlie such mild homocysteinemia, the contribution of dietary and other environmental factors, and the extent to which therapeutic intervention can mitigate such risk. A more detailed discussion of some of the subjects covered in this section can be found in Ref. 343a.

Chronic renal insufficiency is associated with a high risk of premature vascular disease (see citations summarized in Ref. 495a), and with mild elevations of plasma homocyst(e)ine.[495a,495b] The latter can be lowered by administration of folic acid (5 mg orally per day).[495a] The role of mild homocyst(e)inemia in the vascular disease of renal insufficiency, and the possible therapeutic effect of folate, deserve further consideration.

Prenatal Diagnosis

Prenatal diagnosis of cystathionine β-synthase deficiency is feasible in both the first and the second trimester of pregnancy. Extracts of cells cultured from amniotic fluid contain readily detectable activity of cystathionine β-synthase,[440,496,496a] and several pregnancies at risk have been investigated with this method.[94] Fowler and colleagues reported the first diagnosis of an affected fetus.[195] In another pregnancy in which the activity of cystathionine β-synthase in cultured amniotic cells was lower than could confidently be attributed to a heterozygous fetus, assay of phytohemagglutinin-stimulated fetal lymphocytes obtained in the 23d gestational week allowed exclusion of cystathionine β-synthase deficiency.[497] The catalytic activity of cystathionine β-synthase in chorionic villi is insufficient for direct assay of the enzyme.[196] Using extracts of cells grown in tissue culture from chorionic villi, however, one cystathionine β-synthase-deficient fetus and two unaffected fetuses have been diagnosed before the 12th week of gestation.[196]

γ-CYSTATHIONASE DEFICIENCY

In 1959 Harris and his colleagues described a 64-year-old, mentally retarded woman who excreted more than 2 mmol cystathionine daily in her urine.[498] Their studies of this patient, her relatives, and other patients with severe mental retardation led these workers to postulate that this patient had a genetically determined deficiency of γ-cystathionase activity but that the metabolic disorder might have been only fortuitously associated with mental retardation.

The Genetic Defect and Genetic Heterogeneity

Deficient activity of hepatic γ-cystathionase has now been demonstrated in a total of seven cystathioninuric individuals.[140,499–502] Long-term lymphoid cell lines established from peripheral blood leukocytes after stimulation of lymphocytes with phytohemagglutinin have been employed to demonstrate deficient activity of γ-cystathionase in four cystathioninuric subjects,[503–505] one of whom had previously been shown also to have deficient hepatic activity.[140] The deficiency was most marked when cell extracts were assayed without added pyridoxal phosphate.[503,504]

Bittles and Carson[201,506] reported that γ-cystathionase activity was readily detected in eight lines of fibroblasts grown in tissue culture from skin biopsy specimens of control subjects. They found the γ-cystathionase-specific activity in an extract of fibroblasts grown from a cystathioninuric individual to be 15 percent of the mean control specific activity and 31 percent of the lowest control value.[506] Workers in two other laboratories have found either "absent or minimal"[496] or variable, and in some cases undetected,[503,504] activity of this enzyme in control cultured fibroblasts. Although studies of transsulfuration in intact fibroblasts indicate the presence of some γ-cystathionase activity in normal cultured cells of this type,[240] until the reasons for the reported differences in this activity in extracts of control fibroblast lines have been clarified, this system cannot be regarded as reliable for the study of normal human γ-cystathionase or for demonstration of the lack of this enzyme in cystathioninuric individuals.

Homoserine dehydratase activities in the livers of γ-cystathionase-deficient patients are also very low.[500,507] These findings indicate that human γ-cystathionase also possesses homoserine dehydratase activity, as is true of the analogous enzyme from rat liver,[90,508] and that the genetic mutation, or mutations, in the patients studied had affected both activities. No reports have appeared of measurements in γ-cystathionase-deficient patients of the further alternative reactions catalyzed by this enzyme, including cysteine desulfhydrase,[88] homocysteine desulfhydrase,[509] and L-diaminopropionate ammonia lyase.[76]

Several additional enzyme activities involved in sulfur amino acid metabolism have been studied in tissues of cystathioninuric individuals. Methionine adenosyltransferase and cystathionine β-synthase activities were normal in extracts of a single γ-cystathionase-deficient liver.[500] Activities of *S*-adenosylmethionine decarboxylase and of N^5-methyltetrahydrofolate-homocysteine methyltransferase were within the control ranges in extracts of four lines of γ-cystathionase-deficient, long-term lymphoid cells.[504]

As the foregoing summary indicates, enzyme studies have been carried out in relatively few γ-cystathionase-deficient subjects. Nevertheless, the data available indicate differences in the properties of the residual activities of γ-cystathionase (when present) and those of normal γ-cystathionase, and between the residual γ-cystathionase activities of different affected individuals: (1) Residual γ-cystathionase activities have in some cases been stimulated more by the addition of pyridoxal phosphate to the assay reaction mixture than was control γ-cystathionase activity[499,503,504]; in other cases such high stimulations did not occur.[500–502] (2)Residual γ-cystathionase activities from two deficient individuals were sensitized to heat inactivation by pyridoxal phosphate, whereas normal γ-cystathionase was stabilized to such inactivation by pyridoxal phosphate.[505] (3) Immunologic studies of long-term lymphoid lines have shown the absence in one line of γ-cystathionase-deficient cells of material which cross-reacted with rabbit antibody to control human hepatic γ-cystathionase, whereas three such lines did have cross-reacting material. These cross-reacting materials had weak γ-cystathionase activities in the presence of pyridoxal phosphate. More detailed immunologic studies suggested there might be differences between the cross-reacting materials of these three lines.[503,504] As with cystathionine β-synthase deficiency, these results strongly suggest genetic heterogeneity among the lesions which produce γ-cystathionase deficiency and that most mutations causing deficient activity of γ-cystathionase lie in the structural gene for this enzyme.

Additional Patients without Enzyme Data

As discussed above, γ-cystathionase deficiency has been clearly demonstrated in 10 cystathioninuric patients. Without pyridoxine treatment, and on unrestricted diets, these patients excreted from 1000 to 5800 μmol cystathionine daily in their urine. Cystathionine excretion tends to increase with age as dietary methionine intake increases. Based on urinary creatinine, cystathionine excretion ranged from 1400 to 16,300 μmol/g creatinine, being highest in the youngest children.[140,430,499–501,504,506,510–512] A search of published and unpublished records[94] revealed 37 additional patients with cystathionine excretions comparable to the excretions of those proven to be γ-cystathionase-deficient.[142,162,498,511,513–527] Although enzyme assays have not been reported for these patients, their cystathionine excretions, together with the lack of alternative explanations for their cystathioninuria and, in some cases, the familial incidence of this aminoaciduria, have been taken as adequate evidence that all the patients in question have γ-cystathionase deficiency.[94] In this chapter, the 10 patients with proved γ-cystathionase deficiency, as well as the 37 additional patients with presumptive deficiency, are referred to as the γ-cystathionase-deficient group. This group excludes a few additional cystathioninuric patients for whom quantitative data on the extent of the cystathioninuria have not been presented, who had cystathioninuria not permitting clear classification as homozygotes rather than heterozygotes, or for whom more complicated explanations of cystathioninuria have been proposed.[141,143] Also excluded are two brothers who excreted amounts of cystathionine[528] suggesting that they possess a γ-cystathionase activity intermediate between that of severely deficient individuals and that of heterozygotes for γ-cystathionase deficiency. The existence of a γ-cystathionase gene contributing an intermediate amount of activity is implied.[94]

Mode of Inheritance

Enzyme studies indicate an autosomal recessive mode of inheritance for γ-cystathionase deficiency. No quantitative assays of the γ-cystathionase activity in liver of obligate heterozygotes have been published. Pascal and coworkers[504] reported that γ-cystathionase specific activities in extracts of long-term lymphoid lines cultured from five parents of γ-cystathionase-deficient children ranged from 11.2 to 18.9 nmol/mg protein per hour (assayed in the presence of 0.25 m*M* pyridoxal phosphate). The mean was 15.8 ± 1.5 (SE). Twenty-one control lymphocyte lines had a mean specific activity of 25.8 ± 1.7, with an approximate range of 12.5 to 47.5; three cystathioninuric patients who were offspring of the parents in question had specific activities ranging from 3.6 to 7.3. Thus, the parents had intermediate values, but there was extensive overlap with the lower end of the control range.

Cystathionine excretions, measured in a number of parents of γ-cystathionase-deficient subjects under various experimental conditions, are not inconsistent with autosomal recessive inheritance. These results have been summarized elsewhere.[89] Thirty-four parents were studied while on normal diets. Of these, 12 excreted amounts of cystathionine judged by the investigators reporting the results to be abnormally elevated. The excretions ranged from 20 to 270 μmol/g creatinine, values which are small in comparison with those for affected γ-cystathionase-deficient individuals and which overlap extensively the urinary cystathionine excretions subsequently reported by Endres and Seibold for "normal" adults.[144] Sixteen parents received oral methionine loads. Of these, 14 were judged to have abnormal postload increases in cystathionine excretion, suggesting that the heterozygous defect may be more readily identified under these conditions.

Metabolic Sequelae

γ-Cystathionase-deficient patients not only excrete abnormal amounts of cystathionine in their urine but accumulate elevated concentrations of this amino acid in their body fluids and tissues. Plasma cystathionine concentrations have been presented for 17 pyridoxine-responsive patients. In 16, the concentrations were definitely elevated, ranging from 10 to 60 μ*M*,[142,501,511,512,516,520,521,525,526,529] whereas in one patient none was detected.[162] Cystathionine is usually not detected in normal plasma. Two pyridoxine-nonresponsive patients had plasma cystathionine concentrations of 6 to 80 μ*M*.[140,523]

Cystathionine concentrations in cerebrospinal fluid have been 10,[512] 1,[510] and 0.5 μM,[517] and "not detected." Control values were not listed, but only traces (i.e., <1 μ*M*) of cystathionine are present in normal spinal fluid.[530]

Tissues from one patient, obtained postmortem, were examined for cystathionine. The concentrations were: liver, 1.3 to 2.0 μmol/g (control range, 0.05 to 0.9); kidney, 0.56 to 0.82 μmol/g (none detected in control kidney); and frontal lobe of brain, 2.6 to 3.0 μmol/g (control range, 0.22 to 0.35).[409,498] A liver biopsy specimen from a patient not responsive to pyridoxine contained 9.6 μmol/g.[531]

In addition to cystathionine, most γ-cystathionase-deficient patients excrete substantial amounts of *N*-acetylcystathionine,[72,430,532,533] although this compound was not detected in an occasional patient.[526] Published values range from 134 to 474 μmol/day. *N*-Acetylcystathionine presumably arises by the acetylation in vivo of the α-amino group of the 3-carbon moiety of cystathionine.[532]

A number of additional sulfur-containing compounds have been identified in urine from a cystathioninuric girl studied intensively by Kodama and associates.[534] These compounds fall into three groups:

1. *Cystathionine sulfoxide*. Small amounts of this oxidation product of cystathionine were isolated from a large pooled urine sample. It is not certain whether the sulfoxide was formed in vivo or during the isolation procedure.[534]

2. *Compounds formed from either cystathionine or* N-*acetylcystathionine by transamination, followed by either reduction, decarboxylation, or cyclization*. The structure of these compounds and the pathways proposed for their formation have been detailed previously.[89] Recently, two enzymic reactions in the proposed pathways have been studied in vitro: A bovine kidney transaminase acting upon cystathionine to form *S*-(2-oxo-2-carboxyethyl)homocysteine was highly purified and its properties studied.[535] The keto compound may be reduced to the corresponding hydroxy analogue by lactate dehydrogenase, or it may undergo cyclization to a 1,4-thiazepine derivative ring.[536] Each of the products of these pathways is excreted in minor amounts only, as compared with excretion of cystathionine and *N*-acetylcystathionine.

3. *Very minor amounts of* S-*(3-hydroxy-3-carboxy-*n-*propylthio)-homocysteine and* S*(β-carboxyethylthio)-homocysteine*.[533] These compounds are present in homocystinuric urine and are thought to derive from homocystine.[94] Their presence in cystathioninuric urine is unexplained.

Little evidence has emerged to suggest that γ-cystathionase-deficient patients have functional lacks of sulfur-containing metabolites formed distal to the metabolic block. In contrast to the decreased plasma cyst(e)ine concentrations often found in cystathionine β-synthase-deficient patients, plasma cyst(e)ine concentrations have been reported as normal in γ-cystathionase-deficient subjects.[499,512,529] Possible explanations for this difference have been discussed,[89] but there are ample reasons to believe that at least γ-cystathionase-deficient individuals with detected residual activities of this enzyme retain the capacity to metabolize to cysteine and α-ketobutyrate a major portion of the cystathionine formed from a normal dietary intake of methionine.[89]

Rats injected with propargylglycine, an irreversible inhibitor of γ-cystathionase, excrete not only large amounts of cystathionine and *N*-acetylcystathionine, but also secondary products formed by the pathways discussed above: moderate amounts of *S*-(carboxymethyl)homocysteine and minor amounts of *S*-(β-carboxyethyl)cysteine, *S*-(2-hydroxy-2-carboxyethyl)homocysteine, and *S*-(3-hydroxy-3-carboxy-*n*-propyl)cysteine.[537] Thus a convenient experimental animal model is available in which to study the metabolic sequelae of decreased γ-cystathionase activity.

The Pyridoxine Effect and Its Mechanism

γ-Cystathionase deficiency provided the first instance in which, in a human, the major biochemical abnormality due to a defined enzyme defect was clearly shown to be alleviated by administration of large doses of pyridoxine.[510] The majority of γ-cystathionase-deficient patients encountered (33 of the 37 classified in this respect) respond to high intakes of pyridoxine with major decreases in urinary cystathionine excretion. Four patients have shown little or no response. The decrease in urinary cystathionine excretion may be accompanied by an increase in urinary sulfate[510] or by an increase in the ratio of urinary sulfate to total urinary sulfur,[538] although the increment in sulfate is small compared with the basal rate of sulfate excretion and has not been detected in all studies.[520]

Although cystathioninuria is a prominent manifestation of vitamin B_6 deficiency,[152,153] the response in γ-cystathionase-deficient patients is not attributable to correction of a preexisting vitamin B_6 deficiency.[89] The factors affecting pyridoxine responsiveness or nonresponsiveness in γ-cystathionase-deficient patients are strongly reminiscent of the analogous situation in cystathionine β-synthase-deficient patients. Thus: (1) Responsiveness or nonresponsiveness in γ-cystathionase deficiency has so far been constant within sibships.[94] (2) There is a correlation between the presence of detected residual activity of γ-cystathionase and clinical responsiveness to pyridoxine and between the absence of detected residual activity and nonresponsiveness. Adequately sensitive assays have demonstrated low residual activities of γ-cystathionase in liver extracts of three out of three pyridoxine-responsive subjects studied[499,500] (although no activities were detected in a separate family of three γ-cystathionase-deficient pyridoxine-responsive sibs when assays were performed which required at least 6 percent of control activity for detection[501,502]). With cultured cells, activities were detected in one fibroblast line[506] and three long-term lymphoid lines[503,504,539] from four pyridoxine-responsive individuals, but not in the single lymphoid line studied from a pyridoxine-nonresponsive subject.[503,504,539] The residual γ-cystathionase activities in tissue extracts from pyridoxine-responsive subjects have shown variable enhancements on the addition of pyridoxal phosphate to enzyme assay mixtures. In one instance, 0.05×10^{-3} *M* pyridoxal phosphate enhanced activity by only 1.3-fold,[500] whereas in other instances enhancements have been as much as 50-fold[499,504] when unspecified[499] or 0.25 to 1.0 m*M* pyridoxal phosphate[504] was added. In no instance has γ-cystathionase activity been restored to normal by even the highest concentration of pyridoxal phosphate.

A considerable body of evidence suggests that normal humans have a large reserve capacity of γ-cystathionase in comparison to the amount of cystathionine metabolized during intake of a normal diet.[89] As discussed above, pyridoxine responsiveness in γ-cystathionase deficiency is probably dependent on a small residual activity of the deficient enzyme. The steady-state activity of this enzyme is presumably enhanced somewhat when the patient is taking large doses of pyridoxine and becomes sufficient to metabolize the cystathionine arising from a normal methionine intake without accumulation severe enough to produce cystathioninuria. The molecular mechanism (or mechanisms) of the enhancement requires further clarification.

Clinical Manifestations

Following the discovery of γ-cystathionase deficiency in a mentally retarded individual,[498] the search for cystathioninuric patients was initially concentrated on the mentally retarded. The resulting ascertainment bias may have fostered the early impression that γ-cystathionase deficiency is a cause of mental abnormalities. In addition to mental retardation, a wide assortment of other clinical aberrations has been found in individuals with presumptive γ-cystathionase deficiency. Among these are convulsions, hypoplastic genitalia, acromegaly, thrombocytopenia, urinary calculi, nephrogenic diabetes insipidus, and insulin-dependent diabetes mellitus.[94]

It is doubtful, however, that any clinical abnormalities result specifically from γ-cystathionase deficiency. Among the 26 known γ-cystathionase-deficient patients for whom ascertainment bias may be expected to be minimal, only five have clinical aberrations that could be related to the metabolic disorder, and for four of these either additional cystathioninuric sibs are normal, or sibs without severe γ-cystathionase deficiency are equally affected clinically.[94] Even among the four known individuals with pyridoxine-nonresponsive cystathioninuria, in whom the biochemical defect may be more complete than in those with pyridoxine-responsive cystathioninuria, only one is mentally retarded, and he was ascertained by screening conducted because of mental retardation. No clinical information has been published about one, and the remaining two were normal at last follow-up at ages 1[522] or 14 years.[480]

Diagnosis

The characteristic finding in γ-cystathionase deficiency is a specific and easily detectable cystathioninuria. This is most readily demonstrable by amino acid chromatography of urine using a bidimensional technique and ninhydrin staining,[435] or by unidimensional chromatography and a specific sulfur stain such as iodoplatinate reagent.[436] In γ-cystathionase deficiency, metabolites of cystathionine may be present, most notably *N*-acetylcystathionine (see "Metabolic Sequelae," above), but sulfur amino acids such as homocystine will be absent. Should homocystine also be present, consideration should be given to the presence of a homocysteine methylation defect rather than γ-cystathionase deficiency (Table 23-1).

It is important that the urine examined for cystathioninuria be clean and contain a preservative such as thymol or toluene that inhibits bacterial growth. Microorganisms contain γ-cystathionase, an enzyme which cleaves cystathionine to homocysteine and pyruvate. Thus in a contaminated urine sample, cystathionine may be converted to homocyst(e)ine and confusion may result.[72]

Plasma or serum should be analyzed for amino acids using a suitable quantitative technique.[435] In γ-cystathionase deficiency this will reveal cystathionine, an amino acid normally not detected in blood. The methionine concentration will be normal, in contrast to the hypermethioninemia usually seen in patients with cystathionine β-synthase deficiency and also in contrast to the hypomethioninemia which may be noted in association with a homocysteine methylation defect (Table 23-1). The plasma cystine concentration has usually been normal in γ-cystathionase deficiency, again in contrast to cystathionine β-synthase deficiency.

Cystathioninuria per se does not establish the diagnosis of inherited γ-cystathionase deficiency. Cystathioninuria may also occur transiently in the newborn or young infant; in association with liver disease, neuroblastoma, ganglioblastoma, or hepatoblastoma; in vitamin B_6 deficiency; and perhaps even in an occasional individual with thyrotoxicosis (Table 23-1). In transient cystathioninuria of infancy, urinary cystathionine is usually minor in amount and disappears by age 3 months.[142] When cystathioninuria accompanies liver disease or the tumors noted above, the underlying disease is usually clinically apparent.[163,170,171,174] Whenever cystathioninuria is discovered, it is important to rule out these disorders. When cystathioninuria has been established as persistent and of an apparently primary nature, a trial of supplemental pyridoxine should be given to establish whether the disorder is pyridoxine responsive. Initially, oral pyridoxine hydrochloride in amounts of 100 mg/day should be administered and the urine examined after 2 weeks. If there is no response, the dose of pyridoxine hydrochloride should be increased by 100 mg and the urine examined for cystathionine at the end of another 2 weeks.

While the diagnosis can be confirmed by measurement of γ-cystathionase activity in liver obtained by biopsy, even the small risk entailed in a liver biopsy militates against such confirmation of this probably benign disorder. Enzymatic analyses of cultured lymphoid cell lines[503,504] or (perhaps) of fibroblasts cultured from skin[506] are alternative means of diagnosis.

Management

Since γ-cystathionase deficiency is probably a benign disorder, no specific management is indicated. In those individuals responsive to pyridoxine, oral pyridoxine hydrochloride can be given without known risk. The dose has usually been 100 mg or more daily.[512] The amount necessary can best be judged by titration, aimed at eliminating or substantially reducing the cystathioninemia/uria. Conceivably, a low methionine diet could also reduce the accumulation of cystathionine, and might be considered for pyridoxine-nonresponsive patients if further experience indicates that such individuals are at risk for specific clinical complications.

Prevalence and Screening

Among 813,692 newborns screened in Massachusetts by paper chromatography of urine, 12 children with persistent cystathioninuria severe enough to lead to the presumptive diagnosis of γ-cystathionase deficiency were discovered, a prevalence of 1:68,000.[480,540] In Australia, screening of 1,000,000 infants disclosed three subjects with comparably persistent and severe cystathioninuria, a prevalence of 1:333,000.[541]

ADDENDUM

Recent research has such important implications for many aspects of homocysteine metabolism and the role of this amino acid in atherosclerosis that it merits special mention here. Using a method involving extraction of plasma or serum with chloroform:methanol and re-extraction of the organic layer with dilute HCl, McCully and Vezeridis reported that serum samples from each of seven normal humans, male and female, ages 27 to 53 years, contained homocysteine thiolactone. The concentrations ranged from 32 to 6,700 μ*M*, with a mean of 1670 ± 3,060 (SD).[547] This mean is of the order of 100 times the concentration of total plasma homocyst(e)ine previously recognized in normal human plasma (see section on "Metabolic Sequelae" in "Cystathionine β-Synthase Deficiency"). An attempt to repeat the observation in question has yielded negative results.[548] No homocysteine thiolactone was detected in samples from control human subjects using either the organic extraction method described[547] (plasma or serum; n = 18), or direct column amino acid chromatographic analysis of deproteinized plasma (n = 5). Recoveries and sensitivities were such that homocysteine thiolactone would have been detected had it been present at 32 μ*M* in the original samples.[548] Using the organic extraction method, McCully and Vezeridis found, also, that six patients with coronary artery disease and acute myocardial infarction had homocysteine thiolactone concentrations of 1,280 to 47,000 μ*M*, with a mean of 12,500 ± 10,300 (SD), significantly higher than the mean for their normals (p = 0.025).[547] Using the same technique, Dudman and Wilcken were unable to detect homocysteine thiolactone in six patients with myocardial infarcts, in six normal controls, or in three patients with homocystinuria due to cystathionine β-synthase deficiency.[549]

Olszewski and Szostak measured the amounts of total homocysteine (i.e., the sum of homocysteine-cysteine mixed disulfide and twice the homocystine) in samples of hydrolyzed plasma from 26 male survivors of myocardial infarction 2 to 3 months after the acute phase, and 26 healthy males of the same age (30 to 60 years). The homocysteinyl-containing compounds were identified solely on the basis of their elution positions during column chromatography. The mean value for total homocysteine for the patients was 958 ± 84 μ*M* (SEM), about 25 times the mean for the control group (38 ± 11; $p <$ 0.001). Such large differences were found in every patient compared to the controls. Since deproteinized plasma samples contained only low levels of total homocysteine in either group ("several" μ*M*), it was concluded that the homocysteine in hydrolyzed plasma "derived mainly from plasma proteins."[550] Confirmation of these very striking findings will be awaited with interest.

REFERENCES

1. CORNFORTH JW, REICHARD SA, TALALAY P, CARRELL HL, GLUSKER JP: Determination of the absolute configuration at the sulfonium center of S-adenosylmethionine. Correlation with the absolute configuration of the diastereomeric S-carboxymethyl-(S)-methionine salts. *J Am Chem Soc* 99:7292, 1977.
2. KLEE WA, MUDD SH: The conformation of ribonucleosides in solution. The effect of structure on the orientation of the base. *Biochemistry* 6:988, 1967.
3. FOLLMANN H, GREMELS G: Adenine nucleosides in solution: Stabilisation of the *anti*-conformation by C-5′ substituents. *Eur J Biochem* 47:187, 1974.
4. ISHIDA T, MORIMOTO H, INOUE M, FUJIWARA T, TOMITA KI: Three-dimensional x-ray crystal structure of S-adenosyl-L-homocysteine, a potent inhibitor of S-adenosylmethionine-dependent methyltransferases. *JCS Chem Comm* 1:671, 1981.
5. MUDD SH, POOLE JR: Labile methyl balances for normal humans on various dietary regimens. *Metabolism* 24:721, 1975.
6. MUDD SH: The adenosyltransferases, in Boyer PD (ed): *The Enzymes*, 3d ed. New York, Academic, 1973, vol 8, part A, p 121.
7. LOMBARDINI JB, CHOU T-C, TALALAY P: Regulatory properties of adenosine triphosphate-L-methionine S-adenosyltransferase of rat liver. *Biochem J* 135:43, 1973.

7a. LIN CH, CHUNG W, STRICKLAND KP, HUDSON AJ: Characterization of an isozyme of *S*-adenosylmethionine synthetase from rat liver. *Can J Biochem Cell Biol* 62:276, 1984.

8. CANTONI GL: Activation of methionine for transmethylation. *J Biol Chem* 189:745, 1951.
9. CANTONI GL, DURELL J: Activation of methionine for transmethylation. II. The methionine-activating enzyme: Studies on the mechanism of the reaction. *J Biol Chem* 225:1033, 1957.
10. PAN F, TARVER H: Effects on diets and other factors on methionine adenosyltransferase levels in rat liver. *J Nutr* 92:274, 1967.
11. LOMBARDINI JB, COULTER AW, TALALAY P: Analogues of methionine as substrates and inhibitors of the methionine adenosyltransferase reaction: Deductions concerning the conformation of methionine. *Mol Pharmacol* 6:481, 1970.
12. SULLIVAN DM, HOFFMAN JL: Fractionation and kinetic properties of rat liver and kidney methionine adenosyltransferase isozymes. *Biochemistry* 22:1636, 1983.
13. OKADA G, TERAOKA H, TSUKADA K: Multiple species of mammalian S-adenosylmethionine synthetase. Partial purification and characterization. *Biochemistry* 20:934, 1981.

13a. GELLER AM, KOTB MYS, JERNIGAN HM JR, KREDICH NM: Purification and properties of rat lens methionine adenosyltransferase. *Exp Eye Res* 43:997, 1986.

14. ODEN KL, CLARKE S: S-Adenosyl-L-methionine synthetase from human erythrocytes: Role in the regulation of cellular S-adenosylmethionine levels. *Biochemistry* 22:2978, 1983.
15. KOTB M, KREDICH NM: S-Adenosylmethionine synthetase from human lym-

phocytes. Purification and characterization. *J Biol Chem* 7:3923, 1985.

15a. MITSUI K, TERAOKA H, TSUKADA K: Complete purification and immunochemical analysis of *S*-adenosylmethionine synthetase from bovine brain. *J Biol Chem,* in press, 1988.

16. CANTONI GL: Methylation of nicotinamide with a soluble enzyme system from rat liver. *J Biol Chem* 189:203, 1951.

17. MUDD SH, CANTONI GL: Activation of methionine for transmethylation. III. The methionine-activating enzyme of bakers' yeast. *J Biol Chem* 231:481, 1958.

18. HANCOCK RL: S-Adenosylmethionine-synthesizing activity of normal and neoplastic mouse tissues. *Cancer Res* 26:2425, 1966.

19. STEKOL JA: Formation and metabolism of S-adenosyl derivatives of S-alkyl-homocysteines in the rat and mouse, in Shapiro SK, Sclenk F (eds): *Transmethylation and Methionine Biosynthesis.* Chicago, University of Chicago Press, 1965, p 231.

20. PAN F, TARVER H: Comparative studies on methionine, selenomethionine, and their ethyl analogues as substrates for methionine adenosyltransferase from rat liver. *Arch Biochem Biophys* 119:429, 1967.

21. COX R, SMITH RC: Inhibition of S-adenosylmethionine formation by analogues of methionine. *Arch Biochem Biophys* 129:615, 1969.

21a. LOMBARDINI JB, TALALAY P: Formation, functions and regulatory importance of S-adenosyl-L-methionine, in Weber G (ed): *Advances in Enzyme Regulations.* Elmsford, NY: Pergamon, 1971, vol 9, p 231.

22. LIAU MC, LIN GW, HURLBERT RB: Partial purification and characterization of tumor and liver S-adenosylmethionine synthetases. *Cancer Res* 37:427, 1977.

23. HOFFMAN JL, KUNZ GL: Differential activation of rat liver methionine adenosyltransferase isozymes by dimethylsulfoxide. *Biochem Biophys Res Commun* 77:1231, 1977.

24. LIAU MC, CHANG CF, BELANGERL A, GRENIER A: Correlation of isozyme patterns of S-adenosylmethionine synthetase with fetal stages and pathological states of the liver. *Cancer Res* 39:162, 1979.

25. KUNZ GL, HOFFMAN JL, CHIA C-S, STREMEL B: Separation of rat liver methionine adenosyltransferase isozymes by hydrophobic chromatography. *Arch Biochem Biophys* 202:565, 1980.

26. KUNZ GL: *Fractionation and Regulatory Properties of Rat Methionine Adenosyltransferase Isozymes.* Thesis. University of Louisville, 1979.

27. ABE T, OKADA G, TERAOKA H, TSUKADA K: Immunological distinction of S-adenosylmethionine synthethase isozymes from rat liver and kidney. *J Biochem* 91:1081, 1982.

27a. CABRERO C, PUERTA J, ALEMANY S: Purification and comparison of two forms of *S*-adenosyl-L-methionine synthetase from rat liver. *Eur J Biochem* 170:299, 1987.

27b. CABRERO C, ALEMANY S: Conversion of rat liver *S*-adenosyl-L-methionine synthetase from high Mr form to low Mr form by LiBr. *Biochim Biophys Acta,* in press, 1988.

28. TALLAN HH: Methionine adenosyltransferase in man: Evidence for multiple forms. *Biochem Med* 21:129, 1979.

29. MUDD SH, KLEE WA, ROSS PD: Enthalpy changes accompanying the transfer of a methyl group from S-adenosylmethionine and other sulfonium compounds to homocysteine. *Biochemistry* 5:1653, 1966.

30. TABOR H, ROSENTHAL SM, TABOR CW: The biosynthesis of spermidine and spermine from putrescine and methionine. *J Biol Chem* 233:907, 1958.

30a. FAROOQUI JZ, LEE HW, KIM S, PAIK WK: Studies on compartmentation of S-adenosyl-L-methionine in *Saccharomyces cerevisiae* and isolated rat hepatocytes. *Biochim Biophys Acta* 757:342, 1983.

31. MUDD SH: Biochemical mechanisms in methyl group transfer, in Fishman WH (ed): *Metabolic Conjugation and Metabolic Hydrolysis.* New York, Academic, vol 3, 1973, p 297.

32. MUDD SH, EBERT MH, SCRIVER CR: Labile methyl group balances in the human: The role of sarcosine. *Metabolism* 29:707, 1980.

33. HOFFMAN DR, CORNATZER WE, DUERRE JA: Relationship between tissue levels of S-adenosylmethionine, S-adenosylhomocysteine, and transmethylation reactions. *Can J Biochem* 57:56, 1979.

34. HOFFMAN DR, MARION DW, CORNATZER WE, DUERRE JA: S-Adenosylhomocysteine metabolism in isolated rat liver: Effects of L-methionine, L-homocysteine, and adenosine. *J Biol Chem* 255:10822, 1980.

35. CANTONI GL, RICHARDS HH, CHIANG PK: Inhibitors of S-adenosylhomocysteine hydrolase and their role in the regulation of biological methylation, in Usdin E, Borchardt RT, Creveling CR (eds): *Transmethylation.* New York, Elsevier North-Holland, 1979, p 155.

36. DE LA HABA G, CANTONI GL: The enzymatic synthesis of S-adenosyl-L-homocysteine from adenosine and homocysteine. *J Biol Chem* 234:603, 1959.

37. RICHARDS HH, CHIANG PK, CANTONI GL: Adenosylhomocysteine hydrolase. Crystallization of the purified enzyme and its properties. *J Biol Chem* 253:4476, 1978.

38. DOSKELAND SO, UELAND PM: Comparison of some physicochemical and kinetic properties of S-adenosylhomocysteine hydrolase from bovine liver, bovine adrenal cortex and mouse liver. *Biochim Biophys Acta* 708:185, 1982.

39. FUJIOKA M, TAKATA Y: S-Adenosylhomocysteine hydrolase from rat liver. Purification and some properties. *J Biol Chem* 256:1631, 1981.

40. OGAWA H, GOMI T, MUECKLER MM, FUJIOKA M, BACKLUND PS, AKSAMIT RR, UNSON CG, CANTONI G: Amino acid sequence of S-adenosyl-L-homocysteine hydrolase from rat liver as derived from the cDNA sequence. *Proc Natl Acad Sci USA* 84:719, 1987.

41. PALMER JL, ABELES RH: Mechanism for enzymatic thioether formation. Mechanism of action of S-adenosylhomocysteinase. *J Biol Chem* 251:5817, 1976.

41a. PALMER JL, ABELES RH: The mechanism of action of S-adenosylhomocysteinase. *J Biol Chem* 254:1217, 1979.

42. FINKELSTEIN JD, HARRIS B: Methionine metabolism in mammals: Synthesis of S-adenosylhomocysteine in rat tissues. *Arch Biochem Biophys* 159:160, 1973.

43. WALKER RD, DUERRE JA: S-Adenosylhomocysteine metabolism in various species. *Can J Biochem* 53:312, 1975.

44. FINKELSTEIN JD, HARRIS B: Methionine metabolism in mammals: S-adenosylhomocysteine hydrolase in rat intestinal mucosa. *Arch Biochem Biophys* 171:282, 1975.

45. HERSHFIELD MS: Apparent suicide inactivation of human lymphoblast S-adenosylhomocysteine hydrolase by 2′-deoxyadenosine and adenine arabinoside. A basis for direct toxic effects of analogs of adenosine. *J Biol Chem* 254:22, 1979.

46. ABELES RH, TASHJIAN AH, JR, FISH S: The mechanism of inactivation of S-adenosylhomocysteinase by 2′-deoxyadenosine. *Biochem Biophys Res Commun* 95:612, 1980.

47. ABELES RH, FISH S, LAPINSKAS B: S-Adenosylhomocysteinase: Mechanism of inactivation by 2′-deoxyadenosine and interaction with other nucleosides. *Biochemistry* 21:5557, 1982.

48. HOHMAN RJ, VERON M, GUITTON MC: Change in NAD/NADH content of S-adenosyl-L-homocysteine hydrolase upon NAD reversible inactivation by cAMP and 2′-deoxyadenosine. *Curr Top Cell Regul* 26:233, 1985.

49. HERSHFIELD MS, KREDICH NM, OWNBY DR, BUCKLEY R: *In vivo* inactivation of erythrocyte S-adenosylhomocysteine hydrolase by 2′-deoxyadenosine in adenosine deaminase-deficient patients. *J Clin Invest* 63:807, 1979.

50. KAMINSKA JE, FOX IH: Decreased S-adenosylhomocysteine hydrolase in inborn errors of purine metabolism. *J Lab Clin Med* 96:141, 1980.

51. HERSHFIELD MS: Proposed explanation for S-adenosylhomocysteine hydrolase deficiency in purine nucleoside phosphorylase and hypoxanthine-guanine phosphoribosyltransferase-deficient patients. *J Clin Invest* 67:696, 1981.

52. KREDICH NM, HERSHFIELD MS: Perturbations in S-adenosyl-homocysteine and S-adenosyl-methionine metabolism: Effects on transmethylation. *Adv Enzyme Regul* 18:181, 1980.

53. DURELL J, ANDERSON DG, CANTONI GL: The synthesis of methionine by enzymic transmethylation. I. Purification and properties of the tin homocysteine methylpherase. *Biochim Biophys Acta* 26:270, 1957.

54. KLEE WA, RICHARDS HH, CANTONI GL: The synthesis of methionine by enzymic transmethylation, VII. Existence of two separate homocysteine methylpherases in mammalian liver. *Biochim Biophys Acta* 54:157, 1961.

55. TAYLOR RT, WEISSBACH H: N^5-Methyltetrahydrofolate-homocysteine methyltransferases, in Boyer PD (ed): *The Enzymes,* 3d ed. New York, Academic, 1973, vol 9, part b, p 121.

55a. UTLEY CS, MARCELL PD, ALLEN RH, ANTONY AC, KOLHOUSE JF: Isolation and characterization of methionine synthetase from human placenta. *J Biol Chem* 260:13656, 1985.

55b. MELLMAN IS, LIN P-F, RUDDLE FH, ROSENBERG LE: Genetic control of cobalamin binding in normal and mutant cells: Assignment of the gene for 5-methyltetrahydrofolate:L-homocysteine *S*-methyltransferase to human chromosome 1. *Proc Natl Acad Sci USA* 76:405, 1979.

56. RUDIGER H, JAENICKE L: Methionine synthesis: Demonstration of the reversibility of the reaction. *FEBS Lett* 4:316, 1969.

57. MUDD SH: Homocystinuria and homocysteine metabolism: Selected aspects, in Nyhan WL (ed): *Heritable Disorders of Amino Acid Metabolism.* New York, Wiley, 1974, p 429.

58. SCHUH S, ROSENBLATT DS, COOPER BA, SCHROEDER M-L, BISHOP AJ, SEARGEANT LE, HOWARTH JC: Homocystinuria and megaloblastic anemia responsive to vitamin B_{12} therapy. An inborn error of metabolism due to a defect in cobalamin metabolism. *N Engl J Med* 310:686, 1984.

59. SKOVBY F, KRASSIKOFF N, FRANCKE U: Assignment of the gene for cystathionine β-synthase to human chromosome 21 in somatic cell hybrids. *Hum Genet* 65:291, 1984.

60. CHADEFAUX B, RETHORE MO, RAOUL O, CEBALLOS I, POISSONNIER M,

GILGENKRANZ S, ALLARD D: Cystathionine beta synthase: Gene dosage effect in trisomy 21. *Biochem Biophys Res Commun* 128:40, 1985.

61. ARIAS S, PARADISI I, ROLO M: Cystathionine beta-synthase *(CBS)* location excluded from 21pter-q11, but confirmed to 21q, by gene dosage in trisomy 21. *Cytogenet Cell Genet* 40:570, 1985.

62. KRAUS JP, WILLIAMSON CL, FIRGAIRA FA, YANG-FENG TL, MUENKE M, FRANCKE U, ROSENBERG LE: Cloning and screening with nanogram amounts of immunopurified mRNAs: cDNA cloning and chromosomal mapping of cystathionine β-synthase and the β subunit of propionyl-CoA carboxylase. *Proc Natl Acad Sci USA* 83:2047, 1986.

62a. MUNKE M, KRAUS JP, OHURA T, FRANCKE U: The gene for cystathionine β-synthase (CBS) maps to the subtelomeric region on human chromosome 21q and to proximal mouse chromosome 17. *Am J Hum Genet* 42:550, 1988.

63. SKOVBY F, KRAUS JP, ROSENBERG LE: Biosynthesis of human cystathionine β-synthase in cultured fibroblasts. *J Biol Chem* 259:583, 1984.

64. KRAUS J, PACKMAN S, FOWLER B, ROSENBERG LE: Purification and properties of cystathionine β-synthase from human liver. *J Biol Chem* 253:6523, 1978.

65. KRAUS JP, ROSENBERG LE: Cystathionine β-synthase from human liver: Improved purification scheme and additional characterization of the enzyme in crude and pure form. *Arch Biochem Biophys* 222:44, 1983.

66. SKOVBY F, KRAUS JP, ROSENBERG LE: Biosynthesis and proteolytic activation of cystathionine β-synthase in rat liver. *J Biol Chem* 259:588, 1984.

67. KIMURA H, NAKAGAWA H: Studies on cystathionine synthetase: Characteristics of purified rat liver enzyme. *J Biochem (Tokyo)* 69:711, 1971.

68. BROWN FC, GORDON PH: Cystathionine synthase from rat liver: Partial purification and properties. *Can J Biochem* 49:484, 1971.

69. BORCSOK E, ABELES RH: Mechanism of action of cystathionine synthase. *Arch Biochem Biophys* 213:695, 1982.

70. BRAUNSTEIN AE, GORYACHENKOVA EV, TOLOSA EA, WILLHARDT IH, YEFREMOVA LL: Specificity and some other properties of liver serine sulphhydrase: Evidence for its identity with cystathionine β-synthase. *Biochim Biophys Acta* 242:247, 1971.

71. PORTER PN, GRISHAVER MS, JONES OW: Characterization of human cystathionine β-synthase: Evidence for the identity of human L-serine dehydratase and cystathionine β-synthase. *Biochim Biophys Acta* 364:128, 1974.

72. LEVY HL, MUDD SH, UHLENDORF BW, MADIGAN PM: Cystathioninuria and homocystinuria. *Clin Chim Acta* 58:51, 1975.

73. DONALD LJ, WANG HS, HAMERTON JL: Assignment of the gene for cystathionase (CTH) to human chromosome 16. *Cytogenet Cell Genet* 32:268, 1982.

74. MATSUO Y, GREENBERG DM: A crystalline enzyme that cleaves homoserine and cystathionine. I. Isolation procedure and some physicochemical properties. *J Biol Chem* 230:545, 1958.

75. CHURCHICH JE, DUPOURQUE D: Dissociation of cystathionase. *Biochem Biophys Res Commun* 46:524, 1972.

76. MUSHAHWAR IK, KOEPPE RE: Rat liver L-diaminopropionate ammonia lyase: Identification as cystathionase. *J Biol Chem* 248:7407, 1973.

77. BIKEL I, PAVLATOS TN, LIVINGSTON DM: Purification and subunit structure of mouse liver cystathionase. *Arch Biochem Biophys* 186:168, 1978.

78. IGLEHART JD, YORK RM, MODEST AP, LAZARUS H, LIVINGSTON DM: Cystine requirement of continuous human lymphoid cell lines of normal and leukemic origin. *J Biol Chem* 252:7184, 1977.

79. MATSUO Y, GREENBERG DM: A crystalline enzyme that cleaves homoserine and cystathionine. II. Prosthetic group. *J Biol Chem* 230:561, 1958.

80. MATSUO Y, GREENBERG DM: A crystalline enzyme that cleaves homoserine and cystathionine. III. Coenzyme resolution, activators, and inhibitors. *J Biol Chem* 234:507, 1959.

81. OH K-J, CHURCHICH JE: Binding of pyridoxal 5′-phosphate to cystathionase. *J Biol Chem* 248:7370, 1973.

82. GORYACHENKOVA EV, POLYAKOVA LA, YEFREPVA LL, FLORENTIEV VL: Interaction of pyridoxal phosphate analogues with apoenzymes of γ-cystathionase and serine sulphhydrase. *Biochem Biophys Res Commun* 55:1021, 1973.

83. WASHTEIN W, ABELES RH: Mechanism of inactivation of γ-cystathionase by the acetylenic substrate analogue propargylglycine. *Biochemistry* 16:2485, 1977.

84. SILVERMAN RB, ABELES RH: Inactivation of pyridoxal phosphate dependent enzymes by mono- and polyhaloalanines. *Biochemistry* 15:4718, 1976.

85. SILVERMAN RB, ABELES RH: Mechanism of inactivation of γ-cystathionase by β, β, β-trifluoroalanine. *Biochemistry* 16:5515, 1977.

86. ALSTON TA, MURAMATSU H, UEDA T, BRIGHT HJ: Inactivation of γ-cystathionase by β-fluorinated amino acids. *FEBS Lett* 128:293, 1981.

87. FEARON CW, RODKEY JA, ABELES RH: Identification of the active-site residue of γ-cystathionase labeled by the suicide inactivator β, β, β-trifluoroalanine. *Biochemistry* 21:3790, 1982.

88. LOISELET J, CHATAGNER F: Purification et étude de quelques propriétés de la cysteine desulfurase "soluble" (cystathionase) du foie de rat. *Bull Soc Chim Biol* 47:33, 1965.

89. MUDD SH, LEVY HL: Disorders of transsulfuration, in Stanbury JB, Wyngaarden JB, Frederickson DS (eds): *The Metabolic Basis of Inherited Disease,* 4th ed. New York, McGraw-Hill, 1978, p 458.

90. MATSUO Y, GREENBERG DM: A crystalline enzyme that cleaves homoserine and cystathionine. IV. Mechanism of action, reversibility, and substrate specificity. *J Biol Chem* 234:516, 1959.

91. WONG PWK, SCHWARZ V, KOMROWER GM: The biosynthesis of cystathionine in patients with homocystinuria. *Pediatr Res* 2:149, 1968.

92. CHATAGNER F, TIXIER M, PORTEMER C: Biosynthesis of cystathionine from homoserine and cysteine by rat liver cystathionase. *FEBS Lett* 4:231, 1969.

93. TALLAN HH, STURMAN JA, PASCAL TA, GAULL GE: Cystathionine γ-synthesis from homocysteine and cysteine by mammalian tissue. *Biochem Med* 9:90, 1974.

94. MUDD SH, LEVY HL: Disorders of transsulfuration, in Stanbury JB, Wyngaarden JB, Fredrickson DS, Goldstein JL, Brown MS (eds): *The Metabolic Basis of Inherited Disease,* 5th ed. New York, McGraw-Hill, 1983, p 522.

95. STURMAN JA, GAULL GE, RAIHA NCR: Absence of cystathionase in human fetal liver: Is cystine essential? *Science* 169:74, 1970.

96. CASE GL, BENEVENGA NJ: Evidence for S-adenosylmethionine independent catabolism of methionine in the rat. *J Nutr* 106:1721, 1976.

97. MITCHELL AD, BENEVENGA NJ: The role of transamination in methionine oxidation in the rat. *J Nutr* 108:67, 1978.

98. STEELE RD, BENEVENGA NJ: Identification of 3-methylthiopropionic acid as an intermediate in mammalian methionine metabolism *in vitro*. *J Biol Chem* 253:7844, 1978.

99. STEELE RD, BENEVENGA NJ: The metabolism of 3-methylthiopropionate in rat liver homogenates. *J Biol Chem* 254:8885, 1979.

99a. ASCHE GL, BENEVENGA NJ, HAAS LG: Metabolism of L-methionine (MET) and 3-methylthiopropionate (MTP) by the pig. *FASEB J* 2:A1765, 1988.

100. LIVESEY G, LUND P: Methionine metabolism via the transamination pathway in rat liver. *Biochem Soc Trans* 8:540, 1980.

101. LIVESEY G: Metabolism of "essential" 2-oxo acids by liver and a role for branched-chain oxo acid dehydrogenase in the catabolism of methionine, in Walser M, Williamson JR (eds): *Metabolism and Clinical Implications of Branched Chain Amino and Ketoacids.* New York, Elsevier, 1980, p 143.

102. COOPER AJL: Biochemistry of sulfur-containing amino acids. *Ann Rev Biochem* 52:187, 1983.

103. LIVESEY G: Methionine degradation: "anabolic and catabolic." *TIBS* 9:27, 1984.

104. JONES SMA, YEAMAN SJ: Oxidative decarboxylation of 4-methylthio-2-oxobutyrate by branched-chain 2-oxo acid dehydrogenase complex. *Biochem J* 237:621, 1986.

105. FAVIER A, CAILLAT D: Dosage par chromatographie gazeuse avec detection en photometrie de flamme de l'acide alpha-ceto-gamma-methylthiobutyrique urinaire dans les hypermethioninemies. *Clin Chim Acta* 79:419, 1977.

106. GAHL WA, BERNARDINI I, FINKELSTEIN JD, TANGERMAN A, MARTIN JJ, BLOM HJ, MULLEN KD, MUDD SH: Transsulfuration in an adult with hepatic methionine adenosyltransferase deficiency. *J Clin Invest* 81:390, 1988.

107. LASTER L, MUDD SH, FINKELSTEIN JD, IRREVERRE F: Homocystinuria due to cystathionine synthase deficiency: The metabolism of L-methionine. *J Clin Invest* 44:1708, 1965.

108. MARTENSSON J: The occurrence of 4-methylthio-2-hydroxybutyrate in human urine. *Anal Biochem* 154:43, 1986.

109. KAJI H, SAITO N, MURAO M, ISHIMOTO M, KONDO H, GASA S, SAITO K: Gas chromatographic and gas chromatographic-mass spectrometric studies on α-keto- γ-methyl-thiobutyric acid in urine following ingestion of optical isomers of methionine. *J Chromatogr* 221:145, 1980.

110. KAJI H, SAITO K, SAITO N, HISAMURA M, ISHIMOTO M, KONDO H: Simple gas chromatographic analysis of 3-methylthiopropionate in human urine. *J Chromatogr* 272:166, 1983.

111. KAJI H, HISAMURA M, SAITO N, MURAO M: Biochemical aspect of dimethyl sulfide breath test in the studies on methionine metabolism. *Res Commun Chem Pathol Pharmacol* 32:515, 1981.

112. TANAKA K: Personal communication, 1987.

113. ELSAS LJ II: Personal communication, 1987.

114. IBER FL, ROSEN H, LEVENSON SM, CHALMERS TC: The plasma amino acids in patients with liver failure. *J Lab Clin Med* 50:417, 1957.

115. HOROWITZ JH, RYTINS EB, HENDERSON JM, HEYMSFIELD SB, MOFFITT SD,

BAIN RP, CHAWLA RK, BLEIER JC, RUDMAN D: Evidence for impairment of transsulfuration pathway in cirrhosis. *Gastroenterology* 81:668, 1981.

116. GJESSING LR, HALVORSEN S: Hypermethioninaemia in acute tyrosinosis. *Lancet* 2:1132, 1965.

117. SCRIVER CR, CLOW CL, SILVERBERG M: Hypermethioninemia in acute tyrosinosis. *Lancet* 1:153, 1966.

118. PERRY TL, HARDWICK DF, DIXON GH, DOLMAN CL, HANSEN S: Hypermethioninemia: A metabolic disorder associated with cirrhosis, islet cell hyperplasia, and renal tubular degeneration. *Pediatrics* 36:236, 1965.

118a. DUCE AM, ORTIZ P, CABRERO C, MATO JM: *S*-Adenosyl-L-methionine synthetase and phospholipid methyltransferase are inhibited in human cirrhosis. *Hepatology* 8:65, 1988.

118b. CABRERO C, DUCE AM, ORTIZ P, ALEMANY S, MATO JM: Specific loss of the high-Mr form of *S*-adenosyl-L-methionine synthetase in human liver cirrhosis. *Hepatology*, in press, 1988.

119. GAULL GE, RASSIN DK, RAIHA NCR, HEINONEN K: Milk protein quantity and quality in low-birth-weight infants. III. Effects on sulfur amino acids in plasma and urine. *J Pediatr* 90:348, 1977.

120. SNYDERMAN SE, HOLT LE JR, NORTON PM, ROITMAN E, PHANSALKAR SV: The plasma aminogram. I. Influence of the level of protein intake and a comparison of whole protein and amino acid diets. *Pediatr Res* 2:131, 1968.

121. LEVY HL, SHIH VE, MADIGAN PM, KAROLKEWICZ V, CARR JR, LUM A, RICHARDS AA, CRAWFORD JD, MACCREADY RA: Hypermethioninemia with other hyperaminoacidemias. Studies in infants on high-protein diets. *Am J Dis Child* 117:96, 1969.

122. KOMROWER GM, ROBINS AJ: Plasma amino acid disturbance in infancy. I. Hypermethioninaemia and transient tyrosinaemia. *Arch Dis Child* 44:418, 1969.

123. VALMAN HB, BROWN RJK, PALMER T, OBERHOLZER VG, LEVIN B: Protein intake and plasma amino-acids of infants of low birth weight. *Br Med J* 4:789, 1971.

124. GAULL GE, STURMAN JA, RAIHA NCR: Development of mammalian sulfur metabolism: Absence of cystathionase in human fetal tissues. *Pediatr Res* 6:538, 1972.

125. SLAVIK M, LOVENBERG W, KEISER HR: Changes in serum and urine amino acids in patients with progressive systemic sclerosis treated with 6-azauridine triacetate. *Biochem Pharmacol* 22:1295, 1973.

126. HYANEK J, BREMER HJ, SLAVIK M: "Homocystinuria" and [urinary] excretion of β-amino acids in patients treated with 6-azauridine. *Clin Chim Acta* 25:288, 1969.

127. SLAVIK M, SMITH KJ, BLANC O: Decrease of serum pyridoxal phosphate levels and homocystinemia after administration of 6-azauridine triacetate and their prevention by administration of pyridoxine. *Biochem Pharmacol* 31:4089, 1982.

128. EFRON ML, MCPHERSON TC, SHIH VE, WELSH F, MACCREADY RA: D-Methioninuria due to DL-methionine ingestion. *Am J Dis Child* 117:104, 1969.

129. GAULL GE, BENDER AN, VULOVIC D, TALLAN HH, SCHAFFNER F: Methioninemia and myopathy: A new disorder. *Ann Neurology* 9:423, 1980.

130. TSUCHIYAMA A, OYANAGI K, NAKATA F, UETSUJI N, TSUGAWA S, NAKAO T, MORI M: A new type of hypermethioninemia in neonates. *Tohoku J Exp Med* 138:281, 1982.

131. JHAVERI BM, BUIST NRM, GAULL GE, TALLAN HH: Intermittent hypermethioninaemia associated with normal hepatic methionine adenosyltransferase activity: Report of a case. *J Inherited Metab Dis* 5:101, 1982.

132. GAULL GE, TALLAN HH: Methionine adenosyltransferase deficiency: New enzymatic defect associated with hypermethioninemia. *Science* 186:59, 1974.

133. ROSENBLATT DS, COOPER BA, POTTIER A, LUE-SHING H, MATIASZUK N, GRAUER K: Altered vitamin B_{12} metabolism in fibroblasts from a patient with megaloblastic anemia and homocystinuria due to a new defect in methionine biosynthesis. *J Clin Invest* 74:2149, 1984.

134. ROSENBLATT DS, THOMAS IT, WATKINS D, COOPER BA, ERBE RW: Vitamin B_{12} responsive homocystinuria and megaloblastic anemia: Heterogeneity in methylcobalamin deficiency. *Am J Med Genet* 26:377, 1987.

134a. WATKINS D, ROSENBLATT DS: Genetic heterogeneity among patients with methylcobalamin deficiency. Definition of two complementation groups, cblE and cblG. *J Clin Invest* 81:1690, 1988.

134b. COOPER BA, ROSENBLATT DS: Inherited defects of vitamin B_{12} metabolism. *Ann Rev Nutr* 7:291, 1987.

134c. HALLAM LJ, SAYWER M, CLARK ACL, VAN DER WEYDEN MB: Vitamin B_{12}-responsive neonatal megaloblastic anemia and homocystinuria with associated reduced methionine synthase activity. *Blood* 69:1128, 1987.

134d. KOLHOUSE JF, ALLEN RH: Recognition of two intracellular cobalamin binding proteins and their identification as methylmalonyl-CoA mutase and methionine synthetase. *Proc Natl Acad Sci USA* 74:921, 1977.

134e. MELLMAN IS, YOUNGDAHL-TURNER P, WILLARD HF, ROSENBERG LE: Intracellular binding of radioactive hydroxocobalamin to cobalamin-dependent apoenzymes in rat liver. *Proc Natl Acad Sci USA* 74:916, 1977.

134f. ZITTOUN J, FISCHER A, MARQUET J, PERIGNON JL, LAGRUE A, GRISCELLI C: Megaloblastic anemia and immune abnormalities in a patient with methionine synthase deficiency. *Acta Paediatr Scand* 76:991, 1987.

135. SHIN YS, REITER S, ZELGER O, BRUENSTLER I, RUECKER AV: Orotic aciduria, homocystinura, formiminoglutamic aciduria and megaloblastosis associated with formiminotransferase/cyclodeaminase deficiency, in Nyhan WL, Thompson LF, Watts RWE (eds): *Purine and Pyrimidine Metabolism in Man*. New York, Plenum, 1986, p 71.

136. HOLLOWELL JG JR, HALL WK, CORYELL ME, MCPHERSON J JR, HAHN DA: Homocystinuria and organic aciduria in a patient with vitamin B_{12} deficiency. *Lancet* 2:1428, 1969.

137. HIGGINBOTTOM MC, SWEETMAN L, NYHAN WL: A syndrome of methylmalonic aciduria, homocystinuria, megaloblastic anemia and neurologic abnormalities in a vitamin B_{12}-deficient breast-fed infant of a strict vegetarian. *N Engl J Med* 299:317, 1978.

137a. STABLER SP, MARCELL PD, PODELL ER, ALLEN RH, SAVAGE DG, LINDENBAUM J: Elevation of total homocysteine in the serum of patients with cobalamin or folate deficiency detected by capillary gas chromatography–mass spectrometry. *J Clin Invest* 81:466, 1988.

137b. BRATTSTRÖM L, ISRAELSSON B, LINDGARDE F, HULTBERG B: Higher total plasma homocysteine in vitamin B_{12} deficiency than in heterozygosity for homocystinuria due to cystathionine β-synthase deficiency. *Metabolism* 37:175, 1988.

137c. KRISHNASWAMY K: Isonicotinic acid hydrazide and pyridoxine deficiency. *Int J Vitam Res* 44:457, 1974.

138. LEVY HL, MUDD SH: Homocystinuria due to bacterial contamination in pyridoxine-unresponsive cystathioninemia. *Pediatr Res* 7:162, 1973.

139. HARAGUCHI H, IWATANI E, HIROSAWA M, YAMASHITA F, NAGAYAMA T: Cystathioninuria. *Igakunoayumi (Jpn)* 61:72, 1967.

140. TADA K, YOSHIDA T, YOKOYAMA Y, SATO T, NAKAGAWA H, ARAKAWA T: Cystathioninuria not associated with vitamin B_6 dependency: A probably new type of cystathioninuria. *Tohoku J Exp Med* 95:235, 1968.

141. COIGNET J, PASSERON P, LAURENT B, ROUAULT F: A propos d'un cas de cystathionurie avec excretion d'homocystine. *Pediatrie* 26:317, 1971.

142. LYON ICT, PROCOPIS PG, TURNER B: Cystathioninuria in a well baby population. *Acta Paediatr Scand* 60:324, 1971.

143. LAURENT B, COIGNET J: Cystathioninurie: Trouble possible de regulation enzymatique. *Clin Chim Acta* 43:171, 1973.

144. ENDRES W, SEIBOLD H: Renal excretion of cystathionine and creatinine in humans at different ages. *Clin Chim Acta* 87:425, 1978.

145. PRZYREMBEL H, BREMER HJ: Cystathioninuria in premature infants. *Clin Chim Acta* 41:95, 1972.

146. ENDRES W, VOGT R, RIEGEL KP, BREMER HJ: The influence of vitamin B_6 on cystathioninuria in premature infants. *Clin Chim Acta* 86:89, 1978.

147. LEVY HL, MUDD SH, SCHULMAN JD, DREYFUS PM, ABELES RH: A derangement in B_{12} metabolism associated with homocystinemia, cystathioninemia, hypomethioninemia, and methylmalonic aciduria. *Am J Med* 48:390, 1970.

148. SHIH VE, SALAM MZ, MUDD SH, UHLENDORF BW, ADAMS RD: A new form of homocystinuria due to $N^{5,10}$-methylenetetrahydrofolate reductase deficiency. *Pediatr Res* 6:135, 1972.

149. GOODMAN SI, MOE PG, HAMMOND KB, MUDD SH, UHLENDORF BW: Homocystinuria with methylmalonic aciduria: Two cases in a sibship. *Biochem Med* 4:500, 1970.

150. FREEMAN JM, FINKELSTEIN JD, MUDD SH: Folate-responsive homocystinuria and "schizophrenia": A defect in methylation due to deficient 5,10-methylene-tetrahydrofolate reductase activity. *N Engl J Med* 292:491, 1975.

151. HOPE DB: L-Cystathionine in the urine of pyridoxine-deficient rats. *Biochem J* 66:486, 1957.

152. SCRIVER CR, HUTCHISON JH: The vitamin B_6 deficiency syndrome in human infancy: Biochemical and clinical observations. *Pediatrics* 31:240, 1963.

153. PARK YK, LINKSWILER H: Effect of vitamin B_6 depletion in adult man on the excretion of cystathionine and other methionine metabolites. *J Nutr* 100:110, 1970.

154. STURMAN JA, COHEN PA, GAULL GE: Effects of deficiency of vitamin B_6 on transsulfuration. *Biochem Med* 3:244, 1969.

155. FINKELSTEIN JD, CHALMERS FT: Pyridoxine effects on cystathionine synthase in rat liver. *J Nutr* 100:467, 1970.

156. SMOLIN LA, BENEVENGA NJ: Accumulation of homocyst(e)ine in Vitamin B-6 deficiency: A model for the study of cystathionine β-synthase deficiency. *J Nutr* 112:1264, 1982.

157. SMOLIN LA, BENEVENGA NJ: Factors affecting the accumulation of homocyst(e)ine in rats deficient in vitamin B-6. *J Nutr* 114:103, 1984.

158. SMOLIN LA, CRENSHAW TD, KURTYCZ D, BENEVENGA NJ: Homocyst(e)ine

accumulation in pigs fed diets deficient in vitamin B-6: Relationship to atherosclerosis. *J Nutr* 113:2122, 1983.

159. GJESSING LR: Cystathioninuria during a load of thyroxine. *Scand J Clin Lab Invest* 16:680, 1964.

160. FINKELSTEIN JD: Methionine metabolism in mammals: Effects of age, diet, and hormones on three enzymes of the pathway in rat tissues. *Arch Biochem Biophys* 122:583, 1967.

161. CHATAGNER F, JOLLES-BERGERET B, TRAUTMANN O: Hormones thyroidiennes et enzymes de desulfuration de la L-cysteine du foie du rat. *Biochim Biophys Acta* 59:744, 1962.

162. SHAW KNF, LIEBERMAN E, KOCH R, DONNELL GN: Cystathioninuria. *Am J Dis Child* 113:119, 1967.

163. LIEBERMAN E, SHAW KNF, DONNELL GN: Cystathioninuria in galactosemia and certain types of liver disease. *Pediatrics* 40:828, 1967.

164. VON STUDNITZ W: Secondary cystathioninuria. *Acta Paediatr Scand* 58:173, 1969.

165. ENDRES W, WUTTAGE B: Occurrence of secondary cystathioninuria in children with inherited metabolic disorders, liver diseases, neoplasms, cystic fibrosis and celiac disease. *Eur J Pediatr* 129:29, 1978.

166. FRIMPTER GW: Cystathioninuria in a patient with cystinuria. *Am J Med* 46:832, 1969.

167. FRIMPTER GW, GREENBERG AJ: Renal clearance of cystathionine in homozygous and heterozygous cystathioninuria, cystinuria, and the normal state. *J Clin Invest* 46:975, 1967.

168. GJESSING LR: Studies of functional neural tumors. III. Cystathionine in the tumor tissue. *Scand J Clin Lab Invest* 15:479, 1963.

169. GJESSING LR: Studies of functional neural tumors. II. Cystathioninuria. *Scand J Clin Lab Invest* 15:474, 1963.

170. GJESSING LR: Studies of functional neural tumors. IV. Isolation and identification of urinary cystathionine. *Scand J Clin Lab Invest* 15:601, 1963.

171. VON STUDNITZ W: Sulfur-containing amino acids in the urine of patients with tumours from sympathic nervous tissue. *Scand J Clin Lab Invest* 17*(Suppl)*:86, 190, 1965.

172. MUDD SH, FINKELSTEIN JD, IRREVERRE F, LASTER L: Transsulfuration in mammals: Microassays and tissue distributions of three enzymes of the pathway. *J Biol Chem* 240:4382, 1965.

173. MUDD SH, LASTER L, FINKELSTEIN JD, IRREVERRE F: Studies on homocystinuria, in Himwich HE, Kety SS, Smythies JR (eds): *Amines and Schizophrenia*. Elmsford, NY, Pergamon, 1967, p 247.

174. GJESSING LR, MAURITZEN K: Cystathioninuria in hepatoblastoma. *Scand J Clin Lab Invest* 17:513, 1965.

175. VOUTE PA JR, WADMAN SK: Cystathioninuria in hepatoblastoma. *Clin Chim Acta* 22:373, 1968.

176. GEISER CF, SHIH VE: Cystathioninuria and its origin in children with hepatoblastoma. *J Pediatr* 96:72, 1980.

177. GOUT J-P, SERRE J-C, DIETERLEN M, ANTENER I, FRAPPAT P, BOST M, BEAUDOING A: Une nouvelle cause d'hypermethioninemie de l'enfant: Le deficit en S-adenosyl-methionine-synthetase. *Arch Fr Pediatr* 34:416, 1977.

178. FINKELSTEIN JD, KYLE WE, MARTIN JJ: Abnormal methionine adenosyltransferase in hypermethioninemia. *Biochem Biophys Res Commun* 66:1491, 1975.

179. LL GE, TALLAN HH, LONSDALE D, PRZYREMBEL H, SCHAFFNER F, VON BASSEWITZ DB: Hypermethioninemia associated with methionine adenosyltransferase deficiency: Clinical, morphological and biochemical observations on four patients. *J Pediatr* 98:734, 1981.

180. GAHL WA, FINKELSTEIN JD, MULLEN KD, BERNARDINI I, MARTIN JJ, BACKLUND P, ISHAK KG, HOOFNAGLE JH, MUDD SH: Hepatic methionine adenosyltransferase deficiency in a 31-year-old man. *Am J Hum Genet* 40:39, 1987.

180a. KUTZBACH C, STOKSTAD ELR: Mammalian methylenetetrahydrofolate reductase. Partial purification, properties, and inhibition of S-adenosylmethionine. *Biochim Biophys Acta* 250:459, 1971.

180b. FINKELSTEIN JD, KYLE WE, MARTIN JJ, PICK A-M: Activation of cystathionine synthase by adenosylmethionine and adenosylethionine. *Biochem Biophys Res Commun* 66:81, 1975.

181. PRZYREMBEL H: Personal communication, 1986.

182. LONSDALE D: Personal communication, 1986.

183. NATORI Y: Studies on ethionine. VI. Sex-dependent behavior of methionine and ethionine in rats. *J Biol Chem* 238:2075, 1963.

184. FIELD CMB, CARSON NAJ, CUSWORTH DC, DENT CE, NEILL DW: Homocystinuria: A new disorder of metabolism. Abstracts of the Tenth International Congress of Paediatricians (Lisbon), 1962, p 274.

185. CARSON NAJ, NEILL DW: Metabolic abnormalities detected in a survey of mentally backward individuals in Northern Ireland. *Arch Dis Child* 37:505, 1962.

186. GERRITSEN T, VAUGHN JG, WAISMAN HA: The identification of homocystine in the urine. *Biochem Biophys Res Commun* 9:493, 1962.

187. CARSON NAJ, CUSWORTH DC, DENT CE, FIELD CMB, NEILL DW, WESTALL RG: Homocystinuria: A new inborn error of metabolism associated with mental deficiency. *Arch Dis Child* 38:425, 1963.

188. GERRITSEN T, WAISMAN HA: Homocystinuria, an error in the metabolism of methionine. *Pediatrics* 33:413, 1964.

189. SPAETH GL, BARBER GW: Homocystinuria: In a mentally retarded child and her normal cousin. *Trans Am Acad Ophthalmol Otolaryngol* 69:912, 1965.

190. MUDD SH, FINKELSTEIN JD, IRREVERRE F, LASTER L: Homocystinuria: An enzymatic defect. *Science* 143:1443, 1964.

191. MUDD SH, SKOVBY F, LEVY HL, PETTIGREW KD, WILCKEN B, PYERITZ RE, ANDRIA G, BOERS GHJ, BROMBERG IL, CERONE R, FOWLER B, GROBE H, SCHMIDT H, SCHWEITZER L: The natural history of homocystinuria due to cystathionine β-synthase deficiency. *Am J Hum Genet* 37:1, 1985.

192. GOLDSTEIN JL, CAMPBELL BK, GARTLER SM: Cystathionine synthase activity in human lymphocytes: Induction by phytohemagglutinin. *J Clin Invest* 51:1034, 1972.

193. GOLDSTEIN JL, CAMPBELL BK, GARTLER SM: Homocystinuria: Heterozygote detection using phytohemagglutinin-stimulated lymphocytes. *J Clin Invest* 52:218, 1973.

194. FLEISHER LD, BERATIS NG, TALLAN HH, HIRSCHHORN K, GAULL GE: Homocystinuria due to cystathionine synthase (CS) deficiency: Investigations in cultured long-term lymphocytes, fetal skin fibroblasts and amniotic fluid cells. *Pediatr Res* 8:388, 1974.

195. FOWLER B, BORRESEN AL, BOMAN N: Prenatal diagnosis of homocystinuria. *Lancet* 2:875, 1982.

196. KRAUS JP: Personal communication, 1986.

197. UHLENDORF BW, CONERLY EB, MUDD SH: Homocystinuria: Studies in tissue culture. *Pediatr Res* 7:645, 1973.

198. FOWLER B, KRAUS J, PACKMAN S, ROSENBERG LE: Homocystinuria: Evidence for three distinct classes of cystathionine β-synthase mutants in cultured fibroblasts. *J Clin Invest* 61:645, 1978.

199. HEMRAG F, GRIFFITHS R: Enzyme studies in cystathionine β-synthase deficiency: A possible effect of elevated intracellular levels of homocystine in kinetic studies. *J Inherited Metab Dis* 1:171, 1978.

200. FOWLER B, SARDHARWALLA IB: Homocystinuria: Cystathionine synthase activity in cultured skin fibroblasts. International Symposium on Inborn Errors of Metabolism in Humans, Switzerland, 1980, p 20.

201. BITTLES AH, CARSON NAJ: Homocystinuria: Studies on cystathionine β-synthase, S-adenosylmethionine synthase and cystathionase activities in skin fibroblasts. *J Inherited Metab Dis* 4:3, 1981.

202. SEASHORE MR, DURANT JL, ROSENBERG LE: Studies of the mechanism of pyridoxine-responsive homocystinuria. *Pediatr Res* 6:187, 1972.

203. KIM YJ, ROSENBERG LE: On the mechanism of pyridoxine responsive homocystinuria. II. Properties of normal and mutant cystathionine β-synthase from cultured fibroblasts. *Proc Natl Acad Sci USA* 71:4821, 1974.

204. LIPSON MH, KRAUS J, ROSENBERG LE: Affinity of cystathionine β-synthase for pyridoxal 5′-phosphate in cultured cells. *J Clin Invest* 66:188, 1980.

205. FLEISHER LD, LONGHI RC, TALLAN HH, GAULL GE: Cystathionine β-synthase deficiency: Differences in thermostability between normal and abnormal enzyme from cultured human cells. *Pediatr Res* 12:293, 1978.

206. GRIFFITHS R, TUDBALL N: Studies on the use of skin fibroblasts for the measurement of cystathionine synthase activity with respect to homocystinuria. *Clin Chim Acta* 73:157, 1976.

207. LONGHI RC, FLEISHER LD, TALLAN HH, GAULL GE: Cystathionine β-synthase deficiency: A qualitative abnormality of the deficient enzyme modified by vitamin B_6 therapy. *Pediatr Res* 11:100, 1977.

208. SKOVBY F, KRAUS J, REDLICH C, ROSENBERG LE: Immunochemical studies on cultured fibroblasts from patients with homocystinuria due to cystathionine β-synthase deficiency. *Am J Hum Genet* 34:73, 1982.

209. SKOVBY F, KRAUS JP, ROSENBERG LE: Homocystinuria: Biogenesis of cystathionine β-synthase subunits in cultured fibroblasts and in an *in vitro* translation system programmed with fibroblast messenger RNA. *Am J Hum Genet* 36:452, 1984.

210. MCKUSICK VA, HALL JG, CHAR F: The clinical and genetic characteristics of homocystinuria, in Carson NAJ, Raine DN (eds): *Inherited Disorders of Sulphur Metabolism*. London, Churchill Livingstone, 1971, p 179.

211. MCKUSICK VA: *Heritable Disorders of Connective Tissue*, 4th ed. St Louis, CV Mosby, 1972, p 224.

212. FINKELSTEIN JD, MUDD SH, IRREVERRE F, LASTER L: Homocystinuria due to cystathionine synthetase deficiency: The mode of inheritance. *Science* 146:785, 1964.

213. LASTER L, SPAETH GL, MUDD SH, FINKELSTEIN JD: Homocystinuria due to cystathionine synthase deficiency. Combined clinical staff conference at the National Institutes of Health. *Ann Intern Med* 63:1117, 1985.

214. GAULL GE, STURMAN JA, SCHAFFNER F: Homocystinuria due to cystathionine synthase deficiency: Enzymatic and ultrastructural studies. *J Pediatr* 84:381, 1974.

215. BITTLES AH, CARSON NAJ: Tissue culture techniques as an aid to prenatal diagnosis and genetic counselling in homocystinuria. *J Med Genet* 10:120, 1973.

216. FLEISHER LD, TALLAN HH, BERATIS NG, HIRSHHORN K, GAULL GE: Cystathionine synthase deficiency: Heterozygote detection using cultured skin fibroblasts. *Biochem Biophys Res Commun* 55:38, 1973.

217. BRENTON DP, CUSWORTH DC, GAULL GE: Homocystinuria: Metabolic studies on three patients. *J Pediatr* 67:58, 1965.

218. WERDER EA, CURTIUS H-CH, TANCREDI F, ANDERS PW, PRADER A: Homocystinurie. *Helv Paediatr Acta* 21:1, 1966.

219. PERRY TL, HANSEN S, MACDOUGALL L, WARRINGTON PD: Sulfur-containing amino acids in the plasma and urine of homocystinurics. *Clin Chim Acta* 15:409, 1967.

220. REFSUM H, HELLAND S, UELAND PM: Radioenzymic determination of homocysteine in plasma and urine. *Clin Chem* 31:624, 1985.

220a. ARAKI A, SAKO Y: Determination of free and total homocysteine in human plasma by high-performance liquid chromatography with fluorescence detection. *J Chromatogr* 422:43, 1987.

221. GUPTA VJ, WILCKEN DEL: The detection of cysteine-homocysteine mixed disulphide in plasma of normal fasting man. *Eur J Clin Invest* 8:205, 1978.

222. WILCKEN DEL, GUPTA VJ: Cysteine-homocysteine mixed disulphide: Differing plasma concentrations in normal men and women. *Clin Sci* 57:211, 1979.

223. KANG S-S, WONG PWK, BECKER N: Protein-bound homocyst(e)ine in normal subjects and in patients with homocystinuria. *Pediatr Res* 13:1141, 1979.

224. PERRY TL, HANSEN S: Technical pitfalls leading to errors in the quantitation of plasma amino acids. *Clin Chim Acta* 25:53, 1969.

225. KANG S-S, WONG PWK, COOK HY, NORUSIS M, MESSER JV: Protein-bound homocyst(e)ine. A possible risk factor for coronary artery disease. *J Clin Invest* 77:1482, 1986.

225a. STABLER SP, MARCELL PD, PODELL ER, ALLEN RH: Quantitation of total homocysteine, total cysteine, and methionine in normal serum and urine using capillary gas chromatography–mass spectrometry. *Analyt Biochem* 162:185, 1987.

225b. BRATTSTRÖM LE, ISRAELSSON B, JEPPSSON J-O, HULTBERG BL: Folic acid–An innocuous means to reduce plasma homocysteine. *Scand J Clin Lab Invest* 48:215, 1988.

226. SCHNEIDER JA, BRADLEY KH, SEEGMILLER JE: Identification and measurement of cysteine-homocysteine mixed disulfide in plasma. *J Lab Clin Med* 71:122, 1968.

227. SARDHARWALLA IB, JACKSON SH, HAWKE HD, SASS-KORTSAK A: Homocystinuria: A study with low-methionine diet in three patients. *Can Med Assoc J* 99:731, 1968.

228. MALLOY MH, RASSIN DK, GAULL GE: Plasma cyst(e)ine in homocyst(e)inemia. *Am J Clin Nutr* 34:2619, 1981.

229. PERRY TL, HANSEN S: Cystinylglycine in plasma: Diagnostic relevance for pyroglutamic acidemia, homocystinuria, and phenylketonuria. *Clin Chim Acta* 117:7, 1981.

230. SARTORIO R, CARROZZO R, CORBO L, ANDRIA G: Protein-bound plasma homocyst(e)ine and identification of heterozygotes for cystathionine-synthase deficiency. *J Inherited Metab Dis* 9:25, 1986.

231. KANG S-S, WONG PWK, CURLEY K: The effect of D-penicillamine on protein-bound homocyst(e)ine in homocystinurics. *Pediatr Res* 16:370, 1982.

232. SVARDAL A, REFSUM H, UELAND PM: Determination of *in vivo* protein binding of homocysteine and its relation to free homocysteine in the liver and other tissues of the rat. *J Biol Chem* 261:3156, 1986.

233. SMOLIN LA, BENEVENGA NJ: The use of cyst(e)ine in the removal of protein-bound homocysteine. *Am J Clin Nutr* 39:730, 1984.

233a. WILEY VC, DUDMAN NPB, WILCKEN DEL: Interrelations between plasma free and protein-bound homocysteine and cysteine in homocystinuria. *Metabolism* 37:191, 1988.

234. CARSON NAJ, DENT CE, FIELD CMB, GAULL GE: Homocystinuria: Clinical and pathological review of ten cases. *J Pediatr* 66:565, 1965.

235. KENNEDY C, SHIH VE, ROWLAND LP: Homocystinuria: A report in two siblings. *Pediatrics* 36:736, 1965.

236. TADA K, YOSHIDA T, HIRONO H, ARAKAWA T: Homocystinuria: Amino acid pattern of the liver. *Tohoku J Exp Med* 92:325, 1967.

237. CURTIUS H-CH, MARTENET AC, ANDERS PW: Bestimmung von freien Aminosauren im Augenkammerwasser des Menschen bei Homocystinurie-patienten und Kontrollfallen. *Clin Chim Acta* 19:469, 1968.

238. JOCELYN PC: Glutathione metabolism in animals, in Crook EM (ed): *Glutathione*. Cambridge, Cambridge University Press, 1959, p 43.

239. RACKER E: Glutathione-homocystine transhydrogenase. *J Biol Chem* 217:867, 1955.

240. FOWLER B: Transsulphuration and methylation of homocysteine in control and mutant human fibroblasts. *Biochim Biophys Acta* 721:201, 1982.

241. UELAND PM, HELLAND S, BROCH OJ, SCHANCHE JS: Homocysteine in tissues of the mouse and rat. *J Biol Chem* 259:2360, 1984.

242. HELLAND S, UELAND PM: Effect of 2′-deoxycoformycin infusion on S-adenosylhomocysteine hydrolase and the amount of S-adenosylhomocysteine and related compounds in tissues of mice. *Cancer Res* 43:4142, 1983.

243. LEVY HL, SHIH VE, MACCREADY RA: Screening for homocystinuria in the newborn and mentally retarded population, in Carson NAJ, Raine DN (eds): *Inherited Disorders of Sulphur Metabolism.* London, Churchill Livingstone, 1971, p 235.

244. MUDD SH, LEVY HL, MORROW G III: Deranged B_{12} metabolism: Effects on sulfur amino acid metabolism. *Biochem Med* 4:193, 1970.

245. SHIH VE, EFRON ML: Pyridoxine-unresponsive homocystinuria. *N Engl J Med* 283:1206, 1970.

246. GROBE H: Homocystinurie: Klinisches Bild, Behandlung und Ergebnisse bei acht Patienten. *Dtsch Med Wochenschr* 98:1313, 1973.

247. RAO BSSR, NARAYANAN HS, REDDY GNN: Homocystinuria in three Indian children. *Indian J Med Res* 59:569, 1971.

248. DHONDT JL, FARRIAUX JP, GAULL GE, TALLAN H: Diagnostic history of a case of homocystinuria without hypermethioninaemia. *J Inherited Metab Dis* 5 *Suppl* 1:8, 1982.

249. SMOLIN LA, BENEVENGA NJ, BERLOW S: The use of betaine for the treatment of homocystinuria. *J Pediatr* 99:467, 1981.

250. WILCKEN DEL, WILCKEN B, DUDMAN NPB, TYRRELL PA: Homocystinuria—The effects of betaine in the treatment of patients not responsive to pyridoxine. *N Engl J Med* 309:448, 1983.

251. WILCKEN DEL, DUDMAN NPB, TYRRELL PA: Homocystinuria due to cystathionine β-synthase deficiency—The effects of betaine treatment in pyridoxine-responsive patients. *Metabolism* 34:1115, 1985.

252. CAREY MC, FENNELLY JJ, FITZGERALD O: Homocystinuria. II. Subnormal serum folate levels, increased folate clearance and effects of folic acid therapy. *Am J Med* 45:26, 1968.

253. MORROW G III, BARNESS LA: Combined vitamin responsiveness in homocystinuria. *J Pediatr* 81:946, 1972.

254. PERRY TL: Mild elevations of plasma ornithine in homocystinuria. *Clin Chim Acta* 117:97, 1981.

255. DUDMAN NPB, WILCKEN DEL: Increased plasma copper in patients with homocystinuria due to cystathionine β-synthase deficiency. *Clin Chim Acta* 127:105, 1983.

256. DUDMAN NPB, TYRRELL PA, WILCKEN DEL: Homocysteinaemia: Depressed plasma serine levels. *Metabolism* 36:198, 1987.

257. BARBER GW, SPAETH GL: Pyridoxine therapy in homocystinuria. *Lancet* 1:337, 1967.

258. CARSON NAJ, CARRE IJ: Treatment of homocystinuria with pyridoxine: A preliminary study. *Arch Dis Child* 44:387, 1969.

259. WILCKEN B, TURNER B: Homocystinuria: Reduced folate levels during pyridoxine treatment. *Arch Dis Child* 48:58, 1973.

260. MUDD SH, EDWARDS WA, LOEB PM, BROWN MS, LASTER L: Homocystinuria due to cystathionine synthase deficiency: The effect of pyridoxine. *J Clin Invest* 49:1762, 1970.

261. BRENTON DP, CUSWORTH DC: The response of patients with cystathionine synthase deficiency to pyridoxine, in Carson NAJ, Raine DN (eds): *Inherited Disorders of Sulphur Metabolism.* London, Churchill Livingstone, 1971, p 264.

262. GAULL GE, RASSIN DK, STURMAN JA: Enzymatic and metabolic studies of homocystinuria: Effects of pyridoxine. *Neuropaediatrie* 1:199, 1969.

263. BARBER GW, SPAETH GL: The successful treatment of homocystinuria with pyridoxine. *J Pediatr* 75:463, 1969.

264. BOERS GHJ, SMALS AGH, DRAYER JIM, TRIJBELS FJM, LEERMAKERS AI, KLOPPENBORG PW: Pyridoxine treatment does not prevent homocystinemia after methionine loading in adult homocystinuria patients. *Metabolism* 32:390, 1983.

265. FOWLER B, SARDHARWALLA IB: Personal communication, 1981.

266. YOSHIDA T, TADA K, YOKOYAMA Y, ARAKAWA T: Homocystinuria of vitamin B_6 dependent type. *Tohoku J Exp Med* 96:235, 1968.

267. MUDD SH: Diseases of sulphur metabolism: Implications for the methionine-homocysteine cycle, and vitamin responsiveness, in *Sulphur in Biology*. Ciba Foundation Symposium. New York, Elsevier North-Holland, 1980, vol 72 (new series), p 239.

268. MUDD SH: Vitamin-responsive genetic abnormalities. *Adv Nutr Res* 4:1, 1982.

269. CROSS HE: Differential diagnosis and treatment of dislocated lenses. *Birth Defects* 12:335, 1976.

270. FRANCOIS J: Ocular manifestations in aminoacidopathies. *Adv Ophthalmol* 25:28, 1972.

271. HAYASAKA S, ASANO Y, TATEDA H, HOSHI K, KOGA Y: Lens subluxation in homocystinuria. *Acta Ophthalmol (Copenh)* 62:425, 1984.

272. SPAETH GL, BARBER GW: Homocystinuria—Its ocular manifestations. *J Pediatr Ophthalmol* 3:42, 1966.

273. ELKINGTON AR, FREEDMAN SS, JAY B, WRIGHT P: Anterior dislocation of the lens in homocystinuria. *Br J Ophthalmol* 57:235, 1973.
274. JOHNSTON SS: Homocystinuria. *Ophthalmologica* 176:282, 1978.
275. LIEBERMAN TW, PODOS SM, HARTSTEIN J: Acute glaucoma, ectopic lentis and homocystinuria. *Am J Ophthalmol* 61:252, 1966.
276. WILSON RS, RUIZ RS: Bilateral central retinal artery occlusion in homocystinuria. *Arch Ophthalmol* 82:267, 1969.
277. THOMAS RP, HOLLOWELL JG, PETERS HJ, CORYELL ME, LESTER RH: Homocystinuria and ectopic lentis in Negro family. *JAMA* 198:560, 1966.
278. SCHIMKE RN, MCKUSICK VA, HUANG T, POLLACK AD: Homocystinuria. *JAMA* 193:711, 1965.
279. SUDARSHAN A, KOPIETZ L: Corneal changes in homocystinuria. *Ann Ophthalmol* 18:60, 1986.
280. MORREELS CL JR, FLETCHER BD, WEILBAECHER RG, DORST JP: The roentgenographic features of homocystinuria. *Radiology* 90:1150, 1968.
281. SCHEDEWIE H, WILLICH E, GROBE H, SCHMIDT H, MULLER KM: Skeletal findings in homocystinuria: A collaborative study. *Pediatr Radiol* 1:12, 1973.
282. TAMBURRINI O, BARTOLOMEO-DE IURI A, ANDRIA G, STRISCIUGLIO P, DEL GIUDICE E, PALESCANDOLO P, SARTORIO R: Skeletal findings of homocystinuria in childhood. *Radiol Med (Minerva Med)* 1, 1984.
283. THOMAS PS, CARSON NAJ: Homocystinuria: The evolution of skeletal changes in relation to treatment. *Ann Radiol* 21:95, 1978.
284. BRILL PW, MITTY HA, GAULL GE: Homocystinuria due to cystathionine synthase deficiency: Clinical-roentgenologic correlations. *Am J Roentgenol Radium Ther Nucl Med* 121:45, 1974.
285. BRENTON DP: Skeletal abnormalities in homocystinuria. *Postgrad Med J* 53:488, 1977.
286. WESTERMAN MP, GREENFIELD GB, WONG PWK: "Fish vertebrae," homocystinuria, and sickle cell anemia. *JAMA* 230:261, 1974.
287. MACCARTHY JMT, CAREY MC: Bone changes in homocystinuria. *Clin Radiol* 19:128, 1968.
288. SMITH SW: Roentgen findings in homocystinuria. *Am J Roentgenol Radium Ther Nucl Med* 100:147, 1967.
289. GAUDIER B, REMY J, NUYTS JP, CARON-POITREAU C, BOMBART E, FOISSAC-GEGOUX MC: Étude radiologique des signes osseux de l'homocystinurie. *Arch Fr Ped* 26:963, 1969.
290. CARSON NAJ: Homocystinuria: Clinical and biochemical heterogeneity, in Cockburn F, Gitzelmann R (eds): *Inborn Errors of Metabolism in Humans.* England, MTP Press Limited, 1982, p 53.
291. TAMBURRINI O, BARTOLOMEO-DE IURI A, ANDRIA G, STRISCIUGLIO P, DEL GIUDICE E: Short fourth metacarpal in homocystinuria. *Pediatr Radiol* 15:209, 1985.
292. ABBOTT MH, FOLSTEIN SE, ABBEY H, PYERITZ RE: Psychiatric manifestations of homocystinuria due to cystathionine β-synthase deficiency. *Am J Med Genet* 26:959, 1987.
293. BRACKEN P, COLL P: Homocystinuria and schizophrenia. Literature review and case report. *J Nerv Ment Dis* 173:51, 1985.
294. HAGBERG B, HAMBRAEUS L, BENSCH K: A case of homocystinuria with a dystonic neurological syndrome. *Neuropediatrics* 1:337, 1970.
295. KANG ES, BYERS RK, GERALD PS: Homocystinuria: Response to pyridoxine. *Neurology* 20:503, 1970.
296. KAESER AC, RODNIGHT R, ELLIS BA: Psychiatric and biochemical aspects of a case of homocystinuria. *J Neurol Neurosurg Psych* 32:88, 1969.
297. WHITE HH, ROWLAND LP, ARAKI S, THOMPSON HL, COWEN D: Homocystinuria. *Arch Neurol* 13:455, 1965.
298. CAREY MC, DONOVAN DE, FITZGERALD O, MCAULEY FD: Homocystinuria, I. A clinical and pathological study of nine subjects in six families. *Am J Med* 45:7, 1968.
299. DEL GUIDICE E, STRIANO S, ANDRIA G: Electroencephalographic abnormalities in homocystinuria due to cystathionine synthase deficiency. *Clin Neurol Neurosurg* 85:165, 1983.
300. DUNN HG, PERRY TL, DOLMAN CL: Homocystinuria. *Neurology* 16:407, 1966.
301. AUTRET E, RIVRON J, RAMADE J, LEROY J, BOULARD P: Homocystinuria with unusual neurologic features including chorea: A case report. *Ann Pediatr* 29:203, 1982.
302. DAVOUS P, RONDOT P: Homocystinuria and dystonia. *J Neurol Neurosurg Psych* 46:283, 1983.
303. GALE AN, BRENTON DP, CUSWORTH DC, DUCHEN LN, STERN GM: Extrapyramidal disturbance in homocystinuria. *J Med Genet* 19:374, 1982.
304. JACKSON GM, GRISOLIA JS, WOLF PL, JONES OW, BLOOR CM: Postoperative thromboemboli in cystathionine beta-synthase deficiency. *Am Heart J* 108:627, 1984.
305. SCHOONDERWALDT HC, BOERS GHJ, CRUYSBERG JRM, SCHULTE BPM, SLOOFF JL, THIJSSEN HOM: Neurologic manifestations of homocystinuria. *Clin Neurol Neurosurg* 83:153, 1981.
306. WICHERINK-BOL HF, BOERS GHJ, DRAYER JIM, ROSENBUSCH G: Angiographic findings in homocystinuria. *Cardiovasc Intervent Radiol* 6:125, 1983.
307. DEL GIUDICE E, RINALDI E, ANDRIA G: L'omocistinuria da deficit di cistationina sintasi. *Riv Ital Ped* 9:165, 1983.
308. MEYNADIER J, GUILHOU JJ, THOREL M, BARNEON G: Homocystinurie. Etude histologique et ultrastructurale. *Dermatologica (Basel)* 163:34, 1981.
309. PRICE J, VICKERS CFH, BROOKER BK: A case of homocystinuria with noteworthy dermatological features. *J Ment Defic Res* 12:111, 1968.
310. GAULL GE, SCHAFFNER F: Electron microscopic changes in hepatocytes of patients with homocystinuria. *Pediatr Res* 5:23, 1971.
311. GERRITSEN T, WAISMAN HA: Homocystinuria: Absence of cystathionine in the brain. *Science* 145:588, 1964.
312. HURWITZ LJ, CHOPRA JS, CARSON NAJ: Electromyographic evidence of a muscle lesion in homocystinuria. *Acta Paediatr Scand* 57:401, 1968.
313. HOLMGREN G, FALKMER S, HAMBRAEUS L: Plasma insulin content and glucose tolerance in homocystinuria. *Upsala J Med Sci* 78:215, 1973.
314. SCHEDEWIE HK, LIPINSKI C, SCHMIDT H: Elevated growth hormone levels in untreated homocystinuria. Mechanism of tall stature? *Clin Res* 25:69A, 1977.
315. MUNNICH A, SAUDUBRAY JM, DAUTZENBERG MD, PARVY P, OGIER H, GIROT R, MANIGNE P, FREZAL J: Diet-responsive proconvertin (factor VII) deficiency in homocystinuria. *J Pediatr* 102:730, 1983.
316. PALARETI G, SALARDI S, PIAZZI S, LEGNANI C, POGGI M, GRAUSO F, CANIATO A, COCCHERI S, CACCIARI E: Blood coagulation changes in homocystinuria: Effects of pyridoxine and other specific therapy. *J Pediatr* 109:1001, 1986.
316a. BEN DRIDI MF, KAROUI S, KASTALLY R, GHARBI HA, ZAIMI I, BEN OSMAN R: L'homocystinurie. Forme avec thrombose vasculaire et deficit en facteur VII. *Arch Fr Pediatr* 43:41, 1986.
317. SEIDLITZ G: Personal communication, 1982.
318. KOMROWER GM, WILSON VK: Homocystinuria. *Proc R Soc Med* 56:996, 1963.
318a. SCHMIDT H, LUTZ P, KRAUS-MACKIW E: Course studies in homocystinuria cases. *Metab Ophthalmol* 1:189, 1977.
319. PYERITZ RE: Personal communication, 1987.
320. HOPKINS I, TOWNLEY RRW, SHIPMAN RT: Cerebral thrombosis in a patient with homocystinuria. *J Pediatr* 75:1082, 1969.
321. CUSWORTH DC, DENT CE: Homocystinuria. *Br Med Bull* 25:42, 1969.
322. PARRIS WCV, QUIMBY CW: Anesthetic considerations for the patient with homocystinuria. *Anesth Analg* 61:708, 1982.
323. NEWMAN G, MITCHELL JRA: Homocystinuria presenting as multiple arterial occlusions. *Q J Med* 210:251, 1984.
324. HENKIND P, ASHTON N: Ocular pathology in homocystinuria. *Trans Ophthalmol Soc UK* 85:21, 1965.
325. RAMSEY MS, YANOFF M, FINE BS: The ocular histopathology of homocystinuria: A light and electron microscopic study. *Am J Ophthalmol* 74:377, 1972.
326. RAMSEY MS, DICKSON DH: Lens fringes in homocystinuria. *Br J Ophthalmol* 59:338, 1975.
327. MARTENET AC, WITMER R, SPEISER P: Alterations oculaires dans l'homocystinurie. *Ophthalmologica* 154:318, 1967.
328. VANDRESSE JH, DE SAINT HUBERT E, EVRARD P: Homocystinuria and carotid arteriography. *Neuroradiology* 17:57, 1978.
329. GIBSON JB, CARSON NAJ, NEILL DW: Pathological findings in homocystinuria. *J Clin Pathol* 17:427, 1964.
329a. CHOU S-M, WAISMAN HA: Spongy degeneration of the central nervous system: Case of homocystinuria. *Arch Pathol* 79:357, 1965.
330. GAULL GE, CARSON NAJ, DENT CE, FIELD CMB: Homocystinuria: Clinical and pathological description of 10 cases, in Oster J (ed): *Proceedings of the International Copenhagen Congress on the Scientific Study of Mental Retardation.* Copenhagen, 1964, vol 1, p 91.
331. SAITO S, TAMAI Y, MATSUSHITA M: Lipid composition of brain in a patient with mental retardation due to encephalopathy in an infantile period and one due to homocystinuria. *Jpn J Exp Med* 49:257, 1979.
332. WAISMAN HA, GERRITSEN T: Homocystinuria: A metabolic defect associated with mental retardation, in Oster J (ed): *Proceedings of the International Copenhagen Congress on the Scientific Study of Mental Retardation.* Copenhagen, 1964, vol 1, p 507.
333. MCKUSICK VA: *Heritable Disorders of Connective Tissue*, 4th ed. St Louis, CV Mosby, 1972, p 224.
334. GAULL GE: Homocystinuria. *Adv Teratol* 2:101, 1967.
335. ALMGREN B, ERIKSSON I, HEMMINGSSON A,, HILLERDAL G, LARSSON E, ABERG H: Abdominal aortic aneurysm in homocystinuria. *Acta Chir Scand* 144:545, 1978.
336. BROWN JH, ALLISON JB: Effects of excess dietary *dl*-methionine and/or *l*-arginine on rats. *Proc Soc Exp Biol Med* 69:196, 1948.

337. COHEN HP, CHOITZ HC, BERG CP: Response of rats to diets high in methionine and related compounds. *J Nutr* 64:555, 1958.
338. MCCULLY KS: Vascular pathology of homocysteinemia: Implications for the pathogenesis of arteriosclerosis. *Am J Pathol* 56:111, 1969.
339. KANWAR YS, MANALIGOD JR, WONG PWK: Morphologic studies in a patient with homocystinuria due to 5,10-methylenetetrahydrofolate reductase deficiency. *Pediatr Res* 10:598, 1976.
340. BAUMGARTNER R, WICK H, OHNACKER H, PROBST A, MAURER R: Vascular lesions in two patients with congenital homocystinuria due to different defects of remethylation. *J Inherited Metab Dis* 3:101, 1980.
341. DILLON MJ, ENGLAND JM, GOMPERTZ D, GOODEY PA, GRANT DB, HASSEIN HA-A, LINNELL JC, MATTHEWS DM, MUDD SH, NEWNS GH, SEAKINS JWT, UHLENDORF BW, WISE IJ: Mental retardation, megaloblastic anaemia, methylmalonic aciduria, and abnormal homocysteine metabolism due to an error in B_{12} metabolism. *Clin Sci Molec Med* 47:43, 1974.
342. DAYAN AD, RAMSEY RB: An inborn error of vitamin B_{12} metabolism associated with cellular deficiency of coenzyme forms of the vitamin: Pathological and neurochemical findings in one case. *J Neurol Sci* 23:117, 1974.
343. DAYAN AD: Personal communication, 1975.
343a. MUDD SH: Vascular disease and homocysteine metabolism. *Proceedings First Ernhold Lundstrom Symposium,* Malmo, Sweden, June 14–16, 1987; in press, 1988.
344. MCDONALD L, BRAY C, FIELD C, LOVE F, DAVIES B: Homocystinuria, thrombosis, and the blood-platelets. *Lancet* 1:745, 1964.
345. BRENTON DP, CUSWORTH DC, DENT CE, JONES EE: Homocystinuria: Clinical and dietary studies. *Q J Med* 35:325, 1966.
346. BRAY CL: Discussion, in Brett EM: Homocystinuria with epilepsy. *Proc R Soc Med* 59:484, 1966.
347. BRETT EM: Homocystinuria with epilepsy. *Proc R Soc Med* 59:484, 1966.
348. HOLMGREN G, HAMBRAEUS L, LESTRUP E, TANGEN O: The effect of pyridoxine on platelet adhesiveness in homocystinuria. *Neuropaediatrie* 5:402, 1974.
349. HILDEN M, BRANDT NJ, NILSSON IM, SCHONHEYDER F: Investigations of coagulation and fibrinolysis in homocystinuria. *Acta Med Scand* 195:533, 1974.
350. CHASE HP, GOODMAN SI, O'BRIEN D: Treatment of homocystinuria. *Arch Dis Child* 42:514, 1967.
351. HARKER LA, SLICHTER SJ, SCOTT CR, ROSS R: Homocystinemia: Vascular injury and arterial thrombosis. *N Engl J Med* 291:537, 1974.
352. EFRON ML: In discussion of G.E. Gaull, The pathogenesis of homocystinuria. *Am J Dis Child* 113:103, 1967.
353. CLINE JW, GOYER RA, LIPTON J, MASON RG: Adult homocystinuria with ectopia lentis. *South Med J* 64:613, 1971.
354. GRAEBER JE, SLOTT JH, ULANE RE, SCHULMAN JD, STUART MJ: Effect of homocysteine and homocystine on platelet and vascular arachidonic acid metabolism. *Pediatr Res* 16:490, 1982.
355. HAMPTON JR, MITCHELL JRA: A transferable factor causing abnormal platelet behavior in vascular disease. *Lancet* 2:764, 1966.
356. ZWEIFLER AJ, ALLEN RJ: An intrinsic blood platelet abnormality in a homocystinuric boy, corrected by pyridoxine administration. *Thromb Diath Haemorrh* 26:15, 1971.
357. GROBE H, VON BASSEWITZ DB: Thromboembolische Komplikationen und Thrombocytenanomalien bei homocystinurie. *Z Kinderheilkd* 112:309, 1972.
358. GROBE H, BALLEISEN L, STAHL K: Platelet function and morphology in homocystinuria. *Pediatr Res* 13:72, 1979.
359. UHLEMANN ER, TENPAS JH, LUCKY AW, SCHULMAN JD, MUDD SH, SHULMAN NR: Platelet survival and morphology in homocystinuria due to cystathionine synthase deficiency. *N Engl J Med* 295:1283, 1976.
360. HARKER LA, ROSS R, SLICHTER SJ, SCOTT CR: Homocystine induced arteriosclerosis: The role of endothelial cell injury and platelet response in its genesis. *J Clin Invest* 58:731, 1976.
361. HILL-ZOBEL RL, PYERITZ RE, SCHEFFEL U, MALPICA O, ENGIN S, CAMARGO EE, ABBOTT M, GUILARTE TR, HILL J, MCINTYRE PA, MURPHY EA, TSAN MF: Kinetics and distribution of ^{111}indium-labeled platelets in patients with homocystinuria. *N Engl J Med* 307:781, 1982.
362. HILL-ZOBEL RL, SCHEFFEL V, MURPHY EA, TSAN MF: ^{111}-Indium-labeled platelets in homocystinuria. *N Engl J Med* 308:285, 1983.
363. WALL RT, HARLAN JM, HARKER LA, STRIKER GE: Homocysteine induced endothelial cell injury *in vitro:* A model for the study of vascular injury. *Thromb Res* 18:113, 1980.
364. WEIMANN BJ, KUHN H, BAUMGARTNER HR: Effect of homocysteine (Ho) on cultured bovine (BEC) and human (HEC) endothelial cells. *Experientia (Basel)* 36:762, 1980.
364a. STARKEBAUM G, HARLAN JM: Endothelial cell injury due to copper-catalyzed hydrogen peroxide generation from homocysteine. *J Clin Invest* 77:1370, 1986.
365. RODGERS GM, KANE WH: Activation of endogenous factor V by a homocysteine-induced vascular endothelial cell activator. *J Clin Invest* 77:1909, 1986.
365a. GOSPODAROWICZ D, MORAN J, BRAUN D, BIRDWELL C: Clonal growth of bovine vascular endothelial cells: Fibroblast growth factor as a survival agent. *Proc Natl Acad Sci USA* 73:4120, 1976.
365b. PANGANAMALA RV, KARPEN CW, MEROLA AJ: Peroxide mediated effects of homocysteine on arterial prostacyclin synthesis. *Prostaglandins, Leukotrienes and Medicine* 22:349, 1986.
366. DUDMAN NPB, WILCKEN DEL: Homocysteine thiolactone and experimental homocysteinemia. *Biochem Med* 27:244, 1982.
367. DE GROOT PG, WILLEMS C, BOERS GHJ, GONSALVES MD, VAN AKEN WG, VAN MOURIK JA: Endothelial cell dysfunction in homocystinuria. *Eur J Clin Invest* 13:405, 1983.
368. MCCULLY KS, RAGSDALE BD: Production of arteriosclerosis by homocysteinemia. *Am J Pathol* 61:1, 1970.
369. MCCULLY KS, WILSON RB: Homocysteine theory of arteriosclerosis. *Atherosclerosis* 22:215, 1975.
370. REDDY GSR, WILCKEN DEL: Experimental homocysteinemia in pigs: Comparison with studies in sixteen homocystinuric patients. *Metabolism* 31:778, 1982.
371. DONAHUE S, STURMAN JA, GAULL GE: Arteriosclerosis due to homocyst(e)inemia: Failure to reproduce the model in weanling rabbits. *Am J Pathol* 77:167, 1974.
372. HLADOVEC J: Experimental homocystinemia, endothelial lesions and thrombosis. *Blood Vessels* 16:202, 1979.
373. HARKER LA, HARLAN JM, ROSS R: Effect of sulfinpyrazone on homocysteine-induced endothelial injury and arteriosclerosis in baboons. *Circ Res* 53:731, 1983.
373a. RINEHART JF, GREENBERG LD: Arteriosclerotic lesions in pyridoxine-deficient monkeys. *Am J Pathol* 25:481, 1949.
373b. RINEHART JF, GREENBERG LD: Pathogenesis of experimental arteriosclerosis in pyridoxine deficiency. With notes on similarities to human arteriosclerosis. *Arch Pathol* 51:12, 1956.
373c. RINEHART JF, GREENBERG LD: Vitamin B_6 deficiency in the rhesus monkey. With particular reference to the occurrence of arteriosclerosis, dental caries and hepatic cirrhosis. *Am J Clin Nutr* 4:318, 1956.
373d. MUSHETT CW, EMERSON GA: Arteriosclerosis in pyridoxine deficient monkeys and dogs. *Fed Proc* 15:526, 1956.
373e. MANN GV: Blood changes in experimental primates fed purified diets: Pyridoxine and riboflavin deficiency. *Vitam Horm* 26:465, 1968.
374. KRISHNASWAMY K, RAO SB: Failure to produce atherosclerosis in *Macaca radiata* on a high-methionine, high-fat, pyridoxine-deficient diet. *Atherosclerosis* 27:253, 1977.
375. JACKSON CM: Biochemistry of prothrombin activation, in Bloom AL, Thomas DP (eds): *Haemostasis and Thrombosis.* London, Churchill Livingstone, 1981, p 140.
376. JACKSON CM: Mechanisms of prothrombin activation, in Colman RW, Hirsh J, Marder VJ, Salzman EW (eds): *Hemostasis and Thrombosis: Basic Principles and Clinical Practice.* Philadelphia, JB Lippincott, 1982, p 100.
377. RODGERS GM, SHUMAN MA: Prothrombin is activated on vascular endothelial cells by factor Xa and calcium. *Proc Natl Acad Sci USA* 80:7001, 1983.
378. STERN DM, NAWROTH PP, KISIEL W, HANDLEY D, DRILLINGS M, BARTOS J: A coagulation pathway on bovine aortic segments leading to generation of Factor Xa and thrombin. *J Clin Invest* 74:1910, 1984.
379. GIANNINI MJ, COLEMAN M, INNERFIELD I: Antithrombin activity in homocystinuria. *Lancet* 1:1094, 1975.
380. MARUYAMA I, FUKUDA R, KAZAMA M, ABE T, YOSHIDA Y, IGATA A: A case of homocystinuria with low antithrombin activity. *Acta Haem Jpn* 40:267, 1977.
381. BARROWCLIFFE TW, THOMAS DP: Antithrombin III and heparin, in Bloom AL, Thomas DP (eds): *Haemostasis and Thrombosis.* London, Churchill Livingstone, 1981, p 712.
382. ROSENBERG RD: Heparin-antithrombin system, in Colman RW, Hirsh J, Marder VJ, Salzman EW (eds): *Hemostasis and Thrombosis: Basic Principles and Clinical Practice.* Philadelphia, JB Lippincott, 1982, p 962.
383. RATNOFF OD: Activation of Hageman factor by L-homocystine. *Science* 162:1007, 1968.
384. TRAUB W, PIEZ KA: The chemistry and structure of collagen. *Adv Protein Chem* 25:243, 1971.
385. GRANT ME, PROCKOP DJ: The biosynthesis of collagen: Third of three parts. *N Engl J Med* 286:291, 1972.
386. GALLOP PM, BLUMENFELD OO, SEIFTER S: Structure and metabolism of connective tissue proteins. *Ann Rev Biochem* 41:617, 1972.
387. TANZER ML: Cross-linking of collagen. *Science* 180:561, 1973.
388. GALLOP PM, PAZ MA: Posttranslational protein modifications, with special attention to collagen and elastin. *Physiol Rev* 55:418, 1975.

389. SIEGEL RC: Lysyl oxidase. *Int Rev Connect Tissue Res* 8:73, 1979.
390. HARRIS ED JR, SJOERDSMA A: Collagen profile in various clinical conditions. *Lancet* 2:707, 1966.
391. HARRIS ED JR, SJOERDSMA A: Effect of penicillamine on human collagen and its possible application to treatment of scleroderma. *Lancet* 2:996, 1966.
392. KANG AH, TRELSTAD RL: A collagen defect in homocystinuria. *J Clin Invest* 52:2571, 1973.
393. LINDBERG KA, HASSETT A, PINNELL SR: Inhibition of lysyl oxidase by homocysteine: A proposed connective tissue defect in homocystinuria. *J Clin Res* 24:265A, 1976.
394. SIEGEL RC: Collagen cross-linking: Effect of D-penicillamine on cross-linking *in vitro*. *J Biol Chem* 252:254, 1977.
395. SIEGEL RC: The connective tissue defect in homocystinuria (HS). *Clin Res* 23:263a, 1975.
396. SIEGEL RC: The connective tissue defect in homocystinuria (HS). *Arthritis Rheum* 18:425, 1975.
397. PONSETI IV, SHEPARD RS: Lesions of the skeleton and other mesodermal tissues in rats fed sweet-pea *(Lathyrus odoratus)* seeds. *J Bone Jt Surg* 36A:1031, 1954.
398. SELYE H: Lathyrism. *Rev Can Biol* 16:1, 1957.
399. RIVARD GE, LAZERSON J, IZADI P, KIM YJ: Collagen in homocystinuria. *N Engl J Med* 291:1364, 1974.
400. PIRIE A, VAN HEYNINGEN R: *Biochemistry of the Eye*. Springfield, IL, Charles C Thomas, 1956.
401. BUDDECKE E, WOLLENSAK J: Zur Biochemie der Zonulafaser des Rinderauges. *Z Naturforsch* 21B:337, 1965.
402. WOLLENSAK J: Zonula Zinnii. *Fortschr Augenheilkd* 16:240, 1965.
403. IRREVERRE F, MUDD SH, HEIZER WD, LASTER L: Sulfite oxidase deficiency: Studies of a patient with mental retardation, dislocated ocular lenses, and abnormal urinary excretion of S-sulfo-L-cysteine, sulfite, and thiosulfate. *Biochem Med* 1:187, 1967.
404. ORLOWSKI M, MEISTER A: Isolation of highly purified γ-glutamylcysteine synthetase from rat kidney. *Biochemistry* 10:372, 1971.
405. STOKKE O, MARSTEIN S, JELLUM E, LIE SO: Accumulation of pyroglutamic acid (5-oxoproline) in homocystinuria. *Scand J Clin Lab Invest* 42:361, 1982.
406. TALLAN HH, MOORE S, STEIN WH: L-Cystathionine in human brain. *J Biol Chem* 230:707, 1958.
407. WISNIEWSKI K, STURMAN JA, DEVINE E, BROWN WT, RUDELLI R, WISNIEWSKI HM: Cystathionine disappearance with neuronal loss: A possible neuronal marker. *Neuropediatrics* 16:126, 1985.
408. TUDBALL N, BEAUMONT A: Studies on the neurochemical properties of cystathionine. *Biochem Biophys Acta* 588:285, 1979.
409. BRENTON DP, CUSWORTH DC, GAULL GE: Homocystinuria: Biochemical studies of tissues including a comparison with cystathioninuria. *Pediatrics* 35:50, 1965.
410. PERRY TL: Homocystinuria, in Nyhan WL (ed): *Heritable Disorders of Amino Acid Metabolism*. New York, Wiley, 1974, p 395.
411. WILCKEN B, TURNER G: Homocystinuria in New South Wales. *Arch Dis Child* 53:242, 1978.
412. PULLON DHH: Homocystinuria and other methioninemias, in Bickel H, Guthrie R, Hammersen G (eds): *Neonatal Screening for Inborn Errors of Metabolism*. Berlin, Springer-Verlag, 1980, p 29.
413. SHIH VE: Personal communication.
414. SPRINCE H, PARKER CM, JOSEPHS JA JR: Homocysteine-induced convulsions in the rat: Protection by homoserine, serine, betaine, glycine and glucose. *Agents Actions* 1:9, 1969.
415. SPRINCE H, PARKER CM, JOSEPHS JA JR, MAGAZINO J: Convulsant activity of homocysteine and other short-chain mercaptoacids: Protection therefrom. *Ann NY Acad Sci* 166:323, 1969.
416. BLENNOW G, FOLBERGROVA J, NILSSON B, SIESJO BK: Cerebral metabolic and circulatory changes in the rat during sustained seizures induced by DL-homocysteine. *Brain Res* 179:129, 1979.
417. FOLBERGROVA J: Energy metabolism of mouse cerebral cortex during homocysteine convulsions. *Brain Res* 81:443, 1974.
418. WUERTHELE SE, YASUDA RP, FREED WJ, HOFFER BJ: The effect of local application of homocysteine on neuronal activity in the central nervous system of the rat. *Life Sci* 31:2683, 1982.
418a. WALTON NY, TREIMAN DM: Experimental secondarily generalized convulsive status epilepticus induced by D,L-homocysteine thiolactone. *Epilepsy Res* 2:79, 1988.
419. FREED WJ, TAYLOR SP, LUCHINS DJ, WYATT RJ, GILLIN JC: Production of convulsions in mice by the combination of methionine and homocysteine. *Psychopharmacology* 69:275, 1980.
420. HURD RW, HAMMOND EJ, WILDER BJ: Homocysteine induced convulsions: Enhancement by vitamin B_6 and inhibition by hydrazine. *Brain Res* 209:250, 1981.
421. GRIFFITHS R, WILLIAMS DC, O'NEIL C, DEWHURST IC, EKUWEM CE, SINCLAIR CD: Synergistic inhibition of [^{3}H]muscimol binding to calf-brain synaptic membranes in the presence of L-homocysteine and pyridoxal 5'-phosphate. A possible mechanism for homocysteine-induced seizures. *Eur J Biochem* 137:467, 1983.
422. McILWAIN H, POLL JD: Interaction between adenosine generated endogenously in neocortical tissues, and homocysteine and its thiolactone. *Neurochem Int* 7:103, 1985.
423. TUDBALL N, GRIFFITHS R: Biochemical changes in the brain of experimental animals in response to elevated plasma homocystine and methionine. *J Neurochem* 26:1149, 1976.
424. PHILLIS JW: S-Adenosylmethionine excites rat cerebral cortical neurons. *Brain Res* 213:223, 1981.
425. FONLUPT P, ROCHE M, CRONENBERGER L, PACHECO H: La S-adenosyl-L-homocysteine: 1. Inductrice de sommeil. *Can J Physiol Pharmacol* 58:160, 1980.
426. FONLUPT P, ROCHE M, ANDRE A-C, CRONENBERGER L, PACHECO H: La S-adenosyl-L-homocysteine: 2. Anticonvulsivante. *Can J Physiol Pharmacol* 58:493, 1980.
427. SARDA N, DUBOIS M, GHARIB A, VALATX JL, JOUVET M: Increase of paradoxical sleep induced by S-adenosyl-L-homocysteine. *Neurosci Lett* 30:69, 1982.
428. SARDA N, GHARIB A, PACHECO H, JOUVET M: Possible involvement of the S-adenosyl-L-homocysteine metabolites, adenosine and L-homocysteine in sleep in rats. *Neurosci Lett* 66:287, 1986.
429. CANTONI GL: The centrality of S-adenosylhomocysteinase in the regulation of the biological utilization of S-adenosylmethionine, in Borchardt RT, Creveling CR, Ueland PM (eds): *Biological Methylation and Drug Design*. Bethesda, MD: The Human Press, 1986, p 227.
430. STEINMANN B: Personal communication, 1981.
431. SCHATZ RA, WILENS TE, SELLINGER OZ: Decreased transmethylation of biogenic amines after *in vivo* elevation of S-adenosyl-L-homocysteine. *J Neurochem* 36:1739, 1981.
432. SCHATZ RA, WILENS TE, SELLINGER OZ: Decreased *in vivo* protein and phospholipid methylation after *in vivo* elevation of brain S-adenosyl-homocysteine. *Biochem Biophys Res Commun* 98:1097, 1981.
433. BRAND E, HARRIS MM, BILOON S: Cystinuria: The excretion of cystine complex which decomposes in the urine with the liberation of free cystine. *J Biol Chem* 86:315, 1930.
434. SPAETH GL, BARBER GW: Prevalence of homocystinuria among the mentally retarded: Evaluation of a specific screening test. *Pediatrics* 40:586, 1967.
435. SHIH VE: *Laboratory Techniques for the Detection of Hereditary Metabolic Disorders*. Cleveland, CRC Press, 1973.
436. WILCKEN B, TURNER B, BROWN DA: Detection of abnormal sulphur-containing amino acid excretion in a mass urine-screening programme. *Med J Aust* 1:1193, 1972.
437. EFRON ML: Two-way separation of amino acids and other ninhydrin-reacting substances by high-voltage electrophoresis followed by paper chromatography. *Biochem J* 72:691, 1959.
438. MUDD SH, POOLE JR, SIGGERS DC: Unpublished observations.
439. GUTHRIE R: Screening for "inborn errors of metabolism," in the newborn infant—A multiple test program. *Birth Defects* 4:92, 1968.
440. UHLENDORF BW, MUDD SH: Cystathionine synthase in tissue culture derived from human skin: Enzyme defect in homocystinuria. *Science* 160:1007, 1968.
441. GAULL GE, RASSIN DK, STURMAN JA: Pyridoxine-dependency in homocystinuria. *Lancet* 2:1302, 1968.
442. HOLLOWELL JG JR, CORYELL ME, HALL WK, FINDLEY JK, THEVAOS TG: Homocystinuria as affected by pyridoxine, folic acid, and vitamin B_{12}. *Proc Soc Exp Biol Med* 129:237, 1968.
443. GROBE H: Homocystinuria (cystathionine synthase deficiency): Results of treatment in late-diagnosed patients. *Eur J Pediatr* 135:199, 1980.
444. SCHAUMBURG H, KAPLAN J, WINDEBANK A, VICK N, RASMUS S, PLEASURE D, BROWN MJ: Sensory neuropathy from pyridoxine abuse: A new megavitamin syndrome. *N Engl J Med* 309:445, 1983.
445. BERGER A, SCHAUMBURG HH: More on neuropathy from pyridoxine abuse. *N Engl J Med* 311:986, 1984.
446. COHEN M, BENDICH A: Safety of pyridoxine—A review of human and animal studies. *Toxicol Lett* 34:129, 1986.
447. YOSHIDA I, SAKAGUCHI Y, NAKANO M, YAMASHITA F, HITOSHI T: Pyridoxal phospate-induced liver injury in a patient with homocystinuria. *J Inherited Metab Dis* 8:91, 1985.
448. POOLE JR, MUDD SH, CONERLY EB, EDWARDS WA: Homocystinuria due to cystathionine synthase deficiency: Studies of nitrogen balance and sulfur excretion. *J Clin Invest* 55:1033, 1975.
449. Task Force on Dietary Management of Metabolic Disorders. Committee on Nutrition, American Academy of Pediatrics. Report to FDA, Contract 22372-2304. December 1985.

450. ACOSTA PB, ELSAS LJ II: *Dietary Management of Inherited Metabolic Disease: Phenylketonuria, Galactosemia, Tyrosinemia, Homocystinuria, Maple Syrup Urine Disease*. Atlanta, ACELMU Publishers, 1976, p 52.

451. VAN SPRANG FJ, WADMAN SK: Treatment of homocystinuria, in Carson NAJ, Raine DN (eds): *Inherited Disorders of Sulphur Metabolism*. London, Churchill Livingstone, 1971, p 275.

452. PARKINSON MS: Therapeutic problems of adolescent homocystinuria. *Proc R Soc Med* 62:909, 1969.

453. SCHULMAN JD: Approaches to the treatment of inborn errors of sulphur amino acid and peptide metabolism, in Papadatos CJ, Bartsocas CS (eds): *The Management of Genetic Disorders*. New York, AR Liss, 1979, p 201.

454. PERRY TL, HANSEN S, LOVE DL, CRAWFORD LE, TISCHLER B: Treatment of homocystinuria with a low-methionine diet, supplemental cystine, and a methyl donor. *Lancet* 2:474, 1968.

455. KOMROWER GM, SARDHARWALLA IB: The dietary treatment of homocystinuria, in Carson NAJ, Raine DN (eds): *Inherited Disorders of Sulphur Metabolism*. London, Churchill Livingstone, 1971, p 254.

456. CARSON NAJ: Homocystinuria: Trial treatment of a 5-year-old severely retarded child with a natural diet low in methionine. *Am J Dis Child* 113:95, 1967.

457. PERRY TL: Treatment of homocystinuria with a low-methionine diet and supplemental L-cystine, in Carson NAJ, Raine DN (eds): *Inherited Disorders of Sulphur Metabolism*. London, Churchill Livingstone, 1971, p 245.

457a. AMRAM S, PALCOUX JB, MALPUECH G, PLAZONNET MJ, STORME B, MEYER M: Homocystinurie pyridoxino-résistante. A propos d'un cas avec accidents thromboemboliques précoces. *Arch Fr Pediatr* 43:715, 1986.

457b. PULLON DHH: Aspects of treatment of homocystinuria: An illustrative case report. *NZ Med J* 101:10, 1988.

458. SCHULMAN JD, AGARWAL B, MUDD SH, SHULMAN NR: Pulmonary embolism in a homocystinuric patient during treatment with dipyridamole and acetylsalicylic acid. *N Engl J Med* 299:661, 1978.

459. SCHULMAN JD, MUDD SH, SHULMAN NR, LANDVATER L: Pregnancy and thombophlebitis in homocystinuria. *Blood* 56:326, 1980.

460. GROBE H: Homocystinuria and oral contraceptives. *Lancet* 1:158, 1978.

461. FRANCOIS J: Homocystinuria, in Winkelman JE, Crone RA (eds): *Perspectives in Ophthalmology*. Amsterdam, Excerpta Medica, 1970, vol 2, p 81.

462. FROST PM: Anaesthesia and homocystinuria. *Anaesthesia* 35:918, 1980.

463. FUKS AB, KAUFMAN E, GALILI D, GARFUNKEL A: Comprehensive dental treatment under general anesthesia for patients with homocystinuria. *J Dent Child* 47:340, 1980.

464. REGENBOGEN L, ILIE S, ELIAN I: Homocystinuria—A surgical and anesthetic risk. *Metab Pediatr Ophthalmol* 4:209, 1980.

465. CROOKE JW, TOWERS JF, TAYLOR WH: Management of patients with homocystinuria requiring surgery under general anaesthesia. *Br J Anaesth* 43:96, 1971.

466. KOSSOWICZ H: Surgical treatment of dislocated lenses in homocystinuria. *Metab Ophthalmol* 1:121, 1977.

467. GROVER VK, MALHOTRA SK, KAUSHIK S: Anaesthesia and homocystinuria. *Anaethesia* 34:913, 1979.

468. TADA K, TATEDA H, ARASHIMA S, SAKAI K, KITAGAWA T, AOKI K, SUWA S, KAWAMURA M, OURA T, TAKESADA M, KURODA Y, YAMASHITA F, MATSUDA I, NARUSE H: Follow-up study of a nation-wide neonatal metabolic screening program in Japan. *Eur J Pediatr* 142:204, 1984.

469. BICKEL H: Neonatal mass screening for inborn errors of metabolism, in *Recent Progress in Perinatal Medicine and Prevention of Congenital Anamaly*. IYC Commemorative Congress, Oct 21–22, 1979, Tokyo. Ministry of Health and Welfare, Government of Japan, Medical Information Service, Inc, Tokyo, pp 260–269.

470. SARDHARWALLA IB: Personal communication, 1987.

471. LYONS I, VEALE A: Personal communication, 1987.

472. KENNEDY R, STEVENSON J: Personal communication, 1981.

473. CAHALANE S: Personal communication, 1981.

474. ALM J, LARSSON A: Evaluation of a nation-wide neonatal metabolic screening programme in Sweden 1965–1979. *Acta Paediatr Scand* 70:601, 1981.

475. CARSON NAJ: Personal communication, 1980.

476. WHITEMAN PD, CLAYTON BE, ERSSER RS, LILLY P, SEAKINS JWT: Changing incidence of neonatal hypermethioninaemia: Implications for the detection of homocystinuria. *Arch Dis Child* 54:593, 1979.

477. LEVY HL, MITCHELL ML: The current status of newborn screening. *Hosp Pract* 17:89, 1982.

478. THERRELL BL, BROWN LO, DZIUK PE, PETER WP: The Texas newborn screening program. *Tex Med* 79:44, 1983.

479. FOREMAN JW, WALD H, BLUMBERG G, PEPE LM, SEGAL S: Homocystine uptake in isolated rat renal cortical tubules. *Metabolism* 31:613, 1982.

480. LEVY HL: Unpublished observations, 1987.

481. LEVY HL, MADIGAN PM, SHIH VE: Massachusetts metabolic disorders screening program. I. Technics and results of urine screening. *Pediatrics* 49:825, 1972.

482. WATANABE T, KURODA Y, NAITO E, ITO M, TAKEDA E, TOSHIMA K, TOMITA T, MIYAO M, FURUKAWA S: Urinary homocystine levels in a newborn infant with cystathionine synthase deficiency. *Eur J Pediatr* 146:436, 1987.

482a. TOTANI M, SHIMIZU S, YAMADA H, MURACHI T: Screening for neonatal homocystinuria by enzymic determination of homocysteine. *Biochem Soc Trans* 14:1172, 1986.

483. BOERS GHJ, FOWLER B, SMALS AGH, TRIJBELS FJM, LEERMAKERS AI, KLEIJER WJ, KLOPPENBERG PWC: Improved identification of heterozygotes for homocystinuria due to cystathionine synthase deficiency by the combination of methionine loading and enzyme determination in cultured fibroblasts. *Hum Genet* 69:164, 1985.

484. BOERS GH, SMALS AG, TRIJBELS FJ, LEERMAKERS AI, KLOPPENBORG PW: Unique efficiency of methionine metabolism in premenopausal women may protect against vascular disease in the reproductive years. *J Clin Invest* 72:1971, 1983.

485. BRATTSTRÖM LE, HULTBERG BL, HARDEBO JE: Folic acid responsive postmenopausal homocysteinemia. *Metabolism* 34:1073, 1985.

486. KANG S-S: Personal communication, 1987.

487. WILCKEN DEL, WILCKEN B: The pathogenesis of coronary artery disease: A possible role for methionine metabolism. *J Clin Invest* 57:1079, 1976.

488. SARDHARWALLA IB, FOWLER B, ROBINS AJ, KOMROWER GM: Detection of heterozygotes for homocystinuria: Study of sulphur-containing amino acids in plasma and urine after L-methionine loading. *Arch Dis Child* 49:553, 1974.

489. WILCKEN DEL, REDDY SG, GUPTA VJ: Homocysteinemia, ischemic heart disease, and the carrier state for homocystinuria. *Metabolism* 32:363, 1983.

490. MUDD SH, HAVLIK R, LEVY HL, MCKUSICK VA, FEINLEIB M: A study of cardiovascular risk in heterozygotes for homocystinuria. *Am J Hum Genet* 33:883, 1981.

491. BOERS G, SMALS A, KLOPPENBORG P, TRIJBELS F, BAKKEREN J, SCHOONDERWALDT H, FOWLER B, KLEIJER W: Heterozygosity for homocystinuria in premature arterial disease. *N Engl J Med* 314:850, 1986.

492. BRATTSTRÖM LE, HARDEBO JE, HULTBERG BL: Moderate homocysteinemia—A possible risk factor for arteriosclerotic cerebrovascular disease. *Stroke* 15:1012, 1984.

493. MURPHY-CHUTORIAN DR, WEXMAN MP, GRIECO AJ, HEININGER JA, GLASSMAN E, GAULL GE, NG SKC, FEIT F, WEXMAN K, FOX AC: Methionine intolerance: A possible risk factor for coronary artery disease. *J Am Coll Cardiol* 6:725, 1985.

494. SWIFT ME, SHULTZ TD: Relationship of vitamins B-6 and B-12 to homocysteine levels: Risk for coronary artery disease. *Nutr Rep Internat* 34:1, 1986.

495. KANG S-S, WONG PWK, NORUSIS M: Homocysteinemia due to folate deficiency. *Metabolism* 36:458, 1987.

495a. WILCKEN DEL, DUDMAN NPB, TYRRELL PA, ROBERTSON MR: Folic acid lowers elevated plasma homocyst(e)ine in chronic renal insufficiency: Possible implications for prevention of vascular disease. *Metabolism*, in press, 1988.

495b. LAIDLAW SA, SMOLIN LA, DAVIDSON WD, KOPPLE JD: Sulfur amino acids in maintenance hemodialysis patients. *Kidney Int* 32(*Suppl.* 22):S-191, 1987.

496. MUDD SH: Discussion in Carson NAJ, Raine DN (eds): *Inherited Disorders of Sulphur Metabolism*. London, Churchill Livingstone, 1971, p 311.

496a. FLEISHER LD, LONGHI RC, TALLAN HH, BERATIS NG, HIRSCHHORN K, GAULL GE: Homocystinuria: Investigations of cystathionine synthase in cultured fetal cells and the prenatal determination of genetic status. *J Pediatr* 85:677, 1974.

497. FENSOM AH, BENSON PF, CREES MJ, ELLIS M: Prenatal exclusion of homocystinuria (cystathionine β-synthase deficiency) by assay of phytohaemagglutinin-stimulated fetal lymphocytes. *Prenat Diag* 3:127, 1983.

498. HARRIS H, PENROSE LS, THOMAS DHH: Cystathioninuria. *Ann Hum Genet* 23:442, 1959.

499. FRIMPTER GW: Cystathioninuria: Nature of the defect. *Science* 149:1095, 1965.

500. FINKELSTEIN JD, MUDD SH, IRREVERRE F, LASTER L: Deficiencies of cystathionase and homoserine dehydratase activities in cystathioninuria. *Proc Natl Acad Sci USA* 55:865, 1966.

501. HOOFT C, CARTON D, DeSCHRYVER F: Cystathioninemia in three siblings, in Allan JD, Holt HS, Ireland JT, Pollitt RJ (eds): *Enzymopenic Anaemias, Lysosomes and Other Papers*. London, Churchill Livingstone, 1969, p 200.

502. HOOFT C: Personal communication, 1975.

503. PASCAL TA, GAULL GE, BERATIS NG, GILLAM BM, TALLAN HH, HIRSCHHORN K: Vitamin B_6-responsive and -unresponsive cystathioninuria: Two variant molecular forms. *Science* 190:1209, 1975.

504. PASCALL TA, GAULL GE, BERATIS NG, GILLAM BM, TALLAN HH: Cystathionase deficiency: Evidence for genetic heterogeneity in primary cystathioninuria. *Pediatr Res* 12:125, 1978.
505. PASCAL TA, BERATIS NG, TALLAN HH, GAULL GE: Cystathionase deficiency: The effect of cofactor on the stability of normal and abnormal enzyme from lymphoid cell lines. *Enzyme* 24:265, 1979.
506. BITTLES AH, CARSON NAJ: Cystathionase deficiency in fibroblast cultures from a patient with primary cystathioninuria. *J Med Genet* 11:121, 1974.
507. KINT JA, CARTON D: New evidence for the identity of homoserine deaminase and cystathionase in human liver. *Arch Int Physiol Biochem* 79:202, 1971.
508. PASCAL TA, TALLAN HH, GILLAM BM: Hepatic cystathionase: Immunochemical and electrophoretic studies of the human and rat forms. *Biochem Biophys Acta* 285:48, 1972.
509. ROISIN M-P, CHATAGNER F: Purification et étude de quelques propriétés de l'homocysteine desulfhydrase du foie de rat. Identification à la cystathionase. *Bull Soc Chim Biol* 51:481, 1969.
510. FRIMPTER GW, HAYMOVITZ A, HORWITH M: Cystathioninuria. *N Engl J Med* 268:333, 1963.
511. FRIMPTER GW: Cystathioninuria, in Wyngaarden JB, Fredrickson DS (eds): *The Metabolic Basis of Inherited Disease,* 2d ed. New York, McGraw-Hill, 1966, p 409.
512. BERLOW S: Studies in cystathioninemia. *Am J Dis Child* 112:135, 1966.
513. FRIMPTER GW: Personal communication, 1981.
514. HARAGUCHI H, IWATANI E, HIROSAWA M, YAMASHITA F, NAGAYAMA T: Studies on cystathioninuria. *Igakunoayumi (Jpn)* 61:72, 1967.
515. PERRY TL, ROBINSON GC, TEASDALE JM, HANSEN S: Concurrence of cystathioninuria, nephrogenic diabetes insipidus and severe anemia. *N Engl J Med* 276:721, 1967.
516. PERRY TL, HARDWICK DF, HANSEN S, LOVE DL, ISRAELS S: Cystathioninuria in two healthy siblings. *N Engl J Med* 278:590, 1968.
517. PERRY TL: Personal communication, 1981.
518. KODAMA H, YAO K, KOBAYASHI K, HIRAYAMA K, FUJII Y, MIZUHARA S, HARAGUCHI H, HIROSAWA M: New sulfur-containing amino acids in the urine of cystathioninuric patients. *Physiol Chem Phys* 1:72, 1969.
519. NISHIKAWA M, ITO S, SANO K, NISHIOEDA Y, FUJISAWA T, MORI T, SEO K: A case of familial cystathioninuria with goiter and some anomalies. *Endocrinol Jpn* 17:57, 1970.
520. SCOTT CR, DASSELL SE, CLARK SH, CHANG-TENG C, SWEDBERG KR: Cystathioninemia: A benign genetic condition. *J Pediatr* 76:571, 1970.
521. FRIMPTER GW: Recurrent urinary tract calculi possible due to inherited cystathioninuria. *Aerosp Med* 44:1300, 1973.
522. LEVY HL, SHIH VE: Unpublished observations.
523. LEVY HL, MUDD SH, MADIGAN PM: Pyridoxine-unresponsive cystathioninemia. *Pediatr Res* 7:162, 1973.
524. AVRUSKIN TW, KANG ES: Cystathioninuria, mental retardation, and juvenile diabetes mellitus. *Am J Dis Child* 127:250, 1974.
525. WADMAN SK, HEIDEN CVD, VAN SPRANG FJ, VOUTE PA: Primary cystathioninuria and cystathioninuria in patients with neurogenic tumors. Analytical results, in Carson NAJ, Raine DN (eds): *Inherited Disorders of Sulphur Metabolism.* London, Churchill Livingstone, 1971, p 56.
526. WADMAN SK: Personal communication, 1981.
527. BREMER HJ, ENDRES W: Primary cystathioninuria: Methionine load tests and response to pyridoxine. *Helv Paediatr Acta* 27:525, 1972.
528. SCHNEIDERMAN LJ: Latent cystathioninuria. *J Med Genet* 4:260, 1967.
529. MONGEAU J-G, HILGARTNER M, WORTHEN HG, FRIMPTER GW: Cystathioninuria: Study of an infant with normal mentality, thrombocytopenia, and renal calculi. *J Pediatr* 69:1113, 1966.
530. PERRY TL, JONES RT: The amino acid content of human cerebrospinal fluid in normal individuals and in mental defectives. *J Clin Invest* 40:1363, 1961.
531. TADA K, YOSDHIDA T, ARAKAWA T: Free amino acid pattern in the liver from the patients with amino acid disorders: Postmortem diagnosis of inborn errors of amino acid metabolism. *Tohoku J Exp Med* 101:223, 1970.
532. PERRY TL, HANSEN S, LOVE D, FINCH CA: N-Acetylcystathionine: A new urinary amino-acid in congenital cystathioninuria. *Nature* 219:178, 1968.
533. KODAMA H, IKEGAMA T, HIRAYAMA K, MIZUHARA S: Effect of pyridoxine treatment of a cystathioninuric patient on the urinary excretion of some unusual sulfur-containing amino acids. *Clin Chim Acta* 51:29, 1974.
534. KODAMA H, ISHIMOTO Y, SHIMOMURA M, HIROTA T, OHMORI S: Isolation of two new sulfur-containing amino acids from the urine of a cystathioninuric patient. *Physiol Chem Phys* 7:147, 1975.
535. RICCI G, NARDINI M, FEDERICI G, CAVALLINI D: The transamination of L-cystathionine, L-cystine and related compounds by a bovine kidney transaminase. *Eur J Biochem* 157:57, 1986.
536. NARDINI M, KODAMA H, RICCI G, FEDERICI G, CAVALLINI D: Enzymatic production of S-(2-hydroxy-2-carboxyethyl) homocysteine. *Biochem Internat* 11:789, 1985.
537. KODAMA H, SASAKI K, AGETA T: Effect of propargylglycine on cystathionine metabolism in rats. *Biochem Internat* 4:195, 1982.
538. FRIMPTER GW, KOZLOWSKI KK, HORWITH M: Distribution of sulfur in urine of patients with cystathioninuria before and during administration of pyridoxine. *Metabolism* 25:355, 1976.
539. GUARINI L, PASCAL TA, GAULL GE, BERATIS NG: Studies with cystathionase-deficient lymphoid cell lines in culture. *Enzyme* 27:69, 1982.
540. LEVY HL, COULOMBE JT, SHIH VE: Newborn urine screening, in Bickel H, Guthrie R, Hammersen G (eds): *Neonatal Screening for Inborn Errors of Metabolism.* Heidelberg, Springer-Verlag, 1980, p 89.
541. WILCKEN B, SMITH A, BROWN DA: Urine screening for aminoacidopathies: Is it beneficial? *J Pediatr* 97:492, 1980.
542. RODRIJUEZ-ANZA S, LEVY HL: Maternal homocystinuria. *Pediatr Res* 20:271a, 1986.
543. MITCHELL JRA: Personal communication, 1986.
544. BRENTON DP, CUSWORTH DC, BIDDLE SA, GARROD PJ, LASLEY L: Pregnancy and homocystinuria. *Ann Clin Biochem* 14:161, 1977.
545. CARSON D: Personal communication, 1987.
546. CONSTANTINE G, GREEN A: Untreated homocystinuria: A maternal death in a woman with four pregnancies. Case report. *Br J Obstet Gynaecol* 94:803, 1987.
547. McCULLY KS, VEZERIDIS MP: Homocysteine thiolactone in arteriosclerosis and cancer. *Res Commun Chem Pathol Pharmacol* 59:107, 1988.
548. LEVY HL, MATORIN AI, MUDD SH: Unpublished observations, 1988.
549. DUDMAN NPB, WILCKEN DEL: Personal communication, 1988.
550. OLSZEWSKI AJ, SZOSTAK WB: Homocysteine content of plasma proteins in ischemic heart disease. *Atherosclerosis* 69:109, 1988.

CHAPTER **24**

SARCOSINEMIA

C. RONALD SCOTT

1. *Sarcosinemia is a phenotype characterized by increased concentration of sarcosine (N-methylglycine) in plasma and increased excretion of sarcosine in the urine. Sarcosinemia occurs because of a defect in the conversion of sarcosine to glycine that is catalyzed by sarcosine dehydrogenase. A deficiency of sarcosine dehydrogenase can occur because of a genetic alteration in the apoenzyme, a dysfunctioning of a necessary electron transferring flavoprotein, or a severe deficiency of folic acid.*
2. *The formation and degradation of sarcosine occurs in liver and kidney tissue. Sarcosine is enzymatically formed from dimethylglycine by dimethylglycine dehydrogenase (EC 1.5.99.2) and converted to glycine by sarcosine dehydrogenase (EC 1.5.99.1). A small fraction of sarcosine may be generated from glycine by the enzyme glycine methyltransferase (EC 2.1.1.20).*
3. *It was originally reported that sarcosinemia was causally related to mental retardation or neurologic problems. It is most probable that sarcosinemia is a "benign" condition that is unrelated to neurologic symptoms or significant clinical problems.*
4. *Sarcosinemia that occurs from a genetic deficiency of sarcosine dehydrogenase activity is inherited as an autosomal recessive condition. The incidence of sarcosinemia from newborn screening programs that evaluate urine specimens has varied from 1:350,000 (New England) to 1:43,000 (Quebec). The gene has not been cloned, and the chromosomal location is unknown. Detection of heterozygotes by sarcosine-loading studies is unreliable.*

Sarcosinemia is a rare and controversial disorder. Originally described in 1966 in a child with mental retardation, it was assumed that sarcosinemia, similar to phenylketonuria, was responsible for the child's neurologic symptoms.[1] In the following years, additional persons were identified with sarcosinemia who had symptoms of mental disorder; others had congenital defects, and still others were clinically normal. It was subsequently proposed that the finding of sarcosinemia in individuals with neurologic symptoms most likely occurred because of ascertainment bias, i.e., only persons with clinical problems routinely underwent evaluation for alterations in plasma or urine amino acid concentrations. This concept of sarcosinemia being a benign condition is currently the most prevalent belief, but some doubt remains, based on family data and the fact that more than a single biochemical mechanism may account for elevated concentrations of sarcosine in biologic fluid.

The enzymatic error in the most common phenotype of sarcosinemia is sarcosine dehydrogenase. Precise and convincing enzymatic data are lacking in these patients because of the rarity of the clinical condition and the ethical limitations imposed because the enzyme is expressed in liver and kidney tissue only. Genetic data are consistent with an autosomal recessive mode of inheritance. The precise chromosomal localization of the gene for sarcosine dehydrogenase remains to be delineated.

Sarcosinemia is similar to hyperphenylalanemia or homocystinuria in that more than a single enzyme alteration may exist for the biochemical phenotype. Defects of (1) sarcosine dehydrogenase, (2) an electron transfer flavoprotein, or (3) severe folate deficiency are associated with sarcosinemia.

BIOCHEMISTRY OF SARCOSINE

Sarcosine is a unique amino acid whose role in intermediary metabolism exists primarily as a single step in "one-carbon" metabolism. Structurally, sarcosine (*N*-methylglycine) is a glycine molecule that is modified by the addition of a methyl group attached to its nitrogen atom. The compound is normally undetectable in biologic fluids and is not a component of mammalian protein. Sarcosine is formed from the oxidative demethylation of *N, N*-dimethylglycine. The methyl group is removed at the oxidative level of "active" formaldehyde. In the identical manner that sarcosine is formed from *N, N*-dimethylglycine, sarcosine is oxidized by the removal of the methyl group and the formation of glycine and an active 1-carbon fragment (Fig. 24-1). These two sequential steps are believed to occur by two separate enzymatic proteins, dimethylglycine dehydrogenase and sarcosine dehydrogenase.[2,3] The two consecutive oxidative demethylation steps that produce the active 1-carbon fragments are believed to account for the majority of 1-carbon groups available for the formation of an active 1-carbon fragment.[4] These 1-carbon groups react with tetrahydrofolate to form the intermediate N^5, N^{10}-methylenetetrahydrofolate. This activated intermediate of folic acid is available to form the three-carbon of serine by condensation with glycine and for other intermediary processes.

BIOCHEMISTRY OF DIMETHYLGYCINE DEHYDROGENASE AND SARCOSINE DEHYDROGENASE

The reactions that form sarcosine and its subsequent oxidation to glycine occur within the mitochondria.[3,5] The formation of sarcosine is catalyzed by dimethylglycine dehydrogenase (EC 1.5.99.2) and requires folate as cofactor.[5] The oxidation of sarcosine is performed by sarcosine dehydrogenase (EC 1.5.99.1), and it also requires a folate derivative as cofactor. Both enzymes are flavoproteins with a molecular weight of 90,000 for dimethylglycine dehydrogenase and 105,000 for sarcosine dehydrogenase.[6] In isolated rat liver, these proteins are the major folate binding proteins.[7] The primary folate bound to the enzymes is tetrahydropteroylpentaglutamate.[6–8] The affinity for this compound is $K_d = 0.2\ \mu M$, followed by less strong binding by tetrahydrofolate and its 5-formyl and 5-methyl derivatives. The reduced folates bind a hundredfold tighter than fo-

dimethylglycine $(CH_3)_2N\text{-}CH_2\text{-}COOH$ —(1), H_4 PteGlu → 5,10-CH=H_4 PteGlu→ sarcosine $CH_3\text{-}NH\text{-}CH_2\text{-}COOH$ —(2), H PteGlu → 5,10-CH=H_4 PteGlu→ glycine $NH_2\text{-}CH_2\text{-}COOH$ —(3), H PteGlu→ serine $CH_2OH\text{-}HC\text{-}NH_2\text{-}COOH$

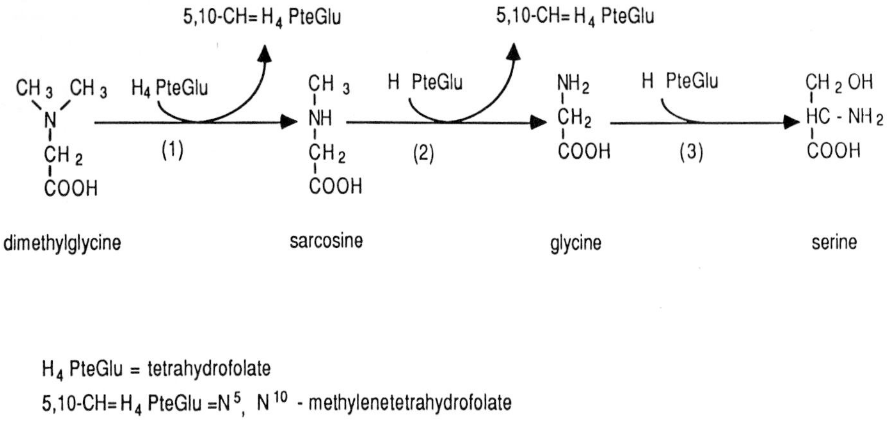

H_4 PteGlu = tetrahydrofolate

5,10-CH=H_4 PteGlu =N^5, N^{10} - methylenetetrahydrofolate

Fig. 24-1 The formation and degradation of sarcosine. (1) Dimethylglycine dehydrogenase, (2) sarcosine dehydrogenase and, (3) serine hydroxymethylase.

late or methyltrexate. Kinetic properties indicate that 1 mol of folate is bound per mole of protein.[9] Similarly, electrophoretic studies show that 1 mol of flavin is bound covalently to 1 mol of protein. Dimethylglycine dehydrogenase demonstrates substrate binding and activity for both dimethylglycine and sarcosine. In addition, *N*-methylalanine and ξ-*N*-methylglycine are also substrates for the reaction. The activity with sarcosine, however, is only 25 percent of that with dimethylglycine. The K_m for dimethylglycine is 0.05 m*M*.[9] The other compounds are significantly poorer substrates. Substrate specificities are assayed with an artificial electron acceptor, phenozinemethosulfate, in the presence of a dye reduction system (2,6-dichloroindophenol).

Sarcosine dehydrogenase and dimethylglycine dehydrogenase have similar binding properties for folates, although the specific properties of the latter enzyme with various folates have not been reported. Sarcosine dehydrogenase does bind sarcosine specifically and does not oxidize other *N*-methyl amino acids. The K_m for sarcosine is 0.5 m*M*.[9]

FORMATION OF "ACTIVE" FORMALDEHYDE

"Active" formaldehyde is formed in the reactions of dimethyl or sarcosine dehydrogenase. The methyl group released by this reaction is used preferentially for incorporation into the 3 carbon of serine.[4] This particular carbon atom participates preferentially in linked enzymatic reactions, and it is called an *active* formaldehyde. Blakely[10] demonstrated that the cosubstrate required by serine hydroxymethyltransferase in the conversion of serine from glycine is 5,10-methylene tetrahydrofolate. A separate enzymatic step converts the released methyl group to 5,10-methylene tetrahydrofolate. The addition of dimethylglycine to its dehydrogenase, prepared with bound [^{3}H]tetrahydrofolate, results in the formation of 5,10-methylene tetrahydrofolate directly. Thus, this compound is formed directly on the protein without undergoing a separate enzymatic reaction. It was postulated that serine hydroxymethylase may be located close to the aforementioned enzymes on the mitochondrial membrane and, thus, have a selective advantage in gaining access to the 5,10-methylene tetrahydrofolate that is formed by the enzymatic action of dimethylglycine and sarcosine dehydrogenase (Fig. 24-2).

SARCOSINE FORMATION FROM GLYCINE

An alternative mechanism for the formation of sarcosine has been proposed.[11] Measurement of the incorporation of the methyl carbon of methionine into sarcosine and serine indicates that 5 to 14 percent of the 1-methyl-[^{14}C]methionine in the diet is converted to sarcosine. In this reaction, methionine is metabolized to *S*-adenosylmethionine, and this compound reacts with glycine to form sarcosine and *S*-adenosylhomocysteine. The enzyme for this reaction is *S*-adenosylmethionine: glycine methyltransferase (EC 2.1.1.20). It is present in liver, kidney, and pancreas tissue in both the adult rabbit and the rat.[12,13] The existence of this pathway in humans has not yet been enzymatically confirmed.

PHYSIOLOGICAL FLUX OF GLYCINE

In a careful clinical study, Mudd and coworkers[14] have measured the rate at which the methyl moiety of methionine is oxidized through the sarcosine pathway. They evaluated two patients with sarcosinemia and sarcosinuria and measured the contribution of methionine, choline, and glycine to the excretion of sarcosine. They concluded that, at a basal metabolic rate, approximately 2 μmol/24 h of sarcosine are formed from choline and excreted in the urine. An increased contribution to sarcosine formation through the 1-carbon cycle did not occur until the total labile methyl intake was near, or exceeded, 13 μmol/24 h. The incremental increase in sarcosine synthesis above the basal rate is most likely due to glycine methylation as a mechanism to remove "excess" labile methyl groups, a process that is shared by both glycine methyltransferase and the sarcosine oxidizing system.

In measuring the flux of the methyl group from methionine, it was estimated that 10.2 μmol/24 h was used for creatine, 1.4 μmol/24 h for transmethylation reactions, 0.5 μmol/24 h for polyamine synthesis, and 2.0 μmol/24 h for sarcosine formation. The total estimated use of labile methyl groups comes to 14.1 μmol/24 h. When the labile methyl intake from dietary sources exceeds this total, the excess is used largely for the formation of sarcosine. This latter response may occur primarily from the methylation of glycine.

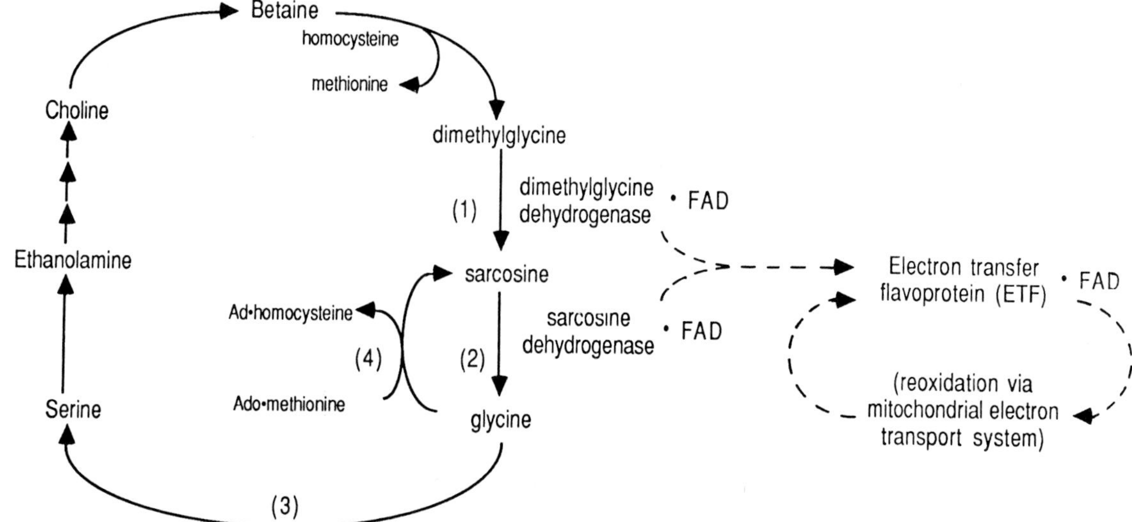

Fig. 24-2 Pathway of the "1-carbon cycle" with sarcosine as an intermediate. Sarcosine may also be formed from glycine [reaction (4)]. The electron transfer flavoprotein (ETF) accepts electrons from dimethyglycine and sarcosine dehydrogenase and, in turn, is reoxidized by the mitochondrial electron transport system. (1) Dimethylglycine dehydrogenase, (2) sarcosine dehydrogenase, (3) serine hydroxymethylase, and (4) S-adenosylmethionine methyltransferase. *(Modified from Mudd et al.[14] Used by permission.)*

RENAL TRANSPORT OF SARCOSINE

Under normal physiological conditions, the existence of sarcosine outside of the liver parenchyma must be quite transitory. An independent renal transport mechanism for sarcosine has not been identified. Glorieux and colleagues[15] studied the renal tubular reabsorption of sarcosine in rat kidney, normal individuals, and persons with sarcosinemia. There are several renal transport systems for related amino acids in humans.[16,17] (See Chap. 102.) The measurement of sarcosine uptake in rat kidney slices in vitro[15] showed that it is partitioned between low K_m and high K_m systems (Fig. 24-3), and it competes with proline and glycine for uptake. These events occur in the slice predominantly at the basolateral membrane.

Similar studies of sarcosine transport have not been performed with human kidney. Renal tubular reabsorption of sarcosine has been measured in humans using normal persons and two patients with sarcosinemia.[15] In the latter there was clear evidence that the majority of the filtered sarcosine is reabsorbed on a high capacity system that is shared by glycine, proline, and hydroxyproline. The estimate for the T_m for filtered sarcosine is 160 μM/min/1.73 M^2.[15]

Fig. 24-3 Michaelis plot of sarcosine uptake by rat kidney slices assigned to low K_m (O) and high K_m (•) systems. The major fraction of sarcosine uptake is achieved by the high K_m system. The K_m values are 0.1 and 3 mM for the low and high K_m systems, respectively. *(From Glorieux et al.[15] Used by permission.)*

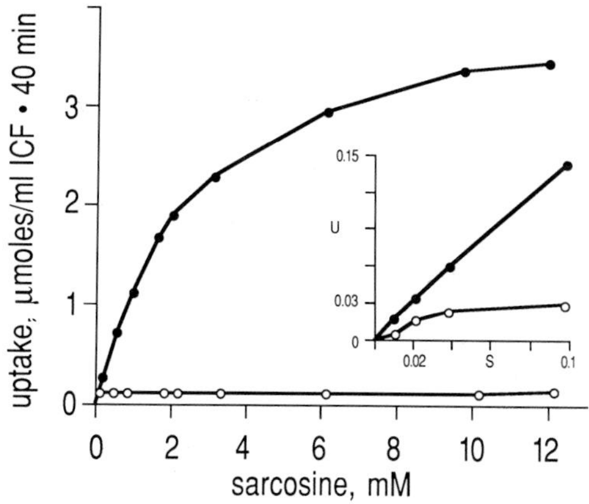

METABOLIC DEFECTS CAUSING SARCOSINEMIA

In humans, the finding of increased sarcosine in blood or urine is a rare event. The phenotype of sarcosinemia or sarcosinuria can occur on the basis of at least three mechanisms: (1) an apparent defect in the holoenzyme of sarcosine dehydrogenase, (2) a mutation in the electron transport flavoprotein that is shared by sarcosine dehydrogenase, dimethylglycine dehydrogenase, and other acyl hydrogenases, and (3) severe folate deficiency.

CLINICAL PHENOTYPE

The original report of sarcosinemia[1] described an infant with mental retardation, hypertonia, and tremors, having an excess of sarcosine in the urine and elevated levels of sarcosine in plasma (15 to 31 mM.) Because the child had mental retardation, it was proposed that the abnormality in sarcosine metabolism was responsible for the mental retardation and contributed perhaps to his other neurologic problems. This concept was reinforced by the finding within the family of an older sibling with similar plasma values of sarcosine and an IQ of 81. Another older sibling, without sarcosinemia, was physically and neurologically normal with an IQ of 101. The oldest boy in this family, however, was physically normal and unaffected with sarcosinemia; his IQ was 81.

In the 5 years following the original description of sarcosinemia, there were five additional reports of sarcosinemic children with clinical problems. Hagge and coworkers[18] reported a child born to Indonesian parents who were first cousins. This child had hepatomegaly but no signs of mental or neurologic abnormalities. Scott and coauthors[19] evaluated a child with mental retardation and growth failure; Willems and associates[20] described two siblings with an unspecified form of dwarfism, and Glorieux et al.[15] reported their evaluations of a child with short stature and normal intelligence. Because of the variation in clinical phenotype and no consistent association between sarcosinemia and mental retardation, Scott and coworkers originally proposed that sarcosinemia was a benign condition that had erroneously been implicated to cause clinical abnormalities because of ascertainment bias.[19] A recent report tends to confirm the concept that sarcosinemia is a benign condition unrelated to any specific neurologic alterations. Levy et al.[21] identified three patients through the newborn screening program in Massachusetts. Clinical and intellectual evaluations between ages 3.8 and 15 years showed they had full-scale IQ scores between 89 and 111 and no neurologic problems.

The literature documents a total of 18 patients with sarcosinemia and sarcosinuria associated with putative deficiency of sarcosine dehydrogenase activity. Twelve were detected because of clinical symptoms, three were identified by a newborn screening of urine amino acids, and three were siblings of original probands (Table 24-1). There is, however, some doubt that sarcosinemia is not completely benign. This is based on three bits of evidence: (1) The IQ of siblings of affected individuals who were detected because of neurologic symptoms is only 74 (group II, Table 24-1). This may have occurred because of low parental IQ or because sarcosine does have some influence on intellectual development. (2) Blom and Fernandes[22] have proposed that some patients may have symptoms of chronic vomiting and poor weight gain as a consequence of their sarcosinemia. Vomiting and poor weight gain have been features of several of the patients detected with sarcosinemia. Blom and Fernandes report a lessening of clinical symptoms from long-term folic acid therapy. (3) There may be more than a single enzymatic defect responsible for sarcosinemia. If such a defect should also include dimethylglycine dehydrogenase, then elevations of both dimethylglycine and sarcosine could occur and theoretically allow for a different clinical phenotype than the phenotype that may exist from sarcosine dehydrogenase deficiency. A deficiency of dimethylglycine dehydrogenase has yet to be described.

Laboratory Data

Sarcosine is not normally detectable in plasma or urine. In patients with sarcosinemia, the concentration in blood ranged from 53 to 760 μmol/liter and urinary excretion from 864 to 7,900 μmol/24 h. The actual quantity of sarcosine excreted in a 24-h period appears to be related to the person's age, body mass, and dietary intake of methyl groups.

Two reports document the concentration of sarcosine in cerebral spinal fluid of affected patients: 5 μ*M* in a 2-year-old male[19] and 17 μM in a 5.8-year-old male.[21] Sarcosine is not normally detectable in spinal fluid.

Hematologic and biochemical assays in patients with sarcosinemia are remarkably scant. It is assumed that such parameters have been measured but are not abnormal.

Sarcosine-Loading Studies

Six patients were studied in this fashion.[1,15,18,19,20,23] If the conversion of sarcosine to glycine is significantly impaired, the rise in plasma sarcosine should be greater than normal and the rise in plasma glycine less. Loading studies in all patients produced this response. Sarcosine concentration peaked at 1 to 1½ h and remained elevated for 5 to 8 h after ingestion. In a 3-month-old infant evaluated by Willems,[20] the infant did not reach maximum plasma values until 3 h after administration. This slow rise may have been related to a slower rate of intestinal absorption for sarcosine in young infants, since a control child of 3 months, unaffected with sarcosinemia, also had a delay in the rise of her serum sarcosine until 3 h after administration.

Glorieux and coworkers calculated the half-life ($t_{1/2}$) of plasma sarcosine to be over 6 h.[15] In four normal persons, the $t_{1/2}$ was about 1½ h. Their patient showed no rise in plasma glycine following sarcosine administration. Patients reported by Scott et al.[19] and by Kang et al.[23] showed a modest rise in plasma glycine following sarcosine administration (Fig. 24-4).

Table 24-1 Summary of Laboratory and Clinical Data of Patients Reported with Sarcosinemia Attributable to Defect in Sarcosine Dehydrogenase (When separated by means of ascertainment, it indicates that the sarcosinemia phenotype is probably independent of mental retardation.)

	Number of patients	*Concentration of sarcosine in plasma μmol/liter*	*Urinary excretion of sarcosine μmol/24° or μmol/mg Cr*	*IQ*	*Clinical problems*	*References*
Group 1 Patients ascertained because of neurologic symptoms	6	157–540	1150–5570 1.5–45	20–75 (x̄ = 49)	Mental retardation, growth delay, vomiting, hypertension, hypoactive, cranial synostosis, syndactyly	1,19, 31,33
Group 2 Sibs of patients in group 1	3	53–326	5320–7891 6.4	74 (est)	Mild mental retardation	1,20,31
Group 3 Patients ascertained without neurologic symptoms or from newborn screening program	9	80–760	864–6740 2.1–9.4	89–116 (x̄ = 103)	None, vomiting, dyslexia, small size, enlarged liver	15,18,20, 21,22

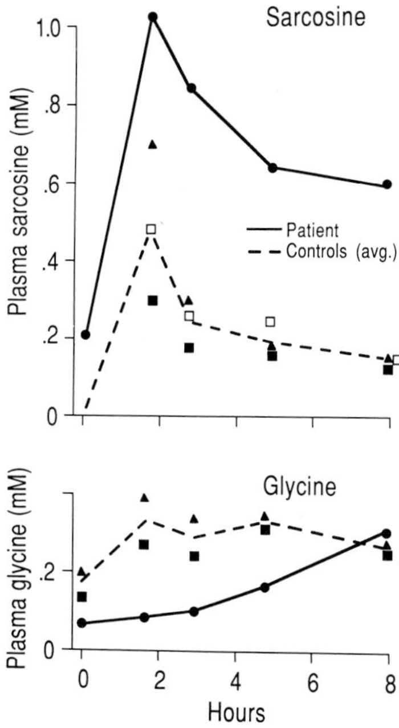

Fig. 24-4 Typical response of plasma sarcosine and glycine concentrations to oral ingestion of 100 mg/kg of sarcosine in child with sarcosinemia. *(From Scott et al.[19] Used by permission.)*

The Enzymatic Error

Quantitative data on enzyme activity from patients with sarcosinemia are scarce. The conversion from sarcosine to glycine requires sarcosine dehydrogenase apoenzyme and the ability to transfer the generated electron to an electron transfer flavoprotein (ETF). There are many steps in this reaction that could be defective. The apoenzyme itself could be affected, or the ability to transfer the electron to its flavoprotein could be impaired. The flavoprotein itself could be altered in its abundance, stability, configuration, or unique ability to bind or accept electrons from sarcosine dehydrogenase. Because of the rarity of the disorder, it is likely that no single mutation is shared by the majority of the patients affected with sarcosinemia. Defects of electron transport should affect sarcosine and dimethylglycine dehydrogenases together.

Gerritsen measured the activity of sarcosine dehydrogenase in a liver biopsy.[24] He found deficient sarcosine dehydrogenase activity. The assay was performed in a manner that did not clarify whether the lesion was in the apoenzyme for sarcosine dehydrogenase or in the ETF.*

Subsequently a second child affected with sarcosinemia had a liver biopsy measured for sarcosine dehydrogenase activity.[25] This assay utilized a mitochondrial-enriched preparation that included phenozinemethosulfate (PMS) as an electron accepter. The specific activity of sarcosine dehydrogenase in this patient was normal. It was concluded that the defect in this particular patient must exist "in or distal to the flavoprotein that acts as the natural electron accepter." No specific data on fatty acid metabolism were given for this patient, an important point in view of subsequent findings that the ETF serving sarcosine dehydrogenase and dimethylglycine dehydrogenase also functions as the electron acceptor for fatty acyl CoA dehydrogenase. Patients with severe deficiencies of ETF have glutaric aciduria and may excrete sarcosine in their urine.[26] Attempts to measure the enzymatic activity of sarcosine dehydrogenase in tissues other than liver has not been successful. Sarcosine oxidation occurs only in liver and kidney; no enzyme activity was detected in skin fibroblasts or peripheral leukocytes.[15,19,27]

*In a previous review article, it was indicated that the in vitro assay system used by Gerritsen included PMS as an electron acceptor in the assay.[25] In a personal communication to H. Mudd,[14] Gerritsen clarified this point, indicating that PMS was not utilized in the assay mixture. Thus, the defect could have involved either the apoenzyme or the ETF.

Inheritance

The precise chromosomal locus of the gene encoding for sarcosine dehydrogenase is unknown. Pedigree studies indicate it is on an autosome. Males and females are affected, and siblings of probands are sometimes affected; at least 3 of 12 siblings had sarcosinuria and sarcosinemia. This frequency is in agreement with an autosomal recessive mode of inheritance. Kang et al.[23] proposed their patient was the offspring of a homozygous (father) × heterozygous (mother) mating. In the family reported by Hagge et al.[18] the parents were first cousins.

Incidence of Sarcosinemia

Incidence of sarcosinemia in the population has been estimated by Levy et al.[21] It is 1 in 350,000 live births ascertained by amino acid screening of urines from newborns (source population: approximately 1×10^6 newborns). Incidence of sarcosinuria is 1 in 43,000 newborns in Quebec (same method of ascertainment.)[28]

Heterozygote Detection

Heterozygote detection has been attempted by sarcosine loading. The assumption is that persons heterozygous for a deficiency of sarcosine dehydrogenase activity may have limited capacity to clear sarcosine from their plasma, and there may be an increased excretion of sarcosine in the urine. Ten obligate heterozygotes have been studied in this manner (Table 24-2). Four of eight obligate heterozygotes showed an elevation in the concentration of sarcosine in their plasma following sarcosine ingestion that was considered above the normal range; the remaining four were within the normal range. Glorieux and associates[15] also measured the rate of sarcosine disappearance from the plasma. Two obligate heterozygotes

Table 24-2 Identification of Obligate Heterozygates for Sarcosinemia by Oral Sarcosine Loading (Each person ingesfed 100 mg/kg body weight of sarcosine in a fasting state. Blood samples were typicaly collected for 12 h following the oral ingestion of sarcosine.)

	Urinary excretion of sarcosine following sarcosine ingestion		*Concentration of sarcosine in plasma following sarcosine ingestion*	
Reference	*Mother*	*Father*	*Mother*	*Father*
Gerritsen[1]	Increased	Normal	Increased	Normal
Hagge[18]	Increased	Increased	Normal	Increased
Willems[20]	Increased	Normal	Increased	Normal
Kang[23]	Increased	Increased	Normal	Increased
Glorieux[15]	(Normal sarcosine renal clearance)		(Slightly prolonged plasma half-life of 2.2 h; normal, 1.6h)	

showed a slightly prolonged sarcosine $t_{1/2}$ (mean value 2.2 h) as compared to $t_{1/2}$ = 1.6 h in controls. These data suggest that the measurement of serum sarcosine concentration following the oral ingestion of sarcosine is not a reliable indicator of the heterozygote state, since only 60 percent of obligate heterozygotes could be detected by this technique.

Quantitation of sarcosine in the urine following sarcosine ingestion has been reported in the parents of five patients. Six of eight heterozygotes showed an increased excretion of urinary sarcosine when compared to control values established for each study. Two of the heterozygotes showed an increased urinary excretion of sarcosine, even though their plasma value remained within the control range. Two of the individuals with normal urinary excretion and normal plasma sarcosine concentration following sarcosine loading studies were fathers of patients. In each case the possibility of nonpaternity was not excluded.[1,20]

Glorieux and coworkers[15] have reported the urinary excretion of sarcosine in terms of renal clearance values for the parents of an affected child. Their renal clearance rates were 9.4 and 9.7 μmol/min per 1.73 M^2 and compared favorably with values of 3.6 to 50.6 μmol/min per 1.73 M^2 for normal adults. There was no obvious alteration in the tubular reabsorptive function of sarcosine in these parents.

SARCOSINEMIA FROM GLUTARIC ACIDEMIA (TYPE II)

Sarcosinemia and sarcosinuria occur in patients with deficiency of either the electron transfer flavoprotein or ETF:ubiquinon oxidoreductase (ETF:QO). Young children with genetic defects of the ETF are classified as glutaric acidemia type II (See Chap. 34). They have recurrent hypoglycemia, metabolic acidosis without ketosis, and significant excretion of organic acids in the urine.[29,30] The urinary organic acid profile reveals lactic, glutaric, 2-hydroxyglutaric, and dicarboxylic acids.[26,29,30] The presence of 2-hydroxy isovaleric acid may give rise to an odor of "sweaty feet." If the deficiency of the ETF is incomplete and allows partial activity of dimethylglycine dehydrogenase and sarcosine dehydrogenase, sarcosine may be formed and detectable in serum and urine.[28,29,30] Not all patients with glutaric acidemia type II have been noted to have detectable sarcosinemia or sarcosinuria.

Glutaric acidemia type II is inherited as a autosomal recessive condition and has been detected prenatally by analysis of organic acids in amniotic fluid[30] and by biochemical evaluation of cultured cells from amniotic fluid.[30]

SARCOSENIMA ASSOCIATED WITH FOLATE DEFICIENCY

A severe deficiency of folic acid may also cause sarcosinemia and sarcosinuria. Tippett and Danks[31] reported a child of 11 months who became folate-deficient on a diet of goat milk alone. Her urine sarcosine concentration was 0.114 to 0.29 mg/mg Cr. Sarcosineuria disappeared upon correction of her folate deficiency. Sarcosinemia and sarcosinuria have also been observed in an infant with severe folate deficiency secondary to congenital folate malabsorption. This male infant had sarcosine values of 14 μM in plasma and 185 μM in urine. His sarcosinemia became undetectable after correction of the folate deficiency.[32]

Further evidence of the interaction of serum folate concentrations on the conversion of sarcosine to glycine is implied in a report by Blom and Fernandez.[22] Sarcosinemia diminished after prolonged folate therapy in their patient, and conversion of sarcosine to glycine improved.

REFERENCES

1. GERRITSEN T, WAISMAN HA: Hypersarcosinemia: An inborn error of metabolism. *N Engl J Med* 275:66, 1966.
2. HOSKINS DD, MACKENZIE CG: Solubilization and electron transfer flavoprotein requirement of mitochondrial sarcosine dehydrogenase and dimethylglycine dehydrogenase. *J Biol Chem* 236:177, 1961.
3. FRISELL WR, MACKENZIE CG: Separation and purification of sarcosine dehydrogenase and dimethylglycine dehydrogenase. *J Biol Chem* 237:94, 1962.
4. MACKENZIE CG, ABELES RH: Production of active formaldehyde in the mitochondrial oxidation of sarcosine. *J Biol Chem* 222:145, 1956.
5. FRISELL WR, CRONIN JR, MACKENZIE CG: Coupled flavoenzymes in mitochondrial oxidation of N-methyl groups. *J Biol Chem* 237:2975, 1962.
6. WITTWER AJ, WAGNER C: Identification of the folate binding proteins of rat liver mitochondria as dimethylglycine dehydrogenase and sarcosine dehydrogenase. Purification and folate-binding characteristics. *J Biol Chem* 256:4102, 1981.
7. WITTWER AJ, WAGNER C: Identification of folate binding protein of mitochondria as dimethylglycine dehydrogenase. *Proc Natl Acad Sci USA* 77:4484, 1980.
8. WITTWER AJ, WAGNER C: Identification of the folate-binding proteins of rat liver mitochondria as dimethylglycine dehydrogenase and sarcosine dehydrogenase. Flavoprotein, nature and enzymatic properties of the purified proteins. *J Biol Chem* 256:4109, 1981.
9. PORTER DH, COOK RJ, WAGNER C: Enzymatic properties of dimethylglycine dehydrogenase and sarcosine dehydrogenase from rat liver. *Arch Biochem Biophys* 243:396, 1985.
10. BLAKLEY RL: A spectrophotometric study of the reaction catalysed by serine transhydroxymethylase. *Biochem J* 77:459, 1960.
11. MITCHELL AD, BENEVENGA NJ: The role of transamination in methionine oxidation in the rat. *J Nutr* 108:67, 1978.
12. KERR SJ: Competing methyltransferase systems. *J Biol Chem* 247:4248, 1972.
13. HEADY JE, KERR SJ: Purification and characterization of glycine N-methyltransferase. *J Biol Chem* 248:69, 1973.
14. MUDD SH, EBERT MH, SCRIVER CR: Labile methyl group balances in the human: The role of sarcosine. *Metabolism* 29:707, 1980.
15. GLORIEUX FH, SCRIVER CR, DELVIN E, MOHYUDDIN F: Transport and metabolism of sarcosine in hypersarcosinemic and normal phenotypes. *J Clin Invest* 50:2313, 1971.
16. SCRIVER CR, EFRON ML, SCHAFER IA: Renal tubular transport of proline, hydroxyproline and glycine in health and in familial hyperprolinemia. *J Clin Invest* 43:374, 1964.
17. SCRIVER CR: Renal tubular transport of proline, hydroxyproline and glycine. III. Genetic basis for more than one mode of transport in human kidney. *J Clin Invest* 47:823, 1968.
18. HAGGE W, BRODEHL J, GELLISSEN K: Hypersacrosinemia. *Pediatr Res* 1:409, 1967.
19. SCOTT CR, CLARK SH, TENG CC, SWEDBERG KR: Clinical and cellular studies of sarcosinemia. *J Pediatr* 77:805, 1970.
20. WILLEMS C, HEUSDEN A, HAINAUT A: Hypersarcosinemic avec sarcosinurie: Étude d'une nouvelle famille. *J Genet Hum* 19:101, 1971.
21. LEVY HL, COULOMBE JT, BENJAMIN R: Massachusetts Metabolic Disorders Screening Program: III. Sarcosinemia. *Pediatrics* 74:509, 1984.
22. BLOM W, FERNANDES J: Folic acid dependent hypersarcosinemia. *Clin Chim Acta* 91:117, 1979.
23. KANG ES, SEYER J, TODD TA, HERRERA C: Variability in the phenotypic expression of abnormal sarcosine metabolism in a family. *Hum Genet* 64:80, 198, 1983.
24. GERRITSEN T: Sarcosine dehydrogenase deficiency, the enzyme defect in hypersarcosinemia. *Helv Paediatr Acta* 27:33, 1972.
25. SCOTT CR: Sarcosinemia, in Nyhan WL (ed): *Heritable Disorders of Amino Acid Metabolism*. New York, Wiley, 1974 p 324.
26. GOODMAN SI, MCCABE ERB, FENNESSEY PV, MACE JC: Multiple acyl-CoA

dehydrogenase deficiency (glutaric aciduria type II) with transient hypersarcosinemia and sarcosinuria: Possible inherited deficiency of an electron transfer flavoprotein. *Pediatr Res* 14:12, 1980.

27. REHBERG ML, GERRITSEN T: Sarcosine metabolism in the rat. *Arch Biochem Biophys* 127:661, 1968.
28. SCRIVER CR, Personal Communication.
29. SWEETMAN L, NYHAN WL, TRAUNER DA, MERRITT TA, SINGH M: Glutaric aciduria type II. *J Pediatr* 96:1020, 1980.
30. BENNETT MJ, CURNOCK DA, ENGEL PC, SHAW L, GRAY RGF, HULL D, PATRICK AD POLLITT RJ: Glutaric aciduria (type II). Biochemical investigation and treatment of a child diagnosed prenatally. *J Inherited Metab Dis* 7:57, 1984.
31. TIPPETT P, DANKS DM: The clinical and biochemical findings in three cases of hypersarcosinemia and one case of transient hypersarcosinuria associated with folic acid deficiency. *Helv Paediatr Acta* 29:261, 1974.
32. SCOTT CR: Unpublished observation.
33. MINAMI R, OLEK K, WARDENBACH P: Hypersarcosinemia with craniostenosis-syndactylism syndrome. *Hum Genet* 28:167, 1975.

CHAPTER **25**

NONKETOTIC HYPERGLYCINEMIA

WILLIAM L. NYHAN

1. *Nonketotic hyperglycinemia is an inborn error of amino acid metabolism in which large amounts of glycine accumulate in body fluids.*
2. *The molecular defect is in the glycine cleavage system, a multienzyme complex with four individual protein components. These components are referred to as the P protein, H protein, T protein, and L protein. In patients with nonketotic hyperglycinemia, defects have been identified in the P protein, the H protein, and the T protein.*
3. *In the classic phenotype life-threatening illness develops in early postnatal life, and most patients die or need to be sustained by mechanical ventilation in the neonatal period. Survivors are very severely mentally retarded and have seizure disorders.*
4. *The high concentration of glycine in the cerebrospinal fluid is a diagnostic feature. The ratio of the concentration in the CSF to that of the plasma is useful in the characterization of this condition. This feature and organic acid analysis of the urine distinguish the disease from other conditions in which there is hyperglycinemia.*

Nonketotic hyperglycinemia is an inborn error of metabolism in which large amounts of glycine are found in body fluids. The concentration of glycine in the cerebrospinal fluid is particularly high, and abnormal organic acids are not present in blood or urine.[1] The disease is distinguished in this way from the various disorders of organic acid metabolism, such as propionic acidemia, in which secondary elevations of glycine content occur. These organic acidemias are generally characterized by the occurrence of repeated episodes of life-threatening illness with massive ketosis. It was because of this clinically distinguishing characteristic that nonketotic hyperglycinemia got its name.[2] Nonketotic hyperglycinemia was first described in detail by Gerritsen et al.[3] The disorder is probably heterogeneous, and patients with relatively mild mental retardation have been seen. However, the classic presentation is of a very young infant with overwhelming illness.[4] Survivors often have intractable seizures, usually with myoclonus, and little or no evidence of cerebral development. The fundamental defect is in the glycine cleavage reaction (Fig. 25-1).

GLYCINE METABOLISM

Glycine is the simplest of the amino acids. It contains two carbon atoms, an amino acid group, and a carboxyl group. Its metabolism is characterized largely by synthetic reactions.[5] Even its major route of catabolism is probably designed to serve a predominantly synthetic function because the cleavage of glycine leads to the formation of a single carbon tetrahydrofolate compound which can serve a variety of synthetic pathways, such as the *de novo* synthesis of purines. Glycine is a nonessential amino acid; it can be synthesized by humans. It is present in high concentrations in collagen and gelatin and is abundant in most animal proteins. The daily intake by the average adult in the United States is 3 to 5 g.

Glycine originally received its name, derived from that of glucose, because it has a sweet taste. It is also a glycogenic amino acid. In a starved animal who is fed glycine, glycogen is laid down in the liver.

Synthetic Reactions Involving Glycine

The metabolism of glycine is concerned largely with its role in synthetic processes, of which there are a number in addition to the synthesis of proteins (Fig. 25-2). Its important role in the synthesis of proteins may involve its ability to permit the construction of proteins with minimal steric restraint. This would facilitate such things as the helical structure of collagen. Approximately 50 percent of dietary glycine is utilized for protein synthesis.[1] Approximately 10 percent is found in the body in nonprotein nitrogen, 40 percent excreted directly in the urine, and 2 to 3 percent in the feces. In experiments using [^{15}C]- or [^{15}N]glycine, most of the label found in proteins is as glycine and serine. Some is in glutamate and aspartate. The extent of conversion of protein serine is about four times that of direct incorporation into protein as glycine.[1] These observations indicate the importance of glycine-serine interconversion.

When labeled glycine is fed, there is a lag of 6 to 8 h before glycogen is formed; the peak is at about 12 h. This suggests that glycine must first be converted to other molecules, which are subsequently converted to glucose. Furthermore, twice as much of the α carbon of glycine appears in glycogen as of the carboxyl carbon. This suggests that there is first a conversion to serine. There is also a lag of 6 to 8 h before the nitrogen of glycine appears in the urine as urea. This delay suggests that glycine participates to a considerable extent in synthetic reactions prior to entering a catabolic pathway.

Glycine plays an important role in the synthesis of purines. It is incorporated intact into what becomes the 4, 5, and 7 positions of the purine ring, and it also provides a source of 1-carbon units for *de novo* purine synthesis (see Chap. 37). This pathway accounts for about a tenth of a percent of glycine metabolized.

Glycine undergoes a series of reactions in which conjugates are formed with acyl derivatives, particularly acyl CoA esters. The most prominent of these is hippuric acid, in which an amide bond that is like the peptide bonds in proteins is formed between benzoic acid and glycine. The acylation of glycine proceeds after formation of a CoA derivative of the carboxyl group of benzoic acid. A similar reaction serves in the detoxification of salicylates through the formation of salicyluric acid, and bile acids are excreted into the intestine in the form of glycine conjugates. Large amounts of isovalerylglycine are found in the urine of patients with isovaleric aci-

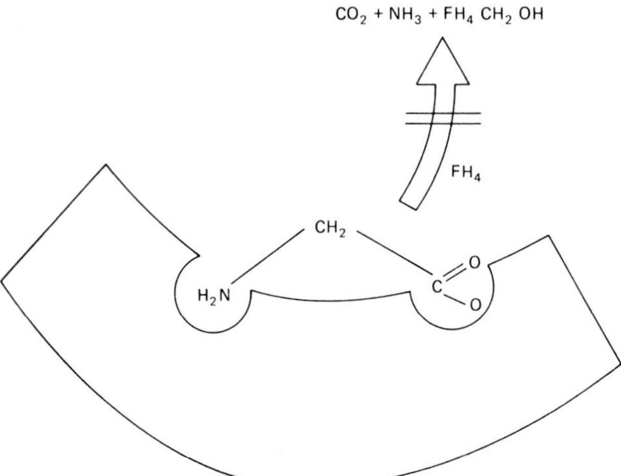

Fig. 25-1 The glycine cleavage reaction, site of the defect in nonketotic hyperglycinemia.

demia,[6] in which condition the conjugation appears to serve a detoxification function. The formation of compounds such as tiglylglycine or hexanoylglycine in other organic acidemias, while diagnostically useful, is probably of little physiological consequence.

Catabolism of Glycine

Many of the catabolic reactions may be in fact primarily synthetic in character. For example, the glycine-succinate reaction is primarily concerned with the synthesis of porphyrins and probably plays no significant part in the degradation of glycine. Similarly, some reversible reactions may be more concerned with the synthesis of glycine than with its catabolism.

The Glycine-Serine Interconversion. The interconversion of glycine and serine (Fig. 25-3) is the most important pathway in the catabolism of glycine. Definitive evidence for conversion of serine to glycine was provided by experiments in which rats were fed serine labeled with ^{15}N and ^{13}C.[1] The ratio of ^{15}N to ^{13}C was the same in hippurate isolated from the urine as in the precursor. This was a strong indication that the conversion was direct. Similarly, when [^{14}C]glycine was fed to rats, the protein of the liver was found to contain labeled serine.[1] [^{13}C]Glycine and [^{14}C]formate were demonstrated to be precursors of serine. Moreover, in human beings labeled serine appears in the blood promptly after the injection of labeled glycine.[1] A variety of observations have indicated that glycine can be converted to serine and that serine can be converted to glycine. However, in long-term feeding experiments[7] in which labeled amino acids were provided until a steady state developed, the evidence suggested that generally there is net conversion of serine to glycine and that glycine serves as a precursor of serine only when there are excess quantities of glycine requiring catabolism. The physiological conversion of glycine to serine is stimulated by large amounts of glycine. Similarly, in *Escherichia coli* the enzyme system which converts glycine to single-carbon units is induced by glycine and repressed by single-carbon units derived from other sources. In the rat experiments the turnover of serine was 35 mmol/kg; that of glycine was 25 mmol/kg.

In studies in which glycine was labeled in the 2 position with carbon 14, the label was found in the 2 and 3 positions of serine.[1] The proportions of carbon 2 of glycine converted to carbon 2 and carbon 3 of serine have generally been found to be about equal.

The system involved in the conversion of glycine to serine was first studied in avian liver and in *Peptococcus glycinophilus*.[1] A close relationship was observed between the production of CO_2 and NH_3 and the synthesis of serine. Pyridoxal phosphate, NAD, and tetrahydrofolic acid were stimulatory. These observations are consistent with the following pathway (FH_4 indicates tetrahydrofolic acid and FH_4CH_2OH its hydroxymethyl derivative):

$$NH_2CH_2COOH + FH_4 + H_2O \rightarrow FH_4CH_2OH + CO_2 + NH_3 \qquad [25\text{-}1]$$

$$FH_4CH_2OH + NH_2CH_2COOH \rightarrow HOCH_2CHNH_2COOH + FH_4 \qquad [25\text{-}2]$$

The overall reaction for the synthesis of serine from glycine by this pathway is

$$2NH_2CH_2COOH + H_2O \rightarrow HOCH_2CHNH_2COOH + CO_2 + NH_3 \qquad [25\text{-}3]$$

Reaction [25-1] is not required for the conversion of glycine to serine by way of reaction [25-2]. Reaction [25-2], catalyzed by serine hydroxymethyl transferase, can proceed from glycine

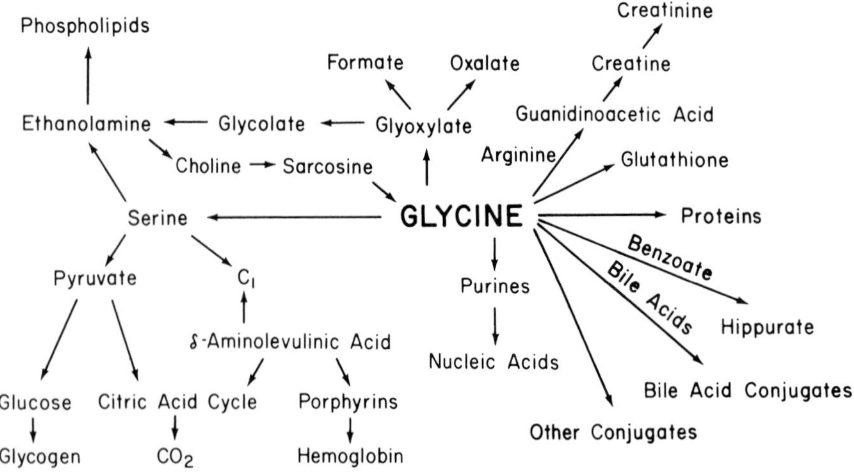

Fig. 25-2 Metabolic pathways of glycine concerned particularly with the synthesis of other molecules.

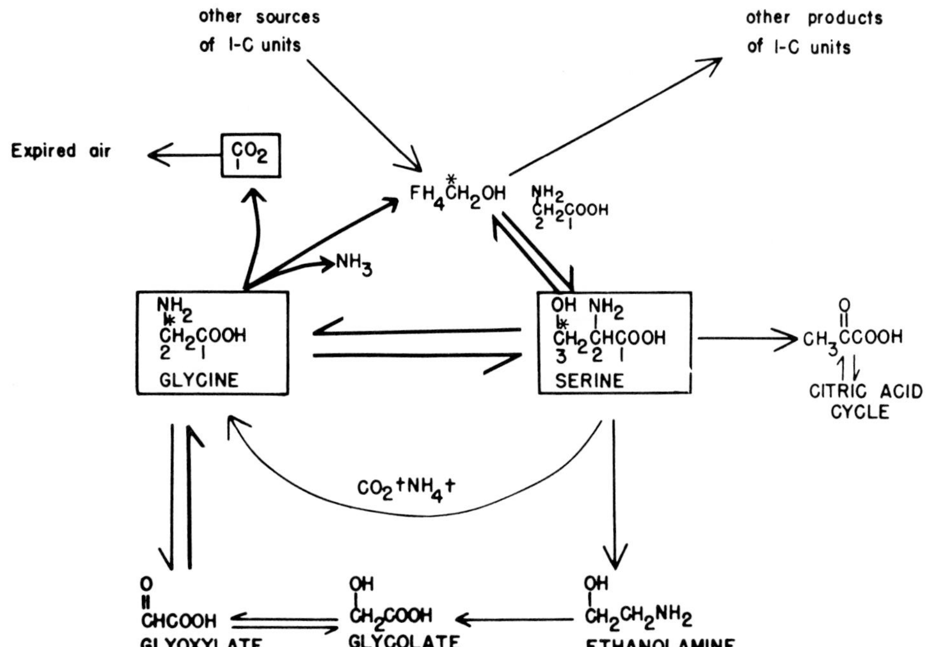

Fig. 25-3 The metabolic interconversion of glycine and serine. The two arrows in the center connecting the glycine and serine boxes indicate that the two molecules are interconvertible by a number of pathways, without specification as to type. The two carbons of glycine are numbered 1 and 2; in this way it is possible to see that carbon 1 and carbon 2 are incorporated directly into the corresponding 1 and 2 carbons of serine. Carbon 2 is also convertible to a tetrahydrofolate derivative, which then becomes carbon 3 of serine. The asterisk has been employed in order to follow this carbon through this reaction sequence. The sequence is reversible. The CO_2-fixation reaction, which produces two molecules of glycine from a molecule of serine, is drawn with the curved arrow below for clarity. FH_4 = tetrahydrofolic acid; 1-C unit = single-carbon unit. *(By permission from Ando et al.,* Pediatric Research *2:254, 1968.)*

and other sources of single carbon units. There are many sources for the CH_2OH of FH_4CH_2OH other than glycine (Fig. 25-3). These constitute the so-called one-carbon pool. Reaction [25-1] requires NAD and pyridoxal phosphate as cofactors. This reaction could serve the catabolism of glycine independently of serine biosynthesis if reaction [25-2] were blocked.

The mechanisms of these two reactions are complex and were shown, in the original studies in *P. glycinophilus*,[1] to involve an enzyme system in which there were four protein components. All four proteins are required to catalyze the overall conversion of glycine to CO_2, NH_3, and an FH_4 derivative. These protein fractions were originally called P_1, P_2, P_3, and P_4 and sometimes E_1, E_2, E_3, and E_4. The four protein components are now known as the P protein, H protein, T protein, and L protein (Fig. 25-4).[5–10] In mammals the glycine cleavage system is entirely mitochondrial. The P protein is a pyridoxal phosphate-dependent glycine decarboxylase. The reaction is reversible. H protein is a heat stable, lipoic acid-containing protein originally designated as a hydrogen carrier protein. This protein has now been established as the aminomethyl carrier protein. Action of both the P and H proteins is required for the formation of CO_2 from glycine. T protein is a tetrahydrofolate-requiring enzyme, a flavoprotein which is reduced in the presence of H protein and glycine and which functions in the presence of the rest of the system to transfer carbon 2 of glycine to FH_4. Its products are NAD and the oxidized lipoic acid-containing H protein. L protein is a lipoamide dehydrogenase.

The H protein is small; it has a molecular weight of about 23,000. It undergoes a protein-protein interaction with the larger P protein, which has a molecular weight of 200,000, to produce a conformational change in the latter that can be observed spectrophotometrically, resulting in activation and enhanced affinity for substrate and leading to the decarboxylation of glycine by the P protein.

Cloning of cDNAs, which probably encode components of the human glycine cleavage system, has recently been undertaken.[11] Antibodies against rat liver P protein and H protein were used to screen a chicken liver cDNA expression library. The resultant positive clones were then used as probes to screen a human cDNA library. A number of human clones have been obtained, and their nature is under exploration.

The glycine-serine interconversion in mammalian systems has been clarified largely through the work of Kikuchi and colleagues.[1,8–10] It can be studied in liver mitochondria by following the CO_2-fixation reaction in which serine and ammonia provide for the synthesis of two molecules of glycine. Carbon 2 of serine and the carbon of bicarbonate are incorporated in a 1:1 ratio into the 2 and carboxyl carbons of glycine. Methylene-FH_4 is effective in replacing serine in the synthesis of glycine. The enzyme preparation also catalyzes the decarboxylation of glycine. The cleavage of glycine requires FH_4. The

Fig. 25-4 The glycine cleavage system.

(P)–CHO + NH_2CH_2COOH ⇌ (P)–CH=NCH_2COOH

(H)<S–S ↓ CO_2

(H)–(S–CH_2NH_2)(SH) + (P)–CHO ⇌ (P)–CH=NCH_2–S–(H)(HS)

(T) ↓ FH_4

5,10-CH_2FH_4 + NH_3 + (H)<(SH)(SH) ⇌ [(L), NAD^+] (H)<S–S + NADH + H^+

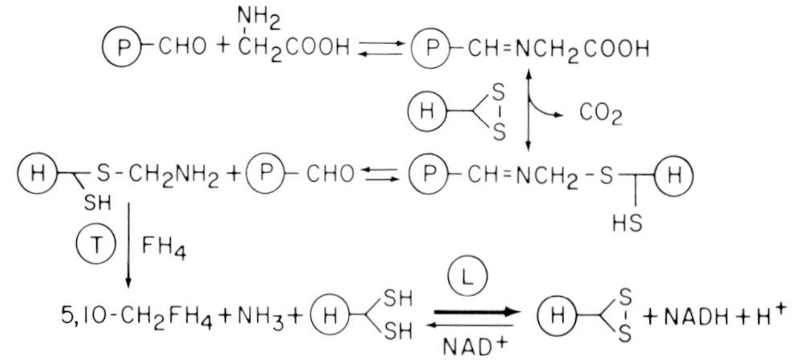

extracts catalyze an exchange between the carboxyl carbon of glycine and CO_2.

Glycine Oxidase and Transaminases. Glycine may be oxidized to glyoxylate, and the conversion is catalyzed by an enzyme which is the same as D-amino acid oxidase.[1] This enzyme has a very high K_m, and it appears unlikely to play a major role in the degradation of glycine. Glyoxylate may also be formed from glycine by transamination,[1] but it is unlikely that these pathways serve significantly in the degradation of glycine because thermodynamic considerations strongly favor the synthesis of glycine rather than its catabolism.[1]

Amino Ketone Formation. δ-Aminolevulinic acid is formed by the condensation of glycine and succinyl CoA, an essential step in the biosynthesis of porphyrins and heme.[1]

$$\begin{array}{l} HOOCCH_2CH_2CO{-}S{-}CoA + CH_2NH_2COOH \\ \rightarrow [HOOCCH_2CH_2COCHNH_2COOH] \\ \qquad \downarrow \rightarrow CO_2 \\ HOOCCH_2CH_2COCH_2NH_2 \end{array} \qquad [25\text{-}4]$$

The α carbon of glycine becomes the δ carbon of δ-aminolevulinic acid, and it is a precursor of a 1-carbon unit. The rest of the compound yields α-ketoglutaraldehyde, which can be converted to α-ketoglutaric acid. Thus, this pathway could operate as a cycle providing the complete oxidation of glycine while regenerating succinate. Although this cycle has been proposed as a major route for the degradation of glycine, studies using ^{14}C-labeled glycine and δ-aminolevulinic acid disclosed that the rate of conversion of glycine to CO_2 was 25 times that of δ-aminolevulinic acid, a finding not consistent with the function of the cycle as a major pathway.[1]

A similar condensation of glycine and acetyl CoA would yield aminoacetone:

$$\begin{array}{l} CH_3CO{-}S{-}CoA + CH_2NH_2COOH \\ \rightarrow CH_3COCH_2NH_2COOH \rightarrow CH_3COCH_2NH_2 + CO_2 \end{array} \qquad [25\text{-}5]$$

The aminoacetone synthesized can be converted by transamination or by the action of monoamine oxidase to methylglyoxal, which could then be converted through a glyoxalase reaction to lactate and ultimately to pyruvate. Thus, the synthesis of this aminoketone could also lead to the complete metabolism of glycine, and this pathway could also operate as a cycle.

Aminoacetone is readily formed from acetyl CoA and glycine in guinea pig liver mitochondria. It has been calculated that conversion to aminoacetone could account for as much as one quarter of the glycine metabolized each day.[1] However, our studies indicated that this is not a major route for the catabolism of glycine in human beings.[1] Following the administration of [^{14}C]glycine, there was no evidence of incorporation of label into aminoacetone. By contrast, there was significant conversion of the label of administered threonine to aminoacetone. Thus in humans the source of urinary aminoacetone is threonine, not glycine.

The Synthesis of Glycine

Glycine is a nonessential amino acid which can be synthesized in a number of ways. These include conversion from serine and transamination of glyoxylate. The CO_2-fixation reaction catalyzed by the glycine cleavage system (Fig. 25-3) is considered to be the major route for the formation of glycine. Glycine could also be synthesized from serine by way of ethanolamine:

$$\begin{array}{ccccc} NH_2 & & NH_2 & & \\ | & & | & & \\ HO\underset{\Delta}{\dot{C}}H_2CHCOOH & \rightarrow & HO\underset{\Delta}{\dot{C}}H_2CH_2 & \longrightarrow & HO\underset{\Delta}{C}H_2CH_2N^+(CH_3)_3 \\ & & \downarrow & & \downarrow \\ & & OH & & \downarrow \\ & & | & & \\ & & \dot{C}H_2COOH & & HOO\underset{\Delta}{C}CH_2NHCH_3 \\ & & \downarrow & & \\ NH_2 & & O & & \\ | & & \| & & \downarrow \\ \dot{C}H_2COOH & \leftarrow & \dot{C}HCOOH & & HOO\underset{\Delta}{C}CH_2NH_2 \end{array} \qquad [25\text{-}6]$$

In the pathway on the left the original hydroxymethyl group of serine becomes the amino carbon of glycine, while conversion of ethanolamine to choline, dimethylglycine, and sarcosine yields a glycine molecule in which the original hydroxymethyl of serine becomes the carboxyl group of glycine. Glycine may also be formed from threonine. In this process threonine is degraded to glycine and acetaldehyde.[1] In the rat one-third to one-fifth of ingested threonine may be converted to glycine.[1]

The Turnover of Glycine

The rate of turnover of glycine has been measured in humans and experimental animals. In the rat glycine is synthesized at the rate of about 2 g/kg per day. In human beings a glycine turnover of 1 g/kg per day was found.[1]

Concentrations of Glycine in Body Fluids

The mean normal concentration of glycine in plasma as measured by column chromatography was 243 ± 20 μM (1.82 ± 0.15 mg/dl).[12] The average adult excretes approximately 1.3 mmol (100 mg) glycine per 24 h, with a range of 0.6 to 1.6 mmol/24 h (50 to 200 mg/24 h).[1] These values amount to 1.3 to 2.6 mmol (0.1 to 0.2 mg) glycine per milligram of creatinine. Similar values have been found in children.[1] The concentration of glycine in cerebrospinal fluid is less than 13 μM (0.1 mg/dl).[1]

CLINICAL FEATURES

The classic phenotype is that of an overwhelming, life-threatening illness in the first days of life.[13–19] This disorder is being diagnosed increasingly in the neonatal intensive care units of major medical centers in this country, and the vast majority of patients about whom we are consulted present in this fashion. It seems more than likely that at least as many infants with this disease die in the neonatal period without benefit of diagnosis.

Most affected infants appear normal at birth and for a short interval, seldom longer than 48 h. Among 25 reported patients,[20] onset was within 4 days in 15, 8 days in one, and not exactly stated but neonatal in 5 more. After this interval, which may or may not await the initiation of protein-containing feedings, the infant develops lethargy and/or convulsions. There may be some vomiting or delayed gastric emptying, but this usually is not prominent. With increasing lethargy there is anorexia leading to failure to feed. The cry may be high in pitch, and poor suck, grasp, and Moro responses are reported. Edema has been observed rarely.[13,19] The state of consciousness deteriorates to deep coma; often within 24 to 48 h of the first symptoms the infant is completely unresponsive and flaccid. Apnea ensues, and unless the baby is intubated and supported by mechanical ventilation, death follows promptly.

A majority of patients die in this early period. Many are ventilated long enough to ascertain the diagnosis; others die despite continued ventilation. In some the initiation of respirations has followed exchange transfusion or peritoneal dialysis. Others have spontaneously begun to breathe without intervention. It is likely that some would improve sufficiently to breathe without assistance if supported long enough. If the ventilator can be discontinued, it is not usually required again. Despite resumption of spontaneous respirations, most patients display virtually no evidence of intellectual development. Many have nearly continuous seizure activity, and may die within the first year. Microcephaly is usually evident.

This course was exemplified by one of the first patients we studied.[13] The patient was diagnosed on the fourth day of life. By that time he was being ventilated. Except for myoclonic jerks, generalized seizures, and persistent hiccuping, there was no movement or spontaneous respiration. Following exchange transfusion, mechanical ventilation was no longer necessary. Nevertheless, the patient made no developmental progress, and at 7 months of age he was unaware of his surroundings, had very few spontaneous movements, and no head control. Tendon reflexes were exaggerated. He died shortly thereafter. A similar course has been reported in a majority of patients.[14–16] This is now considered the classic phenotype. A fulminant course may lead to death as early as 3 weeks despite heroic measures.[16]

Nonketotic hyperglycinemia is common in Finland. In a report of extensive experience with 19 patients,[17] the onset of symptoms was rapid, ranging from 6 h to 21 days, with a mean of 1½ days. In all but one low birth weight infant, symptoms began within the first week. All developed myoclonic jerks and all but four became unresponsive to painful stimuli. All but three developed respiratory failure, and 12 required intubation and assisted ventilation. That respiratory failure was predominantly an early phenomenon was indicated by the fact that infants who survived 3 weeks of age did not have further problems with apnea and survived the first year. This is consistent with experimental observations by DeGroot et al.[18] that glycine is considerably less toxic in animals after the first week of life. Nevertheless, the four patients in the Finnish series who survived beyond the early years were severely retarded, had myoclonic seizures, and were incapable of voluntary movement. Two required gavage feeding. This clinical phenotype of survival into childhood with profound mental retardation was also the case for the patient in the initial report of this disease[3] and in the first patient we described.[21]

The neurologic examination of these childhood suvivors is that of spastic cerebral palsy. Opisthotonos is common. Deep tendon reflexes are exaggerated.

Seizures are prominent in virtually all patients with nonketotic hyperglycinemia.[1,19,22] They range in severity and frequency. Myoclonus is the rule, but grand mal convulsions are also seen. Hiccuping is frequent. The electroencephalogram is usually diffusely abnormal,[23–27] and the pattern may be that of hypsarrhythmia. A pseudoperiodic or burst suppression pattern has been described as more typical,[23–25] in which there are periodic bursts of large-amplitude sharp elements on a low-voltage background. This pattern has also been reported in patients with myoclonic encephalopathy without hyperglycinemia. The burst-suppression pattern characteristic of infancy may change to hypsarrhythmia in later infancy and to multifocal epileptic discharges during wakefulness.[26] The burst-suppression pattern has been observed as early as 30 min after birth.[25] Brain-stem auditory evoked potentials may be abnormal.[26] Atrophy of the brain or hypodensity of the myelin may be seen on CT[28] or MRI scan.

Although most patients resemble those described above, a few have had other presentations. That some of this phenotypic heterogeneity is due to variables other than differences in mutant alleles is suggested by a sibship in which two affected children had phenotypes of variable severity; one had an overwhelming neonatal illness and died at 6 days of age despite exchange transfusion and artificial ventilation; the other was first referred for evaluation of mental retardation at 1 year of age.[29,30]

A few patients have been reported in whom there was only a mild retardation. We studied a family with three affected girls who were only mildly retarded despite biochemical abnormalities indistinguishable from patients with the classic form of the disease.[31] Three other families, each with multiple affected siblings with mild developmental delay, have also been described.[32–34]

We have also encountered in only one patient[35] a very different presentation, as a neurodegenerative disease not unlike Tay-Sachs or Krabbe disease. The patient developed relatively normally for the first months of life, and then in the second half of the first year had a rapid progressive cerebral degeneration course, resembling that of a neurolipidosis. It led to a state of decerebrate rigidity, followed rapidly by death. At autopsy the histopathologic appearance of the brain of this patient was similar to those of other patients with nonketotic hyperglycinemia.

Neutropenia was observed in one patient[13] with nonketotic hyperglycinemia. In this patient the percentage of neutrophils in smears of peripheral blood seldom exceeded 20, and the total neutrophil count was often under 2000 per mm^3 and sometimes well under 1000. However, neutropenia has not regularly been observed in this disease.

The neuropathology of nonketotic hyperglycinemia consists of diffuse alterations in the myelination that normally occurs after birth.[36] There may be vacuolation in the myelin, delay in myelination, or loss of myelin and gliosis. In addition myelin lamellae have been reported in the glial vacuoles.[37] Similar changes have been seen in other aminoacidopathies, including propionic acidemia, PKU, and maple syrup urine disease. In the patient we reported[35] who presented with a clinical picture of cerebral degeneration there was striking cystic degeneration of white matter throughout the cerebrum. Microscopic examination revealed extensive spongy degeneration of white matter and marked gliosis.

BIOCHEMICAL CHARACTERISTICS

Plasma Concentrations

In patients with nonketotic hyperglycinemia the concentration of glycine in the blood is elevated.[1,13,20,32] In Gerritsen's patient[3] the plasma concentration ranged from 920 to 1240 μ*M*. In a series of 31 patients collected from the literature the mean was 1000 ± 457 μ*M*.[32] In 19 Finnish patients the mean concentration was 780 ± 27 μ*M*.[38] Plasma glycine concentration may be lower in some patients. It may also fluctuate considerably in any one patient over time. In the Finnish study the control mean plasma glycine concentration was 200 μ*M*.[38]

Glycine in Urine

The excretion of glycine in the urine by these patients may be enormous. Gerritsen's patient[3] excreted between 1 and 3 g glycine per day at 5 years of age. A normal adult excretes about 100 mg glycine per day[39] or 0.1 to 0.2 mg/mg creatinine. Glycine excretion per milligram creatinine is similar in children.[40,41] In a series of 31 patients of various ages from the literature the range was from 112 mg/day to 1.9 g/day.[33] Because of the large amounts of glycine normally found in the urine, it is possible to overlook a patient with hyperglycinemia when screening the urine for amino acids by paper chromatography or electrophoresis. Also, patients are often studied when acutely ill, not eating, and receiving large amounts of parenterally administered fluids. Under these circumstances the excretion of glycine in hyperglycinemic patients may appear to be normal. Quantitative assay of glycine excretion will usually provide the true answer, but in general it is better to screen for hyperglycinemia using the blood rather than urine, because the blood concentration is seldom brought into the normal range by treatment.

Although there is a common transport system for proline, hydroxyproline, and glycine in human kidney, elevated excretion of proline and hydroxyproline has not been observed in nonketotic hyperglycinemia. This reflects the low affinity of the shared transport system for glycine. The converse does occur; glycine (and hydroxyproline) excretion is increased in hyperprolinemia.[42] (See Chap. 102 for more details of the renal transport of these amino acids.)

Concentrations of Glycine in Cerebrospinal Fluid

Concentrations of glycine are elevated in the cerebrospinal fluid in patients with nonketotic hyperglycinemia. In reported patients concentrations have varied from 130 to 360 μ*M*.[1,13,43,44] In a series of 12 patients summarized from the literature, the mean was 93 μ*M*.[33] In the Finnish series of 19 patients the mean was 93 μ*M*[38] In control subjects the concentration has generally been less than 13 μ*M*.

Perry[43] has pointed out that glycine concentrations in cerebrospinal fluid are particularly elevated in nonketotic hyperglycinemia. The ratio of the CSF concentration to that of the plasma is substantially higher in patients with nonketotic hyperglycinemia than in hyperglycinemic patients with organic acidemia.[43,45] In a series of 12 patients from the literature the mean ratio was 0.17 ± 0.09, while in control individuals the ratio was 0.02[15,24] (Table 25-1). The CSF glycine concentration has been shown to be abnormal in the first 90 min of life,[25] which, along with the early abnormal EEG findings, is consistent with the concept of prenatal damage to the brain in this condition.

Table 25-1 Ratios of the Concentration of Glycine in CSF to that of Plasma

*Patient**	*Ratio*
Control—Perry[43]	0.02
NKH—Perry[43]	0.20–0.33
NKH—Holmgren, lit. (*N* = 12)[33]	0.17 ± 0.009
Holmgren, two patients[33]	0.10, 0.25
NKH—von Wendt et al. (*N* = 19)[17]	0.11
NKH—Holmqvist and Polberger[19]	0.15, 2.52
NKH—Scriver et al.[44]	0.17
NKH—RH[13]	0.30
NKH—TZ[21]	0.10
NKH—Frazier et al., two sibs[32]	0.07, 0.09
NKH—LS[35]	0.07

*NKH = nonketotic hyperglycinemia; the initials are those of three patients reported by the author.

We have observed patients with milder degrees of clinical expression in whom the ratios were, though abnormal, less elevated than in the classic, severe phenotype. We hypothesized that this may be one way in which to characterize clinically heterogeneity of expression. In two reported sibs in which the degree of retardation was mild, the ratios were said to be typical of nonketotic hyperglycinemia.[32] However, as we calculated their ratios in form comparable to those of Perry et al.,[43] the values of 0.065 and 0.086 were considerably lower than Perry's lowest value of 0.2 and were about half the mean literature value.[15,24] In fact we have found values as high as 0.04 in propionic acidemia. On the other hand, in our patient with the atypical course the ratio was 0.07.[35]

Hypooxaluria was initially described as a feature of this syndrome.[3] It is now clear that a diminished excretion of oxalate is not characteristic. Oxalate excretion has been found not to be decreased in a number of patients, including the original patient restudied.[1] Glyoxylate excretion was also normal. These observations provided evidence against the original hypothesis of a defect in glycine oxidase.

Delayed disappearance of glycine from plasma has been observed in loading tests, and there was no appreciable increase in the plasma concentration of serine.[1] By contrast, there was abundant evidence of ready conversion of serine to glycine. The prompt rise and fall in the concentration of serine after a serine load indicated its normal metabolism. However, the glycine concentration rose steadily over a 4-h period. These data are consistent with a defect in the utilization of glycine.

The Molecular Defect

This was first assessed in in vivo studies of the metabolism of glycine designed to evaluate separately the fates of carbon 1 and carbon 2, using [1-^{14}C]glycine or [2-^{14}C]glycine injected separately and intravenously.[46] Collection of expired air permitted measurement of the kinetics of conversion of glycine to CO_2. Serine was isolated from plasma and degraded, and the ^{14}C in the third carbon quantified. Control subjects were studied in the control state and during constant infusion of glycine at a rate which increased the pool to a level comparable to that of patients.

The formation of $^{14}CO_2$ from carbon 1 of glycine was demonstrated to be defective in three patients with nonketotic hyperglycinemia. The curves obtained were virtually identical. The kinetics of the conversion of glycine to plasma serine were similar whether the glycine administered was [1-^{14}C]glycine or [2-^{14}C]glycine. The specific activities of serine in the patients were considerably lower than those of control subjects, and the curves of the patients were so flat that it appeared that different processes were being examined in patients and controls. The process was elucidated through degradation of the isolated serine with periodate. This permitted the selective trapping of carbon 3 as the dimedon derivative. The specific activities of this carbon approximated zero, indicating that there was virtually no conversion of carbon 2 of glycine to carbon 3 of serine in the patients. This conversion was readily made in the control subjects.

The data indicated a primary defect in the metabolism of glycine in nonketotic hyperglycinemia in which the formation of CO_2 from carbon 1 of glycine and the formation of carbon 3 of serine from carbon 2 of glycine were both strikingly defective. These findings are consistent with a block in the glycine cleavage system.

These conclusions were supported by the study of liver homogenates.[1,30,47] In these studies it was found that in patient liver homogenate the rates of conversion of [2-^{14}C]glycine to serine were about equal to those of [1-^{14}C]glycine. In contrast, in control liver the rate of incorporation of [2-^{14}C]glycine to serine was 1.6 times that of [1-^{14}C]glycine. The data indicated that carbon 2 of glycine is normally converted to carbon 2 and 3 of serine, yielding about twice as much isotope enrichment from carbon 2 as from carbon 1, while in the patients carbon 2 of glycine is converted only to carbon 2 of serine. The enzyme has also been studied in autopsied liver by measuring the conversion of [1-^{14}C]glycine to $^{14}CO_2$; this activity was 2 to 4 percent of normal in the patient.[48] We have also studied glycine metabolism in vivo using ^{13}C glycine as a tracer compound; patients with nonketotic hyperglycinemia may be distinguished from control subjects by reduced glycine decarboxylation to respiratory CO_2.[49]

Perry and colleagues[50] observed that the concentration of glycine in brain is elevated in this condition, in contrast to findings in patients with organic acidemia and secondary ketotic forms of hyperglycinemia. Consistent with this, they found that the activity of the glycine cleavage system, as measured by the exchange of $^{14}CO_2$ with glycine, was active in brain but virtually absent in the brain of patients with nonketotic hyperglycinemia.

The biochemical characteristics of the glycine cleavage system in nonketotic hyperglycinemia have now been characterized in a number of patients with different phenotypes.[51–53] Considerable heterogeneity has been encountered; defects have been documented in individual patients in three of the four enzymes of the glycine cleavage system. The first patient studied with the sophisticated techniques developed in Sendai, Japan, was the patient who presented with a phenotype of cerebral degenerative disease.[35] In autopsied liver and brain there was defective activity of both the P protein and the H protein of the glycine cleavage system.[51] The overall activity of glycine cleavage in liver was 2 to 7 percent of control. The activity of the T protein and of lipoamide dehydrogenase, the L protein, were normal. Immunochemical studies using antibody specific to P protein showed that the amount of enzyme protein was normal, as were its kinetic properties. The H protein, the aminomethyl carrier, was considered to be the site of mutant gene expression. Its content was reduced to about 35 percent of control, and it had only two instead of the normal four thiol groups, suggesting that it was devoid of lipoic acid. The purified protein was incapable of reacting with lipoamide dehydrogenase, but reacted with P protein to stimulate some exchange of carbon 1 of glycine with CO_2; its activity in this activation of P protein was only about 4 percent of normal. In sum these data indicated that the H protein was structurally abnormal. The reduction in the activity of the P protein appeared to be secondary as its kinetic properties were unchanged and the amounts of immunoreactive P protein were normal. H protein is required for the catalytic effectiveness of P protein. In fact normally protein-protein interaction between the two enzymes produces a conformational change in the P protein and a change in its absorption spectrum.

Other patients studied have had more usual phenotypes, and all have had defects in the P protein or the T protein.[52,53] Of these, 10 had the classic neonatal presentation and two had a later presentation. These two slower onset patients were sisters who were hypotonic and severely retarded in infancy. Myoclonic jerks were present. The ratio of glycine concentration in the CSF of that in plasma was 0.09 and 0.10 in these two girls and ranged from 0.09 to 0.23 in the classic patients. The actual concentration of glycine in the CSF was lower in the girls with slower onset (42 and 7 μM) than in the classic patients, in whom it ranged from 83 to 280 μM.[53] In all 12 patients the overall activity of the glycine cleavage system was extremely low in the liver and brain tissue studied. However, there was some residual activity in the later onset female sibs, while it was undetectable or nearly so in the more typical patients.

Study of the discrete components revealed defects in the P protein in 7 patients with the typical phenotype; and in the T protein in 2 others (Table 25-2).[52,53] The sisters with the more atypical presentation both had defective activity of the T protein.[53] Immunochemical studies with antibody against the P protein revealed an absence of immunoreactive P protein, consistent with absence of the enzyme protein itself in the patients so far studied.[52] Its activity was undetectable in the tissues of the other patients studied.[53] Thus a virtual absence of the P protein is consistent with the classic nonketotic hyperglycinemia phenotype. In the clinically similar patients with defective T protein, activity was undetectable in liver and brain in one patient[53] and undetectable in brain and extremely low in liver in the other.

It is likely that with further study additional heterogeneity will be uncovered. Virtual absence of activity of any of the components should render the overall cleavage of glycine negligible. Instability of the enzyme at room temperature could lead to spurious reduction in enzyme activity. Therefore, considerable care should be exercised in the storage and assay of tissues. No defects have been observed in the L-protein, but a lipoamide dehydrogenase defect might be expected to have more widespread metabolic effects. It is not clear that the li-

Table 25-2 Clinical and Enzymatic Heterogeneity in Nonketotic Hyperglycinemia

	Site of the defect		
Phenotypes	*P protein*	*T protein*	*H protein*
Classic	8	2	0
Atypical	0	2	0
Degenerative	0	0	1

poamide dehydrogenase of this complex is different genetically from the enzyme involved in the metabolism of pyruvate, 2-ketoglutarate, and the branched chain keto acids. However, patients reported with lipoamide dehydrogenase deficiency and lactic acidemia have had not problems with glycine catabolism.

Differential Diagnosis

In many patients careful assessment of the clinical picture permits the distinguishing of patients with nonketotic hyperglycinemia from those with ketotic hyperglycinemia characteristic of several of the organic acidemias. Even so, we prefer to investigate all hyperglycinemic patients for the accumulation of organic acids, especially propionic and methylmalonic acids. This may be done by examination of the urine for methylcitrate, isovalerylglycine, and other organic acids. Those who do not have organic acidemia or organic aciduria are considered to have nonketotic hyperglycinemia, and for practical purposes the diagnosis is confirmed by assessment of the ratio of glycine concentrations in simultaneously obtained samples of CSF and plasma. The importance of ruling out organic acidemia by analysis of organic acids rather than relying on an absence of ketonuria was highlighted by a patient we reported[54] who had propionic acidemia but presented with hyperglycinemia and overwhelming illness in the absence of ketosis. The distinction is far from academic. Excellent results can be obtained using dietary therapy for patients with propionic acidemia and methylmalonic acidemia, but there is no effective treatment for nonketotic hyperglycinemia. Prompt diagnosis in the neonatal period permits the most informed counsel to the parents.

The differential diagnosis also includes a syndrome in which nonketotic hyperglycinemia is associated with D-glyceric acidemia,[55] which also can be assessed by organic acid analysis. The 2-year-old boy reported had hypotonia from birth that was severe enough to suggest a diagnosis of myasthenia gravis. He developed seizures, and choreiform movements. Mental retardation was severe. Elevated concentrations of glycine were found in blood, urine, and CSF. The excretion of glyceric acid in the urine ranged from 1.5 to 2.5 g/day. The concentration of the compound in the serum was 1200 μM. Assay of D-glyceric acid dehydrogenase in leukocytes was significantly lower in the patient than in controls.[56]

Some time ago Bank and Morrow[57] reported an unusual family in which three brothers with hyperglycinemia had a disorder of the ventral and lateral spinal cord manifested by upper and lower motor neuron signs in both legs and sparing of the sphincters and of sensation. The arms and areas innervated by the cranial nerves were normal. An insidious onset of spasticity and weakness began in childhood and led to atrophy, pes cavus, and contractures. There was ankle clonus and positive Babinski signs. The family was of Lebanese origin, but consanguinity was not noted. There was no urinary methylmalonate, and propionate metabolism was normal in leukocytes. Plasma concentrations of glycine ranged from 610 to 960 μM; the concentration in the CSF was from 21 to 24 μM, and the ratios were 0.035 and 0.025. There was an abnormally blunted rise in serine in plasma after a glycine load, and the conversion of [1-^{14}C]glycine to $^{14}CO_2$ was abnormally low.

A similar patient, also Lebanese, was reported[58] who was found at 4 years of age to have optic atrophy, nystagmus, and mild spastic paraparesis. By 9 years of age, he required braces to assist his ambulation. When studied at 15 years of age, his school performance was age appropriate in a school for the visually handicapped. There was no sphincter involvement, but he had severe, clearly progressive spastic paraparesis and bilateral foot drop. Reflexes were brisk at the knees and absent at the ankles. There was mild vibratory and proprioceptive sensory loss below the knees. Dysmetria of the upper extremities was interpreted as cerebellar in origin, because the spinal involvement spared the arms. This spinocerebellar degeneration was associated with elevated concentrations of glycine in plasma (653 μM), urine (1.3 g/24 h), and CSF (five times the value for normal adults). Following oral administration of glycine, there was little increase in the plasma concentration of serine.

Probably the most frequently encountered etiology of hyperglycinemia in practice today is administration of the anticonvulsant valproate (sodium dipropylacetate, Depakene).[59] In a series of 14 children over 9 months of age, the mean urinary glycine was 552 mg/g creatinine in those receiving valproate, compared to 140 in 52 controls. In 13 in whom serum glycine was measured, the mean was 427 μM, as compared with 237 μM in controls. In two patients in whom the CSF concentration of glycine was measured, it was said to be normal. Furthermore, the glycine concentration of the brain has been reported to be normal in valproate-treated rats.[60] However, more data on humans are required before we can conclude that valproate does not affect central nervous system glycine. Dipropylacetic acid has been found to reduce the actual amount of the glycine cleavage enzyme system in the liver of rats, presumably by an inhibition of enzyme synthesis.[61] The compound gets to the brain where it would be expected to have a similar effect. Certainly a diagnosis of nonketotic hyperglycinemia should be based on determinations not influenced by valproate therapy. On the other hand, we have had the distinct impression that the administration of valproate worsened the status of patients with nonketotic hyperglycinemia. This has been the conclusion of others.[62] However, in two patients valproate was described as the most effective drug for seizure control. A failure to increase the CSF concentration of glycine was cited[63]; in each patient the actual concentrations after treatment were higher, but the differences were small. In one the drug had to be discontinued because of recurrent drug-related neutropenia. It would appear prudent to treat the convulsions of these patients with anticonvulsants other than valproate.

Genetics

Nonketotic hyperglycinemia appears to be a rare autosomal recessive condition. Consanguinity has been reported in two families.[14,29] Multiple affected patients have been reported in some families.[14,29,30] The prevalence is not known. We have estimated it at 1 in 250,000. Many patients must die in infancy undiagnosed. In northern Finland prevalence is 1 in 12,000.[64] Heterozygote detection is not available. However, some minor neurologic findings, alterations in the EEG, and disturbances in vestibular neurophysiology were observed in some of a Finnish series of presumed heterozygotes.[65]

DNA from a few patients with nonketotic hyperglycinemia has been studied with restriction endonucleases and probes made from clones considered to represent the gene.[11] Some polymorphism has been identified, but no family studies have been done to know whether there is linkage that would be useful in heterozygote detection or prenatal diagnosis.

Prenatal diagnosis is not yet available. The glycine cleavage system is not expressed in amniocytes or fibroblasts. The concentrations of glycine and serine in amniotic fluid have been examined,[66] and a pregnancy with an elevated glycine/serine ratio was associated with the birth of an affected infant. However, this test has been shown to be unreliable in a study of 183 amniotic fluids in which the glycine/serine ratios were found to overlap those reported for the hyperglycinemic fetus.[67] Furthermore, although the method was successful in predicting a few additional affected and unaffected fetuses,[68] the small difference between the two sets of values led to doubt as to the reliability of the approach. Even fetal liver biopsy and enzyme assay may be unreliable because the shipment of samples over long distances can result in loss of activity in unaffected fetal liver.

The feasibility of the prenatal diagnosis of nonketotic hyperglycinemia by chorionic villus sampling has been considered based on the demonstration that the glycine cleavage system is present in placenta obtained by abortion at 12 weeks of gestation.[69] The glycine/serine ratio of the involved fetus was not appreciably higher than the control mean. The activity of the glycine cleavage system was shown to be defective in fetal liver and brain. The activity of the system in control placenta at 12 weeks was three to five times that of control placenta at term. The placenta of the fetus at risk had markedly reduced overall activity and no detectable activity of the T protein. The method would require 30 to 50 mg of chorionic villi. A caution is that the enzyme is unstable at room temperature, so samples must be assayed immediately after biopsy or frozen immediately at $-80°C$.

Treatment

The management of nonketotic hyperglycinemia is considerably less than satisfactory. A variety of acute measures in the neonatal period may be lifesaving. Exchange transfusion or peritoneal dialysis may permit the weaning of the patient from ventilator dependency. Presumably hemodialysis would do the same, and it is likely that high-dose benzoate therapy would accomplish the same objective.[44] Whether or not this approach is advisable should be considered in detail with the family.

A number of measures have been employed in long-term management, but they have not appreciably altered the course of the disease.[1,20] Small decreases in the glycine concentration of the serum have been observed following protein restriction, the infusion of N^5-formyltetrahydrofolate (leucovorin), and administration of methionine to provide 1-carbon groups, but the course of the disease does not appear to be altered by these approaches. Bachmann and colleagues[16] have pointed out the potential toxicity of methionine treatment. The content of methionine in the brain of their patient was quite high. Very high levels of methionine in the plasma were reported by others following treatment with methionine.[35,70] Treatment with pyridoxine, formate, or choline also does not result in improvement.[20,70]

Glycine is an inhibitory neurotransmitter.[71] Postsynaptic potentials are reduced by glycine. Although the postsynaptic inhibitory effects of glycine occur predominantly in the spinal cord and brain stem rather than in the cortex,[72] these considerations led to the use of strychnine in the therapy of nonketotic hyperglycinemia. The effects of glycine are similar to those of strychnine, and strychnine blocks glycinergic inhibition.[73] Quite a number of patients have now been treated with strychnine.[71–81] Two reports of modest success have been published.[74,75] However, we and others have treated a number of patients who have failed to respond,[76–80] and the consensus is now that the majority of the patients, including those with the classic form of the disease, do not respond.[79,81] Those who respond appear to have milder atypical phenotypes. In a family with one such variant presentation and a defect in T protein, treatment with strychnine in an older sibling at 9 years of age did not lead to improvement.[78] However, treatment of the younger sibling from birth was associated with a much milder mental retardation than that of the older sibling and an absence of seizures. The younger sibling was also treated with arginine from 9 days of age in an attempt to conjugate glycine to form creatinine, and 250 mg/kg per day of sodium benzoate. These features make it difficult to assess the effect of strychnine, as did the slightly greater residual activity of the glycine cleavage enzyme in the treated sister. Certainly her CSF concentration of glycine was consistently lower than that of the sister, and we would attribute that to an effect of benzoate. Treatment from the neonatal period with strychnine was ineffective in Finnish infants with the classic phenotype.[79]

Our interest in benzoate in the management of nonketotic hyperglycinemia was reawakened by Matalon et al.,[82,83] who developed a three-drug regimen, including sodium benzoate, in a dose of 125 mg/kg per day, a benzodiazepine, diazepam, and choline along with folic acid, to facilitate single carbon unit transfer. This regimen was reported to have a favorable anticonvulsant effect in which seizures stopped, and the patients became more alert and responsible. The authors attributed these effects to the diazepam.

Benzodiazepines compete for glycine receptors in the central nervous system[84] and displace [^{3}H]strychnine from binding to the brain and spinal cord. Further, in a series of benzodiazepines there was a correlation between their rank order of potency and their effectiveness in the competition assay. Flunitrazepam (RO4200) was the most potent. Matalon et al.[82] treated two patients with nonketotic hyperglycinemia with relatively large doses, 1.5 to 3.0 mg/kg per day, of diazepam, along with choline and benzoate. Both patients responded with cessation of previously intractable seizures.

We saw a patient who was being treated with this regimen and who was not seizure-free but was having three to five seizures a day. Cessation of benzoate was followed by a marked increase in the number, to 25 to 30 per day, severity, and duration of the seizures. We then embarked on a systematic approach to the reduction of cerebrospinal fluid concentrations of glycine with maximally tolerated doses of benzoate.[85] Glycine acyltransferase (EC 2.3.1.13), the enzyme that catalyzes the conjugation of glycine with benzoate, is active in mammalian liver but absent in brain,[86] and it is not induced by large quantities of glycine. Therefore, any effect of benzoate on the glycine concentration in brain would have to be exerted through a lowering of concentrations in the blood and subsequent diffusion out of the central nervous system.

We have employed doses of benzoate considerably larger than those previously reported and have consistently achieved a lowering of CSF concentrations of glycine. A statistically significant dose-response relationship was observed. In the first patient studied the CSF concentration of glycine was reduced from 120 to 30 μM. In two others initial concentrations of 367 and 180 were lowered to 50 and 80 μM, respectively. Experience with these three patients has been reported,[85] and experience with three others has been similar. Doses of 250 to 750 mg/kg per day appear to be tolerated by patients with this disorder, and doses of this magnitude are required to alter the CSF concentration of glycine. The clinical result has been a regular diminution in seizures. In some, seizures have ceased. In a patient having virtually continuous seizures, this can certainly improve the sensorium. However, the regimen does not otherwise appear to alter appreciably the course of the disease. In our studies arginine was not effective in lowering CSF concentrations of glycine.

REFERENCES

1. NYHAN WL: Nonketotic hyperglycinemia, in Stanbury JB, Wyngaarden JB, Fredrickson DS (eds): *The Metabolic Basis of Inherited Disease*, 4th ed. New York, McGraw-Hill, 1978, pp 518–527.
2. NYHAN WL, ANDO T, GERRITSEN T: Hyperglycinemia, in Nyhan WL (ed): *Amino Acid Metabolism and Genetic Variation*. New York, McGraw-Hill, 1967, pp 255–265.
3. GERRITSEN T, KAVEGGIA E, WAISMAN HA: A new type of idiopathic hyperglycinemia with hypo-oxaluria. *Pediatrics* 36:882, 1965.
4. NYHAN WL: *Diagnostic Recognition of Genetic Disease*. Philadelphia, Lea & Febiger, 1987, pp 85–95.
5. NYHAN WL: Metabolism of glycine in the normal individual and in patients with non-ketotic hyperglycinaemia. *J Inherited Metab Dis* 5:105, 1982.
6. ANDO T, KLINGBERG WG, WARD AN, RASMUSSEN K, NYHAN WL: Isovaleric acidemia presenting with altered metabolism of glycine. *Pediatr Res* 5:478, 1971.
7. ARNSTEIN HRV, NEUBERGER A: The synthesis of glycine and serine by the rat. *Biochem J* 55:271, 1953.
8. YOSHIDA T, KIKUCHI G: Comparative study on major pathways of glycine and serine catabolism in vertebrate livers. *J Biochem* 72:1503, 1972.
9. KIKUCHI G: The glycine cleavage system: Composition, reaction mechanism, and physiological significance. *Mol Cell Biochem* 1:169, 1973.
10. MOTOKAWA Y, KIKUCHI G: Glycine metabolism by rat liver mitochondria. Reconstitution of the reversible glycine cleavage system with partially purified protein components. *Arch Biochem Biophys* 164:624, 1974.
11. HIRAGA K, KURE S, YAMAMOTO M, TADA K, ISHIGURO Y: Cloning of cDNAS coding for the constituents of the glycine cleavage system from a human liver cDNA library. *Proceedings of the 4th International Congress of Inborn Errors of Metabolism*, Sendai, Japan, May 26–30, 1987.
12. NYHAN WL, YUJNOVSKY AO, WEHR RF: Amino acids and cell growth, in Cheek DB (ed): *Human Growth: Body Composition, Cell Growth, Energy, and Intelligence*. Philadelphia, Lea & Febiger, 1968, pp 396–416.
13. BAUMGARTNER R, ANDO T, NYHAN WL: Nonketotic hyperglycinemia. *J Pediatr* 75:1022, 1969.
14. SIMILA S, VISAKORPI JK: Clinical findings in three patients with nonketotic hyperglycinaemia. *Ann Clin Res* 2:151, 1970.
15. FERDINAND W, GORDON RR, OWEN G: Nonketotic hyperglycinaemia: Clinical findings and amino acid analyses on the plasma of a new case. *Clin Chim Acta* 30:745, 1970.
16. BACHMANN C, MIHATSCH MJ, BAUMGARTNER RE, BRECHBUHLER T, BUHLER UK, OLAFSSON A, OHNACKER H, WICK H: Nicht-ketotische hyperglyzinämie: Perakuter verlauf im Neugeborenenalten. *Helv Paediatr Acta* 26:228, 1971.
17. VON WENDT L, SIMILA S, HIRVASNIEMI A, SUVANTO E: Nonketotic hyperglycinemia. A clinical analysis of 19 Finnish patients. *Monogr Hum Genet* 9:58, 1978.
18. DE GROOT CJ, HOMMES FA, TOUWEN BCL: The altered toxicity of glycine in nonketotic hyperglycinemia. *Hum Hered* 27:178, 1977.
19. HOLMQVIST P, POLBERGER S: Neonatal non-ketotic hyperglycinemia (NKH). Diagnoses and management in two cases. *Neuropediatrics* 16:191, 1985.
20. LANGAN TJ, PUESCHEL SM: Nonketotic hyperglycinemia: Clinical, biochemical, and therapeutic considerations. *Curr Probl Pediatr* 13:1, 1983.
21. ZITER FA, BRAY PF, MADSEN JA, NYHAN WL: The clinical findings in a patient with nonketotic hyperglycinemia. *Pediatr Res* 2:250, 1968.
22. MIGNONE F, BALBO L, VALPREDA A, SCIOLLA N, CHIAPPO GF, GONETTI G: Iperglicinemia non chetosica. Presentazione di un caso. *Minerva Pediatr* 32:111, 1980.
23. AICARDI J, GOUTIERES F: Encéphalopathie myoclonique néonatale. *Rev Electroencephalogr Neurophysiol* 8:99, 1978.
24. MISES J, MOUSSALLI-SALEFRANQUE F, PLOUIN P, TEMAM G, SAUDUBRAY JM: l'E.E.G. dans les hyperglycinémies sans cétose. *Rev Electroencephalogr Neurophysiol* 8:102, 1978.
25. VON WENDT L, SIMILA S, SAUKKONEN A-L, KOIVISTO M, KOUVALAINEN K: Prenatal brain damage in nonketotic hyperglycinemia. *Am J Dis Child* 135:1072, 1981.
26. MARKAND ON, BHUWAN PG, BRANDT IK: Nonketotic hyperglycinemia: Electroencephalographic and evoked potential abnormalities. *Neurology* 32:151, 1982.
27. BERNARDINA BD, DULAC O, FEJERMAN H, DRAVET C, CAPOVILLA G, BONDAVALLI S, COLAMARIA V, ROGER J: Early myoclonic epileptic encephalopathy (E.M.E.E.) *Eur J Pediatr* 140:248, 1983.
28. VALAVANIS A, SCHUBIGER O, HAYEK J: Computed tomography in nonketotic hyperglycinemia. *Comput Tomography* 5:265, 1981.
29. OKKEN A, DE GROOT CJ, HOMMES FA: Nonketotic hyperglycinemia. *J Pediatr* 77:164, 1970.
30. DE GROOT CJ, TROELSTRA HA, HOMMES FA: Nonketotic hyperglycinemia; An in vitro study of the glycine-serine conversion in liver of three patients and the effect of dietary methionine. *Pediatr Res* 4:238, 1970.
31. ANDO T, NYHAN WL, BICKNELL WL, HARRIS R, STERN J: Non-ketotic hyperglycinaemia in a family with an unusual phenotype. *J Inherited Metab Dis* 1:79, 1978.
32. FRAZIER DM, SUMMER GK, CHAMBERLIN HR: Hyperglycinuria and hyperglycinemia in two siblings with mild developmental delays. *Am J Dis Child* 132:777, 1978.
33. HOLMGREN G, BLOMQUIST HK: Non-ketotic hyperglycinemia in 2 sibs with mild psycho-neurological symptoms. *Neuropaediatrie* 8:67, 1977.
34. FLANNERY DB, PELLOCK J, BOUSOUNIS D, HUNT P, NANCE C, WOLF B: Nonketotic hyperglycinemia in two retarded adults: A mild form of infantile nonketotic hyperglycinemia. *Neurology* 33:1064, 1983.
35. TRAUNER DA PAGE T, GRECO C, SWEETMAN L, KULOVICH S, NYHAN WL: Progressive neurodegenerative disorder in a patient with nonketotic hyperglycinemia. *J Pediatr* 98:272, 1981.
36. SHUMAN RM, LEECH RW, SCOTT CR: The neuropathology of the nonketonic and ketonic hyperglycinemias: Three cases. *Neurology* 28:139, 1978.
37. BRUN A, BORJESON M, HULTBERG B, SJÖBLAD S, AKESSON H, LITWIN E: Nonketotic hyperglycinemia: A clinical, biochemical and neuropathologic study including electronic microscopy findings. *Neuropaediatrie* 10:195, 1979.
38. VON WENDT L, SIMILA S, HIRVASNIEMI A, SUVANTO E: Altered levels of various amino acids in blood plasma and cerebrospinal fluid of patients with nonketotic hyperglycinemia. *Neuropaediatrie* 9:360, 1978.
39. STEIN WH: A chromatographic investigation of the amino acid constituents of normal urine. *J Biol Chem* 201:45, 1953.
40. NYHAN WL, BORDEN M, CHILDS B: Idiopathic hyperglycinemia, a new disorder of amino acid metabolism. II. The concentrations of other amino acids in the plasma and their modification by the administration of leucine. *Pediatrics* 27:539, 1961.
41. CHILDS B, NYHAN WL, BORDEN M, BARD L, COOKE RE: Idiopathic hyperglycinemia and hyperglycinuria, a new disorder of amino acid metabolism. *Pediatrics* 27:522, 1961.
42. SCRIVER CR, BERGERON M: Amino acid transport in kidney. The use of mutation to dissect membrane and transepithelial transport, in Nyhan WL (ed): *Heritable Disorders of Amino Acid Metabolism*. New York, Wiley, 1974, pp 515–592.
43. PERRY TL, URQUHART N, MACLEAN J, EVANS ME, HANSEN S, DAVIDSON AGF, APPLEGARTH DA, MACLEOD PJ, LOCK JE: Nonketotic hyperglycinemia. *N Engl J Med* 292:1269, 1975.
44. SCRIVER CR, WHITE A, SPRAGUE W, HORWOOD SP: Plasma-CSF glycine ratio in normal and nonketotic hyperglycinemic subjects. *N Engl J Med* 293:778, 1975.
45. LEVY HL, NISHIMURA RN, ERICKSON AM, JANOWSKA SE: Hyperglycinemia: In vivo comparison of nonketotic and ketotic (propionic acidemic) forms I. CSF glycine concentrations and blood/CSF glycine. *Pediatr Res* 6:400, 1972.
46. ANDO T, NYHAN WL, GERRITSEN T, GONG L, HEINER DC, BRAY PF: Metabolism of glycine in the nonketotic form of hyperglycinemia. *Pediatr Res* 2:254, 1968.
47. TADA K, NARISAWA K, YOSHIDA T, KONNO T, YOKOYAMA Y, NAKAGAWA H, TANNO K, MOCHIZUKI K, ARAKAWA T: Hyperglycinemia: A defect in glycine cleavage reaction. *Tohoku J Exp Med* 98:289, 1969.
48. DINGEON N, ROLLAND MO, DIVRY P, COTTE J: Hyperglycinämie san cétose. Étude biochimique et enzymatique. *Ann Biol Clin* 35:33, 1977.

49. SWEETMAN L, NYHAN WL, KLEIN PD, SZCZEPANIK PA: Glycine-1,2-^{13}C in the investigation of children with inborn errors of metabolism, in Klein PD, Peterson SV (eds): *Proceedings of the 1st International Conference on Stable Isotopes in Chemistry, Biology, and Medicine,* Argonne National Laboratory, Argonne, IL, May 9–11, 1973, Springfield, VA, US Atomic Energy Commission, National Technical Information Service, US Department of Commerce, 1973, pp 404–409.

50. PERRY TL, URQUHART N, HANSEN S: Studies of the glycine cleavage enzyme system in brain from infants with glycine encephalopathy. *Pediatr Res* 11:1192, 1977.

51. HIRAGA K, KOCHI H, HAYASAKA K, KIKUCHI G, NYHAN WL: Defective glycine cleavage system in nonketotic hyperglycinemia. *J Clin Invest* 68:525, 1981.

52. HAYASAKA K, TADA K, KIKUCHI G, WINTER S, NYHAN WL: Nonketotic hyperglycinemia: Two patients with primary defects of P-protein and T-protein, respectively, in the glycine cleavage system. *Pediatr Res* 17:967, 1983.

53. HAYASAKA K, TADA K, NYHAN WL, DANKS DM, HAAN E, NAKAMURA Y, SCHUTGENS RBH, PACKMAN S, SEASHORE MR: Nonketotic hyperglycinemia: Analyses of the glycine cleavage system in typical and atypical cases. *J Pediatr* 110:873, 1987.

54. WADLINGTON WB, KILROY A, ANDO T, SWEETMAN L, NYHAN WL: Hyperglycinemia and propionyl-CoA carboxylase deficiency and episodic severe illness without consistent ketosis. *J Pediatr* 86:707, 1975.

55. BRANDT NJ, RASMUSSEN K, BRANDT S, KØLVRRA S, SCHØNHEYDER F: D-glyceric-acidaemia and non-ketotic hyperglycinaemia. *Acta Paediat Scand* 65:17, 1976.

56. KØLVRRA S, RASMUSSEN K, BRANDT NJ: D-Glyceric acidemia: Biochemical studies of a new syndrome. *Pediatr Res* 10:825, 1976.

57. BANK WJ, MORROW G, III: A familial spinal cord disorder with hyperglycinemia. *Arch Neurol* 27:136, 1972.

58. STEINMAN GS, YUDKOFF M, BERMAN PH, BLAZER-YOST B, SEGAL S: Late-onset nonketotic hyperglycinemia and spinocerebellar degeneration. *J Pediatr* 94:907, 1979.

59. BLENKINSOPP WK, DUPONT PA: Dipropylacetate (valproate) and glycine metabolism. *Lancet* 2:617, 1977.

60. GODIN Y, HEINER L, MARK J, MANDEL P: Effects of DI-n-propylacetate, an anticonvulsive compound, on GABA metabolism. *J Neurochem* 16:869, 1969.

61. KOCHI H, HAWASAKA K, HIRAGA K, KIKUCHI G: Reduction of the level of glycine cleavage system in the rat liver resulting from administration of dipropylacetic acid: An experimental approach to hyperglycinemia. *Arch Biochem Biophys* 198:589, 1979.

62. MELANCON SB, DALLAIRE L, VINCELETTE P, POTIER M, GEOFFROY G: Early treatment of severe infantile glycine encephalopathy (nonketotic hyperglycinemia) with strychnine and sodium benzoate, in Papadatos CJ, Bartsocas CS (eds): *Second International Clinical Genetics Seminar on Management of Genetic Disorders.* Athens, June 1979, New York, AR Liss, 1979, pp 217–229.

63. MacDERMOT K, NELSON W, WEINBERG JA, SCHULMAN JD: Valproate in nonketotic hyperglycinemia. *Pediatrics* 65:624, 1980.

64. VON WENDT L, HIRVASNIEMI A, SIMILA S: Nonketotic hyperglycinemia. A genetic study of 13 Finnish families. *Clin Genet* 15:411, 1979.

65. VON WENDT L, ALANKO H, SORRI M, TOIVAKKA E, SAUKKONEN A-L, SIMILA S: Clinical and neurophysiological findings in heterozygotes for nonketotic hyperglycinemia. *Clin Genet* 19:94, 1981.

66. GARCIA-CASTRO JM, ISALES-FORSYTHE CM, LEVY HL, SHIH VE, LAO-VELEZ CR, GONZALEZ-RIOS MdelC, REYES DE TORRES LC: Prenatal diagnosis of nonketotic hyperglycinemia. *N Engl J Med* 306:79, 1982.

67. MESAVAGE C, NANCE CS, FLANNERY DB, WEINER DL, SUCHY SF, WOLF B: Glycine/serine ratios in amniotic fluid: An unreliable indicator for the prenatal diagnosis of nonketotic hyperglycinemica. *Clin Genet* 23:354, 1983.

68. APPLEGARTH DA, LEVY HL, SHIH VE, MCGILLIVRAY B, WONG JT, TOONE JR, KIRBY LT: Prenatal diagnosis of non-ketotic hyperglycinemia. *Prenat Diagn* 6:257, 1986.

69. HAYASAKA K, TADA K, FUEKI N, TAKAHASHI I, IGARASHI A, TAKABAYASHI T, BAUMGARTNER R: Feasibility of prenatal diagnosis of nonketotic hyperglycinemia: Existence of the glycine cleavage system in placenta. *J Pediatr* 110:124, 1987.

70. TRIJBELS JMF, MONNENS LAH, VanDerZEE SPM, VRENKEN JATh, SENGERS RCA, SCHRETLEN EDAM: A patient with nonketotic hyperglycinemia: Biochemical findings and therapeutic approaches. *Pediatr Res* 8:598, 1974.

71. RANSOM BR: Possible pathophysiology of neurologic abnormalities associated with nonketotic hyperglycinemia. *N Engl J Med* 294:1295, 1976.

72. KELLY JS, KRNJEVIC K: The action of glycine on cortical neurones. *Exp Brain Res* 9:155, 1969.

73. KRNJEVIC K: Chemical nature of synaptic transmission in vertebrates. *Physiol Rev* 54:418, 1974.

74. GITZELMANN R, STEINMANN B, OTTEN A, DUMERMUTH G, HERDAN M, REUBI JC, CUENOD M: Nonketotic hyperglycinemia treated with strychnine, a glycine receptor antagonist. *Helv Paediatr Acta* 32:517, 1977.

75. ARNESON D, CH'IEN LT, CHANCE P, WILROY RS: Strychnine therapy in nonketotic hyperglycinemia. *Pediatrics* 63:369, 1979.

76. MacDERMOTT KD, NELSON W, REICHERT CM, SCHULMAN JD: Attempts at use of strychnine sulfate in the treatment of nonketotic hyperglycinemia. *Pediatrics* 65:61, 1980.

77. WARBURTON D, BOYLE RJ, KEATS JT, VOHR B, PEUSCHEL S, OH W: Nonketotic hyperglycinemia. *Am J Dis Child* 134:273, 1980.

78. HAAN EA, KIRBY DM, TADA K, HAYASAKA K, DANKS DM: Difficulties in assessing the effect of strychnine on the outcome of nonketotic hyperglycinaemia. Observations on sisters with a mild T-protein defect. *Eur J Pediatr* 145:267, 1986.

79. VON WENDT L, SIMILA S, SAUKKONEN A-L, KOIVISTO M: Failure of strychnine treatment during the neonatal period in three Finish children with nonketotic hyperglycinemia. *Pediatrics* 65:1166, 1980.

80. ARENZ B, RISTER M, SANCHEZ A: Strychnin als Therapieversuch der nicht-ketotischen Hyperglycinämie. *Monatsschr Kinderheilkd* 130:621, 1982.

81. CARSON NAJ: Non-ketotic hyperglycinaemia—A review of 70 patients. *J Inherited Metab Dis* 5:126, 1982.

82. MATALON R, MICHALS K, NAIDU S, HUGHES J: Treatment of non-ketotic hyperglycinaemia with diazepam, choline and folic acid. *J Inherited Metab Dis* 5:3, 1982.

83. MATALON R, NAIDU S, HUGHES JR, MICHALS K: Nonketotic hyperglycinemia: Treatment with diazepam—A competitor for glycine receptors. *Pediatrics* 71:581, 1983.

84. YOUNG AB, ZUKIN SR, SNYDER SH: Interaction of benzodiazepines with central nervous glycine receptors: Possible mechanism of action. *Proc Natl Acad Sci* 71:2246, 1974.

85. WOLFF JA, KULOVICH S, YU AL, QIAO C-N, NYHAN WL: The effectiveness of benzoate in the management of seizures in nonketotic hyperglycinemia. *Am J Dis Child* 140:596, 1986.

86. MacDERMOTT KD, NELSON W, SOUTTER V, TOWNE D, SCHULMAN JD: Glycine and benzoate conjugation and glycine acyltransferase activity in the developing and adult rat: Possible relationships to nonketotic hyperglycinemia. *Dev Pharmacol Ther* 3:150, 1981.

CHAPTER **26**

DISORDERS OF ω-AMINO ACIDS IN FREE AND PEPTIDE-LINKED FORMS

CHARLES R. SCRIVER
THOMAS L. PERRY

1. *Five ω-amino acids occur in free forms in mammalian (and human) tissues and body fluids: β-alanine and* R*-β-aminoisobutyric acid* (R*-β-AiB) are pyrimidine catabolites (of uracil and thymine, respectively);* S*-β-AiB is a catabolite of* L*-valine; β-leucine is a precursor of α-leucine; γ-aminobutyric acid (GABA) is a derivative of* L*-glutamate and, to a minor extent, of* L*-ornithine via putrescine.*
2. *β-Alanine and GABA also occur as imidazole dipeptides, which are products of carnosine synthetase activity. The major dipeptides are carnosine (β-alanyl-*L*-histidine), anserine (β-alanyl-1-methyl-*L*-histidine, not a constituent of human tissues), and homocarnosine (γ-aminobutyryl-*L*-histidine, present only in the brain in humans).*
3. *GABA, β-alanine, and carnosine have neurotransmitter functions. Carnosine (and anserine) may act as an intracellular buffer in skeletal muscle during anaerobic glycolysis.*
4. *Several disorders of β-alanine metabolism are known, notably:* (a) *Dihydropyrimidine dehydrogenase deficiency (autosomal recessive) is a disorder of uracil and thymine catabolism (affecting endogenous β-alanine and* R*-β-AiB synthesis). Juvenile-onset patients (four cases) have cerebral dysfunction. Adult-onset probands (two cases) have a pharmacokinetic disorder with CNS signs apparent on exposure to fluorouracil. Deficit enzyme activity can be measured in skin fibroblasts.* (b) *Hyper-β-alaninemia (one case) is accompanied by impaired somatic and neurologic development. A complex hyperaminoaciduria (β-alanine, β-AiB, and taurine) is explained by saturation and inhibition of a β-amino-preferring transport system in the nephron. Elevated levels of β-alanine and GABA occur in plasma and CSF. The putative enzyme deficiency is β-alanine-pyruvate transaminase, which affects GABA metabolism secondarily. Pharmacologic doses of pyridoxine (precursor of a coenzyme for the transaminase) ameliorated the metabolic phenotype.* (c) *A benign disorder (one case) impairing β-alanine catabolism is associated with a characteristic urine metabolite pattern indicative of deficient malonate/methylmalonate semialdehyde dehydrogenase deficiency.*
5. *Hyper-β-AiBuria is a benign "metabolic polymorphism" present in many human populations (5 to 10 percent in whites, 40 to 95 percent in Mongolian-derived populations, but 0 percent in Asian Indians). R-β-AiB is the excreted enantiomer. The enzyme deficiency is hepatic R-β-AiB-pyruvate transaminase inherited as autosomal recessive; heterozygotes have slightly elevated β-AiB excretion and enzyme activity intermediate between that of low excretors (homozygous normal) and high excretors (homozygous mutant).*
6. *There are at least three confirmed or suspected primary disorders of GABA metabolism: (a) Pyridoxine (vitamin B_6) dependency with seizures is autosomal recessive; it has neonatal and delayed onset forms. Seizures respond only to pharmacologic doses of pyridoxine. The postulated mutant enzyme is brain glutamic acid decarboxylase, modified in its binding of coenzyme (pyridoxal-5-phosphate). Vitamin B_6 metabolism is normal in the disorder. (b) GABA-α-ketoglutarate transaminase deficiency was found in three unrelated patients with impaired CNS function. They had accelerated growth and elevated plasma growth hormone levels. Clinical and metabolic phenotypes differentiate the disorder from hyper-β-alaninemia despite the fact that both conditions have impaired GABA and β-alanine catabolism. The enzyme deficiency was documented in lymphocytes and lymphoblasts, and inheritance is autosomal recessive. (c) Succinic semialdehyde dehydrogenase deficiency (4-hydroxybutyricaciduria) has been described in six cases, all with cerebellar signs, muscular hypotonia, and mental retardation. The principal derivative (4-hydroxybutyrate) of the deficient enzyme's substrate accumulates in CSF, plasma, and urine. Deficient dehydrogenase activity was demonstrated in lymphocytes by coupled and direct assays. Inheritance is autosomal recessive.*
7. *Two disorders of dipeptide catabolism (serum carnosinase deficiency, 16 confirmed cases in several pedigrees; homocarnosinosis, four cases in one pedigree) are apparently similar or the same disorder. Although neurologic signs were present in some patients, others were healthy and the association of clinical disease with the metabolic disorder is either a bias of retrospective ascertainment or a consequence of unidentified variables in environment and/or genotype. Both disorders have deficient serum carnosine activity, more extreme in homocarnosinosis. Serum and tissue carnosinase are different enzymes, and tissue carnosinase activity is normal in the disorder. Persistent hypercarnosinuria reflects turnover of endogenous carnosine. Carnosinase-deficient subjects excrete anserine and do not excrete free 1-methyl histidine after ingestion of anserine. Homocarnosine accumulation in CSF is explained by the deficiency of serum carnosinase activity. The disorder is inherited as autosomal recessive. Heterozygotes have partial enzyme deficiency but no metabolic abnormalities.*

   Serum carnosinase activity is low in infancy compared with values in later childhood; maximum normal activity is attained only in puberty. Ontogeny of serum carnosinase activity was responsible for an erroneous diagnosis of the deficiency phenotype in several probands.

This chapter differs from previous versions by the inclusion of several new entities; the corresponding chapter in the previous edition serves an archival role for deleted information, particularly that on membrane transport of the relevant substances. Here we describe current views about the metabolism of β-alanine and β-aminoisobutyric acid (β-AiB), include a brief survey of γ-aminobutyrate (GABA) metabolism, and describe metabolism of the corresponding dipeptides carnosine, anserine, and homocarnosine.

Several disorders affect these substances; some are diseases, while others appear to impose no biologic costs on the variant individuals. We approach them as experiments of nature informative about facets of metabolism, and since they are all apparently Mendelian, they indicate loci at which variant alleles exist in the human gene pool. They include three disorders of β-alanine metabolism: dihydropyrimidine dehydrogenase deficiency, hyper-β-alaninemia, and a sparsely described disorder, putative malonate/methyl malonate semialdehyde dehydrogenase deficiency; three disorders of GABA metabolism: pyridoxine dependency (a putative disorder of GABA homeostasis), GABA-transaminase deficiency, and succinic semialdehyde dehydrogenase deficiency; and one disorder, masking as two, of dipeptide metabolism: serum carnosinase deficiency and homocarnosinosis. The remaining phenotype is hyper-β-AiBuria, an inherited "metabolic polymorphism" in human populations, which also occurs as an acquired phenotype under certain conditions.

In no case has the relevant gene been cloned, and in some the mutant enzyme has only been inferred; hence this is an old-fashioned chapter—describing some inborn errors of metabolism. Our approach is to document each entity and its metabolic phenotype in simple fashion; we leave details about biochemistry of the normal enzymes and processes to the primary literature (cited in detail in Refs. 1 to 3).

β- (AND ω-) AMINO METABOLITES

Five β- or ω-amino carboxylic acids occur in their natural free forms in mammals.

β-Leucine, a precursor of α-L-leucine,[1] has no inherited disorder of its metabolism in humans, and its plasma level is not raised in maple syrup urine disease.[1] An increment in plasma β-leucine occurs in pernicious anemia (24.7 ± 12.4 μmol/l; normal value 4.8 ± 3.1 μmol/l), presumably because leucine-2,3-aminomutase, which converts β- to α-leucine, requires adenosylcobalamine as coenzyme.[1] This finding infers that β-leucine is a normal precursor of α-leucine in humans. β-Leucine metabolism is not discussed further here (see Poston[1] and Griffith[2]). β-Alanine, the simplest of the β-aminomonocarboxylic acids, and *R*-β-AiB are catabolites of uracil and thymine, respectively.[2] *S*-β-AiB is the transamination product of *S*-methymalonic acid semialdehyde, a metabolite of L-valine[2] (see Ref. 2 for other details).

γ-Aminobutyrate (GABA)[3] is the decarboxylation product of L-glutamate. It is a significant metabolite of the nervous system and kidney, and it plays different metabolic roles in the two tissues.

β-Alanine occurs in mammalian tissues principally as the dipeptide carnosine (β-alanyl-L-histidine) and to a lesser extent as anserine (β-alanyl-l-methyl-L-histidine).[2] Anserine is not present in human skeletal muscle. GABA occurs to a minor extent in peptide linkage as homocarnosine (γ-aminobutyryl-L-histidine).

None of these substances occurs in proteins. β-Alanine, GABA, and carnosine are putative neurotransmitters. Chemical structures are shown in Fig. 26-1.

β-ALANINE

Normal Metabolism

(See Ref. 1 for citation of literature.) β-Alanine is an endogenous catabolite of the pyrimidines uracil and cytosine and a precursor of the oxidative substrate acetyl CoA (Fig. 26-2); *R*-βAiB is a metabolic analogue of β-alanine in that it is derived from the pyrimidine thymine, and the enzymes of uracil catabolism are active toward thymine. β-Ureidopropionase [reaction (4), Fig. 26-2] is apparently restricted to liver; hence biosynthesis of free β-alanine (and *R*-β-AiB) from pyrimidines

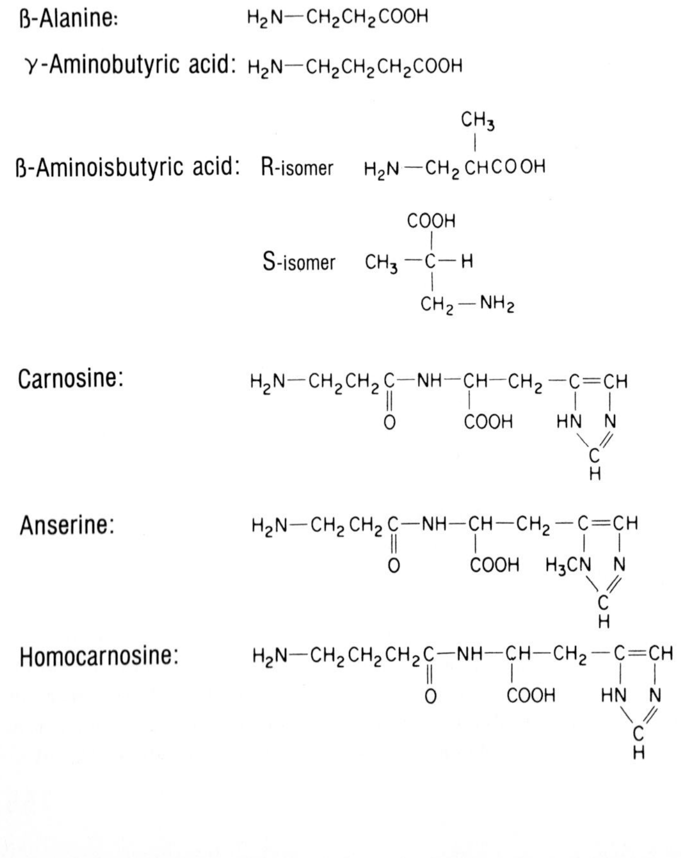

β-Alanine: $H_2N{-}CH_2CH_2COOH$

γ-Aminobutyric acid: $H_2N{-}CH_2CH_2CH_2COOH$

β-Aminoisobutyric acid: R-isomer $H_2N{-}CH_2CH(CH_3)COOH$

S-isomer $CH_3{-}C(H)(COOH){-}CH_2{-}NH_2$

Carnosine: $H_2N{-}CH_2CH_2C({=}O){-}NH{-}CH(COOH){-}CH_2{-}C{=}CH$ (imidazole ring: HN, N, CH)

Anserine: $H_2N{-}CH_2CH_2C({=}O){-}NH{-}CH(COOH){-}CH_2{-}C{=}CH$ (imidazole ring: H_3CN, N, CH)

Homocarnosine: $H_2N{-}CH_2CH_2CH_2C({=}O){-}NH{-}CH(COOH){-}CH_2{-}C{=}CH$ (imidazole ring: HN, N, CH)

Fig. 26-1 Molecular structures of compounds (and related substances) involved in the disorders discussed in the text of this chapter.

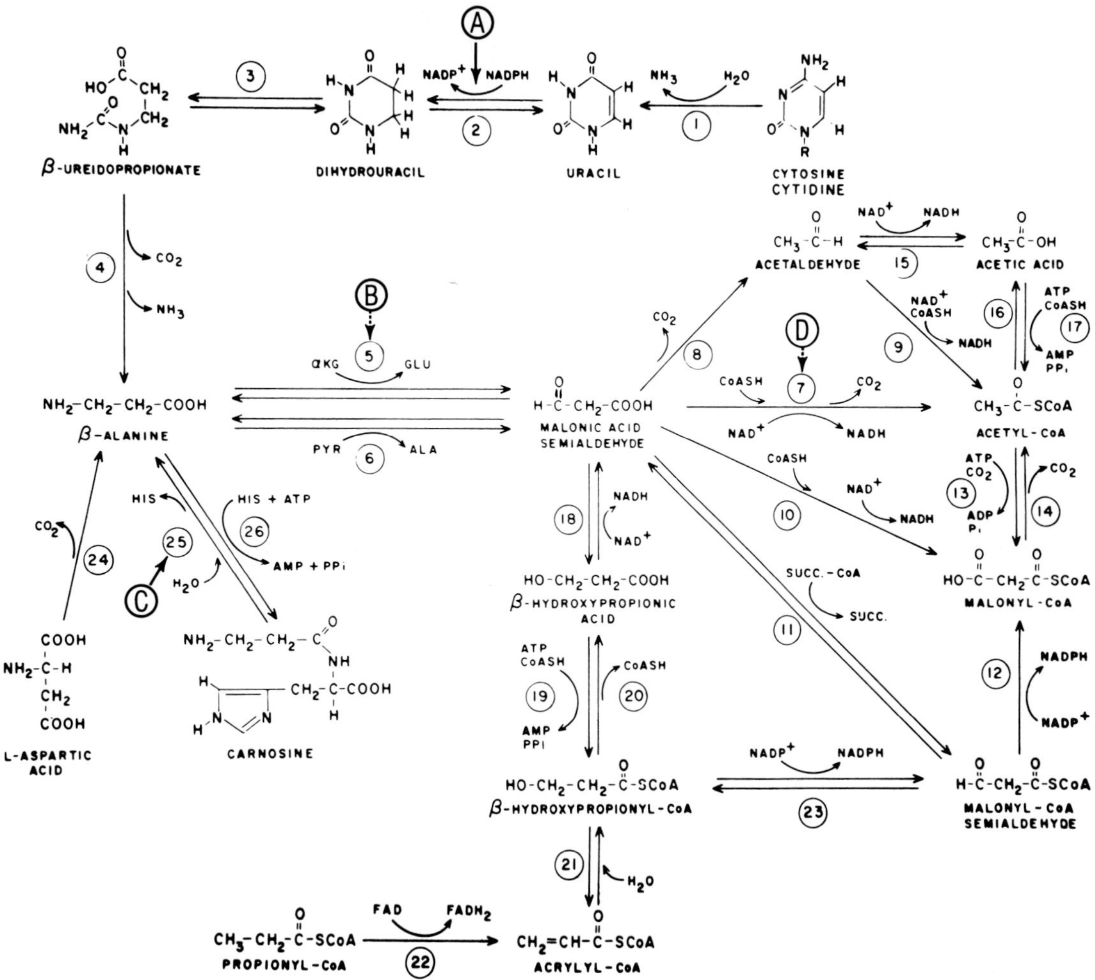

Fig. 26-2 Formation and metabolism of β-alanine. The circled numbers indicate enzymes or metabolic processes: 1 = cytosine ring deamination; 2 = dihydrouracil dehydrogenase; 3 = dihydropyrimidinase; 4 = β-ureidopropionase; 5 = β-alanine-α-ketoglutarate transaminase; 6 = β-alanine-pyruvate transaminase; 7 = malonate semialdehyde dehydrogenase (acetylating); 8 = nonenzymatic or (?) malonate semialdehyde decarboxylase; 9 = acetaldehyde dehydrogenase; 10 = as 9 (?); 11 = succinyl-acetoacetyl CoA transferase; 12 = malonate semialdehyde dehydrogenase; 13 = acetyl CoA carboxylase; 14 = malonyl CoA carboxylase; 15 = aldehyde dehydrogenase; 16 = acetyl CoA hydrolase; 17 = acetyl CoA synthetase; 18 = 3-hydroxypropionate dehydrogenase; 19 = acyl CoA synthetase (?); 20 = 3-hydroxypropionate dehydrogenase; 21 = enoyl CoA hydratase (crotonase); 22 = butyryl CoA dehydrogenase; 23 = 3-hydroxypropionyl CoA dehydrogenase (?); 24 = aspartate decarboxylase (in bacteria) or a minor activity of mammalian cysteine sulfinate decarboxylase and glutamate decarboxylase; 25 = carnosinase; 26 = carnosine synthetase. The circled letters indicate confirmed (solid arrows) or putative (interrupted arrow) enzyme deficiencies in: A = dihydropyrimidine dehydrogenase deficiency (hyperuracil-, thyminuria); B = hyper-β-alaninemia; C = serum carnosinase deficiency (carnosinemia); D = a shared disorder of β-alanine and β-AiB catabolism.[26a] *(Pathway diagram reproduced from Griffith,[2] by permission.)*

may be confined to that tissue. The whole-body pool of β-alanine will depend on the balance between pyrimidine salvage and catabolism in dividing and quiescent cells, respectively, dietary sources of pyrimidines, and delivery of precursors to liver.

Other sources contribute to the β-alanine pool through decarboxylation reactions and by hydrolysis of carnosine and anserine (Fig. 26-2). Aspartate decarboxylation is confined to bacteria but could be a source of β-alanine in humans as an artifact of bacterial metabolism in the large intestine. Mammals form small amounts of β-alanine through a minor activity of cysteine sulfinate decarboxylase and glutamate decarboxylase. Hydrolysis of dipeptides is an important source of the free amino acid during handling of dietary dipeptides and turnover of endogenous dipeptides (see below).

Disposal of free β-alanine is achieved by two major routes. Transamination yields malonic acid semialdehyde [reaction (5), Fig. 26-2]; the subsequent metabolism of this intermediate is complex. Formation of malonyl CoA is not important in humans. [β-^{14}C]Alanine generates $^{14}CO_2$ {from [β-1-^{14}C] alanine, reactions (7) and (8), Fig. 26-2} and a labeled acetyl pool (from [β-2-^{14}C]- and [β-3-^{14}C]alanine). β-Alanine and GABA may share the transaminase (see "Hyper-β-alaninemia," below); β-alanine transaminase requires α-ketoglutarate; the liver enzyme also has activity toward *S*-β-AiB (see below). β-Alanine is also transaminated by a mitochondrial enzyme [reaction (6), Fig. 26-2]. This reaction requires pyruvate. It also transaminates *R*-β-AiB [viz., Fig. 26-4, reaction (4)], and it is the enzyme likely to be involved in the hyper-β-AiBuria (see below).

Disorders of β-Alanine Metabolism

Dihydropyrimidine Dehydrogenase Deficiency. This disorder of pyrimidine catabolism[4–7] impairs endogenous β-alanine synthesis. It is mentioned here because β-alanine homeostasis at critical tissues sites might be abnormal in affected patients. This possibility is not mentioned in the reports.

Four juvenile probands[4–6] and two adult sibs[7] have been reported; one other unreported juvenile case is also mentioned[4]; another cited was later reported.[6] All were found by chemical analysis of urine in symptomatic patients. Urine, plasma, and cerebrospinal fluid levels of uracil, thymine, and 5-hydroxymethyluracil (a metabolite of thymine) are elevated in affected subjects. There is no increment in levels of dihydrouracil and dihydrothymine, and these substances are well metabolized by patients. Uracil and thymine are substrates of the enzyme dihydropyrimidine dehydrogenase (EC 1.3.1.2) [reaction (2), Fig. 26-2]. Combined accumulation of uracil and thymine in the disorder is evidence a shared pathway supports the synthesis of β-alanine and *R*-β-AiB (see above). Deficient activity of the enzyme (0 to 2 percent of control) was demonstrated in leukocytes[4] and skin fibroblasts.[6] The assay is difficult.[7] Heterozygotes have partial deficiency of enzyme activity.[4] This finding, consanguinity of parents,[4] and involvement of both sexes indicates autosomal recessive inheritance of the disorder.

The condition is heterogeneous in clinical expression, and probably it is genetically heterogeneous. Impaired developmental and cerebral dysfunction brought the young probands to notice.[4–6] The adult proposita[7] was diagnosed at 27 years of age when she developed an adverse neurologic reaction to chemotherapy with fluorouracil; her unexposed brother with the same chemical phenotype was otherwise healthy. Accordingly, the condition has pharmacogenetic implications[8] as a *pharmacokinetic* disorder affecting drug disposal. Clinical heterogeneity is associated with metabolic heterogeneity; the early onset (juvenile neurologic) form of dihydropyrimidine dehydrogenase deficiency has urine pyrimidine excretion severalfold higher than the pharmacogenetic form, assuming there is no significant interlaboratory variation in measuring pyrimidines.

Combined *uraciluria-thyminuria* was observed in a child with medulloblastoma.[9] The chemical finding varied with status of the tumor and chemotherapy. Perhaps the patient was heterozygous for dihydropyrimidine dehydrogenase deficiency.

Wadman et al.[5] reported persistent hyperuraciluria in one patient with delayed development and other signs; the underlying pathogenesis was not identified.

Another cause of deficient β-amino acid synthesis occurs in mouse.[10] The C57B1/6 mouse is deficient in β-ureidopropionase activity [reaction (4), Fig. 26-2]. There is no known human counterpart.

Hyper-β-Alaninemia. There is a single published report of this disorder.[11] The proband was diagnosed at 2 months of age; he died in the fifth month with an uncontrolled seizure disorder punctuated by extreme somnolence. Persistent lethargy was observed from birth after a normal delivery in the 38th week of gestation. Fetal movement was obtunded. Seizures appeared at the seventh week of life. The moro and sucking reflexes were impaired, and the infant was continuously somnolent and hypotonic. All anticonvulsant medications were ineffective.

At autopsy, 2 h postmortem, the brain was small (470 g versus 620 ± 71 g), and body length and weight were below the third centile for age. Cerebral ventricles were enlarged, demarcation of white matter was blurred, and there was diffuse edema. Beading of myelin sheaths was the only significant abnormality observed by microscopy. Tissue levels of β-alanine were high (Table 26-1).

The proband was the fourth child of the mother's second marriage. A half-brother and half-sister were healthy. The firstborn of the second marriage was alive and well. The second born (male) died of breathing trouble 4 h after birth. The third pregnancy ended in a miscarriage (third month). The fifth pregnancy resulted in a term stillbirth. No living member of the family had hyper-β-alaninemia. The parents were not consanguineous. The disorder in the proband, if inherited, is probably autosomal recessive.

One other putative proband with hyper-β-alaninemia and a fatal neurologic disease is known (J Sabater, personal communication, 1975).

METABOLIC PHENOTYPE. The normal concentrations of β-alanine in body fluids are <14 μmol/l in plasma, <10 μmol/g total nitrogen in urine, and <0.06 μmol/l in cerebrospinal fluid (CSF) (compiled from Refs. 17, 18, and 54). Levels in the patient were 20 to 51 μmol/l in plasma, fourteen- to one hundredfold increased in urine, and 45 μmol/l in CSF.

There were other metabolic findings in the proband. Free GABA concentration was elevated in plasma (1 to 7 μmol/l; normal, <0.5 μmol/l), urine (25 to 400 μmol/g total nitrogen; normal, 0), and CSF (1 to 2 μmol/l; normal, <0.08 μmol/l). Several tissues (examined 2 h after death at 5 months) had increased concentrations of β-alanine, GABA, and carnosine (Table 26-1). (Carnosine levels in plasma, urine, and CSF were not known to be elevated in life.) During life the urine contained greatly elevated amounts of taurine, β-AiB (isomer not identified), and GABA.

MECHANISM OF HYPERAMINOACIDURIA IN HYPER-β-ALANINEMIA. The hyperaminoaciduria had a combined mechanism: prerenal (overflow) for the β-alanine component and renal (by competition for tubular reabsorption) for the β-AiB and taurine components. Urine and plasma concentrations of β-alanine were directly proportional (Fig. 26-3*A*); urine β-AiB and

Table 26-1 Concentration of β-Alanine, Carnosine, and GABA in Postmortem Tissues of a Patient with Hyper-β-Alaninemia

Tissue	*Source**	*β-Alanine μmol/g wet wt*	*Carnosine, μmol/g wet wt*	*GABA, μmol/g wet wt*
Brain†	Patient	0.20	0.39	3.83
	Control	0	0.02	0.8
Muscle‡	Patient	0.07–0.11	36.1–45.0	0.02
	Control	0.01	6.62–6.84	0
Liver	Patient	0.36	0	0.02
	Control	0.16	0	0
Kidney	Patient	1.12	0	0.24
	Control	—	—	0.03–0.45§

*Postmortem control is an age-matched, male patient with Werdnig-Hoffman disease. Tissues from patient and control were obtained 2 and 3 h, respectively, after death.
†Values indicate total (bound and free) GABA in occipital cortex, deproteinized with picric acid. The patient's value is high for his age when compared with control and published data on infants and children.[12] The wide range of published control values[12–14] reflects techniques of tissue preparation and an age effect, since GABA content of brain increases during human infancy.[12]
‡Deltoid and rectus abdominis.
§Values obtained from Whelan et al.[15] and Zachmann et al.[16]
SOURCE: Reference 10.

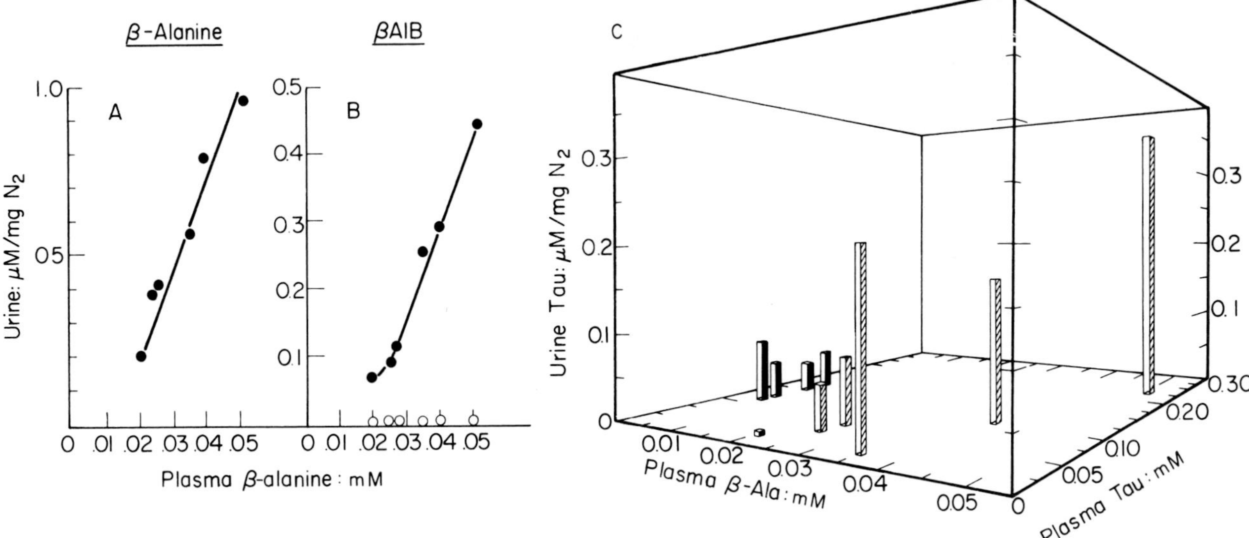

Fig. 26-3 Excretion of β-amino compounds (A, β-alanine; B, β-aminoisobutyric acid; C, taurine) in relation to plasma concentration of β-alanine in the patient with hyper-β-alaninemia. The direct relationship indicates that hyper-β-aminoaciduria reflects interaction at a tubular transport site selective for these compounds. This specific aminoaciduria is of the "combined" type, representing overflow (β-alanine) and renal (βAiB and taurine) mechanisms, the latter by virtue of competitive inhibition by β-alanine. (*Reproduced from Scriver et al.,[11] by permission.*)

plasma β alanine were proportional (Fig. 26-3*B*) without a corresponding increase in plasma β-AiB.[11] Urine taurine was influenced by its own plasma concentration, but it was also proportional to the filtered load of β-alanine (Fig. 26-3*C*). This was an early human example of a combined mechanism for hyperaminoaciduria[19] [others were hyperprolinemia (Chap. 18) and disorders of cationic amino acid catabolism (Chaps. 19 to 21)]. It provided evidence for a β-amino acid-preferring transport system serving reabsorption in the human nephron, as in other mammals.[20–22] A carrier with preference for β-amino acids (including taurine) and low capacity initiates reabsorption from filtrate. It has been characterized in renal brush-border membrane vesicles[23,24] and by microperfusion studies in vivo and in situ in the rat.[25] Assignment of the gene for the system to chromosome 21[25a] is doubtful.

The cause of GABA excretion in the patient was different and more complex. GABA reabsorption in mammalian nephron is accommodated by a low-capacity, GABA-preferring carrier in brush-border membrane which tolerates inhibition by β-alanine.[25,26] Reabsorption of filtered GABA on this carrier would be inhibited by excess β-alanine in the mutant phenotype; it would also experience saturation when the filtered load of GABA was elevated (a combined mechanism). GABA excretion by the proband was not proportional to β-alanine excretion,[11] implying that the source of urinary GABA was not purely from filtrate. Backflux from an intrarenal pool, putatively expanded from time to time in the mutant phenotype, was considered as a likely additional source.[11] GABA is synthesized in kidney (see below). (Other aspects of β-alanine transport by mammalian tissues, including intestine and muscle, were described in Chap. 28 of the previous edition of this text.)

THE ENZYME DEFECT. The deficient enzyme activity was not directly identified in the proband,[11] but impaired oxidation of β-alanine is the likely explanation. There was no apparent excess of malonic semialdehyde in urine[11] (but this was not confirmed on fresh urine by gas chromatography at the time). Accordingly, the block should be at the transamination step.* Two lines of evidence point to this conclusion. Pyridoxine treatment apparently improved the chemical phenotype in vivo[11]; pyrodoxal-5-phosphate is the coenzyme for transaminases, and β-alanine and β-AiB are both transaminated (Figs. 26-2 and 26-3, respectively). β-AiB metabolism was not primarily impaired in the patient. β-Alanine and GABA are transaminated by α-ketoglutarate-requiring enzymes (or isozymes) (EC 2.6.2.19) in liver and brain that are either identical with or similar to each other.[27–30] Concentrations of β-alanine and GABA were elevated in body fluids and tissues of the proband (Ref. 11 and Table 26-1), as they are also in GABA-transaminase deficiency (see below). Assays on any further case should take into account the existence of two β-alanine aminotransferases, with different α-keto acid requirements and cellular locations (see above).

PATHOGENESIS OF CHEMICAL AND CLINICAL FINDINGS. The following is also speculative. Carnosine accumulation in tissues (Table 26-1) was explained by overproduction of dipeptide in the presence of excess β-alanine. The clinical phenotype (hypotonia, hyporeflexia, somnolence, and seizures) was associated with disturbed homeostasis of two inhibitory neurotransmitters (β-alanine, GABA), or three if carnosine is included, which act in cortex, brain stem, and spinal cord. The clinical and chemical phenotypes of hyper-β-alaninemia are different from those of GABA transaminase-deficient patients (see below). This important finding implies that the two conditions have different pathogeneses with different degrees and causes of β-alanine and GABA dishomeostasis.

DIAGNOSIS. The combination of hyper-β-alaninemia and a complex hyperaminoaciduria (comprising β-alanine, β-AiB,

*Deficient activity of malonate/methylmalonate semialdehyde dehydrogenase [reactions (7), Fig. 26-2; (5), Fig. 26-4; and (8), Fig. 26-5) was the presumed cause of increased urinary excretion of β-alanine, β-hydroxypropionate, β-AiB (*R* and *S* enantiomers), and β-hydroxyisobutyrate in a symptomless subject, with unexplained hypermethioninemia developing normally at 4 years of age.[26a]

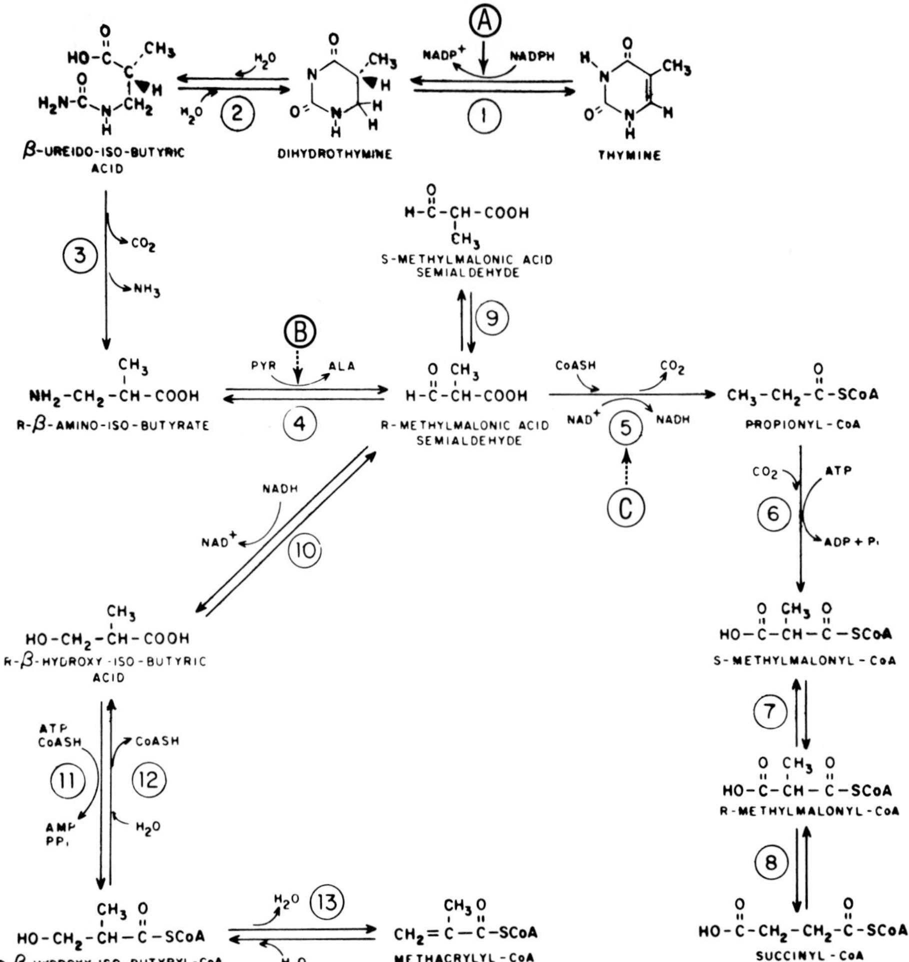

Fig. 26-4 Formation and metabolism of *R*-β-aminoisobutyrate. The circled numbers indicate enzymes or metabolic processes: 1 = dihydrouracil dehydrogenase; 2 = dihydropyrimidinase; 3 = β-ureidopropionase; 4 = β-aminoisobutyrate-pyruvate transaminase; 5 = methylmalonate semialdehyde dehydrogenase (acetylating) (?); 6 = propionyl CoA carboxylase; 7 = methylmalonyl CoA racemase; 8 = methylmalonyl CoA mutase; 9 = nonenzymatic; 10 = 3-hydroxyisobutyrate dehydrogenase; 11 = an acyl CoA synthetase (?); 12 = 3-hydroxyisobutyryl CoA hydrolase; 13 = nonenzymatic for *R* isomers (?). The circled letters indicate confirmed (solid arrow) and putative (interrupted arrow) enzyme deficiencies: A = dihydropyrimidine dehydrogenase deficiency; B = hyper-β-AiBuria; C = a shared disorder of β-alanine and β-AiB catabolism.[26a] *(Pathway diagram reproduced from Griffith,[2] by permission.)*

taurine, and GABA) are suggestive but not diagnostic of the disorder. (See footnote on previous page.) Confirmation that the phenotype is an inborn error requires evidence of deficient enzyme activity (β-alanine-α-ketoglutarate transaminase?). Acquired forms of hyper-β-alaninemia exist, and they also cause β- and ω-aminoaciduria. Certain drugs inhibit the transaminase (e.g., isoniazid, aminooxyacetic acid, and γ-vinyl GABA[31–33]). They produce chemical abnormalities that resemble the congenital disorder. This finding supports the hypothesis that transminase activity is deficient in the latter condition.

Conventional methods for analysis of amino acids will suffice to recognize the chemical phenotype.[11] Plasma amino acid screening in newborns either does not measure β-alanine or is too insensitive. Urine amino acid screening should recognize the chemical phenotype, if it is expressed in the early newborn period, but we do not know that it is.

TREATMENT. There was no response to treatment,[11] with one possible exception. A short course of pyridoxine (10 mg/day) improved the chemical phenotype, but clinical improvement was not observed. The trial was not rigorous.

β-AMINOSOBUTYRIC ACID (β-AiB)

Normal Metabolism

We rely again on the recent review of Griffith[2] and the classic one by Sutton[34] to guide readers to the pertinent literature. β-AiB has a stable chiral structure at the α carbon. The *R* enantiomer [old name D-(−)-β-AiB] derives from thymine (Fig. 26-4), the *S* enantiomer [L-(+)-β-AiB] from L-valine (Fig. 26-5). Early clinical studies[34] placed little emphasis on the chiral form. Chromatographic resolution of the individual enantiomers is a challenge, but it is feasible (see Refs. 2, 4, and 35). Human urine contains *R*-β-AiB almost exclusively, whereas the plasma pool is about 80 percent *S*-β-AiB.[35]

The overview of pyrimidine catabolism in the β-alanine section suffices here to describe synthesis of *R*-β-AiB. The first, second, and third steps of thymine catabolism (Fig. 26-4) and the second, third, and fourth steps of cytosine/uracil catabolism (Fig. 26-2) correspond. Accordingly, the balance between salvage and catabolism of thymine parallels that of β-alanine

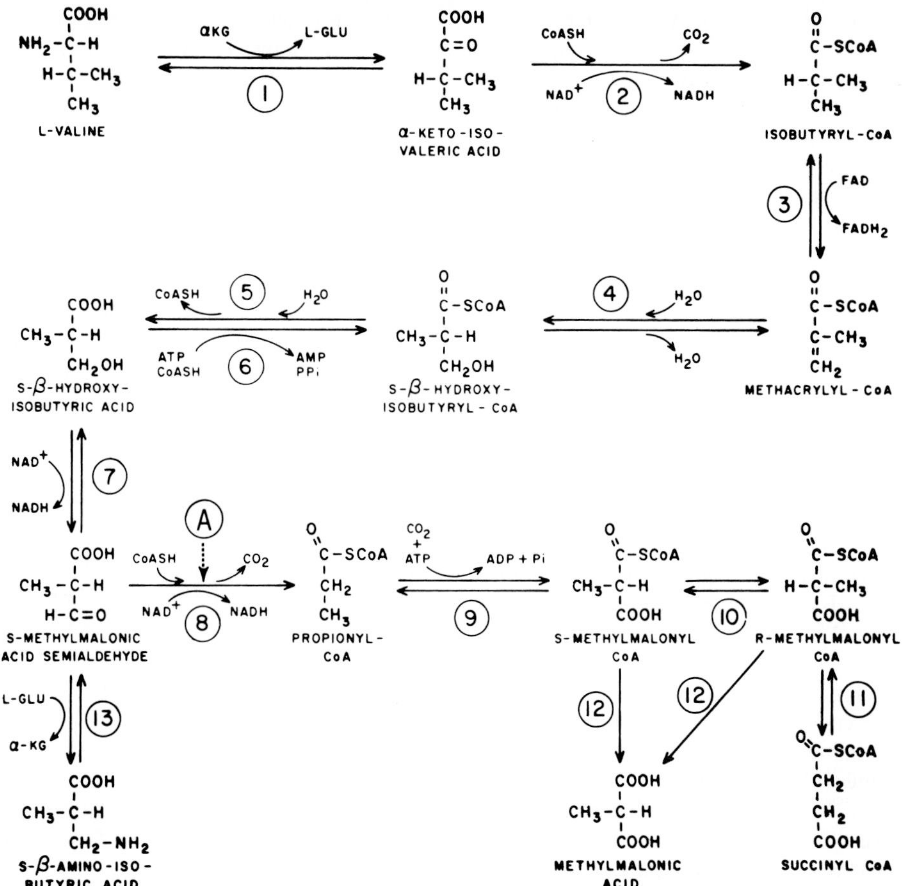

Fig. 26-5 Relationship between L-valine catabolism and S-β-aminoisobutyrate metabolism. The circled numbers indicate the following enzymes: 1 = branched-chain amino acid transaminase(s); 2 = branched-chain α-keto acid dehydrogenase; 3 = isobutyryl CoA dehydrogenase; 4 = enoyl CoA hydratase; 5 = 3-hydroxyisobutyryl CoA hydrolase; 6 = an acyl CoA synthetase (?); 7 = 3-hydroxyisobutyryl CoA dehydrogenase; 8 = methylmalonate semialdehyde dehydrogenase (acylating); 9 = propionyl CoA carboxylase; 10 = methylmalonyl CoA racemase; 11 = methylmalonyl CoA mutase; 12 = thioester hydrolase (?); 13 = S-β-aminoisobutyrate-α-ketoglutarate transaminase. There are inherited disorders of valine catabolism that do not affect β-AiB (see Chap. 22). One disorder[26a] (A) is a putative deficiency of a reaction shared by β-alanine and R- and S-β-AiB. *(Pathway diagram reproduced from Griffith,[2] by permission.)*

(see above). β-Ureidoisobutyric acid or its precursors must be transported to liver to form *R*-β-AiB since β-ureidopropionase is apparently active only in liver.

β-AiB catabolism is glycogenic presumably by the pathway shown [reactions (4) to (8), Fig. 26-4]. The transaminase [reaction (4)] is pyruvate-requiring. MMS dehydrogenase [reaction (5), Fig. 26-4] may be specific for *S*-MMS. Racemization of *R*- to *S*-MMS can occur by a nonenzymatic reaction [reaction (9), Fig. 26-4] and by the reversible pathway between MMS and methacrylyl CoA which, by generating a nonchiral substrate (methyacrylyl CoA), could also yield *S*-MMS from *R*-MMS.

L-Valine, through its catabolite *S*-MMS yields *S*-β-AiB as a by-product of transamination [reaction (13), Fig. 26-5]. The α-ketoglutarate-requiring transaminase also accepts GABA and β-alanine; it is not established that transaminase(s) for *S*-β-AiB and the other substrates are separate entities.[2]

Disorders of β-AiB Metabolism

Dihydropyrimide Dehydrogenase Deficiency. Endogenous synthesis of *R*-β-AiB should be impaired in this disorder[4–7] for the reasons discussed above (see "Disorders of β-Alanine Metabolism"). The significance of this in pathogenesis of the clinical phenotype is unknown.

Hyper-β-AiBuria. Crumpler et al.[36] using paper chromatography identified hyperexcretion of β-AiB in about 5 percent of healthy whites living in London, England. Harris[37] showed the phenotype was inherited in a recessive fashion. The classic review (Ref. 34, deleted after the first edition of this text) addressed several important questions but left in limbo others which can now be answered better.

1. Which enantiomer is excreted? *R*-β-AiB is excreted in excess.[36,38]

2. What is the mutant gene product? There is an impairment of *R*-β-AiB catabolism.[39] The defect is in the pyruvate-requiring transaminase (EC 2.6.1.40).[39a,39b] This finding, obtained from liver samples at autopsy, is compatible with three in vivo studies: high excretors have impaired ability to degrade *R*-β-AiB and thymine; *R*-β-AiB loading increases *R*-β-AiB excretion of high excretors[40] and nonexcretors;[41] valine loading does not increase β-AiB excretion in high excretors.[40] The thymine and *R*-β-AiB loading responses imply that transamination (step 4, Fig. 26-4) is rate limiting in both normal and excretor subjects. The catabolic defect (in high excretors) does not affect β-alanine or GABA homeostasis (see Table 26-3, below).

3. What is the physiological basis of hyper-*R*-β-AiBuria? Plasma β-AiB is slightly elevated in the high-excretor phenotype.[42] The renal tubule has different mechanisms for handling the β-AiB isomers.[39] *S*-β-AiB is filtered at the normal low plasma load (<3 μmol/l)[42] and reabsorbed, albeit inefficiently.[39] *R*-β-AiB is both filtered and "secreted" by tubule cells.[39] Renal clearance of β-AiB usually exceeds the glomerular filtration rate in high excretors, and normal subjects infused with *R*-β-AiB excrete the substance in the same fashion.[39] If the transaminase for the *R*-metabolite is present in kidney (unknown), there would be a primary renal cellular source for urinary *R*-β-AiB, in addition to the augmented filtered load in the variant phenotype.

GENETICS OF HYPER-β-AIBURIA. A clear definition of the hyperexcretor phenotype is elusive, yet upon this depends classification of the phenotype and interpretation of its inheritance. A β-AiB spot of greater intensity than the α-alanine spot, on a two-dimensional paper chromatogram of urine amino acids, is a useful criterion; this amount is equivalent to >70 mg/g creatinine.[37] Column chromatography discriminates normal from hyperexcretors at 20 mg/g creatinine. Acquired variation influences β-AiB excretion (see below); sex is not an important determinant,[34] but age is (higher excretion in children).[34]

Sutton,[34] summarizing several studies, proposed that the trait was autosomal recessive, involving a single pair of alleles (locus unknown) and influenced by other factors (genetic and nongenetic). This implies that heterozygotes do not manifest the phenotype. Others[39b,43,44] showed that heterozygotes are incompletely recessive. The latter finding is compatible with our understanding that *R*-β-AiB metabolism is quite limited, even in normal subjects and with the hypothesis that the transaminase is the rate limiting step. None of the evidence rules out multiple alleles at one locus with different phenotypic effects expressed as hyper-β-AiBuria; polygenic or multifactorial explanations may also be pertinent.

The high-excretor phenotype is a metab. lic polymorphism in human populations[34] (Fig. 26-6) with frequencies up to 10 percent in whites, 15 to 30 percent in blacks, over 40 percent in Orientals, and approaching 95 percent in Southeastern Asians; Asian Indians do not express the phenotype. It is not known whether the polymorphic phenotype is the result of selection or genetic drift.

DIAGNOSIS. Not every high excretor has the genetic form.[2,34] β-AiB excretion is increased transiently in catabolic states, in cancer patients and Down syndrome, and when growth or other events increase pyrimidine turnover. The *R* enantiomer is excreted primarily in these conditions.[36] β-AiB excretion can be used to monitor the clinical progress of certain cancers.[2]

γ-AMINOBUTYRIC ACID (GABA)

It is not our purpose to discuss this vast topic in detail. Readers are referred to a recent review[3] relevant here because of its emphasis on extraneural metabolism of GABA. Only those articles cited in Ref. 3 essential for the discussion of inborn errors are repeated. Three apparent disorders of the GABA pathway (Fig. 26-7) are described here. One (pyridoxine dependency with seizures) is a putative disorder of brain glutamic acid decarboxylation. GABA transaminase deficiency and succinic semialdehyde dehyrodgenase deficiency impair separate steps in the oxidation of GABA. All three disorders cause cerebral dysfunction.

Normal Metabolism

GABA is a major metabolite of brain (Table 26-2), where nearly one-third of synapses are estimated to employ it as an inhibitory neurotransmitter. GABA is also found in several ex-

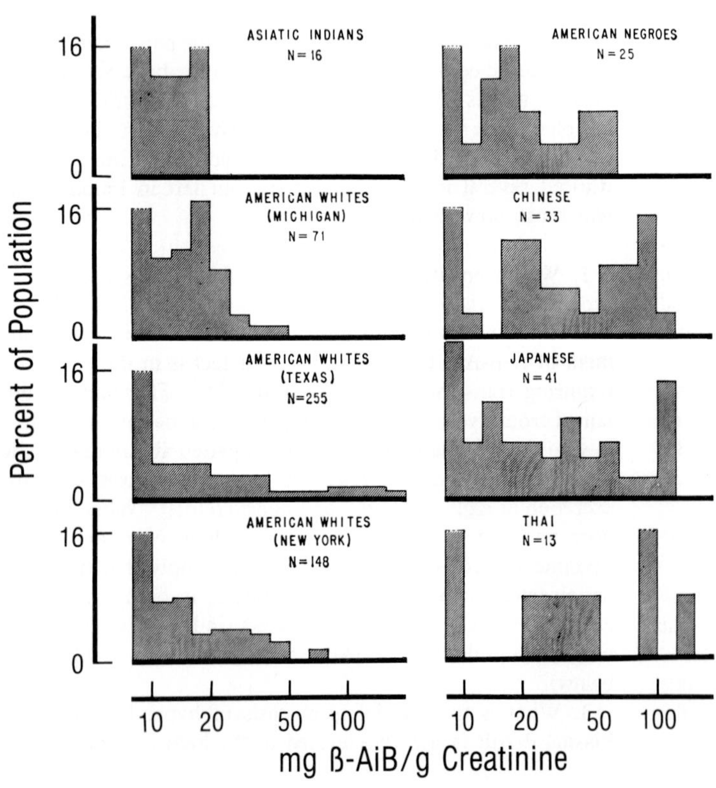

Fig. 26-6 Frequency distribution diagrams of urine β-AiB excretion in various populations. The nonexcretor phenotype value is 20 mg/g creatinine. *(Reproduced, slightly modified, from Sutton,[34] by permission.)*

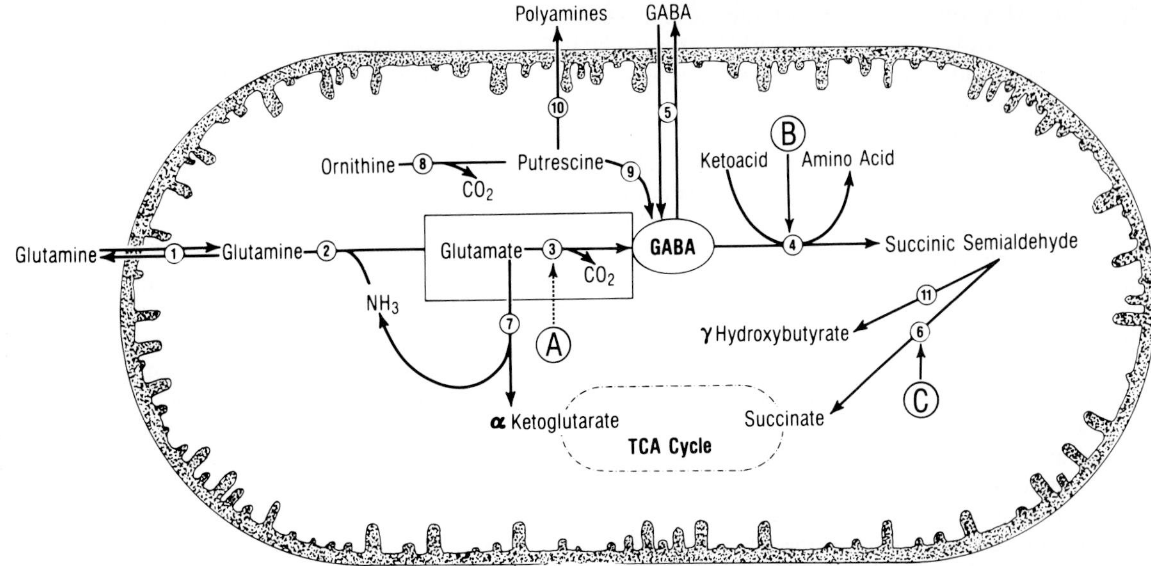

Fig. 26-7 GABA metabolism. Circled numbers indicate enzymes or metabolic processes: 1 = glutamate transport across the inner mitochondrial membrane; 2 = phosphate-dependent glutaminase and ammonia formation; 3 = glutamate decarboxylase and GABA formation (this step is intramitochondrial in kidney and extramitochondrial in brain); 4 = GABA transaminase regenerates glutamate in brain by utilizing α-ketoglutarate as cosubstrate (in kidney, pyruvate may be utilized as well, with net disposal of glutamate by the GABA pathway); 5 = GABA transport (unstudied); 6 = succinic semialdehyde dehydrogenase and succinate formation (commits the carbon chain to oxidative metabolism via the tricarboxylic acid cycle); 7 = glutamate dehydrogenase (major pathway of glutamate disposal during renal ammoniagenesis); 8 = ornithine decarboxylase and putrescine formation; 9 = GABA formation from putrescine (details of the pathway are not fully studied); 10 = polyamine formation from putrescine; 11 = γ-hydroxybutyrate formation (biochemical details and metabolic role not fully studied). Circled letters indicate confirmed (solid arrows) or putative (interrupted arrow) deficiency of enzyme activity: A = Pyridoxine dependency with seizures (deficient binding of pyridoxal-5-phosphate by GAD?); B = GABA-transaminase (α-ketoglutarate requiring) deficiency; C = succinic semialdehyde dehydrogenase deficiency (4-hydroxybutyric aciduria). [Reproduced from Rozen et al.[3] by permission.]

traneural tissues, notably kidney and pancreas islet β cells (Table 26-2). GABA is synthesized in the extraneural tissues, and its presence there is not dependent on interorgan transport.

GABA can be synthesized from L-ornithine and L-glutamate in mammalian tissues (Fig. 26-7); the latter is the more important pathway. Native human brain glutamic acid decarboxylase (GAD) has $M_r \approx 140{,}000$; it appears to be a dimer. It requires pyridoxal-5-phosphate (PALP) as coenzyme. The K_m values (in millimoles) are 1.3 (glutamate) and 13×10^{-5} (PALP). Brain and renal GAD enzymes are different.

The product of GAD action on glutamate is GABA, which acts in brain (see below) at a supramolecular membrane complex by binding to two receptors (site 1, GABA/muscimol receptor, agonist conformation; site 2, GABA/bicuculline receptor, antagonist conformation). GABA binding at sites 1 or 2 is apparently adjacent to a chloride ionophore. GABA modulates membrane chloride permeability.

GABA disposal is a postsynaptic event in brain. Catabolism in brain is initiated by transamination in mitochondria after removal from the synaptic cleft on a high affinity system in the synaptosomal membrane. A glial cell transport system with lower affinity has also been identified. GABA supports oxidative metabolism by its conversion to succinate; two enzymes are required, an α-ketoglutarate-requiring GABA-transaminase (GABA-T) and succinic semialdehyde dehydrogenase (Fig. 26-7).

Table 26-2 Distribution of GABA in Mammalian Tissues

	GABA, nmol/g wet weight		
	Human	*Rat*	*Mouse*
Brain	1860–5690	1900	2610
Ovary	—	590	—
Pancreas	562	41	4
Kidney	440	180	33
Liver	—	30	15
Heart	—	20	—
Testes	—	0	—
Plasma	0.9	0.8	0.5
Thyroid	—	0	—
Muscle	—	0	—

SOURCE: Rozen et al.[3]

Renal Metabolism of GABA. We discuss this aspect because it is relevant to studies of pyridoxine dependency. Renal GABA synthesis by tissue weight is about 30 percent of that in brain in humans. Kidney is the second most important organ with a capacity for GABA synthesis. GABA homeostasis in kidney is maintained by enzymes (GAD and GABA-T) whose properties differ from those of the corresponding brain enzymes. Accordingly, it is likely that different genes control GABA metabolism in brain and kidney.

Renal GABA synthesis is initiated by an enzyme (GAD-II) which differs significantly from that of the principal enzyme in brain (GAD-I). Antibodies to mouse brain GAD do not cross-react with mouse renal GAD. (The reverse experiment has not been reported.) Moreover, there are several functional differences in the properties of the two enzymes (See Refs. 3 and 45). GAD activity and GABA concentration are highest in deep cortex and outer medulla (rat kidney); GAD is enriched in isolated rat proximal tubules relative to whole cortex and glomeruli.[45] Accordingly, the renal tubule is equipped with mechanisms to provide cellular GABA independent of the inefficient but specific transport systems for GABA in kidney.[26]

The renal GABA pathway permits net disposal of glutamate because renal GABA-T accepts pyruvate,[46] whereas brain GABA-T transaminates with α-ketoglutarate specifically (see Ref. 3). GABA-T in kidney appears to be confined to proximal tubule cells of outer medulla (in mouse kidney).[47] The renal GABA pathway accounts for about one quarter of glutamate disposal in rat kidney,[48] acting as a passive arbiter of this process during ammoniagenesis.[46] The role of GABA and the importance of the renal pathway in kidney is clearly not for neurotransmitter activity, but it may serve chloride permeability in the nephron.[3] GABA content and GAD activity increase at birth, relative to the fetal state, in human kidney.[49]

Regulation of GAD Activity. Regional brain GABA correlates with GAD activity. Extrarenal GAD activity and GABA content have not been studied correspondingly. Among the various regulating agents,[3] availability and binding of PALP coenzyme are important. Local synthesis of PALP from pyridoxine (the major dietary form of the vitamin) is influenced by several factors. For example, GABA and biogenic amines inhibit pyridoxal kinase and synthesis of PALP, which is an intracellular metabolite derived from pyridoxine after uptake of the latter. The postnatal increase in brain GAD activity is associated with increased concentration of immunoreactive enzyme. The human renal enzyme has not been studied in this manner. GAD activity in term human kidney is undersaturated with coenzyme.[49]

Disorders of GABA Metabolism

Pyridoxine Dependency. This Mendelian disease (autosomal recessive)[50] is not a proved disorder of GABA metabolism; it is only a hypothesis that brain GABA homeostasis is impaired in affected patients.

Probands with the typical phenotype have severe seizure activity which may begin in utero.[50] A delayed-onset phenotype, which implies that the phenotype may be genetically heterogeneous, has also been reported.[51,52] The seizures are unresponsive to conventional treatments but respond dramatically to pyridoxine at pharmacologic dosages (10 to 100 mg daily); the requirement is permanent. It was this finding, in association with the known importance of GABA as a neuroinhibitor, that provoked the hypothesis of deficient GAD (EC 4.1.1.15) activity in the pyridoxine-dependent seizure phenotype.[50] A second hypothesis was necessary, namely, that GAD binding of PLP was specifically impaired, since there is no impairment of any other PLP-requiring enzyme in probands[50] and there is no evidence that availability of coenzyme is impaired.[50] When GAD activity was found in human kidney (see above and Ref. 50), it was presumed the GAD deficiency hypothesis could be tested. Yoshida and colleagues[53] performed a renal biopsy on a proband and measured renal GAD-activity. They used L-[U-^{14}C]glutamate and measured formation of labeled $^{14}CO_2$ and GABA during a 2-h incubation of kidney homogenate. They found zero GABA synthesis when PALP was not added to homogenate; addition of PALP restored GABA synthesis to normal levels and stimulated CO_2 production more in the patient's tissue than in three control samples. These findings are widely quoted as evidence for deficient GAD activity due to deficient PALP binding by GAD in the phenotype. They also evince skepticism about their relevance for several reasons: (1) Renal GAD and brain GAD-I are not the same enzyme. (2) Complete deficiency of GABA synthesis (0 cpm/μg protein) in proband kidney is a surprising finding. (3) Stimulation of GAD activity in vitro by PALP (measured by formation of CO_2 and GABA) is dependent, in part, on the degree of saturation of native enzyme by PALP in vivo at the time of biopsy; this property varies in normal individuals.[49] Although the findings of Yoshida and colleagues are interesting, their significance remains elusive.

γ-Aminobutyric Acid (GABA) Transaminase Deficiency. Jaeken et al.[54] described two sibs with severe psychomotor retardation, hypotonia, and hyperreflexia. One died at 1 year of age. Both showed abnormally accelerated linear growth. Metabolic studies in the living sib showed increased concentrations in CSF of GABA (4.8 μmol/l; range for 20 control subjects, 0.04 to 0.12), homocarnosine (23.4 μmol/l; control range, 4.0 to 8.7), and β-alanine (0.48 μm/l; control range 0.02 to 0.06). Plasma concentrations of GABA and β-alanine were also increased (2.9 and 23 μmol/l, respectively; corresponding normal values, <0.50, Ref. 14). Increases in the fasting plasma growth hormone level (7.9 to 38.4 ng/ml; normal, <5) were attributed to the growth hormone-releasing effect of GABA.[55] GABA transaminase activity (α-ketoglutarate requiring; EC 2.6.1.19) was deficient in liver biopsy tissue[54] (0.07 μmol/mg protein per hour; range in 10 controls, 0.31 to 0.69) and in lysates of lymphocytes, and Epstein-Barr virus-transformed cultured lymphoblasts (3 percent of control values).[56] GABA transaminase activity in lymphocyte from the parents (obligate heterozygotes) was 15 and 37 percent of the control mean.[56] The evidence implies that inheritance of GABA transaminase deficiency is autosomal recessive, and deficiency of this enzyme was the cause of the disease. Treatment with pharmacologic doses of pyridoxine did not improve the clinical and metabolic phenotypes in the living patient with GABA transaminase deficiency.[54]

Three Different Transaminase-Deficient Phenotypes. The clinical and metabolic phenotypes of GABA transaminase deficiency and hyperβ-alaninemia are different. For example, GABA-transaminase deficiency is associated with accelerated linear growth (it is decreased in hyper-β-alaninemia), and has a CSF level of β-alanine many times less than that in hyper-β-alaninemia. The two diseases provide evidence that the transaminases for GABA and β-alanine are different enzymes, each sharing the alternative substrates and controlled by different genes. Hyper-β-AiBuria is a third putative disorder of transamination.[39a] Table 26-3 summarizes our view of the enzyme phenotypes in the three disorders.

Succinic Semialdehyde Dehydrogenase Deficiency (4-Hydroxybutyric Aciduria). This disease was the subject of a recent symposium.[57–59] Six cases are known;[58] two are sibs, and two probands have consanguineous parents indicating autosomal recessive inheritance of the disorder. The clinical phenotype includes cerebellar signs (ataxia, dysarthria, and ocular dyspraxia), muscular hypotonia, and mental retardation. The cerebellar signs apparently improve with age during childhood. The metabolic phenotype includes urinary excretion of 4-hydroxybutyrate and succinic semialdehyde in elevated amounts; levels of the former are elevated also in plasma and CSF; GABA levels are normal. The enzyme phenotype is deficient succinic semialdehyde dehydrogenase (EC 1.2.1.24) activity.[59,60] The enzyme was measured in lymphocyte lysates, by direct[59] and coupled[60] assays, and normalized to values for propionyl CoA carboxylase in the first case. Patients have

Table 26-3 Transaminases and Apparent Transamination Deficiencies in Hyper-β-Alaninemia, Hyper-β-AiBuria, and GABA-T Deficiency

Substrate			
Primary	*Alternative*	*Preferred keto acid*	*Trait with deficient activity**
S-β-AiB	β-Alanine, GABA	α-Ketoglutarate[2,27,28,30]	—
R-β-AiB	β-Alanine	Pyruvate[2,39a]	β-AiBuria† (confirmed)
β-Alanine	*R*-β-AiB	Pyruvate[2,39a]	—
β-Alanine	GABA, *S*-β-AiB	α-Ketoglutarate[2,27,28,30]	Hyper-β-alaninemia‡ (putative)
GABA	β-ala, β-AiB	α-Ketoglutarate[27,28,30]	GABA-T deficiency§ (confirmed)
GABA	—	Pyruvate (renal)[47]	—

*Confidence that a particular transaminase is impaired in a trait depends on the rigor of investigation

†Studies were done on postmortem liver samples (for enzyme) and urine (for β-AiB value) of Japanese subjects classified as low or high excretors of β-AiB (bimodal distribution).[39a,39b]

‡Putative: No enzyme assays were performed; the hypothesis was based on metabolic data alone.[11]

§Confirmed: GABA-α-ketoglutarate transaminase activity was measured in vitro in liver,[54] lymphocytes,[56] and lymphoblasts[56] of affected probands.

about 10 percent normal mean activity, and parents of patients have 25 to 50 percent normal activity. (The reports are inadequate to discern whether variation in the heterozygote values indicates genetic heterogeneity of deviant gene dosage effects.)

4-Hydroxybutyrate is a normal brain metabolite. Its use in humans as an intravenous anaesthetic was precluded by adverse side effects.[58] L-glutamate is a precursor of the substance in patients with 4-hydroxybutyric aciduria (cited in Ref. 58). The variant metabolic phenotype suggests that the pathway for 4-hydroxybutyrate formation is as shown in Fig. 26-7; a reductase is probably required for conversion of succinic semialdehyde to the corresponding hydroxy acid. The latter probably undergoes β oxidation with formation of 3,4-dihydroxybutyrate and 3-keto-4-hydroxybutyrate. These substances were tentatively identified in urine from a patient with succinic semialdehyde dehydrogenase deficiency.[58]

DIPEPTIDES (CARNOSINE AND OTHER SUBSTANCES)

β-Alanyl-Dipeptide Synthesis

Most β-alanine in the human body occurs as the dipeptide carnosine.[2,61] Skeletal muscle but not cardiac muscle contains carnosine.[62,63] The dipeptide is present in brain, particularly in the primary olfactory pathways; its concentration in olfactory bulbs and olfactory epithelium is maintained by intact pathways for synthesis and hydrolysis of dipeptide. It may play a role as a neurotransmitter.[64]

Carnosine is synthesized by carnosine synthetase, an enzyme which requires ATP during the formation of an enzyme-β-alanyl-adenylate complex. L-Histidine is then united with β-alanine, and the dipeptide (β-alanyl-L-histidine) is released from the enzyme.[65–69]

Skeletal muscle of birds and certain species of mammals, notably the rabbit, rat, and whale, also contain anserine (β-alanyl-1-methyl-L-histidine) (Fig. 26-1). Anserine is absent from human tissues; its appearance in human body fluids is caused by diet[70] and serum carnosinase deficiency (see below). The methyl group of anserine is added to carnosine by the enzyme *S*-adenosyl methionine: carnosine *N*-methyl transferase.[71]

The physiological function of β-alanyl-imidazole dipeptides is not completely understood. They may serve as buffers in stabilizing the pH of muscle contracting anaerobically.[69,72] Carnosine and anserine are potent in vitro activators of myosin ATPase in concentrations comparable to those found in skeletal muscle.[73] The dipeptides also chelate copper.[74] When transported into tissues, they enhance copper uptake and thus may participate in the pathogenesis of Wilson's disease (see Chap. 54).

Co-Enzyme A

β-Alanine is a constituent of coenzyme A in its pantothenate moiety (Fig. 26-1). Incorporation into pantothenic acid does not occur in mammalian tissues. Pantothenate is an essential human nutrient.

β-Alanyl-Dipeptide Catabolism

Carnosine is hydrolyzed by two isozymes, tissue carnosinase and serum (plasma) carnosinase, in human subjects. Human tissue carnosinase differs from the enzyme found in nonhuman tissues.[75–77] The mammalian tissue enzyme is a metalloprotein, and although it is activated in vitro by both manganese and zinc ions, zinc is the metal which appears to occur in the native enzyme.[76]

Tissue carnosinase activity is present in all human tissues so far examined[78,79] being high in kidney, liver, spleen, and brain, and low in skeletal muscle and heart. Human tissue carnosinase is a protein of $M_r \approx 90{,}000$, activated by manganese, with an optimum pH in vitro of 9.5 and a K_m for carnosine of 10 m*M*. It does not hydrolyze anserine or homocarnosine (Table 26-4). Two forms of kidney and brain carnosinase are separable by high resolution anion-exchange chromatography.[78] Only one form can be detected by electrophoretic methods[78] contrary to earlier findings.[80] Human tissues do not possess the homocarnosinase and Mn^{2+}-independent carnosinase identified in rat and hog kidney.[78,79,81]

Serum carnosinase is an entirely different enzyme from human tissue carnosinase[77] (Table 26-4). The former has a higher molecular weight, a lower optimum pH in vitro, and a different K_m value for carnosine; cadmium activates the serum en-

Table 26-4 Properties of Human Carnosinases

Property	Tissue carnosinase	Serum carnosinase
Relative dipeptide-hydrolyzing activity		
Carnosine	100	100
Anserine	0	100
Homocarnosine	0	4
Molecular weight (KDa)	90,000	160,000
Cysteine-containing enzyme	Yes	No
Optimum pH, in vitro	9.5	8.5
Isoelectric point	5.6	4.7
K_m (mM):		
Carnosine	10	4.0
Homocarnosine	—	0.4
Activated by	Mn^{2+}, dithiothreitol	Cd^{2+}, citrate
Inhibited by	EDTA, *p*-hydroxy-mercuribenzoate	EDTA, dithiotreitol

SOURCE: Adapted from data by Lenney et al.[77–79]

zyme twice as effectively as manganese. Human serum carnosinase hydrolyzes anserine and carnosine equally well; homocarnosine hydrolysis by the enzyme is 4 percent that of carnosine.[77] Serum from normal human adults hydrolyzes carnosine under ideal conditions[77] at a rate (42 μmol/ml per hour) about 17 times greater than the average activity previously reported for other assays. Carnosinase activity is very low in serum of the normal infant (Fig. 26-8); it increases gradually to adult values by the age of 13 to 15 years.[77,82,83] Carnosinase activity of the serum type is detectable in human CSF, and in autopsy tissues, in the latter case presumably because of serum contamination.[79]

Related Imidazole Dipeptides

Cetasine (β-alanyl-3-methyl-L-histidine), and anserine, occur in skeletal muscle of fin and sei whales.[84] Homocarnosine (γ-aminobutyryl-L-histidine, Fig. 26-1), was first isolated from bovine brain[85] and later found in brain of several mammalian species, including humans.[86] Homocarnosine does not occur in other human tissues. Homocarnosine and carnosine are both synthesized in mammalian brain by carnosine synthetase[87] in glial cells.[88] Homocarnosine is hydrolyzed by serum carnosinase, but not by the tissue carnosinase in humans.

Human brain contains more homocarnosine than carnosine, the latter occurring in significant quantities only in the olfactory bulb.[89] Homocarnosine concentrations are highest in the dentate and inferior olivary nuclei (>1 mM), intermediate in substantia nigra and globus pallidus, and lowest in frontal cortex, caudate nucleus, and nucleus accumbens.[89,90] The corresponding concentrations are higher in adults than in infants.[90] The physiological role of brain homocarnosine is unknown.

Mammalian tissues contain other ω-amino acid-containing dipeptides: homoanserine (γ-aminobutyryl-L-methylhistidine) in bovine brain,[91] α-(β-alanyl)-lysine in rabbit muscle,[92] α-(γ-aminobutyryl)-lysine,[93] and γ-aminobutyryl-cystathionine[94] in brain of several mammalian species. These γ-aminobutyryl dipeptides occur in human brain[90,94] at low concentrations compared with homocarnosine. The physiological roles of these substances are unknown.

Imidazole Dipeptides in Physiological Fluids and Relation to Diet

Carnosine and anserine are not detectable in fasting plasma, nor are they usually found in significant amounts in the urine of normal subjects consuming diets low in meat. Normal urine contains scores of unidentified ninhydrin-reacting compounds, some of which include β-alanine and imidazoles in peptide linkage.[95]

Normal persons consuming considerable carnosine or anserine in their diet, as they do when they eat chicken or turkey,[70,96–98] excrete these dipeptides in the urine, presumably because they escape complete hydrolysis in the intestine. After absorption they will then appear in blood, from which they can be cleared by glomerular filtration into urine without efficient reclamation by the renal tubule. All forms of meat and poultry, including soup stocks made from meat, contain car-

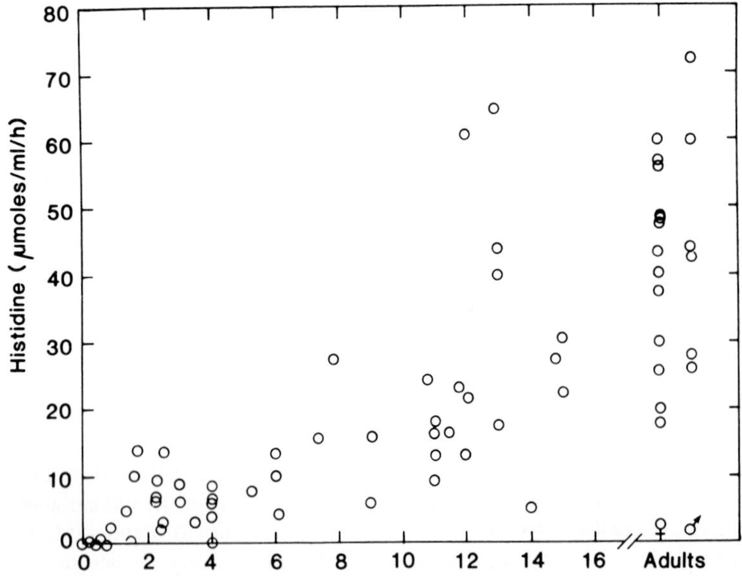

Fig. 26-8 The relationship between serum carnosinase activity (measured by histidine release from carnosine) and age in human controls. (*Reproduced from Lenney et al.,*[77] *by permission.*)

nosine. The most common dietary sources of anserine are the white meat of chicken, and turkey, duck, and rabbit.[70,96]

Subjects fed large amounts of carnosine or anserine may also excrete small amounts of free β-alanine in the urine.[70] Anserine in the diet leads to the appearance of 1-methylhistidine in urine,[70,97,98] except in patients with serum carnosinase deficiency (see below). Renal clearance of 1-methylhistidine is rapid.[99,100] Large amounts of 1-methylhistidine in urine may give a green ferric chloride reaction.[70]

Dietary carnosinuria occurs more readily in infants and young children than in adults, as a consequence of low serum carnosinase activity in the former[77,82,83,101–103] (Fig. 26-8).

Homocarnosine is not detectable in the plasma or urine of normal subjects. It is present in the gray matter of brain,[89,90] its contents being higher in all brain regions in adults than in infants.[89,90] Homocarnosine is almost always detectable in CSF of normal subjects, at higher concentrations in infants and children[104] than in adults.[105] The mean concentration of homocarnosine in the CSF of adults is 1.3 μmol/liter (T. L. Perry, unpublished data) and 8 μmol/liter in normal infants and children under the age of 3½ years.[104] Age-related CSF homocarnosine values are the inverse of age-related serum carnosinase activity; CSF contains serum carnosinase activity.[79]

Disorders of ω-Amino Acid-Containing Peptide Metabolism

Serum Carnosinase Deficiency. Twenty-two patients[83,101,106–114] have been reported with the phenotype of persistent carnosinuria and serum carnosinase deficiency, first observed by Perry et al.;[106] probably only 16 are true cases. The disorder appears to be inherited as an autosomal recessive.

Neurologic signs were described in 14 of 16 true cases. Since clinical manifestations did not necessarily accompany the biochemical phenotype,[83,114] they may reflect an ascertainment bias (retrospective diagnosis while investigating a disease) or unidentified conditions (environmental or of genotype) that have consequences for persons with serum carnosinase deficiency. Neurologic manifestations include myoclonic seizures and psychomotor retardation appearing in the first year of life. Overt manifestations were accompanied by nonspecific electroencephalographic abnormalities. Where the clinical course permitted survival, severe mental retardation, spasticity, and seizures became evident in later infancy and children. Two patients in different pedigrees[83,109,114] were clinically normal at ages from 5 to 8 years. Both were normal sibs of mentally retarded probands with confirmed serum carnosinase deficiency. Only one proband with serum carnosinase deficiency has been discovered as a result of newborn urine screening;[111] at 8 months he had developed normally.

Because serum carnosinase activity is low in young infants (Fig. 26-8), some reported patients probably have an erroneous diagnosis of serum carnosinase deficiency.[101,106,108,111,113,114] Hindsight suggests their low serum carnosinase activity and the associated carnosinuria were probably the normal age-dependent phenomenon.

DIPEPTIDURIA. Carnosine excretion by normal older children and adults on standard diets is negligible (<20 μmol/g creatinine),[115] but it will increase when carnosine-containing diets are ingested, particularly during infancy. Persistence of excessive carnosinuria, even when dietary sources of carnosine are excluded, is a consistent finding in persons with serum carnosinase deficiency. The source of urinary carnosine in these subjects is turnover of endogenous carnosine. The quantity of endogenous carnosine excreted by such persons during ingestion of meat-free diet varies between 0.5 and 1 mmol/g creatinine.[83,106,108]

Anserine also appears in the urine of patients with serum carnosinase deficiency when anserine-containing foods are eaten. This dipeptide is not excreted by persons with serum carnosinase deficiency eating an anserine-free diet, because human tissues do not contain anserine. When normal individuals ingest anserine, they excrete the hydrolysis product 1-methylhistidine.[70] Patients with serum carnosinase deficiency under the same dietary conditions excrete no[83,106] or minimal[108] free 1-methylhistidine.

PLASMA CARNOSINE. Carnosine is absent from the fasting plasma of normal subjects; it appears there at low levels after eating carnosine-containing foods.[106] Measurable concentrations of carnosine were found in the fasting plasma of some patients with serum carnosinase deficiency.[83,106,112] Naming of this disorder *carnosinemia* came from this finding; *serum carnosinase deficiency* is now the recommended name.

CARNOSINE AND HOMOCARNOSINE IN CEREBROSPINAL FLUID. Carnosine is not detectable in normal human CSF. Homocarnosine occurs in the CSF of normal infants and children and at lower levels in the CSF of normal adults.[104,105] "Carnosine" was found in the CSF of two patients with serum carnosinase deficiency;[113] it is more likely that homocarnosine was the substance found in these patients. Five juvenile patients with serum carnosinase deficiency[101,106,114] had normal CSF homocarnosine concentrations.

CARNOSINE AND HOMOCARNOSINE IN TISSUES. Skeletal muscle and brain were examined at autopsy in one subject.[106] Values for carnosine (0.67 to 0.81 μmol/g wet weight in muscle) and homocarnosine (0.14 μmol/g wet weight in brain) were not abnormal. This subject probably did not have inherited serum carnosine deficiency. Another proband[101,106] with true serum carnosinase deficiency had elevated values at the age of 13 years. At autopsy there was no detectable carnosine in nine brain regions, but homocarnosine values were high in the caudate nucleus (0.86 μmol/g wet weight, adult controls, 0.80 ± 0.33 SD) and normal elsewhere. Patients with serum carnosinase deficiency appear not to lack tissue carnosinase. Elevation of homocarnosine content in certain regions of brain is apparently a consequence of serum carnosinase deficiency.

Neuropathologic studies in two patients[109,110] demonstrated axonal degeneration in peripheral nerves, demyelination of pyramidal and spinal cerebellar tracts, Purkinje cell loss, cerebellar gliosis, and neuronal loss in the cerebral cortex. Whether these were incidental findings or a consequence of serum carnosinase deficiency is not known.

SERUM CARNOSINASE ACTIVITY. Several methods have been devised to assay serum carnosinase (EC 3.4.13.3; serum form not distinguished by specific number).[77,80,82,101] The best of these[77] yields higher hydrolysis activity than the others. The values in Fig. 26-8 were obtained with this assay.[77]

Serum carnosinase-deficient probands have low enzyme activity (≈10 percent normal). In vitro mixing experiments, using serum from a proband and a control, yielded the expected combined value.[83,101] Age-related controls must be used to interpret the serum carnosinase value in putative patients. As mentioned above, several subjects,[101,106,108,111,113,114] classified originally as cases of congenital serum carnosinase deficiency, probably had only age-dependent low activity of the serum enzyme. Other diseases cause decrements in serum carnosine activity, and they must be taken into account, for example, urea cycle disorders,[102] muscular dystrophies,[103] and hepatic cirrhosis or hepatoma.[116]

Parents of probands with apparently true serum carnosinase deficiency have partial deficiency of enzyme activity.[83,108,110] The assumption that congenital serum carnosinase deficiency is inherited as an autosomal recessive derives from this evidence.

Homocarnosinosis. Homocarnosinosis has been identified in a single Norwegian pedigree.[117–119] A 69-year-old woman (patient 1) and three of her four children (patients 2, 3, and 4; ages 34 to 41 years) had elevated CSF homocarnosine values. There was no increment of homocarnosine in plasma or urine. The three affected offspring had progressive spastic paraplegia (onset between 6 and 29 years of age), progressive mental deterioration, and retinal pigmentation. Their mother (patient 1) had retained normal neurologic and mental function (when last studied at the age of 72). Two sisters of patient 1; the father of patients 2, 3, and 4; and their sister are healthy and have normal CSF homocarnosine values.[118] Two children, ages 8 and 6 years, of patient 3 are normal; their CSF homocarnosine values have not been determined.[19]

METABOLIC PHENOTYPE. The disorder is characterized by a high homocarnosine value in CSF (50 to 75 μmol/l; normal adult mean, 1.3 ± 1.5 SD). Plasma and urine contained no homocarnosine in the affected subjects, and CSF carnosine was not increased. A follow-up investigation[120] revealed that all four patients excreted substantial amounts of carnosine in their urine (200 to 360 μmol/g creatinine) while they consumed a meat-free diet. After eating anserine-containing foods each patient also excreted large amounts of anserine in urine, but only trace amounts of free 1-methylhistidine.

A brain biopsy, obtained from the nondominant frontal cortex of patient 2 when she was 40 years old,[119] revealed marked atrophy of the cortical tyri and enlargement of the subarachnoid space. There were no abnormal histologic findings. Quick-frozen frontal cortex biopsy material from the same patient contained homocarnosine at levels four times control values.[119] GABA and histidine values were similar in patient and control brain samples. Elevated brain homocarnosine values imply there is no impairment of homocarnosine uptake from CSF.

ENZYME PHENOTYPE. Serum carnosinase activity was measured by the preferred method[77] in patients 2, 3 and 4. Activities were extremely low[121] (0 to 0.3 μmol/l per hour; normal adults, range 18 to 72 μmol/ml per hour). Accordingly, homocarnosinosis resembles serum carnosinase deficiency, of which it may be a more severe form.

Homocarnosine-carnosine synthetase activity was within the normal range for age in a brain biopsy specimen from patient 2.[119] "Homocarnosinase" activity could not be detected in the brain biopsy specimen.[119]

Human serum carnosinase hydrolyzes homocarnosine; tissue carnosinase does not.[77–79] Human CSF has serum carnosinase activity at about 10 percent of the corresponding serum-specific activity.[121] Accordingly, serum carnosinase activity can achieve hydrolysis of homocarnosine in brain, and a severe deficit of serum carnosinase activity in homocarnosinosis[21] could explain homocarnosine accumulation in CSF and brain in the disorder.

SERUM CARNOSINASE DEFICIENCY AND HOMOCARNOSIS: ONE DISORDER? We propose that serum carnosinase deficiency and homocarnosinosis are one disorder. Although CSF homocarnosine values in patients with serum carnosinase deficiency (five subjects) (age 1 to 8 years; 3 to 14 μmol/l) were lower than in the four adults with homocarnosinosis (50 to 75 μmol/l), the lower values in the younger patients can be attributed to the effect of age[90] or to a more severe deficit of hydrolysis activity. Brain and CSF homocarnosine pools are presumably in equilibrium with each other. Impaired hydrolysis of homocarnosine (by serum carnosinase) should cause both brain and CSF homocarnosine to accumulate. We propose, but cannot substantiate, the view that neurologic abnormalities in reported cases with serum carnosinase deficiency and homocarnosinosis are unrelated to the metabolic disorder.

DIAGNOSIS. Carnosinuria (and anserinuria) can be detected by two-dimensional paper chromatography or column chromatography of urine amino acids. When pyridine:acetone:ammonium hydroxide:water (45:30:5:20) is used as the first solvent for partition chromatography, followed by isopropanol:formic acid:water (75:12.5:12.5) as the second solvent, and the sheets are sprayed with ninhydrin-lutidine,[122] carnosine and anserine appear as yellow or tan-yellow spots close to and partially overlapping histidine. The two dipeptides can be conveniently identified if the chromatogram is then counter-sprayed with diazotized sulfanilic acid. When this is done, histidine turns from purple to orange-brown, carnosine turns red, anserine turns grayish blue, and all other ninhydrin-positive spots on the chromatogram are decolorized.[106]

Subjects with carnosinuria should receive a meat- and fowl-free diet for several days to see whether carnosinuria persists in the absence of exogenous sources of the dipeptide. If it does, the patient can be fed white meat of chicken or turkey as a source of anserine. If urine collected after such a meal contains easily detectable 1-methylhistidine, the possibility of serum carnosinase deficiency is excluded.

If carnosinuria persists on a meat-free diet, and if dietary loading with anserine causes excretion of anserine and little or no 1-methylhistidine in urine, serum carnosinase activity should be determined, preferably with the most sensitive method.[77] If serum carnosinase activities are far below the normal age-dependent value (see Fig. 26-8), the homocarnosine concentration of CSF should be measured. An elevated value is a further indication of true serum carnosinase deficiency.

THERAPY. In the absence of good evidence that serum carnosinase deficiency is causally related to neurologic disease, treatment is probably not indicated for this biochemical disorder.

Normal donor plasma infused into a subject with serum carnosinase deficiency over a 45-h period provoked a prompt increment of serum carnosinase activity and a fall in urine carnosine excretion.[108] The effect of the infusion lasted about 24 h. The observation has metabolic but not clinical interest.

Lunde et al.[123] placed two homocarnosinosis patients on a diet very low in histidine for 2½ years. Histidine concentrations in CSF, plasma, and urine declined 90 percent, and CSF homocarnosine values were 30 percent of pretreatment values after 6 months. No clinical improvement occurred. The chemical findings suggests that carnosine is a significant source of histidine in human metabolism (also, see Ref. 2).

GENETICS. Serum carnosinase deficiency is a Mendelian phenotype. Autosomal recessive inheritance is indicated by two pedigrees[106,107,108] where there was parental consanguinity, and in two others where sibs were affected.[83,114] Inheritance of homocarnosinosis in the Norwegian family is also compatible with an autosomal recessive mode, assuming the father of patients 2, 3, and 4 was a heterozygote.

The associated neurologic disorder either has an independent cause of a multifactorial origin in probands with serum carnosinase deficiency. Accordingly, counseling about prognosis in a prospectively identified case is difficult.

REFERENCES

1. POSTON JM: β-leucine and the β-keto pathway of leucine metabolism. *Adv Enzymol* 58:173, 1986.
2. GRIFFITH OW: β-amino acids: Mammalian metabolism and utility as α-amino acid analogues. *Ann Rev Biochem* 55:855, 1986.
3. ROZEN R, GOODYER P R, SCRIVER CR: GABA and taurine. What are metabolites like this doing in places like that? in Freinkel N (ed): *Contemporary Metabolism*. New York, Plenum, 1982, vol 2, pp 189–237.
4. BERGER R, STOKER-DE-VRIES SA, WADMAN SK, DURAN M, BEEMER FA, DEBREE PK, WEITS-BINNERS JJ, PENDERS TJ, VAN DER WOUDE JK: Dihydropyrimidine dehydrogenase deficiency leading to thymine-uraciluria. An inborn error of pyrimidine metabolism. *Clin Chim Acta* 141:227, 1984.
5. WADMAN SK, BEEMER FA, DEBREE PK, DURAN M, VAN GENNIP AH, KETTING D, VAN SPRANG FJ: New defects of pyrimidine metabolism. *Adv Exp Med Biol* 165:109, 1984.
6. BAKKEREN JAJM, DE ABREU RA, SENGERS RCA, GABREELS FJM, MAAS JM, RENIER WO: Elevated urine, blood and cerebrospinal fluid levels of uracil and thymine in a child with dihydrothymine dehydrogenase deficiency. *Clin Chim Acta* 140:247, 1984.
7. TUCHMAN M, STOECKELER JS, KIANG DT, O'DEA RF, RAMNARAINE ML, MIRKIN BL: Familial pyrimidinemia and pyrimidinuria associated with severe fluorouracil toxicity. *N Engl J Med* 313:245, 1985.
8. VESELL ES: Genetic host factors: Determinants of drug response. *N Engl J Med* 313:261, 1985.
9. BERGLUND G, GRETER J, STEEN G, WALDENSTROM J, WASS U: Urinary excretion of thymine and uracil in a two-year old child with a malignant tumor of the brain. *Clin Chem* 25:1325, 1979.
10. DAGG CP, COLEMAN DL, FRASER GM: A gene affecting the rate of pyrimidine degradation in mice. *Genetics* 49:979, 1964.
11. SCRIVER CR, PUESCHEL S, DAVIES E: Hyper-β-alaninemia associated with β-aminoaciduria and γ-aminobutyricaciduria, somnolence and seizures. *N Engl J Med* 274:636, 1966.
12. OKAMURA N, OTSUKU S, KAMEYAMA A: Studies on free amino acids in human brain. *J Biochem* 47:315, 1960.
13. TALLAN HH: A survey of the amino acids and relatea compounds in nervous tissues, in JT Holden (ed): *Amino Acid Pools: Distribution, Formation, and Function of Free Amino Acids*. New York, Elsevier, 1962, p 471.
14. PALO J, SAIFER A, MAZELIS F: Free amino acids in Tay-Sachs and normal human gray matter. *Clin Chim Acta* 22:327, 1968.
15. WHELAN DT, SCRIVER CR, MOHYUDDIN F: Glutamic acid decarboxylase and γ-aminobutyric acid in mammalian kidney. *Nature* 224:916, 1969.
16. ZACHMANN M, TOCCI P, NYHAN WL: The occurrence of γ-aminobutyric acid in human tissues other than brain. *J Biol Chem* 241:1355, 1966.
17. DICKINSON JC, ROSENBLUM H, HAMILTON PB: Ion exchange chromatography of the free amino acids in the plasma of the newborn infant. *Peds* 36:2, 1965.
18. SCRIVER CR, ROSENBERG LE: *Amino Acid Metabolism and Its Disorders*. WB Saunders, Philadelphia, 1973, pp 39–60.
19. SCRIVER CR: The use of human genetic variation to study membrane transport of amino acids in kidney. *Am J Dis Child* 117:4, 1969.
20. GILBERG JT, LORENE YK, ROGERS L, WILLIAMS RJ: The increase in urinary taurine after intraperitoneal administration of amino acids in the mouse. *J Biol Chem* 235:1055, 1960.
21. WILSON OH, SCRIVER CR: Specificity of transport of neutral and basic amino acids in rat kidney. *Am J Physiol* 213:185, 1967.
22. GOLDMAN H, SCRIVER CR: A transport system in mammalian kidney with preference for β-amino compounds. *Pediatr Res* 1:212A, 1967.
23. HAMMERMAN M, SACKTOR B: Transport of β-alanine in renal brush border membrane vesicles. *Biochem Biphys Acta* 509:338, 1978.
24. ROZEN R, TENENHOUSE HS, SCRIVER CR: Taurine transport in renal brush-border-membrane vesicles. *Biochem J* 180:245, 1979.
25. DANTZLER WH, SILBERNAGL S: Renal tubular reabsorption of taurine γ-aminobutyric acid (GABA) and β-alanine studied by continuous microperfusion. *Pflugers Arch* 367:123, 1976.
25a. CONNOLLY BA, GOODMAN HO, SWANTON CH: Evidence for inheritance of a renal beta-amino transport system and its location on chromosome 21. *Am J Hum Genet* 31:43A, 1979.
26. GOODYER PR, ROZEN R, SCRIVER CR: A γ-aminobutyric acid-specific transport mechanism in mammalian kidney. *Bioichem Biophys Acta* 818:45, 1985.
26a. POLLIT RJ, GREEN A, SMITH R: Excessive excretion of β-alanine and of 3-hydroxypropionic, R- and S-3-aminosobutyric, R- and S-3-hydroxyisobutyric and S-2-(hydroxymethyl) butyric acids probably due to a defect in the metabolism of the corresponding malonic semialdehydes. *J Inherited Metab Dis* 8:75, 1985.
27. TAMAKI N, AOYAMA H, KUBO K, IKEDA T, HAMA T: Purification and properties of beta-alanine aminotransferase from rabbit liver. *J Biochem* 92:1009, 1982.
28. BUZENET AM, FAGES C, BLOCH-TARDY M, GONNARD P: Purification and properties of 4-aminobutyrate 2-ketoglutarate aminotransferase from pig liver. *Biochim Biophys Acta* 522:400, 1978.
29. MAITRE M, CIESIELSKI L, CASH C, MANDEL P: Purification and studies on some properties of the 4-aminobutyrata: 2-oxoglutarate transaminase from rat brain. *Eur J Biochem* 52:157, 1975.
30. SCHOUSBOE A, WU J-Y, ROBERTS E: Purification and characterization of the 4-aminobutyrate-2-ketoglutarate transaminase from mouse brain. *Biochemistry* 12:2868, 1973.
31. PERRY TL, HANSEN S: Biochemical effects on man and rat of three drugs which can increase brain GABA content. *J Neurochem* 30:679, 1978.
32. BRANDT NJ, CHRISTENSEN E: ω-aminoaciduria induced by γ-vinyl GABA. *Lancet* 1:450, 1984.
33. SCHECHTER PJ, LEWIS PJ, NEWBERNE JW: γ-vinyl GABA, and GABA and β-alanine transamination. *Lancet* 1:737, 1984.
34. SUTTON HE: β-aminoisobutyricaciduria. In Stanbury JB, Wyngaarden B, Frederickson DS (eds): *The Metabolic Basis of Inherited Disease*, 1st ed. McGraw-Hill, New York, 1960, pp 792–806.
35. SOLEM E, JELLUM E, ELDJARN L: The absolute configuration of β-aminosobutyric acid in human serum and urine. *Clin Chim Acta* 50:393, 1974.
36. CRUMPLER HR, DENT CE, HARRIS H, WESTALL RG: β-Amino isobutyric acid (α-methyl-β-alanine): A new amino acid, obtained from human urine. *Nature* 617:307, 1951.
37. HARRIS H: Family studies on the urinary excretion of β-aminoisobutyric acid. *Ann Eugen* 18:43, 1953.
38. KAKIMOTO Y, ARMSTRONG MD: The preparation and isolation of D-(—)-β-aminosobutyric acid. *J Biol Chem* 236:3283, 1961.
39. ARMSTRONG MD, YATES K, KAKIMOTO Y, TANIGUCHI K, KAPPE T: Excretion of β-aminoisobutyric acid by man. *J Biol Chem* 238:1447, 1963.
39a. KAKIMOTO Y, TANIGUCHI K, SANO I: D-β-aminoisobutyrate:pyruvate aminotransferase in mammalian liver and excretion of β-aminoisobutyrate by man. *J Biol Chem* 244:335, 1969.
39b. TANIGUCHI K, TAKEHIKO T, KAKIMOTO Y: Deficiency of β-aminoisobutyrate:pyruvate aminotransferase in the liver of genetic high excretors of D-β-aminoisobutyrate. *Biochim Biophys Acta* 279:475, 1972.
40. GARTLER SM: A metabolic investigation of urinary β-aminoisobutyric acid excretion in man. *Arch Biochem* 80:400, 1959.
41. SOLEM E: The absolute configuration of beta-aminoisobutyric acid formed by degradation of thymine in man. *Clin Chim Acta* 53:183, 1974.
42. SOLEM E, AGARWAL DP, GOEDDE HW: The determination of β-aminoisobutyric acid in human serum by ion-exchange chromatography. *Clin Chim Acta* 59:203, 1975.
43. YANAI J, KAKIMOTO Y, TSUJIO T, SANO I: Genetic study of beta-aminoisobutyric acid excretion by Japanese. *Am J Hum Genet* 21:115, 1969.
44. SCRIVER CR, ROSENBERG LE: In *Amino Acid Metabolism and Its Disorders*. Philadelphia, WB Saunders, 1973, pp 384–386.
45. GOODYER PR, MILLS M, SCRIVER CR: Properties of γ-aminobutyric acid synthesis by rat renal cortex. *Biochim Biophys Acta* 716:348, 1982.
46. GOODYER PR, LANCASTER G, VILLENEUVE M, SCRIVER CR: The relationship of γ-aminobutyric acid metabolism to ammoniogenesis in renal cortex. *Biochim Biophys Acta* 633:191, 1980.
47. VAN GELDER NM: A possible enzyme barrier for γ-aminobutyric acid in the central nervous system. *Prog Brain Res* 29:259, 1967.
48. LANCASTER G, MOHYUDDIN F, SCRIVER CR, WHELAN DT: A γ-aminobu-

tyrate pathway in mammalian kidney cortex. *Biochim Biophys Acta* 297:229, 1973.

49. LANCASTER GA, MOHYUDDIN F, SCRIVER CR: Ontogeny of L-glutamic acid decarboxylase and γ-aminobutyric acid concentration in human kidney. *Pediatr Res* 9:484, 1975.

50. SCRIVER CR, WHELAN DT: Glutamic acid decarboxylase (GAD) in mammalian tissue outside the central nervous system, and its possible relevance to hereditary vitamin B_6 dependency with seizures. *Ann NY Acad Sci* 166:83, 1969.

51. BANKIER A, TURNER M, HOPKINS IJ: Pyridoxine-dependent seizures—A wider clinical spectrum. *Arch Dis Child* 58:415, 1983.

52. GOUTIERES F, AIRCARDI J: Atypical presentations of pyridoxine-dependent seizures: A treatable cause of intractable epilepsy in infants. *Ann Neurol* 17:117, 1985.

53. YOSHIDA T, TADA K, ARAKAWA T: Vitamin B_6-dependency of glutamic acid decarboxylase in the kidney from a patient with vitamin B_6-dependent convulsion. *Tohoku J Exp Med* 104:195, 1971.

54. JAEKEN J, CASAER P, DECOCK P, CORBEEL L, EECKELS R, EGGERMONT E, SCHECHTER PJ, BRUCHER J-M: Gamma-aminobutyric acid-transaminase deficiency: A newly recognized inborn error of neurotransmitter metabolism. *Neuropediatrics* 15:165, 1984.

55. RACAGNI G, APUD JA, COCCHI D, LOCATELLI V, MULLER EE: Mini-review GABAergic control of anterior pituitary hormone secretion. *Life Sci* 31:823, 1982.

56. GIBSON KM, SWEETMAN L, NYHAN WL, JANSEN I, JAEKEN J: Demonstration of 4-aminobutyric acid aminotransferase deficiency in lymphocytes and lymphoblasts. *J Inherited Metab Dis* 8:204, 1985.

57. RATING D, HANEFELD F, SIEMES H, KNEER J, JAKOBS C, HERMIER M, DIVRY P: 4-hydroxybutyric aciduria: A new inborn error of metabolism. I. Clinical review. *J Inherited Metab Dis* 7:90, 1984.

58. JAKOBS C, KNEER J, RATING D, HANEFELD F, DIVRY P, HERMIER M: 4-hydroxybutyric aciduria: A new inborn error of metabolism. II. Biochemical findings. *J Inherited Metab Dis* 7:92, 1984.

59. GIBSON KM, JANSEN I, SWEETMAN L, NYHAN WL: 4-hydroxybutyric aciduria: A new inborn error of metabolism. III. Enzymology and inheritance. *J Inherited Metab Dis* 7:95, 1984.

60. GIBSON KM, SWEETMAN L, NYHAN WL, JAKOBS C, RATING D, SIEMES H, HANEFELD F: Succinic semialdehyde dehydrogenase deficiency: An inborn error of gamma-aminobutyric acid metabolism. *Clin Chim Acta* 133:33, 1983.

61. CRUSH KC: Carnosine and related substances in animal studies. *Comp Biochem Physiol* 34:3, 1970.

62. SCHMIDT G, CUBILES R: Comparative studies on occurrence of carnosine-anserine fraction in skeletal muscle and heart. *Arch Biochem Biophys* 58:227, 1955.

63. REDDY WJ, HEGSTED DM: Measurement and distribution of carnosine in rat. *J Biol Chem* 237:705, 1962.

64. MARGOLIS FL: Carnosine in the primary olfactory pathway. *Science* 184:909, 1974.

65. KALYANKAR GD, MEISTER A: Enzymatic synthesis of carnosine and related β-alanyl and γ-aminobutyryl peptides. *J Biol Chem* 234:3210, 1959.

66. STENESH JJ, WINNICK T: Carnosine-anserine synthetase of muscle. 4. Partial purification of the enzyme and further studies of β-alanyl peptide synthesis. *Biochem J* 77:575, 1960.

67. MCMANUS JR, BENSON MS: Studies on the formation of carnosine and anserine in pectoral muscle of the developing chick. *Arch Biochem Biophys* 119:444, 1967.

68. DUVIGENEAUD V, BEHRENS O: Carnosine and anserine. *Ergeb Physiol* 41:917, 1939.

69. DAVEY CL: Significance of carnosine and anserine in straited skeletal muscle. *Arch Biochem Biophys* 89:303, 1960.

70. DAVIES E, SCRIVER CR: 1-Methylhistidinuria in man: A festive index, in *Proc Soc Ped Res*, Atlantic City, NJ, 1967, p 134.

71. MCMANUS IR: Enzymatic synthesis of anserine in skeletal muscle by N-methylation of carnosine. *J Biol Chem* 237:1207, 1962.

72. HOCHACHKA PW, MOMMSEN TP: Protons and anaerobisis. *Science* 219:1393, 1983.

73. AVENA RM, BOWEN WJ: Effects of carnosine and anserine on muscle adenosine triphosphatases. *J Biol Chem* 244:1600, 1969.

74. BROWN CE, ANTHOLINE WE: Evidence that carnosine and anserine may participate in Wilson's disease. *Biochem Biophys Res Comm* 92:470, 1980.

75. HANSON HT, SMITH EL: Carnosinase: An enzyme of swine kidney. *J Biol Chem* 179:789, 1949.

76. ROSENBERG A: Purification and some properties of carnosinase of swine kidney. *Arch Biochem Biophys* 88:83, 1960.

77. LENNEY JF, GEORGE RP, WEISS AM, KUCERA CM, CHAN PWH, RINZLER GS: Human serum carnosinase: Characterization, distinction from cellular carnosinase, and activation by cadmium. *Clin Chim Acta* 123:221, 1982.

78. LENNEY JF, PEPPERS SC, KUCERA-ORALLO M, GEORGE RP: Characterization of human tissue carnosinase. *Biochem J* 228:653, 1985.

79. LENNY JF: Carnosinase and homocarnosinosis. *J Oslo City Hosp* 35:27, 1985.

80. MURPHEY WH, PATCHEN L, LINDMARK DG: Carnosinase: A fluorometric assay and demonstration of two electrophoretic forms in human tissue extracts. *Clin Chim Acta* 42:309, 1972.

81. LENNY JF, KAN SC, SIU K, SUGIYAMA GH: Homocarnosinase: A hog kidney dipeptidase with a broader specificity than carnosinase. *Arch Biochem Biophys* 184:257, 1977.

82. VAN MUNSTER PJJ, TRIJBELS JMF, VAN HEESWIJK PJ, SCHUT-JANSEN B, MOERKERK C: A new sensitive method for the determination of serum carnosinase activity using L-carnosine-(1-^{14}C) β-alanyl as substrate. *Clin Chim Acta* 29:243, 1970.

83. MURPHEY WH, LINDMARK DG, PATCHEN LI, HOUSLER ME, HARROD EK, MOSOVICH L: Serum carnosinase deficiency concomitant with mental retardation. *Pediatr Res* 7:601, 1973.

84. NAKAI T, TSUJIGADO N: β-Alanyl dipeptide preparations from whale muscles made by several workers. *J Biochem* 57:812, 1965.

85. PISANO JJ, WILSON JD, COHEN L, ABRAHAM D, UDENFRIEND S: Isolation of γ-aminobutyrylhistidine (homocarnosine) from brain. *J Biol Chem* 236:499, 1961.

86. ABRAHAM D, PISANO JJ, UDENFRIEND S: The distribution of homocarnosine in mammals. *Arch Biochem Biophys* 99:210, 1962.

87. SKAPER SD, DAS S, MARSHALL FD: Some properties of a homocarnosine-carnosine synthetase isolated from rat brain. *J Neurochem* 21:1429, 1973.

88. BAUER K, HALLERMAYER K, SALNIKOW J, KLEINKAUF H, HAMPRECHT B: Biosynthesis of carnosine and related peptides by glial cells in primary culture. *J Biol Chem* 257:3593, 1982.

89. KISH SJ, PERRY TL, HANSEN S: Regional distribution of homocarnosine, homocarnosine-carnosine synthetase and homocarnosinase in human brain. *J Neurochem* 32:1629, 1979.

90. PERRY TL: Cerebral amino acid pools, in Lajtha A (ed): *Handbook of Neurochemistry*, 2d ed. New York, Plenum, 1982, vol I, p 151.

91. NAKAJIMA T, WOLFGRAM F, CLARK WG: The isolation of homoanserine from bovine brain. *J Neurochem* 14:1107, 1967.

92. MATSUOKA M, NAKAJIMA T, SANO I: Identification of α-(β-alanyl)-lysine in rabbit muscle. *Biochim Biophys Acta* 177:169, 1969.

93. NAKAJIMA T, KAKIMOTO Y, KUMON A, MATSUOKA M, SANO I: α-(γ-Aminobutyryl)-lysine in mammalian brain: Its identification and distribution. *J Neurochem* 16:417, 1969.

94. PERRY TL, HANSEN S, SCHIER GM, HALPREN B: Isolation and identification of γ-aminobutyryl-cystathionine from human brain and CSF. *J Neurochem* 29:791, 1977.

95. WESTALL RG: The amino acids and other ampholytes of urine. 3. Unidentified substances expected in normal human urine. *Biochem J* 60:247, 1955.

96. BLOCK WD, HUBBARD RW, STEELE BF: Excretion of histidine and histidine derivatives by human subjects ingesting protein from different sources. *J Nutr* 85:419, 1965.

97. HUBBARD RW, BLOCK WD: Urinary excretion of 1-methylhistidine and histidine in human subjects on low and high protein intake. *Fed Proc* 22:320, 1963.

98. BUTTS JH, FLESHLER B: Anserine, a source of 1-methylhistidine in urine of man. *Proc Soc Exp Biol Med* 118:722, 1965.

99. CUSWORTH DC, DENT CE: Renal clearances of amino acids in normal adults and in patients with aminoaciduria. *Biochem J* 74:550, 1960.

100. SCRIVER CR, DAVIES E: Endogenous renal clearance rates of free amino acids in pre-pubertal children. *Peds* 32:592, 1965.

101. PERRY TL, HANSEN S, LOVE DL: Serum-carnosinase deficiency in carnosinaemia. *Lancet* 1:1229, 1968.

102. BURGESS EA, OBERHOLZER VG, PALMER T, LEVIN B: Plasma carnosinase deficiency in patients with urea cycle defects. *Clin Chim Acta* 61:215, 1975.

103. BANDO K, SHIMOTSUJI T, TOYOSHIMA H, HAYASHI C, MIYAI K: Fluorometric assay of human serum carnosinase activity in normal children, adults and patients with myopathy. *Ann Clin Biochem* 21:510, 1984.

104. PERRY TL, HANSEN S, STEDMAN D, LOVE D: Homocarnosine in human cerebrospinal fluid: An age-dependent phenomenon. *J Neurochem* 15:1203, 1968.

105. PERRY TL, HANSEN S, KENNEDY J: CSF amino acids and plasma-CSF amino acid ratios in adults. *J Neurochem* 24:587, 1975.

106. PERRY TL, HANSEN S, TISCHLER B, BUNTING R, BERRY K: Carnosinemia: A new metabolic disorder associated with neurologic disease and mental defect. *N Engl J Med* 277:1219 1967.

107. PERRY TL: Carnosinemia, in Nyhan WL (ed): *Heritable Disorders of Amino Acid Metabolism*. New York, Wiley 1974, p 293.

108. VAN HEESWIJK PJ, TRIJBELS JMF, SCHRETLEN EDAM, VAN MUNSTER PJJ,

MONNENS LAH: A patient with a deficiency of serum-carnosinase activity. *Acta Paediatr Scand* 58:584, 1969.

109. TERPLAN KL, CARES HL: Histopathology of the nervous system in carnosinase enzyme deficiency with mental retardation. *Neurology* 22:644, 1972.

110. FLEISCHER LD, RASSIN DK, WISNIEWSKI K, SALWEN HR: Carnosinase deficiency: A new variant with high residual activity. *Pediatr Res* 14:269, 1980.

111. GORDON ED JR, COULBOMBE JT, SEPE SJ, LEVY HL: A variant of carnosinemia with normal serum carnosinase activity in an infant. *Pediatr Res* 11:456, 1977.

112. LEININGER ML, CHAPOY P, CHARVET J, VOVAN L, LOUCHET E: La carnosinémie. Première observation française. *Pediatrie* 35:341, 1980.

113. HARTLAGE PL, ROESEL RA, ELLER G, HOMMES FA: Serum carnosinase deficiency: Decreased affinity of the enzyme for the substrate. *J Inherited Metab Dis* 5:13, 1982.

114. COHEN M, HARTLAGE PL, KRAWIECKI N, ROESEL RA, CARTER AL, HOMMES FA: Serum carnosinase deficiency: A non-disabling phenotype? *J Ment Defic Res* 29:383, 1985.

115. TOCCI PM, BESSMAN SP: Histidine peptiduria, in Nyhan WL (ed): *Amino Acid Metabolism and Genetic Variation*. New York, McGraw-Hill, 1967, p 161.

116. BANDO K, ICHIHARA K, TOYOSHIMA H, SHIMOTUJI T, KODA K, HAYASHI C, MIYAI K: Decreased activity of carnosinase in serum of patients with chronic liver disorders. *Clin Chem* 32:1563, 1986.

117. GJESSING LR, SJAASTAD O: Homocarnosinosis: A new metabolic disorder associated with spasticity and mental retardation. *Lancet* 2:1028, 1974.

118. SJAASTAD O, BERSTAD J, GJESDAHL P, GJESSING L: Homocarnosinosis: 2. A familial disorder associated with spastic paraplegia, progressive mental deficiency, and retinal pigmentation. *Acta Neurol Scand* 53:275, 1976.

119. PERRY TL, KISH SJ, SJAASTAD O, GJESSING LR, NESBAKKEN R, SCHRADER H, LOKEN AC: Homocarnosinosis: Increased content of homocarnosine and deficiency of homocarnosinase in brain. *J Neurochem* 32:1637, 1979.

120. LUNDE H, SJAASTAD O, GJESSING L: Homocarnosinosis: Hypercarnosinuria. *J Neurochem* 38:242, 1982.

121. LENNEY JF, PEPPERS SC, KUCERA CM, SJAASTAD O: Homocarnosinosis: Lack of serum carnosinase is the defect probably responsible for elevated brain and CSF homocarnosine. *Clin Chim Acta* 132:157, 1983.

122. PERRY TL, SHAW KNF, WALKER D, REDLICH D: Urinary excretion of amines in normal children. *Peds* 30:576, 1962.

123. LUNDE HA, GJESSING LR, SJAASTAD O: Homocarnosinosis: Influence of dietary restriction of histidine. *Neurochem Res* 11:825, 1986.

PART 5

ORGANIC ACIDS

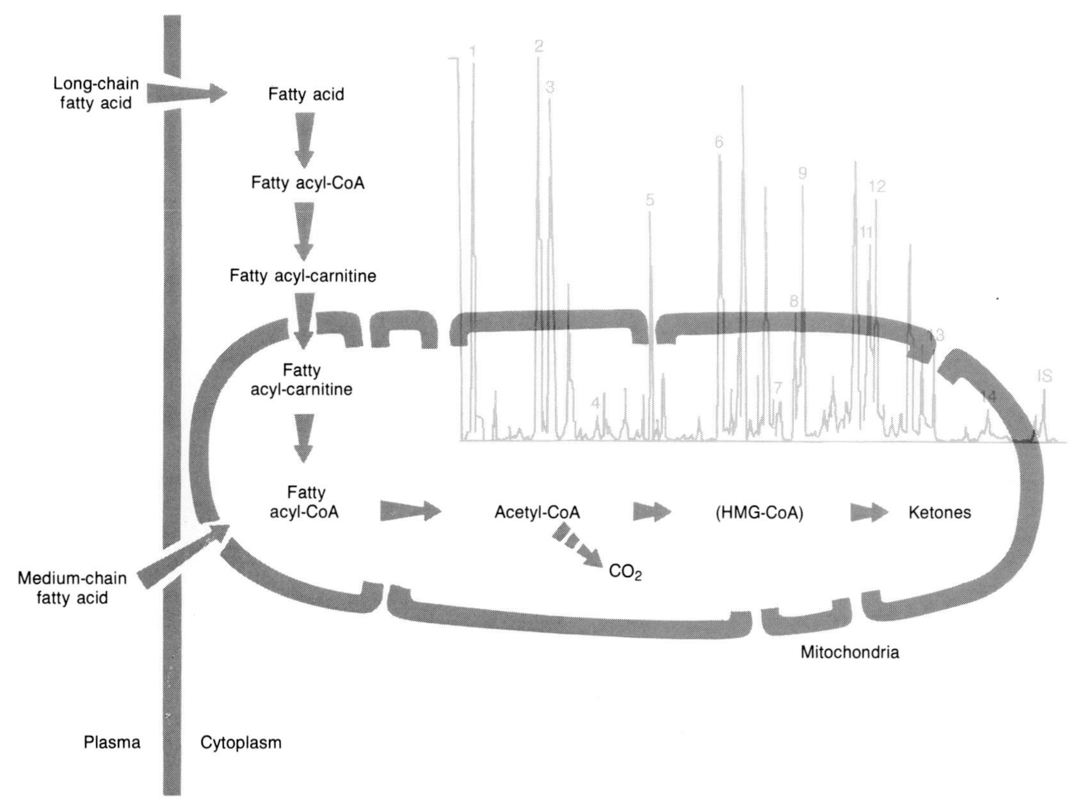

CHAPTER 27

ALCAPTONURIA

BERT N. LA DU

1. *Alcaptonuria is a rare, hereditary, metabolic disease in which homogentisic acid, an intermediary product in the metabolism of phenylalanine and tyrosine, cannot be further metabolized. The metabolic defect causes a characteristic triad of homogentisic aciduria, ochronosis, and arthritis.*
2. *The cause of the disease is a constitutional lack of the enzyme homogentisic acid oxidase. This enzyme normally exists primarily in the liver and kidney. It requires oxygen, ferrous ion, and sulfhydryl groups to open the ring of homogentisic acid.*
3. *The condition is inherited as an autosomal recessive disease. No method for the detection of heterozygotes has been devised.*
4. *The relationships between the metabolic defect and the complications, ochronosis and arthritis, remain a challenging research problem of the future. Even though the lack of homogentisic acid oxidase is no doubt the ultimate cause of these complications, the mechanisms that bring them about are unknown.*

Alcaptonuria is a rare, hereditary, metabolic disease in which the enzyme homogentisic acid oxidase is missing. Because of this defect, homogentisic acid produced during the metabolism of phenylalanine and tyrosine cannot be further metabolized; it therefore accumulates and is excreted in the urine.

If urine containing homogentisic acid is allowed to stand for some time, it gradually turns dark as the acid is oxidized to a melaninlike product (Fig. 27-1). The polymerization is speeded by alkali; this explains why washing diapers of alcaptonuric infants with soap tends to make the stains more intense instead of removing them.

It is not surprising that such an obvious sign as dark urine led to the early recognition of this disease. Several persons reported in the medical literature of the sixteenth and seventeenth centuries who continually passed dark urine are presumed to have had alcaptonuria (see Garrod[1]). It is of interest that an Egyptian mummy dated approximately 1500 B.C. showed the characteristic x-ray changes of alcaptonuria, i.e., extensive intervertebral disk calcification and narrowing of the hip and knee joints.[2] Spectral analysis of pigment obtained from the hip region of the mummy resembled closely the reference pigment obtained by oxidation of homogentisic acid. Although it was not possible to identify homogentisic acid in the tissues, this may well be the earliest case of alcaptonuria.

The first patient in whom the diagnosis was made with certainty was described by Boedeker in 1859.[3] He recognized that the reducing properties of his patient's urine were different from those of urine containing glucose (e.g., it did not reduce bismuth hydroxide), and he observed the darkening of the urine when alkali was added. He used the property of avid oxygen uptake in alkaline solution to give the substance a name.[3]

> . . . *in alkalischer Lösung bei gewöhnlicher Temperature den Sauerstoff begierig zu verschlucken und nannte ihn danach Alcapton (freilich recht barbarisch zusammengesetzt aus dem arabischen* alkali *und dem griechischen* καπτειν, *begierig verschlucken.)*

Two years later,[4] Boedeker spelled it "Alkapton," and since then this condition has been known as *Alkaptonurie* in the Ger-

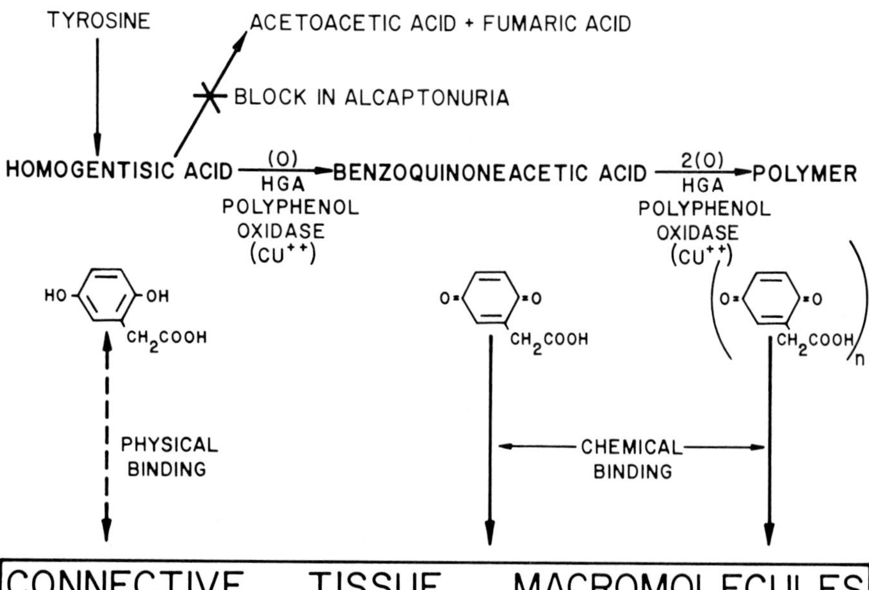

Fig. 27-1 Postulated scheme for the formation of ochronotic pigment in alcaptonuria. (*From Zannoni et al.*[60])

man literature and as *alcaptonurie* in the French. Both *c* and *k* have been used by writers in English.*

Boedeker precipitated homogentisic acid from alcaptonuric urine as the lead salt,[3,5] but he was unable to obtain enough material to purify it and determine its exact chemical structure. He did point out the similarity of its behavior in alkali with that of known hydroxyphenols.

During the following 30 years there was considerable confusion as to the chemical structure of "alkapton." It was variously reported by different groups to be catechol,[6,7] protocatechuic acid,[8] "glycosuric acid,"[9] and uroleucic acid.[10] The various claims and disputes about its composition during this period are well summarized in a review by Knox.[11] The controversy ended and the chemical structure of "alcapton" was firmly established in 1891 by the excellent work of Wolkow and Baumann.[12] They identified it as 2,5-dihydroxyphenylacetic acid and named it *homogentisic acid* because of its close structural relationship to gentisic acid (2,5-dihydroxybenzoic acid). The earlier reports of other substances, such as uroleucic acid, in alcaptonuric urine were shown to be the result of analytic errors from contamination with various normal urinary constituents.[13]

Once the aromatic structure of homogentisic acid was known, it was not long before various suggestions were made as to the source of this unusual urinary product. The known aromatic substances in proteins, tyrosine and phenylalanine, were, of course, the primary suspects (Fig. 27-2). Wolkow and Baumann demonstrated in 1891[12] that feeding either extra tyrosine or a diet high in protein greatly increased the amount of homogentisic acid excreted by an alcaptonuric patient. Even though they were incorrect in believing that the formation of homogentisic acid was due to the activity of bacteria in the intestine, their important observations initiated a number of studies by clinical investigators of that time, who used the metabolic defect in alcaptonuric individuals to determine the pathway by which phenylalanine and tyrosine are metabolized to homogentisic acid. Numerous compounds that were possible intermediary substances in the formation of homogentisic acid were fed to alcaptonuric patients. It was expected that compounds in the metabolic sequence would increase the excretion of homogentisic acid but that those which were not intermediates would fail to do so. On the basis of such studies Neubauer suggested a preliminary scheme of tyrosine metabolism in 1909,[14] the first such scheme for any of the amino acids. In 1928[15], he revised it to incorporate the results obtained during the intervening years (Fig. 27-3). Although a few changes have been made since then, the basic scheme which he postulated has remained essentially unchanged during the last 60 years.

Studies on alcaptonuria have been of great importance in the development of ideas about diseases of metabolism. As a result of his studies on alcaptonuria, Sir Archibald Garrod developed his whole concept of inheritable metabolic diseases. In 1908 he discussed alcaptonuria in one of the Croonian Lectures,[1] and in the following year he expanded his ideas more completely in his classic book, *Inborn Errors of Metabolism.*[13] He thought of alcaptonuria as a metabolic "freak" or "sport," comparable to a structural abnormality, rather than as a disease in the usual sense. He felt that patterns of metabolism varied in each individual according to hereditary background and that alcaptonuria and the other inborn errors of metabolism represented extreme examples of such variant possibilities.[16] He suspected that these variations ultimately might depend upon differences in the activity of specific enzymes, thus anticipating by many years the conclusion of Beadle and Tatum[17] that a single defective gene is correlated with a metabolic block in one enzymatic reaction.

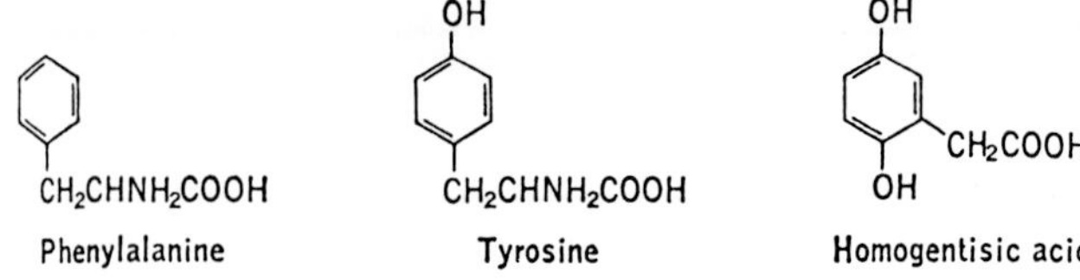

Fig. 27-2 Formulas of phenylalanine, tyrosine, and homogentisic acid.

Fig. 27-3 Scheme of phenylalanine and tyrosine metabolism to homogentisic acid based on feeding experiments with alcaptonuric patients. The dotted arrows show various pathways considered possible by Neubauer;[15] the solid arrows indicate the pathway as it is viewed today. (*From Neubauer.*[15])

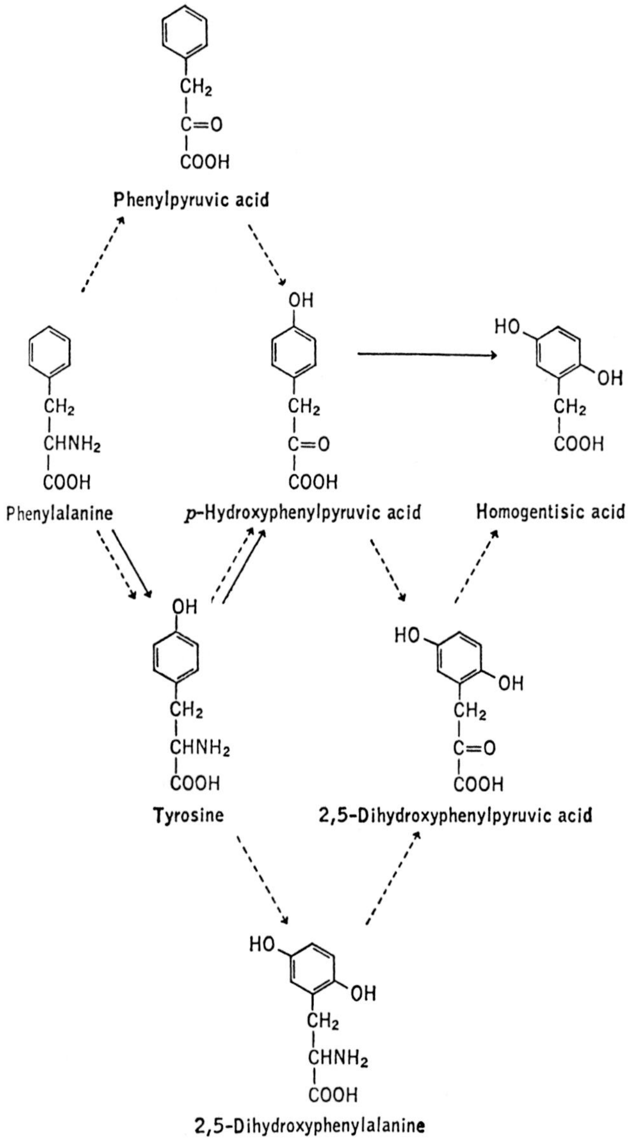

Phenylpyruvic acid

Phenylalanine

p-Hydroxyphenylpyruvic acid

Homogentisic acid

Tyrosine

2,5-Dihydroxyphenylpyruvic acid

2,5-Dihydroxyphenylalanine

*Several medical dictionaries erroneously assume *alkapton* to be derived from *alkali* and the Greek root ἅπτω meaning to seize, to possess; the combination, therefore, meaning "to have an affinity for alkali." *The Oxford English Dictionary*[4] gives the correct origin and indicates that the *k* of alkaptonuria comes from the Greek root κάπτω rather than from alkali. Transliteration of the *k* to *c*, therefore, follows the same pattern used in many words derived from similar Greek roots.

In 1909 Garrod[13] wrote of the probable defect in alcaptonuria:

> We may further conceive that the splitting of the benzene ring in normal metabolism is the work of a special enzyme, that in congenital alcaptonuria this enzyme is wanting, whilst in disease its working may be partially or even completely inhibited. The experiments of G. Embden and others upon perfusion of the liver suggest that organ as the most probable seat of the change.

Garrod's supposition that a specific enzyme is missing in alcaptonuria has been supported through the years by many types of circumstantial evidence and was confirmed in 1958 by direct biochemical assay of alcaptonuric liver preparations.[18]

CLINICAL FEATURES

The cardinal features of alcaptonuria are signs due to the presence of homogentisic acid in the urine, pigmentation of cartilage and other connective tissues, and nearly always, in later years, arthritis.[19] The metabolic disorder does not appear to reduce the normal life span of affected subjects.[20]

Urinary Changes

According to the usual textbook description, people with alcaptonuria give a history of dark urine or urine which turns dark on standing. It should be emphasized that in a large number of alcaptonuric patients this finding is not observed. Many patients have never noted any abnormality in the color of their urine during childhood,[21–23] and diagnosis has been made only after they sought treatment for arthritis during their later years.[22–27] In some cases diagnosis has followed a false positive test for diabetes[22,26] or the finding of the unusual and distinctive x-ray changes in the spine.[28] In others the disease has not been suspected until a surgical procedure has revealed marked pigmentation of the cartilage.[29]

Alcaptonuric individuals on a normal diet void a urine which at first is not an abnormal color and which does not darken for many hours if it remains at an acid pH. This is true even for patients with extensive ochronosis. It appears, therefore, that in those instances in which freshly voided urine turns dark quickly, additional factors must be involved. Two factors that would favor rapid darkening are the excretion of an alkaline urine and a lower concentration than normal of vitamin C and possibly other reducing agents usually present in urine. It is well known that vitamin C protects homogentisic acid against oxidation, and in the past vitamin C has been suggested as a therapeutic agent because of this property.[30]

The unusual findings in alcaptonuric urine can all be attributed to one abnormal constituent, homogentisic acid. No abnormal amino acid pattern[21] or other tyrosine metabolic products are found.[31] It has been reported that an alcaptonuric patient excreting about 7 g homogentisic acid also excreted about 0.5 mg gentisic acid per day.[32] The conversion of small amounts of homogentisic acid to gentisic acid has been demonstrated in homogenates of rabbit liver.[33,34]

The various diagnostic tests for alcaptonuria by urinalysis are all based upon the detection of homogentisic acid through its unusual chemical properties. Its ease of oxidation results in a gradual darkening of the urine downward from the surface until the entire sample is dark brown; this darkening is greatly accelerated by alkali. Further evidence of its ease of oxidation is the behavior of alcaptonuric urine in its reaction with Benedict's sugar reagent. Homogentisic acid not only reduces the copper reagent to yield a yellow-orange precipitate, but it also undergoes darkening because of the alkalinity of the reagent. The net effect is an orange precipitate in a muddy brown solution. The reduction of molybdate is the basis of the Briggs test, commonly used to follow the urinary excretion of homogentisic acid.[35] Reduction of silver in photographic paper emulsion has been used as a qualitative test[36] and as the basis of a quantitative method to measure this acid.[37] Homogentisic acid is not fermented by yeast, and it does not fluoresce under ultraviolet light.

A presumptive diagnosis of alcaptonuria can be made on the basis of the results of these nonspecific tests, but a more specific means for its identification is desirable. In many cases, homogentisic acid has been isolated from the urine after precipitation as the lead salt[31,38] and the product shown to have the correct chemical composition and melting point. Paper chromatography of the urine directly, or of the product obtained by extracting acidified urine with ether, furnishes a simple technique to identify homogentisic acid.[39] A specific enzymatic method has been developed[40] that permits the quantitative analysis of homogentisic acid in urine, blood, and other tissues,[40,41] and a colorimetric method is also available.[42]

Ochronosis

In 1866 Virchow described a peculiar type of generalized pigmentation in the connective tissues of a 67-year-old man.[43] The pigment was gray to bluish black grossly but ochre microscopically, and for this reason, he named the condition *ochronosis*. Although the patient's clinical history is not known, it is quite certain that Virchow described for the first time the generalized pigmentation that gradually develops in alcaptonuria. Actually it was not until nearly 40 years later that Albrecht, in 1902,[44] clearly demonstrated the connection between ochronosis and alcaptonuria. Not long after, Osler diagnosed ochronosis clinically for the first time in two alcaptonuric brothers.[45] He recognized that the pigmentation of the scleras and ears were signs of the same metabolic abnormality that had previously been detected only by changes in the urine. Perhaps it is not unexpected that there was such a delay in the clinical recognition of the ochronotic pigmentation in alcaptonuria. Generally the earliest change that can be detected externally is a slight pigmentation of the scleras or the ears, but these changes are rarely noticeable before the alcaptonuric patient is 20 or 30 years old. The eye pigmentation is usually found about midway between the cornea and outer and inner canthi, at the site of the insertions of the rectus muscles (Fig. 27-4). In addition, a more diffuse pigmentation may also involve the conjunctiva and cornea.[47] The typical pigmentary changes in the ear cartilages similarly occur only in long-standing alcaptonuria. The cartilage is slate blue or gray and feels irregular and thickened. It is first seen in the concha and the antihelix, and later in the tragus. It is sometimes reported that a dusky discoloration, corresponding to the underlying tendons, can be seen through the skin over the hands. The prominence of this pigmentation is variable, and in many instances it is scarcely evident at all. The pigment appears in perspiration; clothing near the axillary regions may be stained, and the skin may have a brownish discoloration in the axillary and genital regions.[28]

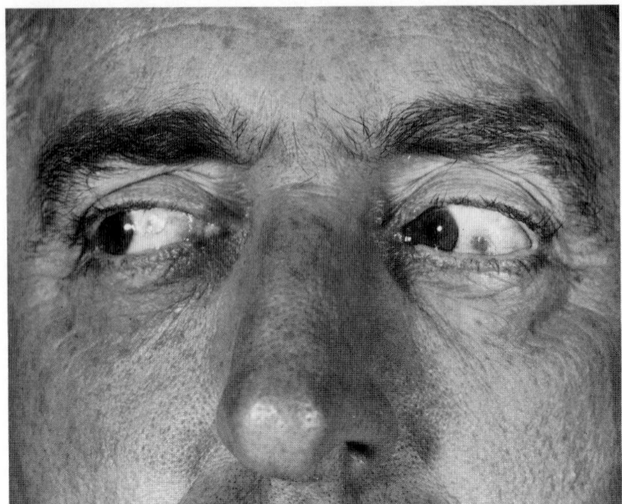

Fig. 27-4 The bilateral deposition of ochronotic pigment in the scleras, best seen in the left eye. (*From Bunim.*[46])

In contrast to these rather minimal findings, the pigmentation observed in the tissues of an elderly alcaptonuric patient at operation or at postmortem is indeed striking.[43,48–51] Cartilage in many areas, particularly the costal, laryngeal, and tracheal cartilage, is densely pigmented and is described as being coal black in some areas. Pigmentation is also present throughout the body in fibrous tissues, fibrocartilage, tendons, and ligaments (Fig. 27-5). To a lesser degree it is also found in the endocardium, the intima of the larger vessels, in various organs such as kidney and lung, and in the epidermis. Microscopic examination shows the pigment to be deposited both intercellularly and intracellularly, and it may be either granular or homogeneous. Electron microscopy of alcaptonuric synovial membranes,[52] hip joint tissue,[53] and articular cartilage[54] shows in greater detail the fragments of cartilage stained with pigment derived from homogentisic acid. Like melanin, the ochronotic pigment is bleached when treated for 24 h with hydrogen peroxide, and it is soluble in alkali, but only slightly soluble in hydrochloric acid. Thus, in many of its chemical characteristics the ochronotic pigment resembles melanin arising from 3,4-dihydroxyphenylalanine (dopa). Unfortunately there is no specific stain to distinguish the ochronotic pigment of alcaptonuria from melanin derived from other sources. Although Fitzpatrick and Lerner[55] state that Becker's silver stain for melanin is not darkened by ochronotic pigment and that the latter is stained intensely black with polychrome methylene blue, Cooper and Moran[50] compared the staining properties of ochronotic pigment and melanin, employing a number of special stains. They concluded that no specific differentiation can be made with any of the stains used. Both pigments were best detected by the Nile blue stains of Lillie.[56] Variations with trichrome, cresyl violet, and the periodic acid-Schiff (PAS) stains seemed to depend mainly upon the differences in the amount of pigment present rather than the type of pigment represented.

Fig. 27-5 Ochronotic pigmentation of the femur of a 56-year-old alcaptonuric patient. (*Courtesy of Dr. H.W. Edmonds of the Washington Hospital Center, Washington, D.C.*)

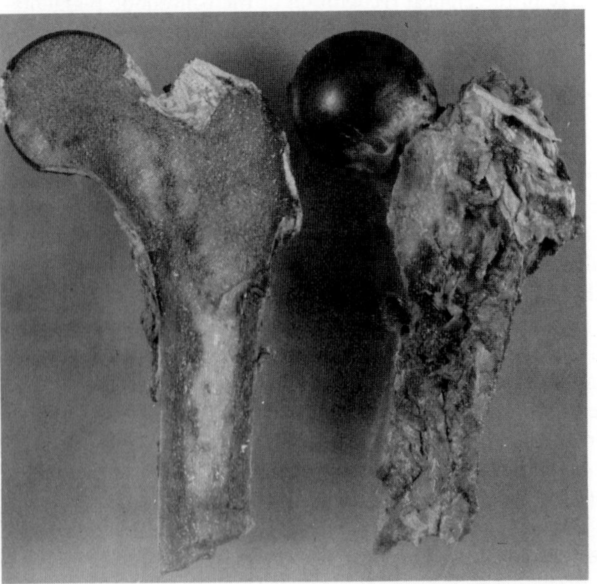

The pigment deposited in ochronosis is presumably a polymer derived from homogentisic acid, but its exact chemical structure has not yet been determined. It is possible that some other constituents, in addition to homogentisic acid, are included in the product, just as melanin obviously contains more than a polymerized dopa unit, i.e., a considerable quantity of sulfur.[57]

The formation of the pigment in the tissues may be entirely nonenzymatic, like the darkening of alcaptonuric urine. Solutions of pure homogentisic acid, made alkaline and aerated with air or oxygen, form a dark-brown product which has an ultraviolet absorption peak at 250 mμ (Milch et al.[58]). Unfortunately, the pigment deposited in the tissues of an alcaptonuric patient with ochronosis has not been analyzed in the same way, and so the relevance of the model polymerization to the in vivo process has not been established. Milch and Titus[59] have suggested that since polymerization of pure homogentisic acid solutions does not proceed at neutral pH and low partial pressure of oxygen (as occurs in cartilage), it is likely that if molecular oxygen is involved in vivo, it involves the participation of an enzyme system present locally. This conclusion assumes not only that the composition steps of formation of the ochronotic pigment would be the same in vivo as in solutions of pure homogentisic acid but that the pigment is both formed and deposited within the cartilage. It is not possible today to say to what degree enzymes play a role in the synthesis of the ochronotic pigmentation in alcaptonuria, although on the basis of their specificity, it seems reasonable to exclude the enzymes involved in the synthesis of melanin by way of dopa.

Mammalian (human, rabbit, and guinea pig) skin and cartilage contain an enzyme called *homogentisic acid polyphenol oxidase* which catalyzes the oxidation of homogentisic acid to an ochronotic-like pigment.[60] Benzoquinoneacetic acid has been identified as an intermediary metabolite in the oxidation. The enzyme is a copper-protein, but it is clearly distinguished from tyrosinase by the finding that tyrosine, dopa, and other catechols are not substrates for the polyphenol oxidase. Earlier studies by La Du and Zannoni[61] demonstrated that ρ-quinones, such as benzoquinoneacetic acid, can form 1,4 addition products with sulfhydryl groups, and Stoner and Blivaiss[62] observed similar derivatives with the amino groups of glycine. Binding and chemical reactions of benzoquinone (or polymers derived from the acid) with the connective tissues may produce important chemical changes that alter tissue constituents and lead to ochronosis and ochronotic arthritis.[63] A possible scheme for the enzymatic oxidation of homogentisic acid and the formation of ochronotic pigment in the connective tissues of alcaptonuric patients is given in Fig. 27-1.

Ochronosis Not Due to Homogentisic Acid

Clinically, ochronosis due to alcaptonuria might possibly be confused with the pigmentation of the skin, nail beds, conjunctivas, and cartilage seen in persons who have taken Atabrine for many months.[64] Of course the history and the failure to find homogentisic acid in the urine should establish the diagnosis.

Another type of acquired ochronosis is that which is secondary to the prolonged use of carbolic acid dressings for chronic cutaneous ulcers.[66–71] This pigmentation is reversible and recedes after medication is discontinued, but this treatment is rarely used today. A related chemical, hydroquinone, is the active ingredient in a number of skin-lightening creams and lotions. Chronic use of these preparations leads to a chemically induced ochronosis.[72–74] Associated inflammatory changes in the treated skin produce papular lesions that persist, although the hyperpigmentation gradually fades after hydroquinone treatment is discontinued.

Nearly all the cases of ochronosis seen now are secondary to alcaptonuria. There are, however, a few puzzling cases of ochronosis in the literature in which exogenous agents, such as phenol, can probably safely be excluded as causative agents and in which the urine is reported to contain no homogentisic acid.[75,76] In the case described by Oppenheimer and Kline,[75] a determined effort to isolate homogentisic acid from the urine was made by Janney.[77] He concluded that this was an example of ochronosis secondary to a melanuria, but no aromatic metabolite related to dopa was identified in the urine. He was able to isolate a melanin-like pigment from the urine and from a prostatic calculus which had, by elementary analysis, much the same values as those reported by Mörner[57] for melanin obtained from the urine and tumor tissue of a patient with a melanosarcoma. It is possible that melanotic tumors might cause a generalized ochronosis also, but it is unlikely that a patient with such a condition would survive long enough for this complication to become evident.[67] In one case of alcaptonuria the ochronotic pigment in the eye was misdiagnosed as a melanosarcoma, and the eye was removed.[78]

On the other hand, instances in which alcaptonuria, unaccompanied by ochronosis, has been diagnosed with certainty are extremely rare. From the nature and completeness of the metabolic defect one would expect that all alcaptonuric patients would develop ochronosis to some degree if they live to middle age. The two patients with alcaptonuria who did not have ochronosis at autopsy[79,80] had extensive tuberculosis. No mention was made of ochronotic changes in their connective tissues, but it is unlikely that if they were present to the degree found in most alcaptonuric patients, they would have gone unnoticed.

Arthritis

"Ochronotic arthritis" is a manifestation of long-standing alcaptonuria. From the case reports in the literature, it appears that alcaptonuric arthritis occurs at an earlier age and is more severe in males than in females,[81] even though the sex incidence of alcaptonuria is roughly equal. This sex difference in ochronotic arthritis is reminiscent of the similar preponderance of gouty arthritis in males. Hench[82] has stated that ochronotic arthritis resembles rheumatoid arthritis clinically but resembles osteoarthritis roentgenographically. The earliest symptoms observed are usually some degree of limitation of motion of the hip, knee joints, or occasionally, the shoulders. There are nearly always periods of acute inflammation which may resemble rheumatoid arthritis, and later there is usually rather marked limitation of motion and ankylosis in the lumbosacral region.

X-rays may reveal changes considered almost pathognomonic of alcaptonuria.[28] The vertebral bodies of the lumbar spine show degeneration of the intervertebral disks with a narrowing of the space and dense calcification of the remaining disk material (Fig. 27-6). This is accompanied to a variable degree by fusion of the vertebral bodies. From the x-ray changes in the lumbar spine alone, it is often possible to be reasonably certain of the diagnosis of alcaptonuria. In contrast to rheumatoid spondylitis, little osteophyte formation and minimal calcification of the intervertebral ligaments are present. The large peripheral joints involved also differ from osteoarthritis in that the degenerative joint changes in ochronotic arthritis are most commonly in the shoulder and hip, whereas such joints as the sacroiliac may be completely spared.

Calcification of the ear cartilage is another sign of the disease that may be observed by x-ray. The large joints affected generally show degenerative osteoarthritic changes with calcified deposits most commonly in the muscle tendons around the large joints. Occasionally free intraarticular bodies are found.[83] By contrast, the smaller joints usually show little or no abnormality.

The common occurrence of arthritis in the general population and the long period before its onset in patients with alcaptonuria no doubt account for the failure of the earlier investigators to appreciate the association of arthritis with alcaptonuria. The first case described by Boedeker was reported to have neuralgia of the lower lumbar spine. The early investigators considered alcaptonuria a completely benign disease without symptoms and of clinical importance only in that it might be misdiagnosed as diabetes. A review of the earlier case reports shows that in most instances osteoarthritis was mentioned, and, indeed, nearly all alcaptonuric patients develop arthritis during their later years. The arthritic complications are often severe and painful and may lead to a completely bedridden existence in later life.

The relationship between the deposition of pigment in the connective tissue and the degenerative changes which occur in some areas of the connective tissues, particularly the cartilage and the intervertebral disks, remains unknown. It has been proposed that the pigment acts as a chemical irritant to accel-

Fig. 27-6 Roentgenograms of the spine showing the typical narrowing and calcification of the intervertebral disks. (*From Bunim.*[46])

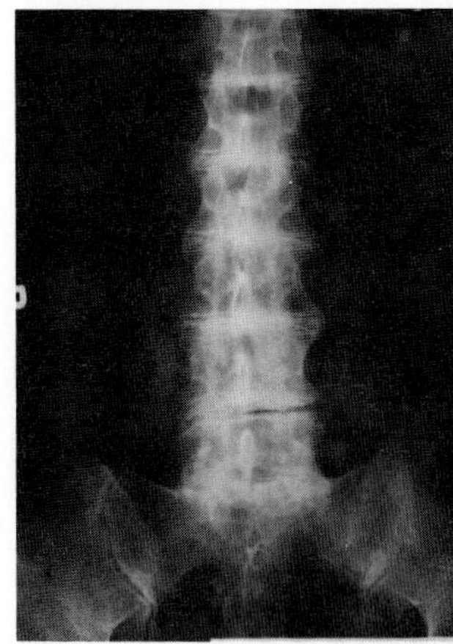

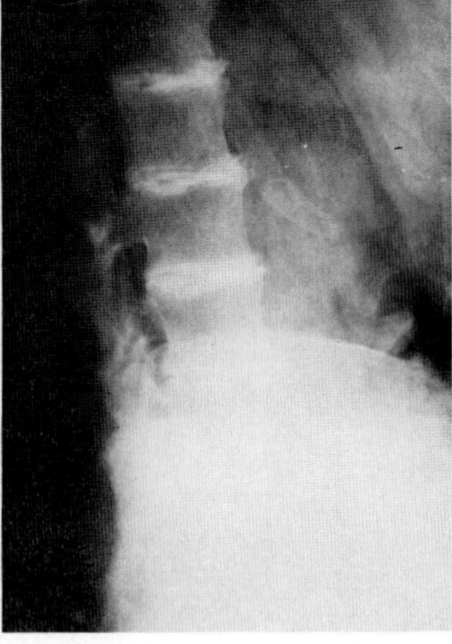

erate a degenerative process in the cartilage, leading to changes similar to those in osteoarthritis.[25,83] The intraarticular injection of homogentisic acid into the knee joints of rabbits produced local lesions in cartilage and the soft tissues resembling those seen in alcaptonuria.[84] It is also possible that either the ochronotic pigment or homogentisic acid itself might inhibit some of the enzyme systems involved in cartilage metabolism. Greiling[85] has shown that low concentrations of the pigment prepared by treating homogentisic acid with alkali inhibit the action of hyaluronidase on chondroitin sulfuric acid and on hyaluronic acid, but homogentisic acid does not act as an inhibitor at the same concentrations. More recently, Dihlmann et al.[86] and Murray et al.[87] have extended these studies and noted the inhibition of several additional enzymes, particularly glutamic dehydrogenase, hexokinase, and malate dehydrogenase by the oxidized, polymerized product of homogentisic acid.

Inhibition of lysyl hydroxylase[87] may be particularly important, since this would reduce the amount of hydroxylysine and the number of cross-linkage bonds, which are essential for the tensile strength of collagen fibers. Reducing agents, such as ascorbic acid and 1,4-dithiothreitol, competitively protect against inhibition of lysyl hydroxylase in the chick embryo, so the actual inhibitory agent may be an oxidation product of homogentisic acid, such as benzoquinoneacetic acid.

Other workers have evaluated the effects of homogentisic acid on articular chondrocytes.[88] Cytotoxic effects were noted with rabbit adult articular chondrocytes at homogentisic acid concentrations of 5 μg/ml or above; effects were seen with fetal articular chondrocytes at concentrations of 1 μg/ml. Another laboratory[89] has shown that hyaline cartilage incubated with the polymerized products of homogentisic acid oxidation develops an increased hardness and decreased elasticity. It is suggested that these changes, along with mechanical stress to the large joints, lead to cartilage destruction.

Other Findings in Alcaptonuria

In addition to the features mentioned above, other complications seem to occur in alcaptonuric patients with a greater frequency than might be anticipated in the general population. The relationship between ochronosis and cardiovascular disease is not clearly established, but a review of the case histo-

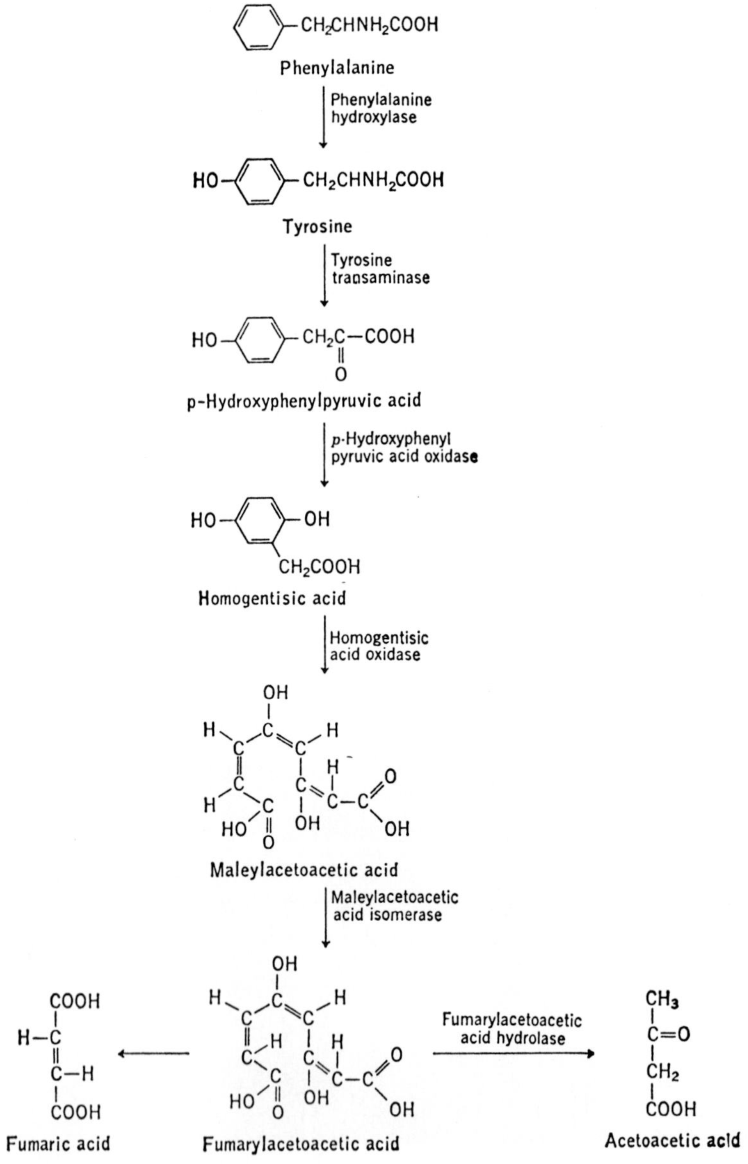

Phenylalanine
Phenylalanine hydroxylase
Tyrosine
Tyrosine transaminase
p-Hydroxyphenylpyruvic acid
p-Hydroxyphenyl pyruvic acid oxidase
Homogentisic acid
Homogentisic acid oxidase
Maleylacetoacetic acid
Maleylacetoacetic acid isomerase
Fumarylacetoacetic acid
Fumarylacetoacetic acid hydrolase
Fumaric acid
Acetoacetic acid

Fig. 27-7 Enzymatic steps in the oxidation of phenylalanine and tyrosine to acetoacetic acid.

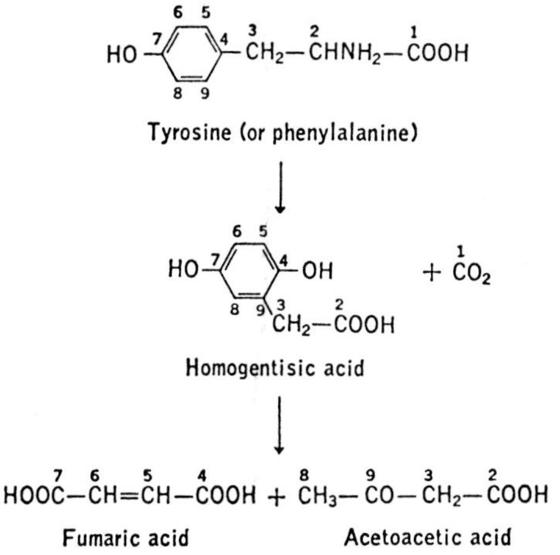

HO–C_6H_4–$\overset{3}{CH_2}$–$\overset{2}{CHNH_2}$–$\overset{1}{COOH}$

Tyrosine (or phenylalanine)

↓

HO–C_6H_3(OH)–$\overset{3}{CH_2}$–$\overset{2}{COOH}$ + $\overset{1}{CO_2}$

Homogentisic acid

↓

$\overset{7}{HOOC}$–$\overset{6}{CH}$=$\overset{5}{CH}$–$\overset{4}{COOH}$ + $\overset{8}{CH_3}$–$\overset{9}{CO}$–$\overset{3}{CH_2}$–$\overset{2}{COOH}$

Fumaric acid   Acetoacetic acid

Fig. 27-8 Fate of each of the carbon atoms of phenylalanine or tyrosine based on experiments with the amino acids labeled with isotopic carbon.

ries of alcaptonuric patients indicates that there is a high incidence of heart disease.[26] In 1910 Beddard[69] tabulated the autopsy findings in 11 cases of ochronosis (none due to treatment with phenol) and found that 8 had chronic mitral and aortic valvulitis, 1 had an aortic aneurysm, and 1 an aneurysm of the left ventricle. Other investigators[48,90] have noted generalized arteriosclerosis and calcification in the heart valves and of the annulus of the aortic and mitral valves.[49,91] Myocardial infarction is a common cause of death in this group.

Other complications reported in alcaptonuric patients are ruptured intervertebral disks[92] and prostatitis[21,26,75,93] or renal stones (see Young[93]). Clinical case reports on new cases of alcaptonuria should be encouraged in order that additional phenomena related to this metabolic disease may be revealed. One case of alcaptonuria with polycythemia,[94] one with nephrocalcinosis,[95] and one with severe renal disease, called "ochronotic nephrosis,"[50] remain isolated examples, presumably because of chance association with other diseases. It should be kept in mind that conditions which favor the expression of alcaptonuria, such as consanguine marriages, would also favor the manifestation of other recessive but unrelated traits.

SYNTHESIS AND DEGRADATION OF HOMOGENTISIC ACID

Biosynthesis

In mammals most of the dietary phenylalanine and tyrosine is oxidized to acetoacetic acid by enzyme systems localized primarily in the liver and kidney. The scheme of this metabolic pathway is shown in Fig. 27-7. Several excellent reviews of phenylalanine and tyrosine metabolism have appeared.[96–99] These may be consulted for the detailed experimental evidence supporting each of the steps in this scheme. As mentioned above, the scheme is based upon the earlier studies with alcaptonuric patients and many animal experiments in vivo. It has been revised and extended particularly during the past 30 years by a large number of experiments on tyrosine metabolism in vitro.

In some of these in vitro studies, isotopically labeled phenylalanine and tyrosine were used to determine the fate of each of the carbon atoms in the aromatic ring and of the side chain.[100–104] The labeled amino acids were incubated with liver slices, and the distribution of the isotope was determined in the products CO_2, acetoacetic acid, and fumaric acid. These experiments showed that two of the four carbon atoms of acetoacetic acid were derived from carbon atoms 2 and 3 of the side chain and that the other two came from the ring. Furthermore, the position of the isotope from the ring carbon atoms indicated that the side chain must have migrated during the oxidation (Fig. 27-8). The isotopic evidence was entirely in agreement with the scheme postulated earlier by Neubauer[15] (Fig. 27-3), to account for the 2,5-dihydroxyphenyl intermediary product, homogentisic acid, from the 4-hydroxyphenyl substrates. This rearrangement was believed to involve a quinol intermediate with a migration of the side chain much like the migration of the methyl group in the oxidation of *p*-cresol[105] (Fig. 27-9). This unusual migration in the oxidation of *p*-hydroxyphenylpyruvic acid to homogentisic acid is, even today, the least understood step of any in the scheme shown in Fig. 27-7. So far, it has not been possible to identify a free intermediate in this step. It appears as though the hydroxylation of the ring and the migration and oxidative decarboxylation of the side chain all take place as a complicated single step.[106–108]

Homogentisic Acid As a Normal Intermediate

The presence of homogentisic acid as a normal intermediate in the scheme deserves further comment. It should be recalled that in 1911 Dakin[109] suggested that not only was homogentisic acid an abnormal urinary product but its formation resulted from the metabolism of tyrosine by an abnormal pathway in alcaptonuria. The main support for this proposal was that when he fed animals and an alcaptonuric patient[110,111] derivatives of phenylalanine and tyrosine (*p*-methylphenylalanine and *p*-methoxyphenylalanine), which because of their *para*-substitute could not form quinol intermediates, he found them to be well metabolized (in his view, by the normal pathway of tyrosine metabolism). He also found that these compounds caused an increase in acetoacetic acid when perfused through dog liver, as did phenylalanine and tyrosine. Although Dakin's results remained unexplained, through the years more and more evidence has accumulated that homogentisic acid is indeed a normal intermediate. For example, it was shown that some homogentisic acid accumulated from tyrosine in rat liver homogenates under certain experimental conditions[39,97]; more recently, it was shown that homogentisic acid accumulated quantitatively from tyrosine or *p*-hydroxyphenylpyruvic acid in preparations of dog liver[112] and human liver[18] in the presence of α,α'-dipyridyl an inhibitor of homogentisic acid oxi-

Fig. 27-9 Formation of quinol intermediate and migration of the substituent (CH_3 in *p*-cresol or side chain) in *p*-hydroxyphenylpyruvic acid oxidation.

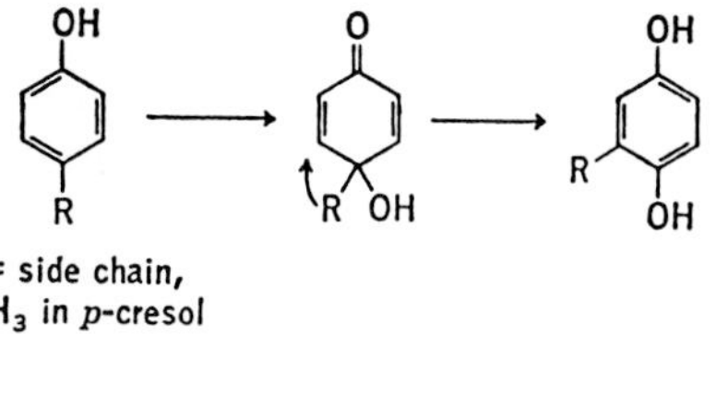

[Structures: OH/R phenol → O/R OH quinol → OH/R/OH hydroquinone]

R = side chain, or CH_3 in *p*-cresol

dase. Homogentisic acid oxidase is widely distributed in nature, and where it occurs, it is associated with the other enzymes involved in the oxidation of tyrosine to acetoacetic acid.

There still remained the problem of explaining Dakin's results. In 1957 Pirrung et al.[113] reinvestigated the ketogenic effect of the tyrosine analogues. They found that *p*-methoxy-DL-phenylalanine is not ketogenic and that neither the L form nor *P*-methoxyphenylalanine was metabolized, although the D isomer was deaminated in dog liver. They attributed the earlier results of Wakeman and Dakin[111] to be the ketogenic effect of the ammonium ion released by the deamination of the D component. (The ketogenic effect of ammonium ion[114] was not known in 1911.) It must also be inferred from these results that Dakin did not have sufficiently sensitive methods to detect the excretion of the unchanged compounds in the urine. The present scheme of tyrosine oxidation (Fig. 27-7) is therefore very much like that of Neubauer (Fig. 27-3) in the steps leading to the formation of homogentisic acid, with the notable exception that neither 2,5-dihydroxyphenylaline nor 2,5-dihydroxyphenylpyruvic acid is now considered a likely intermediate. Both of these compounds produced extra homogentisic acid when fed to alcaptonuric patients,[14,31] but they were found to be inactive as substrates when tested with mammalian liver preparations which oxidize tyrosine or *p*-hydroxyphenylpyruvic acid to homogenistic acid.[18,39,112,115] These results also exclude the alternative pathway suggested by Neuberger in 1947, in which tyrosine would be oxidized first to 2,5-dihydroxyphenylalanine and then either through 2,5-dihydroxyphenylpyruvic acid or 2,5-dihydroxyphenylethylamine to homogentisic acid.[116]

Metabolic Defect in Alcaptonuria

Even though Garrod suggested in 1909[13] that the metabolic defect in alcaptonuria was the absence of the liver enzyme catalyzing the oxidation of homogentisic acid, other possible explanations have been offered from time to time by other workers. At the time Garrod presented his theory, it was quite generally believed that alcaptonuria was due to the formation of homogentisic acid by intestinal organisms. This opinion was based upon an assumption of Wolkow and Baumann[12] that the synthesis of homogentisic acid from tyrosine or phenylalanine was too complicated to be accomplished by human tissues and therefore must have resulted from the action of bacteria in the intestine.

In 1914 Gross[117] presented evidence for an enzymatic defect in alcaptonuria. He reported that homogentisic acid did not disappear when it was incubated with the serum from an alcaptonuric patient, whereas it did disappear when incubated with the serum from normal individuals, presumably because of the presence in normal serum of a homogentisic acid-oxidizing enzyme. A few years later Katsch and Stern[118] suggested that the results of Gross were due not to an enzyme that was missing in alcaptonuric serum but to the presence of an inhibitor in alcaptonuric blood. Both these findings were disputed by Lanyar and Lieb,[119] who pointed out that the previous workers had not controlled the experimental conditions satisfactorily, particularly the pH, and that auto-oxidation of homogentisic acid probably accounted for their results. It is now certain that Gross's results were in error, since plasma contains no detectable homogentisic acid oxidase.[40]

Another proposal as to the nature of the defect was that of Dakin,[109] as discussed above; he considered that the whole pathway to homogentisic acid in alcaptonuric patients is abnormal. Neuberger et al.[31] suggested that perhaps the alcaptonuric kidney differs from the normal kidney in having the capacity to secrete homogentisic acid actively while the normal kidney might not, and that this unusual renal defect might account for the abnormal urinary product (see Dent[120]). However, throughout the last 65 years, Garrod's suggestion that a liver enzyme is missing has been generally considered the most reasonable hypothesis. It was obvious that the net effect would be the same whether the enzyme itself or a vital cofactor were missing or whether there was an inhibitor of the enzyme in alcaptonuric liver.

A careful analysis of the enzymes involved in tyrosine metabolism in normal and alcaptonuric liver showed that only homogentisic acid oxidase is missing in alcaptonuric liver and that all the other enzymes involved in tyrosine metabolism to acetoacetic acid are present and have about the same activity as in normal liver[18,46] (Table 27-1). Evidence was also obtained that the lack of activity is not due to the presence of inhibitor or to the lack of any known cofactor.[18] It now seems reasonable to define the defect in alcaptonuria as the failure to synthesize active homogentisic acid oxidase, and to attribute all the findings in alcaptonuria to this specific enzymatic defect. Whether these individuals form a catalytically inactive protein, differing perhaps only slightly in structure from active homogentisic acid oxidase, or whether they produce no protein at all resembling the enzyme is still unknown.

Later, the opportunity to obtain at autopsy samples of kidney tissue from two alcaptonuric patients made it possible to show that homogentisic acid oxidase is also absent in alcaptonuric kidney, but that the other enzymes involved in the oxidation of tyrosine to acetoacetic acid can easily be detected.[121] Homogentisic acid oxidase could be demonstrated in nonalcaptonuric human kidney autopsy samples. Thus, the genetic defect in alcaptonuria is not limited to the synthesis of homogentisic acid oxidase in liver; it appears to affect the synthesis of the enzyme wherever it is normally present. This is of theoretical interest from the viewpoint of the genetic control and tissue specificity of enzymes,[123,124] and it may be of some practical value in the detection of the carrier trait in relatives of alcaptonuric patients. It might be possible to show a decreased amount of enzyme in carriers of the trait by a direct assay of the enzymes in a tissue more accessible than liver or kidney. This would perhaps be a more accurate means to measure the enzyme than to determine it indirectly by the rate of metabolism of homogentisic acid in a tolerance test.

Table 27-1 Activity of Tyrosine Oxidation Enzymes in Alcaptonuric and Nonalcaptonuric Human Liver Homogenate

	Enzyme activity, μmol substrate oxidized/(h • g) liver	
Enzymes	*Nonalcaptonuric*	*Alcaptonuric*
Tyrosine transaminase	36	32
p-Hydroxyphenylpyruvic acid oxidase	67	46
Homogentisic acid oxidase	268	<0.048
Maleylacetoacetic acid isomerase*	960	780
Fumarylacetoacetic acid hydrolase	288	222

*Units calculated as Δ log density/(h • 0.1 g) wet weight liver.[122]
SOURCE: From La Du et al.[18]

[^{14}C]Carboxyl-labeled homogentisic acid injected intravenously in two alcaptonuric patients was over 90 percent excreted in the urine without change. In contrast, only 3.2 percent was excreted by a control patient, and over 95 percent was oxidized to $^{14}CO_2$ within 12 h.[125] The results support the conclusions from earlier enzymatic studies in vitro and metabolic balance studies in vivo that the enzymatic block is essentially complete in alcaptonuria.

The metabolic abnormality in alcaptonuria is present essentially from birth. Garrod noted in 1901[126] that staining of the diapers was scarcely evident 38 h after birth, although after 52 h they were deeply stained and continued to be thereafter. The reason for the delay in the excretion of homogentisic acid in newborn alcaptonuric patients is probably that the enzyme systems involved in tyrosine oxidation are not completely developed at birth but increase in activity during the first few days after birth.[127] Once established, the defect continues relentlessly throughout life. No therapeutic agent has been found that substantially alters the degree of the defect. The amount of homogentisic acid excreted per day is usually from 4 to 8 g; it can be altered by changing the content of phenylalanine and tyrosine in the diet. In starvation there is a marked decrease in homogentisic acid excretion,[128] as would be expected, although Mittlebach[129] showed that on a diet very low in protein, the alcaptonuric patient continued to excrete some homogentisic acid, presumably from the breakdown of tissue proteins.

Homogentisic Acid Oxidase

The enzymatic step which is missing in alcaptonuria is the further metabolism of homogentisic acid by an oxidative cleavage of the ring to yield maleylacetoacetic acid,[130] which in turn is isomerized enzymatically to fumarylacetoacetic acid[122,131,132] (Fig. 27-7). The next step is hydrolysis to fumaric and acetoacetic acids by an enzyme which appears to be the same as that shown to hydrolyze a number of α,γ-diketo acids by Meister and Greenstein[133] and to hydrolyze triacetic acid.[134,135]

In 1951, Suda and Takeda[136] solubilized an enzyme from a strain of *Pseudomonas* adapted to tyrosine which catalyzed the oxidation of homogentisic acid; they named it *homogentisicase*. They then studied the properties of a similar enzyme from rabbit liver.[137] Homogentisicase, or, as it is more generally called, homogentisic acid oxidase, has been purified to some degree in several laboratories, and many of its properties have been described.[130,138–140] It belongs to the class of oxygenases. In the cleavage of the benzene ring, both oxygen atoms come from atmospheric oxygen, as indicated in experiments with ^{18}O.[141] The enzyme contains essential sulfhydryl groups and requires ferrous iron,[137,142] as do several of the other oxygenases involved in ring cleavage reactions, such as pyrocatechase,[143,144] hydroxyanthranilate oxidase,[145] and protocatechuic acid oxidase[146,147] (see Mason,[148] p. 126). No other cofactors have been clearly implicated in this reaction. Although evidence that one did exist was presented by Suda and Takeda[137] in 1950, it now appears that a protective effect of glutathione may account for the earlier results.[149] There is also general agreement that the previously suggested requirement for ascorbic acid in this enzyme system[150] is an indirect one due to the requirement for ferrous iron. The only function that has been demonstrated for ascorbic acid in this reaction is to maintain iron in the reduced form.[137,151] Homogentisic acid oxidase activity in isolated rat hepatocytes depends upon the oxygen tension.[152] The enzyme is inhibited by various quinones,[139] by sulfhydryl-binding agents,[142] and by metal-chelating agents such as α,α'-dipyridyl and o-phenanthroline,[153] which reacts with ferrous iron.

Homogentisic acid oxidase activity can be measured manometrically, since the oxidation requires the uptake of two atoms of oxygen,[130,154] or it can be measured spectrophotometrically,[130] by following the absorption of the product maleylacetoacetic acid at 330 nm, provided the product is stable under the assay conditions. The enzyme is found in the soluble fraction of liver and kidney,[155] as are all the mammalian enzymes involved in the conversion of tyrosine to acetoacetic acid.[156] Homogentisic acid oxidase activity is highest in liver; there is less activity in kidney; and no significant activity has been found in any of the other tissues so far examined,[140,157] such as blood, salivary glands, germinal epithelium, and muscle. This general distribution pattern has been found in rat, rabbit, guinea pig, and pigeon.[140] In humans, too, it is highest in liver,[18] and appreciable activity is also present in kidney.[121] The liver of the toad, *Buffo marinus,* has as high homogentisic acid oxidase activity as that found in mammalian liver.[158] The presence of the enzyme in some microorganisms adapted to tyrosine has been previously mentioned.[136,159]

The optimal pH for this enzyme is about 7,[137,138] and it is specific for homogentisic acid. Closely related compounds, such as o-hydroxyphenylacetic acid, p-hydroxyphenylacetic acid, and gentisic acid are not oxidized,[138] nor are homogentisic acid ethyl ester and homogentisic acid lactone. The quinone formed by oxidizing homogentisic acid[160] does not appear to be an intermediate in the oxidation,[138] and, in fact, this quinone is an inhibitor of the enzyme.[138,161] The requirement for ferrous iron is apparently specific, since other bivalent metals, such as Co^{2+}, Zn^{2+}, Mg^{2+}, and Mn^{2+}, cannot replace it.[137,161]

A report in the German literature[162] that gentisic acid was less well metabolized in an alcaptonuric patient than in the normal person led Garrod to conclude that the enzyme system defective in alcaptonuria must catalyze the oxidation of some other 2,5-dihydroxyphenyl compounds, as well as homogentisic acid.[1] The specificity of the enzyme rules out this possibility, and the reason for the results in the original study is not known. It is possible that a larger percentage of gentisic acid is excreted as the free acid and less as conjugated derivatives in the alcaptonuric patient because of some inhibitory effect of homogentisic acid on the conjugation of gentisic acid and that for this reason less gentisic acid appeared to be metabolized. However, in one attempt to confirm this finding, the excretion of free gentisic acid was found to be about the same in an alcaptonuric patient as in nonalcaptonuric persons.[163]

Low concentrations of homogentisic acid have been identified in the urine and serum of nonalcaptonuric subjects by gas chromatography–mass spectrometry[164] following the administration of high doses of salicylates. Of course, gentisic acid is a normal, minor metabolite of salicylate; the presence of homogentisic acid is unexpected. The authors propose that gentisic acid or other metabolites of salicylate inhibit homogentisic acid oxidase to account for it.

Intermittent Alcaptonuria

There are a few reports in the literature of intermittent alcaptonuria, or instances in which it is reported that alcaptonuria has spontaneously disappeared (see Galdston et al.[48]). In view of the finding that alcaptonuria is associated with the lack of a specific enzyme, it is difficult to imagine how this hereditary condition would undergo intermittent exacerbations and remissions or a spontaneous cure. Perhaps some of these cases of "alcaptonuria" are misdiagnosed and have some other reducing substance present in the urine. Other cases may be examples in which some agent such as those described below, which can induce experimental alcaptonuria in animals, has altered the activity of the enzymes in this pathway, with resultant homogentisic acid excretion. Any further cases of alcaptonuria of this type should be carefully investigated with the specific methods now available to establish beyond any doubt that homogentisic acid is the reducing substance excreted in the urine. In 1948 Fishberg reported[165] that a patient with autotoxic enterogenous cyanosis excreted up to 0.5 g/day benzoquinoneacetic acid, the quinone corresponding to homogentisic acid. The amount excreted varied in inverse ratio to the ascorbic acid excretion. She also found, on the basis of nonspecific tests, that patients with rheumatic fever and with scurvy excrete a similar quinone capable of producing methemoglobinemia. These results have been questioned by Consden et al.,[166] who found no benzoquinoneacetic acid excreted in scorbutic guinea pigs or in patients with rheumatic fever. They suggest that bacterial activity in the urine leading to nitrite formation may have been responsible for the results of the qualitative tests employed by Fishberg. The excretion of benzoquinoneacetic acid in the case of enterogenous cyanosis cannot be explained in this way. They suggest that the product might have been homogentisic acid which was oxidized to the quinone by nitrite arising from bacterial activity. Others have found nitrite in the urine and blood of patients with enterogenous cyanosis.[167]

Metabolism of Homogentisic Acid

Under normal conditions no homogentisic acid is present in the urine, and none can be detected in plasma by the methods now available.[97] Leaf and Neuberger[168] found that feeding as much as 5 g homogentisic acid to normal adults produced no homogentisic aciduria. However, they found a transitory alcaptonuria following the intravenous injection of 0.3 or 1.0 g homogentisic acid. In these experiments the plasma concentration never rose above 15 mg/100 ml plasma, and it returned to normal values within 30 min.

One might expect to find elevated plasma levels of homogentisic acid in alcaptonuric patients in view of the large quantity of this acid excreted per day. Neuberger et al.[31] found, however, that in a 7-year-old alcaptonuric girl, the fasting plasma level was not more than about 3 mg/100 ml plasma and this level did not increase significantly following the oral administration of 3 g L-phenylalanine. Nevertheless, within 6 h approximately 85 percent of the given amino acid could be accounted for as homogentisic acid in the urine. Neuberger et al. made a very significant observation regarding the excretion of homogentisic acid during this investigation. The plasma clearance data indicated that unless a large fraction of the urinary homogentisic acid were both synthesized and excreted within the kidney, glomerular filtration alone could not begin to account for the rate of homogentisic acid excretion. In fact, the clearance approached 400 to 500 ml/min, about equal to the renal blood flow. Even though it is most unusual for a normally occurring intermediate to be actively secreted by the kidney, this seems to be true of homogentisic acid. This conclusion is in agreement with the earlier observation of Katsch and Metz[169] that intravenous homogentisic acid given to an alcaptonuric subject did not increase the plasma concentration significantly.

Experiments in La Du's laboratory[40] using an enzymatic assay to estimate plasma homogentisic acid have confirmed these conclusions. Alcaptonuric and nonalcaptonuric individuals were found to excrete homogentisic acid rapidly after oral administration, and the renal clearance data indicated active secretion by the kidney. The possibility[31,120] that there might be an important difference in the renal handling of homogentisic acid between normal individuals and alcaptonuric patients can be dismissed.

It appears that two factors serve to keep the plasma, and presumably the tissue, concentrations of homogentisic acid at a low level: the great capacity to metabolize this acid in the liver and kidney and the rapid renal tubular secretion of homogentisic acid. Even in the alcaptonuric patient, the renal mechanism is capable of effectively lowering the plasma level when homogentisic acid is given. This defense mechanism may be highly significant in view of the many years required for ochronosis to appear. It is quite possible that in the alcaptonuric person the tissues are only occasionally flooded with homogentisic acid and that this event has to be repeated many times over a period of years before tissue pigmentation occurs to a significant extent. Benzoquinoneacetic acid may be an intermediate in this process.[170]

Experimental Alcaptonuria and Ochronosis

Spontaneous alcaptonuria has not been found in any species except human beings. Although there is a report by Lewis[171] of a rabbit with urine that darkened upon exposure to air and met some of the qualitative tests for homogentisic acid, the latter was never isolated or positively identified, and the rabbit died without offspring. There are also reports of generalized ochronosis in the bones and connective tissues of cattle, dogs, and horses in which the tissues are described as being black as coal, but again homogentisic acid has never been identified in the urine with certainty.[24,171–173]

Experimental alcaptonuria has been produced in rats and mice by feeding large quantities of phenylalanine or tyrosine (see Table 27-2). It is also reported that vitamin C-deficient guinea pigs fed extra phenylalanine[151,174] or tyrosine[151] excreted homogentisic acid, as well as *p*-hydroxyphenylpyruvic acid and *p*-hydroxyphenyllactic acid. Other workers, however, have found only the latter two compounds and no homogentisic acid in similar experiments with vitamin C-deficient guinea pigs.[185] It should be noted that in some experiments of this type the claim has been made that homogentisic acid was excreted, even though the analytic methods employed would not distinguish between *p*-hydroxyphenyl-pyruvic acid and homogentisic acid.[186]

Experimental alcaptonuria has been produced in rats and mice by feeding large quantities of phenylalanine and tyrosine (see Table 27-2). There is also a report of transitory homogentisic acid excretion after feeding a human volunteer large amounts of L-tyrosine.[180]

Another type of experimental alcaptonuria has been induced in rats by a diet deficient in the sulfur-containing amino acids.[181] This was not corrected by giving ascorbic acid but was reversed by giving cysteine.[182] In this type of experimental al-

Table 27-2 Methods of Producing Experimental Alcaptonuria

Agent	Species	Comment	Reference
Feeding L-phenylalanine	Rats		175–177
	Mice		178
	Guinea pigs	Excreted HGA and PHPP on vitamin C–deficient diet, defect corrected by vitamin C[151]	174, 151
Feeding L-tyrosine	Rats	Believed by authors to be due to adaptive increase in tyrosine transaminase activity, but decrease in homogentisic acid oxidase activity also found	179
	Guinea pigs	On vitamin C–deficient diet; other workers find only PHPP, PHPL, no HGA[185] Defect corrected by ascorbic acid[151] or folic acid[191,192]	150, 151
	Human beings	Large doses over 1 day; 50g; 150g; little or no HGA excreted	180
Diet deficient in sulfur amino acids	Rats	Effects reversed by cystein—not by ascorbic acid	181,182
Diet deficient in tryptophan	Rats	Effects reversed by tryptophan	183
α,α′-Dipyridyl	Guinea pigs	Defect not altered by ascorbic acid	137, 184

NOTE: HGA = homogentisic acid; PHPP = *p*-hydroxyphenylpyruvic acid; PHPL = *p*-hydroxyphenyllactic acid.

captonuria, proportionately less *p*-hydroxyphenylpyruvic acid is excreted than in the type that responds to ascorbic acid.[151]

In addition to the above methods, the finding that homogentisic acid oxidase requires ferrous iron and can be inhibited by α,α′-dipyridyl was used by Suda and Takeda[137] to induce experimental alcaptonuria in guinea pigs. They injected α,α′-dipyridyl and fed extra tyrosine. The excretion of homogentisic acid in these animals was not corrected by administration of vitamin C.

In another investigation, it was found that human volunteers on a vitamin C–deficient diet for several months with frank scorbutic symptoms did not excrete increased amounts of urinary phenols when given 20 g tyrosine orally.[187] This is further evidence that there is no direct requirement for ascorbic acid in homogentisic acid oxidation. It can be concluded that the majority of instances of experimental alcaptonuria are either the result of direct inhibition of homogentisic acid oxidase or are due to an imbalance in the various enzyme reactions sufficient to cause an accumulation of homogentisic acid and its urinary excretion.

Lin and Knox[179] have reported that in experimental alcaptonuria in rats induced by a diet supplemented with extra tyrosine, no homogentisic acid was excreted for the first 3 or 4 days. Following this initial lag period, the degree of homogentisic acid excretion increased during the next several weeks. They attribute these findings of the gradual increase in intensity of the alcaptonuria to an adaptive increase in tyrosine transaminase activity. They believe that this type of alcaptonuria occurs because the relative rate of homogentisic acid formation overbalances the rate of homogentisic acid degradation. Their data also show a significant decrease in liver homogentisic acid oxidase in the experimental group; the decrease may be an important contribution to the resulting alcaptonuria.

It is of interest to recall that the activity of the enzymes in the pathway following homogentisic acid oxidase was approximately normal in alcaptonuric liver (Table 27-1). Since the only known endogenous source of maleylacetoacetic acid is the oxidation of homogentisic acid, it appears that normal levels of the isomerase are produced in the absence of its substrate. Thus it is a constitutive rather than an adaptive enzyme.

Further studies should be mentioned in connection with the "adaptive" changes in the activity of liver tyrosine transaminase. Lin and Knox[188] found that the level of this transaminase could be increased several-fold by injecting rats intraperitoneally with L-tyrosine. Under these conditions the activity of the enzymes later in the pathway was not changed significantly. This adaptation is unusual, since it can also be produced by injecting hydrocortisone, by certain other amino acids, and by propylene glycol.[157] They also found that injections of L-tyrosine were not effective in adrenalectomized animals unless hydrocortisone was also given.

Most attempts to produce experimental alcaptonuria and ochronosis in animals by feeding special diets have met with very limited success. In most instances the inhibition of homogentisic acid oxidase has been inadequate, and only a small fraction of the normal activity is sufficient to prevent the accumulation of the acid and deposition of ochronotic pigment. More recently, prolonged feeding of L-tyrosine has produced some degree of ochronotic pigmentation of the connective tissues in animals. Bondurant and Henry[189] maintained rats on a diet supplemented with 12 percent tyrosine for 40 days. Gross examination of the dissected knee and hip joints revealed no structural abnormalities, but these tissues showed the deposition of pigment in the articular cartilage of the head of the femur and in opposing tibial and patellar surfaces of the knee joint. Microscopic examination showed focal accumulations of dark-brown pigment in the cytoplasm of chondrocytes in the epiphyseal cartilage in some animals.

Blivaiss et al.[190] induced experimental ochronosis in 4-week-old rats by supplementing their diet with 8 percent tyrosine for as long as 28 months. After this time there were ochronotic-like pigment deposits in cartilage, such as the joint capsules, condyles, sternum, and trachea. Pathologic changes were found in the articular cartilage which included abnormal alignment of chrondrocytes with pigment inclusion, fibrillation, and fragmentation, as well as bone denudation. By histochemical techniques, they found an increase in nonsulfated acid mucopolysaccharides in the connective tissues. The histochemical changes were similar to those observed in the patella from a patient with alcaptonuria.

HEREDITARY ASPECTS

The first paper describing the inheritance of alcaptonuria was that of Garrod in 1902,[16] in which he presented evidence that this condition is congenital and familial and that it occurs more often in families in which there are consanguineous marriages. He suggested that alcaptonuria might be transmitted as a single recessive Mendelian trait. He believed that homogentisic acid arose in the normal course of tyrosine metabolism and that consanguineous marriages brought to light a recessive defect in this metabolic process. In 1902 Bateson and Saunders[193] also suggested that the inheritance of a rare recessive factor might explain the incidence of alcaptonuria. These studies on the mode of transmission of alcaptonuria were among the first on hereditary metabolic diseases.

Although in the years immediately following, examples were recorded in which direct transmission (i.e., parent and offspring affected) of alcaptonuria occurred, Garrod believed that these were examples of a heterozygous individual mating with a homozygote. As more family histories were described, the general opinion of the recessive nature of the disease remained unchallenged. In 1932 Hogben et al.[194] carefully summarized all the known cases of alcaptonuria reported up to that time. Again the recessive character of the disease was confirmed in nearly all the families, and it was observed that at least half the affected individuals were the offspring of consanguineous matings. Although there was an unequal sex distribution in their cases—100 males and 46 females—they did not consider this an indication that the condition was semilethal in females. They noted that males were more often the probands in affected families and suggested that the higher incidence in males might be because of the more frequent examination of males. They also noted that among infants there were slightly more females than males, which was in agreement with this explanation. Nevertheless, it is frequently stated in medical texts that the incidence of alcaptonuria is twice as high in males as in females. The paper by Hogben et al. is obviously the source of this information.

Among the families reviewed by Hogben et al. there were some in which a dominant form of alcaptonuria had to be considered. In a family studied by Pieter,[195] the author felt compelled to conclude that a dominant type of alcaptonuria existed. In the end, this conclusion depended upon the predicted opportunity for marriage between homozygous and heterozygous individuals, and the frequency of the heterozygote in the general population, or perhaps more exactly, the incidence of the heterozygote within a selected population. The incidence of alcaptonuria in the general population can be only roughly estimated. At least 600 cases have been described, but this is a conservative number, since new cases are generally not reported unless there are some other special features present. It is reasonably certain, however, that alcaptonuria is less rare than was believed 30 years ago. It is reported[11] that in a study in Northern Ireland by A. C. Stephenson, the incidence of alcaptonuria was from 3 to 5 per million individuals. This would give a considerably higher incidence of heterozygous individuals in the general population than assumed by Hogben et al.[194]

It is important to recall that in the families in which direct transmission of alcaptonuria has been found, the number of consanguineous marriages is very high. One of the best examples of this is the kindred described by Khachadurian and Abu Feisal.[196] In this Lebanese family, there was a total of eight alcaptonuric patients in five successive generations (Fig. 27-10). Careful investigations, however, showed that the grandmothers of the propositus were first cousins and that at least three consanguineous marriages existed in this family. This pedigree is particularly instructive because it illustrates how a recessive trait could appear to be a dominant one unless the entire family pedigree is known.

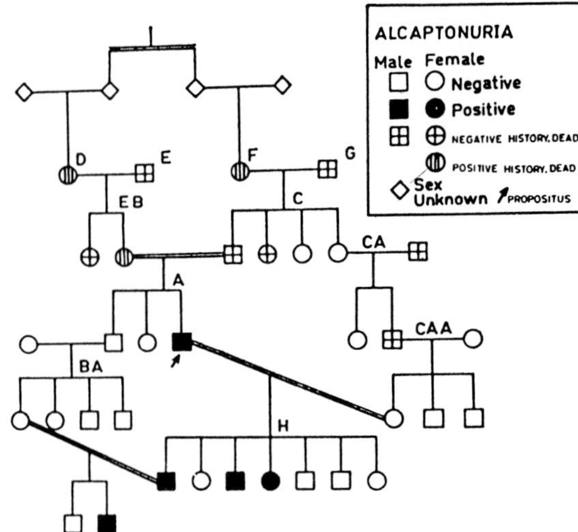

Fig. 27-10 Alcaptonuria in a Lebanese family. (*From A. Khachadurian and K. Abu Feisal.*[196] *Used by permission.*)

At present most, if not all, cases appear to represent the inheritance of a single autosomal recessive gene. This is supported by the biochemical finding that a single enzyme system is inactive in this condition and that only one clinical form of alcaptonuria is known. The few cases in which it has been considered as possibly a dominant form have not shown any clinical differences from the majority of cases.

An unusually high incidence of alcaptonuria has been observed in the Trenčín District of Czechoslovakia, near the Slovakian-Bohemian border.[197] More than 100 alcaptonuric individuals have been identified among the 16,000 inhabitants (see Sršeň et al.[198]). Genetic analysis of the affected families shows a concentration of alcaptonuric patients within specific localities, and the authors propose that the most reasonable explanation is through a founder effect, with genetic drift and inbreeding in the specific isolated hamlets of that region.

The suggestion by Milch[199,200] that alcaptonuria is inherited as a dominant gene with incomplete penetrance seems unnecessarily complicated to explain the data at hand (see Knox[11]). In fact, while the possibility of a dominant type of alcaptonuria cannot be excluded, it should be pointed out that no convincing evidence for it has yet been presented.

The fact that a rare disease with recessive inheritance may be encountered more frequently in selected inbred populations complicates the estimation of the incidence of heterozygotes in the general population. It would be most helpful if a diagnostic test were available to detect the carrier state. In view of the nature of the enzymatic defect in alcaptonuric individuals, one might hope to find approximately one-half of the normal amount of enzyme in the tissues of heterozygous individuals, as is apparently the situation in phenylketonuria[201–203] and galactosemia.[204,205] However, heterozygous carriers of alcaptonuria do not excrete homogentisic acid after an oral loading dose of L-tyrosine,[206] and measurements of the ability to metabolize homogentisic acid by an oral homogentisic acid tolerance test have so far shown no difference between relatives of alcaptonuric patients and normal controls.[207] These results may be due to the tremendous capacity of the liver (see Table 27-1) to metabolize this acid. Perhaps even if this reserve were reduced to one-half, it might not be detected by an oral tolerance test. In fact, assuming a liver weight of 1500 g and assuming that the liver homogentisic acid oxidase is as efficient in vivo as under assay conditions in vitro, it can be calculated that the normal adult liver can metabolize over 1600 g homogentisic acid per day.

In studies related to hereditary tyrosinemia, Laberge et al[208] gave 25 to 100 mg/kg of homogentisic acid to four adult control subjects and two who were obligatory carriers of tyrosemia as an oral tolerance test. The doses of homogentisic acid were rapidly cleared from the plasma, and excreted as free homogentisic acid and as a thioether conjugate, primarily of glutathione. The latter pathway is still another alternative system for removal of homogentisic acid, even if the level of homogentisic acid oxidase were reduced in heterozygous carriers of alcaptonuria.

The chromosomal location of the defective gene related to alcaptonuria has not been identified. A report by Gaucher et al.[209] suggests an association with antigen HLA-B27, based upon the results of studies in a three-generation family with 10 alcaptonuric members. However, in another analysis of 19 unrelated alcaptonuric patients in Czechoslovakia with 11 polymorphic markers by Kaprálik et al.,[210] conflicting evidence of association was observed with blood group systems Duffy, MNSS, and P, and with phosphoglucomutase. Tests for linkage between alcaptonuria and salivary and pancreatic amylases showed no association.[211]

TREATMENT

Attempts to treat alcaptonuria have been directed either toward correcting the underlying metabolic defect or preventing or reversing the pigmentation and arthritis changes. Galdston et al.[48] administered several vitamins, brewers' yeast, tyrosinase, insulin, and adrenocortical extract without altering the amount of homogentisic acid excreted by an alcaptonuric patient. Several groups have studied the effectivness of vitamin C.[30,31,48,212,213] Although it corrects the alcaptonuria induced in guinea pigs by feeding large amounts of tyrosine,[150] it does not change the hereditary type of alcaptonuria.

Other agents, such as vitamin B_{12},[214] cortisone,[3,215,216] and phenylbutazone,[217] are without influence on the metabolic defect. A confusing report by Cope and Kassander[76] that cortisone corrected the metabolic error is difficult to interpret, since the authors claim this was a case of ochronosis without homogentisic acid in the urine.

Now that it is certain that the basic defect is the lack of a specific enzyme, replacement of the missing enzyme is theoretically a therapeutic measure to consider, but this is not practical at present.

In the past it has been suggested that dietary phenylalanine and tyrosine be reduced to decrease the output of homogentisic acid. A severe restriction of the intake of these amino acids is not practical except for brief periods and might be dangerous to the patient if continued over a long time.

Since from a practical standpoint the importance of the metabolic defect is mainly that it leads to pigmentation and arthritic changes, therapeutic measures could be aimed primarily at preventing or correcting these complications of the disease. It is possible, as Sealock et al. have pointed out, that large amounts of ascorbic acid might prevent the deposition of ochronotic pigment[30] even though this does not alter the metabolic defect.

The observation by Murray et al.[87] that ascorbic acid protects lysyl hydroxylase from inhibition (via benzoquinoneacetic acid?) leads to the obvious suggestion that prolonged maintenance of relatively high tissue concentrations of ascorbic acid might delay, and possibly reduce, the degree of pathologic changes in the connective tissues. At least, further clinical experience with this mode of treatment would be worthwhile.

REFERENCES

1. GARROD, AE: The Croonian lecturers on inborn errors of metabolism. Lecture II. Alkaptonuria. *Lancet* 2:73, 1908.
2. STENN, FF, MILGRAM, JW, LEE, SL, WEIGAND, RJ, VEIS, A: Biochemical identification of homogentisic acid pigment in an ochronotic Egyptian mummy. *Science* 197:566, 1977.
3. BOEDEKER C: Ueber das Alcapton; ein neuer Beitrag zur Frage: Welche Stoffe des Harns können Kupferreduction bewirken? *Z Rat Med* 7:130, 1859, p 139.
4. *The Oxford English Dictionary, Supplement*, Oxford, New York, 1933, p 15.
5. BOEDECKER C: Das Alkapton; ein Beitrag zur Frage: Welche Stoffe des Harns konnen aus einer alkalischen Kupferoxydlösung Kupferoxydul reduciren? *Ann Chem Pharmacol* 117:98, 1861.
6. EBSTEIN W, MÜLLER J: Brenzkatechin in dem Urin eines Kindes. *Arch Pathol Anat* 62:554, 1875.
7. FÜRBRINGER PV: Nachtrag über Alkaptonurie. *Berl Klin Wochenschr* 12:390, 1875.
8. SMITH WG: On the occurrence of protocatechuic acid in urine. *Dublin J Med Sci* 73:465, 1882.
9. MARSHALL J: A preliminary notice of a crystalline acid in urine possessing more powerful reducing properties than glucose. *Med News (Philadelphia)* 50:35, 1887.
10. KIRK R: On a new acid found in human urine which darkens with alkalies. *J Anat Physiol London* 23:69, 1889.
11. KNOX WE: Sir Archibald Garrod's "inborn errors of metabolism." II. Alkaptonuria. *Am J Hum Genet* 10:95, 1958.
12. WOLKOW M, BAUMANN E: Über das Wesen der Alkaptonurie. *Z Physiol Chem* 15:228, 1891.
13. GARROD AE: *Inborn Errors of Metabolism*. London, Frowde, Hodder, and Stoughton, 1909.
14. NEUBAUER O: Über den Abbau der Aminosäuren in gesunden und kranken Organismus. *Dtsch Arch Klin Med* 95:211, 1909.
15. NEUBAUER O: Intermediärer Eiweisstoffwechsel. *Handb Norm Pathol Physiol* 5:671, 1928.
16. GARROD AE: The incidence of alkaptonuria: A study in chemical individuality. *Lancet* 2:1616, 1902.
17. BEADLE GW, TATUM EL: Genetic control of biochemical reactions in neurospora. *Proc Natl Acad Sci USA* 27:499, 1941.
18. LA DU BN, ZANNONI VG, LASTER L, SEEGMILLER JE: The nature of the defect in tyrosine metabolism in alcaptonuria. *J Biol Chem* 230:251, 1958.
19. O'BRIEN WM, LA DU BN, BUNIM JJ: Biochemical, pathological, and clinical aspects of alcaptonuria, ochronosis, and ochronotic arthropathy. *Am J Med* 34:813, 1963.
20. SRŠEŇ S, VONDRÁČEK J, SRŠŇOVÁ K, ŠVÁČ J: Analýza dl'žky života alkaptonurických pacientov. (Analysis of the life span of alcaptonuric patients.) *Cas Lek Cesk* 124:1288, 1985.
21. COOPER PA: Alkaptonuria with ochronosis. *Proc R Soc Med* 44:917, 1951.
22. MINNO AM, ROGERS JA: Ochronosis: Report of a case. *Ann Intern Med* 46:179, 1957.
23. YULES JH: Ochronotic arthritis: Report of a case. *Bull N Engl Med Center* 16:168, 1954.
24. MARTIN WJ, UNDERDAHL LO, MATHIESON DR: Alkaptonuria: Report of 3 cases. *Proc Staff Meet Mayo Clin* 27:193, 1952.
25. CRISSEY RE, DAY AJ: Ochronosis: A case report. *J Bone Joint Surg* 32A:688, 1950.
26. SMITH HP, SMITH HP JR: Ochronosis: Report of two cases. *Ann Intern Med* 42:171, 1955.
27. HAMMOND G, POWERS HW: Alkaptonuric arthritis: Report of a case. *Lahey Clin Bull* 11, 18, 1958.
28. POMERANZ MM, FRIEDMAN LJ, TUNICK IS: Roentgen findings in alcaptonuric ochronosis. *Radiology* 37:295, 1941.
29. ROSE GK: Ochronosis. *Br J Surg* 44:481, 1957.
30. SEALOCK RR, GLADSTON M, STEELE JM: Administration of ascorbic acid to an alkaptonuric patient. *Proc Soc Exp Biol Med* 44:580, 1940.
31. NEUBERGER A, RIMINGTON C, WILSON JMG: Studies on alcaptonuria II. Investigations on a case of human alcaptonuria. *Biochem J* 41:438, 1947.

32. SAKAMOTO Y, NAKAMURA K, INAMORI K, IKEDA S, ICHIHARA K: On the formation of gentisic acid. II. *J Biochem (Tokyo)* 44:849, 1957.
33. ICHIHARA K, IKEDA S, SAKAMOTO Y: On the formation of genetisic acid from homogentisic acid by the liver extract. *J Biochem (Tokyo)* 43:129, 1956.
34. KANDA M, WATANABE H, NAKATA Y, HIGASHI T, SAKAMOTO Y: The formation of gentisic acid from homogentisic acid. IV. *J Biochem (Tokyo)* 55:65, 1964.
35. BRIGGS AP: A colorimetric method for the determination of homogentisic acid in urine. *J Biol Chem* 51:453, 1922.
36. FISHBERG EH: The instantaneous diagnosis of alkaptonuria on a single drop of urine. *JAMA* 119:882, 1942.
37. NEUBERGER A: Studies on alcaptonuria. I. The estimation of homogentisic acid. *Biochem J* 41:431, 1947.
38. MEDES G: Modification of Garrod's method for preparation of homogentisic acid from urine. *Proc Soc Exp Biol Med* 30:751, 1933.
39. KNOX WE, LEMAY-KNOX M: The oxidation in liver of L-tyrosine to acetoacetate through *p*-hydroxyphenylpyruvate and homogentisic acid. *Biochem J* 49:686, 1951.
40. SEEGMILLER JE, ZANNONI VG, LASTER L, LA DU BN: An enzymatic spectrophotometric method for the determination of homogentisic acid in plasma and urine. *J Biol Chem* 236:774, 1961.
41. LADU BN, O'BRIEN WM, ZANNONI VG: Studies on ochronosis. I. The distribution of homogentisic acid in guinea pigs. *Arthritis Rheum* 5:81, 1962.
42. LUSTBERG TJ, SCHULMAN JD, SEEGMILLER JE: The preparation and identification of various adducts of oxidized homogentisic acid and the development of a new sensitive colorimetric assay for homogentisic acid. *Clin Chim Acta* 35:323, 1971.
43. VIRCHOW R: Ein Fall von allgemeiner Ochronose der Knorpel und knorpelähnlichen Theile. *Arch Pathol Anat* 37:212, 1866.
44. ALBRECHT H: Ueber Ochronose. *Z Heilk* 23:366, 1902.
45. OSLER W: Ochronosis: The pigmentation of cartilages, sclerotics, and skin in alkaptonuria. *Lancet* 1:10, 1904.
46. BUNIM JJ, MCGUIRE JS JR, HILBISH TF, LASTER L, LA DU BN JR, SEEGMILLER JE: Alcaptonuria: Clinical staff conference at the National Institutes of Health. *Ann Intern Med* 47:1210, 1957.
47. SMITH JW: Ochronosis of the sclera and cornea complicating alkaptonuria: Review of the literature and report of four cases. *JAMA* 120:1282, 1942.
48. GALDSTON M, STEELE JM, DOBRINER K: Alcaptonuria and ochronosis with a report of three patients and metabolic studies in two. *Am Med* 13:432, 1952.
49. LICHTENSTEIN L, KAPLAN L: Hereditary ochronosis: Pathological changes observed in two necropsied cases. *Am J Pathol* 30:99, 1954.
50. COOPER JA, MORAN TJ: Studies on ochronosis. *AMA Arch Pathol* 64:46, 1957.
51. O'BRIEN WM, BANFIELD WG, SOKOLOFF L: Studies on the pathogenesis of ochronotic arthropathy. *Arthritis Rheum* 4:137, 1961.
52. KUTTY MK, IQBAL QM, TEH EC: Ochronotic arthropathy: An electron microscopical study with a view on pathogenesis. *Arch Pathol* 98:55, 1974.
53. GAUCHER A, FAURE G, NETTER P, FLOQUET J, DUHEILLE J: Synovial membrane from ochronotic arthropathy of the hip joint. *Z Rheumatol* 39:231, 1980.
54. MOHR W, WESSINGHAGE D, LENSCHOW E: Die Ultrastruktur von hyalinen Knorpel und Gelenkkapselgewebe bei der alkaptonischen Ochronose. *Z Rheumatol* 39:55, 1980.
55. FITZPATRICK TB, LERNER AB: Biochemnical basis of human melanin pigmentation. *AMA Arch Dermatol* 69:133, 1954.
56. LILLIE RD: A Nile blue staining technic for the differentiation of melanin and lipofuscins. *Stain Technol* 31:151, 1956.
57. MÖRNER KAH: Zur Kenntnis von den Farbostoffen der melanotischen Geschwülste. *Z Physiol Chem* 11:66, 1887.
58. MILCH RA, TITUS ED, LOO TL: Atmospheric oxidation of homogentisic acid: Spectrophotometric studies. *Science* 126:209, 1957.
59. MILCH RA, TITUS ED: Studies of alcaptonuria: Absorption spectra of homogentisic acid-chondroitin sulfate solutions. *Arthritis Rheum* 1:566, 1958.
60. ZANNONI VG, LOMTEVAS N, GOLDFINGER S: Oxidation of homogentisic acid to ochronotic pigment in connective tissue. *Biochim Biophys Acta* 177:94, 1969.
61. LA DU BN, ZANNONI VG: Oxidation of homogentisic acid catalyzed by horseradish peroxidase. *Biochim Biophys Acta* 67:281, 1963.
62. STONER R, BLIVAISS BB: Homogentisic acid metabolism: A 1,4-addition reaction of benzoquinone-2-acetic acid with amino acids and other biological amines. *Fed Proc* 24:656, 1965.
63. LA DU BN, ZANNONI VG: Ochronosis, in Wolman M (ed): *Pigments in Pathology*. New York, Academic, 1969, p 465.
64. SUGAR HS, WADDELL WW: Ochronosis-like pigmentation associated with the use of atabrine. *Ill Med J* 89:234, 1946.
65. LUDWIG GD, TOOLE JF, WOOD JC: Ochronosis from quinacrine (atabrine). *Ann Intern Med* 59:378, 1963.
66. PICK L: Ueber die Ochronose. *Berl Klin Wochenschr* 43:591, 1906.
67. REID E, OSLER W, GARROD AE: On ochronosis. *Q J Med* 1:199, 1908.
68. POPE FM: A case of ochronosis: With a note on the relationship of alkaptonuria to ochronosis by A. E. Garrod. *Lancet* 1:24, 1906.
69. BEDDARD AP: Ochronosis associated with carboluria. *Q J Med* 3:329, 1910.
70. BEDDARD AP, PULMTRE CM: A further note on ochronosis associated with carboluria. *Q J Med* 5:505, 1912.
71. BROGREN N: Case of exogenetic ochronosis from carbolic acid compresses. *Acta Dermatovener* 32:258, 1952.
72. FINDLAY GH, DE BEER HA: Chronic hydroquinone poisoning of the skin from skin-lightening cosmetics. *S Afr Med J* 57:187, 1980.
73. TIDMAN MJ, HORTON JJ, MACDONALD DM: Hydroquinone-induced ochronosis—light and electron microscopic features. *Clin Exp Dermatol* 11:224, 1986.
74 PHILLIPS JI, ISAACSON C, CARMAN H: Ochronosis in Black South Africans who used skin lighteners. *Am J Dermatopathol* 8:14, 1986.
75. OPPENHEIMER BS, KLINE BS: Ochronosis, with a study of an additional case. *Arch Intern Med* 29:732, 1922.
76. COPE CB, KASSANDER P: Cortisone in ochronotic arthritis. *JAMA* 150:997, 1952.
77. JANNEY NW: A study of ochronosis. *Am J Med Sci* 156:59, 1918.
78. SKINSNES OK: Generalized ochronosis: Report of an instance in which it was misdiagnosed as melanosarcoma, with resultant enucleation of an eye. *Arch Pathol* 45:552, 1948.
79. FÜRBRINGER P: Beobachtungen über einen Fall von Alkaptonurie. *Berl Klin Wochenschr* 12:330, 1875.
80. MORACZEWSKI W VON: Ein Fall von Alkaptonurie. *Centr Inn Med* 17:177, 1896.
81. HARROLD AJ: Alkaptonuric arthritis. *J Bone Joint Surg* 38B:532, 1956.
82. HENCH PS: Rheumatism and arthritis: Review of American and English literature of recent years. 9th Rheumatism Review. *Ann Intern Med* 28:310, 1948.
83. SUTRO CJ, ANDERSON ME: Alkaptonuric arthritis: Cause for free intraarticular bodies. *Surgery* 22:120, 1947.
84. MORAN TJ, YUNIS EJ: Studies on ochronosis. 2. Effects of injection of homogentisic acid and ochronotic pigment in experimental animals. *Am J Pathol* 40:359, 1962.
85. GREILING H: Beitrag zur Entstehung der Ochronose bei Alkaptonurie. *Klin Wochenschr* 35:889, 1957.
86. DIHLMANN W, GREILING H, KISTERS R, STUHLSATZ IW: Biochemische und radiologische Untersuchungen zur Pathogense der Alkaptonurie. *Dtsch Med Wochenschr* 95:839, 1970.
87. MURRAY JC, LINDBERG KA, PINNEL SE: In vitro inhibition of chick embryo lysyl hydroxylase by homogentisic acid. *J Clin Invest* 59:1071, 1977.
88. KIRKPATRICK CJ, MOHR W, MUTSCHLER W: Experimental studies on the pathogenesis of ochronotic arthropathy. *Virchows Arch (B)* 47:347, 1984.
89. EBERLE P, MOHR W, CLAES L: Biomechanische Untersuchungen zur Pathgenese der ochronotischen Arthropathie. *Z Rheumatol* 43:249, 1984.
90. COODLEY EL, GRECO AJ: Clinical aspects of ochronosis, with report of a case. *Am J Med* 8:816, 1950.
91. VLAY SC, HARTMAN AR, CULLIFORD AT: Alkaptonuria and aortic stenosis. *Ann Intern Med* 104:446, 1986.
92. EISENBERG H: Alkaptonuria, ochronosis, arthritis, and ruptured intervertebral disk. *AMA Arch Intern Med* 86:79, 1950.
93. YOUNG HH: Calculi of the prostate associated with ochronosis and alkaptonuria. *J Urol* 51:48, 1944.
94. ROSENBAUM H, REVENO WS: Polycythemia and alkaptonuria. *Harper Hosp Bull* 10:36, 1952.
95. GOLDBERG BH, PENSO JS, STERN LM, BERGSTEIN JM: Alcaptonuria and nephrocalcinosis. *J Pediatr* 88:518, 1976.
96. DALGLIESH CE: Metabolism of the aromatic amino acids. *Adv Protein Chem* 10:31, 1955.
97. KNOX WE: The metabolism of phenylalanine and tyrosine, in McElroy WD, Glass HB (eds): *A Symposium on Amino Acid Metabolism*. Baltimore, Johns Hopkins, 1955.
98. LERNER AB: Metabolism of phenylalanine and tyrosine. *Adv Enzymol* 14:73, 1953.
99. MEISTER A: *Biochemistry of the Amino Acids*. New York, Academic, 1957.
100. SCHEPARTZ B, GURIN S: The intermediary metabolism of phenylalanine labeled with radioactive carbon. *J Biol Chem* 180:663, 1949.
101. WEINHOUSE S, MILLINGTON RH: Ketone body formation from tyrosine. *J Biol Chem* 175:995, 1948.
102. WEINHOUSE S, MILLINGTON RH: Ketone body formation from tyrosine. *J Biol Chem* 181:645, 1949.

103. DISCHE R, RITTENBERG D: The metabolism of phenylalanine-4-C^{14}. *J Biol Chem* 211:199, 1954.

104. LERNER AB: On the metabolism of phenylalanine and tyrosine. *J Biol Chem* 181:281, 1949.

105. BAMBERGER E: Über das Verhalten paraalkylierter Phenole gegen das Carosches Reagens. *Ber Dtsch Chem Ges* 36:2028, 1903.

106. SCHWEIZER J, LATTRELL R, HECKLER E: Conversion of p-hydroxyphenylpyruvic acid into homogentisic acid: Possible participation of p-quinol intermediates. *Experientia* 31:1267, 1975.

107. SAITO I, CHUJO Y, SHIMAZU H, YAMANE M, MATSUURA T, CAHNMANN HJ: Nonenzymatic oxidation of p-hydroxyphenylpyruvic acid with singlet oxygen to homogentisic acid. A model for the action of p-hydroxyphenylpyruvate hydroxylase. *J Am Chem Soc* 97:5272, 1975.

108. LEINBERGER R, HULL WE, SIMON H, RETEY J: Steric course of the NIH shift in the enzymic formation of homogentisic acid. *Eur J Biochem* 117:311, 1981.

109. DAKIN HD: The chemical nature of alkaptonuria. *J Biol Chem* 9:151, 1911.

110. DAKIN HD: Experiments relating to the mode of decomposition of tyrosine and of related substances in the animal body. *J Biol Chem* 8:11, 1910.

111. WAKEMAN AJ, DAKIN ID: The catabolism of phenylalanine, tyrosine, and of their derivatives. *J Biol Chem* 9:139, 1911.

112. LA DU BN, ZANNONI VG: The tyrosine oxidation system of liver. II. Oxidation of *p*-hydroxyphenylpyruvic acid to homogentisic acid. *J Biol Chem* 217: 777, 1955.

113. PIRRUNG J, GOTTESMAN L, CRANDALL DI: The metabolism of *p*-methoxyphenylalanine and *p*-methoxyphenylpyruvate. *J Biol Chem* 229:199, 1957.

114. RECKNAGEL RO, POTTER VR: Mechanism of the ketogenic effect of ammonium chloride. *J Biol Chem* 191:263, 1951.

115. EDWARDS SW, HSIA DYY, KNOX WE: The first oxidative enzyme of tyrosine metabolism, *p*-hydroxyphenylpyruvate oxidase. *Fed Proc* 14:206, 1955.

116. NEUBERGER A: Synthesis and resolution of 2:5-dihydroxyphenylalanine. *Biochem* 43:599, 1948.

117. GROSS O: Über den Einfluss des Blutserums des Normalen und des Alkaptonurikers auf Homogentisinsäure. *Biochem Z* 61:165, 1914.

118. KATSCH G, STERN G: Zur Theorie der alkaptonurischen Stoffwechselstřung. *Dtsch Arch Klin Med* 151:329, 1926.

119. LANYAR F, LIEB H: Die quantitative Bestimmung der Homogentisinsäure im Blutserum und in der Milch des Alkaptonurikers. *Z Physiol Chem* 203:135, 1931.

120. DENT CE (ed): Symposium on inborn errors of metabolism. *Am J Med* 22:671, 1957.

121. ZANNONI VG, SEEGMILLER JE, LA DU BN: Nature of the defect in alcaptonuria. *Nature* 193:952, 1962.

122. KNOX SWE, EDWARDS SW: The properties of maleylacetoacetate, the initial product of homogentisate oxidation in liver. *J Biol Chem* 216:489, 1955.

123. HENION WF, SUTHERLAND EW: Immunological differences of phorphorylases. *J Biol Chem* 224:477, 1957.

124. SCHLAMOWITZ M: Immunochemical studies on alkaline phosphatase, in Symposium on Enzymes in Blood. *Ann NY Acad Sci* 75:373, 1958.

125. LUSTBERG TJ, SCHULMAN JD, SEEGMILLER JE: Metabolic fate of homogentisic acid-1-^{14}C (HGA) in alcaptonuria and effectiveness of ascorbic acid in preventing experimental ochronosis. *Arthritis Rheum* 12:678, 1969.

126. GARROD AE: About alkaptonuria. *Lancet* 2:1484, 1901.

127. KRETCHMER O, LEVINE SZ, MCNAMAR H, BARNETT HL: Certain aspects of tyrosine metabolism in the young. I. The development of the tyrosine oxidizing system in human liver. *J Clin Invest* 35:236, 1956.

128. BRAID F, HICKMANS EM: Metabolic study of an alkaptonuric infant. *Arch Dis Child* 4:389, 1929.

129. MITTELBACH F: Ein Beitrag zur Kenntnis der Alkaptonurie. *Dtsch Arch Klin Med* 71:50, 1901.

130. KNOW WE, EDWARDS SW: Homogentisate oxidase of liver. *J Biol Chem* 216:479, 1955.

131. EDWARDS SW, KNOX WE: Homogentisate metabolism: The isomerization of maleylacetoacetate by an enzyme which requires glutathione. *J Biol Chem* 220:79, 1956.

132. RAVDIN RG, CRANDALL DI: The enzymatic conversion of homogentisic acid to 4-fumarylacetoacetic acid. *J Biol Chem* 189:137, 1951.

133. MEISTER A, GREENSTEIN JP: Enzymatic hydrolysis of 2,4-diketo acids. *J Biol Chem* 175:573, 1948.

134. WITTER RF, STOTZ E: The metabolism in vitro of triacetic acid and related diketones. *J Biol Chem* 176:501, 1948.

135. CONNORS WM, STOTZ E: The purification and properties of a triacetic acid-hydrolyzing enzyme. *J Biol Chem* 178:881, 1949.

136. SUDA M, TAKEDA Y: Metabolism of tyrosine. I. Application of successive adaptation of bacteria for the analysis of the enzymatic breakdown of tyrosine. *J Biochem (Tokyo)* 37:375, 1950.

137. SUDA M, TAKEDA Y: Metabolism of tyrosine. II. Homogentisicase. *J Biochem (Tokyo)*37:381, 1950.

138. CRANDALL DI: Homogentisic acid oxidase. II. Properties of the crude enzyme in rat liver. *J Biol Chem* 212:565, 1955.

139. SCHEPARTZ B: Inhibition and activation of the oxidation of homogentisic acid. *J Biol Chem* 205:185, 1953.

140. CRANDALL DI, HALIKIS DN: Homogentisic acid oxidase. I. Distribution in animal tissues and relation to tyrosine metabolism in rat kidney. *J Biol Chem* 208:629, 1954.

141. CRANDALL DI, YASUNOBU K, KRUEGER RC, MASON HS: Oxygen transfer by homogentisate oxidase. *Fed Proc* 17:207, 1958.

142. CRANDALL DI: The ferrous ion activation of homogentisic acid oxidase and other aromatic ring-splitting oxidases, in McElroy WD, Glass HB (eds): *Symposium on Amino Acid Metabolism.* Baltimore, Johns Hopkins, 1955, p 867.

143. SUDA M, HASHIMOTO K, MATSUOKA H, KAMAHORA T: Further studies on pyrocatecase. *J Biochem (Tokyo)* 38:289, 1951.

144. STANIER RY, INGRAHAM JL: Protocatechuic acid oxidase. *J Biol Chem* 210:799, 1954.

145. LONG CL, HILL HN, WEINSTOCK IM, HENDERSON LM: Studies of the enzymatic transformation of 3-hydroxyanthranilate to quinolinate. *J Biol Chem* 211:405, 1954.

146. MAC DONALD DL, STANIER RY, INGRAHAM JL: The enzymatic formation of β-carboxymuconic acid. *J Biol Chem* 210:809, 1954.

147. DAGLEY S, PATEL MD: Microbial oxidation of *p*-cresol and protocatechuic acid. *Biochem J* 60:XXXV, 1955.

148. MASON HS: Mechanisms of oxygen metabolism. *Adv Enzymol* 19:79, 1957.

149. SUDA M: Homogentisic acid oxidizing enzyme. *Med J Osaka Univ, suppl* 8:57, 1958.

150. SEALOCK RR, SILBERSTEIN HE: The control of experimental alcaptonuria by means of vitamin C. *Science* 90:571, 1939.

151. SEALOCK RR, SILBERSTEIN HE: The excretion of homogentisic acid and other tyrosine metabolites by the vitamin C-deficient guinea pig. *J Biol Chem* 135:251, 1940.

152. JONES DP, MASON HS: Metabolic hypoxia: Accumulation of tyrosine metabolites in hepatocytes at low pO_2. *Biochem Biophys Res Commun* 80:477, 1978.

153. SCHEPARTZ B: Intermediate steps in tyrosine metabolism. *Fed Proc* 12:265, 1953.

154. EDWARDS SW, KNOX WE: Homogentisate oxidase from rat liver, in Colowick SP, Kaplan NO (eds): *Methods in Enzymology.* New York, Academic, 1955, vol II, p 292.

155. CRANDALL DL: L-Tyrosine oxidation in rat kidney. *Fed Proc* 13:195, 1954.

156. KNOX WE: p-Hydroxyphenylpyruvate Enol-keto tautomerase, in Colowick SP, Kaplan NO (eds): *Methods in Enzymology,* New York, Academic, 1955, vol II, p 287.

157. LIN ECC, KNOX WE: Specificity of the adaptive response of tyrosine-α-ketoglutarate transaminase in the rat. *J Biol Chem* 233:1186, 1958.

158. LA DU BN, ZANNONI VG: Unpublished observations.

159. JONES JD, SMITH BS, EVANS WC: Homogentisic acid, an intermediate in the metabolism of tyrosine by the aromatic ring-splitting microorganisms. *Biochem J* 51:XI, 1952.

160. MÖRNER CT: Weitere Beiträge zur Chemie der Homogentisinsäure. *Z Physiol Chem* 78:306, 1912.

161. CRANDALL DI: Properties and distribution of homogentisic acid oxidase. *Fed Proc* 12:192, 1953.

162. NEUBAUER O, FALTA W: Über das Schicksal einiger aromatischer Säuren bei der Alkaptonurie. *Z Physiol Chem* 42:81, 1904.

163. LA DU B, et al: Unpublished observations.

164. MONTGOMERY JA, MAMER OA: Profiles in altered metabolism. II: Accumulation of homogentisic acid in serum and urine following acetylsalicylic acid ingestion. *Biomed Mass Spectrom* 5:331, 1978.

165. FISHBERG EH: Excretion of benzoquinoneacetic acid in hypovitaminosis C. *J Biol Chem* 172:155, 1948.

166. CONSDEN R, FORBES HAW, GLYNN LE, STANIER WM: Observations on the oxidation of homogentisic acid in urine. *Biochem J* 50:274, 1951.

167. EVANS AS, ENZER N,EDER HA, FINCH CA: Hemolytic anemia with paroxysmal methemoglobinemia and sulfhemoglobinemia. *AMA Arch Intern Med* 86:22, 1950.

168. LEAF G, NEUBERGER A: The preparation of homogentisic acid and of 2:5-dihydroxyphenylethylamine. *Biochem J*43:606, 1948.

169. KATSCH G, METZ E: Der Nachweis der Homogentisinsäure in Serum des Alkaptonurikers. *Dtsch Arch Klin Med* 157:143, 1927.

170. ZANNONI VG, MALAWISTA SE, LA DU BN: Studies on ochronosis. II. Studies on benzoquinoneacetic acid, a probable intermediate in the connective tissue pigmentation of alcaptonuria. *Arthritis Rheum* 5:547, 1962.

171. LEWIS JH: Alcaptonuria in a rabbit. *J Biol Chem* 70:659, 1926.

172. POULSEN V: Über Ochronose bei Menschen und Tieren. *Beitr Pathol Anat* 48:346, 1910.
173. NILSSON N-G, GRABELL I: A case of bovine ochronosis. *Acta Vet Scand* 18:426, 1978.
174. PAPAGEORGE E, LEWIS HB: Experimental alcaptonuria in the white rat. *J Biol Chem* 123:211, 1938.
175. BUTTS J, DUNN MS, HALLMAN LF: Studies in amino acid metabolism. IV. Metabolism of *dl*-phenylalanine and *dl*-tyrosine in the normal rat. *J Biol Chem* 123:711, 1938.
176. LANYAR F: Über experimentelle Alkaptonurie bei der weissen Ratte. *Z Physiol Chem* 278:155, 1943.
177. LANYAR F: Über experimentelle Alkaptonurie bei der weissen Maus. *Z Physiol Chem* 275:225, 1942.
178. SEALOCK RR, PERKINSON JD JR, BASINSKI DH: Further analysis of the role of ascorbic acid in phenylalanine and tyrosine metabolism. *J Biol Chem* 140:153, 1941.
179. LIN ECC, KNOX WE: Role of enzymatic adaptation in production of experimental alkaphonuria. *Proc Soc Exp Biol Med* 96:501, 1957.
180. ABDERHALDEN E: Bildung von Homogentisinsäure nach Aufnahme grosser Mengen von 1-Tyrosin per os. *Z Physiol Chem* 77:454, 1912.
181. GLYNN LE, HIMSWORTH HP, NEUBERGER A: Pathological states due to deficiency of the sulfur-containing amino acids. *Br J Exp Pathol* 26:326, 1945.
182. NEUBERGER A, WEBSTER TA: Studies on alcaptonuria. 3. Experimental alcaptonuria in rats. *Biochem J* 41:449, 1947.
183. WOODFORD VR, QUAN L, CUTTS F: Experimental alkaptonuria in the rat induced by tryptophan deficiency. *J Biol Chem* 45:791, 1967.
184. SUDA M, TAKEDA Y, SUJISHI K,TANAKA T: Metabolism of tyrosine. III. Relation between homogentisicase, ferrous ion, and L-ascorbic acid in experimental alcaptonuria of guinea pig. *J Biochem (Tokyo)* 38:297, 1951.
185. PAINTER HA, ZILVA SS: The influence of L-ascorbic acid on the disappearance of the phenolic group of L-tyrosine in the presence of guinea pig-liver suspensions. *Biochem J* 46:542, 1950.
186. MALAKAR MC, BANERJEE SN: Effect of glycine or choline chloride on the excretion of homogentisic acid by the tyrosine-fed and scorbutic guinea pigs. *Ann Biochem Exp Med* 15:69, 1955.
187. BARTLEY W, KREBS HA, O'BRIEN JRP: Vitamin C requirement of human adults. Medical Research Council, Special Report Series, London, HM Stationery Office, 1953, no 280, p 27.
188. LIN ECC, KNOX WE: Adaptation of the rat liver tyrosine-α-ketoglutarate transaminase. *Biochim Biophys Acta* 26:85, 1957.
189. BONDURANT RE, HENRY JB: Pathogenesis of ochronosis in experimental alkaptonuria of the white rat. *Lab Invest* 14:62, 1965.
190. BLIVAISS BB, ROSENBERG EF, KUTUZOV H, STONER R: Experimental ochronosis: Induction in rats by long-term feeding with L-tyrosine. *AMA Arch Pathol* 82:45, 1966.
191. WOODRUFF CW, CHERRINGTON ME, STOCKELL AK, DARBY WJ: The effect of pteroylglutamic acid and related compounds upon tyrosine metabolism in the scorbutic guinea pig. *J Biol Chem* 178:861, 1949.
192. WOODRUFF CW, DARBY WJ: An in vivo effect of pteroylglutamic acid upon tyrosine metabolism in the scorbutic guinea pig. *J Biol Chem* 172:851, 1948.
193. BATESON W, SAUNDERS ER: *Report of the Evolution Committee of the Royal Society (London)*, no 1, p 133, 1902.
194. HOGBEN L, WORRALL RL, ZIEVE I: The genetic basis of alkaptonuria. *Proc R Soc Edinb [Biol]* 52:264, 1932.
195. PIETER H: Une famille d'alcaptonuriques. *Presse Med* 33:1310, 1925.
196. KHACHADURIAN A, ABU FEISAL K: Alkaptonuria: Report of a family with seven cases appearing in four successive generations with metabolic studies in one patient. *J Chronic Dis* 7:455, 1958.
197. ČERVEŇANSKÝ J, SITAJ S, URBÁNEK T: Alkaptonuria and ochronosis. *J Bone Joint Surg* 41-A: 1169, 1959.
198. SRŠEŇ S, CIŠARIK F, PÁSZTOR L, HARMEČKO L: Alkaptonuria in the Trenčín District of Czechoslovakia. *Am J Med Genet* 2:159, 1978.
199. MILCH RA: Direct inheritance of alcaptonuria. *Metabolism* 4:513, 1955.
200. MILCH RA: Inheritance of alcaptonuria. *Bull Hosp Joint Dis* 18:103, 1957.
201. HSIA DYY, DRISCOLL KW, TROLL W, KNOX WE: Detection by phenylalanine tolerance tests of heterozygous carriers of phenylketonuria. *Nature (London)* 178:1239, 1956.
202. HSIA DYY, PAINE RS: Phenylketonuria: Detection of the heterozygous carrier. *J Ment Defic Res* 1:53, 1957.
203. KNOX WE, MESSINGER EC: The detection in the heterozygote of the metabolic effect of the recessive gene for phenylketonuria. *Am J Hum Genet* 10:53, 1958.
204. HOLZEL A, KOMROWER GM: A study of the genetics of galactosaemia. *Arch Dis Child* 30:155, 1955.
205. KIRKMAN HN, BYNUM E: Enzymic evidence of a galactosemic trait in patients of galactosemic children. *Ann Hum Genet* 23:117, 1959.
206. ROTH M, FELGENHAUER WR: Recherche de l'excrétion d'acide homogentisique urinaire chez des hétérozygotes pour l'alcaptonurie. *Enzymol Biol Clin* 9:53, 1968.
207. LA DU B: Unpublished observations.
208. LABERGE CA, LESCAULT A, GRENIER A, GAGNE R: "Effet succinylacétone" après surcharges orales d'homogentisate. *Union Med Can* 110:621, 1981.
209. GAUCHER A, POUREL J, RAFFOUX C, FAURE G, NETTER P, STREIFF F: HLA antigens and alkaptonuria. *J Rheumatol 3rd Suppl* 97, 1977.
210. KAPRÁLIK I, CEIZELOVÁ L, NOVAKOVÁ J, POKORNÁ G: Asociacie medzi alkaptonuriou a niektorymi vybranymi polymorfnymi systemami. (Association between alcaptonuria and some selected polymorphic systems.) *Bratisl Lek Listy* 85:194, 1986.
211. SRŠEŇ Š, KAMARYT J, SRŠŇOVÁ K: Studium genovej vazby lokusom alkaptonurickej alely a lokusmi amylazy. (A study of gene linkage between the alkaptonuric allele and amylase loci.) *Cas Lek Cesk* 125:937, 1986.
212. MOSONYI L: A propos de'l'alcaptonurie et de son traitement. *Presse Med* 47:708, 1939.
213. DIAZ CJ, MENDOZA HC, RODRIGUEZ JS: Alkapton, Aceton und Kohlehydratmangel. *Klin Wochenschr* 18:965, 1939.
214. FLASCHENTRÄGER B, HALAWANI A, NABEH I: Alkaptonurie und Vitamin B_{12}. *Klin Wochenschr* 32:131, 1954.
215. BLACK RL: Use of cortisone in alkaptonuria. *JAMA* 155:968, 1954.
216. SUZMAN MM: The clinical application of corticotropin and cortisone therapy: A report of 247 cases. *S Afr Med J* 27:195, 1953.
217. BIGGS TG JR, CANNON E JR: Ochronosis: Report of a case. *J La State Med Soc* 105:395, 1953.

CHAPTER **28**

BRANCHED CHAIN ORGANIC ACIDURIAS

LAWRENCE SWEETMAN

1. Metabolism of the Branched Chain Organic Acids
The essential branched chain amino acids, leucine, isoleucine and valine, are transaminated to the 2-oxo branched chain organic acids and oxidatively decarboxylated to form branched chain acyl-coenzyme A products. Isovaleryl-CoA derived from leucine, 2-methylbutyryl-CoA derived from isoleucine, and isobutyryl-CoA derived from valine are metabolized by separate pathways to intermediates which enter general metabolism. Defects in these pathways cause eight known metabolic disorders called branched chain organic acidurias *(Table 28-10). Inherited deficiencies of all four enzymes of the catabolism of isovaleryl-CoA derived from leucine are known: isovaleric acidemia (isovaleryl-CoA dehydrogenase deficiency), isolated biotin-unresponsive 3-methylcrotonyl-CoA carboxylase deficiency, 3-methylglutaconic aciduria, and 3-hydroxy-3-methylglutaryl-CoA lyase deficiency. Mevalonic aciduria, due to a defect in the biosynthesis of cholesterol from 3-hydroxy-3-methylglutaryl-CoA, is also considered a branched chain organic aciduria. Only one inherited disorder of the catabolism of 2-methylbutyryl-CoA derived from isoleucine is known: 2-methylacetoacetyl-CoA thiolase deficiency. Two disorders of the catabolism of isobutyryl-CoA derived from valine are known: 3-hydroxyisobutyryl-CoA deacylase deficiency and combined 3-hydroxyisobutyric, 3-aminoisobutyric, 3-hydroxypropionic, β-alanine, and 2-ethyl-3-hydroxybutyric aciduria.*

2. Isovaleric acidemia (isovaleryl-CoA dehydrogenase deficiency)
Isovaleryl-CoA dehydrogenase deficiency may present either in the neonatal period as an acute episode of severe metabolic acidosis and ketosis with vomiting which may lead to coma and death or in a chronic intermittent form with episodes of metabolic acidosis. Infants who survive the acute neonatal episode go on to exhibit the chronic form. Neutropenia, thrombocytopenia, or pancytopenia often occurs with acidotic episodes. The odor of "sweaty feet" due to isovaleric acid is usually present during acute episodes. The major metabolic abnormality is a large elevation of isovaleryglycine in urine. Treatment with moderate protein restriction and more recently, with carnitine or glycine generally results in normal development.

3. Isolated 3-Methylcrotonyl-CoA Carboxylase Deficiency
The isolated deficiency of 3-methylcrotonyl-CoA carboxylase is not responsive to biotin and is distinct from the biotin-responsive multiple carboxylase deficiencies due to a deficiency of biotinidase or holocarboxylase synthetase. Patients typically present with acute metabolic acidosis and hypoglycemia. The major abnormal metabolite is 3-hydroxyisovaleric acid in urine. Treatment by modest restriction of dietary protein results in normal development.

4. 3-Methylglutaconic Aciduria
Two forms of 3-methylglutaconic aciduria are known. A mild form with a deficiency of 3-methylglutaconyl-CoA hydratase has speech retardation as its only clinical symptom. The major urinary metabolites are 3-methylglutaconic and 3-hydroxyisovaleric acids. No treatment other than, possibly, modest protein restriction is necessary. A severe form, with normal activity of 3-methylglutaconyl-CoA hydratase, initially permits normal clinical development but at 5 to 11 months causes progressive neurologic deterioration with movement disorders and optic atrophy or neurogenic hearing loss. The major abnormal metabolites are 3-methylglutaconic and 3-methylglutaric acids in urine. The basic biochemical defect is unknown, and no effective treatment has been found.

5. 3-Hydroxy-3-methylglutaryl-CoA lyase deficiency
One-third of patients with 3-hydroxy-3-methylglutaryl-CoA lyase deficiency present in the neonatal period, and two-thirds present between 3 and 11 months with severe hypoglycemia and metabolic acidosis but no ketosis, hyperammonemia, vomiting, and hypotonia which may progress to coma and death. The symptoms resemble Reye syndrome. The major abnormal metabolites are 3-hydroxy-3-methylglutaric, 3-methylglutaconic, and 3-hydroxyisovaleric acids in urine. Treatment by restriction of dietary protein and fat with avoidance of fasting generally leads to normal development.

6. Mevalonic aciduria (mevalonate kinase deficiency)
Patients with the severe form of mevalonic aciduria (mevalonate kinase deficiency) present in the neontal period with anemia, hepatosplenomegaly, gastroenteropathy, failure to thrive, and severe developmental delay. Patients with a milder form show poor muscle development, hypotonia, and ataxia with elevated creatine kinase. There is no metabolic acidosis, and although the defect is in cholesterol biosynthesis, blood cholesterol may be normal. The only metabolic abnormality is an extremely elevated amount of mevalonic acid in urine and plasma.

7. 2-Methylacetoacetyl-CoA thiolase deficiency
In patients with 2-methylacetoacetyl-CoA thiolase deficiency intermittent episodes of severe metabolic acidosis and ketosis begin during the first 2 years of life. These are accompanied by vomiting, often with hematemesis, diarrhea, and coma which may progress to death. The major abnormal urinary metabolites are 2-methyl-3-hydroxybutyric and 2-methylacetoacetic acids, together with butanone from decarboxylation of the latter. Some patients also excrete tiglylglycine. Patients with a milder form may excrete these metabolites only during an episode or with a diagnostic challenge with isoleucine. Treatment by modest restriction of dietary protein generally results in normal development. Several patients who have similar metabolite excretions have been found to have normal 2-methylacetoacetyl-CoA thiolase activities in fibroblasts but deficient metabolism of 2-methylbutyric acid through this pathway in intact fibroblasts.

8. Disorders of valine catabolism
In patients with a disorder of valine catabolism a deficiency of 3-hydroxyisobutyryl-CoA deacylase results in congenital malformations and lack of neurologic development without acidosis. The major abnormal urinary metabolites are not organic acids, but the amino acids S*-(2-carboxypropyl)-cysteine and* S*-(2-carboxypropyl)-cysteamine, which are formed by addition of cysteine to methyacrylyl-CoA, the precursor of 3-hydroxyisobutyryl-CoA. No treatment is known.*

In a person with no clinical symptoms, a presumed deficiency of a semialdehyde dehydrogenase led to elevated excretions of 3-hydroxyisobutyric, 3-aminoisobutyric, 2-ethyl-3-hydroxybutyric and 3-hydroxypropionic acids, together with β-alanine.

CATABOLISM OF THE BRANCHED CHAIN AMINO ACIDS AS BRANCHED CHAIN ORGANIC ACIDS

Transamination and Oxidative Decarboxylation

The initial step in the catabolism of the three branched chain amino acids, leucine, valine, and isoleucine (and also alloisoleucine derived from isoleucine), is the reversible transamination to the branched chain 2-oxo acids as described in Chap. 22. A deficiency of a transaminase causes an elevation of the amino acid with no elevation of the 2-oxo acid or other organic acids metabolites. The second step in the catabolism of the branched chain amino acids is the irreversible oxidative decarboxylation of the 2-oxo acids by branched chain 2-oxo-acid dehydrogenase with formation of branched chain acyl-CoA thioesters with one less carbon than the parent amino and 2-oxo acids, as described in Chap. 22. A deficiency of branched chain 2-oxo acid dehydrogenase causes maple syrup urine disease with an elevation of all of the branched chain amino acids and branched chain 2-oxo acids because the transamination is reversible. The branched chain 2-hydroxy acids may be elevated due to reduction of the elevated branched chain 2-oxo acids, but no other organic acid metabolites of the branched chain 2-oxo acids are elevated.

General Aspects of Branched Chain Acyl-CoA Metabolism

The branched chain acyl-CoA thioesters derived from the three branched chain amino acids are metabolized in a series of steps to simple organic acid intermediates which enter general metabolism. A distinguishing feature of deficiencies of any of these enzymes is that only branched chain organic acid metabolites are elevated; there are no elevations of the branched chain amino acids or branched chain 2-oxo acids because the reaction of branched chain 2-oxo acid dehydrogenase is not reversible. In contrast, many of the catabolic reactions of the branched chain acyl-CoA thioesters after the initial acyl-CoA dehydrogenase reactions are reversible, and as a general consequence the deficiency of an enzyme can cause the elevation of metabolites of many of the intermediates proximal to the deficiency. The elevated acyl-CoA thioesters can also be metabolized by several secondary pathways to a produce a variety of additional metabolites.

DISORDERS OF LEUCINE CATABOLISM

Catabolism of Leucine

The normal pathway for the catabolism of leucine to the common metabolic intermediates acetoacetic acid and acetyl-CoA is shown in Fig. 28-1. Inherited deficiencies of each of the six enzymes in the pathway are known. The four disorders of leucine catabolism considered to be branched chain organic acidurias in this chapter include isovaleric acidemia, isolated 3-methylcrotonyl-CoA carboxylase deficiency, 3-methylglutaconic aciduria, and 3-hydroxy-3-methylglutaryl-CoA lyase deficiency (Table 28-1). The enzymes of the catabolic pathway for leucine are localized in the mitochondria, and their relevant properties are summarized below.

Isovaleryl-CoA Dehydrogenase. The first step of branched chain organic acid metabolism of leucine is the irreversible dehydrogenation of isovaleryl-CoA to 3-methylcrotonyl-CoA catalyzed by isovaleryl-CoA dehydrogenase (Fig. 28-1). The identification of a dehydrogenase specific for isovaleryl-CoA is an outstanding example of how the discovery of an inherited disorder and its detailed characterization can elucidate normal metabolic pathways. It had been thought that a single acyl-CoA dehydrogenase, "butyryl-CoA or green acyl–CoA dehydrogenase," was responsible for the dehydrogenation of short-chain acyl-CoAs in fatty acid oxidation, isovaleryl-CoA in leucine catabolism, 2-methylbutyryl-CoA in isoleucine catabolism, and isobutyryl-CoA in valine catabolism.[1] The identification of the inherited disorder isovaleric acidemia without elevations of other short-chain acids led Tanaka and colleagues to propose the existence of a dehydrogenase specific for isovaleryl-CoA.[2] They confirmed this by demonstrating a deficiency of isovaleryl-CoA dehydrogenase with normal activity of butyryl-CoA dehydrogenase in mitochondria from fibroblasts of patients with isovaleric acidemia.[3] Further confirmation came from separation of isovaleryl-CoA dehydrogenase and butyryl-CoA dehydrogenase from pig liver[4] and from isolation and characterization of isovaleryl-CoA dehydrogenase[5] and four other immunologically distinct acyl-CoA dehydrogenases from rat liver mitochondria.[6]

The cDNA for isovaleryl-CoA dehydrogenase from the rat has been cloned and sequenced.[7] Isovaleryl-CoA dehydrogenase is synthesized on cytosolic free polysomes as a subunit precursor of 45,000 daltons.[8] It is processed to a 43,000-dalton subunit during importation into the mitochondria, where four identical subunits form a tetrameric enzyme of 175,000 daltons located in the matrix or on the inner face of the mitochondrial membrane.[5] It is a flavin enzyme with approximately 1 mol flavin adenine dinucleotide (FAD) per subunit. Electrons from the FAD are accepted by electron-transferring flavoprotein (ETF)[9] and transmitted to coenzyme Q in the mitochondrial electron transport chain by ETF dehydrogenase, an iron-sulfur flavoprotein,[10] as described in Chap. 34. In rat tissues isovaleryl-CoA dehydrogenase is most active in heart, followed by liver, kidney, and skeletal muscle.[11] The activity is present in normal human fibroblasts in culture.[3]

Isovaleryl-CoA dehydrogenase purified from rat liver mitochondria has a high specificity for isovaleryl-CoA, with a K_m of 33 μM, although valeryl-CoA is a poor substrate with a much higher K_m of 400 μM.[5] With substrates at 100 μM, the activity compared to 100 percent for isovaleryl-CoA is 32 percent for valeryl-CoA and only 3.3 percent for butyryl-CoA. The product with isovaleryl-CoA as substrate, 3-methylcrotonyl-CoA, is a competitive inhibitor with a K_i of 100 μM,[5] but it is not known whether this has physiological significance. The stereochemistry of the dehydrogenation reaction has been shown with isotopically labeled compounds to involve removal of the 2-pro-*R* hydrogen of isovaleryl-CoA[12] with anti elimination of hydrogens from C-2 and C-3.[13]

3-Methylcrotonyl-CoA Carboxylase. The product of isovaleryl-CoA dehydrogenase, 3-methylcrotonyl-CoA, is carboxy-

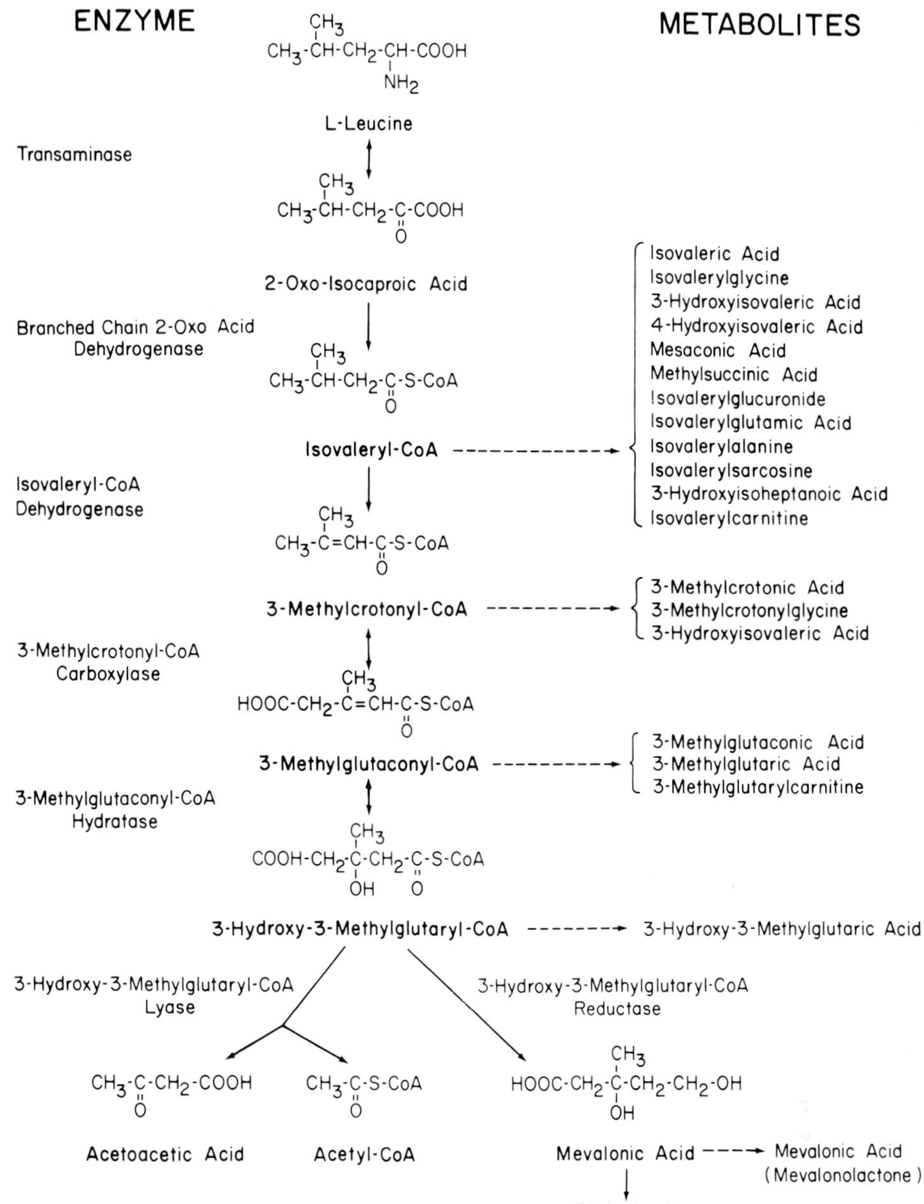

Fig. 28-1 Catabolism of leucine. The structures and names of the intermediates in the pathway for catabolism of leucine are shown in the center, with the names of the enzymes on the left and the metabolites that may be elevated due to a deficiency of the enzymes shown on the right.

lated at the 4 carbon by 3-methylcrotonyl-CoA carboxylase to form 3-methylglutaconyl-CoA (Fig. 28-1). The reaction, extensively studied for the bacterial enzyme, utilizes ATP and bicarbonate, and the product is (*E*)-3-methylglutaconyl-CoA (i.e., a trans double bond).[14] The reaction is reversible. Highly purified 3-methylcrotonyl-CoA carboxylase from bovine kidney mitochondria[15,16] has an approximate molecular weight of 835,000 and may be composed of six protomers. These are two nonidentical subunits, the A subunit of 61,000 daltons and the B subunit of 73,500 daltons, which contains covalently bound biotin,[15,16] and it is likely that the protomer is AB. As in all carboxylases, biotin is attached by an amide bond with an ε-amino group of lysine as described in Chap. 83. The enzyme is associated with the inner membrane of the mitochondria.[17] Normal human fibroblasts and lymphocytes express 3-methylcrotonyl-CoA carboxylase activity (Chap. 83).

3-Methylcrotonyl-CoA carboxylase requires Mg^{2+} and is activated four- to fivefold by K^+ and NH_4^+.[16] The K_m values of bovine kidney 3-methylcrotonyl-CoA carboxylase for the substrates are 82 μ*M* for ATP, 1.8 m*M* for bicarbonate, and 75 μ*M* for 3-methylcrotonyl-CoA. Compared to 3-methylcrotonyl-CoA with a relative velocity of 100 percent, other CoA esters that are substrates are (2*Z*)-3-ethylcrotonyl-CoA with a K_m of 22 μ*M* and relative velocity of 44 percent, *trans*-crotonyl-CoA with a K_m of 225 μ*M* and relative velocity of 27 percent, and acetoacetyl-CoA with a K_m of about 17 μ*M* and a relative velocity of 12 percent.[16] Tiglyl-CoA, which is 2-methylcrotonyl-CoA, is also believed to be a substrate for 3-methylcrotonyl-CoA carboxylase because most patients with disorders of isoleucine catabolism in whom tiglyl-CoA accumulates excrete (*E*)-2-methylglutaconic acid.[18] Butyryl-CoA and propionyl-CoA are not substrates but are weak competitive inhibitors with K_i values of 1.6 m*M* and 1.78 m*M*, respectively.[16]

3-Methylglutaconyl-CoA Hydratase. The product of 3-methylcrotonyl-CoA carboxylase, 3-methylglutaconyl-CoA, is hydrated by a specific enzyme, 3-methylglutaconyl-CoA hydratase, to 3-hydroxy-3-methylglutaryl-CoA (Fig. 28-1). Purified crotonase that hydrates crotonyl-CoA and other 2,3-unsaturated monocarboxylic acid CoA esters has been reported to hydrate 3-methylglutaconyl-CoA,[19] but this activity was re-

Table 28-1 Features of Branched Chain Organic Acidurias

Disorder	*Occurrence*	*Clinical presentation*	*Prominent urinary metabolites*	*Comments*
Isovaleric acidemia	>60 cases	Half with acute neonatal, half with infantile chronic intermittent presentation: vomiting, acidosis, ketosis, lethargy, coma, and death	Isovalerylglycine, 3-hydroxyisovalerate	"Sweaty feet" odor during episodes. Usually normal development with protein restriction, and carnitine or glycine.
3-Methylcrotonyl-CoA carboxylase deficiency	>4 cases	Variable; may include vomiting, acidosis, hypoglycemia, and coma	3-Hydroxyisovalerate, 3-methylcrotonylglycine	Distinct from multiple carboxylase deficiency; does not respond to biotin. Normal development with protein restriction.
3-Methylglutaconic aciduria; hydratase deficiency	2 male sibs	Speech retardation	3-Methylglutaconate, 3-hydroxyisovalerate	Diagnosis requires assay of hydratase.
3-Methylglutaconic aciduria; normal hydratase	7 cases	Normal for months, then a course of neurodegeneration with hypotonia, optic atrophy, usually without acidosis	3-Methylgluctaconate, 3-methylglutarate	Diagnosis requires assay for normal hydratase.
3-Hydroxy-3-methylglutaryl-CoA lyase deficiency	>19 cases	Neonatal or infantile presentation; vomiting, hypotonia, lethargy, coma, acidosis, hypoglycemia without ketosis, and hyperammonemia	3-Hydroxy-3-methylglutarate, 3-methylglutaconate, 3-hydroxyisovalerate	Often presents like Reye syndrome. Diagnosis requires assay of lyase.
3-Hydroxy-3-methylglutaric aciduria; normal lyase	4 cases	Variable; often hyperammonemia	3-Hydroxy-3-methylglutarate, 3-methylglutaconate	Moderate elevation of metabolites. Diagnosis requires assay for normal lyase.
Mevalonic aciduria	4 cases	Variable; may include failure to thrive, gastroenteropathy, hepatosplenomegaly, anemia, and death	Mevalonate	Low or normal blood cholesterol. No acidosis.
2-Methylacetoacetyl-CoA thiolase deficiency	>14 cases	Infantile presentation; intermittent acidosis, ketosis, vomiting, diarrhea, and coma	2-Methyl-3-hydroxybutyrate, 2-methylacetoacetate, sometimes tiglylglycine	Normal development with protein restriction.
3-Hydroxyisobutyryl-CoA deacylase deficiency	1 case	Malformations, failure to thrive, no neurologic development, and death	*S*-(2-carboxypropyl)-cysteine, *S*-(2-carboxypropyl)-cysteamine	No abnormal organic acids.
Semialdehyde dehydrogenase deficiency?	1 case	No clinical symptoms	3-Hydroxyisobutyrate, 3-aminoisobutyrate, 3-hydroxypropionate, β-alanine, 2-ethyl-3-hydroxybutyrate	No acidosis; coincident hypermethioninemia.

moved by repeated recrystallization of crotonase.[20] The specific 3-methylglutaconyl-CoA hydratase has been purified fiftyfold from sheep liver[20] and a hundredfold from beef liver.[21] The enzyme is presumably localized in the mitochondria, as are the other enzymes of leucine catabolism. The activity is expressed in normal human fibroblasts and lymphocytes.[22]

3-Methylglutaconyl-CoA hydratase is highly specific for its unsaturated dicarboxylic acid substrate and does not hydrate the related monocarboxylic acid compounds crotonyl-CoA or 3-methylcrotonyl-CoA.[20] Human fibroblast 3-methylglutaconyl-CoA hydratase has a K_m for (*E*)-3-methylglutaconyl-CoA of 6.9 μ*M*, while the lymphocyte K_m is 9.4 μ*M*.[22] The reaction is reversible with a K_m for dehydration of 3-hydroxy-3-methylglutaryl-CoA of 100 μ*M* for the sheep liver enzyme.[20] At equilibrium the ratio of the hydrated product, 3-hydroxy-3-methylglutaryl-CoA, to substrate 3-methylglutaconyl-CoA, is 5.5.[20] The stereochemistry of the dehydration of 3-hydroxy-3-methylglutaryl-CoA by 3-methylglutaconyl-CoA hydratase has been determined.[23] The product is (*E*)-3-methylglutaconyl-CoA, which would therefore also be the substrate isomer for hydration. The addition and elimination of water is syn in contrast to most enzymatic dehydrations, which are anti.[23] The stereoisomeric product of 3-methylglutaconyl-CoA hydratase is (3*S*)-3-hydroxy-3-methylglutaryl-CoA.

3-Hydroxy-3-Methylglutaryl-CoA Lyase. The product of 3-methylglutaconyl-CoA hydratase, 3-hydroxy-3-methylglutaryl-CoA, is cleaved by 3-hydroxy-3-methylglutaryl-CoA lyase to acetoacetic acid and acetyl-CoA (Fig. 28-1). The lyase has been highly purified from bovine liver.[24] It is a monomeric enzyme of 48,000 daltons[24] and is localized in the mitochondrial matrix.[25] It is most active in liver and kidney, with lesser activity in brain muscle.[25] It is also present in human fibroblasts[26] and leukocytes.[27]

The lyase requires a divalent cation such as Mg^{2+} (K_m of 1 m*M*) and a thiol compound such as glutathione for activity, and the K_m for 3-hydroxy-3-methylglutaryl-CoA is 8.0 μ*M*.[24] The substrate is the (3*S*)-3-hydroxy-3-methylglutaryl-CoA stereoisomer, which is cleaved with inversion of configuration.[23] 3-Hydroxyisovaleryl-CoA and 3-hydroxy-3-methylglutaric acid are not substrates.[28] Although 3-hydroxyglutaryl-CoA is not a substrate, it is a competitive inhibitor with a K_i of 50 μM.[29] The cleavage of 3-hydroxy-3-methylglutaryl-CoA is irreversible.

ROLE OF 3-HYDROXY-3-METHYLGLUTARYL-COA LYASE IN KETOGENESIS. 3-Hydroxy-3-methylglutaryl-CoA lyase functions as a component of the pathway for the catabolism of leucine in the mitochondria of most tissues. In liver the lyase has an additional function, the synthesis of the ketone bodies, acetoacetic acid, and 3-hydroxybutyric acid. There are liver mitochondrial isozymes of acetoacetyl-CoA thiolase which cleave acetoacetyl-CoA to two molecules of acetyl-CoA and a 3-hydroxy-3-methylglutaryl-CoA synthase,[30,31] which condenses acetoacetyl-CoA and acetyl-CoA to form 3-hydroxy-3-methylglutaryl-CoA.[25] 3-Hydroxy-3-methylglutaryl-CoA lyase then cleaves this to acetoacetic acid and acetyl-CoA. The net result of these sequential reactions is that acetoacetyl-CoA is converted to acetoacetic acid and CoA. This sequence of reactions is needed because liver mitochondria have insufficient activity of a deacylase to convert acetoacetyl-CoA directly to acetoacetic acid and CoA.[32] The acetoacetic acid is reduced in part to 3-hydroxybutyric acid, and these ketone bodies, derived from the β oxidation of fatty acids and the catabolism of leucine, enter the bloodstream for metabolism by other tissues. The stereochemistry of the 3-hydroxy-3-methylglutaryl-CoA synthase reaction involves attack of acetyl-CoA on the si face of the carbonyl of acetoacetyl-CoA with formation of the product stereoisomer (3*S*)-3-hydroxy-3-methylglutaryl-CoA,[33] which is the substrate isomer for the lyase. Separate cytosolic acetoacetyl-CoA thiolase and 3-hydroxy-3-methylglutaryl-CoA synthase enzymes are involved in the synthesis of 3-hydroxy-3-methylglutaryl-CoA for the cytosolic synthesis of mevalonic acid and cholesterol,[25] as will be described later.

Isovaleric Acidemia: Isovaleryl-CoA Dehydrogenase Deficiency

Since the first reports of isovaleric acidemia by Tanaka and colleagues in 1966,[2,34] some 45 cases have been reported with sufficient diagnostic criteria to establish the diagnosis. Sibs of these patients who died without a diagnosis but can be presumed to have had this disorder and cases not reported in the literature raise the total number of affected children to more than 60. Thus, this is not an exceedingly rare disorder, although the incidence is uncertain. It has been identified in various ethnic and racial groups. Articles on the earlier cases have been thoroughly reviewed,[35,36] and here reference will be made primarily to cases reported since 1980. Isovaleric acidemia was the first inherited organic acid disorder to be diagnosed by gas chromatography–mass spectrometry of metabolites, which has become the major technique for identification and diagnosis of new as well as recognized disorders.[37,38]

Clinical Aspects. Two clinically different types of isovaleric acidemia have been reported. One-half of the patients present with an acute severe neonatal illness and one-half with a chronic intermittent form. The biochemical defect, a deficiency of isovaleryl-CoA dehydrogenase activity, is the same in both forms, although heterogeneity of mutations occurs (see below).

With the acute form, the infants are well at birth, but at a few days of age (usually at 3 to 6 days, but sometimes as early as the first day or as late as at 14 days) they begin to refuse feeding and vomit, becoming dehydrated, listless, and lethargic.[39–45] They are often hypothermic and may have tremors or twitching and convulsions.[46] A foul odor of "sweaty feet" due to elevated isovaleric acid is commonly noticed. Metabolic acidosis with ketonuria is typical, and most recently reported patients have shown a significant hyperammonemia of 400 to 1200 μM.[41,43–44] Thrombocytopenia and neutropenia[39,41,45] or pancytopenia[47] are common, as is hypocalcemia.[39,41] Typically, the patients become cyanotic, then lapse into a coma, and, finally, die. Death may result from severe ketoacidosis, hemorrhage,[40,41,43] or infections. More than one-half of the patients with the acute form have died, but with rapid diagnosis and recent improvements in therapy, such as administration of glycine[44–47] and carnitine, to be described later, the outcome may be much more favorable. If the patient survives the acute neonatal episode, the subsequent course is that of the chronic intermittent form, and development may be normal.[44–47]

Clinical features of the chronic intermittent form of isovaleric acidemia are well-illustrated by the first two patients[34,48] as well as by more recent cases.[49–57] The first episode of illness usually occurs during the first year of life. Episodes often follow upper respiratory infections or increased intake of protein-rich foods. The recurrent episodes typically involve vomiting, lethargy progressing to coma, acidosis, and ketonuria, and the characteristic odor of "sweaty feet" due to elevated isovaleric acid. The episodes resolve with infusion of glucose and protein restriction. Additional symptoms that may occur with episodes include diarrhea, thrombocytopenia, neutropenia or pancytopenia,[53] and, in some cases, alopecia[51,53] and hyperglycemia.[50] The frequency of episodes is highest during infancy and decreases with increasing age. Most patients with chronic intermittent isovaleric acidemia have normal psychomotor development, but some have developmental delay and mild[34,48] or even severe[52] mental retardation. Many patients have a natural aversion to protein-rich foods. Biochemical diagnostic services are now more generally available so that a diagnosis of isovaleric acidemia often is made with the first episode. By combining early diagnosis with protein restriction and administration of glycine and carnitine, the chances of normal development should improve considerably. The oldest patient, now more than 24 years old,[34,48] although mildly retarded, had only two mild episodes of dizziness, blurred vision, and unsteady gait as a teenager.[48] She tolerated a pregnancy with little difficulty, and there were no ill effects to the offspring.[48]

Biochemical Abnormalities.

ABNORMAL METABOLITES. Isovaleric acidemia derives its name from the elevated concentrations of isovaleric acid found in the patients.[2] The concentrations of isovaleric acid in normal plasma are less than 10 μM. During remission patients may have concentrations of isovaleric acid from normal to 10 times normal (10 to 50 μM), but during severe episodes the levels rise as high as 100 to 500 times normal (600 to 5000 μM). Isovaleric acid has the odor of "sweaty feet." This odor is generally not noticeable during remission but can be quite pronounced during episodes. The amount of isovaleric acid in the urine of patients is much less than in plasma, with the excretion ranging from 8 to 300 μmol/day (normal less than 2 μmol/day).

The major metabolite of isovaleryl-CoA that accumulates

due to the deficiency of isovaleryl-CoA dehydrogenase is not the deacylation (hydrolysis) product, isovaleric acid, but rather an amide product produced by conjugation with the amino group of glycine, isovalerylglycine.[58] This reaction is catalyzed by the mitochondrial enzyme glycine *N*-acylase, whose primary function is the formation of benzoylglycine (hippuric acid) from benzoyl-CoA.[59,60] A variety of acyl-CoAs are substrates for the bovine liver enzyme, which has a K_m for isovaleryl-CoA of 180 μM, about 20 times that for benzoyl-CoA but with comparable maximum velocities for the two substrates.[59] Human liver glycine *N*-acylase has a K_m for isovaleryl-CoA of 672 μM.[60] The excretion of isovaleryglycine by patients with isovaleric acidemia ranges from 2000 to 15,000 μmol/day, compared to normal excretions of less than 15 μmol/day. The excretion is highest during acute episodes but is still very high during remission. Isovalerylglycine appears to be a nontoxic, readily excreted conjugate. The capacity of the glycine *N*-acylase appears to be adequate to remove the amount of isovaleryl-CoA usually produced by the patients so that little is deacylated to isovaleric acid. However, during acute episodes when the amount of isovaleryl-CoA is greatly increased by catabolic crisis, the capacity of glycine *N*-acylase is exceeded, and the level of free isovaleric acid becomes elevated. A second metabolite of isovaleric acid that was identified early is 3-hydroxyisovaleric acid.[61] This is excreted in abnormal amounts only during acute episodes, when there can be as much as 3000 μmol/day, or about 40 percent of the quantity of isovalerylglycine. It is thought to arise from $\omega - 1$ oxidation of elevated free isovaleric acid.

As shown in Fig. 28-1, a large number of additional metabolites of isovaleryl-CoA have now been identified in the urine of patients with isovaleric acidemia. 4-Hydroxyisovaleric acid is believed to be formed by ω oxidation of free isovaleric acid[40,62,63] and can be further oxidized to methylsuccinic acid and then dehydrogenated to mesaconic acid (methylfumaric acid). These oxidation products are only elevated during acute episodes. Isovaleryl-CoA can also form a number of different conjugation products, including isovalerylglucuronide,[64,65] isovalerylglutamic acid,[66] isovalerylalanine and isovalerylsarcosine,[67] and isovalerylcarnitine.[53] Isovaleryl-CoA can also be condensed with acetyl-CoA by 3-oxothiolase to form 3-hydroxyisoheptanoic acid.[68] Of these metabolites, which are only significantly elevated in the urine of patients with isovaleric acidemia during acute episodes, only isovaleryl glucuronide and isovalerylcarnitine are of importance, and their excretions are usually a small fraction of that of isovalerylglycine.

CELL METABOLISM STUDIES. The oxidation of [1-^{14}C]isovaleric acid to $^{14}CO_2$ is deficient in leukocytes of patients with isovaleric acidemia.[2] Similarly, the oxidation of [2-^{14}C]leucine, which is metabolized to [1-^{14}C]isovaleryl-CoA and then to $^{14}CO_2$, is only 1 to 4 percent of normal in fibroblasts cultured from patients.[69,70] Interestingly, the oxidation of [1-^{14}C]leucine, which is a measure of the activity of branched chain 2-oxo-acid dehydrogenase, was modestly decreased in fibroblasts of patients with isovaleric acidemia.[70] This is presumably due to inhibition by isovaleryl-CoA, because high concentrations of isovaleric acid also inhibited this activity in normal fibroblasts. Purified pig kidney branched chain 2-oxo-acid dehydrogenase is markedly inhibited by isovaleryl-CoA.[71] This inhibition does not appear to occur to any significant extent in vivo, because patients do not have elevated levels of the substrate 2-oxoisocaproic acid.

ENZYME DEFICIENCY. Although the pattern of abnormal metabolites and the results of cell metabolism studies strongly indicated that the enzymatic defect in isovaleric acidemia was a deficiency of isovaleryl-CoA dehydrogenase, direct proof of this was not available until 1980 because of the difficulty of measuring the small amount of its activity normally present in cultured human fibroblasts. A sensitive assay was developed based on the release of tritium from [2,3-^{3}H]isovaleryl-CoA by isovaleryl-CoA dehydrogenase with equilibration of the label into water.[4] The isovaleryl-CoA dehydrogenase activity in mitochondria isolated from fibroblasts of patients was shown to be about 13 percent of normal, while their butyryl-CoA dehydrogenase activity was normal.[3] With an improved tritium release assay, the residual activity in nine patients ranged from 0 to 3.5 percent of normal; the amount of residual activity did not correlate with the degree of clinical severity.[72] The K_m for isovaleryl-CoA dehydrogenase for normal fibroblasts was 22 μM. A deficiency of isovaleryl-CoA dehydrogenase in fibroblasts of a patient with isovaleric acidemia has also been demonstrated by a fluorescent ETF-linked assay.[73]

Genetics. The familial occurrence of isovaleric acidemia suggested that it was an inherited disorder.[34] Of 41 well-documented cases of isovaleric acidemia, 58 percent are female and 42 percent are male, which is consistent with autosomal recessive inheritance. The gene for isovaleryl-CoA dehydrogenase has been assigned to the long arm of human chromosome 15, region q12–q15, by Southern blot analysis of DNAs from human-rodent somatic cell hybrids and by *in situ* hybridization.[7] A heterozygote was shown to have less than 50 percent of normal oxidation of [2-^{14}C]leucine in fibroblasts.[69,70] Both the acute neonatal presentation and chronic intermittent forms were present in the same family, suggesting that the clinical heterogeneity may be caused in part by nongenetic factors. Genetic complementation studies of fibroblasts from 12 patients with isovaleric acidemia, half of whom had the severe form and half of whom had the mild intermittent form, indicated involvement of a single locus.[74] The cultured fibroblsts were fused with polyethylene glycol, and complementation in heterokaryons was determined by a macromolecular labeling test of the incorporation of [1-^{14}C]isovaleric acid into macromolecules, which depends on the activity of isovaleryl-CoA dehydrogenase. No complementation was found with fibroblasts from the 12 patients, ruling out intergenic complementation. This is consistent with the fact that the enzyme is a homopolymer of four identical subunits.[5] Molecular heterogeneity of isovaleryl-CoA dehydrogenase in fibroblasts from 15 patients with isovaleric acidemia was shown by labeling the proteins with [^{35}S]methionine, precipitating the enzyme with antirat isovaleryl-CoA dehydrogenase antiserum, and performing sodium dodecyl sulfate polyacrylamide gel electrophoresis.[75] The labeling was done both with rhodamine 6G to prevent processing into mitochondria in order to determine the size of the newly synthesized precursor enzyme and without rhodamine 6G in order to determine the size of the mature processed enzyme in the mitochondria. Five types of variant enzyme were found, with about one-half being variant 1, with normal precursor (45-kDa) and mature (43-kDa) sizes suggesting that the variant 1 alleles have point mutations and are processed normally. Variant 2 had a smaller (42-kDa) precursor, of which very little was processed into a 40-kDa form. Variant 3 was synthesized as a 43-kDa precursor and processed to a 41-kDa form. Variant 4 was synthesized as a 42-

kDa precursor and processed to 40-kDa size. No immunoprecipitable protein was detected with variant 5. Two cell lines were found to be compound heterozygotes for variants 1 and 2. A variety of explanations are possible for the different sizes of variants 2 to 4, but the most likely is premature termination of translation. Variant 5 may have a deletion, very early termination of translation, or a very labile mRNA. It is likely that additional variants will be identified as more patients are studied.

Diagnosis. The diagnosis of isovaleric acidemia requires the analysis of organic acids because the clinical features are common to a number of the organic acidurias. An odor of "sweaty feet" during acute episodes may be suggestive of isovaleric acidemia, but must be distinguished from the similar odor that can occur in glutaric aciduria type II due to the accumulation of butyric, isobutyric, 2-methylbutyric, and isovaleric acids. The odor is generally not present during remission and is not always noticeable during episodes. The possibility of isovaleric acidemia should be considered in neonates or older infants with any combination of refusal to feed, vomiting, lethary, coma, metabolic acidosis, ketosis, hyperammonemia, neutropenia, thrombocytopenia, or pancytopenia. Analysis of volatile short-chain acids in plasma with the demonstration of an elevation of isovaleric acid without elevation of other short-chain acids suggests a diagnosis of isovaleric acidemia. 3-Methylbutyrolactone derived from elevated 4-hydroxyisovaleric acid found in acutely ill patients with isovaleric acidemia may also be detected by analysis of volatile short-chain acids.[63] However, the accurate analysis of the plasma short-chain acids is difficult to perform, is often not readily available, and may not provide a diagnosis of other organic acidurias if the patient proves not to have isovaleric acidemia. Therefore, it is preferable to analyze the urine for nonvolatile organic acids, because isovalerylglycine but not isovaleric acid is always highly elevated in the urine of patients with isovaleric acidemia and most other organic acidemias can be distinguished by their urinary nonvolatile organic acid profiles.[37,38,76,77] The urinary acid profile diagnostic of isovaleric acidemia during an acute episode is a very large elevation of isovalerylglycine (2000 to 9000 mmol per mole creatinine) together with lesser elevations of 3-hydroxyisovaleric acid (1000 to 2000 mmol per mole creatinine). Significant but much smaller amounts (20 to 300 mmol per mole creatinine) of the minor metabolites, 4-hydroxyisovaleric acid, mesaconic acid, methylsuccinic acid, 3-hydroxyisoheptanoic acid, isovalerylglutamic acids, isovalerylglucuronide, isovalerylalanine, and isovalerylsarcosine, may be seen. In addition, nonspecific, large elevations of lactic, 3-hydroxybutyric, and acetoacetic acids are often seen. During remission, the only diagnostic organic acid commonly seen is a large amount of isovalerylglycine (1000 to 3000 mmol per mole creatinine).

High field proton nuclear magnetic resonance (NMR) is a promising new technique for the rapid diagnosis of organic acidurias by direct analysis of a small aliquot of urine; it can readily detect isovalerylglycine.[78–80] Isovaleric acidemia may be especially amenable to diagnosis by NMR because it is the only disorder in which isovalerylglycine is very highly elevated in urine, and this elevation occurs whether the patient is acutely ill or in remission.

The analysis of carnitine esters in urine is a complementary approach to the analysis of organic acids for the diagnosis of isovaleric acidemia. The acyl-CoAs are in equilibrium with their acylcarnitines, and these are readily excreted in the urine. Isovalerylcarnitine in small amounts (10 to 20 mmol per mole creatinine) has been identified in the urine of a patient with isovaleric acidemia during remission.[53] Upon oral administration of 100 mg L-carnitine per kilogram, the excretion of isovalerylcarnitine rose to 3200 mmol per mole creatinine, suggesting that administration of carnitine would increase the reliability of the diagnosis of isovaleric acidemia by the assay of acylcarnitines in urine.

Diagnosis of isovaleric acidemia from assay of the metabolites can be confirmed by assay of fibroblasts for a deficiency of isovaleryl-CoA dehydrogenase by either the tritium release[72] or fluorometric[73] assays. Assay for integrity of the catabolic pathway of leucine by oxidation of [2-^{14}C]leucine[70] or [1-^{14}C]isovaleric acid[69] or by incorporation of [1-^{14}C]isovaleric acid into macromolecules[74] is less conclusive. A deficiency of this pathway is consistent with, but does not prove a deficiency of, isovaleryl-CoA dehydrogenase. However, normal activity of this pathway is not consistent with isovaleric acidemia. Therefore, a patient with Fanconi syndrome reported to have a variant type of isovaleric acidemia[81] who had normal [2-^{14}C]leucine oxidation did not have isovaleric acidemia. This patient had a modest elevation of isovaleric acid in plasma but did not excrete isovalerylglycine, unlike all patients with isovaleric acidemia. Since dicarboxylic acids were increased in urine and no information on other short-chain acids in plasma was reported, it is possible that this patient had glutaric aciduria type II.

Prenatal diagnosis of isovaleric acidemia can be accomplished by assay for isovaleryl-CoA dehydrogenase activity by fluorometric assay or by macromolecular labeling from [1-^{14}C]isovaleric acid in cultured amniocytes, or by stable isotope dilution analysis of elevated isovalerylglycine in amniotic fluid following amniocentesis.[82] Isovalerylglycine was undetectable in 10 normal amniotic fluids and only 0.04 μM in one normal fluid. It was highly elevated at 3.50 and 6.02 μM in the amniotic fluids of two pregnant women with fetuses affected by isovaleric acidemia. It was also slightly elevated, at 0.11 μM, in the amniotic fluids from three pregnancies at risk for but unaffected by isovaleric acidemia. Thus, the accurate quantification of isovalerylglycine in amniotic fluid by stable isotope dilution analysis provides rapid and accurate prenatal diagnosis of isovaleric acidemia. The finding of isovalerylglycine in human amniotic fluid with an affected fetus at 16 weeks suggests that glycine *N*-acylase is active early in human fetal development, in contrast to that of the rabbit and rat, in which species the activity appears perinatally.[83] Isovalerylglycine was present at 1.2 ± 0.5 mmol per mole creatinine in the urine of three pregnant controls; it was the same in one pregnant woman whose fetus was at risk for but unaffected by isovaleric acidemia, but was elevated at 4.0 to 10.7 mmol per mole creatinine in another.[82] In the urine of two pregnant women with fetuses affected with isovaleric acidemia, isovalerylglycine was elevated to 12.5 to 31.1 mmol per mole creatinine. Therefore, analysis of isovalerylglycine in maternal urine is not suitable for prenatal diagnosis.

Treatment. Patients with isovaleric acidemia have been treated during acute episodes with nonspecific procedures appropriate for a number of organic acidurias: glucose infusion to provide calories and reduce endogenous protein catabolism and bicarbonate infusion to control the acidosis.[35,36] Treatment during recovery and remission generally consists of restriction of dietary protein to 1.5 to 2.0 g/(kg·day) to decrease the amount of leucine catabolized to isovaleryl-CoA. This has been effective in decreasing the frequency of episodes, although the wide variation in frequency of episodes among untreated patients and the decreasing frequency with age make it difficult to evaluate accurately the true effectiveness of this and newer modes of therapy. The two newer approaches to treatment, administration of glycine and carnitine, were designed to enhance the removal of isovaleryl-CoA as nontoxic, readily excreted products, isovalerylglycine and isovalerylcarnitine.

Glycine is required for the synthesis of isovalerylglycine by glycine *N*-acylase, and its concentration may be rate-limiting, especially when isovaleryl-CoA is highly elevated during an acute episode. The concentration of glycine in the plasma of patients with isovaleric acidemia tends to decrease during acute episodes, suggesting that insufficient amounts of glycine are available for isovalerylglycine synthesis.[84] Normal tissue levels of glycine are far below the reported K_ms for glycine of the enzyme: 3 m*M* for the beef liver enzyme[59] and 500 m*M* for the human liver enzyme.[60] Increasing the concentration of glycine would be expected to increase the rate at which isovaleryl-CoA is conjugated with glycine to isovalerylglycine. When 250 mg glycine per kilogram body weight was given orally with a leucine challenge to a patient with isovaleric acidemia, the usual rise in plasma isovaleric acid was prevented and the excretion of isovalerylglycine doubled.[84] Chronic therapy with 250 mg glycine/(kg·day) (divided into three doses) and a protein intake of 1.5 g/(kg·day) led to improved weight gain but did not prevent two acute episodes, although their duration was greatly shortened with rectal administration of 200 mg/kg of glycine every 6 h.[84] Two infants were treated with 250 mg glycine per kilogram by nasogastric tube with rapid decreases in metabolite levels but much slower clinical response.[46] Continued oral treatment with 800 mg glycine per day and 1.5 g protein per kilogram gave normal development without additional episodes. Other, similar experiences have been reported.[49,85] A detailed quantitative description of the effects of glycine on the metabolites of isovaleric acid during an acute episode has been published.[51] Benzoic acid, which as its CoA metabolite competes with isovaleryl-CoA for glycine *N*-acylase, prevents the beneficial effect of glycine.[51] Salicylic acid derived from aspirin is also a substrate for glycine *N*-acylase and could also interfere with the synthesis of isovalerylglycine. It would appear to be contraindicated in isovaleric acidemia.

Many patients with isovaleric acidemia were found to have a deficiency of total carnitine and a high percentage of esterified carnitine in plasma and urine.[53,54,86] Some patients have increased urinary excretions of total carnitine with an abnormally high percentage of esterified carnitine.[87] These facts can be accounted for by the equilibrium between isovaleryl-CoA and isovalerylcarnitine catalyzed by carnitine acetyltransferase and the continued loss of isovalerylcarnitine into urine at a rate greater than that for carnitine synthesis. The relative effectiveness of carnitine and glycine in treatment of isovaleric acidemia has been assessed.[53,54] Prior to treatment with carnitine, a patient excreted an amount of isovalerylcarnitine only 0.4 percent that of isovalerylglycine. Treatment orally with 100 mg carnitine per kilogram resulted in a 10 percent decrease in isovalerylglycine excretion and a rise in isovalerylcarnitine to 50 percent the level of isovalerylglycine.[53] When given with a leucine challenge, 2 mmol per kilogram of glycine or of carnitine was similarly effective as judged by the total amount of isovalerylglycine and isovalerylcarnitine excreted. Continued treatment was with 25 mg/(kg·6 h) of L-carnitine without glycine and gave satisfactory results. Another patient has been treated with moderate restriction of protein to 2 g/(kg·day) and L-carnitine, 40 mg/(kg·day) in three divided doses.[54] Excretion of isovalerylglycine remained much higher than that of acylcarnitines, but the patient has grown normally and tolerated an intercurrent illness without ketoacidosis. In this patient, administration of carnitine while the patient was receiving glycine resulted not only in an increase in isovalerylcarnitine excretion but also in a doubling of the excretion of isovalerylglycine.[54] The data are too limited to evaluate whether glycine or carnitine is more effective for the long-term management of isovaleric acidemia. The removal of isovaleric acid as isovalerylglycine with endogenously produced glycine is of primary importance. Restricting the amount of isovaleric acid that must be disposed of by moderate restriction of dietary protein to 1.5 to 2.0 g/(kg·day) is valuable. Treatment with L-carnitine seems appropriate to prevent carnitine deficiency from developing and to provide a second route of isovaleric acid disposal independent of glycine. However, during an acute episode additional treatment with glycine to maximize removal as both isovalerylglycine and isovalerylcarnitine would appear most effective.

A recent study of the catabolism of L-[3-methyl-$^2H_3$]leucine to isovalerylglycine, isovalerylcarnitine, and 3-hydroxyisovaleric acid in a patient with isovaleric acidemia questioned the value of restriction of dietary protein in this disorder.[88] In this study the amount of labeled leucine given was equivalent to the amount of leucine in a low protein diet of 0.75 g/(kg·day). For each of the three urinary metabolites, less than 10 percent was labeled, which indicates that more than 90 percent of the labeled leucine was incorporated into protein. The continued excretion of labeled metabolites after administration of the labeled leucine was stopped reflected turnover of proteins into which the labeled leucine had been incorporated. Thus, at this low level of protein intake the major source of isovaleric acid is the turnover of protein, and the value of protein restriction was questioned. Most patients with isovaleric acidemia are only restricted to 1.5 to 2.0 g protein/(kg·day), and further studies are needed to determine whether or not the fraction of leucine directly metabolized to isovaleric acid metabolites is much higher with higher protein intake.

Other Aspects. The mechanism of the toxicity of isovaleric acid is not known, but it is an inhibitor of succinate:CoA ligase in the tricarboxylic acid cycle and inhibits liver but not muscle mitochondrial oxygen consumption with glutamic, 2-oxoglutaric and succinic acids.[89] Isovaleric acid is an inhibitor of granulopoietic progenitor cell proliferation in bone marrow cultures, with half-maximal inhibition at 1.6 m*M*, and this may account for the neutropenia frequently seen in isovaleric acidemia.[90]

Isolated Deficiency of 3-Methylcrotonyl-CoA Carboxylase

Distinction from Multiple Carboxylase Deficiency. The isolated deficiency of 3-methylcrotonyl-CoA carboxylase that is not responsive to treatment with biotin must be distinguished from the biotin-responsive multiple carboxylase deficiencies that are due to disorders of biotin metabolism (biotinidase deficiency or holocarboxylase synthetase deficiency) and affect all four of the biotin-dependent carboxylases, as discussed in

Chap. 83. In all of these disorders, the major abnormal urinary metabolites are 3-hydroxyisovaleric acid and 3-methylcrotonylglycine due to a deficiency of 3-methylcrotonyl-CoA carboxylase. In the multiple carboxylase deficiencies, these are accompanied by small elevations of metabolites characteristic of propionyl-CoA carboxylase deficiency. Therefore the differential diagnosis of isolated 3-methylcrotonyl-CoA carboxylase deficiency depends on careful analysis of urinary organic acid profiles or on assay of fibroblasts or leukocytes for a deficiency of this enzyme with normal activities of the other carboxylases. It is difficult to determine whether some of the earlier patients had an isolated deficiency of 3-methylcrotonyl-CoA carboxylase because the possibility of multiple carboxylase deficiency was not always ruled out.

The first patient in whom 3-hydroxyisovaleric aciduria and 3-methylcrotonylglycinuria was found[91] was postulated to have a deficiency of 3-methylcrotonyl-CoA carboxylase, although measurement of the enzyme was not reported.[92] Oxidation of [1-^{14}C]isovaleric acid was normal in fibroblasts cultured with and without added biotin.[93] This is not compatible with an isolated deficiency of 3-methylcrotonyl-CoA carboxylase or an abnormal holocarboxylase synthetase, and its is likely that the patient had a deficiency of biotinidase, which is consistent with the cell metabolism studies and the urinary organic acid pattern. The patient was treated with protein restriction and 0.25 mg biotin per day without improvement, but this does not exclude a deficiency of biotinidase, since the required therapeutic dose may be much higher (10 mg biotin per day is the usual dose given to these patients). Four patients with clear indications of isolated 3-methylcrotonyl-CoA carboxylase deficiency have been reported.

Clinical Aspects. There is a wide range of clinical presentations. One female infant developed normally until 5 weeks of age, when she experienced increasing irritability, drowsiness, difficulty in feeding, vomiting, and rapid respiration.[94] She was diagnosed at 11 weeks with metabolic acidosis and infantile spasms, became apneic, and died of a cardiac arrest. Blood glucose was normal, but lactate was elevated. A boy had been well while living in Vietnam on a low protein diet, but at age 5, after moving to the Netherlands and eating a diet higher in protein, began vomiting and was hospitalized with semicoma, metabolic acidosis, moderate hypoglycemia, and some alopecia.[95] He responded to glucose infusion and a high carbohydrate diet but relapsed when protein was increased. Following diagnosis of 3-methylcrotonyl-CoA carboxylase deficiency and restriction of protein intake to 1.8 g/(kg·day), there have been no further episodes, and development is normal. An affected female sib had been asymptomatic in Vietnam for 5 years. Upon moving to the Netherlands, she was diagnosed and treated prophylactically with the same protein restriction and has remained asymptomatic. A female infant had repeated otitis media and presented at 22 months with hypotonia, coma, involuntary movements, and apnea.[96] There was severe hypoglycemia and mild metabolic acidosis. The crisis resolved with glucose infusion, and with treatment by restriction of protein to 2 g/(kg/day) she has remained well. Three previous sibs had died without a diagnosis.

Biochemical Abnormalities.

ABNORMAL METABOLITES. The characteristic abnormal metabolites of the deficiency of 3-methylcrotonyl-CoA carboxylase are 3-hydroxyisovaleric acid and 3-methylcrotonylglycine.[94–96] The acutely ill patient who died had a large elevation of 3-hydroxyisovaleric acid in urine without 3-methylcrotonylglycine and also had a massive excretion of 2-oxoglutaric acid.[94] The second patient excreted massive amounts of 3-hydroxyisovaleric acid (9000 mmol per mole creatinine) and 3-methylcrotonylglycine (400 mmol per mole creatinine), but no detectable 3-methylcrotonic acid upon admission.[95] He and his sib excreted 1700 to 4500 mmol 3-hydroxyisovaleric acid per mole creatinine (normal is less than 20 mmol) and 400 to 1000 mmol 3-methylcrotonylglycine per mole creatinine (normal amount is undetectable) while clinically well on a diet of 1.8 g protein per kilogram per day. The only abnormal metabolite in plasma was 400 to 650 μM of 3-hydroxyisovaleric acid (normal less than 10). The initial urine specimen of the last patient had an enormous elevation of 59,000 mmol 3-hydroxyisovaleric acid per mole creatinine and elevated dicarboxylic acids.[96] Subsequent urinalyses showed high elevations of 3-hydroxyisovaleric acid and 3-methylcrotonylglycine.

The major fate of 3-methylcrotonyl-CoA that accumulates in this disorder is not deacylation to 3-methylcrotonic acid, but appears to be hydration to 3-hydroxyisovaleryl-CoA catalyzed by crotonase (enoyl-CoA hydratase)[19,97,98] and then deacylation to 3-hydroxyisovaleric acid. The K_m of ox liver crotonase for crotonyl-CoA is 20 μM, and at equilibrium the hydrated product is 3.5 times the unsaturated substrate. 3-Methylcrotonyl-CoA is a substrate, and although it is hydrated at 14 percent of the rate of crotonyl-CoA, the equilibrium would favor 3-hydroxyisovaleryl-CoA. A second alternative fate is conjugation with glycine catalyzed by glycine *N*-acylase.[59] The K_m for 3-methylcrotonyl-CoA is 14 μM for the bovine liver enzyme, which is comparable to the K_m for benzoyl-CoA and 10 times lower than the K_m for isovaleryl-CoA.[59] The maximum velocities are comparable for the three substrates. The greater excretion by the patients of 3-hydroxyisovaleric acid than 3-methylcrotonylglycine may reflect the higher activity of crotonase compared to glycine *N*-acylase rather than substrate affinities of the two enzymes.

CELL METABOLISM STUDIES. Fibroblasts from the two sibs had only 2 percent of normal incorporation of [1-^{14}C]isovaleric acid into macromolecules in cultured fibroblasts.[99]

ENZYME DEFICIENCY. The first patient had no detectable activity of 3-methylcrotonyl-CoA carboxylase in mitochondria isolated from autopsy liver with normal activity of propionyl-CoA carboxylase.[91] The two affected sibs had a severe deficiency of 3-methylcrotonyl-CoA carboxylase both in leukocytes and in fibroblasts cultured with different concentration of biotin, while the activities of the other carboxylases were normal.[95] The activity of 3-methylcrotonyl-CoA carboxylase in leukocytes and fibroblasts of the father were less than half of normal, while the activities were within the normal range for the mother. The last patient had a marked deficiency of 3-methylcrotonyl-CoA carboxylase in leukocytes both before and after receiving biotin and in fibroblasts cultured with different concentrations of biotin, while the activity of propionyl-CoA carboxylase was normal.[96]

Genetics. This disorder appears to be inherited as an autosomal recessive trait.

Diagnosis. The possibility of a deficiency of 3-methylcrotonyl-CoA carboxylase should be considered in patients with the typical signs of an organic aciduria and especially in those with hypoglycemia. The diagnosis can be made by finding a large excretion of 3-hydroxyisovaleric acid (greater than 1000 mmol per mole creatinine), often but not always accompanied by elevated 3-methylcrotonylglycine, *without* elevations of isovalerylglycine or the distal metabolites of leucine, 3-methylglutaconic acid or 3-hydroxy-3-methylglutaric acid, and *without* the modest elevations of 3-hydroxypropionic, methylcitric and lactic acids seen in multiple carboxylase deficiency. It should be noted that modest elevations of 3-hydroxyisovaleric acid ranging from 50 to 200 mmol per mole creatinine (normal 1 to 20 mmol) which are seen in patients with severe ketosis of any cause[100] are far lower than the excretions in patients with 3-methylcrotonyl-CoA carboxylase deficiency.

For definitive diagnosis of isolated 3-methylcrotonyl-CoA carboxylase deficiency and exclusion of multiple carboxylase deficiency, the deficit of this enzyme with normal activity of at least one other carboxylase must be shown in leukocytes regardless of treatment with biotin or in fibroblasts regardless of the concentration of biotin in the culture medium.[95,96,101]

Heterozygotes for isolated 3-methylcrotonyl-CoA carboxylase deficiency cannot be reliably diagnosed by assay of the enzyme in leukocytes or cultured fibroblasts.[95]

Prenatal diagnosis of this disorder should be possible by stable isotope dilution analysis for elevated 3-hydroxyisovaleric acid in amniotic fluid, as has been shown for multiple carboxylase deficiency due to an abnormal holocarboxylase synthetase.[102] The prenatal diagnosis by assay for a deficiency of 3-methylcrotonyl-CoA carboxylase in chorionic villus samples or cultured amniocytes should also be possible.[103]

Treatment. Treatment of acute episodes with glucose and bicarbonate infusion and chronic treatment with restriction of dietary protein to 1.8 to 2.0 g/(kg/day) has been effective, giving normal development. Administration of biotin 10 mg/day was without clinical or biochemical effect, as expected with a defect in the 3-methylcrotonyl-CoA carboxylase protein, unlike the response produced in multiple carboxylase deficiency, where the defect is in biotin metabolism. Whenever a patient is diagnosed by analysis of the organic acids, it would be worthwhile to treat with biotin until the precise diagnosis is established by assay of the carboxylases in leukocytes or fibroblasts in case the patient has multiple carboxylase deficiency. Normal persons treated with large doses of biotin have significant increases in the activities of carboxylases in leukocytes,[101] and it is possible that the residual activity of 3-methylcrotonyl-CoA carboxylase in some patients might also be increased by treatment with biotin.

3-Methylglutaconic Aciduria: 3-Methylglutaconyl-CoA Hydratase Deficiency

Only two patients with 3-methylglutaconic aciduria have been shown to have a deficiency of 3-methylglutaconyl-CoA hydratase. These patients will be described first, and the other patients, who are more severely affected clinically and whose basic enzymatic defect is unknown, will be described later.

Clinical Aspects. Two brothers were diagnosed at ages 5 and 7 with speech retardation as their only clinical symptom.[104] One had been comatose for 1 day at age 1 year and had some psychomotor retardation at 2 years. Upon fasting for 18 hours, hypoglycemia and compensated metabolic acidosis occurred in one sib but not the other.

Biochemical Abnormalities.

ABNORMAL METABOLITES. The major abnormal metabolite excreted was 3-methylglutaconic acid, ranging between 500 and 1000 mmole per mole creatinine (normal 6 mmol per mole creatinine).[104] Two isomers are found in urine corresponding to the *E* (trans) and *Z* (cis) isomers. There was four times less excretion of 3-hydroxyisovaleric acid (150 to 250 mmol per mole creatinine, normal 0 to 16) derived from reversibility of the pathway to 3-methylcrotonyl-CoA and hydration. Very small amounts of 3-methylglutaric acid (5 to 10 mmol per mole creatinine, normal level undetectable), derived from hydrogenation of 3-methylglutaconyl-CoA, were excreted. The product of 3-methylglutaconyl-CoA hydratase, 3-hydroxy-3-methylglutaric acid, was excreted in normal amounts (5 to 15 mmol per mole creatinine). The levels of the three abnormal metabolites changed in parallel, increasing twofold with a high protein diet [4 g/(kg·day)] or fasting, decreasing by one-half with a low protein diet (1.5 g/(kg·), and increasing threefold with a challenge of 100 mg leucine per kilogram.

CELL METABOLISM STUDIES. Although the activity of 3-methylglutaconyl-CoA hydratase was very deficient in the fibroblasts of these patients, the incorporation of [1-^{14}C]isovaleric acid into macromolecules was only moderately decreased, to 55 to 65 percent of normal.[99]

ENZYME DEFICIENCY. 3-Hydroxy-3-methylglutaryl-CoA lyase activity was normal in leukocytes of both patients. Activity of 3-methylglutaconyl-CoA hydratase in the reverse reaction, dehydration of 3-hydroxy-3-methylglutaryl-CoA, was too low to be measured in normal leukocytes or fibroblasts.[104] The activity could be measured in normal cells when assayed in the direction of hydration of 3-methylglutaconyl-CoA, and fibroblsts from both sibs were markedly deficient, with activity only 3 percent of normal.[22]

Genetics. On the basis of this one family with two affected male sibs and two unaffected sibs, it is likely that this is an autosomal or X-linked recessive disorder.

Diagnosis. The only clinical symptom is speech retardation. It is uncertain whether this will be a consistent finding in the disorder, but it would be worthwhile to analyze urines of children with speech retardation. Diagnosis of 3-methylglutaconic aciduria can be made by performing quantitative analysis of urinary organic acids and finding a large elevation of 3-methylglutaconic acid (500 to 1000 mmol per mole creatinine) with about 25 percent as much 3-hydroxyisovaleric acid and only 1 percent as much 3-methylglutaric acid but normal excretion of 3-hydroxy-3-methylglutaric acid. A different pattern of metabolite excretions is seen in patients with 3-methylglutaconic aciduria without a deficiency of 3-methylglutaconyl-CoA hydratase: an excretion of 3-methylglutaconic acid of 35 to 600 mmol per mole creatinine and 25 to 40 percent as much 3-methylglutaric acid but no elevation of 3-hydroxyisovaleric acid or 3-hydroxy-3-methylglutaric acid. To distinguish these patients more accurately, it is necessary to assay the activity of 3-methylglutaconyl-CoA hydratase in leukocytes or cultured fibroblasts.[22] The diagnosis cannot be made reliably according to incorporation of [1-^{14}C]isovaleric acid into macromolecules in cultured fibroblasts, since this activity is about 60 percent of normal.[99]

It is not known whether heterozygotes can be diagnosed by

finding intermediate activities of 3-methylglutaconyl-CoA hydratase in leukocytes or cultured fibroblasts.

Prenatal diagnosis should be possible by stable isotope dilution analysis of elevated 3-hydroxyisovaleric acid[102] and 3-methylglutaconic acid in amniotic fluid. 3-Methylglutaconyl-CoA hydratase is likely to be expressed in cultured normal amniocytes, and assay for a deficiency of this enzyme should be suitable for prenatal diagnosis.

Treatment. It is not known whether protein restriction is of clinical benefit in this disorder, but since the excretion of the metabolites varies in proportion to protein intake, it might be worthwhile to evaluate modest restriction of protein to about 1.5 to 2.0 g/(kg·day).

3-Methylglutaconic Aciduria: Normal 3-Methylglutaconyl-CoA Hydratase

Seven patients have been reported with clinical features and organic acid excretions different from those of the two patients with proven deficiency of 3-methylglutaconyl-CoA hydratase. Enzyme assays have shown that two of the patient had normal activity of the enzyme, and cell metabolism studies of four patients also suggest normal hydratase activity. From their metabolite excretions and clinical features it is likely that two patients in whom cell and enzyme studies were not reported also have normal enzyme activity. These seven patients will be discussed together.

Clinical Aspects. The first female patient developed normally until age 9 months, when she ceased to grow.[105] She became hypotonic, had bizarre posturing of the right arm, self-mutilation of the left hand, and seizure activity on EEG, and at age 3 years functioned at a 4-month level. In another family two sibs were normal until 6 months of age.[106] The female patient ceased to develop, showed hyperkinetic movements, and regressed neurologically. She had choreoathetosis at 10 months and optic atrophy by 3.5 years. At 9 years she showed slowly progressive encephalopathy, moderate dementia, hyperkinesia, and spastic paraparesis. The male sibling similarly showed hyperactivity at 6 months, developmental delay at 11 months, and slowly progressive encephalopathy at 6 years with moderate dementia, dyskinetic syndrome, slight spastic paraparesis, pale disk, and neurogenic hearing impairment. A female infant developed normally for 3 months and then had a fever with vomiting, somnolence, and abdominal pain.[107] On recovery she showed failure to thrive, regression of psychomotor development, and hypotonia. At age 2, her findings included severe mental retardation, blindness with optic atrophy, and tapetoretinal degeneration, neurogenic hearing loss, and spastic paraparesis followed by death at 2.5 years. Another female infant developed normally for 5 months and then developed fevers, failure to thrive, and regression of development.[107] At 3 years, she had microcephaly, growth failure, severe mental retardation, optic atrophy, and spastic tetraplegia; death was at age 4 years. Another female infant was treated after birth for intrauterine dystrophy, anemia, and infection.[108] Findings included hypotonia at 6 months, psychomotor retardation, infantile nodding spasms, optic atrophy, and dysplastic features. At 1 year, microcephaly was noted, and there was a compensated metabolic acidosis. The most recent male patient had dysmorphic features, hypospadias, umbilical and inguinal hernias, undescended testes, and talipes equinovarus at birth.[109] At 6 months, he had hepatomegaly, mild developmental delay, truncal hypotonia, and limb spasticity. With viral illnesses, he developed severe metabolic acidosis and ketosis with moderate hyperammonemia.

Biochemical Abnormalities.

ABNORMAL METABOLITES. All seven patients were noted to have elevated excretions of 3-methylglutaconic acid and 3-methylglutaric acid without elevated excretions of 3-hydroxyisovaleric acid and 3-hydroxy-3-methylglutaric acid. The excretions of 3-methylglutaconic acid ranged from 25 to 50 mmol per mole creatinine in the two sibs to as high as 70 to 600 mmol per mole creatinine in other cases.[106–109] These excretions are generally lower than those of the patients with a deficiency of 3-methylglutaconyl-CoA hydratase (500 to 1000 mmol per mole creatinine). The most striking difference is that the latter patients had 25 percent as much 3-hydroxyisovaleric acid as 3-mthylglutaconic acid but only 1 percent as much 3-methylglutaric acid, while the patients with normal enzyme activity excreted 14 to 40 percent as much 3-methylglutaric acid as 3-methylglutaconic acid and had no elevation of 3-hydroxyisovaleric acid. The two elevated urinary metabolites doubled in parallel when a leucine challenge was given,[106] when an overnight fast was observed[107] or with intercurrent illness in conjunction with a high protein diet,[109] and decreased in parallel when protein intake was reduced or stopped.[108] However, in two cases high protein or a leucine challenge failed to increase the excretion of the metabolites.[108,109] With fasting there was a normal ketogenic response,[107] and with an acidotic episode ketosis also occurred.[109] The parents of patients did not show any elevations of the metabolites.[106,107] The two most recent patients also had large excretions of 2-oxoglutaric acid,[108,109] and the most recent case had elevated blood lactate and pyruvate as well.

CELL METABOLISM STUDIES. The oxidation of [2-^{14}C]leucine[107–109] or [1-^{14}C]isovaleric acid[107] was normal in cultured fibroblasts from four of the patients. This suggests that 3-methylglutaconyl-CoA hydratase was normal in these patients. Extensive fibroblast metabolism and enzyme studies in one case showed that there were no abnormalities in fatty acid or pyruvate oxidation or in many tricarboxylic acid–cycle and mitochondrial enzymes.[109]

ENZYME STUDIES. 3-Hydroxy-3-methylglutaryl-CoA lyase was normal in those patients in whom it was assayed.[107–108] Activity of 3-methylglutaconyl-CoA hydratase was normal in both the hydration and dehydration directions in muscle biopsy of the first case.[105] This was confirmed by finding normal activity of the hydratase in cultured fibroblasts of this patient, the next to last patient, and an unreported patient.[110] The basic enzyme defect is currently unknown. The observed metabolite elevations suggest a functional deficiency of 3-methylglutaconyl-CoA hydratase in vivo that may be due to secondary inhibition of the enzyme by a metabolite from an unknown primary enzyme deficiency. Another possibility is that the hydratase activity is normal but that there is a greater flux of 3-methylglutaconyl-CoA than can be metabolized. This flux would be unlikely to come from leucine catabolism. Another possible source is the recycling of intermediates of the cholesterol biosynthetic pathway (at the level of dimethylallyl pyrophosphate) to 3-methylcrotonic acid and hence to 3-methylglutaconic acid via the "mevalonic acid shunt" (Fig. 28-2, p.

805).[111,112] A partial block in cholesterol biosynthesis can lead to the overproduction of very large amounts of intermediates, as occurs in mevalonic aciduria.[113] If a block caused the accumulation of dimethylallyl pyrophosphate, which can be metabolized to 3-methylglutaconyl CoA, it would be far in excess of the amount produced by the catabolism of leucine. Another possible route from mevalonic acid is the dehydration of mevalonic phosphate, dephosphorylation and oxidation of the hydroxyl group to a carboxyl group, producing 3-methylglutaconic acid without going through the acyl-CoA intermediates of the mevalonate shunt. Incorporation of acetate into cholesterol in the most recent patient was normal in fibroblasts cultured in lipid-free medium.[109] This does not completely exclude a possible enzyme deficiency in this pathway because the incorporation of acetate into cholesterol in fibroblasts of a patient with mevalonic aciduria with less than 5 percent of normal mevalonate kinase also approaches normal.[113]

Genetics. Since male and female sibs have been affected, this disorder is likely to be autosomal recessive.

Diagnosis. The diagnosis should be considered in children with initially normal development followed by regression, progressive neuropathy, and usually optic atrophy. Metabolic acidosis generally is absent. The diagnosis can be made by analysis of urinary organic acids, which show an elevation of 3-methylglutaconic acid of 25 to 600 mmol per mole creatinine with about 25 percent as much 3-methylglutaric acid and normal excretion of 3-hydroxyisovaleric acid and 3-hydroxy-3-methylglutaric acid. Some patients also have a large excretion of 2-oxoglutaric acid. Studies of oxidation of leucine or isovaleric acid in fibroblasts are not informative. A specific assay of 3-methylglutaconyl-CoA hydratase is needed to determine whether this enzyme is normal or deficient to completely distinguish the two forms of 3-methylglutaconic aciduria.

Diagnosis of heterozygotes is not possible because metabolite excretions are normal and the affected enzyme is unknown.

Prenatal diagnosis might be possible by accurate stable isotope dilution analysis of the levels of 3-methylglutaconic acid and 3-methylglutaric acid in amniotic fluid.

Treatment. No effective treatment has been found. One patient was treated with a low protein diet for 1 month without improvement.[107] One patient was treated for 2 years with a leucine-restricted diet [150 mg/(kg·day)], which lowered the excretion of 3-methylglutaconic acid and prevented metabolic acidosis and seizures but had no effect on the hypotonia and retardation.[108] Another patient, treated with restriction of protein to 1.5 g/(kg·day) and bicarbonate to control acidosis, has shown no regression.[109]

3-Hydroxy-3-Methylglutaric Aciduria: 3-Hydroxy-3-Methylglutaryl-CoA Lyase Deficiency

Nineteen patients with 3-hydroxy-3-methylglutaric aciduria and documented deficiency of 3-hydroxy-3-methylglutaryl-CoA lyase have been reported since the first patient was diagnosed in 1976,[114] and 12 cases[115] were reviewed recently. Several patients with 3-hydroxy-3-methylglutaric aciduria but normal activity of 3-hydroxy-3-methylglutaryl-CoA lyase will be discussed later.

Clinical Aspects. The age of onset shows a bimodal distribution with about 30 percent of patients presenting between 2 and 5 days of life, 60 percent presenting between 3 and 11 months, and one case presenting as late as at 2 years old. About two-thirds present with vomiting, one-third with hypotonia, and two-fifths with lethargy, which progresses to coma in about 10 percent of the cases. About 10 percent have had seizures during an acute episode. All of the patients have had metabolic acidosis, often very severe with very low blood pHs, and 90 percent have had hypoglycemia, which is often severe. None of the patient have had ketosis, which is consistent since they are deficient in 3-hydroxy-3-methylglutaryl-CoA lyase, which is required for ketone body production. Almost half have had hyperammonemia, sometimes severe, and it is interesting that this is not restricted to neonates as it is in many organic acidurias. Hepatomegaly and elevated transaminases in blood have been seen in half of the patients. Death has occurred in four cases (20 percent)[116–119] and was due to severe hypoglycemia in at least one case.[116] Several patients have had microcephaly,[120,122] but one was microcephalic,[117] Computerized tomography of two severely retarded patients showed cerebral atrophy in one case[117] and hypodensity of white matter in another.[120,121] One patient had mild right hemiparesis.[119] The majority of the patients were developmentally normal.

A number of the patients have either been initially diagnosed with Reye syndrome or described as having symptoms very similar to Reye syndrome.[123–126] A number of other organic acidurias can also present with symptoms similar to Reye syndrome, and it would be worthwhile to analyze the urinary organic acids in all patients with these symptoms. Patients with Reye syndrome do not have the elevations in the urinary organic acids that are found in 3-hydroxy-3-methylglutaric aciduria.

Biochemical Abnormalities.

ABNORMAL METABOLITES. The characteristic abnormal metabolites in urine include 3-hydroxy-3-methylglutaric acid derived from hydrolysis of the 3-hydroxy-3-methylglutaryl CoA that accumulates due to a deficiency of the lyase. This metabolite is derived both from the catabolism of leucine and from the ketone body synthetic pathway from fatty acid oxidation. The average concentration of 3-hydroxy-3-methylglutaric acid in urine is about 1300 mmol per mole creatinine (range, 200 to 4000) when the patients are well and rises to an average of 11,000 mmol per mole creatinine (range, 1500 to 19,000) during metabolic crises. These are very large elevations compared to the normal excretions of 3-hydroxy-3-methylglutaric acid of 50 to 90 mmol per mole creatinine in the first months of life, which decrease to less than 20 mmol per mole creatinine by age 3.[127] Because of the reversibility of 3-methylglutaconyl-CoA hydratase, the excretions of 3-methylglutaconic acid are 70 to 100 percent those of 3-hydroxy-3-methylglutaric acid in affected patients. About 10 percent of the 3-methylglutaconyl-CoA is hydrogenated to 3-methylglutaric acid. Because of the reversibility of 3-methylcrotonyl-CoA carboxylase or because of inhibition by high concentrations of its product, 3-methylglutaconyl-CoA, accumulated 3-methylcrotonyl-CoA is hydrated, leading to a large elevation of the 3-hydroxyisovaleric acid levels corresponding to about 30 to 50 percent of the amount of 3-hydroxy-3-methylglutaric acid. When patients are severely ill, the 3-hydroxyisovaleric acid tends to increase dramatically, and 3-methylcrotonylglycine may also be elevated.[128–130] Elevation of 3-methylcrotonic acid in urine has been reported,[131] but both this compound (also called 3-methyl-2-butenoic acid) and an isomer, 3-methyl-3-butenoic acid, have been shown to be artifacts resulting from decarboxylation of 3-methylglutaconic acid in the gas-chromatographic analysis of 3-methylcrotonic acid.[132,133] It has also been suggested that 3-methylcrotonic acid can arise as an artifact of dehydration of 3-hydroxyisovaleric acid in the gas-chromatographic analysis. There are often secondary elevations of glutaric acid (up to 3000 mmol per mole creatinine) and adipic acid (up to 1100 mmol per mole creatinine) when the patients are acutely ill.[118,119,128,132,134] The glutaric acid may arise from inhibition of glutaryl-CoA dehydrogenase by 3-methylglutaryl-CoA or 3-methylglutaconyl-CoA.

It should be noted that these patients are unable to synthesize ketone bodies, and consequently they never have elevations of acetoacetic acid and 3-hydroxybutyric acid even when fasted or acutely ill. Some patients have had a large elevation of lactic acid during severe episodes.[134]

In common with patients with many other organic acidurias, patients with 3-hydroxy-3-methylglutaric aciduria have been found to have elevated ratios of acylcarnitine to free carnitine in urine.[135] 3-Methylglutarylcarnitine has been identified but not quantified in the urine of patients.[136] No carnitine derivatives of 3-hydroxy-3-methylglutaric, 3-methylglutaconic, or 3-hydroxyisovaleric acids were detected even though these acids are more highly elevated in urine than 3-methylglutaric acid.

CELL METABOLISM STUDIES. Because the pattern of elevated metabolites in urine was very suggestive of a deficiency of 3-hydroxy-3-methylglutaryl-CoA lyase and the substrate was readily available, studies of oxidation of leucine in cells were not done; instead the enzyme was assayed to demonstrate its deficiency directly. Incorporation of [1-^{14}C]isovaleric acid into macromolecules has been studied in cultured fibroblasts from seven patients; all showed the same severe functional deficiency of the leucine catabolic pathway, with a mean activity 5 percent of normal.[99]

ENZYME DEFICIENCY. 3-Hydroxy-3-methylglutaryl-CoA lyase has been shown to be deficient in either fibroblasts,[26] leukocytes,[27] or liver cells[116,125] from all of the reported patients. The amount of residual activity was shown to be essentially the same in fibroblasts of seven patients, with a mean of 1.1 percent of normal (range 0.7 to 1.4 percent), which suggests that the small differences in reported activity are due to differences in methodology and that variations in clinical severity may not be due to differences in the amount of enzyme activity.[99]

Genetics. Approximately equal numbers of males and females are affected, indicating that 3-hydroxy-3-methylglutaric aciduria is inherited as an autosomal recessive trait. Genetic complementation studies with fused fibroblasts from seven patients showed no evidence for different complementation groups.[99] The existence of a single gene for 3-hydroxy-3-methylglutaryl-CoA lyase suggested by the complementation studies is consistent with the fact that the bovine liver enzyme is a monomeric protein.[24]

Diagnosis. The possibility of 3-hydroxy-3-methylglutaryl-CoA lyase deficiency should be considered in neonates and infants presenting with symptoms resembling Reye syndrome, such as lethargy, tachypnea, vomiting, hypoglycemia, hyperammonemia, hepatomegaly, and elevated transaminases in blood, but without ketosis. The first approach to diagnosis is the determination of the urinary organic acid levels for the characteristic pattern of elevated 3-hydroxy-3-methylglutaric acid, 3-methylglutaconic acid, 3-hydroxyisovaleric acid, and 3-methylglutaric acid. Any of the first three acids may be the one most elevated during an acute episode, but with recovery the two predominant acids are 3-hydroxy-3-methylglutaric acid and 3-methylglutaconic acid. Glutaric acid and adipic acid may be highly elevated during severe acidosis, but the glutaric acidurias can be excluded because 3-hydroxy-3-methylglutaric acid and 3-methylglutaconic acid are not elevated in these disorders. 3-Methylcrotonylglycine may or may not be elevated during a crisis, but it is normal between episodes. Two-dimensional NMR can detect 3-hydroxyisovaleric, 3-methylglutaconic, and 3-hydroxy-3-methylglutaric acids in the patients' urine and may be useful for rapid diagnosis.[137] High-performance-liquid-chromatographic (HPLC) analysis of urine with ultraviolet detection has been used to identify and quantify 3-methylglutaconic acid in urine,[138] but as pointed out,[139] this is not sufficient to distinguish between 3-methylglutaconic aciduria and 3-hydroxy-3-methylglutaryl-CoA lyase deficiency. The diagnosis of 3-hydroxy-3-methylglutaryl-CoA lyase deficiency must be demonstrated by direct assay of the enzyme in leukocytes or fibroblasts.

Heterozygotes for 3-hydroxy-3-methylglutaryl-CoA lyase deficiency can usually be diagnosed by finding intermediate activities of the enzyme in leukocytes,[26,140] lymphocytes,[119] or fibroblasts,[119,141] although in some families the activity of obligate heterozygotes is not significantly lower than normal.[122,128]

Prenatal diagnosis of 3-hydroxy-3-methylglutaryl-CoA lyase deficiency has been accomplished by finding elevations of 3-hydroxy-3-methylglutaric, 3-methylglutaconic, and 3-hydroxyisovaleric acids in maternal urine between 23 weeks of gestation and delivery.[140] 3-Methylglutaconic acid was the most elevated metabolite, at about 140 mmol per mole creatinine. It is not certain at what stage of pregnancy elevated urinary metabolites would provide reliable prenatal diagnosis, and, as with other organic acidurias, it would be preferable to accurately quantify the metabolites in amniotic fluid. 3-Hydroxy-3-methylglutaryl-CoA lyase has been demonstrated in cultured normal amniocytes, indicating that prenatal diagnosis by assay for deficiency of this enzyme should be possible.[142] We found levels consistent with a heterozygous fetus in amniocytes from a pregnant woman who gave birth to a healthy child (Sweetman, Gibson, Greene, Blitzer, unpublished). The concentration of 3-hydroxy-3-methylglutaric acid determined by stable isotope dilution gas chromatography–mass spectrometry was normal in the amniotic fluid of this woman. An elevation of this acid and 3-hydroxyisovaleric acid[102] would be expected in amniotic fluid with an affected fetus since elevations were found in maternal urine with an affected fetus.[140]

Treatment. Treatment of acute episodes consists of intravenous administration of glucose to control hypoglycemia and of bicarbonate for acidosis.[123] The first patient, now more than 10 years old, did not receive any special maintenance therapy, but he spontaneously selected a diet low in both protein and fat and has had only minor episodes with normal development.[114,115,123] Patients have been treated by restriction of protein (and hence leucine, a precursor of the elevated metabolites) together with formulas for maple syrup urine disease supplemented with valine and isoleucine to provide 50 to 150 mg leucine per kilogram per day.[121–122,140,143–145] The restriction of fat (a source of acetyl-CoA, a precursor of the elevated metabolites) has been shown to be more effective than restriction of protein in reducing the excretion of metabolites.[117,145] The most appropriate dietary therapy would appear to be restriction of protein to about 1.5 to 2.0 g/(kg·day) with restriction of fat to about 25 percent of caloric intake and hence a high carbohydrate diet. It is important to avoid fasting, which causes hypoglycemia and increases fatty acid oxidation. Acetyl-CoA from fatty acid oxidation cannot be metabolized to ketone bodies due to the deficiency of 3-hydroxy-3-methylglutaryl-CoA lyase. Instead, acetyl-CoA is metabolized in part to 3-hydroxy-3-methylglutaryl-CoA, which results in elevated metabolites and acidosis. Treatment with carnitine may be appropriate to prevent development of carnitine deficiency but is not an effective means of removing elevated metabolites.[136,146] There appears to be some risk in immunizing these infants, because one died[116] and another became ill following immunizations.[122]

3-Hydroxy-3-Methylglutaric Aciduria: Normal 3-Hydroxy-3-Methylglutaryl-CoA Lyase

Not all patients with elevations of some of the urinary metabolites typical of 3-hydroxy-3-methylglutaric aciduria have a deficiency of 3-hydroxy-3-methylglutaryl-CoA lyase, and thus it is essential to determine the activity of this enzyme in all patients with this organic aciduria. A patient with hyperammonemia due to a deficiency of carbamyl-phosphate synthetase deficiency showed modest elevations of 3-hydroxy-3-methylglutaric and 3-methylglutaconic acids which disappeared with protein restriction.[147] Another patient with hyperammonemia but normal urea cycle enzymes had elevations of 3-hydroxy-3-methylglutaric acid (181 mmol per mole creatinine), 3-methylglutaconic cid (463 mmol per mole creatinine), and 3-methylglutaric acid (170 mmol per mole creatinine) but no elevation of 3-hydroxyisovaleric acid and normal activity of 3-hydroxy-3-methylglutaryl-CoA lyase.[148] Except for the modest elevation of 3-hydroxy-3-methylglutaric acid, the quantitative pattern, with 3-methylglutaric acid at 37 percent the amount of the 3-methylglutaconic acid, is rather similar to that of patients with 3-methylglutaconic aciduria with normal activity of 3-methylglutaconyl-CoA hydratase. A sib had hyperammonemia and appeared to have reduced activity of carbamyl-phosphate synthetase.[149] A patient without hyperammonemia but with microcephaly, delayed growth and development, bilateral nerve deafness, and basal ganglia resembling Leigh disease had small elevations of the four characteristic metabolites of 3-hydroxy-3-methylglutaric aciduria but normal 3-hydroxy-3-methylglutaryl-CoA lyase activity.[149] When the patient was relatively well, 3-methylglutaric acid was about 18 percent of 3-methylglutaconic acid and more elevated than 3-hydroxy-3-methylglutaric acid.

Interpretation of these cases is hampered by the lack of quantitative information about the amount and proportions of metabolites during acute episodes and when well. There is no explanation for why this metabolite pattern should be seen in patients with carbamyl-phosphate synthetase deficiency. The last patient more closely resembles those with 3-methylglutaconic aciduria with normal hydratase activity. It is possible that a defect in cholesterol biosynthesis and overload of the leucine catabolic pathway by recycling via the mevalonate shunt could occur. In some patients the limiting enzyme could be 3-hydroxy-3-methylglutaryl-CoA lyase, leading to 3-hydroxy-3-methylglutaric aciduria, and in other patients the limiting enzyme could be 3-methylglutaconyl-CoA hydratase, leading to 3-methylglutaconic aciduria.

Mevalonic Aciduria: Mevalonate Kinase Deficiency

Two patients with mevalonic aciduria have been reported, and two additional patients have been diagnosed recently. Although this disorder is the first recognized defect in the biosynthesis of cholesterol and isoprenoids, it is a branched chain organic aciduria and is related to the other disorders because the initial substrate for the cytosolic pathway is 3-hydroxy-3-methylglutaryl-CoA, which is an intermediate in the mitochondrial pathway for leucine catabolism.

Pathway for Mevalonate and Cholesterol Biosynthesis. The relevant portions of the pathway for the biosynthesis of cholesterol are shown in Fig. 28-2, and the regulatory aspects are discussed more fully in Chap. 48. This pathway is localized in the cytoplasm, and the cytosolic enzymes responsible for the synthesis of 3-hydroxy-3-methylglutaryl-CoA are distinct from the mitochondrial enzymes which are involved in ketone body synthesis. A cytoplasmic acetoacetyl-CoA thiolase interconverts acetyl-CoA and acetoacetyl-CoA, which are then condensed by a cytoplasmic 3-hydroxy-3-methylglutaryl-CoA synthase to form 3-hydroxy-3-methylglutaryl-CoA.[25]

The first enzyme of isoprenoid biosynthesis is 3-hydroxy-3-methylglutaryl-CoA reductase, which reductively decarboxylates the CoA-thioester group of the substrate with NADP to release carbon dioxide, coenzyme A, and 3-*R*-mevalonic acid.[150] This enzyme is highly regulated in its activity by phosphorylation and dephosphorylation and also in its rate of degradation. Its synthesis is controlled at the transcriptional level by end products of isoprenoid biosynthesis and in particular by sterols.[150–152] The reductase reaction is not reversible.

The second step is phosphorylation of the 5-hydroxy group of mevalonic acid with ATP by mevalonate kinase to form 3-*R*-mevalonic acid-5-phosphate.[153–155] The purified porcine liver enzyme has a molecular weight of 104,000 and is composed of two identical subunits.[155] The porcine liver enzyme has a K_m for the natural isomer 3-*R*-mevalonic acid of 50 μM.[154] It is inhibited by geranyl pyrophosphate and farnesyl pyrophosphate.[156]

The next reaction is phosphorylation of mevalonic acid-5-phosphate with ATP by mevalonic acid-5-phosphate kinase to form mevalonic acid-5-pyrophosphate.[153] This is then decarboxylated and dehydrated in an ATP-requiring irreversible reaction by mevalonic acid pyrophosphate decarboxylase to form isopentenyl pyrophosphate. This is in equilibrium with dimethylallyl pyrosphosphate, which has the branched 5-carbon isoprene structure. Isopentenyl pyrophosphate and dimethylallyl pyrophosphate are condensed to form the 10-carbon isoprenoid, farnesyl pyrophosphate. At this point there are branch points to the other isoprenoid end products, dolichol, ubiquinone, heme A, and, via geranyl pyrophosphate and squalene, cholesterol. These end products serve a variety of functions in human metabolism. Cholesterol is an important component of

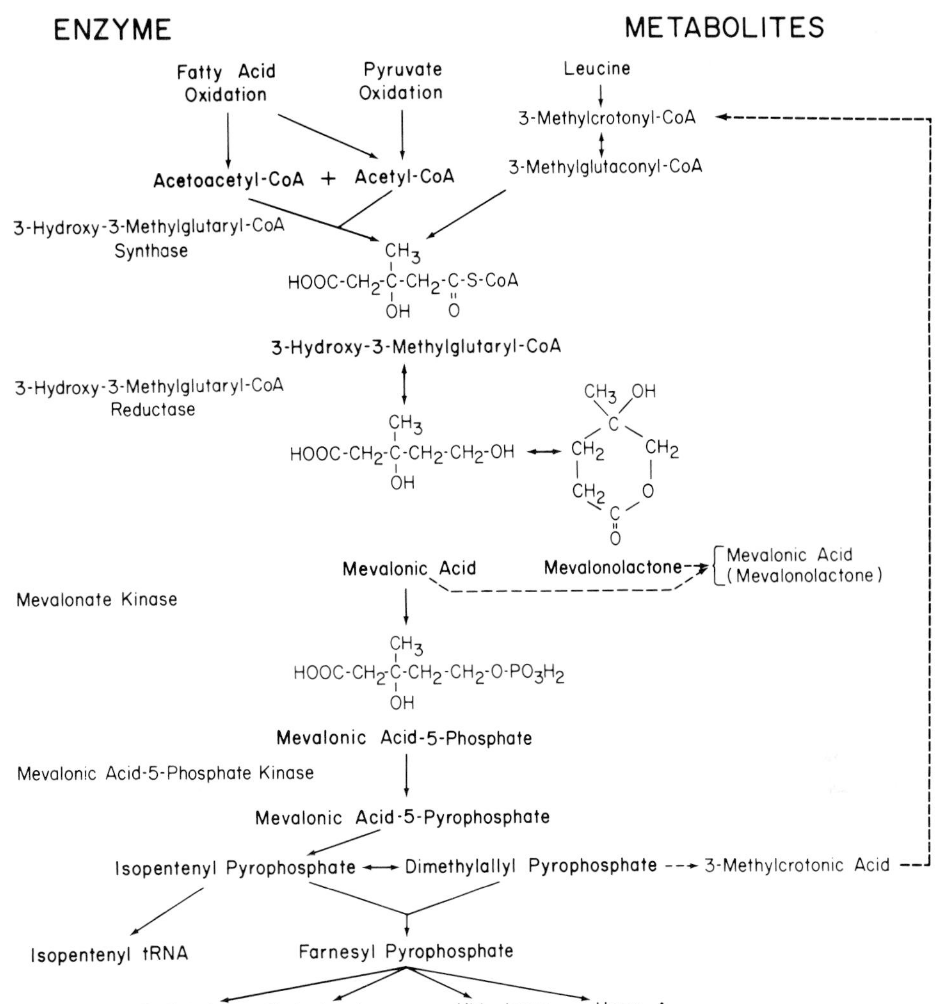

Fig. 28-2 Metabolism of mevalonic acid and biosynthesis of cholesterol. The structures and names of the intermediates in the synthetic pathway for mevalonic acid and cholesterol and other isoprenoids are shown in the center, with the names of the enzymes on the left and the metabolites that may be elevated due to a deficiency of the enzymes shown on the right.

plasma membranes and is a precursor of steroid hormones and bile acids. Dolichol is involved in the synthesis of glycoproteins. Ubiquinone is a component of the electron transport chain in mitochondria.

A mevalonic acid shunt (Fig. 28-2) can recycle mevalonic acid produced from cytosolic 3-hydroxy-3-methylglutaryl-CoA to 3-hydroxy-3-methylglutaryl-CoA in the mitochondria, where it can be cleaved to acetoacetate and acetyl-CoA for ketone body synthesis. Alternatively, these molecules can be transferred to the cytosol for fatty acid synthesis, and ultimately a portion can be oxidized to carbon dioxide.[111,112] This pathway involves the hydrolysis of dimethylallyl pyrophosphate by phosphatases to form dimethylallyl alcohol, which is oxidized sequentially by alcohol and aldehyde dehydrogenases via 3-methylcrotonaldehyde to 3-methylcrotonic acid.[157] After formation of the CoA derivative in the mitochondria, 3-methylcrotonyl-CoA is carboxylated to 3-methylglutaconyl-CoA, hydrated to 3-hydroxy-3-methylglutaryl-CoA and cleaved to acetoacetic acid and acetyl-CoA by the enzymes of the leucine catabolic pathway. About half of the shunting of mevalonic acid to pathways not leading to isoprenoid synthesis occurs in the kidney of the rat.[158] In human beings, the excretion rate of endogenously produced *R*-mevalonic acid is 1.7 μmol/day, or 29 percent of the glomerular filtration rate;[159] in perfused rat kidneys, the excretion rate is 40 to 50 percent of the glomerular filtration rate.[160] Both mevalonic acid and mevalonolactone are readily taken up by cells, but the circulating form in plasma is the salt of mevalonic acid because there is a serum enzyme which catalyzes hydrolysis of the lactone.[161] In human beings the concentrations of mevalonic acid in plasma are about 50 to 100 n*M* and show a circadian rhythm.[162] It is suggested that the intracellular concentration of mevalonic acid is proportional to its rate of synthesis by the highly regulated 3-hydroxy-3-methylglutaryl-CoA reductase and hence proportional to the rate of cholesterol biosynthesis. The assumption that a constant small fraction of this intracellular mevalonic acid diffuses into the plasma would explain the excellent linear correlation between plasma mevalonic acid concentrations and cholesterol biosynthesis.[162]

Clinical Aspects. There is considerable clinical heterogeneity among the two reported patients and the two diagnosed recently. A male neonate had mixed acidosis with diarrhea and fever and remained hospitalized for 7 weeks, requiring transfusions for anemia.[113,163] Cataracts were noted at 2 months. For the first 2 years he had multiple admissions for anemia, infections, seizures, and gastroenteropathy thought to be due to intolerance to cow's milk and fat, but he was not acidotic. He virtually ceased to grow after 6 months. At 2 years he was at a developmental standstill, was hypotonic, and had hyperactive deep-tendon reflexes. Dysplastic features, central cataracts, and hepatosplenomegaly were present. He had an iron deficiency anemia, low serum cholesterol (1.8 to 2.1 m*M*), retarded bone age, and generalized atrophy of the brain. A very high concentration of mevalonic acid was found in his urine. He died at slightly over 2 years following admission with diarrhea, dehydration, hyponatremia, and hypokalemia.

In a subsequent pregnancy a prenatal diagnosis of a female fetus affected with mevalonic aciduria was made, and the pregnancy was terminated at 19 weeks' gestation. The fetus was of normal weight and had no macroscopic or histologic abnormalities.[113,163]

A similar, severely affected patient without dysplastic features was diagnosed recently.[164] The female neonate was noted to have hepatosplenomegaly, thrombocytopenia, anemia, and leukocytosis at birth and to have widened cerebral ventricles. She had gastroenteropathy and failure to thrive. Her serum cholesterol was normal at 1.71 to 3.40 m*M*, and mevalonic acid was highly elevated in plasma and urine. She was still hospitalized at 3½ months, having gained only 700 g over her birth weight of 2200 g while receiving a special formula with casein hydrolysate. Death occurred at 4 months.

A more mildly affected patient has been reported.[165] The male child had frequent upper respiratory infections from age 6 months and elevated liver enzymes in blood at 1 year.[165,166] He had poor muscle development and was hypotonic with elevated creatine kinase at 2½ years. He spoke monotonously, had cerebellar ataxia, and could walk only short distances. A muscle biopsy at 3½ years was normal by light and electron microscopy. Laboratory results were normal at 6 years including serum cholesterol at 3.80 to 5.42 m*M*. The only biochemical abnormality was a large elevation of mevalonic acid in urine. A deficiency of the fat-soluble vitamins A, E, and D was found, along with a low amount of bile acids in feces (but not in blood) and a bile acid pool only 15 percent of normal size. Therapy with bile acids did not lead to clinical improvement, but on treatment with vitamins A, E, and D, there was a decrease in creatine kinase in blood. He attends a normal school.

Another mildly affected patient was diagnosed recently.[167] The male neonate presented with respiratory distress and hepatosplenomegaly. He was lethargic and had anemia, thrombocytopenia, and hyperbilirubinemia. Serum cholesterol was normal at 3.08 m*M*, but mevalonic acid was highly elevated in urine. He had cytomegalovirus in his urine, and his symptoms were consistent with perinatal cytomegalovirus syndrome. On discharge at 6 weeks of age he was doing well.

There are too few recognized patients with this disorder to generalize about the clinical features. Only one patient had dysmorphology, which may not be related to the basic defect. Metabolic acidosis is not a feature of mevalonic aciduria despite the very large production of mevalonic acid. This is due to the high renal clearance of mevalonic acid.

Biochemical Abnormalities. Although the basic defect is in isoprenoid and cholesterol biosynthesis, in general, the levels of cholesterol are normal or only slightly low in serum, and steroid profiles are normal. Bile acid levels in blood were also normal in the one patient studied, but there was a greatly reduced pool size of bile acids.

ABNORMAL METABOLITES. The striking biochemical abnormality in this disorder is the very large elevation of mevalonic acid in urine. Normal excretions in children are 0.2 to 0.3 mmol per mole creatinine.[113] The two patients with the severe phenotype excreted 9000 to 56,000 mmol per mole creatinine, some 50,000 to 200,000 times the normal excretion.[113,164] The two patients with a mild phenotype excreted 1000 to 3600 mmol per mole creatinine, but this is still 5000 to 12,000 times normal.[165,167] Unlike the other branched chain organic acidurias due to defects in catabolic pathways where metabolite excretions show large increases with acidotic episodes, mevalonic aciduria is due to a defect in an anabolic pathway, and each patient showed a fairly constant excretion of mevalonic acid. The very large production of mevalonic acid in these patients is due to a lack of feedback inhibition and repression of the 3-hydroxy-3-methylglutaryl-CoA reductase caused by decreased synthesis of end products. This results in an overproduction of mevalonic acid which is readily cleared by the kidneys.

In the severely affected patients, the plasma levels of mevalonic acid were highly elevated at 440 μm[113] and 70 μ*M*[164] compared to normal levels of 0.026 μ*M*[113] in two children or 0.07 μ*M* in adult controls.[162] Although these levels are 1000 to 9000 times normal, the absolute levels of mevalonic acid are not high enough to cause metabolic acidosis.

No abnormal metabolites other than mevalonic acid have been detected in urine of these patients, suggesting that it is rapidly cleared by the kidneys and not metabolized. The mevalonic acid shunt cannot operate in this disorder because the enzyme deficiency is prior to the synthesis of dimethylallyl pyrophosphate, which is the starting metabolite for the shunt pathway.

CELL METABOLISM STUDIES. The incorporation of [5-^{3}H]mevalonolactone into cholesterol in intact fibroblasts was studied with the cells grown with fetal calf serum (cholesterol and LDL present) and with delipidated serum (LDL and cholesterol removed).[113] In the delipidated medium, where cholesterol synthesis should be maximal, the patient's fibroblasts synthesized about 33 percent as much cholesterol as normal. In the medium with serum, where cholesterol synthesis is depressed by one-half in normal cells, the patient's fibroblasts synthesized cholesterol at 45 percent of the normal rate. In this medium the incorporation of [2-^{14}C]acetate into cholesterol by the patient's fibroblasts was 50 percent of normal.[168] Incorporation into fatty acids was normal, and the content of cholesterol and its esters was also normal in the patient's fibroblasts. Thus, the cells are able to synthesize considerable amounts of cholesterol, but in the absence of exogenous cholesterol, these cells cannot increase synthesis to the same extent as those of normal subjects.

ENZYME DEFICIENCY. The large excretion of mevalonic acid in the urine of the patients suggested three possible sites for an enzyme deficiency (see Fig. 28-2). A deficiency of mevalonate kinase would lead directly to mevalonic aciduria. A deficiency of mevalonic acid-5-phosphate kinase would lead to excess mevalonic acid-5-phosphate which could be dephosphorylated to mevalonic acid by a phosphatase. A deficiency of mevalonic acid-5-pyrophosphate decarboxylase would lead to excess mevalonic acid-5-pyrophosphate which could also be dephosphorylated to mevalonic acid. A convenient assay for mevalonate kinase with [5-^{3}H]mevalonolactone and ATP and separation of the phosphorylated products can provide information about all of these enzymes in normal cells.[169] Lysates of fibroblasts, lymphocytes, or lymphoblasts from all four patients were found to be markedly deficient in the synthesis of both mevalonic acid-5-phosphate and mevalonic acid-5-pyrophosphate, showing that mevalonate kinase was deficient.[113,170,171] The residual activity of mevalonate kinase ranged from 1 to 15 percent of normal, and the amount did not correlate with the clinical severity.[170] The cells of patients were able to metabolize R-[2-^{14}C]mevalonic acid-phosphate and R-[2-^{14}C]mevalonic acid-5-pyrophosphate normally, indicating that the second kinase and the decarboxylase were normal.[113,170] However, it is possible that some future patients with mevalonic aciduria may have deficiencies of either mevalonic acid-5-phosphate kinase or mevalonic acid-5-pyrophosphate decarboxylase.

Genetics. The existence of affected males and females, including one sibship, suggests that mevalonic aciduria is an autosomal recessive disorder. Extensive analyses of the activity of mevalonate kinase in lymphocytes of members of one pedigree are consistent with this.[171]

Diagnosis. With the small number of patients and the wide range of clinical presentations, it is difficult to suggest when this diagnosis should be considered. The patients generally do not have acidosis or low serum cholesterol. Failure to thrive, anemia, gastroenteropathy, and hepatosplenomegaly may be indicators. The diagnosis can be made readily by analysis of urinary organic acids in which mevalonic acid is an overwhelmingly large peak. With most extraction procedures which are acidic, mevalonolactone is formed, and with trimethylsilylation (TMS) a mono-TMS is the major derivative, although some tris-TMS of mevalonic acid may be seen as well as a variety of other minor derivatives. If the derivatization is with methylation, mevalonolactone does not form a methyl ester and may be missed unless a polar gas-chromatographic column is used that will show mevalonolactone and its dehydration product. Accurate quantification of mevalonic acid is difficult due the interconversion of the acid and lactone, and is best accomplished by stable isotope dilution gas chromatography–mass spectrometry.[113] The excretions of mevalonic acid have ranged from 1000 to 55,000 mmol per mole creatinine in affected patients compared to normal excretions of less than 0.3 mmol per mole creatinine. The diagnosis should be confirmed by assay of mevalonate kinase in fibroblasts or lymphocytes since there is the possibility that some patients with mevalonic aciduria may have a defect in either of the two subsequent enzymes in the metabolic pathway.

Heterozygotes can be diagnosed by assay of mevalonate kinase in fibroblasts or lymphocytes where the activity is less than 50 percent of normal and in many cases as low as 20 to 25 percent of normal.[113,171]

Mevalonic aciduria can be diagnosed prenatally by stable isotope dilution analysis of mevalonic acid in amniotic fluid. In a subsequent pregnancy of the mother of the first patient, mevalonic acid was elevated three thousandfold in the amniotic fluid at 16 weeks of gestation, with a concentration of 240 μM compared to normal concentrations of 0.054 to 0.11 μM.[113] Mevalonic acid was also elevated to 35 times normal in maternal urine when assayed by stable isotope dilution, but it would be more reliable to perform a prenatal diagnosis by direct assay of the amniotic fluid. The prenatal diagnosis can also be accomplished by demonstrating a deficiency of mevalonate kinase in cultured amniocytes.[113]

Treatment. A suitable treatment has not been developed. In a mildly affected patient, there was no steatorrhea even though the bile acid pool was very low, and there was no clinical improvement on treatment with bile acids, but there was improvement when the deficiency of the fat-soluble vitamins A, E, and D was corrected. Iron deficiency anemia may be treated with iron. If the failure to thrive is related to poor intestinal absorption of nutrients, parenteral nutrition might be of benefit. A high cholesterol diet might compensate for decreased capacity to synthesize cholesterol. Treatment with ubiquinone might be considered since its synthesis may be impaired. However, there was no lactic acidemia nor any abnormality of muscle mitochondria in the patient as might be expected if the mitochondrial electron transport chain were compromised.

DISORDERS OF ISOLEUCINE CATABOLISM

Catabolism of Isoleucine: The *S* Pathway

The normal pathway for the catabolism of isoleucine is in the mitochondria via intermediates with the *S* stereochemical configuration to the common metabolic intermediates acetyl-CoA and succinyl-CoA, as shown in Fig. 28-3. Inherited deficiencies of five of the eight enzymes in the pathway are known. Of the three known disorders of isoleucine metabolism considered to be branched chain organic acidurias, only one, 2-methylacetoacetyl-CoA thiolase deficiency, will be described in this chapter (Table 28-1). The other two, propionic acidemia and methylmalonic acidemia, are described in Chap. 29. There have been no patients identified with an inherited deficiency of three of the enzymes, 2-methylbranched chain acyl-CoA dehydrogenase, tiglyl-CoA hydratase and 2-methyl-3-hydroxybutyryl-CoA dehydrogenase, which would lead to branched chain organic acidurias.

Isoleucine has two asymmetric carbons and can be converted to a slight extent (via the 2-oxo-acid intermediate) to a diastereoisomer, alloisoleucine. The catabolism of alloisoleucine proceeds via a minor pathway, the *R* pathway, which results in different end products that does the more major *S* pathway for isoleucine. The *R* pathway will be described later.

2-Methylbranched Chain Acyl-CoA Dehydrogenase. The first step of branched chain organic acid metabolism of isoleucine is the irreversible dehydrogenation of 2-methylbutyryl-CoA to tiglyl-CoA (which can also be called 2-methylcrotonyl-CoA), catalyzed by 2-methylbranched chain acyl-CoA dehydrogenase (see Fig. 28-3). This enzyme is distinct from the dehydrogenases acting on the straight-chain acyl-CoA dehydrogenases of fatty acid β oxidation and also from isovaleryl-CoA dehydrogenase in the leucine catabolic pathway.[6] 2-Methylbranched chain acyl-CoA dehydrogenase has been purified from rat liver mitochondria.[172] It is composed of four identical subunits of 41,500 daltons, each containing one FAD, to form a 170,000-dalton enzyme. Electrons from the FAD are transferred to ETF and then to the electron transport chain by ETF dehydrogenase in the same manner as for isovaleryl-CoA dehydrogenase.

The enzyme catalyzes the dehydrogenation of the ethyl group of *S*-2-methylbutyryl-CoA derived from isoleucine to tiglyl-CoA in the major *S* pathway. It catalyzes equally well the dehydrogenation of isobutyryl-CoA (which is 2-methylpropionyl-CoA) derived from valine to methacrylyl-CoA; hence its name.[172] The maximum rate of dehydrogenation of the methyl group of *R*-2-methylbutyryl-CoA derived from alloisoleucine to 2-ethylacrylyl-CoA is only 22 percent of the rate with the *S* isomer. This reaction leads to the minor *R* cata-

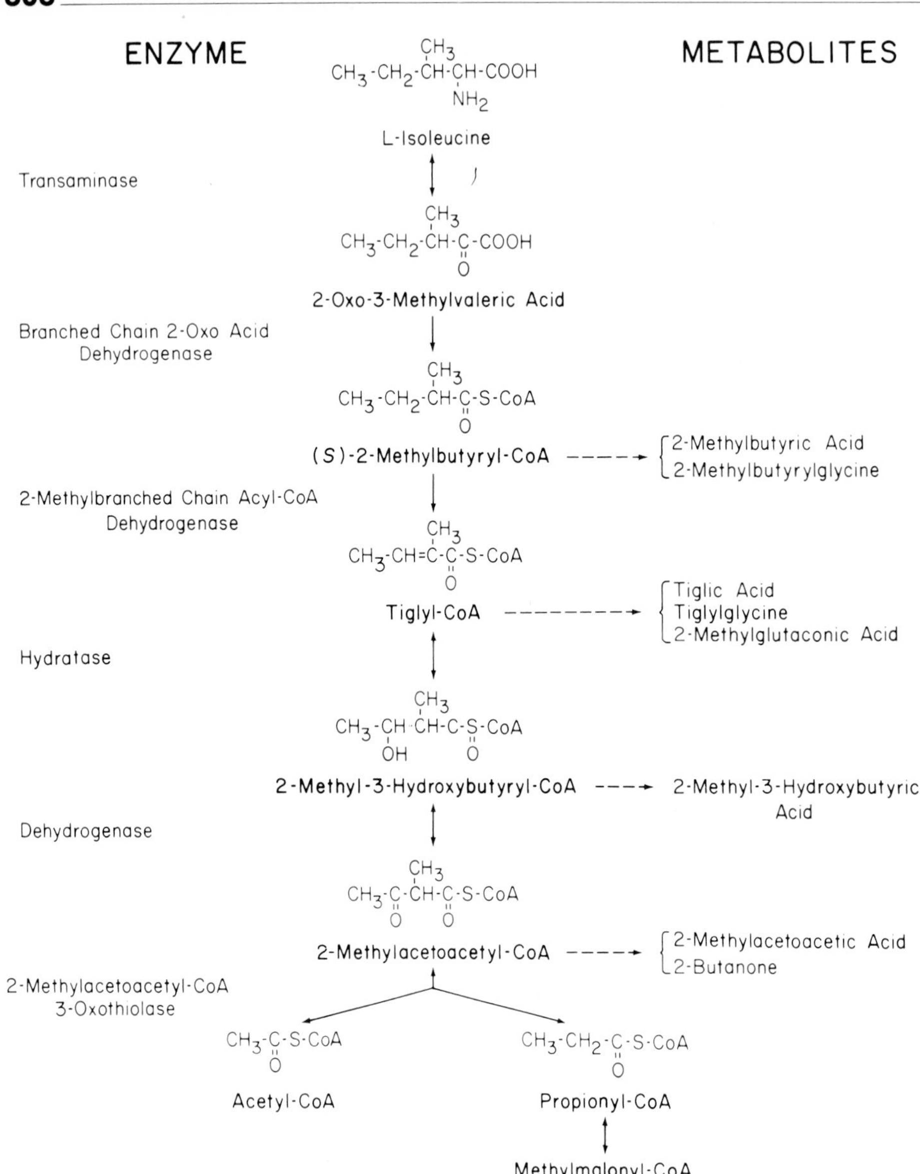

Fig. 28-3 Catabolism of isoleucine. The structures and names of the intermediates in the major *S* pathway for the catabolism of isoleucine are shown in the center, with the names of the enzymes on the left and the metabolites that may be elevated due to a deficiency of the enzymes shown on the right.

bolic pathway, as described later. Other acyl-CoAs are not substrates. The K_m values for the substrates are: 20 μM for *S*-2-methylbutyryl-CoA and 89 μM for isobutyryl-CoA. At equilibrium, the ratio of product to substrate is 4 with *S*-2-methylbutyryl-CoA as substrate and 1 with isobutyryl-CoA as substrate. Tiglyl-CoA, the product of the enzyme with *S*-2-methylbutyryl-CoA as substrate, is a potent competitive inhibitor of the enzyme, with a K_i of 7 μM with *S*-2-methylbutyryl-CoA as substrate and 3 μM with isobutyryl-CoA as substrate. Moderate inhibition is also found with butyryl-CoA, valeryl-CoA, and crotonyl-CoA but not with propionyl-CoA, isovaleryl-CoA, or 3-methylcrotonyl-CoA.

Tiglyl-CoA Hydration. Although the possibility of a hydratase specific for tiglyl-CoA has not been excluded, it is believed that tiglyl-CoA is hydrated to 2-methyl-3-hydroxybutyryl-CoA by crotonase.[19] The crystallized enzyme purified from bovine liver is a 164,000-dalton hexamer of identical subunits[173] which hydrates tiglyl-CoA much more slowly than crotonyl-CoA, but the kinetic constants have not been reported. Sonicated human liver hydrates tiglyl-CoA at 11 percent the rate of hydration of crotonyl-CoA.[174]

2-Methyl-3-Hydroxybutyryl-CoA Dehydrogenase. The oxidation of 2-methyl-3-hydroxybutyryl-CoA to 2-methylacetoacetyl-CoA is catalyzed by an acyl-CoA dehydrogenase (see Fig. 28-3). This may be the dehydrogenase that acts on straight-chain 3-hydroxyacyl-CoA substrates in fatty acid β oxidation, but the possibility of a specific dehydrogenase for this 2-methylbranched substrate has not been excluded.

2-Methylacetoacetyl-CoA Thiolase. 3-Oxothiolases catalyze the reversible cleavage of a 3-oxoacyl-CoA with a CoA to form an acyl-CoA with two fewer carbons and acetyl-CoA.[175] Thus 2-methylacetoacetyl-CoA thiolase interconverts 2-methylacetoacetyl-CoA to propionyl-CoA plus acetyl-CoA (see Fig. 28-3) while acetoacetyl-CoA thiolase interconverts acetoacetyl-CoA to two acetyl-CoAs. There are four types of 3-oxothiolases in mammalian cells, all of them capable of acting on acetoacetyl-CoA, but only one acts on 2-methylacetoacetyl-CoA.[176,177] A cytosolic acetoacetyl-CoA thiolase is specific for acetoacetyl-CoA, is not activated by potassium, is inhibited by CoA but not its other substrates, and functions to synthesize acetoacetyl-CoA from acetyl-CoA for the synthesis of 3-hydroxy-3-methylglutaryl-CoA and cholesterol. A peroxisomal 3-oxoacyl-CoA thiolase has a broad chain length specificity and functions in peroxisomal β oxidation of fatty acids. A similar 3-oxoacyl-CoA thiolase functioning in β oxidation of fatty acids in mitochondria has a broad chain length specificity (maximum activity with 3-oxohexanoyl-CoA), is not stimulated by potassium, and is not inhibited by CoA or high concentrations of the other substrate. In contrast, 2-methylacetoacetyl-CoA thiolase is a mitochondrial enzyme specific for 2-methylacetoacetyl-CoA and acetoacetyl-CoA, is stimulated about fourfold by potassium, and is inhibited by high substrate concentrations but not by CoA.[177,178] Its function in most tissues is the catabolism of isoleucine. In liver it also functions in ketogenesis through the synthesis of acetyl-CoA and acetoacetyl-CoA for 3-hydroxy-3-methylglutaryl-CoA synthesis. The proportions of the thiolase activities with acetoacetyl-CoA as substrate in ox liver is 14 percent cytosolic acetoacetyl-CoA thiolase, 46 percent potassium-stimulable acetoacetyl-CoA (2-methylacetoacetyl-CoA thiolase) thiolase and 40 percent 3-oxoacyl-CoA thiolase.[175]

The potassium-stimulated acetoacetyl-CoA thiolase (2-methylacetoacetyl-CoA thiolase) of ox liver is a tetramer of 169,000 daltons with subunits of 44,000 daltons.[179] The apparent K_ms for the rat liver enzyme are 7 μM for acetoacetyl-CoA (with substrate inhibition above 20 μM) and 21 μM for CoA, and the K_a for potassium is about 1 to 2 mM.[176] The K_m for 2-methylacetoacetyl-CoA is about 100 μM for the purified rat liver enzyme.[177] The rat liver enzyme is 1.6 times more active with 2-methylacetoacetyl-CoA than with acetoacetyl-CoA as substrate. The general 3-oxothiolase of rat liver mitochondria also has some activity with 2-methylacetoacetyl-CoA, this being about 30 percent of that with acetoacetyl-CoA and 7 percent of that with 3-oxohexanoyl-CoA.[177]

Propionyl-CoA and Methylmalonyl-CoA Metabolism. The acetyl-CoA produced by 2-methylacetoacetyl-CoA thiolase enters the general tricarboxylic acid cycle metabolism of the mitochondria. The other product, propionyl-CoA, is first carboxylated to methylmalonyl-CoA, racemized, then isomerized to succinyl-CoA before entering the tricarboxylic acid cycle. These reactions and the disorders resulting from deficiencies of the enzymes are described in Chap. 29. It should be noted that the reactions of the catabolic pathway after the formation of 2-methylbutyryl-CoA are reversible, and the abnormal metabolites found with a deficiency of 2-methylacetoacetyl-CoA thiolases can also be elevated in patients with propionic acidemia or methylmalonic acidemia. In addition, 2-methylacetoacetyl-CoA thiolase can catalyze the condensation of acetyl-CoA and propionyl-CoA to two different products, 2-methylacetoacetyl-CoA (which is reduced to 2-methyl-3-hydroxybutyrate) and 3-oxovaleryl-CoA (and hence 3-hydroxyvalerate) as well as two propionyl-CoAs to 2-methyl-3-oxovaleryl-CoA (and hence 2-methyl-3-hydroxyvalerate). Thus, these additional metabolites can occur in propionic acidemia and methylmalonic acidemia but not in 2-methylacetoacetyl-CoA thiolase deficiency.

Catabolism of Isoleucine: The *R* Pathway

Some of the enzymes of the *S* pathway of isoleucine catabolism can act on the *R* isomers, giving rise to different end products for the two isomers. Isoleucine is transaminated to *S*-2-oxo-3-methylvaleric acid. This can undergo a slow interconversion to *R*-2-oxo-3-methylvaleric acid via an oxo-enol tautomerization.[180] This does not occur to any significant extent with the usual rapid flux through the oxo acid, and hence the *R* pathway is very minor in normal subjects. Significant amounts of the *R* isomer of 2-oxo-3-methylvaleric acid do form in patients with maple syrup urine disease, where the catabolism of the oxo acid is deficient, and this isomer is transaminated to alloisoleucine.[181] However, these patients cannot oxidize the *R*-2-oxo-3-methylvaleric acid to *R*-2-methylbutyric acid, so the *R* pathway does not function even though the precursor is elevated.

R-2-oxo-3-methylvaleric acid is oxidatively decarboxylated by branched chain 2-oxoacid dehydrogenase to *R*-2-methylbutyryl-CoA, which is a substrate for the 2-methylbranched chain acyl-CoA dehydrogenase, although at about 20 percent the rate of the *S* isomer.[172] The product is 2-ethylacrylyl-CoA, which is a homologue of 2-methylacrylyl-CoA in the valine pathway and is metabolized similarly (see Fig. 28-4). After hydration to 2-ethyl-3-hydroxypropionyl-CoA (presumably by crotonase) and deacylation to 2-ethyl-3-hydroxypropionic acid (a portion of which is excreted in urine), it is oxidized to ethylmalonic semialdehyde, then oxidatively decarboxylated to butyryl-CoA. Although butyryl-CoA is normally metabolized to acetyl-CoA, when elevated, it can be carboxylated by propionyl-CoA carboxylase to ethylmalonic acid. The *R* pathway was proposed based on the difference in excretions of the intermediate 2-ethyl-3-hydroxypropionic acid (ethylhydracrylic acid) by patients with various defects in isoleucine catabolism. The pathway was demonstrated by administering deuterium-labeled *R*-2-methylbutyric acid to animals and identifying deuterium-labeled 2-ethyl-3-hydroxypropionic acid and ethylmalonic acid as products.[182] The pathway was shown to proceed primarily from 2-ethyl-3-hydroxypropionic acid through butyryl-CoA to ethylmalonic acid by administration of stable isotopically labeled *RS*-2-methylbutyric acid to hypoglycin-treated rats.[183]

2-Methylacetoacetyl-CoA Thiolase Deficiency

Since the first report of patients with 2-methylacetoacetic and 2-methyl-3-hydroxybutyric aciduria in 1971, 14 patients have been reported with this disorder.[184–198] Although the pattern of metabolites suggested that the defect was in 2-methylacetoacetyl-CoA thiolase (commonly called β-ketothiolase or 3-oxothiolase) and the disorder came to be known as *β-ketothiolase deficiency,* direct demonstration of the enzyme deficiency did not occur until 1982.[177,192] Because β-ketothiolase or 3-oxothiolase is a generic name for a group of enzymes and patients with defects in different thiolases are known who have different clinical presentations and biochemical abnormalities, it would be preferable to use more specific nomenclature. Because the pattern of the organic aciduria is variable, usually with elevated 2-methyl-3-hydroxybutyric acid and often 2-methylacetoacetic acid and butanone but with or without triglylglcine, it would be better to identify this disorder by the enzyme deficiency. Therefore, patients with this disorder will

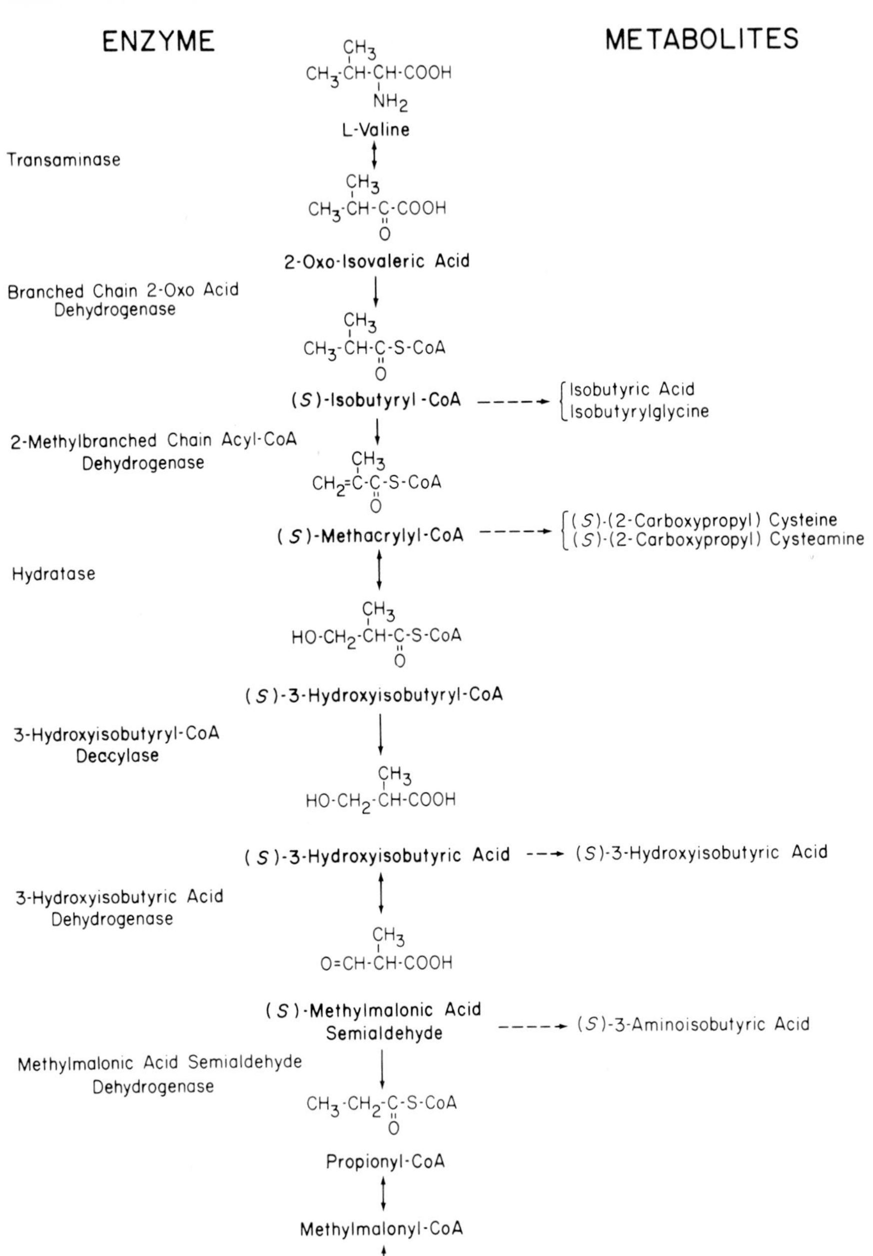

Fig 28-4 Catabolism of valine. The structures and names of the intermediates in the pathway for the catabolism of valine are shown in the center, with the names of the enzymes on the left and the metabolites that may be elevated due to a deficiency of the enzymes shown on the right.

be considered to have *2-methylacetoacetyl-CoA thiolase deficiency* in this chapter. At the end of this section patients with cytoplasmic acetoacetyl-CoA thiolase deficiency will be described briefly.

Clinical Aspects. The clinical features of 2-methylacetoacetyl-CoA thiolase deficiency are quite variable, ranging from frequent severe episodes in infants[184–198] to an asymptomatic course in an adult.[192] The most common features are intermittent severe metabolic acidosis and ketosis with vomiting (often hematemesis), diarrhea (often bloody), and coma following upper respiratory or gastrointestinal infections or increased protein intake.[185,190,193,197] The episodes usually begin between 1 and 2 years of age and can occur every few months. One patient[186,187,191] died with congestive cardiomyopathy at 8 years of age. Several sibs of probands, who were presumably affected, died during acute episodes.[185,189,197] The acute episodes usually resolve with correction of the acidosis with intravenous bicarbonate and glucose, and there is usually no permanent damage, although two patients had developmental retardation[191,197] and another is mentally retarded.[185] Most patients have been treated with moderate restriction of protein, to 1.5 to 2.0 g/(kg·day), which greatly reduced or eliminated severe episodes, and they have developed normally. Several patients have reported severe headaches beginning at 6 to 7 years of age,[188,190] and one patient had ataxia.[191] The father of one patient was shown to have the same severe deficiency of enzyme activity and yet never had symptoms.[192] With prompt correction of the severe acidosis and ketosis during the first episode, the prognosis is excellent for patients diagnosed with 2-methylacetoacetyl-CoA thiolase deficiency and treated with moderate protein restriction.

In one case, the initial diagnosis was of salicylate toxicity because of the similar symptoms and a positive test for salicylates.[189] It was shown that the Trinder method for salicylate detection gives a false positive reaction with the highly elevated amounts of acetoacetic acid that occur in this disorder.

Biochemical Abnormalities.

ABNORMAL METABOLITES. There are considerable variations in the patterns and amounts of abnormal organic acids excreted by patients with a deficiency of 2-methylacetoacetyl-CoA thiolase. In addition, several of the metabolites (2-methylacetoacetic acid, 2-butanone, and tiglylglycine) are difficult to analyze quantitatively by the routine methods for urinary organic acids, requiring special analytical techniques. Thus, the information on the metabolite excretions is fragmentary, and it is difficult to specify a typical quantitative profile. The most characteristic elevated urinary metabolite with a deficiency of 2-methylacetoacetyl-CoA thiolase is 2-methyl-3-hydroxybutyric acid.[185,192,193,197] This is often accompanied by elevated 2-methylacetoacetic acid and its decarboxylation product, 2-butanone. 2-Methylacetoacetic acid is generally not the most elevated metabolite, although it is the substrate for the defective enzyme and might be expected to be most elevated. Rather, due to the reversible reaction of the 3-hydroxyacyl-CoA dehydrogenase and the normal high ratio of NADH to NAD, the reduced compound 2-methyl-3-hydroxybutyric acid is more elevated. Most patients also excrete elevated amounts of tiglylglycine, but some patients do not.[185,192,197] This compound can be elevated due to the accumulation of 2-methyl-3-hydroxybutyryl-CoA, which is in equilibrium with its dehydrated form, tiglyl-CoA. Tiglyl-CoA is a substrate for glycine *N*-acylase, which forms tiglylglycine.[59] The excretion of these metabolites of isoleucine increases during episodes, and they are accompanied by large elevations of acetoacetic acid and 3-hydroxybutyric acid. 2-Methylacetoacetyl-CoA thiolase also functions in the metabolism of acetoacetyl-CoA, and the highly elevated amounts 2-methylacetoacetyl-CoA during episodes can compete with acetoacetyl-CoA for the enzyme, greatly decreasing metabolism of acetoacetyl-CoA and causing an elevation of acetoacetic acid and its reduced product, 3-hydroxybutyric acid. Between episodes, when the accumulation of 2-methylacetoacetyl-CoA is less, the general 3-oxoacyl-CoA thiolase activity is apparently sufficient for normal metabolism of acetoacetyl-CoA, preventing elevations of acetoacetic and 3-hydroxybutyric acids. During ketotic episodes, there are also secondary elevations of dicarboxylic acids such as adipic acid, as occur in any ketotic subject. The elevation of 2-methylacetoacetic acid and acetoacetic acid during episodes can cause a "sweet" odor.

The normal excretion of 2-methyl-3-hydroxybutyric acid is 1-9 mmol per mole creatinine, which can increase to as high as 200 mmol per mole creatinine during ketosis of any cause.[100] Patients with 2-methylacetoacetyl-CoA thiolase deficiency when well often have excretions of 2-methyl-3-hydroxybutyric acid of 200 to 1000 mmol per mole creatinine, which increase to 1000 to 4400 during acute episodes, with high protein intake, or with a challenge of isoleucine.[185,192,193,197] However, more mildly affected patients can have excretions which are in the normal range or up to 700 mmol per mole creatinine when they are well, and show increases that are still within the normal range or up to 300 mmol per mole creatinine when they are ill or challenged with isoleucine.[190,197] There are very few reports of the quantities of 2-methylacetoacetic acid excreted, but these are often about one-tenth to one-fourth of the excretion of 2-methyl-3-hydroxybutyric acid,[185,187] although there may be more 2-methylacetoacetic acid during a challenge with isoleucine,[188] or it may not be detectable in mildly affected patients even with an isoleucine challenge.[190,197] Tiglylglycine as high as 1000 mmol per mole creatinine has been reported,[192,197] but some patients do not excrete tiglyglycine[185,197] except following a load of isoleucine (20 mmol per mole creatinine).[197] 2-Butanone has not been quantified in the urine of patients and was not detectable in some.[192] Small amounts of 2,3-dimethyl-3-hydroxyglutaric acid (3 to 8 mmol per mole creatinine) have been detected.[193,196] This presumably arises from condensation of elevated 2-methylacetoacetyl-CoA with acetyl-CoA catalyzed by mitochondrial 3-hydroxy-3-methylglutaryl-CoA synthase to form 2,3-dimethyl-3-hydroxyglutaryl-CoA.

Only one patient had hyperglycinemia and hyperglycinuria.[187,188,191] This patient also excreted hexanone as well as butanone, which has not been reported for other patients. The activity of 2-methylacetoacetyl-CoA thiolase has not been determined for this patient, and it is possible that there may be some other enzymatic defect.

CELL METABOLISM STUDIES. The oxidation of [U-^{14}C]isoleucine to $^{14}CO_2$ in fibroblasts cultured from patients is less than 50 percent of normal, consistent with a decreased activity of 2-methylacetoacetyl-CoA thiolase.[185,186,189] Recently incorporation of [1-^{14}C]2-methylbutyric acid into macromolecules in cultured fibroblasts from patients was shown to range from 2 to 40 percent of normal.[199] A coupled assay, in which ^3H_2O was incorporated into tiglyl-CoA to form radioactive 2-methyl-3-hydroxybutyryl-CoA and 2-methylacetoacetyl-CoA, which was cleaved by its thiolase to radioactive propionate, was used to show about 10 percent normal activity in leukocyte extracts from a patient.[188]

ENZYME DEFICIENCY. An assay for potassium-stimulated acetoacetyl-CoA thiolase, which is largely a measure of 2-methylacetoacetyl-CoA thiolase but also includes contributions from 3-oxoacyl-CoA thiolase, showed activity of only 12 percent of normal in fibroblasts of a patient.[189] With a similar assay in peripheral mononuclear cells and polymorphonuclear cells, the activity ws 30 to 70 percent of normal.[198] A more specific assay with potassium stimulation and 2-methylacetoacetyl-CoA as substrate[177] showed activity of 0 to 4 percent of normal in fibroblasts from most patients studied,[177,192,195,197] although one more mildly affected patient had 7 percent of normal activity.[197] In these studies, the activity of 3-oxoacyl-CoA thiolase with 3-oxohexanoly-CoA as substrate was normal, while its activity with acetoacetyl-CoA as substrate without potassium stimulation (due to 3-oxoacyl-CoA thiolase activity) was 20 to 50 percent of normal. This indicates that in normal fibroblasts, more than half of the cleavage of acetoacetyl-CoA is done by 2-methylacetoacetyl-CoA thiolase.

A comparison of the activity of 2-methylacetoacetyl-CoA thiolase in sonicates of fibroblasts and the incorporation of [1-^{14}C]-2-methylbutyric acid into macromolecules in intact fibroblasts of patients with metabolite excretions characteristic of a deficiency of the enzyme showed that nine were deficient in both assays.[199] Fibroblasts from four patients, one being the first patient described with this disorder,[184,185] had normal activities of the enzyme but markedly deficient incorporation.[199] A possible explanation might be that an active 2-methylacetoacetyl-CoA thiolase is present in the cytosol but is not properly processed into the mitochondria. This would prevent the normal metabolism of 2-methylbutyric acid in the mitochondria of the intact cells.

Genetics. The inheritance appears to be autosomal recessive. Interestingly, in one pedigree the asymptomatic father was found to be homozygous or perhaps compound heterozygous, while the mother was heterozygous as determined by assay of 2-methylacetoacetyl-CoA thiolase activity in fibroblasts.[192] This could be analogous to the "pseudodeficiency" described for some lysosomal enzyme deficiencies, where activity in vivo is sufficient under most metabolic circumstances despite the in vitro result.

Diagnosis. The diagnosis of 2-methylacetoacetyl-CoA thiolase deficiency should be considered in children presenting with intermittent episodes of severe ketosis and acidosis but without chronic ketosis. The diagnosis of many severely affected patients can be made by analysis of urinary organic acids and finding highly elevated excretions of 2-methyl-3-hydroxybutyric acid (100 to 1000 mmol per mole creatinine), 2-methylacetoacetic acid (25 to 250 mmol per mole creatinine), butanone, and tiglylglycine (70 to 1000 mmol per mole creatinine). However, some patients do not have more than trace amounts of 2-methylacetoacetic acid (and no butanone), and others do not excrete tiglylglycine. An elevation of only 2-methyl-3-hydroxybutyric acid during a ketotic episode is not diagnostic because of the secondary elevation of this acid to levels as high as 200 mmol per mole creatinine in patients with ketosis for any reason.[100] However, the continued elevation of 2-methyl-3-hydroxybutyric acid above 20 mmol per mole creatinine between episodes is strongly suggestive of a deficiency of 2-methylacetoacetyl-CoA thiolase deficiency. There are mildly affected patients who do not have clearly diagnostic elevations of any of the metabolites during or between episodes.[197] These patients can be diagnosed by giving an oral challenge with 100 mg of isoleucine per kilogram and demonstrating an elevation of tiglylglycine to greater than 10 mmol per mole creatinine in the first 8-h urine collected after the challenge.[197] Triglylglycine is not elevated in the urine of controls given an isoleucine challenge. Following the challenge, 2-methyl-3-hydroxy butyric acid is also moderately elevated in the urine of patients with a deficiency of 2-methylacetoacetyl-CoA thiolase, but similar elevations can occur in normal individuals given a challenge.

A definitive diagnosis is made by demonstrating the specific thiolase deficiency in fibroblasts or leukocytes using the specific assay with 2-methylacetoacetyl-CoA and potassium stimulation together with assays for acetoacetyl-CoA and 3-oxoacyl-CoA thiolases.[177,192,195] However, some patients may have normal activity of the enzyme and yet a functional deficiency of the pathway as determined by incorporation of [1-^{14}C]-2-methylbutyric acid into macromolecules in intact cells. Heterozygotes can generally be determined by their decreased enzyme activity.

Prenatal diagnosis should be possible by measurement of the activity of the specific 2-methylacetoacetyl-CoA thiolase in cultured amniocytes if this activity is shown to be deficient in fibroblasts of the proband. Prenatal diagnosis may also be possible in some families for elevated metabolites in amniotic fluid, but considering the large quantitative differences in metabolite excretions in the urine of different patients, it appears that assay of enzyme activity would be more reliable.

Treatment. Treatment of acute acidotic episodes consists of glucose infusion and correction of acidosis.[185,197] Chronic therapy consists of restriction of deitary protein to 1.5 to 2.0 g/(kg·day), which greatly reduces the frequency of episodes or prevents further episodes.[185,187,188,192,193,197,198] If neurologic damage has not occurred during an acidotic episode, the prognosis for normal development is excellent with protein restriction. Unlike many other organic acidurias, increased excretion of acylcarnitines with resulting deficiency of carnitine has not been reported in this disorder. This is presumably due to the fact that acetyl-CoA carnitine transferase has little activity with acyl-CoAs with functional groups such as hydroxyl or carbonyl, as are found in the primary metabolites in 2-methylacetoacetyl-CoA thiolase deficiency. Thus, treatment with carnitine is not likely to be of benefit in this disorder except possibly in patients who excrete tiglylglycine, indicating an elevation of tiglyl-CoA.

Mitochondrial Acetoacetyl-CoA Thiolase Deficiency

A patient with chronic ketosis and lactic acidosis was reported to have a deficiency of a liver mitochondrial potassium-stimulated acetoacetyl-CoA thiolase.[200] The clinical and biochemical features of this patient differed from those of the patients described above, who were believed to have a deficiency of potassium-stimulated 2-methylacetoacetyl-CoA thiolase. The patient, a female, had severe progressive neuropathy and growth retardation at 5 years of age. Growth failure began at 9 months, and ataxia developed at 18 months of age. There was a persistent moderate elevation of lactic acid in blood with a high ratio of lactate to pyruvate, and elevated acetoacetic acid and 3-hydroxybutyric acid with a high ratio of the hydroxy to the oxo acid but normal glucose levels. Urinary organic acids were normal except for elevated lactic, 3-hydroxybutyric, and citric acids, and none of the metabolites of 2-methylacetoacetyl-CoA thiolase deficiency were detectable. The activity of potassium-stimulated acetoacetyl-CoA thiolase in mitochondria of a liver biopsy was 42 percent of normal. Chromatographic separation of the thiolases showed normal activities for the 3-oxoacyl-CoA thiolases but only one peak for potassium-stimulated acetoacetyl-CoA thiolase, compared to two peaks in normal specimens. The activity of 2-methylacetoacetyl-CoA thiolase in cultured fibroblasts was normal as was the cytosolic acetoacetyl-CoA thiolase in liver.[200]

Cytosolic Acetoacetyl-CoA Thiolase Deficiency

Two patients with a deficiency of cytosolic acetoacetyl-CoA thiolase have been reported.[195,201,202] There was delayed motor and mental development, hypotonia, and in one case ataxic and choreiform movements. One patient had moderately elevated lactic and pyruvic acid with a low lactate/pyruvate ratio and normal acetoacetic and 3-hydroxybutyric acid levels and ratio in blood.[201] The other patient had elevated levels of acetoacetate and 3-hydroxybutyrate in blood.[202] The activity of cytosolic acetoacetyl-CoA thiolase in a liver biopsy of the first patient was in the lower range of normal, and abnormal kinetic properties were found with an increased inhibition by CoA resulting in an increase in the apparent K_m for acetoacetyl-CoA.[201] In fibroblasts of the second patient, the activity of acetoacetyl-CoA thiolase was 50 percent of normal, while activities of 2-methylacetoacetyl-CoA thiolase and 3-oxoacyl-CoA thiolase were normal.[202] In agreement with the presumed deficiency of cytosolic acetoacetyl-CoA thiolase which is required for sterol synthesis, the incorporation of acetate into cholesterol was 50 percent of normal in fibroblasts of this patient. Restriction of dietary fat reduced the level of ketone bodies in the blood, but, although there was no further regression, there was no clinical improvement.

DISORDERS OF VALINE CATABOLISM

Catabolism of Valine

The normal pathway for the catabolism of valine is shown in Fig. 28-4. Inherited deficiencies of six of the enzymes are known. Of the four known disorders of valine metabolism considered to be branched chain organic acidurias, only two, 3-hydroxyisobutyryl-CoA deacylase deficiency and methylmalonic semialdehyde dehydrogenase deficiency, will be described in this chapter (Table 28-1). Two others, propionic acidemia and methylmalonic acidemia, are described in Chap. 29. There have been no patients described with an inherited deficiency of three of the enzymes, 2-methylbranched chain acyl-CoA dehydrogenase, methacrylyl-CoA hydratase, and 3-hydroxyisobutyric acid dehydrogenase, which would lead to branched chain organic acidurias. The enzymes of the valine catabolic pathway and their relevant properties are described below.

2-Methylbranched Chain Acyl-CoA Dehydrogenase. This enzyme has been described under isoleucine metabolism (see "2-Methylbranched Chain Acyl-CoA Dehydrogenase") because this enzyme has an identical function in the catabolism of both 2-methylbutyryl-CoA from isoleucine and isobutyryl-CoA (2-methylpropionyl-CoA) from valine.[172] The product of the dehydrogenation of isobutyryl-CoA is methacrylyl-CoA (see Fig. 28-4).

Methacrylyl-CoA Hydration. Purified bovine liver crotonase can hydrate methacrylyl-CoA to 3-hydroxyisobutyryl-CoA.[19,97,98] Human liver sonicates hydrate methacrylyl-CoA at 6 percent of the rate of hydration of crotonyl-CoA, and human fibroblast sonicates can hydrate methacrylyl-CoA.[174] In addition, in aqueous solution there is a reversible nonenzymatic hydration of methacrylyl-CoA to 3-hydroxyisobutyryl-CoA so that these compounds are in equilibrium.[203,204]

3-Hydroxyisobutyryl-CoA Deacylase. Unlike the pathways for catabolism for leucine and isoleucine, where all of the intermediates are CoA esters, in the catabolism of valine, the portion of the pathway between 3-hydroxyisobutyryl-CoA and propionyl-CoA involves the free acids rather than CoA esters (see Fig. 28-4).[203] Thus, a specific deacylase is required to hydrolyze 3-hydroxyisobutyryl-CoA to 3-hydroxyisobutyric acid.[204] The enzyme has been partially purified from pig heart and shows a high substrate specificity for 3-hydroxyisobutyryl-CoA and 3-hydroxypropionyl-CoA.[204] The deacylase is present in human liver and cultured fibroblasts.[174] The reaction is irreversible. The stereoisomer of 3-hydroxyisobutyric acid produced from isobutyric acid in rats has been shown to be the $S(+)$ isomer.[205]

3-Hydroxyisobutyric Acid Dehydrogenase. The 3-hydroxyisobutyric acid produced by the deacylation of 3-hydroxyisobutyryl-CoA is oxidized with NAD as substrate to form methylmalonic semialdehyde (see Fig. 28-4).[206] The enzyme purified two hundredfold from pig kidney is highly specific for both 3-hydroxyisobutyric acid, with a K_m of 120 μM, and NAD, with a K_m of 54 μM.[206] The reaction is reversible, and the equilibrium constant of 0.036 favors reduction of methylmalonic semialdehyde to 3-hydroxyisobutyric acid. The substrate for 3-hydroxyisobutyric acid dehydrogenase in rat liver mitochondria has been shown to be the S (+) isomer.[207] Hexadeuterated isobutyric acid administered to humans leads to the expected excretion of S-3-hydroxyisobutyric acid labeled with five deuteriums.[208] However, it also leads to considerable excretion of S-3-hydroxyisobutyric acid labeled with four deuteriums, and about 20 percent as much R-3-hydroxyisobutyric acid labeled with four deuteriums.[208] The former can be accounted for by the oxidation to S-methylmalonic semialdehyde with loss of a deuterium and reduction back to S-3-hydroxyisobutyric acid with four deuteriums, catalyzed by the reversible 3-hydroxyisobutyric acid dehydrogenase. S-Methylmalonic semialdehyde can undergo spontaneous oxo-enol tautomerism, causing racemization to a mixture of S- and R-methylmalonic semialdehyde, and reduction of the latter forms R-3-hydroxyisobutyric acid.

Methylmalonic Semialdehyde Dehydrogenase. The carboxyl group of S-methylmalonic semialdehyde is decarboxylated to carbon dioxide, and the aldehyde group is oxidized with NAD to a carboxylic acid group which forms a thio ester with CoA to produce propionyl-CoA in a complex reaction catalyzed by methylmalonic semialdehyde dehydrogenase. The mammalian enzyme has not been characterized but is believed to have a mechanism similar to that of the purified bacterial enzyme.[209]

At one time the catabolic pathway of valine was thought to involve direct oxidation of methylmalonic semialdehyde to methylmalonic acid. Studies of the in vivo metabolism of [2-^{13}C]- and [2,3-^{13}C]valine to methylmalonic acid in a patient with methylmalonic acidemia, using NMR analysis of urinary methylmalonic acid, clearly demonstrated that the carboxyl group of methylmalonic semialdehyde was lost, as expected, from metabolism by methylmalonic semialdehyde dehydrogenase to propionyl-CoA with subsequent carboxylation to methylmalonic acid.[210] More extensive studies in rats with stable isotopically labeled isobutyric acid demonstrated the same pathway.[211] Studies of the metabolism of deuterium-labeled $S(+)$-3-hydroxyisobutyric acid and [^{13}C]bicarbonate in rat liver mitochondria also demonstrated decarboxylation of the carboxyl group of methylmalonic semialdehyde.[207]

Propionyl-CoA and Methylmalonyl-CoA Metabolism. The further metabolism of propionyl-CoA derived from valine is by carboxylation to methylmalonyl-CoA and isomerization to succinyl-CoA as described in Chap. 29. Because the formation of propionyl-CoA from methylmalonic acid semialdehyde is irreversible, none of the intermediates of the valine catabolic pathway prior to propionyl-CoA accumulate in patients with propionic acidemia or methylmalonic acidemia.

3-Hydroxyisobutyryl-CoA Deacylase Deficiency

Only one patient has been identified with this disorder.[174,212]

Clinical Aspects. The male infant had dysmorphic features at birth, poor feeding, failure to thrive, hypotonia, and absence of neurologic development.[174] The infant died at 3 months of age, and other findings included vertebral abnormalities, tetralogy of Fallot, and agenesis of the cingulate gyrus and corpus callosum. It is uncertain whether the congenital malformations are a result of the biochemical defect in methacrylyl-CoA metabolism, but methacrylate esters are teratogenic in rats.[213]

Biochemical Abnormalities. Although this can be considered to be a disorder of branched chain organic acid metabolism of valine, no abnormal organic acids are excreted because the accumulated intermediates react with cysteine derivatives to give unusual sulfur amino acids.

ABNORMAL METABOLITES. High voltage electrophoresis of urine showed two unusual amino acids by staining with ninhydrin, and both were positive for sulfur by the iodoplatinate reagent. These were identified as *S*-(2-carboxypropyl)-cysteine and *S*-(2-carboxypropyl)-cysteamine.[212] The former has been identified as a trace component in urine of normal children.[214] Both compounds were detected in tissues from the patient at levels of 1 to 10 nmol per gram tissue.[174] The cysteine adduct is presumably derived from the addition of cysteine across the double bond of methacrylyl-CoA, an intermediate in the catabolism of valine, and the cysteamine adduct could be formed by the decarboxylation of the cysteine adduct. The addition of cysteine and cysteamine to methacrylyl-CoA occurs spontaneously in neutral aqueous solutions.[174] Methacrylyl-CoA would accumulate in tissues of the patient due to the equilibrium between 3-hydroxyisobutyryl-CoA and methacrylyl-CoA catalyzed by crotonase as a result of the demonstrated deficiency of 3-hydroxyisobutyryl-CoA deacylase.

CELL METABOLISM STUDIES. Fibroblasts of the patient, but not normal controls, produced both labeled *S*-(2-carboxypropyl)-cysteine and *S*-(2-carboxypropyl)-cysteamine from either [^{35}S]cysteine or [^{14}C] valine, and the oxidation of [2-^{14}C]valine to $^{14}CO_2$ was markedly deficient in fibroblasts of the patient, indicating a defect in valine catabolism.[174]

ENZYME DEFICIENCY. A deficiency of crotonase could lead to an accumulation of methacrylyl-CoA and the abnormal sulfur amino acids but would be expected to also cause an elevation of crotonic acid, which was not found. Crotonase was normal in the liver and fibroblasts of the patient. 3-Hydroxyisobutyryl-CoA deacylase was shown to be severely deficient in the patient, with 4 percent of normal activity in liver and 20 percent of normal in fibroblats.[174] Fibroblsts of the parents had 40 to 50 percent of normal activity.

Genetics. This is presumably an autosomal recessive disorder because both parents had activities of 3-hydroxyisobutyryl-CoA deaclyase of about 50 percent of normal as would be expected for heterozygotes.[174]

Diagnosis. The diagnosis should be considered in infants with dysmorphic features and skeletal and cardiac malformations, but it is not known whether these will be consistent features of the disorder. There is no acidosis or abnormality of organic acids in this disorder, but two unusual amino acids could be detected by quantitative amino acid analysis. The confirmation of these as sulfur amino acids is best done by high voltage electrophoresis or thin-layer chromatography of urinary amino acids, with abnormal spots detected by ninhydrin confirmed as containing sulfur by reaction with iodoplatinate. Trace amounts of *S*-(2-carboxypropyl)-cysteine are detected in urine of children, but large elevations of this and *S*-(2-carboxypropyl)-cysteamine are unique to the deficiency of 3-hydroxyisobutyryl-CoA deacylase.[212] The identity of these compounds can be confirmed by mass spectrometry.[212] The diagnosis can be confirmed by assay for a deficiency of 3-hydroxyisobutyryl-CoA deacylase in cultured fibroblasts.[174] Heterozygotes can be diagnosed by intermediate levels of activity of the enzyme in fibroblasts. Prenatal diagnosis should be possible because the enzyme activity is expressed in normal cultured amniocytes, and amniocytes from a fetus at risk for this disorder had heterozygous levels of enzyme activity.[174]

Treatment. No treatment has been attempted, and any would likely be ineffective if damage occurs in utero as suggested by the congenital malformations. If one assumes that the toxic intermediate is methacrylyl-CoA, which could cause damage by reaction with cysteine in a variety of proteins, and that the cysteamine adduct is less toxic and excretable, it could be worthwhile to try therapy with cysteamine or phosphocysteamine.

3-Hydroxypropionic, 3-Aminopropionic (β-Alanine), 3-Hydroxyisobutyric, and 3-Aminoisobutyric Aciduria

One child has been reported with a pattern of metabolites strongly suggestive of a deficiency of methylmalonic semialdehyde and malonic semialdehyde dehydrogenase activities.[215,216]

Clinical Aspects. The male infant had episodes of diarrhea and vomiting at 3 weeks and at 9 months of age.[215] A low methionine diet as given starting at 3 weeks of age and was discontinued at 3 years of age. At 4 years of age, eating a regular diet, development is now normal. Loading studies with methionine had no clinical effect.

Biochemical Abnormalities. The infant was found to have hypermethioninemia by newborn screening.[216] He had persistent hypermethioninemia of greater than 1000 μ*M* and elevated excretions of hydroxy and amino acids as described below, but the methionine elevation is probably not related to these because a cousin has hypermethioninemia without the other metabolites.

ABNORMAL METABOLITES. The child has large excretions of the 3-carbon compounds β-alanine (100 to 400 mmol per mole creatinine) and 3-hydroxypropionic acid (500 to 1000 mmol per mole creatinine), the 4-carbon compounds 3-aminoisobutyric acid (β-aminoisobutyric acid, 1000 to 3000 mmol per mole creatinine) and 3-hydroxyisobutyric acid (3000 to 4000 mmol per mole creatinine), and the 5-carbon compound 2-ethyl-3-hydroxypropionic acid (ethylhydracrylic acid or 2-hydroxymethylbutyric acid, 3000 mmol per mole creatinine), but no detectable 2-ethyl-3-aminopropionic acid.[215,216] 3-Aminoisobutyric acid was highly elevated in plasma at 30 μ*M* compared to normal levels of 1.8 to 4.5 μ*M*, and plasma β-alanine was 6 μ*M*.

The metabolites were further characterized as to their chiral configuration. The 3-aminoisobutyric acid was about equally composed of the *S* and *R* isomers while 3-hydroxyisobutyric acid was about 75 percent *S* and 25 percent *R* isomer, and all of the 2-ethyl-3-hydroxypropionic acid was the *S* isomer.[216]

These metabolite elevations are consistent with a deficiency of a dehydrogenase acting on malonic semialdehyde, methylmalonic semialdehyde, and ethylmalonic semialdehyde, but methylmalonic semialdehyde was not detectable in the patient's urine.[216] The precursors of the urinary metabolites were identified by loading studies with valine, which is normally metabolized to *S*-3-hydroxyisobutyric acid,[208] and thymine, which is normally metabolized to *R*-3-aminoisobutyric acid,[217,218] together with about 5 percent as much *S*-3-aminoisobutyric acid.[219] Loading studies in the patient had no effect on the excretion of 3-hydroxypropionic acid, which is a minor metabolite of propionic acid or on the excretion of β-alanine, which comes from degradation of uracil and the peptides carnosine and anserine. Loading with valine caused a large increase in excretion of *S*-3-hydoxyisobutyric acid and had little effect on the excretion of 3-aminoisobutyric acid and no effect on the ratio of *R* to *S* 3-aminoisobutyric acid. The plasma 3-aminoisobutyric acid level (largely the *S* isomer) doubled with the load of valine. This suggests that a small proportion of *S*-methylmalonic semialdehyde derived from valine was transaminated to *S*-3-aminoisobutyric acid and retained in plasma because of efficient renal reabsorption of this isomer.[217,218] Loading with thymine did not increase the plasma 3-aminobutyric acid, which is efficiently excreted, and caused a large increase in *R*-3-aminoisobutyric acid but not 3-hydoxyisobutyric acid in urine. The presence of *R*-3-hydroxybutyric acid in the urine is probably due to some transamination of *R*-3-aminoisobutyric acid to *R*-methylmalonic semialdehyde and reduction. The excreted *S*-2-ethyl-3-hydroxypropionic acid presumably arises from a block at ethylmalonic semialdehyde in the minor *R* pathway of isoleucine metabolism.

CELL STUDIES. Studies with cultured fibroblasts have not been reported.

ENZYME STUDIES. Studies of the enzymes have not been reported. From the metabolite elevations it is likely that there is a deficiency of a dehydrogenase acting on malonic semialdehyde, methylmalonic semialdehyde, and ethylmalonic semialdehyde to form acetyl-CoA, propionyl-CoA, and butyryl-CoA, respectively. Such an enzyme has not been characterized in mammals.

Genetics. The mode of inheritance is unknown.

Diagnosis. There are no clinical symptoms clearly associated with this biochemical disorder. The diagnosis may be made by the detection of the elevated urinary amino acids β-alanine and 3-aminoisobutyric acid and the urinary organic acids 3-hydroxypropionic, 3-hydroxyisobutyric, and 2-ethyl-3-hydroxypropionic acid.

Treatment. No treatment is indicated, as the affected patient is healthy.

REFERENCES

1. BEINERT H: Acyl dehydrogenases from pig and beef liver and beef heart, in Colowick SP, Kaplan No (eds): *Methods in Enzymology.* New York, Academic, 1962, vol V, p 546.
2. TANAKA K, BUDD MA, EFRON ML, ISSELBACHER KJ: Isovaleric acidemia: A new genetic defect of leucine metabolism. *Proc Natl Acad Sci USA* 56:236, 1966.
3. RHEAD WJ, TANAKA K: Demonstration of a specific mitochondrial isovaleryl-CoA dehydrogenase deficiency in fibroblasts from patients with isovaleric acidemia. *Proc Natl Acad Sci USA* 77:580, 1980.
4. RHEAD WJ, HALL CL, TANAKA K: Novel tritium release assays for isovaleryl-CoA and butyryl-CoA dehydrogenases. *J Biol Chem* 256:1616, 1981.
5. IKEDA Y, TANAKA K: Purification and characterization of isovaleryl Coenzyme A dehydrogenase from rat liver mitochondria. *J Biol Chem* 258:1077, 1983.
6. IKEDA Y, DABROWSKI C, TANAKA K: Separation and properties of five distinct acyl-CoA dehydrogenases from rat liver mitochondria. *J Biol Chem* 258:1066, 1983.
7. MATSUBARA Y, KRAUS JP, ITO M, GLASSBERG R, BARTON DE, YANG-FENG T, IKEDA Y, FRANCKE U, TANAKA K: Molecular cloning, nucleotide sequence, and human chromosome assignment of cDNA encoding rat isovaleryl-CoA dehydrogenase. *Am J Human Genet* 41:A228, 1987.
8. IKEDA Y, FENTON WA, TANAKA K: *In vitro* translation and posttranslational processing of four mitochondrial acyl-CoA dehydrogenases. *Fed Proc* 43:2024, 1984.
9. MCKEAN MC, BECKMAN JD, FRERMAN FE: Subunit structure of electron transfer flavoprotein. *J Biol Chem* 258:1866, 1983.
10. RUZICKA FJ, BEINERT H: A new iron-sulfur flavoprotein of the respiratory chain. *J Biol Chem* 252:8440, 1977.
11. RHEAD WJ, DUBIEL B, TANAKA K: The tissue distribution of isovaleryl CoA dehydrogenase in the rat, in Walser M, Williamson JR (eds): *Metabolism and Clinical Implications of Branched Chain Amino and Ketoacids,* New York, Elsevier/North-Holland, 1981, p 47.
12. ABERHART DJ, TANN CH: Substrate stereochemistry of isovaleryl-CoA dehydrogenase: Elimination of the 2-pro-*R* hydrogen in biotin-deficient rats. *Bioorg Chem* 10:200, 1981.
13. ABERHART DJ, FINOCCHIARO G, IKEDA Y, TANAKA K: Substrate stereochemistry of isovaleryl-CoA dehydrogenase II steric course of C-3 hydrogen elimination. *Bioorg Chem* 14:170, 1986.
14. LYNEN F, KNAPPE J, LORCH E, JÜTTING G, RINGELMANN E, LACHANCE JP: Zur biochemischen Funktion des Biotins II Reinigung und Wirkungsweise der beta-Methyl-crotonyl-Carboxylase. *Biochem Z* 335:123, 1961.
15. LAU EP, COCHRAN BC, MUNSON L, FALL RR: Bovine kidney 3-methylcrotonyl-CoA carboxylase and propionyl-CoA carboxylases: Each enzyme contains nonidentical subunits. *Proc Natl Acad Sci USA* 76:214, 1979.
16. LAU EP, COCHRAN BC, FALL RR: Isolation of 3-methylcrotonyl-coenzyme A carboxylase from bovine kidney. *Arch Biochem Biophys* 205:352, 1980.
17. HECTOR ML, COCHRAN BC, LOGUE EA, FALL RR: Subcellular localization of 3-methylcrotonyl-Coenzyme A carboxylase in bovine kidney. *Arch Biochem Biophys* 199:28, 1980.
18. DURAN M, BRUINVIS L, KETTING D, KAMERLING JP, WADMAN SK, SCHUTGENS RBH: The identification of *(E)*-2-methylglutaconic acid, a new isoleucine metabolite, in the urine of patients with beta-ketothiolase deficiency, propionic acidaemia and methylmalonic acidaemia. *Biomed Mass Spectrom* 9:1, 1982.
19. STERN JR, DEL CAMPLILLO A: Enzymes of fatty acid metabolism II. Properties of crystalline crotonase. *J Biol Chem* 218:985, 1956.
20. HILZ H, KNAPPE J, RINGELMANN E, LYNEN F: Methylglutaconase, eine neue Hydratase, die am Stoffwechsel verzweigter Carbonsauren beteiligt ist. *Biochem Z* 329:476, 1958.
21. VILLANUEVA VR, LYNEN F: Une nouvelle méthode de préparation de la méthylglutaconase à partir du foie de boeuf. *C R Acad Sci Paris* 270:3318, 1970.
22. NARISAWA K, GIBSON KM, SWEETMAN L, NYHAN WL, DURAN M, WADMAN SK: Deficiency of 3-methylglutaconyl-Coenzyme A hydratase in two siblings with 3-methylglutaconic aciduria. *J Clin Invest* 77:1148, 1986.
23. MESSNER B, EGGERER H, CORNFORTH JW, MALLABY R: Substrate stereochemistry of the hydroxymethylglutaryl-CoA lyase and 3-methylglutaconyl-CoA hydratase reactions. *Eur J Biochem* 53:255, 1975.
24. STEGINK LD, COON MJ: Stereospecificity and other properties of highly purified beta-hydroxy-beta-methylglutaryl Coenzyme A cleavage enzyme from bovine liver. *J Biol Chem* 243:5272, 1968.
25. CLINKENBEARD KD, REED WD, MOONEY RA, LANE MD: Intracellular localization of the 3-hydroxy-3-methylglutaryl Coenzyme A cycle enzymes in liver. *J Biol Chem* 250:3108, 1975.
26. WYSOCKI SJ, HÄHNEL R: 3-Hydroxy-3-methylglutaric aciduria: Deficiency of 3-hydroxy-3-methylglutaryl Coenzyme A lyase. *Clin Chim Acta* 71:349, 1976.
27. WYSOCKI SJ, HÄHNEL R: 3-Hydroxy-3-methylglutaric aciduria: 3-hydroxy-3-methylglutaryl-Coenzyme A lyase levels in leucocytes. *Clin Chim Acta* 73:373, 1976.
28. BACHHAWAT BK, ROBINSON WG, COON MJ: The enzymatic cleavage of beta-hydroxy-beta-methylglutaryl Coenzyme A to acetoacetic acid and acetyl-CoA. *J Biol Chem* 216:727, 1955.
29. KRAMER PR, MIZIORKO HM: 3-Hydroxy-3-methylglutaryl-CoA lyase: Catalysis of acetyl Coenzyme A enolization. *Biochemistry* 22:2353, 1983.
30. REED WD, CLINKENBEARD KD, LANE MD: Molecular and catalytic properties of mitochondrial (ketogenic) 3-hydroxy-3-methylglutaryl Coenzyme A synthase of liver. *J Biol Chem* 250:3117, 1975.

31. LOWE DM, TUBBS PK: 3-Hydroxy-3-methylglutaryl-coenzyme A synthase from ox liver. *Biochem J* 227:591, 1985.

32. BRADY PS, SCOFIELD RF, OHGAKU S, SCHUMANN WC, BARTSCH GE, MARGOLIS JM, KUMARAN K, HORVAT A, MANN S, LANDAU BR: Pathways of acetoacetate's formation in liver and kidney. *J Biol Chem* 257:9290, 1982.

33. CORNFORTH JW, PHILLIPS GT, MESSNER B, EGGERER H: Substrate stereochemistry of 3-hydroxy-3-methylglutaryl-Coenzyme A synthase. *Eur J Biochem* 42:591, 1974.

34. BUDD MA, TANAKA K, HOLMES LB, EFRON ML, CRAWFORD JD, ISSELBACHER KJ: Isovaleric acidemia-clinical features of a new genetic defect of leucine metabolism. *N Engl J Med* 277:321, 1967.

35. TANAKA K, ROSENBERG LE: Disorders of branched chain amino acid and organic acid metabolism, in Stanbury JB, Wyngaarden JB, Fredrickson DS, Goldstein JL, Brown MS (eds): *The Metabolic Basis of Inherited Disease*, 5th ed. New York, McGraw-Hill, 1983, p 440.

36. TANAKA K: Inborn errors of branched-chain amino acid metabolism, in Odessy R (ed): *Problems and Potential of Branched-Chain Amino Acids in Physiology and Medicine*. New York, Elsevier, 1986, p 201.

37. CHALMERS RA, LAWSON AM: *Organic Acids in Man, The Analytical Chemistry, Biochemistry and Diagnosis of the Organic Acidurias*. London, Chapman and Hall, 1982.

38. GOODMAN SI, MARKEY SP: *Diagnosis of Organic Acidemias by Gas Chromatography-Mass Spectrometry. Laboratory and Research Methods in Biology and Medicine*. New York, AR Liss, 1981, vol 6.

39. NEWMAN CGH, WILSON BDR, CALLAGHAN P, YOUNG L: Neonatal death associated with isovaleric acidemia. *Lancet* 2:439, 1967.

40. TRUSCOTT RJW, MALEGAN D, MCCAIRNS E, BURKE D, HICK L, SIMS P, HALPERN B, TANAKA K, SWEETMAN L, NYHAN WL, HAMMOND J, BUMACK C, HAAN EA, DANKS DM: New metabolites in isovaleric acidemia. *Clin Chim Acta* 110:187, 1981.

41. FISCHER AQ, CHALLA VR, BURTON BK, MCLEAN WT: Cerebellar hemorrhage complicating isovaleric acidemia: A case report. *Neurology* 31:746, 1981.

42. WYSOCKI SJ, FRENCH NP, GRAUAUG A: Organic aciduria associated with isovaleric acidemia. *Clin Chem* 29:1002, 1983.

43. MENDIOLA J, ROBOTHAM JL, LIEHR JG, WILLIAMS JC: Neonatal lethargy due to isovaleric acidemia and hyperammonemia. *Tex Med* 80:52, 1984.

44. WILSON WG, AUDENAERT SM, SQUILLARO EJ: Hyperammonaemia in a preterm infant with isovaleric acidemia. *J Inherited Metab Dis* 7:71, 1984.

45. BEAUVAIS P, PETER MO, BARBIER B: Forme néo-natale de l'acidémie isovalèrique. *Arch Fr Pediatr* 42:531, 1985.

46. COHN RM, YUDKOFF M, ROTHMAN R, SEGAL S: Isovaleric acidemia: Use of glycine therapy in neonates. *N Engl J Med* 299:996, 1978.

47. KELLEHER JF, YUDKOFF M, HUTCHISON R, AUGUST CS, COHN RM: The pancytopenia of isovaleric acidemia. *Pediatrics* 65:1023, 1980.

48. SHIH VE, AUBRY RH, DEGRANDE G, GURSKY SF, TANAKA K: Maternal isovaleric acidemia. *J Pediatr* 105:77, 1984.

49. VELAZQUEZ A, PRIETO EC: Glycine in acute management of isovaleric acidemia. *Lancet* 1:313, 1980.

50. WILLIAMS KM, PEDEN VH, HILLMAN RE: Isovaleric acidemia appearing as diabetic ketoacidosis. *Am J Dis Chil* 135:1068, 1981.

51. SHIGEMATSU Y, SUDO M, MOMOI T, INOUE Y, SUZUKI Y, KAMEYAMA J: Changing plasma and urinary organic acid levels in a patient with isovaleric acidemia during an attack. *Pediatr Res* 16:771, 1982.

52. DURAN M, BRUINVIS L, KETTING D, WADMAN SK, VAN PELT BC, BATENBURG-PLENTER AM: Isovaleric acidemia presenting with dwarfism, cataract and congenital abnormalities. *J Inherited Metab Dis* 5:125, 1982.

53. ROE CR, MILLINGTON DS, MALTBY DA, KAHLER SG, BOHAN TP: L-Carnitine therapy in isovaleric acidemia. *J Clin Invest* 74:2290, 1984.

54. DE SOUSA C, CHALMERS RA, STACEY TE, TRACEY BM, WEAVER CM, BRADLEY D: The response to L-carnitine and glycine therapy in isovaleric acidaemia. *Eur J Pediatr* 144:451, 1986.

55. BAKKEREN JAJM, SENGERS RCA, RUITENBEEK W, TRIJBELS JMF, HOUBEN MLM, VAN DER ZEE SPM: Isovaleriaanzuur-acidemie: Identiek biochemisch beel bij drie patienten met uiteenlopende klinische verschijnselen. *Tijdschr Kindergeneeskd* 50:153, 1982.

56. HYANEK J, ZAPADLO M, ZEMEN J, HOUSTKOVA H, RUBIN A, DURAN M, WADMAN SK, PETOVA J, PISACKA M, KOZICH V, MATOUSOVA M: Izovalerova acidurie. *Cas Lek Cesk* 122:1082, 1983.

57. FLUELER U, GITZELMANN R, STEINMANN B, KUSTER T, NIEDERWIESER A: Azetonämisches Erbrechen als Symptom-Isovaleriansäurekrankheit. *Helv Paediatr Acta Suppl* 47:30, 1982.

58. TANAKA K, ISSELBACHER KJ: The isolation and identification of N-isovalerylglycine from urine of patients with isovaleric acidemia. *J Biol Chem* 242:2966, 1967.

59. BARTLETT K, GOMPERTZ D: The specificity of glycine-*N*-acylase and acylglycine excretion in the organic acidaemias. *Biochem Med* 10:15, 1974.

60. GREGERSEN N, KOLVRAA S, MORTENSEN PB: Acyl-CoA glycine *N*-acyltransferase: *in vitro* studies on the glycine conjugation of straight- and branched chained acyl-CoA esters in human liver. *Biochem Med Exp Biol* 35:210, 1986.

61. TANAKA K, ORR JC, ISSELBACHER KJ: Identification of beta-hydroxyisovaleric acid in the urine of a patient with isovaleric acidemia. *Biochim Biophys Acta* 152:638, 1968.

62. LEHNERT W, NIEDERHOFF H: 4-Hydroxyisovaleric acid: A new metabolite in isovaleric acidemia. *Eur J Pediatr* 136:281, 1981.

63. SHIGEMATSU Y, KIKAWA Y, SUDO M, KIKUCHI K, OHTA S, OKAMATA M: A simple method of determining 4-hydroxyisovaleric acid and its level in a patient with isovaleric acidemia. *Clin Chim Acta* 138:333, 1984.

64. DORLAND L, DURAN M, WADMAN SK, NIEDERWIESER A, BRUINVIS L, KETTING D: Isovalerylglucuronide, a new urinary metabolite in isovaleric acidemia. Identification problems due to rearrangement reactions. *Clin Chim Acta* 134:77, 1983.

65. HINE DG, TANAKA K: The identification and the excretion pattern of isovaleryl glucuronide in the urine of patients with isovaleric acidemia. *Pediatr Res* 18:508, 1984.

66. LEHNERT W: Excretion of N-isovalerylglutamic acid in isovaleric acidemia. *Clin Chim Acta* 116:249, 1981.

67. LEHNERT W: N-isovalerylalanine and N-isovalerylsarcosine: Two new minor metabolites in isovaleric acidemia. *Clin Chim Acta* 134:207, 1983.

68. LEHNERT W: 3-Hydroxyisoheptanoic acid: A new metabolite in isovaleric acidemia. *Clin Chim Acta* 113:101, 1981.

69. SHIH VE, MANDELL R, TANAKA K: Diagnosis of isovaleric acidemia in cultured fibroblasts. *Clin Chim Acta* 48:437, 1973.

70. TANAKA K, MANDELL R, SHIH VE: Metabolism of [1-^{14}C] and [2-^{14}C]leucine in cultured skin fibroblasts from patients with isovaleric acidemia. *J Clin Invest* 58:164, 1976.

71. PETIT FH, YEAMAN SJ, REED LJ: Purification and characterization of branched chain alpha-keto acid dehydrogenase complex of bovine kidney. *Proc Natl Acad Sci USA* 75:4881, 1978.

72. HYMAN DB, TANAKA K: Isovaleryl-CoA dehydrogenase activity in isovaleric acidemia fibroblasts using an improved tritium release assay. *Pediatr Res* 20:59, 1986.

73. FRERMAN FE, GOODMAN SI: Fluorometric assay of acyl-CoA dehydrogenases in normal and mutant human fibroblasts. *Biochem Med* 33:38, 1985.

74. DUBIEL B, DABROWSKI C, WETTS R, TANAKA K: Complementation studies of isovaleric acidemia and glutaric aciduria type II using cultured skin fibroblasts. *J Clin Invest* 72:1543, 1983.

75. IKEDA Y, KEESE SM, TANAKA K: Molecular heterogeneity of variant isovaleryl-CoA dehydrogenase from cultured isovaleric acidemia fibroblasts. *Proc Natl Acad Sci USA* 82:7081, 1985.

76. TANAKA K, WEST-DULL A, HINE DG, LYNN TB, LOWE T: Gas-chromatographic method of analysis for urinary organic acids. II. Description of the procedure, and its application to diagnosis of patients with organic acidurias. *Clin Chem* 26:1847, 1980.

77. SWEETMAN L: Qualitative and quantitative analysis of organic acids in physiologic fluids for diagnosis of the organic acidurias, in Nyhan WL (ed): *Abnormalities in Amino Acid Metabolism in Clinical Medicine*. Norwalk, CT: Appleton-Century-Crofts, 1984, p 419.

78. YAMAGUCHI S, KODA N, ETO Y, AOKI K: Quick screening and diagnosis of organic acidemia by NMR urinalysis. *J Pediatr* 106:620, 1985.

79. ILES RA, HIND AJ, CHALMERS RA: Use of proton nuclear magnetic resonance spectroscopy in detection and study of organic acidurias. *Clin Chem* 31:1795, 1985.

80. LEHNERT W, HUNKLER D: Possibilities of selective screening for inborn errors of metabolism using high-resolution ^{1}H-FT-NMR spectrometry. *Eur J Pediatr* 145:260, 1986.

81. ARNOLD WC, BREWSTER M, BYRNE WJ, BOOTH B: Fanconi syndrome in a patient with a variant of isovaleric acidemia. *Int J Pediatr Nephrol* 7:95, 1986.

82. HINE DG, HACK AM, GOODMAN SI, TANAKA K: Stable isotope dilution analysis of isovalerylglycine in amniotic fluid and urine and its application for the prenatal diagnosis of isovaleric acidemia. *Pediatr Res* 20:222, 1986.

83. JAMES MO, BEND JR: Perinatal development of, and effect of chemical pretreatment on, glycine *N*-acyltransferase activities in liver and kidney of rabbit and rat. *Biochem J* 172:293, 1978.

84. KRIEGER I, TANAKA K: Therapeutic effects of glycine in isovaleric acidemia. *Pediatr Res* 10:25, 1976.

85. YUDKOFF M, COHN RM, PUSHAK R, ROTHMAN R, SEGAL S: Glycine therapy in isovaleric acidemia. *J Pediatr* 92:813, 1978.

86. STANLEY CA, HALE DE, WHITEMAN DEH, COATES PM, YUDKOFF M, BERRY GT, SEGAL S: Systemic carnitine (carn) deficiency in isovaleric acidemia (IVA). *Pediatr Res* 17:296a, 1983.

87. CHALMERS RA, ROE CR, STACEY TE, HOPPEL CL: Urinary excretion of *L*-carnitine and acylcarnitines by patients with disorders of organic acid me-

tabolism: Evidence for secondary insufficiency of *L*-carnitine. *Pediatr Res* 18:1325, 1984.

88. MILLINGTON DS, ROE CR, MALTBY DA, INOUE F: Endogenous catabolism is the major source of toxic metabolites in isovaleric acidemia. *J Pediatr* 110:56, 1987.

89. BERGEN BJ, STUMPF DA, HAAS R, PARKS JK, EGUREN LA: A mechanism of toxicity of isovaleric acid in rat liver mitochondria. *Biochem Med* 27:154, 1982.

90. HUTCHISON RJ, BUNNELL K, THOENE JG: Suppression of granulopoietic progenitor cell proliferation by metabolites of the branched-chain amino acids. *J Pediatr* 106:62, 1985.

91. ELDJARN L, JELLUM E, STOKKE O, PANDE H, WAALER PE: Beta-hydroxyisovaleric aciduria and beta-methylcrotonylglycinuria: A new inborn error of metabolism. *Lancet* 2:521, 1970.

92. STOKKE O, ELDJARN L, JELLUM E, PANDE H, WAALER PE: Beta-methylcrotonyl-CoA carboxylase deficiency: A new metabolic error in leucine degradation. *Pediatrics* 49:726, 1972.

93. STOKKE O, JELLUM E, ELDJARN E: A new metabolic error in the leucine degradation pathway: Beta-hydroxyisovaleric aciduria and beta-methylcrotonylglycinuria, in Stern J, Toothill C (eds): *Organic Acidurias, Proceedings of the Ninth Symposium Society for Study of Inborn Errors of Metabolism,* London, Churchill Livingstone, 1972, p 27.

94. FINNIE MDA, COTTRALL K, SEAKINS JWT, SNEDDEN W: Massive excretion of 2-oxoglutaric acid and 3-hydroxyisovaleric acid in a patient with a deficiency of 3-methylcrotonyl-CoA carboxylase. *Clin Chim Acta* 73:513, 1976.

95. BEEMER FA, BARTLETT K, DURAN M, GHNEIM HK, WADMAN SK, BRUINVIS L, KETTING D: Isolated biotin-resistant 3-methylcrotonyl-CoA carboxylase deficiency in two sibs. *Eur J Pediatr* 138:351, 1982.

96. BARTLETT K, BENNETT MJ, HILL RP, LASHFORD LS, POLLIT RJ, WORTH HGJ: Isolated biotin-resistant 3-methylcrotonyl-CoA carboxylase deficiency presenting with life-threatening hypoglycemia. *J Inherited Metab Dis* 7:182, 1984.

97. STEINMAN HM, HILL RL: Bovine liver crotonase (enoyl coenzyme A hydratase), in Lowenstein JM (ed): *Methods in Enzymology.* New York, Academic, 1975, vol XXXV, p 136.

98. STERN JR: Crotonase, in Boyer PD, Lardy H, Myrback K (eds): *The Enzymes, 2d ed.* New York, Academic, 1961, vol 5, p 511.

99. SOVIK O, SWEETMAN L, GIBSON KM, NYHAN WL: Genetic complementation analysis of 3-hydroxy-3-methylglutaryl-Coenzyme A lyase deficiency in cultured fibroblasts. *Am J Hum Genet* 36:791, 1984.

100. LANDAAS S: Accumulation of 3-hydroxyisobutyric acid, 2-methyl-3-hydroxybutyric acid and 3-hydroxyisovaleric acid in ketoacidosis. *Clin Chim Acta* 64:143, 1975.

101. WOLF B, ROSENBERG LE: Stimulation of propionyl-CoA and beta-methylcrotonyl CoA carboxylase activities in human leukocytes and cultured fibroblasts by biotin. *Pediatr Res* 13:1275, 1979.

102. JAKOBS C, SWEETMAN L, NYHAN WL, PACKMAN S: Stable isotope dilution analysis of 3-hydroxyisovaleric acid in amniotic fluid: Contribution to the prenatal diagnosis of inherited disorders of leucine catabolism. *J Inherited Metab Dis* 7:15, 1984.

103. SWEETMAN FR, GIBSON MK, SWEETMAN L, NYHAN WL: Activity of biotin-dependent and GABA metabolizing enzymes in chorionic villous samples: Potential for 1st trimester prenatal diagnosis. *Prenat Diagn* 6:187, 1986.

104. DURAN M, BEEMER FA, TIBOSCH AS, BRUINVIS L, KETTING D, WADMAN SK: Inherited 3-methylglutaconic aciduria in two brothers—another defect of leucine metabolism. *J Pediatr* 101:551, 1982.

105. ROBINSON BH, SHERWOOD WG, LAMPTY M, LOWDEN JA: Beta-methyl glutaconic aciduria: A new disorder of leucine metabolism. *Pediatr Res* 10:371, 1976.

106. GRETER J, HAGBERG B, STEEN G, SODERHJELM U: 3-Methylglutaconic aciduria: Report on a sibship with infantile progressive encephalopathy. *Eur J Pediatr* 129:231, 1978.

107. HAGBERG B, HJALMARSON O, LINDSTEDT S, RANSNAS L, STEEN G: 3-Methylglutaconic aciduria in two infants. *Clin Chim Acta* 134:59, 1983.

108. LEHNERT W, SCHARF J, WENDEL U: 3-Methylglutaconic and 3-methylglutaric aciduria in a patient with suspected 3-methylglutaconyl-CoA hydratase deficiency. *Eur J Pediatr* 143:301, 1985.

109. HAAN EA, SCHOLEM RD, PITT JJ, WRAITH JE, BROWN GK: Episodes of severe metabolic acidosis in a patient with 3-methylglutaconic aciduria. *Eur J Pediatr* 146:484, 1987.

110. GIBSON KM, SWEETMAN L, NYHAN WL, NARISAWA K, ROTH K, LEHNERT W, ROBINSON B, DURAN M, WADMAN SK: 3-Methylglutaconyl-CoA hydratase deficiency: Two different clinical and enzymatic phenotypes in 3-methylglutaconic aciduria. *Pediatr Res* 19:248A, 1985.

111. EDMOND J, POPJAK G: Transfer of carbon atoms from mevalonate to *n*-fatty acids. *J Biol Chem* 249:66, 1974.

112. BRADY PS, SCOFIELD RF, SCHUMANN WC, OHGAKU S, KUMARAN K, MARGOLIS M, LANDAU BR: The tracing of the pathway of mevalonate's metabolism to other than sterols. *J Biol Chem* 257:10742, 1982.

113. HOFFMANN G, GIBSON KM, BRANDT IK, BADER PI, WAPPNER RS, SWEETMAN L: Mevalonic aciduria—An inborn error of cholesterol and nonsterol isoprene biosynthesis. *N Engl J Med* 314:1610, 1986.

114. FAULL K, BOLTON P, HALPERN B, HAMMOND J, DANKS DM, HÄHNEL R, WILKINSON SP, WYSOCKI SJ, MASTERS PL: Patient with defect in leucine catabolism. *N Engl J Med* 294:1013, 1976.

115. WYSOCKI SJ, HÄHNEL R: 3-Hydroxy-3-methylglutaryl-CoA lyase deficiency: A review. *J Inherited Metab Dis* 9:225, 1986.

116. SCHUTGENS RBH, HEYMANS H, KETEL A, VEDER HA, DURAN M, KETTING D, WADMAN SK: Lethal hypoglycemia in a child with a deficiency of 3-hydroxy-3-methylglutarylcoenzyme A lyase. *J Pediatr* 94:89, 1979.

117. WALTER JH, CLAYTON PT, LEONARD JV: 3-Hydroxy-3-methylglutaryl-CoA lyase deficiency. *J Inherited Metab Dis* 9:287, 1986.

118. DIVRY P, ROLLAND MO, TEYSSIER J, COTTE J, FORMOSINHO FERNANDES MC, TAVARES DE ALMEIDA I, DA SILVEIRA C: 3-Hydroxy-3-methylglutaric aciduria combined with 3-methylglutaconic aciduria: A new case. *J Inherited Metab Dis* 4:173, 1981.

119. ZOGHBI HY, SPENCE JE, BEAUDET AL, O'BRIEN WE, GOODMAN CJ, GIBSON KM: Atypical presentation and neuropathological studies in 3-hydroxy-3-methylglutaryl-CoA lyase deficiency. *Ann Neurol* 20:367, 1986.

120. LISSON G, LEUPOLD D, BECHINGER D, WALLESCH C: CT findings in a case of deficiency of 3-hydroxy-3-methylglutaryl-CoA lyase. *Neuroradiology* 22:99, 1981.

121. LEUPOLD D, BOJASCH M, JAKOBS C: 3-Hydroxy-3-methylglutaryl-CoA lyase deficiency in an infant with macrocephaly and mild metabolic acidosis. *Eur J Pediatr* 138:73, 1982.

122. STACEY TE, de SOUSA C, TRACEY BM, WHITELAW A, MISTRY J, TIMBRELL P, CHALMERS RA: Dizygotic twins with 3-hydroxy-3-methylglutaric aciduria; unusual presentation, family studies and dietary management. *Eur J Pediatr* 144:177, 1985.

123. SHILKIN R, WILSON G, OWLES E: 3-Hydroxy-3-methylglutaryl Coenzyme A lyase deficiency: Follow-up of first described case. *Acta Paediart Scand* 70:265, 1981.

124. LEONARD JV, SEAKINS JWT, GRIFFIN NK: Beta-hydroxy-beta-methylglutaric aciduria presenting as Reye's syndrome. *Lancet* 1:680, 1979.

125. ROBINSON BH, OEI J, SHERWOOD WG, SLYPER AH, HEININGER J, MAMER OA: Hydroxymethylglutaryl CoA lyase deficiency: Features resembling Reye syndrome. *Neurology* 30:714, 1980.

126. GREENE C, BLITZER M, BRONFIN D, SHAPIRA E: 3-Hydroxy-3-methylglutaric aciduria presenting as Reye syndrome in an infant. *Clin Res* 34:241A, 1986.

127. LIPPE G, GALSIGNA L, RANCESCONI M, ZORZI C, DEANA R: Age-dependent excretion of 3-hydroxy-3-methylglutaric acid (HMG) and ketone bodies in the urine of full-term and pre-term newborns. *Clin Chim Acta* 126:291, 1982.

128. WILSON WG, CASS MB, SOVIK O, GIBSON MK, SWEETMAN L: A child with acute pancreatitis and recurrent hypoglycemia due to 3-hydroxy-3-methylglutaryl-CoA lyase deficiency. *Eur J Pediatr* 142:289, 1984.

129. FAULL KF, BOLTON PD, HALPERN B, HAMMOND J, DANKS DM: The urinary organic acid profile associated with 3-hydroxy-3-methylglutaric aciduria. *Clin Chim Acta* 73:553, 1976.

130. WYSOCKI SJ, HÄHNEL R: 3-Methylcrotonylglycine excretion in 3-hydroxy-3-methylglutaric aciduria. *Clin Chim Acta* 86:101, 1978.

131. WYSOCKI SJ, WILKINSON SP, HÄHNEL R, WONG CYB, PANEGYRES PK: 3-Hydroxy-3-methylglutaric aciduria, combined with 3-methylglutaconic aciduria. *Clin Chim Acta* 70:399, 1976.

132. DURAN M, KETTING D, WADMAN SK, JAKOBS C, SCHUTGENS RBH, VEDER HA: Organic acid excretion in a patient with 3-hydroxy-3-methylglutaryl-CoA lyase deficiency: Facts and artefacts. *Clin Chim Acta* 90:187, 1978.

133. JAKOBS C, BOJASCH M, DURAN M, KETTING D, WADMAN SK, LEUPOLD D: 3-Methyl-3-buteneoic acid: An artefact in the urinary metabolic pattern of patients with 3-hydroxy-3-methylglutaryl-CoA lyase deficiency. *Clin Chim Acta* 106:85, 1980.

134. GREEN CL, CANN HM, ROBINSON BH, GIBSON KM, SWEETMAN L, HOLM J, NYHAN WL: 3-Hydroxy-3-methylglutaric aciduria. *J Neurogenet* 1:165, 1984.

135. CHALMERS RA, ROE CR, TRACEY BM, STACEY TE, HOPPEL L, MILLINGTON DS: Secondary carnitine insufficiency in disorders of organic acid metabolism: Modulation of acyl-CoA/CoA ratios by L-carnitine *in vivo*. *Biochem Soc Trans* 11:724, 1983.

136. ROE CR, MILLINGTON DS, MALTBY DA: Identification of 3-methylglutarylcarnitine: A new diagnostic metabolite of 3-hydroxy-3-methylglutaryl-Coenzyme A lyase deficiency. *J Clin Invest* 77:1391, 1986.

137. ILES RA, JAGO JR, WILLIAMS SR, CHALMERS RA: 3-Hydroxy-3-methylglu-

taryl-CoA lyase deficiency studied using 2-dimensional proton nuclear magnetic resonance spectroscopy. *FEBS Lett* 203:49, 1986.

138. BUCHANAN DN, THOENE JG: Photodiode array detection of liquid chromatographic profiling of carboxylic acids in physiological fluids: 3-hydroxy-3-methylglutaric aciduria. *Clin Chem* 32:169, 1986.

139. WILKINSON SP, WYSOCKI SJ, HÄHNEL R: Diagnosing 3-hydroxy-3-methylglutaric acidura. *Clin Chem* 32:1615, 1986.

140. DURAN M, SCHUTGENS RBH, KETEL A, HEYMANS H, BERNTSSEN MWJ, KETTING D, WADMAN SK: 3-Hydroxy-3-methylglutaryl coenzyme A lyase deficiency: Postnatal management following prenatal diagnosis by analysis of maternal urine. *J Pediatr* 95:1004, 1979.

141. GIBSON KM, SWEETMAN L, NYHAN WL, PAGE TM, GREENE C, CANN HM: 3-Hydroxy-3-methylglutaric aciduria: A new assay of 3-hydroxy-3-methylglutaryl-CoA lyase using high performance liquid chromatography. *Clin Chim Acta* 126:171, 1982.

142. HÄHNEL R, WYSOCKI SJ: Potential prenatal diagnosis of 3-hydroxy-3-methylglutaryl-Coenzyme A lyase deficiency. *Clin Chim Acta* 111:287, 1981.

143. FRANCOIS B, BACHMANN C, SCHUTGENS RBH: Glucose metabolism in a child with 3-hydroxy-3-methylglutaryl-coenzyme A lyase deficiency. *J Inherited Metab Dis* 4:163, 1981.

144. NORMAN EJ, DENTON MD, BERRY HK: Gas-chromatographic/mass spectrometric detection of 3-hydroxy-3-methylglutaryl-CoA lyase deficiency in double first cousins. *Clin Chem* 28:137, 1982.

145. BERRY HK, SUCHY F, HUNT M, NORMAN E: Treatment of 3-hydroxy-3-methylglutaric aciduria in first cousins, in Walser M, Williamson JR (eds): *Metabolism and Clinical Implications of Branched Chain Amino and Keto Acids*. New York, Elsevier/North-Holland, 1981, p 405.

146. DASOUKI M, BUCHANAN D, MERCER N, GIBSON KM, THOENE J: 3-Hydroxy-3-methylglutaric aciduria: Response to carnitine therapy and fat and leucine restriction. *J Inherited Metab Dis* 10:142, 1987.

147. APPLEGARTH DA, MacLEOD PM, TOONE JR, KIRBY LT, MacLEAN JR, MAMER OA, MONTGOMERY JA: Organic acids and Reye's syndrome. *Lancet* 1:1147, 1979.

148. TRUSCOTT RJW, HALPERN B, WYSOCKI SJ, HÄHNEL R, WILCKEN B: Studies on a child suspected of having a deficiency in 3-hydroxy-3-methylglutaryl-CoA lyase. *Clin Chim Acta* 95:11, 1979.

149. HAMMOND J, WILCKEN B: 3-Hydroxy-3-methylglutaric, 3-methylglutaconic and 3-methylglutaric acids can be non-specific indicators of metabolic disease. *J Inherited Metab Dis* 7:*Suppl* 2, 117, 1984.

150. SCHROEPFER GJ JR: Sterol Biosynthesis. *Annu Rev Biochem* 50:585, 1981.

151. GOLDSTEIN JL, BROWN MS: Progress in understanding the LDL receptor and HMG-CoA reductase, two membrane proteins that regulate the plasma cholesterol. *J Lipid Res* 25:1450, 1984.

152. BROWN MS, GOLDSTEIN JL: Multivalent feedback regulation of HMG CoA reductase, a control mechanism coordinating isoprenoid synthesis and cell growth. *J Lipid Res* 21:505, 1980.

153. LEVY HR, POPJAK G: Studies on the biosynthesis of cholesterol 10, mevalonic kinase and phosphomevalonic kinase from liver. *Biochem J* 75:417, 1960.

154. BEYTIA E, DORSEY JK, MARR J, CLELAND WW, PORTER JW: Purification and mechanism of action of hog liver mevalonic kinase. *J Biol Chem* 245:5450, 1970.

155. LEE CS, O'SULLIVAN WJ: An improved purification procedure, an alternative assay and activation of mevalonate kinase by ATP. *Biochim Biophys Acta* 747:215, 1983.

156. DORSEY JK, PORTER JW: The inhibition of mevalonic kinase by geranyl and farnesyl pyrophosphates. *J Biol Chem* 243:4667, 1968.

157. CRISTOPHE J, POPJAK G: Studies on the biosynthesis of cholesterol: XIV. The origin of prenoic acids from allyl pyrophosphates in liver enzyme systems. *J Lipid Res* 2:244, 1961.

158. EDMOND J, FOGELMAN AM, POPJAK G: Mevalonate metabolism: Role of the kidneys. *Science* 193:154, 1976.

159. KOPITO RR, BRUNENGRABER H: (R)-mevalonate excretion in human and rat urines. *Proc Natl Acad Sci USA* 77:5738, 1980.

160. BRUNENGRABER H, WEINSTOCK SB, STORY DL, KOPITO RR: Urinary clearance and metabolism of mevalonate by the isolated perfused rat kidney. *J Lipid Res* 22:916, 1981.

161. WILEY MH, HULING S, SIPERSTEIN MD: Conversion of mevalonolactone to its open-chain salt by a serum enzyme. *Biochem Biophys Res Commun* 88:605, 1979.

162. PARKER TS, MCNAMARA DJ, BROWN CD, KOLB R, AHRENS EH JR, ALBERTS AW, TOBERT J, CHEN J, DE SCHEPPER PJ: Plasma mevalonate as a measure of cholesterol synthesis in man. *J Clin Invest* 74:795, 1984.

163. SWEETMAN L, HOFFMANN G, GIBSON KM, BADER PI, WAPPNER RS, BRANDT IK: Mevalonic aciduria: A newly recognized inborn error of cholesterol biosynthesis. *Pediatr Res* 19:322A, 1985.

164. de KLERK JBC, DURAN M, BROUWERS HAA, BRUINVIS L, KETTING D: Personal communication.

165. BERGER R, SMIT GPA, SCHIERBEEK H, BIJSTERVELD K, LE COULTRE R: Mevalonic aciduria: An inborn error of cholesterol biosynthesis? *Clin Chim Acta* 152:219, 1985.

166. SMIT GPA: Personal communication.

167. BRANDT IK, WAPPNER RS: Personal communication.

168. HOFFMANN G, GIBSON KM, KOHLSCHUTTER A, SWEETMAN L, NYHAN WL: Pathobiochemical effects of mevalonate kinase deficiency on lipid composition and cholesterol biosynthesis in intact fibroblasts. *Pediatr Res* 20:330A, 1986.

169. HARWOOD HJ JR, RODWELL VW: HMG-CoA reductase kinase: Measurement of activity by methods that preclude interference by inhibitors of HMG-CoA reductase activity or by mevalonate kinase. *J Lipid Res* 23:754, 1982.

170. GIBSON KM: Personal communication.

171. GIBSON KM, HOFFMANN G, NYHAN WL, SWEETMAN L, BRANDT IK, WAPPNER RS, BADER PI: Mevalonic aciduria: An inborn error of cholesterol biosynthesis due to mevalonate kinase deficiency. *J Inherited Metab Dis* 10(*Suppl* 2):282, 1987.

172. IKEDA Y, TANAKA K: Purification and characterization of 2-methyl-branched chain acyl-Coenzyme A dehydrogenase, an enzyme involved in the isoleucine and valine metabolism, from rat liver mitochondria. *J Biol Chem* 258:9477, 1983.

173. HASS GM, HILL RL: The subunit structure of crotonase. *J Biol Chem* 244:6080, 1969.

174. BROWN GK, HUNT SM, SCHOLEM R, FOWLER K, GRIMES A, MERCER JFB, TRUSCOTT RM, COTTON RGH, ROGERS JG, DANKS DM: Beta-hydroxyisobutyryl coenzyme A deacylase deficiency: A defect in valine metabolism associated with physical malformations. *Pediatrics* 70:532, 1982.

175. MIDDLETON B: The existence of ketoacyl-CoA thiolases of differing properties and intracellular location in ox liver. *Biochem Biophys Res Commun* 46:508, 1972.

176. MIDDLETON B: The oxoacyl-Coenzyme A thiolases of animal tissues. *Biochem J* 132:717, 1973.

177. MIDDLETON B, BARTLETT K: The synthesis and characterisation of 2-methylacetoacetyl coenzyme A and its use in the identification of the site of the defect in 2-methylacetoacetic and 2-methyl-3-hydroxybutyric aciduria. *Clin Chim Acta* 128:291, 1983.

178. MIDDLETON B: 3-Ketoacyl-CoA thiolases of mammalian tissues, in Lowenstein JM (ed): *Methods in Enzymology*. New York, Academic, 1975, vol XXXV, p 128.

179. GEHRING U, RIEPERTINGER C: Dissoziation und Rekonstitution der Thiolase. *Eur J Biochem* 6:281, 1968.

180. WEINBERG RB, WALSER M: Racemization and amination of the keto-analog of isoleucine in the intact dog. *Biochem Med* 17:164, 1977.

181. MATHEWS DE, BEN-GALIM E, HAYMOND MW, BIER DM: Alloisoleucine formation in maple syrup urine disease: Isotopic evidence for the mechanism. *Pediatr Res* 14:854, 1980.

182. MAMER OA, TJOA SS, SCRIVER CR, KLASSEN GA: Demonstration of a new mammalian isoleucine catabolic pathway yielding an *R* series of metabolites. *Biochem J* 160:417, 1976.

183. BARETZ BH, LOLLO CP, TANAKA K: Metabolism in rats *in vivo* of *RS*-2-methylbutyrate and *n*-butyrate labeled with stable isotopes at various positions. *J Biol Chem* 254:3468, 1979.

184. DAUM RS, LAMM PH, MAMER OA, SCRIVER CR: A "new" disorder of isoleucine metabolism. *Lancet* 2:1289, 1971.

185. DAUM RS, SCRIVER CR, MAMER OA, DELVIN E, LAMM P, GOLDMAN H: An inherited disorder of isoleucine catabolism causing accumulation of alpha-methylacetoacetate and alpha-methyl-beta-hydroxybutyrate, and intermittent metabolic acidosis. *Pediatr Res* 7:149, 1973.

186. KEATING JP, FEIGIN RD, TENENBAUM SM, HILLMAN RE: Hyperglycinemia with ketosis due to a defect in isoleucine metabolism: A preliminary report. *Pediatrics* 50:890, 1972.

187. HILLMAN RE, KEATING JP: Beta-ketothiolase deficiency as a cause of the "ketotic hyperglycinemia syndrome." *Pediatrics* 53:221, 1974.

188. GOMPERTZ D, SAUDUBRAY JM, CHARPENTIER C, BARTLETT K, GOODEY PA, DRAFFAN GH: A defect in L-isoleucine metabolism associated with alpha-methyl-beta-hydroxybutyric and alpha-methylacetoacetic aciduria: Quantitative in vivo and in vitro studies. *Clin Chim Acta* 57:269, 1974.

189. ROBINSON BH, SHERWOOD WG, TAYLOR J, BALFE JW, MAMER OA: Acetoacetyl CoA thiolase deficiency: A cause of severe ketoacidosis in infancy simulating salicylism. *J Pediatr* 95:228, 1979.

190. HALVORSEN S, STOKKE O, JELLUM E: A variant form of 2-methyl-3-hydroxybutyric and 2-methylacetoacetic aciduria. *Acta Paediatr Scand* 68:123, 1979.

191. HENRY CG, STRAUSS AW, KEATING JP, HILLMAN RE: Congestive cardio-

myopathy associated with beta-ketothiolase deficiency. *J Pediatr* 99:754, 1981.

192. SCHUTGENS RBH, MIDDLETON B, v.d. BLIJ JF, OORTHUYS JWE, VEDER HA, VULSMA T, TEGELAERS WHH: Beta-ketothiolase deficiency in a family confirmed by in vitro enzymatic assays in fibroblasts. *Eur J Pediatr* 139:39, 1982.

193. BENNETT MJ, LITTLEWOOD JM, MacDONALD A, POLLITT RJ, THOMPSON J: A case of beta-ketothiolase deficiency. *J Inherited Metab Dis* 6:157, 1983.

194. GRAY RGF, LOWTHER GW, LITTLEWOOD JM, MIDDLETON B, BENNETT MJ: A case of 2-methylacetoacetyl CoA thiolase deficiency with coincidental chromosome abnormalities. *J Med Genet* 21:397, 1984.

195. MIDDLETON B, GRAY RGF, BENNETT MJ: Two cases of beta-ketothiolase deficiency: A comparison. *J Inherited Metab Dis* 7:*(Suppl 2)*:131, 1984.

196. POLLITT RJ: The occurrence of substituted 3-methyl-3-hydroxyglutaric acids in urine in propionic acidaemia and in beta-ketothiolase deficiency. *Biomed Mass Spectrom* 10:253, 1983.

197. MIDDLETON B, BARTLETT K, ROMANOS A, GOMEZ VASQUEZ J, CONDE C, CANNON RA, LIPSON M, SWEETMAN L, NYHAN WL: 3-Ketothiolase deficiency. *Eur J Pediatr* 144:586, 1986.

198. HIYAMA K, SAKURA N, MATSUMOTO T, KUHARA T: Deficient beta-ketothiolase activity in leucocytes from a patient with 2-methylacetoacetic aciduria. *Clin Chim Acta* 155:189, 1986.

199. IDEN P, SOVIK O, MIDDLETON B, GIBSON KM, SWEETMAN L: Unpublished observation.

200. HARTLAGE P, ELLER G, CARTER L, ROESEL A, HOMMES F: Mitochondrial acetoacetyl-CoA thiolase deficiency. *Biochem Med Metabolic Biol* 36:198, 1986.

201. DE GROOT CJ, LUIT-DE HAAN G, HULSTAERT CE, HOMMES FA: A patient with severe neurologic symptoms and acetoacetyl-CoA thiolase deficiency. *Pediatr Res* 11:1112, 1977.

202. BENNETT MJ, HOSKING GP, SMITH MF, GRAY RGF, MIDDLETON B: Biochemical investigations on a patient with a defect in cytosolic acetoacetyl-CoA thiolase, associated with mental retardation. *J Inherited Metab Dis* 7:125, 1984.

203. ROBINSON WG, NAGLE R, BACHHAWAT BK, KUPIECKI FP, COON MJ: Coenzyme A thiol esters of isobutyric, methacrylic, and beta-hydroxyisobutyric acids as intermediates in the enzymatic degradation of valine. *J Biol Chem* 224:1, 1957.

204. RENDINA G, COON MJ: Enzymatic hydrolysis of the coenzyme A thiol esters of beta-hydroxypropionic and beta-hydroxyisobutyric acids. *J Biol Chem* 225:523, 1957.

205. AMSTER J, TANAKA K: Isolations and identification of *S*(+)-3-hydroxyisobutyric acid in the urine of rats loaded with isobutyric acid. *Biochem Biophys Acta* 585:643, 1979.

206. ROBINSON WG, COON MJ: The purification and properties of beta-hydroxyisobutyric dehydrogenase. *J Biol Chem* 225:511, 1957.

207. YOSHINO M, SWEETMAN L, NYHAN WL, CRAIG JC, GRUENKE L: Metabolism of deuterated 3-hydroxyisobutyrate in rat liver. *Proc Jpn Soc Biomed Mass Spectrom* 5:97, 1981.

208. MANNING NJ, POLLITT RJ: Tracer studies of the interconversion of *R*- and *S*-methylmalonic semialdehydes in man. *Biochem J* 231:481, 1985.

209. BANNERJEE D, SANDERS LE, SOKATCH JR: Properties of purified methylmalonate semialdehyde dehydrogenase of *Pseudomonas aeruginosa*. *J Biol Chem* 245:1828, 1970.

210. TANAKA K, ARMITAGE IA, RAMSDELL HS, HSIA YE, LIPSKY SR, ROSENBERG LE: [^{13}C]Valine metabolism in methylmalonic acidemia using nuclear magnetic resonance: Propionate as an obligate intermediate. *Proc Natl Acad Sci USA* 72:3692, 1975.

211. BARETZ BH, TANAKA K: Metabolism in rats *in vivo* of isobutyrates labeled with stable isotopes at various positions: Identification of propionate as an obligate intermediate. *J Biol Chem* 253:4203, 1978.

212. TRUSCOTT RJW, MALEGAN D, MCCAIRNS E, HALPERN B, HAMMOND J, COTTON RGH, MERCER JFB, HUNT S, ROGERS JG, DANKS DM: Two new sulphur-containing amino acids in man. *Biomed Mass Spectrom* 8:99, 1981.

213. SINGH RR, LAWRENCE WH, AUTIAN J: Embryonic-fetal toxicity and teratogenic effects of a group of methyacrylate esters in rats. *J Dent Res* 51:1632, 1972.

214. OHMORI S, SHIMOMURA T, AZUMI T, MIZUHARA S: S-(beta-carboxy-n-propyl)-L-cysteine and S-(beta-carboxyethyl)l-cysteine in urine. *Biochem Z* 343:9, 1965.

215. CONGDON PJ, HAIGH D, SMITH R, GREEN A, POLLITT RJ: Hypermethioninaemia and 3-hydroxyisobutyric aciduria in an apparently healthy baby. *J Inherited Metab Dis* 4:79, 1981.

216. POLLITT RJ, GREEN A, SMITH R: Excessive excretion of beta-alanine and of 3-hydroxypropionic, *R*- and *S*-3-aminobutyric, *R*- and *S*-3-hydroxyisobutyric and *S*-2-(hydroxymethyl)butyric acids probably due to a defect in the metabolism of the corresponding malonic semialdehydes. *J Inherited Metab Dis* 8:75, 1985.

217. SOLEM E, JELLUM E, ELDJARN L: The absolute configuration of beta-aminoisobutyric acid in human serum and urine. *Clin Chim Acta* 50:393, 1974.

218. SOLEM E: The absolute configuration of beta-aminoisobutyric acid formed by degradation of thymine in man. *Clin Chim Acta* 53:183, 1974.

219. van GENNIP AH, KAMERLING JP, de BREE PK, WADMAN SK: Linear relationship between the *R*- and the *S*-enantiomers of beta-aminoisobutyric acid in human urine. *Clin Chim Acta* 116:261, 1981.

CHAPTER **29**

DISORDERS OF PROPIONATE AND METHYLMALONATE METABOLISM

LEON E. ROSENBERG
WAYNE A. FENTON

1. *Propionyl-CoA, formed in the catabolism of several essential amino acids (isoleucine, valine, methionine, threonine), odd-chain fatty acids, and cholesterol, is metabolized primarily by enzymatic conversion to methylmalonyl-CoA, which is subsequently isomerized to succinyl-CoA. This sequence depends on the activity of several enzymes (Fig. 29-2); propionyl-CoA carboxylase, methylmalonyl-CoA racemase, and methylmalonyl-CoA mutase. Propionyl-CoA carboxylase requires biotin as a cofactor, while methylmalonyl-CoA mutase requires a cobalamin (vitamin B_{12}) coenzyme, adenosylcobalamin (AdoCbl).*
2. *Propionyl-CoA carboxylase and methylmalonyl-CoA mutase are oligomeric enzymes. Propionyl-CoA carboxylase is composed of nonidentical subunits (α and β); biotin binds to the α subunit. The holocarboxylase contains four α and four β subunits ($\alpha_4\beta_4$). The α subunit is encoded by a gene on chromosome 13 in human beings; the β subunit by a gene on chromosome 3. Methylmalonyl-CoA mutase is a dimer of identical subunits (α_2); encoded by a gene on chromosome 6.*
3. *Inherited deficiency of propionyl-CoA carboxylase activity in human beings results from genetically distinct defects at four loci. Isolated deficiency is caused by mutations at the α and β loci coding for the carboxylase subunits. Deficiency of multiple biotin-dependent carboxylases occurs in two forms—one resulting from deficiency of holocarboxylase synthetase (the enzyme which attaches biotin to apocarboxylase subunits); the other from deficiency of biotinidase (the enzyme which cleaves biotin from the lysine residue in the carboxylase to which the biotin is attached). Multiple carboxylase deficiency is discussed in detail in Chap. 83.*
4. *Isolated deficiency of propionyl-CoA carboxylase, a major cause of the "ketotic hyperglycinemia syndrome," results in the accumulation of propionate in blood and of β-hydroxypropionate, methylcitrate, tiglylglycine, and unusual ketone bodies in urine. Two complementation groups,* pccA *and* pccBC, *have been defined among propionyl-CoA carboxylase–deficient patients. These groups correspond to mutations affecting genes coding for the α subunit and the β subunit, respectively, of the carboxylase apoprotein. Clinically, the disorder is characterized by severe metabolic ketoacidosis, which often appears in the neonatal period and which requires vigorous alkali therapy and protein restriction.*
5. *Multiple carboxylase deficiency leads to impaired activity of four biotin-dependent enzymes: acetyl-CoA carboxylase, propionyl-CoA carboxylase, β-methylcrotonyl-CoA carboxylase, and pyruvate carboxylase. The clinical hallmarks of this disorder include ketoacidosis, a diffuse erythematous skin rash, alopecia, seizures, hypotonia, and developmental retardation.*
6. *Inherited deficiency of methylmalonyl-CoA mutase activity in human beings is caused by mutations at many different loci. Isolated deficiency results from mutations at the apomutase locus and at two loci coding for gene products required, specifically, for the biosynthesis of AdoCbl. Combined deficiency of mutase and of the other major cobalamin-dependent enzyme in mammalian cells,* N^5*-methyltetrahydrofolate:homocysteine methyltransferase, result from inherited defects in cobalamin transport and from three distinct defects in the intracellular pathway of cobalamin coenzyme synthesis affecting the synthesis of both AdoCbl and methylcobalamin (MeCbl), the coenzyme required by the above mentioned methyltransferase. These several defects in intracellular cobalamin metabolism are discussed in detail in Chap. 82.*
7. *Neonatal or infantile metabolic ketoacidosis is the clinical hallmark of isolated methylmalonyl-CoA mutase deficiency. Cells from some apomutase-deficient children have no functional mutase (designated* mut°*); cells from others contain a structurally altered mutase with reduced affinity for AdoCbl and with reduced stability* (mut^-)*. Such children exhibit methylmalonic acidemia and methylmalonic aciduria that do not respond to cobalamin supplementation but can sometimes be treated effectively with dietary protein restriction.*
8. *Two abnormalities in adenosylcobalamin synthesis only (designated* cblA *and* cblB*) lead to impaired methylmalonyl-CoA mutase activity and in a clinical and chemical picture virtually identical to that seen in apomutase-deficient children. In most but not all patients with these defects, pharmacologic supplements of cyanocobalamin or hydroxocobalamin produce distinct reduction in methylmalonate accumulation and offer a valuable therapeutic adjunct to dietary protein limitation.*
9. *Three other distinct mutations, designated* cblC, cblD, *and* cblF, *lead to impaired synthesis of AdoCbl and MeCbl, and, accordingly to deficient activity of methylmalonyl-CoA mutase and homocysteine:*N^5*-methyltetrahydrofolate methyltransferase. Such children have methylmalonic aciduria and homocystinuria. Many children with* cblC *mutation appear to be more severely affected clinically than the two known sibs in the* cblD *group. Major clinical problems in* cblC *patients include*

Nonstandard abbreviations used in this chapter are: AdoCbl = adenosylcobalamin; Cbl = cobalamin; *cbl* = cobalmin locus (*cblA, cblB*, etc.); CN-Cbl = cyanocobalamin; CPS I = carbamyl phosphate synthetase I; CRM = cross-reacting material; H_4 folate = tetrahydrofolate; IF = intrinsic factor; MeCbl = methylcobalamin; Me-H_4folate = N^5-methyltetrahydrofolate; NAG = *N*-acetyl glutamate; OH-Cbl = hydroxocobalamin; *pcc* = propionyl-CoA carboxylase locus *(pccA, pccB)*; and TC (I, II, or III) = transcobalamin (I, II, or III).

failure to thrive, developmental retardation, and such hematologic abnormalities as megaloblastic anemia and macrocytosis. The precise defect in the cblC *and* cblD *patients is not yet known, but it involves an early step in the intracellular metabolism of cobalamins. The defect in* cblF *cells involves impaired efflux of free cobalamin from lysosomes.*

10. *The discriminating biochemical features of the known forms of inherited methylmalonic acidemia are shown in Table 29-5.*
11. *All of the disorders of propionate and methylmalonate metabolism for which there are adequate data are inherited as autosomal recessive traits. Heterozygotes for the following mutations can be detected:* pccA; mut°, mut⁻; *and* cblB. *Genetic complementation analyses with somatic cell heterokaryons have been particularly useful in demonstrating genetic heterogeneity and in confirming the existence of autosomal recessive inheritance among the propionic acidemias and the methylmalonic acidemias.*
12. *Prenatal detection of fetuses with propionyl-CoA carboxylase deficiency, methylmalonyl-CoA apomutase deficiency, and defective synthesis of adenosylcobalamin has been accomplished using cultured amniotic cells and chemical determinations on amniotic fluid or maternal urine.*

Methylmalonic acid and its immediate precursor, propionic acid, are detectable in normal human blood, urine, and cerebrospinal fluid only in trace amounts. The minuscule quantities of these compounds in extracellular fluids have obscured, until recently, the key role that these acids play in human metabolism. Biochemists investigating animal nutrition have been interested in propionate metabolism for more than 25 years, because ruminants derive most of their energy requirements from the oxidation of propionate and acetate produced by bacterial fermentation in their rumens.[1] Although propionate and methylmalonate are of little quantitative importance in human beings as direct sources of energy, these acids, found intracellularly largely as their coenzyme A (CoA) esters, are vital intermediates in the catabolism of fat and protein.

Several independent, and seemingly unrelated, lines of evidence drew the attention of the physician and the clinical investigator to the study of propionate and methylmalonate metabolism. In 1959 and 1960, several groups reported that adenosylcobalamin (AdoCbl), one of the coenzyme forms of cobalamin (vitamin B_{12}), is an essential cofactor in the enzyme conversion of L-methylmalonyl-CoA to succinyl-CoA.[2–4] Shortly thereafter, patients with acquired cobalamin deficiency were shown to excrete large amounts of methylmalonic acid in the urine.[5,6] The methylmalonic aciduria was rapidly reversed by administration of physiologic doses of cobalamin and was attributed to an acquired block in methylmalonate catabolism caused by inadequate amounts of the needed cobalamin coenzyme.

In 1961, Childs and associates[7] described a young boy with recurrent attacks of severe ketoacidosis who had elevated concentrations of glycine and several other amino acids in his blood and urine. A series of detailed metabolic studies demonstrated that the attacks were precipitated by protein feeding and more specifically by ingestion of the branched chain amino acids, methionine, and threonine. Since elevation in plasma glycine level was the most striking biochemical abnormality, the disorder was called *ketotic hyperglycinemia*. Recent evidence indicates that this disorder is caused by an inherited defect in the catabolism of propionate, not by a primary abnormality in glycine utilization or biosynthesis.[8,9]

Since 1967, a number of critically ill children have been described who draw these seemingly disparate observations together and focus attention on the enzymes and coenzymes that regulate the pathway responsible for the formation of propionate and its conversion to succinate. Oberholzer,[10] Stokke,[11] and their colleagues described infants with profound metabolic acidosis and hyperglycinemia (or hyperglycinuria) who excrete huge amounts of methylmalonic acid in the urine but who were not cobalamin-deficient. Subsequently, Rosenberg and his colleagues[8] reported that urine from the index patient with ketotic hyperglycinemia and from his affected sister contained no methylmalonic acid. This observation indicated that primary methylmalonic acidemia and ketotic hyperglycinemia were different disorders with identical clinical manifestations.[8]

The latter group and Lindblad et al.[123,13] also described children with ketoacidosis and methylmalonic acidemia who were not cobalamin-deficient but who responded to administration of pharmacologic doses of cyanocobalamin or its coenzyme with a marked fall in concentration of urinary methylmalonic acid. The index patient[8] was subsequently shown to suffer from a primary defect in AdoCbl synthesis,[14,15] not from a defect of the apoenzyme which catalyzes the conversion of methylmalonyl-CoA to succinyl-CoA.

These observations, and others which will be discussed in detail subsequently, emphasize that numerous inherited abnormalities in the metabolic pathway for propionate and methylmalonate occur, and that these defects lead to profound illness and, in many cases, death due to a disturbed acid-base balance or developmental failure. The study of these disorders has led to important insights in our understanding of the role of this pathway in human beings and has illustrated, once again, that a group of clinically identical disorders can be produced by several different mutations affecting the synthesis of related apoenzymes and coenzymes. Several reviews of this subject matter have appeared.[16–18]

BIOCHEMICAL PATHWAYS

Propionate Metabolism

Formation of Propionate and Methylmalonate. Most of the propionic acid utilized by ruminant animals is formed by bacterial fermentation in the rumen.[1] By contrast, nonruminant mammals derive nearly all their propionate from the catabolism of lipid and protein. As noted in Fig. 29-1, catabolism of the branched chain amino acid isoleucine leads to the formation of propionyl-CoA, as does the degradation of methionine and threonine.[19] Studies with [^{13}C]valine in a patient with methylmalonic acidemia[20] and with the valine catabolite [^{13}C]isobutyrate in rats[21] indicate that valine is also a propionate precursor and is not catabolized directly to methylmalonyl-CoA, as suggested earlier. Catabolism of these amino acids accounts for much of the propionate formed in humans, but other sources are known. β-Oxidation of fatty acids with an odd number of carbon atoms ultimately leads to the formation of 1 mol propionyl-CoA per mole of fatty acid.[22] Degradation of the side chain of cholesterol also leads to the synthesis of propionyl-CoA, but this pathway appears to be of little quantitative significance.[23]

Methylmalonyl-CoA is synthesized from two sources (Fig. 29-1). Catabolism of thymine accounts for only a small amount of the intracellular methylmalonyl-CoA compared to that

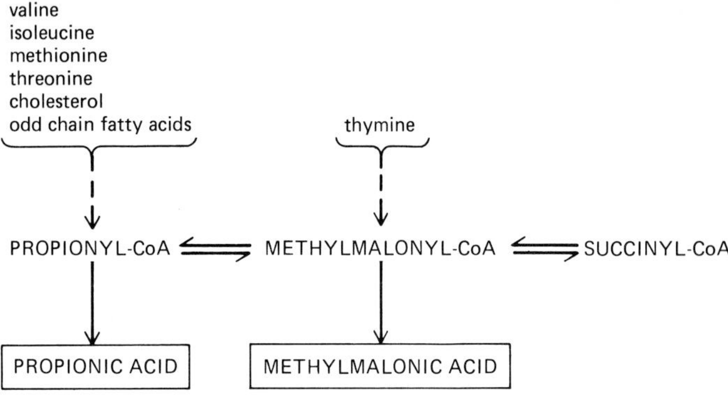

Fig. 29-1 Precursors of and major catabolic pathway for propionate and methylmalonate. The free acids are derived from their CoA esters by hydrolysis. A number of clinical disorders arise from errors at various steps in these pathways. Broken arrows indicate the presence of several reactions.

formed from the carboxylation of propionyl-CoA. Propionate has long been known to be glycogenic in animals,[24] but the pathway by which propionate is converted to carbohydrate became clear only when Lardy and Adler demonstrated that liver mitochondria contain enzymes which synthesize succinate from propionate.[24] The discovery in 1955 that methylmalonate is an intermediate in the formation of succinate from propionate (Fig. 29-1) provided an important further step in the characterization of this pathway.[25,26]

Kaziro and Ochoa first defined the individual steps of propionate catabolism in animal tissues and characterized the enzymes involved.[22] Propionyl-CoA, formed either by the degradative reactions discussed above or by the enzymatic esterification of propionate itself,[27] may be considered the precursor of this reaction sequence (Fig. 29-2). Three enzymatic reactions are responsible for the conversion of propionyl-CoA to succinyl-CoA. The first involves the carboxylation of propionyl-CoA to methylmalonyl-CoA,[27,28] a reaction catalyzed by propionyl-CoA carboxylase (EC 6.4.1.3). Although two stereoisomers of methylmalonyl-CoA are known, only the D form is produced in the carboxylation reaction.[29,30] This isomer is not a substrate for the subsequent mutase reaction and must be racemized to the L configuration by another enzyme, methylmalonyl-CoA racemase (EC 5.1.99.1).[31] The third reaction, catalyzed by methylmalonyl-CoA mutase (EC 5.4.99.2), isomerizes L-methylmalonyl-CoA to succinyl-CoA.[32] The latter compound enters the tricarboxylic acid cycle and is ultimately glycogenic because of its conversion to pyruvate by way of oxaloacetate. The sum of all these reactions may be written as follows:

$$\text{Propionate} + \text{ATP} \rightarrow \text{pyruvate} + 4\text{H} + \text{ADP} + \text{P}_i \quad [29\text{-}1]$$

In bacteria, propionate is formed from pyruvate by reversal of the reaction sequence just described,[22] but in mammalian systems the equilibrium of the system is far in the direction of propionate catabolism rather than biosynthesis.

Apoenzymes

Propionyl-CoA Carboxylase. This enzyme, first crystallized from pig heart,[33] has been purified to homogeneity from bovine kidney[34] and human liver.[35,36] The enzyme is composed of nonidentical subunits (α and β), and the required cofactor, biotin, is bound exclusively to the larger (or α) subunit. The molecular weights for the human enzyme are ~540,000 for the native form, 72,000 for the α subunit, and 56,000 for the β subunit. Each mole of enzyme contains 4 mol of biotin. This is consistent with other evidence that the native enzyme is a tetramer of protomers, each protomer containing a single α and a single β subunit. The native enzyme thus appears to have an $(\alpha\beta)_4$ quaternary structure. Several groups have shown that the carboxylation of propionyl-CoA is a two-step reaction.[22] In the first step, which requires ATP and Mg^{2+} and is stimulated by K^+, bicarbonate is attached to the ureido nitrogen of the apoenzyme-biotin complex (Fig. 29-3), forming a carboxybiotin-apoenzyme intermediate. This complex, in turn, reacts with propionyl-CoA and transfers the carboxyl group from biotin to the second carbon of propionyl-CoA, forming D-methylmalonyl-CoA. As with several other biotin-catalyzed carbon dioxide fixation reactions, the biotin molecule is directly responsible for the transfer of the carboxyl group.[37]

As is the case for most nuclear-encoded mitochondrial proteins, the α and β subunits are synthesized on free cytoplasmic polyribosomes as larger precursors, bearing cleavable amino-terminal leader peptides.[38,39] These leaders direct the α and β precursors to mitochondria and are cleaved after import into that organelle. Presumably, assembly of the mature α and β subunits into the oligomeric holoenzyme occurs after mitchondrial import and removal of the leader peptides has occurred.

Recently, cDNAs for the α and β subunits have been cloned and isolated from human liver[40,41] and rat liver[42,43] libraries. Using these cDNAs as probes, the locus for the human α subunit was localized to chromosome 13[40] and that for

Fig. 29-2 Enzymatic details of major catabolic pathway for propionyl-CoA and methylmalonyl-CoA. Succinyl-CoA has several metabolic fates, including oxidation through the tricarboxylic acid cycle and condensation with glycine to form δ-aminolevulinic acid. Two coenzymes act in the reaction sequence: biotin in the carboxylation of propionyl-CoA, and adenosylcobalamin (AdoCbl) in the isomerization of L-methylmalonyl-CoA to succinyl-CoA.

$H_2C{-}CH_3$ / CO-S-CoA + HCO_3^- ⇌ (Biotin, ATP, Mg^{++}; Propionyl-CoA Carboxylase) COOH / $HC{-}CH_3$ / CO-S-CoA ⇌ (Methylmalonyl-CoA Racemase) COOH / $H_3C{-}CH$ / CO-S-CoA ⇌ (Adenosylcobalamin; Methylmalonyl-CoA Mutase) COOH / $H_2C{-}CH_2$ / CO-S-CoA

PROPIONYL-CoA — D-METHYLMALONYL-CoA — L-METHYLMALONYL-CoA — SUCCINYL-CoA

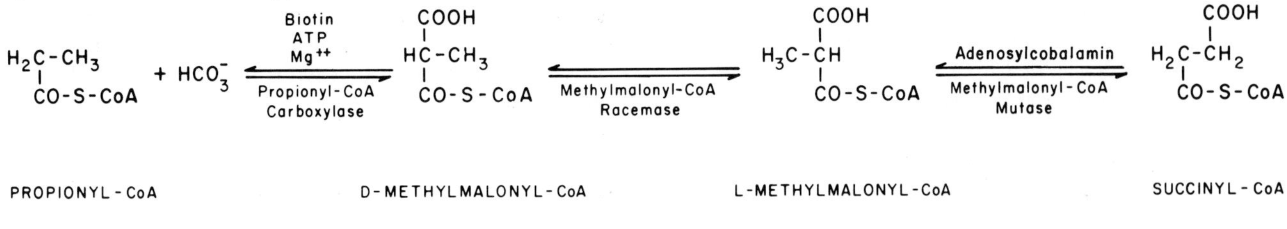

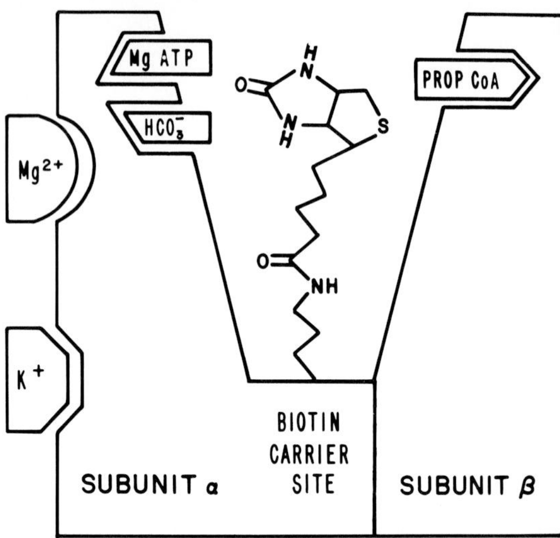

Fig. 29-3 A proposed model for the mammalian propionyl-CoA carboxylase protomer containing two nonidentical subunits (α and β), a biotin carrier site, and multiple substrate and effector sites. See text for details.

the β subunit to the long arm of chromosome 3.[40,42] RNA blot hybridization studies revealed a 2.9-kb mRNA species coding for the α chain and a major 2.0-kb species coding for the β chain.[40,43] These studies revealed further that the β-subunit leader peptide is a positively charged, 40- to 42-residue-long species[43] and that the four crucial residues around the biotin binding site of the α subunit (Ala-Met-Lys-Met) have been strictly conserved from prokaryotes to human beings.[41]

Methylmalonyl-CoA Racemase. This enzyme owes its discovery to the observation that methylmalonyl-CoA synthesized chemically is a substrate for the mutase reaction (Fig. 29-2), whereas methylmalonyl-CoA formed enzymatically from the carboxylation of propionyl-CoA will not react with the mutase unless it is first heated. Ultimately the demonstration that heating converts D-methylmalonyl-CoA to DL-methylmalonyl-CoA led to the conclusion that only the L form of the ester will react with the mutase enzyme. This interpretation was confirmed by separating mutase activity from racemase activity using Sephadex chromatography.[22,31,44] The racemase has been purified extensively from sheep liver.[31] It has no known cofactor requirements and catalyzes the conversion of D- to L-methylmalonyl-CoA by inducing a shift in the α-hydrogen atom.[31,44]

Methylmalonyl-CoA Mutase. In 1955, Flavin et al.[25] and Katz and Chaikoff[26] observed independently that the isomerization of methylmalonyl-CoA to succinyl-CoA was catalyzed by an enzyme found in sheep kidney and rat liver. The chemical analogy between this isomerization reaction and the isomerization of glutamate to β-methylaspartate in bacteria,[45] along with the demonstration by Barker and his colleagues[46,47] that a coenzyme form of cobalamin was needed for the latter reaction, led to the finding in several laboratories that a cobalamin coenzyme is also required for the isomerization of methylmalonyl-CoA.[2-4] The enzyme, originally called *methylmalonyl-CoA isomerase* but now designated *methylmalonyl-CoA mutase*, was first crystallized from sheep kidney and bacteria. More recently, it has been purified to homogeneity from human placenta[48] and human liver.[49] From both human sources, the enzyme appears to be a dimer (MW ~145,000 to 150,000) of identical subunits (MW ~72,000 to 77,000). The holoenzyme contains 1 mol adenosylcobalamin (AdoCbl) per mole of subunit, the cobalamin cofactor being very tightly bound to the apoenzyme (estaimted K_m of the sheep kidney enzyme for AdoCbl $\sim 2 \times 10^{-8} M$). The human enzyme displays complex kinetics with regard to the binding of methylmalonyl-CoA[49] and AdoCbl,[50] leading to the thesis that the active sites of the dimeric enzyme are not equivalent.[50] In this regard it is significant that hydroxocobalamin (OH-Cbl) appears to act as both a competitive and an irreversible inhibitor of human mutase.[50,51]

Figure 29-2 shows that the isomerization reaction could occur by transfer of either the free carboxyl group or the CoA-carboxyl radical. Studies using isotopically labeled methylmalonyl-CoA demonstrated convincingly that it is the CoA-carboxyl group that is transferred[52] through an intramolecular isomerization.[53,54] The exact role of the cobalamin coenzyme in the isomerization reaction remains undefined, but the mechanism surely involves cleavage of the carbon-cobalt bond followed by transfer of hydrogen from the substrate to the 5′-deoxyadenosyl fragment produced by the cleavage reaction.[55]

The mutase subunit is synthesized as a larger cytoplasmic precursor, bearing a 3- to 4-kDa cleavable leader peptide.[56] In a cell-free system, the precursor is imported by mitchondria via an energy-dependent mechanism and cleaved to its mature form by a divalent cation–dependent protease. In intact cells, the precursor is rapidly ($t_{1/2}$ = 6 to 9 min) converted to its mature form.[56]

Recently, cDNAs encoding human mutase have been cloned from liver and placenta libraries.[56a,56b] The DNA sequence predicts a leader peptide 32 amino acids long that is strongly positively charged (4 Arg, 2 Lys, 1 Glu).[56b] Analysis of Southern blots of DNA from human/hamster somatic cell hybrids and *in situ* hybridization, using the mutase cDNAs as probes, mapped the human gene for mutase and the MUT locus to region 6p12-p21.2 and uncovered one highly informative RFLP.[56a] Preliminary analysis of *mut* cell lines indicates that some have reduced amounts of mutase mRNA.[56c]

Alternative Pathways of Propionate Metabolism

Although the catabolism of propionate to succinate through methylmalonate is the major pathway for propionate utilization in mammalian systems, alternative pathways exist. Propionyl-CoA can replace acetyl-CoA as a "primer" for long-chain fatty acid synthesis[57] and lead to the formation of odd-chain fatty acids, notably heptanoate, nannanoate, and undecanoate. There are also alternative catabolic mechanisms, one of which is described in Fig. 29-4.[22] The first step in this sequence involves the formation of the α,β-unsaturated fatty acid acrylyl-CoA, which may be subsequently hydrated, leading to the formation of either lactyl-CoA or β-OH-propionyl-CoA. The former compound is hydrolyzed to lactate, thus providing a second means by which propionate may be converted to pyruvate. Catabolism of β-OH-propionyl-CoA leads ultimately to the synthesis of acetyl-CoA or β-alanine, compounds discussed elsewhere in this volume. In addition, propionyl-CoA may condense with oxaloacetate to form methylcitrate in a reaction analogous to the biosynthesis of citric acid from acetyl-CoA and oxaloacetate.[58] These alternative pathways are of little quantitative significance in normal subjects but become much more prominent in patients with blocks in the major pathway of propionate metabolism.[59,60]

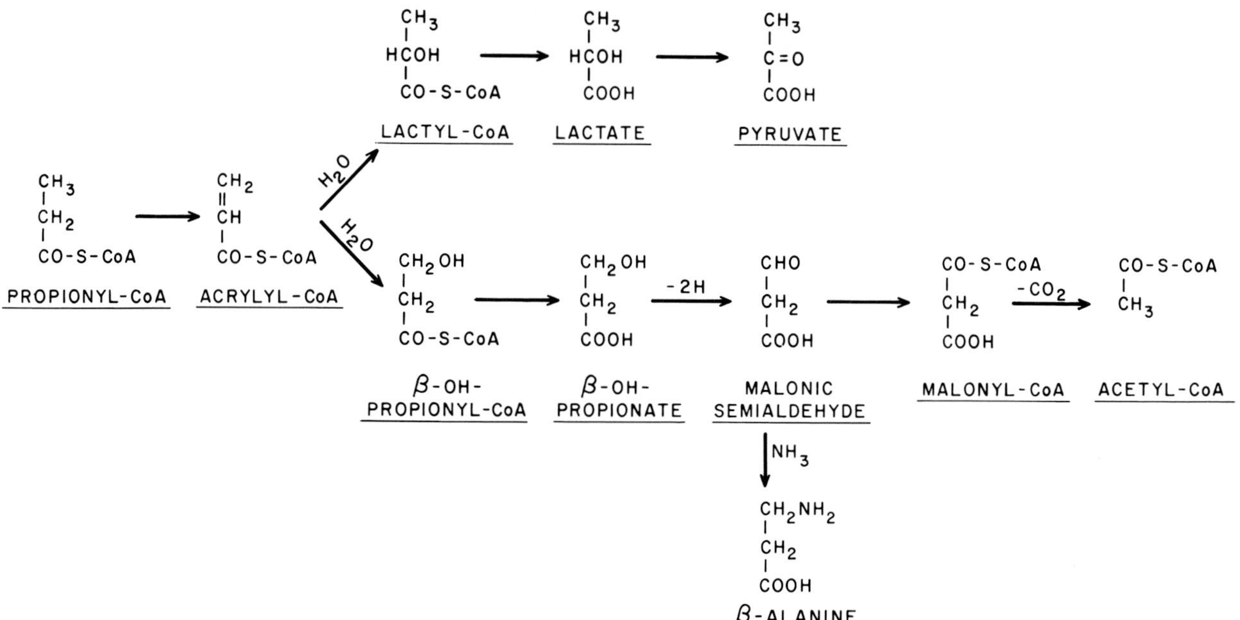

Fig. 29-4 Minor pathways of propionate catabolism. Note that both pathways can ultimately generate acetyl-CoA. The significance of these minor pathways is discussed in the text.

Coenzymes

Biotin. Biotin is widely distributed in plants and animal tissues and is readily synthesized by a variety of microorganisms. It was first isolated from egg yolk in 1936 by the Dutch biochemist Kögl, and its structure was defined soon thereafter by duVigneaud and colleagues. Our understanding of this water-soluble cofactor is inextricably linked with the evolution of our knowledge concerning avidin, an egg white protein which binds biotin most tightly. Comprehensive reviews on biotin[61,62] and on biotin-dependent enzymes[63,64] exist. Biotin metabolism and its disorders are discussed extensively in Chap. 83.

STRUCTURE AND FUNCTION. Biotin (Fig. 29-3) is a relatively simple molecule, being composed of fused imidazole and thiophene rings to which is attached an *n*-valeric acid side chain. It has a molecular weight of 244. Like many other water-soluble vitamins, biotin functions as a cofactor in enzyme-catalyzed reactions. Specifically, biotin is a prosthetic group for four mammalian enzymes, each of which catalyzes the carboxylation of its substrate (Fig. 29-5). One of these biotin-dependent carboxylases, acetyl-CoA carboxylase, is cytosolic and catalyzes the key step in long-chain fatty acid biosynthesis—the formation of malonyl-CoA from acetyl-CoA. The three other biotin-dependent carboxylases are found in the mitchondrial matrix, where they catalyze critical steps in amino acid degradation (β-methylcrotonyl-CoA carboxylase), organic acid rearrangement (propionyl-CoA carboxylase), or gluconeogenesis (pyruvate carboxylase). The sequence of partial reactions by which these biotin-requiring enzymes carry out their functions appear to be similar (Fig. 29-3 and Fig. 29-5). First, biotin is covalently attached to an ϵ-amino group of a lysine residue on the apoprotein;[63,64] this reaction is catalyzed by an enzyme(s) called *holocarboxylase synthetase* found in the cytosol and mitochondria of animal cells.[63,65] It has not been determined whether the biotin-binding carboxylase subunits destined for mitchondria are biotinylated in the cytosol or in mitochondria. Next, an activated carboxyl group (bound to one of the carboxylase subunits) is transferred to a ureido nitrogen

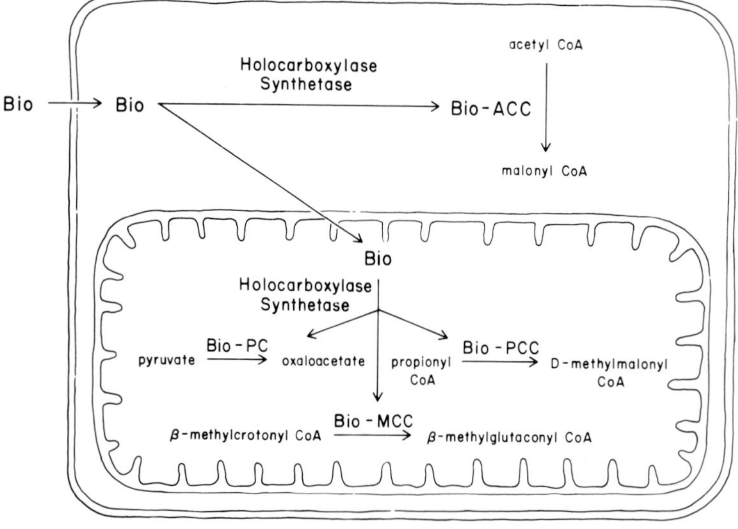

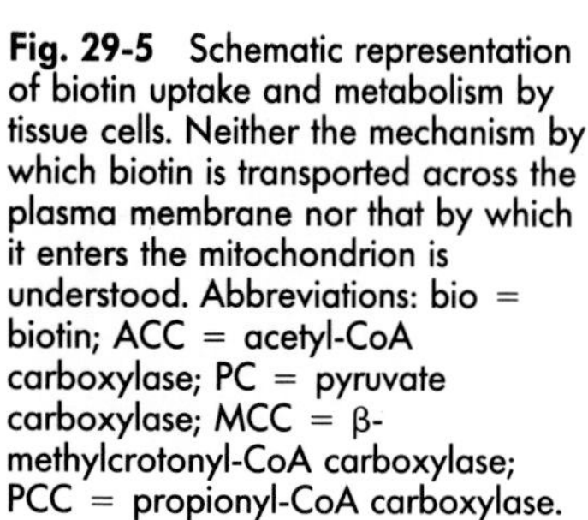

Fig. 29-5 Schematic representation of biotin uptake and metabolism by tissue cells. Neither the mechanism by which biotin is transported across the plasma membrane nor that by which it enters the mitochondrion is understood. Abbreviations: bio = biotin; ACC = acetyl-CoA carboxylase; PC = pyruvate carboxylase; MCC = β-methylcrotonyl-CoA carboxylase; PCC = propionyl-CoA carboxylase.

group of biotin, forming carboxybiotin. Finally, the carboxyl is shuttled to the substrate bound to the other carboxylase subunit, thereby completing the carboxylation and regenerating the cofactor. It seems likely that the several biotin-dependent carboxylases owe their substrate specificity to their respective substrate-binding subunits. It is likely that each carboxylase contains a unique bicarbonate-binding subunit, or domain, as well.

Biotin remains bound to the carboxylases until they turn over. Upon the degradation of the proteins, biotin is released from small biotinylated peptides or from biocytin (biotinyl lysine) by the enzyme biotinidase. The latter enzyme, widely distributed in tissues and most abundant in serum, has recently been purified to homogeneity.[66,67]

ABSORPTION AND DISTRIBUTION. It seems likely that free biotin is formed in the intestinal lumen, either by enzymatic hydrolysis of ingested, tissue-bound biotin or by release from intestinal microorganisms. Biotinidase may play a role in releasing biotin from foods.[68] Whereas saturable, sodium-dependent systems for biotin transport and absorption have been demonstrated in hamster[69,70] and rat[71] intestine, the physiologic mode of biotin absorption remains unclear. It may well be that such absorption occurs via mediated and nonmediated systems.[71,72] Biotin transport in blood has received little attention. Hence, it is not clear whether specific plasma-binding proteins for the vitamin exist. Given the latter situation, it is not surprising that information regarding uptake of biotin by tissue cells is sparse. It is not clear whether biotin is taken up by cells free or protein-bound, whether uptake is receptor-mediated, or whether endocytosis is involved.

BIOTIN DEFICIENCY. Spontaneous biotin deficiency has almost never been reported in humans, probably because the daily requirement is very small (estimated at ~20 μg/day) and because intestinal microorganisms synthesize sufficient amounts of the cofactor even in the absence of nutritional sources. Biotin deficiency has been reported recently, however, in a patient with the "short bowel syndrome" being fed exclusively by parenteral alimentation.[73] Experimental biotin deficiency has been produced in animals and humans by ingestion of large amounts of egg white, which contains the potent biotin binder aviden.[74] Under these conditions, four experimental human subjects developed cutaneous pallor, dermatitis, depression, lassitude, muscle pains, hyperesthesia, and finally anemia and electrocardiographic changes. All these symptoms and signs were reversed rapidly by administration of 150 to 300 μg biotin daily for several days. In animals, experimental biotin deficiency has been shown to produce decreased activity of biotin-dependent carboxylases in tissues.[61–63]

Cobalamin (Vitamin B_{12}). The structure and function of this compound have intrigued students of human biology since 1926, when Minot and Murphy demonstrated that oral administration of crude liver extract was effective in the treatment of pernicious anemia.[75] In 1948, this "anti-pernicious anemia factor" was isolated from liver and kidney[76,77] and was named *vitamin B_{12}*. Administration of as little as 1 μg of the vitamin daily was shown to prevent relapse of pernicious anemia. Although the vitamin is widely distributed in animal tissues, there is strong evidence that it is synthesized only in microoragnisms found in soil, water, or the rumen and intestine of animals. Metabolism of cobalamin and inherited defects in its metabolism are discussed extensively in Chap. 82.

STRUCTURAL FEATURES. The isolation of vitamin B_{12} culminated in the elucidation of its three-dimensional structure by Hodgkin and coworkers using x-ray crystallographic techniques.[78] Vitamin B_{12} or, as it is now officially designated, *cobalamin*, is composed of a central cobalt atom (Co) surrounded by a planar corrin ring and a complex side chain extending down from the corrin plane consisting of a 5,6-dimethylbenzimidazole group, a ribose molecule, and phosphate moiety (Fig. 29-6). The benzimidazole is linked to the cobalt atom through one of its nitrogens, while the phosphate is bonded to the D member of the corrin ring. The molecule is completed by coordinate linkage from the corrin plane of one of several different radicals to the cobalt nucleus. Thus, cyanocobalamin or, more strictly, α-(5,6-benzimidazolyl)-cobamide cyanide is formed by the attachment of a cyanide radical to the cobalt atom. Although this compound is the most common commercial form of the vitamin, it is an artifact of isolation and does not occur naturally in microorganisms, plants, or animal tissues. Many other cobalamins have been formed by replacement of the cyanide radical, but only three have been isolated from mammalian tissue: hydroxocobalamin, methylcobalamin, and adenosylcobalamin. The latter two compounds are unique for two reasons: They are the only two compounds in nature known to have a direct carbon-cobalt bond, and they are the only two forms of cobalamin known to act as specific coenzymes in mammalian systems.

The structure and nomenclature of the cobalamins are further complicated by oxidation and reduction of the cobalt atom. In hydroxocobalamin the cobalt atom is trivalent [cob(III)alamin], and this compound has been called *vitamin B_{12a}*. When the cobalt is reduced to a divalent state [cob(II)alamin], the molecule is called vitamin B_{12r}, and in the monovalent state cob(I)alamin it is called *vitamin B_{12s}*. These

Fig. 29-6 Structure of adenosylcobalamin (AdoCbl). R = CH_2CONH_2; R′ = $CH_2CH_2CONH_2$. Other radicals which may be coordinately linked to the cobalt atom include CH_3 (methylcobalamin), OH^- (hydroxocobalamin), and CN^- (cyanocobalamin). *(Reproduced from Babior,[55] with permission of the author and publisher.)*

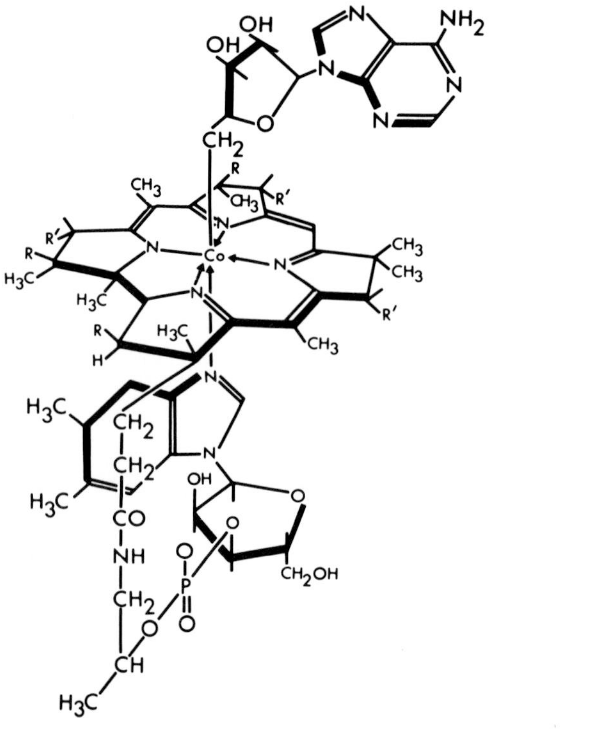

oxidation-reduction states are important, since there appear to be specific reductase enzymes which sequentially convert cob(III)alamin to cob(I)alamin, with cob(II)alamin acting as an intermediate.[79] The cobalt atom must be reduced to its monovalent state prior to formation of methylcobalamin or adenosylcobalamin.

COBALAMIN COENZYMES. In 1958, Barker and his colleagues demonstrated that the glutamate mutase reaction in *Clostridium tetanomorphum* required vitamin B_{12}[45] and, more specifically, that the active coenzyme form of the vitamin was adenosylcobalamin.[46,47] One year later, Smith and Monty reported that the analogous isomerization of methylmalonyl-CoA to succinyl-CoA was defective in the liver of cobalamin-deficient rats.[2] They suggested that cobalamin is a cofactor for the latter isomerization system, a thesis born out by Gurnani et al.[3] and Stern and Friedmann,[4] who showed in vitro that the activity of methylmalonyl-CoA mutase in liver from cobalamin-deficient animals could be restored to normal by addition of adenosylcobalamin, but not by cyanocobalamin or other vitamin B_{12} analogues (see Fig. 29-7). For several years, because adenosylcobalamin was the only known coenzyme form of vitamin B_{12}, it was designated *coenzyme* B_{12}.

In 1966, Weissbach and his colleagues[80] demonstrated that methylcobalamin (MeCbl) is a cofactor in the complex series of reactions by which homocysteine is remethylated to methionine (Fig. 29-7). This reaction requires *S*-adenosylmethionine and N^5-methyltetrahydrofolate (Me-H_4folate), as well as the methyltransferase apoenzyme and methylcobalamin. The exact mechanism of homocysteine remethylation has not been defined precisely but probably involves the following sequence: Me-H_4folate is converted to tetrahydrofolate (H_4folate) by transferring its methyl group to a cobalamin prosthetic group of the methyltransferase apoenzyme; in turn, the methyl group is transferred from MeCbl to homocysteine, leading to the formation of methionine.[81,82] This sequence of reactions, which is relevant to the manifestations of various inborn errors of cobalamin metabolism and to the interrelationships between folate and cobalamins, will be discussed in more detail in Chaps. 81 and 82.

Fig. 29-7 Reactions catalyzed by cobalamin coenzymes in mammalian tissues. Note the specificity of adenosylcobalamin for the isomerization of methylmalonyl-CoA and of methylcobalamin for the methylation of homocysteine. Me-H_4folate = N^5-methyltetrahydrofolate; H_4folate = tetrahydrofolate.

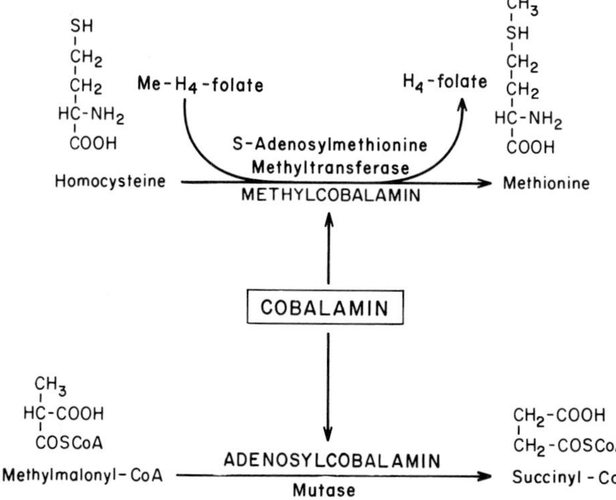

The conversion of methylmalonyl-CoA to succinyl-CoA and the methylation of homocysteine to methionine are the only cobalamin-dependent reactions that have been demonstrated conclusively in mammalian systems. Poston has reported that AdoCbl acts as a cofactor in the enzymatic reaction by which α-leucine is isomerized to β-leucine,[83] but this has not yet been confirmed in other laboratories. In microorganisms several other apoenzymes require adenosylcobalamin:[55,84] glutamate mutase; diol dehydrase; glycerol dehydrase; ethanolamine ammonia-lyase; and ribonucleotide reductase. In addition, MeCbl catalyzes the formation of methane and acetic acid and the fermentation of lysine in bacteria, but the specific enzymes that catalyze these reactions are not known.

COBALAMIN ABSORPTION AND DISTRIBUTION. The cobalamin vitamins have a unique and highly specialized mechanism of intestinal absorption that has been reviewed in detail recently.[85,86] The ability to transport physiologic quantities of the vitamin depends on the combined action of gastric, ileal, and pancreatic components. The gastric substance, called *intrinsic fctor (IF)* by Castle, who first demonstrated its existence, is a glycoprotein that binds cobalamins in the intestinal lumen. IF, which has been isolated and characterized extensively,[85] is synthesized by gastric parietal cells. Evidence obtained in vitro[87,88] and in vivo[89] suggests that three events precede the formation of IF-cobalamin (Cbl) in the gut lumen. First, cobalamins are released from dietary protein in the acid environment of the stomach. Second, cobalamins bind to "R" proteins of salivary and gastric origin; these R proteins are members of a family of glycoproteins with high affinity for cobalamins. Third, pancreatic proteases digest the R proteins, thereby liberating cobalamins in the upper small intestine, where they are complexed to IF. Subsequently, the IF-Cbl complex interacts through its protein moiety with specific ileal receptor sites in the presence of calcium ions. In this process the IF-Cbl complex is dissociated and the vitamin is transported across the ileal membrane into the portal blood. Once in the bloodstream, the free vitamin is bound by at least three different globulins, designated *transcobalamin I (TC I), transcobalamin II (TC II),* and *transcobalamin III (TC III)* (see Refs. 85, 90, and 91 for reviews). TC I and TC III are glycoproteins of the R family which carry the majority of cobalamin found in plasma; their physiologic role, however, is still unclear. TC II, a β-globulin, is the transport protein for newly absorbed vitamin. When labeled cobalamin is administered intravenously or orally, most of the labeled vitamin is immediately bound to TC II and disappears from the plasma in a few hours.[92,93] Only a small fraction binds to TC I, and this component turns over very slowly. Surprisingly, MeCbl is the major circulating cobalamin species, accounting for 60 to 80 percent of total plasma cobalamin; OH-Cbl and AdoCbl make up the remainder.[94] Since over 90 percent of total plasma cobalamin is bound to TC I, it is clear that most of the circulating MeCbl travels with this R binder. This unusual cobalamin distribution pattern is puzzling, particularly in the face of evidence indicating that AdoCbl accounts for ~70 percent of total hepatic cobalamins, whereas MeCbl constitutes a mere 1 to 3 percent.[94] This preponderance of AdoCbl is also present in such other tissues as erythrocytes, kidney, and brain. The physiologic significance of these widely different fractional amounts of cobalamin compounds in extracellular and intracellular compartments remains obscure.

TC II also facilitates cobalamin uptake by mammalian tissues. Finkler and Hall[95] showed that CN-Cbl bound to TC II was accumulated by HeLa cells much more rapidly than free CN-Cbl or CN-Cbl bound to TC I, IF, or other binding proteins. Such TC II–mediated uptake was subsequently confirmed in a variety of cell types, both in vivo and in culture (liver, kidney, heart, spleen, lung, small intestine, cultured fibroblasts, Chinese hamster ovary cells, mouse L cells, lymphoma cells, and phytohemagglutinin-stimulated lymphocytes) (see Ref. 86 for a review). These findings, coupled with the observations in vivo that TC II disappeared from plasma as TC II–cobalamin was absorbed,[96] and appeared in lysosomal fractions of hepatic[97] and kidney cells,[98] led to the proposal that the circulating TC II–Cbl complex is recognized by a specific, widely distributed plasma membrane receptor. This notion is now supported by considerable experimental evidence (Fig. 29-8). Using ^{125}I-labeled TC II–Cbl complexes, Youngdahl-Turner and associates[99] showed that the complex binds to a specific, high-affinity ($K_a \sim 10^{10}\ M^{-1}$) cell surface receptor on cultured skin fibroblasts through a membrane site which recognizes TC II, and by a mechanism dependent on Ca^{2+}. They showed further that the TC II–Cbl complex is then internalized intact via adsorptive endocytosis,[100] and that the degradation of TC II and release of Cbl from the complex occur as a result of lysosomal protease activity.[99,100] Cobalamin then exits from the lysosome by processes that are poorly understood, and is either converted to MeCbl and bound to the methyltransferase in the cytosol or enters the mitochondrion, where, after reduction and adenosylation, it is bound to methylmalonyl-CoA mutase.[101,102]

The intricate process just described is surely the most widely distributed physiologic means by which mammalian cells obtain cobalamins, but it is not the only means. Hepatocytes, for instance, contain a surface receptor for asialoglycoproteins, and this receptor interacts with TC I–Cbl (and perhaps TC III–Cbl) complexes, thereby providing a second potential means by which this particular tissue obtains cobalamins.[103] Finally, there is growing evidence that at least some tissues are capable of taking up free (unbound) cobalamin if the concentration of unbound vitamin is raised to sufficiently high concentrations. In cultured fibroblasts this uptake process for free cobalamin is saturable, Ca^{2+}-independent, and sensitive to inhibitors of protein synthesis and sulfhydryl reagents.[104] Its functional role, under most circumstances, is probably negligible.

COENZYME BIOSYNTHESIS AND COMPARTMENTATION. Since methylmalonyl-CoA mutase, the mammalian enzyme dependent on AdoCbl, is a mitochondrial protein[105] whereas the MeCbl-dependent methyltransferase is cytoplasmic,[106] it becomes important to relate the cellular biology of the vitamin to its cellular and molecular chemistry. Significant progress in this direction is being made. The chemical pathway of AdoCbl synthesis was defined initially in bacteria.[79,107] Three enzymes were required for coenzyme synthesis, two reductases and an adenosyltransferase. The reductases are flavoproteins which require NAD as a cofactor. The first (EC 1.6.99.8) is responsible for converting cob(III)alamin, i.e. hydroxocobalamin, to cob(II)alamin and the second (EC 1.6.99.9) for catalyzing the further reduction to cob(I)alamin. The latter compound and ATP are substrates for an adenosyltransferase (EC 2.5.1.17) which completes the synthesis of AdoCbl. Neither of the reductases has been purified extensively, but the adenosyltransferase has. It has a pH optimum of 8, requires Mn^{2+}, and has a k_m of $1 \times 10^{-5}\ M$ for cob(I)alamin and $1.6 \times 10^{-5}\ M$ for ATP.[107] The biosynthetic steps leading to MeCbl formation are not as clear. They may involve a concerted reduction-methylation sequence on or around the methyltransferase apoenzyme.[108,109]

Evidence is accumulating which indicates that mammalian cell metabolism of cobalamin may proceed by a very similar set of reactions (see Fig. 29-8). In 1964 Pawalkiewicz et al.[110] showed that human liver and kidney homogenates could convert CN-Cbl to AdoCbl. Several years later, AdoCbl synthesis from OH-Cbl was observed in HeLa cell extracts incubated with ATP and a reducing system which presumably bypassed the enzymatic reduction of OH-Cbl [cob(III)alamin] to cob(II)alamin.[111] Subsequently, Mahoney and Rosenberg[112] demonstrated the synthesis of both AdoCbl and MeCbl by intact human fibroblasts growing in a tissue culture medium containing OH-[^{57}Co]Cbl. This system was subsequently characterized in cell extracts.[113,114] As with the HeLa cell system, chemical reductants were employed to bypass both cobalamin reductases.[114] Such extracts synthesized AdoCbl, thereby

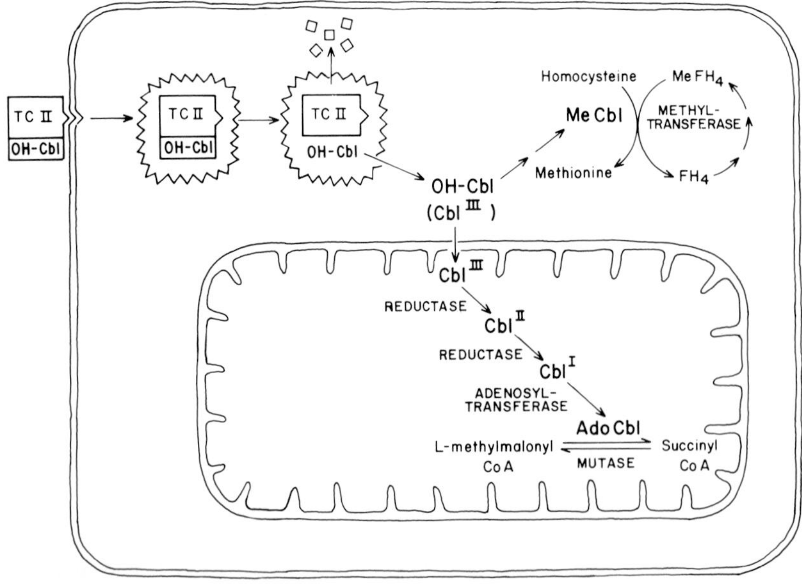

Fig. 29-8 General pathway of the cellular uptake and subcellular compartmentation of cobalamins, and of the intracellular distribution and enzymatic synthesis of cobalamin coenzymes. Abbrevations: TC II = transcobalamin II; OH-Cbl = hydroxocobalamin; MeCbl = methylcobalamin; AdoCbl = adenosylcobalamin; Cbl^{III}, Cbl^{II}, Cbl^{I} = cobalamins with cobalt valence of 3^+, 2^+, and 1^+, respectively.

demonstrating that the adenosyltransferase found in bacteria also exists in normal human cells. These experiments also revealed that the adnosyltransferase was mitochondrial in location, implying that both the synthesis and cofactor activity of AdoCbl take place in this organelle. It seems almost certain, as shown in Fig. 29-8, that MeCbl synthesis takes place in the cytosol.

METABOLIC ABNORMALITIES IN COBALAMIN DEFICIENCY. The biochemical abnormalities in plasma and urine of patients with cobalamin deficiency reflect the dysfunction of the enzymes dependent on cobalamin coenzymes. The first relevant observation in this context was the demonstration by Cox and White[5] and by Barness and his colleagues[6] that methylmalonic acid excretion in the urine was distinctly increased in cobalamin-deficient patients with classic pernicious anemia. The methylmalonic aciduria in these patients was reversed rapidly by administration of physiologic doses of cobalamin, indicating that repletion of cobalamin stores restored the methylmalonyl-CoA mutase reaction to normal. Later, Cox et al. reported that patients with cobalamin deficiency also have distinctly increased amounts of propionic acid in the urine, this abnormality again being reversed by treatment.[115] Interestingly, they also found excessive amounts of acetic acid in the urine of cobalamin-deficient subjects. The mechanism of this abnormality is not clear, since acetate does not participate in the major pathway of propionate catabolism. The finding could, of course, reflect increased utilization of the alternative pathways of propionate metabolism in the face of a block in the major pathway, since each of the alternative routes leads eventually to the formation of acetyl-CoA (Fig. 29-4). Excessive excretion of homocystine has also been documented in cobalamin-deficient patients,[116,117] as has combined methylmalonic aciduria and homocystinuria.[118] The latter report is particularly interesting since it documents congenital but not hereditary cobalamin deficiency due, in this instance, to acquired cobalamin deficiency in the offspring of a strictly vegetarian mother also deficient in the vitamin.

Biochemical studies in an animal model, the cobalamin-deficient pig, have yielded other significant biochemical findings. Cardinale and his colleagues[119] noted that, as expected, the concentrations of total cobalamin and of adenosylcobalamin were markedly reduced in the liver, kidney, and brain of cobalamin-deficient pigs. They also observed that the methylmalonyl-CoA mutase apoenzyme content appeared to be increased. The latter finding suggests the possibility of a feedback control system between apoenzyme and coenzyme that must be explored further.

DISEASE STATES

The Propionic Acidemias

In 1961, Childs et al.[7] described a male infant with episodic metabolic ketoacidosis, protein intolerance, and remarkably elevated plasma glycine concentration. More than 100 children with similar clinical and biochemical findings have since been described. Many of these children were subsequently found to have methylmalonic acidemia;[120] a few had β-ketothiolase deficiency (see Chap. 28). However, the patient described by Childs et al. and many reported subsequently have propionic acidemia due to a primary and specific deficiency of propionyl-CoA carboxylase activity (Fig. 29-2). This conclusion was derived independently from the description of a patient with massive propionate accumulation in blood,[121] from another with impaired propionate oxidation in leukocytes[9] and defective carboxylase activity in fibroblast extracts,[122] and from a third with both propionic acidemia and defective carboxylase activity.[123] We now recognize that propionyl-CoA carboxylase deficiency also occurs in children with inherited abnormalities in biotin metabolism leading to deficiency of multiple biotin-dependent carboxylases (see Chap. 83). Hence, we must now use the term *propionic acidemias* to refer to this heterogeneous group of related inborn errors. As will be discussed subsequently, a similar kind of heterogeneity exists among the *methylmalonic acidemias*.

Propionyl-CoA Carboxylase Deficiency.

CLINICAL MANIFESTATIONS. E.G., the patient described by Childs, Nyhan, et al.[7,124,125] presented with dehydration, lethargy, and coma on the first day of life. He was found to be severely ketoacidotic and responded slowly to massive alkali replacement. The clinical course was characterized by recurrent attacks of ketoacidosis, precipitated by infections or protein ingestion, and by developmental retardation, electroencephalographic abnormalities, and osteoporosis. The patient had episodic neutropenia and thrombocytopenia prior to death at age 7. A sister (A.G.) also became ketotic and acidotic during the first 4 days of life, but the course of her condition has been modified dramatically because of the extensive experience gained in studying her brother. Although she has had mild attacks of ketoacidosis during intercurrent infections, maintenance on a low protein diet has resulted in little need for hospital care and normal somatic and mental development up to age 15 years.[126]

In 1968, Hommes and his colleagues[121] described a male infant with hyperventilation, areflexia, and grunting at age 60 h. There was a profound metabolic acidosis (arterial pH 6.98), and in spite of administration of massive amounts of sodium bicarbonate and tris(hydroxymethyl)aminomethane (THAM), the infant died on the fifth day of life. Leukocytes and platelets were normal. Postmortem examination showed only a fatty liver and degeneration of Purkinje cells and the granular layer of the cerebellum.

Subsequent descriptions of patients with this form of propionic acidemia have confirmed that most patients present in the newborn period with severe metabolic acidosis manifested by refusal to feed, vomiting, lethargy, and hypotonia; dehydration, seizures, and hepatomegaly occur less often.[127,128] It should be emphasized that other patients have presented later, either with episodic ketoacidosis or with developmental retardation uncomplicated by attacks of ketosis or acidosis.[129] Interestingly, still other children with almost complete deficiency of propionyl-CoA carboxylase activity in cultured fibroblast extracts have had no clinical abnormalities whatever and have been identified during family studies.[130] No satisfactory explanation for this striking lack of clinical-enzymatic correlation exists at present.

Based on a survey of 65 patients with propionic acidemia, Wolf et al.[128] reported that the clinical course of symptomatic patients is characterized by repeated relapses—usually precipitated by excessive protein intake, constipation, or intercurrent infection. Management of these children has been quite difficult, and neurologic sequellae have been common. Among the neurologic complications often observed, developmental delay, focal and general seizures, cerebral atrophy, and EEG abnormalities have been the most prominent. These authors also emphasized that leukopenia and thrombocytopenia, perhaps due to marrow suppression by one or more of the toxic metabolites produced, is not uncommon.

BIOCHEMICAL ABNORMALITIES. Childs and Nyhan[7,124,125,131] studied their index patient extensively. Because of the hyperglycinemia, they focused their attention on the pathways of glycine formation and utilization but found no consistent abnormalities. Normal hemoglobin concentration in the peripheral blood indicated that the pathway from glycine to δ-aminolevulinic acid was not blocked. Slices of the patient's liver incorporated [^{14}C]glycine into protein and carbon dioxide as well as slices of rat liver did. Salicylate and benzoate were normally conjugated with glycine, and the glutathione concentration of whole blood was normal. Although the rate of conversion of tritiated glycine to serine in vivo was slower than in controls, this difference may have reflected the enlarged glycine pool rather than a specific block in the conversion of glycine to serine.[131]

Several observations suggested an abnormality in the catabolism of the branched chain amino acids, methionine, and threonine: Plasma concentrations of valine, isoleucine, and leucine were elevated intermittently; administration of leucine, valine, isoleucine, threonine, and methionine each precipitated attacks of ketoacidosis, but no other amino acids were toxic. Menkes[132] reported that the urine contained large amounts of butanone (a 4-carbon ketone which is a by-product of isoleucine catabolism) and the longer-chain ketones, pentanone and hexanone. These long-chain ketones were not detected in the urine of patients with ketosis due to diabetes, starvation, or ketogenic diets. Since isoleucine, valine, threonine, and methionine are all precursors of propionate, a defect in propionate metabolism seemed likely, but patient E.G. died before any other studies of propionate catabolism could be performed. Subsequently, Hsia et al.[9] demonstrated a striking defect in propionate catabolism in A.G., the affected sister of E.G. When leukocytes isolated from her peripheral blood were incubated with [3-^{14}C]propionate, negligible quantities of $^{14}CO_2$ were evolved compared to values in controls, but her cells oxidized methylmalonate and succinate normally. Identical findings were obtained using fibroblasts grown in tissue culture. These data showed that the primary metabolic defect in E.G. and A.G. was in the conversion of propionyl-CoA to D-methylmalonyl-CoA, a reaction catalyzed by propionyl-CoA carboxylase. This conclusion was confirmed subsequently by assay of carboxylase activity in fibroblast extracts.[122]

In their child with lethal neonatal acidosis, Hommes et al.[121] found that the serum propionic acid concentration was 400 mg/dl (5.4 m*M*), a value more than 100 times that reported in normal infants. The liver contained fatty acids with 15 and 17 carbon atoms in addition to the even-chain fatty acids found in control livers. From these data, Hommes et al. also postulated a defect in propionyl-CoA carboxylation in their patient.

Subsequent investigations have confirmed and extended these early findings. Analysis of body fluids in several additional patients[58-60,123] showed that propionate accumulation in blood and urine occurs regularly, its magnitude being related to the severity of the clinical course and the time at which sampling is performed. Ando and colleagues have stressed that other propionate derivatives also accumulate in urine. These include methylcitrate, which is probably formed from the intramitochondrial condensation of propionyl-CoA with oxalacetate;[58] propionylglycine, which results from the conjugation of propionate with glycine;[59] β-hydroxypropionate, an intermediate in one of the alternative pathways of propionate catabolism[60] (Fig. 29-4); and tiglic acid,[133] an isoleucine catabolite several steps proximal to the block. Although the exact amounts of these compounds in urine have not always been determined, they appear to account for a small fraction of the propionate pool that accumulates in vivo in this disease. Their presence may be important in mitigating the toxic effects of propionate excess.

Other compounds, not directly concerned with the propionate pathway, have also been found in significantly increased amounts. In addition to hyperglycinemia and hyperglycinuria, which were discussed earlier, marked hyperammonemia has been documented in several patients,[128,134] and a distinct correlation between plasma propionate and blood ammonia has been noted in two patients.[135]

THE ENZYMATIC DEFECT. The molecular pathology in propionyl-CoA carboxylase deficiency is both complex and interesting. Cell extracts from a number of affected patients share a common finding, namely, reduction in propionyl-CoA carboxylase activity to 1 to 5 percent of that in controls.[136-138] Such enzymatic dysfunction reflects different mutations at a minimum of two loci, because complementation studies with heterokaryons formed between pairs of affected cell lines demonstrate the existence of two major complementation groups (designated *pccA* and *pccBC*).[139,140] The *pccBC* class, too, is heterogeneous, being subdivided into *pccB* and *pccC*. These findings are supported by independent biochemical observations which show that *pccA* and *pccBC* mutants can be distinguished by differences in thermostability, affinity for the effector K^+, and their responses to the addition of avidin.[137] Moreover, cell extracts from obligate heterozygotes of the *pccA* class have about 50 percent of control propionyl-CoA carboxylase activity, while those of heterozygotes of the *pccBC* class have carboxylase activity indistinguishable from that in controls.[138] The simplest way to account for this biochemical and genetic heterogeneity is to propose that the two major classes of *pcc* mutants correspond to structural alterations of the two nonidentical subunits (α and β) of the carboxylase molecule (see Fig. 29-2 and related discussion).

This hypothesis now has ample experimental confirmation. Based on studies using immunoprecipitation and gel electrophoresis, Lamhonwah et al.[141] showed that fibroblast extracts from *pccA* mutants had little or no α chain of propionyl-CoA carboxylase. They showed further[142] that *pccA* mutants lacked the mRNA for α chain but contained β-chain mRNA. Thus, it is clear that carboxylase deficiency in *pccA* mutants reflects deficient synthesis of α chains and that *pccBC* mutants have defective β-chain formation. Significantly, neither *pccA* nor *pccBC* lines have residual immunotitratable cross-reacting material (i.e., all lines are CRM^- for carboxylase), implying that the small amount of residual enzyme activity observed in all *pcc* mutants is produced by other carboxylases, not by propionyl-CoA carboxylase itself.[143]

PATHOLOGIC PHYSIOLOGY. A defect in the carboxylation of propionate provides a satisfactory explanation for many of the findings reported in this disorder. This defect would be expected to lead to an elevated concentration of propionate in the blood and an inability of leukocytes to catabolize propionate to carbon dioxide. Since isoleucine, valine, threonine, and methionine are precursors of propionate, such a block should also lead to the observed protein and specific amino acid intolerance. The appearance of long, odd-chain fatty acids in the liver suggests that when propionyl-CoA carboxylation is blocked, odd-chain fatty acid biosynthesis may be augmented because propionyl-CoA is the "primer" for such compounds. Finally, the presence of such compounds as butanone, methylcitrate, β-hydroxypropionate, propionylglycine, and tiglic acid very likely results from reversal of reactions proximal to the primary carboxylase block or from increased utilization of alternative pathways. It is not at all clear from the foregoing why some patients have a severe and often life-threatening course and others are mildly affected clinically. Major differences in dietary protein or in alternate mechanisms for propionate disposal are possible explanations for the wide clinical spectrum, but the prominent intrafamilial differences in severity are not easily explained this way.[130] Further, several other features of the disease are not adequately explained by the block in propionate catabolism. The ketosis produced in E.G. by leucine is not understood, since this amino acid is not catabolized to propionate. It is, however, ketogenic in normal subjects, suggesting that its effect in E.G. was nonspecific. The cause for the hyperglycinemia seen in many, but not all, of these patients has not been adequately defined. Because the infant described by Hommes et al.[121] with massive propionic acidemia never showed hyperglycinemia, the latter cannot be ascribed simply to the acidosis or ketosis. Numerous theses have been put forth. One or more products of isoleucine catabolism may interfere with glycine cleavage or glycine-serine interconversion.[131,144,145] Ando et al.[58] speculated that methylcitrate cleavage in the cytosol may yield propionate and glyoxylate, the latter being used as a substrate for glycine overproduction. Impaired glycine conjugation systems have been suggested, but no data in support of this notion have been forthcoming. Since plasma glycine concentration may rise in sick children with negative nitrogen balance of many causes,[146] the hyperglycinemia may be nonspecific. The hyperammonemia often observed in this disorder has been the subject of considerable recent investigation. It appears very likely that this secondary but clinically important finding results from inhibition of the first enzyme of the urea cycle, mitochondrial carbamyl phosphate synthetase (CPS I), by the organic acids and CoA esters which accumulate intramitochondrially behind the block in propionyl-CoA carboxylation. This conclusion rests on the following data from studies with experimental animals and animal tissues: Propionate inhibits ureagenesis in rat liver slices when ammonia, but not citrulline or aspartate, is the nitrogen-donating substrate;[147] administration of sufficiently large amounts of propionate or methylmalonate to produce hyperammonemia in rats is associated with a marked fall in hepatic concentration of *N*-acetyl glutamate (NAG),[148] the required allosteric effector of CPS I, probably by competitively inhibiting NAG synthetase.[149] That such CPS I inhibition occurs in vivo as well as in vitro is supported by case reports which describe selective impairment of CPS I activity in the livers of patients with propionic acidemia[150] or methylmalonic acidemia.[151]

GENETICS. The presence of two affected sibs, one of each sex, in the index family with this condition suggested autosomal recessive inheritance. This suggestion has been amply supported for both the *pccA* and *pccBC* classes. (1) Several families in each class with two or more affected sibs have been described. (2) Propionyl CoA-carboxylase activity in cultured skin fibroblast extracts from both parents of affected children in the *pccA* class have about 50 percent of normal propionyl-CoA carboxylase activity.[122,138] (3) Complementation testing with heterokaryons formed between cell lines of several carboxylase-deficient patients has revealed that the enzyme defect behaves as a recessive in culture.[139]

As mentioned earlier, it is now clear that the *pccA* mutants result from abnormalities in the structure and function of the α subunit of propionyl-CoA carboxylase, while the complex *pccBC* mutants owe their enzyme deficiency to abnormalities in the β subunit. The *pccB* and *pccC* subclasses occur, most likely, due to intragenic complementation.

One further genetic issue deserves mention. Why do cells from individuals heterozygous for *pccA* mutations have the expected half-normal carboxylase activity while cells from *pccBC* heterozygotes display normal carboxylase activity? The answer appears to be that the β-chain subunit is made in distinct excess of the α subunit. Thus, even reducing β-chain presence by half (as occurs in *pccBC* heterozygotes) still yields sufficient β chains to assemble with the normally synthesized α chains.

DIAGNOSIS AND TREATMENT. A defect in propionate carboxylation must be considered in any child who develops ketosis or acidosis in the neonatal period. Other inborn errors of metabolism must be ruled out, as must the more common causes of acidosis in the newborn period. Determinations of propionic acid in blood or urine and studies of propionyl-CoA carboxylase activity in leukocyte or fibroblast extracts are required for such definitive diagnosis. The latter test is, in fact, the only absolutely specific one, since propionate accumulation can occur in patients with defects of methylmalonate metabolism as well as in those with propionyl-CoA carboxylase deficiency. Such assays on cord blood leukocytes should allow immediate diagnosis in a high-risk newborn. Prenatal diagnosis has been accomplished reliably by measuring carboxylase activity in cultured amniotic fluid cells,[153] by measuring [^{14}C]propionate fixation in amniotic fluid cells,[154] or by measuring methylcitrate in amniotic fluid.[155]

A low protein diet [0.5 to 1.5 g/(kg·day)] or one selectively reduced in the content of propionate precursors appears to be the best treatment for the disorder at this time. Such diets will minimize the number of attacks of ketoacidosis but will not necessarily prevent them or allow normal development in all patients. Attacks of ketoacidosis should be treated vigorously by withdrawing all dietary protein and administering sodium bicarbonate parenterally. Since propionyl-CoA carboxylase requires biotin as a coenzyme, it is possible that some patients may improve when given supplementary biotin, but no clear example of a biotin-responsive patient with isolated propionyl-CoA carboxylase deficiency has yet been documented. Whereas patients with specific propionyl-CoA carboxylase deficiency do not respond to biotin supplements, their cells often show some increase in enzyme activity,[156] indicating that a trial of biotin supplementation may still be worthwhile in patients with this disorder. Dramatic biotin responsiveness has been described in several children in whom propionyl-CoA carboxylase deficiency as part of the constellation now called *multiple carboxylase deficiency* (see below and Chap. 83).

One additional therapeutic adjunct deserves mention. Roe and Bohan reported marked, transient clinical improvement in a child with propionic acidemia given a single oral dose (100 mg/kg) of L-carnitine.[157] Because this child's urinary hippurate concentration rose markedly after carnitine, because free plasma carnitine was reduced in three other patients with propionic acidemia,[158] and because urinary propionylcarnitine was present in large amounts in such patients,[158] these workers proposed that patients with propionic acidemia have a relative carnitine deficiency. Subsequently, Wolff et al.[159] observed that L-carnitine supplements significantly reduced the ketogenic response to fasting in patients with propionic acidemia. Thus, it appears that long-term L-carnitine supplementation in these patients warrants serious consideration. To date, no results of such long-term treatment with carnitine have been published.

Multiple Carboxylase Deficiency. In 1971, Gompertz et al.[160] reported a male infant (J.R.) thought to have specific deficiency of the mitochondrial, biotin-dependent enzyme β-methylcrotonyl-CoA carboxylase (see Chap. 28 and Fig. 29-5). This infant developed a diffuse, erythematous skin rash at age 5 weeks and was admitted to the hospital at age 5 months because of a worsening rash, recurrent vomiting, irritability, and a mild metabolic acidosis. His urine, which smelled like "tom cats' urine," was analyzed for organic acids and was found to contain large excesses of β-methylcrotonylglycine, tiglylglycine, and β-hydroxyisovaleric acid. When he was given 10 mg biotin (about 100 times the estimated human requirement) by mouth daily for several days, the rash, vomiting, irritability, and abnormal urine metabolites all disappeared dramatically. Several years later, it became clear that J.R. had multiple—not specific—carboxylase deficiency: His reanalyzed urine contained metabolites characteristic of propionyl-CoA carboxylase deficiency as well as β-methylcrotonyl-CoA carboxylase deficiency[161]; his cultured fibroblast extracts were deficient in pyruvate carboxylase[162] as well as propionyl-CoA and β-methylcrotonyl-CoA carboxylase;[163,163] and supplementation of the fibroblast growth medium with biotin led to complete correction of the deficiency of all three biotin-dependent enzymes.[162–164] Subsequently, nearly 50 children with multiple carboxylase deficiency have been described (see Chap. 83). These children are now known to suffer from one of two known defects in biotin metabolism. One group of 11 children is deficient in holocarboxylase synthetase activity.[165–168] These children tend to present in the first days or weeks of life with feeding difficulties, hypotonia, lethargy, and seizures; some have a diffuse skin rash and/or alopecia. A second, larger group is deficient in biotinidase activity.[169–171] These children usually present later in life (mean age of onset, 3 months) with a variety of neurologic problems (seizures, hypotonia, developmental delay, hearing loss, optic atrophy). Both groups respond dramatically to biotin supplements (10 mg daily) with prompt and sustained clinical improvement. Thus, multiple carboxylase deficiency differs markedly from isolated propionyl-CoA carboxylase deficiency in response to biotin and, hence, in long-term prognosis. It should be emphasized, however, that clinical presentations may be very similar. For this reason urinary metabolite identification is of important therapeutic significance.

The Methylmalonic Acidemias

In 1967, Oberholzer,[10] Stokke,[11] and their colleagues described critically ill infants with profound metabolic ketoacidosis and developmental retardation who accumulated huge amounts of methylmalonate in their blood and urine. These children had none of the hematologic or neurologic stigmata of cobalamin deficiency, failed to respond to cobalamin supplements, and excreted much larger amounts of methylmalonate than those observed in patients with pernicious anemia.[6,7] They were presumed to have a congenital defect of methylmalonyl-CoA racemase or of the methylmalonyl-CoA mutase apoenzyme (Fig. 29-2). Shortly thereafter, Rosenberg,[172] Lindblad,[12,13] and their coworkers reported children with similar clinical presentations whose methylmalonic aciduria responded dramatically to pharmacologic but not physiologic amounts of cyanocobalamin or adenosylcobalamin (AdoCbl). Such children were found subsequently to have a primary defect of AdoCbl synthesis which resulted in impaired mutase activity.[14,15] The array of different biochemical and clinical disturbances of methylmalonate metabolism was broadened still further in 1969 and 1970, when Mudd,[173] Goodman,[174] and their associates described children with methylmalonic aciduria whose clinical and chemical findings differed from those described above: Ketoacidosis was not present, and the increased methylmalonate excretion was accompanied by homocystinuria, cystathioninuria, and hypomethioninemia. This biochemical constellation was interpreted as evidence for defective synthesis of both cobalamin coenzymes, wtih secondary impairment of AdoCbl-dependent methylmalonyl-CoA mutase and MeCbl-dependent homocysteine:N^5-methyltetrahydrofolate methyltransferase (Fig. 29-7). These early descriptions, coupled with a growing body of data to be discussed subsequently, have demonstrated many different biochemical bases for inherited forms of methylmalonic acidemia: two distinct defects of the mutase apoenzyme—one producing complete mutase deficiency (*mut*°), the other partial deficiency (*mut*⁻); two distinct defects of AdoCbl synthesis only—one probably due to deficiency of a mitochondrial Cbl reductase (*cblA*), the other to deficiency of mitochondrial cob(I)alamin adenosyltransferase (*cblB*); and three distinct defects of AdoCbl and MeCbl synthesis due to abnormal cystosolic or lysosomal metabolism of cobalamins (*cblC*, *cblD*, and *cblF*). Those patients with lesions producing methylmalonic acidemia only (*mut*°, *mut*⁻, *cblA*, *cblB*) share many clinical features and will be discussed as a group; discussion of the much smaller group of patients whose lesions produce methylmalonic acidemia and homocystinuria (*cblC*, *clbD*, and *cblF*) will follow. For a more detailed comparison of the several inherited defects in cobalamin metabolism, the reader is directed to Chap. 82.

Methylmalonyl-CoA Mutase Deficiency.

CLINICAL AND LABORATORY PRESENTATION. More than 100 children with isolated mutase deficiency have been documented. Although, as mentioned above, there are four known etiologies for such deficiency, the clinical findings in affected patients from the four etiologic groups are remarkable more for their similarities than for their differences. We surveyed[175] the natural history in 45 such patients; 15 were *mut*°; 5 were *mut*⁻; 14 were *cblA*, and 11 were *cblB*. There were approximately equal numbers of males and females in each group. Information was obtained from questionnaires completed by the patients' physicians, published reports, unpublished communications, and personal experience. The most common signs and symptoms at the onset of clinical difficulty were lethargy, failure to thrive, recurrent vomiting, dehydration, respiratory distress, and muscular hypotonia (Table 29-1). Little interclass difference was observed for these major clinical manifestations or for such less common ones as developmental retardation, hepatomegaly, or coma. Patients in the *mut*° class, however, presented earlier than those in the other groups (Fig. 29-9). Whereas 80 percent of children in the *mut*°

Table 29-1 Clinical Presentation in 45 Patients with Methylmalonic Acidemia

	Mutant class				
Signs and symptoms at onset	*cblA*	*cblB*	*mut⁻*	*mut°*	*Total*
Lethargy	78	83	100	85	84
Failure to thrive	75	86	40	77	73
Recurrent vomiting	58	86	80	77	73
Dehydration	64	86	100	62	71
Respiratory distress	89	67	50	55	67
Muscular hypotonia	44	57	33	91	63
Developmental retardation	36	33	25	65	47
Hepatomegaly	11	67	0	57	41
Coma	50	29	40	38	40

SOURCE: From Matsui et al.[175] Numerical values represent percentages of patients in each group.

class became ill during the first week of life, less than half of the children in the three other groups presented during this interval. Furthermore, clinical onset occurred in ~90 percent of *mut°* patients before the end of the first month, whereas onset beyond the first month was observed in an appreciable fraction of patients in each of the other groups.

The laboratory findings in affected patients at the time that methylmalonic acidemia (with or without aciduria) was first documented are shown in Table 29-2. As expected, serum cobalamin concentrations were routinely normal. Metabolic acidosis, with blood pH values as low as 6.9 and serum bicarbonate concentrations as low as 5 meq/liter, was observed in the majority of patients in all four groups. Ketonemia or ketonuria was found in ~80 percent of patients with hyperammonemia being only slightly less common—occurring in ~70 percent of affected patients. Leukopenia, thrombocytopenia, and anemia were the only other manifestations that were noted in 50 percent or more of this group of patients. Earlier case reports (reviewed in Ref. 176) reported that hypoglycemia occurs in about 40 percent of affected patients. Inadvertently, this parameter was not assessed in the recent survey.

It should be mentioned that mutase deficiency is not always associated with serious clinical consequences. Ledley et al.[177] reported eight children, between ages 18 months and 13 years, who had methylmalonate accumulation in blood and urine but were without symptoms. Presumably, these apomutase-deficient patients have an enzyme defect so "leaky" that homeostasis is not interfered with.

Fig. 29-9 Age at clinical onset in 45 patients with methylmalonic acidemia. Inset numbers denote percentages of patients in each group. *(From Matsui et al.[175])*

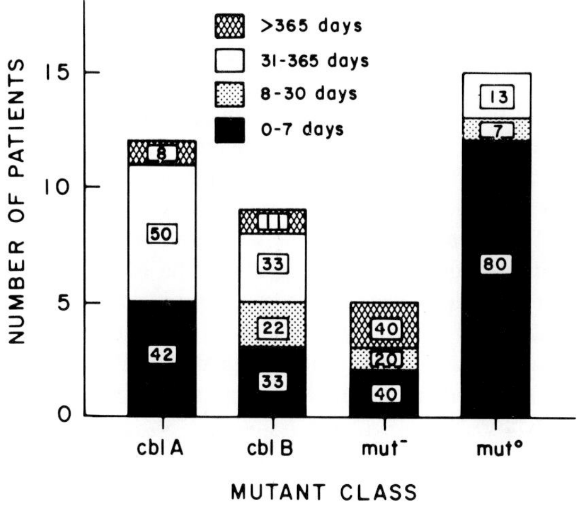

CHEMICAL ABNORMALITIES IN VIVO. Large amounts of methylmalonic acid have appeared in the urine or blood of all reported patients. Whereas normal children and adults excrete less than 5 mg methylmalonate daily, children with isolated methylmalonic acidemia have excreted from 240 to 5700 mg in a 24-h period. Their plasma concentrations of methylmalonate, undetectable in normal subjects, have ranged from 2.6 to 34 mg/dl. In those few patients in whom it was measured, the cerebrospinal fluid concentration of methylmalonate equaled that of plasma (see Ref. 176 for references to early case reports). No relationship between the quantities of methylmalonate acumulated in body fluids and the etiology of mutase deficiency (i.e., apoenzyme versus coenzyme deficiency) has been reported. Methylmalonate is surely the major, but not the only, abnormal metabolite found in body fluids of these patients. Since propionyl-CoA carboxylation is reversible, propionate and some of its precursors (butanone) or metabolites (β-hydroxypropionate and methylcitrate) also accumulate in blood and urine,[8,58,59,178,179] their amounts being small compared to that of methylmalonate.

Several groups have studied the relationship between protein or amino acid loading and methylmalonate accumulation in these patients. Without exception, administration of protein or those amino acids known to be precursors of propionate and methylmalonate, such as methionine, threonine, valine, or isoleucine, has resulted in augmented methylmalonate accumulation and, in some instances, ketosis or acidosis.[8,10–12] When cobalamin-responsive patients are given supplements of this vitamin, such augmentation by methylmalonate precursors is lessened considerably.[180] All these findings suggest that patients with discrete defects at the mutase step have a major block in the utilization of methylmalonyl-CoA which is expressed as methylmalonate accumulation.

LOCALIZATION OF ENZYMATIC DEFECTS. Since the conversion of propionate to succinate is blocked in each of the methylmalonic acidemias, an early screening test for these disorders measured the ability of intact peripheral blood leukocytes or cultured fibroblasts to oxidize [^{14}C]propionate to $^{14}CO_2$ and compared this with the oxidation of [^{14}C]succinate to $^{14}CO_2$.[172] By including estimation of [^{14}C]methylmalonate oxidation as well, this test can distinguish between deficiency of propionyl-CoA carboxylase and of methylmalonyl-CoA mutase. More re-

Table 29-2 Laboratory Findings in 45 Patients with Methylmalonic Acidemia

	Mutant class				
Finding at clinical onset	*cblA*	*cblB*	*mut⁻*	*mut°*	*Total*
Normal serum cobalamin	100	100	100	100	100
Metabolic acidosis	100	88	100	85	92
Ketonemia and/or ketonuria	78	67	100	85	81
Hyperammonemia	50	83	80	75	71
Hyperglycinemia and/or -glycinuria	70	83	40	70	68
Leukopenia	70	45	60	62	60
Anemia	10	45	0	58	55
Thrombocytopenia	75	45	40	40	50

SOURCE: From Matsui et al.[175] Numerical values represent percentages of patients in each group.

cently, incorporation of [^{14}C]propionate into trichloroacetic acid-precipitable material by intact cultured cells has replaced the more cumbersome $^{14}CO_2$ evolution technique.[181,182] Further discrimination among the methylmalonic acidemias has depended on studies of cobalamin uptake and AdoCbl formation by intact cultured fibroblasts, on assays of mutase activity in cell extracts, and on genetic complementation studies with cultured cell heterokaryons.

MUTASE APOENZYME DEFICIENCY. Morrow and colleagues[183] provided the first evidence in vitro for apoenzyme abnormalities and for biochemical heterogeneity among the methylmalonic acidemias. In four patients who had died, they studied mutase activity in liver homogenates by measuring the conversion of DL-[^{3}H]methylmalonyl-CoA to [^{3}H]succinyl-CoA (Table 29-3). Activity was barely detectable in three and showed no response when AdoCbl was added at concentrations sufficient to saturate the normal enzyme. In the fourth, mutase activity was restored to control values by AdoCbl. These findings were interpreted as evidence for a mutase apoenzyme defect in the first three patients and for defective AdoCbl synthesis in the fourth. These findings were confirmed subsequently in studies with cultured fibroblasts.[184] Cells from the first three patients synthesized AdoCbl normally but had much reduced mutase activity in extracts regardless of the amount of AdoCbl added; cells from the fourth had a distinct defect in AdoCbl synthesis.

Subsequently, it has become clear that two general types of apomutase defects exist. In one type, designated *mut°* and constituting about two-thirds of the *mut* complementation group, mutase activity in extracts of cultured fibroblasts is undetectable (<0.1 percent of control), even when assayed in the presence of AdoCbl concentrations greatly in excess of that normally required to saturate the enzyme.[184-186] When cross-reacting material (CRM) was sought under steady state conditions in cell lines from 21 such patients by radioimmunoassay, 12 had no immunologically identifiable mutase protein (CRM$^-$), while 9 had reduced amounts of CRM ranging from 1 to 40 percent of that found in control extracts.[187] In a follow-up study,[188] cells from this group of patients were pulse-labeled to determine how amounts of newly synthesized mutase protein detected by specific immunoprecipitation compared with the CRM values obtained under steady state conditions. As expected, all CRM$^+$ mutants had easily detectable newly synthesized mutase. Of 11 CRM$^-$ lines, however, 5 had amounts of newly synthesized mutase ranging from barely detectable to nearly half that seen in controls. Thus, some apomutase mutations lead to the synthesis of unstable mutase proteins, which are rapidly degraded intracellularly. One other result of this study bears mention. Using a pulse-chase experimental protocol, mitochondrial import and cleavage of the apomutase precursor was studied in control lines and in 38 lines from *mut* mutants which synthesized mutase protein. In one of the 38 mutant lines, an amino-terminal deletion resulted in failure of the mutant mutase to be taken up by mitochondria.

The second type, designated *mut*$^-$, involves a structurally abnormal mutase apoenzyme. The mutant apoenzymes in these cell extracts retain maximally 2 to 75 percent of control activity, have a K_m for AdoCbl approximately 200 to 5000 times normal, show a normal K_m for methylmalonyl-CoA, and exhibit increased thermolability relative to control enzyme.[185,186,189] By radioimmunoassay, the amount of immunologically reactive mutase protein in these extracts ranges from 20 to 100 percent of control.[187] Since pairwise crosses between *mut°* and *mut*$^-$ yield noncomplementing heterokaryons, it seems likely that both mutant types reflect abnormalities of the locus coding for the apomutase structural gene.[185,186] This conclusion is further supported by the identification of affected individuals who appear to be *mut°*/*mut*$^-$ compound heterozygotes—a finding expected for allelic mutations.[186] Finally, it should be mentioned that the only patient thus far reported to have methylmalonyl-CoA racemase deficiency[190] has been restudied subsequently and shown conclusively to be a *mut*$^-$ mutant biochemically and genetically.[16]

Table 29-3 Methylmalonyl-CoA Mutase Activity in Liver Homogenates from Patients with Methylmalonic Acidemia

	*Enzymatic activity**	
Subjects	*Without added AdoCbl*	*With added AdoCbl* (4×10^{-5} M)
Controls (3)	535–866	799–1058
Patients		
1	1	3
2	8	33
3	3	7
4	80	1368

*Assayed by measuring conversion of DL-[^{3}H]methylmalonyl-CoA to [^{3}H]succinyl-CoA. Values expressed as picomoles of succinate formed per milligram protein per 30 min.
SOURCE: Adapted from Morrow et al.[183]

DEFECTIVE SYNTHESIS OF ADENOSYLCOBALAMIN. A series of observations by Rosenberg,[14] Mahoney,[15] and their colleagues on the fibroblasts of the index patient with cobalamin-responsive methylmalonic acidemia led to the demonstration of a primary defect in AdoCbl synthesis (Fig. 29-10): (1) Such cells were unable to oxidize propionate or methylmalonate in a medium containing 25 to 50 pg/ml cobalamin and under these conditions, the cell content of adenosylcobalamin was only 10 percent of normal.[14] (2) Supplementation of the medium to 250,000 pg/ml raised the AdoCbl content to that of controls and led to a distinct increase in propionate oxidation.[14] (3) Such intact cells were unable to convert OH-[^{57}Co]Cbl to Ado[^{57}Co]Cbl, although they took up the labeled vitamin normally and had no abnormality in synthesizing the other cobalamin coenzyme, MeCbl.[15] (4) Mutase activity in cell-free extracts supplemented with AdoCbl was normal.[14] (5) Cell-free extracts from this line synthesized AdoCbl normally when incubated with OH-[^{57}Co]Cbl, ATP, and a reducing system designed to bypass cob(III)alamin reductase and cob(II)alamin reductase and to measure only cob(I)alamin adenosyltransferase (Fig. 29-8).[113] Subsequent biochemical[113] and genetic complementation[191-193] studies again showed two distinct mutant classes among patients whose intact cells are unable to synthesize AdoCbl normally, thereby leading to deficient holomutase activity. One class, which contains the index responsive patient just described and is designated *cblA*, is very likely characterized by deficiency of one of the mitochondrial cobalamin reductases. The second, designated *cblB*, has been shown to result from a specific deficiency of cob(I)alamin adenosyltransferase.[114]

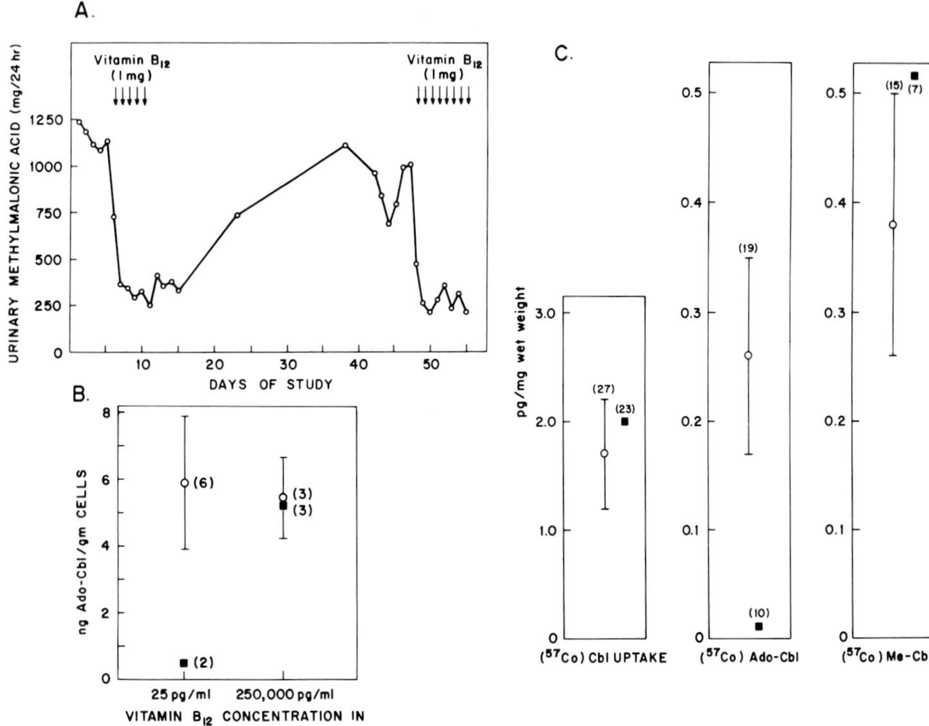

Fig. 29-10 The trail of evidence in the index patient with cobalamin-responsive methylmalonic acidemia. A. Fall in urinary methylmalonate excretion after intramuscular administration of 1 mg cyanocobalamin daily. Treatment with smaller quantities of cyanocobalamin (50 to 250 μg daily) produced no response in methylmalonate excretion. B. Reduced content of adenosylcobalamin (AdoCbl) in the patient's cultured skin fibroblasts (■) compared to controls (○) when propagated in medium containing 25 pg/ml cobalamin, and restoration to normal AdoCbl content when cells were grown in a medium containing 250,000 pg/ml cobalamin. C. Defective accumulation of [^{57}Co]AdoCbl by the patient's intact fibroblasts (■) grown in a medium containing [^{57}Co]OH-Cbl. Note that uptake of [^{57}Co]Cbl and formation of MeCbl are normal (○). *(Figures adapted from Rosenberg,[14] Mahoney,[15] and colleagues.)*

PATHOPHYSIOLOGY. All studies in vivo and in vitro in patients with methylmalonic acidemia due to specific methylmalonyl-CoA mutase deficiency indicate that the primary block in the conversion of methylmalonyl-CoA to succinyl-CoA explains admirably the accumulation of methylmalonate in blood and urine, the augmentation of methylmalonate excretion and the precipitation of ketosis by protein, amino acids, or propionate, and the excretion of long-chain ketones formed in the catabolism of branched chain amino acids. The primary block does not explain several important physiologic disturbances: the acidosis, hypoglycemia, hyperglycinemia, and hyperammonemia. Oberholzer et al.[10] pointed out that the concentration of methylmalonate in the blood (no more than 2 m*M*) could not alone explain the acidosis, and suggested other possibilities. They proposed that an accumulation of coenzyme A "trapped" intracellularly as methylmalonyl-CoA could lead to an insufficiency of this widely utilized coenzyme and secondarily to impaired carbohydrate metabolism and subsequent acidosis. Alternatively, they suggested that methylmalonyl-CoA, a known inhibitor of pyruvate carboxylase,[194] could interfere with gluconeogenesis and lead directly to hypoglycemia and indirectly to excessive catabolism of lipid, with ketosis and acidosis. Halperin et al.[195] showed that methylmalonate inhibited the transmitochondrial shuttle of malate and argued that impairment of this key step in gluconeogenesis could lead to hypoglycemia. As discussed earlier for deficiencies of β-ketothiolase (see Chap. 28) and propionyl-CoA carboxylase, the mechanism of the hyperglycinemia and hyperammonemia so often observed in children with any one of these disorders probably reflects inhibition of the intramitochondrial glycine cleavage enzyme and of CPS I, respectively, by the accumulated organic acids or their CoA esters.[144,145,147–151] Thus, as shown in Fig. 29-11, each of the major secondary abnormalities in the propionic and methylmalonic acidemias can be explained satisfactorily by inhibition of specific intramitochondrial processes by the accumulated organic acids and esters.

By comparing and contrasting the findings in patients with isolated mutase deficiency with those in patients with cobalamin deficiency (as in classic pernicious anemia), it should be possible to shed some light on the mechanism responsible for the hematologic and neurologic abnormalities in the latter disorder. Thus, the absence of megaloblastic anemia in any patient with isolated mutase deficiency militates against any involvement of this enzyme in the typical megaloblastosis seen in cobalamin deficiency. Similarly, the cerebellar and posterior column abnormalities so often encountered in cobalamin-deficient patients have never been observed in patients with methylmalonic acidemia due to specific mutase dysfunction. Therefore, the notion that neurologic dysfunction in pernicious anemia reflects aberrant incorporation of odd-chain or branched chain fatty acids into myelin because of a block in the propionate pathway has little to recommend it. It appears likely, then, that abnormalities in the cobalamin-dependent methyltransferase account for the hematologic and neurologic abnormalities in cobalamin-deficient patients. This matter will be discussed further when we consider that group of patients with methylmalonic acidemia and homocystinuria.

As mentioned earlier, however, about half of the reported patients with isolated methylmalonic acidemia show pancytopenia.[175] A recent report suggests that methylmalonate inhibits growth of marrow stem cells in a concentration-dependent fashion.[196] Further studies of this sort will be of interest.

GENETIC CONSIDERATIONS. Each of the four etiologic bases for specific methylmalonyl-CoA mutase deficiency (*mut°*,

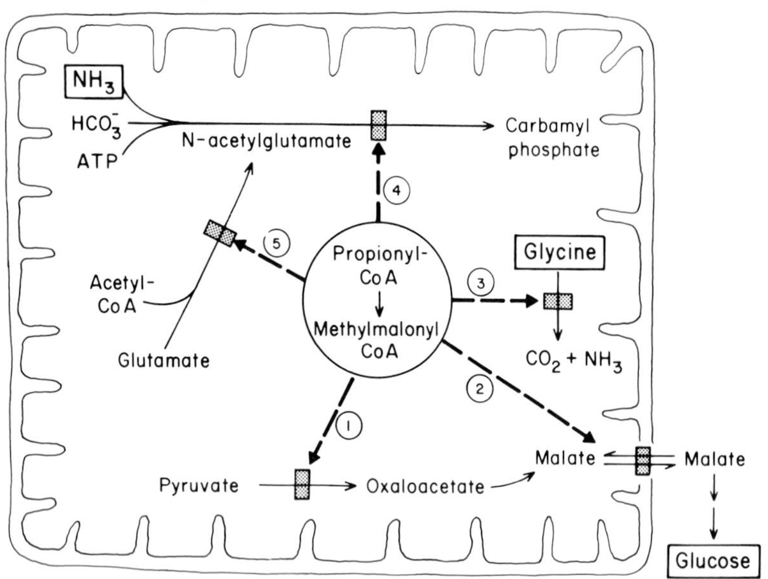

Fig. 29-11 Proposed mechanisms of hypoglycemia, hyperglycinemia, and hyperammonemia in patients with inherited deficiencies of β-ketothiolase (see Chap. 28), propionyl-CoA carboxylase, or methylmalonyl-CoA mutase. Inhibitory effects of the enlarged intramitochondrial pools of acyl-CoA esters (such as propionyl-CoA) or their respective free acids on selected mitochondrial functions are shown by the numbered dashed lines corresponding to the following enzymatic or shuttle-mediated reactions: (1) pyruvate carboxylase; (2) the transmitochondrial malate shuttle; (3) the glycine cleavage enzyme; (4) carbamyl phosphate synthetase I; and (5) *N*-acetylglutamate synthetase. See text for discussion.

mut$^-$, *cblA*, and *cblB*) is almost certainly inherited as an autosomal recessive trait. This conclusion is based on the following findings: First, approximately equal numbers of affected males and females are encountered in each group.[175] Second, no instance of vertical transmission from affected parent to affected child has been reported. Third, interclass heterokaryons formed between cell lines from different etiologic groups (i.e., *mut*° × *cblA*) complement each other, whereas intraclass heterokaryons (i.e., *mut*° × *mut*°) do not; thus, each mutant class behaves as a recessive in culture.[191–193] Fourth, cell lines from heterozygotes for the *mut*°, *mut*$^-$, and *cblB* mutations show partial mutase apoenzyme deficiency[186] and partial adenosyltransferase deficiency,[114] respectively. And fifth, among a large group of *mut* mutants studied, some have inherited a genetically different mutant allele from each parent—thereby being compound heterozygotes (i.e., *mut*°/*mut*$^-$) rather than true homozygotes (i.e., *mut*°/*mut*°).[186]

It is not yet possible to define with any precision the prevalence of these disorders in the general population. A survey of newborns in Massachusetts has suggested that methylmalonic acidemia may occur in 1:48,000 infants.[197] Since this study screened urines from ingants ages 3 to 4 weeks, and since it is known that many children with methylmalonic acidemia die in the first week of life from ketoacidosis or hyperammonemia or both, the true prevalence must be considerably greater.

DIAGNOSIS, TREATMENT, AND PROGNOSIS. Since simple colorimetric assays for urinary methylmalonate and more complex gas-liquid chromatographic assays for serum and urinary methylmalonate are now available, it should no longer be difficult to make a diagnosis of methylmalonic acidemia once this condition is considered. Other sources of neonatal or infantile ketoacidosis must be ruled out. If excessive amounts of methylmalonate are found in the urine, cobalamin deficiency can be excluded by direct measurement of serum cobalamin concentration. Confirmation and etiolgoic designation (i.e., *mut* or *cbl*) depend on more laborious studies with cultured cells and extracts therefrom;[16] such laboratory confirmation should and can be regionalized. Prenatal detection of methylmalonic acidemia has been accomplished on several occasions in two different ways: by measurement of methylmalonate in amniotic fluid and maternal urine at midtrimester[198,199] and by studies of mutase activity and cobalamin metabolism in cultured amniotic fluid cells.[191,199,200] Mutase apoenzyme[199,200] and AdoCbl synthesis[181,198] deficiencies have been identified in these ways.

Two treatment regimens for children with methylmalonic acidemia exist and should be employed in tandem. A diet restricted in protein (or a special formula restricted in amino acid precursors of methylmalonate) should be instituted as soon as such life-threatening problems as ketoacidosis, hypoglycemia, or hyperammonemia have been addressed; and supplementary cobalamin [1 to 2 mg cyanocobalamin (CN-Cbl) or hydroxocobalamin (OH-Cbl) intramuscularly daily for several days] should be given as soon as the diagnosis of methylmalonic acidemia is made (or even seriously considered). Such measures should decrease the circulating concentrations of methylmalonate and propionate. Even cobalamin-unresponsive children with delayed development have been shown to improve markedly when treated with careful dietary protein restriction.[201,202] As discussed earlier for patients with propionyl-CoA carboxylase deficiency, Roe and associates[157,158,203] have pointed out that L-carnitine supplements may be a useful therapeutic adjunct in patients with methylmalonic acidemia, presumably by repleting intracellular and extracellular stores of free carnitine which are depleted in affected patients because of complexing with methylmalonyl-CoA and propionyl-CoA.

Our previously mentioned survey[175] suggests that both the response to cobalamin supplements and the long-term outcome in affected patients depend considerably on the nature of the biochemical lesion causing the methylmalonic acidemia. As shown in Fig. 29-12, essentially none of the children designated *mut*° or *mut*$^-$ responded to cobalamin supplements with a distinct fall in blood or urinary methylmalonate, whereas over 90 percent of the *cblA* and about 40 percent of the *cblB* patients showed such a response. Given the complete absence of mutase activity in cells from the *mut*° group, it is not surprising that they were regularly cobalamin-unresponsive in vivo. The disappointing absence of response in four *mut*$^-$ patients presumably means that even parenteral cobalamin supplements could not drive tissue concentrations of AdoCbl sufficiently high to increase significantly their mutase holoenzyme activity. That fraction (~60 percent) of *cblB* pa-

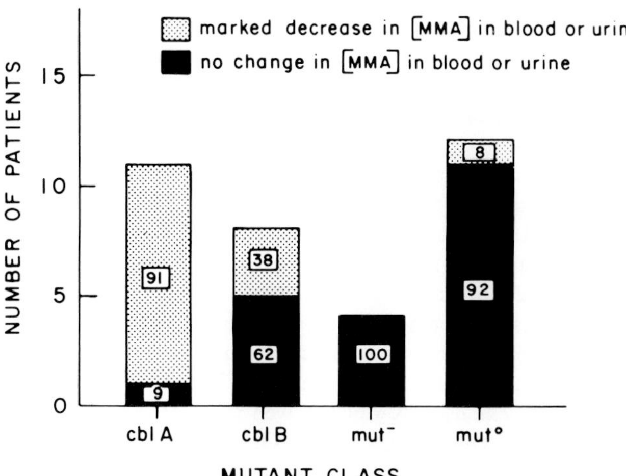

Fig. 29-12 Biochemical response to cobalamin supplementation in 45 patients with methylmalonic acidemia. MMA refers to the concentration of methylmalonate. The supplementation protocol generally employed 1 mg CN-Cbl parenterally daily for 7 to 14 days. Inset numbers denote the percentage of patients in each group. *(From Matsui et al.*[175]*)*

tients unresponsive to cobalamin supplements presumably has such complete adenosyltransferase deficiency that AdoCbl synthesis cannot be augmented by cobalamin supplements, as apparently it can in the *cblB* patients with "leaky" mutations that permit responsiveness in vivo. Patients in the *cblA* group were uniformly responsive, suggesting either that the responsible mutations are leaky, thereby allowing mass action to result in more AdoCbl synthesis, or that alternative pathways of cobalamin reduction which require high substrate concentrations exist in cells. It should be emphasized that responsiveness in vivo does not mean complete correction of mutase deficiency. Studies with cultured cells from a variety of patients with methylmalonic acidemia[16,193] suggest that raising holomutase activity to only ~10 percent of normal values by supplementing the growth medium with OH-Cbl results in distinct augmentation of propionate pathway activity (or, conversely, in a distinct decrease in the magnitude of the metabolic block). Some patients, unresponsive to CN-Cbl or OH-Cbl in vivo, might be expected to respond to AdoCbl itself, but no published reports documenting the efficacy of this logical alternative exist at present.

The long-term outlook for affected patients is revealing. As noted in Fig. 29-13, the *mut*° group has the poorest prognosis, with 60 percent deceased and 40 percent distinctly impaired developmentally at the time of the survey. In sharp contrast, the *cblA* patients (i.e., that group biochemically most responsive to cobalamin supplements) had the best outcome—~70 percent were alive and well at ages up to 14 years. The *cblB* and *mut*⁻ groups were intermediate, with about equal fractions in each group being found in the alive and well, the alive and impaired, or the deceased category. It is interesting, albeit anecdotal, that the index patient in the *cblA* group (now 20 years old) discontinued cobalamin supplements at age 9 years in spite of our advice to the contrary. In the ensuing 11 years, his development and general health have remained excellent despite the accumulation of very large amounts of methylmalonate in the blood and urine. Perhaps, as in some other inherited metabolic disorders, treatment of methylmalonic acidemia is most critical during the early years of life. If this experience is borne out by others, it makes expert clinical management in the early weeks or months of life most important. Finally, the feasibility of prenatal therapy with cobalamin supplements has also been demonstrated. Ampola et al.[199] showed that administration of cobalamin supplements to a woman carrying a cobalamin-responsive, affected fetus resulted in significant reduction in maternal excretion of methylmalonate. The utility of this provocative observation must await the demonstration that prenatal damage occurs if therapy is withheld.

Combined Deficiency of Methylmalonyl-CoA Mutase and Homocysteine:Methyltetrahydrofolate Methyltransferase.

CLINICAL AND LABORATORY PRESENTATIONS. More than a dozen children with inherited methylmalonic acidemia and homocystinuria have been reported. Most of these patients have been the subject of individual case reports;[174,204–217] three have not yet been formally reported. Cells from these children comprise three biochemically and genetically distinct complementation groups, designated *cblC*, *cblD*, and *cblF*.[113,191,192,218]

As noted in Table 29-4, detailed clinical information is available on 17 children (nine males; eight females) in the *cblC* group. Clinical findings have varied widely among patients in this group. Most of the early-described patients presented in the first 2 months of life because of failure to thrive, poor feeding, or lethargy. Subsequent reports have emphasized that some patients have a much delayed onset of symptoms: a 4-year-old with fatigue, delirium, and spasticity;[210] a 14-year-old with the rather sudden onset of dementia and myelopathy.[209] Thus, regardless of age, neurologic manifestations are prominent. Most, but not all, of these patients have had hematologic abnormalities characterized by megaloblastosis and macrocytic anemia; hypersegmented polymorphonuclear leukocytes and thrombocytopenia have been observed less often. Significantly, serum cobalamin and folate concentrations were normal in each child.

The single reported patient in the *cblF* group (a female) presented during the first 2 weeks of life with stomatitis, seizures, and hypotonia. She developed poorly and was clearly delayed when diagnosed at 8 months of age.[217] No hematologic abnormalities were found. In sharp contrast, neither of the brothers in the *cblD* group[174] had any clinically significant problems until much later in life. The older brother came to medical attention because of severe behavioral pathology and

Fig. 29-13 Long-term outcome in 45 patients with methylmalonic acidemia. The ages of the patients surveyed ranged from a few weeks to 14 years. *(From Matsui et al.*[175]*)*

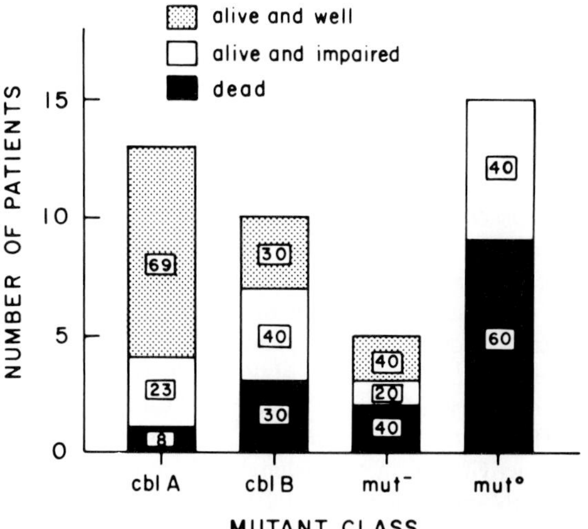

Table 29-4 Clinical and Laboratory Features of Patients with Methylmalonic Acidemia and Homocystinuria

	Mutant class		
Finding	*cblC*	*cblD*	*cblF*
Clinical			
Sex (male/female)	9/8	2/0	0/1
Neonatal onset	10/17	0/2	1/1
Failure to thrive	9/17	0/2	1/1
Developmental retardation	9/17	1/2	1/1
Seizures	4/17	0/2	1/1
Feeding difficulties	5/17	0/2	1/1
Laboratory			
Normal serum cobalamin	17/17	2/2	1/1
Anemia	11/17	0/2	0/1
Megaloblastic marrow	8/17	0/2	0/1
Hypersegmented PMN	2/17	0/2	0/1
Thrombocytopenia	2/17	0/2	0/1
Complications			
Hemolytic episodes	4/17	0/2	0/1
Congestive failure	3/17	0/2	0/1
Thromboemboli	0/17	1/2	0/1
Current status			
Living and well	2/17	1/2	0/1
Living and impaired	11/17	1/2	1/1
Deceased	4/17	0/2	0/1

SOURCE: Information obtained from published case reports[174,204–217] and personal communications. Numerical ratios denote patients showing particular finding/total number of patients in each mutant class.

moderate mental retardation at 14 years of age. He had, as well, a poorly defined neuromuscular problem involving his lower extremities. His then 2-year-old brother was aysmptomatic, although biochemically affected. No hematologic abnormalities have been noted in either sib.

CHEMICAL ABNORMALITIES IN VIVO. In addition to the methylmalonic aciduria and homocystinuria which characterize this group of patients, some have shown hypomethioninemia and cystathioninuria. This constellation of chemical abnormalities, plus the normal serum cobalamin values, led to the proposal,[173,204] which will be discussed in detail subsequently, that these children suffered from a defect in cellular metabolism of cobalamins such that both cobalamin-dependent enzyme activities (mutase and methyltransferase, see Fig. 29-7) were deficient. The methylmalonic aciduria in these children is distinctly less severe than that encountered in children with isolated mutase deficiency (see above). Further, the single *cblF* patient had no detectable homocystinuria despite a cellular deficit in methyltetrahydrofolate:homocysteine methyltransferase activity. Moreover, neither hyperglycinemia nor hyperammonemia has been reported in any of the *cblC*, *cblD*, or *cblF* patients.

LOCALIZATION OF DEFECTIVE CELLULAR METABOLISM OF COBALAMINS. It has long been clear that patients in the *cblC* and *cblD* groups have a defect in cellular metabolism of cobalamins. This conclusion is based on the following data: Total cobalamin content of liver, kidney, and cultured fibroblasts is markedly reduced;[173,205,219,220] the ability of cultured cells to retain ^{57}Co-labeled CN-Cbl[221] or to convert ^{57}Co-labeled CN-Cbl or OH-Cbl to AdoCbl and MeCbl is markedly impaired;[15,192] activity of methylmalonyl-CoA mutase and of homocysteine:N^5-methyltetrahydrofolate methyltransferase in cultured cells is deficient, such deficiency being improved by supplementation of the growth medium with OH-Cbl;[192,193,222] and the mutase and methyltransferase apoenzymes in cells from affected patients appear to be normal.[173,174,192,193,223] The precise nature of the metabolic defect in the *cblC* and *cblD* classes remains elusive, but considerable progress has been made. Since these mutant cells demonstrate normal receptor-mediated adsorptive endocytosis of the TC II–Cbl complex and normal intralysosomal hydrolysis of TC II,[16,99,100,192] perusal of Fig. 29-8 makes it clear that the defects in the *cblC* and *cblD* cells must affect some step or steps subsequent to cellular uptake, common to the synthesis of both coenzymes and prior to the binding of the cobalamin coenzymes to their respective apoproteins. Significantly, *cblC* (and, to a lesser extent, *cblD*) cells use CN-Cbl less well than OH-Cbl[222,224] and are unable to convert CN-Cbl to OH-Cbl, a step shown in normal cells to be a metabolic prerequisite for the synthesis of both AdoCbl and MeCbl.[224] The latter results have been interpreted as evidence for a defect in a cytosolic cob(III)alamin reductase, which is required for reducing cobalamin's trivalent cobalt prior to alkylation.[224] More direct assays of such a putative reductase in extracts of *cblC* and *cblD* cells will be necessary to confirm or deny this thesis. Finally, it should be mentioned that the distinction between the *cblC* and *cblD* classes is based first and foremost on complementation studies which define the two classes as unique.[192] Their biochemical differences appear to be quantitative rather than qualitative, with the *cblC* group having more severe metabolic derangements (and, pari passu, more severe clinical involvement) than the sibs designated *cblD* (Table 29-5).

Studies using cultured fibroblasts from the single reported patient in the *cblF* group are of particular interest. As with cells from *cblC* and *cblD* patients, both mutase and methyltransferase activities were impaired and AdoCbl and MeCbl contents were reduced. In contrast to the *cblC* and *cblD* mutants, however, the *cblF* cells accumulated unmetabolized non-protein-bound cyanocobalamin in lysosomes. These findings indicate that *cblF* cells are deficient in the mediated process by which cobalamin vitamers exit from lysosomes after being taken up by receptor-mediated endocytosis.

The panorama of mutations leading to methylmalonic aciduria is shown in Fig. 29-14 juxtaposed to those seen in inherited forms of propionic acidemia.

PATHOPHYSIOLOGY. The megaloblastic anemia so commonly observed in the *cblC* patients almost surely reflects the enzymatic distrubance of the homocysteine: N^5-methyltetrahydrofolate methyltransferase. This can be stated with some assurance since patients with isolated methylmalonyl-CoA mutase deficiency (*mut°*, *mut⁻*, *cblA*, *cblB*) more severe than that encountered in the *cblC* patients exhibit no such hematologic dysfunction. The early and severe CNS abnormalities encountered in the *cblC* group probably reflect the methyltransferase abnormality as well, in that such patients do not have the severe metabolic ketoacidosis that probably accounts for the CNS problems in patients with mutase deficiency only. Thus, patients with severe, inherited dysfunction in the synthesis of both cobalamin coenzymes resemble closely patients with exogenous cobalamin deficiency—both groups having prominent hematologic and neurologic manifestations resulting from the blocked methyltransferase system.

GENETIC CONSIDERATIONS. Because equal numbers of affected males and affected females exist in the *cblC* group (Table 29-4), because females have been as seriously affected as

Table 29-5 Salient Biochemical Features of Cultured Fibroblasts from Patients with the Various Methylmalonic Acidemias

Biochemical parameter	Mutant class*						
	mut°	*mut⁻*	*cblA*	*cblB*	*cblC*	*cblD*	*cblF*
Studies with intact cells							
[^{14}C]propionate oxidation	−	−	−	−	−	−	−
[^{14}C]MeTHF fixation	+	+	+	+	−	−	−
MeCbl synthesis	+	+	+	+	−	−	−
AdoCbl synthesis	+	+	−	−	−	−	−
Conversion of CN-Cbl to OH-Cbl	+	+	+	+	−	±	−
Lysosomal efflux of free Cbl	+	+	+	+	+	+	−
Enzyme activities in cell extracts†							
Mutase holoenzyme	−	−	−	−	−	−	
Mutase total enzyme	−	±	+	+	+	+	
Methyltransferase holoenzyme	+	+	+	+	−	−	−
Methyltransferase total enzyme	+	+	+	+	±	±	±
Cob(I)alamin adenosyltransferase	+	+	+	−	+	+	+

*+ = normal; − = markedly deficient or undetectable; ± = partially deficient.
†*Holoenzyme* is defined as that enzyme activity measured in the absence of added cofactor; *total enzyme* is that activity measured in the presence of saturating concentrations of cofactor.
Abbrevations: MeTHF = N^5-methyltetrahydrofolate; MeCbl = methylcobalamin; AdoCbl = adenosylcobalamin; CN-Cbl = cyanocobalamin; OH-Cbl = hydroxocobalamin.

males, and because cells from affected patients behave as recessives in complementation studies,[191] it seems safe to predict that this disorder is inherited as an autosomal recessive trait. The mode of inheritance of the *cblD* and the *cblF* mutations cannot yet be defined, because of the paucity of known patients. Identification of heterozygotes for the *cblC, cblD,* or the *cblF* has not yet been accomplished. One additonal contribution of the somatic cell genetic studies used to characterize these disorders deserves mention. The locus coding for the human methyltransferase structural gene has been mapped to chromosome 1 using human/hamster hybrids.[223]

DIAGNOSIS, TREATMENT, AND PROGNOSIS. The combination of methylmalonic aciduria, homocystinuria, and normal serum cobalamin concentrations is the triad needed to distinguish patients in the *cblC, cblD,* or *cblF* groups from those with isolated mutase deficiency; with such other causes of homocystinuria as cystathionine synthase deficiency or $N^{5,10}$-methylenetetrahydrofolate reductase deficiency; with cobalamin deficiency; or with the *cblE* and *cblG* mutations affecting only the methyltransferase enzyme (see Chaps. 81 and 82). Such distinctions, easily confirmed by cell studies, are critical because appropriate therapy depends on making them. Whereas exogenous cobalamin deficiency will respond dramatically to

Fig. 29-14 Summary scheme of inherited defects of propionate and methylmalonate metabolism. The circled numbers and their key signify the nine general sites at which abnormalities have been identified. Abbrevations: PCC = propionyl-CoA carboxylase; MCC = β-methylcrotonyl-CoA carboxylase; PC = pyruvate carboxylase; ACC = acetyl-CoA carboxylase; MUT = methylmalonyl-CoA mutase; Cbl^{III} = cob(III)alamin (e.g., OH-Cbl); Cbl^{I} = cob(I)alamin; AdoCbl = adenosylcobalamin; MeCbl = methylcobalamin; MHM = methyltetrahydrofolate:homocysteine methyltransferase.

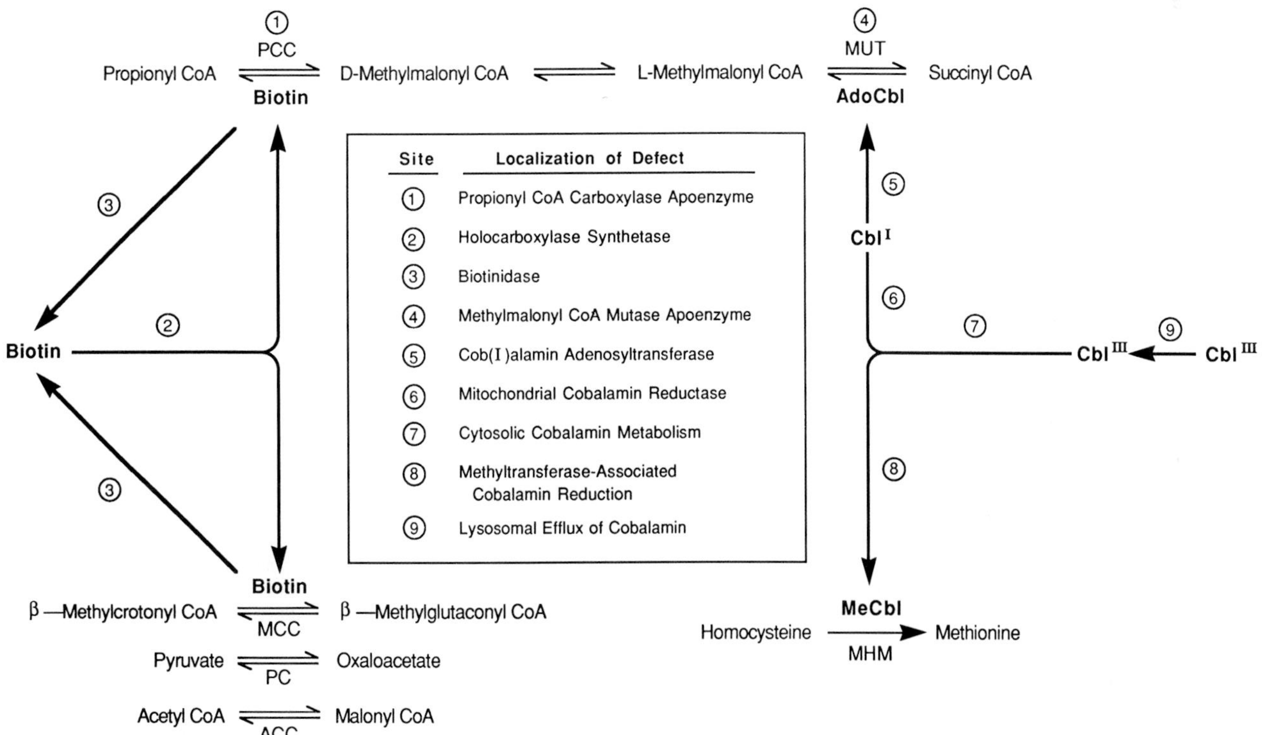

physiologic amounts of cobalamin and certain forms of homocystinuria will respond to supplements of pyridoxine or folate (see Chaps. 23 and 81), successful management of *cblC*, *cblD*, *cblE*, or *cblF* patients probably demands administration of very large amounts (up to 1 mg daily) of OH-Cbl.[174,206,208–210,217] Such treatment has resulted in dramatic decreases in urinary methylmalonate (and less dramatic decreases in urinary homocystine) in those patients who have received it. In fact, early diagnosis and prompt institution of therapy with cobalamin supplements may be the only way to change the outcome of these patients which, in the case of the *cblC* group, has been dismal thus far. Four of the six earliest reported *cblC* patients died at ages 7 weeks,[204] 3 months (personal communication), 4 months,[207] and 7 years,[205] respectively. Severe hemolytic anemia has been a major complication in the deceased *cblC* patients, as has congestive heart failure. Thromboemboli, so often encountered in patients with homocystinuria due to cystathionine synthase deficiency have, thus far, been documented only in the older of the two *cblD* brothers, and this complication was not noted until he reached 18 years of age. Until patients with those defects of cobalamin metabolism affecting AdoCbl and MeCbl synthesis (*cblC*, *cblD*, *cblF*) are diagnosed before birth or soon therafter and treated immediately with cobalamin supplements, we will not know whether the poor outcome in this group can be modified significantly. Documentation of such experience will be particularly important in assessing the clinician's ability to modify the natural history of these disorders.

REFERENCES

1. MARSTON HR, ALLEN SH, SMITH RM: Primary metabolic defect supervening on vitamin B_{12} deficiency in the sheep. *Nature* 190:1085, 1961.
2. SMITH RM, MONTY KJ: Vitamin B_{12} and propionate metabolism. *Biochem Biophys Res Commun* 1:105, 1959.
3. GURNANI S, MISTRY SP, JOHNSON BC: Function of vitamin B_{12} in methylmalonate metabolism. I. Effect of a cofactor form of B_{12} on the activity of methylmalonyl-CoA isomerase. *Biochim Biophys Acta* 38:187, 1960.
4. STERN JR, FRIEDMANN DC: Vitamin B_{12} and methylmalonyl-CoA isomerase I. Vitamin B_{12} and propionate metabolism. *Biochem Biophys Res Commun* 2:82, 1960.
5. COX EV, WHITE AM: Methylmalonic acid excretion: Index of vitamin-B_{12} deficiency. *Lancet* 2:853, 1962.
6. BARNESS LA, YOUNG D, MELLMAN WJ, KAHN SB, WILLIAMS WJ: Methylmalonate excretion in patient with pernicious anemia. *N Engl J Med* 268:144, 1963.
7. CHILDS B, NYHAN WL, BORDEN M, BARD L, COOKE RE: Idiopathic hyperglycinemia and hyperglycinuria: New disorder of amino acid metbolism. I. *Pediatrics* 27:522, 1961.
8. ROSENBERG LE, LILLJEQVIST A-C, HSIA YE: Methylmalonic aciduria: An inborn error leading to metabolic acidosis, long-chain ketonuria and intermittent hyperglycinemia. *N Engl J Med* 278:1319, 1968.
9. HSIA YE, SCULLY KJ, ROSENBERG LE: Defective propionate carboxylation in ketotic hyperglycinaemia. *Lancet* 1:757, 1969.
10. OBERHOLZER VC, LEVIN B, BURGESS EA, YOUNG WF: Methylmalonic aciduria: An inborn error of metabolism leading to chronic metabolic acidosis. *Arch Dis Child* 42:492, 1967.
11. STOKKE O, ELDJARN L, NORUM KR, STEEN-JOHNSEN J, HALVORSEN S: Methylmalonic aciduria: A new inborn error of metabolism which may cause fatal acidosis in the neonatal period. *Scand J Clin Lab Invest* 20:313, 1967.
12. LINDBLAD B, OLIN P, SVANBERG B, ZETTERSTRÖM R: Methylmalonic acidemia. *Acta Paediatr Scand* 57:417, 1968.
13. LINDBLAD B, LINDSTRAND K, SVANBERG B, ZETTERSTRÖM R: The effect of cobamide coenzyme in methylmalonic acidemia. *Acta Paediatr Scand* 58:178, 1969.
14. ROSENBERG LE, LILLJEQVIST A-C, HSIA YE, ROSENBLOOM FM: Vitamin B_{12} dependent methylmalonicaciduria: Defective B_{12} metabolism in cultured fibroblasts. *Biochem Biophys Res Commun* 37:607, 1969.
15. MAHONEY MJ, ROSENBERG LE, MUDD SH, UHLENDORF BW: Defective metabolism of vitamin B_{12} in fibroblasts from patients with methylmalonicaciduria. *Biochem Biophys Res Commun* 44:375, 1971.
16. WILLARD HF, ROSENBERG LE: Inherited deficiencies of methylmalonyl CoA mutase activity: Biochemical and genetic studies in cultured skin fibroblasts, in Hommes FA (ed): *Models for the Study of Inborn Errors of Metabolism*. Amsterdam, Elsevier North-Holland, 1979, p 297.
17. ROSENBERG LE: The inherited methylmalonic acidemias: A model system for the study of vitamin metabolism and apoenzyme-coenzyme interactions (Milner Lecture), in Belton NR, Toothill C (eds): *Transport and Inherited Disease*. Lancaster, England, MTP Press Ltd, pp 3–32, 1981.
18. WOLF B, FELDMAN GL: The biotin dependent carboxylase deficiencies. *Am J Hum Genet* 34:699, 1982.
19. MEISTER A: *Biochemistry of the Amino Acids*. New York, Academic, 1965, pp 674, 729, 753.
20. TANAKA K, ARMITAGE IM, RAMSDELL HS, HSIA YE, LIPSKY SR, ROSENBERG LE: [^{13}C]Valine metabolism in methylmalonic acidemia using nuclear magnetic resonance: Propionate as an obligate intermediate. *Proc Natl Acad Sci USA* 72:3692, 1975.
21. BARETZ BH, TANAKA K: Metabolism in rats *in vivo* of isobutyrates labeled with stable isotopes at various positions: Identification of propionate as an obigate intermediate. *J Biol Chem* 253:4203, 1978.
22. KAZIRO Y, OCHOA S: The metabolism of propionic acid. *Adv Enzymol* 26:283, 1964.
23. DANIELSSON H: Present status of research on catabolism and excretion of cholesterol. *Adv Lipid Res* 1:335, 1963.
24. LARDY HA, ADLER J: Synthesis of succinate from propionate and bicarbonate by soluble enzymes from liver mitochondria. *J Biol Chem* 219:935, 1956.
25. FLAVIN M, ORTIZ PJ, OCHOA S: Metabolism of propionic acid in animal tissues. *Nature* 176:823, 1955.
26. KATZ J, CHAIKOFF IL: The metabolism of propionate by rat liver slices and the formation of isosuccinic acid. *J Am Chem Soc* 77:2659, 1955.
27. FLAVIN M, OCHOA S: Metabolism of propionic acid in animal tissues. I. Enzymatic conversion of propionate to succinate. *J Biol Chem* 229:965, 1957.
28. TIETZ A, OCHOA S: Metabolism of propionic acid in animal tissues. V. Purification and properties of propionyl carboxylase. *J Biol Chem* 234:1394, 1959.
29. SPRECHER M, CLARK MJ, SPRINSON DB: The absolute configuration of methylmalonyl-CoA and stereochemistry of the methylmalonyl-CoA mutase reaction. *Biochem Biophys Res Commun* 15:581, 1964.
30. RETEY J, LYNEN F: The absolute configuration of methylmalonyl-CoA. *Biochem Biophys Res Commun* 16:358, 1964.
31. MAZUMDER R, SASAKAWA T,KAZIRO Y, OCHOA S: Metabolism of propionic acid in animal tisses. IX. Methylmalonyl coenzyme A racemase. *J Biol Chem* 237:3065, 1962.
32. BECK WS, FLAVIN M, OCHOA S: Metabolism of propionic acid in animal tissues. III. Formation of succinate. *J Biol Chem* 229:997, 1957.
33. KAZIRO Y, OCHOA S, WARNER RC, CHEN J: Metabolism of propionic acid in animal tissues. VIII. Crystalline propionyl carboxylase. *J Biol Chem* 236:1917, 1961.
34. LAU EP, COCHRAN BC, MUNSON L, FALL RR: Bovine kidney 3-methylcrotonyl-CoA and propionyl-CoA carboxylases: Each enzyme contains nonidentical subunits. *Proc Natl Acad Sci USA* 76:214, 1979.
35. KALOUSEK F, DARIGO MD, ROSENBERG LE: Isolation and characterization of propionyl-CoA carboxylase from normal human liver: Evidence for a protomeric tetramer of nonidentical subunits. *J Biol Chem* 255:60, 1980.
36. GRAVEL RA, LAM KF, MAHURAN D, KRONIS A: Purification of human liver propionyl-CoA carboxylase by carbon tetrachloride extraction and monomeric avidin affinity chromatography. *Arch Biochem Biophys* 201:669, 1980.
37. MISTRY SP, DAKSHINAMURTI K: Biochemistry of biotin. *Vitam Horm* 22:1, 1964.
38. KRAUS JP, KALOUSEK F, ROSENBERG LE: Biosynthesis and mitochondrial processing of the β subunit of propionyl CoA carboxylase from rat liver. *J Biol Chem* 258:7245, 1983.
39. ROSENBERG LE, FENTON WA, HORWICH AL, KALOUSEK F, KRAUS JP: Targeting of nuclear-encoded proteins to the mitochondrial matrix: Implications for human genetic defects. *Ann NY Acad Sci* 488:99, 1986.
40. LAMHONWAH AM, BARANKIEWICS TJ, WILLARD HF, MAHURAN DJ, QUAN F, GRAVEL RA: Isolation of cDNA clones coding for the α and β chains of human propionyl-CoA carboxylase: Chromosomal assignments and DNA polymorphisms associated with *PCCA* and *PCCB* genes. *Proc Natl Acad Sci USA* 83:4864, 1986.
41. LAMHONWAH AM, QUAN F, GRAVEL RA: Sequence homology around the biotin-binding site of human propionyl-CoA carboxylase and pyruvate carboxylase. *Arch Biochem Biophys* 254:631, 1987.
42. KRAUS JP, WILLIAMSON CL, FIRGAIRA FA, YANG-FENG TL, MUNKE M,

FRANCKE U, ROSENBERG LE: Cloning and screening with nanogram amounts of immunopurified messenger RNAs: cDNA cloning and chromosomal mapping of cystathionine β-synthase and the β-subunit of propionyl CoA carboxylase. *Proc Natl Acad Sci USA* 83:2047, 1986.

43. KRAUS JP, FIRGAIRA F, NOVOTNY J, KALOUSEK F, WILLIAMSON C, OHURA T, ROSENBERG LE: Coding sequence of the precursor of the β subunit of rat propionyl-CoA carboxylase. *Proc Natl Acad Sci USA* 83:8049, 1986.

44. OVERATH P, KELLERMAN GM, LYNEN F, FRITZ HP, KELLER HJ: Zum Mechanismus der Umlagerung von Methylmalonyl-CoA in Succinyl-CoA. II. Verusche zur Wirkungweise von Methylmalonyl-CoA-Isomerase und Methylmalonyl-CoA-Racemase. *Biochem Z* 335:500, 1962.

45. BARKER HA, SMYTH RD, WAWSZKIEWICZ EJ, LEE MN, WILSON RM: Enzymatic preparation and characterization of an α-L-β-methylaspartic acid *Arch Biochem Biophys* 78:468, 1958.

46. BARKER HA, WEISSBACH H, SMYTH RD: A coenzyme containing pseudovitamin B_{12}. *Proc Natl Acad Sci USA* 44:1093, 1958.

47. WEISSBACH H, TOOHEY J, BARKER HA: Isolation and properties of B_{12} coenzymes containing benzimidazole or dimethylbenzimidazole. *Proc Natl Acad Sci USA* 45:521, 1959.

48. KOLHOUSE JF, UTLEY C, ALLEN RH: Isolation and characterization of methylmalonyl-CoA mutase from human placenta. *J Biol Chem* 255:2708, 1980.

49. FENTON WA, HACK AM, WILLARD HF, GERTLER A, ROSENBERG LE: Purification and properties of methylmalonyl CoA mutase from human liver. *Arch Biochem Biophys* 214:815, 1982.

50. WILLARD HF, ROSENBERG LE: Interactions of methylmalonyl CoA mutase from normal human fibroblasts with adenosylcobalamin and methylmalonyl CoA: Evidence for nonequivalent active sites. *Arch Biochem Biophys* 200:130, 1980.

51. WILLARD HF, ROSENBERG LE: Effect of cobalamin supplementation in culture on methylmalonyl CoA mutase activity in normal and mutant human fibroblasts: Inhibition of apoenzyme and holoenzyme by hydroxocobalamin. Submitted.

52. EGGERER H, STADTMAN ER, OVERATH P, LYNEN F: Zum Mechanismus der durch Cobalamin-Coenzym katalysierten Umlagerung von Methylmalonyl-CoA in Succinyl-CoA. *Biochem Z* 333:1, 1960.

53. KELLERMEYER RW, WOOD HG: Methylmalonyl isomerase: A study of the mechanism of isomerization. *Biochemistry* 1:1124, 1962.

54. PHARES EF, LONG MV, CARSON SF: An intramolecular rearrangement in the methylmalonyl isomerase reaction as demonstrated by positive and negative mass analysis of succinic acid. *Biochem Biophys Res Commun* 8:142, 1962.

55. BABIOR BM: Cobamides as cofactors: Adenosylcobamide dependent reactions, in Babior BM (ed): *Cobalamin Biochemistry and Pathophysiology*. New York, Wiley, 1975, p. 141.

56. FENTON WA, HACK AM, HELFGOTT D, ROSENBERG LE: Biogenesis of the mitochondrial enzyme methylmalonyl CoA mutase: Synthesis and processing of a precursor in a cell-free system and in cultured cells. *J Biol Chem* 259:6616, 1984.

56a. LEDLEY FD, LUMETTA M, NGUYEN PN, KOLHOUSE JF, ALLEN RH: Molecular cloning of L-methylmalonyl-CoA mutase: Gene transfer and analysis of *mut* cell lines. *Proc Natl Acad Sci USA* 85:3518, 1988.

56b. JANSEN R, KALOUSEK F, FENTON WA, ROSENBERG LE, LEDLEY FD: Cloning of full length methylmalonyl CoA mutase sequences from a cDNA library by polymerase chain reaction. (In preparation.)

56c. LEDLEY FD, LUMETTA MR, ZOGHBI HY, VanTUINEN P, LEDBETTER SA, LEDBETTER DH: Mapping of human methylmalonyl CoA mutase (MUT) locus on chromosome 6. *Am J Hum Genet* 42:839, 1988.

57. LYNEN F: Biosynthesis of saturated fatty acids. *Fed Proc* 20:941, 1961.

58. ANDO T, RASMUSSEN K, WRIGHT JM, NYHAN WL: Isolation and identification of methylcitrate, a major metabolic product of propionate in patients with propionic acidemia. *J Biol Chem* 247:2200, 1972.

59. RASMUSSEN K, ANDO T, NYHAN WL, HULL D, COTTOM D, WADLINGTON W, KILROY AW: Excretion of propionylglycine in propionic acidemia. *Clin Sci* 42:665, 1972.

60. ANDO T, RASMUSSEN K, NYHAN WL, HULL D: 3-Hydroxypropionate: Significance of β-oxidation of propionate in patients with propionic acidemia and methylmalonic acidemia. *Proc Natl Acad Sci USA* 69:2807, 1972.

61. SEBRELL WH, HARRIS RS: Biotin, in *The Vitamins: Chemistry, Physiology, Pathology Methods*. New York, Academic, 1978, p 261.

62. MURTHY PNA, MISTRY SP: Biotin. *Prog Food Nutr Sci* 2:405, 1977.

63. MOSS J, LANE MD: The biotin-dependent enzymes. *Adv Enzymol* 35:321, 1971.

64. WOOD HG, BARDEN RE: Biotin enzymes. *Ann Rev Biochem* 46:385, 1978.

65. MURTHY PNA, MISTRY SP: *In vitro* synthesis of propionyl-CoA holocarboxylase by a partially purified mitochondrial preparation from biotin-deficient chicken liver. *Can J Biochem* 52:800, 1974.

66. CRAFT DV, GOSS NH, CHANDRAMOULI N, WOOD HG: Purification of biotinidase from human plasma and its activity on biotinyl peptides. *Biochemistry* 24:2471, 1985.

67. CHAUHAN J, DAKSHINAMURTI K: Purification and characterization of human serum biotinidase. *J Biol Chem* 261:4268, 1986.

68. WOLF B, HEARD GS, MCVOY JS, RAETZ HM: Biotinidase deficiency: The possible role of biotinidase in the processing of dietary protein-bound biotin. *J Inherited Metab Dis* 7:121, 1984.

69. SPENCER RP, BRODY KR: Biotin transport by small intestine of rat, hamster, and other species. *Am J Physiol* 206:633, 1964.

70. BERGER E, LONG E, SEMENZA G: The sodium activation of biotin absorption in hamster small intestine *in vitro*. *Biochim Biophys Acta* 255:873, 1972.

71. BOWMAN BB, SELHUB J, ROSENBERG IH: Intestinal absorption of biotin in the rat. *J Nutr* 116:1266, 1986.

72. GORE J, HOINARD C, MAINGAULT P: Biotin uptake by isolated rat intestinal cells. *Biochim Biophys Acta* 856:357, 1986.

73. MOCK DM, DeLORIMER AA, LIEBMAN WM, SWEETMAN L, BAKER H: Biotin deficiency: An unusual complication of parenteral alimentation. *N Engl J Med* 304:820, 1981.

74. SYDENSTRICKER VP, SINGAL SA, BRIGGS AP, DeVAUGHN NM: Preliminary observations on "egg white injury" in man and its cure with a biotin concentrate. *Science* 95:176, 1942.

75. MINOT GR, MURPHY LP: Treatment of pernicious anemia by a special diet. *JAMA* 87:470, 1926.

76. SMITH EL: Purification of anti-pernicious anemia factors from liver. *Nature* 161:638, 1948.

77. RICKES EL, BRINK NG, KONIUSZY FR, WOOD TR, FOLKERS K: Crystalline vitamin B_{12}. *Science* 107:396, 1948.

78. HODGKIN DC, KAMPER J, MacKAY M, PICKWORTH J, TRUEBLOOD KN, WHITE JG: Structure of vitamin B_{12}. *Nature* 178:64, 1956.

79. WALKER GA, MURPHY S, HEUNNEKENS FH: Enzymatic conversion of vitamin B_{12} to adenosyl-B_{12}: Evidence for the existence of two separate reducing systems. *Arch Biochem Biophys* 134:95, 1969.

80. WEISSBACH H, TAYLOR R: Role of vitamin B_{12} in methionine biosynthesis. *Fed Proc* 25:1649, 1966.

81. TAYLOR RT, WEISSBACH H: Enzymatic synthesis of methionine: Formation of a radioactive cobamide enzyme with N^5 methyl-^{14}C-tetrahydrofolate. *Arch Biochem Biophys* 119:572, 1967.

82. TAYLOR RT, WEISSBACH H; *Escherichia coli* B N^5-methyltetrahydrofolate-homocysteine vitamin-B_{12} transmethylase: Formation and photolability of a methylcobalamin enzyme. *Arch Biochem Biophys* 123:109, 1968.

83. POSTON JM: Leucine 2,3-aminomutase, an enzyme of leucine catabolism. *J Biol Chem* 251:1859, 1976.

84. POSTON JM, STADTMAN TC: Cobamides as cofactors: Methylcobamides and the synthesis of methionine, methane and acetate, in Babior BM (ed): *Cobalamin Biochemistry and Pathophysiology*. New York, Wiley, 1975, p 111.

85. DONALDSON RM JR: Intrinsic factor and the transport of cobalamin, in Johnson LR (ed): *Physiology of the Gastrointestinal Tract*. New York, Raven, 1981 pp 959–973.

86. SENNETT C, MELLMAN IS, ROSENBERG LE: Transmembrane transport of cobalamin in prokaryotic and eukaryotic cells. *Ann Rev Biochem* 50:1053, 1981.

87. ALLEN RH, SEETHARAM B, PODELL E, ALPERS DH: Effect of proteolytic enzymes on the binding of cobalamin to R protein and intrinsic factor. In vitro evidence that a failure to partially degrade R protein is responsible for cobalamin malabsorption in pancreatic insufficiency. *J Clin Invest* 61:47, 1978.

88. ALLEN RH, SEETHARAM B, ALLEN NC, PODELL ER, ALPERS DH: Correction of cobalamin malabsorption in pancreatic insufficiency with a cobalamin analogue that binds with high affinity to R protein but not to intrinsic factor. In vivo evidence that a failure to partially degrade R protein is responsible for cobalamin malabsorption in pancreatic insufficiency. *J Clin Invest* 61:1628, 1978.

89. MARCOULLIS G, PARMENTIER Y, NICOLAS J-P, JIMENZ M, GERARD P: Cobalamin malabsorption due to nondegradation of R proteins in the human intestine: Inhibited cobalamin absorption in exocrine pancreatic dysfunction. *J Clin Invest* 66:430, 1980.

90. ALLEN RH: Human vitamin B_{12}-transport proteins. *Prog Hematol* 9:57, 1975.

91. ELLENBOGEN LE: Uptake and transport of cobalamins. *Int Rev Biochem* 27:45, 1979.

92. HALL CA, FINKLER AE: The dynamics of transcobalamin. II. A vitamin B_{12} binding substance in plasma. *J Lab Clin Med* 65:459, 1965.

93. HOM BL: Plasma turnover of ^{57}cobalt-vitamin B_{12} bound to transcobalamin I and II. *Scand J Haematol* 4:321, 1967.

94. LINNELL JC: The fate of cobalamins *in vivo*, in Babior BM (ed): *Cobalamin: Biochemistry and Pathophysiology*. New York, Wiley, 1975, p 287.

95. FINKLER AE, HALL CA: Nature of the relationship between vitamin B_{12} binding and cell uptake. *Arch Biochem Biophys* 120:79, 1967.

96. TAN CH, HANSEN HJ: Studies on the site of synthesis of transcobalamin II. *Proc Soc Exp Biol Med* 127:740, 1968.

97. PLETSCH QA, COFFEY JW: Properties of the proteins that bind vitamin B_{12} in subcellular fractions of rat liver. *Arch Biochem Biophys* 151:157, 1972.

98. NEWMARK P, NEWMAN GE, O'BRIEN JRP: Vitamin B_{12} in the rat kidney: Evidence for an association with lysosomes. *Arch Biochem Biophys* 141:121, 1970.

99. YOUNGDAHL-TURNER P, ROSENBERG LE, ALLEN RH: Binding and uptake of transcobalamin II by human fibroblasts. *J Clin Invest* 61:133, 1978.

100. YOUNGDAHL-TURNER P, MELLMAN IS, ALLEN RH, ROSENBERG LE: Protein mediated vitamin uptake: Adsorptive endocytosis of the trancobalamin II-cobalamin complex by cultured human fibroblasts. *Exp Cell Res* 118:127, 1979.

101. MELLMAN IS, YOUNGDAHL-TURNER P, WILLARD HF, ROSENBERG LE: Intracellular binding of radioactive hydroxocobalamin to cobalamin-dependent apoenzymes in rat liver. *Proc Natl Acad Sci USA* 74:916, 1977.

102. KOLHOUSE JF, ALLEN RH: Recognition of two intracellular cobalamin binding proteins and their identification as methylmalonyl-CoA mutase and methionine synthetase. *Proc Natl Acad Sci USA* 74:921, 1977.

103. BURGER RL, SCHNEIDER RJ, MEHLMAN CS, ALLEN RH: Human plasma R-type vitamin B_{12} binding protein. II. The role of transcobalamin I, transcobalamin III and the normal granulocyte vitamin B_{12}-binding protein in the plasma transport of vitamin B_{12}. *J Biol Chem* 250:7707, 1975.

104. BERLINER N, ROSENBERG LE: Uptake and metabolism of free cyanocobalamin by cultured human fibroblasts from controls and a patient with transcobalamin II deficiency. *Metabolism* 30:230, 1981.

105. FRENKEL DP, KITCHENS RL: Intracellular localization of hepatic propionyl-CoA carboxylase and methylmalonyl-CoA mutase in humans and normal and vitamin B_{12} deficient rats. *Br J Haematol* 31:501, 1975.

106. WANG FK, KOCH J, STOKSTAD EL: Folate coenzyme pattern, folate linked enzymes and methionine biosynthesis in rat liver mitochondria. *Biochem Z* 246:458, 1967.

107. VITOLS E, WALKER GA, HUENNEKENS FM: Enzymatic conversion of vitamin B_{12} to a cobamide coenzyme, α(5,6-dimethylbenzimidazolyl) deoxyadenosylcobamide (adenosyl-B_{12}). *J Biol Chem* 241:1455, 1966.

108. ERTEL R, BROT N, TAYLOR R, WEISSBACH H: Studies on the nature of the bound cobamide in *E. coli* N^5-methyltetrahydrofolate-homocysteine transmethylase. *Arch Biochem Biophys* 126:353, 1968.

109. TAYLOR RT, WEISSBACH H: *E. coli* B N^5-methyltetrahydrofolate-homocysteine methyltransferase: Sequential formation of bound methylcobalamin with *S*-adenosyl-L-methionine and N^5-methyltetrahydrofolate. *Arch Biochem Biophys* 129:728, 1969.

110. PAWALKIEWICZ J, GORNA M, FENRYCH W, MAGAS S: Conversion of cyanocobalamin in vivo and in vitro into its coenzyme form in humans and animals. *Ann NY Acad Sci* 112:641, 1964.

111. KERWAR SS, SPEARS C, MCAUSLAN B, WEISSBACH H: Studies on vitamin B_{12} metabolism in HeLa cells. *Arch Biochem Biophys* 142:231, 1971.

112. MAHONEY MJ, ROSENBERG LE: Synthesis of cobalamin coenzymes by human cells in tissue culture. *J Lab Clin Med* 78:302, 1971.

113. MAHONEY MJ, HART AC, STEEN VD, ROSENBERG LE: Methylmalonicacidemia: Biochemial heterogeneity in defects of 5′-deoxyadenosylcobalamin synthesis. *Proc Natl Acad Sci USA* 72:2799, 1975.

114. FENTON WA, ROSENBERG LE: The defect in the *cbl B* class of human methylmalonic acidemia: Deficiency of cob(I)alamin adenosyltransferase activity in extracts of cultured fibroblasts. *Biochem Biophys Res Commun* 98:283, 1981.

115. COX EV, ROBERTSON-SMITH D, SMALL M, WHITE AM: The excretion of propionate and acetate in vitamin B_{12} deficiency. *Clin Sci* 35:123, 1968.

116. SHIPMAN RT, TOWNLEY RRW, DANKS DM: Homocystinuria, Addisonian pernicious anaemia, and partial deletion of a G chromosome. *Lancet* 2:693, 1969.

117. HOLLOWELL JG JR, HALL WK, CORYELL ME, MCPHERSON J JR, HAHN DA; Homocystinuria and organic aciduria in a patient with vitamin-B_{12} deficiency. *Lancet* 2:1428, 1969.

118. HIGGINBOTTOM MC, SWEETMAN L, NYHAN WL: A syndrome of methylmalonic aciduria, homocystinuria, megaloblastic anemia and neurologic abnormalities in a vitamin B_{12}-deficient breast-fed infant of a strict vegetarian. *N Engl J Med* 299:317, 1978.

119. CARDINALE GJ, DREYFUS PM, AULD P, ABELES RH: Experimental vitamin B_{12} deficiency: Its effect on tissue vitamin B_{12}-coenzyme levels and on the metabolism of methylmalonyl-CoA. *Arch Biochem Biophys* 131:92, 1969.

120. MORROW G, BARNESS LA, AUERBACH VH, DI GEORGE AM, ANDO T, NYHAN WL: Observations on the coexistence of methylmalonic acidemia and glycinemia. *J Pediatr* 74:680, 1969.

121. HOMMES FA, KUIPERS JRG, ELEMA JD, JANSE JF, JONXIS JJP: Propionicacidemia, a new inborn error of metabolism. *Pediatr Res* 2:519, 1968.

122. HSIA YE, SCULLY KJ, ROSENBERG LE: Inherited propionyl-CoA carboxylase deficiency in "ketotic hyperglycinemia." *J Clin Invest* 50:127, 1971.

123. GOMPERTZ D, STORRS CN, BAU DCK, PETERS TJ, HUGHES EA: Localization of enzyme defect in propionicacidemia. *Lancet* 1:1140, 1970.

124. NYHAN WL, BORDEN M, CHILDS B; Idiopathic hyperglycinemia: A new disorder of amino acid metabolism. II. The concentrations of other amino acids in the plasma and their modification by the administration of leucine. *Pediatrics* 27:539, 1961.

125. CHILDS B, NYHAN WL: Further observations of a patient with hyperglycinemia. *Pediatrics* 33:403, 1964.

126. BRANDT IK, HSIA YE, CLEMENT DH, PROVENCE SA: Propionicacidemia (ketotic hyperglycinemia): Dietary treatment results in normal growth and development. *Pediatrics* 53:391, 1974.

127. NYHAN WL, ANDO T, RASMUSSEN K: Ketotic hyperglycinemia, in Stern J, Toothill C (eds): *Organic Acidurias*. London, Churchill Livingstone, 1972, p 1.

128. WOLF B, HSIA YE, SWEETMAN L, GRAVEL R, HARRIS DJ, NYHAN WL: Propionic acidemia: A clinical update. *J Pediatr* 99:835, 1981.

129. MAHONEY MJ, HSIA YE, ROSENBERG LE: Propionyl-CoA carboxylase deficiency (propionicacidemia): A cause of non-ketotoic hyperglycinemia, abstracted. *Pediatr Res* 5:395, 1971.

130. WOLF B, PAULSEN EP, HSIA YE: Asymptomatic propionyl CoA carboxylase deficiency in a 13-year-old girl. *J Pediatr* 95:563, 1979.

131. NYHAN WL, CHILDS B; Hyperglycinemia. V. The miscible pool and turnover rate of glycine and the formation of serine. *J Clin Invest* 43:2404, 1964.

132. MENKES JH: Idiopathic hyperglycinemia: Isolation and identification of three previously undescribed urinary ketones. *J Pediatr* 69:413, 1966.

133. NYHAN WL, ANDO T, RASMUSSEN K, WADLINGTON W, KILROY AW, COTTOM D, HULL D: Tiglic aciduria in propionicacidema. *Biochem J* 126:1035, 1972.

134. HSIA YE: Inherited hyperammonemic syndromes. *Gastroenterology* 67:347, 1974.

135. WOLF B, HSIA YE, TANAKA K, ROSENBERG LE: Correlation between serum propionate and blood ammonia concentrations in propionic acidemia. *J Pediatr* 93:471, 1978.

136. HSAI YE, SCULLY KJ, ROSENBERG LE: Human propionyl CoA carboxylase: Some properties of the partially purified enzyme in fibroblasts from controls and patients with propionic acidemia. *Pediatr Res* 13:746, 1979.

137. WOLF B, HSIA YE, ROSENBERG LE: Biochemical differences between mutant propionyl-CoA carboxylases from two complementation groups. *Am J Hum Genet* 30:455, 1978.

138. WOLF B, ROSENBERG LE: Heterozygote expression in propionyl coenzyme A carboxylase deficiency: Differences between major complementation groups. *J Clin Invest* 62:931, 1978.

139. GRAVEL RA, LAM K-F, SCULLY KJ, HSIA YE: Genetic complementation of propionyl-CoA carboxylase deficiency in cultured human fibroblasts. *Am J Hum Genet* 29:378, 1977.

140. WOLF B, WILLARD HF, ROSENBERG LE: Kinetic analysis of genetic complementation in heterokaryons of propionyl CoA carboxylase-deficient human fibroblasts. *Am J Hum Genet* 32:16, 1980.

141. LAMHONWAH AM, LAM KF, TSUI F, ROBINSON B, SAUNDERS ME, GRAVEL RA: Assignment of the α and β chains of human propionyl-CoA carboxylase to genetic complementation groups. *Am J Hum Genet* 35:889, 1983.

142. LAMHONWAH AM, GRAVEL RA: Propionic-acidemia: Absence of alpha chain mRNA in fibroblasts from patients of the *pccA* complementation group. *Am J Hum Genet*, 41:1124, 1987.

143. KALOUSEK F, ORSULAK MD, ROSENBERG LE: Absence of cross-reacting material in isolated propionyl CoA carboxylase deficiency: Nature of residual carboxylating activity. *Am J Hum Genet* 35:409, 1983.

144. HILLMAN RE, SOWERS LH, COHEN JL: Inhibition of glycine oxidation in cultured fibroblasts by isoleucine. *Pediatr Res* 7:945, 1973.

145. HILLMAN RE, OTTO EF: Inhibition of glycine-serine interconversion in cultured human fibroblasts by products of isoleucine catabolism. *Pediatr Res* 8:941, 1974.

146. SNYDERMAN SE, HOLT CE, NORTON PM, ROITMAN E, PHANSALKAR SV: The plasma aminogram. I. Influence of the level of protein intake and a comparison of whole protein and amino acid diets. *Pediatr Res* 2:131, 1968.

147. GLASGOW AM, CHASE HP: Effect of propionic acid on fatty acid oxidation and ureagenesis. *Pediatr Res* 10:683, 1976.

148. STEWART PM, WALSER M: Failure of the normal ureagenic response to amino acids in organic acid loaded rats: A proposed mechanism for the hyperammonemia of propionic and methylmalonic acidemia. *J Clin Invest* 66:484, 1989.

149. COUDE FX, SWEETMAN L, NYHAN WL: Inhibition by propionyl CoA of *N*-

acetylglutamate synthetase in rat liver mitochondria. *J Clin Invest* 64:1544, 1979.

150. KIRKMAN HN, KIESEL JL: Congenital hyperammonemia, abstracted, *Pediatr Res* 3:358, 1969.

151. HARRIS DJ, YANG BJ-Y, SNODGRASS PJ: Carbamyl phosphate synthetase deficiency: A possible transient phenocopy of dysautonomia. *Am J Hum Genet* 29:52A, 1977.

152. OHURA T, KRAUS JP, ROSENBERG LE: Molecular analysis of propionic acidemia. *Am J Hum Genet*, 41:A13, 1987.

153. GOMPERTZ D, GOODEY PA, THOM H, RUSSELL G, JOHNSTON AW, MELLOR DH, MacLEAN MW, FERGUSON-SMITH ME, FERGUSON-SMITH MA: Prenatal diagnosis and family studies in case of propionicacidemia. *Clin Genet* 8:244, 1975.

154. WILLARD HF, AMBANI LM, HART AC, MAHONEY MJ, ROSENBERG LE: Rapid prenatal and postnatal detection of inborn errors of propionate, methylmalonate, and cobalamin metabolism: A sensitive assay using cultured cells. *Hum Genet* 34:277, 1976.

155. SWEETMAN L, WEYLER W, SHAFAI T, YOUNG PE, NYHAN WL: Prenatal diagnosis of propionic acidemia. *JAMA* 242:1048, 1979.

156. WOLF B: Reassessment of biotin-responsiveness in "unresponsive" propionyl CoA carboxylase deficiency. *J Pediatr* 97:964, 1980.

157. ROE CR, BOHAN TP: L-carnitine therapy in propionic acidemia. *Lancet* 1:1411, 1982.

158. ROE CR, MILLINGTON DS, MALTBY DA, BOHAN TP: L-carnitine enhances excretion of propionyl *coenzyme A* as propionylcarnitine in propionic acidemia. *J Clin Invest* 73:1785, 1984.

159. WOLFF JA, CARROLL JE, THUY LP, PRODANOS C, HAAS R, NYHAN WL: Carnitine reduces ketogenesis in patients with disorders of propionate metabolism. *Lancet* 1:289, 1986.

160. GOMPERTZ D, DRAFFAN GH, WATTS JL, HULL D: Biotin-responsive β-methylcrotonyl-glycinuria. *Lancet* 2:22, 1971.

161. SWEETMAN L, BATES SP, HULL D, HYHAN WL: Propionyl-CoA carboxylase deficiency in a patient with biotin-responsive 3-methylcrotonyl-glycinuria. *Pediatr Res* 11:1144, 1977.

162. SAUNDERS M, SWEETMAN L, ROBINSON B, ROTH K, COHN R, GRAVEL RA: Biotin-response organicaciduria. Multiple carboxylase defects and complementation studies with propionicacidemia in cultured fibroblasts. *J Clin Invest* 64:1695, 1979.

163. BARTLETT K, GOMPERTZ D: Combined carboxylase defect: Biotin-responsiveness in cultured fibroblasts. *Lancet* 2:804, 1976.

164. WEYLER W, SWEETMAN L, MAGGIO DC, NYHAN WL: Deficiency of propionyl-CoA carboxylase and methylcrotonyl-CoA carboxylase in a patient with methylcrotonylglycinuria. *Clin Chim Acta* 76:321, 1977.

165. BURI BJ, SWEETMAN L, NYHAN WL: Mutant holocarboxylase synthetase: Evidence for the enzyme defect in early infantile biotin-responsive multiple carboxylase deficiency. *J Clin Invest* 68:1491, 1981.

166. GHNEIM HK, BARTLETT K: Mechanism of biotin-responsive combined carboxylase deficiency. *Lancet* 1:1187, 1982.

167. SAUNDERS ME, SHERWOOD WG, DUTHIE M, SURH L, GRAVEL RA: Evidence for a defect of holocarboxylase synthetase activity in cultured lymphoblasts from a patient with biotin-responsive multiple carboxylase deficiency. *Am J Hum Genet* 34:590, 1982.

168. BURRI BJ, SWEETMAN L, NYHAN WL: Heterogeneity of holocarboxylase synthetase in patients with biotin-responsive multiple carboxylase deficiency. *Am J Hum Genet* 37:426, 1985.

169. WOLF B, BRIER RE, ALLEN RJ, GOODMAN SI, KIEN CL: Biotinidase deficiency: The enzymatic defect in late-onset multiple carboxylase deficiency. *Clin Chim Acta* 131:272, 1983.

170. GAUDRY M, MUNNICH A, AGOIER H, MARSAC C, MARQUET A, SAUDUBRAY JM, MITCHELL G, CAUSSE M, FREZAL J: Deficient liver biotinidase activity in multiple carboxylase deficiency. *Lancet* 2:397, 1983.

171. WOLF B, HEARD GS, SECOR MCVOY JR, GRIER RE: Biotinidase deficiency. *Ann NY Acad Sci* 447:529, 1985.

172. ROSENBERG LE, LILLJEQVIST A, HSIA YE: Methylmalonicaciduria: Metabolic block localization and vitamin B_{12} dependency. *Science* 162:805, 1968.

173. MUDD SH, LEVY HL, ABELES RH: A derangement in B_{12} metabolism leading to homocystinemia, cystathioninemia and methylmalonicaciduria. *Biochem Biophys Res Commun* 35:121, 1969.

174. GOODMAN SI, MOE PG, HAMMOND KB, MUDD SH, UHLENDORF BW: Homocystinuria with methylmalonic aciduria: Two cases in a sibship. *Biochem Med* 4:500, 1970.

175. MATSUI SM, MAHONEY MJ, ROSENBERG LE: The natural history of the inherited methylmalonic acidemias. *N Engl J Med* 308:857, 1983.

176. ROSENBERG LE: Disorders of propionate, methylmalonate and cobalamin metabolism, in Stanbury JB, Wyngaarden JB, Fredrickson DS (eds): *The Metabolic Basis of Inherited Disease,* 4th ed. New York, McGraw-Hill, 1978, p 411.

177. LEDLEY FD, LEVY HL, SHIH VE, BENJAMIN R, MAHONEY MJ: Benign methylmalonic aciduria. *N Engl J Med* 311:1015, 1984.

178. ANDO T, RASMUSSEN K, NYHAN WL, DONNELL GN, BARNES ND: Propionicacidemia in patients with ketotic hyperglycinemia. *J Pediatr* 78:827, 1971.

179. STOKKE O, JELLUM E, ELDJARN L, SCHNITLER R: The occurrence of β-hydroxy-*n*-valeric acid in a patient with propionic and methylmalonic acidemia. *Clin Chim Acta* 45:391, 1973.

180. HSIA YE, SCULLY K, LILLJEQVIST A-CH, ROSENBERG LE: Vitamin B_{12} dependent methylmalonicaciduria. *Pediatrics* 46:497, 1970.

181. WILLARD HF, AMBANI LM, HART AC, MAHONEY MJ, ROSENBERG LE: Rapid prenatal and postnatal detection of inborn errors of propionate, methylmalonate, and cobalamin metabolism: A sensitive assay using cultured cells. *Hum Genet* 34:277, 1976.

182. MORROW G, REVSIN B, MATHEWS C, GILES H: A simple rapid method for prenatal detection of defects in propionate metabolism. *Clin Genet* 10:218, 1976.

183. MORROW G, BARNESS LA, CARDINALE GJ, ABELES RH, FLAKS JG: Congenital methylmalonic acidemia: Enzymatic evidence for two forms of the disease. *Proc Natl Acad Sci USA* 63:191, 1969.

184. MORROW G, MAHONEY MJ, MATHEWS C, LEBOWITZ J: Studies of methylmalonyl coenzyme A carbonylmutase activity in methylmalonic acidemia. I. Correlation of clinical, hepatic and fibroblast data. *Pediatr Res* 9:641, 1975.

185. WILLARD HF, ROSENBERG LE: Inherited deficiencies of human methylmalonyl CoA mutase activity: Reduced affinity of mutant apoenzyme for adenosylcobalamin. *Biochem Biophys Res Commun* 78:927, 1977.

186. WILLARD HF, ROSENBERG LE: Inherited methylmalonyl CoA mutase apoenzyme deficiency in human fibroblasts: Evidence for allelic heterogeneity, genetic compounds, and codominant expression. *J Clin Invest* 65:690, 1980.

187. KOLHOUSE JF, UTLEY C, FENTON WA, ROSENBERG LE: Immunochemical studies on cultured fibroblasts from patients with inherited methylmalonic acidemia. *Proc Natl Acad Sci USA* 84:1421, 1981.

188. FENTON WA, HACK AM, KRAUS JP, ROSENBERG LE: Immunochemical studies of fibroblasts from patients with methylmalonyl-CoA mutase apoenzyme deficiency: Detection of a mutation interfering with mitochondrial import. *Proc Natl Acad Sci USA* 84:1421, 1987.

189. MORROW G III, REVSIN B, CLARK R, LEBOWITZ J, WHELAN DT: A new variant of methylmalonic acidemia: Defective coenzyme-apoenzyme binding in cultured fibroblasts. *Clin Chim Acta* 85:67, 1978.

190. KANG ES, SNODGRASS PJ, GERALD PS: Methylmalonyl-CoA racemase defect: Another cause of methylmalonicaciduria. *Pediatr Res* 6:875, 1972.

191. GRAVEL RA, MAHONEY MJ, RUDDLE FH, ROSENBERG LE: Genetic complementation in heterokaryons of human fibroblasts defective in cobalamin metabolism. *Proc Natl Acad Sci USA* 72:3181, 1975.

192. WILLARD HF, MELLMAN IS, ROSENBERG LE: Genetic complementation among inherited deficiencies of methylmalonyl-CoA mutase activity: Evidence for a new class of human cobalamin mutant. *Am J Hum Genet* 30:1, 1978.

193. WILLARD HF, ROSENBERG LE: Inborn errors of cobalamin metabolism: Effect of cobalamin supplementation in culture on methylmalonyl CoA mutase activity in normal mutant human fibroblasts. *Biochem Genet* 17:57, 1979.

194. UTTER MF, KEECH DB, SCRUTTEN ML: A possible role for acetyl-CoA in the control of gluconeogenesis, in Webber G (ed): *Advances in Enzyme Regulation.* New York, Pergamon, 1964, vol 2, p 49.

195. HALPERIN ML, SCHILLER CM, FRITZ IB: The inhibition by methylmalonic acid of malate transport by the dicarboxylate carrier in rat liver mitochondria. *J Clin Invest* 50:2276, 1971.

196. INOUE S, KREIGER I, SARNAIK A, RAVINDRANATH Y, FRACASSA M, OTTENBREIT MJ: Inhibition of bone marrow stem cell growth *in vitro* by methylmalonic acid: A mechanism for pancytopenia in a patient with methylmalonic acidemia. *Pediatr Res* 15:95, 1981.

197. COULOMBE JT, SHIH VE, LEVY HL: Massachusetts metabolic disorders screening program. II. Methylmalonic aciduria. *Pediatrics* 67:26, 1981.

198. MORROW G, SCHWARTZ RH, HALLOCK JA, BARNESS LA: Prenatal detection of methylmalonic acidemia. *J Pediatr* 77:120, 1970.

199. AMPOLA MG, MAHONEY MJ, NAKAMURA E, TANAKA K: Prenatal therapy of a patient with vitamin B_{12} responsive methylmalonic acidemia. *N Engl J Med* 293:313, 1975.

200. MAHONEY MJ, ROSENBERG LE, LINDBLAD B, WALDENSTROM J, ZETTERSTROM R: Prenatal diagnosis of methylmalonic aciduria. *Acta Paediatr Scand* 64:44, 1975.

201. NYHAN WL, FAWCETT N, ANDO T, RENNERT OM, JULIUS RL: Response to dietary therapy in B_{12} unresponsive methylmalonic acidemia. *Pediatrics* 51:539, 1973.

202. SATOH T, NARISAWA K, IGARASHI Y, SAITOH T, HAYASAKA K, ICHINOHA-

ZAMA Y, ONODERA H, TADA K, OOHARA K: Dietary therapy in two patients with vitamin B_{12}-unresponsive methylmalonic acidemia. *Eur J Pediatr* 135:305, 1981.

203. ROE CR, HOPPEL CL, STACEY TE, CHALMERS RA, TRACEY BM, MILLINGTON DS: Metabolic response to carnitine in methylmalonic aciduria. *Arch Dis Child* 58:916, 1983.

204. LEVY HL, MUDD SH, SCHULMAN JD, DREYFUSS PM, ABELES RH: A derangement in B_{12} metabolism associated with homocystinemia, cystathioninemia, hypomethioninemia and methylmalonic aciduria. *Am J Med* 48:390, 1970.

205. DILLON MJ, ENGLAND JM, GOMPERTZ D, GOODEY PA, GRANT DB, HUSSEIN HA, LINNEL JC, MATHEWS DM, MUDD SH, NEWNS GH, SEAKINS JWT, UHLENDORF BW, WISE IJ: Mental retardation, megaloblastic anemia, methylmalonic aciduria and abnormal homocysteine metabolism due to an error in vitamin B_{12} metabolism. *Clin Sci Mol Med* 47:43, 1974.

206. ANTHONY M, MCLEAY AC: A unique case of derangement of vitamin B_{12} metabolism. *Proc Aust Assoc Neurol* 13:61, 1976.

207. BAUMGARTNER ER, WICK H, MAURER R, EGLI N, STEINMANN B: Congenital defect in intracellular cobalamin metabolism resulting in homocystinuria and methylmalonic aciduria. *Helv Paediatr Acta* 34:465, 1979.

208. CARMEL R, BEDROS AA, MACE JW, GOODMAN SI: Congenital methylmalonic aciduria-homocystinuria with megaloblastic anemia: Observations on response to hydroxocobalamin and on the effect of homocysteine and methionine on the deoxyuridine suppression test. *Blood* 55:570, 1980.

209. SHINNAR S, SINGER HS: Cobalamin C mutation (methylmalonic aciduria and homocystinuria) in adolescence. *N Engl J Med* 311:451, 1984.

210. MITCHELL GA, WATKINS D, MELANCON SB, ROSENBLATT DS, GEOFFROY G, ORQUIN J, HOMSY MB, DALLAIRE L: Clinical heterogeneity in cobalamin C variant of combined homocystinuria and methylmalonic aciduria. *J Pediatr* 108:410, 1986.

211. COGAN DG, SCHULMAN J, PORTER RJ, MUDD SH: Epileptiform ocular movements with methylmalonic aciduria and homocystinuria. *Am J Ophthalmol* 90:251, 1980.

212. LINNEL JC, MIRANDA B, BHATT HR, DOWTON SB, LEVY HL: Abnormal cobalamin metabolism in a megaloblastic child with homocystinuria, cystathioninuria and methylmalonic aciduria. *J Inherited Metab Dis (Suppl 2)* 6:127, 1980.

213. MAMLOCK RJ, ISENBERG JN, RASSIN DN: A cobalamin metabolic defect with homocystinuria, methylmalonic aciduria and macrocytic anemia. *Neuropediatrics* 17:94, 1986.

214. RAVINDRANATH Y, KRIEGER I: Vitamin-B_{12} (Cbl) and folate interrelationship in a case of homocystinuria-methylmalonic (HC-MMA)-uria due to genetic deficiency. *Pediatr Res* 18:247a, 1984.

215. RIBES A, VILASECA A, BRIONES P: Methylmalonic aciduria with homocystinuria. *J Inherited Metab Dis (Suppl* 3) 7:129, 1984.

216. ROBB RM, DOWTON SB, FULTON AB, LEVY HL: Retinal degeneration in vitamin B_{12} disorder associated with methylmalonic aciduria and sulfur amino acid abnormalities. *Am J Ophthalmol* 97:691, 1984.

217. ROSENBLATT DS, LAFRAMBOISE R, PICHETTE J, LANGEVIN P, COOPER BA, COSTA T: New disorder of vitamin B_{12} metabolism (cobalamin F) presenting as methylmalonic aciduria. *Pediatrics* 78:51, 1986.

218. WATKINS D, ROSENBLATT DS: Failure of lysosomal release of vitamin B_{12}: A new complementation group causing methylmalonic aciduria (cblF). *Am J Hum Genet* 39:404, 1986.

219. LINNELL JC, MATTHEWS DM, MUDD SH, UHLENDORF BW, WISE IJ: Cobalamins in fibroblasts cultured from normal control subjects and patients with methylmalonic aciduria. *Pediatr Res* 10:179, 1976.

220. BAUMGARTNER ER, WICK H, LINNEL JC, GAULL GE, BACHMANN C, STEINMANN B: Congenital defect in intracellular cobalamin metabolism resulting in homocystinuria and methylmalonic aciduria. *Helv Paediatr Acta* 34:483, 1979.

221. ROSENBERG LE, PATEL L, LILLJEQVIST A: Absence of an intracellular cobalamin binding protein in cultured fibroblasts from patients with defective synthesis of 5′-deoxyadenosylcobalamin and methylcobalamin. *Proc Natl Acad Sci USA* 72:4617, 1975.

222. MUDD SH, UHLENDORF BW, HINDS KR, LEVY HL: Deranged B_{12} metabolism: Studies of fibroblasts grown in tissue culture. *Biochem Med* 4:215, 1970.

223. MELLMAN IS, LIN P-F, RUDDLE FH, ROSENBERG LE: Genetic control of cobalamin binding in normal and mutant cells: Assignment of the gene for 5-methyltetrahydrofolate:L-homocysteine *S*-methyltransferase to human chromosome 1. *Proc Natl Acad Sci USA* 76:405, 1979.

224. MELLMAN I, WILLARD HF, YOUNGDAHL-TURNER P, ROSENBERG LE: Cobalamin coenzyme synthesis in normal and mutant human fibroblasts: Evidence for a processing enzyme activity deficient in *cbl C* cells. *J Biol Chem* 254:11847, 1979.

225. ROSENBLATT DS, HOSACK A, MATIASZUK NV: Defect in vitamin B_{12} release from lysosomes: Newly described inborn error of vitamin B_{12} metabolism. *Science* 228:1319, 1985.

CHAPTER **30**

ORGANIC ACIDEMIAS DUE TO DEFECTS IN LYSINE OXIDATION: 2-Ketoadipic Acidemia and Glutaric Acidemia

STEPHEN I. GOODMAN
FRANK E. FRERMAN

1. *2-Ketoadipic acid, an intermediate in the metabolism of L-lysine, hydroxy-L-lysine, and L-tryptophan, undergoes successive oxidative decarboxylations by 2-ketoadipic dehydrogenase and glutaryl-CoA dehydrogenase to form glutaryl-CoA and crotonyl-CoA, respectively.*
2. *Deficiency of 2-ketoadipic dehydrogenase causes 2-ketoadipic acidemia, a condition characterized by accumulation and excretion of 2-ketoadipic, 2-aminoadipic, and 2-hydroxyadipic acids, probably without adverse phenotypic effects.*
3. *Deficiency of glutaryl-CoA dehydrogenase causes glutaric acidemia (type I), a disorder characterized clinically by dystonia and dyskinesia which appears during the first years of life; chemically by (usually) excretion of glutaric and 3-hydroxyglutaric acids in urine; and pathologically by neuronal degeneration of the caudate and putamen. Abnormalities of CT and MRI scans may be present before the onset of symptoms.*
4. *Glutaryl-CoA dehydrogenase deficiency is inherited as an autosomal recessive trait, and identification of heterozygous carriers may be possible by demonstrating intermediate enzyme activities in cultured fibroblasts and peripheral leukocytes.*
5. *Prenatal diagnosis is possible by demonstrating increased concentrations of glutaric acid in amniotic fluid or glutaryl-CoA dehydrogenase deficiency in cultured amniocytes.*
6. *There is no effective treatment, although a few patients have responded to riboflavin, to dietary restriction of lysine, and to the γ-aminobutyric acid (GABA) analogue baclofen.*

BIOCHEMISTRY

Steps in the conversion of L-lysine to 2-ketoadipic acid, and defects in this pathway, have been discussed in Chap. 21. 2-Ketoadipic acid, which is also an intermediate in the oxidation of hydroxy-L-lysine and L-tryptophan, is converted to crotonyl-CoA, an intermediate in fatty acid oxidation, by the sequential action of two enzymes, 2-ketoadipic dehydrogenase and glutaryl-CoA dehydrogenase (Fig. 30-1). Inherited defects in these proteins cause 2-ketoadipic acidemia and glutaric acidemia, respectively.

2-Ketoadipic dehydrogenase is a mitochondrial enzyme, and has not been separated from 2-ketoglutaric dehydrogenase (EC 1.2.4.1), the citric acid cycle enzyme which forms succinyl-CoA.[1] The enzyme has at least three subunits analogous to those of pyruvate dehydrogenase (see Chap. 32), i.e., a thiamine-containing E-1 subunit which decarboxylates 2-ketoadipic acid to active glutaraldehyde (and possibly also 2-ketoglutaric acid to active succinaldehyde), an E-2 transacetylase, and an E-3 lipoamide dehydrogenase. It is likely that the E-3 subunit is the same protein as the E-3 subunit of pyruvate dehydrogenase and branched chain ketoacid dehydrogenase, and it may also form part of the glycine cleavage enzyme. Electrons from 2-ketoadipic dehydrogenase are transferred into complex I of the respiratory chain via the NADH dehydrogenase complex.

Glutaryl-coenzyme A dehydrogenase (EC 1.3.99.7) is one of eight primary flavoprotein dehydrogenases of the mitochondrial matrix whose electrons are transferred to ubiquinone in the respiratory chain via electron transfer flavoprotein (ETF) and ETF:ubiquinone oxidoreductase. Disorders of these enzymes, and the enzymes themselves, are discussed in Chaps. 24, 28, and 34.

Glutaryl-CoA dehydrogenase has been purified to homogeneity by the criterion of a single band on denaturing polyacrylamide gel electrophoresis. The homogeneous enzymes from *Pseudomonas fluorescens*[2] and pork liver mitochondria[3] catalyze the oxidative decarboxylation of glutaryl-CoA to crotonyl-CoA and carbon dioxide. By analogy with octanoyl-CoA dehydrogenase,[4] the dehydrogenase flavin, FAD, is reduced to the two-electron-reduced (hydroquinone) form. Enzyme-bound FAD hydroquinone is reoxidized in discrete steps by two equivalents of ETF, the flavin of each being reduced to the one-electron-reduced (semiquinone) form.[3] This scheme is shown in Fig. 30-2.

The interaction of glutaryl-CoA dehydrogenase with ETF requires precise protein-protein interactions, probably by the binding of an anionic domain on the dehydrogenase to a cationic domain on ETF.[5] The domains which bind to substrate and to ETF may be quite distinct, since it is possible to modify glutamic acid residues on octanoyl-CoA dehydrogenase, a quite similar enzyme, so that the enzyme retains the ability to oxidize substrate and to transfer electrons to artificial electron acceptors but is unable to reduce ETF.[6]

It is not known whether glutaconyl-CoA is a transient intermediate in the reaction, although this has been proposed (see below), and there are data to suggest that glutaconyl-CoA can be decarboxylated by a partially purified preparation of glu-

Nonstandard abbreviations used in this chapter are: CT = coaxial tomography; ETF = electron transport flavoprotein; GABA = gamma aminobutyric acid; GAD = glutamic acid decarboxylase; MRI = magnetic resonance imaging.

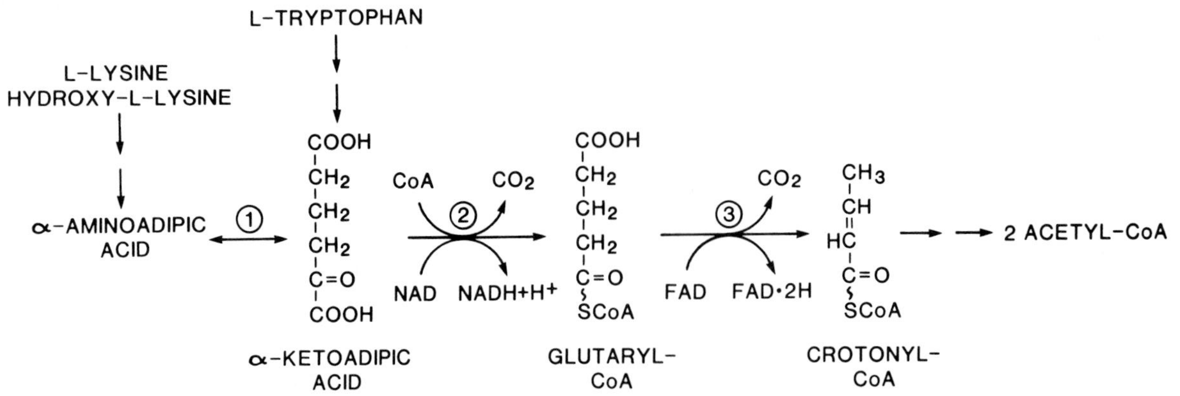

L-TRYPTOPHAN
L-LYSINE
HYDROXY-L-LYSINE
α-AMINOADIPIC ACID ① α-KETOADIPIC ACID (COOH–CH2–CH2–CH2–C=O–COOH)
② CoA, NAD → CO_2, NADH+H+
GLUTARYL-CoA (COOH–CH2–CH2–CH2–C=O–SCoA)
③ FAD → CO_2, FAD·2H
CROTONYL-CoA (CH3–CH=HC–C=O–SCoA) → → 2 ACETYL-CoA

Fig. 30-1 Synthesis and oxidation of 2-ketoadipic acid in mammals. 1 = 2-aminoadipic acid transaminase; 2 = 2-ketoadipic dehydrogenase; 3 = glutaryl-CoA dehydrogenase.

taryl-CoA dehydrogenase from *Pseudomonas fluorescens*.[7] However, when radiolabeled glutaryl-CoA is oxidized by the mammalian enzyme, the sole radiolabeled reaction products are crotonyl-CoA and carbon dioxide, and no labeled glutaconyl-CoA or 3-hydroxyglutaryl-CoA is detected.[3,8]

Like the other characterized flavoprotein acyl-CoA dehydrogenases, native glutaryl-CoA dehydrogenase from pork liver mitochondria appears to be a homotetramer, with each subunit containing one equivalent of ionically bound and easily dissociable flavin adenine nucleotide (FAD). The molecular weight of the pork subunit is approximately 47 kDa, and the molecular weight of the human subunit may be some 20 to 30 percent larger.[3] The purified pork liver enzyme has K_m values of 3.3 μM and 1.1 μM for glutaryl-CoA and ETF, respectively, when assayed fluorometrically at 25°C. Under these conditions, glutaryl-CoA is oxidized at the rate of 330 mol/min per mole of enzyme and ETF semiquinone is formed at the rate of 860 mol/min per mole of enzyme, in agreement with the reaction scheme showing 2:1 stoichiometry between substrate oxidized and ETF semiquinone formed. At 37°C, assayed with methylene blue as the electron acceptor and determining $^{14}CO_2$ release, the rate of glutaryl-CoA oxidation is 850 mol/min per mole of enzyme. The pork enzyme slowly transfers reducing equivalents from hexanoyl-, octanoyl-, butyryl-, and isovaleryl-CoA to ETF, but only at high concentrations of these alternative substrates. All of these coenzyme A esters competitively inhibit decarboxylation of glutaryl-CoA.[3]

Investigation of the chemical mechanism of glutaryl-CoA dehydrogenase by Gomes et al.[2] suggests initial formation of an α carbanion as the result of proton abstraction by a base catalyst on the enzyme, followed by transfer of the β hydrogen as a hydride ion to the flavin, to yield the proposed glutaconyl-CoA intermediate (Fig. 30-3). An initial proton abstraction of this type is apparently common in the mechanisms of acyl-CoA dehydrogenases.[9] That glutaconyl-CoA is an intermediate is suggested by the observation that glutaconyl-CoA can be decarboxylated by a partially purified preparation of the bacterial enzyme.[7] Carbon dioxide is not released from the intermediate in the absence of an electron acceptor for the reduced dehydrogenase flavin.[2] The proton of the ω-methyl group of the crotonyl-CoA product is apparently derived from the α proton, since solvent protons are not incorporated into this position, while the β proton of the substrate exchanges with solvent via the flavin.[2] A similar proton shift occurs when octanoyl-CoA dehydrogenase catalyzes the conversion of 3,4-pentadieneoyl-CoA to 2,4-pentadieneoyl-CoA without net oxidation, probably by forming an N-5 covalent adduct of the flavin.[10]

The enzyme is also inhibited by methylenecyclopropylacetyl-CoA,[11] the metabolite of hypoglycin A which is probably responsible for Jamaican vomiting sickness. When methylenecyclopropylacetyl-CoA is dehydrogenated, the transient α-carbanion product leads to opening of the cyclopropyl ring, forming a compound which reacts covalently and irreversibly with enzyme-bound flavin, and it thus acts as an active-site-directed inhibitor.[12]

The activity of glutaryl-CoA dehydrogenase can be measured in several ways. The simplest and most sensitive assay utilizes [1,5-^{14}C] glutaryl-CoA as substrate (Fig. 30-4), measuring release of $^{14}CO_2$.[8] Another radioassay measures the release of tritium from carbon 3 of [2,3,4-^{3}H] glutaryl-CoA as it equilibrates with solvent water.[11] In both of these assays artificial electron acceptors, methylene blue in the first instance and phenazine methosulfate in the second, are used to regenerate oxidized dehydrogenase. Glutaryl-CoA dehydrogenase activity can also be assayed by following the disappearance of ETF flavin fluorescence as it is reduced to the semiquinone.[3] This assay, though far less sensitive, is unlike the others in that it is potentially sensitive to alterations of the enzyme domain that interacts with ETF.

2-KETOADIPIC ACIDEMIA

2-Ketoadipic acidemia is an inborn error of lysine, tryptophan, and hydroxylysine metabolism which may have no clin-

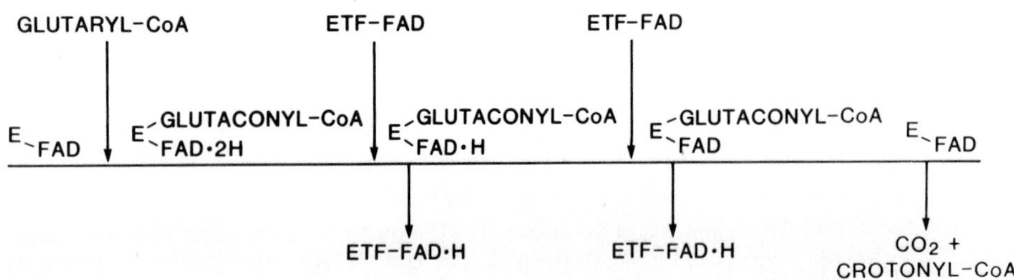

Fig. 30-2 Catalytic mechanism of glutaryl-CoA dehydrogenase. The sequence in which carbon dioxide and crotonyl-CoA leave the protein is not known.

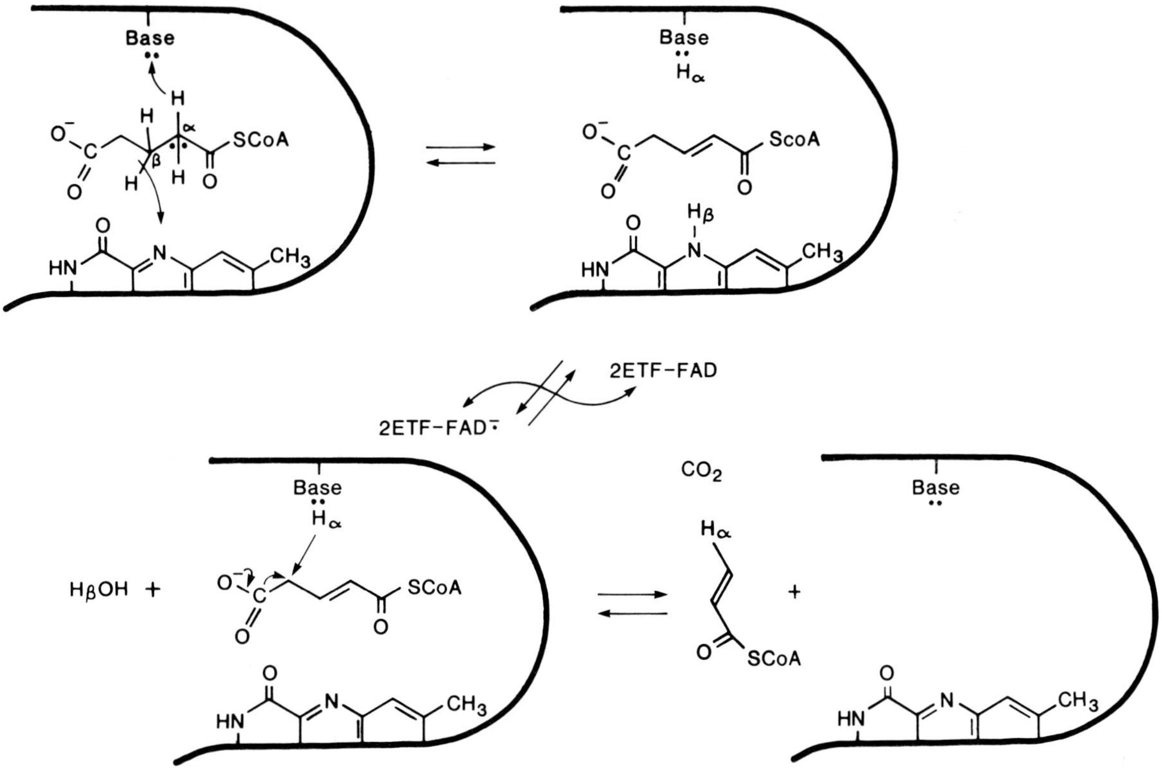

Fig. 30-3 Proton transfers during catalysis by glutaryl-CoA dehydrogenase, showing exchange of β proton with solvent, and transfer of α proton to ω carbon of crotonyl-CoA.

ical significance. It is probably due to deficiency of the E-1 or E-2 component of 2-ketoadipic acid dehydrogenase, and is manifested by the accumulation and excretion of 2-aminoadipic, 2-ketoadipic, and 2-hydroxyadipic acids. Inheritance is probably as an autosomal recessive trait.

Several affected individuals have been described. These include a 14-month-old girl with hypotonia, intermittent metabolic acidosis, and motor and developmental delay[13]; a 14-year-old retarded boy and his normal sister[14]; a 9-year-old boy with a mild learning disability and his normal brother[15,16]; a 10-year-old retarded girl[17]; a 9-year-old boy with psychomotor retardation and a history of seizures[18]; and a 7-year-old girl with developmental delay and cerebellar ataxia.[19] Three additional patients, apparently normal siblings aged 8, 13, and 15 years, are also known.[20] These observations suggest that the condition is not deleterious and that the large number of individuals with developmental delay and other neurologic symptoms are accounted for by sampling bias.

Almost all probands were identified when prominent spots of 2-aminoadipic acid were noted on amino acid chromatography of urine, with subsequent investigations demonstrating 2-aminoadipic acidemia and increased urine concentrations of 2-ketoadipic and 2-hydroxyadipic acid. 2-Hydroxyglutaric acid is observed in urine in some patients, possibly because 2-ketoglutaric dehydrogenase and 2-ketoadipic dehydrogenase are the same enzyme. Small amounts of glutaric acid are also detected in the urine, almost certainly because of spontaneous decarboxylation of 2-ketoadipic acid.[18]

Fig. 30-4 Assay of glutaryl-CoA dehydrogenase by $^{14}CO_2$ release from [1,5-^{14}C]glutaryl-CoA. In most assays X = methylene blue or phenazine methosulfate.

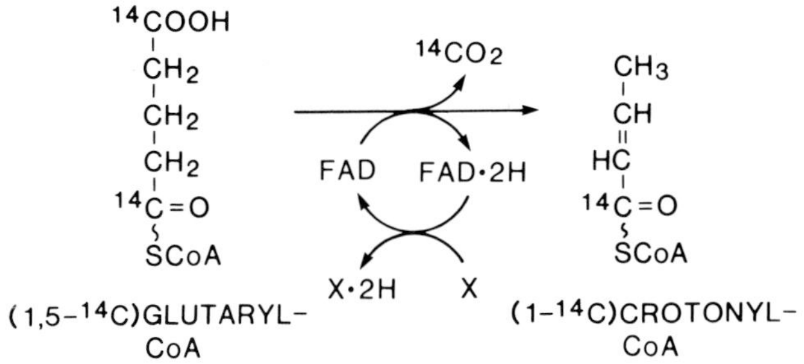

The accumulated metabolites suggest a block in 2-ketoadipic dehydrogenase, and intact mutant fibroblasts are almost totally unable to oxidize 2-amino [1-^{14}C] adipic and 2-keto [1-^{14}C] adipic acid to $^{14}CO_2$,[18,21] but a defect in 2-ketoadipic dehydrogenase has not been demonstrated directly. If 2-ketoadipic dehydrogenase and 2-ketoglutaric dehydrogenase are indeed the same, it is not clear how so central a defect can produce so mild a phenotype. This incongruity suggests that the two enzymes may be different.

In view of the fact that the condition may have no clinical consequences, treatment and antenatal diagnosis may be of little import, although protein restriction to 1.5 g/kg per day is reported to have produced some clinical improvement in one patient, perhaps leading to improved interaction between the child and his parents.[17]

Inheritance as an autosomal recessive trait is inferred from the pedigrees, and there is no evidence that heterozygous carriers can be distinguished from control subjects. The incidence is not known.

GLUTARIC ACIDEMIA (TYPE I)

Introduction

Glutaric acidemia is a recently recognized inborn error which is characterized clinically by progressive dystonia and dyskinesia in childhood, pathologically by striatal degeneration, in particular of the caudate and putamen, and biochemically by tissue deficiency of glutaryl-CoA dehydrogenase. Large quantities of glutaric and 3-hydroxyglutaric acids are usually present in urine. The disorder is transmitted as an autosomal recessive trait. Treatment by dietary restriction of glutarigenic amino acids (lysine, tryptophan, and hydroxylysine), by supplementation with riboflavin, or by drugs like baclofen and valproic acid does not usually alter the course of the disease, and most patients die during the first decade of life.

Clinical Manifestations

Patients, some of whom have been followed carefully from birth because of macrocephaly, appear to develop normally for up to 2 years. In most cases the disease first becomes apparent when a minor infection is followed by the sudden appearance of hypotonia, loss of head control, seizures, opisthotonus, grimacing, fisting, tongue thrusting, rigidity, and dystonia (Fig. 30-5), and recovery is slow and incomplete. In other patients onset is not acute, and motor delay, hypotonia, dystonia, and dyskinesia develop gradually during the first few years of life. After onset, the neurologic course is usually one of slow progression punctuated by acute episodes of ketosis, vomiting, hepatomegaly, and coma and convulsions brought on by infection, with relative preservation of intellect. Episodes of unexplained high fever are frequent, and may be due to consistent and unabated activity of large skeletal muscles. Death usually occurs during the first decade, often after an intercurrent infection or during a Reye syndrome–like episode.[22–36]

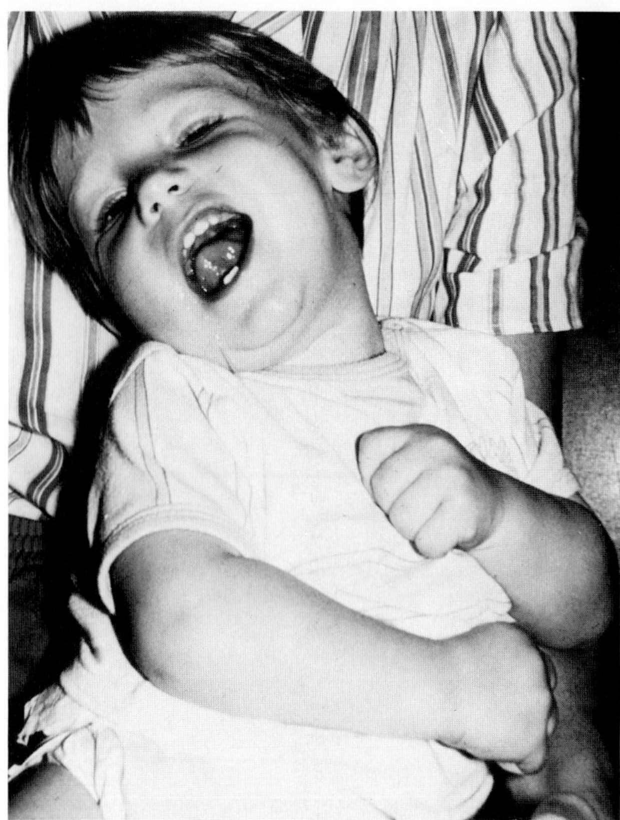

Fig. 30-5 A 13-month-old boy with glutaric acidemia, showing dystonia of face, tongue, neck, back, arms, and hands. This child did not have abnormal urine organic acids. *(Courtesy of Dr. I. Bergman.)*

Most routine laboratory studies, including serum electrolytes and pH, are normal except during acute episodes. Metabolic acidosis may appear during acute episodes associated with infection, often with hypoglycemia, ketosis and ketonuria, hyperammonemia, and elevation of serum transaminases.[26,37,38] Routine studies of cerebrospinal fluid are also normal.

Urine organic acids are abnormal in most cases, but patients without organic aciduria may be just as severely affected clinically.[30,36] When abnormal, the organic acid pattern is characteristic (Fig. 30-6), showing large quantities of glutaric acid (up to 22 mg/per milligram of creatinine), lesser amounts of 3-hydroxyglutaric acid (up to 0.7 mg/per milligram of creatinine), and occasionally small amounts of glutaconic acid.[39] The possible origin of these compounds is discussed below. Excretion of glutaconic acid becomes prominent and often exceeds that of 3-hydroxyglutaric during acute ketotic episodes, when large amounts of 3-hydroxybutyric, acetoacetic, adipic,

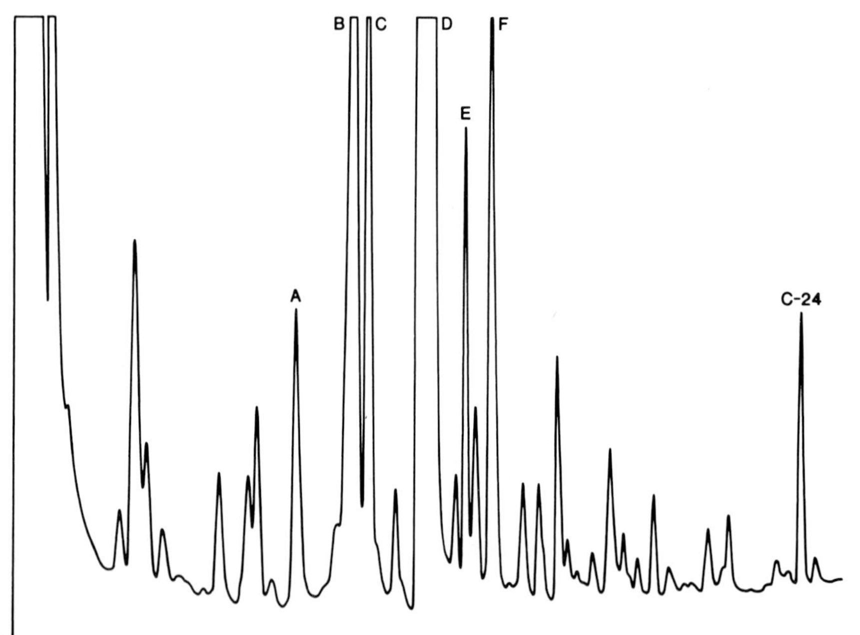

Fig. 30-6 Urine organic acids in glutaric acidemia. A = malonic (internal standard), B = urea, C = succinic, D = glutaric, E = unknown (not glutaconic), F = 3-hydroxyglutaric. *(From S.I. Goodman and S.P. Markey,* Diagnosis of Organic Acidemias by Gas Chromatogrphy-Mass Spectrometry, *Alan R. Liss Inc., New York, 1981. Used by permission.)*

suberic, and sebacic acids are also found.[26,37,38] Increased concentrations of glutaric acid, usually 0.1 to 2.5 mg/dl, are also found in blood and cerebrospinal fluid.[22,23,27,29]

Amino acids in blood and urine are usually normal, but during acute episodes 2-aminoadipic acid may be greatly elevated in plasma and the urine may show a generalized aminoaciduria, with special prominence of glutamine, glutamic acid, 2-aminoadipic acid, and saccharopine.[26,37] Similar changes have been described in some patients with Reye syndrome and are not diagnostic.

CT scans are usually abnormal, with dilatation of the lateral ventricles and widening of cortical sulci often noted within days of the onset of neurologic symptoms.[31–33] Areas of decreased density of white matter around the frontal and occipital horns, and decreased density of the caudate and putamen, have also been noted. Three patients who were followed closely from the onset of symptoms with serial CT scans and magnetic resonance imaging (MRI)[36] showed marked and early increases in cerebrospinal fluid anterior to the temporal lobes and within the sylvian fissures; these changes precede the onset of symptoms, and were noted in an infant with macrocephaly and mild hypertonia and no movement disorder, who was found to have the typical organic aciduria and glutaryl-CoA dehydrogenase deficiency in fibroblasts.[40] Significant atrophy of the caudate may be noted late in the course of the disease (Fig. 30-7).

Diagnosis

Because most clinical chemistry parameters are normal between acute episodes, activity of glutaryl-CoA dehydrogenase in leukocytes or fibroblasts should be measured in all children with progressive dystonia and dyskinesia, even if their urine organic acid levels are normal. Enzyme activity varies from 0 to 10 percent of normal in affected patients when measured by decarboxylation of [1,5-^{14}C] glutaryl-CoA[22] or by tritium release from [2,3,4-^{3}H] glutaryl-CoA,[11] and this result establishes the diagnosis.

When abnormal, urine organic acid analysis shows large quantities of glutaric, 3-hydroxyglutaric, and (occasionally) glutaconic acids. When 3-hydroxyglutaric acid is identified, the diagnosis is almost certain, since it has not been found in any other condition. Analysis of urine organic acids in glutaric acidemia type II shows an increase in 2-hydroxyglutaric acid[41] and not in 3-hydroxyglutaric acid.

Chemical Pathology

Glutaric acid concentrations have been increased in all tissues which have been examined, including liver, brain, kidney, cardiac and skeletal muscle, and aqueous humor.[29,34,37] Determination of the latter, which is easily possible at autopsy, has been suggested as useful for postmortem diagnosis.[34] The concentration of glutaric acid in brain may be different in different areas; in one patient it was 0.67 μmol per gram wet weight in frontal cortex and 1.25 μmol per gram wet weight in basal ganglia.[29] In another patient, the glutaric acid concentration in frontal cortex was 0.83 μmol per gram wet weight (it is normally undetected).[37] Glutaconic acid has not been detected in brain, even when large amounts of the compound were being excreted in urine just before death.[37]

The concentrations of γ-aminobutyric acid (GABA) were extremely low in the caudate (0.60 μmol per gram wet weight; normal, 3.03 ± 0.83) and putamen (0.87 μmol per gram wet weight; normal, 5.69 ± 0.75) of one patient, and correlated with severe deficiency of neuronal glutamate decarboxylase and neuronal cell death in these areas. Enzyme activities, and the concentrations of GABA, were much nearer to the normal range in frontal, occipital, and cerebellar cortex.[29]

Anatomic Pathology

Minimal and possibly insignificant changes in the striatum were observed in one affected abortus of 23 weeks' gestation.[42] Histologic changes were also minimal, with moderate fatty changes in the neurons of the caudate in one patient[34] and increased numbers of astrocytes in the putamen in another,[36] in two severely affected patients who died at about 1 year of

Fig. 30-7 Computered tomography (CT) and magnetic resonance imaging (MRI) scans of brain in glutaric acidemia. *Left:* CT scan of 10-month-old boy, 3 months after the onset of movement disorder, showing loss of cerebral volume, most notable in the temporal lobes, and widening of Sylvian fissures. *(Courtesy of Dr. I. Bergman.) Middle:* CT scan of a 5-month-old boy without movement disorder but with abnormal urine organic acids and glutaryl-CoA dehydrogenase deficiency, showing the same changes. *(Courtesy of Dr. S. Seshia.) Right:* MRI scan of a 3-year-old girl, showing cortical atrophy, dilated lateral ventricles, and shrinkage and increased intensity of the caudate and putamen, suggesting fibrosis.

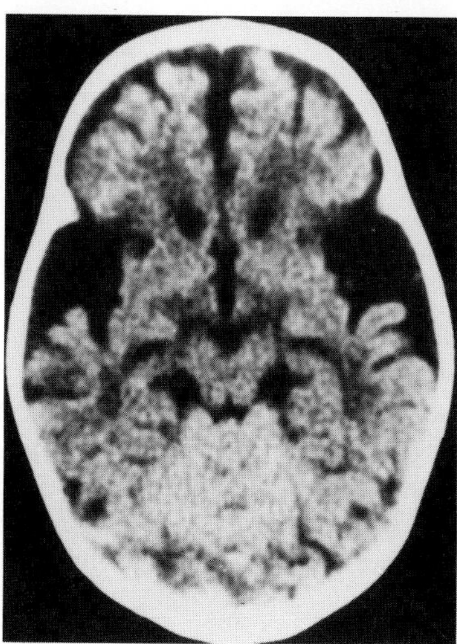

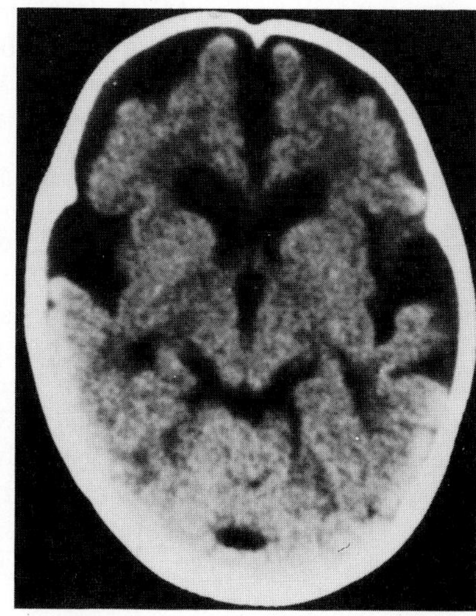

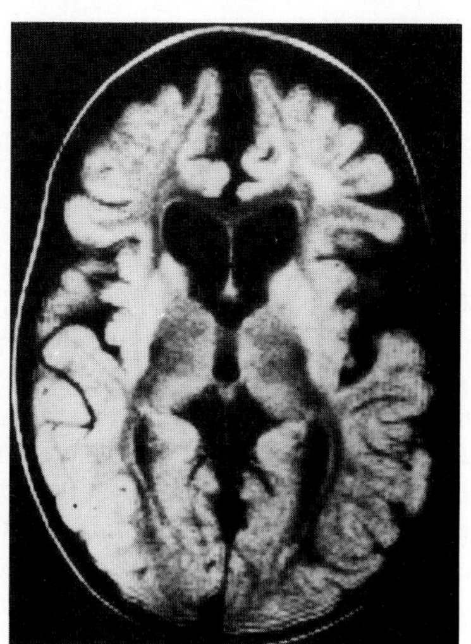

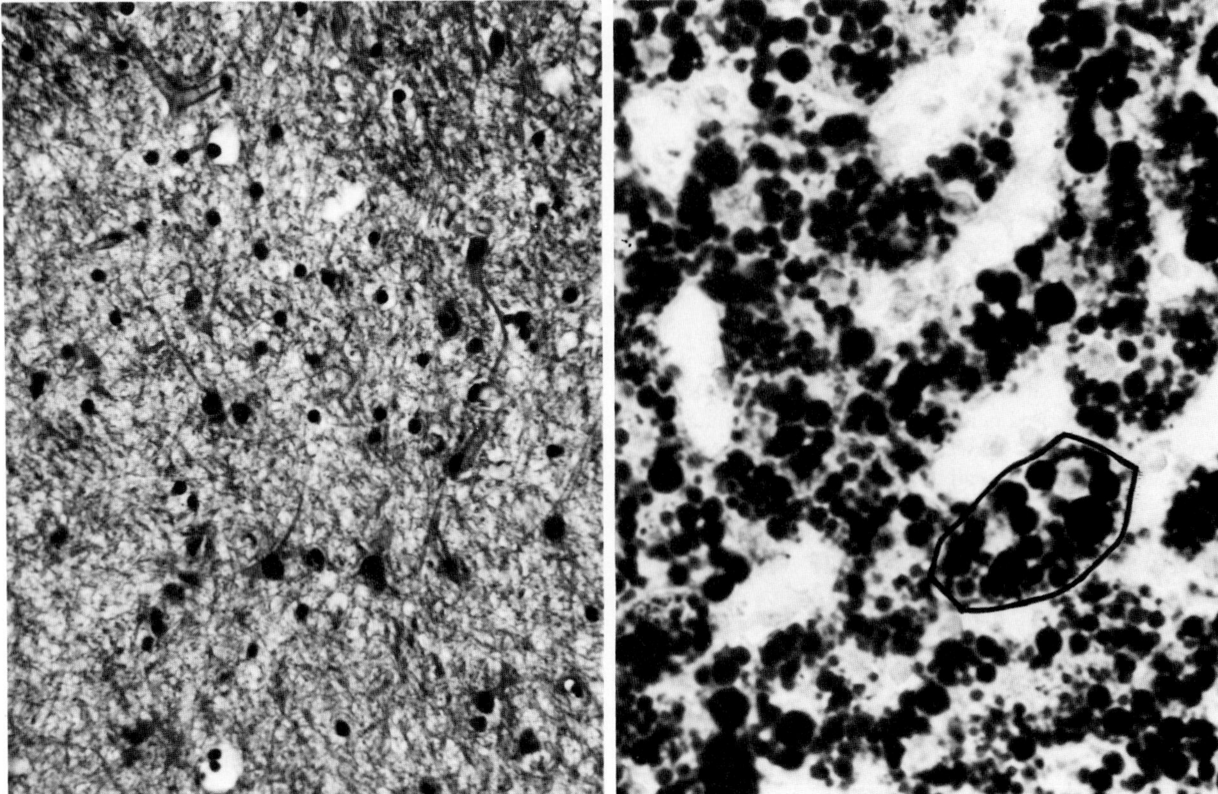

Fig. 30-8 Histologic section of the caudate nucleus from a 10-year-old boy with glutaric acidemia, showing almost total neuronal loss and replacement by gliotic tissue. H&E; original magnification ×300. *(Courtesy of Dr. M.D. Norenberg.) Right:* Section of liver from the same patient, showing large and small fatty droplets in hepatocytes. A single cell is outlined at right. Osmic acid–fixed, unstained; original magnification ×400. *(Courtesy of Dr. R.H. Shikes.)*

age. Changes were much more marked in two patients who died at 3 and 10 years[29,37]; in both patients there was severe neuronal loss and extensive fibrous gliosis in the caudate and putamen (Fig. 30-8). Severe degeneration of the caudate and putamen has been seen in several additional but unpublished cases; some of these patients also showed degeneration of the globus pallidus and marked spongy degeneration of cortical white matter. It is apparent that the striatum bears the brunt of neurotoxicity in this disorder and that whatever its cause, clinical evidence of striatal dysfunction occurs well before the appearance of histologic abnormality.

Of the few patients who have been autopsied, most have also shown microvesicular fatty infiltration of liver parenchymal cells (Fig. 30-8), cells of the proximal renal tubule, and myocardium.[34,36,37] These changes are not pathognomonic, as they are seen in several other disorders, including Reye syndrome, other organic acidemias, and disorders of the urea cycle.

Incidence

There are no accurate incidence figures because neonatal screening for this disorder is not performed and because cases may not be diagnosed. Over 20 patients have been described since the initial description of the condition in 1975, and more than 20 others are known to us in North America alone. The disease is certainly not rare, and its incidence in Sweden has been estimated to be about the same as that of phenylketonuria, i.e., about 1 in 30,000.[28]

Genetics

Pedigree analysis, which shows that males and females are affected with approximately equal frequency, suggests inheritance as an autosomal recessive trait, and this is confirmed by the presence of intermediate glutaryl-CoA dehydrogenase activities in leukocytes and fibroblasts from the parents of patients.[27,43,44] Enzyme activities in the few carriers examined to date appear to be somewhat below half normal, a finding which may be due to decreased stability of an enzyme tetramer composed of normal and mutant subunits. Heterozygous carriers are normal chemically as well as clinically, and two such carriers did not excrete glutaric acid in urine even following oral loads (410 μmol/kg three times a day) of L-lysine.[22]

There has not been sufficient experience with carrier detection to know its reliability. This is of particular concern in families in which the index case and/or obligate heterozygotes are not available.

Prenatal Diagnosis

Prenatal diagnosis of an affected fetus has been made on at least one occasion, with the affected pregnancy being characterized by an increased concentration of glutaric acid in the amniotic fluid (4.35 to 13.3 μg/ml; normal <0.39 μg/ml) and by decreased activity of glutaryl-CoA dehydrogenase in cultured amniotic cells.[42] The diagnosis was confirmed by the presence of large quantities of glutaric acid in fetal liver (17 μg per gram wet weight), brain (112 μg per gram wet weight), and kidney (70.2 μg per gram wet weight), as well as by decreased enzyme activity in liver and kidney. There has been no published experience with cells grown from chorionic villus sampling, but prenatal diagnosis based on enzyme deficiency in these cells should be possible. As stated above, the affected fetus also showed some minimal and possibly significant histologic abnormalities in the brain, but histopathology was otherwise unremarkable.

Genetic Heterogeneity

Since some glutaric acidemia patients appear to have more activity of glutaryl-CoA dehydrogenase in cultured fibroblasts than others,[44] with the residual enzyme activity correlating with disease severity, there are probably at least two different mutant alleles at the glutaryl-CoA dehydrogenase locus. The cDNA sequence which encodes the protein has not been cloned, however, and there is no information on the specific mutations which cause the disease.

Pathogenesis

Almost total deficiency of glutaryl-CoA dehydrogenase is found in glutaric acidemia tissues, including cultured fibroblasts and amniocytes, peripheral leukocytes, liver, brain, and kidney. Enzyme deficiency in cultured fibroblasts and partial deficiency in obligate heterozygotes establishes inherited glutaryl-CoA dehydrogenase deficiency as the cause of the condition.

The excretion of glutaric acid is probably due to accumulation of the substrate of the deficient enzyme, glutaryl-CoA, and hydrolysis of this metabolite to the free acid by intracellular thioesterases. It is not yet clear why 3-hydroxyglutaric and glutaconic acids accumulate in this condition, but several lines of evidence indicate that it is not due to deficiency of only the decarboxylase function of glutaryl-CoA dehydrogenase, with release of glutaconyl-CoA and hydration to 3-hydroxyglutaryl-CoA. These include the fact that glutaconyl-CoA has never been demonstrated to be a reaction product in the system, as well as direct evidence that mutant glutaryl-CoA dehydrogenase cannot dehydrogenate its substrate. Specifically, no radiolabeled reaction products are formed when mutant liver enzyme is reacted with [1,5-^{14}C] glutaryl-CoA,[37] and glutaric acidemia fibroblasts do not dehydrogenate [2,3,4-^{3}H] glutaryl-CoA.[11]

Another possibility is that glutaconyl-CoA is formed from glutaryl-CoA by mitochondrial octanoyl-CoA dehydrogenase or by peroxisomal glutaryl-CoA oxidase.[45] The observation that glutaconic and 3-hydroxyglutaric acids are not excreted in glutaric acidemia type II, in which all mitochondrial flavoprotein dehydrogenases are deficient because of a defect in electron transport but in which peroxisomal oxidases are apparently normal, favors the mitochondrial origin of glutaconyl-CoA, and thus of 3-hydroxyglutaryl-CoA, in this disease.

The cause of striatal dysfunction and degeneration in the condition is not understood but may be due to accumulation of glutaric acid, which is toxic to striatal cells in culture.[46]

Glutaric, glutaconic, and 3-hydroxyglutaric acids are competitive inhibitors of neuronal glutamic acid decarboxylase (GAD), the enzyme responsible for γ-aminobutyric acid (GABA) biosynthesis, and the K_i of glutarate, i.e., $1.3 \times 10^{-3} M$,[47] approximates the concentration in which the compound is found in brain in glutaric acidemia. The low concentrations of GABA in the caudate and putamen of the one patient in which they were measured[29] may lend some support to this possibility. However, it is not known how inhibition of GAD could produce the neuronal loss which eventually occurs, and the decreased GAD activity and GABA concentration in the striatum might be secondary to cell death from some other cause, as probably occurs in Huntington's chorea.[48]

Another possibility is that glutarate toxicity results from repeated depolarization of glutamate receptors. Kainic acid, a glutamic acid analogue, causes neuronal degeneration when injected into rat striatum, probably because it somehow potentiates the action of glutamic acid as a neurotransmitter.[49] This could cause cell death by hyperpolarization. High affinity uptake of glutamic acid by synaptosomes is inhibited 80 percent by 10 mM glutaric acid[50] but not at all by a 0.1-mM concentration,[51] but it is not known if the 1.0- to 1.5-mM concentrations found in brain in glutaric acidemia can inhibit glutamate uptake and thus cause high and possibly stimulatory concentrations of the neurotransmitter to be retained within the synaptic cleft.

Another possible pathogenetic mechanism involves quinolinic acid. This intermediate in the metabolism of tryptophan in brain (Fig. 30-9) is a potent neurotoxin when injected directly into the central nervous system of experimental animals,[52] and neurons are so sensitive to its effects that even endogenous concentrations may be toxic.[53] It is possible that the block in glutaryl-CoA dehydrogenase could increase the intracellular concentration of quinolinic acid to toxic levels and cause tissue damage.[54]

It should be noted that the manifestations of glutarate toxicity on striatal cells in culture are not the same as those due to kainic acid and quinolinic acid. Kainic and quinolinic acids are toxic to cortical-striatal cultures only when synapses are well established,[55] while glutaric acid causes neurodegenera-

Fig. 30-9 The two pathways of tryptophan metabolism in brain: one through glutaryl-CoA and one through quinolinic acid. The inherited block in type I glutaric acidemia is indicated by the bar. The open arrow indicates a hypothetical increase in the production of quinolinic acid and related metabolites in this disorder.

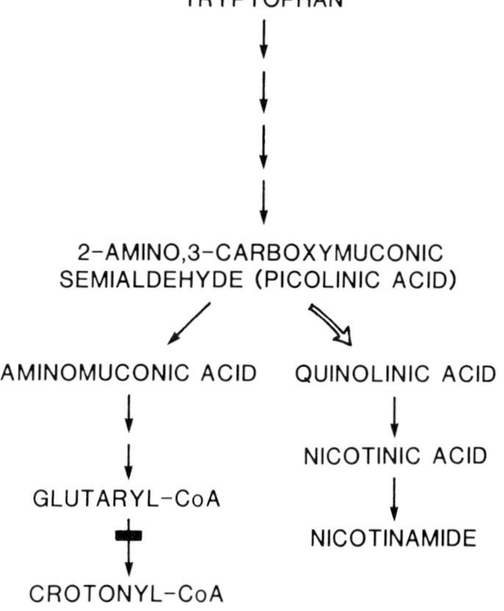

tive changes even before synapses are well established.[46] Neuronal degeneration in the condition may therefore be on a totally different basis.

The cause of the fatty changes seen at autopsy in the liver, kidneys, and heart is likewise not known, and may merely be an indication of nonspecific mitochondrial toxicity, as in Reye syndrome. The observation of severe ketosis during Reye syndrome–like episodes in this condition suggests that carnitine deficiency, if present, does not seriously affect the capacity of the liver to oxidize long-chain fatty acids. It is also possible that glutaconic acid, which is excreted in large amounts during ketotic episodes, is a mitochondrial toxin; excretion may rise during ketotic episodes because the enoyl-CoA intermediates of fatty acid oxidation competitively inhibit hydration of glutaconyl- to 3-hydroxyglutaryl-CoA. Whatever its cause, the accumulation of 2-aminoadipic acid and saccharopine observed during acute episodes appears to relate more to general mitochondrial dysfunction than to backup of metabolites proximal to glutaryl-CoA, because the same abnormalities have been described in Reye syndrome.[56,57]

Treatment

A diet low in protein or lysine, one of three glutarigenic amino acids, quickly and drastically reduces glutaric acid excretion, but usually without clinical improvement.[22,27,34] In one patient, clear reduction of irritability and hypertonus accompanied an approximately fifty-fold decrease in glutarate excretion,[28] and a diet low in lysine and tryptophan produced increased motor ability and lessening of hyperkinesia in three Danish patients.[58] A challenge with protein-rich foods produced exacerbation of dyskinesia and dystonia in these patients.

Observations of low free and esterified carnitine in plasma of patients with glutaric acidemia,[33,35] probably because of urinary losses as glutarylcarnitine, led to trials to determine the effects of supplementary carnitine. Increases in plasma levels of both free and esterified carnitine were noted, but there was no change in clinical status.[35]

Riboflavin on the order of 200 to 300 mg/day has also been tried, with the rationale that increased FAD might stabilize the mutant enzyme. Again the experience is varied; two groups reported no clinical effect with 200 mg/day,[33,34] and one reported a decrease in glutaric acid excretion and obvious clinical benefit with 300 mg/day.[58]

Observations that glutaric, glutaconic, and 3-hydroxyglutaric acid inhibit neuronal glutamate decarboxylase[47] and that glutamate decarboxylase activity and γ-aminobutyric acid (GABA) concentrations are low in the basal ganglia of glutaric acidemia patients[29] have prompted treatment with pharmacologic agents that increase GABA concentrations in brain. The two agents that have been tried are baclofen and valproic acid.

It was originally thought that baclofen, i.e., β-(4-chlorophenyl)GABA, activated GABA receptors, but it has since been learned that it activates neurons which are normally inhibited by this neurotransmitter.[59,60] Thus, any effect it has on this disorder may not relate to a GABA-like function. Baclofen therapy has been tried in several patients, again with variable results. In some patients there has been no effect whatever,[34] but Brandt has reported significant improvement in two of three Danish patients given 2 mg/kg per day, even when administration was controlled in a double blind fashion.[58] Effects varying from "none" to "questionable" have been observed in several additional patients, but we know of no other case in which the effects were as dramatic as those noted in the Danish patients.

Valproic acid therapy has also been tried in several patients, with the rationale that the drug causes selective increase of GABA in synaptic areas by inhibiting GABA transaminase or succinic semialdehyde dehydrogenase, or by inhibiting GABA uptake by glial cells and nerve endings. Some improvement of one patient on valproic acid has been reported.[33]

It should be apparent that treatment is generally unsatisfactory, possibly because irreversible damage has already been done to the striatum by the time the diagnosis is established. A low protein diet, riboflavin, and either valproic acid or baclofen should probably be tried in all patients, and this should be combined with rapid treatment of acidosis and hypoglycemia during intercurrent infections.

REFERENCES

1. HIRASHIMA M, HAYAKAWA T, KOIKE M: Mammalian α-keto acid dehydrogenase complexes II. An improved procedure for the preparation of 2-oxyglutarate dehydrogenase complex from pig heart muscle. *J Biol Chem* 242:902, 1976.
2. GOMES B, FENDRICH G, ABELES RH: Mechanism of action of glutaryl-CoA and butyryl-CoA dehydrogenases. Purification of glutaryl-CoA dehydrogenase. *Biochemistry* 20:1481, 1981.
3. LENICH AC, GOODMAN SI: The purification and characterization of glutaryl-coenzyme A dehydrogenase from porcine and human liver. *J Biol Chem* 261:4090, 1986.
4. GORELICK RJ, SHOPFER LM, BALLOU DP, MASSEY V, THORPE C: Interflavin oxidation-reduction reactions between pig kidney general acyl CoA dehydrogenase and electron transferring flavoprotein. *Biochemistry* 24:6830, 1985.
5. FRERMAN FE, MIELKE DM, HUHTA K: The functional role of carboxyl residues in an acyl CoA dehydrogenase. *J Biol Chem* 255:2199, 1980.
6. BECKMANN JD, FRERMAN FE: The effects of pH, ionic strength and chemical modifications on the reaction of electron transfer flavoprotein with an acyl CoA dehydrogenase. *J Biol Chem* 258:7563, 1983.
7. NUMA S, ISHIMURA Y, NAKAZAWA T, OKAZAKI T, HAYAISHI O: Enzymic studies on the metabolism of glutarate in *Pseudomonas*. *J Biol Chem* 239:3915, 1964.
8. BESRAT A, POLAN CE, HENDERSON LM: Mammalian metabolism of glutaric acid. *J Biol Chem* 244:1461, 1969.
9. WALSH C: Scope of chemical redox transformations catalyzed by flavoenzymes, in Massey V, Williams CH (eds): *Flavins and Flavoproteins, Developments in Biochemistry*. New York, Elsevier/North-Holland, 1982, vol 21, p 121.
10. WENZ A, GHISLA S, THORPE C: Reaction of general acyl-CoA dehydrogenase with 3,4-pentadienoyl-CoA, in Massey V, Williams CH (eds): *Flavins and Flavoproteins, Developments in Biochemistry*. New York, Elsevier/North-Holland, 1982, vol 21, p 605.
11. HYMAN DB, TANAKA K: Specific glutaryl-CoA dehydrogenating activity is deficient in cultured fibroblasts from glutaric aciduria patients. *J Clin Invest* 73:778, 1984.
12. WENZ A, THORPE C, GHISLA S: Inactivation of general acyl-CoA dehydrogenase from pig kidney by a metabolite of hypoglycin A. *J Biol Chem* 256:9809, 1981.
13. PRZYREMBEL H, BACHMANN D, LOMBECK I, BECKER K, WENDEL U, WADMAN SK, BREMER HJ: Alpha-ketoadipic aciduria, a new inborn error of lysine metabolism; biochemical studies. *Clin Chim Acta* 58:257, 1975.
14. WILSON RW, WILSON CM, GATES SC, HIGGINS JV: α-Ketoadipic aciduria: A description of a new metabolic error in lysine-tryptophan degradation. *Pediatr Res* 9:522, 1975.
15. FISCHER MH, GERRITSEN T, OPITZ JM: α-Aminoadipic aciduria, a non-deleterious inborn metabolic defect. *Humangenetik* 24:265, 1974.
16. FISCHER MH, BROWN RR: Tryptophan and lysine metabolism in alpha-aminoadipic aciduria. *Am J Med Genet* 5:35, 1980.
17. CASEY RE, ZELESKI WA, PHILP M, MENDELSON IS, MACKENZIE SL: Biochemical and clinical studies of a new case of α-aminoadipic aciduria. *J Inherited Metab Dis* 1:129, 1978.
18. DURAN M, BEEMER FA, WADMAN SK, WENDEL U, JANSSEN B: A patient with α-ketoadipic and α-aminoadipic aciduria. *J Inherited Metab Dis* 7:61, 1984.

19. VIANEY-LIAUD C, DIVRY P, COTTE J, TEYSSIER G: α-Aminoadipic and α-ketoadipic aciduria: Detection of a new case by a screening program using two dimensional thin layer chromatography of amino acids. *J Inherited Metab Dis* 8 *Suppl* 2:133, 1985.
20. WILCKEN B: Personal communication.
21. WENDEL U, RÜDIGER HW, PRZYREMBEL H, BREMER HJ: Alpha-amino-adipic aciduria: Degradation studies with fibroblasts. *Clin Chim Acta* 58:271, 1975.
22. GOODMAN SI, MARKEY SP, MOE PG, MILES BS, TENG CC: Glutaricaciduria; a "new" disorder of amino acid metabolism. *Biochem Med*12:12, 1975.
23. GREGERSEN N, BRANDT NJ, CHRISTENSEN E, GRÓN I, RASMUSSEN K, BRANDT S: Glutaric aciduria: Clinical and laboratory findings in two brothers. *J Pediatr* 90:740, 1977.
24. KYLLERMAN M, STEEN G: Intermittently progressive dyskinetic syndrome in glutaric aciduria. *Neuropadiatrie* 8:397, 1977.
25. BRANDT NJ, BRANDT S, CHRISTENSEN E, GREGERSEN N, RASMUSSEN K: Glutaric aciduria in progressive choreo-athetosis. *Clin Genet* 13:77, 1978.
26. FLORET D, DIVRY P, DINGEON N, MONNET P: Acidurie glutarique: Une nouvelle observation. *Arch Fr Pediat* 36:462, 1979.
27. WHELAN DT, HILL R, RYAN ED, SPATE M: L-Glutaric acidemia: Investigation of a patient and his family. *Pediatrics* 63:88, 1979.
28. KYLLERMAN M, STEEN G: Glutaric aciduria. A "common" metabolic disorder? *Arch Fr Pediatr* 37:279, 1980.
29. LEIBEL RL, SHIH VE, GOODMAN SI, BAUMAN ML, MCCABE ERB, ZWERDLING RG, BERGMAN I, COSTELLO C: Glutaric acidemia: A metabolic disorder causing progressive choreoathetosis. *Neurology* 30:1163, 1980.
30. HELLSTRÖM B: Progressive dystonia and dyskinesia in childhood: A review of some recent advances. *Acta Paediatr Scand* 71:177, 1982.
31. DUNGER DB, SNODGRASS GJAI: Glutaric aciduria type I presenting with hypoglycaemia. *J Inherited Metab Dis* 7:122, 1984.
32. AICARDI J, GOUTIERES F, SAUDUBRAY JM, OGIER H: CT scans of infants with glutaric aciduria. *Dev Med Child Neurol* 27:401, 1985.
33. STUTCHFIELD P, EDWARDS MA, GRAY RGF, CRAWLEY P, GREEN A: Glutaric aciduria type I misdiagnosed as Leigh's encephalopathy and cerebral palsy. *Dev Med Child Neurol* 27:514, 1985.
34. BENNETT MJ, MARLOW N, POLLITT RJ, WALES JKH: Glutaric aciduria type I: Biochemical investigations and postmortem findings. *Eur J Pediatr* 145:403, 1986.
35. SECCOMBE DW, JAMES L, BOOTH F: L-Carnitine treatment in glutaric aciduria type I. *Neurology* 36:264, 1986.
36. BERGMAN I, FINEGOLD D, GARTNER JC, ZITELLI BJ, CLASSEN D, SCARANO J, ROE C, STANLEY C, GOODMAN SI: Acute profound dystonia in infants with glutaric acidemia. *Pediatrics* (in press).
37. GOODMAN SI, NORENBERG MD, SHIKES RH, BRESLICH DJ, MOE PG: Glutaric aciduria: Biochemical and morphologic considerations. *J Pediatr* 90:746, 1977.
38. GREGERSEN N, BRANDT NJ: Ketotic episodes in glutaryl-CoA dehydrogenase deficiency (glutaric aciduria). *Pediatr Res* 13:977, 1979.
39. STOKKE O, GOODMAN SI, THOMPSON JA, MILES BS: Glutaric aciduria; presence of glutaconic and β-hydroxyglutaric acids in urine. *Biochem Med* 12:386, 1975.
40. YAGER JY, McCLARTY BM, SESHIA SS: CT scan findings in gluteric aciduria, type I. *Dev Med Child Neurol* (in press).
41. GOODMAN SI, STENE DO, MCCABE ERB, NORENBERG MD, SHIKES RH, STUMPF DA, BLACKBURN GK: Glutaric acidemia type II: Clinical, biochemical, and morphologic considerations. *J Pediatr* 100:946, 1982.
42. GOODMAN SI, GALLEGOS DA, PULLIN CJ, HALPERN B, TRUSCOTT RJW, WISE G, WILCKEN B, RYAN ED, WHELAN DT: Antenatal diagnosis of glutaric acidemia. *Am J Hum Genet* 32:695, 1980.
43. GOODMAN SI, KOHLHOFF JG: Glutaric aciduria: Inherited deficiency of glutaryl-CoA dehydrogenase activity. *Biochem Med* 13:138, 1975.
44. CHRISTENSEN E, BRANDT NJ: Studies on glutaryl-CoA dehydrogenase in leucocytes, fibroblasts and amniotic fluid cells. The normal enzyme and the mutant form in patients with glutaric aciduria. *Clin Chim Acta* 88:267, 1978.
45. VAMECQ J, DE HOFFMAN E, VAN HOOF F: Mitochondrial and peroxisomal metabolism of glutaryl-CoA. *Eur J Biochem* 146:663, 1985.
46. WHETSELL WO: The use of organotypic tissue culture for study of amino acid neurotoxicity and its antagonism in mammalian CNS. *Clin Neuropharm* 7 (*Suppl* 1):452, 1984.
47. STOKKE O, GOODMAN SI, MOE PG: Inhibition of brain glutamate decarboxylase by glutarate, glutaconate, and β-hydroxyglutarate: Explanation of the symptoms in glutaric aciduria. *Clin Chim Acta* 66:411, 1976.
48. APPEL SH: Membrane defects in Huntington's disease, in Chase TN, Wexler NS, Barbeau A (eds): *Huntington's Disease, Advances in Neurology*. New York, Raven, 1979, vol 23, p 387.
49. COYLE JT, LONDON ED, BIZIERE K, ZACZEK R: Kainic acid neurotoxicity: Insights into the pathophysiology of Huntington's disease, in Chase TN, Wexler NS, Barbeau A (eds): *Huntington's Disease, Advances in Neurology*. New York, Raven, 1979, vol 23, p 593.
50. BENNETT JP, LOGAN WJ, SNYDER SH: Amino acids as central nervous transmitters: The influence of ions, amino acid analogues, and ontogeny on transport systems for L-glutamic and L-aspartic acids and glycine into central nervous synaptosomes of the rat. *J Neurochem* 21:1533, 1973.
51. BALCAR VJ, JOHNSTON GAR: The structural specificity of the high affinity uptake of L-glutamate and L-aspartate by rat brain slices. *J Neurochem* 19:2657, 1972.
52. SCHWARCZ R, WHETSELL WO, MANGANO RM: Quinolinic acid: An endogenous metabolite that produces axon-sparing lesions in rat brain. *Science* 219:316, 1983.
53. MCGEER EG, SINGH E: Neurotoxic effects of endogenous materials: Quinolinic acid, L-pyroglutamic acid and TRH. *Exp Neurol* 86:410, 1984.
54. HEYES MP: Hypothesis: A role for quinolinic acid in the neuropathology of glutaric aciduria type I. *Can J Neurol Sci* 14:441, 1987.
55. WHETSELL WO, SCHWARCZ R: The organotypic tissue culture model of corticostriatal system used for examining amino acid neurotoxicity and its antagonism: Studies on kainic acid, quinolinic acid and (−)2-amino-7-phosphonoheptanoic acid. *J Neural Transm Suppl* 19:53, 1983.
56. KANG ES, GERALD PS: Hyperammonemia and Reye's syndrome. *N Engl J Med* 286:1216, 1972.
57. SHIH VE, GLICK TH, BERCU BB: Lysine metabolism in Reye's syndrome. *Lancet* 2:163, 1974.
58. BRANDT NJ, GREGERSEN N, CHRISTENSEN E, GRØN IH, RASMUSSEN K: Treatment of glutaryl-CoA dehydrogenase deficiency (glutaric aciduria). *J Pediatr* 94:669, 1979.
59. DAVIDOFF RA, SEAR ES: The effects of lioresal on synaptic activity in the isolated spinal cord. *Neurology* 24:957, 1974.
60. FUKUDA H, KUDO Y, ONO H: Effect of β-(p-chlorophenyl)-GABA (Baclofen) on spinal synaptic activity *Eur J Pharmacol* 44:17, 1977.

CHAPTER **31**

GLUTATHIONE SYNTHETASE DEFICIENCY AND OTHER DISORDERS OF THE γ-GLUTAMYL CYCLE

ALTON MEISTER
AGNE LARSSON

1. *Severe glutathione synthetase deficiency, an inborn error of glutathione metabolism, is associated with massive urinary excretion of 5-oxoproline, elevated levels of 5-oxoproline in the blood and cerebrospinal fluid, severe metabolic acidosis, tendency toward hemolysis, and defective central nervous system function. A block at this step of the γ-glutamyl cycle leads to generalized glutathione deficiency. Glutathione normally regulates its own biosynthesis by inhibiting γ-glutamylcysteine synthetase, the enzyme that catalyzes the first step in the synthesis of glutathione. Therefore, a marked reduction of glutathione levels leads to increased formation of γ-glutamylcysteine, which is converted to 5-oxoproline by the action of γ-glutamyl cyclotransferase (Fig. 31-1). The overproduction of 5-oxoproline exceeds the capacity of 5-oxoprolinase to convert this substrate to glutamate, and some of the 5-oxoproline formed is therefore excreted in the urine. Glutathione synthetase deficiency leads to a modified γ-glutamyl cycle in which there is a futile synthesis of γ-glutamylcysteine followed by its conversion to 5-oxoproline and cysteine.*
2. *A milder form of glutathione synthetase deficiency, apparently restricted to the erythrocyte, is associated with decreased erythrocyte glutathione levels and well-compensated hemolytic disease. 5-Oxoprolinuria does not occur in this condition. This inborn error is associated with synthesis of an unstable glutathione synthetase molecule. Turnover of the defective but active enzyme is sufficiently rapid in most tissues to compensate for the defect; however, this is not true for the erythrocyte in which protein synthesis does not take place.*
3. *Deficiency of γ-glutamylcysteine synthetase has been described in two sibs with hemolytic anemia, spinocerebellar degeneration, peripheral neuropathy, myopathy, and aminoaciduria. There was generalized glutathione deficiency and marked deficiency in the synthesis of γ-glutamyl cysteine.*
4. *Patients with inborn deficiency of γ-glutamyl transpeptidase exhibit central nervous system involvement, glutathionemia, and urinary excretion of substantial amounts of glutathione, as well as of γ-glutamylcysteine and cysteine moieties.*
5. *Individuals with inborn deficiency of 5-oxoprolinase excrete moderate amounts of 5-oxoproline in their urine and have higher than normal plasma levels of 5-oxoproline. The patients thus far studied do not have acidosis or other symptoms clearly related to the biochemical defect.*

GLUTATHIONE BIOCHEMISTRY AND PHYSIOLOGY

Glutathione (L-γ-glutamyl-L-cysteinylglycine) is present in virtually all mammalian tissues. It is found intracellularly in millimolar concentrations; plasma and urine contain much lower levels. The intracellular level of glutathione is much greater than that of cysteine and cystine; glutathione therefore seems to serve as a storage form of cysteine moieties.

Glutathione has two characteristic structural features: a γ-glutamyl linkage and a sulfhydryl group. These moieties of the tripeptide facilitate its participation in an impressive number and variety of functions. Glutathione participates in transhydrogenation reactions that are involved in the formation and maintenance of the sulfhydryl groups of other molecules (e.g., coenzyme A, various enzymes, and other proteins). Glutathione provides reducing capacity for various reactions, e.g., the formation of deoxyribonucleotides by ribonucleotide reductase. Glutathione functions in the detoxication of hydrogen peroxide, other peroxides, and free radicals. It also plays a role in detoxication of a variety of foreign compounds which interact with glutathione and which are ultimately excreted in the urine or feces in the form of mercapturic acids. Analogous derivatives of glutathione are formed with endogenous metabolites, e.g., in the metabolism of leukotrienes, prostaglandins, steroids, and melanins. There is evidence that the γ-glutamyl moiety of glutathione functions in the transport of amino acids (especially cystine and certain other neutral amino acids) and possibly also of peptides and amines.

The synthesis and degradation of glutathione take place by reactions of the γ-glutamyl cycle (Fig. 31-2). Since this cycle leads to the synthesis of glutathione, its function is closely connected with the several metabolic and physiological functions that are performed by this ubiquitous tripeptide. Glutathione is of importance in the function of the central nervous system; it is notable that many of the patients with defects of the γ-glutamyl cycle are mentally retarded and exhibit other brain defects. The functions and metabolism of glutathione have been reviewed.[1–5]

The intracellular synthesis of glutathione from its constituent amino acids, which occurs in virtually all mammalian tissues, takes place by reactions (1) and (2).[6]

$$\text{L-Glutamate} + \text{L-cysteine} + \text{ATP} \xrightarrow[\text{synthetase}]{\gamma\text{-glutamylcysteine}} \text{L-}\gamma\text{-glutamyl-L-cysteine} + \text{ADP} + P_i \quad (1)$$

$$\text{L-}\gamma\text{-Glutamyl-L-cysteine} + \text{glycine} + \text{ATP} \xrightarrow[\text{synthetase}]{\text{glutathione}} \text{glutathione} + \text{ADP} + P_i \quad (2)$$

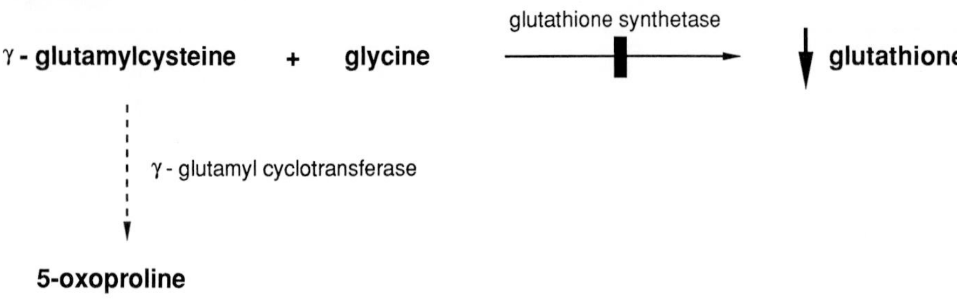

Fig. 31-1 In 5-oxoprolinuria, glutathione synthetase is blocked. The consequent deficiency of glutathione (a feedback inhibitor of γ-glutamylcysteine synthetase) leads to an excessive production of γ-glutamylcysteine, the γ-glutamyl moiety of which is converted to 5-oxoproline by γ-glutamyl cyclotransferase.

Patients who exhibit deficiency of the synthesis of glutathione are of three general types:[7,8]

1. Those with glutathione synthetase deficiency in whom the defect appears to be restricted to the erythrocytes.

2. Those in whom glutathione synthetase deficiency is generalized. Patients of this type exhibit increased urinary excretion of 5-oxoproline (synonyms: L-pyroglutamate, L-2-pyrrolidone-5-carboxylate). For this reason, this condition was initially called 5-oxoprolinuria (or pyroglutamic aciduria). This disease is interesting because the enzymatic block greatly reduces synthesis of glutathione, which normally inhibits γ-glutamylcysteine synthetase by feedback control. The block thus increases the activity of the latter enzyme, and it is this effect which leads to the massive accumulation and excretion of 5-oxoproline (Fig. 31-1). Sixteen patients with this disorder have been described.

3. Those with γ-glutamylcysteine synthetase deficiency; two such patients have been described.

It is interesting to note that although the three groups of patients listed above are deficient in either of the enzymes required for glutathione synthesis and exhibit markedly reduced levels of erythrocyte glutathione, they differ substantially with respect to other biochemical findings and in their clinical manifestations. Such patients must be distinguished from those who have enzymatic defects such as glucose-6-phosphate dehydrogenase deficiency in whom glutathione can be synthesized from its constituent amino acids at a normal rate, but in whom there is a deficiency in ability to maintain glutathione in the reduced form (see Chap. 91).[9]

Two other inborn errors of glutathione metabolism involve steps in its metabolism. The enzyme γ-glutamyl transpeptidase catalyzes the initial step in the degradation of glutathione. This enzyme catalyzes the transfer of the γ-glutamyl moiety of glutathione to an amino acid or other acceptor (which may be glutathione itself). Cystine is among the best acceptors of the γ-glutamyl moiety.

$$\text{Glutathione} + \text{L-cystine} = \text{L-}\gamma\text{-glutamyl-L-cystine} + \text{L-cysteinylglycine} \quad (3)$$

Another reaction of the γ-glutamyl cycle is that catalyzed by 5-oxoprolinase.

$$\text{5-Oxo-L-proline} + \text{ATP} + 2H_2O \rightarrow \text{L-glutamate} + \text{ADP} + P_i \quad (4)$$

Several individuals who have deficiencies of the enzymes that catalyze reactions (3) and (4) have been reported.

Fig. 31-2 The γ-glutamyl cycle.

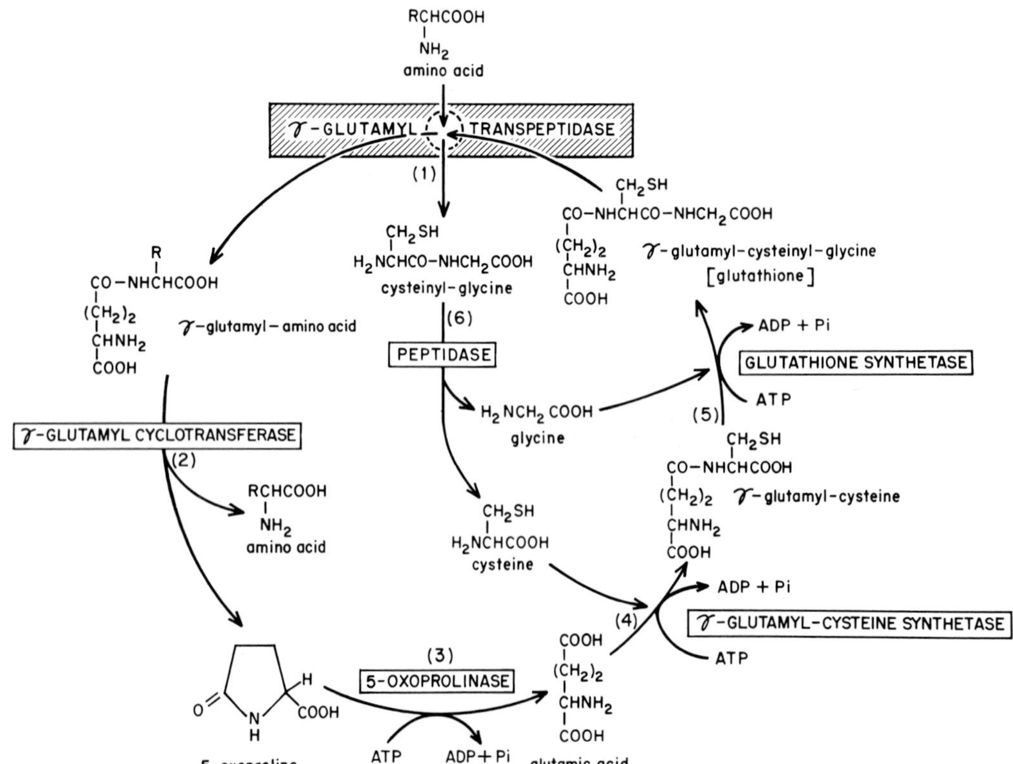

THE γ-GLUTAMYL CYCLE

The synthesis of glutathione and its utilization are linked by a series of six enzyme-catalyzed reactions which have been termed the γ-glutamyl cycle (Fig. 31-2).[2,5,10] Synthesis of glutathione takes place within cells by reactions (4) and (5) (Fig. 31-2). Glutathione is transported (exported) and becomes a substrate of γ-glutamyl transpeptidase, an enzyme bound to the external surfaces of certain cells. The action of γ-glutamyl transpeptidase leads to formation of γ-glutamyl amino acids and cysteinylglycine. The latter is cleaved by dipeptidase to form cysteine and glycine. γ-Glutamyl amino acids, formed in the transpeptidation reaction, are substrates of the intracellular enzyme γ-glutamyl cyclotransferase. Evidence for the transport of γ-glutamyl amino acids into cells has been obtained (see below). γ-Glutamyl cyclotransferase converts certain γ-glutamyl amino acids into the corresponding free amino acids and 5-oxoproline. 5-Oxoproline is decyclized to yield glutamate [Reaction (3)/(Fig. 31-2)]. The equilibrium between 5-oxoproline and glutamate at pH values near neutrality markedly favors cyclization,[11–13] and thus energy is required for decyclization. The mechanism of the coupling between ATP cleavage and that of the internal peptide bond of 5-oxoproline is now becoming understood. The reaction involves formation of an enzyme-bound phosphorylated derivative of 5-oxoproline, which is converted via γ-glutamyl phosphate to glutamate.[14,15]

γ-Glutamyl transpeptidase is localized in the epithelia of tissues that are extensively involved in transport, e.g., the nephron, choroid plexus, jejunum, and ciliary body.[16] Although purified preparations of γ-glutamyl transpeptidase can catalyze hydrolysis of glutathione and other γ-glutamyl compounds, there is much evidence that transpeptidation is a major function of the enzyme in vivo.[2,17] When the purified enzyme is incubated with glutathione and a mixture of amino acids that closely approximates the amino acid composition of plasma, about half of the glutathione utilized participates in transpeptidation with amino acids.[17] It is interesting to note that glutathione itself can serve as an acceptor substrate. When purified γ-glutamyl transpeptidase is incubated with various concentrations of glutathione (4 μM to 50 mM), the initial rates of formation of γ-glutamyl-glutathione are substantial at all concentrations of glutathione studied and are greater than the rates of formation of glutamate (indicating hydrolysis) at physiological intracellular concentrations of glutathione (1 to 10 mM).[18] It is notable that γ-glutamyl-glutathione has been found in bile, and evidence has been obtained that it is also formed in kidney.[18] The most active amino acid acceptors of the γ-glutamyl moiety include cystine,[19] glutamine, methionine, and other neutral amino acids.[20]

γ-Glutamyl transpeptidase is localized on the outer surface of the cell membrane, whereas glutathione is found predominantly intracellularly. The finding of an enzyme on one side of a membrane and of its substrate on the other led to the postulate that there must be a mechanism for transporting intracellular glutathione to the membrane-bound enzyme[21]; as discussed below, there is now much evidence for such transport (i.e., export). When γ-glutamyl transpeptidase is inhibited in vivo by treating animals with inhibitors of this enzyme, extensive glutathionuria results.[22] These and other studies[5,23] show that transported renal glutathione is a substrate of the transpeptidase. Transport of glutathione also occurs in other tissues with transpeptidase activity. Thus, transport of glutathione is a discrete step in the γ-glutamyl cycle. Export of glutathione and glutathione disulfide by cells has been observed in liver perfusion studies[24] and in cells grown in culture.[25–27] Export of glutathione is a general cellular phenomenon. Many cells normally export glutathione (rather than glutathione disulfide). This has been demonstrated in studies on a variety of mammalian cells (See Ref. 1, pages 1 to 22). Thus, glutathione, which is the major (>99.5 percent) intracellular form, is also the major export form. (Under certain experimental conditions involving use of oxidizing agents, export of glutathione disulfide has been observed, and it has been postulated that export of glutathione disulfide may function as an emergency system in the presence of extreme oxidative stress.) The normal cellular export of glutathione functions to provide a supply of thiols to the cell membrane and to its immediate environment. This serves in cellular protection and, for example, may function to protect against lipid peroxidation and to reduce the oxy radical form of α-tocopherol. In some cells, export of glutathione functions as part of a transport system for amino acids and as a recovery system for cysteine moieties.

In the kidney and other sites with high transpeptidase activity intracellular glutathione is transported to the membrane-bound enzyme, and the products of enzyme action are taken up by the cell. Tissues that have low transpeptidase activity transport glutathione to the extracellular fluid and plasma. When an inhibitor of glutathione synthesis such as buthionine sulfoximine[28] is given, there is a decrease in the tissue levels of glutathione, and this leads to decreased plasma glutathione levels. The prompt decline in the levels of glutathione in the liver and kidney that follow administration of an inhibitor of glutathione synthesis reflects the rapid turnover of glutathione in these tissues. Such turnover is very largely due to export of glutathione, which continues after glutathione synthesis is stopped. The rate of decline in glutathione level decreases markedly when the level reaches 15 to 20 percent of the initial value. That the value decreases very slowly from this level to zero reflects sequestration of glutathione within the mitochondria. Mitochondria do not synthesize glutathione but obtain it by transport from the cytoplasm.[29]

When an inhibitor of transpeptidase is given, plasma glutathione levels increase. Plasma glutathione levels are normally in the micromolar range (rat, ≈ 35 μM; human, 1 to 3 μM).[30] Most of the plasma glutathione is supplied by the liver, which also exports some glutathione to the bile. Glutathione is removed from plasma by the action of transpeptidase, much of which is located in the kidney. Kidney uses glutathione that is transported from renal cells (intraorgan cycle) as well as glutathione present in the plasma. The transport of glutathione from renal cells to the renal tubule accounts for about 80 percent of the tubular glutathione; the remainder comes from the plasma via glomerular filtration. Experiments on anephric animals treated with transpeptidase inhibitor show that about two-thirds of the plasma glutathione is used by the kidney and the remainder by extrarenal transpeptidase.[31] Since about 80 percent of arterial plasma glutathione is removed during passage through the kidney, there must be a mechanism distinct from glomerular filtration for removing glutathione. The nonfiltration mechanism was at first thought to involve transport of glutathione across the basolateral circulation of the kidney.[32] However, it is now clear that the nonfiltration mechanism involves the activity of γ-glutamyl transpeptidase located in the basolateral circulation.[33–35] Studies with several types of isotopically labeled glutathione failed to detect net basolateral transport of glutathione; these studies showed that there is extensive breakdown of glutathione by the actions of basolateral γ-glutamyl transpeptidase and dipeptidase. No net basolateral transport of γ-glutamyl amino acids was detected in these studies, supporting the view that the transport of γ-glutamyl amino acids into renal cells takes place on the tubular side.[35] As noted above, kidney and probably other cells have a transport mechanism for γ-glutamyl amino acids which is separate from those that transport free amino acids. Such transport has been shown in vivo[36] and in vitro using kidney slices.[37] The membrane transport of γ-glutamyl amino acids may be analogous to the transport of certain other dipeptides.[38]

The γ-glutamyl amino acid transport system appears to be part of a mechanism for the recovery and transport of cysteine moieties. In this pathway, γ-glutamylcystine is formed by the action of γ-glutamyl transpeptidase on glutathione and cystine.[19] The apparent K_m value for L-cystine as an acceptor substrate of the transpeptidase is about 30 μM, whereas the plasma concentration of cystine is in the range 30 to 60 μM. γ-Glutamylcystine is readily transported into renal cells where it is reduced to form cysteine and γ-glutamylcysteine.[39] The latter can be used directly as a substrate of glutathione synthetase, thus providing an alternative pathway of glutathione biosynthesis. These and other studies, which show that γ-glutamyl amino acids are transported into cells, usually more rapidly than the corresponding free amino acids, support the γ-glutamyl cycle hypothesis of amino acid transport. Thus, a major function of γ-glutamyl transpeptidase seems to be connected with the recovery of cellular cystine. An important function of the γ-glutamyl cycle is thus to provide glutathione for export, a process which may be essential for cell membrane protection. It is likely that the in vivo transport of other γ-glutamyl amino acids such as γ-glutamyl methionine and γ-glutamyl glutamine is accompanied by conversion to 5-oxoproline and the corresponding free amino acids.

Several modifications of the scheme given in Fig. 31-2 have been considered.[2,5,23] For example, γ-glutamyl amino acids might be hydrolyzed to some extent to yield glutamate and free amino acids. Successive transpeptidation reactions may occur; γ-glutamyl amino acids can serve as acceptors of the γ-glutamyl group, leading to formation of di-γ-glutamyl amino acids. It is of interest that γ-glutamyl cyclotransferase is most active toward the L-γ-glutamyl derivatives of the L isomers of several amino acids, e.g., glutamine, methionine, alanine, cysteine, cystine, and serine. The enzyme is also highly active toward a variety of di-γ-glutamyl amino acids, which may be formed by the action of transpeptidase.[40]

Studies on the activities of the several enzymes of the γ-glutamyl cycle suggest that the reaction catalyzed by 5-oxoprolinase may be the slowest step and may therefore be rate limiting. However, there seems to be sufficient 5-oxoprolinase to maintain the 5-oxoproline levels in various mammalian tissues at relatively low steady-state values (20 to 50 μM).[41–43] Even a complete block of 5-oxoprolinase activity does not stop the function of the γ-glutamyl cycle since glutamate can be produced by other pathways, such as hydrolysis of glutamine and transamination or reductive amination of α-ketoglutarate.

γ-Glutamylcysteine synthetase is nonallosterically inhibited by glutathione.[44] Studies on the rat kidney enzyme indicated that glutathione is a competitive inhibitor with respect to glutamate; the apparent K_i value for glutathione (2.3 mM) is about equivalent to the concentration of glutathione in rat kidney. γ-Glutamyl-α-aminobutyrate and γ-glutamyl-α-aminobutyrylglycine inhibit the enzyme much less than do the corresponding sulfhydryl compounds, suggesting that glutathione also binds to another site on the enzyme and that its sulfhydryl group is involved in such binding. Glutathione may bind to both the glutamate and the cysteine binding sites of the enzyme. The data on kidney γ-glutamylcysteine synthetase activity thus show that this enzyme is inhibited by glutathione under conditions similar to those that prevail in vivo, indicating a physiologically significant feedback control mechanism. This appears to be a general mechanism since inhibition by glutathione of γ-glutamylcysteine synthetase from erythrocytes[45,46] and liver[47] has also been observed. The biosynthesis of glutathione is affected by other metabolic phenomena, especially by variation of the intracellular levels of cysteine. The apparent K_m value for L-cysteine for γ-glutamylcysteine synthetase is about 0.3 mM, a value not far from the usual intracellular levels of cysteine.

As discussed in this chapter, several types of blocks of the γ-glutamyl cycle have been observed in humans. Animal models of several of these diseases have been produced by use of specific enzyme inhibitors.[48] Thus, administration of a competitive inhibitor of 5-oxoprolinase to mice leads to an appreciable increase in the tissue levels of 5-oxoproline and to urinary excretion of this compound. When an L-amino acid was given together with the inhibitor, there was a substantial increase of 5-oxoproline accumulation and excretion.[42] Administration of amino acids increases transpeptidation and thus the amount of 5-oxoproline formed by γ-glutamyl cyclotransferase. Similar results were obtained in studies in which animals were also given inhibitors of γ-glutamylcysteine synthetase, indicating that the formation of 5-oxoproline by the combined activities of γ-glutamylcysteine synthetase and γ-glutamyl cyclotransferase is not normally a major pathway for 5-oxoproline formation; however, such a pathway occurs in 5-oxoprolinuria, as discussed below.

Administration of small amounts of amino acids does not affect glutathione levels[49] because there is rapid resynthesis of glutathione; however, administration of larger amounts of amino acids may decrease renal glutathione levels.[50] This reduction does not occur after giving inhibitors of γ-glutamyl transpeptidase. When a competitive inhibitor of γ-glutamyl cyclotransferase is given to animals, there is a marked decrease in the 5-oxoproline level of the kidney, and studies with a model substrate showed that this is due to in vivo inhibition of γ-glutamyl cyclotransferase.[51] γ-Glutamylcysteine synthetase may be inhibited in vivo by giving the specific inhibitor buthionine sulfoximine.[28] Methionine sulfoximine also inhibits this enzyme[52] as well as glutamine synthetase.[53] However, buthionine sulfoximine inhibits only the synthesis of glutathione. α-Ethylmethionine sulfoximine specifically inhibits glutamine synthetase and has no effect on γ-glutamylcysteine synthetase.[54] Experimental animals treated with inhibitors of γ-glutamyl transpeptidase exhibit biochemical phenomena which are similar to those observed in patients with γ-glutamyl transpeptidase deficiency (see below).

The development of selective inhibitors of glutathione biosynthesis and of other reactions of the γ-glutamyl cycle has made it possible to modulate the metabolism of glutathione.[55–59,133] Several approaches have been developed that lead to increased cellular levels of glutathione.[39,60–67] Glutathione levels may be increased by administration of L-2-oxothiazolidine-4-carboxylate, which is a good substrate of 5-oxoprolinase. It is effectively transported into cells and converted to cysteine, which is used for glutathione synthesis.[60–63] Administration of γ-glutamylcystine (and similar compounds) leads to increased renal levels of glutathione.[39] Although glutathione itself is not effectively transported into cells, half-esters (ethyl, isopropyl, etc.) of glutathione (γ-glu-cySH-gly-ester) are rapidly transported into cells and are deesterified intracellularly.[64–66] In general, an increase in the glutathione level of a cell makes it more resistant to certain antitumor agents and also more resistant to radiation and oxidative effects. On the other hand, therapy that decreases cellular glutathione levels promotes sensitivity to certain drugs, radiation, and oxygen. Of much interest, certain tumor cells that have become resistant to radiation and to certain anticancer agents have been found to have developed high levels of glutathione; treatment with buthionine sulfoximine decreases the cellular glutathione levels and resensitizes these cells to anticancer drugs and to radiation. It is thus evident that modulation of the metabolism of glutathione may provide a means to selectively destroy or protect cells.[56–59,133]

INBORN ERRORS OF GLUTATHIONE METABOLISM

Severe Glutathione Synthetase Deficiency (5-Oxoprolinuria)

The first patient with this inborn error of metabolism was reported in 1970 by Jellum et al.[68] The patient was a 19-year-old boy of normal height and weight who had been mentally retarded since childhood. He showed signs of organic cerebral damage with spastic quadraparesis and cerebellar disturbances. Abnormalities included increased resistance to passive movement, predominantly of the pyramidal type, retarded voluntary movements, pronounced tremor, and impaired coordination. Speech was simple, childlike, and dysarthric. His IQ (Wechsler) was about 60. At age 17, the patient was treated surgically for a diaphragmatic hernia,[69] and postoperatively he developed life-threatening acidosis, which was successfully treated with daily infusions containing potassium and bicarbonate ions. Later he was maintained on oral sodium bicarbonate.

The most remarkable biochemical finding was excretion between 24 and 34.5 g (0.19 to 0.27 mol) of 5-oxoproline per day in his urine. Urinary excretion of urea was 11.8 g/day, a value considered to be 35 to 45 percent of that normally expected. The urinary 5-oxoproline was identified by thin layer chromatography, gas-liquid chromatography, and mass spectrometry. The serum contained 5-oxoproline and another glutamic acid derivative which was not identified.

The patient became jaundiced and seriously ill immediately after birth, but recovered spontaneously. During childhood he exhibited various neurologic symptoms which were progressive. In retrospect, it appears that he had chronic metabolic acidosis, which was compensated until the surgical procedure was carried out.

Hagenfeldt et al.[70] described the second patient found to have this disease. This female infant developed severe metabolic acidosis on the third day of life. Acidosis was corrected by intravenous administration of sodium bicarbonate; discontinuation of treatment led to return of acidosis. Subsequently, the patient has been treated continuously with sodium bicarbonate. Examination at age 11 and 14 months showed no neurologic or other abnormalities, and psychomotor development was normal. The patient excreted between 48 and 54 mmol of 5-oxoproline per day. It was established that this was 5-oxo-L-proline by assays done with L-glutamate dehydrogenase after conversion of 5-oxoproline to glutamate by acid hydrolysis. The plasma level of 5-oxoproline was 4.5 m*M*. Aminoaciduria was not found, nor were any unusual peptides detected in the urine. On the third day of life, the hemoglobin concentration was 15 g/dl blood; the level of hemoglobin decreased continuously to 7 to 8 g/dl at age 3 weeks. The anemia disappeared spontaneously after 2 months, although some reticulocytosis was observed. At age 2 years 10 months, there was a mild macrocytic anemia with a hemoglobin concentration of 8.5 to 11.5 g/dl. At this age, development was normal, there were no neurologic symptoms, and the electroencephalogram and motor nerve conduction velocity were normal.

A third case of this disease (the younger sister of the second patient) was studied by Larsson et al.[71] This case is instructive because the diagnosis was made at birth. Increased urinary excretion of 5-oxoproline was observed during the first day of life, and increased levels of 5-oxoproline were also found in the amniotic fluid at birth. The acid-base balance of this patient was normal for 4 h after birth, but she then developed metabolic acidosis, and by age 20 h, the blood pH had decreased to 7.3. Both this patient and her older sister exhibited an increased rate of hemolysis. These two siblings have been carefully followed up to puberty.[72,73] They were found to exhibit a progressive decline in their results on different psychometric tests, which indicated mild mental retardation. Neurologic examinations did not reveal abnormalities, but both patients gave pathologic responses in electroretinograms with decreased or abolished oscillatory potentials.

The Enzymatic Defect and Mechanism of 5-Oxoprolinuria

The enzyme defect in this inborn error of metabolism was identified by determinations of enzyme activities carried out on the cultured skin fibroblasts of patient 2, erythrocytes from patient 2 and from her younger sister (patient 3), and placenta obtained at the delivery of patient 3.[74] Studies on several enzyme activities of the placenta and cultured skin fibroblasts of these patients and controls are summarized in Table 31-1. The activities of γ-glutamylcysteine synthetase and of γ-glutamyl cyclotransferase of the placenta of patient 3 were similar to control values. However, the glutathione synthetase activity of the placenta was only about 2 percent of controls. Extracts of the cultured fibroblasts from patient 3 contained activities of γ-glutamylcysteine synthetase, γ-glutamylcyclotransferase, and 5-oxoprolinase that were somewhat greater than the corresponding activities found in fibroblasts obtained from a 1.5-year-old control subject. In contrast, the glutathione synthetase activity of the patient's fibroblasts was less than 5 percent of that of the controls. Studies on the erythrocytes of patients 2 and 3, their parents, and controls are summarized in Table 31-2. Erythrocytes from the patients and their parents had γ-glutamylcysteine synthetase and γ-glutamylcyclotransferase activity similar to those in control samples. However, a marked deficiency of glutathione synthetase was found in erythrocytes from the patients. The values were about 5 to 10 percent of those of control samples. The erythrocyte glutathione synthetase of the father was appreciably less, and the value for the mother's erythrocytes was somewhat lower than that of controls. Determinations of glutathione synthetase activity of mixtures of extracts obtained from patients in the

Table 31-1 Enzyme Activities of Placenta and Cultured Fibroblasts of Patients with 5-Oxoprolinuria*

	Placenta		*Fibroblasts*	
Enzyme activity	*Patient*	*Control*	*Patient*	*Controls*
γ-Glutamylcysteine synthetase	79	63	83	47
Glutathione synthetase	1.7	77	<2.0	46,72
γ-Glutamyl cyclotransferase	198	163	83	40
5-Oxoprolinase	. . .	. . .	6.1	3.5

*The activities are expressed as nanomoles per hour per milligram of protein.
SOURCE: Wellner et al.[74]

control subjects gave strictly additive results. The erythrocytes from patients 2 and 3 were found to have very low concentrations of glutathione. Similarly, the placenta (patient 3) contained 0.16 m*M* glutathione (control, 0.56 m*M*).

The enzyme studies indicated a marked deficiency of glutathione synthetase activity in several types of tissue obtained from two patients with this disorder. The deficiency was found in erythrocytes, placenta, and cultured skin fibroblasts and indicated that a generalized glutathione synthetase deficiency was responsible for a generalized deficiency of glutathione. It is notable that the erythrocytes of the father and possibly also of the mother of the patients exhibited glutathione synthetase activity intermediate between those of the patients and of the control subjects. This suggests that the condition, which is apparently an autosomal recessive, may be detected in heterozygotes (see also Ref. 75).

An understanding of the way in which a block of glutathione synthetase can produce 5-oxoprolinuria involves consideration of the γ-glutamyl cycle and certain properties of the enzymes involved. Glutathione is not a substrate of γ-glutamyl cyclotransferase, and therefore this tripeptide may accumulate in cells in substantial concentrations, as it does under normal conditions. In contrast, γ-glutamylcysteine is an excellent substrate of γ-glutamyl cyclotransferase as well as of γ-glutamyl transpeptidase and glutathione synthetase (Fig. 31-3). The normal tissue concentration of γ-glutamylcysteine is very low, perhaps less than 1 percent of that of glutathione. It is possible that normally γ-glutamylcysteine is protected from the action of γ-glutamyl cyclotransferase, perhaps by close linkage between the two synthetases or by compartmentalization within the cell.[10] The affinity of glutathione synthetase for γ-glutamylcysteine may be greater than the affinities of the other enzymes that act on this substrate. Since γ-glutamylcysteine is a good substrate for γ-glutamyl transpeptidase,[20] this dipeptide might serve in place of glutathione as a γ-glutamyl donor in transpeptidation reactions with amino acids [reaction (3), Fig. 31-3]. However, γ-glutamylcysteine which is not used for glutathione synthesis or for transpeptidation reactions would be converted to 5-oxoproline and cysteine [Reaction (4), Fig. 31-3]. A block in glutathione synthesis would lead to 5-oxoprolinuria if more than normal amounts of γ-glutamylcysteine were formed and converted to 5-oxoproline by the action of γ-glutamyl cyclotransferase, and if the overproduction of 5-oxoproline exceeded the capacity of 5-oxoprolinase to convert this substrate to glutamate.[10] This indeed seems to be the mechanism of 5-oxoprolinuria. It appears that γ-glutamylcysteine synthetase normally functions at substantially less than its maximal capacity because of feedback inhibition of glutathione. In the absence or marked reduction in the cellular level of glutathione there is increased formation of γ-glutamylcysteine, which is efficiently converted to 5-oxoproline.

This is an interesting example of a metabolic block that prevents the synthesis of a compound which functions normally as a feedback inhibitor. The compound that accumulates as a result of the block is derived from the immediate precursor of the feedback inhibitor. The metabolic defect in this disease therefore leads to a modified γ-glutamyl cycle (Fig. 31-4) in which γ-glutamylcysteine synthesis is followed by its conversion to 5-oxoproline and cysteine. In the modified cycle, γ-glutamylcysteine replaces glutathione as a γ-glutamyl donor for transpeptidation reactions, and cysteine is recycled. The modified γ-glutamyl cycle proposed for this condition is mediated by the action of only four enzymes; neither cysteinylgylcinase nor glutathione synthetase activity is involved. It would be interesting to learn whether patients with 5-oxoprolinuria have any abnormalities involving the metabolism of glycine.

Early studies on the first patient found to have this inborn error led to consideration of the idea that the patient had a defect in one of the steps in the urea cycle. Although this possibility was later discarded, some interesting studies on the patient were reported. It was found that administration of ammonium bicarbonate, sodium glutamate, or glutamine did not influence the urinary excretion of 5-oxoproline.[76–78] There was an apparent correlation between the excretion of urinary ammonia and 5-oxoproline; the molar excretion of ammonium was about half that of 5-oxoproline even when the urinary pH was brought to the alkaline range by oral administration of sodium bicarbonate. When this patient was given an intravenous infusion containing a mixture of 19 amino acids, the blood levels of the amino acids increased substantially, about as expected, and the urinary excretion of 5-oxoproline increased about twofold.

Studies in which this patient and a control subject were

Table 31-2 Enzyme Activities and Glutathione Content of Erythrocytes from 5-Oxoprolinuria Patients, Their Parents, and Controls

		Glutathione synthetase	*γ-Glutamylcysteine synthetase*	*γ-Glutamyl cyclotransferase*	
	Age, yr	*nmol/(h · mg hemoglobin)*			*Glutathione, mM**
Patient 2	0.25	1.5	58	44	<0.01
Patient 3	3	1.3	59	44	<0.01
Father	30	8.6	50	40	
Mother	30	12	52	41	
Control ♀	4	24	61	39	
Control ♂	36	15	61	41	

*Normal range, 1 to 2 m*M*.
SOURCE: Wellner et al.[74]

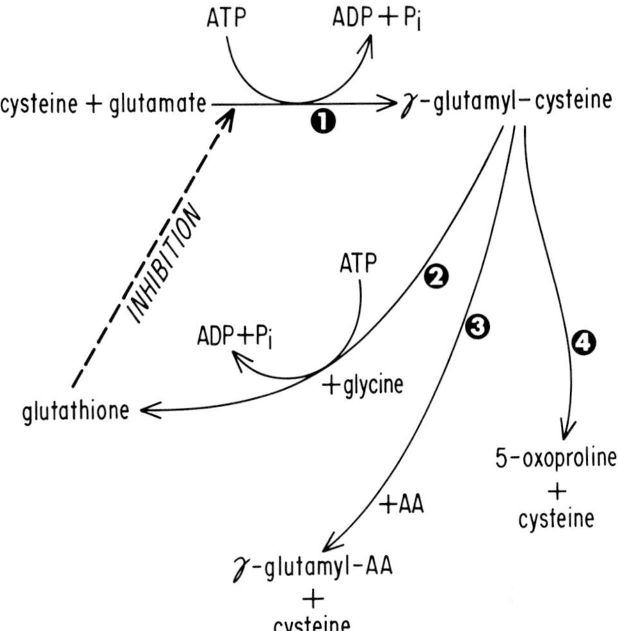

Fig. 31-3 Metabolic interrelationships in glutathione biosynthesis. (1) γ-Glutamylcysteine synthetase; (2) glutathione synthetase; (3) γ-glutamyl transpeptidase; (4) γ-glutamyl cyclotransferase. *(From Richman and Meister.[44] Used by permission.)*

given an intraveneous injection of a tracer dose of uniformly labeled 5-oxo-L-[^{14}C]proline and in which the excretion of radioactive respiratory carbon dioxide was determined seemed to be consistent with the idea that the patient had a block at the 5-oxoprolinase step of the γ-glutamyl cycle. However, this idea was withdrawn on the basis of later studies.[77] Recalculation of these data indicated that endogenous production of 5-oxoproline is about 62 to 80 g/day, or more than twice the amount excreted in the urine. Similarly, studies in which the second patient was given radioactive 5-oxoproline showed a daily synthesis of about 210 mmol of 5-oxoproline, of which about 50 mmol was excreted in the urine, indicating an endogenous utilization of 5-oxoproline of about 75 percent.[70] Thus, studies on patients 1 and 2 are in accord with the explanation for 5-oxoprolinuria given above. It is evident that 5-oxoproline accumulation exceeds the capacity of 5-oxoprolinase to convert this compound to glutamate.

Certain observations made on the first patient may be understood in terms of the modified γ-glutamyl cycle (Fig. 31-4). The marked increase in this patient's urinary excretion

Fig. 31-4 Modified γ-glutamyl cycle in 5-oxoprolinuria. *(From Wellner et al.[74] Used by permission.)*

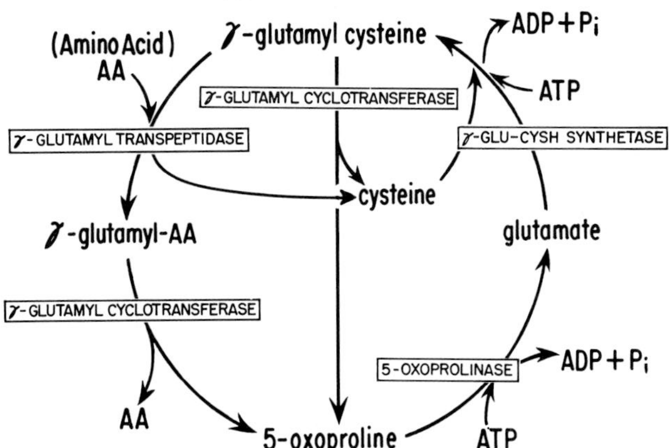

of 5-oxoproline following intravenous administration of amino acids may have represented an increase in transpeptidation in response to the increase in amino acid levels, followed by a corresponding increase in conversion of γ-glutamyl amino acids into 5-oxoproline, with "overflow" of the latter compound into the urine. An analogous situation has been observed in studies on mice.[42]

Pathophysiology and Other Considerations of Glutathione Synthetase Deficiency

A total of 16 patients with severe glutathione synthetase deficiency associated with 5-oxoprolinuria have thus far been recognized in several different countries.[79] Ten of the sixteen patients were male, and three pairs of sibs with this disorder have been observed.

Some general conclusions about the known cases of severe glutathione synthetase deficiency may be drawn. All of them show markedly decreased erythrocyte glutathione synthetase activity levels and also decreased erythrocyte glutathione levels. Most exhibit an increased rate of hemolysis and some degree of central nervous system involvement. However, even in the small group of patients thus far studied, there is considerable variability in the chemical and clinical findings reflecting substantial biochemical heterogeneity, as has been noted in a number of other inborn errors of metabolism. It will be of importance to establish whether all the patients carry the same mutant allele for glutathione synthetase. Preliminary studies on erythrocyte extracts from two patients showed that the mutant enzyme exhibited normal affinity for its substrates,[71] but somewhat different results were obtained in another study.[80] It will be of importance to isolate the enzymes and to determine the nucleotide sequences of the normal and mutant glutathione synthetase genes.

Metabolic acidosis due to accumulation of the acid, 5-oxoproline, is usually the first symptom. Correction of acidosis by therapy with bicarbonate or citrate is essential. This is of particular importance because hyperbilirubinemia is a common complication, and acidosis increases the risk of bilirubin encephalopathy. It is possible that some of the neurologic symptoms observed in patients with this condition may be due to bilirubin toxicity. Neonatal hyperbilirubinemia is common in these patients because they exhibit an increased rate of hemolysis which is directly associated with decreased levels of glutathione in the erythrocytes. The tendency for these patients to exhibit increased rate of hemolysis is evidenced by reticulocytosis, decreased plasma levels of haptoglobin, or increased levels of carbomonoxy-hemoglobin.

Two of the patients were found to exhibit an apparent increased susceptibility to bacterial infections. In one patient, the recurrent episodes of bacterial infections were associated with neutropenia and defective granulocyte function.[81] This defect was corrected by administration of large doses of vitamin E.[82,83]

Symptoms relating to the central nervous system affect both intellectual and motor functions. This was particularly striking in the first patient, but this patient received no therapy for acidosis for the first 17 years of his life. Patients 2 and 3, who were treated constantly for acidosis, exhibited a progressive decline in mental ability. Although progressive mental retardation appears to be a general finding in these patients, the degree of severity varies.

The extent of 5-oxoprolinuria also appears to vary considerably, but the reported data are difficult to compare.[79] The excretion of 5-oxoproline in some patients is much less than that observed in the first patient. Although detection and quantitation of 5-oxoproline in urine and plasma is quite feasible, a reliable procedure for mass screening is not yet available (see Refs. 83 and 84). It may be noted that 5-oxoproline does not react with ninhydrin. A rapid screening method for blood glutathione levels has been devised in which dried spots of blood on filter paper are treated with 5,5′-dithiobis(2-nitrobenzoic acid).[85,86] This test or a modification of it may be of value in detecting patients who have lower than normal levels of erythrocyte glutathione.

Patients with severe glutathione synthetase deficiency (and also those with the milder form of this condition; see below) exhibit increased rates of hemolysis and in this respect resemble patients with glucose-6-phosphate dehydrogenase deficiency.[9] Consequently it has been recommended that such patients avoid exposure to certain drugs and food products known to precipitate hemolytic crises in patients with glucose-6-phosphate dehydrogenase deficiency.[8] Such recommendations are amply justified by experience with drugs such as acetaminophen whose detoxication involves reaction with glutathione. Cells with decreased levels of glutathione are known to be more sensitive to the effects of radiation, oxygen, and certain drugs.[2] In this respect it is of interest that cells obtained from patients with glutathione synthetase deficiency were more sensitive to ionizing radiation than normal cells as revealed by DNA breakage or clonogenic survival.[87,88] The oxygen enhancement ratio was markedly decreased in such cells. Similarly, there is evidence that lymphocytes from patients with glutathione synthetase deficiency are more sensitive to metabolites of acetaminophen.[89,90,91] It is interesting to note that the lymphocytes of subjects who are heterozygous for glutathione synthetase deficiency are also more sensitive than controls.[92] These considerations suggest the importance of exercising caution with respect to oxygen therapy, radiation, and certain drugs in the management of patients with glutathione synthetase deficiency.

Treatment of glutathione synthetase deficiency by administration of α-tocopherol has been considered. Defective granulocyte function was found to be corrected by administration of massive doses of α-tocopherol.[81] Impaired erythrocyte survival has been observed in a patient with glutathione synthetase deficiency. Both this patient and one with glucose-6-phosphate dehydrogenase deficiency were found to exhibit increased reticulocyte counts when given α-tocopherol.[83] Treatment of patients with glutathione synthetase deficiency with large doses of vitamin E may have protective effects on blood cells, but protective effects on the central nervous system have not yet been observed. In one patient such therapy did not prevent psychomotor retardation at 2 to 3 years of age.[93]

Therapy of glutathione synthetase deficiency has also been attempted with oral administration of glutathione and 2-mercaptopropionylglycine.[72] Such therapy did not affect urinary excretion of 5-oxoproline, plasma levels of 5-oxoproline, acid-base balance, and erythrocyte glutathione levels. Similar negative findings were observed after administration of *N*-acetylcysteine.[94]

Recent studies have indicated that glutathione monoesters are efficiently transported into many cells, whereas glutathione itself is not.[64–66] Thus, after administration of glutathione monoesters to mice, increased glutathione levels have been found in liver, kidney, and other tissues. However, no increase in the overall glutathione concentration of the brain was observed. Although therapy with glutathione monoesters may be of some value to patients with glutathione synthetase deficiency, the apparent inability of this compound to cross the blood-brain barrier would seem to limit its usefulness in therapy designed to prevent central nervous system damage. On the other hand, administration of L-2-oxothiazolidine-4-carboxylate has been found to increase cysteine levels in mouse brain.[95] This type of therapy might conceivably raise total thiol levels of the brain, but whether cysteine could replace glutathione in protection of the central nervous system is not known.

Incubation of fibroblasts from a patient with 5-oxoprolinuria with L-serine and borate (a combination known to inhibit γ-glutamyl transpeptidase[96]) caused more than a twofold increase in the content of cellular glutathione.[97] (A similar result was observed in the kidneys of mice treated with serine and borate.[50]) Such treatment decreased the formation of 5-oxoproline from glutamate in 5-oxoprolinuric fibroblasts.[97] The suggestion that inhibition of γ-glutamyl transpeptidase may be a useful approach to elevating the effects of glutathione synthetase deficiency needs to be further explored. However, it should be noted that inhibition of γ-glutamyl transpeptidase leads to increased extracellular levels of glutathione and that intracellular levels of glutathione are generally unaffected or decreased somewhat in experimental systems.[67]

Another therapy that has been considered consists of partial inhibition of γ-glutamylcysteine synthetase. Moderate doses of buthionine sulfoximine might decrease the overproduction of γ-glutamylcysteine (without stopping synthesis of glutathione completely), and thus decrease 5-oxoproline formation and ameliorate acidosis.[98] This approach appears to suffer from the disadvantage that γ-glutamylcysteine may conceivably substitute for glutathione in certain cellular processes. It would seem undesirable to inhibit the initial step in glutathione biosynthesis with patients who have a marked deficiency of this tripeptide. The possibility that γ-glutamylcysteine may be a substitute for glutathione with patients with glutathione synthetase deficiency needs to be considered. The report[68] of an unidentified glutamic acid derivative in the urine of patient 1 is consistent with accumulation of γ-glutamylcysteine. However, accumulation of γ-glutamylcysteine has not been seen in other patients. It has been reported that in normal fibroblasts γ-glutamylcysteine accumulates substantially, in fact to about 30 percent of the glutathione levels.[99] There is, however, some variability in regard to this finding, and further studies need to be carried out.

The activity of thioredoxin and of its reductase was normal in extracts of skin fibroblasts obtained from patients with severe glutathione synthetase deficiency. These findings suggest that the levels of glutathione and thioredoxin are regulated independently.[100] Similar results were obtained with fibroblasts obtained from a cystinotic patient. The activities of CuZn superoxide dismutase, Mn superoxide dismutase, catalase, and glutathione peroxidase were found to be in the normal range in studies in cultured fibroblasts from patients with severe glutathione synthetase deficiency.[101]

Some additional and intriguing observations were made on the first patient when he was 24 years old.[102] His condition had gradually deteriorated neurologically, and he began to have frequent seizures. He continued to be treated with sodium bicarbonate and was also given potassium salts, chlorpromazine, and clonazepam. The glutathione synthetase activity of his erythrocytes was found to be less than 2 percent of that of controls. Remarkably, it was found that his erythrocytes were loaded with free amino acids in concentrations that were 5 to 100 times the normal levels. Thus, marked elevations in the concentrations of threonine, serine, asparagine, glutamate, proline, glycine, alanine, valine, methionine, isoleucine, leucine, tyrosine, phenylalanine, tryptophan, ornithine, lysine, histidine, and arginine were found in three different specimens of the patient's blood. The erythrocytes contained no detectable glutathione at the time of analysis. On at least two occasions, a substantial amount of methionine sulfoxide was found in the erythrocytes. After the deproteinized extracts of the patients erythrocytes were hydrolyzed in 6 *M* hydrochloric acid in vacuo for 16 h at 105°C, analyses of the hydrolysates revealed increases in a number of amino acids that could not be accounted for by hydrolysis of glutathione, 5-oxoproline, glutamine, and asparagine. No such amino acid accumulation occurred in the patient's skeletal muscle, in which the glutathione level was found to be 3 percent of normal. A repetition of this study carried out above 1 year after the initial observations were made showed erythrocyte glutathione levels that were 5 to 10 percent of normal. At this time much lower levels of amino acids were found, although several continue to be present in elevated concentrations.[103] Similar studies were later carried out on patients 2 and 3[104] and on another patient with 5-oxoprolinuria.[105] The erythrocytes of these patients contained glutathione levels that were 2 to 17 percent of normal. There were only minor changes in the amino acid levels.

There is as yet no satisfactory explanation for the marked concentration of amino acids in the erythrocytes found at one time during the life of the first patient. Several possible explanations have been given,[102–104,106] but none of these seems consistent with all the currently available facts about glutathione metabolism and function. Although it has been suggested that there is a relationship between the level of erythrocyte glutathione and the remarkable accumulation of free amino acids (and apparently also of peptides) into erythrocytes, the nature of this relationship is not clear, and other explanations for the findings are conceivable.

The first patient died at age 28. Pathologic examination of his brain showed selective atrophy of the granule cell layer of the cerebellum and focal lesions in the frontoparietal cortex and bilaterally in the visual cortex and the thalamus. The type and distribution of the lesions resembled those seen after mercury intoxication, and it was therefore suggested that treatment with an antioxidant might be of value in severe glutathione synthetase deficiency.[107]

Glutathione Synthetase Deficiency without 5-Oxoprolinuria

In this condition, glutathione synthetase deficiency appears to be restricted to the erythrocyte. A large family with a number of members with decreased erythrocyte glutathione levels and well-compensated hemolytic disease was described,[108,109] and later two unrelated patients with hemolytic anemia and decreased erythrocyte glutathione levels were reported.[110] A similar patient was found to have a marked deficiency of erythrocyte glutathione synthetase activity. The erythrocytes from the patients and children of these patients had glutathione synthetase activity levels that were about half of those of controls.[111] This latter patient, as well as his heterozygous relatives, had normal levels of erythrocyte γ-glutamylcysteine synthetase activity. More recently, two brothers with erythrocyte glutathione synthetase deficiency have been described.[112] It thus appears that this genetic defect has been found in at least four families and is inferred on the basis of indirect evidence to occur in other families. All these patients have well-compensated hemolytic anemia. Three had enlarged spleens. There was no indication of neonatal jaundice in these patients, and there is no report of neurologic deficiency. Later studies on several patients showed that they do not have 5-oxoprolinuria.[113] The leukocytes and cultured skin fibroblasts obtained from one of the patients have been investigated.[80] These cells were found to have significant levels of glutathione synthetase activity and also of glutathione. Much lower values for the corresponding levels in erythrocytes were found. It was reported that the enzyme activity of the patient's leukocytes and fibroblasts was less stable on storage at 4°C and after dialysis than found in controls. In another study[112] two sibs with erythrocyte glutathione synthetase deficiency who had only about 3 percent of the normal level of glutathione in the erythrocytes had normal levels of glutathione in their leukocytes.

It appears that, in the mild form of glutathione synthetase deficiency, the genetic lesion leads to synthesis of an unstable glutathione synthetase molecule. The rate of replacement of such a defective, but active, enzyme would appear to be sufficiently great in most tissues to compensate for the defect. However, such a compensatory mechanism would not be possible in the erythrocyte in which the protein synthesis does not take place. It seems likely that the same enzyme protein is synthesized in all the cells of the patient, but isolation and examination of the enzyme is still to be carried out.

It is of interest that observations made on two siblings with this disorder revealed the associated finding of decreased erythrocyte glutathione-*S*-transferase activity.[112] This may indicate that glutathione-*S*-transferase is stabilized by glutathione and that it becomes unstable when cellular levels of glutathione decrease substantially.

γ-Glutamylcysteine Synthetase Deficiency

This inborn error has thus far been reported only in two sibs.[114,115] These patients exhibit a syndrome of hemolytic anemia, spinocerebellar degeneration, peripheral neuropathy, myopathy, and aminoaciduria associated with glutathione deficiency. One patient, examined initially at age 27, had mild hemolytic anemia associated with erythrocyte glutathione deficiency. The only physical abnormalities were absent reflexes in the lower extremities. Two years later, this patient developed psychotic behavior and a decrease in blood hemoglobin after receiving a sulfonamide for a urinary tract infection. By age 35, she had developed mild ataxia with impaired coordination and dysmetria in both extremities. Her brother, at age 29, had hemolytic anemia and erythrocyte glutathione deficiency. By age 36, he developed muscular weakness, ataxia, and decreased vibratory and position sensation in both upper and lower extremities with dysmetria and dysdiadochokinesis. Deep-tendon reflexes were absent or sluggish, and by age 37 he developed irregular staccato speech and painful myoclonic spasms of his right foot and calf.

Both patients had erythrocyte glutathione levels that were less than 3 percent of normal. The glutathione content of the peripheral leukocytes was less than one-half normal, and the glutathione content of the muscle was about 25 percent of normal. There was a marked reduction of γ-glutamylcysteine synthetase activity of the erythrocytes,[10,115] and both patients exhibited generalized amino aciduria.[10,115]

In contrast to the patients with severe glutathione synthetase deficiency, the patients with γ-glutamylcysteine synthetase deficiency have a severely impaired ability to synthesize γ-glutamyl compounds. Thus, whereas a block of glutathione synthetase leads to a modified γ-glutamyl cycle in which transpeptidation is possible with γ-glutamylcysteine, a block of γ-glutamylcysteine synthetase would be expected to markedly reduce the activity of the γ-glutamyl cycle. The finding of amino aciduria in these patients is therefore of interest. Further studies on amino acid transport in these patients would be desirable, as would similar studies on animal models of this disease, which might be produced by administration of buthionine sulfoximine or a similar compound that inhibits γ-glutamylcysteine synthetase. It is of interest that administration of buthionine sulfoximine to experimental animals has been found to produce cataracts, decreased response of lymphocytes to mitogens, increased response to teratogenic compounds, and still other effects (see Refs. 2, 56, 57, 133, and 134).

γ-Glutamyl Transpeptidase Deficiency

Two patients with apparently generalized γ-glutamyl transpeptidase have been described in detail,[116,117] and three others have been described very briefly or are under investigation.[118,119] One patient is a moderately retarded man first studied at the age of 33, who was found to excrete glutathione in his urine and to have glutathionemia.[116] Subsequent studies on this patient's cultured skin fibroblasts showed an extreme decrease in the activity of γ-glutamyl transpeptidase.[120] His excretion amounted to about 850 mg of glutathione per day. His serum amino acid levels were reported to be normal except for a reduction in the sum of asparagine and glutamine and a comparable increase in glutamic acid, which was thought to reflect hydrolysis of glutamine to glutamate during sample storage and preparation. (This conclusion may not be valid, since nonenzymatic destruction of glutamine at pH values near neutrality leads to formation of 5-oxoproline rather than glutamate.) Renal absorption was calculated to be normal for 14 amino acids, but fell slightly below the normal range for serine, tyrosine, phenylalanine, and the sum of asparagine and glutamine.[120] The data are consistent with deficiency of glutamine transport. The percentage of excretion of glutamine plus asparagine was about fivefold higher than the corresponding values for four other amino acids (serine, alanine, tyrosine, and methionine), which were slightly above normal. The uptake kinetics for cystine, glutamine, methionine, and alanine were determined in studies on the cultured fibroblasts from this patient. No significant differences were found in the kinetics of uptake for each of these as compared with the results obtained with fibroblasts from a normal individual. The levels of phenylalanine, cystine, and cysteine in the mutant cells were significantly increased.[121]

Another patient with γ-glutamyl transpeptidase deficiency is a mentally retarded young woman with severe behavioral problems.[117] No γ-glutamyl transpeptidase activity was detected in the urine, plasma, or cultured skin fibroblasts, but a slight activity was reported for the leukocytes. There was substantial glutathionuria and glutathionemia.

The initial reports on the patients discussed above with γ-glutamyl transpeptidase deficiency stated that amino acid analysis of the patients' urine did not show unusual features other than the presence of glutathione. However, the reported data on one patient indicate some degree of cystinuria.[117] Additional studies[122] of the urine of the second patient disclosed a substantial amount of γ-glutamylcysteine and of cysteine moieties. Both compounds were present in disulfide form. Amino acid analysis of the urine was carried out after treatment with dithiothreitol and 2-vinylpyridine. A similar approach had previously been used in mice treated with inhibitors of γ-glutamyl transpeptidase.[22] The urine of mice whose transpeptidase activity was markedly inhibited by administration of L-γ-glutamyl-(*o*-carboxy)phenylhydrazide or of AT-125 contained high concentrations of glutathione (3 to 28 m*M*) and about half as much γ-glutamylcyst(e)ine and cyst(e)ine. The finding of markedly increased urinary excretion of glutathione, cysteine, and γ-glutamylcysteine moieties in γ-glutamyl transpeptidase deficiency in humans and in animals suggests that the physiological function of γ-glutamyl transpeptidase is associated with the metabolism or transport (or both) of these sulfur-containing compounds. At least three pathways could account for the appearance of urinary γ-glutamylcysteine: (1) γ-glutamylcysteine formed intracellularly by γ-glutamylcysteine synthetase might be translocated from cells to the extracellular fluid and the glomerular filtrate; (2) the small amount of active transpeptidase present in both the patient and experimental animal may catalyze the extracellular formation of γ-glutamylcyst(e)ine from glutathione and cyst(e)ine; and (3) γ-glutamylcyst(e)ine may be formed by cleavage of the cys-gly bond of glutathione (or of glutathione disulfide).

Pathway 1 is unlikely since there are two highly active intracellular enzymes (glutathione synthetase and γ-glutamyl cyclotransferase) that can utilize this dipeptide. Furthermore, in 5-oxoprolinuria the excess γ-glutamylcysteine formed intracellularly is effectively converted into 5-oxoproline by γ-glutamyl cyclotransferase, and little if any γ-glutamylcysteine is found extracellularly. In addition, the absence of 5-oxoprolinuria in γ-glutamyl transpeptidase deficiency indicates that there is little or no increase in the intracellular level of γ-glutamylcysteine. Pathway 3 appears to be excluded by studies,[123] which also support pathway 2. The evidence strongly suggests that transpeptidation between glutathione and cystine occurs in vivo and also that this reaction constitutes a significant physiological function of the enzyme. The finding of the 2-vinylpyridine derivatives of cysteine and γ-glutamylcysteine after treatment of the urine of the patient with dithiothreitol and 2-vinylpyridine is consistent with the presence of γ-glutamylcystine in the urine. (γ-Glutamylcysteine has also been found in the urine of the other patient[116] described above.[124]) Accumulation of γ-glutamylcystine and excretion of this compound would be expected if the rate of γ-glutamylcystine formation exceeded that of its transport into cells. The transport of γ-glutamyl amino acids has been found to be inhibited by high concentrations of glutathione.[36,37] The appearance of large amounts of γ-glutamylcystine may therefore reflect an inhibitory effect of glutathione on the transport of γ-glutamylcystine in the patients. (Intracellular reduction of γ-glutamylcystine would lead to formation of γ-glutamylcysteine and cysteine, both of which are substrates of glutathione biosynthesis, as discussed above.[39]) This interpretation is strongly supported by studies (see above[39]) which show that administration of γ-glutamylcystine to experimental animals leads to increased renal levels of glutathione. The findings also indicate that γ-glutamyl transpeptidase activity is not completely absent in patients found to have deficiency of this enzyme, nor is the activity of the enzyme abolished in experimental animals treated with potent transpeptidase inhibitors. Thus, the biochemical findings on the patients described above closely resemble those made on experimental animals treated with inhibitors of γ-glutamyl transpeptidase.

Another patient reported briefly was subsequently shown to have a deficiency of γ-glutamyl transpeptidase.[119] Two additional cases (sisters aged 13 and 11) have recently been identified, but detailed information is currently available.

5-Oxoprolinase Deficiency

Three individuals with 5-oxoprolinase deficiency have been reported.[125,126] Two of these,[125] brothers age 16 and 11, had enterocolitis and urolithiasis (a stone from one patient contained calcium oxalate and carbonate) and exhibited excessive excretion of 5-oxo-L-proline (39 to 71 mmol/day). One patient had a plasma 5-oxoproline level of about 0.18 m*M*. These individuals had normal erythrocyte glutathione levels and did not exhibit acidosis, neurologic symptoms, or hemolysis. The glutathione synthetase activities of their erythrocytes, leukocytes, and cultured skin fibroblasts were within normal limits. The γ-glutamyl cyclotransferase activity and the activity of γ-glutamylcysteine synthetase of their erythrocytes were also within normal limits. The cultured skin fibroblasts of both individuals and the leukocytes of one of them exhibited very low levels of 5-oxoprolinase. In the cultured fibroblasts the activity was about 2 percent of that of controls, whereas the activity found in the cells of the parents of these individuals had a level that was intermediate between those of the individuals and the controls. Addition of extracts prepared from the patient's cells to those of controls gave additive results. The affinity of glutathione synthetase for γ-glutamyl-α-aminobutyrate was normal, and feedback inhibition of γ-glutamylcysteine synthetase by glutathione was also normal.

A third individual found to have 5-oxoprolinase deficiency was discovered in the course of study of her child, who had prolinemia and birth defects.[126] The mother excreted large quantities of 5-oxoproline (28.6 ± 1.55 mmol/day). The father and the child had daily urinary 5-oxoproline excretion that was less than 1 mmol/day. The mother's plasma 5-oxoproline level was nine times greater than that of the controls. The erythrocyte glutathione synthetase activities of the mother and child were normal, and kinetic analysis showed no decrease in apparent affinity for ATP and glycine. The mother's blood glutathione level was normal. A skin biopsy from the deltoid region of her arm and her cultured skin fibroblasts had about 2 percent of the 5-oxoprolinase activity of controls. Oral proline loading tests were performed on the father, mother, and child. Although the plasma proline values after the load were no different in the mother, father, and child from that in the controls, the family members all excreted pipecolic acid after the proline load. Lysine loading in the mother and child did not produce pipecolic acid excretion. The individual with 5-oxoprolinase deficiency (the mother) was apparently healthy; her IQ was 67.

The clinical findings in the first two patients[125] are quite different from those found in the third.[126] The urinary excretion of 5-oxoproline was about the same in all these patients as was the level of 5-oxoprolinase in their cultured skin fibroblasts. The findings indicate that 5-oxoprolinase is an inherited recessive trait, but the associated clinical and biochemical phenomena need to be further studied before definite conclusions can be reached.

These patients do not appear to have abnormalities of amino acid transport, nor do they have acidosis, apparently because accumulation of 5-oxoproline is not very large. Although 5-oxoprolinase deficiency would be expected to decrease conversion of 5-oxoproline to glutamate, a deficiency of glutamate would not be expected. Glutamate is available from the diet and also by reductive amination and transamination of α-ketoglutarate. Thus, a deficiency of glutathione would not be expected, nor has it been found. The total daily excretion of 5-oxoproline by these patients (29 to 71 mmol) must be taken as minimal estimates of the amount of glutathione that is metabolized per day via 5-oxoproline. The total formation of 5-oxoproline is undoubtedly much greater than such calculated minimal values because these patients do not have a complete lack of 5-oxoprolinase. The levels of 5-oxoprolinase activity in various tissues of the patients are not yet known. The situation may be analogous to that seen in patients who have a deficiency in one of the urea cycle enzymes, but who nevertheless can synthesize urea at a substantial rate (see Chap. 20).

It should be noted that increased urinary 5-oxoproline has been observed in patients with severe burns or patients that have Stevens-Johnson syndrome.[127] Possibly in these conditions there is increased metabolism of collagen, fibrinogen, or other proteins that contain substantial amounts of *N*-terminal 5-oxoproline. 5-Oxoproline can also be of dietary origin[128]; certain infant formulas may contain proteins modified by preparation that have increased 5-oxoproline content. Patients with homocystinuria have been reported to have increased urinary excretion of 5-oxoproline.[129] The mechanism underlying increased excretion of 5-oxoproline is thought to be related to the ability of γ-glutamylcysteine synthetase to use homocysteine as a substrate. The γ-glutamyl homocysteine formed is a substrate for γ-glutamyl cyclotransferase, thus leading to 5-oxoproline formation. 5-Oxoproline excretion appears to occur when plasma level of homocystine is above 0.2 m*M*. It should be noted that normal human urine contains variable amounts of 5-oxo-D-proline (formed by enzymatic cyclization of D-glutamate, which probably arises from dietary or bacterial sources,[12,13]) and this may complicate the interpretation of analyses of urine for 5-oxoproline. Normal human skin contains large amounts of 5-oxoproline.[130,131] Somewhat elevated levels of 5-oxo-L-proline and 5-oxo-D-proline have been found in the plasma of patients with renal insufficiency.[132]

MUTATIONS IN ORGANISMS OTHER THAN HUMANS

As discussed elsewhere,[1,134] several mutant microorganisms that have blocks in the biosynthesis of glutathione are known. Glutathione-related mutants of sheep are also known; one type involves decreased erythrocyte γ-glutamyl cysteine synthetase. In another there is decreased transport of cysteine into the erythrocyte.[1,79]

REFERENCES

1. LARSSON A, ORRENIUS S, HOLMGREN A, MANNERVIK B (eds): *Functions of Glutathione—Biochemical, Physiological, Toxicological and Clinical Aspects.* New York, Raven, 1983.
2. MEISTER A, ANDERSON ME: Glutathione. *Annu Rev Biochem* 52:711, 1983.

3. SIES H, WENDEL A (eds): *Glutathione, Functions in Liver and Kidney*, Berlin, Heidelberg, New York, Springer-Verlag, 1978.
4. JAKOBY WB, ARIAS I (eds): *Workshop on Glutathione, Krok Symposium, Santa Barbara, Calif, June 2–3, 1975*. New York, Raven, 1976.
5. MEISTER A: On the cycles of glutathione metabolism and transport, in Horecker B, Stadtman E (eds): *Symposium on Biological Cycles (Honoring Sir Hans A Krebs). Curr Top Cell Regul* 18:21, 1981.
6. MEISTER A: Glutathione synthesis, in *The Enzymes*, 3d ed 1974, vol 10, p 671.
7. MEISTER A: The γ-glutamyl cycle: Diseases associated with specific enzymatic deficiencies. *Ann Intern Med* 81:247, 1974.
8. LARSSON A: 5-Oxoprolinuria and other inborn errors related to the γ-glutamyl cycle, in Belton NR, Toothill C (eds): *Transport and Inherited Disease*, Lancaster, MTP Press, 1981, pp 277–306.
9. BEUTLER E: Glucose-6-phosphate Dehydrogenase Deficiency. Chap 74 in this volume.
10. MEISTER A: On the enzymology of amino acid transport. *Science* 180:33, 1973.
11. WILSON H, CANNAN RK: The glutamic acid–pyrrolidonecarboxylic acid system. *J Biol Chem* 119:309, 1937.
12. MEISTER A, BUKENBERGER MW: Enzymic conversoin of D-glutamic acid to D-pyrrolidone carboxylic acid by mammalian tissues. *Nature* 194:557, 1962.
13. MEISTER A, BUKENBERGER MW, STRASSBURGER M: The optically specific enzymatic cyclization of D-glutamate. *Biochem Z* 338:217, 1963.
14. SEDDON AP, MEISTER A: Trapping of an intermediate in the reaction catalyzed by 5-oxoprolinase. *J Biol Chem* 261:11538, 1986.
15. LI L-Y, SEDDON A, MEISTER A: ^{18}O Studies on the 5-oxoprolinase reaction. Evidence for a tetrahedral intermediate. *J Biol Chem* 262:11020, 1987.
16. MEISTER A, TATE SS, ROSS LL: Membrane bound γ-glutamyl transpeptidase, in Martinosi A (ed): *The Enzymes of Biological Membranes*. New York, Plenum, 1976, vol 3, pp 315–347.
17. ALLISON D, MEISTER A: Evidence that transpeptidation is a significant function of γ-glutamyl transpeptidase. *J Biol Chem* 256:2988, 1981.
18. ABBOTT WA, GRIFFITH OW, MEISTER A: γ-Glutamyl-glutathione: Natural occurrence and enzymology, *J Biol Chem* 261:13657, 1986.
19. THOMPSON GA, MEISTER A: Utilization of L-cystine by the γ-glutamyl transpeptidase γ-glutamyl cyclotransferase pathway. *Proc Natl Acad Sci USA* 72:1985, 1975.
20. TATE SS, MEISTER A: Interaction of γ-glutamyl transpeptidase with amino acids, dipeptides, and derivatives and analogs of glutathione. *J Biol Chem* 249:7593, 1974.
21. MEISTER A: Current status of the γ-glutamyl cycle, in *Functions of Glutathione in Liver and Kidney*. Berlin, Heidelberg, New York, Springer-Verlag, 1978, pp. 43–59.
22. GRIFFITH OW, MEISTER A: Translocation of intracellular glutathione to membrane-bound γ-glutamyl transpeptidase as a discrete step in the γ-glutamyl cycle: Glutathionuria after inhibition of transpeptidase. *Proc Natl Acad Sci USA* 76:268, 1979.
23. MEISTER A, TATE SS: Glutathione and related γ-glutamyl compounds: Biosynthesis and utilization. *Annu Rev Biochem* 45:559, 1976.
24. BARTOLI GM, SIES H: Reduced and oxidized glutathione efflux from liver. *FEBS Lett* 86:89, 1978.
25. GRIFFITH OW, NOVOGRODSKY A, MEISTER A: Translocation of glutathione from lymphoid cells that have markedly different γ-glutamyl transpeptidase activities. *Proc Natl Acad Sci USA* 76:2249, 1979.
26. BANNAI S, TSUKEDA H: The export of glutathione from human diploid cells in culture. *J Biol Chem* 254:3444, 1979.
27. DETHMERS JK, MEISTER A: Glutathione export by human lymphoid cells: Depletion of glutathione by inhibition of its synthesis decreases export and increases sensitivity to irradiation. *Proc Natl Acad Sci USA* 78:7492, 1981.
28. GRIFFITH OW, MEISTER A: Potent and specific inhibition of glutathione synthesis by buthionine sulfoximine (S-n-butyl homocysteine sulfoximine). *J Biol Chem* 254:7558, 1979.
29. GRIFFITH OW, MEISTER A: Origin and turnover of mitochondrial glutathione. *Proc Natl Acad Sci USA* 82:4668, 1985.
30. ANDERSON ME, MEISTER A: Dynamic state of glutathione in blood plasma. *J Biol Chem* 255:9530, 1980.
31. GRIFFITH OW, MEISTER A: Glutathione: Interorgan translocation, turnover and metabolism. *Proc Natl Acad Sci USA* 76:5606, 1979.
32. HABERLE D, WAHLLANDER A, SIES H: Assessment of the kidney function in maintenance of plasma glutathione concentration and redox state in anesthetized rats. *FEBS Lett* 108:335, 1979.
33. SPATER HW, PORUCHYNSKY MS, QUINTANA N, INOUE M, NOVIKOFF AB: Immunocytochemical localization of γ-glutamyltransferase in rat kidney with protein A-horseradish peroxidase. *Proc Natl Acad Sci USA* 79:3547. 1982.
34. ANDERSON ME, BRIDGES RJ, MEISTER A: Direct evidence for inter-organ transport of glutathione and that the non-filtration renal mechanism for glutathione utilization involves γ-glutamyl transpeptidase. *Biochem Biophys Res Commun* 96:848, 1980.
35. ABBOTT WA, BRIDGES RJ, MEISTER A: Extracellular metabolism of glutathione accounts for its disappearance from the basolateral circulation of the kidney. *J Biol Chem* 259:15393, 1984.
36. GRIFFITH OW, BRIDGES RJ, MEISTER A: Transport of γ-glutamyl amino acids: Role of glutathione and γ-glutamyl transpeptidase. *Proc Natl Acad Sci USA* 76:6319, 1979.
37. BRIDGES RJ, MEISTER A: γ-Glutamyl amino acids; transport and conversion to 5-oxoproline in the kidney. *J Biol Chem* 260:7304, 1985.
38. Peptide transport and hydrolysis. *CIBA Foundation Symposium, New Series*, New York, Elsevier North-Holland, Excerpta Medica, vol 50, 1977.
39. ANDERSON ME, MEISTER A: Transport and direct utilization of γ-glutamylcyst(e)ine for glutathione synthesis. *Proc Natl Acad Sci USA* 80:707, 1983.
40. TANIGUCHI N, MEISTER A: γ-Glutamyl cyclotransferase from rat kidney: Sulfhydryl groups and isolation of a stable form of the enzyme. *J Biol Chem* 253:1799, 1978.
41. VAN DER WERF P, MEISTER A: The metabolic formation and utilization of 5-oxo-L-proline (L-pyroglutamate, L-pyrrolidone carboxylate). *Adv Enzymol* 43:519, 1975.
42. VAN DER WERF P, STEPHANI RA, MEISTER A: Accumulation of 5-oxoproline in mouse tissues after inhibition of 5-oxoprolinase and administration of amino acids: Evidence for function of the γ-glutamyl cycle. *Proc Natl Acad Sci USA* 71:1026, 1974.
43. SEKURA R, MEISTER A: Glutathione turnover in the kidney. Considerations relating to the γ-glutamyl cycle and the transport of amino acids. *Proc Natl Acad Sci USA* 71:2969, 1974.
44. RICHMAN P, MEISTER A: Regulation of γ-glutamylcysteine synthetase by nonallosteric feedback inhibition by glutathione. *J Biol Chem* 250:1422, 1975.
45. JACKSON RC: Studies in the enzymology of glutathione metabolism in human erythrocytes. *Biochem J* 111:309, 1969.
46. LARSSON A, MATTSSON B: On the mechanism of 5-oxoproline overproduction in 5-oxoprolinuria. *Clin Chim Acta* 67:245, 1976.
47. WENDEL A: Biosynthesis of glutathione, in Flohé L, Benöhr H Ch, Sies H, Waller HD, Wendel A (eds): *Symposium on Glutathione, Tübingen, March, 1973. Stuttgart, Thieme, 1973, pp. 69–71.*
48. MEISTER A: New aspects of glutathione biochemistry and transport; Selective alteration of glutathione metabolism; William C. Rose Award in Biochemistry Lecture, June 4, 1984, *Fed Proc* 43:3031, 1984.
49. PALEKAR AG, TATE SS, MEISTER A: Decrease in glutathione levels of kidney and liver after injection of methionine sulfoximine into rats. *Biochem Biophys Res Commun* 62:651, 1975.
50. GRIFFITH OW, BRIDGES RJ, MEISTER A: Evidence that the γ-glutamyl cycle functions in vivo using intracellular glutathione: Effects of amino acids and selective inhibition of enzymes. *Proc Natl Acad Sci USA* 75:5405, 1978.
51. BRIDGES RJ, GRIFFITH OW, MEISTER A: L-γ-(Threo-β-methyl)glutamyl-L-α-aminobutyrate, a selective substrate of γ-glutamyl cyclotransferase: Inhibition of enzyme activity by β-aminoglutaryl-L-α-aminobutyrate. *J Biol Chem* 255:10787, 1980.
52. RICHMAN PG, ORLOWSKI M, MEISTER A: Inhibition of γ-glutamylcysteine synthetase by L-methionine-S-sulfoximine. *J Biol Chem* 248:6684, 1973.
53. RONZIO R, MEISTER A: Phosphorylation of methionine sulfoximine by glutamine synthetase. *Proc Natl Acad Sci USA* 59:164, 1968.
54. GRIFFITH OW, MEISTER A: Differential inhibition of glutamine and γ-glutamylcysteine synthetases by α-alkyl analogs of methionine sulfoximine that induce convulsions. *J Biol Chem* 253:2333, 1978.
55. ABBOTT WA, MEISTER A: Modulation of γ-glutamyl transpeptidase activity by bile acids. *J Biol Chem* 258:6193, 1983.
56. MEISTER A: New developments in glutathione metabolism and their potential application in therapy. *Hepatology* 4:739, 1984.
57. MEISTER A: The fall and rise of cellular glutathione levels: Enzyme-based approaches, in Levine RL, Ginsburg A (eds): *Current Topics in Cellular Regulation*. International Symposium on the Molecular Basis of Cellular Regulation in Honor of Earl Stadtman and Thressa Stadtman, May 3–5, 1984. New York, Academic, 1985, vol 26, pp 383–394.
58. MEISTER A: Modulation of intracellular levels of glutathione, in Valeriote F, Baker L (eds): *Biochemical Modulators: Experimental and Clinical Approaches, Annual Cancer Symposium, Detroit, June 13–14, 1985*. Boston, Martinus Nijhaus, 1986, pp 245–275.
59. MEISTER A: Novel drugs that affect glutathione metabolism, in *Mechanisms of Drug Resistance in Neoplastic Cells, Part II, Enzymatic Basis of Drug Resistance*, New York, Academic, 1988, pp. 99–126.
60. WILLIAMSON JM, MEISTER A: Stimulation of hepatic glutathione formation

by administration of L-2-oxothiazolidine-4-carboxylate, A 5-oxo-L-prolinase substrate. *Proc Natl Acad Sci USA* 78:936, 1981.

61. WILLIAMSON JM, MEISTER A: New substrates of 5-oxo-L-prolinase. *J Biol Chem* 257:12039, 1982.

62. WILLIAMSON JM, BOETTCHER B, MEISTER A: An intracellular cysteine delivery system that protects against toxicity by promoting glutathione synthesis. *Proc Natl Acad Sci USA* 79:6246, 1982.

63. MEISTER A: Metabolism and transport of glutathione and of other γ-glutamyl compounds, in Larsson A, Orrenius S, Holmgren A, Mannervik B (eds): *Fifth Karolinska Institute Nobel Conference: Functions of Glutathione-Biochemical, Physiological and Toxicological Aspects, Skokloster, Sweden (Mary 23-27, 1982)*. New York, Raven, 1983, pp 1–22.

64. PURI RN, MEISTER A: Transport of glutathione, as γ-glutamylcysteinylglycyl ester, into liver and kidney. *Proc Natl Acad Sci USA* 80:5258, 1983.

65. WELLNER VP, ANDERSON ME, PURI RN, JENSEN GL, MEISTER A: Radioprotection by glutathione ester; Transport of glutathione ester into human lymphoid cells and fibroblasts. *Proc Natl Acad Sci USA* 81:4732, 1984.

66. ANDERSON ME, POWRIE F, PURI RN, MEISTER A: Glutathione monoethyl ester; Preparation, uptake by tissues, and conversion to glutathione. *Arch Biochem Biophys* 239:538, 1985.

67. ANDERSON ME, MEISTER A: Inhibition of γ-glutamyl transpeptidase and glutathionuria produced by γ-glutamyl amino acids. *Proc Natl Acad Sci USA* 83:5029, 1986.

68. JELLUM E, KLUGE T, BORRESEN HC, STOKKE O, ELDJARN L: Pyroglutamic aciduria—A new inborn error of metabolism. *Scand J Clin Lab Invest* 26:327, 1970.

69. KLUGE T, BORRESEN HC, JELLUM E, STOKKE O, ELDJARN L, FRETHEIM B: Esophageal hiatus hernia and mental retardation: Life-threatening postoperative metabolic acidosis and potassium deficiency linked with a new inborn error of nitrogen metabolism. *Surgery* 71:104, 1972.

70. HAGENFELDT L, LARSSON A, ZETTERSTROM R: Pyroglutamic aciduria. Studies of an infant with chronic metabolic acidosis. *Acta Paediatr Scand* 63:1, 1974.

71. LARSSON A, ZETTERSTROM R, HAGENFELDT L, ANDERSON R, DREBORG S, HORNELL H: Pyroglutamic aciduria (5-oxoprolinuria), an inborn error in glutathione metabolism. *Pediatr Res* 8:852, 1974.

72. LARSSON A, WACHTMEISTER L, von WENDT L, ANDERSSON R, HAGENFELDT L, HERRLIN K-M: Ophthalmological, psychometric and therapeutic investigation in two sisters with hereditary glutathione synthetase deficiency (5-oxoprolinuria). *Neuropediatrics* 16:131, 1985.

73. GUSTAFSSON J, LARSSON A, MÅRTENSSON J: A therapeutic trial with N-acetylcysteine in two sisters with hereditary glutathione synthetase deficiency (5-oxoprolinuria), *J Inherited Metab Dis*, in press, 1988.

74. WELLNER VP, SEKURA R, MEISTER A, LARSSON A: Glutathione synthetase deficiency, an inborn error of metabolism involving the γ-glutamyl cycle in patients with 5-oxoprolinuria (pyroglutamic aciduria). *Proc Natl Acad Sci USA* 71:2505, 1974.

75. LARSSON A, ZETTERSTROM R, HORNELL H, PORATH U: Erythrocyte glutathione synthetase in 5-oxoprolinuria: Kinetic studies of the mutant enzyme and detection of heterozygotes. *Clin Chim Acta* 73:19, 1976.

76. ELDJARN L, JELLUM E, STOKKE O: Pyroglutamic aciduria: Studies on the enzymic block and on the metabolic origin of pyroglutamic acid. *Clin Chim Acta* 40:461, 1972.

77. ELDJARN L, JELLUM E, STOKKE O: Pyroglutamic aciduria, in Hommes FA, Van Den Bern CJ (eds): *Inborn Errors of Metabolism*. New York, Academic, 1973, pp 255–260.

78. ELDJARN L, STOKKE O, JELLUM E: Pyroglutamic aciduria. A new inborn error of metabolism possibly in the "γ-glutamyl cycle" proposed for amino acid transport, in Stern J, Toolhill C (eds): *Organic Acidurias*. Baltimore, Williams & Wilkins, 1972, pp 113–120.

79. LARSSON A: Hereditary disorders relating to glutathione deficiency, in Dolphin D, Paulson R, Avramovic O (eds): *Coenzymes and Cofactors*. New York, Wiley, 1988.

80. SPIELBERG SP, GARRICK MD, CORASH LM, BUTLER J, DeB, TIETZE F, GORGERS LV, SCHULMAN JD: Biochemical heterogeneity in glutathione synthetase deficiency. *J Clin Invest* 61:1417, 1978.

81. BOXER LA, OLIVER JM, SPIELBERG SP, ALLEN JM, SCHULMAN JD: Protection of granulocytes by vitamin E in glutathione synthetase deficiency. *N Engl J Med* 301:901, 1979.

82. SPIELBERG SP, BUTLER J, DeB, MacDERMOTT K, SCHULMAN JD: Treatment of glutathione synthetase deficient fibroblasts by inhibiting γ-glutamyl transpeptidase activity with serine and borate. *Biochem Biophys Res Commun* 89:504, 1979.

83. SPIELBERG SP, BOXER LA, CORASH LM, SCHULMAN JD: Improved erythrocyte survival with high-dose vitamin E in chronic hemolyzing G6PD and glutathione synthetase deficiencies. *Ann Intern Med* 90:53, 1979.

84. SPIELBERG SP, BOXER LA, OLIVER JM, ALLEN JM, SCHULMAN JD: Oxidative damage to neutrophils in glutathione synthetase deficiency. *Br J Haematol* 42:215, 1979.

85. ORFANOS AP, NAYLOR EW, GUTHRIE R: Ultramicromethod for estimation of total glutathione in dried blood spots on filter paper. *Anal Biochem* 104:70, 1980.

86. GARRICK MD, ORFANOS AP, ROGERS L, NAYLOR EW, GUTHRIE R: A simple screening test for reduced glutathione in filter paper spots of blood. *J Pediatr* 98:265, 1981.

87. RÉVÉSZ L: Review: The role of endogenous thiols in intrinsic radioprotection. *Int J Radiat Biol* 47:361, 1985.

88. MIDANDER J: Oxygen enhancement ratios for glutathione-deficient human fibroblasts determined from the frequency of radiation induced micronuclei. *Int J Radiat Biol* 42:195, 1–82.

89. SPIELBERG SP: Acetaminophen toxicity in human lymphocytes in vitro. *J Pharmacol Exp Ther* 213:395, 1980.

90. SPIELBERG SP, GORDON GB: Glutathione synthetase-deficient lymphocytes and acetaminophen toxicity. *Clin Pharmacol Ther* 29:51, 1981.

91. SPIELBERG SP, GORDON GB: Nitrofurantoin cytotoxicity; in vitro assessment of risk based on glutathione metabolism. *J Clin Invest* 67:37, 1981.

92. SPIELBERG S: Acetaminophen toxicity in lymphocyte heterozygous for glutathione synthetase deficiency. *Can J Physiol Pharmacol* 63:468, 1985.

93. LARSSON A, HAGENFELDT L: Hereditary glutathione synthetase deficiency in man, in Larsson A, Orrenius S, Holmgren A, Mannervik B (eds): *Functions of Glutathione—Biochemical, Physiological, Toxicological and Clinical Aspects*. New York, Raven, 1983, pp 317–324.

94. MÅRTENSSON J, GUSTAFSSON J, LARSSON A: Effect of short-term long-dosage N-acetyl cysteine supplementation on glutathione and sulphur amino acids in subjects with hereditary glutathione synthetase deficiency. *J Inherited Metab Dis*, in press, 1988.

95. ANDERSON ME, MEISTER AM: Unpublished data, 1987.

96. REVEL JP, BALL EG: The reaction of glutathione with amino acids and related compounds as catalyzed by γ-glutamyl transpeptidase. *J Biol Chem* 234:577, 1959.

97. SPIELBERG SP, BUTLER J DeB, MacDERMOT K, SCHULMAN JD: Treatment of glutathione synthetase deficient fibroblasts by inhibiting γ-glutamyl transpeptidase activity with serine and borate. *Biochem Biophys Res Commun* 89:504, 1979.

98. GRIFFITH OW, LARSSON A, MEISTER A: Inhibition of γ-glutamyl-cysteine synthetase by cystamine: An approach to a therapy of 5-oxoprolinuria (Pyroglutamic aciduria). *Biochem Biophys Res Commun* 79:919, 1977.

99. LARSSON A, MATTSSON B, HAGENFELDT L, MOLDÉUS P : Glutathione synthetase deficient human fibroblasts in culture. *Clin Chim Acta* 135:57, 1983.

100. LARSSON A, HOLMGREN A, BRATT I: Thioredoxin and glutathione in cultured fibroblasts from human cases with 5-oxoprolinuria and cystinosis. *FEBS Lett* 87:61, 1978.

101. MARKLUND SL, MIDANDER J, WESTMAN G: CuZn superoxide dismutase, Mn superoxide dismutase, catalase and glutathione peroxidase in glutathione-deficient human fibroblasts. *Biochim Biophys Acta* 798:302, 1984.

102. MARSTEIN S, JELLUM E, HALPERN B, ELDJARN L, PERRY TL: Biochemical studies of erythrocytes in a patient with pyroglutamic acidemia (5-oxoprolinemia). *N Engl J Med* 295:406, 1976.

103. MARSTEIN S, PERRY TL: Studies of amino acid content and transport in glutathione-deficient erythrocytes from a patient with pyroglutamic acidemia (5-oxoprolinemia). *Clin Chim Acta* 109:13, 1981.

104. HAGENFELDT L, LARSSON A, ANDERSSON R: The γ-glutamyl cycle and amino acid transport. *N Engl J Med* 299:587, 1978.

105. MENDELSON IS, ZALESKI WA, CAZSEY RE, CHRISTIE EJ, WELLNER VP, MEISTER A: Ataxia in 5-oxoprolinuria: Is there a connection between the γ-glutamyl cycle and GABA function? *Eleventh International Congress of Biochemistry*, Toronto, Canada, 1979.

106. BEUTLER E: Glutathione deficiency, pyroglutamic acidemia and amino acid transport. Editorial, *N Engl J Med* 295:441, 1976.

107. SKULLERUD K, MARSTEIN S, SCHRADER H, BRUNDELET PJ, JELLUM E: The cerebral lesions in a patient with generalized glutathione deficiency and pyroglutamic aciduria (5-oxoprolinuria). *Acta Neuropathol (Berl)* 52:235, 1980.

108. OORT M, LOOS JA, PRINS HR: Hereditary absence of reduced glutathione in the erythrocytes—A new clinical and biochemical entity? *Vox Sang* 6:370, 1961.

109. PRINS HK, OORT M, LOOS JA, ZURCHER C, BECKERS T: Congenital nonspherocytic hemolytic anemia associated with glutathione deficiency of the erythrocytes. *Blood J Hematol* 27:145166, 1966.

110. BOIVIN P, GALAND C: La synthese du glutathion au cours de l'anemia hemolytique congenitale avec deficit en glutathion reduit. *Nouv Rev Fr Hematol* 5:707, 1965.

111. MOHLER DN, MAJERUS PW, MINNICH V, HESS CE, GARRICK MD: Glutathi-

one synthetase deficiency as a cause of hereditary hemolytic disease. *N Engl J Med* 283:1253, 1970.

112. BEUTLER E, GELBART T, PEGELOW C: Erythrocyte glutathione synthetase deficiency leads not only to glutathione but also to glutathione-S-transferase deficiency. *J Clin Invest* 77:38, 1986.

113. BOIVIN P: Personal communication.

114. KONRAD PN, RICHARDS F II, VALENTINE WN, PAGLIA D: γ-Glutamylcysteine synthetase deficiency. *N Engl J Med* 286:557, 1972.

115. RICHARDS F II, COOPER MR, PEARCE LA, COWAN RJ, SPURR CL: Familial spinocerebellar degeneration, hemolytic anemia, and glutathione deficiency. *Arch Intern Med* 124:534, 1974.

116. GOODMAN SI, MACE JW, POLLACK S: Serum γ-glutamyl transpeptidase deficiency. *Lancet* 234, 1971.

117. WRIGHT EC, STERN J, ERSSER R, PATRICK AD: Glutathionuria: γ-glutamyl transpeptidase deficiency. *J Inherited Metab Dis* 2:3, 1979.

118. O'DALY S: An abnormal sulphydryl compound in urine. *Ir J Med Sci* 578, 1968.

119. HAMMOND J: Personal communication, 1986.

120. SCHULMAN JD, GOODMAN SI, MACE JW, PATRICK AD, TIETZE F, BUTLER EJ: Glutathionuria: Inborn error of metabolism due to tissue deficiency of γ-glutamyl transpeptidase. *Biochem Biophys Res Commun* 65:68, 1975.

121. PELLEFIGURE F, BUTLER JDeB, SPIELBERG SP, HOLLENBERG MD, GOODMAN SI, SCHULMAN JD: Normal amino acid uptake by cultured human fibroblasts does not require γ-glutamyl transpeptidase. *Biochem Biophys Res Commun* 73:997, 1976.

122. GRIFFITH OW, MEISTER A: Excretion of cysteine and γ-glutamylcysteine moieties in human and experimental animal γ-glutamyl transpeptidase deficiency. *Proc Natl Acad Sci USA* 77:3384, 1980.

123. GRIFFITH OW, BRIDGES RJ, MEISTER A: Formation of γ-glutamylcyst(e)ine in vivo is catalyzed by γ-glutamyl transpeptidase. *Proc Natl Acad Sci USA* 78:277, 1981.

124. GRIFFITH OW, MEISTER A: Unpublished data.

125. LARSSON A, MATTSSON B, WAUTERS EAK, VAN GOOL JD, DURAN M, WADMAN SK: 5-Oxoprolinuria due to hereditary 5-oxoprolinase deficiency in two brothers—A new inborn error of the γ-glutamyl cycle. *Acta Paediatr Scand* 70:301, 1981.

126. RØSEL RA, HOMMES FA, SAMPER L: Pyroglutamic aciduria (5-oxoprolinuria) without glutathione synthetase deficiency and with decreased pyroglutamate hydrolase activity. *J Inherited Metab Dis* 4:89, 1981.

127. THAM R, NYSTRÖM I, HOLMSTEDT B: Identification by mass spectrometry of pyroglutamic acid as a peak in the gas chromatography of human urine. *Biochem Pharmacol* 17:1735, 1968.

128. OBERHOLTZER VG, WOOD CBS, PALMER T, HARRISON BM: Increased pyroglutamic acid levels in patients on artificial ducts. *Clin Chim Acta* 62:299, 1975.

129. JELLUM E, MARSTEIN S, SKULLERUD K, MUNTHE E: Glutathione in pyroglutamic aciduria (5-oxoprolinuria) and rheumatoid arthritis, in Larsson A, Orrenius S, Holmgren A, Mannervik B (eds): *Functions of Glutathione—Biochemical, Physiological, Toxicological, and Clinical Aspects,* New York, Academic, 1983, pp 347–353.

130. PASCHER G: Die wasserloslichen bestandteile der peripheren hornschicht (Hautoberflache). Quantitative analysen. III, α-pyrrolidoncarbonsaure. *Arch Klin Exp Dermatol* 203:234, 1956.

131. LADEN L, SPITZER R: Identification of a natural moisturizing agent in skin. *J Soc Cosmet Chem* 18:351, 1967.

132. PALEKAR AG, TATE SS, SULLIVAN J, MEISTER A: Accumulation of 5-oxo-L-proline and 5-oxo-D-proline in the blood plasma in end stage renal disease. *Biochem Med* 14:339, 1975.

133. MEISTER A, Selective modification of glutathione metabolism. *Science* 220:471, 1983.

134. MEISTER A, Metabolism and function of glutathione, in Dolphin D, Poulson R, Avramovic O (eds): *Coenzymes and Cofactors.* New York, Wiley, 1988, chap. 1.

CHAPTER **32**

LACTIC ACIDEMIA

BRIAN H. ROBINSON

1. The lactic acid that circulates in the human body is the product of the anaerobic metabolism of glucose which takes place primarily in red cells, skin, kidney medulla, and white skeletal muscle. Some of it is oxidized by red muscle and kidney cortex, but the bulk of it is taken up by the liver and made into glucose. Lactate is always produced by reduction of pyruvate through lactate dehydrogenase and is always removed by a reversal of this process. Deficiency of both the H and the M subunit forms of lactate dehydrogenase are known, but they are relatively benign conditions. The oxidative metabolism of pyruvate proceeds through pyruvate dehydrogenase, the Krebs cycle, and the respiratory chain, whereas anabolic utilization proceeds primarily through pyruvate carboxylase. A defect in any of these pathways may lead to inadequate removal of pyruvate and lactate from the circulation, and a condition of lactic acidemia results.

2. Deficiency of the pyruvate dehydrogenase complex is the most common of the disorders leading to lactic acidemia. It can be due to a defect in the E_1, the E_3, or the pyruvate dehydrogenase phosphatase component of the complex. There is a graded spectrum of presentation of the E_1 pyruvate decarboxylase deficiency, which shows a partial correlation with residual activity remaining in the pyruvate dehydrogenase complex. The presentation varies from overwhelming lactic acidemia in the neonatal period to moderate or mild lactic acidemia accompanied by psychomotor retardation or ataxic episodes. The E_3 lipoamide dehydrogenase defect leads to deficient activity not only in the pyruvate dehydrogenase complex but also in the α-ketoglutarate and branched chain ketoacid dehydrogenase complexes. Pyruvate dehydrogenase phosphatase deficiency has been documented in four patients, three of them presenting with Leigh disease and the fourth with unremitting lactic acidemia. The most common pathologic feature of deficiency of the pyruvate dehydrogenase complex is the development of cystic lesions in the cerebral cortex, basal ganglia, and brain stem.

3. Pyruvate carboxylase deficiency presents in two ways. In the simple (A) form of the disease, the patient presents in the first few months of life with a mild to moderate lactic acidemia and delayed development. In the more complex (B) form of the disease, the patient presents soon after birth with a severe lactic acidemia accompanied by hyperammonemia, citrullinemia, and hyperlysinemia. The patients of this latter group rarely survive to 3 months of age. There is good evidence to suggest that patients in the A group have some residual pyruvate carboxylase activity while those in the B group have no activity at all. Some patients in the B group have absence of both mRNA and pyruvate carboxylase protein in cultured skin fibroblasts. Patients of the A group who survive are severely mentally retarded. This seems to be due to loss of cerebral neurons, despite the fact that in normal individuals there is pyruvate carboxylase activity in astrocytes but not in neurons. This suggests that pyruvate carboxylase has an essential anaplerotic role in astrocytes and that its absence deprives the neuron of an obligatory nutrient normally supplied by astrocyte metabolism.

4. Defects in the mitochondrial respiratory chain associated with chronic lactic acidemia have been reported in both children and adults. These defects, usually documented in muscle biopsy tissue, cover a wide spectrum of clinical presentation and have been ascribed to abnormalities in all four complexes of the respiratory chain. The best documentation for primary genetically determined lesions exists for defects in complex I (NADH-CoQ reductase) and complex IV (cytochrome oxidase). These patients present with chronic lactic acidemia, often with accompanying neurologic problems.

5. There is a group of patients for whom lactic acidemia and the presence of ragged red fibers seen in muscle histology are common features with spongy degeneration of the central nervous system, sensorineural hearing loss, dementia, and short stature. This group can be subdivided into three entities: the syndrome of Kearns-Sayre (KSS), the syndrome of myoclonic epilepsy with ragged red fibers (MERRF), and the syndrome of mitochondrial myopathy, encephalopathy, lactic acidosis, and strokelike episodes (MELAS). Though KSS is usually nonfamilial, MELAS and MERRF are familial, very often with the possibility of maternal transmission in the inheritance pattern. In this group, the mitochondrial proliferation which is responsible for the ragged red fiber appearance in muscle is almost certainly a response to energy production problems in the muscle fiber. Some of these patients may be shown to have mitochondrial respiratory chain defects, while in others the problem may result from a microangiopathy in the form of muscle and brain capillary occlusion.

6. Two defects in the Krebs cycle have been defined. One occurs at the α-ketoglutarate dehydrogenase complex and the other at fumarase. The patients with pyruvate dehydrogenase (E_3) deficiency have a defect in the α-ketoglutarate dehydrogenase complex activity, but isolated deficiency of the α-ketoglutarate dehydrogenase complex has also been described in two sibs. These patients, who exhibited increased excretion of α-ketoglutaric acid in the urine, initially displayed delayed development and then regression of acquired skills. Fumaric aciduria has been described in five patients, three of whom were shown to have fumarase deficiency. Two infants had severe psychomotor retardation; one was a mentally retarded 3½ year old, and two were mentally retarded adults. In two of the patients, the fumarase deficiency was demonstrated in cultured skin fibroblasts.

Several inborn errors of metabolism present with a metabolic acidosis in which the major anionic contributing species is lactate. In others where acidosis is not a problem, the blood lactate level is elevated above normal either on a chronic or an acute basis. For the most part these elevations of lactic acid are secondary, such as is seen in propionic acidemia, methyl-

Nonstandard abbreviations used in this chapter are: KSS = Kearns-Sayre syndrome; LDH = lactate dehydrogenase; MELAS = mitochondrial myopathy, encephalopathy, lactic acidosis, and strokelike episodes; MERRF = myoclonic epilepsy with ragged red fibers; PDH = pyruvate dehydrogenase; PEPCK = phosphoenolpyruvate carboxykinase; PFK = phosphofructokinase; and TPP = thiamine pyrophosphate

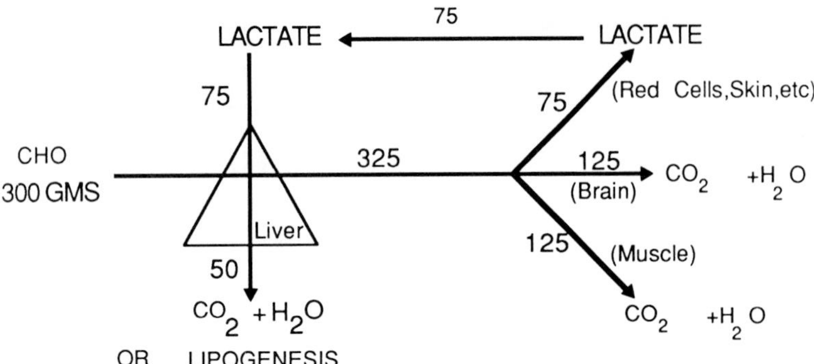

Fig. 32-1 Disposition of ingested carbohydrate in an average 70-kg adult in a 24-h period. Values for different branches of metabolic activity are given in grams per 24 h. See text for details.

malonic acidemia, hydroxymethylglutaric aciduria, and the fatty acid oxidation defects[1] (see Chaps. 28, 29, and 33), occurring because of interference with coenzyme A (CoA) metabolism in relation to its important function in the pyruvate dehydrogenase complex. Fortunately these secondary lactic acidemias are easily distinguishable by the presence of unusual organic acids in the urine. Excessive lactic acid production also occurs in many other nongenetic conditions associated with blood vessel occlusion, asphyxia, liver disease, and other pathologic conditions which are not always easy to distinguish from the inborn errors which are primary causes of lactic acidemia. In order to understand how lactic acid accumulation occurs, it is necessary to understand the dynamics of lactate production and utilization in the human body.

THE NORMAL METABOLISM OF PYRUVATE AND LACTATE

The Fed State

In the fed state, the average (70-kg) male adult ingests 300 g of carbohydrates per day. Of this 300 g, perhaps 50 g is utilized by the liver for a variety of purposes (glycogen synthesis, energy provision, lipogenesis, etc.) leaving 250 g to be utilized in the periphery (Fig. 32-1). Another 125 g is used by the brain and 125 g by muscle. Additional output of 75 g of glucose from the liver occurs as a result of gluconeogenesis from lactate. This output of 75 g of glucose from the liver is not oxidized to CO_2 and H_2O but is converted in glycolytic tissues to lactate and released into the circulation. Small amounts of lactic acid are also released from brain and white muscle, and much of this lactate is reconverted to glucose in the liver, a small amount being oxidized by red muscle. This conversion of glucose to lactate in the periphery and reconversion of lactate to glucose in the liver is known as the Cori cycle. It is this cycle that is responsible for the turnover of the pool of lactate in the body fluids.[2,3] The major difference that must be appreciated between the adult considered above and the pediatric patient is that the higher brain-to-body weight ratio in a child causes a higher proportion of hepatic glucose output to be used by the brain (Fig. 32-2). The above models for carbohydrate metabolism in the fed state are oversimplified summaries of the average disposition of carbon atoms in a 24-h period, but they do help us put in perspective the relative importance of carbon flow, especially in relation to flux through gluconeogenesis and through oxidative metabolism.

The Fasted State

In the fasted state, major changes occur: (1) fatty acids are substituted as the major fuel for muscle and liver, (2) a major new carbohydrate source from muscle breakdown is available in the form of amino acid as gluconeogenic precursors (mostly alanine), and (3) glycerol derived from triglyceride breakdown contributes to gluconeogenesis (Fig. 32-3). The activity of the Cori cycle and oxidation of glucose remain unchanged in the early stages of fasting.[2,3] As fasting continues, the reliance of the brain on carbohydrate fuels diminishes as ketone body oxidation is substituted as an energy source.[4] This allows the rate of muscle breakdown, which is rapid in the early stages of fasting, to slow down, thus conserving lean body mass. Again this situation is somewhat different for pediatric subjects. Their relatively large brain weight and relatively small lean body mass mean that children are much more prone than adults to the development of hypoglycemia in the fasting situation.[5] The above considerations should lead us to the following series of conclusions about the metabolism of pyruvate and lactate, which are summarized below with reference to Fig. 32-4:

1. In the fed state, 50 to 90 percent of the ingested carbohydrate that gets oxidized to CO_2 and H_2O will be utilized by the brain, the proportion being high in infants and low in adults.

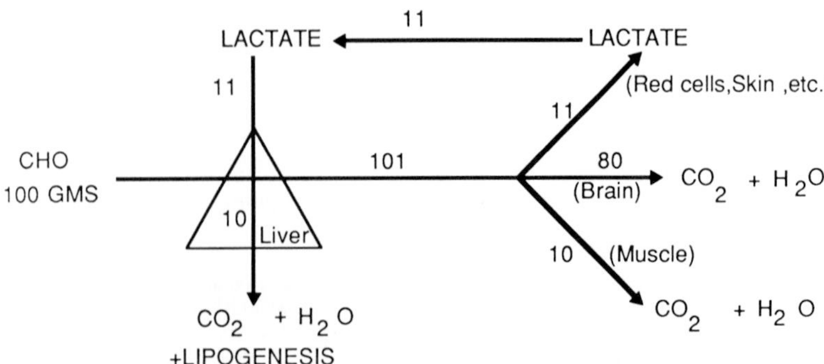

Fig. 32-2 Disposition of ingested carbohydrate in a 24-h period in a 10-kg infant. Values for different branches of metabolic activity are given in grams per 24 h. See text for details.

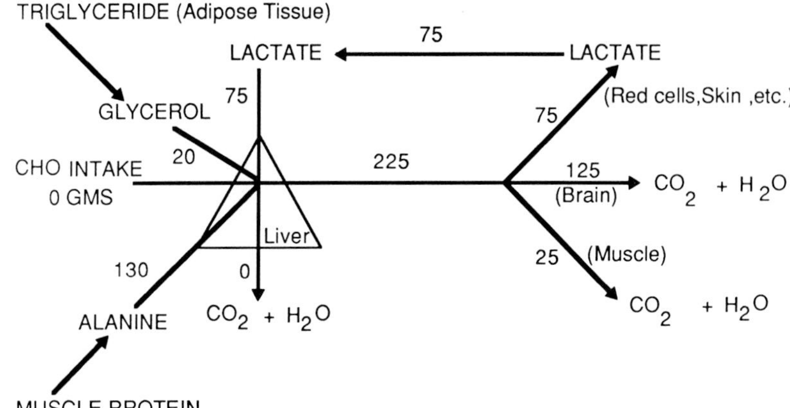

Fig. 32-3 Sources and disposition of carbohydrate after 24 h fasting in a 70-kg adult. Carbohydrate is derived from triglyceride glycerol, from muscle protein breakdown, or from lactate and is utilized primarily by brain. Values are given for different branches of metabolic activity in grams of carbohydrate per 24 h.

2. In the fasted state, the brain is the major site of oxidation of glucose produced by the liver.

3. As a result of items 1 and 2, the activity of the pyruvate dehydrogenase complex, the citric acid cycle, and the respiratory chain are essential to the normal working of the human central nervous system.

4. Normal liver pyruvate carboxylase and phosphoenolpyruvate carboxykinase function are essential for the maintenance of glucose output in the fasting state.

Anaerobic Production of Pyruvate and Lactate

For most cell types, providing the oxygen supply is adequate, the bulk of ATP requirements is generated by oxidation of pyruvate, fatty acids, or ketone bodies through the oxidation of acetyl CoA in the tricarboxylic acid cycle. However, as mentioned above, there are some cell types that preferentially derive their energy supply from glycolytic activity, with oxidative metabolism playing a minor role. In such tissues the end products of metabolism are pyruvic and lactic acids. Some tissues, such as blood, have either very few (white cells) or no (red cells) mitochondria, and thus a glycolytic mode of metabolism is obligatory. Other tissues have such a high glycolytic capacity that oxidative metabolism is suppressed, a phenomenon known as the Crabtree effect (Fig. 32-5).

In the oxidative cell types like liver, red muscle, and kidney cortex, the products of mitochondrial oxidative phosphorylation (ATP and citrate) act to curtail the activity of the glycolytic pathway by bringing about allosteric inhibition of phosphofructokinase. There are two species of phosphofructokinase (PFK) present in these cell types in varying proportions, an L type which predominates in liver and an M type which predominates in muscle. Both of these species are controlled tightly by the allosteric activators 5′AMP and fructose 2,6-bisphosphate and by the allosteric inhibitors ATP and citrate so that glycolytic flow is highly regulated.[6] In skin fibroblasts, platelets, lymphocytes, brain, and kidney medulla, a distinct form of phosphofructokinase (PFK-F) occurs which has no allosteric activators and is weakly inhibited by ATP and citrate.[7] In cells types where PFK-F predominates, glycolysis is a very important factor in ATP generation, and in these cells lactate production occurs in the presence of adequate supplies of both respiratory substate and oxygen. This unregulated PFK-F also is present in significant amounts in fetal tissues and in tumor cells, where glycolysis is again a prominent mode of energy production.[7,8]

In the normal individual who is well oxygenated and well perfused, the blood lactate is between 1 and 2 m*M* and does not change appreciably with fasting, feeding, or any of the simple infectious diseases. We have already seen that hepatic removal of 75 g lactic acid per 24 h[9] occurs out of a daily lactic acid production of 115 g/day.[10] Of this, 29 g is produced by red cells, 29 g by skin, 17 g by brain, 16 g by skeletal muscle (white), 8 g by intestinal mucosa, and 15 g by renal medulla.[9,10] Thus, about 40 g of lactic acid is removed extrahepatically, mostly by oxidation in red muscle and kidney cortex. The contribution of white skeletal muscle to lactic acid production over and above the normal daily total lactic acid

Fig. 32-4 The metabolic fates of pyruvate. Pyruvate can be converted to phosphoenolpyruvate (PEP), oxaloacetate (OAA), acetyl coenzyme A (AcCoA), alanine, or lactate. The enzymes involved are pyruvate kinase (PK), phosphoenolpyruvate carboxykinase (PEPCK), pyruvate dehydrogenase (PDH), pyruvate carboxylase (PC) alanine aminotransferase (AAT), and lactate dehydrogenase (LDH).

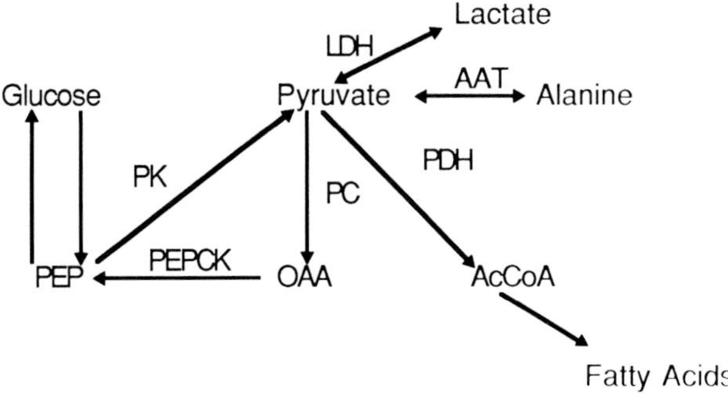

Fig. 32-5 The two modes of cellular energy metabolism. On the left the glycolytic mode generates the majority of cellular ATP requirements by metabolizing glucose or glycogen to lactate. On the right the oxidative mode generates the majority of cellular ATP requirements by oxidation of pyruvate, fatty acids, and ketone bodies in the mitochondria.

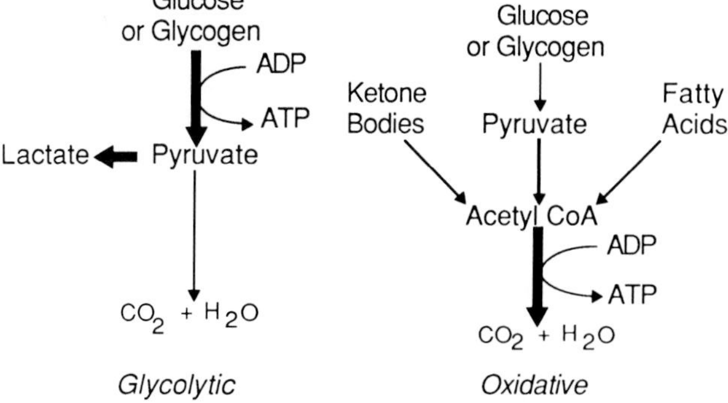

production may be considerable when the subject is involved in explosive exercise such as sprinting. Hermansen et al.[11] showed in a group of athletes that three bouts of sprinting to exhaustion in a 12-min period generated a mean blood lactic acid level of 22 m*M* at the end of the third bout of exercise. If the athletes then rested, 6 to 8 h was required to remove the lactic acid load and return the blood lactate to normal, but if the subjects followed the explosive exercise with a period of jogging, then the lactic acid load was removed more rapidly. This experiment illustrates that the normal route for the removal of a lactic acid load via the liver is rather slow,[12] but the alternative route of removal by direct oxidation in muscle is very efficient.[11]

A variety of problems associated with circulatory failure, shock, blood vessel occlusion, and asphyxia result in an ensuing transient or chronic lactic acidemia.[12] This arises because of lack of sufficient oxygenation of the tissues, a situation in which production of ATP by oxidative phosphorylation is curtailed and rising intracellular levels of 5′AMP, ADP, NH_4^+, and inorganic phosphate trigger a rapid degradation of glycogen to form lactate.[13] In this situation there is usually a much increased blood lactate-to-pyruvate ratio, indicative of the more reduced intracellular conditions prevailing in hypoxia.[12]

THE ENZYMES OF PYRUVATE METABOLISM

Pyruvate is metabolized through four main enzyme systems in the human body: lactate dehydrogenase, alanine aminotransferase, pyruvate carboxylase, and the pyruvate dehydrogenase complex (Fig. 32-4). Alanine aminotransferase is not discussed in detail here because deficiency of this enzyme in humans has not been reported. Its main function in overall metabolism is to provide (1) the catalytic function in the fed state, whereby nitrogen derived from branched chain amino acid oxidation can be donated to pyruvate and returned to the liver for fixation, and (2) the catalytic function in fasting, whereby 3-carbon units derived from muscle protein breakdown to amino acids can be aminated and directed to the liver for gluconeogenesis.[4]

Lactate Dehydrogenase

Lactate dehydrogenase exists in two subunit forms: an H form, which predominates in heart, and an M form, which predominates in skeletal muscle. The active form of the enzyme is a tetramer such that in most tissues a spectrum of isoenzymic forms appear, to include H_4, H_3M, H_2M_2, H_1M_3, and M_4.[15] Separate deficiencies have been described for the two subunit forms of this enzyme. In one case report, four sibs were totally lacking detectable activity of the M subunit form of the enzyme, and all activity detected in red cells, white cells, and muscle was of the H_4 form.[16] One sib had pigmenturia and easy fatigue on exercise. Ischemic exercise of the forearm led to an exaggerated pyruvic acidemia and to a muted elevation of blood lactic acid.

Since muscle damage was evident in this patient, we must conclude that the residual H_4 isoenzyme of lactic dehydrogenase (LDH) present in exercising muscle must have had less than adequate activity to sustain NADH reoxidation rates, thus leading to an early curtailment of glycolysis and loss of intramuscular ATP. Deficiency of the H subunit was described in a 64-year-old man with moderately impaired glucose tolerance and slight elevation of cholesterol.[17]

Pyruvate Dehydrogenase

Composition of the α-Keto Acid Dehydrogenase Complexes. The three α-keto acid dehydrogenase complexes are made up of three basic functional types of catalytic protein: E_1, an α-keto acid decarboxylase forming hydroxyalkyl thiamine pyrophosphate (TTP)-E_1 and CO_2; E_2, an acyl transferase forming acyl CoA; and E_3, dihydrolipoyl dehydrogenase, a flavin-requiring enzyme forming NADH. Lipoyl groups covalently attached through lysine to the E_2 backbone act to transfer both hydrogen and acyl groups between the different component enzymes of the complex.[18,19] Each functional component of a complex is present in multiples in a working undissociated complex such that the actual molecular weight will be several million. Thus the molecular weight of the bovine heart pyruvate dehydrogenase (PDH) complex is 8.5 million, made up of 30 units of E_1, 60 units of E_2, and six units of E_3. The E_1 unit is an $\alpha_2\beta_2$ tetramer with subunits of 41,000 and 36,000 daltons for α and β, respectively. The E_2 is a monomer which gives an apparent M_r of 74,000 on SDS polyacrylamide gel electrophoresis, though its true molecular weight is closer to 52,000.[18] The E_3 dihydrolipoyl dehydrogenase or lipoamide dehydrogenase is a dimer whose subunit molecular weight is 55,000. In contrast the E_1 component of the α-ketoglutarate dehydrogenase complex is a dimer of subunit molecular weight 118,000; the E_2, transuccinylase, is 48,000; and the E_3 subunit is again 55,000. The branched chain α-keto acid dehydrogenase complex bears a striking resemblance to the PDH complex. Its E_1 component is an $\alpha_2\beta_2$ tetrameric structure with molecular weights of 47,000 and 38,000 for α and β subunits, respectively. The E_2 component is 51,000, and the E_3 is again 55,000.[20] The E_3 component of each of the complexes is almost certainly identical, being encoded by the same gene in prokaryotic cells[21] (Fig. 32-6).

The branched chain α-keto acid dehydrogenase complex also resembles the pyruvate dehydrogenase complex in that both can radically change their overall catalytic activity in response to the phosphorylation and dephosphorylation of the $E_1\alpha$ subunit.[19,22,23] Pyruvate dehydrogenase kinase is a dimer of two dissimilar subunits of M_r = 45,000 and 48,000,[18] which catalyzes phosphorylation of serine residues in at least two positions on the $E_1\alpha$ protein, rendering the complex inactive. The kinase is strongly inhibited by pyruvate and by ADP so that the complex tends to stay more active either when rates of ATP turnover are high or when pyruvate concentrations are high.[18,19] The same groups are dephosphorylated by the action of PDH phosphatase, a dimer (M_r = 50,000 and 98,000) which is weakly bound to the complex.[18,19] This phosphatase requires Mg^{2+} ($K_{0.5}$ = 1 m*M*) and Ca^{2+} ($K_{0.5}$ = 1 μ*M*) for full activity, and this activation by Ca^{2+} ions is thought to be physiologically important in muscle and heart under condition of increased workload (Fig. 32-7).

Though both α subunits are identical in each PDH-E_1 tetramer, phosphorylation of only one seems to be sufficient to obtain 99 percent inactivation of the complex. Phosphorylation can and does take place to the extent of three serine sites per α subunit, but the physiological significance of this process is not clear.[18,19] The amount of PDH complex present in the active nonphosphorylated form in vivo is known for labo-

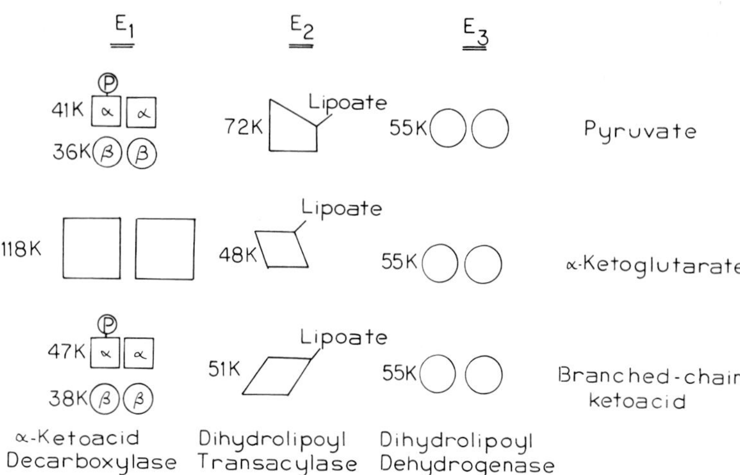

Fig. 32-6 Composition of the α-keto acid dehydrogenase complexes. See text for explanation.

ratory animals but not for humans (Table 32-1). These figures do change depending on the physiological state. In starvation and diabetes, the percentage activity falls to one-half or one-third of that in the fed state, depending on the length of exposure to the catabolic state.[3] The percentage activity of heart and skeletal muscle PDH complex may rise three- to fourfold after the commencement of heavy exercise.[3,19,24] In the former case, the increasing oxidation of fats brought about by a catabolic hormonal milieu leads to high intramitochondrial NADH/NAD and acetyl CoA/CoA ratios, which have a stimulating effect on the PDH kinase and lead to a decrease in overall activity of the complex. In the case of heavy exercise, increasing concentrations of ADP, pyruvate, and Ca^{2+} have the dual effect of activating the phosphatase and inhibiting the kinase, thus leading to an increase in the overall activity of the complex. The percentage of the pyruvate dehydrogenase complex in the active form can also be increased by the use of dichloroacetate, a pyruvate analogue and an effective inhibitor of PDH kinase.[25]

Disorders of the Pyruvate Dehydrogenase Complex. There are three defects which have been documented to occur in the pyruvate dehydrogenase complex, the most common being the deficiency of the E_1-pyruvate decarboxylase. Patients deficient in the E_3-dihydrolipoyl dehydrogenase and in pyruvate dehydrogenase phosphatase have been described but are comparatively rare.

Pyruvate Decarboxylase Deficiency. There are technical difficulties associated with the measurement of the activity of the

Fig. 32-7 Control of activity in the pyruvate dehydrogenase (PDH) complex. The complex exists in a nonphosphorylated active form or a phosphorylated inactive form. The phosphorylation is catalyzed by a kinase, which is inhibited by ADP, pyruvate, dichloroacetate-increased mitochondrial $NAD^+/NADH$, and CoA/AcCoA. The dephosphorylation is catalyzed by a phosphatase which is activated by Ca^{2+} and Mg^{2+}

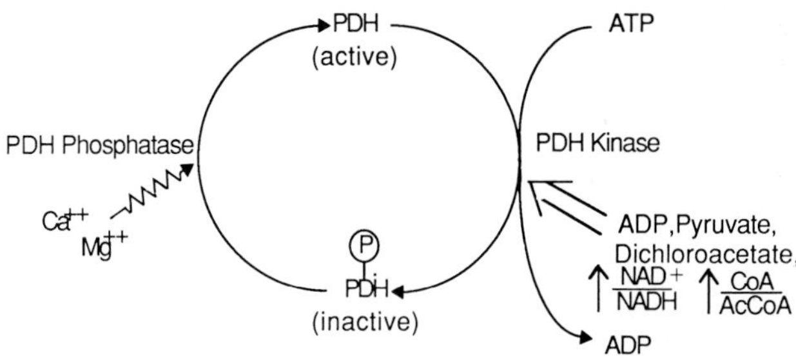

pyruvate dehydrogenase complex and its subcomponents in tissue taken at postmortem because of the lability of the complex unless tissue is frozen in liquid N_2 and stored at $-70°C$ or below. The measurement of these activities in fibroblasts, pioneered by Blass,[26–28] allowed for the unequivocal documentation of pyruvate dehydrogenase deficiency as an entity. The first cases described were deficient in pyruvate decarboxylase, the first component of the complex.[26–30] We have reviewed 30 cases that have emerged from our lactic acidemia screening program and another 24 cases that are described in the literature.[31] The findings are summarized in Table 32-2. Patients with deficiency of the pyruvate dehydrogenase complex (E_1) can present with symptoms at any time from birth to 4 years of age. The percentage residual activity varies from 1 percent upward. Because pyruvate dehydrogenase is a highly regulated and flux-generating step in metabolism, it is not unusual to see symptomatic patients with 50 percent activity. In general, heterozygotes have normal or close to normal activity of the complex. The majority of patients have chronic lactic acidemia, and the severity of the lactic acidemia correlates very well with the clinical presentation. On the other hand, the residual activity of the pyruvate dehydrogenase complex does not correlate well with either the severity of the lactic acidemia or the severity of clinical presentation. The patients fit into three broad categories from the point of view of their viability and their clinical problems (Table 32-2).

In the first category we have grouped together those patients who died before 6 months of age, a total of 13 cases. These patients in general had low residual activity of the complex and chronic severe lactic acidemia.[30–35] Four members of this group were shown at autopsy to have agenesis of the corpus callosum.[31,32] Cystic lesions were present in white matter of the brain in two of these patients and in both white and gray matter in another two patients.[31] In the second category we have grouped 35 patients who survived beyond 6 months

Table 32-1 Percentage of the Pyruvate Dehydrogenase Present in the Active Form in Various Tissues of the Rat in the Fed State

% active PDH	*Tissue*
62	Brain[23]
23	Liver[3]
15	Skeletal muscle[24]
21	Heart[25]
61	Kidney[3]

Table 32-2 Summary of Clinical Findings of Patients with Pyruvate Decarboxylase Deficiency (total patients 54)*

Neonatal and infant deaths (13), all dead	*Psychomotor retardation (35)*		*Ataxia only (6), all living†*
	12 died 10 mo–3 yr	*23 still living*	
Death due to overwhelming lactic acidosis before 6 mo 2 with documented white matter cystic lesions postmortem 2 with cystic lesions in both gray and white matter 4 with agenesis of the corpus callosum, one of this group with external olivary nuclei[30–35]	9 with pathology of the brain stem and basal ganglia typical of Leigh disease 2 with cystic lesions in the basal ganglia and the cerebral hemispheres 1 with cerebral cystic lesions only[31,36–42]	12 with structural brain damage on CT 2 with brain-stem and basal ganglia hypodensities 7 with cerebral hypodensities only; of the other 11 patients: 3 microcephalic, 2 with seizures, 2 with ataxia[27,31,32,40,43–45]	All with ataxia only, made symptomatic by high carbohydrate in diet[31,40,45–47] All boys
% Activity = 12.8 ± 4.0(13)	% Activity = 21.8 ± 3.2(12)	% Activity = 31.6 ± 3.7(23)	% Activity = 27.6 ± 7.7(6)

*Values are given as the mean ± standard error of the mean for each group as a percentage of control activity, the number of patients being given in parentheses.
†Probably a group with an X-linked defect, $E_1\alpha$ and $E_1\beta$ subunits allocated to chromosomes X and 3, respectively (*Robinson & Willard, unpub.*).

but had psychomotor retardation. In all these patients it was chronic lactic acidemia of a mild to moderate nature (3 to 6 m*M*) and delayed development which brought them to the attention of a physician and led to eventual diagnosis. Twelve of these patients died between 10 months and 3 years of age, nine of them showing areas of necrosis in the basal ganglia and brain stem typical of Leigh disease.[31,36–42] The other three patients who died also had cystic lesions, two with the lesions present in the basal ganglia and the cerebral white matter and one with white matter lesions alone.[31] Twenty-three patients with psychomotor retardation were still alive, 12 with CT-documented structural brain damage, the most common being manifest as hypodensities in the cerebral hemispheres seen in seven patients.[31] Two had brain stem and basal ganglia hypodensities typical of Leigh disease and two had brain stem, basal ganglia, and cerebral hypodensities.[31] Of the remaining 11 patients some exhibited microcephaly,[40,43,44] seizures,[45] or ataxia.[32,40] In the third category we placed six patients who were only mildly affected, having either chronic or episodic ataxia and being otherwise mentally and developmentally normal.[31,40,45–47] These patients tended to have blood lactates only marginally elevated, but their symptoms were aggravated by carbohydrate ingestion.

Correlation of the Clinical Presentation with the Deficit in Activity. Although measurements have been made of the E_1-decarboxylase component in skin fibroblasts using a ferricyanide-linked assay system,[26–31] the results were thought not to be reliable because this reaction proceeds at a rate 30 to 50 times slower than the rate exhibited by the total complex.[48] In addition, because the E_1, E_2, E_3 complex of enzymes works as a functional unit, measurement of a single component may not reflect its ability to interact with the rest of the complex components. For this reason the activity of the complex is probably a better reflection of residual activity, although E_1, E_2, and E_3 activities must be measured separately to locate the defective catalytic component in the complex. Despite these caveats there remains a poor correlation between severity of clinical presentation and residual activity of the pyruvate dehydrogenase complex. How does this variability arise, and can we make at least some deductions about the relationship between the enzyme defect and the disease?

First, the patients who suffer an early death from overwhelming acidosis before 6 months of life tend to be clustered at the lower end of the range of pyruvate dehydrogenase complex activities.[31] In these children the deficit is severe enough to cause a chronic, unremitting acidosis which is difficult to control. The four patients with agenesis of the corpus callosum fall into this group. Second, a group of patients with less severe lactic acidemia survive, but they develop slowly both physically and mentally. Some of these patients die in the infancy or childhood, while some survive to the second decade. These patients develop a variety of symptoms that may include seizures and ataxic episodes or spastic quadriplegia. The variety of symptoms exhibited depends at least to some extent on the damage caused in the brain by absence of PDH complex activity, and this again is variable. In some patients there may be cerebral atrophy, but more often the damage is manifest in the formation of cystic lesions in the cerebral cortex, cerebellum, basal ganglia, or brain stem.[31] A third group of patients, usually with greater than 20 percent residual activity of the complex, have mild lactic acidemia and ataxic episodes associated with carbohydrate intolerance. Last, the incidence of facial dysmorphism is spread across the spectrum of patients, and its features resemble those of fetal alcohol syndrome.[31] Typically this facial appearance is one of a narrowed head with frontal bossing, wide nasal bridge, an upturned nose, long filtrum, and flared nostrils.[31,49–51] We have suggested that the reason for this parallel between fetal alcohol syndrome dysmorphism and the dysmorphism found in patients with PDH complex deficiency may be that a common mechanism is involved. In fetal alcohol syndrome, acetaldehyde from the maternal circulation inhibits pyruvate dehydrogenase in the fetus, thus causing malformation. In PDH complex deficiency the endogenous low activity of the complex in the fetus causes the same facial malformations.[31]

The damage sustained in thiamine deficiency (Wernicke encephalopathy) and in some cases of PDH complex deficiency is located in the areas of the greatest metabolic activity of the brain, the brain stem and basal ganglia.[52] We have calculated that the actual activity of PDH complex present in the brain is barely enough to support the maximal observed rates of glucose oxidation[47] for the whole brain. A partial deficit in PDH complex in terms of high energy demand would have to be compensated for by excess glycolysis and excess lactic acid production. Chronic situations arising from this problem may lead to neuronal cell death because of either localized lactic acidosis or intracellular ATP depletion or both. Thus, necrotic lesions develop in areas where there is heavy energy demand or perhaps poor vascularization available to remove the lactic acid produced. Alternatively, neuronal death from this situation may be more generalized, leading to cerebral atrophy and apparent dilation of the ventricles. Several patients with PDH complex deficiency have shown clinical improvement or at least have demonstrated more stability on a high fat, low carbohydrate diet which is ketogenic.[31,43,45,46] The provision of ketone bodies as an alternative oxidative substrate to pyruvate for brain mitochondria appears to compensate at least in part for the PDH complex deficit. Some patients also seem to benefit from thiamine administration, though except in one case,[32] the effect does not seem to be due to a direct thiamine or thiamine pyrophosphate dependency of the PDH complex defect.[31] The response is more likely to result from the fact that elevated levels of thiamine pyrophosphate cause activation of the residual PDH complex activity.[53] Dichloroacetate administration also has been shown to be useful in patients, especially in an acidotic crisis, again because activation of the residual PDH complex takes place.[54,55] The variable clinical presentation of patients with similar percentage deficits in the PDH complex is at first sight disconcerting and has led to the expression of difficulty in attempts to make a rational approach to this defect.[49] The basic problem is the lack of correlation of in vitro enzymatic data with the clinical spectrum. The answers to the problem are probably multifactorial and may revolve around three variables: the difficulty of birth, the age of detection and institution of treatment, and the different subunit defects possible in the E_1 protein. Taking the first of these variables, a child with a partial PDH complex defect experiencing a hypoxic insult during the birth process may develop localized central nervous system lactic acid concentrations which cause irreversible neuronal damage. This level of hypoxia in a normal child may cause somewhat milder lactic acid accumulations which are rapidly removed when normal oxygenation is established. There is evidence from the dysmorphism and the cases of brain malformation that some effect of the deficit may actually occur in utero, and this again may be variable depending on oxygenation of the fetus. The second variable, the age of detection and possible treatment, is important because of the known beneficial effect of a ketogenic diet. In a case of two sibs with the same defect, treatment of the second sib with the diet from an early age resulted in milder symptoms than in the elder sib.[56] Thiamine administration may also be beneficial in this context. The third variable still awaits true definition. We do not know with complete certainty whether all E_1 defects are located on $E_1\alpha$, although there is a suggestion in some patients that this is the case.[34,41,57] It is possible that, because the facility for activation-deactivation by phosphorylation-dephosphorylation resides in the α subunit, a defect in $E_1\alpha$ is more damaging than one in $E_1\beta$. The answer to these questions awaits answers from molecular biologic approaches since cDNAs have been isolated for $E_1\alpha$ in two laboratories.[57,58] Preliminary observations suggest that a small number of patients have a defect which limits the production of mRNA for $E_1\alpha$.[57]

Lipoamide Dehydrogenase Deficiency: Combined α-Keto Acid Dehydrogenase Complex Deficiency. Combined deficiency of the α-keto acid dehydrogenase complexes is a comparatively rare entity, there being only six well-documented cases in the world literature.[59–65] Surprisingly, none of the affected children presented at birth, but they developed lactic acidemia that became troublesome at a few months of age. Since the data indicate that the α-keto acid dehydrogenase complexes include only the E_3 component in common,[21] it is appropriate that the E_3 component, otherwise known as lipoamide dehydrogenase, is found to be deficient in most cases of the combined defect. The fact that all complexes are deficient is consistent with the fact that elevations of pyruvate, lactate, α-ketoglutarate, and branched chain amino acids are observed in blood samples from these patients.[59,60,62,64] The branched chain amino acids are not elevated to the extent seen in classic maple syrup urine disease. Urine organic acids typically show elevated lactate, pyruvate, α-hydroxybutyrate, α-hydroxyisovalerate, and α-ketoglutarate.[61,63,66] In one case α-ketoisocaproic acid was present in addition to these other acids.[64] When postmortem examination of the brain was carried out,[59,60,61] myelin loss and cavitation were found in discrete areas of the basal ganglia, thalamus, and brain stem. The cerebral cortex appeared to be free of pathology.

The diagnosis was made initially by measuring activity of the α-keto acid dehydrogenase complexes in tissues or in fibroblasts.[59–61] In four of the six known cases, the combined defect in the complexes is definitely the result of a defect in lipoamide dehydrogenase,[59–61,63] which was between 0 and 20 percent of the activity found in controls. In another two cases, despite the fact that the α-keto acid dehydrogenases were deficient to the extent of 25 percent of normal, lipoamide dehydrogenase activity was 59 and 63 percent normal.[62,65] This anomalous situation could be explained if it is postulated that the abnormal protein can carry out the lipoamide dehydrogenase reaction, but the ability of these E_3 proteins to interact with the E_2 transacetylases is affected by the mutation.[62]

Pyruvate Dehydrogenase Phosphatase Deficiency

In a small number of cases with congenital lactic acidemia, a defect was demonstrated in the enzyme which activates the PDH complex by removing phosphate groups from $E_1\alpha$ serine residues. Three cases, two reported by Sorbi and Blass[67] and one by De Vivo et al.,[68] had a clinical picture typical of Leigh disease, while a fourth patient described by Robinson and Sherwood[69] died at age 6 months after a course of unremitting lactic acidosis. Two of the cases[68,69] showed poor reactivation of the PDH complex after inactivation by incubation with ATP in postmortem tissues. The other cases[67] showed a normal activity of the complex in fibroblasts in the native state, but no activation could be demonstrated after incubation of the fibroblasts with dicholoroacetate. None of the methods used in these studies was a direct assay of the activity of pyruvate dehydrogenase phosphatase activity. A method was described by Wicking et al.[34] for measuring PDH phosphatase activity in fibroblasts by the release of ^{32}P from added ^{32}P-labeled PDH phosphate. This is a more direct method of measurement and should be able to detect abnormal activity of this enzyme.

Pyruvate Carboxylase

Enzymology. Pyruvate carboxyase is a biotin-containing protein of subunit molecular weight M_r = 125,000, each active enzyme molecule consisting of four tightly bound identical subunits. Each subunit has one molecule of covalently bound biotin and possesses binding sites for pyruvate, ATP, HCO_3, and acetyl CoA.[70–72] The enzyme is almost totally dependent on the presence of acetyl CoA as an allosteric activator for activity. As the first enzyme in the gluconeogenic pathway, it is activated in conditions where fatty acids are mobilized and acetyl CoA is generated.[73]

Pyruvate carboxylase is widely viewed as the major regulatory enzyme and the flux-generating step in the pathway of gluconeogenesis,[73] being regulated by the relative acetyl CoA/

CoA and ATP/ADP ratios in liver mitochondria.[74] This enzyme is always intramitochondrial and has its highest activity in liver and kidney, where its role in gluconeogenesis is important. It is found in lesser amounts in other tissues such as brain, muscle, adipocytes, and fibroblasts where its function is believed to be anaplerotic.[75–77] In these tissues it plays a role in the maintenance of 4-carbon intermediates in the citric acid cycle.[78] Partial length cDNA clones have been obtained for pyruvate carboxylase by two groups of investigators.[79,80]

Human Deficiency. The known instability of pyruvate carboxylase in suboptimal conditions of preservation and storage plagued the early attempts to define the nature of human pyruvate carboxylase deficiency.[81] Many reports were based on measurements of enzyme activity in liver biopsy or postmortem liver specimens, and though some of these cases were undoubtedly bona fide cases of pyruvate carboxylase deficiency, some almost certainly were not. Early reports associated pyruvate carboxylase deficiency with subacute necrotizing encephalomyelopathy (Leigh disease).[82] In a series of nine patients with Leigh disease, skin fibroblast pyruvate carboxylase was examined and found to be normal.[82] In five of the patients, the diagnosis of Leigh disease was confirmed at autopsy, and in eight the urine inhibitor of thiamine triphosphate synthesis was present. Hommes et al. reviewed a number of cases where diagnosis of pyruvate carboxylase deficiency was made on liver tissue obtained by biopsy or at postmortem.[81] The majority of these determinations are reported as single measurements and many of them have low or undetectable activity. In one case,[83] detailed measurements of the kinetics of pyruvate carboxylase activity were made, and it was found that a low K_m component of the enzyme was missing. In the partially purified human enzyme, it has been shown that there are two kinetic components, one with a low K_m and one with a high K_m for pyruvate.[84] This type of defect is difficult to test for and may not be detected in single-measurement assay systems for enzyme activity.

The demonstration that pyruvate carboxylase activity could be measured in cultured skin fibroblasts led to the accurate definition of the clinical sequelae of pyruvate carboxylase deficiency.[76,77,85] There appear to be two distinct groups of patients who have been identified using the highly reproducible cultured skin fibroblast assay (Table 32-3). This initially became evident because the patients presenting with pyruvate carboxylase deficiency in North America (group A) had a simple presentation of lactic acidemia and psychomotor retardation,[85–92] while the patients presenting in France and the United Kingdom (group B) had a more complex biochemical presentation with lactic acidemia, hyperammonemia, citrullinemia, and hyperlysinemia.[89,90,93–98] Those in group B all presented in the neonatal period and died before 3 months of age compared with the longer survival of group A. Group B patients also demonstrated a redox disturbance, the cytosolic compartment being more reduced, as evidenced from an increased ratio of blood lactate to pyruvate, and the mitochondrial compartment being more oxidized, as judged by a higher ratio of blood acetoacetate to β-hydroxybutyrate. Both group A and group B patients exhibit hyperalaninemia and hyperprolinemia and have less than 5 percent pyruvate carboxylase activity in their fibroblasts compared to controls. Proximal renal tubular acidosis was present in three of the group A cases, and 8 of the 13 group A cases were full-blooded North American Indian children, six from either the Manitoba or Ontario Ojibway and two from the Saskatchewan Cree.

The biotin-containing enzymes present in cultured skin fibroblasts can be visualized either by [^{3}H]biotin labeling (Fig. 32-8) or by [^{35}S]streptavidin blotting. In both cases the cell proteins are separated by sodium dodecylsulfate (SDS) polyacrylamide gel electrophoresis.[88–90] When this was done with fibroblasts from patients with pyruvate carboxylase deficiency, it was found that the patients with group A presentation showed the same 125-kDa band corresponding to the subunits of pyruvate carboxylase. However many of the patients in group B showed no band for pyruvate carboxylase but normal bands for the α subunit of propionyl CoA carboxylase (73 kDa) and the α subunit of methyl crotonyl CoA carboxylase

Table 32-3 The Presentation of Human Pyruvate Carboxylase (PC) Deficiency

	Group A (13 cases)	*Group B (11 cases)*
Origin	8 Amerindian, 1 Canadian Italian parents, 3 U.S. Caucasian, 1 Japanese	2 Canadian (1 with Egyptian parents), 4 French, 2 U.K., 1 West German, 1 Saudi Arabian, 1 Swede
Presentation	Metabolic acidosis Delayed neurologic development	Metabolic acidosis Hepatomegaly
Age of presentation	Birth to 5 months	Neonatal
Survival	2 survive to 5 years; severe mental retardation	All dead within 3 months
Biochemical	α-Ketoglutarate in urine Lactic acidosis mild with severe attacks on infection	α-Ketoglutarate in urine Lactic acidosis chronically severe
Pyruvate carboxylase activity	<5% control	<5% control
Lactate/pyruvate ratio	Normal	Elevated (X5)
Acetoacetate/3HOB ratio	Normal?	Elevated (X5)
Blood ammonia	Normal	Elevated (X5)
Alanine	Elevated	Elevated
Citrulline	Normal	Elevated (X5)
Lysine	Normal	Elevated
Proline	Elevated	Elevated
PC [^{3}H]biotin protein (125 kDa)	Present	Absent in 6/10 cases
PC immunoreactive protein	Present	Absent in 6/10 cases
PC mRNA	Present	Absent in 4/10 cases
	Refs. 85 to 92 +3 unpublished cases*	Refs. 93 to 98 +3 unpublished cases*

*Studied by the author (BHR).

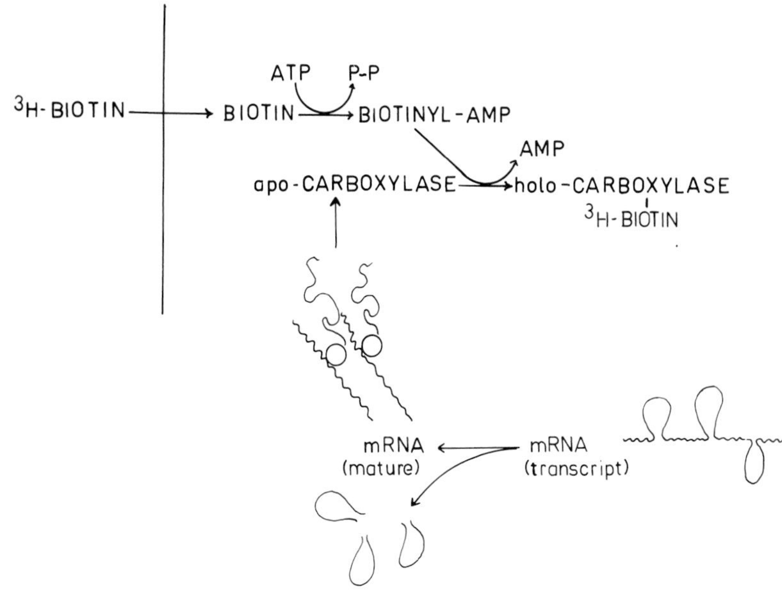

Fig. 32-8 Incorporation of [^{3}H]biotin into carboxylase protein. The mRNA for carboxylase produces a translated apocarboxylase which must incorporate activated biotin in the form of biotinyl-AMP with the release of 5′AMP. The resulting holocarboxylase protein has [^{3}H]biotin covalently attached at a lysine residue.

(75 kDa)[89,90] (Fig. 32-9). Immunoprecipitation of labeled protein from cells preincubated with [^{35}S]methionine also showed absence of the 125-kDa protein in some of the group B patients when anti-pyruvate carboxylase antiserum was used.[89,90] Finally, Northern blotting with a cloned cDNA probe[79] for pyruvate carboxylase showed absent mRNA in four of the six group B patients who lacked a demonstrable pyruvate carboxylase protein.[90]

In trying to correlate the biochemical symptoms of those patients with the physical and molecular facts about pyruvate carboxylase that arise from the study of the patients' skin fibroblasts, it is evident that in one group of patients, group A, all patients produce a biotin-containing 125-kDa pyruvate carboxylase protein that has little activity. In group B there are two groups of patients who are different in molecular terms, those who produce a 125-kDa biotin-containing pyruvate carboxylase protein and those who do not. However, all group B patients are more severely affected with death in infancy, and they have a complex biochemical disturbance affecting pyruvate metabolism, the urea cycle, and intracellular redox states.[90] What then determines whether pyruvate carboxylase deficiency presents with the simple phenotype of lactic acidemia or with the complex phenotype of lactic acidemia, citrullinemia, and hyperammonemia? Since we know that the pyruvate carboxylase gene is not expressed in all cases in which the presentation is the complex group B phenotype, we can associate this phenotype with total absence of activity. Thus we can hypothesize that the other patients in group B who have expression of pyruvate carboxylase protein must also have total absence of activity to attain this phenotype. Where there is expression of the enzyme with the milder group A phenotype, we must assume that there is enough residual activity in the mutant pyruvate carboxylase to ameliorate the most severe symptoms of the deficiency, but not enough to prevent lactic acidemia and psychomotor retardation.

Fig. 32-9 [^{3}H]Biotin labeling of proteins in cultured skin fibroblasts. Cultured skin fibroblasts were incubated with [^{3}H]biotin as described in Ref. 88. Proteins were extracted and run on sodium dodecylsulfate, 7% polyacrylamide gels, and the position of [^{3}H]biotin-labeled proteins detected by fluorography. Lanes 1 and 8 are from a control cell line (C); lanes 2, 4, 5, 6, and 7 are cell lines from patients with presentation B of pyruvate carboxylase deficiency; and lane 3 is a cell line from a patient with presentation A of pyruvate carboxylase deficiency.

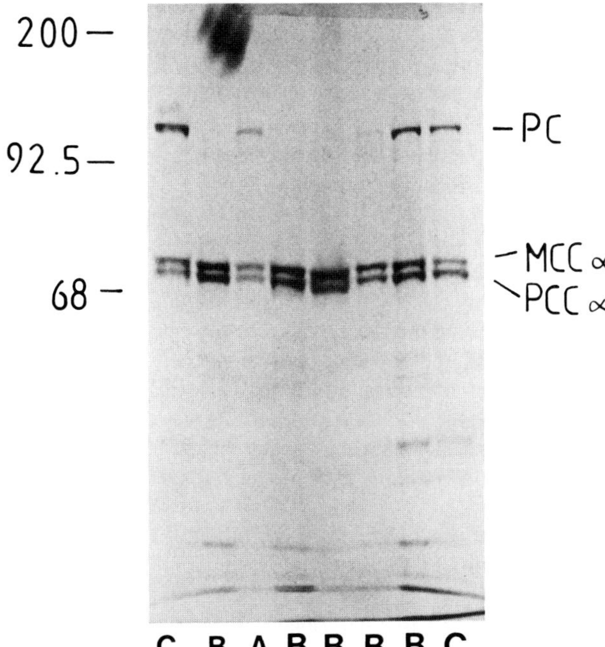

That all patients with pyruvate carboxylase deficiency develop lactic acidemia is almost certainly due to a failure of the Cori cycle and, in times of starvation, also a failure of gluconeogenesis itself. Patients in both groups have been documented with hypoglycemic episodes, though this is not a major problem.[89] The group B patients with the complex presentation show features which are suggestive of depletion of intracellular aspartate and oxaloacetate.[93–95] In the urea cycle, aspartate is the second nitrogen donor, and low levels would cause the accumulation of both citrulline and ammonia (Fig. 32-10). Aspartate is also an essential component of the shuttle system responsible for the transport of reducing equivalents from the cytosol to the mitochondria.[99] Electrogenic ejection of aspartate from mitochondria is necessary to maintain the typically very oxidized NAD^+/NADH ratio in the cytosol as opposed to the very reduced NAD^+/NADH ratio in the mitochondrial compartment. A lack of aspartate would result in the cytosol becoming more reduced and the mitochondria becoming more oxidized, exactly the situation seen in the

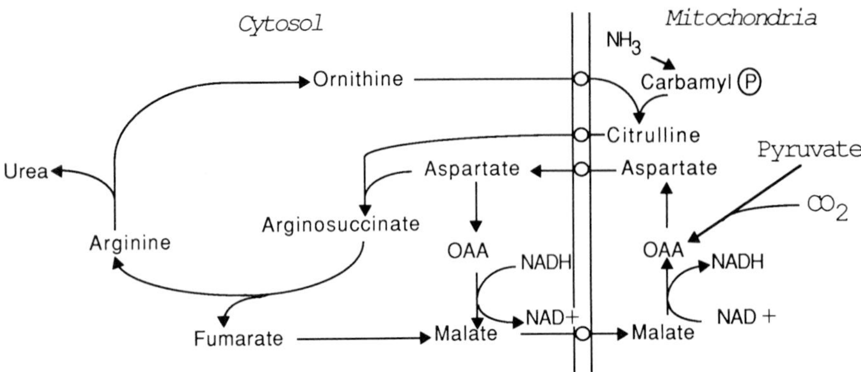

Fig. 32-10 Anaplerotic role of pyruvate carboxylase in the liver.

group B patients with the complex phenotype. Thus it would seem that pyruvate carboxylase activity in the group B patients is so low that it cannot sustain oxaloacetate and aspartate levels. The few tissue measurements of pyruvate carboxylase activity that have been done in liver have yielded 6.2, 17.2, and 0.0 percent of control values for three group A patients and 0.3 and 0.3 percent for two group B patients.[77,85,87,93]

Pathology. The pathology of pyruvate carboxylase deficiency has been documented in one group A and two group B cases and is primarily present in liver and brain. Hepatomegaly, which is seen frequently in this defect, seems to be due to lipid droplet accumulation in hepatocytes.[77,85,97,98] In one group A case, hyperplasia of hepatocyte endoplasmic reticulum was seen,[77] and the architecture of liver mitochondria had an abnormal appearance with increased matrix density, increased matrix granule size, and dilatation of intracrystal space.[98] The central nervous system pathology common to both group A and B patients consists of very poor myelination and paucity of neurons in the cerebral cortex, gliosis, ventricular enlargement, thinning of the corpus callosum, and proliferation of astrocytes.[77,93,98] In both group B patients that came to autopsy there was additional damage in the form of cavitated infarcts or cysts present in the cerebral cortex.[93,98] In one case, microscopic examination of the kidney showed diffuse vacuolation of the kidney tubules.[77] The appearance of cerebral cortex in pyruvate carboxylase deficiency suggests that myelination is not taking place, that neuronal death is occurring, and that a virtual developmental arrest of the brain is the net result. Thus pyruvate carboxylase is obviously essential for normal brain development, and this is related to its anaplerotic (Greek derivation meaning "filling up") role in metabolism. It has recently been documented that pyruvate carboxylase activity is plentiful in astrocytes but is low or absent in neurons.[100] Current evidence suggests that neurotransmitter pools are replenished in part by *de novo* synthesis within the presynaptic terminals and that glutamine derived metabolically from astrocytes appears to be a major metabolic precursor of the transmitter pools for both glutamate and γ-aminobutyric acid (GABA). The anaplerotic formation of glutamine is thought to occur using pyruvate carboxylation as the initial step, and this can only take place in astrocytes. Thus in an individual lacking pyruvate carboxylase activity, the neurons will lose their ability to be replenished with glutamine from astrocytes, and depletion of 4- and 5-carbon intermediates in the neuron may result in neuronal death. To compound this problem, the lack of the anaplerotic function of pyruvate carboxylase in myelin lipid synthesis at the same time leads to poor or absent myelin formation. The absence of these two essential roles of pyruvate carboxylase in the anaplerotic processes of brain metabolism undoubtedly is a major contributor to the pathology seen in the central nervous system in this disorder. Children who survive with this defect are grossly mentally retarded and often have accompanying seizure activity. This lack of a key anaplerotic enzyme may also be the cause of abnormalities seen in kidney and of accumulation of lipid in type 1 skeletal muscle fibers, in addition to the urea cycle and redox abnormalities previously mentioned.

Heterozygote Detection and Prenatal Diagnosis. The activity of pyruvate carboxylase in the cultured skin fibroblasts from normal individuals varies over quite a wide range. For this reason, although it may be possible to identify heterozygotes for this defect within a family, it is not possible to do this in the general population.[87,101] To add to the confusion there is a report of a patient with a 50 percent deficiency of pyruvate carboxylase in skin fibroblasts who had severe chronic lactic acidemia.[102] This patient had a kinetic defect in the enzyme that was perhaps similar to a case described earlier.[83] This type of defect awaits a clearer definition in both enzymatic and clinical terms.

Prenatal diagnosis of an affected child with pyruvate carboxylase deficiency has been reported on two occasions. Both families had already had a child who died with the group B complex presentation of the defect.[103,104] In one case the absence of [^{3}H]biotin-labeled protein was demonstrated in amniocytes.[104]

Phosphoenolpyruvate Carboxykinase Deficiency

A defect in this enzyme is rarely reported as a cause of lactic acidemia in childhood. The enzyme exists in two compartments in two distinct isoenzymic forms, and for this reason the diagnosis of a suspected deficiency of either one of the two isoenzymes is difficult. Three cases of phosphoenolpyruvate carboxykinase (PEPCK) deficiency have been documented where the assay of activity was carried out with a liver homogenate.[105,106] In another group of cases the cytosolic PEPCK in liver was measured and found to be deficient.[107] In two cases the defect was defined by measurement of PEPCK in cultured skin fibroblasts.[56,77] Since it has been shown that the majority of PEPCK present in fibroblasts is mitochondrial in origin, the detection of 15[56] and 16 percent[78] of normal activity in these cases was suggestive of deficiency of mitochondrial PEPCK. This was confirmed by the demonstration of 6 percent of normal activity in the mitochondria from fibroblasts of one patient.[56,109]

Both of the children described with mitochondrial PEPCK deficiency had lactic acidemia, hypoglycemia, hypotonia, hepatomegaly, and failure to thrive.[56,108,109] One patient had more severe symptoms, and in addition had peripheral edema, disordered liver function, and episodes of unexplained pyrexia. She died at age 6 months.[108] The other patient with mitochondrial PEPCK deficiency had survived to age 10 years with some continuing muscular weakness and hypotonia. These latter symptoms are most likely due to a lack of mitochondrial PEPCK in muscle, where it is thought to play an essential role in the regulation of the pool size of 4-carbon intermediates.[78] The cytosolic form of PEPCK is subject to induction and repression, being induced by catabolic states and repressed by anabolic states.[110] There is a strong suggestion in the cases described by Vidnes and Sovik[107] that the hypoglycemia and low cystolic PEPCK seen in this group of neonates was a result of hyperinsulinism, a condition that would repress cytosolic PEPCK expression in the liver. Hepatomegaly and hypoglycemia were present in two infants described by Hommes et al.[106] with 5 and 10 percent of control PEPCK activity. Localization of the site of the PEPCK was not attempted in postmortem liver samples from these children, both having succumbed to uncontrollable hypoglycemic episodes. Interestingly, one of these children had the inexplicable hypertriglyceridemia and hypercholesterolemia that was evident in the child we described.[56,106,109]

LACTIC ACIDEMIA AND RESPIRATORY CHAIN DEFECTS

There is an equilibrium set up between the redox couple NAD^+/NADH in the cytosol and NAD^+/NADH in the mitochondrial compartment in all cells so far investigated. This equilibrium is catalyzed by the "shuttle" system shown in Fig. 32-11. The processes of glycolysis and respiration are always linked through this equilibrium, the NAD^+/NADH ratio being always much higher in the cytosol than in the mitochondria because of the electrogenic expulsion of aspartate[111,112] from the mitochondrial compartment. When the respiratory chain is deprived of oxygen, the NAD^+/NADH ratio in the mitochondria is decreased and by equilibrium the cytosolic NAD^+/NADH also becomes more reduced. This combination of increased cytosolic reducing power, inability to oxidize pyruvate, and demand for ATP synthesis leads to substantial increases in glycolysis, in lactate and pyruvate production, and in lactate/pyruvate ratio. Since any interference with or abnormality in the respiratory chain would bring about a similar metabolic state, it would be expected that genetic defects in the components of the respiratory chain would present as some form of lactic acidemia.

Fig. 32-11 The mitochondrial "aspartate shuttle system" for transporting cytosolic reducing equivalents into the mitochondria. ASP = aspartate; OG = α-ketoglutarate; GLU = glutamate; OAA = oxaloacetate; MAL = malate; f_p = flavoprotein; and aa_3 = cytochrome aa_3.

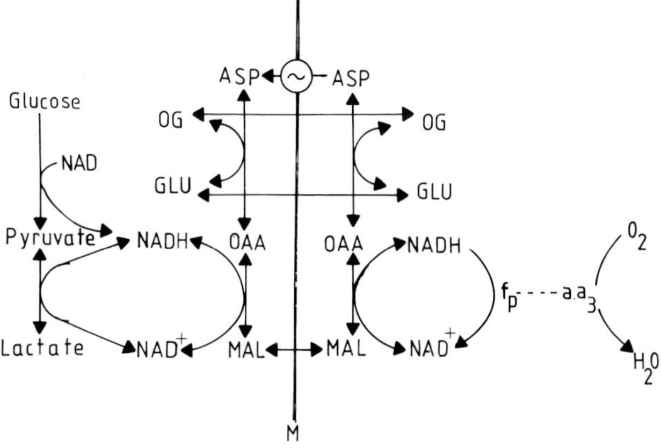

Protein Composition of the Respiratory Chain

The mitochondrial respiratory chain which is capable of transferring electrons from reduced pyridine and flavin nucleotides to oxygen is a highly organized system located in the inner mitochondrial membrane. At the same time the aforementioned process of respiration is coupled by a chemiosmotic mechanism to the phosphorylation of ADP to ATP.[113] The inner mitochondrial membrane can be treated with detergents to release five complexes which together make up the respiratory chain and phosphorylating systems: complex I, or NADH-coenzyme Q reductase; complex II, or succinate-coenzyme Q reductase; complex III, or coenzyme QH_2-cytochrome c reductase; complex IV, or cytochrome c oxidase; and complex V, the ATP synthetase[113] (Fig. 32-12).

Each complex of the respiratory chain is made up of a number of protein components, 25 for complex I, 4 to 5 for complex II, 9 to 10 for complex III, 13 for complex IV, and 12 to 14 for complex V.[113,114] The majority of these components are coded for by nuclear DNA, synthesized on cytoplasmic ribosomes, and transported into mitochondria. However, certain components are encoded by mitochondrial DNA and synthesized *in situ* on mitochondrial ribosomes. Thus seven components of complex I, cytochrome b in complex III, the three main catalytic components of complex IV, and two of the components of complex V are encoded in the mitochondrial genome[115,116] (Table 32-4). Tissue-specific forms of some of the subunits of cytochrome oxidase, complex IV, have been reported, but this has not been demonstrated to occur within the other complexes.[114]

Defects in Respiratory Chain Complexes

Defects in the mitochondrial respiratory chain have been reported in both children and adults in association with chronic lactic acidemia. These defects are usually documented in muscle biopsy tissue and cover a wide spectrum of clinical presentations.[117–119]

Complex I. The original group of patients reported with complex I deficiency based on examination of muscle mitochondria isolated from muscle biopsies had generalized weakness, exercise intolerance, and lactic acidemia.[120–124] A single patient

Table 32-4 Polypeptide Composition of the Mitochondrial Respiratory Chain

Complex	*Function*	*Polypeptide subunits*	*Subunits encoded by mitochondrial DNA*
I	NADH CoQ reductase	25	7
II	Succinate CoQ reductase	4–5	0
III	$CoQH_2$-cyt c reductase	9–10	1
IV	Cytochrome oxidase	13	3
V	Oligomycin sensitive ATPase	12–14	2

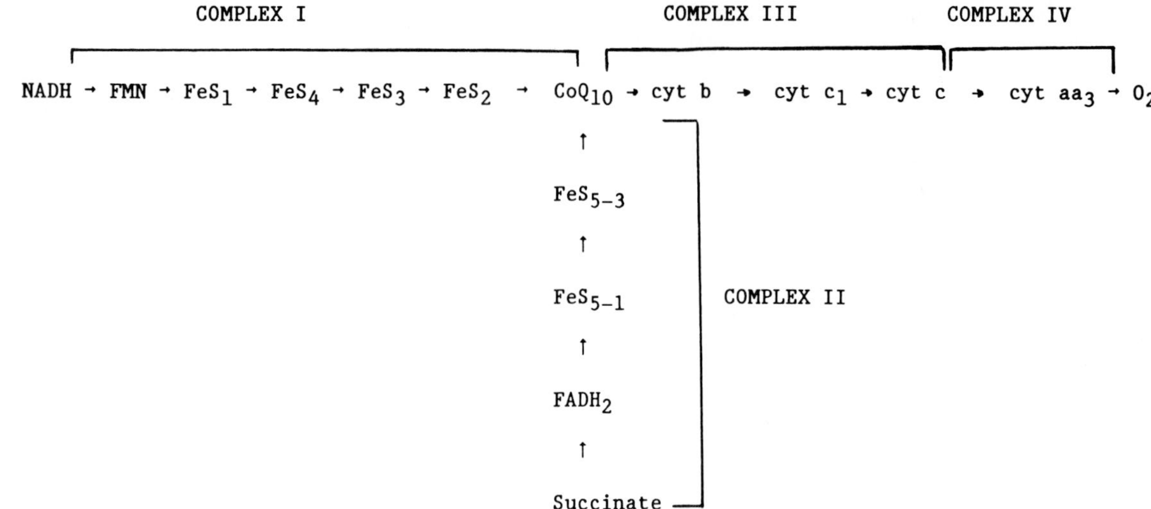

Fig. 32-12 The four complexes of the mitochondrial respiratory chain.

documented by Moreadith et al.[125] had infantile lactic acidosis and died at a few months of age. Mitochondria prepared from a number of tissues were deficient in rotenone-sensitive NADH-cytochrome c reductase ranging from mild deficiency in kidney to total deficiency in skeletal muscle. Electron-spin resonance spectroscopy of liver submitochondrial particles revealed nearly complete absence of the iron sulfur cluster signals typical of complex I. In support of this, it was also demonstrated by immunoblotting that the 75- and 13-kDa polypeptides of complex I, which are thought to be iron-sulfur proteins, were reduced or absent in the mitochondria of this patient. It has been shown that this type of defect can be demonstrated in cultured skin fibroblasts.[126,127] Four patients have been described with complex I defects on the basis of abnormal redox state and deficient rotenone-sensitive NAD-cytochrome c reductase in fibroblast mitochondria.[127,128] These patients presented with infantile lactic acidosis, high rates of blood lactate to pyruvate, anorexia, tachypnea, and hypotonia. They died at 2 weeks, 4 weeks, 6 weeks, and 7 months. The three who survived the neonatal period had an abnormal EEG, and in two there was frank seizure activity. One was examined at autopsy and showed necrosis of subcortical white matter and dysmyelination.[128] The residual activity of the respiratory chain between NADH and cytochrome c in these cases varied between 14 and 21 percent of normal (Table 34-5).

Complex II. Only two sibs have been reported as being deficient in complex II. A 7-year-old boy and a 9-year-old girl showed progressive encephalomyopathy with dementia, myoclonic seizures, and small stature. A muscle biopsy showed mitochondrial aggregates and excessive lipid droplets in muscle fibers. In muscle mitochondria it was found that the activity of succinate cytochrome c reductase was deficient while succinate dehydrogenase activity was normal. The activities of NADH-cytochrome c reductase and cytochrome oxidase were also found to be normal. This places the defect somewhere between succinate dehydrogenase and coenzyme Q_{10} in complex II.[129]

Complex III. The group of patients reported with this defect display some heterogeneity. The earliest cases reported in 1970 were those of a father and son (ages 46 and 16) who represented with the combination of proximal weakness, areflexia, ataxia, progressive external ophthalmoplegia, and dementia.[130] Another case in an adult with ophthalmoplegia showed limb weakness, premature fatigue, ptosis, and dysphagia.[131] The other five patients described also had combinations of muscular weakness, ataxia, exercise intolerance, and ocular myopathy.[132–135] Most of them noted problems initially in childhood which worsened with age.

In biochemical terms, this group is also heterogeneous. In isolated muscle mitochondria, five had a deficiency of reducible cytochrome b[130,132–134] and one had combined deficiency of cytochrome b and c_1,[135] while in the others the cytochrome spectrum was normal.[131] In all these cases there was deficient succinate cytochrome c reductase and rotenone-sensitive NADH-cytochrome c reductase.

Finally, in one unusual recent case it was demonstrated that both deficient NADH-coenzyme Q reductase and succinate-coenzyme Q reductase occured in muscle mitochondria.[136] The patient had seizure activity from the seventh day of life, and at 17 months of age this boy was mentally retarded and suffered from myoclonus and abnormal ocular movements. The authors suggested that the defect resided at the level of coenzyme Q, perhaps due to a change in the lipid or protein environment.[136] Where looked for, the defect in one patient was found not to be expressed in cultured skin fibroblast mitochondria.[134,137]

Complex IV. The reported defects in complex IV are the most numerous and the most varied. In a recent review, DiMauro et al.[138] classified nine different presentations of patients with cytochrome oxidase deficiency (Table 32-5). In some of these, such as Menkes disease, the muscle complex IV defect is almost certainly secondary, in that particular instance due to low intracellular copper levels rather than a primary defect in cytochrome oxidase itself.[139]

A frequently reported clinical picture is a fatal infantile myopathy with renal dysfunction. The patients presented in the neonatal period with lactic acidosis, hypotonia, hyporeflexia, respiratory failure, and DeToni-Fanconi-Debré syndrome.[140–145] In this group of patients, cytochrome oxidase activity and reducible cytochrome aa_3 were absent from muscle, partially absent in kidney, but normal in liver, heart, and brain. The defect was not demonstrable in fibroblasts. Of the seven patients described with this subtype of complex IV deficiency, six died

Table 32-5 Reported Defects in the Complexes of the Respiratory Chain

Complex I	*Complex II*	*Complex III*	*Complex IV*
*a.** Infantile Severe lactic acidemia Death before 1 yr Hypotonia, anorexia, apnea *b.*† Adults Lactic acidemia, generalized weakness, and exercise intolerance	†2 cases only—sibs Progressive encephalomyopathy, dementia, myoclonic seizures, and small stature No increased blood lactate	*a.*† Adult History of muscular weakness and exercise intolerance plus combinations of lactic acidemia, ophthalmoplegia, ptosis, dysphagia, and ataxia *b.*† Infantile One case with combined Complex I and Complex III deficiency Lactic acidemia	*a.*† Fatal infantile myopathy with DeToni-Fanconi-Debré syndrome *b.**† Fatal infantile mitochondrial myopathy with cardiomyopathy and lactic acidemia *c.*† Benign infantile mitochondrial myopathy and lactic acidemia, reversible *d.**† Subacute necrotizing encephalomyelapathy (Leigh disease) *e.*† Adult chronic progressive external ophthalmoplegia, 1/7 lactic acidemia *f.**† Kearns-Sayre syndrome, lactic acidemia *g.*† Menkes disease

*Diagnosed in cultured skin fibroblasts.
†Diagnosed in muscle.

before age 4 months and one died at 8 months after prolonged assisted ventilation.[138,145] The fact that two patients were sibs[144] and that in two other families there had been previous sibs who died in infancy with similar symptoms[140,143] strongly points to genetic determination of this defect. The fact that this defect is exclusively confined to a lack of activity of the cytochrome oxidase complex in muscle tissue has led to the suggestion by Kuhn-Nentwig and Kadenbach[146] that a nuclear encoded subunit of the complex which is specifically expressed in skeletal muscle postnatally may be the defective entity.

A similar suggestion has been made to explain the course of benign infantile mitochondrial myopathy.[147,148] Two patients presented at 2 and 6 weeks of age with hypotonia, hyporeflexia, and lactic acidosis. In both cases muscle biopsies were performed which showed accumulations of lipid droplets, glycogen, and mitochondria with deficient activity of cytochrome oxidase.[147,148] What is unusual about these cases is that, over an 18-month period, the patients slowly but spontaneously recovered, and this was concomitant with a return to normal activity of muscle cytochrome oxidase.[147,148]

A combination of skeletal and cardiac myopathy was described in two patients with complex IV deficiency[149,150] in muscle. In one of the two patients cardiac cytochrome oxidase was found to be normal at autopsy despite the clinical cardiomyopathy and deficient skeletal muscle enzyme.[150] A similar patient was studied by us recently in collaboration with Chang and Di Mauro. This patient had a fatal hypertrophic cardiomyopathy, skeletal myopathy, and lactic acidosis and died at 3 weeks of age. In this patient muscle cytochrome oxidase was 14 percent of normal, and activity in cultured skin fibroblasts was 37 percent of normal. Moreover, the skin fibroblasts had an abnormally high lactate/pyruvate ratio, indicative of the presence of a respiratory chain defect. Deficient liver cytochrome oxidase was reported in a child who died at 9 months of age, while a second cousin died of infantile myopathy with deficient cytochrome oxidase and absence of reducible cytochrome b and aa_3.[151]

Perhaps the largest and best documented of the groups of patients with complex IV deficiency are those that present with the diagnosis of subacute necrotizing encephalomyelopathy (Leigh disease).[117–119,128] Ten patients altogether have been described in this category; the defect was detected initially in cultured skin fibroblasts in seven cases and in muscle in three cases.[40,128,152,153] In three of the patients diagnosed in fibroblasts, the defect was also documented in muscle.[40,128] The deficit in activity was associated with 17 to 28 percent residual activity of cytochrome oxidase in cultured skin fibroblasts,[40,128] and similar residual activities were found in liver, muscle, and brain.[40,128,152,153] These patients presented between 10 months and 5 years of age with hypotonia, dysphagia, and a mild lactic acidemia. From this initial presentation, which is often accompanied by delayed development, there is a gradual loss of acquired motor functions.[128] Nystagmus and intention tremor often develop during this regressive period.[40,128,152] Death often results from apnea. In those patients where postmortem examination of the brain was possible, the necrotic and cystic lesions in the brain stem and basal ganglia typical of Leigh disease were found.[40]

Mitochondrial Myopathy, Ragged Red Fibers, and Lactic Acidemia. Many of the reports of patients having defects in the mitochondrial respiratory chain are accompanied by descriptions of the abnormal ultrastructural appearance of the muscle mitochondria. In addition to these morphologic abnormalities, a situation is often described which suggests that mitochondrial proliferation has taken place.[117,118] The distinct pattern given by such subsarcolemmal mitochondrial aggregates after muscle sections have been treated with Gomori trichrome stain[154] has given rise to the term "ragged red fibers" to describe this condition.[155]

There is a group of patients for whom the presence of ragged red fibers and lactic acidemia is a common feature together with spongy degeneration of the central nervous system, sensorineural hearing loss, dementia, and short stature[156] (Table 32-6).

This group is composed of patients who have either Kearns-Sayre syndrome (KSS), the syndrome of myoclonus epilepsy with ragged red fibers, or the syndrome of mitochondrial myopathy, encephalopathy, lactic acidosis, and strokelike episodes. The Kearns-Sayre syndrome can be distinguished from the other two by the presence of external ophthalmoplegia, retinal degeneration, heart block, and a high CSF protein.[157] Cases of this syndrome are sporadic, with one reported exception. Both MELAS and MERRF on the other hand are familial, and the most unusual feature of MERRF is myoclonic epilepsy.[118,158] There is also considerable evidence in some

Table 32-6 Clinical and Laboratory Features in Three Syndromes with Mitochondrial Encephalomyopathy*

Features	*KSS*	*MERRF*	*MELAS*
Dementia	+	+	+
Short stature	+	+	+
Sensorineural hearing loss	+	+	+
Lactic acidosis	+	+	+
Weakness	+	+	+
Ragged-red fibers	+	+	+
Spongy degeneration	+	+	+
Episodic vomiting	−	−	+
Cortical blindness	−	−	+
Hemiparesis, hemianopia	−	−	+
Positive family history	−	+	+
Seizures	−	+	+
Myoclonus	−	+	−
Ataxia	+	+	−
Ophthalmoplegia	+	−	−
Retinal degeneration	+	−	−
Heart block	+	−	−
CSF protein > 100 mg/dl	+	−	−

*KSS = Kearns-Sayre syndrome; MERRF = myoclonus epilepsy with ragged-red fibers; MELAS = mitochondrial encephalopathy, myopathy, lactic acidosis, and strokelike episodes; CSF = cerebrospinal fluid.
SOURCE: Adapted from DiMauro et al.[156]

kindreds that MERRF inheritance is non-Mendelian, and some pedigrees suggest maternal inheritance.[156,159] MELAS patients resemble those with MERRF and KSS in that they do not present until the second or third decade. There is often short stature, but the distinguishing feature is the recurrence of episodes which resemble strokes in that there is hemiparesis, hemaniopsia, or cortical blindness often accompanied by headache, seizures, and vomiting.[160–162] Very often the mothers of these patients are affected by sensorineural hearing loss or subclinical myopathy.[161] In one case with features of MELAS, it was demonstrated that there was a swelling of the endothelial cells and a thickening of the basal lamina of muscle capillaries,[163] suggesting occlusion of the vessels. Similar cases with vessel occlusion in MELAS have been documented by Stadhouders[164] and ourselves.[165] It was suggested that ischemia was the cause of development of ragged red fibers in this case. On the other hand lack of coenzyme Q_{10}[156] and cytochrome oxidase deficiency[165,166] have been described in patients with Kearns-Sayre syndrome.

In the majority of cases of MELAS, MERRF, and Kearns-Sayre syndrome, investigations of the mitochondrial respiratory chain components in muscle reveal no consistent abnormalities.[160] In a total of four cases which had symptoms typical of MELAS or MERRF, a defect in complex I has been documented in muscle mitochondria.[165,167,168] In two of the patients there was an additional feature of a ventricular cardiomyopathy.[165,167] These patients all developed symptoms early, between 2 and 6 years of age, with simple exercise intolerance. Approaching puberty, these patients developed either myoclonic seizures or strokelike episodes. The average activity of the four patients was 11 percent of normal; succinate cytochrome c reductase was normal in all cases, but there was also a reduction in cytochrome oxidase activity in every case, the average being between 28 and 68 percent of control activity. The difference between the results in these cases and those reported earlier may be that mitochondria were isolated from muscle tissue before determination of respiratory chain activity in these cases. In the earlier cases analysis was carried out with muscle that had been frozen in liquid N_2.[160] Mitochondrial proliferation was observed in muscle in some of the cases with documented lesions of the respiratory chain but with a different clinical picture.[130,132,140,141] Ragged red fibers and mitochondrial proliferation can be produced in experimental animals by reduction of the energy supply of the tissue either by infusion of uncoupling agents[169] or by induced hypoxia.[170] Thus the appearance of ragged red fibers in a group of muscle fibers may be a physiological response either to oxygen deprivation or to abnormal or inefficient functioning of the respiratory chain. By using serial sectioning techniques, Sengers et al. found that affected fibers show the ragged red appearance over a limited region of their length[117] and that these regions occur in zones. Capillary proliferation also occurs in these zones with the ragged red appearance.[117] This may occur in response to capillary occlusion.[163] This has been observed in adult chronic progressive external ophthalmoplegia, another disease in which ragged red fibers are seen.[117,171] As a further complication, it also seems that ragged red fibers in chronic progressive external ophthalmoplegia stain very poorly for cytochrome oxidase, suggesting that increased synthesis of fully active complex IV of the respiratory chain does not accompany mitochondrial proliferation.[171]

In summary, it would seem that mitochondrial proliferation is a response to the occurrence of energy production problems in the muscle fiber. This can take place either in response to a microangiopathy, which deprives the fibers of oxygen, or in response to an inherited defect in the mitochondrial energy production system. Where exactly the MELAS, MERRF, Kearns-Sayre group of patients fits into this picture is not clear at present. There is considerable overlap between these patient groups, and some have features which make it impossible to place them definitively in any one category.

KREBS CYCLE DEFECTS

There are reports of patients with lactic acidemia where studies on cultured skin fibroblasts revealed a defective Krebs cycle turnover as judged by the oxidation of [3-^{14}C]pyruvate to [$^{14}CO_2$].[40,56] These patients had normal activities of the pyruvate dehydrogenase complex and pyruvate carboxylase. Clinically they were all ataxic though there was a disparity in age with two patients being 1½ years old[45] and two patients being 10 and 11 years old[56] at the time of reporting. Two of the patients had seizures and a third had involuntary movements. Three of them had delayed neurologic development. The reason for the defective Krebs cycle turnover was not defined further in any of these patients. None of them had abnormal organic acids in the urine. There are two Krebs cycle abnormalities that have been definitively localized, one at α-ketoglutarate dehydrogenase and one at fumarase.

Isolated Deficiency of the α-Ketoglutarate Dehydrogenase Complex

It was pointed out above that patients with lipoamide dehydrogenase deficiency exhibit deficiency of all three α-keto acid dehydrogenase complexes, including the α-ketoglutarate dehydrogenase complex. Isolated deficiency of the α-ketoglutarate dehydrogenase complex has been described in two affected sibs whose parents were first cousins.[172] The first male sib presented with delayed development. This boy was able to walk with an unsteady gait by the age of 30 months, but this ability was lost by age 3 years. Muscular hypotonia and choreoathetoid movements were noted at this time. By 5 years of age the child was immobile and exhibited signs of spasticity. The younger female sib exhibited a similar course up to age 3 years. Despite the loss of acquired motor skills in both sibs, it was thought that the development at the emotional and cognitive levels was not primarily affected. Excretion of α-ketoglutaric acid in the urine of both children was 15 to 100 times normal, and both were shown to have increased levels of blood α-ketoglutarate. A mild elevation of blood lactate was evident in the older child. Activity of the α-ketoglutarate dehydrogenase complex was about 30 percent of normal in skin fibroblasts, while the activity of the E_1 α-ketoglutarate decarboxylase was thought to be normal. Since the E_3 lipoamide dehydrogenase activity was also normal, the authors concluded that the defect lay in the E_2 transuccinylase portion of the complex.[172]

Deficiency of Fumarase (Fumarate Hydratase)

Five patients have been described who exhibited consistent fumaric aciduria, three of them with documented fumarase deficiency. Whelan et al.[173] described two mentally retarded adults with large amounts of fumaric acid in the urine. Because the plasma fumaric acid levels showed only a mild elevation compared with controls, the urinary abnormality was thought to be due to a renal tubular resorption defect specific for fumaric acid. Fumarase activity was not measured in these cases. The other three cases were documented in children. The patient with the most severe case exhibited cyanotic spells and hypothermia on the first day of life and at 2 weeks was aphagic and lethargic with a blood lactate of 3.7 m*M*.[174] A CT scan showed cerebral atrophy. At three months microcephaly and failure to thrive were evident, and visual fixation was absent. The lactate/pyruvate ratio was elevated, and the urine showed increased amounts of fumarate, succinate, citrate, and oxalate. A muscle biopsy showed increased numbers of subsarcolemmal mitochondria but no ragged red fibers. The EEG was abnormal, and opisthotonic posturing developed. At 8 months of age the child died while being treated with antibiotics for otitis media. Fumarase activity was 20 percent of normal or less in both liver and muscle tissue homogenates and in liver and muscle mitochondria.[174] A second patient, the male infant of a first cousin marriage, exhibited microcephaly, hypotonia, and severe developmental delay at age 1 year.[175] There were large amounts of succinate, fumarate, and α-ketoglutarate in the urine. Cultured skin fibroblasts had 20 percent of normal fumurase activity, and the activity was decreased both in the cytosolic and mitochondrial forms of the enzyme. In this case, analysis of extracts of cultured skin fibroblasts with isoelectric focusing revealed only one band of mitochondrial origin compared to the six bands of diverse origin present normally. The fourth patient was a 3½-year-old mentally retarded girl with excessive amounts of fumarate, succinate, and α-ketoglutarate in the urine. Increased fumarate was present in plasma and CSF.[176] There was 1.8 percent of normal fumarase activity present in cultured skin fibroblasts.

Though these patients were somewhat different in their presentation, it is of interest that in at least one of them both the mitochondrial and cytosolic forms of fumarase were affected. Edwards and Hopkinson[177] discovered an asymptomatic human fumarase electrophoretic variant, and both the cytosolic and mitochondrial forms of the enzyme were affected. This confirmed the proposal that both isoenzymes were encoded by the same autosomal gene.[178] Both isoenzymes are thought to be tetrameric (M_r = 180,000), the mature subunits having a relative molecular weight of 45,000.[179] Translation of rat liver mRNA in vitro produces two distinct fumarase proteins, one at M_r = 45,000 and one at M_r = 50,000.[180] The larger species is incorporated into rat liver mitochondria in a process involving proteolytic cleavage to M_r = 45,000. Thus rat liver mRNA contains two separate messages for fumarase, probably derived from the same gene by differential splicing.[180] O'Hare and Doonan[181] examined the tryptic peptides of cytosolic and mitochondrial fumarase isolated from pig liver and found that 58 tryptic peptides were present in common for both enzymes, while two were unique to the mitochondrial and five were unique to the cytosolic form of the enzyme. The *N*-terminal amino acid sequence was different for the two isoenzymes. Extrapolating from this information, we can predict that it would be possible to have mutations which affect either mitochondrial or cytosolic forms of the enzyme in isolation, but more likely both forms of the enzyme would be affected by a single mutation.

THE DIFFERENTIAL DIAGNOSIS OF LACTIC ACIDEMIA

The patient with lactic acidemia presents one of the more difficult diagnostic problems in the area of genetic metabolic disease. It is important to assemble as much biochemical and pathologic information as possible on the patient and, together with the clinical signs and symptoms, this will help pinpoint the diagnosis. The basic measurements required are as follows: (1) blood lactate, pyruvate, 3-hydroxybutyrate, acetoacetate; (2) quantitative serum amino acids; (3) urine organic acids done by gas chromatography/mass spectrometry; (4) fasting blood glucose, lactate, and 3-hydroxybutyrate; (5) muscle biopsy in some cases. A flow chart for diagnosis is shown in Fig. 32-13.

Since lactic acid elevation occurs in many of the organic acidurias, these diagnoses should be ruled out in the early stages of investigation by gas chromatography/mass spectrometry analysis of the urine organic acids (See Chaps. 27 to 36, 82 and 83). Almost any of the organic acidurias can present with an increased blood lactate because of interference with CoA metabolism. Similarly, hypoglycemia in the organic acidurias can develop because of depression of the levels of acetyl CoA, the allosteric activator of pyruvate carboxylase. Fatty acid oxidation defects similarly produce a combination of lactic acidemia, hypoglycemia, and dicarboxylic aciduria.[182] Most cases of biotinidase and multiple carboxylase deficiency will probably be detected at this stage by the presence of unusual organic acids, since both defects can present with lactic acid accumulation. The presence of alopecia, dermatitis, and persistent *Candida* infections should also pinpoint most but not all biotinidase and multiple carboxylase deficiency cases (Chap. 83).

The ratio of lactate to pyruvate in the blood is one of the most helpful indicators of the underlying problem and may determine the directions of further investigation. A lactate/pyruvate ratio of below 25, which we consider to be in the normal range, points in the direction of a defect either in pyruvate dehydrogenase or one of the gluconeogenic enzymes, while a consistently raised lactate/pyruvate ratio especially of 35 and

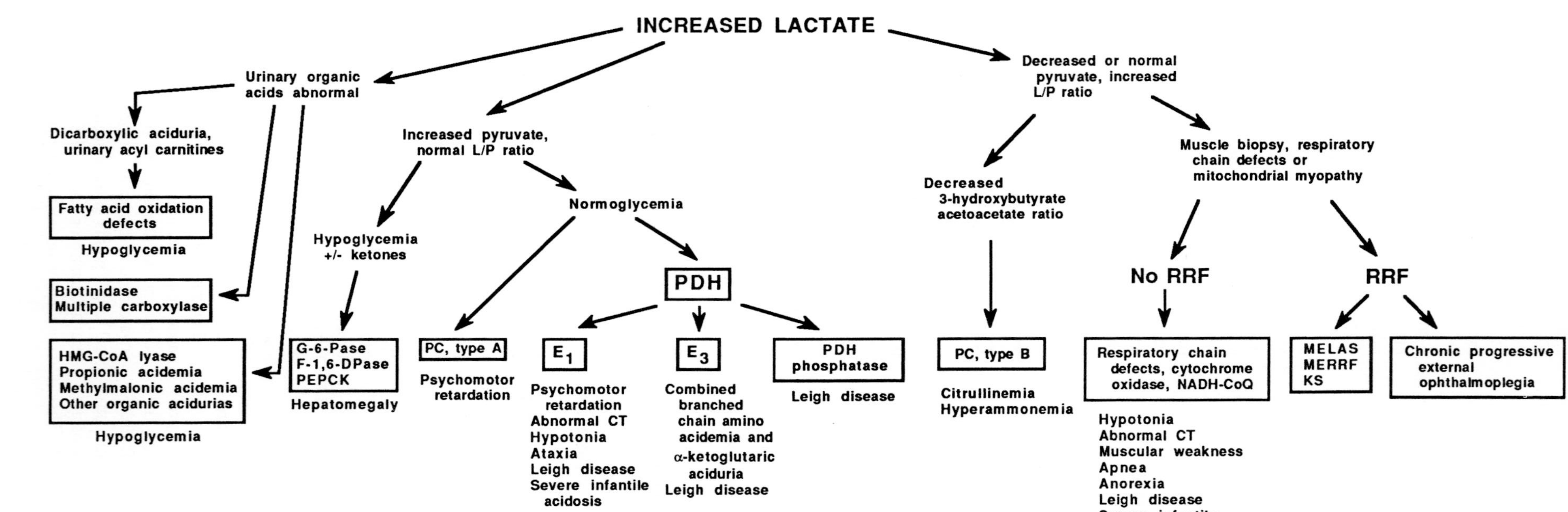

Fig. 32-13 Flow chart for the differential diagnosis of lactic acidemia. See text for detailed explanation. Diagram starts with the observation of increased blood lactic acid. Disease entities or categories are highlighted in boxes.

above is indicative of either pyruvate carboxylase (type A) deficiency, a respiratory chain defect, or in some cases a mitochondrial myopathy.[89,128,161–163]

Taking the normal lactate/pyruvate ratio group first, a further differential can be obtained using the response to fasting. A defect in any of the enzymes of the gluconeogenic pathway results in a tendency toward fasting hypoglycemia accompanied by a blood lactate which is higher than in the fed state. The severity of the hypoglycemia experienced is in the order glucose-6-phosphatase > fructose-1,6-bisphosphatase > phosphoenolpyruvate carboxykinase > pyruvate carboxylase. Hepatomegaly usually accompanies the gluconeogenic defects, the severity being in the same order as above. In occasional cases neither fasting hypoglycemia nor hepatomegaly is observed in pyruvate carboxylase deficiency (type A).[86] Muscular hypotonia is present in phosphoenolpyruvate carboxykinase deficiency and pyruvate carboxylase deficiency[108,109] but not in glucose-6-phosphatase or fructose-1,6-bisphosphatase deficiency. Psychomotor retardation is present in all pyruvate carboxylase (type A)-deficient patients and in most cases of PDH complex deficiency.[31,86] Ataxic episodes are a common occurrence, and hypotonia is present in nearly all cases of PDH complex deficiency. Many patients with PDH complex deficiency manifest a neurodegenerative course with loss of acquired milestones.[31] Differential diagnosis between E_1 and E_3 subtypes of PDH complex deficiency can be made by observing the presence of elevated plasma branched chain amino acids in the E_3 subtype.

An increased ratio of blood lactate to pyruvate which is accompanied by a decreased ratio of 3-hydroxybutyrate to acetoacetate is indicative of type B pyruvate carboxylase deficiency.[86,93] The presentation of this will be infantile and should not be considered in an older child. It can be confirmed by the presence of elevated plasma citrulline and lysine which is accompanied by hyperammonemia. Mild elevations of ammonia have also been observed in PDH complex (E_1 type) deficiency.[54]

An increased ratio of blood lactate to pyruvate which is accompanied by an increased ratio of 3-hydroxybutyrate to acetoacetate (>2:1) is indicative of a respiratory chain defect or in some cases a mitochondrial myopathy. On the other hand, the presence of ragged red fibers in the muscle is typical of a mitochondrial myopathy, and if this is accompanied by dementia, short stature, and sensorineural hearing loss, this would place the patient in the MELAS, MERRF, Kearns-Sayre group of disorders.[156] This group of patients is typically older, many of them being in the second or third decade of life. Ragged red fibers are also seen occasionally in patients with the mitochondrial respiratory chain defects. These patients have muscular weakness, hypotonia, failure to thrive, and anorexia. Many present as infants or neonates, but other reported cases have an adult onset. CT scanning or nuclear magnetic resonance imaging can be helpful. In both the PDH complex defects and the respiratory chain defects the cystic lesions and areas of necrosis that develop in the brain stem and basal ganglia may be detectable.[31,40,128] Further, in PDH complex deficiency, enlarged ventricles and cerebral atrophy may also be evident.[31]

This outline will give the clinician an idea of the approximate diagnosis of the patient concerned. The final diagnosis must, of course, be confirmed by measurement of enzyme activity where possible in leukocytes, cultured skin fibroblasts, or muscle or liver biopsy, depending on the identity of the suspected defect.

REFERENCES

1. TANAKA K, ROSENBERG LE: Disorders of branched chain–amino acid and organic acid metabolism, in Stanbury JB, Wyngaarden JB, Frederickson DS, Goldstein JL, Brown MS (eds): *The Metabolic Basis of Inherited Disease*. New York, McGraw-Hill, 1983, p 440.
2. NEWSHOLME EA, LEECH AR: in *Biochemistry for the Medical Sciences*, New York, Wiley, 1983, p 448.
3. RANDLE PJ, SUGDEN PH, KERBEY AL, RADCLIFFE PM, HUTSON NJ: Regulation of pyruvate oxidation and the conservation of glucose. *Biochem Soc Symp* 43:47, 1978.
4. AHLBORG O, FELIG P: Lactate and glucose exchange across the forearm, legs, and splanchnic bed during and after prolonged leg exercise. *J Clin Invest* 69:45, 1982.
5. CHAUSSAIN JL, GEORGES P, OLIVE G, JOB JC: Glycemic response to 24-hour fast in normal children and children with ketotic hypoglycemia. 2. Hormonal and metabolic changes. *J Pediatr* 85:776, 1974.
6. KAHN A, MEIENHOFER MC, COTTREAU D, LAGRANGE JC, DREYFUS JC: Phosphofructokinase (PFK) isozymes in man. *Hum Genet* 48:93, 1979.
7. MEIENHOFER MC, COTTREAU D, DREYFUS JC, KAHN A: The kinetic properties of human F_4 phosphofructokinase. *FEBS Lett* 110:219, 1980.
8. DAVIDSON M, COLLINS M, BYRNE J, VORA S: Alterations in phosphofructokinase isoenzymes during early human development. *Biochem J* 214:703, 1983.
9. KREISBERG RA: Glucose-lactate interrelations in man. *N Engl J Med* 287:132, 1973.
10. KREISBERG RA, PENNINGTON LF, BOSHELL BR: Lactate turnover and gluconeogenesis in normal and obese humans. *Diabetes* 19:53, 1970.
11. HERMANSEN L, MACHLUM S, PRUETT EDR, VAGI O, WALDUM H, WESSEL-AAS T: Lactate removal at rest and during exercise, in Howald H, Poortman JR (eds): *Metabolic Adaptation to Prolonged Physical Exercise*. Basel, Birkhauser Verlag, 1975, p 101.
12. KREBS HA, WOODS HF, ALBERTI KGMM: Hyperlactataemia and lactic acidosis, in Marks V, Hales CN (eds): *Essays in Medical Biochemistry*. London, William Clowes, 1975, vol 1, p 81.
13. NEWSHOLME EA, LEECH AR: in *Biochemistry for the Medical Sciences*. New York, Toronto, Wiley, 1983, p 229.
14. FELIG P: Amino acid metabolism in man. *Annu Rev Biochem* 44:993, 1975.
15. KAPLAN NO, EVERSE J: Regulatory characteristics of lactate dehydrogenases. *Adv Enzyme Regul* 10:323, 1972.
16. KANNO T, SUDO K, TAKEUCHI I, KANDA S, HONDA N, NISHIMURA Y, OYAMA K: Hereditary deficiency of lactate dehydrogenase M-subunit. *Clin Chim Acta* 108:267, 1980.
17. KITAMURA M, IIJIMA N, HASHIMOTO F, HIRATSUKA A: Hereditary deficiency of the subunit H of lactate dehydrogenase. *Clin Chim Acta* 34:419, 1971.
18. REED LJ: Regulation of mammalian pyruvate dehydrogenase complex by a phosphorylation-dephosphorylation cycle. *Curr Top Cell Regul* 18:95, 1981.
19. RANDLE PJ: Mitochondrial 2-oxoacid dehydrogenase complexes of animal tissues. *Philos Trans R Soc Lond, Series B*, 302:47, 1983.
20. PAXTON R, HARRIS RA: Isolation of rabbit liver branched-chain α-ketoacid dehydrogenase and regulation by phosphorylation. *J Biol Chem* 257:14433, 1982.
21. GUEST RJ: Gene-protein relationships of the α-keto-acid dehydrogenase complexes of *Escherichia coli* K_{12}: Chromosomal location of the lipoamide dehydrogenase gene. *J Gen Microbiol* 80:523, 1974.
22. LINN TE, PETTIT FH, HUCHO F, REED LJ: Keto acid dehydrogenase complexes. XI. Comparative studies of the regulatory properties of the pyruvate dehydrogenase complexes from kidney, heart and liver mitochondria. *Proc Natl Acad Sci USA* 64:227, 1969.
23. MCALLISTER A, ALLISON SP, RANDLE PJ: Effects of dichloroacetate on the metabolism of glucose, pyruvate, acetate, 3-hydroxybutyrate and palmitate. *Biochem J* 134:1067, 1973.
24. HOGG SA, TAYLOR SI, RUDERMAN NB: Pyruvate dehydrogenase activity in starvation, diabetes and exercise. *Biochem J* 158:203, 1976.
25. WHITEHOUSE S, COOPER RH, RANDLE PJ: Mechanism of activation of pyruvate dehydrogenase by dichloroacetate and other halogenated carboxylic acids. *Biochem J* 141:761, 1974.
26. BLASS JP, AVIGAN J, UHLENDORF BW: A defect of pyruvate decarboxylase in a child with an intermittent movement disorder. *J Clin Invest* 49:423, 1970.
27. BLASS JP, KARK RAP, ENGEL WK: Clinical studies of a patient with pyruvate decarboxylase deficiency. *Arch Neurol* 25:449, 1971.
28. BLASS JP, LONSDALE D, UHLENDORF BW, HAM E: Intermittent ataxia with pyruvate decarboxylase activity. *Lancet* 1:1302, 1971.

29. FARMER TW, VEATH L, MILLER AL, O'BRIEN J, ROSENBERG RN: Pyruvate decarboxylase deficiency in a patient with subacute necrotizing encephalomyelopathy. *Neurology* 23:429, 1973.

30. FARREL DF, CLARK AF, SCOTT CR, WENNBERG RP: Absence of pyruvate decarboxylase activity in man. A cause of congenital lacticacidosis. *Science* 187:1082, 1975.

31. ROBINSON BH, MACMILLAN H, PETROVA-BENEDICT R, SHERWOOD WG: Variable clinical presentation in patients with deficiency of the pyruvate dehydrogenase complex. A review of 30 cases with a defect in the F component of the complex. *J Pediatr* 111:525, 1987.

32. WICK H, SCHWEIZERK K, BAUMGARTNER R: Thiamine dependency in a patient with congenital lactic acidemia due to pyruvate dehydrogenase deficiency. *Agents Actions* 7:405, 1977.

33. STROMME JH, BORUD O, MOE PJ: Fatal lactic acidosis in a newborn attributable to a congenital defect of pyruvate dehydrogenase. *Pediatr Res* 10:60, 1976.

34. WICKING CA, SCHOLEM RD, HUNT SM, BROWN GK: Immunochemical analysis of normal and mutant forms of human pyruvate dehydrogenase. *Biochem J* 239:89, 1986.

35. MATSUO M, OOKITA K, TAKEMINE H, KOIKE K, KOIKE M: Fatal case of pyruvate dehydrogenase deficiency. *Acta Paediatr Scand* 74:140, 1985.

36. EVANS OB: Pyruvate decarboxylase deficiency in subacute necrotizing encephalomyelopathy. *Arch Neurol* 38:515, 1981.

37. PAPANASTASIOU D, LEHNERT W, SCHUCHMANN L, HOMMES FA: Chronic lactic acidosis in an infant. *Helv Paediatr Acta* 35:253, 1980.

38. HANSEN TL, CHRISTENSEN E, BRANDT NJ: Studies on pyruvate carboxylase, pyruvate decarboxylase and lipoamide dehydrogenase in subacute necrotizing encephalomyelopathy. *Acta Paediatr Scand* 71:263, 1982.

39. TOSHIMA K, KURODA Y, HASHIMOTO T, ITO M, WATANABE T, MIYAO M, KUNIO II: Enzymologic studies and therapy of Leigh's disease associated with pyruvate decarboxylase deficiency. *Pediatr Res* 16:430, 1982.

40. MIYABAYASHI S, ITO T, NARISAWA K, IINUMA K, TADA K: Biochemical studies in 28 children with lactic acidosis in relation to Leigh's encephalomyelopathy. *Eur J Pediatr* 143:278, 1985.

41. HO L, HU CWC, PACKMAN S, PATEL MS: Deficiency of the pyruvate dehydrogenase component in pyruvate dehydrogenase complex-deficient human fibroblasts. Immunological identification. *J Clin Invest* 78:844, 1986.

42. OHTAKE M, TAKADA G, MIYABAYASHI S, ARAI N, TADA K, MONNADA S: Pyruvate decarboxylase deficiency in a patient with Leigh's encephelomyopathy. *Tohoku J Exp Med* 137:379, 1982.

43. CEDERBAUM SD, BLASS JP, MINKOFF N, BROWN WJ, COTTON ME, HARRIS SH: Sensitivity to carbohydrate in a patient with familial intermittent lacticacidosis and pyruvate dehydrogenase deficiency. *Pediatr Res* 10:713, 1976.

44. BLASS JP, SCHULMAN JD, YOUNG DS, HOM E: An inherited defect affecting the tricarboxylic acid cycle in a patient with congenital lacticacidosis. *J Clin Invest* 51:1845, 1972.

45. FALK RE, CEDERBAUM SD, BLASS JP, GIBSON GE, KARK RAP, CARREL RE: Ketonic diet in the management of pyruvate dehydrogenase deficiency. *Pediatrics* 58:713, 1976.

46. EVANS O: Episodic weakness in pyruvate decarboxylase deficiency. *J Pediatr* 105:961, 1984.

47. KODAMA S, YAS R, NINOMIYA M, GOJI K, TAKAHASHI T, MONSHITA Y, MATSUO T: The effect of high fat diet on pyruvate decarboxylase deficiency without involvement of the central nervous system. *Brain Dev* 5:381, 1983.

48. STANSBIE D, WALLACE SJ, MARSAC C: Disorders of the pyruvate dehydrogenase complex. *J Inherited Metab Dis* 9:105, 1986.

49. ROBINSON BH: The lactic acidemias, in Lloyd JK, Scriver CR (eds): *Genetic and Metabolic Disease in Pediatrics*. London, Butterworth, 1985, p 111.

50. MCKAY N, PETROVA-BENEDICT R, THOENE J, BERGEN B, WILSON W, ROBINSON B: Three cases of lactic acidemia due to pyruvate decarboxylase (E_1) deficiency with evidence of protein polymorphism in the α subunit of the enzyme. *Eur J Pediatr* 144:445, 1986.

51. ROBINSON BH, SHERWOOD WG: Lactic acidemia, the prevalence of pyruvate decarboxylase deficiency. *J Inherited Metab Dis 7:Suppl* 1, 69, 1984.

52. REYNOLDS SF, BLASS JP: A possible mechanism for selective cerebellar damage in partial pyruvate dehydrogenase deficiency. *Neurology* 26:625, 1976.

53. HOMMES FA, BERGER R, LUIT-DE HAAN G: The effect of thiamine treatment on the activity of pyruvate dehydrogenase. Relation to the treatment of Leigh's encephalomyelopathy. *Pediatr Res* 7:616, 1973.

54. MCCORMICK K, VISCARDI RM, ROBINSON BH, HEININGER J: Partial pyruvate decarboxylase deficiency with profound lacticacidosis and hyperammonemia: Responses to dichloroacetate and benzoate. *Am J Med Genet* 22:291, 1985.

55. KURODA Y, ITO M, TOSHIMA K, TAKEDA E, NAITO E, HWANG TJ, HASHIMOTO T, MIYAO M, MASUDA M, YAMASHITA K, ADACHI T, SUZUKI Y, NISHIYAMA K: Treatment of chronic congenital lacticacidosis by oral administration of dichloroacetate. *J Inherited Metab Dis* 9:244, 1986.

56. ROBINSON BH, TAYLOR J, SHERWOOD WG: The genetic heterogeneity of lactic acidosis: Occurrence of recognizable inborn errors of metabolism in a pediatric population with lacticacidosis. *Pediatr Res* 14:956, 1980.

57. DAHL H, HUNT SM, HUTCHISON WM, BROWN GK: The Human Pyruvate Dehydrogenase Complex: Isolation of cDNA clones for the $E_1\alpha$ subunit, sequence analysis and characterization of the mRNA. *J Biol Chem* 262:7398, 1987.

58. DE MEIRLEIR L, MCKAY N, ROBINSON BH: Isolation of a full length cDNA clone for the $E_1\alpha$-subunit of pyruvate dehydrogenase. *J Biol Chem* 263:1991, 1988.

59. ROBINSON BH, TAYLOR J, SHERWOOD WG: Deficiency of dihydrolipoyl dehydrogenase. A cause of congenital lactic acidosis in infancy. *Pediatr Res* 11:1198, 1978.

60. TAYLOR J, ROBINSON BH, SHERWOOD WG: A defect in branched-chain amino acid metabolism in a patient with congenital lacticacidosis due to dihydrolipoyl dehydrogenase deficiency. *Pediatr Res* 12:60, 1978.

61. ROBINSON BH, TAYLOR J, KAHLER SG, KIRKMAN HN: Lacticacidemia, neurological deterioration and carbohydrate dependence in a girl with dihydrolipoyl dehydrogenase deficiency. *Eur J Pediatr* 136:35, 1981.

62. MUNNICH A, SAUDUBRAY JM, TAYLOR J, CHARPENTIER C, MARSAC C, ROCCHICCIOLI F, AMEDEE-MANESME O, COUDE FX, FREZAL J, ROBINSON BH: Congenital lactic acidosis, α-ketoglutaric aciduria and variant form of maple syrup urine disease due to a single enzyme defect. Dihydrolipoyl dehydrogenase deficiency. *Acta Paediatr Scand* 71:167, 1982.

63. MATALON R, STUMPF DA, MICHALS K, HART RD, PARKS JK, GOODMAN SI: Lipoamide dehydrogenase deficiency with primary lactic acidosis: Favorable response to treatment with oral lipoic acid. *J Pediatr* 104:65, 1984.

64. KUHARA T, SHINKA T, INQUE Y, MATSUMOTO M, YOSHINO M, SAKAGUCHI Y, MATSUMOTO I: Studies of urinary organic acid profiles of a patient with dihydrolipoyl dehydrogenase deficiency. *Clin Chim Acta* 133:133, 1983.

65. OTULAKOWSKI G, NYHAN W, SWEETMAN L, ROBINSON BH: Immunoextraction of lipoamide dehydrogenase from cultured skin fibroblasts in patients with combined α-ketoacid dehydrogenase deficiency. *Clin Chim Acta* 152:27, 1985.

66. SWEETMAN L, NYHAN W: Personal communication re patient documented in Ref. 65.

67. SORBI S, BLASS JP: Abnormal activation of pyruvate dehydrogenase in Leigh disease fibroblasts. *Neurology* 32:555, 1982.

68. DE VIVO DC, HAYMOND MW, OBERT KA, NELSON JS, PAGLIARA AS: Defective activation of the pyruvate dehydrogenase complex in subacute necrotizing encephalomyelopathy (Leigh disease). *Ann Neurol* 6:483, 1979.

69. ROBINSON BH, SHERWOOD WG: Pyruvate dehydrogenase phosphate deficiency: A cause of chronic congenital lacticacidosis in infancy. *Pediatr Res* 9:935, 1975.

70. BARDIN RE, TAYLOR BL, OSOHASHI I: Structural properties of pyruvate carboxylase from chicken liver and other sources. *Proc Natl Acad Sci USA* 72:4308, 1975.

71. WALLACE JC, EASTERBROOK-SMITH SB: in Keech DB, Wallace JC (eds): *Pyruvate Carboxylase*. Boca Raton, FL, CRC Press, 1985, p 65.

72. SCRUTTON MC, WHITE MD: Purification and properties of human liver pyruvate carboxylase. *Biochem Med* 9:271, 1974.

73. BARRIT GJ: in Keech DB, Wallace JC (eds): *Pyruvate Carboxylase*. Boca Raton, FL, CRC Press, 1985, p 141.

74. VON GLUTZ G, WALTER P: Regulation of pyruvate carboxylation by acetyl CoA in rat liver mitochondria. *FEBS Lett* 72:299, 1976.

75. CRABTREE B, HIGGINS SJ, NEWSHOLME EA: The activities of pyruvate carboxylase, phosphoenolpyruvate carboxykinase and fructose 1,6,diphosphatase in muscles from vertebrates and invertebrates. *Biochem J* 130:391, 1972.

76. ATKIN BM, BUIST NRM, UTTER M, LEITER AB, BANKER BQ: Pyruvate carboxylase deficiency and lactic acidosis in a retarded child without Leigh's disease. *Pediatr Res* 13:109, 1979.

77. ATKIN BM, UTTER MF, WEINBERG MB: Pyruvate carboxylase and phosphoenolpyruvate carboxykinase activity in leucocytes and fibroblasts from a patient with pyruvate carboxylase deficiency. *Pediatr Res* 13:38, 1979.

78. LEE SH, DAVIS JE: Carboxylase and decarboxylation reactions anapleurotic flux and removal of citric acid cycle intermediates in skeletal muscle. *J Biol Chem* 254:420, 1979.

79. LAMHONWAH A, QUAN F, GRAVEL RA: Sequence homology around the biotin-binding site of human propionyl-CoA carboxylase and pyruvate carboxylase. *Arch Biochem Biophys* 254:631, 1987.

80. FREYTAG SO, COLLIER KJ: Molecular cloning of a cDNA for human pyruvate carboxylase. *J Biol Chem* 259:12831, 1984.

81. HOMMES FA, SCHRIJVER J, DIAS TH: Pyruvate carboxylase deficiency, studies on patients and on an animal model system, in Burman D, Holton

JB, Pennock CA (eds): *Inherited Disorders of Carbohydrate Metabolism.* Baltimore, University Park Press, 1979, p 239.

82. MURPHY JV, ISOHASHI F, WEINBERG MB, UTTER MT: Pyruvate carboxylase deficiency—An alleged biochemical cause of Leigh's disease. *Pediatrics* 88:401, 1981.

83. BRUNETTE MG, DELVIN E, HAZEL B, SCRIVER CR: Thiamine-responsive lactic acidosis in a patient with deficient low K_m pyruvate carboxylase activity in liver. *Pediatrics* 50:702, 1972.

84. SCRUTTON MC, WHITE MD: Purification and properties of human liver pyruvate carboxylase. *Biochem Med* 9:271, 1974.

85. DEVIVO D, HAYMOND MW, LECKIE MP, BUSSMANN YL, MCDOUGAL DB, PAGLIARA AS: Clinical and biochemical implications of pyruvate carboxylase deficiency. *J Clin Endocrinol Metab* 45:1281, 1977.

86. ROBINSON BH, OEI J, SHERWOOD WG, APPLEGARTH D, WONG L, HAWORTH J, GOODYER P, CASEY R, ZALESKI LA: The molecular basis for the two different clinical presentations of classical pyruvate carboxylase deficiency. *Am J Hum Genet* 36:283, 1984.

87. HAWORTH JC, ROBINSON BH, PERRY TL: Lactic acidosis due to pyruvate carboxylase deficiency. *J Inherited Metab Dis* 4:57, 1981.

88. ROBINSON BH, OEI J, SAUNDERS M, GRAVEL R: [^{3}H]biotin-labeled proteins in cultured human skin fibroblasts from patients with pyruvate carboxylase deficiency. *J Biol Chem* 258:6660, 1983.

89. GRAVEL RA, ROBINSON BH: Biotin-dependent carboxylase deficiences (propionyl-CoA and pyruvate carboxylases). *Ann NY Acad Sci* 447:225, 1985.

90. ROBINSON BH, OEI J, SAUDUBRAY JM, MARSAC C, BARTLETT K, QUAN F, GRAVEL R: The French and North American phenotypes of pyruvate carboxylase deficiency. Correlation with biotin containing protein by ^{3}H-biotin incorporation, ^{35}S-streptavidin labelling, and Northern blotting with a cloned cDNA probe. *Am J Hum Genet* 40:50, 1987.

91. TSUCHIYAMA A, OYANAGI K, HIRANO S, TACHI N, SOGAWA H, WAGATSUMA K, NAKAO T, TSUGAWA S, KAWAMURA Y: A case of pyruvate carboxylase deficiency with later prenatal diagnosis of an unaffected sibling. *J Inherited Metab Dis* 6:85, 1983.

92. OIZUMI J, DONNEL GN, NG WG, MULIVOR PR, GREENE AE, CORIELL LL: Congenital lactic acidosis associated with pyruvate carboxylase deficiency. Repository identification No. GM 6056. *Cytogenet Cell Genet* 38:80, 1984.

93. SAUDUBRAY JM, MARSAC C, CHARPENTIER C, CATHELINEAU L, BESSON LM, LEROUX JP: Neonatal congenital lactic acidosis with pyruvate carboxylase deficiency in two siblings. *Acta Paediatr Scand* 65:717, 1976.

94. COUDE FX, OGIER H, MARSAC C, MUNNICH A, CHARPENTIER C, SAUDUBRAY JM: Secondary citrullinemia with hyperammonemia in four neonatal cases of pyruvate carboxylase deficiency. *Pediatrics* 68:914, 1981.

95. CHARPENTIER C, TETAU JM, OGIER H, SAUDUBRAY JM, COUDE FX, LEMONNIER A: Amino acid profile in pyruvate carboxylase deficiency: Comparison with some other metabolic disorders. *J Inherited Metab Dis [Suppl]* 5:11, 1982.

96. BARTLETT K, GHNEIM HK, STIRK JH, DALE G, ALBERTI KGMM: Pyruvate carboxylase deficiency. *J Inherited Metab Dis [Suppl]* 7:74, 1984.

97. GRETER J, GUSTAFSSON J, HOLME E: Pyruvate carboxylase deficiency with urea cycle impairment. *Acta Paediatr Scand* 74:982, 1985.

98. WONG LTK, DAVIDSON GF, APPLEGARTH DA, DIMMICK JE, NORMAN MG, TOONE JR, PIRIE G, WONG J: Biochemical and histologic pathology in an infant with cross-reacting material (negative) pyruvate carboxylase deficiency. *Pediatr Res* 20:274, 1986.

99. ROBINSON BH, HALPERIN ML: Transport of reduced nicotinamide adenine dinucleotide into mitochondria of white adipose tissue. *Biochem J* 116:229, 1970.

100. SHANK RP, BENNETT GS, FREYTAG SO, CAMPBELL GL: Pyruvate carboxylase: An astrocyte-specific enzyme implicated in the replenishment of amino acid neurotransmitter pools. *Brain Res* 329:364, 1985.

101. ATKIN B: Carrier detection of pyruvate carboxylase deficiency in fibroblasts and lymphocytes. *Pediatr Res* 13:1101, 1979.

102. HANSEN TL, CHRISTENSEN E, WILLEMS JL, TRIJBELS JMF: A mutation of pyruvate carboxylase in fibroblasts from a patient with severe, chronic lactic acidaemia. *Clin Chim Acta* 131:39, 1983.

103. MARSAC C, AUGERAU GL, FELDMAN G, WOLF B, HANSEN TL, BERGER R: Prenatal diagnosis of pyruvate carboxylase deficiency. *Clin Chim Acta* 119:121, 1982.

104. ROBINSON BH, TOON JR, PETROVA-BENEDICT R, DIMMICK JE, OEI J, APPLEGARTH DA: Prenatal diagnosis of pyruvate carboxylase deficiency. *Prenat Diagn* 5:67, 1985.

105. FISER RH JR, MELSHER HL, FISHER DA: Hepatic phosphoenolpyruvate carboxylase (PEPCK) deficiency. A new cause of hypoglycemia in childhood. *Pediatr Res* 10:60, 1974.

106. HOMMES FA, BENDIEN K, ELEMA JD, BREMER HJ, LOMBECK I: Two cases of phosphoenolpyruvate carboxykinase deficiency. *Acta Paediatr Scand* 65:233, 1976.

107. VIDNES J, SOVIK O: Gluconeogenesis in infancy and childhood. III. Deficiency of the extramitochondrial form of hepatic phosphoenolpyruvate carboxykinase in a case of persistent neonatal hypoglycemia. *Acta Paediatr Scand* 65:307, 1976.

108. CLAYTON PT, HYLAND K, BRAND M, LEONARD JV: Mitochondrial phosphoenolpyruvate carboxykinase deficiency. *Eur J Pediatr* 145:46, 1986.

109. ROBINSON BH, TAYLOR J, KAHLER S: Mitochondrial phosphoenolpyruvate carboxykinase deficiency in a child with lactic acidemia, hypotonia and failure to thrive. *Am J Hum Genet* 31:60A, 1979.

110. HANSON R, GARBER AJ: Phosphoenolpyruvate carboxykinase, its role in gluconeogenesis. *Am J Clin Nutr* 25:1010, 1972.

111. KREBS HA: Pyridine nucleotides and rate control. *Symp Soc Exp Biol* 17:299, 1973.

112. WILLIAMSON JR, SAFER B, LANOUE K, SMITH CM, WALAJTYS E: Mitochondrial-cytosolic interactions in cardiac tissue: Role of malate-aspartate cycle in the removal of glycolytic NADH from the cytosol. *Symp Soc Exp Biol* 17:241, 1973.

113. HATEFI Y: The mitochondrial electron transport and oxidative phosphorylation system. *Annu Rev Biochem* 54:1015, 1985.

114. JARAUSCH J, KADENBACH B: Tissue-specificity overrides species-specificity in cytoplasmic cytochrome c oxidase polypeptides. *Hoppe-Seyler's Z Physiol Chem* 363:1133, 1982.

115. CHOMYN A, MARIOTTINI P, CLEETER MWJ, RAGAN CI, MATSUNO-YAGI A, HATEFI Y, DOOLITTLE RF, ATTARDI G: Six unidentified reading frames of human mitochondrial DNA encode components of the respiratory-chain NADH dehydrogenase. *Nature* 314:592, 1984.

116. CHOMYN A, CLEETER MWJ, RAGAN CI, RILEY M, DOOLITTLE RF, ATTARDI G: URF6, the last unidentified reading frame of human mtDNA, codes for an NADH dehydrogenase subunit. *Science* 234:614, 1986.

117. SENGERS RCA, STADHOUDERS AM, TRIJBELS JMF: Mitrochondrial myopathies. Clinical, morphological and biochemical aspects. *Eur J Pediatr* 141:192, 1984.

118. CORNELIO F, DiDONATO S: Myopathies due to enzyme deficiencies. *J Neurol* 232:329, 1985.

119. DiMAURO S, ZEVIANI M, BONILLA E, BRESOLIN N, NAKAGAWA M, MIRANDA FA, MOGGIO M: Cytochrome c oxidase deficiency. *Trans Biochem Soc* 13:651, 1985.

120. MORGAN-HUGHES JA, DARVENIZA P, LANDON DN, LAND JM, CLARK JB: A mitochondrial myopathy with a deficiency of respiratory chain NADH-CoQ reductase activity. *J Neurol Sci* 43:27, 1979.

121. BUSCH HFM, SCHOLTE HR, ARTS WF, LUYT-HOUWEN IEM: A mitochondrial myopathy with a respiratory chain defect and carnitine deficiency, in Busch HFM, Jennekens FGI, Scholte HR (eds): *Mitochondria and Muscular Diseases.* Mefar, Beetsterzwaag, 1981, p 207.

122. PRICK MJJ, GABREELS FJM, RENIER WO, TRIJBELS JMF, SENGERS RCA, SLOOFF JL: Progressive infantile poliodystrophy. Association with disturbed pyruvate oxidation in muscle and liver. *Arch Neurol* 38:767, 1981.

123. LAND JM, HOCKADAY JM, HUGHES JT, ROSS BD: Childhood mitochondrial myopathy with ophthalmoplegia. *J Neurol Sci* 51:371, 1981.

124. LAND JM, MORGAN-HUGHES JA, CLARK J: Mitochondrial myopathy. Biochemical studies revealing a deficiency of NADH-cytochrome b reductase activity. *J Neurol Sci* 50:1, 1981.

125. MOREADITH RW, BATSHAW ML, OHNISHI T, KERR D, KNOX B, JACKSON D, HRUBAN R, OLSON J, REYNAFARJE B, LEHNINGER AL: Deficiency of the iron sulfur clusters of mitochondrial reduced nictotinamide adenine dinucleotide-ubiquinone oxidoreductase (Complex I) in an infant with congenital lactic acidosis. *J Clin Invest* 74:685, 1984.

126. ROBINSON BH, MCKAY N, GOODYER P, LANCASTER G: Defective intramitochondrial NADH oxidation in skin fibroblasts from an infant with fatal neonatal lactic acidemia. *Am J Hum Genet* 37:983, 1985.

127. ROBINSON BH, WARD J, GOODYER P, BEAUDET A: Respiratory chain defects in the mitochondria of cultured skin fibroblasts from three patients with lactic acidemia. *J Clin Invest* 77;1422, 1986.

128. ROBINSON BH, DE MEIRLEIR L, GLERUM M, SHERWOOD G, BECKER L: Clinical presentation of patients with mitochondrial respiratory chain defects in NADH-coenzyme Q reductase and cytochrome oxidase: Clues to the pathogenesis of Leigh disease. *J Pediatr* 110:216, 1987.

129. RIGGS JE, SCHOCHET SS, FAKADEJ AV, PAPADIMITRIOU A, DiMAURO S, CROSBY TW, GUTMAN L, MOXLEY RT: Mitochondrial encephalomyopathy with decreased succinate-cytochrome-c-reductase activity. *Neurology* 34:48, 1984.

130. SPIRO AJ, MOORE CL, PRINEAS JW, STRASBERG PM, RAPIN I: A cytochrome related inherited disorder of the nervous system and muscle. *Arch Neurol* 23:103, 1970.

131. MORGAN-HUGHES JA, HAYES DJ, CLARK JB: Mitochondrial myopathies, in Serratrie G, Cross D, Desnuelle C (eds): *Neuromuscular Diseases,* New York, Raven Press, 1984, p 79.

132. MORGAN-HUGHES JA, DARVENIZA P, LANDON DN, LAND JM, CLARK JB: A

mitochondrial myopathy with deficiency of respiratory chain NADH-CoQ reductase activity. *J Neurol Sci* 43:27, 1979.

133. MORGAN-HUGHES JA, HAYES DJ, CLARK JB, LANDON DN, SWASH M, STARK RJ, RUDGE P: Mitochondrial encephalomyopathies. Biochemical studies in two cases revealing defects in the respiratory chain. *Brain* 105:553, 1982.

134. DARLEY-USMAR VM, KENNAWAY NG, BUIST NRM, CAPALDI RA: Deficiency in ubiquinone cytochrome c reductase in a patient with mitochondrial myopathy and lactic acidosis. *Proc Natl Acad Sci USA* 80:5103, 1983.

135. HAYES DJ, LECKY BRF, LANDON DN, MORGAN-HUGHES JA, CLARK JB: A new mitochondrial myopathy, biochemical studies revealing a deficiency in the cytochrome bc complex (complex III) of the respiratory chain. *Brain* 107:1165, 1984.

136. FISCHER JC, RUITENBEEK W, GABREELS FJM, JANSSEN AJM, RENIER WO, SENGERS RCA, STADHOUDERS AM, TER LAAK HJ, TRIJBELS JMF, VEERKAMP JH: A mitochondrial encephalomyopathy: The first case with an established defect at the level of coenzyme Q. *Eur J Pediatr* 144:441, 1986.

137. DARLEY-USMAR VM, WATANABE M, UCHIYAMA Y, KONDO I, KENNAWAY NG, GRONKE L, HAMAGUCHI H: Mitochondrial myopathy: Tissue-specific expression of a defect in ubiquinol-cytochrome c reductase. *Clin Chim Acta* 158:253, 1986.

138. DiMAURO S, ZEVIANI M, BONILLA E, BRESOLIN N, NAKAGAWA M, MIRANDA AF, MOGGIO M: Cytochrome c oxidase deficiency. *Trans Biochem Soc* 13:651, 1985.

139. FRENCH JH, SHERARD ES, LUBELL H, BROTZ M, MOORE CL: Trichopoliodystrophy 1. Report of a case and biochemical studies. *Arch Neurol* 26:229, 1972.

140. VAN BIERVLIET JPGM, BRUINVIS L, KETTING D, De BREE PK, VAN DER HEIDEN C, WADMAN SK: Hereditary mitochondrial myopathy with lactic acidemia, a DeToni-Fanconi-Debré syndrome, and a defective respiratory chain in voluntary striated muscles. *Pediatr Res* 11:1088, 1977.

141. DiMAURO S, MENDELL JR, SAHENK Z, BACHMAN D, SCARPA A, SCOFIELD RM, REINER C: Fatal infantile mitochondrial myopathy and renal dysfunction due to cytochrome-c oxidase deficiency. *Neurology* 30:795, 1980.

142. HEIMAN-PATTERSON TD, BONILLA E, DiMAURO S, FOREMAN J, SCHOTLAND DL: Cytochrome c oxidase deficiency in a floppy infant. *Neurology* 32:898, 1982.

143. MINCHOM PE, DORMER RL, HUGHES IA, STANSBIE D, CROSS AR, HENDRY GA, JONES OTG, JOHNSON MA, SHERRATT HSA, TURNBULL DM: Fatal infantile mitochondrial myopathy due to cytochrome-c-oxidase deficiency. *J Neurol Sci* 60:453, 1983.

144. MULLER-HOCKER J, PONGRATZ D, DEUFEL TH, TRIJBELS JMF, ENDRES W, HUBNER G: Fatal lipid storage myopathy with deficiency of cytochrome c oxidase and carnitine. *Virchows Arch (A)* 399:11, 1983.

145. ZEVIANI M, NONAKA I, BONILLA E, OKINO E, MOGGIO M, JONES S, DiMAURO S: Fatal infantile mitochondial myopathy and renal dysfunction caused by cytochrome c oxidase deficiency: Immunological studies in a new patient. *Ann Neurol* 17:414, 1985.

146. KUHN-NENTWIG L, KADENBACH B: Isolation and properties of cytochrome c oxidase from rat liver and quantification of immunological differences between isozymes from various rat tissues with subunit-specific antisera. *Eur J Biochem* 149:147, 1985.

147. DiMAURO S, NICHOLSON JF, HAYS AP, EASTWOOD AB, PAPADIMITRIOU A, KOENIGSBERGER R, DeVIVO DC: Benign infantile mitochondrial myopathy due to reversible cytochrome c oxidase deficiency. *Ann Neurol* 14:226, 1983.

148. ZEVIANI M, PETERSON P, SEVIDEI S, BONILLA E, DiMAURO S: Benign reversible muscle cytochrome oxidase deficiency. *Neurology* 37:64, 1987.

149. SENGERS RCA, TRIJBELS JMF, BAKKEREN JAJM, RUITENBEEK W, FISCHER JC, JANSSEN AJM, STADHOUDERS AM, TER LAAK HJ: Deficiency of cytochrome b and aa_3 in muscle from a floppy infant with cytochrome oxidase deficiency. *Eur J Pediatr* 141:178, 1984.

150. RIMOLDI M, BOTTACCHI E, ROSSI L, CORNELIO T, UZIEL G, Di DONATO S: Cytochrome c oxidase deficiency in muscles of a floppy infant without mitochondrial myopathy. *J Neurol* 27:201, 1982.

151. BOUSTANY RN, APRILLE JR, HALPERIN J, LEVY H, DELONG GR: Mitochondrial cytochrome deficiency presenting as a myopathy with hypotonia, external ophthalmoplegia and lactic acidosis in an infant and as fatal hepatopathy in a second cousin. *Ann Neurol* 14:462, 1983.

152. WILLEMS JL, MONNENS AH, TRIJBELS JMF, VEERKAMP JH, MEYER EAFH, VAN DAM K, VAN HAELST U: Leigh's encephalomyopathy in a patient with cytochrome c oxidase deficiency of muscle tissue. *Pediatrics* 60:850, 1977.

153. HOGANSON GE, PAULSON DJ, CHUN R, SUFIT RL, SHUG AL: Deficiency of muscle cytochrome oxidase in Leigh's Disease. *Pediatr Res* 18:22A, 1984.

154. ENGEL WK, CUNNINGHAM GG: Rapid examination of muscle tissue: An improved trichrome stain method for fresh frozen biopsy sections. *Neurology* 13:919, 1963.

155. OLSON W, ENGEL WK, WALSH GO, EINAUGLER R: Oculocraniosomatic neuromuscular disease with "ragged-red" fibres. *Arch Neurol* 26:193, 1972.

156. DiMAURO S, BONILLA E, ZEVIANI M, NAKAGAWA M, DeVIVO DC: Mitochondrial myopathies. *Ann Neurol* 17:521, 1985.

157. BERENBERG RA, PELLOCK JM, DiMAURO S, SCHOTLAND DL, BONILLA E, EASTWOOD A, VICALE CT, BEHRENS M, CHUTORIAN A, ROWLAND LP: Lumping or splitting? "Ophthalmoplegia-plus" or Kearns-Sayre syndrome? *Ann Neurol* 1:37, 1977.

158. FUKUHARA N, TOKIGUCHI S, SHIRAKAWA S, TSUBAKI T: Myoclonus epilepsy associated with ragged red fibres: Disease entity or syndrome? Light- and electron-microscopic studies of two cases and review of the literature. *J Neurol Sci* 47:117, 1980.

159. ROSING HS, HOPKINS LC, WALLACE DC, EPSTEIN CM, WEIDENHEIM K: Maternally inherited mitochondrial myopathy and myoclonic epilepsy. *Ann Neurol* 17:228, 1985.

160. PAVLAKIS SG, PHILLIPS PC, DiMAURO S, DeVIVO DC, ROWLAND LP: Mitochondrial myopathy, encephalopathy, lactic acidosis, and strokelike episodes: A distinctive clinical syndrome. *Ann Neurol* 16:481, 1984.

161. YAMAMOTO T, BEPPU H, TSUBAKI T: Mitochondrial encephalomyopathy: Fluctuating symptoms and CT. *Neurology* 34:1456, 1984.

162. KURIYAMA M, IGATA A: Mitochondrial encephalopathy, lactic acidosis and strokelike syndrome (MELAS). *Ann Neurol* 18:625, 1985.

163. KOBAYASHI Y, MIYABAYASHI S, TAKADA G, NARISAWA K, TADA K, YAMAMOTO TY: Ultrastructural study of the childhood mitochondrial myopathy syndrome associated with lactic acidosis. *Eur J Pediatr* 139:25, 1982.

164. STADHOUDERS AM: Personal communications.

165. ROBINSON BH, SHERWOOD WG, TEIN I, BECKER L: In preparation.

166. YORIFUJI S, OGASAHARA S, TAKAHASHI M, TARUI S: Decreased activities in mitochondrial inner membrane electron transport system in muscle from patients with Kearns-Sayre syndrome. *J Neurol Sci* 71:65, 1985.

167. KOBAYASHI M, MORISHITA H, SUGIYAMA N, YOKOCHI K, NAKANO M, WADA Y, HOTTA Y, TERAUCHI A, NONAKA I: Two cases of NADH-coenzyme Q reductase deficiency: Relationship to MELAS syndrome. *J Pediatr* 110:223, 1987.

168. YAMAMOTO M, SATO T, ANNO M, UJIKE H, TAKEMOTO M: Mitochondrial myopathy, encephalopathy, lactic acidosis and strokelike episodes with recurrent abdominal symptoms. *J Neurol Neurosurg Psychiatry* 50:1475, 1987.

169. MELMED C, KARPATI G, CARPENTER S: Experimental mitochondrial myopathy produced by *in vivo* uncoupling of oxidative phosphorylation. *J Neurol Sci* 26:305, 1981.

170. HEFFNER RR, BARRON SA: The early effects of ischemia upon skeletal muscle mitochondria. *J Neurol Sci* 38:295, 1978.

171. JOHNSON MA, TURNBULL DM, DICK DJ, SHERRAT HSA: A partial deficiency of cytochrome c oxidase in chronic progressive external ophthalmoplegia. *J Neurol Sci* 60:31, 1983.

172. KOHLSCHUTTER A, BEHBEHANI A, LANGENBECK U, ALBANI M, HEIDEMANN P, HOFFMANN G, KLEINEKE J, LEHNERT W, WENDEL U: A familial progressive neurodegenerative disease with 2-oxoglutaric aciduria. *Eur J Pediat* 138:32, 1982.

173. WHELAN DT, HILL RE, MCCLORRY S: Fumaric aciduria: A new organic aciduria, associated with mental retardation and speech impairment. *Clin Chim Acta* 132:301, 1983.

174. ZINN AB, KERR DS, HOPPEL CL: Fumarase deficiency: A new cause of mitochondrial encephalomyopathy. *N Engl J Med* 315:469, 1986.

175. PETROVA-BENEDICT R, ROBINSON BH, STACEY TE, MISTRY J, CHALMERS RA: Deficient fumarase activity in an infant with fumaricacidemia and its distribution between the different forms of the enzyme seen on isolectric focussing. *Am J Hum Genet* 40:257, 1987.

176. CHRISTENSEN E, BRANDT NJ, SKOVBY S, DJEMES B: Fumaric aciduria due to fumarase deficiency. *J Inherited Metab Dis* (in press 1988).

177. EDWARDS YH, HOPKINSON DA: Further characterisation of the human fumarase variant FH 2-1. *Ann Hum Genet Lond* 43:103, 1979.

178. TOLLEY E, CRAIG I: Presence of two forms of fumarase (fumarate hydratase E.C. 4.2.1.2) in mammalian cells: Immunological characterisation and genetic analysis in somatic cell hybrids. Confirmation of the assignment of a gene necessary for the enzyme expression to numeric chromosome 1. *Biochem Genet* 13:867, 1975.

179. HILL RL, TEIPEL JW: Fumarase and crotonase, in Boyer P (ed): *The Enzymes*. New York, Academic, 1971, vol 5, p 539.

180. ONO H, YOSHIMURA N, SATO N, TUBOI S: Translocation of protein into rat liver mitochondria: Existence of two different precursor polypeptides of liver fumarase and import of the precursor into mitochondria. *J Biol Chem* 260:3402, 1985.

181. O'HARE MC, DOONAN S: Purification and structural comparisons of the cytosolic and mitochondrial isoenzymes of fumarase from pig liver. *Biochim Biophys Acta* 827:127, 1985.

182. VIANEY-LIAUD C, DIVRY P, GREGERSON N, MATHIEU M: The inborn errors of fatty acid oxidation. *J Inherited Metab Dis* 10:*Suppl* 1, 159, 1987.

CHAPTER **33**

ACYL-CoA DEHYDROGENASE DEFICIENCIES

CHARLES R. ROE
PAUL M. COATES

1. *The pathway of fatty acid β oxidation in mitochondria plays a major role in energy production during periods of fasting. Fatty acids are mobilized from adipose tissue, taken up from the circulation by liver and by other tissues, and activated to form acyl-CoA esters in the cytoplasm. They traverse the mitochondrial membrane as carnitine esters and become reesterified to form CoA esters within the mitochondrial matrix. β Oxidation of the acyl-CoA proceeds through four sequential steps mediated by acyl-CoA dehydrogenases, enoyl-CoA hydratases, 3-hydroxyacyl-CoA dehydrogenases, and 3-ketoacyl-CoA thiolases, resulting in the transfer of electrons to electron transfer flavoprotein (ETF), the release of acetyl-CoA, and the formation of a chain-shortened acyl-CoA which can reenter the β-oxidation spiral. As the acyl-CoA becomes shorter, the first step of each turn of the spiral is mediated by acyl-CoA dehydrogenases with different, but overlapping, chain-length specificities: long-chain (LCAD), medium-chain (MCAD), and short-chain (SCAD). The other steps in the pathway appear also to have some degree of chain length specificity.*

2. *Three inherited defects have been described within the β-oxidation pathway, each due to deficiency of one of the acyl-CoA dehydrogenases: LCAD, MCAD, and SCAD deficiency. Each is inherited in an autosomal recessive manner.*

3. *MCAD deficiency is the most common defect in the pathway. It has been described in more than 65 children, most of whom present within the first 2 years of life with recurrent episodes of hypoglycemia provoked by fasting. Ketosis is inappropriately low for the degree of circulating free fatty acids, and there is increased urinary excretion of medium-chain fatty acid metabolites: dicarboxylic acids (adipic, suberic, and sebacic acids), glycine conjugates (hexanoyl-, phenylproionyl-, and suberylglycine), and carnitine esters (decenoyl-, octanoyl-, octenoyl-, and hexanoylcarnitine). Patients have low carnitine levels in plasma, skeletal muscle, and liver, with an increased proportion of esterified carnitine, secondary to this metabolic block. Hepatomegaly may occur with marked microvesicular or macrovesicular fat infiltration of hepatocytes and altered mitochondrial ultrastructure. Between episodes, patients with MCAD deficiency can appear quite normal. Therapy includes avoidance of fasting with or without reduction in dietary fat intake and* L*-carnitine supplementation, which can be increased during episodes of viral infection. MCAD deficiency may be mistaken for Reye syndrome in the young infant, and it has been implicated in cases of sudden infant death. Several asymptomatic patients with MCAD deficiency also have been identified, some of whom have subsequently developed symptoms requiring treatment. The defect can be demonstrated by measurement of MCAD activity in fibroblasts and leukocytes, and heterozygotes can be detected, so that screening of family members can be performed readily. Affected siblings can also be identified by analysis of urinary acylcarnitines. Prenatal diagnosis of MCAD deficiency has been carried out by measurement of MCAD activity in cultured amniotic fluid cells.*

4. *LCAD deficiency has been identified in six patients. It shares a number of clinical features with MCAD deficiency, with recurrent episodes of hypoglycemia, vomiting, and coma triggered by fasting; however, some patients have had a much more severe course with significant compromise of skeletal and cardiac muscle function. As in MCAD deficiency, there is a failure of ketosis in the fasting state, a secondary carnitine deficiency, and increased urinary excretion of dicarboxylic acids. Hepatomegaly, with fatty infiltration and altered hepatocyte mitochondrial ultrastructure, has been observed. Hypertrophic cardiomyopathy and chronic skeletal muscle weakness have been evident in some patients. The enzyme defect can be demonstrated in fibroblasts and leukocytes, and heterozygotes can be detected.*

5. *SCAD deficiency has been reported in four patients. Two of them had an early episode of lethargy and metabolic acidosis associated with increased ethylmalonate excretion, following a period of decreased oral intake. A third patient had no episodes of illness provoked by fasting; instead, she was chronically weak during the first 2 years of life, with low muscle carnitine levels and evidence of fatty infiltration of muscle and liver. All three patients had a deficiency of SCAD which could be demonstrated in fibroblasts. A fourth patient presented in middle age with lipid storage myopathy and low muscle carnitine levels, whose SCAD deficiency was expressed in muscle but not in fibroblasts.*

6. *As experience has been gained with the study of patients with acyl-CoA dehydrogenase deficiencies, other patients have been recognized with obvious defects in fatty acid oxidation, but with normal acyl-CoA dehydrogenase activities. Given the complexity of this pathway, it is likely that other enzyme defects in β oxidation will be described.*

7. *Alterations in carnitine status have been observed in all of the acyl-CoA dehydrogenase deficiencies, as well as in other defects of mitochondrial metabolism. Reduced plasma and/or tissue levels of carnitine, coupled with the demonstration that the spe-*

Nonstandard abbreviations used in this chapter are: γ-BB = γ-butyrobetaine; γ-BBA = γ-butyrobetaine aldehyde; CNS = central nervous system; CPK = creatine phosphokinase; CPT = carnitine palmityltransferase; DCPIP = dichlorophenolindophenol; ETF = electron transfer flavoprotein; FAB-MS = fast atom bombardment–mass spectrometry; HMG-CoA = hydroxymethylglutaryl-CoA; HTML = hydroxytrimethyllysine; LCAD = long-chain acyl-CoA dehydrogenase; MCAD = medium-chain acyl-CoA dehydrogenase; MCT = medium-chain triglycerides; PEP = phosphoenolpyruvate; PMS = phenazine methosulfate; SCAD = short-chain acyl-CoA dehydrogenase; TCA = tricarboxylic acid; TML = trimethyllysine; TPN = total parenteral nutrition.

cies of acylcarnitine excreted in urine reflects the site of metabolic block, suggests that carnitine plays a role in the removal of toxic intermediates of organic acid metabolism in several of these disorders.

INTRODUCTION AND HISTORICAL PERSPECTIVE

Disorders of fatty acid oxidation are relative newcomers to the arena of inborn errors of metabolism. The first well-documented disorders were described in the mid-1970s in patients with skeletal muscle weakness or exercise-induced rhabdomyolysis and abnormalities in muscle fatty acid metabolism associated with muscle carnitine deficiency[1] or carnitine palmityltransferase (CPT) deficiency.[2] Shortly thereafter, the syndrome of systemic carnitine deficiency was identified; in this disorder, plasma, muscle, and liver carnitine levels were low and fatty acid metabolism in muscle and sometimes liver was impaired.[3] Characterization of another group of inborn errors of mitochondrial fatty acid oxidation began in 1982–83 with the description by three different groups of investigators of medium-chain acyl-CoA dehydrogenase (MCAD) deficiency[4–7] in patients with disorders of fasting adaptation. Within the last few years, long-chain acyl-CoA dehydrogenase (LCAD) deficiency[8] and short-chain acyl-CoA dehydrogenase (SCAD) deficiency[9–11] have also been described.

Stanley[12] noted that fatty acid oxidation disorders may have escaped attention, in part because this pathway does not play a major role in energy production under nonfasting conditions. Thus, defects in fatty acid oxidation may be clinically silent until relatively late in fasting. Another factor contributing to the delay in their recognition is that routine laboratory tests, other than qualitative urinary ketone analysis, do not provide clues about potential defects in the fatty acid oxidation pathway. Methods to identify abnormal metabolites of fatty acids using gas chromatography and mass spectrometry have been available only since the mid-1970s; it is in large measure the availability of these techniques that has permitted the identification of patients with defects in fatty acid oxidation.

In this chapter, we review the clinical, laboratory, pathologic, and metabolic findings in patients with disorders of fatty acid oxidation resulting from deficiency of each of the acyl-CoA dehydrogenases (Fig. 33-1). One of these defects, the inherited deficiency of MCAD, has emerged as a common metabolic disease, implicated in some cases of the sudden infant death syndrome and in infantile Reye syndrome. Because abnormalities in carnitine status are a common feature of patients with all of these disorders, we also include details of the relationship between carnitine metabolism and fatty acid metabolism. Finally, it has become apparent that there are patients with many of the features of an acyl-CoA dehydrogenase deficiency who do not, in fact, have one of these defects. Other sites of potential defect in the pathway of fatty acid β oxidation are discussed in light of the clinical and laboratory information that has emerged about such patients.

Fig. 33-1 The reaction catalyzed by mitochondrial acyl-CoA dehydrogenase (ACD). A double bond is inserted between the α and β carbons, with two electrons transferred to electron transfer flavoprotein (ETF).

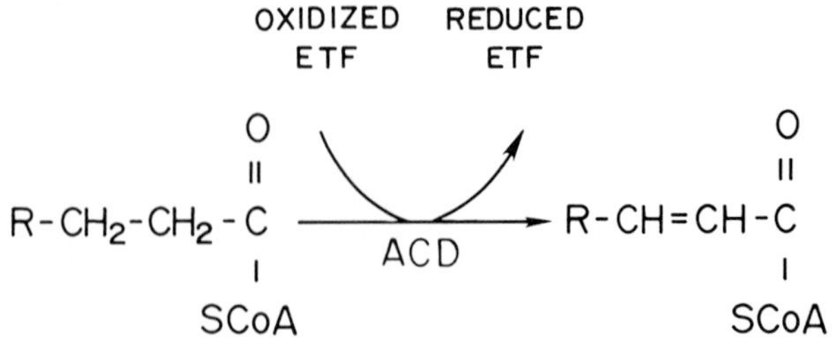

OXIDIZED ETF → REDUCED ETF

$$R\text{-}CH_2\text{-}CH_2\text{-}\overset{O}{\overset{\|}{C}}\text{-}SCoA \xrightarrow{ACD} R\text{-}CH{=}CH\text{-}\overset{O}{\overset{\|}{C}}\text{-}SCoA$$

FATTY ACID OXIDATION

The pathways of fatty acid oxidation and ketogenesis have been reviewed elsewhere.[13,14] In this section we will outline the major steps in these pathways, with particular emphasis on the role of the acyl-CoA dehydrogenases in mitochondrial β oxidation.

Mobilization, Tissue Uptake, and Activation

Fatty acids are mobilized from adipose tissue stores and are transported in the circulation primarily bound to albumin. During periods of fasting, fatty acids become the predominant substrate for energy production via oxidation in liver, cardiac muscle, and skeletal muscle. The brain does not directly utilize fatty acids for oxidative metabolism, but readily oxidizes ketone bodies derived from the partial oxidation of fatty acids by the liver. During prolonged aerobic exercise, fatty acid oxidation accounts for 60 percent of muscle oxygen consumption.[15]

Fatty acids are taken up by the liver and by other tissues by concentration-dependent mechanisms which are poorly understood but may include both saturable carrier-mediated uptake and nonsaturable diffusion.[16] Once inside the cell (Fig. 33-2), fatty acids are activated to form coenzyme A (CoA) esters through the action of the cytoplasmic enzyme(s) acyl-CoA synthase. The acyl-CoA esters can serve as substrates for triglyceride, phospholipid, and cholesteryl ester synthesis, but under fasting conditions, they are largely directed toward mitochondrial β oxidation. In order to traverse the mitochondrial membrane, long-chain acyl-CoA esters must first be transesterified to carnitine by the outer mitochondrial membrane enzyme, carnitine palmityltransferase I (CPT I). The transmembrane transfer of acylcarnitines is mediated by carnitine translocase. Within the mitochondrial matrix, acylcarnitines are reesterified to form CoA esters by carnitine palmityltransferase II (CPT II). Medium-chain and short-chain fatty acids traverse the mitochondrial membrane as free acids without the need for carnitine esterification; they then are activated to form acyl-CoA esters within the mitochondrial matrix.

Mitochondrial β-Oxidation Spiral and Electron Transfer

It is the acyl-CoA ester which enters the pathway of mitochondrial β oxidation (Fig. 33-3). With each turn of the β-oxidation spiral, the chain length of a saturated acyl-CoA is shortened by 2 carbons as an acetyl-CoA moiety is released. In most tissues, such as muscle and heart, acetyl-CoA is oxidized in the tricarboxylic acid cycle to carbon dioxide and water. In liver and to a much smaller extent, kidney, acetyl-CoA produced from β oxidation is largely converted to ketone bodies, β-hydroxybutyrate and acetoacetate, via the hydroxymethylglutaryl-CoA (HMG-CoA) pathway (see "Hepatic Ketogene-

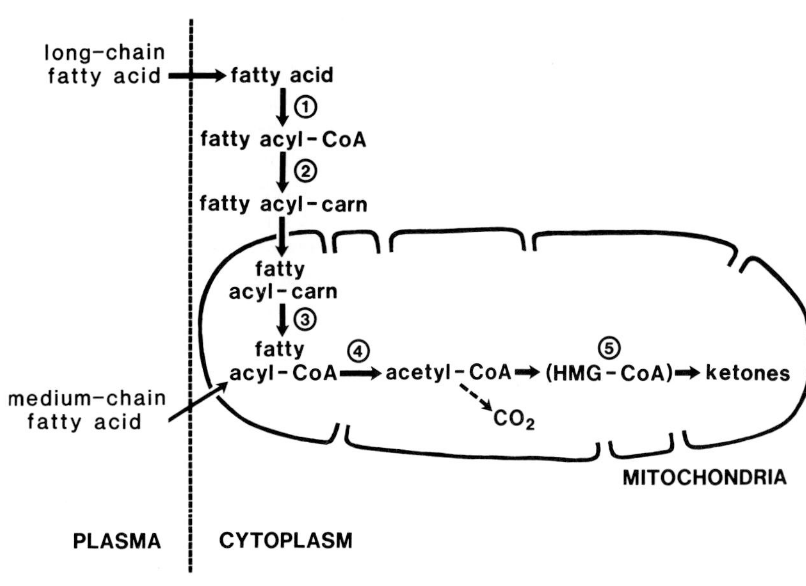

Fig. 33-2 Pathway of fatty acid entry, activation, mitochondrial uptake, β oxidation, and ketogenesis in liver. The vertical dashed line denotes the liver cell membrane. Numbers indicate the sequence of reactions: 1 = fatty acid activation by acyl-CoA synthase to form acyl-CoA esters; 2 = fatty acyl-CoA transesterification to carnitine by carnitine palmityltransferase (CPT) I prior to mitochondrial translocation; 3 = reesterification of acylcarnitine to fatty acyl-CoA by CPT II; 4 = the β-oxidation spiral, each turn of which yields acetyl-CoA, which can be oxidized in the TCA cycle to CO_2 (broken line with arrow) or can become available for reactions depicted by 5, the hydroxymethylglutaryl (HMG)-CoA pathway to form ketone bodies. Medium-chain fatty acids can traverse the mitochondrial membrane as free acids without the requirement for carnitine-mediated transport. *(Courtesy of C.A. Stanley.)*

sis," below); these are then exported for final oxidation by other tissues such as brain.

Each turn of the spiral of β oxidation is mediated by a sequence of enzymes (Fig. 33-3), some of which are known to exhibit specificity for the chain length of the acyl-CoA moiety. For a typical saturated acyl-CoA such as palmityl-CoA (C_{16}), the sequence of four enzyme steps is: acyl-CoA dehydrogenase, enoyl-CoA hydratase, 3-hydroxyacyl-CoA dehydrogenase, and 3-ketoacyl-CoA thiolase.

The series of chain-length-specific acyl-CoA dehydrogenase enzymes are flavoproteins;[17,18] in the process of inserting a double bond between the α and β carbons of an acyl-CoA moiety, and hence forming the corresponding enoyl-CoA, they transfer the electrons generated by dehydrogenation to electron transfer flavoprotein (ETF).[19] In turn, reduced ETF is oxidized by ETF:ubiquinone oxidoreductase (ETF dehydrogenase) and coenzyme Q, with the ultimate transfer of electrons to the electron transport chain; details of the reactions involving ETF and ETF dehydrogenase are covered in Chap. 32. The second reaction in β oxidation involves hydration of the enoyl-CoA catalyzed by enoyl-CoA hydratase (crotonase), with formation of an L-3-hydroxyacyl-CoA. One or more enzymes called 3-hydroxyacyl-CoA dehydrogenase catalyze the oxidation of the hydroxy group to a keto group in an NAD^+-dependent reaction. The final reaction, catalyzed by one or more enzymes called *3-ketoacyl-CoA thiolase* (or 3-oxoacyl-CoA thiolase), is cleavage of the α,β bond in the presence of reduced CoA. The two products of this reaction are acetyl-

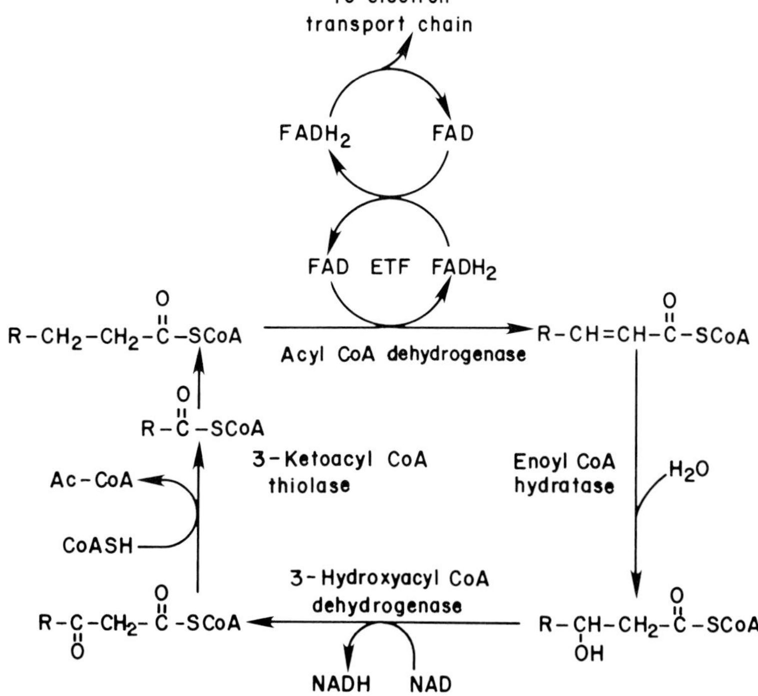

Fig. 33-3 Spiral of fatty acyl-CoA β oxidation in mitochondria. An acyl-CoA enters the spiral, whereupon acyl-CoA dehydrogenase inserts a double bond, forming an enoyl-CoA and transferring electrons to ETF. Enoyl-CoA hydratase adds water across the double bond to form a 3-hydroxyacyl-CoA, which is oxidized by an NAD-linked 3-hydroxyacyl-CoA dehydrogenase to form a 3-ketoacyl-CoA. In the presence of free coenzyme A (CoASH), 3-ketoacyl-CoA thiolase cleaves the α,β bond to yield acetyl-CoA and an acyl-CoA moiety, now 2 carbons shorter, which can reenter the spiral.

CoA and an acyl-CoA now 2 carbons shorter than the original substrate (e.g., palmityl-CoA, a 16-carbon acyl-CoA, yields acetyl-CoA and myristyl-CoA, with 14 carbons).

Acyl-CoA compounds can cycle through β oxidation as many times as it is possible to generate acetyl-CoA fragments (e.g., palmityl-CoA can make as many as seven cycles through β oxidation). As the molecule becomes shorter, it will be recognized preferentially by one of three acyl-CoA dehydrogenase enzymes with different chain-length specificity. The straight-chain acyl-CoA dehydrogenases, the related flavoproteins, isovaleryl-CoA dehydrogenase, 2-methylbranched chain acyl-CoA dehydrogenase, and electron transfer flavoprotein have been purified and characterized in several laboratories.[20-31] There have been multiple reports of the substrate specificity of the acyl-CoA dehydrogenases.[20,24,25,27,31] There is considerable overlap among these enzymes, but in liver, LCAD catalyzes the first reaction in β oxidation of acyl-CoA moieties ranging in length from 18 carbons down to 12 carbons; MCAD recognizes a broad range of acyl-CoA compounds from 14 carbons down to 4 carbons in length; SCAD recognizes only 4- and 6-carbon compounds. There is evidence to support the existence of chain-length-specific enoyl-CoA hydratase and 3-hydroxyacyl-CoA dehydrogenase enzymes in mammalian tissues,[13,32-35] but these have not yet been characterized in human beings. There are at least two mitochondrial enzymes with 3-ketoacyl-CoA thiolase activity, one specific for acetoacetyl-CoA and another with broader chain-length specificity.[36,37] In addition, there is a cytosolic acetoacetyl-CoA thiolase involved in cholesterol biosynthesis.[36]

Enzymes Required for Odd-Chain and Unsaturated Fatty Acid Oxidation

Odd-chain acyl-CoA compounds are oxidized by the same series of reactions described above, until the 3-carbon moiety, propionyl-CoA, is formed, which is degraded by the biotin-dependent enzyme, propionyl-CoA carboxylase.[16]

Unsaturated acyl-CoA compounds are also oxidized by the same series of reactions, until the double bond is reached (Fig. 33-4). Further oxidation requires the activity of two additional enzymes, 3-*cis*, 2-*trans*-enoyl-CoA isomerase and 2,4-dienoyl-CoA reductase, followed by enoyl-CoA hydratase and the remainder of the β-oxidation pathway.[13,16]

Hepatic Ketogenesis

Liver is virtually the only tissue which can channel the product of fatty acid β oxidation, acetyl-CoA, into ketone body formation[13] (Fig. 33-2). Especially under conditions of fasting, when carbohydrate stores are depleted, the rate of hepatic ketogenesis is increased. Its purpose is to provide an auxiliary source of substrate for brain oxidative metabolism, sparing glucose oxidation and thus preventing proteolysis. The pathway of hepatic ketogenesis is depicted in Fig. 33-5. Two acetyl-CoA molecules can condense to form acetoacetyl-CoA; this compound can also be derived directly from β oxidation in the last turn of the spiral. The enzyme, HMG-CoA synthase, catalyzes the synthesis of HMG-CoA from acetoacetyl-CoA and acetyl-CoA. HMG-CoA lyase cleaves HMG-CoA to form acetoactate and acetyl-CoA. Acetoacetate is reduced to D-3-hydroxybutyrate by the NAD^+-linked 3-hydroxybutyrate dehydrogenase within mitochondria.

Microsomal and Peroxisomal Oxidation

Omega (ω) oxidation of fatty acids is known to occur in liver microsomes through the action of a cytochrome P_{450}–linked mixed function oxygenase which catalyzes ω hydroxylation in the presence of molecular oxygen and NADPH. An NAD^+-dependent oxidation subsequently converts the ω-hydroxy fatty acid into a dicarboxylic acid. The resulting dicarboxylic acid can be transported to the mitochondrial matrix or to peroxisomes for β oxidation.[38] Commonly, dicarboxylic acids are formed because mitochondrial β oxidation is overloaded (e.g., in diabetic ketoacidosis) or genetically impaired, and they are rapidly and quantitatively excreted in urine (see below). They are also present in the urine of patients fed a diet high in medium-chain triglycerides (MCT).[39] A similar hydroxylation reaction is thought to occur at the $(\omega - 1)$ position, possibly using the same microsomal oxygenase pathway.[38,40]

Alpha (α) oxidation occurs in microsomes and degrades fatty acids one carbon at a time; 3-methylbranched chain fatty acids such as phytanic acid (3,7,11,15-tetramethylhexadecanoic acid) require an α-oxidation step which uses NADPH and molecular oxygen.[13,16]

Peroxisomal oxidation of fatty acids shares a number of key features with the mitochondrial process: it is a β-oxidation scheme leading to thiolytic cleavage of the α,β bond, and acetyl-CoA is one of the products. It differs from mitochondrial oxidation in some key features: transport of long-chain acyl-CoA into peroxisomes does not require carnitine; the first step is catalyzed by a long-chain acyl-CoA oxidase (not a dehydrogenase), which generates no reducing equivalents; the second and third steps are carried out by a bifunctional enzyme; and peroxisomal β oxidation is thought to proceed only to the medium-chain acyl-CoA level. Details of the pathways of peroxisomal metabolism and the clinical disorders associated with peroxisomal dysfunction are covered in Chap. 57.

Regulation of Fatty Acid Oxidation

The regulation of fatty acid oxidation in mammalian tissues by hormones, competing substrates, cofactors, and diet has been reviewed extensively elsewhere[13,14,16] and is discussed in Chap. 10. Numerous studies in mammalian tissues have related rates of fatty acid oxidation to the concentrations of free fatty acids mobilized from adipose tissue which are hence available for oxidative metabolism. In the transition from the fed to the fasted state, the liver converts itself from being an organ of glucose uptake and fatty acid synthesis to one of glucose production, fatty acid oxidation, and ketogenesis.

Hormonal control of fatty acid oxidation is exerted at the level of substrate mobilization from adipose tissue and by indirect effects on the activity of CPT I. Insulin inhibits lipolysis in adipose tissue, thereby decreasing the level of free fatty acids available for oxidative metabolism; it also stimulates acetyl-CoA carboxylation and lipogenesis in the liver, in turn increasing tissue levels of malonyl-CoA, an inhibitor of CPT I, thereby inhibiting fatty acid oxidation. Glucagon stimulates hepatic fatty acid oxidation indirectly, by inhibiting acetyl-CoA carboxylase, which in turn reduces tissue levels of malonyl-CoA, thereby promoting fatty acid oxidation. In the fed state, in which the glucagon insulin ratio is low, the liver directs fatty acid metabolism toward synthesis. Under these conditions, oxidation of fatty acids is suppressed by the high tissue levels of malonyl-CoA. In the fasting state, elevation of

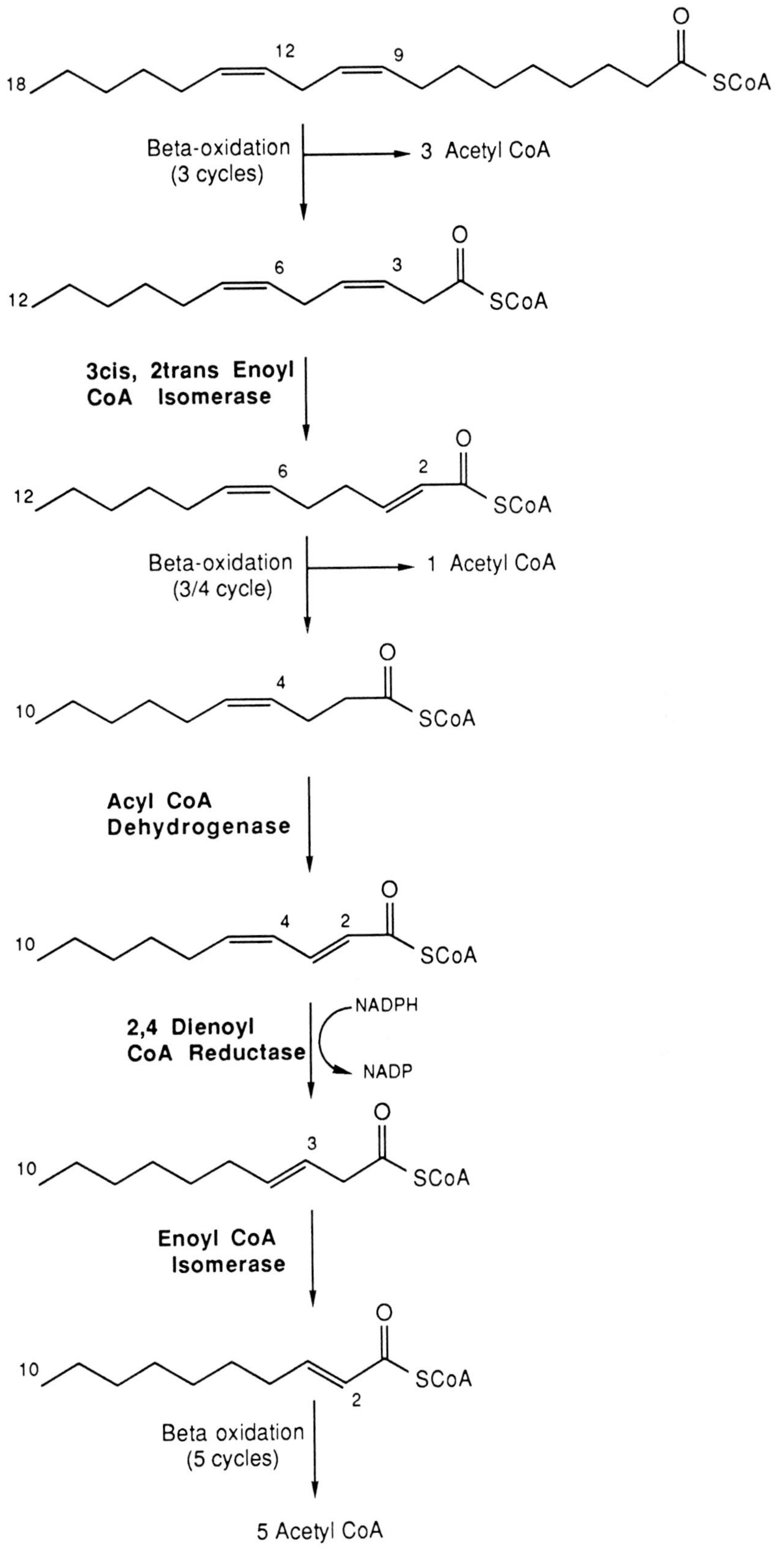

Fig. 33-4 Unsaturated fatty acyl-CoA β oxidation. A polyunsaturated fatty acid (e.g., linoleate) can make three turns of the β-oxidation spiral until the first double bond is in the 3 position. A 3-*cis,* 2-*trans*-enoyl-CoA isomerase puts the double bond in the 2 position, permitting the completion of another turn of β oxidation, until the second double bond is reached at the 4 position. Medium-chain acyl-CoA dehydrogenase inserts another double bond in the 2 position. 2,4-Dienoyl-CoA reductase reduces this series of double bonds, leaving one double bond in the 3 position. Finally, 3-*cis,* 2-*trans*-enoyl-CoA isomerase converts this to a 2-enoyl CoA for further oxidation. *(Courtesy of D.E. Hale.)*

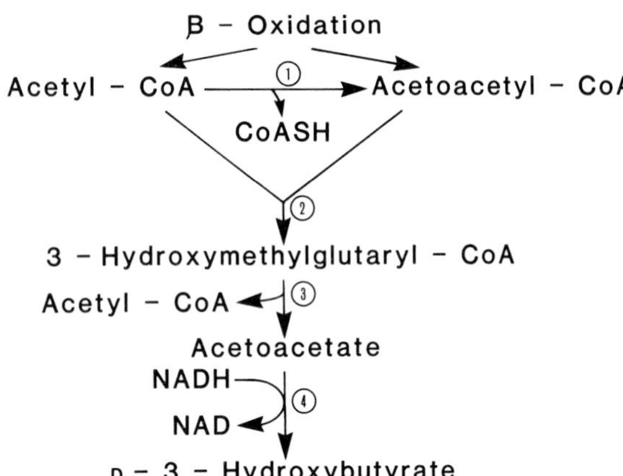

Fig. 33-5 Hydroxymethylglutaryl (HMG)-CoA pathway for ketone body formation. Two molecules of acetyl-CoA condense to form acetoacetyl-CoA via acetyl-CoA acetyltransferase (Reaction 1). Acetoacetyl-CoA, together with acetyl-CoA, is converted to HMG-CoA by HMG-CoA synthase (Reaction 2). Acetoacetate and acetyl-CoA are released by cleavage of HMG-CoA via HMG-CoA lyase (Reaction 3). Acetoacetate is reduced to D-3-hydroxybutyrate by 3-hydroxybutyrate dehydrogenase (Reaction 4).

the glucagon insulin ratio suppresses malonyl-CoA synthesis and consequently directs fatty acids toward mitochondria for oxidation. Further details of the relationships between fatty acid oxidation and glucose metabolism are presented in Chap. 10.

CARNITINE BIOSYNTHESIS AND METABOLISM

Synthesis and Metabolism

The biosynthesis of L-carnitine (β-hydroxy-γ-*N*-trimethylammonium butyrate) has been well-described[41]; the major steps in its synthesis are shown in Fig. 33-6. Peptide-bound lysine residues are methylated to trimethyllysine (TML) residues by the nuclear enzyme methylase III; *S*-adenosylmethionine is specifically required as the methyl donor.[42] Proteins with TML residues are degraded in lysosomes[43] and the released TML is hydroxylated in the mitochondria to hydroxy-TML (HTML) by 6-*N*-trimethyllysine, 2-oxoglutarate dioxygenase (TML hydroxylase). HTML is then converted to γ-butyrobetaine aldehyde (γ-BBA) and glycine by 3-hydroxy-6-*N*-trimethyllysine aldolase, which appears to be the same as the enzyme, serine hydroxymethyl transferase, involved in folate metabolism.[44] This pyridoxal phosphate–requiring enzyme is found in both mitochondria and cytosol, with the latter being most abundant. Increased concentrations of glycine reverse the reaction. γ-BBA is then dehydrogenated to γ-butyrobetaine (γ-BB) by the enzyme trimethylaminobutyraldehyde dehydrogenase. The final step of synthesis to L-carnitine is catalyzed by γ-butyrobetaine, 2-oxoglutarate dioxygenase (γ-butyrobetaine hydroxylase), which is also cytosolic and is distinct from the mitochondrial 6-*N*-trimethyllysine, 2-oxoglutarate dioxygenase. Both dioxygenase enzymes require Fe^{2+}, ascorbate, and 2-oxoglutarate.[41] Cofactor availability can affect carnitine biosynthesis. It is noteworthy that scorbutic animals have 50 percent less carnitine in heart and skeletal muscle than do controls.[46] Similarly, the pyridoxal phosphate antagonist 1-amino-D-proline markedly reduces carnitine biosynthesis in the rat.[47]

The carnitine biosynthetic pathway traverses various cellular compartments from nucleus to lysosome to mitochondrion and finally, cytosol. The tissue capability for this synthesis is varied. Liver and kidney are capable of the complete synthesis of carnitine in human beings, while skeletal muscle and heart are able to synthesize γ-BB, but must export this intermediate for final hydroxylation to L-carnitine by kidney or liver. Brain appears to have its own enzymatic systems for carnitine biosynthesis. Huth et al.[48] demonstrated carnitine uptake by brain slices, although others[49,50] were unable to demonstrate uptake of labeled carnitine into the central nervous system from the plasma in vivo. In human beings the kidney appears to play a major role in carnitine synthesis from TML and has significantly greater specific activity of γ-butyrobetaine, 2-oxoglutarate dioxygenase than does liver.[51]

In addition to endogenous synthesis, tissue carnitine stores can be replenished by dietary intake. Meat products, especially red meat, and dairy products are rich in L-carnitine.

The only known metabolic fate for L-carnitine is the formation of acylcarnitines effected by several carnitine acyltransferases. Unlike D-carnitine, the L isomer is not degraded to smaller molecular forms; however, bacterial degradation in the gastrointestinal tract does result in the removal of the quaternary end of the molecule, producing trimethylamine. This compound is normally oxidized by hepatic trimethylamine oxidase and excreted in the urine.[41] Children receiving large oral doses of L-carnitine (>300 mg/kg/24 h) may produce trimethylamine in excess of the capacity of the oxidase, causing an iatrogenic acquired trimethylaminuria. The result is a social complication—a body odor like rotten fish—but no toxicity. The odor disappears as the dose is reduced.

Functions

L-Carnitine appears to have several functions.[41,52,53] The best known is its role in the transport of long-chain fatty acyl-CoA compounds as acylcarnitines into the mitochondrial matrix where the reactivated long-chain fatty acyl-CoA is subjected to the cycles of *β* oxidation. Furthermore, carnitine is involved in the transport of acetyl groups as acetylcarnitine between the mitochondrial matrix and the cytosolic compartment. A third function, namely detoxification, is suggested by the finding that acylcarnitine excretion in the urine of patients with defects in acyl-CoA metabolism mirrors the acyl-CoA species which would be predicted to accumulate in the face of the metabolic block. This is described in some detail below (see "Carnitine Deficiency Syndromes") and specifically in relation to defects in fatty acid oxidation (see "MCAD").

These functions are mediated by the carnitine acyltransferases, specifically carnitine palmityltransferase(s) and carnitine acetyltransferase, respectively.[41] A third enzyme, carnitine octanoyltransferase, is considered responsible for the formation of medium-chain length acylcarnitines within the mitochondrial matrix.[54]

Carnitine Deficiency Syndromes

A considerable literature devoted to disorders in which carnitine deficiency is a cardinal feature has appeared since the first description of a patient with muscle carnitine deficiency by

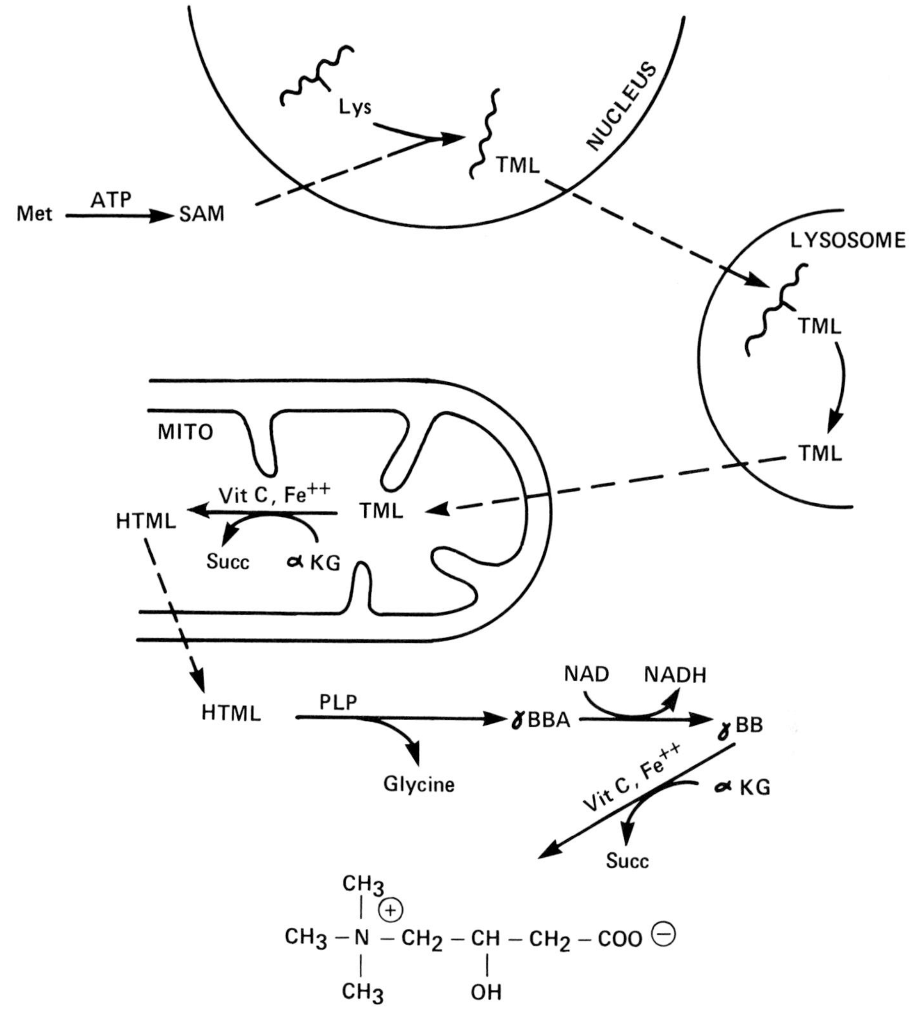

Fig. 33-6 Pathway of carnitine biosynthesis. See text for details. Additional abbreviations: α-KG = α-ketoglutarate (2-oxoglutarate); Lys = lysine; Met = methionine; PLP = pyridoxal phosphate; SAM = S-adenosylmethionine; Succ = succinate.

Engel and Angelini in 1973.[1] Two years later, Karpati et al.[3] described a patient in whom carnitine deficiency was demonstrated in plasma and liver as well as in muscle; this was referred to as systemic carnitine deficiency. More recently, with the availability of improved techniques to analyze acylcarnitines, there has been renewed interest in determining the underlying abnormality or abnormalities in patients with carnitine deficiency. It now appears that a number of metabolic disorders have an associated carnitine deficiency;[53,55–65] furthermore, a specific acylcarnitine species accumulates and is excreted in many of these disorders. The mechanisms responsible for carnitine deficiency in these disorders are complex and heterogeneous; thus, the designation of muscle versus systemic carnitine deficiency has lost much of its utility in diagnosis.

In some disorders (e.g., the renal Fanconi syndrome), the inability to conserve carnitine at the renal level offers a reasonable explanation for carnitine deficiency, namely *excessive urinary loss*.[57] The possibility that renal loss is the mechanism of carnitine deficiency in the organic acidurias is supported only by the identification of characteristically abnormal species in the urine. In several of these disorders, however, the actual quantities of free carnitine and acylcarnitines excreted per kilogram of body weight per 24 h are much less than in normals. This is best illustrated by the findings in untreated patients with isovaleric acidemia[61] and MCAD deficiency,[62,63] who have a marked reduction in plasma free carnitine associated with decreased excretion of total carnitine. Renal loss therefore is not an adequate explanation for carnitine deficiency in these disorders; the integrity of carnitine biosynthesis may be compromised.

In diseases such as propionic acidemia and methylmalonic aciduria, the levels of total carnitine in plasma and urine are often normal. This is due to an increase in the short- to medium-chain acylcarnitine fraction in both plasma and urine, with an associated reduction in the free carnitine level. Thus, in these disorders, although the *total* amount of carnitine may be normal, the bulk of it is esterified, mostly as propionylcarnitine.[64,65] Thus, this is not a true "deficiency" state; rather it is a *relative insufficiency of carnitine to meet metabolic needs*. Oral supplementation with L-carnitine results in increased excretion of propionylcarnitine and elevation of the free carnitine fraction, suggesting that more carnitine is needed to handle the large quantities of propionyl-CoA being produced. The transesterification reaction forming propionylcarnitine is most likely mediated by carnitine acetyltransferase; substrate specificity studies have revealed that its preferred substrate is propionyl-CoA.[66]

Analysis of urinary carnitine status in the various organic acidurias revealed an increased ratio of acylcarnitines to free carnitine in many of those disorders.[58] This observation suggested that the acyl-CoA intermediates which accumulate in these disorders were being excreted as their carnitine esters; however, routine chemical analysis does not identify the acyl moiety of the carnitine ester. Acylcarnitines are a difficult class of compounds to detect for a number of reasons: they are thermolabile, and therefore not amenable to ordinary gas chromatography; they do not contain a chromophore, which therefore limits the choices of detection methods; and they are zwitterions containing a quaternary amine. With these properties in mind, mass spectometric methods for the detection, characterization, and quantitation of acylcarnitines have been developed.[59,67]

Fast atom bombardment–mass spectrometry (FAB-MS) is a soft ionization technique carried out at room temperature which provides the means to detect signals corresponding to the intact acylcarnitine molecules. Fig. 33-7*A* demonstrates the methyl esters of acylcarnitines in urine over a mass range. FAB-MS permits identification of, in this case, the methyl ester of the normally detected species, acetylcarnitine [mass-to-charge ratio (m/z) 218], as well as the methyl esters of octanoylcarnitine (m/z 302), etc. The sensitivity of detection with currently available techniques is ≥50 nmol per milliter of urine. The signals for acetyl- and propionylcarnitine are specific, whereas acylcarnitines of greater chain length contain isomers for which the FAB signal would be identical. More detailed confirmation of structure and differentiation of isomers has been achieved using other analytical techniques such as tandem mass spectrometry (Fig. 33-7*B*), liquid chromatography–mass spectrometry, and hydrolysis of acylcarnitines followed by gas chromatography of the liberated acids (Fig. 33-7*C*).[60]

These techniques were first applied to patients with propionic acidemia and methylmalonic aciduria. In both of these conditions, propionylcarnitine is the abnormal species excreted, in contrast to the species normally excreted, acetylcarnitine. Further studies using these techniques revealed an interesting correlation between the species of acylcarnitine excreted and the corresponding enzyme deficiency: the acylcarnitines excreted in the urine reflected the acyl-CoA compounds which would be predicted to accumulate above the block in the metabolic pathway. These disorders and their characteristic acylcarnitines are presented in Table 33-1.[60]

Early studies involving oral carnitine administration to enhance urinary excretion of these acylcarnitine species suggested that carnitine enhances the excretion of toxic acyl-CoA compounds (e.g., propionyl-CoA in propionic acidemia) as acylcarnitines, while preserving the intramitochondrial acyl-CoA:CoASH ratio. Associated with the increased excretion of acylcarnitine was an increase in the production of hippurate (benzoyglycine), which is produced from benzoyl-CoA and glycine in a reaction catalyzed by glycine-*N*-acylase. This finding suggested that the formation of acylcarnitines from the accumulated CoA esters released free coenzyme A (CoASH) for utilization in other reactions (i.e., hippurate formation). Figure 33-8 depicts this detoxification role mediated by mitochondrial carnitine acyltransferases, as it might operate in the organic acidurias.[53,60]

Carnitine supplementation in normal individuals results in a ratio of urinary acylcarnitine to total carnitine of 0.3, and the species excreted is acetylcarnitine. Children with propionic acidemia or methylmalonic aciduria receiving a large oral dose of L-carnitine (200 mg/kg/day) seldom reduce that ratio to less than 0.5; more commonly, they excrete 60 to 70 percent of

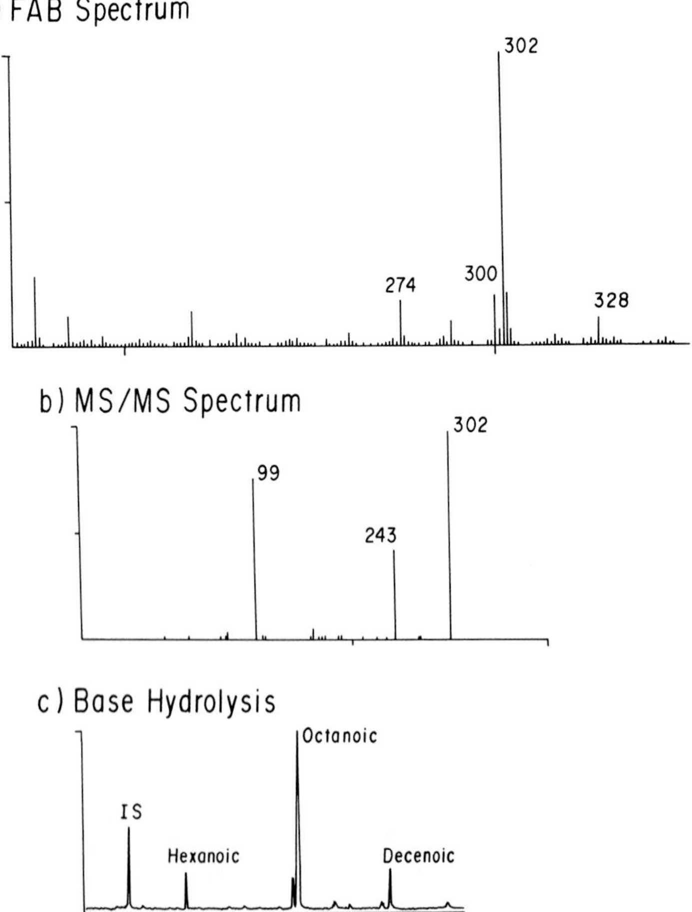

Fig. 33-7 Characterization of urinary acylcarnitines by mass spectrometry. *A.* Fast atom bombardment–mass spectrometry (FAB-MS) analysis of acylcarnitines in the urine of a patient with medium-chain acyl-CoA dehydrogenase (MCAD) deficiency, revealing the methyl ester of the major acylcarnitine species, octanoylcarnitine, with m/z 302; the normal species, acetylcarnitine, with m/z 218 is markedly reduced. *B.* Tandem mass spectrometry (MS/MS) generates a fragmentation pattern of the m/z 302 ion, resulting in a daughter ion at m/z 243; m/z 99 ion is a fragment common to all acylcarnitines. *C.* GC-MS analysis of acids liberated from the acylcarnitines by mild alkaline hydrolysis. IS = internal standard.

Table 33-1 Acylcarnitine Profiles in Organic Acidurias

Disorder	*Acylcarnitine*
Normal	Acetyl
Reye syndrome	Acetyl
MSUD*	Acetyl
Lactic acidosis/ketosis	Acetyl
Propionic acidemia	Propionyl
Methylmalonic aciduria	Propionyl
Isovaleric acidemia	Isovaleryl
β-Ketothiolase deficiency	Tiglyl
MCAD deficiency	Hexanoyl
	Octanoyl
	Octenoyl
	Decenoyl
LCAD deficiency	Acetyl
	(plasma LC)
HMG-CoA lyase deficiency	3-Methylglutaryl
	Isobutyryl
	Isovaleryl
	2-Methylbutyryl
Glutaric aciduria type I	Glutaryl
Glutaric aciduria type II	Butyryl
(mild and infantile forms)	2-Methylbutyryl
	Isobutyryl
	Isovaleryl
	Hexanoyl
	Octanoyl
	Glutaryl

*Abbreviations: HMG = 3-hydroxy-3-methylglutaryl; LC = long-chain; MSUD = maple syrup urine disease.
SOURCE: Modified from Ref. 60.

total carnitine in the form of acylcarnitines. This suggests that even higher doses of L-carnitine are required to meet metabolic needs. At doses of L-carnitine greater than 200 mg/kg/day, bacterial degradation of carnitine in the intestine produces trimethylamine and thereby becomes an important route of loss of ingested L-carnitine. Furthermore, unpublished studies suggest that only about 15 percent of an oral dose is absorbed and utilized (C.L. Hoppel, personal communication). Therefore, oral administration may be inadequate to provide carnitine to meet the needs for conjugation of propionyl-CoA. When these children are ill, therefore, intravenous administration of L-carnitine is likely to be far more beneficial.

These examples of carnitine deficiency and insufficiency are typical of genetic disorders associated with blocks in the mitochondrial oxidation of acyl-CoA compounds. In addition, there are many circumstances in which *acquired carnitine deficiency* occurs.[41,52] Children requiring hemodialysis or total parenteral nutrition (TPN) develop a secondary carnitine deficiency. Why children or adults on TPN should have carnitine deficiency is not clear, particularly since adequate lysine and cofactors are supplied parenterally. There are reports of clinically significant carnitine deficiency, in association with a switch from milk-based to soy protein–based formula and in association with a strict vegetarian diet. In these instances, dietary carnitine supplementation provided dramatic clinical response.[52] Reduced lysine in the diet, such as may occur in the dietary management of glutaric aciduria type I, or associated with severe malnutrition, theoretically can result in carnitine deficiency. Deficiency of vitamin C and pyridoxine,[41] which are cofactors in carnitine biosynthesis, may result in carnitine deficiency.

Children treated with valproate (Depakene) for seizure disorders are also prone to develop a toxicity syndrome with associated carnitine deficiency.[68,69] They may develop a Reye syndrome–like disease, with dicarboxylic aciduria and an increase in serum transaminases and hyperammonemia. Although valproyl-CoA is a substrate for acylcarnitine formation, valproylcarnitine represents only 10 percent of the acylcarnitine fraction in the urine.[70] Valproate is known to inhibit hepatic fatty acid oxidation at the medium-chain level;[71] however, only trace amounts of octanoylcarnitine have been observed by liquid chromatography–mass spectrometry analysis in the urine of patients receiving valproate.[70] Since β oxidation is affected, perhaps the mechanism is similar to that causing carnitine deficiency in the MCAD and LCAD enzyme defects (see below).

As noted above, there have been numerous reports of a disorder characterized as systemic carnitine deficiency since it was first described in 1975.[3] The clinical presentation resembled Reye syndrome, with hypoglycemia and lethargy leading to coma and possibly death. The basis of this disorder was thought to be defective carnitine biosynthesis, and it therefore was considered a primary carnitine deficiency. The early definition was "when (deficiency) is not known to be associated with another identifiable systemic illness that might deplete tissue carnitine stores."[72] Further studies of these patients implicated renal loss of carnitine as responsible for the deficiency state. Experiments to assess the integrity of carnitine biosynthesis by infusing methyl-[^{3}H]TML revealed normal or increased production and excretion of [^{3}H]-carnitine in these patients.[73] Since TML is mainly taken up by the kidney in human beings, that part of the renal biosynthetic pathway appeared intact. Biopsy of liver and assay of the enzymes involved in the transformation of TML to carnitine revealed slightly reduced activity of 6-*N*-trimethyllysine-2-oxoglutarate dioxygenase which produces HTML.[74] Unfortunately, in these cases, no quantitation of carnitine excretion was made in

Fig. 33-8 The role of carnitine in detoxification within mitochondria in the organic acidurias. Short-chain (SC) acyl-CoA compounds produced from the partial oxidation of long-chain (LC) fatty acids or branched chain (BC) amino acids are transesterified to carnitine via carnitine acetyltransferase, liberating free coenzyme A (CoASH) and SC-acylcarnitine which can be exported from the mitochondria. Supplementation with L-carnitine enhances this process. The sites of the inborn errors which result in the abnormal accumulation of SC acyl-CoA compounds are indicated by the asterisks (*).

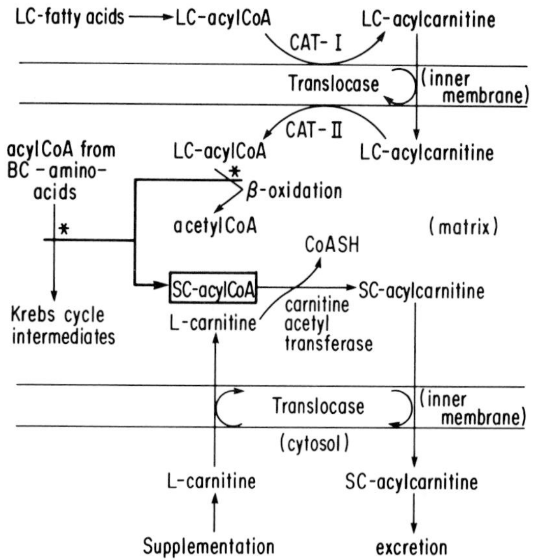

order to determine if increased renal loss was responsible for the deficiency state. Although acylcarnitines can inhibit the proximal tubular reabsorption of free carnitine, the net amount of total carnitine excreted in these patients, in retrospect, was probably reduced. These results should be viewed in light of the fact that all of the patients with systemic carnitine deficiency in these reports[75,76] have MCAD deficiency.[77,78] It would appear, therefore, that systemic carnitine deficiency in those patients does not represent a primary defect in carnitine biosynthesis.

Other patients have been described with hypoketotic hypoglycemia or with significant cardiomyopathy and severe skeletal muscle weakness, associated with systemic carnitine deficiency, who have required high doses of L-carnitine to maintain normal plasma levels and presumably tissue levels.[79–81] While the specific abnormality in some of these patients has not yet been identified, Stanley et al.[81a] demonstrated that some patients, including the patient in Ref. 81, have a primary defect in carnitine transport which can be identified in cultured fibroblasts. Other patients may represent examples of primary defects in carnitine biosynthesis. Actual defects in the pathway from protein-bound lysine to carnitine have not yet been clearly identified, although one might predict that such disorders would be characterized by defective mitochondrial β oxidation in liver, skeletal muscle, and cardiac muscle, as well as impaired renal function.

GENETIC DEFECTS IN ACYL-CoA DEHYDROGENASE ACTIVITIES

MCAD Deficiency

Clinical Presentations. Since the first patients with MCAD deficiency were described in 1982–83,[4–7] more than 85 patients have been identified (Refs. 62, 63, 77, and 82–94 and unpublished observations). Several patients who had been previously described with disorders of fasting adaptation[95–97] have since been found to have MCAD deficiency (Ref. 88; D.E. Hale and P.M. Coates, unpublished observations).

While there is no "typical" presentation of MCAD deficiency, there are some common features of the disease which should be noted.[12] The child with MCAD deficiency often presents with an episode of vomiting and lethargy following a period of fasting. There may have been a prior viral infection (upper respiratory, gastrointestinal) and decreased oral intake. There is occasionally a history of previous similar episodes. On presentation to the emergency room, the child may be comatose; blood glucose will be low and often there will be no (or trace) ketones in the urine. Blood ammonia levels and liver function tests may be abnormal. Intravenous infusion with 10% dextrose will generally cause rapid improvement. The child will be asymptomatic between episodes, and further episodes can be prevented by providing an adequate caloric intake.

There is, however, considerable variation in the clinical presentation of MCAD deficiency, as described below; sudden infant death syndrome,[83,83a] recurrent Reye syndrome,[75,94] and episodic hypoglycemic coma[97] have all been described in MCAD deficiency; patients have also been described who are completely asymptomatic.[77,89] The following case descriptions illustrate the phenotypic heterogeneity associated with MCAD deficiency.

Case 1 A 12-month-old female was well and developmentally normal until she developed an upper respiratory infection 3 days prior to admission. Vomiting began 36 h prior to and continued until admission precipitated by the onset of lethargy. She was found to have severe hypoglycemia (1 mg/dl), mild hyperammonemia (55 μM), slightly elevated SGOT (84 IU/liter), and mild metabolic acidosis. She responded rapidly to glucose administration and was tentatively diagnosed as being in stage 0 of Reye syndrome on the basis of these findings. There were no siblings, and the parents were unrelated.

Case 2 A 13-month-old female (patient R − 1 in Ref. 62) developed an upper respiratory infection associated with fever. During the ensuing 24 to 48 h, she vomited repeatedly, became lethargic and then unconscious, and she had two seizures. Upon admission, her blood glucose was 22 mg/dl, CSF glucose was 7 mg/dl, blood ammonia was 66 μM, SGOT was 224 IU/liter, and she had mild metabolic acidosis. Her liver was 2 cm below the right costal margin, and her urine revealed small ketones. She was considered to have stage II Reye syndrome and was treated accordingly. Her intracranial pressure increased transiently during the hospital course, but responded to mannitol. Her recovery was complicated by complex partial seizures, but her development was normal. Her parents were unrelated, and the family history was notable for a male sibling who had died suddenly and unexpectedly in the crib at the age of 7 months and who on postmortem examination had cerebral edema and fatty liver.

Case 3 A male was well until 23 months of age, when he developed a stomach virus which progressed to vomiting, lethargy, and seizures. He was hyperammonemic (253 μM) and hypoglycemic (10 mg/dl). He died 4 days after admission with the diagnosis of Reye syndrome. His parents were unrelated. He had two male siblings, one of whom died suddenly at 18 months of age following a respiratory illness; the other was well at 3½ years of age. He also had an infant female sibling. Biochemical evaluation of this patient and his two surviving siblings revealed that they all had MCAD deficiency. Subsequently, the female has been hospitalized twice with Reye syndrome–like illnesses.[63]

Case 4 A 21-month-old female[92] was entirely normal and had received all immunizations without incident. She developed a "stomach virus" which resulted in refractory vomiting, and proceeded to lethargy, seizures, coma, and death on arrival at the hospital after an illness of 48 h. Autopsy revealed fatty infiltration of the liver and cerebral edema. Her diagnosis was considered to be sudden infant death syndrome rather than Reye syndrome. There were no siblings. One year later, these unrelated parents had a male child who appeared entirely normal. This asymptomatic child was found to have MCAD deficiency by examination of acylcarnitines in urine and by measurement of acyl-CoA dehydrogenase activities in his fibroblasts. Liver from the postmortem examination of the sibling contained increased octanoylcarnitine, in contrast to control livers, in which the major acylcarnitine species was acetylcarnitine.

Case 5 A white female,[75] at the age of 11 months, developed an upper respiratory infection. Two days later, she began vomiting; on the fourth day, she became lethargic, limp, and unresponsive. On admission, she was semistuporous and had irregular respirations with periods of apnea. Laboratory studies revealed: blood glucose 15 mg/dl, blood ammonia 57 μM, SGOT 105 IU/liter, SGPT 102 IU/liter. Mechanical ventilation was begun, and she was given intravenous dextrose therapy. She became alert and active within 12 h. A similar illness occurred at 4½ years of age, and she again improved with intravenous dextrose therapy. A percutaneous liver biopsy showed diffuse microvesicular fatty degeneration, which was interpreted as consistent with Reye syndrome. Evaluation at 5 years of age revealed an alert, intelligent girl with mild weakness of the proximal muscles of all four extremities.

Case 6 A white 18-year-old girl (patient T − 1 in Ref. 77) had been followed since early childhood for recurrent episodes of illness precipitated by fasting and characterized by severe lethargy and vomiting. Her history revealed that she had suffered her first episode at 13 months of age. Beginning at 4 years of age, these episodes occurred nearly monthly for 6 months. On each occasion, she was hospitalized and improved within several hours of receiving intravenous fluids and dextrose. She rarely became hypoglycemic during these episodes. An admission at 5 years of age was precipitated by weakness, lethargy, and vomiting after an overnight fast. She was afebrile, limp, and moderately dehydrated. Her liver was not enlarged. Laboratory studies revealed: blood glucose 46 mg/dl, blood urea nitrogen 21 mg/dl, SGOT 32 IU/liter. A fasting study showed evidence of reduced ketogenesis (0.32 m*M* β-hydroxybutyrate) despite high plasma free fatty acid levels (4.1 m*M*). Following the recognition that her illness was precipitated by fasting for more than 12 to 16 h, her parents were instructed to avoid prolonged periods without feeding and, in the ensuing 13 years, this has successfully prevented all but rare recurrences of her illness. At 18 years of age, she is physically and intellectually normal. She has no evidence of muscle weakness.

The family history is commonly characterized by the loss of a sibling who carried the diagnosis of either Reye syndrome or sudden infant death syndrome. If this has occurred, attempts should be made to obtain autopsy information, since that child may have had the cerebral edema and fatty liver commonly encountered in MCAD deficiency. Postmortem diagnosis either by acylcarnitine measurement or by specific enzyme assay (see below) may be possible if tissue has been stored frozen.

Initial Laboratory Findings. The initial laboratory studies usually include serum electrolytes, glucose, ammonia, transaminases, and urinalysis. Although there may be a mild metabolic acidosis, a large anion gap is unusual and, if present, often indicates superimposed lactic acidosis. Hypoglycemia is usually present, but normal or borderline glucose levels have been observed in lethargic patients with MCAD deficiency, suggesting that the central nervous system manifestations are not due entirely to hypoglycemia. Therefore, the diagnosis of MCAD deficiency should not be excluded on this basis alone. Ammonia levels in the blood are usually only mildly elevated (50 to 100 μM; normal <50 μM), but have been observed as high as 253 μM. Similarly, there is a mild (two- to fourfold) elevation in serum transaminases. MCAD deficiency was originally described as a nonketotic hypoglycemia,[7,98] but urine ketones have been occasionally observed and confirmed by gas chromatography–mass spectrometry (GC-MS) in acutely ill children with MCAD deficiency. It would be more precise to consider this a hypoketotic condition, since there is an inappropriately low degree of ketosis for the level of circulating free fatty acid substrate. It should be noted that the urinalysis could also be characterized by "small ketones" if the child has ingested aspirin recently.

If the child has the appropriate clinical presentation and all of the preliminary laboratory studies are consistent (hypoglycemia, little or no urine ketones, increased transaminases, and a mild increase in ammonia), then the diagnosis of MCAD deficiency appears plausible. This clinical history alone gives sufficient cause to proceed with more specific diagnostic testing, including GC-MS of organic acids, carnitine assays, acylcarnitine analysis, and specific enzyme assay (see below).

Definitive evaluation of the child with MCAD deficiency for both diagnosis and pretreatment status should include: capillary GC-MS of urinary organic acids, assessment of carnitine status, acylcarnitine identification (e.g., by FAB-MS), and specific enzyme assay in either fibroblasts or white blood cells. Except for the enzyme assay, the other studies can be obtained quickly so that early decisions regarding patient management and the exclusion of other disorders from the differential diagnosis can be made.

Organic Acid Analysis. Figure 33-9 shows the results of GC-MS analysis of urine from a patient with MCAD deficiency. The substrate specificity of the enzyme dictates the metabolites that will be observed when it is deficient;[98,99] specifically, all are of medium-chain length (C_6 to C_{12}). The major compounds that would be expected to accumulate in tissues during periods of stress and lipolysis include the following CoA thioesters: hexanoyl-, octanoyl-, octenoyl-, decanoyl-, decenoyl-, and dodecanoyl-. When mitochondrial β oxidation is limited by MCAD deficiency, partially oxidized medium-chain fatty acids, such as octanoic acid and especially 4-decenoic acid, may accumulate, and have been identified in plasma from MCAD-deficient patients.[100] Alternative pathways, such as ω and $(\omega - 1)$ oxidation and peroxisomal β oxidation, become involved, resulting in the production of medium-chain dicarboxylic acids, adipic ($C_{6:0}$), suberic ($C_{8:0}$), dehydrosuberic ($C_{8:1}$), sebacic ($C_{10:0}$), dehydrosebacic ($C_{10:1}$), and dodecane-

Fig. 33-9 Capillary GC-MS analysis of urinary organic acids in a patient with MCAD deficiency when sick *(A)* and well *(B)*. Peaks: 1 = lactate; 2 = 3-hydroxybutyrate; 3 = acetoacetate; 4 = octanoate; 5 = 5-hydroxyhexanoate; 6 = adipate; 7 = hexanoylglycine; 8 = dehydrosuberate; 9 = suberate; 10 = citrate; 11 = dehydrosebacate; 12 = sebacate; 13 = 3-hydroxydecanedioic; 14 = suberylglycine; IS = internal standard.

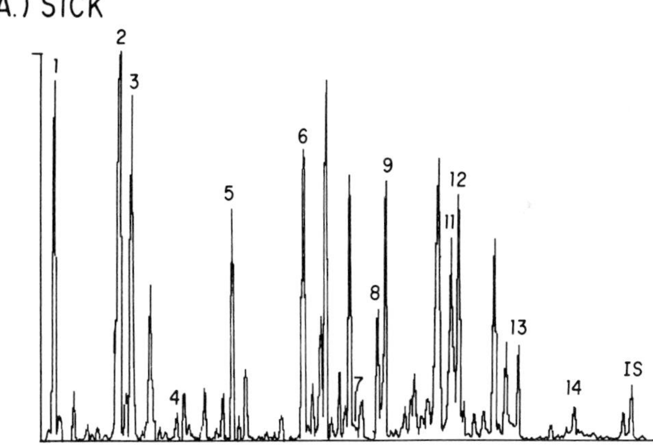

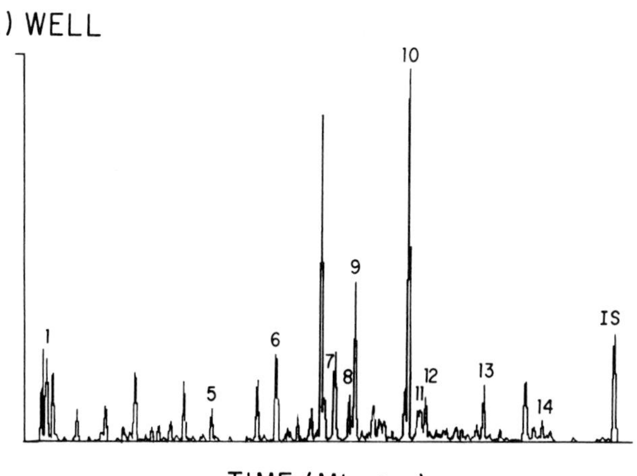

dioic ($C_{12:0}$). Analysis of urine by GC-MS will reveal most of these dicarboxylic acids. The corresponding ($\omega-1$)-hydroxy acids (5-hydroxyhexanoate and 7-hydroxvoctanoate) also may be present in urine of these patients. Among the most specific findings are the glycine conjugates, phenylpropionylglycine, hexanoylglycine, and suberylglycine.[98,98a] This reflects the substrate specificity of the mitochondrial glycine-*N*-acylase, which cannot conjugate glycine with octanoyl-CoA but is active with hexanoyl-CoA and suberyl-CoA.[99] It should be noted that suberylglycine may be overlooked if a packed column GC is used for the analysis, because it co-elutes with 4-hydroxyhippurate; these compounds can be separated by capillary GC. Furthermore, suberylglycine is not present in large quantities except when the patient is ill, and it may be overlooked when one employs methods that do not use mass spectrometry or even when one uses capillary GC-MS, but fails to examine small peaks for the presence of this key metabolite.

Unlike diseases such as methylmalonic aciduria, isovaleric acidemia, etc., the concentrations of abnormal urinary metabolites in MCAD deficiency vary greatly. The characteristic acylglycines, the less specific dicarboxylic acids, and ($\omega-1$)-hydroxy acids may all be below detection levels for capillary GC-MS if the patient is in the fed state (Fig. 33-9). When urine organic acids are analyzed by capillary GC-MS at the time the patient is ill, levels of acetoacetate and 3-hydroxybutyrate, if present, will be reduced relative to the extent of dicarboxylic aciduria and the abnormal metabolites will be prominent in the urine. Obviously, samples obtained close to admission will be more informative. It should be emphasized that dicarboxylic acid excretion itself, and even ($\omega-1$)-hydroxy fatty acid excretion, are not diagnostic of MCAD deficiency; they have been observed in other diseases (such as diabetic ketoacidosis), or following the administration of MCT. In the latter setting, only saturated dicarboxylic acids are excreted, in contrast to both saturated and unsaturated forms seen in MCAD deficiency.[94] Furthermore, the relative concentrations of the C_6, C_8, and C_{10} dicarboxylic acids differ between MCAD deficiency and MCT feeding; in MCAD deficiency, these tend to be present with $C_6 > C_8 > C_{10}$, while the reverse is usually found in the urine of patients fed MCT.[39,101]

Table 33-2 Carnitine Status in MCAD Deficiency

	Father	*Mother*	*S-1*	*S-3*	*Controls*
Baseline plasma carnitine (μmol/L)					
Total	59	52	17	47	46 ± 10
Free	53	42	12	33	37 ± 8
Acid-soluble	3	7	4	10	6 ± 4
Acid-insoluble	3	3	1	4	4 ± 2
Baseline urinary carnitine excretion (μmol/kg/24 h)					
Total	6.46	2.97	0.92	4.46	5.4 ± 1.7
Free	3.53	0.88	0.16	1.98	3.0 ± 1.0
Acyl	2.93	2.10	0.76	2.48	2.4 ± 0.8
Species	acetyl	acetyl	N.D.	octanoyl	acetyl
Effect of maternal carnitine supplementation on urinary carnitine excretion (μmol/kg/24 h) in the mother and in the breast-feeding infant					
Total	—	41.29	—	29.36	—
Free	—	24.85	—	15.62	—
Acyl	—	16.44	—	13.74	—
Species	—	acetyl	—	octanoyl	—

N.D. = not detectable, but octanoylcarnitine identified following L-carnitine oral load.

SOURCE: Modified from Ref. 63; S-1 and S-3 are affected sibs.

Carnitine Status and Acylcarnitine Species. Many of the observations regarding plasma and urinary carnitine levels encountered in a family with children having MCAD deficiency (Case 3) are shown in Table 33-2.[63] These measurements were made by a radioenzymatic assay[102] after plasma acylcarnitines had been separated into an acid-soluble fraction (short- and medium-chain acylcarnitines) and an acid-insoluble fraction (long-chain acylcarnitines). Since long-chain acylcarnitines are not readily excreted, urinary acylcarnitines are found mainly in the acid-soluble fraction. Fluctuations in the levels of free and acylcarnitines occur normally in plasma and urine. When a normal individual is fasted, there is a reduction in plasma free carnitine and a corresponding increase in the acid-soluble fraction due to increased production of acetyl-CoA from β oxidation and its conversion to acetylcarnitine. The total plasma carnitine concentration may remain unchanged.[7]

An affected child who is not symptomatic at the time of testing and is receiving normal dietary intake typically has low total plasma carnitine levels, as illustrated by patient S − 1 in Table 33-2. This results from a reduction in plasma free carnitine, since acylcarnitines in plasma are usually elevated. Urinary free carnitine relative to creatinine may also be reduced and associated with a relative increase in acylcarnitines. The ratio of urinary acylcarnitine to free carnitine is normally ≤ 4. In many children with MCAD deficiency this ratio is significantly increased. However, absolute carnitine excretion (μmol/kg/24 h) is frequently decreased. These reductions parallel the reported concentrations of carnitine in tissues. Six untreated cases of MCAD deficiency (including three cases originally described as having systemic carnitine deficiency) were characterized by tissue levels of carnitine 16 to 42 percent of normal in liver and 16 to 25 percent of normal in muscle.[7,75,76]

An affected, breast-fed infant studied prior to onset of symptoms may have quite normal plasma carnitine levels (patient S − 3 in Table 33-2). Human breast milk contains L-carnitine at a concentration of roughly 50 μM with nearly undetectable acylcarnitines. It is currently presumed that this dietary source of L-carnitine provides much of the infant's requirement in the early months of life, at a time when the capacity for carnitine biosynthesis may be relatively underdeveloped.[52] That carnitine is transported in breast milk from mother to infant has been demonstrated by enhanced excretion of both free and acylcarnitines by the infant following administration of oral carnitine to the mother (patient S-3 in Table 33-2). There are currently no data to indicate when a carnitine deficiency state first occurs relative to the onset of symptoms.

The identification of acylcarnitine species excreted by MCAD-deficient children[58,62,63,100] is of greater value in diagnosis than is the measurement of total or even esterified carnitine levels and, in some instances, is more sensitive and specific than capillary GC-MS analysis of urinary organic acids. The child with MCAD deficiency has a highly specific acylcarnitine profile (Fig. 33-7*A*) which includes: m/z 274, corresponding to the methyl ester of hexanoylcarnitine; m/z 300, octenoylcarnitine; m/z 302, octanoylcarnitine; and m/z 328, decenoylcarnitine. These species can be quantitated using isotope dilution mass spectrometry with deuterated internal standards; the acylcarnitine FAB profile is so specific, however, that quantitation is only useful for investigative purposes. The m/z 302 signal for octanoylcarnitine dominates the profile in urine from most patients with MCAD deficiency, and characteristically there is very little signal corresponding to the normal species, acetylcarnitine. This latter observation is consistent with the reduced capacity to produce acetyl-CoA in this β-oxidation defect.

Table 33-2 (Case 3) demonstrates that octanoylcarnitine was dominant in the urine of both a sick child (S-2)[63] and a presymptomatic infant (S-3), both of whom had substantial amounts of acylcarnitines in the urine. Of particular note is the other presymptomatic sibling, S-1, who was carnitine-deficient but in whose urine strong signals for acylcarnitines were not obvious. Following carnitine supplementation of this infant (100 mg/kg), the FAB-MS profile was identical with that seen in Fig. 33-6*A*. Children who are deficient in carnitine may excrete insufficient levels of acylcarnitines for FAB-MS detection. Administration of an oral carnitine load (100 mg/kg) results in a rapid increase in urinary acylcarnitine and is a useful noninvasive method for diagnosis without risk. It is equally useful for detection of affected siblings.

FAB-MS is also useful for postmortem detection of MCAD deficiency in autopsy liver, since acylcarnitines appear to be stable (Fig. 33-10). Families who have lost a child to the sudden infant death syndrome or Reye syndrome, for example, may have the opportunity for postmortem diagnosis and counseling for future pregnancies if this analysis is performed.[92]

The parents of MCAD-deficient patients have normal plasma and urine carnitine levels. Table 33-2 shows that when the mother of an MCAD-deficient child was given a carnitine load, there was more than fivefold increased excretion of total carnitine, reflected in both the free and acylcarnitine fractions. The increment in acylcarnitine was due to the normally detected species, acetylcarnitine, confirming that abnormal acyl-CoA compounds are not significantly increased in vivo in the heterozygote.

Pathologic Findings. The primary pathologic findings in MCAD-deficient patients include light microscopic and ultrastructural changes mainly in liver, but alterations have been observed in other tissues. Cerebral edema is noted post mortem in most cases.[7,63,89,90] Hepatic light microscopic alterations in MCAD deficiency are essentially limited to steatosis, which may be either macro- or microvesicular in nature.[90] In some cases, the microvesicular fat accumulation has been indistinguishable from that seen in Reye syndrome. In those instances, however, ultrastructural studies have clearly demonstrated that the generalized mitochondrial changes characteristic of Reye syndrome were not present. Specifically, the matrix swelling and rarefaction commonly seen in hepatic mitochondria of patients with Reye syndrome have not been observed in mitochondria from patients with MCAD deficiency. Increased matrix density and intracristal widening gave the mitochondria of two out of five MCAD-deficient patients a condensed appearance. In one of the five patients, there were so-called crystalloids in the matrix, associated with an increased number of cristae and with enlargement and abnormal shape of the mitochondria. Two of the five patients had normal mitochondrial ultrastructure. Condensed mitochondria have been described in other disease states, and crystalloids have been noted in mitochondria from patients with carnitine-deficient myopathy, as well as in other myopathies.[103]

Fatty Acid Oxidation in Fibroblasts From Patients with MCAD Deficiency. Defects in the pathway of fatty acid β oxidation, including MCAD deficiency, have been identified indirectly by measuring the products of ^{14}C-labeled fatty acid oxidation.[4,6,77,89,100,104–106] Substantial differences among the methods employed by various investigators make direct comparisons very difficult, but for the most part, fibroblasts from patients with MCAD deficiency oxidize [1-^{14}C]octanoic acid at approximately 20 percent of control rates, whether the product measured is $^{14}CO_2$ alone (Table 33-3) or $^{14}CO_2$ plus ^{14}C-labeled acid-soluble intermediates. Few studies of [1-^{14}C]octanoic acid oxidation have been performed on cells from obligate heterozygotes, but these have been completely normal (Ref. 89; P.M. Coates and D.E. Hale, unpublished observations).

Table 33-3 demonstrates that cells from MCAD-deficient patients have apparently normal rates of oxidation when [1-^{14}C]palmitic acid is used as the labeled substrate, while [6-^{14}C]-, [16-^{14}C]-, and [^{14}C(U)]palmitic acid are all oxidized at significantly diminished rates compared to controls.[77] These findings reflect the chain-length specificity of MCAD; since

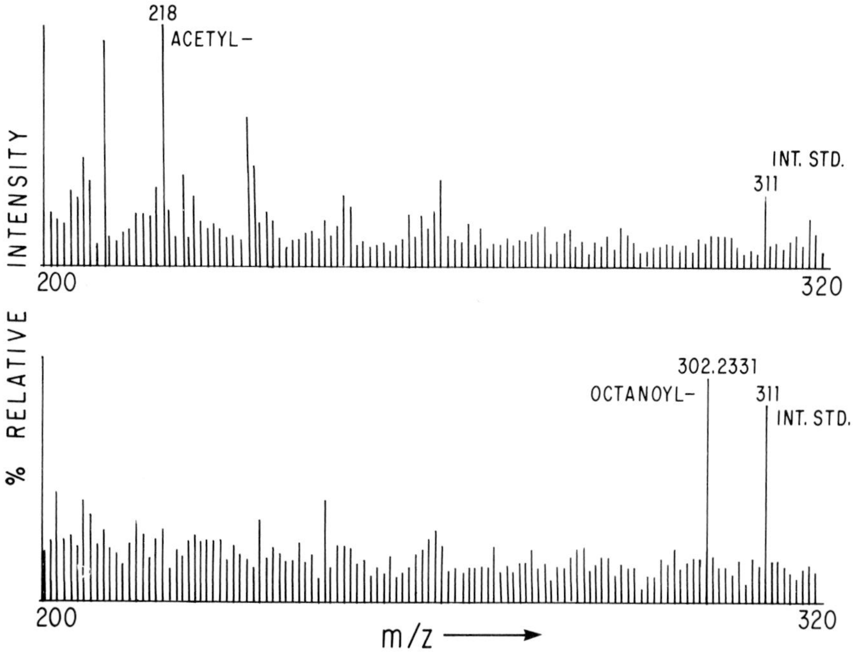

Fig. 33-10 Postmortem diagnosis of MCAD deficiency in liver tissue by FAB-MS analysis. Acetylcarnitine (m/z 218) is the dominant species in the control liver *(top)*, whereas octanoylcarnitine (m/z 302.2331) is the most prominent species in the MCAD-deficient liver *(bottom)*. Int Std = internal standard ([$^2H_9$]octanoylcarnitine, m/z 311).

Table 33-3 Fatty Acid Oxidation in Cultured Fibroblasts from Patients with MCAD Deficiency and LCAD Deficiency

Substrate	*MCAD deficiency*	*LCAD deficiency*	*Controls*
[1-^{14}C]-butyric	44.0 ± 3.0 (3)*	33.0 (1)	35.0 ± 13.0 (10)
[1-^{14}C]-octanoic	3.0 ± 0.2 (5)	10.0 (1)	15.1 ± 3.7 (10)
[1-^{14}C]-palmitic	13.4 ± 0.3 (5)	6.7 (1)	14.5 ± 1.5 (10)
[6-^{14}C]-palmitic	4.7 ± 0.6 (3)	N.T.†	9.2 ± 3.1 (4)
[16-^{14}C]-palmitic	0.9 ± 0.4 (3)	0.8 (1)	6.3 ± 2.1 (4)
[^{14}C(U)]-palmitic	6.9 ± 0.4 (5)	3.0 (1)	15.0 ± 1.0 (4)

*nmol $CO_2/10^6$ cells/h, mean ± S.D. for the number of subjects in parentheses.
†N.T. = not tested.
SOURCE: Modified from Refs. 8, 77.

the [1-^{14}C] label in palmitic acid is removed in the first turn of the β-oxidation spiral, MCAD can have no substantial activity toward the 16-carbon acyl-CoA molecule. As the palmitic acid is sequentially degraded, each turn of the spiral will become increasingly dependent on the activity of MCAD to permit normal flux through the pathway; if MCAD is deficient, the ability of mitochondria to cleave acetyl-CoA groups at and beyond the level of the medium chain is substantially impaired. A short-chain fatty acid, such as [1-^{14}C]butyric acid can enter the β-oxidation sequence beyond the metabolic block and hence is oxidized at a normal rate. This is in spite of the fact that the contribution of MCAD toward butyryl-CoA dehydrogenation is considerable, at least in vitro. An unexplained aspect of the results of oxidation studies done in cells from MCAD-deficient patients is that their rate of octanoate β oxidation is appreciable (20 percent), despite the virtual absence of MCAD acitivty. It is likely that medium-chain fatty acids which fail to be oxidized normally in mitochondria undergo alternative metabolism.

In some instances, MCAD deficiency has been inferred from profoundly reduced rates of [1-^{14}C]octanoic acid oxidation in fibroblasts. While this method should provide a good screening test for defects in fatty acid oxidation, it suffers from variability in rates of oxidation and high background rates. Given that there are multiple enzymes in β oxidation with some degree of chain-length specificity, it cannot be stated with certainty that a significant reduction in the oxidation of a fatty acid such as octanoate will specifically detect MCAD deficiency.

Recently, Moon and Rhead[107] described a method for detecting defects in fatty acid oxidation based on the formation of ^3H_2O from [9,10(n)-^{3}H]palmitic acid. In cells from three MCAD-deficient patients, the rate of ^3H_2O production was approximately 20 percent of control rates, comparable to those seen using ^{14}C-labeled fatty acid substrates. This assay has several advantages, including a reduced sample requirement, which make it potentially useful for demonstrating defects in fatty acid metabolism. By coupling this assay with an in vitro complementation strategy, the authors could distinguish MCAD-deficient, carnitine palmityltransferase–deficient, LCAD-deficient, ETF-deficient, and ETF dehydrogenase–deficient cells. As noted later in this chapter (see "Other Defects in Fatty Acid Oxidation"), this method may provide an initial screening method to detect abnormalities in oxidation.

Enzymatic Diagnosis of MCAD Deficiency. The specific enzyme defect has been demonstrated in cultured skin fibroblasts[4–6,77,82,86,88,90,93,94,108–110] and peripheral mononuclear leukocytes;[77,111] the diagnosis has also been made in liver,[7,78,83,89] heart,[83a] and skeletal muscle.[78,112] Four general types of methods have been used in different laboratories to measure MCAD and other acyl-CoA dehydrogenase activities. The first is based on the transfer of electrons to the physiological acceptor, electron transfer flavoprotein (ETF), under anaerobic conditions.[77,109] Oxidized ETF is intensely fluorescent; it is reduced by electrons transferred from the acyl-CoA during the dehydrogenation reaction, and the fluorescence of ETF declines at a rate proportional to the transfer of electrons.[7,77,109] The second is based on the transfer of electrons to artificial electron receptors, such as dichlorophenolindophenol (DCPIP) or phenazine methosulfate (PMS), either directly or as a terminal acceptor from ETF.[6] The third employs GC-MS techniques to measure the concentration of enoyl-CoA, the metabolite formed by dehydrogenation of acyl-CoA.[4] The fourth measures the formation of tritiated water from the ^{3}H released as a [2,3-^{3}H]acyl-CoA substrate undergoes dehydrogenation.[88,113] Results obtained for the detection of MCAD deficiency in fibroblasts using octanoyl-CoA as substrate in all four assay systems are shown in Table 33-4.

With the ETF-based assay (Refs. 77, 90, 108–111; D.E. Hale and P.M. Coates, unpublished observations), MCAD activity measured with octanoyl-CoA as substrate has been generally less than 10 percent of control levels in fibroblasts from MCAD-deficient patients. Levels in cells from 65 patients ranged from 0.01 to 0.47 nmol ETF reduced per minute per milligram of protein, compared to controls which ranged from 3.65 to 5.01 nmol ETF reduced per minute per milligram of protein, but there was no obvious association between the residual MCAD activity and the severity of clinical disease in these patients. Comparable results have been obtained using the tritium-release assay and the artificial dye reduction assay, both described by Rhead and colleagues.[6,88] The single ion monitoring GC-MS method[4,85,86] gives similar results, but the residual enzyme activity in MCAD-deficient fibroblasts has ranged up to 30 percent of control levels.

Dehydrogenase activities toward other acyl-CoA compounds have been measured in cells from MCAD-deficient patients. Limited data indicate that isovaleryl-CoA dehydrogenase activity is normal in cells from these patients. Table 33-5 demonstrates that LCAD activity, measured using palmityl-CoA as substrate in the ETF-based assay, is generally within the normal range. This finding confirms previous reports by others who have examined the substrate specificity of MCAD[28] that this enzyme has no substantial activity toward long-chain acyl-CoA compounds such as palmityl-CoA. This latter finding was further substantiated[114] in experiments using a monospecific antibody against MCAD; control fibroblasts incubated with anti-MCAD lost all of their activity toward octanoyl-CoA as substrate, while the activity toward palmityl-CoA was unaffected.

By contrast, dehydrogenase activity toward butyryl-CoA as substrate was reduced to 50 percent of control levels in cells

Table 33-4 MCAD Deficiency in Cultured Fibroblasts Demonstrated Using Octanoyl-CoA as Substrate by Four Different Methods

Assay principle (units of enzyme activity)	*Whole cells (C) or mitochondria (M)*	*Controls (n)*	*Patients (n)*	*Ref.*
ETF-Based	C	4.11 ± 0.38 (65)	0.25 ± 0.11 (40)	77; unpubl.
(nmol ETF reduced · min^{-1} · mg	C	2.71 ± 0.72 (9)	0.25; 0.09 (2)	109
$protein^{-1}$, mean ± SD)				
Tritium-Release	C	57 ± 4.0 (10)	4.5 ± 0.6 (6)	88
(pmol ^3H_2O) formed · min^{-1} · mg	M*	1,376 ± 215 (4)	66 ± 10 (4)	88
$protein^{-1}$, mean ± SEM)				
ETF-Linked Dye Reduction	M†	1,850 ± 434 (6)	134 ± 34 (7)	6
(pmol DCPIP reduced · min^{-1} · mg				
$protein^{-1}$, mean ± SEM)				
SIM-GC/MS	C	30 ± 12.1 (5)	11.8 (1)	4
(nmol enoyl-CoA formed · h^{-1} · mg	C	39 (5)	12.0 (1)	85
$protein^{-1}$, mean ± SD)	C	29 ± 8.8 (4)	4.7; 2.3 (2)	86

*Assayed in the presence of 10 m*M* phenazine methosulfate.
†Assayed in the presence of 0.2 m*M* n-ethylmaleimide.

from MCAD-deficient patients.[6,77,110] These data suggested that MCAD has substantial activity toward short-chain acyl-CoA compounds. This may be a function of the assay system employed, since less overlap was observed in MCAD substrate specificity when a tritium-release assay was employed with butyryl-CoA as substrate.[88] The overlap in substrate specificity has been further demonstrated by experiments in control cells treated with anti-MCAD where, in addition to completely inhibiting octanoyl-CoA dehydrogenation, the antibody inhibited 50 percent of the activity toward butyryl-CoA.[114] Cells from parents had intermediate levels of activity toward butyryl-CoA as substrate (Table 33-5). Data similar to these have been obtained for purified human liver MCAD; Finocchiaro et al. demonstrated using an ETF-based assay that MCAD had substantial activity toward butyryl-CoA as substrate.[18]

The only substantial experience in MCAD heterozygote detection has been gained using the ETF reduction assay. Table 33-5 demonstrates that cells from parents of MCAD-deficient patients have intermediate levels of MCAD activity using octanoyl-CoA as substrate, consistent with their being heterozygous for an autosomal recessive trait. The mean residual enzyme activity is 49.5 percent of control levels, ranging from 35 to 67 percent; there has been no overlap between heterozygote levels and either control or affected levels of MCAD activity. This has important ramifications in terms of genetic counseling and diagnosis (see below).

Inheritance. All available data indicate that MCAD deficiency is inherited as an autosomal trait; patients are homozygous for an abnormal allele at the MCAD locus (or are genetic compounds with two different abnormal alleles), and their parents are heterozygous for the abnormal allele(s). With the exception of a single family in which the father and several children appeared to have MCAD deficiency,[89] the parents in all other families tested have half-normal levels of MCAD activity and are clinically asymptomatic.

Biochemical and Molecular Aspects. Finocchiaro et al.[18] have purified MCAD, as well as other acyl-CoA dehydrogenase activities, from human liver. The native molecular weight of MCAD was estimated to be 178,000 by gel filtration. The enzyme is a homotetramer, with a subunit molecular weight of approximately 44,000. Each subunit contains 1 molecule of flavin adenine dinucleotide (FAD).

Ikeda et al.[110] examined the biosynthesis of MCAD in control and in MCAD-deficient fibroblasts; using a rabbit antirat MCAD antibody which cross-reacted with human MCAD,[110,115] they demonstrated that the human MCAD subunit is synthesized on cytoplasmic ribosomes as a 50-kDa precursor, with a leader peptide sequence of 4kDa; the mature enzyme subunit, once translocated to the mitochondrial matrix, has a molecular weight of 46kDa. Among 13 human MCAD-deficient cultures, in which residual enzyme activity toward octanoyl-CoA ranged from 6 to 13 percent of control levels, the MCAD precursor was synthesized and processed to the mature MCAD, and both were indistinguishable in size from the corresponding precursor and mature forms of MCAD in control cells. These data suggested that the mutation(s) causing MCAD deficiency, at least in these 13 patients, was likely to be a point mutation affecting the catalytic activity of the enzyme. More recently, a single patient was identified[115a] with a 12-base-pair insertion in the region of the MCAD gene encoding the mitochondrial transit peptide, resulting in a virtual failure of mitochondrial uptake of the MCAD precursor. If this preliminary report is confirmed, it represents the first report of a mitochondrial leader sequence

Table 33-5 Acyl-CoA Dehydrogenase Activities in Fibroblasts and Leukocytes from Patients with MCAD Deficiency, Their Parents, and Controls Measured in an ETF-Based Assay

Subjects	*Palmityl-CoA*	*Octanoyl-CoA*	*Butyryl-CoA*
Patients	2.12 ± 0.25 (39)*	0.25 ± 0.11 (40)	0.95 ± 0.16 (39)
Parents	2.21 ± 0.27 (14)	2.01 ± 0.41 (16)	1.56 ± 0.16 (14)
Controls	2.19 ± 0.22 (142)	4.17 ± 0.37 (142)	2.20 ± 0.26 (126)

*nmol ETF reduced/min/mg protein, mean ± S.D. for the number of subjects in parentheses.

mutation in humans. These results are quite different from the extensive molecular heterogeneity demonstrated for the isovaleryl-CoA dehydrogenase deficiency in patients with isovaleric acidemia[116] and for the ETF deficiency in some patients with glutaric aciduria type II.[117]

Matsubara et al.[118,118a,118b] have cloned the cDNAs encoding rat and human MCAD and have assigned the human gene to the short arm of chromosome 1, band p31.

Pathogenesis. MCAD, a critical enzyme in mitochondrial β oxidation, is deficient in this disorder. Fasting and/or an infectious prodrome can precipitate hypoglycemia and lethargy leading to coma. The secondary metabolic consequences of this defect have not been clearly identified; however, there is substantial information available from controlled fasting studies and from the analysis of urinary metabolite excretion profiles[7,12,58,60,62,63,94,98–100] which permits speculation on the sequence of metabolic events and their potential consequences, and formulation of a rationale upon which treatment can be developed.

The primary consequence of illness associated with fasting and lipolysis in the MCAD-deficient patient is the accumulation of medium-chain length (C_6 to C_{12}) acyl-CoA intermediates within the mitochondrion. Analysis of urinary acylcarnitines suggests that octanoyl-CoA is the predominant intermediate and that very little acetyl-CoA is present. Unregulated lipolysis therefore results in extraordinary accumulation of acyl-CoA compounds at the expense of free CoASH, which does not exchange between the mitochondrial and cytosolic compartments. Thus, increased acyl-CoA production results in decreased availability of CoASH for other important mitochondrial reactions. The ratio of acyl-CoA to CoASH in the mitochondrion exerts regulatory control over pyruvate dehydrogenase[119] and α-ketoglutarate dehydrogenase.[120] When this ratio is elevated, both enzyme systems are inhibited, resulting in a reduced rate of conversion of pyruvate to acetyl-CoA; furthermore, flux through the tricarboxylic acid (TCA) cycle is reduced since citrate synthesis is compromised and flux from α-ketoglutarate to succinyl-CoA is impeded. Succinyl-CoA ligase is also inhibited by octanoate, as well as by other acyl-CoA intermediates.[121] When there is accumulation of acyl-CoA intermediates, mitochondrial β oxidation is inhibited;[13] the expected result would be fatty acid incorporation into triglycerides. In MCAD deficiency, during periods of lipolysis, it would be predicted that fat would accumulate in liver, dicarboxylic acids would be produced via microsomal ω oxidation and peroxisomal β oxidation, and acetyl-CoA production would be inadequate.

The consequences of "inadequate" acetyl-CoA have significant secondary effects on ketone body production in the liver, on flux through the TCA cycle, on regulation of fatty acid oxidation in the mitochondrion, and on the efficiency of gluconeogenesis (Fig. 33-11). The reasons for considering these in MCAD-deficient patients are: (1) there is diminished ketone body formation from long-chain and medium-chain fatty acid substrates in liver homogenates;[7] and (2) acylcarnitine excretion in the untreated patient is greatly reduced and composed mainly of medium-chain acylcarnitines, instead of the normal acetylcarnitine.[63]

Acetyl-CoA is a substrate, along with oxaloacetate, for the citrate synthase reaction. Inadequate amounts of either substrate would result in diminished citrate synthesis. Citrate may be viewed as a precursor of oxaloacetate; in light of the known inhibition of α-ketoglutarate dehydrogenase by an elevated acyl-CoA/CoASH ratio, flux through the TCA cycle can be compromised. Furthermore, there are two major ways by which acetyl-CoA can be transported from the mitochondrial to the cytosolic compartment—as citrate and as acetylcarnitine. The consequence of decreased availability of citrate for transport to the cytosol has bearing on the regulation of both fatty acid oxidation and gluconeogenesis. When citrate is in sufficient quantity, it is transported to the cytosol, where it is converted into acetyl-CoA and oxaloacetate by the citrate lyase reaction. The latter may be converted to malate or to phosphoenolpyruvate (PEP). These possibilities would have effects both on the redox state and on gluconeogenesis. Acetyl-CoA produced from citrate by the citrate lyase reaction then serves as a substrate for acetyl-CoA carboxylase. This enzyme is responsible for synthesis of malonyl-CoA, the primary regulator of CPT I. Citrate is not only the source of substrate for the acetyl-CoA carboxylase, but it is also its primary activator. Therefore, decreased acetyl-CoA in the mitochondrion reduces the amount of citrate available to both activate and provide substrate for the acetyl-CoA carboxylase. The result is a reduction in malonyl-CoA concentration, which thereby permits unregulated entry of fatty acids into the mitochondrion and, in MCAD deficiency, increased production of the medium-chain-length acyl-CoA intermediates.

A further consequence of inadequate acetyl-CoA inside the mitochondrion relates to pyruvate carboxylase. This biotin-dependent enzyme converts pyruvate to oxaloacetate and is critical for gluconeogenesis. The oxaloacetate produced by this reaction is reduced to malate, which may shuttle to the cytosolic compartment where it is reconverted to oxaloacetate. This is a substrate for the PEP carboxykinase reaction, leading to PEP and ultimately glucose. Reduction in acetyl-CoA would affect this pathway, since acetyl-CoA is the primary activator of pyruvate carboxylase. Compromise of this pathway in MCAD deficiency, although not proven, suggests an etiology for the hypoglycemia observed in this disorder.

The clinical presentation and many of the routine laboratory observations found in MCAD-deficient patients are often indistinguishable from those found in Reye syndrome. Observations by Mamunes[122] focused interest on lipolysis as a major feature of Reye syndrome, but more interesting was the reported elevation of octanoate in plasma samples from some of these children with Reye syndrome. Trauner developed an animal model involving infusion of octanoate in rabbits which produced many of the pathologic findings of Reye syndrome.[123] In 1980, Ogburn et al.[124] reported additional studies of fatty acids in patients with Reye syndrome, but failed to observe any significant elevation of octanoate in plasma. Although many studies were carried out exploring the "octanoate model" of Reye syndrome, their real applications were not realized until 1983, when MCAD deficiency was first recognized.

The encephalopathy and cerebral edema observed in MCAD deficiency may result from mechanisms similar to those in the octanoate model of Reye syndrome.[123,125] Studies carried out in the 1950s revealed that acyl compounds with three or more carbons have significant encephalopathic properties and are associated with the electroencephalographic changes often observed in "metabolic disorders."[126] The greater the chain length of the acyl-CoA, the more rapidly coma occurred. Similarly, acyl compounds of this type, e.g., propionate, octanoate, palmitate, etc., enter the central nervous system (CNS) at rates increasing with longer carbon chain length. These observations indicate the potential for

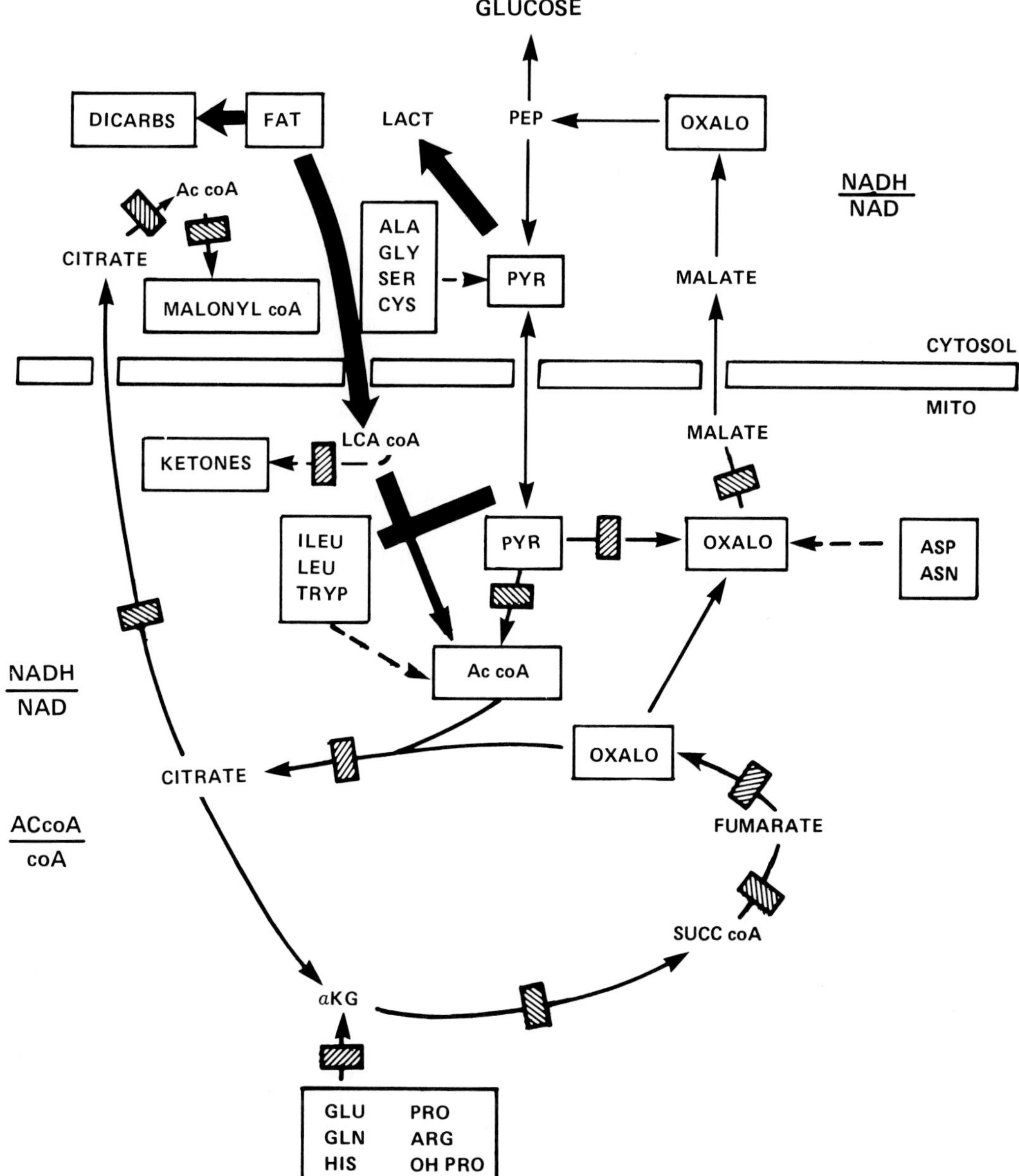

Fig. 33-11 Metabolic consequences of MCAD deficiency. Shaded blocks indicate metabolic steps which would be compromised. These include: ketone body production, citrate production, malonyl-CoA synthesis, TCA cycle activities, malate production.

rapid accumulation of fatty acids within the CNS. This accumulation may be further compromised by octanoate-induced inhibition of the choroid plexus organic anion uptake system, which is largely responsible for egress of these compounds from the CNS.[126] Octanoate is produced in increasing quantities during lipolysis in MCAD-deficient patients; it then reaches the plasma compartment and ultimately the CNS. Experimentally induced octanoic acidemia has been shown to damage neuronal mitochondria, leading to distension, separation of mitochondrial cristae, and loss of matrix integrity.[125] There is an associated depression of energy metabolism resulting in decreased availability of high energy phosphate compounds.[127] The final result in the seriously ill MCAD-deficient patient may be cerebral edema. It should be noted in this regard that, while hypoglycemia is a very common finding in MCAD deficiency, coma in these patients is not entirely due to low blood glucose levels; it is evident from fasting studies[7] that these patients can become ill and can lose consciousness while still normoglycemic. It is likely that these symptoms represent a toxic effect of the accumulated fatty acids or their metabolites.

Management and Treatment. As noted elsewhere, there is extensive phenotypic heterogeneity associated with MCAD deficiency. The first patients identified with the disease had severe, recurrent episodes of illness resembling Reye syndrome which were provoked by fasting. Common symptoms included vomiting and lethargy, which progressed rapidly to coma in the most severe cases. Although hypoglycemia was often present and glucose administration ameliorated the clinical picture in many instances, it has been noted repeatedly that glucose levels in plasma can be normal or only moderately reduced when these patients are ill.[7,12] This suggests that toxic fatty acid intermediates themselves can evoke clinical symptoms.

Because of the nature of this particular metabolic defect, situated in the middle of a pathway that, at least in liver, is generally only activated under conditions of fasting stress (as in infection), the management of MCAD-deficient patients includes the avoidance of fasting, even though some patients tolerate fasting well. Once it has been recognized that the patient has a disorder of fatty acid oxidation, the frequency of further episodes may be reduced by ensuring regular and adequate caloric intake with a diet moderately high in carbohydrate.

It is evident from Case 6 above that some patients with MCAD deficiency have been able to withstand repeated fasting insults; as long as these episodes are appropriately treated with intravenous glucose administration, the long-term outlook for some patients is good.[77] Case 6, in particular, has no apparent residua from her multiple episodes; she is reported to be healthy, active, and mentally alert and to have no skeletal muscle weakness. There do appear to be considerable differences, however, among patients in their ability to tolerate fasting; Case 6 became ill if she forgot to eat breakfast, while B-2, the asymptomatic brother of patient B-1,[7] withstood a 36-h controlled fast without any signs of clinical illness. It is important, therefore, to tailor recommendations about time between meals to particular children. As noted below, the first episode of illness in children with MCAD deficiency generally does not occur before 5 months of age. It is at about that time that many children are weaned from a regular feeding schedule around the clock to a schedule which permits an overnight fast.

The role of L-carnitine supplementation in the management of patients with MCAD deficiency is analogous to the use of glycine and L-carnitine supplementation in isovaleric acidemia.[61] The primary defect in both disorders is enzymatic. Hence, supplementation with carnitine, as with glycine in isovaleric acidemia, will not correct the enzyme abnormality and therefore would not be expected to ameliorate the failure of fasting ketogenesis. On the other hand, carnitine represents a useful conjugation pathway for the removal of potentially toxic intermediates which accumulate under conditions of fasting stress in patients with MCAD deficiency. Acyl-CoA intermediates are known to inhibit other metabolic pathways and to alter the intramitochondrial acyl-CoA/CoASH ratio. This ratio can be influenced by supplementing with L-carnitine in the acute setting, as suggested by the enhanced excretion of medium-chain-length acylcarnitines following supplementation. This allows removal of octanoate from tissues while restoring CoASH levels, without increasing plasma octanoate levels. Long-term carnitine supplementation of patients with MCAD deficiency is currently under evaluation, in association with dietary fat reduction and avoidance of fasting. Chronic supplementation with carnitine in several patients with MCAD deficiency has been associated with tolerating chickenpox without hospitalization. Chronic therapy (25 mg/kg four times daily) is probably useful in preventing deterioration in the face of infection, but its role during periods of health is likely to be less important. Reconsideration of the cascade of metabolic events in this disorder would indicate the utility of maintaining carnitine levels to deal with sudden illness.

Counseling, Family Screening, and Prenatal Diagnosis. MCAD deficiency has emerged as a common cause of clinical disease resembling Reye syndrome, especially in the first 2 years of life,[125] and it has been implicated in cases of sudden infant death syndrome,[128] but accurate estimates of its frequency in the population have not been made. Its approximate frequency in the United Kingdom, based upon several indirect lines of evidence, is between 1 in 10,000 and 1 in 25,000 (M.J. Bennett, personal communication), making MCAD deficiency a common hereditary metabolic disorder, with heterozygotes present in the population at an estimated frequency of perhaps 1 to 2 percent.

The case descriptions above suggest that there is significant phenotypic heterogeneity in MCAD deficiency, even within the same family. The causes of this heterogeneity are unknown. It is possible, given the array of potentially available alternative pathways for the detoxification of accumulated organic acid intermediates, that the efficiency of these pathways may be of great importance in modulating the effect of these intermediates; there is likely to be considerable interindividual variation in the activity of these pathways. The children may have only one episode of illness or multiple recurrences or in some cases appear to be asymptomatic. There is little doubt that the first episode can be devastating, resulting in sudden death. Families with MCAD deficiency have been studied in which there are affected, but asymptomatic, siblings.[63,77,89] In some cases (Case 3), the "asymptomatic" siblings subsequently became symptomatic. Review of the currently available literature and experiences of major laboratories testing for MCAD deficiency revealed that of 43 families identified with this disorder, one-third had one or more unexplained sibling deaths. In a few of these, the diagnosis of MCAD deficiency was made post mortem.[83,89,92] Of the 65 children in these 43 families, there were 22 deaths. Figure 33-12 illustrates the age of onset and mortality associated with initial occurrence of symptoms in this group of 65 children. The earliest onset of symptoms was at 1 week of age. The greatest frequency of presentation occurs between 5 and 24 months of age. There is only one report of first symptoms at age 7 years. Furthermore, there appears to be less recurrent illness after 4 years. Similarly, symptoms requiring repeated hospitalization in the second decade are rare. Since the disorder has only recently been defined, the long-term course is not yet clear, and the effects of pregnancy on affected females are yet to be determined.

The mortality rate is significant. In the first year of life, 4 of 30 children (13 percent) died with their first episode. After 12 months of age, 15 of 35 children (43 percent) died with their first episode. Significantly, 3 children first identified with MCAD deficiency at 2, 5, and 6 months of age died with a recurrence between 26 and 30 months of age. There appears to be a period between 15 and 26 months of age during which mortality is extremely high (59 percent).

These data suggest that: (1) children with MCAD deficiency are at risk for death with either the initial or later illness; (2) "asymptomatic" siblings may have symptoms subsequently; and (3) the risk of death is greatest between 15 and 26 months of age.

Asymptomatic siblings of patients with MCAD deficiency can be evaluated in two ways. Urinary acylcarnitines can be examined following oral administration of a test dose of L-carnitine (100 mg/kg); this has the advantage of being noninvasive, as the analysis can be done directly in urine, but it will not discriminate between heterozygotes and normals. Patients with MCAD deficiency excrete octanoylcarnitine, especially following an oral carnitine load. Roe et al.[63] used this strategy to make the diagnosis of MCAD deficiency in an asymptomatic 8-week-old sibling of two children who had died, one with sudden unexplained death at 18 months and the other at 23 months of a Reye-like syndrome. Similarly, they identified a 4-week-old male infant whose sister died suddenly at age 21 months. This girl was shown also to have MCAD deficiency by the identification of octanoylcarnitine in postmortem liver.[92] Enzyme activity can be measured in leukocytes or fibroblasts; this has the advantage that heterozygous individuals

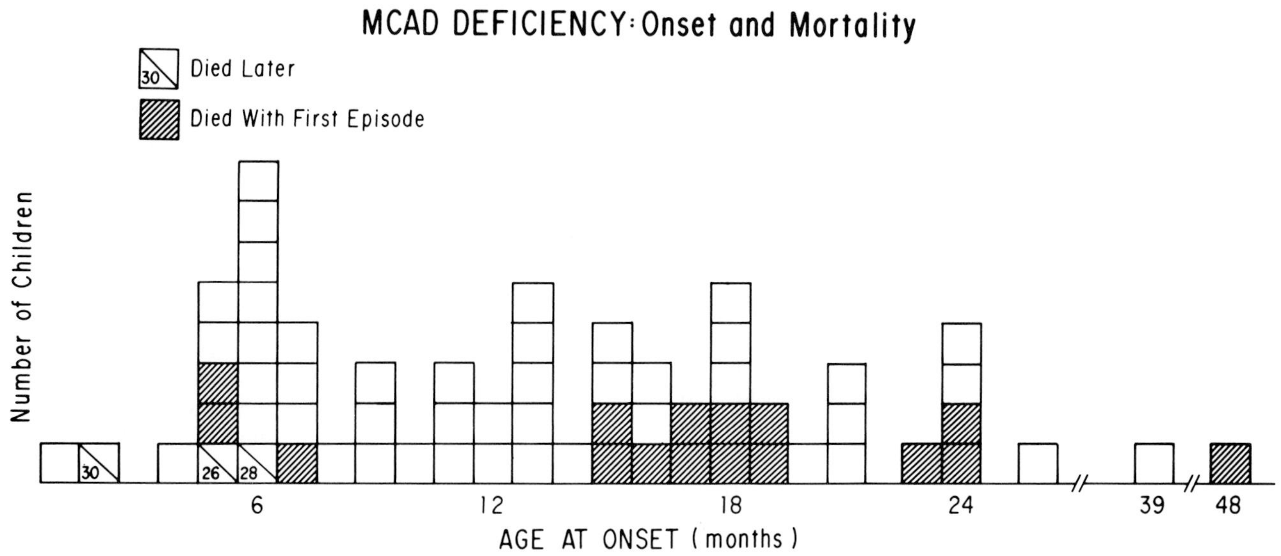

MCAD DEFICIENCY: Onset and Mortality

Died Later

Died With First Episode

Number of Children

AGE AT ONSET (months)

Fig. 33-12 Age at onset and incidence of mortality among 65 children with MCAD deficiency in 43 families. Each square represents one patient. Open symbol = survived episode. Open symbol with number = survived first episode but died during later episode at age shown (in months). Shaded symbol = died during first episode.

can be distinguished from controls as well as from those with MCAD deficiency. Among nine siblings of four MCAD-deficient patients, Coates et al. (Ref. 77; unpublished observations) identified two with MCAD deficiency, three with heterozygote levels of enzyme activity, and four with control levels.

Given that the frequency of heterozygotes may approach 1 percent and that the disease carries the potential for sudden death, attention should also be given to the screening of siblings of the parents, and extending the screening to unrelated spouses of those siblings if the latter are found to be heterozygotes.

Bennett et al.[93] reported the prenatal diagnosis of MCAD deficiency in the third pregnancy of a woman whose first child had died unexpectedly at 18 months of age; postmortem studies of this infant's liver had revealed MCAD deficiency.[83] MCAD activity, measured using octanoyl-CoA as substrate in an ETF-based assay, was absent from amniotic fluid cells obtained at 15 weeks of gestation. The family elected to continue the pregnancy, and the diagnosis was confirmed in cultured fibroblasts obtained shortly after birth. In another family, Bennett et al.[129] made the prenatal diagnosis of MCAD deficiency by measuring $^{14}CO_2$ production from [1-^{14}C]octanoic acid in cultured amniotic fluid cells. Thus, prenatal diagnosis of this disorder is possible, and should be considered as an option for the early detection of an affected fetus; however, it is likely that prenatal diagnosis will rarely be sought for the purpose of pregnancy termination, since disease associated with this defect is often preventable by appropriate management and intervention during episodes of fasting stress. On the other hand, there may well be families in which parents feel unable to cope with a second affected child. At the very least, prenatal diagnosis offers the earliest possible detection of an affected child, so that appropriate treatment strategies can be instituted.

LCAD Deficiency

Clinical Presentations. Six patients have been identified with LCAD deficiency since the defect was described in three infants in 1985.[8] At that time, the authors noted that one of two siblings originally reported by Naylor[130] had the same enzyme defect. Since that time, another patient (W.F. Schwenk, M.W. Haymond, and D.E. Hale, personal communication) and the sibling of Naylor's patient (Ref. 131; D.E. Hale and P.M. Coates, unpublished observations) have been documented to have LCAD deficiency by specific enzyme assay. This disorder shares some features with MCAD deficiency, but patients with LCAD deficiency have, in addition, unique findings.[132] The two cases presented here point out the marked clinical differences observed among the few patients described.

Case 1 A white male (patient R-1 in Ref. 8) was born by cesarian section to a 39-year-old mother and her 41-year-old husband, her third cousin. At 36 h of age, he had a cardiorespiratory arrest from which he was resuscitated. He gained weight poorly, had frequent episodes of emesis, and at 6 weeks of age was demonstrated to have grade III gastroesophageal reflux. At 10 weeks, he developed a viral illness with diarrhea and lethargy, for which he was placed on a clear liquid diet. He became obtunded over the next 36 h. Upon his admission to hospital, examination revealed a hypotonic, unresponsive infant with hepatomegaly, hypoglycemia (25 mg/dl), and no ketones in urine. Blood ammonia was 180 μM, bicarbonate was 18 meq/liter, and liver function tests were normal. He had a second cardiorespiratory arrest requiring resuscitation and ventilation. A chest x-ray and echocardiogram showed hypertrophic cardiomyopathy. A liver biopsy showed extensive macrovesicular fat infiltration. Plasma carnitine was 10 μM, all of this carnitine was esterified. Liver carnitine was 110 nmol per gram wet weight, compared to normals of 730 to 1800 nmol per gram wet weight. He was placed on a high carbohydrate, low fat diet supplemented with L-carnitine (100 mg/kg/day), with gradual improvement over the next several months. By the age of 12 months, cardiac hypertrophy resolved. He has continued to have episodes of illness two to four times per year. At 5 years of age, he is microcephalic, moderately hypotonic, and delayed in gross motor, social, and verbal development.

Case 2 A 22-year-old white female (patient HC in Refs. 8,130) had several unexplained episodes of lethargy and coma associated with fasting, hypoglycemia, and dicarboxylic aciduria but without ketonuria during the first few years of life. The eldest of six siblings, she was born to healthy unrelated parents. Pregnancy, delivery, and early development were unremarkable. At 18 months of age, she began to experience periods of lethargy and unresponsiveness; these occurred as frequently as once a month, almost invariably precipitated by an upper respiratory infection. During a hospitalization at 24 months for such an episode, hepatomegaly was noted, and a liver biopsy showed marked fatty infiltration, moderate lymphocytic infiltration, and perilobular fibrosis. At age 5 years, she was hospitalized after an episode during which she became lethargic, then comatose and unresponsive. Her blood glucose was 20 mg/dl, blood ammonia was 62 μM, blood urea nitrogen was 31 mg/dl, total CO_2 was 14.8 mM, pH was 7.37, and her urine was negative for ketones. She received IV glucose, which prompted her recovery. Glucose infusion was discontinued; the next morning she again became lethargic, although her blood glucose was 69 mg/dl. On a ketogenic diet, she became hypoglycemic and vomited at 8 h; no ketones were found in her urine. Electroencephalogram was normal. Over the next several years, she had periodic episodes of hypoglycemia and lethargy which were aggravated by a low carbohydrate diet.

Further investigation was prompted by recurrent episodes of fatigue and muscle soreness, beginning in the second decade. On admission at 20 years of age, at a time when she was clinically well, blood glucose and electrolytes were normal. She had dicarboxylic aciduria (C_6, C_8, and C_{10} acids, both saturated and unsaturated). Her plasma total carnitine level was 10.6 μM, of which 4.4 was free carnitine, 0.4 was short-chain acylcarnitine, and 5.8 was long-chain acylcarnitine. Urinary carnitine excretion (μmol/kg/24 h) was 1.2 total, 0.1 free, and 1.1 acyl, compared to controls of 5.4, 3.0, and 2.4, respectively. The major species excreted was acetylcarnitine. Her serum creatine phosphokinase (CPK) was 374 IU/liter, compared to controls of $<$130 IU/liter. Electrocardiogram and chest x-ray were normal. Echocardiography was normal with no evidence of left ventricular dysfunction. Radionuclide angiogram showed a normal ejection fraction, with normal wall motion at rest or upon exercise. Since that time, she has experienced further episodes of fatigue and muscle soreness, during which CPK levels ranged from 6400 to 32,200 IU/liter; only the highest level was associated with frank myoglobinuria. These episodes appeared to follow either emotional stress or periods of decreased dietary intake. Although none of these episodes was associated with obvious hypoglycemia, treatment with 10% IV glucose resulted in a reduction of her CPK level, resolution of her dicarboxylic aciduria, and cessation of her muscle discomfort.

The age at first episode was 2.5 to 6 months in five of the patients and 18 months in patient HC; with the exception of HC, this is earlier than is commonly seen in MCAD deficiency. Reye syndrome was not considered in any of these patients, although a preceding viral illness leading to lethargy and coma associated with hepatomegaly, hyperammonemia, and elevated liver enzymes has been frequently demonstrated in these patients.[8,90,130,132] All but one have had multiple episodes.

In three of the six patients (A-1, J-1, R-1 in Ref. 8) the clinical similarities to MCAD deficiency include: recurrent episodes of coma, vomiting, and hypoglycemia brought on by fasting. In these patients, by contrast with the typical MCAD-deficient child, the illness was more severe, had earlier onset, and was associated with a striking involvement of cardiac and skeletal muscle. One patient has died, and the other two have significant developmental delay associated with muscle weakness and hypotonia.

In the other three patients (Refs. 8,130; M.W. Haymond, personal communication; authors' unpublished observations), the clinical course during the first few years of life was reminiscent of MCAD deficiency, with one or more episodes of vomiting and hypoglycemia. By contrast to the other three patients, however, these three patients are alive; two of them are in their twenties, and one is 6 years of age; none have had evidence of cardiomyopathy. One of these patients (HC) has begun to experience attacks of muscle pain and myoglobinuria reminiscent of CPT deficiency (see Chap. 117), but her sister (JC) has had no clinical disease referrable to her metabolic abnormality since about 4 years of age. The third patient (M.W. Haymond, personal communication) has had numerous episodes of viral illness associated with elevated CPK levels, muscle cramps, and myoglobinuria. She has never become hypoglycemic during these epidoses; between episodes, she is well and her CPK level is in the normal range.

Initial Laboratory Findings. Upon fasting or when clinically ill, these patients are hypoglycemic, hypoketotic, and acidotic, and they have abnormal liver function tests and hyperuricemia. In two of these patients, serum CPK was elevated during periods of fasting stress. The urinary organic acid profile reveals reduced or absent ketones and evidence of dicarboxylic aciduria. In addition to the C_6 to C_{10} dicarboxylic aciduria typical of MCAD-deficient patients, there was evidence for the excretion of longer-chain C_{12} and C_{14} dicarboxylic acids in two patients.[130] Suberylglycine, phenylpropionylglycine, and hexanoylglycine excretion have not been observed in LCAD deficiency.[8,98a]

Carnitine Status. As in MCAD deficiency, patients with LCAD deficiency have had a secondary carnitine deficiency; muscle, liver, and plasma carnitine levels in patient R-1 were all low,[8] and plasma carnitine levels in other patients have been low. Urinary carnitine excretion is low when these patients are ill; short-chain acylcarnitines, chiefly acetylcarnitine, are the major excretion products.[60] This latter finding is in contrast to the urinary carnitine ester profiles of patients with other defects in mitochondrial metabolism, in which the predominant acylcarnitine corresponds to the acyl-CoA derivative that accumulates proximal to the metabolic block (Table 33-1). Long-chain acylcarnitines are not readily excreted by the kidney.

Pathologic Findings. Hepatic light microscopic alterations[90] include: panlobular steatosis, with both macrovesicular and microvesicular droplets; portal fibrosis; absence of necrosis or cholestasis. Liver from one patient had electron microscopic findings similar to those seen in MCAD deficiency, namely mitochondrial matrix density with widening of the intracristal space.

Cardiac enlargement and ECG evidence of hypertrophic cardiomyopathy have been documented in three cases.[8] In two of them who have survived to 5 years of age, there has been gradual resolution of the cardiac hypertrophy. Both of these patients, however, remain hypotonic and developmentally delayed.

Diagnosis of LCAD Deficiency. The enzyme defect has been demonstrated in cultured fibroblasts from six patients and in leukocytes from two of them (Table 33-6). Using an ETF-based assay with palmityl-CoA as substrate, cells from the patients had less than 8 percent of control levels of LCAD activity (range, 5 to 10 percent). In spite of the marked clinical heterogeneity in this small group of patients, there were no apparent differences among them in residual LCAD activity. Dehydrogenase activities towards octanoyl-CoA and butyryl-CoA in cells from these patients have been essentially normal; the modest, but significant, 10 percent reduction in octanoyl-

Table 33-6 Acyl-CoA Dehydrogenase Activities in Cultured Fibroblasts from Patients with LCAD Deficiency, Their Parents, and Controls Measured in an ETF-Based Assay

Subjects	*Palmityl-CoA*	*Octanoyl-CoA*	*Butyryl-CoA*
Patients	0.18 ± 0.04 (6)*	3.56 ± 0.29 (6)	2.08 ± 0.30 (6)
Parents	1.08 ± 0.27 (8)	N.T.†	N.T.
Controls	2.17 ± 0.20 (65)	4.11 ± 0.38 (65)	2.15 ± 0.22 (61)

*nmol ETF reduced/min/mg protein, mean ± S.D. for the number of subjects in parentheses.
†N.T. = not tested.

CoA dehydrogenation in LCAD-deficient cells suggests that there is little activity of LCAD toward substrates of medium-chain length, at least under the conditions of assay. It should be noted that the enzyme defect could be detected in liver of one patient,[8] but the assay of LCAD in liver should be done at low protein concentrations, since high concentrations obscure the LCAD defect by as-yet unknown mechanisms (D.E. Hale, personal communication).

Parents' fibroblasts and leukocytes had approximately 50 percent of control LCAD activity (Table 33-6), consistent with heterozygosity for an autosomal trait. Four asymptomatic siblings of two of these patients have been screened: one had normal LCAD activity, and three had activities within the heterozygote range.

Defective oxidation of ^{14}C-labeled fatty acids has been demonstrated in fibroblasts from several of these patients.[8] Table 33-3 demonstrates that LCAD-deficient cells oxidize [^{14}C(U)]palmitic acid at roughly 20 percent of control rates. This is in contrast to the oxidation of this substrate at approximately 50 percent of control rates that is seen in cells from MCAD-deficient patients. The oxidation of [1-^{14}C]palmitic acid is impaired, although the residual oxidative activity toward this substrate is higher than would be expected based upon the location of the metabolic block; this may reflect the contribution of other routes of oxidative degradation (e.g., peroxisomal) to the metabolism of this fatty acid. Octanoic acid and butyric acid oxidation are within normal limits, reflecting the fact that LCAD has no substantial activity toward medium-chain or short-chain fatty acids.

Rhead and colleagues[107,131] also demonstrated impaired oxidation in fibroblasts from patients with LCAD deficiency using [9,10(n)-^{3}H]palmitate as substrate. They made the further observation that cells from the patient with a more severe presentation (R-1 in Ref. 8) had substantially increased ability to oxidize this substrate than did cells from the two patients with a milder presentation (HC and JC in Ref. 130), in spite of the fact that cells from all three patients had virtually the same residual LCAD activity (<10 percent).

Biochemical and Molecular Aspects. Ikeda et al.[27] have purified LCAD from rat liver mitochondria, where its native molecular weight was estimated to be 180,000 by gel filtration. Like MCAD, LCAD is a homotetramer, with a subunit molecular weight of 45,000; each subunit contains 1 molecule of FAD. Its purification from human sources has not been reported, and there are as yet no data regarding the molecular aspects of LCAD deficiency.

Pathogenesis. To date, only a few patients with LCAD deficiency have been described; hence, little information is available about the pathogenesis of disease associated with this enzyme defect. One can speculate that by analogy with the MCAD defect, a failure of fatty acid oxidation at this step would have far-reaching effects on other metabolic pathways, including impaired energy production during periods of fasting stress, and toxic effects of the long-chain acyl-CoA intermediates which accumulate within mitochondria. The adenine nucleotide translocase, for example, an important site for regulation of oxidative phosphorylation, is sensitive to inhibition by long-chain acyl-CoA esters.[133] Three pieces of information point directly to the potential role of peroxisomal β oxidation and microsomal ω oxidation in disposing of accumulated acyl-CoA intermediates in LCAD deficiency. First, [1-^{14}C]palmitic acid oxidation is only reduced by about 50 percent in fibroblasts from LCAD-deficient patients, suggesting that the first cycle of β oxidation, while impaired, is not severely affected. Second, the only prominent acylcarnitine species excreted in urine of these patients is acetylcarnitine. Third, there is a significant medium-chain dicarboxylic aciduria.

Treatment and Counseling. As is the case with MCAD deficiency, this disorder should be regarded as potentially fatal. There are no obvious clues to the diagnosis of LCAD deficiency, except those which point to a defect in fatty acid oxidation: inappropriately low ketosis in the face of hypoglycemia; dicarboxylic aciduria; low plasma carnitine levels with a high proportion of long-chain acylcarnitines. Further evidence for a defect in long-chain fatty acid oxidation might come from the demonstration of severe skeletal muscle weakness and cardiac enlargement. As noted below, however (see "Other Defects in Fatty Acid Oxidation"), these findings may be observed in other patients who do not have LCAD deficiency. Management should be aimed at avoiding fasting, maintaining a high carbohydrate intake, frequent feeding, and treating episodes of illness with IV glucose. The role of carnitine supplementation in this disorder has not been assessed systematically. It is possible that MCT feeding might provide a route for administering calories, since medium-chain fatty acids enter the β-oxidation spiral below the metabolic block. Obviously, this should be attempted only after ruling out a defect of medium-chain fatty acid oxidation such as MCAD deficiency.

Currently, the only way to make the diagnosis of LCAD deficiency is to measure acyl-CoA dehydrogenase activities in fibroblasts or leukocytes[8] or, possibly, to perform the complementation analysis using [9,10(n)-^{3}H]palmitic acid.[107] Given that it is a life-threatening illness, diagnosis should be made as early as possible, so that appropriate modifications of formula and feeding schedule can be made. Asymptomatic siblings can be tested by measurement of LCAD activity in fibroblasts and leukocytes.

Given that acyl-CoA dehydrogenase activities can be readily measured in cultured amniotic fluid cells,[93] it should be possible to carry out the prenatal diagnosis of LCAD deficiency. This has not yet been attempted. There are as yet no data on the frequency of LCAD deficiency.

SCAD Deficiency

Clinical Presentations. SCAD deficiency has been identified in only a few patients, and the clinical and laboratory findings are variable, as demonstrated in the following three case presentations.

Case 1 A female infant (neonate II in Ref. 10) was born to unrelated parents. She had five normal male sibs. After a normal delivery, she began cow's milk formula on day 2. On day 3, she fed poorly, began to vomit, and became lethargic and hypertonic. Blood glucose was 38 mg/dl, she was acidotic (pH 7.28) and hyperammonemic (399 μM), while other laboratory values were essentially normal. After 12 h on IV glucose, her SGOT was 211 IU/liter, SGPT was 77 IU/liter, and ammonia was 298 μM. In spite of continuing improvement in blood glucose, ammonia, and pH, she became progressively more lethargic, unresponsive, and hypotonic, and had worsening respiratory effort. Organic acid analysis showed lactic acidosis, ketosis, and increased butyrate, ethylmalonate, and adipate excretion. On day 5, she had fixed, dilated pupils, no spontaneous movement, and a brain scan showed little blood flow. She died on day 6. Postmortem examination revealed cerebral edema, hepatosplenomegaly with fatty changes, cholestasis, and focal hepatocellular necrosis.

Case 2 Coates et al.[11] described a female infant of unrelated parents whose early postnatal life was complicated by poor feeding and frequent emesis. During the first year of life, she exhibited poor weight gain, developmental delay, progressive skeletal muscle weakness, hypotonia, and microcephaly. Skeletal muscle biopsy was unremarkable, except for minor generalized lipid accumulation in type I fibers. She never had episodes of hypoglycemia, rarely had organic aciduria, had low-normal plasma carnitine levels, but had 50 percent of control levels of muscle carnitine, 75 percent of which was esterified. She responded poorly to a fat-restricted diet supplemented with L-carnitine. Developmental testing at 21 months revealed significant motor, cognitive, developmental, and language delay. Increasing difficulty with poor oral intake necessitated insertion of a gastrostomy tube at 23 months. At 32 months, she showed significant weight gain and overall improvement in strength.

Case 3 A 46-year-old woman[9] with no previous neuromuscular disorders presented with persistent weakness in the left arm and in both legs, which was exacerbated by mild exertion. Neurologic examination revealed a proximal myopathy, which was confirmed by electromyography. Serum creatine kinase was normal. There was excess neutral lipid in type I fibers of skeletal muscle, but no other abnormalities were detected. Muscle carnitine levels were low (25 percent of control) with an increased proportion of acylcarnitine to free carnitine. Plasma carnitine levels were low-normal. The major urinary metabolite was ethylmalonate; fasting was not associated with hypoglycemia, and blood ketone body levels were elevated. Her muscle weakness did not respond to treatment with either carnitine or prednisolone.

Pathologic Findings. In Case 3, pathologic findings were limited to muscle and included lipid vacuolization, especially in type I fibers.[9] In Case 2, in spite of the fact that the patient's clinical manifestations were largely muscular, there was only minor lipid accumulation in muscle;[11] her liver showed extensive ultrastructural evidence of lipid droplets, both micro- and macrovesicular in nature, and mitochondrial changes reminiscent of those seen in MCAD deficiency, namely, crystalloids and increased matrix density (P.M. Coates and S.D. Douglas, unpublished observations). Case 1 had fatty changes in her liver at autopsy.

Enzymatic Diagnosis. Cultured skin fibroblasts from these patients were assayed for acyl-CoA dehydrogenase activities (Table 33-7). With butyryl-CoA as substrate, cells from Cases 1 and 2, and another patient described by Amendt et al. (neonate I in Ref. 10) had 50 percent of control levels of enzyme activity, all of which was inhibited by incubation of the cells with anti-MCAD antibody. Activity toward palmityl-CoA was normal in cells from all three patients. The patients of Cases 1 and 2 had normal activities toward octanoyl-CoA as substrate. These data demonstrated that they had a specific SCAD deficiency and provided further evidence for the overlapping substrate specificity of MCAD. Cultured fibroblasts from the parents of Case 2 had intermediate levels of SCAD, consistent with their being heterozygous for an autosomal trait. Studies of cells from members of the other families were not performed.

Skeletal muscle SCAD activity in Case 3, measured with butyryl-CoA as substrate,[9] was 25 percent of control levels; acyl-CoA dehydrogenase activities toward longer-chain substrates (octanoyl-, decanoyl-, dodecanoyl- and palmityl-CoA) were well within normal limits. SCAD activity in this patient's fibroblasts was normal, however, when measured in an ETF-based assay by Coates et al.[11] and in a tritium-release assay by Amendt et al.[10] While careful study of this enzyme in other tissues from the patient of Case 3 could not be performed, the data suggested that this patient had a SCAD deficiency isolated to muscle, although a variant form of a multiple acyl-CoA dehydrogenation defect has not been ruled out completely.

Biochemical and Molecular Aspects. Finocchiaro et al.[18] have purified SCAD from human liver. Its native molecular weight was estimated to be 168,000 by gel filtration. Like MCAD, SCAD is a homotetramer, with a subunit molecular weight of 41,000; each subunit contains 1 molecule of FAD. Ozasa et al.[134] reported the molecular cloning and nucleotide sequence of cDNA encoding rat liver SCAD. The human gene has been assigned to chromosome 12, region q22-qter.[134a]

Pathogenesis. The pathogenesis of disease associated with SCAD deficiency presents some puzzling aspects. There is not as yet a common thread among the patients who have been described with this defect. The patient of Case 3 described by Turnbull et al.[9] and another patient with similar findings[135] appear to have an isolated muscle SCAD deficiency, while the other three patients[10,11] have an enzyme defect which is expressed in fibroblasts. Because of its location in the pathway of β oxidation, it seems unlikely that a defect in SCAD would

Table 33-7 Acyl-CoA Dehydrogenase Activities in Cultured Fibroblasts from a Patient with SCAD Deficiency (Case 2), Her Parents, and Controls Measured in an ETF-Based Assay

			Butyryl-CoA			
Subjects	*Palmityl-CoA*	*Octanoyl-CoA*	*Alone*	*+IgG*	*+anti-MCAD*	*+anti-SCAD*
Patient	2.35*	4.01	1.09	0.78‡	0.08	0.72
Parents	N.T.†	4.09;4.37	1.61;1.57	N.T.	N.T.	N.T.
Controls	2.17 ± 0.20 (65)	4.11 ± 0.38 (65)	2.17 ± 0.22 (61)	1.52	0.69	0.69

*nmol ETF reduced/min/mg protein, mean ± S.D. for the number of subjects in parentheses.
†N.T. = not tested.
‡Enzyme activity decays with time at room temperature; hence, a control experiment was run, incubating cells with nonimmune IgG.

directly affect energy production from fatty acid oxidation, since at least three-quarters of a long-chain fatty acid would have been degraded before it reached this step. This is supported by the finding that under conditions of fasting stress, the patients described were capable of a ketogenic response. The effect of this metabolic block, however, appears to be profound, although it does not affect all patients similarly. Whether this reflects disruption of the normal acyl-CoA:CoASH ratio or whether butyrate can accumulate to toxic levels in the face of this block remains to be determined.

Counseling. Currently, the only way to make the diagnosis of SCAD deficiency is to measure acyl-CoA dehydrogenases directly in muscle or in fibroblasts in the presence of an antibody which inhibits the activity of MCAD toward the short-chain substrate, butyryl-CoA. Limited data indicate that heterozygotes for SCAD deficiency can be detected; hence, testing of family members should be possible. Likewise, prenatal diagnosis of SCAD deficiency is theoretically possible, but it has not yet been attempted.

OTHER DEFECTS IN FATTY ACID OXIDATION

Defects of other enzymes have been identified which have a considerable impact on flux through the β-oxidation pathway. CPT deficiency impairs the entry of long-chain acyl-CoA compounds into mitochondria[2,136,137] and is more fully described in Chap. 117. Abnormalities in the structure and function of ETF and of ETF dehydrogenase have been associated with a spectrum of disorders (multiple acyl-CoA dehydrogenation defects, ethylmalonic-adipic aciduria, glutaric aciduria type II) in which the dehydrogenation of numerous substrates (fatty acyl-CoA, isovaleryl-CoA, isobutyryl-CoA, 2-methylbranched chain acyl-CoA, glutaryl-CoA, and sarcosine) is impaired,[117,138–141] as detailed in Chap. 32. Deficiency of the HMG-CoA lyase affects ketone body formation from acetyl-CoA and has been associated with a Reye syndrome–like disease,[142,143] which in some respects resembles MCAD deficiency.[12] It is more fully described in Chap. 28. Acetoacetyl-CoA thiolase deficiency[144–146] has been demonstrated in several patients with metabolic acidosis and significant ketosis, occasionally associated with hypoglycemia. As noted earlier, patients with primary defects in carnitine transport can present with clinical and biochemical evidence of impaired β-oxidation.[81a]

Unexplained Defects in Fatty Acid Oxidation

Within the last few years, patients have been reported who have many clinical and laboratory features consistent with a defect in fatty acid oxidation who have been shown not to have an acyl-CoA dehydrogenase deficiency. Given the complexity of the β-oxidation spiral (Fig. 33-3), the fact that the other enzymes in the pathway—enoyl-CoA hydratases, 3-hydroxyacyl-CoA dehydrogenases, and 3-ketoacyl-CoA thiolases—have been proven or suggested to exist in multiple forms with different chain length specificity, and the fact that the complete oxidation of unsaturated fatty acids requires additional enzyme-mediated steps, it would not be surprising to find defects elsewhere in fatty acid oxidation.

Bennett et al.[147] reported a patient with a defect in fibroblast short-chain fatty acid oxidation whose clinical and laboratory findings were remarkably like those described for patients with SCAD deficiency described by Amendt et al.,[10] but her fibroblasts had normal SCAD activity.[11]

Patients have been described with many of the features of LCAD deficiency, including fasting intolerance, dicarboxylic aciduria, and muscle weakness, but who excrete hydroxydicarboxylic and hydroxymonocarboxylic acids in their urine (Refs. 148–151; authors' unpublished observations). The specific location of the hydroxyl group, reported to be in the 3-position of long-chain fatty acids in these patients, may well be an important clue to the site of their enzyme defect. While the excretion of long-chain and medium-chain hydroxydicarboxylic acids may occur in a number of disorders, including diabetic ketoacidosis[152] and Werdnig-Hoffmann disease,[153] the presence of these compounds should raise the possibility of a defect in fatty acid oxidation, either primary or secondary, at the level of 3-hydroxyacyl-CoA dehydrogenase.

While the major part of this chapter has focused on defects of the acyl-CoA dehydrogenases, and especially MCAD, there is emerging evidence available to warrant the further investigation of possibly inherited defects in the many other enzymes of saturated and unsaturated fatty acid oxidation in human beings. The availability of techniques for the identification of fatty acid metabolites in urine and in plasma coupled with the careful study of the enzymes of β oxidation should lead to exciting new information about this metabolic pathway.

REFERENCES

1. ENGEL AG, ANGELINI C: Carnitine deficiency of human skeletal muscle with associated lipid storage myopathy: A new syndrome. *Science* 179:899, 1973.
2. DIMAURO S, DIMAURO PMM: Muscle carnitine palmityltransferase deficiency and myoglobinuria. *Science* 182:929, 1973.
3. KARPATI G, CARPENTER S, ENGEL AG, WATTERS G, ALLEN J, ROTHMAN S, KLASSEN G, MAMER OA: The syndrome of systemic carnitine deficiency: Clinical, morphologic, biochemical, and pathophysiologic features. *Neurology* 25:16, 1975.
4. KOLVRAA S, GREGERSEN N, CHRISTENSEN E, HOBOLTH N: In vitro fibroblast studies in a patient with C_6-C_{10}-dicarboxylic aciduria: Evidence for a defect in general acyl-CoA dehydrogenase. *Clin Chim Acta* 126:53, 1982.
5. DIVRY P, DAVID M, GREGERSEN N, KOLVRAA S, CHRISTENSEN E, COLLET JP, DELLAMONICA C, COTTE J: Dicarboxylic aciduria due to medium chain acyl CoA dehydrogenase defect. A cause of hypoglycemia in childhood. *Acta Paediatr Scand* 72:943, 1983.
6. RHEAD WJ, AMENDT BA, FRITCHMAN KS, FELTS SJ: Dicarboxylic aciduria: Deficient [1-^{14}C] octanoate oxidation and medium-chain acyl-CoA dehydrogenase in fibroblasts. *Science* 221:73, 1983.
7. STANLEY CA, HALE DE, COATES PM, HALL CL, CORKEY BE, YANG W, KELLEY RI, GONZALES EL, WILLIAMSON JR, BAKER L: Medium-chain acyl-CoA dehydrogenase deficiency in children with non-ketotic hypoglycemia and low carnitine levels. *Pediatr Res* 17:877, 1983.
8. HALE DE, BATSHAW ML, COATES PM, FRERMAN FE, GOODMAN SI, SINGH I, STANLEY CA: Long-chain acyl coenzyme A dehydrogenase deficiency: An inherited cause of nonketotic hypoglycemia. *Pediatr Res* 19:666, 1985.
9. TURNBULL DM, BARTLETT K, STEVENS DL, ALBERTI KGMM, GIBSON GJ, JOHNSON MA, MCCULLOCH AJ, SHERRATT HSA: Short-chain acyl-CoA dehydrogenase deficiency associated with a lipid-storage myopathy and secondary carnitine deficiency. *N Engl J Med* 311:1232, 1984.
10. AMENDT BA, GREENE C, SWEETMAN L, CLOHERTY J, SHIH V, MOON A, TEEL L, RHEAD WJ: Short-chain acyl-CoA dehydrogenase deficiency: Clinical and biochemical studies in two patients. *J Clin Invest* 79:1303, 1987.
11. COATES PM, HALE DE, FINOCCHIARO G, TANAKA K, WINTER SC: Genetic deficiency of short-chain acyl-coenzyme A dehydrogenase in cultured fibroblasts from a patient with muscle carnitine deficiency and severe skeletal muscle weakness. *J Clin Invest* 81:171, 1988.
12. STANLEY CA: New genetic defects in mitochondrial fatty acid oxidation and carnitine deficiency. *Adv Pediatr* 34:59, 1987.

13. BREMER J, OSMUNDSEN H: Fatty acid oxidation and its regulation, in Numa S (ed): *Fatty Acid Metabolism and Its Regulation*. Amsterdam, Elsevier, 1984, p 113.
14. MCGARRY JD, FOSTER DW: Regulation of hepatic fatty acid oxidation and ketone body production. *Annu Rev Biochem* 49:395, 1980.
15. AHLBORG G, FELIG P, HAGENFELDT L, HENDLER R, WAHREN J: Substrate turnover during prolonged exercise in man. Splanchnic and leg metabolism of glucose, free fatty acids, and amino acids. *J Clin Invest* 53:1080, 1974.
16. SCHULZ H: Oxidation of fatty acids, in Vance DE, Vance JE (eds): *Biochemistry of Lipids and Membranes*. Menlo Park, CA, Benjamin/Cummings, 1985, p 116.
17. BEINERT H: Acyl dehydrogenases from pig and beef liver and beef heart, in Colowick SP, Kaplan NO (eds): *Methods in Enzymology*. New York, Academic, 1962, vol 5, p 546.
18. FINOCCHIARO G, ITO M, TANAKA K: Purification and properties of short chain acyl-CoA, medium chain acyl-CoA, and isovaleryl-CoA dehydrogenases from human liver. *J Biol Chem* 262:7982, 1987.
19. CRANE FL, BEINERT H: On the mechanism of dehydrogenation of fatty acyl derivatives of coenzyme A. II. The electron-transferring flavoprotein. *J Biol Chem* 218:717, 1956.
20. CRANE FL, MII S, HAUGE JG, GREEN DE, BEINERT H: On the mechanism of dehydrogenation of fatty acyl derivatives of coenzyme A. I. The general fatty acyl coenzyme A dehydrogenase. *J Biol Chem* 218:701, 1956.
21. HAUGE JG, CRANE FL, BEINERT H: On the mechanism of dehydrogenation of fatty acyl derivatives of coenzyme A. III. Palmityl CoA dehydrogenase. *J Biol Chem* 219:727, 1956.
22. HALL CL, KAMIN H: The purification and some properties of electron transfer flavoprotein and general acyl coenzyme A dehydrogenase from pig liver mitochondria. *J Biol Chem* 250:3476, 1975.
23. THORPE C, MATTHEWS RG, WILLIAMS CH: Acyl-coenzyme A dehydrogenase from pig kidney. Purification and properties. *Biochemistry* 18:331, 1979.
24. DAVIDSON B, SCHULZ H: Separation, properties, and regulation of acyl coenzyme A dehydrogenases from bovine heart and liver. *Arch Biochem Biophys* 213:155, 1982.
25. DOMMES V, KUNAU WH: Purification and properties of acyl coenzyme A dehydrogenases from bovine liver. Formation of 2-trans, 4-cis-decadienoyl coenzyme A. *J Biol Chem* 259:1789, 1984.
26. SHAW L, ENGEL PC: The purification and properties of ox liver short-chain acyl-CoA dehydrogenase. *Biochem J* 218:511, 1984.
27. IKEDA Y, OKAMURA-IKEDA K, TANAKA K: Purification and characterization of short-chain, medium-chain, and long-chain acyl-CoA dehydrogenases from rat liver mitochondria. Isolation of the holo- and apoenzymes and conversion of the apoenzyme to the holoenzyme. *J Biol Chem* 260:1311, 1985.
28. IKEDA Y, DABROWSKI C, TANAKA K: Separation and properties of five distinct acyl-CoA dehydrogenases from rat liver mitochondria. Identification of a new 2-methyl branched chain acyl-CoA dehydrogenase. *J Biol Chem* 258:1066, 1983.
29. HUSAIN M, STEENKAMP DJ: Electron transfer flavoprotein from pig liver mitochondria. A simple purification and re-evaluation of some of the molecular properties. *Biochem J* 209:541, 1983.
30. GORELICK RJ, MIZZER JP, THORPE C: Purification and properties of electron-transferring flavoprotein from pig kidney. *Biochemistry* 21:6936, 1982.
31. FURUTA S, MIYAZAWA S, HASHIMOTO T: Purification and properties of rat liver acyl-CoA dehydrogenases and electron transfer flavoprotein. *J Biochem* 90:1739, 1981.
32. SCHULZ H: Long chain enoyl coenzyme A hydratase from pig heart. *J Biol Chem* 249:2704, 1974.
33. STERN JR, DEL CAMPILLO A: Enzymes of fatty acid metabolism: II. Properties of crystalline crotonase. *J Biol Chem* 218:985, 1956.
34. EL-FAKHRI M, MIDDLETON B: The existence of two different L-3-hydroxacyl-coenzyme A dehydrogenases in rat tissues. *Biochem Soc Trans* 7:392, 1979.
35. NOYES BE, BRADSHAW RA: L-3-Hydroxyacyl coenzyme A dehydrogenase from pig heart muscle. I. Purification and properties. *J Biol Chem* 248:3052, 1973.
36. MIDDLETON B: The oxoacyl-coenzyme A thiolases of animal tissues. *Biochem J* 132:717, 1973.
37. STAACK H, BINSTOCK JF, SCHULZ H: Purification and properties of a pig heart thiolase with broad chain length specificity and comparison of thiolases from pig heart and Escherichia coli. *J Biol Chem* 253:1827, 1978.
38. GREGERSEN N, MORTENSEN PB, KOLVRAA S: On the biologic origin of C_6-C_{10}-dicarboxylic and C_6-C_{10}-ω-1-hydroxy monocarboxylic acids in human and rat with acyl-CoA dehydrogenation deficiencies: in vitro studies on the ω- and ω-1-oxidation of medium-chain (C_6-C_{12}) fatty acids in human and rat liver. *Pediatr Res* 17:828, 1983.
39. WHYTE RK, WHELAN D, HILL R, MCCLORRY S: Excretion of dicarboxylic and ω-1 hydroxy fatty acids by low birth weight infants fed with medium-chain triglycerides. *Pediatr Res* 20:122, 1986.
40. BJORKHEM I, DANIELSSON H: ω- and ω-1-Oxidation of fatty acids by rat liver microsomes. *Eur J Biochem* 17:450, 1970.
41. BREMER J: Carnitine-metabolism and functions. *Physiol Rev* 63:1420, 1983.
42. PAIK WK, KIM S: Solubilization and partial purification of protein methylase III from calf thymus nuclei. *J Biol Chem* 245:6010, 1970.
43. LABADIE J, DUNN WA, ARONSON NN: Hepatic synthesis of carnitine from protein-bound trimethyl-lysine. Lysosomal digestion of methyl-lysine-labelled asialo-fetuin. *Biochem J* 160:85, 1976.
44. HULSE JD, ELLIS SR, HENDERSON LM: Carnitine biosynthesis: β-hydroxylation of trimethyllysine by an α-ketoglutarate-dependent mitochondrial dioxygenase. *J Biol Chem* 253:1654, 1978.
45. ERBE RW: Genetic aspects of folate metabolism. *Adv Hum Genet* 9:293, 1979.
46. NELSON PJ, PRUITT RE, HENDERSON LL, JENNESS R, HENDERSON LM: Effect of ascorbic acid deficiency on the in vivo synthesis of carnitine. *Biochim Biophys Acta* 672:123, 1981.
47. DUNN WA, ARONSON NN, ENGLARD S: The effect of 1-amino-D-proline on the production of carnitine from exogneous protein-bound trimethyllysine by the perfused rat liver. *J Biol Chem* 257:7948, 1982.
48. HUTH PJ, SCHMIDT MJ, HALL PV, FARIELLO RG, SHUG AL: The uptake of carnitine by slices of rat cerebral cortex. *J Neurochem* 36:715, 1981.
49. BROOKS DE, MCINTOSH JEA: Turnover of carnitine by rat tissues. *Biochem J* 148:439, 1975.
50. KIM CS, PRATT RM, ROE CR: Maternal and fetal tissue distribution of L-carnitine in pregnant mice. *J Histochem Cytochem*, submitted, 1988.
51. REBOUCHE CJ, ENGEL AG: Significance of renal γ-butyrobetaine hydroxylase for carnitine biosynthesis in man. *J Biol Chem* 255:8700, 1980.
52. REBOUCHE CJ, PAULSON DJ: Carnitine metabolism and function in humans. *Annu Rev Nutr* 6:41, 1986.
53. STUMPF DA, PARKER WD, ANGELINI C: Carnitine deficiency, organic acidemias, and Reye's syndrome. *Neurology* 35:1041, 1985.
54. BIEBER LL, LYSIAK W: Characteristics and functions of short-chain and medium-chain carnitine acyltransferases, in Borum PR (ed): *Clinical Aspects of Human Carnitine Deficiency*. New York, Pergamon, 1986, p 157.
55. ALLEN RJ, WONG P, RATHENBERG SP, DIMAURO S, HEADINGTON JT: Progressive neonatal leukoencephalomyopathy due to absent methylenetetrahydrofolate reductase, responsive to treatment. *Ann Neurol* 8:211, 1980.
56. MULLER-HOCKER J, PONGRATZ D, DUEFEL T, TRIJBELS JMF, ENDRES W, HUBNER G: Fatal lipid storage myopathy with deficiency of cytochrome-c-oxidase and carnitine. *Virchows Arch (A)* 399:11, 1983.
57. BERNARDINI I, RIZZO WB, DALAKAS M, BERNAR J, GAHL WA: Plasma and muscle free carnitine deficiency due to renal Fanconi syndrome. *J Clin Invest* 75:1124, 1985.
58. CHALMERS RA, ROE CR, STACEY TE, HOPPEL CL: Urinary excretion of 1-carnitine and acylcarnitines by patients with disorders of organic acid metabolism: Evidence for secondary insufficiency of 1-carnitine. *Pediatr Res* 18:1325, 1984.
59. MILLINGTON DS, ROE CR, MALTBY DA: Application of high resolution fast atom bombardment and constant B/E ratio linked scanning to the identification and analysis of acylcarnitines in metabolic disease. *Biomed Mass Spectrom* 11:236, 1984.
60. ROE CR, MILLINGTON DS, MALTBY DA: Diagnostic and therapeutic implications of acylcarnitine profiling in organic acidurias associated with carnitine insufficiency, in Borum PR (ed): *Clinical Aspects of Human Carnitine Deficiency*. New York, Pergamon, 1986, p 97.
61. ROE CR, MILLINGTON DS, MALTBY DA, KAHLER SG, BOHAN TP: L-Carnitine therapy in isovaleric acidemia. *J Clin Invest* 74:2290, 1984.
62. ROE CR, MILLINGTON DS, MALTBY DA, BOHAN TP, KAHLER SG, CHALMERS RA: Diagnostic and therapeutic implications of medium-chain acylcarnitines in the medium-chain acyl-CoA dehydrogenase deficiency. *Pediatr Res* 19:459, 1985.
63. ROE CR, MILLINGTON DS, MALTBY DA, KINNEBREW P: Recognition of medium-chain acyl-CoA dehydrogenase deficiency in asymptomatic siblings of children dying of sudden infant death or Reye-like syndromes. *J Pediatr* 108:13, 1986.
64. ROE CR, MILLINGTON DS, MALTBY DA, BOHAN TP, HOPPEL CL: L-carnitine enhances excretion of propionyl coenzyme A as propionylcarnitine in propionic acidemia. *J Clin Invest* 73:1785, 1984.
65. ROE CR, HOPPEL CL, STACEY TE, CHALMERS RA, TRACEY BM, MILLINGTON DS: Metabolic response to carnitine in methylmalonic aciduria. An effec-

tive strategy for elimination of propionyl groups. *Arch Dis Child* 58:916, 1983.

66. MARKWELL MAK, TOLBERT NE, BIEBER LL: Comparison of the carnitine acyltransferase activities from rat liver peroxisomes and mitochondria. *Arch Biochem Biophys* 176:479, 1976.

67. GASKELL SJ, GUENAT C, MILLINGTON DS, MALTBY DA, ROE CR: Differentiation of isomeric acylcarnitines using tandem mass spectrometry. *Anal Chem* 58:2801, 1986.

68. OHTANI Y, ENDO F, MATSUDA I: Carnitine deficiency and hyperammonemia associated with valproic acid therapy. *J Pediatr* 101:782, 1982.

69. BAHL JJ, BRESSLER R: The pharmacology of carnitine. *Annu Rev Pharmacol Toxicol* 27:257, 1987.

70. MILLINGTON DS, BOHAN TP, ROE CR, YERGEY AL, LIBERATO DJ: Valproylcarnitine: A novel drug metabolite identified by fast atom bombardment and thermospray liquid chromatography–mass spectrometry. *Clin Chim Acta* 145:69, 1985.

71. BECKER CM, HARRIS RA: Influence of valproic acid on hepatic carbohydrate and lipid metabolism. *Arch Biochem Biophys* 223:381, 1983.

72. REBOUCHE CJ, ENGEL AG: Primary systemic carnitine deficiency: I. Carnitine biosynthesis. *Neurology (NY)* 31:813, 1981.

73. ENGEL AG, REBOUCHE CJ, WILSON DM, GLASGOW AM, ROMSHE CA, CRUSE RP: Primary systemic carnitine deficiency. II. Renal handling of carnitine. *Neurology (NY)* 31:819, 1981.

74. REBOUCHE CJ, ENGEL AG: In vitro analysis of hepatic carnitine biosynthesis in human systemic carnitine deficiency. *Clin Chim Acta* 106:295, 1980.

75. GLASGOW AM, ENG G, ENGEL AG: Systemic carnitine deficiency simulating recurrent Reye syndrome. *J Pediatr* 96:889, 1980.

76. CRUSE RP, DI MAURO S, TOWFIGHI J, TREVISAN C: Familial systemic carnitine deficiency. *Arch Neurol* 41:301, 1984.

77. COATES PM, HALE DE, STANLEY CA, CORKEY BE, CORTNER JA: Genetic deficiency of medium-chain acyl coenzyme A dehydrogenase: Studies in cultured skin fibroblasts and peripheral mononuclear leukocytes. *Pediatr Res* 19:671, 1985.

78. ZIERZ S, ENGEL AG, ROMSHE CA: Assay of acyl-CoA dehydrogenases in muscle and liver and identification of four new cases of medium-chain acyl-CoA dehydrogenase deficiency associated with systemic carnitine deficiency. *Muscle Nerve* 9*(Suppl)*:193, 1986.

79. CHAPOY PR, ANGELINI C, BROWN WJ, STIFF JE, SHUG AL, CEDERBAUM SD: Systemic carnitine deficiency—A treatable inherited lipid-storage disease presenting as Reye's syndrome. *N Engl J Med* 303:1389, 1980.

80. TRIPP ME, KATCHER ML, PETERS HA, GILBERT EF, ARYA S, HODACH RJ, SHUG AL: Systemic carnitine deficiency presenting as familial endocardial fibroelastosis. A treatable cardiomyopathy. *N Engl J Med* 305:385, 1981.

81. WABER LJ, VALLE D, NEILL C, DIMAURO S, SHUG A: Carnitine deficiency presenting as familial cardiomyopathy: A treatable defect in carnitine transport. *J Pediatr* 101:700, 1982.

81a. STANLEY CA, TREEM WR, COATES PM, HALE DE, FINEGOLD DN: "Primary carnitine deficiency" due to a defect in carnitine transport. *Pediatr Res* 23:397A, 1988.

82. WABER L, FRANCOMANO C, BRUSILOW S, VALLE D, FRERMAN F, GOODMAN S: Medium chain acyl-CoA dehydrogenase (MCD) deficiency. *Pediatr Res* 18:302A, 1984.

83. HOWAT AJ, BENNETT MJ, VARIEND S, SHAW L: Deficiency of medium chain fatty acylcoenzyme A dehydrogenase presenting as the sudden infant death syndrome. *Br Med J* 288:976, 1984.

83a. ALLISON F, BENNETT MJ, VARIEND S, ENGEL PC: Acylcoenzyme A dehydrogenase deficiency in heart tissue from infants who died unexpectedly with fatty change in the liver. *Br Med J* 296:11, 1988.

84. DEL VALLE JA, GARCIA MJ, MERINERO B, PEREZ-CERDA C, ROMAN F, JIMENEZ A, UGARTE M, MARTINEZ-PARDO M, LUDENA C, CAMERERO C, DEL OLMO R, DURAN M, WADMAN SK: A new patient with dicarboxylic aciduria suggestive of medium-chain acyl-CoA dehydrogenase deficiency presenting as Reye's syndrome. *J Inherited Metab Dis* 7:62, 1984.

85. DIVRY P, VIANEY-LIAUD C, COTTE J: Gas chromatography–mass spectrometry (GC-MS) diagnosis of two cases of medium-chain acyl-CoA dehydrogenase deficiency. *J Inherited Metab Dis* 7 *(Suppl* 1):44, 1984.

86. BOUGNERES PF, ROCCHICCIOLI F, KOLVRAA S, HADCHOUEL M, LALAU-KERALY J, CHAUSSAIN JL, WADMAN SK, GREGERSEN N: Medium-chain acyl-CoA dehydrogenase deficiency in two siblings with a Reye-like syndrome. *J Pediatr* 106:918, 1985.

87. HOWAT AJ, BENNETT MJ, VARIEND S, SHAW L, ENGEL PC: Defects of metabolism of fatty acids in the sudden infant death syndrome. *Br Med J* 290:1771, 1985.

88. AMENDT BA, RHEAD WJ: Catalytic defect of medium-chain acyl-coenzyme A dehydrogenase deficiency. Lack of both cofactor responsiveness and biochemical heterogeneity in eight patients. *J Clin Invest* 76:963, 1985.

89. DURAN M, HOFKAMP M, RHEAD WJ, SAUDUBRAY JM, WADMAN SK: Sudden child death and "healthy" affected family members with medium-chain acyl-coenzyme A dehydrogenase deficiency. *Pediatrics* 78:1052, 1986.

90. TREEM WR, WITZLEBEN CA, PICCOLI DA, STANLEY CA, HALE DE, COATES PM, WATKINS JB: Medium-chain and long-chain acyl CoA dehydrogenase deficiency: Clinical, pathologic and ultrastructural differentiation from Reye's syndrome. *Hepatology* 5:1270, 1986.

91. VAN GENNIP AH, BAKKER HD, DURAN M, VAN OUDHEUSDEN LJ: The diagnosis and treatment of a patient with medium-chain acyl-CoA dehydrogenase deficiency: Overnight fasting does not result in the expected urinary metabolite profile. *J Inherited Metab Dis* 9 *(Suppl* 2):293, 1986.

92. ROE CR, MILLINGTON DS, MALTBY DA, WELLMAN RB: Post-mortem recognition of inherited metabolic disorders from specific acylcarnitines in tissue in cases of sudden infant death. *Lancet* 1:512, 1987.

93. BENNETT MJ, ALLISON F, POLLITT RJ, MANNING NJ, GRAY RGF, GREEN A, HALE DE, COATES PM: Prenatal diagnosis of medium-chain acyl-CoA dehydrogenase deficiency in family with sudden infant death. *Lancet* 1:440, 1987.

94. TAUBMAN B, HALE DE, KELLEY RI: Familial Reye-like syndrome: A presentation of medium-chain acyl-coenzyme A dehydrogenase deficiency. *Pediatrics* 79:382, 1987.

95. TRUSCOTT EJW, HICK L, PULLIN C, HALPERN B, WILCKEN B, GRIFFITHS H, SILINK M, KILHAM H, GRUNSEIT F: Dicarboxylic aciduria: The response to fasting. *Clin Chim Acta* 94:31, 1979.

96. CHALMERS RA, LAWSON AM, WHITELAW A, PURKISS P: Twin siblings with a Reye's-like syndrome associated with an abnormal organic aciduria, hypoglycemia, diarrhea, and vomiting with close similarities to Jamaican vomiting sickness. *Pediatr Res* 14:1097, 1980.

97. COLLE E, MAMER OA, MONTGOMERY JA, MILLER JD: Episodic hypoglycemia with ψ-hydroxy fatty acid excretion. *Pediatr Res* 17:171, 1983.

98. GREGERSEN N, KOLVRAA S, RASMUSSEN K, MORTENSEN PB, DIVRY P, DAVID M, HOBOLTH N: General (medium-chain) acyl-CoA dehydrogenase deficiency (non-ketotic dicarboxylic aciduria): Quantitative urinary excretion pattern of 23 biologically significant organic acids in three cases. *Clin Chim Acta* 132:181, 1983.

98a. RINALDO P, O'SHEA J, TANAKA K: Stable isotope dilution method for diagnosis of medium chain acyl-CoA dehydrogenase deficiency. *Lancet* 2:1158, 1987.

99. GREGERSEN N: The acyl-CoA dehydrogenation deficiencies. *Scand J Clin Lab Invest* 45 *(Suppl* 174):1, 1985.

100. DURAN M, MITCHELL G, DE KLERK JBC, DE JAGER JP, HOFKAMP M, BRUINVIS L, KETTING D, SAUDUBRAY JM, WADMAN SK: Octanoic acidemia and octanoylcarnitine excretion with dicarboxylic aciduria due to defective oxidation of medium-chain fatty acids. *J Pediatr* 107:397, 1985.

101. MORTENSEN PB, GREGERSEN N: Medium-chain triglyceride medication as a pitfall in the diagnosis of non-ketotic C_6-C_{10}-dicarboxylic acidurias. *Clin Chim Acta* 103:33, 1980.

102. BRASS EP, HOPPEL CL: Carnitine metabolism in the fasting rat. *J Biol Chem* 253:2688, 1978.

103. ENGEL AG, BANKER BQ, EIBEN RM: Carnitine deficiency: Clinical, morphological, and biochemical observations in a fatal case. *J Neurol Neurosurg Psychiatry* 40:313, 1977.

104. SAUDUBRAY JM, COUDE FX, DEMAUGRE F, JOHNSON C, GIBSON KM, NYHAN WL: Oxidation of fatty acids in cultured fibroblasts: A model system for the detection and study of defects in oxidation. *Pediatr Res* 16:877, 1982.

105. VEERKAMP JH, VAN MOERKERK HTB, BAKKEREN JAJM: An accurate and sensitive assay of [^{14}C] octanoate oxidation and its application on tissue homogenates and fibroblasts. *Biochim Biophys Acta* 876:133, 1986.

106. CHALMERS RA, ENGLISH N: Fatty acid oxidation in cultured skin fibroblasts from patients with inherited disorders of fatty acid metabolism: Studies on the specificity of acyl-CoA dehydrogenases. *Biochem Soc Trans* 15:489, 1987.

107. MOON A, RHEAD WH: Complementation analysis of fatty acid oxidation disorders. *J Clin Invest* 79:59, 1987.

108. COATES PM, HALE DE, STANLEY CA, GLASGOW AM: Systemic carnitine deficiency simulating Reye syndrome. *J Pediatr* 105:679, 1984.

109. FRERMAN FE, GOODMAN SI: Fluorometric assay of acyl-CoA dehydrogenases in normal and mutant human fibroblasts. *Biochem Med* 33:38, 1985.

110. IKEDA Y, HALE DE, KEESE SM, COATES PM, TANAKA K: Biosynthesis of variant medium chain acyl-CoA dehydrogenase in cultured fibroblasts from patients with medium chain acyl-CoA dehydrogenase deficiency. *Pediatr Res* 20:843, 1986.

111. HALE DE, CRUSE RP, ENGEL A: Familial systemic carnitine deficiency. *Arch Neurol* 42:1133, 1985.

112. HUIJMANS JGM, SCHOLTE HR, BLOM W, LUYT-HOUWEN IEM, PRZYREMBEL

H: Enzymatic evidence for a medium-chain acyl-CoA dehydrogenase deficiency in muscle of a patient with hypoketotic hypoglycemic dicarboxylic aciduria. *Pediatr Res* 18:1978, 1984.

113. RHEAD WJ, HALL CL, TANAKA K: Novel tritium release assays for isovaleryl-CoA and butyryl-CoA dehydrogenases. *J Biol Chem* 256:1616, 1981.

114. HALE DE, FINOCCHIARO G, COATES PM, TANAKA K: Substrate chain length specificity of the residual enzyme activity in medium chain acyl-CoA dehydrogenase (MCAD) deficient cells: Study using specific antibodies. *Pediatr Res* 20:329A, 1986.

115. IKEDA Y, TANAKA K: Immunoprecipitation and electrophoretic analysis of four human acyl-CoA dehydrogenases and electron transfer flavoprotein using antibodies raised against the corresponding rat enzymes. *Biochem Med Metab Biol* 37:329, 1987.

115a. KELLEY DP, ALPERS R, HEUSEL J, STRAUSS AM: Molecular analysis of inherited medium-chain acyl-CoA dehydrogenase deficiency. *Clin Res* 36:404A, 1988.

116. IKEDA Y, KEESE SM, TANAKA K: Molecular heterogeneity of variant isovaleryl-CoA dehydrogenase from cultured isovaleric acidemia fibroblasts. *Proc Natl Acad Sci USA* 82:7081, 1985.

117. IKEDA Y, KEESE SM, TANAKA K: Biosynthesis of electron transfer flavoprotein in a cell-free system and in cultured human fibroblasts: Defect in the alpha subunit synthesis is a primary lesion in glutaric aciduria type II. *J Clin Invest* 78:997, 1986.

118. MATSUBARA Y, KRAUS JP, YANG-FENG TL, FRANCKE U, ROSENBERG LE, TANAKA K: Molecular cloning of cDNAs encoding rat and human medium-chain acyl-CoA dehydrogenase and assignment of the gene to human chromosome 1. *Proc Natl Acad Sci USA* 83:6543, 1986.

118a. MATSUBARA Y, KRAUS JP, OZASA H, GLASSBERG R, FINOCCHIARO G, IKEDA Y, MOLE J, ROSENBERG LE, TANAKA K: Molecular cloning and nucleotide sequence of cDNA encoding the entire precursor of rat liver medium chain acyl coenzyme A dehydrogenase. *J Biol Chem* 262:10104, 1987.

118b. KELLY DP, KIM JJ, BILLADELLO JJ, HAINLINE BE, CHU TW, STRAUSS AW: Nucleotide sequence of medium-chain acyl-CoA dehydrogenase in mRNA and its expression in enzyme-deficient human tissue. *Proc Natl Acad Sci USA* 84:4068, 1987.

119. DENTON RM, MCCORMACK JG, OVIASU OA: Short-term regulation of pyruvate dehydrogenase activity in the liver, in Hue L, Van de Werve G (eds): *Short-Term Regulation of Liver Metabolism*. Amsterdam, Elsevier, 1981, p 159.

120. POGSON CI, MUNOZ-CLARES RA, ELLIOTT KRF, KEAN EA, LLOYD P, SMITH SA: Interactions of amino acids with gluconeogenesis, in Hue L, Van de Werve G (eds): *Short-Term Regulation of Liver Metabolism*. Amsterdam, Elsevier, 1981, p 339.

121. PARKER WD, HAAS R, STUMPF DA, EGUREN LA: Effects of octanoate on rat brain and liver mitochondria. *Neurology (Cleveland)* 33:1374, 1983.

122. MAMUNES P, DEVRIES GH, MILLER CD, DAVID RB: Fatty acid quantitation in Reye's syndrome, in Pollack JD (ed): *Reye's Syndrome*. New York, Grune and Stratton, 1974, p 245.

123. TRAUNER DA, ADAMS H: Intracranial pressure elevations during octanoate infusion in rabbits: An experimental model of Reye's syndrome. *Pediatr Res* 15:1097, 1981.

124. OGBURN PL, SHARP H, LLOYD-STILL JD, JOHNSON SB, HOLMAN RT: Abnormal polyunsaturated fatty acid patterns of serum lipids in Reye's syndrome. *Proc Natl Acad Sci USA* 79:908, 1982.

125. HEUBI JE, PARTIN JC, PARTIN JS, SCHUBERT WK: Reye's syndrome: Current concepts. *Hepatology* 7:155, 1987.

126. KIM CS, O'TUAMA LA, MANN JD, ROE CR: Effect of increasing carbon chain length on organic acid transport by the choroid plexus: A potential factor in Reye's syndrome. *Brain Res* 259:340, 1983.

127. MCCANDLESS DW: Octanoic acid-induced coma and reticular formation energy metabolism. *Brain Res* 335:131, 1985.

128. ANON: Sudden infant death and inherited disorders of fat oxidation. *Lancet* 2:1073, 1986.

129. BENNETT MJ, ALLISON F, LOWTHER GW, GRAY RGF, JOHNSTON DI, FITZSIMMONS JS, MANNING NJ, POLLITT RJ: Prenatal diagnosis of medium-chain acyl-coenzyme A dehydrogenase deficiency. *Prenat Diagn* 7:135, 1987.

130. NAYLOR EW, MOSOVICH LL, GUTHRIE R, EVANS JE, TIECKELMANN H: Intermittent non-ketotic dicarboxylic aciduria in two siblings with hypoglycemia: An apparent defect in β-oxidation of fatty acids. *J Inherited Metab Dis* 3:19, 1980.

131. AMENDT BA, TEEL L, RHEAD WJ: Long chain acyl-CoA dehydrogenase (LCADH) deficiency (LCD): Clinical and biochemical heterogeneity in three patients. *Pediatr Res* 21:339A, 1987.

132. STANLEY CA, COATES PM: Inherited defects of fatty acid oxidation which resemble Reye's syndrome, in Pollack JB (ed): Reye's syndrome IV. *J Natl Reye's Syndrome Found* 5:190, 1985.

133. TAGER JM, WANDERS RJA, GROEN AK, KUNZ W, BOHNENSACK R, KUSTER U, LETKO G, BOHME G, DUSZYNSKI J, WOJTCZAK L: Control of mitochondrial respiration. *FEBS Lett* 151:1, 1983.

134. OZASA H, IKEDA Y, FINOCCHIARO G, MATSUBARA Y, TANAKA K: Molecular cloning and nucleotide sequence of cDNA encoding rat liver short chain acyl-CoA dehydrogenase. *Am J Hum Genet* 41:A232, 1987.

134a. BARTON DE, YANG-FENG TL, FINOCCHIARO G, OZASA H, TANAKA K, FRANCKE U: Short chain acyl-CoA dehydrogenase (ACADS) maps to chromosome 12 (q22-qter) and electron transfer flavoprotein (ETFA) to 15 (q23-q25). *Cytogenet Cell Genet* 46:577, 1987.

135. DIDONATO S, CORNELIO F, GELLERA C, PELUCHETTI D, RIMOLDI M, TARONI F: Short-chain acyl CoA dehydrogenase-deficient myopathy, with secondary carnitine deficiency. *Muscle Nerve* 9(*Suppl*):178, 1986.

136. BOUGNERES PF, SAUDUBRAY JM, MARSAC C, BERNARD O, ODIEVRE M, GIRARD J: Fasting hypoglycemia resulting from hepatic carnitine palmitoyl transferase deficiency. *J Pediatr* 98:742, 1981.

137. ZIERZ S, ENGEL AG: Regulatory properties of a mutant carnitine palmitoyltransferase in human skeletal muscle. *Eur J Biochem* 149:207, 1985.

138. GOODMAN SI, MCCABE ERB, FENNESSEY PV, MACE JW: Multiple acyl-CoA dehydrogenase deficiency (glutaric aciduria type II) with transient hypersarcosinemia and sarcosinuria; possible inherited deficiency of an electron transfer flavoprotein. *Pediatr Res* 14:12, 1980.

139. GREGERSEN N, KOLVRAA S, RASMUSSEN K, CHRISTENSEN E, BRANDT NJ, EBBESEN F, HANSEN FH: Biochemical studies in a patient with defects in the metabolism of acyl-CoA and sarcosine: Another possible case of glutaric aciduria type II. *J Inherited Metab Dis* 3:67, 1980.

140. AMENDT BA, RHEAD WJ: The multiple acyl-coenzyme A dehydrogenation disorders, glutaric aciduria type II and ethylamlonic-adipic aciduria. Mitochondrial fatty acid oxidation, acyl-coenzyme A dehydrogenase, and electron transfer flavoprotein activities in fibroblasts. *J Clin Invest* 78:205, 1986.

141. FRERMAN FE, GOODMAN SI: Deficiency of electron transfer flavoprotein or electron transfer flavoprotein: Ubiquinone oxidoreductase in glutaric acidemia type II fibroblasts. *Proc Natl Acad Sci USA* 82:4517, 1985.

142. SCHUTGENS RBH, HEYMANS H, KETEL A, VEDER HA, DURAN M, KETTING D, WADMAN SK: Lethal hypoglycemia in a child with a deficiency of 3-hydroxy-3-methylglutarylcoenzyme A lyase. *J Pediatr* 94:89, 1979.

143. ROBINSON BH, OEI J, SHERWOOD WG, SLYPER AH, HEININGER J, MAMER OA: Hydroxymethylglutaryl CoA lyase deficiency: Features resembling Reye syndrome. *Neurology* 30:714, 1980.

144. HARTLAGE P, ELLER G, CARTER L, ROESEL A, HOMMES F: Mitochondrial acetoacetyl-CoA thiolase deficiency. *Biochem Med Metab Biol* 36:198, 1986.

145. LEONARD JV, MIDDLETON B, SEAKINS JWT: Acetoacetyl CoA thiolase deficiency presenting as ketotic hypoglycemia. *Pediatr Res* 21:211, 1987.

146. YAMAGUCHI S, ORII T, SAKURA N, MIYAZAWA S, HASHIMOTO T: Defect in biosynthesis of mitochondrial acetoacetyl-CoA thiolase in cultured fibroblasts from a boy with 3-ketothiolase deficiency. *J Clin Invest* 81:813, 1988.

147. BENNETT MJ, GRAY RGF, ISHERWOOD DM, MURPHY N, POLLITT RJ: The diagnosis and biochemical investigation of a patient with a short-chain fatty acid oxidation defect. *J Inherited Metab Dis* 8(*Suppl* 2):135, 1985.

148. GLASGOW AM, ENGEL AG, BIER DM, PERRY LW, DICKIE M, TODARO J, BROWN BI, UTTER MF: Hypoglycemia, hepatic dysfunction, muscle weakness, cardiomyopathy, free carnitine deficiency and long-chain acylcarnitine excess responsive to medium chain triglyceride diet. *Pediatr Res* 17:319, 1983.

149. RIUDOR E, RIBES A, BORONAT M, SABADO C, DOMINGUEZ C, BALLABRIGA A: A new case of C_6-C_{14} dicarboxylic aciduria with favourable evolution. *J Inherited Metab Dis* 9(*Suppl* 2):297, 1986.

150. POLLITT RJ, LOSTY H, WESTWOOD A: 3-Hydroxydicarboxylic aciduria: A distinctive type of intermittent dicarboxylic aciduria of possible diagnostic significance. *J Inherited Metab Dis* 10(*Suppl* 2):266, 1987.

151. KELLEY RI, MORTON DH: 3-Hydroxyoctanoic aciduria: Identification of a new organic acid in the urine of a patient with non-ketotic hypoglycemia. *Clin Chim Acta*, 1988, in press.

152. GRETER J, LINDSTEDT S, SEEMAN H, STEEN G: 3-Hydroxydecanedioic acid and related homologues: Urinary metabolites in ketoacidosis. *Clin Chem* 26:261, 1980.

153. KELLEY RI, SLADKY JT: Dicarboxylic aciduria in an infant with spinal muscular atrophy. *Ann Neurol* 20:734, 1986.

CHAPTER **34**

GLUTARIC ACIDEMIA TYPE II AND DEFECTS OF THE MITOCHONDRIAL RESPIRATORY CHAIN

FRANK E. FRERMAN
STEPHEN I. GOODMAN

1. *The mitochondrial respiratory chain is a series of multiprotein complexes which couple the reactions of electron transport to energy-requiring synthesis of ATP. In addition to the main respiratory chain, which is reduced by NADH and succinate, there exist a number of "side chains" through which electrons from acyl-CoA thioesters and several other low molecular weight substrates enter the main chain.*
2. *Some proteins of the respiratory chain are encoded by nuclear genes while others, mainly components of complexes I, III, and IV, are encoded by mitochondrial genes.*
3. *While several disorders are thought to be inherited in the mitochondrial genome and expressed as defects in the main respiratory chain, associated protein abnormalities which are both specific and inherited have not been demonstrated in most instances. Two phenotypes which are likely due to such defects are Leber hereditary optic neuropathy and certain skeletal muscle myopathies.*
4. *Electron transfer flavoprotein (ETF) and ETF-ubiquinone oxidoreductase (ETF-QO) are nuclear encoded proteins which constitute the side chain through which electrons from flavoprotein acyl-CoA dehydrogenases, dimethylglycine dehydrogenase, and sarcosine dehydrogenase enter the respiratory chain. Inherited deficiency of these proteins causes glutaric acidemia type II, a disorder characterized by typical organic aciduria and a wide variety of phenotypic manifestations depending on the severity and location of the enzyme block.*
5. *Complete deficiency of ETF or ETF-QO causes nonketotic hypoglycemia and metabolic acidosis in early infancy, and death within the first week of life. Deficiency of ETF-QO is frequently associated with a syndrome of congenital defects, with renal cysts and dysplasia being the most frequent single abnormality.*
6. *Known primary defects include those in ETF-QO and in the α subunit of ETF; both are inherited as autosomal recessive traits. No patient has been described with a primary defect in the ETF β subunit.*
7. *Prenatal diagnosis is possible by demonstrating abnormal organic acids, usually glutarate, in amniotic fluid.*
8. *There is no effective treatment for patients who present with symptoms in early infancy. Treatment with riboflavin, L-carnitine, and diets restricted in fat and protein may be effective in less severely affected patients.*

BIOCHEMISTRY OF THE MAIN RESPIRATORY CHAIN

In eukaryotic cells, multiprotein complexes in the inner mitochondrial membrane couple the oxidative, energy-yielding reactions of electron transport with the energy-requiring synthesis of ATP in a process known as *oxidative phosphorylation.* Various components of this system also act as proton transporters, and electron flow results in directional translocation of protons to the cytoplasmic side of the inner membrane, resulting in an electrochemical gradient of protons between the two compartments. The free energy of this gradient is enzymatically transduced by H^+-ATPase to the synthesis of ATP.[1] The transmembrane arrangement and the proton translocating activity of some components of the electron transferring complexes are consistent with this mechanism for the conservation of redox energy. The entire electron transport–oxidative phosphorylation system is the subject of two recent reviews.[2,3]

In addition to the main respiratory chain (Fig. 34-1), which is reduced by NADH and succinate, there are "side chains" through which electrons are transferred into the main chain from acyl-CoA thioesters,[4] glycerol phosphate,[5,6] and other substrates. Except for the segment from cytochrome c to oxygen, which is irreversible in driving the formation of the β, γ-phosphate anhydride bond of ATP, the reactions are reversible and electrons can equilibrate among various components of the main and side chains.[7–9]

The coenzymes of the redox proteins that mediate electron transfers in the main respiratory chain and its branches do not dissociate from the apoproteins during a catalytic cycle. Some, but not all, are covalently bound to the apoproteins, e.g., succinic and sarcosine dehydrogenases contain covalently bound FAD,[10,11] and c-type cytochromes contain covalently bound heme.[12,13] A coenzyme in the respiratory chain can exhibit widely different oxidation-reduction potentials and physical-chemical properties depending on the microenvironment provided by its apoprotein. The specific electron carriers in the respiratory chain are flavoproteins, iron-sulfur proteins, ubiquinone, cytochromes, and protein-bound copper.

Nonstandard abbreviations used in this chapter are: BAL = British anti-Lewisite; DCCD = dicyclohexylcarbodiimide; DCPIP = dichlorophenol indophenol; DMGDH = dimethylglycine dehydrogenase; ETF = electron transport flavoprotein; ETF-QO = electron transport flavoprotein-ubiquinone oxidoreductase; LHON = Leber hereditary optic neuropathy; SDH = sarcosine dehydrogenase; UHBDT = 5-undecyl-6-hydroxy-4,7-hydroxynaphtho-quinone.

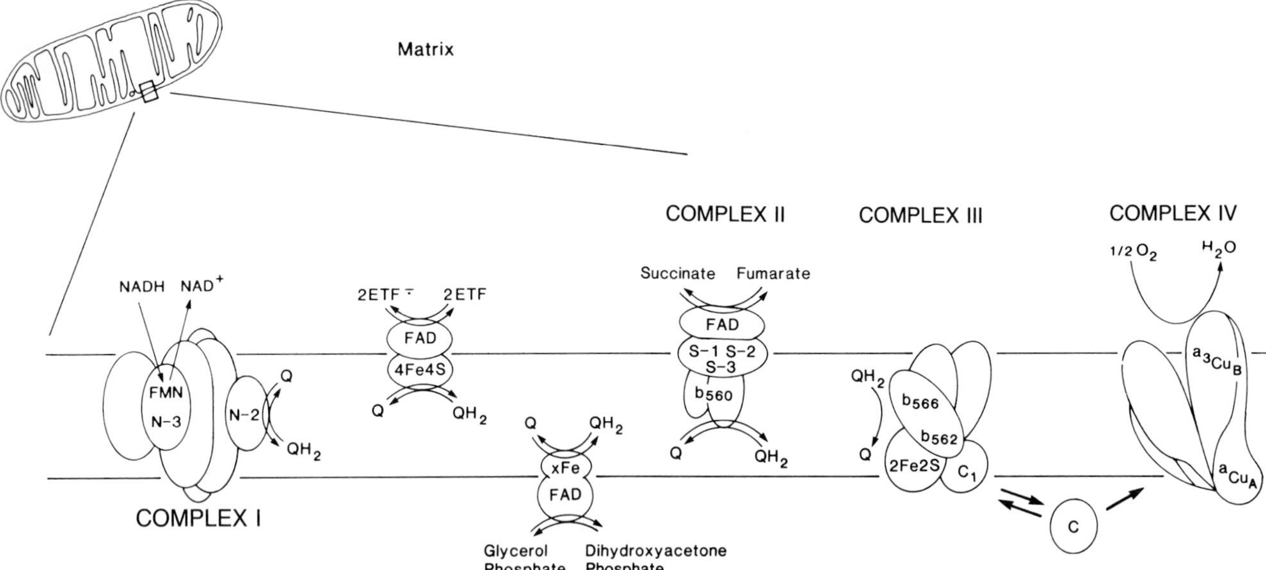

Fig. 34-1 Reactions and topography of the mitochondrial respiratory chain, and the ETF/ETF-QO and glycerol phosphate dehydrogenase branches, showing the better characterized prosthetic groups. Some iron-sulfur clusters in complexes I and II are indicated according to the nomenclature in Refs. 2 and 3. The ubiquinone (Q) and ubiquinol (QH_2) reactants and products of individual complexes and oxidoreductases are shown as part of the ubiquinone pool;[94] protein-bound ubisemiquinone species in complexes I, II, and III are not shown.

Flavins

Because the flavin prosthetic group may exist in any of three redox states—i.e., the oxidized flavin; the one-electron-reduced state, or flavin semiquinone; and the two-electron-reduced state, or flavin hydroquinine (Fig. 34-2)—flavoproteins are particularly well suited as electron input sites for the respiratory chain. Interactions between flavin and apoenzyme determine which redox states are stable in a particular protein.[14] For example, the flavins of mitochondrial acyl-CoA dehydrogenases oscillate between oxidized, two-electron-reduced, and one-electron-reduced states,[15] but in peroxisomal acyl-CoA oxidases, which catalyze the same transformation of acyl-CoA substrates, the flavin oscillates only between the oxidized and two-electron-reduced forms.[16] There are several titratable groups in the isoalloxazine ring of flavins at physiologic pH, and the pK_as of these groups may be perturbed by binding to apoproteins, altering the properties of the flavin. The redox states and protonic equilibria of flavin are shown in Fig. 34-2, and their ionization states in flavoprotiens can be distinguished by characteristic optical absorption, electron paramagnetic resonance (EPR), and resonance Raman spectra.[17–19] The red anionic flavin semiquinones have increased absorbance in the 370-nm region and decreased absorbance in the 450-nm region, relative to oxidized flavin (Fig. 34-3*A*), while neutral flavin semiquinones have a broad, featureless absorption band with a maximum in the 560-nm region and decreased absorbance in the 450-nm region (Fig. 34-3*B*). Fig. 34-4 shows how

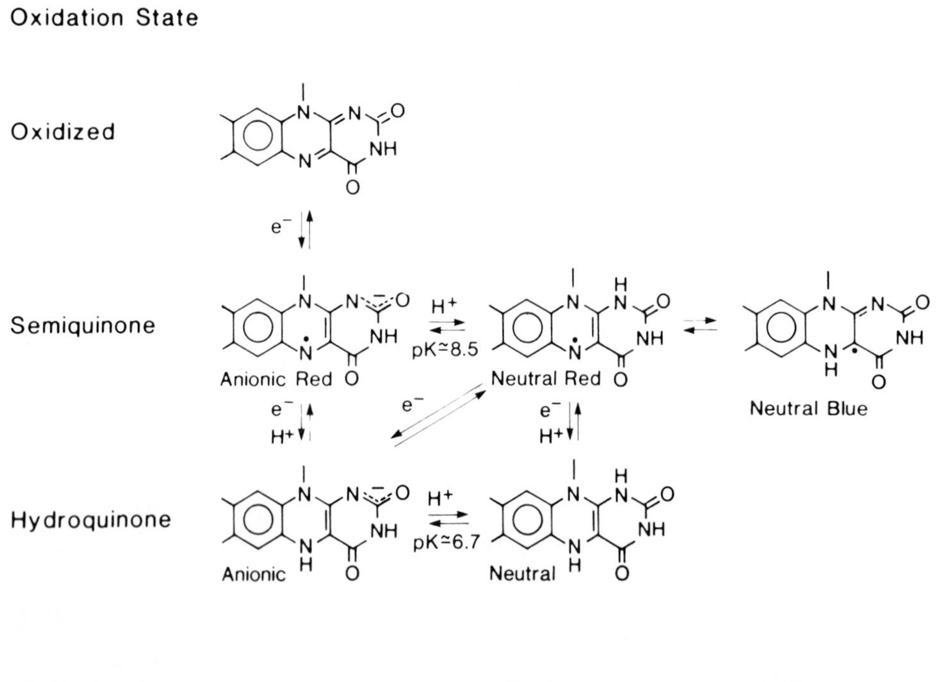

Oxidation State

Oxidized

Semiquinone

Anionic Red — H^+, pK≈8.5 — Neutral Red — Neutral Blue

Hydroquinone

Anionic — H^+, pK≈6.7 — Neutral

Fig. 34-2 Oxidized and one- and two-electron-reduced states of the flavin isoalloxazine system, and protonic equilibria of the reduced, i.e., semiquinone and hydroquinone, states.

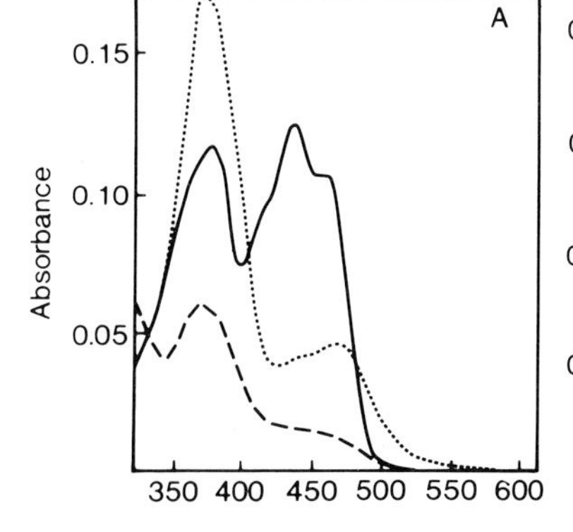

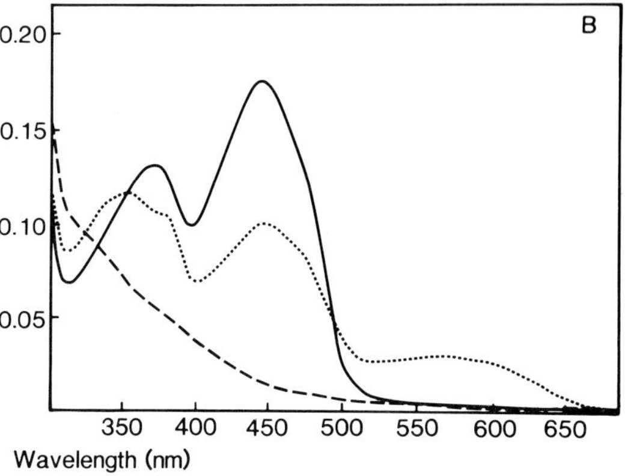

Fig. 34-3 Absorption spectra of flavin (FAD) prosthetic groups in pork liver electron transfer flavoprotein (*A*) and general acyl-CoA dehydrogenase (*B*). The spectra of the oxidized (—), semiquinone (···), and hydroquinone (---) forms of the photochemically reduced proteins are shown.

apoproteins may stabilize neutral and anionic flavin semiquinones. The apoprotein also modulates the oxidation-reduction potential of the bound flavin, which varies from about −320 mV in NADH dehydrogenase[2] to about 0 mV in electron transfer flavoprotein-ubiquinone oxidoreductase.[4]

Iron-Sulfur Clusters

Iron-sulfur clusters are the most abundant prosthetic groups in the electron transport system, and the structures of the tetrahedral 2Fe2S and cubane 4Fe4S clusters that are the most common in mammalian systems are shown in Fig. 34-5.[20] 3Fe*x*S clusters have also been described.[21] Like flavins, the properties of iron-sulfur clusters are modulated by their apoproteins, and the oxidation-reduction potentials of 2Fe2S clusters in proteins in complex I differ from those in complex III by at least 250 mV. A similar difference in the potentials of 4Fe4S clusters is observed between certain proteins of complex I and electron transfer flavoprotein:ubiquinone oxidoreductase.[2,4] Physiologically, iron-sulfur clusters accept and donate single electrons.

Hemes

The structures of the A, B, and C heme prosthetic groups of the respiratory chain cytochromes are shown in Fig. 34-6. The effect of protein ligands on the properties of the heme are illustrated by the distinct absorption spectra and oxidation-reduction potentials possessed by the b cytochromes associated with complex II and complex III.[2,3,22,23] Also, the physical-chemical properties of the b cytochromes of complex III may be altered during protein purification, presumably by modification of the protein microenvironments due to loss of phospholipid.[24]

Fig. 34-4 Stabilization of flavin semiquinones by amino acid side chains of apoproteins. In *A* the negative charge in the N-1–C-2 region of the anion semiquinone is stabilized by a proton-donating group, and in *B* the N-5 nitrogen in the neutral semiquinone is protonated by a proton-donating group on the protein.

NADH-Ubiquinone Oxidoreductase (Complex I)

Complex I contains 26 polypeptides, which range in molecular weight from approximately 75 to 5 kDa,[25] and some may not be required for catalytic activity. The major polypeptides are present in approximately equimolar amounts[26] and form a structural unit, since antiserum against only a few of them precipitates the entire complex, except for a 42-kDa polypeptide, from detergent-solubilized submitochondrial particles.[27] Complex I contains flavin mononucleotide (FMN), nonheme iron equimolar with acid labile sulfur, and variable amounts of phospholipid and ubiquinone.[2,3] Although the function of the bound ubiquinone is unknown, ubisemiquinone has been detected in complex I reduced with NADH, and its Q-band EPR spectrum suggests that the radical is bound to protein.[28] There is evidence that the FMN is bound to a 57-kDa polypeptide[29] which is buried in the membrane and which is not accessible to labeling with membrane-impermeable reagents;[27] the polypeptides that bear the iron-sulfur clusters are also buried in the interior of the complex.[30] Three other polypeptides (75, 49, and 30 kDa) traverse the membrane and are labeled from both sides of the membrane by nonpermeating reagents.[27]

The number and types of iron-sulfur clusters in complex I remain a subject of intense investigation. With some exceptions, the same clusters have been identified in whole mitochondria, submitochondrial particles, isolated complex I, and in a soluble, high molecular weight NADH dehydrogenase[31–37] which is similar to complex I with respect to the FMN/Fe ratio, but which lacks the capacity to reduce ubiquinone.[36] All these preparations contain five NADH-reducible iron-sulfur centers, designated N-1b, N-2, N-3, N-4, and N-5, and the midpoint oxidation-reduction potentials, stoichiometries relative to FMN, and qualitative natures of these clusters are listed in Table 34-1. Although several other iron-sulfur centers have been detected in complex I, their concentrations relative to FMN are low and they are not reduced by NADH, and they may not be intrinsic components of NADH-ubiquinone oxidoreductase.[38] Analysis by EPR spectroscopy has permitted the assignment of some iron-sulfur clusters to specific poly-

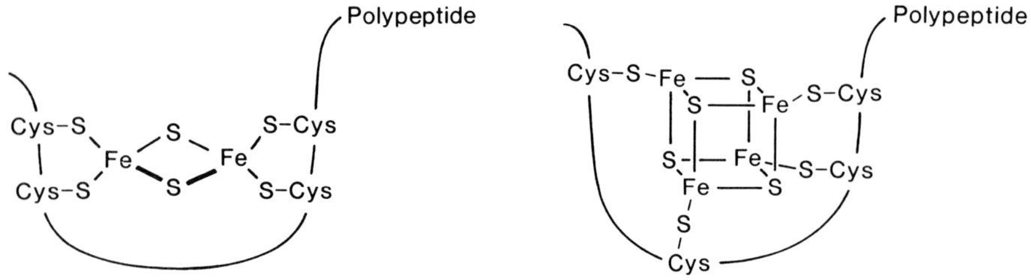

Polypeptide

Cys-S, S, S-Cys; Fe, Fe; Cys-S, S, S-Cys

Polypeptide

Cys-S-Fe — S; S — Fe-S-Cys; S — Fe — S-Cys; Fe — S; S; Cys

Fig. 34-5 Structures of the binuclear (2Fe2S) and tetranuclear (4Fe4S) clusters of iron-sulfur proteins of the respiratory chain.

peptides or subfractions, but some of these assignments are considered tentative.[39,40]

The complexity of NADH-Q oxidoreductase has hindered detailed description of the electron transfer mechanism and the mechanism of energy conservation at site I. The 26-polypeptide complex is capable of rotenone-sensitive reduction of ubiquinone and rotenone-insensitive reduction of ferricyanide. Ferricyanide reduction and NADH oxidation may occur at the same or overlapping sites since these substrates exhibit mutual competitive inhibition.[41] The soluble high molecular weight NADH dehydrogenase (see above), which is unable to reduce ubiquinone, may be functionally similar to soluble succinate dehydrogenase, which requires two integral membrane proteins to perform this function.[42,43] When incorporated into liposomes, complex I catalyzes directional translocation of protons during NADH oxidation consistent with its role in site I phosphorylation,[44] but the specific proton carriers in the complex are not known. The three polypeptides that traverse the membrane might be involved in this function. The midpoint potential of the N-2 iron-sulfur cluster is dependent on pH (and phosphate) potential,[45] and this observation indicates that an ionizable group on the protein is protonated and deprotonated during oxidation-reduction, suggesting a role for the protein in proton movements (Equation 34-1).

$$H_nX_{red} \rightleftarrows X_{ox} + nH^+ + ne^- \qquad (34\text{-}1)$$

Of the 26 peptides that constitute complex I, 19 are encoded by nuclear genes, while the mitochondrial genome codes for 7;[46,47] these 7 genes comprise about 60 percent of the human mitochondrial genome (Fig. 34-7).

Succinate-Ubiquinone Oxidoreductase (Complex II)

Highly purified preparations of succinate-ubiquinone oxidoreductase from bovine heart mitochondria contain four polypeptides, which are designated $C_{II\text{-}1}$ (74 kDa), $C_{II\text{-}2}$ (27 kDa), $C_{II\text{-}3}$ (15.5 kDa), and $C_{II\text{-}4}$ (13.5 kDa).[10,42,43,48–51] The complex contains FAD covalently bound to the 74-kDa subunit, three iron-sulfur clusters (S-1, S-2, and S-3), a b-type cytochrome (cytochrome b_{560}), and variable amounts of ubiquinone and phospholipid depending on the method of preparation. The iron-sulfur centers and covalently bound FAD are located in succinate dehydrogenase, a soluble fraction which contains $C_{II\text{-}1}$ and $C_{II\text{-}2}$ and which does not have ubiquinone oxidoreductase activity. Soluble succinic dehydrogenase can bind to dehydrogenase-depleted submitochondrial particles to reconstitute succinate oxidase activity.[52] The S-1 and S-2 centers are thought to be in close proximity in $C_{II\text{-}1}$ and $C_{II\text{-}2}$, and one of these proteins probably also contains the S-3 center.[53,54] The S-2 center, which can be reduced with dithionite but not succinate, has such a low potential that its role in succinate oxidation has been questioned.[54] It is not clear if the trinuclear (3FexS) cluster of S-3 functions as such, or if it is an inactive degradation product of a tetranuclear cluster.[21,55] A similar 3FexS cluster is found in the four-subunit succinic dehydrogenase complex of *Escherichia coli.*[56]

$C_{II\text{-}3}$ and $C_{II\text{-}4}$ are intrinsic membrane proteins which are required for ubiquinone reduction;[42,43] they are part of the structural and enzymatic complex and are immunoprecipitated, along with $C_{II\text{-}1}$ and $C_{II\text{-}2}$, by antiserum specific for $C_{II\text{-}1}$.[42] The function and subunit localization of cytochrome b_{560} in complex II is not clear; its apparent molecular weight is 14,000, which suggests that the heme is associated with one of the low molecular weight proteins. Bovine heart cytochrome b_{560} was recently isolated with the two subunits (Q-binding proteins) that convert succinic dehydrogenase to succinate-ubiquinone oxidoreductase.[57] Cytochrome b_{560}, even in reconstituted succinate-ubiquinone oxidoreductase, was not reduced by succinate, but was reduced by NADH in the presence of NADH dehydrogenase. Further, the reduced cytochrome was oxidized by fumarate in the presence of succinic dehydrogenase. Thus, this cytochrome is not in the pathway

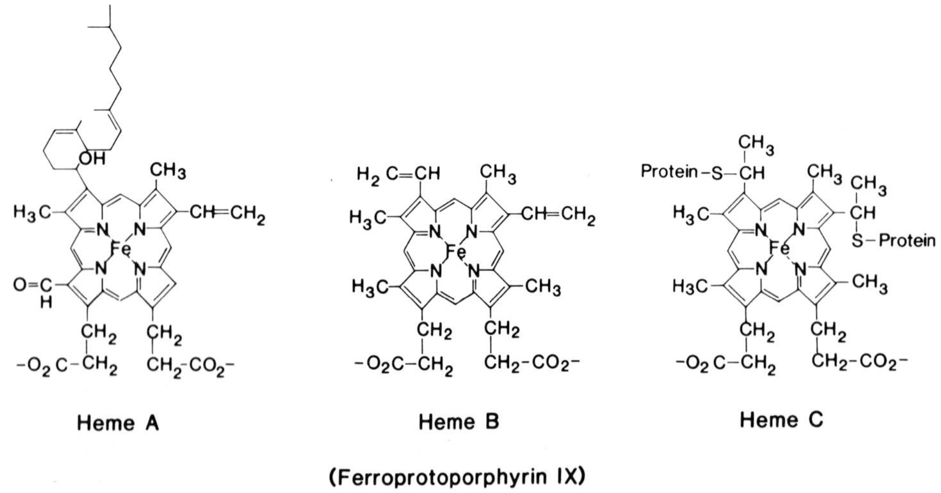

Heme A

Heme B

(Ferroprotoporphyrin IX)

Heme C

Fig. 34-6 Structures of the heme prosthetic groups of the cytochromes of the respiratory chain.

Table 34-1 NADH-Reducible Iron-Sulfur Clusters of Complex I

Cluster	Type	Redox potential at pH7, mV	Cluster-containing subunit, mol wt	Cluster:FMN ratio
N-lb	2Fe2S	−245	24,000	1
N-2	2Fe4S	−20	—	1
N-3	4Fe4S	−245	51,000	1
N-4	4Fe4S	−245	(30,000 or 49,000)	1
N-5	—	−270	—	0.25

of electron transfer from succinate to ubiquinone, but its function in fumarate reduction by NADH suggests a regulatory role in electron transport and oxidative phosphorylation.[57]

Ubiquinol–Cytochrome c Oxidoreductase (Complex III)

Complex III isolated from bovine heart mitochondria contains seven or eight polypeptides with apparent molecular weights ranging from 50 kDa to 6.4 kDa and four redox active centers, i.e., cytochrome b_{562}, cytochrome b_{566}, cytochrome c_1, and the Rieske iron-sulfur protein. The largest subunits are designated core proteins 1 and 2. The cytochrome b centers are present in the same molar concentrations, but have different absorption maxima and oxidation-reduction potentials.[22,23,58] Because the mitochondrial genome contains only a single complex III cytochrome b gene, the two centers are apparently on the same protein.[59] The molecular weight of the b cytochrome, deduced from its DNA sequence, is about 44 kDa,[59] but most gel electrophoresis systems give it a somewhat lower apparent molecular weight.[60] Molecular modeling based on the nucleotide sequence indicates that the cytochrome b protein could span the inner mitochondrial membrane up to nine times,[22] and recent data indicates that the two heme prosthetic groups are approximately 20 Å apart.[61] Cytochrome c_1, a 28-kDa protein, has an oxidation-reduction potential of +250 mV and binds cytochrome c and the iron-sulfur protein.[58,62,63] The Rieske iron-sulfur protein has a molecular weight of 25 kDa, and contains a 2Fe2S cluster with an oxidation-reduction potential of +280 mV.[64,65] Cytochrome c_1 and the Rieske protein are exposed on the cytosolic side of the inner mitochondrial membrane,[66] and the b cytochromes are buried within the membrane.[49] The high molecular weight core subunits are exposed to the matrix compartment and appear to have no function in electron transport;[67,68] the core proteins are not present in ubiquinol–cytochrome c reductase from photosynthetic organisms and *Paracoccus denitrificans*.[69,70]

Complex III translocates protons during electron transport and has a transmembrane arrangement, in accord with its function in site-2 oxidative phosphorylation.[71,72] The complex appears to be a dimer in electron micrographs of two-dimensional crystals, and one model for its reaction mechanism involves a functional dimer, but the complex is active even when clearly monomeric.[73–75]

Electron transport through complex III is branched rather than linear. The branched nature of electron flow in the complex was initially suggested by Mitchell to explain the 2:1 stoichiometric ratio of directionally translocated protons to transferred electrons.[76] The proposed mechanism is known as the Q cycle, and employs ubiquinone (Q) both as an electron and a proton carrier. Modified Q cycles and the sites of action of inhibitors which helped establish current models[65,77] for the

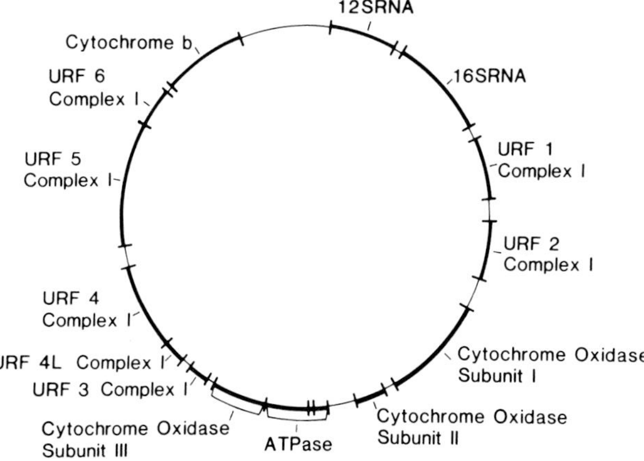

Fig. 34-7 The human mitochondrial genome. Sequences initially designated as unidentified reading frames (URF) are now known to encode respiratory proteins in Complex I. (See Refs. 46, 47, 95, and 96.)

mechanism of complex III are shown in Fig. 34-8. Both models involve (1) a pair of quinone reaction sites, Q_o and Q_i, that are functionally situated on opposite sides in the membrane, and (2) generation of a low potential ubisemiquinone reductant of cytochrome b_{566}. In the model shown in Fig. 34-8*A*, one electron is transferred from ubiquinol (QH_2) to the iron-sulfur protein, and the resulting low potential ubisemiquinone reduces cytochrome b_{566}. These oxidations at the Q_o center release two protons to the cytosolic compartment. At Q_i, which is the quinone reductase center, the high potential cytochrome b_{562} reduces ubiquinone to ubiquinol in two steps via a ubisemiquinone intermediate. The result is that half of the electron equivalents from the initial ubiquinol oxidation are returned to ubiquinol in the quinone/quinol pool. In a second model (Fig. 34-8*B*), a dehydrogenase operates in conjunction with complex III to generate the initial quinol reductant,[65] but it is now clear that the complex can turn over with a quinol substrate even in the absence of dehydrogenase,[78] and such mechanisms have been criticized on these grounds.[79] The net reactions in both models account for the observed stoichiometry of two protons translocated per electron transferred, for oxidant-induced reduction of cytochrome b,[80] and for inhibition of cytochrome c_1 reduction by British anti-Lewisite (BAL), which destroys the iron-sulfur cluster.[81–83] Both models also account for inhibition of cytochrome b_{566} reduction by myxothiazole, which binds at a site near b_{566} and the iron-sulfur center.[84,85] Depending on the accumulation of ubiquinol, b_{562} may still be reduced at the Q_i site by ubiquinol in the quinol/quinone pool.[86] The mechanism involves displacement of the ubisemiquinone at the Q_o center.[87,88] Inhibitors such as 5-undecyl-6-hydroxy-4,7-hydroxynaphtho-quinone (UHBDT) inhibit reoxidation of the iron-sulfur center and reduction of b_{566}.[89] UHBDT binds to the reduced iron-sulfur protein, displacing ubiquinol and increasing the potential of the cluster by 100 mV. Antimycin inhibits quinone reduction at the Q_i site such that b cytochromes are reduced but reduction of cytochrome c_1 is inhibited.[84,90] The two functional species of ubisemiquinone in these models have been demonstrated by EPR spectroscopy.[91]

Cytochrome Oxidase (Complex IV)

Cytochrome c mediates electron transfer between complex III and complex IV. The heme cleft in the cytochrome c molecule

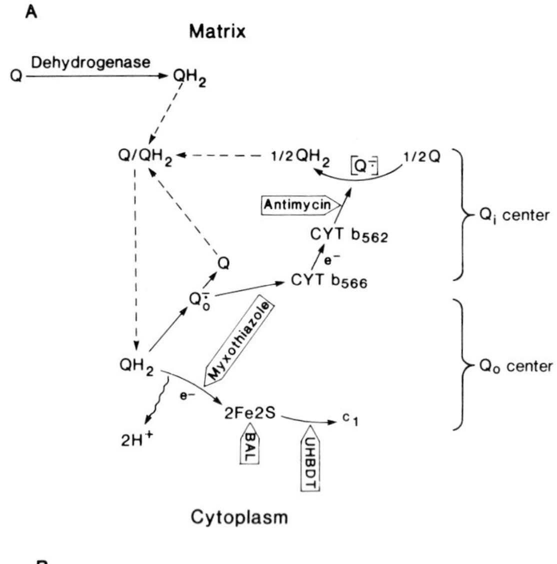

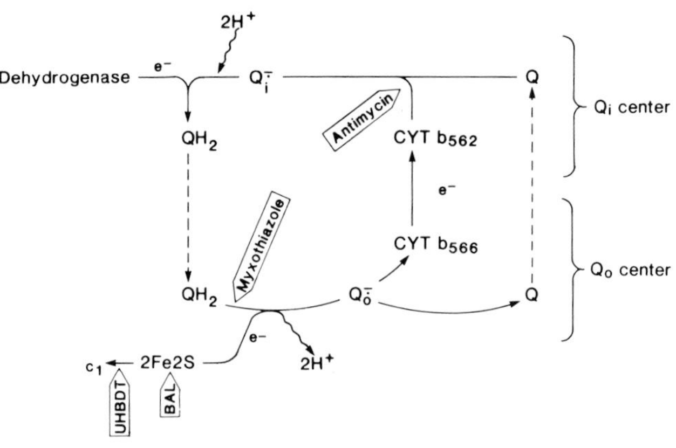

Fig. 34-8 Models of the Q cycle for electron transfer and proton translocation by complex III. Solid arrows indicate direct electron transfer reactions, and dashed arrows indicate diffusion of ubiquinone species within the membrane. Q/QH_2 indicates the mobile ubiquinone pool. Arrows show sites of action of the inhibitors antimycin, myxothiazole, British anti-Lewisite (BAL), and 5-undecyl-6-hydroxy-4,7-hydroxynaphthoquinone (UHBDT). *(Adapted from Rich;[77] B from Trumpower.[65])*

is surrounded by lysine residues (Fig. 34-9) which interact electrostatically with cytochrome c_1 and with subunit II of cytochrome oxidase.[92] Since there is but one site for electron transfer on the cytochrome c molecule, it must act as an electron shuttle between complex III and complex IV in the intramembranal space. Kinetic analysis of this reaction indicates that cytochrome c functions as a mobile pool,[93] and it therefore performs the same function played by ubiquinone in the lipid phase of the inner mitochondial membrane.[94]

Bovine heart cytochrome oxidase contains ten polypeptides, of which subunits I, II, and III are encoded by mitochondrial genes.[95,96] The complex catalyzes the four-electron reduction of molecular oxygen to water, and contains four redox-active prosthetic groups, i.e., two copper atoms and two equivalents of heme A. All four prosthetic groups are located in subunits I and II.[97,98] Subunit I is the most likely site of cytochrome a_3 and Cu_B, which are in close proximity.[99–101] Subunit II appears to contain the binding sites for cytochrome a and Cu_A, which are near the binding site for cytochrome c,[99] and this is consistent with the finding that subunit II is exposed on the cytosolic side of the membrane.[49,102] Further, cytochrome a and Cu_A are rapidly reduced by ferrocytochrome c, while cytochrome a_3 and Cu_B are reduced more slowly.[103] Finally, EPR spectroscopy indicates that both Cu_A and cytochrome a are on the cytosolic side of the membrane and that Cu_B and cytochrome a_3 are located distant from this membrane surface.[104,105] Subunit III can be removed from the enzyme without loss of significant electron transfer activity or major changes in absorption spectrum,[106] and has been implicated in redox-linked proton translocation.[106–108] Consistent with this role as a proton channel,[106] the polypeptide traverses the inner membrane and, when a specific glutamate residue is chemically modified with dicyclohexylcarbodiimide (DCCD), proton translocation is inhibited, but electron transport is not.[107,108] The primary sequence around this residue bears a striking homology to the sequence near a DCCD-reactive glutamate residue in a membrane protein which forms the proton channel of the bovine proton-translocating mitochondrial ATPase.[109]

INHERITED DEFECTS IN THE MAIN RESPIRATORY CHAIN

Inherited defects in proteins of the mitochondrial respiratory chain are thought to be the cause of Leber hereditary optic neuropathy and several mitochondrial myopathies, but extensive discussion of these conditions is not warranted because defects that are both specific and inherited have not yet been demonstrated. The fact that some respiratory chain proteins

Fig. 34-9 Three-dimensional structure of mitochondrial cytochrome c. The domains of lysine residues 13, 27, 72, and 87, which surround the heme crevice and contribute to electrostatic binding of protein reductants and oxidants, are superimposed on the protein backbone.[92] The heme prosthetic group and ligands to the iron are shown in bold. *(Adapted from F Salemme, Structure and function of cytochromes c, Ann Rev Biochem **46:**299, 1977. Used by permission.)*

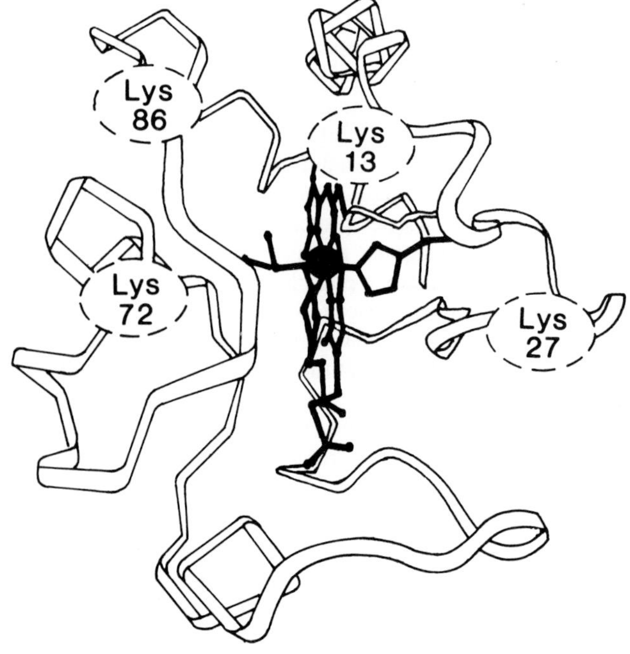

are encoded in the mitochondrion (Fig. 34-7) has made recognition of these conditions particularly difficult.

Defects of mitochondrial-encoded proteins should show maternal inheritance, reflecting the fact that all of the mitochondria in the fertilized egg derive from the ovum.[110] Moreover, unless random segregation of mitochondria with normal and mutated genomes, i.e., mitotic segregation, in a "carrier" mother creates an ovum in which there are no mutant mitochondria, all maternal offspring will receive mutant genes. Whether or not these offspring are affected, and how severely, will be determined by mitotic segregation during embryogenesis and by the number of mutated genes that are required to disturb the function of a particular cell. For instance, it is possible that mutations of some mitochondrial genes will disturb cell function only when very few normal mitochondrial genomes are present; mitotic segregation will create this situation only rarely, carriers of the defects will usually be normal, and the clinical condition might appear to be sporadic instead of inherited. Mutations of other mitochondrial genes might disturb cellular function even when many normal mitochondrial genomes are present; carriers of these mutations would be affected much more often and the familial nature of the disease would be recognized more readily. Even in these cases, however, tissue differences in the proportions of normal and mutant mitochondrial genomes might make the phenotype extremely variable, even within a single kindred.

The respiratory chain is so central to normal cell function that total deficiency of a nuclear-coded protein might well be lethal, and the early onset of symptoms and multiple congenital anomalies exhibited by infants with glutaric acidemia type II due to complete deficiency of ETF-QO, a protein somewhat outside the main respiratory chain, suggests that this is indeed the case. Autosomal recessive diseases with later onsets may thus be due to incomplete defects, which may be difficult to identify and study. Some of the nuclear-coded respiratory chain proteins, e.g., some cytochrome c oxidase subunits,[111] are tissue-specific, and defects in these proteins might be identifiable only in certain tissues. In spite of difficulties in case finding and studying defective respiratory chain proteins, two groups of disorders have been identified which are almost certainly due, at least on some occasions, to inherited defects of these proteins.

Leber hereditary optic neuropathy (LHON) is the best example of a human disorder transmitted as a maternal trait, and typical pedigrees (Fig. 34-10) have now been described which conform to this pattern of inheritance.[112–114] The usual manifestation of the disease is sudden loss of central vision and blindness, with severe bilateral optic atrophy and large central scotomas, usually in young adults. The condition affects many more males than females. In several pedigrees there are individuals with other neurologic abnormalities, such as dystonia, skeletal muscle myopathy, and mental retardation, apparently transmitted in the same manner.[112,114] Bilateral necrosis of the caudate and putamen has been described in several subjects with neurologic symptoms.[46]

The pedigrees are most consistent with mitochondrial inheritance, but some offspring of affected women are not affected, and there are women who clearly transmit the disease to offspring without being affected themselves. These phenomena, and the existence of subjects with neurologic manifestations in LHON pedigrees, have been explained on the basis of mitotic segregation. The preponderance of affected males in these pedigrees has not been explained. The specific defect or defects which can cause this disorder are not known, but maternal inheritance points to deficiency of one of the mitochondrially encoded respiratory chain proteins. Restriction fragments of mitochondrial DNA have been examined in certain pedigrees, but in most instances have not shown differences between affected and unaffected individuals.[114] Recently, Wallace and colleagues described a missense mutation (Arg_{340} →

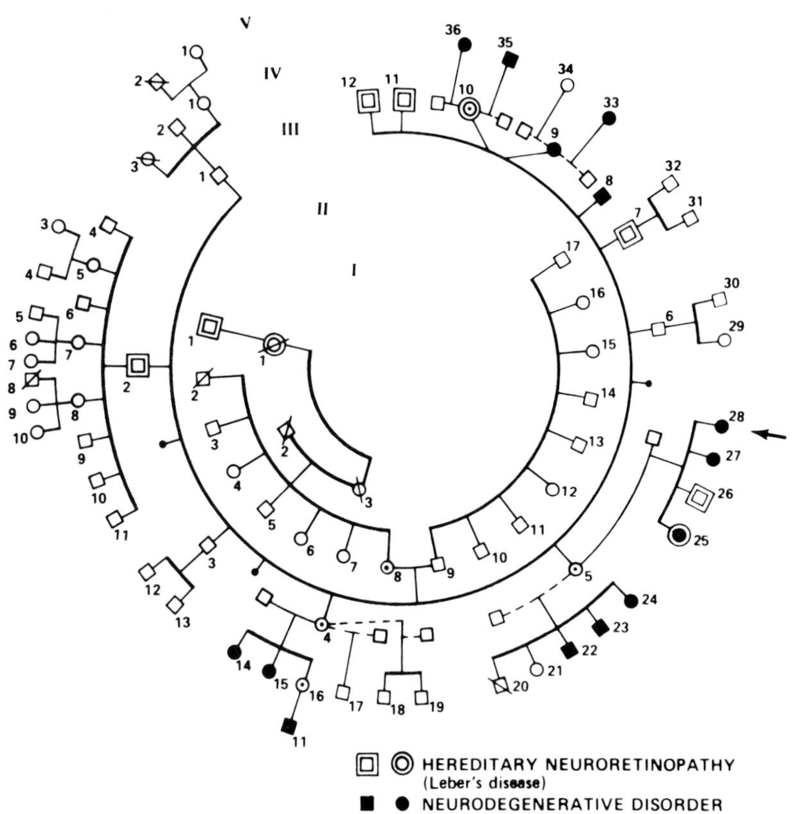

Fig. 34-10. Transmission of Leber hereditary optic neuropathy and a dystonic neurodegenerative disorder as maternal traits in the same family. *(From Novotny et al.[114] Used by permission.)*

His) in the mitochondrially encoded subunit 4 of NADH dehydrogenase (complex I) in 9 of 11 LHON pedigrees.[192] The functional consequence of this subtle alteration remains to be determined.

The other clinical phenotypes widely thought to be due to inherited defects of respiratory chain proteins are the so-called mitochondrial myopathies, and several defects have been demonstrated in these patients. Mitochondrial myopathies are a group of disorders characterized by (usually) late onset of proximal muscle weakness, the presence of ragged red fibers when skeletal muscle is stained with Gomori trichrome (Fig. 34-11), and abnormalities of mitochondrial ultrastructure on electron microscopy. Lactic acidosis, neurologic symptoms, and cardiomyopathy may also be present. Defects in complex I,[115–117] complex III,[118–122] and complex IV[123,124] have been identified in the skeletal muscle mitochondria of several patients, usually by polarigraphic assay of oxygen consumption, spectral measurements of cytochromes, and occasionally by direct assays of activities of various complexes. Defects in these complexes have also been identified in infants with severe disease who usually die before the age of 1 year.[125–128] Mitochondrial proteins have been studied by Western blot analysis in only a few patients. One infant with hypotonia, congenital lactic acidosis, and cardiomyopathy had almost total absence of the iron-sulfur clusters of complex I (Table 34-1) in liver mitochondria,[125] with immunoblot analysis showing complete absence of two of the polypeptide constituents of the iron-protein fragment.[129] The most likely cause of this observation was thought to be inability to properly assemble complex I, but the primary defect was not identified. In an adult female with lactic acidosis, progressive muscle weakness, and a defect in complex III, immunoblot analysis of skeletal muscle mitochondria showed deficiency of several nuclear- and mitochrondrial-encoded complex III proteins,[121,122] but these defects were not detected in cultured fibroblasts.[130] These results are also consistent with a primary defect leading to decreased stability of the complex, but again the defect was not defined. Recent reports describe deletions of up to 5.9 kb in skeletal muscle but not in lymphocyte mitochondrial DNA from about 40 percent of patients with mitochondrial myopathies.[193,194]

It should be clear that inherited defects of the main respiratory chain do indeed exist in human beings, but that they are difficult to study and they are not yet clearly defined. It would appear that improved definition and understanding of these conditions will come about only when biochemical and recombinant DNA techniques are used together to identify defects in particular proteins, and to correlate these defects with abnormalities in mitochondrial and nuclear DNA.

BIOCHEMISTRY OF THE ETF/ETF-QO SIDE CHAIN

Mitochondrial oxidation of fatty acids and several amino acids involves acyl-CoA intermediates which are oxidized to 2,3-enoyl-CoA thioesters by specific flavin-containing acyl-CoA dehydrogenases (see Chaps. 28, 30, and 33). Choline is catabolized via *N,N*-dimethylglycine and sarcosine by two specific *N*-methyl dehydrogenases[131,132] which contain covalently bound FAD and dissociable folate cofactors.[133] Electron transfer from these enzymes to the main respiratory chain is mediated by ETF and ETF-QO (Fig. 34-1).

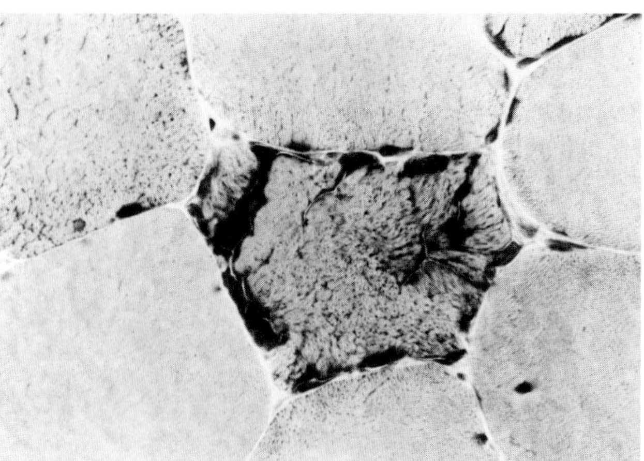

Fig. 34-11 Cross-section of human skeletal muscle. The fiber in the center shows dark clumps of mitochondria which stain red with modified trichrome. The jagged, white lines are cracks due to increased lipid. Modified trichrome; original magnification ×800. *(Courtesy of Dr. S.P. Ringel.)*

Electron Transfer Flavoprotein

Porcine electron transfer flavoprotein is the best characterized mammalian ETF; it is a soluble matrix protein which exists as a 60-kDa heterodimer and contains a single, noncovalently bound, FAD prosthetic group.[134–139] The α and β subunits have molecular weights of 32 kDa and 28 kDa, respectively. Unlike most protein-bound flavins, the flavin in ETF is highly fluorescent[140] and, when chemically reduced, the protein stabilizes an anion semiquinone which is far less fluorescent than the oxidized flavin;[141] this decrease in ETF flavin fluorescence on reduction has been employed to assay the primary flavoprotein dehydrogenases and ETF-QO.[142,143] Immunologic analysis by Western blotting and immunoprecipitation of radiolabeled human fibroblast proteins indicate that the subunits of human ETF have approximately the same apparent molecular weights as the porcine and rat proteins.[144,145] The α subunit is synthesized as a 35-kDa precursor which is processed to the mature subunit during translocation into the mitochondrion, but the β subunit is apparently synthesized as the mature polypeptide.[145] The functions of the subunits in the reductive and oxidative half-reactions of ETF and the precise location of the flavin are not known.

The reactions between ETF and primary flavoprotein dehydrogenases, and between ETF and ETF-QO involve electrostatic interactions, with ϵ-amino groups of ETF providing a cationic domain that reacts with carboxylate groups on the primary dehydrogenases and ETF-QO.[141,146,147] ETF does not form a stable complex with the primary dehydrogenases, but coulombic forces contribute to the formation of a Michaelis complex between the two proteins.

The oxidation-reduction states of octanoyl-CoA dehydrogenase and ETF in the reductive half-reaction have been defined by pre-steady state and steady state spectrophotometric analysis,[15] and the mechanism of this half-reaction is shown in Equations 34-2 to 34-4.

$$DH_{2e^-}\cdot 2,3\text{-enoyl CoA} + ETF_{ox} \rightleftharpoons DH_{1e^-}\cdot 2,3\text{-enoyl CoA} + ETF_{1e^-} \quad (34\text{-}2)$$

$$DH_{1e^-}\cdot 2,3\text{-enoyl CoA} + ETF_{ox} \rightleftharpoons DH_{ox}\cdot 2,3\text{-enoyl CoA} + ETF_{1e^-} \quad (34\text{-}3)$$

$$DH_{ox}\cdot 2,3\text{-enoyl CoA} \rightleftharpoons DH_{ox} + 2,3\text{-enoyl CoA} \quad (34\text{-}4)$$

Electrons are transferred from the two-electron-reduced dehydrogenase flavin to two ETF molecules in two separate one-electron transfers to yield two molecules of one-electron-reduced ETF. In the case of octanoyl-CoA dehydrogenase, the one-electron-reduced dehydrogenase flavin is stabilized by the tightly bound enoyl-CoA product,[148] and this is probably true of all ETF-linked dehydrogenases, because all that have been studied reduce ETF flavin to the semiquinone. Thus, while the flavin of primary dehydrogenases apparently oscillates between the zero-, one-, and two-electron-reduced states during physiological electron transport, that of ETF oscillates only between the zero- and one-electron-reduced states.

Electron Transfer Flavoprotein-Ubiquinone Oxidoreductase

ETF-QO was initially detected in EPR spectra as an unknown iron-sulfur cluster signal on the oxygen side of the rotenone inhibition site in mitochondria and submitochondrial particles reduced with NADH,[9] and was purified by following the EPR signal after solubilizing the protein from beef heart mitochondria and submitochondrial particles.[4,149] The purified protein contained one equivalent of FAD and four equivalents of non-heme iron and acid-labile sulfur per 68-kDa monomer, and the iron-sulfur cluster was reduced by ETF in the presence of butyryl-CoA and acyl-CoA dehydrogenase under anaerobic conditions. The protein has also been purified from pork liver submitochondrial particles,[143] and has been demonstrated in human liver and fibroblasts by Western blotting using antisera prepared against the pork enzyme.[144] Consistent with the presence of a single flavin and 4Fe4S cluster, the protein takes up three electrons when chemically reduced, but enzymatic reduction proceeds only to the two-electron-reduced form, with the flavin in the semiquinone state.[4,143] Resonance Raman spectroscopy of the iron-sulfur cluster is consistent with the assignment of an 4Fe4S cluster and, based on studies with metal-flavin chelates, the flavin is not coordinated with the iron in the cluster.[150]

Extensive study of ETF-QO was limited for some time by the lack of a sensitive catalytic assay, but three such assays are now available. ETF-QO can be assayed by following reduction of the ubiquinone homologue Q_1 in a system containing an acyl-CoA substrate, purified acyl-CoA dehydrogenase, and ETF. The turnover number measured in the glutaryl-CoA-ubiquinone reductase reaction is 55 per second.[151] ETF-QO also catalyzes the equilibration of ETF redox states under anaerobic conditions according to Equation 34-5.[143]

$$2\ ETF_{1e^-} \rightleftarrows ETF_{2e^-} + ETF_{ox} \qquad (34\text{-}5)$$

In the forward reaction, i.e., disproportionation of ETF semiquinone, the turnover number is about 200 per second at pH 7.4. This number represents the minimal rate of ETF semiquinone oxidation by ETF-QO. ETF-QO is more easily assayed fluorometrically in the reverse reaction, i.e., by comproportionation of ETF_{ox} and ETF_{2e^-}. The turnover number in this direction is about 100 per second. This assay can also be utilized to assay the crude soluble or particulate ETF-QO.[144] ETF-QO has also been assayed in submitochondrial particles and in the particulate fraction of human fibroblasts as an NADH-ETF reductase.[152] Under anaerobic conditions and in the presence of antimycin, NADH reduces ETF to the semiquinone. The reaction is inhibited by rotenone and antibody to ETF-QO and requires the ubiquinone pool. Unlike succinic dehydrogenase, ETF-QO can stabilize a ubisemiquinone intermediate in the two-step reduction of ubiquinone without the presence of other proteins.

GLUTARIC ACIDEMIA TYPE II

Glutaric acidemia type II, or multiple acyl-CoA dehydrogenation deficiency, is a recently described inborn error characterized clinically by nonketotic hypoglycemia and metabolic acidosis; pathologically by fatty degeneration of liver parenchymal cells, renal tubular epithelium, and myocardium; and biochemically by the accumulation and excretion of oxidation products of all substrates normally oxidized by mitochondrial flavin-containing acyl-CoA dehydrogenases. Oxidation of these substrates by intact cells and mitochondria is decreased, but in vitro activity of acyl-CoA dehydrogenases is normal. In most cases the disorder is due to deficiency of either electron transfer flavoprotein (ETF) or ETF:ubiquinone oxidoreductase (ETF-QO), but in some it may be due to an as yet undefined abnormality in flavin metabolism or transport. Complete deficiency of ETF-QO is often associated with congenital anomalies, the most frequent and characteristic being cysts and dysplasia of the kidneys. All forms of the disease appear to be transmitted as autosomal recessive traits. Most patients with severe disease do not survive the first few weeks of life.

Clinical Manifestations

Patients with glutaric acidemia type II fall into one of three groups, each consistent within a family. These have been designated as (1) neonatal onset with congenital anomalies, (2) neonatal onset without anomalies, and (3) mild or later onset. The first two groups are sometimes said to have multiple acyl-CoA dehydrogenation deficiency, severe (MADD:S) and the third to have multiple acyl-CoA dehydrogenation deficiency, mild (MADD:M), or ethylmalonic-adipic aciduria.

Neonatal onset patients with congenital anomalies are often premature and present during the first 24 to 48 h of life with hypotonia, hepatomegaly, severe hypoglycemia, and metabolic acidosis, and (often) an odor similar to that present in isovaleric acidemia (see Chap. 28), i.e., the odor of sweaty feet. In some patients the kidneys are palpably enlarged, and there may be facial dysmorphism (high forehead and low-set ears, hypertelorism, hypoplastic mid face, etc.), rocker-bottom feet, muscular defects of the anterior abdominal wall, and anomalies of the external genitalia, including hypospadias and chordee. Most such patients die within the first week of life.[153,158] In other patients congenital anomalies are not noted on physical examination, and renal cysts are discovered only at autopsy.[159–162]

Infants without congenital anomalies usually develop hypotonia, tachypnea and metabolic acidosis, hepatomegaly, hypoglycemia, and a "sweaty feet" odor within the first few days of life, many of them within the first 24 h. The few patients with this form of the disease that have survived beyond the first week of life because of prompt diagnosis and treatment have died within a few months, usually with severe cardiomyopathy. A few other infants have been hypoglycemic in the newborn period, and only later developed typical episodes of

Reye syndrome-like illnesses, and these patients have survived somewhat longer.[153,163–168]

The course and age at presentation of later onset glutaric acidemia type II, or ethylmalonic-adipic aciduria, is extremely variable. The first patient to be described with this form of the condition had intermittent episodes of vomiting, hypoglycemia, and acidosis beginning at 7 weeks of age,[169,170] and another was totally symptom-free during childhood, presenting in adult life with episodic vomiting, hypoglycemia, hepatomegaly, and proximal myopathy.[171]

Several other patients with episodic disease beginning during the first few years of life have been described,[172–174] as well as two others with progressive lipid storage myopathy and carnitine deficiency.[152,175,176] One such patient was originally reported as a case of systemic carnitine deficiency, and was only later shown to have had deficiency of ETF-QO.[152,176]

Routine laboratory evaluation shows severe metabolic acidosis, often with an increased anion gap, mild or moderate hyperammonemia (usually $< 200\ \mu M$), and severe hypoglycemia without ketonuria or ketonemia. Serum transaminases may be elevated, and prothrombin and partial thromboplastin times may be prolonged. Plasma lactic acid is usually elevated. Chest x-ray may show cardiac enlargement, and echocardiography may show evidence of hypertrophic cardiomyopathy. Abdominal ultrasound or CT scan may show renal cysts (Fig. 34-12).

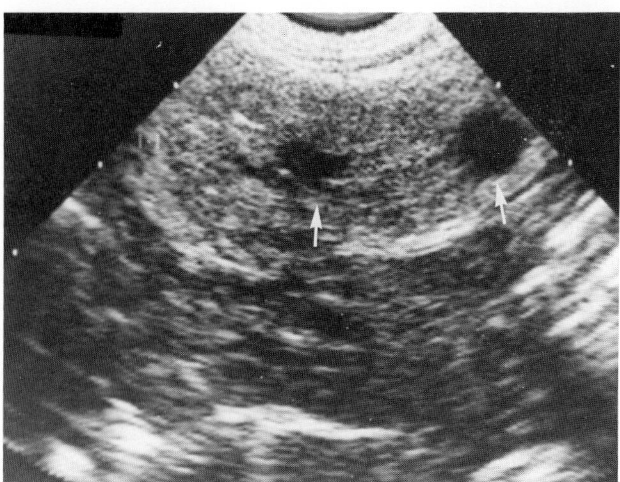

Fig. 34-12 Abdominal ultrasound showing renal cysts in a 2-day-old infant with glutaric acidemia type II due to ETF-QO deficiency. *(Courtesy of Dr. C. Greenberg.)*

Urine organic acid analysis is abnormal, showing various combinations of short-chain volatile acids (e.g., isovaleric, isobutyric, 2-methylbutyric); glutaric, ethylmalonic, 3-hydroxyisovaleric, 2-hydroxyglutaric, 5-hydroxyhexanoic, adipic, suberic, sebacic, and dodecanedioic acids; and isovalerylglycine, isobutyrylglycine, and 2-methylbutyrylglycine (Fig. 34-13). 3-Hydroxybuyric and acetoacetic acids are either not seen or are not prominent. Organic acids are also significantly elevated in serum and cerebrospinal fluid.

Generalized aminoacidemia and aminoaciduria, often with marked increases in proline and hydroxyproline, are common in neonatal onset patients, and elevations of sarcosine in serum and urine are especially frequent in patients with later onset.

Carnitine concentrations in plasma may be normal or low, but acylcarnitine esters in urine may be significantly increased.[177] Treatment of one patient with oral carnitine produced a large increase in several acylcarnitine esters in urine, including acetylcarnitine, isobutyrylcarnitine, isovalerylcarnitine, hexanoylcarnitine, butyrylcarnitine, and propionylcarnitine.[152]

Diagnosis

The presence of the characteristic organic acid pattern in urine from a newborn with nonketotic hypoglycemia and metabolic acidosis establishes the diagnosis as glutaric acidemia type II. A very similar organic aciduria occurs in Jamaican vomiting sickness,[178] which occurs only after ingestion of unripe ackees and thus only in areas of the world in which the fruit is eaten.

Diagnosis in late onset cases may be considerably more difficult because metabolic acidosis, the usual indication for examining urine organic acids, may not be present. Further, the organic aciduria in such patients is considerably less pronounced and is often intermittent, being present only during acute episodes. The finding of 2-hydroxyglutaric aciduria in such patients is a useful diagnostic point, and serves to distinguish the condition from glutaric acidemia (glutaryl-CoA dehydrogenase deficiency), in which 3-hydroxyglutaric is excreted. Some patients with mild glutaric acidemia type II bear a strong phenotypic resemblance to children with von Gierke's disease, and liver biopsy will be avoided only if the absence of ketonemia and ketonuria is noted.

Whole fibroblast metabolism of a variety of radiolabelled compounds may be examined in an attempt to solidify the diagnosis, and this can be done by measuring oxidation of various ^{14}C-compounds, e.g., [1-^{14}C]palmitate, [1-^{14}C]octanoate, [1-^{14}C]butyrate, [1,5-^{14}C]glutarate, [2-^{14}C]lysine, [2-^{14}C]leucine, etc., to $^{14}CO_2$, or incorporation of ^{14}C from appropriate labeled precursors into lipid or protein. Another method assays oxidation of [1,5-^{14}C]glutaryl-CoA to $^{14}CO_2$ in the absence of artificial electron acceptor, when oxidation is totally dependent on the presence of endogenous ETF and ETF-QO.[179,180] However, since there is more than one cause of the glutaric acidemia type II, specific diagnosis can be established only by demonstrating deficiency of ETF or ETF-QO in fibroblasts or other appropriate tissues, e.g., liver, or by showing that cells

Fig. 34-13 Urine organic acids in an infant with glutaric acidemia type II. A = lactic, B = malonic (internal standard), C = ethylmalonic, D = glutaric, E = adipic, F = 2-hydroxyglutaric, G = suberic, H = sebacic, I = dodecanedioic. *(From S.I. Goodman and S.P. Markey,* Diagnosis of Organic Acidemias by Gas Chromatography-Mass Spectrometry, *Alan R. Liss Inc., New York, 1981. Used by permission.)*

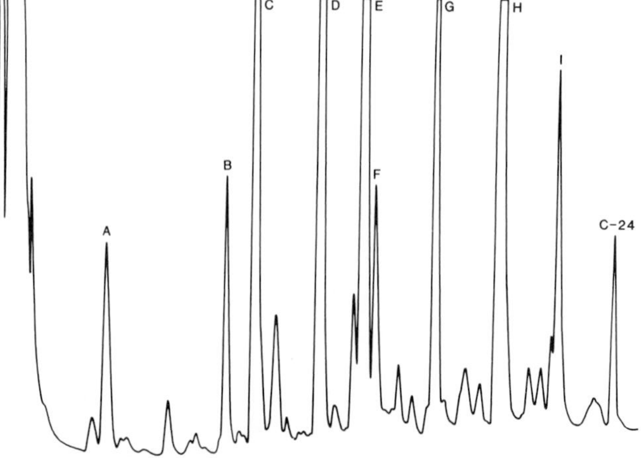

from a particular patient do not complement cells with a known biochemical defect.

Measuring ETF activity in fibroblasts is difficult, but two recently described spectrophotometric assays make this somewhat easier. The first procedure follows the reduction of dichlorophenol indophenol (DCPIP) in the presence of a tissue source of ETF and substrate concentrations of octanoyl-CoA and octanoyl-CoA dehydrogenase,[181] and the other follows the reduction of Q_1, a ubiquinone analogue, in the presence of tissue and substrate concentrations of octanoyl-CoA, octanoyl-CoA dehydrogenase, and ETF-QO.[182] The latter employs substrate concentrations of ETF-QO and therefore requires preparation of an additional reagent enzyme, but has the advantages of being more sensitive than dye reduction assays and being potentially sensitive to alterations of ETF at the domain which interacts with ETF-QO.

ETF-QO can be measured in fibroblasts and other tissues by catalyzed comproportionation of oxidized and two-electron-reduced (hydroquinone) forms of ETF,[143] or by NADH-ETF reductase activity.[152] In both of these assays the loss of ETF flavin fluorescence is followed as oxidized ETF is reduced to ETF semiquinone.

In some cases the specific defect can be demonstrated by showing deficient ETF or ETF-QO antigen in appropriate tissues, either by Western blot analysis[144] or by radiolabeling cells followed by immunoprecipitation.[145]

Glutaric acidemia type II fibroblasts also show a defect in the ability to release tritium from [9,10(*n*)-^{3}H]palmitic acid into cell water, and mutant fibroblasts may be assigned to complementation groups based on their ability to correct the defect in another cell line after polyethylene glycol–induced cell fusion.[183] Such procedures can quickly and accurately identify the enzyme defect in a test cell line without the need to grow the large numbers of cells that are necessary to assay specific enzymes. There is the additional advantage that if there are forms of glutaric acidemia type II due to mutations of proteins other than ETF and ETF-QO, cells with defects in the same protein can be identified as such without the need to identify the particular protein that is mutated.

Enzyme Defects

In some patients glutaric acidemia type II is due to inherited deficiency of ETF-QO, and in others it is due to inherited deficiency of ETF. Deficiency of ETF or ETF-QO can cause all three clinical forms of the disease. However, severe disease with anomalies is only rarely associated with ETF deficiency.[183a]

Deficiency of ETF-QO antigen was first demonstrated in membranes of liver mitochondria obtained from a female infant with polycystic kidneys and multiple additional congenital anomalies,[156] and ETF-QO antigen deficiency was then confirmed in fibroblasts[144] from this child and from two additional infants in whom renal cysts were discovered at autopsy.[159–162] There was almost total deficiency of ETF-QO in these cell lines, as assayed by catalyzed comproportionation of oxidized and two-electron-reduced ETF, with enzyme activity in four parent fibroblast lines being intermediate between patient and control values.[144] These results established inheritance of ETF-QO deficiency as an autosomal recessive trait. Less severe deficiency of ETF-QO, assayed both by catalyzed comproportionation of oxidized and reduced ETF and by NADH-ETF reductase, has been demonstrated in a patient with a late onset form of the disease.[152]

Deficiency of ETF antigen was first noted in fibroblast lines from two affected newborns without congenital anomalies. In one cell line both α and β-ETF subunits were deficient, and the very small amount of α-ETF that could be detected was slightly smaller than normal. In the other line the β-ETF subunit was normal in size and amount while the α-ETF subunit appeared to be smaller than normal.[144] Subsequent studies of ETF biosynthesis in these lines showed virtually no biosynthesis of precursor α-ETF subunit in the first line, while in the second line the precursor α-ETF subunit appeared to be about 1000-Da smaller than normal. Two weak bands of precursor α-ETF, one of normal size and one slightly smaller than normal, were demonstrated in cells from a third patient with severe disease without congenital anomalies.[145] Biosynthesis of β-ETF appeared normal in all three fibroblasts lines. Almost total deficiency of ETF catalysis has now been demonstrated in these cells, and in cells of yet another affected newborn without anomalies, and partial deficiency has been demonstrated in fibroblasts from several patients with late onset disease.[181] Hybridization studies have shown that all of these cell lines form one complementation group, indicating that the primary defects in all involve the same gene.[183]

While the above studies appear to show that inherited defects of the α-ETF subunit can be a cause of glutaric acidemia type II, no patient has yet been described with a primary defect in the β subunit.

Some glutaric acidemia type II cells have normal ETF and ETF-QO activities[182] and, since severe riboflavin deficiency can produce a quite similar organic aciduria in rats, the disease in such patients might be due to a defect in FAD biosynthesis or transport. There are, however, no instances in which such defects have been conclusively demonstrated. The central role of flavoproteins in cytosolic, microsomal, mitochondrial, and peroxisomal function suggests that early or complete blocks in FAD biosynthesis would be lethal, but the effects of a less severe block in FAD biosynthesis, or of an as yet undescribed transport system which might move FAD from the cytoplasm into mitochondria, are more difficult to predict. A defect in cytoplasmic FAD biosynthesis could lead to FAD deficiency in both peroxisomes and mitochondria, and might explain why certain patients with glutaric acidemia type II resemble those with Zellweger syndrome,[182] in which peroxisomal dysfunction is prominent (see Chap. 57). Defects of this type should affect only mitochondrial (and peroxisomal) processes which are flavoprotein-dependent, and should especially affect proteins with low affinity for FAD or which, like ETF and glutaryl-CoA dehydrogenase, are unstable in its absence.

Pathology

All patients autopsied to date have shown severe microvesicular fatty changes in liver parenchymal cells, cells of the proximal renal tubule, and myocardium, but these changes are not diagnostic. Renal anomalies, when present, may be dramatic. The kidneys may be so large that they fill the abdomen, and cysts may occupy all of the cortex and medulla.[157,158,184] Dysplastic changes are present in some cases, but not all (Fig. 34-14).

Brain has been examined in six patients. In two cases there was focal dysplasia of the cerebral cortex with bilateral reduction in the number of gyri in the frontal, parietal, and temporal lobes, with numerous warty protrusions on the temporoparietal cortex, and microscopic evidence of abnormal neuronal migration.[184] Abnormal neuronal migration was observed in three additional patients[185,186] but not in a fourth,[157] in whom the sole finding on routine examination was a reduced number of Purkinje cells in the cerebellar cortex. Electron microscopy in this patient showed moderately electron-dense, membrane-limited cytoplasmic bodies, and it was suggested that these might be characteristic, if not pathognomonic.

Concentrations of glutaric acid are increased in several tissues, including liver and kidney, and detection of this compound in postmortem tissue has established the diagnosis in several cases, one of them including an infant with fatty changes in the liver that were prominent enough to have suggested a diagnosis of Wolman disease (see Chap. 64).

Incidence

The disorder is not screened for in the newborn period, and there are no accurate figure about incidence. Many reports of the condition have appeared since its first description in 1975,[163] and it is probably one of the more common inborn errors. It is certainly not rare.

Genetics

Demonstration of the ETF-QO deficiency in some patient fibroblasts, with enzyme activities in parents intermediate between patient and control values,[144] established inheritance of this form of the disease as autosomal recessive, and more recent reports of the condition show a more nearly expected ratio of affected males and females.

The occurrence of defects in a α-ETF biosynthesis in both males and females, even in the same family, suggests that α-subunit deficiency is inherited as an autosomal recessive trait. As stated above, there is to date no description of disease due to deficiency of only the ETF β subunit.

Many of the first glutaric acidemia type II patients to be described were male, prompting speculation that the disorder was inherited as an X-linked trait. The family history of one affected newborn was particularly striking, with two maternal uncles dying in infancy of what might well have been the same disorder, and this strongly suggested X-linked recessive inheritance.[161] Glutaric acidemia type II in the proband, however, was later shown to be due to ETF-QO deficiency,[144] which is an autosomal recessive trait, and the death of the two maternal uncles may have been caused by ornithine transcarbamylase deficiency, another disorder that was present in the family.[187]

Prenatal Diagnosis

Prenatal diagnosis has been established on several occasions by demonstrating large amounts of glutaric acid in amniotic fluid and/or impaired substrate oxidation by whole cultured amniocytes.[166,167,188,189] Confirmation of predictions that the fetus would be affected has been made by showing deficient substrate oxidation in whole fetal fibroblasts, by demonstrating the presence of large, cystic kidneys in ETF-QO-deficient fetuses (Fig. 34-14), or, in two instances, by showing that fetuses which had been allowed to proceed to term indeed had the disease.

Genetic Heterogeneity

Since glutaric acidemia type II can be caused by mutations in ETF and ETF-QO, and possibly by defects in FAD biosynthesis or transport, there is clearly a considerable degree of genetic heterogeneity within the condition. There are probably several mutant alleles at the ETF-QO and α-ETF loci, because different mutant fibroblasts have different amounts of ETF and ETF-QO activity and antigen,[144,152] and this correlates with disease severity. Also, ETF activity in one mutant cell line could be increased by FAD,[181] perhaps suggesting the existence of a mutant enzyme with diminished coenzyme binding. Studies of ETF α-subunit biosynthesis by ETF-deficient mutant cell lines also indicate that there are several different mutant alleles.[145] One mutant allele appears to make no precursor whatever, as though there were a nonsense mutation near the 5′ end of the mRNA; one appears to synthesize a precursor of normal molecular weight, as though there were a single amino acid substitution; and another appears to synthesize a shortened precursor, as though a mutation close to the 3′ end of the mRNA caused premature termination of translation. The cDNA sequences which encode ETF-QO and the ETF α and β subunits have not been cloned, and there is no information available about the specific mutations that cause the disease.

Pathogenesis

Deficiency of ETF or ETF-QO in severely affected patients is almost complete, resulting in functional deficiency of all mitochondrial flavoprotein dehydrogenases and accumulation of their substrates, probably including dimethylglycine and sarcosine. Some excreted acids, like glutaric, probably derive from simple hydrolysis of the accumulated coenzyme A ester, but most have a more complex origin which involves carboxylation, ω or $(\omega - 1)$ oxidation in microsomes, β oxidation in peroxisomes, and glycine conjugation, either alone or in combination. For example, microsomal ω oxidation of accumulated long-chain acyl-CoAs probably creates long-chain dicarboxylic esters, with subsequent β oxidation in peroxisomes generating the C_{12} (dodecanedioic), C_{10} (sebacic), C_8 (suberic), and C_6 (adipic) acids.

Sarcosine is frequently found in serum and urine of less severely affected patients, but not in patients with acute neonatal onset, perhaps for the following reason: Sarcosine is synthesized by dimethylglycine dehydrogenase (DMGDH) and metabolized by sarcosine dehydrogenase (SDH). Both enzymes transfer flavin-bound electrons to ETF, and sarcosine biosynthesis might be blocked in complete ETF (or ETF-QO) deficiency. With less severe deficiency of ETF or ETF-QO, sarcosine would accumulate if its rate of oxidation was slower than its rate of biosynthesis. The apparent K_m of DMGDH and SDH for their substrates is 0.5 and 1.0 mM, respectively,[133] which would favor sarcosine accumulation if the enzyme turnover numbers were similar.

Limited availability of acetyl-CoA from β oxidation of fatty acids, with decreased synthesis of *N*-acetylglutamate (Chap. 30) and reduced allosteric activation of pyruvate carboxylase (Chap. 32), may be important in causing hyperammonemia

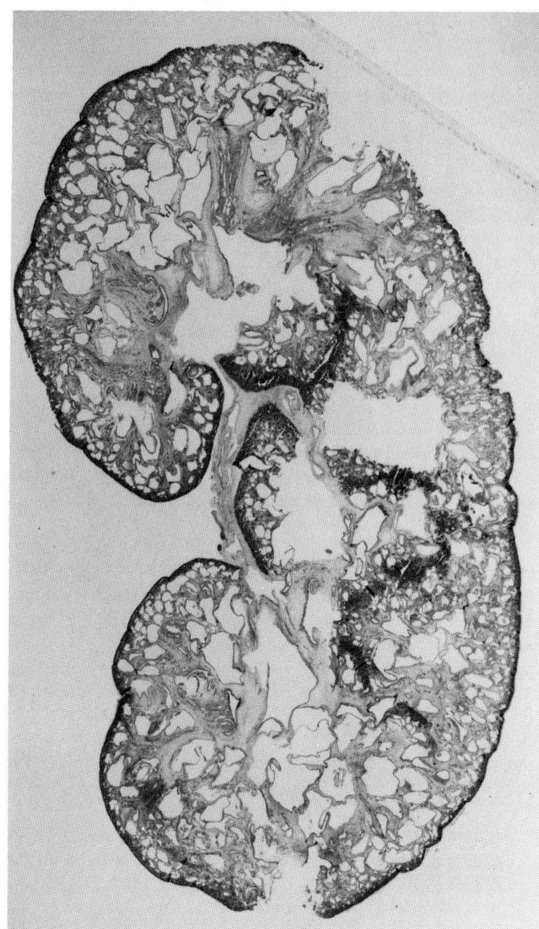

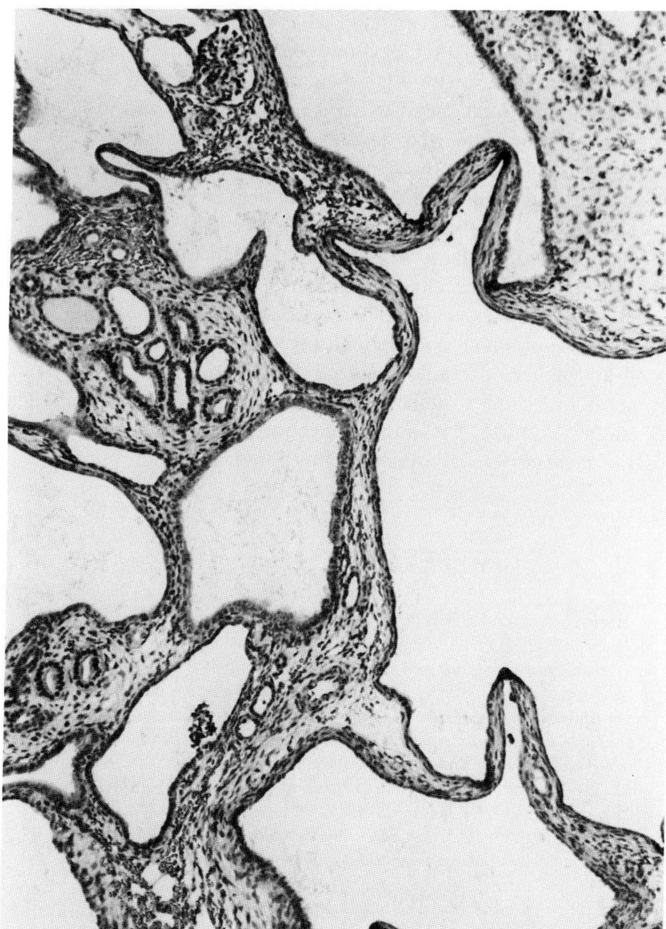

Fig. 34-14 Kidney of a 19-week fetus with glutaric acidemia type II due to ETF-QO deficiency. *Left:* Not magnified. *Right:* Cysts derived from Bowman's capsule and renal tubules, with interstitial tissue resembling primitive mesenchyme. Both kidneys showed the same features. H&E; original magnification ×50. *(Courtesy of Dr. Y.E. Hsia.)*

and hypoglycemia. Decreased generation of NADH could also limit gluconeogenesis by decreasing glyceraldehyde-phosphate dehydrogenase activity. Hyperammonemia may contribute to the encephalopathy that occurs during acute episodes, but high circulating levels of toxic short-chain fatty acids and reduced levels of ketone bodies may also play a role. The heart's inability to oxidize long-chain fatty acids, and the decreased availability of ketone bodies, deprives it of preferred energy sources, perhaps causing cardiomyopathy.

It is clear that loss of carnitine esters of organic acids in the urine can lead to depletion of carnitine stores, but the role that carnitine deficiency plays in pathogenesis is not clear. In severely affected infants, for example, complete deficiency of ETF or ETF-QO would preclude mitochondrial β oxidation of fatty acids, even in the presence of normal carnitine stores. Carnitine deficiency appears more likely to play a role in the pathogenesis of late onset glutaric acidemia type II; in these patients, who presumably have marginally adequate rates of β oxidation, carnitine depletion could further impair β oxidation by decreasing uptake of long-chain fatty acids into skeletal muscle mitochondria, leading to fat accumulation and myopathy.

The cause of abnormal fetal development in complete ETF-QO deficiency is not known, but the presence of congenital anomalies suggests a specific toxic effect of one of the accumulated metabolites or the need for ETF-QO, or this part of the electron transport chain, in certain developmental processes. The similarity of the renal lesions to those seen in riboflavin deficiency and in the Zellweger syndrome has been noted,[185] but remains unexplained. The lack of anomalies in the few patients with complete ETF deficiency that are known is puzzling, since ETF-QO accepts electrons only from ETF, and the results of the metabolic block should be the same in both conditions. There is, however, more residual oxidation of fatty acids in mutant cells with ETF deficiency than in those with ETF-QO deficiency,[181] and the presence of very small amounts of ETF activity in "ETF-deficient" cell lines may in some way prevent the development of anomalies.

Treatment

Most patients that present within a few days of birth, even those without multiple anomalies, die within the first few months of life. Diets low in fat and protein, with supplementation of carnitine and riboflavin, have been tried without success. Intravenous administration of methylene blue (2 mg/kg per dose) has been tried in one instance, with apparent clinical improvement and almost total clearing of organic aciduria, but the child died soon after the therapeutic trial was terminated.[190] Such treatment assumes that the artificial electron acceptor will enter mitochondria, remove flavin-bound electrons from acyl-CoA dehydrogenases, and lessen substrate accumulation behind the metabolic block.

Treatment with riboflavin, carnitine, and diets low in protein and fat has been somewhat more successful when applied to patients with milder or later onset disease. Treatment with oral riboflavin (100 to 300 mg/day) has been particularly effective in a few patients, including a woman who developed organic aciduria and sarcosinuria only during pregnancy and intercurrent infection, and who without treatment had had six consecutive offspring die by 3 months of age.[173–175,191] With riboflavin treatment during pregnancy, she delivered two normal offspring.[191] The primary defects in these patients have not been identified. Patients with defects in flavin metabolism or transport should be excellent candidates for such treatment, but there may also be patients whose defects in ETF and ETF-QO, both of which contain ionically bound FAD, might respond to higher intramitochondrial FAD concentrations. This might overcome a defect in coenzyme binding, or the FAD might stabilize the mutant electron transferase just enough to increase its activity above a required threshold.

REFERENCES

1. HAMAMOTO T, KAGAWA Y: H^+-ATPase as an energy-converting enzyme, in Martonosi AN (ed): *The Enzymes of Biological Membranes, Bioenergetics of Electron and Proton Transport*, New York, Plenum, 1985, vol 4, p 149.
2. HATEFI J, RAGAN CI, GALANTE YM: The enzymes and enzyme complexes of the mitochondrial oxidative phosphorylation system, in Martonosi AN (ed): *The Enzymes of Biological Membranes, Bioenergetics of Electron and Proton Transport*, New York, Plenum, 1985, vol 4, p 1.
3. HATEFI Y: The mitochondrial electron transport and oxidative phosphorylation system. *Ann Rev Biochem* 54:1015, 1985.
4. RUZICKA FJ, BEINERT H: A new iron-sulfur flavoprotein of the respiratory chain: A component of the fatty acid β oxidation pathway. *J Biol Chem* 252:8440, 1977.
5. COTTINGHAM IR, RAGAN CI: The reconstitution of L-3-glycerophosphate-cytochrome c oxidoreductase from L-3-glycerophosphate dehydrogenase, ubiquinone-10 and ubiquinol-cytochrome c oxidoreductase. *Biochem J* 192:19, 1980.
6. GARRIB A, MCMURRAY WC: Purification and characterization of glycerol-3-phosphate dehydrogenase (flavin-linked) from rat liver mitochondria. *J Biol Chem* 261:8042, 1986.
7. ERNSTER L, LEE I-Y, NORLING B, PERSSON B: Studies with ubiquinone-depleted submitochondrial particles. Essentially of ubiquinone for the interaction of succinic dehydrogenase, NADH dehydrogenase and cytochrome b. *Eur J Biochem* 9:299, 1969.
8. LOW H, VALLIN I: Succinate-linked diphosphopyridine nucleotide reduction in submitochondrial particles. *Biochim Biophys Acta* 69:361, 1963.
9. OHNISHI T, WILSON DF, ASAKURA T, CHANCE B: Studies on iron-sulfur proteins in the site I region of the respiratory chain in pigeon heart mitochondria and submitochondrial particles. *Biochem Biophys Res Comm* 46:1631, 1972.
10. DAVIS KA, HATEFI Y: Succinic dehydrogenase. I. Purification, molecular properties and substructure. *Biochemistry* 10:2509, 1971.
11. COOK RJ, MISONO KS, WAGNER C: The amino acid sequences of the flavin-peptides of dimethylglycine dehydrogenase and sarcosine dehydrogenase from rat liver mitochondria. *J Biol Chem* 260:12998, 1985.
12. WAKABAYASHI S, MATSUBARA H, KIM CH, KING TE: Structural studies of bovine heart cytochrome c_1. *J Biol Chem* 257:9335, 1982.
13. MARGOLIASH E, SCHEJTER A: Cytochrome c. *Adv Protein Chem* 21:113, 1966.
14. MASSEY V, HEMMERICH P: Active-site probes of flavoproteins. *Biochem Rev* 8:246, 1980.
15. GORELICK RJ, SCHOPFER LM, BALLOU DP, MASSEY V, THORPE C: Interflavin oxidation-reduction reactions between pig kidney general acyl-CoA dehydrogenase and electron transferring flavoprotein. *Biochemistry* 24:6830, 1985.
16. JIANG Z-Y, THORPE C: Acyl-CoA oxidase from Candida tropicalis. *Biochemistry* 22:3752, 1983.
17. GHISLA S, MASSEY V, LHOSTE J-M, MAYHEW SG: Fluorescence and optical characteristics of reduced flavines and flavoproteins. *Biochemistry* 13:589, 1974.
18. EHRENBERG A, MÜLLER F, HEMMERICH P: Basicity, visible spectra and electron spin resonance of flavosemiquinone anions. *Eur J Biochem* 2:286, 1967.
19. MCFARLAND JT: Resonance Raman spectroscopy of flavins and flavoproteins, in Spiro TG (ed): *Biological Applications of Resonance Raman Spectroscopy*. New York, Wiley, 1987, vol 2, p 211.
20. BEINERT H, ALBRACHT SPJ: New insights, ideas and unanswered questions concerning iron-sulfur clusters in mitochondria. *Biochim Biophys Acta* 683:245, 1982.
21. SINGER TP, RAMSEY RR: Iron-sulfur clusters in mitochondrial enzymes, in Martonosi AN (ed): *The Enzymes of Biological Membranes. Bioenergetics of Electron and Proton Transport*. New York, Plenum, 1985, vol 4, p 301.
22. MAHLER HR, PERLMAN PS: Cytochrome b of the respiratory chain, in Martonosi AN (ed): *The Enzymes of Biological Membranes. Bioenergetics of Electron and Proton Transport*. New York, Plenum, 1985, vol 4, p 195.
23. VON JAGOW G, SEBALD W: b-Type cytochromes. *Ann Rev Biochem* 49:281, 1980.
24. SALERNO JC, YOSHIDA S, KING TE: Effects of protein-protein and protein-lipid interactions on heme site conformation in the mitochondrial b cytochromes. *J Biol Chem* 261:5480, 1986.
25. HERON C, SMITH S, RAGAN CI: An analysis of the polypeptide composition of bovine heart mitochondrial NADH-ubiquinone oxidoreductase by two-dimensional polyacrylamide-gel electrophoresis. *Biochem J* 181:435, 1979.
26. RAGAN CI: The molecular organization of NADH dehydrogenase, in Roodyn DB (ed): *Subcellular Biochemistry*. New York, Plenum, 1980, vol 7, p 267.
27. SMITH S, RAGAN CI: The organization of NADH dehydrogenase polypeptides in the inner mitochondrial membrane. *Biochem J* 185:315, 1980.
28. SUZUKI H, KING TE: Evidence of an ubiquinone radical(s) from the NADH-ubiquinone reductase of the mitochondrial respiratory chain. *J Biol Chem* 258:352, 1983.
29. CHEN S, GUILLORY RJ: Studies on the interaction of arylazido-β-alanyl NAD^+ with the mitochondrial NADH dehydrogenase. *J Biol Chem* 256:8318, 1981.
30. EARLEY FGP, RAGAN CI: Identification of the subunits of bovine heart mitochondrial NADH dehydrogenase that are exposed to the phospholipid bilayer by photolabeling with 5-iodonaphthyl azide. *Biochem J* 191:429, 1980.
31. ORME-JOHNSON NR, HANSEN RE, BEINERT H: Electron paramagnetic resonance-detectable electron acceptors in beef heart mitochondria. *J Biol Chem* 249:1922, 1974.
32. OHNISHI T, BLUM H, GALANTE YM, HATEFI Y: Iron-sulfur clusters studied in NADH-ubiquinone oxidoreductase and in soluble NADH dehydrogenase. *J Biol Chem* 256:9216, 1981.
33. ALBRACHT SPJ, SUBRAMANIAN J: The number of Fe atoms in the iron-sulfur centers of the respiratory chain. *Biochim Biophys Acta* 462:36, 1977.
34. ALBRACHT SPJ, DOOIJEWAARD G, LEEUWERIK FJ, VANSWOL B: EPR signals of NADH-Q oxidoreductase. Shape and intensity. *Biochim Biophys Acta* 459:300, 1977.
35. ALBRACHT SPJ, LEEUWERIK FJ, VANSWOL B: The stoichiometry of the iron-sulfur clusters 1a, 1b and 2 of NADH-Q oxidoreductose as present in beef heart submitochondrial particles. *FEBS Lett* 104:197, 1979.
36. PAECH C, REYNOLDS JG, SINGER TP, HOLM RH: Structural identification of iron-sulfur clusters in respiratory chain-linked NADH dehydrogenase. *J Biol Chem* 256:3167, 1981.
37. KOWAL AT, MORNINGSTAR JE, JOHNSON MK, RAMSAY R, SINGER TP: Spectroscopic characterization of the number and type of iron-sulfur clusters in NADH: ubiquinone oxidoreductase. *J Biol Chem* 261:9239, 1986.
38. BEINERT H: Iron sulfur centers of the mitochondrial electron transfer system, in Lovenberg W (ed): *Iron-Sulfur Proteins, Structure and Metabolic Mechanisms*. New York, Academic, 1977, vol 3, p 61.
39. RAGAN CI, GALANTE YM, HATEFI Y: Purification of three iron-sulfur proteins from the iron-protein fragment of mitochondrial NADH-ubiquinone oxidoreductase. *Biochemistry* 21:2518, 1982.
40. OHNISHI T, RAGAN CI, HATEFI Y: EPR studies of iron-sulfur clusters in isolated subunits and subfractions of NADH-ubiquinone oxidoreductase. *J Biol Chem* 260:2782, 1985.
41. DOOIJEWAARD G, SLATER EC: Steady state kinetics of high molecular weight (type I) NADH dehydrogenase. *Biochim Biophys Acta* 440:1, 1976.
42. ACKRELL BAC, BALL MB, KEARNEY EB: Peptides from complex II active in reconstitution of succinate-ubiquinone reductase. *J Biol Chem* 255:2761, 1980.
43. YU C-A, YU L: Isolation and properties of a mitochondrial protein that converts succinic dehydrogenase into succinate-ubiquinone oxidoreductase. *Biochemistry* 19:3579, 1980.
44. RAGAN CI, HINKLE PC: Ion transport and respiratory control in vesicles formed from reduced nicotinamide adenine dinucleotide coenzyme Q reductase and phospholipids. *J Biol Chem* 250:8472, 1975.
45. INGLEDEW WJ, OHNISHI T: An analysis of some thermodynamic properties of iron-sulfur centers in site I of mitochondria. *Biochem J* 186:111, 1980.

46. CHOMYN A, MARIOTTINI P, CLEETER MWJ, RAGAN CI, MATSUNO-YAGI A, HATIFI Y, DOOLITTLE RF, ATTARDI G: Six unidentified reading frames of human mitochondrial DNA encode components of the respiratory chain NADH dehydrogenase. *Nature* 314:592, 1985.

47. CHOMYN A, CLEETER MWJ, RAGAN IC, RILEY M, DOOLITTLE RF, ATTARDI G: URF 6, last unidentified reading frame of human mtDNA, codes for an NADH dehydrogenase subunit. *Nature* 234:614, 1986.

48. TUSHURASHVILI PR, GAVRIKOVA EV, LEDNEV AN, VINOGRADOV AD: Studies on the succinic dehydrogenase system. Isolation and properties of the mitochondrial succinate-ubiquinone reductase. *Biochim Biophys Acta* 809:145, 1985.

49. CAPALDI RA: Arrangement of proteins in the mitochondrial inner membrane. *Biochim Biophys Acta* 694:291, 1982.

50. CAPALDI RA, SWEETLAND J, MERLI A: Polypeptides in the succinate-coenzyme Q reductase segment of the respiratory chain. *Biochemistry* 16:5707, 1977.

51. HANSTEIN WG, DAVIS KA, GALAMBOR MA, HATEFI Y: Succinic dehydrogenase. II. Enzymatic properties. *Biochemistry* 10:2517, 1971.

52. ACKRELL BAC, KEARNEY EB, COLES CJ: Isolation of reconstitutively active succinic dehydrogenase in highly purified state. *J Biol Chem* 252:6963, 1977.

53. OHNISHI T: Mitochondrial iron-sulfur flavoprotein dehydrogenases, in Capaldi RA (ed): *Membrane Proteins in Energy Transduction*. New York, Marcel Dekker, 1979, p 1.

54. OHNISHI T, SALERNO JC: Iron-sulfur clusters in the mitochondrial electron transport chain, in Spiro TG (ed): *Iron-Sulfur Proteins*. New York, Wiley, 1982, vol 4, p 285.

55. ACKRELL BAC, KEARNEY EB, MIMS WB, DEISACH J, BEINERT H: Iron-sulfur cluster 3 of beef heart succinic-ubiquinone oxidoreductase is a 3-iron cluster. *J Biol Chem* 259:4015, 1984.

56. CONDON C, CAMMACK R, PATIL DS, OWEN P: The succinic dehydrogenase of Escherichia coli. Immunochemical resolution and biophysical characterization of a 4-subunit enzyme complex. *J Biol Chem* 260:9427, 1985.

57. YU L, XU J-X, HALEY PE, YU C-A: Properties of bovine heart mitochondrial cytochrome b_{560}. *J Biol Chem* 262:1137, 1987.

58. NELSON BD, GELLERFORS P: The redox properties of the cytochromes of purified complex III. *Biochim Biophys Acta* 357:358, 1974.

59. WIDGER WR, CRAMER WA, HERRMANN RG, TREBST A: Sequence homology and structural similarity between cytochrome b of mitochondrial complex III and the chloroplast b_6-f complex: Position of the cytochrome b hemes in the membrane. *Proc Natl Acad Sci USA* 81:674, 1984.

60. SCHAGGER H, LINK TA, ENGEL WD, VON JAGOW G: Isolation of the eleven protein subunits of the bc_1 complex from beef heart. *Methods Enzymol* 126:224, 1986.

61. OHNISHI T, VON JAGOW G: Topographical location of redox active centers in the energy coupling site II. *Biophys J* 47:241a, 1985.

62. STONEHUERNER J, O'BRIEN P, GEREN L, MILLET F, STEIDL J, YU L, YU C-A: Identification of the binding site on cytochrome c_1 for cytochrome c. *J Biol Chem* 260:5392, 1985.

63. SHIMOMURA Y, NISHIKIMI M, OZAWA T: Novel purification of cytochrome c_1 from mitochondrial complex III. *J Biol Chem* 260:10575, 1985.

64. RIESKE JS: Composition, structure and function of complex III of the respiratory chain. *Biochim Biophys Acta* 456:195, 1976.

65. TRUMPOWER BL: Function of the iron-sulfur proteins of the cytochrome bc_1 segment of electron transfer and energy conservation reactions of the mitochondrial respiratory chain. *Biochim Biophys Acta* 639:129, 1981.

66. BEATTIE D, CLEJAN L, CHEN Y-S, LIN C-I, SIDHU A: Orientation of complex III in the yeast mitochondrial membrane: Labeling with $[^{125}I]$diazobenzene-sulfonate and functional studies with the decyl analog of coenzyme Q as substrate. *J Bioenerg Biomembr* 13:357, 1981.

67. BELL RL, SWEETLAND J, LUDWIG B, CAPALDI RA: Labeling of complex III with $[^{35}S]$diazobenzenesulfonate: Orientation of this electron transfer segment in the mitochondrial inner membrane. *Proc Natl Acad Sci USA* 76:741, 1979.

68. GUTWENIGER H, BISSON R, MONTECUCCO C: Membrane topology of beef heart ubiquinone cytochrome c reductase (complex III). *J Biol Chem* 256:11132, 1981.

69. HAUSKA G, HURTE E, GABELLINI N, LOCKAU W: Comparative aspects of quinol-cytochrome c/plastocyanin oxidoreductase. *Biochim Biophys Acta* 726:97, 1983.

70. YANG X, TRUMPOWER BL: Purification of a three subunit ubiquinol-cytochrome c oxidoreductase complex from Paracoccus denitrificans. *J Biol Chem* 261:12282, 1986.

71. LEUNG KH, HINCKLE PC: Reconstitution of ion transport and respiratory control in vesicles formed from reduced coenzyme Q-cytochrome c reductase and phospholipids. *J Biol Chem* 250:8467, 1975.

72. WICKSTRÖM MKF, KRAB K: Respiration linked H^+ translocation in mitochondria: Stoichiometry and mechanism. *Curr Top Bioenergetics* 10:51, 1980.

73. LEONARD K, WINGFIELD P, ARAD T, WEISS H: Three dimensional structurte of ubiquinol:cytochrome c reductase from Neurospora mitochondria determined by electron microscopy of membrane crystals. *J Mol Biol* 149:259, 1981.

74. DEVRIES S, ALBRACHT SPJ, BERDEN JA, MARRES CAM, SLATER EC: The effect of pH, ubiquinone depletion and myxothiazole on the reduction kinetics of the prosthetic groups of ubiquinol:cytochrome c oxidoreductase. *Biochim Biophys Acta* 723:91, 1983.

75. CROFTS AR: The mechanism of the ubiquinol:cytochrome c oxidoreductases of mitochondria and Rhodopseudomonas sphaeroides, in Martonosi AN (ed): *The Enzymes of Biological Membranes. Bioenergetics of Electron and Proton Transport*, New York, Plenum, 1985, vol 4, p 347.

76. MITCHELL P: Possible molecular mechanisms of the proton motive function of cytochrome systems. *J Theoret Biol* 62:327, 1976.

77. RICH PR: Perspectives on Q-cycles. *J Bioenerg Biomembr* 18:145, 1986.

78. VAN ARK G, RAPP AK, BERDEN JA, SLATER EC: Kinetics of cytochrome b reduction in submitochondrial particles. *Biochim Biophys Acta* 637:34, 1981.

79. GARLAND PB, CLEGG RA, BOXER D, DOUONIC JA, HADDOCK BA: Proton-translocating nitrate reductase of Escherichia coli, in Quagliariello E, Papa S, Palmieri F, Slater EC, Siliprandi N (eds): *Electron Transfer Chains and Oxidative Phosphorylation*. Amsterdam, Elsevier, 1975, p 351.

80. WIKSTRÖM M, KRAB K, SARASTE M: Proton translocating cytochrome complexes. *Ann Rev Biochem* 50:623, 1980.

81. SLATER EC, DEVRIES S: Identification of the BAL-labile factor. *Nature* 288:717, 1980.

82. EDWARDS CA, BOWYER JR, TRUMPOWER BL: Function of the iron-sulfur protein of the cytochrome bc_1 segment in electron transfer reactions of the mitochondrial respiratory chain. *J Biol Chem* 257:3705, 1982.

83. SHIMOMURA Y, NISHIKIMI M, OZAWA T: Isolation and reconstitution of the iron-sulfur protein in ubiquinol-cytochrome c oxidoreductase complex. *J Biol Chem* 259:14059, 1984.

84. VON JAGOW G, ENGEL WD: Complete inhibition of electron transfer from ubiquinol to cytochrome b by the combined action of antimycin and myxothiazole. *FEBS Lett* 136:19, 1981.

85. VON JAGOW G, LJUNGDAHL PO, GRAF P, OHNISHI T, TRUMPOWER BL: An inhibitor of mitochondrial respiration which binds to cytochrome b and displaces quinone from the iron-sulfur protein of the cytochrome bc_1 complex. *J Biol Chem* 259:6318, 1984.

86. TANG H, TRUMPOWER BL: Triphasic reduction of cytochrome b and the protonmotive Q cycle pathway of electron transfer in the cytochrome bc_1 complex of the mitochondrial respiratory chain. *J Biol Chem* 261:6209, 1986.

87. TRUMPOWER BL, HAGGERTY JG: Inhibition of electron transfer in the cytochrome bc_1 segment of the mitochondrial respiratory chain by a synthetic analog of ubiquinone. *J Bioenerg Biomembr* 12:151, 1980.

88. BOWYER JR, EDWARDS CA, OHNISHI T, TRUMPOWER BL: An analog of ubiquinone which inhibits respiration by binding to the iron-sulfur protein of the cytochrome bc_1 segment of the mitochondrial respiratory chain. *J Biol Chem* 257:8321, 1982.

89. MATSURA K, BOWYER JR, OHNISHI T, DUTTON PL: Inhibition of electron transfer by 3-alkyl-2-hydroxy-1,4-naphthoquinones in the ubiquinol-cytochrome c oxidoreductases of Rps. Sphaeroides and mammalian mitochondria. *J Biol Chem* 258:1571, 1983.

90. OHNISHI T, TRUMPOWER BL: Differential effects of antimycin on ubisemiquinone bound in different environments in isolated succinate cytochrome c reductase complex. *J Biol Chem* 255:3278, 1980.

91. DEVRIES S, ALBRACHT SPJ, BERDEN JA, SLATER EC: A new species of bound ubisemiquinone anion in QH_2:cytochrome c oxidoreductase. *J Biol Chem* 256:11996, 1981.

92. KOPPENOL WH, MARGOLIASH E: The asymmetric distribution of charges on the surface of horse cytochrome c: Functional implications. *J Biol Chem* 257:4426, 1982.

93. FROUD RJ, RAGAN CI: Cytochrome c mediated electron transfer between ubiquinol-cytochrome c reductase and cytochrome c oxidase. Kinetic evidence for a mobile cytochrome c pool. *Biochem J* 217:551, 1984.

94. KRÖGER A, KLINGENBERG M: The kinetics of the redox reactions of ubiquinone related to the electron-transport activity in the respiratory chain. *Eur J Biochem* 34:358, 1973.

95. WALLACE DC: Structure and organization of organelligenomes. *Microbiol Rev* 46:208, 1982.

96. ANDERSON S, BANKIER AT, BARRELL BG, DEBRUIJN MHL, COULSON AR, DROUIN J, EPERON IC, NIERLICH DP, ROE BA, SANGER F, SCHRIRER PH, SMITH AJH, STADEN R, YOUNG IG: Sequence and organization of the human mitochondrial genome. *Nature* 290:457, 1981.

97. WINTER DB, BRUYNINCKX WJ, FOULKE FG, GRINICH NP, MASON HS: Lo-

cation of heme A on subunits I and II and Cu on subunit II of cytochrome oxidase. *J Biol Chem* 255:11408, 1980.

98. FREEDMAN JA, TRACY RP, CHAN SP: Heme-associated subunit complex of cytochrome c oxidase identified by a new two-dimensional gel electrophoresis. *J Biol Chem* 254:4305, 1979.

99. WIKSTRÖM M, SARASTE M, PENTTILÄ T: Relationships between structure and function in cytochrome oxidase, in Martonosi AN (ed): *The Enzymes of Biological Membranes. Bioenergetics of Electron and Proton Transport.* New York, Plenum, 1985, vol 4, p 111.

100. TWEEDLE MF, WILSON LJ, GARCIA-INIQUEZ L, BABCOCK GT, PALMER G: Electronic state of heme in cytochrome oxidase III. The magnetic susceptibility of beef heart cytochrome oxidase and some of its derivatives from 7-200K. Direct evidence for antiferromagnetically coupled Fe (III)/Cu (II) pair. *J Biol Chem* 253:8065, 1978.

101. MOSS TH, SHAPIRO E, KING TE, BEINERT H, HARTZELL CR: The magnetic susceptibility of cytochrome oxidase in the 4.2-1.5K range. *J Biol Chem* 253:8072, 1978.

102. MICHEL B, BOSSHARD HR: Spectroscopic analysis of the interaction between cytochrome c and cytochrome c oxidase. *J Biol Chem* 259:10085, 1984.

103. ANTALIS TM, PALMER G: Kinetic characterization of the interaction between cytochrome oxidase and cytochrome c. *J Biol Chem* 257:6194, 1982.

104. AZZI A: Cytochrome c oxidase. Towards a clarification of its structure, interactions and mechanism. *Biochim Biophys Acta* 594:231, 1980.

105. OHNISHI T, LOBRUTTO R, SALERNO JC, BRUCKNER RC, FREY TG: Spatial relationship between cytochrome a and a_3. *J Biol Chem* 257:14821, 1982.

106. PROCHASKA LJ, REYNOLDS KA: Characterization of electron transfer and proton translocation activities in bovine heart mitochondrial cytochrome c oxidase deficient in subunit III. *Biochemistry* 25:781, 1986.

107. CASEY RP, THELEN M, AZZI A: Dicyclohexylcarbodiimide binds specifically and covalently to cytochrome c oxidase while inhibiting its H^+-translocating activity. *J Biol Chem* 255:3994, 1980.

108. PROCHASKA LJ, BISSON R, CAPALDI RA, STEFFENS GCM, BUSE G: Inhibition of cytochrome c oxidation function by dicyclohexylcarbodiimide. *Biochim Biophys Acta* 637:360, 1981.

109. SEBALD W, MACHLEIDT W, WACHTER E: N,N′-Dicyclohexylcarbodiimide binds specifically to a single glutamyl residue of the proteolipid subunit of the mitochondrial adenosine triphosphatases from Neurospora crassa and Saccharomyces cerevisiae. *Proc Natl Acad Sci USA* 77:785, 1980.

110. FINE PEM: Mitochondrial inheritance and disease. *Lancet* 2:659, 1978.

111. MERLE P, KADENBACH B: Kinetic and structural differences between cytochrome c oxidases from beef liver and heart. *Eur J Biochem* 125:239, 1982.

112. WALLACE DC: A new manifestation of Leber's disease and a new explanation for the agency responsible for its unusual pattern of inheritance. *Brain* 93:121, 1980.

113. ERICKSON RP: Leber's optic atrophy: A possible example of maternal inheritance. *Am J Hum Genet* 24:348, 1972.

114. NOVOTNY EJ, SINGH G, WALLACE DC, DORFMAN LJ, LOUIS A, SOGG RL, STEINMAN L: Leber's disease and dystonia: A mitochondrial disease. *Neurology* 36:1053, 1986.

115. MORGAN-HUGHES JA, DARVENIZA P, LANDON DN, LAND JM, CLARK JB: A mitochondrial myopathy with a deficiency of respiratory chain NADH-CoQ reductase activity. *J Neurol Sci* 43:27, 1979.

116. LAND JM, MORGAN-HUGHES JA, CLARK JB: Mitochondrial myopathy: Biochemical studies revealing a deficiency of NADH-cytochrome b reductase activity. *J Neurol Sci* 50:1, 1981.

117. MORGAN-HUGHES JA, HAYES DJ, CLARK JB, LANDON DN, SWASH M, STARK RJ, RUDGE P: Mitochondrial encephalomyopathies: Biochemical studies in two cases revealing defects in the respiratory chain. *Brain* 105:553, 1982.

118. SPIRO AJ, MOORE CL, PRINEAS JW, STRASBERG PM, RAPIN I: A cytochrome-related inherited disorder of the nervous system and muscle. *Arch Neurol* 23:103, 1970.

119. MORGAN-HUGHES JA, DARVENIZA P, KAHN SN, LANDON DN, SHERRATT RM, LAND JM, CLARK JB: A mitochondrial myopathy characterized by deficiency in reducible cytochrome b. *Brain* 100:617, 1977.

120. HAYES JD, LECKY BRF, LANDON DN, MORGAN-HUGHES JA, CLARK JB: A new mitochondrial myopathy: Biochemical studies revealing a deficiency in the cytochrome b-c_1 complex (complex III) of the respiratory chain. *Brain* 107:1165, 1984.

121. DARLEY-USMAR VM, KENNAWAY NG, BUIST NRM, CAPALDI RA: Deficiency in ubiquinone cytochrome c reductase in a patient with mitochondrial myopathy and lactic acidosis. *Proc Natl Acad Sci USA* 80:5103, 1983.

122. KENNAWAY NG, BUIST NRM, DARLEY-USMAR VM, PAPADIMITRIOU A, DIMAURO S, KELLEY RI, CAPALDI RA, BLANK NK, D'AGOSTINO A: Lactic acidosis and mitochondrial myopathy associated with deficiency of several components of complex III of the respiratory chain. *Pediatr Res* 18:991, 1984.

123. JOHNSON MA, TURNBULL DM, DICK DJ, SHERRATT HSA: A partial deficiency of cytochrome c oxidase in chronic progressive external ophthalmoplegia. *J Neurol Sci* 60:31, 1983.

124. SERVIDEI S, LAZARO RP, BONILLA E, BARRON KD, ZEVIANI M, DIMAURO S: Mitochondrial encephalomyopathy and partial cytochrome c oxidase deficiency. *Neurology* 37:58, 1987.

125. MOREADITH RW, BATSHAW ML, OHNISHI T, KERR D, KNOX B, JACKSON D, HRUBAN R, OLSON J, REYNAFARJE B, LEHNINGER AL: Deficiency of the iron-sulfur clusters of mitochondrial reduced nicotinamide-adenine dinucleotide-ubiquinone oxidoreductase (complex I) in an infant with congenital lactic acidosis. *J Clin Invest* 74:685, 1984.

126. PAPADIMITRIOU A, NEUSTEIN HB, DIMAURO S, STANTON R, BRESOLIN N: Histiocytoid cardiomyopathy of infancy: Deficiency of reducible cytochrome b in heart mitochondria. *Pediatr Res* 18:1023, 1984.

127. ROBINSON BH, WARD J, GOODYER P, BEAUDET A: Respiratory chain defects in the mitochondria of cultured skin fibroblasts from three patients with lacticacidemia. *J Clin Invest* 77:1422, 1986.

128. DIMAURO S, ZEVIANI M, BONILLA E, BRESOLIN N, NAKAGAWA M, MIRANDA AF, MOGGIO M: Cytochrome c oxidase deficiency. *Biochem Soc Trans* 13:651, 1985.

129. MOREADITH RW, CLEETER MWJ, RAGAN CI, BATSHAW ML, LEHNINGER AL: Congenital deficiency of two polypeptide subunits of the iron-protein fragment of mitochondrial complex I. *J Clin Invest* 79:463, 1987.

130. DARLEY-USMAR VM, WATANABE M, UCHIYAMA Y, KONDO I, KENNAWAY NG, GRONKE L, HAMAGUCHI H: Mitochondrial myopathy: Tissue-specific expression of a defect in ubiquinol-cytochrome c reductase. *Clin Chim Acta* 158:253, 1986.

131. BEINERT H, FRISELL WR: The functional identity of the electron-transferring flavoproteins of the fatty acyl coenzyme A and sarcosine dehydrogenase systems. *J Biol Chem* 237:2988, 1962.

132. FRISELL WR, MACKENZIE CG: Separation and purification of sarcosine dehydrogenase and dimethylglycine dehydrogenase. *J Biol Chem* 237:94, 1962.

133. WITTWER AJ, WAGNER C: Identification of the folate-binding proteins of rat liver mitochondria as dimethylglycine dehydrogenase and sarcosine dehydrogenase. Flavoprotein nature and enzymatic properties of the purified proteins. *J Biol Chem* 256:4109, 1981.

134. CRANE FL, BEINERT H: On the mechanism of dehydrogenation of fatty acyl derivatives of coenzyme A. II. The electron-transferring flavoprotein. *J Biol Chem* 218:717, 1956.

135. HUSAIN M, STEENKAMP DJ: Electron transfer flavoprotein from pig liver mitochondria. A simple purification and re-evaluation of some of the molecular properties. *Biochem J* 209:541, 1983.

136. GORELICK RJ, MIZZER JP, THORPE C: Purification and properties of electron transferring flavoprotein from pig kidney. *Biochemistry* 21:6936, 1982.

137. MCKEAN MC, BECKMANN JD, FRERMAN FE: Subunit structure of electron transfer flavoprotein. *J Biol Chem* 258:1866, 1983.

138. BEINERT H: Electron-transferring flavoprotein, in Boyer PD, Lardy H, Myrbäck K (eds): *The Enzymes.* New York, Academic, 1963, vol 7, part A, p 467.

139. HUSAIN M, STANKOVICH MT, FOX BG: Measurement of the oxidation-reduction potentials for one-electron and two-electron reduction of electron transfer flavoprotein from pig liver. *Biochem J* 219:1043, 1984.

140. HALL CL, KAMIN H: The purification and some properties of electron transfer flavoprotein and general fatty acyl CoA dehydrogenase from pig liver mitochondria. *J Biol Chem* 250:3476, 1975.

141. BECKMANN JD, FRERMAN FE: The effects of pH, ionic strength and chemical modifications on the reaction of electron transfer flavoprotein with an acyl coenzyme A dehydrogenase. *J Biol Chem* 258:7563, 1983.

142. FRERMAN FE, GOODMAN SI: Fluorometric assay of acyl CoA dehydrogenases in normal and mutant fibroblast lines. *Biochem Med* 33:38, 1985.

143. BECKMANN JD, FRERMAN FE: Electron transfer flavoprotein-ubiquinone oxidoreductase from pig liver. Molecular, catalytic and redox properties. *Biochemistry* 24:3913, 1985.

144. FRERMAN FE, GOODMAN SI: Deficiency of electron transfer flavoprotein or electron transfer flavoprotein ubiquinone oxidoreductase in glutaric acidemia type II fibroblasts. *Proc Natl Acad Sci USA* 82:4517, 1985.

145. IKEDA Y, KEESE SM, TANAKA K: Biosynthesis of electron transfer flavoprotein in a cell-free system and in cultured human fibroblasts. Defect in the alpha subunit synthesis is a primary lesion in glutaric aciduria type II. *J Clin Invest* 78:997, 1986.

146. FRERMAN FE, MIELKE DM, HUHTA K: The functional role of carboxyl residues in an acyl-CoA dehydrogenase. *J Biol Chem* 255:2199, 1980.

147. BECKMANN JD, FRERMAN FE: Interaction of electron transfer flavoprotein

and electron transfer flavoprotein ubiquinone oxidoreductase. *Biochemistry* 24:3922, 1985.

148. MIZZER JP, THORPE C: Stabilization of the red semiquinone form of pig kidney general acyl-CoA dehydrogenase by acyl coenzyme A derivatives. *Biochemistry* 20:4965, 1981.

149. RUZICKA FJ, BEINERT H: A new membrane iron-sulfur flavoprotein of the mitochondrial electron transfer system. The entrance point of the fatty acyl dehydrogenase pathway? *Biochem Biophys Res Commun* 66:622, 1975.

150. SCHMIDT J, BECKMANN JD, FRERMAN FE, MCFARLAND JT: Resonance Raman spectra of ETF dehydrogenase. *Biochem Biophys Res Commun* 113:784, 1983.

151. STEENKAMP DJ, RAMSAY RR, HUSAIN M: Reactions of ETF and ETF:Q oxidoreductase, in Bray RC, Engel PC, Mayhew SG (eds): *Flavins and Flavoproteins*. Berlin, Walter de Gruyter, 1984, p 459.

152. DIDONATO S, FRERMAN FE, RIMONDI M, RINALDO P, TARONI F, WEISMANN UN: Systemic carnitine deficiency due to lack of electron transfer flavoprotein:ubiquinone oxidoreductase. *Neurology* 36:957, 1986.

153. SWEETMAN L, NYHAN WL, TRAUNER DA, MERRITT TA, SINGH M: Glutaric aciduria type II. *J Pediatr* 96:1020, 1980.

154. LEHNERT W, WENDEL U, LINDENMAIER S, BÖHM N: Multiple acyl-CoA dehydrogenation deficiency (glutaric aciduria type II), congenital polycystic kidneys, and symmetric warty dysplasia of the cerebral cortex in two brothers. I. Clinical, metabolical, and biochemical findings. *Eur J Pediatr* 139:56, 1982.

155. GOODMAN SI, REALE M, BERLOW S: Glutaric acidemia type II: A form with deleterious intrauterine effects. *J Pediatr* 102:411, 1983.

156. GOODMAN SI, FRERMAN FE: Glutaric acidaemia type II (Multiple acyl-CoA dehydrogenation deficiency). *J Inherited Metab Dis* 7 *Suppl* 1:33, 1984.

157. HARKIN JC, GILL WL, SHAPIRA E: Glutaric acidemia type II: Phenotypic findings and ultrastructural studies of brain and kidney. *Arch Pathol Lab Med* 110:399, 1986.

158. CHALMERS RA, TRACY BM, KING GS, PETTIT B, ROCCHICCIOLI F, SAUDUBRAY JM, GRAY RGF, BOUÉ J, KEELING JW, LINDENBAUM BH: The prenatal diagnosis of glutaric aciduria type II, using quantitative gc-ms. *J Inherited Metab Dis* 8 *Suppl* 2:145, 1985.

159. GREGERSEN N, KØLVRAA S, RASMUSSEN K, CHRISTENSEN E, BRANDT NJ, EBBESEN F, HANSEN, FH: Biochemical studies in a patient with defects in the metabolism of acyl-CoA and sarcosine: Another possible case of glutaric aciduria type II. *J Inherited Metab Dis* 3:67, 1980.

160. BRANDT NJ: Personal communication.

161. COUDE FX, OGIER H, CHARPENTIER C, THOMASSIN G, CHECOURY A, AMEDEE-MANESME O, SAUDUBRAY JM, FREZAL J: Neonatal glutaric aciduria type II: An X-linked recessive inherited disorder. *Hum Genet* 59:263, 1981.

162. MITCHELL G, SAUDUBRAY JM, GUBLER MC, HABIB R, OGIER H, FREZAL J, BOUE J: Congenital anomalies in glutaric aciduria type 2. *J Pediatr* 104:961, 1984.

163. PRZYREMBEL H, WENDEL U, BECKER K, BREMER HJ, BRUINVIS L, KETTING D, WADMAN SK: Glutaric aciduria type II: Report on a previously undescribed metabolic disorder. *Clin Chim Acta* 66:227, 1976.

164. GOODMAN SI, MCCABE ERB, FENNESSEY PV, MACE JW: Multiple acyl-CoA dehydrogenase deficiency (glutaric aciduria type II) with transient hypersarcosinemia and sarcosinuria: Possible inherited deficiency of an electron transfer flavoprotein. *Pediatr Res* 14:12, 1980.

165. GOODMAN SI, STENE DO, MCCABE ERB, NORENBERG MD, SHIKES RH, STUMPF DA, BLACKBURN GK: Glutaric acidemia type II: Clinical, biochemical, and morphologic considerations. *J Pediatr* 100:946, 1982.

166. NIEDERWIESER A, STEINMANN B, EXNER U, NEUHEISER F, REDWEIK U, WANG M, RAMPINI S, WENDEL U: Multiple acyl-CoA dehydrogenation deficiency (MADD) in a boy with nonketotic hypoglycemia, hepatomegaly, muscle hypotonia and cardiomyopathy: Detection of N-isovalerylglutamic acid and its monoamide. *Helv Paediatr Acta* 38:9, 1983.

167. BENNETT MJ, CURNOCK DA, ENGEL PC, SHAW L, GRAY RGF, HULL D, PATRICK AD, POLLITT RJ: Glutaric aciduria type II. Biochemical investigation and treatment of a child diagnosed prenatally. *J Inherited Metab Dis* 7:57, 1984.

168. MOOY PD, PRZYREMBEL H, GIESBERTS MAH, SCHOLTE HR, BLOM W, VAN GELDEREN HH: Glutaric aciduria type II: Treatment with riboflavine, carnitine and insulin. *Eur J Pediatr* 143:92, 1984.

169. TANAKA K, MANTAGOS S, GENEL M, SEASHORE MR, BILLINGS BA, BARETZ BH: New defect in fatty-acid metabolism with hypoglycemia and organic aciduria. *Lancet* 2:986, 1977.

170. MANTAGOS S, GENEL M, TANAKA K: Ethylmalonic-adipic aciduria: In vivo and in vitro studies indicating deficiency of activities of multiple acyl-CoA dehydrogenases. *J Clin Invest* 64:1580, 1979.

171. DUSHEIKO G, KEW MC, JOFFE BI, LEWIN JR, MANTAGOS S, TANAKA K: Recurrent hypoglycemia associated with glutaric aciduria type II in an adult. *N Engl J Med* 301:1405, 1979.

172. VERGEE ZH, SHERWOOD WG: Multiple acyl-CoA dehydrogenase deficiency: A neonatal onset case responsive to treatment. *J Inherited Metab Dis* 8 *Suppl* 2:137, 1985.

173. GREEN A, MARSHALL TG, BENNETT MJ, GRAY RGF, POLLITT RJ: Riboflavin responsive ethylmalonic-aciduria. *J Inherited Metab Dis* 8:67, 1985.

174. GREGERSEN G, WINTZENSEN H, KØLVRAA S, CHRISTENSEN E, CHRISTENSEN MF, BRANDT NJ, RASMUSSEN K: C_6-C_{10}-Dicarboxylic aciduria: Investigation of a patient with riboflavin responsive multiple acyl-CoA dehydrogenation defects. *Pediatr Res* 16:861, 1982.

175. DE VISSER M, SCHOLTE HR, SCHUTGENS RBH, BOLHUIS PA, LUYT-HOUWEN IEM, VAANDRAGER-VERDUIN MHM, VEDER HA, OEY PL: Riboflavin-responsive lipid-storage myopathy and glutaric aciduria type II of early adult onset. *Neurology* 36:367, 1986.

176. CORNELIO F, DIDONATO S, PELUCHETTI D, BIZZI A, BENTAGNOLIO B, D'ANGELO A, WIESMANN U: Fatal cases of lipid storage myopathy with carnitine deficiency. *J Neurol Neurosurg Psychiatry* 40:170, 1977.

177. CHALMERS RA, ROE CR, STACEY TE, HOPPEL CL: Urinary excretion of L-carnitine and acylcarnitines by patients with disorders of organic acid metabolism: Evidence for secondary insufficiency of L-carnitine. *Pediatr Res* 18:1325, 1984.

178. TANAKA K, KEAN EA, JOHNSON B: Jamaican vomiting sickness: Biochemical investigation of two cases. *N Engl J Med* 295:461, 1976.

179. CHRISTENSEN E, KØLVRAA S, GREGERSEN N: Glutaric aciduria type II: Evidence for a defect related to the electron transfer flavoprotein or its dehydrogenase. *Pediatr Res* 18:663, 1984.

180. CHRISTENSEN E: Glutaryl-CoA dehydrogenase activity determined with intact electron-transport chain: Application to glutaric aciduria type II. *J Inherited Metab Dis* 7 *Suppl* 2:103, 1984.

181. AMENDT BA, RHEAD WJ: The multiple acyl-coenzyme A dehydrogenation disorders, glutaric aciduria type II and ethylmalonic-adipic aciduria: Mitochondrial fatty acid oxidation, acyl-coenzyme A dehydrogenase, and electron transfer flavoprotein activities in fibroblasts. *J Clin Invest* 78:205, 1986.

182. LOEHR J, FRERMAN FE, GOODMAN SI: A new form of glutaric acidemia type II (GA2). *Pediatr Res* 21:291A, 1987.

183. MOON A, RHEAD WJ: Complementation analysis of fatty acid oxidation disorders. *J Clin Invest* 79:59, 1987.

183a. MITCHELL G, VALLE D, FRERMAN FE, GOODMAN SI: Unpublished data.

184. BÖHM N, UY J, KIEẞLING M, LEHNERT W: Multiple acyl CoA dehydrogenation deficiency (glutaric aciduria type II), congenital polycystic kidneys, and symmetric warty degeneration of the cerebral cortex in two newborn brothers. II Morphology and pathogenesis. *Eur J Pediatr* 139:60, 1982.

185. HOGANSON G, BERLOW S, GILBERT EF, FRERMAN F, GOODMAN S, SCHWEITZER L: Glutaric acidemia type II and flavin-dependent enzymes in morphogenesis, in Gilbert EF, Opitz JM (eds): *Genetic Aspects of Developmental Pathology. Birth Defects.* New York, AR Liss, 1987, vol 23, p 65.

186. GREENBERG C: Personal communication.

187. SAUDUBRAY JM: Personal communication.

188. MITCHELL G, SAUDUBRAY JM, BENOIT Y, ROCCHICCIOLI F, CHARPENTIER C, OGIER H, BOUÉ J: Antenatal diagnosis of glutaricaciduria type II. *Lancet* 1:1099, 1983.

189. JACOBS C, SWEETMAN L, WADMAN SK, DURAN M, SAUDUBRAY JM, NYHAN WL: Prenatal diagnosis of glutaric aciduria type II by direct chemical analysis of dicarboxylic acids in amniotic fluid. *Eur J Pediatr* 141:153, 1984.

190. HARPEY JP, CHARPENTIER C, COUDÉ M: Methylene-blue for riboflavin-unresponsive glutaricaciduria type II. *Lancet* 1:391, 1986.

191. HARPEY JP, CHARPENTIER C, GOODMAN SI, DARBOIS Y, LEFÉBVRE G, SEBBAH J: Multiple acyl-CoA dehydrogenase deficiency occurring in pregnancy and caused by a defect in riboflavin metabolism in the mother. *J Pediatr* 103:394, 1983.

192. WALLACE DC, SINGH G, LOTT MT, HODGE JA, SCHURR TG, LEZZA AMS, ELSAS LJ II, NIKOSKELAINEN EK: Mitochondrial DNA mutation associated with Leber's hereditary optic neuropathy. *Science*, in press.

193. HOLT IJ, HARDING AE, MORGAN-HUGHES JA: Deletions of mitochondrial DNA in patients with mitochondrial myopathies. *Nature* 331:717, 1988.

194. LESTIENNE P, PONSOT G: Kearns-Sayre syndrome with muscle mitochondrial DNA deletion. *Lancet* i:885, 1988.

CHAPTER 35

PRIMARY HYPEROXALURIAS

RICHARD E. HILLMAN

1. *Primary hyperoxaluria is a general term for two rare genetic disorders characterized clinically by recurrent calcium oxalate nephrolithiasis and nephrocalcinosis, frequently leading to progressive renal insufficiency and death before the age of 20. Symptoms of renal stone disease begin usually before the age of 5, although there are variations in age of onset and in severity of clinical symptoms. Calcium oxalate deposits may be found in extrarenal tissues, a pathologic condition termed* oxalosis.
2. *Primary hyperoxaluria is characterized biochemically by the continuous excessive synthesis and excretion of oxalic acid. The demonstration of different patterns of urinary organic acid excretion has allowed classification of this disease into two specific types. In type I (glycolic aciduria), excessive amounts of glyoxylic and glycolic acids are also found in the urine. In type II (L-glyceric aciduria), large amounts of L-glyceric acid but normal amounts of glyoxylic and glycolic acids are excreted.*
3. *In type I primary hyperoxaluria, the excessive synthesis of oxalate and glycolate results from deficiency of the hepatic peroxisomal enzyme alanine:glyoxylate aminotransferase (EC 2.6.1.44). Immunoblotting of the enzyme provides evidence for genetic heterogeneity with some patients expressing a normal-sized mutant enzyme monomer while others lack both enzyme activity and antigen.*
4. *In type II primary hyperoxaluria, a defect in hydroxypyruvate metabolism results in its excessive reduction to L-glyceric acid, catalyzed by lactic dehydrogenase. A deficiency of leukocyte D-glyceric dehydrogenase has been demonstrated in four patients with this disorder.*
5. *The cause of excessive oxalate synthesis in primary hyperoxaluria type II has not been completely clarified. Studies suggest that hydroxypyruvate accumulation, secondary to D-glyceric dehydrogenase deficiency, may indirectly increase oxalate synthesis from glyoxylate. The reduction of hydroxypyruvate to L-glycerate enhances the oxidation of glyoxylate to oxalate in the coupled reaction catalyzed by lactic dehydrogenase.*
6. *The inheritance of both types of primary hyperoxaluria appears to be autosomal recessive. This conclusion is based on genetic analyses in type I and on limited studies of heterozygotes in both type I and type II.*
7. *Treatment of primary hyperoxaluria is directed toward decreasing oxalate excretion by inhibition of oxalate synthesis and toward increasing calcium oxalate solubility at a given urinary concentration of oxalate. Pyridoxine in large doses has been successful in reducing oxalate synthesis in a few patients with primary hyperoxaluria type I. Inhibitors of oxalate synthesis from glyoxylate have been effective in vitro, but their efficacy has not been established in vivo. Renal homotransplantation has not proved successful in the management of chronic renal insufficiency complicating primary hyperoxaluria in most cases.*

Primary hyperoxaluria refers to at least two inherited disorders characterized by recurrent calcium oxalate nephrolithiasis, chronic renal failure, and early death from uremia. The true incidence of these disorders is not known. There is considerable clinical variation in the disease. Some patients are classified as having the neonatal form, which leads to death before age 1[1]; most patients have renal failure by age 20,[2,3] but some are not diagnosed until an older age and have a slower course of progression of the disease.[4] Because the criteria for diagnosis have been based mainly on urinary studies and not on direct enzymatic measurements, patients also exist who have been described with still more limited disease.[5]

Biochemically two enzymatic deficiencies have been discerned. Primary hyperoxaluria type I, the most common form of this disease, is indicated by the finding of oxalic, glycolic, and glyoxylic acids in the urine.[6] This disease has recently been shown[7,8] and confirmed[9] to be a defect in the peroxisomal enzyme alanine:glyoxylate aminotransferase. Primary hyperoxaluria type II is a much rarer disorder. It is characterized by the excretion of oxalic and L-glyceric acids in the urine in excess, but of normal glycolic acid excretion.[10] A defect in hydroxypyruvate metabolism has been demonstrated.[11]

The primary hyperoxalurias must be distinguished from secondary causes of increased oxalate in the urine. These secondary causes include ingestion of various substances including ascorbic acid and ethylene glycol, pyridoxine deficiency, increased ingestion of oxalate itself, and probably most commonly, hyperabsorption of oxalate—the *enteric hyperoxaluria syndrome*. Now that the pathways leading to oxalate are better understood, it is probable that other inherited causes of primary hyperoxaluria will be found in the future.

HISTORY

The presence of characteristic oxalate crystals in certain broad-leaved plants has been recognized for about 200 years. In the early nineteenth century, calcium oxalate was recognized in renal stones[12] and then in normal human urine.[13] Primary hyperoxaluria was first described by Lepoutre in 1925.[14] The first detailed report of a case appeared in 1950 following postmortem examination.[15] The first case diagnosed during life was in 1953.[16] The familial nature of the disease was soon recognized.[17,18] However, it was not until the pioneering studies of Smith and colleagues and of Williams and colleagues in the 1960s that these disorders became better understood and clearly distinguished from secondary causes of hyperoxaluria. Some of their extensive studies are covered in greater depth in previous editions of this book than in the present review, and the reader is referred there.[19] These workers showed that hyperoxaluria type I was due to a defect in glyoxylate metabolism and suggested that the defect was due to a deficiency of transamination of glyoxylate to glycine.[6] In 1967 Koch et al.[20]

Nonstandard abbreviation used in this chapter is: LDH = lactate dehydrogenase.

reported that hyperoxaluria type I was associated with a defect in the cytosolic form of 2-oxoglutarate:glyoxylate carboligase. However, in the last year the original concept of a defect in transamination has been clearly defined and confirmed.[7–9] The proposed defect in type II disease[11] has not been confirmed in additional patients,[21] but appears to involve hydroxypyruvate and serine metabolism, specifically the enzyme glyceric acid dehydrogenase. Elucidation of the exact cause of the hyperoxaluria in type II disease is not directly explained by this defect and calls for further investigation.

BIOCHEMISTRY OF OXALATE

Chemistry

The role of oxalic acid in biology is unknown. It is probably an end product of metabolism whose importance to medicine and the pathogenesis of disease comes primarily from its relative insolubility in water. Thus, like cystine, it appears to cause problems by precipitating from solution; in oxalosis the event occurs in the kidney, joints, the male gametic tract, and elsewhere. Oxalate is present in high concentrations in leafy plants such as spinach, rhubarb, cocoa, and tea as well as many common ornamental plants.[22,23] The presence of oxalate in house plants has caused them to be labeled as toxic.[24] It is possible that oxalate crystals add stability to the leaf structure.

Oxalic acid is a relatively strong dicarboxylic acid; the pK_1 is 1.27, and the pK_2, 4.27.[25] The free acid is soluble in water at 8.7 g/100 g. It forms a wide variety of salts, the most important of which, from the biologic point of view, is calcium oxalate. The calcium salt has a very low solubility in water. At neutral or alkaline pH, the solubility is only 0.67 mg/100 g. Solubility of the salt is greatly affected by its ionic environment as well as the pH of the solution. A variety of compounds and metal ions are known to inhibit the precipitation of the crystals. This subject will be returned to in "Treatment."

Biology of Oxalate and Glyoxylate

Primary oxaluria is one of the growing number of peroxisomal diseases discussed at length elsewhere in this volume. It is impossible to come to a clear understanding of these disorders without consideration of the role of the peroxisome in the metabolism of oxalate and glyoxylate. De Duve[26,27] suggested that the peroxisome might be a "fossil organelle," perhaps dispensible in modern organisms. He also pointed out, "One cannot overlook the fact that peroxisomes have persisted throughout evolution. It is difficult not to assume that selective pressure has favored their retention and therefore they perform some function wherever found."

Biologists have long recognized the importance of physical compartments in separating those metabolic pathways having common intermediates, so as to separate the reactions that would otherwise compete for these compounds. Physical compartments may also restrict certain toxic or reactive metabolites for general access to the cell contents. Here it should be noted that oxalate is probably produced primarily from glyoxyate after that compound leaves the peroxisome[28]; the L-glyceric acid generated in type II disease can only be produced extraperoxisomally.[29] Thus, the major metabolic consequences of these enzymatic defects occur because intermediates in metabolism normally isolated in the peroxisome are allowed to interact with extraperoxisomal enzymes.

Organelles with the cytologic characteristics of peroxisomes were first termed *microbodies* by Rhodin in 1954,[30] who described them in the proximal tubule cells of mouse kidney. The term *microbody* has been accepted as the generic term for a diverse but related group of organelles which vary in important respects from tissue to tissue and species to species. Mollenhauser et al.[31] noted the cytologic similarities between mammalian microbodies and organelles observed in a wide variety of plant species. De Duve and his colleagues[32–34] are credited with advancing the biochemical characterization of microbodies in rat liver. They demonstrated that these organelles (from rat liver) contained a number of oxidases which transfer hydrogen atoms from a donor to molecular oxygen, forming hydrogen peroxide. However, the work done on the two plant microbodies, termed the *glyoxisome* and the *leaf microbody*, is most relevant to the present discussion.

In 1967, Breidenbach and Bevers[35–37] discovered that in fatty seed storage tissue, enzymes of the glyoxylate cycle were associated with a subcellular particle distinct from mitochondria. They adopted the term *glyoxisome*[38] to indicate the functional significance of the compartmentalization of this phase of the gluconeogenic process. The second particle was reported by Tolbert and coworkers,[39–41] who characterized yet another subclass of microbodies found in the chlorophyllous tissues of higher plants and called them *leaf microbodies* or *peroxisomes* because of their primary location. These tissues, which lack the glyoxylate bypass enzymes and therefore are incapable of gluconeogensis from fat, have a metabolic role in the glycolate pathway in photosynthetic tissues.[42] It is interesting to compare the wide distribution of microbodies in plants with their more limited distribution in animals.[43] Microbodies in birds, amphibians, fishes, and mammals are most apparent in kidney and liver. Not all of the enzymes found in the production and metabolism of glyoxylate have yet been found in mammalian tissues. However, the pathway as originally described in *Tetrahymena* by Hogg,[44] and subsequently in a wide variety of plants and fungi, provides a framework for our understanding of the primary hyperoxalurias.

The Peroxisomal Pathways for Glycine and Serine Metabolism

The pathways for glycine and serine metabolism in the peroxisome (Fig. 35-1) can be thought of as parallel two-step reactions, the oxidation of α-hydroxy acids to α-keto acids and their subsequent transamination to amino acids. In plants the pathway leading to glycine is usually referred to as the *glycolate pathway* and the pathway leading to serine as the *glycerate pathway*. Each is named for the initial α-hydroxy acid. The glycine and serine produced are transported outside the peroxisome to the mitochondria, where they can be interconverted by the glycine cleavage reaction and by serine hydroxymethyltransferase (see Chap. 25). The glycolate and glycerate pathways are part of the oxidative photosynthetic carbon cycle of photorespiration in plants.[45,46] In mammals a comparable part of the pathway has not yet been demonstrated.

In the pathway leading to glycine, the reactions for the oxidation of glycolate to glyoxylate and glyoxylate conversion to glycine are present in leaf and liver peroxisomes.[29] (See Fig. 35-2.) However, the α-hydroxy acid oxidase in these tissues

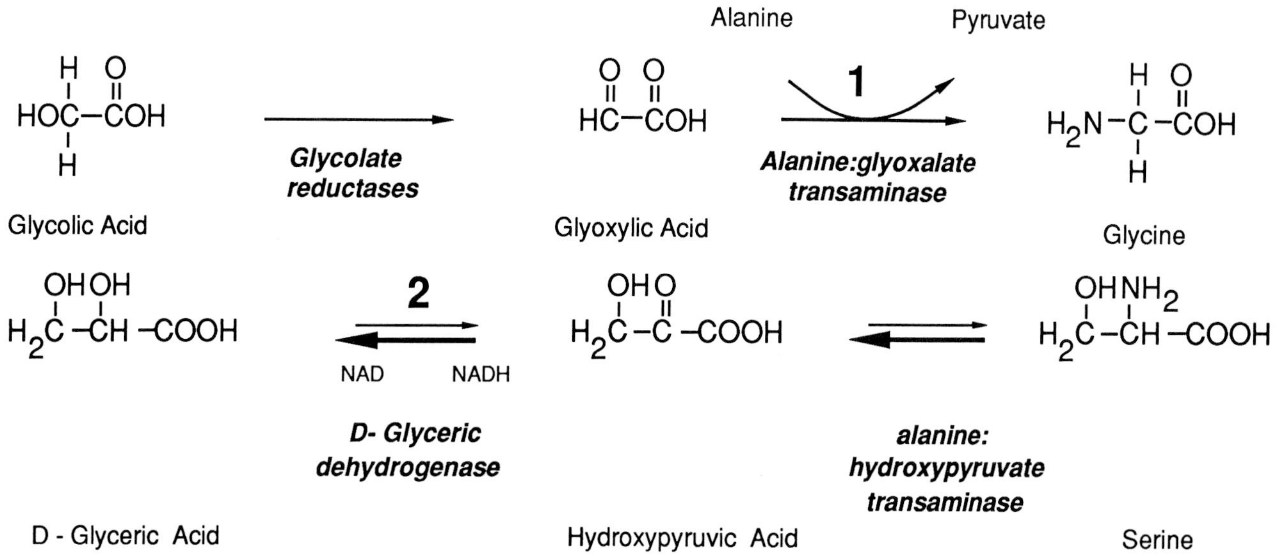

Fig. 35-1 Peroxisomal pathways for glycine and serine metabolism. Numbers indicate the locations of defects in the two primary hyperoxalurias: 1 = type I disease, alanine:glyoxylate aminotransferase deficiency; 2 = type II disease, D-glyceric acid dehydrogenase deficiency. Glycine and serine must leave the peroxisome to undergo interconversion and complete the pathway.

appears quite different than the oxidase present in kidney.[47] In rat liver and leaves, the enzyme oxidizes glycolate (C2) and lactate (C3), but is much less active with C4 and C5 α-hydroxy acids. The oxidase in kidney peroxisomes oxidizes only long-chain α-hydroxy acids and L-amino acids. Thus the origin of glyoxylate in the kidney peroxisome cannot be from glycolate.

Several different aminotransferases have been reported to convert glyoxylate to glycine. However, as discussed under pathogenesis of hyperoxaluria type I, alanine:glyoxylate aminotransferase[48] seems to be most important. This enzyme requires pyridoxal phosphate coenzyme.[49,50]

In leaf peroxisomes two aminotransferases[42] are needed for the interconversion of hydroxypyruvate and serine. One, serine-glyoxylate aminotransferase, is irreversible and links the glycerate pathway and the glycolate pathway during photorespiration. The second reversible enzyme is active in the absence of photosynthesis. In mammals, including humans,[51] the conversion is believed to occur primarily by a reversible alanine:hydroxypyruvate transaminase. Unfortunately, these studies were done before the role of the peroxisome was recognized and must be confirmed. Reduction of hydroxypyruvate to glycerate is catalyzed by a NADH-dependent dehydrogenase.[52] This enzyme is quite active in mammals[53] and has been shown to be stimulated by a variety of dietary factors.[54]

The knowledge of the direction of the normal flux through these pathways is crucial to our understanding of the pathophysiology of the hyperoxalurias. The glycine pathway will be considered first. In plants, glycolate is the product of carboxylase-oxygenase oxidation of ribulose diphosphate to phosphoglycolate[55–57] which is then hydrolyzed by a specific phosphatase to free glycolate.[58] Glyoxylate, in addition to its formation from glycolate, is also generated as part of the glyoxylate pathway (see below). Thus, in plants, the predominant flux is in the direction of glycine formation and is linked to serine metabolism by serine-glyoxylate aminotransferase. In mammals, particularly humans, the normal direction of the flux is less clear. Smith et al.[59] have demonstrated the conversion of both [1-^{14}C]glycolate and [1-^{14}C]glyoxylate to $^{14}CO_2$ and [^{14}C]glycine in both normal humans and those with hyperoxaluria. Their detection of considerable amounts of [^{14}C]glycine, following administration of tracer amounts of these compounds, suggests the flux normally flows toward glycine. Moreover, patients with either primary or secondary hyperglycinemias (discussed in Chap. 25) do not have hyperglyoxyluria or hyperoxaluria,[60] again suggesting that this is the predominant flux. On the other hand, when Crawhall et al.[61] loaded patients with [1-^{13}C]glycine, tracer was found in oxalate, suggesting that reversal of the pathway is possible. Moreover, because the fractional contribution of glycine to oxalate synthesis was unchanged in a patient with primary hyperoxaluria, these authors suggested that an alternate pathway might be responsible for the conversion of glycine to oxalate. The concept of alternate pathways leading from glycine to oxalate was supported by the studies of Dean et al.,[62] who gave both [1-^{13}C] and [2-^{13}C] glycine to a patient. Their results were thought to be consistent with two pathways, one with direct conversion of glycine to glyoxylate and the second by way of glycine conversion to serine. Serine can be converted to glycolate via ethanolamine and glycolaldehyde. Thus, in human beings it appears that the flux is probably toward glycine under normal conditions. The only real difficulty with this concept is that little evidence exists to support a source of glycolate or glyoxylate other than glycine or ascorbic acid. Yet the existence of primary hyperoxalurias suggests that such a source must be present.

The pathway leading to D-glycerate from serine is an alternate gluconeogenic process in leaf peroxisomes. During photorespiration, carbon flows from glycolate to glycine to serine to D-glycerate.[41] However, in the dark, because the glycolate pathway is not operational and serine-glyoxylate aminotransferase is not active, the pathway is reversed and serves as a major source of serine. Presumably in human beings, the pathway also is driven toward D-glycerate under normal conditions. Because the aminotransferase reaction is reversible in

Fig. 35-2 The glyoxylate shunt pathway. Succinate and malate must move from the peroxisome to the mitochondria for further metabolism. Glyoxylate may be further metabolized in the peroxisome to glycine or in the cytosol to oxalate.

1. *Isocitrate lyase*
   Isocitrate → Glyoxylate + Succinate
2. *Malate synthase*
   Glyoxylate + Acetyl CoA → Malate

humans,[51,52] and because no counterpart of the dark regulated serine:glyoxylate aminotransferase is known to exist, the direction of the flux may change more than in plants. It should be kept in mind, however, that if a counterpart of this enzyme does exist in humans linking the glycolate and glycerate pathways, it might explain the hyperoxaluria seen in type II disease.

The Glyoxylate Cycle

The glyoxylate cycle has not been described in human beings and the guinea pig fetus is the only mammal in which it has been reported to exist.[63] It is considered here because the source of the glycolate and glyoxylate which accumulate in type I hyperoxaluria is not defined in human beings. The glyoxylate cycle is a logical source of glyoxylate, and evidence suggesting its presence in mammalian systems should be sought. This alternate pathway of acetate catabolism, if present, would also be of interest in patients with other peroxisomal disorders and might explain their frequent complication of calcium oxalate deposits. It might also be a mechanism to explain some of the variation seen in disorders of fatty acid metabolism.

Like mammalian tissues, except in the storage tissues of fatty seeds, higher plants cannot utilize acetate, or long-chain fatty acids catabolized to acetate, as a source of carbon for gluconeogenesis.[38] In the seed storage tissue and perhaps elsewhere a pathway is present that permits conversion of acetate into gluconeogenic four-carbon dicarboxylic acids.[38] This process requires the presence of two unique enzymes, isocitrate lyase and malate synthase, referred to as the glyoxylate bypass enzymes. The glyoxisomal enzymes together with enzymes of the tricarboxylic acid cycle present in the glyoxisomes or in the mitochondria make up the glyoxylate cycle.

These unique glyoxylate bypass enzymes were first described by Hogg in *Tetrahymena*.[44] Their widest description has been in plants and fungi. Both of the glyoxylate bypass enzymes, isocitrate lyase and malate synthase, and all of the essential enzymes of the tricarboxylic acid cycle are localized in the glyoxisomes in fat-storing seeds and in *Tetrahymena*. Interestingly, these two enzymes are located in the mitochondria of the worm *Turbatrix aceti*.[64,65] They were not believed to be present in other animals. However, activity has been reported in fetal guinea pig liver.[63]

The tricarboxylic acid cycle and the glyoxylate cycle can be thought of as alternate pathways for energy utilization of acetate. Both the tricarboxylic acid cycle and the glyoxylate cycle use the same reactions to produce isocitrate from acetyl-CoA and oxaloacetate but beyond that they differ. The tricarboxylic acid cycle leads to the formation of succinate and CO_2 by successive decarboxylations. The glyoxylate cylce cleaves isocitrate directly to give succinate and the 2-carbon fragment glyoxylate. Glyoxylate can then condense with a second acetyl CoA molecule to form malate. Thus, two molecules of acetyl-CoA are converted to a single 4-carbon dicarboxylic acid that can be further metabolized.

The glyoxylate pathway is a gluconeogenic process, but only after transfer of its metabolic products to the mitochondria. Succinate cannot be metabolized by glyoxisomes and must be exported to the mitochondria to be oxidized to malate and oxaloacetate, with the concomitant conservation of energy. Malate formed by malate synthase also diffuses from the glyoxisome to the cytoplasm and into the mitochondria where it can undergo a variety of reactions including shunting to pyruvate and to gluconeogenesis.

Sources of Oxalic Acid

The only proven direct precursors of oxalic acid in human beings are glyoxylate and ascorbic acid. Most of the other compounds described as precursors to oxalate act through initial conversion to glycine and glyoxylate. (See Fig. 35-3.) Nonetheless, many questions remain about possible alternative pathways. Tryptophan has been described as a source of oxalate in humans.[66] Although the pathway probably leads through glyoxylate, studies in perfused rat liver suggest that tryptophan conversion to oxalate may not involve serine,[67] a necessary step in the pathway to glyoxalate. Also in the rat, glycolate as well as glyoxylate appear to be precursors of oxalate.[68] Phenylalanine and tyrosine also give rise to oxalate in the rat.[69]

Ascorbic acid is a precursor of oxalate in many animals,[70–72] including human beings,[73–75] and orally ingested ascorbic acid can be shown to be converted to urinary oxalate. Approximately 35 to 50 percent of normally excreted oxalate is derived from ascorbic acid based on the isotope studies.[74] The pathway from ascorbic acid to oxalate is not known in its entirety. Ascorbic acid is not significantly oxidized to CO_2 in humans.[75] It is probably first oxidized to dehydroascorbate and then hydrolyzed to 2.3-diketogluconic acid with subsequent conversion to oxalate and L-threose. It should be noted that this proposed pathway is highly analogous to the photorespiratory pathway of photosynthesis. Synthesis of oxalate from ascorbate must be saturated under normal conditions because ingestion of relatively large amounts of ascorbic acid (less than 4 g) does not increase urinary oxalate.[73] Ingestion of more than 4 g increases urinary oxalate excretion.

Several different enzymes have been postulated to be responsible for the oxidation of glyoxylate to oxalate.[76] Glycolic acid oxidase, the enzyme which oxidizes glycolate to glyoxylate, has some affinity for its product.[77,78] However, the rate and affinity of the enzyme for glyoxylate largely prohibits any important role in normal metabolism.[79,80] D-Amino acid oxidases including what was once called glycine oxidase also have some activity, particularly in kidney.[81,82] Again the kinetic constants of the reaction are not consistent with a major role in oxalate production in human beings. Xanthine oxidase also has some activity,[83] but patients with a defect in this reaction and patients receiving allopurinol (a xanthine oxidase inhibitor) do not have decreased oxalate excretion.[19] Human and animal data support the role of lactate dehydrogenase (LDH) as the major enzyme catalyzing the conversion of glyoxylate to oxalate.[84–86] The affinity of LDH for glyoxylate is sufficiently

Fig. 35-3 Extraperoxisomal reactions important to glyoxylate metabolism. Interconversion of glycine and serine occurs in the mitochondria. Oxidation of glyoxylate to oxalate is believed to occur in the cytosol. Hydroxypyruvate is converted to L-glyceric acid by LDH. The product in the peroxisome is D-glyceric acid. THFj = tetrahydrofolate.

1. *Serine hydroxymethyltransferase*
   Serine + methylene THF → glycine
2. *Glycine cleavage reaction*
   Glycine + THF → methylene THF
3. *Glyoxylate oxidation*
   Glyoxylate → oxalate
4. *Hydroxypyruvate reduction by LDH*
   Hydroxypyruvate → L-glycerate

high, and the linkage of glyoxylate oxidation to NAD reduction has been confirmed.[87]

Absorption of Oxalate

Although oxalic acid is present in large amounts in many plant tissues, very little is normally absorbed. The content of oxalate in a typical diet has been reported as from 97 to 930 mg/day.[22,23] The wide range reflects the difficulty of measuring oxalate in foods as well as differences in intake. Early studies showed that only 2.3 to 4.5 percent of ingested oxalate was absorbed by normal fasting subjects.[88] Using [^{14}C]oxalic acid tracers, absorption has been reported as high as 12 percent in normal humans in the fasting stage.[89] The amount of oxalate absorbed is dependent on the particular salt present in the gastrointestinal tract. Sodium oxalate is more soluble and more easily absorbed than calcium oxalate, the normal component of plant tissues. In patients with small bowel disease and steatorrhea, the decreased availability of calcium ions may allow more oxalate absortion.[90] (See "Secondary Causes of Hyperoxaluria," below.)

Oxalate absorption usually has been considered a passive process. However, Hatch et al.[91] reported that net oxalate absorption occurs in the distal rabbit colon under conditions which suggested that oxalate transport was an active process. The presence of oxalate transporters on the brush border of the rabbit ileum has also been demonstrated.[92] In the ileum oxalate can be transported in exchange either for OH or Cl ions. pH and Cl gradients stimulated oxalate uptake over a wide range of oxalate concentrations. Considering that a physiological role for oxalate is not known, the reason for this transport process is unclear. It may, however, contribute to the secondary hyperoxaluria in the enteric hyperoxaluria syndrome.

Excretion of Oxalate

Oxalate is excreted almost exclusively in the urine,[93] with little evidence for fecal loss of endogenously produced oxalate in human beings. In the dog,[94] net tubular secretion of oxalate has been demonstrated with an oxalate/inulin ratio averaging 1.28. Renal clearance of oxalate was measured in normal adults and in patients with primary hyperoxaluria (types I and II) by Williams et al.[95] using an isotopic oxalate method similar to that used by Cattell et al.[94] in the dog. The calculated oxalate/inulin ratio of 1.6 did not differ significantly between patients and controls indicating that net secretion also occurs in human beings. Weinman et al.[96] using micropuncture techniques demonstrated the secretion of oxalate in the early proximal tubule, with bidirectional flow in the midproximal tubule of the rat nephron.

Catabolism of Oxalate

There is no evidence that oxalate is further metabolized in humans.[97] Labeled oxalate given intravenously to normal humans does not label respiratory CO_2, and 89 to 99 percent is recovered unchanged in the urine. Moreover, rat studies using radiolabeled oxalate failed to demonstrate conversion of oxalate to hippurate, suggesting that reduction to glyoxylate and transamination to glycine does not occur. Since oxalate may be metabolized by microorganisms by direct decarboxylation or intermediate formation of oxalyl-CoA,[98] it is possible that small amounts of oxalate may be degraded in the human colon. A recent paper[99] suggests that the amount degraded may be greater than previously considered. The normal synthetic rate of oxalate calculated from its pool size (3.5 to 6.1 mg) and turnover rate (biologic half-time of 2.2 to 2.8 h) is 24 to 46 mg/day.[97] This figure agrees closely with the normal urinary excretory rate.

GENETIC DISORDERS OF GLYOXYLATE METABOLISM

Clinical Features*

Distinctions between neonatal, childhood, and adult forms of primary hyperoxaluria type I have not been well-delimited. Though most patients develop symptoms before age 5,[1] the range of presentation extends into the thirties and forties.[100–105] Approximately 10 percent of the cases present before age 1[101] and are usually classified as neonatal primary oxaluria. The distinction between neonatal and later onset forms of the disease can now be made on the basis of residual enzyme activity,[102] suggesting that the severity of the disease does correlate with residual enzyme activity. Family studies[106,107] suggest the disease tends to present at approximately the same age in each affected family member, but the number of reports of multiple patients in pedigrees is too scanty to prove that genetic heterogeneity exists. At this time, confirmation of diagnosis by enzyme assay has been achieved in only a few patients. Symptoms are present for less than 10 years in over 90 percent of patients who die of the disease. Over 80 percent die of renal failure before they reach the age of 20.[19] As expected for a disease inherited as an autosomal recessive, the sex ratio is approximately 1:1.

The majority of patients present with classic symptoms of calcium oxalate nephrolithiasis, either typical renal colic or asymptomatic hematuria. Some male infants have required meatotomies for relief of blockage from small concretions. Other patients develop uremia without a previous history of nephrolithiasis. Short stature is common and may be caused by secondary renal tubular acidosis.[108] A number of patients with hyperoxaluria do not show the typical pattern of onset or progression of the disease.[109–112] Their disease may manifest initially in adult life even after the age of 40. None of these late onset patients have had enzymatic confirmation of diagnosis, and urinary oxalate excretion has been measured reliably in only a few. Thus, the diagnosis of primary hyperoxaluria has not always been established conclusively.

Other rarer clinical manifestations of primary hyperoxaluria include acute arthritis and symptoms referable to cardiac involvement.[109–112] Attacks of joint pain have been diagnosed as gout frequently in this disease. Although this feature has been observed most commonly during the uremic phase of the disease, some patients have had both hyperuricemia and joint symptoms before the onset of renal insufficiency. Since calcium oxalate crystals have been found in synovial membranes, it has been suggested that joint symptoms in these patients may be secondary to calcium oxalate crystallization in joint fluid. In some patients with primary hyperoxaluria the devel-

*Adapted and updated from the chapter in the fifth edition of this book by H.E. Williams and L.H. Smith.

opment of complete atrioventricular block has been related to the deposition of calcium oxalate crystals near the myocardial conduction system, a pathologic feature substantiated in several reports.[113–116] These patients may also exhibit severe peripheral vascular insufficiency.[117]

There are no specific physical findings in patients with primary hyperoxaluria. Growth retardation reflects renal failure. In the early stages of the disease the development of hydronephrosis may lead to palpable renal enlargement. Calcium oxalate crystals in the eye have been reported in some patients,[118–120] although many other patients have been examined carefully for such crystals with negative results.

Roentgenographic features are confined largely to the genitourinary tract and skeletal system with urolithiasis and nephrocalcinosis most frequently reported.[121] Radiopaque calcium oxalate densities are observed both in the collecting system of the kidneys and within the renal parenchyma. In the uremic phase of the disease bone changes consistent with secondary hyperparathyroidism and other forms of renal osteodystrophy may develop.

Primary oxaluria type II has only been reported in four persons from two families.[10] In three of the cases calcium oxalate nephrolithiasis developed before the age of 2. In the remaining patient the first symptoms did not develop until age 24. All four had intermittent microscopic hematuria, but none developed renal insufficiency in spite of symptoms for over 15 years in two. The oldest patient developed insulin-requiring diabetes mellitus at age 34.

Pathogenesis of Type I Primary Hyperoxaluria

Type I disease is characterized by the excretion of oxalate, glyoxylate, and glycolic acid and is often referred to as glycolic aciduria.[2] The defect in this disease is in the glycolic acid pathway. (See Fig. 35-4.) The metabolism of intravenously administered radiolabeled glyoxylate is diminished, as measured by expired respiratory CO_2, and the urinary excretion of labeled glyoxylate, oxalate, and glycolate is increased.[6] Similar results are obtained with labeled glycolate. Glyoxylate accumulates and is oxidized to oxalic acid probably outside the peroxisome. Recently, Danpure and Jennings[7,8] clearly demonstrated that the defect is in the peroxisomal enzyme, alanine:glyoxylate aminotransferase (EC 2.6.1.44), and this work has now been confirmed by Wanders et al.[9] Additional immunoblot studies of human liver tissue provide evidence for genetic heterogeneity, with three patients expressing a normal-sized enzyme monomer (CRM^+) while nine other patients lacked enzyme (CRM^-).[9a] Earlier studies[122–124] had failed to demonstrate this defect due to a variety of factors; either the wrong transaminating agent (glutamine) or the wrong compartment (mitochondria or cytosol) was studied. The new data are consistent with the plant model and also with the in vitro and in vivo studies in human beings.

Even though the enzyme deficiency is now defined, the source of the glyoxylate which is converted to oxalate is not clear. Atkins et al.[125] used [^{13}C]ascorbic acid to demonstrate that the pool size, turnover rate, and metabolic conversion of ascorbate to urinary oxalate were similar in a control subject and in two patients with primary hyperoxaluria. Less than 10 percent of the oxalate was derived from ascorbate. Administration of large amounts of ascorbate to patients with primary hyperoxaluria failed to increase urinary oxalate. Thus, the glyoxylate must be derived either from glycine or from the glyoxylate and glycolate pathways. As previously described, the equilibrium between glycine and glyoxylate is far in the direction of glycine. In addition, the major transaminase converting glycine and glyoxylate is defective in this disorder. It is possible that glycine could be transaminated to glyoxylate by another transaminase or oxidized by D-amino acid oxidase. Conversion certainly does occur, as demonstrated by the studies previously cited[61,62] showing that under equilibrium conditions, about 40 percent of oxalate is derived from glycine. However, the same studies did not show a difference between patients and normals and were interpreted to mean that the fractional contribution of glycine to oxalate was not increased in patients. Therefore, it must be concluded that the glycolate and glyoxylate pathways are the source of the glyoxylate and that enzymes similar to those known to exist in other organisms will be found in mammals including human beings.

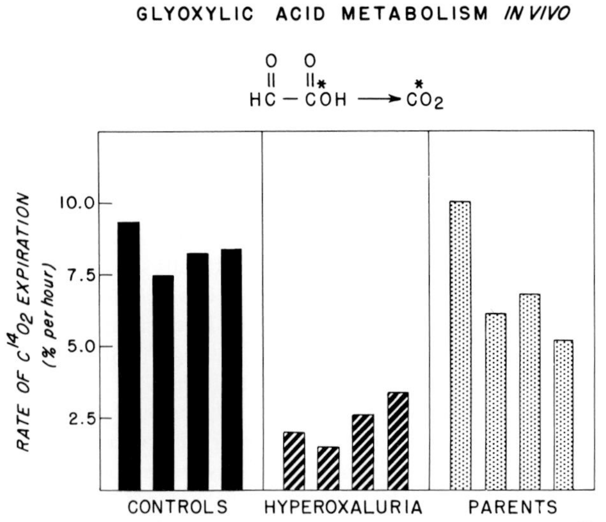

GLYOXYLIC ACID METABOLISM *IN VIVO*

Fig. 35-4 Metabolism of glyoxylic acid. (*From Frederick et al.*[59] *used with permission.*)

Pathogenesis of Primary Hyperoxaluria Type II

Hyperoxaluria type II is characterized by excessive excretion in the urine of oxalic acid and L-glyceric acid but neither glycolic acid or glyoxylic acid.[10,11] L-Glyceric acid is an extraperoxisomal product. D-Glyceric acid is the product of the peroxisomal portion of the glyceric acid pathway. To date, only four patients in two pedigrees have been described.

The major source of both D- and L-glyceric acid in both plants and animals is hydroxypyruvate produced by transamination of serine.[54] Within the peroxisome or glyoxisome, hydroxypyruvate is reduced by the enzyme D-glycerate dehydrogenase to D-glycerate.[53] This enzyme uses NADPH or NADH as hydrogen donors. The K_m for hydroxypyruvate is quite low ($4.5 \times 10^{-5} M$) and the equilibrium is far in the direction of the reduced product. In mammalian systems L-glyceric acid is the product of reduction of hydroxypyruvate by lactic dehydrogenase in the presence of NADH.[29] The K_m for L-glyceric acid is as low as that for L-lactic acid. This enzyme is not found in peroxisomes, and hydroxypyruvate must diffuse out of the cell to be reduced to L-glyceric acid rather than D-glyceric acid. Equilibrium of the reaction catalyzed by LDH is also in the direction of the reduced product. Since L-glyceric acid is not found in the urine of normal people, this finding in type II hyperoxaluria suggests that a defect in the normal metabolism of hydroxypyruvate to D-glycerate is the primary aberration in this disorder.

In vivo and in vitro studies have supported this view. [1-^{14}C]Hydroxypyruvate given intravenously to a patient with type II disease[10] resulted in approximately 15 percent of the isotope being recovered as L-glyceric acid. The activity of D-glycerate dehydrogenase was measured in leukocyte preparations from four patients with type II disease (see Fig. 35-5), the two parents of the three sibs with this disorder, and 14 normal controls by Williams and Smith.[10] No enzyme activity was detectable in leukocytes from the four patients. Enzyme activity was low in leukocytes from the mother but was within the normal range in the father. One patient with type I disease was also measured and was normal. This enzyme deficiency explains the hyperglyceric aciduria in these patients but does not explain the hyperoxaluria.

Several possible explanations can be given for the increased oxalate levels. The first is that hydroxypyruvate and/or L-glyceric acid can be metabolized directly to oxalic acid without passing through the glycolate pathway. Animal studies with [3-^{14}C]hydroxypyruvate have suggested a precursor-product relationship.[126] However, similar data do not exist for human beings and other evidence suggests that the origin of the oxalate is glyoxylate. A second possibility is that hydroxypyruvate inhibits glyoxylate reduction to glycolate. This reasoning would explain the lack of glycolate in the urine with type II disease, but because the prevailing flux is from glycolate to glyoxylate to glycine this would not explain the hyperoxaluria. A third possibility is that hydroxypyruvate accumulation stimulates the conversion of glyoxylate to oxalate. A patient with type II disease given [1-^{14}C]glyoxylate incorporated excessive amounts of label into oxalate when compared with controls. In this instance one would expect oxalate to be elevated without an increase in either glyoxylate or glycolate. In studies on

Fig. 35-5 D-Glyceric acid dehydrogenase activity in leukocytes from four patients with L-glyceric aciduria (primary hyperoxaluria type II), parents of three sibs with this syndrome, and control subjects. *(From Williams and Smith.[10] Used with permission.)*

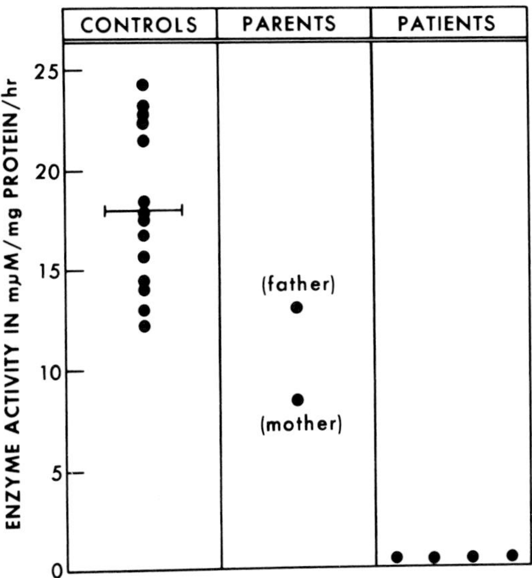

human erythrocytes and leukocytes and in partially purified LDH preparations,[127–129] it has been demonstrated that hydroxypyruvate increases oxalate synthesis and diminishes glycolate synthesis from glyoxylate, presumably through enhanced formation of NADH. Another possible explanation of the hyperoxaluria comes from plant studies. It is possible that direct linkage exists between the glycolate and glycerate pathways in mammals as it does in plants. If linkage did occur by a serine:glyoxylate aminotransferase as it does in photosynthesis or by some other mechanism, then the accumulation of hydroxypyruvate in and of itself might prevent the normal metabolism of glyoxylate and the shunting of this compound to oxalate.

Secondary Causes of Hyperoxaluria

Besides the two inherited causes of hyperoxaluria discussed in this chapter (primary hyperoxaluria type I and II), several secondary causes of increased oxalate excretion and precipitation in tissue have been documented. As noted below in "Diagnosis," none of these secondary disorders is associated with increases in the other characteristic organic acids seen in the primary diseases.

Under extreme conditions, the ingestion of excess oxalate may lead to hyperoxaluria in normal individuals. Hyperoxaluria can be produced in experimental animals by feeding oxalate in large quantities and oxalate poisoning has been reported in human beings. The presence of oxalate in the leaves of many plants is the main reason that they are classified as toxic. Because the absorption of oxalate is so low, this is an extremely rare cause of hyperoxaluria.

Ethylene glycol ingestion[130–133] is a far more common cause of secondary hyperoxaluria, at least in children. Ethylene glycol is rapidly converted to glycolate in the human and leads to extensive precipitation of calcium oxalate in the renal tubules leading to renal insufficiency. In one case seen in our institution, no ethylene glycol could be detected in body fluids 1 h after an ingestion. At that time, oxaluria was already severe.

Hyperoxaluria and nephrocalcinosis have been reported after the administration of the anesthetic agent methoxyflurane,[134–137] with resultant transient renal failure. This agent is presumably oxidized directly to oxalate.

Pyridoxine deficiency in experimental animals leads to hyperoxaluria and oxalosis.[138–140] Pyridoxine is a necessary cofactor for the enzyme alanine:glyoxylate aminotransferase, and deficiency produces a disease mimicking primary hyperoxaluria type I.[141] It is possible that some of the published reports of relatively late presenting cases of hyperoxaluria in humans may represent pyridoxine deficiency.

Enteric hyperoxaluria is one of the most interesting secondary causes of hyperoxaluria in human beings. It has been observed in patients with inflammatory bowel disease[142–146] and in patients who have had extensive resections of their intestines.[147–150] The syndrome also has been recognized in patients with fat malabsorption secondary to a variety of diseases of the bowel.[151–158] Oxalate and other fatty acids in the bowel compete for calcium ions. In the face of fat malabsorption, more of the oxalate is found as salts more soluble than calcium oxalate. This hypothesis is supported by studies in vitro of oxalate solubility in the presence of fatty acids.[159,160] Patients with this syndrome hyperabsorb dietary oxalate.[161] Absorption may reach 40 percent or more of the ingested oxalate as compared to 10 percent or less in normal individuals. Unlike patients with the primary hyperoxalurias, dietary manipulations, use of medium-chain triglycerides, reduction of dietary oxalate, and adminsitration of oral calcium supplements may return oxalate excretion to normal.

A number of studies have emphasized the role of the colon in the enteric hyperoxaluria syndrome.[98] The finding that certain bile acids and fatty acids may stimulate the transport of oxalate across the colonic mucosa has stressed colonic uptake as an important factor in this entity. Recently, a newly recognized species of bacteria that metabolizes oxalic acid has been isolated from human colons.[99] The cultural counts in normal human feces were as high as 10^7 colonies per gram of stool. Eight patients with jejunoileal bypasses, however, had far fewer colonies of this organism. The authors of this report believe that the lack of metabolism of oxalate in the bypass patients may have an important contribution to their hyperoxaluria.

DIAGNOSIS

The single most important finding in the diagnosis is increased urinary excretion of oxalate in the absence of pyridoxine deficiency, a history of ingestion of ethylene glycol or an oxalate precursor, or bowel disease causing fat malabsorption. Routine urinalysis and the sighting of oxalate crystals in the urinary sediment rarely are helpful although in one case seen in this institution the diagnosis was suggested on that basis. Such crystals are often present in normal individuals and those with calcium stones from other causes. Urinary oxalate excretion in normal human urine varies between 10 and 50 mg/24 h measured by the isotope dilution method.[162–164] Other methods give somewhat different values. When corrected for body surface area, the urine oxalate excretion is remarkably similar in children and adults.[59] In our laboratory we have used 30 mg/m^2/24 h as an upper limit of normal in children. In patients with primary hyperoxaluria studied by Smith et al.[162] urinary oxalate excretion averaged 240 mg/24 h with some values in excess of 400 mg/24 h. Smith and Williams state that it is extremely unusual to find levels below 100 mg/24 h in a patient with these disorders in the absence of renal failure.[19] Measurements of serum oxalate concentrations have proved extremely difficult,[165–173] and in one study[170] only one of six subjects with primary hyperoxaluria had serum oxalate levels above the normal range. However, generally elevated levels of oxalate have been documented in both patients with primary hyperoxaluria and in patients with renal failure from other causes.

The measurement of the other organic acids excreted in excess in these disorders provides the means to distinguish type I from type II and to separate them from secondary causes of hyperoxaluria. Unfortunately glyoxylic acid is quite labile and difficult to measure. This may explain why some patients with type I disease are not found to have elevations of glyoxylic acid in their urine.[162] However, under proper conditions the glyoxylic and glycolic acids[174] in type I disease and glyceric acid[175] in type II disease can be shown to be elevated. In our own laboratory we have used a combination of isotope dilution and capillary gas chromatography–mass spectroscopy for this purpose.

Now that the deficient enzyme in type I disease has been identified, enzyme diagnosis should be possible in these patients. However, alanine-glyoxylate aminotransferase has thus far only been detected in human liver and not in fibroblasts, making direct enzymatic diagnosis a difficult undertaking.[176] If the enzyme deficiency in type II disease is confirmed, it may be that leukocytes can be utilized for diagnostic assays.

The extrarenal deposit of calcium oxalate crystals is common in the primary hyperoxalosis syndromes but can also be seen in a number of other disorders including a variety of other peroxisomal disorders. Calcium oxalate crystals are found in the kidney in several conditions including chronic glomerulonephritis, chronic pyelonephritis, renal tubular acidosis, and acute tubular necrosis. Smith and Williams state that although oxalosis may be much more extensive in patients with the primary hyperoxalurias than in other disorders, it is often difficult in the individual case to use the extent of calcium oxalate deposit as a diagnostic tool.

TREATMENT

As of this writing, proposed treatment regimens have moderated the course of patients with hyperoxaluria, but, in the more severe cases, have not prevented most of the consequences of the disease, including renal failure. Treatment can be considered in four categories: prevention of stone formation and calcium oxalate precipitation, treatment of renal failure, attempts to limit precursors of oxalate and glyoxlyate conversion to oxalate, and attempts to stimulate or replace the missing enzyme activity. Treatment of renal failure will not be considered in this review. Treatment of hyperoxaluria has been recently reviewed by Smith.[177]

The attempts to prevent stone formation have followed the treatment of other disorders which involve calcium oxalate stone formation. This topic has also been recently reviewed.[178] Most of the efforts have involved ways to increase the solubility of calcium oxalate.[179–183] High fluid intake and alkalinization remain the mainstays of this approach. Other helpful therapy has included the use of other trace metal ions[179] and colloids.[180] These treatments may be of benefit in the management of patients with nongenetic hyperoxaluria but are not effective in preventing renal failure in type I disease.

Several attempts have been made to limit oxalate and its precursors. The use of benzoic acid to conjugate with glycine has been attempted by several authors without major effect. This is consistent with the more recent knowledge of the metabolic pathway and the now described metabolic defects. Attempts to limit oxalate absorption are quite effective in patients with enteric hyperoxaluria and may play a role in milder cases of primary hyperoxaluria. Hemodialysis, used because of the renal failure, can remove large quantities of both oxalate and its precursors.[184] Attempts to prevent the oxidation of glyoxylate to oxalate have thus far not met with much success.

The enzyme deficiency in type I disease involves a pyridoxine-dependent reaction. The use of large doses of pyridoxine does seem to decrease oxalate excretion at least in the milder cases and is consistent with the partial cofactor dependency seen in a variety of other disorders involving pyridoxal phosphate–requiring enzymes. Pyridoxine should be tried in these patients.[185–189] Finally, organ transplantation[190–196] has produced some hope for these patients, both as a primary means of treating renal failure and for enzyme replacement. Renal transplantation by itself appears not to be sufficient because of the rapid accumulation of oxalate in the transplanted kidney. However, recently a combined liver-kidney transplant was shown to result in substantial reduction in plasma and urinary oxalate concentrations to levels just above the normal range 8 months after the surgery.[197] Long-term follow-up will be required to evaluate this potentially promising therapy.

REFERENCES

1. DeZEGHER FE, WOLFF ED, VD HEIJDEN AJ, SUKHAI RN: Oxalosis in infancy. *Clin Nephrol* 22:114, 1984.
2. WILLIAMS HE, SMITH LH JR: Disorders of oxalate metabolism. *Am J Med* 45:715, 1968.
3. HELIN I: Primary hyperoxaluria. An analysis of 17 Scandinavian patients. *Scand J Urol Nephrol* 14:61, 1980.
4. WALLS J, MORLEY AR, KERR DNS: Primary hyperoxaluria and renal transplantation. *J Urol* 111:398, 1974.
5. COCHRAN M, HODGKINSON A, ZAREMBSKI PM, ANDERSON CK: Hyperoxaluria in adults. *Br J Surg* 55:121, 1968.
6. FREDERICK EW, RABKIN MT, SMITH LH JR: Primary hyperoxaluria: A defect in glyoxylate metabolism. *J Clin Invest* 41:1358, 1962.
7. DANPURE CJ, JENNINGS PR: Peroxisomal alanine:glyoxylate aminotransferase deficiency in primary hyperoxaluria type I. *FEBS Letters* 201:20, 1986.
8. DANPURE CJ, JENNINGS PR, WATTS RWE: Enzymological diagnosis of primary hyperoxaluria type I by measurement of hepatic alanine:glyoxylate aminotransferase activity. *Lancet* 1:289, 1987.
9. WANDERS RJA, van ROERMUND CWT, WESTRA R, SCHUTGENS RBH, VAN DER ENDE MA, TAGER JM, MONNENS LAH, BAADENHUYSEN H, GOVAERTS L, PRZYREMBEL H, WOLFF ED, BLOM W, HUIJMANS JGM, VAN LAERHOVEN FGM: Alanine:glyoxylate aminotransferase and the urinary excretion of oxalate and glycollate in hyperoxaluria type I and the Zellweger syndrome. *Clin Chim Acta* 165:311, 1987.

9a. WISE PJ, DANPURE CJ, JENNINGS PR: Immunological heterogeneity of hepatic alanine: Glyoxalate aminotransferase in primary hyperoxaluria type 1. *FEB* 222:17, 1987.

10. WILLIAMS HE, SMITH LH JR: L-Glyceric aciduria: A new genetic variant of primary oxaluria. *N Engl J Med* 278:233, 1968.
11. WILLIAMS HE, SMITH LH JR: L-Glyceric aciduria, in Hodgkinson A, Nordin BEC (eds): *Renal Stone Research Symposium.* London, Churchill Livingstone, 1969, p 309.
12. WOLLASTON WH: On cystic oxide, a new species of urinary calculus. *Philos Trans (Lond)* 100:223, 1810.
13. DONNE MA: Tableau de differents depots de matieres salines et de substance organiees qui se font dans les urines, presentatant les caracteres propre a les distinguer entre eux et a reconnaitre leure nature. *CR Acad Sci (D) (Paris)* 6:19, 1838.
14. LEPOUTRE C: Calculs multiples chez un enfant. Infiltration due parenchyme renal par des cristaux. *J Urol* 20:424, 1925.
15. DAVID JS, KLINGBERG WG, STOWELL RE: Nephrolithiasis and nephrocalcinosis with calcium oxalate crystals in kidneys and bones. *J Pediatr* 36:343, 1950.
16. NEWNS GH, BLACK JA: A case of calcium oxalate nephrocalcinosis. *Great Ormond St J* 5:40, 1953.
17. DANIELS RA, MICHELS R, AISEN P, GOLDSTEIN G: Familial hyperoxaluria. *Am J Med* 29:820, 1960.
18. APONTE GE, FETTER TR: Familial idiopathic oxalate nephrocalcinosis. *Am J Clin Pathol* 24:1363, 1954.
19. WILLIAMS HE, SMITH RH JR: Primary hyperoxaluria, in Stanbury JB, Wyngaarden JB, Fredrickson DS, Golstein JL, Brown MS (eds): *The Metabolic Basis of Inherited Disease,* 5th ed. New York, McGraw-Hill, 1983, p 204.
20. KOCH J, STOKSTAD ELR, WILLIAMS HE, SMITH LH JR: Deficiency of 2-oxoglutarate:glyoxylate carboligase activity in primary hyperoxaluria. *Proc Natl Acad Sci USA* 57:1123, 1967.
21. YENDT ER, COHANIM M: Response to a physiologic dose of pyridoxine in type I primary hyperoxaluria. *N Engl J Med* 312:953, 1985.
22. ZAREMBSKI PM, HODGKINSON A: The oxalic acid content of English diets. *Br J Nutr* 16:627, 1962.
23. ZARENBSKI PM, HODGKINSON A: The determination of oxalic acid in food. *Analyst* 85:698, 1962.
24. CHRISTENSEN HE, LUGENBYHL TT, CAROLL BS: *The Toxic Substances List.* USHEW, Rockwells, 1974.
25. DEAN JA: *Lange's Handbook of Chemistry.* New York, McGraw-Hill, 1979.
26. DE DUVE C: Evaluation of the peroxisome. *Ann NY Acad Sci* 168:369, 1969/70.
27. DE DUVE C, BAUDHUIN P: Peroxisomes (microbodies and realted particles). *Physiol Rev* 46:323, 1966.
28. BANNER MR, ROSALKI SB: Glyoxylate as a substrate for lactate dehydrogenase. *Nature* 213:726, 1967.
29. TOLBERT NE: Metabolic pathways in peroxisomes and glyoxysomes. *Annu Rev Biochem* 50:133, 1981.
30. RHODIN J: Cited in Breidenbach RW: Microbodies, in Bonner J, Varner JE (eds): *Plant Physiology.* New York, Academic, 1976.
31. MOLLENHAUSER HH, MORRE DJ, KELLY AG: The widespread occurrence of plant cytosomes resembling animal microbodies. *Protoplasma* 62:44, 1966.
32. LEIGHTON F, POOLE B, LAZAROW PB, DEDUVE C: The synthesis and turnover of rat liver peroxisomes. I. Fractionation of peroxisome proteins. *J Cell Biol* 41:521, 1969.
33. DE DUVE C: Peroxisomes and related particles in historical perspective. *Ann NY Acad Sci* 386:1, 1982.
34. POOLE B, LEIGHTON F, DE DUVE C: The synthesis and turnover of rat liver peroxisomes. II. Turnover of peroxisome proteins. *J Cell Biol* 41:536, 1969.
35. BREIDENBACH RW, BEVERS H: Association of the glyoxylate cycle enzymes in a novel subcellular particle from castor bean endosperm. *Biochem Biophys Res Commun* 27:462, 1967.
36. BREIDENBACH RW, BEVERS H: Characterization of glyoxysomes from castor bean endosperm. *Biochem Biophys Res Commun* 27:462, 1967.
37. HUANG AHC, BEEVERS H: Isolation of microbodies from plant tissues. *Plant Physiol* 48:637, 1971.
38. BEEVERS H: Microbodies in higher plants. *Annu Rev Plant Physiol* 30:159, 1979.
39. TOLBERT NE, OESER H, YAMAZAKI RK, HAGEMAN RH, KISAKI T: A survey of plants for leaf peroxisomes. *Plant Physiol* 44:135, 1969.
40. TOLBERT NE: Microbodies, peroxisomes and glyoxysomes. *Annu Rev Plant Physiol* 22:45, 1971.
41. TOLBERT NE, YAMAZAKI RK, DESER A: Localization and properties of hydroxypyruvate and glyoxylate reductases in spinach leaf particles. *J Biol Chem* 245:5129, 1970.
42. YAMAZAKI RK, TOLBERT NE: Enzymic characterization of leaf peroxisomes. *J Biol Chem* 245:5137, 1970.
43. HRUBAN Z, RECHCIGL M JR: Microbodies and related particles. Morphology, biochemistry, and physiology. *Int Rev Cytol Suppl* 1:1, 1969.
44. HOGG JF: The nature and function of peroxisomes (microbodies, glyoxysomes). *Ann NY Acad Sci* 168:281, 1969.
45. HUANG A, BEEVERS H: Localization of enzymes within microbodies. *J Cell Biol* 58:379, 1973.
46. MASTERS C, HOLMES R: Peroxisomes: New aspects of cell physiology and biochemistry. *Physiol Rev* 57:816, 1977.
47. McGROARTY E, HSICH B, WIED D, TOLBERT NE: Alpha hydroxy acid oxidation by peroxisomes. *Arch Biochem Biophys* 161:194, 1974.
48. HOCKADAY TDR, CLAYTON JE, SMITH LH JR: The metabolic error in primary hyperoxaluria. *Arch Dis Child* 40:485, 1965.
49. TAKADA Y, MORI T, NOGUCHI T: The effect of vitamin B6 deficiency on alanine:glyoxylate aminotransferase isoenzymes in rat liver. *Arch Biochem Biophys* 229:1, 1984.
50. FABER SR, FEITLER WW, BLEILER RE, OHLSON MA, HODGES RE: The effects of an induced pyridoxine deficiency on excretion of oxalic and xanthurenic acids in the urine. *Am J Clin Nutr* 12:406, 1963.
51. CHEUNG GP, COTROPIA JP, SALLACH HJ: Comparative studies of enzymes related to serine metabolism in fetal and adult liver. *Biochim Biophys Acta* 170:334, 1968.
52. WALSH DA, SALLACH JH: Comparative studies on pathways for serine biosynthesis in animal tissues. *J Biol Chem* 24:4068, 1966.
53. WILLIS JE, SALLACH JH: Evidence for mammalian d-glyceric dehydrogenase. *J Biol Chem* 237:910, 1962.
54. FALLON JH, HACKNEY EJ, BYRNE WL: Serine biosynthesis in rat liver: Regulation of enzyme concentration by dietary factors. *J Biol Chem* 241:4157, 1966.
55. BOWES G, OGREN WL: Oxygen inhibition and other properties of soybean ribulose 1,5-diphosphate carboxylase. *J Biol Chem* 247:2171, 1972.
56. TOLBERT NE: Leaf peroxisomes. *Ann NY Acad Sci* 386:254, 1982.
57. LORIMER G: The carboxylation and oxygenation of ribulose 1,5-biphosphate: The primary events in photosynthesis. *Annu Rev Plant Physiol* 32:340, 1981.
58. RANDELL DD, TOLBERT NE, GREMEL D: 3-phosphoglycerate phosphate in plants II. *Plant Physiol* 48:480, 1971.
59. FREDERICK EW, RABKIN MT, RICHIE RH JR, SMITH LH JR: Studies on primary hyperoxaluria. I. In vivo demonstration of a defect in glyoxylate metabolism. *N Engl J Med* 269:821, 1963.
60. HILLMAN RE, KEATING JP: Beta-ketothiolase deficiency as a cause of the ketotic hyperglycinemia syndrome. *Pediatrics* 53:221, 1973.

61. CRAWHALL JC, SCOWEN EF, WATTA RWE: Conversion of glycine to oxalate in primary hyperoxaluria. *Lancet* 2:806, 1959.
62. DEAN BM, WATTS RWE, WESTWICK WJ: The conversion of [1-13C] glycine and [2-13C] glycine to [13C] oxalate in primary hypeoxaluria: Evidence for the existence of more than one metabolic pathway from glycine to oxalate in man. *Clin Sci* 35:325, 1968.
63. JONES CT: Is there a glyoxylate cycle in the liver of the fetal guinea pig? *Biochem Biophys Res Commun* 95:849, 1980.
64. MCKINLEY MP, FIELD LA, TRELEASE RN: Multiple forms of isocitrate lyase in the matrix of Turbatrix aceti mitochondria. *Arch Biochem Biophys* 197(1):253, 1979.
65. MCKINLEY MP, TRELEASE RN: Coexistence of isocitrate lyase and NADP-isocitrate dehydrogenase in Turbatrix aceti mitochondria. *Biochem Biophys Res Commun* 81(2):434, 1978.
66. FARAGALLA FF, GERSHOFF SN: Occurrence of C14-oxalate in rat urine after administration of C14-tryptophane. *Proc Soc Exp Biol Med* 114:602, 1963.
67. LIAO LL, RICHARDSON KE: The metabolism of oxalate percursors in isolated perfused rat livers. *Arch Biochem Biophys* 153:438, 1972.
68. LIAO LL, RICHARDSON KE: The synthesis of oxylate from hydroxypyruvate by isolated perfused rat liver. The mechanism of hyperoxaluria in 1-glyceric aciduria. *Biochim Biophys Acta* 538:76, 1978.
69. LIAO LL, RICHARDSON KE: The inhibition of oxalate biosynthesis in isolated perfused rat liver by dl-phenyllactate and n-heptanoate. *Arch Biochem Biophys* 154:68, 1973.
70. CURTIN CO, KING CG: The metabolism of ascorbic acid-1-14-C and oxalic acid-14C in the rat. *J Biol Chem* 216:539, 1955.
71. BANAY M, DIMANT E: On the metabolism of 1-ascorbic acid in the scorbutic guinea pig. *Biochim Biophys Acta* 59:313, 1962.
72. ART AF, VonSCHUCHING S, ENNS T: 1-Ascorbic-1-C14 acid catabolism in the rhesus monkey. *Nature* 193:1178, 1962.
73. TAKENOUGHI K, ASO K, KAWASE K, ICHIKAWA H, SHIOMI T: On the metabolites of ascorbic acid, especially oxalic acid, eliminated in urine, following the administration of large amounts of ascorbic acid. *J Vitamin (Kyoto)* 12:49, 1966.
74. HELLMAN L, BURNS JJ: Metabolism of 1-ascorbic acid 1-14C in man. *J Biol Chem* 230:923, 1958.
75. BAKER EM, SAARI JC, TOLBERT BM: Ascorbic acid metabolism in man. *Am J Clin Nutr* 190:371, 1966.
76. GIBBS DA: The separation and characterization of the enzymes which oxidize glyoxlate to oxalate in the liver. *Clin Sci* 41:3P, 1971.
77. SMITH LH JR, BUER RL, CRAIG JC, WILLIAMS HE: Inhibition of oxalate synthesis: in Vitro studies using analogues of ostalate and glycolate. *Biochem Med* 6:317, 1972.
78. RICHARDSON KE, TOLBERT NE: Oxidation of glyoxylic acid to oxalic acid by glycolic acid oxidase. *J Biol Chem* 236:1280, 1961.
79. ZELITCH I: Oxidation and reduction of glycolic and glyoxylic acids in plants. II. Glyoxylic acid reductase. *J Biol Chem* 201:719, 1953.
80. ZELITCH I, GOTTO AM: Properties of a new glyoxylate reductase from leaves. *Biochem J* 84:541, 1962.
81. WATTS RWE, CRAWHALL JC: The first glycine metabolic pool in man. *Biochem J* 73:277, 1959.
82. RATNER S, NOCITO V, GREEN DE: Glycine oxidase. *J Biol Chem* 152:119, 1944.
83. GIBBS DA, WATTS RWE: An investigation of the possible role of xanthine oxidase in the oxidation of glyoxylate and oxalate. *Clin Sci* 31:285, 1966.
84. CRAWHALL JC, WATTS RWE: The metabolism of glyoxylate by human and rat liver mitochondria. *Biochem J* 85:163, 1963.
85. SAWAKI S, HATTORI N, MORIKAWA N, YAMADA K: Oxidation and reduction of glyoxylate by lactase dehydrogenase. *J Vitamin (Kyoto)* 13:93, 1967.
86. ANDERSON SR, FLORINI JR, VESTLING CS: Rat liver lactate dehydrogenase. III. Kinetics and specificity. *J Biol Chem* 239:2991, 1964.
87. SAWAKI S, HATTORI N, YAMADA K: Reduction of nicotinamide adenine dinucleotide by glyoxylate in animal organs. *J Vitamin (Kyoto)* 13:93, 1966.
88. ARCHER HE, DORMER AE, SCOWEN EF, WATTS TWE: Studies on the urinary excretion of oxalate by normal subjects. *Clin Sci* 16:405, 1957.
89. ERNEST DL, JOHNSON G, WILLIAMS HE, ADMIRAND WH: Hyperoxaluria in patients with ileal resection: An abnormality in dietary oxalate absorption. *Gasteroenterology* 66:1114, 1975.
90. CHADWICK VS, MODHA K, DOWLING RH: Mechanism for hyperoxaluria in patients with ileal dysfunction. *N Engl J Med* 289:172, 1973.
91. HATCH M, FREEL RW, GOLDNER AM, EARNEST DL: Oxalate and chloride absorption by the rabbit colon: Sensitivity to metabolic and anion transport inhibitors. *Gut* 25:232, 1984.
92. KNICKELBEIN RG, ARONSON PS, DOBBINS JW: Oxalate transport by anion exchange across rabbit ileal brush border. J Clin Invest 77:170, 1986.
93. OSSWALD H, HAUTMAN R: Renal elimination kinetics and plasma half-life of oxalate in man. *Urol Int* 34:440, 1979.
94. CATTELL WR, SPENCER G, TAYLOR GW, WATTS RWE: The mechanism of the renal excretion of exalate in the dog. *Clin Sci* 22:43, 1962.
95. WILLIAMS HE, JOHNSON GA, SMITH LH JR: The renal clearance of oxalate in normal subjects and patients with primary hyperoxaluria. *Clin Sci* 41:219, 1962.
96. WEINMAN EJ, FRANKFURT SJ, INCE A, SANSOM S: Renal tubular transport of organic acids. *J Clin Invest* 61:801, 1978.
97. AKCAY T, ROSE GA: The real and apparent plasma oxalate. *Clin Chim Acta* 101:305, 1980.
98. GOLDKIND L, CAVE DR, JAFFIN B, BLISS CM, ALLISON MJ: Bacterial oxalate metabolism in the human colon—A possible factor in enteric hyperoxaluria. *Gastroenterology* 90:1431, 1986.
99. ALLISON MJ, COOK HM, MILNE DB, GALLAGHER S, CLAYMAN RV: Oxalate degradation by gastrointestinal bacterial from humans. *J Nutr* 116:455, 1986.
100. BOQUIST L, LINDQUIST B, OSTBERG Y, STEEN L: Primary oxalosis. *Am J Med* 54:673, 1973.
101. MORRIS MC, CHAMBERS TL, EVANS PWG, MALLESON PN, PINCOTT JR, ROSE GA: Oxalosis in infancy. *Arch Dis Child* 57:224, 1982.
102. WANDERS RJA and SCHUTGENS RBH: Personal communication.
103. HOLMGREN G, HORNSTROM T, JOHNANSSON S, SAMUELSON G: Primary hyperoxaluria (glycolic acid variant): A clinical and genetical investigation of eight cases. *UPS J Med Sci* 83:65, 1978.
104. McLAURIN AW, BEISEL WR, McCORMICK GJ, SCALETTER R, HERMAN RH: Primary hyperoxaluria. *Ann Intern Med* 55:70, 1961.
105. STAUFFER M: Oxalosis: Report of a case, with a review of the literature and discussion of the pathogenesis. *N Engl J Med* 263:386, 1960.
106. DIGAARD H, SODERHJELM L, HOGLUND NJ, WERNER I: Familial oxalosis II. *Acta Soc Med Upsala* 68:55, 1963.
107. SHEPARD TH II, LEE LW, KREBS EG: Primary hyperoxaluria. II. Genetic studies in a family. *Pediatrics* 25:869, 1960.
108. LAGRUE G, LAUDAT MH, MEYER P, SAPIR M, MILLLIEZ P: Oxalose familiale avec acidose hyperchloremique secondaire. *Semin Hop Paris* 35:2023, 1959.
109. BOQUIST L, LINDQVIST B, OSTERG Y, STEEN L: Primary oxalosis. *Am J Med* 54:673, 1973.
110. CHISHOLM GD, HEARD BE: Oxalosis. *Br J Surg* 50:78, 1962.
111. BURKE EC, BAGGENSTOSS AH, OWEN CA JR, POWER MH, LOHR OW: Oxalosis, *Pediatrics* 15:383, 1955.
112. HALL EG, SCOWEN EF, WATTS RWE: Clinical manifestations of primary hyperoxaluria. *Arch Dis Child* 35:108, 1960.
113. COLTART DJ, HUDSON REB: Primary oxalosis of the heart: A cause of heart block. *Br Heart J* 33:315, 1971.
114. PIKULA B, PLAMENAC P, CURFCIC B, NIKULIN A: Myocarditis caused by primary oxalosis in a 4 year old child. *Virchows Arch (A)* 358:99, 1973.
115. BENNETT B, ROSENBLUM C: Calcium oxalate crystals in the myocardium in uremic patients. *Lab Invest* 10:947, 1961.
116. WEST RR, SALYER WR, HUTCHINS GM: Adult-onset primary oxalosis with complete heart block. *Johns Hopkins Med J* 133:195, 1973.
117. ARBUS GS, SNIDERMAN S: Oxalosis with peripheral gangrene. *Arch Pathol* 97:107, 1974.
118. BULLOCK JD, ALBERT DM, SKINNER HCW, MILLER WH, GALLA JH: Calcium oxalate retinopathy associated with generalized oxalosis: X-ray diffraction and electron microscopic studies of crystal deposits. *Invest Ophthalmol* 13:256, 1974.
119. CAINE R, ALBERT DM, LAHAV M, BULLOCK J: Oxalate retinopathy: An experimental model of a flecked retina. *Invest Ophthalmol* 14:359, 1975.
120. TOUSSAINT D, VEREERSTRAETEN P, GOFFIN P, VANLANDUYT P, JEDWAB J, LEGRAND JM: Primary hyperoxaluria. Clinical, histological and crystallographic study of the ocular lesions. *Arch Ophthalmol (Paris)* 36:97, 1976.
121. DAY DL, SCHEINMAN JI, MAHAN J: Radiological aspects of primary hyperoxaluria. *Am J Roentgenology* 146:395, 1986.
122. CRAWHALL JC, WATTS RWE: The metabolism of [1-14C]-glyoxylate by the liver mitochondria of patients with primary hyperoxaluria and nonhyperoxaluric subjects. *Clin Sci* 23:163, 1962.
123. DEAN BM, GRIFFIN WJ, WATTS RWE: Primary hyperoxaluria. *Lancet* 1:406, 1966.
124. DEAN BM, WATTS RWE, WESTWICH WJ: Metabolism of [1-14C] glyoxylate, [1-14C] glycolate, [1-14C] glycine, and [2-14C] glycine by homogenates of kidney and liver tissue from hyperoxaluric and control subjects. *Biochem J* 106:701, 1967.
125. ATKINS GL, DEAN BM, GRIFFIN WJ, SCOWEN EF, WATTS RWE: Quantitative aspects of ascorbic acid metabolism in patients with primary hyperoxaluria. *Clin Sci* 29:305, 1965.
126. RICHARDSON KE, KIAO LI: Formation of oxalate from hydroxypyruvate by isolated perfused rat liver. *Fed Proc* 32:565, 1973.

127. SMITH LH JR, BAUER RL, WILLIAMS HE: Oxalate and glycolate synthesis by hemic cell. *J Lab Clin Med* 78:245, 1971.
128. ZEWE V, FROMM HJ: Kinetic studies of rabbit muscle lactate dehydrogenase. II. Mechanism of the reaction. *Biochemistry* 4:782, 1965.
129. FISHER V, WATTS RWE: The metabolism of glyoxylate in blood from normal subjects and patients with primary hyperoxaluria. *Clin Sci* 34:97, 1968.
130. WACKER WEC, HAYNES H, DRUYAN R, FISHER W, COLEMAN JE: Treatment of ethylene glycol poisoning with ethyl alcohol. *JAMA* 194:1231, 1965.
131. LYON ES, BORDEN TA, VERMEULLEN CW: Experimental oxalate lithiasis produced with ethylene glycol. *Invest Urol* 4:143, 1966.
132. PARRY MF, WALLACH R: Ethylene glycol poisoning. *Am J Med* 47:143, 1974.
133. FRIEDMAN EA, GREENBERG JB, MERRIL JP, DAMMIN GJ: Consequences of ethylene glycol poisoning. *Am J Med* 32:891, 1962.
134. FRASCINO JA, VANAMEE P, ROSEN PP: Renal oxalosis and azotemia after methoxyflurane anesthesia. *N Engl J Med* 283:676, 1970.
135. MAZZE RI, COUSINS MJ: Methoxyflurane anesthesia. *Arch Pathol* 92:484, 1971.
136. AUFDERHEIDE AC: Renal tubular calcium oxalate crystal deposition: Its possible relation to methoxyflurane anesthesia. *Arch Pathol* 92:162, 1971.
137. BERGSTRAND A, COLLSTE LG, FRANKSSON C, GLAS JE, LOFSTROM B, MAGNUSSON G, NORDENSTAM H, WERNER B: Oxalosis in renal transplants following methoxyflurane anesthesia. *Br J Anesth* 44:569, 1972.
138. GERSHOFF SN, FARAGALLA FF, NELSON DA, ANDRUS SB: Vitamin B6 deficiency and oxalate nephrocalcinosis in the cat. *Am J Med* 27:72, 1959.
139. RUNYAN TJ, GERSHOFF SN: The effect of Vitamin B6 deficiency in rats on the metabolism of oxalic acid precursors. *J Biol Chem* 240:1889, 1965.
140. GERSHOFF SN: Vitamin B6 and oxalate metabolism. *Vitam Horm* 27:558, 1974.
141. GIBBS D, WATTS RWE: The action of pyridoxine in primary hyperoxaluria. *Clin Sci* 38:2277, 1970.
142. ADMIRAND W, EARNEST D, WILLIAMS HE: Hyperoxaluria and bowel disease. *Trans Assoc Am Physicians* 84:307, 1972.
143. ADMIRAND WH: Hyperoxaluria and bowel disease. *N Engl J Med* 286:1412, 1972.
144. SMITH LH, FROMM H, HOFMANN AF: Acquired hyperoxaluria, nephrolithiasis, and intestinal disease: Description of a syndrome. *N Engl J Med* 286:1371, 1972.
145. DOWLING RH, ROSE GA, SUTOR DJ: Hyperoxaluria and renal calculi in ileal disease. *Lancet* 1:1103, 1971.
146. EARNEST DL: Enteric hyperoxaluria. *Adv Intern Med* 24:407, 1979.
147. CHADWICK VS, MODHA K, DOWLING RH: Pathogenesis of secondary hyperoxaluria in ileal resection. *Gut* 13:840, 1972.
148. STAUFFER JO, HUMPHREYS MH, WEIR GJ: Acquired hyperoxaluria with regional enteritis after ileal resection: Role of dietary oxalate. *Ann Intern Med* 79:383, 1973.
149. ANDERSSON H, FILIPSSON S, HULTEN L: Urinary oxalate excretion related to ileocolic surgery in patients with Crohn's disease. *Scand J Gastroenterol* 12:465, 1978.
150. HOLST J, PEDERSEN J, SITTEN J: The effect of calcium on hyperoxaluria following jejunoileal bypass in morbid obesity. *Scand J Gastroenterol* 14:97, 1979.
151. CASPARY WE, TONISSEN J, LANKISCH PG: "Enteral" hyperoxaluria. Effect of cholestyramine, calcium neomycin and bile acids on intestinal oxalate absorption in man. *Acta Hepatogastroenterol (Stuttg)* 24:193, 1977.
152. STAUFFER JQ: Hyperoxaluria and intestinal disease. The role of steatorrhoea and dietary calcium in regulating intestinal oxalate absorption. *Am J Dig Dis* 22:921, 1977.
153. MODIGIANI R, LABAYLE D, AYMES C, DENVIL R: Evidence for excessive absorption of oxalate by the colon in enteric hyperoxaluria. *Scand J Gasteroenterol* 13:187, 1978.
154. STAUFFER JQ: Hyperoxaluria and calcium oxalate nephrolithiasis after jejunoileal bypass. *Am J Clin Nutr* 30:64, 1977.
155. BARILLA DE, NOTZ C, KENNEDY D, PAK CY: Renal oxalate excretion following oral oxalate loads in patients with ilial disease and with renal and absorptive hypercalciurias. Effect of calcium and magnesium. *Am J Med* 64:579, 1978.
156. MARSHALL RW, COCHRAN M, HODGKINSON A: Relationships between calcium and oxalic acid intake in the diet and their excretion in the urine of normal and renal-stone-forming subjects. *Clin Sci* 43:91, 1972.
157. DOBBINS JW, BINDER HJ: Importance of the colon in enteric hyperoxaluria. *N Engl J Med* 296:298, 1977.
158. BINDER HJ: Intestinal oxalate absorption. *Gastroenterology* 57:441, 1974.
159. SCHWARTZ SE, STAUFFER JO, BURGESS LW, CHENEY M: Oxalate uptake by everted sacs of rat colon. Regional differences and the effects of pH and ricinoleic acid. *Biochim Biophys Acta* 593:404, 1980.
160. DOBBINS JW, BINDER HJ: Effect of bile salts and fatty acids on the colon absorption of oxalate. *Gastroenterology* 70:1096, 1976.
161. PANZA E, SANGALETTI O, GHIRAROSI C, PORRO GB: Urinary oxalate recovery after oral oxalic load—An alternative method to the quantitative determination of stool fat for the diagnosis of lipid malabsorption. *Ital J Gastroenterology* 18:62, 1986.
162. HOCKADAY TDR, FREDERICK EW, CLAYTON JE, SMITH LH JR: Studies on primary hyperoxaluria. II. Urinary oxalate, glycolate and glyoxylate measurement by isotope dilution method. *J Lab Clin Med* 65:677, 1965.
163. PRENEN JAC, OEI HY, MEES EJD: Indirect estimation of plasma oxalate usine C14 oxalate. *J Nucl Med* 27:571, 1986.
164. SCHEINMAN JI, MILLINGTON DS, GALE DA, ROE C: Assay for urine and plasma oxalate by GC/MS isotope dilution. *Kidney Int* 29:202, 1986.
165. KSIDAS GP, ROSE GA: Measurement of plasma oxalate in healthy subjects and in patients with chronic renal failure using immobilized oxalate oxidase. *Clin Chim Acta* 154:49, 1986.
166. HODGKISON A: Determination of oxalic acid in biological material. *Clin Chem* 16:547, 1970.
167. GIBBS DA, WATTS RWE: The variation of urinary oxalate excretion with age. *J Lab Clin Med* 73:901, 1969.
168. BARBER HH, GALLIMORE EJ: The metabolism of oxalic acid in the animal body. *Biochem J* 34:144, 1940.
169. CRAWHALL JC, WATTS RWE: The oxalate content of human plasma. *Clin Sci* 20:357, 1961.
170. ZAREMBSKI PM, HODGKINSON A: The renal clearance of oxalic acid in normal subjects and in patients with primary hyperoxaluria. *Invest Urol* 1:87, 1963.
171. ZAREMBSKI PM, HODGKISON A: Fluorimetric determination of oxalic acid in blood and other biological material. *Biochem J* 96:717, 1965.
172. ELDER TD, WYNGVAARDEN JB: The biosynthesis and turnover of oxalate in normal and hyperoxaluric subjects. *J Clin Invest* 39:1337, 1960.
173. RUSSELL JC, CHAMBERS M: A specific assay for plasma oxalate. *Clin Biochem* 6:22, 1973.
174. NIEDERWIESER A, MATASOVIC A, LEUMANN EP: Glycolic acid in urine. A colorimetric method with values in normal adult controls and in patients with primary hyperoxaluria. *Clin Chim Acta* 89:13, 1978.
175. WILLIAMS HE, SMITH LH JR: Identification and determination of glyceric acid in human urine. *J Lab Clin Med* 71:495, 1968.
176. WANDES RJA, SHUTGENS RBH: Personal communication.
177. SMITH LH: Primary hyperoxaluria, the effect of long term treatment. *Urol Res* 14:95, 1986.
178. BUTZ M, KLAN R, KARADZIC G: First long-term results of oxalate stone prevention by alkali citrate. *Urol Res* 14:95, 1986.
179. ELLIOT JS, EUSEBIO E: Calcium oxalate solubility: The effect of trace metals. *Invest Urol* 4:428, 1967.
180. MACLAGAN NF, ANDERSON AJ: Some observations on urinary colloids in relation to renal calculi. *Br J Urol* 30:269, 1958.
181. HOWARD JE, THOMAS WC JR: Control of crystallization in urine. *Am J Med* 45:693, 1968.
182. SILVER L, BRUDLER H: Use of magnesium oxide in management of familial hyperoxaluria. *J Urol* 106:274, 1971.
183. THOMAS WC JR, MILLER GH JR: Inorganic phosphates in the treatment of renal calculi. *Mod Treat* 4:494, 1967.
184. SAXON A: Hemodialysis for oxaluric renal failure. *N Engl J Med* 288:526, 1973.
185. LYON ES, BORDEN TA, ELLIS JE, VERMEULEN CW: Calcium oxalate lithiasis produced by pyridoxine deficiency and inhibition with high magnesium diets. *Invest Urol* 4:133, 1966.
186. GERSHOFF SN, PRIEN EL: Effect of daily MgO and vitamin B6 administration to patients with recurrent oxalate kidney stones. *Am J Clin Nutr* 20:393, 1967.
187. WATTS RW, CHALMERS RA, GIBBS DA, LAWSON AM, PRUKISS P, SPELLACY E: Studies on some possible biochemical treatments of primary hyperoxaluria. *Q J Med* 48:259, 1979.
188. SOLOMONS CC, GOODMAN SI, RILEY CM: Treatment of hyperoxaluria. *N Engl J Med* 277:1425, 1967.
189. FABER SR, FEITLER WW, BLEILER RE, OHLSON MA, HODGES RE: The effects of an induced pyridoxine and panthothenic acid deficiency on excretions of oxalic and xanthurenic acids in the urine. *Am J Clin Nutr* 12:406, 1963.
190. DEOHAR SD, TUNG KSK, ZUHLKE V, NAKAMOTO S: Renal homotransplantation in a patient with priamry familial oxalosis. *Arch Pathol* 87:118, 1969.
191. KLAUWERS J, WOLF PL, COHN R: Failure of renal transplantation in primary oxalosis. *JAMA* 209:551, 1969.
192. SAXON A, BUSCH GJ, MERRILL JP, FRANCO V, WILSON RE: Renal transplantation in primary hyperoxaluria. *Arch Intern Med* 133:464, 1974.
193. KOCH B, IRVINE AH, BARR JR, POZNANSKI WJ: Three kidney transplanta-

tions in a patient with primary hereditary hyperoxaluria. *Can Med Assoc J* 106:1323, 1972.

194. LEUMANN EP, WEGMANN W, LARGIADER F: Prolonged survival after renal transplantation in primary hyperoxaluria of childhood. *Clin Nephrol* 9:29, 1978.

195. HALVERSTADT DB, WENZL JE: Primary hyperoxaluria and renal transplantation. *J Urol* 111:398, 1974.

196. WATTS RW, MORGAN SH, PURKISS P, MANSELL MA, BAKER LR, BROWN CB: Timing of renal transplantation in the management of pyridoxine-resistant type I primary hyperoxaluria. *Transplantation* 45:1143, 1988.

197. WATTS RW, CALNE RY, ROLLES K, DANPURE CJ, MORGAN SH, MANSELL MA, WILLIAMS R, PURKISS P: Successful treatment of primary hyperoxaluria type I by combined hepatic and renal transplantation. *Lancet* II:474, 1987.

CHAPTER **36**

DISORDERS OF GLYCEROL METABOLISM

EDWARD R. B. McCABE

1. *Glycerol kinase deficiency is an X-linked inborn error of metabolism characterized by hyperglycerolemia and glyceroluria, and "pseudohypertriglyceridemia" (if the laboratory measures triglycerides by quantitation of glycerol released after lipolysis). Glycerol kinase deficiency has been subdivided into three clinical forms according to phenotype: (1) the microdeletion form, also called the infantile or complex glycerol kinase deficiency syndrome, distinguished by involvement of the glycerol kinase (GK) locus and the closely linked Xp21 loci for congenital adrenal hypoplasia (AHC) and/or Duchenne muscular dystrophy (DMD); (2) the juvenile form, associated with vomiting, acidemia, and stupor presenting in the toddler age group; and (3) the benign or adult form, detected incidentally with pseudohypertriglyceridemia. All patients with phenotypic involvement of the AHC, GK, and DMD loci have had some degree of developmental delay, but this has not been observed among individuals with the juvenile or benign forms. The juvenile and benign forms apparently represent isolated glycerol kinase deficiency.*
2. *Patients with the glycerol intolerance syndrome have episodes of sweating, irritability, confusion, marked lethargy, and coma. Hypoglycemia and seizures are variably observed. Episodes can be precipitated by glycerol ingestion or infusion. Patients may outgrow these episodes. Each of the three individuals investigated has had a history of prematurity. Measurements of glycerol kinase activity have been normal. Diminished hepatic fructose-1,6-diphosphatase activity and increased sensitivity of this enzyme to inhibition of glycerol-3-phosphate have been reported. These observations have prompted speculation that this syndrome may represent an unusual sensitivity to the hypoglycemic effects of glycerol-3-phosphate, possibly due to delayed maturation of enzymes of the glycerol metabolic pathway.*
3. *The diagnosis of glycerol kinase deficiency is routinely confirmed by documentation of the enzyme deficiency in leukocytes, fibroblasts, liver, and/or transformed lymphoblastoid cell lines. Kidney and small intestine are also deficient in glycerol kinase activity.*
4. *Because of the relatively high frequency of microdeletions in this chromosomal region, all patients with Duchenne muscular dystrophy and developmental delay should be evaluated for adrenal hypoplasia and insufficiency and for glycerol kinase deficiency.*
5. *Management is most critical for the patients with adrenal hypoplasia and insufficiency, since all the deaths seem to have resulted from Addisonian crises. They require glucocorticoid and mineralocorticoid treatment. Patients with vomiting, acidemia, and stupor associated with glycerol kinase deficiency or the glycerol intolerance syndrome should be placed on a low fat (i.e., glycerol-restricted) diet with avoidance of prolonged fasts.*
6. *The gene order surrounding the GK locus is: Xpter...AHC-GK-DMD-OTC...cen. Molecular genetic studies indicate that the GK locus maps between the DNA probes L1.4 (DXS68) and J-Bir (DXS270).*

INTRODUCTION AND HISTORICAL PERSPECTIVE

Glycerol ($C_3H_8O_3$; molecular weight 92.09), also known as glycerin or 1,2,3-propanetriol, is a hygroscopic, clear, colorless, syrupy liquid. The term *glycerol* is derived from the Greek *glykeros* ("sweet") via the French *glycerine*, reflecting its taste.

Glyceroluria was described originally in 1967 in four mentally retarded patients among a group of 900 screened for polyhydric alcohol excretion.[1] Serum glycerol concentrations of these patients were similar to those of controls.[1,2] The glycerol intolerance syndrome was described in 1975 in a 3-year-old boy with episodic confusion, drowsiness, nausea, vomiting, and loss of consciousness associated with glycerol ingestion or infusion; this patient did not have hyperglycerolemia or glyceroluria and had normal leukocyte glycerol kinase activity.[3]

Deficiency of glycerol kinase (Fig. 36-1) was reported in 1977[4] in two brothers with hyperglycerolemia, glyceroluria, psychomotor retardation, spasticity, osteoporosis, Duchenne-type dystrophic myopathy, and adrenal hypoplasia.[4–6] Glycerol kinase deficiency was documented independently in 1978[7] in a pedigree which included a 70-year-old proband, originally described with "idiopathic hyperglycerolemia,"[8] his clinically normal brother, and his 21-year-old grandson. Subsequent pedigrees confirmed the X-linked inheritance of glycerol kinase deficiency.[9] Glycerol kinase maps to the Xp21 region, and patients with the phenotype which includes congenital adrenal hypoplasia, glycerol kinase deficiency, and dystrophic myopathy are now recognized to represent a microdeletion syndrome.[10–27]

Glycerol is a neutral compound, and, therefore, glycerol kinase deficiency is not an organic acidemia. However, this disorder is frequently considered with the organic acidemias because the diagnosis is often made following urine organic acid

Nonstandard abbreviations used in this chapter are: AHC = congenital adrenal hypoplasia; cGPDH:NAD = cytoplasmic NAD-linked glycerol-3-phosphate dehydrogenase; DMD = Duchenne muscular dystrophy; GC/MS = gas chromatography/mass spectrometry; GK = glycerol kinase; mGPDH:FAD = mitochondrial FAD-linked glycerol-3-phosphate dehydrogenase; mGPDH:NAD = mitochondrial NAD-linked glycerol-3-phosphate dehydrogenase; OTC = ornithine transcarbamylase; pGPDH:NAD = peroxisomal NAD-linked glycerol-3-phosphate dehydrogenase. See text and tables for genotype and phenotype designations.

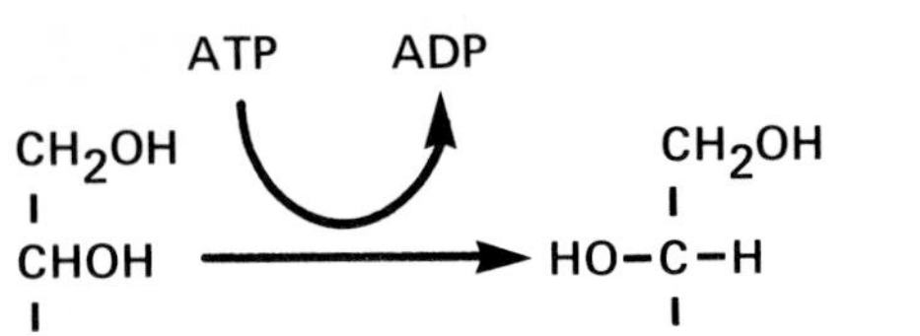

Glycerol $\quad$ *sn*-Glycerol-3-phosphate

Fig. 36-1 The glycerol kinase reaction.

analysis by gas chromatography/mass spectrometry (GC/MS) performed for evaluation of acute deterioration with shock and acidemia from the congenital adrenal hypoplasia or as part of a general metabolic evaluation or workup for "pseudohypertriglyceridemia."[4–6,9,28–31] Pseudohypertriglyceridemia results from the elevated free glycerol in the blood of these patients, which interferes with the routine measurement of triglycerides based on quantitation of glycerol liberated by lipolysis.[31]

BIOCHEMISTRY AND PHYSIOLOGY OF GLYCEROL METABOLISM

Sources and Fates of Glycerol

The metabolism of glycerol is shown in Fig. 36-2. The sources of glycerol include endogenous breakdown of triglycerides and other glycerolipids and production of glycerol from glucose, protein, lactate, or pyruvate (a process which has been termed *glyceroneogenesis*); the exogenous source is uptake of glycerol from dietary fats after release during digestion.[32–41] Glycerol has been shown to support glycogenesis in various systems, including whole animals,[42–44] liver,[45] and white blood cells.[46] Increased serum glucose and/or gluconeogenesis following glycerol administration has been demonstrated in experimental animals,[40,44,47–52] in normal humans,[53–55] in neonates,[56] and in various pathologic situations including diabetes mellitus and prediabetes,[53,57–60] ketotic hypoglycemia,[55,61] and certain of the glycogenoses.[54,62] Glycerol serves as a precursor for synthesis of glycerolipids which include the acyl-glyceride derivatives, phosphatidic acid, and other glycerol phospholipids such as phosphatidylinositide and the polyphosphoinositides.[40,63–69] Glycerol is a source for dihydroxyacetone phosphate, which is the immediate precursor of ether lipid synthesis in the peroxisome.[70–73] Glycerol may also be metabolized to lactate,[46,74,75] oxalate,[75] and protein[76] and may be oxidized to carbon dioxide.[38,40]

Pathway of Glycerol Metabolism

The three principal enzymes in the glycerol pathway which are discussed in this section include glycerol kinase (ATP: glycerol-3-phosphotransferase, EC 2.7.1.30), the cytoplasmic NAD-dependent glycerol-3-phosphate dehydrogenase (*sn*-glycerol-3-phosphate:NAD$^+$2-oxidoreductase, EC 1.1.1.8), and the mitochondrial FAD-linked glycerol-3-phosphate dehydrogenase (*sn*-glycerol-3-phosphate:(acceptor) 2-oxidoreductase, EC 1.1.99.5). The literature is confusing with respect to the cytoplasmic glycerol-3-phosphate dehydrogenase, using the designations EC 1.1.1.8 and EC 1.1.1.94 arbitrarily. These Enzyme Commission numbers refer to *sn*-glycerol-3-phosphate:NAD$^+$2-oxidoreductase (EC 1.1.1.8) and *sn*-glycerol-3-phosphate:NAD(P)$^+$2-oxidoreductase (EC 1.1.1.94).[77] Most workers have assayed with NAD$^+$ or NADH and have not attempted to distinguish between these two enzymes. The following convention is used in this chapter to discriminate between the cytoplasmic and mitochondrial enzymes: cGPDH:NAD specifies the cytoplasmic, NAD-linked enzyme and mGPDH:FAD specifies the mitochondrial, FAD-linked enzyme. Additional activities are indicated as follows: the mitochondrial, NAD-linked activity as mGPDH:NAD and the peroxisomal, NAD-linked enzyme as pGPDH:NAD (see below).

Glycerol Kinase. Glycerol kinase catalyzes the phosphorylation of glycerol by ATP to yield the products glycerol-3-phosphate and ADP[78] (Fig. 36-1). This enzymatic reaction has been demonstrated in a number of tissues or cells, including liver,[65,66,79–98] kidney,[99–103] circulating leukocytes,[4,7,76] intestinal mucosa,[104] brain,[105–107] adrenal gland,[108,109] adipose tissue,[110–128] thyroid gland,[129] cardiac and skeletal muscle,[130,131] lung,[132] mammary gland,[133] spermatozoa,[134–136] and fibroblasts.[6,76,95] Glycerol kinase activity has also been demonstrated in Epstein-Barr virus-transformed lymphoblastoid cell lines,[21] in rat hepatomas and cultured Novikoff rat hepatoma cells,[137,138] and in adenoma alveolar type II cells.[139] In considering these transformed tumor cells, it is of note that the Rous sarcoma virus transforming gene pp60^{src}, a 60-kDa phosphoprotein which phosphorylates protein substrates on tyrosine residues using GTP or ATP, shows ATP-dependent glycerol kinase activity.[140] A related, 54-kDa protein, pp54^{src}, shows similar glycerol kinase activity, as does the catalytic subunit of cAMP-dependent protein kinase.[141,142] The physiological significance of the glycerol kinase activity of these protein kinases remains in question because of the relatively high K_m for glycerol.[140,141] Glycerol kinase has also been investigated in bacteria,[78,143] with considerable work in *Escherichia coli*,[144–154] including cloning and characterization of the gene,[155–157] and in *Bacillus stearothermophilus*.[158] Studies have also been carried out in fungi,[78,159,160] in particular *Candida mycoderma*,[84,161,162] in *Neurospora crassa*[163] and in protozoa with investigations in *Tetrahymena*,[164] and in *Leishmania*[165] and *Trypanosoma brucei*,[166,167] where it is localized to the peroxisomelike glycosomes.

The properties of glycerol kinase vary considerably, depending on its source and the assay conditions used. While not reproducibly observed by all investigators, dihydroxyacetone and UTP may serve as alternative substrates, and glycerol-3-phosphate, AMP, and ADP as inhibitors of glycerol kinase in liver.[78,80,84,85,168,169] Additional inhibitors of glycerol kinase activity include D,L-1-chloro-2-3-propanediol (α-chlorhydrin),[170] (±)-2,3-dihydroxypropyl dichloroacetate,[171] and 1-thioglycerol.[172] Glycerol kinase activity is increased in liver and adipose tissue in response to hyperinsulinemia produced by insulin injection[88,115] or by hypothalamic lesion,[173] and this may be etiologically related to the elevated enzyme activity observed in the homozygous genetically obese (ob/ob) mice.[41] Castration leads to a decreased glycerol kinase activity, and this is reversed by testosterone injection.[174]

NAD-Linked Glycerol-3-Phosphate Dehydrogenases. cGPDH:NAD catalyzes the reverisble oxidation of glycerol-3-

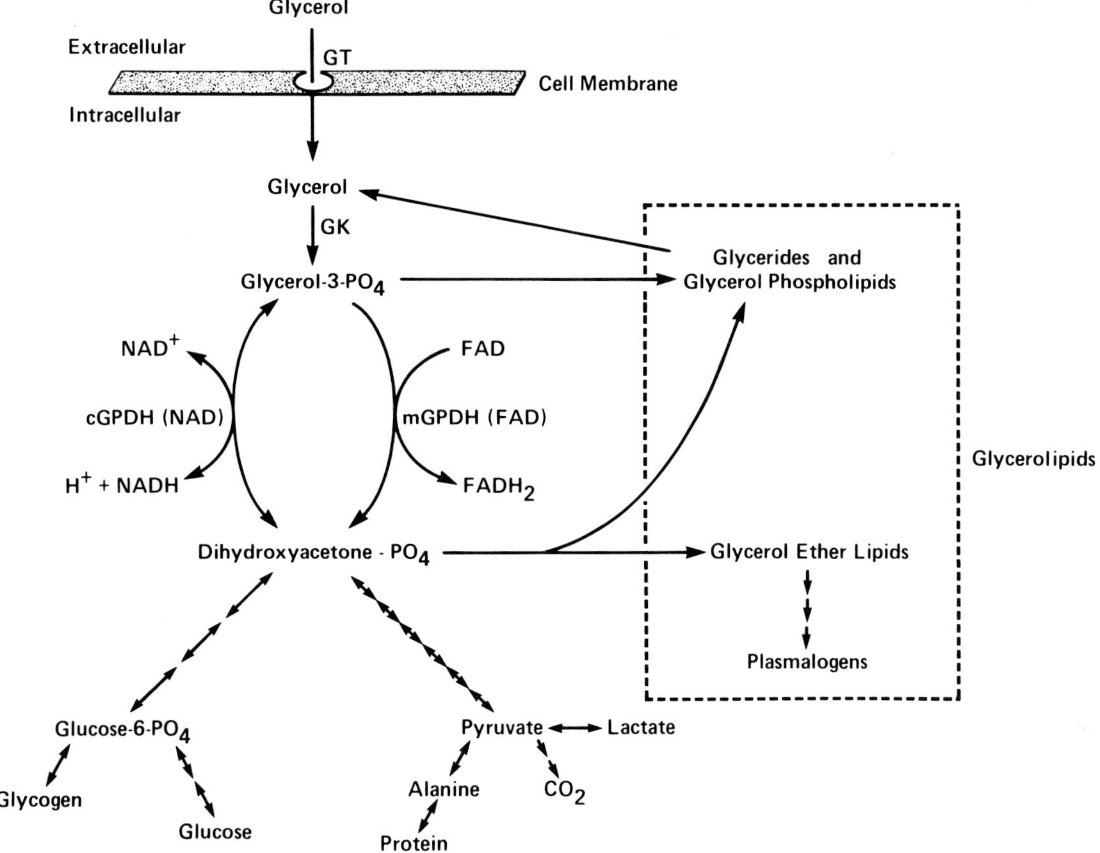

Fig. 36-2 Pathway of glycerol metabolism. GT = glycerol transporter; GK = glycerol kinase; cGPDH:NAD = cytoplasmic, NAD-linked glycerol-3-phosphate dehydrogenase; mGPDH:FAD = mitochondrial, FAD-linked glycerol-3-phosphate dehydrogenase.

phosphate to dihydroxyacetone phosphate with reduction of NAD^+ to NADH + H^+. This enzyme was originally described in muscle extracts[175,176] and was crystallized from muscle.[177] Nearly 90 percent of the total activity in the rat is found in skeletal muscle, but cGPDH:NAD has also been described in liver, kidney, smooth muscle, cardiac muscle, and adipose tissue.[41,178] Glucocorticoids induce increased synthesis of the enzyme in cultured glial cells.[179] Glucocorticoids have a similar effect on cGPDH:NAD activity in cultured rat heart cells,[180] but triiodothyronine (T_3) results in decreased enzyme activity in rat heart cells in culture.[181] Investigations of rat glioma C6 cells using a cDNA for cGPDH:NAD indicate that regulation by glucocorticoids is at the transcriptional level.[182] This cDNA hybridized to 4.7-kb mRNA from rat muscle, rat brain, mouse liver, and C6 cells.[182] A mouse genomic clone for this enzyme also was isolated.[183]

An NAD-linked glycerol phosphate dehydrogenase (mGPDH:NAD) was described in rat liver mitochondria with properties very similar to the cytosolic enzyme.[184] In contrast to the cytosolic enzyme, mGPDH:NAD responded to thyroid status in a manner similar to mGPDH:FAD (see below); i.e., thyroidectomy decreased the activity of the mitochondrial oxidoreductase, and T_3 treatment restored the enzyme activity.[184]

An NAD-linked peroxisomal glycerol phosphate dehydrogenase (pGPDH:NAD), with properties differing from the cytosolic enzyme, has also been described.[185,186] The activity of pGPDH:NAD increased under conditions associated with increased peroxisomal fatty acid β oxidation.[186] The peroxisomal oxidoreduction was proposed to play a role in a glycerol-3-phosphate shuttle involving the movement of reducing equivalents between peroxisomes, cytoplasm, and mitochondria (Fig. 36-3).[185,186]

FAD-Linked Glycerol-3-Phosphate Dehydrogenase. The mitochondrial FAD-linked enzyme catalyzes the irreversible oxidation of glycerol-3-phosphate to dihydroxyacetone phosphate. Phenazine methosulfate can serve directly as an artificial electron acceptor.[187] This enzyme was originally described in frog muscle[188] and has a broad tissue distribution in mammals.[41] In the rat the highest specific activity was in testicular mitochondria,[189] although the activity of this enzyme was quite low in human testis.[190] Other tissues with mGPDH:FAD activity include skeletal muscle, lung, spleen, intestine, brain, placenta, adipose tissue, aorta, and leukocytes.[41,191,192] This enzyme is considered to be localized to the outer surface of the inner mitochondrial membrane.[41,193] The activity of mGPDH:FAD responds to glucocorticoids and thyroid hormone in a manner inversely related to that of cGPDH:NAD. Activity of mGPDH:FAD increases after adrenalectomy[194] or administration of thyroid hormone.[195–197]

Glycerol Transport. Glycerol transport in red blood cells occurs by facilitated diffusion, presumably mediated by a specific carrier which is sensitive to inhibition by Cu^{2+} and other heavy metal ions.[41,198,199] Ethylene glycol acts as a competitive inhibitor for this transport process.[200–202] Transport of glycerol was investigated also in normal hepatocytes[97] and tumor cells,

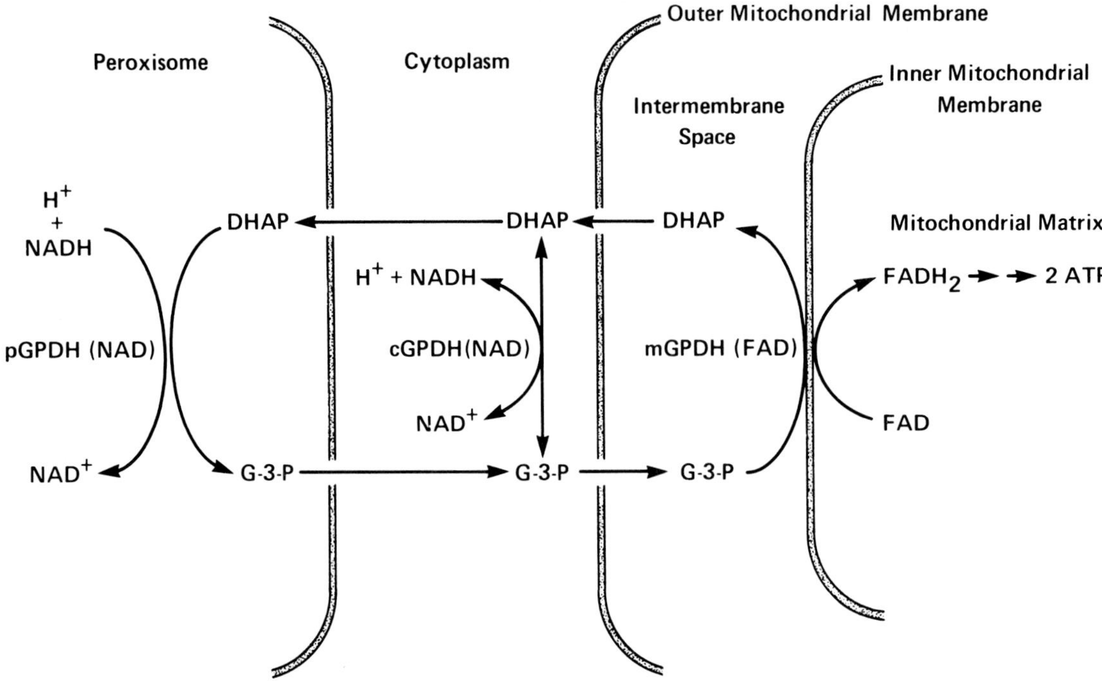

Fig. 36-3 Glycerol phosphate shuttle showing potential communications between peroxisomes, cytoplasm, and mitochondria. *(Adapted from Tolbert[185] and Newsholme and Start.[208])*

including Novikoff rat hepatoma, Hela, and HEP-2 cells.[138] The transport process for glycerol was distinct from that for glucose.[97,138] Glycerol uptake was measured in perfused rat liver under steady-state conditions, and it was concluded that uptake across the hepatic cell membrane was an important factor in the regulation of glycerol metabolism.[203]

Compartmentation of Glycerol Metabolism

Glycerol Phosphate Shuttle. Reducing equivalents serve as energy currency to the cell, since these provide the mitochondria with substrate for oxidative phosphorylation. However, mitochondria are impermeable to the pyridine nucleotides,[204] and indirect pathways, or "shuttles," are used for the transfer of these reducing equivalents from the cytoplasm to the mitochondrial electron transfer chain.[205] One such mechanism is the glycerol phosphate shuttle[205–207] (Fig. 36-3). Glycerol-3-phosphate moves from the cytoplasm through the outer mitochondrial membrane to the intermembrane space, where it serves as a substrate for mGPDH:FAD on the outer surface of the inner mitochondrial membrane.[41,193] Dihydroxyacetone phosphate formed by mGPDH:FAD exits the intermembrane space where cGPDH:NAD completes the cycle with production of glycerol-3-phosphate. The directionality of this cycle is ensured by the nonequilibrium reaction catalyzed by the mitochondrial dehydrogenase: the NADH equivalent of the cytoplasm, with a potential P:O ratio (ratio of the number of moles of ATP formed per atom of oxygen consumed) of 3 is utilized by mGPDH:FAD, yielding a P:O ratio of only 2, with loss of the additional energy presumably as heat.[205,208] Additional options such as glycolysis, gluconeogenesis, and glycerolipid synthesis are available to the intermediates of this shuttle, and, as in any cyclic pathway, the intermediates withdrawn for these metabolic alternatives must be replenished in order for the cycle to continue.

The glycerol phosphate shuttle is clearly important in the energy supply to insect flight muscles.[209,210] Mutations in *Drosophila melanogaster* leading to deficient mGPDH:FAD result in loss of ability to fly.[211] Glycerol phosphate can serve as a mitochondrial respiratory substrate for a number of tissues, including brain, liver, adipose tissue, intestine, skeletal muscle, aorta, and placenta.[191,212–219] In one study in liver, the glycerol phosphate shuttle accounted for 40 percent of the reducing equivalent flux from the cytoplasm to the mitochondria,[216] and this shuttle appears to play a role in managing the increased reducing equivalents associated with ethanol oxidation.[220–222] The presence of a peroxisomal glycerol phosphate dehydrogenase (see above) has led to the proposal that there may be a peroxisomal glycerol phosphate shuttle, which would move reducing equivalents generated by fatty acid oxidation out of the peroxisome as glycerol phosphate, and that this might be continuous with the cytoplasmic-mitochondrial shuttle, with reoxidation of glycerol phosphate generated in the peroxisome.[185] The functional role of the mitochondrial glycerol phosphate shuttle in mammals has been questioned, primarily because of studies indicating a limited capacity of the shuttle in a number of tissues.[41,205,223,224]

Glycerol Kinase Binding to Porin on the Outer Mitochondrial Membrane. The term *ambiquitous* (meaning "both places," in analogy with *ubiquitous*, or "all places") was coined to refer to enzymes with rapid and reversible changes in intracellular distribution.[225] Enzymes considered in this category have included hexokinase,[225,226] aldolase,[227] glyceraldehyde-3-phosphate dehydrogenase,[227] and glycerol kinase.[96,109,228–231] Glycerol kinase may be found in either the cytosolic or particulate fraction with differences in subcellular distribution dependent on the tissue, developmental stage, and metabolic state.[95,96,108,109,228–232] In the particulate fraction, glycerol kinase is present in microsomes and mitochondria, and the mitochondrial bound activity varies with the metabolic state of the animal.[96,230] The mitochondrial receptor for glycerol kinase is porin, the pore forming protein of the outer mitochondrial membrane[96,228,230,233–235] (Fig. 36-4). Porin is identical with the hexokinase binding protein[228,236,237] and is an important channel for movement of adenine nucleotides across the outer mitochondrial membrane.[238] These features explain the competition between mitochondrially bound hexokinase and added glycerol kinase for mitochondrially generated ATP.[229,239,240] The activity of mitochondrially bound glycerol kinase is stimulated by the respiratory substrates ADP and succinate and is inhibited by atractyloside, which blocks the adenine nucleotide carrier of the inner mitochondrial membrane; i.e., glycerol kinase bound to the outer mitochondrial membrane may utilize ATP generated within the mitochondrion.[96,109,231] The reaction product, glycerol-3-phosphate, promotes release of bound glycerol kinase from porin in liver and adrenal,[96,109,231] and apparent K_m's for ATP and for glycerol are lower for the bound enzyme than for that in the supernatant.[109,231] Similarly, mitochondrial hexokinase is specifically solubilized by its product, glucose-6-phosphate,[226,241] utilizes mitochondrially generated ATP,[242-246] and has a K_m for ATP which is lower than that for the soluble enzyme.[226] Therefore, glycerol kinase, like hexokinase, meets the criteria for an ambiquitous enzyme, with rapid and reversible changes in intracellular distribution dependent on cellular energy status and metabolite levels, and with distinct kinetic properties dependent on this distribution.[231]

Fig. 36-4. Model for functional compartmentation of glycerol kinase to porin on the outer mitochondrial membrane. *(From McCabe.[229] Used by permission of Academic Press.)*

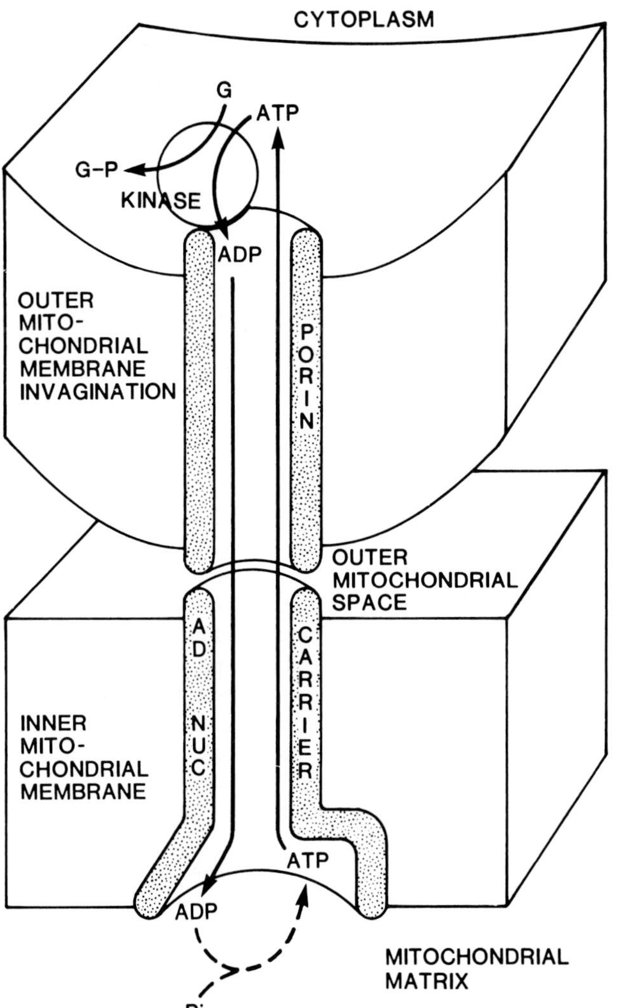

The reversible and regulable juxtaposition of an ADP-producing kinase with an ADP-permeable pore suggested the possibility of concerted formation and transport of ADP into the intermembrane space through this pore, and ADP could continue to the mitochondrial matrix through the adenine nucleotide carrier of the inner membrane.[229] It was suggested that contact sites between the inner and outer mitochondrial membranes might delimit microcompartments within the intermembrane space.[230,234] The binding of these kinases to the outer mitochondrial membrane and the formation of intermembrane microcompartments become processes which control communication between cytoplasmic and mitochondrial energy production and regulate availability of substrates for alternative metabolic processing.[229-231] It is known that mammalian mitochondria are capable of synthesizing glycerophospholipids from glycerol and ATP, and the involvement of bound glycerol kinase in a microcompartmented system has been proposed.[247]

Physiology of Glycerol Metabolism

It is generally recognized that the splanchnic region, and in particular the liver and kidney, represent the principal sites of glycerol metabolism in mammals.[33,41] However, it has been asserted that circulating leukocytes and thrombocytes contribute significantly to the metabolism of glycerol in humans.[248] It is not coincidental that these tissues represent the bulk of the glycerol kinase activity in the body. The best evidence that glycerol kinase represents the primary entry of glycerol into metabolism is finding glyceroluria and hyperglycerolemia in patients with glycerol kinase deficiency.

Studies in lean and obese subjects showed that there was a direct correlation between plasma glycerol concentration and glycerol turnover, and that both were increased in obese subjects when compared with lean individuals.[38] The free fatty acid/glycerol turnover ratio in lean individuals was 4.7:1, differing from the theoretical ratio of 3:1 and indicating incomplete hydrolysis of triglycerides[38]; alternatively, this could be explained by intracellular reutilization of a portion of the glycerol released by hydrolysis. Glycerol did not contribute more than 10 percent of the total respiratory CO_2.[38] Glycerol contribution to gluconeogenesis became substantial under conditions of starvation,[38,249] with glycerol providing 38 percent of the new glucose from protein or glycerol in lean individuals and 79 percent in the obese. Increases in the hepatic activities of glycerol kinase and glycerol-3-phosphate dehydrogenase during starvation were considered to be important for the increased utilization of glycerol released by lipolysis for gluconeogenesis.[250]

During pregnancy there is a decreased utilization of glycerol by maternal extrahepatic tissues, associated with a decreased half-life of tracer glycerol and increased gluconeogenesis from this substrate by the maternal liver.[251,252] The fetus is able to respond to maternal fasting and to fetal norepinephrine injection with mobilization of glycerol.[253] The mother is able to supply glycerol to the fetus across the placenta, and the fetus is able to utilize circulating glycerol for gluconeogenesis and glycogen synthesis.[254] The blood glycerol concentration rises rapidly in the postnatal period in premature and term infants.[255,256] The effect of intrauterine asphyxiation on the concentration of blood glycerol is unclear from differing studies.[257,258] In the postnatal period, stress (such as a series of heel pricks or cold exposure) results in elevated blood glycerol.[259,260] Intravenously administered glycerol was eliminated more rapidly in the first day of life in small for gestational age compared with appropriate for gestational age infants and was eliminated most rapidly at 3 to 5 weeks of age, with term and premature infants showing similar rates of elimination at that age.[56] Malnutrition during lactation results in a decrease in the offspring of the hepatic activities of glycerol kinase, cGPDH:NAD, and mGPDH:FAD, suggesting that nutritional deprivation might limit the capacity of the liver to use glycerol in such offspring.[261] Animals malnourished after weaning showed striking deficits in gluconeogenic capacity compared with control animals, and these differences were attributed to hepatic accumulation of phosphorylated glycerol metabolites and their inhibiting effects on the pathway of gluconeogenesis.[262]

Studies in rat and hamster showed a dramatic rise in glycerol kinase activity during the neonatal period, but these studies measured the activity of this enzyme only in the supernatant.[263–266] Investigations in human fetuses and newborns did not show similar developmental changes in glycerol kinase when activity was examined in the whole homogenate.[232,267] There was a marked change in the particulate bound fraction of this enzyme from 91 percent bound in the fetus to 7 percent bound in the infant, the latter being similar to values observed in adults.[108,232] Activity of cGPDH:NAD paralleled the increase in supernatant glycerol kinase activity in the rat, and both enzyme activities increased in response to hydrocortisone and thyroxine, although the oxidoreductase response to thyroxine was smaller.[265] A second, chromatographically distinct form of cGPDH:NAD was reported in neonatal mice.[268]

Diagnostic and Therapeutic Uses of Glycerol

Glycerol is used as an osmotic agent for treatment of increased intraocular and intracerebral pressure,[269,270] as a substrate for the evaluation of disorders of carbohydrate metabolism,[54,61,62] and as a component of emollient solutions, ointments, purgatives, suppositories, and other medications.[32] Our experience indicates that exogenous glycerol is a frequent explanation of glyceroluria, and this possibility should be considered even in the face of hyperglycerolemia.

GLYCEROL KINASE DEFICIENCY

Hyperglycerolemia (McKusick MIM #30703) is also known as glycerol kinase deficiency and GK1 deficiency.[271] Glycerol kinase deficiency can be subdivided into three clinical forms by phenotype. The infantile form, or complex glycerol kinase deficiency syndrome,[14,28,229,272] is now recognized as a microdeletion syndrome[10–27] involving not only the glycerol kinase locus, but also the congenital adrenal hypoplasia and/or Duchenne muscular dystrophy loci in the Xp21 region.[271] There are two phenotypes which appear to have isolated involvement of the GK locus, the juvenile form[28,272] associated with vomiting, acidemia, and stupor presenting in the toddler age group, and the benign, or adult, form[28,229,272] detected incidentally with pseudohypertriglyceridemia.[31]

In this chapter glycerol kinase associated microdeletions will be shortened to "microdeletion form" to designate those patients with involvement of the GK locus and one or more linked loci. It is clear that DMD is a separate locus from GK and AHC.[17–27,273–275] There is also very strong evidence that GK and AHC are distinct loci. This evidence includes patients and families with the juvenile and benign forms of glycerol kinase deficiency and others with isolated congenital adrenal hypoplasia without glycerol kinase deficiency or Duchenne muscular dystrophy.[9] But the most compelling evidence involves patients with Xp21 microdeletions who have either isolated congenital adrenal hypoplasia[276] or glycerol kinase deficiency and Duchenne muscular dystrophy with normal adrenal function.[26]

In order to be as specific as possible in designating the information available about patients, the conventions developed for human gene nomenclature are used,[277] and are adapted to describe these microdeletions. Capital letters are used to designate genes, alleles, and phenotypes. Genes and alleles are italicized, and an asterisk (*) is used to separate the gene from allele designation. Phenotype symbols have the same characters as gene and allele symbols, and the asterisk is omitted. The symbol for regional deletion, CR, for chromosome region, is used when more than one locus is involved. Regional cytogenetic identification (e.g., Xp21) is incorporated into the symbol, but it is capitalized. Microdeletions are designated by the initial one or two letters of the deleted loci (two used to prevent confusion with previous genetic designations), arranged from Xpter to the centromere. The designations are two or three letters in length and delimit the known extent of the microdeletion. For example, the genotype designation for a male with AHC, GK deficiency, and DMD is *AGDCR*XP21/Y* and the phenotype designation is AGDCR XP21; since in this chapter it is understood that the microdeletions are in the Xp21 region, phenotype designations are frequently shortened to the initial five characters, e.g., AGDCR. A deletion limited to a single locus is designated by the gene symbol for that locus followed by CR; e.g., the gene symbol for a cytogenetic deletion involving only congenital adrenal hypoplasia is *AHCCR*XP21*. Gene symbols for the juvenile and benign alleles of glycerol kinase deficiency are *GK*JUV* and *GK*BEN*, respectively. The gene symbols referred to in this chapter are summarized in Table 36-1.

Clinical Aspects

Microdeletion Form Involving AHC, GK, and DMD Loci. Two brothers with this AGDCR phenotype were originally described with glycerol kinase deficiency in 1977,[4] although the association with congenital adrenal hypoplasia was not recognized until later.[6] To date at least 18 individuals in 14 families have been described with this phenotype, with an additional six individuals who died prior to the recognition of this syndrome but are suspected to have had this diagnosis.[4,6,9,12–22,25,27,273,278–280] All but one of these patients has been male.[9] One additional male dying in the neonatal period also had ornithine transcarbamylase deficiency and the AGOCR microdeletion phenotype.[10,11]

A summary was compiled of the clinical findings in 17 patients with microdeletion phenotypes of whom 15 had the AGDCR or AGOCR phenotype.[279] Among these 15 patients, the following features were observed with frequencies determined from the cases in which a comment was made about the particular feature: psychomotor retardation (12/12); short

Table 36-1. Summary of Designations for Gene Symbols

	Loci			
Gene symbol	*AHC*	*GK*	*DMD*	*OTC*
*AGOCR*XP21*	DEL	DEL	DEL	DEL
*AGDCR*XP21*	DEL	DEL	DEL	NL
*AGKCR*XP21*†	DEL	DEL	NL	NL
*GDCR*XP21*	NL	DEL	DEL	NL
*AHCCR*XP21*	DEL	NL	NL	NL
*DMDCR*XP21*	NL	NL	DEL	NL
*GK*JUV*	NL	JUV	NL	NL
*GK*BEN*	NL	BEN	NL	NL

Abbreviations: BEN = benign allele of glycerol kinase deficiency; DEL = deleted; JUV = juvenile allele of glycerol kinase deficiency; NL = normal.
†AGKCR is used instead of AGCR to avoid confusion with the existing designation, AG, used by some for the alpha globin gene family.[271]

stature (10/12); abnormal genitalia (6/13); osteoporosis (6/13); and characteristic facies with strabismus (6/13), wide-set eyes, and drooping mouth (4/13); or dysmorphic facies (1/13, the individual with AGOCR). The abnormal genitalia include anorchia and cryptorchidism and most likely are related to the gonadotropin deficiency associated with X-linked cytomegalic congenital adrenal hypoplasia.[278,279,281] Similarly, psychomotor retardation may be seen in patients with congenital adrenal hypoplasia.[6,276,281] The clinical features of these patients, including the facial resemblance of several of them, indicate that this is a clinically recognizable syndrome.[279]

There is an extremely high frequency of neonatal and early childhood deaths from unrecognized adrenal insufficiency in these families. Since all the documented patients with the AGDCR phenotype living beyond the neonatal period have been developmentally delayed,[18,25,279] this would suggest that any patient with Duchenne muscular dystrophy and developmental delay should have adrenal function evaluated. If this phenotype is ascertained in one family member, then collateral relatives should also be pursued and evaluated.

Microdeletion Form Involving AHC and GK Loci. Four families have been described with this AGKCR phenotype, including five fully documented patients and seven suspected; all were male.[9,13,17,19,21,23,24]

In the first family described with the AGKCR phenotype, in addition to the four boys who were suspected of having this phenotype because of death at 21 days to 2 years of age associated with adrenal hypoplasia, there were three male neonates who died of unexplained causes and a fourth male who was "slow" and died at 3 years of age.[9] One of the living boys in the first family was diagnosed prenatally by reduced maternal estriol levels because of the known family history of X-linked adrenal hypoplasia, and despite initiation of steroid replacement therapy in the immediate perinatal period, he was developmentally delayed.[9,282] These boys had normal serum creatine kinase values and no evidence of myopathy.[17] The affected child in the second family was the son of Algerian second cousins; three older brothers died early in life.[21] The living boy presented with hypoglycemia in the neonatal period; the diagnosis of glycerol kinase deficiency with adrenal hypoplasia was made and steroid therapy begun. Serum creatine kinase values were normal on repeated measurement, and he had no evidence of the McLeod phenotype or chronic granulomatous disease. Psychomotor development was reported to be normal.[21] The clinical descriptions of the other two boys have been brief, but one died unexpectedly at 12 months of age during a respiratory infection and had glyceroluria, psychomotor retardation, and adrenocortical insufficiency.[23] The other was a 26-year-old with adrenal aplasia, hypogonadism, and glycerol kinase deficiency.[24]

The family histories of these patients and the high frequency of unexplained early deaths indicate that any patient with evidence of glycerol kinase deficiency, whether or not developmentally delayed, should have adrenal function evaluated.

Microdeletion Form Involving GK and DMD Loci. Two brothers have been described with the GDCR phenotype.[26] Both boys had initial recognition of muscle weakness at 1 year of age. Progressive muscle weakness, elevated serum creatine kinase and aldolase activities, and characteristic muscle histology led to the diagnosis of Duchenne muscular dystrophy in the older brother. The younger boy also had elevated serum creatine kinase values. Both experienced multiple recurring episodes of vomiting beginning at 11 to 12 years of age. The younger boy required hospitalization for intractable vomiting on several occasions, and dehydration, severe metabolic acidemia (arterial pH 7.01, total CO_2 2 to 3 m*M*), and ketonuria were documented. Both showed hyperglycerolemia, glyceroluria, and glycerol kinase deficiency. Normal adrenal function and reserve were documented in both patients by fasting cortisol and ACTH levels, and cosyntropin challenges. They were placed on a low fat, low glycerol diet with no subsequent episodes of vomiting or acidemia during the ensuing nine months. These episodes and the response to dietary restriction of glycerol are similar to the observations in patients with the juvenile form of isolated glycerol kinase deficiency.[28,283]

Isolated Glycerol Kinase Deficiency. There are two clinical subtypes of isolated glycerol kinase deficiency referred to previously as the juvenile and the benign, or adult, forms of glycerol kinase deficiency.[28,229,272]

Two unrelated boys with hyperglycerolemia, glyceroluria, and glycerol kinase deficiency were reported with the juvenile form (GK JUV), each presenting with an initial episode of vomiting, acidemia, and somnolence or stupor progressing to unconsciousness on occasion.[28,283] The patient reported by Eriksson et al.[283] was hospitalized at ages 4, 6, 7, 8.5, and 9 years with fever, vomiting, and diarrhea interpreted as viral gastroenteritis. These episodes were associated with metabolic acidemia: pH 7.2 to 7.31, standard bicarbonate 13.9 to 17.1 meq/liter, and base excess −10.5 to −12.9 meq/liter. On a separate occasion at age 8 years, he experienced two grand mal seizures unassociated with one of these episodes, for which he was placed on phenytoin. EEG at that time showed Rolandic spikes in central and parietal right hemisphere. Normal studies included serum creatine kinase and intravenous corticotropin-stimulation test. Growth and mental development were considered normal. A maternal granduncle had epilepsy. Organic acid analysis revealed glyceroluria.

The second patient[28] presented at age 4 2/12 years with vomiting, acidemia, hypotonia, fever, and unresponsiveness after ingestion of mouthwash. This episode and those at 4 10/12 and 5 years were associated with pH 7.01 to 7.32 and bicarbonate 3.0 to 3.5 meq/liter. Ketonuria was documented during one episode. Physical and neurologic exams were normal at 6 4/12 years. EEG was normal at 6 4/12 and 8 years except for a single 1-s burst of diffuse bilateral polyspike and wave discharge. A muscle biopsy examined by light and electron microscopy was remarkable only for increased numbers of morphologically normal mitochondria. Serum creatine kinase, cortisol, and ACTH were normal. Intelligence was above average at age 7 years with IQ by WISC of 145 and by Stanford-Binet of 122. Pseudohypertriglyceridemia led to his diagnosis. A low fat diet (<30 percent of total calories) was associated with no subsequent episodes at the time of the report, suggesting that the episodes might be related to glycerol ingestion. Family history was positive for hypertension, diabetes, hypertriglyceridemia, myocardial infarction, and cerebrovascular accident. Concordance between the clinical symptomatology and glycerol kinase deficiency has not been conclusively established in the juvenile form. However, the resemblance of the clinical presentations between these two patients and those with glycerol intolerance is intriguing, as is the similarity between the acute episodes in these patients and those described in the two brothers with microdeletions involving the GK and DMD loci (GDCR phenotype).

Eight adult males in four families have been described with the benign, or adult, phenotype (GK BEN).[7,31,284,285] Hyperglycerolemia was noted in a mother of three glycerol kinase-deficient sons in one of these families,[285] and the daughter of one of the men had intermediate glycerol kinase activity.[31] The proband in each of these families was ascertained incidentally with pseudohypertriglyceridemia.[31] Hyperglycerolemia was recognized, because the apparent hypertriglyceridemia was not consistent with the subsequent workup for hyperlipidemia or because the individual did not respond as expected to hyperlipidemia management. The men with this biochemical abnormality ranged in age from 18 to 76 years. Associated medical problems included mild diabetes mellitus,[7,285] myocardial infarctions,[7] laryngeal carcinoma *in situ*,[7] osteoarthritis,[7] herpes zoster ophthalmicus,[7] diarrhea,[285] and a positive family history of diabetes mellitus.[7] Two probands were discovered during routine medical evaluation and were in good health.[31,284] This was an older and relatively healthy population, and while workup of these patients for myopathy and adrenal function was not described, there was no clinical evidence of these features.

Other Patients. Additional patients have been described with a phenotype involving the AHC and DMD loci without measurement of glycerol kinase activity. A Japanese boy presented with vomiting, weight loss, hyponatremia (116 meq/liter), and hyperkalemia (7.5 meq/liter) at age 23 days.[286] Adrenal insufficiency was documented and treated, and an adrenal scintigram showed bilateral absence of the adrenal glands. Serum creatine kinase was elevated, a muscle biopsy was consistent with Duchenne muscular dystrophy, and his clinical course was characteristic of this disorder. He developed generalized seizures, unconsciousness, and apnea after 1 week of insufficient medication and died at age 3 5/12 years. Autopsy findings confirmed the adrenal hypoplasia. Two brothers were reported who had adrenal insufficiency and hypoplasia, dystrophic myopathy with elevated serum creatine kinase, severe psychomotor retardation, failure to thrive, and megalocornea.[287] Family history included an institutionalized older sister with seizures and mental retardation, a brother with encopresis, and a normal sister. Glycerol kinase activity was not measured in these three patients with congenital adrenal hypoplasia and dystrophic myopathy, but they would be expected to have glycerol kinase deficiency if the gene loci are ordered AHC, GK, and DMD.

Management

Patients with adrenal insufficiency, i.e., those with the AGDCR and the AGKCR microdeletion phenotypes, must be managed in the same way as those with isolated congenital adrenal hypoplasia. This requires replacement doses of a glucocorticoid, such as hydrocortisone, and therapeutic doses of a mineralocorticoid, such as 9α-fluorocortisol (Florinef). Those patients who have died with these AHC-associated phenotypes, died prior to diagnosis or at times when steroid doses were reduced to subtherapeutic ranges.

The patients with dystrophic myopathy require supportive management. It must be noted that not all these patients have the classic Duchenne muscular dystrophy phenotype, and early counseling and management must recognize that the course of the myopathy is variable and may be mild.

One of the two individuals with the juvenile phenotype associated with vomiting, acidemia, and stupor in the toddler period was placed on a low fat (i.e., low glycerol) diet, and subsequent episodes were not observed.[28] Similar responses were observed in the two brothers with microdeletions involving the GK and DMD loci.[26] A direct relationship between the dietary change and lack of subsequent episodes cannot be ascertained by these limited trials. However, dietary restriction of glycerol should be considered in patients with glycerol kinase deficiency and episodic vomiting and acidemia if these symptoms are not attributable to adrenal insufficiency.

Key to the management of these patients is careful documentation of the phenotype. Those individuals with the benign form of isolated glycerol kinase deficiency require no intervention.

Diagnosis

Patients with glycerol kinase deficiency have uniformly evidenced hyperglycerolemia and glyceroluria. The glyceroluria frequently comes to attention during the general metabolic evaluation, which includes urine organic acid analysis by GC/MS. The glyceroluria is substantial in these patients, leading to contamination of the organic acid fraction by the neutral compound, glycerol, when a solvent extraction procedure is used.[4,29] If ion exchange chromatography is used in preparation of the specimen for GC/MS,[29,30] glycerol may not be seen with the organic acids but will be present in the neutral fraction.[4] Even using solvent extraction procedures, at least two individuals with glycerol kinase deficiency have had negative initial urine screens for glycerol.[280,283] If glyceroluria is suspected, it is preferable for the GC/MS screen to be performed in a laboratory which has had previous experience in the evaluation of these patients. Quantitation of the urinary concentrations of glycerol in these patients has resulted in values of 41 to 345 m*M* (normal ≤ 0.2 m*M*),[9,16–18,278,279,283] 90 to 193 mmol/mmol creat (normal not detectable),[280] or 140 to 360 mmol per 24 h (normal < 1 mmol per 24 h).[7,31,284,285]

Hyperglycerolemia may come to attention during evaluation of pseudohypertriglyceridemia,[31] which in fact represents elevated free glycerol in the blood. Different methods of serum triglyceride measurement may give discrepant results, depending on whether the routine clinical laboratory method which measures glycerol released after lipolysis is used, or alternatively, a method which relies upon solvent extraction and colorimetry is used, which does not show interference by water-soluble compounds, such as free glycerol.[7] The hyperglycerolemia in these individuals has been measured in plasma and serum and has ranged from 1.8 to 8.3 m*M* (normal = 0.2 to 0.27 m*M*).[4,9,16,18,22,26,28,31,278,279,283–285] No differences in degree of glyceroluria or hyperglycerolemia were noted between the different phenotypes described above, and the values vary considerably, even within the same individual.

The deficiency of glycerol kinase activity has been documented in a number of tissues including intact and disrupted leukocytes,[4,7,22,24,31,76,278,283,285] liver,[6,76,284] kidney,[6,76] small intestine,[6] intact and disrupted fibroblasts,[6,9,16,17,21,24,26,28,68,76,278–280,283] Epstein-Barr virus transformed lymphoblastoid cell lines,[21] and cultured amniotic fluid cells.[23] These assays have used radiochemical or spectrophotometric methods to measure glycerol conversion to glycerol-3-phosphate, to CO_2, to protein, or to phosphoglycerides and triacylglycerols. The radiochemical assay of glycerol kinase activity[4,6,21,76] has been superior to the spectrophotometric assay in our hands. The incorporation of labeled glycerol into trichloroacetic acid precipitable counts *in situ* in intact cells[21,28,76,279,280] has been used in parallel with the in vitro assay for diagnostic purposes. Incorporation of labeled glycerol into glycerolipids also discriminates between patients and controls quite well.[68]

Prenatal diagnosis has been successfully performed for glycerol kinase deficiency. One patient with a microdeletion involving the AHC and GK loci, AGKCR, was diagnosed *in utero* using maternal estriol measurements before glycerol kinase deficiency was recognized in this family,[282] and two pregnancies at risk for AGDCR were diagnosed to be normal using this approach.[288] Glycerol kinase activity is present in amniocytes.[288] A 26-year-old woman, with a previous son who died at age 12 months with the AGKCR microdeletion phenotype, underwent amniocentesis at 18 weeks of pregnancy.[23] Radiochemical assay of glycerol kinase activity in homogenates of cultured amniocytes revealed the enzyme deficiency. Total amniotic fluid glycerol (free and triglyceride bound) was 1.740 ± 0.037 m*M*, which was 9.0 standard deviations above the control mean and twice the highest control concentration. Analysis of DNA from cultured amniotic fluid cells and the aborted fetus confirmed the diagnosis of an affected fetus. Exclusion of the *AGOCR*XP21/Y* genotype in a fetus was performed using molecular genetic techniques.[11] These studies show that there are several different approaches to prenatal diagnosis of glycerol kinase deficiency. If amniotic fluid glycerol concentration is used, it would be valuable to compare free and total glycerol concentrations with controls.

Genetics

The GK locus maps to the Xp21 region,[10–27] and the gene order is Xpter...AHC-GKD-DMD...cen (Fig. 36-5). This gene order is based on the clinical and molecular genetic evaluation of patients with isolated and complex involvement of these loci as summarized in Fig. 36-5.[12–26,273–276] The clinical data are consistent with X-linked inheritance.

Many of these patients have cytogenetic or DNA evidence of deletions. The largest deletion detected was in a patient with *AGOCR*XP21/Y* in whom cytogenetic analysis showed 46XY del (X)(p11.2→p21).[10] Patients with AGDCR and AGKCR have had deletions limited to Xp21, and where sublocalization was possible these seem to involve the Xp21.2→p21.3 region.[13–15,17,18,21,22] Other patients with AGDCR have had normal cytogenetic studies.[6,16,23,24,279] Even at the DNA level, not all the patients with AGDCR or AGKCR have evidenced deletions.[16,21] Those with involvement of the DMD locus may be expected to have deletions detectable with the DMD cDNA probes,[275] but results with these probes have not yet been reported. Examination of DNA from nine patients with these microdeletions has allowed the mapping of the GK locus to the region bounded by the probes L1.4 (DXS68) and J-Bir (DXS270)[21] (Table 36-2). The deletions among other patients with *AGKCR*XP21/Y* are consistent with this localization.[11–14,16–20,23–27,273] Additional information regarding the genomic organization of the DMD locus and the relationship of this locus to previously available probes provides a more distal limit to the map interval for the GK locus, i.e., telomeric to the deletion in patient DL 66.6 and to the 3′ terminus of the DMD cDNA.[275] Patients with the GK JUV and GK BEN phenotypes have shown no deletions with the currently available probes[21] and presumably have smaller mutations affecting the GK locus.

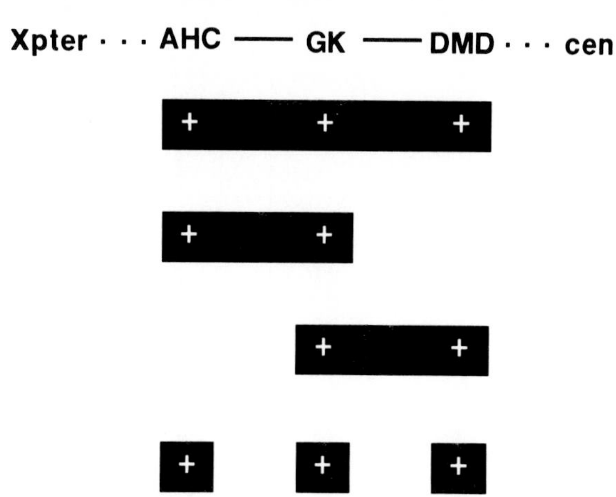

Fig. 36-5. Summary of clinical phenotypes involving the loci surrounding GK. This allows ordering of the AHC, GK, and DMD loci.

Pathogenesis

Biochemical comparison of fibroblasts from indivduals with the AGDCR and GK BEN phenotypes showed no dramatic differences with respect to substrate kinetics, and no evidence of complementation was observed between these cell lines.[76] Elevations of the apparent K_m for glycerol with no change in the apparent K_m for ATP, compared with controls, was observed in liver, kidney, leukocytes, and fibroblasts from the AGKCR patients and in fibroblasts from the GK BEN individual,[76] but since the GK locus is apparently deleted in the AGDCR patients, it would now seem that this most likely reflects the kinetic properties of a genetically unrelated activity. Differences were noted in the incorporation of labeled glycerol into acid-precipitable material, but not in in vitro enzymatic activity between an individual with the AGKCR phenotype and another with the GK JUV phenotype, suggesting functional residual activity in the cells from the patient with the more limited phenotype.[28] The compartmental organization of glycerol kinase and the regulation of this compartmentation

Table 36-2 Summary of Phenotype, Cytogenetics, and DNA Data from Francke et al.[21]

			DNA hybridization results												
Phenotype	*Patient*	*Cytogenetics*	*DXS43 D2*	*DXS41 99-6*	*DXS67 B24*	*DXS28 C7*	*DXS68 L1.4*	*DXS270 J-Bir*	*DXS164 pERT87*	*DXS206 XJ1.1*	*DXS142 pERT84*	*DXS84 754*	*DXS148 CX5.7*	*OTC*	*References*
AGDCR XP21															
	CM	46,XY	+	+	+	+	+	+	+	+	+	+			6, 21
	RB	ND	+	+	+	+	+	+	+	+	+	+		+	21, 281
	MK	ND	+	+	+	+	+	−	+	+	+	+		+	21, 281
	SA	46,XY,del(X) (p21→p21)			+	+	+	−	−	−	−	−	−	+	15, 21
	MM	46,XY,del(X) (p21→p21)	+	+	−	−	−	−	−	−	+	+			21, 280
AGKCR XP21															
	RW	46,XY,del(X) (p21.2→p21.3)	+	+	−	−	−	+	+	+	+	+			9, 13, 17, 19, 21
	YB	46,XY,del(X) (p21→p21)			+	+	+	+	+	+	+	+	+		21
GK JUV															
	MR	ND	+	+	+	+	+	+	+	+	+	+			21, 28
GK BEN															
	DD	ND	+	+	+	+	+	+	+	+	+	+			7, 21

NOTE: ND = no data available.

led to speculation that the pathogenesis of glycerol kinase deficiency involved the interruption of this compartmentation, resulting in disruption of cellular energetics and/or synthetic processes including glycerophospholipid synthesis, and that the phenotypic variability resulted from pleiotropic effects of mutations at the GK locus.[6,229,231,247,271]

The possibility that the association between glycerol kinase deficiency and the other phenotypic features was not causal, but rather coincidental, was considered early in the description of this disorder, and it was hypothesized that these features might represent distinct, but closely linked, loci on the X chromosome.[6,9,76,229] It is now quite clear that this is a microdeletion syndrome with involvement of discrete AHC, GK, and DMD loci.[9–27,274–276]

Patients with the GDCR and GK JUV phenotypes have episodic vomiting and acidemia, which may respond to dietary limitation of glycerol.[26,28,283] Patients with AGDCR have similar episodes, but these episodes are attributed to the adrenal insufficiency. The two boys with GK JUV were the only affected individuals in their families, and it was not possible to evaluate the genetic concordance between glycerol kinase deficiency and their clinical features, though the similarities between these unrelated boys were quite striking.[28,283] We could speculate that episodic vomiting and acidosis are associated with more significant mutations in the GK locus than those in the GK BEN individuals and that the vomiting and acidemia of individuals with AGKCR and AGDCR may result from involvement of the GK as well as the AHC locus. Alternatively, these episodes may be unrelated to genotype in those individuals without AHC involvement or may be related by as yet unrecognized mechanism(s), e.g., one or more independent, undefined loci. Additional clinical experience and molecular genetic detail will be required to resolve this point.

Psychomotor retardation is seen frequently in the microdeletion patients with glycerol kinase deficiency including AGDCR and AGKCR individuals.[9,17,23,279] Only one patient with AGKCR was reported to be developmentally normal.[21,25] A patient with a microdeletion involving the AHC locus, but not the GK or DMD locus, also had developmental delay.[276] The size of these microdeletions is substantial[21,25,27,276,279] and may interrupt loci important to brain development. Individuals with isolated glycerol kinase deficiency, GK JUV or GK BEN, have been intellectually normal.[28,31,283–285] There is an association between Duchenne muscular dystrophy and developmental delay,[289] and the pathogenesis of psychomotor retardation of those patients with the AGDCR or GDCR microdeletion phenotypes could be related through involvement of the DMD locus. The recent observations of expression of the DMD locus in the brain will lead to additional investigation to define the cells in which this is expressed (e.g., vascular smooth muscle versus brain parenchyma) and the relationship between expression and brain development.[290,291]

Other Causes of Glyceroluria or Hyperglycerolemia

Glyceroluria was observed in four mentally retarded individuals of a group of 900 surveyed.[1] One of these had Down syndrome, and three were reported to have cerebral palsy. Subsequently glyceroluria was recognized in a normal female.[2] Plasma glycerol concentrations were not elevated (patients, 0.06 to 0.10 m*M;* controls, 0.02 to 0.08 m*M*),[1] suggesting that these patients did not have generalized glycerol kinase deficiency.[6]

Twenty boys with Duchenne muscular dystrophy were screened for glyceroluria, and one was positive.[18] His urinary glycerol ranged from 3.2 to 10 m*M* with a mean of 7.7 m*M*, which was 40 times the upper limit of normal ($\leq$0.2 m*M*) but was less than the concentration in the glycerol kinase-deficient patient (300 m*M*) examined by these same authors and was less than the values reported for other patients (see "Diagnosis," above). Serum glycerol was normal (0.15 m*M;* normal $\leq$ 0.2 m*M*), and fibroblast glycerol kinase activity was above the control range for their laboratory. This patient had no evidence of mental retardation, adrenal hypoplasia, or cytogenetic or molecular deletions.

Hyperglycerolemia may be seen in patients with diabetes mellitus and hyperthyroidism.[6] The reported values are only several-fold above controls, and in our experience, even with poorly controlled patients with diabetes mellitus, the value in hyperglycerolemia has not been similar to that in glycerol kinase deficiency. Therapeutic doses of glycerol may result in substantial hyperglycerolemia and glyceroluria.[6,269]

Our experience in a metabolic screening laboratory indicates that the most common cause of glyceroluria not associated with glycerol kinase deficiency is contamination of the specimen by exogenous glycerol. Sources of contamination, especially in a "bagged" specimen collected from an infant, include glycerol-containing perineal lotions and glycerin suppositories.

GLYCEROL INTOLERANCE SYNDROME

Glycerol intolerance was initially described in a 3-year-old boy who presented at 11 months of age with the first of a series of episodes of pallor, sweating, and inability to be aroused.[3] Blood glucose was 29 mg/dl, and he improved with glucose administration; he was ketonuric. Subsequent episodes occurred in the fasting and nonfasting state, and included sweating, confusion, irritability, and marked lethargy. He weighed 2722 g at birth and was 3 weeks premature. There was a possible history of hypoglycemia in two of four paternal uncles. Intelligence and muscle tone were both normal. Oral glycerol tolerance tests were associated with similar episodes and, variably, with hypoglycemia. Hyperglycerolemia was seen only with glycerol loading. Only 1 percent of the glycerol was excreted in the urine. An unusual response of the patient's serum dopamine β-hydroxylase after oral glycerol prompted speculation regarding altered response of this patient's sympathetic nervous system to glycerol.[292] Intravenous glycerol tolerance testing was associated with rapid loss of consciousness within 4 min of start of the infusion. A generalized convulsive jerk was followed by coma, unreactive constricted pupils, pallor, sweating, and decreased response to pain, but no hypoglycemia. After 1 h, he returned to normal. Similar doses of glycerol were not associated with these problems in other children or adults. In the patient's leukocytes, accumulation of phosphorylated products of glycerol, oxidation of glycerol-3-phosphate, and activity of fructose-1,6-diphosphatase were normal. He was placed on a low fat diet and improved, although episodes continued with increased fat intake, infection, or emotional crisis.

Two other patients, one male and one female, have subsequently been reported with the glycerol intolerance syndrome.[293,294] Both were premature: 2300 g at 36 weeks and 1850 g at 34 weeks, respectively. The boy had an episode of hypoglycemia at age 16 h, then had consistent morning irritability relieved by food, and at 4 ½ years he was hypoglycemic with vomiting and seizures following milk ingestion after one overnight fast.[293] A similar episode with coma was observed 1 month later after a 12-h fast. A liver biopsy revealed mitochondrial swelling and occasional mitochondrial inclusions. On a low fat diet with frequent snacks, he remained well over the ensuing 2 years. The girl had her first hypoglycemic episode at age 5 months.[294] Seizures were not observed with all these episodes, and no food intolerances were appreciated. She had a positive family history for chronic seizure disorder and a mentally retarded second cousin. At 5 9/12 years she was begun on a regimen of frequent feedings with avoidance of fatty foods and long fasts, and a brief regimen of folic acid administration. She had an improved tolerance to fasting and to glycerol after 6 weeks on folic acid therapy. She developed normally, and at 15 4/12 years had an improved response to a glycerol tolerance test.

Hepatic activities of fructose-1.6-diphosphatase were less than one-third of control values in both of the latter patients.[293,294] Hepatic cGDP:NAD and mGPD:FAD were also measured and found to be decreased in the boy; glycerol kinase was among the enzymes with normal activities in this patient.[293] His hepatic fructose-1,6-diphosphatase was more sensitive to inhibition by glycerol-3-phosphate than controls.[293] The girl's leukocyte fructose-1,6-diphosphatase activity improved after folic acid treatment and was normal at 15 4/12-years.

It has been suggested that the glycerol intolerance syndrome represents a sensitivity to the hypoglycemic effects of glycerol-3-phosphate, possibly due to delayed maturation of enzymes of the pathway of glycerol metabolism.[262,293,294] The exaggerated hypoglycemic response of malnourished weanling rats to glycerol-3-phosphate[262] and the suggestion that the glycerol intolerance syndrome may represent delayed maturation of glycerol metabolism are interesting in view of the fact that the three reported patients were all born prematurely. Improvement of the patients with age might represent the decreasing metabolic demands of the liver with age.[294] The clinical similarity between the patients with glycerol intolerance and those with the juvenile form of isolated glycerol kinase deficiency is quite striking. This prompted speculation that, although glycerol kinase activity was normal in the glycerol-intolerant patients, compartmentation of this enzyme could be disrupted.[229,231]

The glycerol intolerance syndrome should be considered in the differential diagnosis of the child with fasting or nonfasting hypoglycemia or in the patient with unusual clinical or glycemic response to glycerol, medium chain triglycerides, or dietary fat.

REFERENCES

1. PITKANEN E, PALO J: Increased excretion of glycerol in four patients with mental retardation. *Ann Med Exp Fenn* 45:90, 1967.
2. PALO J, SERVO C, PITKANEN E, TAMMISTO P: Increased urinary excretion of glycerol: Metabolic studies on a patient. *Clin Chim Acta* 80:391, 1977.
3. MACLAREN NK, COWLES C, OZAND PT, SHUTTEE R, CORNBLATH M: Glycerol intolerance in a child with intermittent hypoglycemia. *J Pediatr* 86:43, 1975.
4. McCABE ERB, FENNESSEY PV, GUGGENHEIM MA, MILES BS, BULLEN WW, SCEATS DJ, GOODMAN SI: Human glycerol kinase deficiency with hyperglycerolemia and glyceroluria. *Biochem Biophys Res Commun* 78:1327, 1977.
5. McCABE ERB, GUGGENHEIM MA, FENNESSEY PV, O'BRIEN D, MILES BS, GOODMAN SI: Glyceroluria, psychomotor retardation, spasticity, dystrophic myopathy and osteoporosis in a sibship. *Pediatr Res* 11:527, 1977.
6. GUGGENHEIM MA, McCABE ERB, ROIG M, GOODMAN SI, LUM GM, BULLEN WW, RINGEL SP: Glycerol kinase defieincy with neuromuscular, skeletal, and adrenal abnormalities. *Ann Neurol* 7:441, 1980.
7. ROSE CI, HAINES DSM: Familial hyperglycerolemia. *J Clin Invest* 61:163, 1978.
8. ROSE CI, HAINES DSM: Idiopathic hyperglycerolemia. *Ann R Coll Phys Surg Can* 9:53, 1976.
9. BARTLEY JA, MILLER DK, HAYFORD JT, McCABE ERB: The concordance of X-linked glycerol kinase deficiency with X-linked adrenal hypoplasia in two families. *Lancet* 2:733, 1982.
10. HAMMOND J, HOWARD NJ, BROOKWELL R, PURVIS-SMITH S, WILCKEN B, HOOGENRAAD N: Proposed assignment of loci for X-linked adrenal hypoplasia and glycerol kinase genes. *Lancet* 1:54, 1985.
11. OLD JM, BRIAND PL, PURVIS-SMITH S, HOWARD NJ, WILCKEN B, HAMMOND J, PEARSON P, CATHELINEAU L, WILLIAMSON R, DAVIES KE: Prenatal exclusion of ornithine transcarbamylase deficiency by direct gene analysis. *Lancet* 1:73, 1985.
12. WIERINGA B, HUSTINX T, SCHERES J, HOFKER M, ROPERS HH, TER HAAR B: Glycerol kinase deficiency syndrome explained as X-chromosomal deletion. *Cytogenet Cell Genet* 40:777, 1985.
13. PATIL SR, BARTLEY JA, MURRAY JC, IONASESCU VV, PEARSON PL: X-linked glycerol kinase, adrenal hypoplasia and myopathy maps at Xp21. *Cytogenet Cell Genet* 40:720, 1985.
14. WIERINGA B, HUSTINX T, SCHERES J, REINIER W, TER HAAR B: Complex glycerol kinase deficiency syndrome explained as X-chromosomal deletion. *Clin Genet* 27:522, 1985.
15. SAITO F, GOTO J, KAKINUMA H, NAKAMURA F, MURAYAMA S, NAKANO I, TONOMURA A: Inherited Xp21 deletion in a boy with complex glycerol kinase deficiency syndrome. *Clin Genet* 29:92, 1986.
16. DUNGER DB, DAVIES KE, PEMBREY M, LAKE B, PEARSON P, WILLIAMS D, WHITFIELD A, DILLON MJD: Deletion of the X chromosome detected by direct DNA analysis in one of two unrelated boys with glycerol kinase deficiency, adrenal hypoplasia, and Duchenne muscular dystrophy. *Lancet* 1:585, 1986.
17. BARTLEY JA, PATIL S, DAVENPORT S, GOLDSTEIN D, PICKENS J: Duchenne muscular dystrophy, glycerol kinase deficiency, and adrenal insufficiency associated with Xp21 interstitial deletion. *J Pediatr* 108:189, 1986.
18. CLARKE A, ROBERTS SH, THOMAS NST, WHITFIELD A, WILLIAMS J, HARPER PS: Duchenne muscular dystrophy with adrenal insufficiency and glycerol kinase deficiency: High resolution cytogenetic analysis with molecular, biochemical and clinical studies. *J Med Genet* 23:501, 1986.
19. VAN OMMEN GJB, VERKERK JMH, HOFKER MH, MONACO AP, KUNKEL LM, RAY P, WORTON R, WIERINGA B, BAKKER E, PEARSON PL: A physical map of 4 million bp around the Duchenne muscular dystrophy gene on the human X-chromosome. *Cell* 47:499, 1986.
20. KENWRICK S, PATTERSON M, SPEER A, FISCHBECK K, DAVIES K: Molecular analysis of the Duchenne muscular dystrophy region using pulsed field gel electrophoresis. *Cell* 48:351, 1987.
21. FRANCKE U, HARPER JF, DARRAS BT, COWAN JM, McCABE ERB, KOHLSCHUTTER A, SELTZER WK, SAITO F, GOTO J, HARPEY J-P, WISE JE: Congenital adrenal hypoplasia, myopathy and glycerol kinase deficiency: Molecular genetic evidence for deletions. *Am J Hum Genet* 40:212, 1987.
22. KAKINUMA H, NAKAMURA F, MURAYAMA S, GOTO J, NAKANO I, SAITO F, OHTAKE A, TAKAYANAGI M, NAKAJIMA H: A case with the infantile type of glycerol kinase deficiency. *Acta Paediatr Jpn* 29:465, 1987.
23. BORRESEN A-L, HELLERUD C, MOLLER P, SOVIK O, BERG K: Prenatal diagnosis associated with a DNA deletion on the short arm of the X-chromosome. *Clin Genet* 32:254, 1987.
24. GOONEWARDENA P, DAHL N, RITZEN M, PETTERSSON U: Deletion in Xp associated with glycerol kinase deficiency, adrenal aplasia and hypogonadotropic hypogonadism. *Cytogenet Cell Genet*, 46:621, 1987.
25. CHELLY J, MARLHENS F, VAN OMMEN GJB, DUTRILLAUX B, HARPEY JP, FARDEAU M, KAPLAN JC: Mapping of glycerol kinase (GK) and congenital adrenal hypoplasia (AHC) between J66-H1 (in DMD locus) and L1 (DXS68). *Cytogenet Cell Genet* 46:592, 1987.
26. DAVIES KE, PATTERSON M, KENWRICK SM, BELL M, SLOAN HR, WESTMAN JA, ELSAS LJ, MAHAN J: Fine mapping of glycerol kinase deficiency and adrenal hypoplasia within Xp21 on the short arm of the human X chromosome. *Am J Med Genet*, 29:557, 1988.
27. SELTZER WK, McCABE ERB: Glycerol kinase deficiency: Association with Duchenne muscular dystrophy, adrenal insufficiency and mental retardation, in Rowland LP (ed): *Molecular Genetics and Clinical Neurology*. New York, Oxford University Press, 1988, in press.
28. GINNS EI, BARRANGER JA, McCLEAN SW, SCHAEFER E, BRADY RO, YOUNG R, GOODMAN SI, McCABE ERB: Juvenile form of glycerol kinase deficiency with episodic vomiting, acidemia and stupor. *J Pediatr* 104:736, 1984.

29. GOODMAN SI, MARKEY SP: *Diagnosis of Organic Acidemias by Gas Chromatography—Mass Spectrometry.* New York, AR Liss, 1981.
30. CHALMERS RA, LAWSON AM: *Organic Acids in Man—Analytical Chemistry, Biochemistry and Diagnosis of the Organic Acidurias.* New York, Chapman and Hall, 1982.
31. GOUSSAULT Y, TURPIN E, NEEL D, DREUX C, CHANN B, BAKIR R, ROUFFY J: "Pseudohypertriglyceridemia" caused by hyperglycerolemia due to congenital enzyme deficiency. *Clin Chim Acta* 123:269, 1982.
32. HANKE ME: The physiological action of glycerol, in Miner CS, Dalton NN (eds): *Glycerol.* New York, Reinhold, 1953, p 402.
33. BORCHGREVINK CF, HAVEL RJ: Transport of glycerol in human blood. *Proc Soc Exp Biol Med* 113:946, 1963.
34. SHAFRIR E, GORIN E: Release of glycerol in conditions of fat mobilization and deposition. *Metabolism* 12:58, 1963.
35. HAVEL RJ: Some influences of the sympathetic nervous system and insulin in mobilization of fat from adipose tissue: Studies of the turnover rates of free fatty acids and glycerol. *Ann NY Acad Sci* 131:91, 1965.
36. BALLARD FJ, HANSON RW, LEVEILLE GA: Phosphoenolpyruvate carboxykinase and the synthesis of glyceride-glycerol from pyruvate in adipose tissue. *J Biol Chem* 242:2746, 1967.
37. BJORNTORP P, BERGMAN H, VARNAUSKAS E, LINDHOLM B: Lipid mobilization in relation to body composition in man. *Metabolism* 18:840, 1969.
38. BORTZ WM, PAUL P, HAFF AC, HOLMES WL: Glycerol turnover and oxidation in man. *J Clin Invest* 51:1537, 1972.
39. RESHEF L, MEYUHAS O, BOSHWITZ CH, HANSON RW, BALLARD FJ: Physiological role and regulation of glyceroneogenesis in rat adipose tissue. *Isr J Med Sci* 8:372, 1972.
40. SHREEVE WW: *Physiological Chemistry of Carbohydrates in Mammals.* Philadelphia, Saunders, 1974, p 298.
41. LIN ECC: Glycerol utilization and its regulation in mammals. *Annu Rev Biochem* 46:765, 1977.
42. CATRON LF, LEWIS HB: The formation of glycogen in the liver of the young white rat after the oral administration of glycerol. *J Biol Chem* 84:553, 1929.
43. SHAPIRO I: Studies on ketosis. V. The comparative glycogenic and ketolytic action of glucose and some carbohydrate intermediates. *J Biol Chem* 108:373, 1935.
44. DOERSCHUK AP: Some studies on the metabolism of glycerol-1-^{14}C. *J Biol Chem* 193:39, 1951.
45. ASHMORE J, RENOLD AE, NESBETT FB, HASTINGS AB: Studies on carbohydrate in rat liver slices. V. Glycerol metabolism in relation to substrates in normal and diabetic tissue. *J Biol Chem* 215:153, 1955.
46. NOBLE EP, STJERNHOLM RL, WEISBERGER AS: Carbohydrate metabolism in the leukocytes. I. The pathway of two- and three-carbon compounds in the rabbit polymorphonuclear leukocyte. *J Biol Chem* 235:1261, 1960.
47. VOEGTLIN C, THOMPSON JW, DUNN ER: Hyperglycemia produced by glycerol. *J Biol Chem* 64:639, 1925.
48. CHAMBERS WH, DEUEL HJ: Animal calorimetry. XXX. The metabolism of glycerol in phlorizen diabetes. *J Biol Chem* 65:21, 1925.
49. NIKKILA EA, OJALA K: Gluconeogenesis from glycerol in fasting rats. *Life Sci* 3:243, 1964.
50. BERGMAN EN: Glycerol turnover in the nonpregnant and ketotic pregnant sheep. *Am J Physiol* 215:865, 1968.
51. ROBINSON JA, NEWSHOLME EA: The effects of dietary conditions on glycerol uptake by rat liver and kidney-cortex slices. *Biochem J* 112:449, 1969.
52. WINKLER B, RATHGEB I, STEELE R, ALTSZULER N: Conversion of glycerol to glucose in the normal dog. *Am J Physiol* 219:497, 1970.
53. WISHNOFSKY M, KANE AP, SPITZ WC, MICHALOVER S, BYRON CS: Influence of glycerol on glycemia in normal and diabetic individuals. *J Lab Clin Med* 26:526, 1940.
54. SENIOR B, LORIDAN L: Studies of liver glycogenoses with particular reference to the metabolism of intravenously administered glycerol. *N Engl J Med* 279:958, 1968.
55. VIDNES J, SOVIK O: Gluconeogenesis in infancy and childhood. *Acta Paediatr Scand* 65:297, 1976.
56. WOLF H, MELICHAR V, MICHAELIS R: Elimination of intravenously administered glycerol from the blood of newborns. *Biol Neonate* 12:162, 1968.
57. FERBER J, RABINOWITSCH S: Increase in blood sugar following the ingestion of glycerol. *Am J Med Sci* 177:827, 1929.
58. D'ALENA P, FERGUSON W: Adverse effects after glycerol orally and parenterally. *Arch Ophthalmol* 75:201, 1966.
59. PELKONEN R, NIKKILA EA, KEKKI M: Metabolism of glycerol in diabetes mellitus. *Diabetologia* 3:1, 1967.
60. SEARS ES: Nonketotic hyperosmolar hyperglycemia during glycerol therapy for cerebral edema. *Neurology* 26:89, 1976.
61. SENIOR B, LORIDAN L: Gluconeogenesis and insulin in the ketotic variety of childhood hypoglycemia and in control children. *J Pediatr* 74:529, 1969.
62. SENIOR B, LORIDAN L: Functional differentiation of glycogenoses of the liver with respect to the use of glycerol. *N Engl J Med* 279:965, 1968.
63. MARINETTI GV: Biosynthesis of triglycerides, in Dawson RMC, Rhodes DN (eds): *Comprehensive Biochemistry. Lipid Metabolism.* New York, Wiley, 1964, vol 18, p 71.
64. ROGNSTAD R, CLARK DG, KATZ J: Pathways of glyceride glycerol synthesis. *Biochem J* 140:249, 1974.
65. LAMB RG, WOOD CK, LANDA BM, GUZELIAN PS, FALLON HJ: Studies of the formation and release of glycerolipids by primary monolayer cultures of adult rat hepatocytes. *Biochem Biophys Acta* 489:318, 1977.
66. WOOD CK, LAMB RG: The effect of ethanol on glycerolipid biosynthesis by primary monolayer cultures of adult rat hepatocytes. *Biochim Biophys Acta* 572:121, 1979.
67. FARESE RV: Phosphoinositide metabolism and hormone action. *Endocr Rev* 4:78, 1983.
68. BARTLEY JA, WARD R: Glycerol kinase deficiency inhibits glycerol utilization in phosphoglyceride and triacylglycerol biosynthesis. *Pediatr Res* 19:313, 1985.
69. RASMUSSEN H: The calcium messenger system. *N Engl J Med* 314:1094, 1986.
70. HAJRA AK, AGRANOFF BW: Acyl dihydroxyacetone phosphate—Characterization of a ^{32}P-labeled lipid from guinea pig liver mitochondria. *J Biol Chem* 243:1617, 1968.
71. HAJRA AK: Biosynthesis of glycerolipids via acyldihydroxyacetone phosphate. *Biochem Soc Trans* 5:34, 1977.
72. HAJRA AK, BISHOP JE: Glycerolipid biosynthesis in peroxisomes via the acyl dihydroxyacetone phosphate pathway. *Ann NY Acad Sci* 386:170, 1982.
73. BALLAS LM, LAZAROW PB, BELL RM: Glycerolipid synthetic capacity of rat liver peroxisomes. *Biochim Biophys Acta* 795:297, 1984.
74. ESMANN V: Dihydroxyacetone as an intermediate during the metabolism of glycerol and glyceraldehyde in leukocytes from rat. *Acta Chem Scand* 22:2281, 1968.
75. ROFE AM, JAMES HM, BAIS R, EDWARDS JB, CONYERS RA: The production of (^{14}C)-oxalate during the metabolism of (^{14}C)-carbohydrates in isolated rat hepatocytes. *Aust J Exp Biol Med Sci* 58:103, 1980.
76. McCABE ERB, SADAVA D, BULLEN WW, SELTZER WK, McKELVEY HA, ROSE CI: Human glycerol kinase deficiency: Enzyme kinetics and fibroblast hybridization. *J Inherited Metab Dis* 5:177, 1982.
77. INTERNATIONAL UNION OF BIOCHEMISTRY: *Enzyme Nomenclature 1984.* Orlando, Academic, 1984.
78. THORNER JW, PAULUS H: Glycerol and glycerate kinases, in Boyer D (ed): *The Enzymes* New York, Academic, 1973, vol VIII, p 487.
79. KENNEDY EP: Synthesis of phosphatides in isolated mitochondria. *J Biol Chem* 201:399, 1953
80. BUBLITZ C, KENNEDY EP: Synthesis of phosphatides in isolated mitochondria. III. The enzymatic phosphorylation of glycerol. *J Biol Chem* 211:951, 1954.
81. BUBLITZ C, KENNEDY EP: A note on the asymmetrical metabolism of glycerol. *J Biol Chem* 211:963, 1954.
82. WIELAND O, SUYTER M: Glycerokinase: Isolierung und eigenschaften des enzyms. *Biochem Z* 329:320, 1957.
83. BUBLITZ C, WIELAND O: Glycerokinase, in Colowick SP, Kaplan NO (eds): *Methods in Enzymology.* New York, Academic, 1962, vol V, p 354.
84. GRUNNET N, LUNDQUIST F: Kinetics of glycerol kinases from mammalian liver and *Candida mycoderma. Eur J Biochem* 3:78, 1967.
85. ROBINSON J, NEWSHOLME EA: Inhibition of liver glycerol kinase by adenosine monophosphate and L-alpha-glycerophosphate. *Biochem J* 104:70P, 1967.
86. TEPPERMAN HM, TEPPERMAN J: Adaptive changes in alpha-glycerophosphate-generating enzymes in rat liver. *Am J Physiol* 214:67, 1968.
87. ROBINSON J, NEWSHOLME EA: Some properties of hepatic glycerol kinase and their relation to the control of glycerol utilization. *Biochem J* 112:455, 1969.
88. KAMPF SC, SEITZ HJ, TARNOWSKI W: Regulation of glycerol metabolism. I. Hormonal and metabolic control of rat liver glycerol kinase activity. *Hoppe-Seyler's Z Physiol Chem* 351:32, 1970.
89. LECH JJ: Glycerol kinase and glycerol utilization in trout (*Salmo gairdneri*) liver. *Comp Biochem Physiol* 34:117, 1970.
90. KRAUSE R, WOLF H: Glyzerokinase der schweineleber. I. Allgemeine und kinetische eigenschaften des enzyms. *Acta Biol Med Ger* 33:385, 1974.
91. KRAUSE R, WOLF H: Glyzerokinase der schweineleber. II. Postnatale entwicklung und intrazellulare verteilung des enzyms. *Acta Biol Med Ger* 33:393, 1974.
92. SCHNEIDER PB: Activation of bovine liver glycerol kinase by ethanol. *Biochim Biophys Acta* 397:110, 1975.

93. GARDNER LB, REISER S: Serum glycerol and hepatic glycerokinase activity in the carbohydrate-sensitive BHE strain of rat. *Proc Soc Exp Biol Med* 153:158, 1976.
94. DIVAKARAN P: Regulation of liver lipogenic enzymes by dietary fats. *Experientia* 32:1128, 1976.
95. SELTZER WK, BULLEN WW, McCABE ERB: Human glycerol kinase: Comparison of properties from fibroblasts and liver. *Life Sci* 32:1721, 1983.
96. OSTLUND AK, GOHRING U, KRAUSE J, BRDICZKA D: The binding of glycerol kinase to the outer membrane of rat liver mitochondria: Its importance in metabolic regulation. *Biochem Med* 30:231, 1983.
97. LI C-C, LIN ECC: Glycerol transport and phosphorylation by rat hepatocytes. *J Cell Physiol* 117:230, 1983.
98. PITTNER RA, FEARS R, BRINDLEY DN: Effects of cyclic AMP, glucocorticoids and insulin on the activities of phosphatidate phosphohydrolase, tyrosine aminotransferase and glycerol kinase in isolated rat hepatocytes in relation to the control of triacylglycerol synthesis and gluconeogenesis. *Biochem J* 225:455, 1985.
99. KALCKAR H: Phosphorylation in kidney tissue. *Enzymologia* 2:47, 1937.
100. KALCKAR H: LXXVIII. The nature of phosphoric esters formed in kidney extracts. *Biochem J* 33:631, 1939.
101. ACKERMAN RH: Auswirkungen parenteraler glycerinzufuhr auf die glycerokinase-aktivitat und den adenosintriphosphatspiegel in der niere von ratten. *Res Exp Med (Berl)* 166:251, 1975.
102. WIRTHENSOHN G, VANDEWALLE A, GUDER WG: Renal glycerol metabolism and the distribution of glycerol kinase in rabbit nephron. *Biochem J* 198:543, 1981.
103. BURCH HB, HAYS AE, McCREARY MD, COLE BR, CHI MM, DENCE CN, LOWRY OH: Relationships in different parts of the nephron between enzymes of glycerol metabolism and the metabolite changes which result from large glycerol loads. *J Biol Chem* 257:3676, 1982.
104. HAESSLER HA, ISSELBACHER KJ: The metabolism of glycerol by intestinal mucosa. *Biochem Biophys Acta* 73:427, 1963.
105. JENKINS BT, HAJRA AK: Glycerol kinase and dihydroxyacetone kinase in rat brain. *J Neurochem* 26:377, 1976.
106. TILDON JT, STEVENSON JH, OZAND PT: Mitochondrial glycerol kinase activity in rat brain. *Biochem J* 157:513, 1976.
107. KANEKO M, KUROKAWA M, ISHIBASHI S: Binding and function of mitochondrial glycerol kinase in comparison with those of mitochondrial hexokinase. *Arch Biochem Biophys* 237:135, 1985.
108. SELTZER WK, McCABE ERB: Human and rat adrenal glycerol kinase: Subcellular distribution and bisubstrate kinetics. *Mol Cell Biochem* 62:43, 1984.
109. SELTZER WK, McCABE ERB: Subcellular distribution and kinetic properties of soluble and particulate-associated bovine adrenal glycerol kinase. *Mol Cell Biochem* 64:51, 1984.
110. KOSCHINSKY T, GRIES FA, HERBERG L: Glycerol kinase activity in isolated fat cells of BHob mice. *Horm Metab Res* 2:185, 1970.
111. KOSCHINSKY T, GRIES FA: Glycerin-kinase und lipolyse des menschlichen fettgewebes in abhangigkeit vom relativen korpergewicht. *Hoppe-Seyler's Z Physiol Chem* 352:430, 1971.
112. KOSCHINSKY T, GRIES FA, HERBERG L: Regulation of glycerol kinase by insulin in isolated fat cells and liver of Bar Harbor obese mice. *Diabetologia* 7:316, 1971.
113. THENEN SW, MAYER J: Adipose tissue glycerokinase activity in genetic and acquired obesity in rats and mice. *Proc Soc Exp Biol Med* 148:953, 1975.
114. MARTIN RJ, LAMPREY PM: Early development of adipose cell lipogenesis and glycerol utilization in Zucker obese rats. *Proc Soc Exp Biol Med* 149:35, 1975.
115. PERSICO PA, CERCHIO M, JEFFAY H: Glycerokinase in mammalian adipose tissue: Stimulation by lipogenic substances. *Am J Physiol* 228:1868, 1975.
116. THENEN SW, MAYER J: Hyperinsulinemia and fat cell glycerokinase activity in obese (ob/ob) and diabetic (db/db) mice. *Horm Metab Res* 8:80, 1976.
117. BERTIN R: Glycerokinase activity and lipolysis regulation in brown adipose tissue of cold acclimated rats. *Biochimie* 58:431, 1976.
118. RYALL RL, GOLDRICK RB: Glycerokinase in mammalian adipose tissue. *Lipids* 12:272, 1977.
119. O'FLAHERTY EJ, McCARTY CP: Alteration of rat adipose tissue metabolism associated with dietary chromium supplementation. *J Nutr* 108:321, 1978.
120. BARRERA LA, HO R: Adipose glycerol kinase: Low molecular weight protein has two Michaelis constants for glycerol. *Biochem Biophys Res Commun* 86:145, 1979.
121. TAYLOR WM, GOLDRICK RB, ISHIKAWA T: Glycerokinase in rat and human adipose tissue: Response to hormonal and dietary stimuli. *Horm Metab Res* 11:280, 1979.
122. HO RJ, FAN C-C, BARRERA LA: Comparison of adipose glycerol kinase of hyperglycemic obese mice and lean litter-mates. *Mol Cell Biochem* 27:89, 1979.
123. BERNFELD P: Glycerokinase levels in adipose tissues of obese hamsters. *Prog Exp Tumor Res* 24:139, 1979.
124. KAPLAN M, LEVEILLE GA: Development of lipogenesis and insulin sensitivity in tissues of the ob/ob mouse. *Am J Physiol* 240:E101, 1981.
125. STERN JS, HIRSCH J, DREWNOWSKI A, SULLIVAN AC, JOHNSON PR, COHN CK: Glycerol kinase activity in adipose tissue of obese rats and mice: Effects of diet composition. *J Nutr* 113:714, 1983.
126. CHAKRABARTY K, CHAUDHURI B, JEFFAY H: Glycerokinase activity in human brown adipose tissue. *J Lipid Res* 24:381, 1983.
127. BERTIN R, ANDRIAMIHAJA M, PORTET R: Glycerokinase activity in brown and white adipose tissues of cold-adapted obese Zucker rats. *Biochimie* 66:569, 1984.
128. CHAKRABARTY K, TAUBER JW, SIGEL B, BOMBECK CT, JEFFAY H: Glycerokinase activity in human adipose tissue as related to obesity. *Int J Obes* 8:609, 1984.
129. SCHNEIDER PB: Thyroidal glycerol kinase. *Endocrinology* 86:687, 1970.
130. ROBINSON J, NEWSHOLME EA: Glycerol kinase activities in rat heart and adipose tissue. *Biochem J* 104:2C, 1967.
131. NEWSHOLME EA, TAYLOR K: Glycerol kinase activities in muscles from vertebrates and invertebrates. *Biochem J* 112:465, 1969.
132. FISHER A, CHANDER A: Glycerol kinase activity and glycerol metabolism of rat granular pneumocytes in primary culture. *Biochim Biophys Acta* 711:128, 1982.
133. McBRIDE OW, KORN E: Presence of glycerokinase in guinea pig mammary gland and the incorporation of glycerol into glycerides. *J Lipid Res* 5:442, 1964.
134. MOHRI H, MOHRI T, ERNSTER L: Isolation and enzyme properties of the midpiece of bull spermatozoa. *Exp Cell Res* 38:217, 1965.
135. MOHRI H, MASAKI J: Glycerokinase and its possible role in glycerol metabolism of bull spermatozoa. *J Reprod Fertil* 14:179, 1967.
136. MOHRI H, HASEGAWA S, MASAKI J: Seasonal changes in glycerol kinase activity of goat spermatozoa. *Biol Reprod* 2:352, 1970.
137. HARDING JW, PYERITZ EA, MORRIS HP, WHITE HB: Proportional activities of glycerol kinase and glycerol-3-phosphate dehydrogenase in rat hepatomas. *Biochem J* 148:545, 1975.
138. LI C-C, LIN ECC: Uptake of glycerol by tumor cells and its control by glucose. *Biochem Biophys Res Commun* 67:677, 1975.
139. WYKLE RL, KRAEMER WF: Glycerol kinase activity in adenoma alveolar type II cells. *FEBS Lett* 78:83, 1977.
140. GRAZIANI Y, ERIKSON E, ERIKSON RL: Evidence that the Rous sarcoma virus transforming gene product is associated with glycerol kinase activity. *J Biol Chem* 258:2126, 1983.
141. RICHERT ND, BLITHE DL, PASTAN I: Properties of the *src* kinase purified from Rous sarcoma virus-induced rat tumors. *J Biol Chem* 257:7143, 1982.
142. RICHERT ND: Phosphorylation of glycerol by cAMP-dependent protein kinase: Comparison with *src* kinase. *Biochem Int* 6:63, 1983.
143. HAYASHI S, LIN ECC: Capture of glycerol by cells of *Escherichia coli*. *Biochim Biophys Acta* 94:479, 1965.
144. HAYASHI S, LIN ECC: Product induction of glycerol kinase in *Escherichia coli*. *J Mol Biol* 14:515, 1965.
145. LIN ECC: Glycerol dissimilation and its regulation in bacteria. *Annu Rev Microbiol* 30:535, 1976.
146. HAYASHI S-I, LIN ECC: Purification and properties of glycerol kinase from *Escherichia coli*. *J Biol Chem* 242:1030, 1967.
147. ZWAIG N, KISTLER WS, LIN ECC: Glycerol kinase, the pacemaker for the dissimilation of glycerol in *Escherichia coli*. *J Bacteriol* 102:753, 1970.
148. THORNER JW, PAULUS H: Composition and subunit structure of glycerol kinase from *Escherichia coli*. *J Biol Chem* 246:3885, 1971.
149. DE RIEL JK, PAULUS H: Subunit dissociation in the allosteric regulation of glycerol kinase from *Escherichia coli*. 1. Kinetic evidence. *Biochemistry* 17:5134, 1978.
150. DE RIEL JK, PAULUS H: Subunit dissociation in the allosteric regulation of glycerol kinase from *Escherichia coli*. 2. Physical evidence. *Biochemistry* 17:5141, 1978.
151. DE RIEL JK, PAULUS H: Subunit dissociation in the allosteric regulation of glycerol kinase from *Escherichia coli*. 3. Role in desensitization. *Biochemistry* 17:5146, 1978.
152. ORR GA, SIMON J, JONES SR, CHIN GJ, KNOWLES JR: Adenosine 5′-0-([gamma-^{18}O] gamma-thio) triphosphate chiral at the gamma-phosphorus: Stereochemical consequences of reactions catalyzed by pyruvate kinase, glycerol kinase, and hexokinase. *Proc Natl Acad Sci USA* 75:2230, 1978.
153. BLATTLER WA, KNOWLES JR: Stereochemical course of the phosphokinases. The use of adenosine [gamma-(S)-^{16}O,^{17}O,^{18}O] triphosphate and mechanistic consequences for the reactions catalyzed by glycerol kinase,

hexokinase, pyruvate kinase, and acetate kinase. *Biochemistry* 18:3927, 1979.

154. PLIURA DH, SCHOMBURG D, RICHARD JP, FREY PA, KNOWLES JR: Stereochemical course of a phosphokinase using a chiral [^{18}O] phosphorothioate. Comparison with the transfer of a chiral [^{16}O, ^{17}O, ^{18}O] phosphoryl group. *Biochemistry* 19:325, 1980.

155. CONRAD CA, STEARNS GW, PRATER WE, RHEINER JA, JOHNSON JR: Characterization of a *glpK* transducing phage. *Mol Gen Genet* 193:376, 1984.

156. PETTIGREW DW: Inactivation of *Escherichia coli* glycerol kinase by 5,5′-dithiobis(2-nitrobenzoic acid) and N-ethylmaleimide: Evidence for nucleotide regulatory binding sites. *Biochemistry* 25:4711, 1986.

157. PETTIGREW DW, MA D-P, CONRAD CA, JOHNSON JR: *Escherichia coli* glycerol kinase: Cloning and sequencing of the *glpK* gene and the primary structure of the enzyme. *J Biol Chem* 263:135, 1988.

158. SCAWEN MD, HAMMOND PM, COMER MJ, ATKINSON T: The application of triazine dye affinity chromatography to the large-scale purification of glycerokinase from *Bacillus stearothermophilus*. *Anal Biochem* 132:413, 1983.

159. JENNINGS DH: Polyol metabolism in fungi. *Adv Microb Physiol* 25:149, 1984.

160. CHOPRA A, KHULLER GK: Lipid metabolism in fungi. *CRC Crit Rev Microbiol* 11:209, 1984.

161. BERGMEYER H-U, HOLZ G, KAUDER EM, MOLLERING H, WIELAND O: Kristallisierte glycerokinase aus *Candida mycoderma*. *Biochem Z* 333:471, 1961.

162. EISENTHAL R, HARRISON R, LLOYD WJ: Specificity of glycerol kinase. *Biochem J* 141:305, 1974.

163. PYLE JE, HOWE HB: Uptake and dissimilation of glycerol by wild type and glycerol nonutilizing strains of *Neurospora crassa*. *Mol Gen Genet* 189:166, 1983.

164. LAVINE JE, ROBERTS CT, MORSE DE: Glucose regulation of specific gene expression is altered in a glucokinase-deficient mutant of *Tetrahymena*. *Mol Cell Biochem* 48:45, 1982.

165. HART DT, OPPERDOES FR: The occurrence of glycosomes (microbodies) in the promastigote stage of four major *Leishmania* species. *Mol Biochem Parasitol* 13:159, 1984.

166. HAMMOND DJ, AMAN RA, WANG CC: The role of compartmentation and glycerol kinase in the synthesis of ATP within the glycosome of *Trypanosoma brucei*. *J Biol Chem* 260:15646, 1985.

167. MISSET O, BOS OJM, OPPERDOES FR: Glycolytic enzymes of *Trypanosoma brucei*. *Eur J Biochem* 157:441, 1986.

168. BARMAN TE: *Enzyme Handbook*. New York, Springer-Verlag, 1969, vol 1, p 401.

169. GRUNNET N: Inhibition of glycerol kinase by α-glycerophosphate. *Biochem J* 119:927, 1970.

170. BROOKS DE: The interaction of α-chlorohydrin with glycerol kinase. *J Reprod Fertil* 56:593, 1979.

171. TISDALE MJ, THREADGILL MD: (±)-2,3-Dihydroxypropyl dichloroacetate, an inhibitor of glycerol kinase. *Cancer Biochem Biophys* 7:253, 1984.

172. SELTZER WK, DHARIWAL G, McKELVEY HA, McCABE ERB: 1-Thioglycerol: Inhibitor of glycerol kinase activity in vitro and in situ. *Life Sci* 39:1417, 1986.

173. KASEMSRI S, BERNARDIS LL, CHLOUVERAKIS C, SCHNATZ JD: The incorporation of ^{14}C-glycerol into adipose tissue lipids of weanling rats with hypothalamic obesity. *Proc Soc Exp Biol Med* 141:38, 1972.

174. FATHIPOUR A, PRIDHAM JB: Control of glycerokinase activity by sex hormones. *Biochem Soc Trans* 2:1116, 1974.

175. VON EULER H, ADLER E, GUNTHER G: Über die komponenten der dehydrasesysteme. XV. Zur kenntnis der dehydrierung von alpha-glycerinphosphor saure in tierkorper. *Hoppe-Seyler's Z Physiol Chem* 249:1, 1937.

176. ADLER E, VON EULER H, HUGHES W: Über die komponenten der dehydrasesysteme; glycerophosphat-dehydrase. Oxydoreduction in muskel. *Hoppe-Seyler's Z Physiol Chem* 252:1, 1938.

177. BARANOWSKI T: Crystalline glycerophosphate dehydrogenase from rabbit muscle. *J Biol Chem* 180:535, 1949.

178. McGINNIS JF, DE VELLIS J: Glycerol-3-phosphate dehydrogenase isoenzymes in human tissues: Evidence for a heart specific form. *J Mol Cell Cardiol* 11:795, 1979.

179. McGINNIS JF, DE VELLIS J: Glucocorticoid regulation in rat brain cell cultures—Hydrocortisone increases the rate of synthesis of glycerol phosphate dehydrogenase in C6 gliomia cells. *J Biol Chem* 253:8483, 1978.

180. FREERKSEN DL, HARTZELL CR: Glucocorticoid stimulation of metabolism and glycerol-3-phosphate dehydrogenase activity in cultured heart cells. *J Cell Physiol* 126:206, 1986.

181. FREERKSEN DL, SCHROEDL NA, HARTZELL CR: Triiodothyronine depresses NAD-linked glycerol-3-phosphate dehydrogenase activity of cultured neonatal rat heart cells. *Arch Biochem Biophys* 228:474, 1984.

182. KUMAR S, SACHAR K, HUBER J, WEINGARTEN DP, DE VELLIS J: Glucocorticoids regulate the transcription of glycerol phosphate dehydrogenase in cultured glial cells. *J Biol Chem* 260:14743, 1985.

183. IRELAND RC, KOTARSKI MA, JOHNSTON LA, STADLER U, BIRKENMEIER E, KOZAK LP: Primary structure of the mouse glycerol-3-phosphate dehydrogenase gene. *J Biol Chem* 261:11779, 1986.

184. NOTSU Y, OMURA S, YOSHIMOTO A, TOMITA K: An NAD-linked alpha-glycerophosphate dehydrogenase in rat liver mitochondria and its response to thyroid hormone. *J Biochem* 72:447, 1972.

185. TOLBERT NE: Metabolic pathways in peroxisomes and glyoxysomes. *Annu Rev Biochem* 50:133, 1981.

186. GEE R, TOLBERT NE: Glycerol phosphate dehydrogenase in rat and mouse liver peroxisomes. *Ann NY Acad Sci* 386:417, 1982.

187. RINGLER RL, SINGER TP: α-L-Glycerophosphate dehydrogenase from pig brain, in Colowick SP, Kaplan NO (eds): *Methods in Enzymology*. New York, Academic, 1962, vol 5, p 432.

188. MEYERHOF O: Über die Atmung der froschmuskulatur. *Pfluegers Arch* 175:20, 1919.

189. LEE Y-P, LARDY HA: Influence of thyroid hormones on L-α-glycerophosphate dehydrogenase and other dehydrogenases in various organs of the rat. *J Biol Chem* 240:1427, 1965.

190. SCHENKMAN JB, RICHERT DA, WESTERFELD WW: α-Glycerophosphate dehydrogenase activity in rat spermatozoa. *Endocrinology* 76:1055, 1965.

191. KALRA VK, BRODIE AF: The presence of the glycerol phosphate shuttle and energy dependent transhydrogenase in aortic mitochondria. *Biochem Biophys Res Commun* 51:414, 1973.

192. JEMELIN M, FREI J: Leukocyte energy metabolism. III. Anaerobic and aerobic ATP production and related enzymes. *Enzym Biol Clin* 11:289, 1970.

193. KLINGENBERG M: Localization of the glycerol-phosphate dehydrogenase in the outer phase of the mitochondrial inner membrane. *Eur J Biochem* 13:247, 1970.

194. HENLEY KS, KAWATA H, PINO ME: Effect of adrenalectomy on rat liver mitochondria. *Endocrinology* 73:366, 1963.

195. SELLINGER OZ, LEE K-L: The induction of mitochondrial α-glycerophosphate dehydrogenase by thyroid hormone: Evidence for enzyme synthesis. *Biochim Biophys Acta* 91:183, 1964.

196. LEE Y-P, TAKEMORI AE, LARDY HA: Enhanced oxidation of α-glycerophosphate by mitochondria of thyroid-fed rats. *J Biol Chem* 234:3051, 1959.

197. LARDY HA, LEE Y-P, TAKEMORI A: Enzyme responses to thyroid hormones. *Ann NY Acad Sci* 86:506, 1960.

198. CARLSEN A, WIETH JO: Glycerol transport in human red cells. *Acta Physiol Scand* 97:501, 1976.

199. YAEGER Y, NATHAN I, DVILANSKY A, MEYERSTEIN N: Permeability of fresh and stored human erythrocytes to glycerol and its acylated derivatives. *Experientia* 35:1673, 1979.

200. JACOBS MH: A case of apparent physiological competition between ethylene glycol and glycerol. *Biol Bull* 107:314, 1954.

201. HUNTER FR: Facilitated diffusion in human erythrocytes. *Biochim Biophys Acta* 211:216, 1970.

202. CAINELLI SR, CHUI A, McCLURE JD, HUNTER FR: Facilitated diffusion in erythrocytes of mammals. *Comp Biochem Physiol* 48A:815, 1974.

203. SESTOFT L, FLERON P: Kinetics of glycerol uptake by the perfused rat liver: Membrane transport, phosphorylation and effect on NAD redox level. *Biochim Biophys Acta* 375:462, 1975.

204. LEHNINGER AL: Phosphorylation coupled to oxidation of dihydrodiphosphopyridine nucleotide. *J Biol Chem* 190:345, 1951.

205. NEWSHOLME EA, LEECH AR: *Biochemistry for the Medical Sciences*. New York, Wiley, 1983.

206. BUCHER T, KLINGENBERG M: Wege des wasserstoffs in der lebendigen organisation. *Angew Chem* 245:552, 1958.

207. ESTABROOK RW, SACKTOR B: α-Glycerophosphate oxidase of flight muscle mitochondria. *J Biol Chem* 233:1014, 1958.

208. NEWSHOLME EA, START C: *Regulation in Metabolism*. New York, Wiley, 1973.

209. SACKTOR B: The role of mitochondria in respiratory metabolism of flight muscle. *Annu Rev Entomol* 6:103, 1961.

210. SACKTOR B: Regulation of intermediary metabolism with special reference to control mechanisms in insect flight muscle. *Adv Insect Physiol* 7:267, 1970.

211. BEWLEY GC, LUCCHESI JC: Origin of α-glycerophosphate dehydrogenase isozymes in *Drosophila melanogaster* and their functional relationship in the α-glycerophosphate cycle. *Biochem Genet* 15:235, 1977.

212. SACKTOR B, PACKER L, ESTABROOK RW: Respiratory activity of brain mitochondria. *Arch Biochem Biophys* 80:68, 1959.

213. SURANYI EM, HEDMAN R, LUFT R, ERNSTER L: Reconstruction of the glycerol-1-phosphate cycle with subcellular fractions from rat skeletal muscle. *Acta Chem Scand* 17:877, 1963.

214. KLEITKE B, WOLLENBERGER A: Reconstruction of the glycerophosphate cycle in suspensions of rat brain mitochondria. *J Neurochem* 16:1629, 1969.
215. GALTON DJ: Regulation of supply of glycerol phosphate for lipogenesis in human adipose tissue. *Clin Sci* 36:505, 1969.
216. BERRY MN, KUN E, WERNER HV: Regulatory role of reducing-equivalent transfer from substrate to oxygen in the hepatic metabolism of glycerol and sorbitol. *Eur J Biochem* 33:407, 1973.
217. LAMARTINIERE CA, WEISS G: The role of the glycerolphosphate shuttle in heterogeneous liver mitochondria. *Hoppe-Seyler's Z Physiol Chem* 355:1549, 1974.
218. SWIERCZYNSKI J, SCISLOWSKI P, ALEKSANDROWICZ Z: Regulation of α-glycerophosphate dehydrogenase activity in human term placental mitochondria. *Biochim Biophys Acta* 452:310, 1976.
219. SCHILLER CM: Flow of reducing equivalents into intestinal mitochondria. *Metabolism* 28:105, 1979.
220. CURSTEDT T: Deuterium labeling of glycerol-3-phosphate during metabolism of [1-$^2H_2$]-ethanol in rats. *Eur J Biochem* 49:355, 1974.
221. WILLIAMSON JR, OHKAWA K, MEIJER AJ: Regulation of ethanol oxidation in isolated rat liver cells, in Thurman RG, Yonetani T, Williamson JR, Chance B (eds): *Alcohol and Aldehyde Metabolizing Systems.* New York, Academic, 1974, p 365.
222. POSO AR: Influence of the activity of mitochondrial α-glycerophosphate oxidase on the L-alpha-glycerophosphate shuttle during ethanol oxidation. *FEBS Lett* 83:285, 1977.
223. WU BC, ARGUS MF, ARCOS JC: Differential decrease of "shuttle" enzymes of extramitochondrial $NADH_2$ oxidation of heart muscle during progressive thiamine deficiency. *Proc Soc Exp Biol Med* 133:808, 1970.
224. CARNICERO HH, MOOR CL, HOBERMAN HD: Oxidation of glycerol 3-phosphate by the perfused rat liver. *J Biol Chem* 247:418, 1972.
225. WILSON JE: Ambiquitous enzymes: Variation in the intracellular distribution as a regulatory mechanism. *Trends Biochem Sci* 3:124, 1978.
226. WILSON JE: Brain hexokinase, the prototype ambiquitous enzyme. *Curr Top Cell Regul* 16:1, 1980.
227. WINZOR DJ, WARD LD, NICHOL LW: Quantitative considerations of the consequences of an interplay between ligand binding and reversible adsorption of a macromolecular solute. *J Theor Biol* 98:171, 1982.
228. FIEK C, BENZ R, ROOS N, BRDICZKA D: Evidence for the identity between the hexokinase binding protein and the mitochondrial porin in the outer membrane of the rat liver mitochondria. *Biochim Biophys Acta* 688:429, 1982.
229. McCABE ERB: Glycerol kinase deficiency: An inborn error of compartmental metabolism. *Biochem Med* 30:215, 1983.
230. BRDICZKA D, KNOLL G, RIESINGER I, WEILER U, KLUG G, BENZ R, KRAUSE J: Microcompartmentation at the mitochondrial surface: Its function in metabolic regulation, in Brautbar N (ed): *Myocardial and Skeletal Muscle Bioenergetics.* New York, Plenum, 1986, p 55.
231. McCABE ERB, SELTZER WK: Glycerol kinase deficiency: Compartmental considerations regarding pathogenesis and clinical heterogeneity, in Brautbar N (ed): *Myocardial and Skeletal Muscle Bioenergetics.* New York, Plenum, 1986, p 481.
232. SADAVA D, DEPPER M, GILBERT M, BERNARD B, McCABE ERB: Development of enzymes of glycerol metabolism in human fetal liver. *Biol Neonate* 52:26, 1987.
233. BENZ R: Porin from bacterial and mitochondrial outer membranes. *CRC Crit Rev Biochem* 19:145, 1985.
234. OHLENDIECK K, RIESINGER I, ADAMS V, KRAUSE J, BRDICZKA D: Enrichment and biochemical characterization of boundary membrane contact sites from rat-liver mitochondria. *Biochim Biophys Acta* 860:672, 1986.
235. KRAUSE J, HAY R, KOWOLLIK C, BRDICZKA D: Cross-linking analysis of yeast mitochondrial outer membrane. *Biochim Biophys Acta* 860:690, 1986.
236. FELGNER PL, MESSER JL, WILSON JE: Purification of a hexokinase-binding protein from the outer mitochondrial membrane. *J Biol Chem* 254:4944, 1979.
237. LINDEN M, GELLERFORS P, NELSON BD: Pore protein and the hexokinase-binding protein from the outer membrane of rat liver mitochondria are identical. *FEBS Lett* 141:189, 1982.
238. ROOS N, BENZ R, BRDICZKA D: Identification and characterization of the pore forming protein in the outer membrane of rat liver mitochondria. *Biochim Biophys Acta* 686:204, 1982.
239. ROSE IA, WARMS JVB: Mitochondrial hexokinase—Release, rebinding and location. *J Biol Chem* 242:1635, 1967.
240. FELGNER PL: Studies on the physiological raison d'être of mitochondrial hexokinase. *Fed Proc* 32:488, 1973.
241. CHOU AS, WILSON JE: Purification and properties of rat brain hexokinase. *Arch Biochem Biophys* 151:48, 1972.
242. GOTS RE, GORIN FA, BESSMAN SP: Kinetic enhancement of bound hexokinase activity by mitochondrial respiration. *Biochem Biophys Res Commun* 49:1249, 1972.
243. GOTS RE, BESSMAN SP: The functional compartmentation of mitochondrial hexokinase. *Arch Biochem Biophys* 163:7, 1974.
244. BESSMAN SP, BORREBAEK B, GEIGER PJ, BEN-OR S: Mitochondrial creatine kinase and hexokinase—Two examples of compartmentation predicted by the hexokinase mitochondrial binding theory of insulin action, in Srere PA, Estabrook RW (eds): *Microenvironments and Metabolic Compartmentation.* New York, Academic, 1978, p 111.
245. INUI M, ISHIBASHI S: Functioning of the mitochondrial-bound hexokinase in rat brain in accordance with the generation of ATP inside the organelle. *J Biochem* 85:1151, 1979.
246. BESSMAN SP, GEIGER PJ: Compartmentation of hexokinase and creatine phosphokinase, cellular regulation, and insulin action. *Curr Top Cell Regul* 16:55, 1980.
247. SELTZER WK, FIRMINGER H, KLEIN J, PIKE A, FENNESSEY P, McCABE ERB: Adrenal dysfunction in glycerol kinase deficiency. *Biochem Med* 33:189, 1985.
248. TIBBLING G: Glycerol uptake in leukocytes and thrombocytes. *Scand J Clin Lab Invest* 26:185, 1970.
249. OWEN DE, FELIG P, MORGAN AP, WAHREN J, CAHILL GF: Liver and kidney metabolism during prolonged starvation. *J Clin Invest* 48:574, 1969.
250. HARDING JW, PYERITZ EA, COPELAND ES, WHITE HB: Role of glycerol 3-phosphate dehydrogenase in glyceride metabolism. *Biochem J* 146:223, 1975.
251. GILBERT M, RICQUIER D: Glycerol metabolism in the pregnant and virgin rats. *Biol Neonate* 31:36, 1977.
252. CHAVES JM, HERRERA E: In vivo glycerol metabolism in the pregnant rat. *Biol Neonate* 37:172, 1980.
253. JAMES E, MESCHIA G, BATTAGLIA FC: A-V differences of free fatty acids and glycerol in the ovine umbilical circulation. *Proc Soc Exp Biol Med* 138:823, 1971.
254. GILBERT M: Origin and metabolic fate of plasma glycerol in the rat and rabbit fetus. *Pediatr Res* 11:95, 1977.
255. PERSSON B, GENTZ J: The pattern of blood lipids, glycerol and ketone bodies during the neonatal period, infancy and childhood. *Acta Paediatr Scand* 55:353, 1966.
256. MELICHAR V, WOLF H: Postnatal changes in the blood serum content of glycerol and free fatty acids in premature infants—Influence of hypothermia and of respiratory distress. *Biol Neonate* 11:50, 1967.
257. SABATA V, WOLF H, LAUSMANN S: Glycerol levels in the maternal and umbilical cord blood under various conditions. *Biol Neonate* 15:123, 1970.
258. CHRISTENSEN NC: Concentrations of triglycerides, free fatty acids and glycerol in cord blood of newborn infants with a birthweight of ≤2700 grams. *Acta Paediatr Scand* 66:43, 1977.
259. STUBBE P, WOLF H: The effect of stress on growth hormone, glucose and glycerol levels in newborn infants. *Horm Metab Res* 3:175, 1971.
260. PRIBYLOVA H, RYLANDER E: Free fatty acids, glycerol, glucose and β-hydroxybutyrate of plasma of infants protected from cooling and exposed to cold at various times after birth. *Biol Neonate* 20:425, 1972.
261. WAPNIR RA, MANCUSI VJ: Glycerol metabolism in experimental malnutrition during lactation. *Biochem Med* 27:374, 1982.
262. WAPNIR RA, STIEL L: Regulation of gluconeogenesis by glycerol and its phosphorylated derivatives. *Biochem Med* 33:141, 1985.
263. HAHN P, GREENBER R: The development of pyruvate kinase, glycerol kinase and phosphoenolpyruvate carboxykinase activities in liver and adipose tissue of the rat. *Experientia* 24:428, 1968.
264. VERNON RG, WALKER DG: Glycerol metabolism in the neonatal rat. *Biochem J* 118:531, 1970.
265. WARD CJ, WALKER DG: Regulation of enzyme development for glycerol utilization by neonatal rat liver. *Biol Neonate* 23:403, 1973.
266. SEITZ HJ, PORSCHE E, TARNOWSKI W: Glycerol kinase–A regulatory enzyme of gluconeogenesis? *Acta Biol Med Ger* 35:141, 1976.
267. MELICHAR V, RAZOVA M: Glycerokinase in brain and liver of low birthweight newborns. *Acta Paediatr Scand* 65:10, 1976.
268. CHAN AK, THOMPSON EA: Appearance of a second form of hepatic glycerol-3-phosphate dehydrogenase during neonatal development in the mouse. *Arch Biochem Biophys* 207:96, 1981.
269. FRANK MSB, NAHATA MC, HILTY MD: Glycerol: A review of its pharmacology, pharmacokinetics, adverse reactions, and clinical use. *Pharmacotherapy* 1:147, 1981.
270. BAYER AJ, PATHY MS, NEWCOMBE R: Double-blind randomised trial of intravenous glycerol in acute stroke. *Lancet* 1:405, 1987.
271. McKUSICK VA: *Mendelian Inheritance in Man—Catalogs of Autosomal Dominant, Autosomal Recessive, and X-linked Phenotypes,* 7th ed. Baltimore, The Johns Hopkins University Press, 1986.

272. McCABE ERB: Glycerol kinase deficiency, in Buise ML (ed): *Birth Defects Encyclopedia*. New York, AR Liss, 1988, in press.

273. HOFKER MH, BERGEN AAB, SKRAASTAD MI, BAKKER E, FRANCKE U, WIERINGA B, BARTLEY J, VAN OMMEN GJB, PEARSON PL: Isolation of a random cosmid clone, which defines a new polymorphic locus DXS148 near the locus for Duchenne muscular dystrophy. *Hum Genet* 74:275, 1986.

274. MONACO AP, NEVE RL, COLLETTI-FEENER C, BERTELSON CJ, KURNIT DM, KUNKEL LM: Isolation of candidate cDNAs for portions of the Duchenne muscular dystrophy gene. *Nature* 323:646, 1986.

275. KOENIG M, HOFFMAN EP, BERTELSON CJ, MONACO AP, FEENER C, KUNKEL LM: Complete cloning of the Duchenne muscular dystrophy (DMD) cDNA and preliminary genomic organization of the DMD gene in normal and affected individuals. *Cell* 50:509, 1987.

276. YATES JRW, GILLARD EF, COOKE A, COLGAN JM, EVANS TJ, FERGUSON-SMITH MA: A deletion of Xp21 maps congenital adrenal hypoplasia distal to glycerol kinase deficiency. *Cytogenet Cell Genet,* 46:723, 1987.

277. SHOWS TB, McALPINE PJ, BOUCHEIX C, COLLINS FS, CONNEALLY PM, FREZAL J, GERSHOWITZ H, GOODFELLOW PN, HALL JG, ISSITT P, JONES CA, KNOWLES BB, LEWIS M, McKUSICK VA, MEISLER M, MORTON NE, RUBINSTEIN P, SCHANFIELD MS, SCHMICKEL RD, SKOOLNICK MH, SPENCE AM, SUTHERLAND GR, TRAVER M, VAN CONG N, WILLARD HF: Guidelines for human gene nomenclature—An international system for human gene nomenclature (ISGN, 1987). *Cytogenet Cell Genet,* 46:11, 1987.

278. RENIER WO, NABBEN FAE, HUSTINX TWJ, VEERKAMP JH, OTTEN BJ, TER LAAK HJ, TER HAAR BGA, GABREELS FJM. Congenital adrenal hypoplasia, progressive muscular dystrophy, and severe mental retardation, in association with glycerol kinase deficiency, in male sibs. *Clin Genet* 24:243, 1983.

279. WISE JE, MATALON R, MORGAN AM, McCABE ERB: Phenotypic features of patients with congenital adrenal hypoplasia and glycerol kinase deficiency. *Am J Dis Child* 141:744, 1987.

280. KOHLSCHUTTER A, WILLIG HP, SCHLAMP D, KRUSE K, McCABE ERB, SCHAFER HJ, BECKENKAMP G, ROHKAMM R: Infantile glycerol kinase deficiency—A condition requiring prompt identification—Clinical, biochemical, and morphological findings in two cases. *Eur J Pediatr* 146:575, 1987.

281. ZACHMANN M, ILLIG R, PRADER A: Gonadotropin deficiency and cryptorchidism in three prepubertal brothers with congenital adrenal hypoplasia. *J Pediatr* 97:255, 1980.

282. HENSLEIGH PA, MOORE WV, WILSON K, TULCHINSKY D: Congenital X-linked adrenal hypoplasia. *Obstet Gynecol* 52:228, 1978.

283. ERIKSSON A, LINDSTEDT S, RANSNAS L, VON WENDT L: Deficiency of glycerol kinase (EC2.7.1.30). *Clin Chem* 29:718, 1983.

284. POMETTA D, SUENRAM A, VON DER WEID N, WIDMANN JJ: Liver glycerokinase deficiency in man with hyperglycerolaemia and hypertriglyceridaemia. *Eur J Clin Invest* 14:103, 1984.

285. WIRTH A, HEUCK CC, BIEGER W, SCHLIERF G: Pseudo-hypertriglyceridamie bei glycerokinase-mangel. Dtsch Med Wochenschr 110:843, 1985.

286. TOYOFUKU T, TAKASHIMA S, NAGAFUJI H, WATANABE T: An autopsy case of Duchenne type muscular dystrophy with congenital adrenal hypoplasia. *Brain Dev* 3:241, 1981.

287. PETRYKOWSKI WV, BECKMANN R, BOHM N, KETELSEN U-P, ROPERS HH, SAUER M: Adrenal insufficiency, myopathic hypotonia, severe psychomotor retardation, failure to thrive, constipation and bladder ectasia in 2 brothers: Adrenomyodystrophy. *Helv Paediatr Acta* 37:387, 1982.

288. WILLIAMSON R, PATIL S, BARTLEY J, GREENBERG F: Prenatal evaluation for glycerol kinase deficiency (GKD) associated with congenital adrenal hypoplasia. *Am J Hum Genet* 36:200S, 1984.

289. MOSER H: Duchenne muscular dystrophy: Pathogenetic aspects and genetic prevention. *Hum Genet* 66:17, 1984.

290. HOFFMAN EP, BROWN RH, KUNKEL LM: Dystrophin: The protein product of the Duchenne muscular dystrophy locus. *Cell* 51:919, 1987.

291. CHAMBERLAIN JS, PEARLMAN JA, MUZNY DM, GIBBS RA, RANIER JE, REEVES AA, CASKEY CT: Expression of the murine Duchenne muscular dystrophy gene in muscle and brain. *Science* 239:1416, 1988.

292. KARAHASANOGLU AM, TILDON JT, OZAND PT, MacLAREN NK: Glycerol-induced changes in human serum dopamine beta-hydroxylase activity. *Biochem Pharmacol* 27:2369, 1978.

293. WAPNIR RA, LIFSHITZ F, SEKARAN C, TEICHBERG S, MOAK SA: Glycerol-induced hypoglycemia: A syndrome associated with multiple liver enzyme deficiencies. Clinical and in vitro studies. *Metabolism* 31:1057, 1982.

294. FORT P, WAPNIR RA, DE ROSAS F, LIFSHITZ F: Long-term evolution of glycerol intolerance syndrome. *J Pediatr* 106:453, 1985.

PART 6

PURINES AND PYRIMIDINES

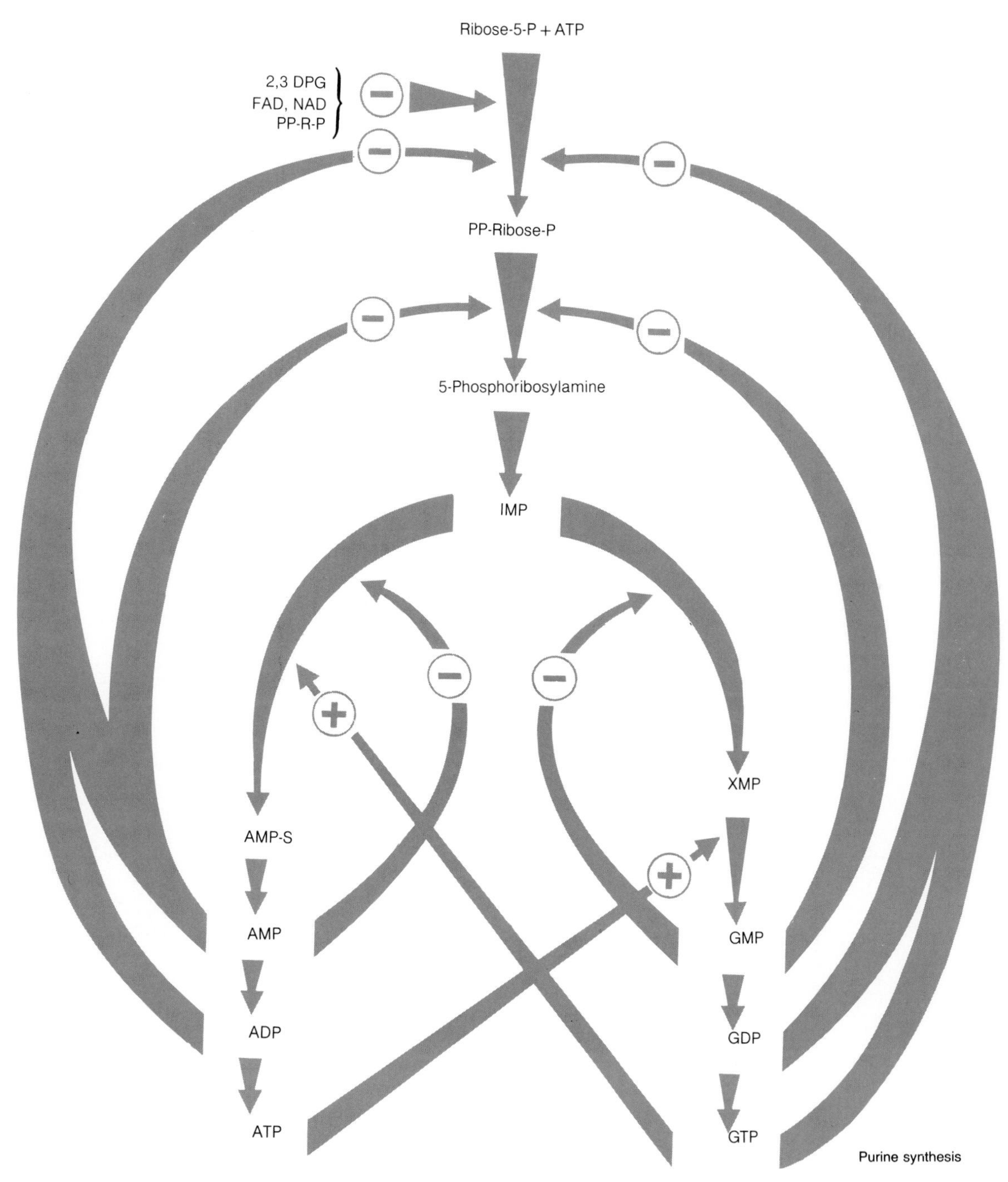

Purine synthesis

CHAPTER 37

HYPERURICEMIA AND GOUT

THOMAS D. PALELLA
IRVING H. FOX

1. Gout is a clinical syndrome characterized by hyperuricemia, recurrent attacks of acute arthritis, and, in some cases, tophaceous deposits of monosodium urate. The arthritis may progress to a chronic, debilitating form. Nephropathy is common in gout. In some instances it may represent a complication of gout although more commonly it is due to comorbid causes. Uric acid nephrolithiasis also occurs frequently and may precede gouty arthritis.

2. Hyperuricemia may be defined on either a physicochemical basis or on the basis of statistical distributions of serum urate values in a population. Different methods of urate measurement yield different results. The uricase method is considered superior to the phosphotungstic acid method, which may overestimate true plasma urate levels by 0.4 to 1.0 mg/dl. The limit of solubility of monosodium urate in extracellular fluid is 7.0 mg/dl (uricase method) at 37°C. Thus, in a physicochemical sense, hyperuricemia exists when serum concentrations of urate exceed this value. Hyperuricemia defined on a statistical basis exists when serum urate levels exceed the mean plus two standard deviations in healthy age- and sex-matched populations. Using this definition, hyperuricemia is present in men when the serum urate level exceeds 7.0 mg/dl and in women when it is greater than 6.0 mg/dl. Also, serum urate concentrations in excess of 7.0 mg/dl carry increased risk of gouty arthritis or renal stones.

3. There is considerable variability of plasma urate values among various population samples. Serum urate also varies with age, sex, body weight, and surface area. The prevalence of gout and nephrolithiasis correlates strongly with the height of the mean serum urate concentration.

4. Acute gout is triggered by crystals of monosodium urate which initiate an inflammatory response. Serum or synovial fluid supersaturated with monosodium urate is a necessary but not sufficient precondition for developing acute gout. A variety of other factors participate in the regulation of the deposition of monosodium urate in human tissue. Inflammatory mediators, such as complement components and interleukin 1, participate in producing the typical clinical picture.

5. Uric acid is the ultimate degradative product of purine metabolism in humans. Human purine metabolism is a complex series of biochemical pathways which may be conveniently compartmentalized. The synthesis of the purine ring from nonpurine precursors is referred to as "de novo *purine synthesis." This pathway results in the formation of inosinic acid, the parent purine compound. Preformed purine bases from the diet or from endogenous catabolism may be reutilized through the salvage pathways. Inosinic acid is converted to other purines via the nucleotide interconversion pathways. Finally, purines are catabolized to uric acid by a series of reactions referred to as "the degradative pathway." These interrelated pathways are regulated at several levels.*

6. The majority of uric acid is excreted by the kidneys. Under normal conditions, only trace amounts of purine and oxypurine bases and nucleosides are present in the urine. Approximately one-third of the daily production of uric acid is eliminated through the gut, where uricolysis by intestinal microorganisms occurs. Extrarenal disposition of uric acid is increased in renal failure and often in gouty subjects with normal renal function.

7. The serum urate concentration is a function of both synthetic and degradative rates. Thus, hyperuricemia may occur on the basis of either overproduction or underexcretion of uric acid. Either of these mechanisms may be primary or the secondary result of a concurrent condition. Excessive dietary intake of purines is a rare cause of hyperuricemia.

8. Primary gout is a form of the disease that is attributable to an inborn error of metabolism. The category is biochemically and genetically heterogeneous. The largest subgroup consists of patients in whom the biochemical defect is as yet undefined but pedigree analysis suggests an inherited cause. Many patients in this group can be shown to produce uric acid excessively, when studied by techniques for assessment of turnover of uric acid or of rate of incorporation of labeled precursors into uric acid. In many subjects there is a reduction in fractional renal urate clearance. In addition to genetic factors, dietary excesses and alcohol ingestion often appear to be important.

9. Reduction of fractional renal urate clearance is most readily demonstrable in gouty patients when serum urate concentration values are artificially raised. The defect is most prominent in those patients with normal 24-h urinary uric acid excretion values. Some patients appear to exhibit this defect as the major or even the sole basis of hyperuricemia. This defect is present in many overproducers of uric acid, although not in patients with hypoxanthine-guanine phosphoribosyltransferase (HPRT) deficiency, or with overactive variants of 5-phosphoribosyl-1-pyrophosphate (PP-ribose-P) synthetase.

10. Three distinct genetically determined enzymatic defects have been defined that lead to marked hyperuricemia at an early age. These are glucose-6-phosphatase deficiency (von Gierke glycogen storage disease), hyoxanthine-guanine phosphoribosyltransferase deficiency (complete and partial), and phosphoribosylpyrophosphate synthetase variants with increased catalytic activity. In the last two of these, markedly excessive production of purines appears to result from elevated intracellular levels of PP-ribose-P, a key substrate of the initial reaction of the purine pathway.

11. In population studies hyperuricemia appears to be multifacto-

Nonstandard abbreviations used in this chapter are: AMP-S = adenylosuccinic acid; APRT = adenine phosphoribosyltransferase; 2,3-DPG = 2,3-diphosphoglycerate; HPRT = hypoxanthine-guanine phosphoribosyltransferase; IMP = inosinic acid; PP-ribose-P = 5-phosphoribosyl-1-pyrophosphate; THFA = tetrahydrofolic acid; XMP = xanthosine 5′-monophosphate; ZMP = 5-amino-4-imidazolecarboxamide 5′-monophosphate.

rial and attributable to a combination of genetic and nongenetic factors. Genetic factors may include both cumulative gene action and single-gene effects. In studies of families or isolates the latter sometimes suggest autosomal dominant factors, sometimes sex-linked factors. Known enzymatic abnormalities associated with hyperuricemia are of several genetic types. HPRT deficiency and PP-ribose-P synthetase superactivity are X-linked. Glucose-6-phosphatase deficiency is an autosomal recessive trait.

12. *Specific therapy is available to treat gout. Anti-inflammatory therapy is used to treat the acute attack or to prevent it. Antihyperuricemic therapy is given to lower the serum urate level into the normal range. Increased renal excretion of uric acid is induced with uricosuric drugs. Decreased production of uric acid is achieved with allopurinol by its inhibition of xanthine oxidase.*

Gout is a disease that represents a triumph of medical research. Potent treatments have been developed since 1950 which dramatically modify the natural history of the disease.

Prior to 1950 gout was a major problem for which there was no effective therapy. In fact, this disease has received considerable attention for over 2000 years.[1] Gout has afflicted the rich and famous[2] as well as the poor and obscure, and may be responsible for modifying the course of history.[3] The modern era of the history of gout began with Thomas Sydenham's description of his own disease during the 1600s.[1] During the next two centuries the chemical basis of gout, urate in tophi and blood and uric acid in kidney stones, was elucidated. Development of standard methods of measurement of uric acid, the elucidation of purine biochemistry, the discovery of inborn errors of metabolism leading to gout, and the development of effective therapies to reduce the serum urate concentration constitute the major advances in the conquest of gout.

Knowledge of the regulation of purine biochemistry gained through the intensive studies of the metabolic basis of gout has been important. For example, the discovery of hypoxanthine-guanine phosphoribosyltransferase deficiency as an inherited form of gout[4,5] has provided an important model for the study of inborn errors in metabolism. The 20 years from the clinical description of the Lesch-Nyhan syndrome[1] and the initial elucidation of its enzymatic basis[6] to the definition of its molecular basis at the level of DNA[7] witnessed major accomplishments. These spectacular advances notwithstanding, the metabolic basis for gout in the majority of patients remains unclear.

Definitions

Gout may be defined as a heterogenous group of diseases found exclusively in man, which in their full development are manifest by (a) an increase in the serum urate concentration; (b) recurrent attacks of a characteristic type of acute arthritis, in which crystals of monosodium urate monohydrate are demonstrable in leukocytes of synovial fluid; (c) aggregated deposits of monosodium urate monohydrate (tophi) occurring chiefly in and around the joints of the extremities and sometimes leading to severe crippling and deformity; (d) renal disease involving glomerular, tubular, and interstitial tissues and blood vessels; and (e) uric acid urolithiasis. These manifestations can occur in different combinations. (*Wyngaarden and Kelley.*[8])

Hyperuricemia must be distinguished from *gout.* While only a minority of hyperuricemic patients ever become gouty, all patients with gout have hyperuricemia at some stage in their clinical course. In one study only 12 percent of 200 hyperuricemic patients developed gout.[9]

Confusion regarding the definition of hyperuricemia is the result of different methods used for the measurement of serum urate.[1] In general, automated analyzers give more reproducible results than do manual methods. The phosphotungstic acid method is less specific, is interfered with by other reducing substances in the plasma, and overestimates the true plasma urate levels by 0.4 to 1.0 mg/dl as compared to the uricase differential spectrophotometric method. The latter is considered the method of choice for research determinations.

Using the uricase differential spectrophotometric method, the serum urate value is theoretically elevated when it exceeds 7.0mg/dl, the limit of solubility of monosodium urate in serum at 37°C. Epidemiologically, an elevated serum urate concentration is defined as a value exceeding the upper limit of the mean serum urate value plus two standard deviations in a healthy sex- and age-matched population. In most studies, the upper limit has been rounded off at 7.0 mg/dl in men and 6.0 mg/dl in women. Furthermore, a serum urate value in excess of 7.0 mg/dl confers an increased risk of gouty arthritis or renal stones. When methods are used for measuring uric acid that are not specific for urate, the upper limit of normal is higher than 7.0 mg/dl.[1]

Epidemiology

The serum urate concentration varies with age and sex (Fig. 37-1).[10] Children of both sexes normally have a serum urate concentration of 3 to 4 mg/dl. At puberty, males exhibit a further elevation in the serum urate concentration of 1 to 2 mg/dl, which is generally sustained throughout life, while females exhibit little, if any, change in the serum urate concentration at this time. At the menopause, serum urate concentrations in women rise and approach the values for adult males. More recent large population studies have confirmed the influence of age and sex upon urate concentrations which are normally distributed among both males and females.[11–13] Mean urate levels of adult male volunteers in a longitudinal study of human aging rose steadily during a 17-year period.[14]

A number of factors contribute to the serum urate level. The mechanism of the lower serum urate levels in females as compared to males is related to a higher fractional excretion of urate secondary to lower tubular urate postsecretory reabsorption[15] (see Chap. 106). Although changes in plasma 17β-estradiol do not modify this,[15] increases in testosterone/estradiol ratios are associated with hyperuricemia.[16] Ethnic variations also influence serum urate concentration. For example, indigenous Pacific island inhabitants have a significantly higher mean serum urate level[1,13] than do other populations. Studies have also implicated anthropometric and social factors, including high levels of academic achievement. Physiological determinants of serum urate levels during adolescence include sexual and skeletal maturation in early stages and body composition (skin-fold thickness and body mass index), blood pressure, and hematocrit in later stages.[12] In adults, serum urate levels correlate strongly with serum creatinine, body weight or body mass index, height, age, urea nitrogen, blood pressure, and alcohol intake[13,17–19] and less strongly with serum calcium, SGOT, serum magnesium, and serum cholesterol.[13] Variation of the degree of urate binding

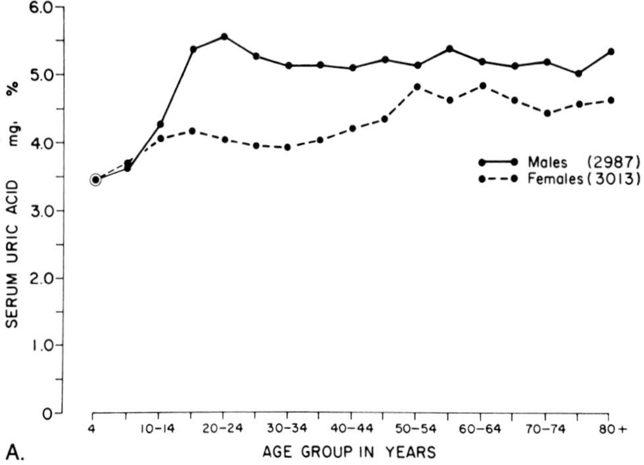

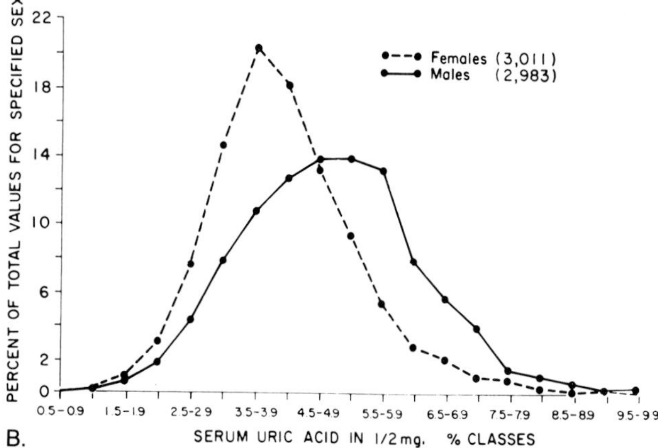

Fig. 37-1 Serum urate levels in a population. *A.* The distribution of serum urate values in Tecumseh, 1959–1960, is indicated. *B.* The influence of age and sex on the mean serum urate concentration in Tecumseh, 1959–1960. *(From Mikkelson et al.*[10] *By permission of* American Journal of Medicine.)

to plasma proteins is no longer considered a significant determinant of plasma urate level or the predisposition toward gout.[1]

The annual incidence of gout varies from 0.20 to 0.35 per 1000, with an overall prevalence of 2 to 2.6 per 1000.[19–21] The prevalence increases with age and serum urate concentration.[18,19] For example, the prevalence is 15 per 1000 in males in the 35-to-44 age range.[18] The annual incidence rate of gout is 4.9 percent for urate levels greater than 9 mg/dl, 0.5 percent for 7.0 to 8.9 mg/dl, and 0.1 percent for less than 7.0 mg/dl.[22] For serum urate values greater than 9 mg/dl, the cumulative incidence of gout reaches 22 percent after 5 years[22] (Fig. 37-2).

CLINICAL DESCRIPTION

Symptomatic hyperuricemia includes acute gouty arthritis, chronic gout, and renal disease. These complications of hyperuricemia result from the precipitation of uric acid in body fluids and tissues, the occurrence of which depends upon the physical properties of uric acid. Uric acid is a trioxypurine with oxygen at positions 2, 6, and 8 of the purine ring (Fig. 37-3). It is a weak acid, ionized at position 9 with a p*K*a of 5.75 and at position 3 with a p*K*a of 10.3. The degree of ionization of uric acid is related to pH by the Henderson-Hasselbalch equation. Thus, at pH 5.75, 50 percent of the uric acid is ionized as urate and 50 percent is nonionized as the free acid. At pH 4.75, 91 percent of uric acid is nonionized, whereas at pH 6.75, 91 percent is ionized. In plasma at pH 7.4, uric acid is 98 percent ionized as urate. Therefore, pH determines the form of uric acid which is deposited.

In body tissues at physiological pH, sodium urate is deposited, whereas in urine, which generally has a lower pH, uric acid is precipitated. Sodium concentration also influences solubility. According to the solubility law for univalent salts, the concentration of anion in a saturated solution varies inversely with cation concentration. For estimations of solubility, the concentration of sodium in serum is approximately 140 meq/liter, whereas in urine the sodium concentration is assumed to be that of the urate anion. The theoretical solubility limit in serum therefore is 6.4 mg/dl, which is considerably less than the solubility of urate in urine at the same pH; on the other hand, urine is saturated with uric acid at concentrations of 15 mg/dl at pH 5.0, 22 mg/dl at pH 6.0, 158 to 200 mg/dl at pH 7.0, and 1520 mg/dl at pH 8.0.[23]

The most common complication of hyperuricemia is the development of gouty arthritis. Gout usually passes through four states: asymptomatic hyperuricemia, acute gouty arthritis, intercritical gout, and chronic tophaceous gout. The phase of asymptomatic hyperuicemia ends with the first attack of gouty

Fig. 37-2 Cumulative incidence of gouty arthritis by prior urate levels. The numbers (n) refer to the number of examination intervals for each group. *(From Campion et al.*[22] *By Permission of* American Journal of Medicine.)

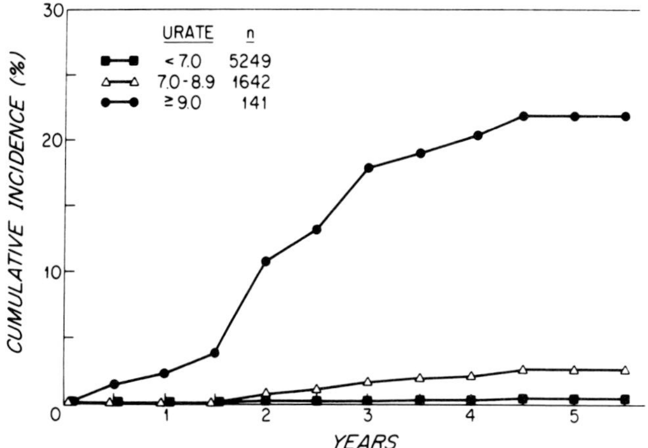

Fig. 37-3 Ionization of uric acid. The weakly acidic nature of uric acid is due to ionization of hydrogen atoms. Ionization at position 9 (pK_a = 5.75) is shown above. The ionized forms of uric acid readily form salts. In extracellular fluids in which sodium is the principal cation, about 98 percent of uric acid is in the form of the monosodium salt at pH 7.4. The crystals, which form in the synovial fluid or the tophi of gouty patients when solubility limits are exceeded, are composed of monosodium urate monohydrate.

pK_a=5.75
H^+

URIC ACID

URATE ION

arthritis or urolithiasis. While only a minority of patients with hyperuricemia will ever develop gout, in most instances when gout does develop, it is after 20 to 30 years of sustained hyperuricemia.[1]

Acute Gout

The pattern of clinical gout is one of acute attacks of exquisitely painful arthritis. Initially, arthritis is monoarticular and associated with few constitutional symptoms. Later, the attacks tend to be polyarticular and fever is common. Each episode lasts a variable, but limited, period of time. Between episodes, there are intervals of complete freedom from symptoms. Attacks eventually recur at shorter intervals and resolve incompletely. The peak age of onset of acute gouty arthritis is between the fourth and sixth decades.[1] There is a marked predominance for males with a peak age of onset at 50 years.

In 85 to 90 percent of first attacks a single joint will be involved. In most patients, the initial attack of gout occurs acutely during apparent excellent health. In at least one-half of initial acute attacks the first metatarsophalangeal joint will be the site of the paroxysm (podagra). Ninety percent of gouty patients experience acute attacks in the great toe at some time during the course of their disease. Next in order of frequency as sites of initial involvement are the insteps, ankles, heels, knees, wrists, fingers, and elbows. Commonly the first attack begins at night. Within a few hours the affected joint becomes hot, dusky red, and extremely tender and may progress to resemble a bacterial cellulitis. Systemic signs of inflammation may include leukocytosis, fever, and elevation of the erythrocyte sedimentation rate.

Sydenham[24] gave the classic description of the acute attack:

> The victim goes to bed and sleeps in good health. About two o'clock in the morning he is awakened by a severe pain in the great toe; more rarely in the heel, ankle, or instep. This pain is like that of a dislocation, and yet the parts feel as if cold water were poured over them. Then follow chills and shivers and a little fever. The pain, which was at first moderate, becomes more intense. With its intensity the chills and shivers increase. After a time this comes to its full height, accommodating itself to the bones and ligaments of the tarsus and metatarsus. Now it is a violent stretching and tearing of the ligaments—now it is a gnawing pain—and now a pressure and tightening. So exquisite and lively meanwhile is the feeling of the part affected, that it cannot bear the weight of bedclothes nor the jar of a person walking in the room. The night is passed in torture, sleeplessness, turning of the part affected, and perpetual change of posture; the tossing about of the body being as incessant as the pain of the tortured joint, and being worse as the fit comes on. Hence the vain effort by change of posture, both in the body and the limb affected, to obtain an abatement of the pain.

The course of untreated acute gout is highly variable. Mild attacks may subside in several hours or persist for only a day or two. Several attacks may last days to weeks. Resolution is usually complete, and the patient is once again perfectly well.

Acute gouty arthritis is best diagnosed by examining synovial fluid from the acutely inflamed joint for monosodium urate crystals in polymorphonuclear leukocytes under a polarizing microscope with first-order red compensator. The crystals are negatively birefringent and appear yellow when oriented parallel to the axis of the compensator and blue when oriented perpendicular to it. The crystals appear needlelike with blunted ends. Several arthritic diseases can have a clinical onset similar to acute gout. These include infection, pyrophosphate arthropathy, seronegative arthritis, trauma, and others. Thus, identification of urate crystals is critical.[25]

There are a number of less common presentations of acute gout. Although acute gout is classically monoarticular, polyarticular gout occurs and may be especially confusing since some patients are normouricemic on presentation.[26–28] These patients usually have a past history of acute gout, tophi, and involvement of joints in the lower extremities. Gout may also occur in Heberden nodes and erosive osteoarthritis and be easily overlooked.[29,30] The simultaneous occurrence of gout and septic arthritis can be clinically confusing, with the former masking the latter.[31–33] Finally, hyperuricemia and gout occur frequently in Paget disease[34] and uncommonly in Down syndrome.[35]

Drugs may precipitate acute gout by either increasing or decreasing serum urate levels acutely. The occurrence of gout following the initiation of antihyperuricemic therapy is well-established. Drug-induced gout secondary to increased serum urate levels occurs in association with diuretic therapy, intravenous heparin, and cyclosporin.[36–40] Diuretic therapy in the elderly appears to be a particularly important precipitating factor for gouty arthritis.[36,38,40,41] A goutlike arthritis has been reported following cimetidine and ranitidine therapy.[42,43]

Acute gout is the prototype for crystal-induced synovitis[1,44] (Fig. 37-4). Serum or synovial fluid supersaturated with monosodium urate is a necessary, but not sufficient, precondition for the development of acute gouty arthritis. Additional factors may regulate the deposition of urate in human tissues. These include lower intra-articular temperature, the presence of proteoglycans, changes in pH, trauma, aging, and disequilibrium resulting from extracellular fluid reabsorption from a joint space at a faster rate than urate.

There have been a number of recent advances in the understanding of urate-related crystal-induced synovitis. An important role for the complement system in this process has been suggested by the monosodium urate–mediated C-reactive protein–dependent or IgG-dependent depletion of complement from plasma.[45–47] In excess of 30 crystal-associated polypeptides have been identified including Clq, Clr, Cls, fibronectin, fibrinogen, IgG, lysosomal enzymes, and apolipoproteins.[45,48–50] Crystal-bound apolipoprotein B inhibits synovitis by blocking phagocytosis, superoxide generation, and neutrophil cytolysis.[49,50] These properties of lipoproteins may be related to inhibition of the physical association of crystals with cell membranes. The latter may explain why crystals occur in asymptomatic joints (see below).

The neutrophil remains the central focus of crystal-induced synovitis, although a role has been proposed for platelet mediators as well. The neutrophil is attracted by a crystal-induced chemotactic factor, which is degraded after binding to its specific receptor.[51] There is no correlation between crystal size, shape, or number and the intensity of inflammation.[52] Protein-coated crystals of sodium urate are taken up within the phagosomes of polymorphs and merge with lysosomes. Crystals bind to the lysosomal membrane which subsequently lyses. Monosodium urate crystals have a high negative surface potential and the crystal-membrane interaction is probably electrostatic.[53–55] Crystals stimulate oxygen radical formation by neutrophils.[47,48,56,57] The release of lysosomal mediators together with release of superoxide anion augments the local inflammatory response. The stimulation of oxygen radical for-

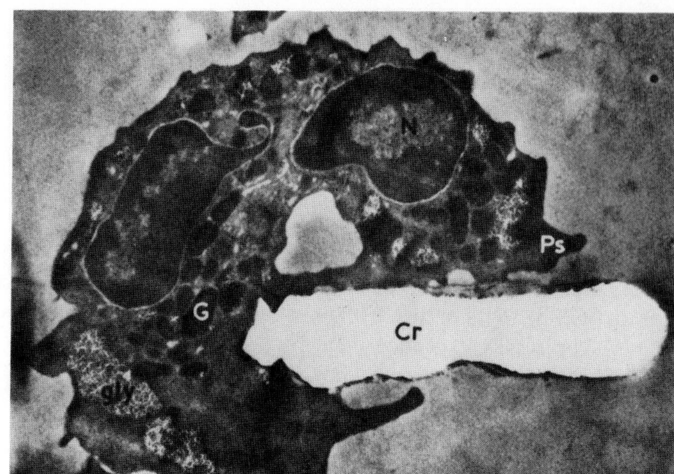

Fig. 37-4 Polymorphonuclear leukocyte ingesting a urate crystal (Cr). The pseudopodia (Ps) appear to be holding the crystal. Note that the cytoplasm is devoid of granules. N = nucleus; G = granule; gly = glycogen. × = 11,700. *(From Rajan et al.*[576] *By permission of* Annals of Rheumatic Disease.)

mation is inhibited by supernatants of polymorphonuclear leukocytes exposed to monosodium urate crystals.[57] Since polymorphonuclear leukocyte lysis occurs during crystal-induced synovitis, this provides one explanation for the self-limitation of acute gouty attacks.

Other factors released from polymorphonuclear leukocytes mediate urate-induced inflammation. They include leukotriene B_4, kinins, latent collagenase, kallikrein, prostaglandin E_2, and 6-keto-prostaglandin$F_1\alpha$ and interleukin 1.[58–62] The metabolism and deactivation of leukotriene B_4, an important mediator of local inflammation, are partially inhibited by monosodium urate crystals, thus potentiating its activity.[58] Hageman factor (factor XII) is not essential for the development of crystal-induced synovitis, since gout occurs in the setting of deficiency of this factor.[63] The interaction of urate crystals with mononuclear phagocytes stimulates the production of interleukin 1, the peptide mediator of fever and other features of inflammation.[62] The dissemination of this hormonelike substance accounts for many of the systemic effects of acute gouty arthritis, including fever, peripheral neutrophilia, acute-phase reactants, and polyarticular inflammation (Fig. 37-5).

Interval Gout

Typically, symptoms remit completely between attacks. The intervals between gouty attacks are called *intercritical periods.* Most patients experience a second attack within 6 months to 2 years of their first. If untreated, the attacks increase in frequency. The patient later may be febrile, and the arthritis becomes polyarticular.

The diagnosis of gout in a hyperuricemic patient with a past history of acute attacks of monoarthritis may be difficult or inconclusive during the intercritical phase. Aspiration of an asymptomatic metatarsophalangeal joint or knee joint may demonstrate extracellular urate crystals.[64–68] Joint fluid obtained from gouty patients during the intercritical phase revealed monosodium urate crystals in 12.5 to 58 percent of knees and in 52 percent of metatarsophalangeal joints.[67,68] In renal failure this test is limited by false-positive results. Postmortem detection of crystals in 4 to 18 percent of synovial fluids obtained from first metatarsophalangeal joints remains difficult to explain, there being no significant association with antecedent gouty arthritis.[69,70]

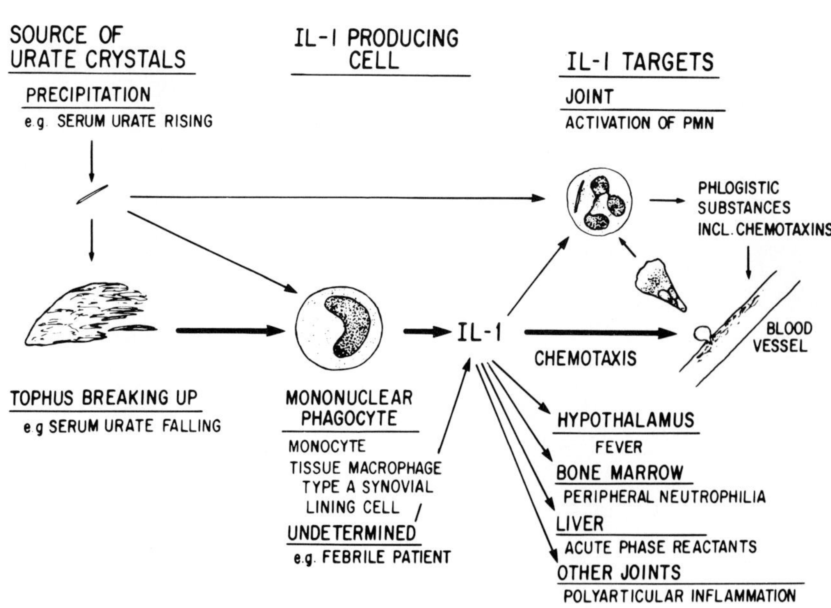

Fig. 37-5 Role of interleukin (IL-1) 1 in acute gouty arthritis. The diagram shows how the interaction of urate crystals with mononuclear phagocytes may initiate and help to propagate the more familiar interaction of crystals with polymorphonuclear leukocytes (PMN) that characterizes gouty inflammation. Sufficient dissemination of interleukin 1 may also account for such generalized manifestations of the inflammatory response as fever, peripheral neutrophilia, acute-phase reactants, and polyarticular inflammation. Since IL-1 is chemotactic for PMN, PMN are not essential for the initiation of inflammation; urate crystals and resident mononuclear phagocytes may suffice *(thick arrows).* A tophus breaking up may be an especially strong stimulus to IL-1 production. *(From Malawista et al.*[62] *By permission of* Arthritis and Rheumatism.)

Chronic Gout

After many years, a third stage of chronic arthritis occurs. Deposit of monosodium urate around joints increases, bony erosion occurs, and joint destruction with chronic joint swelling and pain results. This process progresses slowly to a crippling disease in which acute exacerbations decrease in frequency and severity.

Chronic tophaceous gout develops after a period of chronic gout. Before the development of effective anithyperuricemic therapy, visible tophi occurred after an average of 12 years of gout. A chronically expanded urate pool leads to crystalline deposits of urate in cartilage, synovial membranes, tendons, and soft tissues. Tophi may be located in the helix of the ear, in fingers, hands, knees, feet, on the ulnar surface of the forearm, or in the olecranon bursa[1,44] (Figs. 37-6 and 37-7). Unusual locations of tophi include heart valves,[71–74] eyes,[75,76] spine, with neurologic disorders,[77–81] and peripheal nerves, with entrapment.[82–84] Eventually, grotesque deformation of the hands and feet leads to crippling.[1]

The overall incidence of tophaceous gout has declined to as low as 3 percent of affected patients,[85] but in one recent study 35 percent of male veterans had tophi upon physical examination.[86] This group was characterized by an early age of onset (40.5 years), long duration of disease (18.7 years), four attacks per year, mean urate value of 9.2 mg/dl, and a high frequency (71 percent) of polyarticular episodes. Tophi generally develop only in long-standing gout, but rarely they develop without a preceding history of acute gouty arthritis.[87] Elderly patients with impaired renal function receiving anti-inflammatory and urate-retaining drugs are also at high risk for tophaceous gout.

Radiologic Changes

Soft tissue swelling, osteopenia, and aseptic necrosis occur as nonspecific radiographic manifestations early in the disease. With long standing disease, tophi accumulate and lead to nodulated soft tissue densities in the feet, hands, elbows, ankles, and knees. Bony erosions are common in chronic gout, occur in association with tophi, and have a round or oval shape, sclerotic border, punched-out appearance, and an overhanging edge of bone (Fig. 37-8). Erosions occur most often and characteristically in the first metatarsophalangeal joint.[44]

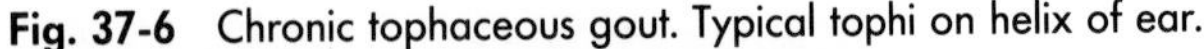

Fig. 37-6 Chronic tophaceous gout. Typical tophi on helix of ear.

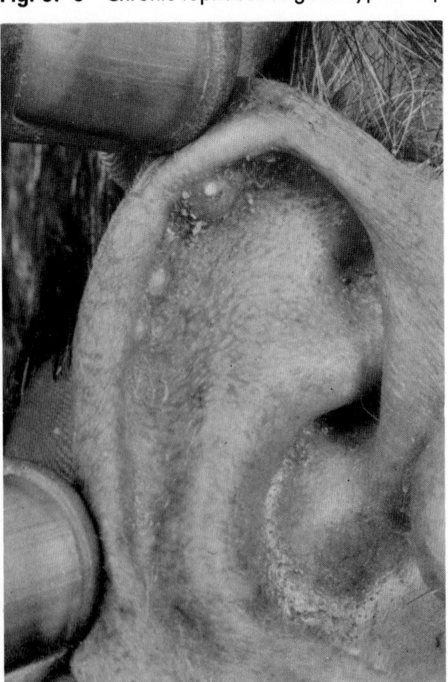

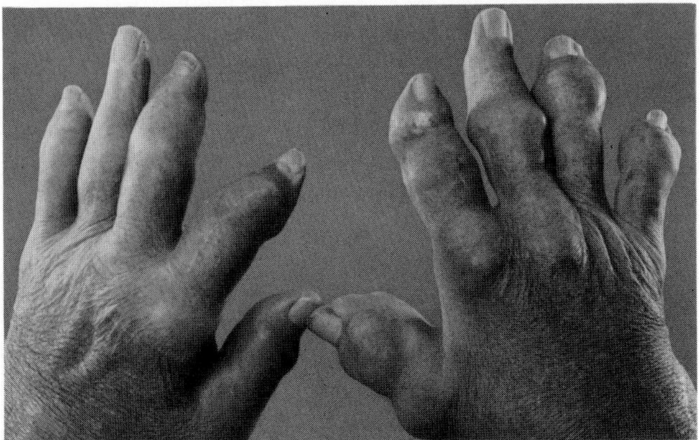

Fig. 37-7 Chronic tophaceous gout. Deformities of the hands are related to tophaceous deposits.

Renal Disease

Renal disease is the second most frequent complication of hyperuricemia. Several types of renal disease occur. The first, urate nephropathy, is attributed to the deposition of monosodium urate crystals in the renal interstitial tissue and is thought to be associated with chronic hyperuricemia. In contrast, uric acid nephropathy is caused by elevated concentrations of uric acid in the urine and appears clinically as either acute uric acid nephropathy or uric acid calculi. This class of renal disease results from formation of uric acid crystals in the collecting tubules, pelvis, or ureter with subsequent impairment of urine flow. In addition, calcium oxalate nephrolithia-

Fig. 37-8 Chronic tophaceous gout. X-ray of hand shows evidence of a tophus and erosions.

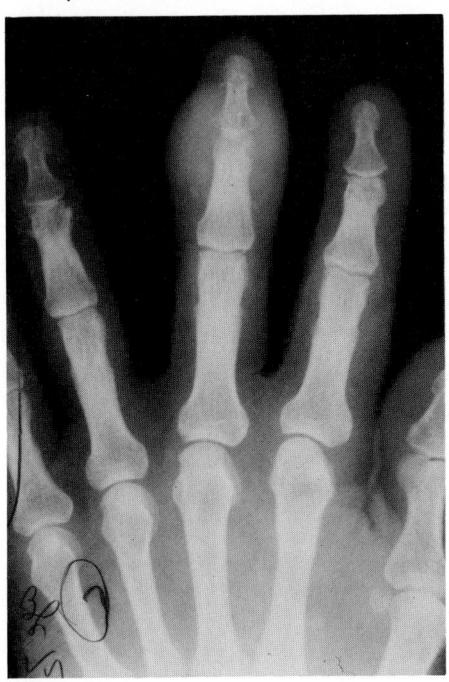

sis occurs more commonly in patients with hyperuricemia or gout than in normouricemic subjects.

Urate Nephropathy. Although urate nephropathy appears to be a distinct entity, it is not believed to be an important contributor to declining renal function in the majority of patients with gout. The deposition of urate crystals in the interstititum of the medulla and pyramids with a surrounding giant cell reaction is a distinctive histologic characteristic of the gouty kidney. Some 20 to 40 percent of patients with gout have albuminuria, which is usually mild and often intermittent. The inability to generate a maximally concentrated urine, is one of the earliest manifestations of urate nephropathy and occurs before any change in the serum creatinine concentration. Although up to one-third of patients with gout are hypertensive, a number of abnormalities in renal function—such as reduced glomerular filtration rate, proteinuria, and reduced renal concentrating ability—are observed in gouty patients even when hypertensive patients are eliminated from the study population.[1,44]

Renal failure now accounts for 10 percent of deaths of gouty patients.[1,44] Although it is clear that renal disease is associated with gout, it is not evident to what extent this is related to hyperuricemia alone and the associated deposition of monosodium urate in the renal tissue. Indeed, most available evidence suggests that moderate hyperuricemia per se has little, if any, harmful effect on renal function.[88–92] Other factors, such as coexistent hypertension, chronic lead exposure, ischemic heart disease, or primary preexistent renal insufficiency may be more important than urate in the pathogenesis of the lesion previously considered to be "urate nephropathy."[91–96] Although increasing age does lead to deterioration of renal function in both gouty and control populations,[89–92] this phenomenon is accentuated in gouty subjects,[89] especially in the presence of hypertension, ischemic heart disease, or preexistent renal disease.[92] On the other hand, extreme hyperuricemia, serum urate concentrations in excess of 13 mg/dl in men or 10 mg/dl in women, may be implicated in the etiology of renal damage.[88] These extremes of hyperuricemia typically result from inherited enzyme deficiencies which cause urate overproduction, fulminating gout, and blood dyscrasias with oliguria and urolithiasis.[92] Indeed, the gouty kidney, as described by Garrod,[95] is a rarity at the present time.

More recently, the relationship between gout and monosodium urate deposition in the kidney has been questioned. Two studies have documented a substantial incidence of renal urate deposition not associated with clinical gout.[1] In one study, 17 of 62 patients dying of renal insufficiency had renal medullary tophi, which were attributed to the hyperuricemia of chronic renal insufficiency. Only four of these patients had ever experienced attacks of articular gout. In another study, medullary microtophi were found in 8 percent of unselected subjects at autopsy. While these deposits were most frequently associated with a history of gout or the presence of preexisting nongouty renal disease, in 26 percent of patients no etiology was evident. Both studies suggest that in some instances urate deposition in the renal medulla may be a consequence rather than the direct cause of renal failure. Factors other than hyperuricemia clearly contribute to renal deposition, although the precise nature is unclear at present.

Foley and Weinman[96] have concluded from these data that chronic hyperuricemia rarely leads to significant renal disease and that urate nephropathy is therefore not a distinct clinical entity. They suggest that administration of anti-inflammatory drugs in gouty arthritis leads to deterioration of renal function and thus exacerbates existing renal disease.

Acute Uric Acid Nephropathy. Acute renal failure may also result from precipitation of uric acid crystals in the collecting ducts and ureters.[44] This syndrome, the *acute tumor lysis syndrome*, has been defined as hyperuricemia, lactic acidosis, hyperkalemia, hyperphosphatemia, and hypocalcemia and occurs in aggressive, rapidly proliferating tumors, including lymphoproliferative disorders and metastic medulloblastoma.[97–100] This complication commonly results from rapid turnover of malignant cells, often during chemotherapy. Massive amounts of nucleic acids and nucleotides liberated during cytolysis are rapidly converted to uric acid. Marked hyperphosphatemia contributes to this syndrome by phosphate precipitation.[97] Acute or chronic renal failure may also result from uric acid overproduction due to an enzymopathy such as hypoxanthine-guanine phosphoribosyltransferase deficiency.[101]

The pathogenesis of acute renal failure in uric acid nephropathy is related to the precipitation of uric acid in the distal tubules and collecting ducts, which are the sites of maximal acidification and concentration of the urine. Typically, hyperuricemia is marked, with a mean serum urate level of 20 mg/dl (range: 12 to 36 mg/dl). Oliguria or even anuria, as well as azotemia, occur. Gravel or sand is often noted in the urine. The ratio of uric acid to creatinine in the urine of these patients typically exceeds 1.0, whereas in patients with other causes of acute renal failure, it is 0.4 ± 0.3.[44] Urinary uric acid/creatinine ratios exceed unity in hypercatabolic and hyperbilirubinemic states with lower serum urate levels (11.0 ± 0.9 mg/dl).[102]

Renal Calculi. Uric acid calculi account for approximately 10 percent of all stones in patients in the United States and range from as low as 5 percent in some countries to 40 percent in countries such as Israel and Australia.[1,44] Renal stones occur in 10 to 25 percent of patients with primary gout, a prevalence more than 1000 times greater than that in the general population. The likelihood of stones in a given patient with gout increases with the serum urate concentration and with urinary uric acid excretion. It reaches 50 percent with a serum urate value of 13 mg/dl or above or with urinary uric acid excretion rates in excess of 1100 mg/dl. The risk for the development of urolithiasis in established gouty arthritis is about 1 percent per year and in asymptomatic hyperuricemia is about 0.27 percent per year.[88]

Although renal calculi are uncommon in gout secondary to lead nephropathy, the incidence of renal calculi in other patients with secondary gout may be as high as 42 percent. In this setting, urolithiasis tends to occur after vigorous cytolytic therapy. The high incidence of uric acid calculi in secondary gout is related to higher serum urate levels and urinary uric acid excretion in this group.[103] Plasma urate is greater than 10 mg/dl in 30 percent of patients with primary gout and in 75 percent of patients with secondary gout. Urinary uric acid is greater than 800 mg/day in 22 percent of patients with primary gout and in 37 percent of patients with secondary gout. Uric acid stones also occur in patients with no history of gouty arthritis, but only approximately 20 percent of this group are hyperuricemic. This may be related to a lower fasting urine pH.[103]

Other forms of stone disease are associated with hyperuricemia and gout. Gouty subjects have an increased incidence of stones containing calcium. Additional studies have demonstrated that about 30 percent of patients with recurrent calcium stone disease have either hyperuricemia or hyperuricaciduria. Patients with recurrent calcium oxalate stones consume greater quantities of dietary purines than normal subjects, excrete larger quantities of uric acid even with dietary purine restriction, and have higher renal clearances of uric acid. Patients with pure calcium calculi or both calcium and uric acid calculi have urine supersaturated with calcium or calcium and uric acid, respectively.[104] Allopurinol therapy significantly reduces recurrent formation of calcium oxalate stones.[105–107] This observation supports an etiologic association between formation of uric acid and calcium oxalate calculi.

Gout and cystinurea are also related.[103,108] Up to 50 percent of cystinuric patients with nephrolithiasis are hyperuricemic, and a similar percentage have mixed stones of cystine and uric acid.[103] Xanthine and oxipurinol calculi have been reported in patients with Lesch-Nyhan syndrome on allopurinol therapy.[109]

Other Nephropathy in Gout.

FAMILIAL URATE NEPHROPATHY. Several families have been reported in which there is (1) a high incidence of hyperuricemia with gout beginning at an unusually young age, (2) involvement of females or involvement of both sexes with hypertension, (3) progressive renal disease leading to death before the age of 40, (4) no evidence for any metabolic abnormality which increases uric acid production, and (5) frequently, an autosomal dominantly inherited disorder.[110–118] These patients are unusual for several reasons. Although hyperuricemia and gout may be familial and associated with progressive renal disease, it is unusual for renal disease to be the cause of early death in primary gout. In addition, although hyperuricemia may eventually occur in renal disease of any type, it is uncommon for the hyperuricemia of chronic renal failure to be associated with gout. Usually these patients with familial urate nephropathy do not exhibit other features suggestive of hereditary renal disease.[119,120] Specific diagnosis may be relevant since stabilization of renal function has occurred in some patients following allopurinol therapy.[111]

Hyperuricemia has been associated with other types of familial nephropathy such as medullary cystic disease[113] and focal tubulointerstitial disease.[121] It is possible that the primary interstitial nephropathy leads to a relatively selective defect in uric acid excretion causing hyperuricemia. The possibility that renal disease is the primary event in other families should not be overlooked.

POLYCYSTIC KIDNEY DISEASE. About one-third of patients with polycystic kidney disease have gout.[122,123] Furthermore, hyperuricemia and gouty arthritis precede the development of renal failure.[122–124] Although the basis for this association is unclear, altered renal handling of uric acid may be an early manifestation of the underlying renal lesion.

LEAD INTOXICATION. Hyperuricemia and gout are well-recognized complications of chronic lead intoxication. While a renal defect appears to be present, it has not been well-defined. Campbell and associates[94] have reported that patients with primary gout have elevated blood lead levels when compared to age- and sex-matched controls despite the absence of a history of overt lead exposure. This suggests that occult chronic lead intoxication may be etiologic in some patients with primary gout. There is also evidence that patients with gout and renal impairment have an increased quantity of mobilizable lead as compared to gouty patients with normal renal function. This observation suggests a potentially important role for lead in the pathogenesis of gouty nephropathy.[93] On the other hand, in a study of patients with a history of moonshine (home-distilled spirit) ingestion, no correlation was found between the degree of depression in uric acid or creatinine clearance and amount of lead excretion following EDTA infusion.[125]

More recent studies of saturnine gout indicate that the occurrence of gouty arthritis varies considerably. Among veterans of U.S. Armed Services more than 50 percent of patients with a diagnosis of plumbism had gout, and gout secondary to lead intoxication afflicted 36 percent of all gouty patients.[126] In another setting only 6 percent of lead-intoxicated adults had gout, while 20 percent complained of arthralgias.[127] Despite the occurrence of larger quantities of mobilizable lead in hypertensives with renal impairment as compared to hypertensives with normal renal function,[128] lead was not apparently important in the pathogenesis of the renal disease in hypertensive gouty patients.[129] However, there is good evidence to suggest that the presence of gout in chronic renal failure is a useful marker for chronic lead poisoning.[130–132] This latter combination of events together with alcoholism is proposed to have caused a disorder severe enough to be blamed for the fall of the Roman Empire.[133]

Factors other than renal abnormalities may account for the frequent occurrence of gout in lead intoxication. The addition of lead to a urate solution induces nucleation of lead urate at lower concentrations than is required for the nucleation of lead urate at lower concentrations than is required for the nucleation of monosodium urate.[134] In addition, lead urate crystals can serve as nucleation sites for monosodium urate. In contrast, the inhibition of guanine aminohydrolase by lead is difficult to relate to the etiology of gout in lead intoxication.[135]

Associated Disorders

There are a number of disorders which occur frequently in association with hyperuricemia and gout.[1]

Hyperlipidemia. Hyperuricemia occurs in 82 percent of hypertriglyceridemic patients, and hypertriglyceridemia is present in 75 to 84 percent of patients with gout.[1] The association of hyperuricemia with hypercholesterolemia is not as clear-cut.[1] Types IIa, IIb, and IV hyperlipidemia were observed with frequencies of 13, 15, and 69 percent, respectively.[136] There are associated decreases in high density lipoprotein cholesterol (HDL_c) and very low density lipoprotein (VLDL) apo C-II.[136–142] The mechanisms for these changes are not clear but include a relationship to excessive sucrose intake,[143] genetic linkage,[144] excessive ethanol intake,[136] obesity, and defective clearance of triglyceride.[145] Since these lipid abnormalities are not present in first-degree relatives of gouty subjects, the abnormalities appear to be a reflection of the patient's lifestyle rather than genetic factors.[146]

Hypertension. Hypertension is present in 25 to 50 percent of patients with gout.[1] One the other hand, hyperuricemia has been reported in 22 to 38 percent of untreated hypertensives.[147–149] This is significantly greater than the prevalence of hyperuricemia in an unselected population. The prevalence of gout in hypertension has been variously reported, ranging from 2 to 12 percent.[148,150]

The serum urate concentration correlates inversely with renal blood flow and urate clearance, and directly with renal, as well as total peripheral, vascular resistance.[151–154] Therefore, the association of hypertension and hyperuricemia may be related to reduction of renal blood flow in the former condition. It has also been proposed that an elevation of the serum urate concentration may be an indicator of renal vascular involvement in essential hypertension. Weight changes are important modifiers of hypertension and hyperuricemia. Loss of weight often improves both conditions.[155,156]

Obesity. Body weight is a major determinant of serum urate levels.[1,15] Elevated body weight is associated with hyperuricemia, and gouty patients are on average 17.8 percent overweight.[1] Obesity is a common factor relating hyperlipidemia, hypertension, diabetes, and atherosclerosis, as well as hyperuricemia.[1]

Atherosclerosis and Vascular Accidents. The association of hyperuricemia with coronary artery disease is controversial.[1] In a retrospective study of the cause of death in patients with gout treated with antihyperuricemic drugs,[157] cerebrovascular disease and cardiovascular disease accounted for more than 50 percent of the mortality. The majority of these patients had either hypertension or hyperlipidemia. It is likely that in patients with hyperuricemia, clinical correlates such as hypertension, diabetes mellitus, hyperlipidemia, and obesity[9,89,157–160] may all contribute to the observed association between elevated serum urate concentration and arteriosclerosis. Numerous studies have suggested tht hyperuricemia is an independent risk factor for cardiovascular mortality.[161–164] However, using multivariate analysis serum urate levels do not add independently to the prediction of coronary heart disease.[164,165] Recent studies indicate that platelet aggregation and adhesion are not enhanced by hyperuricemia, eliminating this potential mechanism associating hyperuricemia and vascular disease.[165,166]

Hyperglycemia and Diabetes Mellitus. Gouty arthritis occurs in 0.1 to 9.0 percent of diabetic subjects, while hyperuricemia occurs in 2 to 50 percent of diabetics.[1] Despite these observtions there is no epidemiologic relationship between gout and diabetes. In fact, the mean urate level is lower in diabetes, perhaps secondary to the uricosuric effect of hyperlgycemia.[1]

Ethanol Consumption. Alcohol consumption has long been associated with hyperuricemia and, in susceptible persons, with the precipitation of acute gouty arthritis.[1] Although early studies indicated that a decrease in the renal excretion of uric acid could account for ethanol-induced hyperuricemia,[167–170] an increase in uric acid production is now recognized to be the more important factor. Ethanol increases uric acid production by accelerating the turnover of ATP.[171,172] Beer may have more potent effects upon uric acid production because of its guanosine content.[173] The basis for this disorder is discussed in the context of the mechanisms of hyperuricemia later in this chapter.

Acute Illness. Studies of acutely ill patients in intensive care units indicate that markedly elevated serum urate levels in the range of 20 mg/dl are associated with a poor prognosis[174] and hypotensive events.[175] This is likely related to two events. First, ischemic tissue stimulates the degradation of ATP to purine end products, thus enhancing the synthesis of uric acid. The finding of elevated levels of ATP degradation products in the plasma of patients with adult respiratory distress syndrome provides evidence for this mechanism.[176] Second, the conversion of hypoxanthine to uric acid by xanthine oxidase during ischemia produces oxidant radicals.[177] The latter are themselves associated with tissue injury. Thus, inhibition of xanthine oxidase with allopurinol may be a useful therapy in this setting. The metabolic basis for this disorder is also discussed in the context of mechanisms of hyperuricemia later in this chapter.

The substantial antioxidant properties of uric acid have been the subject of speculation.[178–183] It is possible that these properties may counteract the potent oxidant properties of xanthine oxidase during uric acid synthesis.

Pregnancy. Maternal urate levels normally decrease during pregnancy until the twenty-fourth week and then increase until 12 weeks after delivery.[184–186] Hyperuricemia occurs in pre-eclampsia and eclampsia[184–192] due to a decrease in the renal clearance of urate. Perinatal mortality is markedly increased when maternal serum urate levels are elevated, generally in association with early onset pre-eclampsia.[190,191] The highest mortality occurs when the serum urate levels exceed 6.0 mg/dl and diastolic blood pressure is greater than 110 mmHg.[190]

Labor itself is associated with an increased serum urate level.[193] Blood urea levels increase as well, suggesting that diminished renal clearance causes the hyperuricemia of parturition. The serum urate level remains elevated for 1 to 2 days postpartum.[194] Increased production of urate may occur as well, although direct evidence for this is lacking.

Negative Disease Associations. A negative association exists between gout and specific rheumatic disorders such as systemic lupus erythematosus,[195–197] rheumatoid arthritis,[198–201] and amyloidosis.[202,203] The basis for the decreased concurrence of these disorders is not known. Several explanations have been proposed. Lupus erythematosus and rheumatoid arthritis are more common in women, in whom gout is less likely to occur. Acute gout is difficult to distinguish from flares of other rheumatic diseases. The low synovial fluid complement occurring in these diseases may inhibit the expression of clinical gout. Futhermore, treatment with large doses of aspirin is often used, which would delay or prevent the onset of gout due to the uricosuric effect of a high concentration of salicylate. In addition, there is evidence for an immunosuppressive effect of hyperuricemia in rheumatoid arthritis and for antiinflammatory properties of rheumatoid factor in gout. Patients with rheumatoid arthritis and persistent hyperuricemia above 7.5 mg/dl have minimally active disease.[204] Hyperuricemia inhibits mononuclear cell production of rheumatoid factor, suggesting one possible mechanism.[205] Furthermore, since the interaction of crystal-bound IgG with Fc receptors is important in the pathogenesis of acute attacks of gout, rheumatoid factor may block the reaction inhibiting crystal-induced inflammation.[206]

BIOCHEMICAL BASIS

Biochemistry of Purines

The overall scheme of human purine metabolism is depicted in Fig. 37-9. This representation is conveniently divided into interfacing compartments: (1) *de novo* purine synthesis; (2) salvage of preformed purine bases; (3) nucleotide interconversions, and (4) degradation. The regulation of purine metabolism centers around ribonucleotide biosynthesis at the levels of *de novo* synthesis from nonpurine precursors and reutilization of preformed purines by the salvage of bases and nucleosides. Thus, the parent compound, the purine ring, is the logical starting point in the examination of purine metabolism.

Biosynthesis of the Purine Nucleus. The purine nucleus consists of fused pyrimidine and imidazole rings.[8] This base is the parent compound for all purines, and the origins of its individual atoms have been defined in a variety of prokaryotic and eukaryotic systems.[207–215] The enumeration of the constituent atoms of the purine ring and their origins are depicted in Fig. 37-10. The biosynthetic pathways whereby nonpurine precursors are combined to form the purine ring are referred to as "*de novo* purine synthesis." The reactions comprising *de novo* synthesis of purines are virtually invariant in bacteria, yeast, birds, and mammals.[8]

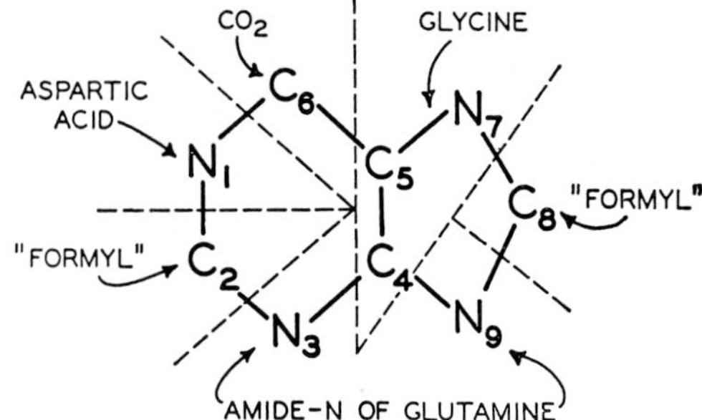

Fig. 37-10 Origins of the atoms of the purine ring.

Fig. 37-9 Overview of human purine metabolism. Human purine metabolism is focused on the synthesis of purine ribonucleotides. There are two major pathways leading to purine ribonucleotide synthesis. One is purine biosynthesis *de novo* from nonpurine precursors, including amino acids, in the diet. The second is the purine salvage pathway by which purine bases and nucleosides, including purines contained in the diet, can be resynthesized to ribonucleotides. Purine ribonucleotides may be interconverted from the monophosphate derivatives to the diphosphate and triphosphate derivatives as well as to the cyclic nucleotide derivatives. These compounds are essential components of intermediary metabolism. Purine ribonucleotides can act as substrates for a number of different pathways. The ribonucleoside diphosphate derivatives are converted to the deoxyribonucleoside diphosphate derivatives and are substrates for DNA synthesis. Adenosine triphosphate is a substrate for the cellular transmethylation cycle to form S-adenosylmethionine. During cellular transmethylation, S-adenosylhomocysteine and then adenosine are formed, and adenosine feeds into the pathway of purine nucleotide degradation. Purine ribonucleoside triphosphates are substrates for RNA synthesis, and nucleotides are products of RNA degradation. Purine ribonucleoside monophosphates are the main substrates for the pathway of purine nucleotide degradation. This is the pathway by which purine nucleotides are converted in humans to uric acid. The pathway of purine nucleotide degradation is supplied from the degradation of ribonucleotides, the dietary intake of purines, the degradation of deoxyribonucleotides, and the formation of adenosine from cellular transmethylation. The final step in the pathway of purine nucleotide degradation is the formation of uric acid, the main excretory product of the pathway. Small amounts of nucleosides and bases may be excreted into the urine. As noted on the pathway, nucleosides and bases can be salvaged back to ribonucleotide derivatives. *(From Fox.[448] By permission of Harper & Row.)*

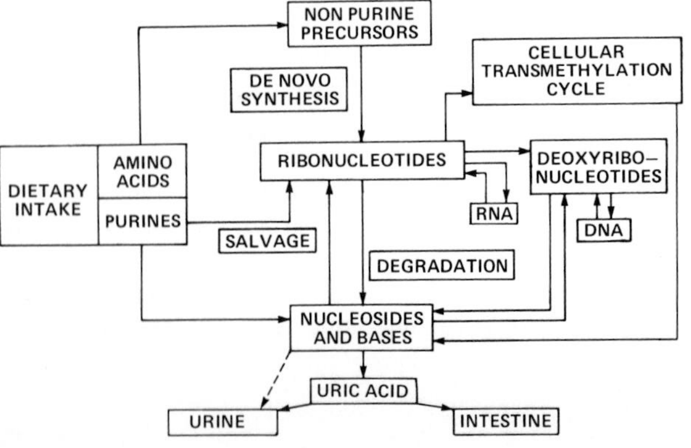

The first reaction in purine synthesis *(de novo)* is the formation of an important regulatory intermediate, 5-phosphoribosyl-α-1-pyrophosphate (PP-ribose-P).[216,217] The importance of this compound in purine metabolism is twofold: PP-ribose-P condenses with L-glutamine in the first committed step of the *de novo* pathway,[218] and PP-ribose-P serves as the phosphoribosyl donor in salvage reactions whereby purine bases are converted into ribonucleotides.[219,220]

In a reaction catalyzed by PP-ribose-P synthetase, the terminal pyrophosphate of ATP is transferred to carbon 1 of ribose-5-phosphate.[216] Magnesium and inorganic phosphate are required cofactors in this reaction.[221] This enzyme is regulated by negative feedback inhibition by purine and pyrimidine nucleotides.[222]

$$\text{Ribose-5-phosphate} + \text{ATP} \xrightarrow{Mg^{2+}} \alpha\text{-PP-ribose-P} + \text{AMP} \quad (37\text{-}1)$$

The first committed step in *de novo* synthesis generates 5-β-phosphoribosyl-1-amine.[215,218,223] In this irreversible reaction, which is catalyzed by the enzyme amidophosphoribosyltransferase, the amide group of glutamine displaces pyrophosphate from PP-ribose-P.[224] In the process, the substituents are inverted such that a β linkage is generated.[218]

$$\alpha\text{-PP-ribose-P} + \text{glutamine} + H_2O \xrightarrow{Mg^{2+}} \beta\text{-phosphoribosylamine} + \text{glutamic acid} + PP_i \quad (37\text{-}2)$$

Alternative reactions leading to the formation of phosphoribosylamine have been described in bacterial, avian, and mammalian cell extracts.[225–228] Their physiological importance is uncertain.

Subsequent reactions in the *de novo* pathway form the purine ring as summarized in Fig. 37-11. In the next reaction,[3] a second ATP is consumed in the formation of 5′-phosphoribosylglycineamide.[229,230] This compound contains the fundamental constituents of a nucleotide, i.e., a nitrogenous base, a sugar, and a phosphoric acid moiety.[8]

$$\text{Phosphoribosylamine} + \text{glycine} + \text{ATP} \xrightarrow{Mg^{2+}} 5'\text{-phosphoribosylglycineamine} + \text{ADP} + P_i \quad (37\text{-}3)$$

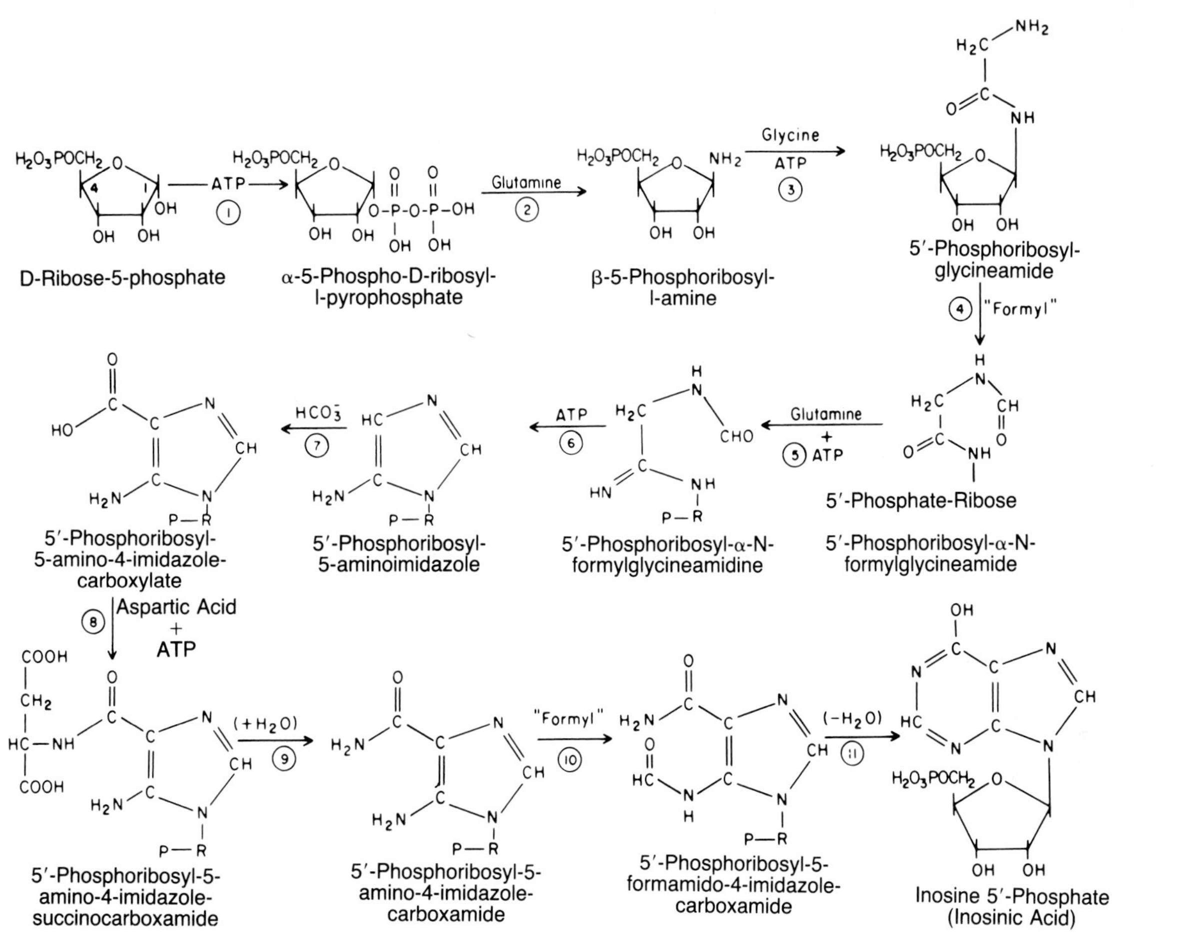

D-Ribose-5-phosphate — ATP (1) → α-5-Phospho-D-ribosyl-l-pyrophosphate — Glutamine (2) → β-5-Phosphoribosyl-l-amine — Glycine, ATP (3) → 5′-Phosphoribosyl-glycineamide — (4) "Formyl" → 5′-Phosphoribosyl-α-N-formylglycineamide — Glutamine + ATP (5) → 5′-Phosphoribosyl-α-N-formylglycineamidine — ATP (6) → 5′-Phosphoribosyl-5-aminoimidazole — HCO_3^- (7) → 5′-Phosphoribosyl-5-amino-4-imidazole-carboxylate — (8) Aspartic Acid + ATP → 5′-Phosphoribosyl-5-amino-4-imidazole-succinocarboxamide — $(+H_2O)$ (9) → 5′-Phosphoribosyl-5-amino-4-imidazole-carboxamide — "Formyl" (10) → 5′-Phosphoribosyl-5-formamido-4-imidazole-carboxamide — $(-H_2O)$ (11) → Inosine 5′-Phosphate (Inosinic Acid)

Fig. 37-11 Biosynthesis of the purine ring. The encircled numbers in this figure and in Fig. 37-12 refer to the numbered reactions in the text.

In Step 4, the purine synthetic pathway interfaces with one-carbon metabolism via N^5, N^{10}-methenyl tetrahydrofolic acid (THFA), which donates a "formyl" unit to the stepwise growth of the purine ring.[231,232]

$$\text{Phosphoribosylglycineamide} + N^5, N^{10}\text{-methenyl-THFA} + H_2O \longrightarrow 5'\text{-phosphoribosyl-}\alpha\text{-}N\text{-formylglycineamide} + \text{THFA} + H^+ \quad (37\text{-}4)$$

Glutamine then donates its amide group to form 5′-phosphoribosyl-α-*N*-formylglycineamidine.[233,234] The third ATP molecule consumed in *de novo* synthesis is the energy source in ths reaction:

$$5'\text{-phosphoribosylformylglycineamide} + \text{glutamine} + \text{ATP} + H_2O \xrightarrow{Mg^{2+}} 5'\text{-phosphoribyosyl-}\alpha\text{-}N\text{-formylglycineamidine} + \text{glutamic acid} + \text{ADP} + P_i \quad (37\text{-}5)$$

In the presence of K^{2+} and Mg^{2+}, a fourth ATP is consumed as the imidazole ring closes:[235]

$$5'\text{-phosphoribosyl-}\alpha\text{-}N\text{-formylglycineamidine} + \text{ATP} \xrightarrow{Mg^{2+}K^+} 5'\text{-phosphoribosyl-5-aminoimidazole} + \text{ADP} + P_i \quad (37\text{-}6)$$

Reversible carboxylation of C-4 of the imidazole ring by bicarbonate occurs next.[236] This carboxyl condenses with aspartic acid, consuming the fifth molecule of ATP.[232] Rapid hydrolysis of this intermediate occurs yielding a compound one carbon short of a complete purine ribonucleotide:

$$5'\text{-Phosphoribosylaminoimidazole} + CO_2 \longrightarrow 5'\text{-Phosphoribosyl-5-amino-4-imidazolecarboxylate} \quad (37\text{-}7)$$

$$5'\text{-Phosphoribosyl-5-amino-4-imidazolecarboxylate} + \text{aspartate} + \text{ATP} \xrightarrow{Mg^{2+}} 5'\text{-phosphoribosyl-5-amino-4-imidazolesuccinocarboxamide} + \text{ADP} + P_i \quad (37\text{-}8)$$

$$5'\text{-Phosphoribosyl-5-amino-4-imidazolesuccinocarboxamide} \rightleftarrows \text{fumarate} + 5'\text{-phosphoribosyl-5-amino-4-imidazolecarboxamide} \quad (37\text{-}9)$$

Once again, a one-carbon unit is provided by a folic acid derivative, N^{10}-formyl-THFA, which supplies C-2 of the purine nucleus.[237,238]

$$5'\text{-Phosphoribosyl-5-amino-4-imidazolecarboxamide} + N^{10}\text{-formyl-THFA} \overset{K^+}{\rightleftarrows} 5'\text{-Phosphoribosyl-5-foramido-4-imidazolecarboxamide} + \text{THFA} \quad (37\text{-}10)$$

Ring closure occurs by the exclusion of a water molecule, yielding the parent purine compound, inosinic acid (IMP).

$$5'\text{-Phosphoribosyl-5-formamido-4-imidazolecarboxamide} \longrightarrow \text{IMP} + H_2O \quad (37\text{-}11)$$

Nucleotide Interconversions and Catabolism. All purine ribonucleotides and deoxyribonucleotides derive from IMP.[8] These reactions are summarized in Fig. 37-12, wherein interconversion, catabolic, and salvage reactions are depicted. The major purine ribonucleotides involved in nucleic acid synthesis are adenosine 5′-monophosphate (AMP) and guanosine 5′-monophosphate (GMP).

AMP derives from IMP in two steps:[239,240]

$$\text{IMP} + \text{L-aspartate} + \text{GTP} \xrightleftharpoons{Mg^{2+}} \text{AMP-S} + \text{GDP} + P_i \quad (37\text{-}12)$$

$$\text{AMP-S} \rightleftharpoons \text{AMP} + \text{fumarate} \quad (37\text{-}13)$$

Reaction 37-12 is noteworthy because GTP is the energy source for the synthesis of adenylosuccinic acid (AMP-S).[241] The reversible cleavage of AMP-S is catalyzed by the same enzyme which catalyzes reaction 37-9, adenylosuccinase (or, alternatively, adenylosuccinate synthetase).[242]

A two-step energy-consuming series of reactions converts IMP to GMP through formation of the intermediate, xanthosine 5′-monophosphate (XMP).[243,244] ATP provides the energy whereby the NH_2 of glutamine is transferred to C-2 of XMP to form GMP:[245,246]

$$\text{IMP} + \text{NAD}^+ + H_2O \xrightarrow{K^+} \text{XMP} + \text{NADH} + H^+ \quad (37\text{-}14)$$

$$\text{XMP} + \text{glutamine} + \text{ATP} \xrightarrow{Mg^{2+}} \text{GMP} + \text{glutamic acid} + \text{AMP} + PP_i \quad (37\text{-}15)$$

Mononucleotides are converted to nucleosides by a variety of enzymes falling into two broad classes: (1) nonspecific phosphatases and (2) 5′-nucleotidases:[247–251]

$$\text{Purine mononucleotides} + H_2O \longrightarrow \text{purine nucleoside} + P_i \quad (37\text{-}16)$$

Purine nucleosides may be further catabolized by phosphorolysis via purine nucleoside phosphorylase.[252] In this reversible reaction, the synthetic direction is favored at equilibrium.

$$\text{Purine nucleoside} \rightleftharpoons \text{purine base} + \text{ribose-1-P} \quad (37\text{-}17)$$

Purine nucleoside phosphorylase from erythrocytes cleaves guanosine, inosine, and, less effectively, xanthosine. It does not split adenosine.[252] Adenosine is phosphorolyzed by a specific adenosine phosphorylase found only in mycoplasma.[253]

AMP deaminase converts AMP to IMP with the liberation of ammonia:[1]

$$\text{AMP} \longrightarrow \text{IMP} + NH_3 \quad (37\text{-}18)$$

Adenosine, chiefly derived from *S*-adenosylhomocystine (yet another interface with one-carbon metabolism) is converted to inosine reversibly via adenosine deaminase.[254]

$$\text{Adenosine} \longrightarrow \text{inosine} + NH_3 \quad (37\text{-}19)$$

Adenosine kinase converts to adenosine to AMP, consuming ATP in the process.[255,256]

$$\text{Adenosine} + \text{ATP} \xrightarrow{Mg^{2+}} \text{AMP} + \text{ADP} \quad (37\text{-}20)$$

Salvage Pathways. *De novo* purine synthesis is metabolically expensive. A minimum of six ATP molecules are consumed per purine nucleotide formed.[1] Catabolized nucleotides can be salvaged, however, in two distinct ways. As noted above, purine nucleoside phosphorylase catalyzes a freely reversible re-

Fig. 37-12 Biosynthesis of purine ribonucleotides, ribonucleosides, and bases.

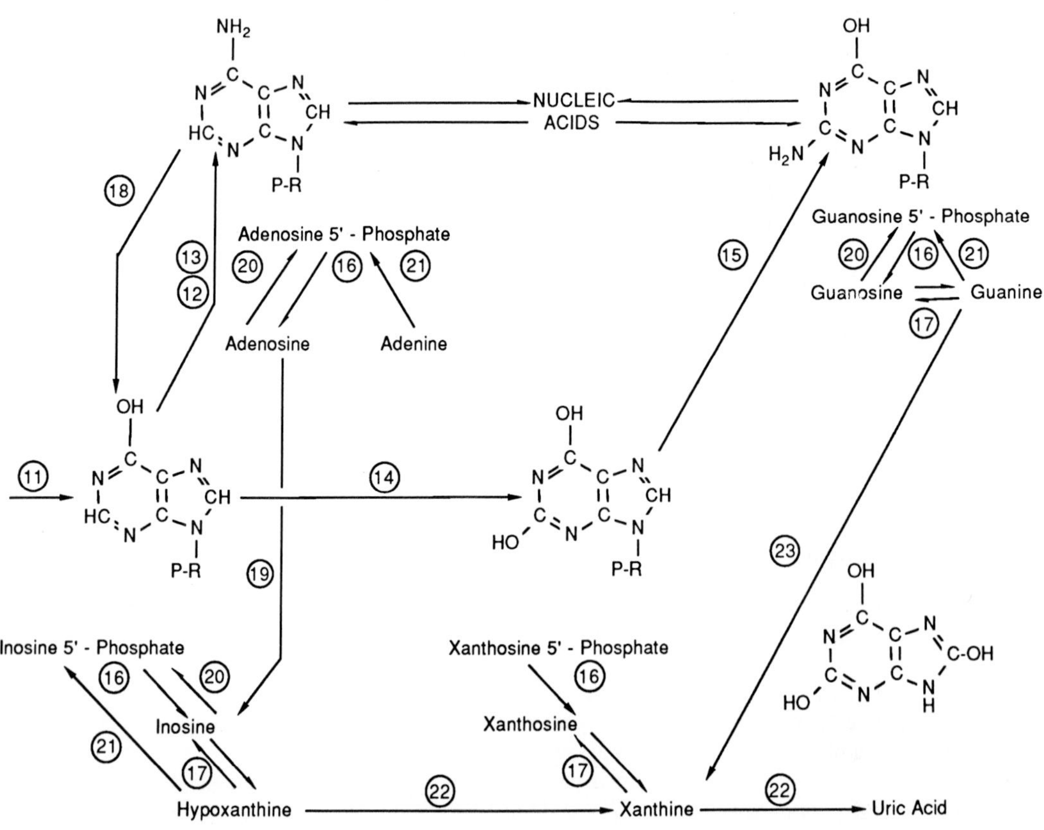

action in which nucleosides are converted to corresponding base and ribose-1-phosphate. The K_{eq} for this reaction lies in the synthetic direction and, therefore, favors nucleoside formation rather than degradation.[252] Such nucleosides may be rephosphorylated by the action of purine kinases.[255–259] These two reactions have the following general form:

$$\text{Purine base} + \text{ribose-1-P} \rightleftharpoons \text{Purine nucleoside} \quad (37\text{-}17)$$

$$\text{Purine nucleoside} + \text{ATP} \longrightarrow \text{Purine nucleotide} + \text{ADP} \quad (37\text{-}20a)$$

This two-step pathway consumes one molecule of ATP and, therefore, is much more efficient than resynthesis by way of the *de novo* pathway.

The second general mechanism whereby the purine nucleus is salvaged is via the actions of phosphoribosyltransferases.[260,261] In these reactions, the free bases condense with PP-ribose-P, forming ribonucleotides in a single step. Phosphoribosyltransferase reactions have the following general form:

$$\text{Purine base} + \text{PP-ribose-P} \xrightarrow{Mg^{2+}} \text{Purine mononucleotide} + PP_i \quad (37\text{-}21)$$

In mammalian species, two different purine phosphoribosyltransferases exist. Adenine phosphoribosyltransferase (APRT) converts adenine to AMP.[260] It will also accept aminoimidazolecarboxamide and a variety of adenine analogues.[1,260] Hypoxanthine-guanine phosphoribosyltransferase (HPRT) converts hypoxanthine and guanine to IMP and GMP, respectively.[8,261] This enzyme also catalyzes the conversion of xanthine to XMP at a much less efficient rate.[261] A variety of purine analogues including 6-thioguanine and allopurinol are converted to their respective ribonucleotides as well.[262] Deficiency states of both HPRT and APRT in humans have been described and are discussed more fully below and in Chap. 38 and 39, respectively.

5-Amino-4-imidazolecarboxamide-5′-monophosphate (ZMP) is an intermediate in the *de novo* pathway which under certain conditions is also salvaged. The nucleotide ZTP was first discovered in folate deficient *Salmonella typhimurium*.[263] Subsequently, ZTP was shown to accumulate in a variety of eukaryotic cells incubated with Z-riboside. Although no biological function has yet been determined for ZTP in eukaryotic cells, situations under which this metabolite accumulates have been associated with the arrest of growth in mammalian fibroblasts.[264] ZTP is synthesized in a one-step reaction in which the pyrophosphate moiety of PP-ribose-P is transferred to ZMP. This reaction is reversibly catalyzed by PP-ribose-P synthetase.[265] This unusual route of synthesis is the only known example of reversal of the usual direction of the reactions catalyzed by PP-ribose-P synthetase. ZTP is normally undetectable in human erythrocytes, although elevated levels of ZTP have been determined in red blood cells from subjects with the Lesch-Nyhan syndrome.[266] These subjects were not folate-deficient but did have the mild macrocytic anemia often seen in complete HPRT deficiency. ZTP is involved in a variety of other metabolic pathways (Fig. 37-13).

Physiologically, the phosphoribosyltransferase pathways are the most active in the salvage of preformed purine bases.[1,8] The origin of these bases is from endogenous catabolism of purines, nucleic acid breakdown, and the exogenous intake or administration of purine compounds. The two-step nucleoside phosphorylase-nucleoside kinase pathway does not appear to be very active in most tissues under normal conditions.[1]

On the other hand, adenine nucleotides participate in a physiologically active pathway that has been termed *the adenosine cycle* (Fig. 37-14).[267] In this series of reactions AMP is converted to adenosine by the action of 5′-nucleotidases. Adenosine formed in this manner may be rephosphorylated to AMP by adenosine kinase. ATP is the phosphate donor in this reaction, and ADP is generated as a result. At first glance this cycle appears to be futile, but recent evidence indicates it may subserve important physiological roles with respect to the generation of adenosine available to specific cell surface receptors mediating a wide variety of cellular events.[267] This cycle may also be important in the homeostatic maintenance of the cellular "energy charge."

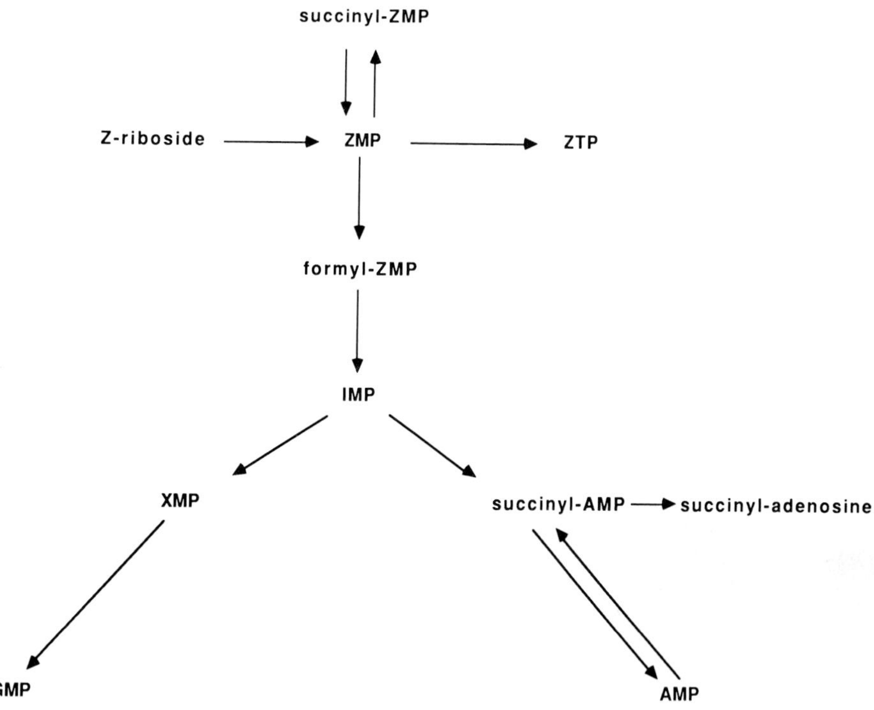

Fig. 37-13 Metabolism of Z nucleotides. *Z* refers to the base 5-amino-4-imidazolecaboxamide. *Z-riboside* is ribosyl-5-amino-4-imidazolecarboxamide. *ZMP* is 5′-phosphoribosyl-5-amino-4-imidazolecarboxamide and is the product of Reaction 9 in Fig. 37-11.

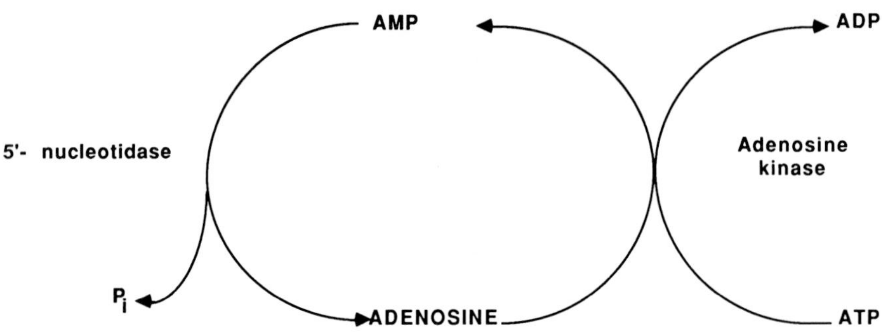

Fig. 37-14 The adenosine cycle.

$$\text{“Energy charge”} = \frac{\text{ATP} + \frac{1}{2}\,\text{ADP}}{\text{ATP} + \text{ADP} + \text{AMP}}$$

Atkinson has proposed that the energy charge of a cell acts as a composite metabolic regulator of a variety of biosynthetic events, including the synthesis of PP-ribose-P.[268] This ratio is sensitive to the relative amounts of the various adenine nucleotides, each of which participates in the adenosine cycle.

An alternative adenosine cycle had been proposed previously: adenosine → inosine → hypoxanthine → IMP → AMP-S → AMP → adenosine.[269] The physiological activity of this cycle, as well as its role, is unclear. Since IMP generated in this fashion may be converted to GMP, it provides a potential source of guanyl nucleotides.[1]

Synthesis of Uric Acid. Xanthine oxidase is a flavoprotein containing both iron and molybdenum which oxidizes a wide variety of purines and pteridines.[270,271] A soluble form of the enzyme having dehydrogenase activity (xanthine dehydrogenase or D form[272] has been isolated from a variety of sources.[272–275] The D form is converted to the oxidase form (D form) by the oxidation of thiol groups in the protein, especially in the presence of high concentrations of oxygen.[276–278] It is the O form of xanthine oxidase that is responsible for the formation of uric acid as the final metabolic product in human purine metabolism. This enzyme converts hypoxanthine to xanthine and xanthine to uric acid:

$$\text{Hypoxanthine} + H_2O + 2O_2 \longrightarrow \text{xanthine} + 2O_2^- + 2H^+ \quad (37\text{-}22a)$$

$$\text{Hypoxanthine} + H_2O + O_2 \longrightarrow \text{xanthine} + H_2O_2 \quad (37\text{-}22b)$$

$$\text{Xanthine} + H_2O + 2O_2 \longrightarrow \text{uric acid} + 2O_2^- + 2H^+ \quad (37\text{-}22c)$$

or

$$\text{Xanthine} + H_2O + O_2 \longrightarrow \text{uric acid} + H_2O_2 \quad (37\text{-}22d)$$

Superoxide anion or hydrogen peroxide are thus generated.[279] Hydrogen peroxide may then be converted to free hydroxyl radicals:

$$Fe^{2+} + H_2O_2 \longrightarrow Fe^{3+} + OH^- + OH^{\cdot}$$

These compounds, O_2^-, H_2O_2, and OH^-, are important mediators of inflammation and tissue destruction. Xanthine oxidase may have a significant pathophysiological role in states of ischemia or tissue injury that lead to accentuated adenine nucleotide breakdown.[177]

In humans, xanthine oxidase activity is found in substantial quantities only in the liver and small intestine.[1,270] Trace amounts of activity are found in other tissues, but none is detectable in leukocytes, erythrocytes, or fibroblasts in tissue culture.[8] However, the enzyme protein is detected by sensitive immunohistochemical techniques in endothelial cells where xanthine oxidase has been postulated to have a role in defense against injury and microbial invasion.[280] These same studies localize xanthine oxidase activity to hepatic sinusoidal lining cells in the liver which explains the abundance of enzyme activity in that organ.[280] Although trace quantities of free purine bases are excreted in human urine, the majority of the catabolic products of purine metabolism are converted in the liver to uric acid and excreted in that form.[281] Deficiency of xanthine oxidase in humans results in xanthinuria, in which xanthine and hypoxanthine are the final products of purine metabolism. Xanthine oxidase and xanthinuria are discussed in Chap. 42.

An alternative route of uric acid synthesis via uric acid ribonucleoside has been described.[281–284] The biological significance of this pathway remains unclear.

Regulation of Purine Biosynthesis

Several lines of evidence suggest that the first committed step in purine biosynthesis is condensation of L-glutamine and PP-ribose-P to form phosphoribosylamine.[1,285] Phosphoribosylamine is the first specific precursor of purines whence *de novo* purine synthesis proceeds in a direct manner to formation of inosinic acid from which all other purines are subsequently derived. The enzyme catalyzing this initial reaction, amidophosphoribosyltransferase, is subject to regulation by the end products of purine metabolism, i.e., purine ribonucleotides. The rate at which purine biosynthesis proceeds is controlled at this step by PP-ribose-P: high intracellular concentrations of PP-ribose-P accelerate purine biosynthesis, whereas depletion of this substrate slows the rate of *de novo* synthesis.[1,8,286] Thus, glutamine is rate-limiting for purine synthesis only under very restricted conditions.[1,8] The regulation of the enzyme catalyzing this reaction is discussed in greater detail below.

Another putative site for regulation of *de novo* purine synthesis may be at a multienzyme complex consisting of the enzymes catalyzing Reaction 4 (phosphoribosylglycineamide for myltransferase) and Reaction 37-10 (phosphoribosylaminoimidazolecarboxamide formyltransferase) together with formyl-methenyl-methylene-tetrahydrofolate synthetase and serine transhydroxymethylase.[287,288] A direct regulatory role for this complex in purine synthesis *de novo* has yet to be established.

Phosphoribosylpyrophosphate Synthetase (PP-ribose-P Synthetase). PP-ribose-P synthetase is an allosteric enzyme with a subunit molecular weight of approximately 33,200.[221,289,290] The smallest native form of this enzyme from human red blood cells has a molecular weight of approximately 65,000 and consists of two subunits of identical molecular weights.[289] This enzyme has an absolute requirement for inorganic phosphate as an allosteric activator. The enzyme requires magnesium ATP as a substrate.[221,222,289,290]

Magnesium ATP, in saturating concentrations, aggregates the enzyme into two high molecular weight forms of molecular weights ranging from 65,000 to 1,040,000.[289,290] These very large forms are the active states of the enzyme in vivo.[290] The other substrate, ribose-5-phosphate, does not affect the state of aggregation of the enzyme. The enzyme is modified extensively after translation leading to marked electrophoretic heterogeneity.[291] The gene encoding PP-ribose-P synthetase is on the X chromosome.[292] Human variants of PP-ribose-P synthetase having supernormal activity has been described in human subjects with gout.[293–298] These superactive forms of the enzyme appear to result from structural gene mutations.

The regulation of PP-ribose-P synthetase activity is complex and depends upon the concentrations of substrates, allosteric activators, end products of reactions in which PP-ribose-P is a substrate, and other specific phosphate-containing compounds. These are summarized in Fig. 37-15. There are at least three regulatory sites in PP-ribose-P synthetase. As evidence in support of this: (1) ADP inhibits the enzyme competitively with respect to magnesium ATP;[221,222] (2) 2,3-diphosphoglycerate (2,3-DPG) inhibits the enzyme competitively with respect to ribose-5-phosphate;[222] and (3) a variety of nucleotides inhibit the enzyme noncompetitively with respect to both substrates.[222,299] In the last mechanism of inhibition, nucleotide di- and triphosphates are the most potent inhibitors of the enzyme.[299,300] Since availability of PP-ribose-P controls the first committed step of purine synthesis, as noted above, regulation of this enzyme is an important determinant of overall purine synthesis. The variety of mechanisms whereby PP-ribose-P synthetase is inhibited are collectively referred to as *heterogeneous metabolic pool inhibition*.[1]

The product of this reaction, α-phosphoribosyl-1-pyrophosphate (PP-ribose-P), is clearly an important regulatory intermediate in purine biosynthesis. The rate at which it is synthesized by PP-ribose-P synthetase, its subsequent interaction with amidophosphoribosyltransferase, and its utilization in the salvage pathway reactions yield at least three different sites for a regulatory role. Physiologic steady state levels of PP-ribose-P, which are determined by rates of both production and utilization, are near or equal to the K_m of amidophosphoribosyltransferase.[301–304] Availability of this compound, therefore, determines to some extent the rate at which the cell commits to purine synthesis *de novo*.

Fig. 37-15 Feedback controls of sequential reactions of purine biosynthesis, catalyzed by PP-ribose-P synthetase and amidophosphoribosyltransferase. The first has at least three regulatory sites, the second at least two, as described in the text.

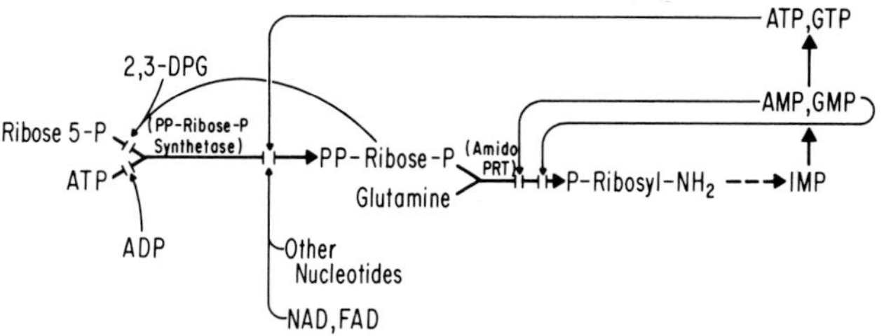

Amidophosphoribosyltransferase. Amidophosphoribosyltransferase is an important enzyme which has been studied in a variety of systems.[305–310] The enzyme has an absolute requirement for PP-ribose-P as substrate. Although glutamine appears to be the major amino donor, ammonia and certain other amines may substitute.[224,311] Like PP-ribose-P synthetase, this enzyme is allosteric and has an absolute requirement for a divalent cation.[224] PP-ribose-P binds first to the enzyme, which induces a conformation change and activation of the enzyme.[306,307] There is cooperativity in the binding of PP-ribose-P with Hill coefficients ranging from 1.1 to 3.0.[311] Inorganic phosphate is a competitive inhibitor of PP-ribose-P as well as a potentiator of nucleotide inhibition and a factor in reducing cooperativity of PP-ribose-P binding.[306,310]

The site at which glutamine binds to the human form of this enzyme is distinct from the ammonia site, since blocking the glutamine binding site with covalently bound analogues does not reduce ammonia utilization.[311] These sites apparently interact, however.

All forms of amidophosphoribosyltransferase studied to date are extremely labile when studied in vitro because of inactivation by oxygen.[309,312–315] PP-ribose-P and a variety of nucleotides protect the enzyme from oxygen inactivation presumably by interaction with the iron-sulphur center of the enzyme.[309,313,314] It is this thiometallic region which is the site of inactivation by oxidation and is indispensable for catalysis.[314,315]

Purine ribonucleotides inhibit amidophosphoribosyltransferase in an allosteric fashion[316] (Fig. 37-15). This inhibition is fairly specific for purine 5′-ribonucleotides and is competitive with respect to PP-ribose-P. Evidence suggests, however, that inhibitors bind at sites distinct from the substrate binding sites. In contrast to PP-ribose-P synthetase, monophosphates are more effective inhibitors than diphosphates, which are in turn more potent inhibitors than triphosphates.[306,309,317] Also, unlike PP-ribose-P synthetase, in which there is no synergism between ribonucleotide inhibitors, synergism is prominent in the control of amidophosphoribosyltransferase.[306,307,317] This synergy is dependent upon differing substituents at position 6 on the purine ring since combinations of 6-amino- and 6-hydroxyribonucleotides are synergistic, while mixtures of ribonucleotides substituted with the same group at position 6 are merely additive.[318] Synergistic inhibition by mononucleotides is completely overridden by very high concentrations of PP-ribose-P.[318] Human amidophosphoribosyltransferase exists in large and small molecular weight forms.[319] These two forms have molecular weights of approximately 133,000 and 270,000, respectively. In the absence of PP-ribose-P and ribonucleotides, the two forms are in equilibrium.[320] It is the small molecular weight form that is active.[319,320] Purine nucleotides associate the enzyme into its inactive high molecular weight form, while the substrate P-ribose-PP dissociates the enzyme into its active subunits (Fig. 37-16). This enzyme has been studied from a variety of sources and has been reviewed extensively in the previous edition.[1]

Considerable evidence indicates that these initial enzymes in purine *de novo* biosynthesis, i.e., PP-ribose-P synthetase and amidophosphoribosyltransferase, are coordinated with respect to their regulation.[320] The major determinants of this coordination are the intracellular concentrations of PP-ribose-P and

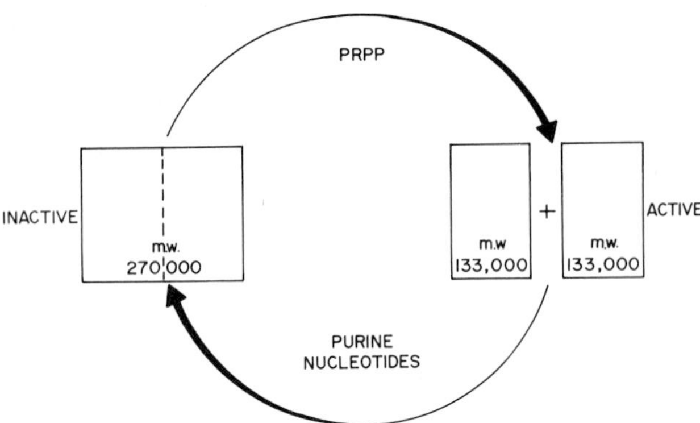

Fig. 37-16 Model of interconversion of small (active) and large (inactive) forms of amidophosphoribosyltransferase. *(Courtesy of Dr. E.W. Holmes, Duke University Medical Center.)*

purine nucleotides. By comparison of the regulatory influences on these two enzymes (see Fig. 37-12), a delicate and carefully balanced system is evident.

Purine Ribonucleotide Interconversions. The next major site of regulation of purine ribonucleotide synthesis is at the level of control of interconversions. As noted above, there are a variety of reaction series by which the various nucleotides are interconverted. Each of these reactions is regulated by the nucleotide end product, which typically inhibits the first enzyme in the pathway.[1] The conversion of IMP to AMP is inhibited by the products of the reaction, AMP and GDP.[242,321] Correspondingly, the synthesis of GMP from IMP is inhibited by GMP in the two-step process which requires ATP as energy donor.[322] Thus, availability of GTP and ATP, each of which controls the synthesis of the other nucleotide, as well as inhibition by products of the reactions with respect to their own biosynthesis likely regulates the steady state levels of adenyl and guanyl nucleotides.

AMP can ultimately be converted back to GMP via conversion to IMP by AMP deaminase (see below). The purine nucleotide cycle of muscle involves conversion of AMP to IMP and resynthesis of AMP. This cycle is responsible for release of ammonia during muscle contraction. Deficiency of AMP deaminase in human muscle results in myopathy (Chap. 41).

Ribonucleotide Degradation. In vivo and in vitro evidence indicates that nucleotide breakdown is regulated in a complex manner.[323–325] When cultured ascites tumor cells are incubated with 2-deoxyglucose or glucose, these compounds are rapidly phosphorylated by ATP.[325] The abrupt decrease of ATP concentrations due to its rapid utilization results in elevations of AMP and IMP. These nucleotides are dephosphorylated to purine nucleosides by 5′-nucleotidases and are subsequently either catabolized or reutilized.

Regulation of nucleotide degradation is critically controlled by AMP deaminase (Reaction 18) and 5′-nucleotidases (Reaction 16). AMP deaminase is an allosteric enzyme which is activated by ATP and ADP and inhibited by GTP and P_i.[1,8] Release of inhibition of AMP deaminase results in accelerated production of uric acid. Regulation at the level of dephosphorylation is more complex and is the focus of intensive investigation. At least three soluble 5′-nucleotidase activities have been described.[326–329] One form has a micromolar K_m for both AMP and IMP and is inhibited by nucleotides.[326,328] A second form, isolated from a wide variety of sources, hydrolyzes IMP and GMP preferentially but with millimolar K_m values for these substrates.[249,330–335] This "high K_m" form is activated by ATP and ADP and inhibited by inorganic phosphate. Finally, nonspecific phosphatases cleave AMP and have millimolar K_m values.[1] This activity is inhibited by inorganic phosphate.

Although the interactions of these enzymatic activities are incompletely understood at present, their catalytic and regulatory properties indicate that nucleotides themselves, especially ATP and ADP, as well as inorganic phosphate, are key modulators of nucleotide catabolism. Intracellular ATP and ADP levels activate AMP deaminase and the "high K_m" nucleotidase, while they inhibit "low K_m" nucleotidase.[326,327,336] In addition, the relative levels of these nucleotides determine the rates of AMP formation by adenylate kinase. GTP activates high K_m nucleotidase, but inhibits AMP deaminase and low K_m nucleotidase activity.[249,327,336]

Inorganic phosphate levels are also critical.[337–339] P_i (1 to 5 m*M*) inhibits AMP deaminase, high K_m 5′-nucleotidase, and nonspecific phosphatases, but not low K_m nucleotidases. Examination of ATP degradation in cellular systems employing different substrates such as deoxyglucose, rotenone, or dinitrophenol reveals marked differences in degradative patterns.[338–339] The latter two compounds cause increased P_i levels, and ATP degrades through adenosine. The use of 2-deoxyglucose decreases P_i levels and causes degradation by AMP deaminase.

The interplay of these enzymatic activities and metabolites requires further careful elucidation in cell-free systems as well as in cultured cell and animal models. Additionally, differences may exist among various tissues which reflect the metabolic requirements subserving individual organ function.

URIC ACID METABOLISM

Production of Uric Acid

The major determinants of purine synthesis are: (1) rate of *de novo* purine synthesis; (2) rates of purine salvage; (3) rate of exogenous supply of purine metabolic products. The elimination of purines is controlled by the rates of: (1) nucleotide breakdown; (2) synthesis of uric acid; and (3) purine excretion in urine and by extrarenal routes. Thus, the overall rate of purine synthesis reflects the difference between purine intake and *de novo* synthesis and excretion of purine metabolic products. In practice, these variables are complex and interrelated, making it very difficult to assess synthetic rates in intact organisms. Estimates of the minimal level of purine production have been obtained by severe dietary restriction of purine intake in humans. A very wide distribution of these rates in normal adults is seen. Correspondingly, urinary uric acid excretions also vary widely, since they are a reflection of overall purine production. Values for urinary uric acid excretion in 24 h are defined on a statistical basis under controlled conditions of dietary intake on the basis of the mean plus or minus two standard deviations. On isocaloric, purine-free diets, the value in normal adult men was 418 ± 70 mg in one study[340] and 426 ± 81 mg in another.[341]

In gouty subjects, urinary uric acid values vary even more widely. In patients with primary gout, values as low as 150 mg in 24 h to greater than 2400 mg in 24 h have been demonstrated.[1] Low values are seen in subjects with renal defects as the bases of primary gout. Levels of excretion of uric acid in excess of 2 SD above the mean value of a normal population (600 mg and above) represent states of overproduction.[341] Due to the impracticality of putting patients on purine-free diets for several days prior to the collection of 24-h urine sample, a value from a subject on a regular diet in excess of 1000 mg/day is considered definitely abnormal, while values ranging from 800 to 1000 mg in 24 h are considered borderline. Elevation of urinary uric acid in excess of 1000 mg/day is evidence of overproduction of urate. A proportion of hyperuricemic subjects whose 24-h excretion of urate is between 800 to 1000 mg/day are also overproducers of urate. Overexcretion of uric acid in the absence of hyperuricemia does not necessarily imply overproduction of urate and may reflect increased renal clearance of uric acid.

Sustained overexcretion of uric acid is a marker for increased synthesis of purines *de novo*. Normal excretion of uric acid in a gouty subject does not exclude the possibility of overproduction, however, since renal impairment may alter the evident excretor status of the patient. In such subjects, extrarenal disposal of urate is increased and may account for the majority of urate turnover. Probably fewer than 10 percent of subjects with primary gout overproduce urate.[1]

Previously, urate production and disposition have been investigated by turnover studies and the administration of radioactive precursors to gouty and nongouty subjects. These studies provide direct insight into the functional significance of the evaluation of serum urate and urinary uric acid levels. Although briefly reviewed here, this subject is more extensively reviewed in the previous edition of this chapter.[1]

Measurement of Uric Acid Synthesis In Vivo

Body Fluid Purines. Body fluid purine levels are usually measured by high pressure liquid chromatography and indicate relative changes in the rate of urate synthesis. An elevation of the serum urate level and the urinary uric acid excretion suggests increased production of urate. An elevation of the serum urate level together with increases in plasma and urine precursors of urate (hypoxanthine, xanthine, and inosine) provides evidence for increased synthesis of urate as well. Similarly, a diminution of the serum urate level and urine uric acid excretion indicates a reduction in urate synthesis. The latter may occur in association with inherited blocks of uric acid synthesis (xanthine oxidase or purine nucleoside phosphorylase deficiency) or with pharmacologic block (allopurinol at xanthine oxidase or high dose azathioprine at amidophosphoribosyltransferase).

Uric Acid Pool Size and Turnover. Since intravenously administered radiolabeled uric acid mixes readily with the endogenous pool of urate in the body, isotope dilution may be used to estimate both uric acid pool size and the rate of its turnover.[342] A detailed explanation of the technique as well as the calculation of pool size and turnover rate is presented in the previous edition of this chapter.[1]

In normal men, the rapidly miscible pool of uric acid ranges from 866 to 1587 mg with an average value of 1200 mg.[8,343] When body weight is taken into account, the average pool size is 16.3 mg/kg (range 11.0 to 20.3 mg/kg).[344] In gouty subjects, employing a single compartment model, the rapidly miscible pools of uric acid are substantially larger, ranging from 2000 to 4000 mg in patients without apparent tophi[343,344] and from 18,000 to 31,000 mg in subjects with severe tophaceous disease.[345] However, these represent only a minor fraction of the total urate pool since a "second compartment" of urate, presumably in tissue and not readily miscible, is apparent upon careful analysis.[345,346] This second pool may be huge when compared to the rapidly miscible pool. In one subject with severe tophaceous gout, the insoluble pool was estimated to be 300 times larger than the miscible pool.[346]

The turnover rate of uric acid, estimated from the rate of disappearance of labeled uric acid from the miscible pool, averages from 695 to 743 mg/day (range 513 to 1108 mg/day).[1] A production rate of 343 ± 36 mg/(m^2/day) was calculated from these data. Thus, a quantity of uric acid enters the miscible pool which is in excess of that recovered in the urine by as much as 100 to 365 mg/day.[343,347] This excess represents the fraction of uric acid disposed by uricolysis in the gut.

Turnover rates are elevated in gouty subjects who overexcrete uric acid,[343] and may exceed 2000 mg/day.[5] In normoexcretors with gout, turnover rates vary substantially, and the considerable variations in turnover rate overlap with the normal range. In Scott's study, gouty subjects had turnover rates averaging 800 ± 130 mg/24 h compared to 693 ± 112 mg/24 h in nongouty controls.[344]

Incorporation of Labeled Precursors into Uric Acid. The availability of radiolabeled nonpurine precursors of uric acid has been used as a sensitive means of measuring uric acid production. Radiolabeled glycine, ammonium, formate and 4-aminoimidazole-5-carboxamide have been employed to this end. Similarly, purine precursors of uric acid, such as hypoxanthine and adenine, have also been used to estimate degradative rates and fluxes through nucleotide pools. After administration of the labeled compound, urinary uric acid is isolated, and the amount of incorporated radioisotope is measured.[348,349]

When [^{15}N]- or [^{14}C]glycine is fed to nongouty subjects, the specific activity of urinary uric acid peaks between 48 and 72 h after administration.[348,349] Gouty subjects show a different pattern, with isotope enrichment occurring earlier and to a higher degree than in normal controls, reflecting accelerated urate production.[348–351]

Results of studies performed between 1957 and 1980 are summarized in Fig. 37-17. Virtually all gouty overexcretors and the majority of normoexcretors with primary gout overincorporate radiolabeled glycine into urinary uric acid when compared to controls. Thus, in primary gout, urate production varies widely.

Intravenously infused [^{14}C]adenine is incorporated into the adenine nucleotide pool. As this pool is turned over, radiolabeled purine end products are produced which reflect the amount of adenine nucleotide degraded. Rates of adenine nucleotide degradation may thus be directly assessed in vivo by quantitation of the urinary excretion of radioactivity.[352,353] Since the amount of degradation of [^{14}C]adenine nucleotides to [^{14}C]uric acid is dependent upon hypoxanthine salvage, this technique allows quantitation of the contribution of hypoxanthine reutilization in normal subjects in comparison with HPRT-deficient individuals. The mean cumulative excretion of radioactivity 7 days after [^{14}C]adenine infusion in normal subjects is 5.6 percent of the infused radioactivity. The mean cumulative excretions of radiolabel for partially HPRT-deficient subjects and for subjects with the Lesch-Nyhan syndrome were 12.9 percent and 22.3 percent, respectively.[352] The latter subjects have a diminished or absent ability to reutilize hypoxanthine. The difference in radioactivity excretion

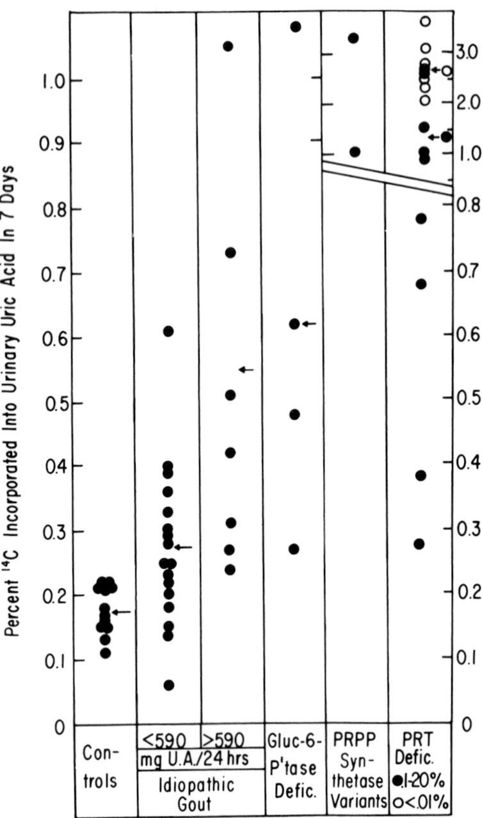

Fig. 37-17 Summary of values of cumulative incorporation of ^{14}C into urinary uric acid in control and gouty subjects reported from 1957 through 1980.

between normal subjects and HPRT-deficient patients suggests that up to 75 percent of hypoxanthine is normally reutilized each day.

Excretion of Uric Acid

Renal Handling of Uric Acid. The renal mechanism of uric acid excretion in normal human subjects is discussed in Chap. 106. Therefore, only a brief synopsis pertinent to hyperuricemia and gout is presented here.

Glomerular ultrafiltration of uric acid has been shown to occur by direct analysis of fluid obtained from the urinary space of Bowman.[354,355] The degree to which urate is bound to serum proteins in vivo influences its filtration. Although as much as 30 percent of urate is protein-bound in vitro,[356] in vivo studies indicate that no more than 5 percent is likely to be bound to protein.[357,358] It is therefore unlikely that protein binding significantly affects filtration of urate.

Less than 10 percent of the filtered load of urate is ultimately excreted in urine,[340] indicating that net reabsorption of uric acid occurs in the nephron. In animal studies the major site of urate reabsorption has been localized to the proximal tubule.[359–364] Other studies have suggested additional reabsorption sites in the distal tubule,[360,361] in the ascending limb of the loop of Henle,[365] and in the collecting duct.[366] The existence of distal reabsorption in the human nephron is unresolved.

Tubular secretion of urate in the human kidney was initially demonstrated in a hypouricemic subject whose clearance of urate was in excess of his inulin clearance.[367] Subsequent studies have confirmed this observation in normal subjects.[368] Urate appears to be secreted in the proximal tubule in human beings[369] and is likely mediated by an energy-dependent organic acid transport system.[370] Tubular secretion of urate may be the single most important mechanism in establishing urinary urate excretion.[371–373]

The relative contributions of reabsorption and secretion of urate in the human kidney are difficult to estimate. Previously the pyrazinamide suppression test was employed to distinguish between reabsorptive and secretory contributions to urine urate concentrations.[374] For a variety of reasons, reviewed in Ref. 375, the pyrazinamide suppression test is no longer considered a valid technique. A more complicated model of the renal handling of urate has been proposed, the *postsecretory reabsorptive model,* which agrees closely with a variety of observations regarding the renal handling of uric acid.[371,376–378] In this model, there are two sites for urate reabsorption in the proximal nephron, separated by the urate secretory site. This model represents the best explanation to date for the accumulated observations on renal urate handling in human beings. In support of this model is the description of a subject with renal wasting of urate.[379] Additionally, in two kindreds with familial hyperuricemia due to diminished urate clearance, it was proposed that the defect was due to increased postsecretory reabsorption.[117] The relative fluxes of urate through each component remain undetermined, and authentication of their existence awaits direct demonstration using micropuncture and isolated nephron techniques.

Extrarenal Excretion of Uric Acid. When [^{15}N]uric acid is injected into normal subjects, only 75 perent of the radiolabel is recovered in the urine.[343] Furthermore, as noted above, turnover studies of uric acid indicate that the quantity of uric acid synthesized per day exceeds urinary excretion.[380] Thus, an extrarenal route is available for the disposition of a substantial fraction of uric acid.

Approximately 25 percent of ^{15}N is recovered in urinary allantoin, urea, and ammonia and fecal nitrogen when [^{15}N]uric acid is administered intravenously,[342,347] indicating uricolysis has taken place. Other studies have localized the site of uricolysis within the intestines.[380] A substantial portion of ^{15}N derived from orally administered labeled uric acid is recoverable within intestinal bacteria.[380] Intestinal bacteria contain enzymes capable of uricolysis,[347] and antimicrobial-induced bacteriostasis in a normal subject virtually eliminated the degradative products of uric acid in excretory products.[1,380]

Trace amounts of uricolysis can occur in certain human tissues, such as leukocytes, which contain peroxidases capable of destroying uric acid.[381] An insignificant fraction of uric acid may be metabolized in this manner.

In gouty subjects, a smaller fraction of intravenously injected radiolabeled uric acid is recovered in the urine than in nongouty subjects.[380,382] Thus, intestinal uricolysis is enhanced in gouty subjects. This, in turn, reflects greater than normal quantities of uric acid entering the gut in secretions.[343] This effect is secondary to elevated urate levels and in subjects with severe renal insufficiency may be the major route of urate excretion.[346] The elimination of a substantially greater than normal fraction of uric acid in the gut implies that measurement of urinary excretion of uric acid in the hyperuricemic subject is underestimated to a greater degree than in normouricemic individuals.

MECHANISMS OF HYPERURICEMIA

Serum urate levels reflect the difference between production of uric acid and its excretion via renal and extrarenal routes. Hyperuricemia and gout may be conveniently classified on the basis of increased urate production or decreased excretion. In a substantial portion of subjects, both mechanisms may be simultaneously operative (Table 37-1). Within each major classification, the principal mechanism may be regarded as primary or secondary. The term *primary hyperuricemia* is used to describe those states in which the principal metabolic abnormality is elevation of the serum urate. Although the specific inborn error resulting in hyperuricemia is known in only a minority of cases, primary hyperuricemia presumably arises from inherited abnormalities in purine metabolism and the renal handling of urate. *Secondary hyperuricemia* refers to those conditions in which a distinct pathologic state or administration of a pharmacologic agent directly results in an elevation of the serum urate. In the following discussion, the metabolic bases underlying each mechanism will be examined independently.

Table 37-1 Pathogenesis of Hyperuricemia and Gout

- Increased production of urate
  - Primary hyperuricemia
    - Idiopathic
    - Elevated intracellular PP-ribose-P
      - Hypoxanthine-guanine phosphoribosyltransferase (HPRT) deficiency
        - Complete (Lesch-Nyhan syndrome)
        - Partial (Kelley-Seegmiller syndrome)
      - PP-ribose-P synthetase variants with supernormal activity
    - Decreased hypoxanthine reutilization
  - Secondary hyperuricemia
    - Accelerated ATP degradation
      - Glycogen storage diseases (types I, III, V, VII)
      - Tissue hypoxia
      - Ethanol intake
    - Increased nucleic acid turnover
      - Blood dyscasias
      - Malignancies
      - Psoriasis
    - Excessive purine intake
- Decreased excretion of urate
  - Primary hyperuricemia
    - Decreased filtered load
    - Increased tubular reabsorption
    - Decreased tubular secretion
  - Secondary hyperuricemia
    - Reduced renal functional mass–chronic renal insufficiency
    - Increased tubular reabsorption
      - Dehydration
      - Diabetes insipidus
      - Diuretics
    - Decreased tubular secretion
      - Conditions associated with elevated levels of β-hydroxybutyrate and acetoacetate
        - Starvation
        - Diabetic ketoacidosis
      - Conditions associated with hyperlacticacidemia
        - Acute ethanol ingestion
        - Eclampsia
        - Tissue hypoxia
    - Mechanism not established
      - Lead nephropathy
      - Associated with drug administration
      - Pyrazinamide
      - Salicylates (low dose)
      - Ethambutol
      - Diuretics
      - Nicotinic acid

Primary Hyperuricemia due to Urate Overproduction

Radioisotopic studies in human subjects with hyperuricemia and gout have demonstrated that overproduction of uric acid occurs with a frequency approximating 10 percent in gouty subjects. In many of these subjects, overproduction of uric acid is a secondary consequence of a specific inborn error of metabolism. In a considerable fraction, however, the mechanism resulting in primary overproduction of uric acid is unknown. This group of disorders constitutes *idiopathic primary gout*, and the underlying mechanisms are discussed in this section. Secondary overproduction of uric acid is discussed in a separate section.

Examination of potential mechanisms for primary idiopathic overproduction of urate begins with an examination of the rate-limiting step. Both substrates for this reaction, l-glutamine and PP-ribose-P, have been implicated in the possible pathogenesis of primary overproduction of uric acid. Examination of both of these substrates is reviewed extensively in the previous edition of this chapter.[1] In this discussion, we will summarize the salient features.

Elevated Phosphoribosylpyrophosphate Levels. As early as 1960, Wyngaarden proposed that elevation of intracellular concentrations of PP-ribose-P was the basis for overproduction of uric acid in some subjects with primary hyperuricemia (Fig. 37-18).[383] Two enzymatic abnormalities provide examples of mechanisms by which intracellular PP-ribose-P levels may be increased. In PP-ribose-P synthetase overactivity, overproduction of PP-ribose-P itself drives *de novo* synthesis. In HPRT deficiency, on the other hand, underutilization of PP-ribose-P by this salvage enzyme leads to accumulation of the unused substrate which subsequently activates amidophosphoribosyltransferase and accelerates *de novo* synthesis. Although this hypothesis has been confirmed for these two rare enzymopathies, the role of excess PP-ribose-P in the majority of patients with primary overproduction of uric acid remains undetermined.

Attempts to relate elevated intracellular concentrations of PP-ribose-P to overproduction of uric acid require examina-

Fig. 37-18 Schematic summary of human purine metabolism. Accelerated *de novo* purine synthesis caused by increased intracellular concentrations of nonpurine precursors.

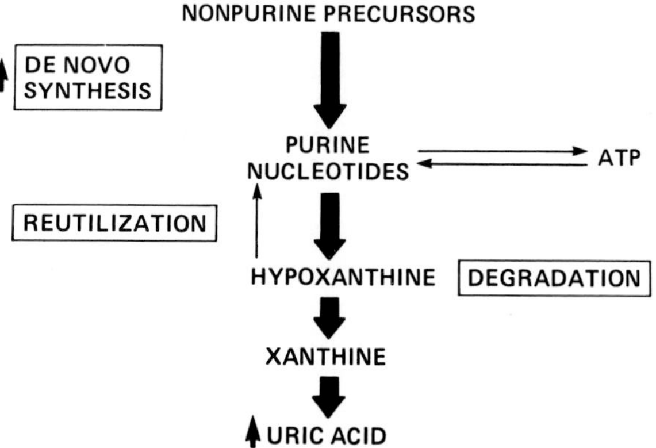

tion of the intracellular concentrations of PP-ribose-P, its rate of production, and its turnover. These aspects of metabolism of PP-ribose-P in mammalian cells have recently been reviewed.[384] PP-ribose-P is a rate-limiting substrate for *de novo* purine synthesis because rates of purine synthesis are directly proportional to intracellular PP-ribose-P levels which modulate the activity of the rate-determining enzyme amidophosphoribosyltransferase.[1]

In subjects with PP-ribose-P synthetase overactivity, PP-ribose-P concentrations in erythrocytes and cultured fibroblasts from affected individuals are elevated.[294,385–388] Furthermore, the rate of PP-ribose-P generation is accelerated in those cells, providing convincing evidence that elevated levels of PP-ribose-P result from increased PP-ribose-P production rather than from decreased utilization.[294,385–388] Indeed, these findings suggest that an elevated rate of PP-ribose-P synthesis itself accelerates the *de novo* pathway, leading to a surfeit of purines which results in overproduction of purines.

In subjects with severe HRPT deficiency, erythrocyte and fibroblast PP-ribose-P levels are elevated as well.[1,8,388] PP-ribose-P concentrations may be elevated in heterozygous carriers of HPRT deficiency whose enzyme activities are in the intermediate range.[389] However, red blood cell PP-ribose-P concentrations may be normal in some heterozygotes despite evidence of abnormal purine metabolism including hyperuricemia and hyperuricaciduria.[389] These data argue that other factors contribute to the overproduction of urate in HPRT deficiency or that erythrocyte PP-ribose-P levels are not representative of other tissues.

PP-ribose-P metabolism has been studied extensively in subjects with primary overproduction of urate without either of these enzymatic disorders.[383,390–392] The rate of turnover of PP-ribose-P has been assessed by the administration of radioactive glucose, which is ultimately incorporated into PP-ribose-P by way of the pentosemonophosphate shunt.[391] The subsequent administration of imidazole acetic acid (IAA) allows sampling of the pool of PP-ribose-P labeled in such a fashion. In the liver, IAA combines with PP-ribose-P to form IAA ribonucleotide, which is subsequently degraded to the riboside and excreted in the urine.[1] Using this technique, gouty overexcretors of uric acid have markedly increased PP-ribose-P turnover rates in contrast to gouty subjects who excrete normal amounts of uric acid. Since this technique depends upon determination of the specific activity of PP-ribose-P, the normal turnover rates in the normoexcretors may be artifactual due to isotope dilution. Subjects with gout who were evaluated by this method showed clear increases in PP-ribose-P turnover, lending support to the hypothesis that excessive PP-ribose-P metabolism may result in overproduction of uric acid despite any absence of knowledge of the metabolic defect itself.

Further evidence to support this hypothesis derives from measurement of intracellular concentrations of PP-ribose-P in cultured fibroblasts of gouty subjects who overproduce uric acid.[388] Elevated intracellular levels of PP-ribose-P were found in patients with superactivity of PP-ribose-P synthetase and cells derived from subjects with HPRT deficiency, as expected. Furthermore, Becker demonstrated elevated levels of PP-ribose-P in cells derived from seven gouty overproducers without one of these enzyme defects. In two cases, the elevated PP-ribose-P levels were apparently the effect of accelerated production of ribose-5-phosphate.[388] Again, the underlying metabolic basis has not been determined.

When other cells are examined, the data are more heterogeneous. While concentrations of PP-ribose-P are above normal in the erythrocytes of patients with PP-ribose-P synthetase overactivity and with severe HPRT deficiency, this is not always the case in gouty subjects who overproduce uric acid.[389] In general, erythrocyte PP-ribose-P levels are normal in the latter subjects and do not relate to the serum or urinary uric acid concentrations.[392,393] More importantly, normal erythrocyte concentrations of PP-ribose-P do not predict concentrations in other tissues such as the liver.[1]

The regulation of PP-ribose-P synthesis by changes in carbohydrate metabolism is relevant to metabolic disorders. PP-ribose-P concentrations in liver have a diurnal variation and are responsive to dietary, hormonal, and pharmacologic manipulations.[394] In states of carbohydrate excess and lipogenesis, flux through the pentosemonophosphate shunt is increased, and therefore ribose-5-phosphate production is accelerated,[395] which makes it potentially available for PP-ribose-P synthesis. These observations provide a basis for the relationships between obesity, hypertriglyceridemia, and hyperuricemia.[143] In addition, the rapid removal of ATP provides metabolic pressure to overproduce purines following fructose infusion in normal subjects and during hypoglycemia and hyperglucagonemia in patients with glycogen storage disease type I. The release of amidophosphoribosyltransferase inhibition by decreased intracellular concentration of ATP stimulates *de novo* purine synthesis.

L-Glutamine in Primary Hyperuricemia and Gout. In addition to PP-ribose-P, L-glutamine is a substrate involved in the rate-determining step of *de novo* purine synthesis. Thus, L-glutamine concentrations are potentially rate-limiting. Indirect evidence for this mechanism has been provided in several studies.[396–398] Numerous studies designed to directly define the role of L-glutamine are inconclusive (reviewed in Ref. 1). At present, a specific defect in glutamate or glutamine metabolism cannot be implicated in primary hyperuricemia and gout.

Decreased Reutilization of Hypoxanthine. In a normal subject, hypoxanthine may either be reutilized to IMP or oxidized to uric acid. Reutilization of hypoxanthine is the result of its conversion to IMP by HPRT. In HPRT-deficient subjects, the only metabolic fate available to hypoxanthine is oxidation. Studies employing [^{14}C]adenine (see above) indicate that approximately 75 percent of the hypoxanthine formed each day is salvaged by HPRT.[352,353] These studies also indicate that a greater fraction of urinary oxypurines results from decreased reutilization of hypoxanthine in HPRT-deficient subjects when compared to normal controls. This mechanism acts in concert with the acceleration of *de novo* purine synthesis caused by elevated PP-ribose-P levels to produce the profound overproduction of urate which characterizes this disorder (Fig. 37-19). This mechanism has not been evaluated in primary overproducers of uric acid without a demonstrable enzyme disorder.

Secondary Hyperuricemia due to Urate Overproduction

Disorders of ATP Metabolism. Disordered ATP metabolism is manifested by accelerated breakdown of ATP and resultant decreases in intracellular ATP concentrations. There are two major mechanisms by which net ATP degradation is acceler-

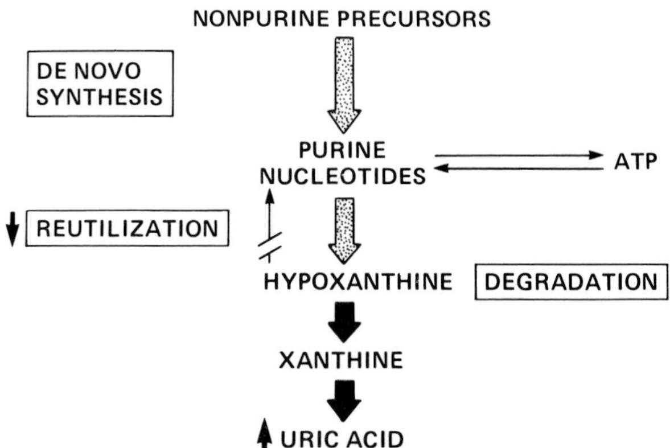

Fig. 37-19 Schematic summary of human purine metabolism in HPRT-deficient states. In addition to accelerated *de novo* synthesis of purine nucleotides, diminished reutilization of hypoxanthine contributes to overproduction of uric acid when HPRT activity is decreased or absent.

ated: increased ATP breakdown and decreased ATP synthesis.[251,399,400]

ATP is formed primarily in mitochondria by the following reaction:

$$3ADP + 3P_i + \tfrac{1}{2} O_2 + NADH + H^+ \rightarrow 3ATP + 4H_2O + NAD^+$$

Thus, decreased supply of O_2, P_i, or NADH will diminish the rate of ATP synthesis.[399] Normal cellular function requires continual resynthesis of ATP from ADP, the principal product of energy-requiring reactions which consume ATP. Thus, either an impairment in ATP-synthetic capacity or rapid consumption of ATP in excess of synthetic capacity results in degradation of adenine nucleotides to inosine, hypoxanthine, xanthine, and uric acid (Fig. 37-20).

Accelerated degradation of ATP by these two mechanisms has been evaluated in two experimental models. These models provide the physiological basis for several pathologic conditions in which secondary hyperuricemia occurs as a result of disordered ATP degradation.

Experimental Models of Accelerated ATP Degradation.

FRUCTOSE-INDUCED HYPERURICEMIA. The ability to label the adenine nucleotide pool allows direct examination of ATP degradation in vivo. Such studies are important models of disease states in which ATP degradation is accelerated. One such model is the intravenous infusion of fructose.[401] Upon infusion of fructose, there is a rapid and marked increase in plasma and urinary purine levels. The serum urate increases by 30 to 40 percent and plasma hypoxanthine, xanthine, and inosine levels rise markedly within 15 min.[402] There is also a rapid increase in urinary uric acid, hypoxanthine, xanthine, and inosine excretion. These findings indicate that fructose infusion triggers dramatic purine catabolism.

The model to explain these abrupt changes in purine levels is based upon accelerated ATP degradation (Fig. 37-21). Fructose is rapidly phosphorylated in the liver to fructose-1-phosphate, which consumes ATP and traps inorganic phosphate. Since inorganic phosphate is required by mitochondria to resynthesize ATP from ADP, when P_i levels drop, ATP synthesis diminishes. Alternatively, ATP may be synthesized from two ADP molecules, leading to elevation of the intracellular AMP concentration. The decrease in ATP and P_i concentrations releases inhibition of AMP degradation, and the production of inosine, hypoxanthine, xanthine, and uric acid increases abruptly. In support of this model is the direct demonstration of a drop in hepatic ATP levels after fructose infusion.[251]

Fructose infusion after administration of [^{14}C]adenine may be used to assess the capacity of nucleotide catabolism to accelerate in response to changes in ATP levels. In normal subjects, there is a 7.5 mmol per gram of creatinine increase in total urinary purines during the 3 h after fructose infusion. Urinary radioactivity increases five- to tenfold above the baseline, indicating catabolism of ATP.[251] Patients with partial or

Fig. 37-20 Schematic summary of human purine metabolism. Accelerated degradation of ATP (or diminished ATP synthesis) increases purine nucleotide degradation, resulting in overproduction of uric acid.

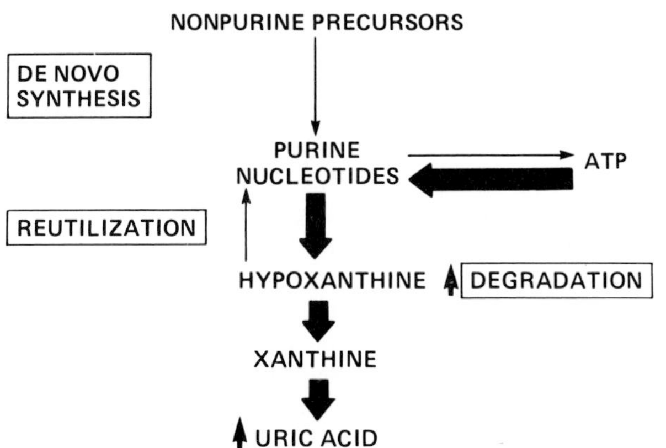

Fig. 37-21 Mechanism of fructose-induced purine nucleotide degradation. Fructose triggers rapid breakdown of purine nucleotides to uric acid in the liver. Phosphorylation of fructose to fructose-1-phosphate causes ATP to be degraded to ADP. Fructose-1-phosphate tends to accumulate and thus traps inorganic phosphate. ADP is converted back to ATP by the mitochondrial electron transport system or glycolysis, which use inorganic phosphate, or by adenylate kinase. The reaction with adenylate kinase also forms AMP. Net result is a diminution of intracellular ATP and inorganic phosphate and buildup of AMP. Elevated AMP concentrations also lead to increased IMP concentration. Dephosphorylation by 5′-nucleotidase is triggered. If AMP and IMP concentrations are high enough, then nonspecific phosphatase can be activated. Once dephosphorylation is activated, there is a cascade of nucleotide degradation through catabolic pathways leading to increased synthesis of uric acid and accounting for hyperuricemia and elevated urinary excretion of inosine, hypoxanthine, xanthine, and uric acid. - - - - = inhibition. Vertical arrows beside ATP, P, and AMP = changes caused by fructose infusion. *(From Fox.[251] By permission of* Metabolism.)

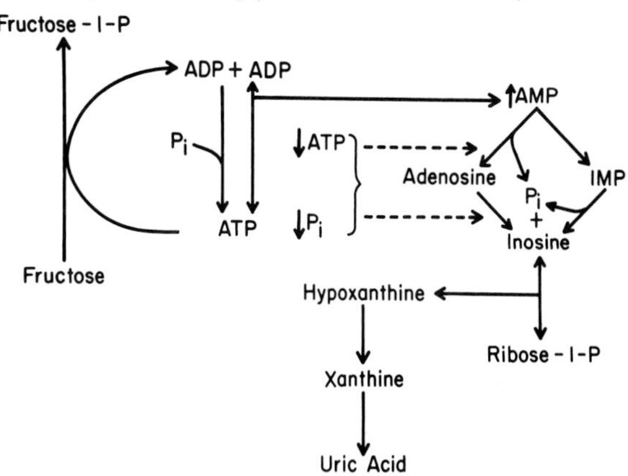

complete HPRT deficiency states show increases of 18.6 and 17.3 mmol per gram of creatinine, respectively.[352,353]

The measurement of body fluid purines and radioactivity originating from ATP has been used to examine the pathogenesis of hyperuricemia in a variety of pathologic states in which accelerated ATP degradation contributes to elevations of serum urate, including glycogen storage diseases and ethanol-induced hyperuricemia.[171,172,403–405]

STRENUOUS MUSCULAR EXERCISE. A second experimental model for hyperuricemia resulting from accelerated ATP breakdown is strenuous muscular exercise.[406] Strenuous muscular exercise leads to hyperuricemia.[406–408] Although dehydration and hyperlacticacidemia reduce urate excretion and contribute to the rise in serum urate, production of increased amounts of uric acid is a major factor in this form of secondary hyperuricemia. When normal subjects are exercised to exhaustion, ATP levels in muscle decrease by 40 percent.[406] This decline in tissue ATP levels correlates with a threefold rise in plasma and urinary oxypurine levels.[406] This overproduction of purines is a consequence of increased ATP degradation (Fig. 37-22). ATP is consumed rapidly during muscle contraction. During exercise to exhaustion, ATP consumption exceeds ATP synthetic capacity, resulting in degradation of adenine nucleotides to oxypurines.

Examples of pathologic conditions resulting in hyperuricemia from disordered ATP metabolism are listed in Table 37-2. The pathophysiology of hyperuricemia in some of these disorders has been reviewed[399,400] and is briefly summarized here.

Fig. 37-22 ATP metabolism in muscle. During muscle contraction ATP is converted to ADP and other purine nucleotides. The purine nucleotide cycle from AMP to IMP to AMP is active during muscle contraction. Oxygen, inorganic phosphate (P_i), and glucose oxidation or fatty acid oxidation are required for regeneration of ATP. Ischemic exercise tends to cause ATP to degrade by limiting availability of oxygen and fuel sources. There is a resultant degradation of ATP to adenosine, inosine, and hypoxanthine in muscle. Xanthine and uric acid are formed in the liver by oxidation of hypoxanthine (- - -). Any disorder limiting oxidation of glucose or fatty acid fuel sources may accelerate ATP degradation. *(From Bertorini et al.[433] By permission of Neurology.)*

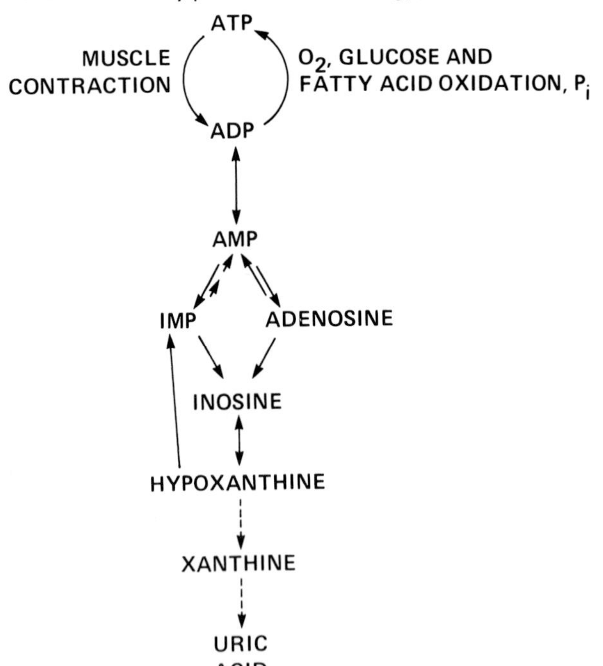

Table 37-2 Conditions Resulting in Disordered ATP Metabolism

Increased ATP degradation
Models
Fructose infusion
Exercise
Ethanol ingestion
Glucose-6-phosphatase deficiency
Hereditary fructose intolerance
Fructose-1,6-diphosphatase deficiency
Decreased ATP synthesis
Tissue hypoxia
Ischemia
Hypoxemia
Metabolic myopathies
Hypophosphatemia

Increased ATP Degradation in Disease States.

ETHANOL-INDUCED HYPERURICEMIA. Two mechanisms for the hyperuricemia associated with ethanol ingestion have now been well-documented: decreased rate of renal excretion secondary to hyperlacticacidemia and increased urate production secondary to accelerated ATP degradation. Ethanol ingestion results in increased urinary uric acid excretion, doubling of urate turnover, and an increase in oxypurine excretion.[171] Ethanol infusion after in vivo labeling of the adenine nucleotide pool by [^{14}C]adenine administration results in a 150 percent increase in urine radioactivity and a 400 percent increase in urinary oxypurine excretion. This indicates that increased ATP degradation to uric acid precursors has occurred. A model to explain this observation based on ethanol and ATP metabolism has been proposed (Fig. 37-23). Ethanol is converted to acetate, which is then converted to acetylcoenzyme A. Acetylcoenzyme A synthesis consumes ATP, which is converted to AMP. AMP may be recycled to ATP or degraded. Ethanol ingestion may thus result in accelerated turnover of ATP to a degree sufficient to account for a significant increase in uric acid synthesis. This model has been directly tested by infusion of acetate into normal volunteers after [^{14}C]adenine infusion, which also resulted in accelerated ATP degradation and increased oxypurine excretion.[172] These studies provide evidence which supports the hypothesis that ethanol-induced hyperuricemia is caused, in part, by accelerated ATP turnover.

GLUCOSE-6-PHOSPHATASE DEFICIENCY. Hyperuricemia, gout, and renal calculi are important features of glucose-6-phosphatase deficiency (glycogen storage disease, type I). Accelerated ATP turnover has now been clearly shown to the basis for overproduction of urate in this disorder.[403]

Accelerated ATP degradation in response to hypoglycemia and the release of glucagon has been proposed as a cause for uric acid overproduction in glucose-6-phosphatase deficiency (Fig. 37-24).[251,404,405] The activation of glycogen phosphorylase by glucagon leads to glycogenolysis and formation of glucose-6-phosphate. In the absence of glucose-6-phosphatase, only limited quantities of free glucose can be formed in the liver, probably from debrancher enzyme activity.[409] Continuing formation of phosphorylated sugars[410] leads to trapping of inorganic phosphate and depletion of ATP.[404] Under these conditions, purine nucleoside monophosphates accumulate and in turn are degraded to uric acid. An analogous mechanism underlies the hyperuricemia accompanying disorders of fructose

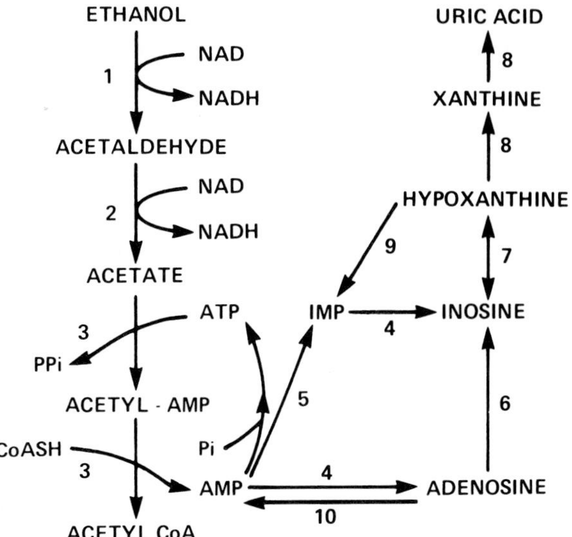

Fig. 37-23 Mechanism of accelerated turnover of ATP during ethanol administration. Ethanol is converted to acetate. Formation of acetylcoenzyme A (acetyl-CoA) consumes ATP. If a small proportion of AMP that is formed is not salvaged back to ATP, AMP may be degraded, leading to increased production of oxypurines (hypoxanthine and xanthine) and uric acid. 1 = Alcohol dehydrogenase; 2 = aldehyde dehydrogenase; 3 = acetyl-CoA synthetase; 4 = 5′-nucleotidase; 5 = AMP deaminase; 6 = adenosine deaminase; 7 = purine nucleoside phosphorylase; 8 = xanthine oxidase; 9 = hypoxanthine phosphoribosyltransferase; and 10 = adenosine kinase. PP_i (inorganic pyrophosphate), P_i (inorganic phosphate), and IMP (inosine monophosphate). *(From Faller and Fox.*[171] *By permission of* New England Journal of Medicine.)

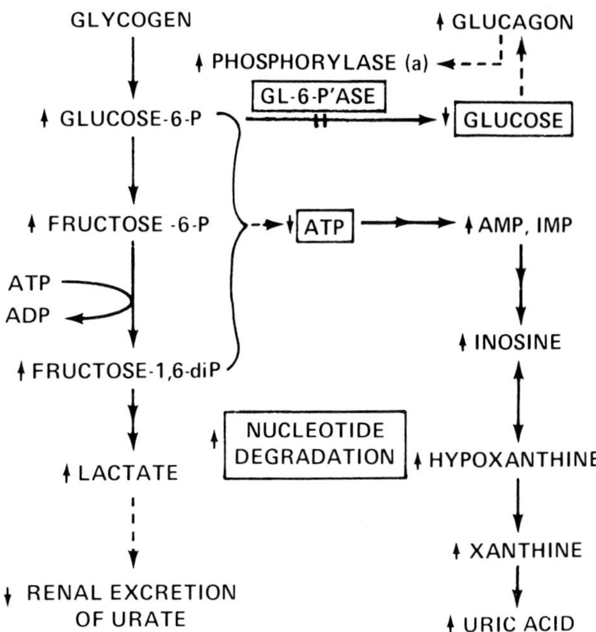

Fig. 37-24 Hypothetical mechanism linking hypoglycemia to hyperuricemia in glucose-6-phosphatase deficiency. Hypoglycemia stimulates release of glucagon. This activates hepatic glycogen phosphorylase, which degrades glycogen with trapping of phosphate in phosphorylated sugars. Cellular depletion of ATP occurs and increases intracellular concentrations of purine monophosphates, which are subsequently degraded to uric acid. The phosphorylated sugars are converted to lactate which may block the renal excretion of urate. IMP = inosine monophosphate. *(From I.H. Fox,* Metabolism: Clinical and Experimental *30:616, 1981. By permission.)*

metabolism[251,411] and the accelerated ATP degradation following fructose infusion in subjects with normal enzyme activity.[401,412–414]

This model is supported by experimental evidence. Correction of hypoglycemia suppresses plasma glucagon levels and reverses cellular glucopenia. Sustained normalization of blood sugar by either intravenous or intragastric infusion of nutritional supplements corrects the metabolic abnormalities, including hyperuricemia and growth retardation of children with glucose-6-phosphatase deficiency.[403,415–422] Acidosis, hyperlipidemia, and hyperuricemia are improved by continuous intravenous glucose infusion.[403] Plasma glucagon concentrations were lowered during this therapy and in previous experiments.[403,415,423] These findings are consistent with the hypothesis that glucagon stimulates uric acid production. However, since hypoglycemia was eliminated, it is difficult to attribute the changes in uric acid levels to the reduction in glucagon levels alone.

Glucagon administration increases the serum urate levels in patients with glucose-6-phosphatase deficiency.[404] Pharmacologic doses of intravenous glucagon lowered hepatic ATP content and increased hepatic concentrations of phosphorylated sugars. These metabolic alterations accompanied an acute rise in the serum urate level. The association between glucagon injection and uric acid metabolism is further supported by the observations that pharmacologic doses of glucagon elevate serum urate levels and the urinary concentrations of oxypurines, uric acid, and radioactivity originating from labeled ATP.[403]

Central to this model linking hypoglycemia to purine degradation is the concept that endogenous release of hypoglycemia counterregulatory hormones should activate ATP breakdown to uric acid in patients with glucose-6-phosphatase deficiency. Untreated patients have elevated glucagon levels,[403,415,423] which may be a response to chronic hypoglycemia.[419,424] The hypothesis that it is the elevation of plasma glucagon concentration that causes the hyperuricemia of glucose-6-phosphatase deficiency was supported by examining the responses to suppression of glucagon levels during the infusion of somatostatin.[403] Infusion of somatostatin lowered the plasma glucagon level and simultaneously reduced the serum urate level, urinary uric acid, oxypurine, and radiolabeled purine excretion as compared with the values observed during a saline infusion under identical conditions. These changes provide evidence that activation of ATP degradation to uric acid is regulated in part by the increase in endogenous plasma glucagon levels.

Decreased ATP Synthesis.

TISSUE HYPOXIA. Massive hyperuricemia has been observed in acutely ill patients in whom tissue hypoxia on the basis of either ischemia or hypoxemia was a prominent feature.[174–176,251,425] Indeed, in such severely ill patients, serum urate concentrations were substantially higher in nonsurvivors (mean serum urate of 20.7 mg/dl) compared to survivors (mean serum urate of 7.1 mg/dl).[174,175] In most nonsurvivors, evaluation of urinary excretion of urate suggested overproduction of urate. In severely hypoxemic patients, elevated plasma levels of hypoxanthine, xanthine, and inosine have been documented reflecting accelerated ATP degradation. In these conditions, tissue hypoxia, as well as impaired supply of nutrients, results in impairment of resynthesis of ATP. Therefore, ATP degrades to purine end products including uric acid. These studies provide evidence for the association between hypoxia, impaired ATP metabolism, hyperuricemia, and a grave prognosis.

METABOLIC MYOPATHIES. Hyperuricemia has been observed in several conditions in which muscle metabolism is impaired. These include: glycogen storage disease type III (debranching enzyme deficiency);[426,428] glycogen storage disease type V (muscle phosphorylase deficiency);[428–430] glycogen storage disease type VII (muscle phosphofructokinase deficiency);[428,429,431] and myoadenylate deaminase deficiency.[432] In all of these disorders there is impairment of the metabolic pathways providing substrates necessary for ATP synthesis (Fig. 37-25). Thus, when ATP is consumed by muscular activity, accelerated degradation of adenine nucleotides occurs.[406] Indirect evidence for this hypothesis has been obtained in these disorders by exercise testing. In subjects with these disorders, normal exercise and ischemic exercise cause increased release of ATP degradation products (including inosine, hypoxanthine, and xanthine) compared to normal individuals.[428–433] The degradation of these compounds to uric acid thus leads to hyperuricemia. Excessive release of ATP degradation products following ischemic exercise occurs in carnitine palmityltransferase deficiency and myoadenylate deaminase deficiency and could potentially cause hyperuricemia.[432,433] Therefore, myogenic hyperuricemia may be explained by decreased ATP synthetic capacity.

Increased Nucleic Acid Turnover. Hyperuricemia often accompanies disease states such as hemolytic anemia,[434–437] myeloproliferative disorders,[438–440] multiple myeloma,[441] and secondary polycythemia.[442,443] All of these conditions are characterized by accelerated turnover of bone marrow cells.[444,445] In these conditions, the excessive nucleic acid synthesis that occurs utilizes massive amounts of purine nucleotides. As purine nucleotide concentrations fall, their feedback inhibitory influence diminishes and *de novo* purine synthesis increases. Accelerated turnover of nucleic acid and nucleotides leads in turn to hyperuricemia and hyperuricaciduria. Particularly dramatic increases in serum urate and urinary uric acid are often seen during treatment of myeloproliferative disorders when lysis of malignant cells releases massive amounts of nucleotides.

Accelerated Nucleotide Degradation. Rapid nucleotide degradation may be operative in some subjects with primary overproduction of urate. Two instances of accelerated deamination of AMP have been described[446,447] and provide indirect evidence for this hypothesis. Primary overproduction of uric acid may occur as a result of AMP deaminase that is resistant to its physiological inhibitors, P_i and GTP, causing increased degradation of adenylate nucleotides.[1] The postmortem examination of the liver of a gouty subject showed partial resistance to inhibition of AMP deaminase by GTP at concentrations capable of inhibiting this enzyme normally.[447]

Excessive Dietary Purine Intake. Ingestion of large amounts of foods particularly rich in nucleoproteins may also contribute to hyperuricemia.[448,449] This is a very uncommon cause of hyperuricemia.

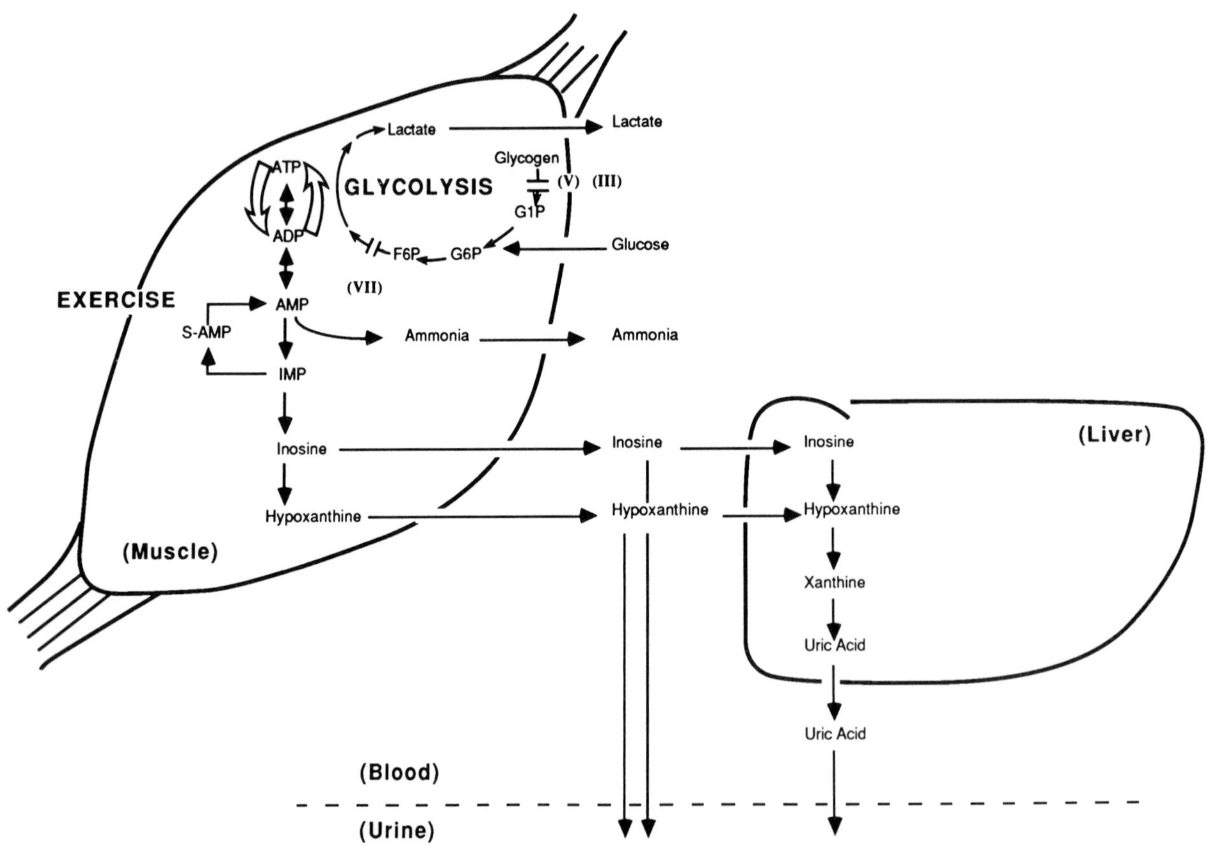

Fig. 37-25 Mechanism of myogenic hyperuricemia in glycogen storage diseases. *(From Mineo et al.[428] By permission of New England Journal of Medicine.)*

Primary Hyperuricemia due to Decreased Urate Excretion

Decreased uric acid excretion remains the most common cause of hyperuricemia and gout. The hyperuricemic subject who excretes less than 250 to 300 mg of uric acid in 24 h while on a purine-free diet is, by definition, an underexcretor of uric acid.[1]

Underexcretion of uric acid may occur on either a primary or secondary basis. Several studies have clearly demonstrated that gouty subjects with primary underexcretion of uric acid have lower uric acid clearance rates than nongouty subjects (see Table 43-17, Ref. 343).[340,450–455] When urinary urate excretion rate (expressed in milligrams per minute) is evaluated as a function of the plasma urate concentration in both gouty and nongouty individuals, the shapes of the curves are identical, but the curve of gouty individuals is shifted such that they appear to require serum urate concentrations 1.7 mg/dl higher than normal subjects to obtain equivalent excretion rates (Fig. 37-26).[451,455,456,457] The same phenomenon is observed when the C_{urate}/C_{inulin} ratio is examined.[340,451,456,545] Elevations of the plasma urate level by infusion of lithium urate or by exogenous administration of RNA increases this ratio in both normal and gouty subjects.[453,460] However, in gouty subjects, a higher plasma urate level is required to obtain a clearance ratio identical to normals. The vast majority of subjects with idiopathic gout demonstrate this renal defect, the mechanism of which is unknown.[1] This shift in the uric acid clearance ratio curve can be accounted for by any of three possibilities: (1) decreased filtration of uric acid, (2) enhanced reabsorption, or (3) diminished secretion. No single mechanism has been established as the basis for primary underexcretion of urate, although decreased tubular excretion of urate is favored at present.

Fig. 37-26 Urate excretion at varying concentrations of plasma urate. Urinary urate is expressed in mg/(min • 100 ml of glomerular filtrate). The slopes of the normal (○- - - - -○) and gout (●—●) regressions are not significantly different from each other. The average gouty individual must have a serum urate 1.7 mg/dl higher than normal in order to equal the normal rate of urate excretion. *(From P.A. Simkin.[456])*

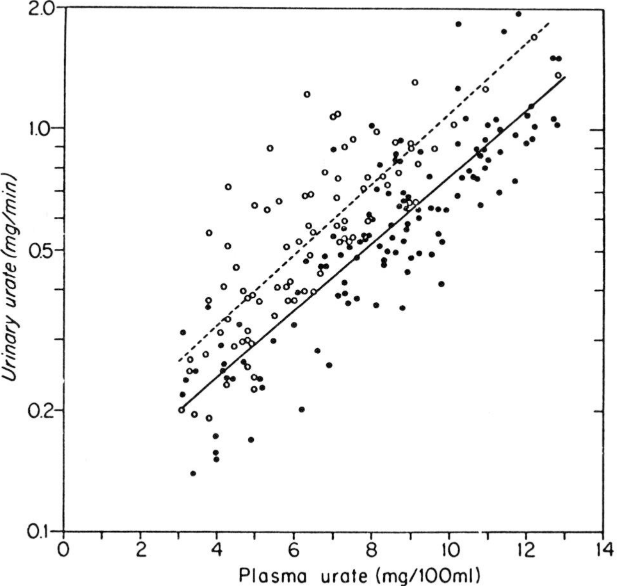

Decreased Filtration. Theoretically, enhanced protein binding of urate could decrease its filtration even in the presence of a normal glomerular filtration rate. A group of hyperuricemic subjects from New Zealand were reported to have increased binding of urate.[458] However, no data regarding urate clearance were included in this report. Thus, there is no direct evidence to support this mechanism of hyperuricemia.

Enhanced Reabsorption. The administration of pyrazinamide results in a transient reduction of urinary excretion of uric acid without affecting glomerular filtration rate.[459,460] This is due to inhibition of tubular secretion of uric acid.[461,462] In humans, the increase in urinary uric acid secretion caused by infusion of lithium urate is suppressed by pyrazinamide.[463] This is the basis of the pyrazinamide suppression test[377] which was previously used to evaluate the relative contributions of tubular reabsorption and secretion to urate excretion. The underlying assumption of the test was that pyrazinamide blocks tubular secretion of urate completely without affecting tubular reabsorption. In the original construction of the model, no allowance for postsecretory reabsorption was made. Thus, the pyrazinamide suppression test grossly underestimates tubular urate secretion.[377,464,465] Originally, data derived from gouty subjects using the pyrazinamide suppression test were interpreted to indicate that decreased secretion of urate in primary underexcretors was responsible for hyperuricemia. Reinterpretation of this data taking postsecretory reabsorption into account suggeted that enhanced reabsorption was the mechanism responsible for hyperuricemia in these gouty subjects.[371,377,464,465] At present, this reinterpretation must be considered equivocal and any conclusion drawn from it tentative at best. There is little direct evidence supporting enhanced reabsorption of urate as the principal mechanism of hyperuricemia on the basis of primary underexcretion.

Decreased Secretion. More recent studies of the renal handling of urate in gouty subjects in which the four-component model was taken into account in the experimental design suggest diminished tubular secretion of urate in underexcretors.[371,373] Rieselbach showed that when plasma urate concentrations were lowered, underexcretors exhibited a secretory rate similar to that of controls.[473] This finding suggested that underexcretors have impaired tubular secretion of urate which normalizes when serum urate levels are decreased.[466] These data raise the question of whether hyperuricemia is the cause or the result of the apparent tubular defect. This question has been addressed by careful analysis of gouty subjects using the pyrazinamide suppression test to assess postsecretory absorption and the probenicid test to evaluate secretory rates. Probenicid inhibits postsecretory reabsorption. Puig et al.[372,467] were able to demonstrate a diminished uricosuric response from probenicid in gouty underexcretors. Furthermore, the tubular urate secretory rate was not influenced by serum urate levels. These data provide strong indirect evidence that a defect in urate tubular secretion is the cause of hyperuricemia in primary underexcretors, but concomitant abnormalities in urate excretion cannot be excluded on the basis of these studies alone. A complete understanding of the mechanisms of primary underexcretion of urate awaits direct evidence of the type obtained by micropuncture analysis.

Secondary Hyperuricemia due to Decreased Urate Excretion

Decreased Glomerular Filtration Rate. The reduced nephron population in chronically diseased kidneys represents perhaps the most common mechanism whereby the clearance of uric acid is decreased.[1] In severe renal disease, there is a striking increase in the fractional excretion of filtered urate. Thus, in the diseased kidney, glomerular filtration assumes the principal homeostatic role for the maintenance of urate excretion.[468] With declining glomerular filtration rate, this mechanism becomes unavailable, and hyperuricemia ensues. The hyperuricemia of renal failure is perhaps the most common pathologic mechanism for secondary renal hyperuricemia.

Increased Reabsorption. Conditions associated with contraction of the extracellular volume result in hyperuricemia due to enhanced reabsorption of urate as well as decreased glomerular filtration rate.[448,469] Conditions such as dehydration, diabetes insipidus, and diuretic therapy are commonly associated with hyperuricemia on this basis.

Diuretic-induced hyperuricemia is particularly common, accounting for as much as 20 percent of all hyperuricemia in hospitalized patients.[9] Some 75 percent of all diuretic-treated subjects exhibit hyperuricemia.[470] Diuretics may induce hyperuricemia by several mechanisms. The principal mechanism involves salt and water losses resulting in volume contraction and enhanced urate reabsorption.[471–473] Thus, hyperuricemia in the setting of diuretic therapy is not the direct effect of the drug on the tubule but a secondary result of volume loss. Additionally, furosemide induces sufficient lacticacidemia to inhibit tubular secretion of urate secondarily.[474]

Decreased Tubular Secretion. Certain organic acids share tubular secretory sites with urate.[1] A variety of organic acids competitively inhibit uric acid excretion in animals and humans. Thus, conditions associated with elevated blood levels of these acids result in hyperuricemia. These include lactate,[130] β-hydroxybutyrate and acetoacetate,[475] branched chain keto acids,[476] and salicylate at low concentrations.[477] The effects of these acids on urate excretion have been interpreted as resulting from the inhibition of tubular secretion.[477,478] Micropuncture studies have provided direct evidence for impaired urate secretion in this setting.[479]

Undetermined Mechanisms. Other drugs affect the renal clearance of urate including pyrazinamide,[480] ethambutol,[481] nicotinic acid,[482,483] methoxyflurane,[484] levodopa,[485] cyclosporin A,[486] catecholamines and β-adrenoreceptor blockers,[487] theophylline,[488] and warfarin.[489] Also, several nonsteroidal anti-inflammatory drugs—diflunisal, azapropazone, indomethacin—decrease the renal clearance of urate.[490] The mechanisms whereby renal clearance of urate is reduced by these pharmacologic agents are undetermined and probably complex. For instance, nicotinic acid reduces urate clearance[483] and depletes PP-ribose-P in erythrocytes but stimulates *de novo* purine synthesis.[482,474]

Chronic lead intoxication has long been recognized as a cause of gout.[491–494] Lead intoxication results in hyperuricemia because of impaired renal excretion of urate.[93,492] Although increased reabsorption may be responsible based on the pyrazinamide suppression test, the relative roles of reabsorption and secretion of uric acid in "saturnine gout" remain undetermined.[93]

GENETIC BASIS

Idiopathic Gout and Hyperuricemia

Galen was the first physician to recognize the familial nature of gout. Modern studies report a wide variation of familial incidence rates ranging from 6 to 72 percent.[1,495,496] A review of five published series examining the familial incidence of gout suggests the incidence of gout averages 20 percent among hyperuricemic relatives of gouty subjects.[497] These data strongly suggested that hyperuricemia segregated according to the presence or absence of a dominant autosomal allele.[498,499] Estimates of the penetrance of this putative dominant allele are 84 percent in heterozygous males and 14 percent in heterozygous females.[499]

There are also population studies that support the single dominant gene hypothesis. Studies in England,[500] in Pittsburgh,[501,502] of Filipino males living in the United States,[503] and of residents of the Mariana Islands[504] all showed bimodal distributions of serum uric acid values.

Other investigators have challenged the single autosomal dominant gene hypothesis arguing that hyperuricemia is a polygenic trait.[505,506] Reexamination of Smyth's original kindreds by Neel failed to provide convincing evidence for bimodality in the distribution of serum urate values that had previously been reported.[506] Thus, he concluded that the hypothesis of multifactorial inheritance was considered at least as likely as the autosomal dominant gene hypothesis.

More recently, linkage analysis has been applied to familial hyperuricemia in families with familial hypertriglyceridemia.[137,144] Linkage of these two disorders suggests the close association of the genes responsible for both phenotypes. Similar linkage has been noted in some kindreds with familial nephropathies.[118,121,506] Interestingly, familial hypouricemia has also been linked to abnormalities in lipid metabolism.[137] It seems likely that primary gout is due to both single gene abnormalities and polygenic mechanisms in different kindreds.

Large population studies on a variety of homogeneous and heterogeneous populations have also indicated strong hereditary determinants of hyperuricemia.[10,501,507] These studies also suggest a polygenic origin for hyperuricemia. An examination of Blackfoot and Pima Indians indicates that some of the genes involved in polygenic transmission were autosomal dominants while others were X-linked dominants.[1] In two other large population studies, there was no evidence of bimodality of urate concentrations in frequency histograms, favoring a multifactorial inheritance pattern.[10,507]

In precocious gout, i.e., severe gout of early onset, the probability of a positive family history is increased. Gout thus illustrates the theme that early onset multifactorial disease is likely to be more severe, is more difficult to manage, and is likely to have an overt genetic component.[507a]

A synthesis of all available data suggests that serum uric acid concentrations are under the control of multiple genes. The probability of detecting dominant genes may well be a function of the basis of selection of the group for study. Complete understanding of the heredity of hyperuricemia awaits definition of the exact biochemical mechanisms in each family. The techniques of molecular genetics should speed the resolution of this interesting problem.

Gout Associated with Specific Inborn Errors

Superactive Variants of Phosphoribosylpyrophosphatase Synthetase. The syndrome of overactivity of PP-ribose-P synthetase was first described in 1972 by Sperling.[293,294] The first subjects to be described were brothers who had the early onset of severe hyperuricemia, renal colic, and gout. The serum urate concentration in the proband was 13.6 mg/dl, and his urinary excretion of uric acid was 2400 mg/24 h. This overproduction of uric acid reflected a markedly accelerated rate of PP-ribose-P synthesis[293] which was subsequently shown to be due to a variant form of superactive PP-ribose-P synthetase with altered kinetic properties.[508] The enzyme was found to be relatively insensitive to inhibition by the nucleotides GDP, ADP, and AMP as well as 2,3-DPG.[385,508,509] Thus, the enzyme was resistant to control by nucleotides at their normal intracellular concentrations, but catalytic activity per molecule was normal.

Subsequent to this description, at least seven kindreds have been described in which purine overproduction is the result of excessive rates of PP-ribose-P synthesis due to abnormalities of the synthetase.[1,296,510–512] Clinically, all affected subjects had severe hyperuricemia and hyperuricaciduria. Gout and nephrolithiasis were of precocious onset, usually in the second or third decades. Additionally, the gout tends to be unusually severe. Metabolic studies confirmed the massive acceleration of PP-ribose-P synthesis in red cells and cultured fibroblasts in every subject. However, investigation of the kinetic, catalytic, and regulatory properties of the different variants displayed remarkable heterogeneity.

In the second kindred described, PP-ribose-P synthetase activity was three times that found in normal erythrocytes.[296,297] Increased enzyme activity (maximal velocity) was seen at all concentrations of inorganic phosphate tested. Additionally, the enzyme had normal affinities for substrates and normal responsiveness to purine nucleotide end-product inhibition. Immunologic studies employing antibody inhibition titration showed an increased specific activity of the enzyme with a normal number of enzyme molecules per erythrocyte. Thus, the structural alterations of this enzyme resulted in enhanced catalytic activity rather than the abnormal regulatory behavior of the synthetase.

Yet another subject provided the prototype of the third variant of PRPP synthetase overactivity.[509] The defect in this kindred is an increased affinity of PP-ribose-P synthetase for the substrate ribose-5-phosphate. Because of this kinetic abnormality, the mutant form of the enzyme catalyzes the synthesis of PP-ribose-P at a faster than normal rate at any concentration of ribose-5-phosphate below saturation.

A fourth variant of PP-ribose-P overactivity studied by Becker reflects a combination of both abnormal resistance of the enzyme to feedback inhibition by purine nucleotides as well as a hyperbolic, rather than sigmoidal, activation curve with increasing phosphate concentrations.[297] This mutant enzyme, therefore, has both regulatory and catalytic abnormalities. Other mutant enzymes have been characterized in which the synthetase is defective in its response to competitive inhibition by ADP and the essential activator, inorganic phosphate.[298]

Some interesting disease associations have been described with PP-ribose-P synthetase overactivity. Among these is a patient with this enzymopathy and the temporally related onset of symmetric lipomatosis.[513] However, this subject had a brother with presumed primary gout but without lipomatosis, and PP-ribose-P synthetase activity was reported to be normal in an unrelated patient with benign symmetric lipomatosis. More recently, PP-ribose-P phosphate synthetase superactivity has been associated with deafness.[514] This relationship has now been observed in more than one kindred. Hearing loss in these subjects appears to be sensorineural although its relationship to the enzymopathy is not understood. Further evidence that PP-ribose-P synthetase may perform a critical role in neural development or function is provided by the description of hypouricemic subjects deficient in PP-ribose-P activity who were severely mentally retarded with progressive electroencephalographic abnormalities.[515,516] However, synthetase activity was normal in fibroblasts derived from these subjects (M.A. Becker, unpublished data).

There is strong evidence that PP-ribose-P synthetase variants with superactivity result from mutations of the structural gene. Studies of superactive enzymes have provided evidence for structural alterations underlying superactivity such as diminished thermal stability and altered electrophoretic properties.[517] Furthermore, enzyme superactivity is transmitted as an X-linked trait,[518,519] and the gene encoding PP-ribose-P synthetase has been localized to the long arm of chromosome X.[292] To date, however, the demonstration of altered primary structure of the enzyme protein itself has not been accomplished, but the weight of evidence suggests structural gene mutations as the basis for enzyme superactivity.

There is also evidence that there may be selective expression of PP-ribose-P synthetase superactivity in some cells. Lymphoblast lines derived from individuals with PP-ribose-P synthetase overactivity showed phenotypic differences when compared to cultured fibroblasts derived from the same individuals.[517] In lymphoblast lines derived from subjects with catalytic defects, normal enzyme activity, PP-ribose-P concentrations, and rates of purine synthesis were found. The enzyme in lymphoblasts from a subject with combined catalytic and regulatory defects showed restoration of normal maximal reaction velocity in lymphoblasts, but continued to express purine nucleotide inhibitor resistance. A second regulatory defect in substrate binding was also demonstrable in lymphoblasts that was identical to the enzyme defect from fibroblasts derived from the same patients. Thus, it seems that variant forms of PP-ribose-P synthetase from lymphoblasts of patients with catalytic superactivity differ both structurally and functionally from their fibroblast counterparts. This does not appear to be the case, however, when the variant enzyme has regulatory defects, in which case the lymphoblast enzyme appears both structurally and functionally identical to that of fibroblasts.

Irrespective of the nature of the mechanism underlying enzyme overactivity, the result of all types of defects is an excessive rate of generation of PP-ribose-P. As reviewed above, elevated PP-ribose-P levels drive *de novo* biosynthesis resulting in overexcretion of purines (Fig. 37-18). Although the prevalence of this defect is not known, it is probably rare.

Hypoxanthine-Guanine Phosphoribosyltransferase Deficiency. The virtually complete deficiency of HPRT activity is associated with a syndrome of mental and growth retardation, choreoathetosis, spasticity, and a bizarre compulsion to self-mutilate.[4,5] This condition is known as the *Lesch-Nyhan syndrome*. There is a dramatic overproduction and overexcretion of uric acid in these patients, and uric acid nephrolithiasis and gout occur as a result. The gene encoding HPRT is on the long arm of the X chromosome, and the disease is transmitted in classic X-linked manner. The Lesch-Nyhan syndrome is discussed in detail in Chap. 38.

Shortly after the description of HPRT deficiency in the Lesch-Hyhan syndrome, adult patients with primary overproduction of uric acid and severe gout were found to have partial deficiency of HPRT activity.[6] Partial HPRT deficiency is also discussed in Chap. 38.

Subjects with partial HPRT deficiency develop severe gouty arthritis at an early age and often have renal stones and crystalluria. Neurologic dysfunction occurs in a minority, and when present tends to be mild. These patients do not self-mutilate. This condition is known as *Kelley-Seegmiller syndrome*. Both Lesch-Nyhan syndrome and Kelley-Seegmiller syndrome have been studied extensively at the molecular level, and these HPRT deficiency states are among the most valuable genetic models for inborn errors yet described. The metabolic basis for overproduction of purines and the subsequent hyperuricemia and hyperuricaciduria are discussed above (Fig. 37-19). The basis for the neurologic dysfunction remains unclear.

Purine Enzymopathies and Neurologic Disease. Defective function of several purine nucleotide synthetic enzymes have now been associated with various forms of neurologic dysfunction. As noted above, HPRT deficiency results in Lesch-Nyhan syndrome, PP-ribose-P synthetase deficiency has been associated with mental retardation, while overactivity of the enzyme can be accompanied by sensorineural hearing loss. Recently, the inherited deficiency of adenylosuccinase has been associated with psychomotor retardation and autism[520] and other forms of neurobehavioral dysfunction including epilepsy, spastic tetraplegia, and hydrocephaly. Diagnosis of this disorder depends upon detection of large amounts of succinyloaminoimidazolecarboxamide riboside (succinyl Z-riboside) and succinyloadenosine in the urine by thin-layer chromatography or cation-exchange chromatography[521] (Fig. 37-13). These experiments of nature offer opportunities to examine critical features of neural development as it relates to purine metabolism.

Glycogen Storage Disease.

GLUCOSE-6-PHOSPHATASE DEFICIENCY (VON GIERKE'S, TYPE I). Hyperuricemia and gout occur frequently in glucose-6-phosphatase deficiency.[404,405,409,410,522–530] The hyperuricemia results from both a decreased renal clearance of urate secondary to lacticacidemia[522–524] and ketonemia[410] and increased production of uric acid[251,410,541,542] (Fig. 37-24).

MYOGENIC HYPERURICEMIA. Hyperuricemia has been reported in patients with three glycogen storage diseases with muscle involvement either in the basal state or following exercise.[429,431,531–538] This abnormality has been observed in debranching enzyme deficiency (type III), myophosphorylase deficiency (type V), and muscle phosphofructokinase deficiency (type VII). The mechanism for this disorder is related to excessive ATP degradation in muscle tissue during exercise secondary to decreased formation of carbohydrate substrates necessary for ATP synthesis (Fig. 37-25).

TREATMENT

The existence of hyperuricemia, a common biochemical abnormality, requires investigation to discern the cause. In deciding whether treatment is appropriate, it is also important to determine if the patient is symptomatic as a result of the hyperuricemia. Therapy is appropriate for gout, renal calculi associated with hyperuricemia, or hyperuricaciduria, as well as for the prevention of acute uric acid nephropathy.

Asymptomatic Hyperuricemia

Two main arguments for the treatment of asymptomatic hyperuricemia revolve around the possibilities that hyperuricemia causes renal damage or is a risk factor for coronary artery disease.

Studies have suggested that hyperuricemia per se has little, if any, harmful effect on renal function.[1,44,88–94] When renal function does deteriorate in patients with gout, it is correlated with increasing age and the development of associated disease such as independently occurring nephropathy, hypertension with nephrosclerosis, diabetes with nephropathy, renal arteriosclerosis, increased mobilizable lead, or renal calculi with pyelonephritis. Clinically significant azotemia attributable to hyperuricemia does not occur with serum urate levels less than 13 mg/dl in men and 10 mg/dl in women.[88] A 10 percent decrease in the creatinine clearance has been attributed to the gouty state alone.

While hyperuricemia has been proposed as a cardiovascular risk factor, this putative relationship may be the result of the association of hyperuricemia with hypertension. It has been clearly shown that there is a high incidence of hyperuricemia in hypertension and vice versa.[1,147–154] Increased renal vascular and total peripheral resistance parallel rising serum urate concentrations. Therefore, essential hypertension may lead to an elevation in the serum urate concentration, which is an indicator of renal vascular involvement, and the hypertension itself may be the major risk factor for coronary artery disease. In patients with hyperuricemia, additional risk factors such as diabetes mellitus, increasing age, hyperlipidemia, and obesity may also contribute to the association between elevated serum urate concentration and coronary artery disease.

The decision to treat hyperuricemia uncomplicated by articular gout, urolithiasis, or nephropathy is an exercise in clinical judgment. Differences of opinion reflect the paucity of firm data on hyperuricemia as an independent risk factor for hypertension, atherosclerosis, and renal disease. In our opinion, asymptomatic hyperuricemia is important only as it predisposes toward symptomatic hyperuricemia, which is associated with articular gout, tophi, urate nephropathy, uric acid or calcium oxalate stones, and acute uric acid nephropathy. Therefore, the risks associated with asymptomatic hyperuricemia are equivalent to the statistical risks of development of these manifestations and their consequences.

The magnitude of the risk of articular gout or tophi is related to the degree and duration of hyperuricemia and the sex and age of the patient. Gouty arthritis and tophi are treatable and reversible whenever they occur and by themselves are not life-threatening. It is reasonable to withhold antihyperuricemic therapy until gouty arthritis occurs. Similarly, antihyperuricemic therapy should not be instituted as prophylaxis against the development of stone disease but should be started promptly with discovery of a stone in the hyperuricemic or hyperuricaciduric patient. The yearly risk of stone formation in asymptomatic hyperuricemia is less than 0.27 percent.[88]

We recommend consideration of antihyperuricemic therapy in the asymptomatic hyperuricemic subject in three specific clinical situations. First, treatment should be considered in patients with hyperuricemia that is persistent and is characterized by a serum urate concentration above 13 mg/dl. This level is not ordinarily achieved by altered renal function alone and thus usually predicts some degree of uric acid overproduction and its potential complications. This serum urate concentration may have some nephrotoxic properties.[88] Second, treatment should be considered in the patient excreting more than 1100 mg uric acid per 24 h since these patients have as high as a 50 percent risk for forming a uric acid calculus.[1,44] Finally, patients about to receive cytolytic therapy that is expected to lead to substantial cell killing should be treated with allopurinol to prevent acute uric acid nephropathy.

Gouty Arthritis

The therapeutic aims in gout are to terminate the acute attack as promptly and gently as possible; to prevent recurrences of acute gouty arthritis; to prevent or reverse complications of the disease resulting from deposition of sodium urate crystals in joints, kidneys, or other sites; to prevent or reverse associated features of the illness that are also deleterious, such as obesity, hypertriglyceridemia, or hypertension; and to prevent formation of renal calculi.[539]

In considering these aims, an important distinction must be made between the management of the acute inflammatory manifestations on the one hand and the control of hyperuricemia (and hyperuricaciduria) on the other. Drugs that are highly effective in the treatment of acute gout are generally of no value in the control of hyperuricemia; conversely, those drugs useful in the control of hyperuricemia are of no immediate value in the treatment of the acute gouty attack.

Anti-Inflammatory Therapy. Acute gouty arthritis can be effectively treated in most instances with intravenous colchicine or oral indomethacin. Virtually any nonsteroidal anti-inflammatory drug or intra-articular corticosteroids may be used as well. Irrespective of the anti-inflammatory treatment used, the earlier such therapy is initiated after onset of the acute attack, the more effective it will be.

Intravenous (IV) colchicine is highly effective if used within 24 to 48 h of the onset of an attack of acute gouty arthritis. It is most commonly utilized in a hospital setting. When 2 mg is diluted into 20 ml of isotonic saline solution and infused slowly and carefully into a vein, the patient should receive relief in 6 to 12 h. If a dramatic response is not observed within 6 h, 1 mg diluted appropriately may be repeated every 6 h up to a total dose of 4 mg during any one attack. If a patient has been receiving prophylactic colchicine on a long-term basis, no more than 2 mg should be given IV at the time of the acute attack. Care should be taken not to infiltrate colchicine into the extravascular space, since extravasation can lead to inflammation and necrosis. Gastrointestinal side effects such as nausea, vomiting, diarrhea, and abdominal pain do not occur with IV colchicine if oral colchicine therapy is stopped before the institution of the IV program. Leukopenia is a serious potential complication, particularly in the patient receiving previous maintenance colchicine or in the patient with hepatic or renal disease. Indeed, IV colchicine should be considered contraindicated in the patient with leukopenia or substantial hepatic or renal disease. Although quite effective, oral colchicine is not generally recommended because of the frequency of nausea, vomiting, and diarrhea.

While colchicine remains efficaceous, the reports of severe bone marrow toxicity and death[540–543] and myopathy and neuropathy[544] indicate that the drug should be used with caution, if at all, to treat acute gouty arthritis. It is containdicated when there is significant kidney or liver disease, which provide major pathways of metabolism and excretion. Alternative effective therapy is currently available with nonsteroidal anti-inflammatory drugs. Indomethacin, naproxen, fenoprofen, ibuprofen, indoprofen, sulindac, piroxicam, and others may be used in standard dosages. If therapy with the usual drugs is not possible or contraindicated, intra-articular corticosteroids are useful in the treatment of acute gout limited to a single joint or bursa.

Prophylactic Therapy. Acute gouty arthritis may develop in any patient with hyperuricemia. Episodes of gouty arthritis may also occur during the first 6 to 12 months after initiation of antihyperuricemic therapy. Prophylactic therapy with low-dose oral colchicine, 0.6 mg twice per day, is helpful in any patient with a history of gout. In the patients who cannot tolerate low-dose colchicine, indomethacin, 25 mg twice per day, is also effective. Prophylactic therapy can be discontinued 6 to 12 months after the last attack, assuming that the serum urate concentration has been in the normal range and all visible urate deposits have disappeared.

A recent reappraisal of colchicine prophylaxis confirms its efficacy.[545] Its mechanism of action is most likely the suppression of chemotactic factor release by synovial lining cells.

Antihyperuricemic Therapy. Antihyperuricemic drugs are the definitive means for controlling hyperuricemia. While it is important to control and prevent acute attacks of gouty arthritis with anti-inflammatory agents, it is the long-term control of hyperuricemia that ultimately modifies the natural history of the gouty diathesis. In general, the aim of antihyperuricemic therapy is to reduce the serum urate concentration below 6 mg/dl, which is well below the concentration (6.4 mg/dl) at which monosodium urate saturates extracellular fluid.[539]

Reduction of the serum urate concentration is achieved pharmacologically by increasing the renal excretion of uric acid or by decreasing its synthesis. The drugs most widely used to increase uric acid excretion are probenecid and sulfinpyrazone; others including benzbromarone, benziodarone, and zoxazolamine have also been used in Europe. For reducing uric acid synthesis, allopurinol is the most effective drug available. The choice of an antihyperuricemic drug should have a rational basis, because the treatment of hyperuricemia and gout is ordinarily continued indefinitely. Although allopurinol has gained increasing use in the treatment of hyperuricemia, there remains an important place for uricosuric compounds.

In patients with gout who excrete less than 700 mg of uric acid per day, a reduction in serum urate concentration can be achieved equally well with allopurinol or a uricosuric drug such as probenecid or sulfinpyrazone. Either of these agents may prevent the deterioration of renal function in patients with primary gout.[539] There is no clear evidence that uricosuric drugs are superior to the inhibitors of xanthine oxidase or vice versa in preventing renal damage from hyperuricemia in subjects with a normal excretion of uric acid and no history of renal calculi. All other things being equal, a uricosuric drug might be tried first, since these agents are known to be relatively safe on the basis of more than 30 years of clinical use. A reasonable candidate for treatment with a uricosuric drug is a gouty patient with the following features: no tophi, younger than 60 years, normal renal function, creatinine clearance greater than 80 ml/min, normal 24-h urinary uric acid excretion (less than 700 mg/24 h), and no history of renal calculi.[539] Clearly, a large proportion of gouty patients meet all of these criteria. Cost and convenience of administration have become the more important concerns.

URICOSURIC DRUGS. Uricosuric drugs are weak organic acids that increase the renal clearance of uric acid by inhibiting renal tubular reabsorption of uric acid at a postsecretory site. Therapy with uricosuric drugs is started at a low dose to minimize the risk of renal calculi associated with the transient increase in uric acid excretion. The maintenance of adequate urine flow and alkalinization of the urine with oral sodium bicarbonate (2 to 6 g/day) or sodium citrate (Scholl's solution, 20 to 60 ml/day) further diminish the possibility of uric acid stone formation but are probably unnecessary in most patients. Sulfinpyrazone is started at a dose of 50 mg twice per day, increasing in a few days to 100 mg three or four times each day. The maximum effective dose is 800 mg/day. Probenecid is started at a dose of 250 mg twice per day, increasing after several weeks to 500 to 1000 mg two or three times each day. The maximum effective dose is 3 g/day.

Probenecid and sulfinpyrazone are effective for most gouty patients. From 75 to 80 percent of patients with tophaceous gout have demonstrated improvement. In the remaining 20 percent of patients whose conditions are not brought under ideal control, failure is a result of drug intolerance, concomitant salicylate ingestion, or impaired renal function. Salicylate ingestion at any dose blocks the uricosuric effect of probenecid and sulfinpyrazone. When the glomerular filtration rate is below 20 to 30 ml/min, most uricosuric drugs are ineffective. The exception is benzbromarone, which may have some antihyperuricemic activity with impaired renal function.

The major side effects of uricosuric drugs include skin rash, precipitation of acute gouty arthritis, gastrointestinal intolerance, and uric acid calculus formation. Probenecid has a calciuric action in gouty patients.[546] This complication of probenecid therapy reinforces the contraindication for use in gouty patients with nephrolithiasis. Beyond this probenecid should not be used in hyperuricemic cystinuric patients because of increased cystine, and decreased cysteine-penicillamine mixed disulfide and penicillamine disulfide metabolites.[547] Uricosuric drugs alter the transport of other organic acids across cell membranes, resulting in numerous drug interactions. For example, the renal excretion of penicillin and ampicillin is decreased by probenecid, and thus the half-life of these antibiotics is prolonged. The half-life of rifampin is also prolonged because the hepatic uptake of rifampin is impaired by probenecid. Finally, autoimmune hemolytic anemia has been reported with probenecid therapy.[548,549]

Other new drugs have uricosuric properties. These include diflunisal, azapropazone, and amflutizole.[550–554] It is unclear whether these will be therapeutically efficaceous.

XANTHINE OXIDASE INHIBITORS. Allopurinol inhibits uric acid synthesis. The serum urate concentration is decreased by allopurinol due to inhibition of xanthine oxidase, the enzyme which catalyzes the oxidation of hypoxanthine to xanthine and uric acid (Fig. 37-27). Allopurinol is itself a substrate for xanthine oxidase and is oxidized to oxipurinol. In fact, 6 h after a single dose of allopurinol, it is no longer detectable in the plasma and only oxipurinol is present.[1,555] The latter actively inhibits xanthine oxidase.

By virtue of its being a structural analogue of hypoxanthine, allopurinol [4-hydroxypyrazido(3,4-*d*)pyrimidine] undergoes complex interconversions (Fig. 37-28).[1,555] There are three pathways of metabolism. Allopurinol can be converted to a nucleoside 5′-monophosphate derivative [1-*N*(5′-phosphoribosyl)allopurinol]. This can be dephosphorylated to a nucleoside derivative [1-*N*(5′-ribosyl)allopurinol]. The latter compound can also be formed directly from allopurinol by the reaction of purine nucleoside phosphorylase. The major pathway of allopurinol metabolism is oxidation to oxipurinol.

Oxipurinol is a structural analogue of xanthine and has four distinct pathways of metabolism. In parallel to allopurinol xanthine is a substrate for hypoxanthine-guanine phosphoribosyltransferase and purine nucleoside phosphorylase. The purine nucleotide and nucleoside derivatives are similarly formed. In contrast to allopurinol, oxipurinol is also a substrate for orotate phosphoribosyltransferase and pyrimidine nucleoside phosphorylase. The compounds formed are 7-*N*(5′-phosphoribosyl)-oxipurinol and 7-*N*(5′-ribosyl)oxipurinol.

Allopurinol and its derivatives have multiple effects upon purine and pyrimidine metabolism.[1,555] Xanthine oxidase is potently inhibitied by allopurinol and oxipurinol. Allopurinol is a competitive inhibitor, and both allopurinol and oxipurinol produce pseudoirreversible inactivation of xanthine oxidase.

Fig. 37-27 Effect of allopurinol on uric acid formation in human beings. Purine nucleotides are eventually degraded to hypoxanthine, xanthine, and uric acid. Final steps are catalyzed by xanthine oxidase. Allopurinol is converted to oxipurinol by this enzyme. Both compounds inhibit xanthine oxidase. Effects on plasma and urinary concentrations are indicated as increase, decrease, or no substantial change.

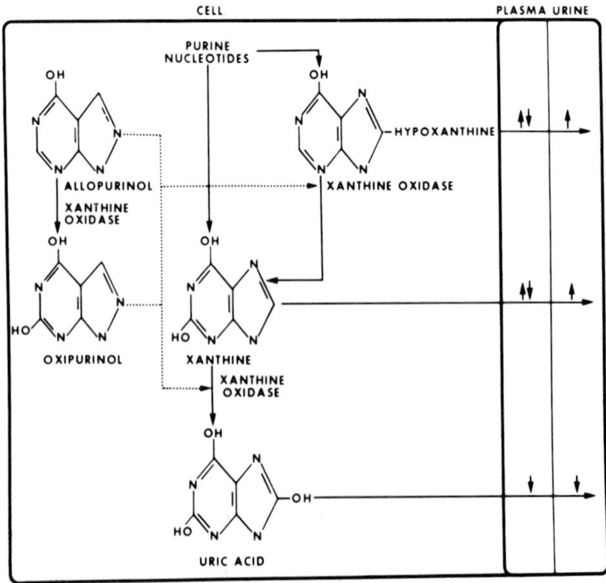

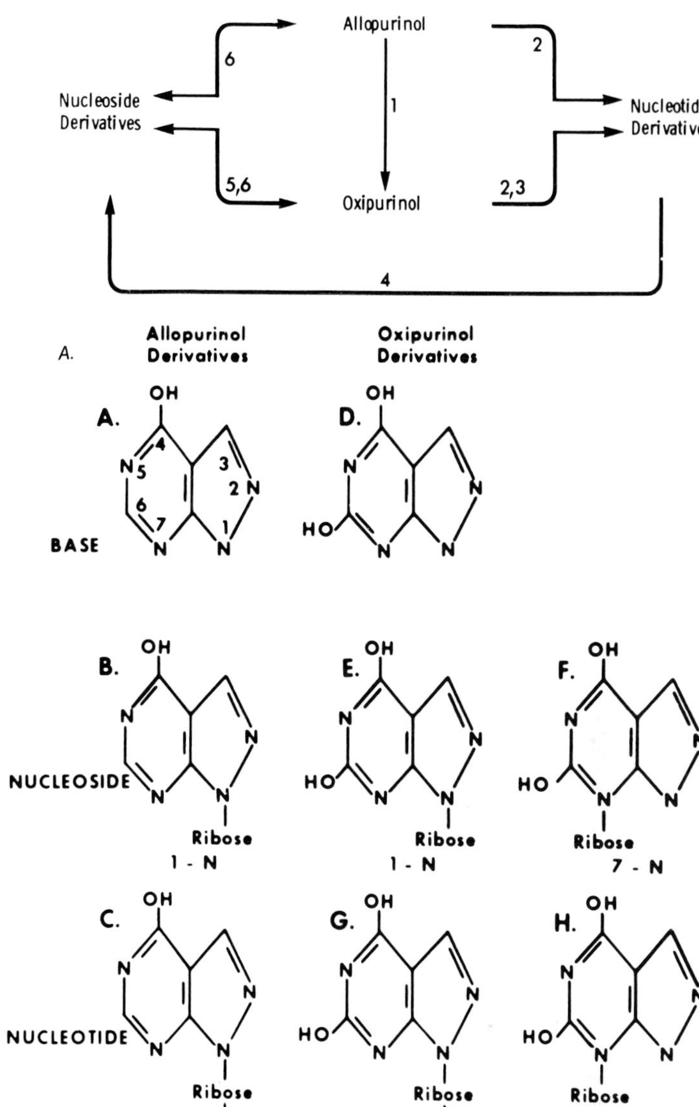

Fig. 37-28 Allopurinol metabolism in humans. *A.* Allopurinol undergoes a complex series of metabolic alterations. Allopurinol is oxidized to oxipurinol. Small quantities of these compounds are converted to the nucleoside and nucleotide derivatives. The reactions are catalyzed by the enzymes indicated: 1 = xanthine oxidase; 2 = hypoxanthine-guanine phosphoribosyltransferase; 3 = orotate phosphoribosyltransferase; 4 = 5′-nucleotidase; 5 = pyrimidine nucleoside phosphorylase; 6 = purine nucleoside phosphorylase. *B.* The structure of the allopurinol metabolites are outlined. Oxipurinol has two types of derivatives, the 7-N or 1-N, depending on whether metabolism occurred by orotate phosphoribosyltransferase or hypoxanthine-guanine phosphoribosyltransferase, respectively.

The result is a buildup of hypoxanthine and xanthine in body fluids and a pharmacologic xanthinuria. Increased urinary excretion of orotic acid and orotidine during allopurinol therapy has been related to inhibition of *de novo* pyrimidine synthesis at orotidylic decarboxylase by allopurinol ribonucleotide. Allopurinol therapy also decreases total urinary purine excretion either by inhibition of *de novo* purine synthesis by nucleotide derivatives of allopurinol and oxipurinol[1,555] or by causing the enhanced reutilization of hypoxanthine with a secondary decrease of *de novo* purine synthesis.[353] The decrease in total urinary purine excretion described during allopurinol therapy requires hypoxanthine-guanine phosphoribosyltransferase deficiency and is not observed with a deficiency of this enzyme.[1] This produces a pharmacogenetic abnormality.

The usual daily dose is 300 mg; occasionally, in particularly resistant cases, 600 mg/day may be necessary. Allopurinol may be taken in a single daily dose. In renal failure the half-life of oxipurinol, the active metabolite of allopurinol, is prolonged. Therefore, the dose should be reduced in the rare patient with renal insufficiency who requires antihyperuricemic therapy. Within 1 to 2 days of allopurinol administration, the serum urate concentration begins to decrease, reaching a minimum value within 7 to 14 days. After 3 to 6 months of normouricemia, a reduction in the frequency of gouty attacks may be expected. An apparent failure of allopurinol to decrease the serum urate concentration to the desired level is more often related to a lack of patient compliance than to ineffectiveness of the drug.

Allopurinol has proven to be highly effective for more than 20 years of observation.[555] Recent studies of the half-life of oxipurinol indicate a monoexponential decay with a half-life ranging from 12.2 to 17.3 h.[556–558] The half-life can be markedly increased to 49.9 h with a low protein diet.[558] Therefore, in protein-malnourished patients, the dose of allopurinol should probably be reduced. Parenteral and rectal administration are desirable for patients unable to ingest oral medication. However, the drug is limited by poor solubility.[557] The latter may be improved with a prodrug approach by N_1-acyclomethyl derivatives of allopurinol.[559]

The precipitation of acute gouty arthritis is the most common side effect of allopurinol therapy. Adverse reactions to allopurinol occurred in about 3.5 percent of a large hospital population.[560] Half of these patients had skin rashes; it remains unclear whether allopurinol or another drug was the cause. After the exclusion of skin reactions, the most common abnormalities are hematologic, diarrhea, and drug fever. However, the life-threatening toxicity syndrome, consisting of an erythematous desquamative skin rash, fever, hepatitis, eosinophilia, and worsening renal function, is noteworthy.[561–562] The usual setting for this syndrome is a standard dose of allopurinol in the face of impaired renal function. This disorder, which has a mortality of approximately 25 perent, should be avoided by using allopurinol for appropriate indications and reducing the dose of allopurinol to the minimum required to keep the serum urate level below 6.0 mg/dl. Other reactions include gastrointestinal intolerance, leukopenia, vasculitis, and interstitial nephritis. Xanthine lithiasis or xanthine crystalluria is unusual and has been observed only in patients who have received massive cytolytic tumor therapy or have hypoxanthine-guanine phosphoribosyltransferase deficiency. Side effects of allopurinol therapy are most common in patients with renal insufficiency.

Several drug-drug interactions involving allopurinol are important clinically. The effects of compounds that are inactivated by xanthine oxidase, such as 6-mercaptopurine and azathioprine, will be potentiated by allopurinol administration. An increased incidence of bone marrow suppression has been observed in patients taking allopurinol who are also receiving cyclophosphamide.[1,539] Allopurinol has been shown to reduce the activity of hepatic microsomal drug-metabolizing enzymes and thus to prolong the half-lives of antipyrine and dicumarol. Allopurinol also enhances the activity of warfarin sodium. Finally, a threefold increase in the incidence of ampicillin-induced skin rash has been observed in patients receiving allopurinol; the basis for this is unclear.

Allopurinol and a uricosuric drug may be used together to further reduce the serum urate concentration in the unusual patient incompletely responsive to either agent alone. Uricosuric drugs increase the clearance of oxipurinol and decrease the excretion of oxypurines. The half-life of probenecid is prolonged by about 50 percent by allopurinol, possibly due to the inhibitory effect of this latter compound on microsomal drug-metabolizing enzymes. Despite these interactions, it is generally acceptable to use both drugs together at their usual dosage.[1,539]

Table 37-3 Purine-Free Diet: Sample Menu (2500 Calories, 70 g Protein)*

Household measure		*Gram weight*
Breakfast		
Orange juice	1 cup	240
Cream of wheat	1 cup	240
2% Milk	1 cup	240
Egg	1	55
Toast	2 slices	45
Margarine	2 teaspoons	10
Jelly	1 tablespoon	20
Sugar	2 teaspoons	10
Coffee (decaffeinated)		
Lunch		
Grilled cheese sandwich		
Bread	2 slices	45
Cheese	2 ounces	60
Margarine	2 teaspoons	10
Apple	1 medium	150
Celery sticks	1 large stalk	50
Sugar	1 teaspoon	5
Coffee (decaffeinated)		
Supper		
Spaghetti		
Tomato sauce	½ cup	135
Spaghetti noodles	1 cup	150
Broccoli	⅔ cup	100
Tossed salad		
Lettuce	1 serving	100
Tomato	½ small	50
Italian dressing	2 tablespoons	30
French bread	1 slice	20
Margarine	2 teaspoons	10
Peaches, canned	½ cup	100
2% Milk	1 cup	240
Sugar	1 teaspoon	5
Coffee (decaffeinated)		
Snack		
Banana	1 medium	150

*Typical diet used for research purposes at the Clinical Research Center, University Hospital, University of Michigan, Ann Arbor, Michigan.

SOURCE: Courtesy of Constance Hydrich, Head Dietitian, Clinical Research Center.

DIETARY MANAGEMENT. Dietary purines are normally extensively absorbed and converted to their end product in the gut,[563–565] where there is a substantial quantity of purine catabolic enzymes, including xanthine oxidase. Adenine seems to be handled differently, and a significant proportion of unaltered adenine is absorbed and incorporated into liver, kidney, heart, and spleen.[564,565] Administration of AMP and GMP to normal humans leads to expansion of the uric acid pool, increased daily turnover of uric acid, rise in the renal clearance of uric acid, and no inhibition of endogenous urate synthesis.[566]

A diet restricted in purine content will normally reduce the urinary excretion of uric acid by 200 by 400 mg/day and lower the mean serum urate value only about 1 mg/100 ml.[1,44] The latter is ineffective from a therapeutic point of view. In some patients the reduction is even greater. For example, increased serum urate levels, hyperuricosuria, dysuria, and uric acid crystalluria have been associated with the substantial purine content in high-dose pancreatic extract therapy in cystic fibrosis.[567,568] Under these specific conditions reduction of pancreatic enzyme therapy dose decreases serum urate levels and urinary uric acid.

Severe dietary purine restriction is not often necessary, unless renal function is very poor and the control of hyperuricemia with drugs is unsatisfactory. A typical low purine diet is proposed in Table 37-3. Unfortunately, the low purine diet may be atherogenic in this setting. In addition, a diet with a high fructose content may increase the levels of both uric acid and triglycerides.[143,401,412,569–571]

Renal Disease

The major treatable renal diseases related to hyperuricemia are acute uric acid nephropathy and nephrolithiasis.

Acute Uric Acid Nephropathy. Acute uric acid nephropathy may be effectively prevented in patients at high risk by alkalinizing the urine above pH 6.5, maintaining high urine flow, and prophylactically administering allopurinol.[44,539] These measures decrease the uric acid concentration and increase uric acid solubility.

More detailed studies of the acute tumor lysis syndrome indicate that despite allopurinol therapy urinary uric acid may still increase, and urinary excretion of xanthine can increase to concentrations capable of precipitating xanthine nephropathy.[572] Alternative approaches using increased destruction of uric acid seem indicated. The administration of urate oxidase appears promising in prophylaxis against renal damage.[1,573,574]

Polyethylene glycol-conjugated uricase may be particularly useful, since it has a prolonged half-life and appears to be non-antigenic.[573]

If the patient develops acute renal failure, the rapid application of preventive measures may reverse the problem. If this fails, the only effective therapy is hemodialysis, which is 10 to 20 times more effective than peritoneal dialysis in clearing uric acid, since uric acid crosses the peritoneum relatively poorly.[44]

Nephrolithiasis. Uric acid stones may be managed with alkalinization of urine to pH 6.0 to 6.5 to increase uric acid solubility, allopurinol therapy, high fluid intake (2 to 3 liters/day), and dietary purine reduction to decrease uric acid concentration. A reduction of dietary purines, high urine flow, and allopurinol therapy may be useful in some patients with recurrent calcium oxalate stones and disorders of uric acid metabolism.[44]

Allopurinol causes a significant reduction in calcium oxalate stone frequency when there is an associated hyperuricemia or hyperuricaciduria.[104–107] However, it does not seem effective in patients with calcium stones in the absence of hyperuricemia or hyperuricaciduria.[575]

Supported by grants from the United States Public Health Service AM2R01 19675, 5MO1 RR42, and RO1 DK19045. Dr. Palella is the recipient of an Arthritis Investigator Award from the Arthritis Foundation. The authors wish to thank Ardith Listeman, Jeanne Schmaltz, and Holly Gibson for excellent typing of the manuscript.

REFERENCES

1. WYNGAARDEN JB, KELLEY WN: Gout, in Stanbury JB, Wyngaarden JB, Fredrickson DS, Goldstein JL, Brown MS (eds): *The Metabolic Basis of Inherited Disease,* 5th ed. New York, McGraw-Hill, chap 50, p 1043, 1983.
2. APPELBOOM T, BENNETT JC: Gout of the rich and famous. *J Rheum* 13:618, 1986.
3. COPEMAN WS: Historical aspects of gout. *Clin Orthop* 71:14, 1980.
4. LESCH M, NYHAN WL: A familial disorder of uric acid metabolism and central nervous system function. *Am J Med* 36:561, 1964.
5. KELLEY WN, GREENE ML, ROSENBLOOM FM, HENDERSON JF: Hypoxanthine-guanine phosphoribosyltransferase deficiency in gout. *Ann Intern Med* 70:155, 1969.
6. KELLEY WN, ROSENBLOOM FM, HENDERSON JF, SEEGMILLER JE: A specific enzyme defect in gout associated with overproduction of uric acid. *Proc Natl Acad Sci USA* 57:1735, 1967.
7. WILSON JM, STOUT JT, PALELLA TD, DAVIDSON BL, KELLEY WN, CASKEY CT: A molecular survey of hypoxanthine-guanine phosphoribosyltransferase deficiency in man. *J Clin Invest* 77:188, 1986.
8. WYNGAARDEN JB, KELLEY WN: *Gout and Hyperuricemia.* New York, Grune and Stratton, 1976, pp 1–512.
9. PAULUS HE, COUTTS A, CALABRO JJ, KLINENBERG JR: Clinical significance of hyperuricemia in routinely screened hospitalized men. *J Am Med Assoc* 211:277, 1970.
10. MIKKELSON WM, DODGE HJ, VALKENBURG H: The distribution of serum uric acid values in a population unselected as to gout or hyperuricemia: Tecumseh, Michigan, 1959–1960. *Am J Med* 39:242, 1965.
11. AKIZUKI S: Serum uric acid levels among thirty-four thousand people in Japan. *Ann Rheum Dis* 41:272, 1982.
12. HARLAN WR, CORNONI-HUNTLEY J, LEAVERTON PE: Physiologic determinants of serum urate levels in adolescence. *Pediatrics* 63:569, 1979.
13. HARLAN WR, HULL AL, SCHMOUDER RP, THOMPSON FE, LARKIN FA, LANDIS JR: Dietary intake and cardiovascular risk factors, part II. Serum urate, serum cholesterol, and correlates, in *Vital and Health Statistics, United States, 1971–75.* Public Health Service, Washington, DC, March 1983, Series 11, no 227, DHHS Publ no (PHS) 83-1677.
14. GLYNN RJ, CAMPION EW, SILBERT JE: Trends in serum uric acid levels 1961–1980. *Arthritis Rheum* 26:87, 1983.
15. ANTON FM, GARCIA-PUIG J, RAMOS T, GONZALEZ P, ORDAS J: Sex differences in uric acid metabolism in adults: Evidence for a lack of influence of estradiol-17 beta (E_2) on the renal handling of urate. *Metabolism* 35:343, 1986.
16. MARINELLO E, GIUSEPPE R-S, MARCOLONGO R: Plasma follicle-stimulating hormone, luteinizing hormone, and sex hormones in patients with gout. *Arthritis Rheum* 28:127, 1985.
17. KUNTZ D, CHRETIEN JM, RYCKEWAERT A: Distribution and correlations of serum uric acid in two French adult populations. *Semin Hop Paris* 55:241, 1979.
18. ZALOKAR J, LELLOUCH J, CLAUDE JR: Serum urate and gout in 4663 young male workers. *Semin Hop Paris* 57:664, 1981.
19. NISHIOKA K, MIKANAGI K: Hereditary and environmental factors influencing the serum uric acid throughout ten years population study in Japan. *Adv Exp Med Biol* 122A:155, 1980.
20. CURRIE WJC: Prevalence and incidence of the diagnosis of gout in Great Britain. *Ann Rheum Dis* 38:101, 1979.
21. AKIZUKI S: A population study of hyperuricemia and gout in Japan: Analysis of sex, age and occupational differences in thirty-four thousand people living in Nagano Prefecture. *Ryumachi* 22:201, 1982.
22. CAMPION EW, GLYNN RJ, DELABRY LO: Asymptomatic hyperuricemia: The risks and consequences. *Am J Med* 82:422, 1987.
23. WILCOX WR, KHALAF A, WEINBERGER A, KIPPEN I, KLINENBERG JR: Solubility of uric acid and monosodium urate. *Med Biol Eng* 10:522, 1972.
24. SYDENHAM T: *The Works of Thomas Sydenham,* translated from the Latin by RG Lathan, London, New Sydenham Society, vol II, p 124, 1850.
25. HUSKISSON EC, BALME HW: Pseudopodagra: Differential diagnosis of gout. *Lancet* 1:269, 1972.
26. HADLER NM, FRANCK WA, BRESS NM, ROBINSON DR: Acute polyarticular gout. *Am J Med* 56:715, 1974.
27. RADDATZ DA, MAHOWALD ML, BILKA PJ: Acute polyarticular gout. *Ann Rheum Dis* 42:117, 1983.
28. MODY GM, NAIDOO PD: Gout in South African blacks. *Ann Rheum Dis* 43:394, 1984.
29. SIMKIN PA, CAMPBELL PM, LARSON EB: Gout in Heberden's nodes. *Arthritis Rheum* 26:94, 1983.
30. PARHAMI N, GREENSTEIN N, JUOZEVICIUS JL: Erosive osteoarthritis and gout: Gout in 36 joints. *J Rheum* 11:469, 1986.
31. BAER PA, TENNENBAUM J, FAM AG, LITTLE H: Coexistent septic and crystal arthritis. Report of four cases and literature review. *J Rheum* 13:604, 1986.
32. BOULWARE DW, LOPEZ M, GUM OB: Tuberculous Podagra. To the editor. *J Rheum* 12:1022, 1985.
33. O'CONNELL PG, MILBURN BM, NASHEL DJ: Coexistent gout and septic arthritis: A report of two cases and literature review. *Clin Exp Rheum* 3:265, 1985.
34. FRANCK WA, BRESS NM, SINGER FR, KRANE SM: Rheumatic manifestations of Paget's disease of bone. *Am J Med* 56:592, 1974.
35. CIOMPI ML, BAZZICHI LM, BERTOLUCCI D, MAZZONI MR, BARBIERI P, MENCACCI S, MACCHIA D, MARIANI G: Uric acid metabolism in two patients with coexistent Down's syndrome and gout. *Clin Rheum* 3:229, 1984.
36. WORDSWORTH BP, MOWAT AG: Rapid development of gouty tophi after diuretic therapy. *J Rheum* 12:376, 1985.
37. KHALIFA P, SERENI D, BOISSONNAS A, CREMER GA, LAROCHE C: Attacks of gout and thromboembolic disease: Role of heparin therapy. *Ann Intern Med* 136:582, 1985.
38. TILLER DJ, HALL BM, HORVATH JS, DUGGIN GG, THOMPSON JF: Gout and hyperuricemia in patients on cyclosporin and diuretics (letter). *Lancet* 1:453, 1985.
39. SCHOUSBOE JT, DAVEY K, GILCHRIST NL, SAINSBURY R: Chronic polyarticular gout in the elderly: A report of six cases. *Age Ageing* 15:8, 1986.
40. MYERS OL, MONTEAGUDO FSE: Gout in females: An analysis of 92 patients. *Clin Exp Rheum* 3:105, 1985.
41. MacFARLANE DG, DIEPPE PA: Diuretic-induced gout in elderly women. *Br J Rheum* 24:155, 1985.
42. EINARSON TR, TURCHET EN, GOLDSTEIN JE, MACNAY KR: Gout-like arthritis following cimetidine and ranitidine. *Drug Intell Clin Pharm* 19:201, 1985.
43. DARCY PF: Gout-like arthritis after cimetidine and ranitidine. *Pharm Int* 6:191, 1985.
44. KELLEY WN, FOX IH: Gout and related disorders of purine metabolism. In Kelley WN, Harris ED Jr, Ruddy S, Sledge CB (eds): *Textbook of Rheumatology,* 2d ed. Philadelphia, Saunders, p 1359, 1985.
45. TERKELTAUB R, TENNER AJ, KOZIN F, GINSBERG MH: Plasma protein binding by monosodium urate crystals. *Arthritis Rheum* 26:775, 1983.
46. FIELDS TR, ABRAMSON SB, WEISMANN G, KAPLAN AP, GHEBREHIWET B:

Activation of the alternative pathway of complement by monosodium urate crystals. *Clin Immunol Immunopathol* 26:249, 1983.

47. RUSSELL IJ, PAPAIOANNOU C, MCDUFFIE FC, MACINTYRE S, KUSHNER I: Effect of IgG and C-reactive protein on complement depletion by monosodium urate crystals. *J Rheum* 10:425, 1983.

48. CHERIAN PV, SCHUMACHER HR JR: Immunochemical and ultrastructural characterization of serum proteins associated with monosodium urate crystals (MSU) in synovial fluid cells from patients with gout. *Ultrastruct Pathol* 10:209, 1986.

49. TERKELTAUB R, CURTISS LK, TENNER AJ, GINSBERG MH: Lipoproteins containing apoprotein B are a major regulator of neutrophil responses to monosodium urate crystals. *J Clin Invest* 73:1719, 1984.

50. TERKELTAUB R, SMELTZER D, CURTISS LK, GINSBERG MH: Low density lipoprotein inhibits the physical interaction of phlogistic crystals and inflammatory cells. *Arthritis Rheum* 29:363, 1986.

51. SPILBERG I, MEHTA J: Binding characteristics of radioiodinated crystal-induced chemotactic factor to human neutrophils. *J Lap Clin Med* 104:939, 1984.

52. ANTOMMATTEI O, SCHUMACHER HR, REGINATO AJ, CLAYBURNE G: Prospective study of morphology and phagocytosis of synovial fluid monosodium urate crystals in gouty arthritis. *J Rheum* 11:741, 1984.

53. BURT HM, KALKMAN PH, MAULDIN D: Membranolytic effects of crystalline monosodium urate monohydrate. *J Rheum* 10:440, 1983.

54. HERRING FG, LAM EWN, BURT HM: A spin label study of the membranolytic effects of crystalline monosodium urate monohydrate. *J Rheum* 13:623, 1986.

55. BURT HM, EVANS E, LAM EWN, GEHRS PF, HERRING FG: Membranolytic effects of monosodium urate monohydrate: Influence of grinding. *J Rheum* 13:778, 1986.

56. HIGSON FK, JONES OTG: Oxygen radical production by horse and pig neutrophils induced by a range of crystals. *J Rheum* 11:735, 1984.

57. ROSEN MS, BAKER DG, SCHUMACHER HR JR, CHERIAN PV: Products of polymorphonuclear cell injury inhibit IgG enhancement of monosodium urate-induced superoxide production. *Arthritis Rheum* 29:1473, 1986.

58. RAE SA, DAVIDSON EM, SMITH MJH: Leukotriene B_4, an inflammatory mediator in gout. *Lancet* 2:1122, 1982.

59. DAMAS J, REMACLE-VOLON G, ADAM A: Inflammation in the rat paw due to urate crystals. Involvement of the kinin system. *Arch Pharm* 325:76, 1984.

60. WIGLEY FM, FINE IT, NEWCOMBE DS: The role of the human synovial fibroblast in monosodium urate crystal-induced synovitis. *J Rheum* 10:602, 1983.

61. DUFF GW, ATKINS E, MALAWISTA SE: The fever of gout: Urate crystals activate endogenous pyrogen production from human and rabbit mononuclear phagocytes. *Trans Assoc Am Phys* 96:234, 1983.

62. MALAWISTA SE, DUFF GW, ATKINS E, CHEUNG HS, MCCARTY DJ: Crystal-induced endogenous pyrogen production. A further look at gouty inflammation. *Arthritis Rheum* 28:1039, 1985.

63. LONDINO AV JR, LUPARELLO FJ: Factor XII deficiency in a man with gout and angioimmunoblastic lymphadenopathy. *Arch Intern Med* 144:1497, 1984.

64. WEINBERGER A, SCHUMACHER HR: Urate crystals in asymptomatic metatarsophalangeal joints. *Ann Intern Med* 91:56, 1979.

65. ROUAULT T, CALDWELL DS, HOLMES EW: Aspiration of the asymptomatic metatarsophalangeal joint in gout patients and hyperuricemic controls. *Arthritis Rheum* 25:209, 1982.

66. GORDON TP, BERTOUCH JV, WALSH BR, BROOKS PM: Monosodium urate crystals in asymptomatic knee joints. *J Rheum* 9:967, 1982.

67. KENNEDY TD, HIGGENS CS, WOODROW DF, SCOTT JT: Crystal deposition in the knee and great toe joints of asymptomatic gout patients. *J Soc Med* 77:747, 1984.

68. BOMALASKI JS, LLUBERAS G, SCHUMACHER HR JR: Monosodium urate crystals in the knee joints of patients with asymptomatic nontophaceous gout. *Arthritis Rheum* 29:1480, 1986.

69. WALL B, AGUDELO CA, TESSER JRP, MOUNTZ J, HOLT D, TURNER RA: An autopsy study of the prevalence of monosodium urate and calcium pyrophosphate dihydrate crystal deposition in first metatarsophalangeal joints. *Arthritis Rheum* 26:1522, 1983.

70. MOENS C, MOENS D, MOENS PH: Prevalence of monosodium urate and calcium pyrophosphate dihydrate crystals in postmortem knee synovial fluid. *Arthritis Rheum* 28:1319, 1985.

71. JAWORSKI RC, GIBSON M: Tophaceous aortic valve: A case report. *Pathology* 15:197, 1983.

72. CURTISS EI, MILLER TR, SHAPIRO LS: Pulmonic regurgitation due to valvular tophi. *Circulation* 67:699, 1983.

73. SCALAPINO JN, EDWARDS WD, STECKELBERG JM, WOOTEN RS, CALLAHAN JA, GINSBURG WW: Mitral stenosis associated with valvular tophi. *Mayo Clin Proc* 59:509, 1984.

74. GAWOSKI JM, BALOGH K, LANDIS WJ: Aortic valvular tophus: Identification by x-ray diffraction of urate and calcium phosphates. *J Clin Pathol* 38:873, 1985.

75. MARTINEZ-CORDERO E, BARREIRA-MAERCADO E, KATONA G: Eye tophi deposition in gout. Letters to the editor. *J Rheum* 11:471, 1986.

76. FERRY AP, SAFIR A, MELIKIAN HE: Ocular abnormalities in patients with gout. *Ann Ophthalmol* 17:632, 1985.

77. LAGIER R, MACGEE W: Spondylodiscal erosions due to gout: Anatomico-radiological study of a case. *Ann Rheum Dis* 42:350, 1983.

78. AARON SL, MILLER JDR, PERCY JS: Tophaceous gout in the cervical spine. *J Rheum* 11:862, 1984.

79. JACOBS SR, EDEIKEN J, RUBIN B, DEHORATIUS RJ: Medically reversible quadriparesis in tophaceous gout. *Arch Phys Med Rehab* 66:188, 1985.

80. VARGA J, GIAMPAOLO C, GOLDENBERG DL: Tophaceous gout of the spine in a patient with no peripheral tophi: Case report and review of the literature. *Arthritis Rheum* 28:1312, 1985.

81. STEPAN J, SVAB V, KOLAR J, SUSTA A, CAP F: The spine and polytopic hyperostoses in gout and hyperuricemia. *Radiology* 23:371, 1983.

82. GREEN EJ, DILWORTH JH, LEVITIN PM: Tophaceous gout. An unusual cause of bilateral carpal tunnel syndrome. *J Am Med Assoc* 237:2747, 1977.

83. DELANEY P: Gouty neuropathy. *Arch Neurol* 40:823, 1983.

84. AKIZUKI S, MATSUI T: Entrapment neuropathy caused by tophaceous gout. *J Hand Surg* 9:331, 1984.

85. O'DUFFY JD, HUNDER GG, KELLY PJ: Decreasing prevalence of tophaceous gout. *Mayo Clin Proc* 50:227, 1975.

86. NAKAYAMA DA, BARTHELEMY C, CARRERA G, LIGHTFOOT RW JR, WORTMANN RL: Tophaceous gout: A clinical and radiographic assessment. *Arthritis Rheum* 27:468, 1984.

87. HOLLINGWORTH P, SCOTT JT, BURRY HC: Nonarticular gout: Hyperuricemia and tophus formation without gouty arthritis. *Arthritis Rheum* 26:98, 1983.

88. FESSEL WJ: Renal outcomes of gout and hyperuricemia. *Am J Med* 67:74, 1979.

89. GIBSON T, HIGHTON J, POTTER C: Renal impairment and gout. *Ann Rheum Dis* 39:417, 1980.

90. BERGER L, YU T-F: Renal function in gout. IV. An analysis of 524 gouty subjects including long-term follow-up studies. *Am J Med* 59:605, 1975.

91. YU T-F, BERGER L, DORPH DJ: Renal function in gout. V. Factors influencing renal hemodynamics. *Am J Med* 67:766, 1979.

92. YU T-F, BERGER L: Renal function in gout: Its association with hypertensive vascular disease and intrinsic renal disease. *Am J Med* 72:95, 1982.

93. BATUMAN V, MAESAKA JK, HADDAD B, TEPPER E, LANDY E, WEDEEN RP: The role of lead in gout nephropathy. *N Engl J Med* 304:520, 1981.

94. CAMPBELL BC, MOORE MR, GOLDBERG A: Subclinical lead exposure: A possible cause of gout. *Br Med J* 2:1403, 1978.

95. GARROD AB: *A Treatise on Gout and Rheumatic Gout,* 3d ed. London, Longman, Green, 1876.

96. FOLEY RJ, WEINMAN EJ: Review: Urate neuropathy. *Am J Med Sci* 288:208, 1984.

97. COHEN LF, BALOW JE, POPLACK DG: Acute tumor lysis syndrome: A review of 37 patients with Burkitt's lymphoma. *Am J Med* 68:486, 1980.

98. TOMLINSON GC, SOLBERG LA JR: Acute tumor lysis syndrome with metastatic medulloblastoma. A case report. *Cancer* 53:1783, 1984.

99. BOCCIA RV, LONGO DL, LIEBER ML, JAFFE ES, FISHER RI: Multiple recurrences of acute tumor lysis syndrome in an indolent non-Hodgkin's lymphoma. *Cancer* 56:2295, 1985.

100. ANDREOLI SP, CLARK JH, MCGUIRE WA, BERGSTEIN JM: Purine excretion during turnover lysis in children with acute lympocytic leukemia receiving allopurinol: Relationship to acute renal failure. *J Pediatr* 109:292, 1986.

101. BATCH JA, RIEK RP, GORDON RB, BURKE JR, EMMERSON BT: Renal failure in infancy due to over-production of urate. *Aust NZ J Med* 14:852, 1984.

102. TUNGSANGA K, BOONWICHIT D, LEKHAKULA A, SITPRIJA V: Urine uric acid and urine creatinine ratio in acute renal failure. *Arch Intern Med* 144:934, 1984.

103. YU TF: Review article. Urolithiasis in hyperuricemia and gout. *J Urol* 126:424, 1981.

104. MILLMAN S, STRAUSS AL, PARKS JH, COE FL: Pathogenesis and clinical course of mixed calcium oxalate and uric acid nephrolithiasis. *Kidney Int* 22:366, 1982.

105. MASCHIO G, TESSITORE N, DANGELO A, FABRIS A, PAGANO F, TASCA A, GRAZIANI G, AROLDI A, SURIAN M, COLUSSI G, MANDRESSI A, TRINCHIERI A, ROCCO F, PONTICELLI C, MINETTI L: Prevention of calcium nephrolithiasis with low dose thiazide, amiloride and allopurinol. *Am J Med* 71:623, 1981.

106. PAK C, PETERS P, HURT G, KADESKY M, FINE M, REISMAN D, SPLANN F,

CARAMELA C, FEEMAN A, BRITTON F, SAKHAEE K, BRESLAU NA: Is selective therapy of recurrent nephrolithiasis possible? *Am J Med* 71:615, 1981.

107. ETTINGER B, TANG A, CITRON JT, LIVERMORE B, WILLIAMS T: Randomized trial of allopurinol in the prevention of calcium oxalate calculi. *N Engl J Med* 27:1386, 1986.

108. SMITH A, WILCKEN B: Homozygous cystinuria in New South Wales. A study of 110 individuals with cystinuria ascertained by methods other than neonatal screening. *Med J Aust* 141:500, 1984.

109. BROCK WA, GOLDEN J, KAPLAN GW: Xanthine calculi in the Lesch-Nyhan syndrome. *J Urol* 130:157, 1983.

110. DUNCAN H, DIXON AS: Gout, familial hyperuricemia and renal diseases. *Q J Med* 113:127, 1960.

111. BENNETT RM, CHAIT A, LEWIS B: Familial hyperuricemia and hypertriglyceridemia. *Ann Rheum Dis* 32:497, 1973.

112. CARR AA: Colchicine toxicity. *Arch Intern Med* 115:29, 1965.

113. THOMPSON GR, WEISS JJ, GOLDMAN RT: Familial occurrence of hyperuricemia, gout and medullary cystic disease. *Arch Intern Med* 138:1614, 1978.

114. MASSARI PU, HSU CH, BARNES RV, FOX IH, GIKAS PW, WELLER JM: Familial hyperuricemia and renal disease. *Arch Intern Med* 140:680, 1980.

115. SIMMONDS HA, CAMERON JS, POTTER CF: Renal failure in young subjects with familial gout. *Adv Exp Med Biol* 122A:15, 1980.

116. SIMMONDS HA, WARREN DJ, CAMERON JS: Familial gout and renal failure in young women. *Clin Nephrol* 14:176, 1980.

117. STAPLETON FB, NYHAN WL, BORDEN M: Renal pathogenesis of familial hyperuricemia: Studies in two kindreds. *Pediatr Res* 15:1447, 1981.

118. MacDERMOT KD, ALLSOP J, WATTS, RW: The rate of purine synthesis de novo in blood mononuclear cells in vitro from patients with familial hyperuricaemic nephropathy. *Clin Sci* 67:249, 1984.

119. WHALEN RE, MCINTOSH HD: The spectrum of hereditary renal diseases. *Am J Med* 33:282, 1962.

120. PERKOFF GR: The hereditary renal diseases. *N Engl J Med* 277:79, 1967.

121. LEUMANN EP, WEGMANN W: Familial nephropathy with hyperuricemia and gout. *Nephron* 34:51, 1983.

122. RIVERA JV, MARTINEZ-MALDONADO MM, RAMIREZ DE ARELLANO GA, EHRLICH L: Association of hyperuricemia and polycystic kidney disease. *Bol Assoc Med* 57:251, 1965.

123. NEWCOMBE DS: Gouty arthritis and polycystic kidney disease. *Ann Intern Med* 79:605, 1973.

124. RIVERA JV: Gout and polycystic disease of kidney. *Ann Intern Med* 80:427, 1974.

125. REYNOLDS PP, KNAPP MJ, BARAF HSB, HOLMES EW: Moonshine and lead: Relationship to the pathogenesis of hyperuricemia in gout. *Arthritis Rheum* 26:1057, 1983.

126. HALLA JT, BALL GV: Saturnine gout: A review of 42 patients. *Semin Arthritis Rheum* 11:307, 1982.

127. CULLEN MR, ROBINS JM, ESKENAZI B: Adult inorganic lead intoxication: Presentation of 31 new cases and a review of recent advances in the literature. *Medicine (Baltimore)* 62:221, 1983.

128. BATUMAN V, LANDY E, MAESAKA JK, WEDEEN RP: Contribution of lead to hypertension with renal impairment. *N Engl J Med* 309:17, 1983.

129. WRIGHT LF, SAYLOR RP, CECERE FA: Occult lead intoxication in patients with gout and kidney disease. *J Rheum* 11:517, 1984.

130. CRASWELL PW, PRICE J, BOYLE PD, HEAZLEWOOD VJ, BADDELEY H, LLOYD HM, THOMAS BJ, THOMAS BW: Chronic renal failure with gout: A marker of chronic lead poisoning. *Kidney Int* 26:319, 1984.

131. BEHRINGER D, CRASWELL P, MOHL C, STOEPPLER M, RITZ E: Urinary lead excretion in uremic patients. *Nephron* 42:323, 1986.

132. COLLEONI N, DAMICO G: Chronic lead accumulation as a possible cause of renal failure in gouty patients. *Nephron* 44:32, 1986.

133. NRIAGU JO: Occasional notes. Saturnine gout among Roman aristocrats. Did lead poisoning contribute to the fall of the empire? *N Engl J Med* 308:660, 1983.

134. TAK HK, WILCOX WR, COOPER SM: The effect of lead upon urate nucleation. *Arthritis Rheum* 224:1291, 1981.

135. FARKAS WR, STANOWITZ T, SCHNEIDER M: Saturnine gout: Lead induced formation of guanine crystals. *Science* 99:786, 1978.

135. JIAO S, KAMEDA K, MATSUZAWA Y, TARUI S: Hyperlipoproteinaemia in primary gout: Hyperlipoproteinaemic phenotype and influence of alcohol intake and obesity in Japan. *Ann Rheum Dis* 45:308, 1986.

137. LASKARZEWSKI PM, KHOURY P, MORRISON JA, KELLY K, GLUECK CJ: Familial hyper- and hypouricemias in random and hyperlipidemic recall cohorts. *Metabolism* 32:230, 1983.

138. MacFARLANE DG, MIDWINTER CA, DIEPPE PA, BOLTON CH, HARTOG M: Demonstration of an abnormality of C apoprotein of very low density lipoprotein in patients with gout. *Ann Rheum Dis* 44:390, 1985.

139. ULREICH A, KOSTNER GM, PFEIFFER KP, SEDLMAYR P, RAINER F: Serum lipids and lipoproteins in patients with primary gout. *Rheumatol Int* 5:73, 1985.

140. FERNS GA, LANHAM J, STOCKS J, RITCHIE C, KATZ J, GALTON DJ: The measurement of high density lipoprotein subfractions in patients with primary gout using a simple precipitation method. *Ann Clin Biochem* 22:526, 1985.

141. PHILLIPI T, BARRETT-CONNOR E: Fasting plasma glucose, uric acid, and triglycerides as predictors of the ratio of total cholesterol to HDLC. *Am J Clin Pathol* 82:329, 1984.

142. JACOBELLI S, ARTEAGA A, BIDEGAIN F: Cholesterol distribution among lipoprotein fractions in patients with gout and normal controls. *J Rheum* 13:774, 1986.

143. FOX IH, JOHN D, DEBRUYNE S, DWOSH I, MARLISS EB: Hyperuricemia and hypertriglyceridemia: Metabolic basis for the association. *Metabolism* 34:741, 1985.

144. FERNS GA, LANHAM J, GALTON DJ: The association between primary gout and hypertriglyceridemia may be due to genetic linkage. *Monogr Atheroscler* 13:121, 1985.

145. NAITO HK, MacKENZIE AH: Secondary hypertriglyceridemia and hyperlipoproteinemia in patients with primary asymptomatic gout. *Clin Chem* 25:371, 1979.

146. DARLINGTON LG, SLACK J, SCOTT JT: Family study of lipid and purine levels in gout patients. *Ann Rheum Dis* 41:253, 1982.

147. CANNON PJ, STASON WB, DEMARTINI FE: Hyperuricemia in primary and renal hypertension. *N Engl J Med* 275:457, 1966.

148. BRECKENRIDGE A: Hypertension and hyperuricemia. *Lancet* 1:15, 1966.

149. GARRICK R, BAUER GE, EWAN CE: Serum uric acid in normal and hypertensive Australian subjects: From a continuing epidemiological survey on hypertension commenced in 1955. *Aust NZ J Med* 2:351, 1972.

150. DOLLERY CT, DUNCAN H, SCHUMER B: Hyperuricemia related to treatment of hypertension. *Br Med J* 2:832, 1960.

151. MESSERLI FH, FROHLICH ED, DRESLINSKI GR: Serum uric acid in essential hypertension: An indicator of renal vascular involvement. *Ann Intern Med* 93:817, 1980.

152. PREBIS JW, GRUSKIN AB, POLINSKY MS: Uric acid in childhood essential hypertension. *J Pediatr* 98:702, 1981.

153. SIMON NM, SMUCKER JE, O'CONNOR VJ JR: Differential uric acid excretion in essential and renal hypertension. *Circulation* 39:121, 1969.

154. SAITO I, SARUTA T, KONDO K: Serum uric acid and the renin-angiotensin system in hypertension. *J Am Geriatr Soc* 26:241, 1978.

155. HEYDEN S, BORHANI NO, TYROLER HA, SCHNEIDER KA, LANGFORD HG, HAMES CG, HUTCHINSON R, OBERMAN A: The relationship of weight change to changes in blood pressure, serum uric acid, cholesterol and glucose in the treatment of hypertension. *J Chronic Dis* 38:281, 1985.

156. The Hypertension Detection and Follow-up Program Cooperative Research Group: Mortality findings for stepped-care and referred-care participants in the hypertension detection and follow-up program, stratified by other risk factors. *Prev Med* 14:312, 1985.

157. NISHIOKA K, MIKANAGI K: A retrospective study on the cause of death, in Japan, of patients with gout. *Ryumachi* 21:29, 1981.

158. JOHNSON MW, MITCH WE: The risks of asymptomatic hyperuricemia and the use of uricosuric diuretics. *Drugs* 21:220, 1981.

159. TWEDDALE MG, FODOR JG: Elevated serum uric acid: A cardiovascular risk factor. *Nephron* 23:3, 1979.

160. FESSEL WJ: High uric acid as an indicator of cardiovascular disease, independent from obesity. *Am J Med* 68:401, 1980.

161. REUNANEN A, TAKKUNEN H, KNEKT P, AROMAA A: Hyperuricemia as a risk factor for cardiovascular mortality. *Acta Med Scand* 668:49, 1982.

162. PETERSON B, TRELL E: Raised serum urate concentration as risk factor for premature mortality in middle aged men: Relation to death from cancer. *Br Med J* 287:7, 1983.

163. BEARD JT: Serum uric acid and coronary heart disease. *Am Heart J* 106:397, 1983.

164. BRAND FN, MCGEE DL, KANNEL WB, STOKES III J, CASTELLI WP: Original contributions: Hyperuricemia as a risk factor of coronary heart disease: The Framingham study. *Am J Epidemiol* 121:11, 1985.

165. MacFARLANE DG, SLADE R, HOPES PA, HARTOG MH: A study of platelet aggregation and adhesion in gout. *Clin Exp Rheum* 1:63, 1983.

166. CIOMPI ML, DECATERINA R, BERTOLUCCI D, BERNINI W, MICHELASSI C, LABBATE A: Uric acid levels and platelet function in humans. An in-vivo ex-vivo study. *Clin Exp Rheum* 1:143, 1983.

167. LIEBER CS, DAVIDSON CS: Some metabolic effects of ethanol accumulation. *Am J Med* 33:319, 1962.

168. LIEBER CS, JONES DP, LOSOWSKY MS, DAVIDSON CS: Interrelation of uric acid and ethanol metabolism in man. *J Clin Invest* 41:1863, 1962.

169. BECK LH: Clinical disorders of uric acid metabolism. *Med Clin North Am* 65:401, 1981.

170. YU T-F, SIROTA JH, BERGER L, HALPERN M, GUTMAN AB: Effect of sodium

lactate infusion on urate clearance in man. *Proc Soc Exp Biol Med* 96:809, 1957.

171. FALLER J, FOX IH: Ethanol induced hyperuricemia: Evidence for increased urate production by activation of adenine nucleotide turnover. *N Engl J Med* 307:1598, 1982.

172. PUIG JG, FOX IH: Ethanol induced activation of adenine nucleotide turnover. Evidence for a role of acetate. *J Clin Invest* 74:936, 1984.

173. GIBSON T, RODGERS AV, SIMMONDS HA, TOSELAND P: Beer drinking and its effect on uric acid. *Br J Rheum* 23:203, 1984.

174. WOOLLISCROFT JO, COLFER H, FOX IH: Hyperuricemia in acute illness: A poor prognostic sign. *Am J Med* 72:58, 1982.

175. WOOLLISCROFT JO, FOX IH: Increased body fluid purines during hypotensive events: Evidence for ATP degradation. *Am J Med* 81:472, 1986.

176. GRUM CM, SIMON RH, DANTZKER DR, FOX IH: Biochemical indicators of cellular hypoxia in critically ill patients: Evidence for ATP degradation. *Chest* 88:763, 1985.

177. McCORD J: Oxygen-derived free radicals in postischemic tissue injury. *N Engl J Med* 312:159, 1985.

178. AMES BN, CATHCART R, SCHWIERS E, HOCHSTEIN P: Uric acid provides an antioxidant defense in humans against oxidant- and radical-caused aging and cancer: A hypothesis. *Proc Natl Acad Sci USA* 78:6858, 1981.

179. SMITH RC, LAWING L: Antioxidant activity of uric acid and 3-N-ribosyluric acid with unsaturated fatty acids and erythrocyte membranes. *Arch Biochem Biophys* 223:166, 1983.

180. SMITH RC, NUNN V: Prevention by 3-N-ribosyluric acid of the oxidation of bovine hemoglobin by sodium nitrite. *Arch Biochem Biophys* 232:348, 1984.

181. KITTRIDGE KJ, WILLSON RL: Uric acid substantially enhances the free radical-induced inactivation of alcohol dehydrogenase. *Fed Eur Biochem Soc* 170:162, 1984.

182. MEADOWS J, SMITH RC, REEVES J: Uric acid protects membranes and linolenic acid from ozone-induced oxidation. *Biochem Biophys Res Commun* 137:536, 1986.

183. MEADOWS J, SMITH RC: Uric acid protection of nucleobases from ozone-induced degradation. *Arch Biochem Biophys* 246:838, 1986.

184. BOYLE JA, CAMPBELL S, DUNCAN AM, GREIG WR, BUCHANAN WW: Serum uric acid levels in normal pregnancy with observations on the renal excretion of urate in pregnancy. *J Clin Pathol* 19:501, 1966.

185. HILL LM: Subject review. Metabolism of uric acid in normal and toxemic pregnancy. *Mayo Clin Proc* 53:743, 1978.

186. LIND T, GODFREY KA, OTUN H: Changes in serum uric acid concentrations during normal pregnancy. *Br J Obstet Gynecol* 91:128, 1984.

187. SCHAFFER NK, DILL LV, CADDEN JF: Uric acid clearance in normal pregnancy and pre-eclampsia. *J Clin Invest* 22:201, 1943.

188. SEITZCHIK J: Observations on the renal tubular reabsorption of uric acid. *Am J Obstet Gynecol* 65:981, 1953.

189. CARSWELL W, SEMPLE PF: The effect of frusemide on uric acid levels in maternal blood, fetal blood and amniotic fluid. *J Obstet Gynecol* 81:472, 1974.

190. REDMAN CWG, BEILIN LJ, BONNAR J, WILKINSON RH: Plasma-urate measurements in predicting fetal death in hypertensive pregnancy. *Lancet* 1:1370, 1976.

191. HAECKEL R, RIEDEL H, BUTTNER J: Estimation of decision criteria for the uric acid concentration for the early diagnosis of gestosis. *J Clin Chem Clin Biochem* 19:173, 1981.

192. LIEDHOLM H, MONTAN S, ABERG A: Risk grouping of 113 patients with hypertensive disorders during pregnancy, with respect to serum urate, proteinuria and time of onset of hypertension. *Acta Obstet Gynecol Scand Suppl* 118:43, 1984.

193. CRAWFORD MD: The effect of labour on plasma uric acid and urea. *J Obstet Gynecol* 46:540, 1939.

194. HAMILTON WFD, ROBERTSTON GS, CAMPBELL D: Changes in serum uric acid concentrations after caesarean section using methyoxyflurane. *Br J Anaesth* 47:508, 1975.

195. LALLY EV, PARKER VS, KAPLAN SR: Acute gouty arthritis and systemic lupus erythematosus. *J Rheum* 9:308, 1982.

196. MOIDEL RA, GOOD AE: Coexistent gout and systemic lupus erythematosus. *Arthritis Rheum* 24:969, 1981.

197. WALL BA, AGUDELO CA, WEINBLATT ME: Acute gout and systemic lupus erythematosus: Report of 2 cases and literature review. *J Rheum* 9:305, 1982.

198. JESSEE EF, TOONE E, OWEN DS: Coexistent rheumatoid arthritis and chronic tophaceous gout. *Arthritis Rheum* 23:244, 1980.

199. ATDJIAN M, FERNANDEZ-MADRIS F: Coexistence of chronic tophaceous gout and rheumatoid arthritis. *J Rheum* 8:989, 1981.

200. RIZZOLI AJ, TRUJEQUE L, BANKHURST AD: The coexistence of gout and rheumatoid arthritis: Case reports and a review of the literature. *J Rheum* 7:316, 1980.

201. WALLACE DJ, KLINENBERG JR, MORHAIM D: Coexistent gout and rheumatoid arthritis. *Arthritis Rheum* 22:81, 1979.

202. RUBINOW A, SONNENBLICK M: Amyloidosis secondary to polyarticular gout. *Arthritis Rheum* 24:1425, 1981.

203. LEVO Y, SHALEV O, ROSENMANN E: Gout and amyloidosis. *Ann Rheum Dis* 39:589, 1980.

204. AGUDELO CA, TURNER RA, PANETTI M, PISKO E: Does hyperuricemia protect from rheumatoid inflammation? A clinical study. *Arthritis Rheum* 27:443, 1984.

205. GORDON TP, AHERN MJ, REID C, ROBERTS-THOMSON PJ: Studies on the interaction of rheumatoid factor with monosodium urate crystals and case report of coexistent tophaceous gout and rheumatoid arthritis. *Ann Rheum Dis* 44:384, 1985.

206. TURNER RA, PISKO EJ, AGUDELO C, COUNTS GB, FOSTER SL, TREADWAY WJ: Uric acid effects on in vitro models of rheumatoid inflammatory and autoimmune processes. *Ann Rheum Dis* 42:338, 1983.

207. BARNES FW, SHOENHEIMER R: On biological synthesis of purines and pyrimidines. *J Biol Chem* 151:123, 1943.

208. SHEMIN D, RITTENBERG D: On the utilization of glycine for uric acid synthesis in man. *J Biol Chem* 167:875, 1947.

209. BUCHANAN JM, SONNE JC, DELLUVA AM: Biologic precursors of uric acid. II. The role of lactate, glycine, and carbon dioxide as precursors of the carbon chain and nitrogen atom 7 of uric acid. *J Biol Chem* 173:81, 1948.

210. KARLSON JL, BARKER HA: Biosynthesis of uric acid labeled with radioactive carbon. *J Biol Chem* 177:597, 1949.

211. SONNE JC, BUCHANAN JM, DELLUVA AM: Biological precursors of uric acid. I. The role of lactate, acetate and formate in synthesis of the ureido groups of uric acid. *J Biol Chem* 173:69, 1948.

212. HEINRICH MR, WILSON DW: Biosynthesis of nucleic acid components studied with C^{14}. I. Purines and pyrimidines in the rat. *J Biol Chem* 186:447, 1950.

213. SONNE JC, LIN I, BUCHANAN JM: Biosynthesis of the purines. IX. Precursors of the nitrogen atoms of the purine ring. *J Biol Chem* 220:369, 1956.

214. LEVENBERG B, HARTMAN SC, BUCHANAN JM: Biosynthesis of the purines. X. Further studies in vitro on the metabolic origin of nitrogen atoms 1 and 3 of the purine ring. *J Biol Chem* 220:379, 1956.

215. GOLDTHWAIT DA, PEABODY RA, GREENBERG GR: On the mechanism of synthesis of glycinamideribotide and its formylderivative. *J Biol Chem* 221:569, 1956.

216. KORNBERG A, LIEBERMAN I, SIMMS ES: Enzymatic synthesis and properties of 5-phosphoribosylpyrophosphate. *J Biol Chem* 215:389, 1955.

217. REMY CN, REMY WT, BUCHANAN JM: Biosynthesis of the purines. VIII. Enzymatic synthesis and utilization of 5-phosphoribosylpyrophosphate. *J Biol Chem* 217:885, 1955.

218. HARTMAN SC, BUCHANAN JM: Biosynthesis of the purines. XXI. 5-phosphoribosylpyrophosphateamidotransferase. *J Biol Chem* 233:451, 1958.

219. FLAKS JC, ERWIN MJ, BUCHANAN JM: Biosynthesis of the purines. XVI. The synthesis of adenosine 5′-phosphate and 5′-amino-4-imidazole-carboxamide ribotide by a nucleotide pyrophosphorylase. *J Biol Chem* 228:201, 1957.

220. LUKENS LN, HERRINGTON KA: Enzymatic formation of 6-mercaptopurine ribotide. *Biochim Biophys Acta* 24:432, 1957.

221. FOX IH, KELLEY WN: Human phosphoribosylpyrophosphate synthetase: Distribution, purification and properties. *J Biol Chem* 246, 1971.

222. FOX IH, KELLEY WN: Human phosphoribosylpyrophosphate synthetase: Kinetic mechanism and end-product inhibition. *J Biol Chem* 247:2126, 1972.

223. GOLDTHWAIT DA: 5-Phosphoribosylamine, a precursor of glycinamide ribotide. *J Biol Chem* 222:1051, 1956.

224. HARTMAN SC: Phosphoribosylpyrophosphate amidotransferase: Purification and general catalytic properties. *J Biol Chem* 238:3024, 1963.

225. HOLMES EW, KING G, LEYVA A, SINGER SC: A purine auxotroph deficient in phosphoribosylpyrophosphate amidotransferase and phosphoribosylpyrophosphate aminotransferase activities with normal activity of ribose-5-phosphate aminotransferase. *Proc Natl Acad Sci USA* 73:2458, 1976.

226. NIERLICH DP, MAGASANIK B: Alternative first steps of purine biosynthesis. *J Biol Chem* 236:PC32, 1961.

227. LE GAL M-L, LE GAL Y, ROCHE J, ET AL: Purine biosynthesis: Enzymatic formation of ribosylamine-5-phosphate from ribose-5-phosphate and ammonia. *Biochem Biophys Res Commun* 27:618, 1967.

228. REEM G: Enzymatic synthesis of 5′-phosphoribosylamine from ribose-5-phosphate and ammonia. Alternative first step in purine biosynthesis. *J Biol Chem* 243:5695, 1968.

229. HARTMAN SC, LEVENBERG B, BUCHANAN JM: Biosynthesis of the purines. XI. Structure, enzymatic synthesis, and metabolism of glycinamide ribotide and (α-N-formyl)glycinamide ribotide. *J Biol Chem* 221:1057, 1956.

230. HARTMAN SC, BUCHANAN JM: Biosynthesis of the purines. XXII. 2-

Amino-N-ribosylacetamide-5'phosphate kinosynthetase. *J Biol Chem* 233:456, 1958.

231. WARREN L, BUCHANAN JM: Biosynthesis of the purines. XIX. 2-Amino-N-ribosylacetamide-5'-phosphate (glycinamide ribotide) transformylase. *J Biol Chem* 229:613, 1957.

232. WARREN L, FLAKS JG, BUCHANAN JM: Biosynthesis of the purines. XX. Integration of enzymatic transformylation reactions. *J Biol Chem* 229:627, 1957.

233. MIZOBUCHI K, BUCHANAN JM: Biosynthesis of the purines: Isolation and characterization of formylglycinamide ribonucleotide amidotransferase-glutamyl complex. *J Biol Chem* 243:4853, 1968.

234. MIZOBUCHI K, KENYON GL, BUCHANAN JM: Binding of formylglycinamide ribonucleotide and adenosine triphosphate to formylglycinamide ribonucleotide amidotransferase. *J Biol Chem* 243:4863, 1968.

235. LEVENBERG B, BUCHANAN JM: Biosynthesis of the purines. XII. Structure, enzymatic synthesis, and metabolism of 5-aminoimidazole ribotide. *J Biol Chem* 224:1005, 1957.

236. LUKENS LN, BUCHANAN JB: Further intermediates in the biosynthesis of inosinic acid de novo. *J Am Chem Soc* 79:1511, 1957.

237. FLAKS JG, WARREN L, BUCHANAN JM: Biosynthesis of the purines. XVII. Further studies of the inosinic acid transformylase system. *J Biol Chem* 228:215, 1957.

238. FLAKS JG, ERWIN MJ, BUCHANAN JM: Biosynthesis of the purines. XVII. 5'-amino-1-ribosyl-4-imidazolecarboxamide 5'-phosphate transformylase and inosinicase. *J Biol Chem* 229:603, 1957.

239. CARTER CE, COHEN CH: The preparation and properties of adenylosuccinase and adenylosuccinic acid. *J Biol Chem* 222:17, 1956.

240. JOKLIK WK: Adenine succinic acid and adenylosuccinic acid from mammalian liver: Isolation and identification. *Biochem J* 66:333, 1957.

241. LIEBERMAN I: Enzymatic synthesis of adenosine 5'-phosphate from inosine 5'-phosphate. *J Biol Chem* 223:327, 1956.

242. VAN DER WEYDEN M, KELLEY WN: Human adenylosuccinate synthetase. Partial purification, kinetic and regulatory properties of the enzyme. *J Biol Chem* 249:7282, 1974.

243. MAGASANIK B, MOYED HS, GEHRING LB: Enzymes essential for the biosynthesis of nucleic acid guanine: Inosine-5'-phosphate dehydrogenase of Aerobacter aerogenes. *J Biol Chem* 226:339, 1957.

244. LAGERVIST U: Biosynthesis of guanosine 5'-phosphate. I. Xanthosine 5'-phosphate as an intermediate. *J Biol Chem* 233:138, 1958.

245. LAGERVIST U: Biosynthesis of guanosine 5'-phosphate. II. Amination of xanthosine 5'-phosphate by purified enzymes from pigeon liver. *J Biol Chem* 233:143, 1958.

246. ABRAMS R, BENTLEY M: Biosynthesis of nucleic acid purines. III. Guanosine 5'-phosphate formation from xanthosine 5'-phosphate and 1-glutamine. *Arch Biochem* 79:81, 1959.

247. ITOH R, MITSUI A, TSUSHIMA K: 5'-nucleotidase of chicken liver. *Biochim Biophys Acta* 146:151, 1967.

248. ITOH R, MITSUI A, TSUCHIMA K: Properties of 5'-nucleotidase from hepatic tissue of higher animals. *J Biochem* 63:165, 1968.

249. VAN DEN BERGHE G, VAN POTTELSBERGHE C, HERS H-G: A kinetic study of the soluble 5'-nucleotidase of rat liver. *Biochem J* 162:611, 1977.

250. FOX IH: Degradation of purine nucleotides. In Kelley WN, Weiner IM (eds): *Uric Acid.* New York, Springer-Verlag, 1978, pp 93–124.

251. FOX IH: Metabolic basis for disorders of purine nucleotide degradation. *Metabolism* 30:616, 1981.

252. KRENITSKY TA, ELION GB, HENDERSON AM, HITCHINGS GH: Inhibition of human purine nucleoside phosphorylase: Studies with intact erythrocytes and the purified enzyme. *J Biol Chem* 243:2876, 1968.

253. HATANAKA M, DEL GIUDICE R, LONG C: Adenine formation from adenosine by mycoplasmas: Adenosine phosphorylase activity. *Proc Natl Acad Sci USA* 72:1401, 1975.

254. KREDICH NM, HERSHFIELD MS: Adenosine deaminase deficiency, in Stanbury JB, Wyngaarden JB, Fredrickson DS, Godlstein JL, Brown MS (eds): *The Metabolic Basis of Inherited Disease,* 5th ed. New York, McGraw-Hill, 1983, chap 53, p 1157.

255. ANDRES CM, FOX IH: Purification and properties of human placental adenosine kinase. *J Biol Chem* 254:11288, 1979.

256. PALELLA TD, ANDRES CM, FOX IH: Human placental adenosine kinase. *J Biol Chem* 255:5264, 1980.

257. PIERRE RJ, LEPAGE GA: Formation of inosine-5'-monophosphate by a kinase in cell-free extracts of Ehrlich ascites cells in vivo. *Proc Soc Exp Biol Med* 127:432, 1968.

258. WADA Y, ARAKAWA T, KOIZUMI K: Lesch-Nyhan syndrome: Autopsy findings and in vitro study of incorporation of C-8-inosine into uric acid, guanosine-monophosphate and adenosine-monophosphate in the liver. *Tohoku J Exp Med* 95:253, 1968.

259. HURLEY MC, PALELLA TD, FOX IH: Human placental deoxyadenosine and deoxyguanosine phosphorylating activity. *J Biol Chem* 258:15021, 1983.

260. FLAKS JG, ERWIN MJ, BUCHANAN JM: Biosynthesis of the purines. VI. The synthesis of adenosine 5'-phosphate and 5'-amino-4-imidazole-carboxamide ribotide by a nucleotide pyrophosphorylase. *J Biol Chem* 228:201, 1957.

261. KELLEY WN, ROSENBLOOM FM, HENDERSON JF, SEEGMILLER JE: Xanthine phosphoribosyltransferase in man: Relationship to hypoxanthine-guanine phosphoribosyltransferase. *Biochem Biophys Res Comm* 28:340, 1967.

262. McCOLLISTER RJ, GILBERT WR JR, ASHTON DM, WYNGAARDEN JB: Pseudo-feedback inhibition of purine synthesis by 6-mercaptopurine ribonucleotide and other purine analogues. *J Biol Chem* 239:1560, 1964.

263. BOCHNER BR, AMES BN: ZTP (5-amino 4-imidazole carboxamide riboside 5'-triphosphate): A proposed alarmone for 10-formyl-tetrahydrofolate deficiency. *Cell* 26:929, 1982.

264. THOMAS CB, MEADE JC, HOLMES EW, SWAIN JL: Aminoimidazole carboxamide ribonucleoside toxicity. A model for the study of pyrimidine starvation. *J Cell Physiol* 107:335, 1982.

265. SABINA RL, HOLMES EW, BECKER MA: The enzymatic synthesis of 5-amino-4-imidazolecarboxamide riboside triphosphate (ZTP). *Science* 223:1193, 1984.

266. SIDI Y, MITCHELL BS: Z-nucleotide accumulation in erythrocytes from Lesch-Nyhan patients. *J Clin Invest* 76:2416, 1985.

267. FOX IH, KELLEY WN: The role of adenosine and deoxyadenosine in mammalian cells. *Annu Rev Biochem* 47:655, 1978.

268. ATKINSON DE: The energy charge of the adenylate pool as a regulatory parameter: Interaction with feedback modifiers. *Biochemistry* 7:4030, 1968.

269. CHAN T-S, ISHI K, LONG C, GREEN H: Purine excretion by mammalian cells deficient in adenosine kinase. *J Cell Physiol* 81:315, 1973.

270. BERGMANN F, DIKSTEIN S: Studies on uric acid and related compounds. III. Observations on the specificity of mammalian xanthine oxidase. *J Biol Chem* 223:765, 1956.

271. BRAY RC: Molybdenum iron-sulfur flavin hydrolases and related enzymes, in Boyer RD (ed): *The Enzymes.* 3d ed. New York, Academic, 1975, vol 12, p 229.

272. WAUD WR, RAJAGOPALAN KV: The mechanism of conversion of rat liver xanthine dehydrogenase from an NAD^+-dependent form (type D) to an O_2-dependent form (type O). *Arch Biochem Biophys* 172:265, 1976.

273. DELLA CORTE E, STIRPE F: The regulation of rat liver xanthine oxidase. Involvement of thiol groups in the conversion of the enzyme activity from dehydrogenase (type D) into oxidase (type O) and purification of the enzyme. *Biochem J* 126:739, 1972.

274. ROUSSOS GG: Xanthine oxidase from bovine small intestine. *Methods Enzymol* 12:5, 1967.

275. BRUDER G, HEID H, JARASCH E-D, KEENAN TW, MATHER IH: Characteristics of membrane-bound and soluble forms of xanthine oxidase from milk and endothelial cells of capillaries. *Biochim Biophys Acta* 701:357, 1982.

276. NAKAMURA M, KUREBAYASHI H, YAMAZAKI I: One-electron and two-electron reductions of acceptors by xanthine oxidase and xanthine dehydrogenase. *J Biochem* 83:9, 1978.

277. KAMINSKI ZW, JEZEWSKA MM: Involvement of a single thiol group in the conversion of the NAD^+-dependent activity of rat liver xanthine oxidoreductase to the O_2-dependent activity. *Biochem J* 207:341, 1982.

278. BATTELLI MG: Enzymic conversion of rat liver xanthine oxidase from dehydrogenase (D-form) to oxidase (O-form). *FEBS Lett* 113:47, 1980.

279. LYNCH RE, FRIDOVICH I: Effects of superoxide on the erythrocyte membrane. *J Biol Chem* 253:1838, 1982.

280. JARASCH E-D, BURDER G, HEID HW: Significance of xanthine oxidase in capillary endothelial cells. *Acta Physiol Scand Suppl* 548:39, 1986.

281. DAVIS AR, NEWTON EB, BENEDICT SR: The combined uric acid in beef blood. *J Biol Chem* 54:595, 1922.

282. FALCONER R, GULLAND JM: Constitution of the purine nucleosides. VIII: Uric acid riboside. *J Chem Soc* p 1369, 1939.

283. FORREST HS, HATFIELD D, LAGOWSKI JM: Uric acid riboside. I: Isolation and reinvestigation of the structure. *J Chem Soc* p 963, 1961.

284. COHEN A, DOYLE D, MARTIN DW JR, AMMANN AN: Abnormal purine metabolism and purine overproduction in a patient deficient in purine nucleoside phosphorylase. *N Engl J Med* 295:1449, 1976.

285. HENDERSON JR, KHOO KY: Synthesis of 5-phosphoribosyl-1-pyrophosphate from glucose in Ehrlich ascites tumor cells in vitro. *J Biol Chem* 240:2349, 1965.

286. KELLEY WN, FOX IH, WYNGAARDEN JB: Essential role of phosphoribosylpyrophosphate (PRPP) in regulation of purine biosynthesis in cultured human fibroblasts. *Clin Res* 18:457, 1970.

287. CAPERELLI CA, BENKOVIC PA, CHETTUR G, BENKOVIC SJ: Purification of a complex catalyzing folate cofactor synthesis and transformylation in de novo purine biosynthesis. *J Biol Chem* 255:1885, 1980.

288. SMITH GK, MUELLER WT, WASSERMAN GF, TAYLOR WD, BENKOVIC SJ:

Characterization of the enzyme complex involving the folate-requiring enzymes of de novo purine biosynthesis. *Biochemistry* 19:4313, 1980.

289. BECKER MA, MEYER LJ, HUISMAN WH, LAZAR C, ADAMS WB: Human erythrocyte phosphoribosylpyrophosphate synthetase: Subunit analysis and states of subunit association. *J Biol Chem* 252:3911, 1977.

290. MEYER LJ, BECKER MA: Human erythrocyte phosphoribosylpyrophosphate synthetase: Dependence of activity on state of subunit association. *J Biol Chem* 252:3919, 1977.

291. LEBO RV, MARTIN DW JR: Electrophoretic heterogeneity of 5-phosphoribosyl-1-pyrophosphate synthetase within and among humans. *Biochem Genet* 16:905, 1978.

292. BECKER MA, YEN RCK, ITKIN P: Regional localization of the gene for human phosphoribosylpyrophosphate synthetase on the X chromosome. *Science* 203:1016, 1979.

293. SPERLING O, EILAM G, PERSKY-BROSH S, DE VRIES A: Accelerated erythrocyte 5-phosphoribosyl-1-pyrophosphate synthesis: A familial abnormality associated with excessive uric acid production and gout. *Biochem Med* 6:310, 1972.

294. DE VRIES A, SPERLING O: Familial gouty malignant uric acid lithiasis due to mutant phosphoribosylpyrophosphate synthetase. *Urologe A* 12:153, 1973.

295. BECKER MA, KOSTEL PJ, MEYER LJ, SEEGMILLER JE: Human phosphoribosylpyrophosphate synthetase: Increased enzyme specific activity in a family with gout and excessive purine synthesis. *Proc Natl Acad Sci USA* 70:2749, 1973.

296. BECKER MA, MEYER LJ, SEEGMILLER JE: Gout with purine overproduction due to increased phosphoribosyl-pyrophosphate synthetase activity. *Am J Med* 55:232, 1973.

297. BECKER MA, RAIVIO KO, BAKAY B, ADAMS WB, NYHAN WL: Variant human phosphoribosylpyrophosphate synthetase altered in regulatory and catalytic functions. *JClin Invest* 65:109, 1980.

298. LEJEUNE E, BOUVIER M, MOUSSON B, LLORCA G, BALTASSAT P: Anomalies de la phosphoribosylpyrophosphate synthetase dans deuxcas de goutte a debut precose. *Rev Rhum* 46:457, 1979.

299. GREEN CD, MARTIN DW JR: Characterization of a feedback resistant phosphoribosylpyrophosphate synthetase from cultured, mutagenized hepatoma cells that overproduce purines. *Proc Natl Acad Sci USA* 70:3698, 1973.

300. ROTH DG, SHELTON E, DENEL TF: Purification and properties of phosphoribosylpyrophosphate synthetase from rat liver. *J Biol Chem* 249:291, 1974.

301. FOX IH, WYNGAARDEN JB, KELLEY WN: Depletion of erythrocyte phosphoribosylpyophosphate in man, a newly observed effect of allopurinol. *N Engl J Med* 283:1177, 1970.

302. VAN MARIS AGCCM, TAX WJM, OEI TL, DE BRUYN CHMM, KLEIN F, GEERTS SJ, VEERKAMP JH, VALKENBURG HA: Phosphoribosylpyrophosphate and enzymes of purine metabolism in erythrocytes from young hyperuricemic males. *Biochem Med* 23:263, 1980.

303. KELLEY WN, FOX IH, WYNGAARDEN JB: Regulation of purine biosynthesis in cultured human cells. I. Effects of orotic acid. *Biochim Biophys Acta* 215:512, 1970.

304. LALLANE M, HENDERSON JF: Effects of hormones and drugs on phosphoribosylpyrophosphate concentrations in mouse liver. *Can J Biochem* 53:394, 1975.

305. WYNGAARDEN JB: Glutamine phosphoribosylpyrophosphate amidotransferase, in Horecker B, Stadtman E (eds): *Current Topics in Cellular Regulation.* New York, Academic, 1972, vol 5, p 135.

306. HOLMES EW, MCDONALD JA, MCCORD JM, WYNGAARDEN JB, KELLEY WN: Human glutamine phosphoribosylpyrophosphate amidotransferase: Kinetic and regulatory properties. *J Biol Chem* 248:144, 1973.

307. WOOD AW, SEEGMILLER JE: Properties of 5-phosphoribosyl-1-pyrophosphate amidotransferase from human lymphoblasts. *J Biol Chem* 2487:138, 1973.

308. REEM GH: Enzymatic synthesis of phosphoribosylamine in human cells. *J Biol Chem* 249:1696, 1974.

309. HOLMES EW: Kinetic, physical, and regulatory properties of amidophosphoribosyltransferase. *Adv Enzyme Regul* 44:215, 1981.

310. KOVARSKY J, EVANS MC, HOLMES EW: Regulation of human amidophosphoribosyltransferase: Interaction of orthophosphate, PP-ribose-P and purine ribonucleotides. *Can J Biochem* 56:334, 1978.

311. KING GL, BOUNOUS CG, HOLMES EW: Human placental amidophosphoribosyltransferase. Comparison of the kinetics of glutamine and ammonia utilization. *J Biol Chem* 253:3933, 1978.

312. WONG JY, MEYER E, SWITZER RL: Glutamine phosphoribosylpyrophosphate amidotransferase from Bacillus subtilis. A novel iron-sulfur protein. *J Biol Chem* 252:7424, 1977.

313. ITAKURA M, MEADE J, HOLMES EW: Protection of amidophosphoribosyltransferase from O_2 inactivation in the cell: A potential mechanism for controlling purine biosynthesis. *Fed Proc* 38:671, 1979.

314. ITAKURA M, HOLMES EW: Human amidophosphoribosyltransferase. An oxygen-sensitive iron-sulfur protein. *J Biol Chem* 254:333, 1979.

315. AVERIL BA, DWIREDI A, DEBRUNNER P, VOLLMER SJ, WONG JY, SWITZER RL: Evidence for a tetra-nuclear iron-sulfur center in glutamine phosphoribosylpyrophosphate amidotransferase from Bacillus subtilis. *J Biol Chem* 255:6007, 1980.

316. WYNGAARDEN JB, ASHTON DM: The regulation of activity of phosphoribosylpyrophosphate amidotransferase by purine ribonucleotides: A potential feedback control of purine biosynthesis. *J Biol Chem* 234:1492, 1959.

317. CASKEY CT, ASHTON DM, WYNGAARDEN JB: The enzymology of feedback inhibition of glutamine phosphoribosylpyrophosphate amidotransferase by purine ribonucleotides. *J Biol Chem* 239:2570, 1964.

318. GRINDEY GB, LOWE JK, DIVEKAR AY, JAKALA MT: Potentiation by guanine nucleosides on the growth-inhibitory effects of adenosine analogs on L1210 and sarcoma 180 cells in culture. *Cancer Res* 36:379, 1976.

319. SINGER SC, HOLMES EW: Human glutamine phosphoribosylpyrophosphate amidotransferase: Hysteretic properties. *J Biol Chem* 252:7959, 1977.

320. ITAKURA M, SABINA RL, HEALD PW, HOLMES EW: Basis for control of purine biosynthesis by purine ribonucleotides. *J Clin Invest* 67:994, 1981.

321. WYNGAARDEN JB, GREENLAND RA: The inhibition of succinoadenylate kinosynthetase of Escherichia coli by adenosine and guanosine 5′-monophosphates. *J Biol Chem* 238:1054, 1963.

322. MAGER J, MAGASANIK B: Guanosine 5′-phosphate reductase and its role in the interconversion of purine nucleotides. *J Biol Chem* 235:1474, 1960.

323. HERS H-G: The mechanism of adenosine triphosphate depletion in the liver after a fructose load. A kinetic study of liver adenylate deaminase. *Biochem J* 162:601, 1977.

324. ZOREF E, DE VRIES A, SPERLING O: Kinetic aspects of purine metabolism in cultured fibroblasts. A comparative study of cells from patients overproducing purines due to HGPRT deficiency and PRPP synthetase superactivity. *Monogr Hum Genet* 10:96, 1978.

325. LOMAX CA, BAGNARA AS, HENDERSON JF: Studies of the regulation of purine nucleotide catabolism. *Can J Biochem* 53:231, 1975.

326. MADRID-MARINA V, FOX IH: Human placental cytoplasmic 5′-nucleotidase. Kinetic properties and inhibition. *J Biol Chem* 261:444, 1986.

327. KAMINSKA-BERRY J, MADRID-MARINA V, FOX IH: Purification and properties of human placental cytoplasmic 5′-nucleotide. *J Biol Chem* 261:449, 1986.

328. NAITO Y, TSUSHIMA K: Cytosol 5′-nucleotidase from chicken liver. Purification and some properties. *Biochim Biophys Acta* 438:159, 1976.

329. FRITZSON P: Nucleotidase activities in the soluble fraction of rat liver homogenate. Partial purification and properties of a 5′-nucleotidase with pH optimum 6.3. *Biochim Biophys Acta* 178:534, 1969.

330. FRITZSON P: Regulation of nucleotidase activities in animal tissues. *Adv Enzyme Regul* 16:43, 1978.

331. CARSON DA, KAYE J, WASSON DB: The potential importance of soluble deoxynucleotidase activity in mediating deoxyadenosine toxicity in human lymphoblasts. *J Immunol* 126:348, 1981.

332. CARSON DA, WASSON WB: Characterization of an adenosine 5′-triphosphate- and deoxyadenosine 5′-triphosphate-activated nucleotidase from human malignant lymphocytes. *Cancer Res* 42:4321, 1982.

333. BAGNARA AS, HERSHFIELD MS: Mechanism of deoxyadenosine-induced catabolism of adenine ribonucleotides in adenosine deaminase-inhibited human T lymphoblastoid cells. *Proc Natl Acad Sci USA* 79:2673, 1982.

334. EDWARDS NL, MANFREDI J, REMBECKI R, FOX IH: Regulation of purine metabolism by plasma membrane and cytoplasmic 5′-nucleotidases. *Am J Physiol* 243:C270, 1982.

335. FOX IH, MARCHANT PJ: Purine catabolism in man: Inhibition of 5′-phosphomonesterase activities from placental microsomes. *Can J Biochem* 54:1055, 1976.

336. LOMAX CA, HENDERSON JF: Adenosine formation and metabolism during adenosine triphosphate catabolism in Ehrlich ascites tumor cells. *Cancer Res* 33:2825, 1973.

337. BARANKIEWICZ J, BATTELL ML, HENDERSON JF: Role of orthophosphate concentration in the regulation of ribose phosphate synthesis and purine metabolism in Ehrlich ascites tumor cells. *Can J Biochem* 55:834, 1977.

338. BARANKIEWICZ J, COHEN A: Nucleotide catabolism and nucleoside cycles in human thymocytes. *Role of orthophosphate. Biochem J* 219:197, 1984.

339. MATSUMOTO SS, RAIVIO K, SEEGMILLER JE: Adenine nucleotide degradation during energy depletion in human lymphoblasts. Adenosine accumulation and adenylate energy charge correlation. *J Biol Chem* 254:8956, 1979.

340. GUTMAN AB, YU T-F: Renal function in gout: With a commentary on the renal regulation of urate excretion and the role of the kidney in the pathogenesis of gout. *Am J Med* 23:600, 1957.

341. SEEGMILLER JE, GRAYZEL AI, LASTER L, LIDDLE L: Uric acid production in gout. *J Clin Invest* 40:1304, 1961.
342. BENEDICT JD, FORSHAM PH, STETTEN D JR: The metabolism of uric acid in the normal and gouty human studies with the aid of isotopic uric acid. *J Biol Chem* 181:183, 1949.
343. WYNGAARDEN JB, KELLEY WN: Gout, in Stanbury JB, Wyngaarden JB, Fredrickson DS (eds): *The Metabolic Basis of Inherited Disease,* 4th ed. New York, McGraw-Hill, 1978, p 916.
344. SCOTT JT, HOLLOWAY VP, GLASS HI, ARNOT RN: Studies of uric acid pool size and turnover rate. *Ann Rheum Dis* 28:366, 1969.
345. BENEDICT JD, FORSHAM PH, ROCHE M, SOTOWAY J, STETTEN D JR: The effect of salicylates and adrenocorticotrophic hormone on the miscible pool of uric acid in gout. *J Clin Invest* 29:1104, 1950.
346. SORENSEN LB: The pathogenesis of gout. *Arch Intern Med* 109:379, 1962.
347. WYNGAARDEN JB, STETTEN D JR: Uricolysis in normal man. *J Biol Chem* 203:9, 1953.
348. BENEDICT JD, ROCHE M, YU T-F, BIEN EJ, GUTMAN AB, STETTEN D JR: Incorporation of glycine nitrogen into uric acid in normal and gouty man. *Metabolism* 1:3, 1952.
349. BENEDICT JD, YU T-F, BIEN EJ, GUTMAN AB, STETTEN D JR: A further study of the utilization of dietary glycine nitrogen for uric acid synthesis in gout. *J Clin Invest* 32:775, 1953.
350. WYNGAARDEN JB: Overproduction of uric acid as the cause of hyperuricemia in primary gout. *J Clin Invest* 36:1508, 1957.
351. WYNGAARDEN JB: Normal glycine-C^{14} incorporation into uric acid in primary gout. *Metabolism* 7:374, 1958.
352. EDWARDS NL, RECKER D, FOX IH: Overproduction of uric acid in hypoxanthine-guanine phosphoribosyltransferase deficiency. *J Clin Invest* 63:922, 1979.
353. EDWARDS NL, RECKER D, AIROZO D, FOX IH: Enhanced purine salvage during allopurinol therapy: An important pharmacologic property in humans. *J Lab Clin Med* 98:673, 1981.
354. ROCH-RAMEL F, DIEZI-CHOMETY F, DE ROUGEMONT D, TELLIER M, WIDMER J, PETERS G: Renal excretion of uric acid in the rat: A micropuncture and microperfusion study. *Am J Physiol* 230:768, 1976.
355. ROCH-RAMEL F: Renal excretion of uric acid in mammals. *Clin Nephrol* 12:1, 1979.
356. CAMPION DW, BLUESTONE R, KLINENBERG JR: Uric acid: Characterization of its interaction with human serum albumin. *J Clin Invest* 52:2383, 1973.
357. HOLMES EW, BLONDET P: Urate binding to serum albumin: Lack of influence on renal clearance of uric acid. *Arthritis Rheum* 22:737, 1979.
358. KELTON JG, ULAN R, STILLER C, HOLMES E: Comparison of chemical composition of peritoneal fluid and serum: A method for monitoring dialysis patients and a tool for assessing binding to serum proteins in vivo. *Ann Intern Med* 89:67, 1978.
359. ABRAMSON RG, LEVITT MF: Micropuncture study of uric acid transport in rat kidney. *Am J Physiol* 228:1597, 1975.
360. GREGER R, LANG F, DEETJEN P: Handling of uric acid by the rat kidney. II. Microperfusion studies on bidirectional transport of uric acid in the proximal tubule. *Pfluegers Arch* 335:257, 1972.
361. GREGER R, LANG F, DEETJEN P: Handling of uric acid by the rat kidney: I. Microanalysis of uric acid in proximal tubular fluid. *Pfluegers Arch* 324:279, 1971.
362. KRAMP RA, LASSITER WE, GOTTSCHALK CW: Urate 2-^{14}C transport in the rat nephron. *J Clin Invest* 50:35, 1971.
363. ROCH-RAMEL F, BOUDRY JF: Tubular fate of 2-^{14}C urate: Microperfusion experiments. *Fed Proc* 30:338, 1971.
364. ROCH-RAMEL F, WEINER IM: Excretion of urate by the kidneys of Cebus monkeys: A micropuncture study. *Am J Physiol* 224:1369, 1973.
365. GREGER R, LANG F, DEETJEN P: Urate handling by the rat kidney. IV. Reabsorption in the loops of Henle. *Pfluegers Arch* 351:115, 1974.
366. DIAMOND HS, MEISEL AD: Postsecretory reabsorption of urate in man. *Arthritis Rheum* 18(6):805, 1975.
367. PRAETORIUS E, KIRK JE: Hypouricemia: With evidence for tubular elimination of uric acid. *J Lab Clin Med* 35:865, 1950.
368. GUTMAN AB, YU T-F, BERGER L: Tubular secretion of urate in man. *J Clin Invest* 38:1778, 1959.
369. PODEVIN R, ARDAILLOU R, PAILLARD F, FONTANELLE J, RICHET G: Étude chex l'homme de la cinetique d'apparition dans l'urine de l'acide urique 2-^{14}C. *Nephron* 5:134, 1968.
370. WEINER IM, MUDGE GH: Renal tubular mechanisms for excretion of organic acids and bases. *Am J Med* 36:743, 1964.
371. LEVINSON DJ, SORENSON LB: Renal handling of uric acid in gouty and normal subjects: Evidence for a 4-component system. *Ann Rheum Dis* 39:173, 1980.
372. PUIG JG, ANTON FM, JIMENEZ ML, GUITIERREZ PC: Renal handling of uric acid in gout: Impaired tubular transport of urate not dependent on serum urate values. *Metabolism* 35:1147, 1986.
373. REISELBACH RE, SORENSON LB, SHELP WD, STEELE TH: Diminished renal urate secretion per nephron as a basis for primary gout. *Ann Intern Med* 73:359, 1970.
374. STEELE TH, RIESELBACH RE: The renal mechanism for urate homeostasis in normal man. *Am J Med* 43:868, 1967.
375. HOLMES EW, KELLEY WN: The renal pathophysiology of gout, in Kurtzman NA, Martinez-Moldonado M (eds): *Pathophysiology of the Kidney.* Springfield, IL, Charles C. Thomas, 1977, p 696.
376. STEELE TH, BONER G: Origins of the uricosuric response. *J Clin Invest* 52:1368, 1973.
377. STEELE TH: Urate secretion in man: The pyrazinamide suppression test. *Ann Intern Med* 79:734, 1973.
378. DIAMOND HS, PAOLINO JS: Evidence for a post-secretory reabsorptive site for uric acid in man. *J Clin Invest* 52:1491, 1973.
379. TOFUKU Y, MITSUHIKO K, TAKEDA R: Hypouricemia due to renal urate wasting. *Nephron* 30:39, 1982.
380. SORENSEN LB: The elimination of uric acid in man studied by means of C^{14}C-labeled uric acid. *Scand J Clin Lab Invest* 12:1, 1960.
381. HOWELL RR, WYNGAARDEN JB: On the mechanism of peroxidation of uric acids by hemoproteins. *J Biol Chem* 235:3544, 1960.
382. BUZARD J, BISHOP C, TALBOTT JH: The fate of uric acid in the normal and gouty human being. *J Chronic Dis* 2:42, 1955.
383. WYNGAARDEN JB: Gout, in Stanbury JB, Wyngaarden JB, Fredrickson DS (eds): *Metabolic Basis of Inherited Disease.* New York, McGraw-Hill, 1960, p 679.
384. BECKER MA, RAVIO KO, SEEGMILLER JE: Synthesis of phosphoribosylpyrophosphate in mammalian cells. *Enzymology* 49:281, 1979.
385. HERSHKO A, HERSHKO C, MAGER J: Increased formation of 5'-phosphoribosyl-1-pyrophosphate in red blood cells of some gouty patients. *Isr J Med Sci* 4:939, 1968.
386. BECKER MA, LOSMAN MJ, WILSON J, SIMMONDS HA: Superactivity of human phosphoribosylpyrophosphate synthetase due to altered regulation by nucleotide inhibitors and inorganic phosphate. *Biochim Biophys Acta* 882:168, 1986.
387. BECKER MA, MEYER LJ, WOOD AW, SEEGMILLER JE: Purine overproduction in man associated with increased phosphoribosylpyrophosphate synthetase activity. *Science* 179:1123, 1973.
388. BECKER MA: Patterns of phosphoribosylpyrophosphate and ribose-5-phosphate concentration and generation in fibroblasts from patients with gout and purine overproduction. *J Clin Invest* 57:308, 1976.
389. EMMERSON BT, WYNGAARDEN JB: Purine metabolism in heterozygous carriers of hypoxanthine-guanine phosphoribosyltransferase deficiency. *Science* 166:1533, 1979.
390. JONES OW JR, ASHTON DM, WYNGAARDEN JB: Accelerated turnover of phosphoribosylpyrophosphate, a purine nucleotide precursor, in certain gouty subjects. *J Clin Invest* 41:1805, 1962.
391. KATZ J, ROGNSTAD R: The labeling of pentose phosphate from glucose-^{14}C and estimation of the rates of transaldolase, transketolase, the contribution of the pentose cycle, and ribosephosphate synthesis. *Biochemistry* 6:2227, 1967.
392. FOX IH, KELLEY WN: Phosphoribosylpyrophosphate (PRPP) in man: Biochemical and clinical significance. *Ann Intern Med* 74:242, 1971.
393. VAN MARIS AGCCM, TAX WJM, OEI TL, DEBRUYN CHMM, KLEIN F, GEERTS SJ, VEERKAMP JH, VALKENBURG HA: Phosphoribosylpyrophosphate and enzymes of purine metabolism in erythrocytes from young hyperuricemic males. *Biochem Med* 23:263, 1980.
394. LALANNE M, HENDERSON JF: Effects of hormones and drugs on phosphoribosylpyrophosphate concentrations in mouse liver. *Can J Biochem* 53:394, 1975.
395. KREBS HA, EGGLESTON LV: The regulation of the pentose phosphate cycle in rat liver, in Weber G (ed): *Advances in Enzyme Regulation.* Oxford, Pergamon, 1974, vol 12, p 421.
396. RAIVIO KO, SEEGMILLER JE: Role of glutamine in purine synthesis and interconversions. *Clin Res* 19:161, 1971.
397. BIEN EJ, YU I-F, BENEDICT JD, GUTMAN AB, STETTEN D JR: The relation of dietary nitrogen consumption to the rate of uric acid synthesis in normal and gouty man. *J Clin Invest* 32:778, 1953.
398. FEIGELSON M, FEIGELSON P: Relationships between hepatic enzyme induction, glutamate formation, and purine nucleotide biosynthesis in glucocorticoid action. *J Biol Chem* 241:5819, 1966.
399. FOX IH: Adenosine triphosphate degradation in specific disease. *J Lab Clin Med* 106:101, 1985.
400. FOX IH, PALELLA TD, KELLEY WN: Hyperuricemia: A marker for cell energy crisis. *N Engl J Med* 317:111, 1987.

401. FOX IH, KELLEY WN: Studies on the mechanism of fructose induced hyperuricemia in man. *Metabolism* 21:713, 1972.

402. MATEOS FA, PUIG JG, JIMENEZ ML, FOX IH: Hereditary xanthinuria. Evidence for enhanced hypoxanthine salvage. *J Clin Invest* 79(3):847, 1987.

403. COHEN JL, VINIK A, FULLER J, FOX IH: Hyperuricemia in glycogen storage disease type I: Contributions by hypoglycemia and hypophosphatemia to increased urate production. *J Clin Invest* 78:251, 1985.

404. GREENE HL, WILSON FA, HEFFERAN P, TERRY AB, MORAN JR, SLONIM AE, CLAUS TH, BURR IM: ATP depletion, a possible role in the pathogenesis of hyperuricemia in glycogen storage disease type I. *J Clin Invest* 62:321, 1978.

405. ROE TF, KOGUT MD: The pathogenesis of hyperuricemia in glycogen storage disease, type I. *Pediatr Res* 11:664, 1977.

406. SUTTON JR, TOEWS CJ, WARD GR, FOX IH: Purine metabolism during strenuous muscular exercise in man. *Metabolism* 29:254, 1980.

407. NASRALLA S, AL-KHALIDI V: Nature of purines excreted in urine during muscular exercise. *J Appl Physiol* 19:246, 1964.

408. KNOCHEL JB, DOTIN LN, HAMBURGER RJ: Heat stress, exercise, and muscle injury: Effects on urate metabolism. *Ann Intern Med* 81:321, 1972.

409. TSALIKIAN E, SIMMONS P, HOWARD C, HAYMOND MW: Near normal glucose production in type I GSD. *Pediatr Res* 16:265A, 1982.

410. HOWELL RR: The interrelationship of glycogen storage disease and gout. *Arthritis Rheum* 8:780, 1965.

411. GITZELMANN R, STEINMANN B, VAN DEN BERGHE G: Essential fructosuria, hereditary fructose intolerance and fructose 1,6-diphosphatase deficiency, in Stanbury JB, Wyngaarden JB, Fredrickson DS (eds): *The Metabolic Basis of Inherited Disease*, 5th ed. New York, McGraw-Hill, 1983, p 118.

412. PERHEENTUPA J, RAIVIO K: Fructose-induced hyperuricemia. *Lancet* II:528, 1967.

413. WOODS HF, EGGLESTON LV, KREBS HA: The cause of hepatic accumulation of fructose-l-phosphate on fructose loading. *Biochem J* 119:501, 1970.

414. RAIVIO KO, BECKER MA, MEYER LJ, GREENE ML, NUKI G, SEEGMILLER JE: Stimulation of human purine synthesis de novo by fructose infusion. *Metab Clin Exp* 24:861, 1975.

415. SLONIM AE, LACY WW, TERRY A, GREENE HL, BURR IM: Nocturnal intragastric therapy in type I glycogen storage disease: Effect on hormonal and amino acid metabolism. *Metab Clin Exp* 28:707, 1979.

416. CRIGLER JF, FOLKMAN J: Glycogen storage disease: New approaches to therapy. *Ciba Found Symp* 55:331, 1978.

417. GREENE HL, SLONIM AE, O'NEILL JA, BURR IM: Continuous nocturnal intragastric feeding for management of type I glycogen storage disease. *N Engl J Med* 294:423, 1976.

418. DAVISDON AGF, WONG TK, KIRBY L, TZE WJ, RIGG JM, APPLEGARTH DA: Glycogen storage disease type I: Effect of continuous nocturnal nasogastric feeding. *Monogr Hum Genet* 9:29, 1978.

419. EHRLICH RM, ROBINSON BH, FREEDMAN HH, HOWARD NJ: Nocturnal intragastric infusion of glucose in management of defective gluconeogenesis with hypoglycemia. *Am J Dis Child* 132:241, 1978.

420. PEARLMAN M, AKER M, SLONIM AE: Successful treatment of severe type I glycogen storage disease with neonatal presentation by nocturnal intragastric feeding. *J Pediatr* 94:772, 1979.

421. GREENE HL, SLONIM AE, BURR IM, MORAN JR: Type I glycogen storage disease: Five years of management with nocturnal intragastric feeding. *J Pediatr* 96:590, 1980.

422. BENKE PJ, GOLD S: Uric acid metabolism in therapy of glycogen storage disease type I. *Pediatr Res* 12:204, 1978.

423. OKADA S, SEINO Y, KODAMA H, YUTAKA T, INUI K, ISHIDA M, YABUUCHI M, SEINE Y: Insulin and glucagon secretion in hepatic glycogenoses. *Acta Paediatr Scand* 68:735, 1979.

424. GERICH JE, SCHNEIDER V, DIPPE SE, LANGLOIS M, NOACCO C, KARAM J, FORSHAM P: Characterization of the glucagon response to hypoglycemia in man. *J Clin Endocrinol Metab* 38:77, 1974.

425. BRAUNWALD E, KLONER RA: Myocardial reperfusion: A double-edged sword? *J Clin Invest* 76:1713, 1985.

426. BRUNBERG JB, MCCORMICK WF, SHOECHET SS: Type III glycogenosis. An adult with diffuse weakness and muscle wasting. *Arch Neurol* 25:171, 1971.

427. MURASE T, IKEDA H, MURO T, NAKAO K, SUGITA H: Myopathy associated with type III glycogenosis. *J Neurol Sci* 20:287, 1973.

428. MINEO I, KONO N, HARA N, TAKAO S, YAMADA Y, KAWACHI M, KIYOKAWA H, WANG YL, TARUI S: Myogenic hyperuricemia: A common clinical feature of glycogenosis types III, V and VII. *N Engl J Med* 317:75, 1987.

429. MINEO I, KONO N, SHIMIZU T, HARA N, YAMADA Y, SUMI S, NONAKA K, TARUI S: Excess purine degradation in exercising muscles of patients with glycogen storage disease types V and VII. *J Clin Invest* 76:556, 1985.

430. BROOKS MH, PATTERSON VH, KAISER KK: Hypoxanthine and McArdle disease. A clue to metabolic stress in the working forearm. *Muscle Nerve* 6:204, 1983.

431. KONO N, MINEO I, SHIMIZU T, HARA N, YAMADA Y, NONAKA K, TARUI S: Increased plasma uric acid after exercise in muscle phosphofructokinase deficiency. *Neurology* 36:106, 1986.

432. SABINA RL, SWAIN JL, OLANOW CW, BRADLEY WG, FISHBEIN WN, DIMAURO S, HOLMES EW: Myoadenylate deaminase deficiency. Functional and metabolic abnormalities associated with disruption of the purine nucleotide cycle. *J Clin Invest* 73:720, 1984.

433. BERTORINI TE, SHIVELY V, TAYLOR B, PALMIERI GMA, FOX IH: ATP degradation products after ischemic exercise: Hereditary lack of phosphorylase or carnitine palmityltransferase. *Neurology* 35:1355, 1985.

434. BALL GV, SORENSEN LB: Pathogenesis of hyperuricemia and gout in sickle cell anemia. *Arthritis Rheum* 13:846, 1970.

435. GOLD MS, WILLIAMS JC, SPIVACK M, GRANN V: Sickle cell anemia and hyperuricemia. *JAMA* 206:1572, 1968.

436. MARCH HW, SCHYLEN SM, SCHWARTZ SE: Mediterranean hemopathic syndromes (Cooley's anemia) in adults: Study of a family with unusual complications. *Am J Med* 13:46, 1952.

437. PAIK CH, ALAVI I, DUNEA G, WEINER L: Thalassemia and gouty arthritis. *JAMA* 213:296, 1970.

438. HICKLING RA: Gout, leukaemia, and polychythaemia. *Lancet* 1:57, 1953.

439. TALBOTT JH: *Gout*. New York, Grune and Stratton, 1957.

440. YU T-F: Secondary gout associated with myeloproliferative diseases. *Arthritis Rheum* 8:765, 1965.

441. BRONSKY D, BERNSTEIN A: Acute gout secondary to multiple myeloma: A case report. *Ann Intern Med* 41:820, 1954.

442. SOMERVILLE J: Gout in cyanotic congenital heart disease. *Br Heart Med* 23:31, 1961.

443. ZIMMER JG, DEMIS DJ: Associations between gout, psoriasis, and sarcoidosis: With consideration of their pathologic significance. *Ann Intern Med* 64:786, 1966.

444. LYNCH EC: Uric acid metabolism in proliferative diseases of the marrow. *Arch Intern Med* 109:639, 1962.

445. TALBOTT JH: Gout and blood dyscrasias. *Medicine* 38:173, 1959.

446. HERS H-G, VAN DEN BERGHE G: Enzyme defect in primary gout. *Lancet* 1:585, 1979.

447. VAN DEN BERGHE G, HERS H-G: Abnormal AMP deaminase in primary gout. *Lancet* 2:1090, 1980.

448. FOX IH: Disorders of purine and pyrimidine metabolism, in Spittell JA (ed): *Clinical Medicine*. Philadelphia, Harper & Row, 1982, p 1.

449. WILSON D, BEYER A, BISHOP C, TALBOTT JH: Urinary uric acid excretion after the ingestion of isotopic yeast nucleic acid in the normal and gouty human. *J Biol Chem* 209:227, 1954.

450. NUGENT CA, MACDIARMID WD, TYLER FH: Renal excretion of urate in patients with gout. *Arch Intern Med* 113:115, 1964.

451. SEEGMILLER JE, GRAYZEL AI, HOWELL RR, PLATO C: The renal excretion of uric acid in gout. *J Clin Invest* 41:1094, 1962.

452. LATHEM W, RODNAN GP: Impairment of uric acid excretion in gout. *J Clin Invest* 41:1955, 1962.

453. HOUPT JB, OGRYZLO MA: Persistence of impaired uric acid excretion in gout during reduced synthesis with allopurinol. *Arthritis Rheum* 7:316, 1964.

454. SNAITH ML, SCOTT JT: Uric acid clearance in patients with gout and normal subjects. *Ann Rheum Dis* 30:285, 1971.

455. SIMKIN PA: Uric acid excretion in patients with gout. *Arthritis Rheum* 22:98, 1979.

456. SIMKIN PA: Urate excretion in normal and gouty men, in Miller MM, Kaiser E, Seegmiller JE (eds): *Purine Metabolism in Man* II. New York, Plenum, 1977, p 41.

457. WYNGAARDEN JB: Gout. *Adv Metab Disord* 2:2, 1965.

458. CAMPION DW, OLSEN RW, CAUGHEY D, BLUESTONE R, KLINENBERG JR: Does increased free serum urate concentration cause gout? *Clin Res* 23:261A, 1975.

459. STEELE TH, RIESELBACK RE: The renal mechanism for urate homeostasis in normal man. *Am J Med* 43:868, 1967.

460. YU T-F, BERGER L, STONE DJ, WOLF J, GUTMAN AB: Effects of pyrazinamide and pyrazinoic acid on urate clearance and other discrete renal functions. *Proc Soc Exp Biol Med* 96:264, 1957.

461. YU T-F, BERGER L, GUTMAN AB: Suppression of the tubular secretion of urate by pyrazinamide in the dog. *Proc Soc Exp Biol Med* 107:905, 1961.

462. DAVIS BB, FIELD JB, RODNAN GP, KEDES LH: Localization and pyrazinamide inhibition of distal transtubular movement of uric acid-2-^{14}C with a modified stop-flow technique. *J Clin Invest* 44:716, 1965.

463. YU T-F, BERGER L, GUTMAN AB: Renal function in gout. II. Effect of uric acid loading on renal excretion of uric acid. *Am J Med* 33:829, 1962.

464. RIESELBACH RE, STEELE TH: Influence of the kidney upon urate homeostasis in health and disease. *Am J Med* 56:665, 1974.

465. DIAMOND HS, PAOLINO JS: Evidence for a post-secretory reabsorptive site for uric acid in man. *J Clin Invest* 52:1491, 1973.

466. BOSS GR, SEEGMILLER JE: Hyperuricemia and gout. *N Engl J Med* 300:1459, 1979.

467. PUIG GJ, ANTON MF, SANZ MA, GASPAR G, LESMES A, RAMOS T, VAZQUEZ OJ: Renal handling of uric acid in normal subjects by means of the pyrazinamide and probenecid tests. *Nephron* 35:183, 1983.

468. STEELE TH, RIESELBACH RE: The contribution of residual nephrons within the chronically diseased kidney to urate homeostasis in man. *Am J Med* 43:876, 1967.

469. FEINSTEIN EI, QUION VH, KAPTEIN EM, MASSRY SG: Severe hyperuricemia in patients with volume depletion. *Am. J. Nephrology* 4(2):77, 1984.

470. DEMARTINI FE, WHEATON EA, HEALEY LA, LARAGH JH: Effect of chlorothiazide on the renal excretion of uric acid. *Am J Med* 32:572, 1962.

471. STEELE TH: Evidence for altered renal urate reabsorption during changes in volume of the extracellular fluid. *J Lab Clin Med* 74:228, 1969.

472. STEELE TH, OPPENHEIMER S: Factors affecting urate excretion following diuretic administration in man. *Am J Med* 47:564, 1969.

473. SUKI WN, EKNOYAN G, MARTINEZ-MALDONADO M: Tubular sites and mechanisms of diuretic action. *Ann Rev Pharmacol* 13:91–106, 1973.

474. HOLMES EW: Clinical gout and the pathogenesis of hyperuricemia, in McCarty DJ (ed): *Arthritis and Allied Conditions*, 10th ed. Philadelphia, Lea & Febiger, 1985, p 1445.

475. GOLDFINGER S, KLINENBERG JR, SEEGMILLER JE: Renal retention of uric acid induced by infusion of beta-hydroxybutyrate and acetoacetate. *N Engl J Med* 272:351, 1965.

476. SCHULMAN JD, LUSTBERG TJ, KENNEDY JL, MUSELES M, SEEGMILLER JE: A new variant of maple syrup urine disease (branched chain ketoaciduria): Clinical and biochemical evaluation. *Am J Med* 49:118, 1970.

477. YU T-F, GUTMAN AB: Study of the paradoxical effects of salicylate in low, intermediate and high dosage on the renal mechanisms for excretion of urate in man. *J Clin Invest* 38:1298, 1959.

478. GUTMAN AB, YU T-F: Renal mechanisms for regulation of uric acid excretion, with special reference to normal and gouty man. *Semin Arthritis Rheum* 2:1, 1972.

479. GERGER R, LANG F, DEETJEN P: Handling of uric acid by rat kidney. II. Microperfusion studies on bidirectional transport of uric acid in the proximal tubule. *Eur J Physiol* 335:257, 1972.

480. WEINER IM, TINKER JP: Pharmacology of pyrazinamide: Metabolic and renal function studies related to the mechanism of drug-induced urate retention. *J Pharmacol Exp Ther* 180:411, 1972.

481. POSTLETHWAITE AE, BARTEL AG, KELLEY WN: Hyperuricemia due to ethambutol. *N Engl J Med* 286:761, 1972.

482. BECKER MA, RAIVIO KO, MEYER LJ, SEEGMILLER JE: The effects of nicotinic acid on human purine metabolism. *Clin Res* 21:616, 1973.

483. GERSHON SL, FOX IH: Pharmacologic effects of nicotinic acid on human purine metabolism. *J Lab Clin Med* 84:179, 1974.

484. HAMILTON WFD, ROBERTSON GS: Changes in serum uric acid related to the dose of methoxyflurane. *Br J Anaesth* 46:54, 1974.

485. HONDA H, GINDIN RA: Gout while receiving levodopa for Parkinsonism. *JAMA* 219:55, 1972.

486. PALESTINE AG, NUSSENBLATT RB, CHAN CC: Side effects of systemic cyclosporine in patients not undergoing transplantation. *Am J Med* 77:652, 1984.

487. SUGINO H, KAGOSHIMA M, KATAGIRI S: Effects of some drugs on plasma uric acid in rats—Actions of catecholamines and beta-blocking agents. *Nippon Yakurigaku Zasshi* 84:293, 1984.

488. MORITA Y, NISHIDA Y, KAMATANI N, MIYAMOTO T: Theophylline increases serum uric acid levels. *J Allergy Clin Immunol* 74:707, 1984.

489. MENON RK, MIKHAILIDIS DP, BELL JL, KERNOFF PB, DADDONA P: Warfarin administration increases uric acid concentrations in plasma. *Clin Chem* 32:1557, 1986.

490. TIITINEN S, NISSILA M, RUUTSALO HM, ISOMAKI H: Effect of nonsteroidal anti-inflammatory drugs on the renal excretion of uric acid. *Clin Rheumatol* 2:233, 1983.

491. BALL GV, MORAN JM: Chronic lead ingestion and gout. *South Med J* 61:21, 1968.

492. BALL GV, SORENSEN LB: Pathogenesis of hyperuricemia in saturnine gout. *N Engl J Med* 280:1199, 1969.

493. EMMERSON BT: Chronic lead neuropathy: The diagnostic use of calcium EDTA and the association with gout. *Aust Ann Med* 12:310, 1963.

494. RICHET G, ET AL: Le rein du saturnisme chronique. *Rev Fr Etudes Clin Biol* 9:188, 1964.

495. COHEN J: Gout, in Copeman WSC (ed): *Textbook of the Rheumatic Diseases*. Edinburgh, Livingstone, 1955, p 361.

496. TALBOTT JH: Gout. *J Chronic Dis* 1:338, 1955.

497. SMYTH CJ: Hereditary factors in gout: A review of recent literature. *Metabolism* 6:218, 1957.

498. SMYTH CJ, COTTERMAN CW, FREYBERG RH: The genetics of gout and hyperuricemia: Analysis of nineteen families. *J Clin Invest* 27:749, 1948.

499. STECHER RM, HERSH AH, SOLOMAN WM: The heredity of gout and its relationship to familial hyperuricema. *Ann Intern Med* 31:595, 1949.

500. LAWRENCE JS: Heritable disorders of connective tissue. *Proc R Soc Med* 53:522, 1960.

501. COBB S: Hyperuricemia in executives, in *The Epidemiology of Chronic Rheumatism*. Philadelphia, Davis, 1963, vol 1, p 182.

502. DUNN JP, BROOKS GW, MAUSNER J, RODNAN GP, COBB S: Social class gradient of serum uric acid levels in man. *JAMA* 185:431, 1963.

503. DECKER JL, LANE JJ JR, REYNOLDS WE: Hyperuricemia in a Filipino population. *Arthritis Rheum* 5:144, 1962.

504. BURCH TA, O'BRIEN WM, REED R, KURLAND LT: Hyperuricemia and gout in Mariana Islands. *Ann Rheum Dis* 25:114, 1966.

505. HAUGE M, HARVALD B: Heredity in gout and hyperuricemia. *Acta Med Scand* 152:247, 1955.

506. NEEL JV, RAKIC MT, DAVIDSON RI, VALKENBURG HA, MIKKELSEN WM: Studies on hyperuricemia. II. A reconsideration of the distribution of serum uric acid values in the families of Smyth, Cotterman, and Freyberg. *Am J Hum Genet* 17:14, 1965.

507. HALL AP, BARRY PE, DAWBER TR, MCNAMARA M: Epidemiology of gout and hyperuricemia: A long-term population study. *Am J Med* 42:27, 1967.

507a. CHILDS B, SCRIBER CR: Age at onset and causes of disease. *Perspect Biol Med* 29:437, 1986.

508. SPERLING O, PERSKY-BROSH S, BOER P, DE VRIES A: Human erythrocyte phosphoribosylpyrophosphate synthetase mutationally altered in regulatory properties. Biochem Med 7:389, 1973.

509. HENDERSON JF, ROSENBLOOM FM, KELLEY WN, SEEGMILLER JE: Variations in purine metabolism of cultured skin fibroblasts from patients with gout. *J Clin Invest* 47:1511, 1968.

510. NISHIDA Y, AKAOKA I, HORIUCHI Y: Altered isoelectric property of a superactive 5-phosphoribosyl-1-pyrophosphate (PRPP) synthetase in a patient with clinical gout. *Biomed Med* 26:387, 1981.

511. AKAOKA I, FUJIMORI S, KAMATANI N, TAKEUCHI F, YANO E, NISHIDA Y, HASHIMOTO A, HORIUCHI Y: A gouty family with increased phosphoribosylpyrophosphate synthetase activity: Case reports, familial studies, and kinetic studies of the abnormal enzyme. *J Rheumatol* 8:563, 1981.

512. SPERLING O, BOER P, BROSH S, ZOREF E, DE VRIES A: Overproduction disease in man due to enzyme feedback resistance mutation. *Enzyme* 23:1, 1978.

513. ITKIN P, WOO S, BECKER MA: Human phosphoribosylpyrophosphate synthetase: Radioimmunochemical quantitation in erythrocytes and fibroblasts. *J Lab Clin Med* 104:96, 1984.

514. SIMMONDS HA, WEBSTER DR, LINGAM S, WILSON J: An inborn error of purine metabolism, deafness and neurodevelopmental abnormality. *Neuropediatrics* 16:106, 1985.

515. WADA Y, NISHIMURA Y, TANABU M, YOSHIMURA Y, IINUMA K, YOSHIDA T, ARAKAWA T: Hypouricemic, mentally retarded infant with a defect of 5-phosphoribosyl-1-pyrophosphate synthetase of erythrocytes. *Tohoku J Exp Med* 113:149, 1974.

516. IINUMA K, WADA Y, ONUMA A, TANABU M: Electroencephalographic study of an infant with phosphoribosylpyrophosphate synthetase deficiency. *Tohoku J Exp Med* 116:53, 1975.

517. LOSMAN M, RIMON D, KIM M, BECKER MA: Selective expression of phosphoribosylphosphate synthetase superactivity in human lymphoblast lines. *J Clin Invest* 76:1657, 1985.

518. ZOREK EA, DE VRIES A, SPERLING O: X-linked pattern of inheritance of gout due to mutant feedback resistant phosphoribosylpyrophosphate synthetase. *Adv Exp Med Biol* 76A:287, 1977.

519. YEN RCK, ADAMS WB, LAZAR C, BECKER MA: Evidence for X-linkage of human phosphoribosylpyrophosphate synthetase. *Proc Natl Acad Sci USA* 75:782, 1978.

520. JACKEN J, VAN DEN BERGHE G: An infantile autistic syndrome characterised by the presence of succinylpurines in body fluids. *Lancet* 2:1058, 1984.

521. DE BREE PK, WADMAN SK, DURAN M, DE JONGE F: Diagnosis of inherited adenylosuccinase deficiency by thin-layer chromatography of urinary imidazoles and by automated cation exchange column chromatography of purines. *Clin Chim Acta* 156:279, 1986.

522. HOWELL RR, ASHTON DM, WYNGAARDEN JB: Glucose-6-phosphatase deficiency glycogen storage disease. Studies on the interrelationships of carbohydrate, lipid and purine abnormalities. *Pediatrics* 29:553, 1962.

523. JEANDET J, LESTRADET H: L'hyperlactacidemie, cause probable de l'hy-

peruricemie dans la glycogenase hépatique. *Rev Fr Etud Clin Biol* 6:71, 1961.

524. FINE RN, STRAUSS J, DONNELL GN: Hyperuricemia in glycogen-storage disease type I. *Am J Dis Child* 112:572, 1966.

525. ALEPA FP, HOWELL RR, KLINENBERG JR, SEEGMILLER JE: Relationships between glycogen storage disease and tophaceous gout. *Am J Med* 42:58, 1967.

526. JAKOVCIC S, SORENSEN LB: Studies of uric acid metabolism in glycogen storage disease associated with gouty arthritis. *Arthritis Rheum* 10:129, 1967.

527. KELLEY WN, ROSENBLOOM FM, SEEGMILLER JE, HOWELL RR: Excessive production of uric acid in type I glycogen storage disease. *J Pediatr* 72:488, 1968.

528. KOLB OF, DE LALLA RS, GORMAN JW: The hyperlipidemias in disorders of carbohydrate metabolism, serial lipoprotein studies in diabetic acidosis with xanthomatosis and in glycogen storage disease. *Metab Clin Exp* 4:310, 1955.

529. JEUNE M, CHARRAT A, BERTRAND J: Polycori hépatique, hyperuricemic et goutte. *Arch Fr Pediatr* 14:897, 1957.

530. JEUNE M, FREANCOIS R, JARLOT B: Contribution a l'étude des polycories glycogeniques du foie. *Rev Int Hepatol* 9:1, 1959.

531. AGAMANOLIS D, ASKARI AD, DI MAURO S, HAYS A, KUMAR K, LIPTON M, RAYNOR A: Muscle phosphofructokinase deficiency. Two cases with unusual polysaccharide accumulation and immunologically active enzyme protein. *Muscle Nerve* 3:456, 1980.

532. HAYS AP, HALLETT M, DELFS J, MORRIS BM, SOTREL A, SHEVCHUNK MM: Muscle phosphofructokinase deficiency. Abnormal polysaccharide in a case of late-onset myopathy. *Neurology* 31:1077, 1981.

533. ZANELLA A, MARIANI M, MEOLA G, FAGNANI G, SIRCHIA G: Phosphofructokinase (PFK) deficiency due to a catalytically inactive mutant M-type subunit. *Am J Hematol* 12:215, 1982.

534. VORA S, DAVIDSON M, SEAMAN C, MIRANDA AF, NOBLE NA, KOUICHI RT, FRENKEL EP, DIMAURO S: Heterogeneity of the molecular lesions in inherited phosphofructokinase deficiency. *J Clin Invest* 72:1995, 1983.

535. FOGELFELD L, SAROVA-PINHAS I, MEYTES D: Glycogen storage disease type VII myopathy (Tarui) associated with hemolysis and gout. *J Neurol* 232*(suppl)*:186, 1985.

536. BRUNBERG JB, MCCORMICK WF, SCHOCHET SS: Type III glycogenosis. An adult with diffuse weakness and muscle wasting. *Arch Neurol* 25:171, 1971.

537. MURASE T, IKEDA H, MURO T, NAKAO K, SUGITA H: Myopathy associated with type III glycogenosis. *J Neurol Sci* 20:287, 1973.

538. DI MAURO S, MIRANDA AF, KHAN S, GITLIN K, FRIEDMAN R: Human muscle phosphoglycerate mutase deficiency: Newly discovered metabolic myopathy. *Science* 212:1277, 1981.

539. FOX IH, KELLEY WN: Management of gout. *JAMA* 242:361, 1979.

540. FREEMAN DL: Frequent doses of intravenous colchicine can be lethal. *N Engl J Med* 309:310, 1983.

541. STANLEY MW, TAUROG JD, SNOVER DC: Fatal colchicine toxicity: Report of a case. *Clin Exp Rheum* 2:167, 1984.

542. FERRANNINI E, PENTIMONE F: Marrow aplasia following colchicine treatment for gouty arthritis. *Clin Exp Rheum* 2:173, 1984.

543. NEUSS MN, MCCALLUM RM, BRENCKMAN WD, SILBERMAN HR: Long-term colchicine adminstration leading to colchicine toxicity and death. *Arthritis Rheum* 29:448, 1986.

544. KUNCL RW, DUNCAN G, WATSON D, ALDERSON K, ROGAWSKI MA, PEPER M: Colchicine myopathy and neuropathy. *N Engl J Med* 316:1562, 1987.

545. YU TF: The efficacy of colchicine prophylaxis in articular gout. A reappraisal after 20 years. *Arthritis Rheum* 12:256, 1982.

546. WEINBERGER A, LIBERMAN UA, SPERLING O, SCHINDEL B, PINKHAS J: Calciuric effect of probenecid in gouty patients. *Isr J Med Sci* 19:377, 1983.

547. YU TF, ROBOZ J, JOHNSON S, KAUNG C: Studies on the metabolism of D-penicillamine and its interaction with probenecid in cystinuria and rheumatoid arthritis. *J Rheum* 11:467, 1984.

548. SOSLER SD, BEHZAD O, GARRATTY G, LEE CL, POSTOWAY N, KHONO O: Immune hemolytic anemia associated with probenecid. *Am J Clin Pathol* 84:391, 1985.

549. KICKLER TS, BUCK S, NESS P, SHIRLEY RS, SHOLAR PW: Probenecid induced immune hemolytic anemia. *J Rheum* 13:208, 1986.

550. FERRACCIOLI G, SPISNI A, AMBANELLI U: Hypouricemic action of diflunisal in gouty patients: In vitro and in vivo studies. *J Rheum* 11:330, 1984.

551. THOMAS AL, MAJOOS FL, NUKI G: Preliminary studies with azapropazone in gout and hyperuricemia. *Eur J Rheumatol Inflamm* 6:149, 1983.

552. WILLIAMSON PJ, ENE MD, ROBERTS CJ: A study of the potential interactions between azapropazone and frusemide in man. *Br J Clin Pharm* 18:619, 1984.

553. GIBSON T, SIMMONDS HA, ARMSTRONG RD, FAIRBANKS LD, RODGERS AV: Azapropazone: A treatment for hyperuricemia and gout? *Br J Rheum* 23:44, 1984.

554. WORTMANN RL, RIDOLFO AS, LIGHTFOOT RW JR, FOX IH: Antihyperuricemia properties of amflutizole in gout. *J Rheum* 12:540, 1985.

555. RUNDLES RW: The development of allopurinol. *Arch Intern Med* 145:1492, 1985.

556. BREITHAUPT H, TITTEL M: Kinetics of allopurinol after single intravenous and oral doses. *Eur J Clin Pharm* 22:77, 1982.

557. APPELBAUM SJ, MAYERSOHN M, DORR RT, PERRIER D: Allopurinol kinetics and bioavailability. Intravenous, oral and rectal administration. *Cancer Chemother Pharmacol* 8:93, 1982.

558. BERLINGER WG, PARK GD, SPECTOR R: The effect of dietary protein on the clearance of allopurinol and oxypurinol. *N Engl J Med* 313:771, 1985.

559. BUNDGAARD H, FALCH E: Improved rectal and parenteral delivery of allopurinol using the prodrug approach. *Arch Pharm Chem Sci Ed* 13:39, 1985.

560. MCINNES GT, LAWSON DH, JICK H: Acute adverse reactions attributed to allopurinol in hospitalized patients. *Ann Rheum Dis* 40:245, 1981.

561. HANDE KR, NOONE RM, STONE WJ: Severe allopurinol toxicity. Description and guidelines for prevention in patients with renal insufficiency. *Am J Med* 76:47, 1984.

562. SINGER JZ, WALLACE SL: The allopurinol hypersensitivity syndrome. Unnecessary morbidity and mortality. *Arthritis Rheum* 29:82, 1986.

563. SONODA T, TATIBANA M: Metabolic fate of pyrimidines and purines in dietary nucleic acids ingested by mice. *Biochim Biophys Acta* 521:55, 1978.

564. HO CY, MILLER KV, SAVAIANO DA, CRANE RT, ERICSON KA, CLIFFORD AJ: Absorption and metabolism of orally administered purines in fed and fasted rats. *J Nutr* 109:1377, 1979.

565. SAVAIANO DA, HO CY, CHU V, CLIFFORD AJ: Metabolism of orally and intravenously administered purines in rats. *J Nutr* 110:1793, 1980.

566. LOFFLER W, GROBNER W, MEDINA R, ZOLLNER N: Influence of dietary purines on pool size, turnover, and excretion of uric acid during balance conditions. *Res Exp Med* 181:113, 1982.

567. STAPLETON FB, KENNEDY J, NOUSIA-ARVANITAKIS S, LINSHAW MA: Hyperuricosuria due to high-dose pancreatic extract therapy in cystic fibrosis. *N Engl J Med* 295:246, 1976.

568. SACK J, BLAU H, GOLDFARB D, BEN-ZARAY S, KATZNELSON D: Hyperuricosuria in cystic fibrosis patients treated with pancreatic enzyme supplements. A study of 16 patients in Israel. *Isr J Med Sci* 16:417, 1980.

569. NARINS RG, WEISBERG JS, MEYERS AR: Effects of carbohydrate on uric acid metabolism. *Metabolism* 23:455, 1974.

570. BODE JC, ZELDER O, RUMPELT HJ, WITTKAMO U: Depletion of liver adenosine phosphates and metabolic effects of intravenous infusion of fructose or sorbital in man and in the rat. *Eur J Clin Invest* 3:436, 1973.

571. EMMERSON BT: Effect of oral fructose on urate production. *Ann Rheum Dis* 33:276, 1974.

572. HANDE KR, HIXSON CV, CHABNER BA: Postchemotherapy purine excretion in lymphoma patients receiving allopurinol. *Cancer Res* 41:2273, 1981.

573. DAVIS S, PARK YK: Hypouricaemic effect of polyethyleneglycol modified urate oxidase. *Lancet* 1:281, 1981.

574. MASERA G, JANKOVIC M, ZURLO MG, LOCASCIULLI A, ROSSI MR, UDERZO C, RECCHIA M: Urate-oxidase prophylaxis of uric acid-induced renal damage in childhood leukemia. *J Pediatr* 100:152, 1982.

575. SANCHEZ-BAYLE M, GARCIA-VAO C, RAMO-MANCHENO C, VAZQUEZ-MARTUL M: Hyperuricemia and increase in postsecretory reabsorption of uric acid. *Nephron* 43:151, 1986.

576. RAJAN KT: Observations on phagocytosis of urate crystals by polymorphonuclear leukocytes. *Ann Rheum Dis* 34:54, 1975.

CHAPTER 38

HYPOXANTHINE PHOSPHORIBOSYLTRANSFERASE DEFICIENCY: The Lesch-Nyhan Syndrome and Gouty Arthritis

J. TIMOTHY STOUT
C. THOMAS CASKEY

1. *The Lesch-Nyhan syndrome results from a complete deficiency of the purine salvage enzyme hypoxanthine phosphoribosyltransferase (HPRT). The disease is characterized by hyperuricemia, choreoathetosis, spasticity, mental retardation, and self-mutilation. Patients with a partial deficiency of HPRT have hyperuricemia and gouty arthritis but are spared most of the neurologic sequelae of the Lesch-Nyhan syndrome.*
2. *Patients with the Lesch-Nyhan syndrome are clinically normal at birth. Developmental delay is evident by 6 months of age, and choreiform movements appear within the first year. Self-mutilation is present in 85 percent of patients with the disease and may begin as early as age 1 year or as late as 16 years. Autopsies of Lesch-Nyhan patients fail to detect any consistent pathologic changes other than these associated with chronic hyperuricemia.*
3. *Hyperuricemia associated with HPRT deficiency may lead to nephrolithiasis, uric acid crystalluria, tophi formation, obstructive uropathy, or, eventually, a form of gouty arthritis. Allopurinol (10 mg/kg per day, maximum dose 800 mg/day) reduces serum uric acid levels and prevents most of the sequelae of hyperuricemia. There is no effective therapy for the neurologic complications of the Lesch-Nyhan syndrome.*
4. *Functional HPRT is a 217 amino acid protein and is encoded by a single gene on the X chromosome (Xq26-q27). The gene is divided into nine exons which are dispersed over ≈44 kb of genomic DNA. Four autosomal pseudogenes are present within the human genome. One three-allele* Bam*H1 restriction fragment length polymorphism has been described for the X-linked gene.*
5. *HPRT is expressed in all tissues at low levels. Elevated levels are present in the basal ganglia where the rate of* de novo *purine synthesis is low. The specific relationship(s) between HPRT deficiency and neurologic dysfunction are unknown.*
6. *Mouse and human HPRT gene promoter sequences lack "CAAT" and "TATAA" elements 5′ to the initiation sites. Both genes have extremely G-plus-C-rich promoters which contain several GGCGGG or CCGCCC direct repeats. Hypomethylation of CpG clusters within the first intron and hypermethylation of sites within the 3′ portion of the gene correlate with gene activity.*
7. *The genetic lesions which result in HPRT deficiency are heterogeneous. Six point mutations, three complete gene deletions, two partial deletions, one insertion, and one endoduplication of exons have been described. The majority of mutations (85 percent) do not represent major gene alterations and are probably the result of point mutations or small deletions.*
8. *Affected hemizygous males inherit the mutant allele from asymptomatic carrier females or are the result of* de novo *germ line mutation. Carrier detection is possible through fibroblast, lymphoblast, or hair follicle tests. HPRT activity is normal in erythrocytes from carrier females. Prenatal diagnosis by enzyme assay or DNA analysis is possible with amniocytes or chorionic villus samples.*

The enzyme hypoxanthine phosphoribosyltransferase (HPRT, EC 2.4.2.8) catalyzes the metabolic salvage of the purine bases hypoxanthine and guanine.[1,2] In 1967 Seegmiller et al. identified HPRT deficiency as the genetic defect in the X-linked Lesch-Nyhan syndrome.[3] Clinical heterogeneity is associated with HPRT deficiency. Complete deficiency of enzyme activity is associated with the Lesch-Nyhan syndrome, characterized by hyperuricemia, choreoathetoid movements, spasticity, hyperreflexia, mental retardation, and compulsive self-injurious behavior.[4] Partial HPRT deficiency is associated with increased *de novo* purine synthesis and hyperuricemia, which results in nephrolithiasis and gouty arthritis.[5,6] Approximately 20 percent of patients with partial HPRT deficiency exhibit spasticity, cerebellar ataxia, and mild mental retardation but do not become self-mutilating.[7] The molecular cloning of the HPRT gene has permitted the characterization of its mutations, identification of female carriers, and improved prenatal diagnosis.[8–16] Mouse models of HPRT deficiency have been developed.[17–18]

Nonstandard abbrevations used in this chapter are: AMPRT = amidophosphoribosyltransferase; APRT = adenine phosphoribosyltransferase; ES cells = embryonic stem cells; HPRT = hypoxanthine phosphoribosyltransferase; PCR = polymerase chain reaction; PP-ribose-P = 5′-phosphoribosyl-1-pyrophosphate; and PRA = phosphoribosylamine.

CLINICAL PHENOTYPES

Neurologic Dysfunction

The clinical abnormalities associated with HPRT deficiency are absent at birth.[3,19,20] Developmental delay is evident in Lesch-Nyhan patients within ages 3 to 6 months; pyramidal and extrapyramidal motor involvements become apparent within the first year.[4,21–24] These latter findings begin as fine athetoid movements of the hands and feet and later become choreiform in nature.[24–29] Alternatively, patients may present with poor head control due to hypotonia and subsequently develop hyperkinetic movements dominated by chorea and dystonia.[3,4,20] These patients will usually go on to develop hypertonia and spasticity (Fig. 38-1).

Dysarthria is one of the most disabling symptoms of the Lesch-Nyhan syndrome and frequently confounds attempts to accurately assess mental development.[7,23,27] While mental retardation is associated with the Lesch-Nyhan syndrome, attempts should be made to distinguish between definite retardation and an inability to communicate. One Lesch-Nyhan patient was determined to have a normal IQ when psychometric tests were designed to account for disorders of speech and movement.[30] In general, patients with the Lesch-Nyhan syndrome are moderately retarded; IQ values usually range from 40 to 80.

Fig. 38-1 An 8-year-old patient with the Lesch-Nyhan syndrome. When the protective mouthguard was removed from this patient, he began to bite his lower lip and buccal mucosa.

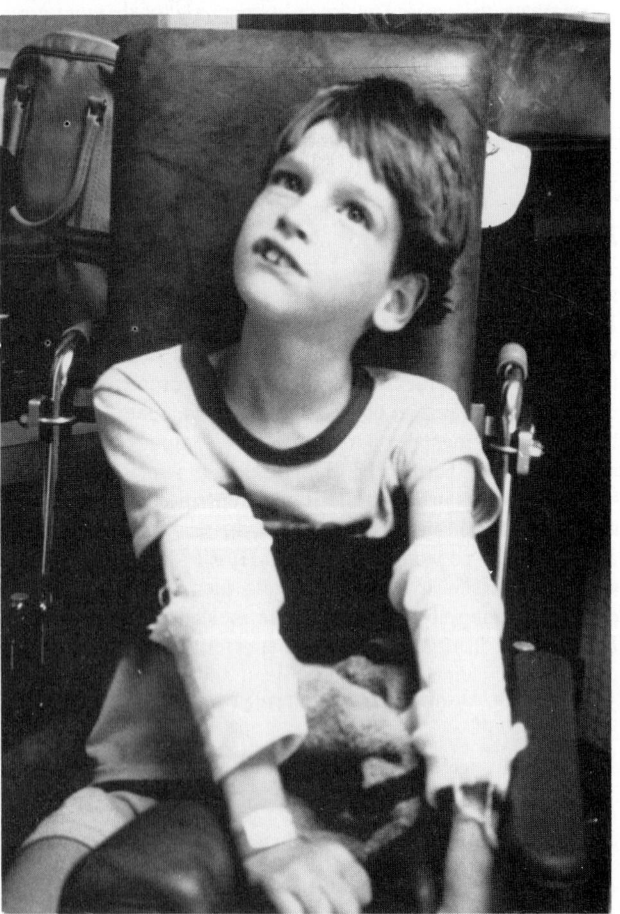

The most intriguing symptom of patients with the Lesch-Nyhan syndrome is a compulsive tendency toward self-injurious behavior, a trait observed in 85 percent of cases.[4,31] The age of onset of self-mutilation has been as early as age 1 year and as late as 16 years (mean = 3.5 years). Frequently it is the development of this symptom that results in the correction of an erroneous diagnosis of cerebral palsy.[32] The Lesch-Nyhan syndrome should be considered as part of the differential diagnosis in males with athetotic cerebral palsy who do not have a history of perinatal injury.[33]

Patients begin by biting their lips and/or buccal mucosa; this frequently progresses to the biting of fingers and hands. This destructive urge is often so severe that arm splint restraints or dental extraction are needed to prevent serious injury. Lesch-Nyhan patients may also attempt to injure themselves by hitting their heads against nearby objects such as walls, bed rails, or even examiners. The tendency to self-mutilation may exhibit quite a variable course (Fig. 38-2).[7,34] Patients may be aggressively mutilative for weeks or months at a time and then return to normal behavioral patterns. Unfortunately, the onset or cessation of periods of self-mutilation cannot be predicted by changes in biochemical or other behavioral parameters. The degree of self-mutilation can also vary on a day-to-day basis and may be exacerbated by aggravating environmental events. Usually these patients attempt to injure any exposed or unrestrained part of their body, but some patients demonstrate an unusual aggressive predilection for a group of fingers or one arm. In these patients, limbs that are not targets for self-mutilation may be left unrestrained. While the course of self-mutilation is variable, this behavior is less pronounced in patients older than 10 to 12 years of age. Patients with partial HPRT deficiency do not exhibit mutilatory behavior.

While routine studies of cerebral spinal fluid are normal in these patients, levels of specific neural transmitters and their metabolites have been reported to be altered.[35] When serial determinations of spinal fluid homovanillic acid and 5-hydroxyindoleacetic acid were made in four Lesch-Nyhan patients over a 5-year period, homovanillic acid levels were lower than the mean value for age-matched controls in 18 of 19 samples.[36] Other studies demonstrated that patients have decreased levels of 3-methoxy-4-hydroxy phenylethylene glycol.[37] These results suggest that reduced dopamine and norepinephrine turnover may be important in the pathogenesis of the disease. Spinal fluid levels of 5-hydroxyindoleacetic acid are normal or are slightly elevated, suggesting no consistent change in serotonin turnover. Electromyograms and electroencephalograms are typically normal in these patients.[20] Seizure activity in affected males is usually attributable to an event unrelated to HPRT deficiency such as birth anoxia, hypocalcemia, or hypoglycemia.[7,19,26] One patient with partial HPRT deficiency had a history of seizures.[6]

Growth retardation has been described in Lesch-Nyhan but may reflect a nutritional deficit rather than a primary manifestation of the disease (Table 38-1).[32,38] Delays in motor, social, and speech development have been described and are presumably due to dysarthria and mental retardation.[34] Evidence of spasticity, cerebellar ataxia, and mild mental retardation can be found in approximately 20 percent of patients with partial HPRT deficiency.[6] Approximately 50 percent of patients with partial deficiency have evidence of mental retardation without accompanying cerebellar symptoms.

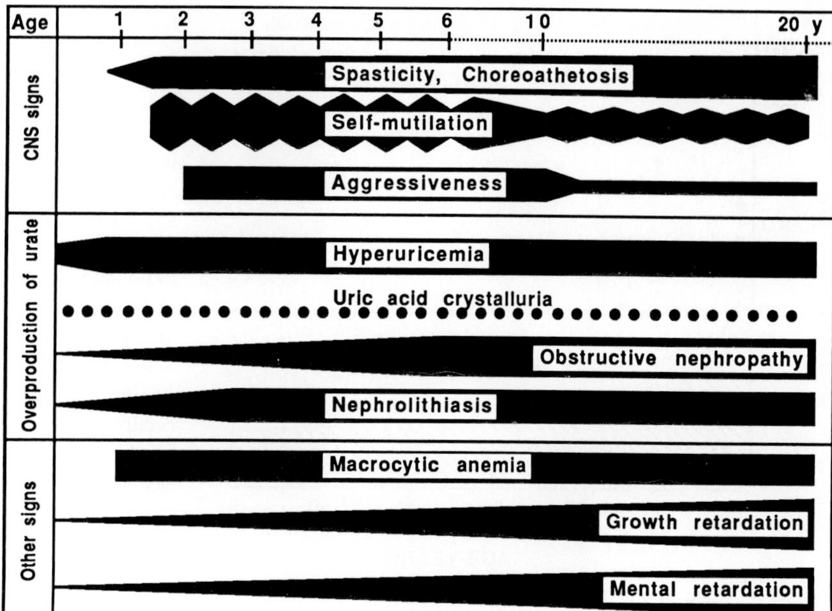

Fig. 38-2 Clinical course of the Lesch-Nyhan syndrome. *(Adapted from Mizuno.[32])*

Hyperuricemia and Renal Dysfunction

Hyperuricemia is common in patients with partial or complete HPRT deficiency and is associated with an increase in the rate of *de novo* purine synthesis.[4,6,7] Lymphoblasts or fibroblasts from controls and from Lesch-Nyhan patients exhibit accelerated *de novo* synthesis when cultured in hypoxanthine-depleted media, but only normal cells reduce the rate of *de novo* synthesis upon the addition of exogenous hypoxanthine.[7,39–43] The inability of Lesch-Nyhan cells to convert intracellular hypoxanthine to inosinic acid (IMP) leads to the cellular loss of hypoxanthine. The rapid conversion of hypoxanthine to uric acid by hepatocyte xanthine oxidase results in relatively mild elevations of hypoxanthine in the serum of these patients. Uric acid excretion is dramatically increased and ranges from 25 to 184 mg/kg of body weight per 24 h (normal = 1 to 14 mg/kg of body weight per 24 hours).[3,5,6] Patients with partial HPRT deficiency excrete uric acid at levels approaching those seen in patients with the Lesch-Nyhan syndrome.

Quantitation of urinary uric acid relative to urinary creatine was developed as a screening test for HPRT deficiency.[44] Figure 38-3 demonstrates elevated ratios of uric acid to creatine in urine samples obtained from patients with the Lesch-Nyhan syndrome or with partial HPRT deficiency. Further studies have suggested that the uric acid/creatine ratio, when used to estimate urate overproduction and predict HPRT deficiency, may result in a significant number of false positives because of diurnal variation in urinary uric acid excretion.[45]

Hyperuricemia in these patients frequently leads to uric acid crystalluria, nephrolithiasis, and obstructive nephropathy. The occasional observation of orange crystals in the diapers of affected males rarely leads to early diagnosis.[7,24] While patients with either partial or complete HPRT deficiency are hyperuricemic, it is unusual for patients with the Lesch-Nyhan syndrome to develop gouty arthritis. Greater than 80 percent of patients with partial HPRT deficiency will eventually develop gouty arthritis during the disease course. This frequency is somewhat lower for patients in Japan, perhaps reflecting

Table 38-1 Clinical Features of the Lesch-Nyhan Syndrome

						Developmental level			Physical growth		
Case	*Chronological age, yr:mo*	*Duration of follow-up, yr:mo*	*Initial diagnosis*	*Onset of self-mutilation, yr:mo*	*Cause of death*	*Motor, yr:mo*	*Social, yr:mo*	*Speech, yr:mo*	*Height age, % control*	*Weight age, % control*	*Bone age*
1	19:0	16:11	CP	1:10		0:8	3:0	2:6	9:0 (47.4)	5.6 (28.9)	18:0
2	15:4	14:10	CP	3:0	Pneumonia	0:6	1:0	1:6	7.6 (48.9)	6:0 (39.1)	13:0
3	19:5	18:7	CP	3:6	Sudden death	1:0	6:0	6:0	10:6 (54.1)	9:0 (46.4)	19:0
4	13:9	9:9	CP	3:0	Pneumonia	0:4	0:6	0:10	8:6 (61.8)	4:0 (29.1)	10:0
5	19:6	18:10	CP	2:4		0:7	3:0	2:6	10:0 (51.3)	8:0 (41.0)	17:6
6	12:3	11:10	CP	1:3		0:6	1:6	2:0	6:0 (49.0)	5.6 (44.9)	10:6
7	13:3	9:3	CP, UTI	2:6		0:6	7:0	7:0	9.6 (71.7)	6:0 (45.3)	12:0
8	11:9	9:5	CP	2:0		0:6	2:0	2:0	5:6 (46.8)	4:0 (34.0)	10:6
9	7.5	5:11	CP/renal hypoplasia	1:8	Sudden death	0:6	1:6	1:6	4:6 (60.7)	2:6 (33.7)	6:0
10	8.0	3:3	CP	2:0		0:7	3:0	3:0	3:0 (37.5)	2:6 (31.3)	7:0

NOTE: CP = cerebral palsy; UTI = urinary tract infection.
SOURCE: Mizuno.[32]

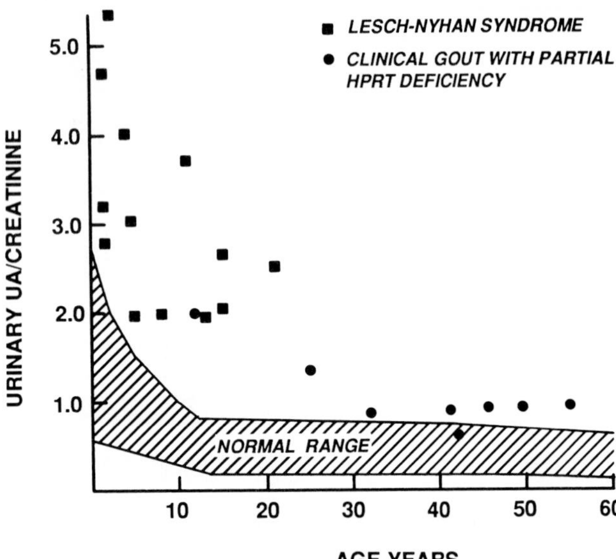

Fig. 38-3 Ratio of uric acid to creatinine concentration in purine samples obtained from patients with the Lesch-Nyhan syndrome and those with gout and a partial HPRT deficiency. The normal range represents ± 2 SD in a total of 284 control subjects of various ages. *(From Kaufman et al.*[44]*)*

dietary or genetic differences.[32] Hyperuricemia can be adequately controlled by the inhibition of xanthine oxidase with allopurinol.

Hematologic Dysfunction

Hematologic abnormalities have been associated with the Lesch-Nyhan syndrome. In 1979, Catel and Schmidt reported an HPRT-deficient patient with a megaloblastic anemia.[46] Others have confirmed macrocytic and megaloblastic changes in Lesch-Nyhan syndrome.[6,29,47–50] While these patients have low serum folate levels, perhaps due to increased folate consumption during *de novo* purine synthesis, the megaloblastic anemia in one patient failed to respond to folate therapy.[51] The Lesch-Nyhan syndrome has also been associated with hemolytic anemia and abnormal platelet morphology.[52–54] Electron microscopy of platelets from one patient with complete HPRT deficiency revealed decreased organization of marginal bundle structures, but clotting abnormalities have not been described.[53] Increased levels of red cell glutathione have also been associated with the Lesch-Nyhan syndrome,[55] but a relationship between glutathione and this disorder remains speculative.

Patients with the Lesch-Nyhan syndrome have normal numbers of peripheral T lymphocytes, normal delayed hypersensitivity reactions, and normal responses to phytohemagglutinin.[56,57] Serum IgM, IgA, and IgE are within normal limits.[56–59] The percentage of B lymphocytes, IgG levels, and serum-isohemagglutinin titers are subnormal,[7,56] suggesting HPRT deficiency may interfere with the proliferation and/or function of B lymphocytes. Leukocyte dysfunction may represent an important clinical aspect of the Lesch-Nyhan syndrome, since overwhelming infection is frequently the cause of death.

Pathology

Autopsies of patients with the Lesch-Nyhan syndrome fail to detect any consistent pathologic changes other than those associated with hyperuricemia.[7,24,27,60–62] Patients often have bilaterally shrunken kidneys, urate or xanthine nephrolithiasis, and dengenerative changes secondary to obstructive uropathy.[7] Routine histologic examination of brain tissue has not revealed consistent findings. One investigation described periodic acid-Schiff positive deposits in the ganglion cells of the nucleus olivaris.[63] These deposits did not stain with sudan-III and were not fluorescent in the presence of ultraviolet light. When formol-fixed tissue from the nucleus olivaris from this patient was examined with electron microscopy, circumscribed accumulations of a relatively homogenous substance were found in the dilated smooth endoplasmic reticulum. The identity of this material and its relevance to the disease remain unclear. Other inconsistent findings in brain tissue from patients with this disease include mild brownish pigmentation of the cerebral cortex, generalized thinning of the cerebellar cortex, and a loss of cells in the granular layer.[7,60,64]

NORMAL BIOCHEMISTRY AND PHYSIOLOGY

Properties of the Normal Enzyme

Enzymology. Hypoxanthine phosphoribosyltransferase catalyzes the condensation of 5′-phosphoribosyl-1-pyrophosphate (PP-ribose-P) and the purine bases hypoxanthine and guanine in the formation of 5′-IMP and 5′-GMP, respectively (Fig. 38-4).[1,2,65,66] HPRT is found in all cells as a soluble, cytoplasmic, nonglycosylated enzyme and usually accounts for 0.005 to 0.04 percent of total cellular protein.[7,67,68] This enzyme catalyzes the salvage of hypoxanthine and guanine, which are precursors in DNA and RNA synthesis and in the synthesis of cofactors which function in a wide range of enzymatic reactions. Adenine phosphoribosyltransferase (APRT) catalyzes a similar salvage of adenine.

Human erythrocyte HPRT Michaelis constants for guanine and hypoxanthine are 5 and 17 μM, respectively; K_m values for PP-ribose-P range from 55 to 200μ M, depending on the source of enzyme.[69–72] HPRT requires magnesium, and the specific mechanism of catalysis is greatly influenced by the Mg^{2+}/PP-ribose-P ratio.[73] Under physiological conditions, the enzyme first binds PP-ribose-P and then the purine base in the establishment of a short-lived ternary complex. The phosphoribosyl moiety is transferred to the base, and the enzyme and nucleotide dissociate, presumably with the release of pyrophosphate. While PP-ribose-P is the only useful ribosyl donor in this reaction, HPRT can bind and ribosylate a wide range of toxic purine analogues. The ability of HPRT to phosphoribosylate purine analogues is the basis for cell selection protocols which allow the recovery of HPRT-deficient cells.[74,75]

HPRT is one of 10 related phosphoribosyltransferases which are found in many oragnisms and participate in the biosynthesis of purines, pyrimidines, histidine, and tryptophan. Functionally and structurally similar HPRT proteins have been characterized from hamster, mouse, rat, and human

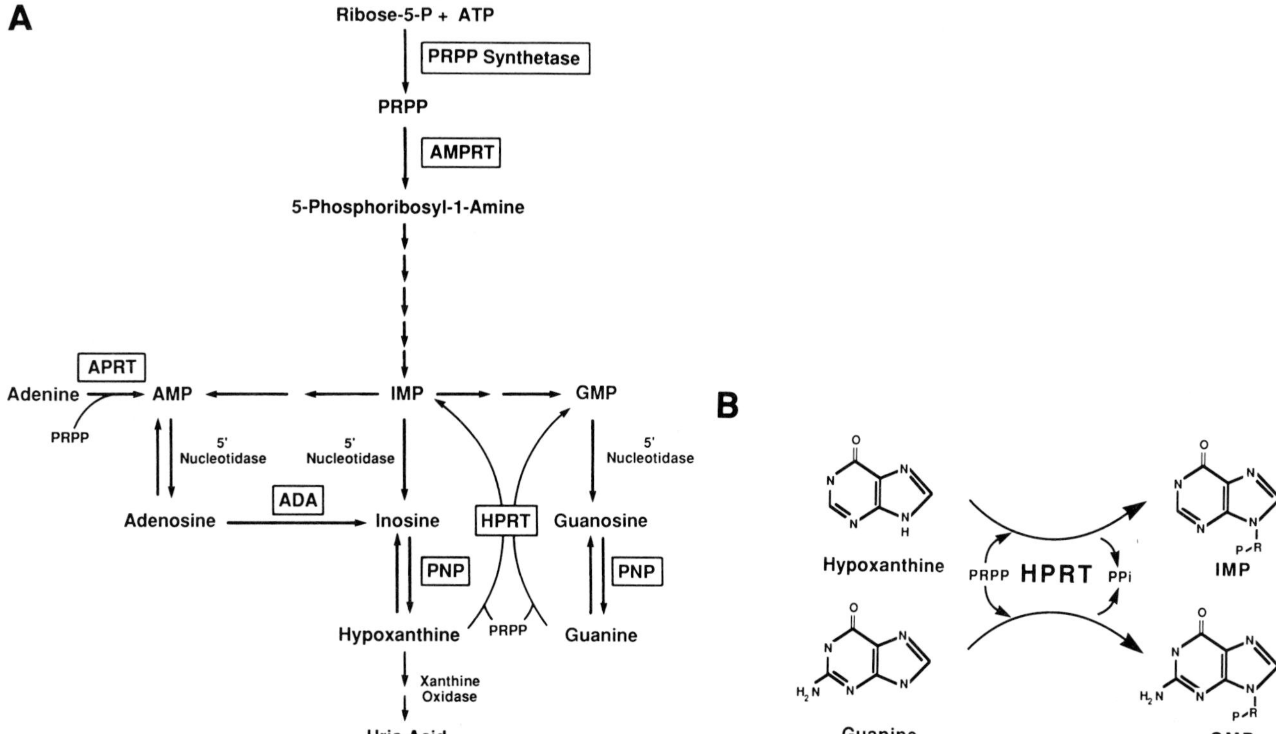

Fig. 38-4 A. Purine synthetic pathway. AMPRT = amidophosphoribosyltransferase; APRT = adenine phosphoribosyltransferase; HPRT = hypoxanthine phosphoribosyltransferase; ADA = adenosine deaminase; PNP = purine nucleoside phosphorylase. B. Reactions catalyzed by HPRT.

sources.[67,76–79] Yeast HPRT has been purified and is a single enzyme capable of recognizing guanine, hypoxanthine, and xanthine.[80,81] The protozoan *Leishmania donovani* is dependent on three salvage enzymes for purine homeostasis since it lacks the enzymes needed for *de novo* purine synthesis.[82] One transferase recognizes adenine, a second enzyme binds hypoxanthine or guanine, and a third, xanthine. *Salmonella typhimurium* and *Escherichia coli* use independent enzymes for conversion of hypoxanthine and guanine to IMP and GMP.[83–85]

Enzyme Structure. Wilson et al. determined the amino acid sequence of human HPRT and demonstrated that each monomer contains 217 amino acids equal to a mass of 24,470 daltons.[86] Cross-linking studies and isoelectric focusing of human-mouse heteropolymers indicate that the native enzyme is a tetramer of identical subunits (Fig. 38-5).[87,88] Human HPRT exhibits substantial electrophoretic heterogeneity, a fact attrib-

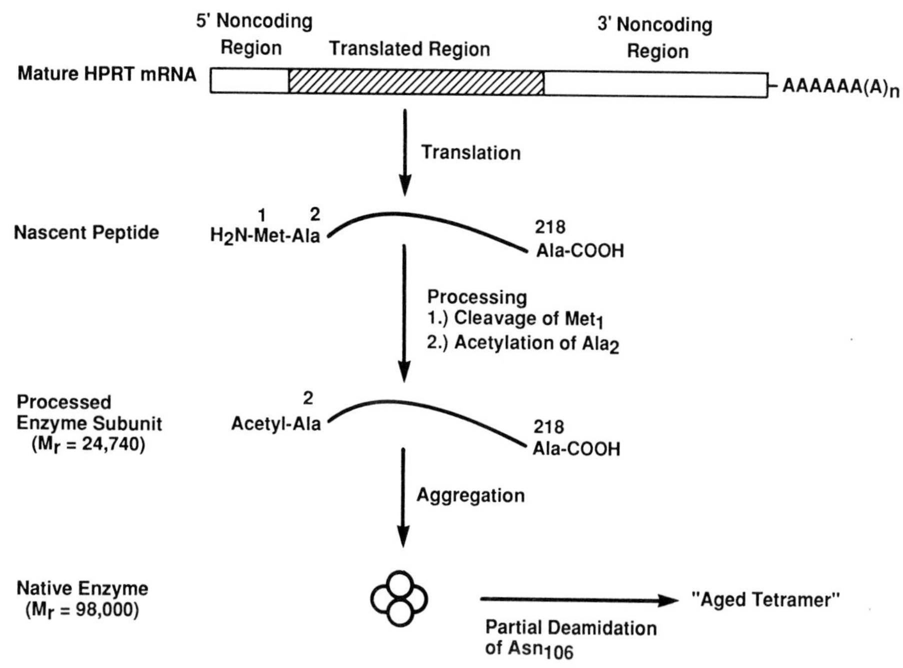

Fig. 38-5 Maturation pathway of HPRT protein. (*From Wilson et al.*[15])

uted to posttranslational modification.[89–92] The removal of the N-terminal methionine residue results in an alanine N terminus.[86] Partial deamidation of the asparagine residue at position 106 occurs in a time-dependent fashion and may be related to protein turnover.[15,86,93,94]

HPRT is one of 10 catalytically related phosphoribosyltransferases. Based on presumed functional similarities between these enzymes, Musick predicted that common structural features may represent shared substrate or catalytic sites.[95] Comparison of the primary structures of three phosphoribosyltransferases (human HPRT, adenosine triphosphate phosphoribosyltransferase from *S. typhimurium,* and glutamine PP-ribose-P amidotransferase from *E. coli*) revealed a common 34-residue span between the human and the *E. coli* enzymes.[96] When the amino acids from these enzymes were compared in terms of properties thought to control protein folding, a substantial correlation suggested the presence of a common structural domain. This analysis predicted the presence of a dinucleotide fold that is likely to be involved in substrate binding. Sequence analysis of mutant HPRT proteins, whose kinetic abnormalities were well defined, was subsequently used to predict the hypoxanthine/guanine and PP-ribose-P binding sites.[15,97–99]

Tissue Distribution. HPRT is present in all mammalian tissues at relatively low levels with the exception of the CNS.[6,100–102] Quantitation of regional CNS levels indicates that in rats and humans the basal ganglia have the highest levels of enzyme and mRNA.[6,100,102] It has been suggested that this region of the brain has an inherently limited ability to synthesize purines *de novo,* i.e., a capacity that may be insufficient to meet metabolic needs at certain stages of development.[100,102–104] Perhaps under these conditions purine salvage becomes particularly important. An inverse relationship between *de novo* synthesis and salvage has been described in other tissues as well. Erythrocytes, platelets, and bone marrow cells produce little amidophosphoribosyltransferase (AMPRT, the rate limiting enzyme in *de novo* purine synthesis), yet are rich in HPRT.[105–108] It is tempting to speculate that differences in purine salvage and *de novo* synthesis may affect CNS nucleotide pools and thereby be related to the neuropathology of the Lesch-Nyhan syndrome.

Regulation of Purine Metabolism

Nearly all living organisms are able to synthesize nucleotides *de novo* from simple precursors. Once formed, these nucleotides are able to participate in the synthesis of DNA and RNA or serve as coenzymes in many enzymatic reactions. After nucleotides are metabolized in such reactions, the free purine bases can be reconverted directly to their nucleotide form by the appropriate phosphoribosyltransferase in the presence of PP-ribose-P (Fig. 38-4). Ninety percent of free purines in humans are recycled in this manner.[109]

Purine *de novo* biosynthesis is usually represented by a linear reaction sequence which begins with the formation of phosphoribosylamine (PRA) from glutamine and PP-ribose-P and ends with the cyclodehydration of 5′-phophoribosyl-5-formamido-4-imidazole carboxamide in the formation of inosinic acid (IMP) (Fig. 38-4).[1,2,65,66,110] PP-ribose-P is generated by the pyrophosphorylation of α-D-ribose-5-phosphate by the enzyme PP-ribose-P synthetase at the expense of ATP. All together, six high energy phosphate groups are utilized in the formation of a single IMP molecule from D-ribose-5-phosphate. ATP and GTP are synthesized from inosinic acid by independent branch pathways.

There appear to be at least two levels of regulatory control of *de novo* synthesis (Fig. 38-4). The first involves regulation of the pathway leading to IMP synthesis; the second involves regulation of the branch pathways from IMP to AMP and GMP. It is generally accepted that the rate of purine *de novo* biosynthesis is controlled primarily by the activity of amidophosphoribosyltransferase (AMPRT), the enzyme which catalyzes the formation of PRA from glutamine and PP-ribose-P.[111,112] This enzyme is a bivalent regulatory enzyme, which is inhibited by ATP, ADP, AMP or by GTP, GDP, or GMP.[113–117] Each of these two types of nucleotides bind to separate allosteric sites on the enzyme and promote formation of a metabolically inactive aggregate of 270,000 daltons.[118] This inhibition appears to be cumulative, so that the enzyme is maximally inhibited when both types of nucleotides are present.[119] PP-ribose-P promotes disaggregation to the active form of 133,000 daltons, which probably consists of five or six identical subunits of 24,500 daltons.[120–122]

Cellular levels of PP-ribose-P are governed by the relative activity of PP-ribose-P synthetase and by the rate of PP-ribose-P utilization.[123,124] Since PP-ribose-P acts to activate AMPRT, increased levels of PP-ribose-P drive purine *de novo* synthesis forward. Patients with a mutant, overactive PP-ribose-P synthetase or elevated cellular levels of PP-ribose-P have higher rates of purine *de novo* synthesis.[125–127] Patients who lack HPRT activity consume less PRPP, resulting in high cellular levels of PRPP and increased *de novo* purine synthesis.[40,124,128]

The second level of regulation of *de novo* purine biosynthesis involves regulation of the branch pathways from IMP to AMP and GMP. Each of the end products of these branch pathways coordinately stimulates the other pathway by serving as a reactive phosphate donor. The conversion of IMP to adenylosuccinic acid, a precursor to ATP, requires GTP. The conversion of xanthylic acid to GMP requires ATP. Thus, an excess of either nucleotide accelerates the pathway leading to the synthesis of the other nucleotide. In addition to this coordinated system of branch pathway regulation, AMP and GMP are able to negatively affect their own synthesis by directly inhibiting the conversion of inosinic acid to adenylosuccinic acid or xanthylic acid, respectively.[129–133] Finally, AMP and GMP inhibit their respective salvage enzymes, thus directly promoting nucleotide catabolism.[134,135]

Characteristics of the Normal HPRT Gene

Structure. Human and rodent HPRT proteins are each encoded by single X-chromosomal sequences. The human HPRT gene has been localized to Xq26-q27, the mouse gene to band XA6, and the hamster gene to distal Xp.[14,136–140] Four nonexpressed pseudogenes have been detected in human DNA.[12] Southern analysis of DNA from somatic cell hybrids indicates that two of these sequences are located on chromosome 11, one on chromosome 3, and another in the region 5p13-q11.[12,141] Pseudogenes have been identified in mouse and hamster DNA but have not been characterized. These human pseudogenes presumably arise from processed HPRT mRNA and, consequently, lack promoters.

The cloning of the HPRT cDNA was simplified by the isolation of a mouse neuroblastoma cell line, NBR4, that expresses high levels of a mutant HPRT gene.[142] In vitro studies of this mutant revealed a tenfold elevation of a mutant HPRT protein, and a twenty- to fiftyfold overproduction of HPRT mRNA.[68] A differential hybridization strategy that employed NBR4 cDNA and cDNA from the parental cell line was used to isolate the first HPRT cDNA recombinants.[8] These initial probes were used to isolate a full-length mouse HPRT cDNA, which contained an open reading frame of 654 nucleotides preceded by 100 nucleotides of 5′ untranslated sequence and followed by 550 nucleotides of 3′ untranslated sequence. Extensive cross-species homology simplified the subsequent isolation of hamster and human HPRT cDNA full-length clones.[143,144]

An alternative approach succeeded in the isolation of λ-phage recombinants which contained portions of the human HPRT gene.[10] Mouse cells lacking HPRT were transfected with human genomic DNA, and primary HPRT positive transfectants were isolated by growth in selective media containing hypoxanthine, aminopterin, and thymidine. DNA from primary transfectants was used to generate secondary transfectants from which genomic recombinant libraries were generated. One of these clones, found to contain human-specific *Alu*I repetitive sequences, was used to screen a human cDNA library and identified a nearly full-length human HPRT cDNA recombinant clone.[11]

The nucleic acid sequence of these human HPRT cDNA clones is in perfect agreement with the amino acid sequence of human erythrocyte HPRT. The human cDNA open reading frame begins with an ATG initiation codon, codes for a protein of 218 amino acids, and ends with a TAA termination codon. Cleavage of the initial methionine from the nascent polypeptide had been shown to be a postantranslational event which results in the functional 217 amino acid monomer.[86] Northern analysis of RNA isolated from wild-type human, mouse, or hamster cells revealed messages of approximately 1600 nucleotides in length for each species.[16,144] Sequence comparison between these cDNAs indicates that homology between these three species is greater than 95 percent in the protein coding region and 80 percent in 5′ and 3′ nontranslated segments. The differences between mouse and human nucleotide sequence result in seven amino acid substitutions, five of which are conservative amino acid changes.

The isolation of these cDNA recombinants permitted the characterization of mouse and human HPRT gene structure. Analysis of overlapping λ-phage recombinants indicates that mouse and human HPRT genes each have nine exons dispersed over 34 and 44 kb of genomic DNA, respectively (Fig. 38-6).[9,12] The intron/exon boundaries are identical for both species. The nine exons range in length from 18 to 593 bp for the mice and from 18 to 637 bp for humans; differences are accounted for by nontranslated sequence. The major difference in size between these genes is due to differences in intron length, which range from 0.2 to 10.5 kb in the mouse genome and from 0.17 kb to 13.8 kb in humans. Primer extension and S1 nuclease mapping experiments demonstrated multiple transcription start sites for the mouse and human genes.[9,13] In addition, two independent hamster cDNA clones were found to have 3′ untranslated regions of different lengths, suggesting that more than one class of processed mRNA may be produced.[144]

RFLPs at the HPRT Locus. Mutant alleles can be followed within a family by association with a readily identifiable RFLP. Polymorphism within the HPRT locus has been identified only with the restriction endonuclease *Bam*HI.[145,146] Polymorphism involves the presence of a 22- or 12-kb fragment and the presence of a 25- or 18-kb fragment. Only three patterns of fragments have been observed: (1) a 22-kb/25-kb pair, (2) a 12-kb/25-kb pair, and (3) a 22-kb/18-kb pair. An analysis of the origin of these polymorphisms is shown in Fig. 38-7. Frequencies in an unselected white population are 0.77 for the 22/25 pair, 0.16 for the 12/25, and 0.7 for 22/18, resulting in an average heterozygosity of 38 percent. Most X chromosomes contain a single 22-kb (5′) and a single 25-kb (3′) fragment. In some individuals, the 22-kb allele is converted to a 12-kb allele, while in others the 25-kb allele is replaced by an 18-kb allele. The 22/18-kb pattern may be more prevalent in oriental populations.[147]

An additional two-allele *Taq*I RFLP has been reported for an anonymous sequence (DXS10) separate from, but closely linked to, the HPRT gene (95 percent confidence limits $\theta <$ 15 centimorgans).[148] These alleles are represented as 5- or 7-kb bands on Southern blots and have frequencies of 0.67 and 0.33, respectively. The RFLP patterns from both the *Bam*HI (HPRT) and *Taq*I (DXS10) polymorphisms can be combined to establish six haplotypes. A recent survey of 24 HPRT-deficient patients demonstrated that the most frequent haplotype, the 22/25/5 pattern, was found in 19 patients (79 percent).[149] The 22/25/7 pattern was detected in three patients (12.5 percent), while the 12/25/5 and 22/18/5 patterns were each seen in a single patient (4 percent).

Regulation of Gene Expression

HPRT is expressed in most mouse and human tissues at relatively low levels. Elevated levels are detectable in the basal ganglia (0.1 to 0.4 percent of total protein). The genetic signals responsible for this variable pattern of expression are beginning to be studied. Mouse and human HPRT promoters lack the "CAAT" and "TATAA" sequences immediately 5′ to the initiation site.[9,13] Both genes have extremely G-plus-C-rich promoters. Approximately 80 percent of the 250 bp immediately 5′ to the initiation codon are G or C residues, while the

Fig. 38-6 Human mouse HPRT gene structure. Stippled areas represent 5′ and 3′ noncoding sequence; black areas represent coding sequence. *(From Melton et al.[9] and Patel et al.[12])*

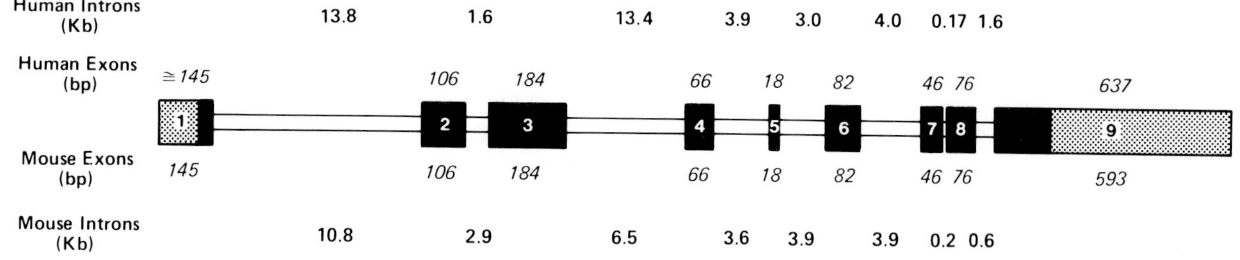

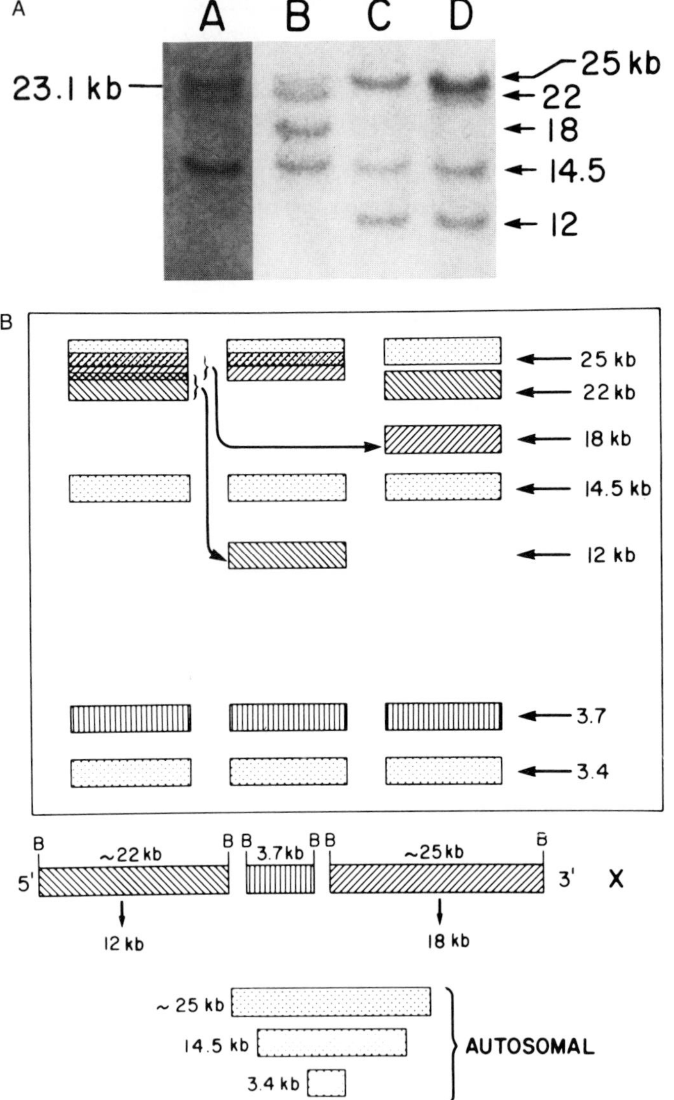

Fig. 38-7 A. Southern analysis of *Bam*HI-digested DNA from three unrelated male patients (lanes A, B, and C) and from the mother of one patient (lane D). *(From Nussbaum et al.*[145]*)* B. Schematic diagram of the Southern blot patterns of *Bam*HI-digested DNA from males with or without the 18- and 12-kb polymorphisms. *(From Nussbaum et al.*[146]*)*

G-plus-C content of the coding sequence is 46 percent. S1 nuclease protection and primer extension experiments demonstrated multiple transcription initiation sites. The 5′ termini of human HPRT mRNAs show little or no obvious preference for a particular initiation point and begin from 104 to 169 bp upstreams from the ATG codon.[13] The mouse HPRT mRNA has three major initiation sites which occur 84, 90, and 117 bp 5′ to the ATG initiation codon.[9,150]

The mouse HPRT promoter consists of a complex series of direct repeats, which include two tandem 12-bp repeats flanked by two imperfect 18-bp repeats.[9,150] Within each 12-bp repeat is the hexanucleotide GGCGGG. Deletion analysis of this promoter demonstrated that the removal of the first copies of the 18- and 12-bp repeats had no effect on expression, while removal of the second 12-bp repeat drastically reduced normal initiation.[150] The human HPRT promoter is arranged in a similar fashion with several copies of the hexanucleotide CCGCCC or its inverted complement, GGGCGG. This hexanucleotide motif is present twice in the 21-bp repeats of the SV40 promoter and has been shown to be crucial for the binding of the transcriptional factor Sp1.[151–153]

Similar promoters have been described for other genes. The human adenosine deaminase gene lacks 5′ "CAAT" and "TATAA" sequences and contains a G-plus-C-region with 5 GGGCGG repeats.[154] The human phosphoglycerate kinase gene has 8-bp direct repeats in the 5′ flanking region and shows approximately 80 percent homology for the 31 nucleotides immediately 5′ to the HPRT gene.[155] Analogous promoter structures have been reported for the human dihydrofolate reductase and the 3-hydroxy-3-methylglutaryl coenzyme A reductase genes.[156–158] Each of these genes are expressed in a wide range of tissues at low levels.

Deletion analysis of the human HPRT promoter suggests that additonal factors may play a role in transcription control. In cultured cell selection experiments, the removal of 122 nucleotides (from between 356 and 234 bp 5′ from the ATG initiation codon) enhanced gene expression, suggesting these sequences may play a negative regulatory role.[159] Negative regulatory sequences have been described for a number of eukaryotic genes, including the human immunoglobulin heavy chain gene, the rat α-fetoprotein gene, the chicken lysozyme gene, and the Drosophila *heldup-a* gene.[160–163] As of now, it is unclear how this element might regulate HPRT gene expression. Such sequences may represent binding sites for promoter-specific transcription factors or may represent local perturbations in DNA conformation which negatively affect transcription. A more detailed characterization of both the mouse and human HPRT promoters is needed to answer these questions.

The G-plus-C-rich nature of the 5′ portion of these genes raises the possibility that DNA methylation may participate in the control of gene expression. The methylation of cytosine residues within CpG clusters has been implicated in the control of a number of genes and may affect the maintenance of X-chromosome inactivation. Since there are 46 and 35 such clusters within the 400 bp 5′ to the translation start site of the human and mouse HPRT genes, analysis of individual sites of methylation has been difficult. Yen and coworkers suggested that patterns of methylation, rather than methylation of specific sites, correlate with HPRT gene activity.[164] By using methylation-sensitive restriction enzymes to analyze DNA from somatic cell hybrids containing active, inactive, or reactivated X chromosomes, they demonstrated that hypomethylation of the active or reactivated X chromosome correlates well with HPRT gene expression. Other studies showed that the CpG clusters of the active HPRT gene are not only undermethylated, but are also hypersensitive to MspI, DNaseI, and S1 nuclease, further supporting the idea that these sites are "open" to transcriptional activation.[165,166] Two specific regions with different patterns of methylation may be important in HPRT gene regulation. One region, within the first intron of the gene, includes four sites that are unmethylated when carried on the active X chromosome and methylated when carried on the inactive X.[167] Furthermore, these sites revert from the hypermethylated state to the hypomethylated state in reactivated genes. The converse pattern is observed in a second region, which includes several sites in the 3′ portion of the gene extending from exon 3 to exon 9. These sites are completely methylated on the active X and completely unmethylated on the inactive X.

The temporal relationship between the methylation of the CpG clusters within the first intron of the mouse HPRT gene and X inactivation has recently been studied.[168] These sequences are unmethylated prior to X inactivation and do not become methylated X until several days after inactivation has taken place. These results suggest that methylation of these sites does not play a role in the primary events of X inactivation, but the data do not rule out a potential role in the maintenance of X inactivation. While differences in methylation exist between active and inactive X chromosomes, no cause-and-effect relationship has been established, and many questions concerning transcriptional repression versus chromosome inactivation remain unanswered.

As stated previously, HPRT is variably expressed in all tissues. The genetic signals responsible for the elevated levels of HPRT mRNA detected in tissues of the CNS have not been defined. A number of different mechanisms which influence mRNA synthesis or stability may be involved. Potential mechanisms include: (1) interactions between tissue specific trans-acting factors and positive or negative regulatory elements of the HPRT gene, (2) variations in DNA methylation patterns in genes from different tissues, or (3) signals within the MRNA itself, which may affect tissue-specific synthesis or stability. The possibility that sequences within the HPRT mRNA might affect tissue variability was suggested by studies of transgenic mice that express a human HPRT minigene.[169] Recombinant molecules tht contained the human HPRT cDNA flanked by the mouse metallothionein promoter (5′) and the human growth hormone polyadenylation signal (3′) were injected into single cell mouse embryos in an attempt to produce mice capable of expressing the human HPRT protein. Four separate lines of transgenic mice expressed the human enzyme variably in many tissues, but expression was consistently elevated in brain tissue. Southern analysis of DNA from these mice showed that each mouse line had a different transgene integration site. Breeding experiments proved that for at least three of the four mouse lines the human gene had integrated into a mouse autosome. Whether preferential expression of the fusion gene in the CNS of these mice resulted from innate regulatory qualities of the human cDNA or was the result of anomalous, vector-influenced effects is not known.

MUTANT PHENOTYPE AND GENOTYPE

Mutant Forms of HPRT

Since the description of the familial nature of the Lesch-Nyhan syndrome and its biochemical etiology, HPRT deficiency has been a model for the study of X-linked disease. The first descriptions of HPRT deficiency distinguished those patients with no detectable activity (Lesch-Nyhan patients) from those patients with depressed, but detectable, levels of enzyme activity (patients with gouty arthritis).[3,5,6,170] HPRT mutations were described initially on the basis of altered protein or enzymatic parameters such as thermolability, altered electrophoretic mobility, altered kinetic properties, or diminished reactivity with anti-HPRT antibodies.[3,4,6,171–179] This approach was limited to those mutants with residual HPRT activity and excluded most patients with the Lesch-Nyhan syndrome.

The elucidation of the normal HPRT amino acid sequence permitted the comparison of HPRT peptide sequence from patients with residual protein. Structural alterations were detected by comparative mapping of tryptic peptides, and the sequences of these aberrant peptides were determined by manual Edman degradation reactions. One of the first mutants examined, $HPRT_{Toronto}$, was isolated from a gouty patient with 34 percent of wild-type HPRT activity.[78] Sequence analysis revealed a glycine-for-arginine substitution at amino acid position 50. Additional mutant forms of HPRT isolated from gouty patients included $HPRT_{London}$ (a substitution of leucine for serine at position 109) and $HPRT_{Munich}$ (a substitution of arginine for serine at position 103).[15,99] $HPRT_{Kinston}$ was the first mutant protein isolated from a patient with the Lesch-Nyhan syndrome.[97] This mutant differs from the normal enzyme by a substitution of asparagine for arginine at position 193. It became evident from these studies that HPRT deficiency is the result of a heterogenous group of mutations.[180,181]

The cloning and sequencing of the HPRT cDNA allowed a prediction of the base changes which could account for these mutations. For $HPRT_{Toronto}$, a single C-to-G base change in the arginine codon could explain this substitution and would result in the abolishment of the *Taq*I restriction endonuclease recognition site within the HPRT gene. Southern blot analysis of *Taq*I-digested DNA from this patient clearly demonstrated the predicted alteration in length of the restriction fragment in this allele (Fig. 38-8).[182] A normal 2-kb restriction fragment was replaced by a 4-kb fragment in DNA from the affected male, while DNA from an unaffected brother had a normal restriction pattern. Southern blots of DNA from heterozygotes (the patient's mother and sister) revealed both the normal and abnormal restriction fragments.

To study the relation between these amino acid substitutions and the apparent alterations in the catalytic activity of these proteins, the location of mutations in $HPRT_{Munich}$, $HPRT_{London}$, and $HPRT_{Toronto}$ was compared with the pre-

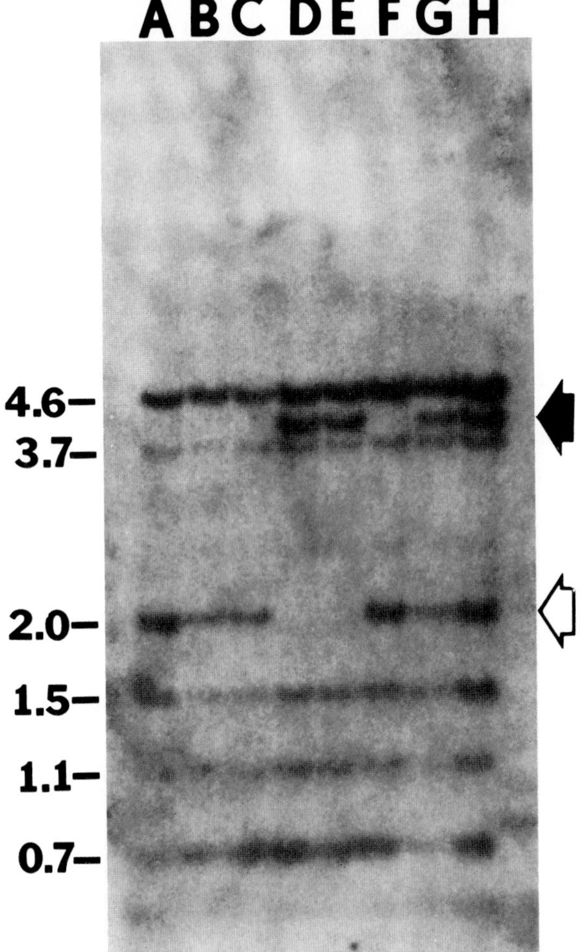

Fig. 38-8 Southern analysis of *TaqI*-digested normal and mutant ($HPRT_{Toronto}$) DNA. Lane A, DNA from cultured lymphoblasts from an $HPRT^{+}$ patient with four X chromosomes; lanes B and C, DNA from cultured lymphoblasts of two control individuals; lane D, DNA from cultured lymphoblasts from the propositus ($HPRT_{Toronto}$); lane E, DNA from leukocytes from the propositus; lane F, DNA from leukocytes from an unaffected brother of the propositus; lane G, DNA from leukocytes from the mother of the propositus; lane H, DNA from leukocytes from the daughter of the propositus. *(From Wilson et al.*[182]*)*

dicted tertiary structure of the normal enzyme (Fig. 38-9).[95,96] The amino acid substitution in $HPRT_{London}$ is located within a predicted β turn that connects two regions near the proposed hypoxanthine binding site. This prediction is in agreement with the slight decrease in binding of hypoxanthine observed for this mutant. The replacement of serine by arginine in $HPRT_{Munich}$ occurs within a proposed dinucleotide fold, a position which may contribute directly to the formation of the hypoxanthine binding site. Such a change might be expected to interfere with the binding of hypoxanthine and the catalytic activity of the enzyme without affecting the binding of PP-ribose-P, a fact consistent with the 100-fold increase in the Michaelis constant for hypoxanthine for this protein. The amino acid substitution of glycine for arginine in $HPRT_{Toronto}$ occurs in an α-helix region distant from the postulated binding sites for PP-ribose-P for hypoxanthine and, as one would predict, the Michaelis constants for these substrates are unchanged in this variant.

Protein sequence comparison provided useful initial information about the molecular basis of HPRT deficiency but had limited general usefulness since 73 percent of Lesch-Nyhan patients fail to have a detectable protein in cell extracts.[149] The cloning of the HPRT gene provided new insight into the mutational alterations at the locus.

Genetic Alterations

The first survey of HPRT gene structure involved the Southern analysis of DNA from 28 unrelated Lesch-Nyhan patients using four different restriction endonucleases (*Bam*HI, *Bgl*II, *Pst*I, and *Msp*I) and a full-length HPRT cDNA probe.[16] Twenty-three patients had restriction patterns identical with that found among normal controls. Five patients (18 percent) had restriction fragment patterns indicative of major gene alterations (Fig. 38-10). These alterations included a total gene deletion, two distinct 3′ deletions, one insertion mutation, and an endoduplication of exons. None of the deletions or insertion mutants produced a detectable HPRT mRNA. HPRT mRNA from the patient with the exon duplication was approximately 200 nucleotides larger than wild-type RNA, a size consistent with the duplication of exons 2 and 3.

Since that initial report, an additional 25 HPRT deficient patients (17 Lesch-Nyhan patients and eight with gouty arthritis) have been studied by Southern and Northern analysis.[149,183] All the patients with gouty arthritis had reduced enzyme levels and normal Southern and Northern blot patterns. Of the 17 Lesch-Nyhan patients studied, Southern analysis revealed two complete gene deletions. Two patients were found to have normal Southern patterns but reduced levels of HPRT mRNA. Of the remaining 13 patients, 12 had normal Southern and Northern studies.

The final patient is an intriguing case of a female with the Lesch-Nyhan syndrome.[184] This Japanese patient presented with the typical clinical and enzymic features of males with the Lesch-Nyhan syndrome. Northern analysis of RNA from this patient revealed no HPRT mRNA in fibroblasts or lymphoblasts.[185] Karyotype and Southern analysis demonstrated that the patient had two cytologically normal X chromosomes but only one copy of the HPRT gene. Southern blots of the parental DNA revealed two apparently normal HPRT genes in the mother and one apparently normal HPRT gene in the father. Assay of HPRT activity in hair follicles and fibroblasts from the mother demonstrated that she was not a carrier of a defective HPRT gene. While the deletion in this patient involved the entire HPRT gene, it did not extend to the DXS10 locus, an anonymous locus closely linked to the HPRT gene. Somatic cell hybrids were used to show that the deletion was associated with the maternal X chromosome, and that the paternal X chromosome was constitutively inactive. Thus, the combination of a deletion within a maternal gamete and an inactive paternal X chromosome resulted in the Lesch-Nyhan syndrome in this female.

Genetic heterogeneity among Lesch-Nyhan patients was recently addressed using Southern, Northern, kinetic, and immunoquantitative data.[149] Using these parameters to create a composite picture for each patient, 14 of 24 patients were shown to have unique genetic features. This suggests that the Lesch-Nyhan syndrome is the result of a heterogeneous group of mutations, presumably many of which are the result of single DNA base pair changes. Methods have been developed to identify and characterize these point mutations and improve diagnostic accuracy.

An RNase A cleavage technique has been used to define the location of mutations in five patients who have wild-type

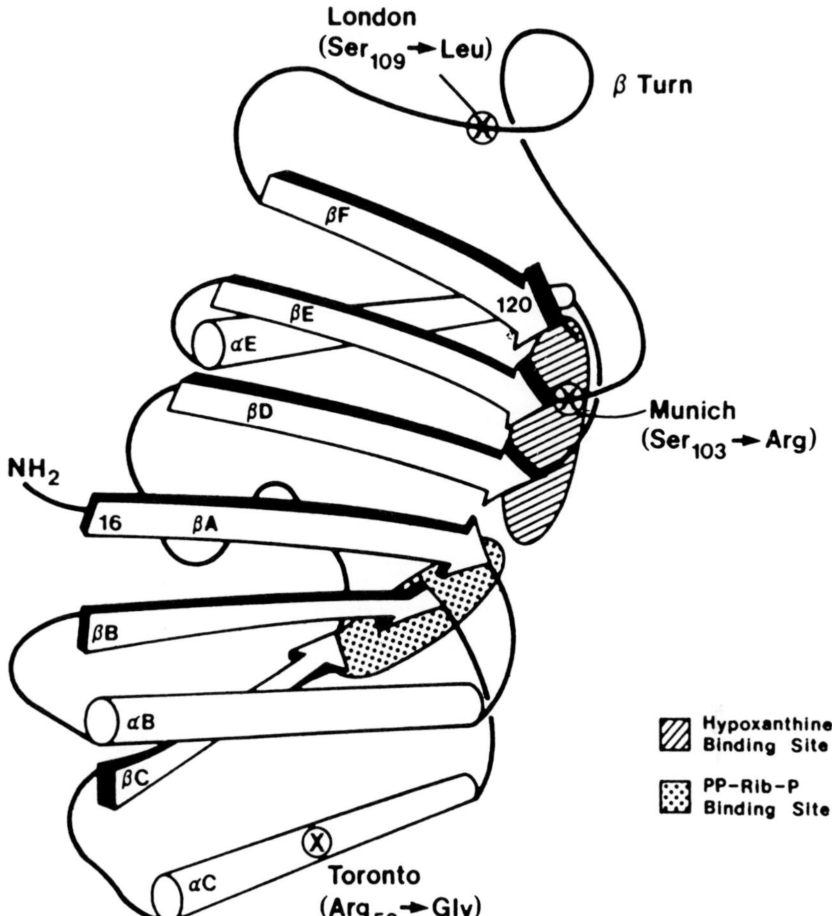

Fig. 38-9 Relationship of structural and functional abnormalities for three HPRT mutants ($HPRT_{London}$), ($HPRT_{Munich}$), and ($HPRT_{Toronto}$). *(From Wilson et al.[15])*

Southern and Northern blot patterns.[186–188] This assay technique provides a test for exact complementarity of a particular nucleotide sequence with a radiolabeled probe and can detect point mutations without prior knowledge of the precise location of the lesion. The basis of the RNase A cleavage assay is that some single base mismatch sites in RNA:RNA or RNA:DNA hybrids will be susceptible to cleavage by RNase A (Fig. 38-11). By this technique, labeled wild-type HPRT RNA probes, which are complementary to HPRT mRNA, are allowed to anneal with RNA isolated from Lesch-Nyhan patients. Polyadenylated messages hybridized to labeled probes are isolated by further hybridization to polyuridylic acid affinity paper and are treated with RNase A, an enzyme which will digest single-stranded regions of RNA but will not degrade double stranded hybrids. Single-base mismatches within the double-stranded regions will be cleaved in approximately 30 to 50 percent of cases. Mismatches that result from deletions, insertions, or other rearrangements which cause the probe to

Fig. 38-10 Summary of HPRT gene alterations. *(From Yang et al.[16])*

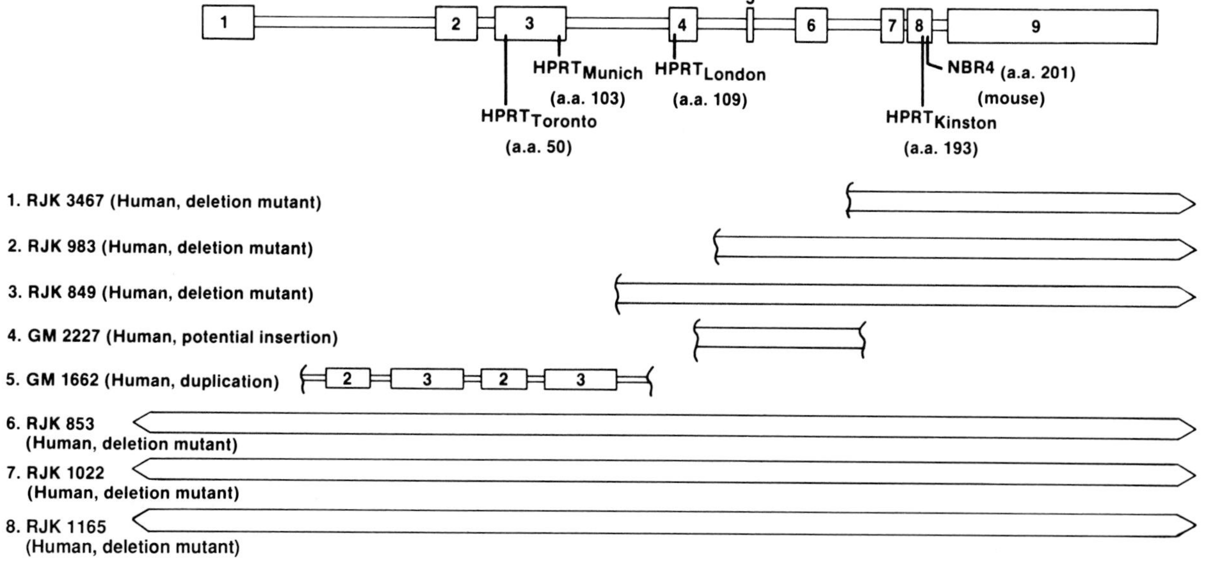

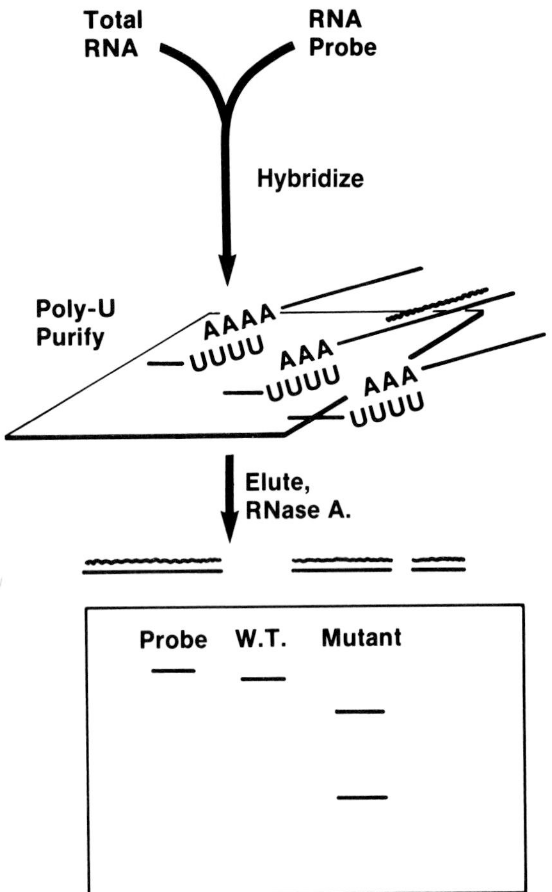

Fig. 38-11 Schematic diagram of RNAse A cleavage analysis using purification with polyuridylic acid-bound affinity paper. *(From Gibbs and Caskey.[188])*

loop out are readily detected. Cleaved products are separated by electrophoresis through polyacrylamide or agarose gels and are compared with wild-type and HPRT mRNA negative controls (Fig. 38-12). In this way, a single RNA probe can be used to detect the presence of mismatched basis, or a pair of overlapping probes can be used to locate the mutation unambiguously.

When RNA from 14 unrelated Lesch-Nyhan patients was examined, five of these samples revealed distinctive RNase A cleavage patterns (Fig. 38-13).[188] Two of the five cases were shown to have deletions within the HPRT message that were undetectable by routine Northern blots. The remaining three variants represented either HPRT point mutants or very small deletions. Each of these five patients had wild-type Southern and Northern blot patterns. The RNase A cleavage assay in combination with Southern and Northern analysis allows HPRT mutation detection in 50 percent of all cases of the Lesch-Nyhan syndrome.

Further refinement and simplification of mutation detection has been achieved by use of a polymerase chain reaction technique (PCR). This method uses oligonucleotide probes of opposite polarity that flank a particular region of the genome. These oligonucleotides prime repetitive rounds of synthesis of DNA complementary to that region.[189,190] Oligonucleotide probes may be designed so that unique restriction enzymes cleave at the ends of these "amplification units" and thus facilitate their direct cloning. Areas identified as a site of mutation by RNase A cleavage can be rapidly recovered from genomic DNA by PCR amplification and characterized by DNA sequence analysis.[191] The sensitivity and specificity of these new techniques allows the detection and characterization of a heterogenous group of point mutations with ease.

Associated Biochemical Changes

A number of other enzyme alterations have been observed with the Lesch-Nyhan syndrome. These secondary events may be the result of effects on the rate of *de novo* biosynthesis or protein turnover. Adenine phosphoribosyltransferase, the enzyme responsible for the salvage of adenine, is increased in erythrocytes of patients with complete or partial HPRT deficiency.[3,4,170,192,193] Elevated cellular levels of PP-ribose-P found in Lesch-Nyhan erythrocytes may account for this alteration, since PP-ribose-P has been shown to stabilize APRT in vitro.[92,124,128,194,195] APRT levels in HPRT deficient fibro-

Fig. 38-12 RNAse A cleavage patterns of normal (HeLa) and Lesch-Nyhan HPRT mRNAs. *A.* Summary of antisense RNA probes used to locate sites of mutation within HPRT messages. *B.* RNAse A cleavage studies of mRNA isolated from unrelated patients RJK894 and RJK906. DNA and RNA from these patients revealed normal Southern and Northern blotting patterns. Hybridized samples were treated with RNAse A (2 μg/ml, lane A; or 10 μg/ml, lane B). RNA from RJK894 cells protected fragments of 495 and 190 bp with probe 2. With probe 1, RNA from RJK894 cells protected fragments of 190 and 160 hp, while RNA from RJK906 cells protected fragments of 225 and 125 bp. See Fig. 38-13 for further interpretation. *(From Gibbs and Caskey.[188])*

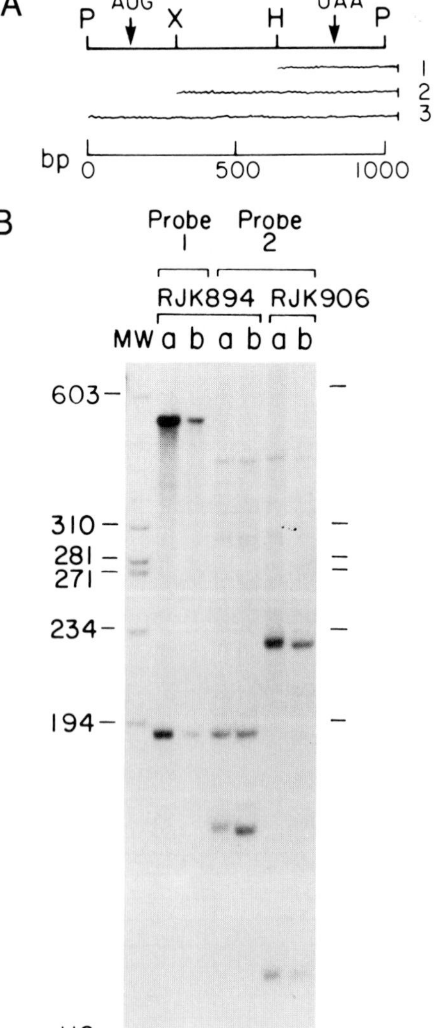

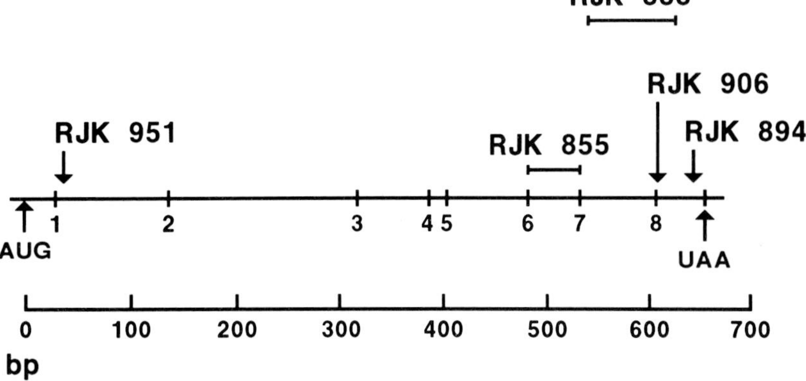

Fig. 38-13 Summary of mutation sites in Lesch-Nyhan HPRT mRNAs detected by RNAse A cleavage. *(From Gibbs and Caskey.[188])*

blasts, lymphoblasts, and neuroblastoma cells are normal, in spite of elevated levels of PP-ribose-P.[41,192,196,197] A similar tissue-specific elevation in enzyme activity has been described for inosine-5′-monophosphate dehydrogenase (IMP dehydrogenase).[198,199] This enzyme is elevated in erythrocytes, but not in leukocytes, fibroblasts, or muscle cells from patients with the Lesch-Nyhan syndrome. This may be due to the relatively high concentration of 2,3-diphosphoglycerate in erythrocytes.[200] The removal of 2,3-diphosphoglycerate by prolonged dialysis of hemolysates from normal or Lesch-Nyhan patients results in equal IMP dehydrogenase levels in both preparations. In contrast, monoamine oxidase, which degrades biogenic amines, has been reported to be found in decreased levels in HPRT-deficient neuroblastoma cells and in skin fibroblasts from patients with the Lesch-Nyhan syndrome.[201–205] The assignment of the monoamine oxidase A and B genes to the X chromosome has raised the possibility that the HPRT and monoamine oxidase genes may be coordinately regulated, but direct evidence is lacking.[206] Three reports have demonstrated a two- to fourfold increase in the activity of PP-ribose-P synthetase in fibroblasts or lymphoblasts from HPRT-deficient patients as well as in HPRT-deficient rat hepatoma cells.[207–209] PP-ribose-P synthetase activity in Lesch-Nyhan erythrocytes is normal but may be elevated in red cells of patients with gout.[7,210]

Animal Models of HPRT Deficiency

Despite the well characterized clinical phenotype associated with HPRT deficiency and an exhaustive search for potential animal models, no animal equivalent of the Lesch-Nyhan syndrome was found until 1987. Early attempts at producing such a model involved the administration of caffeine, a methylxanthine, to rats. This was shown to produce self-mutilatory behavior similar to that seen in males with the Lesch-Nyhan syndrome.[211] Other investigators demonstrated that this behavior could be elicited in rats which had undergone unilateral destruction of nigrostriatal dopaminergic pathways and were postoperatively treated with the dopamine analogue, 6-hydroxydopamine.[212,213] The ability of various dopamine agonists to induce abnormal movements and self-mutilative behavior in monkeys has also been examined.[214] In these studies, surgical denervation of nigrostriatal dopamine neurons was performed when the monkeys were 2 to 4 years old. Eight to twelve years after surgery, administration of mixed dopamine agonists such as L-dopa, apomorphine, or abeorphine caused self-mutilative biting of the contralateral forelimb digits and spasticity of the contralateral hindlimb. This behavior was elicited by dopamine agonists, which stimulated D_1, but not D_2, receptors and was prevented by the administration of D_1 antagonists such as fluphenazine. These and other studies suggested that the self-mutilatory behavior seen in these animals was mediated by D_1 dopamine receptor pathways.[215–217] These models exhibited some degree of self-mutilation but had normal HPRT levels and lacked many of the other neurologic findings associated with the Lesch-Nyhan syndrome.

Recently two independent approaches have been taken to develop an authentic model for HPRT deficiency in the mouse. The first approach involved the selection of $HPRT^-$ embryonal stem (ES) cells to produce $HPRT^+/HPRT^-$ chimeric animals.[218,219] ES cells are derived from early mouse embryos and remain undifferentiated in culture. When these cells are microinjected into mouse blastocysts, they differentiate and produce a chimeric embryo composed of two cell populations, one from the host embryo and one from the donor ES cells. Donor ES cells in these chimeric animals contribute to gonadal tissue and can become part of the germ line. Two groups produced lines of $HPRT^-$ ES cells, which were introduced into developing blastocysts to generate $HPRT^-$ chimeric animals.[17,18] When male ES cells were introduced into female host embryos, the resultant chimeras were frequently phenotypically male. Sperm from these animals reflected the donor genotype and were able to transmit the defective HPRT gene. Female offspring from these chimeric males were heterozygous for the deficiency and were bred to produce HPRT-deficient males.

Another strategy employed to generate partial HPRT deficiency in mice involved the use of antisense of HPRT mRNA (RNA complimentary to the endogenous HPRT message). Previous experiments had demonstrated that the constitutive expression of HPRT antisense RNA in cultured cells resulted in a substantial decrease in the levels of HPRT synthesis.[220,221] Presumably, antisense transcripts inhibit HPRT synthesis by annealing with the endogenous HPRT mRNA, thus preventing normal RNA processing or translation. Antisense templates placed under the transcriptional control of the inducible metallothionein promoter were microinjected into fertilized mouse eggs to generate transgenic animals able to produce high levels of antisense HPRT RNA. Upon administration of Cd^{2+} or Zn^{2+}, these mice have approximately a 50 percent reduction in the levels of HPRT in regions of the CNS that express the antisense transgene.[222]

It is interesting to note that male mice with complete HPRT deficiency produced using the ES-cell method are phenotypically normal without any of the metabolic or neurologic symptoms associated with the Lesch-Nyhan syndrome. The cause(s) of this unexplained lack of symptoms remains a mystery. The data obtained from rats treated with 6-hydroxydopamine suggest that a reduction of dopamenergic pathways in the nigrostriatal region may be responsible for the mutilation seen in the Lesch-Nyhan syndrome.[212,217] It is possible that these neurons in the mouse basal ganglia are less dependent on purine salvage for normal arborization and function, and thus self-mutilation is not evident in the HPRT-deficient state. Alternatively, metabolic differences between mouse and human neural systems may account for this difference. The accumulation of the toxic intermediates of purine metabolism in the developing human cells has been proposed as a mechanism for neural dysfunction in the Lesch-Nyhan syndrome. It is tempting to speculate that the enzyme uricase, found at high levels in mouse but not human tissues, may prevent the development of sustained hyperuricemia and the buildup of toxic intermediates.

PATHOPHYSIOLOGY

Pathophysiology of Neurologic Symptoms

The specific relationship between the neurologic symptoms associated with the Lesch-Nyhan syndrome and HPRT deficiency remains unclear. Recent biochemical and histologic studies suggest that inappropriate development of nigrostriatal dopaminergic neurons may be important.[35,217] Three lines of evidence implicate cells of the basal ganglia in pathogenesis. First, the involuntary movement seen in diseases of the extrapyramidal motor system are essentially those observed in patients with the Lesch-Nyhan syndrome. By 6 months of age, most patients with the Lesch-Nyhan syndrome begin to demonstrate pyramidal and extrapyramidal motor involvement initially characterized by fine athetoid movements of the hands and feet. These movements later gain a choreiform character similar to that seen in patients with caudate and putamen lesions. Normally, a balance is thought to exist between dopaminergic suppressor and facilitative mechanisms of the extrapyramidal motor systems.[223,226] Destruction of a particular extrapyramidal nucleus is usually associated with an imbalance of these mechanisms and can be correlated clinically with the appearance of a specific form of involuntary movement, such as those seen with the Lesch-Nyhan syndrome. Athetosis and choreiform movements are seen with lesions of the caudate and putamen. Perhaps an imbalance of these mechanisms is related to the dopamine-agonist-induced self-mutilation observed in surgically denervated monkeys.[214,216] Since guanine nucleotides participate in the regulation of dopamine receptor-agonist binding, it is possible that HPRT deficiency affects GTP pools and dopaminergic function.[227,228]

Second, postmortem analysis of brain tissue from Lesch-Nyhan patients reveals that indices of dopamine function are reduced by 70 to 90 percent in the basal ganglia.[35,37,229,230] Levels of dopamine, homovanillic acid, and dihydroxyphenylacetic acid, and activities of dopa decarboxylase and tyrosine hydroxylase have all been reported to be low in these patients.[35,226] Dopaminergic cell bodies in the substantia nigra of rats are as numerous in neonates as they are in adults, but their density in the prenatal substantia is low. This suggests that nigrostriatal dopaminergic terminal arborization occurs during the period of neonatal rapid brain growth. If normal development of these cells is particularly dependent on efficient purine salvage, either for rapid cell division or for proper differentiation, HPRT deficiency may result in aberrant function.

Third, dissection and biochemical analysis of normal postmortem human brain tissue reveals high levels of HPRT in the area of the basal ganglia.[102,103] Levels of AMPRT are lowest in this area, suggesting that this region may be particularly dependent on purine salvage. The significance of this final point has been criticized since these data were obtained from adult brain tissue.[122] Other studies have shown that the activities of AMPRT and APRT remain steady or decrease slightly between birth and maturity, while HPRT activity increases over time.[231–233] Data which compare the ratio of HPRT to AMPRT with age show that the highest value for this ratio occurs after dopaminergic synaptogenesis.[122] These observations suggest that purine *de novo* synthesis is able to meet the needs of growth and differentiation but that purine salvage becomes important later, possibly in the maintenance of GTP homeostasis.

Other metabolites have been examined for their effects on dopamine and catecholamine regulation in the Lesch-Nyhan syndrome. Inosine and hypoxanthine have been shown to be inhibitors of diazepam binding in the central nervous system and thus may act as neurologic modulators.[234] Altered levels of cyclic GMP, glycine, and glutamine have also been reported in Lesch-Nyhan patients, but the mechanisms through which they might mediate the neurodysfunction associated with this disease are unclear.[104,201,235–237]

Hyperuricemia

Hyperuricemia in these patients is associated with an increase in the rate of *de novo* purine synthesis.[4,6,7] This increase is probably due to the combined effects of decreased feedback inhibition by nucleotide end products and cellular loss of hypoxanthine. Radiolabeled glycine administered to patients with the Lesch-Nyhan syndrome is rapidly incorporated into uric acid.[7,31] Quantitation of labeled uric acid in urine collected over 7 days from these patients reveals levels which may be as much as 20 times normal.

The inability of Lesch-Nyhan cells to convert intracellular hypoxanthine to IMP leads to cellular loss and subsequent conversion of hypoxanthine to uric acid by hepatocyte xanthine oxidase. Normally, xanthine is excreted in excess of hypoxanthine. In Lesch-Nyhan patients, because hypoxanthine is not salvaged, a substantial increase in the excretion of hypoxanthine relative to xanthine is observed.[238,239]

Two mechanisms to explain increased *de novo* purine synthesis in HPRT-deficient cells have been proposed. The first suggests that low levels of intracellular IMP and GMP result in decreased inhibition of *de novo* synthesis.[115,118] Low levels of these end products favor the metabolically active form of AMPRT and accelerate *de novo* synthesis. The second proposal maintains that increased *de novo* synthesis is a result of increased levels of intracellular PP-ribose-P.[40,123,124] Cells which lack HPRT fail to consume PP-ribose-P in normal purine salvage reactions. The resulting increase in intracellular PP-ribose-P favors the metabolically active form of AMPRT, presumably resulting in an acceleration of *de novo* purine synthesis.[120,121]

Genetics

The first evidence that the Lesch-Nyhan syndrome was X-linked came from pedigree analysis of affected families and was included in the original report by Lesch and Nyhan.[4] After the link between the Lesch-Nyhan syndrome and HPRT was determined, mouse-human somatic cell hybrids were used to demonstrate synteny between HPRT and two genes on the long arm of the X chromosome, glucose-6-phosphate dehydrogenase and phosphoglycerate kinase.[136,139,240] Subsequent mapping localized the human HPRT gene to Xq26-q27.[14] Because the Lesch-Nyhan syndrome is an X-linked recessive disease, affected individuals are typically male. Female carriers of this disease are asymptomatic, and Lesch-Nyhan males fail to reproduce. The disease appears to occur with equal frequency in a wide range of racial group, and there is no greater frequency within inbred populations.[7]

Many individuals with the Lesch-Nyhan syndrome have parents who are not carriers of the disease. New mutations may account for as many as one-third of all cases of such X-linked disorders which limit reproductivity.[241] Such estimates are based on the predictions of Haldane and are calculated by the formula $\mu = [x(1 - f)]/3$, where μ is the mutation rate, x is the incidence of diseased males within the male population, and f relates to the effective fertility of diseased males. Since males with the Lesch-Nyhan syndrome do not reproduce, $f = 0$. Genetic equilibrium is thus dependent on the sporadic occurrence of a heterogenous group of new mutations within a stationary population. If there is no difference in the rate of mutation within male and female germ cells, then approximately one-third of all affected males per generation would represent new mutations and would have homozygous, normal (noncarrier) mothers. The detection of these new mutations is of obvious importance to the clinician trying to estimate the risk of recurrence within an affected family.

To test the hypothesis that one-third of all cases of the Lesch-Nyhan syndrome are the results of new mutation, Francke et al. compiled the results of carrier detection tests on mothers and maternal grandmothers from 54 families with a single affected child.[242] These tests suggested that 11 of 54 affected males were the result of new mutations. Fewer than the expected one-third of cases were shown to be the result of new mutation. Further study revealed that 10 of the heterozygous mothers were carriers of new mutations. In four of five cases in which the heterozygous mother of an affected individual represented a new mutation, the age of the parents of the heterozygote was considerably higher than the mean parental age in the population, suggesting the possibility of a parental age affect on the frequency of X-linked mutations. Molecular analysis of mutations should make these studies more precise and thus determine the validity of the earlier conclusions.

The first documentation of a new mutation at the molecular level involved family studies of the Lesch-Nyhan patient GM1662, whose mutation involved an endoduplication of exons 2 and 3.[16] Southern analysis disclosed that an abnormal 4.1-kb *Bgl*II band characteristic of the duplication mutation was present in the propositus, his mother, and two sisters, but was absent in his maternal grandmother (Fig. 38-14). These data indicate that this mutation originated in the germ line of a maternal grandparent and gave rise to an asymptomatic carrier female. Since that original description, the origin of mutation in two additional patients has been determined.[243] Both events involved deletion of all or part of the HPRT gene in maternal gametes. Molecular analysis of the origins of these mutations in families will permit the identification of paternal and maternal gametic mutations as well as help determine the mechanisms of mutations for each.

DIAGNOSIS AND TREATMENT

Clinical Diagnosis

A number of clinical signs which precede the onset of self-mutilation are evident in patients with the Lesch-Nyhan syndrome. Neurologic dysfunction may become apparent within the first year as these patients develop choreoathetosis.[4,21] Patients usually present with hypotonia which may progress to a spastic hypertonic dystonia. Dysarthria, growth and mental retardation, and ataxia may also be evident.[7] The first signs of hyperuricemia may be uric acid crystalluria. Nephrolithiasis and obstructive nephropathy, while rarely the presenting complaint in patients with the Lesch-Nyhan syndrome, may be the first manifestation of disease in patients with partial HPRT deficiency.

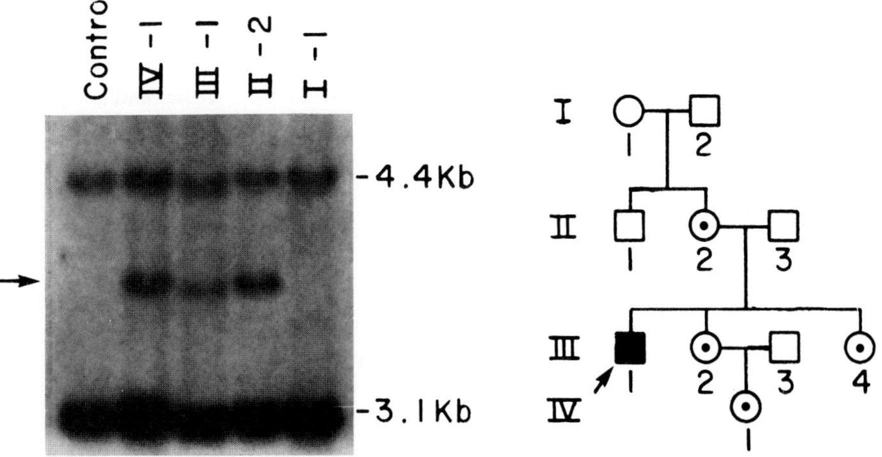

Fig. 38-14 Molecular analysis of HPRT gene alteration in the family of patient GM1662. A Southern blot of *Bgl*II-digested DNA from maternal grandmother (I-1), mother (II-2), and niece (IV-1) of proband (III-1). The arrow indicates a 4.1-kb *Bgl*II band associated with the gene alteration in GM1662. *(From Yang et al.[16])*

Despite these early signs, the clinical diagnosis of the Lesch-Nyhan syndrome is rarely made prior to the development of auto-aggressive behavior. Self-mutilation resulting in the actual loss of tissue is very suggestive of the Lesch-Nyhan syndrome; its onset warrants the immediate quantitation of erythrocyte or fibroblast HPRT.

Prenatal diagnosis of the Lesch-Nyhan syndrome by enzyme assay or DNA analysis of extracts from cultured amniocytes or chorionic villus samples is possible.[244–247] Diagnosis with chorionic material is possible hours after sampling and can be accomplished during the first trimester of the pregnancy at risk.

Carrier Detection

Female carriers of the Lesch-Nyhan syndrome cannot be reliably detected by clinical evaluation. Carrier detection is most reliable in instances where DNA analysis is diagnostic. This occurs when the mutation can be detected directly or when an RFLP is informative for the offspring of known heterozygotes. RFLP analysis is usually not helpful in determining whether antecedents in the family are carriers or not. When informative, DNA analysis circumvents the problems associated with tests dependent on random X inactivation. Heterozygotes may demonstrate a moderate increase in the rate of *de novo* purine synthesis but are clinically asymptomatic.[4,7,248,249]

When DNA analysis is not diagnostic, carrier status is usually determined by techniques designed to exploit the fact that random X inactivation results in two populations of cells ($HPRT^+$ and $HPRT^-$) in carrier females. Using cultured fibroblasts and hair follicles, it has been possible to demonstrate that obligate heterozygotes are mosaics in terms of HPRT activity; some cells contain the X chromosome that bears the mutant HPRT allele, others carry the normal X chromosome.[250–253] Several studies have shown that the mutant allele is not present at the expected frequency in lymphocytes and erythrocytes from proven heterozygotes.[254,255] This is apparently due to an *in vivo* selection against HPRT-deficient cells in the presence of normal erythrocytic or lymphocytic cells. The nature of this selection process is not clearly understood. Study of cultured phytohemagglutinin-stimulated lymphocytes revealed that $HPRT^-$ lymphocytes constituted 5 to 10 percent of the total lymphocyte population in three young sisters of a male with the Lesch-Nyhan syndrome.[256] No $HPRT^-$ cells could be recovered from similarly treated lymphocytes from the mother of this patient, a known heterozygote, suggesting that the selection phenomenon may not be absolute and may be age-related. Selection against $HPRT^-$ cells is not seen in all tissues. Single hair follicles exhibit a large degree of clonal growth, and study of follicles from carrier females reveals three types of follicles: one type with normal HPRT activity, another type with no HPRT, and a minor third type with intermediate HPRT activity due to the presence of both $HPRT^+$ and $HPRT^-$ cells. This method for determining carrier status is rapid, relatively inexpensive, but not infallible, and should be supported by cultured skin fibroblast data when time permits. Recently, we have used EBV-transformed lymphoblasts to determine carrier status.[257] In this assay 8-azaguanine is used to detect a small population of $HPRT^-$ lymphoblasts in heterozygous females. Detailed data are not yet available to document whether this method is more sensitive or reliable than other approaches. In contrast to earlier reports, this assay does not appear to be affected by the age of the heterozygote.[256]

Therapy

Hyperuricemia associated with HPRT deficiency can be effectively controlled by the inhibition of xanthine oxidase with allopurinol.[7] Allopurinol reduces serum and urine uric acid levels and thus prevents uric acid crystalluria, urate nephropathy, nephrolithiasis, and gouty arthritis. Patients with partial HPRT deficiency treated with this drug are able to lead relatively disease-free lives. Unfortunately, allopurinol has no effect on the neurologic sequelae of the Lesch-Nyhan syndrome.

A lack of understanding of the basis of neural dysfunction in these patients has slowed attempts to develop useful therapy. Neither the specific cell types involves in pathogenesis nor the developmental stage at which irreversible damage occurs are known. Early attempts at therapy were directed toward the pharmacologic alteration of nucleotide pools. Administration of GMP, IMP, AMP, guanosine, inosine, or 2,6-diaminopurine were all shown to be of no therapeutic value.[6,20,29] Although two patients treated from birth with adenine developed the CNS abnormalities associated with the Lesch-Nyhan syndrome, one older patient showed a striking improvement in his megaloblastic anemia following adenine therapy.[45,258–261] In each case, 2,8-dioxyadenine nephrotoxicity prompted the discontinuation of therapy.[262] The administration of large doses of PP-ribose-P and hypoxanthine to a patient found to have a kinetically abnormal HPRT protein led to no apparent improvement in this patient's disease.[7] In addition to purine therapy, folate, glutamine, and magnesium were each shown to be of no benefit to Lesch-Nyhan patients.[263–267] Because L-5-hydroxytryptophan had been shown to reduce aggressive behavior in rats, this drug was administered to four patients with the Lesch-Nyhan syndrome.[268] Oral administration of this drug led to complete control of self-mutilation in each patient, but this behavior returned 15 h after the discontinuation of treatment.[269] Carbidopa and 5-hydroxytryptophan were used in combination and were reported to have a transient beneficial effect; however, each patient suffered a sustained relapse within 1 to 3 months despite continued treatment. Blood exchange transfusion was attempted in one patient, and although erythrocyte HPRT activity did not fall below 10 percent of normal for more than 90 days, no improvement in motor function or self-mutilation was detected.[259] Other ineffective attempts at therapy have included orotic acid, α-methyl-dopa, thiopropazate, chlorpromazine, and L-tryptophan.[7,259,268] One patient treated with carbidopa and levodopa showed a marked improvement in mutilatory behavior and no longer required restraints.[37] Another patient showed improvement with tetrabenazine, a monoamine depleting drug. Diazepam, haloperidol, and phenobarbital each appear to be helpful in treating the hyperactive behavior and chorea seen in these patients.[268] How these drugs interact with the GTP-dependent dopaminergic nervous system in these patients is unclear. Behavior modification therapy in a 2-year-old patient was reported to reduce self-mutilation for as long as 6 months.[270]

The ultimate goal is the management of inborn errors of metabolism at the genetic, rather than symptomatic, level. The devastating nature of the Lesch-Nyhan syndrome, the lack of therapeutic alternatives, and the development of efficient gene transfer techniques have made this disease a prototype for the study of gene replacement therapy. The transfer of an expressible HPRT cDNA molecule into HPRT-deficient cells was first accomplished in 1983.[143,271] The expression of a human HPRT cDNA in cultured fibroblasts from Lesch-Nyhan patients led to a metabolic correction of the deficiency. Studies involving the microinjection of human HPRT cDNA sequences into mouse embryos suggested that these minigenes could become stable components of the recipient genome.[169] These transgenes were expressed in a variety of tissues and were able to be transmitted to progeny in a Mendelian fashion.

Recently, naturally occurring RNA and DNA viruses have been used as vectors for gene transfer.[272] The unique structure and capabilities of viruses make them an ideal gene transfer system in mammalian cells. Retroviruses are RNA viruses whose life cycle depends on the integration, replication, and expression of their genetic material in host cells. This system is efficient (100 percent of cells infected carry an integrated copy of the gene), and many cell types refractory to other methods of gene transfer can be infected with these viruses.

Infection of cultured Lesch-Nyhan cells with amphotrophic retroviruses containing the human HPRT cDNA resulted in the production of an enzymatically active HPRT.[271] Expression of HPRT of these cells led to the partial correction of associated metabolic abnormalities such as elevated purine excretion and increased intercellular hypoxanthine. Several studies have suggested that these retroviruses are able to infect cultured bone marrow cells which can then be transplanted into receptive hosts.[273–276] In the first of these studies, HPRT virus production was detected in mouse spleen and bone marrow cells as long as 133 days after transplantation.[273] Human protein was detected in spleen cells for 2 months. While these studies suggest that retroviral vectors may be an efficient mechanism for gene transfer, it is not clear if introduction of HPRT into bone marrow cells will influence the neurologic dysfunction in patients. One bone marrow transplantation in a 22-year-old male resulted in engraftment, but no definite change in neurologic status occurred.[277] Questions concerning the tissue specificity and temporal requirements for HPRT gene expression as well as the safety and stability of this method of gene transfer need to be resolved prior to human experimentation.[278–281]

REFERENCES

1. KORNBERG A, LIEBERMAN I, SIMS ES: Enzymatic synthesis of purine nucleotides. *J Biol Chem* 215:417, 1955.
2. KORN ED, REMY CN, WASILEYKO HC, BUCHANAN JM: Biosynthesis of nucleotides from bases by partially purified enzymes. *J Biol Chem* 217:875, 1955.
3. SEEGMILLER JE, ROSENBLOOM FM, KELLEY WN: An enzyme defect associated with a sex-linked human neurological disorder and excessive purine synthesis. *Science* 155:1682, 1967.
4. LESCH M, NYHAN WL: A familial disorder of uric acid metabolism and central nervous system function. *Am J Med* 36:561, 1964.
5. KELLEY WN, ROSENBLOOM RM, HENDERSON JR, SEEGMILLER JE: A specific enzyme defect in gout associated with overproduction of uric acid. *Proc Natl Acad Sci USA* 57:1735, 1967.
6. KELLEY WN, GREENE ML, ROSENBLOOM FM, HENDERSON JF, SEEGMILLER JE: Hypoxanthine-guanine phosphoribosyltransferase in gout. *Ann Intern Med* 70:155, 1969.
7. KELLEY WN, WYNGAARDEN JB: Clinical syndromes associated with hypoxanthine guanine phosphoribosyltransferase deficiency, in Stanbury JB, Wyngaarden JB, Frederickson DS, Goldstein JL, Brown MS (eds): *The Metabolic Basis of Inherited Disease*, 5th ed. New York, McGraw-Hill, 1983, p 1115.
8. BRENNAND J, CHINAULT AC, KONECKI DS, MELTON DW, CASKEY CT: Cloned cDNA sequences of the hypoxanthine guanine phosphoribosyltransferase gene from a mouse neuroblastoma cell line found to have amplified genomic sequences. *Proc Natl Acad Sci USA* 79:1950, 1982.
9. MELTON DW, KONECKI DS, BRENNAND J, CASKEY CT: Structure expression and mutation of the hypoxanthine phosphoribosyltransferase gene. *Proc Natl Acad Sci USA* 81:2147, 1984.
10. JOLLY DJ, ESTY AC, BERNARD HV, FRIEDMANN T: Isolation of a genomic clone partially encoding human hypoxanthine phosphoribosyltransferase. *Proc Natl Acad Sci USA* 79:5038, 1982.
11. JOLLY DJ, OKAYAMA H, BERG P, ESTY AC, FILPULA D, BOHLEN P, JOHNSON GG, SCIVELY JE, HUNKAPILLAR T, FRIEDMANN T: Isolation and characterization of a full-length expression cDNA for human hypoxanthine phosphoribosyltransferase. *Proc Natl Acad Sci USA* 80:477, 1983.
12. PATEL PI, NUSSBAUM RL, FRAMSON PE, LEDBETTER D, CASKEY CT, CHINAULT AC: Organization of the HPRT gene and related sequences in the human genome. *Somatic Cell Mol Genet* 10:483, 1984.
13. PATEL PI, FRAMSON PE, CASKEY CT, CHINAULT AC: Fine structure of the human hypoxanthine phosphoribosyltransferase gene. *Mol Cell Biol* 6:393, 1986.
14. PAI GS, SPRENKLE JA, DO TT, MARENI CE, MIGEON BK: Localization of loci for HPRT and glucose-6-phosphate dehydrogenase and biochemical evidence for non-random X-chromosome expression from studies of a human X-autosome translocation. *Proc Natl Acad Sci USA* 77:2810, 1980.
15. WILSON JM, YOUNG AB, KELLEY WN: Hypoxanthine guanine phosphoribosyltransferase deficiency. The molecular basis of the clinical syndrome. *N Engl J Med* 309:900, 1983.
16. YANG TP, PATEL PI, CHINAULT AC, STOUT JT, JACKSON LG, HILDEBRAND BM, CASKEY CT: Molecular evidence for new mutation in the HPRT locus in Lesch-Nyhan patients. *Nature* 310:412, 1984.
17. HOOPER M, HARDY K, HANDYSIDE A, HUNTER S, MONK M: HPRT deficient (Lesch-Nyhan) mouse embryos derived from germline colonisation by cultured cells. *Nature* 326:292, 1987.
18. KUEHN MR, BRADLEY A, ROBERTSON EJ, EVANS MJ: A potential animal model for Lesch-Nyhan syndrome through introduction of HPRT mutations into mice. *Nature* 326:295, 1987.
19. MARKS JF, BAUM J, JEKKE DK, KAY JL, MacFARLEN A: Lesch-Nyhan syndrome treated from the early neonatal period. *Pediatrics* 42:357, 1968.
20. BERMAN PH, BALIS ME, DANCIS J: Congenital hyperuricemia, an inborn error of purine metabolism associated with psychomotor retardation, athetosis, and self-mutilation. *Arch Neurol* 20:44, 1969.
21. DREIFUSS FE, NEWCOMBE DS, SHAPIRO SL, SHEPPARD GL: X-linked primary hyperuricemia (hypoxanthine-guanine phosphoribosyltransferase deficiency encephalopathy). *J Ment Defic Res* 12:100, 1968.
22. MUNSAT TL, KLINENBERG J, CARREL RE, MENKES J: Defects in purine metabolism and neurologic disease. *Bull Los Angeles Neurol Soc* 33:101, 1968.
23. MICHENER WM: Hyperuricemia and mental retardation with athetosis and self-mutilation. *Am J Dis Child* 113:195, 1967.
24. HOEFNAGEL D, ANDREW ED, MIREAULT NG, BERNDT WO: Hereditary choreoathetosis, self-mutilation, and hyperuricemia in young males. *N Engl J Med* 273:130, 1965.
25. RILEY JD: Gout and cerebral palsy in three-year-old boy. *Arch Dis Child* 35:293, 1960.
26. HOEFNAGEL D: Seminars on the Lesch-Nyhan syndrome: Discussion. *Fed Proc* 27:1045, 1967.
27. PARTINGTON MW, HENNEN BKE: The Lesch-Nyhan syndrome: Self-destructive biting, mental retardation, neurological disorder and hyperuricemia. *Dev Med Child Neurol* 9:563, 1967.
28. VAN BOGAERT L, DAMME JV, VERSCHUEREN M: Sur un syndrome professif d'hypertonie extrapyramidale avec osteoarthropathies goutteuses chez deux freres. *Rev Neurol (Paris)* 114:15, 1966.
29. ROSENBERG D, MONNET P, MAMELLE JL, COLONBEL M, SALLE B, BOVIER-LAPIERRE M: Encephalopathie avec troubles due metabolisme des purines. *Presse Med* 76:2333, 1968.
30. SCHERZER AL, ILSON JB: Normal intelligence in the Lesch-Nyhan syndrome. *Pediatrics* 44:116, 1969.
31. NYHAN WL, OLIVER WJ, LESCH M: A familial disorder of uric acid metabolism and central nervous system function. II. *J Pediatr* 67:257, 1965.
32. MIZUNO T: Long-term follow-up of ten patients with Lesch-Nyhan syndrome. *Neuropediatrics* 17:158, 1986.
33. MITCHELL G, MCINNES RR: Differential diagnosis of cerebral palsy: Lesch-Nyhan syndrome without self-mutilation. *Can Med Assoc J* 130:1323, 1984.
34. BAKAY B, NISSINEN E, SWEETMAN L, FRANCKE U, NYHAN WL: Utilization of purines by an HPRT variant in an intelligent, nonmutilative patient with features of the Lesch-Nyhan syndrome. *Pediatr Res* 13:1365, 1979.
35. LLOYD KG, HORNYKIEWICZ O, DAVIDSON L, SHANNAK K, FARLEY I, GOLD-

STEIN M, SHIBUYA M, KELLEY WN, FOX IH: Biochemical evidence of dysfunction of brain neurotransmitters in the Lesch-Nyhan syndrome. *N Engl J Med* 305:1106, 1981.

36. SIVERSTEIN FS, JOHNSTON MV, HUTCHINSON RJ, EDWARDS NL: Lesch-Nyhan syndrome: CSF neurotransmitter abnormalities. *Neurology* 35:907, 1985.

37. JANKOVIC J, CASKEY CT, STOUT JT, BUTLER IJ: Lesch-Nyhan syndrome: A study of motor behavior and cerebrospinal fluid neurotransmitters. *Ann Neurol* 23:466, 1988.

38. SKYLER JS, NEELON FA, ARNOLD WJ, KELLEY WN, LEBOVITZ HE: Growth retardation in the Lesch-Nyhan syndrome. *Acta Endocrinol (Copenh)* 75:3, 1974.

39. HERSHFIELD MS, SEEGMILLER JE: Regulation of *de novo* purine synthesi: in human lymphoblasts. *J Biol Chem* 252:6002, 1977.

40. ROSENBLOOM FM, HENDERSON JF, CALDWELL IC, KELLEY WN, SEEGMILLER JE: Biochemical basis of accelerated purine biosynthesis *de novo* in human fibroblasts lacking hypoxanthine-guanine phosphoribosyltransferase. *J Biol Chem* 243:1166, 1968.

41. NUKI G, LEVER J, SEEGMILLER JE: Biochemical characteristics of 8-azaguanine resistant human lymphoblast mutants selected in vitro, in Sperling O, DeVries A, Wyngaarden JB (eds): *Purine Metabolism in Man.* New York, Plenum, 1975, p 255.

42. SPERLING O, BROSH S, DE VRIES A: Synthesis of purine nucleotides in leukocytes from normal and hypoxanthine-guanine phosphoribosyltransferase-deficient subjects. *Isr J Med Sci* 11:1221, 1975.

43. ROSENBLOOM FM, HENDERSON JF, KELLEY WN, SEEGMILLER JE: Accelerated purine biosynthesis *de novo* in skin fibroblasts deficient in hypoxanthine-guanine phosphoribosyltransferase activity. *Biochim Biophys Acta* 166:258, 1968.

44. KAUFMAN JM, GREENE ML, SEEGMILLER JE: Urine uric acid to creatinine ratio: Screening test for disorders of purine metabolism. *J Pediatr* 73:583, 1968.

45. WORTMANN RL, FOX IH: Limited value of uric acid to creatinine ratios in estimating uric acid excretion. *Ann Intern Med* 93:822, 1980.

46. CATEL W, SCHMIDT J: Über familiare gichtische Diathese in Verdundung mit zerebralen and renalen Symptomen bei einem Kleinkind. *Dtsch Med Wochenschr* 84:2145, 1959.

47. VAN DER ZEE SPM, MONNENS LAH, SCHRETLEN EDAM: Hereditary disorder of purine metabolism with cerebral affection and megaloblastic anemia. *Ned Tijdschr Geneeskd* 112:1475, 1968.

48. MARIE J, ROYER P, RAPPAPORT R: Hyperuric neurologiques, renaux et sanguinis. *Arch Fr Pediatr* 24:501, 1967.

49. MANZKE H: Hyperuricemie mit cerebralparese syndrom eines hereditaren Purenstoffwechselleidens. *Helv Paediatr Acta* 22:258, 1967.

50. HERNANDEZ-NIETO L, BRITO-BARRASO ML, NYHAN WL: Megaloblastic anemia in Lesch-Nyhan disease. *Sangre* 29:476, 1984.

51. VAN DER ZEE SPM, SCHRETLEN EDAM, MONNENS LAH: Megaloblastic anemia in the Lesch-Nyhan syndrome. *Lancet* 1:1427, 1968.

52. SCHNEIDER W: The Lesch-Nyhan syndrome as a rare cause of hemolytic anemia. *Acta Med Austriaca* 6:202, 1979.

53. RIVARD GE, IZADI T, LAZERSON J, MCLAREN GD, PARKER C, FISH CH: Functional and metabolic studies of platelets from patients with Lesch-Nyhan syndrome. *Br J Haemtol* 31:45, 1975.

54. SCHNEIDER W, MORGENSTERN E, REIMERS HJ: Disassembly of microtubules in the Lesch-Nyhan syndrome? *Clin Wochenschr* 57:181, 1979.

55. VALENTINE WN, PAGLIA DE: Syndromes with increased red cell glutathione (GSH). *Hemoglobin* 4:799, 1980.

56. ALLISON AC, WATTS RWE, HOVI T, WEBSTER ADB: Immunological observations on patients with Lesch-Nyhan syndrome, and on the role of *de novo* purine synthesis in lymphocyte transformation. *Lancet* 2:1179, 1975.

57. DE BRUYN C, GAUSSET P, DUCHATEAU J, VAMOS E, KULAKOWSKI S, DELESPESSE G: Immunological studies on Lesch-Nyhan patients. *Adv Exp Med Biol* 122b:321, 1979.

58. CZLONKOWSKA A, ZDZIENICKA-TULCZYNSKA E: Immunology of the Lesch-Nyhan syndrome. *Lancet* 1:863, 1976.

59. SEEGMILLER JE, WATANABE T, SHREIER MH, WALDMANN TA: Immunological aspects of purine metabolism. *Adv Exp Med Biol* 76:412, 1977.

60. SEEGMILLER JE: Summary: Pathology and pathologic physiology. *Fed Proc* 27:1042, 1968.

61. BASSERMANN R, GUTENSOHN W, SPRINGMANN JS: Pathological and immunological observations in a case of Lesch-Nyhan syndrome. *Eur J Pediatr* 132:93, 1979.

62. SASS JK, ITABASHI HH, DEXTER RA: Juvenile gout with brain involvement. *Arch Neurol* 13:639, 1965.

63. WARZOK R, SCHWESINGER G, KNAPP A, SEIDLITZ F: Neuropathological findings in the Lesch-Nyhan syndrome. *Zentralbl Allg Pathol* 126:95, 1982.

64. CRUSSI FG, ROBERTSON DM, HISCOX JL: The pathological condition of the Lesch-Nyhan syndrome. *Am J Dis Child* 118:501, 1969.

65. BUCHANAN JM, HARTMAN SC: Enzymatic reactions in synthesis of the purines. *Adv Enzymol* 21:199, 1959.

66. BUCHANNAN JM: The enzymatic synthesis of the purine nucleotides. *Harvey Lect* 54:104, 1960.

67. GUTENSOHN W, GUROFF G: Hypoxanthine guanine phosphoribosyltransferase from rat brain (purification, kinetic properties, development, and distribution). *J Neurochem* 19:2139, 1972.

68. MELTON DW, KONECKI DS, LEDBETTER DH, HEJTMANCIK JF, CASKEY CT: In vitro translation of hypoxanthine guanine phosphoribosyltransferase mRNA: Characterization of a mouse neuroblastoma cell line that has elevated levels of hypoxanthine guanine phosphoribosyltransferase protein. *Proc Natl Acad Sci USA* 78:6977, 1981.

69. HAGEN C: Effect of purine analogues on IMP-pyrophosphorylase. *Biochim Biophys Acta* 293:105, 1973.

70. HENDERSON JF, BROX LW, KELLEY WN, ROSENBLOOM FM, SEEGMILLER JE: Kinetic studies of hypoxanthine guanine phosphoribosyltransferase. *J Biol Chem* 243:2514, 1968.

71. KRENITSKY TA, PAPAIOANNOU R, ELION GB: Human hypoxanthine phosphoribosyltransferase. I. Purification, properties and specificity. *J Biol Chem* 244:1263, 1969.

72. MCDONALD JA, KELLEY WN: Lesch-Nyhan syndrome: Altered kinetic properties of a mutant enzyme. *Science* 171:689, 1971.

73. SALERNO C, GIACOMELLO A: Human hypoxanthine guanine phosphoribosyltransferase. The role of magnesium ion in phosphoribosylpyrophosphate utilizing enzyme. *J Biol Chem* 256:3671, 1981.

74. SZYBALSKI W, SZYBALSKA EH: Drug sensitivity as a genetic marker for human cell lines. *Univ Mich Med Bull* 28:277, 1962.

75. STUTTS P, BROCKMAN RW: A biochemical basis for resistance of L1210 mouse leukemia to 6-thioguanine. *Biochem Pharmacol* 12:97, 1963.

76. ARNOLD WJ, KELLEY WN: Human hypoxanthine guanine phosphoribosyltransferase: Purification and subunit structure. *J Biol Chem* 246:7398, 1971.

77. CHIANG CS: Characterization of HPRT mutations in cultured Chinese hamster cells. PhD thesis, Baylor College of Medicine, Houston TX, 1977.

78. HUGHES SH, WAHL GM, CAPECCHI MR: Purification and characterization of mouse hypoxanthine guanine phosphoribosyltransferase. *J Biol Chem* 250:120, 1975.

79. OLSEN AS, MILMAN G: Chinese hamster hypoxanthine guanine phosphoribosyltransferase. *J Biochem* 249:4030, 1974.

80. DE GROODT A, WHITEHEAD EP, HESLOT H, PIORIER L: The substrate specificity of purine phosphoribosyltransferases in *Schizosaccharomyces pompe*. *Biochem J* 122:415, 1971.

81. SCHMIDT R, WIEGAND H, REICHERT U: Purification and characterization of the hypoxanthine guanine phosphoribosyltransferase from *Saccharomyces cerevisiae*. *Eur J Biochem* 93:355, 1979.

82. TUTTLE JV, KRENITSKY TA: Purine phosphoribosyltransferase from *Leishmania donovani*. *J Biol Chem* 255:909, 1980.

83. CHOU JY, MARTIN RG: Purine phosphoribosyltransferases of *Salmonella typhimurim*. *J Bacteriol* 112:1010, 1972.

84. GOTS JS, BENSON LE, SHUMAS SR: Genetic separation of hypoxanthine and guanine-xanthine phosphorbosyltransferase activities by deletion mutations in *Salmonella tryphimurium*. *J Bacteriol* 112:910, 1972.

85. MILLER RL, RAMSEY GA, KRENITSKY TA, ELTON GB: Guanine phosphoribosyltransferase from *Escherichia coli*, specificity and properties. *Biochemistry* 11:4723, 1972.

86. WILSON JM, TARR GE, MAHONEY WC, KELLEY WN: Human hypoxanthine guanine phosphoribosyltransferase: Complete amino acid sequence of the erythrocyte enzyme. *J Biol Chem* 257:10987, 1982.

87. HOLDEN JA, KELLEY WN: Human hypoxanthine phosphoribosyltransferase: Evidence for tetrameric structure. *J Biol Chem* 253:4459, 1978.

88. JOHNSON GG, EISENBERG LR, MIGEON BR: Human and mouse hypoxanthine guanine phosphoribosyltransferase: dimers and tetramers. *Science* 203:174, 1979.

89. OLSEN AS, MILMAN G: Human hypoxanthine phosphoribosyltransferase: Purification and properties. *Biochemistry* 21:960, 1977.

90. OLSEN AS, MILMAN G: Subunit molecular weight of human hypoxanthine guanine phosphoribosyltransferase. *J Biol Chem* 249:4038, 1974.

91. DAVIES MR, DEAN BM: The heterogeneity of erythrocyte IMP: Pyrophosphate phosphoribosyltransferase and purine nucleoside phosphorylase by isoelectric focusing. *FEBS Lett* 18:283, 1971.

92. BAKAY B, NYHAN WL: Hetereogeneity of hypoxanthine guanine phosphoribosyltransferase from human erythrocytes. *Arch Biochem Biophys* 168:26, 1975.

93. WILSON JM, BAUGHER BW, LANDA LE, KELLEY WN: Human hypoxanthine

guanine phosphoribosyltransferase: Purification and characterization of mutant forms of the enzyme. *J Biol Chem* 256:10306, 1981.

94. ZANNIS VI, GUDAS LH, MARTIN DW JR: Characterization of the subunit composition of HGPRTase from human erythrocytes and cultured fibroblasts. *Biochem Genet* 18:1, 1980.

95. MUSICK WDL: Structural features of the phosphoribosyltransferases and their relationship to human deficiency disorders of purine and pyrimidine metabolism. *CRC Crit Rev Biochem* 11:1, 1981.

96. ARGOS P, HANEI M, WILSON JM, KELLEY WN: A possible nucleotide-binding demain in the tertiary fold of phosphoribosyltransferases. *J Biol Chem* 258:6430, 1983.

97. WILSON JM, KELLEY WN: Molecular basis of hypoxanthine guanine phosphoribosyltransferase deficiency in a patient with the Lesch-Nyhan syndrome. *J Clin Invest 71:1331, 1983.*

98. WILSON JM, KOBAYASHI R, FOX IH, KELLEY WN: Human hypoxanthine guanine phosphoribosyltransferase: Molecular abnormality in a mutant form of the enzyme ($HPRT_{Toronto}$). *J Biol Chem* 258:6458, 1983.

99. WILSON JM, TARR GE, KELLEY WN: Human hypoxanthine guanine phosphoribosyltransferase: An amino acid substitution in a mutant form of the enzyme isolated from a patient with gout. *Proc Natl Acad Sci USA* 80:870, 1983.

100. ALLSOP J, WATTS RWE: Activities of amidophosphoribosyltransferase and purine phosphoribosyltransferases and the phosphyribosylpyrophosphate content of rat central nervous system at different stages of development. *J Neurol Sci* 46:221, 1980.

101. KRENITSKY TA: Tissue distribution of purine ribosyl and phosphoribosyltransferases in the rhesus monkey. *Biochim Biophys Acta* 179:506, 1969.

102. HOWARD WJ, KERSON LA, APPEL SH: Synthesis de novo of purines in slices of rat brain and liver. *J Neurochem* 17:121, 1970.

103. ROSENBLOOM FM, KELLEY WN, MILLER J, HENDERSON JF, SEEGMILLER JE: Inherited disorder of purine metabolism: Correlation between central nervous system dysfunction and biochemical defects. *JAMA* 202:175, 1967.

104. MCKERAN RO, HOWELL A, ANDREWS TM, WATTS RWE, ARLETT CF: Observations on the growth in vitro of myeloid progenitor cells and fibroblasts from hemizygotes and heterozygotes for "complete" and "partial" HGPRT deficiency, and their relevance to the pathogenesis of brain damage in the Lesch-Nyhan syndrome. *J Neurol Sci* 22:183, 1974.

105. FONTENELLE LJ, HENDERSON JF: An enzymatic basis for the inability of erythrocytes to synthesize purine ribonucleotides *de novo*. *Biochim Biophys Acta* 177:175, 1969.

106. HOLMES H, ROSENBERG MC: Adenine nucleotide metabolism of blood platelets. III. Adenine phosphoribosyltransferase and nucleotide formation from exogenous adenine. *Biochim Biophys Acta* 157:266, 1968.

107. LAJTHA LG, VANE JR: Dependence of bone marrow cells on the liver for purine supply. *Nature* 182:191, 1958.

108. LOWY BA, RAMOT B, LONDON IM: The biosynthesis of ATP and GTP in the rabbit erythrocyte in vivo and in vitro. *J Biol Chem* 235:2929, 1960.

109. LEHNINGER A: *Biochemistry*, 2d ed., New York, Worth, 1978, p 742.

110. GUTMAN AB, YU TF: Uric acid metabolism in normal man and in primary gout. *N Engl J Med* 273:252, 1965.

111. WYNGAARDEN JB, ASHTON DM: The regulation of activity of phosphoribosylpyrophosphate amidotransferase by purine ribonucleotides: A potential feedback control of purine biosynthesis. *J Biol Chem* 234:1492, 1959.

112. MAPES JP, KREBS HA: Rate-limiting factors in urate synthesis and gluconeogenesis in avian liver. *Biochem J* 172:193, 1978.

113. NIERLICK DP, MAGASANIK B: Regulation of purine ribonucleotide synthesis by end product inhibition: The effect of adenine and guanine ribonucleotides on the 5′-phosphoribosylpyrophosphate amidotransferase of *Aerobacter aerogenes*. *J Biol Chem* 240:358, 1965.

114. CASKEY CT, ASHTON DM, WYNGAARDEN JB: The enzymology of feedback inhibition of glutamine phosphoribosylpyrophosphate amidotransferase by purine ribonucleotides. *J Biol Chem* 239:270, 1964.

115. HOLMES EW, MCDONALD JA, MCCORD MM, WYNGAARDEN JB, KELLEY WN: Human glutamine phosphoribosylpyrophosphate amidotransferase: Kinetic and regulatory properties. *J Biol Chem* 248:144, 1973.

116. HENDERSON JF: Feedback inhibition of purine biosynthesis in ascites tumor cells. *J Biol Chem* 237:2631, 1962.

117. WOOD AW, SEEGMILLER JE: Properties of 5-phosphoribosyl-1-pyrophosphate amidotransferase from human lymphoblasts. *J Biol Chem* 248:138, 1973.

118. HOLMES EW, WYNGAARDEN JB, KELLEY WN: Human glutamine phosphoribosylpyrophosphate amidotransferase: Two molecular forms interconvertible by purine ribonucleotide and phosphoribosylpyrophosphate. *J Biol Chem* 248:6035, 1973.

119. ITAKURA M, SABINA RL, HEALD PW, HOLMES EW: Basis for the control of purine biosynthesis by purine ribonucleotides. *J Clin Invest* 67:994, 1981.

120. UDOM A, HOLMES EW: Purification and characterization of human amidophosphoribosyltransferase. *Z Klin Chem Klin Biochem* 20:428, 1982.

121. RUPPEN ME, SWITZER RL: Degredation of the *Bacillus subtilis* glutamine phosphoribosylpyrophosphate amidotransferase in vivo. *J Biol Chem* 258:2843, 1983.

122. WATTS REW: Some regulatory and integrative aspects of purine nucleotide biosynthesis and its control: An overview. *Adv Enzyme Regul* 21:33, 1983.

123. KELLEY WN, FOX IH, WYNGAARDEN JB: Essential role of phosphoribosylpyrophosphate (PRPP) in regulation of purine biosynthesis in cultured human fibroblasts. *Clin Res* 18:457, 1970.

124. FOX IH, KELLEY WN: Phosphoribosylpyrophosphate in man: Biochemical and clinical significance. *Ann Intern Med* 74:424, 1971.

125. BECKER LA, LOSMAN MJ, ITKIN P, SINKIN PA: Gout with superactive phosphoribosylpyrophosphate synthetase due to increased enzyme catalytic rate. *J Lab Clin Med* 99:495, 1982.

126. ZOREF E, DE VRIES A, SPERLING O: Kinetic aspects of purine metabolism in cultured fibroblasts. A comparative study of cells from patients overproducing purines due to HGPRT deficiency and PRPP synthetase superactivity. *Monogr Hum Genet* 10:96, 1978.

127. ZOREF E, DE VRIES A, SPERLING O: Mutant feedback-resistant phosphoribosylpyrophosphate synthetase associated with purine overproduction and gout. Phosphoribosylpyrophosphate and purine metabolism in cultured fibroblast. *J Clin Invest* 56:1093, 1985.

128. GREENE ML, BOYLE JA, SEEGMILLER JE: Substrate stabilization: Genetically controlled reciprocal relationship of 2 human enzymes. *Science* 167:337, 1970.

129. MAGASANIK B, KARIBIAN D: Purine nucleotide cycles and their metabolic role. *J Biol Chem* 235:2672, 1960.

130. MAGER J, MAGASANIK B: Guanosine 5′-phosphate reductase and its role in the interconversion of purine nucleotides. *J Biol Chem* 235:1474, 1960.

131. WYNGAARDEN JB, GREENLAND RA: The inhibition of succinoadenylate kinosynthetase of *Escherichia coli* by adenosine and guanosine 5′ monophosphates. *J Biol Chem* 238:1054, 1963.

132. VAN DER WEYDEN MB, KELLEY WN: Human adenylosuccinate synthetase: Partial purification kinetic and regulatory properties of the enzyme from placenta. *J Biol Chem* 249:7282, 1974.

133. HOLMES EW, PEHKLE DM, KELLEY WN: The role of human inosinic acid dehydrogenase in the control of purine biosynthesis *de novo*. *Biochem Biophys Acta* 364:209, 1974.

134. HENDERSON JF: Kinetic properties of hypoxanthine-guanine and adenine phosphoribosyltransferase. *Fed Proc* 27:1053, 1968.

135. KRENITSKY TA, PAPAIOANNOU R, ELION GB: Human hypoxanthine phosphoribosyltransferase. I. Purification, properties and specificity. *J Biol Chem* 244:1263, 1969.

136. LYON MF, ZENTHON J, BURTENSHAW MD, EVANS EP: Localization of the HPRT locus by *in situ* hybridization and distribution of loci on the mouse-X-chromosome. *Cytogenet Cell Genet* 44:163, 1987.

137. FARRELL SA, WORTON RG: Chromosome loss is responsible for segregation at the HPRT locus in Chinese hamster cell hybrids. *Somatic Cell Genet* 3:539, 1977.

138. FENWICK RG: Reversion of a mutation affecting the molecular weight of HGPRT: intragenic suppression and localization of X-linked gene. *Somatic Cell Genet* 6:477, 1980.

139. SHOWS TB, BROWN JA: Localization of genes coding for PGK, HPRT, and G6PD on the long arm of the X chromosome in somatic cells hybrids. *Cytogenet Cell Genet* 14:426, 1975.

140. FRANCKE U, TAGGART RT: Comparative gene mapping: Order of loci of X chromosome is different in mice and humans. *Proc Natl Acad Sci USA* 77:3595, 1980.

141. DOBROVIC A, GAREAU T, SEIFERT AM, MASSING K, BRADLEY WE: A *Hind*III RFLP for the HPRT pseudogene on chromosome 3 (HPRT P1). *Nucleic Acids Res* 15:1346, 1987.

142. MELTON DW: Cell-fusion induced mouse neuroblastoma HPRT revertants with variant enzyme and elevated HPRT protein levels. *Somatic Cell Genet* 1:331, 1981.

143. BRENNAND J, KONECKI DS, CASKEY CT: Expression of human and Chinese hamster hypoxanthine guanine phosphoribosyltransferase cDNA recombinants in cultured Lesch-Nyhan and Chinese hamster fibroblasts. *J Biol Chem* 258:9593, 1983.

144. KONECKI DS, BRENNAND J, FUSCOE JC, CASKEY CT, CHINAULT AC: Hypoxanthine guanine phosphoribosyltransferase genes of mouse and Chinese hamster: Construction and sequence analysis of cDNA recombinants. *Nucleic Acids Res* 10:6763, 1982.

145. NUSSBAUM RL, CROWDER WE, NYHAN WL, CASKEY CT: A three-allele re-

striction fragment length polymorphism of the hypoxanthine phosphoribosyltransferase locus in man. *Proc Natl Acad Sci USA* 80:4035, 1983.

146. NUSSBAUM RL, BRENNAND J, CHINAULT AC, FUSCOE JC, KONECKI DS, MELTON D, CASKEY CT: Molecular analysis of the hypoxanthine phosphoribosyltransferase locus, in Caskey CT, White R (eds): *Banbury Report 14: Recombinant DNA Applications to Human Disease*. Cold Spring Harbor, Cold Spring Harbor Laboratory, 1983, p 88.

147. NUSSBAUM RL, STOUT JT, CASKEY CT: Unpublished observations.

148. BOGGS BA, NUSSBAUM RL: Two anonymous X-specific human sequences detecting restriction fragment length polymorphisms in the region Xq26-qter. *Somatic Cell Mol Genet* 10:607, 1984.

149. WILSON JM, STOUT JT, PALELLA TD, DAVIDSON BL, KELLEY WN, CASKEY CT: A molecular survey of hypoxanthine-guanine phosphoribosyltransferase deficiency in man. *J Clins Invest* 77:188, 1986.

150. MELTON DW, MCEWAN C, MCKIE AB, REID AM: Expression of the mouse HPRT gene: Deletional analysis of the promoter region of an X chromosome linked housekeeping gene. *Cell* 44:319, 1986.

151. HANSEN U, SHARP PA: Sequences controlling in vitro transcription of SV40 promoters. *EMBO J* 2:2293, 1983.

152. DYNAN WS, TJIAN R: Isolation of transcription factors that discriminate between different promoters recognized by RNA polymerase II. *Cell* 32:669, 1983.

153. DYNAN WS, TJIAN R: The promoter-specific transcription factors Spl binds to upstream sequences SV40 early promoter. *Cell* 35:79, 1983.

154. VALERIO D, DUYVESTEYN MGC, DEKKER BMM, WEEDA G, BERKVENS TM, VAN DER VOORN L, VAN ORMANDT H, VAN DER EB AJ: Adenosine deaminase: Characterization and expression of a gene with a remarkable promoter. *EMBO J* 4:437, 1985.

155. SINGER S, KEITH DH, TANI K, SIMMER RL, SHIVELY L, LINDSAY S, YOSHIDA A, RIGGS AD: Sequence of the promoter region of the gene for human X-linked 3-phosphoglycerate kinase. *Gene* 32:409, 1984.

156. CHEN MJ, SHIMADA T, MOULTON AD, CLINE A, HUMPHRIES RK, MAIZEL J, NIENHUIS AW: The functional human dihydrofolate reductase gene. *J Biol Chem* 259:3922, 1984.

157. REYNOLDS GA, BASUS K, OSBORNE TF, CHIN DJ, GIL G, BROWN MS, GOLDSTEIN JL, LUSKEY KL: HMG Co-A reductase: A negatively regulated gene with unusual promoter and 5′ untranslated regions. *Cell* 38:275, 1984.

158. REYNOLDS GA, GOLDSTEIN JL, BROWN MS: Multiple mRNAs for 3-hydroxy-3-methylglutaryl coenzyme A reductase determined by multiple transcription initiation sites and intron splicing sites in the 5′ untranslated region. *J Biol Chem* 260:10369, 1985.

159. PATEL PI, TSAO TY, CASKEY CT, CHINAULT AC: 5′ Regulatory elements of the human HPRT gene, in Granner D, Rosenfeld MG, Chang S (eds): *Transcriptional Control Mechanisms*. New York, Alan R. Liss, 1987, p 45.

160. IMLER JL, LEMAIRE C, WASYLYK C, WASYLYK B: Negative regulation contributes to tissue specificity of the imunoglobulin heavy-chain enhancer. *Mol Cell Biol* 7:2558, 1987.

161. MUGLIA L, ROTHMANDENES LB: Cell type-specific negative regulatory element in the control region of the rat alpha-fetoprotein gene. *Proc Natl Acad Sci USA* 83:7653, 1986.

162. STEINER C, MULLER M, BAMIAHMAD A, RENKAWITZ R: Lysozyme gene activity in chicken macrophages is controlled by positive and negative regulatory elements. *Nucleic Acids Res* 15:4163, 1987.

163. MATTOX WW, DAVIDSON N: Isolation and characterization of the beadex locus of Drosophila melanogaster: A putative cis-acting negative regulatory element for the heldup-a gene. *Mol Cell Biol* 4:1343, 1984.

164. YEN PH, PATEL PI, CHINAULT AL, MOHANDAS T, SHAPIRO LJ: Differential methylation of hypoxanthine phosphoribosyltransferase genes on active and inactive human X-chromosomes. *Proc Natl Acad Sci USA* 81:1759, 1984.

165. WOLF SF, JOLLY DJ, LUNNEN KD, FRIEDMANN T, MIGEON BR: Methylation of the hypoxanthine phosphoribosyltransferase locus on the human X-chromosome inactivation. *Proc Natl Acad Sci USA* 81:2806, 1984.

166. WOLF SF, MIGEON BR: Clusters of CpG dinucleotides implicated by nuclease hypersensitivity as control elements of housekeeping genes. *Nature* 314:467, 1985.

167. LOCKE LF, MELTON DW, CASKEY CT, MARTIN GR: Methylation of the mouse HPRT gene differs on the active and inactive X chromosomes. *Mol Cell Biol* 6:914, 1986.

168. LOCKE LF, TAKAGI N, MARTIN GR: Methylation of the HPRT gene on the inactive X occurs after chromosome inactivation. *Cell* 48:39, 1987.

169. STOUT JT, CHEN HY, BRENNAND J, CASKEY CT, BRINSTER RL: Expression of human HPRT in the central nervous system in transgenic mice. *Nature* 317:250, 1985.

170. KELLEY WN: Hypoxanthine-guanine phosphoribosyltransferase deficiency in the Lesch-Nyhan syndrome and gout. *Fed Proc* 27:1047, 1968.

171. SPERLING O, BOER P, EILAM G, DEVRIES A: Altered kinetic properties of erythrocyte phosphoribosylpyrophosphate synthetase in excessive purine production. *Eur J Clin Biol Res* 17:703, 1972.

172. BALIS ME, YIP LC, YU TF, GUTMAN AB, COX R, DANCIS J: Unstable HPRTase in subjects with abnormal urinary oxypurine excretion, in Sperling O, DeVries A, Wyngaarden JB (eds): *Purine Metabolism in Man*. New York, Plenum, 1974, p 195.

173. BAKAY B, NYHAN WL: Activation of variants of hypoxanthine-guanine phosphoribosyltransferase by the normal enzyme. *Proc Natl Acad Sci USA* 69:2523, 1972.

174. BAKAY B, NYHAN WL: Electrophoretic properties of hypoxanthine-guanine phosphoribosyltransferase in erythrocytes of subjects with Lesch-Nyhan syndrome. *Biochem Genet* 6:139, 1972.

175. GUTENSOHN W, JAHN H: Partial deficiency of hypoxanthine-phosphoribosyltransferase: Evidence for a structural mutation in a patient with gout. *Eur J Clin Invest* 9:43, 1979.

176. KELLEY WN, MEADE JC: Studies on hypoxanthine-guanine phosphoribosyltransferase in fibroblasts from patients with the Lesch-Nyhan syndrome: Evidence for genetic heterogeneity. *J Biol Chem* 246:2953, 1971.

177. BENKE PM, HERRICK N: Azaguanine-resistance as a manifestation of a new form of metabolic overproduction of uric acid. *Am J Med* 52:547, 1972.

178. MCDONALD JA, KELLEY WN: Lesch-Nyhan syndrome: Altered kinetic properties of mutant enzyme. *Science* 171:689, 1971.

179. ARNOLD WJ, MEADE JC, KELLEY WN: Hypoxanthine-guanine phosphoribosyltransferase: Characteristics of the mutant enzyme in erythrocytes from patients with the Lesch-Nyhan syndrome. *J Clin Invest* 51:1805, 1972.

180. WILSON JM, BAUGHER BW, MATTES PM, DADDONA PE, KELLEY WN: Human hypoxanthine-guanine phosphoribosyltransferase. Demonstration of structural variants in lymphoblastoid cells derived from patients with a deficiency of the enzyme. *J Clin Invest* 69:706, 1982.

181. WILSON JM, BAUGHER BW, KELLEY WN: Hypoxanthine-guanine phosphoribosyltransferase in human lymphoblastoid cells: Confirmation of 4 structural variants and demonstration of a new variant ($HPRT_{Ann\ Arbor}$). *Adv. Exp Med Biol* 165:33, 1984.

182. WILSON JM, FROSSARD P, NUSSBAUM RL, CASKEY CT, KELLEY WN: Human hypoxanthine guanine phosphoribosyltransferase: Detection of a mutant allele by restriction endonuclease analysis. *J Clin Invest* 72:767, 1983.

183. GORDON RB, STOUT JT, EMMERSON BT, CASKEY CT: Molecular studies of hypoxanthine-guanine phosphoribosyltransferase mutations in 6 Australian families. *Aust NZ J Med* 17:424, 1987.

184. OGASAWARA N, KASHIWAMATA S, OISHI H, HARA K, WATANABE K, MIYAZAKI S, KUMAGAI T, HAKAMAD S: Hypoxanthine-guanine phosphoribosyltransferase (HGPRT) deficiency in a girl. *Adv Exp Med Biol* 165:13, 1984.

185. OGASAWARA N, STOUT JT, CASKEY CT: Unpublished observations.

186. MYERS RM, MANIATIS T: Recent advances in the development of methods for detecting single-base substitution associated with human genetic diseases. *Cold Spring Harbor Symp Quant Biol* 51:275, 1986.

187. MYERS RM, LARIN Z, MANIATIS T: Detection of a single-base substitution by ribonuclease cleavage at mismatches in RNA:DNA duplexes. *Science* 230:1242, 1985.

188. GIBBS RA, CASKEY CT: Identification and localization of mutations at the Lesch-Nyhan locus by RNAse A cleavage. *Science* 236:303, 1987.

189. SAIKI RK, SCHARF S, FALOONA FA, MULIS KB, HORN GT, ERLICK HA, ARNHEIM N: Enzymatic amplification of beta-globin genomic sequences and restriction site analysis for diagnosis of sickle cell anemia. *Science* 230:1350, 1985.

190. MULLIS KB, FALOONA FA: Specific synthesis of DNA in vitro via a polymerase catalyzed chain reaction. *Methods Enzymol* 155:335, 1987.

191. VERES G, GIBBS RA, SCHERER SE, CASKEY CT: The molecular basis of the sparse fur mouse mutation. *Science* 237:415, 1987.

192. KELLEY WN: Studies on the adenine phosphoribosyltransferase enzyme in human fibroblasts lacking hypoxanthine-guanine phosphoribosyltransferase. *J Lab Clin Med* 77:33, 1971.

193. RUBIN CS, BALIS ME, PIOMELLI S, BERMAN PH, DANCIS J: Elevated AMP pyrophosphorylase activity in congenital IMP pyrophosphorylase deficiency (Lesch-Nyhan disease). *J Lab Clin Med* 74:732, 1969.

194. YIP LC, DANCIS J, METHIESON B, BALIS ME: Age induced changes in adenosine monophosphate: Pyrophosphate phosphoribosyltransferase from normal and Lesch-Nyhan erythrocytes. *Biochemistry* 13:2558, 1974.

195. GORDON RB, THOMPSON L, EMMERSON BT: Erythrocyte phosphoribosylpyrophosphate concentrations in heterozygotes for hypoxanthine-guanine phosphoribosyltransferase deficiency. *Metabolism* 23:921, 1974.

196. WOOD AW, BECKER MA, MINNA JD, SEEGMILLER JE: Purine metabolism in normal and thioguanine-resistant neuroblastoma. *Proc Natl Acad Sci USA* 70:3880, 1973.

197. WOOD AW, BECKER MA, SEEGMILLER JE: Purine nucleotide synthesis in

lymphoblasts cultured from normal subjects and a patient with Lesch-Nyhan syndrome. *Biochem Genet* 9:261, 1973.

198. PEHLKE DM, MCDONALD JA, HOLMES EW, KELLEY WN: Inosinic acid dehydrogenase activity in the Lesch-Nyhan syndrome. *J Clin Invest* 51:1398, 1972.

199. SWEETMAN L, NYHAN WL: Further studies of the enzyme composition of mutant cells in X-linked uric aciduria. *Arch Intern Med* 130:214, 1974.

200. LOMMEN EJP, DE ABREU RA, TRIJBELS JMF, SCHRETLEN EDAM: The IMP dehydrogenase catalysed reaction in erythrocytes of normal individuals and patients with hypoxanthine-guanine phosphoribosyltransferase deficiency. *Acta Paediatr Scand* 63:140, 1974.

201. SKAPER SD, SEEGMILLER JE: Hypoxanthine-guanine phosphoribosyltransferase mutant glioma cells: Diminished monoamine oxidase activity. *Science* 194:1171, 1976.

202. ROTH JA, BREAKEFIELD XO, CASTIGLIONE CM: Monamine oxidase and catechol-o-methyltransferase in cultured human skin fibroblasts. *Life Sci* 19:1705, 1976.

203. BREAKEFIELD XO, CASTIGLIONE CM, EDELSTEIN SB: Monoamine oxidase activity decreased in cells lacking hypoxanthine phosphoribosyltransferase activity. *Science* 192:1018, 1976.

204. SINGH S, WILLER I, KLUSS EM, GOEDDE HW: Monoamine oxidase and catechol-o-methyltransferase activity in cultured fibroblasts from patients with maple syprup urine disease, Lesch-Nyhan syndrome and healthy controls. *Clin Genet* 15:153, 1979.

205. EDELSTEIN SB, CASTIGLIONE CM, BREAKEFIELD XO: Monoamine oxidase activity in normal and Lesch-Nyhan fibroblasts. *J Neurochem* 31:1247, 1978.

206. KOCHERSPERGER LM, PARKER EL, SICILIANO M, DARLINGTON GJ, DENNEY IM: Assignment of genes for the human monoamine oxidases A and B to the X chromosome. *J Neurosci Res* 16:601, 1986.

207. MARTIN DW, GRAF LH, MCROBERTS JA, HARRISON TM: Evidence that the gene for hypoxanthine-guanine phosphoribosyltransferase controls the concentration of the enzyme, phosphoribosylphosphate synthetase, abstracted. *Clin Res* 23:263A, 1975.

208. REEM GH: Purine metabolism in murine virus-induced erythroleukemic cells during differentiation in vitro. *Proc Natl Acad Sci USA* 72:1630, 1975.

209. TORRELIO BM, PAZ MA: Increased phosphoribosylpyrophosphate synthetase activity in fibroblasts of hypoxanthine-guanine phosphoribosyltransferase deficient patients. *Biochem Biophys Res Commun* 87:380, 1979.

210. HARDWELL TR, BRAVEN J, SHAW S, WHITTAKER M: Phosphoribosylpyrophosphate synthetase and glutathione reductase in erythrocytes from hyperuricaemic and gout patients. *Clin Chim Acta* 126:217, 1982.

211. BOYD EM, DOLMAN M, KNIGHT LM, SHEPPARD EP: The chronic oral toxicity of caffeine. *Can J Physiol Pharmacol* 43:995, 1965.

212. UNGERSTEDT U: Postsynaptic supersensitivity after 6-hydroxydopamine induced degeneration of the nigrostriatal dopamine system. *Acta Physiol Scand (suppl)* 367:69, 1971.

213. BREESE GR, BAUMEISTER AA, MCCOWEN TJ, EMERICK SG, FRYE GD, CROTTY K, MUELLER RA: Behavioral differences between neonatal and adult 6-hydroxydopamine-treated rats to dopamine agonists: Relevance to neurological symptoms in clinical syndromes with reduced brain dopamine. *J Pharmacol Exp Ther* 231:343, 1984.

214. GOLDSTEIN M, KUGA S, KUSANO N, MELLER E, DANCIS J, SCHWARCZ R: Dopamine agonist induced self-mutilative biting behavior in monkeys with unilateral ventromedial tegmental lesions of the brainstem: Possible pharmacological model for Lesch-Nyhan syndrome. *Brain Res* 367:114, 1986.

215. GOLDSTEIN M, CEASAR P, ANAGNOSTE B, BATTISTA AF: Lesions of the nigrostriatal dopamine pathway: Effects on the storage and metabolism of striatal dopamine. *Pharmacol Ther* 2B:89, 1976.

216. GOLDSTEIN M, KUGA S: Dopamine (DA) agonist induced compulsive biting (CB) behavior in monkeys: Animal model for Lesch-Nyhan syndrome. *Soc Neurosci Abstr* 10:239, 1984.

217. GOLDSTEIN M, ANDERSON LT, REUBEN R, DANCIS J: Self mutilation in Lesch-Nyhan disease is caused by dopaminergic denervation. *Lancet* 1:338, 1985.

218. GOSSLER A, DOETSCHMAN T, KORN R, SERFLING E, KEMLER R: Transgenesis by means of blastocyst-derived embryonic stem cell lines. *Proc Natl Acad Sci USA* 83:9065, 1986.

219. KAUFMAN MH, EVENS MJ, ROBERTSON EJ, BRADLEY A: Influence of injected pluripotential (EK) cells on haploid diploid parthenogenetic development. *J Embryol Exp Morphol* 80:75, 1984.

220. STOUT JT, CASKEY CT: Antisense RNA inhibition of endogenous genes. *Methods Enzymol* 151:519, 1987.

221. STOUT JT: Antisense RNA inhibition of cellular HPRT synthesis. Ph.D. thesis. Houston, TX, Baylor College of Medicine, 1987.

222. MUNIR MI, ROSSITER BFJ, CASKEY CT: Antisense inhibition of HPRT in vitro and in vivo. Banbury Report, Cold Spring Harbor, Cold Spring Harbor Laboratory (in press).

223. FAHN S: Biochemistry of basal ganglia. *Adv Neurol* 14:59, 1976.

224. LEFKOWITZ RJ, CARON MC, STILES GL: Mechanisms of membrane-receptor regulation: Biochemical physiological, and clinical insights derived from studies of the adrenergic receptors. *N Engl J Med* 310:1570, 1984.

225. LEFF SE, HAMBLIN MW, CREESE I: Interactions of dopamine agonists with brain D_1 receptors labeled by ^3H-antagonists: Evidence for the presence of high and low affinity agonist-binding states. *Mol Pharmacol* 27:171, 1985.

226. SILVERSTEIN FS, JOHNSTON MV, HUTCHINSON RJ, EDWARDS NL: Lesch-Nyhan syndrome: CSF neurotransmitter abnormalities. *Neurology* 35:907, 1985.

227. CREESE I, USDIN TB, SNYDER SH: Dopamine receptor binding regulated by guanine nucleotides. *Mol Pharmacol* 16:69, 1979.

228. SEEMAN P: Brain dopamine receptors. *Pharmacol Rev* 32:299, 1981.

229. ROCKSON S, STONE R, VAN DER WEYDEN M, KELLEY WN: Lesch-Nyhan syndrome: Evidence for abnormal adrenergic function. *Science* 186:934, 1974.

230. LAKE CR, ZIEGLER MG: Lesch-Nyhan syndrome: Low dopamine-B-hydroxylase activity and diminished sympathetic response to stress and posture. *Science* 196:905, 1977.

231. BLOOM FE: The role of cyclic nucleotides in central synaptic function. *Rev Physiol Biochem Pharmacol* 74:1, 1975.

232. MCKERIN RO, WATTS RWE: Purine metabolism and cell physiology, in O'Riordan JLH (ed): *Recent Advances in Endocrinology and Metabolism.* Edinburgh, Churchill Livingston, 1978, p 219.

233. WATTS RWE, SPELLACY E, GIBBS DA, ALLSOP J, MCKERAN RO, SLAVEN GE: Clinical, post-mortem, biochemical and therapeutic observations on the Lesch-Nyhan syndrome with particular reference to the neurological manifestations. *Q J Med* 51:43, 1982.

234. SKOLNICK PN, MARANGOS PJ, GOODWIN FK, EDWARDS M, PAUL S: Identification of inosine and hypoxanthine as endogenous inhibitors of [^3H] diazepam binding in the central nervous system. *Life Sci* 23:1473, 1978.

235. ROUFOGALIS BD, THORNTON M, WADE DN: Nucleotide requirement of dopamine sensitive adenylate cyclase in synaptosomal membranes from the striatum of rat brain. *J Neurochem* 27:1533, 1976.

236. NIEOULLON A, CHERAMY A, GLOWINSKI J: Nigral and striatal dopamine release under sensory stimuli. *Nature* 269:340, 1977.

237. SWEETMAN L, BORDE M, KULOVICH S, KAUFMAN I, NYHAN WL: Altered excretion of 5-hydroxyindoleacetic acid and glycine in patients with the Lesch-Nyhan disease, in Muller MM, Kaiser E, Seegmiller JE (eds): *Purine Metabolism in Man II: Regulation of Pathways and Enzyme Defects.* New York, Plenum, 1977, p 398.

238. BALIS ME, KRAKOFF IH, BERMAN PH, DANCIS J: Urinary metabolites in congenital hyperuricosuria. *Science* 156:1122, 1967.

239. BALIS ME: Aspects of purine metabolism. *Fed Proc* 27:1067, 1968.

240. RICCIUTI FC, RUDDLE FH: Assignment of nucleoside phosphorylase to D-14 and localization of X-linked loci in man by somatic cell genetics. *Nature New Biol* 241:180, 1973.

241. HALDANE JBS: The rate of spontaneous mutation of a human gene. *J Genet* 31:317, 1935.

242. FRANCKE U, WINTER TM, LIN DM, BAKAY B, SEEGMILLER JE, NYHAN WL: Use of carrier detection tests to estimate male to female ratio of mutation rates in Lesch-Nyhan disease, in Hook EB, Porter IH (eds): *Population and Biological Aspects of Human Mutations.* New York, Plenum, 1981, p 431.

243. STOUT JT, CASKEY CT: Unpublished observations.

244. GIBBS DA, HEADHOUSE-BENSON CM, WATTS RWE: Family studies of the Lesch-Nyhan syndrome: The use of a restriction fragment length polymorphism (RFLP) closely linked to the disease gene for carrier state and prenatal diagnosis. *J Inherited Metab Dis* 9:45, 1986.

245. GIBBS DA, MCFADYEN IR, CRAWFURD Md'A, de MUICK-KEIZER EE, HEADHOUSE-BENSON CM, WILSON TM, FARRANT PH: First trimester prenatal diagnosis of Lesch-Nyhan syndrome. *Lancet* 2:1180, 1984.

246. BOYLE JA, RAIVIO KO, ASTRIN KH, SCHULMAN JD, GRAF ML, SEEGMILLER JE, JACOBSEN CB: Lesch-Nyhan syndrome: Preventative control by prenatal diagnosis. *Science* 169:688, 1970

247. STOUT JT, JACKSON LG, CASKEY CT: First trimester diagnosis of Lesch-Nyhan syndrome: Applications to other disorders of purine metabolism. *Prenat Diagn* 5:183, 1985.

248. EMMERSON BT: Urate metabolism in heterozygotes of HGPRTase deficiency, in Sperling O, De Vries A, Wyngaarden JB (eds): *Purine Metabolism in Man.* New York, Plenum, 1974, p 237.

249. EMMERSON BT, THOMPSON CH, WALLACE DC: Partial deficiency of hypo-

xanthine-guanine phosphoribosyltransferase: Intermediate enzyme deficiency in heterozygote red cells. *Ann Intern Med* 76:285, 1972.

250. GARTLER SM, SCOTT RC, GOLDSTEIN JL, CAMPBELL B: Lesch-Nyhan syndrome: Rapid detection of heterozygotes by the use of hair follicles. *Science* 172:572, 1971.

251. GOLDSTEIN JL, MARKS JF, GARTLER SM: Expression of two X-linked genes in human hair follicles of double heterozygotes. *Proc Natl Acad Sci USA* 68:1425, 1971.

252. SILVERS DN, COX P, BALIS ME, DANCIS J: Detection of heterozygotes in Lesch-Nyhan disease by hair-root analysis. *N Engl J Med* 286:390, 1972.

253. FRANCKE U, BAKAY B, NYHAN WL: Detection of heterozygous carriers of the Lesch-Nyhan syndrome by electrophoresis of hair root lysates. *J Pediatr* 82:472, 1973.

254. MCDONALD JA, KELLEY WN: Lesch-Nyhan syndrome: Absence of the mutant enzyme in erythrocytes of heterozygote for both normal and mutant hypoxanthine-guanine phosphoribosyltransferase. *Biochem Genet* 6:21, 1972.

255. DANCIS J, BERMAN PH, HANSEN V, BALIS ME: Absence of mosaicism in the lymphocyte in X-linked congenital hyperuricosuria. *Life Sci* 7:587, 1968.

256. ALBERTINI RJ, DEMARS R: Mosaicism of peripheral blood lymphocyte populations in females heterozygous for the Lesch-Nyhan mutation. *Biochem Genet* 11:397, 1974.

257. STOUT JT, CASKEY CT: Unpublished observation.

258. SPERLING O, BROSH S, BOER P, LIBERMAN UA, DE VRIES A: Urinary xanthine stones in an allopurinol-treated gouty patient with partial deficiency of hypoxanthine-guanine phosphoribosyltransferase. *Isr J Med Sci* 14:288, 1978.

259. WATTS RWE, MCKERAN RO, BROWN E, ANDRES TM, GRIFFITHS MI: Clinical and biochemical studies on treatment of Lesch-Nyhan syndrome. *Arch Dis Child* 49:693, 1974.

260. VAN DER ZEE SPM, LOMMEN EJP, TRIJBELS JMF, SCHRETLEN EDAM: The influence of adenine on the clinical features and purine metabolism in the Lesch-Nyhan syndrome. *Acta Paediatr Scand* 59:259, 1970.

261. DEMUS A, KAISER W, SCHAUB J: The Lesch-Nyhan syndrome. Metabolic studies during administration of adenine. *Z Kinderheilkd* 114:119, 1973.

262. PHILIPS FS, THIERSCH JB, BENDICH A: Adenine intoxication in relation to *in vivo* formation and deposition of 2,8-dioxyadenine in renal tubules. *J Pharmacol Exp Ther* 104:20, 1952.

263. BENKE PJ, ANDERSON J: Use of folic acid, adenine, and bicarbonate in newborn twins with the Lesch-Nyhan syndrome. *Pediatr Res* 3:356, 1969.

264. BENKE PJ, HERRICK N, SMITEN L, ARADINE C, LAESSIG R, WOLCOTT GJ: Adenine and folic acid in the Lesch-Nyhan syndrome. *Pediatr Res* 7:729, 1973.

265. GHADIMI H, BHALLA CK, KIRSCHENBAUM DM: The significance of the deficiency state in Lesch-Nyhan disease. *Acta Paediatr Scand* 59:233, 1970.

266. WOOD MH, FOX RM, VINCENT L, REYE C, O'SULLIVEN WJ: The Lesch-Nyhan syndrome: Report of three cases. *Aust NZ J Med* 2:57, 1972.

267. BENKE PH, HERBERT A, HERRICK N: *In vitro* effects of magnesium ions on mutant cells from patients with the Lesch-Nyhan syndrome. *N Engl J Med* 289:446, 1973.

268. MIZUNO TI, YUGARI Y: Self-mutilation in Lesch-Nyhan syndrome. *Lancet* 1:761, 1974.

269. NYHAN WL, JOHNSON HG, KAUFMAN IA, JONES KL: Serotonergic approaches to the modification of behavior in the Lesch-Nyhan syndrome. *Appl Res Ment Retard* 1:25, 1980.

270. MCGREEVY P, ARTHUR M: Effective behavioral treatment of self-biting by a child with Lesch-Nyhan syndrome. *Dev Med Child Neurol* 29:536, 1987.

271. MILLER AD, JOLLY DJ, FRIEDMANN T, VERMA IM: A transmissible retrovirus expressing human hypoxanthine phosphoribosyltransferase (HPRT): Gene transfer into cells obtained from humans deficient in HPRT. *Proc Natl Acad Sci USA* 80:4709, 1983.

272. GLUZMAN Y: *Eukaryotic Viral Vectors*. Cold Spring Harbor, NY, Cold Spring Harbor Press, 1982, p 221.

273. MILLER AD, ECKNER RJ, JOLLY DJ, FRIEDMANN T, VERMA IM: Expression of a retrovirus encoding human HPRT in mice. *Science* 255:630, 1984.

274. WILLIS R, JOLLY DJ, MILLER AD, PLENT M, ESTY A, ANDERSON P, CHANG HC, JONES O, SEEGMILLER JE, FRIEDMANN T: Partial phenotypic correction of human Lesch-Nyhan (hypoxanthine-guanine phosphoribosyltransferase deficient) lymphoblasts with a transmissible retroviral vector. *J Biol Chem* 259:7842, 1984.

275. NELSON DL, CHANG SM, HENKEL-TIGGES J, WAGER-SMITH K, BELMONT JW, CASKEY CT: Gene replacement therapy for inborn error of purine metabolism. *Cold Spring Harbor Symp Quant Biol* 51:1065, 1986.

276. CHANG SM, WAGER-SMITH K, TSAO TY, HENKEL-TIGGES J, VAISHNAV S, CASKEY CT: Construction of a defective retrovirus encoding the human hypoxanthine phosphoribosyltransferase cDNA and its expression in cultured cells in mouse bone marrow. *Mol Cell Biol* 7:854, 1987.

277. NYHAN WL, PARKMAN R, PAGE T, GRUBER HE, PYATI J, JOLLY D, FRIEDMANN T: Bone marrow transplantation in Lesch-Nyhan disease. *Adv Exp Med Biol* 195(A):167, 1986.

278. CASKEY CT: Genetic therapy: Somatic gene transplants. *Hosp Pract* 8:181, 1987.

279. BELMONT JW, CASKEY CT: Developments leading to human gene therapy, in Kucherlapati R (ed): *Gene Transfer* New York, Plenum, 1986, p 411.

280. HUMAN GENE THERAPY SUBCOMMITTEE, NIH RECOMBINANT DNA ADVISORY COMMITTEE: The design and submission of human somatic cell gene therapy protocols. *Recomb DNA Tech Bull* 9:221, 1986.

281. JOLLY DJ: The role of the HPRT gene in human disease. *Horiz Biochem Biophys* 8:123, 1986.

CHAPTER 39

ADENINE PHOSPHORIBOSYLTRANSFERASE DEFICIENCY AND 2,8-DIHYDROXYADENINE LITHIASIS

H. ANNE SIMMONDS
AMRIK S. SAHOTA
KAREL J. VAN ACKER

1. *Adenine phosphoribosyltransferase (APRT) deficiency is an inherited disorder of purine metabolism. The enzyme defect results in an inability to salvage the purine base adenine, which, in the absence of any other significant pathway of metabolism in humans, is oxidized via the 8-hydroxy intermediate by xanthine oxidase to 2,8-dihydroxyadenine (2,8-DHA). This produces crystalluria and the possible formation of kidney stones due to the excretion of excessive amounts of this insoluble purine.*

2. *Two types of defect have been identified in 2,8-DHA stone formers, depending on the level of residual APRT in erythrocyte lysates. Those with virtually undetectable enzyme activity (type I), found predominantly in Caucasians, are homozygotes or compound heterozygotes for null alleles designated APRT*Q0. Those with significant APRT activity (type II), found only in Japan to date, are considered to have a mutant allele designated APRT*J.*

3. *Clinical symptoms—colic, hematuria, urinary tract infection, and dysuria—are due to 2,8-DHA stone formation, or crystalluria, and may be present from birth. Approximately 15 percent of homozygotes for either type of defect have been completely symptomless. A minority presented with acute renal failure, some of whom have suffered permanent and severe renal damage requiring dialysis, indicating a wide spectrum of clinical expression of the defect. Two-thirds of the cases have been children.*

4. *Except for the excretion of adenine and its metabolites, no other biochemical abnormalities have been recorded so far. Purine production and excretion are considered normal, indicating that APRT is not vital for the overall control of purine metabolism in humans. Neither homozygotes nor heterozygotes show any evidence of immunodeficiency.*

5. *Normally, adenine metabolites account for 20 to 30 percent of the total purine excretion, even on a low purine intake. The main source of endogenous adenine is probably the polyamine pathway, of which adenine is a metabolic by-product. However, adenine-rich foods may be a precipitating factor in the expression of the more severe clinical manifestations of the defect.*

6. *2,8-DHA is protein-bound. Adenine and 2,8-DHA are secreted by the human kidney. Both factors tend to minimize toxicity in tissues other than the kidney in vivo. Exogenous adenine is itself toxic in different in vitro systems and has produced 2,8-DHA nephrotoxicity in a variety of animal models and also in humans with normal APRT activity.*

7. *Heterozygotes for the type I defect have generally had no clinical or biochemical abnormality. APRT activity in hemolysates was about 25 percent, rather than the expected 50 percent of normal, but intact red cells showed normal conversion of adenine at physiological concentrations of substrate and phosphate. Cells from homozygotes, but not heterozygotes, with the type I defect were resistant to the deleterious effects of 2,6-diaminopurine and other analogues. Immunochemical and electrophoretic analyses of APRT from patients with the complete deficiency and their families have provided evidence for a variety of mutations on the structural gene coding for the enzyme.*

8. *APRT from homozygotes for the type II deficiency showed a reduced affinity for 5-phosphoribosyl-1-pyrophosphate (PP-ribose-P) compared with the normal enzyme. The mutant enzyme also displayed sigmoidal rather than hyperbolic kinetics and altered heat stability depending on the absence or presence of PP-ribose-P. The specific activity in hemolysates from type II homozygotes was approximately 25 percent of normal, but intact cells showed no conversion of adenine under physiological conditions and were resistant to the effects of 2,6-diaminopurine and other analogues. APRT from type II heterozygotes, like the enzyme from type I heterozygotes, displayed normal physicochemical properties. These two types of heterozygotes could be distinguished only by intact cell studies.*

9. *The amino acid sequence of erythrocyte APRT has been determined. The enzyme is a dimer with a subunit molecular weight of 19,481. The gene coding for human APRT is located on chromosome 16q. The gene has been isolated from a genomic lambda phage library using cloned rodent genes as probes. The cloned gene is similar in size and intron-exon arrangement to the rodent genes. There is a* Taq*I polymorphic site within the gene. Detailed analysis of APRT deficiency at the gene level has not yet been carried out.*

10. *The defect is inherited in an autosomal recessive manner. A relatively high frequency of heterozygosity has been noted in several Caucasian population studies (0.4 to 1.1 per hundred). The type II defect had a similar frequency. This suggests that homozygosity for the defect may be more prevalent than is cur-*

Nonstandard abbreviations used in this chapter are: ADA = adenosine deaminase; APRT = adenine phosphoribosyltransferase; 2,8-DHA = 2,8-dihydroxyadenine; 2-HA = 2-hydroxyadenine; HPLC = high performance liquid chromatography; PNP = purine nucleoside phosphorylase; PP-ribose-P = 5-phosphoribosyl-1-pyrophosphate.

rently recognized, presumably due to the wide range of clinical expression coupled with the problems of diagnosis.

11. *Diagnosis of the defect has presented problems in the past. 2,8-DHA stones were previously confused with uric acid because of the structural similarity of these purines, which leads to identical chemical reactivity. Homozygotes may be identified by the characteristic 2,8-DHA crystals in the urine. The diagnosis can be established by the adenine and the 2,8-DHA excreted in the urine; from the 2,8-DHA in kidney stones (identified by ultraviolet, infrared, and mass spectrometry, or by x-ray crystallography); and by the absence of functional APRT activity in intact erythrocytes. The last is impossible if transfusion has formed an essential part of the treatment.*
12. *Treatment has included dietary purine restriction and a high fluid intake. Allopurinol has prevented further 2,8-DHA excretion and stone formation. It is suggested that the use of alkali be avoided. Renal transplantation has been successful in one case.*

Deficiency of the purine salvage enzyme adenine phosphoribosyltransferase (APRT: EC 2.4.2.7) is inherited as an autosomal recessive trait. The chief clinical manifestation directly related to the metabolic defect is 2,8-dihydroxyadenine (2,8-DHA) urolithiasis. This is not an invariable finding but, when present, can lead to serious complications. The stones were previously mistaken for uric acid stones.[1-3] Thirty-two homozygotes with no detectable erythrocyte lysate APRT activity, two-thirds of them males, have been identified.[1-19] This type of defect, found predominantly in Caucasians to date, is referred to as the type I, or APRT*Q0 defect (see "Nomenclature of the Mutant Forms," below). Initially the defect was reported only in children,[1] but adults now constitute one-third of the cases detected. An additional 31 cases have been identified among kindreds containing 2,8-DHA stone formers with erythrocyte lysate APRT activity approximately 25 percent of normal. This type of partial APRT deficiency linked with disease is referred to as the type II, or APRT*J defect, and has been found exclusively in Japan so far.[20-25]

CLINICAL FEATURES

Clinical symptoms in APRT deficiency occur only when 2,8-DHA stones or crystals are formed as a consequence of the enzyme defect (Fig. 39-1). The clinical situation may vary from benign to life-threatening.[1-25] 2,8-DHA crystalluria can occur without clinical symptoms, and the abnormality is then detected only during family investigations.[4,7,25] Brief case histories representing the most extreme forms of expression and details of the first 10 patients are recorded in the previous edition of this text.[1] The main characteristics of these patients and the more recent cases now reported with the type I (APRT*Q0) defect and the additional families from Japan, the majority of whom have the type II (APRT*J) defect, are summarized below.

PATTERN OF EXPRESSION OF APRT DEFICIENCY

The age of onset of symptoms has varied from birth to 50 years of age for the type I defect,[1,18] or 72 years for the type II defect.[25] The time from onset to correct diagnosis in earlier cases sometimes took up to 23 years.[1] In those patients with 2,8-DHA urolithiasis, the whole scale of symptoms associated with stone formation was observed: fever from urinary tract infection, macroscopic hematuria, dysuria, urinary retention, and abdominal colic. In a few cases, acute anuric renal failure drew attention to the underlying lithiasis.[1] Three cases have progressed to chronic renal insufficiency requiring maintenance dialysis[1,6,8,25]; two have subsequently had renal transplants,[6,8] only only of which was successful. In the initial cases, once the diagnosis of urolithiasis had been made, it took considerable time before the exact nature of the stone was recognized and appropriate treatment given. Most stones were considered to be uric acid stones, either on the grounds of chemical analysis[1] or because of their radiolucency, together with the reported presence of "uric acid" crystals in the urine.[10] In recent cases the use of more appropriate techniques and better knowledge of the disease has shortened the time from recognition of the urolithiasis to diagnosis of APRT deficiency. Laxity of the joints observed in two sibs has been shown to be inherited independently of APRT deficiency.[4]

Heterozygotes with the type I defect have approximately 25 percent of normal APRT activity and have never had any specific clinical symptoms. The first report of 2,8-DHA stone formation by an apparent heterozygote in Japan,[20] therefore, aroused considerable interest. The possibility that this case may have had fictitiously raised erythrocyte APRT levels because of other factors such as a blood transfusion, as in an earlier patient,[6] was excluded. The subsequent finding of many similar cases in Japan and enzyme kinetic data established that these cases were in fact homozygous for type II APRT deficiency due to an abnormal gene product which was nonfunctional in intact cells, as discussed below.

BIOCHEMICAL FEATURES OF APRT DEFICIENCY

Subjects with complete APRT deficiency generally have normal levels of uric acid in plasma and urine, although slightly raised levels were noted initially.[1] Total urinary purine end product (uric acid + precursor oxypurines and adenine derivatives) has also been normal (0.05 to 0.1 mmol/kg per 24 h), with adenine metabolites making up to 20 to 30 percent of this total.[5-7,16,17] Three different adenine derivatives are excreted in the urine: adenine itself, 8-hydroxyadenine (8-HA), and 2,8-dihydroxyadenine (2,8-DHA) in the proportion of approximately 1:0.03:1.5, as shown by several different reports.[1] The excretion of 8-HA in APRT deficiency confirms earlier studies in vitro[26] that adenine, unlike hypoxanthine, is oxidized by xanthine oxidase via the 8-, not the 2-hydroxy, intermediate (Fig. 39-1). No other abnormal purines or pyrimidines have been detected in plasma and urine, and heterozygotes do not excrete detectable amounts of adenine or its metabolites.[1]

Erythrocytes from both homozygotes and heterozygotes for type I APRT deficiency have normal ATP and 5-phosphoribosyl-1-pyrophosphate (PP-ribose-P) levels.[27,28] The former observation indicates that the erythrocyte must maintain its adenine nucleotide pool predominantly through the action of adenosine kinase.[27] The latter, together with the normal PP-ribose-P synthetase activity[27] and purine production,[1] suggests

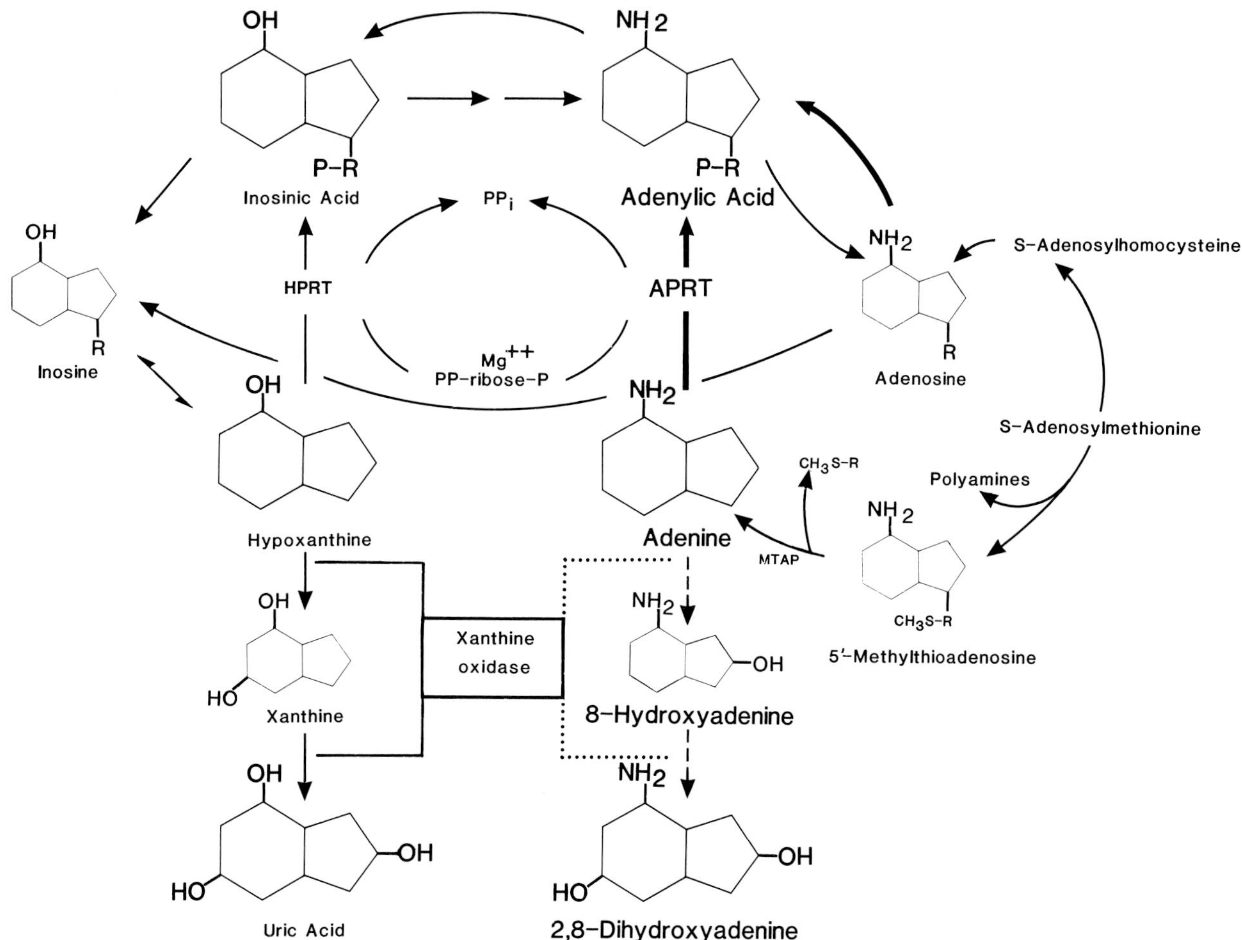

Fig. 39-1 Diagram showing the metabolic pathways for the formation and disposal of adenine and adenosine in humans, compared with those for hypoxanthine. Adenine is normally converted by APRT to adenylic acid (AMP). In the absence of APRT it is oxidized by xanthine oxidase (dotted lines) via the 8-hydroxy intermediate (8-HA) to 2,8-dihydroxyadenine (2,8-DHA). Significant amounts of adenine are not formed from adenosine by the action of purine nucleoside phosphorylase in intact cells in vitro. Formation of adenine from 5-methylthioadenosine has been demonstrated, indicating that the polyamine pathway, and not purine metabolism, is the likely source of adenine formation in vivo. APRT = adenine phosphoribosyltransferase; HPRT = hypoxanthine-guanine phosphoribosyltransferase; MTAP = 5-methylthioadenosine phosphorylase; CH_3S-R = 5-methylthioribose.

that APRT, unlike its companion salvage enzyme hypoxanthine-guanine phosphoribosyltransferase (HPRT),[29] is not critical for cellular economy and that adenine salvage is not vital for the overall regulation of purine metabolism in humans.[1] Apart from the abnormal adenine metbolites excreted, all other biochemical and hematologic factors studied have been normal in homozygotes.[1-19] No detailed metabolic studies in the Japanese patients have been published.

Immunology. Lymphocyte function has been investigated in homozygotes from two Caucasian families and heterozygotes in their immediate kindred.[5,30] T- and B-cell function were within normal limits as judged from E-rosette formation, lymphocyte membrane immunoglobulins, cutaneous sensitivity tests, serum immunoglobulins, and lymphocyte transformation studies after stimulation with phytohemagglutinin, pokeweed mitogen, or concanavalin A. C3, C4, and total hemolytic complement were also normal. From these studies it can be concluded that APRT is not essential for normal immune function. Also from the clinical standpoint, and unlike two other enzyme defects in purine metabolism (see Chap. 40), APRT deficiency is not characterized by an increased susceptibility to recurrent infection.[1]

TYPES OF APRT DEFICIENCY

Three mutant forms of APRT have now been identified. These are: (1) partial APRT deficiency not apparently associated with any specific form of disease; (2) complete enzyme deficiency linked with 2,8-DHA urolithiasis (type I defect), which appears to be the common form of the disorder in Caucasians; (3) partial deficiency with 2,8-DHA urolithiasis (type II defect), so far found only in the Japanese population.

Detection of Mutant Forms of the Enzyme

Enzyme assays in erythrocyte lysates alone will not distinguish among the various mutant forms of the enzyme[21-23] and can be misleading in a transfused patient.[6] Homozygotes and heterozygotes for the two conditions leading to 2,8-DHA lithiasis can be identified by a combination of assays based on: (1) APRT activity in blood cells, cultured lymphocytes, or fibroblasts[1,25,28,31-33]; (2) adenine uptake by intact cells[24,27,34,35]; (3) sensitivity of cultured cells to adenine analogues[22,23,36]; and (4) analysis of urine for adenine and its oxidation products by high performance liquid chromatography (HPLC) and other analytical techniques.[1,37]

Nomenclature of the Mutant Forms

In line with international nomenclature,[38] the normal APRT allele has been designated APRT*1, the mutant allele(s) coding for the complete deficiency APRT*Q0, and the mutant allele coding for the Japanese variant APRT*J.[21] In this nomenclature, the Q0 designation implies a null allele with enzyme quantity of zero. It is understood that Q0 may represent a number of different alleles at a molecular level. Patients with complete APRT deficiency are described as homozygotes for alleles of the APRT*Q0 type, recognizing that these may represent compound heterozygotes and that there may be multiple APRT*Q0 alleles at a molecular level. Those with the Japanese variant are considered to be homozygous for the APRT*J allele,[21,23] although homozygosity is not proven at a molecular level. Again, these designations do not imply that the two alleles in a given genotype are identical at a molecular level. The genetics of these disorders is discussed later. Individuals with the genotype APRT*J/APRT*Q0 have not been identified with certainty.[21]

Partial APRT Deficiency

Partial APRT deficiency was initially identified in Caucasian patients during screening for hypoxanthine-guanine phosphoribosyltransferase (HPRT) deficiency[1,28,39–42] (see Chap. 38). Enzyme activity was approximately 25 percent of normal in hemolysates, but the activity in cultured fibroblasts was normal.[28,40] Decreased enzyme activity was observed in leukocytes from some patients but not others.[28] Initial observations linking partial APRT deficiency with hyperuricemia and gout[39–42] and disturbances in lipid metabolism[40] were not substantiated[1,28,31]; these conditions were considered to be found with equal frequency in family members with normal APRT activity as well as in the general population. However, recent studies have highlighted further cases, with the extremely unusual combination of adolescent gout, affecting young females as well as males, in several families with partial APRT deficiency,[43] suggesting further investigation in kindreds with the latter combination of rare events is warranted.

Type I (APRT*Q0) Deficiency

Detailed studies have now been reported from 12 countries in 32 subjects with complete APRT deficiency (genotype APRT*Q0/APRT*Q0).[1–19,43] This includes 10 patients from Japan, the largest single national group.[25] Five such subjects have so far been asymptomatic.[43] In general, APRT activity in erythrocyte lysates from the above homozygotes has varied from essentially undetectable in some[3,7–9] to extremely low, but measurable, in others.[4,5] This led to the suggestion that the latter group might represent partial enzyme deficiency in comparison with a similar situation in HPRT deficiency.[8] Studies in intact erythrocytes from these patients failed to detect AMP synthesis from adenine under any incubation conditions,[27] confirming homozygosity for the defect and suggesting that intact cells may be a better guide to enzyme competence than cell extracts.[35]

At physiological levels of adenine and phosphate, AMP synthesis in intact erythrocytes from heterozygotes for the type I (APRT*Q0) defect was indistinguishable from that in controls,[27] despite APRT activity of much less than 50 percent of normal in lysed cells.[4,5] The majority of Caucasian heterozygotes have had erythrocyte enzyme levels of about 25 percent of the normal mean.[1,28,40–45] Lymphocytes and fibroblasts from type I homozygotes also lacked APRT activity, and heterozygotes had intermediate levels.[7,27,44,45]

Type II (APRT*J) Deficiency

2,8-DHA urolithiasis associated with partial APRT (type II) deficiency in cell extracts has been found only in Japan so far. These patients are homozygous for the mutant allele APRT*J. Among 41 Japanese cases identified during family studies in kindreds with 2,8-DHA urolithiasis, 31 had partial APRT deficiency.[20–25,46–48] Four of these cases were asymptomatic.[25] Patients with this type of disorder had considerable APRT activity in hemolysates (about 25 percent of normal) and T-cell extracts (about 50 percent of normal).[22,24] They could not therefore be distinguished from heterozygotes for complete APRT deficiency on the basis of lysate enzyme assay alone.[24,48] However, cultured T cells from these patients were resistant to the adenine analogue 6-methylpurine, whose cytotoxicity is dependent on APRT.[21,22] This indicates that, although the enzyme can be detected in cell extracts in APRT*J homozygotes, it is apparently not functional in intact cells, or in vivo. Intact erythrocytes from these patients incorporated only minimal amounts of radioactive adenine,[24] indicating that severe impairment in adenine metabolism in APRT*J homozygotes is shown not only in viable T cells but also in erythrocytes.[21,24]

Distinction Between Mutant Forms of the Enzyme in Heterozygotes

Since cells from heterozygotes for the type I deficiency are sensitive to 6-methylpurine,[22] 6-methylpurine toxicity and adenine uptake can be used to distinguish them from type II homozygotes. Cells from heterozygotes for the type II deficiency are also sensitive to 6-methylpurine and have variable levels of APRT activity, ranging from 25 to 100 percent of normal.[21,25] Type II heterozygotes cannot, therefore, be distinguished from type I heterozygotes by enzyme assay, adenine uptake, or analogue resistance.[21,22,24,25] A distinction between the groups can, however, be made by exposing transformed B-cell lines to 2,6-diaminopurine following treatment with the mutagen *N*-methyl-*N'*-nitro-*N*-nitrosoguanidine (nitrosoguanidine) to inactivate the normal APRT allele.[23] Cell extracts of clones growing in diaminopurine from type I heterozygotes had no detectable APRT activity, whereas clones from type II heterozygotes had significant enzyme activity.[23]

PROPERTIES OF THE NORMAL ENZYME

APRT catalyzes the formation of 5'-AMP (adenylic acid) and pyrophosphate (PP_i) from adenine and PP-ribose-P. Since AMP can also be formed by the *de novo* pathway (Fig. 39-1), APRT is generally referred to as a salvage enzyme. In humans and higher animals, APRT appears to provide the only mechanism by which free adenine can be converted to the nucleotide form. In some prokaryotes and lower eukaryotes, adenine can be deaminated to hypoxanthine by adenine aminohydrolase,[49] which can then enter the nucleotide pool via HPRT. The properties of APRT from human and other mammalian sources have been reviewed.[50–54]

Assay Methods and Stability. A wide variety of methods have been used to assay APRT in cell extracts. The majority of procedures employ radioactive adenine and differ from one another only in the way substrate and product are separated.[32,55–57] Methods based on HPLC have also been used.[58–60] APRT activity is relatively stable in crude extracts, but it declines quite rapidly in more purified preparations. This can be prevented to some extent by the addition of Mg^{2+} and PP-ribose-P to the enzyme preparation.[57] PP-ribose-P also protects against enzyme inactivation by sonication during cell disruption, as well as during freezing and thawing.[61] The enzyme is extremely heat labile, losing up to 56 percent of activity after 4 min at 56°C.[62] PP-ribose-P, but not adenine, has a protecting effect against thermal inactivation.[62,63] PP-ribose-P might stabilize APRT by inducing a conformational change in the enzyme.

Tissue Distribution. APRT is widely distributed in humans, and studies of its activity in different tissues have generally been undertaken as a supplement to HPRT analyses.[64] APRT activity in erythrocyte lysates from the vast majority of subjects is in the range 16 to 32 nmol/h per milligram of hemoglobin (or protein).[1] This is about one-third of the corresponding HPRT activity.[29] Both enzyme activities are of the same order of magnitude in leukocytes, platelets, and fibroblasts.[28,65–67] The highest APRT activity is found in liver where it exceeds HPRT activity threefold.[64] It is also in similar excess over HPRT in muscle, but here both activities are extremely low. APRT activity in brain is about one-tenth that of HPRT.[64]

It is generally assumed that APRT is a soluble, cytoplasmic enzyme,[57] but studies with membrane vesicles from erythrocytes[68] and lymphocytes[69] suggest that, at least in these cell types, a small proportion of the enzyme activity might be loosely bound to the cell membrane. Some of the HPRT and PP-ribose-P synthetase activity from lymphocytes may also be membrane associated.[69]

Kinetic and Electrophoretic Properties. The K_m for adenine for the human erythrocyte enzyme is in the range 1.1 to 2.7 μM.[28,39,50,70] The K_m for PP-ribose-P is Mg^{2+} dependent and is in the range 6 to 29 μM.[28,39,50,70] Mg^{2+} is the most effective cofactor, but activity is also observed with some other divalent cations.[71] The enzyme also shows a burst of activity at 0°C in the absence of Mg^{2+} [57] and has maximal activity over the pH range 7.4 to 9.5,[57,70] but is rapidly inactivated at pH values below 5.[51] The equilibrium constant for the reaction for the Erlich ascites tumor enzyme favors AMP synthesis, but reversibility of the reaction has been demonstrated. The APRT reaction mechanism has not been investigated in detail, but the available evidence suggests that AMP formation proceeds as an ordered sequential reaction.[71,72]

APRT is strongly inhibited by both products of the reaction (Fig. 39-1), inhibition by AMP being competitive with respect to PP-ribose-P and noncompetitive with respect to adenine.[71] K_i values of 7.5 to 30.0 μM for AMP have been reported for the Erlich tumor enzyme.[71] Inhibition by PP_i is noncompetitive with respect to both substrates.[71,72] K_i for PP_i for the tumor enzyme was 0.5 mM.[52] In addition to AMP, APRT from several sources is also inhibited by other mono-, di-, and triphosphates, with GMP being the most effective.[52,73] This nonspecific inhibition is in contrast to HPRT, for which AMP is not an inhibitor.[74] Low concentrations of ATP (250 μM) have been reported to stimulate the Erlich tumor enzyme, whereas higher concentrations were inhibitory.[75] The erythrocyte enzyme was inhibited by Hg^{2+}, *p*-chloromercurobenzoate, and iodoacetate,[71] but the latter two reagents had no effect on the monkey liver enzyme.[76] Sulfhydryl reducing agents such as dithiothreitol also had no effect on the monkey enzyme.[76]

APRT from human tissues migrates as a single band in starch or polyacrylamide gels, but electrophoretic variants have been observed.[28,77,78] Under identical electrophoretic conditions, human APRT migrates faster than HPRT.[77] The human enzyme also migrates faster than the monkey and mouse enzymes but slower than the hamster enzyme.[77,78] The isoelectric point of the human erythrocyte enzyme is 4.8.[57]

Amino Acid Sequence. APRT from human erythrocytes has been purified to near homogeneity (22,000- to 55,000-fold purification with 9 to 25 percent recovery) by a combination of ion-exchange and affinity chromatography.[34,52,79] The placental enzyme has also been purified about 8000-fold with a recovery of 15 percent.[80] The amino acid sequence of the erythrocyte enzyme has been determined.[81] The N-terminal amino acid is not methionine but acetylated alanine. The enzyme is a dimer with 179 amino acid residues per subunit. The calculated subunit molecular weight is 19,481. The amino acid sequence and the molecular weight are in agreement with that predicted from the cDNA nucleotide sequence.[82] Earlier chromatographic studies showed that the enzyme was a dimer of apparently identical subunits with a molecular weight of about 18,000.[1]

Role of APRT in Adenine Transport

Adenine penetrates human and other mammalian cells rapidly, but it is not clear whether APRT is involved in this process (for review, see Refs. 83 to 86). Some studies have suggested that uptake of adenine and other purine bases occurs by active transport involving phosphoribosyltransferases.[87,88] The presence of low levels of membrane-bound APRT activity (see "Tissue Distribution," above) has been cited as evidence for this.[68,69] Other studies have indicated that adenine enters the cell by facilitated diffusion and is subsequently phosphoribosylated by APRT.[89–93] Still other studies were unable to distinguish between these two possibilities.[34,91] Evidence based on kinetics, inhibitors of transport and of APRT, and mutants with partial and complete APRT deficiency strongly suggest that adenine is transported as the free base and is subsequently metabolized by APRT.[84–86,90,91] Evidence from Novikoff hepatoma cells suggests the transport system for adenine is different from that for hypoxanthine and guanine.[89]

Adenine Analogues as Substrates for APRT

In addition to adenine, many adenine analogues are substrates for APRT. Adenine, however, has a much higher affinity for APRT than any of the analogues,[76] which include 4-amin-5-imidazolecarboxamide, 4-aminopyrazolo(3,4-*d*)pyrimidine (pyrazoloadenine), 8-azaadenine, 4-carbamoylimidazolium-5-

olate, 2,6-diaminopurine, 2-fluoroadenine, 6-methylaminopurine, and 6-methylpurine.[57,76,93,94] Once converted into nucleotides, these analogues are often toxic to cells. Analogue metabolites may also inhibit other enzymes of purine metabolism, as in the inhibition of IMP dehydrogenase by the nucleotide of 4-carbamoylimidazolium-5-olate.[95]

Diaminopurine and azaadenine are the most widely used analogues for selecting resistant cells.[36,54] Cells resistant to one analogue are usually cross-resistant to the others. Cells resistant to the toxic effects of adenine analogues are generally defective in APRT activity. However, some diaminopurine-resistant mouse lymphoma cells have been shown to have normal APRT activity.[96] Also, mouse teratocarcinoma cells, resistant to diaminopurine and lacking APRT activity, have been reported to incorporate adenine into the nucleotide pool.[97] These observations suggest the presence of modified forms of the enzyme, or other pathways for adenine metabolism, and need to be substantiated.

PROPERTIES OF THE MUTANT ENZYMES

Partial APRT Deficiency

Studies of the mutant enzyme in heterozygotes with the type I defect showed normal physicochemical characteristics.[1,28,40] However, an unusually high degree of heat stability[50] and minor differences in the isoelectric pattern[28] have been observed. Studies with intact cells showed normal sensitivity of cultured fibroblasts to 8-azaadenine and almost normal incorporation of adenine into nucleotides.[28] The half-life of circulating erythrocytes was also generally normal.[28] Reports of an abnormally short half-life in some heterozygotes[28] may be due to abnormal degradation of APRT in the erythrocyte aging process.[98] These observations suggest that the mutant allele does not give rise to a significantly altered active protein, although minor structural differences may be present in some individuals.[28,50]

Type 1 (APRT*Q0) Deficiency

Detailed immunochemical and electrophoretic analyses of APRT have been carried out in hemolysates from 30 patients (four homozygotes and 26 heterozygotes) in six unreleated families with the APRT*Q0 (type I) defect.[44] APRT activity and immunoreactive protein in homozygotes was less than 1 percent of control values. APRT activity in the heterozygotes was approximately 25 percent of normal, but the level of immunoreactive protein ranged from 22 percent to normal. The enzyme from all heterozygotes had the same isoelectric point except in one patient who had both the normal and a more acidic form of the enzyme. In another study, no cross-reacting material was found in the erythrocytes of an APRT-deficient child.[34] APRT activity and immunoreactive protein have also been characterized in erythrocytes and lymphoblastoid cell lines in 18 subjects from another family with the APRT*Q0 deficiency.[45] Levels of APRT activity and immunoreactive protein in the two homozygotes were again less than 1 percent of normal. The mean APRT activity in hemolysates from 10 heterozygotes was 28 percent of normal and the mean cross-reacting material 34 percent of normal. Corresponding values in lymphoblasts were 46 and 41 percent of normal, respectively. The above studies suggest that in the homozygotes for the type I defect, either very little enzyme is synthesized, or it is degraded very rapidly. These data provide evidence for a variety of mutations in the structural gene for APRT, in agreement with earlier suggestions in presumptive heterozygotes.[28]

As mentioned above, the specific activity of APRT in hemolysates from the APRT*Q0 heterozygotes is generally about 25 percent of normal rather than the more usual 50 percent. A model has been proposed to account for this[44] based on the assumptions that the native APRT dimer can be formed by the random aggregation of monomer subunits and that the normal-mutant (hybrid) dimer is either inactive or unstable in vivo. The three dimer combinations (normal-normal, normal-mutant, mutant-mutant) would be formed in the ratio 1:2:1. If only the normal-normal dimer is active, this would account for the 25 percent of normal activity observed in heterozygotes.[44] However, the above model is not in accord with the observation that APRT activity in lymphoblasts from heterozygotes is approximately 50 percent of normal, unless it is assumed that the hybrid dimer is more stable in lymphoblasts than in erythrocytes.[45] Alternatively, the expression of the normal allele might be increased in lymphoblasts, while either the mutant allele is not expressed or its product is labile.[45]

Type II (APRT*J) Deficiency

APRT from homozygotes for the APRT*J (type II) deficiency had reduced affinity for PP-ribose-P compared with the normal enzyme, but the affinity for adenine was unchanged.[21,46] The mutant enzyme showed sigmoidal rather than hyperbolic kinetics with respect to PP-ribose-P. The Hill coefficient for the mutant enzyme from the four families studied was close to 2 compared with 1 for the normal enzyme. The $S_{0.5}$ value for PP-ribose-P for the normal enzyme was 2.9 μM, but it was in the 47 to 82 μM range for the mutant enzyme.[21,46] Partially purified mutant enzyme from the four families was more heat stable than the normal enzyme in the absence of PP-ribose-P, but more heat labile in the presence of PP-ribose-P. PP-ribose-P stabilized the normal enzyme against heat inactivation, but the mutant enzyme was insensitive to stabilization.[21,46] Normal and mutant enzymes were equally inhibited by the product AMP. Immunochemical characterization of the type II mutant enzyme has not been reported.

APRT ACTIVITY IN OTHER DISORDERS

Erythrocyte APRT activity is elevated in most patients with partial as well as complete HPRT deficiency.[29] Increased APRT activity is found in HPRT-deficient hemolysates even after dialysis.[62] The intracellular concentration of PP-ribose-P is also raised in these disorders. Increased APRT activity has also been found in brain and liver,[64] but not in cultured fibroblasts.[99] It has been proposed that the increased levels of PP-ribose-P in HPRT deficiency stabilize APRT in vivo and that this leads to a diminished rate of degradation of the enzyme and an increased specific activity.[63] However, one kindred with partial HPRT deficiency was found to have normal erythrocyte APRT and PP-ribose-P levels.[100]

APRT activity and PP-ribose-P levels are also increased in erythrocytes in purine nucleoside phosphorylase (PNP) deficiency,[101,102] but PP-ribose-P levels are normal in fibroblasts.[101] Erythrocyte APRT activity is also raised in hereditary orotic aciduria, but PP-ribose-P levels are normal in this disorder.[103,104] The raised APRT levels in hereditary orotic aciduria have been related to increased synthesis rather than diminished degradation.[105] These apparent contradictions suggest that explanations other than PP-ribose-P stabilization should be sought for the raised erythrocyte APRT activity in HPRT and PNP deficiency.

The description of Lesch-Nyhan families with partial deficiency of both APRT and HPRT, but with normal PP-ribose-P levels,[106] also cannot be explained by the above hypothesis. Elevated erythrocyte APRT levels have been noted in newborns,[107] in patients with megaloblastic anemia and reticulocytosis,[108] and in renal failure[109] confirming the general pattern of increased enzyme activity in young erythrocytes. HPRT and PNP activities are within the normal range for homozygotes and heterozygotes for APRT deficiency.[1]

An increase in APRT activity has been observed in partial trisomy of chromosome 16q22.2→qter.[110] The increased activity might be a reflection of increased gene dosage, as has been suggested.[111] APRT activity was increased twofold in human colorectal carcinoma cells compared with that in normal colon mucosa,[112] but it was low or absent in lymphocytes and fibroblasts from Bloom syndrome.[113]

GENETICS OF APRT DEFICIENCY

Mode of Inheritance

Family studies in patients with partial APRT deficiency originally suggested that the inheritance of APRT deficiency was autosomal recessive and that the patients were heterozygous for the defect.[28,31,39–42] Extensive studies in one large kindred (Fig. 39-2) containing two homozygotes and 17 heterozygotes for type I APRT deficiency have confirmed the autosomal mode of inheritance for this defect.[114] Studies in a second large kindred[115] and the immediate family members of other homozygotes with this deficiency also supported this mode of inheritance.[1] The inheritance pattern of both types of APRT deficiency in 2,8-DHA stone formers in Japan—the complete (type I) form and the partial (type II) form—is also autosomal recessive.[25,46]

The majority of patients homozygous for type I APRT deficiency have been Caucasian, including an Arab[5] and an Asian family (unpublished), but the finding of the defect in some Japanese families suggests that it is not restricted to certain ethnic groups. Consanguinity has been observed in the families of two homozygous individuals.[5,20] As mentioned above, in the Caucasian population the genotype APRT*Q0/APRT*Q0 is associated with urolithiasis, whereas in the Japanese population two genotypes are associated with urolithiasis, APRT*Q0/APRT*Q0 and APRT*J/APRT*J.[21] The frequency of the type II defect in Japan is approximately the same as that of the type I deficiency.[25]

It is likely that the APRT*J allele represents a single mutational event, even though Japanese patients with this disorder come from three different islands far removed from each other.[21,23] It is well established that families with a deficiency of the related enzyme, HPRT, carry different mutations.[116] It is not clear why the mutant allele APRT*J is found only in Japan and is a relatively common form of the disorder in this population. The allele frequency may simply be the result of genetic drift or a founder effect in the ancestral population of Japan, since the mutation is only slightly deleterious.[21] The defect in one Caucasian kindred[114] has been traced back to at least the early 1800s (Fig. 39-2), but similar studies do not yet exist in the Japanese families.

Fig. 39-2 Pedigree of patient 1[1,4] and his asymptomatic sib showing the recessive mode of inheritance and the high penetrance also noted in the kindred of other homozygotes, and the absence of any other heterozygote in the father's kindred, suggesting a spontaneous mutation. The numbers refer to the level of APRT activity in lysed erythrocytes for the heterozygotes. The high proportion of members with enzyme levels approximately 25 percent of the control mean (24.4 ± 4.8 nmol/h per milligram of hemoglobin) was also a feature in other kindreds.

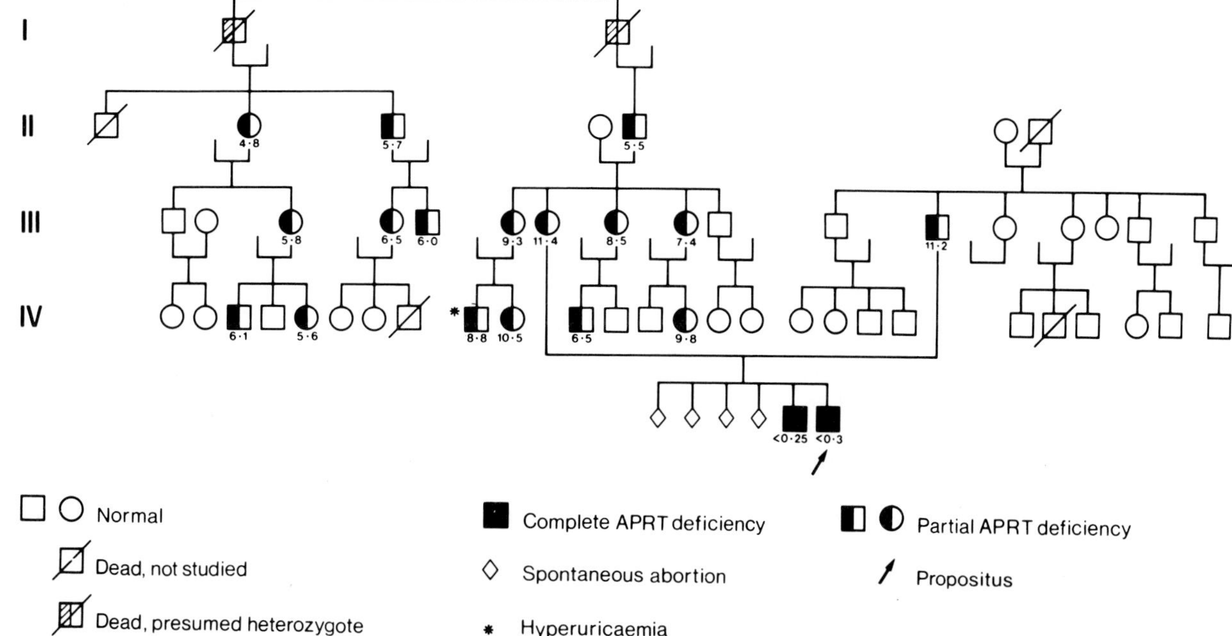

Frequency of Heterozygosity

The frequency of heterozygosity for APRT deficiency in different Caucasian populations has been estimated to be 0.4 to 1.1 percent.[17,28,39,42,43,109,117] This is a relatively high frequency and is in accord with the abnormally high rate of mutation at the APRT locus in cultured mammalian cells.[54] Studies with Chinese hamster ovary cells suggest that the high mutation frequency may be due to a deletion of one of the alleles and a possible mutational hot spot in the other.[118]

The frequency of heterozygosity given above would suggest homozygosity for the genotype APRT*Q0/APRT*Q0 of the order of 1 in 250,000 to 1 in 33,000. This is of similar incidence to some of the common autosomal recessive disorders. It is surprising, therefore, that complete APRT deficiency as a disease entity was recognized only just over 10 years ago. The potentially lethal nature of the defect when unrecognized or misdiagnosed as in some homozygotes,[6,8,23] the asymptomatic status in other homozygotes, and the difficulties of diagnosis may have contributed to lack of adequate recognition in the past.[1,25,114] The possibility that death may occur in utero is supported by the four spontaneous abortions (Fig. 39-2) in family 2.[1,4] Future awareness should allow determination of the real prevalence of homozygosity in the Caucasian population and establish whether the defect is more frequent than its recent description suggests. However, only one 2,8-DHA stone was identified in two European studies, each involving detailed analysis of over 1000 stones,[1] which would tend to exclude inaccurate diagnosis as the reason for the lower numbers of 2,8-DHA stone formers identified compared with Japan.[25]

THE APRT GENE

The gene for human APRT has been mapped to the long arm of chromosome 16.[119,120] More recently, the gene has been localized to position 16q24.[132] This location is distal to the haptoglobin gene (HP) and the fragile site at 16q23.2 (FRA16D), making the gene order HP-FRA16D-APRT-qter.[121]

The human APRT gene has been isolated from a genomic λ phage library using cloned hamster and mouse APRT genes as probes.[122,123] The gene was shown to be functional by its ability to transfer human APRT activity to APRT-deficient rodent cells in a phage-mediated transfection assay. Digestion of the recombinant phage with restriction enzymes generated a number of fragments, but only a 2.8-kb *BglII-ClaI* fragment had transfecting activity.[124] A 2.2-kb *BamHI* fragment, located within the 2.8-kb fragment, has been used as a probe to isolate APRT cDNA by screening human cDNA libraries.[82] There is a *TaqI* polymorphic site near the middle of the 2.2-kb *BamHI* fragment.[123,124]

Both the genomic and the cDNA regions of the human APRT gene have been sequenced.[82] The gene contains five exons and four introns. The total length of the gene is 2.8 kb, including the 5′ flanking region (0.6 kb) and the 3′ untranslated region (0.2 kb). The cDNA sequence is 0.9 kb long. The amino acid sequence deduced from the cDNA is in full agreement with that obtained from peptide mapping.[81] There is a high degree of homology in the protein coding regions of the human and rodent genes, as well as some homology with the *Escherichia coli* gene.[125–127] There is no significant similarity in the 5′ flanking, 3′ untranslated, or the intron sequences between the human and the rodent genes.[82,125–127] The introns in the human gene are located at the same positions as in the rodent genes, although they vary somewhat in size.

The human gene contains five GC-rich boxes in the promoter region, and the mouse gene contains three such boxes.[82,125] These boxes probably are the binding sites for Spl and other transcriptional factors that facilitate the binding of RNA polymerase to DNA.[128] A striking feature of the human and mouse genes is the way CpG dinucleotides are distributed within the gene. Although the mammalian genome is about 40 percent G + C, the frequency of occurrence of these dinucleotides is lower than expected and is nonrandom.[82] In the human and mouse genes these dinucleotides are overrepresented at the 5′ end, but are underrepresented at the 3′ end.[82] By comparison the distribution of GpC dinucleotides is relatively constant over the length of both genes.[82] The function of these dinucleotides is not fully understood, but they may be involved in transcriptional regulation of the gene.[129] Like some other housekeeping genes, the promoter region of the human APRT gene lacks TATA and CCAAT sequences.[82,130]

MOLECULAR ANALYSIS OF APRT DEFICIENCY

The availability of the cloned gene and the polymorphism associated with it should prove valuable for molecular analysis of APRT deficiency, but studies of this nature have not been carried out so far. Preliminary analysis of DNA from two APRT-deficient brothers (patients 1 and 2, previous edition of this text[1]) and an unrelated heterozygote did not reveal any gross deletions or insertions as being responsible for the mutant phenotype.[123] The pattern of *TaqI* digestion of DNA from these patients was also similar to that from normal subjects.[123] More recently, *TaqI* polymorphism has been observed in a Japanese patient who is homozygous for the mutant allele APRT*J.[131] Studies on restriction enzyme and nucleotide sequence analysis of DNA from several other APRT-deficient patients are in progress.[132,133]

NEPHROTOXICITY AND STONE FORMATION

The nephrotoxicity of 2,8-DHA is due to its insolubility at any pH. Solubility in water at pH 6.5 is 1.53 ± 0.04 mg/liter (approximately 9×10^{-6}M).[134] Unlike uric acid, a significant increase in solubility does not occur within the physiological pH range for human urine.[1] Human urine at 37°C appears to exhibit enhanced capacity for solubilizing 2,8-DHA. Solubility in vitro is 2.68 ± 0.84 mg/liter at pH 5.0 and 4.97 ± 1.49 mg/liter at pH 7.8.[134] 2,8-DHA may remain supersaturated in urine in vitro at levels of 40.38 ± 3.33 mg/liter for 16 h, while levels as high as 96 mg/liter have been noted in vivo in patients receiving oral adenine.[134] Levels up to 80 mg/liter have been noted in a growing asymptomatic homozygote,[17] confirming supersaturation in vivo of 2,8-DHA in APRT deficiency. Varying ability to supersaturate the urine may thus explain the existence of affected and asymptomatic sibs in several families.[4,7,25] The apparent lack of 2,8-DHA toxicity to other tissues in vivo may be related to the high degree of protein binding[135] coupled with the active secretion of 2,8-DHA by the human kidney[136]; 92 percent of a high dose of [^{14}C]2,8-DHA was recovered in the urine of rats 24 h after IV injection. High retention with very high specific activity was found only in the kidney,[137] confirming this hypothesis.

The nephrotoxicity of 2,8-DHA was first noted, as early as 1898, during the feeding of adenine to animals.[138] Nephrotoxicity of 2,8-DHA has been demonstrated in most mammalian species, the severity varying with the route and length of time of adenine administration and with the species.[139–144] The threshold varies, the pig tolerating the highest doses.[139] In all species little 2,8-DHA was formed at doses below 10 mg/kg.[139–142] With increasing dosage, insoluble yellowish spheres of 2,8-DHA appeared in the urine with crystals in tubular lumens.[138–143] Higher doses and longer periods produced extensive deposits not only within tubules, but also within the interstitium, with progressive renal failure and death.[140–143] Renal pathology in these animal studies corresponded closely with the findings in patient 5[1,6] (Fig. 39-3) and confirmed acute intratubular crystal deposition as the primary event in this nephropathy.[145]

Adenine and Red Cell Preservation

Much of the work in this field has been related to the investigation of the potential toxicity of blood to which adenine has been added to prolong its shelf life from 3 to 5 weeks,[145,146] a practice which commenced in Sweden and the western United States and is now quite common.[147] Administration of adenine equivalent to 10 to 15 mg/kg apparently does not produce 2,8-DHA crystals in normal humans.[146–150] A fatal instance occurred in a patient receiving a massive dose (equivalent to 150 mg/kg) who developed impaired renal function. Intratubular birefringent rosette-shaped crystals were found at autopsy.[148] Although 10 to 15 mg/kg is considered nontoxic,[146–151] the possibility that toxicity could occur in some heterozygotes for APRT deficiency should be considered, particularly in view of the possibly high frequency of the defect in the population.

In Vitro Toxicity of Adenine

Many studies relating to the in vitro toxicity of adenine have been carried out. Toxicity, as measured by inhibition of cell growth (using various parameters—cell number, protein content, thymidine uptake, etc.), has been observed in human fibroblasts, lymphocytes, and cervical carcinoma cells, as well as cell types from other mammalian species (reviewed in Ref. 152). A number of studies have compared adenine toxicity in parental cell lines and in strains resistant to adenine analogues. Despite resistance to 2,6-diaminopurine, an APRT mutant of the WI-L2 human lymphoblast line with <1 percent of APRT activity was sensitive to the toxic effects of adenine.[153] Similar results were reported for diaminopurine-resistant mouse L cells,[154] suggesting that adenine itself, in the absence of APRT, is toxic to cells. Since most cell types used lacked xanthine oxidase activity, adenine oxidation products were unlikely to be responsible for the observed toxicity. One study suggested that adenine may be inhibitory to lymphocyte-mediated cytolysis through elevation of *S*-adenosylhomocysteine levels.[155]

Adenine Toxicity in Vivo

Recent studies in mice showed that adenine was immunosuppressive in both the plaque assay and skin allograft models.[156] Since this effect could also be induced by 2-hydroxyadenine (2-HA) and abrogated by allopurinol, it was considered that 2-HA could contribute to the immunosuppressive activity.[156] However, the normal clinical and immunologic status of two homozygous sibs,[4] despite 12 years of allopurinol therapy[17,43] in the younger brother (in whom adenine accumulation could occur), must argue against significant adenine toxicity in vivo. Presumably rapid excretion by an active kidney secretory

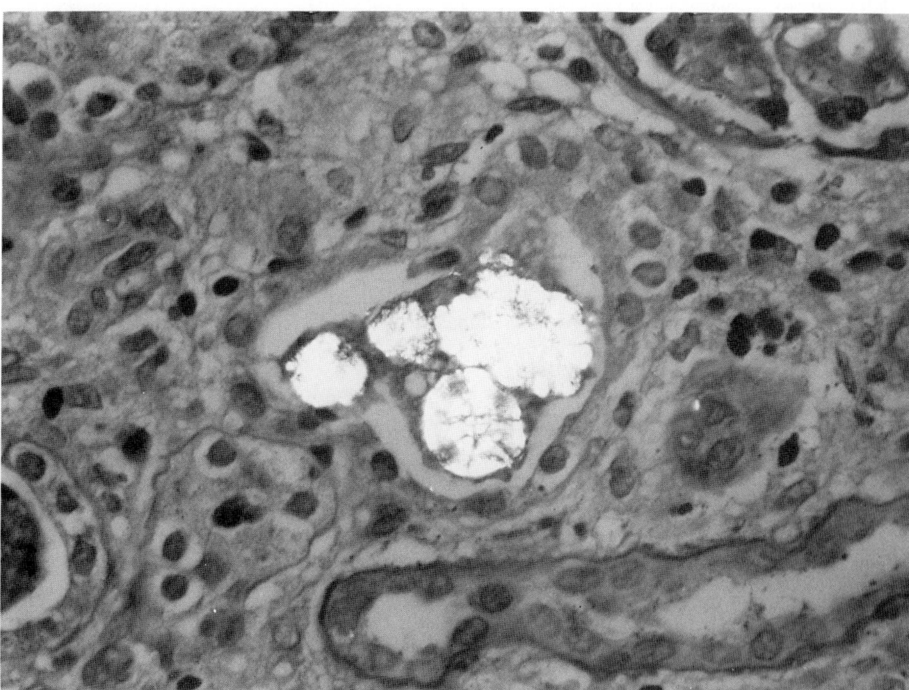

Fig. 39-3 Photomicrograph of renal biopsy ×800 (original magnification) from patient 3,[1,6] stained by periodic acid-Schiff technique and photographed in semipolarized light. Several large crystals are seen within the lumen of a distended, atrophied, cortical tubule (center). There is greatly increased interstitial connective tissue with lymphocytes; within this tissue is a reactive multinucleate giant cell (right) which has formed around a further small crystal. *(Courtesy of JR Pincott, M.D., FRC Path.)*

mechanism[136] ensures that circulating adenine levels are low. The absence of detectable 2-HA in humans suggests the existence of species differences in the metabolism of adenine, as well as in the distribution of xanthine oxidase.[157] Repeated follow-up studies in a homozygote on allopurinol, originally presenting with severe renal damage and eventually requiring dialysis and transplantation,[158] have not shown evidence of any long-term toxicity or immunodeficiency, although there have been several presentations in coma.[6]

ADENINE METABOLISM IN HUMANS

Adenine Metabolism and the Regulation of Purine Production in Humans

Studies with [^{14}C]adenine have contributed to our understanding of adenine metabolism in animals and humans.[135,137,144,159–161] In one study in the rabbit[159] less than 10 percent of the label was incorporated into nucleic acids, but extensive incorporation into the soluble nucleotides occurred, predominantly in the kidney and small intestine, with little in the brain or skeletal muscle. Large amounts of free adenine and hypoxanthine were excreted within 24 h in the urine, the former with the same specific activity. Thus the body pools of adenine must normally be very small. A slow subsequent rate of isotope elimination reflected the incorporation and turnover of body mononucleotide pools. Similar results have been found in humans.[150]

Earlier isotope studies have shown an identical pattern and have demonstrated inhibition of *de novo* purine synthesis by adenine in normal and gouty humans.[160,161] This reduced purine synthesis did not result in diminished uric acid excretion. This was explained in part by a prompt conversion of adenine to uric acid.[160] The clinical use of adenine in the Lesch-Nyhan syndrome has been based on the assumption, derived from such experiments, that adenine causes feedback inhibition of purine synthesis.[161] Adenine therapy has proved generally ineffective in the Lesch-Nyhan syndrome[162–166] and has actually precipitated 2,8-DHA nephropathy in spite of simultaneous allopurinol therapy.[165,166] Other studies have demonstrated that adenine-induced reduction in *de novo* synthesis is a transitory phenomenon, due to diminution in the pool of available PP-ribose-P.[167] This is in accord with other data and with the general ineffectiveness of therapy.[163] Furthermore, a loading test for the diagnosis of latent hyperuricemia in patients who form oxalate stones, based on the rapid catabolism of approximately 1 g of adenine and guanine to uric acid, is further proof that adenine will increase uric acid levels rather than correct them.[168] This practice is equally dangerous, with its real risk of nephrotoxicity.

Origin of the Adenine in APRT Deficiency

The ubiquitous distribution of the APRT enzyme in human tissue had long been puzzling in view of extremely low adenine levels in blood (1.13 ± 0.41 μM; 0.64 ± 0.15 μM; 0.07 μM[149,169,170]) and almost undetectable levels,[1,171] or less than 1.5 mg (11 μmol) per 24 h, in the urine of normal humans.[169,172] The finding that homozygotes for APRT deficiency eliminated up to 100 mg (740 μmol) of adenine and its oxidation products per 24 h[1] was thus of particular interest, since pathways for adenine production involving purine metabolism appeared to be lacking in humans (Fig. 39-1).

Adenosine Phosphorylase. Unlike hypoxanthine and guanine, no significant pathway for the formation of adenine from adenosine (or vice versa) via PNP has been demonstrated in mammalian cells[27,173,174] as distinct from bacterial and other cells.[49,175] The high activity of APRT in normal cells had made it difficult to study this point. Studies in intact cells from APRT-deficient homozygotes (forming an effective adenine trap) have thus been extremely useful and have confirmed the insignificance of this pathway in either direction in humans.[27] Some activity of adenosine phosphorylase was demonstrated in one study in APRT-deficient erythrocyte lysates, but the measurement required high and unphysiological substrate levels, which are unlikely to be of importance in vivo.[7]

The original description of adenine (and traces of 2,8-DHA) excretion in ADA deficiency[170] suggested significance for this pathway in vivo. The adenine was subsequently shown in reality to be deoxyadenosine degraded in the cationic systems used.[171] Studies with ADA-deficient intact erythrocytes have also failed to demonstrate any significant PNP activity with adenine or adenosine as substrate.[176]

Dietary Sources of Adenine. The alternative possibility that the adenine metabolites excreted in the urine in APRT deficiency were derived from the diet was excluded when detailed studies of the effect of dietary purine restriction demonstrated only a slight reduction in total.[1] This suggested an endogenous origin for most of the adenine compounds excreted. Nevertheless, diet is probably an important precipitating factor in the most severe clinical expression of the defect, as indicated by the acute renal failure and permanent renal damage in a child[6] fed a diet rich in adenine-containing compounds.[177]

Polyamine Pathway and Endogenous Adenine

The polyamine pathway, of which adenine is a metabolic by-product (Fig. 39-1), now appears to be the main source of endogenous adenine in humans (reviewed in Refs. 1 and 178). Recent studies have demonstrated the production in vitro of adenine from 5′-methylthioadenosine through the action of 5′-methylthioadenosine phosphorylase in human cells.[179,180] This enzyme, which has an absolute requirement for phosphate, catalyzes the last step of this pathway and has been found in different mammalian tissues,[178] including lymphocytes. The erythrocyte enzyme has a specific activity in the range 6 to 14 nmol/h per milligram of hemoglobin.[179] Further support for the production of adenine via this route in vivo comes from in vitro studies in cells deficient in 5′-methylthioadenosine where no conversion of 5′-methylthioadenosine to adenine or adenine nucleotides could be demonstrated compared with control cells.[179,180]

The polyamine pathway is active in dividing and regenerating tissue.[178] The level of adenine metabolites excreted by homozygotes would be consistent with the normal activity of this pathway.[1] Detailed studies over 12 years in two homozygotes have shown a remarkable constancy in the daily excretion of adenine metabolites as a percentage of the total daily purine excretion (20 to 30 percent). Both tend to parallel the increase in body weight, which would support the polyamine pathway as the source of endogenous adenine.[43]

DIAGNOSIS OF 2,8-DHA LITHIASIS

Homozygotes for the type I or type II defect can be identified by the characteristic yellow-brown, round, urinary crystals of 2,8-DHA, which resemble leucine crystals (Fig. 39-4). 2,8-DHA is an analogue of uric acid, indistinguishable from it in routine chemical testing.[1] It reacts mole for mole as uric acid in colorimetric analysis (phosphomolybdate and murexide tests). The two compounds may also be confused, if only the alkaline ultraviolet spectrum is examined or when stone material is analyzed by thermogravimetric analysis. Both stones are radiolucent.[1] These factors have been responsible for the earlier and frequent misdiagnosis of the stones as "uric acid" stones.[1]

Simple guidelines for correct stone identification include the macroscopic appearance of the stones. 2,8-DHA stones are whitish to pale gray, rough, and friable, in contrast to uric acid stones which are generally yellowish, smooth, hard, and difficult to crush. 2,8-DHA is resistant to the action of uricase[3,17] and will also be separated in the acid, but not the alkaline, fraction by a technique employing wet chemistry. Final confirmation may be obtained from infrared spectrometry, mass spectrometry, x-ray crystallography, and the ultraviolet spectrum in both acid and alkali.[1] The diagnosis of uric acid stones should always be suspect, especially in children who are otherwise normal. The stones are generally 95 to 98 percent 2,8-DHA, the remainder being predominantly uric acid.[1,25]

Diagnosis of Asymptomatic Subjects

The finding of the characteristic 2,8-DHA crystals in the urine deposit (Fig. 39-4) is also diagnostic of the defect in asymptomatic homozygotes, as is the excretion of adenine compounds in the urine.[1] Isotachophoresis is superior to HPLC[1,37] in this regard. Coelution problems with methylated xanthine derivatives may lead to a false adenine peak when using HPLC in subjects not on caffeine-free diets.[37] A method for the detection of 2,8-DHA by HPLC has also been published.[181] The estimation of APRT activity in erythrocyte lysates will identify both homozygotes and heterozygotes for APRT deficiency. Intact cell studies will be essential to separate heterozygotes for the type I defect from homozygotes for the type II defect. The defect in the latter cannot be established by any other means. It should again be stressed that false and near-normal results may be obtained if (as in case 5 in the previous edition of this

Fig. 39-4 Microscopy of urinary crystals. *A.* Microcrystals of 2,8-DHA in the freshly passed urine from an asymptomatic homozygote[1,4] collected on a Millipore filter at 37°C and viewed by polarized light. *B.* Round brown crystals in urine of a boy with 2,8-DHA stones.[9] *C.* Scanning electron micrograph of crystals. *(B and C courtesy of J. Joost, M.D., and the publishers of* Urology.*)*

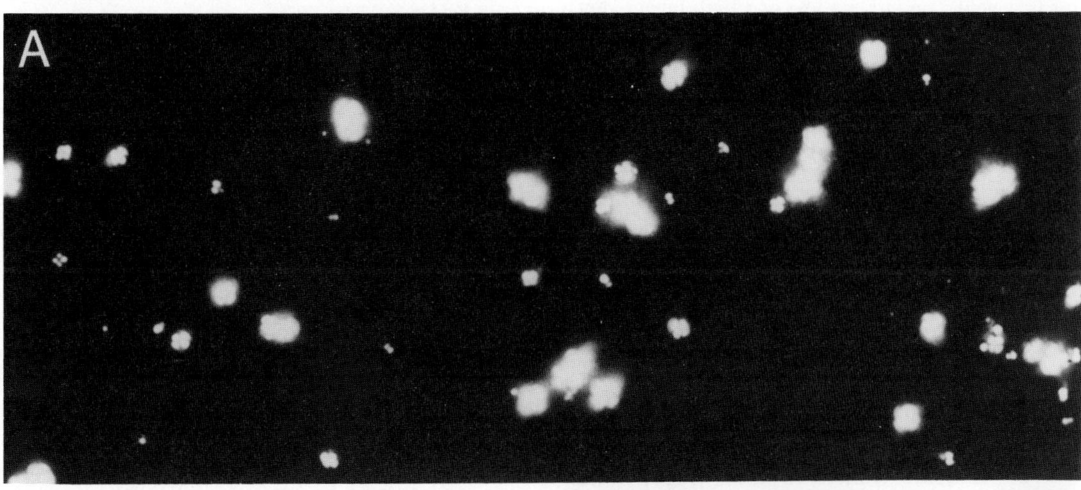

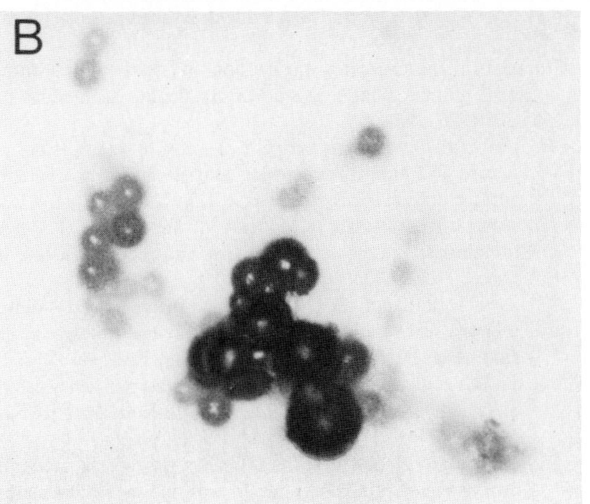

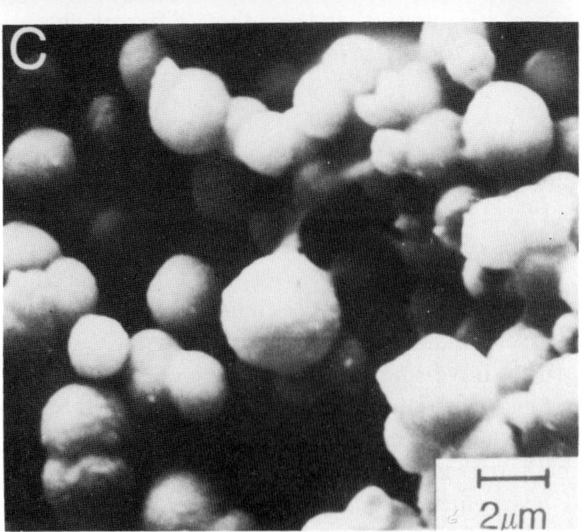

text[1]) the clinical condition on admission has necessitated blood transfusion.[6,23] A simple technique using dried blood spots, which could be of use in screening for the defect, has been reported.[33]

TREATMENT AND PROGNOSIS

Diet. In all homozygotes, particularly those with urolithiasis, a low purine diet is recommended[4] since dietary adenine can contribute to the severity of the clinical manifestation. A child[6] presenting initially in acute renal failure and subsequently in coma on several occasions was from a commune consuming diets rich in lentils and other grain and vegetable extracts, all foods with a reputedly high adenine content.

Therapy. 2,8-DHA formation may be controlled by allopurinol, but some 8-HA is still excreted.[4,6,7,15] Allopurinol therapy has not reduced the total level of adenine compounds excreted by homozygotes (still 20 to 30 percent of total purine excretion),[17,43] but it has rearranged the proportion so that adenine becomes the major urinary component.[4,6,7,15,17] One study also showed that allopurinol was ineffective in reducing the absorption of dietary purine in homozygotes, in contrast to its apparently beneficial effect in this regard in controls.[1] This indicates that dietary purine restriction should always be advised in APRT deficiency. The apparent lack of effect of allopurinol on total oxypurine excretion (xanthine plus hypoxanthine plus uric acid), on either a low or a high purine diet, was questioned in another report,[7] but unfortunately urinary xanthine and hypoxanthine were not measured.

Allopurinol at 10 mg/kg per day has eliminated 2,8-DHA from the urine in most cases.[1] The dose has had to be reduced to 5 mg/kg per day in children (100 mg/day in adults) with permanent renal damage.[6] Where there was evidence of further decline in renal function, the dose has been reduced to 5 mg/kg (100 mg for adults) three times a week.[158] The reason for this is the well-documented retention of oxpurinol (the active metabolite of allopurinol) in renal failure, with the associated risk of bone marrow depression and other undesirable side effects.[182] When possible, plasma oxipurinol levels should be monitored, and dosage adjusted accordingly.[182] A careful watch should be kept on all hematologic factors. A high fluid intake is encouraged, and the use of allopurinol without alkali is advised.[4,9,43] The solubility of 2,8-DHA is not altered within the physiological pH range.[3,7] Indeed, three different observations have suggested that use of alkali may even be contraindicated.[4,5,9]

Prognosis. The prognosis clearly depends on the renal function remaining at the time of diagnosis.[1,6,17,25,43] Two patients with terminal renal failure have had replacement of renal function by transplantation, which was successful in only one of them.[158] Therefore the importance of early diagnosis and treatment must be stressed. The possibility of any long-term adverse effects of xanthine oxidase inhibition, with its attendant potential for increasing circulating adenine levels, particularly where renal function is impaired, appears unlikely. Homozygotes with normal renal function now followed for 9 to 12 years, both treated and untreated, have shown normal growth and development.[43]

ADDENDUM

Initial biochemical studies suggested that a single mutation might be responsible for the type II deficiency.[21,23] More extensive family and molecular genetic studies appear to confirm this.[183,184] Molecular studies of a patient with type I APRT deficiency (the propositus in Fig. 39-4) indicate a three-base deletion in exon 5 leading to removal of a phenylalanine residue in the coding sequence.[185] The other allele contains an insertion of a single nucleotide adjacent to the splice junction at the 5′ end of the fourth intron leading to aberrant splicing and absence of exon 4 in mRNA. Studies of a type II homozygote identified a T to C substitution in exon 5 causing a Met_{136}→Thr missense mutation.[184] This defect was found by RNAse mapping in six other type II homozygotes but not in a Japanese type I homozygote. The mutation is within the putative PP-ribose-P binding region,[126] and may be responsible for the increased K_m for PP-ribose-P in type II deficiency.

REFERENCES

1. SIMMONDS HA, VAN ACKER KJ: Adenine phosphoribosyltransferase deficiency: 2,8-Dihydroxyadenine lithiasis, in Stanbury JB, Wyngaarden JB, Fredrickson DS, Goldstein JL, Brown MS (eds): *The Metabolic Basis of Inherited Disease,* 5th ed. New York, McGraw-Hill, 1983, p 1144.
2. SIMMONDS HA, VAN ACKER KJ, CAMERON JS, SNEDDEN W: The identification of 2,8-dihydroxyadenine, a new component of urinary stones. *Biochem J* 157:485, 1976.
3. DEBRAY H, CARTIER P, TEMSTET A, CENDRON J: Child's urinary lithiasis revealing a complete deficit in adenine phosphoribosyltransferase. *Pediatr Res* 10:762, 1976.
4. VAN ACKER KJ, SIMMONDS HA, POTTER CF, CAMERON JS: Complete deficiency of adenine phosphoribosyltransferase: Report of a family. *N Engl J Med* 297:127, 1977.
5. BARRATT TM, SIMMONDS HA, CAMERON JS, POTTER CF, ROSE GA, ARKELL DG, WILLIAMS DI: Complete deficiency of adenine phosphoribosyltransferase. A third case presenting as renal stones in a young child. *Arch Dis Child* 54:25, 1979.
6. GREENWOOD MC, DILLON MJ, SIMMONDS HA, BARRATT TM, PINCOTT JR, METREWELLI C: Renal failure due to 2,8-dihydroxyadenine urolithiasis. *Eur J Pediatr* 138:346, 1982.
7. CARTIER P, HAMET M, VINCENS A, PERIGNON JL: Complete adenine phosphoribosyltransferase (APRT) deficiency in two siblings: Report of a new case, in Rapado A, Watts RWE, De Bruyn CHMM (eds): *Purine Metabolism in Man.* New York, Plenum, 1980, vol III, 122A, p 343.
8. SCHABEL F, DOPPLER W, HIRSCH-KAUFFMAN M, GLATZL J, SCHWEIGER M, BERGER H, HEINZ-ERIAN P: Hereditary deficiency of adenine phosphoribosyltransferase. *Paediatr Paedol* 15:233, 1980.
9. JOOST J, DOPPLER W: The 2,8-dihydroxyadenine stone in childhood. *Urology* 20:67, 1982.
10. GAULT MH, SIMMONDS HA, SNEDDEN W, DOW D, CHURCHILL DN, PENNEY H: Urolithiasis due to 2,8-dihydroxyadenine in an adult. *N Engl J Med* 305:1570, 1981.
11. OSADA T, INCUE T, HIRANO A, TANAKA K, OGITA Z, ISOBE M, HAYASHI S: A case of 2,8-dihydroxyadenine lithiasis revealing a complete deficit in adenine phosphoribosyltransferase. *Clin Urol (Jpn)* 34:981, 1980.
12. WITTEN FR, MORGAN JE, FOSTER JG, GLENN JF: 2,8-Dihydroxyadenine urolithiasis: Review of the literature and report of a case in the United States. *J Urol* 130:938, 1983.
13. ASPER R, SCHMUCKI O: Diagnostik und therapie der 2,8-dihydroxyadenine lithiasis, in Gasser G, Vahlensieck W (eds): *Pathogenese und Klinik der Harnsteine.* Darmstadt, Steinkopff Verlag, 1982, vol IX, p 274.
14. SZONYI P, BERENI M, TOTH J: A rare enzyme deficiency causing formation of 2,8-dihydroxyadenine (purine body) calculi. *Int Urol Nephrol* 17:231, 1985.
15. CHEVET D, LE POGAMP P, GIE S, GARY J, DAUDON M, HAMET M: 2,8-Dihydroxyadenine (2,8-DHA) urolithiasis in an adult—complete adenine

phosphoribosyltransferase deficiency—family study. *Kidney Int* 26:226, 1984.

16. CHRISTENSEN E, BRANDT NJ, LAXDAL T: Adenine phosphoribosyltransferase deficiency: A case diagnosed by GC-MS identification of 2,8-dihydroxyadenine in urinary crystals. *J Inherited Metab Dis* 10:187, 1987.
17. SIMMONDS HA: 2,8-dihydroxyadenine lithiasis. *Clin Chim Acta* 160:103, 1986.
18. MAMYAK MJ, FRENSILLI FJ, MILLER HC: 2,8-dihydroxyadenine urolithiasis: Report of an adult case in the United States. *J Urol* 137:312, 1987.
19. JUNG P, BOMMERT R, JESBERGER H-J: 2,8-dihydroxyadenine lithiasis: A case with a complete deficiency of adenine phosphoribosyltransferase. *Klin Wochenschr* 65 (*Suppl* X):12, 1987.
20. KURODA M, MIKI T, KIYOHARA H, USAMI M, NAKAMURA T, KOTAKE T, TAKEMOTO M, SONODA T: Urolithiasis composed of 2,8-dihydroxyadenine due to partial deficiency of adenine phosphoribosyltransferase. *Jpn J Urol* 71:283, 1980.
21. FUJIMORI S, AKAOKA I, SAKAMOTO K, YAMANAKA H, NISHIOKA K, KAMATANI N: Common characteristics of mutant adenine phosphoribosyltransferase from four separate Japanese families wtih 2,8-dihydroxyadenine urolithiasis associated with partial enzyme deficiencies. *Hum Genet* 7:171, 1985.
22. KAMATANI N, TAKEUCHI F, NISHIDA Y, YAMANAKA H, NISHIOKA K, TATARA K, FUJIMORI S, KANEKO K, AKAOKA I, TOFUKU Y: Severe impairment in adenine metabolism with a partial deficiency of adenine phosphoribosyltransferase. *Metabolism* 34:164, 1985.
23. KAMATANI N, KUROSHIMA S, TERAI C, KAWAI K, MIKANAGI K, NISHIOKA K: Selection of human cells having two different types of mutations in single cells: Application to the diagnosis of the heterozygous state for a unique type adenine phosphoribosyltransferase deficiency. *Hum Genet* 76:148, 1987.
24. TAKEUCHI F, MATSUTA K, MIYAMOTO T, ENOMOTO S, FUJIMORI S, AKAOKA I, KAMATANI N, NISHIOKA K: Rapid method for the diagnosis of partial adenine phosphoribosyltransferase deficiency causing 2,8-dihydroxyadenine urolithiasis. *Hum Genet* 71:167, 1985.
25. KAMATANI N, TERAI C, KUROSHIMA S, NISHIOKA K, MIKANAGI K: Genetic and clinical studies on 19 families with adenine phosphoribosyltransferase deficiencies. *Hum Genet* 75:163, 1987.
26. WYNGAARDEN JB, DUNN JT: 8-Hydroxyadenine as the metabolic intermediate in the oxidation of adenine to 2,8-dihydroxyadenine by xanthine oxidase. *Arch Biochem Biophys* 70:150, 1957.
27. DEAN BM, PERRETT D, SIMMONDS HA, SAHOTA A, VAN ACKER KJ: Adenine and adenosine metabolism in intact erythrocytes deficient in adenosine monophosphate-pyrophosphate phosphoribosyltransferase: A study of two families. *Clin Sci Mol Med* 55:407, 1978.
28. FOX IH, LA CROIX S, PLANET G, MOORE M: Partial deficiency of adenine phosphoribosyltransferase in man. *Medicine (Baltimore)* 56:515, 1977.
29. KELLEY WN, WYNGAARDEN JB: Clinical syndromes associated with hypoxanthine-guanine phosphoribosyltransferase deficiency, in Stanbury JB, Wyngaarden JB, Fredrickson DS, Goldstein JL, Brown MS (eds): *The Metabolic Basis of Inherited Disease,* 5th ed. New York, McGraw-Hill, 1983, p 1115.
30. STEVENS WJ, PEETERMANS ME, VAN ACKER KJ: Immunological investigation in adenine phosphoribosyltransferase (APRT) deficiency. *Clin Exp Immunol* 36:364, 1979.
31. JOHNSON LA, GORDON RB, EMMERSON BT: Adenine phosphoribosyltransferase: A simple spectrophotometric assay and the incidence of mutation in the normal population. *Biochem Genet* 15:256, 1977.
32. BANHOLZER P, GROBNER W, in Bergmeyer HV (ed): *Methods of Enzymatic Analysis,* 3d ed. Weinheim, Verlag Chemie, 1983, vol 3, p 393.
33. NISHIDA Y, MIYAMOTO T: Simple screening methods for hypoxanthine-guanine phosphoribosyltransferase and adenine phosphoribosyltransferase deficiencies using dried blood spots on filter paper. *Ann Clin Biochem* 23:529, 1986.
34. DOPPLER W, HIRSCH-KAUFFMAN M, SCHABEL F, SCHWEIGER M: Characterization of the biochemical basis of a complete deficiency of the adenine phosphoribosyltransferase (APRT). *Hum Genet* 54:404, 1981.
35. FAIRBANKS LD, SIMMONDS HA, WEBSTER DR. Use of intact erythrocytes in the diagnosis of inherited purine and pyrimidine disorders. *J Inherited Metab Dis* 10:174, 1987.
36. STEGLICH C, DeMARS R: Mutations causing deficiency of APRT in fibroblasts cultured from humans heterozygous for mutant APRT alleles. *Somatic Cell Genet* 8:115, 1982.
37. MORRIS GS, SIMMONDS HA: Use of a fundamental elution protocol for the development of a reverse phase HPLC method enabling rapid simultaneous determination of purines, pyrimidines and allied compounds commonly found in biological fluids. *J Chromatogr* 344:101, 1985.
38. SHOWS TB, ALPER CA, BOOTSMA D: International system for human gene nomenclature. *Cytogenet Cell Genet* 25:96, 1979.
39. KELLEY WN, LEVY RI, ROSENBLOOM FM, HENDERSON JF, SEEGMILLER JE: Adenine phosphoribosyltransferase deficiency—A previously undescribed genetic defect in man. *J Clin Invest* 47:2281, 1968.
40. FOX IH, MEADE JC, KELLEY WN: Adenine phosphoribosyltransferase deficiency in man. Report of a second family. *Am J Med* 55:614, 1973.
41. DELBARRE F, AUSCHER C, AMOR B, DE GERY A, CARTIER P, HAMET M: Gout with adenine phosphoribosyltransferase deficiency. *Biomedicine* 21:82, 1974.
42. EMMERSON BT, GORDON RB, THOMPSON L: Adenine phosphoribosyltransferase deficiency: Its inheritance and occurrence in a female with gout and renal disease. *Aust NZ J Med* 5:440, 1975.
43. SIMMONDS HA: 2,8-dihydroxyadenine lithiasis—Epidemiology, Pathogenesis and Therapy, in *Verhandlungen der deutschen Gesellschaft für innere Medizin,* Munich. JF Bergman Verlag, 1986, vol 92, p 503.
44. WILSON JM, DADDONA PE, SIMMONDS HA, VAN ACKER KJ, KELLER WN: Human adenine phosphoribosyltransferase: Immunochemical quantitation and protein blot analysis of mutant forms of the enzyme. *J Biol Chem* 257:1508, 1982.
45. O'TOOLE TE, WILSON JM, GAULT MH, KELLEY WN: Human adenine phosphoribosyltransferase: Characterisation from subjects with a deficiency of enzyme activity. *Biochem Genet* 21:1121, 1983.
46. FUJIMORI S, AKAOKA I, TAKEUCHI F, KANAYAMA H, TATARA K, NISHIOKA K, KAMATANI N: Altered kinetic properties of a mutant adenine phosphoribosyltransferase. *Metabolism* 35:187, 1986.
47. KAMATANI N: Personal communication, 1987.
48. NOBORI T, YAMANAKA H, KAMATANI N, NISHIOKA K, MIKANAGI K: The prevalence of metabolic disorders in Japan, in Nyhan WL, Thompson LF, Watts RWE (eds): *Purine and Pyrimidine Metabolism in Man.* New York, Plenum, 1986, vol V, 195A, p 35.
49. ZIELKE CL, SUELTER CH: Purine, purine nucleoside, and purine nucleotide aminohydrolases, in Boyer PD (ed): *The Enzymes,* 3d ed. New York, Academic, 1971, vol 5, p 47.
50. HENDERSON JF, MILLER HR, KELLEY WN, ROSENBLOOM FM, SEEGMILLER JE: Kinetic studies of mutant human erythrocyte adenine phosphoribosyltransferase. *Can J Biochem* 46:703, 1968.
51. RAIVIO KO, SEEGMILLER JE: The role of phosphoribosyltransferase in purine metabolism, in Horecker BL, Stadtman ER (eds): *Current Topics in Cellular Regulation.* London, Academic, 1970, p 201.
52. ARNOLD WJ: Purine salvage enzymes, in Kelley WN, Weiner IM (eds): *Uric Acid.* Berlin, Springer-Verlag, 1978, p 61.
53. MUSICK WDL: Structural features of the phosphoribosyltransferases and their relationship to the human deficiency disorders of purine and pyrimidine metabolism. *CRC Crit Rev Biochem* 11:1, 1981.
54. TAYLOR MW, SIMON AE, KOTHARI RM: The APRT system, in Gottesman MM (ed): *Molecular Cell Genetics.* New York, Wiley, 1985, p 311.
55. CARTIER P, HAMET M: Les activités purine-phosphoribosyltransferiques des globules rouges humains. Technique de dosage. *Clin Chim Acta* 20:205, 1968.
56. HOFFEE PA, JONES ME (eds): *Methods in Enzymology.* New York, Academic, 1978, vol 51, p 558.
57. ARNOLD WJ, KELLEY WJ: Adenine phosphoribosyltransferase, in Hoffee PA, Jones ME (eds): *Methods in Enzymology.* New York, Academic, vol 51, 1978, p 568.
58. VASQUEZ B, BIEBER AL: High performance liquid chromatography: A tool for study of enzyme reactions involving purines and purine nucleotides. *Anal Biochem* 79:52, 1977.
59. FAIRBANKS LD, GODAY A, MORRIS GS, BROLSMA MFJ, SIMMONDS HA, GIBSON T: Rapid determination of purine enzyme activity in intact and lysed cells using high performance liquid chromatography with and without radiolabelled substrates. *J Chromatogr* 276:427, 1983.
60. RYLANCE HJ, WALLACE RC, NUKI G: Adenine phosphoribosyltransferase: Assay using high performance liquid chromatography. *Clin Chim Acta* 148:267, 1985.
61. ZOREF E, SPERLING O, DE VRIES A: Stabilisation by PRPP of cellular purine phosphoribosyltransferases against inactivation by freezing and thawing: Study of normal and hypoxanthine-guanine phosphoribosyltransferase deficient human fibroblasts, in Sperling O, De Vries A, Wyngaarden JB (eds): *Purine Metabolism in Man.* New York, Plenum, 1974, vol 41A, p 15.
62. BASHKIN P, SPERLING O, SCHMIDT R, SZEINBERG A: Resistance of erythrocyte adenine phosphoribosyltransferase in the Lesch-Nyhan syndrome to destabilisation to heat by hypoxanthine, in Sperling O, De Vries A,

Wyngaarden JB (eds): *Purine Metabolism in Man*. New York, Plenum, 1974, vol 41A, p 215.

63. GREENE ML, BOYLE JA, SEEGMILLER JE: Substrate stabilization: Genetically controlled reciprocal relationship of two human enzymes. *Science* 167:887, 1970.

64. ROSENBLOOM FM, KELLEY WN, MILLER J, HENDERSON JF, SEEGMILLER JE: Inherited disorder of purine metabolism. Correlation between central nervous system dysfunction and biochemical defects. *JAMA* 202:103, 1967.

65. SMITH JL, OMURA GA, KRAKOFF JH, BALIS EM: IMP and AMP pyrophosphate phosphoribosyltransferase in leukemic and normal human leukocytes. *Proc Soc Exp Biol Med* 136:1299, 1971.

66. JERUSHALMY Z, SPERLING O, PINKHAS J, KRYNSKA M, DE VRIES A: Enzymes of purine metabolism in platelets. Phosphoribosylpyrophosphate synthetase and purine phosphoribosyltransferase. *Adv Exp Med Biol* 41:159, 1973.

67. RIVARD G, IZADI P, LAZERSON J, MCLAREN JD, PARKER C, FISH CH: Functional and metabolic studies of platelets from patients with Lesch-Nyhan syndrome. *Br J Haematol* 31:245, 1975.

68. DE BRUYN CHMM, OEI TL: Purine phosphoribosyltransferases in human erythrocyte ghosts, in Muller MM, Kaiser E, Seegmiller JE (eds): *Purine Metabolism in Man*. New York, Plenum, 1977, vol II, 76A, p 139.

69. YIP LC, CHANG V, BALIS EM: Membrane-associated purine metabolising enzyme activities of human peripheral blood cells. *Biochemistry* 21:6972, 1982.

70. DEAN M, WATTS RWE, WESTWICK WJ: Human erythrocyte AMP pyrophosphate phosphoribosyltransferase (EC 2.4.2.7). *FEBS Lett* 1:179, 1968.

71. SRIVASTAVA SK, BEUTLER E: Purification and kinetic studies of adenine phosphoribosyltransferase from human erythrocytes. *Arch Biochem Biophys* 142:426, 1971.

72. HORI M, HENDERSON JF: Kinetic studies of adenine phosphoribosyltransferase. *J Biol Chem* 241:3404, 1966.

73. HENDERSON JF, HORI M, PALSER HM, GADD REA: Kinetic studies of inhibition of adenine phosphoribosyltransferase by guanylate. *Biochim Biophys Acta* 268:70, 1972.

74. KRENITSKY TA, PAPAIOANNOU R, ELION GB: Human hypoxanthine phosphoribosyltransferase. 1. Purification, properties and specificity. *J Biol Chem* 244:1263, 1969.

75. MURRAY AW, WONG PCL: Stimulation of adenine phosphoribosyltransferase by adenosine triphosphate and other nucleoside triphosphates. *Biochem J* 104:669, 1967.

76. KRENITSKY TA, NEIL SM, ELION GB, HITCHINGS GH: Adenine phosphoribosyltransferase from monkey liver. *J Biol Chem* 244:4779, 1969.

77. BAKAY B, NYHAN WN: The separation of adenine and hypoxanthine-guanine phosphoribosyl transferase isoenzymes by disc gel electrophoresis. *Biochem Genet* 5:81, 1971.

78. MOWBRAY S, WATSON B, HARRIS H: A search for electrophoretic variants of human adenine phosphoribosyltransferase. *Ann Hum Genet* 36:153, 1972.

79. SAHOTA A, CHESNUT K, MA Z, TAYLOR MW: Unpublished results, 1986.

80. CHESNUT K, MA Z, SAHOTA A, TAYLOR MW: Unpublished results, 1986.

81. WILSON JM, O'TOOLE TE, ARGOS P, SHEWACH DS, DADDONA PE, KELLEY WN: Human adenine phosphoribosyltransferase: Complete amino acid sequence of the erythrocyte enzyme. *J Biol Chem* 261:13677, 1986.

82. BRODERICK TP, SCHAFF DA, BERTINO AM, DUSH MK, TISCHFIELD JA, STAMBROOK PJ: Comparative anatomy of the human APRT gene and enzyme: Nucleotide sequence divergence and conservation of a non-random CpG dinucleotide arrangement. *Proc Natl Acad Sci USA* 84:3349, 1987.

83. BERLIN RD, OLIVER JM: Membrane transport of purine and pyrimidine bases and nucleosides in animal cells, in Bourne GH, Danielli JF, Jeon KW (eds): *International Review of Cytology*. New York, Academic, 1975, p 287.

84. SIROTNAK FM, CHELLO PL, BROCKMAN RW: Potential for exploitation of transport systems in anticancer drug design, in DeVita VT Jr, Busch H (eds): *Methods in Cancer Research*. New York, Academic, 1979, vol XVI, p 381.

85. PLAGEMANN PGW, WOHLHUETER RM: Permeation of nucleosides, nucleic acid bases, and nucleotides in animal cells, in Bronner F, Kleinzeller A (eds): *Current Topics in Membranes and Transport*. New York, Academic, 1980, p 225.

86. WOHLHUETER RM, PLAGEMANN PGW: The roles of transport and phosphorylation in nutrient uptake in cultured animal cells, in Bourne GH, Danielli JF, Jeon KW (eds): *International Review of Cytology*. New York, Academic, 1980, p 171.

87. BENKE PJ, HERRICK N, HERBERT A: Transport of hypoxanthine in fibroblasts with normal and mutant hypoxanthine-guanine phosphoribosyltransferase. *Biochem Med* 8:309, 1973.

88. EPSTEIN J, LITTLEFIELD JW: Hypoxanthine transport in normal and hypoxanthine guanine phosphoribosyltransferase (HGPRT) deficient diploid human lymphoblasts. *Exp Cell Res* 106:247, 1977.

89. ZYLKA JM, PLAGEMANN PGW: Purine and pyrimidine transport by cultured Novikoff cells. Specificities and mechanism of transport and relationship to phosphoribosylation. *J Biol Chem* 250:5756, 1975.

90. WITNEY FR, TAYLOR MW: Role of adenine phosphoribosyltransferase in adenine uptake in wild-type and APRT mutants of CHO. *Biochem Genet* 16:917, 1978.

91. CARTIER PH: Adenine uptake by isolated rat thymocytes. *J Biol Chem* 255:4574, 1980.

92. SIXMA JJ, HOLMSEN H, TRIESCHNIGG ACM: Adenine nucleotide metabolism of blood platelets. VIII. Transport of adenine into human platelets. *Biochem Biophys Acta* 298:460, 1973.

93. KOYAMA H, KODAMA H: Adenine phosphoribosyltransferase deficiency in cultured mouse mammary tumor FM3A cells resistant to 4-carbamoylimidazolium-5-olate. *Cancer Res* 42:4210, 1982.

94. TAYLOR MW, SAHOTA A: Cellular resistance to adenine analogues, in Gupta RS (ed): *Drug Resistance in Mammalian Cells*. Boca Raton, FL, CRC Press (1988, in press).

95. FUKUI M, INABA M, TSUKAGOSHI S, SAKURAI Y: New anti-tumor imidazole derivative, 5-carbamoyl-1-H-imidazol-4-yl piperonylate, as an inhibitor of purine synthesis and its activation by adenine phosphoribosyltransferase. *Cancer Res* 42:1098, 1983.

96. PAERATAKUL U, TAYLOR MW: Unpublished results, 1986.

97. TURKER MS, TISCHFIELD JA, RABINOVITCH P, STAMBROOK PJ, TRILL JJ, SMITH AC, OGBURN CE, MARTIN GM: Differentiation alters the unstable expression of adenine phosphoribosyltransferase in mouse teratocarcinoma cells. *J Exp Pathol* 2:299, 1986.

98. YIP LC, DANCIS J, MATHIESON B, BALIS NE: Age-induced changes in adenosine monophosphate pyrophosphate phosphoribosyltransferase and inosine monophosphate pyrophosphate phosphoribosyltransferase from normal and Lesch-Nyhan erythrocytes. *Biochemistry* 13:2558, 1974.

99. KELLEY WN: Studies on the adenine phosphoribosyltransferase enzyme in human fibroblasts lacking hypoxanthine-guanine phosphoribosyltransferase. *J Lab Clin Med* 77:33, 1971.

100. EMMERSON BT, GORDON RB: HGPRT deficiency with normal erythrocyte PRPP and APRT activity, in Nyhan WL, Thompson LF, Watts RWE (eds): *Purine and Pyrimidine Metabolism in Man*. New York, Plenum, 1986, vol V, 195A, p 163.

101. COHEN A, DOYLE D, MARTIN DW, AMMANN AJ: Abnormal purine metabolism and purine overproduction in a patient deficient in purine nucleoside phosphorylase. *N Engl J Med* 295:1449, 1976.

102. SIMMONDS HA, FAIRBANKS LD, MORRIS GS, MORGAN G, WATSON AR, TIMMS P: Central nervous system dysfunction and erythrocyte guanosine triphosphate depletion in purine nucleoside phosphorylase deficiency. *Arch Dis Child* 62:385, 1987.

103. FOX IH, KELLEY WN: Observations of altered intracellular phosphoribosylpyrophosphate (PP-ribose-P) in human diseases, in Sperling O, De Vries A, Wyngaarden JB (eds): *Purine Metabolism in Man*. New York, Plenum, 1974, vol 41B, p 471.

104. SIMMONDS HA, WEBSTER DR, BECROFT DMO, POTTER CF: Purine and pyrimidine metabolism in hereditary orotic aciduria: Some unexpected effects of allopurinol. *Eur J Clin Invest* 10:33, 1980.

105. WILSON JM, DADDONA PE, OTOADESE T, KELLEY WN: Adenine phosphoribosyltransferase in patients with disorders of purine and pyrimidine metabolism. *J Lab Clin Med* 99:163, 1982.

106. ITIABA K, MELANCON SB, DALLAIRE L, CRAWHALL JC: Adenine phosphoribosyltransferase deficiency in association with subnormal hypoxanthine phosphoribosyltransferase in families of Lesch-Nyhan patients. *Biochem Med* 19:252, 1978.

107. BORDEN M, NYHAN WL, BAKAY B: Increased activity of adenine phosphoribosyltransferase in erythrocytes of normal newborn infants. *Pediatr Res* 8:31, 1974.

108. FOX IH, DOTTEN DA, MARCHANT PJ, LA CROIX S: Acquired increases of human erythrocyte purine enzymes. *Metabolism* 25:571, 1976.

109. STENZEL A, BANHOLZER P, REITER S, GROBNER W, ZOLLNER N, HEGEMAN M, PFAB R: Activity of adenine phosphoribosyltransferase (APRT) in patients with renal failure and urolithiasis, in Schwille PO, Smith LH, Robertson WG, Vahlensieck W (eds): *Urolithiasis and Clinical Research*. New York, Plenum, 1985, p 347.

110. RETHORE M-O, LAFOURCADE J, COUTURIER J, HARPEY JP, HAMET M, ENGLER R, ALCINDOR LG, LEJEUNE J: Increased activity of adenine phosphoribosyl transferase in a child trisomic for 16q22.2→16qter due to malsegregation of a t(16;21)(q22.2;q22.2)pat. *Ann Genet* 25:36, 1982.

111. MARIMO B, GIANNELLI F: Gene dosage effect in human trisomy 16. *Nature* 256:204, 1975.

112. NATSUMEDA Y, LUI MS, EMRANI J, FADERAN MA, REARDON MA, EBLE JN, GLOVER JL, WEBER G: Purine enzymology of human colon carcinomas. *Cancer Res* 45:2556, 1985.

113. MARTINEZ-VALDEZ H, LONG TC, ANDRES AJ, TAYLOR MW: Low adenine nucleotide pools in Bloom's syndrome may reflect a defective salvage purine biosynthesis. *Pediatr Res* 19:764, 1985.

114. VAN ACKER KJ, SIMMONDS HA, POTTER CF, SAHOTA A: Inheritance of adenine phosphoribosyltransferase (APRT) deficiency, in Rapado A, Watts RWE, De Bruyn CHMM (eds): *Purine Metabolism in Man.* New York, Plenum, 1980, vol III, 122A, p 349.

115. GAULT MH, O'TOOLE T, WILSON JM, PAYNE RH, ITTEL TH, SIMMONDS HA, CHURCHILL DN, MORGAN F: Urolithiasis in a large kindred deficient in adenine phosphoribosyltransferase (APRT), in Schwille PO, Smith LH, Robertson WG, Vahlensieck W (eds): Urolithiasis and related clinical research. New York, Plenum, 1985, p 9.

116. WILSON JM, YOUNG AB, KELLEY WN: Hypoxanthine-guanine phosphoribosyltransferase deficiency: The molecular basis of the clinical syndromes. *N Engl J Med* 309:900, 1983.

117. SRIVASTAVA SK, VILLACORTE D, BEUTLER E: Correlation between adenylate metabolising enzymes and adenine nucleotide levels of erythrocytes during blood storage in various media. *Transfusion* 12:190, 1972.

118. SIMON AE, TAYLOR MW, BRADLEY WEC: Mechanism of mutation at the APRT locus in Chinese hamster ovary cells: Analysis of heterozygotes and hemizygotes. *Mol Cell Biol* 3:1703, 1983.

119. KAHAN B, HELD KR, DEMARS R: The locus for human adenine phosphorphoribosyltransferase on chromosome no. 16. *Genetics* 78:1143, 1974.

120. TISCHFIELD JA, RUDDLE FH: Assignment of the gene for adenine phosphoribosyltransferase to human chromosome 16 by mouse-human somatic cell hybridization. *Proc Natl Acad Sci USA* 71:45, 1974.

121. FRATINI A, SIMMERS RN, CALLEN DF, HYLAND VJ, TISCHFIELD JA, STAMBROOK PJ, SUTHERLAND GR: A new location for the human adenine phosphoribosyltransferase gene (APRT) distal to the haptoglobin (HP) and fra(16)(q23)(FRA16D) loci. *Cytogenet Cell Genet* 43:10, 1986.

122. MURRAY AM, DROBETSKY E, ARRAND JE: Cloning the complete human adenine phosphoribosyl transferase gene. *Gene* 31:233, 1984.

123. STAMBROOK PJ, DUSH MK, TRILL JJ, TISCHFIELD JA: Cloning of a functional human adenine phosphoribosyltransferase (APRT) gene: Identification of a restriction fragment length polymorphism and preliminary analysis of DNAs from APRT-deficient families and cell mutants. *Somatic Cell Mol Genet* 10:359, 1984.

124. TISCHFIELD JA, TRILL JJ, DUSH MK, STAMBROOK PJ: Polymorphism within the human adenine transferase (APRT) locus. *Genetics* 107:s107, 1984.

125. DUSH MK, SIKELA JM, KHAN SA, TISCHFIELD JA, STAMBROOK PJ: Nucleotide sequence and organisation of the mouse adenine phosphoribosyltransferase gene: Presence of a coding region common to animal and bacterial phosphoribosyltransferases that has a variable intron/exon arrangement. *Proc Natl Acad Sci USA* 82:2731, 1985.

126. HERSHEY HV, TAYLOR MW: Nucleotide sequence and deduced amino acid sequence of *Escherichia coli* adenine phosphoribosyltransferase and comparison with other analogous enzymes. *Gene* 43:287, 1986.

127. NALBANTOGLU J, PHEAR GA, MEUTH M: Nucleotide sequence of hamster adenine phosphoribosyltransferase (APRT) gene. *Nucleic Acids Res* 14:1914, 1986.

128. BRIGGS MR, KADONAGA JT, BELL SP, TIJIAN R: Purification and biochemical characterization of the promoter specific transcription factor, Sp1. *Science* 234:47, 1986.

129. KESHET I, YISRAELI J, CEDAR H: Effect of regional DNA methylation on gene expression. *Proc Natl Acad Sci USA* 82:2560, 1985.

130. PARK J-H, HERSHEY HV, TAYLOR MW: Housekeeping genes, in Simonsen CC, Shepard M (eds): *Molecular Genetics of Mammalian Cells.* New York, Macmillan, 1986, p 79.

131. TISCHFIELD JA, BEHZADIAN MA, BRODERICK TP, STAMBROOK PJ: The human adenine phosphoribosyltransferase (APRT) gene and APRT deficiency in Japan. Proceedings of the 4th International Congress on Inborn Errors of Metabolism (1987).

132. O'TOOLE T, KELLEY WN: Personal communication, 1987.

133. TISCHFIELD J: Personal communication, 1987.

134. PECK CC, BAILEY FJ, MOORE GL: Enhanced solubility of 2,8-dihydroxyadenine (DOA) in human urine. *Transfusion* 17:383, 1977.

135. STERN IJ, COSMAS F, GARVIN PJ: The occurrence and binding of 2,8-dioxyadenine in plasma. *Transfusion* 13:382, 1972.

136. ERICSON A, GROTH T, NIKLASSON F, DE VERDIER C-H: Plasma concentration and renal excretion of adenine and 2,8-dihydroxyadenine after administration of adenine in man. *Scand J Clin Lab Invest* 40:1, 1980.

137. DEVENUTO F, WILSON SM, BILLINGS TA, SHIELDS CE: In vivo distribution of injected 14-C-dioxyadenine in tissues and organs of normal rats. *Transfusion* 16:24, 1976.

138. MINKOWSKI O: Untersuchungen zur physiologie und pathologie der harnsaure bei saugetieren. *Arch Exp Pathol Pharmakol* 41:375, 1898.

139. CAMERON JS, SIMMONDS HA, CADENHEAD A, FAREBROTHER D: Metabolism of intravenous adenine in the pig, in Miller MM, Kaiser E, Seegmiller JE (eds): *Purine Metabolism in Man.* New York, Plenum, 1977, vol II, 76A, p 496.

140. SHIELDS CE, LOPAS H, BIRNDORF NI: Investigation of nephrotoxic effects of adenine and its metabolic product 2,8-dioxyadenine, on primates (Macaca Irus). *J Clin Pharmacol* 10:316, 1970.

141. KLAIN GJ, MEIKLE AW, SULLIVAN FJ, ROGERS GB: Metabolic effects of dietary adenine in kidney of rats. *Fed Proc* 29:366, 1970.

142. LINDBLAD G, JANSSON G, FALK J: Adenine toxicity: A three-week intravenous study in dogs. *Acta Pharmacol Toxicol (Copenh)* 32:246, 1973.

143. YOKOZAWA T, ZHENG PD, OURA H, KOIZUMI F: Animal model of adenine-induced chronic renal failure in rats. *Nephron* 44:230, 1986.

144. BARTLETT GR: Formation of oxyadenine metabolites in the rabbit after intravenous administration of adenine. *Transfusion* 17:351, 1972.

145. FAREBROTHER DA, PINCOTT JR, SIMMONDS HA, WARREN DJ, DILLON MJ, CAMERON JS: Uric acid crystal induced nephropathy: Evidence for a specific renal lesion in a gouty kindred. *J Pathol* 135:159, 1981.

146. WESTMAN BJM: Serum creatinine and creatinine clearance after transfusion with ACD adenine blood and ACD blood. *Transfusion* 12:371, 1972.

147. HOGMAN CF, ANDREEN M, ROSEN I, AKERBLOM O, HELLSING K: Haemotherapy with red cell concentrates and a new red-cell storage medium. *Lancet* 1:269, 1983.

148. FALK JS, LINDBLAD GTO, WESTMAN BJM: Histopathological studies on kidneys from patients treated with large amounts of blood preserved with ACD-adenine. *Transfusion* 12:376, 1972.

149. DE VERDIER CH, ERICSON A, NIKLASSON F, WESTMAN M: Adenine metabolism in man. 1. After intravenous and peroral administration. *Scand J Clin Lab Invest* 37:567, 1977.

150. BARTLETT GR: Metabolism by man of intravenously administered adenine. *Transfusion* 17:367, 1977.

151. ROTH GJ, MOORE CL, KLINE WE, POSKITT TR: The renal effect of intravenous adenine in humans. *Transfusion* 15:116, 1975.

152. HENDERSON JF, SCOTT FW: Inhibition of animal and invertebrate cell growth by naturally occurring purine bases and ribonucleosides. *Pharmacol Ther* 8:539, 1980.

153. HERSHFIELD MS, SNYDER FF, SEEGMILLER JE: Adenine and adenosine are toxic to human lymphoblast mutants defective in purine salvage enzymes. *Science* 197:1284, 1977.

154. BLAIR DGR, PAESHER SJ, CROSS DC: Toxicity of adenine and purine analogues to 2,6-diaminopurine sensitive and resistant L-strain mouse cells. *Can J Microbiol* 16:775, 1970.

155. ZIMMERMAN TP, WOLBERT G, DUNCAN GS, ELION GB: Adenosine analogues as substrates and inhibitors of S-adenosylhomocysteine hydrolase in intact lymphocytes. *Biochemistry* 19:2252, 1980.

156. CHALMERS AH, ROTSTEIN T, MOHAN RAO M, MARSHALL VR, COLEMAN M: Studies of the mechanism of immunosuppression with adenine. *Int J Immunopharmacol* 7:433, 1985.

157. SIMMONDS HA, GODAY A, MORRIS GS: Superoxide radicals, immunodeficiency and xanthine oxidase activity: Man is not a mouse! *Clin Sci* 68:561, 1985.

158. SIMMONDS HA, CAMERON JS, BARRATT TM, DILLON MJ, MEADOW SR, TROMPETER RS: Acute renal failure as a presenting symptom in hypoxanthine-guanine (HGPRT) and adenine phosphoribosyltransferase (APRT) deficiency. *J Inherited Metab Dis* 11:in press, 1988.

159. BARTLETT GR: Metabolism of intravenously administered adenine and inosine in the rabbit, in Chaplin H Jr, Jaffe ER, Lenford C, Valeri CR (eds): *Preservation and Red Blood Cells.* Washington, DC, National Academy of Science, 1973, p 215.

160. WYNGAARDEN JB, SEEGMILLER JE, LASTER L, BLAIR AE: Utilization of hypoxanthine, adenine and 4-amino-5-imidazolecarboximide for uric acid synthesis in man. *Metabolism* 8:455, 1959.

161. SEEGMILLER JE, KLINENBERG JR, MILLER J, WATTS RWE: Suppression of glycine-15N incorporation into urinary uric acid by adenine-8-13C in normal and gouty subjects. *J Clin Invest* 47:1193, 1968.

162. VAN DER ZEE SPM, LOMMEN EJP, TRIJBELS JMF, SCHRETLEN EDAM: The influence of adenine on the clinical features and purine metabolism in the Lesch-Nyhan syndrome. *Acta Paediatr Scand* 59:259, 1970.

163. WATTS RWE, MCKERAN RO, BROWN E, ANDREWS TM, GRIFFITHS MI: Clinical and biochemical studies on treatment of Lesch-Nyhan syndrome. *Arch Dis Child* 49:693, 1974.

164. BEYER P, BIETH D, LUTZ D, GEISERT J, BOILLETOT A: Une nouvelle obser-

vation du syndrome de Lesch-Nyhan: Essai de traitement par l'adenine. *Arch Fr Pediatr* 32:293, 1975.

165. DEMUS A, KAISER W, SCHAUB J: The Lesch-Nyhan syndrome. Metabolic studies during administration of adenine. *Eur J Pediatr* 114:119, 1973.

166. CECCARELLI M, CIOMPI ML, PASERO G: Acute renal failure during adenine therapy in Lesch-Nyhan syndrome, in Sperling O, De Vries A, Wyngaarden JB (eds): *Purine Metabolism in Man.* New York, Plenum, 1974, vol 41B, p 671.

167. MARKO P, GERLACH E, ZIMMER HG, PECHAN I, CREMER T, TRENDELLENBURG C: Interrelationship between salvage pathway and synthesis de novo of adenine nucleotides in kidney slices. *Hoppe-Seyler's Z Physiol Chem* 350:1669, 1969.

168. SCHNEEBURGER W, BACH D, HESSE A, VAHLENSIECK W: Circadian excretion of uric acid on a standard diet and purine load in Ca-oxalate stone formers and healthy controls, in Smith LH, Robertson WG, Finlayson B (eds): *Urolithiasis: Clinical and Basic Research.* New York, Plenum, 1981, p 51.

169. HAMET M: Le microdosage de l'adenine par une methode de cinetique enzymatique-dilution isotopique. *Ann Biol Clin* 33:131, 1975.

170. MILLS CG, SCHMALSTIEG FC, TRIMMER KB, GOLDMAN AS, GOLDBLUM RM: Purine metabolism in adenosine deaminase deficiency. *Proc Natl Acad Sci USA* 73:2867, 1976.

171. SIMMONDS HA, SAHOTA A, POTTER CF, CAMERON JS: Purine metabolism and immunodeficiency: Urinary purine excretion as a diagnostic screening test in adenosine deaminase and purine nucleoside phosphorylase deficiency. *Clin Sci Mol Med* 54:579, 1978.

172. KELLEY WN, WYNGAARDEN JB: Effect of dietary purine restriction, allopurinol, and oxipurinol on urinary excretion of ultraviolet absorbing compounds. *Clin Chem* 16:707, 1970.

173. ZIMMERMAN TP, GERSTEN NB, ROSS AF, MIECH RP: Adenine as a substrate for purine nucleoside phosphorylase. *Can J Biochem* 49:1050, 1971.

174. SNYDER FF, HENDERSON JF: Alternative pathways of deoxyadenosine and adenosine metabolism. *J Biol Chem* 248:5899, 1973.

175. HAMET M, BONISSOL C, CARTIER P: Activities of enzymes of purine and pyrimidine metabolism in nine mycoplasma species, in Rapado A, Watts RWE, De Bruyn CHMM (eds): *Purine Metabolism in Man.* New York, Plenum, 1980, vol III, 122B, p 231.

176. SAHOTA A, SIMMONDS HA, POTTER CF, WATSON JG, HUGH-JONES K, PERRETT D: Adenosine and deoxyadenosine metabolism in the erythrocytes of a patient with adenosine deaminase deficiency, in Rapado A, Watts RWE, De Bruyn CHMM (eds): *Purine Metabolism in Man.* New York, Plenum, 1980, vol III, 122A, p 397.

177. CLIFFORD AJ, STORY DL: Levels of purines in foods and their metabolic effects in rats. *J Nutr* 106:435, 1975.

178. WILLIAMS-ASHMAN HG, SEIDENFELD J, GALETTI P: Trends in the biochemical pharmacology of 5′-deoxy-5′-methylthioadenosine. *Biochem Pharmacol* 31:277, 1982.

179. SAHOTA A, WEBSTER DR, POTTER CF, SIMMONDS HA, RODGERS AV, GIBSON T: Methylthioadenosine phosphorylase activity in human erythrocytes. *Clin Chim Acta* 128:283, 1983.

180. KAMATANI N, KUBOTA M, WILLIS EH, FRINCKE LA, CARSON D: 5′-methylthioadenosine is the major source of adenine in human cells, in De Bruyn CHMM, Simmonds HA, Muller MM (eds): *Purine Metabolism in Man.* New York, Plenum, 1984, vol IV, 165B, p 83.

181. CHUNG TG, KANAZAWA, SAITO A: Determination of 2,8-dihydroxyadenine in urine by high performance anion-exchange liquid chromatography. *J Chromatogr* 1983:277, 300.

182. SIMMONDS HA, CAMERON HS, MORRIS GS, DAVIES PM: Allopurinol in renal failure and the tumour lysis syndrome. *Clin Chim Acta* 160:189, 1986.

183. KAMATANI N, TERAI C, KUROSHIMA S, NISHIOKA N, MIKANAGI K: Genetic and clinical studies on 19 families with adenine phosphoribosyltransferase deficiencies. *Hum Genet* 75:163, 1987.

184. HIDAKA Y, TARLE SA, FUJIMORI S, KAMATANI N, KELLEY WN, PALELLA TD: Human adenine phosphoribosyltransferase deficiency. Demonstration of a single mutant allele common to the Japanese. *J Clin Invest* 81:945, 1988.

185. HIDAKA Y, PALELLA TD, O'TOOLE TE, TARLE SA, KELLEY WN: Human adenine phosphoribosyltransferase. Identification of allelic mutations at the nucleotide level as a cause of complete deficiency of the enzyme. *J Clin Invest* 80:1409, 1987.

CHAPTER **40**

IMMUNODEFICIENCY DISEASES CAUSED BY ADENOSINE DEAMINASE DEFICIENCY AND PURINE NUCLEOSIDE PHOSPHORYLASE DEFICIENCY

NICHOLAS M. KREDICH
MICHAEL S. HERSHFIELD

1. *Heritable deficiency of either adenosine deaminase (ADA) or purine nucleoside phosphorylase (PNP) causes abnormalities in purine nucleoside metabolism that are selectively toxic to lymphocytes and result in immune deficiency disease. Most patients with ADA deficiency are severely lymphopenic and lack both cell-mediated (T-cell) and humoral (B-cell) immunity, resulting in severe combined immunodeficiency disease (SCID). PNP-deficient children have a severe defect in cell-mediated immunity but either normal or hyperactive humoral immunity.*

2. *Both conditions are inherited in an autosomal recessive manner and result from mutations in structural genes located on chromosomes 20q (ADA) and 14q (PNP). ADA-deficient SCID has been identified in children from approximately 100 families; 21 cases of PNP deficiency have been reported. Diagnosis is made by finding an absence of enzyme activity in an hemolysate of the patient's erythrocytes. Heterozygotes for both conditions have normal immune function and approximately one-half normal erythrocyte enzyme levels. Prenatal diagnosis can be established by measuring enzyme activity in amniotic cells or chorionic villi.*

3. *Levels of the ADA substrates adenosine and deoxyadenosine are elevated in the plasma and deoxyadenosine is elevated in the urine of ADA-deficient children. dATP is markedly elevated in erythrocytes and variably elevated in peripheral blood mononuclear cells. ATP may be decreased to 50 percent of normal in erythrocytes. Erythrocyte S-adenosylhomocysteine hydrolase activity is markedly diminished in ADA deficiency, owing to its irreversible "suicide like" inactivation by deoxyadenosine. PNP-deficient children are hypouricemic and hypouricosuric but excrete abnormally large amounts of total purines as the PNP substrates inosine, guanosine, deoxyinosine, and deoxyguanosine; plasma levels of these nucleosides are elevated. In erythrocytes dGTP may be detectable and the level of GTP may be decreased.*

4. *Several biochemical mechanisms may contribute to the immune defect in ADA deficiency by impairing lymphocyte differentiation, viability, or function:* (a) *dATP may accumulate preferentially in lymphocytes, particularly in immature T cells. In dividing lymphocytes dATP inhibits ribonucleotide reductase, which leads to inhibition of DNA replication and cell division.* (b) *Accumulation of dATP activates AMP deaminase and IMP nucleotidase, which may lead to selective depletion of cellular ATP.* (c) *In nondividing, mature T cells dATP accumulation may cause DNA strand breaks to accumulate, which can activate nuclear poly(ADP-ribose) synthetase and deplete NAD.* (d) *S-Adenosylhomocysteine, which may accumulate as a result of increased adenosine levels and inactivation of S-adenosylhomocysteine hydrolase by deoxyadenosine, may inhibit vital S-adenosylmethionine-mediated transmethylation reactions. Accumulation of dGTP in T lymphocytes with resultant inhibition of ribonucleotide reductase and DNA replication has been proposed as an explanation for the T-cell defect in PNP deficiency.*

5. *Untreated, ADA-deficient children usually die before age 2 from overwhelming infection. Bone marrow transplantation from an HLA-identical donor is the preferred treatment and can result in complete or partial immune reconstitution. Transplantation of T-cell-depleted bone marrow from a haploidentical donor has also been used successfully in some patients. Enzyme replacement therapy in the form of repeated transfusions with irradiated erythrocytes from normal donors has improved immune function in some ADA-deficient children. Bovine ADA modified by covalent attachment of polyethylene glycol (PEG-ADA) has a prolonged circulating time in animals and reduced immunogenicity compared with unmodified bovine ADA. In initial clinical trials in ADA-deficient children chronic weekly intramuscular injection of PEG-ADA maintained high levels of plasma ADA activity, corrected the biochemical abnormalities caused by ADA deficiency, and restored immune function. Transplantation and erythrocyte transfusion therapy have been used in PNP deficiency with limited success. Both ADA deficiency and PNP deficiency are likely candidates for attempts at gene replacement therapy.*

INTRODUCTION AND HISTORY

The immune system consists of two major functional arms: cell-mediated immunity, effected primarily by a class of lymphocytes termed *T cells;* and humoral immunity, mediated by antibodies produced by a class of lymphocytes termed *B cells* and by their plasma-cell descendents. Although these two divisions are interdependent, primary immune defects occur

Nonstandard abbreviations used in this chapter include: ADA = adenosine deaminase; ALL = acute lymphoblastic leukemia; dNTP = deoxynucleoside triphosphate; EHNA = *erythro*-9-(2-hydroxy-3-nonyl)adenine; GVHD = graft-versus-host disease; IL = interleukin; LTR = long terminal repeat sequences encoding transcriptional control elements at each end of integrated retroviral DNA; MLC = mixed lymphocyte culture; PEG = polyethylene glycol; PNP = purine nucleoside phosphorylase; PRPP = phosphoribosylpyrophosphate; SCID = severe combined immunodeficiency disease.

that dramatically affect one form of immunity while leaving the other relatively intact. Severe combined immunodeficiency disease (SCID) refers to a life-threatening impairment of both cell-mediated and humoral immunity.[1]

Although several different types of heritable, or primary, immunodeficiency disease had been recognized and categorized on the basis of clinical and pathologic criteria, none had ever been associated with a specific, known molecular defect until 1972, when Eloise Giblett and her collaborators[2] described two patients with SCID and virtually complete absence of erythrocyte adenosine deaminase (ADA). As Dr. Giblett relates the story,[3] she was testing genetic marker systems in blood, including ADA, as part of a project evaluating patients receiving human transplants. A specimen from a 2-year-old child with SCID who was being considered for a bone marrow transplant was found to lack ADA; shortly thereafter a second SCID patient, unrelated to the first, was also found to be deficient in ADA. Within a year four additional ADA-deficient SCID patients were described by other investigators,[4–6] making it clear that these two conditions are closely related.

Dr. Giblett and her colleagues then established a screening program in which other enzymes of purine and pyrimidine metabolism were assayed in patients with various immune disorders. In 1975 these efforts were rewarded with the discovery of the first case of purine nucleoside phosphorylase (PNP) deficiency, found in a 5-year-old girl with a defect in cellular immunity but with apparently normal humoral immunity.[7] Additional cases were soon reported by others.[8–12]

CLINICAL ASPECTS

As the historical account suggests, the most conspicuous clinical consequence of heritable ADA and PNP deficiency is immunodeficiency, manifested as a predisposition to recurrent and persistent infections. Almost all ADA-deficient patients have SCID, whereas a T-cell defect predominates in PNP-deficient individuals, who have impaired cellular immunity and normal or even hyperactive B-cell function. The recognized clinical spectrum of each of these diseases has broadened as patients with atypical or milder forms of immunodeficiency have been found to be enzyme-deficient. The diagnosis should be ruled out in children presenting with virtually any degree of cellular or humoral immunodeficiency even as late as at 3 to 5 years of life.

ADA Deficiency

Severe Combined Immunodeficiency. SCID is a rare disorder that is caused by at least several different primary genetic defects.[1] The condition is X-linked in approximately one-third of cases and has an autosomal recessive mode of inheritance in the others. Of the latter approximately one-half are due to ADA deficiency.[13]

Approximately 85 to 90 percent of ADA-deficient patients present with a form of SCID that cannot be distinguished clinically from the disease found in patients with normal ADA.[14,15] In some instances the defect is ascertained at birth because of an older sibling, often deceased, with suspected or proven immunodeficiency. In most cases the immune defect is present in partial or complete form at birth, or at least at 1 to 2 months of age, which may be the earliest that a clinical picture of recurrent infection prompts an evaluation of immune function. Initially, infection involves those areas with greatest exposure to organisms, i.e., the skin and the gastrointestinal, and respiratory systems. A variety of infectious agents are encountered, including various bacteria, fungi, viruses, and protozoa, both ordinary and opportunistic pathogens. *Pneumocystis carinii* pneumonia and giant-cell pneumonia occur frequently. Candidiasis is almost invariably present, usually first as just "diaper rash," then as a more extensive infection involving skin, oral and esophageal mucosa, and vagina. Diarrhea, which is believed to be secondary to abnormal intestinal flora, is a common feature and may seriously compromise nutrition. Vaccination with live viruses may be fatal, and transfusion with unirradiated blood may cause graft-versus-host disease. Physical growth and development are delayed in most SCID patients. Unless special measures are taken, these children usually die from overwhelming infection and sepsis before 2 years of age. ADA-deficient SCID patients who survive beyond early childhood may develop chronic pulmonary insufficiency from recurrent pneumonia. They are also at increased risk of developing lymphomas, usually of B-cell origin, which may be related to infection with Epstein-Barr virus or cytomegalovirus.

For the most part, physical findings are unremarkable except for evidence of infection and the absence of lymph nodes and pharyngeal lymphoid tissue. Prominence of the costochondral junctions, a so-called rachitic rosary, may also be noted in ADA deficiency.[14] Three patients have been described with various neurologic abnormalities including spasticity, head lag, movement disorders, nystagmus, and inability to focus.[16,17] Although the relationship of these disturbances to ADA deficiency is unclear, their improvement with enzyme replacement therapy[17] suggests that loss of ADA leads to an accumulation of toxic metabolites that can disturb neurologic function.[17] Fine, sparse hair, anatomic malformations of the urinary tract and transient renal tubular acidosis have also been reported,[14] but it is not clear whether these findings are secondary to chronic infection or if their association with ADA deficiency is only coincidental.

In contrast to these ADA-deficient patients who present with classic SCID, the remaining 10 to 15 percent have a milder disease characterized by later age of onset and relative sparing of humoral immunity. In several cases immune function was found to deteriorate over the course of months or years until typical SCID prevailed, implying a cumulative effect of ADA deficiency on the immune system.[18–20]

Radiographic Features. X-ray studies show, as in other forms of SCID, absence of a thymic shadow and suggest diminution or lack of adenoids. Cupping and flaring of the anterior rib ends has been described in patients with a "rachitic rosary."[21] Other x-ray abnormalities include: pelvic dysplasia; shortening of the vertebral transverse processes with flattening or convexity of their ends; platyspondyly; and unusually thick growth arrest lines.[21] None of these x-ray changes are specific for ADA deficiency and in our present state of knowledge may be construed as "nonspecific" reactions to metabolic insult.[22]

Laboratory Findings. Lymphopenia ranging from severe to moderate is present with absolute lymphocyte counts usually less than 500 per milliliter. Eosinophilia has been reported in some patients, but other blood elements are usually normal in number. Abnormal platelet function in vitro has been described.[23,24] Lymphocytes, when present, usually lack the surface markers by which B cells and T cells are routinely identified. Skin tests for delayed hypersensitivity to *Candida*, streptokinase, streptodornase, dinitrochlorobenzene, and other agents are negative. In vitro lymphocyte responses to lectins such as phytohemagglutinin, pokeweed mitogen, and concanavalin A, to specific antigens, and to allogeneic cells are attenuated or absent. Total immunoglobin levels may be only slightly depressed at birth owing to the maternal contribution of IgG, but IgM and IgA, which ordinarily do not pass the placental barrier, are often absent. IgG levels decline as maternal antibodies are cleared, and by 1 or 2 months of age pronounced hypogammaglobulinemia signals the patient's lack of humoral immunity. Antibody responses to specific antigens such as tetanus toxoid and ϕX174 bacteriophage usually cannot be elicited, and blood group isoagglutinins are absent in patients with SCID.

ADA deficiency is most conveniently diagnosed by the demonstration of very low or immeasurable levels of ADA activity in an erythrocyte hemolysate. Occasionally a patient will have received red cell transfusions before the possibility of ADA deficiency was considered. In this situation the finding of appreciable levels of dATP in red cells (more than 20 μmol per milliliter packed erythrocytes; see "Metabolism" below) strongly suggests ADA deficiency. The diagnosis may then be confirmed by assaying ADA activity in blood mononuclear cells. Alternatively, if the child is too lymphopenic, sufficient nucleated cells may be obtained from 1 to 2 ml of heparinized bone marrow.

Pathology. Early studies on thymic histopathology suggested a significant difference between ADA-deficient patients and SCID patients with normal ADA.[25] In the latter group the thymus was described as embryonal with small nests of undifferentiated epithelial cells and an absence of Hassall bodies, a picture presumed to represent a defect in the early stages of thymic differentiation. In contrast, the thymus in several ADA-deficient children showed areas of differentiated epithelium and Hassall bodies, suggesting some degree of normal thymic development and subsequent involution. A later study, however, failed to find consistent differences between these two groups of SCID patients.[22]

A number of abnormalities have been noted in the cartilaginous growth plates of ADA-deficient children that differ from those seen in other metaphyseal chrondrodysplasias and correspond to the x-ray abnormalities already described.[26,27] A lack of proliferative cells, necrotic chondrocytes, and absent or disordered column formation are found in the hypertrophic zone, while hypertrophic chondrocytes may be seen in resting cartilage. Poor trabecular formation and interrupted areas of calcified cartilage with abrupt transition of cartilage to bone are also observed. Mesangial sclerosis in renal glomeruli and adrenal gland cortical sclerosis have been noted.[27]

Partial ADA Deficiency. Shortly after the first description of ADA deficiency in SCID, a report appeared of a 10-year-old !Kung tribesman in South-West Africa who lacked erythrocyte ADA while retaining normal immune function.[28] Subsequent studies showed that this individual, who appears to be homozygous for a mutant ADA allele common among the !Kung (gene frequency of about 0.11),[29] has ADA activities in his erythrocytes, leukocytes, and cultured fibroblasts that are approximately 2, 10, and 26 percent, respectively, of normal.[30] Immune function was still normal when reevaluated at age 18.[31]

Since this initial case report, at least ten additional immunocompetent individuals have been found with deficiency of erythrocyte ADA, a condition referred to as *partial ADA deficiency*.[32–39] Most of these have been ascertained through a newborn screening program in New York State. As in the !Kung tribesman, ADA levels in erythrocytes in all these individuals are very low or unmeasurable, but they can be measured in lymphocytes or fibroblasts, ranging between 2 and 70 percent of normal. In most instances this ADA activity has been shown to differ from normal with respect to heat lability, electrophoretic mobility, or both. By these criteria at least seven different ADA activities, presumably representing different mutant alleles for the enzyme, have been identified in individuals with partial ADA deficiency.[33,39,40]

The absence of erythrocyte ADA in partial ADA deficiency is believed to be due to the time-dependent inactivation of a relatively unstable mutant enzyme in cells that cannot synthesize new protein. The reduced levels of ADA found in other tissues apparently are adequate to preserve immune function—at least in most instances. One child with partial ADA deficiency was noted to develop a transient decrease in IgG at 5 months of age,[34] and another was diagnosed at 8 years of age because of the development of combined immunodeficiency.[36] Peripheral blood mononuclear cells from the latter child had only 2 percent of normal ADA activity, suggesting this level is near the threshold required for normal immune function.

Elevated Erythrocyte ADA Activity. Hereditary hemolytic anemia with erythrocyte ADA levels that are 40 to 85 times normal has been reported in three unrelated families.[41–43] Lymphocyte ADA levels and immune function are normal. The nonspherocytic, Coombs' negative anemia is probably due to diminished levels of erythrocyte ATP that result from increased AMP catabolism and a decrease in adenine nucleotide synthesis from adenosine.[43] A pedigree analysis of one family showed an autosomal dominant mode of inheritance,[41] and biochemical studies of all three families indicate that erythrocytes contain an increased amount of catalytically and immunologically normal ADA.[41,43,44,45]

PNP Deficiency

PNP deficiency has been reported in 21 children from 13 different families.[7–12,46–54] The clinical feature common to all has been a defect in cellular immunity, and except for two unrelated children,[54] humoral immunity has been either normal or hyperactive. Children have presented between 4 months and 9 years of age—usually with infections involving skin, lung, middle ear and mastoids, and urinary tract. In keeping with current concepts regarding the role of cellular immunity, infections with nonbacterial agents such as *Candida albicans*, varicella, vaccinia, and cytomegalovirus have been the most common and troublesome in these patients. Although some individuals received live virus immunization without complication, two children developed generalized vaccinia, which for one proved fatal.[10] Neurologic abnormalities have been noted in about one-half of cases and include spastic diplegia or tetraparesis, head lag, hypotonia, developmental delay, and irritability.[8,12,47,49–53] In at least six children these problems were noted prior to any recognized defect in cell-mediated immunity[49,52,53] indicating they represent effects of purine nucleoside phosphorylase deficiency per se rather than complications secondary to central nervous system infection.

X-rays may show absence of thymic shadow, but none of the bone abnormalities characteristic of ADA deficiency have been noted in PNP-deficient patients. Anemia has occurred in several children and at one point was the most conspicuous feature in the first PNP-deficient patient described, whose hypoplastic bone marrow had earlier suggested a diagnosis of Diamond-Blackfan syndrome.[7] Autoimmune hemolytic anemia has been observed in five patients.[11,12,50,51,53] One patient died at 2.5 years of age of a B-immunoblastic-type malignant lymphoma.[47]

Studies of immune function in PNP deficiency show lymphopenia, a paucity of peripheral T cells as determined by E-rosetting with sheep erythrocytes and by reactivity with monoclonal antibodies against T-cell membrane antigens, diminished or absent lymphocyte responses to phytohemagglutinin and allogeneic cells, and negative skin tests for delayed hypersensitivity. One patient, diagnosed retrospectively, suffered a fatal graft-versus-host reaction following transfusion with unirradiated whole blood.[8,55] Tests of humoral immunity typically show normal levels of immunoglobulins, isohemagglutinins, and specific antibodies. Depressed levels of serum immunoglobulins have been reported in one child, and markedly depressed IgM responses to immunizations in another.[54] One patient has had idiopathic thrombocytopenic purpura requiring treatment with steroids,[54] and another has been reported with rheumatoid factor, a positive lupus erythematosus (LE) preparation, antinuclear antibody, and a positive Coombs' test.[46] These findings and the occurrence of autoimmune hemolytic anemia in five patients has led to speculation that impairment of T-suppressor-cell activity in PNP deficiency may lead to a hyperactive state of humoral immunity.

Assays of erythrocyte lysates and other tissues show only trace-to-immeasurable levels of PNP activity. Most patients have marked hypouricemia and hypouricosuria, but actually excrete excessive amounts of total purine, which are found in the urine as inosine, guanosine, 2′-deoxyinosine, 2′-deoxyguanosine, and uric acid 9-*N*-riboside.[56] High levels of inosine and guanosine are found in patients' serums as well (see "Metabolism" below).

GENETIC ASPECTS

ADA Deficiency

Genetics and Chemistry of the Normal Enzyme. Adenosine deaminase catalyzes the irreversible deamination of adenosine and 2′-deoxyadenosine to inosine and 2′-deoxyinosine, respectively (Fig. 40-1). The highest levels of ADA activity are found in thymus and other lymphoid tissues.[57–61] Levels are higher in immature cortical thymocytes compared with medullary thymocytes and mature T lymphocytes; a decrease in ADA activity with stage of maturation was also found in B cells.[62–65]

The enzyme exists in many different physical forms, which can be accounted for by a combination of genetic polymorphism and a system of isozymes generated by posttranslational modifications and binding to a noncatalytic glycoprotein. The use of specific histochemical stains for enzyme activity has allowed characterization of ADA isozymes by their mobility during starch gel electrophoresis.[66] The pattern given by

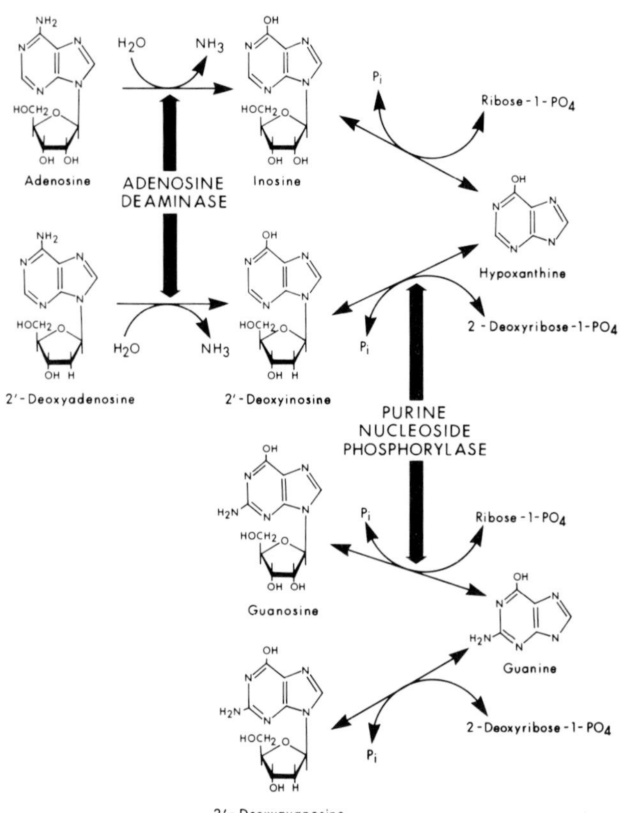

Fig. 40-1 Reactions catalyzed by ADA and PNP.

erythrocyte lysates is relatively simple, consisting of one major and two minor bands, and has been used extensively to study ADA genetic polymorphism. In the phenotype designated ADA 2, each of the three erythrocyte isozymes has a slightly slower anodal mobility than that of its counterpart in the predominant ADA 1 phenotype. A combination of the two patterns is seen in the ADA 2-1 phenotype indicating codominant expression of two alleles, designated ADA^1 and ADA^2, at an autosomal locus. This conclusion has been confirmed by pedigree analyses.[66] Thus ADA 1, ADA 2, ADA 2-1 are the phenotypes corresponding to the genotypes ADA^1/ADA^1, ADA^2/ADA^2, and ADA^2/ADA^1, respectively. ADA^2 is much less common than ADA^1 and has a gene frequency of 0.03 to 0.11 in populations described as "Negro," "English," and "Asian Indian."[66]

Examination of tissues other than erythrocytes shows more complicated isozyme patterns, which in large part are tissue-specific.[57] These "tissue isozymes" are of higher molecular weight than the erythrocyte enzymes[57,67] and arise from interaction of the ADA catalytic moiety with a protein termed *binding protein* or *complexing protein*.[68] Variations in the carbohydrate content of binding protein may account for the different tissue isozymes noted on electrophoresis.[69,70] The erythrocyte isozymes contain no binding protein and presumably reflect posttranslational modifications of the catalytic subunit itself.[71,72]

The catalytic moiety of ADA from several human tissues has been purified to homogeneity and is a single polypeptide chain with an estimated molecular weight of 36,000 to 44,000.[71–74] The purified human erythrocyte enzyme has a K_m for adenosine of 52 μM.[72] The ADA locus has been assigned to the long arm of human chromosome 20,[75] more specifically to 20q13.11.[76,77] The binding protein also has been extensively purified[70,73] and is a dimer with a native molecular weight of about 190,000. One native molecule of binding protein has been found to bind two molecules of catalytic ADA.[70] A physiological role for binding protein has not been conclusively established, but its presence on the cell surface of fibroblasts[78] and in the brush border region of proximal renal tubules[79] has prompted speculation that it may contribute to extracellular adenosine catabolism by binding ADA to the outer cell surface, or that it may be involved in the renal clearance of monomeric ADA.[80] Genes on chromosomes 2 and 6 are both required for the expression of binding protein in cultured cells.[81,82]

cDNA sequences of normal human ADA have been cloned and characterized in several different laboratories.[83–88] The amino acid sequence deduced from cDNA nucleotide sequences corresponds to a 40,762-dalton peptide containing 363 amino acids and agrees with that obtained from analyses of peptides representing approximately 73 percent of the total ADA protein.[83,88] The amino-terminal methionine is believed to be removed by posttranslational processing to give a mature ADA peptide of only 362 residues.[87]

The ADA gene itself has been cloned[89,90] and completely sequenced.[90] Spanning a total of 32 kb, it consists of 12 exons, ranging in size between 62 and 325 base pairs, and 11 introns, one of which is more than 15 kb in length (Fig. 40-2). The 135-base pair region immediately 5′ to the putative transcription start site is very rich in G and C residues (82 percent) and lacks the TATA and CAAT sequences found in the promoter regions of many other eukaryotic genes.[91] These features are characteristic of a class of genes termed "housekeeping" genes because of their expression, usually at low levels, in virtually all cells. Examples include the mouse and human genes for hypoxanthine phosphoribosyltransferase,[92–94] the hamster gene for 3-hydroxy-3-methylglutaryl-coenzyme A reductase,[95] the gene for human 3-phosphoglycerate kinase,[96] and the mouse and human genes for dihydrofolate reductase.[97,98] The promoter regions of the ADA gene and of other housekeeping genes are also noteworthy for the presence of multiple copies of the sequence GGGCGG or the inverse sequence, CCGCCC. Such sequences are also found in the promoter regions of SV40 early and late genes, where they have been shown to interact with the eukaryotic transcription factor Sp1.[99,100] Sp1 has also been shown to bind to and stimulate transcription from the promoter region of the mouse dihydrofolate reductase gene[101] suggesting that it may be involved in the expression of ADA and other housekeeping genes as well.

The Primary Genetic Defect. Protein and enzymologic studies using patient tissues have not only helped to delineate the genetic defect in ADA deficiency but have also contributed to our understanding of the relatedness of ADA isozymes. The finding that ADA-deficient children lack both erythrocyte and tissue isozymes indicates that a component common to these forms of ADA is missing or defective.[102] A minor adenosine deaminase activity has been described in the spleen, serum, and cultured lymphoblasts from ADA-deficient and normal individuals that differs from the major enzyme with respect to molecular weight, sensitivity to ADA inhibitors, immunologic reactivity, and K_m value for adenosine.[103–105] The reactivity of this enzyme at physiological adenosine concentrations is very low and probably represents a spurious aminohydrolase activity of some unknown enzyme. Binding protein is normal in

Fig. 40-2 Genes for human ADA and PNP. Exons are shown as *shaded* regions, introns as *open*. The scale is not proportional to nucleotide length. *(From the data of Wiginton et al.*[90] *for the ADA gene and Williams et al.*[154,155] *for the PNP gene.)*

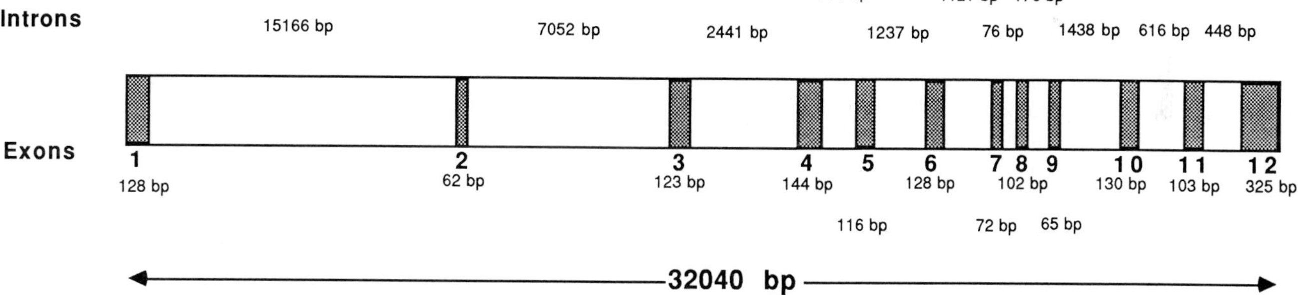

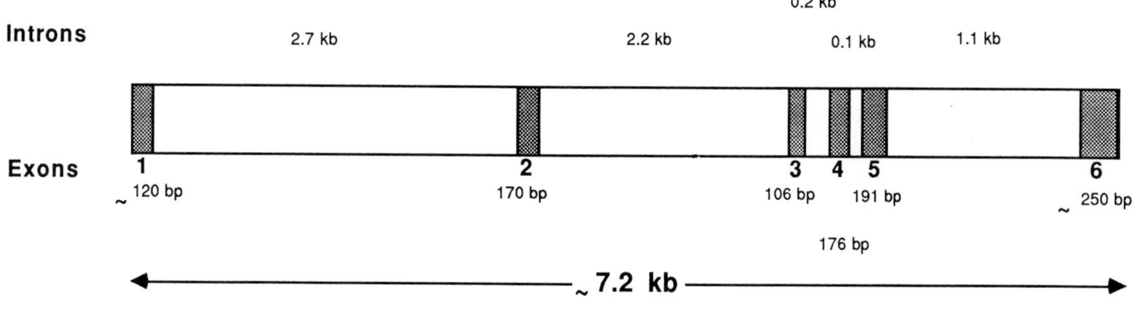

ADA deficiency as determined by direct assays[106] and by the fact that addition of tissue extracts from an ADA-deficient child to normal erythrocyte enzyme results in the formation of tissue isozymes.[107]

ADA proteins from a number of immunodeficient patients have been characterized; they react with antibody to the normal enzyme but differ with respect to electrophoretic mobility, heat stability, rates of degradation, levels of immunologically cross-reacting material, and kinetic parameters in those cases where residual activity can be measured.[106,108–115] A considerable degree of heterogeneity has been demonstrated among these mutant proteins, which is probably responsible in part for the variability in expression of SCID in ADA deficiency. The range of differences with respect to mutant proteins and clinical manifestations is even greater when individuals with partial ADA deficiency are included.[32,35,39,40,116]

The availability of cDNA probes derived from normal ADA mRNA has made it possible to measure gene expression in cultured cells from ADA-deficient individuals. All but one of the cell lines that have been investigated by Northern blot analyses have shown normal or increased levels of ADA mRNA,[85,87,115–119] suggesting that most mutations causing ADA deficiency are point mutations in the coding portion of the ADA gene. The exception is a cell line that does not produce detectable ADA mRNA and appears to be homozygous for a deletion in exon 1.[120] All of the mRNAs characterized by Northern blot analyses are of normal length, i.e., approximately 1.6 kb, except one of 1.45 kb,[119] which lacks exon 4 sequences.[121] A mutation affecting pre-mRNA splicing is thought to be responsible for this defect.

Thus far, a total of six mutant ADA alleles from four different cell lines have been characterized by cDNA sequencing (Table 40-1). Five have been shown to have a single base change in the second position of a codon resulting in amino acid substitutions that presumably decrease ADA catalytic activity, protein stability, or both;[121–123] one cDNA lacks all of exon 4.[121] Two altered codons causing amino acid substitutions have been noted in the same allele in cell line GM2471. The substitution at amino acid residue 80 of an arginine for a lysine is termed "conservative" because both are basic amino acids, and an ADA minigene engineered to contain this change alone has been shown to code for an enzymatically active protein.[123] It is likely, therefore, that the mutation at codon 304 (leucine → arginine) is responsible for the ADA defect associated with this allele in GM2471. Comparison of a number of normal and mutant ADA sequences has also shown the presence of several "silent polymorphisms" consisting of nucleotide differences that result in synonymous codons, e.g., $AAG_{lysine} \rightarrow AAA_{lysine}$ (summarized in Ref. 121). The presence of such silent polymorphisms in the alleles from GM2756 and GM2825A that have the same mutation in codon 329 (Table 40-1) proves that these alleles are not identical.[121]

Prevalence, Inheritance, and Prenatal Diagnosis. More than 60 families with ADA-deficient SCID have been reported, and the total number identified may be close to 100. The actual prevalence of this condition has not been determined, but is probably less than one in 1 million births.[124]

As expected from our knowledge of the molecular genetics of ADA, family studies have shown an autosomal recessive mode of inheritance for ADA-deficient SCID with most obligate heterozygotes having approximately half-normal levels of erythrocyte ADA. Because of an overlap between normal individuals and some obligate heterozygotes, erythrocyte ADA levels are not entirely reliable for the identification of carriers.[125] ADA levels in cultured skin fibroblasts and amniotic cells are too variable to be useful in heterozygote detection.[108]

Occasionally ADA polymorphism can be exploited to identify carriers of a mutant or "null" gene as was demonstrated in a family where three sibs with ADA 1 phenotypes were born to ADA 1 and ADA 2 parents.[126] One would have expected ADA 2-1 offspring in this situation; therefore the ADA 2 parent (in this case the mother) must have contributed a "null" gene. Similar cases have been reported in families of ADA-deficient children.[127,128]

Although unsuitable for the detection of carriers, assay of ADA in cultured amniotic cells has been used successfully in the prenatal diagnosis of ADA deficiency.[129–131] By means of a sensitive microradioassay ADA can be measured in as few as 1000 cells within 14 days after amniocentesis.[132] ADA deficiency and the carrier state have also been detected by assay of ADA in fetal blood[133] and in chorionic villi.[134,135] The major advantage of these two methods is that they can provide a diagnosis within hours of sample collection. Prenatal diagnosis of ADA deficiency has been accomplished through fetoscopy

Table 40-1 Mutations Described in Defective ADA Alleles

Cell line or patient	*Codon position*	*Codon change*	*Amino acid change*	*Reference*
GM1715	101	CGG → CAG	Arginine → glutamine	122
GM2471	80*	AAA → AGA	Lysine → arginine	123
GM2471 (same allele)	304*	CTG → CGG	Leucine → arginine	123
GM2756 (first allele)	211	CGT → CAT	Arginine → histidine	121
GM2756 (second allele)	329†	GCG → GTG	Alanine → valine	121
GM2825A (first allele)	329†	GCG → GTG	Alanine → valine	121
GM2825A (second allele)		mRNA lacks exon 4 sequences		121
R.P. (both alleles)		No mRNA; deletion of exon 1		120

*The leucine → arginine change at codon 304 is probably the major cause of loss of enzyme activity, since the lysine → arginine at codon 80 is considered a "conservative" change.[123]

†The same mutation is responsible for the defect in these two alleles, but the alleles themselves are not identical. The GM2756 allele has a silent polymorphism in the codon for Ser-110, and the GM2825 allele has a silent polymorphism in the codon for Val-178.[121]

and examination of fetal blood for lymphocytes reactive with monoclonal antibodies specific for T cells.[136]

PNP Deficiency

Genetics and Chemistry of the Normal Enzyme. Purine nucleoside phosphorylase catalyzes the reversible phosphorolysis of inosine, guanosine, and their 2′-deoxy derivatives to give either hypoxanthine or guanine and the appropriate pentose-1-phosphate (Fig. 40-1). K_m values of 44 to 60 μM have been reported for these nucleosides with the human erythrocyte enzyme.[137,138] Although the equilibrium constant in the direction of nucleoside formation is rather high (K_{eq} is 54 for inosine and 2′-deoxyinosine formation[139,140]), intracellular phosphorolysis occurs readily, probably owing to inorganic phosphate concentrations that are higher than those of ribose-1-phosphate or 2-deoxyribose-1-phosphate and efficient metabolism of hypoxanthine and guanine. The mammalian enzyme has no significant activity with adenosine as a substrate.[141] Hence, both ADA and PNP are required in the sequential degradation of adenosine and 2′-deoxyadenosine to hypoxanthine.

Human PNP has been extensively purified from several different tissues including erythrocytes,[138,142–144] placenta,[145] granulocytes,[146] and cultured fibroblasts.[147] In each case the native enzyme has been found to be a trimer composed of subunits with identical molecular weights. The erythrocyte enzyme has a native molecular weight of 87,000 to 94,000 with a subunit molecular weight of 30,000 to 32,000.[143,144,148] Similar values have been reported for the enzymes isolated from other tissues. The chromosomal locus for human PNP is at 14q13.[149,150]

As in the case of ADA, electrophoretic separations of native PNP show an extensive system of isozymes, which arise from a common gene product and vary from one tissue to another.[151] Although variant alleles of PNP have been described, they are very rare, and the locus is not polymorphic in the populations tested.[151] There is no evidence for a noncatalytic, PNP-binding protein. The most complicated pattern is found in erythrocytes, where at least seven isozymes can be demonstrated. Isozymes with a slower anodal mobility predominate in young erythrocytes, and older cells have greater amounts of the more rapidly migrating species.[152] The patterns in placenta, granulocytes, and cultured fibroblasts are much simpler, consisting of only two or three isozymes, which correspond to the slowest erythrocyte bands. From these findings it has been suggested that the slowest migrating band is the primary gene product, or at least most closely related to such, and that other bands arise from time-dependent, posttranslational modifications,[152] which are likely to be more extensive in erythrocytes than in tissues with a significant rate of protein turnover.

The separation of erythrocyte PNP subunits by isolectric focusing has shown four major and two minor forms with the same molecular weights, but with different isoelectric points.[143] Given a trimeric structure and the estimated charge differences between the four major components, one would predict the generation of 12 electrophoretically distinguishable native isozymes if all combinations of subunits were permitted. The fact that only seven are usually noted may be due to technical difficulties in obtaining sufficient resolution and sensitivity.

cDNA sequences for human PNP have been cloned from HeLa cells[153] and sequenced.[154] The open reading frame thought to represent the PNP coding region contains 289 codons and corresponds to a 32,153-dalton peptide with a deduced amino acid content similar to that found from an analysis of purified human erythrocyte PNP. The structural organization of the PNP gene has been determined from cloned genomic DNA from a normal individual[154] and from a PNP-deficient patient.[155] Exon sequences were found to extend over a distance of about 7 kb and were interspersed by five introns ranging from 0.1 to almost 3 kb in length (Fig. 40-2). The promoter region of the PNP gene has not been sequenced.

The Primary Genetic Defect. Patients from two unrelated families have been found to have residual erythrocyte PNP activities that differ from each other and from normal with respect to kinetic parameters, isoelectric point, and sensitivity to sulfhydryl reagents.[156,157] Two patients from one of these families have PNP with an altered electrophoretic mobility, 0.5 percent of normal enzyme activity, and about 50 percent of normal reactivity with specific antibody.[156,158] Studies of obligate heterozygotes have shown varying amounts of immunologically reacting protein with little or no enzyme activity, indicating the presence of catalytically inactive PNP protein.[158,159] In one family, a mutant protein could not be demonstrated in the patient, but was present in both consanguineous parents.[158,160,161] Two-dimensional protein gels and peptide maps of the PNP purified from the parents showed the presence of an altered subunit,[160,162] which subsequently was shown to be due to a mutation in codon 89 from $GAA_{glutamate}$ to AAA_{lysine}.[155]

Prevalence, Inheritance, and Prenatal Diagnosis. PNP deficiency is an autosomal recessive disorder, which must be considered very rare since it has been reported in only 21 children from 13 different families. In most cases erythrocyte PNP levels are half-normal in obligate heterozygotes. The presence of a low serum urate level in a child with recurrent infections or with autoimmune hemolytic anemia should suggest PNP deficiency. PNP deficiency has been correctly excluded in a fetus at risk by assay of cultured amniotic cells,[163] and the feasibility of measuring PNP in chorionic villi has also been demonstrated.[135]

METABOLISM

Purine Nucleosides

Giblett[3] attributes the earliest suggestion of a relationship between ADA and lymphocyte function to Wintrobe,[164] who speculated that because they were rich in ADA, lymphocytes might be "instrumental in the destruction of toxic products . . . of metabolism." Indeed, ADA and some PNP substrates are cytotoxic.[165,166] Understanding the basis for selective lymphopenia in ADA and PNP deficiencies requires an understanding of the normal metabolism of purine nucleosides, the effects of the enzyme deficiencies on their metabolism by lymphoid and nonlymphoid cells, and knowledge of the biochemical actions of nucleosides that operate in the enzyme-deficient states.

In normal individuals, the plasma concentration of adenosine is in the range of 0.05 to 0.4 μM. Levels of other purine ribo- and deoxyribonucleosides are even lower, and are usually reported as undetectable. Purine nucleoside excretion in urine is normally negligible. For comparison, plasma urate is 200 to 450 μM, and about 2 to 4 mmol uric acid is excreted daily. The flux of adenosine,[167] and probably other purine nucelosides, through plasma is very high. The low levels of nucleosides in plasma and urine reflect their rapid equilibration across cell membranes and efficient metabolism by cells.

Dietary purine nucleosides are probably catabolized and excreted without gaining access to the circulation.[168,169] The possibility that absorption might be increased in ADA- or PNP-deficient patients has not been studied. Nucleotides and nucleic acids of senescent hematopoietic cells may be a significant extracellular source of nucleoside production, particularly purine deoxyribonucleosides.[170] The surfaces of endothelial cells and some other cell types possess ectonucleotidase and ecto-ATPase activities capable of degrading extracellular nucleotides to nucleosides.[171,172] Nucleosides enter and exit cells very rapidly by means of a bidirectional, nonconcentrative facilitated diffusion transporter located in the plasma membrane and by less well characterized transport systems.[173–177]

Within cells purine nucleosides exist at low concentrations; they are generated as transient intermediates in the catabolism, interconversion, and normal metabolic turnover of nucleotides, nucleic acids, and *S*-adenosylhomocysteine. Participation of ectonucleotidases in the metabolism of intracellular nucleotides has been questioned.[178–180] Several lysosomal and cytoplasmic nucleotidases and phosphatases with differing catalytic and regulatory properties have been identified in diverse tissues,[181–187] including lymphocytes.[188,189] The physiological roles of cytoplasmic nucleotidases have not been clearly defined, though they may be involved, along with ADA, PNP, and other enzymes of nucleoside and nucleotide metabolism, in substrate cycles that subserve metabolic regulation.[190] Deficiency of ADA or PNP would interrupt cycles in which they participate, resulting in accumulation of potentially toxic ADA and PNP substrates.

Release of adenosine by adipose tissue,[191] hepatocytes,[192] well-oxygenated liver,[193,194] and other tissues may reflect the operation of substrate cycles that involve dephosphorylation of AMP, presumably catalyzed by a cytoplasmic 5′-nucleotidase.[192,195] However, deamination to form IMP, rather than dephosphorylation to form adenosine, is the major route of AMP catabolism, both under normal metabolic conditions,[181,188,196–199] and in cells made anoxic or exposed to other conditions that increase ATP breakdown.[178,181,199–201] Inosine production via dephosphorylation of IMP, which may be part of an "inosinate cycle" that involves PNP but not ADA, has been demonstrated with cultured lymphoblasts and fibroblasts.[197,202,203] In contracting skeletal muscle deamination of AMP is the first step of the "purine nucleotide cycle," which involves neither ADA nor PNP (discussed in Chap. 41).

Adenosine is formed in all cells from the hydrolysis of *S*-adenosylhomocysteine, which is a byproduct of *S*-adenosylmethionine-dependent methyl transfer reactions. Metabolic balance studies, in which the intake and excretion of methylated compounds were determined in normal adults, indicate that 14 to 23 mmol adenosine are generated from *S*-adenosylhomocysteine daily.[204] Hepatic methylation of guanidinoacetic acid to form creatine alone accounts for about 85 percent of the total. In other tissues a variety of transmethylation reactions involving nucleic acids, proteins, phospholipids, biogenic amines, and other methyl acceptors account for the remainder of the adenosine derived from this route. Hydrolysis of *S*-adenosylhomocysteine accounted for nearly all adenosine released from the isolated, normoxic guinea pig heart.[205]

Adenosine may be either phosphorylated to AMP by adenosine kinase or deaminated to inosine by ADA. The K_m values for adenosine of human adenosine kinase range from 0.4 to 3 μM,[206–208] considerably less than K_m values reported for human ADA, 25 to 74 μM.[67,72,209,210] In most tissue and cell extracts that have been studied, the total activity of ADA exceeds that of adenosine kinase. In intact human lymphocytes[211] and WI-L2 B lymphoblastoid cells[198] phosphorylation of adenosine exceeded deamination at a range of levels of exogenous adenosine from below 0.5 to 5 μM. As the concentration of adenosine increases, adenosine kinase becomes saturated and is also subject to both substrate and product inhibition.[175,206,212,213] In rat liver cleavage of adenosine to adenine occurred only at 0.25 percent of the rates of deamination or phosphorylation.[214] These studies indicate that in normal individuals phosphorylation is the major route of adenosine metabolism.

Kinases for inosine, guanosine, and deoxyinosine do not occur in mammalian cells, and significant phosphorylation of deoxyguanosine probably occurs only in PNP deficiency (discussed below). These nucleosides are normally metabolized exclusively by phosphorolysis to purine bases, which may either be reconverted to nucleotides by hypoxanthine-guanine phosphoribosyltransferase, or oxidized by xanthine oxidase to uric acid.

Deoxynucleosides and Deoxynucleotides

It has been proposed that cellular deoxynucleoside triphosphate (dNTP) pools may be regulated in part by substrate cycles involving deoxynucleotide phosphatase(s) and deoxynucleoside kinases.[215] Such cycles could be a source of deoxyadenosine or deoxyguanosine in ADA and PNP deficiency. In contrast to AMP, dAMP is a very poor substrate for AMP deaminase, and catabolism of dAMP in T lymphoblasts has been shown to proceed almost exclusively by dephosphorylation to produce deoxyadenosine.[188,201,216] Excretion of deoxyadenosine by ADA-deficient or inhibited cultured T and B lymphoblasts has been demonstrated.[217,218] In mouse T lymphoblasts, GMP could be degraded either by deamination or by dephosphorylation, but dGMP was catabolized exclusively by dephosphorylation to produce deoxyguanosine.[219]

Deoxyadenosine can be phosphorylated by purified adenosine kinase[206,220–223] and by deoxycytidine kinase, which can also catalyze deoxyguanosine phosphorylation.[208,224–227] Adenosine kinase uses deoxyadenosine as substrate much less efficiently than adenosine; human adenosine kinase has a K_m for adenosine of 0.3 to 3 μM, compared with 135 to 540 μM for deoxyadenosine.[206–208,223] For various preparations of deoxycytidine kinase, K_m values for deoxycytidine have ranged from 0.7 to 16 μM,[224,225,228] compared with 120 to 730 μM for deoxyadenosine[208,224,225,227] and 0.3 to 3 mM for deoxyguanosine.[224–226] Phosphorylation of both purine deoxynucleosides by deoxycytidine kinase is strongly inhibited by dCTP.[224] A mitochondrial kinase with a K_m of 6 μM for deoxyguanosine but without activity toward deoxycytidine has been isolated from calf thymus.[226] Other less well characterized kinases with activity toward deoxyadenosine or deoxyguanosine have been isolated from various tissues.[227,229,230]

The relative contributions of adenosine kinase and deoxycytidine kinase to the phosphorylation of purine deoxynucleoides has been evaluated in intact lymphoblastoid cells, which contain substantial amounts of both activities. In the case of S49 mouse T lymphoma cells[231] and the human B-cell line WI-L2,[208,232] loss of adenosine kinase diminished the toxicity of deoxyadenosine and eliminated the ability of deoxyadenosine to cause dATP pool expansion; loss of deoxycytidine kinase had little effect on either deoxyadenosine toxicity or dATP accumulation. In the CEM human T-cell line both deoxycytidine kinase and adenosine kinase were active in phosphorylating deoxyadenosine, with deoxycytidine kinase predominating at low concentrations of deoxyadenosine, and adenosine kinase at higher.[233-235] Mutational loss of deoxycytidine kinase eliminated[235,236] and exogenous deoxycytidine blocked[233,237-240] dGTP accumulation from deoxyguanosine in T-cell lines. In isolated normal human thymocytes deoxycytidine was able to completely block accumulation of dATP and dGTP from their deoxynucleoside precursors.[241]

The K_m of ADA for deoxyadenosine is in the range of 7 to 40 μM, comparable to that for adenosine, and the maximal rate of its deamination by ADA is 30 percent that of adenosine.[67,210,242] Consistent with the relative activities of ADA versus adenosine kinase and deoxycytidine kinase toward deoxyadenosine, deamination was by far the major route of deoxyadenosine metabolism in studies of several mouse tissues and human erythrocytes.[243] By using kinetic constants determined in extracts of rat thymocytes, it was calculated that the ratio of deamination to phosphorylation would be >2000:1 at 0.1 μM deoxyadenosine, and >200:1 even at 1 mM; analogous ratios for adenosine were 3:1 and 80:1.[242] The major route of deoxyguanosine metabolism by cultured T and B lymphoblasts was phosphorolysis, though the concentration dependence of metabolism was not studied.[244,245] However, the K_m of deoxyguanosine for human erythrocyte PNP, 44 μM,[246] is considerably lower than that for deoxycytidine kinase, and in lymphoid cells the activity of PNP far exceeds that of the kinase.[60,246,248] Taken together, available data indicate that in normal cells deoxyadenosine and deoxyguanosine are probably metabolized almost entirely by deamination and phosphorolysis, respectively. Phosphorylation only plays a significant role in their metabolism in ADA and PNP deficiency.

Metabolic Abnormalities in Plasma, Erythrocytes, and Urine of ADA- and PNP-Deficient Patients

In ADA-deficient patients, plasma levels and excretion of urate are in the normal range.[249] Since inosine is a significant precursor of urate, this is a further indication that IMP dephosphorylation rather than deamination of adenosine is the major metabolic source of inosine. The plasma concentrations of adenosine and deoxyadenosine are variable, but are usually elevated to between 0.5 and 10 μM, with that of adenosine usually being the higher. Urinary excretion of deoxyadenosine is invariably elevated, and considerably greater than excretion of adenosine, reflecting the more efficient cellular reutilization of adenosine compared with deoxyadenosine (Table 40-2). Urine of ADA-deficient patients also contains elevated levels of methylated and incompletely characterized derivatives of adenosine.[250-253]

The first metabolic studies of ADA-deficient children reported elevated levels of ATP, not dATP, in erythrocytes and lymphocytes.[16,251] Failure to identify dATP resulted from the use of enzymatic assays or chromatographic methods that did not distinguish ATP from dATP, and from the lability of deoxyadenosine and its nucleotide derivatives during prolonged exposure to acidic conditions of extraction or chromatographic analysis. The concentration of dATP in ADA-deficient red cells often equals or exceeds that of ATP. In the first reports of dATP accumulation, Coleman et al.[254] found 157 nmol dATP per 10^9 erythrocytes, compared with <0.1 nmol in normal erythrocytes, and Cohen et al.[255] found 340 to 1100 nmol dATP per milliliter of packed red cells in three immunodeficient, ADA-deficient children, compared with <20 nmol/ml packed cells in an ADA-deficient but immunocompetent child, and 8 nmol/ml in control erythrocytes. Elevated levels of dATP have been found in the red cells of ADA-deficient fetuses at 16 to 17 weeks of gestation[136,249] and in cord blood at birth.[249,256] The level of erythrocyte dATP rises after birth. In dizygotic ADA-deficient twin boys, levels of total deoxyadenosine nucleotides (dAXP) rose from 253 and 289 nmol per milliliter of packed erythrocytes in cord blood to 725 and 630 nmol per milliliter in venous erythrocytes 10 days after birth (M. S. Hershfield, unpublished).

In the most severely enzyme deficient patients, erythrocyte ATP is decreased; it may approach one-half the concentration of ATP in red cells of normal individuals.[257-260] The activity of S-adenosylhomocysteine hydrolase is invariably decreased to <10 percent, and frequently to <2 percent of normal.[259-261]

In PNP deficiency, plasma urate concentration and urinary excretion of uric acid are decreased owing to the metabolic block. Plasma inosine is usually >20 μM and may exceed 100 μM; plasma guanosine, deoxyinosine, and deoxyguanosine range from 1 to 30 μM (Table 40-2). Urinary levels of all four PNP substrates, the end products of purine catabolism in this setting, are elevated and their total exceeds the normal excretion of uric acid.[56,250] Normally undetectable in red cells, dGTP in the range of 2 to 11 nmol per milliliter of packed cells has been found in patients with PNP deficiency (Refs. 53, 262, 263; M. S. Hershfield, unpublished). Depletion of GTP to about 10 percent of normal in red cells has also been observed.[53,263,264]

Aside from erythrocytes, there is only limited information regarding dATP pool expansion in either lymphoid or nonlymphoid hematopoietic cells of ADA-deficient patients; dGTP pool expansion has never been demonstrated in nonerythroid cells of PNP-deficient patients. Marked dATP pool expansion (770 and 1760 pmol per 10^6 cells; normal, 2 to 4 pmol per 10^6 cells) was found on two occasions in peripheral blood mononuclear cells of one ADA-deficient patient who had been receiving red cell transfusions for over a year at the time of the study.[265] However, in a later report of the same patient followed over a 40-month period, the level of dATP in blood mononuclear cells was 10 ± 3.9 pmol per 10^6 cells, compared with a normal value of 5.3 ± 1.3 pmol per 10^6 cells.[266] Interestingly, dATP was found to be elevated (40 to 80 pmol per 10^6 cells) in functioning lymphocytes of donor origin isolated from the blood of an ADA-deficient patient who had undergone successful transplantation.[267] The dATP pool was about 2 percent of the ATP pool in nucleated cells, representing a mixture of mostly immature nonlymphoid hematopoetic cells, from the bone marrow of one ADA-deficient patient, while in red cells from the same marrow sample dATP content was 70 percent of the ATP pool size.[259]

Table 40-2 Purine Compounds in Plasma, Serum, and Urine of ADA- and PNP-Deficient Patients

*A. Plasma or serum, ADA and PNP deficiency**

Compound	*Controls μM*	*ADA deficiency, μM*	*PNP deficiency, μM*	*References*
Adenosine	<0.05–0.4	<0.1–10		249, 255, 256, 261, 457
Inosine	Undetectable		14–115	7, 8, 12, 56, 158, 249, 453, 458
Guanosine	Undetectable		6–29	8, 53, 158, 461
Deoxyinosine	Undetectable		2–19	53
Deoxyguanosine	Undetectable		2–14	53
Urate	220 ± 60	80–260	Trace—150	7, 12, 53, 56, 249, 458, 461

*B. Urine, ADA deficiency**

	Uric acid	*Adenosine*	*Deoxyadenosine*	*References*
Control, μmol/24 h		<2	Undetectable	
ADA deficiency, μmol/24 h		<2–5.6	60–124	265, 459
Control, μmol/g uric acid		<4.2	<0.6	460
ADA deficiency, μmol/g uric acid		5.7	193	
Control, μ*M*		<0.3, 5.4 ± 4.5	<2, <0.01	251, 314
ADA deficiency, μ*M*		1.38, 5.6	300, 68	
Control, mmol/mol creatinine	400–1000	<1	<1	249
ADA deficiency, mmol/mol creatinine	460–1600	10.3 ± 20.4	140 ± 74	249
		4.5 ± 1.2	50 ± 16	252

*C. Urine, PNP deficiency**

Compound	*Controls, mmol/24 h (mmol/g creatinine)*	*PNP deficiency mmol/24 h (mmol/g creatinine)*	*References*
Inosine	Undetectable	1.3–4.3 (4.5–17)	7, 12, 53, 56, 250, 458, 459, 461
Deoxyinosine	Undetectable	1.7, 0.4 (2.8–4.7)	53, 56, 250, 459
Guanosine	Undetectable	0.61–2.3 (1.4–7.7)	7, 12, 53, 56, 250, 458, 459, 461
Deoxyguanosine	Undetectable	0.82, 0.53 (2.3–3.6)	53, 56, 250, 459
Uric acid	(2.8–5.2)†	0.01–1.19 (0.16–3.13)	7, 12, 53, 56, 250, 458, 459, 461
Uric acid equivalents (mg/mg creatinine)	0.48–0.88†	1.9–5.1	7, 12, 56, 250, 458, 459, 461

*Data have, where possible, been recalculated for purposes of comparison of values in common units.
†Data for children from M.E. Balis, I.H. Krakoff, P.H. Berman, J. Dancis, *Science* 156:1122, 1967.

PATHOGENESIS

Overview of Experimental Systems

The severe lymphopenia of children with ADA and PNP deficiencies has limited biochemical and functional studies of their lymphoid cells. Epstein-Barr virus (EBV) transformed B-cell lines derived from these patients have been used to study purine nucleoside metabolism and toxicity. However, most investigation has involved ADA-expressing cells treated with potent ADA inhibitors such as EHNA [*erythro*-9-(2-hydroxy-3-nonyl)adenine], coformycin, and 2′-deoxycoformycin, which have inhibitory constants of 1.6×10^{-9}, 10^{-11}, and 2.5×10^{-12} M, respectively.[268] Less potent inhibitors of PNP with K_i values in the 10^{-5} to 10^{-7} M range have now been developed.[269,270] One of these, 8-aminoguanosine, has been used to study the basis for the toxicity of PNP substrates to cultured cells.[240,244,271–273] Somatic cell genetic approaches, employing mutant and hybrid lymphoblastoid cell lines, have been used to define the enzymatic basis for purine deoxynucleoside activation to cytotoxic deoxynucleotides, the basis for differing abilities of T- and B-cell lines to accumulate these nucleotides, and the mechanism of deoxynucleotide toxicity to dividing cells. Nucleoside kinase–deficient mutants have also been used to assess the toxicity due to effects of adenosine and deoxyadenosine on the catabolism of *S*-adenosylhomocysteine.

A consistent observation of in vitro studies is that ADA or PNP inhibition alone is not particularly toxic to lymphoid cells in the absence of exogenous ADA or PNP substrates. This reflects the limited production of deoxyadenosine and deoxyguanosine by living cells and the capacity of adenosine kinase to metabolize endogenously generated adenosine. When ADA is inhibited or deficient, exogenous adenosine is usually toxic in the range of 5 to 50 μ*M*, and deoxyadenosine in the range 0.2 to 50 μ*M*. Deoxyguanosine toxicity to PNP-deficient or inhibited lymphoid cells is manifest in the range of about 1 to 50 μ*M*. Variation in sensitivity is related to differences among cell types and species in the way nucleosides are metabolized or exert their effects and to differences in experimental design. Though important in identifying toxic actions of nucleosides, in vitro models cannot establish the relative importance of particular actions in contributing to the immune defects in ADA- and PNP-deficient patients.

The potent ADA inhibitor 2′-deoxycoformycin has been used to treat patients with lymphoid malignancies. At doses used clinically 2′-deoxycoformycin inhibits ADA very effectively and within a few days causes lymphopenia affecting nonmalignant as well as malignant lymphocytes.[274–279] In some patients, toxicity to nonlymphoid organs occurs which may result from inhibition of AMP deaminase as well as of ADA by higher concentrations of 2′-deoxycoformycin,[280–282] or from the ability of some cells to phosphorylate 2′-deoxycoformycin to a slight extent.[283] Although 2′-deoxycoformycin therapy is not an entirely valid model of the inherited enzyme deficiency, monitoring the biochemical consequences of its use in humans has nevertheless provided very useful information regarding the in vivo operation of potentially pathogenic mechanisms in ADA deficiency, and at least in some patients it has provided insight into possible effects of ADA deficiency on early stages in lymphoid differentiation.

Specific Mechanisms of Adenosine and Deoxyadenosine Toxicity

The major toxic effects of adenosine, deoxyadenosine, and their metabolites that have been considered as potential causes of the immune deficiency in ADA deficiency are summarized in Fig. 40-3.

Cyclic AMP as Mediator of Adenosine Toxicity. Adenosine has widespread physiological effects on cellular and organ function. The effects of adenosine include its actions as a regulator of blood flow; as an inhibitor of platelet aggregation, lipolysis, and neurotransmitter release; as a modulator of β-adrenoreceptor and insulin-mediated responses; as a stimulator of steroidogenesis and histamine release; and as an inhibitor of superoxide and hydrogen peroxide release from neutrophils. These actions are mediated through plasma membrane–associated adenosine receptors, which are coupled to adenylate cyclase and possibly to other cAMP-independent second messenger systems (for reviews see Refs. 284–287). Subtypes of adenosine receptors have been designated as A1 and A2, based on ability to inhibit (A1) or stimulate (A2) adenylate cyclase, and according to their sensitivity to adenosine analogue agonists. The A1 receptor has been isolated and shown to be coupled to a guanine nucleotide-binding protein.[288] The A2 receptor, which is found on lympocytes and most other hematopoietic cells, has not yet been isolated.

The ability of adenosine to increase levels of cAMP in lymphocytes raised the possibility that cAMP might mediate the toxicity of adenosine to lymphocytes in ADA deficiency. The reader may refer to the previous edition of this chapter for a review of experimental evidence for and against this hypothesis. Most of this evidence indicates that cAMP is not responsible for the growth-inhibitory effects of adenosine to ADA-inhibited lymphoid cells and cell lines. There is presently no indication that any of the physiologic responses affected by adenosine are abnormal in children with ADA deficiency. This may reflect adaptation to chronically elevated levels of extracellular adenosine.

Inhibition of Pyrimidine Synthesis by Adenosine. The ability of adenosine to cause depletion of cellular pyrimidine nucleotides was one of the first mechanisms proposed as the cause of lymphopenia in ADA deficiency[289] (the reader is referred to the previous version of this chapter for other references in the literature pertinent to this topic). Pyrimidine depletion in vitro requires the phosphorylation of adenosine, and appears to be due to inhibition of phosphoribosylpyrophosphate (PRPP) synthetase. This blocks *de novo* synthesis of pyrimidine nucleotides at the level of PRPP-dependent conversion of orotic acid to orotidylic acid. In some cell lines, growth inhibition by adenosine could be prevented by exogenous uridine or loss of adenosine kinase. However, uridine did not prevent the ability of adenosine to block the response of human peripheral blood lympocytes to mitogens,[290,291] and adenosine toxicity to a human B-cell line was not diminished significantly by loss of adenosine kinase activity or by addition of uridine.[292] Normal levels of UTP and CTP in blood mononuclear cells and normal excretion of orotic acid were found in studies of an ADA deficient child.[293,294] Thus there is no evidence that pyrimidine starvation occurs in vivo in ADA deficiency.

dATP and dGTP Toxicity. Lymphoblast mutants with defective nucleoside transport or inability to phosphorylate deoxyadenosine and deoxyguanosine show greatly reduced sensitivity to these nucleosides, evidence that phosphorylation, presumably to the deoxynucleoside triphosphate, is the pri-

Fig. 40-3 Effects of adenosine and deoxyadenosine that have been considered as potential causes of immune dysfunction in ADA deficiency. AdoHcy = S-Adenosylhomocysteine; AXP = adenosylnucleotides.

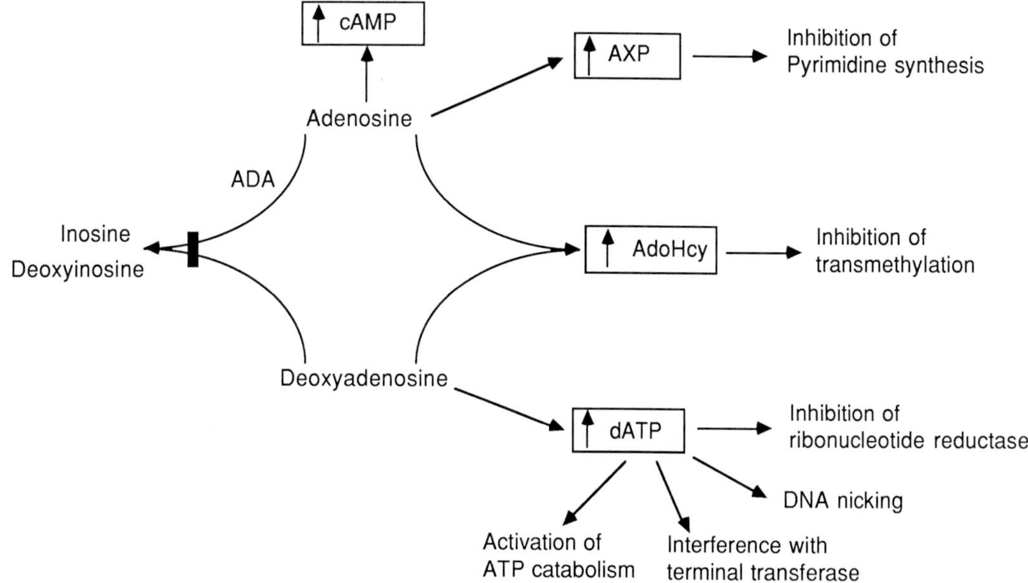

mary cause of toxicity.[208,231,232,235,236] Studies with deoxyguanosine using cell lines that possess normal or incompletely inhibited PNP activity are more difficult to interpret because salvage of guanine, produced by phosphorolysis of deoxyguanosine or guanosine, can expand the GTP pool, which also causes growth inhibition, particularly to B-cell lines.[240,244,295,296] Nevertheless, deoxyguanosine is generally more toxic than guanosine or guanine to T-cell lines, and mutant cell lines deficient in PNP or hypoxanthine phosphoribosyltransferase remain sensitive to deoxyguanosine but not to guanosine or guanine.[236,239,297]

Deoxycytidine kinase is largely confined to lymphoid tissues in the rat and mouse, with highest activity in the thymus.[298] A similar distribution was found in autopsy tissues obtained from human infants.[60,233] Freshly isolated human thymocytes have relatively high levels of purine deoxynucleoside kinase activities.[64,299] Based on this tissue distribution, it was suggested that accumulation of dATP in ADA deficiency and of dGTP in PNP deficiency should be confined to lymphoid tissue.[60] However, dATP accumulation is not an exclusively lymphoid phenomenon in vivo as indicated by the fact that erythrocytes, which contain adenosine kinase but virtually no deoxycytidine kinase, accumulate massive amounts of dATP in ADA-deficient patients. Other tissues from these patients have not been systematically examined, but dATP was present in nonlymphoid tissues in autopsy material from a child with inherited ADA deficiency,[300] and in two patients who died during treatment with 2′-deoxycoformycin, elevated dATP levels were present in both kidney and liver, and exceeded dATP levels in spleen.[278]

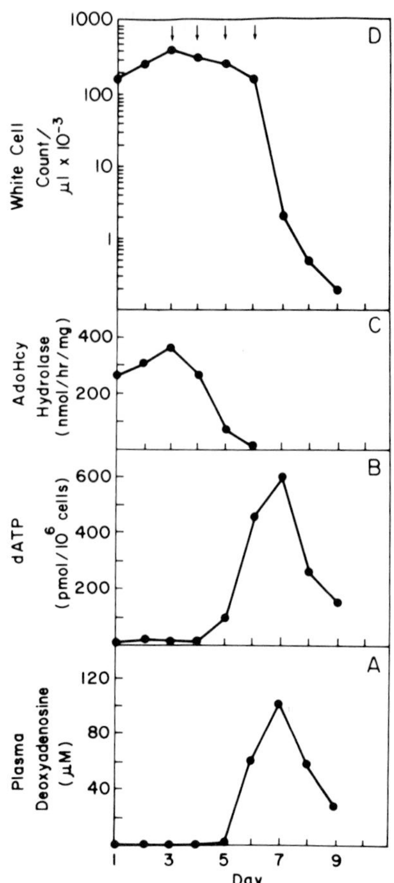

Fig. 40-4 Correlation of plasma deoxyadenosine concentration *(A)* with lymphoblast dATP levels *(B)*, lymphoblast S-adenosylhomocysteine hydrolase activity *(C)*, and white blood cell count *(D)* in a 13-year-old male with refractory T-cell leukemia during treatment with the ADA inhibitor 2′-deoxycoformycin. Complete inhibition of lymphoblast ADA was achieved on day 5. The peak concentration of deoxyadenosine was 104 µ*M* (day 7). In contrast the highest concentration of plasma adenosine achieved was 2.1 µ*M* on day 4 (not shown). Arrows in the figure indicate days on which leukapheresis was performed to lower the white cell count, prior to the onset of cell lysis on day 6. *(From Mitchell, Koller, and Heyn.[274] Used by permission.)*

DIFFERENTIAL ACCUMULATION OF dATP AND dGTP BY T AND B CELLS. It has been observed that, in general, T lymphoblastoid cell lines are more sensitive than B-cell lines to deoxyadenosine, and this correlates with the greater ability of T-cell lines to accumulate dATP.[237,248,297,301–305] T-cell acute lymphoblastic leukemia (ALL) has been more responsive to treatment with 2′-deoxycoformycin than non-T ALL, and this also correlates with ability of circulating malignant T lymphoblasts to accumulate dATP in vivo (Fig. 40-4).[274–278,306] Similarly, the greater toxicity of deoxyguanosine to T- than B-cell lines has been associated with the ability of T-cell lines to accumulate dGTP.[237,239,262,271,297,304,307–310] These differences between T- and B-cell lines cannot be explained by differences in their levels of nucleoside kinase activities[233,235] and appear, instead, to be due to the ability of B lymphoblasts to rapidly catabolize deoxynucleotides.[305,311,312] Both resistance to deoxyadenosine and ability to catabolize intracellular dATP were dominantly expressed in hybrid cell lines formed by fusion of human T and B lymphoblasts.[248]

Ecto-5′-nucleotidase,[305,311] which is higher in B- than T-cell lines, and an ecto-ATPase[313] have been proposed as the dNTP catabolic enzyme of B cells, but the presence or absence of the activities of these enzymes has not correlated well with sensitivity of lymphoblastoid cell lines to deoxynucleosides or with their ability to accumulate dATP or dGTP.[307,314–316] A cytoplasmic deoxynucleotidase has been partially purified from WI-L2 human B lymphoblasts.[312] Its K_m values for deoxynucleoside monophosphates were in the range of 300 to 600 µ*M*, much higher than the intracellular concentrations of these deoxynucleotides. The activity varied widely among lymphoblastoid cell lines, with no more than a threefold difference in extracts of T- and B-cell lines. At present the enzyme(s) responsible for dNTP catabolism in B-cell lines has not been clearly identified.

Based on the above studies of malignant T- and Epstein-Barr virus–transformed B lymphoblasts, it was postulated that T lymphocytes, but not B cells or presumably nonlymphoid cells, would be able to trap deoxyadenosine and deoxyguanosine as dATP and dGTP. This could account for the cellular immune defects in ADA and PNP deficiencies and the sparing of B-cell function both in PNP deficiency and in 10 to 15 percent of patients with ADA deficiency.[60,231,262,308,310] The distinction between T and B cells is less clear-cut at present. Some B-cell lines accumulate dATP and dGTP as efficiently as T-cell lines,[245,317] and among malignant T and B cells, the ability to accumulate deoxynucleotides may be related to the degree of maturity. Relatively mature malignant cells from patients with chronic T- and B-cell leukemia and hairy cell leukemia have very limited ability to accumulate dATP and dGTP, though these leukemias may respond to treatment with 2′-deoxycoformycin.[316,318,319]

Freshly isolated human thymocytes, both dividing and nondividing, efficiently accumulate dATP and dGTP from deoxyadenosine and deoxyguanosine and are very sensitive to the toxicity of these nucleosides.[241,299,320–322] Compared with immature thymocytes, mature circulating T cells have very small dNTP pools and only limited ability to trap deoxynucleosides as dNTPs.[299,316,321–323] ADA-inhibited B cells from peripheral blood or tonsil accumulated dATP efficiently when incubated with deoxyadenosine;[322,324] they did not accumulate dGTP from deoxyguanosine.[299] In a colony assay, both T and B cells derived from peripheral blood of normal individuals were equally sensitive to deoxyadenosine and adenosine when ADA was inhibitied.[325]

INHIBITION OF RIBONUCLEOTIDE REDUCTASE. In dividing cells, dNTP synthesis *de novo* occurs via the reduction of ADP, GDP, CDP, and UDP to their respective 2′-deoxy derivatives, catalyzed by single enzyme, ribonucleotide reductase (EC 1.17.4.1). This is a stringently regulated process that maintains dNTP pools at approximately 1 percent of the levels of corresponding NTP pools, sufficient to support only a few minutes of DNA replication. Ribonucleotide reductase is composed of nonidentical subunits, M1, an effector binding subunit, and M2, which contains nonheme iron and a unique tyrosyl radical essential for catalytic activity. A balanced production of DNA precursors is achieved by complex allosteric effects of dATP, dGTP, dTTP, and ATP, which bind to the M1 subunit[326–333] (see Fig. 6 in Ref. 320). ATP is a general activator and dATP a general inhibitor of the reduction of all four substrates. dGTP and dTTP inhibit CDP reduction, and dGTP also inhbits UDP reduction. Reduction of ADP and GDP is stimulated by dGTP and dTTP, respectively. K_i values for dATP as an inhibitor of the reduction of CDP, UDP, GDP, and ADP were 40, 55, 1500, and 4 μM for the enzyme purified from the Molt-4 human T-cell line.[334] K_i values for dGTP as an inhibitor of CDP and UDP reduction by this enzyme were 25 to 47 μM and 1.5 to 4.3 μM.

Numerous studies between 1959 and 1976 (reviewed in the previous version of this chapter) identified inhibition of ribonucleotide reductase, particularly of CDP reduction, as a cause of inhibition of DNA synthesis when nonlymphoid mammalian cells are incubated with either deoxyadenosine, deoxy guanosine, or thymidine. Since the discovery in 1977 of dATP accumulation in cells of ADA-deficient patients, similar observations have been made in studies of deoxyadenosine and deoxyguanosine toxicity to mouse and human lymphoblastoid cell lines.[166,218,231,236,238,273,308,335–337] In these studies the toxicity of deoxyadenosine and deoxyguanosine have been associated with depletion of appropriate dNTP pools, and toxicity has been prevented by addition of deoxycytidine. T lymphoblast mutants with increased levels of ribonucleotide reductase or with a reductase resistant to inhibition by dATP or dGTP show decreased sensitivity to deoxyadenosine or deoxyguanosine.[218,236,335,336] These findings have led to the hypothesis that the T-cell defects in ADA and PNP deficiencies result from inhibition or ribonucleotide reductase by dATP and dGTP, leading to inhibition of DNA replication.

In many of the studies cited above, a role for reductase inhibition in mediating deoxyadenosine and deoxyguanosine toxicity has been inferred by demonstrating a decrease in dCTP pools or a protective effect of deoxycytidine, presumed to result from maintenance of dCTP pools. However, the degree of protection by deoxycytidine is variable and may be due to inhibition of the phosphorylation of purine deoxynucleosides by deoxycytidine kinase (discussed above). In ADA-inhibited[338] and PNP-inhibited[273] human CEM T lymphoblasts, low micromolar concentrations of deoxyadenosine and deoxyguanosine, respectively, halted growth in the G1, rather than the S phase of the cell cycle, which seems inconsistent with the expected consequence of inhibition of the synthesis of DNA precursors. On the other hand, the finding that deoxyadenosine- and deoxyguanosine-resistant T lymphoblast mutants (including some derived from CEM) have altered ribonucleotide reductase activity strongly implicates inhibition of reductase as the major cause of growth inhibition. It has been speculated that purine dNTP accumulation may preferentially inhibit ribonucleotide reductase activity in cells at the G1/S boundary, possibly by preventing the reductase from associating with other proteins involved in a hypothetical complex required for initiation of replicative DNA synthesis.[273,336]

ATP Depletion. Depressed erythrocyte ATP levels were found in children with inherited ADA deficiency.[257,258] The significance of this finding was not appreciated until it was reported that a dramatic fall in erythrocyte ATP, associated with hemolysis, occurs in patients undergoing treatment with 2′-deoxycoformycin (Fig. 40-5).[277] A fall in the ATP content of circulating T lymphoblasts has also been found during treatment with 2′-deoxycoformycin.[339] In both inherited and 2′-deoxycoformycin-induced ADA deficiency there appears to be a reciprocal relationship between the levels of ATP and dATP in red cells. Hemolysis associated with half-normal levels of red cell ATP, which could not be explained by hemolytic mechanisms other than ATP depletion, has been reported in one child with inherited ADA deficiency.[259] Hemolytic anemia due to decreased levels of erythrocyte ATP has also been reported in patients with an inherited marked elevation in red cell ADA activity, which limits the ability of red cells to efficiently phosphorylate adenosine.[41]

The mechanism of deoxyadenosine-induced ATP catabolism was investigated in ADA-inhibited human T lymphoblasts.[188] Breakdown of ATP was dependent on dATP accumulation (it did not occur in nucleoside kinase–deficient cells) and proceeded via the deamination of AMP to IMP, followed by dephosphorylation of IMP. Activation of selective adenine ribonucleotide catabolism by deoxyadenosine phosphorylation could be accounted for by the findings that dAMP was much less active than AMP as a substrate for AMP deaminase, while dATP was as effective as ATP as a potent activator of both AMP deaminase and a cytoplasmic 5′-IMP nucleotidase. Coformycin, an inhibitor of AMP deaminase as well as ADA, permitted dATP accumulation, but prevented ATP breakdown in the presence of deoxyadenosine.

NAD Depletion and DNA Nicking. Treatment with 2′-deoxycoformycin causes rapid depletion of nonmalignant circulating lymphocytes,[275] which are largely nondividing cells. In vitro, deoxyadenosine is most effective in blocking the mitogenic response of ADA-inhibited lymphocytes when it is added during the first 24 h of incubation,[340] prior to the onset of DNA replication, when ribonucelotide reductase activity is very low.[341,342] In addition, low micromolar concentrations of deoxyadenosine kill unstimulated, ADA-inhibited T lymphocytes.[320,343] These observations are clearly inconsistent with the ribonucleotide reductase hypothesis of dATP toxicity.

Killing of unstimulated lymphocytes by deoxyadenosine was accompanied by dATP accumulation and ATP depletion, and all of these effects were diminished by deoxycytidine. ATP

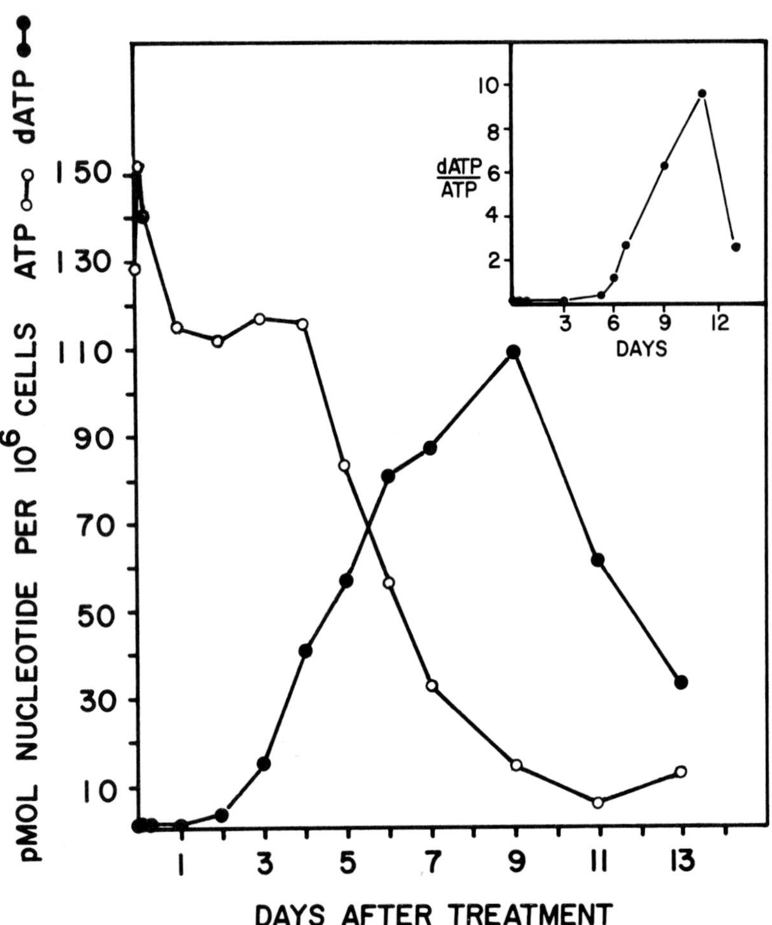

Fig. 40-5 Changes in ATP (open circles) and dATP (filled circles) in erythrocytes of a patient during treatment with 2′-deoxycoformycin. The insert shows ratios of the concentrations of dATP to ATP. *(From Siaw, Mitchell, Koller, Coleman, and Hutton.[277] Used by permission.)*

depletion was initially postulated to be the mechanism of cell death.[343] A different mechanism was later proposed based on evidence that resting lymphocytes normally contain DNA strand breaks, which are rapidly rejoined after addition of mitogens,[344,345] and also on the observation that deoxyadenosine caused accumulation of single strand breaks in DNA of unstimulated human T cells.[346] Seto et al.[347] showed that treatment of resting lymphocytes with deoxyadenosine not only induced DNA strand breaks but also depleted NAD (as well as ATP). The NAD depletion was attributed to activation of the chromatin-associated enzyme poly-ADP-ribose synthetase, which uses NAD as a substrate and is activated by DNA strand breaks.[348,349] When assessed over a 24- to 48-h period of culture, NAD depletion and the rate of loss of viability could be diminished by treatment with high concentrations (5 mM) of nicotinamide, a precursor of NAD, or of 3-aminobenzamide, an inhibitor of poly(ADP-ribose) synthetase, as well as other enzymes and metabolic processes.[350–352] Based on these findings, it was proposed that dATP in some manner caused a defect in DNA repair in resting cells, which stimulated NAD utilization for poly(ADP-ribose) formation, exceeding the ability of resting lymphocytes to maintain NAD pools; depletion of NAD would then cause a fall in ATP and cell death.[347]

In a patient with hairy cell leukemia who responded to treatment with 2′-deoxycoformycin, neither an increase in dATP, a decrease in ATP, nor DNA strand breaks were detected in circulating hairy cells during serial observations over the first 72 h of treatment.[319] Although these findings do not provide support for the DNA nicking and NAD depletion hypothesis, these malignant cells may differ from resting lymphocytes in their capacity to synthesize NAD or to repair DNA. We are not aware of other studies of this mechanism in vivo in patients undergoing treatment with 2′-deoxycoformycin, or in patients with inherited ADA deficiency.

***S*-Adenosylhomocysteine Toxicity.** Postsynthetic modification by *S*-adenosylmethionine-mediated transmethylation affects the processing or functioning of DNA, all classes of RNA and proteins, and is involved in the synthesis or further metabolism of various small molecules, including creatine, neurogenic amines, and certain phospholipids.[353,354] Methylation has been implicated in specialized cellular processes including the regulation of gene expression and cellular differentiation;[355–358] leukocyte chemotaxis;[359,360] and activation of macrophages[361] and lymphocytes.[362] Inhibition of transmethylation has been shown to interfere with these processes and to contribute to the cytotoxic effects of adenosine and deoxyadenosine in dividing lymphoid cells.

S-adenosylhomocysteine is a product (Fig. 40-6) of all transmethylation reactions, and a potent inhibitor, competitive with *S*-adenosylmethionine, of virtually all methyltransferases. K_i values for *S*-adenosylhomocysteine range from 10^{-7} to 10^{-5} M and are frequently lower than K_m values for *S*-adenosylmethionine.[353,354] Normal operation of methylation-dependent processes requires efficient catabolism of *S*-adenosylhomocysteine, which in mammalian cells is accomplished by hydrolysis to adenosine and homocysteine, catalyzed by *S*-adenosylhomocysteine hydrolase (EC 3.3.1.1).[363] This reaction is reversible and thermodynamically unfavorable (K_{eq} of 1.4×10^{-6} M). Moreover, *S*-adenosylhomocysteine hydrolase has a high affinity for adenosine: for the human enzyme the K_m is 1 μM in the *S*-adenosylhomocysteine synthesis reaction and the K_d is 0.2 to 0.5 μM for adenosine binding in the absence of homocysteine.[364,365] Because of these characteristics, catabo-

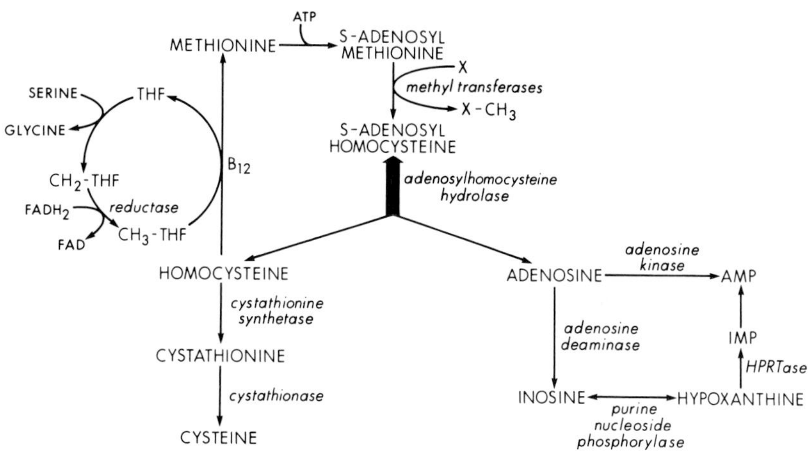

Fig. 40-6 The transmethylation pathway showing the relationships between methionine, homocysteine, and adenosine metabolism. Because of the reversibility of the S-adenosylhomocysteine hydrolase reaction, an increase in adenosine concentration, as would occur from a lack of ADA, is accompanied by a higher steady state level of S-adenosylhomocysteine, a potent inhibitor of methyl transfer reactions. THF = tetrhydrofolate; X = any of several methyl acceptors.

lism of *S*-adenosylhomocysteine depends on both adequate levels of cellular hydrolase activity and efficient metabolism of adenosine and homocysteine. Under normal conditions, deamination and phosphorylation of adenosine and removal of homocysteine via transsulfuration and remethylation (Chap. 23) permit the ratio *S*-adenosylmethionine/*S*-adenosylhomocysteine to be kept at 10:1 or greater. This ratio, sometimes called the *methylation index,* is a useful indicator of the capacity of a cell to transmethylate, both because of the competitive effects of *S*-adenosylmethionine and *S*-adenosylhomocysteine and because the basal concentration of *S*-adenosylmethionine varies among cell types.

In ADA deficiency, two mechanisms can limit the ability to degrade *S*-adenosylhomocysteine. First, elevated levels of adenosine drive the *S*-adenosylhomocysteine hydrolase–catalyzed reaction in the direction of *S*-adenosylhomocysteine formation.[366] Second, deoxyadenosine irreversibly inactivates purified *S*-adenosylhomocysteine hydrolase with kinetics characteristic of "suicide" inactivation[367] (Fig. 40-7). The inactivation constant, K_I, for deoxyadenosine was found to be 66 μM, and V_{max} to be approximately 0.12 per minute. Inactivation by deoxyadenosine and another adenosine analogue, adenine arabinoside, involves the reduction of the enzyme-bound NAD cofactor that is essential for catalytic activity.[368–372]

S-Adenosylmethionine turnover occurs in resting as well as dividing lymphocytes, and the pool size of *S*-adenosylmethionine increases sharply within 2 h after lymphocytes are exposed to mitogens.[373] In ADA-inhibited lymphoblasts[366,374] and mitogen-stimulated lymphocytes[375] concentrations of adenosine that blocked proliferation (10 to 50 μM) caused three- to twentyfold increases in *S*-adenosylhomocysteine, lowering the ratio of *S*-adenosylmethionine to *S*-adenosylhomocysteine from ≥10 to ≤3, accompanied by inhibition of both DNA and RNA methylation. Homocysteine enhanced the toxicity of adenosine by greatly accentuating *S*-adenosylhomocysteine accumulation. Studies of the toxicity of adenosine and homocysteine to adenosine kinase–deficient human lymphoblasts indicate that growth inhibition results from *S*-adenosylhomocysteine accumulation per se and not from potential effects of adenosine mediated by its phosphorylation or its interaction with adenylate cyclase.[292,374] Inactivation of *S*-adenosylhomocysteine hydrolase by deoxyadenosine caused *S*-adenosylhomocysteine accumulation and growth inhibition in ADA-inhibited lymphoblasts that are incapable of deoxyadenosine phosphorylation.[208]

These effects of adenosine and deoxyadenosine have been shown to operate in vivo during treatment with 2′-deoxycoformycin for lymphoid leukemias.[274,306,376] In circulating lymphoblasts, the concentration of *S*-adenosylhomocysteine increased by up to twenty- to thirtyfold and the ratio *S*-adenosylmethionine/*S*-adenosylhomocysteine (the methylation index) fell from approximately 40:1 to 3 to 4:1.[306,376] The rise in lymphoblast levels of *S*-adenosylhomocysteine began before maximal (80 to 95 percent) hydrolase inactivation and was accompanied by an abrupt fall in plasma homocysteine, suggesting that reversal of the hydrolase reaction caused by adenosine was responsible, as well hydrolase inactivation by deoxyadenosine. Some evidence of impaired methylation of newly synthesized RNA was observed, the degree of inhibition corresponding to the decrease in the methylation index (Fig. 40-8).[306]

Accumulation of dATP is probably the primary cause of the cytolytic effect of 2′-deoxycoformycin treatment in patients with T-cell ALL. As noted earlier, more mature malignant T and B cells of patients with chronic lymphocytic and hairy cell leukemias accumulate dATP very poorly, yet respond to treatment with relatively low doses of 2′-deoxycoformycin. In one such patient with chronic T-cell leukemia, circulating malignant cells accumulated no detectable dATP and showed minimal change in levels of ATP. However, *S*-adenosylhomocy-

Fig. 40-7 Kinetics of inactivation of human lymphoblast S-adenosylhomocysteine hydrolase by deoxyadenosine. The rate of loss of enzyme activity is first-order and saturates at high concentrations of deoxyadenosine, indicating that inactivation proceeds from an enzyme-deoxyadenosine complex. Other studies established that deoxyadenosine binds to the enzyme active site and that inactivation is irreversible, consistent with a suicidelike process. *(From Hershfield.[367] Used by permission.)*

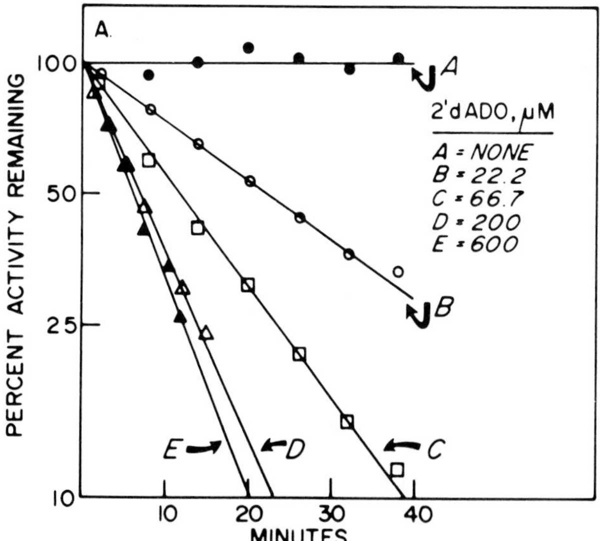

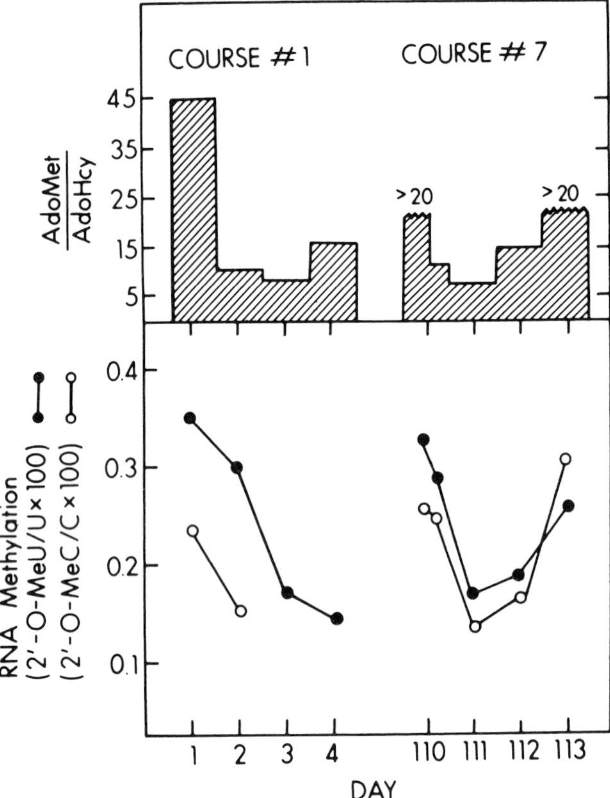

Fig. 40-8 Effects of 2′-deoxycoformycin treatment on lymphoblast methylation index and RNA methylation in a patient with T-cell acute leukemia. Two courses of treatment are depicted. The *upper panel* shows the methylation index (AdoMet/AdoHcy) in circulating lymphoblasts. The *lower panel* shows the ability of the same circulating lymphoblasts to methylate RNA. For the latter, lymphoblasts were incubated with [^{3}H]uridine and then radioactivity found in 2′-O-methyluridine and 2′-O-methylcytidine residues in newly synthesized RNA was expressed as a percent of label incorporated into the total uridylate and cytidylate residues from which the methylated residues are derived. The first point in each sequence represents a zero-time control value obtained just before administration of 2′-deoxycoformycin. The abbreviations are: 2′-O-MeU/U = ratio of 2′-O-methyluridine to uridine in RNA; 2′-O-MeC/C = ratio of 2′-O-methylcytidine to cytidine in RNA; AdoMet = S-adenosylmethionine; AdoHcy = S-adenosylhomocysteine. *(From Hershfield, Kredich, Koller, Mitchell, Kurtzberg, Kinney, and Falletta.*[306] *Used by permission).*

steine hydrolase activity in these cells fell by about 60 percent and accumulation of *S*-adenosylhomocysteine occurred, with a decline in the methylation index from 47:1 to 6:1.[318]

Erythrocytes of ADA-deficient children have less than 2 percent of normal *S*-adenosylhomocysteine hydrolase activity, presumably the result of inactivation by deoxyadenosine in vivo.[259–261,377] Nucleated cells from bone marrow of three ADA-deficient patients were found to have normal amounts of immunologically reactive *S*-adenosylhomocysteine hydrolase protein, but with a specific activity approximately 15 percent of normal (Refs. 259,378; M.S. Hershfield, unpublished). There are presently no data regarding *S*-adenosylhomocysteine levels in nucleated cells of children with ADA deficiency. Hydrolase activity is also decreased to 15 to 20 percent of normal in erythrocytes from children with PNP deficiency.[377,379] Of the PNP substrates, inosine was found to be both a weak substrate and a weak inactivator of *S*-adenosylhomocysteine hydrolase, with K_m and K_I values of 9.3 m*M* and 5.9 m*M*, respectively.[379]

The gene for human *S*-adenosylhomocysteine hydrolase has been mapped to the long arm of chromosome 20, which also bears the locus for the ADA gene.[380,381] It has been speculated that in view of the dependence of *S*-adenosylhomocysteine hydrolase activity on ADA activity in vivo, there may have been some selective advantage in physical linkage of the ADA and hydrolase genes during their evolution.[380]

Other in Vitro Effects of ADA Deficiency. In addition to effects on replicative DNA synthesis, it has been suggested[254] that a marked increase in the dATP pool could modify the product of terminal deoxynucleotidyl transferase, a template-independent DNA polymerase found in thymic lymphocytes and in bone marrow lymphoid progenitors which may play some role in generating immunologic diversity.[382–387] In the presence of manganese, dATP, but not other dNTPs, is also a potent inhibitor of terminal transferase.[388]

As little as 1 μ*M* deoxyadenosine, but not adenosine or deoxyguanosine, inhibited RNA synthesis in unstimulated, ADA-inhibited human blood lymphocytes.[389] Inhibition of RNA synthesis occurred within 4 h and was associated with dATP accumulation but not ATP depletion. In ADA-inhibited CEM T cells radiolabeled deoxyadenosine was incorporated into the 3′-OH terminal position of polyadenylated segments of cytoplasmic poly(A)$^+$ RNA.[390] In a cell-free system, *S*-adenosylhomocysteine inhibited the initiation of transcription by RNA polymerase II but did not block polymerization of preinitiated RNA.[391] The concentration of *S*-adenosylhomocysteine required for this effect was >100 μ*M*, while 1 to 10 μ*M* inhibited mRNA cap methylation. It was suggested that *S*-adenosylhomocysteine might influence the stability of the initiation complex by some mechanism other than inhibition of methylation.

At the level of lymphocyte function, a number of phenomena have been reported to be influenced by purine nucleosides. Brief exposure of normal human CD4$^+$ T helper cells to adenosine induced a rapid expression of CD8 antigen followed by development of suppressor activity, an effect thought to be mediated through adenosine receptors.[392,393] As little as 1 μ*M* deoxyadenosine inhibited the function of human blood–derived T cells in a mixed lymphocyte culture (MLC) assay, and in MLC-activated T cells somewhat higher concentrations blocked interleukin (IL) 2 production and expression of the IL-2 receptor; addition of IL-2 did not overcome the antiproliferative effect of deoxyadenosine.[394]

Dysregulation, rather than absence of lymphocytes, may be more important a factor in PNP deficiency in view of the autoimmune phenomena described in some patients. Deoxyguanosine blocked antigen-induced human T suppressor cell activity at micromolar concentrations, but much higher concentrations were required to block nonproliferative T helper cell function and the differentiation and proliferation of B lymphocytes.[304] Administration of deoxyguanosine abrogated the development of suppressor T cells in mice.[395–397]

Differentiation. Formation of erythroid, myeloid, and T lymphoid colonies from committed human marrow progenitors was equally sensitive to micromolar concentrations of deoxyadenosine in the presence of nontoxic concentrations of 2′-deoxycoformycin.[398] Identical results were obtained with peripheral blood–derived progenitors.[325] In the latter study adenosine was only slightly less toxic than deoxyadenosine, and both nucleosides were equally toxic to T- and B-cell colony formation and to both helper and suppressor T-cell colonies. When cells were exposed to 2′-deoxycoformycin and deoxyadenosine for various times before continuing culture in the absence of nucleosides, deoxyadenosine was more toxic to T-cell than to myeloid colonies.[399] When normal human marrow cells were cultured in spleen cell–conditioned medium to enhance their survival in vitro, 2′-deoxycoformycin and adenosine killed nondividing T cells but did not affect the viability or ability to differentiate hematopoietic progenitor cells; in contrast 2′-deoxycoformycin and deoxyadenosine killed both T cells and nonlymphoid progenitors.[400]

Incubation of precursor cells from the bone marrow of children with SCID with normal thymic epithelium but not fibroblasts induced erythrocyte rosette receptor expression. With precursors from ADA-deficient patients, but not from children with other forms of SCID, an ADA inhibitor blocked erythrocyte rosette receptor expression; this block could be reversed by addition of ADA.[401] This was interpreted as demonstrating a requirement for ADA at the earliest stage of T-cell differentiation.

Although direct in vitro study of the effects of nucleosides on proliferation and differentiation of pluripotent stem cells is not yet possible, some potentially informative observations have been made of patients with stem-cell leukemias. The abrupt conversion from a T lymphoblastoid to a myeloid phenotype has occurred in close association with 2′-deoxycoformycin therapy in two patients who were considered to have stem-cell leukemias.[376,402] In one of these patients[376] phenotypic conversion occurred within 3 to 4 days of a 3-day infusion of 2′-deoxycoformycin. Cytogenetic evidence showed that pretreatment T lymphoblasts and postconversion myeloid cells arose from the same clone. Accumulation of both dATP and *S*-adenosylhomocysteine occurred in leukemia cells during treatment. These observations and other considerations suggested that biochemical effects of ADA inhibition had induced a change in the direction of differentiation of a malignantly transformed, pluripotent stem cell from lymphoid to myeloid. In vitro studies with the patient's leukemia cells and with a cell line derived from them showed that both were capable of multilineage differentiation.[376,403] Treatment of the cell line in its undifferentiated state with deoxyadenosine, adenosine, and with nucleoside analogues that specifically inhibit *S*-adenosylhomocysteine hydrolase induced the expression of myeloid characteristics.[403,404] Based on these observations it was proposed that the absence of lymphoid lineages in ADA deficiency might be explained by biochemical effects that selectively interfered with lymphoid differentiation at the stage of a pluripotent stem cell.

Purine Overexcretion in PNP Deficiency

The hypouricemia and hypouricosuria that occur in PNP deficiency are easily explained by the block in synthesis of the uric acid precursors hypoxanthine and guanine. These bases are also substrates for hypoxanthine phosphoribosyltransferase, so that a major salvage pathway for purine nucleotide synthesis is also eliminated by complete PNP deficiency. As with primary deficiency of hypoxanthine phosphoribosyltransferase (Chap. 38), the metabolic consequence of impaired purine salvage in PNP deficiency is also overproduction of purines *de novo*. This is manifested by an overexcretion of the end products of purine catabolism, the nucleoside substrates for PNP.[56] For example, a 10-kg PNP-deficient child excreted in 24 h 0.08 mmol uric acid, and 1.78, 0.71, 0.40, and 0.53 mmol each of inosine, guanosine, deoxyinosine, and deoxyguanosine, with total purine excretion of 3.59 mmol. A 12.8-kg control child excreted 0.92 mmol total purines, 95 percent as uric acid.[250] Thus far no clinical consequences of this purine overproduction have been noted, which reflects the greater solubility of nucleosides compared with uric acid and the distribution among four rather than production of one molecular species.

In hypoxanthine phosphoribosyltransferase deficiency two mechanisms may cause purine overproduction: diminished synthesis of feedback inhibitory nucleotides and increased intracellular PRPP, both of which regulate the rate of purine nucleotide synthesis by the *de novo* pathway (Chap. 37). Markedly elevated PRPP concentrations are found in cultured fibroblasts of patients with hypoxanthine phosphoribosyltransferase deficiency, but fibroblasts from a PNP-deficient patient had normal levels of PRPP.[56] A model that may account for these differences in PRPP levels and for the common overproduction of purines in the two diseases has been proposed which is based on the different ways that the two enzyme deficiencies affect operation of the inosinate cycle[197] (Fig. 40-9). In hypoxanthine phosphoribosyltransferase deficiency reutilization of purine bases derived from the phosphorolysis of PNP substrates is deficient, but salvage of the other product, ribose-1-phosphate, after isomerization to ribose-5-phosphate, can still occur, resulting in an increase in steady state concentration of PRPP. In PNP deficiency there is an equal block in salvage of both the purine base and ribosyl moieties of PNP substrates, so that this source of excess PRPP is eliminated. In both disorders there is a block in salvage synthesis of feedback inhibitory purine nucleotides, and this could account for the increased activity of the *de novo* pathway in each case.

Basis for Selective Immune Dysfunction in ADA and PNP Deficiencies

Despite the body of information regarding the metabolism and actions of ADA and PNP substrates, there is not yet a precise understanding of the causes of immune deficiency in patients with ADA and PNP deficiency. Attempts to account for the "purinogenic" immunodeficiency diseases in terms of a single mechanism, such as inhibition of ribonucleotide reductase, seem overly reductionist in view of the multiplicity of biochemical actions of purine nucleosides and evidence of effects on virtually every stage of lymphoid development, from the still uncommitted pluripotent stem cell to the mature, circulating lymphocyte.

ATP and GTP function not only as precursors of RNA and phosphate donors, but also as effectors that modify the function of cell surface hormone receptors and proteins in all cellular compartments. In contrast dATP and dGTP serve much more limited functions, which may all be related to DNA metabolism in the nucleus. Purine deoxyribosyl metabolites could potentially act as structural analogue inhibitors of reactions that have evolved with specificity for their purine ribosyl counterparts. Examples of such pathologic analogue effects are the inactivation of *S*-adenosylhomocysteine hydrolase by deoxyadenosine and the ability of dATP to activate ATP catabolism. The toxic inhibition of ribonucleotide reductase by excessive pools of dATP and dGTP represents the abnormal accentuation of a physiologic regulatory mechanism in which these metabolites are effectors.

In the face of selective pressure to avoid detrimental substrate analogue effects, cells appear to have evolved sophisti-

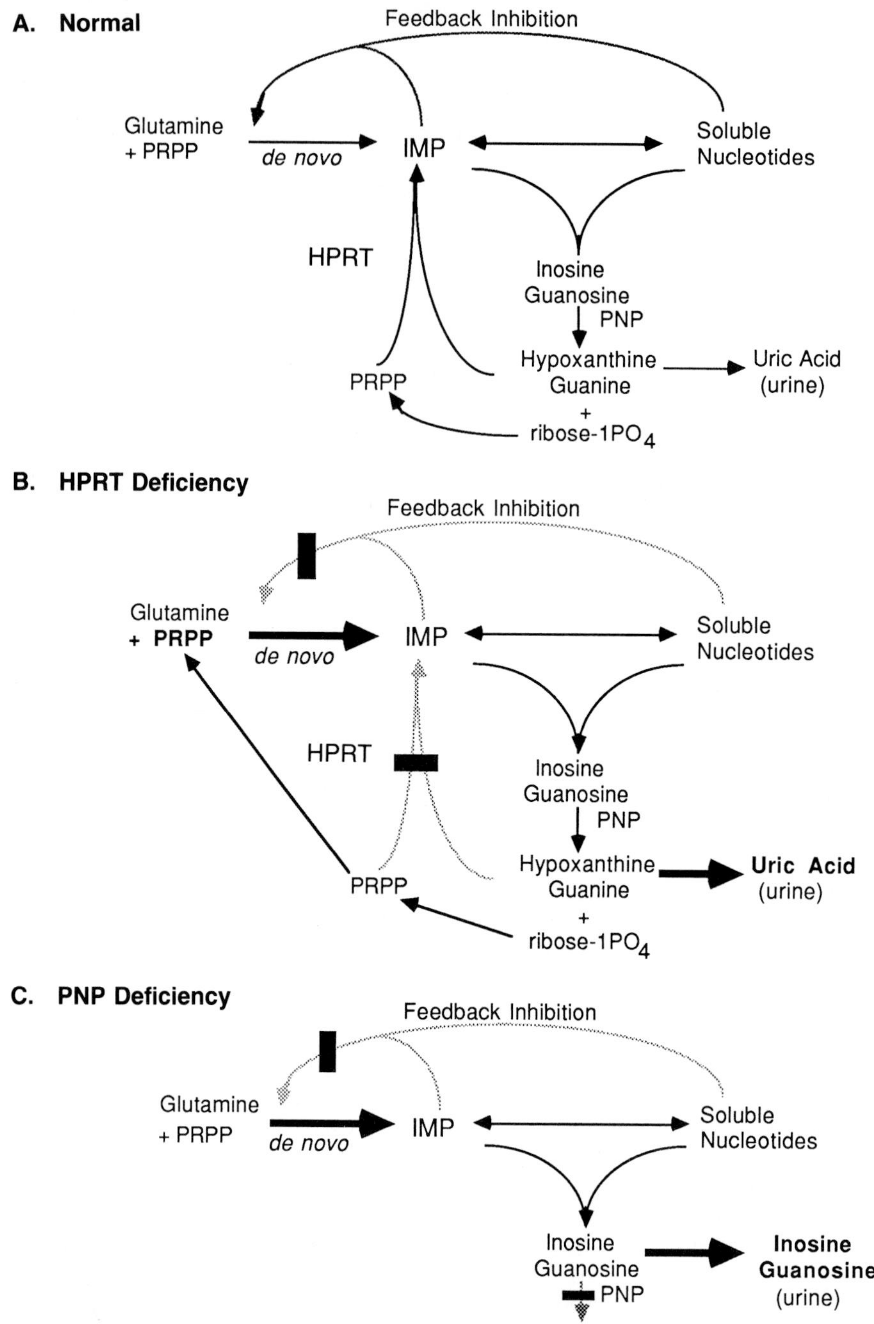

Fig. 40-9 Schema depicting factors that may affect the cellular content of phosphoribosylpyrophosphate (PRPP), purine nucleotide synthesis, and the urinary excretion of purines in *A.* normal individuals, in patients with genetic deficiencies of *B.* hypoxanthine phosphoribosyltransferase (HPRT), and *C.* purine nucleoside phosphorylase (PNP). In normal individuals there is a "balanced" reutilization, via HPRT-catalyzed IMP synthesis, of the ribose and purine base moieties generated by PNP-catalyzed phosphorolysis of inosine and guanosine, with a fraction of the hypoxanthine and guanine being converted to uric acid. In HPRT deficiency virtually all of the hypoxanthine and guanine are converted to uric acid, while the ribose-1-PO4 generated by the PNP reaction continues to be reutilized by cells, contributing to an increased steady state concentration of PRPP. Both increased PRPP concentration and diminished salvage synthesis of feedback-inhibitory nucleotides result in enhanced synthesis of purine nucleotides via the *de novo* pathway. In PNP deficiency inosine and guanosine, rather than uric acid, are the end products of purine catabolism. There is an equivalent block in formation, and hence reutilization, of both the ribose and purine bases ordinarily generated by the PNP reaction. Therefore, there is no increase in steady state concentration of PRPP in cells capable of purine synthesis *de novo*, and the diminished salvage synthesis of feedback-inhibitory nucleotides alone accounts for enhanced synthesis *de novo* of purine nucleotides. *(Modified from Hershfield and Seegmiller.[197] Used by permission.)*

cated mechanisms for limiting the size of purine deoxyribonucleoside and deoxyribonucleotide pools. The regulatory properties of ribonucleotide reductase and the relative inefficiency of purine deoxynucleoside kinases are examples of such mechanisms. The expression of high levels of ADA and PNP in lymphoid cells at certain stages of differentiation may represent additional, lineage-specific mechanisms, perhaps needed to protect differentiating lymphocytes during intrathymic development, when programmed cell death on a massive scale[405] may generate high levels of potentially toxic nucleosides. Given the unique role of gene rearrangement and somatic mutation in the development of T and B cells, it is also possible that accumulation of deoxyribosyl metabolites may interfere with DNA recombination or repair enzymes (one possibility being terminal transferase) which are uniquely essential to lymphoid differentiation. It is intriguing that a form of SCID in mice, which is not due to ADA or PNP deficiency, appears to be caused by a defect in a recombinase involved in rearrangement of antigen receptor genes.[406]

TREATMENT

As in all immunodeficiency states, supportive care consisting of varying degrees of isolation and antisepsis combined with vigorous antibiotic therapy for specific infections is essential. It is particularly important to avoid exposure to common childhood viral illnesses such as varicella, and immunization with live virus is contraindicated. Administration of immunoglobulin is used in ADA-deficient children with SCID and may prove useful in the management of certain infections in children with PNP deficiency. Specific forms of therapy are discussed below.

Transplantation

Bone marrow transplantation from a histocompatible donor is the treatment of choice for children with SCID or other life-threatening primary T-cell defects. Unfortunately, HLA-identical donors are usually not available, and until recently, transplantation with marrow from nonidentical donors has been associated with fatal graft-versus-host disease (GVHD). Improved techniques for removing postthymic T cells from bone marrow aspirates now allow the use of HLA-haploidentical donor marrow with high rates of engraftment and minimal risk from GVHD.[407–409] ADA-deficient patients have been successfully treated with bone marrow from HLA-identical and haploidentical donors[54,408–412] but may not respond as well as SCID patients with normal ADA.[408,409,412] It has been speculated that partial correction of metabolic abnormalities by donor cells may allow development of host T cells to the point where they reject the transplant; conversely, it is possible that continued abnormalities in adenosine and 2′-deoxyadenosine metabolism[413] may impede the development of transplanted stem cells. T-cell numbers and in vitro function were improved in a PNP-deficient patient following bone marrow transplantation from a haploidentical donor, but it was not clear that these changes were due to the transplant since engraftment could not be demonstrated.[54]

Fetal liver and thymus transplantation have been used with limited success in ADA deficiency[18,414,415] and in a single patient with PNP deficiency, who eventually died of a lymphosarcoma.[55] In one child with ADA deficiency, transfusion of peripheral blood lymphocytes from an HLA-AB identical parent resulted in engraftment and marked improvement in T-cell function and clinical status.[416] Thymosin and other thymic peptide hormones have been used with little or no long-term success in patients with ADA or PNP deficiency.[54,417,418] Improved laboratory measurements of T-cell function were noted in one ADA-deficient patient only with a combination of erythrocyte transfusion (see below) and thymosin.[419]

Engraftment after tissue transplantation for ADA deficiency has been characterized by chimerism for circulating lymphocytes. T cells are virtually always of donor origin, but in some patients B cells do not engraft and continue to be derived from host stem cells. Transient erythrocyte chimerism has been reported in two patients.[411,414] Erythrocyte dATP levels after successful engraftment have ranged from completely normal[411] to levels higher than those found prior to transplantation.[416] In two patients erythrocyte dATP levels were markedly reduced following bone marrow transplantation but still remained ten- to fiftyfold higher than normal.[413] Decreases in urinary excretion of adenosine and deoxyadenosine were also noted, but plasma adenosine levels were as high as in untreated patients. *S*-adenosylhomocysteine hydrolase levels were about 20 percent of normal.[413]

Enzyme Replacement

Although dATP, *S*-adenosylhomocysteine, and dGTP cannot easily cross cell membranes, they are in metabolic equilibrium with nucleoside substrates of ADA and PNP, which can equilibrate rapidly with plasma via the cell membrane–associated nucleoside transporter. Thus, circulating ADA and PNP in plasma should be capable of depleting enzyme-deficient cells of toxic metabolites, provided sufficient enzyme activity could safely and conveniently be maintained. The feasibility of enzyme replacement therapy for ADA deficiency was first suggested by the finding that the mitogenic response of blood lymphocytes from a patient was stimulated by addition of ADA to the culture medium.[420]

The ability to use circulating enzyme would overcome one potential limitation to enzyme replacement therapy: the need for targeted delivery and cellular uptake.[421,422] Other major barriers to enzyme replacement therapy are the short circulating life of purified cytoplasmic proteins and the potential immunogenicity of the administered enzyme if it must be obtained from a nonhuman source. To overcome these problems, the approach that was first taken to treat ADA deficiency consisted of transfusion of frozen, irradiated (to reduce the risk of graft-versus-host disease) red cells from normal donors.[16] Erythrocyte ADA can be increased to near normal by transfusions repeated at 2- to 4-week intervals; this activity decays with a half-life of 3 to 4 weeks. This treatment schedule decreased plasma levels of adenosine[255] and deoxyadenosine[17,419] and urinary excretion of deoxyadenosine.[17] Reductions in erythrocyte dATP of 90 percent or more have been observed[17,255,266,423] and reflect both the metabolic state of the transfused cells and loss of dATP from remaining ADA-deficient cells. Transfusion therapy improved immune function and clinical status in some children,[16,17,419,423] but the response has been transient or inadequate in others.[266,418,424–426] A review of ten patients showed that the five whose response was judged good had residual T- and B-cell function prior to treatment, while four who did not respond had no residual function.[427]

Two of the five patients who initially responded to transfusion therapy subsequently died, one of varicella pneumonia after several years of treatment (U. Sorensen, personal communication) and the second of refractory hemolytic anemia due to sensitization to a ubiquitous minor erythrocyte antigen (R. Hirschhorn, personal communication). The other three children each developed iron overload, indicated by markedly increased serum transferrin levels and documented in one patient by liver biopsy,[431] requiring a decrease in the frequency of transfusions and treatment with deferoxamine. Transfusions were discontinued at 10 to 12 years of age, when each of the three began receiving enzyme replacement therapy with polyethylene glycol–modified ADA (see below). In addition to sensitization to red cell antigens and iron overload, chronic red cell transfusion exposes immunodeficient patients to the risks of acquiring hepatitis, Epstein-Barr virus, and other viral infections. The treatment requires hospitalization and may be uncomfortable and traumatic, as well as inconvenient. Partial exchange transfusion in young patients must be carefully monitored to avoid circulatory embarrassment. Erythrocyte transfusion has been considered a "holding action" treatment for ADA-deficient patients for whom transplantation is ineffective or is considered inadvisable by their parents or the physicians involved in their care.[13,15,427]

A novel solution to the problems of immunogenicity and the short circulating life of injected enzymes involves modification of the purified enzyme by covalent attachment of the inert polymer monomethoxypolyethylene glycol (PEG) through lysine residues. This modification can greatly slow the clearance of proteins from the circulation, diminish immunogenicity, and prevent degradation by proteases and binding by antibody.[428,429] These effects presumably result from the increased size of the modified enzyme and from steric effects of the flexible, bulky, and hydrophilic PEG molecules. Attachment of PEG of average molecular weight 5000 to approximately 60 percent of the 22 lysine residues of bovine ADA diminished its immunogenicity and increased its circulating half-life from <30 min to ~30 h in mice.[430] These results, and the lack of toxicity of PEG-ADA in animals, suggested its use for treatment of ADA deficiency.

Published results of clinical testing of PEG-ADA replacement therapy for from 3 to 10 months are available in three patients with ADA deficiency.[260,431] Additional data have been obtained from continued treatment of these three patients for up to 2.5 years (M.S. Hershfield, R. Buckley, R. Kobayashi, U. Sorensen, unpublished) and from three others for more than a year (M.S. Hershfield, A. Rubinstein, R. Hirschhorn, unpublished results). PEG-ADA is readily absorbed after intramuscular injection, reaching peak levels in plasma in 24 to 48 h, after which plasma ADA activity declines with a half-life of approximately 3 to 5 days. Weekly injection of 15 to 20 units of PEG-ADA per kilogram of body weight maintains blood ADA activity at one to three times (trough to peak) the normal level of blood ADA. The enzyme is not appreciably taken up by blood cells.

In each of the six patients now undergoing treatment, PEG-ADA replacement therapy has reversed almost completely the major metabolic abnormalities associated with ADA deficiency (Fig. 40-10*A* and *B*): in erythrocytes levels of adenosine nucleotides have increased to normal, and levels of deoxyadenosine nucleotides have decreased so as to be nearly undetectable (5 to 15 nmol per milliliter of packed erythrocytes); *S*-adenosylhomocysteine hydrolase activity has returned to normal in both red cells and nucleated bone marrow cells. The degree of correction in these abnormalities was greater than had been seen while these children were receiving red cell transfusions.

Evidence of improvement in vitro tests of immune function has taken as little as 3 weeks and as long as 4 to 5 months to appear (Fig. 40-10*C*). This lag is similar to that encountered after haploidentical bone marrow transplantation and may also be related to both the severity of the preexisting immunodeficiency and the age at which replacement therapy was begun. The mitogenic response of blood mononuclear cells increased dramatically to near-normal levels in all six patients, although responses have fluctuated during treatment. In contrast, while receiving transfusion therapy responses in four of the patients to mitogens did not exceed 10 percent of normal. The percentage of T cells among blood mononuclear cells increased, though the children remained somewhat lymphopenic, and the ratio of $CD4^+$ to $CD8^+$ cells was normal. Improvement in B-cell function took somewhat longer to appear. In the first two patients, treated for 29 months and 24 months, immunoglobulin levels increased and the responses to immunization with tetanus, diphtheria and bacteriophage ϕX174 were near normal, whereas before treatment there was no production of specific antibody. No toxicity or allergic reactions were observed. Using an ELISA technique, circulating antibodies to native, but not PEG-modified, bovine ADA are detectable in the plasma of some patients (M. Nucci, unpublished). The significance of this finding is not clear since the circulating life of the modified enzyme has not been affected in any patient, and in some patients such antibodies could be detected before PEG-ADA therapy was begun.

While the clinical response to treatment is still being evaluated, PEG-ADA therapy appears to improve immunologic function and is considerably more convenient than transfusion therapy, and it avoids the risks of transmitting virus infection, producing sensitization to red cell antigens, and causing iron overload. On the other hand, the long-term effects of receiving a few milligrams of PEG-modified protein each week over the course of a lifetime cannot now be predicted. Nevertheless, the experience with PEG-ADA has clearly been more successful than previous attempts at enzyme replacement therapy for inherited diseases of metabolism. At present the use of PEG modification strategy would seem to be limited to other diseases in which toxic cellular metabolites are in equilibrium with plasma.

Attempts have been made to treat four PNP-deficient patients by red cell transfusion. No improvement was noted in two patients.[432,433] Limited improvement in percentage of T cells and in mitogenic response was seen in the other two.[434,435] In the latter children there was marked decrease in urinary excretion of PNP substrates and total purines, an increase in plasma and urinary urate, and reduction in red cell dGTP.[435] Based on these results, the development of PEG-PNP for treatment of PNP deficiency would appear a reasonable goal.

Metabolite Replacement

Correction of a putative dCTP deficiency by oral or parenteral administration of deoxycytidine has been attempted in a total of four individuals with ADA deficiency[418,427,436] and in two patients with PNP deficiency.[49,434,437] The only significant effects of this form of therapy were transient improvements in laboratory measurements of T-cell function in one ADA-deficient patient[436] and in one patient with PNP deficiency.[437] Some improvements in in vitro T-cell function were noted in two patients receiving oral uridine, but not in a third.[46,417]

SOMATIC CELL GENE THERAPY

A mechanism for evaluating somatic cell gene therapy clinical protocols has been established.[438] Selected patients with ADA and PNP deficiencies, presumably those who have not responded to, or are not candidates for, more conventional therapy, are considered likely subjects for early trials of gene therapy.[439,440] The following limited discussion deals with preclinical studies of techniques that might be used to treat these patients.

Several observations suggest that introduction of a functional human ADA gene into bone marrow stem cells of patients with ADA deficiency might correct their immune defect, even if normal expression of the transferred gene were not achieved: (1) Allogeneic bone marrow transplantation can reconstitute the immune system in ADA-deficient SCID patients. (2) The reappearance of functional lymphocytes in patients receiving PEG-ADA replacement therapy indicates the presence of endogenous stem cells capable of normal lymphoid differentiation. (3) Immune function is normal in individuals with partial ADA deficiency whose lymphocytes express as little as 2 to 5 percent of normal ADA activity. Conversely, overexpression of ADA activity is not likely to be harmful, based on experience with patients with inherited overexpression of ADA in erythroid cells. (4) Expression of ADA is likely to confer resistance to toxic ADA substrates and a strong survival advantage to lymphoid progeny of transformed stem cells. Similar considerations may apply to PNP deficiency.

Since lymphohematopoietic stem cells account for ≤0.1 per-

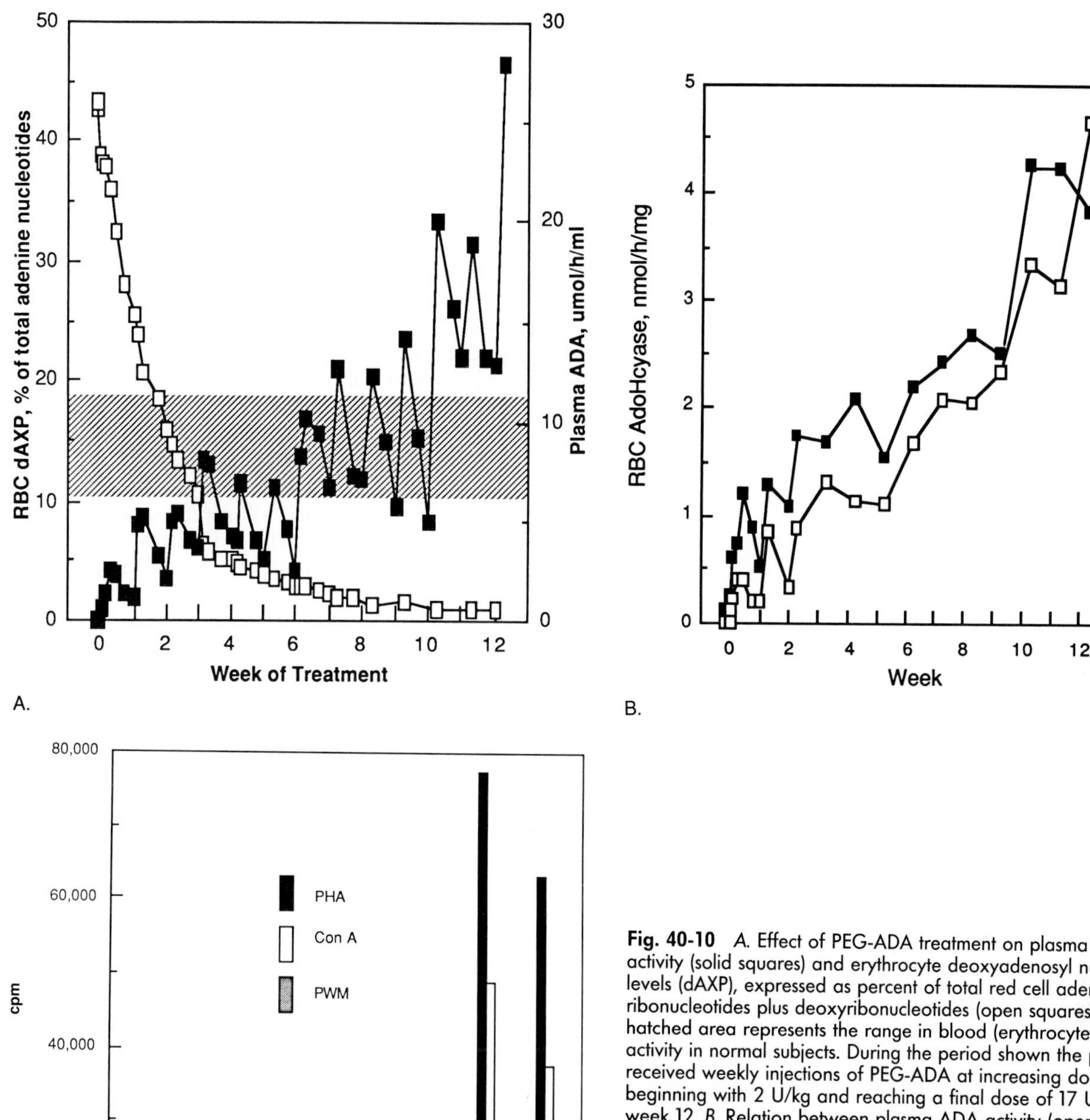

Fig. 40-10 *A.* Effect of PEG-ADA treatment on plasma ADA activity (solid squares) and erythrocyte deoxyadenosyl nucleotide levels (dAXP), expressed as percent of total red cell adenine ribonucleotides plus deoxyribonucleotides (open squares). The hatched area represents the range in blood (erythrocyte) ADA activity in normal subjects. During the period shown the patient received weekly injections of PEG-ADA at increasing doses, beginning with 2 U/kg and reaching a final dose of 17 U/kg at week 12. *B.* Relation between plasma ADA activity (open squares) and erythrocyte *S*-adenosylhomocysteine hydrolase activity (AdoHcyase, solid squares) in the same patient. Values were determined 24 to 48 h after injection of PEG-ADA, and correspond to peak levels of plasma ADA activity in *A. C.* Proliferative response of peripheral blood mononuclear cells to mitogens during treatment with PEG-ADA. The data are from the same patient. Proliferation is measured as counts per minute (cpm) of [^{3}H]thymidine incorporated per 10^5 cells. Values for normal controls ranged from 70,000 to 153,000 for PHA; 73,000 to 125,000 for Con A; and 30,000 to 60,000 for PWM. PHA = phytohemagglutinin; Con A = concanavalin A; PWM = pokeweed mitogen. *(From Hershfield, Buckley, Greenberg, Melton, Schiff, Hatem, Kurtzberg, Kobayashi, Kobayashi, and Abuchowski.[260] Used by permission.)*

cent of marrow nucleated cells, very efficient transfer of genetic material into target cells may be essential to the chances for successful gene therapy of ADA and PNP deficiency. At present only vectors derived from retroviruses are capable of high efficiency gene transfer (for review see Refs. 441, 442). Murine leukemia viruses and Maloney sarcoma virus have been exploited as vectors in experimental models of gene therapy because of their well-characterized biology and the existence of amphotropic strains capable of infecting human cells.[443] Upon entering a cell, which must be undergoing replication, retroviral single stranded RNA is transcribed by virion-associated reverse transcriptase into double stranded DNA, which then circularizes and integrates randomly and stably into the host genome as a provirus. Signals for integration are present in terminally repeated segments of the viral genome, called LTRs, which also contain promoter and enhancer sequences that regulate expression of contiguous genes, located between the LTRs, that encode the viral core proteins *(gag)*, reverse transcriptase *(pol)*, and envelope proteins *(env)*. The retrovirus life cycle is completed when genomic RNA, replicatively transcribed from the integrated provirus, combines with the *gag*, *pol*, and *env* gene products to yield infectious virus that buds nonlytically from the host.

Most of the region between the LTRs can be removed from cloned proviral DNA and replaced with the gene(s) to be transferred. The resulting recombinant genome can be propagated by introduction into a "packaging" cell line that possesses an integrated "helper" provirus, which provides the trans-acting *gag*, *pol*, and *env* products necessary for infectious virion assembly. By using mutant helper virus that lacks a specific cis-acting sequence (called *psi*) necessary for packaging of its own RNA, high titer preparations of infectious retroviral vectors can be prepared free of helper virus.[443,444] Such vectors retain the ability to infect target cells, undergo reverse transcription, integrate, and express the inserted gene(s), but they cannot replicate since they lack *gag*, *pol*, and *env* genes. In addition to the cDNA of therapeutic interest (ADA or PNP), vectors may carry a "dominant selectable" gene that confers a conditional advantage on cells in which it is expressed. Exposure of infected target cells to the selective conditions permits enrichment and easy identification of cells in which the vector has integrated. Examples of selectable markers include the bacterial gene for neomycin resistance (neo^R) and cDNA for methotrexate-resistant dihydrofolate reductase. Expression of the inserted gene(s) may be under control of the viral LTR regulatory sequences, or alternatively, an "internal" promoter can be placed adjacent to the 5′ terminus of the insert. For example, the SV40 virus early promoter and metallothionein promoter have been used to drive expression of the ADA and PNP genes.

Using various retroviral vector constructs, cDNA for human ADA has been introduced into cultured murine fibroblasts,[445,446] murine lymphoid cell lines,[446,447] and human T-cell (HTLV-I transformed) and B-cell (EBV transformed) lines derived from ADA-deficient patients.[448] In each case stable in vitro expression of the human ADA cDNA was easily demonstrated, often without preselection. Human PNP activity has been expressed in cell lines transformed with plasmid vectors carrying cDNA for human PNP.[449] However, gene transfer efficiencies were low compared to results obtained with retroviral vectors, which were also used to express human PNP in vitro in murine bone marrow cells.[450]

Retrovirus vector–mediated ADA gene transfer and expression have been examined in more direct models of gene therapy in mice and primates. Human ADA cDNA linked to an SV40 promoter was expressed in myeloid progenitor cells and their progeny after infected mouse bone marrow was cultured in vitro.[451] However, when infected marrow was injected into lethally irradiated mice, little or no ADA gene expression was detected in regenerating spleen hematopoietic colonies, either with ADA genes linked to the SV40 promoter[447] or to the mouse metallothionein promoter;[450] the ADA gene was not expressed even in colonies in which the intact, integrated provirus could be demonstrated. Irradiated cynomolgus monkeys could be rescued by transplantation of autologous marrow that had been infected with a retrovirus vector carrying human ADA cDNA linked to an SV40 promoter. However, only very limited transfer and transient expression of the vector ADA gene was detected in circulating hematopoietic cells.[452] These experiments suggest that upon differentiation in vitro stem cells may lose their ability to recognize a particular promoter or that signals in the viral LTR interfere with their recognition in stem cells. Further studies may lead to discovery of promoters that remain active in stem cells. In addition, retroviral vectors have been developed that possess deletions of viral promoter and enhancer sequences within 3′ LTR. Upon integration these vectors yield a provirus that is transcriptionally inactive, which appears to allow expression of inserted genes to be directed more effectively by internal promoters.[453,454] The use of such "self-inactivating" vectors may diminish the possibility of activating cellular oncogenes at the site of integration, which is a potential risk of gene therapy.

Another approach to gene therapy involves the grafting or implantation of cloned, differentiated cells, such as fibroblasts, that have been transduced with the gene of interest in vitro.[455,456] Cultured fibroblasts from an ADA-deficient patient expressed 12 times the normal level of ADA activity following infection with a retroviral vector containing cDNA for human ADA linked to an SV40 promoter.[456] It was proposed that if this level of expression were maintained after reimplantation into an ADA-deficient patient, 4×10^8 transduced fibroblasts could provide as much ADA activity as a unit of red cells. The usefulness of this approach will depend on the life span of the cell used to deliver the ADA or PNP gene, the level of gene expression, and the access of toxic metabolites to the cell. The ability to define exactly the structure of the integrated vector and its effects on the cloned cells that are to be implanted would be advantageous. This technique would not require efficient gene delivery, so that use of retroviral vectors might be avoided.

REFERENCES

1. ROSEN FS, WEDGWOOD RJ, EIBL M, AIUTI F, COOPER MD, GOOD RA, GRISCELLI C, HANSON LA, HITZIG WH, MATSUMOTO S, SELIGMANN M, SOOTHILL JF, WALDMANN TA: Primary immunodeficiency diseases: Report of a World Heatlh Organization scientific group. *Clin Immunol Immunopathol* 40:166, 1986.
2. GIBLETT ER, ANDERSON JE, COHEN F, POLLARA B, MEUWISSEN HJ: Adenosine deaminase deficiency in two patients with severely impaired cellular immunity. *Lancet* 2:1067, 1972.
3. GIBLETT ER: ADA and PNP deficiencies: How it all began. *Ann NY Acad Sci* 451:1, 1985.
4. DISSING J, KNUDSEN JB: Adenosine deaminase deficiency and combined immunodeficiency syndrome. *Lancet* 2:1316, 1972.
5. OCHS HD, YOUNT JE, GIBLETT ER, CHEN SH, SCOTT CR, WEDGWOOD RJ: Adenosine-deaminase deficiency and severe combined immunodeficiency syndrome. *Lancet* 1:1393, 1973.
6. POLLARA B, PICKERING RJ, MEUWISSEN HJ: Combined immunodeficiency disease and adenosine deaminase deficiency, an inborn error of metabolism. *Pediatr Res* 7:362, 1973.
7. GIBLETT ER, AMMANN AJ, WARA DW, SANDMAN R, DIAMOND LK: Nucleoside-phosphorylase deficiency in a child with severely defective T-cell immunity and normal B-cell immunity. *Lancet* 1:1010, 1975.
8. STOOPS JW, ZEGERS BJM, HENDRICKX GFM, SIEGENBEEK VAN HEUKELOM LH, STAAL GEJ, DE BREE PK, WADMAN SK, BALLIEUX RE: Purine nucleoside phosphorylase deficiency associated with selective cellular immunodeficiency. *N Engl J Med* 296:651, 1977.
9. BIGGAR WD, GIBLETT ER, OZERE RL, GROVER BD: A new form of nucleoside phophorylase deficiency in two brothers with defective T-cell function. *J Pediatr* 92:354, 1978.
10. VIRELIZIER JL, HAMET M, BALLET JJ, REINERT P, GRISCELLI C: Impaired defense against vaccinia in a child with T-lymphocyte deficiency associated with inosine phosphorylase defect. *J Pediatr* 92:358, 1978.
11. CARAPELLA-DE LUCA E, AIUTI F, LACARELLI P, BRUNI L, BARONI CD, IMPERATO C, ROOS D, ASTALDI A: A patient with nucleoside phosphorylase deficiency, selective T-cell deficiency, and autoimmune hemolytic anemia. *J Pediatr* 93:1000, 1978.
12. RICH KC, ARNOLD WJ, PALELLA T, FOX IH: Cellular immune deficiency with autoimmune hemolytic anemia in purine nucleoside phosphorylase deficiency. *Am J Med* 67:172, 1979.
13. HIRSCHHORN R: Inherited enzyme deficiencies and immunodeficiency: Adenosine deaminase (ADA) and purine nucleoside phosphorylase (PNP) deficiencies. *Clin Immunol Immunopathol* 40:157, 1986.

14. HIRSCHHORN R: Clinical delineation of adenosine deaminase deficiency, in Elliot K, Whelan J (eds): *Enzyme Defects and Immune Dysfunction, Ciba Foundation Symposium 68*, New York, Excerpta Medica, 1979, p 35.

15. POLMAR SH: Metabolic aspects of immunodeficiency disease. *Semin Hematol* 17:30, 1980.

16. POLMAR SH, STERN RC, SCHWARTZ AL, WETZLER EM, CHASE PA, HIRSCHHORN R: Enzyme replacement therapy for adenosine deaminase deficiency and severe combined immunodeficiency. *N Engl J Med* 295:1337, 1976.

17. HIRSCHHORN R, PAPAGEORGIOU PS, KESARIWALA HH, TAFT LT: Amelioration of neurologic abnormalities after "enzyme replacement" in adenosine deaminase deficiency. *N Engl J Med* 303:377, 1980.

18. ACKERET C, PLUSS HJ, HITZIG WH: Hereditary severe combined immunodeficiency. *Pediatr Res* 10:67, 1976.

19. HIRSCHHORN R: Defects of purine metabolism in immunodeficiency diseases, in Schwartz RS (ed): *Progress in Clinical Immunology*. New York, Grune & Stratton, 1977, vol 3, p 67.

20. COHEN F, CEJKA J, CHANG C-H, BROUGH AJ, ROWE BJ, GAINES PJ: Adenosine deaminase deficiency and immunodeficiency, in Pollara B, Pickering RJ, Meuwissen HJ, Porter IH (eds): *Inborn Errors of Specific Immunity*. New York, Academic, 1979, p 401.

21. WOLFSON JJ, CROSS VF: The radiographic findings in 49 patients with combined immunodeficiency, in Meuwissen HJ, Pickering RJ, Pollara B, Porter IH (eds): *Combined Immunodeficiency Disease and Adenosine Deaminase Deficiency: A Molecular Defect*. New York, Academic, 1975, p 225.

22. HIRSCHHORN R, VAWTER GF, KIRKPATRICK JA JR, ROSEN FS: Adenosine deaminase deficiency: Frequency and comparative pathology in autosomally recessive severe combined immunodeficiency. *Clin Immunol Immunopathol* 14:107, 1979.

23. SCHWARTZ AL, POLMAR SH, STERN RC, COWAN DH: Abnormal platelet aggregation in severe combined immunodeficiency disease with adenosine deaminase deficiency. *Br J Haematol* 39:189, 1978.

24. LEE CH, EVANS SP, ROZENBERG MC, BAGNARA AS, ZIEGLER JB, VAN DER WEYDEN MB: In vitro platelet abnormality in adenosine deaminase deficiency and severe combined immunodeficiency. *Blood* 53:465, 1979.

25. HUBER J, KERSEY J: Pathologic features, in Meuwissen HJ, Pickering RJ, Pollara B, Porter IH (eds): *Combined Immunodeficiency Disease and Adenosine Deaminase Deficiency: A Molecular Defect*. New York, Academic, 1975, p 279.

26. CEDERBAUM SD, KAITILA I, RIMOIN DL, STIEHM ER: The chondro-osseous dysplasia of adenosine deaminase deficiency with severe combined immunodeficiency. *J Pediatr* 89:737, 1976.

27. RATECH H, GRECO MA, GALLO G, RIMOIN DL, KAMINO H, HIRSCHHORN R: Pathologic findings in adenosine deaminase-deficient severe combined immunodeficiency. *Am J Pathol* 120:157, 1985.

28. JENKINS T: Red-blood-cell adenosine deaminase deficiency in a "healthy" Kung individual. *Lancet* 2:736, 1973.

29. JENKINS T, LANE AB, NURSE GT, HOPKINSON DA: Red cell adenosine deaminase (ADA) polymorphism in Southern Africa, with special reference to ADA deficiency among the !Kung. *Ann Hum Genet* 42:425, 1979.

30. JENKINS T, RABSON AR, NURSE GT, LANE AB: Deficiency of adenosine deaminase not associated with severe combined immunodeficiency. *J Pediatr* 89:732, 1976.

31. JENKINS T, LANE AB: The red cell adenosine deaminase polymorphism in Southern African populations with particular reference to the !Kung of Tsumkwe, Southwest Africa/Nambia, in Pollara B, Pickering RJ, Meuwissen HJ, Porter IH (eds): *Inborn Errors of Specific Immunity*. New York, Academic, 1979, p 73.

32. HIRSCHHORN R, ROEGNER V, JENKINS T, SEAMAN C, PIOMELLI S, BORKOWSKY W: Erythrocyte adenosine deaminase deficiency without immunodeficiency. Evidence of an unstable mutant enzyme. *J Clin Invest* 64:1130, 1979.

33. PERIGNON JL, HAMET M, BROYER M, GRISCELLI C, LENOIR G, CARTIER P: Primary hyperoxaluria and adenosine deaminase deficiency without immunodeficiency. *Int J Pediatr Nephrol* 1:26, 1980.

34. BORKOWSKI W, GERSHON AA, SHENKMAN L, HIRSCHHORN R: Adenosine deaminase deficiency without immunodeficiency: Clinical and metabolic studies. *Pediatr Res* 14:885, 1980.

35. DADDONA PE, MITCHELL BS, MEUWISSEN HJ, DAVIDSON BL, WILSON JM, KOLLER CA: Adenosine deaminase deficiency with normal immune function. *J Clin Invest* 72:484, 1983.

36. AMMANN AJ, COWAN MJ, MARTIN DW, WARA DW: Dipyridamole and intravenous deoxycytidine therapy in a patient with adenosine deaminase deficiency. in Wedgwood RJ, Rosen FS, Paul NW (eds): *Primary Immunodeficiency Diseases, March of Dimes Birth Defects*. New York, AR Liss, 1983, p 117.

37. SCHMALSTEIG FC, MILLS GC, TSUDA H, GOLDMAN AS: Severe combined immunodeficiency in a child with a healthy adenosine deaminase deficient mother. *Pediatr Res* 17:935, 1983.

38. HART SL, LANE AB, JENKINS T: Partial adenosine deaminase deficiency: Another family from southern Africa. *Hum Genet* 74:307, 1986.

39. HIRSCHHORN R, ELLENBOGEN A: Genetic heterogeneity in adenosine deaminase (ADA) deficiency: Five different mutations in five new patients with partial ADA deficiency. *Am J Genet* 38:13, 1986.

40. HIRSCHHORN R, MARTINIUK F, ROEGNER-MANISCALCO V, ELLENBOGEN A, PERIGNON JL, JENKINS T: Genetic heterogeneity in partial adenosine deaminase deficiency. *J Clin Invest* 71:1887, 1983.

41. VALENTINE WN, PAGLIA DE, TARTAGLIA AP, GILSANZ F: Hereditary hemolytic anemia with increased red cell adenosine deaminase (45- to 70-fold) and decreased adenosine triphosphate. *Science* 195:783, 1977.

42. MIWA S, FUJII H, MATSUMOTO N, NAKATSUJI T, ODA S, ASANO H, ASANO S: A case of red-cell adenosine deaminase overproduction associated with hereditary hemolytic anemia found in Japan. *Am J Hematol* 5:107, 1978.

43. PERIGNON JL, HAMET M, BUC HA, CARTIER PH, DERYCKE M: Biochemical study of a case of hemolytic anemia with increased (85-fold) red cell adenosine deaminase. *Clin Chim Acta* 124:205, 1982.

44. FUJII H, MIWA S, TANI K, FUJINAMI N, ASANO H: Overproduction of structurally normal enzyme in man: Hereditary haemolytic anaemia with increased red cell adenosine deaminase activity. *Br J Haematol* 51:427, 1982.

45. CHOTTINER EG, CLOFT HJ, TARTAGLIA AP, MITCHELL BS: Elevated adenosine deaminase activity and hereditary hemolytic anemia: Evidence of abnormal translational control of protein synthesis. *J Clin Invest* 79:1001, 1987.

46. AMMAN AJ: Immunologic abberations in purine nucleoside phosphorylase deficiencies, in Elliot K, Whelan J (eds): *Enzyme Defects and Immune Dysfunction, Ciba Foundation Symposium 68*. New York, Excerpta Medica, 1979, p 55.

47. WATSON AR, EVANS DI, MARSDEN HB, MILLER V, ROGERS PA: Purine nucleoside phosphorylase deficiency associated with a fatal lymphoproliferative disorder. *Arch Dis Child* 56:563, 1981.

48. ZUBAY JM, De La CONCHA EG, LUDEÑA C, LOZANO C, PASCUAL-SALCEDO D, BOOTELLO A, GONZALEZPORQUÉ P: B cell hyperactivity and abnormalities in T cell markers and immunoregulatory function in a patient with purine nucleoside phosphorylase deficiency. *Clin Exp Immunol* 50:610, 1982.

49. WATSON AR, SIMMONDS HA, WEBSTER RD, LAYWARD L, EVANS DIK: Purine nucleoside phosphorylase (PNP) deficiency: A therapeutic challenge. *Adv Exp Med Biol* 196A:53, 1984.

50. MCGINNISS MH, WASNIOWSKA K, ZOPF DA, STRAUS SE, REICHERT CM: An erythrocyte Pr auto-antibody with sialoglycoprotein specificity in a patient with purine nucleoside phosphorylase deficiency. *Transfusion* 25:131, 1985.

51. SIMMONDS HA, FAIRBANKS LD, MORRIS GS, TIMMS P, SINGH B, BOLD A: Erythrocyte GTP depletion in PNP deficiency presenting with haemolytic anaemia and hypouricemia. *Adv Exp Med Biol* 195A:481, 1986.

52. RIJKSEN G, KUIS W, WADMAN SK, SPAAPEN LJM, DURAN M, VOORBROOD BS, STAAL GEJ, STOOP JW, ZEGERS BJM: A new case of purine nucleoside phosphorylase deficiency: Enzymologic, clinical and immunologic characteristics. *Pediatr Res* 21:137, 1987.

53. SIMMONDS HA, FAIRBANKS LD, MORRIS GS, MORGAN G, WATSON AR, TIMMS P, SINGH B: Central nervous system dysfunction and erythrocyte guanosine triphosphate depletion in purine nucleoside phosphorylase deficiency. *Arch Dis Child* 62:385, 1987.

54. MARKERT ML, HERSHFIELD MS, SCHIFF RI, BUCKLEY RH: Adenosine deaminase and purine nucleoside phosphorylase deficiencies: Evaluation of therapeutic interventions in eight patients. *J Clin Immunol* 7:389, 1987.

55. STOOP JW, EIJSVOOGEL VP, ZEGERS BJM, BLOK-SCHUT B, VAN BEKKUM DW, BALLIEUX RE: Selective severe cellular immunodeficiency: Effect of thymus transplantation and transfer factor administration. *Clin Immunol Immunopathol* 6:289, 1976.

56. COHEN A, DOYLE D, MARTIN DW Jr, AMMANN AJ: Abnormal purine metabolism and purine overproduction in a patient deficient in purine nucleoside phosphorylase. *N Engl J Med* 295:1449, 1976.

57. EDWARDS YH, HOPKINSON DA, HARRIS H: Adenosine deaminase in human tissues. *Ann Hum Genet* 35:207, 1971.

58. ADAMS A, HARKNESS RA: Adenosine deaminase activity in thymus and other human tissues. *Clin Exp Immunol* 26:647, 1976.

59. VAN DER WEYDEN MB, KELLEY WN: Human adenosine deaminase: Distribution and properties. *J Biol Chem* 251:5448, 1976.

60. CARSON DA, KAYE J, SEEGMILLER JE: Lymphospecific toxicity in adenosine deaminase deficiency and purine nucleoside phosphorylase deficiency: Possible role of nucleoside kinase(s). *Proc Natl Acad Sci USA* 74:5677, 1977.

61. HIRSCHHORN R, MARTINIUK F, ROSEN FS: Adenosine deaminase activity

in normal tissues and tissues from a child with severe combined immunodeficiency and adenosine deaminase deficiency. *Clin Immunol Immunopathol* 9:287, 1978.

62. BARTON R, MARTINIUK F, HIRSCHHORN R, GOLDSCHNDEIDER I: Inverse relationship between adenosine deaminase and purine nucleoside phosphorylase in rat lymphocyte populations. *Cell Immunol* 49:208, 1980.

63. CHECHIK BE, SCHRADER WP, MINOWADA J: An immunomorphologic study of adenosine deaminase distribution in human thymus tissue, normal lymphocytes, and hematopoietic cell lines. *J Immunol* 126:1003, 1981.

64. MA DDF, SYLWESTROWICZ TA, GRANGER S, MASSAIA M, FRANKS R, JANOSSY G, HOFFBRAND AV: Distribution of terminal deoxynucleotidyl transferase and purine degradative and synthetic enzymes in subpopulations of human thymocytes. *J Immunol* 129:1430, 1982.

65. CHECHIK BE, SCHRADER P, PERETS A, FERNANDES B: Immunohistochemical localization of adenosine deaminase distribution in human benign extrathymic lymphoid tissues and B-cell lymphomas. *Cancer* 53:70, 1984.

66. SPENCER N, HOPKINSON DA, HARRIS H: Adenosine deaminase polymorphism in man. *Ann Hum Genet* 32:9, 1968.

67. AKEDO H, NISHIHARA H, SHINKAI K, KOMATSU K, ISHIKAWA S: Multiple forms of human adenosine deaminase. I Purification and characterization of two molecular species. *Biochim Biophys Acta* 276:257, 1972.

68. NISHIHARA H, ISHIKAWA S, SHINKAI K, AKEDO H: Multiple forms of human adenosine deaminase. II Isolation and properties of a conversion factor from human lung. *Biochim Biophys Acta* 302:429, 1973.

69. SWALLOW DM, EVANS L, HOPKINSON DA: Several of the adenosine deaminase isozymes are glycoproteins. *Nature* 269:261, 1977.

70. DADDONA PE, KELLEY WN: Human adenosine deaminase binding protein. Assay, purification, and properties. *J Biol Chem* 253:4617, 1978.

71. SCHRADER WP, STACY AR, POLLARA B: Purification of human erythrocyte adenosine deaminase by affinity column chromatography. *J Biol Chem* 251:4026, 1976.

72. DADDONA PE, KELLEY WN: Human adenosine deaminase: Purification and subunit structure. *J Biol Chem* 252:110, 1977.

73. SCHRADER WP, STACY AR: Purification and subunit structure of adenosine deaminase from human kidney. *J Biol Chem* 252:6409, 1977.

74. WIGINTON DA, COLEMAN MS, HUTTON JJ: Purification, characterization and radioimmunoassay of adenosine deaminase from human leukemic granulocytes. *Biochem J* 195:389, 1981.

75. TISCHFIELD JA, CREAGAN RP, NICHOLS EA, RUDDLE FH: Assignment of a gene for adenosine deaminase to human chromosome 20. *Hum Hered* 24:1, 1974.

76. PHILLIP T, LENOIR G, ROLLAND MO, PHILLIP I, HAMET N, LAURAS B, FRAISSE J: Regional assignment of the ADA locus 20q13.2 qter by gene dosage studies. *Cytogenet Cell Genet* 27:187, 1980.

77. PETERSEN MB, TRANEBJAERG L, TOMMERUP N, NYGAARD P, EDWARDS H: New assignment of the adenosine deaminase gene locus to chromosome 20q13.11 by study of a patient with interstitial deletion 20q. *J Med Genet* 24:93, 1987.

78. ANDY RJ, KORNFELD R: The adenosine deaminase binding protein of human skin fibroblasts is located on the cell surface. *J Biol Chem* 257:7922, 1982.

79. SCHRADER WP, BRYER PJ: Characterization of an insoluble adenosine deaminase complexing protein from human kidney. *Arch Biochem Biophys* 215:107, 1982.

80. SCHRADER WP, HARDER CM, SCHRADER DK, WEST CA: Metabolism of different molecular forms of adenosine deaminase intravenously infused into the rabbit. *Arch Biochem Biophys* 230:158, 1984.

81. KOCH G, SHOWS TB: A gene on human chromosome 6 functions in assembly of tissue-specific adenosine deaminase isozymes. *Proc Natl Acad Sci USA* 75:3876, 1978.

82. KOCH G, SHOWS TB: Somatic cell genetics of adenosine deaminase expression and severe combined immunodeficiency disease in humans. *Proc Natl Acad Sci USA* 77:4211, 1980.

83. ORKIN SH, DADDONA PE, SHEWACH DS, MARKHAM AF, BRUNS GA, GOFF SC, KELLEY WN: Molecular cloning of human adenosine deaminase gene sequences. *J Biol Chem* 258:12753, 1983.

84. VALERIO D, DUYVESTEYN MGC, MEERA KAHN P, GUERTS van KESSEL A, de WAARD A, van der EB AJ: Isolation of cDNA clones for human adenosine deaminase. *Gene* 25:231, 1984.

85. WIGINTON DA, ADRIAN GS, FRIEDMAN D, PARKER-SUTTLE D, HUTTON JJ: Cloning of cDNA sequences of human adenosine deaminase. *Proc Natl Acad Sci USA* 80:7481, 1983.

86. WIGINTON DA, ADRIAN GS, HUTTON JJ: Sequence of human adenosine deaminase cDNA including the coding region and a small intron. *Nucl Acid Res* 12:2439, 1984.

87. DADONNA PE, SHEWACH DS, KELLEY WN, ARGOS P, MARKHAM AF, ORKIN SH: Human adenosine deaminase: cDNA and complete primary amino acid sequence. *J Biol Chem* 259:12101, 1984.

88. DADONNA PE, ORKIN SH, SHEWACH DS, KELLEY WN: cDNA and amino acid sequence of human adenosine deaminase. *Ann NY Acad Sci USA* 451:238, 1985.

89. VALERIO D, DUYVESTEYN MGC, DEKKLER BMM, WEEDA G, BERKVENS TM, van der VOORN L, van ORMONDT H, van der EB AJ: Adenosine deaminase: Characterization and expression of a gene with a remarkable promoter. *EMBO J* 4:437, 1985.

90. WIGINTON DA, KAPLAN DJ, STATES JC, AKESON AL, PERME CM, BILYK IJ, VAUGHN AJ, LATTIER DL, HUTTON JJ: Complete sequence and structure of the gene for human adenosine deaminase. *Biochemistry* 25:8234, 1986.

91. BREATHNACH R, CHAMBON P: Organization and expression of eucaryote split genes coding for proteins. *Annu Rev Biochem* 50:349, 1981.

92. MELTON DW, KONECKI DS, BRENNAND J, CASKEY CT: Structure, expression and mutation of the hypoxanthine phosphoribosyltransferase gene. *Proc Natl Acad Sci USA* 81:2147, 1984.

93. KIM SH, MOORES JC, DAVID D, RESPESS JG, JOLLY DJ, FRIEDMANN T: The organization of the human HPRT gene. *Nucl Acids Res* 14:3103, 1986.

94. PATEL PI, FRAMSON PE, CASKEY CT, CHINAULT AC: Fine structure of the human hypoxanthine phosphoribosyltransferase gene. *Mol Cell Biol* 6:393, 1986.

95. REYNOLDS GA, BASU SK, OSBORNE TF, CHIN DJ, GIL G, BROWN MS, GOLDSTEIN JL, LUSKEY KL: HMG CoA reductase: A negatively regulated gene with unusual promoter and 5′ untranslated regions. *Cell* 38:275, 1984.

96. SINGER-SAM J, KEITH DH, TANI K, SIMMER RL, SHIVELY L, LINDSAY S, YOSHIDA A, RIGGS AD: Sequence of the promoter region of the gene for human X-linked 3-phosphoglycerate kinase. *Gene* 32:409, 1984.

97. CROUSE GF, SIMONSEN CC, McEWAN BN, SCHIMKE RT: Structure of amplified normal and variant dihydrofolate reductase genes in mouse sarcoma S180 cells. *J Biol Chem* 257:7887, 1982.

98. CHEN MJ, SHIMADA T, MOULTON AD, CLINE A, HUMPHRIES RK, MAIZEL J, NIENHUIS AW: The functional human dihydrofolate reductase gene. *J Biol Chem* 259:3933, 1984.

99. DYNAN WS, TIJAN R: Isolation of transcription factors that discriminate between different promoters recognized by RNA polymerase II. *Cell* 32:669, 1983.

100. DYNAN WS, TIJAN R: The promoter-specific transcription factor Spl binds to upstream sequences in the SV40 early promoter. *Cell* 35:79, 1983.

101. DYNAN WS, SAZER S, TIJAN R, SCHIMKE RT: Transcription factor Spl recognizes a DNA sequence in the mouse dihydrofolate reductase promoter. *Nature* 319:246, 1986.

102. HIRSCHHORN R, LEVYTAKA V, POLLARA B, MEUWISSEN HJ: Evidence for control of several different tissue-specific isozymes of adenosine deaminase by a single genetic locus. *Nature* 246:200, 1973.

103. SCHRADER WP, POLLARA B, MEUWISSEN HJ: Characterization of the residual adenosine deaminase activity in the spleen of a patient with combined immunodeficiency disease and adenosine deaminase deficiency. *Proc Natl Acad Sci USA* 75:446, 1978.

104. RATECH H, HIRSCHHORN R: Serum adenosine deaminase in normals and in a patient with adenosine deaminase deficient-severe combined immunodeficiency. *Clin Chim Acta* 115:341, 1981.

105. DADDONA PE, KELLEY WN: Characteristics of an aminohydrolase distinct from adenosine deaminase in cultured human lymphoblasts. *Biochim Biophys Acta* 653:280, 1981.

106. DADDONA PE, FROHMAN MA, KELLEY WN: Human adenosine deaminase and its binding protein in normal and adenosine deaminase-deficient fibroblast cell strains. *J Biol Chem* 255:5681, 1980.

107. HIRSCHHORN R: Conversion of human erythrocyte-adenosine deaminase activity to different tissue specific isozymes. Evidence for a common catalytic unit. *J Clin Invest* 55:661, 1975.

108. CHEN SH, SCOTT CR, SWEDBERG DR: Heterogeneity for adenosine deaminase deficiency: Expression of the enzyme in cultured skin fibroblasts and amniotic fluid cells. *Am J Hum Genet* 27:46, 1975.

109. HIRSCHHORN R, BERATIS N, ROSEN FS: Characterization of residual enzyme activity in fibroblasts from patients with adenosine deaminase deficiency and combined immunodeficiency: Evidence for a mutant enzyme. *Proc Natl Acad Sci USA* 73:213, 1976.

110. CARSON DA, GOLDBLUM R, SEEGMILLER JE: Quantitative immunoassay of adenosine deaminase in combined immunodeficiency disease. *J Immunol* 118:270, 1977.

111. DADDONA PE, FROHMAN MA, KELLEY WN: Radioimmunochemical quantitation of human adenosine deaminase. *J Clin Invest* 64:798, 1979.

112. WIGINTON DA, HUTTON JJ: Immunoreactive protein in adenosine deaminase deficient human lymphoblast cell lines. *J Biol Chem* 257:3211, 1982.

113. HERBSCHLEB-VOOGT E, PEARSON RL, VOSSEN JM, MEERA KHAN P: Basic defect in the expression of adenosine deaminase in ADA-SCID disease investigated through the cells of an obligate heterozygote. *Hum Genet* 56:379, 1981.

114. HERBSCHLEB-VOOT E, SCHOLTEN JW, MEERA KHAN P: Basic defect in the

expression of adenosine deaminase in ADA-SCID. II. Deficiency of ADA-CRM detected in heterozygote human-Chinese hamster cell hybrids. *Hum Genet* 63:121, 1983.

115. VALERIO D, DUYVESTEYN MGC, van ORMONDT H, MEERA KHAN P, van der EB AJ: Adenosine deaminase (ADA) deficiency in cells derived from humans with severe combined immunodeficiency disease is due to an aberration of the ADA protein. *Nucleic Acids Res* 12:1015, 1984.

116. DADDONA PE, DAVIDSON BL, PERIGNON JL, KELLEY WN: Genetic expression in partial adenosine deaminase deficiency: mRNA levels and protein turnover for the enzyme variants in human B-lymphoblast cell lines: *J Biol Chem* 260:3875, 1985.

117. ADRIAN GS, HUTTON JJ: Adenosine deaminase messenger RNAs in lymphoblast cell lines derived from leukemic patients and patients with hereditary adenosine deaminase deficiency. *J Clin Invest* 71:1649, 1983.

118. ADRIAN GS, WIGINTON DA, HUTTON JJ: Structure of adenosine deaminase mRNAs from normal and adenosine deaminase-deficient human cell lines. *Mol Cell Biol* 4:1712, 1984.

119. ADRIAN GS, WIGINTON DA, HUTTON JJ: Characterization of normal and mutant adenosine deaminase messenger RNAs by translation and hybridization to a cDNA probe. *Hum Genet* 68:169, 1984.

120. MARKERT ML, HERSHFIELD MS, WIGINTON DA, STATES JC, WARD FE, BIGNER SH, BUCKLEY RH, KAUFMAN RE, HUTTON JJ: Identification of a deletion in the adenosine deaminase gene in a child with severe combined immunodeficiency. *J Immunol* 138:3203, 1987.

121. AKESON AL, WIGINTON DA, STATES JC, PERME CM, DUSING MR, HUTTON JJ: Mutations in the human adenosine deaminase gene that affect protein structure and RNA splicing. *Proc Natl Acad Sci USA* 84:5947, 1987.

122. BONTHRON DT, MARKHAM AF, GINSBERG D, ORKIN SH: Identification of a point mutation in the adenosine deaminase gene responsible for immunodeficiency. *J Clin Invest* 76:894, 1985.

123. VALERIO D, DEKKER BMM, DUYVESTEYN MGC, van der VOORN L, BERKVENS TM, van ORMONDT H, van der EB AJ: One adenosine deaminase allele in a patient with severe combined immunodeficiency contains a point mutation abolishing enzyme activity. *EMBO J* 5:113, 1986.

124. HIRSCHHORN R: Incidence and prenatal detection of adenosine deaminase deficiency and purine nucleoside phosphorylase deficiency, in Pollara B, Pickering RJ, Meuwissen HJ, Porter IH (eds): *Inborn Errors of Specific Immunity*. New York, Academic, 1979, p 5.

125. SCOTT CR, CHEN SH, GIBLETT ER: Detection of the carrier state in combined immunodeficiency disease associated with adenosine deaminase deficiency. *J Clin Invest* 53:1194, 1974.

126. BRINKMANN B, BRINKMAN M, MARTIN H: A new allele in red cell adenosine deaminase polymorphism: ADA°. *Hum Hered* 23:603, 1973.

127. CHEN SH, SCOTT CR, GIBLETT ER: Adenosine deaminase: Demonstration of a "silent" gene associated with combined immunodeficiency disease. *Am J Hum Genet* 26:103, 1974.

128. CHEN SH, SCOTT CR, GIBLETT ER, LEVIN AS: Adenosine deaminase deficiency: Another family with a "silent" ADA allele and normal ADA activity in two heterozygotes. *Am J Hum Genet* 29:642, 1977.

129. HIRSCHHORN R, BERATIS N, ROSEN FS, PARKMAN R, STERN R, POLMAR S: Adenosine-deaminase deficiency in a child diagnosed prenatally. *Lancet* 1:73, 1975.

130. HIRSCHHORN R: Prenatal diagnosis and heterozygote detection in adenosine deaminase deficiency, in Güttler F, Seakins JWT, Harkness RA (eds): *Inborn Errors of Immunity and Phagocytosis* Lancaster, MTP Press, 1979, p 121.

131. ZIEGLER JB, VAN der WEYDEN MB, LEE CH, DANIEL A: Prenatal diagnosis for adenosine deaminase deficiency. *J Med Genet* 18:154, 1981.

132. AITKEN DA, KLEIJER WJ, NIERMEIJER MF, HERBSCHLEB-VOOGT E, GALJAARD H: Prenatal detection of a probable heterozygote for ADA deficiency and severe combined immunodeficiency disease using a microradioassay. *Clin Genet* 17:293, 1980.

133. SIMMONDS HA, FAIRBANKS LD, WEBSTER DR, RODECK CH, LINCH DC, LEVINSKY RJ: Rapid prenatal diagnosis of adenosine deaminase deficiency and other purine disorders using fetal blood. *Biosci Rep* 3:31, 1983.

134. AITKEN DA, GILMORE DH, FREW CA, FERGUSON-SMITH ME, CARTY MJ, CHATFIELD WR: Early prenatal investigation of a pregnancy at risk of adenosine deaminase deficiency using chorionic villi. *J Med Genet* 23:52, 1986.

135. DOOLEY T, FAIRBANKS LD, SIMMONDS HA, RODECK CH, NICOLAIDES KH, STEWART P, MORGAN G, LEVINSKY RJ: First trimester diagnosis of adenosine deaminase deficiency. *Prenat Diag* 7:561, 1987.

136. LINCH DC, LEVINSKI RJ, RODECK CH, MACLENNAN KA, SIMMONDS HA: Prenatal diagnosis of three cases of severe combined immunodeficiency: Severe T cell deficiency—during the first half of gestation in fetuses with adenosine deaminase deficiency. *Clin Exp Immunol* 56:223, 1984.

137. LEWIS AS, LOWY BA: Human erythrocyte purine nucleoside phosphorylase: Molecular weight and physical properties. A Theorell-Chance catalytic mechanism. *J Biol Chem* 254:9927, 1979.

138. KIM BK, CHA S, PARKS RE Jr: Purine nucleoside phosphorylase from human erythrocytes. I Purification and properties. *J Biol Chem* 243:1763, 1968.

139. KALKAR HM: The enzymatic synthesis of purine ribosides. *J Biol Chem* 167:477, 1947.

140. FRIEDKIN M: Desoxyribose-1-phosphate. II The isolation of crystalline desoxyribose-1-phosphate. *J Biol Chem* 184:449, 1950.

141. ZIMMERMAN TP, GERSTEN NB, ROSS RF, MIECH RP: Adenine as substrate for purine nucleoside phosphorylase. *Can J Biochem* 49:1050, 1971.

142. AGARWAL RP, PARKS RE Jr: Purine nucleoside phosphorylase from human erythrocytes. IV. Crystallization and some properties. *J Biol Chem* 244:644, 1969.

143. ZANNIS V, DOYLE D, MARTIN DW Jr: Purification and characterization of human erythrocyte purine nucleoside phosphorylase and its subunits. *J Biol Chem* 253:504, 1978.

144. OSBORNE WR: Human red cell purine nucleoside phosphorylase. Purification by biospecific affinity chromatography and physical properties. *J Biol Chem* 255:7089, 1980.

145. GHANGAS G, REEM GH: Characterization of the subunit structure of human placental nucleoside phosphorylase by immunochemistry. *J Biol Chem* 254:4233, 1979.

146. WIGINTON DA, COLEMAN MS, HUTTON JJ: Characterization of purine nucleoside phosphorylase from human granulocytes and its metabolism of deoxyribonucleosides. *J Biol Chem* 255:6663, 1980.

147. ZANNIS VI, GUDAS LG, MARTIN DW Jr: Characterization of the subunits of purine nucleoside phosphorylase from cultured normal human fibroblasts. *Biochem Genet* 17:621, 1979.

148. STOECKLER JE, AGARWAL RP, AGARWAL KC, SCHMID K, PARKS RE Jr: Purine nucleoside phosphorylase from human erythrocytes: Physiochemical properties of the crystalline enzyme. *Biochemistry* 17:278, 1978.

149. CREAGAN RP, TAN YH, CHEN S, TISCHFIELD JA, RUDDLE FJ: Mouse/human somatic cell hybrids utilizing human parental cells containing a (14:22) translocation: Assignment of the gene for nucleoside phosphorylase to chromosome 14, in Bergsma D (ed): *Human Gene Mapping*. New York, The National Foundation, 1973.

150. AITKEN DA, FERGUSON-SMITH MA: Regional assignment of nucleoside phosphorylase by exclusion to 14q13. *J Med Genet* 18:158, 1981.

151. EDWARDS YH, HOPKINSON DA, HARRIS H: Inherited variants of human nucleoside phosphorylase. *Ann Hum Genet* 34:395, 1971.

152. TURNER BM, FISHER RA, HARRIS H: An association between the kinetic and electrophoretic properties of human purine-nucleoside-phosphorylase isozymes. *Eur J Biochem* 24:288, 1971.

153. GODDARD JM, CAPUT D, WILLIAMS SR, MARTIN DW Jr: Cloning of human purine nucleoside phosphorylase cDNA sequences by complementation in *Escherichia coli*. *Proc Natl Acad Sci USA* 80:4281, 1983.

154. WILLIAMS SR, GODDARD JM, MARTIN DW Jr: Human purine nucleoside phosphorylase cDNA sequence and genomic clone characterization. *Nucleic Acids Res* 12:5779, 1984.

155. WILLIAMS SR, GEKELER V, McIVOR RS, MARTIN DW Jr: A human purine nucleoside phosphorylase deficiency caused by a single base change. *J Biol Chem* 262:2332, 1987.

156. FOX IH, ANDRES CM, GELFAND EW, BIGGAR D: Purine nucleoside phosphorylase deficiency: Altered kinetic properties of a mutant enzyme. *Science* 197:1084, 1977.

157. WORTMANN RL, ANDRES CM, KAMINSKA J, GELFAND EW, ARNOLD W, RICH K, FOX IH: Biochemical heterogeneity in purine nucleoside phosphorylase deficiency. *Arthritis Rheum* 21:603, 1978.

158. OSBORNE WR, CHEN SH, GIBLETT ER, BIGGAR WD, AMMANN AA, SCOTT CR: Purine nucleoside phosphorylase deficiency. Evidence for molecular heterogeneity in two families with enzyme-deficient members. *J Clin Invest* 60:741, 1977.

159. OSBORNE WR, SCOTT CR: Purine nucleoside phosphorylase deficiency. Measurement of variant protein in four families with enzyme-deficient members by an enzyme-linked immunoabsorbant assay. *Am J Hum Genet* 32:927, 1980.

160. GUDAS LJ, ZANNIS VI, CLIFT SM, AMMAN AJ, STAAL GE, MARTIN DW Jr: Characterization of mutant subunits of human purine nucleoside phosphorylase. *J Biol Chem* 253:8916, 1978.

161. GIBLETT ER: Adenosine deaminase and purine nucleoside phosphorylase deficiency: How they were discovered and what they may mean, in Elliot K, Whelan J (eds): *Enzyme Defects and Immune Dysfunction, Ciba Foundation Symposium 68*, New York, Excerpta Medica, 1979, p 3.

162. MCROBERTS JA, MARTIN DW Jr: Submolecular characterization of a mutant purine-nucleoside phosphorylase. *J Biol Chem* 255:5605, 1980.

163. CARAPELLA DE LUCA E, STEGAGNO M, DIONISI VICI C, PAESANO R, FAIR-

BANKS LD, MORRIS GS, SIMMONDS HA: Prenatal exclusion of purine nucleoside phosphorylase deficiency. *Eur J Pediatr* 145:51, 1986.

164. WINTROBE MM: *Clinical Hematology*, 4th ed. Philadelphia, Lea & Febiger, 1959, p 222.

165. HENDERSON JF, SCOTT FW: Inhibition of animal and invertebrate cell growth by naturally occurring purine bases and ribonucleosides. *Pharmacol Ther* 8:539, 1980.

166. HENDERSON JF, FRASER WS, LOWE JK: Toxicity of nturally occurring purine deoxyribonucleosides. *Pharmacol Ther* 8:573, 1980.

167. MOSER GH, SCHRADER J: Half-life of adenosine in human blood. Effects of dipyridamole. *Eur J Physiol* 407 (*suppl* 1): S37, 1986.

168. SONODA T, TATIBANA M: Metabolic fate of pyrimidines and purines in dietary nucleic acids ingested by mice. *Biochem Biophys Acta* 521:55, 1978.

169. WILSON D, BEYER A, BISHOP C, TALBOTT JH: Urinary uric acid excretion after ingestion of isotopic yeast nucleic acid in the normal and gouty human. *J Biol Chem* 209:227, 1954.

170. CHAN TS: Purine excretion by mouse peritoneal macrophages lacking adenosine deaminase activity. *Proc Natl Acad Sci USA* 76:925, 1979.

171. PEARSON JD, COADE SB: Kinetics of endothelial cell ectonucleotidases, in Gerlach E, Becker BF (eds): *Topics and Perspectives in Adenosine Research.* Berlin, Heidelberg, Springer-Verlag, 1987, p 145.

172. GERLACH E, BECKER BF, NEES S: Formation of adenosine by vascular endothelium: A homeostatic and antithrombogenic mechanism? in Gerlach E, Becker BF (eds): *Topics and Perspectives in Adenosine Research.* Heidelberg, Springer-Verlag, 1987, p 309.

173. PATERSON ARP, BABB LR, PARAN JH, CASS CE: Inhibition by nitrobenzylthioinosine of adenosine uptake by asynchronous HeLa cells. *Mol Pharmacol* 13:1147, 1977.

174. COHEN A, ULLMAN B, MARTIN DW Jr: Characterization of a mutant mouse lymphoma cell with deficient transport of purine and pyrimidine nucleosides. *J Biol Chem* 254:112, 1979.

175. PLAGEMANN PGW: Transport and metabolism of adenosine in human erythrocytes: Effects of transport inhibitors and regulation by phosphate. *J Cell Physiol* 128:491, 1986.

176. PATERSON ARP, JAKOBS ES, NG CYC, ODEGARD RD, ADJEI AA: Nucleoside transport inhibition in vitro and in vivo, in Gerlach E, Becker BF (eds): *Topics and Perspectives in Adenosine Research.* Berlin, Heidelberg, Springer-Verlag, 1987, p 89.

177. JARVIS SH: Kinetics and molecular properties of nucleoside transporters in animal cells, in Gerlach E, Becker BF (eds): *Topics and Perspectives in Adenosine Research.* Berlin, Heidelberg, Springer-Verlag, 1987, p 102.

178. NEWBY AC: Role of adenosine deaminase, ecto-(5′-nucleotides) and ecto-(non-specific phosphatase) in cyanide-induced adenosine monophosphate catabolism in rat polymorphonuclear leucocytes. *Biochem J* 186:907, 1980.

179. EDWARDS NL, RECKER D, MANFREDI J, REMBECKI R, FOX I: Regulation of purine metabolism and cytoplasmic 5′-nucleotidases. *Am J Physiol* 243:270, 1982.

180. NEWBY AC, WORKU Y, MEGHJI G: Critical evaluation of the role of ecto- and cytosolic 5′-nucleotidase in adenosine formation, in Gerlach E, Becker BF (eds): *Topics and Perspectives in Adenosine Research.* Berlin, Heidelberg, Springer-Verlag, 1987, p 155.

181. VAN DEN BERGHE G, VAN POTTELSBERGHE C, HERS H-G: A kinetic study of the soluble 5′-nucleotidase of rat liver. *Biochem J* 162:611, 1977.

182. FRITZSON P: Regulation of nucleotide activities in animal tissues. *Adv Enzyme Regul* 16:43, 1978.

183. ITOH R: Purification and some properties of cytosol 5′-nucleotidase from rat liver. *Biochem Biophys Acta* 657:402, 1981.

184. MONTERO JM, FES JB: Purification and characterization of bovine brain 5′-nucleotidase. *J Neurochem* 39:982, 1982.

185. ITOH R, OKA J, OZASA H: Regulation of rat heart cytosol 5′-nucleotidase by adenylate energy charge. *Biochem J* 235:847, 1986.

186. MADRID-MARINA V, FOX IH: Human placental cytoplasmic 5′-nucleotidase. *J Biol Chem* 261:444, 1986.

187. COLLINSON AR, PEUHKURINEN KJ, LOWENSTEIN JM: Regulation and function of 5′-nucleotidase, in Gerlach E, Becker BF (eds): *Topics and Perspectives in Adenosine Research.* Berlin, Heidelberg, Springer-Verlag, 1987, p 133.

188. BAGNARA AS, HERSHFIELD MS: Mechanism of deoxyadenosine-induced catabolism of adenine ribonucleotides in adenosine deaminase-inhibited human T lymphoblastoid cells. *Proc Natl Acad Sci USA* 79:2673, 1982.

189. CARSON DA, WASSON DB: Characterization of an adenosine 5′-triphosphate- and deoxyadenosine 5′-triphosphate-activated nucleotidase from human malignant lymphocytes. *Cancer Res* 42:4321, 1982.

190. NEWSHOLME EA, CHALLISS RAJ, CRABTREE B: Substrate cycles: Their role in improving sensitivity in metabolic control. *Trends Biochem Sci* 9:277, 1984.

191. SCHWABE U, EBERT R, ERBLER HC: Adenosine release from isolated fat cells and its significance for the effects of hormones on cyclic 3′,5′-AMP levels and lipolysis. *Naunyn-Schmiedebergs Arch Pharmacol* 276:133, 1973.

192. BONTEMPS F, VAN DEN BERGHE G, HERS H-G: Evidence for a substrate cycle between AMP and adenosine in isolated hepatocytes. *Proc Natl Acad Sci USA* 80:2829, 1983.

193. LERNER MH, LOWY BA: Formation of adenosine in rabbit liver and its role as a direct precursor of erythrocyte nucleotides. *J Biol Chem* 249:259, 1974.

194. PRITCHARD JB, O'CONNOR N, OLIVER JM, BERLIN RD: Uptake and supply of purine compounds by the liver. *Am J Physiol* 229:967, 1975.

195. CHAN T-S, ISHII K, LONG C, GREEN H: Purine excretion by mammalian cells deficient in adenosine kinase. *J Cell Physiol* 81:315, 1973.

196. BROX LW, HENDERSON JF: The "adenosine cycle" is not a significant route of purine metabolism in mammalian cells. *Can J Biochem* 54:200, 1976.

197. HERSHFIELD MS, SEEGMILLER JE: Regulation of de novo purine synthesis in human lymphoblasts. Similar rates of de novo synthesis during growth by normal cells and mutants deficient in hypoxanthine-guanine phosphoribosyltransferase activity. *J Biol Chem* 252:6002, 1977.

198. SNYDER FF, TRAFZER RJ, HERSHFIELD MS, SEEGMILLER JE: Elucidation of aberrant purine metabolism. Application of hypoxanthine-guanine phosphoribosyltransferase—and adenosine kinase deficient mutants, and IMP dehydrogenase—and adenosine deaminase-inhibited human lymphoblasts. *Biochem Biophys Acta* 609:492, 1980.

199. MATSUMOTO SS, RAIVIO KO, SEEGMILLER JE: Adenine nucleotide degradation during energy depletion in human lymphoblasts. Adenosine accumulation and adenylate energy charge correlation. *J Biol Chem* 254:8865, 1979.

200. LOMAX CA, HENDERSON JF: Adenosine formation and metabolism during adenosine triphosphate catabolism in Ehrlich ascites tumor cells. *Can Res* 33:2825, 1973.

201. BARANKIEWICZ J, COHEN A: Evidence for distinct catabolic pathways for adenine ribonucleotides and deoxyribonucleotides in human T lymphoblastoid cells. *J Biol Chem* 259:15178, 1984.

202. BARANKIEWICZ J, GELFAND EW, ISSEKUTZ A, COHEN A: Evidence for active purine nucleoside cycles in human mononuclear cells and fibroblasts. *J Biol Chem* 257:11597, 1982.

203. WILLIS RC, KAUFMAN AH, SEEGMILLER JE: Purine nucleotide reutilization by human lymphoblast lines with aberrations of the inosinate cycle. *J Biol Chem* 259:4157, 1984.

204. MUDD HS, POOLE JR: Labile methyl balances for normal humans on various dietary regimens. *Metabolism* 24:721, 1975.

205. LLOYD HGE, SCHRADER J: The importance of the transmethylation pathway for adenosine metabolism in the heart, in Gerlach E, Becker BF (eds): *Topics and Perspectives in Adenosine Research.* Berlin, Heidelberg, Springer-Verlag, 1987, p 199.

206. PALELLA TD, ANDRES CM, FOX IH: Human placental adenosine kinase: Kinetic mechanism and inhibition. *J Biol Chem* 255:5264, 1980.

207. MEYSKENS FL, WILLIAMS HE: Adenosine metabolism in human erythrocytes. *Biochim Biophys Acta* 240:170, 1971.

208. HERSHFIELD MH, KREDICH NM: Resistance of an adenosine kinase-deficient human lymphoblastoid cell line to effects of deoxyadenosine on growth, S-adenosylhomocysteine hydrolase inactivation, and dATP accumulation. *Proc Natl Acad Sci USA* 77:4292, 1980.

209. OSBORNE WRA, SPENCER N: Partial purification and properties of the common inherited forms of adenosine deaminase from human erythrocytes. *Biochem J* 133:117, 1973.

210. AGARWAL RP, SAGAR SM, PARKS RE Jr: Adenosine deaminase from human erythrocytes: Purification and effects of adenosine analogs. *Biochem Pharmacol* 24:693, 1975.

211. SNYDER FF, MENDELSOHN J, SEEGMILLER JE: Adenosine metabolism in phytohemagglutinin-stimulated human lymphocytes. *J Clin Invest* 58:654, 1976.

212. HENDERSON JF, MIKOSHIBA A, CHU SY, CALDWELL IC: Kinetic studies of adenosine kinase from Ehrlich ascites tumor cells. *J Biol Chem* 247:1972, 1972.

213. HAWKINS CF, KYD JM, BAGNARA AS: Adenosine metabolism in human erythrocytes: A study of some factors which affect the metabolic fate of adenosine in intact red cells in vitro. *Arch Biochem Biophys* 202:380, 1980.

214. DIVEKAR AY: Adenosine phosphorylase activity as distinct from inosine-guanosine phosphorylase activity in sarcoma 180 cells and rat liver. *Biochim Biophys Acta* 422:15, 1976.

215. NICANDER B, REICHARD P: Evidence for the involvement of substrate cycles in the regulation of deoxyribonucleoside triphosphate pools in 3T6 cells. *J Biol Chem* 260:9216, 1985.

216. VALENTINE WN, PAGLIA DE, CLARKE S, MORIMOTO BH, NAKATANI M, BROCKWAY R: Adenine ribo- and deoxyribonucleotide metabolism in hu-

man erythrocytes, B- and T-lymphocyte cell lines, and monocyte-macrophages. *Proc Natl Acad Sci USA* 82:6682, 1985.

217. IIZASA T, KUBOTA M, CARSON DA: Differential production of deoxyadenosine by human T and B lymphoblasts. *J Immunol* 131:1776, 1983.

218. KUBOTA M, CARRERA CJ, WASSON DB, CARSON DA: Deoxynucleoside overproduction in deoxyadenosine-resistant, adenosine deaminase-deficient human histiocytic lymphoma cells. *Biochim Biophys Acta* 804:37, 1984.

219. BARANKIEWICZ J, COHEN A: Evidence for distinct catabolic pathways for deoxy-GTP and GTP in purine nucleoside phosphorylase-deficient mouse T lymphoblasts. *J Biol Chem* 260:4565, 1985.

220. MILLER RL, ADAMCZYK DL, MILLER WH: Adenosine kinase from rabbit liver: Purification by affinity chromatography and properties. *J Biol Chem* 254:2339, 1979.

221. MILLER RL, ADAMCZYK DA, MILLER WH, KOSZALKA GW, RIDEOUT JL, BEACHMAN LM, CHAO EY, HAGGERTY JJ, KRENITSKY TA, ELION GB: Adenosine kinase from rabbit liver: II. Substrate and inhibitor specificity. *J Biol Chem* 254:2346, 1979.

222. ANDRES CM, FOX IH: Purification and properties of human placental adenosine kinase. *J Biol Chem* 254:11388, 1979.

223. HURLEY MC, LIN B, FOX IH: Regulation of deoxyadenosine and nucleoside analog phosphorylation by human placental adenosine kinase. *J Biol Chem* 260:15675, 1985.

224. IVES DH, DURHAM JP: Deoxycytidine kinase: Kinetics and allosteric regulation of the calf thymus enzyme. *J Biol Chem* 245:2285, 1970.

225. KRENITSKY TA, TUTTLE JV, KOSZALKA GW, CHEN IS, BEACHMAN LM, RIDEOUT JL, ELION GB: Deoxycytidine kinase from calf thymus: Substrate and inhibitor specificity. *J Biol Chem* 251:4055, 1976.

226. GOWER WR, CARR MC, IVES DH: Deoxyguanosine kinase: Distinct molecular forms in mitochondria and cytosol. *J Biol Chem* 254:2180, 1979.

227 HURLEY MC, PALELLA TD, FOX IH: Human placental deoxyadenosine and deoxyguanosine phosphorylating activity. *J Biol Chem* 258:15021, 1983.

228. MOMPARLER RL, FISCHER GA: Mammalian deoxynucleoside kinase I. Deoxycytidine kinase: Purification, properties and kinetic studies with cytosine arabinoside. *J Biol Chem* 243:2498, 1968.

229. KRYGIER V, MOMPARLER RL: Mammalian deoxynucleoside kinase. II. Deoxyadenosine kinase: Purification and properties. *J Biol Chem* 246:2745, 1971.

230. KRYGIER V, MOMPARLER RL: Mammalian deoxynucleoside kinase. III. Deoxyadenosine kinase: Inhibition by nucleotides and kinetic studies. *J Biol Chem* 246:2752, 1971.

231. ULLMAN B, GUDAS LJ, COHEN A, MARTIN DW Jr: Deoxyadenosine metabolism and cytotoxicity in cultured mouse T lymphoma cells: A model for immunodeficiency disease. *Cell* 14:365, 1978.

232. ULLMAN B, LEVINSON BB, HERSHFIELD MS, MARTIN DW Jr: A biochemical genetic study of the role of specific nucleoside kinases in deoxyadenosine phosphorylation by cultured human cells. *J Biol Chem* 256:848, 1981.

233. CARSON DA, KAYE J, WASSON DB: Differences in deoxyadenosine metabolism in human and mouse lymphocytes. *J Immunol* 124:8, 1980.

234. HERSHFIELD MS, KREDICH NM: Effects of adenosine deaminase inhibition of transmethylation, in Tattersall MNH, Fox RM (eds): *Nucleosides and Cancer Treatment*. New York, Academic, 1981, p 161.

235. HERSHFIELD MS, FETTER JE, SMALL WC, BAGNARA AS, WILLIAMS SR, ULLMAN B, MARTIN DW Jr, WASSON DB, CARSON DA: Effects of mutational loss of adenosine kinase and deoxycytidine kinase on deoxyATP accumulation and deoxyadenosine toxicity in cultured CEM cells. *J Biol Chem* 257:6380, 1982.

236. ULLMAN B, GUDAS LJ, CLIFT SM, MARTIN DW Jr: Isolation and characterization of purine-nucleoside phosphorylase-deficient T-lymphoma cells and secondary mutants with altered ribonucleotide reductase: Genetic model for immunodeficiency, disease. *Proc Natl Acad Sci USA* 76:1074, 1979.

237. MITCHELL BS, MEJIAS E, DADDONA PE, KELLEY WN: Purinogenic immunodeficiency diseases: Selective toxicity of deoxyribonucleosides for T cells. *Proc Natl Acad Sci USA* 75:5011, 1978.

238. WILSON JM, MITCHELL BS, DADDONA PE, KELLEY WN: Purinogenic immunodeficiency diseases: Differential effects of deoxyadenosine and deoxyguanosine on DNA synthesis in human T lymphoblasts. *J Clin Invest* 64:1475, 1979.

239. OSBORNE WRA, SCOTT CR: The metabolism of deoxyguanosine and guanosine in human B and T lymphoblasts. *Biochem J* 214:711, 1983.

240. SPAAPEN LJM, RIJKERS GT, STAAL GEJ, RIJKSEN G, WADMAN SK, STOOP JW, ZEGERS BJM: The effect of deoxyguanosine on human lymphocyte function I. Analysis of the interference with lymphocyte proliferation in vitro. *J Immunol* 132:2311, 1984.

241. COHEN A, BARANKIEWICZ J, LEDERMAN HM, GELFAND E: Purine and pyrimidine metabolism in human thymocytes. *J Biol Chem* 258:12334, 1983.

242. SNYDER FF, LUKEY T: Purine ribonucleoside and deoxyribonucleoside metabolism in thymocytes. *Adv Exp Med Biol* 122B:259, 1980.

243. SNYDER FF, HENDERSON JF: Alternative pathways of deoxyadenosine and adenosine metabolism. *J Biol Chem* 248:5899, 1973.

244. SIMMONDS HA, GODAY A, MORRIS GS, BROLSMA MFJ: Metabolism of deoxynucleosides by lymphocytes in long-term culture deficient in different purine enzymes. *Biochem Pharmacol* 33:763, 1984.

245. GODAY A, SIMMONDS HA, MORRIS GS, FAIRBANKS LD: B cells as well as T cells form deoxynucleotides from either deoxyadenosine or deoxyguanosine. *Clin Exp Immunol* 56:39, 1984.

246. STOECKLER JD, CAMBOR C, PARKS RE Jr: Human erythrocyte purine nucleoside phorphorylase: Reaction with sugar modified nucleoside substrates. *Biochemistry* 19:102, 1980.

247. NORTH ME, NEWTON CA, WEBSTER ADB: Phosphorylation of deoxyguanosine by B and T lymphocytes: Evidence against selective trapping of deoxyguanosine by T lymphocytes in purine nucleoside phosphorylase deficiency. *Clin Exp Immunol* 42:523, 1980.

248. KURTZBERG J, HERSHFIELD MS: Determinants of deoxyadenosine toxicity in hybrids between human T- and B-lymphoblasts as a model for the development of drug resistance in T-cell acute lymphoblastic leukemia. *Cancer Res* 45:1579, 1985.

249. MORGAN C, LEVINSKY RJ, HUGH-JONES K, FAIBANKS LD, MORRIS GS, SIMMONDS HA: Heterogeneity of biochemical, clinical and immunological parameters in severe combined immunodeficiency due to adenosine deaminase deficiency. *Clin Exp Immunol* 70:491, 1987.

250. SIMMONDS HA, SAHOTA A, POTTER CF, CAMERON JS, WADMAN SK: Purine metabolism and immunodeficiency: Urinary purine excretion as a diagnostic screening test in adenosine deaminase and purine nucleoside phosphorylase deficiency. *Clin Sci Mol Med* 54:579, 1978.

251. KUTTESCH JF, SCHMALSTIEG FC, NELSON JA: Analysis of adenosine and other adenine compounds in patients with immunodeficiency diseases. *J Liquid Chromatogr* 1:97, 1978.

252. MILLS GC, GOLDBLUM RM, NEWKIRK KE, SCHMALSTIEG FC: Urinary excretion of purines, purine nucleosides, and pseudouridine in adenosine deaminase deficiency. *Biochem Med* 20:180, 1978.

253. HIRSCHHORN R, RATECH H, RUBINSTEIN A, PAPAGEORGIOU P, KESARWALA H, GELFAND E, ROEGNER-MANISCALCO V: Increased excretion of modified adenine nucleosides by children with adenosine deaminase deficiency. *Pediatr Res* 16:362, 1982.

254. COLEMAN MS, DONOFRIO J, HUTTON JJ, HAHN L, DAOUD A, LAMPKIN B, DYMINSKY J: Identification and quantitation of adenine deoxynucleotides in erythrocytes of a patient with adenosine deaminase deficiency and severe combined immunodeficiency. *J Biol Chem* 253:1619, 1978.

255. COHEN A, HIRSHHORN R, HOROWITZ SD, RUBINSTEIN A, POLMAR SH, HONG R, MARTIN DW: Deoxyadenosine triphosphate as a potentially toxic metabolite in adenosine deaminase deficiency. *Proc Natl Acad Sci USA* 75:472, 1978.

256. HIRSCHHORN R, ROEGNER V, RUBINSTEIN A, PAPAGEORGIOU P: Plasma deoxyadenosine, adenosine, and erythrocyte deoxyATP are elevated at birth in an adenosine deaminase-deficient child. *J Clin Invest* 65:768, 1980.

257. SIMMONDS HA, SAHOTA A, POTTER CF, PERRETT D, HUGH-JONES K, WATSON JG: Purine metabolism in adenosine deaminase deficiency, in Elliot K, Whelan J (eds): *Enzyme Defects and Immune Dysfunction, Ciba Foundation Symposium 68*. New York, Excerpta Medica, 1979, p 255.

258. SIMMONDS HA, LEVINSKY RJ, PERRETT D, WEBSTER DR: Reciprocal relationship between erythrocyte ATP and deoxy-ATP levels in inherited ADA deficiency. *Biochem Pharmacol* 31:947, 1982.

259. HERSHFIELD MS, KURTZBERG J, AIYAR VN, SUH EJ, SCHIFF R: Abnormalities in *S*-adenosylhomocysteine hydrolysis, ATP catabolism, and lymphoid differentiation in adenosine deaminase deficiency. *Ann NY Acad Sci* 451:78, 1985.

260. HERSHFIELD MS, BUCKLEY RH, GREENBERG ML, MELTON AL, SCHIFF R, HATEM C, KURTZBERG J, MARKERT ML, KOBAYASHI RH, KOBAYASHI AL, ABUCHOWSKI A: Treatment of adenosine deaminase deficiency with polyethylene glycol-modified adenosine deaminase. *N Engl J Med* 316:589, 1987.

261. HERSHFIELD MS, KREDICH NM, OWNBY DR, OWNBY H, BUCKLEY R: *In vivo* inactivation of erythrocyte *S*-adenosylhomocysteine hydrolase by 2′-deoxyadenosine in adenosine deaminase-deficient patients. *J Clin Invest* 63:807, 1979.

262. COHEN A, GUDAS LJ, AMMANN AJ, STAAL GEJ, MARTIN DW Jr: Deoxyguanosine triphosphate as a possible toxic metabolite in the immunodeficiency associated with purine nucleoside phosphorylase deficiency. *J Clin Invest* 61:1405, 1978.

263. SIMMONDS HA, WATSON AR, WEBSTER DR, SAHOTA A, PERRETT D: GTP depletion and other erythrocyte abnormalities in inherited PNP deficiency. *Biochem Pharmacol* 31:941, 1982.

264. SIDI Y, MITCHELL BS: Z-nucleotide accumulation in erythrocytes from Lesch-Nyhan patients. *J Clin Invest* 76:2416, 1985.

265. DONOFRIO J, COLEMAN MS, HUTTON JJ, DAOUD A, LAMPKIN B, DYMINSKI J: Overproduction of adenine deoxynucleosides and deoxynucleotides in adenosine deaminase deficiency with severe combined immunodeficiency disease. *J Clin Invest* 62:884, 1978.

266. HUTTON JJ, WIGINTON DA, COLEMAN MS, FULLER SA, LIMOUZE S, LAMPKIN BC: Biochemical and functional abnormalities in lymphocytes from an adenosine deaminase deficient patient during enzyme replacement therapy. *J Clin Invest* 68:413, 1981.

267. RICH KC, RICHMAN CM, MEJIAS E, DADDONA PA: Immunoreconstitution by peripheral blood leukocytes in adenosine deaminase-deficient severe combined immunodeficiency. *J Clin Invest* 66:389, 1980.

268. AGARWAL RP, SPECTOR T, PARKS RE Jr: Tight-binding inhibitors-IV. Inhibition of adenosine deaminases by various inhibitors. *Biochem Pharmacol* 26:359, 1977.

269. STOECKLER JD, CAMBOR C, KUHNS V, CHU S-H, PARKS RE JR: Inhibition of purine nucleoside phosphorylase. *Biochem Pharmacol* 31:163, 1982

270. STOECKLER JD, EALICK SE, BUGG CE, PARKS RE JR: Design of purine nucleoside phosphorylase inhibitors. *Fed Proc* 45:2773, 1986.

271. KAZMERS IS, MITCHELL BS, DADONNA PE, WOTRING LL, TOWNSEND LB, KELLEY WN: Inhibition of purine nucleoside phosphorylase by 8-aminoguanosine: Selective toxicity for T lymphoblasts. *Science* 214:1137, 1981.

272. DE FOUW NJ, MA DDF, MICHALEVICZ R, GRAY DA, HOFFBRAND AV: Differential cytotoxicity of deoxyguanosine and 8-aminoguanosine for human leukemic cell lines and normal bone marrow progenitor cells. *Hematol Oncol* 2:189, 1984.

273. MANN GJ, FOX RM: Deoxyadenosine triphosphate as a mediator of deoxyguanosine toxicity in cultured T lymphoblasts. *J Clin Invest* 78:1261, 1986.

274. MITCHELL BS, KOLLER CA, HEYN R: Inhibition of adenosine deaminase results in cytotoxicity to T lymphoblasts in vivo. *Blood* 56:556, 1980.

275. SMYTH JF, PAINE RM, JACKMAN AL, HARRAP KR, CHASSIN MM, ADAMSON RH, JOHNS DG: The clinical pharmacology of the adenosine deaminase inhibitor 2′-deoxycoformycin. *Cancer Chemother Pharmacol* 5:93, 1980.

276. PRENTICE HG, GANESHAGURU K, BRADSTOCK KF, GOLDSTONE AH, SMYTH JF, WONKE B, JANOSSY G, HOFFBRAND AV: Remission induction with the adenosine deaminase inhibitor 2′-deoxycoformycin in thy$^-$ lymphoblastic leukemia. *Lancet* 2:170, 1980.

277. SIAW MFE, MITCHELL BS, KOLLER CA, COLEMAN MS, HUTTON JJ: ATP depletion as a consequence of adenosine deaminase inhibition in man. *Proc Natl Acad Sci USA* 77:6157, 1980.

278. GREVER MR, SIAW MFE, JACOB WF, NEIDHART JA, MISER JS, COLEMAN MS, HUTTON JJ, BALCERZAK SP: The biochemical and clinical consequences of 2′-deoxycoformycin in refractory lymphoproliferative malignancy. *Blood* 57:406, 1981.

279. Proceedings of the Conference on 2′-deoxycoformycin. *Cancer Treatment Symposia* 1984, vol 2.

280. DEBATISSE M, BUTTIN G: The control of cell proliferation by preformed purines: A genetic study. II. Pleiotropic manifestations and mechanisms of a control exerted by adenylic purines on PRPP synthesis. *Somatic Cell Genet* 3:513, 1977.

281. AGARWAL RP, PARKS RE Jr: Potent inhibition of muscle 5′-AMP deaminase by the nucleoside antibiotics coformycin and deoxycoformycin. *Biochem Pharmacol* 26:663, 1977.

282. HENDERSON JF, BROX L, ZOMBOR G, HUNTING D, LOMAX CA: Specificity of adenosine deaminase inhibitors. *Biochem Pharmacol* 26:1967, 1977.

283. SIAW MFE, COLEMAN MS: In vitro metabolism of deoxycoformycin in human T lymphoblastoid cells: Phosphorylation of deoxycoformycin and incorporation into cellular DNA. *J Biol Chem* 259:9426, 1984.

284. BERNE RM, RALL TW, RUBIO R: *Regulatory Function of Adenosine*. The Hague, Nijhoff, 1983.

285. DALY JW: Adenosine receptors. *Adv Cyclic Nucleotide Phosphorylation Res* 19:29, 1985.

286. STILES GL: Adenosine receptors: structure, function and regulation. *Trends Physiol Sci* 7:486, 1986.

287. GERLACH E, BECKER BF: *Topics and Perspectives in Adenosine Research*. Berlin, Heidelberg, Springer-Verlag, 1987.

288. STILES GL: The A1 adenosine receptor: Solubilization and characterization of a guanine nucleotide-sensitive form of the receptor. *J Biol Chem* 260:6728, 1985.

289. GREEN H, CHAN T-S: Pyrimidine starvation induced by adenosine in fibroblasts and lymphoid cells: Role of adenosine deaminase. *Science* 182:836, 1973.

290. HARRAP KR, PAINE RM: Adenosine metabolism in cultured lymphoid cells. *Adv Enzyme Regul* 15:169, 1977.

291. CARSON DA, SEEGMILLER JE: Effect of adenosine deaminase inhibition upon human lymphocyte blastogenesis. *J Clin Invest* 57:274, 1976.

292. HERSHFIELD MS, SNYDER FF, SEEGMILLER JE: Adenine and adenosine are toxic to human lymphoblast mutants defective in purine salvage enzymes. *Science* 197:1284, 1977.

293. SCHMALSTIEG FC, NELSON JA, MILLS GC, MONAHAN TM, GOLDMAN AS, GOLDBLUM RM: Increased purine nucleotides in adenosine deaminase-deficient lymphocytes. *J Pediatr* 91:48, 1977.

294. MILLS GC, SCHMALSTIEG FC, NEWKIRK KE, GOLDBLUM RM: Cytosine and orotic acid in urine of immunodeficient children. *Clin Chem* 25:419, 1979.

295. ITOH K, UCHINO H: Control of pyrimidine biosynthesis in human lymphocytes. Inhibitory effect of guanine and guanosine on induction of enzymes for pyrimidine biosynthesis de novo in phytohemagglutinin-stimulated lymphocytes. *J Biol Chem* 251:1427, 1976.

296. SIDI Y, MITCHELL BS: 2′-Deoxyguanosine toxicity for B and mature T lymphoid cell lines is mediated by guanine ribonucleotide accumulation. *J Clin Invest* 74:1640, 1984.

297. OCHS UH, CHEN S-H, OCHS HD, OSBORNE WRA, SCOTT CR: Deoxyribonucleoside toxicity on adenosine deaminase and purine nucleoside phosphorylase positive and negative cultured lymphoblastoid cells, in Pollara B, Pickering RJ, Meuwissen HJ, Porter IH (eds): *Inborn Errors of Specific Immunity*. New York, Academic, 1979, p 191.

298. DURHAM JP, IVES DH: Deoxycytidine kinase I. Distribution in normal and neoplastic tissues and interrelationships of deoxycytidine and 1 β-D-arabinofuranosylcytidine phosphorylation. *Mol Pharmacol* 5:358, 1969.

299. COHEN A, LEE JWW, DOSCH H-M, GELFAND EW: The expression of deoxyguanosine toxicity in T lymphocytes at different stages of maturation. *J Immunol* 125:1578, 1980.

300. COLEMAN MS, DANTON MJ, PHILLIPS A: Adenosine deaminase and immune dysfunction. *Ann NY Acad Sci* 451:54, 1985.

301. HORIBATA K, HARRIS AW: Mouse myelomas and lymphomas in culture. *Exp Cell Res* 60:61, 1970.

302. REYNOLDS EC, HARRIS AW, FINCH LR: Deoxyribonucleoside triphosphate pools and differential thymidine sensitivities of cultured mouse lymphoma and myeloma cells. *Biochim Biophys Acta* 561:110, 1979.

303. CARSON DA, KAYE J, SEEGMILLER JE: Differential sensitivity of human leukemic T cell lines and B cell lines to growth inhibition by deoxyadenosine. *J Immunol* 121:1726, 1978.

304. GELFAND EW, LEE JJ, DOSCH HM: Selective toxicity of purine deoxynucleosides for human lymphocyte growth and function. *Proc Natl Acad Sci USA* 76:1998, 1979.

305. CARSON DA, KAYE J, MATSUMOTO S, SEEGMILLER JE, THOMPSON L: Biochemical basis for the enhanced toxicity of deoxyribonucleosides toward malignant human T cell lines. *Proc Natl Acad Sci USA* 76:2430, 1979.

306. HERSHFIELD MS, KREDICH NM, KOLLER CA, MITCHELL BS, KURTZBERG J, KINNEY TR, FALLETTA JM: *S*-Adenosylhomocysteine catabolism and basis for acquired resistance during treatment of T-cell acute lymphoblastic leukemia with 2′-deoxycoformycin alone and in combination with 9-β-D-arabinofuranosyladenine. *Cancer Res* 43:3451, 1983.

307. FOX RM, TRIPP EH, PIDDINGTON SK, TATTERSALL MHN: Sensitivity of leukemic human null lymphocytes to deoxynucleosides. *Cancer Res* 40:3383, 1980.

308. CHAN T-S: Deoxyguanosine toxicity on lymphoid cells as a cause for immunosuppression in purine nucleoside phosphorylase deficiency. *Cell* 14:523, 1978.

309. OCHS UH, CHEN S-H, OCHS HD, OSBORNE WRA, SCOTT CR: Purine nucleoside phosphorylase deficiency: A molecular model for selective loss of T cell function. *J Immunol* 122:2424, 1979.

310. GUDAS LJ, ULLMAN B, COHEN A, MARTIN DW Jr: Deoxyguanosine toxicity in a mouse T lymphoma: Relationship to purine nucleoside phosphorylase-associated immune dysfunction. *Cell* 14:531, 1978.

311. WORTMANN RL, MITCHELL BS, EDWARDS NL, FOX IH: Biochemical basis for differential deoxyadenosine toxicity to T and B lymphoblasts: Role for 5′-nucleotidase. *Proc Natl Acad Sci USA* 76:2434, 1979.

312. CARSON DA, KAYE J, WASSON DB: The potential importance of soluble deoxynucleotidase activity in mediating deoxyadenosine toxicity in human lymphoblasts. *J Immuol* 126:348, 1981.

313. FOX RM, PIDDINGTON SK, TRIPP EH, TATTERSALL MHN: Ecto-ATPase deficiency in cultured human T and null leukemic lymphocytes: A biochemical basis for thymidine sensitivity. *J Clin Invest* 68:544, 1981.

314. THOMPSON LF, SEEGMILLER JE: Adenosine deaminase deficiency and severe combined immunodeficiency disease. *Adv Enzymol* 51:167, 1980.

315. MITCHELL BS, EDWARDS NL: Purine metabolizing enzymes as predictors of lymphoblast sensitivity to deoxyadenosine. *J Lab Clin Med* 104:414, 1984.

316. SIDI Y, EDWARDS NL, WINKLER C, BUNN P, MITCHELL BS: Differential metabolism of deoxyribonucleosides by leukaemic T cells of immature and mature phenotype. *Br J Haem* 61:125, 1985.

317. LEE N, RUSSELL N, GANESHAGURU K, JACKSON BFA, PIGA A, PRENTICE HG, FOA R, HOFFBRAND AV: Mechanisms of deoxyadenosine toxicity in human

lymphoid cells in vitro: Relevance to the therapeutic use of inhibitors of adenosine deaminase. *Br J Haematol* 56:107, 1984.

318. MITCHELL BS, SIDI Y, HERSHFIELD M, KOLLER CA: Biochemical consequences of adenosine deaminase inhibition in vivo. *Ann NY Acad Sci* 451:129, 1985.

319. JOHNSTON JB, BEGLEITER A, PUGH L, LEITH MK, WILKINS JA, CAVERS DJ, ISRAELS LG: Biochemical changes induced in hairy-cell leukemia following treatment with the adenosine deaminase inhibitor 2′-deoxycoformycin. *Cancer Res* 46:2179, 1986.

320. KEFFORD RF, FOX RM: Purine deoxyribonucleoside toxicity in nondividing cells. *Cancer Res* 42:324, 1982.

321. COHEN A, BARANKIEWICZ J, GELFAND E: Roles of alternative synthetic and catabolic purine pathways in T lymphocyte differentiation. *Ann NY Acad Sci* 451:26, 1985.

322. GODAY A, SIMMONDS HA, MORRIS GS, FAIRBANKS LD: Human B lymphocytes and thymocytes but not peripheral blood mononuclear cells accumulate high dATP levels in conditions simulating ADA deficiency. *Biochem Pharmacol* 34:3561, 1985.

323. GRUBER H, COHEN A, REDELMAN D, BLUESTEIN H: Levels of dATP in ADA-inhibited human peripheral blood B and T lymphocytes cultured in deoxyadenosine. *Ann NY Acad Sci* 45:315, 1985.

324. GRUBER HE, COHEN A, FIRESTEIN GS, REDELMAN D, BLUESTEIN HG: Deoxy-ATP accumulation in adenosine deaminase-inhibited human T and B lymphocytes. *Adv Exp Med Biol* 195A:503, 1986.

325. BROX LW, POLLOCK E, BELCH A: Adenosine and deoxyadenosine toxicity in colony assay systems for human T-lymphocytes, B-lymphocytes, and granulocytes. *Cancer Chemother Pharmacol* 9:49, 1982.

326. NORDENSKJÖLD BA, SKOOG L, BROWN NC, REICHARD P: Deoxyribonucleotide pools and deoxyribonucleic acid synthesis in cultured mouse embryo cells. *J Biol Chem* 245:5360, 1970.

327. REICHARD P: Control of deoxyribonucleotide synthesis *in vitro* and *in vivo*. *Adv Enzyme Regul* 10:3, 1972.

328. WALTERS RA, TOBEY RA, RATLIFF RL: Cell-cycle dependent variations of deoxyribonucleoside triphosphate pools in Chinese hamster cells. *Biochim Biophys Acta* 319:336, 1973.

329. THELANDER L, REICHARD P: Reduction of ribonucleosides. *Annu Rev Biochem* 48:133, 1979.

330. ERIKSSON S, THELANDER L, AKERMAN M: Allosteric regulation of calf thymus ribonucleoside diphosphate reductase. *Biochemistry* 18:2948, 1979.

331. ERIKSSON S, CARAS IW, MARTIN DW, JR: Direct photoaffinity labeling of an allosteric site on subunit protein M1 of mouse ribonucleotide reductase by dTTP. *Proc Natl Acad Sci USA* 79:81, 1982.

332. HUNTING D, HENDERSON JF: Models of the regulation of ribonucleotide reductase and their evaluation in intact mammalian cells. *CRC Crit Rev Biochem* 13:325, 1983.

333. NUTTER LM, CHENG Y-C: Nature and properties of mammlian ribonucleoside diphosphate reductase. *Pharmacol Ther* 26:191, 1984.

334. CHANG C-H, CHEN Y-C: Effects of nucleoside triphosphates on human ribonucleotide reductase from molt-4F cells. *Cancer Res* 39:5087, 1979.

335. ULLMAN B, CLIFT SM, GUDAS LJ, LEVINSON BB, WORMSTED MA, MARTIN DE Jr: Alterations in deoxyribonucleotide metabolism in cultured cells with ribonucleotide reductase activities refractory to feedback inhibition by 2′-deoxyadenosine triphosphate. *J Biol Chem* 255:8308, 1980.

336. WADDELL D, ULLMAN B: Characterization of a cultured human T-cell line with genetically altered ribonucleotide reductase activity. *J Biol Chem* 258:4226, 1983.

337. ALBERT D, BLUESTEIN HG, THOMPSON L, SEEGMILLER JA: The mechanism of inhibition and "reversal" of mitogen-induced lymphocyte activation in a model of adenosine deaminase deficiency. *Cell Immunol* 86:510, 1984.

338. FOX RM, KEFFORD RF, TRIPP EH, TAYLOR IW: G1-Phase arrest of cultured human leukemic T-cells induced by deoxyadenosine. *Cancer Res* 41:5141, 1981.

339. YU AL, BAKAY B, KUNG FH, NYHAN WL: Effects of 2′-deoxycoformycin on the metabolism of purines and the survival of malignant cells in a patient with T-cell leukemia. *Cancer Res* 41:2677, 1981.

340. UBERTI J, LIGHTBODY JJ, JOHNSON RM: The effect of nucleosides and deoxycoformycin on adenosine and deoxyadenosine inhibition of human lymphocyte activation. *J Immunol* 123:189, 1979.

341. MUNCH-PETERSEN B, TYRSTED G, DUPONT B: The deoxyribonucleoside 5′-triphosphate (dATP and dTTP) pools in phytohemagglutinin-stimulated and non-stimulated human lymphocytes. *Exp Cell Res* 79:249, 1973.

342. TYRSTED G, GAMULIN V: Cytidine 5′-diphosphate reductase activity in phytohemagglutinin stimulated human lymphocytes. *Nucleic Acids Res* 6:305, 1979.

343. CARSON DA, WASSON DB, LAKOW E, KAMATANI N: Possible metabolic basis for the different immunodeficient states associated with genetic deficiencies of adenosine deaminase and purine nucleoside phosphorylase. *Proc Natl Acad Sci USA* 79:3848, 1982.

344. JOHNSTONE AP, WILLIAMS GT: Role of DNA breaks and ADP-ribosyl transferase activity in eukaryotic differentiation demonstrated in human lymphocytes. *Nature* 300:368, 1982.

345. JOHNSTONE AP: Rejoining of DNA strand breaks is an early nuclear event during the stimulation of quiescent lymphocytes. *Eur J Biochem* 140:401, 1984.

346. BROX L, NG A, POLLOCK E, BELCH E: DNA strand breaks induced in human T-lymphocytes by the combination of deoxyadenosine and deoxycoformycin. *Cancer Res* 44:934, 1984.

347. SETO S, CARRERA CJ, KUBOTA M, WASSON DB, CARSON DA: Mechanism of deoxyadenosine and 2-chlorodeoxyadenosine toxicity to nondividing human lymphocytes. *J Clin Invest* 75:377, 1985.

348. BENJAMIN RC, GILL DM: ADP-ribosylation in mammalian cell ghosts. Dependence of poly(ADP-ribose) synthesis on strand breakage in DNA. *J Biol Chem* 255:10493, 1980.

349. BENJAMIN RC, GILL DM: Poly(ADP-ribose) synthesis in vitro programmed by damaged DNA. A comparison of DNA molecules containing different types of strand breaks. *J Biol Chem* 255:10502, 1980.

350. MILAM KM, CLEAVER JE: Inhibitors of poly(adenosine diphosphate-ribose) synthesis: Effect on other metabolic processes. *Science* 223:589, 1984.

351. HUNTING DJ, GOWANS BJ, HENDERSON JF: Specificity of inhibitors of poly(ADP-ribose) synthesis. Effects on nucleotide metabolism in cultured cells. *Mol Pharmacol* 28:200, 1985.

352. CLEAVER JE, MILAM KM, MORGAN WF: Do inhibitor studies demonstrate a role for poly(ADP-ribose) in DNA repair? *Radiat Res* 101:16, 1985.

353. SALVATORE F, BOREK E, ZAPPIA V, WILLIAMS-ASHMAN HG, SCHLENK F: *The Biochemistry of S-Adenosylmethionine*. New York, Columbia University Press, 1977.

354. BORCHARDT RT, USDIN E, CREVELING CR: *Biochemistry of S-Adenosylmethionine and Related Compounds*. London, Macmillan, 1982.

355. HOLLIDAY R, PUGH JE: DNA modification mechanisms and gene activity during development. *Science* 187:226, 1975.

356. RAZIN A, RIGGS AD: DNA methylation and gene function. *Science* 210:604, 1980.

357. JONES PA, TAYLOR SM: Cellular differentiation, cytidine analogs and DNA methylation. *Cell* 20:85, 1980.

358. HOLLIDAY R: The inheritance of epigenetic defects. *Science* 238:163, 1987.

359. O'DEA RF, VIVEROS OH, AXELROD J, ASWANIKUMAR S, SCHIFFMAN E, CORCORAN BA: Rapid stimulation of protein carboxymethylation in leukocytes by a chemotactic peptide. *Nature* 272:462, 1978.

360. PIKE MC, KREDICH NM, SNYDERMAN R: Requirement of S-adenosyl-L-methionine-mediated methylation for human monocyte chemotaxis. *Proc Natl Acad Sci USA* 75:3928, 1978.

361. BONVINI E, HOFFMAN T, HEBERMAN RB, VARESIO L: Selective augmentation by recombinant interferon-g of the intracellular content of S-adenosyl-methionine in murine macrophages. *J Immunol* 136:2596, 1986.

362. HIRATA F, TOYOSHIMA S, AXELROD J, WAXDAL MJ: Phospholipid methylation: A biochemical signal modulating lymphocyte mitogenesis. *Proc Natl Acad Sci USA* 77:862, 1980.

363. DE LA HABA G, CANTONI GL: The enzymatic synthesis of *S*-adenosyl-L-homocysteine from adenosine and homocysteine. *J Biol Chem* 234:603, 1959.

364. HERSHFIELD MS, KREDICH NM: *S*-Adenosylhomocysteine hydrolase is an adenosine-binding protein: A target for adenosine toxicity. *Science* 202:757, 1978.

365. HERSHFIELD MS, AIYAR VN, PREMAKUMAR R, SMALL WC: *S*-Adenosylhomocysteine hydrolase from human placenta. *Biochem J* 230:43, 1985.

366. KREDICH NM, MARTIN DW Jr: Role of *S*-adenosylhomocysteine in adenosine-mediated toxicity in cultured mouse T-lymphoma cells. *Cell* 12:931, 1977.

367. HERSHFIELD MS: Apparent suicide inactivation of human lymphoblast *S*-adenosylhomocysteine hydrolase by 2′-deoxyadenosine and adenosine. *J Biol Chem* 254:22, 1979.

368. HERSHFIELD MS: Alternate reactions of *S*-adenosylhomocysteine hydrolase. *Fed Proc* 39:1858, 1980.

369. ABELES RH, TASHJIAN AH, FISH S: The mechanism of inactivation of *S*-adenosylhomocysteinase by 2′-deoxyadenosine. *Biochem Biophys Res Commun* 95:612, 1980.

370. ABELES RH, FISH S, LAPINSKAS B: *S*-Adenosylhomocysteinase: Mechanism of inactivation by 2′-deoxyadenosine and interaction with other nucleosides. *Biochemistry* 21:5557, 1982.

371. HELLAND S, UELAND PM: Inactivation of *S*-adenosylhomocysteine hydrolase by 9-β-D-arabinofuranosyladenine in intact cells. *Cancer Res* 42:1130, 1982.

372. HERSHFIELD MS, SMALL WC, PREMAKUMAR R, BAGNARA AS, FETTER JE: Inactivation of *S*-adenosylhomocysteine hydrolase: Mechanism and occurrence in vivo in disorders of purine nucleoside catabolism, in Borchardt

RT, Usdin E, Creveling CR (eds): *Biochemistry of S-Adenosylmethionine and Related Compounds.* London, Macmillan, 1982, p 657.

373. GERMAN DC, BLOCH CA, KREDICH NM: Measurements of *S*-adenosylmethionine and L-homocysteine metabolism in cultured human lymphoid cells. *J Biol Chem* 258:10997, 1983.

374. KREDICH NM, HERSHFIELD MS: *S*-Adenosylhomocysteine toxicity in normal and adenosine kinase-deficient lymphoblasts of human origin. *Proc Natl Acad Sci USA* 76:2450, 1979.

375. JOHNSTON JM, KREDICH NM: Inhibition of methylation by adenosine in adenosine deaminase-inhibited, phytohemagglutinin-stimulated human lymphocytes. *J Immunol* 123:97, 1979.

376. HERSHFIELD MS, KURTZBERG J, MOORE JO, WHANG-PENG J, HAYNES BF: Conversion of a stem cell leukemia from T-lymphoid to a meyloid phenotype by the adenosine deaminase inhibitor 2′-deoxycoformycin. *Proc Natl Acad Sci USA* 81:253, 1984.

377. KAMINSKA JE, FOX IH: Decreased *S*-adenosylhomocysteine hydrolase in inborn errors of purine metabolism. *J Lab Clin Med* 96:141, 1980.

378. HERSHFIELD MS, AIYAR VN, CHAFFEE S, CURTIS S, GREENBERG ML: Probes for examining the structure and function of human S-adenosylhomocysteine hydrolase, and for isolation of cDNA, in Borchardt RT, Creveling CR, Ueland PM (eds): *Biological Methylation and Drug Design.* Clifton NJ, Humana Press, 1986, p 253.

379. HERSHFIELD MS: Proposed explanation for *S*-adenosylhomocysteine hydrolase deficiency in purine nucleoside phosphorylase and hypoxanthine guanine phosphoribosyltransferase-deficient patients. *J Clin Invest* 67:696, 1981.

380. HERSHFIELD MS, FRANCKE U: The human genes for *S*-adenosylhomocysteine hydrolase and ADA are syntenic on chromosome 20. *Science* 216:739, 1982.

381. MOHANDAS T, SPARKES RS, SUH EJ, HERSHFIELD MS: Regional localization of the human genes for S-adenosylhomocysteine hydrolase (cen → q131) and adenosine deaminase (q131 → qter) on chromosome 20. *Hum Genet* 66:292, 1984.

382. BOLLUM FJ: Terminal deoxynucleotidyl transferase: Biological studies. *Adv Enzymol* 47:347, 1978.

383. CHANG LMS: Development of terminal deoxynucleotidyl transferase activity in embryonic calf thymus gland. *Biochem Biophys Res Commun* 44:124, 1971.

384. KUNG PC, SILVERSTONE AE, MC CAFFREY RP, BALTIMORE D: Murine terminal deoxynucleotidyl transferase: Cellular distribution and response to cortisone. *J Exp Med* 141:855, 1975.

385. GREGOIRE KE, GOLDSCHNEIDER I, BARTON RW, BOLLUM FJ: Intracellular distribution of terminal deoxynucleotidyl transferase in rat bone marrow and thymus. *Proc Natl Acad Sci USA* 74:3993, 1977.

386. BALTIMORE D: Is terminal deoxynucleotidyl transferase a somatic mutagen in lymphocytes? *Nature* 248:409, 1974.

387. BOLLUM FJ: Terminal deoxynucleotidyl transferase: Source of immunological diversity? in Zahn R (ed): *Karl-August-Forster-Lectures.* Wiesbaden, Franz Steiner Verlag, 1975, vol 14, p 1.

388. MODAK MJ: Biochemistry of terminal deoxynucleotidyl transferase. Mechanism of manganese-dependent inhibition by deoxyadenosine 5′-triphosphate and biological implications. *Biochemistry* 12:2679, 1979.

389. MATSUMOTO SS, YU J, YU AL: Inhibition of RNA synthesis by deoxyadenosine plus deoxycoformycin in resting lymphocytes. *J Immunol* 131:2762, 1983.

390. KEFFORD RF, FOX RM, MCCAIRNS E, FAHEY D, MUSCAT GEO, ROWE PB: Terminal incorporation of 2′-deoxyadenosine into polyadenylate segments of polyadenylated RNA in G1-phase-arrested human T lymphoblasts. *Cancer Res* 43:2252, 1983.

391. JOVE R, MANLEY JL: Transcription initiation by RNA polymerase II is inhibited by *S*-adenosylhomocysteine. *Proc Natl Acad Sci USA* 79:5842, 1982.

392. BIRCH RE, POLMAR SH: Pharmacologic modification of immunoregulatory T-lymphocytes I. Effect of adenosine, H_1 and H_2 histamine agonists upon T-lymphocyte regulation of B-lymphocyte differentiation in vitro. *Clin Exp Immunol* 48:218, 1982.

393. BIRCH RE, ROSENTHAL AK, POLMAR SH: Pharmacologic modification of immunoregulatory T-lymphocytes II. Modulation of T-lymphocyte cell surface characteristics. *Clin Exp Immunol* 48:231, 1982.

394. RUERS TJM, BUURMAN WA, van der LINDEN CJ: 2′-Deoxycoformycin and deoxyadenosine affect IL 2 production and IL 2 receptor expression of human T cells. *J Immunol* 138:116, 1987.

395. DOSCH H-M, MANSOUR A, COHEN A, SHORE A, GELFAND EW: Inhibition of suppressor T-cell development following deoxyguanosine administration. *Nature* 285:494, 1980.

396. BRIL H, van den AKKER TW, MOLENDIJK-LOK BD, BIANCHI ATJ, BRENNER R: Influence of 2′-deoxyguanosine upon the development of DTH effector T cells and suppressor T cells in vivo. *J Immunol* 132:599, 1984.

397. LELCHUK R, COOKE A, PLAYFAIR JHL: Differential sensitivity to 2′-deoxyguanosine of antigen-specific and nonspecific suppressor T cells in delayed hypersensitivity. *Cell Immunol* 72:202, 1982.

398. AYE MT, DUNN JV, YANG WC: Studies on the effect of deoxyadenosine on deoxycoformycin-treated myeloid and lymphoid stem cells. *Blood* 60:872, 1982.

399. RUSSELL NH, CARRON J, HOFFBRAND AV, BELLINGHAM AJ: The relative sensitivity of peripheral blood T-lymphocyte colony forming cells and bone marrow CFU-GM to deoxyadenosine and 2′-deoxycoformycin. *Leukemia Res* 9:315, 1985.

400. FABIAN I, WILLIAMS Z: The effect of deoxycoformycin on bone marrow cells treated with adenosine and deoxyadenosine and hematopoietic growth factors. *Hum Immunol* 21:81, 1988.

401. SHORE A, DOSCH H-M, GELFAND EW: Role of adenosine deaminase in the early stages of precursor T cell maturation. *Clin Exp Immunol* 44:152, 1981.

402. MURPHY SB, STASS S, KALWINSKY D, RIVERA G: Phenotypic conversion of acute leukemia from T-lymphoblastic to myeloblastic induced by therapy with 2′-deoxycoformycin. *Br J Haematol* 55:285, 1983.

403. KURTZBERG J, BIGNER SH, HERSHFIELD MS: Establishment of the DU.528 human lymphohematopoietic stem cell line. *J Exp Med* 162:1561, 1985.

404. HERSHFIELD MS, KURTZBERG J, CHAFFEE S, GREENBERG ML, HAYNES BJ: Effects of purine nucleosides on differentiation in stem cell leukemia, in Aarbakke J, Chiang PK, Koeffler HP (eds): *The Biology and Pharmacology of Tumor Cell Differentiation.* Clifton, NJ, Humana Press, 1987, p 251.

405. SCOLLAY RG, BUTCHER EC, WEISSMAN IL: Thymus cell migration. Quantitative aspects of cellular traffic from the thymus to the periphery in mice. *Eur J Immunol* 10:210, 1980.

406. SCHULER W, WELLER IJ, SCHULER A, PHILLIPS RA, ROSENBERT N, MAK TW, KEARNEY JF, PERRY RP, BOSMA MJ: Rearrangement of antigen receptor genes is defective in mice with severe combined immunodeficiency. *Cell* 46:963, 1986.

407. REISNER Y, KAPOOR N, KIRKPATRICK D, POLLACK MS, CUNNINGHAM-RUNDLES S, DUPONT B, HODES MZ, GOOD RA, O'REILLY RJ: Transplantation for severe combined immunodeficiency with HLA-A,B,D,DR incompatible parental marrow cells fractionated by soybean agglutinin and sheep red blood-cells. *Blood* 61:341, 1983.

408. FRIEDRICH W, GOLDMANN SF, EBELL W, BLUTTERS-SAWATZKI R, GAEDECKE G, RAGHAVACHAR A, PETER HH, BELOHRADSKY B, KRETH W, KUBANEK B, KLEIHAUER E: Severe combined immunodeficiency: Treatment by bone marrow transplantation in 15 infants using HLA-haploidentical donors. *Eur J Pediatr* 144:125, 1985.

409. BUCKLEY RH, SCHIFF SE, SAMPSON HA, SCHIFF RI, MARKERT ML, KNUTSEN AP, HERSHFIELD MS, HUANG AT, MICKEY GH, WARD FE: Development of immunity in human severe primary T cell deficiency following haploidentical bone marrow stem cell transplantation. *J Immunol* 136:2398, 1986.

410. PARKMAN R, GELFAND EW, ROSEN FS, SANDERSON A, HIRSCHHORN R: Severe combined immunodeficiency and adenosine deaminase deficiency. *N Engl J Med* 292:714, 1975.

411. CHEN SH, OCHS HD, SCOTT CR, GIBLETT ER, TINGLE AJ: Adenosine deaminase deficiency: Disappearance of adenine deoxynucleotides from a patient's erythrocytes after successful marrow transplantation. *J Clin Invest* 62:1386, 1978.

412. FISCHER A, FRIEDRICH W, LEVINSKY R, VOSSEN J, GRISCELLI C, KUBANEK B, MORGAN G, WAGEMAKER G, LANDAIS P: Bone-marrow transplantation for immunodeficiencies and osteopetrosis: European survey, 1968–1985. *Lancet* 2:1080, 1986.

413. HIRSCHHORN R, ROEGNER-MANISCALCO V, KURITSKY L, ROSEN FS: Bone marrow transplantation only partially restores purine metabolites to normal in adenosine deaminase-deficient patients. *J Clin Invest* 68:1387, 1981.

414. KEIGHTLEY RG, LAWTON AR, COOPER MD, YUNIS EJ: Successful fetal liver transplantation in a child with severe combined immunodeficiency. *Lancet* 2:850, 1975.

415. HONG R, SCHULTE-WISSERMANN H, HOROWITZ S, BORZY M, FINLAY J: Cultured thymic epithelium in severe combined immunodeficiency. *Transplant Proc* 10:201, 1978.

416. RICH KC, RICHMAN CM, MEJIAS E, DADDONA P: Immunoreconstitution by peripheral blood leukocytes in adenosine deaminase-deficient severe combined immunodeficiency. *J Clin Invest* 66:389, 1980.

417. AMMAN AJ, WARA DW, ALLEN T: Immunotherapy and immunopathologic studies in a patient with nucleoside phosphorylase deficiency. *Clin Immunol Immunopathol* 10:262, 1978.

418. DAVIES EG, LEVINSKY RJ, WEBSTER DR, SIMMONDS HA, PERRETT D: Effect of red cell transfusions, thymic hormone and deoxycytidine in severe

combined immunodeficiency due to adenosine deaminase deficiency. *Clin Exp Immunol* 50:303, 1982.

419. RUBINSTEIN A, HIRSCHHORN R, SICKLICK M, MURPHY RA: *In vivo* and *in vitro* effects of thymosin and adenosine deaminase on adenosine-deaminase-deficient lymphocytes. *N Engl J Med* 300:387, 1979.

420. POLMAR SH, WETZLER EM, STERN RC, HIRSCHHORN R: Restoration of in vitro lymphocyte responses with exogenous ADA in a patient with severe combined immunodeficiency. *Lancet* 2:743, 1975.

421. DESNICK RJ, THORPE SR, FIDDLER MB: Toward enzyme therapy for lysosomal storage diseases. *Physiol Rev* 56:57, 1976.

422. DESNICK RJ, GRABOWSKI GA: Advances in the treatment of inherited metabolic diseases. *Adv Hum Genet* 11:281, 1981.

423. DYMINSKI JW, DAOUD A, LAMPKIN BC, LIMOUZE S, DONOFRIO J, COLEMAN MS, HUTTON JJ: Immunological and biochemical profiles in response to transfusion therapy in an adenosine deaminase-deficient patient with severe combined immunodeficiency disease. *Clin Immunol Immunopathol* 14:307, 1979.

424. SCHMALSTEIG FC, MILLS GC, NELSON JA, MAY LT, GOLDMAN AS, GOLDBLUM RM: Limited effect of erythrocyte and plasma infusions in adenosine deaminase deficiency. *J Pediatr* 93:597, 1978.

425. TSUCHIYA S, ARAI N, KUDO M, KONNO T, TADA K, YOKOYAMA S: Effect of adenosine deaminase replacement therapy on a child with adenosine deaminase deficiency with severe combined immunodeficiency disease. *Tohoku J Exp Med* 128:251, 1979.

426. ZIEGLER JB, LEE CL, van der WEYDEN MB, BAGNARA AS, BEVERIDGE J: Severe combined immunodeficiency and adenosine deaminase deficiency: Failure of enzyme replacement therapy. *Arch Dis Child* 55:452, 1980.

427. POLMAR SH: Enzyme replacement and other biochemical approaches to the therapy of adenosine deaminase deficiency, in Elliot K, Whelan J (eds): *Enzyme Defects and Immune Dysfunction, Ciba Foundation Symposium 68*. New York, Excerpta Medica, 1979, p 213.

428. ABUCHOWSKI A, van ES T, PALCZUK NC, DAVIS FF: Alteration of immunological properties of bovine serum albumin by covalent and attachment of polyethylene glycol. *J Biol Chem* 252:3578, 1977.

429. ABUCHOWSKI A, MCCOY JR, PALCZUK NC, van ES T, DAVIS FF: Effect of attachment of polyethylene glycol on immunogenicity and circulating life of bovine liver catalase. *J Biol Chem* 252:3582, 1977.

430. DAVIS S, ABUCHOWSKI A, PARK YK, DAVIS FF: Alteration of the circulating life and antigenic properties of bovine adenosine deaminase in mice by attachment of polyethylene glycol. *Clin Exp Immunol* 46:649, 1981.

431. LEVY Y, HERSHFIELD MS, FERNANDEZ-MEJIA C, POLMAR SH, SCUDIERY D, BERGER M, SORENSEN RU: Adenosine deaminase deficiency with late onset of recurrent infections: Response to treatment with polyethylene glycol-modified adenosine deaminase (PEG-ADA). *J Pediatr* 113:312, 1988.

432. SANDMAN R, AMMANN AJ, GROSE C, WARA DW: Cellular immunodeficiency associated with nucleoside phosphorylase deficiency. *Clin Immunol Immunopathol* 8:247, 1977.

433. GELFAND EW, DOSCH H-M, BIGGAR WD, FOX IH: Partial purine nucleoside phosphorylase deficiency: Studies of lymphocyte function. *J Clin Invest* 61:1071, 1978.

434. ZEGERS BJM, STOOP JW, STAAL GEJ, WADMAN SK: An approach to the restoration of T cell function in a purine nucleoside phosphorylase deficient patient, in Elliot K, Whelan J (eds): *Enzyme Defects and Dysfunction, Ciba Foundation Symposium 68*, New York, Excerpta Medica, 1979, p 231.

435. RICH KC, MEJIAS E, FOX IH: Purine nucleoside phosphorylase deficiency: Improved metabolic and immunologic function with erythrocyte transfusions. *N Engl J Med* 303:973, 1980.

436. COWMAN MJ, WARA DW, AMMANN AJ: Deoxycytidine therapy in two patients with adenosine deaminase deficiency and severe immunodeficiency disease. *Clin Immunol Immunopathol* 37:30, 1985.

437. STOOP JW, ZEGERS BJM, SPAAPEN LJM, KUIS W, ROORD JJ, RIJKERS GT, STAAL GEJ, RIJKSEN G, DURAN M, WADMAN SK: The effect of deoxycytidine and tetrahydrouridine in purine nucleoside phosphorylase deficiency. *Adv Exp Med Biol* 165A:61, 1984.

438. Department of Health and Human Services, National Institutes of Health: Recombinant DNA research; request for public comment on points to consider in the design and submission of human somatic-cell gene therapy protocols. *Federal Register* 50:2945, 1985.

439. ANDERSON WF: Prospects for human gene therapy. *Science* 226:401, 1984.

440. FLETCHER J: Ethical issues in and beyond prospective clinical trials of human gene therapy. *J Med Philos* 10:293, 1985.

441. BERNSTEIN A, BERGER S, HUSZAR D, DICK J: Gene transfer with retrovirus vectors, in Setlow K, Hollaender A (eds): *Genetic Engineering: Principles and Methods*. New York, Plenum, 1985, vol 7, p 235.

442. GILBOA E, EGLITIS MA, KANTOFF PW, ANDERSON WF: Transfer and expression of cloned genes using retroviral vectors. *Biotechniques* 4:504, 1986.

443. CONE RD, MULLIGAN RC: High efficiency gene transfer into mammalian cells: Generation of helper-free recombinant retrovirus with broad mammalian host range. *Proc Natl Acad Sci USA* 81:6349, 1984.

444. MANN R, MULLIGAN RC, BALTIMORE DB: Construction of a retrovirus packaging mutant and its use to produce helper-free defective retrovirus. *Cell* 33:153, 1983.

445. VALERIO D, DUYVESTEYN MGC, van der EB AJ: Introduction of sequences encoding functional human adenosine deaminase into mouse cells using a retroviral shuttle system. *Gene* 34:163, 1984.

446. FRIEDMAN RL: Expression of human adenosine deaminase using a transmissable murine retrovirus vector system. *Proc Natl Acad Sci USA* 82:703, 1985.

447. WILLIAMS DA, ORKIN SH, MULLIGAN RC: Retrovirus-mediated transfer of human adenosine deaminase gene sequences into cells in culture and into murine hematopoietic cells in vivo. *Proc Natl Acad Sci USA* 83:2566, 1986.

448. KANTOFF PW, KOHN DB, MITSUYA H, ARMENTANO D, SIEBERG M, ZWIEBEL JA, EGLITIS MA, MCLACHLIN JR, WIGINTON DA, HUTTON JJ, HOROWITZ SD, GILBOA R, BLAESE DA, ANDERSON WF: Correction of adenosine deaminase deficiency in cultured human T and B cells by retrovirus-mediated gene transfer. *Proc Natl Acad Sci USA* 83:6563, 1986.

449. McIVORS RS, GODDARD JM, SIMONSEN CC, MARTIN DW Jr: Expression of a cDNA sequence encoding human purine nucleoside phosphorylase in rodent and human cells. *Mol Cell Biol* 5:1349, 1985.

450. McIVOR RS, JOHNSON MJ, MILLER AD, PITTS S, WILLIAMS SR, VALERIO D, MARTIN DW Jr, VERMA IM: Human purine nucleoside phosphorylase and adenosine deaminase: Gene transfer into cultured cells and murine hematopoietic stem cells by using recombinant amphotropic retroviruses. *Mol Cell Biol* 7:838, 1987.

451. BELMONT JW, HENKEL-TIGGES J, CHANG SMW, WAGER-SMITH K, KELLEMS RE, DICK JE, MAGLI MC, PHILLIPS RA, BERNSTEIN A, CASKEY CT: Expression of human adenosine deaminase in murine haematopoietic progenitor cells following retroviral transfer. *Nature 322:385, 1986.*

452. KANTOFF PW, GILLIO A, MCLACHLIN JR, BORDIGNON C, EGLITIS MA, KERNAN NA, MOEN RC, KOHN DB, YU S-F, KARSON E, KARLSSON S, ZWIEBEL JA, GILBOA E, BLAESE RM, NIENHUIS A, O'REILLY RJ, ANDERSON WF: Expression of human adenosine deaminase in non-human primates after retroviral mediated gene transfer. *J Exp Med* 166:219, 1987.

453. YU S-F, VON RUDEN T, KANTOFF PW, GARBER C, SEIBERG M, RUTHER U, ANDERSON WF, WAGNER EF, GILBOA E: Self-inactivating retroviral vectors designed for transfer of whole genes into mammalian cells. *Proc Natl Acad Sci USA* 83:3194, 1986.

454. HAWLEY RG, COVARRUBIAS L, HAWLEY T, MINTZ B: Handicapped retroviral vectors efficiently transduce foreign genes into hematopoietic stem cells. *Proc Natl Acad Sci USA* 84:2406, 1987.

455. SELDEN RF, SKOSKIEWICZ MJ, HOWIE KB, RUSSELL PS, GOODMAN HM: Implantation of genetically engineered fibroblasts into mice: Implications for gene therapy. *Science* 236:714, 1987.

456. PALMER TD, HOCK RA, OSBORNE WRA, MILLER AD: Efficient retrovirus-mediated transfer and expression of a human adenosine deaminase gene in diploid skin fibroblasts from an adenosine deaminase-deficient human. *Proc Natl Acad Sci USA* 84:1055, 1987.

457. MILLS GC, SCHMALSTIEG FC, TRIMMER KB, FOLDMAN AS, GOLDBLUM RM: Purine metabolism in adenosine deaminase deficiency. *Proc Natl Acad Sci USA* 73:2867, 1976.

458. EDWARDS NL, GELFAND EW, BIGGAR D, FOX IH: Partial deficiency of purine nucleoside phosphorylase: Studies of purine and pyrimidine metabolism. *J Lab Clin Med* 91:736, 1978.

459. SIMMONDS HA, WATSON JG, HUGH-JONES K, PERRETT D, SAHOTA A, POTTER CF: Deoxynucleoside excretion in adenosine deaminase deficiency and purine nucleoside phosphorylase deficiency, in Pollara B, Pickering RJ, Meuwissen HJ, Porter IH (eds): *Inborn Errors of Specific Immunity*. New York, Academic, 1979, p 377.

460. HIRSCHHORN R, PAPAGEORGIOU P, RUBINSTEIN A, ROSEN FS: Transfusion vs. bone marrow transplantation in combined immunodeficiency. *Clin Res* 27:507A, 1979.

461. SIEGENBEEK VAN HEUKELOM LH, AKERMANN JWN, STAHL JEJ, DE BRUYN CHMM, STOOP JW, ZEGERS BJM, DE BREE PK, WADMAN SK: A patient with purine nucleoside phosphorylase deficiency: Enzymological and metabolic aspects. *Clin Chim Acta* 74:271, 1977.

CHAPTER 41

MYOADENYLATE DEAMINASE DEFICIENCY

RICHARD L. SABINA
JUDITH L. SWAIN
EDWARD W. HOLMES

1. *Muscle AMP deaminase (EC 3.5.4.6) deficiency is a relatively benign disorder characterized clinically by muscle fatigue following exercise. More than 130 patients have been characterized, and it has also been demonstrated in approximately 2 percent of muscle biopsy specimens submitted for pathologic examination for a wide array of indications.*
2. *Two distinct forms of this myopathy have been proposed. Primary (inherited) deficiency presents clinically as exercise-related cramps and myalgias only, while secondary (acquired) deficiency is associated with a wide array of other neuromuscular or rheumatologic disorders.*
3. *The primary enzyme deficiency appears to be inherited as an autosomal recessive trait, although this has not yet been clearly established. Of all reported cases, males outnumber females 2 to 1. A similar predominance of affected males exists in secondary (acquired) enzyme deficiency as well.*
4. *Of the reported patients, 88 percent have had easy fatigability, cramps, or myalgias following exercise. Patients exhibit muscle dysfunction only, and AMP deaminase activity is normal in other tissues.*
5. *When patients with myoadenylate deaminase deficiency exercise, their skeletal muscle does not accumulate NH_3 and IMP, as occurs in normal subjects.*
6. *The myopathy in patients with primary adenylate deaminase deficiency indicates that this enzyme and the purine nucleotide cycle, of which it is one component, play an important role in skeletal muscle metabolism during exercise.*

The purine nucleotide cycle (Fig. 41-1), of which the adenylate deaminase (AMP deaminase) reaction is one component, is thought to play an important role in skeletal muscle function for several reasons. The activities of all three enzymes in the purine nucleotide cycle are several-fold greater in skeletal muscle than any other organ, and the activity of AMP deaminase is approximately 100 times greater than that of the other two enzymes.[1-3] During exercise, NH_3 production and inosine monophosphate (IMP) content of skeletal muscle increase in proportion to the work performed by the muscle,[1-8] indicating increased AMP deaminase activity under these conditions. Activation of myoadenylate deaminase and increased flux through the purine nucleotide cycle during exercise lead to an increase in energy production through the generation of intermediates for the citric acid cycle from amino acids and through stimulation of glycolysis.[1-7] Thus, one might anticipate that a high grade deficiency of myoadenylate deaminase activity and disruption of the purine nucleotide cycle could lead to skeletal muscle dysfunction.

In 1978 Fishbein et al. described five patients with a history of skeletal muscle dysfunction following mild to moderate exercise.[9] In these patients myoadenylate deaminase activity was virtually absent. Up to the present, 133 additional patients with myoadenylate deaminase deficiency have been described.[9-27] Data from several institutions suggest that this myopathy may be relatively common, since approximately 2 percent of all biopsies submitted for pathologic evaluation have been found to be deficient in AMP deaminase activity.[9,11,18]

CLINICAL FEATURES

The clinical features and laboratory abnormalities associated with myoadenylate deaminase deficiency are summarized in Table 41-1. Sixty-eight percent of patients are male; 88 percent of patients develop fatigue, cramps, or myalgias following moderate to vigorous exercise. Myoglobinuria following strenuous exercise has been reported in only one patient. The median age at the time of diagnosis of myoadenylate deaminase deficiency is 32 years, with a range of 1.5 to 70 years. Of patients noted, 23 percent had onset of symptoms in childhood and 26 percent as teenagers. These figures are not significantly different upon separation of patients into presumed primary and secondary deficiency (see "Clinical Spectrum and Variability," below).

Increased serum creatine kinase activity has been found in 52 percent of patients. In a number of cases serum creatine kinase activity was normal at rest and increased into the abnormal range only following exercise. Electromyogram (EMG) may be normal, but minor abnormalities have been described in some patients undergoing this test. Results of muscle bi-

Fig. 41-1 Purine nucleotide cycle. S-AMP refers to adenylsuccinate.

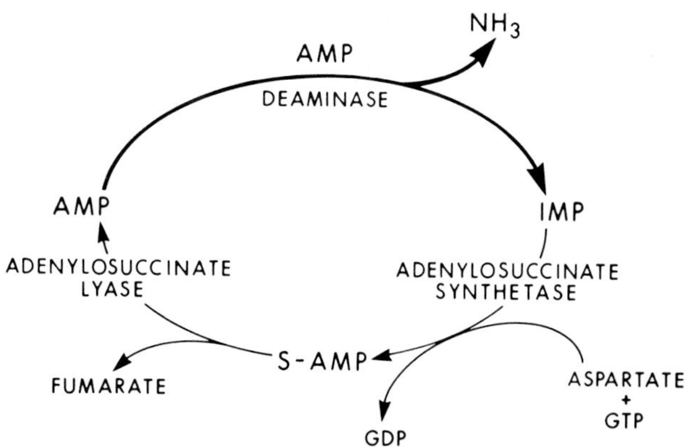

Table 41-1 Clinical Features and Laboratory Abnormalities

- Clinical features of AMP deaminase deficiency
  - Sex: 87 male/128 total
  - Age at time of diagnosis
    - Mean: 32 years
    - Median: 30 years
    - Range: <1 to 70 years
  - Age at time of onset of symptoms
    - Infancy (<2 years): 1 out of 35 (3%)
    - Childhood (2–12): 8 out of 35 (23%)
    - Teenage (13–19): 9 out of 35 (26%)
    - Young adult (20–40): 8 out of 35 (23%)
    - Older adult (<40): 9 out of 35 (26%)
  - Postexercise symptoms
    - Easy fatigue, cramps, myalgia: 49 out of 56 (88%)
  - Other clinical diagnoses (presumably secondary deficiency)
    - Dystrophy: 10
    - Neuropathy: 9
    - Polymyositis: 8
    - Atrophy: 7
    - Collagen vascular disease: 3
    - Amyotrophic lateral sclerosis: 2
    - Progressive systemic sclerosis: 2
    - Dermatomyositis: 2
    - Hypotonia: 2
    - Type I atrophy: 2
    - Hypokalemic periodic paralysis: 1
    - Kugelberg-Welander syndrome: 1
    - Others: 7
- Laboratory abnormalities in patients with AMP deaminase deficiency
  - Elevated serum CPK*: 30 out of 58 (52%)
  - Failure to produce NH_3 on ischemic testing: 115 out of 115 (100%)
  - Negative histochemical stain for AMP deaminase: 120 out of 120 (100%)
  - Diminished (<0.2–15.7% of normal) AMP deaminase activity on direct assay: 111 out of 111 (100%)

*CPK = creatine phosphokinase.

opsy, examined by routine histochemical stains and electron microscopy, have varied from no pathologic findings to mild abnormalities in distribution of fiber type, with or without minimal changes in fiber size. Histochemical stain for AMP deaminase activity has been negative in all patients tested, and myoadenylate deaminase residual activity varies from virtually absent (<0.2) to 15.7 percent of control. The percent residual activity may be helpful in distinguishing primary from secondary deficiency (see Table 41-2 and Ref. 22). No NH_3 is produced following ischemic forearm exercise in patients with myoadenylate deaminase deficiency, and this test has been used to screen patients for this enzyme deficiency. This test is not specific for myoadenylate deaminase deficiency, but it does appear to be a sensitive screening procedure since all patients with this enzyme deficiency fail to produce NH_3 during ischemic forearm exercise, whereas lactate production is normal.

CLINICAL SPECTRUM AND VARIABILITY

Myoadenylate deaminase deficiency presents a confusing clinical picture. Not all patients with an absence of AMP deaminase activity on muscle biopsy present with exercise-related symptoms. For example, three patients had clinical findings consistent with a primary neurologic disorder—amyotrophic lateral sclerosis and Kugelberg-Welander syndrome. The first patient reported with myoadenylate deaminase deficiency was diagnosed as having primary hypokalemic periodic paralysis. Two patients with myoadenylate deaminase deficiency first sought medical attention for muscle symptoms at approximately 70 years of age following an influenzalike illness. Another patient presented at 1.5 years of age with delayed motor and speech development, as well as prominent hypotonia. Associated rheumatologic disorders include collagen vascular disease, progressive systemic sclerosis, and polyarthralgias. In addition, asymptomatic individuals have been reported with deficient myoadenylate deaminase activity.[18] It is not clear what relationship, if any, the deficiency of myoadenylate deaminase activity bears to the neuromuscular and rheumatologic disorders exhibited in approximately one-half of all reported patients with myoadenylate deaminase deficiency. However, Fishbein's recent data suggest that there may be two distinct forms of myoadenylate deaminase deficiency.[22] As summarized in Table 41-2, patients with myoadenylate deaminase deficiency have been classified as either primary (inherited) or secondary (acquired) based on their clinical presentation, level, and immunoreactivity of residual activity, and relative activities of other muscle-specific enzymes.

Although this hypothesis needs to be rigorously tested, it holds promise for clarifying the clinical picture associated with myoadenylate deaminase deficiency. As is discussed in subsequent sections of this chapter, the postexercise symptoms experienced by the great majority (88 percent) of patients may be explained by primary deficiency of myoadenylate deaminase and disruption of the purine nucleotide cycle. The deficiency of myoadenylate deaminase activity found in patients with the clinical diagnosis of other neuromuscular and rheu-

Table 41-2 Characteristics of Proposed Alternative Forms of Myoadenylate Deaminase Deficiency

	Primary myoadenylate deaminase deficiency	*Secondary myoadenylate deaminase deficiency*
Clinical presentation	Exercise-related aches, cramps, and pains	Other neuromuscular manifestations
Residual activity	<2.0% of control*	Up to 15% of control
Immunoreactivity of residual activity	Not precipitated by muscle-specific antiserums	Precipitated by muscle-specific antiserums
Other muscle-specific enzymatic activities	Unaffected	Also reduced (i.e., creatine phosphokinase, adenylate kinase)

*Residual activity in muscle of patients with presumptive primary deficiency is accompanied by a comparable decrease in AMP deaminase peptide in immune precipitation and Western blot analyses.
SOURCE: Taken from Fishbein.[22]

matologic diseases may represent the coincidental finding of a relatively common enzyme deficiency in patients in whom muscle biopsy is performed as a routine part of their diagnostic evaluation. Alternatively, the depression of myoadenylate deaminase and other muscle-specific enzymatic activities in secondary deficiency, as suggested by Fishbein, could reflect a regulatory derangement in muscle-specific gene expression as a consequence of other pathologic neuromuscular and rheumatologic abnormalities. Whichever explanation, clinical presentation in these patients includes symptoms of the associated disorder as well as those related to myoadenylate deaminase deficiency.

The severity and age of onset of postexercise symptoms are variable in patients with myoadenylate deaminase activity. The reactions catalyzed by AMP deaminase and the other enzymes in the purine nucleotide cycle (Fig. 41-1) play an important role in the metabolism of the fast-twitch glycolytic fiber following vigorous exercise (see "Purine Nucleotide Cycle," below). This series of reactions also appears to play a role in the metabolism of slow-twitch oxidative fibers.[28] Some of the variability in postexercise symptoms associated with myoadenylate deaminase deficiency may be related to individual differences in the proportion of fast-twitch glycolytic versus slow-twitch oxidative fibers in a given muscle group and the extent to which the purine nucleotide cycle contributes to energy production in each fiber type. In addition, long-standing deficiency of AMP deaminase, as in the inherited defect, may be associated with adaptive changes in other metabolic pathways which could ameliorate symptoms.

The pattern of inheritance of AMP deaminase deficiency has not been clearly defined, possibly because of confusion between primary and secondary deficiency states. This is reflected in the literature, where limited family studies have suggested X-linked,[18] autosomal recessive,[27] and autosomal dominant inheritance.[18] However, reduced levels of AMP deaminase activity relative to controls have been reported in presumed heterozygotes, suggesting an autosomal recessive mode of inheritance.[18,27] This matter should be resolved when appropriate nucleic acid probes for human myoadenylate deaminase become available.

PURINE NUCLEOTIDE CYCLE

Three enzymes participate in the purine nucleotide cycle (Fig. 41-1): AMP deaminase (AMP aminohydrolase) (EC 3.5.4.6), adenylosuccinate synthetase (EC 6.3.4.4), and adenylosuccinate lyase (EC 4.3.2.2). At first glance this series of reactions might appear to be a futile cycle, i.e., AMP → IMP → AMP. However, each turn of the cycle results in the utilization of one molecule of aspartate and guanosine triphosphate (GTP) and the production of one molecule of guanosine diphosphate (GDP), fumarate, and NH_3. Before discussing the potential role(s) this cycle plays in muscle function, it may be helpful to review the data which establish that flux through the cycle increases in skeletal muscle during exercise.

Several laboratories have shown that the purine nucleotide cycle is operative in vivo.[2–7,20,28] Biopsies obtained from the hind limbs of rodents following nerve stimulation or treadmill running demonstrate the following sequence of biochemical changes: (1) In fast-twitch glycolytic muscle the ATP concentration falls when the capacity for energy production by substrate oxidation is exceeded. (2) The resultant increase in AMP and adenosine diphosphate (ADP) production coupled with the decreases in adenosine triphosphate (ATP) concentration leads to an increase in AMP deaminase activity (see "AMP Deaminase Isoforms," below). (3) IMP accumulates in an amount that is almost stoichiometric with the decrease in adenine nucleotides. (4) NH_3 content of the muscle increases stoichiometrically with IMP, and spillover of additional NH_3 into the blood leads to an increase in plasma NH_3 concentration. (5) Aspartate concentration in the muscle falls while the concentrations of fumarate, malate, and citrate increase. This sequence of events demonstrates that AMP deaminase activity increases in muscle following vigorous exercise, and activation of this enzyme in turn leads to increased flux through the purine nucleotide cycle. These experiments establish a central role for AMP deaminase in the control of flux through this cycle.

It has been difficult to quantify flux through the purine nucleotide cycle, and consequently it has been difficult to estimate the extent to which flux is increased during exercise. Several studies indicate that flux through the cycle is increased substantially during exercise. Meyer et al.[5] have shown that blood NH_3 concentration increases 5.5 times in the rat following vigorous exercise. This magnitude of increase in blood NH_3 cannot be accounted for by the stoichiometric conversion of ATP to IMP and suggests that a substantial proportion of the NH_3 released into the blood is derived from aspartate through the purine nucleotide cycle. Aragon and Lowenstein[3] have demonstrated that citrate, isocitrate, and succinate concentrations in muscle increase following exercise, and that at least 72 percent of this expansion of the pool of citric acid cycle intermediates is derived from aspartate via the purine nucleotide cycle. These studies demonstrate that the IMP which accumulates in skeletal muscle during exercise is continuously recycled to AMP and back to IMP. Reconstitution experiments with muscle extracts have documented simultaneous flux through both "arms," i.e., AMP → IMP + NH_3 and IMP + aspartate + GTP → → AMP + fumarate + GDP, of the purine nucleotide cycle, and the flux through the cycle is controlled by adenylate energy charge.[29] These results taken together support the conclusion that flux through both arms of the purine nucleotide cycle increases during exercise.

During the rest period following vigorous muscle contraction, IMP is converted first to adenylosuccinate and then to AMP.[3,5–7] Since the capacity for ATP synthesis is greater than the rate of ATP utilization in resting muscle, any AMP formed from IMP is rapidly phosphorylated to ATP. Thus, the IMP which accumulates during exercise is used to restore the ATP pool during rest. In most studies the ATP pool is fully replenished after 15 to 30 min of rest.[3,5–7,30,31]

Sequential muscle biopsies have also been obtained in human subjects at rest, following exercise, and during the period of recovery.[30] Changes in IMP and adenine nucleotide content of human skeletal muscle are similar to those reported in animal experiments.[3,5–7] Blood NH_3 concentration increases following vigorous exercise, and the increase in NH_3 concentration is proportional to the work load.[32–34] Ischemic forearm exercise also leads to NH_3 production by human skeletal muscle.[9,13,15,24–27] These results indicate that AMP deaminase activity and flux through the purine nucleotide cycles are increased in human skeletal muscle, much as in rodent skeletal muscle, following exercise.

Several mechanisms have been proposed to explain the role of the purine nucleotide cycle in muscle function. One hypothesis is that the increase in flux through the purine nucleotide cycle during exercise serves to maintain the adenylate energy charge of the myocyte under these conditions.[2,35,36] The adenylate energy charge would be maintained through the following mechanism: The increase in AMP deaminase activity that occurs during exercise would prevent AMP accumulation following ATP catabolism, and this in turn would displace the adenylate kinase reaction toward ATP formation. A second hypothesis is that the local production of NH_3 acts in conjunction with the decrease in ATP to stimulate the activity of phosphofructokinase and enhance the rate of glycolysis.[36] It has also been suggested that the increase in IMP concentration may contribute to activation of glycogen phosphorylase and further enhance glycolysis.[37] However, normal lactate accumulation reported in exercising AMP deaminase-deficient skeletal muscle[9,23–25,27] documents that a disruption of the purine nucleotide cycle does not lead to any significant changes in flux through the glycolytic pathway. Still another hypothesis is that the generation of fumarate, malate, and citrate from aspartate provides a mechanism by which intermediates of the citric acid cycle could be replenished during a time of increased demand for ATP production.[3] Finally, the accumulation of IMP may provide a mechanism for preserving the pool of purine nucleotides during exercise, and this reservoir of IMP may be used to replete the ATP pool rapidly during recovery.[15] These proposed mechanisms are not mutually exclusive, and more than one, or all, may have validity.

It is not clear which fiber type, i.e., glycolytic or oxidative, is more dependent on the purine nucleotide cycle for maintenance of energy production. In fast-twitch glycolytic fibers, ATP depletion and flux through the purine nucleotide cycle are readily evident following anaerobic exercise protocols.[5–7] One might postulate that AMP deaminase plays a role in maintaining energy charge in these fiber types by preventing AMP accumulation and by any positive effects which NH_3 and IMP accumulation have on enhanced glycolysis. In slow-twitch oxidative fibers, ATP levels are usually maintained during aerobic exercise protocols,[5–7] suggesting the purine nucleotide cycle is of little importance in these types of fibers. However, inhibition of adenylosuccinate lyase activity is associated with rapid onset of fatigue in stimulation protocols which simulate aerobic exercise.[28,38] We might conclude from these studies that the purine nucleotide cycle is important for production of citric acid cycle intermediates for enhanced oxidative metabolism during aerobic exercise even when ATP levels are not markedly reduced. Thus it is not unexpected that AMP deaminase deficiency might lead to dysfunction of both glycolytic and oxidative muscle fibers. What is unexpected is how mild and variable the symptoms are in many patients with AMP deaminase deficiency. While there is no explanation for this at present, one might speculate that inherited deficiency of AMP deaminase may be compensated for by adaptive changes in other metabolic pathways, while abrupt interruption of flux through the purine nucleotide cycle with pharmacologic agents does not permit adaptive changes, and muscle dysfunction is more severe and reproducible under these circumstances. Alternatively, residual activity (i.e., as much as 15 percent of control) may be sufficient for low-level functioning of the purine nucleotide cycle to such a degree that severe symptoms are alleviated.

Table 41-3 Exercise-Related Metabolic Abnormalities Associated with Myoadenylate Deaminase Deficiency

Observation	*Reference*
Submaximal exercise	
Impaired increase in plasma NH_4 and plasma purines	39, 40
↓ Adenylate catabolism (intracellular)	41
↓ IMP accumulation (intracellular)	41
Maximal exercise	
↓ Adenylate catabolism	20
↓ IMP accumulation	20
↑ Adenosine production	20
↑ Energy substrate (i.e., ATP, CP) depletion per unit work	20

EXERCISE-RELATED METABOLIC AND FUNCTIONAL ABNORMALITIES IN PATIENTS WITH MYOADENYLATE DEAMINASE DEFICIENCY

Various exercise protocols have been employed to analyze changes in metabolites and muscle performance in patients with myoadenylate deaminase deficiency.[20,39–41] Relative to control individuals, patients with myoadenylate deaminase deficiency exhibit a number of exercise-related derangements in metabolism (Table 41-3). Many of these are predicted effects of a block in deamination of AMP and confirm a biochemical disruption of the purine nucleotide cycle as a consequence of myoadenylate deaminase deficiency.

Functional abnormalities (i.e., diminished endurance and enhanced depletion of high-energy phosphate pools per unit of work) have been reported in patients with myoadenylate deaminase deficiency during vigorous aerobic bicycle exercise,[20] whereas no significant differences from control individuals were observed after a less intense protocol employing ischemic forearm exercise.[41]

AMP DEAMINASE ISOFORMS

There are several isoenzymes of AMP deaminase. Different tissues contain varying proportions of these isoenzymes, and the properties of these isoenzymes are quite distinct.[42–44] At least three isoenzymes of AMP deaminase have been identified in the rat on the basis of kinetic, physical, and immunologic properties as well as differences in peptide maps. Isoenzyme A, referred to as myoadenylate deaminase, is found only in skeletal muscle and diaphragm; isoenzyme B is the predominant form in liver, kidney, and testes; isoenzyme C is the only isoenzyme found in heart muscle; and hybrids of isoenzymes B and C are found in brain, lung, and spleen.[42–44] In humans, there are reportedly four isoenzymes of AMP deaminase,[45] and as in rodents, one is found exclusively in skeletal muscle. Studies in patients with AMP deaminase deficiency suggest that some, if not all, of these isoenzymes are products of different transcripts. Skeletal muscle is the only tissue deficient in AMP deaminase activity in patients with myopathic symptoms.[9,13,46] Deficiency of AMP deaminase activity restricted to erythrocytes has been described in several asymptomatic families in Japan.[47]

During the course of development, the total amount of AMP deaminase activity in a given tissue may vary, as well as the relative distribution among isoenzyme species.[48–54] In rat skeletal muscle, total AMP deaminase activity increases as much as eightfold from birth to adulthood,[54,55] and during intrauterine development in rat and humans, there is a switch in AMP deaminase isoforms produced in skeletal muscle at different stages of development.[53,54] Fast-twitch white (type IIb) fibers contain three- to tenfold more AMP deaminase activity[56] and mRNA[57] than slow-twitch red (type I) fibers. Although some studies have suggested that red and white skeletal muscle contain different isoenzymes of AMP deaminase,[58] others have found little difference in the kinetic properties, and possible isoenzyme type, during development.[44] A shift in isoenzyme type has also been observed when myocytes are grown in culture,[49] and this may explain the finding of AMP deaminase activity in primary myoblasts grown in culture from a muscle biopsy specimen of a patient with well-documented myoadenylate deaminase deficiency.[13]

Myoadenylate deaminase (isoenzyme A) has been purified to homogeneity from many mammalian sources, including humans.[59–61] The native molecular weight of the enzyme from rat skeletal muscle is reportedly 238,000, and following treatment with denaturing agents such as guanidine hydrochloride or sodium dodecylsulfate, the enzyme dissociates into a single polypeptide with a reported molecular weight of approximately 60,000.[60] The enzyme from rabbit skeletal muscle reportedly has a native molecular weight of approximately 270,000 and is composed of a single subunit of approximately 69,000.[61] However, recent evidence has suggested that these analyses may have been performed on partially proteolyzed protein. Purification in the presence of protease inhibitors yields a subunit molecular weight of approximately 80,000 in the rat and a native molecular weight of 320,000.[54] Nevertheless, all data are consistent with the conclusion that AMP deaminase from skeletal muscle is composed of four polypeptide chains, and tryptic maps suggest that these subunits are identical. The amino acid composition of this protein is not unusual, and it does not appear to contain substantial amounts of carbohydrate.

AMP deaminase is closely associated with contractile proteins in the myocyte. Histochemical studies have demonstrated that AMP deaminase is bound to the myofibril in the region of the A band[62] and that 2 mol of native enzyme bind to 1 mol of myosin.[63] AMP deaminase binds to a specific region of rabbit myosin heavy chain, i.e., heavy meromyosin or subfragment 2, and the association between AMP deaminase and myosin may play a role in controlling the activity of this enzyme (see below). It is interesting to note that the rat 80,000 AMP deaminase peptide binds much more tightly to myosin than the 66,000 proteolyzed fragment.[64]

AMP deaminase from skeletal muscle is a complex allosteric enzyme, the activity of which is influenced by many ligands. Human myoadenylate deaminase exhibits a high degree of specificity for 5′-AMP.[59,65] The velocity with 5′-dAMP is only 4 percent of that with 5′-AMP, and essentially no deaminase activity is observed with ATP, ADP, 3′-AMP, 2′-AMP, or adenosine. Other isoenzymes of AMP deaminase exhibit varying degrees of activity with these potential substrates.[65]

Studies in vitro and in vivo suggest that myoadenylate deaminase exhibits a striking increase in activity in muscle during exercise (see "Purine Nucleotide Cycle," above). Reconstitution experiments that attempt to mimic conditions found in resting muscle in vivo suggest that AMP deaminase is inhibited by as much as 80 to 90 percent under these conditions, while conditions which mimic contracting muscle are associated with marked increases in AMP deaminase activity and flux through the purine nucleotide cycle.[65,66] Many factors that affect myoadenylate deaminase activity in vitro have been identified: adenylate energy charge; ratio of purine nucleoside triphosphates to diphosphates to monophosphates; concentration of K^+, H^+, Pi, and creatine phosphate; and binding to myosin.[29,44,60,62,67,68] Changes in one or more of these variables are thought to lead to the release of inhibition of AMP deaminase and the increase in activity of this enzyme during exercise.

It is not established how each of the above factors influences AMP deaminase activity, but the data obtained by Ashby and Frieden[68] from kinetic and binding studies have led these investigators to propose a model that explains many of the regulatory properties of this enzyme. They suggest that the enzyme has three distinct types of purine nucleotide binding sites: a catalytic site that binds AMP, an inhibitory site that binds purine nucleoside triphosphates, and a stimulatory site that binds all types of purine nucleotides, but binds diphosphates in preference to monophosphates, and monophosphates in preference to triphosphates. K^+ ions affect the activity of the enzyme through cooperative effects on the catalytic site. Nucleoside triphosphates (ATP and GTP) bind avidly to the inhibitory site and produce indirect effects on cooperativity at the catalytic site. Nucleoside diphosphates and monophosphates (ADP, GDP, AMP, and GMP) bind avidly to the stimulatory site and indirectly decrease the affinity of the inhibitory site for nucleoside triphosphates. IMP, a product of the reaction, also binds to the stimulatory site and may under some conditions lead to enzyme activation. In resting muscle, purine nucleoside triphosphates are present in considerable excess relative to diphosphates and monophosphates. Following vigorous work, nucleoside triphosphate content decreases, producing a lower concentration of ligands for binding at the inhibitory site. Nucleoside diphosphate and monophosphate content increases, leading to higher ligand concentrations for binding at the stimulatory site and secondarily decreasing the affinity of the inhibitory site for nucleoside triphosphates. AMP content increases, providing more substrate and probably enhanced enzyme activity by binding of this monophosphate at the stimulatory site. This model accommodates a close correlation between the increase in AMP deaminase activity and the drop in adenylate energy charge that occurs with exercise.[30,69] The drop in myocyte pH that follows exercise also contributes to the increase in AMP deaminase activity, especially in fast-twitch glycolytic fibers.[70] The pH optimum for this enzyme (i.e., pH 6.5) reflects the role of metabolic acidosis in AMP deaminase activation.[71] Changes in creatine phosphate concentration probably do not play a role in controlling the activity of this enzyme.[72] The effect of AMP deaminase binding to myosin on the control of enzyme activity has not been thoroughly evaluated, but may prove to be important since the myosin components participating in this reaction bind to the nucleoside triphosphate, or inhibitory site, of AMP deaminase.[63]

A number of potent inhibitors of AMP deaminase have been identified and may prove useful in defining the role of this enzyme in muscle function. Coformycin and 2′-deoxycoformycin, potent inhibitors of adenosine deaminase, are less potent inhibitors of AMP deaminase (K_i of 2×10^{-8}M and 4×10^{-7}M, respectively).[73] The nucleotide derivatives, coformycin-5′-phosphate and 2′-deoxycoformycin-5′-phosphate, are considerably more potent inhibitors of AMP deaminase (K_i of 6×10^{-11}M and 1×10^{-9}M, respectively).[74]

AMP DEAMINASE GENE AND TRANSCRIPTS

The preceding discussion predicts that different AMP deaminase transcripts will be found to explain the different AMP deaminase isoforms produced in different tissues. Studies examining regulation of AMP deaminase gene expression are still in their infancy since a nucleic acid probe for this gene has become available only recently.

A cDNA corresponding to the AMP deaminase isoform produced in skeletal muscle has been cloned from a rat muscle library.[57] Southern blots of rat genomic DNA analyzed with this cDNA have identified only one Bam H1 restriction fragment, ≈20 kb, which hybridizes with this probe, suggesting AMP deaminase is not encoded by a family of genes like muscle proteins such as myosin heavy chain. AMP deaminase coding sequences have been highly conserved during evolution, as evidenced by probing genomic DNA from species as diverse as yeasts and humans. Comparison of predicted amino acid sequences for yeast and rat skeletal muscle AMP deaminase demonstrate an overall 44 percent sequence identity, confirming the conservation of AMP deaminase during evolution.

RNA analyses have demonstrated a 2.5-kb transcript which hybridizes with this probe, and this transcript is only found in skeletal muscle.[57] An 80,000 AMP deaminase peptide, which is also unique to skeletal muscle, increases in abundance as the abundance of this 2.5-kb transcript increases during muscle development.[57] In the embryo and many nonmuscle tissues of the adult animal a 3.4-kb transcript hybridizes with this cDNA probe.[75] These tissues contain an AMP deaminase peptide which is distinct from that found in skeletal muscle. During muscle development in vivo and during differentiation of L6 rat myoblasts in vitro the 3.4-kb transcript and its accompanying peptide first increase in abundance and then decline as the myocyte matures. Paralleling the decline in the 3.4-kb transcript and its accompanying peptide, the 2.5-kb transcript and its accompanying peptide increase in abundance. Since AMP deaminase is apparently encoded by a single gene in rat, these data suggest multiple transcripts are derived from this gene in response to tissue-specific signals which are produced by a developmentally controlled program.

These results provide a basis for beginning to understand inherited and acquired deficiencies of AMP deaminase. As pointed out earlier, primary myoblast cultures from a patient with deficient myoadenylate deaminase activity in his skeletal muscle exhibited normal AMP deaminase activity in myoblasts. This apparently contradictory result can be explained by the rodent studies if undifferentiated human myoblasts are also shown to produce a nonmuscle AMP deaminase transcript and peptide. Since the deficiency of AMP deaminase is restricted to skeletal muscle in myopathic patients, it is likely that the defect in these patients will be restricted to a transcript which is unique to skeletal muscle. By analogy to the rodent studies, this could result from a defect in a developmental switch leading to increased production of the muscle-specific transcript, failure of normal mechanisms which control translation of this transcript, or structural mutations in exons or noncoding sequences unique to this transcript. Alternatively, acquired deficiency appears to be the result of a generalized reduction in several muscle-specific enzymatic activities (see Table 41-2), although AMP deaminase activity is affected to a greater degree.[22] This might be the expected result from a generalized regulatory derangement in transcription, transcript switching, or translation of several muscle-specific genes. When a human cDNA probe becomes available, it should be possible to distinguish between these several mechanisms which might lead to primary-versus-secondary myoadenylate deaminase deficiency.

TREATMENT

There are no therapies which are unequivocally documented to be effective in treating myoadenylate deaminase deficiency. Based on limited biochemical data from muscle biopsies, it was originally hypothesized that therapeutic programs aimed at enhancing the rate of replenishment of the ATP pool might be beneficial in these patients. One approach successful in increasing the rate of ATP synthesis in myocardium of the rat is the administration of ribose.[76] Ribose increases the rate of synthesis of phosphoribosylpyrophosphate (PP-ribose-P) through increasing the availability of ribose-5-phosphate. The increases in PP-ribose-P content of the cell could enhance salvage and *de novo* synthesis of purine nucleotides. Oral ribose (2 to 60 g/day) has been administered to patients deficient in myoadenylate deaminase reportedly leading to enhanced stamina[77] and diminished exercise-related symptoms[25] in some, while being ineffective in others.[78] The biochemical basis for the therapeutic effect of ribose is unclear, as no biochemical data have been generated from the use of this compound in these patients.

REFERENCES

1. LOWENSTEIN JM: Ammonia production in muscle and other tissues: The purine nucleotide cycle. *Physiol Rev* 52:382, 1972.
2. LOWENSTEIN JM, GOODMAN MN: The purine nucleotide cycle in skeletal muscle. *Fed Proc* 37:2308, 1978.
3. ARAGON JJ, LOWENSTEIN JM: The purine-nucleotide cycle: Comparison of the levels of citric acid cycle intermediates with the operation of the purine nucleotide cycle in rat skeletal muscle during exercise and recovery from exercise. *Eur J Biochem* 110:371, 1980.
4. GOODMAN MN, LOWENSTEIN JM: The purine nucleotide cycle: Studies of ammonia production by skeletal muscle in situ and in perfused preparations. *J Biol Chem* 252:5054, 1977.
5. MEYER RA, DUDLEY GA, TERJUNG RL: Ammonia and IMP in different skeletal muscle fibers after exercise in rats. *J Appl Physiol* 49:1037, 1980.
6. MEYER RA, TERJUNG RL: AMP deamination and IMP reamination in working skeletal muscle. *Am J Physiol* 239:C32, 1980.
7. MEYER RA, TERJUNG RL: Differences in ammonia and adenylate metabolism in contracting fast and slow muscle. *Am J Physiol* 237:C111, 1979.
8. BROOKE MH, CHOKSI R, KAISER KK: Inosine monophosphate production is proportional to muscle force in vitro. *Neurology* 36:288, 1986.
9. FISHBEIN WN, ARMBRUSTMACHER VW, GRIFFIN JL: Myoadenylate deaminase deficiency: A new disease of muscle. *Science* 200:545, 1978.
10. ENGEL AG, POTTER CS, ROSEVEAR JW: Nucleotides and adenosine monophosphate deaminase activity of muscle in primary hypokalaemic periodic paralysis. *Nature* 202:670, 1964.
11. SCHUMATE JB, KATNIK R, RUIZ M, KAISER K, FRIEDEN C, BROOKE MH, CARROLL JE: Myoadenylate deaminase deficiency. *Muscle Nerve* 2:213, 1979.
12. FISHBEIN WN, GRIFFIN JL, MAGARAJAN K, WINKERT JW, ARMBRUSTMACHER VW: Myoadenylate deaminase deficiency: Association with collagen disease. *Clin Res* 27:37A, 1979.
13. DiMAURO S, MIRANDA AF, HAYS AP, FRANCK WA, HOFFMAN GS, SCHOENFELDT RS, SINGH N: Myoadenylate deaminase deficiency: Muscle biopsy and muscle culture in a patient with gout. *J Neurol Sci* 47:191, 1980.
14. SCHUMATE JB, KAISER KK, CARROLL JE, BROOKE MH: Adenylate deaminase deficiency in a hypotonic infant. *J Pediatr* 96:885, 1980.
15. SABINA RL, SWAIN JL, PATTEN BM, ASHIZAWA T, O'BRIEN WE, HOLMES EW: Disruption of the purine nucleotide cycle: A potential explanation for

muscle dysfunction in myoadenylate deaminase deficiency. *J Clin Invest* 66:1419, 1980.

16. MERCELES R, MARTIN JJ, DEHAENE I, DEVARSY TH, VAN DEN BERGHE G: Myoadenylate deaminase deficiency in a patient with facial and limb girdle myopathy. *J Neurol* 225:157, 1981.
17. SCHOLTE HR, BUSCH HFM, LUYT-HOUWEN IEM: Familial AMP deaminase deficiency with skeletal muscle Type I atrophy and fatal cardiomyopathy. *J Inherited Metab Dis* 4:169, 1981.
18. KELEMAN J, RICE DR, BRADLEY WG, MUNSAT TL, DiMAURO S, HOGAN EL: Familial myoadenylate deaminase deficiency and exertional myalgia. *Neurology* 32:857, 1982.
19. HAYES DI, SUMMERS BA, MORGAN-HUGHES JA: Myoadenylate deaminase deficiency or not? Observations on two brothers with exercise-induced muscle pain. *J Neurol Sci* 53:125, 1982.
20. SABINA RL, SWAIN JL, OLANOW CW, BRADLEY WG, FISHBEIN WN, DiMAURO S, HOLMES EW: Myoadenylate deaminase deficiency: Functional and metabolic abnormalities associated with disruption of the purine nucleotide cycle. *J Clin Invest* 73:720, 1984.
21. GERTLER PA, JACOBS RP: Myoadenylate deaminase deficiency in a patient with progressive systemic sclerosis. *Arthritis Rheum* 27:586, 1984.
22. FISHBEIN WN: Myoadenylate deaminase deficiency: Inherited and acquired forms. *Biochem Med* 33:158, 1985.
23. LALLY EV, FRIEDMAN JH, KAPLAN SR: Progressive myalgias and polyarthralgias in a patient with myoadenylate deaminase deficiency. *Arthritis Rheum* 28:1298, 1985.
24. GOEBEL HH, BARDOSI A, CONRAD B, KUHLENDAHL HD, DiMAURO S, RUMPF KW: Myoadenylate deaminase deficiency. *Klin Wochenschr* 64:342, 1986.
25. ZOLLNER N, REITER S, GROSS M, PONGRATZ D, REIMERS CD, GERBITZ K, PAETZKE I, DEUFEL T, HUBNER G: Myoadenylate deaminase deficiency: Successful symptomatic therapy by high dose oral administration of ribose. *Klin Wochenschr* 64:1281, 1986.
26. HELLER SL, KAISER KK, PLANER GJ, HAGBERG JM, BROOKE MH: McArdle's disease with myoadenylate deaminase deficiency: Observations in a combined enzyme deficiency. *Neurology* 37:1039, 1987.
27. SINKELER SPT: Myoadenylate deaminase deficiency: A study of its clinical significance. Dissertation, University of Nijmegen, The Netherlands, 1987.
28. FLANAGAN WF, HOLMES EW, SABINA RL, SWAIN JL: Importance of the purine nucleotide cycle to energy production in skeletal muscle. *Am J Physiol* 251:C795, 1986.
29. MANFREDI JP, HOLMES EW: Control of the purine nucleotide cycle in extracts of rat skeletal muscle: Effects of energy state and concentrations of cycle intermediates. *Arch Biochem Biophys* 233:515, 1984.
30. SAHLIN K, PALMSKOG G, HULTMAN E: Adenine nucleotide and IMP content of the quadriceps muscle in man after exercise. *Pflugers Arch* 374:193, 1978.
31. HETTLEMAN BD, SABINA RL, DREZNER MK, HOLMES EW, SWAIN JL: Defective adenosine triphosphate synthesis: An explanation for skeletal muscle dysfunction in phosphate-deficient mice. *J Clin Invest* 72:582, 1983.
32. WILKERSON JE, BATTERSON DL, HORVATH SM: Exercise-induced changes in blood ammonia levels in humans. *Eur J Appl Physiol* 37:255, 1977.
33. BABIJ P, MATTHEWS SM, RENNIE MJ: Changes in blood ammonia, lactate, and amino acids in relation to workload during bicycle ergometer exercise in man. *Eur J Appl Physiol* 50:405, 1983.
34. KATZ A, BROBERG S, SAHLIN K, WAHREN J: Muscle ammonia and amino acid metabolism during dynamic exercise in man. *Clin Physiol* 6:365, 1986.
35. TORNHEIM K, LOWENSTEIN JM: The purine nucleotide cycle: Interactions with oscillations of the glycolytic pathway in muscle extracts. *J Biol Chem* 249:3241, 1974.
36. TORNHEIM K, LOWENSTEIN JM: The purine nucleotide cycle: Control of phosphofructokinase and glycolytic oscillations in muscle extracts. *J Biol Chem* 250:6304, 1975.
37. ARAGON JJ, TORNHEIM K, LOWENSTEIN JM: On a possible role of IMP in the regulation of phosphorylase activity in skeletal muscle. *FEBS Lett* 117:*suppl* K56, 1980.
38. SWAIN JL, HINES JJ, SABINA RL, HARBURY OL, HOLMES EW: Disruption of the purine nucleotide cycle by inhibition of adenylosuccinate lyase produces skeletal muscle dysfunction. *J Clin Invest* 74:1422, 1984.
39. PATTERSON YH, KAISER KK, BROOKE MH: Exercising muscle does not produce hypoxanthine in adenylate deaminase deficiency. *Neurology* 33:784, 1983.
40. SINKELER SPT, JOOSTEN EMG, WEVERS RA, BINKHORST RA, OERLEMAUS FT, VAN BENNEKOM CA, COERWINKEL MM, OEI TL: Ischaemic exercise test in myoadenylate deaminase deficiency and McArdles disease: Measurement of plasma adenosine, inosine, and hypoxanthine. *Clin Sci* 70:399, 1986.
41. SINKELER SPT, BINKHORST RA, JOOSTEN EMG, WEVERS RA, COERWINKEL MM, OEI TL: AMP deaminase deficiency: Study of the human skeletal muscle purine metabolism during ischaemic isometric exercise. *Clin Sci* 72:475, 1987.
42. OGASAWARA N, GOTO H, YASUKAZU Y, WATANABE T: Distribution of AMP-deaminase isozymes in rat tissue. *Eur J Biochem* 87:297, 1978.
43. OGASAWARA N, GOTO H, WATANABE T: Isozymes of rat AMP deaminase. *Biochim Biophys Acta* 403:530, 1975.
44. SOLANO C, COFFEE CJ: Differential response of AMP deaminase isoenzymes to changes in the adenylate energy charge. *Biochem Biophys Res Commun* 85:564, 1978.
45. OGASAWARA N, GOTO H, YAMADA Y, WATANABE T, ASANO T: AMP deaminase isozymes in human tissues. *Biochim Biophys Acta* 714:298, 1982.
46. FISHBEIN WN, DAVID JI, NAGARAJON K, WINKERT JW, FOELLMER JW: Immunologic distinction of human muscle adenylate deaminase from the isozyme in human peripheral blood cells: Implications for myoadenylate deaminase deficiency. *Arch Biochem Biophys* 205:360, 1980.
47. OGASAWARA N, GOTO H, YAMADA Y, NISHIGAKI I, ITOH T, HASEGAWA I: Complete deficiency of AMP deaminase in human erythrocytes. *Biochem Biophys Res Commun* 122:1344, 1984.
48. KENDRICK-JONES J, PERRY SV: The enzymes of adenine nucleotide metabolism in developing skeletal muscle. *Biochem J* 103:207, 1967.
49. SAMMONS DW, CHILSON OP: AMP deaminase: Stage-specific isoenzymes in differentiating chick muscle. *Arch Biochem Biophys* 191:561, 1978.
50. KALETHA K: Regulatory properties of 14-day embryo and adult hen skeletal muscle AMP deaminase. *Biochim Biophys Acta* 759:99, 1983.
51. KALETHA K, SKLANDOWSKI A: Regulatory properties of 14-day embryo and adult hen heart AMP deaminase. *Int J Biochem* 16:75, 1984.
52. SPYCHALA J, KALETHA K, MAKAREWICZ W: Developmental changes of chicken liver AMP deaminase. *Biochem J* 231:329, 1985.
53. KALETHA K, SPYCHALA J, NOWAK G: Developmental forms of human skeletal muscle AMP deaminase. *Experientia* 43:440, 1987.
54. MARQUETANT R, DESAI NM, SABINA RL, HOLMES EW: Evidence for sequential expression of multiple AMP deaminase isoforms during skeletal muscle development. *Proc Natl Acad Sci USA* 84:2345, 1987.
55. KALETHA K: Changes of the heat sensibility of AMP-deaminase from rat skeletal muscle in the course of postnatal development. *Int J Biochem* 6:471, 1975.
56. WINDER WW, TERJUNG RL, BALDWIN KM, HOLLOSZY JO: Effect of exercise on AMP deaminase and adenylosuccinase in rat skeletal muscle. *Am J Physiol* 227:1411, 1974.
57. SABINA RL, MARQUETANT R, DESAI NM, KALETHA K, HOLMES EW: Cloning and sequence of rat myoadenylate deaminase cDNA: Evidence for tissue-specific and developmental regulation. *J Biol Chem* 262:12397, 1987.
58. RAGGI A, BERGAMINI C, RONCA G: Isozymes of AMP deaminase in red and white skeletal muscles. *FEBS Lett* 58:19, 1975.
59. MAKAREWICZ W, STANKIEWICZ A: Purification of AMP-deaminase from human skeletal muscle on 5′-AMP sepharose 4B. *Int J Biochem* 7:245, 1976.
60. COFFEE CJ: AMP deaminase from rat skeletal muscle. *Methods Enzymol* 51:490, 1978.
61. BOOSMAN A, CHILSON OP: Subunit structure of AMP-deaminase from chicken and rabbit skeletal muscle. *J Biol Chem* 251:1847, 1976.
62. ASHBY B, FRIEDEN C, BISCHOFF R: Immunofluorescent and histochemical localization of AMP deaminase in skeletal muscle. *J Cell Biol* 81:361, 1979.
63. ASHBY B, FRIEDEN C: Interaction of AMP aminohydrolase with myosin and its subfragments. *J Biol Chem* 252:1869, 1977.
64. MARQUETANT R, SABINA RL, HOLMES EW: Evidence for a non-catalytic domain in AMP deaminase which influences binding to myosin heavy chain. Manuscript submitted.
65. STANKIEWICZ A, SPYCHALA J, MAKAREWICZ W: Comparative studies on muscle AMP-deaminase—III. Substrate specificity of the enzymes from man, rabbit, rat, hen, frog and pikeperch. *Comp Biochem Physiol B* 66:529, 1980.
66. COFFEE CJ, SOLANO C: Rat muscle 5′-adenylic acid aminohydrolase. *J Biol Chem* 252:1606, 1977.
67. WHEELER TJ, LOWENSTEIN JM: Adenylate deaminase from rat muscle: Regulation by purine nucleotides and orthophosphate in the presence of 150mM KC1. *J Biol Chem* 254:8994, 1979.
68. ASHBY B, FRIEDEN C: Adenylate deaminase. Kinetic and binding studies on the rabbit muscle enzyme. *J Biol Chem* 253:8728, 1978.
69. SUTTON JR, TOEWS CJ, WARD GR, FOX IH: Purine metabolism during strenuous muscle exercise in man. *Metabolism* 29:254, 1980.
70. DUDLEY GA, TERJUNG RL: Influence of acidosis on AMP deaminase activity in contracting fast-twitch muscle. *Am J Physiol* 248:C43, 1985.
71. SOLANO C, COFFEE CJ: Comparison of AMP deaminase from skeletal muscle of acidotic and normal rats. *Biochim Biophys Acta* 582:369, 1979.

72. WHEELER TJ, LOWENSTEIN JM: Creatine phosphate inhibition of adenylate deaminase is mainly due to pyrophosphate. *J Biol Chem* 254:1484, 1979.
73. AGARWAL RP, PARKS RE JR: Potent inhibition of muscle 5′-AMP deaminase by the nucleoside antibiotics coformycin and deoxycoformycin. *Biochem Pharmacol* 26:663, 1977.
74. FRIEDEN C, GILBERT HR, MILLER RL: Adenylate deaminase: Potent inhibition by 2′-deoxycoformycin 5′-phosphate. *Biochem Biophys Res Commun* 91:278, 1979.
75. SABINA RL, HOLMES EW: Developmentally regulated transcript switching of AMP deaminase during myogenesis. Manuscript in preparation.
76. ZIMMER HG, GERLACH E: Stimulation of myocardial adenine nucleotide biosynthesis by pentoses and pentitols. *Pflugers Arch* 376:223, 1978.
77. PATTEN BM: Beneficial effect of D-ribose in a patient with myoadenylate deaminase deficiency. *Lancet* 1:1071, 1982.
78. LECKY BRF: Failure of D-ribose in myoadenylate deaminase deficiency. *Lancet* 1:193, 1983.

CHAPTER **42**

HEREDITARY XANTHINURIA

EDWARD W. HOLMES
JAMES B. WYNGAARDEN

1. *Xanthinuria is a rare disorder characterized by the replacement of uric acid by xanthine and hypoxanthine in urine. When dietary purines are restricted, there is a virtual absence of uric acid in serum and urine. The disorders of purine metabolism can be subdivided into two types. Classic xanthinuria, or isolated deficiency of xanthine oxidase, has been reported in 58 well-documented cases, 38 of them in males. In about two-thirds of these cases, the patients were asymptomatic and the metabolic defect was an incidental finding. In the remaining one-third of the subjects, xanthine calculi of the urinary tract developed. In four, a myopathy was present associated in three with crystalline deposits of hypoxanthine and xanthine in muscle. Recurrent polyarthritis was noted in three patients, but crystals have not been demonstrated in synovial fluid or tissue.*
2. *A new subtype of xanthinuria has been described in which the deficiency of xanthine oxidase is associated with a deficiency of another molybdenum-containing enzyme, sulfite oxidase. Fifteen patients have been reported to have a combined deficiency of these two enzymes as a result of defects in molybdenum metabolism. In these individuals the neurologic symptoms attributable to sulfite oxidase deficiency overshadow the symptoms of xanthine oxidase deficiency. This disorder is discussed in Chap. 56.*
3. *There is a gross deficiency of xanthine oxidase activity in xanthinuria. Jejunal, hepatic, and renal tissue, as well as colostrum, show absent or extremely low enzyme activity toward hypoxanthine, xanthine, and xanthopterin with either oxygen or NAD as the electron acceptor.*
4. *Several additional patients have formed xanthine stones in childhood and may have xanthinuria. Many of the adults who have formed xanthine stones have clearly not had a defect in xanthine oxidase activity, for in several instances normal or elevated serum uric acid levels were found. Circumstantial evidence, such as the finding of xanthine deposits in the renal parenchyma in one case, suggests that xanthine excretion may have been excessive in a few, but this is unproved.*
5. *All available data on genetic factors are consistent with an autosomal recessive pattern of inheritance. In two families some of the presumed obligate heterozygotes showed moderate increases in urinary oxypurine excretion, although they had normal levels of uric acid in serum and in urine.*

Hereditary xanthinuria is a rare disorder characterized by a gross deficiency of xanthine oxidase activity in the tissues, by the excretion of xanthine and hypoxanthine as the chief end products of purine metabolism, and by low concentrations of uric acid in serum and urine. There are well-documented reports of more than 50 patients with this disorder.[1–36] Although the true prevalence of xanthinuria is not known, discovery of three cases in a random survey of 137,194 serum urate analyses suggests a prevalence of 1 in 45,000.[32]

About 40 cases of xanthine stones have been recorded since they were first identified by Marcet in 1817.[37] In some patients, chiefly adults, serum or urinary uric acid values were normal, and xanthine was only a minor component of the calculus. At least seven xanthine stones occurred in subjects under age 15 who may have had hereditary xanthinuria, but since xanthine excretion studies were not performed, the relationship is uncertain.[38–49]

CLINICAL FEATURES

Xanthinuria can be subdivided into two types. Classic xanthinuria, or isolated deficiency of xanthine oxidase, has been recognized since 1954. There have been 58 patients with well-documented xanthinuria of the classic form described in the literature, and the clinical features and biochemical findings in these patients are summarized in Table 42-1. In 1978 Duran et al.[33] described a new subtype of xanthinuria in which the deficiency of xanthine oxidase was associated with a deficiency of sulfite oxidase. The clinical presentation of patients with the combined deficiencies of xanthine oxidase and sulfite oxidase encompasses the clinical and biochemical features of classical xanthinuria and those of isolated sulfite oxidase deficiency. This disorder is discussed in detail in Chap. 56.

In classic xanthinuria only about one-third of the patients describe symptoms referable to the deficiency of xanthine oxidase. Thus, the majority of the patients are asymptomatic and are usually discovered by the finding of a very low serum urate concentration during investigation of presumably unrelated medical problems or during screening tests in a population health survey. In one-third of the subjects xanthine calculi of the urinary tract developed; in one subject it led to mild calyceal clubbing and in another to hydronephrosis and eventual nephrectomy. Symptomatic xanthinuric infants have irritability, intermittent hematuria, and occasional orange-brown staining of their diapers. In four xanthinuric adults a myopathy was present, associated in three with crystalline deposits of xanthine and hypoxanthine. Recurrent polyarthritis was noted in three patients. It has been suggested that this symptom may represent crystal-induced synovitis,[50] but neither hypoxanthine nor xanthine crystals have been demonstrated in synovial fluid or tissue.

In patients with combined deficiencies of xanthine oxidase and sulfite oxidase the clinical features of sulfite oxidase deficiency[51–53] overshadow those of xanthine oxidase deficiency. These patients have severe neurologic abnormalities

Because there have been few new developments in our understanding of xanthinuria, we are reprinting this chapter from the fifth edition with minor revisions and updating. The Editors.

Table 42-1 Clinical Features and Biochemical Data on Reported Cases of Classic Xanthinuria (Isolated Deficiency of Xanthine Oxidase)

	Patients			Controls	
	(Number)	*Mean*	*Range*	*Mean*	*Range*
Clinical features:	(58)				
Age, years		30.7	0.5–80		
Sex, % male		66			
Renal calculi, %		30			
Myopathy, %		6.9			
Arthropathy, %		5.1			
Plasma purines:*					
Urate, mg/dl	(58)	0.47	0–1.44	†	
Hypoxanthine, μ*M*	(7)	6.6	1.6–11.9	2.5 ±	1.0‡
Xanthine, μ*M*	(7)	18.1	6.8–25.5	1.4 ±	0.7‡
Urinary excretion:					
Uric acid, mg/24 h		22.9	0–81.2		
Oxypurines, mg/24 h		316.9	55–557		
Oxypurines that are xanthine, %		79	42–95		
Xanthine oxidase activity, % of control:					
Liver	(6)	0–10			
Jejunum	(11)	0–5.7			
Rectum	(1)	25			
Kidney	(1)	10			
Colostrum	(1)	0			

*The molecular weight of uric acid is 168.1; xanthine, 152.1; hypoxanthine, 136.1.
†Normal serum urate values vary with age and sex; however, 99 percent of the normal population have values >2 mg% (see Chap. 37 of this book).
‡From Boulieu et al.,[32b] who studied 11 individuals.

which include mental retardation, major motor seizures, and cerebral atrophy. In addition they have ocular lens dislocation.

Illustrative Cases

Case 1 In 1954 Dent and Philpot[1] described a 4½-year-old girl with hematuria who passed a smooth oval calculus weighing 0.9 g. It was nonopaque to x-rays, contained only traces of calcium and magnesium, and was almost ash-free. In the murexide test it gave a reddish-brown color quite unlike that of uric acid. By paper chromatography, extracts of the stone matched xanthine exactly. Xanthine excretion was 176 mg/day, or 607 mg per gram of creatinine. Uric acid excretion was 30 mg/day, and plasma urate was 0.5 mg/dl.

This patient was restudied at age 9 by Dickinson and Smellie.[2] She had no further calculi but had developed clubbing of the calyces of the left kidney. As measured by specific enzymatic methods, plasma oxypurines were 0.75 mg/dl, and plasma uric acid was 0.2 mg/dl. The renal clearance of oxypurines was 94 ml/min per 1.73 m^2 body surface area, a value equivalent to 82 percent of the simultaneous endogenous creatinine clearance (normal is 10 to 20 percent). When the patient was given a low purine diet, uric acid was not detectable in fresh urine and plasma. Urinary hypoxanthine was equivalent to 10 to 20 percent of xanthine.

At age 14 a pyelogram showed some persistent clubbing of the left renal calyces, with reduction of size of the left kidney (10.5 cm) compared with the right (14 cm). At age 19 she was normotensive and in good health.[50]

Case 2 In 1964 Engleman and colleagues[3,4] described a 23-year-old black woman suffering from pheochromocytoma and heart failure who was found to have a very low serum urate value. In addition, she was mentally retarded, with an IQ of 53, had congenital skeletal abnormalities, and on a later admission, exhibited a glucose-6-phosphate dehydrogenase deficiency.[50] There was no clinical or radiologic evidence of urinary calculi. Further study disclosed diminished amounts of uric acid and increased quantities of oxypurines in both serum and urine. The renal clearance of oxypurines was 87 percent of the endogenous creatinine clearance. The increased excretion of uric acid which normally follows the ingestion of 5-amino-4-imidazole carboxamide was replaced by an approximately equivalent increase in the urinary excretion of xanthine.[4] With three different assays, xanthine oxidase activities of the patient's jejunal mucosa and liver corresponded to no more than 0.1 percent of activities found in specimens from control subjects. No evidence was found for an inhibitor of xanthine oxidase in intestinal mucosa or blood.[3,4] By age 27 she had developed muscle cramps in her legs following walking or strenuous exercise. A muscle biopsy specimen contained numerous crystals which were identified as xanthine and hypoxanthine.[10,54]

Case 3 Bradford et al.[8] described a 62-year-old Puerto Rican woman, with a 30-year history of mild psoriasis, who entered Bellevue Hospital because of acute monoarticular arthritis. This became migratory and polyarticular, affecting ankles, knees, elbows, wrists, and hands over a 6-week period, with fever to 104°F (40°C). The etiology of the arthritis was not established, but the finding of a serum uric acid of 0.8 to 1.1 mg/dl prompted study of xanthinuria. On a low purine diet, urinary uric acid ranged from 0 to 38.5 mg/day; urinary xanthine, from 125 to 325 mg/day; and urinary hypoxanthine, from 27 to 76 mg/day.

Case 4 In 1969, Chalmers et al.[9] reported a 31-year-old black male from Guyana who had been an active athlete until 3 years earlier, when he developed "tight sensations" at the back of both thighs and calves. Examination disclosed no vascular abnormalities, and the neurologic findings were normal except for universally sluggish reflexes and absent ankle jerks. Muscle strength was normal, no muscle tenderness was found at rest or following exertion, and there was no myotonia, but the calves felt firmer than normal. The finding of a very low serum urate value led to further investigation in the hospital, where the mean of four determinations was 0.78 mg/dl. Plasma oxypurines, calculated as xanthine, were 0.29 mg/dl. Urinary excretion values were uric acid, 12 to 52 mg; xanthine, 245 mg; and hypoxanthine, 19 mg/24 h. No xanthine oxidase activity was demonstrated by histochemical techniques in a jejunal biopsy specimen. Electromyographic studies were in keeping with a diffuse myopathic process. Four muscle biopsies were performed over a period of 12 months. A striking feature was the unusually high average diameter of muscle fibers, which also showed increased numbers of centrally placed muscle nuclei. A few of the fibers contained intensely staining rodlike inclusions, which on electron microscopy consisted of aggregations of electron-dense material, much of which was crystalline in appearance. By polarized light, phase contrast, and interference microscopy, the optical properties of the crystals were compatible with their being hypoxanthine and xanthine.[10,54] Identification of crystals from this patient and from the patient of case 2 was subsequently accomplished by high-resolution mass spectrometry.[55]

Case 5 In 1986 Carpenter et al.[32e] reported an infant who developed irritability, sleeplessness, and gross hematuria at 5 to 6 months of age. The mother noted occasional orange-brown staining of the diaper. The physical examination was normal with growth parameters in the 50th percentile for age. Serum uric acid was 0.5 mg/dl. An excretory urogram and abdominal ultrasonography demonstrated a stone in the left renal pelvis. The stone was removed surgically, and chemical analysis showed that it was pure xanthine. Despite increased fluid intake, a second stone formed in the left renal pelvis over the next month. Allopurinol, 25 mg twice a day, had no effect on serum hypoxanthine/xanthine ratios and symptoms persisted. The drug was discontinued after 2 weeks. Subsequently, the infant's diet was switched from a soy formula to an unrestricted dietary intake including cow's milk. Coincident with this change in diet, the infant's symptoms subsided.

Case 6 In 1978 Duran et al.[33,34] described a 3-week-old female who had all of the biochemical features of xanthinuria, i.e., hypouricemia (0.2 to 1.1 mg/dl), hypouricosuria (11.8 mg of uric acid excreted per gram of creatinine), increased excretion of oxypurines (817 mg xanthine and 144 mg of hypoxanthine per gram of creatinine), and virtual absence of xanthine oxidase activity (not detectable in jejunum, 6 percent of control in liver). This patient was different from the classic patient with xanthinuria in that she had severe neurologic abnormalities. The patient was admitted to the hospital because of feeding difficulties since birth. Examination at that time demonstrated typical tonic-clonic seizures, nystagmus, enophthalmus, bilateral ocular lens dislocation, and a ring of Brushfield spots. The skull was asymmetric with frontal bossing. Electroencephalogram showed diffuse irregularities, and the pneumoencephalogram demonstrated widened ventricles and periventricular atrophy.[35] Liver biopsy demonstrated a deficiency of sulfite oxidase activity as well as of xanthine oxidase activity. In addition, the urine of this patient contained excessive quantities of sulfite, *S*-sulfocysteine, taurine, and thiosulfate. Sulfate, the product of the sulfite oxidase reaction, was diminished in the urine of this patient. These neurologic findings and abnormalities of sulfur metabolism are typical of those described in patients with an isolated deficiency of sulfite oxidase.[51–53] Subsequent studies have provided an explanation for the combined deficiency of xanthine oxidase and sulfite oxidase in this patient.[35] Both of these enzymes require a molybdenum cofactor for catalytic activity (see below), and this cofactor was not found in the liver of this patient even though the serum concentration of molybdenum was normal. Follow-up studies in this patient have revealed no improvement in clinical symptoms in spite of numerous manipulations of sulfur content of the diet. At age 14 months small brownish concretions were noticed on her diaper and the calculi were proved to be xanthine stones.[33]

Case 7 In 1979 Abumrad et al.[36] described a 20-year-old male with the short bowel syndrome maintained for 18 months on total parenteral nutrition who developed hypouricemia (1 mg/dl) and hypouricosuria (100 mg uric acid excreted per day). Following infusion of commercially available amino acid solutions he experienced headaches, night blindness, irritability, lethargy, and became comatose. Urinary excretion of sulfite and thiosulfate were increased while excretion of sulfate was decreased. Treatment with ammonium molybdate reversed the biochemical abnormalities in purine and sulfur metabolism, and relieved the neurologic symptoms. It was suggested from these results that acquired deficiency of molybdenum led to a decrease in the activity of both xanthine oxidase and sulfite oxidase. This conclusion is supported by studies with rats made molybdenum-deficient by feeding tungsten.[56,57] These animals develop simultaneous deficiencies of xanthine oxidase and sulfite oxidase activities.

Comment The association of xanthinuria and pheochromocytoma in case 2 is probably fortuitous. Plasma from eight other patients with pheochromocytoma studied by Engleman et al.[4] contained normal amounts of uric acid, and urine from the xanthinuric patient of Dent and Philpot contained normal amounts of catecholamines and their metabolites.[1] In the patient of Frezal et al.[7] urinary excretion of vanillylmandelic acid was normal.

The association of xanthinuria and hemochromatosis in one patient is also probably coincidental.[5] In 4 of 11 patients with proved hemochromatosis in whom serum uric acid values were available, the values were normal.[5] The patient with xanthinuria described by Engleman and associates[4] developed iron deficiency anemia and hypoferremia that responded promptly to oral iron administration. Seegmiller and associates[58] later found a normal absorption of ^{59}Fe and a normal incorporation of absorbed iron into erythrocytes of this patient.

Case 5 emphasizes the difficulty of diagnosing renal colic in infants. Pediatricians should consider nephrolithiasis as a cause of chronic irritability, particularly if there is a history of hematuria or discoloration of the urine.

The association of xanthine oxidase and sulfite oxidase deficiencies is not fortuitous. Since both of these enzymes require a molybdenum cofactor for catalytic activity and since studies with experimental animals have demonstrated that molybdenum deficiency leads to the simultaneous loss of both activities,[56,57] there is a sound biochemical explanation for the associated loss of xanthine oxidase and sulfite oxidase activities in patients with molybdenum deficiency or a defect in the synthesis of molybdenum cofactor (see below and Chap. 56).

XANTHINE OXIDASE

Oxidation of hypoxanthine to xanthine and xanthine to uric acid (Fig. 42-1) may be catalyzed by either *xanthine oxidase* (EC 1.2.3.2), in which case oxygen is the terminal electron acceptor, or *xanthine dehydrogenase* (EC 1.2.1.37), in which case NAD functions as the electron acceptor. Although xanthine oxidase and xanthine dehydrogenase have been given separate numbers by the Enzyme Commission, it is not clear that these two activities are distinct proteins. Xanthine dehydrogenase from a number of mammalian sources can be converted to xanthine oxidase by treatments such as incubation at 37°C for several hours or limited proteolysis with trypsin.[59–64a] Apparently, oxidation of reduced sulfhydryls to disulfides is one mechanism by which the dehydrogenase can be converted to an oxidase, since the dehydrogenase activity can be restored by incubation of the oxidase with reductants such as dithiothreitol or dithioerythritol.[60–64] Conversion of the dehydrogenase to an oxidase by trypsin treatment is associated with the loss of a peptide of approximately 20,000 daltons which is rich in reduced sulfhydryl content and is essential for dehydrogenase activity.[63] Purification procedures in the past which did not protect the enzyme from oxidation or proteolysis may account for the failure of earlier reports to recognize that the great majority of the enzyme activity was present in the form of a dehydrogenase rather than an oxidase.

Other studies also suggest that xanthine oxidase activity is derived in vitro from xanthine dehydrogenase. When both activities have been purified from rat liver the enzymes are indistinguishable in their absorption spectra, cofactor composition, and electrophoretic behavior on 5 percent polyacrylamide gels.[59] These observations, combined with the reports that both xanthine oxidase and xanthine dehydrogenase activities are reduced or absent in tissues from xanthinuric subjects, suggest that both activities are the product of one gene. How-

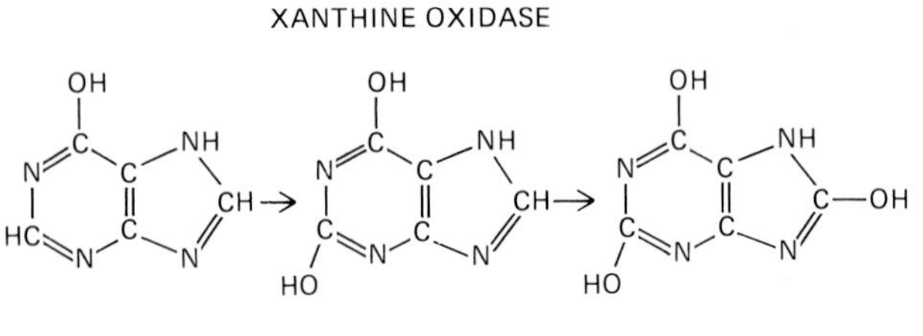

XANTHINE OXIDASE

Hypoxanthine Xanthine Uric Acid

Fig 42-1 Conversion of hypoxanthine to xanthine and of xanthine to uric acid by xanthine oxidase. Structures are shown in their lactim forms.

ever, it may be premature to conclude that all of the xanthine oxidase activity detected in tissue extracts is derived from an in vitro transformation of the xanthine dehydrogenase. A recent study has reported that as much as 20 percent of the xanthine oxidase activity found in the intestine of mice is immunologically and catalytically different from the xanthine oxidase produced in vitro from xanthine dehydrogenase.[64] This study raises the possibility that some of the xanthine oxidase activity detected in extracts may be distinct from xanthine dehydrogenase. Possibly this non-xanthine dehydrogenase–related xanthine oxidase activity accounts for some of the residual activity found in tissue extracts from xanthinuric subjects.

Data from several laboratories indicate that oxidation of hypoxanthine and xanthine in most mammalian tissues is catalyzed in vivo by the xanthine dehydrogenase activity.[50,59–64] In extracts from human liver the dehydrogenase activity is substantially greater than the oxidase activity. This suggests that NAD rather than oxygen is the primary electron acceptor in vivo in humans.[50,62] Consequently, it would be more correct to state that xanthinuria results from a deficiency of xanthine dehydrogenase activity, but inasmuch as the bulk of the literature on the subject refers to the enzyme as "xanthine oxidase" and since assays of its activity in tissues of xanthinuric subjects have almost exclusively examined its oxidase function, we will retain the more common name in this discussion. In the limited cases where both activities have been determined in the tissues of xanthinuric subjects, both the xanthine oxidase and dehydrogenase activities have been markedly reduced or absent.

Substrate Specificity

Xanthine oxidase is not a highly discriminating enzyme. It attacks a variety of substrates, including aldehydes, pteridines, and purines other than hypoxanthine and xanthine. 6-Mercaptopurine[64a] is oxidized to 6-thiouric acid. Allopurinol is oxidized to oxipurinol (alloxanthine).[65–67] Aldehyde oxidase (EC 1.2.3.1), a closely related molybdenum enzyme, may also catalyze the oxidation of allopurinol to oxipurinol.[68] Xanthine oxidase does not attack methylxanthines other than the 1-methyl compound.[69] The human liver enzyme oxidizes 7-methylguanine to 7-methyl-8-hydroxyguanine.[70]

Molecular Weight and Cofactors

The molecular weight of the enzyme from milk is 275,000[71,72] to 300,000;[73] from pig liver, 288,000;[74] and from chicken liver, 300,000.[75] The bovine milk enzyme can be dissociated into subunits of 150,000 daltons in guanidine hydrochloride or acid.[73] Amino acid analyses of the purified milk enzyme disclose no unusual percentage composition.[76]

Bovine milk xanthine oxidase contains 2 g-atom molybdenum, 2 FAD residues, 8 g-atom nonheme iron, and 8 mol labile sulfide per molecular weight of 300,000.[77] Different Mo/FAD/Fe ratios have been reported for the enzyme obtained from mammalian intestine and liver and from avian liver,[78] but these differences may reflect inadvertent removal of cofactors during purification.

As pointed out earlier molybdenum is an essential cofactor for xanthine oxidase activity,[56,57,79] and deficiency of the molybdenum cofactor can result in the clinical picture of xanthinuria.[33–36] Recent studies have identified the molybdenum cofactor from xanthine oxidase as a novel pterin with an unknown substitution at the 6 position.[80] Activity of the cofactor requires that the pterin moiety be present in a reduced form. This cofactor is stored in the outer membrane of the mitochondria.[81] In one xanthinuric patient who has been carefully studied no molybdenum cofactor could be detected in hepatic tissue.[35] Liver extract from this patient had no detectable xanthine oxidase activity even though the apoprotein was readily observable on immunodiffusion plates. The xanthine oxidase apoprotein could not be activated by incubation in vitro with molybdenum cofactor. Since the molybdenum cofactor required for xanthine oxidase activity is identical with that required for sulfite oxidase activity,[80] it is not surprising that patients with dietary deficiency of molybdenum or congenital absence of molybdenum cofactor exhibit the simultaneous loss of xanthine oxidase and sulfite oxidase activities.[33–36]

Flavin-free enzyme is devoid of xanthine oxygen reductase activity and can be reconstituted by a short incubation with FAD.[82]

Mechanism of Action

The complexity of xanthine oxidase approaches that of enzyme systems with multiple intermediates, such as the respiratory chain. Electron flow during purine oxidation is first to molybdenum, which is reduced from valence of +6 to +5 or +4, from molybdenum to iron sulfide to FAD, and terminally from $FAD \cdot H_2$ to oxygen or, anaerobically, to methylene blue, cytochrome c, NAD, or other acceptor.[79,82,83] Under anaerobic conditions lower valence states of molybdenum are detected.[77] The inhibitory action of allopurinol and oxypurinol apparently involves complex formation with enzyme-bound molybdenum in the Mo^{4+} state and is dependent upon prior reduction of the enzyme by substrate.[67] Binding studies with [^{14}C]oxypurinol suggests that 1 mol purine is bound per mole of molybdenum, and therefore that there are two active sites per molecule of enzyme.[67] This accords with the observation that the enzyme can be dissociated into halves.[73]

Distribution and Synthesis

The distribution of xanthine oxidase in mammalian and avian tissues varies from species to species.[62,84] In most mammals, liver and small-intestinal mucosa are rich sources. In human beings these are the only tissues that normally show abundant xanthine oxidase activity, although significant traces of activity exist in kidney, spleen, and skeletal and heart muscle.[85] Activity has been detected inconstantly in marrow of leukemic children,[86] but not in circulating normal leukocytes.[85] Although activity is undetectable in serum of normal persons, individuals with acute infectious hepatitis and jaundice may have striking levels of activity in serum.[87,88] Xanthine oxidase has also been detected in the urine from patients with urinary tract infections, but not in sterile urine.[89,90] Xanthine oxidase is regularly present in human milk.

Hepatic xanthine oxidase activity falls sharply with induced dietary deficiencies of iron or molybdenum in experimental animals.[91] Hepatic xanthine oxidase levels can be altered tenfold by changes of dietary protein intake in the rat.[92] Restoration of normal values following a shift from a low to a normal protein diet involves accelerated synthesis of new enzyme protein. In human beings[93] hepatic xanthine oxidase activity is increased two- to fourfold following feeding of RNA, hypoxanthine, or 2-ethylamino-1,3,4-thiadiazole, or by the infusion of fructose.

Regulation of hepatic synthesis and degradation of xanthine oxidase have been studied in a number of animal models. Results of studies in an avian model suggest that synthesis is proportional to levels of messenger RNA, and formation of the active enzyme follows synthesis of an inactive precursor.[94] Degradation is preceded by the formation of a second inactive enzyme species.[94] The following agents or conditions have been demonstrated to affect xanthine oxidase synthesis or degradation or both in chicken liver: dietary protein, dietary amino acids, starvation, insulin, carbamyl reagents which are vitamin B_6 antagonists such as hydrazine and amino-oxyacetate, 6-aminonicotinamide, reserpine, monoamine oxidase inhibitors, and melatonin (reviewed in Ref. 94). In mammalian systems the following agents or conditions have been shown to alter hepatic xanthine oxidase activity: increase in dietary protein intake,[92] vitamin E deficiency,[95] malignant transformation,[96] and androgen/estrogen balance.[97]

METABOLIC DEFECTS IN XANTHINURIA

Xanthine Oxidase Activity

The findings of Dent and Philpot[1] that xanthine had replaced uric acid as the chief end product of purine metabolism in their patients, and of Dickinson and Smellie[2] that the plasma level of oxypurines was elevated, pointed toward a deficiency of xanthine oxidase activity in xanthinuria. Watts, Engleman, and associates[3] subsequently demonstrated less than 0.1 percent of normal activity in jejunal mucosa and liver biopsy material from their patient. Activity was deficient using xanthine, hypoxanthine, or xanthopterin as substrate and was not restored by addition of FAD, molybdenum, or ferric iron. Xanthine dehydrogenase activity measured with addition of methylene blue as electron acceptor was also missing. Residual activity was abolished by heating the homogenate to 100°C for several minutes and by the inhibitors allopurinol and pteridylaldehyde.

Deficiency of hepatic, intestinal, renal, or milk xanthine oxidase activity has been reported in 16 additional patients. Assay values have ranged from "no detectable activity" to more than 10 percent of control values (25 percent of control values in rectal mucosa). In a postpartum patient with xanthinuria, enzyme activity was missing in colostrum.[98] The report of missing activity in leukocytes in a Spanish family[16] is difficult to evaluate, since Watts et al.[85] were unable to detect any xanthine oxidase activity in intact or sonicated leukocytes from normal subjects. Assay methods differed in the various laboratories, and limits of accuracy and sensitivity were not given. Accordingly, it is not yet known whether the apparent variations in levels of residual activity represent methodological limitations, heterogeneity of the genetic and molecular defect, or assay of a xanthine oxidase–like activity which is unrelated to xanthine dehydrogenase.

Xanthine oxidase is not expressed in normal human cultured skin fibroblasts.

Muscle Hypoxanthine and Xanthine Content

Concentrations of hypoxanthine and xanthine in skeletal muscle of two patients have been determined by Parker, Snedden, and Watts[55,99] using quantitative high-resolution mass spectrometry. The results are given in Table 42-2. In another patient oxypurine content of muscle was also found increased.[25]

Plasma Purine Concentration Values

Normal plasma contains from 0.1 to 0.3 mg oxypurines per deciliter,[100,101] of which hypoxanthine appears to be the major component. Plasma oxypurine concentrations have been recorded in 26 xanthinuric patients and have ranged from 0.1 to 0.96 mg/dl, with a mean of 0.56 mg/dl (Table 42-1). In one patient in whom the plasma oxypurines were analyzed separately, 90 percent was xanthine;[17] while in another patient only 35 percent was xanthine.[28]

Serum uric acid concentrations ranged from 0 to 1.44 mg/dl with a mean of 0.47 mg/dl (Table 42-1). On a purine-restricted diet virtually all values were less than 1.0 mg and were often less than 0.5 mg/dl. An exception is the patient of Terhorst,[11] commented on below.

Purine Excretion

Urinary excretion of xanthine normally ranges from 4.1 to 8.6 mg/day (average 6.1) and of hypoxanthine from 5.9 to 13.2 mg/day (average 9.7).[102] Auscher et al.[21] report an increased quantity of 7-methylguanine (10 mg) and no detectable 7-methyl-8-hydroxyguanine in the urine of their xanthinuric subject. Castro-Mendoza et al.[16] report a sixfold increase in urinary adenine in one of their subjects. Adenine and guanine excretions have been normal whenever measured in other xanthinuric subjects.[16,21,22]

In reported cases of xanthinuria the excretion of hypoxanthine plus xanthine ranged from 55 to 557 mg/day with a mean of 317 mg/day (Table 42-1). Uric acid excretion ranged from 0 to 81 mg/day with a mean of 23 mg/day. The urinary uric acid is at least in part of endogenous origin, for in the patient of Engleman et al. [^{14}C]xanthine given intravenously was converted to [^{14}C]uric acid found in serum and urine. It was cal-

Table 42-2 Concentration of Hypoxanthine and Xanthine in Skeletal Muscle from Xanthinuric and Control Subjects

Subject	*Hypoxanthine, ng/mg dry wt*	*Xanthine, ng/mg dry wt*
Patient	350 ± 40	315 ± 30
Control	22 ± 3	<50
Patient	240 ± 30	450 ± 40
Control	29 ± 3	<50

SOURCE: Parker et al.[55]

culated that the low level of xanthine oxidase activity detected in liver and intestinal mucosa was sufficient to account for the small amounts of uric acid excreted, 2 to 12 mg/day.[4]

An exceptional case was reported by Terhorst[11] of a man with a serum urate concentration of 3.15 mg/dl who excreted 670 mg xanthine per day, but also 269 mg uric acid per day. Xanthine oxidase activity was not measured. Presumably his degree or type of deficiency of xanthine oxidase differs from most other reported patients.

In all patients the urinary excretion of xanthine has greatly exceeded that of hypoxanthine (average 79 percent xanthine, range 42 to 95 percent) (Table 42-1). The ratio of xanthine to hypoxanthine is reduced in some xanthinuric subjects given allopurinol[4,22] but not in others.[21] The predominance of xanthine may be attributable to a low level of residual activity of xanthine oxidase in some subjects.

An additional and perhaps more important explanation for the preponderance of urinary xanthine has emerged from isotope dilution studies of the dynamics of the miscible pools of hypoxanthine and xanthine in two xanthinuric patients. Engleman et al.[4] calculated an immediate xanthine pool of 144 mg, with a turnover of 264 mg/day. Their patient excreted 126 mg xanthine and only 52 mg hypoxanthine. In a second patient (Table 42-3), Bradford et al.[8] showed that the initial pool of xanthine was 73 mg and of hypoxanthine, 118 mg. Daily turnovers of these pools were calculated to be 276 and 960 mg, respectively. Of these quantities 79 percent of the xanthine turnover (219 mg) was excreted in urine, compared with only 5.7 percent of the hypoxanthine turnover (54 mg). Qualitatively similar results were obtained by Ayvazian and Skupp,[103] who found utilization of administered purines greatest with adenine, intermediate with hypoxanthine, and least with xanthine.

These data disclose a considerable reutilization, or "salvage," of hypoxanthine, but little reutilization of xanthine in the tissues of human beings. Although the same phosphoribosyltransferase which efficiently catalyzes the conversion of hypoxanthine and guanine to their respective ribonucleotides also catalyzes the reutilization of xanthine, it does so at less than 1 percent of the rate of the reaction with hypoxanthine.[104] Accordingly, a much larger percentage of xanthine produced each day is permanently lost from the purine nucleotide pool, and in the absence (or severe deficiency) of xanthine oxidase activity is excreted unchanged.

Renal Handling of Xanthine

Studies showing a renal clearance of oxypurines approaching that of the glomerular filtration rate in the original patient of Dent and Philpot suggested to Dickinson and Smellie[2] that there were two metabolic defects, one of xanthine oxidase deficiency and another of renal tubular reabsorption of xanthine.

Table 42-3 Dimensions and Turnover of Purine Pools in a Xanthinuric Patient

Purine	*Miscible pool, mg*	*Turnover, mg/day*	*Urinary excretions, mg/day*	*Turnover excreted/day, %*
Hypoxanthine	118	960	54.5	5.7
Xanthine	72.5	276	219	79
Uric acid	19	11	6.5	61

SOURCE: Bradford et al.[8]

A high renal clearance of oxypurines was also found in the patient of Engleman and associates.[4] However, when serum oxypurine levels were raised in normal subjects to those found in xanthinuria, either by administration of a xanthine oxidase inhibitor[105] or by infusion of xanthine,[4] the clearance of oxypurines rose from normal values of 0.1 to 0.2 of the filtered load to 0.7 to 1.9 times the endogenous creatinine clearance. The high clearances found in xanthinuria may therefore be regarded as a normal response to the elevated serum levels of oxypurines. It is not necessary to postulate a separate tubular defect in handling of xanthine.

IDENTIFICATION OF XANTHINE STONES

Xanthine stones are rare. Hsieh and Hsu[49] found 1 pure xanthine calculus in 760 cases of urinary calculi. Herring[106] found four stones containing xanthine among 10,000 urinary calculi. Of these, one was pure xanthine (possibly the one obtained from Hsieh and Hsu), and three contained 5 to 19 percent xanthine.

The majority of xanthine stones have been described as brownish or brown-yellow, smooth, round or oval, friable, easily cut with a razor, and white and laminated inside. A few have been irregular in shape. They have ranged in size from a few millimeters in diameter to the size of a hen's egg[38] and in weight from "a few grains" to 3 g[18] or more.[45] Xanthine stones are nonopaque to x-rays unless calcium is trapped within the stone.

A variety of methods have been used for identification of xanthine in the stone. Most of these leave much to be desired, and identification should be based upon the highly sensitive and specific methods now available, including differential spectrophotometry, paper and column chromatography, and x-ray crystallography.[49] Methods for detection of xanthine in stones are given elsewhere.[107] A detailed description of the two types of crystal structure found in xanthine stones is given by Hsieh and Hsu.[49]

Other Cases of Xanthine Stones

Xanthine stones have been found in patients ranging from 2 to 72 years of age.[38–49] Three-quarters of the subjects have been males. Two-thirds of the xanthine stones have been "pure" and one-third, "mixed." The mixed stones have frequently contained uric acid, calcium oxalate, or phosphate in addition to xanthine.

Except in the patients described in Table 42-1, urinary excretion of xanthine has not been measured, nor has hypouricemia been reported in any other patient with xanthine stones. The level of blood or serum urate has been normal[39,45,48] or even somewhat high[44] in the few patients studied, all of them adults. In two Duke Hospital patients who had passed mixed xanthine–uric acid stones, excretions of xanthine and of other urinary purines[108] were normal, and serum uric acid levels were not low. A third subject, a woman who had passed stones since early childhood, had pure xanthine stones at age 28. No uric acid analyses were performed, and she has since been lost to follow-up.

It is clear that not all patients who form xanthine stones have a deficiency of xanthine oxidase activity. Among the patients with xanthine stones are several about whom a strong suspicion exists that xanthine excretion may have been elevated.

Taylor and Taylor[45] reported a 60-year-old male who had xanthine stones weighing 12 g. If xanthine excretion were normal in this subject (6 mg/day), these stones would represent quantitative precipitation and retention of the cumulative urinary xanthine excretion of 6 years. In addition, seven cases of xanthine stone formation have involved children under age 15, an age group in which the suspicion of an underlying metabolic defect is high. For example, the 2-year-old Taiwanese girl from whom surgeons removed a pure xanthine stone weighing 0.2 g[49] may very well have xanthinuria. Unfortunately the critical studies required to establish the presence or absence of xanthinuria have not been performed in these subjects.

Ichikawa[47] reported a 44-year-old male who had a left nephrectomy after a lengthy history of hematuria and negative study for urinary calculi. The kidney was grossly normal but on palpation was studded with numerous small nodules. The cut surface disclosed many small holes with brownish, granular concentrations, which were round or oval, smooth, and friable. Chemical tests showed these to be xanthine, and some tubules contained xanthine casts.

GENETICS

Of the 58 known patients with xanthinuria, 19 have been females and 39 males. Only 3 have been blacks. The xanthinuric subject examined by Dent and Philpot[1] had 13 relatives who showed no abnormal excretion values of xanthine and had normal urinary values of uric acid. These included an only sister, both parents, and three surviving grandparents. None gave a history of renal stone, and the parents were not related. The paternal aunts and the three children of the patient of Ayvazian[5] had ample uric acid in urine; urinary oxypurines were not measured. The mother of the patient of Engleman and associates had normal uric acid and oxypurine levels in plasma and urine and normal xanthine oxidase activity in jejunal mucosa.[4] The patient has no sibs, and the father was not available for study. All three sibs of the patient of Sperling et al.[13] had normal plasma urate values.

The family reported by Cifuentes-Delatte and Castro-Mendoza[6] included two brothers with near total replacement of urinary uric acid by xanthine and a sister who excreted 60 to 83 mg oxypurines per day in addition to 371 to 421 mg uric acid per day. In a second Spanish family described by Castro-Mendoza et al.,[16] oxypurine excretion was normal in all sibs and offspring of xanthinuric subjects. In the study of a large xanthinuric kindred by Wilson and Tapia,[20] 3 of 21 possible heterozygotes tested (Fig. 42-2) showed elevated urinary excretion values of oxypurines: 73, 38, and 116 mg/day on a low purine diet. All had normal plasma and urinary uric acid values.

Temperville et al.[29] studied a kindred with three xanthinuric subjects and found no relationship between the deficiency of xanthine oxidase and HLA type or the blood groups ABO, Rh, Pi, and Gm.

All known data are consistent with the interpretation that xanthinuria is an autosomal recessive disorder. No abnormalities have been detected in most of the presumed obligate heterozygotes, but in two families some possible heterozygotes showed elevated urinary oxypurine excretion values. These findings, taken together with the variable range of residual enzyme activity values, indicate probable heterogeneity of the genetic and molecular defect.

A deficiency of xanthine oxidase activity, probably genetic, has been discovered in a dachshund that produced xanthine urinary stones.[109]

TREATMENT

Prevention of xanthine stone formation in predisposed individuals depends upon recognition of the low solubility of xanthine in acid solutions. The pK_{a1} of xanthine is 7.7, and the pK_{a2} is 10.6.[110] Dent and Philpot[1] found that 100 ml normal urine at 26°C dissolved 6.7, 6.5, and 16.5 mg xanthine at a pH of 5.8, 7.0, and 8.1, respectively.

A high fluid intake and maintenance of a large urinary volume would appear to be indicated, as in all instances of stone formation. Oral alkali may be useful in specific instances, but the hazards of continuous alkali therapy must be borne in mind. Furthermore, alkalinization produces only a modest increase in the solubility of xanthine compared with its effect upon uric acid (Table 42-4).[50,111] Although xanthine excretion

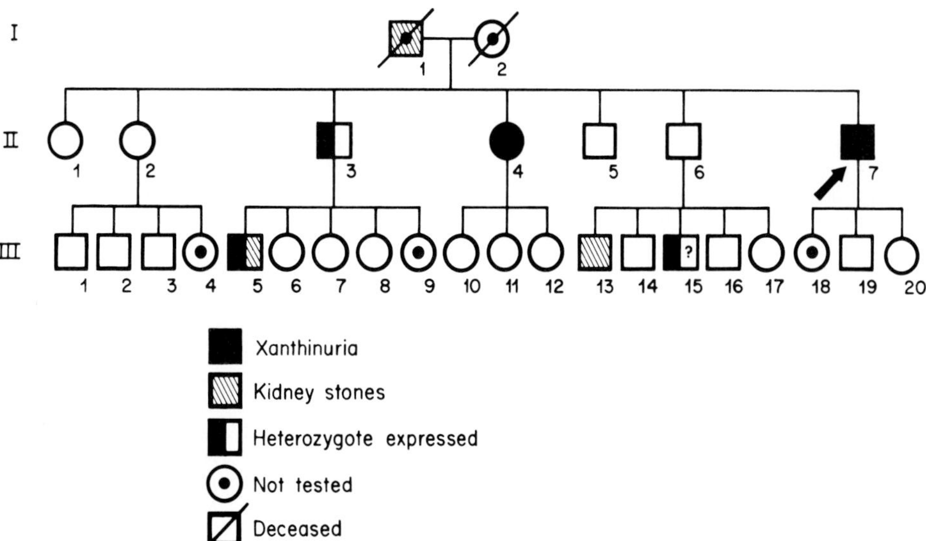

Fig 42-2 Kindred of a family with hereditary xanthinuria in which heterozygote expression was found. *(From Wilson and Tapia.[20] Used by permission.)*

Table 42-4 Solubility of Purines in Body Fluids

Fluid	*pH*	*Uric acid, mg/100 ml*	*Xanthine, mg/100 ml*	*Hypoxanthine, mg/100 ml*
Serum	7.4	7	10	115
Urine	5	15	5	140
Urine	7	200	13	150

SOURCE: Klinenberg et al.[111]

is independent of diet in normal subjects,[108] dietary purines would no doubt add to the burden of xanthine excretion and should be limited. Allopurinol therapy in high doses reversed the xanthine/hypoxanthine ratio in two patients[4,22] and might be useful in xanthinuric people with xanthine stones and residual xanthine oxidase activity. The potential advantage of substitution of the more soluble hypoxanthine for a portion of xanthine is clear from Table 42-4. Methylxanthines, such as caffeine and theophylline, are very much more soluble than xanthine and are not metabolized by xanthine oxidase. It is unnecessary to prohibit their use in xanthinuric subjects.

In managing patients with a combined deficiency of xanthine oxidase and sulfite oxidase, the neurologic symptoms resulting from sulfite oxidase deficiency are more devastating clinically than those resulting from xanthine oxidase deficiency. Consequently, most attention has been focused on the treatment of the neurologic symptoms and correction of the sulfite oxidase deficiency. In the patient reported by Abumrad et al.[36] treatment with 300 to 500 μg ammonium molybdate per day replaced the dietary deficiency of molybdenum, corrected the disorders of both purine and sulfur metabolism, and markedly ameliorated the neurologic symptoms attributed to sulfite oxidase deficiency. The patient with no detectable molybdenum cofactor in the liver was treated with oral ammonium molybdate (200 μg/day) without significant improvement in biochemical parameters or neurologic symptoms.[35] Allopurinol therapy with $NaHCO_3$ supplements was also tried in this patient because of xanthine calculi, but there was no reduction in the incidence of xanthine calculi or change in the ratio of xanthine to hypoxanthine in the urine. Restriction of methionine and cysteine reduced urinary output of abnormal sulfur metabolites but had no demonstrable effect on clinical symptoms during a short therapeutic trial.

REFERENCES

1. DENT CE, PHILPOT GR: Xanthinuria, an inborn error (or deviation) of metabolism. *Lancet* 1:182, 1954.
2. DICKINSON CJ, SMELLIE JM: Xanthinuria. *Br Med J* 2:1217, 1959.
3. WATTS RWE, ENGLEMAN K, KLINENBERG JR, SEEGMILLER JE, SJOERDSMA A: The enzyme defect in a case of xanthinuria. *Biochem J* 90:4P, 1964.
4. ENGLEMAN K, WATTS RWE, KLINENBERG JR, SJOERDSMA A, SEEGMILLER JE: Clinical, physiological, and biochemical studies of a patient with xanthinuria and pheochromocytoma. *Am J Med* 37:839, 1964.
5. AYVAZIAN JH: Xanthinuria and hemochromatosis. *N Engl J Med* 270:18, 1964.
6. CIFUENTES-DELATTE L, CASTRO-MENDOZA HJ: Xanthinuria familiar. *Rev Clin Esp* 107:244, 1967.
7. FREZAL J, MALASSENET R, CARTIER P, FESSARD C, ROY C, REY J, LAMY M: Sur un cas de xanthinurie. *Arch Fr Pediatr* 24:129, 1967.
8. BRADFORD MJ, KRAKOFF IH, LEEPER R, BALIS ME: Study of purine metabolism in a xanthinuric female. *J Clin Invest* 47:1325, 1968.
9. CHALMERS RA, JOHNSON M, PALLIS C, WATTS RWE: Xanthinuria with myopathy (with some observations on the renal handling of oxypurines in the disease). *Q J Med* 38:493, 1969.
10. CHALMERS RA, WATTS RWE, BITENSKY L, CHAYEN J: Microscopic studies on crystals in skeletal muscle from two cases of xanthinuria. *J Pathol* 99:45, 1969.
11. TERHORST B: Xanthinsteine und Xanthinurie: Ein kasuistischer Beitrag. *Z Urol Nephrol* 62:37, 1969.
12. KUTTER D, HUMBEL R, BISDORFF J: Biochemische Untersuchungen bei einem typischen Fall von Xanthinurie. *Dtsch Med Wochenschr* 95:1269, 1970.
13. SPERLING O, LIBERMAN UA, FRANK M, DEVRIES A: Xanthinuria: An additional case with demonstration of xanthine oxidase deficiency. *Am J Clin Pathol* 55:351, 1971.
14. CURNOW DH, MASAREL JR, CULLEN KM, MCCALL MG: Xanthinuria discovered in population screening. *Br Med J* 1:403, 1971.
15. CLERC M, BARBIER M: Le calcul renal d'un sujet déficitaire en xanthine-oxydase. *Bull Soc Pathol Exot* 64:527, 1971.
16. CASTRO-MENDOZA HJ, CIFUENTES-DELATTE LC, RAPADO YAR: Una neuva observación de xanthinuria familiar. *Rev Clin Exp* 124:341, 1972.
17. SORENSEN LB, TESAR JT, ELLMAN MH, COLWELL N: A new case of xanthinuria. *Am J Med* 53:690, 1972.
18. FRAYHA RA, SALTI IS, HAICLAR GIA, AL-KHALIDI U, HEMADY K: Hereditary xanthinuria and xanthine urolithiasis: An additional 3 cases. *J Urol* 109:871, 1973.
19. DE VOOGHT HJ, VON DE KAMP JJP, VAN GERDEREN HH, BERNINI LF, BOOGAART AM: Een xanthinesteen by een kind met xanthinurie: Enkele beschouwingen over een Zeldaure "inborn error of metabolism." *Ned Tijdschr Geneeskd* 117:976, 1973.
20. WILSON DM, TAPIA HK: Xanthinuria in a large kindred, in Sperling D, DeVries A, Wyngaarden JB (eds): *Purine Metabolism in Man.* Plenum, New York, 1974, p 343.
21. AUSCHER C, PASQUIER C, MERCIER N, DELBARRE F: Urinary excretion of 6 hydroxylated metabolite and oxypurines in a xanthinuric man given allopurinol or thiopurinol, in Sperling D, DeVries A, Wyngaarden JB (eds): *Purine Metabolism in Man.* New York, Plenum, 1974, p 663.
22. HOLMES EW, MASON DH, GOLDSTEIN LI, BLOUNT RE, KELLEY WN: Xanthine oxidase deficiency: Studies in a previously unreported case. *Clin Chem* 20:1076, 1974.
23. SIMMONDS HA, LEVIN B, CAMERON JS: Variations in allopurinol metabolism by xanthinuric subjects. *Clin Sci Mol Med* 47:173, 1974.
24. RAPADO A, CASTRO-MENDOZA HJ, CASTRILLO JM, FRUTOS M, CIFUENTES-DELATTE L: Xanthinuria as a cause of hypouricemia in liver disease. *Br Med J* 11:560, 1975.
25. ISAACS H, HEFFRON JJA, BERMAN L, BADENHORST M, PICKERING A: Xanthine, hypoxanthine, and muscle pain. Histochemical and biochemical observations. *S Afr Med J* 49:1035, 1975.
26. KITAMURA T, KAWAMURA T, KITAGAWA R, OGAWA A: Xanthine stone and xanthinuria associated with retrocaval ureter: Report of a case and a review of the literature. *Jpn J Urol* 67:670, 1976.
27. AUSCHER C, PASQUIER C, DE GERY A, WEISSENBACH R, DELBARRE D: Xanthinuria: Study of a large kindred with familial urolithiasis and gout. *Biomed Exp* 27:57, 1977.
28. CARTIER P, PERIGNON JL: Xanthinuria. *Nouv Presse Med* 7:1381, 1978.
29. TEMPERVILLE B, GODIN M, DUBOIS D, FILLASTRE JP: A propos de trois observations de xanthinurie familiale: Revue de la littérature. *Semin Hop Paris* 55:1899, 1979.
30. MITNICK PD, BECK LH: Hypouricemia and malignant neoplasms. *Arch Intern Med* 139:1186, 1979.
31. CURIEL P, BANDINELLI R: Pregnancy in a woman with xanthinuria: Study of amniotic fluid uric acid. *Am J Obstet Gynecol* 134:721, 1979.
32. MORIMI PL, BANDINELLI R, CURIEL P: Hypouricemia and xanthinuria. Observation of 3 cases. *Minerva Med* 70:873, 1979.

32a. KOJIMA T, NISHINA T, KITAMURA M, HOSOYA T, NISHIOKA K: Biochemical studies on the purine metabolism of four cases with hereditary xanthinuria. *Clin Chim Acta* 137:189, 1984.

32b. BOULIEU R, BORY C, BALTASSAT P, DIVRY P: Hypoxanthine and xanthine concentrations determined by high performance liquid chromatography in biological fluids from patients with xanthinuria. *Clin Chim Acta* 142:83, 1984.

32c. MATEOS FA, PUIG JG, JIMENEZ ML, FOX IH: Hereditary xanthinuria: Evidence for enhanced hypoxanthine salvage. *J Clin Invest* 79:847, 1987.

32d. BENNETT MJ, CARPENTER KH, HILL PG: Asymptomatic xanthinuria detected as a result of routine analysis of serum for urate. *Clin Chem* 31:492, 1985.

32e. CARPENTER TO, LEBOWITZ RL, NELSON D, BAUER S: Hereditary xanthinuria presenting in infancy with nephrolithiasis. *J Pediatr* 109:307, 1986.

33. DURAN M, BEEMER FA, HEIDEN CVD, KORTELAND J, DE BREC PK, BRINK M, WADMAN SK: Combined deficiency of xanthine oxidase and sulfite oxidase: A defect of molybdenum metabolism or transport. *J Inherited Metab Dis* 1:175, 1978.
34. HEIDEN CVD, BEEMER FA, BRINK W, WADMAN SK, DURAN M: Simultaneous occurrence of xanthine oxidase and sulfite oxidase deficiency. A

molybdenum dependent inborn error of metabolism. *Clin Biochem* 12:206, 1979.

35. JOHNSON JL, WAUD WR, RAJAGOPALAN KV, DURAN M, BEEMER FA, WADMAN SK: Inborn errors of molybdenum metabolism: Combined deficiencies of sulfite oxidase and xanthine dehydrogenase in a patient lacking the molybdenum cofactor. *Proc Natl Acad Sci USA* 77:3715, 1980.
36. ABUMRAD NN, SCHNEIDER AJ, STEEL DR, ROGERS LS: Acquired molybdenum deficiency. *Clin Res* 27:774A, 1979.
37. MARCET A: *An Essay on the Chemical History and Medical Treatment of Calculous Disorders*. 2d ed., rev. and enlarged. London, Strahan and Spottiswoode for Longman, 1819.
38. KRETSCHMER HL: Xanthine calculi: Report of a case and a review of the literature. *J Urol* 38:183, 1937.
39. RATNER M, STRASBERG A: A case of xanthine calculosis. *Can Med Assoc J* 40:350, 1939.
40. HYMAN A, LEITER HE: A case of xanthine calculi. *J Mount Sinai Hosp* 8:84, 1941.
41. BUTT AJ, HOLLIMAN HE JR: Xanthine calculus: A case report. *J Urol* 52:89, 1944.
42. GERSH IJ, MELTZER HL: Xanthine urinary calculi: Two cases. *J Urol* 55:169, 1946.
43. BERMAN LS: Twenty-second case of xanthine urinary calculus. *J Urol* 60:420, 1948.
44. PEARLMAN CK: Xanthine urinary calculus. *J Urol* 64:799, 1950.
45. TAYLOR WN, TAYLOR JN: Xanthine calculus: Case report. *J Urol* 68:659, 1952.
46. MACKEY JF JR: Xanthine calculus. *Mo Med* 50:617, 1953.
47. ICHIKAWA T: Xanthine calculi of kidney. *J Urol* 72:770, 1954.
48. JORDON H: Multiple Xanthinsteinbildung: Bericht über einen Fall. *Dtsch Z Verdau Stoffwechselkr* 15:143, 1955.
49. HSIEH HF, HSU TC: Xanthine calculus: A case report. *J Formosan Med Assoc* 62:83, 1963.
50. SEEGMILLER JE: Hereditary xanthinuria, in Bondy PK, Rosenberg LE (eds): *Duncan's Diseases of Metabolism*. Philadelphia, Saunders, 1974, p 739.
51. MUDD SH, IRREVERRE F, LASTER L: Sulfite oxidase deficiency in man: Demonstration of the enzymatic defect. *Science* 156:1599, 1967.
52. IRREVERRE F, MUDD SH, KEIZER WD, LASTER L: Sulfite oxidase deficiency: Studies of a patient with mental retardation, dislocated lenses, and abnormal urinary excretion of S-sulfo-L-cysteine, sulfite, and thiosulfate. *Biochem Med* 1:187, 1967.
53. SHIH VE, ABROMS IF, JOHNSON JL, CARNEY M, MANDELL R, ROBB RM, CLOHERTY JP, RAJAGOPALAN KV: Sulfite oxidase deficiency: Biochemical and clinical investigations of a hereditary metabolic disorder in sulfur metabolism. *N Engl J Med* 297:1022, 1977.
54. CHALMERS RA, WATTS RWE, PALLIS C, BITENSKY L, CHAYEN J: Crystalline deposits in striped muscle in xanthinuria. *Nature* 221:170, 1969.
55. PARKER R, SNEDDEN W, WATTS RWE: The mass-spectrometric identification of hypoxanthine and xanthine ("oxypurines") in skeletal muscle from two patients with congenital xanthine oxidase deficiency (xanthinuria). *Biochem J* 115:103, 1969.
56. JOHNSON JL, RAJAGOPALAN KV, COHEN HJ: Molecular basis of the biological function of molybdenum. Effect of tungsten on xanthine oxidase and sulfite oxidase in the rat. *J Biol Chem* 249:859, 1974.
57. COHEN HJ, JOHNSON JL, RAJAGOPALAN KV: Molecular basis of the biological function of molybdenum. Developmental patterns of sulfite oxidase and xanthine oxidase in the rat. *Arch Biochem Biophys* 164:440, 1974.
58. SEEGMILLER JE, ENGLEMAN K, KLINENBERG JR, WATTS RWE, SJOERDSMA A: Xanthine oxidase and iron. *N Engl J Med* 270:534, 1964.
59. STIRPE E, DELLA CORTE E: The regulation of rat liver xanthine oxidase: Conversion in vitro of the enzyme activity from dehydrogenase (type D) to oxidase (type O). *J Biol Chem* 244:3855, 1969.
60. DELLA CORTE E, STIRPE F: The regulation of rat liver xanthine oxidase: Involvement of thiol groups in the conversion of the enzyme activity from dehydrogenase (type D) into oxidase (type O) and purification of the enzyme. *Biochem J* 126:739, 1972.
61. BATELLI MG, LORENZONI E, STIRPE F: Milk xanthine oxidase type D (dehydrogenase) and type O (oxidase). *Biochem J* 131:191, 1973.
62. KRENITSKY TA, TUTTLE JV, CATTAU EL JR, WONG P: A comparison of the distribution and electron acceptor specificities of xanthine oxidase and aldehyde oxidase. *Comp Biochem Physiol* 49B:687, 1974.
63. WAUD WR, RAJAGOPALAN KV: The mechanism of conversion of rat liver xanthine dehydrogenase from an NAD^+-dependent form (type D) to an O_2-dependent form (type O). *Arch Biochem Biophys* 172:365, 1976.
64. KRENITSKY TA, TUTTLE JV: Xanthine oxidase activities: Evidence for two catalytically different types. *Arch Biochem Biophys* 185:370, 1978.
64a. SILBERMAN HR, WYNGAARDEN JB: 6-Mercaptopurine as substrate and inhibitor of xanthine oxidase. *Biochim Biophys Acta* 47:178, 1961.
65. FEIGELSON P, DAVIDSON JD, ROBINS RK: Pyrazolopyrimidines as inhibitors and substrates of xanthine oxidase. *J Biol Chem* 226:993, 1957.
66. ELION GB: Enzymatic and metabolic studies with allopurinol. *Ann Rheum Dis* 25:608, 1966.
67. MASSEY V, KOMAI H, PALMER G, ELION G: On the mechanism of inactivation of xanthine oxidase by allopurinol and other pyrazolo [3,4-d] pyrimidines. *J Biol Chem* 245:2837, 1970.
68. HUH K, YAMAMOTO I, GOHDA E, IWATA H: Tissue distribution and characteristics of xanthine oxidase and allopurinol oxidizing enzymes. *Jpn J Pharmacol* 26:719, 1976.
69. DE RENZO EC: Chemistry and biochemistry of xanthine oxidase. *Adv Enzymol* 17:293, 1956.
70. SKUPP S, AYVAZIAN JH: Oxidation of 7-methylguanine by human xanthine oxidase. *J Lab Clin Med* 73:909, 1969.
71. ANDREWS P, BRAY RC, EDWARDS P, SHOOTER KV: The chemistry of xanthine oxidase. II. Ultracentrifuge and gel-filtration studies on the milk enzyme. *Biochem J* 93:627, 1964.
72. HART LI, MCGARTOLL MA, CHAPMAN HR, BRAY RC: The composition of milk xanthine oxidase. *Biochem J* 116:851, 1970.
73. NELSON CA, HANDLER P: Preparation of bovine xanthine oxidase and the subunit structures of some iron flavoproteins. *J Biol Chem* 243:5368, 1968.
74. BRUMBY PE: Ph.D. thesis. University of Sheffield, 1963.
75. RAJAGOPALAN KV, HANDLER P: Purification and properties of chicken liver xanthine dehydrogenase. *J Biol Chem* 242:409, 1967.
76. BRAY RC, MALMSTROM BG: The chemistry of xanthine oxidase. 12. The amino acid composition. *Biochem J* 93:633, 1964.
77. MASSEY V, BRUMBY PE, KOMAI H, PALMER G: Studies on milk xanthine oxidase: Some spectral and kinetic properties. *J Biol Chem* 244:1682, 1969.
78. MEHLER AH: *Introduction to Enzymology*. New York, Academic, 1957, p 178.
79. BRAY RC, CHISHOLM J, HART LI, MERIWETHER LS, WATTS DC: Studies on the composition and mechanism of action of milk xanthine, in Slater EC (ed): *Flavines and Flavoproteins*. Amsterdam, Elsevier, 1966, p 117.
80. JOHNSON JL, HAINLINE BE, RAJAGOPALAN KV: Characterization of the molybdenum cofactor of sulfite oxidase, xanthine oxidase, and nitrate reductase. *J Biol Chem* 255:1783, 1980.
81. JOHNSON JL, JONES HP, RAJAGOPALAN KV: In vitro reconstitution of demolybdosulfite oxidase by a molybdenum cofactor from rat liver and other sources. *J Biol Chem* 252:4994, 1977.
82. KOMAI H, MASSEY V, PALMER G: The preparation and properties of deflavo xanthine oxidase. *J Biol Chem* 244:1692, 1969.
83. OLSON JS, BALLOU DP, PALMER G, MASSEY V: The mechanism of action of xanthine oxidase. *J Biol Chem* 249:4363, 1974.
84. AL-KHALIDI UAS, CHAGLASSIAN TH: The species distribution of xanthine oxidase. *Biochem J* 97:318, 1965.
85. WATTS RWE, WATTS JEM, SEEGMILLER LE: Xanthine oxidase activity in human tissues and its inhibition by allopurinol (4-hydroxypyrazolo [3,4-d] pyrimidine). *J Lab Clin Med* 66:688, 1965.
86. DUNN JT, WYNGAARDEN JB: Unpublished data.
87. SHAMMA'A MH, NASRALLAH S, CHAGLASSIAN T, KACHADURIAN AK, AL-KHALIDI UAS: Serum xanthine oxidase: A sensitive test of acute liver injury. *Gastroenterology* 48:226, 1965.
88. GILER S, SPERLING O, BROSCH S, URCA I, DEVRIES A: Serum xanthine oxidase in jaundice. *Clin Chim Acta* 63:37, 1975.
89. GILER S, HENIG EF, URCA I, SPERLING O, DEVRIES A: Urine xanthine oxidase activity in urinary tract infection. *J Clin Pathol* 31:444, 1978.
90. MORGAN EJ: The distribution of xanthine oxidase. *Biochem J* 20:1282, 1926.
91. BRAY RC: Xanthine oxidase, in Boyer P, Lardy H, Myrbach K (eds): *The Enzymes*, 2d ed. New York, Academic, 1963, vol VII, p 533.
92. ROWE PB, WYNGAARDEN JB: The mechanism of dietary alterations in rat hepatic xanthine oxidase levels. *J Biol Chem* 241:5571, 1966.
93. MARCOLONGO R, MARINELLO E, POMPUCCI G, PAGANI R: The role of xanthine oxidase in hyperuricemic states. *Arthritis Rheum* 17:430, 1974.
94. THOMPSON JM, NICKELS JS, FISHER JR: Synthesis and degradation of xanthine dehydrogenase in chick liver: In vivo and in vitro studies. *Biochim Biophys Acta* 568:157, 1979.
95. CATIGNANI GL, CHYTIL F, DARBY WJ: Vitamin E deficiency: Immunochemical evidence for increased accumulation of liver xanthine oxidase. *Proc Natl Acad Sci USA* 71:1966, 1974.
96. PRAJDA N, MORRIS HP, WEBER G: Imbalance of purine metabolism in hepatomas of different growth rates as expressed in behavior of xanthine oxidase. *Cancer Res* 36:4639, 1976.
97. LEVINSON DJ, CHALKER D: Rat hepatic xanthine oxidase activity. Age and sex specific differences. *Arthritis Rheum* 23:77, 1980.
98. OLIVER I, SPERLING O, LIBERMAN UA, FRAN M, DEVRIES A: Deficiency of

xanthine oxidase activity in colustrum of xanthinuric female. *Biochem Med* 5:279, 1971.

99. PARKER R, SNEDDEN W, WATTS RWE: The quantitative determination of hypoxanthine and xanthine ("oxypurines") in skeletal muscle from two patients with congenital xanthine oxidase deficiency (xanthinuria). *Biochem J* 116:317, 1970.

100. SEGAL S, WYNGAARDEN JB: Plasma glutamine and oxypurine content in patients with gout. *Proc Soc Exp Biol Med* 88:342, 1955.

101. JORGENSEN S: Hypoxanthine and xanthine accumulated in stored human blood: Determination of relative amounts by spectrophotometry. *Acta Pharmacol Toxicol* 11:265, 1955.

102. WEISSMANN B, BROMBERG PA, GUTMAN AB: The purine bases of human urine. II. Semiquantitative estimation and isotope incorporation. *J Biol Chem* 224:423, 1957.

103. AYVAZIAN JH, SKUPP S: The study of purine utilization and excretion in a xanthinuric man. *J Clin Invest* 44:1248, 1965.

104. KELLEY WN, ROSENBLOOM FM, HENDERSON JF, SEEGMILLER JE: Xanthine phosphoribosyltransferase in man. Relationship to hypoxanthine-guanine phosphoribosyltransferase. *Biochem Biophys Res Commun* 28:340, 1967.

105. KLINENBERG JR, GOLDFINGER S, MILLER J, SEEGMILLER JE: The effectiveness of a xanthine oxidase inhibitor in the treatment of gout. *Arthritis Rheum* 6:779, 1963.

106. HERRING LC: Observations on the analysis of ten thousand urinary calculi. *J Urol* 88:545, 1962.

107. WYNGAARDEN JB: Xanthinuria, in Stanbury JB, Wyngaarden JB, Fredrickson DS (eds): *The Metabolic Basis of Inherited Disease,* 1st ed. New York, McGraw-Hill, 1960, p 761.

108. WEISSMANN B, BROMBERG PA, GUTMAN AB: The purine bases of human urine. 1. Separation and identification. *J Biol Chem* 224:407, 1957.

109. DELBARRE F, HOLTZER A, AUSCHER C: Xanthine urinary lithiasis in a dachshund: Deficiency, probably genetic, of the xanthine oxidase system. *C R Acad Sci [D] (Paris)* 269:1449, 1969.

110. BERGMANN F, DIKSTEIN S: The relationship between spectral shifts and structural changes in uric acids and related compounds. *J Am Chem Soc* 77:691, 1955.

111. KLINENBERG JR, GOLDFINGER SF, SEEGMILLER JD: The effectiveness of a xanthine oxidase inhibitor allopurinol in the treatment of gout. *Ann Intern Med* 62:639, 1965.

CHAPTER **43**

HEREDITARY OROTIC ACIDURIA AND OTHER DISORDERS OF PYRIMIDINE METABOLISM

D. PARKER SUTTLE
DAVID M. O. BECROFT
DIANNE R. WEBSTER

1. *There are three specific enzyme defects described in pyrimidine metabolism. The first defect, hereditary orotic aciduria, is in the* de novo *synthetic pathway. This autosomal recessive disorder results from a severe deficiency of the last two activities in the pathway, orotate phosphoribosyltransferase and orotidine-5'-monophosphate decarboxylase. Although orotic aciduria was originally thought to be unique because of the loss of two enzymes, it is now known that these activities reside in separate domains of a single polypeptide coded for by a single gene. This bifunctional protein, uridine-5'-monophosphate synthase, has been purified, the amino acid sequence determined by cDNA sequencing, and the gene localized to human chromosome 3q13.*
2. *There are 13 patients known with hereditary orotic aciduria; all have had a macrocytic hypochromic megaloblastic anemia and orotic acid crystalluria. Other features have included renal tract obstruction by crystals, cardiac malformations, and strabismus. Infections have been a problem in some, associated with various abnormalities in in vitro tests of immune function. One patient had severe congenital abnormalities. Twelve have been treated with uridine, and all have responded. Those who are now young adults remain well but require continued therapy.*
3. *The other two disorders involve defects in the pyrimidine degradative pathway. Deficiency of pyrimidine-5'-nucleotidase causes hemolytic anemia, possibly due to accumulation in erythrocytes of pyrimidine nucleotides, mostly uridine triphosphate (UTP) and cytidine triphosphate (CTP). The disorder is transmitted in an autosomal recessive manner, and there is no specific treatment available. Deficiency of dihydropyrimidine dehydrogenase causes an increase in the levels of uracil and thymine in blood and urine. This deficiency is detected in a variety of clinical situations including pediatric metabolic screens for neurologic and other problems, neuroblastoma, and adverse reactions to 5-fluorouracil, and also is found in asymptomatic relatives of detected cases. The enzyme deficiency is transmitted in an autosomal recessive fashion, and there is some doubt whether there is a causal relationship between the deficiency and the symptoms.*
4. *Pyrimidines and purines are the building blocks of DNA and RNA and are thus required for the retention and transmission of genetic information. In addition, they function in the formation of coenzymes and active intermediates in carbohydrate and phospholipid metabolism. Purines and pyrimidines have two routes for nucleotide formation, the* de novo *pathway, which begins with ribose-phosphate, amino acids, CO_2, and ammonia; and the salvage pathway, which takes free bases and nucleosides back to nucleotides.* De novo *and salvage pathways are balanced and connected through the enzymes which convert the basic purine or pyrimidine ring structure to other nucleosides and nucleotides, and the enzymes which degrade the nucleotides to β-amino acids, CO_2, and ammonia.*
5. *In contrast to the large number of defects in purine metabolism[1-6] only three defects in pyrimidine metabolism have been documented: hereditary orotic aciduria (McKusick 25890, 25892), hemolytic anemia due to pyrimidine-5'-nucleotidase deficiency (McKusick 26612), and dihydropyrimidine dehydrogenase deficiency, or pyridinemia (McKusick 27427). Purine metabolism has an easily recognizable, easily measurable end product in uric acid. Alteration in uric acid levels directly reflect alterations in the enzymes of purine metabolism. There is no equivalent compound in pyrimidine metabolism.*

PYRIMIDINE ENZYMES

The enzymes of pyrimidine metabolism are summarized in Table 43-1, and a diagram of the interrelationship between the enzymes of *de novo* synthesis, interconversion, salvage, and degradation is given in Fig. 43-1. The body requirement for pyrimidines can be met either by synthesis from small molecules or by reutilization of preformed pyrimidines available from body cell turnover or dietary sources (Figs. 43-1 and 43-2). *De novo* pyrimidine synthesis has been estimated at 4 to 16 mmol/day,[7] or 450 to 700 mg/day, approximately equal to

Nonstandard abbreviations used in this chapter include: AECE-6AZUMP = 5-{2-{*N*-(aminoethyl) carbamyl}ethyl}-6-azauridine-5'-monophosphate; ATC = aspartate transcarbamylase; 5AZOA = 5-azaorotic acid; 6AZUR = 6-azauridine; BA = barbituric acid; CAD = the multifunctional protein containing domains for carbamyl-phosphate synthase, aspartate transcarbamylase, and dihydro-orotase activity, also called multienzyme pyr 1-3; CPS = carbamyl-phosphate synthetase; DHO = dihydro-orotase; DHODH = dihydro-orotate dehydrogenase; DHPDH = dihydropyrimidine dehydrogenase; FIGLU = formiminoglutamic acid; 5FU = 5-fluorouracil; HPLC = high performance liquid chromatography; OA = orotic acid; ODC = orotidine-5'-monophosphate decarboxylase; OMP = orotidine-5'-monophosphate; OPRT = orotate phosphoribosyltransferase; PF = pyrazofurin, 3,β-D-ribofuranosyl-4-hydroxypyrazole-5-carboxamide; PNMK = pyrimidine nucleoside monophosphate kinase; PRPP = 5-phosphoribosyl-1-pyrophosphate; P5N = pyrimidine-5'-nucleotidase; SDS-PAGE = sodium dodecyl sulfate-polyacrylamide gel electrophoresis; UMP = uridine-5'-monophosphate; UMPS = uridine-5'-monophosphate synthase. In addition, patients with UMPS deficiency are referred to by their initials (see Table 43-2).

Table 43-1 Enzymes of the Pyrimidine *De Novo* Synthetic, Biosynthetic, Salvage, and Catabolic Pathways*

Enzyme number	*Name*	*Abbreviation*	*EC number*
De novo synthetic			
1–3	Multienzyme pyr 1–3 (CPS-ATC-DHO)	CAD	
1	Carbamyl-phosphate synthase	CPS	2.7.2.9
2	Asparate transcarbamylase	ATC	2.1.3.2
3	Dihydro-orotase	DHO	3.5.2.3
4	Dihydro-orotate dehydrogenase	DHODH	1.3.3.1
5, 6	UMP synthase (multienzyme pyr 5,6) (OPRT-ODC)	UMPS	
5	Orotate phosphoribosyltransferase	OPRT	2.4.2.10
6	Orotidine-5′-monophosphate decarboxylase	ODC	4.1.1.23
Biosynthetic			
7	Uridine (pyrimidine) monophosphate kinase		2.7.4.14
8	Ribonucleoside-diphosphate reductase		1.17.4.1
9	Pyrimidine diphosphate kinase		2.7.4.6
10	Thymidylate synthetase		2.1.1.45
11	Thymidine monophosphate kinase		2.7.4.9
12	Cytidine triphosphate synthetase		6.3.4.2
13	RNA nucleotidyltransferase		2.7.7.6
14	DNA nucleotidyltransferase		2.7.7.7
Salvage			
15	Uridine kinase		2.7.1.48
16	Uridine phosphorylase		2.4.2.3
17	Thymidine kinase		2.7.1.21
18	Thymidine phosphorylase		2.4.2.4
19	Deoxycytidine kinase		2.7.1.74
Catabolic			
20	Cytidine deaminase		3.5.4.5
21	Deoxycytidine monophosphate deaminase		3.5.4.12
22	Dihydropyrimidine dehydrogenase	DHPDH	1.3.1.2
23	Hydropyrimidine hydrase (dihydropyrimidine amidohydrolase)		
24	Ureidopropionase		
25	Pyrimidine-5′-nucleotidase	P5N	3.1.3.5
26	Orotidine-5′-monophosphate phosphohydrolase		

*Enzyme numbers used throughout refer to those given in this table and in Figs. 43-1, 43-2, 43-8, and 43-9.

the daily purine requirement.[8] There are a number of excellent reviews and sources of information on basic pyrimidine biochemistry.[9–13]

De Novo Synthesis

The six activities of *de novo* pyrimidine biosynthesis in animals are coded by three structural genes. The first gene codes for a large multifunctional protein containing the first three activities of the pathway, carbamyl-phosphate synthetase (CPS, enzyme 1 on Figs. 43-1 and 43-2), aspartate transcarbamylase (ATC, enzyme 2) and dihydro-orotase (DHO, enzyme 3). The second gene codes for dihydro-orotate dehydrogenase (DHODH, enzyme 4). The third gene codes for the last two activities of the *de novo* pathway, orotate phosphoribosyltransferase (OPRT, enzyme 5) and orotidine-5′-monophosphate decarboxylase (ODC, enzyme 6).

Carbamyl-phosphate synthase, **A**spartate transcarbamylase, and **D**ihydro-orotase are contained in a single polypeptide (CAD, or pyr 1-3) with a molecular weight of approximately 220,000 daltons.[14–17] This cytosolic multifunctional protein appears to be composed of three distinct catalytic domains in the following arrangements: NH_2-DHO-CPS-ATC-COOH.[18,19] Sedimentation analysis and chemical cross-linking studies indicate the native form of the protein consists of stable trimers and hexamers of the basic polypeptide.[14,20,21] The hexamers have an open planar appearance by electron microscopy and can associate to form higher oligomeric forms.[21] Treatment of the CAD protein with staphylococcal proteinase results in cleavage of the protein but no loss in activity. One fragment of 182,000 daltons contains CPS and DHO. A 42,000-dalton fragment retains the ATC activity.[22] Similar results were obtained when the CAD protein was digested with elastase,[23] and the ATC domain was shown to self-associate and form well-defined oligomers.

The CAD gene spans a region of more than 25 kb and has over 30 introns.[24] The size of the mRNA coding for the CAD protein is 7.9 kb.[25] The ATC is coded by a 2.2-kb piece from the 3′ end of the total CAD message. Transformation of bacteria defective in ATC activity with this cDNA fragment results in complementation of the defect. Sequence homology is noted between the hamster and *Escherichia coli* ATC at the areas of the protein structure that are critical to catalysis.[19]

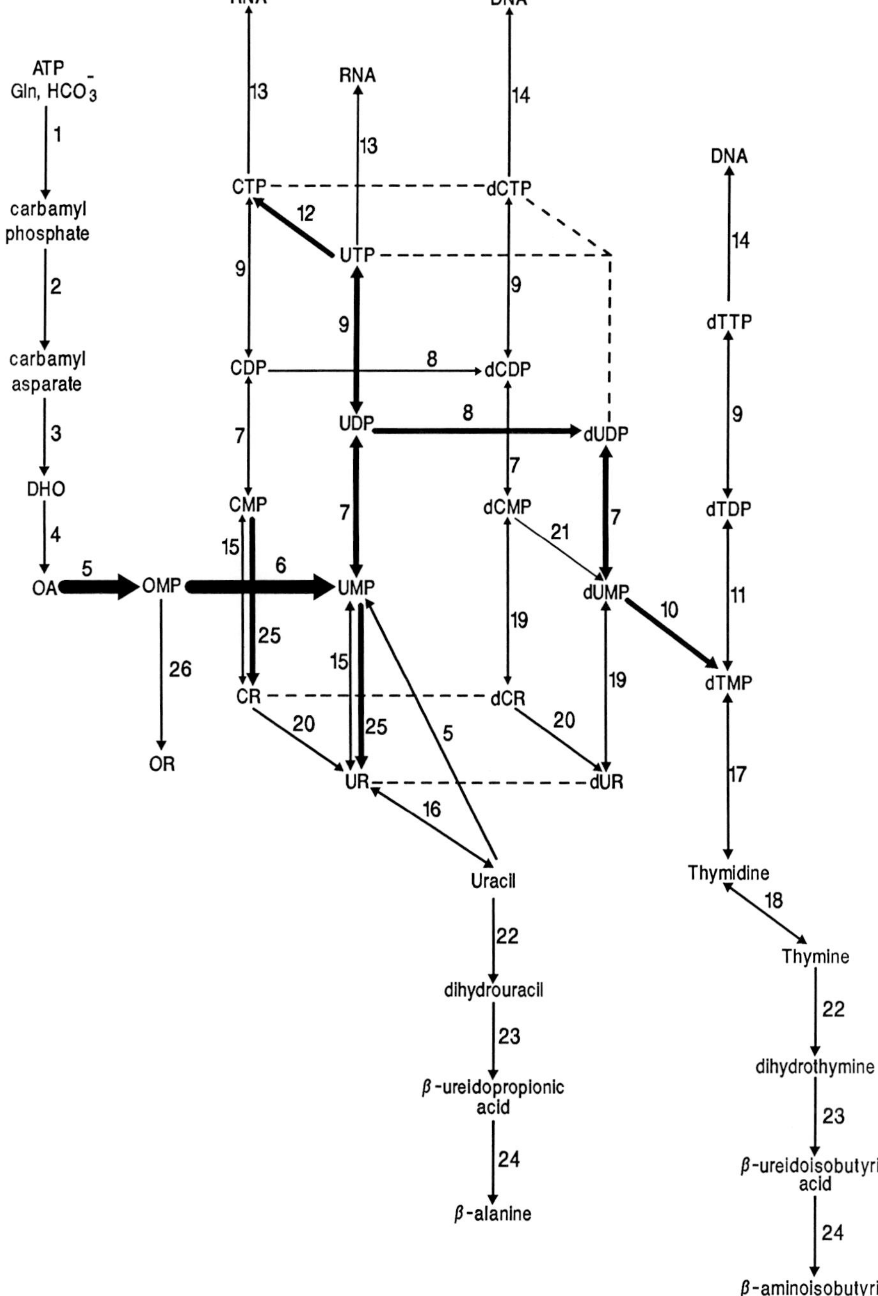

Fig. 43-1 Diagram indicating the interrelationship of *de novo* pyrimidine synthesis, conversion of UMP to other ribo- and deoxyribonucleotides, salvage from cell turnover or dietary sources, and degradation. The ribonucleosides and ribonucleotides form the left face of the interconversion box. The deoxynucleosides and deoxynucleotides form the right face of the box. Uridine nucleosides and nucleotides form the front face and cytidine nucleosides and nucleotides form the back face of the box. Thymidine nucleotides parallel the deoxy face of the box. Hereditary orotic aciduria is caused by the functional absence of enzymes 5 and 6 (UMPS); pyrimidine-5′-nucleotidase deficiency by the absence of enzyme 25 (P5N); and dihydropyrimidine dehydrogenase deficiency by the absence of enzyme 22 (DHPDH).

The first activity, CPS, produces carbamyl phosphate from glutamine and CO_2, and two molecules of ATP (Fig. 43-2). This activity is referred to as CPS II to distinguish it from CPS I, the mitochondrial enzyme of liver and kidney which produces carbamyl phosphate from ammonia and CO_2 for utilization in the urea cycle. Because of the presence of the next two activities of the complex, almost all the carbamyl phosphate produced by CPS II is used for pyrimidine synthesis. The activity of CPS is the rate-limiting step in the *de novo* synthesis of UMP except when ATP levels are increased at a time when uridine nucleotides and phosphoribosyl pyrophosphate (PRPP) levels are low. Under these conditions orotic acid (OA) accumulates and OPRT is the rate-limiting reaction.[11] Increased availability of carbamyl phosphate produced by CPS I in various urea cycle deficiencies causes vast increases in the rate of *de novo* pyrimidine synthesis.[26] The next activities are aspartate transcarbamylase, which catalyzes the irreversible formation of carbamylaspartate from carbamyl phosphate and aspartate, and dihydro-orotase, which effects ring closure to form dihydro-orotic acid (Fig. 43-2).

Dihydro-orotate dehydrogenase (DHODH) catalyzes the oxidation of dihydro-orotic acid to OA. This protein is located on the outer surface of the inner membrane of the mitochondrion. The activity of DHODH is lower when assayed in crude tissue preparations than the activity found with isolated mitochondria. The lower activity appears to be due to the rapid conversion of OA to orotidine-5′-monophosphate (OMP) by UMP synthase when OA is measured as the end point of the reaction.[27]

UMP synthase (UMPS, pyr 5,6) is a bifunctional protein containing the activities OPRT and ODC in a single polypeptide of 52,199 daltons. OPRT utilizes PRPP to add the ribose-5′-monophosphate moiety to OA and produce OMP. ODC releases CO_2 from OMP to produce uridine-5′-monophosphate

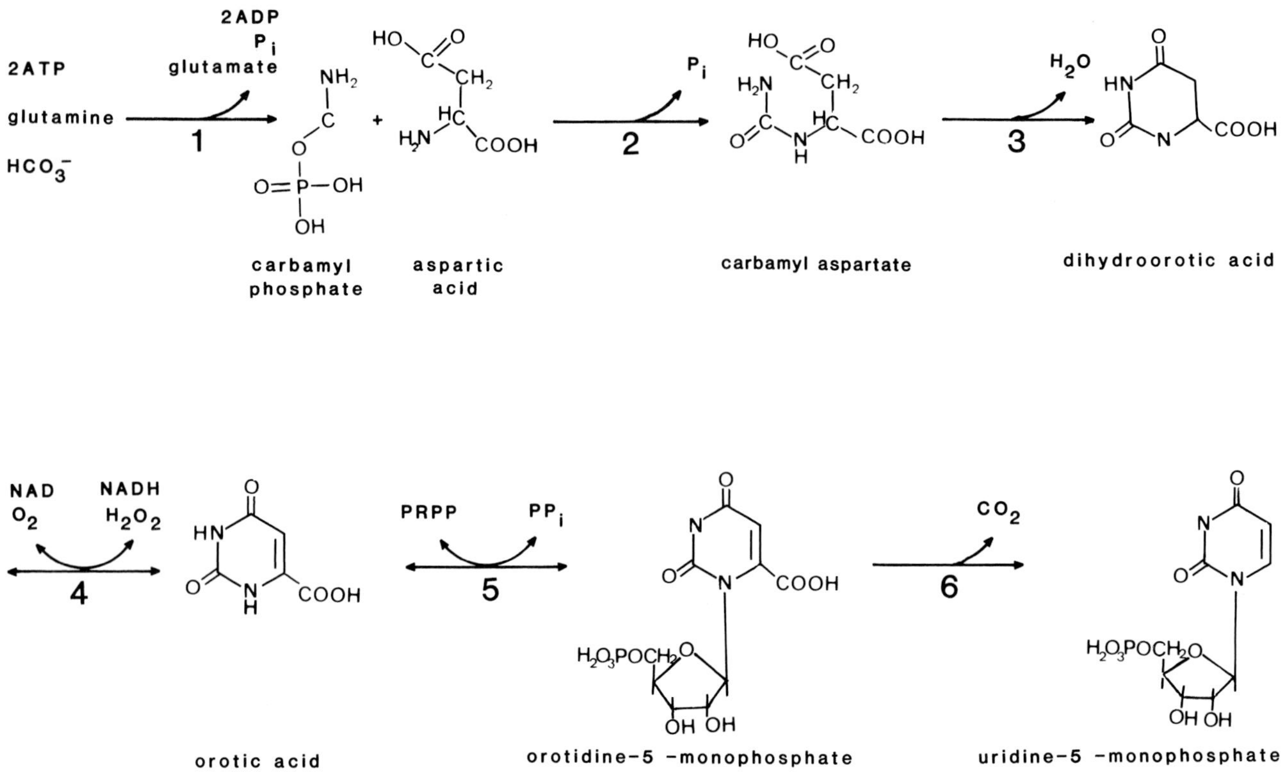

2ATP, glutamine, HCO_3^- —1→ (2ADP, P_i, glutamate) carbamyl phosphate + aspartic acid —2→ (P_i) carbamyl aspartate —3→ (H_2O) dihydroorotic acid

(NAD, O_2) —4→ (NADH, H_2O_2) orotic acid —5→ (PRPP, PP_i) orotidine-5 -monophosphate —6→ (CO_2) uridine-5 -monophosphate

Fig. 43-2 Chemical structure of the intermediates of the *de novo* pyrimidine biosynthetic pathway. Enzyme numbers refer to Table 43-1.

(UMP) (Fig. 43-2). This enzyme will be discussed in detail later in the chapter.

Interconversion

The pyrimidine nucleus in UMP may be converted to all the other required pyrimidine nucleotides, or these may be salvaged from dietary sources or cell turnover (Table 43-1, Fig. 43-1). Pyrimidine mononucleotides are further phosphorylated by pyrimidine monophosphate kinase (enzyme 7) and pyrimidine diphosphate kinase (enzyme 9). Cytidine nucleotides are formed by the action of cytidine triphosphate synthetase (enzyme 12) from uridine triphosphate. Reduction of ribonucleotides to deoxyribonucleotides is by the action of ribonucleoside diphosphate reductase (enzyme 8), which forms dUMP and dCDP. The thymidine nucleotides are formed by thymidylate synthetase (enzyme 10), which produces dTMP from dUMP. 5,10-Methylene-5,6,7,8-tetrahydrofolate is a cofactor for the reaction. dTMP may be further phosphorylated by thymidine monophosphate kinase (enzyme 11). Triphosphate nucleotides form DNA and RNA by the action of the appropriate nucleotidyltransferases (enzymes 13 and 14).

Pyrimidine Salvage

De novo synthesis requires 5 mol ATP for each mole of UMP produced, whereas reutilization of uridine from cell turnover or dietary sources costs only 1 mol ATP per mole of UMP. Studies in rat hepatoma and human breast cancer cells have shown that the rate of *de novo* synthesis is substantially reduced when exogenous uridine is supplied,[28,29] and the mechanism for this control may be an alteration of the amount of OPRT enzyme produced.[28] The amount of salvage in the breast cancer cells was controlled by the size of the uridine nucleotide pool.[29] Although *de novo* pyrimidine synthesis has been estimated (4 to 16 mmol/day[7]) to be approximately equal to the daily purine requirement,[8] it is possible to supply the greater part of the pyrimidine requirement through the salvage pathway, as is done in the treatment of hereditary orotic aciduria. Uptake studies in human leukemic cells have shown that in these cells (most at G_1 or G_0) the salvage pathway was 100 to 300 times more active than the *de novo* pathway; however, it was calculated that up to 70 percent of the pyrimidine requirement could be met from *de novo* synthesis and that about 30 percent of the requirement in normal bone marrow was from this source.[30] The major enzymes of pyrimidine salvage include uridine kinase (enzyme 15), which phosphorylates both uridine and cytidine, deoxycytidine kinase (enzyme 19), and thymidine kinase (enzyme 17).

Degradation

The pyrimidine degradative pathway proceeds in parallel through uridine and thymidine. Cytidine is deaminated to uridine by cytidine deaminase (enzyme 20), and uridine is reduced to uracil by uridine phosphorylase (enzyme 16) (uridine + $P_i \rightarrow$ uracil + ribose-1-phosphate). Although this reaction is reversible in vitro, it appears not to form uridine from uracil in vivo in humans, as evidenced by the unsuccessful use of uracil in the treatment of hereditary orotic aciduria.[31] Recent studies indicate that lymphoblasts are unable to salvage pyrimidine bases. While lymphocytes can synthesize deoxyuridine and thymidine from bases, it is only at high and nonphysiological concentrations, and neither cell can form uridine from uracil.[32] Thymidine phosphorylase is a separate enzyme (enzyme 18) which also catabolizes deoxyuridine nucleotides via dTMP. Following the formation of uracil and thymine, dihydropyrimidine dehydrogenase (DHPDH, enzyme 22) reduces them to dihydrouracil and dihydrothymine, whence dihydropyrimidine hydrase and ureidopropionase (enzymes 23 and 24) convert dihydrouracil to β-ureidopropionic acid and then β-alanine and dihydrothymine to β-ureidoisobutyric acid and then β-aminoisobutyric acid. It has been suggested that a potential degradative pathway exists as a reversal of the steps of *de novo* synthesis, but this is not quantitatively important in humans.[33,34]

ENZYMOLOGY OF UMP SYNTHASE

Purification and Characterization

The early attempts to isolate either OPRT or ODC from mammalian sources resulted in the coordinated purification of both activities.[35–41] It was therefore postulated that the two activities form a complex. In all of these studies OPRT was the more labile, and its activity was often lost in later stages of purification while the ODC activity remained. There were at least two reports that the two activities could be separated. Kasbekar and colleagues reported separation of the activities by starch gel electrophoresis.[37] Brown and O'Sullivan reported the separation of a 62,000-dalton complex into two 20,000-dalton subunits with ODC activity and two 13,000-dalton subunits with OPRT activity following treatment of the complex with guanidine hydrochloride.[42] Formation of higher molecular weight complexes was associated with increased thermal stability and was induced by orotic acid and competitive inhibitors. An early observation that the activity of ODC in fibroblasts was an exponential function of the amount of protein suggested that there may be an equilibrium between subunits and enzyme aggregate.[43]

The association of the two activities throughout all the purification procedures and the coordinate increase in both activities in the presence of competitive inhibitors caused speculation that the complex was a multifunctional protein that contained two domain centers.[11] Evidence to confirm the bifunctional nature came from: (1) the purification of a single peptide that retained both activities; (2) the characterization of cells resistant to inhibitors of ODC that had coordinately increased levels of OPRT and overproduction of a single protein; and (3) the isolation, sequencing and expression of a single cDNA that contains sequences for both OPRT and ODC domains.

The UMPS protein was first purified to apparent homogeneity from mouse Ehrlich ascites cells.[44] The purification steps included streptomycin sulfate treatment, ammonium sulfate precipitation, and affinity chromatography through 5-{2-{*N*-(2-aminoethyl)carbamyl}ethyl} - 6 - azauridine - 5′ - monophosphate (AECE-6AZUMP) coupled to agarose and phosphocellulose. The AECE-6AZUMP was synthesized by the procedure of Brody and Westheimer,[45] who had used the compound coupled to carboxymethyl-agarose to purify the ODC enzyme from yeast.

The protein recovered from the columns gave a single band in polyacrylamide gel electrophoresis with a molecular weight of about 51,500. The protein contained both OPRT and ODC activities. The ratio of ODC to OPRT was increased about five-fold in the purified preparation due to loss of OPRT activity. The more stable ODC activity was purified 2300-fold by this procedure. The activities cosedimented in sucrose density gradients at 3.7 S. Two-dimensional electrophoresis revealed two bands with isoelectric points of 5.85 and 5.65. Assays of the protein in the isoelectrofocusing gel showed that each band contained both activities. The pI of the protein is 7.17. As yet the physiological significance of the isoenzyme forms has not been determined.

More recently the UMPS protein has been similarly purified from human placenta.[46] Following two affinity chromatography steps (Dye Matrix green A and phosphocellulose), the enzyme is more than 99 percent pure. The human enzyme has a similar molecular weight and isoenzyme pattern to the murine enzyme.

Substantiating evidence that the two activities, OPRT and ODC, reside within a single polypeptide chain came from enzyme studies in pyrazofurin (PF, 3,β-D-ribofuranosyl-4-hydroxypyrazole-5-carboxamide) and 6-azauridine (6AZUR)–resistant cells that had coordinate increases in both OPRT and ODC activities.[47–49] PF (a C-nucleoside antibiotic) and 6AZUR are metabolized to monophosphates by adenosine kinase[50,51] and uridine kinase,[52] respectively. The monophosphates are specific inhibitors of ODC. In PF-resistant rat hepatoma cells the activities of both OPRT and ODC were coordinately increased fortyfold over wild type levels.[53] Similar increases in the two activities were seen in 6AZUR-resistant mouse lymphoma cell lines.[48] In the rat hepatoma cell lines grown in the absence of PF, there was a gradual loss of both activities until their levels were only three- to fourfold above wild type cells. Analysis of cell extracts by sodium dodecyl sulfate polyacrylamide gel electrophoresis (SDS-PAGE) revealed only a single band of approximately 55,000 daltons that was increased in the PF-resistant cells and subsequently decreased in the revertant cells.[53] Two-dimensional gel electrophoresis of extracts from sensitive and resistant cells showed overproduction of two spots in the resistant cells with the same molecular weight of 55,000, but different isoelectric points.[54] These two overproduced proteins correspond to the two isoenzyme forms found in the mouse ascites enzyme.[44] Antibodies prepared against the affinity-purified mouse ascites UMPS protein were used in Western blot analysis to conclusively demonstrate that this band is UMPS. The overproduction of the UMPS protein is the result of an amplification of the UMPS gene.[55]

Conformation

In studies of mouse Ehrlich ascites cells, it has been demonstrated that UMPS protein exists in three different species or conformations as determined by sucrose density gradient sedimentation and gel filtration chromatography.[56,57] Conformation states with $s_{20,w}$ values of 3.6 S, 5.1 S, and 5.6 S are found depending on the effector molecules in the environment. Since distinct peaks can be distinguished on sucrose gradients, the different forms of the protein are not in rapid equilibrium. The monomer form of the protein has an $S_{20,w}$ value of 3.6 S. In the presence of substrates, products, or their analogues, a 5.1-S dimer is formed. A third species of 5.6 S is formed in the presence of nucleotide monophosphates or their analogues, OMP being the most efficient. The formation of the dimer appears to be the result of binding of the ligand molecule to the ODC catalytic site.[56] The stronger this binding, the lower the amount required to convert the monomer to the dimer form. In the presence of dithiothreitol and the absence of either substrates or products, the larger conformations are converted back to the 3.6-S monomer. The predicted interactions of the monomer units of UMPS are illustrated diagramatically in Fig. 43-3.

Kinetic studies of UMPS have shown that ODC activity is predominantly associated with the 5.6-S dimer.[58] The OPRT activity is found in all three forms of the protein. The 5.1- and 5.6-S dimers are probably conformationally different. The data could be explained by the presence of a regulatory site separate from the two catalytic sites. The function of the monomer-dimer system could be to control enzyme activity or to enhance stability of the protein. Regulation of the monomer-dimer transitions may therefore be physiologically significant.

Domain Structure

The tertiary structure of multifunctional proteins is now generally accepted to consist of autonomous globular domains connected by peptide bridges.[59] The globular structural domains are relatively protease-resistant compared to the polypeptide linker that is often protease-sensitive. With limited proteolytic digestion it is often possible to separate the structural domains of the multifunctional protein and study individual catalytic steps.

Limited proteolysis of UMPS with elastase or trypsin produces fragments that maintain catalytic activity.[39,60] In one study, such digestion resulted in only a slight decrease in ODC activity, but OPRT activity was no longer detectable. Analysis of the digest on SDS-PAGE showed only a single band of 28,500 daltons. This size is similar to the yeast ODC protein that has an apparent molecular weight of 27,500.[61] The ODC domain was isolated from digest using immobilized trypsin,[60] and found to be much less stable than the ODC activity of the undigested UMPS protein. This may reflect an inherent stability in the conformation of UMPS as a bifunctional protein. This increased instability in the isolated domains has also been observed in the multifunctional CAD protein.[23] These studies indicate that while the isolated domains have the functional and structural nature of the intact multifunctional protein, interdomain interactions stabilize the tertiary structure.

The domain structure of the UMPS protein was also demonstrated by the expression of a murine UMPS cDNA in ODC-deficient bacteria.[62] The cDNA was selected from a murine cDNA library prepared in λgt10 by hybridization with a rat UMPS probe. A fragment of 1600 bp was inserted into an expression vector (pUC12) and used to transform strains of bacteria that were deficient in ODC activity. Bacterial colonies that grew in the absence of uracil were shown to express the murine ODC domain by immunotitration assays and by immunoblot analysis. The expressed ODC protein had a molecular weight of 26,000 to 27,300.

In further studies, the cDNA encoding the ODC domain was inserted into a yeast expression vector and used to transform ODC-deficient yeast.[63] Selected yeast transformants expressed the ODC domain and had a high specific activity for ODC. Compared to intact UMPS or the ODC domain isolated by proteolytic digestion, the ODC domain expressed in yeast has a lower affinity for the substrate OMP and the inhibitor 6AZUMP. The expressed ODC domain was able to form dimers in the presence of ligands which bind at the catalytic site as measured by sucrose gradient analysis. This indicates that the ODC domains contain a dimerization surface. There was no evidence for the formation of an altered dimer comparable to the 5.6-S species associated with intact UMPS. Thus the expressed ODC domain does not appear to contain the regulatory site predicted from the studies of purified UMPS protein.[63]

Fig. 43-3 Schematic representation of the three conformational states of UMP synthase. The dimerization and conformational alteration of the UMP synthase monomer unit. Each monomer is composed of an OPRT and an ODC domain joined by a linker peptide. 1 = OPRT catalytic site; 2 = ODC catalytic site; 3 = pyrimidine nucleotide–binding regulatory site. E_f^- = anionic effector molecules other than OMP; PyrMP = pyrimidine ribonucleoside monophosphates. *(From E.E. Floyd and M.E. Jones,[60] Biol Chem 260:9443, 1985, Figure 9.)*

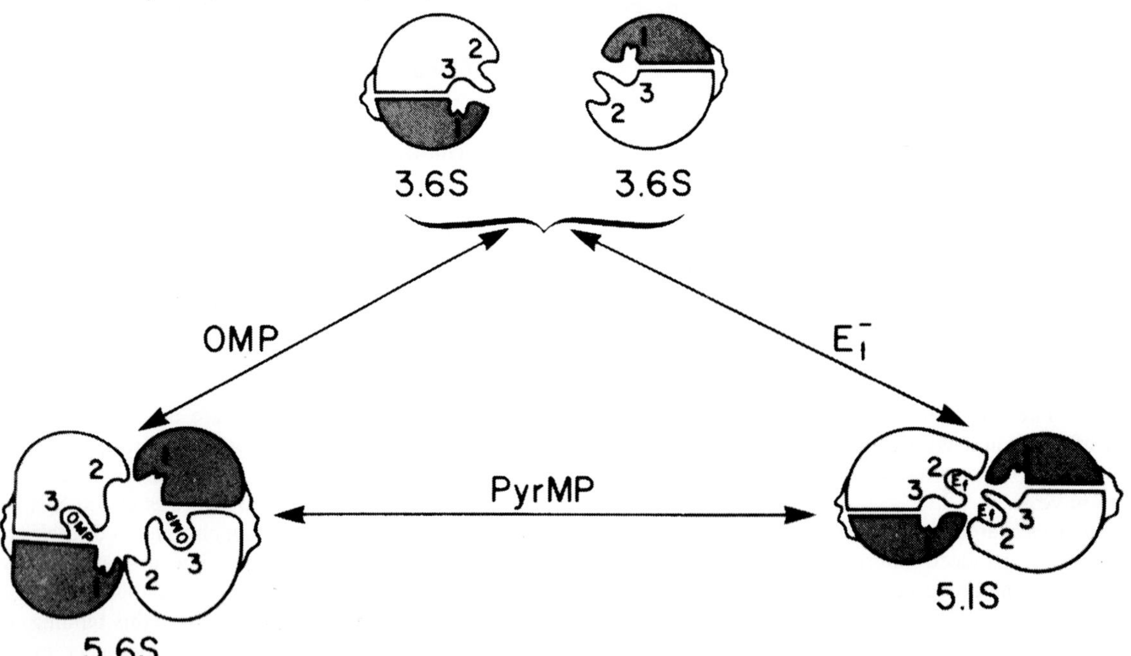

OPRT Reaction Mechanism

Studies of yeast OPRT have demonstrated that the involvement of metal ions in the reaction may be at more than one site.[64,65] It has also been postulated that the reaction may proceed through a BiBi ping pong kinetic mechanism. The first half of the reaction may be formation of an active ribosylphosphate-enzyme intermediate from PRPP with release of pyrophosphate from the α_1' position. The second half would involve formation of a β_1'-glycosidic bond between orotate and the ribose-phosphate moiety on the enzyme to form OMP. The reaction mechanism must be more complex than double displacement, because stereochemical inversion occurs.[66]

Channeling of OMP

In the metabolism of OA to UMP the possibility exists that the intermediate product, OMP, would be "channeled" from the OPRT catalytic site to the ODC site. Channeling would mean that no OMP would diffuse away from UMPS to form a free pool of OMP.[67] To determine if channeling was occurring, Traut and Jones[68] measured the amount of UMP formed from OA in the presence of exogenous OMP. Although strict channeling of OMP was found not to occur at high concentrations of exogenous OMP, the results were interpreted as showing partial channeling at all concentrations of OMP studied. One purpose of the channeling could be to protect the OMP from degradation by nucleotidases.[69] The presence of OMP channeling by UMPS has been disputed by McClard and Shokat,[70] who used a computer modeling analysis of the Traut and Jones data to show that the experimentally observed amounts of UMP produced from exogenous OMP were as predicted. The question of channeling of OMP in UMPS is presently unresolved.

MOLECULAR BIOLOGY OF UMP SYNTHASE

cDNA Selection

The first isolation of a UMPS cDNA was from rat hepatoma cells (3924A) selected in multiple steps for resistance to PF.[53,55] These cells had levels of UMPS activity approximately fortyfold that of sensitive cells. Comparison of cell extracts on SDS-PAGE showed overproduction of a protein of approximately 55,200 daltons which was confirmed as UMPS using antibody prepared to the mouse Ehrlich ascites UMPS. In vitro translation of mRNA from the PF-resistant cells showed that the UMPS mRNA was present at increased levels. It was then determined that the UMPS gene is amplified approximately fourteen-fold in the PF-resistant cells.[55]

The increased level of UMPS mRNA in the PF-resistant rat cells provided a significant advantage in the selection of a cDNA clone for UMPS.[55] Poly(A)+ mRNA from these cells was further enriched for UMPS mRNA by size fractionation on sucrose density gradients. The partially purified mRNA fraction was used to produce a cDNA library that was inserted into the plasmid vector pBR322 using the G-C tailing technique. Recombinant plasmids with inserts complementary to UMPS sequences were selected by differential hybridization to single-stranded cDNA prepared from wild type and resistant cell poly(A)+ mRNA. Recombinants that demonstrated increased hybridization to the PF-resistant cell cDNA were then tested further for hybrid selection of UMPS mRNA.[55]

cDNA probes for the human UMPS mRNA were selected from a λgt10 library generated with mRNA from a T-cell leukemic cell line, HPB-ALL.[71] The human UMP synthase-specific clone was selected by cross-hybridization with the rat sequence described above.[72] A fragment of this rat UMPS probe was also used to select a murine cDNA encompassing the ODC domain of UMPS from Erhlich ascites cells.[62]

Analysis of mRNA and Gene Structure

The size of the mRNA for human UMPS was determined by Northern blot analysis of mRNA from HeLa cells and a PF-resistant HeLa line to be approximately 2.0 kb.[72] The UMPS mRNA in the PF-resistant rat hepatoma cell line was estimated to be about 1.8 kb.[53] The minimum size of the human UMPS gene containing the coding region can be estimated to be a minimum of 15 kb, based on the size of genomic fragments that contain sequences for the 5′ and 3′ ends of the coding region of the mRNA.[54]

Sequence of Complete Coding Region. The complete coding region of the human UMPS mRNA has been determined by sequencing of cDNAs and a 5′-genomic fragment containing the ATG initiation codon.[73] The UMPS protein is composed of 480 amino acids with a molecular weight of 52,199. The bifunctional nature of the UMPS protein is clearly demonstrated by comparison of its amino acid sequence with that of the monofunctional proteins (OPRT) from *E. coli*,[74] ODC from yeast,[61] and the murine ODC domain.[62] Between the murine ODC domain and the yeast ODC sequence 52 percent of the amino acid residues are identical. If amino acids that have similar hydration potential are considered equivalent, these sequences are 75 perccent homologous.[62] The amino acid sequence of the murine ODC domain is 90 percent identical with the carboxy-terminal 259 amino acids of the human UMPS protein.[73] Within this region there are only 26 nonidentical amino acids and 7 of these are neutral substitutions (i.e., changes between Ala or Gly and Ile, Leu, or Val).

Homology of the OPRT Domain with *E. Coli*. Alignment of the *E. coli* monofunctional OPRT with the amino-terminal 214 amino acids of the UMPS protein gives several regions of strong homology. In the region between residues 96 and 155, the two sequences are 43 percent identical, and if amino acids of similar hydration potential are considered equivalent, this region is 73 percent homologous.[73] This region of the OPRT domain includes a stretch of amino acids that is highly conserved in a set of mammalian and prokaryotic enzymes that have the phosphoribosyltransferase function in common (Fig. 43-4).[73,75–77] This sequence has been predicted to be part of a phosphoribosyltransferase catalytic site.[78] Thus, it appears that the UMPS enzyme in mammals is the result of a fusion process that occurred between the separate genes for OPRT and ODC that are present in the lower eukaryotes and prokaryotes.

```
OPRT  116  G E T C L I I E D V V T S G S S V L E T
HPRT  126  G K N V L I V E D I I D T G K T M Q T L
APRT  120  G Q R V V V V D D L L A T G G T M N A A
```

Fig. 43-4 Amino acid sequence comparison of human phosphoribosyltransferase enzymes. The putative catalytic site is aligned for three human phosphoribosyltransferase (PRT) enzymes: orotate PRT, hypoxanthine PRT, and adenine PRT. Positions of identical or neutral amino acid substitutions are boxed. The numbers indicate the position of the glycine residue in the respective protein sequence. *(From D.P. Suttle, B.Y. Bugg, J.K. Winkler and J.J. Kanalas,[73] Proc. Natl. Acad. Sci. USA 85:1754, 1988.)*

Expression of Recombinant cDNA Vector in Urd$^-$C Cells. The most convincing proof that a DNA sequence encodes a specific protein is by expression of the sequence and production of the protein. The complete coding region for UMP synthase, including a 450-base pair stretch of nontranslated 3′ region, was inserted into a mammalian shuttle vector and transfected into Urd$^-$C cells.[79] Urd$^-$C cells were selected for resistance to 5-fluorouracil (5FU) and are deficient in both OPRT and ODC, requiring uridine in the medium for growth.[80] Isolated colonies of transfected cells were selected for their ability to grow in the absence of uridine. Enzyme assays of the selected cells show ODC activity to be two- to fourfold higher than that found in the V79 cell line of Chinese hamster lung cells.[79] This experiment gave definitive evidence that the cDNA sequence is sufficient to code for both OPRT and ODC activity.

Chromosome Location of UMPS Gene

The chromosomal location of the UMPS gene was initially determined through the use of somatic cell hybrids between human lymphocytes and the mutant Urd$^-$C Chinese hamster cells.[80–81] Hybrid cells were isolated that did not require uridine for growth and were sensitive to 5FU. These cells were analyzed cytogenetically for chromosome 3 and for concordance between the human ODC activity and chromosome-specific markers (ACY-1, β-galactosidase, D3S1, and transferrin receptor). Very high concordance was demonstrated between the presence of the long arm of chromosome 3, transferrin receptor, human ODC activity, and uridine independent growth, providing strong evidence for the location of the UMPS gene on the long arm of chromosome 3.[81] The location of the gene was later narrowed to 3cen-3q21 by analysis of deletion mutants in hamster-human hybrids containing chromosome 3 as the only human chromosome.

In order to sublocalize the UMPS gene on the long arm of chromosome 3, *in situ* hybridization of the human UMPS cDNA probe to human metaphase spreads of lymphocytes was carried out.[82] Analysis of the spreads showed 20 percent of the silver grains to be localized in the region 3q13. By this procedure the UMPS gene is positioned between the transferrin receptor and the D3S1 DNA sequence. No other region of significant hybridization was detected, indicating only one locus for the UMPS gene sequence.

PYRIMIDINE METABOLISM

Transport. OA is not transported into nucleated cells, but there is a high capacity, nonsaturable transport system for OA into erythrocytes, with the rate-limiting step being the conversion of OA to UMP.[83] If nucleated cells (fibroblasts, lymphoblasts) are incubated with erythrocytes, the erythrocytes take up OA and excrete uridine into the medium, where it is utilized by the nucleated cells.[83]

Uridine enters animal cells by means of a carrier-mediated nucleoside transport process[84–86] which is concentrative.[87,88] Uridine transport in murine splenocytes involves cotransport.[88] It has been difficult to measure rates of transport separate from the rate of uridine utilization, but modern techniques[86] indicate that the kinetic parameters for transport are about 100 times that for phosphorylation, while the first-order rate constants are about the same. This means that in rat hepatoma cells at physiological (less than 10 μM) concentrations of uridine, uridine is phosphorylated inside the cell at about 70 percent of its rate of entry into the cell, so neither phosphorylation nor transport is rate-limiting and the cells effectively deplete the medium of substrate. At higher concentrations, phosphorylation becomes rate-limiting and intracellular uridine concentrations approach those in the medium. Also at higher concentrations (10 to 30 μM) the rate of uptake decreases with time, possibly due to some feedback inhibition or depletion of substrate.[86] Uracil, 5FU, and thymine are transported into rat intestine by an active process that requires Na^+.[89]

Utilization. Levels of pyrimidine nucleotides in cultured and blood cells have been measured by high performance liquid chromatography (HPLC).[90–93] The UTP level is 100 to 300 pmol per 10^6 cells, 10 to 20 percent of the level of ATP. Exogenous uridine is rapidly incorporated into nucleotides in nucleated cells but not in erythrocytes, and the increased uracil nucleotide pool size may be associated with a reduction in *de novo* synthesis.[28,29]

Differential incorporation of labeled OA and uridine into UMP in rat hepatoma cells has indicated that there may be two or three separate UTP pools, one formed from *de novo* synthesis that is used for RNA incorporation and uridine sugar nucleotide production and one from pyrimidine salvage, which is the primary source of cytidine nucleotides. The two pools are interconnected.[94] Compartmentation of UTP pools but not of the CTP pool has also been demonstrated in rat hepatocytes. Expansion of the UTP and CTP pools did not alter the amount of OA incorporation into RNA.[95] Double-label studies of perfused rat liver slices and measurement of OA, uracil, uridine, and UMP have also indicated marked compartmentalization of uridine, uracil, and UMP.[96]

It has been suggested that PRPP availability may coordinate purine and pyrimidine metabolic activity, since it is an important intermediate in both systems.[33] Pyrimidine nucleotides are increased in cells from patients with Lesch-Nyhan syndrome, and PRPP is elevated in these cells.[97] Reduction in pyrimidine synthesis in erythrocytes by adenosine may be mediated by PRPP since adenosine does not inhibit OPRT or ODC, but these experiments were at high adenosine concentrations.[98]

Pharmacologic Inhibition of UMPS

The usual pharmacologic effect of inhibitors of UMPS is to increase the urinary excretion of OA and orotidine. Paradoxically, there is often a concomitant increase in the measured level of OPRT and ODC activity in blood cells. A similar increase is also seen in human fibroblasts grown in the presence of various drugs or enzyme inhibitors, including allopurinol and oxipurinol, 5-azaorotic acid (5AZOA), 6AZUR, and barbituric acid (BA).[99–101]

Allopurinol. Allopurinol and its metabolite oxipurinol cause orotic aciduria and orotidinuria while increasing OPRT and ODC activity in patients. In vitro these compounds (or their metabolites) inhibit OPRT and/or ODC. Early reports indicated allopurinol caused substantial increases in levels of urinary OA and orotidine in gouty patients and control subjects.[102–104] Normal subjects receiving 200 to 300 mg allopurinol per day showed an increase in urinary orotidine from <3 mg/day to 24 to 55 mg/day and in OA from <2 mg/day to 6 to 30 mg/day.[104] Allopurinol (800 mg/day) and oxipurinol (800 mg/day) reduced expired [^{14}C]CO_2 from [7-^{14}C]-OA and increased urinary metabolite excretion. It was suggested that the inhibitory compound may be oxipurinol-1-ribotide or oxipurinol-7-ribotide.[105]

Allopurinol-induced orotic aciduria can be reduced by dietary pyrimidines, RNA, or RNA hydrolysates, and by dietary purines.[106] Pigs given allopurinol showed increased urinary levels of orodidine and OA, but these declined with time even though the allopurinol dose was kept constant.[107]

Allopurinol also causes increased levels of erythrocyte OPRT and ODC activity, with exposure times varying from a few days to 2 weeks.[102,103, 108–110] The increase of ODC activity with allopurinol was not associated with a reduction of ODC inhibition in vivo in either nucleated cells or erythrocytes. Data are consistent with enzyme activation, stabilization of the enzyme in the extraction procedure,[108,109] or to stabilization of enzymes in the aging erythrocyte.[103] It was suggested that there may be "pseudosubstrate" stabilization of UMPS by oxipurinol ribonucleotide, synthesized by OPRT.

A concentration-dependent increase in OPRT and ODC in fibroblasts and lymphoblasts incubated with oxipurinol occurred within 2 to 3 h, implying enzyme stabilization during extraction from the cells or direct activation of enzyme rather than inhibition of normal enzyme catabolism. Oxipurinol incubated with lymphoblasts caused inhibition of OA incorporation within 90 min, and OPRT and ODC activity increased within this time.[111] This is consistent with oxipurinol ribonucleotide alteration of quaternary structure and increased stability and activity of the enzyme complex.

Rat liver studies suggested allopurinol is converted to an inhibitor which promotes formation of a higher molecular weight, more stable form of UMPS.[112] In 1975 Grobner and colleagues showed that allopurinol ribonucleotide and oxipurinol-7-ribonucleotide cause alterations in the molecular weight form of UMPS, so that the most stable forms predominate. Thus, the apparent increase in enzyme activity is related to the stabilization of an enzyme complex during lysis and extraction.[113]

Allopurinol ribonucleotide inhibits ODC in dialyzed erythrocyte lysate.[104] A compound which inhibits ODC is produced when erythrocytes from normal, OPRT-deficient, and HPRT-deficient individuals are incubated with oxipurinol. This required PRPP, and implied the inhibitory compound was oxipurinol-1-ribotide or oxipurinol-7-ribotide.[105] OA excretion is also increased in xanthinuric patients, who do not form oxipurinol, implying allopurinol-1-ribotide also inhibits ODC in vivo, although not as effectively as the oxipurinol nucleotides.[114] High levels of oxipurinol-7-ribotide have been found in renal failure, and this has been correlated with high levels of plasma, urine, and erythrocyte orotidine.[115]

Allopurinol reduces PRPP in fibroblasts and OA utilization in normal and HPRT-deficient fibroblasts. Oxipurinol does not alter PRPP, but reduces OA incorporation into acid-precipitable material. Neither compound altered uridine incorporation.[116,117] Oxipurinol increased ODC in fibroblasts, including OPRT-deficient cells.[101]

6-Azauridine. 6AZUR is converted to 6-azauridine-5′-monophosphate (6AZUMP) by uridine kinase.[52] In its monophosphate form, 6AZUR is a competitive inhibitor of the ODC activity of UMPS. Inhibition of UMPS by 6AZUR has been demonstrated in tumor slices, cell-free preparations, yeast, and leukocytes.[118–120] The inhibition is reversible and pH-dependent.[120]

Intravenous 6AZUMP given to chronic myelogenous leukemia patients (180 to 240 mg/(kg/day) produced 8 to 19 mmol OA per day and 5 to 9 mmol orotidine per day. Three patients had [6-^{14}C]OA infused and its incorporation into pseudouridine determined. *De novo* pyrimidine production was 4 to 16 mmol/day. Patients given [7-^{14}C]OA and 6AZUR excreted 50 to 66 percent of label as OA, 3 to 13 percent as orotidine, 1 to 7 percent as other urine compounds, and 14 to 26 percent as expired CO_2. They showed a sevenfold increase in *de novo* pyrimidine production with 6AZUR, but a decrease in UMP production estimated by respiratory expired isotopic CO_2.[7] In other similar studies increased orotic aciduria and enzyme inhibition in leukocytes were observed.[120,121] Clinical response to 6AZUR was correlated with inhibition of UMPS in intact leukocytes, but no effect on UMPS could be shown in cell-free systems. Development of drug resistance was correlated with lack of enzyme inhibition in intact leukocytes. Urinary excretion of OA and orotidine did not correlate with enzyme inhibition or antileukemic effects.[122,123]

Mouse tumor response to 6AZUR did correlate with in vitro inhibition of OA decarboxylation by tissue slices, but after initial suppression of OA metabolism, enzyme activity returned to pretreatment levels despite continued 6AZUR.[124] Response to 6AZUR did not correlate with inhibition of UMPS in other mouse tumors.[125] Mouse salivary glands stimulated with isoproterenol have increased incorporation of OA into RNA and thymidine into DNA, both of which are inhibited by 6AZUR, but uridine incorporation into RNA was not inhibited.[126] 6AZUR reduced OA incorporation into RNA in cat brain.[127]

Stabilization of UMPS Protein. Human fibroblasts grown in $10^{-5}M$ 6AZUR had increased specific activities of ODC and OPRT.[99,128] The increase in enzyme activity occurred also when cytidine was present in the cultures. Pinsky and Krooth[99] found that direct addition of 6AZUMP to human fibroblast extracts inhibited the activity of ODC, but inhibition could be overcome by excess OMP. The activity obtained with addition of excess substrate was no higher than in extracts assayed without addition of the drug. Mixtures of extracts from cells grown with or without 6AZUR had an average value for the enzyme, and dialysis of extracts grown in the presence or absence of 6AZUR did not alter the enzyme specific activity. These results were interpreted as indicating the increased ODC activity was due to increased enzyme in the cell.

The same workers also showed that 5AZOA (which inhibits OPRT but not ODC) in the culture medium increased both activities in fibroblast extracts. The concentrations of 5AZOA used did not inhibit cell growth. BA also had no effect on growth but augmented enzyme activity levels. They suggested that dihydro-orotic acid may be the active precursor that stimulates OPRT and ODC activities.[100]

Barbituric Acid. Barbituric acid (BA) competitively inhibits dihydro-orotate dehydrogenase (DHODH) and OPRT (directly or indirectly), and has been shown to increase OPRT and ODC in human fibroblasts. It was suggested that the molecule active in augmenting enzyme activity may be dihydro-orotic acid.[100] The ribonucleotide of BA, 6-hydroxyuridine-5′-monophosphate, inhibits uridine monophosphate kinase and is a powerful competitive inhibitor of ODC. BA is a competitive inhibitor itself of ODC if PRPP is present.[129]

Niedzwicki[130] evaluated 80 pyrimidine base analogues as inhibitors of OPRT and found 4,6-dihydroxypyrimidine to be a potent inhibitor of the enzyme activity. 5-Azauridine, 5-aza-orotic acid, and BA inhibited ODC significantly only after preincubation with PRPP and $MgCl_2$ in the presence of cytosol.

5-Fluorouracil. 5FU can be metabolized to 5FUMP by the action of OPRT in the presence of PRPP.[39,131,132] OPRT will utilize 5FU or orotate as a substrate with similar efficiency.[39] The conversion of 5FUMP to 5FdUMP or 5FUTP is required for cytotoxicity. 5FdUMP acts as an inhibitor of thymidylate synthase, which is required for the production of dTMP *de novo*. 5FUTP can be incorporated into RNA.

Cells in culture can be selected for resistance to the cytotoxic action of 5FU.[48,80,128,133] The 5FU-resistant cells are deficient in OPRT and ODC activity. The level of activity of the remaining enzyme in the resistant cells varies from undetectable[80] to up to 50 percent.[133] The level of 5FU resistance should correlate inversely with the amount of OPRT activity in the cells.

Purines. Adenosine toxicity to cultured mammalian cells has been associated with increased purine nucleotide pools and decreased pyrimidine nucleotide pools. The toxic effects are reversible by the addition of uridine to the culture medium and are thought to be mediated by PRPP concentration changes.[51,134,135] Altered PRPP concentration was correlated with inhibition of UMPS by adenosine in fibroblasts and erythrocytes.[98] Recent work suggests that the effect of adenosine at low concentrations (less than 10 μM in lymphoid cells) is depletion of PRPP, UTP and CTP, and a G_1-S transition block, while higher concentrations neither inhibit cell growth nor alter nucleotide levels.[136,137]

HEREDITARY OROTIC ACIDURIA—UMP SYNTHASE DEFICIENCY

There are several inherited diseases in which excessive amounts of orotic acid may be excreted in the urine, but the term *hereditary orotic aciduria* was first applied to a case of UMPS deficiency[138] and is best restricted to that deficiency. Homozygous UMPS deficiency is rare in human beings, and we know of only 13 cases for review, of which 12 have been established by direct measurement. These cases are summarized in Table 43-2. Huguley and colleagues reported the first case in 1959, J.P., a child who died at age 2 years 9 months, before enzyme assays were performed.[139] The authors' prediction of the nature of the metabolic defect was later confirmed by the demonstration of partial deficiencies of OPRT and ODC in the child's parents and other presumed family heterozygotes.[123,138,140] By 1973 six further cases with confirmed enzyme deficiency had been reported: D.G., J.P., T.H., D.B., K.P., and P.M., summarized as cases 2 to 7 in Table 43-2.[31,108,141–148] We have excluded from our series the last two cases in Table 56-1 of the fifth edition of this text[33,149,150] because the enzyme deficiencies were not confirmed. We agree with the comments in the previous edition of this text and by the author of one of the reports[151] that they appear to represent different disorders. We know of only four cases with confirmed enzyme deficiency reported since 1973: Y.S., R.S., XX, and D.M.[152–155] Our inquiries to individuals or organizations likely to know of additional cases produced information on two other enzymatically confirmed but unpublished cases born in the 1980s, H.B. and Y.F.[156,157] From our review of the information available on each of the 13 cases, we conclude that a majority of homozygotes for UMPS deficiency will have a uniform clinical presentation in which the major features will be megaloblastic anemia and OA crystalluria frequently associated with some degree of physical and intellectual retardation. These features will respond to appropriate pyrimidine replacement therapy, and uncomplicated cases have a good prognosis in the short term.

There is a notable lack of published follow-up information on those patients who initially did well. For this reason and as a basis for discussion of the clinical manifestations in all 13 cases, we will first summarize the history of D.G. This patient is the longest-known survivor, the first to be treated with uridine and the subject of a number of reports of clinical and laboratory studies over the years.[31,73,79,101,128,142,143,148,158–162] We also directed inquiries to the authors of the previous reports on six patients likely to be surviving to age 15 years or more, and we received information on P.M., D.M., T.H., and J.P.[163–166] This information confirmed our impression of a good long-term prognosis for the "typical" case. However, a minority of cases have additional features, particularly congenital malformations and immune deficiencies, which may adversely affect this prognosis. These variations occur with sufficient frequency to suggest that they are not coincidental but are the result of a poorly understood heterogeneity in the UMPS gene or its expression.

Case Report

D.G., male, mother Maori/part white, father white, was born in October 1961.[142] His birth weight was 4.15 kg. He grew normally until about 3 months of age, when he became pale and lethargic and his motor development slowed. At 13 months he was admitted to hospital with bronchopneumonia which responded promptly to antibiotics. During this admission he was found to be severely anemic (hemoglobin 46 g/liter) and leukopenic. His bone marrow showed megaloblastosis, and he had a low serum iron level. Treatment with iron, folic acid, cobalamin, pyridoxine, and thyroxine caused a slight rise in the hemoglobin level, but the marrow remained megaloblastic. At 17 months he was assessed at a children's hospital when his weight (9.5 kg) was below the 3d percentile. He was pale, had expressionless facies, and an alternating convergent strabismus. His hair was sparse, short, and fine and his nails had not grown during previous months. He showed little interest in his surroundings, could not sit up, but was able to maintain a sitting position. He did not say words. Psychometric assessment indicated abilities in the 7- to 11-month

Table 43-2 **Cases of Hereditary Orotic Aciduria–UMPS Deficiency**

*Name**	*Sex*	*Age at presentation*	*Presenting features*	*MA*	*CR*	*OU*	*GD*	*DD*	*MAL*	*SQ*	*CM*	*MI*	*ID*	*Age at treatment*	*Age at last report*	*Status*	*Refs.*
1 J.R.	M	3 m	Pallor, diarrhea	+	+	−	−	+	+		−	+		18 m	21 m	Dead	138 to 140
2 D.G.	M	3 m	Pale, retarded development	+	+	−	+	+		+	−	+	−	19 m	26 y	Well	31, 142, 143, 160
3 J.P.	M	10 m	Weakness, anemia, poor development	+	+	+	−	+		+	?	−		20 m	25 y	Well	144, 166
4 T.H.	F	2 m	Anemia strabismus	+	+	−	+	−		+	+	−		11 m	21 y	Well	145, 165
5 D.B.	F	7 y	Fatigue, hematuria, back & flank pain	+	+	+	−	−			?	−		7 y	8 y	Well	148
6 K.P.	M	1 d	Multiple malformations	+	+	+		+			+	+		4 m	6 m	Dead	146, 147
7 P.M.	M	6 m	Failure to thrive, anemia	+	+	−	+	+				−		6 m	19 y	Well	146, 147, 163
8 D.M.	M	6 m	Cough, anemia, failure to thrive	+	+	+	+	+				−		2 y	15 y	Well	155, 164
9 Y.S.	M	7 y	Diarrhea, hematuria, stomatitis, anemia	+	+	−	+	−	+			+	+	7 y	8 y	Dead	152, 153, 175
10 R.S.	F	3 m	Sib of Y.S.; pallor, transient diarrhea	+		−	−	−				−	+	3 m	7 y	Well	152, 153, 175, 176
11 XX	F		Anemia, failure to thrive	+		−	+	+		+					9 y		154
12 H.B.	F	4 d	Congenital heart disease	+	+	−	−	+			+	−	+	18 m	3 y	Well	156
13 Y.F.	F	1 m	Congenital heart disease, anemia, failure to thrive	+	+	−	+				+	−	+	3 m	15 m	Well	157

*Number shown indicates the case number.
Abnormalities abbreviations:
MA = megaloblastic anemia; MAL = malabsorbtion
CR = crystalluria; SQ = squint
OU = obstruct uropathy; CM = cardiac malformation (? = heart murmur was present which may have been hemic)
GD = growth deficiency; MI = major infections
DD = developmental delay; ID = immune dysfunction (refers to the results of lab studies)
NOTE: + = a feature is documented as present
− = a feature is documented as absent
XX = patient's name is unknown

range. The spleen was just palpable. There was no glossitis or specific neurologic findings. His peripheral blood had a hemoglobin of 80 g/liter with normal platelet, neutrophil, and lymphocyte counts. The erythrocytes showed a marked degree of anisocytosis and poikilocytosis with numerous macrocytes up to 16 μm in diameter and other morphological abnormalities consistent with megaloblastosis (Fig. 43-5A). Many macrocytes were hypochromic. The bone marrow was megaloblastic with a predominance of erythroid cells. Serum vitamin B12 and folate levels were above normal for age. Urine specimens were clear when fresh but when left to stand for several hours produced an abundant white flocculent precipitate which microscopic analysis revealed to be colorless, fine, needle-shaped crystals (Fig. 43-6). A feature of the deposit was the firm adherence of the particles to the sides of glass containers. This deposit was identified as OA. There was an average of 1.5 g OA excreted daily during the initial period of assessment. Orotidine, carbamylaspartate, and dihydro-orotate were also increased in the urine. Studies initiated before treatment showed the activities of OPRT and ODC were very low in his erythrocytes and cultured fibroblasts, and there was no ODC activity demonstrable in leukocytes. Later studies showed that growth of cultured skin fibroblasts was stimulated by addition of uridine or cytidine to the culture medium.[162]

His initial treatment is summarized in Fig. 43-7. Cytidylic acid, 2.6 mmol/day orally for 12 days, caused only a slight rise in hemoglobin and no change in red cell morphology. There was a decrease in the average daily OA excretion to 58 percent of the pretreatment level. An equivalent dose of uridine, 3.1 mmol/day orally in five doses, had similar slight effects, but there was a marked response when uridine was increased to 6.1 mmol/day (150 mg/kg/day). There was a prompt reticulocytosis and return of blood hemoglobin levels to normal. The bone marrow became normoblastic, and erythrocytes were normal (Fig. 43-5B). OA excretion decreased to a mean of 0.30 g/day, 26 percent of the pretreatment level, and was not further reduced by temporary doubling of the dose of uridine. Previously elevated levels of aspartate transcarbamylase (ATC) and dihydro-orotase (DHO) in red cells returned to normal with therapy.[167] The clinical response was impressive, with a rapid improvement in his color, activity, alertness, and appetite, and immediate weight gain. There was a sudden spurt in the growth of his hair and nails. At 2 years he began to feed himself; he spoke single words at 2 years 2 months; and he walked at 2 years 5 months.

This clinical improvement was maintained but after 8 months of treatment, because of weight gain, his oral uridine dose had fallen to 100 mg/kg/day. At this uridine level there were signs of hematological relapse which were reversed by increasing uridine to 150 mg/kg/day (in three doses). This has been the recommended dose of uridine during the next two decades except for a short and unsuccessful trial of uracil as alternative therapy (Fig. 43-5C).[31] His progress during these years has been monitored clinically, hematologically, and by assay of urinary OA levels. In the first 18 months of treatment his weight increased from the 3d to the 90th percentile, after which this growth spurt diminished, and he has maintained average adult height and weight. He has had the usual child-

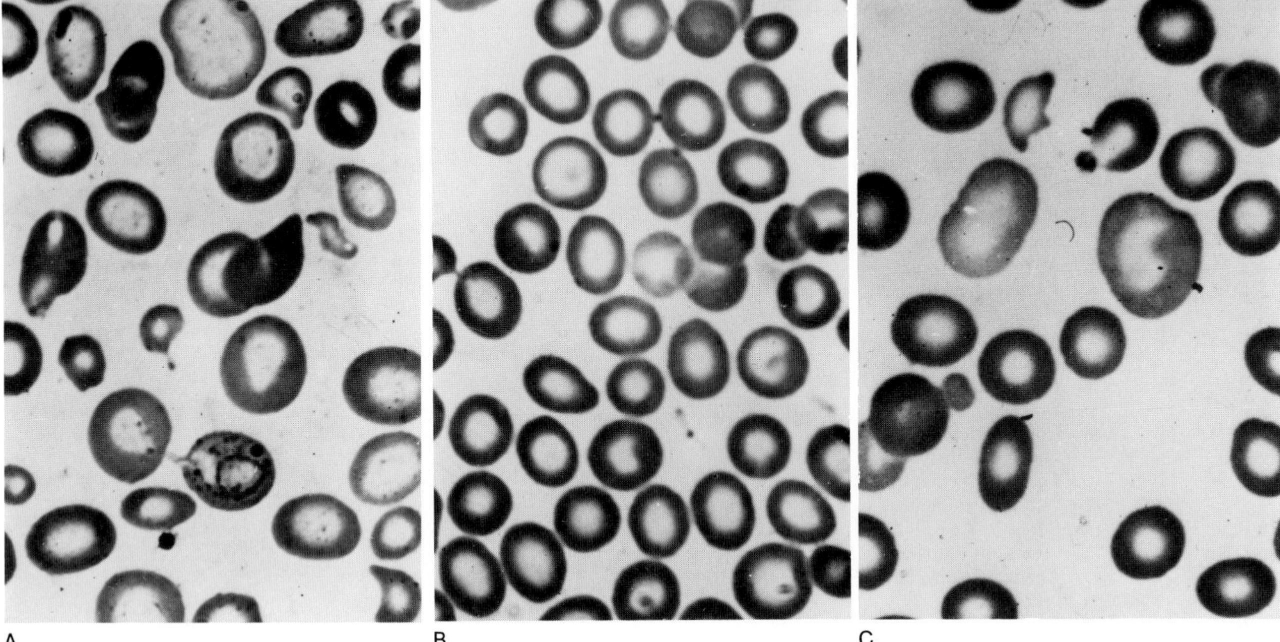

Fig. 43-5 A. Blood film from D.G. before treatment with uridine. *B.* Blood film after 6 months of treatment with uridine. C. Blood film during relapse on uracil therapy.

hood infections, including measles, but no major illnesses. His intelligence at the last formal assessment at age 7 years was in the range of 73 to 81 on the Weschler scale, and his subsequent performance suggests he is functioning at or above this level. He had normal schooling, is currently in steady employment as a warehouseman-driver, appears well-adjusted socially, and is married, without children.

His compliance with treatment has been variable. When taking uridine, although not necessarily at the recommended dose, he has blood hemoglobin levels in the range 115 to 135 g/liter (average 120 g/liter), and there is minimal anisocytosis of red cells with normal white cell and platelet counts. The mean urinary OA excretion has been 0.38 mmol/mmol creatinine. Periodically he has stopped taking his uridine and has presented after ill-defined time intervals with recurrences of macrocytosis, hemoglobin levels falling to as low as 68 g/liter, and urinary OA excretion as high as 3.2 mmol/mmol creatinine. He has felt some loss of energy during these episodes, but there have been no urinary or other specific symptoms.

Fig. 43-6 Sediment of crystalline orotic acid in the urine of patient D.G.

His urine has normal cell and protein content, and at various times his creatinine clearance, urinary concentrating capacity, and intravenous pyelogram have been normal.[160]

A more detailed in vivo study of purine and pyrimidine metabolism and the effect of allopurinol was made when he was 17 years old.[160,161] Uridine therapy and a caffeine-free diet were maintained while the effects of oral allopurinol and diets with high or low nucleoprotein content were investigated. Allopurinol produced up to a 70 percent reduction in urinary OA excretion and more than a 50 percent reduction in the previously elevated urinary uric acid and oxypurine excretion, irrespective of the purine content of the diet. The study confirmed that allopurinol could reduce the excretion of potentially crystal-forming components in the urine, but this treatment was not continued because he has had no urinary symptoms and has normal renal function. Further studies of the relationship of purines and pyrimidines to immune function were undertaken in 1983 and 1984 following reports[152,153] of abnormal cellular immunity in other cases of hereditary orotic aciduria. These studies of immune function in D.G. were undertaken during periods of compliance and noncompliance with uridine therapy. All results were normal and consistent with the clinical impression of his immunologic competence and general good health.[143,158,160]

Clinical Diagnosis

Megaloblastic Anemia. Children with hereditary orotic aciduria have had a variety of clinical presentations. In all cases the eventual detection of an anemia with the subsequent identification of bone marrow megaloblastosis has predicated the biochemical investigations leading to the confirmed diagnosis. Anemia has been initially detected at ages ranging from 1½ months to 7 years. Initial hemoglobin levels in nine cases presenting between 3 months and 7 years of age were in the range 60 to 80 g/liter. D.G., J.P., and H.B.[142,144,156] had more severe anemia, including one infant with a hemoglobin of 52 g/liter when only 1½ months old. The anemia has been of moderate severity and not rapidly progressive in several patients followed for a period of months before they received pyrimidine

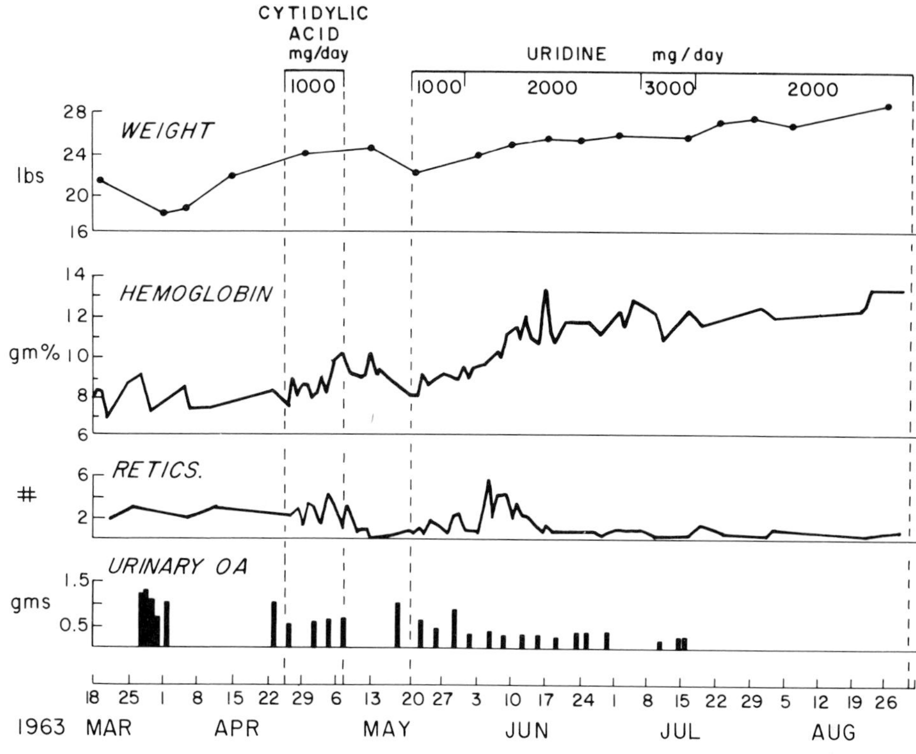

Fig. 43-7 Changes in weight, hemoglobin, reticulocytes, and urinary OA in patient D.G. during treatment with cytidylic acid and with uridine.

replacement therapy. In some cases the anemia has improved after treatment with various vitamins, steroids and hematinics but without reversal of megaloblastosis. Rapid falls in hemoglobin occurred in the terminal phases of illness in J.R. and Y.S.[139,152,153] Reticulocyte counts have been in the normal to low range. Most reports have described or illustrated striking abnormalities of erythrocyte morphology including severe anisocytosis, poikilocytosis, and other cytologic abnormalities indicative of marrow megaloblastosis (Fig. 43-5). Anisocytosis and macrocytosis of this degree is very unusual in young children, and will be easily detected by modern blood cell analyzers. Several authors have commented on the degree of associated hypochromia (Fig. 43-5) despite normal serum iron levels or iron therapy. The total leukocyte counts have usually been low at presentation, and this has been reflected to varying degrees by neutropenia and lymphopenia, with counts being less than 2.0×10^6 per liter. A few patients have had normal or even higher neutrophil and lymphocyte counts prior to specific therapy, while in others the neutropenia or lymphopenia was intermittent. Platelet counts have been normal in all cases. Bone marrows, when differentials have been reported, have had 60 to 80 percent of normal levels of erythroid precursors and megaloblastic changes which in most cases have been considered atypical but in others were not commented on as differing from those of megaloblastosis of other causes. Myeloid precursors and megakaryocytes have been specified as having megaloblastic features in some cases.

The differential diagnosis of the anemia is mainly from other causes of megaloblastosis in infancy and early childhood.[168,169] The more common "nutritional" megaloblastic anemias due to dietary deficiencies or congenital or acquired defects in absorption of folate or vitamin B_{12} will usually be considered first, and in most reported cases of hereditary orotic aciduria were readily excluded by measurement of plasma folate and vitamin B_{12} levels and/or by the failure to obtain a response to therapeutic amounts of folate or cobalamin. The hematologic problem that has emerged in many cases is the further investigation of a "refractory" megaloblastic anemia. We do not intend to review in detail the conditions of childhood in which there may be associated megaloblastosis unrelated to folate or vitamin B_{12} deficiency. These include the leukemias and other forms of dyshematopoiesis, anemias responsive to pyridoxine or thiamine, drug-induced megaloblastosis, Lesch-Nyhan syndrome, and the inborn errors of folate or vitamin B_{12} metabolism. The latter are discussed in detail in Chaps. 81 and 82 of this volume and may have clinical features similar to those described for hereditary orotic aciduria, including onset in infancy of megaloblastic anemia, retarded motor and intellectual development, and sparse hair. Differentiation from hereditary orotic aciduria will be based on the additional clinical and biochemical features detailed in Chaps. 81 and 82 and more specifically the absence of orotic aciduria. Orotic aciduria has been described in a child with formimino transferase–cyclodeaminase deficiency.[170] This might cause diagnostic difficulty, but the slight increase in OA excretion (6.4 to 21.4 mmol/creatinine) was considerably less than that in UMPS deficiency and formiminoglutamic acid (FIGLU) excretion was increased. The child in whom Niemann and colleagues[149] diagnosed hereditary orotic aciduria had a megaloblastic anemia responsive to high doses of folic and folinic acid, and although OA crystals were demonstrable, this was after in vitro concentration of urine samples. FIGLU excretion was increased, and this patient is more likely to have an inborn error of folate metabolism than UMPS deficiency and has been excluded from our list of cases. We also exclude a child with presumed PRPP-synthetase deficiency[150] who had megaloblastic anemia, severe mental retardation, and hyperuricemia and excreted small amounts of OA in the urine. Both megaloblastosis and orotic aciduria disappeared after ACTH treatment.[151]

Orotic Acid Crystalluria and Obstructive Uropathy. The excretion of large amounts of OA in the urine is a constant feature of UMPS deficiency. OA is present in the urine in amounts that may result in crystalluria both within the urinary tract and, more consistently, in urine specimens. Urine may be clear initially but on standing produces deposits similar to those illustrated in Fig. 43-7. Methods for the quantification of urinary OA, including distinguishing between hereditary orotic aciduria and orotic aciduria from other causes, will be presented in the following section on laboratory diagnosis. Although orotic aciduria from other causes may reach levels comparable with those associated with UMPS deficiency, symptoms resulting from OA crystalluria have been reported only with UMPS deficiency. OA crystalluria has been of diagnostic importance in six of the 13 cases. The resulting symptoms were a very important factor leading to the identification of the underlying metabolic error in the first reported case J.R.[139] When J.R. became dehydrated, he suffered from precipitation of crystals in his bladder and episodes of ureteral obstruction that required forcing fluids for relief. K.P. developed urethral obstruction when aged 4 months which required catheterization for relief.[146] The mother of D.M. noted a whitish discharge in the urine which left a powdery substance in the diaper. D.M. developed urethral obstruction at 22 months and required meatotomy.[155,164] Patient J.P. at 19 months old[144] had an upper respiratory tract infection followed by hematuria, crystalluria, oliguria, and azotemia. An intravenous pyelogram showed intrarenal retention of radiopaque material in the kidney which was interpreted as due to blockage of collecting tubules by crystals. Both D.B. and Y.S. presented at age 7 years[148,152,153] with hematuria presumably caused by crystals injuring the renal tract. A preceding history of back pain in D.B. is likely to have been due to intermittent partial obstruction of the upper urinary tract. Thus, OA crystalluria may have important clinical manifestations in hereditary orotic aciduria although a slight majority of cases have had no urinary symptoms.

Growth Deficiency. A history of weight loss or "failure to thrive" is common but not invariable in hereditary orotic aciduria. D.G. had a typical history of above-average birthweight and failure to thrive in later infancy, so that by 1 year his weight was below the 3d percentile for his age. Six of the affected children whose birthweight is known were delivered at term and averaged 3.3 kg, and three more that were delivered prematurely had average birthweights for their gestations of 30 to 35 weeks. Five of the 13 affected children had weights at or below the 3d percentiles for ages ranging between 3 months and 7 years. In addition, XX[154] failed to thrive in infancy, and the weight of T.H. dropped from the 50th to the 10th percentiles between 6 and 9 months of age.[145] In contrast, J.R. was described as well-developed and well-nourished at 9 months of age[139] and J.P., D.B., and H.B. had weights above the 25th percentile for age when 10 months, 7 years, and 23 months old.[144,148,156] R.S. had normal growth in early infancy.[152,153] Body heights have not been severely affected.

Intellectual and Motor Impairment. Developmental delay was not observed during the first year of life of J.R., the first patient with hereditary orotic aciduria,[139] but has been noted in at least six subsequent cases before specific therapy was begun. Assessment after therapy of D.G., J.P., and P.M.[144,146] suggested there may have been permanent effects on the developing nervous system which might have been prevented by earlier treatment. However, both the frequency and specificity of this developmental delay remain in doubt. Formal assessments have been made in three young children before treatment: D.G. at 17 months had abilities in the 7- to 11-month range; J.P. at 1 year old was functioning at a 66 percent level as assessed by Gessell development testing;[144] and P.M. at 5 months old was functioning at the 3-month-old level.[141] Before treatment XX and D.M. were described as having poor development at 5 months and 2 years of age, respectively.[154,164] H.B. had marked developmental delay at 18 months old, although a previous episode of bacterial meningitis may have contributed.[156] The central nervous system effects were difficult to assess in K.P.,[146] who was severely handicapped, with multiple congenital malformations and hypertonia from birth until death in infancy. In contrast, there are five affected children in whom developmental delay was either excluded or not mentioned at time of presentation. Those with normal development included two 7-year-olds, D.B. and Y.S., one of whom (D.B.) had an IQ of 133 on the Stanford-Binet intelligence scale.

The assessment of the level of retardation in some infants may have been affected adversely by an associated effect on their muscular or motor function. Weakness, hypotonia, lack of activity, and sluggish movements have received special comment in some affected infants, as has the prompt reversal of these features with specific therapy. The effect may be progressive, as P.M. had good head control at age 5 weeks but lost the control at age 4 months.[146] An unusually high incidence of strabismus may be another manifestation of abnormal motor activity. Strabismus has been recorded in four children, described in three as alternating or bilateral[142,144,145] and as unilateral in one.[154] D.G.'s strabismus resolved spontaneously as he grew older, and surgical correction was performed in T.H.[145] The incidence of strabismus in the general population has been conservatively estimated at 5 percent.[171]

Prenatal Development and Malformations. The normal birthweights for gestation of children with hereditary orotic aciduria has been commented on above and suggests that there are no major effects on late fetal development. There is stronger evidence that there may be an effect during organogenesis causing an increased incidence of malformations, particularly cardiac. Systolic cardiac murmurs reported in some anemic children were not commented on further and probably were hemic. Four cases had stronger evidence for a cardiac abnormality. H.B. had a severe abnormality, including pulmonary atresia, hypoplastic right ventricle, and a large atrial septal defect, for which a Blalock-Taussig shunt had been performed.[156] Further evaluation of the cardiac murmur in T.H. indicated a probable interventricular septal defect.[145] K.P. had other malformations in addition to a presumed intraventricular septal defect and died without a necropsy.[146] Y.F. received digoxin through the first year of life, presumably because of a persistent cardiac problem.[157] This is an unusual incidence when structural heart defects overall have an incidence of 6 to 7 per 1000 births.[172–173]

Minor congenital abnormalities, outward torsion of the left tibia, and coloboma of the eyelid were each noted in a single case. K.P. was the only case with multiple congenital defects. He had defects of the thoracic and abdominal musculature which caused herniation of the lung into the supraclavicular regions along with umbilical and inguinal hernias. There was dorsolumbar kyphoscoliosis and a scaphoid skull and severe hypertonia, and the infant was grossly handicapped from birth. This spectrum of skeletal muscle abnormalities, including a pleural "dome" in the neck, closely resemble those of amyoplasia, a nonfamilial form of muscular abnormality causing multiple congenital contractures.[174]

Malabsorption. There are theoretical reasons for believing that the untreated genetic defect might have an effect on epithelial function in the gastrointestinal tract, but the majority of cases have shown no evidence of this. The two exceptional cases had other factors that may have contributed to the observed malabsorption. Diarrhea with bulky stools suggestive of malabsorption was the presenting symptom in the first reported case of hereditary orotic aciduria.[139] However, a recurrence of diarrhea late in the patient's course was attributed to the high phosphate and salt content of the yeast extract that had induced hematologic remission. Another affected child[152,153] also had periods of diarrhea and chronic stomatitis during the first years of his life, but an underlying immunodeficiency and infection may have contributed to these symptoms. His diarrhea recurred after 3 months of apparently successful treatment with oral and intramuscular uridine. Severe diarrhea associated with intestinal candidiasis, partial intestinal villous atrophy, and malabsorption developed. Parenteral nutrition was instituted, but the patient died of meningitis.

Immunodeficiency. The majority of cases of hereditary orotic aciduria did not have undue susceptibility to infection before or after treatment, although two of the first seven reported patients died from infection. The description of immune dysfunction in purine nucleoside phosphorylase deficiency and adenosine deaminase deficiency[33] raised the possibility of an analogous propensity in UMPS deficiency.

Girot and colleagues reported two siblings who had UMPS deficiency with impaired cell-mediated immunity, although humoral immunity was normal.[152,153,175] Y.S. had increased serum IgG levels and severe lymphopenia before treatment. He had depressed leukocyte proliferative response to mitogens and depressed cell-mediated lymphocytolysis. Plasma-cell generation by pokeweed mitogen was impaired and did not improve with the addition of uridine to the culture system. These findings were not altered when the patient received uridine therapy, which resulted in only a poor clinical response. He developed diarrhea, malabsorption, and intestinal candidiasis, and died from purulent meningitis. R.S., his sister, tested before uridine therapy, had similar abnormal results. In addition, T-cell subsets were markedly abnormal (OKT3 13 percent, normal 68 to 86 percent, OKT4 1 percent, normal 46 to 51 percent, and OKT8 5 percent, normal 27 to 36 percent) and only slightly higher after uridine therapy.[152,153,175] After 3 more years of uridine therapy, T3, T4, and T8 lymphocytes have returned to normal. Proliferative responses to mitogens and antigens remain normal, but the T-cell-mediated lymphocytolysis is still profoundly decreased.[176]

Patient H.B., who had complex congenital heart disease, had studies of immune function before treatment.[156] Mitogen stimulation studies showed abnormal lymphocyte proliferative responses to concanavalin A and pokeweed mitogen, but normal response to phytohemagglutinin. Serum immunoglobins were depressed (IgG 251 mg/100 ml, IgM 52 mg/100 ml, and IgA <6.6 mg/100 ml), but except for IgA returned to normal after uridine treatment. The pretreatment lymphocyte phenotype was abnormal. She had an episode of bacterial meningitis at 7 months of age but responded to treatment and has shown no further evidence of susceptibility to infection.[156]

An unpublished case patient, Y.F., also had normal humoral immunity but an impaired cell-mediated immunity. This was characterized by a decreased number of total circulating lymphocytes and by a decrease in delayed skin reactivity to phytohemagglutinin. This patient is doing well.[157]

D.G. has had normal immunity on and off therapy. No abnormalities have been identified in serum immunoglobin levels, phytohemagglutinin lymphocyte proliferative responses, T-cell subsets, B lymphocytes (identified by surface immunoglobin), positive recall of delayed hypersensitivity responses to *Candida*, purified protein derivative, or mumps antigen.[143,158] He remains in good health. It has been suggested that differences in residual enzyme activity may account for the difference in immune response between D.G. and Y.S. or R.S.[175] It is possible that the periods D.G. was off uridine therapy were too short to allow immunologic parameters to return to a true pretreatment state. The studies in H.B. clearly show abnormal immune parameters before treatment which became normal after 3 months of therapy.[156] Although three patients died of infection, there were alternative predisposing factors. These included severe malabsorption and anemia when uridine therapy could not be maintained in two of the cases, and severe handicap with multiple congenital abnormalities in the third.

To summarize present knowledge of immune function in hereditary orotic aciduria:

1. In vitro studies have shown abnormalities, but these have been inconsistent in parameters affected.
2. There is a suggestion that these abnormalities are reduced by therapy and after long-term therapy remain normal during short periods of hematologic relapse.
3. Most cases will not show clinical evidence of increased susceptibility to infection either before or after treatment.
4. These specific immune defects may have been contributory to the deaths from infection in three cases, in combination with other predisposing factors.

Further elucidation of the contribution of impaired *de novo* pyrimidine synthesis to immune dysfunction will only be obtained by detailed studies of immune function performed on any new cases of hereditary orotic aciduria before and after treatment.

Treatment

Pyrimidines. Pyrimidine replacement therapy has proved effective in the majority of cases of hereditary orotic aciduria.

Uridine. The nucleoside uridine has been used for all patients except J.R. The salvage pathway for uridine utilization has been discussed previously. Uridine can be taken as a mildly bitter but otherwise flavorless powder and appears to have no gastrointestinal or other side effects at the doses used. D.G. responded to 150 mg uridine per kilogram body weight per day given orally in five divided doses. Eight further patients treated with oral doses of between 100 and 200 mg/kg/day have shown improvement in their anemias, disappearance of megaloblastosis, decrease in orotic aciduria, and immediate improvement in strength, activity, alertness, and general well-being. At 2 years old, D.G. showed early bone marrow relapse when his uridine dose fell to 100 mg/kg/day, although other patients have responded to lower uridine amounts. Uridine at

50 mg/kg/day was sufficient to produce hematological and clinical remission in R.S.,[152,153] and a similar effect of 300 mg/day in XX at 5 months old[154] probably represents a similar response to a lesser dose.

In Y.S. there was no response to oral uridine at a dose increasing from 75 to 150 mg/kg/day over a 9-month period.[152,153] He is the only patient known to have been treated with intramuscular uridine. The previous oral dose of 150 mg/kg/day, divided approximately equally between the oral and intramuscular routes, stabilized the hemoglobin level, improved the bone marrow to show only minimal megaloblastosis, and decreased orotic aciduria, but leukopenia persisted.

The rate of relapse after stopping uridine appears to be relatively slow. The return of orotic aciduria to pretreatment levels and full hematologic relapse took 3 weeks when D.G.'s uridine was replaced by uracil. The dependency on uridine is lifelong. D.G., after 20 years, and T.H., aged 21 years still showed hematologic relapse and increased orotic aciduria when uridine was stopped, either intentionally or against advice.[165] However, the dose of uridine required to maintain remission may be less in later life. We doubt D.G.'s compliance with his recommended dose of 150 mg/kg/day (9 g/day), and T.H. is said to be under good control on a dose of approximately 0.5 to 1 g/day.[165]

The decision that D.G. should take uridine five or three times daily was arbitrary, because there was no available information on uridine pharmacokinetics or on the presumed cumulative effect of "pyrimidine starvation," which might allow less frequent dosage. A recent pharmacokinetic study of oral uridine in six healthy volunteers and three patients with advanced colorectal cancer at doses of 0.3 to 12 g/m^2 found peak plasma uridine levels of 13 to 87 μmol/liter at 2 to 3 h. The area under the concentration-time curve increased linearly with dose between 48 and 476 μmol/h/liter. The total plasma clearance varied between 25 and 76 ml/kg/min while the volume of distribution was 4.3 to 16.6 ml/kg. The mean residence time was 200 to 300 min. Dose-limiting toxicity was diarrhea at 12 g/m^2. Plasma uracil increased from 4 h at doses of 8 to 12 g/m^2.[177] Another normal adult taking 9 g daily (in three doses with meals) attained blood levels of 20 to 60 μmol/liter (mean 40 μmol/liter) compared with a mean of 6 μmol/liter pretreatment.[178] Normal blood levels of uridine in adults are approximately 2 to 10 μmol/liter. D.G. has had levels between 30 and 50 μmol/liter while in hematologic remission.[143]

The bioavailability of oral uridine in healthy adults was 7 percent relative to a 1-h infusion.[177] Also in mice given 350 and 3500 mg/kg orally, the uridine levels were 7 percent of a subcutaneous dose.[179] Since bioavailability is low, defects in intestinal absorption or increased degradation could be an important limitation on treatment. Information on this point would have been of particular interest in Y.S.,[152,153] who had no response to a long trial of a seemingly adequate oral dose of uridine. He had a history of episodic diarrhea, and late in his illness there was evidence of malabsorption and partial intestinal villous atrophy. Circulating uridine is assumed to diffuse readily into cells and appears to be well conserved. There are no relevant published studies in hereditary orotic aciduria, but in cancer patients, infused uridine had a terminal half-life of 118 min,[180] and this was independent of the uridine dose. Peak plasma levels did increase with dose. Infused uridine at large doses (up to 12 g/m^2) was excreted 24 percent unchanged and 3 percent as uracil.[180] Weissman has shown that uridine is normally reutilized in humans and that the renal clearance is 0.5 to 2 percent of the creatinine clearance.[181] D.G. excreted 2 to 7 percent of his daily dose as uridine and uracil.[161] A normal adult also excreted less than 5 percent of a daily dose at the usual therapeutic level.[178]

In previously untreated patients, the effective dose of uridine should be sought by gradually increasing the daily dose. Well-controlled trials are needed to determine the frequency of the dose and to determine the dosage and frequency in older patients. Treatment can be monitored by occasional checks on hemoglobin and erythrocyte morphology. Urinary orotic acid levels can also be measured, but in retrospect, this was not essential for D.G.'s management.

Other Pyrimidines. A yeast extract containing uridylic and cytidylic acids was effective in inducing hematological and clinical remission in J.R.[139] The maximum dose used provided about 6 mmol of the nucleotides per day. This dose of about 0.6 mmol/kg/day was equal in molar terms to uridine at 150 mg/kg/day. The response could not be maintained because the yeast extract was poorly tolerated and caused diarrhea which seemed directly related to the dose. The diarrhea was assumed to be due to the high phosphate and salt content of the yeast extract. D.G. showed a reduction in orotic aciduria in response to treatment with cytidylic acid at 900 mg per day orally in six doses continued for 12 days (0.26 mmol/kg/day). This is a further indication that pure nucleotides in higher weight (equimolar) doses could be as effective as uridine, but their cost is much greater and their effect may involve degradation to nucleosides before absorption. A prolonged trial of uracil at 2.5 g/day (approximately 2 mmol/kg/day) was ineffective in J.R.[139] A trial of uracil when D.G. was 4 years old was similarly unsuccessful. Frank relapse occurred with a daily oral dose of 3 g (1.3 mmol/kg/day), followed by prompt remission with the reintroduction of oral uridine at 0.6 mmol/kg/day.[31] Assuming that uracil is adequately absorbed, the lack of response is consistent with other information suggesting that the normal utilization of uracil through salvage pathways is less efficient than that of uridine (see "Pyriumidine Metabolism"). If OPRT is important for normal uracil salvage, this would be impaired in hereditary orotic aciduria. There is in vitro evidence that uridine had a much greater stimulating effect on D.G.'s cultured fibroblasts than did uracil.[43,101,128]

Allopurinol. Allopurinol increases blood OPRT and ODC activities in humans (see earlier) and has been given to three patients with hereditary orotic aciduria. Allopurinol 2.2 mmol/day for 6 days did not increase OPRT or ODC activity in D.G.'s erythrocytes, but urine OA was markedly reduced in parallel with a significant reduction in urate excretion.[160] This reduction was possibly caused by in vivo enzyme stabilization by allopurinol or a metabolite. No orotidine was observed in the urine at any time during this study.[160] Allopurinol in two other cases did not decrease urinary OA but caused an increase in orotidinuria.[108] Uridine alone reduces orotic aciduria to a level where there appear to be no long-term effects on the renal tract or renal function. Allopurinol at present does not have a therapeutic role.

Nonspecific Therapy. Patients with orotic aciduria have received a variety of hematinics and vitamins, but the only consistent response has been to adrenal corticosteroids. Reticulocytosis and improvement in anemia to near-normal hemoglobin levels were obtained in J.R. with cortisone and prednisone, 10 to 51 mg/day,[139] and in J.P. with prednisone,

30 mg/day.[144] The bone marrows remained megaloblastic in both cases. When steroids were stopped, hemoglobin levels fell sharply in both, but there was a second response when these were reintroduced. Conversely, 1 mg/kg/day prednisone over 6 weeks had no clinical or hematologic effect in Y.S.[152,153] Amelioration of anemia by adrenal steroids has been reported in pernicious anemia and in megaloblastic anemia of other causes.[168] The mode of action of steroids in these situations has been described as complex and probably not the same in all patients,[168] and therefore the effect in hereditary orotic aciduria may be nonspecific. Possible modes of action include improved absorption or availability of pryimidines from dietary sources and increased salvage from increased cell catabolism.

Prognosis

Reversal of megaloblastosis and reduction of orotic aciduria with uridine is not necessarily an indication that the effects of the metabolic defect have been ameliorated in other tissues, nor does monitoring these parameters exclude the possibility of other long-term sequelae. Two of the 12 hereditary orotic aciduria patients treated with uridine in childhood died as described above. The other 10 were in hematologic remission and clinically improved at the time case reports were published or available to us; in most cases this was after a treatment period of 2 years or less. Therefore, we inquired about the current status of all surviving patients and obtained information in varying detail in five cases: D.G., now aged 26 years, T.H., now 21 years,[165] P.M., now 19 years,[163] D.M., now 15 years,[164] and S.R., now 7 years.[176] All were well physically and there was no mention of recurrence of anemia, urinary symptoms, or other medical complications while uridine treatment was maintained. The question of whether there is long-term impairment if treatment is delayed or uridine does not reach the central nervous system[31] is not completely resolved. One patient who was not regarded as retarded before treatment in early childhood (T.H.) was later assessed as having an intelligence quotient in the 75 to 80 range. This low result surprised the physician who had been following the clinical course.[165] Other treated patients have shown no late deterioration and even those whose early development had appeared retarded have achieved a normal education and lifestyle. Growth and sexual development have been normal, but no comment can be made on fertility. Therefore, the prognosis into early adult life is excellent in the majority of cases, even when early treatment is delayed. This good prognosis may be modified by severe congenital malformations (K.P. and H.B.) or by undue susceptibility to infection (J.R. and Y.S.).

Biochemical Features

Urinary Orotic Acid. The simplest method for measurement of urinary OA is that of Rogers and Porter,[182] but this colorimetric method is subject to interference from a variety of compounds.[183] Interfering compounds are unlikely to be a problem when OA is measured for the diagnosis or monitoring of therapy in hereditary orotic aciduria because the concentrations involved are high. The specificity of this method can be increased by the use of a nonbrominated blank sample.[184] Both OA and orotidine are measured unless these compounds are separated chromatographically before analysis. A more specific method, e.g., chromatographic[185–187] or isotope dilution,[188] should be used when a precise measurement is needed for determination of carrier status in hereditary orotic aciduria or the urea cycle disorders.

Urinary excretion of orotic acid is less than 10 μmol/mmol of creatinine[183,185,189–192] in normal individuals. The level is higher in newborns than in older children[183,185,189,190,193] The range is 1.3 to 5.3 μmol/mmol of creatinine in newborns, 1.0 to 3.2 in children 2 weeks to 1 year old, and 0.5 to 3.3 in children from 1 to 10 years old.[183] Van Gennip reports urine OA 3.9 to 20.3 μmol/liter in six children aged 0.3 to 5.9 years.[187] OA excretion is about half normal in periods of starvation.[191,194]

In contrast, urine OA levels in hereditary orotic aciduria are several orders of magnitude greater than normal. Levels have been reported in seven untreated cases: J.R., aged 9 months, 9.6 mmol/24 h;[139] D.G., aged 17 months, 4.4 and 8.6 mmol/24 h, and at 23 years, 1.4, 3.2, and 1.9 mmol/mmol of creatinine;[142,143] J.P., aged 11 months, 6.0 mmol/24 h;[144] P.M., 1.8 mmol/24 h;[146] Y.S., aged 7 years, 5.4 mmol/24 h;[152] R.S., aged 3 months, 1.0 mmol/24 h;[152] Y.F. at 3 months, about 1.9 mmol/day;[157] H.B., aged 18 months, 5.6 mmol/mmol of creatinine.[156] Orotidine has been very low to undetectable except in P.M. (weight 5 kg), who excreted 1.8 mmol OA per day and 0.2 mmol orotidine per day before treatment.

Other Causes of Orotic Aciduria. Orotic aciduria has been reported in a number of other metabolic diseases and as a consequence of pharmacologic agents.

UREA CYCLE DEFECTS. These are discussed elsewhere in this volume (Chap. 20).[26] They are the only metabolic diseases in which the magnitude of the orotic aciduria is comparable to that observed in UMPS deficiency. Blocks in the urea cycle after CPS I can cause accumulation of intramitochondrial carbamyl-phosphate. This diffuses into the cytosol and is thus available for the *de novo* pyrimidine synthetic pathway. In ornithine transcarbamylase deficiency, argininosuccinate synthetase deficiency (citrullinemia), and argininemia,[195] urine OA levels are increased and can be comparable to those found in hereditary orotic aciduria. The levels can be 3 to 10 mmol OA per millimole of creatinine in hemizygous affected males and 0.1 to 9 mmol per millimole of creatinine in heterozygotes.[195] These conditions can be differentiated from hereditary orotic aciduria as they are associated with hyperammonemia and abnormal plasma amino acid levels. In addition, the raised levels of OA are accompanied by raised levels of uridine and uracil, which are not found in untreated hereditary orotic aciduria.

Heterozygous carriers for these disorders are often detected by their slightly raised urine OA concentrations, especially after high protein meals or amino acid loading,[26] but this is not always the case.[196] Normal individuals also show a slight increase in OA after high protein meals or amino acid loading, but the increase is of smaller magnitude. Amino acid induced orotic aciduria has also been observed in rats.[197]

LYSINURIC PROTEIN INTOLERANCE. Patients with this inherited disorder of diamino acid transport (Chap. 100) may have increased urine OA concentrations (controls—mean 7.9, range 6.5 to 10.8 μmol/mmol of creatinine; homozygotes—mean 44, range 0.7 to 639 μmol/mmol of creatinine on a self-chosen diet). All had orotic aciduria outside the control range following alanine loading. The postulated mechanism for this is the same as that in the urea cycle enzyme defects.[198]

FORMIMINOTRANSFERASE/CYCLODEAMINASE DEFICIENCY. A moderate orotic aciduria (6.4 to 21.4 μmol/mmol of creatinine) has been described in this condition and attributed to increased pyrimidine synthesis.[170] It is possible that orotic aciduria of this magnitude is present in other disorders of folate metabolism or absorption, where the OA crystalluria was not apparent until the urine was concentrated.[149]

PRPP SYNTHETASE DEFICEINCY. A single, 11-month-old patient had a urine excretion of 0.2 mmol OA per day. This child had persistently low levels of uric acid in body fluids, low erythrocyte PRPP concentrations, and markedly decreased PRPP synthetase activity in erythrocytes.[150]

OTHER PURINE METABOLIC DISORDERS. There is a report that children with purine nucleoside phosphorylase deficiency[199] have raised levels of urinary OA, although this has not been confirmed by other workers.[159,200] One patient studied on various purine and pyrimidine dietary supplements and allopurinol had urinary OA and orotidine excretions sometimes within, and sometimes just outside, the normal range.[187] Children with adenosine deaminase deficiency[159,201] have normal levels of urinary OA. Some other immunodeficiency conditions may have slightly increased urinary OA.[201]

PREGNANCY. In one study, slight to moderate increases in urinary OA and orotidine have been found in pregnancy,[202] but in another study, no difference in OA levels was found between pregnant and nonpregnant women.[189]

DRUGS. Allopurinol given in regular doses to gouty patients has been found to increase urine OA and orotidine levels; 200 to 400 mg/day of allopurinol produced 0.09 to 0.42 mmol orotidine per day and 0.05 to 0.19 mmol OA per day.[102,108] A similar effect was found with oxipurinol.

The monophosphate form of 6AZUR inhibits the ODC activity of UMPS, resulting in an accumulation of orotidine and OA. In patients with nonterminal malignant disease, 6AZUR at 70 mg/day resulted in urinary OA of 0.12 mmol/day. Doses of 450 mg 6AZUR per day resulted in excretion of 0.42 mmol OA per day and 1.12 mmol orotidine per day.[121] Another study reported that 180 to 240 mg/kg/day 6AZUR gave 8 to 19 mmol OA per day and 5 to 9 mmol orotidine per day.[7] When normalized for body weight, the amount of OA excreted with 6AZUR-induced orotic aciduria may be greater than that found in hereditary orotic aciduria. The major difference is that since 6AZUMP inhibits ODC, significant amounts of orotidine are also excreted.[121] Patients receiving both 6AZUR and uridine excreted less OA and orotidine than when 6AZUR was given alone.[121]

Blood Orotic Acid. OA levels in blood have not been used in the diagnosis of hereditary orotic aciduria. The concentration of OA in normal plasma is less than 0.5 μM, and the high performance liquid chromatography (HPLC) technology for the measurement has been available only in the last decade. Since D.G. on treatment has OA levels around 20 to 30 μM,[143] it is probable that untreated levels would be at least as high. Increased blood OA could then be helpful in diagnosis. Blood OA is increased in the urea cycle defects,[203] but as in the urine, uracil and uridine levels are also increased and hyperammonemia is present. The observation of fractional orotate clearances greater than 1 in hereditary orotic aciduria and ornithine carbamyltransferase deficiency[203] suggests the presence of an active renal secretory mechanism for OA is involved.

Other Pyrimidine Metabolites. Dihydro-orotic acid was undetectable in urine from normal adults, normal children, and patients J.P. and D.M. Carbamylaspartate concentrations were slightly increased in hereditary orotic aciduria.[155]

There is no information on levels of other pyrimidines in untreated hereditary orotic aciduria. Urine uracil is normally undetectable (less than 6 μmol per millimole of creatinine).[204,205] A wider range in measurement of all these compounds is obtained when the measurement is not corrected for the concentration of urine or the size of the child. In six children aged between 0.3 and 5.9 years, van Gennip reports urine values of orotidine 9 to 26 μM, uridine $<44\ \mu M$, uracil 30 to 90 μM, and pseudouridine $<601\ \mu M$.[187]

Plasma pyrimidines can be measured by simple HPLC techniques.[187,203] Care should be taken to ensure peak identity and purity as with all HPLC methods. Serum and plasma uridine is normally in the range 2 to 10 μM[180,203,206,207] and is not affected by fasting.[206] Plasma uracil is less than 0.5 μM.[203–205] Plasma OA is normally less than 0.5 μM.[203]

A microbiologic assay measuring blood "uridine + uracil" indicated that about 15 μM of these compounds was present,[208] while a recent HPLC method involving extraction and derivatization gave uridine levels about 2 μM and uracil about 8 μM.[209] CSF uridine levels have been measured at 3.3 μM (2 SD, range 0.6 to 6.3 μM) in newborn infants and 1.6 μM (2 SD, range 0.3 to 8.2 μM) in adults. Amniotic fluid uridine is 0.8 to 2.7 μM and OA is 0.19 to 0.37 μM in pregnancies with no identified risk factors.[211,188] The same authors report 0.33 to 0.84 μM uracil levels but do not report either uridine or pseudouridine present. It is possible these compounds may have been hydrolyzed to uracil by the derivatization process used.

Purine metabolites have not been studied in most cases of hereditary orotic aciduria reported to date. At age 17 years, D.G.'s plasma urate was 160 and 140 μM on a low purine diet, and he excreted 4.30 and 6.03 mmol urate per 24 h on the same diet. At age 23 years, on a normal diet, his plasma urate was 130 μM, and urine urate 2.5 mmol/24 h. Plasma and urine hypoxanthine and xanthine were not abnormal.[143,160] These results give fractional urate clearance ($C_{urate}/C_{creatinine}$) of 14.7 and 18.3 at age 17 years and 14.3 at age 23 years. This high fractional (and absolute) urate clearance could be due to the uricosuric action of OA.[212] It has been suggested that this results from the competition between urate and orotate for the same transport mechanism for tubular resorption.[121]

Conversely, J.R. showed a slight rise in urine urate excretion while OA excretion declined during the initial course of nucleotide treatment.[139] The increased urine urate may have been caused by increased dietary purine taken with the nucleotide preparation.[213] J.P. had normal urinary urate following a histidine load.[144] Fallon and coworkers note the absence of hyperuricemia or any abnormality of urate clearance in members of the R. family.[123]

Enzymes. The two activities of UMPS catalyze the conversion of OA to OMP and OMP to UMP.

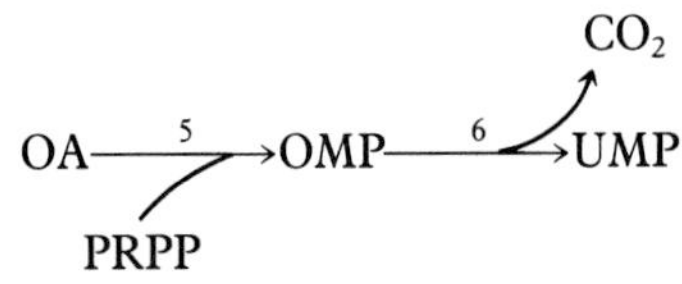

The most commonly used assay of OPRT and ODC activity is the release of $^{14}CO_2$ from labeled OA or OMP. The activities can be measured separately or together. OPRT activity is determined when OA is the substrate and OMP is the measured product, or if CO_2 release or UMP is quantitated in the presence of added ODC. ODC activity is determined when OMP is the substrate and CO_2 release or UMP is quantitated. UMPS activity, i.e., both activities combined, is measured when OA is the substrate and CO_2 release or UMP is quantitated in the absence of added ODC. Since the specific acitivity of ODC is at least two-fold greater than OPRT in the normal UMPS protein,[47] OPRT is the rate-limiting step in the combined reaction. Thus, assays of UMPS activity usually reflect the level of OPRT activity. However, this would not be the case if the endogenous ODC activity were deficient or inhibited.

These assays are usually done on lysed cell preparations at high substrate concentrations. It is also possible to separate and quantitate substrate and/or products by HPLC.[214] In interpreting mesurements of OPRT in tissue extracts it is necessary to consider possible competition for PRPP by other enzymes, especially hypoxanthine phosphoribosyltransferase.[214] PRPP levels are not increased in hereditary orotic aciduria erythrocytes measured directly[215] or by adenine utilization.[143]

Erythrocytes. It is difficult to compare results between laboratories, as different measures of erythrocyte or hemolysate amount and different methods of lysate preparation are used. Standard methods for preparation of lysates for enzyme assays have been suggested.[216] Standardization is important for these enzymes because their activity levels are much higher in younger than in older cell populations.

Erythrocyte OPRT is about 130 nmol/h/ml of erythrocytes and ODC about 280 nmol/h/ml of erythrocytes.[103] Other estimates include: UMPS in 19 normal controls, 2.4 to 14.9 nmol/h per 10^9 erythrocytes;[145] UMPS 1.35 ± 0.43, OPRT 1.7 ± 0.99, and ODC 4.2 ± 2.2 nmol/min/ml of erythrocytes;[154] OPRT 34 to 109 and ODC 52 to 285 nmol/h/ml of red cells;[160] OPRT, 131 ± 35 and ODC 288 ± 77 nmol/h/ml of erythrocytes;[103] OPRT 923 and ODC 152, 107 nmol/h/mg of hemoglobin;[148] OPRT 0.12 ± 0.06 and ODC 0.13 ± 0.06 nmol/h/mg of erythrocyte protein for adults and OPRT 0.26 ± 0.16 and ODC 0.18 ± 0.15 nmol/h/mg of erythrocyte protein for children.[108]

Some patients have had small but measurable OPRT and ODC activities (D.G., K.P., D.B., Y.F., T.H., H.B.; Refs. 142, 145, 146, 148, 156, 157) in erythrocytes. J.P. had ODC "markedly reduced" in erythrocytes.[144] Y.S. and R.S. had undetectable OPRT and low ODC.[152,153]

In 1971 Fox demonstrated coordinate activity between erythrocyte OPRT and ODC activities and showed specific activity decreases with increased erythrocyte age.[103] This was confirmed by a study that showed that the net orotidylate activity was directly related to the maturity of the peripheral erythrocyte population.[217] The relationship of cell age to enzyme activity has also been shown for adenosine phosphoribosyl transferase,[218] glucose-6-phosphate dihydrogenase,[217] and UMP kinase.[219] The decrease in enzyme activity with cell age observed in children with reticulocytosis is much greater than in individuals without measurable reticulocytosis.[178] As has been found for other enzymes, the amount of the increase per percent reticulocytes is less in cells from cord blood than from older individuals.[220]

Levels of OPRT and ODC are elevated in patients with congenital hypoplastic anemia.[221] ODC is elevated in Diamond-Blackfan anemia to about the same extent as in cord blood or hemolytic anemia.[222] UMPS activity is reduced in vitamin B_{12} and folate deficiency, possibly due to a population of older erythrocytes.

Other Tissues. It is possible to measure OPRT and ODC in saliva, but there is a wide range of normal values, and it was not possible to distinguish levels found in a UMPS heterozygote from normal levels.[140] There is measurable UMPS in amniocentesis-derived cells.[154] The activity in white cells was OPRT 0.79 and 0.87 and ODC 4.3, and 5.1 nmol/h/mg of leukocyte protein.[160] Control liver samples had OPRT, 0.79 and 1.9; ODC, 5.4, 4.1, and 3.6, and UMPS, 0.83, 1.5, and 2.4 nmol/h/5 mg wet liver.[145]

Fibroblasts from hereditary orotic aciduria patients also have had low enzyme activity,[101,128,148,154,162,223] but these activities are variable and depend on the culture growth.[162] The low levels are close to blank values and difficult to interpret.

Other Enzymes in UMPS Deficiency. DHO was not different from normal in fibroblasts from D.G. and J.P.,[162] and DHODH was also normal in fibroblasts from the same patients and not altered by growth in BA or 6AZUR.[226]

The Molecular Defect in UMP Synthase Deficiency

As previously discussed, cells from most patients with UMPS deficiency have low but detectable enzyme activity. The residual OPRT and ODC activities in fibroblasts from J.P. and D.G. are thermolabile and nondialyzable.[162] Fibroblasts from T.H. have residual ODC more thermolabile and of different electrophoretic mobility than the enzyme from normal cells, but with the same kinetic characteristics, suggesting a structural gene mutation.[223]

The ODC activity in fibroblasts from P.M. and D.G. increased several-fold when cells were grown with barbituric acid (BA) or oxipurinol.[101,128] Cells from D.G. show increased enzyme activity when grown with dihydro-orotic acid,[99,100] 6AZUR, or 5AZOA. This increase in activity is not prevented when cytidine is added to the growth media. D.G. and J.P. cells are more sensitive to adenosine than normal cells, but this can be prevented by addition of uridine or cytidine.

Fibroblasts from D.G., D.B., and XX have recently been characterized for defects in the gene or mRNA for UMPS.[224] Normal fibroblasts were used as the control. Southern blot analysis of DNA digested with five different restriction enzymes revealed no alteration of the UMPS gene in the deficient cells. In each case the restriction pattern was quite simple with only two to five fragments. The minimum total fragment size of approximately 15 kb can be used as an estimate of the size of the UMPS gene.

The amount of UMPS mRNA was estimated by quantification of the amount of UMPS probe hybridizing to cell mRNA. There was no significant decrease in the quantity of UMPS mRNA in the orotic aciduria cells.[224] Northern blot analysis showed the mRNA to be of the same size in the deficient cells as in normal cells. An S1 nuclease analysis of the mRNA did not reveal any alteration in the structure, sequence, or processing of the UMP synthase mRNA. From these studies it is confirmed that the orotic aciduria cells do express the UMPS gene at normal levels, that the mRNA transcript is stable, and that the mRNA is processed in a manner that results in the proper size for the mature mRNA.

Both polyclonal and monoclonal antibodies to the purified human UMPS have been developed.[225] In fibroblasts derived from patient D.G., it has been demonstrated by immunblotting techniques that a UMPS protein is synthesized and comigrates with the normal protein in polyacrylamide gel electrophoresis.[225] In the absence of substrate, the deficient cell UMPS exhibits an altered pattern of inactivation at 57°C. This is similar to the results reported above by Worthy et al.,[223] which showed alterations in enzyme stability in cells from orotic aciduria patient T.H. These results provide evidence that the UMPS deficiency is the result of the production of a structurally altered protein.

The hypothesis is put forth[224] that the defect may result from an altered amino acid sequence that has changed the ability of the subunits to form the 5.6-S altered dimer conformation necessary for optimal ODC activity (see discussion under "Conformation"). Alteration of the amino acids that form the interacting surface(s) of the monomer could result in weakened association and loss of stability of the dimer. If the active form of the enzyme in vivo is the dimer, the inability of the protein to form competent dimers could greatly reduce the catalytic activity. The addition of inhibitors which increase functional activity might stabilize or induce the formation of the 5.6-S altered dimer.

Orotic Aciduria Type II

In all cases of orotic aciduria except one, a deficiency in both OPRT and ODC activities has been reported. One patient (P.M.) has been referred to as having "type II" hereditary orotic aciduria[146] because the first measured values of erythrocyte enzyme activity (after 3 months of uridine therapy) were OPRT 0.83 and 0.24 nmol/h/mg of protein (one high and one normal value), while ODC was barely detectable. At 2 years of age, while on uridine therapy, OPRT was 0.005 nmol/h/ml of red blood cells (10 to 15 percent of normal), and ODC was 0.005 nmol/h/mg of red blood cell protein[147] and was undetectable in fibroblasts.[141] Later assays measured fibroblast ODC at 0.02 nmol/h/mg of protein.[101] At 13 years he had detectable OPRT and no ODC in erythrocytes. The finding of normal OPRT was corroborated by high urine orotidine excretion. When OPRT levels decreased, orotidine excretion was also reduced.

Even though it has now been shown that a single gene encodes the bifunctional protein UMPS, it may still follow that a single activity can be deficient without effect on the other. The work of Jones and coworkers has demonstrated that the ODC activity is predominantly associated with the 5.6-S altered dimer form, whereas the OPRT activity is found in all of the conformations of the enzyme.[56–58] Thus if dimer formation were blocked or otherwise inhibited, ODC activity would be lost or diminished while OPRT activity might be unaffected. For deficiency in both activities, one could postulate an altered amino acid sequence that would result in a protein that does not form the proper monomer configuration. An alternative would be a mutation that results in a protein that is more susceptible to proteolytic action or that is more heat labile.

Prenatal Diagnosis

There are no reports of prenatal diagnosis of hereditary orotic aciduria. In a further pregnancy in the mother of Y.S. and R.S. normal UMPS activity was found in chorionic villi and amniocytes.[176] The pregnancy concluded with the delivery of a child with normal erythrocyte enzyme activities. There are no strong grounds for termination of affected pregnancies because most infants are normal at birth and have a good prognosis following simple treatment. Maternal uridine supplementation might be considered, although, if intended for prevention of malformations, this would have to be initiated before fetal diagnosis is currently possible. It is unlikely that OA levels in amniotic fluid would be diagnostic. Ornithine transcarbamylase deficiency is another condition with postnatal orotic aciduria, and OA, orotidine, uridine or uracil were undetectable in amniotic fluid from a pregnancy with an affected male fetus.[227]

Neonatal Diagnosis

None of the cases of hereditary orotic aciduria to date have been diagnosed in the neonatal period. McClard and colleagues report exclusive neonatal diagnosis in an unaffected sib of XX, case 11,[154] and prenatal diagnosis of an unaffected child was confirmed by OPRT and ODC measurements after birth in another case.[176] It seems likely that an increase of urinary OA would be detectable soon after birth. Care would need to be exercised in interpretation of OPRT and ODC levels in the presence of the neonatal reticulocytosis, as discussed earlier.

Pathogenesis of Clinical Features of Hereditary Orotic Aciduria

Precursor Toxicity. The urinary excretion of OA is in amounts which imply a marked increase over the normal rate of OA synthesis. This may cause obstructive uropathy, and probably has a uricosuric effect. Blood levels of OA are only slightly increased, and there is no information on whether or not intracellular levels would be sufficiently elevated to exert some of the known pharmacologic effects of OA.

OA has been used therapeutically as a pyrimidine source in the treatment of neonatal jaundice, myocardial infarction, pernicious anemia,[228] and degenerative retinal diseases.[229] Oral OA reduces both blood urate and cholesterol levels.[229] OA inhibits *de novo* purine synthesis, probably by depleting intracellular PRPP,[230] and has been used as a therapeutic agent in gout.[212,228] OA has had pharmacologic use to lower plasma β-lipoprotein and triglyceride.[228] This is in contrast to the production of grossly fatty livers in rats receiving diets supplemented with OA. These animals have an associated increase in uridine nucleotides and reduced adenine nucleotides. Both the biochemical changes and the fatty liver are prevented by the addition of allopurinol to the diet.[231] In contrast to liver, OA-supplemented diets do not disturb nucleotide metabolism and lipoprotein secretion in rodent intestinal mucosa, which may be because OPRT and ODC activities are low or absent in these tissues.[232] All the latter effects of OA are likely to be related to its further metabolism to OMP and UMP causing nucleotide imbalance or PRPP depletion.[33] Therefore the enzymatic block in hereditary orotic aciduria should be protective, probably explaining the lack of corresponding effects in the disease.

Product Deficiency. The depletion of pyrimidine nucleotides is assumed to be the cause of the majority of clinical features of the disorder. Again, there are no direct measurements of the severity of this depletion, and it is not known whether all tissues are affected equally. The consistent occurrence of bone marrow megaloblastosis is a strong indication of important consequences at the cellular level. Megaloblastosis is evidence of slowed DNA synthesis per unit time and of the arrest of the process of cell division, particularly in S phase.[233] There are lesser effects on RNA synthesis, giving the characteristic asynchronous "young nucleus–old cytoplasm" appearance at all stages of erythrocyte maturation.[233] Kelley[33] has postulated that certain reported cytologic variations from the usual pattern in megaloblastosis in hereditary orotic aciduria might be because RNA synthesis is more severely affected, but not all observers regard the megaloblastosis as atypical. The defective DNA synthesis in megaloblastic states is usually present in all proliferating cells and is particularly marked in rapidly dividing cells such as those in the alimentary tract and vagina.[168,233] This could account for the malabsorption in some of the treated cases of hereditary orotic aciduria and the intestinal villous atrophy observed in one patient. It also could account for D.G.'s deficient hair and nail growth, although this has been recorded in only one other case.[146] There are some inconstant features of hereditary orotic aciduria in which the possible contribution of genetic variation in enzyme function cannot be separated from the modifying effects of pyrimidines obtained from dietary and salvage sources or from chance events unrelated to the genetic defect. Growth deficiency responds immediately to therapy, but this may be an indirect effect of improved appetite, motor activity, or general well-being rather than a reversal of pyrimidine "starvation." The difficulty of assessing intellectual impairment as either a short- or long-term effect of the disease has been referred to above. There is no firm theoretical basis for effects of the metabolic error on the developing nervous system. Some other inborn errors of metabolism causing megaloblastosis may be associated with mental retardation,[33] and there may be periods at which the developing brain has critical requirements for pyrimidine synthesis. This appears to be the case during restorative brain growth after undernutrition in neonatal animals.[234] Recent work has shown that UTP and UDP are important in relaxation of pial vessels, which may have implications in maintenance of brain circulation.[235]

Girot and colleagues[153,175] drew an analogy between the pathogenesis of the immune deficiencies in their patients with hereditary orotic aciduria and the immune deficiency associated with inherited deficiencies of two enzymes of the purine degradative pathway, adenosine deaminase and purine nucleoside phosphorylase. Selective toxicity of the metabolites deoxyadenosine and deoxyguanosine in T lymphocytes is the currently favored explanation for the pathogenesis of the immune impairment in the latter deficiencies.[4] There is no reason to believe that defects in the *de novo* pyrimidine biosynthetic pathway cause analogous accumulation of toxic metabolites. Alternatively, it has been suggested that pyrimidine starvation associated with adenosine deaminase deficiency may be a cause of immune dysfunction, since adenosine causes OA accumulation and pyrimidine nucleotide depletion in cultured cells. Not all experiments support this theory,[98] but dietary nucleotide depletion has been associated with reduction in cell-mediated immunity in mice.[236] The mechanism for this may be associated with low circulating pyrimidine levels causing low dCTP pools and reduced cell proliferation.[137,237]

No features of the disease have been related to defective synthesis of specific cofactors. Depletion of UDP-sugars and CDP-choline, necessary for galactose utilization and glycogen formation, or depletion of CDP-ethanolamine, necessary for phospholipid synthesis, might be the basis for the skeletal muscle weakness in some cases.

The pathogenesis of cardiac and other malformations, if these are caused by the enzyme deficiency, will depend on the relative roles of *de novo* synthesis and transplacental supply of maternal pyrimidines in the embryo and fetus, which may change through gestation.[238] Normal birth weights for gestation in hereditary orotic aciduria imply there is no pyrimidine starvation during late gestation. Studies in sheep have shown that 40 to 60 percent of uridine in fetal blood is maternally derived,[239] and a similar effect in humans could protect the fetus with UMPS deficiency in later pregnancy, although the levels of blood uridine in the heterozygous mother are not known. If these levels are lower than normal or if the maternal diet is deficient in pyrimidines, then fetal pyrimidine starvation might result. The conceptus may be at greater risk earlier in gestation, particularly during organogenesis, when malformations could be induced. There is a "normal" megaloblastic phase of erythropoiesis in the embryo prior to the commencement of hepatic blood formation[168] which may indicate susceptibility to additional deficiencies during that phase. 6AZUR is an inhibitor of ODC and is a potent teratogen when given during organogenesis.[240] 6AZUR administered to pregnant women induced degenerative changes in placental trophoblast at gestations of 1½ to 2½ months but not at older gestational age,[241] as a further indication that certain tissues have particular susceptibility to enzyme deficiencies early in pregnancy.

Genetics

Cases of hereditary orotic aciduria have been widely distributed geographically, and include patients of Polynesian, Oriental, white, American Indian, and black origin. Immunologic, molecular, biochemical, and genetic evidence indicates that the structural gene coding for UMPS activity is located on the long arm of chromosome 3 in the region 3q13.[81,82] This is consistent with the presumption of autosomal recessive inheritance of hereditary orotic aciduria.[138,141,145,147] based on the facts that patients with hereditary orotic aciduria have been both male (seven cases) and female (six cases), that one family had two siblings affected, and that it is possible to assign heterozygote status by biochemical observation.

Heterozygote detection is not simple in UMPS deficiency. Early family studies showed that obligate heterozygotes had blood enzyme levels or urinary OA levels clearly different from those of normal individuals.[33] Investigation of the family of J.R. suggested 18 of 45 family members were heterozygotes on the basis of reduced red cell UMPS activity.[138] There was no overlap in individual values between presumed normal and presumed heterozygotes. Heterozygotes had enzyme levels less than 1.5 nmol UMPS per hour per 10^9 erythrocytes. Presumed heterozygotes also had urine screening test ratios equal to or above 2 SD from the normal mean.[182] They were assigned as normal individuals with enzyme assays above 1.7, with a normal range ($n = 19$) of 2.4 to 14.9 nmol UMPS per hour per 10^9 erythrocytes. OA excreted in heterozygotes was clearly increased above controls levels, but orotidine excretion was about the same.[242]

McClard and colleagues have shown obligate heterozygote OPRT and ODC levels intermediate between a single homozygote and a single control in fibroblasts and erythrocytes,[154] and Tubergen also showed fibroblast OPRT and ODC levels intermediate between control (n = 2) and homozygous (n = 3) levels.[148] Urinary OA levels from these individuals were at the top of the normal range or higher.

However, Fox et al. showed that the frequency histogram for erythrocyte ODC was non-Gaussian and that the levels of both OPRT and ODC in obligate heterozygotes overlapped the lower end of the normal distribution.[147] This observation has been confirmed by other workers.[33,178] Fox suggests that assignation of heterozygote status should require both a low enzyme activity and a raised urine OA level.[147] The combined criterion is necessary since there are many other causes of slightly elevated urine OA.

Gene Frequency. A survey of 1358 mentally retarded subjects found two individuals who had repeatedly abnormal screening tests for urine OA and low OPRT and ODC activities. One had a parent with similar biochemical findings. These results would give a gene frequency with 95 percent confidence limits of 1:188 to 1:5607. No apparent heterozygotes were found in a study of 200 specimens from blood bank donors.[33] An unrelated apparently heterozygous individual was found during family studies of T.H.[145] This data implies the gene frequency is relatively high, which is at variance with the small number of documented cases of hereditary orotic aciduria. It has been suggested that the surviving cases represent a mild variant of the condition and that the more severe forms are lethal in utero. UMPS deficiency has been reported in cattle,[243] and recent work has suggested that homozygosity is lethal in the species in utero, perhaps due to embryonic resorption sometime before 40 days into pregnancy.[244] A large family study of patient J.R. failed to show any increase in spontaneous abortions over four generations.[138]

PYRIMIDINE-5′-NUCLEOTIDASE DEFICIENCY

Enzymology

Pyrimidine-5′-nucleotidase (P5N, enzyme 25, Fig. 43-1; sometimes called UMP hydrolase) catalyzes the dephosphorylation of pyrimidine-5′-ribomonophosphates to the corresponding nucleosides (Fig. 43-8). The enzyme was first identified in the soluble fraction of erythrocytes.[245,246] It has been separated from acid phosphatase and electrophoretically characterized.[247,248] P5N does not dephosphorylate purine nucleotides or the 2′-, 3′-, or cyclic pyrimidine nucleotides. The activity with thymidine monophosphate (TMP) is about half that found with UMP and CMP (K_ms 0.33 mM, UMP; 0.15 mM, CMP; and 1.0 mM, TMP).[246] The pH optimum is 7.5,[245,249] and the enzyme is most stable between pH 6 and 7.5.[249] Optimal activity requires the presence of magnesium and cannot be achieved with manganese. The enzyme is heat-sensitive and inhibited by AMP, some purine bases, purine and pyrimidine nucleosides, divalent cations of heavy metals, and agents active against sulfhydryl groups.[246]

Purification. The enzyme has been purified 250,000-fold by DEAE-cellulose chromatography, ammonium sulfate precipitation, gel filtration through Sephacryl S-200, and isoelectric focusing. Electrophoresis of the purified fraction revealed two major and two faint bands.[249] The enzyme has a pI of 5.0. The molecular weight was estimated by gel filtration to be 28,000 daltons. The purified enzyme has a K_m of 10 μM for CMP. This was lower than that measured in hemolysates (10 μM versus 40 μM), suggesting the possible presence of an inhibitor in the preparations.[249]

Isozymes. More recent reports indicate that specific isozymes of P5N exist. Erythrocytes from classic P5N-deficient patients that exhibited the expected loss of activity with UMP or CMP as substrate had activity with TMP as substrate.[250,251] Hydrolytic activity of erythrocytes from a P5N-deficient patient toward TMP and dUMP led Swallow[252] to postulate two separate structural gene loci, and the gene for the enzyme which hydrolyzes deoxynucleotides has been localized to the long arm of chromosome 17.[253]

Further evidence for a number of isozymes came from the study of four more families.[254] Somatic cell hybridization studies showed the presence of two isozymes catalyzing UMP hydrolysis, one of which is more active against deoxynucleotides.[255] Recent work by Hirono and colleagues[251] suggests there may be two totally separate enzymes of similar molecular weight, only one of which is important in the hydrolysis of nucleotides in the developing erythrocyte.

One isozyme (MW 52,000) separated from normal erythrocytes is active for UMP and CMP, but not for TMP. Two other isozymes (MW 52,000 and 48,000) were more active for TMP than for UMP or CMP.[256] The isoelectric points were 5.22, 4.90, and 4.68, respectively. None of these isozymes appear to correspond with the high purified enzyme of Torrance et al. (pI 5.0 and MW 28,000).[249]

A 5′-nucleotidase that is specific for OMP has been isolated from mouse liver microsomes.[257] This enzyme has negligible activity for UMP, CMP, dTMP, or purine monophosphates. The molecular weight is estimated to be 53,000. This activity may be responsible in part for the low levels of intracellular OMP and the accumulation of orotidine in cells treated with 6-AZUR.

Studies in rat hepatocytes suggest an immature form (M_r 67,000) which converts to a mature form (M_r 72,000). The half-life of the enzyme after the level reached plateau was 22.8 h.[258]

Clinical Studies

Presentation. P5N deficiency as a cause of hereditary hemolytic anemia was reported first by Valentine and colleagues in 1974.[245] They described four members of three kindreds who had hemolytic anemia with splenomegaly, and erythrocytes having prominent basophilic stippling. By 1980, 33 cases from 24 unrelated families had been reported.[259] Presentation is with a mild to moderate, usually well-compensated anemia. Splenomegaly is usually present, and sometimes hepatomegaly is noted. Hemoglobin concentrations are around 10 g/dl with reticulocytosis and marrow hyperplasia. There is unconjugated hyperbilirubinemia, increased erythrocyte glutathione, and decreased serum haptoglobins. There may be exacerbations during acute infections or pregnancy. Two siblings reported by Hansen and colleagues[260] had hemolysis, hemoglobinuria, and enlarged kidneys with considerable iron accumulation. The association with mental retardation in a minority of cases is of uncertain significance. The presenting details of 23 patients are summarized by Paglia et al.[259]

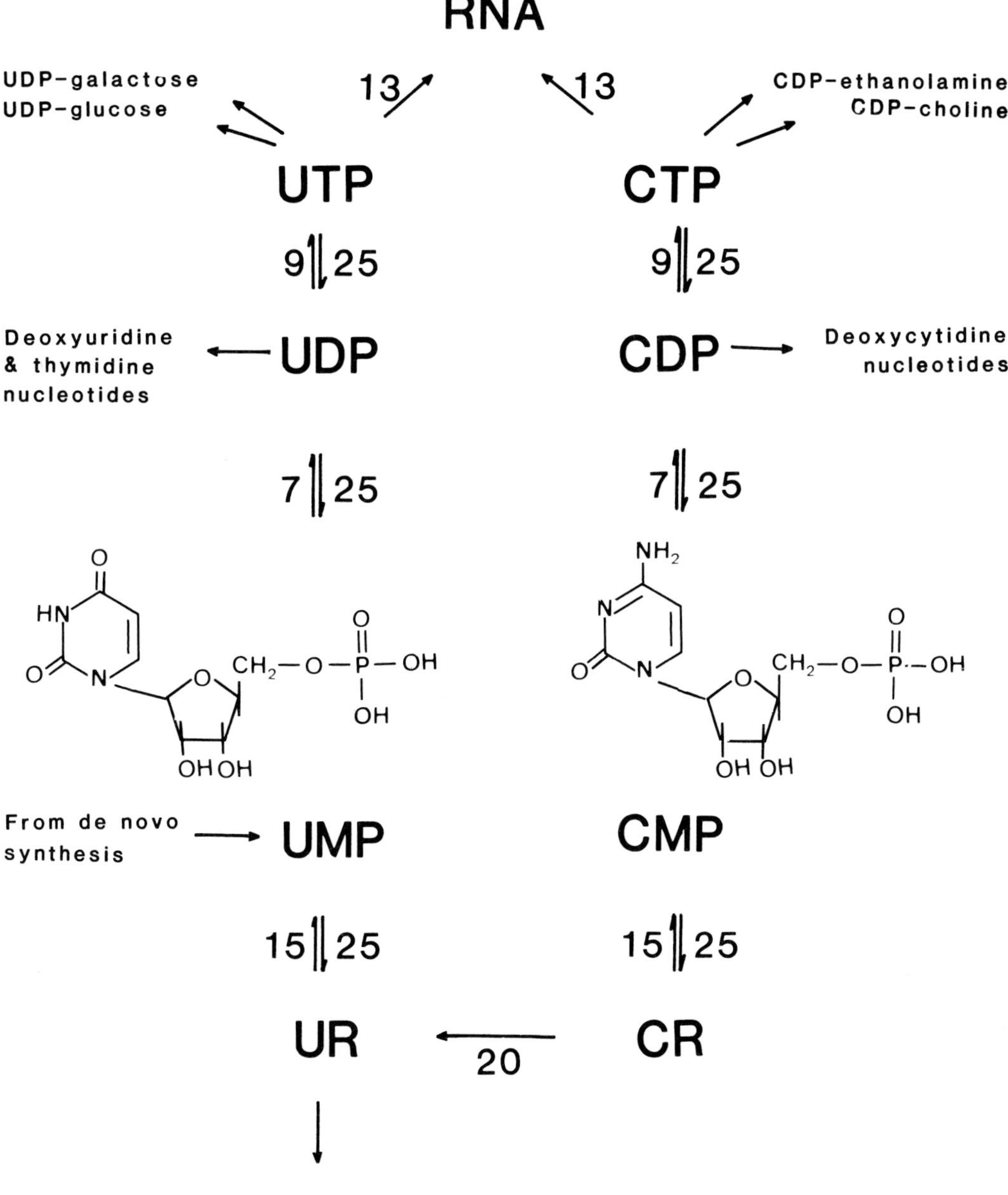

Fig. 43-8 Chemical structure of intermediates involved in pyrimidine-5′-nucleotidase deficiency. Enzyme numbers refer to Table 43-1.

Diagnosis. The diagnosis is often suspected because of basophilic stippling of erythrocytes and may be made simply by measurement of the ultraviolet (UV) absorption spectrum of deproteinized erythrocytes. The presence of high levels of cytidine and uridine ribonucleotides causes a pronounced shift in the UV absorption maximum and magnitude. Control extracts had a maximum absorbance at pH 2.0 between 255 to 260 nm, while patient extracts had maxima at 266 to 270 nm.[245] This may be confirmed by chromatographic separation of erythrocyte nucleotides.[261] Quantification of erythrocyte nucleotides (Table 43-3) shows large increases in cytidine nucleotides and cytidine phosphodiesters (3 to 4 m*M*). Smaller but substantial increases are seen in uridine nucleotides and nucleotide sugars (2 to 3 m*M*). Levels of purine nucleotides are not elevated.

Diagnosis may be confirmed by measurement of erythrocyte enzyme activity. Affected individuals have activity from 0 to 30 percent of normal mean. However, these levels are sometimes difficult to interpret, as the enzyme is much more active in young cells[259,268] and patients typically have 5 to 25 percent reticulocytes. It is necessary to prepare erythrocytes free of leukocytes and platelets by a standard methodology so as to obtain preparations of equivalent density and hence cell age. The enzyme may be assayed by separation of [^{14}C] CMP from cytidine by binding of the CMP to the barium sulfate precipitate that forms in the deproteinization procedure. The soluble cytidine can then be counted.[216,249] The products of the enzyme assay may also be quantified by chemical, other radiochemical,[262,263] or chromatographic methods.[249,264–267] A comprehensive discussion of methodology has been written by Paglia and colleagues.[259]

Treatment. There is no specific treatment at present for P5N deficiency, and there is no improvement with splenectomy. The erythrocyte hemolysis is probably caused by the accumulated pyrimidine nucleotides, and it has been shown that

Table 43-3 Erythrocyte Nucleotide Levels (μmol/liter) in Pyrimidine-5′-Nucleotidase Deficiency in Two Patients and Three Different Control Series[265,271,272]

	Patients (2)	Controls (3)		
Nucleotide	*Ref. 271*	*Ref. 270*	*Ref. 272*	*Ref. 271*
AMP	1.73, 1.87	0.084		1.41–2.04
ADP	0.16, 0.18	0.610	0.260	0.13–0.19
ATP	0.01, 0.01	1.063	1.270	0.01–0.02
IMP	<0.02, <0.02			<0.02
GMP	<0.01, <0.01			<0.01
GDP	0.02, 0.02		0.017	0.01–0.03
GTP	0.08, 0.07		0.060	0.05–0.09
UMP	0.05, 0.04		0.108	<0.01
UDP	0.10, 0.08	0.276	0.024	<0.01
UTP	0.94, 0.86	0.220	0.380	<0.01
CMP	0.09, 0.07	0.757	0.025	<0.01
CDP	0.35, 0.31	0.278	0.130	<0.01
CTP	1.74, 1.54	0.831	0.770	<0.01
UDP-glucose	0.66, 0.61	0.237	0.310	<0.10
UDP-*N*-Ac-glucosamine	0.61, 0.59			<0.01
CDP-choline	1.51, 1.50		0.930	<0.05
CDP-ethanolamine	0.57, 0.56		0.410	<0.01
NAD	0.09, 0.09			0.04–0.07

most of these nucleotides come from circulating preformed pyrimidines.[269] Kinetic analysis suggests that most of the pyrimidines are likely to be from orotate rather than from uridine, so a likely prospect for therapy of this condition is an inhibitor or orotate transport across erythrocyte membranes.[261] A trial of allopurinol in one patient increased the levels of erythrocyte pyrimidine nucleotides after 2 to 3 weeks. This is consistent with allopurinol in vivo inhibition of UMPS, increase of circulating orotate, increased orotate salvage, and therefore, increased pyrimidine nucleotides.[269]

Pathophysiology. The striking biochemical abnormality is the vastly increased amounts of erythrocyte pyrimidine nucleotides. Chromatographic separation and quantification (Table 43-3) showed that the increase was greater for the cytidine nucleotides,[270–272] and although the mononucleotides are closest to the enzyme block, the increase is greatest in the trinucleotides. The cytidine diphosphodiesters, CDP-ethanolamine and CDP-choline, were identified by Fourier transform–nuclear magnetic resonance and mass spectrometry.[272] These are found in high concentration, although no abnormality was reported in erythrocyte membrane phospholipids in one patient.[272] Lachant and coworkers[273] have studied pyrimidine nucleoside monophosphate kinase (PNMK, enzyme 7) activity in P5N deficiency. The enzyme has about double the activity in young cells compared with older erythrocytes, and is increased about fourfold in patients with P5N deficiency. PNMK activity in normal hemolysates is increased by UMP and CDP-ethanolamine. This suggests that in P5N deficiency increase of PNMK activity by UMP causes accumulation of UDP and CDP, which are subsequently phosphorylated by pyrimidine nucleoside diphosphate kinase (enzyme 9) to accumulate as triphosphates.[273]

Erythrocytes have been shown to readily increase uridine nucleotides when incubated with orotate,[274] and this increase goes into a separate cell compartment from the increase after uridine incubation.[275] Erythrocytes of two patients were found to have decreased pentose phosphate shunt activity. UTP and CTP inhibited glucose-6-phosphate dehydrogenase and pentose phosphate shunt activity about 50 percent at 5.5 m*M*, suggesting this may contribute to the pathogenesis of hemolysis.[276] Further kinetic analysis indicated that the K_is are above the intraerythrocytic concentrations in P5N deficiency and that it is unlikely this was a contributory factor in the hemolysis.[277]

It has been suggested that since pyrimidine nucleotides avidly bind magnesium, the hemolytic anemia may be due to a state of functional magnesium depletion in erythrocytes. The addition of 6 to 10 m*M* magnesium to intact red cells from a patient with P5N deficiency did not improve the autohemolysis test, the incubated Heinz body assay, or the rate of glucose oxidation by the pentose phosphate shunt. This lack of effect may have been due to the slow rate of uptake by the red cells.[273]

Genetics

A large family study could not identify all carriers by enzyme kinetic studies, electrophoresis, chromatographic examination of nucleotide extracts, or measurement of enzyme in cells of different ages due to overlap of obligate heterozygote with the normal range.[279] P5N activity was the same in males and females.[268]

Although it has been suggested that the disease is more common in Askenazim and blacks, it has also been reported in South Africans,[248] Norwegians,[260] Turks,[278] and Spaniards.[279] There are several reports of families with different P5N enzyme mutants. Hirono[251] reports three families with different kinetic-thermostability properties: P5N Kunamoto, Nagano, Kurume. Japanese families with different mutations are also reported by Fujii[280] (P5N Kagushima) and Rosa[247,248] (P5N Ishida). A Guadaloupe family was found to have about 14 percent normal activity.

Acquired Pyrimidines-5′-Nucleotidase Deficiency

In 1975, Paglia and colleagues[281] noted the similarity of the hematologic picture in lead poisoning to that in hereditary P5N deficiency. In 1976[282] they found reduced nucleotidase activity and increased pyrimidine nucleotides in erythrocytes in patients with lead poisoning. The severity of the enzyme inhibition was correlated with blood lead levels.[283] Lieberman and Gordon-Smith reported decreased P5N and increased glutathione in a variety of myeloproliferative disorders.[284] No correlation was found between the P5N and glutathione levels.

DIHYDROPYRIMIDINE DEHYDROGENASE DEFICIENCY

Dihydropyrimidine dehydrogenase (DHPDH) catalyzes the rate-limiting step in the degradation of the pyrimidine bases uracil and thymine. This NADPH-dependent reaction converts the bases to their dihydro derivatives (enzyme 22, Fig. 43-1). The dihydrouracil and dihydrothymine are then further catabolized to CO_2 and β-alanine or β-aminoisobutyric acid respectively (Fig. 43-9).

Enzymology

Purification. The enzyme has been partially purified from several sources including bacteria, rat, mouse, and beef liver.[285–288] DHPDH has been purified to apparent homogeneity from rat liver.[289] The native molecular weight was estimated to be 220,000 by calibrated gel filtration and by sedimentation equilibrium ultracentrifugation. Analysis of the purified protein by SDS-PAGE showed only a single band of approximately 110,000 daltons, suggesting that the enzyme is a dimer of two identical subunits. Each mole of enzyme contains 4 mol FAD (flavin adenine dinucleotide) and 3 mol iron.[289] DHPDH activity is decreased in regenerating and differentiating rat liver, rat hepatomas, and colon tumor in mouse.[290–292]

Kinetics. The pH optimum for the reaction is 7.4, with an apparent K_m of 2.6 μM for thymine and 1.8 μM for uracil in the presence of NADPH. Very similar values have been determined for ammonium sulfate precipitated liver extracts.[289] The rates of degradation for 5′-substituted analogues were highest for 5-fluorouracil and 5-bromouracil and lowest for 5-nitrouracil. The degradation rate of uracil was slightly faster than for thymine but significantly slower than for 5-fluorouracil. Uridine is a noncompetitive inhibitor of pyrimidine base degradation in vitro, with total inhibition of 5FU degradation at 10 μM. Thymidine was a less potent inhibitor of the reaction.[293]

Clinical Presentation

Deficiency of DHPDH has been documented in nine patients. Clinical details of these are given in Table 43-4 (patients 1 to 9). Patients 10 and 11 have had similarly elevated levels of uracil and thymine in body fluids but no enzyme studies.[293–300]

This enzyme deficiency does not have well-defined clinical effects, and most affected individuals have been detected in circumstances that could be coincidental. Only one case had a medical problem immediately after birth.[294] Other probands were investigated later in childhood for nonspecific variable neurologic resons. 5FU toxicity was the presenting feature in one case.[293] However, 4 children had late-onset, atypical seizures, and these may be a manifestation of the enzyme deficiency. Wilcken comments on the neonatal case: "The clinical presentation of our patient was quite different from other reported cases, no other patient had the striking alterations in tone and muscular incoordination or hepatomegaly. Nor do the other patients described resemble each other clinically, and it is possible the clinical findings are unrelated to the deficient activity of dihydropyrimidine dehydrogenase. . . . It is possible that the other patients did not have such completely deficient activity in liver as did our patient."[294]

Diagnosis

Uracil-thyminuria may be identified by measurement of urine pyrimidines by HPLC[205,295,296] or gas-chromatographic[294,295,297] techniques. A simple thin-layer chromatographic screening method has been described.[301] The results may be confirmed by measurement of plasma pyrimidines and leukocyte enzyme studies. High concentrations of uracil are also excreted in urea cycle defects, but this is accompanied by increased urine uridine and OA.[26]

Localization of the enzyme block in the original patient was made by oral loading studies. Most (75 percent) of the dose of uracil and thymine was excreted unchanged, while only 7 percent of dihydrouracil and 40 percent of dihydrothymine (given

Fig. 43-9 Chemical structure of the intermediates of the pyrimidine degradative pathway. Enzyme numbers refer to Table 43-1.

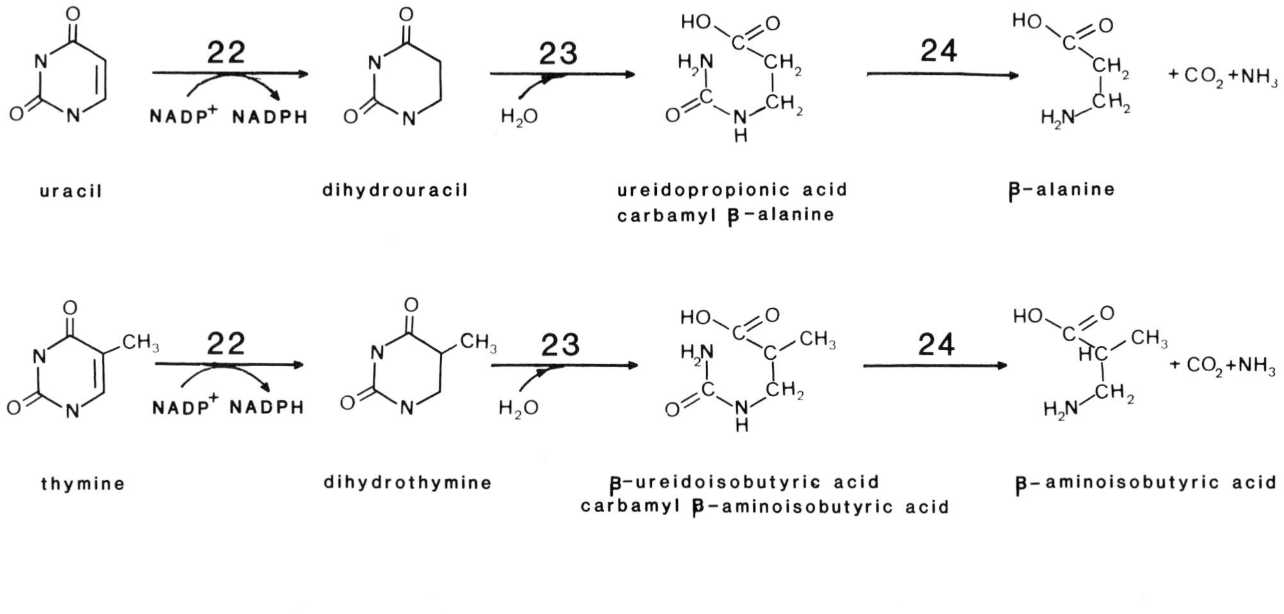

uracil → (22; NADP⁺ → NADPH) dihydrouracil → (23; H_2O) ureidopropionic acid / carbamyl β-alanine → (24) β-alanine + CO_2 + NH_3

thymine → (22; NADP⁺ → NADPH) dihydrothymine → (23; H_2O) β-ureidoisobutyric acid / carbamyl β-aminoisobutyric acid → (24) β-aminoisobutyric acid + CO_2 + NH_3

Table 43-4 Presentation of Cases of DHPDH Deficiency

Patient	Sex	Age	Presentation	Reference
1 R.E.	M	4 yr	Seizures, petit mal from 1½ yr, solitary behavior, autistic behavior, normal IQ, speech retardation, growth problems	296, 297
2 M.S.	F	14 yr	Mental retardation at 14 yr, epileptic absences from 5–6 yr, solitary behavior, hypohydrotic ectodermal dysplasia	296, 297
3 B.B.	M	15 mo	Developed feeding difficulties at 15 mo, growth retardation, microcephaly, retarded motor development	296, 297
4 M.M.	M	3 days	Hypertonia, hyperreflexia from birth, not sucking, fixing, or following, hepatomegaly (fatty liver, normal brain at postmortem) neuromuscular incoordination	294
5	M	6 yr	Epileptic seizures from 3 yr, microcephaly	295
6	F	Adult	Mother of case 5, epilepsy under treatment during pregnancy	205, 299
7	M	?	Brother of case 5, presumed normal	205, 299
8	M	2 yr	Ataxia and neurologic symptoms preceeding diagnosis of medulloblastoma	298
9	F	22 mo	Developmental problems	300
10	F	27 yr	Cancer of the breast 5FU treatment, severe CNS toxicity	299
11	M	?	Brother of case 10, presumed asymptomatic	299

as a mixture of R and S forms) were not metabolized. The diagnosis of DHPDH deficiency in patients 1 to 5 and 9 was made when urine organic acid gas chromatography, run as part of a screening protocol for inborn errors of metabolism, showed the presence of high concentrations of uracil and thymine. DHPDH activity was subsequently determined in fibroblasts or liver tissue. There is no absolute evidence, but it seems likely on theoretical grounds that the reported severe 5FU toxicity was caused by the enzyme deficiency.[293] One child with a medulloblastoma showed high urinary thymine and uracil levels. There may be pyrimidine as well as purine overproduction by neoplastic tissue, but six other children with neoplastic disease produced normal or only slightly elevated urine uracil and thymine.[298]

Treatment

No treatment specific for the enzyme defect or consequences of the defect has been described.

Pathophysiology

The specific increase of uracil and thymine in urine has led to the identification of this disorder. Body fluid measurements and enzyme activities are summarized in Table 43-5. Urine concentrations of uracil in DHPDH deficiency are greater than 100 mmol/mol of creatinine (normal less than 8[205,296] and of thymine greater than 80 mmol/mol of creatinine (normal

Table 43-5 Blood and Urine Pyrimidine Levels and Associated Enzyme Activities in Dihydropyrimidine Dehydrogenase Deficiency

	Urine, mmol/mol creatinine		Plasma, μmol/liter		
Patient	Uracil	Thymine	Uracil	Thymine	Enzyme activity, nmol/h/mg protein
1	519	339	nd	nd	0.04 leukocyte
2	226	271	nd	nd	0.01 leukocyte
3	1187	848	nd	nd	<0.01 leukocyte
4	157	111*	nd	nd	<0.05 liver
5	594	187	24	19	0.01 fibroblast
6	263	89	15	13	0.01 fibroblast
7	nd	nd	30	16	0.03
8	220	120	nd	nd	2.5 fibroblast
9	239	35	nd	nd	<0.01 leukocyte
10	100	114	6	12	nd
11	111	83	8	19	nd
Control	0.8–3.4†	not det†	<1†	<1†	1.01–4.46
Leukocytes†	<8‡	<6‡	0.2‡	not det‡	0.51–0.83 fibroblast‡ 4.4, 5.6 fibroblast§

*Ref. 163.
†Ref. 296.
‡Refs. 205, 299.
§Ref. 298.
nd = not done; not det = not detectable

less than 6[205,296]). Similarly, plasma concentrations of uracil and thymine are several-fold greater than normal, 8 μM compared to less than 1 μM.[205,296]

Patients 1 to 3 also excreted large amounts of 5-hydroxymethyluracil, a metabolite of thymine,[297] but this was undetectable in patient 9. Urine OA was normal in one patient[295] and urine urate normal in another patient.[294] Patients 1 and 2 had low levels of DHPDH activity in leukocytes, and patients 3 and 9 had an undetectable level. Fibroblast DHPDH activity was about half normal in patient 8, 1 to 2 percent of control activity in patient 5, while liver enzyme was undetectable in patient 4 (Table 43-5).

Genetics

There is no published information on incidence or gene frequency of DHPDH deficiency. Three of the eleven affected individuals listed in Table 43-5 appear to be asymptomatic. It is possible that the deficiency is more frequent than the number of reported cases would indicate and may be most often detected coincidentally. Severe 5FU toxicity may be a manifestation of the deficiency to be added to other examples of pharmacogenetic conditions.[302] There seems to be equal sex distribution. Family studies indicate probable autosomal recessive inheritance, but carrier detection may not be reliable. Heterozygotes may have reduced DHPDH in fibroblasts, although two of six parents studied had enzyme levels within the normal range.[297] Patient 6, the mother of patient 5, has an enzyme level similar to that of her affected child. There is no report on enzyme level in the father.

REFERENCES

1. See Chap. 37, Vol. I.
2. See Chap. 38, Vol. I.
3. See Chap. 39, Vol. I.
4. See Chap. 40, Vol. I.
5. See Chap. 41, Vol I.
6. See Chap. 42, Vol. I.
7. BONO VH, WEISSMAN SM, FREI E: The effect of 6-azauridine administration on de novo pyrimidine production in chronic myelogenous leukemia. *J Clin Invest* 43:1486, 1964.
8. SMITH LH JR: Pyrimidine metabolism in man. *N Engl J Med* 238:764, 1973.
9. HENDERSON JF, PATERSON ARP: *Nucleotide Metabolism. An Introduction.* New York, Academic, 1973.
10. CIHAK A, REUTTER W: in *Orotic Acid.* Great Britain, MTP Press, 1980.
11. JONES ME: Regulation of pyrimidine and arginine biosynthesis in mammals, in Weber G (ed): *Advances in Enzyme Regulations.* Oxford, New York, Pergamon, 1971, p 19.
12. SHAMBAUGH GE: Pyrimidine biosynthesis. *Am J Clin Nutr* 32:1290, 1979.
13. MAKOFF AJ, RADFORD A: Genetics and biochemistry of carbamoyl phosphate biosynthesis and its utilisation in the pyrimidine biosynthetic pathway. *Microbiol Rev* 42:307, 1978.
14. COLEMAN PF, SUTTLE DP, STARK GR: Purification from hamster cells of the multifunctional protein that initiates de novo synthesis of pyrimidine nucleotides. *J Biol Chem* 252:6379, 1977.
15. MORI M, TATIBANA M: Purification of homogeneous glutamine-dependent carbamly phosphate synthetase from ascites hepatoma cells as a complex with aspartate tanscarbamylase and dihydroorotase. *J Biochem* 78:239, 1975.
16. JARRY BP: Purification of asparatate transcarbamylase from Drosophila melanogaster. *Eur J Biochem* 87:633, 1978.
17. DAVIDSON JN, PATTERSON D: Alteration in structure of multifunctional protein from Chinese hamster ovary cells defective in pyrimidine biosynthesis. *Proc Natl Acad Sci USA* 76:1731, 1979.
18. DAVIDSON JN, NISWANDER LA: Partial cDNA sequence to a hamster gene corrects defects in Escherichia coil pyrB mutant. *Proc Natl Acad Sci USA* 80:6897, 1983.
19. SHIGESADA K, STARK GR, MALEY JA, NISWANDER LA, DAVIDSON JN: Construction of a cDNA to the hamster CAD gene and its application toward defining the domain for aspartate transcarbamylase. *Mol Cell Biol* 5:1735, 1985.
20. MORI M, TATIBANA M: Multi-enzyme complex of glutamine-dependent carbamoyl-phosphate synthase with aspartate carbamoyltransferase and dihydroorotase from rat ascites-hepatoma cells. Purification, molecular properties and limited proteolysis. *Eur J Biochem* 86:381, 1978.
21. LEE L, KELLY RE, PASTRA-LANDIS SC, EVANS DR: Oligomeric structure of the multifunctional protein CAD that initiates pyrimidine biosynthesis in mammalian cells. *Proc Natl Acad Sci USA* 82:6802, 1985.
22. RUMSBY PC, CAMPBELL PC, NISWANDER LA, DAVIDSON JN: Organization of a multifunctional protein in pyrimidine biosynthesis. *Biochem J* 217:435, 1984.
23. GRAYSON DR, EVANS DR: The isolation and characterization of the aspartate transcarbamylase domain of the multifunctional protein, CAD. *J Biol Chem* 258:4123, 1983.
24. PADGETT RA, WAHL GM, STARK GR: Structure of the gene for CAD, the multifunctional protein that initiates UMP synthesis in Syrian hamster cells. *Mol Cell Biol* 2:293, 1982.
25. WAHL GM, PADGETT RA, STARK GR: Gene amplification causes overproduction of the first three enzymes of UMP synthesis in N-(phosphonacetyl)-L-aspartate-resistant hamster cells. *J Biol Chem* 264:8679, 1979.
26. See Chap. 20, Vol. I.
27. DILEEPAN K, KENNEDY J: Rapid conversion of newly-synthetised orotate to uridine-5-monophosphate by rat liver cytosolic enzymes. *FEBS Lett* 153:1, 1983.
28. HOOGENRAAD NJ, LEE DC: Effect of uridine on de novo pyrimidine biosynthesis in rat hepatoma cells in culture. *J Biol Chem* 249:2763, 1974.
29. KARLE JM, COWAN KH, CHISENA CA, CYSYK RL: Uracil nucleotide synthesis in a human breast cancer cell line (MCF-7) and in two drug-resistant sublines that contain increased levels of enzymes of the de novo pyrimidine pathway. *Mol Pharmacol* 30:136, 1986.
30. SUGIURA Y, FUJIOKA S, YOSHIDA S: Biosynthesis of pyrimidine nucleotides in human leukemic cells. *Jpn J Cancer Res* 77:664, 1986.
31. BECROFT DMO, PHILLIPS LI, SIMMONDS A: Hereditary orotic aciduria: Long term therapy with uridine and a trial of uracil. *J Pediatr* 75:885, 1969.
32. PERIGNON J-L, BORIES DM, HOULLIER A-M, THUILLIER L, CARTIER PH: Metabolism of pyrimidine bases and nucleosides by pyrimidine-nucleoside phosphorylases in cultured cells. *Biochim Biophys Acta* 928:130, 1987.
33. KELLEY WN: Hereditary orotic aciduria, in JB Stanbury, JB Wyngaarden, DS Fredrickson, JL Goldstein, Brown MS (eds): *The Metabolic Basis of Inherited Disease*, 5th ed. New York, McGraw-Hill, 1983, p 1202.
34. REICHARD P: The enzymatic synthesis of pyrimidines. *Adv Enzymol* 21:623, 1959.
35. SHOAF WT, JONES ME: Uridylic acid synthesis in Ehrlich ascites carcinoma. Properties, subcellular distribution, and nature of enzyme complexes of the six biosynthetic enzymes. *Biochemistry* 12:4039, 1973.
36. HATFIELD D, WYNGAARDEN JB: 3-Ribosylpurines I. Synthesis of (3-ribosyluric acid) 5′-phosphate and (3-ribosylxanthine) 5′-phosphate by a pyrimidine ribonucleotide pyrophosphorylase of beef erythrocytes. *J Biol Chem* 239:2580, 1964.
37. KASBEKAR DK, NAGABHUSHANAM A, GREENBERG DM: Purification and properties of orotic acid-decarboxylating enzymes from calf thymus. *J Biol Chem* 239:4245, 1964.
38. APPEL SH: Purification and kinetic properties of brain orotidine 5′-phosphate decarboxylase. *J Biol Chem* 243:3924, 1968.
39. REYES P, GUGANIG ME: Studies on a pyrimidine phosphoribosyltransferase from murine leukemia P1534J. *J Biol Chem* 250:5097, 1975.
40. BROWN GK, FOX RM, O'SULLIVAN WJ: Interconversion of different molecular weight forms of human erythrocyte orotidylate decarboxylase. *J Biol Chem* 250:7352, 1975.
41. KAVIPURAPU PR, JONES ME: Purification, size, and properties of the complex of orotate phosphoribosyltransferase:orotidylate decarboxylase from mouse Ehrlich ascites carcinoma. *J Biol Chem* 251:5589, 1976.
42. BROWN GK, O'SULLIVAN WJ: Subunit structure of the orotate phosphoribosyltransferase-orotidylate decarboxylase complex from human erythrocytes. *Biochemistry* 16:3235, 1977.
43. KROOTH RS, PAN Y-L, PINSKY L: Studies of the orotidine 5′-monophosphate decarboxylase activity of crude extracts of human cells. *Biochem Genet* 8:133, 1973.

44. MCLARD RW, BLACK MJ, LIVINGSTONE LR, JONES ME: Isolation and initial characterization of the single polypeptide that synthesizes uridine 5′-monophosphate from orotate in Ehrlich ascites carcinoma. Purification by tandem affinity chromatography of uridine-5′-monophosphate synthase. *Biochemistry* 19:4699, 1980.
45. BRODY RS, WESTHEIMER FH: The purification of orotidine-5′-phosphate decarboxylase from yeast by affinity chromatography. *J Biol Chem* 254:4238, 1979.
46. LIVINGSTONE LR, JONES ME: The purification and preliminary characterization of UMP synthase from human placenta. *J Biol Chem* 262:15726, 1987.
47. SUTTLE DP, STARK GR: Coordinate overproduction of orotate phosphoribosyltransferase and orotidine-5′-phosphate decarboxylase in hamster cells resistant to pyrazofurin and 6-azauridine. *J Biol Chem* 254:4206, 1979.
48. LEVINSON BB, ULLMAN B, MARTIN DW JR: Pyrimidine pathway variants of cultured mouse lymphoma cells with altered levels of both orotate phosphoribosyltransferase and orotidylate decarboxylase. *J Biol Chem* 254:4396, 1979.
49. SUTTLE DP, WEBER G: Coordinate overproduction of orotate phosphoribosyltransferase and orotidylate carboxylase in hepatoma cells resistant to pyrazofurin and 6-azauridine. *XI International Congress of Biochemistry*, A318, 1979.
50. SUTTLE DP, HARKRADER RJ, JACKSON RC: Pyrazofurin-resistant hepatoma cells deficient in adenosine kinase. *Eur J Cancer* 17:43, 1981.
51. ISHII K, GREEN H: Lethality of cultured mammalian cells by interference with pyrimidine biosynthesis. *J Cell Sci* 13:429, 1973.
52. PASTERNACK CA, HANDSCHUMACHER RE: The biochemical activity of 6-azauridine: Interference with pyrimidine metabolism in transplantable mouse tumors. *J Biol Chem* 234:2992, 1959.
53. SUTTLE DP: Increased levels of UMP synthase protein and mRNA in pyrazofurin-resistant rat hepatoma cells. *J Biol Chem* 258:7707, 1983.
54. SUTTLE DP: Unpublished data.
55. KANALAS JJ, SUTTLE DP: Amplification of the UMP synthase gene and enzyme overproduction in pyrazofurin-resistant rat hepatoma cells. Molecular cloning of a cDNA for UMP synthase. *J Biol Chem* 259:1848, 1984.
56. TRAUT TW, JONES ME: Interconversion of different molecular weight forms of the orotate phosphoribosyltransferase Orotidine-5′-phosphate decarboxylase enzyme complex from mouse Erlich ascites cells. *J Biol Chem* 254:1143, 1979.
57. TRAUT TW, PAYNE RC, JONES M-E: Dependence of the aggregation and conformation states of uridine 5′-phosphate synthase on pyrimidine nucleotides. Evidence for a regulatory site. *Biochemistry* 19:6062, 1980.
58. TRAUT TW, PAYNE RC: Dependence of the catalytic activities on the aggregation and conformation states of uridine 5′-phosphate synthase. *Biochemistry* 19:6068, 1980.
59. BISSWANGER H, SCHMINCKE-OTT E (eds): *Multifunctional Proteins*. New York, Wiley, 1980, p. 1.
60. FLOYD EE, JONES ME: Isolation and characterization of the orotidine 5′-monophosphate decarboxylase domain of the multifunctional protein uridine 5′-phosphate synthase. *J Biol Chem* 260:9443, 1985.
61. ROSE M, GRISAFI P, BOTSTEIN D: Structure and function of the yeast URA3 gene: Expression in Escherichia coli. *Gene* 29:113, 1984.
62. OHMSTEDE C-A, LANGDON SD, CHAE C-B, JONES ME: Expression and sequence analysis of a cDNA encoding the orotidine 5′-monophosphate decarboxylase domain from Ehrlich ascites uridylate synthase. *J Biol Chem* 261:4276, 1986.
63. LANGDON SD, JONES ME: Study of the kinetic and physical properties of the orotidine-5′-monophosphate decarboxylase domain from mouse UMP synthase produced in Saccharomyces cerevisiae. *J Biol Chem* 262:13359, 1987.
64. VICTOR J, LEO-MENSAH A, SLOAN DL: Divalent metal ion activation of the yeast orotate phosphoribosyltransferase catalysed reaction. *Biochemistry* 18:3597, 1979.
65. SYED DB, STRAUSS RS, SLOAN DL: Orotate phosphoribosyltransferase and hypoxanthine/guanine phosphoribosyltransferase from yeast: Nuclear magnetic relaxation studies of enzyme-bound phosphoribosyl 1-pyrophosphate. *Biochemistry* 26:1051, 1987.
66. VICTOR J, GREENBERG LG, SLOAN DL: Studies of the kinetic mechanism of orotate phosphoribosyltransferase from yeast. *J Biol Chem* 254:2647, 1979.
67. TRAUT TW: UMP synthase: The importance of quaternary structure in channeling intermediates. *TIBS* 7:255, 1982.
68. TRAUT TW, JONES ME: Kinetic and conformational studies of the orotate phosphoribosyltransferase: Orotidine-5′-phosphate decarboxylase enzyme complex from mouse Ehrlich ascites cells. *J Biol Chem* 252:8374, 1977.
69. TRAUT TW: Significance of the enzyme complex that synthesizes UMP in Ehrlich ascites cells. *Arch Biochem Biophys* 200:590, 1980.
70. MCCLARD RW, SHOKAT K: Does the bifunctional protein uridylate synthase actually "channel" orotidine 5′-phosphate (OMP)? *Biochemistry* 26:3378, 1987.
71. WIGINTON DA, ADRIAN GA, FRIEDMAN RL, SUTTLE DP, HUTTON JJ: Cloning of cDNA sequences of human adenosine deaminase. *Proc Natl Acad Sci USA* 80:7481, 1983.
72. KANALAS JJ, HUTTON JJ, SUTTLE DP: Characterization of pyrazofurin-resistant HeLa cells with amplification of UMP synthase gene. *Somatic Cell Mol Genet* 11:359, 1985.
73. SUTTLE DP, BUGG BY, WINKLER JK, KANALAS JJ: Molecular cloning and nucleotide sequence for the complete coding region of human UMP synthase. *Proc Natl Acad Sci USA* 85:1754, 1988.
74. POULSON P, JENSEN KF, VALENTIN-HANSEN P, CARLSSON P, LUNDBERG LG: Nucleotide sequence of the *Escherichia coli pyrE* gene and of the DNA in front of the protein-coding region. *Eur J Biochem* 135:223, 1983.
75. DUSH MK, SIKELA JM, KHAN SA, TISCHFIELD JA, STAMBROOK PJ: Nucleotide sequence and organization of the mouse adenine phosphoribosyltransferase gene: Presence of a coding region common to animal and bacterial phosphoribosyltransferases that has a variable intron/exon arrangement. *Proc Natl Acad Sci USA* 82:2731, 1985.
76. HERSHEY HV, TAYLOR MW: Nucleotide sequence and deduced amino acid sequence of Escherichia coli adenine phosphoribosyltransferase and comparison with other analogous enzymes. *Gene* 43:287, 1986.
77. BRODERICK TP, SCHAFF DA, BERTINO AM, DUSH MK, TISCHFIELD JA, STAMBROOK PJ: Comparative anatomy of the human APRT gene and enzyme: Nucleotide sequence divergence and conservation of a nonrandom CpG dinucleotide arrangement. *Proc Natl Acad Sci USA* 84:3349, 1987.
78. ARGOS P, HANEI M, WILSON JM, KELLY WN: A possible nucleotide-binding domain in the tertiary fold of phosphoribosyltransferases. *J Biol Chem* 258:6450, 1983.
79. STEPANIK P, BUGG B, SUTTLE DP: Construction of a UMP synthase (UMPS) expression vector capable of selection, amplification, and deamplification. *FASEB J* 2:A4828, 1988.
80. PATTERSON D: Isolation and characterization of 5-fluorouracil-resistant mutants of Chinese hamster ovary cells deficient in the activities of orotate phosphoribosyltransferase and orotidine 5′-monophosphate decarboxylase. *Somatic Cell Genet* 6:101, 1980.
81. PATTERSON D, JONES C, MORSE H, RUMSBY P, MILLER Y, DAVIS R: Structural gene coding for multifunctional protein carrying orotate phosphoribosyltransferase and OMP decarboxylase activity is located on the long arm of human chromosome 3. *Somatic Cell Genet* 9:359, 1983.
82. QUMSIYEH MB, VALENTINE M, SUTTLE DP: Unpublished data.
83. BERMAN P, HARLEY EH: Orotate uptake and metabolism by human erythrocytes. *Adv Exp Biol Med* 165A:367, 1984.
84. YOUNG JD, JARVIS SM: Nucleoside transport in animal cells. *Bioscience Rep 3:309, 1983.*
85. PLAGEMANN PGW: Nucleotide pools of Novikoff rat hepatoma cells growing in suspension culture. I. Kinetics of incorporation of nucleosides into nucleotide pools and pool sizes during growth cycle. *J Cell Physiol* 77:213, 1971.
86. PLAGEMANN PGW, WOHLHEUTER RM: Nucleoside transport in mammalian cells and interaction with intracellular metabolism, in Berne RM, Rall TW, Rubio R (eds): *Regulatory Function of Adenosine*. The Hague, Martinus Nijhoff, 1983, p 179.
87. DARNOWSKI JW, HANDSCHUMACHER RE: Tissue uridine pools: Evidence in vivo of a concentrative mechanism for uridine uptake. *Cancer Res* 46:3490, 1986.
88. DARNOWSKI JW, HOLDRIDGE C, HANDSCHUMACHER RE: Concentrative uridine transport by murine splenocytes: Kinetics, substrate specificity, and sodium dependency. *Cancer Res* 47:2614, 1987.
89. BRONK JR, HASTEWELL JG: The transport of pyrimidines into tissue rings cut from rat small intestine. *J Physiol* 382:475, 1987.
90. TAYLOR MW, KOTHARI RM, HOLLAND GD, MARTINEZ-VALDEZ H, ZEIGE G: A comparison of purine and pyrimidine pools in Bloom's syndrome and normal cells. *Cancer Biochem Biophys* 7:19, 1983.
91. PETERS GJ, DE ABREU RA, OOSTERHOF A, VEERKAMP JH: Concentration of nucleotides and deoxynucleotides in peripheral and phytohemaggutinin-stimulated mammalian lymphocytes. Effects of adenosine and deoxyadenosine. *Biochim Biophys Acta* 759:7, 1983.
92. DE KORTE D, HAVERKORTE WA, ROOS D, VAN GENNIP A: Anion-exchange high performance liquid chromatography method for the quantitation of nucleotides in human blood cells. *Clin Chim Acta* 148:185, 1985.
93. DE KORTE, HAVERKORTE WA, VAN GENNIP AH, ROOS D: Nucleotide profiles of normal human blood cells determined by high performance liquid chromatography. *Anal Biochem* 147:197, 1985.

94. LOSMAN MJ, HARLEY EH: Evidence for compartmentation of uridine nucleotide pools in rat hepatoma cells. *Biochim Biophys Acta* 521:762, 1978.

95. RASENACK J, PAUSCH J, GEROK W: *De novo* pyrimidine biosynthesis in isolated rat hepatocytes. *J Biol Chem* 260:4145, 1985.

96. TSENG JK, GURPIDE E: Compartmentalisation of uridine and uridine 5'-monophosphate in rat liver slices. *J Biol Chem* 248:5634, 1973.

97. NUKI G, ASTRIN K, BRENTON D, CRUIKSHANK M, LEVER J, SEEGMILLER JE: Purine and pyrimidine nucleotides in some mutant human lymphoblasts, in *Purine and Pyrimidine Metabolism, Ciba Foundation Symposium 48.* Amsterdam, Elsevier, 1977, p 127.

98. FOX IH, BURK L, PLANET G, GOREN M, KAMINSKA J: Pyrimidine nucleotide biosynthesis. A study of normal and purine-enzyme deficient cells. *J Biol Chem* 253:6794, 1978.

99. PINSKY L, KROOTH RS: Studies on the control of pyrimidine biosynthesis in human diploid cell strains, I. Effect of 6-azauridine on cellular phenotype. *Proc Natl Acad Sci USA* 57:925, 1967.

100. PINSKY L, KROOTH RS: Studies on the control of pyrimidine biosynthesis in human diploid cell strains, II. Effects of 5-azaorotic acid, barbituric acid and pyrimidine precursors on cellular phenotype. *Proc Natl Acad Sci USA* 57:1267, 1967.

101. KROOTH RS, LAM GFM, CHEN KIANG SY: Oxipurinol and orotic aciduria: Effect on the orotidine-5'-monophosphate decarboxylase activity of cultured human fibroblasts. *Cell* 3:55, 1974.

102. KELLEY WN, BEARDMORE TD: Allopurinol: Alteration of pyrimidine metabolism in man. *Science* 169:388, 1970.

103. FOX RM, WOOD MH, O'SULLIVAN WJ: Studies on the co-ordinate activity and lability of orotidylate phosphoribosyltransferase and decarboxylase in human erythrocytes, and the effect of allopurinol administration. *J Clin Invest* 50:10050, 1971.

104. BEARDMORE TD, FOX IH, KELLEY WN: Effect of allopurinol on pyrimidine metabolism in the Lesch-Nyhan syndrome. *Lancet* ii:830, 1970.

105. BEARDMORE TD, KELLEY WN: Mechanism of allopurinol-mediated inhibition of pyrimidine biosynthesis. *J Lab Clin Med* 78:696, 1971.

106. GROBNER W, ZOLLNER N: The Influence of dietary purines and pyrimidines on human pyrimidine biosynthesis. *Klin Wochenschr* 61:1191, 1983.

107. HATFIELD PJ, SIMMONDS HA, CAMERON JS, JONES AS, CADENHEAD A: Effects of allopurinol and oxonic acid on pyrimidine metabolism in the pig. *Adv Exp Med Biol* 41B:637, 1974.

108. BEARDMORE TD, CASHMAN JS, KELLEY WN: Mechanism of allopurinol-mediated increase in pyrimidine metabolism in man. *J Clin Invest* 51:1823, 1972.

109. BEARDMORE TD, KELLEY WN: Effects of allopurinol and oxipurinol on pyrimidine biosynthesis in man. *Adv Exp Med Biol* 41:609, 1974.

110. FOSTER DM, LEE CS, O'SULLIVAN WJ: Allopurinol and enzymes of de novo pyrimidine biosynthesis. *Biochem Med* 7:61, 1973.

111. BECKER MA, ARGUBRIGHT KF, FOX RM, SEEGMILLER JE: Oxipurinol-associated inhibition of pyrimidine synthesis in human lymphoblasts. *Mol Pharmacol* 10:657, 1974.

112. BROWN GK, FOX RM, O'SULLIVAN WJ: Alteration of quaternary structural behaviour of an hepatic orotate phosphoribosyltransferase-orotidine-5'-phosphate decarboxylase complex in rats following allopurinol therapy. *Biochem Pharmacol* 21:2469, 1972.

113. GROBNER W, KELLEY WN: Effect of allopurinol and its metabolic derivatives on the configuration of human orotate phosphoribosyltransferase and orotidine 5'-phosphate decarboxylase. *Biochem Pharmacol* 24:379, 1975.

114. REITER S, ZOLLNER N, BRAUN S, KNEDEL M: Allopurinol-induced orotic-aciduria in a xanthinuric patient not forming allopurinol. *Klin Wochenschr* 65 (*suppl* X):13, 1987.

115. DAVIES PM, SIMMONDS HA, MULLIGAN PE: Orotidine accumulates in the erythrocytes of patients with renal failure or gout during allopurinol therapy. *Klin Wochenschr* 65 (*suppl* X):10, 1987.

116. KELLEY WN, FOX IH, BEARDMORE TD, MEADE JC: Allopurinol and oxipurinol: Alteration of purine and pyrimidine metabolism in cell culture. *Ann NY Acad Sci* 179:588, 1971.

117. KELLEY WN, BEARDMORE TD, FOX IH, MEADE JC: Effect of allopurinol and oxipurinol on pyrimidine synthesis in cultured human fibroblasts. *Biochem Pharmacol* 20:1471, 1971.

118. HANDSCHUMACHER RE, PASTERNAK CA: Inhibition of orotidylic acid decarboxylase, a primary site of carcinostasis by 6-azauracil. *Biochem Biophys Acta* 30:451, 1958.

119. CARDØSO SS, CALABRESI P, HANDSCHUMACHER RE: Alterations in human pyrimidine metabolism as a result of therapy with 6-azauridine. *Cancer Res* 21:1551, 1961.

120. HANDSCHUMACHER RE: Orotidylic acid decarboxylase: Inhibition studies with azauridine 5'-phosphate. *J Biol Chem* 235:2917, 1960.

121. FALLON HJ, FREI E, BLOCK J, SEEGMILLER JE: The uricosuria and orotic aciduria induced by 6-azauridine. *J Clin Invest* 40:1906, 1961.

122. FALLON HJ, FREI E, FREIREICH EJ: Correlations of biochemical and clinical effects of 6-azauridine in patients with leukemia. *Am J Med* 33:526, 1962.

123. FALLON HJ, LOTZ M, SMITH LH: Congenital orotic aciduria: Demonstration of an enzyme defect in leukocytes and comparison with drug-induced orotic aciduria. *Blood* 20:700, 1962.

124. CONN HO, CREASEY WA, CALABRESI P: Effect of 6-azauridine on plasma cell tumours of mice: Correlation of antitumour effect with inhibition of orotic acid metabolism. *Cancer Res* 27:618, 1967.

125. BRUEMMER NC, HOLLAND JF, SHEEHE PR: Drug effects on a target metabolic pathway and on mouse tumour growth: Azauridine and decarboxylation of orotic acid-7-C^{14}. *Cancer Res* 22:113, 1962.

126. ROUX JM, HOOGENRAAD NJ, KRETCHMER N: Biosynthesis of pyrimidine nucleotides in mouse salivary glands stimulated with isoproterenol. *J Biol Chem* 248, 1196, 1973.

127. WELLS W, GAINES D, KOENIG H: Studies of pyrimidine nucleotide metabolism in the central nervous system I. Metabolic effects and metbolism of 6Azauridine. *J Neurochem* 10:709, 1963.

128. KROOTH RS: Molecular models for pharmacological tolerance and addiction. *Ann NY Acad Sci* 179:548, 1971.

129. POTVIN BW, STERN HJ, MAY SR, LAM GF, KROOTH RS: Inhibition by barbituric acid and its derivatives of the enzymes in rat brain which participate in the synthesis of pyrimidines ribotides. *Biochem Pharm* 27:655, 1978.

130. NIEDZWICKI JG, ILTZSCH MH, EL KOUNI MH, CHA S: Structure-activity relationship of pyrimidine base analogs as ligands of orotate phosphoribosyltransferase. *Biochem Pharmacol* 33:2383, 1984.

131. ARDALAN B, GLAZER R: An update on the biochemistry of 5-fluorouracil. *Cancer Treatment Reviews* 8:157, 1981.

132. KESSEL D, HALL TC, PEYES P: Metabolism of uracil and 5-fluorouracil in P388 murine leukemia cells. *Mol Pharmacol* 5:481, 1969.

133. MULKINS MA, HEIDELBERGER C: Isolation of fluoropyrimidine-resistant murine leukemic cell lines by one step mutation and selection. *Cancer Res* 42:956, 1982.

134. GREEN H, CHAN T-S: Pyrimidine starvation induced by adenosine in fibroblasts and lymphoid cells; role of adenosone deaminase. *Science* 182:836, 1973.

135. DANKS MK, SCHOLAR EM: Regulation of phosphoribosylpyrophosphate synthetase by endogenous purine and pyrimidine compounds and synthetic analogs in normal and leukemic white blood cells. *Biochem Pharmacol* 31:1687, 1982.

136. VAN DER KRAAN PM, VAN ZANDVOORT PM, DE ABREU RA, VAN BAAL JM, BAKKEREN JAJM: Inhibition of lymphoid cell growth by adenine ribonu cleotide accumulation. The role of phosphoribosylpyrophosphate-depletion induced pyrimidine starvation. *Biochim Biophys Acta* 927:213, 1987.

137. FALLER J, PALELLA TD, DEAN P, FOX IH: Altered cell cycle distributions of cultured human lymphoblasts during cytotoxicity related to adenosine derminase inhibition. *Metabolism* 33:369, 1984.

138. FALLON HJ, SMITH LH JR, GRAHAM JB, BURNETT CH: A genetic study of hereditary orotic aciduria. *N Engl J Med* 270:878, 1964.

139. HUGULEY CM, BAIN JA, RIVERS SL, SCOGGINS RB: Refractory megaloblastic anaemia associated with excretion of orotic acid. *Blood* 14:615, 1959.

140. SMITH LH JR, SULLIVAN M, HUGULEY CM: Pyrimidine metabolism in man. IV The enzymatic defect of orotic aciduria. *J Clin Invest* 40:656, 1961.

141. SOUTTER JB, YU JS, LOVRIC A, STAPLETON T: Hereditary orotic aciduria. *Aust Paediatr J* 6:47, 1970.

142. BECROFT DMO, PHILLIPS LI: Hereditary orotic aciduria and megaloblastic anaemia: A second case with response to uridine. *Br Med J* 1:547, 1965.

143. BECROFT DMO, WEBSTER DR, SIMMONDS HA, FAIRBANKS LD, WILSON JD, PHILLIPS LI: Hereditary orotic aciduria: Further biochemistry. *Adv Exp Med Biol* 195A:67, 1986.

144. HAGGARD ME, LOCKHART LH: Megaloblastic anemia and orotic aciduria. A hereditary disorder of pyrimidine metabolism responsive to uridine. *Am J Dis Child* 113:733, 1967.

145. ROGERS LE, WARFORD LR, PATTERSON B, PORTER FS: Hereditary orotic aciduria. I. A new case with family studies. *Pediatrics* 42:415, 1968.

146. FOX RM, O'SULLIVAN WJ, FIRKIN BG: Orotic aciduria, Differing enzyme patterns. *Am J Med* 47:332, 1969.

147. FOX RM, WOOD MH, ROYSE-SMITH D, O'SULLIVAN WJ: Hereditary orotic aciduria: Types I and II. *Am J Med* 55:791, 1973.

148. TUBERGEN DG, KROOTH RS, HEYN RM: Hereditary orotic aciduria with normal growth and development. *Am J Dis Child* 118:864, 1969.

149. NEIMANN N, NAJEAN Y, SCIALOM C, BOULARD M, PIERSON M, BERNARD J: Étude d'un cas d'anemie megaloblastique de l'enfant avec excretion anormale d'acide orotique. *Nouv Rev Fr Hematol* 5:445, 1963.

150. WADA Y, NISHIMURA Y, TANABU M, YOSHIMURA Y, IINUMA K, YOSHIDA T,

ARAKAWA T: Hypouricemic, mentally retarded infant with a defect of 5-phosphoribosyl-1-pyrophosphate synthetase of erythrocytes. *Tohoku J Exp Med* 113:149, 1974.

151. WADA Y: Personal communication.

152. GIROT R, DURANDY A, PERIGNON J-L, GRISCELLI C: Hereditary orotic aciduria: A defect of pyrimidine metabolism with cellular immunodeficiency. *Birth Defects* 19:313, 1983.

153. GIROT R, HAMET M, PERIGNON J-L, GUESNU M, FOX RM, CARTIER P, DURNADY A, GRISCELLI C: Cellular immune deficiency in two siblings with hereditary orotic aciduria. *N Engl J Med* 308:700, 1983.

154. MCCLARD RW, BLACK MJ, JONES ME, YOUNG SR, BERKOWITZ GP: Neonatal diagnosis of orotic aciduria: An experience with one family. *J Pediatr* 102:85, 1983.

155. SMITH LH JR, GILMOUR L: Determination of urinary carbamylaspartate and dihydro-orotate in normal subjects and in patients with hereditary orotic aciduria. *J Lab Clin Med* 86:1047, 1975.

156. ALVARADO CS: Personal communication.

157. SUCHI M: Personal communication.

158. BECROFT DMO, PHILLIPS LI, WEBSTER DR, WILSON JD: Absence of immune deficiency in hereditary orotic aciduria. *N Engl J Med* 310, 1333, 1984.

159. SIMMONDS HA, POTTER CF, SAHOTA A, CAMERON JS, WEBSTER DR, BECROFT DMO: Absence of orotic aciduria in adenosine deaminase deficiency and purine nucleoside phosphorylase deficiency. *Clin Exp Immunol* 34:42, 1978.

160. SIMMONDS HA, WEBSTER DR, BECROFT DMO, POTTER CF: Purine and pyrimidine metabolism in hereditary orotic aciduria: Some unexpected effects of allopurinol. *Eur J Clin Invest* 10:333, 1980.

161. WEBSTER DR, SIMMONDS HA, POTTER CF, BECROFT DMO: Purine and pyrimidine metabolism in hereditary orotic aciduria during a 15 year follow-up study. *Adv Exp Med Biol* 122B:203, 1980.

162. HOWELL RR, KLINENBERG JR, KROOTH RS: Enzyme studies on diploid cell strains developed from patients with hereditary orotic aciduria. *Johns Hopkins Med J* 120:81, 1967.

163. WILCKEN B: Personal communication.

164. LAHEY ME: Personal communication.

165. PATTERSON RB: Personal communication.

166. HAGGARD ME: Personal communication.

167. SMITH LH JR, HUGULEY CM JR, BAIN JA: Hereditary orotic aciduria, in Stanbury JB, Wyngaarden JB, Fredrickson DS (eds): *The Metabolic Basis of Inherited Disease,* 2d ed. New York, McGraw-Hill, 1966, p 739.

168. CHANARIN I: *The Megaloblastic Anemias,* 2d ed. Oxford, Blackwell, 1979.

169. NATHAN DG, OSKI FA: The megaloblastic anemias, in Nathan DG, Oski FA (eds): *Hematology of Infancy and Childhood,* 2d ed. Philadelphia, Saunders, 1974.

170. SHIN YS, REITER S, ZELGER O, BRUNSTLER I, V RUCKER A: Orotic aciduria, homocystinuria, formiminoglutamic aciduria and megaloblastosis associated with the formiminotransferase/cyclodeaminase deficiency. *Adv Exp Med Biol* 195A:71, 1986.

171. REINEKE RD: Current concepts in opthalmology. Strabismus. *N Engl J Med* 300:1139, 1979.

172. INSLEY J: The heritability of congenital heart disease. *Br Med J* 294:662, 1987.

173. KENNA AP, SMITHELLS RW, FIELDING DW: Congenital heart disease in Liverpool: 1960–1969. *Q J Med* 44:17, 1975.

174. REID COMV, HALL JG, ANDERSON C, BOCIAN M, CAREY J, COSTA T, CURRY C, GREENBERG F, HORTON W, JONES M, LAFER C, LARSON E, LUBINSKY M, MCGILLIVRAY B, PEMBRY M, POPKIN J, SELLER M, SIEBERT V, VERHAGEN A: Association of amyoplasia with gastroschisis, bowel atresia, and defect of muscular layer of the trunk. *Am J Med Genet* 24:701, 1986.

175. GIROT R, DURANDY A, PERIGNON J-L, GRISCELLI C: Absence of immune deficiency in hereditary orotic aciduria. *N Engl J Med* 310:1334, 1984.

176. PERIGNON J-L: Personal communication.

177. PETERS JG, VAN GROENINGEN C, NADAL JG, LEYVA A, LAURENSSE E, PINEDO HM: Metabolism, excretion and bioavailability of orally administered uridine in man. *Klin Wochenschr* 65 (*suppl* X):15, 1987.

178. WEBSTER DR, SIMMONDS HA, BECROFT DMO: Unpublished observations.

179. KLUBES P, GEFFEN DB, CYSYK RL: Comparison of the bioavailability of uridine in mice after either oral or parenteral administration. *Cancer Chemother Pharmacol* 17:236, 1987.

180. LEYVA A, VAN GROENINGEN CJ, KRAAL I, PETERS JG, LANKELMA J, PINEDO HM: Phase I and pharmacokinetic studies of high-dose uridine intended for rescue from 5-fluorouracil toxicity. *Cancer Res* 44:5928, 1984.

181. WEISSMAN SM, LEWIS M, KARON M: The metabolism of isotopically labelled uracil and uridine in man. *Metabolism* 12:60, 1963.

182. ROGERS LE, PORTER FS: Hereditary orotic aciduria II: A urinary screening test. *Pediatrics* 42:423, 1968.

183. HARRIS ML, OBERHOLZER VG: Conditions affecting the colorimetry of orotic acid and orotidine in urine. *Clin Chem* 26:473, 1980.

184. KAMOUN P, COUDE M, DEPRUN C, RABIER D: Source of error in the assay of urinary orotic acid. *Clin Chem* 33:713, 1987.

185. GLASGOW AM: A new method for measuring urinary orotic acid. *Am J Clin Pathol* 77:452, 1982.

186. REITER S, SIMMONDS HA, WEBSTER DR, WATSON AR: On the metabolism of allopurinol. Formation of allopurinol-1-riboside in purine nucleoside phosphorylase deficiency. *Biochem Pharmacol* 32:2167, 1983.

187. VAN GENNIP AH, VAN BREE-BLOM EJ, GRIFT J, DE BREE PK, WADMAN SK: Urinary purines and pyrimidines in patients with hyperammonemia of various origins. *Clin Chim Acta* 104:227, 1980.

188. JAKOBS C, SWEETMAN L, NYHAN WL, GRUENKE L, CRAIG JC, WADMAN SK: Stable isotope dilution analysis of orotic acid and uracil in amniotic fluid. *Clin Chim Acta* 143:123, 1984.

189. GLASGOW AM, LARSEN JW: Urinary orotic acid in pregnancy. *Am J Obstet Gynecol* 149:464, 1984.

190. BACHMANN C, COLOMBO JP: Determination of orotic acid in children's urine. *J Clin Chem Clin Biochem* 18:293, 1980.

191. JEEVANANDAM M, SHOEMAKER JD, HOROWITZ GD, LOWRY SF, BRENNAN MF: Orotic acid excretion during starving and after refeeding in normal men. *Metabolism* 34:325, 1985.

192. VISEK WJ, LONG DA, WELLIK DL, NELSON RA: Urinary orotic acid (uoa) compared to other urinary metabolites for adult volunteers. *Fed Proc* 39:1116, 1980.

193. TAX WJM, VEERKAMP JH, SCHRETLEN EDAM: The urinary excretion of orotic acid and orotidine, measured by isotope dilution assay. *Clin Chim Acta* 90:217, 1978.

194. VISEK WJ, SHOEMAKER JD: Orotic acid, arginine and hepatotoxicity. *J Am Coll Nutr* 5:153, 1986.

195. BACHMANN C, COLOMBO JP: Diagnostic value of orotic acid in heritable disorders of the urea cycle and hyperammonemia due to organic acidurias. *Eur J Paediatr* 134:109, 1980.

196. BECROFT DMO, BARRY DMJ, WEBSTER DR, SIMMONDS HA: Failure of protein loading tests to identify heterozygosity for ornithine carbamolytransferase deficiency. *J Inherited Metab Dis* 7:157, 1984.

197. HATCHWELL LC, MILNER JA: Amino-acid induced orotic aciduria. *J Nutr* 108:578, 1978.

198. RAJANTIE J: Orotic aciduria in lysinuric protein intolerance: Dependence on urea cycle intermediates. *Pediatr Res* 15:115, 1981.

199. COHEN A, STAHL GE, AMMANN AJ, MARTIN DW JR: Orotic aciduria in two unrelated patients with inherited deficiencies of purine nucleoside phosphorylase deficiency. *J Clin Invest* 60:491, 1977.

200. EDWARDS NL, GELFAND EW, BIGGAR D, FOX IH: Partial deficiency of purine nucleoside phosphorylase: Studies of purine and pyrimidine metabolism. *J Lab Clin Med* 91:736, 1978.

201. MILLS GC, SCHMALSTEIG FC, NEWKIRK KE, GOLDBLUM RM: Cytosine and orotic acid in urine of immunodeficient children. *Clin Chem* 25:419, 1979.

202. WOOD MH, O'SULLIVAN WJ: The orotic aciduria of pregnancy. *Am J Obstet Gynecol* 116:57, 1973.

203. WEBSTER DR, SIMMONDS HA, BARRY DMJ, BECROFT DMO: Purine and pyrimidine metabolites in ornithine carbamoyltransferase deficiency. *J Inherited Metab Dis* 4:27, 1981.

204. WADMAN SK, BEEMER FA, DE BREE PK, DURAN M, VAN GENNIP AH, KETTING D, VAN SPRANG FJ: New defects of pyrimidine metabolism. *Adv Exp Med Biol* 165A:109, 1982.

205. DE ABREU RA, BAKKEREN JAJM, BRAAKHEKKE J, GABREELS FJM, MAAS JM, SENGERS RCA: Dihyrothymine dehydrogenase deficiency in a family, leading to elevated levels of uracil and thymine. *Adv Exp Med Biol* 195A:77, 1986.

206. KARLE JM, ANDERSON LW, DIETRICK DD, CYSYK RL: Determination of serum and plasma uridine levels in mice rats and humans by high pressure liquid chromatography. *Anal Biochem* 109:41, 1980.

207. CHAN TCK, MARKMAN M, CLEARY S, HOWELL SB: Plasma uridine changes in cancer patients treated with the combination of dipyridamole and N-phosphonoacetyl-L-aspartate. *Cancer Res* 46:3168, 1986.

208. PARRY TE, BLACKMORE JA: Serum "uracil + uridine" levels in pernicious anaemia. *Br J Haematol* 34:567, 1976.

209. YOSHIDA S, HIROSE S: Use of 4-bromomethyl-7-methoxycoumarin for derivatisation of pyrimidine compounds in serum analysed by high-performance liquid chromatography with fluorimetric detection. *J Chromatogr* 383:61, 1986.

210. HARKNESS RA, LUND RJ: Cerebrospinal fluid concentrations of hypoxanthine, xanthine, uridine and insoine: High concentrations of the ATP metabolite hypoxanthine after hypoxia. *J Clin Pathol* 36:1, 1983.

211. HARKNESS RA, GEIRSSON RT, MCFADYEN IR: Concentrations of hypoxanthine, xanthine, uridine and urate in amniotic fluid at caesarean section

and the association of raised levels with prenatal risk factors and foetal distress. *Br J Obstet Gynaecol* 90:815, 1983.

212. DELBARRE F, AUSCHER C: Traitement de la goutte par l'acide uracil-6-carboxylique et ses derives. *Presse Med* 71:11765, 1963.

213. ZOLLNER N, GROBNER W: Dietary feedback regulation of purine and pyrimidine biosynthesis in man, in *Purine and Pyrimidine Metabolism, Ciba Foundation Symposium 48*. Amsterdam, Elsevier, 1977.

214. CHUNG SH, SLOAN DL: Enzymatic kinetic analyses that employ high performance liquid chromatography. Competition between orotate- and hypoxanthine/guanine phosphoribosyltransferase for a common substrate. *J Chromatogr* 371:71, 1986.

215. FOX IH, KELLEY WN: Phosphoribosylpyrophosphate in man: Biochemical and clinial significance. *Ann Intern Med* 74:424, 1971.

216. BEUTLER E, BLUME KG, KAPLAN JC, LOHR GW, RAMOT B, VALENTINE WN: International committee for standardisation in haematology: Recommended methods for red cell enzyme analysis. *Br J Haematol* 35:331, 1977.

217. VAN DER WEYDEN MB, COOPER M, FIRKIN BG: Altered erythrocyte pyrimidine activity in vitamin B_{12} or folate deficiency. *Br J Haematol* 42:85, 1979.

218. BORDEN M, NYHAN WL, BAKAY B: Increased activity of adenine phosphoribosyltransferase in erythrocytes of normal newborn infants. *Pediatr Res* 8:31, 1974.

219. TENG Y-S, CHEN S-H, GIBLETT ER: Red cell uridine monophosphate kinase: Effects of red cell aging on the activity of the two UMPK gene products. *Am J Hum Genet* 28:138, 1986.

220. KONRAD P, VALENTINE WN, PAGLIA DE: Enzymatic activities and glutathione content of erythrocytes in the newborn: Comparison with red cells of older normal subjects and those with comparative reticulocytosis. *Acta Haematol* 48:193, 1972.

221. ZIELKE HR, OZAND PT, LUDDY RE, ZINKHAM WH, SCHWARTZ AD, SEVDALIAN DA: Elevation of pyrimidine enzyme activities in the rbc of patients with congenital hypoplastic anemia and their parents. *Br J Haematol* 42:381, 1979.

222. GLADER B, BACKER K: Comparative activity of erythrocyte adenosine deaminase and orotidine decarboxylase in Diamond-Blackfan anemia. *Am J Hematol* 23:135, 1986.

223. WORTHY TE, GROBNER W, KELLEY WN: Hereditary orotic aciduria: Evidence for a structural gene mutation. *Proc Natl Acad Sci USA* 71:3031, 1974.

224. WINKLER JK, SUTTLE DP: Analysis of UMP synthase gene and mRNA structure in hereditary orotic aciduria fibroblasts. *Am J Hum Genet* 43:86, 1988.

225. PERRY ME, JONES ME: Studies of UMP synthase in orotic aciduria fibroblasts. *Fed Proc* 46(6):309, 1987.

226. WUU K-D, KROOTH RS: Dihydroorotic acid dehydrogenase activity of human diploid cell strains. *Science* 160:539, 1968.

227. RODECK CH, PATRICK AD, PEMBREY ME, TZANNATOS C, WHITFIELD AE: Fetal liver biopsy for prenatal diagnosis of ornithine carbamoyltransferase deficiency. *Lancet* ii:297, 1982.

228. O'SULLIVAN WJ: Orotic acid. *Aust NZ J Med* 3:417, 1973.

229. COLLIPP PJ: Orotic acid, inosine and nucleotides in the treatment of degenerative retinal diseases: A double blind study. *Curr Ther Res* 41:135, 1987.

230. KELLEY WN, FOX IH, WYNGAARDEN JB: Regulation of purine biosynthesis in cultured human cells. I. effects of orotic acid. *Biochem Biophys Acta* 215:512, 1970.

231. WINDMUELLER HG, VAN EULER LH: Prevention of orotic acid induced fatty liver with allopurinol. *Proc Soc Exp Biol Med* 136:98, 1971.

232. RAISONNIER A, BOUMA ME, SALVAT C, INFANTE R: Metabolism of orotic acid: Lack of orotate phosphoribosyltransferase in rat intestinal mucosa. *Eur J Biochem* 188:565, 1981.

233. HERBERT V: Biology of disease. Megaloblastic anemias. *Lab Invest* 52:3, 1985.

234. WEISCHEL ME, CLARK BR: Pyrimidine metabolism during restorative brain growth after neonatal undernutrition in the rat. *Pediatr Res* 11:293, 1977.

235. HARDEBO JE, KAHRSTROM J, OWMAN C, SALFORD LG: Endothelium dependent relaxation by uridine tri-and diphosphate in human pial vessels. *Blood Vessels* 24:150, 1987.

236. VAN BUREN CT, KULKARNI AD, SCHANDLE VB, RUDOLPH FB: The influence of dietary nucleotides on cell-mediated immunity. *Transplantation* 36:350, 1983.

237. BHALLA K, GRANT S: Effect of deoxycytidine on the in vitro response of human leukemia cells to inhibitors of de novo pyrimidine biosynthesis. *Cancer Chemother Pharmacol* 19:226, 1987.

238. GALOFRE A, KRETCHMER N: Biosynthesis of pyrimidine by various organs of the chick during embryogenesis. *Pediatr Res* 4:55, 1970.

239. GURPIDE E, TSENG J, ESCARCENA L, FAHNING M, GIBSON C, FEHR P: Feto-maternal production and transfer of progesterone and uridine in sheep. *Am J Obstet Gynecol* 113:21, 1972.

240. GUTOVA M, ELIS J, RASKOVA H: Teratogenic effect of 6-azauridine in rats. *Teratology* 4:287, 1971.

241. VOJTA M, JIRASEK J: 6-Azauridine-induced changes of the trophoblast of early human pregnancy. *Clin Pharmacol Ther* 7:162, 1966.

242. LOTZ M, FALLON HJ, SMITH LH JR: Excretion of orotic acid and orotidine in heterozygotes of congenital orotic aciduria. *Nature* 197:194, 1963.

243. ROBINSON JL, DRABNIK MR, DOMBROWSKI DB, CLARK JH: Consequences of UMP synthase deficiency in cattle. *Proc Natl Acad Sci USA* 80:321, 1983.

244. HARDEN KK, ROBINSON JL: Deficiency of UMP synthase in dairy cattle: A model for hereditary orotic aciduria. *J Inherited Metab Dis* 10:201, 1987.

245. VALENTINE WN, FINK K, PAGLIA DE, HARRIS SR, ADAMS WS: Hereditary hemolytic anemia with human erythrocyte pyrimidine 5'-nucleotidase deficiency. *J Clin Invest* 54:866, 1974.

246. PAGLIA DE, VALENTINE WN: Characteristics of a pyrimidine-specific 5'-nucleotidase in human erythrocytes. *J Biol Chem* 250:7973, 1975.

247. ROSA R, ROCHANT H, DREYFUS B, VALENTIN C, ROSA J: Electrophoretic and kinetic studies of human erythrocytes deficient in pyrimidine 5'-nucleotidase. *Hum Genet* 38:209, 1977.

248. ROSA R, VALENTIN C, ROSA J: Electrophoretic characterization of pyrimidine 5'-nucleotidase of human erythrocytes and its distinction from acid phosphatase. *Clin Chim Acta* 79:115, 1977.

249. TORRANCE J, WEST C, BEUTLER E: A simple rapid radiometric assay for pyrimidine 5'-nucleotidase. *J Lab Clin Med* 90:563, 1977.

250. PAGLIA DE, VALENTINE WN, KEITT AS, BROCKWAY RA, NAKATANI M: Pyrimidine nucleotidase deficiency with active dephosphorylation of dTMP: Evidence for existence of thymidine nucleotidase in human erythrocytes. *Blood* 62:1147, 1983.

251. HIRONO A, FUJII H, MIYAJIMA H, KAWAKATSU T, HIYOSHI Y, MIWA S: Three families with hereditary hemolytic anemia and pyrimidine 5'-nucleotidase deficiency: Electrophoretic and kinetic studies. *Clin Chim Acta* 130:189, 1983.

252. SWALLOW MMD, AZIZ I, HOPKINSON DA, MIWA S: Analysis of human erythrocyte 5'-nucleotidases in healthy individuals and a patient deficient in pyrimidine 5'-nucleotidase. *Ann Hum Genet* 47:19, 1983.

253. WILSON DL, SWALLOW DM, POVEY S: Assignment of the gene for uridine 5'-monophosphate phosphohydrolase (UMPH2) to the long arm of chromosome 17. *Ann Hum Genet* 50:223, 1986.

254. PAGLIA DE, VALENTINE WN, BROCKWAY RA: Identification of thymidine nucleotidase and deoxyribonucleotidase activities among normal isozymes of 5'-nucleotidase in human erythrocytes. *Proc Natl Acad Sci USA* 81:588, 1984.

255. HOPKINSON DA, SWALLOW DM, TURNER VS, AZIZ I: Evidence for a distinct deoxypyrimidine 5'-nucleotidase in human tissues. *Adv Exp Med Biol* 165A:535, 1984.

256. ODA T, NAGAO M, SHIRONO K, KAGIMOTO T, TAKATSUKI K: Isozymes of human erythrocyte pyrimidine 5'-nucleotidase. *J Lab Clin Med* 106:646, 1985.

257. EL KOUNI MH, CHA S: Isolation and partial characterization of a 5'-nucleotidase specific for orotidine-5'-monophosphate. *Proc Natl Acad Sci USA* 79:1037, 1982.

258. BARON MD, LUZIO JP: The synthesis and turnover of 5'-nucleotidase in primary cultured hepatocytes. *Biochim Biophys Acta* 927:81, 1987.

259. PAGLIA DE, FINK K, VALENTINE WN: Additional data from two kindreds with genetically-induced deficiencies of erythrocyte pyrimidine nucleotidase. *Acta Hematol* 63:262, 1980.

260. HANSEN TWR, SIEP M, DE VERDIER C-H, ERICSON A: Erythrocyte pyrimidine 5'-nucleotidase deficiency. Report of 2 new cases, with a review of the literature. *Scand J Hematol* 31:122, 1983.

261. HARLEY EH, BERMAN P: Diagnostic and therapeutic approaches in pyrimidine 5'-nucleotidase deficiency. *Adv Exp Med Biol* 165A:1003, 1984.

262. BUC H, KAPLAN J-C: A radioassay for pyrimidine-5'-nucleotidase activity. *Clin Chim Acta* 85:193, 1978.

263. ELLIMS PH, BAILEY L, VAN DER WEYDEN MB: An improved method for the determination of human erythrocyte pyrimidine 5'-nucleotidase activity. *Clin Chim Acta* 88:99, 1978.

264. TORRANCE JD, KARABUS CD, SHNIER M, MELTZER M, KATZ J, JENKINS T: Haemolytic anaemia due to erythrocyte pyrimidine 5'-nucleotidase deficiency. Report of the first South African family. *S Afr Med J* 52:671, 1977.

265. TORRANCE JD, WULFSOHN MS, MILLS W: Problems encountered in measuring erythrocyte pryimidine 5'-nucleotidase activity. *Anal Biochem* 126:235, 1982.

266. SAKAI T, YANAGIHARA S, USHIO K: Determination of 5′-nucleotidase activity in human erythrocytes and plasma using high performance liquid chromatography. *J Chromatogr* 239:717, 1982.

267. ZEREZ CR, TANAKA KR: A continuous spectrophotometric assay for pyrimidine 5′-nucleotidase. *Anal Biochem* 151:282, 1985.

268. TORRANCE JD, WHITTAKER D, JENKINS T: Erythrocyte pyrimidine 5′-nucleotidase. *Br J Haematol* 45:585, 1980.

269. HARLEY EH, HEATON A, WICOMB W: Pyrimidine metabolism in hereditary erythrocyte pyrimidine 5′-nucleotidase deficiency. *Metabolism* 27:1743, 1978.

270. TORRANCE JD, WHITTAKER D: Distribution of erythrocyte nucleotides in pyrimidine 5′-nucleotidase deficiency. *Br J Haematol* 43:423, 1979.

271. ERICSON A, DE VERDIER C-H, HANSEN TWR, SIEP M: Erythrocyte nucleotide pattern in two children in a Norwegian family with pyrimidine 5′-nucleotidase deficiency. *Clin Chim Acta* 134:25, 1983.

272. SWANSON MS, MARKIN RS, STOHS SJ, ANGLE CR: Identification of cytidine diphosphodiesters in erythrocytes from a patient with pyrimidine nucleotidase deficiency. *Blood* 63:665, 1984.

273. LACHANT NA, ZEREZ CR, TANAKA KR: Pyrimidine nucleoside monophosphate hyperactivity in hereditary pyrimidine 5′-nucleotidase deficiency. *Br J Haematol* 66:91, 1987.

274. HARLEY EH, SACKS S, BERMAN P, COHEN L, SIMMONDS HA, FAIRBANKS LD, BLACK D: Source and fate of circulating pyrimidines. *Adv Exp Med Biol* 195A:109, 1986.

275. HARLEY EH, ZETLER P, NEAL S: Kinetics and compartmentation of erythrocyte pyrimidine metabolism. *Adv Exp Med Biol* 122B:217, 1980.

276. TOMODA A, NOBLE NA, LACHANT NA, TANAKA KR: Hemolytic anemia in hereditary pyrimidine 5′-nucleotidase deficiency: Nucleotide inhibition of G6PD and the pentose phosphate shunt. *Blood* 60:1212, 1982.

277. ODA E, ODA S, TOMODA A, LACHANT NA, TANAKA KR: Hemolytic anemia in hereditary pyrimidine 5′-nucleotidase deficiency. II. Effect of pyrimidine nucleotides and their derivatives on glycolytic and pentose phosphate shunt enzyme activity. *Clin Chim Acta* 141:93, 1984.

278. OZSOYLU S, GURGEY A: A case of hemolytic anemia due to erythrocyte pyrimidine 5′-nucleotidase deficiency. *Acta Hematol* 66:56, 1981.

279. VIVES-CORRONS JL, MONTSERRAT-COSTA E, ROZMAN C: Hereditary hemolytic anemia with erythrocyte pyrimidine 5′-nucleotidase deficiency in Spain. Clinical, biological and familial studies. *Hum Genet* 34:285, 1976.

280. FUJII H, NAKASHIMA K, MIWA S, NOMURA K: Electrophoretic and kinetic studies of a mutant red cell pyrimidine 5′-nucleotidase. *Clin Chim Acta* 95:98, 1979.

281. PAGLIA DE, VALENTINE WN, DAHLGREN JG: Effects of low-level lead exposure on pyrimidine 5′-nucleotidase and other erythrocyte enzymes. *J Clin Invest* 56:1164, 1975.

282. VALENTINE WN, PAGLIA DE, FINK K, MADOKORO G: Lead poisoning. Association with hemolytic anemia, basophilic stippling, erythrocyte pyrimidine 5′-nucleotidase deficiency and intraerythrocytic accumulation of pyrimidines. *J Clin Invest* 58:926, 1976.

283. PAGLIA DE, VALENTINE WN, FINK K: Lead poisoning. Further observations on erythrocyte pyrimidine nucleotidase deficiency and intracellular accumulation of pyrimidine nucleotides. *J Clin Invest* 60:1362, 1977.

284. LIEBERMAN JE, GORDON-SMITH EC: Red cell pyrimidine 5′-nucleotidase and glutathione in myeloproliferative and lymphoproliferative disorders. *Br J Haematol* 44:425, 1980.

285. CAMPBELL LL: Reductive degradation of pyrimidines. III. Purification and properties of dihydrouracil dehydrogenase. *J Biol Chem* 227:693, 1957.

286. GRISOLIA S, CARDOSO SS: The purification and properties of hydropyrimidine dehydrogenase. *Biochem Biophys Acta* 25:430, 1957.

287. FRITZSON P: Properties and assay of dihydrouracil dehydrogenase of rat liver. *J Biol Chem* 235:719, 1960.

288. SANNA Y, HOLZED M, SCHMIKE RT: Studies of a mutation affecting pyrimidine degradation in inbred mice. *J Biol Chem* 245:5668, 1970.

289. SHIOTANI T, WEBER G: Purification and properties of dihydrothymine dehydrogenase from rat liver. *J Biol Chem* 256:219, 1981.

290. POTTER VR, POTIT HC, ONO T, MORRIS HP: The comparative enzymology and cell origin of rat hepatoma. I. Deoxycytidylate deaminase and thymine degradation. *Cancer Res* 20:1255, 1960.

291. FRITZSON P: Delayed synthesis of uracil-degrading enzymes in regenerating rat liver. *Biochem Biophys Acta* 91:374, 1964.

292. QUEENER SF, MORRIS HP, WEBER G: Dihydrourical dehydrogenase activity in normal, differentiating, and regenerating liver and in hepatomas. *Cancer Res* 31:1004, 1971.

293. TUCHMAN M, STOECKELER JS, KIANG DT, O'DEA RF, RAMNARAINE ML, MIRKEN BL: Familial pyridinaemia and pyrimidinuria associated with severe fluorouracil toxicity. *N Engl J Med* 313:245, 1985.

294. WILCKEN B, HAMMOND J, BERGER R, WISE G, JAMES C: Dihydropyrimidine dehydrogenase deficiency—A further case. *J Inherited Metab Dis* 8 *suppl* 2:115, 1985.

295. BAKKEREN JAJM, DE ABREU RA, SENGERS RCA, GABREELS FJM, MAAS JM, RENIER WO: Elevated urine, blood and cerebrospinal fluid levels of uracil and thymine in a child with dihydrothymine dehydrogenase deficiency. *Clin Chim Acta* 140:247, 1984.

296. WADMAN SK, BERGER R, DURAN M, DE BREE PK, STOKER-DE VRIES SA, BEEMER FA, WEITS-BINNERTS JJ, PENDERS TJ, VAN DER WOUDE JK: Dihydropyrimidine dehydrogenase deficiency leading to Thymine-uraciluria. An inborn error of pyrimidine metabolism. *J Inherited Metab Dis* 8 *suppl* 2:113, 1985.

297. BERGER R, STOKER-DE VRIES SA, WADMAN SK, DURAN M, BEEMER FA, DE BREE PK, WEITS-BINNERTS JJ, PENDERS TJ, VAN DER WOUDE JK: Dihydropyrimidine dehydrogenase deficiency leading to thymine-uraciluria. An inborn error of pyrimidine metabolism. *Clin Chim Acta* 141:227, 1984.

298. BERGLUND G, GRETER J, LINDSTEDT S, STEEN G, WALDENSTROM J, WASS U: Urinary excretion of thymine and uracil in a two-year-old child with a malignant tumor of the brain. *Clin Chem* 25:1325, 1979.

299. DE ABREU RA, BAKKEREN JAJM, BRAAKHEKKE J, GABREELS FJM, MAAS JM, SENGERS RCA: Dihydrothymine dehydrogenase deficiency in a family, leading to elevated levels of uracil and thymine. *Adv Exp Med Biol* 195A:77, 1986.

300. VAN GENNIP AH, BAKKER HD, ZOETEKOUW A, ABELING NGGM: A new case of thymine-uraciluria. *Klin Wochenschr* 65(*suppl* X):14, 1987.

301. VAN GENNIP AH, VAN NOORDENBERG-HUISTRA DY, DE BREE PK, WADMAN SK: Two dimensional thin-layer chromatography for the screening of disorders of purine and pyrimidine metabolism. *Clin Chim Acta* 86:7, 1978.

302. VESSELL ES: Genetic host factors: Determinants of drug response. *N Engl J Med* 313:261, 1985.

PART 7

LIPOPROTEIN AND LIPID METABOLISM DISORDERS

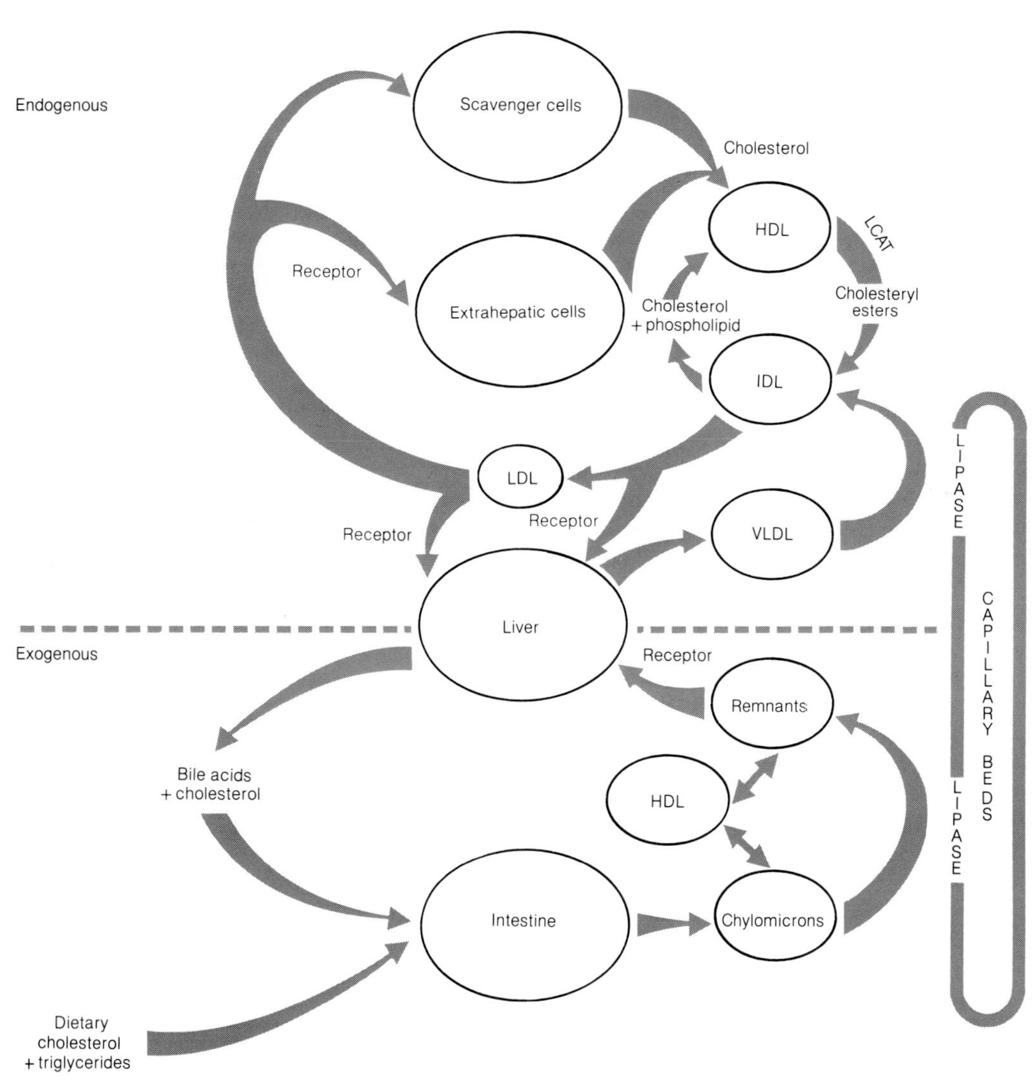

CHAPTER **44A**

INTRODUCTION: Structure and Metabolism of Plasma Lipoproteins

RICHARD J. HAVEL
JOHN P. KANE

Although it was appreciated at the turn of the century that the lipids of plasma are solubilized by protein,[1] it was another 28 years before the first lipoproteins, high density lipoproteins (HDL), were isolated.[2] During the comprehensive efforts to isolate human plasma proteins during World War II, lipoproteins of low density and β electrophoretic mobility were clearly identified and separated from HDL with α mobility.[3] Within the next decade, the major antigenic determinants of α and β lipoproteins were shown to be distinct.[4,5] Studies of their hydrodynamic behavior demonstrated the existence of the larger, less dense very low density lipoproteins (VLDL) and intermediate density lipoproteins (IDL)[6]; it was established that a strongly antigenic protein was common to these lipoproteins and low density lipoproteins (LDL).[7] The presence of glutamic acid as the principal N terminal in LDL[8,9] and one of several in VLDL[10] gave chemical support to the concept that one protein, distinct from the principal proteins in HDL, is virtually the only apolipoprotein in LDL and is present with significant amounts of other apolipoproteins in VLDL. This common protein constituent of LDL and its lipoprotein precursors was termed apolipoprotein (apo) B to distinguish it from the protein moiety of HDL (apo A) and the newly recognized proteins of VLDL (apo C).

Current knowledge of the processes of lipid transport in the blood owes much to discoveries of major gene mutations affecting the apolipoproteins, key enzymes that control lipid transport, and cellular receptors that recognize specific apolipoproteins. Indeed, it is difficult to imagine how this field could have reached its present state in the absence of these discoveries, which resulted from clinical investigations of patients manifesting qualitative or quantitative abnormalities of the plasma lipoproteins.

Despite extraordinary advances during the last few years, the basis of much of the variation in lipoprotein concentrations among humans remains poorly understood. However, the primary structure of almost all the proteins that direct the processes of lipid transport in blood plasma is now known, and the discovery of polymorphisms among these proteins holds much promise for elucidating this variation.

To facilitate understanding of the disorders described in this section, a brief overview of lipoprotein structure, composition, and metabolism is given here (for more extensive discussions, see Refs. 11 to 13). The general clinical approach to determining the presenting phenotype is also included (see also Refs. 14 and 15).

GENERAL STRUCTURE AND CLASSIFICATION OF PLASMA LIPOPROTEINS

The lipoproteins normally present in blood plasma vary widely in size, but virtually all appear to be microemulsions.[16] Lipoprotein particles are thus spherical and contain a central core of nonpolar lipids (primarily triglycerides and cholesteryl esters) and a surface monolayer of polar lipids (primarily phospholipids) and apoproteins. Unesterified cholesterol is also present mainly in the surface monolayer, but with increasing particle size it distributes progressively into the core. Small amounts of the nonpolar lipids also distribute into the monolayer in accordance with their phase behavior. Most of the protein components of the monolayer, like the phospholipids, have amphipathic (detergentlike) properties. These properties are conferred by regions containing both polar and nonpolar amino acid residues, which are often distributed on opposite sides of an α helix.[11] The association of the polar lipids and proteins with lipoproteins is thus driven by hydrophobic forces whereby the fatty acyl chains and the nonpolar amino acid side chains are excluded from the aqueous environment. With the exception of the B apoproteins, the apoproteins, together with unesterified cholesterol, have appreciable water solubility and can exchange readily between lipoprotein particles or with other lipid surfaces. Phospholipids and the nonpolar lipids have little potential for exchange but may be transferred between lipoproteins by specific transfer proteins.

Most of the apolipoproteins possess repeated amphipathic helical regions (apoproteins A-I, A-II, A-IV, C-I, C-II, C-III, and E). These proteins belong to a multigene family in which the coding regions are composed of tandem repeats of 11 codons, indicating that these genes evolved through duplications of a primordial gene.[17] Some of these proteins, however, do not belong to this family and contain few amphipathic helices.

Nonstandard abbreviations used in this chapter are: apo = apolipoprotein; HDL = high density lipoproteins; IDL = intermediate density lipoproteins; LCAT = lecithin:cholesterol acyltransferase; LDL = low density lipoproteins; and VLDL = very low density lipoproteins.

Table 44A-1 Characteristics of Plasma Apolipoproteins in Normal Fasting Humans

	Plasma concentration		*Distribution in lipoproteins, mol %†*					
	mg/dl	*mol %**	*HDL*	*LDL*	*IDL*	*VLDL*	*Major tissue source*	*Molecular weight of amino acid chain*
Apo A-I	130	43	100				Liver and intestine	29,016
Apo A-II	40	22	100					17,414
Apo A-IV								44,465
Apo B-48							Intestine	240,800
Apo B-100	80	5		82	8	2	Liver	512,723
Apo C-I	6	9	97		1	2	Liver	6,630
Apo C-II	3	3	60		10	30		8,900
Apo C-III	12	13	60	10	10	20		8,800
Apo D	10	5	100					19,000
Apo E-II, Apo E-III, Apo E-IV	5	2	50	10	20	20	Liver	34,145

*Based on total plasma concentration.
†For each apoprotein.
SOURCE: Modified from Ref. 11, by permission of the publisher.

The B apoproteins (B-100 and B-48), which are by far the largest of the apolipoproteins and are the products of a single gene, evidently derive their lipophilicity in large part from stretches of hydrophobic amino acid residues and amphipathic β structure (see Chap. 44B). Apo D (a member of the α_{2u}-globulin gene family which includes retinol-binding protein) and the cholesteryl ester transfer protein (which possesses no known family relationships) also contain many nonpolar amino acid residues.[18,19] The failure of apo B to transfer between lipoprotein particles is presumably related to the large number of nonpolar amino acid side chains that penetrate the surface monolayer. The smaller apo D and the cholesteryl ester transfer protein have relatively low affinities for lipoproteins and can be dissociated by procedures such as ultracentrifugation. Some properties of the apolipoproteins and their origin and distribution in plasma lipoproteins are summarized in Table 44A-1.

The density of lipoprotein particles is inversely related to their size, reflecting the relative amounts of low density, nonpolar core lipid and high density, surface protein present. Based on density and certain compositional and functional properties, the lipoproteins are usually separated into six main classes (Table 44A-2). The two largest classes contain mainly triglycerides in their cores. These are the chylomicrons, secreted from enterocytes, in which the B apoprotein is primarily or exclusively apo B-48, and the VLDL, secreted by hepatocytes, which contain apo B-100. The two smallest lipoprotein classes, LDL and HDL, contain mainly cholesteryl esters in their cores. The mature forms of these particles are not secreted directly from cells but rather are produced by metabolic processes within the blood plasma. LDL are produced as end products of the metabolism of VLDL. Components of HDL are secreted with chylomicrons and VLDL and also independently as HDL precursors. The fifth class, IDL, which contain appreciable amounts of both triglycerides and cholesteryl esters in their core, is produced during the conversion of VLDL to LDL. The composition of the major lipoprotein classes is summarized in Table 44A-3.

In certain pathologic states, lipoproteins with a different structure, the lamellar lipoproteins, are found. These particles lack a nonpolar core and are composed of a bilayer of lipids and proteins, as in cell membranes. They occur in two distinct forms: disks and vesicles. In the disks, amphipathic apoproteins are thought to comprise a peripheral annulus.[20] These particles occur in familial lecithin:cholesterol acyltransferase (LCAT) deficiency and in liver diseases in which this enzyme is deficient. Similar particles, found in perfusates of isolated livers and in intestinal and peripheral lymph, are thought to represent a form of nascent HDL. The vesicles are composed of a lipid bilayer with apoproteins adsorbed to the surface. In biliary obstruction, such particles ("lipoprotein X") are formed as a result of reflux of biliary lipids into the blood.[21] Similar particles also occur in familial LCAT deficiency (see Chap. 46).

Table 44A-2 Physical Properties of Human Plasma Lipoprotein Classes

Class	*Density g/ml*	*Electrophoretic mobility*	*Diameter nm*	*Molecular weight*
Chylomicrons	0.93	Remains at origin	75–1200	$50–1,000 \times 10^6$
VLDL	0.93 –1.006	Pre-β-lipoproteins	30–80	$10–80 \times 10^6$
IDL	1.006–1.019	Slow pre-β-lipoproteins	25–35	$5–10 \times 10^6$
LDL*	1.019–1.063	β-Lipoproteins	18–25	2,300,000
HDL_2	1.063–1.125	β-Lipoproteins	9–12	360,000
HDL_3	1.125–1.210	β-Lipoproteins	5–9	175,000

*A small but variable fraction of LDL is complexed via disulfide bonding to a larger glycoprotein, apo(a), constituting a subclass known as the Lp(a) lipoprotein (see Chap. 44B).

Table 44A-3 Chemical Composition of Normal Human Plasma Lipoproteins

	Surface components			*Core lipids*	
	Cholesterol	*Phospholipids*	*Apolipoprotein*	*Triglycerides*	*Cholesteryl esters*
Chylomicrons	2	7	2	86	3
VLDL	7	18	8	55	12
IDL	9	19	19	23	29
LDL	8	22	22	6	42
HDL_2	5	33	40	5	17
HDL_3	4	35	55	3	13

NOTE: Surface components and core lipids given as percentage of dry mass.

KEY ENZYMES OF LIPOPROTEIN-LIPID TRANSPORT

Three enzymes have important roles in lipoprotein-lipid transport: lipoprotein lipase, hepatic lipase, and LCAT (Table 44A-4). Lipoprotein lipase and hepatic lipase are members of a multigene family that includes pancreatic lipase.[22,23]

Lipoprotein lipase is synthesized in a variety of tissues, but most is present in adipose tissue and striated muscle (see Chap. 45). The enzyme is synthesized in tissue parenchymal cells and is secreted and transported to the endothelial surface of blood capillaries, where it is bound to heparan sulfate. Lipoprotein lipase is required for the efficient hydrolysis of triglycerides in chylomicrons and most VLDL particles. Its action requires the presence of an activator protein, apo C-II, on the surface of the lipoproteins. In adipose tissue, enzyme activity is induced by insulin and is high in anabolic conditions. In muscle, particularly red skeletal muscle and cardiac muscle, the activity remains high or increases under catabolic conditions. These changes in activity contribute to the storage of triglyceride fatty acids in adipose tissue in the postprandial state and help to provide these fatty acids to contracting muscles in the postabsorptive state.

Hepatic lipase resembles lipoprotein lipase in acting at cell surfaces, presumably bound to heparan sulfate. It is synthesized in hepatocytes and is transported to hepatic endothelial cells and perhaps to endothelial cells in the adrenal and gonads as well.[23] Its function is less well defined than that of lipoprotein lipase, but it appears to participate in the lipolysis of VLDL and IDL during the later stages of the formation of LDL and in the hydrolysis of phospholipids and triglycerides in HDL.[24] Its activity is increased by androgens and reduced by estrogens.

LCAT is responsible for the synthesis of virtually all cholesteryl esters in plasma lipoproteins (see Chap. 46). LCAT is synthesized in hepatocytes and secreted into the blood where it acts on species of HDL to esterify cholesterol with a fatty acyl residue of phosphatidyl choline (lecithin). In some mammals, including humans, the product cholesteryl esters are rapidly transferred to acceptor lipoproteins by the cholesteryl ester transfer protein.[25] The major normal acceptor is LDL, but VLDL and HDL also derive their cholesteryl esters by this route. Apo D is closely associated with the HDL species on which LCAT acts. By analogy with retinol-binding protein, apo D is thought to possess a cleft that constitutes a binding site for cholesterol.[18] The system comprising LCAT, cholesteryl ester transfer protein, and apo D is thought to have a key role in the process of *reverse cholesterol transport*, by which cholesterol is transported from extrahepatic cells to hepatocytes.[25]

LIPOPROTEIN RECEPTORS

The terminal catabolism of lipoproteins that contain B apolipoproteins occurs by receptor-mediated endocytosis (see Chap. 48). The mechanism of the terminal catabolism of HDL particles is less well understood. The only well-defined lipoprotein receptor is the LDL receptor, which mediates the endocytosis of particles containing apo B-100 (partially catabolized VLDL, IDL, and LDL). Like other receptors that mediate endocytosis of macromolecules, the LDL receptor is a transmembrane protein. The lipoprotein particles bound to the receptor are endocytosed via coated pits on the plasma membrane. The lipoproteins become dissociated from the receptor in the acidic internal environment of endosomes and

Table 44A-4 Key Enzymes of Plasma Lipid Transport

Enzyme	*Molecular weight of amino acyl chain*	*Major tissue source*	*Substrates*
Lipoprotein lipase	50,394	Adipose tissue (adipocytes); striated muscle	Triglycerides and phospholipids of chylomicrons and large VLDL
Hepatic lipase	53,222	Liver (hepatocytes)	Triglycerides and phospholipids of small VLDL, IDL, and large HDL
Lecithin-cholesterol acyltransferase	47,090	Liver	Cholesterol and phosphatidylcholine of species of HDL

are eventually catabolized in secondary lysosomes. The receptor separates from the endosome in prelysosomal compartments and recycles to the cell surface for another round of endocytosis. The number of LDL receptors in cells is tightly regulated by the availability of cholesterol. Release of unesterified cholesterol from lysosomes leads to down-regulation of the LDL receptor. Release of cholesterol also down-regulates β-hydroxy-β-methylglutaryl CoA reductase, the major rate limiting enzyme of cholesterol biosynthesis. These events contribute to maintenance of cellular cholesterol concentrations within narrow limits.

The terminal catabolism of partially degraded chylomicrons appears also to be mediated by receptor-dependent endocytosis.[26] It is thought that a unique chylomicron remnant receptor mediates this process, but no distinct receptor protein has been isolated. HDL particles bind with high affinity to sites on cell surfaces. This binding appears to be regulated by cellular cholesterol concentrations, but it is not known whether the interaction is mediated by a specific protein on the plasma membrane or reflects a nonspecific association of lipoprotein particles with the cell surface. In either case, the binding event does not appear to mediate a pathway leading to lysosomal catabolism of the entire HDL particle.[26]

Certain lipoproteins in which the protein components are modified covalently are taken up into cells by a "scavenger" receptor that mediates endocytosis and lysosomal catabolism. There is little evidence that this receptor, which is present mainly on endothelial cells and macrophages, participates in the normal metabolism of plasma lipoproteins.[26]

LIPOPROTEIN METABOLISM

Biosynthesis and Catabolism of Lipoproteins Containing Apo B

Chylomicrons and VLDL are synthesized and assembled in the endoplasmic reticulum of enterocytes and hepatocytes, respectively, then transported to the Golgi apparatus where the nascent lipoproteins are packaged in secretory vesicles and delivered into the extracellular space by exocytosis (see Chap. 44B). Chylomicrons enter lacteals in the intestinal villi, and VLDL pass through the fenestrae of the hepatic sinusoidal endothelium to enter the blood.

Nascent chylomicrons contain newly absorbed fatty acids as triglycerides; their protein components, synthesized in enterocytes, include apo B-48 and the A apoproteins (A-I, A-II, A-IV). After secretion, they acquire C apoproteins and apo E by transfer from HDL (Fig. 44A-1). Chylomicrons, delivered via the thoracic duct into the blood, bind to lipoprotein lipase on the surface of capillary endothelial cells, where most of the triglycerides are rapidly hydrolyzed together with some of the surface glycerophosphatides. Concomitantly, some phospholipids and the A apoproteins are transferred to HDL. With these changes, the particles gradually lose their affinity for C apoproteins, which are also transferred to HDL; the residual particle, now called a *chylomicron remnant*, having lost 80 to 90 percent of its triglycerides, is released into the blood. The remnant then binds to receptors on hepatocytes where, after

Fig. 44A-1 Chylomicron pathway. Dietary triglycerides are hydrolyzed in the intestine by pancreatic lipase to fatty acids (FFA) and monoglycerides (MG) which are reesterified to form triglycerides (TG) in intestinal mucosal cells. Triglycerides are assembled in the endoplasmic reticulum with other lipids and proteins to form the core of nascent chylomicrons (shaded areas). Dietary cholesterol is likewise largely esterified in these cells and incorporated into the core of the particles (black areas). After completion of assembly in the Golgi apparatus, nascent chylomicrons are secreted into the interstitium of intestinal villi and enter lacteals. There, and after entry into the blood, the proteins synthesized in the absorptive cells (apo B-48 and the A apoproteins) are augmented by transfer of apo E and C apoproteins from HDL. The first step in chylomicron catabolism takes place in extrahepatic tissues where most of the triglycerides are rapidly hydrolyzed by lipoprotein lipase to yield chylomicron remnants (see text). The remnants, which retain their component cholesteryl esters, are released from the enzyme and are then taken up by receptors on the surface of hepatocytes that recognize a binding domain on apo E. The remnants are endocytosed and catabolized in lysosomes, from which cholesterol can enter metabolic pathways in hepatocytes, including excretion into the bile. *(From R. J. Havel, Approach to the patient with hyperlipidemia, Med Clin North Am 66:319–333, 1982. Used by permission of the publisher.)*

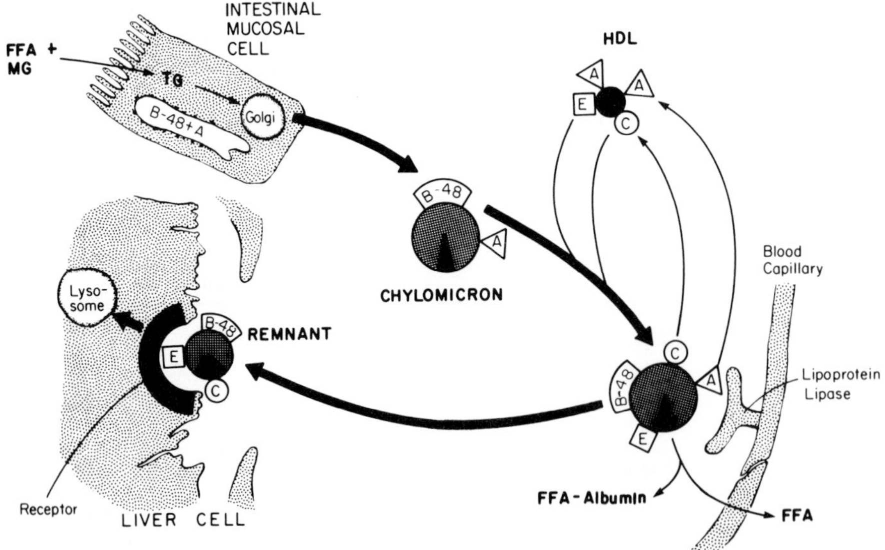

endocytosis, all components of the particle are hydrolyzed in lysosomes. During the first step of chylomicron metabolism in extrahepatic tissues, most of the triglyceride fatty acids enter adipocytes for storage or cells of other tissues for oxidation. In addition, some of the released fatty acids become bound to plasma albumin and are transported to a variety of tissues, including the liver. During the second step of chylomicron metabolism, the residual triglycerides and virtually all dietary cholesterol are delivered to hepatocytes. The cholesterol released from lysosomes in hepatocytes can enter pathways leading to formation of bile acids, be secreted into the bile as such, be incorporated in nascent lipoproteins, or be esterified with a long-chain fatty acid and stored in lipid droplets within the cell.

VLDL provide a pathway for export from hepatocytes of excess triglycerides (derived from lipogenesis, from plasma free fatty acids, or from chylomicron remnants taken up from the blood), which would otherwise be stored within the cell. In humans, it is thought that nascent VLDL normally contain few cholesteryl esters because the activity of the hepatocytic cholesterol esterifying enzyme, acyl CoA-cholesterol acyltransferase, is low. As they enter the blood, nascent VLDL contain newly synthesized apo B-100 and small amounts of E and C apoproteins. Additional amounts of the latter proteins are added after secretion, as in the case of nascent chylomicrons (Fig. 44A-2). Thereafter, the initial phase of metabolism resembles that of chylomicrons: hydrolysis by lipoprotein lipase and the formation of VLDL remnants. The rate of hydrolysis of VLDL triglycerides is slower than that of chylomicron triglycerides. This is thought to be related to the smaller size of the average VLDL particle, which can bind fewer lipoprotein lipase molecules than the larger chylomicron particle. The normal residence time for chylomicron triglycerides in the blood is 5 to 10 min, whereas for VLDL triglycerides it is 15 to 60 minutes.

VLDL remnants interact with hepatocytic LDL receptors via apo E. The presence of several molecules of apo E on the remnant particles results in high affinity binding and rapid removal of the remnants from the blood. This is especially the case for larger VLDL particles, which tend to yield large remnants. Smaller VLDL particles yield smaller remnants, with fewer molecules of apo E; these have lower affinity for hepatocytic LDL receptors and remain longer in the blood. The smaller remnants include particles that are isolated as IDL. Many of these particles are further processed, probably by lipolysis involving hepatic lipase, to form LDL. LDL contain little or no apo E but can bind to the LDL receptor monovalently via component apo B-100.

Although nascent VLDL contain apo E, the binding domain is not initially exposed for interaction with LDL receptors. During the formation of VLDL remnants and particularly with the loss of C apoproteins, the binding domain becomes exposed, permitting uptake by LDL receptors. Similarly, the binding domain of apo B is not exposed in nascent

Fig. 44A-2 VLDL-LDL pathways. The formation of VLDL in hepatocytes resembles that of chylomicrons in intestinal absorptive cells. VLDL provide a pathway for exit of surplus fatty acids as triglycerides (shaded areas in lipoprotein particles) from the liver (see text). VLDL also transport cholesteryl esters from the liver (black areas), but most of these esters are synthesized by LCAT in species of HDL and transferred to the VLDL particles in the blood. The liver synthesizes a larger form of apo B (B-100) than the B-48 protein synthesized in the intestine and also synthesizes apo E and C apoproteins, which enter the blood with nascent VLDL. As with chylomicrons, most VLDL triglycerides are hydrolyzed in extrahepatic tissues by lipoprotein lipase to yield remnant particles. LDL receptors on hepatocytes recognize apo E on VLDL remnants and mediate the endocytosis of a substantial fraction of these particles. Some, however, are further processed, presumably by a lipase on hepatic cell surfaces, to yield LDL. LDL can be taken up into the hepatocytes by these same receptors (which recognize apo B-100) or by LDL receptors on extrahepatic cells, but unlike their remnant precursors which have a short life span, LDL circulate in the blood for days (see text). *(From R. J. Havel, Approach to the patient with hyperlipidemia, Med Clin North Am 66:319–333, 1982. Used by permission of the publisher.)*

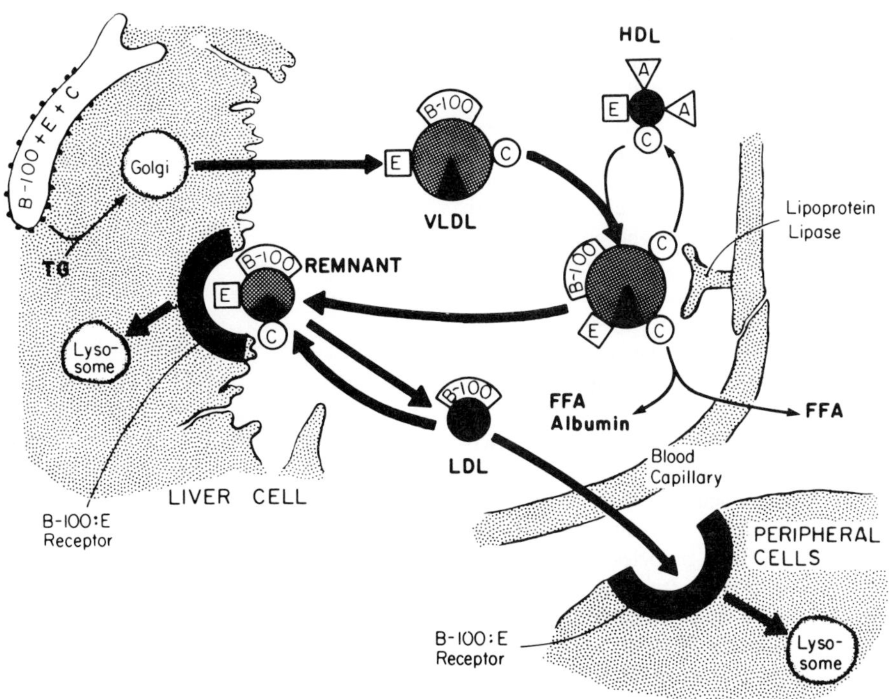

VLDL but eventually becomes exposed during lipolysis, so that as apo E is lost, the particle retains some affinity for the LDL receptor. The relatively low affinity of LDL as compared with that of VLDL remnants presumably accounts for the long residence time of LDL particles (about 3 days) compared with that of VLDL remnants (minutes to hours).

The endocytosis of chylomicron remnants into hepatocytes is also mediated by apo E, and, as in the case of nascent VLDL, exposure of the binding domain of apo E requires lipolysis, accompanied by loss of C apoproteins. In contrast to the situation with VLDL, particles lacking apo E (equivalent to LDL) are not formed during the lipolysis of chylomicron remnants. In addition, the B-48 protein of chylomicrons lacks the receptor-binding domain present in apo B-100 and consequently is not thought to participate in remnant uptake into the liver (see Chap. 47).

In most mammals, the majority of VLDL remnants is taken up efficiently into the liver, and only a small fraction is converted to LDL. In humans, more remnants, perhaps about one-half, are eventually converted to LDL. Whereas remnants are taken up almost entirely into the liver, some LDL particles are taken up into the extrahepatic tissues, mainly via the LDL receptor. Normally, the liver is also the principal site of removal of LDL from the blood. In general, the higher the activity of hepatocytic LDL receptors, the greater the efficiency of removal of VLDL remnants and the lower the fraction of remnants converted to LDL (see Chap. 48).

Formation of HDL and Plasma Cholesterol Transport

The A apoproteins (mainly apo A-I and apo A-II) are the major protein components of plasma HDL. In the intestine, these proteins are secreted in part as components of nascent chylomicrons, but some are also secreted as nascent HDL (see Chap. 49). Nascent HDL are also secreted from hepatocytes; these contain apo E as well as the A apoproteins. The mode of assembly of nascent HDL and the form in which they enter the blood are poorly understood, but they first appear in lymph and blood as lamellar disks or small micellar aggregates. In the plasma, surface components of triglyceride-rich lipoproteins, including phospholipids, cholesterol, and certain apoproteins, are transferred to HDL during lipolysis. Phosphatidyl choline and cholesterol in certain species of HDL are acted upon by LCAT to yield lysolecithin and cholesteryl ester. The former is transferred to albumin and removed from the blood, whereas the latter is transferred to other lipoprotein particles via the cholesteryl ester transfer protein. The nonpolar cores of plasma lipoproteins thereby become enriched in cholesteryl esters. In humans, almost all the cholesteryl esters in each major lipoprotein class are produced in this way. In the case of HDL, nascent particles are transformed into spherical microemulsions with a core of cholesteryl esters, and small HDL particles increase in size by acquisition of core lipid or by interparticle fusions.[27] In humans, efficient lipolysis is associated with increasing size of HDL particles, reflecting the transfer of surface components to HDL from triglyceride-rich lipoproteins and, possibly, stimulation of cholesterol esterification. Larger HDL particles are referred to as HDL_2; smaller HDL particles in human plasma are called HDL_3.

The cholesterol substrate for LCAT is derived not only from the surface of plasma lipoproteins but also from the plasma membrane of cells.[25] When large amounts of cholesterol are available on the surface of lipoproteins (for example, when the chemical potential of cholesterol on the surface of remnants is high), the fraction of cellular cholesterol used by LCAT falls. Cellular cholesterol is transferred mainly to species of small HDL particles that contain apo A-I but no apo A-II. This cholesterol is available for utilization by those HDL species to which LCAT is bound.

The esterification of cholesterol by LCAT removes lipoprotein and cellular cholesterol by trapping it within the apolar cores of plasma lipoproteins. Removal of these lipoproteins by the liver (for example, during receptor-mediated uptake of remnants of trigylceride-rich lipoproteins and LDL into hepatocytes) completes a pathway of "reverse cholesterol transport" by which cholesterol synthesized in or delivered to extrahepatic cells is delivered to the site from which cholesterol can be excreted in the bile (Fig. 44A-3).

Cholesterol in HDL particles may also be delivered to the liver directly in several ways.[26] One of these is a poorly defined process that involves selective uptake of cholesteryl esters without endocytosis of HDL particles per se. In addition, hy-

Fig 44A-3 The process of reverse cholesterol transport, whereby cholesterol in extrahepatic cells is delivered to the liver, is mediated largely by LCAT bound to species of HDL particles. In the presence of apo A-I, the principal cofactor protein for LCAT, cholesterol (C) transferred to these particles from the surface of cells or from other lipoprotein particles is esterified with a fatty acyl moiety derived from phosphatidyl choline (lecithin) to yield cholesteryl esters (CE). Apo D, also present in this HDL species, here called the cholesteryl ester transfer complex, may participate in this process (see text). The cholesteryl esters produced are rapidly transferred to other lipoproteins, including LDL and remnant particles that can be taken up into hepatocytes by receptor-mediated endocytosis. There, after lysosomal hydrolysis, the cholesterol can be excreted into the bile, as such or after conversion to bile acids. The esterification of cholesterol by LCAT creates a gradient which permits cellular cholesterol to be transferred into the blood. Other pathways for reverse cholesterol transport exist (see text), but the pathway shown here in which newly synthesized cholesteryl esters are tranferred to LDL and remnants is thought to predominate in humans. (*From R. J. Havel, Approach to the patient with hyperlipidemia, Med Clin North Am 66:319–333, 1982. Used by permission of the publisher.*)

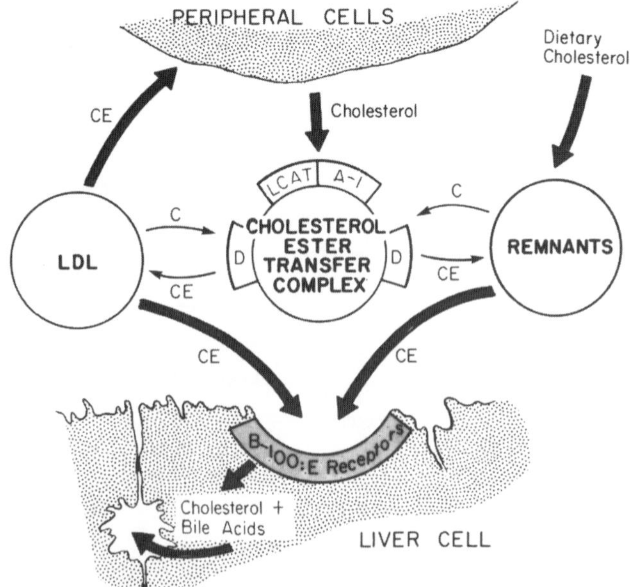

Table 44A-5 Normal Values (mg per dl) for Total Cholesterol

	White males			*White females (sex hormone nonusers)*		
		Percentiles			*Percentiles*	
Age, yr	*Mean*	*5*	*95*	*Mean*	*5*	*95*
0–4	155	114	203	156	112	200
5–9	160	121	203	163	126	205
10–14	158	119	202	160	124	201
15–19	150	113	197	157	119	200
20–29	174	129	231	167	125	219
30–39	197	142	262	180	135	236
40–49	209	155	272	198	150	259
50–59	213	157	277	224	167	293
60–69	213	159	275	231	171	300
70–79	206	153	265	230	169	292
80+	207	144	275	222	165	279

drolysis of HDL phospholipids by hepatic lipase, by increasing the chemical potential of cholesterol, may promote net transfer of cholesterol from the surface of HDL to the liver. The activity of hepatic lipase is inversely related to the concentration of HDL_2 in plasma, and it has been proposed that hydrolysis of HDL phosphatidyl choline on the surface of liver cells promotes the uptake of cholesteryl esters as well as cholesterol and lysophosphatidylcholine into the liver. In the process, HDL_2 is converted to HDL_3. Finally, the small fraction of HDL particles that contains apo E may be taken up into hepatocytes via the receptors that recognize this protein.

DEFINITION AND CLASSIFICATION OF HYPERLIPIDEMIA

The concentrations of lipids in blood plasma and in the major lipoprotein classes are continuous, widely distributed functions in the population. Hence, any definition of hyperlipidemia is necessarily arbitrary. For diagnostic purposes, the concentration of total cholesterol and triglycerides in blood plasma and the concentration of total cholesterol in major lipoprotein classes form the basis for clinical classification of hyperlipidemia and hyperlipoproteinemia. Hypolipidemia and hypolipoproteinemia are similarly classified. Arbitrarily, values in the upper and lower 5 percent of the distribution are usually taken to define an abnormality, but prevalence of the monogenic disorders considered here increases at more restrictive cutoff points. Age- and sex-specific values for American and Canadian populations based upon data from the Lipid Research Clinics Program are shown in Tables 44A-5 to 44A-8.

In general, VLDL triglyceride concentrations are highly correlated with triglyceride levels in plasma and provide a useful estimate of VLDL concentration, but it must be remembered that the composition of VLDL varies considerably, even in the absence of a lipoprotein disorder. Chylomicrons contribute little to triglycerides in plasma obtained during the postabsorptive state except when the lipoprotein lipase system is deficient or overwhelmed. The presence of chylomicrons is simply evaluated by the presence of a creamy layer on the surface of plasma or serum that has been stored overnight in the cold.

LDL cholesterol normally accounts for about two-thirds of plasma total cholesterol, but the correlation between the two is insufficient for use of plasma levels as an index of LDL concentration. LDL cholesterol is usually estimated from the difference between plasma and HDL cholesterol, with an additional correction for VLDL cholesterol, which is usually estimated to be one-fifth of the plasma triglyceride level. The correlation with directly measured LDL cholesterol is good

Table 44A-6 Normal Values (mg per dl) for Total Triglycerides

	White males			*White females (sex hormone nonusers)*		
		Percentiles			*Percentiles*	
Age, yr	*Mean*	*5*	*95*	*Mean*	*5*	*95*
0–4	56	29	99	64	34	112
5–9	56	30	101	60	32	105
10–14	66	32	125	75	36	131
15–19	78	37	148	72	39	124
20–29	108	45	225	74	37	138
30–39	137	52	293	82	40	163
40–49	152	57	324	101	46	203
50–59	147	58	303	120	54	248
60–69	140	58	279	129	58	241
70–79	129	58	263	131	59	237
80+	132	55	255	135	60	242

Table 44A-7 Normal Values (mg per dl) for LDL Cholesterol

	White males			*White females (sex hormone nonusers)*		
		Percentiles			*Percentiles*	
Age, yr	*Mean*	*5*	*95*	*Mean*	*5*	*95*
5–9	93	67	126	100	67	133
10–14	96	62	130	96	66	134
15–19	97	65	149	100	69	146
20–29	116	73	163	106	68	158
30–39	132	83	190	113	72	168
40–49	141	89	198	128	81	189
50–59	143	83	211	150	96	219
60–69	143	87	208	159	97	227
70–79	136	81	202	157	98	330

Table 44A-8 Normal Values (mg per dl) for HDL Cholesterol

	White males			*White females (sex hormone nonusers)*		
		Percentiles			*Percentiles*	
Age, yr	*Mean*	*5*	*95*	*Mean*	*5*	*95*
5–9	56	39	73	53	33	72
10–14	54	37	73	52	35	70
15–19	45	29	68	52	33	74
20–29	45	30	64	55	35	77
30–39	44	27	64	56	35	81
40–49	44	29	67	57	35	87
50–59	45	27	67	59	34	87
60–69	46	28	70	57	35	85
70–79	47	29	84	55	34	79

except in conditions such as familial dysbetalipoproteinemia in which the composition of VLDL is altered or in patients with very high triglyceride levels. However, in such individuals, LDL levels are almost always depressed. For more accurate estimation of LDL cholesterol, VLDL are first removed by ultracentrifugation of plasma at its native small molecule density (1.006 g/ml). Thus, after subtraction of HDL cholesterol, the calculated LDL fraction includes IDL ($1.006 < d < 1.019$ g/ml). This is satisfactory in most situations because "true" LDL ($1.019 < d < 1.063$ g/ml) are present in much higher concentrations than IDL. However, in some pathologic states, IDL levels may be substantial, and the usual method becomes inaccurate. In addition, LDL separated by ultracentrifugation include a small but variable amount of the Lp(a) lipoprotein, in which the B apoprotein of LDL is complexed with the apo(a) protein (see Chap. 44B).

HDL levels are most commonly measured as the cholesterol remaining in plasma after precipitation of VLDL, IDL, and LDL with a polyanion such as heparin or phosphotungstate in the presence of a divalent cation. HDL cholesterol is an imperfect measure of total HDL mass or particle number because of the heterogeneity of HDL size and composition. In addition, with increasing plasma triglyceride levels, HDL become progressively enriched in triglycerides at the expense of cholesteryl esters. The low HDL cholesterol levels in most hypertriglyceridemic patients reflect mainly this phenomenon and a predominance of small HDL_3 particles and, to a lesser extent, a reduction of HDL particle number.[28] The number of HDL particles is better reflected by measurement of the major protein of HDL, apo A-I, in whole plasma.

With the presence of abnormal lipoproteins, as in LCAT-deficiency states, measurement of unesterified (free) cholesterol concentrations as well as total cholesterol may be useful. There are few clinical indications, however, for estimation of other plasma lipids such as phospholipids. Lipoprotein electrophoresis can help to document the presence of abnormal lipoproteins, especially when applied to ultracentrifugally separated fractions such as VLDL, but it is seldom needed for diagnosis of the genetic disorders discussed in this section.

The initial measurements of plasma triglycerides, LDL cholesterol, and HDL cholesterol, together with a qualitative estimate of chylomicronemia, are usually sufficient to determine the nature and severity of hyperlipidemia. This is commonly expressed as a lipoprotein "phenotype," which denotes the class or classes of lipoproteins whose concentration is abnormal. With this information, the physician should exclude abnormalities reflecting systemic disorders associated with al-

Table 44A-9 Hyperlipidemic Disorders

Generic designation and elevated lipoprotein class	*Synonym*	*Primary disorders*	*Secondary disorders**
Exogenous hyperlipemia (chylomicrons)	Type 1	Familial lipoprotein lipase deficiency C-II apolipoprotein deficiency Unclassified	Dysglobulinemias Systemic lupus erythematosus
Endogenous hyperlipemia (VLDL)	Type IV	Familial hypertriglyceridemia (mild form) Familial multiple lipoprotein-type hyperlipidemia Sporadic hypertriglyceridemia Tangier disease	Diabetic hyperlipemia† Glycogenosis, type I Lipodystrophies Dysglobulinemias Uremia Hypopituitarism Nephrotic syndrome (Diabetes mellitus)‡
Mixed hyperlipemia (VLDL + chylomicrons)	Type V	Familial hypertriglyceridemia (severe form) Familial lipoprotein lipase deficiency C-II apolipoprotein deficiency	(Alcoholism) (Estrogen use) (Glucocorticoid use) (Stress-induced)
Hypercholesterolemia (LDL)	Type II-a	Famlial hypercholesterolemia (LDL receptor defects) Familial multiple lipoprotein-type hyperlipidemia Polygenic hypercholesterolemia (includes exogenous hypercholesterolemia)	Nephrotic syndrome Hypothyroidism Dysglobulinemias Cushing syndrome Acute intermittent porphyria
Combined hyperlipidemia (LDL + VLDL)	Type II-b	Familial multiple lipoprotein-type hyperlipidemia Unclassified	Nephrotic syndrome Hypothyroidism Dysglobulinemias Cushing syndrome (Glucocorticoid use) (Stress-induced)
Remnant hyperlipidemia (β-VLDL)	Type III	Familial dysbetalipoproteinemia Unclassified	Hypothyroidism Systemic lupus erythematosus
Lamellar hyperlipoproteinemia (Vesicular and discoidal lipoproteins)	—	Familial lecithin:cholesterol acyltransferase deficiency	Cholestasis (with LP-X) Hepatic failure (with lamellar HDL)

*All conditions associated with elevated VLDL or β-VLDL are aggravated by hypertrophic obesity.
†Denotes mixed hyperlipemia caused by severe, prolonged insulin deficiency.
‡Parentheses indicate conditions that frequently aggravate a primary hyperlipemia but seldom cause hyperlipemia *de novo*. These conditions cause some cases of primary hypertriglyceridemia (mild form) to present as mixed hyperlipemia.
SOURCE: Reprinted by permission from R. J. Havel, Approach to the patient with hyperlipidemia, *Med Clin North Am* 66:319–333, 1982.

Table 44A-10 Monogenic Disorders of the Plasma Lipoproteins

Apolipoprotein disorders	
Apo A-I (49, 50)*	A-I deficiency (3 types)
	$A\text{-}I_{Milano}$
	Tangier disease
Apo B (44B)	Classic abetalipoproteinemia (B-100 + B-48 absence)
	Familial hypobetalipoproteinemia
	Normotriglyceridemic abetalipoproteinemia (selective deficiency of apo B-100)
	Hypobetalipoproteinemia with apo B-37
	Chylomicron retention disease
Apo C-II (45)	C-II deficiency (multiple mutants)
Apo E (47)	E deficiency
	Dysfunctional apo E (multiple mutants)
Enzyme disorders	
Lipoprotein lipase (45)	Lipoprotein lipase deficiency
	Lipoprotein lipase inhibitor
Hepatic lipase (49)	Hepatic lipase deficiency
Lecithin:cholesterol acyltransferase (46)	LCAT deficiency (multiple mutants)
	Fish eye disease
Receptor disorders	
LDL receptor (48)	Familial hypercholesterolemia (multiple mutants)
Transfer protein disorders	
Cholesteryl ester transfer protein (49)	Cholesteryl ester transfer protein deficiency

*Chapter numbers in parentheses.

tered lipoprotein concentrations (Table 44A-9). Well-defined monogenic disorders account for only a small fraction of the primary hyperlipoproteinemias, and all the monogenic hypolipoproteinemias are rare (Table 44A-10). In some cases, other clinical information, especially the presence of xanthomas of skin or tendons, narrows the diagnostic possibilities and occasionally permits a specific diagnosis to be made (Table 44A-11). For example, the presence of xanthomas of the Achilles tendons in a patient with a very high LDL cholesterol level usually establishes the diagnosis of familial hypercholesterolemia. However, for most of the disorders considered here, special diagnostic tests to detect abnormal amounts or structure of apolipoproteins or enzymes of lipid transport are needed.

Most apoproteins can be estimated in whole plasma by immunoassay. However, qualitative abnormalities of apolipoproteins and gross changes in their concentration are usually evaluated by electrophoresis of apolipoproteins from ultracentrifugally separated lipoprotein fractions. Electrophoresis is performed in polyacrylamide gels containing sodium dodecyl sulfate or by isoelectric focusing. The activities of lipoprotein lipase and hepatic lipase are usually estimated in blood plasma obtained after intravenous injection of heparin, which releases these enzymes from their binding sites on cell surfaces. The activity of lipases and LCAT is usually assayed with artificial emulsions or liposomes containing radioactive substrate. Immunoassays for these enzymes and assay of LDL receptor activity in freshly isolated leukocytes or in cultured fibroblasts are currently available in only a few research laboratories. The application of these diagnostic tests is described in the chapters that follow.

Table 44A-11 Associations of Visible Xanthomas and Lipid Infiltrates with Lipoprotein Disorders

Xanthoma	*Genetic disorder*	*Secondary disorder*
Eruptive	Familial lipoprotein lipase deficiency	Diabetic hyperlipemia
	C-II apolipoprotein deficiency	Cholestasis
	Familial lipoprotein lipase inhibitor	Lipodystrophies
	Familial hypertriglyceridemia	Glycogenosis type I
	(severe forms or aggravated by alcohol, estrogen use, or diabetes)	Monoclonal gammopathies
Tuberoeruptive	Familial hypertriglyceridemia (as above)	Cholestasis
	Familial dysbetalipoproteinemia	Monoclonal gammopathies
Tuberous	Familial dysbetalipoproteinemia	Monoclonal gammopathies
	Familial hypercholesterolemia	
	Cerebrotendinous xanthomatosis	
Tendinous	Familial hypercholesterolemia	
	Familial dysbetalipoproteinemia	
	Phytosterolemia	
	Cerebrotendinous xanthomatosis	
Planar		
Palmar-digital creases	Familial dysbetalipoproteinemia	Cholestasis
Intertriginous	Familial hypercholesterolemia (homozygotes)	
Diffuse	A-I apolipoprotein deficiency	Monoclonal gammopathies
Subcutaneous	Familial hypercholesterolemia	Monoclonal gammopathies
	Phytosterolemia	
Xanthelasma*	Familial hypercholesterolemia	Monoclonal gammopathies
	Familial dysbetalipoproteinemia	
	Phytosterolemia	
	Cerebrotendinous xanthomatosis	
Corneal arcus*	Familial hypercholesterolemia	
	Phytosterolemia	
Tonsillar	Tangier disease	

*May occur in normolipidemic individuals.

REFERENCES

1. NERKING J: *Fetteiweissverbindungen. Pfluegers Arch* 85:330, 1901.
2. MACHEBOEUF MA: Recherches sur les phosphoaminolipides et les sterides du serum et du plasma sanguins. *Bull Soc Chim Biol* 11:268, 1929.
3. ONCLEY JL, SCATCHARD G, BROWN A: Physical-chemical characteristics of the certain proteins of normal human plasma. *J Phys Chem* 51:184, 1947.
4. LEVINE L, KAUFFMAN DL, BROWN RK: The antigenic similarity of human low density lipoproteins. *J Exp Med* 102:105, 1955.
5. ALADJEM F, LEIBERMAN M, GOFMAN JW: Immunochemical studies on human plasma lipoproteins. *J Exp Med* 105:49, 1957.
6. GOFMAN JW, LINDGREN FT, ELLIOTT H: Ultracentrifugal studies on lipoproteins of human serum. *J Biol Chem* 179:973, 1949.
7. BRINER WW, RIDDLE JW, CORNWELL DG: Studies on the immunochemistry of human low density lipoproteins utilizing an hemoglutination technique. *J Exp Med* 110:113, 1959.
8. SHORE B: C- and N-terminal amino acids of human serum lipoproteins. *Arch Biochem Biophys* 71:1, 1957.
9. RODBELL M: N-terminal amino acid and lipid composition of lipoproteins from chyle and plasma. *Science* 127:701, 1958.
10. GUSTAFSON A, ALAUPOVIC P, FURMAN RH: Studies of the composition and structure of serum lipoproteins: Physical-chemical characterization of phospholipid-protein residues obtained from very-low-density human serum lipoproteins. *Biochim Biophys Acta* 87:767, 1964.
11. GOTTO AM JR, POWNALL HR, HAVEL RJ: Introduction to the plasma lipoproteins. *Methods Enzymol* 128:3, 1986.
12. HAVEL RJ: Origin, metabolic fate and metabolic function of plasma lipoproteins in Steinberg D, Olefsky JM (eds): *Contemporary Issues in Endocrinology and Metabolism*. New York, Churchill Livingstone, 1987, vol 3, p 117.
13. EISENBERG S: High density lipoprotein metabolism. *J Lipid Res* 25:1017, 1984.
14. HAVEL RJ: Approach to the patient with hyperlipidemia. *Med Clin North Am* 66(2):319, 1982.
15. BROWN WV, GINSBERG H: Classification and diagnosis of the hyperlipidemias, in Steinberg D, Olefsky JM (eds): *Contemporary Issues in Endocrinology and Metabolism*. New York; Churchill Livingstone, 1987, vol 3, p 143.
16. EDELSTEIN C, KÉZDY F, SCANU AM, SHEN BW: Apolipoproteins and the structural organization of plasma lipoproteins: Human plasma high density lipoprotein-3. *J Lipid Res* 20:143, 1979.
17. LUO C-C, LI W-H, MOORE MN, CHAN L: Structure and evolution of the apolipoprotein multigene family. *J Mol Biol* 187:325, 1986.
18. DRAYNA D, FIELDING C, MCLEAN J, BAER B, CASTRO G, CHEN E, COMSTOCK L, HENZEL W, KOHR W, RHEE L, WION K, LAWN R: Cloning and expression of human apolipoprotein D cDNA. *J Biol Chem* 261:16535, 1986.
19. DRAYNA D, JARNAGIN AS, MCLEAN J, HENZEL W, KOHR W, FIELDING C, LAWN R: Cloning and sequencing of human cholesteryl ester transfer protein cDNA. *Nature* 327:632, 1987.
20. TALL AR, SMALL DM, DECKELBAUM RJ, SHIPLEY G: Structure and thermodynamic properties of high density lipoprotein recombinants. *J Biol Chem* 252:4702, 1977.
21. FELKER TE, HAMILTON RL, VIGNE J-L, HAVEL RJ: Properties of lipoproteins in blood plasma and liver perfusates of rats with cholestasis. *Gastroenterology* 83:652, 1982.
22. WION KL, KIRCHGESSNER TG, LUSIS AJ, SCHOTZ JC, LAWN RM: Human lipoprotein lipase complementary DNA sequence. *Science* 235:1638, 1987.
23. KOMAROMY MC, SCHOTZ MC: Cloning of rat hepatic lipase cDNA: Evidence for a lipase gene family. *Proc Natl Acad Sci USA* 84:1526, 1987.
24. JACKSON RL: Lipoprotein lipase and hepatic lipase, in Boyer PD (ed): *The Enzymes*. New York, Academic Press, 1984, vol 16, p 141.
25. FIELDING CJ, FIELDING PE: Cholesterol transport between cells and body fluids. *Med Clin North Am* 66(2):363, 1982.
26. HAVEL RJ, HAMILTON RL: Hepatocytic lipoprotein receptors and intracellular lipoprotein catabolism. *Hepatology*, in press.
27. NICHOLS AV, BLANCHE PJ, GONG EL, SHORE VG, FORTE TM: Molecular pathways in the transformation of model discoidal lipoprotein complexes induced by lecithin:cholesterol acyltransferase. *Biochim Biophys Acta* 834:285, 1985.
28. PHILLIPS NR, HAVEL RJ, KANE JP: Serum apolipoprotein A-I levels: Relationship to lipoprotein lipid levels and selected demographic variables. *Am J Epidemiol* 116:302, 1982.

CHAPTER **44B**

DISORDERS OF THE BIOGENESIS AND SECRETION OF LIPOPROTEINS CONTAINING THE B APOLIPOPROTEINS

JOHN P. KANE
RICHARD J. HAVEL

1. *Very low density lipoproteins (VLDL) and chylomicrons, which transport triglycerides to peripheral tissues via the bloodstream, are major lipoprotein secretory products of the liver and intestine, respectively. Each class of these lipoproteins contains a protein of very high molecular weight (a B apolipoprotein) which is essential for the secretion of the lipoprotein particle and which has very high affinity for lipids, remaining with the lipoprotein complex throughout its metabolic processing in plasma or lymph.*
2. *There are two translation products of a single structural gene for B apolipoproteins. The predominant, if not exclusive, B apoprotein of VLDL and low density lipoproteins (LDL) is apolipoprotein (apo) B-100, a single polypeptide chain of over 4500 amino acid residues and the full-length translation product of the gene. The predominant and perhaps exclusive species of apo B in chylomicrons is apo B-48, a single chain of 2152-amino acid residues homologous to the amino-terminal portion of apo B-100. This protein is translated from mRNA containing a single base substitution, which produces a stop codon corresponding to residue 2153 of apo B-100. Several disorders are now recognized in which the secretion of apo B–containing lipoproteins is abnormal.*
3. *Abetalipoproteinemia is a recessive disorder characterized by the absence of VLDL and LDL from plasma. Fat malabsorption is severe and triglyceride accumulation occurs in enterocytes and, to some extent, in liver. Acanthocytosis of erythrocytes is common. Spinocerebellar ataxia with degeneration of the fasciculus cuneatus and fasciculus gracilis, peripheral neuropathy, degenerative pigmentary retinopathy, and ceroid myopathy all appear to be secondary to defects of transport of tocopherol in blood. It is likely that mechanisms underlying the failure to secrete VLDL and chylomicrons will differ among kindreds; however, in studies on a few patients to date, both apo B mRNA and protein have been identified within hepatocytes, suggesting the presence of defective processing or secretion of the gene product. Treatment involves reduction of dietary fat and supplementation with tocopherol to prevent progression of the neuromuscular and retinal degenerative disease.*
4. *In the homozygous state, clinical manifestations of familial hypobetalipoproteinemia are indistinguishable from those of abetalipoproteinemia: acanthocytosis, neuromuscular disability, and malabsorption. Clinically, this disorder is distinguished from recessive abetalipoproteinemia by the appearance of hypolipidemia in heterozygotes. Studies on a few patients have revealed decreased content of apo B mRNA and protein in hepatocytes.*
5. *Disorders involving truncated forms of apo B-100: In normotriglyceridemic abetalipoproteinemia, chylomicrons appear to be formed normally, but LDL are absent from plasma. VLDL contain a truncated form of apo B-100. Acanthocytosis and ataxia can occur, and plasma tocopherol levels are very low. The inability to form LDL presumably reflects the requirement for sequence in the carboxy-terminal region of apo B-100 in this transformation. Another form of truncated B apoprotein leading to a B protein shorter than the B-48 chain (B-37) has been described in one kindred in combination with another genetic determinant of hypolipidemia. The abnormal B proteins are found in VLDL, chylomicrons, and on a lipoprotein particle found in the high density interval upon ultracentrifugation.*
6. *Hypolipoproteinemia with selective deletion of apo B-48 (chylomicron retention disease) is characterized by fat malabsorption and the absence of chylomicrons in plasma after fat ingestion. Apo B-100 is found in LDL; however, total LDL levels are about half of normal. Acanthocytosis and neurologic manifestations occur in some patients. The defect appears to be recessive. Large amounts of B-48 protein have been detected in enterocytes suggesting that this disorder is probably based on a selective defect in processing of apo B-48 or in the secretion pathway for chylomicrons.*
7. *Familial combined hyperlipidemia is probably the most prevalent genetically determined disorder of lipoproteins now recognized and appears to carry a significant increased risk of coronary arteriosclerosis. It appears to be an autosomal dominant trait with high penetrance which leads to elevated levels of VLDL, LDL, or both in plasma. The phenotypic pattern can shift among these types with time. Preliminary studies suggest that increased production of VLDL may be a common underlying metabolic characteristic.*
8. *In Lp(a) hyperlipoproteinemia, the Lp(a) lipoprotein contains an LDL-like microemulsion particle containing apo B-100 linked to a high molecular weight glycoprotein, Lp(a)-specific protein, which is a translation product of a gene that has evolved from the plasminogen structural gene. The origins of this protein are not known with certainty; however, it is synthesized in liver, at least. Whether it is secreted in a VLDL-like particle is unknown, but in serum of fasted individuals, virtually all of the Lp(a) protein is associated with LDL-like particles. Levels of this lipoprotein in plasma vary up to a hundredfold among individuals, suggesting that major heritable factors may be influencing its production rate. High levels of Lp(a) lipoprotein in plasma appear to correlate with increased risk of coronary artery disease.*

Nonstandard abbreviations used in this chapter are: ABL-HDL_4 = abnormal-HDL_4; ACAT = acyl-CoA:cholesterol O-acyltransferase; apo = apoprotein or apolipoprotein; CD = circular dichroism; FCH = familial combined hyperlipidemia; IDL = intermediate density lipoproteins; LCAT = lecithin:cholesterol acyltransferase; LDL = low density lipoproteins; LPL = lipoprotein lipase; and VLDL = very low density lipoproteins.

Absence of VLDL and LDL in abetalipoproteinemia was described in 1960. Studies of this disorder have provided some of the best evidence that apo B is required for the normal assembly and secretion from the liver and small intestine of lipoproteins that contain it. Additional genetic disorders involving apo B have been described subsequently, including familial hypobetalipoproteinemia, normotriglyceridemic abetalipoproteinemia, and chylomicron retention disease, in all of which the synthesis or secretion of one or more of the lipoproteins containing apo B is impaired. The pathogenesis of these disorders has remained poorly understood, primarily because the characterization of B apoproteins, which are large and water-insoluble, proved to be exceedingly difficult. Recently, considerable progress has been made. The primary structure of the B apolipoproteins has been elucidated by sequence analysis of cDNA. The normal biosynthesis of B apoproteins, their assembly with lipid, their secretion from hepatocytes and enterocytes, and the regulation of these processes are being investigated intensively.

The characterization of apo B proceeded very slowly, in contrast to that of the small apolipoproteins. Chief among the obstacles to its chemical manipulation was its extreme self-association upon the removal of lipids.[1] Soluble, lipid-free preparations were achieved only by chemical modification such as succinylation of apo B in intact LDL, followed by extraction of lipids, or by laborious extractions in the presence of chaotropic or amphipathic compounds such as guanidinium hydrochloride, sodium deoxycholate, or SDS.[1-3] A further obstacle was the marked susceptibility of the molecule to scission by proteases from serum, or microbial proteases acquired casually during purification. Thus, a number of investigators reported the isolation of putative protomeric units varying in estimated molecular weight from 8000 to over 250,000 daltons.[1] However, studies designed to inhibit self-association and protease attack yielded apparent molecular weights of 549,000 daltons by SDS gel electrophoresis in one report[4] and 387,000 daltons by ultracentrifugal analysis, gel permeation chromatography in guanidinium hydrochloride, and SDS gel electrophoresis in another report,[5] indicating that the apo B of LDL is indeed one of the largest proteins found in mammals.

STRUCTURE OF APO B

Apo B in Lipoproteins

Recognition of Multiple Forms of Apo B. In 1981 Kane et al. reported the presence of two primary forms of apo B in human plasma and thoracic duct lymph.[4] One, found in LDL and VLDL, had an apparent molecular weight of 549,000 daltons, whereas the other, found in chylomicrons of thoracic duct lymph and in plasma after a fatty meal, had an apparent molecular weight of 264,000 daltons. The amino acid compositions were distinct, but immunochemical cross-reactivity was prominent. In order to facilitate comparison of apparent molecular weights of apo B species, a centile system of nomenclature was proposed in which the predominant form of apo B in human LDL is termed apo B-100 and each other species or fragment of apo B is assigned a centile designation reflecting its apparent M_r relative to apo B-100 (Fig. 44B-1). In this system the smaller species of human apo B was designated apo

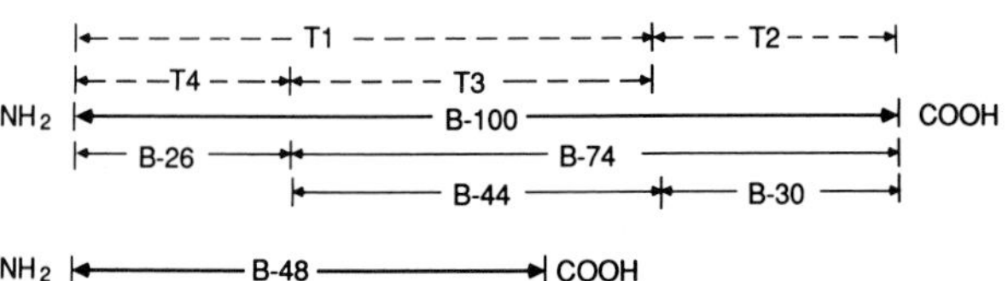

Fig. 44B-1 B apolipoproteins and their large proteolytic fragments. The proteins and fragments are aligned according to sequence, with the amino termini of the B-100 and B-48 proteins indicated at left. Thrombin-derived fragments are indicated with broken lines, above the B-100 line; kallikrein-derived fragments with solid lines, below the B-100 line.

B-48. Although different terms have been applied by others, the centile system has proved useful for description of enzymatic fragments and partial deletion gene products.

The Molar Representation of Apo B Species in Lipoproteins. As described below, the distribution of the primary species of apo B among the lipoproteins of plasma in humans appears to resemble that found in most mammals. That is, apo B-100 appears in liver-derived triglyceride-rich lipoproteins and in LDL exclusively, whereas apo B-48 is the predominant, if not exclusive, B apolipoprotein produced by the intestine of adult animals. One other class of particles, the Lp(a) lipoproteins, also appears to contain apo B-100 as the sole B-apoprotein species linked to Lp(a) apoprotein by disulfide bridging.[6,7]

Calculations based upon the chemical composition of LDL[8-11] have suggested that LDL particles contain about 7×10^5 daltons of protein. However, most such calculations do not include corrections for hydration or relative chromogenicity of proteins used as standards and therefore overestimate the content of apo B. A content of 540×10^3 daltons per particle has been found, based on amino acyl mass,[12] a value that would accommodate with reasonable agreement one copy of apo B per particle. This is supported by the observation, in individuals heterozygous for a polymorphism of apo B, that a specific discriminating monoclonal antibody is capable of precipitating only approximately half of the LDL particles,[13] indicating that the product of only one allele is present on each. Strong additional evidence comes from studies of the stoichiometries of the reactions of eight anti-apo B monoclonal antibodies with LDL.[14] The stoichiometries ranged from 0.5 to 1.2 moles of antibody per particle of LDL, with a mean of 0.75.

Determination of the number of copies of apo B-48 per chylomicron particle is a much more formidable task because of the extreme heterogeneity of particle size, the relatively small percentage of total mass attributed to B protein, and the likelihood of contamination with VLDL. A content of 4.8×10^5 daltons of B protein per particle has been reported,[15] a figure that would nearly accommodate two copies of apo B-48. Because of the multiple uncertainties of measurement in this analysis, further studies will be required to establish this point with conviction.

Disposition of Apo B in Lipoproteins. Virtually all the data available on the conformation of B apoproteins and their relationship to lipids in lipoproteins have been obtained by study of LDL and VLDL. Some inference may be drawn for apo B-48 based on its sequence homology with apo B-100, but direct observation will be required to determine its conformation in chylomicrons with confidence. B apoprotein is thought to be disposed largely at the interface of the surface monolayer with the aqueous environment, hydrophobic side chains interacting with lipid, and hydrophilic side chains extending into the aqueous phase. This model is supported by the relative completeness of modification of hydrophilic side chains by hydrophilic reagents, and accessibility to trypsin.[16,17] Nuclear magnetic resonance imaging (NMR) studies indicate constraint by apo B-100 on the phospholipids of LDL.[18] It appears that apo B-100 is also capable of constraining the motion of core cholesteryl esters, either directly or indirectly, because scission of the protein by trypsin in native LDL causes an increase of disorder as detected by reduction of induced circular dichroism (CD) of a carotene probe.[19] Analyses of CD indicate that apo B in LDL contains approximately 41 percent helix, 22 percent β structure, 20 percent β turns, and 17 percent random coil structure.[20–23] Allowing for the CD contribution of non-B apoproteins, it appears that apo B-100 is somewhat more helical in VLDL than in LDL.[24]

Studies of recombination of delipidated apo B-100 with lipids have shed useful light on the nature of its interaction with lipid. Krieger et al.[25] were able to produce an apo B-100:phospholipid complex in which hydrophobic core lipids could be replaced, re-forming LDL-like particles. Further evidence of affinity of apo B for surface phospholipids is the association of apo B-100 with lecithin to form complexes in which the protein conformation resembles that of native LDL.[26] Apo B-100 solubilized with deoxycholate forms a complex with dimyristoylphosphatidylcholine liposomes,[27] which has less thermal stability, however, than native LDL.

Delipidated apo B-100 also recombines with microemulsions to form LDL-like particles.[28,29] Thermal analysis revealed that apo B influences the transitions of core lipids in the recombinant particles and that greater thermal stability of the protein was achieved in the microemulsion complexes than when complexed with phospholipid alone.[28] Secondary structure of the protein in these complexes was similar to that in LDL. Recombination of proteolytic fragments of apo B-100 with microemulsions of phospholipid and cholesteryl esters indicates that lipid-binding properties are broadly distributed within the apo B molecule. Virtually all of the polypeptides over 5000 daltons in arrays of fragments produced by three endoproteases bind to microemulsion particles, yielding LDL-like particles with similar helicity to native LDL but with less beta conformation.[30]

Structure of Apo B and Its Gene

Cloning of Apo B. The application of molecular genetic techniques to elucidate the structure of apo B was retarded by the chemical intractability of the B proteins. Because of their strong self-association, the isolation of internal peptides for sequencing was extremely difficult. Attempts at immunoselection of polysomes were unsuccessful in several laboratories, as were early attempts to translate apo B mRNA either in vitro or in frog oocytes. The first cDNA sequence for B protein was reported by Lusis et al.[31] These authors identified a clone by antibody screening of rat hepatic cDNA libraries and reported a short sequence in the carboxy-terminal portion of the protein. They reported an mRNA of approximately 20 kb in both liver and intestine. A message of similar length was quickly reported by others in human, monkey, and baboon liver,[32,33] in Hep G2 cells,[34] and in human and monkey intestine.[33] A message of approximately half that length was also observed in intestine by several of the groups, along with varying amounts of mRNA of intermediate lengths. Sequences of additional cDNA clones were then rapidly reported by several groups.[33,35–41] One series of overlapping clones yielded the sequence of the carboxy-terminal third of the B-100 protein.[33] Another[40,41] yielded the sequence of the amino-terminal third of the protein and that of a 27-amino acid signal peptide sequence. Analysis of genomic DNA in the 5′ flanking region revealed two classic promotor elements, a TATA box 29 nucleotides upstream of the ATG transcription initiation site, and a CAAT box 31 nucleotides upstream from the TATA box. A further sequence associated with promotors, CCGCCC, is repeated twice in the 80 bases preceding the ATG site.[40,41] The entire cDNA sequence has subsequently been reported by several laboratories,[42–47] establishing apo B-100 as a single polypeptide chain.

Sequence of Apo B-100 Inferred from cDNA. The availability of complete sequence data for the 4536 amino acid residues of apo B-100 permits analysis of both overall and local properties of the protein. Its mean calculated hydrophobicity (0.916 kcal per residue) approaches that of integral membrane proteins and appreciably exceeds that of other known apolipoproteins. The carboxyl-terminal region has an especially high hydrophobicity, even though no long sequences of hydrophobic residues are present. At least 12 hydrophobic regions with membrane-associated or membrane-spanning capability are distributed over the length of the molecule. Theoretical calculations of the maximum content of secondary structure are consistent with observations based on circular dichroic measurements. There are relatively few typical amphipathic helices compared with some other apolipoproteins, but one region in which the typical charge distribution and helix-forming potential exists to form classic amphipathic helices occurs between residues 2000 and 2600. Four regions rich in proline probably form amphipathic β sheets.[44,48] Of the 25 cysteine residues present, 12 occur in the B-26 region of the protein near the amino terminus, suggesting that this region contains tertiary structure stabilized by disulfide bridges. In agreement with the location of epitopes of monoclonal antibodies that block interaction of apo B-100 with the apo B-100:E receptor (see below), the peptide sequence from residue 3345 to 3381 partially restores binding of trypsinized VLDL, indicating that at least a portion of the receptor-binding domain is at that site.[43]

The Apo B Gene. A number of studies have located the apo B gene on the short arm of chromosome 2.[33,35,39,49–51] The entire gene comprises over 43 kb[52–54] with 29 exons. The introns are concentrated in the 5′ portion of the gene. Two extremely long exons of 1906 and 7572 bp are found in the 3′ terminal region of the gene, suggesting that exon fusion may have occurred in phylogeny.

Origin of B-48. Examination of Southern blots indicates that there is but one copy of the apo B gene in the human genome. Furthermore, the phenotypes of apo B-100 and apo B-48 always correspond with respect to an allelic polymorphism detected by monoclonal antibody MB19.[55] Thus, apo B-48 and apo B-100 appear to be transcripts of this single gene, an uncommon mechanism in vertebrates. By comparison of peptide arrays, internal sequences, and epitopes of focal polyclonal antibodies, apo B-48 appears to be totally homologous with the amino-terminal portion of apo B-100.[56–58a] The region of the gene corresponding to the C terminus of apo B-48, however, contains no intron. Likewise, there is no evidence of exon shuffling. Thus, conventional alternate splicing of mRNA cannot account for the production of apo B-48. Instead, the appearance in intestinal cDNA of a single base substitution leading to the stop codon (TAA) in place of (CAA) for glutamine at codon 2153 appears to reveal the mechanism.[58–60a] The finding that the C-terminal sequence of apo B-48 is Met-Ile, which corresponds to codons 2151 and 2152 in native apo B-100, provides confirmation of the site and the mechanism for termination.[60] Polyadenylation occurs at several sites after the stop codon, giving rise to a predominant 7.5-kb message in addition to a range of messages extending up to 19 kb. Oligonucleotide probe studies suggest that virtually all of the full-length message in intestine contains the stop codon. The stop codon is absent from genomic DNA.[59] Thus, its appearance in intestinal mRNA must be the result of a tissue-specific editing phenomenon.

General Properties of B Apoproteins in Lipoproteins

As described below, both apo B-100 and apo B-48 appear to play essential roles in the organization and secretion of their respective lipoproteins from liver and intestinal epithelium, as evidenced by the absence of corresponding lipoproteins in abetalipoproteinemia. Furthermore, some portion of apo B, which is deleted from the carboxy-terminal region in disorders associated with truncated B proteins, is essential to the normal processing of VLDL to LDL.[61,220] A singular property of B apolipoproteins is their extremely high affinity for the lipid moieties of their respective lipoproteins: essentially no unbound apoprotein exists in plasma. The heparin-binding property, common to both primary forms of apo B,[62–65] may play an important role in the hydrolysis of circulating triglycerides by lipoprotein lipase and could facilitate the activity of hepatic lipase. Subfractions of heparin with high affinity for LDL also bind thrombin, apo E, and the antithrombin III:thrombin complex with high affinity.[64] Proteolysis of apo B-100 in LDL results in enhanced heparin binding while reducing interaction with the B-100:E receptor, indicating that the principal heparin-binding sites are not involved in receptor-ligand interaction.[66] Apo B-100 appears to contain seven heparin interactive sites[65] distributed rather evenly through the length of the chain, three of which are also present in apo B-48.

The receptor-binding domain for the B-100:E receptor appears to reside in the portion of B-100 that is not homologous with B-48. Monoclonal antibodies that block binding react with the nonhomologous portion of B-100.[38,67,68,188] Apo E–deficient remnants of chylomicrons and VLDL bind poorly to the receptor,[69] as do remnants of chylomicrons from individuals homozygous for apo E-2, which is defective with respect to receptor binding.[63] Thrombin proteolysis which attacks receptor-interactive apo E eliminates binding.[70] Apo B tends to be cleaved as well, but such scission, at least in LDL, does not inhibit binding. Restoration of intact apo E restores binding of the triglyceride-rich particles. Kallikrein proteolysis of LDL also does not interfere with receptor-binding function.[71] Thus Apo B of VLDL is not a ligand for the LDL receptor,[38] which suggests that conformational changes attendant to intravascular lipolysis are required to establish this domain.[195] Although the exact site and nature of the receptor-binding domain are not yet elucidated, a cluster of arginine and lysine residues near the junction of two of the thrombin fragments of apo B-100 (T2 and T3) is the most likely region and is in keeping with the earlier demonstration that chemical modification of either lysine or arginine residues effectively blocks binding of LDL.[72,73] The carbohydrate moiety of LDL does not appear to be involved in binding.[74]

Proteolysis of Apo B

Both kallikrein and thrombin cleave apo B-100, producing large fragments which have been useful in sequence determination. They promise to be of much further use in localizing sites of biochemical interest because of the large molecular weights of the B proteins. Furthermore, the sites of scission are likely to delineate functional domains of these proteins. Kane et al.[4] noted the presence of two apparent complementary fragments of apo B-100 in human LDL of "approximately" 144×10^3 and "approximately" 407×10^3 daltons, which they designated apo B-26 and apo B-74 in the centile system of nomenclature. Although each showed immunochemical cross-reactivity with apo B-100, they had no common determinants. Their amino acid compositions and molecular weights were in good agreement with their being scission products of apo B-100, and the amino terminal sequence of the B-26 fragment placed it at the amino terminus of apo B-100.[40] Cardin et al. demonstrated that human kallikrein produces similar fragments from apo B-100 in LDL[75] and that a second scission point appears in the B-74 fragment with further incubation.[76] Determination of the amino terminal sequence of the B-74 fragment[77] places the scission site at residue 1297 of apo B-100, a typical site for cleavage by kallikrein (Phe-Lys-Ser). Numerous additional kallikrein scission sites occur in delipidated apo B-100, which suggests that they are in regions that are unexposed in native LDL.[71] Thus, the site dividing B-26 and B-74 probably occurs on an exposed loop connecting the cysteine-rich B-26 domain to the remainder of apo B-100. The addition of inhibitors of kallikrein to freshly drawn blood inhibits these proteolytic events,[76] suggesting that little or no cleavage of apo B by kallikrein occurs in vivo. The observation that C1 esterase inhibitor is the natural inhibitor of this reaction[78] suggests that LDL apo B of individuals deficient in that protein may be subject to scission in vivo.

Thrombin, too, cleaves apo B-100 of LDL, and, to a lesser extent, apo B of VLDL into large fragments. The primary fragments T1 and T2 were at first confused with B-74 and B-26, respectively, because they have similar molecular weights. However, the scission sites are on opposite ends of the B-100 chain (Refs. 33,79; Fig. 44B-1). T1 is cleaved further into two polypeptides, T3 and T4. T2 and T3 remain joined by a disulfide bridge unless reduced.[44]

Topology and Polymorphisms of Apo B in Lipoproteins

Immunochemical heterogeneity of LDL was first detected in the form of alloantibodies that appeared in the serum of individuals who had received multiple transfusions.[80] Five sets of alleles referred to as the Ag system have been identified,[81] each compatible with codominant transmission of a genomic polymorphism at a unique locus. Some of these traits show interesting genoclines in multinational studies. It has not been established whether some of the allotypes represent alterations in the carbohydrate moiety of apo B-100, however. A monoclonal antibody can discriminate between the homozygous and heterozygous states for one allelic pair, Ag(c) and Ag(g).[82,83]

Because a large number of individuals have been tested by the alloantibody technique, it is likely that most, or all, of the widely distributed polymorphisms affecting exposed regions of the protein have been detected in this fashion. It will be important for investigators searching for uncommon polymorphisms of B proteins by protein mapping or for those seeking restriction fragment length polymorphisms of DNA to correlate the data with the polymorphisms of the Ag system. Groups of monoclonal antibodies that react more readily with intermediate density lipoprotein (IDL) and VLDL than with LDL or with LDL and IDL more than with VLDL have been identified,[84,111] consistent with other evidence that apo B undergoes substantial conformational change as VLDL are transformed to LDL.

More than 60 differences in DNA sequence for apo B have been reported,[52] a number of which correspond to restriction fragment length polymorphisms. One such polymorphism detected with *Xba*I in a small series of Caucasian males appeared to correlate with hypertriglyceridemia.[85] Another, detected by *Eco*RI, corresponds to a lysine to glutamate substitution in apo B-100. The Ag(x) allele has been linked to an *Xba*I polymorphism, indicating that at least this Ag determinant represents a variation in protein sequence.[86] An *Eco*RI site, heterogeneous polymorphisms detected with *Msp*I, and *Xba*I polymorphism have been reported to correlate with myocardial infarction in a small series of Caucasians, apparently without affecting levels of lipids or apo B in plasma.[87] Because the correlations of restriction fragment length polymorphisms with pathophysiological processes are very sensitive to factors such as ethnicity, the study of large population samples will be required to relate genomic polymorphisms to disease with confidence. This approach, however, offers the prospect of valuable insights into pathophysiological mechanisms.

BIOSYNTHESIS OF LIPOPROTEINS CONTAINING APOLIPOPROTEIN B

Assembly and Secretion of Lipoprotein Particles

The secretion of lipoproteins containing apo B follows the pathway identified for other proteins in constitutive secretory cells. Like other secreted proteins, apo B-100 and apo B-48 are synthesized on attached ribosomes of the endoplasmic reticulum. The typical signal peptide of 27 amino acids[40] is presumably cleaved cotranslationally. By immunoelectron microscopy, apo B has been identified in rat hepatocytes associated with ribosomes and elsewhere in the rough endoplasmic reticulum.[88] However, particles resembling nascent VLDL associated with the immunoreactive apo B are evident only at the smooth-surfaced termini of this organelle. Since similar particles lacking apo B immunoreactivity are also seen in cisternae of the smooth endoplasmic reticulum, it has been proposed that nascent VLDL particles are formed in the smooth endoplasmic reticulum (possibly by a process of budding inward from the organelle membrane)[89] and that these particles then migrate to junctions with the rough endoplasmic reticulum where apo B is added.[88] Similar observations have been made for nascent chylomicrons in mucosal cells of human jejunum.[90] In both cells, the nascent particles are transported either via transition vesicles that arise from the endoplasmic reticulum or, via a specialized tubular system, to the Golgi apparatus, where the protein components may be further processed and eventually are terminally glycosylated in the *trans*-cisternae. The particles accumulate in the expanded ends of the *trans*-cisternae, which are thought to bud off as secretory vesicles that migrate to and fuse with the cell membrane (the basolateral membrane in enterocytes and the microvillous membrane in hepatocytes), resulting in exocytosis of the nascent lipoproteins.[91]

In pulse-chase experiments, the translation of apo B-100 in chicken hepatocytes[92] and human hepatoma cells[93] has been found to require about 10 to 14 min, transport to the Golgi apparatus 5 to 10 min, and secretion from the cell another 10 min. Newly synthesized phospholipids (mainly phosphatidylcholine) seem to be added to the nascent particle in two stages: the first shortly after translation, prior to acquisition of newly synthesized triglycerides, and the second much later, presumably in the Golgi apparatus.[94] Key enzymes of phosphatidylcholine synthesis (CTP:phosphocholine transferase and CDPcholine phosphotransferase) are present at high activity in hepatocytic Golgi membranes of rats.[94] When translation of apo B in chicken hepatocytes is terminated prematurely by addition of puromycin, newly secreted VLDL contain truncated forms of apo B, which evidently can sustain the secretory mechanism.[92] On the other hand, at least in one form of recessive human abetalipoproteinemia, apo B is synthesized in normal or increased amounts in hepatocytes, but lipoprotein particles are not secreted.[95] In hepatocytes and enterocytes from one affected individual, apo B has been found by immunogold labeling in cisternae and secretory vesicles of the Golgi apparatus.[96] In rats treated with orotic acid for 1 week or more, secretion of particles containing apo B from the liver is virtually abolished, but secretion of chylomicrons from the intestine is unaffected. In these animals, large lipoprotein particles accumulate in the endoplasmic reticulum near the cis side of the Golgi apparatus.[97] Although these particles contain apo B,[98] transfer to the Golgi apparatus is evidently blocked, and terminal glycosylation does not occur. Prevention of terminal glycosylation by administration of tunicamycin, however, does not inhibit secretion of VLDL from the liver.[92]

Recent studies suggest that apolipoprotein B-100 remains attached to the endoplasmic reticulum for some time after its synthesis has been completed, with regions of the protein remaining susceptible to enzymatic attack from the exterior of the membrane.[93] One model, consistent with much of the available data, would have completed apo B chains remain associated with newly synthesized phospholipids and cholesteryl esters (the biosynthetic enzymes for which reside in the rough endoplasmic reticulum) within the membrane of the endoplasmic reticulum. The forming triglyceride droplet would arise elsewhere in a specialized portion of the smooth endoplasmic reticulum.[91] These two elements would join at the smooth-surfaced termini of the rough endoplasmic reticulum to form a complex that would eventually be released into the lumen, perhaps in connection with incremental additions of phospholipid in the Golgi apparatus.

Properties of Nascent Lipoprotein Particles

VLDL. Nascent lipoproteins have been isolated from Golgi apparatus–rich fractions of the liver of several species.[91] Some of these fractions may have been contaminated with multivesicular bodies and other endosomal structures that contain lipoproteins taken up into the liver by receptor-mediated endocytosis, making it difficult to evaluate their properties.[99] Apo B–containing particles isolated from Golgi-rich fractions from rat liver in which endosomal contamination is very limited have been shown to be almost entirely VLDL that resemble in size and composition those found in blood plasma.[91] VLDL isolated from perfusates of isolated livers also resemble Golgi VLDL in most respects.[91]

Rat plasma VLDL contain appreciable amounts of a B apoprotein the size of apo B-48 as well as apo B-100, and both of these are secreted by the liver in this species.[100] The B-48 protein is also secreted in a particle in the HDL density range; secretion of this particle is not abolished in rats fed orotic acid.[97] By contrast, in other species (monkeys and rabbits) in which apo B-100 is virtually the sole apo B component of plasma VLDL, only this form of apo B is secreted by the liver.[100] Although Golgi VLDL also contain apo E and the several C apoproteins found in plasma VLDL,[91] the content of C apoproteins is considerably lower in Golgi VLDL.[101] All of the proteins found in Golgi VLDL appear to be newly synthesized; there is no evidence that plasma apolipoproteins can be reutilized in the assembly of the nascent particles. Golgi VLDL also differ from plasma VLDL with respect to the lipids of the particle surface; Golgi VLDL contain less unesterified cholesterol and more phospholipids.[101] When Golgi VLDL are incubated with blood plasma from which VLDL have been removed by ultracentrifugation, they acquire C apoproteins from HDL.[101] They also acquire cholesterol and lose phospholipids by transfers with other lipoproteins so that they then closely resemble plasma VLDL in surface composition. In rats, Golgi and perfusate VLDL contain an appreciable complement of cholesteryl esters, reflecting the high activity of acyl-CoA:cholesterol O-acyltransferase (ACAT) in this species.[101,102] In several animals in which the activity of this enzyme is low, Golgi and perfusate VLDL contain much lower amounts of cholesteryl esters than those of blood plasma.[103,104] In such animals, most cholesteryl esters in VLDL are derived from the action of lecithin:cholesterol acyltransferase (LCAT) on species of HDL and transferred to VLDL by a specific transfer protein.[100] In all species, triglycerides are the major constituent of nascent VLDL, accounting for 50 percent or more of particle mass.

In humans, the activity of hepatic ACAT is low,[105] and cholesteryl esters are readily transferred to VLDL by the cholesteryl ester transfer protein.[106] Therefore, nascent human VLDL presumably resemble those of species like the rabbit, which contain few cholesteryl esters.

Chylomicrons. It has been considerably more difficult to isolate nascent chylomicrons from enterocytes, but it is thought that, like nascent VLDL, the size and core lipid composition of triglyceride-rich lipoproteins secreted from enterocytes are similar to those of lymph chylomicrons. Chylomicrons isolated from prenodal intestinal lymph are changed least from those secreted from the cells, but some modification of surface components clearly occurs in the interstitial space and lacteals, since plasma HDL and other lipoproteins are present at these sites.[107] In the several mammalian species examined, apo B-48 has been found to be the sole form of apo B present in chylomicrons.[100] The other major apoproteins of nascent chylomicrons of rats are apo A-I and apo A-IV which, although synthesized in the liver as well, are present in only trace amounts in nascent VLDL.[102,107,108] This difference between chylomicrons and VLDL is not solely a matter of the large size of chylomicrons during active fat absorption, since the protein composition of small chylomicrons secreted in the absence of dietary fat is not appreciably different.[108] Apo E and the C apoproteins are also present on intestinal lymph chylomicrons of rats, but they are thought to be acquired mainly from HDL after secretion since synthesis of these proteins by enterocytes is very limited.[107] However, both rat and human enterocytes appear to have some capacity to synthesize C apoproteins.[109] Acquisition of apoproteins from HDL continues after chylomicrons enter the blood plasma, and some of the A apoproteins may concomitantly be transferred to HDL, together with some chylomicron phospholipids.[108] In addition to the apoproteins found in rat lymph chylomicrons, human plasma chylomicrons contain a proline-rich protein normally found predominantly as an oligomer in a lipid-poor form in blood plasma.[110]

Specificity of Apo B Synthesis in Liver and Intestine. The nature of the B apoproteins synthesized by human liver and intestine has been the subject of several recent studies. Apo B-100 is by far the predominant form of apo B in plasma VLDL. Only apo B-100 has been found to accumulate in media of a human hepatoma cell line (Hep G2).[112] Furthermore, newly synthesized apo B in samples of human liver consists exclusively of apo B-100, in the fetus as well as adults.[113] The type of apo B synthesized by human intestine is less clear. Apo B-48 is the predominant form of apo B in human thoracic duct lymph chylomicrons.[4] Although apo B-100 is present, this could reflect the presence of lipoproteins derived from hepatic lymph. Apo B has been localized in normal human enterocytes, particularly the apical regions, with monoclonal antibodies that react exclusively with epitopes on apo B-100 as well as with those that recognize regions common to apo B-100 and apo B-48.[96] By contrast, monoclonal antibodies that recognize both apo B-100 and B-48, but not those that recognize apo B-100 alone, identified apo B in isolated enterocytes from patients with chylomicron retention disease.[114] The only form of newly synthesized apo B identified in experiments with isolated human jejunal enterocytes from normal adults was apo B-48.[113] However, newly synthesized apo B-100 was also found in enterocytes from fetuses up to the sixteenth week of gestation.[113]

This current evidence indicates that apo B-100 is the sole form of apo B synthesized in human liver. Whereas apo B-48 is the predominant form of apo B synthesized in human intestine, apo B-100 may also be synthesized, at least in the fetus.

Hepatic Production of LDL. The lipoproteins that accumulate in media of Hep G2 cells have been characterized in several laboratories. In most but not all cases, newly synthesized apo B-100 has been found to accumulate predominantly in LDL particles,[115–117] although more VLDL particles containing apo B-100 accumulate when fatty acids are present in the incubation medium.[116] These observations have been interpreted to suggest that LDL as well as VLDL are normally secreted from the liver of humans, consistent with data obtained in some kinetic studies of apo B metabolism.[118] Most studies of apo B kinetics of normal individuals have suggested that apo B is secreted solely in VLDL particles and that LDL arise from VLDL (see Chap. 44A). Cultured human hepatocytes appear to secrete mainly VLDL,[119] and it is possible that secretion of LDL from Hep G2 cells is a peculiarity of this cell line. Alternatively, newly secreted VLDL particles may be degraded by hepatic lipase, which is also secreted from Hep G2 cells.[120] Kinetic studies of apo B metabolism in rabbits[121] and other species[122] have also been interpreted to indicate that LDL particles are secreted by the liver independent of VLDL. However, in rabbits, other studies challenge this interpretation.[123] Furthermore, virtually all apo B–containing lipoproteins isolated from Golgi fractions or isolated perfusates of rabbit liver are VLDL.[104] However, LDL-sized particles are secreted from perfused livers of cholesterol-fed animals and in certain other pathologic states.[91,124] Currently, the question of independent secretion of LDL from human liver, which is important for our understanding of the pathophysiology of a number of disorders involving apo B, remains open. Available evidence suggests that VLDL are the sole or major form in which apo B is secreted from the liver of normal individuals. Additional information is needed for patients with diseases affecting the synthesis or catabolism of apo B.

Regulation of Secretion of Chylomicrons and VLDL

Plasticity of VLDL and Chylomicrons in Lipid Transport. As evidenced by the absence of chylomicrons and VLDL in classic abetalipoproteinemia, apo B-100 and apo B-48 are required for these lipoproteins to be assembled and secreted. As described above, nascent VLDL contain a single copy of apo B-100, whereas nascent chylomicrons may contain two copies of apo B-48. This constancy evidently applies to all VLDL particles, regardless of their size.[125] Increased transport of triglycerides can be accomplished by expansion of the core of chylomicrons or VLDL without a necessary increase in the number of particles synthesized and secreted. Feeding fat to rats for up to 48 h increases the transport of triglycerides in intestinal lymph chylomicrons by a factor of 20, but transport of apo B is increased no more than twofold.[107] This is accomplished by increasing mean particle diameter about 2.5 times. Synthesis of apo B-48 in jejunal and ileal enterocytes is not altered when rats are fed isocaloric diets containing no fat or up to 30 percent by weight of triglycerides.[126] Thus, transport of dietary fat seems to be accomplished mainly by incorporating many more triglyceride molecules into chylomicron particles, which continue to be synthesized and secreted independently of dietary fat absorption. Similarly, in the liver, the size of secreted VLDL increases in response to increased rates of hepatic triglyceride synthesis. This is evident from rates of accumulation of apo B and triglycerides in perfusates of isolated livers from rats fed carbohydrate-rich diets.[127,128] In fetal guinea pigs, livers accumulate fat toward the end of gestation as a result of the uptake of large amounts of free fatty acids transported across the placenta.[129] VLDL secreted then become very large, approaching the size of chylomicrons normally secreted after administration of a dietary fat load.[130]

The core of VLDL can also expand to accommodate more cholesteryl esters in animals fed cholesterol-rich diets.[91] This is particularly striking in animals such as the rabbit and guinea pig, in which cholesterol feeding is accompanied by accumulation of large amounts of cholesteryl esters in the liver. Under these conditions, some newly secreted VLDL contain many more cholesteryl ester molecules than can be accommodated in a particle the size of LDL (~200 Å in diameter). Consequently, removal of VLDL triglycerides by lipolysis yields particles whose diameter and density remain predominantly in the VLDL or IDL range. Although these particles, like LDL, contain little triglyceride, they may retain substantial amounts of apo E and some C apoproteins.

Regulation of Apo B Synthesis. Although the upstream region of the apo B gene contains a number of potential regulatory elements,[52] little is yet known about the regulation of apo B gene transcription or translation in either liver or intestine. The concentration of apo B-100 mRNA was found to be increased severalfold in liver from two patients with abetalipoproteinemia.[95] Insulin inhibits synthesis and secretion of apo B from cultured rat hepatocytes.[131,132] Synthesis of apo B in Hep G2 cells is increased by high concentrations of estrogens, paralleled by occupancy of type II (low affinity) estrogen receptors.[133] Cholesterol reportedly stimulates the secretion of apo B from cultured human hepatocytes.[119] By contrast, in rat enterocytes, synthesis of apo B-48 is inversely related to sustained alterations of mucosal cholesterol flux, but increased triglyceride flux does not affect synthesis of apo B-48.[126]

ABETALIPOPROTEINEMIA

Early Descriptions

The first description of this syndrome appeared in 1950.[134] Bassen and Kornzweig[134] described an 18-year-old female with an atypical pigmented retinopathy and abnormalities of red cell morphology not previously described. The "star-shaped" erythrocytes that abounded in peripheral blood were noted to form rouleaux very poorly. Ataxia and loss of deep-tendon reflexes were also present. During childhood the patient was thought to have celiac disease, based on the presence of chronic diarrhea. The appearance of similar erythrocytes and retinopathy in the patient's brother, of consanguineous parentage, and the absence of findings in the parents suggested recessive inheritance of a rare allele. In 1952 Jampel and Falls,[135] studying another case with acanthocytosis, fat malabsorption, retinopathy, and advanced neurologic disability, made the critical observation that the content of cholesterol in the serum was extremely low. They also observed, using free electrophoresis, that the β-globulin fraction of serum proteins, then known to be associated with cholesterol transport, was deficient. This discovery linked the malabsorption of fat to impaired lipid transport in plasma. Hypocholesterolemia was soon found in another case,[136] and in 1960 three laboratories demonstrated the absence of β- and pre-β-migrating lipoproteins from plasma.[137–139] Preparative ultracentrifugation confirmed the absence of LDL. The presence of normal pancreatic lipase activity and bile acid levels in duodenal contents[137] and of high levels of free fatty acids in stool[138] indicated that the malabsorption involved fat and that the defect must be at the level of the intestinal epithelium. Thus, with these key observations, a syndrome had emerged, encompassing fat malabsorption, acanthocytosis, retinopathy, and progressive neurologic disease. Though not all patients described subsequently had all of these features at the time they were studied, the absence of β-lipoproteins was at once a unifying feature and the first clue to mechanisms underlying the disease.

Lipoproteins and Lipid Transport in Abetalipoproteinemia

Structure and Composition of Plasma Lipoproteins. As techniques for isolation and identification of plasma lipoproteins improved, it became apparent that the lipoproteins that were absent from blood in abetalipoproteinemia included chylomicrons and all the lipoprotein particles of the VLDL cascade, that is, all the lipoproteins that contain B apolipoproteins.[140–144] Because these lipoproteins normally bear most of the cholesterol and triglycerides in plasma, the levels of both classes of lipids are markedly reduced. Plasma triglyceride levels are frequently only a few milligrams per deciliter. Cholesterol levels are usually less than half of normal, and often only 20 to 45 mg/dl. Plasma triglyceride levels fail to rise after ingestion of fat, although some polyunsaturated fatty acids eventually appear in plasma.[144] The content of exogenous polyunsaturated fatty acids such as linoleate is decreased in plasma and in adipose tissue, reflecting inefficiency in the uptake of dietary fat into the body.[144] There is a striking shift away from the normal distribution of generic species of phospholipids in plasma. The relative content of phosphatidylcholine is decreased and that of sphingomyelin is increased.[140,145]

Examination of the lipoproteins of blood showed the presence of some lipoprotein material in the ultracentrifugal density intervals in which chylomicrons, VLDL, IDL, and LDL are found (Fig. 44B-2). However, virtually all efforts to detect circulating apo B by immunochemical means have been unsuccessful.[146–148] In one study, serum from patients with abetalipoproteinemia appeared to contain a substance that inhibited antigen-antibody reaction between azo LDL and antiserum against azo LDL, but did not inhibit the reaction of nonderivatized LDL with its antiserum, an observation that as yet remains unexplained.[149]

Among the lipoproteins of the $d < 1.006$ g/ml and $1.006 < d < 1.063$ g/ml ultracentrifugal fractions, apo A-I is a major constituent,[147,148] but apo A-II and E apoproteins are also present.[148] As with the other lipoproteins of abetalipoprotein-

Fig. 44B-2 Electron-microscopic appearance of abnormal serum lipoproteins in two forms of hypolipidemia and in Lp(a) hyperlipidemia. *(Original magnification indicated.)* *A.* "Square packing" lipoproteins from the LDL density interval in recessive abetalipoproteinemia. ×195,000. *(Courtesy of Dr. Trudy Forte.)* *B.* Lipoproteins of the LDL density interval from a patient with normotriglyceridemic abetalipoproteinemia, showing irregular outlines and some cuboidal forms. × 180,000. *C.* Lipoproteins of the d<1.006 g/ml fraction of serum in normotriglyceridemic abetalipoproteinemia. ×180,000. *(Courtesy of Dr. Mary Malloy.)* *D.* Lipoproteins of the HDL density interval from a patient with hyper Lp(a) lipoproteinemia, showing numerous Lp(a) particles among normal-appearing HDL particles. ×180,000. Lipoproteins in all panels are visualized by negative staining with phosphotungstate.

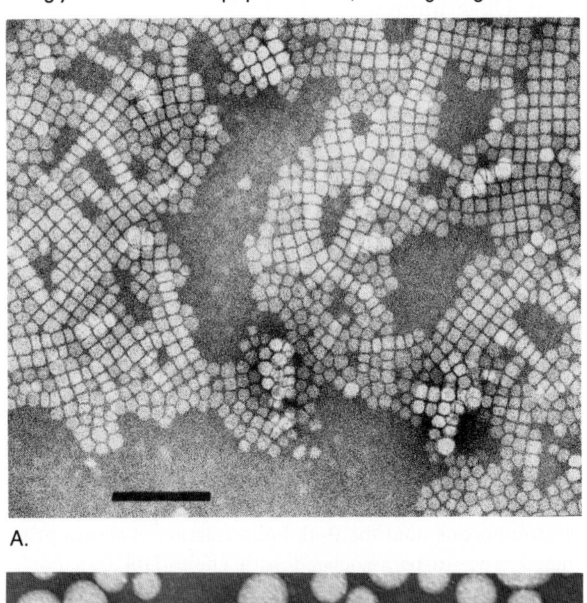

A.

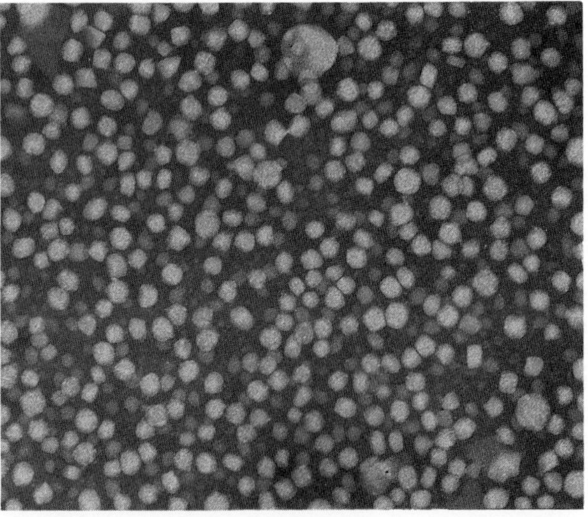

B.

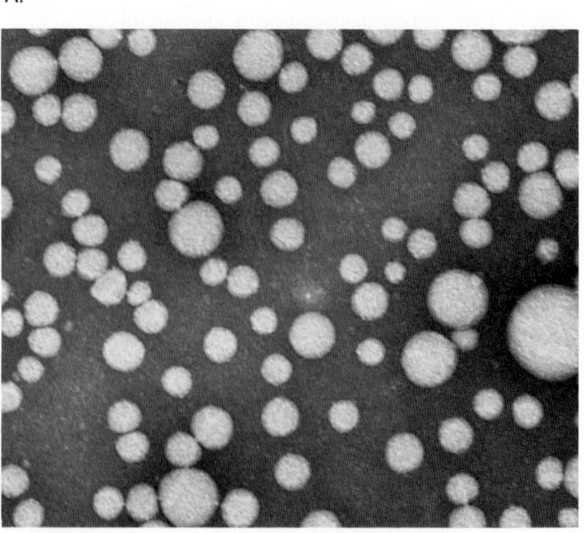

C.

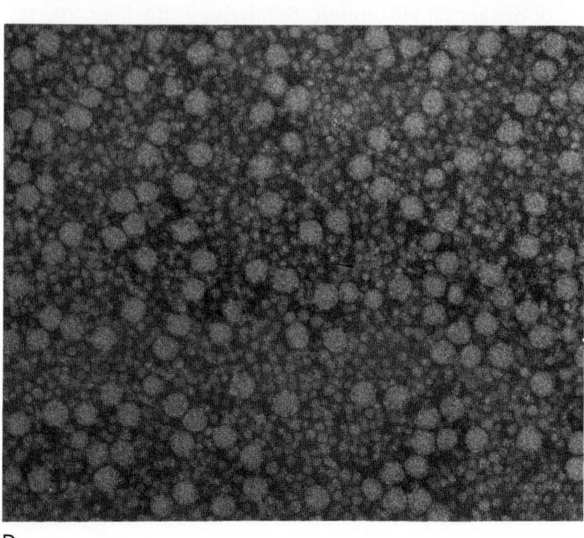

D.

emia, the most anionic isoform of apo C-III, apo C-III_2, which carries two residues of sialic acid, is the only isoform present in the LDL interval.[146–148] This pattern is also observed when VLDL secretion from liver is inhibited by administration of orotic acid, suggesting that the more highly sialated form of apo C-III may enter plasma via pathways other than by the secretion of VLDL, perhaps via secretion of HDL. The lipoproteins of the LDL and VLDL density intervals in abetalipoproteinemia have a distinct cuboidal, square-packing appearance with an 80- to 90-Å periodicity[148,150] (Fig. 44B-2). A possible mechanism for the development of square-packing particles of this type is suggested by the observation that when bovine HDL acquire dimyristoylphosphatidylcholine, they lose a portion of their complement of apo A-I, becoming less dense and assuming cuboidal shape.[151] Like the more abundant HDL particles, the lipoproteins of the LDL density interval show a decreased ratio of lecithin to sphingomyelin (nearly 1 in contrast to a normal ratio of 2). Nearly one-half of the cholesterol is unesterified, compared with less than one-third in normal LDL.[148]

The HDL density interval contains about one-half the normal amount of lipoprotein mass. As with the lipoproteins of lower density, the HDL have an abnormally high ratio of free to esterified cholesterol (0.7 compared with 0.3) and a lecithin: spingomyelin ratio of about 5:4 (compared with a normal ratio of about 8:1).[148] By electron microscopy they resemble normal HDL except that they tend to larger particle diameters.[150,151] Rate zonal ultracentrifugation shows that most of the particles have the flotation characteristics of HDL_2, with mean diameters of 135 Å. A second population has mean diameters of about 100 Å, and a third, designated ABL-HDL_4 and not previously described in normal individuals, is also spherical, with a mean diameter of 60 Å. Apo A-I is the predominant protein constituent of all three particle types. Apo A-II comprises about one-eighth of the apoprotein mass of the HDL_2-like fraction and about one-third of that of the ABL-HDL_4. All the isoforms of apo A-II are present, but their distribution differs from the normal pattern.[152] Apo E is almost as abundant in the HDL_2-like particles as apo A-II, and it is present to the extent of 1 to 3 percent of protein mass in the HDL_3-like particles, but in only trace amounts in the ABL-HDL_4 particle.[153]

Because apolipoproteins, especially apo E, may become dissociated from lipoprotein particles during ultracentrifugation, it is important to verify their distribution among lipoprotein particles by nonultracentrifugal techniques. Using gel permeation chromatography, Gibson et al.[154] found that apo E was not associated with the LDL-size particles of abetalipoproteinemia, indicating that its appearance in the HDL particles was not a consequence of the disintegration during ultracentrifugation of particles of lower density. Much of the apo E appears to be present in the form of an apo E:apo A-II disulfide-bridged dimer.[155] The apolipoproteins that appear in plasma in abetalipoproteinemia all appear to be structurally normal. Absence of the nonsialated and monosialated forms of apo C-III characterize the HDL species as well as the lipoproteins of lower density.

Viewed mechanistically, the circulating lipoproteins in abetalipoproteinemia reflect the lack of transport of both exogenous (chylomicron) and endogenous (VLDL) triglycerides. Thus, the lipid constituents that are normally transferred to HDL in the course of intravascular lipolysis are lacking. Also, the transport of dietary cholesterol into the body is impaired. The appearance of most of the normal apolipoproteins other than the two molecular forms of apo B indicates that they can be secreted independently of the apo B–containing lipoproteins, the exception being the apo C-III_0 and apo C-III_1 isoforms. Sphingomyelin, which normally is acquired from tissues by HDL and transferred to apo B–containing lipoproteins,[156] accumulates in HDL. Free cholesterol also accumulates in HDL, perhaps as a consequence of the lack of appropriate acceptor particles for the transfer of cholesteryl esters generated by the LCAT reaction. The accumulation of lipid in some of the HDL particles causes a reordering and loss of a portion of the complement of apo A-I, forming particles that enter the low density interval. Though further metabolic studies are needed, preliminary data suggest that the synthesis of apo A-I is reduced to two-thirds of normal but that its catabolic rate is normal.[157]

Activities of Lipoprotein Lipase and LCAT. Lipoprotein lipase (LPL) activity has been found to be very low in abetalipoproteinemia.[144,158] Illingworth found heparin-releasable activities of LPL and hepatic lipase to be reduced to about one-half of normal.[159] It is likely that this is due to a reduced induction of the enzymes due to fat malabsorption itself. It is recognized that extremely low dietary intake of fat[160] or malabsorption[161] results in appreciable reduction in lipoprotein lipase activity. A possible role for gastric inhibitory peptide in this induction is suggested by increased release of the peptide during fat ingestion[162] and stimulation by the hormone of lipoprotein lipase secretion by preadipocytes.[163]

Decreased LCAT activity likewise has been observed in abetalipoproteinemia.[147,148,164] This may be due in part to the relatively poor substrate activity of HDL_2.[165] However, the observation that the addition of normal LDL results in marked stimulation of cholesterol esterification in plasma from patients with abetalipoproteinemia[166] suggests that deficiency of acceptor lipoproteins is a major factor.

Sterol Metabolism and the Interaction of Plasma Lipoproteins with Receptors. Several studies of total body synthesis of cholesterol in abetalipoproteinemia have been reported. In two of these studies,[167,168] essentially normal rates of about 15 mg/(kg/day) were observed. In two other subjects,[169] rates somewhat higher were observed, which could be accounted for by the impaired reabsorption of biliary cholesterol alone. In long-term cholesterol turnover studies in two individuals, Goodman et al.[170] showed rates of cholesterol production of 0.82 and 0.89 g/day, well within the normal range. The data fit a three-pool model well. As expected, the most rapidly exchanging pool was markedly reduced, whereas the total exchangeable cholesterol pool was essentially normal. Studies in freshly isolated lymphocytes from one patient with abetalipoproteinemia showed cholesterol synthesis to be normal,[171] but in others an elevated rate was observed.[172,173] The activity of β-hydroxy-β-methylglutaryl-CoA reductase was found to be normal in hair roots from one subject.[174] Freshly isolated mononuclear cells from one patient were found to bind and degrade LDL at a rate comparable to that of cells from normal individuals.[175]

The delivery of cholesterol to cells in abetalipoproteinemia is apparently accomplished with efficiency via apo E–containing HDL particles.[173,176,177] These particles compete effectively with LDL for binding and endocytosis via the B-100:E LDL receptors, downregulating the receptors. Apo E–containing HDL from subjects with abetalipoproteinemia were capable of inducing a three- to fivefold increase in the cholesteryl ester content of cultured fibroblasts,[177] indicating their effectiveness in the delivery of cholesterol to peripheral cells. The increased efficiency of apo E as a receptor ligand and the increased content of cholesterol compared with normal HDL allows plasma in abetalipoproteinemia to deliver cholesterol to the periphery with the same efficiency as would occur at an LDL cholesterol level of approximately 100 mg/dl.

Thus, delivery of cholesterol to peripheral cells appears, in general, to be nearly normal in the absence of VLDL and LDL. In the adrenal cortex, delivery of cholesterol also appears to be normal in the basal state, but the maximum secretion of cortisol is less than normal in the face of corticotropin stimulation.[178,179] Similarly, the production of progesterone during the luteal phase of the menstrual cycle appears to have been abnormally low in one patient.[180] Thus, the extraction of cholesterol from plasma via the abnormal lipoproteins appears to be insufficient to support maximum steroidogenesis. In spite of this, at least one patient has carried a pregnancy to term, delivering a normal infant.[181]

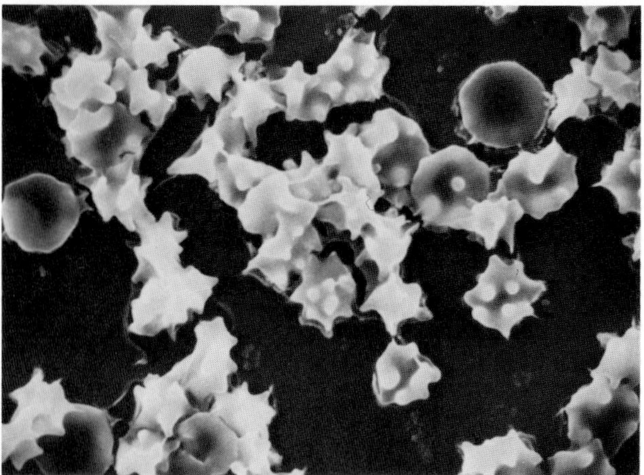

Fig. 44B-3 Acanthocytosis of erythrocytes from a patient with homozygous recessive abetalipoproteinemia. *(Scanning electron micrograph courtesy of Dr. Mary Malloy.)*

Clinical Features

Hematologic Manifestations. The markedly abnormal form of erythrocytes has attracted the attention of investigators since the earliest descriptions of the disorder. Singer et al.[182] created the term *acanthrocytosis* (from *acantha*, "thorn" in Greek), which soon became modified to *acanthocytosis*.

Acanthocytes comprise from 50 percent to virtually all of circulating erythrocytes (Fig. 44B-3). However, they are not found in bone marrow, suggesting that the membranous changes leading to malformation are acquired by contact with plasma. Their structure strongly inhibits rouleaux formation, leading to extremely low erythrocyte sedimentation rates.[183] The lipid composition of their envelopes reflects the abnormal composition of the plasma lipoproteins in this disorder.[184–187] The contents of total phospholipids and cholesterol are greater than in normal cells, and the sphingomyelin lecithin ratio is increased dramatically, from 0.9 to over 1.4. The fatty acid compositions of phosphatidylcholine and phosphatidylserine appear normal, but there is a shift to more saturated fatty acids among the sphingomyelins.[186] The erythrocytes apparently assume the acanthocytic form because of a maldistribution of lipids between the two bilayer leaflets.[189] The redundant exterior leaflet drives outward curvature, a phenomenon that is rapidly reversible in the presence of chlorpromazine, which expands the cytoplasmic leaflet.

Red cell survival is frequently shortened,[136,190,191] and hyperbilirubinemia[136,140,190] has been described. Many patients have demonstrated erythroid hyperplasia[136,145,192,193] and reticulocytosis,[141,197] suggesting that erythropoiesis per se is not notably impaired by abetalipoproteinemia.

Anemia and Abnormalities of Hemostasis. Severe anemia has been described in a number of children with abetalipoproteinemia,[182,190,194,196] many of whom appear to respond to replacement therapy with iron or folic acid.[197–199] It is likely that most cases of severe anemia principally reflect deficiencies of iron, folate, and perhaps other nutrients secondary to fat malabsorption, but probably not deficiency of vitamin B_{12}.[145,190] Autohemolysis of erythrocytes, which appears to result from accelerated hydroperoxidation of olefinic fatty acids secondary to tocopherol deficiency, may also contribute to the anemia.[149,187,197,200,201]

A number of descriptions of cases in which vitamin K deficiency resulted in significant prothrombin deficiency[187,193,194,197,202,203] have appeared in the literature. In two other cases, significant gastrointestinal bleeding was present in infancy or childhood, associated with severe vitamin K deficiency.[204,205]

Like erythrocytes, the platelet membranes show compositional changes, notably an increase in free cholesterol.[206] Because the lipoproteins bearing apo B-100 appear to stimulate platelet aggregation and serotonin release in response to collagen and adenosine diphosphate, it might be expected that the platelet response in abetalipoproteinemia would be lower than normal. However, HDL from patients with abetalipoproteinemia have been found to bind to platelets, activating them as LDL normally do.[207] This finding is of particular interest in view of the fact that normal HDL inhibit platelet reactiveness to those stimuli. It is likely that the apo E–containing HDL are the particles responsible for the stimulatory effect.

Gastrointestinal Manifestations. Malabsorption of fat is a central pathophysiological feature of abetalipoproteinemia. It is usually observed in the neonatal period, with vomiting, diarrhea, and failure to gain weight normally. It is no doubt the chief reason for the somatic underdevelopment described in the majority of cases. Radiographic examination of the intestine frequently demonstrates clumping of contrast material.[138,190,208] The intestinal symptoms correlate directly with the amount of fat in the diet and tend to diminish over the years, reflecting in part a striking aversion of many patients to dietary fat.

Studies of Intestinal Absorption. Despite the inability to secrete chylomicrons, some absorption of long-chain fatty acids occurs.[145,187,209] Some fatty acids, especially polyunsaturated, are probably transported directly to the liver as free fatty acids. Lysosomal hypertrophy has been described with fat feeding, suggesting that some alternative processes are induced. In adult life, loss of fatty acids in stool may represent as little as 20 percent of the ingested mass. The chronic excretion of fatty acids is apparently enough to induce oxalate urolithiasis, however,[210] which might be prevented by increasing dietary calcium intake.

In normal individuals, vitamin A is esterified in the enterocyte and its esters are secreted into the intestinal lymphatics in chylomicrons.[211] The absorption of vitamin A is diminished in patients with abetalipoproteinemia.[187,191,192] Although the concentration in plasma tends to be low,[141,212–214] administration of supplemental vitamin results in normal levels in plasma, by as yet unknown mechanisms.

Unlike vitamins A and K, where even modest supplementation serves to achieve normal plasma levels, the transport of tocopherol is severely inhibited in abetalipoproteinemia.[215–217] Normally, tocopherol enters plasma via the chylomicrons and, apparently, directly via the portal system also.[218] The bulk of blood tocopherol is found in LDL, which deliver the vitamin, at least in part, to peripheral tissues by endocytosis via the B-100:E receptor.[219] The abnormal lipoproteins of abetalipoproteinemia appear incapable of incorporating normal amounts of tocopherol even in the face of relatively large oral supplements[217] or even intramuscular injection. Massive supplementation, however, somehow increases the flux into the body, eventually increasing the tocopherol content of adipose tissue appreciably.[215] Low plasma and tissue levels of tocopherol in normotriglyceridemic abetalipoproteinemia,[220] where chylomicrons are apparently formed normally, suggest that LDL play a vital role in the transport of tocopherol and that the impairment of transport in abetalipoproteinemia is not entirely due to failure to produce chylomicrons.

The Intestinal Mucosa. Yellowish discoloration of duodenal mucosa has been observed on endoscopy.[221] The findings in biopsy specimens are highly characteristic. Unlike celiac disease, with which abetalipoproteinemia has been frequently confused, the villi are formed normally. Extensive hyaline vacuolization of the villus cells is evident when stained conventionally;[141,208] however, lipophilic stains reveal the vacuoles to be filled with lipid.[187,197] The lipid content of the mucosa is several times normal,[197] even when no fat has been ingested for days. Electron microscopy reveals numerous fat droplets within the mucosal cells.[222] However, they are not clearly within the Golgi apparatus as are the fat droplets seen during normal fat absorption. They do not accumulate in the Golgi zone and are not clearly surrounded by membrane. Immunofluorescence studies in intestinal mucosal biopsies from several individuals with abetalipoproteinemia have failed to demonstrate apo B, a finding compatible with a structural gene defect for apo B.[223,224] However, the finding of immunoreactive material with antibodies to apo B in hepatic and intestinal cells in another case of abetalipoproteinemia[96] suggests that defects in posttranslational processing or transport may also lead to abetalipoproteinemia.

Hepatic Manifestations. Despite the inability of the liver to secrete VLDL, abnormalities of liver function are uncommon in abetalipoproteinemia. Two patients have had abnormal levels of transaminases in serum.[145,226] However, accumulation of lipid droplets in hepatocytes has also been observed.[145,209] Frank cirrhosis has been described in only a few cases and appears to be related to treatment with medium-chain triglycerides.[226,227] Liver tissue from an adult not treated with medium-chain triglycerides was found to have numerous lipid droplets within hepatocytes. They were not membrane-bound, nor were they associated with the Golgi apparatus. No fibrosis was present.[228]

Neuromuscular Manifestations. The neurologic manifestations of abetalipoproteinemia have placed it among the hereditary spinocerebellar degenerative syndromes (Fig. 44B-4). In fact, it is only the recognition of disordered lipoprotein metabolism that has permitted a clear separation of abetalipoproteinuria from the other disorders of that group. Early cases were frequently considered variants of Friedreich ataxia. In retrospect, many of the reported cases of Friedreich ataxia with pigmented retinopathy must have been abetalipoproteinemia. Prior to the advent of aggressive tocopherol therapy, the onset of neurologic disease usually began in the first or second decade of life and often progressed to catastrophic disability, though some patients inexplicably escaped serious affliction until much later. The most characteristic degenerative sites in the nervous system are the large sensory neurons of the spinal ganglia and their heavily myelinated axons, which enter the cord lateral to the posterior funiculus. The pathologic appearance is that of an axonopathy.[193,194,229] Extensive demyelination of the fasciculus cuneatus and fasciculus gracilis may occur.[193,194]

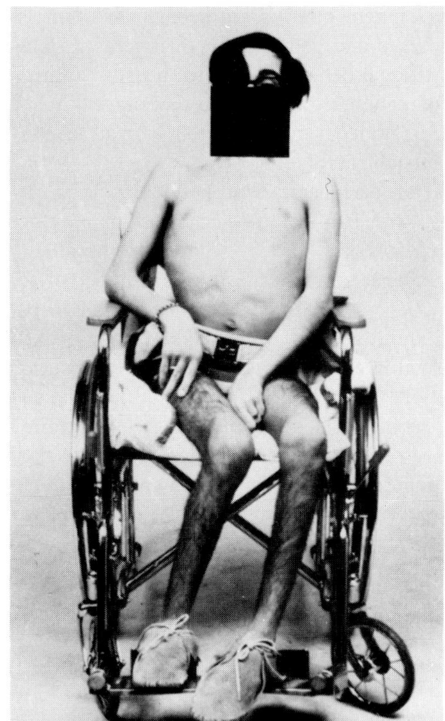

Fig. 44B-4 A 17-year-old patient with abetalipoproteinemia with generalized weakness, kyphoscoliosis, and lordosis. *(Courtesy of Drs. Peter Herbert, Gerd Assmann, Antonio M. Gotto, Jr., and Donald Fredrickson.)*

The first neurologic signs are diminution in intensity of deep-tendon reflexes, which may appear in the first few years of life,[191,198] probably due primarily to loss of function in spinocerebellar pathways and posterior columns. Vibratory sense and proprioception tend to be lost progressively, and an ataxic gait appears. The Romberg sign is frequently present. Untreated patients are often unable to stand unaided by the third decade. Movements may become highly dysmetric, and dysarthia may become severe. Muscle contractures are common, leading to pes cavus and equinovarus, and kyphoscoliosis.

The presence of Babinski responses in some patients has been attributed to pyramidal tract disease;[134,145,193] however, spastic paralysis is not seen. Mental retardation or dullness has been described in a number of cases. However, attribution of this phenomenon to the metabolic defect of abetalipoproteinemia is difficult because specific neuropathologic evidence of cerebral cortical disease is lacking. Furthermore, the slow neuromuscular development observed in neonates is often associated with steatorrhea and general growth failure and may reflect multiple nutritional deficiencies. Also, because approximately one-third of patients described to date appear to be the products of consanguineous matings, other rare alleles may be responsible for mental retardation.

Clinical evidence of peripheral neuropathy has been described infrequently, but has included classic stocking-glove distribution of hypesthesia.[138,141,230,231] Patients frequently show diminished response to local anesthetics. Studies of somatosensory conduction revealed abnormalities in 9 of 10 patients with abetalipoproteinemia, whereas brainstem-evoked potentials were normal in all 9 patients.[232] Marked diminution in amplitude of sensory potentials has been found in tibial and sural nerves, with slowing of conduction velocity. Electromyographic studies have revealed evidence of denervation of skeletal muscle.[233] In general, the cranial nerves are spared, but oculomotor nerve involvement and denervation of the tongue have been observed.[231]

The principal finding in biopsies of sural nerves has been loss of large myelinated fibers. Paranodal demyelination appears to correlate with the severity and duration of disease, whereas unmyelinated fibers appear to be relatively unaffected.[233] In all, there is a striking resemblance between the neurologic lesions of abetalipoproteinemia and those encountered in various malabsorption syndromes involving tocopherol deficiency[234–237] and in vitamin E–deficient animals.[238–241] The appearance of a metastatic glioma in an adult patient with abetalipoproteinemia has raised the interesting possibility that the deficiency of tocopherol may have led to free radical–mediated mutagenesis in the central nervous system.[204]

Muscle weakness is a frequent feature of abetalipoproteinemia, but the clinical determination that myopathy is present tends to be obscured by the frequent presence of denervative neuropathy. Myopathy characterized by the presence of ceroid pigment in the muscle fibers has been described, however, in a 26-year-old man.[242] The granules reacted with periodic acid–Schiff reagent and were electron-dense and autofluorescent, resembling closely the ceroid pigment observed in the muscle tissue of tocopherol-deficient animals. Cardiomyopathy leading to death has been described in a 10-year-old.[194] Again, the pathologic appearance of perinuclear deposits of lipochrome pigment suggested tocopherol deficiency.

Ophthalmic Manifestations. The most prominent ophthalmic abnormality in abetalipoproteinemia is pigmentary retinal degeneration, which clinically resembles other forms of retinitis pigmentosa not associated with deficiency of lipoproteins. Commonality of mechanism with the neurologic abnormalities in abetalipoproteinemia is suggested by the general observation that the more severe examples of retinopathy tend to occur in individuals with severe neurologic disability.[134,135,141,231] Major pathologic features are loss of photoreceptors, loss of pigment epithelium, and relative preservation of submacular pigment epithelium. Lipofuscin pigment is present, and macrophagelike cells which invade the retina contain trilaminar structures that probably represent ingested lipofuscins.[243,244] These retinal alterations closely resemble the retinopathy of experimental tocopherol deficiency.[238,245,246] Deficiency of vitamin A may also contribute to the retinopathy of abetalipoproteinemia. This is suggested by clinical descriptions of improvement in dark adaptation and electrophysiological behavior of the retina with vitamin A supplementation.[247–250] Because retinitis pigmentosa is not typical of the pathology observed in experimental vitamin A deficiency[251,252] or in human vitamin A deficiency,[253] it appears that vitamin A probably does not play a central role in the retinal disease in abetalipoproteinemia. The observation that progression of retinopathy has been described in the face of vitamin A supplementation[254] tends to support this view. Thus, it is likely, especially in the light of the abundance of lipofuscin pigment in the retina, that tocopherol deficiency plays a central role in the process, though vitamin A supplements may be of some benefit.

The onset of symptoms is variable. Visual acuity has been significantly compromised during the first decade in a few cases,[141,199,225] though many cases have been asymptomatic until adulthood. Loss of night vision is frequently a presenting symptom,[134,255] and loss of color vision has also been described.[243] The retinopathy often produces slowly enlarging annular scotomas with macular sparing, such that patients are relatively unaware of the progression of the disease. Complete loss of vision can ultimately occur. Many patients develop nystagmus, which is probably a reflection of the loss of visual acuity.

Ophthalmoplegia has been described in a number of cases.[190,191,230,231,243,255,256] A neural basis for this symptom is suggested by the occurrence of primary aberrant regeneration of the oculomotor nerve.[231] Ptosis[141,191] and anisocoria[181,193,221] likewise are most likely the result of neuropathy. Although lenticular opacities are frequently encountered in other forms of retinitis pigmentosa, they are observed infrequently in abetalipoproteinemia.

Associated Clinical Abnormalities. A number of diverse clinical abnormalities have been described in isolated cases or in a few instances. Among these are aminoaciduria,[198] hypogammaglobulinemia,[187,212] extra digits and webbing of the fingers,[256] deformities of the digits,[134,136,243,257] and microcephaly.[257] It is likely that these abnormalities either reflect other independent recessive states or some effect of the gestational environment. On the other hand, hypoalbuminemia[255] and low levels of γ-globulins[187,212] may reflect severe calorie and amino acid malabsorption, and acrodermatitis enteropathica[258] is probably due to deficiency of essential fatty acids.

Genetics

The molecular genetic relationships of many of the disorders discussed in this chapter are unclear at the present time; some represent defects at the apolipoprotein B locus, and others may not. Abetalipoproteinemia has now been recognized in individuals of white, black, Near Eastern, Asian, Malay, and Mexican origin; a disproportionate fraction appears to be of Jewish descent. The pedigrees described to date are compatible with a recessive mode of inheritance. There are no reported instances of an affected parent and child. The allele or alleles responsible must be rare, because about one-third of reported cases are attributed to consanguineous matings. A number of affected females have been reported. It is of interest, however, that males outnumber females about 6:4, suggesting either some mechanism involving sex influence or, alternatively, multiple defects including an X-linked mechanism, operative in a small fraction of cases. Few karyotypes have been reported.[199,212]

Studies of the apo B gene have been carried out in four patients with classic abetalipoproteinemia, who represented three kindreds.[259] By Southern blot analysis, using probes for 30 kb of the apo B-100 gene, all four were shown to have grossly normal structural genes. Polyadenylated mRNA for apo B was present in five- to sixfold the normal amount in liver biopsies of two patients, suggesting that apo B-100 is inducible and that the primary defect in these subjects does not involve the expression of the gene. Furthermore, a B-100–like protein was detected in the biopsy material, indicating that the defect does not block the synthesis of apo B-100–like material. The defect in the patients described appears to involve the processes by which apo B-100 is modified posttranslationally or by which it is incorporated into lipoproteins and secreted into plasma, although defects in the structural gene may account for cases in which apo B is not detectable.[223,224]

Treatment

Clinical experience has shown conclusively that the gastrointestinal symptoms respond to restriction of triglycerides containing long-chain fatty acids. Fatty acids derived from medium-chain triglycerides do not require the formation of chylomicrons for absorption but are transported mainly by albumin as free fatty acids via the hepatic portal system. They are an energy substrate for liver but are not necessary nutrients. Reports of hepatic fibrosis associated with their use in two patients with abetalipoproteinemia[226,227] suggest that they should not be used routinely. However, in extremely malnourished infants, temporary use might be undertaken as long as liver function is followed carefully.

The assessment of the effects of tocopherol supplementation in treatment of abetalipoproteinemia has required prolonged observation. However, it is now apparent that such supplementation does inhibit the progression of the neurologic disease and probably leads to some regression of symptoms, even if commenced in adulthood.[249,260–265] The retinopathy[250,266] can also be prevented if therapy is started early, or stabilized if disease is already present when therapy commences. The myopathy, too, appears to be reversed with tocopherol treatment.[264] Further support for the rationale of therapy with tocopherol comes from similar observations on the effect of tocopherol in other malabsorption states that produce clinical effects in the central nervous system similar to those associated with abetalipoproteinemia.[267] Until the reliability and safety of parenteral vitamin E preparations are established, treatment will require the use of large oral doses of the vitamin. Originally recommended at 100 mg/(kg·day), it is now apparent that much larger doses are well-tolerated and may be of greater benefit. Concentrated preparations now permit the convenient administration of 1000 to 2000 mg/day to infants and 5000 to 10,000 mg/day to older children and adults. In view of the low blood levels of vitamin A and carotene in untreated patients, supplementation with water-soluble preparations of vitamin A would appear to be a reasonable adjunct to treatment with vitamin E. Because vitamin D has its own transport mechanism and because signs and symptoms of deficiency are lacking in abetalipoproteinemia, no specific therapy appears necessary in this regard. Supplementation with vitamin K should be undertaken if bruising, bleeding, or hypoprothrombinemia are present.

FAMILIAL HYPOBETALIPOPROTEINEMIA

Early Descriptions

One of the first examples of the syndrome of hypobetalipoproteinemia was a child born to parents who both had abnormally low levels of cholesterol in serum.[137] A few years later a sibship in which three brothers had hypocholesterolemia without any of the classic clinical findings of abetalipoproteinemia was described.[268] In 1969 Mars et al. described a kindred in which nine individuals with hypocholesterolemia were found in three generations.[269] The propositus was a 37-year-old woman with ataxia and resistance to local anesthetics. She showed only minimal increases in plasma triglycerides after the ingestion of fat, and abnormal fat droplet accumulation was seen in jejunal biopsy specimens taken after a 12-h fast. All nine of the individuals with serum cholesterol levels below 100 mg/dl had acanthocytosis. Another kindred was described in the same year in which two generations were affected, again suggesting a dominant mode of inheritance.[270] Over the next 7 years, individuals with hypobetalipoproteinemia were identified in five additional kindreds.[271–274]

In 1974[275,276] it was reported that individuals with complete absence of apo B–containing lipoproteins could be found in kindreds containing individuals with hypobetalipoproteinemia. This led to the discrimination of a new autosomal disorder in which low levels of LDL and minimal sequelae are present in the heterozygous state and in which the homozygous state is clinically indistinguishable from homozygous recessive abetalipoproteinemia. This concept was soon supported by additional case reports.[277,278]

Lipoprotein Composition and Metabolism

In the heterozygous state serum cholesterol levels range from 40 to 180 mg/dl, averaging about 90 mg/dl. Serum triglycerides range from 15 mg/dl into the normal range. Unlike in patients with abetalipoproteinemia, the ratio of free to esterified cholesterol in plasma is normal, as is the distribution of fatty acids in phospholipids and cholesteryl esters.[268–270,279] The composition of LDL appears normal, as does its hydrodynamic and optical behavior.[271] The levels of LDL in plasma are probably best compared with those of family members to control for other genetic determinants and diet. Compared with first-degree relatives, heterozygotes appear to have clearly distinguishable LDL levels, usually 50 percent or less of the mean for the unaffected members.[270,271,273] HDL cholesterol levels appear to be widely scattered over the normal range.[269,270,272,273,275,279–281] LDL lipid composition appears to be normal.[270,273]

In the homozygous state the lipoprotein pattern closely resembles that in homozygous recessive abetalipoproteinemia. Lipoproteins with β or pre-β mobility are absent upon electrophoresis of serum, and chylomicrons do not appear after fat feeding.[137,275,276] Scant amounts of cuboidal lipoproteins containing apo A-I, like those of recessive abetalipoproteinemia, are found in the LDL density interval,[282] and the apoprotein composition of HDL also resembles that of recessive abetalipoproteinemia.[155] Several groups have failed to detect apo B by conventional immunochemical assays,[275,278,283] but one group has reported extremely low concentrations of apo B (about 0.02 percent of normal) after 3000-fold concentration of ultracentrifugal fractions.[280] In contrast to normals, it was detected in the high density interval as well as in the $1.006<d<1.063$ fraction. The fact that a faint band of appropriate apparent molecular weight was observed in SDS gels suggests that apo B-100 was indeed present.

Cholesterol synthesis was found to be moderately increased in one patient with homozygous hypobetalipoproteinemia: 15 mg/(kg·day) versus 8 mg/(kg·day) in controls.[278] Absorption of cholesterol from the gastrointestinal tract was below normal. The increases in cholesterogenesis could be accounted for by decreased absorption of biliary cholesterol in this case.

Several studies have suggested that production rates for VLDL and LDL are low and that catabolism is normal.[271,284] Detailed studies of sterol balance and VLDL kinetics in a patient with a variant form of hypobetalipoproteinemia revealed a striking increase in bile acid synthesis. Production rates of both triglycerides and apo B in VLDL were normal; however, the direct removal of VLDL from plasma appeared to be very high.[281] Thus, in this case the primary defect may be the overproduction of bile acids with attendant upregulation of B-100:E receptors in the liver, leading to abstraction of VLDL from blood before they are converted to LDL. Whether such a mechanism will be common among individuals with hypobetalipoproteinemia will require further study. It is likely that multiple defects may emerge, leading to this phenotype, among them primary disorders of VLDL production.

In two unrelated subjects with homozygous hypobetalipoproteinemia, the apo B gene was present without major derangements. Hepatic mRNA for apo B was of normal size, but was present in abnormally small quantities. Apo B was detectable in hepatocytes in smaller than normal amounts but was undetectable in plasma.[284a] In two other cases, truncated forms of apo B were detected.[284b] One truncated protein of 1799 residues, resulting from a single base deletion, was detectable at low levels in VLDL and LDL in plasma. The other truncated protein of 1305 residues resulted from a premature stop codon but was not detectable in plasma.

Clinical Features

Hematologic Manifestations. Several instances of acanthocytosis have been described[276,283] in heterozygotes, but usually the fraction of the red cells affected is lower than in recessive abetalipoproteinemia. That some subtle changes in erythrocytes may be present is suggested by the finding of extremely low erythrocyte sedimentation rates in other individuals in whom frank acanthocytosis was not seen. Homozygous patients, however, have all had acanthocytosis. The content of free cholesterol is increased, as is the ratio of sphingomyelin to phosphatidylcholine, and the content of linoleate is low among the esterified fatty acids of plasma. Prothrombin deficiency has been observed in homozygotes in two instances,[275,276] with significant hemorrhage in one subject.

Gastrointestinal Manifestations. In heterozygotes there has been only limited clinical evidence of impaired fat absorption.[269,284c] Minor abnormalities of intestinal mucosa were described in one case[269] but were not found in others,[268,273,281] and the absorption of dietary fat appears to proceed normally.[270,275] However, prolonged chylomicronemia after meals suggests that the rate of chylomicron release may be abnormal in some subjects.[284] Similarly, the appearance of a limited steatosis of liver in one case may indicate impaired release of VLDL.[268]

The histologic findings in homozygous subjects are in general indistinguishable from those in homozygous recessive abetalipoproteinemia, with numerous fat droplets in the intestinal epithelium[137,275,277] and liver.[275] Chylomicrons are absent from plasma after a fat meal,[137,275–277] and fat is found in abnormal amounts in the stool.[275,276]

Neuromuscular Manifestations. In contrast to the hematologic and gastrointestinal manifestations, neurologic disease can be found in heterozygotes.[268,270,272,284c,285] Absent or diminished deep-tendon reflexes are most frequently described, but ataxia and proprioceptive deficits have also been observed. In the few cases reported to date, neurologic disease in homozygotes appears to be less severe than it is in recessive abetalipoproteinemia.[275,276,278]

Ophthalmic Manifestations. Classic retinitis pigmentosa has been reported in several cases of hypobetalipoproteinemia,[284c] including the patient with increased bile acid synthesis.[281] Some structural abnormalities of the retina have been described in two others[281,286] who had no impairment of visual acuity. Typical retinitis has also been described in homozygotes.[254,269]

Genetics

Cases of European, Asian, and Near Eastern origin have now been reported. Data from family studies to date are consistent with monogenic transmission of an autosomal allele or alleles. The highly varied plasma levels of LDL in heterozygotes, even within kindreds, suggest that expression is modified significantly by other determinants.

It is probable that different mechanisms underlie the phenotype of hypobetalipoproteinemia in different kindreds. In contrast to results in a small number of patients with abetalipoproteinemia who were found to have abundant mRNA and protein for apo B within hepatocytes, two apparently unrelated patients homozygous for hypobetalipoproteinemia were found to have a lower content of mRNA and protein for apo B in hepatocytes than is found in normal hepatocytes.[368] The apo B gene was of normal size, and no major aberrations of its sequence were detectable. More detailed studies of the gene sequence will be required to identify the mechanism precisely; however, these data suggest that the disorder in these patients is due to either a regulatory defect or a local defect in the apo B gene that leads to defective splicing, nuclear processing, or stability of the message.

Treatment

Treatment for the disease of the homozygote is the same as for recessive abetalipoproteinemia: restriction of dietary fat and aggressive supplementation of vitamin E. In heterozygotes restriction of fat in the diet would appear judicious if evidence of malabsorption or oxalate urolithiasis is present.

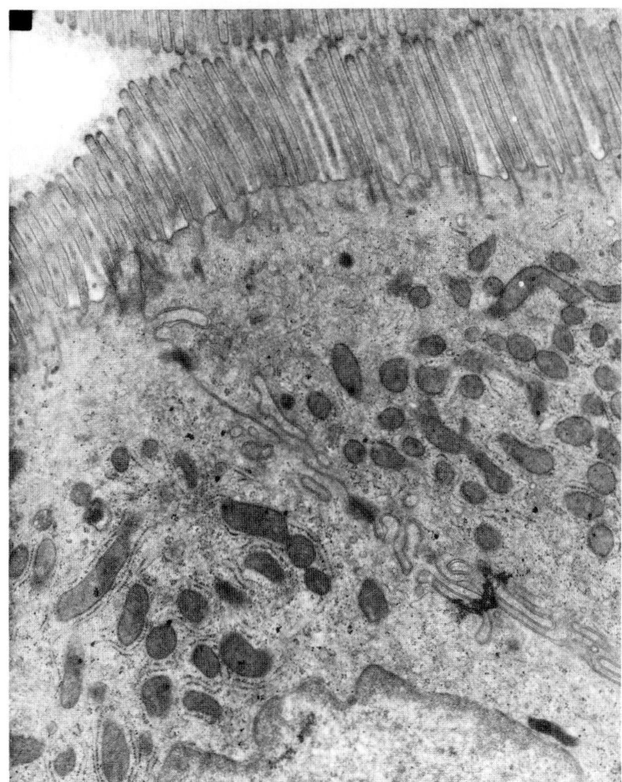

Fig. 44B-5 Electron-microscopic appearance of intestinal epithelium in normotriglyceridemic abetalipoproteinemia. Biopsy was taken 16 h following a fat-rich meal. *(Electron microscopy courtesy of Dr. Albert L. Jones.)*

Because heterozygotes can indeed develop neurologic disease, they, too, should receive concerted supplementation with vitamin E.

NORMOTRIGLYCERIDEMIC ABETALIPOPROTEINEMIA

In 1981, Malloy et al. reported a new disorder in which LDL were absent from plasma but chylomicrons were present after fat feeding.[220] Serum cholesterol levels remained around 25 mg/dl, whereas serum triglycerides rose from 30 mg/dl to 250 mg/dl after fat feeding and to 76 mg/dl after feeding of a high carbohydrate, low fat diet for 5 days. Jejunal biopsy showed no retention of lipid in intestinal epithelium 16 h after a fat meal (Fig. 44B-5). The patient, an 8-year-old female, was obese. She had esotropia, genu valgum, and a wide-based, ataxic gait. She was retarded, with a mental age of 2 to 3 years. Dark-adapted retinograms showed low normal responses. On a typical American diet her excretion of fat in the stool averaged 10 g/day. Her serum carotene level was low (31 μ/dl), but vitamin A levels were normal. When she was first studied, tocopherol was undetectable in plasma, but increased into the normal range with oral supplementation with 400 mg of tocopherol per day. Over several years of observation while she received tocopherol supplementation, her ataxia improved significantly.

Analysis of lipoproteins showed spherical particles resembling VLDL in serum after a 12-h fast. Very small amounts of somewhat cuboidal lipoprotein particles were present in the LDL density interval, along with larger spherical particles of ~300 Å diameter, resembling VLDL remnants (Fig. 44B-2). In contrast to abetalipoproteinemia and homozygous hypobetalipoproteinemia, spherical particles with diameters and hydrodynamic properties typical of HDL_3 predominated in the HDL density interval.

Each of the lipoprotein fractions showed an increase in the ratio of sphingomyelin to phosphatidylcholine similar to that in recessive abetalipoproteinemia. Apolipoproteins C-I, C-II, C-III, E, A-I, and A-II were present, but the apo C-III_0 and apo C-III_1 isoforms were present at very low levels. The total apo A-I content of plasma was 96 mg/dl. The proline-rich apolipoprotein and apo D were also present.

The signal difference between this disorder and previously recognized forms of abetalipoproteinemia is the presence of the B-48 protein, which presumably explains the ability to absorb fat and form chylomicrons. Recent improvements in resolution and mapping of B apoproteins on gels have permitted the detection of a slightly larger B protein in the serum of this patient in addition to apo B-48. Therefore, it appears that some genetic process leading to truncation of the B-100 protein just beyond the normal terminus of apo B-48 may be the mechanism underlying this disorder.[287] Thus, some of the triglyceride-rich particles in plasma are probably of hepatic origin. If so, the abbreviated apo B-100 present appears to lack the ability to produce normal LDL particles. Examination of genomic DNA from the patient's leukocytes failed to detect any major deletions; hence, it is likely that some mechanism, such as a point substitution leading to an inappropriate stop codon, may underlie this disorder. In a second case, detected in infancy, some apparent B-100 protein was found, but subsequently disappeared.[288] This finding must be interpreted with caution because apo B-48 can form dimers that migrate like authentic apo B-100 in SDS gels. In this patient, the lipoprotein findings closely resembled those of the case reported earlier except that HDL_2 became more prominent than HDL_3 after 18 months of age. Despite the appearance of chylomicrons in plasma, fat absorption was very poor. No retinopathy or neuropathy was detected up to the age of 20 months. A third case presenting with malabsorption and acanthocytosis in infancy has been reported.[289] Duodenal mucosa cells, obtained after a 16-h fast, and hepatocytes both contained fat droplets. Serum cholesterol levels ranged from 27 to 38 mg/dl and triglyceride levels from 63 to 119 mg/dl. An apo B-48–like protein was present in plasma, but no apo B-100 was detectable. In contrast to the case in which the less sialated forms of apo C-III were present but not in normal abundance,[220] apo C-III_1 was undetectable. Because fat malabsorption was present, it is possible that in addition to the inability to produce or secrete apo B-100, there is some limitation of the ability to secrete apo B-48. The child's parents had normal plasma lipoproteins, indicating that this is a recessive disorder.

HYPOBETALIPOPROTEINEMIA WITH A TRUNCATED FORM OF B PROTEIN APO B-37

In 1979 Steinberg et al. described a previously unrecognized form of hypolipidemia with very low levels of LDL, normal plasma levels of triglyceride, hypobetalipoproteinemia, and mild fat malabsorption.[290] Serum cholesterol levels in the proband varied only between 33 and 42 mg/dl and triglyceride levels between 61 and 103 mg/dl, despite wide variations in his diet. There was no neurologic disease, and only rare acanthocytes were observed. The apo B content of the lipoproteins of the LDL density interval was only 7.4 mg/dl, and that of the VLDL interval was 0.9 mg/dl. The HDL interval contained apo B as well, unlike normal plasma. The plasma levels of apo A-I and apo A-II were somewhat low at 77 and 17 mg/dl, respectively. Apo $C\text{-}III_1$ was undetectable in any of the lipoproteins. Triglyceride turnover measured by [^{3}H]glycerol kinetics showed delay and diminished secretion followed by slow decay from plasma. Chylomicron kinetics studied by the technique of constant duodenal infusion reflected a removal defect. Neutral sterol excretion was found to be about twice normal.

Further studies in this kindred by Young et al.[61] have demonstrated a truncated form of apo B, apo B-37 in the centile system of nomenclature for the B proteins. It was found in chylomicrons as well as in particles that may be hepatogenous VLDL, along with apparently normal apo B-100. In contrast with apo B-100, apo B-37 was found in the HDL density interval as well, on particles discrete from typical HDL.[290a] The amino-terminal sequence of apo B-37 is identical to that of B-100 and B-48, and reaction with a battery of monoclonal antibodies allowed the conclusion that it has common sequence with apo B-100 and B-48 up to its carboxy terminus. Studies in the kindred reveal two alleles that influence levels of LDL in plasma.[291] The foreshortened B-37 product results from a short deletion in the apo B structural gene which produces a premature stop codon.[284b] A second allele appears to cause reduced levels of apo B-100 in plasma. By use of a monoclonal antibody that recognizes a common polymorphism of apo B, it was possible to show that apo B-100 and apo B-48 were the products of a single allele, whereas apo B-37 was the sole product of the other. Several individuals in the kindred were shown to be compound heterozygotes, while others were heterozygotes for one or the other mutant allele.

HYPOBETALIPOPROTEINEMIA WITH SELECTIVE DELETION OF APO B-48 (CHYLOMICRON RETENTION DISEASE)

In 1961 Anderson et al. reported an infant in whom fat malabsorption was present and fat droplets abounded in the intestinal epithelial cells[292] (Fig. 44B-6). Chylomicrons were absent from plasma after meals, and both LDL and HDL levels were low, as were plasma levels of fat-soluble vitamins and carotenoids. Soon, additional reports of an apparent defect of lipid transport within the enterocyte appeared.[293–295] Bouma et al. studied three young adults and four children.[296] All presented with severe diarrhea in childhood and had varying degrees of growth retardation. Serum cholesterol levels ranged from 33 to 116 mg/dl, with all but one below 95 mg/dl. The diagnosis was established by the finding of fat-laden enterocytes in small bowel biopsies. Monoclonal antibodies directed at apo B-48 reacted intensely with the enterocytes of patients, but those reactive with apo B-100 and not apo B-48 showed no binding. LDL levels in plasma were about one-half of normal, as was the plasma content of apo B and apo A-I. The LDL were found to be enriched in triglycerides. The triglyceride content of plasma increased after a fat meal, but no chylomicronemia ever appeared. A protein with an apparent molecular weight appropriate for B-100 was found in LDL. All isoforms of apo C-III and apo E were found in the very low density interval. Apolipoproteins A-I, A-II, and A-IV were present in plasma. An abnormally large percentage of the apo A-I appeared to be in the pro A-I form, and semiquantitative analysis suggested that the relative content of apo E and apo E:apo A-II dimer was increased. In a study of eight additional subjects, Roy et al. also found increased amounts of immunoreactivity in enterocytes with antibodies against apo B.[297] All patients showed severe growth retardation, steatorrhea, and malnutrition. Three had hypoalbuminemia, and five had undetectably low levels of vitamin E in plasma. One had mild acanthocytosis, and neurologic symptoms were present in three patients who were in the second decade of life. Deep-tendon reflexes were diminished or absent, and vibratory sense was diminished. Among three patients, one was clearly retarded and two were

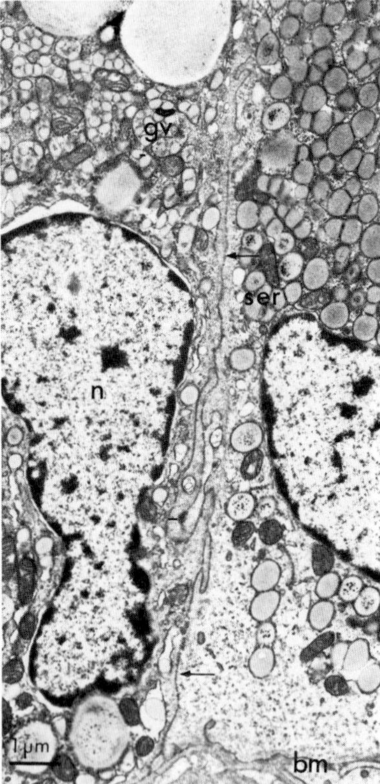

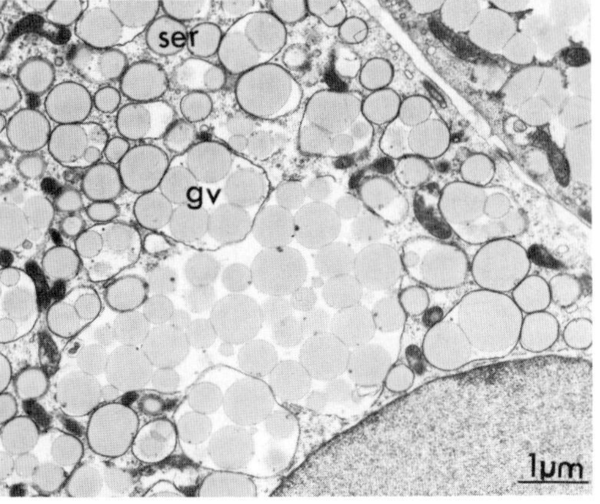

Fig. 44B-6 Electron-photomicrographic appearance of intestinal epithelium in chylomicron retention disease. *(Courtesy of Dr. Claude Roy.) Left panel:* Accumulation of lipid droplets in the supranuclear region of the cell. n = nucleus; ser = endoplasmic membranes; gv = possible Golgi vesicle; bm = basement membrane. *Right panel:* Clustering of lipid droplets within membranous structure in the supranuclear region.

considered to have low-normal intelligence. Four patients tested had a mild defect in visual perception of the blue-yellow axis, and four of five tested had mild abnormalities of retinal function. None of the patients had retinitis pigmentosa.

Following a fat load, plasma triglyceride levels rose only about 10 mg/dl, and levels of LDL apo B and apo A-I in HDL were unchanged. Activities of lipoprotein lipase and hepatic lipase after heparin injection were significantly lower than in control children. Total LDL apo B levels in plasma averaged 61 mg/dl, compared with 76 mg/dl in controls. Total apo A-I levels were more strikingly abnormal, with an average of 50 mg/dl in comparison with 137 mg/dl in the plasma of controls. The LDL were found to be markedly depleted in cholesterol (22 percent of mass as compared with 41 percent in control LDL), and somewhat enriched in triglyceride, phospholipid, and protein. The relative cholesterol content of HDL was halved (23 to 11 percent), with a nearly twofold increase in phospholipid (24 to 43 percent). The percentage of total plasma phospholipid represented by sphingomyelins was moderately higher (20 versus 17 percent), and the percentage of phosphatidylcholine was lower (66 percent) than in normals (71 percent).[298] As in other forms of fat malabsorption, essential fatty acid levels were lower among total plasma fatty acids than in normals.

Levy and coworkers[298] studied in vitro explants obtained by intestinal biopsy in short-term culture. Total protein synthesis appeared normal in the explants, but glycosylation was significantly decreased in comparison with normal control tissue. A monoclonal antibody to apo B-100 reacted with a protein from an extract of explant tissue, labeling a band which co-migrated precisely with authentic apo B-48. Secretion of triglyceride into the medium by explants of tissue from patients with the disorder was impaired in comparison with normal tissue, though phospholipid secretion appeared normal.[298] These results strongly suggest that apo B-48 synthesis may be normal in this disorder, but the formation and secretion of chylomicrons are impaired, perhaps as part of a generalized defect in glycosylation.

The finding of several kindreds with multiple affected sibs establishes the familial nature of this disorder, and the lack of vertical transmission of the phenotype suggests it is a recessive trait. The presence of the disorder in females indicates it is not predominantly X-linked, but the predominance of males (6:2 in the two largest kindreds reported) suggests that complex mechanisms of inheritance could exist. Treatment should include restriction of dietary fat, especially in infancy. The appearance of neurologic manifestations in several patients indicates that supplementation with vitamin E and perhaps vitamin A should be maintained in all cases.

FAMILIAL COMBINED HYPERLIPIDEMIA (FAMILIAL MULTIPLE-TYPE HYPERLIPOPROTEINEMIA)

Familial combined hyperlipidemia (FCH) was first identified in studies of hyperlipidemia among survivors of myocardial infarction and their relatives.[299–303] Patients may present with any of three phenotypes: elevated levels of VLDL, elevated levels of LDL, or increases in the levels of both lipoproteins in plasma. Unlike familial hypercholesterolemia, hyperlipidemia appears in only 10 to 20 percent of patients in childhood, usually in the form of hypertriglyceridemia.[302] The disorder is rarely if ever associated with xanthomas unless additional genetic determinants of hyperlipidemia are present. The phenotypic pattern may change over time. If all three phenotypes are considered equivalent in studying the kindreds of affected individuals, the trait appears to be transmitted as a Mendelian dominant with high penetrance.[299,301] Homozygosity for the trait may result in severe hypertriglyceridemia.[304] Mating of a hypertriglyceridemic patient with a normal spouse can produce an offspring with a predominant increase in LDL levels, and, conversely, the mating of a hypercholesterolemic patient with a normal spouse has been shown to produce hypertriglyceridemic offspring.[299]

Perhaps the most striking abnormality of plasma lipoproteins in this disorder is the marked elevation of apo B content of plasma.[304] The levels of VLDL and LDL appear to have a reciprocal relationship. VLDL composition is within the normal range, but VLDL particles tend to be smaller than normal. The ratio of apo A-I to apo A-II is below normal, independent of VLDL levels. Some but not all patients have been found to have dense, cholesteryl ester–depleted LDL of small diameter.[304–306] Since most of these patients also have elevated levels of triglycerides, it is possible that the abnormalities in LDL composition, size, and density are the result of transfer and exchange of core constituents between VLDL and LDL.

The finding, by several groups, of an appreciably increased rate of production of B apoprotein may signal the underlying metabolic abnormality in this disorder.[307–310] Secretion of triglycerides in VLDL also appears to be increased.[307,311] The increased production of VLDL could lead to an expanded plasma pool of VLDL in some individuals, but in others with more efficient lipolysis, it might result in increased levels of LDL, providing a basis for the multiple phenotypic expressions. Modeling of kinetic data suggests that in FCH the removal of LDL from plasma may be different than it is in normal subjects or in patients with familial hypercholesterolemia.[312,313] However, the LDL receptors of cultured fibroblasts appear to be normal in FCH.[314] The primary defect could lie in the regulation of secretion of VLDL per se, or of apo B-100, or in a metabolic pathway involved in the triglyceride economy of the liver. It is possible that this disorder constitutes a syndrome in which increased VLDL production is a response to any of several such stimuli. The appearance of glucose intolerance and obesity in a number of individuals with this disorder[299,303] suggests that the hyperlipidemia that results from a genetic determinant for increased VLDL production may be amplified by such additional factors. It is also possible that some individuals with this disorder may not be appreciably hyperlipidemic if removal of LDL is very efficient. The relationship of FCH to the overproduction of VLDL apo B associated with normal plasma content of LDL in some patients with coronary artery disease[315] and to disorders in which small, dense LDL are present in the absence of hypertriglyceridemia[316] will need to be investigated in this light.[305,315]

Although surveys adequate to establish accurately the prevalence of this disorder have not been conducted, clinical experience suggests that it is at least five times as prevalent as familial hypercholesterolemia, occurring in about 1 percent of the North American population. The predilection toward coronary artery disease among patients with this disorder makes it the most prominent known metabolic cause of premature atherosclerosis.[317]

LP(a) HYPERLIPOPROTEINEMIA

Recognition of Lp(a) Lipoprotein

In 1963, Berg described a new antigenic component, Lp(a), among human plasma lipoproteins.[318] Initially it was thought that the antigen was present in about one-third of individuals. With the advent of more sensitive assays, it is apparent that the serum of virtually all humans contains this antigen,[319–321] but in highly varying amounts. Recently, considerable sequence homology between Lp(a) protein and plasminogen has been demonstrated. Earlier immunoassays may therefore have measured plasminogen to some extent as well as the Lp(a) protein. With this reservation, data accumulated in large subject groups indicate that the content of Lp(a) antigen can vary as much as a hundredfold among individuals, is similar in men and women, and is remarkably stable over time.[319,322] Levels of Lp(a) antigen appear to correlate with the content of apoprotein B in plasma.[313] Whereas the distribution of Lp(a) levels in Caucasians is highly skewed toward the lower values, the levels in black men are roughly twice as high and are distributed in a gaussian fashion.[322] The range of Lp(a) levels among the Japanese appears to be similar to that among whites.[324] Among men, Lp(a) antigen levels are correlated with LDL cholesterol levels, but the correlation was found to disappear upon subtraction of the cholesterol content attributable to Lp(a), whereas the correlation was found to persist in women.[325] Correlations between levels of Lp(a) and LDL cholesterol have also been observed in both men and women in a survey of a European population.[324]

Lp(a) Lipoproteins and Heart Disease

A number of early studies showed an association between plasma Lp(a) levels and coronary heart disease.[323,326–332] At about the same time, a relationship between the content of the "sinking pre-β lipoproteins" (observed on electrophoresis of lipoproteins of the $d > 1.006$ g/ml fraction of plasma) with risk of coronary heart disease was becoming evident. These lipoproteins had also been observed as a pre-β_1 lipoprotein band on electrophoresis of whole serum.[333] As the identity of these lipoproteins with Lp(a) became established,[334,335] it became clear that sinking pre-β bands are visible only in serums with the highest (top 5 to 10 percent) levels of Lp(a) antigen.[334,336] Thus, studies in which the risk of coronary disease has been related to detectable sinking pre-β lipoproteins segregate out only patients with the highest levels of Lp(a) lipoproteins. Nonetheless, the presence of such a band correlated with a relative risk of 1.7 in a large cohort of Japanese-American men in Hawaii.[336]

Using an electroimmunoassay for Lp(a) antigen, Kostner et al. found a doubled incidence of Lp(a) values above 50 mg/dl among survivors of myocardial infarction compared with controls.[337] Also, using an electroimmunoassay, Dahlén et al. showed a significant relationship between the risk of angiographically determined coronary vascular disease and Lp(a) levels in women and in men under 55 years of age.[325] Studies of serum Lp(a) levels in a cohort of Japanese-Americans who had suffered myocardial infarctions and population-based controls showed a significant, independent association in the upper quartile of Lp(a) levels that diminished markedly with age.[338] In another study of angiographically determined coronary arteriosclerosis, a 2.7-fold increase in risk was associated with a sixfold increase in levels of Lp(a) antigen.[339] In this study, the risk increment increased sharply with concomitant increases in LDL cholesterol.

Structure of Lp(a) Lipoproteins

Detailed studies of the structures of Lp(a) lipoproteins were initially hampered by the tendency of these lipoproteins to become denatured under conditions which do not appear to affect the structure of LDL. From initial immunochemical studies of the Lp(a) lipoproteins it was known that they contain material cross-reactive with apo B as well as an Lp(a)-specific antigen. Further studies then established that there were two principal proteins, one corresponding to the apo B of LDL and the other an unrelated, heavily glycosylated protein responsible for the Lp(a) reactivity.[340,341] Heterogeneity of Lp(a) particles became apparent when subpopulations with different hydrodynamic properties were discovered.[342] Later, differing densities of Lp(a) particle populations were attributed to the content of Lp(a)-specific proteins of different molecular weights.[343,344] Three commonly occurring isoforms of the protein were found in particle subpopulations of different densities,[343,344] from one to two species being evident in the plasma of a single individual.[343] Six isoforms have now been identified on the basis of their apparent molecular weights.[345] It appears that the presence of Lp(a) proteins of widely differing molecular weights may account for the variation in buoyant densities of Lp(a) lipoproteins. The distribution of modal densities ranges from 1.047 to 1.1 g/ml.[343] The Lp(a)-specific protein has been found to occur with molecular weights varying from 280×10^3 to more than 600×10^3 daltons,[6,7,346,347] all of which are immunochemically cross-reactive.[347] The Lp(a) protein has been found to be bound to the apo B moiety by disulfide bridging.[6,340,343] It does not appear to interact significantly with the lipids of the Lp(a) lipoprotein particles. When subjected to reduction, the Lp(a) protein dissociates as a water soluble entity, leaving behind an LDL-like particle [Lp(a)−] which retains the apo B-100 moiety.[7] After trypsinization most of the fragments of apo B adhere to the lipids, whereas the fragments of Lp(a) are dispersed in the aqueous medium.[344]

The cDNA sequence corresponding to the Lp(a)-specific protein of a single patient has now been obtained.[348,349] The sequence commenced with an apparent signal peptide of 19 residues, and then a segment highly homologous to the kringle 4 structure of plasminogen, which was followed by a 37-fold tandem repeat of kringle 4–like domains, one domain homologous to the kringle 5 domain, and then a domain related to the serine protease moiety of plasminogen, but lacking the proteolytic scission point for activation. The variation in molecular weights among Lp(a) proteins may be due to differences in the number of tandem repeated domains of the kringle 4 type. Whereas the kringle regions of proteases involved in regulation of the clotting process bind readily to fibrin, the analogous structures in Lp(a) appear to be modified in ways that would be expected to interrupt such binding. Arginine residues critical to binding have been deleted from all but one kringle 4 structure, and all have potential sites for *N* glycosylation.

Metabolism of Lp(a) Lipoproteins

The mRNA of Lp(a) protein is represented in cDNA libraries of hepatic origin, but the immediate secretory products of liver which bear this protein are not yet known. Lp(a) protein occurs in a disulfide complex with apo B-100 in the largest triglyceride-rich lipoproteins in plasma after a fat meal. This raises the possibility that Lp(a) protein may originate in the intestine,[350] though that would appear to require the concomitant secretion of apo B-100. Alternatively, VLDL particles of large diameter, containing the Lp(a) protein, could be secreted by the liver in response to an increased flux of chylomicron remnants. Lp(a) lipoprotein does not appear to originate via VLDL or by transfer of the Lp(a) protein from VLDL to LDL. Injection of VLDL radiolabeled in the apo B-100 moiety into individuals with substantial plasma levels of Lp(a) lipoprotein does not produce labeled Lp(a) lipoproteins.[351] Likewise injection of similarly labeled LDL into an individual with extremely high levels of Lp(a) lipoproteins failed to produce detectable labeling of Lp(a) lipoprotein.[352] Also, radioiodinated Lp(a) lipoprotein does not transfer to other classes of lipoproteins when injected into humans.[353] The production rate appears to be the principal determinant of plasma levels; the average half-life of injected Lp(a) was 3.3 days.

Several studies have indicated that Lp(a) lipoproteins bind competitively to LDL receptors.[354,355] Electron-microscopic evidence of localization in coated pits has been obtained.[355] In one study, two species of Lp(a) lipoproteins with different modal densities were found to bind to fibroblast receptors with affinity equal to that of LDL,[356] but in two other studies Lp(a) was found to be bound with lower affinity than LDL.[346,357] In one of the latter, removal of the Lp(a) protein by reduction resulted in increased uptake of the Lp(a)− particle.[346] In at least one study, however, uptake of Lp(a) lipoprotein by fibroblasts appeared to take place via pathways not involving the LDL receptor.[358]

Genetics

Evidence for autosomal dominant inheritance of high levels of Lp(a) protein in plasma has been obtained in several studies.[359–361] In another, polygenic factors appeared to dominate.[362] In twin studies, the heritability was found to approach 100 percent.[363] In a study of a large pedigree, the data best fit the model of a dominant major gene effect with a polygenic background.[364] Incongruent levels in spouses indicated that environmental factors have little effect. The gene frequency for the dominant major gene was found to be 0.10. At this point, the number of alleles that can alter the production rate of Lp(a) lipoproteins is uncertain.

Clinical Presentation

Because the Lp(a) lipoproteins are distributed continuously in the population, the definition of clinically significant levels is circumstantial and arbitrary. However, no other lipoprotein species has so great a range of levels in plasma. For the majority of individuals, Lp(a) levels appear to represent a graded factor which may be semi-independent of other lipoproteins with respect to risk of arteriosclerotic heart disease. However, because Lp(a) lipoproteins appear to share the receptor-mediated removal pathway with LDL, Lp(a) levels in the population must reflect to some extent the efficiency of removal of LDL. Individuals at the high extreme of Lp(a) levels, however, may have manifestations due in appreciable part to the Lp(a) lipoproteins themselves. Subcutaneous xanthomas, unlike any xanthomas observed so far in other forms of hyperlipoproteinemia, may be a unique stigma of markedly high circulating levels of Lp(a) lipoproteins (Fig. 44B-7). Such patients also may have exuberent tendinous xanthomas and severe arteriosclerosis of the coronary and carotid vessels. Extremely high levels of Lp(a) lipoproteins may be found in individuals with familial hypercholesterolemia.[365] It is possible that these individuals possess the gene or genes that cause a high production rate of Lp(a) lipoproteins, which then accumulate in plasma due to impaired removal via the LDL receptors. Severe arteriosclerotic disease may possibly be due to effects of the Lp(a) lipoproteins on thrombogenesis or thrombolysis as well as the increased burden of atherogenic lipoproteins entering the arterial intima. Understanding of the pharmacologic management of hyper Lp(a) lipoproteinemia is incomplete as yet, but alteration of the fractional catabolic rate of LDL by the use of bile acid–binding resins was reported to be ineffective in individuals with moderate elevations of Lp(a) levels.[366] Niacin, however, appears to have some effect,[367] perhaps by reducing the production rate of Lp(a) lipoproteins in liver.

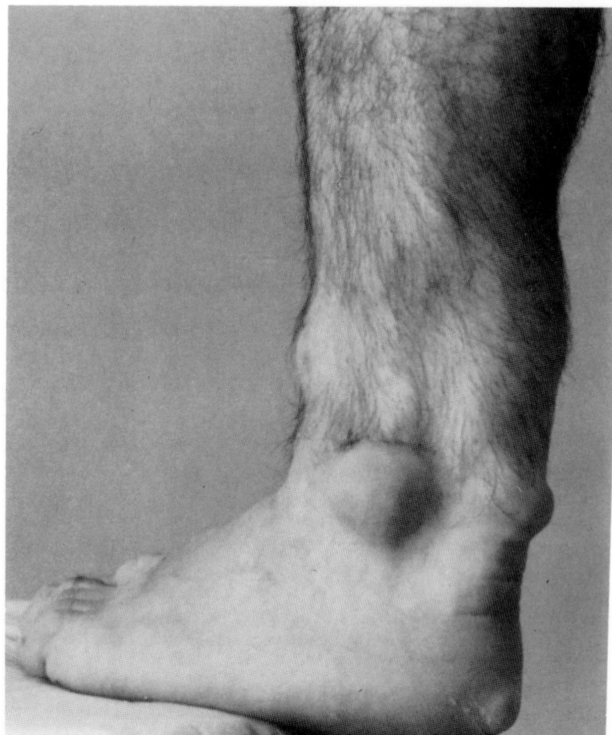

Fig. 44B-7 Massive tendinous and subcutaneous xanthomas in a patient with familial hypercholesterolemia and Lp(a) hyperlipoproteinemia. *(Courtesy of Dr. David Klonoff.)*

REFERENCES

1. KANE JP: Apolipoprotein B: Structural and metabolic heterogeneity. *Annu Rev Physiol* 45:637,1983.
2. WALSH MT, ATKINSON D: Solubilization of low-density lipoprotein with sodium deoxycholate and recombination of apoprotein B with dimyristoyl-phosphatidylcholine. *Biochemistry* 22:3170, 1983.
3. WALSH MT, ATKINSON D: Reassembly of low-density lipoproteins. *Methods Enzymol* 128:582, 1986.
4. KANE JP, HARDMAN DA, PAULUS HE: Heterogeneity of apolipoprotein B. Isolation of a new species from human chylomicrons. *Proc Natl Acad Sci USA* 77:2465, 1980.
5. ELOVSON J, JACOBS JC, SCHUMAKER VN, PUPPIONE DL: Molecular weights of apoprotein B obtained from human low-density lipoprotein (apoprotein B-PI) and from rat very low density lipoprotein (apoprotein B-PIII). *Biochemistry* 24:1569, 1985.
6. GAUBATZ JW, HEIDEMAN C, GOTTO AM JR, MORRISETT JD, DAHLÉN GH: Human plasma lipoprotein (a). *J Biol Chem* 258:4582, 1983.
7. FLESS GM, ZUM MALLEN ME, SCANU AM: Isolation of apolipoprotein(a) from lipoprotein(a). *J Lipid Res* 26:1224, 1985.
8. HAMMOND MG, FISHER WR: The characterization of a discrete series of low density lipoproteins in the disease, hyper-pre-β-lipoproteinemia. *J Biol Chem* 246:5454, 1971.
9. MJOS OD, FAERGEMAN O, HAMILTON RL, HAVEL RJ: Characterization of remnants produced during the metabolism of triglyceride-rich lipoproteins of blood plasma and intestinal lymph in the rat. *J Lipid Res* 16:603, 1975.
10. EISENBERG S, RACHMILEWITZ D: Interaction of rat plasma very low density lipoprotein with lipoprotein lipase-rich (postheparin) plasma. *J Lipid Res* 16:341, 1975.
11. REDGRAVE TG, CARLSON LA: Changes in plasma very low density and low density lipoprotein content, composition, and size after a fatty meal in normo- and hypertriglyceridemic man. *J Lipid Res* 20:217, 1979.
12. KANE JP, HARDMAN DA: Unpublished observations.
13. ROBINSON MT, SCHUMAKER VN, BUTLER R, BERG K, CURTISS LK: Ag(c) recognition by a monoclonal antibody. *Arteriosclerosis* 6:341, 1986.
14. WIKLUND O, DYER CA, TSAO BP, CURTISS LK: Stoichiometric binding of apolipoprotein B-specific monoclonal antibodies to low density lipoproteins. *J Biol Chem* 260:10956, 1985.
15. BHATTACHARYA S, REDGRAVE TG: The content of apolipoprotein B in chylomicron particles. *J Lipid Res* 22:820, 1981.
16. MARGOLIS S, LANGDON RG: Studies on human β_1-lipoprotein. II. Chemical modifications. *J Biol Chem* 241:477, 1966.
17. SCANU A, POLLARD H, READER J: Properties of human serum low density lipoproteins after modification by succinic anhydride. *J Lipid Res* 9:342, 1968.
18. LUND-KATZ S, PHILLIPS M: Packing of cholesterol molecules in human low-density lipoprotein. *Biochemistry* 25:1562, 1986.
19. CHEN GC, CHAPMAN MJ, KANE JP: Secondary structure and thermal behavior of trypsin-treated low density lipoproteins from human serum: A circular dichroic study. *Biochim Biophys Acta* 754:51, 1983.
20. SCANU A, HIRZ R: Human serum low-density lipoprotein protein: Its conformation studied by circular dichroism. *Nature* 218:200, 1968.
21. GOTTO AM, LEVY RI, FREDRICKSON DS: Observations on the conformation of human beta lipoprotein: Evidence for the occurrence of beta structure. *Proc Natl Acad Sci USA* 60:1436, 1968.
22. CHEN GC, KANE JP: Temperature dependence of the optical activity of human serum low density lipoprotein. The role of lipids. *Biochemistry* 14:3357, 1975.
23. CHEN GC, KANE JP: Circular dichroic analysis of lipoprotein lipids. *Methods Enzymol* 128:519, 1986.
24. CHEN GC, KANE JP: Secondary structure in very low density and intermediate density lipoproteins of human serum. *J Lipid Res* 20:481, 1979.
25. KREIGER M, BROWN MS, FAUST JR, GOLDSTEIN JL: Replacement of endogenous cholesteryl esters of low density lipoprotein with exogenous cholesteryl linoleate. *J Biol Chem* 253:4093, 1978.
26. WATT RM, REYNOLDS JA: Interaction of apolipoprotein B from human serum low-density lipoprotein with egg yolk phosphatidylcholine. *Biochemistry* 20:3897, 1981.
27. GINSBERG GS, SMALL DM, ATKINSON D: Microemulsions of phospholipids and cholesterol esters. *J Biol Chem* 257:8216, 1982.
28. GINSBERG GS, WALSH MT, SMALL DM, ATKINSON D: Reassembled plasma low-density lipoproteins. *J Biol Chem* 259:6667, 1984.
29. LUNDBERG B, SUOMINEN L: Preparation of biologically active analogs of serum low density lipoproteins. *J Lipid Res* 25:550, 1984.
30. CHEN GC, HAMILTON RL, KANE JP: Unpublished observations.
31. LUSIS AJ, WEST R, MEHRABIAN M, REUBEN MA, LeBOEUF RC, KAPTEIN JS, JOHNSON DF, SCHUMAKER VN, YUHASZ MP, SCHOTZ MC, ELOSON J: Cloning and expression of apolipoprotein B, the major protein of low and very low density lipoproteins. *Proc Natl Acad Sci USA* 82:4597, 1985.
32. DEEB SS, MOTULSKY AG, ALBERS JJ: A partial cDNA clone for human apolipoprotein B. *Proc Natl Acad Sci USA* 82:4983, 1985.
33. KNOTT TJ, RALL SC, INNERARITY TL, JACOBSON SF, URDEA MS, LEVY-WILSON B, POWELL LM, PEASE RJ, EDDY R, NAKAI H, BYERS M, PRIESTLY LM, ROBERTSON E, RALL LB, BETSHOLTZ C, SHOWS TB, MAHLEY RW, SCOTT J: Human apolipoprotein B: Structure of carboxyl-terminal domains, sites of gene expression, and chromosomal localization. *Science* 230:37, 1985.
34. CARLSSON P, OLLOFSSON SO, BONDJERS G, DARNFORS C, WIKLUND O, BJURSELL G: Molecular cloning of human apolipoprotein B cDNA. *Nucleic Acids Res* 13:8813, 1985.
35. LAW SW, LACKNER KJ, HOSPATTANKAR AV, ANCHORS JM, SAKAGUCHI AY, NAYLOR SL, BREWER HB JR: Human apolipoprotein B-100: Cloning, analysis of liver mRNA, and assignment of the gene to chromosome 2. *Proc Natl Acad Sci USA* 82:8340, 1985.
36. WEI C-F, CHEN S-H, YANG C-Y, MARCEL YL, MILNE RW, LI W-H, SPARROW JT, GOTTO AM JR, CHAN L: Molecular cloning and expression of partial cDNAs and deduced amino acid sequence of a carboxyl-terminal fragment of human apolipoprotein B-100. *Proc Natl Acad Sci USA* 82:7265, 1985.
37. HUANG L-S, BOCK SC, FEINSTEIN SI, BRESLOW JL: Human apolipoprotein B cDNA clone isolation and demonstration that liver apolipoprotein B mRNA is 22 kilobases in length. *Proc Natl Acad Sci USA* 82:6825, 1985.
38. KRUL ES, TIKKANEN MJ, COLE TG, DAVID JM, SCHONFELD G: Roles of apolipoproteins B and E in the cellular binding of very low density lipoproteins. *J Clin Invest* 75:361, 1985.
39. DEEB SS, DISTECHE C, MOTULSKY AG, LEBO RV, KAN YW: Chromosomal localization of the human apolipoprotein B gene and detection of homologous RNA in monkey intestine. *Proc Natl Acad Sci USA* 83:419, 1986.
40. PROTTER AA, HARDMAN DA, SCHILLING JW, MILLER J, APPLEBY V, CHEN GC, KIRSHER SW, MCENROE G, KANE JP: Isolation of a cDNA clone containing the amino terminal region of human apolipoprotein B. *Proc Natl Acad Sci USA* 83:1467, 1986.
41. PROTTER AA, HARDMAN DA, SATO KY, SCHILLING JW, YAMANAKA M, HART YJ, HJERRILD KA, CHEN GC, KANE JP: Analysis of cDNA clones encoding the entire B-26 region of human apolipoprotein B. *Proc Natl Acad Sci USA* 83:5678, 1986.
42. KNOTT TJ, WALLIS SC, POWELL LM, PEASE RJ, LUSIS AJ, BLACKHART B, MCCARTHY BJ, MAHLEY RW, LEVY-WILSON B, SCOTT J: Complete cDNA and derived protein sequence of human apolipoprotein B-100. *Nucleic Acids Res* 14:7501, 1986.
43. YANG C-Y, CHEN S-H, GIANTURCO SH, BRADLEY WA, SPARROW JT, TANIMURA M, LI W-H, SPARROW DA, DeLOOF H, ROSSENEU M, LEE F-S, GU Z-W, GOTTO AM JR, CHAN L: Sequence, structure, receptor-binding domains and internal repeats of human apolipoprotein B-100. *Nature* 323:738, 1986.
44. KNOTT JT, PEASE RJ, POWELL LM, WALLIS SC, RALL SC, INNERARITY TL, BLACKHART B, TAYLOR WH, MARCEL Y, MILNE R, JOHNSON D, FILLER M, LUSIS AJ, MCCARTHY BM, MAHLEY RW, LEVY-WILSON B, SCOTT J: Complete protein sequence and identification of structural domains of human apolipoprotein B. *Nature* 323:734, 1986.
45. LAW SW, GRANT SM, HIGUCHI K, HOSPATTANKAR A, LACKNER K, LEE N, BREWER HB JR: Human liver apolipoprotein B-100 cDNA: Complete nucleic acid and derived amino acid sequence. *Proc Natl Acad Sci USA* 83:8142, 1986.
46. CHEN S-H, YANG C-Y, CHEN P-G, STEZER D, TANIMURA M, LI W-H, GOTTO AM JR, CHAN L: The complete cDNA and amino acid sequence of human apolipoprotein B-100. *J Biol Chem* 261:12918, 1986.
47. CLADARAS C, HADZOPOULOU-CLADARAS M, NOLTE RT, ATKINSON D, ZANNIS VI: The complete sequence and structural analysis of apolipoprotein B: Relationship between apo B-100 and apo B-48 forms. *EMBO J* 5:3495, 1986.
48. SCOTT J, PEASE RJ, POWELL LM, WALLIS SC, MCCARTHY BJ, MAHLEY RW, LEVY-WILSON B, KNOTT TJ: Human apolipoprotein B: complete cDNA sequence and identification of structural domains of the protein. *Biochem Soc Trans* 15:195, 1987.
49. CHAN L, VAN TUINEN P, LEDBETTER DM, DAYER SP, GOTTO AM JR, CHEN SH: The human apolipoprotein B-100 gene: A highly polymorphic gene that maps to the short arm of chromosome 2. *Biochem Biophys Res Commun* 133:248, 1985.
50. BARNI N, TALMUD PJ, CARLSSON P, AZOULAY M, DARNFORS C, HARDING D, WEIL D, GRZESCHIK KH, BJURSELL G, JUNIEN C, WILLIAMSON R, HUMPHRIES SE: The isolation of genomic recombinants for the human apoli-

poprotein B gene and the mapping of three common DNA polymorphisms of the gene—A useful marker for human chromosome 2. *Hum Genet* 73:313, 1986.

51. HUANG L-S, MILLER DA, BRUNS GAP, BRESLOW JL: Gene mapping of the human apo B to chromosome 2 p and demonstration of a two-allele restriction fragment length polymorphism. *Proc Natl Acad Sci USA* 83:646, 1986.

52. BLACKHART BD, LUDWIG EM, PIEROTTI VR, CAIATI L, ONASCH MA, WALLIS SC, POWELL L, PEASE R, KNOTT TJ, CHU M-L, MAHLEY RW, SCOTT J, MCCARTHY BJ, LEVY-WILSON B: Structure of the human apolipoprotein B gene. *J Biol Chem* 261:15364, 1986.

53. LUDWIG EH, BLACKHART BD, PIEROTTI VR, CAIATI L, FORTIER C, KNOTT T, SCOTT J, MAHLEY RW, LEVY-WILSON B, MCCARTHY BJ: DNA sequence of the human apolipoprotein B gene. *DNA* 6:363, 1987.

54. WAGENER R, PFITZNER R, STOFFEL W: Studies on the organization of the human apolipoprotein B-100 gene. *Biol Chem Hoppe Seyler* 368:419, 1987.

55. YOUNG SG, BERTICS SJ, SCOTT TM, DUBOIS BW, CURTISS LK, WITZTUM JL: Parallel expression of the MB 19 genetic polymorphism in apoprotein B-100 and apoprotein B-48. *J Biol Chem* 261:2995, 1986.

56. MILNE RW, MARCEL YL: The use of monoclonal antibodies to probe human apolipoprotein B structure and function. *Can J Cell Biol* 63:906, 1984.

57. HARDMAN DA, PROTTER AA, CHEN GC, SCHILLING JW, SATO KY, LAU K, YAMANAKA M, MIKITA T, MILLER J, CRISP T, MCENROE G, SCARBOROUGH RM, KANE JP: Structural comparison of human apo B-48 and B-100. *Biochemistry* 26:5478, 1987.

58. POWELL LM, WALLIS SC, PENSE RJ, EDWARDS YH, KNOTT TJ, SCOTT J: A novel form of tissue-specific RNA processing produces apolipoprotein B-48 in intestine. *Cell* 50:831, 1987.

58a. INNERARITY TL, YOUNG SG, POKSAY KS, MAHLEY RW, SMITH RS, MILNE RW, MARCEL YL, WEISGRABER KH: Structural relationship of human apolipoprotein B-48 to apolipoprotein B-100. *J Clin Invest* 80:1794, 1987.

59. CHEN S-H, HABIB G, YANG C-Y, GU Z-W, LEE BR, WANG S-A, SILBERMAN SR, CAI S-J, DESLYPERE JP, ROSSENEU M, GOTTO AM JR, LI W-H, CHAN L: Apolipoprotein B-48 is the product of a messenger RNA with an organ-specific in-frame stop codon. *Science* 238:363, 1987.

60. HARDMAN DA, PROTTER AA, SCHILLING JW, KANE JP: Carboxyl terminal analysis of human B-48 protein confirms the novel mechanism proposed for chain termination. *Biochem Biophys Res Commun* 107:616, 1987.

60a. HOSPATTANKAR AV, HIGUCHI K, LAW SW, MEGLIN N, BREWER HB JR: Identification of a novel in-frame translational stop codon in human intestine apo B mRNA. *Biochem Biophys Res Commun* 148:279, 1987.

61. YOUNG SG, BERTICS SJ, CURTISS LK, WITZTUM JL: Characterization of an abnormal species of apolipoprotein B, apo B-37, associated with familial hypobetalipoproteinemia. *J Clin Invest* 80:1850, 1987.

62. IVERIUS P-H: The interaction between human plasma lipoproteins and connective tissue glycosaminoglycans. *J Biol Chem* 247:2607, 1972.

63. MAHLEY RW, WEISGRABER KH, INNERARITY TL: Interaction of plasma lipoproteins containing apolipoproteins B and E with heparin and cell surface receptors. *Biochim Biophys Acta* 575:81, 1979.

64. CARDIN AD, BARNHART RL, WITT KR, JACKSON RL: Reactivity of heparin with the human plasma heparin-binding proteins thrombin, antithrombin III, and apolipoproteins E and B-100. *Thromb Res* 34:541, 1984.

65. WEISGRABER KH, RALL SC JR: Human apolipoprotein B-100 heparin-binding sites. *J Biol Chem* 262:11097, 1987.

66. CARDIN AD, RANGANATHAN S, HIROSE N, WALLHAUSSER L, HARMONY JAK, JACKSON RL: Effect of trypsin treatment on the heparin- and receptor-binding properties of human plasma low density lipoproteins. *Biochemistry* 25:5258, 1986.

67. HUI DY, INNERARITY TL, MILNE RW, MARCEL YL, MAHLEY RW: Binding of chylomicron remnants and beta very low density lipoproteins to hepatic and extrahepatic lipoprotein receptors: A process independent of apolipoprotein B-48. *J Biol Chem* 259:15060, 1984.

68. MARCEL YL, INNERARITY TL, SPILMAN C, MAHLEY RW, PROTTER AA, MILNE RW: Mapping of human apolipoprotein B antigenic determinants. *Arteriosclerosis* 7:166, 1987.

69. SCHAEFER EJ, GREGG RE, GHISELLI G, FORTE TM, ORDOVAS JM, ZECH LA, BREWER HB JR: Familial apolipoprotein E deficiency. *J Clin Invest* 78:1206, 1986.

70. BRADLEY WA, GIANTURCO SH: Apo E is necessary and sufficient for the binding of large triglyceride-rich lipoproteins to the LDL receptor, apo B is unnecessary. *J Lipid Res* 27:40, 1986.

71. YAMAMOTO M, RANGANATHAN S, KOTTKE B: Structure and function of human low density lipoproteins: Studies using proteolytic cleavage by plasma kallikrein. *J Biol Chem* 260:8509, 1985.

72. MAHLEY RW, INNERARITY TL, PITAS RE, WEISGRABER KH, BROWN JH, GROSS E: Inhibition of lipoprotein binding to cell surface receptors of fibroblasts following selective modification of arginyl residues in arginine-rich and B apoproteins. *J Biol Chem* 252:7279, 1977.

73. WEISGRABER HK, INNERARITY TL, MAHLEY RW: Role of the lysine residues of plasma lipoproteins in high affinity binding to cell surface receptors on human fibroblasts. *J Biol Chem* 253:9053, 1978.

74. SHIREMAN RB, FISHER WR: The absence of a role for the carbohydrate moiety in the binding of apolipoprotein B to the low density lipoprotein receptor. *Biochim Biophys Acta* 572:537, 1979.

75. CARDIN AD, JACKSON RL, DONALDSON VH, CHAO J, MARGOLIUS HS: Processing of apolipoprotein B-100 of human plasma low density lipoproteins by tissue and plasma kallikreins. *Adv Exp Biol* 198:(Part A)195, 1986.

76. CARDIN AD, WITT RK, CHAO J, MARGOLIUS HS, DONALDSON VH, JACKSON RL: Degradation of apolipoprotein B-100 of human plasma low density lipoproteins by tissue and plasma kallikreins. *J Biol Chem* 259:8522, 1984.

77. HARDMAN DA, GUSTAFSON A, SCHILLING JW, DONALDSON FH, KANE JP: Scission of human apolipoprotein B-100 by kallikrein: Characterization of the cleavage site. *Biochem Biophys Res Commun* 137:821, 1986.

78. GUSTAFSON A, KANE JP, HAVEL RJ: Determinants of kallikrein proteolysis of apolipoprotein B-100 in human blood plasma. *Eur J Clin Invest* 18:75, 1988.

79. CARDIN AD, PRICE CA, HIROSE N, KRIVANEK MA, BLANKENSHIP DT, CHAO J, MAO SJT: Structural organization of apolipoprotein B-100 of human plasma low density lipoproteins: Comparison to B-48 of chylomicrons and very low density lipoproteins. *J Biol Chem* 261:16744, 1986.

80. BLUMBERG BS, BERNANKE D, ALLISON AC: A human lipoprotein polymorphism. *J Clin Invest* 41:1936, 1962.

81. BÜTLER R, BÜTLER-BRUNNER E, SCHERZ R, PFLUGSHAUPT R: The Ag system of low density lipoproteins—An updating, in Peeters H (ed): *Protides of the Biological Fluids.* New York, Pergamon, 1977, p 255.

82. SCHUMAKER VN, ROBINSON MT, CURTISS LK, BÜTLER R, SPARKES RS: Antiapoprotein B monoclonal antibodies detect human low density lipoprotein polymorphism. *J Biol Chem* 259:6423, 1984.

83. YOUNG SG, BERTICS SJ, CURTISS LK, CASAL DC, WITZTUM JL: Monoclonal antibody MB19 detects genetic polymorphism in human apolipoprotein B. *Proc Natl Acad Sci USA* 83:1101, 1986.

84. TSAO BP, CURTISS LK, EDGINGON TS: Immunochemical heterogeneity of human plasma apolipoprotein B II. Expression of apolipoprotein B epitopes on native lipoproteins. Evidence that both apoproteins are products of the same gene. *J Biol Chem* 257:15222, 1982.

85. LAW A, POWELL LM, BRENT M, KNOTT TJ, ALTMAN DG, RAJPUT J, WALLIS SC, PEASE J, PRIESTLY LM, SCOTT J, MILLER AJ, MILLER NE: Common DNA polymorphism within coding sequence of apolipoprotein B gene, associated with altered lipid levels. *Lancet* 1:1301, 1986.

86. BERG K, POWELL LM, WALLIS SC, PEASE R, KNOTT TJ, SCOTT J: Genetic linkage between the antigenic group (Ag) variation and the apolipoprotein B gene: Assignment of the Ag locus. *Proc Natl Acad Sci USA* 83:7367, 1986.

87. HEGELE RA, HUANG L-S, HERBERT PN, BLUM CB, BURING JE, HENNEKENS CH, BRESLOW JL: Apolipoprotein B-gene DNA polymorphisms associated with myocardial infarction. *N Engl J Med* 315:1509, 1986.

88. ALEXANDER CA, HAMILTON RL, HAVEL RJ: Subcellular localization of "B" apoprotein of plasma lipoproteins in rat liver. *J Cell Biol* 69:241, 1976.

89. NORUM KR, BERG T, HELGERUD P, DREVON CA: Transport of cholesterol. *Physiol Rev* 63:1343, 1983.

90. CHRISTENSEN UJ, RUBIN CE, CHEUNG MC, ALBERS JJ: Ultrastructural immunolocalization of apolipoprotein B within human jejunal absorptive cells. *J Lipid Res* 24:1229, 1983.

91. HAMILTON RL: Hepatic secretion of plasma lipoproteins, in Glaumann H, Peters T Jr, Redman C (eds): *Plasma Protein Secretion by the Liver.* New York, Academic, 1983, p 357.

92. JANERO DR, SIUTA-MANGANO P, MILLER KW, LANE MD: Synthesis, processing, and secretion of hepatic very low density lipoprotein. *J Cell Biochem* 24:131, 1984.

93. OLOFSSON S-O, BOSTROM K, CARLSSON P, BOREN J, WETTESTEN M, BJURSELL G, WIKLUND O, BONDJERS GP: Structure and biosynthesis of apolipoprotein B. *Am Heart J* 113:446, 1987.

94. HIGGINS JA, FIELDSEND JK: Phosphatidylcholine synthesis for incorporation or for secretion as plasma lipoproteins by Golgi membranes of rat liver. *J Lipid Res* 28:1268, 1987.

95. LACKNER KJ, MONGE JC, GREGG RE, HOEG JM, TRICHE TJ, LAW SW, BREWER HB JR: Analysis of the apolipoprotein B gene and messenger ribonucleic acid in abetalipoproteinemia. *J Clin Invest* 78:1707, 1986.

96. DULLAART RPF, SPEELBERG B, SCHUMANN H-J, MILNE RW, HAVEKES LM, MARCEL YL, GEUZE HJ, HOLSHOF MM, ERKELENS DW: Epitopes of apolipoprotein B-100 and B-48 in both liver and intestine. Expression and

evidence for local synthesis in recessive abetalipoproteinemia. *J Clin Invest* 78:1397, 1986.

97. HAMILTON RL, GUO LS, FELKER TE, HAVEL RJ: Nascent high density lipoproteins from liver perfusates of orotic acid-fed rats. *J Lipid Res* 27:967, 1986.
98. POTTENGER LA, GETZ GS: Serum lipoprotein accumulation in the liver of orotic acid-fed rats. *J Lipid Res* 12:450, 1971.
99. HORNICK CA, HAMILTON RL, SPAZIANI E, ENDERS GH, HAVEL RJ: Isolation and characterization of multivesicular bodies from rat hepatocytes: An organelle distinct from secretory vesicles of the Golgi apparatus. *J Cell Biol* 100:1558, 1985.
100. HAVEL RJ: Metabolism of triglyceride-rich lipoproteins, in Schettler FD (ed): *Atherosclerosis VI*. Berlin-Heidelberg, Springer-Verlag, 1983, p 480.
101. HAMILTON RL: Synthesis and secretion of plasma lipoproteins, in Holmes EW, Paoletti R, Kritchevsky D (eds): *Pharmacological Control of Lipid Metabolism*. New York, Plenum, 1972, p 7.
102. HAMILTON RL, WILLIAMS MC, FIELDING CJ, HAVEL RJ: Discoidal bilayer structure of nascent high density lipoproteins from perfused rat liver. *J Clin Invest* 58:667, 1976.
103. GUO LSS, HAMILTON RL, OSTWALD R, HAVEL RJ: Secretion of nascent lipoproteins and apolipoproteins by perfused livers of normal and cholesterol-fed guinea pigs. *J Lipid Res* 23:543, 1982.
104. HORNICK CA, KITA T, HAMILTON RL, KANE JP, HAVEL RJ: Secretion of lipoproteins from the liver of normal and Watanabe heritable hyperlipidemic rabbits. *Proc Natl Acad Sci USA* 80:6096, 1983.
105. ERICKSON SK, COOPER AJ: Acyl-coenzyme A:cholesterol acyltransferase in human liver. In vivo detection and some characteristics of the enzyme. *Metabolism* 29:991, 1980.
106. FIELDING CJ, FIELDING PE: Cholesterol transport between cells and body fluids. Role of plasma lipoproteins and the plasma cholesterol esterification system. *Med Clin North Am* 66:363, 1982.
107. IMAIZUMI K, HAVEL RJ, FAINARU M, VIGNE J-L: Origin and transport of the A-I and arginine-rich apolipoproteins in mesenteric lymph of rats. *J Lipid Res* 19:1038, 1978.
108. IMAIZUMI K, FAINARU M, HAVEL RJ: Composition of proteins of mesenteric lymph chylomicrons in the rat and alterations produced upon exposure of chylomicrons to blood serum and serum proteins. *J Lipid Res* 19:712, 1978.
109. SCHONFELD G, GRIMME H, ALPERS D: Detection of apolipoprotein C in human and rat hepatocytes. *J Cell Biol* 86:562, 1980.
110. SATA T, HAVEL RJ, KOTITE L, KANE JP: New protein in human blood plasma, rich in proline, with lipid-binding properties. *Proc Natl Acad Sci USA* 73:1063, 1976.
111. TIKKANEN MI: Immunogenetic polymorphism of apolipoprotein B in humans: Studies with a monoclonal anti-Ag(c) antibody. *Am Heart J* 113:428, 1987.
112. RATH JM, ROTHBLAT GH, SPARKS CE: Lipoprotein apoprotein synthesis by human hepatoma cells in culture. *Biochim Biophys Acta* 666:294, 1981.
113. GLICKMAN RM, ROGERS M, GLICKMAN JN: Apolipoprotein B synthesis by human liver and intestine in vitro. *Proc Natl Acad Sci USA* 83:5296, 1986.
114. BOUMA M-E, BEUCIER I, AGGERBECK L-P, INFANTE R, SCHMITZ J: Hypobetalipoproteinemia with accumulation of an apo B-like protein in intestinal cells. *J Clin Invest* 78:398, 1986.
115. THRIFT RN, FORTE TM, CAHOON BE, SHORE VE: Characterization of lipoproteins produced by the human liver cell line, Hep G2, under defined conditions. *J Lipid Res* 27:236, 1986.
116. ELLSWORTH JL, ERICKSON SK, COOPER AD: Very low density and low density lipoprotein synthesis and secretion by the human hepatoma cell line Hep G2: Effects of free fatty acid. *J Lipid Res* 27:858, 1986.
117. TAM S-P, ARCHER TK, DEELEY RG: Effects of estrogen on apolipoprotein secretion by the human hepatocarcinoma cell line, Hep G2. *J Biol Chem* 260:1670, 1985.
118. HAVEL RJ: The formation of LDL: Mechanisms and regulation. *J Lipid Res* 25:1570, 1984.
119. KOSYKH VA, PREOBRAZHENSKY SN, FUKI IV, ZAIKINA OE, TSIBULSKY VP, REPIN VS, SMIRNOV VN: Cholesterol can stimulate secretion of apolipoprotein B by cultured human hepatocytes. *Biochim Biophys Acta* 836:385, 1985.
120. BELCHER JB, ERICKSON SK, FROST PH, FIELDING PE, HAVEL RJ: Human hepatoma cells in culture synthesize and secrete enzymatically and immunologically detectable hepatic triacylglycerol lipase. *Fed Proc* 45:1673, 1987.
121. GHISELLI G: Evidence that two synthetic pathways contribute to the apolipoprotein B pool of the low density lipoprotein fraction of rabbit plasma. *Biochim Biophys Acta* 711:311, 1982.
122. HUFF MW, TELFORD DE: Direct synthesis of low-density lipoprotein apoprotein B in the miniature pig. *Metabolism* 34:36, 1985.
123. YAMADA N, SHAMES DM, STOUDEMIRE JB, HAVEL RJ: Metabolism of lipoproteins containing apolipoprotein B-100 in blood plasma of rabbits: Heterogeneity related to the presence of apolipoprotein E. *Proc Natl Acad Sci USA* 83:3479, 1986.
124. JOHNSON FL, SWIFT LL, RUDEL LL: Nascent lipoproteins from recirculating and nonrecirculating liver perfusates and from hepatic Golgi apparatus of African green monkeys. *J Lipid Res* 28:549, 1987.
125. KANE JP, SATA T, HAMILTON RL, HAVEL RJ: Apoprotein composition of very low density lipoproteins in human serum. *J Clin Invest* 56:1622, 1975.
126. DAVIDSON NO, MAGUN AM, BRASITUS TA, GLICKMAN RM: Intestinal A-I and B-48 metabolism: Effects of sustained alterations in dietary triglyceride and mucosal cholesterol flux. *J Lipid Res* 28:388, 1987.
127. SCHONFELD G, PFLEGER B: Utilization of exogenous free fatty acids for the production of very low density lipoprotein triglyceride by livers of carbohydrate-fed rats. *J Lipid Res* 12:614, 1971.
128. DAVIS RA, ENGELHORN SC, PANGBURN SH, WEINSTEIN DB, STEINBERG D: Very low density lipoprotein synthesis and secretion by cultured rat hepatocytes. *J Biol Chem* 254:2010, 1979.
129. BØHMER T, HAVEL RJ, LONG JA: Physiological fatty liver and hyperlipemia in the fetal guinea pig: Chemical and ultrastructural characterization. *J Lipid Res* 13:371, 1972.
130. BØHMER T, HAVEL RJ: Genesis of fatty liver and hyperlipemia in the fetal guinea pig. *J Lipid Res* 16:454, 1975.
131. PATSCH W, FRANZ S, SCHONFELD G: Role of insulin in lipoprotein secretion by cultured hepatocytes. *J Clin Invest* 71:1161, 1983.
132. SPARKS CE, SPARKS JD, BOLOGNINO M, SALHANICK A, STRUMPH PS, AMATRUDA JM: Insulin effects on apolipoprotein B lipoprotein synthesis and secretion by primary cultures of rat hepatocytes. *Metabolism* 35:1128, 1986.
133. TAM S-P, ARCHER TK, DEELEY RG: Biphasic effects of estrogen on apolipoprotein synthesis in human hepatoma cells: Mechanisms on antagonism by testosterone. *Proc Natl Acad Sci USA* 83:3111, 1986.
134. BASSEN FA, KORNZWEIG AL: Malformation of the erythrocytes in a case of atypical retinitis pigmentosa. *Blood* 5:381, 1950.
135. JAMPEL RS, FALLS HF: Atypical retinitis pigmentosa, acanthocytosis, and heredogenerative neuromuscular disease. *Arch Ophthalmol* 59:818, 1958.
136. DRUEZ G: Un nouveau cas d'acanthocytose; Dysmorphie erythrocytaire congenitale avec retinite, troubles nerveux et stigmates degeneratifs. *Rev Hematol* 14:3, 1959.
137. SALT HB, WOLFF OH, LLOYD JK, FOSBROOKE AS, CAMERON AH, HUBBLE DV: On having no beta-lipoprotein: A syndrome comprising abetalipoproteinemia, acanthocytosis, and steatorrhea. *Lancet* 2:325, 1960.
138. LAMY M, FREZAL J, POLONOVSKI J, REY J: L'Absence congenitale de beta lipoproteines. *CR Soc Biol (Paris)* 154:1974, 1960.
139. MABRY CC, DI GEORGE AM, AUERBACH VH: Studies concerning the defect in a patient with acanthocytosis. *Clin Res* 8:371, 1960.
140. JONES JW, WAYS P: Abnormalities of high density lipoproteins in abetalipoproteinemia. *J Clin Invest* 46:1151, 1967.
141. SCHWARTZ JF, ROWLAND LP, EDER H, MARKS PA, OSSERMAN EF, HIRSCHBERG E, ANDERSON H: Bassen-Kornzweig syndrome: Deficiency of serum beta-lipoprotein. *Arch Neurol* 8:438, 1963.
142. LEVY RI, FREDRICKSON DS, LASTER L: The lipoproteins and lipid transport in abetalipoproteinemia. *J Clin Invest* 45:531, 1966.
143. FREDRICKSON DS, LEVY RI, LINDGREN FT: A comparison of heritable abnormal lipoprotein patterns as defined by two different techniques. *J Clin Invest* 47:2446, 1968.
144. BARNARD G, FOSBROOKE AS, LLOYD JK: Neutral lipids of plasma and adipose tissue in abetalipoproteinemia. *Clin Chim Acta* 28:417, 1970.
145. HOOGHWINKEL GJM, BRUYN GW: Congenital lack of β-lipoproteins. A study of blood phospholipids in a patient and his family. *J Neurol Sci* 3:374, 1966.
146. GOTTO AM, LEVY RI, JOHN K, FREDRICKSON DS: On the nature of the protein defect in abetalipoproteinemia. *N Engl J Med* 284:813, 1971.
147. KOSTNER G, HOLASEK A, BOHLMANN HG, THIEDE H: Investigation of serum lipoproteins and apoproteins in abetalipoproteinemia. *Clin Sci Mol Med* 46:457, 1974.
148. SCANU AM, AGGERBECK LP, KRUSKI AW, LIM CT, KAYDEN HJ: A study of the abnormal lipoproteins in abetalipoproteinemia. *J Clin Invest* 53:440, 1974.
149. LEES RS: Immunological evidence for the presence of B protein (apoprotein of β-lipoprotein) in normal and abetalipoproteinemic plasma. *J Lipid Res* 8:396, 1967.
150. FORTE T, NICHOLS AV: Application of electron microscopy to the study of plasma lipoprotein structure. *Adv Lipid Res* 10:1, 1972.
151. FORTE TM, REN CL, NORDHAUSEN RW, NICHOLS AV: Formation of phospholipid-rich HDL: A model for square-packing lipoprotein particles

found in interstitial fluid and in abetalipoproteinemia plasma. *Biochim Biophys Acta* 834:386, 1985.

152. SCHMITZ G, ILSEMANN K, MELNIK B, ASSMANN G: Isoproteins of human apolipoprotein A-II: Isolation and characterization. *J Lipid Res* 24:1021, 1983.

153. DECKELBAUM RJ, EISENBERG S, OSCHRY Y, COOPER M, BLUM C: Abnormal high density lipoproteins of abetalipoproteinemia: Relevance to normal HDL metabolism. *J Lipid Res* 23:1274, 1982.

154. GIBSON JC, RUBENSTEIN A, BROWN WV, GINSBERG HN, GRETEN H, NORUM R, KAYDEN H: Apo E-containing lipoproteins in low or high density lipoprotein deficiency. *Arteriosclerosis* 5:371, 1985.

155. HERBERT PN, HEINER RJ, BAUSSERMAN LL, HENDERSON LO, MUSLINER TA: Abetalipoproteinemia and hypobetalipoproteinemia.: Questions still exceed insights, in Gotto AM Jr, Smith LC, Allen B (eds): *Atherosclerosis V: Proceedings of the Fifth International Symposium on Atherosclerosis.* New York, Springer-Verlag, 1980, p 684.

156. BLUMENFELD OO, SCHWARTZ E, ADAMANY AM: Efflux of phospholipids from cultured aortic smooth muscle cells. *J Biol Chem* 254:7183, 1979.

157. SHEPHERD J, CASLAKE M, FARISH E, FLECK A: Chemical and kinetic study of the lipoproteins in abetalipoproteinemic plasma. *J Clin Pathol* 31:382, 1978.

158. KUO PT, BASSETT DR, DI GEORGE AM, CARPENTER GG: Lipolytic activity of post-heparin plasma in hyperlipemia and hypolipemia. *Circ Res* 16:221, 1965.

159. ILLINGWORTH DR, ALAM SS, ALAM NA: Lipoprotein lipase and hepatic lipase activity after heparin administration in abetalipoproteinemia and hypobetalipoproteinemia. *Metabolism* 32:869, 1983.

160. FREDRICKSON DS, ONO D, DAVIS LL: Lipolytic activity of post heparin plasma in hypertriglyceridemia. *J Lipid Res* 4:24, 1963.

161. SLACK J, NAIR S, TRAISMAN H, et al: Lipoprotein lipase in cystic fibrosis of the pancreas. *J Lab Clin Med* 59:302, 1962.

162. FALKO JM, CROCKETT SE, CATALAND S, et al: Gastric inhibitory peptide stimulated by fat ingestion in man. *J Clin Endocrinol Metab* 41:260, 1975.

163. ECKEL RH, FUJIMOTO WY, BRUNZELL JD: Gastric inhibitory polypeptide enhanced lipoprotein lipase activity in cultured preadipocytes. *Diabetes* 28:1141, 1979.

164. COOPER RA, GULBRANDSEN CL: The relationship between serum lipoproteins and red cell membranes in abetalipoproteinemia: Deficiency of lecithin:cholesterol acyltransferase. *J Lab Clin Med* 78:323, 1971.

165. FIELDING CJ, FIELDING PE: Purification and substrate specificity of lecithin-cholesterol acyltransferase from human plasma. *FEBS Lett* 15:355, 1971.

166. SUBBAIAH PV: Requirement of low density lipoproteins for the lysolecithin acyltransferase activity in human plasma: Assay of enzyme activity in abetalipoproteinemic patients. *Metabolism* 31:294, 1982.

167. MYANT NB, REICHL D, LLOYD JK: Sterol balance in a patient with abetalipoproteinaemia. *Atherosclerosis* 29:509, 1978.

168. KAYDEN HJ: Abetalipoproteinemia—Abnormalities of serum lipoproteins, in Peeters H (ed): *Protides of the Biological Fluids (Proceedings of the 25th Coll, Bruges, 1977).* Oxford, Pergamon, 1978, p 271.

169. ILLINGWORTH DR, CONNOR WE, LIN DS, DI LIBERTI J: Lipid metabolism in abetalipoproteinemia: A study of cholesterol absorption and sterol balance in two patients. *Gastroenterology* 78:68, 1980.

170. GOODMAN DS, DECKELBAUM RJ, PALMER RH, DELL RB, RAMAKRISHNAN R, DELPRE G, BEIGEL Y, COOPER M: Cholesterol turnover and metabolism in two patients with abetalipoproteinemia. *J Lipid Res* 24:1605, 1983.

171. REICHL D, MYANT NB, LLOYD JK: Surface binding and catabolism of low-density lipoprotein by circulating lymphocytes from patients with abetalipoproteinaemia with observations on sterol synthesis in lymphocytes from one patient. *Biochim Biophys Acta* 530:124, 1978.

172. HO YK, FAUST JR, BILHEIMER DW, BROWN MS, GOLDSTEIN JL: Regulation of cholesterol synthesis by low density lipoprotein in isolated human lymphocytes. *J Exp Med* 145:1531, 1977.

173. ILLINGWORTH DR, ALAM NA, SUNDBERG EE: Cholesterol and steroid hormone metabolism in abetalipoproteinemia, in Schettler G, Gotto AM Jr, Middelhoff G, Habenicht AJR, Jurutka KR (eds): *Atherosclerosis.* New York, Springer, 1982, p 852.

174. BRANNAN PG, GOLDSTEIN JL, BROWN MS: 3-hydroxy-3-methylglutaryl coenzyme A reductase activity in human hair roots. *J Lipid Res* 16:7, 1975.

175. LEES AM, LEES RS: Low density lipoprotein degradation by mononuclear cells from normal and dyslipoproteinemic subjects. *Proc Natl Acad Sci USA* 80:5098, 1983.

176. ILLINGWORTH DR, ALAM NA, SUNDBERG EE, HAGEMENAS FC, LAYMAN DL: Regulation of low density lipoprotein receptors by plasma lipoproteins from patients with abetalipoproteinemia. *Proc Natl Acad Sci USA* 80:3475, 1983.

177. INNERARITY TL, BERSOT TP, ARNOLD KS, WEISGRABER KH, DAVIS PA, FORTE TM, MAHLEY RW: Receptor binding activity of high-density lipoproteins containing apoprotein E from abetalipoproteinemic and normal plasma. *Metabolism* 33:186, 1984.

178. ILLINGWORTH DR, KENNY TA, ORWOLL ES: Adrenal function in heterozygous and homozygous hypobetalipoproteinemia. *J Clin Endocrinol Metab* 54:27, 1982.

179. ILLINGWORTH DR, KENNY TA, CONNOR WE, ORWOLL ES: Corticosteroid production in abetalipoproteinemia: Evidence for an impaired response to ACTH. *J Lab Clin Med* 100:115, 1982.

180. ILLINGWORTH DR, CORBIN DK, KEMP ED, KEENAN EJ: Hormone changes during the menstrual cycle in abetalipoproteinemia. Reduced luteal phase progesterone in a patient with homozygous hypobetalipoproteinemia. *Proc Natl Acad Sci USA* 79:6685, 1982.

181. EHLERS N, HANSEN HJ: Abetalipoproteinemia: Ocular involvement in a Danish case. *Acta Ophthalmol* 59:747, 1981.

182. SINGER K, FISHER B, PERLSTEIN MA: Acanthrocytosis: A genetic erythrocytic malformation. *Blood* 7:577, 1952.

183. KAYDEN HJ, BESSIS M: Morphology of normal erythrocyte and acanthocyte using Nomarski optics and the scanning electron microscope. *Blood* 35:427, 1970.

184. PHILLIPS GB: Quantitative chromatographic analysis of plasma and red blood cell lipids in patients with acanthocytosis. *J Lab Clin Med* 59:357, 1962.

185. WAYS P, REED CF, HANAHAN DJ: Red-cell and plasma lipids in acanthocytosis. *J Clin Invest* 42:1248, 1963.

186. IIDA H, TAKASHIMA Y, MAEDA S, SEKIYA T, KAWADE M, KAWAMURA M, OKANO Y, NOZAWA Y: Alterations in erythrocyte membrane lipids in abetalipoproteinemia: Phospholipid and fatty acyl composition. *Biochem Med* 32:79, 1984.

187. BACH C, POLONOVSKI J, POLONOVSKI C, LELUC R, JOLLY G, MOSZER M: L'Absence congenitale de β-lipoproteines: Une nouvelle observation. *Arch Fr Pediatr* 24:1093, 1967.

188. MARCEL Y, HOGUE TR JR, MILNE R: Mapping of antigenic determinants of human apolipoprotein B using monoclonal antibodies against low density lipoproteins. *J Biol Chem* 257:13165, 1982.

189. LANGE Y, STECK TL: Mechanism of red blood cell acanthocytosis and echinocytosis in vivo. *J Membr Biol* 77:153, 1984.

190. MIER M, SCHWARTZ SO, BOSHES B: Acanthocytosis, pigmentary degeneration of the retina and ataxic neuropathy: A genetically determined syndrome with associated metabolic disorder. *Blood* 5:1586, 1960.

191. WAYS P, REED CF, HANAHAN DJ: Red cell and plasma lipids in acanthocytosis. *J Clin Invest* 42:1248, 1963.

192. FARQUHAR JW, WAYS P: Abetalipoproteinemia, in Stanbury JB, Wyngaarden JB, Fredrickson DS (eds): *The Metabolic Basis of Inherited Disease,* 2d ed. New York, McGraw-Hill, 1966, p 509.

193. SOBREVILLA LA, GOODMAN ML, KANE CA: Demyelinating central nervous system disease, macular atrophy and acanthocytosis (Bassen-Kornzweig syndrome). *Am J Med* 37:821, 1964.

194. DISCHE MR, PORRO RS: The cardiac lesions in Bassen-Kornzweig syndrome. *Am J Med* 49:568, 1970.

195. BRADLEY WA, WHANG S-LC, KARLIN JB, LIN AHY, PRASAD SC, GOTTO AM JR, GIANTURCO SH: Low density lipoprotein receptor binding determinants switch from apolipoprotein E to apolipoprotein B during conversion of hypertriglyceridemic very-low-density lipoproteins to low density lipoproteins. *J Biol Chem* 259:14728, 1984.

196. LEYLAND FC, FOSBROOKE AS, LLOYD JK, SEGALL MM, TAMIR I, TOMKINS R, WOLFF OH: Use of medium-chain triglyceride diets in children with malabsorption. *Arch Dis Child* 44:170, 1969.

197. WAYS PO, PARMENTIER CM, KAYDEN HJ, JONES JW, SAUNDERS DR, RUBIN CE: Studies on the absorptive defect for triglyceride in abetalipoproteinemia. *J Clin Invest* 46:35, 1967.

198. BECROFT DMO, COSTELLO JM, SCOTT PJ: Abetalipoproteinemia (Bassen-Kornzweig syndrome). *Arch Dis Child* 40:40, 1965.

199. FORSYTH CC, LLOYD JK, FOSBROOKE AS: A-beta-lipoproteinaemia. *Arch Dis Child* 40:47, 1965.

200. SIMON ER, WAYS P: Incubation hemolysis and red cell metabolism in acanthocytosis. *J Clin Invest* 43:1311, 1964.

201. KAYDEN HJ, SILBER R: The role of vitamin E deficiency in the abnormal autohemolysis of acanthocytosis. *Trans Assoc Am Physicians* 78:334, 1965.

202. CABALLERO FM, BUCHANAN GR: Abetalipoproteinemia presenting as severe vitamin K deficiency. *Pediatrics* 65:161, 1980.

203. ILLINGWORTH DR, CONNOR WE, MILLER RG: Abetalipoproteinemia: Report of two cases and review of therapy. *Arch Neurol* 37:659, 1980.

204. NEWMAN RP, SCHAEFER EJ, THOMAS CB, OLDFIELD EH: Abetalipoproteinemia and metastatic spinal cord glioblastoma. *Arch Neurol* 41:554, 1984.

205. MALLOY MJ: Unpublished observation.

206. SHASTRI KM, CARVALHO ACA, LEES RS: Platelet function and platelet lipid

composition in the dyslipoproteinemias. *J Lipid Res* 21:467, 1980.

207. AVIRAM M, DECKELBAUM RJ, BROOK JG: Platelet function in a case of abetalipoproteinemia. *Atherosclerosis* 57:313, 1985.

208. WEINSTEIN MA, PEARSON KD, AGUS SG: Abetalipoproteinemia. *Radiology* 108:269, 1973.

209. ISSELBACHER KJ, SCHEIG R, PLOTKIN GR, CAUFIELD JB: Congenital beta-lipoprotein deficiency: An hereditary disorder involving a defect in the absorption and transport of lipids. *Medicine* 43:347, 1964.

210. GRISE B, LELUYER B, MITROFANOFF D: Lithiase oxalique associée à une abêtalipoproteinémie. A propos d'un cas. *Chir Pediatr* 24:411, 1983.

211. HUANG HS, GOODMAN DS: Vitamin A and carotenoids. I. Intestinal absorption and metabolism of ^{14}C-labeled vitamin A alcohol and betacarotene in the rat. *J Biol Chem* 240:2839, 1965.

212. BELANGER M, TREMBLAY M, LAPOINTE JR: Absence congénitale des bêta-lipoprotéines; Syndrome rare et bizarre. Nouvelle observation. *Laval Med* 42:332, 1971.

213. WALLIS K, GROSS M, ZAIDMAN JL, JULSARY A, SZEINBERG A, KOOK A: Tocopherol therapy in acanthocytosis. *Pediatrics* 48:669, 1971.

214. BIERI JG, HOEG JM, SCHAEFER EJ, ZECH LA, BREWER B: Vitamin A and vitamin E replacement in abetalipoproteinemia. *Ann Intern Med* 100:238, 1984.

215. KAYDEN HJ, HATAM LJ, TRABER MG: The measurement of nanograms of tocopherol from needle aspiration biopsies of adipose tissue: Normal and abetalipoproteinemic subjects. *J Lipid Res* 24:652, 1983.

216. MULLER DPR, HARRIES JT, LLOYD JK: Vitamin E therapy in a-betalipoproteinemia. *Arch Dis Child* 45:715, 1970.

217. MULLER DPR, HARRIES JT, LLOYD JK: The relative importance of the factors involved in the absorption of vitamin E in children. *Gut* 15:966, 1974.

218. MACMAHON MT, NEALE G, THOMPSON GR: Lymphatic and portal venous transport of α-tocopherol and cholesterol. *Eur J Clin Invest* 1:288, 1971.

219. TRABER MG, KAYDEN HJ: Vitamin E is delivered to cells via the high affinity receptor for low density lipoprotein. *Am J Clin Nutr* 40:747, 1984.

220. MALLOY MJ, KANE JP, HARDMAN DA, HAMILTON RL, DALAL K: Normotriglyceridemic abetalipoproteinemia. Absence of the B-100 apoprotein. *J Clin Invest* 67:1441, 1981.

221. DELPRE G, KADISH U, GLANTZ I, AVIDOR I: Endoscopic assessment in abetalipoproteinemia (Bassen-Kornzweig Syndrome). *Endoscopy* 10:59, 1978.

222. DOBBINS WO III: An ultrastructural study of the intestinal mucosa in congenital betalipoprotein deficiency with particular emphasis upon the intestinal absorptive cell. *Gastroenterology* 50:195, 1966.

223. GLICKMAN RM, GREEN PHR, LEES RS, LUX SE, KILGORE A: Immunofluorescence studies of apolipoprotein B in intestinal mucosa. *Gastroenterology* 76:288, 1979.

224. GREEN PH, LEFKOWITCH JH, GLICKMAN RM, RILEY JW, QUINET E, BLUM C: Apolipoprotein localization and quantitation in the human intestine. *Gastroenterology* 83:1223, 1982.

225. COGAN DG, RODRIGUES M, CHU FC, SCHAEFFER ELT: Ocular abnormalities in abetalipoproteinemia. *Ocular Pathol Clin* 91:991, 1984.

226. PARTIN JS, PARTIN JC, SCHUBERT WK, MCADAMS AJ: Liver ultrastructure in abetalipoproteinemia: Evolution of micronodular cirrhosis. *Gastroenterology* 67:107, 1974.

227. ILLINGWORTH DR, CONNOR WE, MILLER RG: Abetalipoproteinemia. Report of two cases and review of therapy. *Arch Neurol* 37:659, 1980.

228. AVIGAN MI, ISHAK KG, GREGG RE, HOOFNAGLE JH: Morphologic features of the liver in abetalipoproteinemia. *Hepatology* 4:1223, 1984.

229. BRIN MF, NELSON JS, ROBERTS WC, MARQUARDT MD, SUSWANKOSAI P, PETITO CK: Neuropathology of abetalipoproteinemia: A possible complication of the tocopherol (vitamin E) deficient state. *Neurology [Suppl]* 33:142, 1983.

230. KORNZWEIG AL, BASSEN FA: Retinitis pigmentosa, acanthocytosis, and heredogenerative neuromuscular disease. *Arch Opthalmol* 58:183, 1957.

231. COHEN DA, BOSLEY TM, SAVINO PJ, SERGOTT RC, SCHATZ JI: Primary aberrant regeneration of the oculomotor nerve. *Arch Neurol* 42:821, 1985.

232. BRIN MF, PEDLEY TA, LOVELACE RE, EMERSON RG, GOURAS P, MACKAY C, KAYDEN HJ, LEVY J, BAKER H: Electrophysiologic features of abetalipoproteinemia: Functional consequences of vitamin E deficiency. *Neurology* 36:669, 1986.

233. WICHMAN A, BUCHTHAL F, PEZESHKPOUR GH, GREGG RE: Peripheral neuropathy in abetalipoproteinemia. *Neurology* 35:1279, 1985.

234. WERLIN SL, HARB JM, SWICK H, BLANK E: Neuromuscular dysfunction and ultrastructural pathology in children with chronic cholestasis and vitamin E deficiency. *Ann Neurol* 13:291, 1983.

235. KOBAYASHI Y, TAZAWA Y, NAKAGAWA M, SUZUKI H, KONNO T, YAMAMOTO TY: Ultrastructural changes in skeletal muscle of a patient with familial intrahepatic cholestasis associated with vitamin E deficiency. *Tohoku J Exp Med* 142:337, 1984.

236. HARDING AE, MATTHEWS S, JONES S, ELLIS CJK, BOOTH IW, MULLER DPR: Spinocerebellar degeneration associated with a selective defect of vitamin E absorption. *N Engl J Med* 313:32, 1985.

237. STUMPF DA, SOKOL R, BETTIS D, et al: Clinical picture mimicking Friedreich's ataxia associated with vitamin E deficiency and normal fat absorption. *Neurology [Suppl]* 35:145, 1985.

238. HAYS KC: Retinal degeneration in monkeys induced by deficiencies of vitamin E or A. *Invest Ophthalmol* 13:499, 1974.

239. ROBINSON WG JR, KUWABARA T, BIERI JG: Deficiencies of vitamin E and A in the rat: Retinal damage and lipofuscin accumulation. *Invest Ophthalmol Vis Sci* 19:1030, 1980.

240. NELSON JS: Pathology of vitamin E deficiency, in Machlin L (ed): *Vitamin E: A Comprehensive Treatise.* New York, Dekker, 1980, p 397.

241. NELSON JS, FITCH CD, FISCHE VW, BROUN GD, CHOU AC: Progressive neuropathologic lesions in vitamin E deficient rhesus monkeys. *J Neuropathol Exp Neurol* 40:166, 1981.

242. KOTT E, DELPRE G, KADISH U, DZIATELOVSKY M, SANDBANK U: Abetalipoproteinemia (Bassen-Kornzweig Syndrome). *Acta Neuropathol (Berl)* 37:255, 1977.

243. KHACHADURIAN AK, FREYHA R, SHAMMA'A MM, BAGHDASSARIAN SA: A-betalipoproteinemia and colour blindness. *Arch Dis Child* 46:871, 1971.

244. VON SALLMANN L, GELDERMAN AH, LASTER L: Ocular histopathologic changes in a case of a-beta-lipoproteinemia (Bassen-Kornzweig syndrome). *Doc Ophthalmol* 26:451, 1969.

245. ROBISON WG JR, KUWABARA T, BIERI JG: The roles of vitamin E and unsaturated fatty acids in the visual process. *Retina* 2:263, 1982.

246. ROBISON WG JR, KUWABARA T, BIERI JG: Vitamin E deficiency and the retina: Photoreceptor and pigment epithelial changes. *Invest Ophthalmol Vis Sci* 18:683, 1979.

247. GOURAS P, CARR RE, BUNKEL RD: Retinitis pigmentosa in abetalipoproteinemia: Effects of vitamin A. *Invest Ophthalmol* 10:784, 1971.

248. SPERLING MA, HILES DA, KENNERDELL JS: Electroretinographic responses following vitamin A therapy in a-beta-lipoproteinemia. *Am J Ophthalmol* 73:342, 1972.

249. BIERI JG, HOEG JM, SCHAEFER EJ, ZECH LA, BREWER B: Vitamin A and vitamin E replacement in abetalipoproteinemia. *Ann Intern Med* 100:238, 1984.

250. BISHARA S, MERIN S, COOPER M, AZIZ G, DELPRE G, DECKELBAUM RJ: Combined vitamin A and E therapy prevents retinal electrophysiological deterioration in abetalipoproteinemia. *Br J Ophthalmol* 12:767, 1971.

251. DOWLING JE: Nutritional and inherited blindness in the rat. *Exp Eye Res* 3:348, 1964.

252. SCOTT PP, GREAVES JP, SCOTT MG: Nutritional blindness in the cat. *Exp Eye Res* 3:357, 1964.

253. RODGER RC: The ocular effects of vitamin A deficiency in man in the tropics. *Exp Eye Res* 3:367, 1964.

254. WOLFF OH, LLOYD JK, TONKS EL: A-beta-lipoproteinaemia with special reference to the visual defect. *Exp Eye Res* 3:439, 1964.

255. SPERLING MA, HENGSTENBERG F, YUNIS E, KENNY FM, DRASH AL: Abetalipoproteinemia: Metabolic, endocrine, and electron-microscopic investigations. *Pediatrics* 48:91, 1971.

256. FRIEDMAN IS, COHN H, ZYMORIS M, GOLDMAN AMG: Hypocholesterolemia in idiopathic steatorrhea. *Arch Intern Med* 105:112, 1960.

257. BOHLMANN HG, THIEDE H, ROSENSTIEL K, HERDEMERTEN S, PANITZ D, TACKMANN W: A-β-Lipoproteinämie bei drei Geschwistern. *Dtsch Med Wochenschr* 97:892, 1972.

258. ZAIDMAN JL, JULSARY A, KOOK AI, SZEINBERG A, WALLIA K, AZIZI E: Abetalipoproteinemia in acrodermatitis enteropathica. *N Engl J Med* 284:1387, 1971.

259. LACKNER KJ, MONGE JC, GREGG RE, HOEG JM, TRICHE TJ, LAW SW, BREWER HB JR: Analysis of the apolipoprotein B gene and messenger ribonucleic acid in abetalipoproteinemia. *J Clin Invest* 78:1707, 1986.

260. KAYDEN HJ, TRABER MG: Clinical, nutritional, and biochemical consequences of apolipoprotein B deficiency. *Adv Exp Med Biol* 201:67, 1986.

261. MULLER DPR, LLOYD JK, BIRD AC: Long-term management of abetalipoproteinemia. *Arch Dis Child* 52:209, 1977.

262. AZIZI E, ZAIDMAN JL, ESCHAR J, SZEINBERG A: Abetalipoproteinemia treated with parenteral and oral vitamins A and E, and with medium chain triglycerides. *Acta Paediatr Scand* 67:797, 1978.

263. MULLER DPR, LLOYD JK, WOLFF OH: Vitamin E and neurological function. *Lancet* 1:225, 1983.

264. HEGELE RA, ANGEL A: Arrest of neuropathy and myopathy in abetalipoproteinemia with high dose vitamin E therapy. *Can Med Assoc J* 12:41, 1985.

265. MULLER DPR, LLOYD JK: Effect of large oral doses of vitamin E on the neurological sequelae of patients with abetalipoproteinemia. *Ann NY Acad Sci* 393:133, 1982.

266. RUNGE P, MULLER DPR, MCALLISTER J, CALVER D, LLOYD JK, TAYLOR D:

Oral vitamin E supplements can prevent the retinopathy of abetalipoproteinemia. *Br J Ophthalmol* 70:166, 1986.

267. SUNG JM, PARK SH, MASTRI AR, WARWICK WJ: Axonal dystrophy in the gracile nucleus in congenital biliary atresia and cystic fibrosis (mucoviscidosis): Beneficial effect of vitamin E therapy. *J Neuropathol Exp Neurol* 39:584, 1980.

268. VAN BUCHEM FSP, POL G, DE GIER J, BOTTCHER CJF, PRIES C: Congenital-β-lipoprotein deficiency. *Am J Med* 40:794, 1966.

269. MARS H, LEWIS LA, ROBERTSON AL JR, BUTKUS A, WILLIAMS GH JR: Familial hypo-β-lipoproteinemia: A genetic disorder of lipid metabolism with nervous system involvement. *Am J Med* 46:886, 1969.

270. RICHET G, DUREPAIRE H, HARTMANN L, OLLIER M-P, POLONOVSKI J, MAITROT B: Hypolipoproteinémie familiale asymptomatique predominant sur les bêtalipoprotéines. *Presse Med* 77:2045, 1969.

271. LEVY RI, LANGER T, GOTTO AM, FREDRICKSON DS: Familial hypobetalipoproteinemia, a defect in lipoprotein synthesis. *Clin Res* 18:539, 1970.

272. MAWATARI S, IWASHITA H, KUROIWA Y: Familial hypo-β-lipoproteinemia. *J Neurol Sci* 16:93, 1972.

273. FOSBROOKE A, CHOKSEY S, WHARTON B: Familial hypo-β-lipoproteinemia. *Arch Dis Child* 48:729, 1973.

274. BROWN BJ, LEWIS LA, MERCER RD: Familial hypobetalipoproteinemia: Report of a case with psychomotor retardation. *Pediatrics* 54:111, 1974.

275. COTTRILL C, GLUECK CJ, LEUBA V, MILLET F, PUPPIONE D, BROWN WV: Familial homozygous hypobetalipoproteinemia. *Metabolism* 23:779, 1974.

276. BIEMER JJ, MCCAMMON RE: The genetic relationship of abetalipoproteinemia and hypobetalipoproteinemia: A report of the occurrence of both diseases within the same family. *J Lab Clin Med* 85:556, 1975.

277. FEIT J-P, DAVID M, MACABEO V, DIVRY P, BERNARD J-C, LAMBERT D, BEUCLER I, JEUNE M: L'Abetalipoprotéinemie. Étude clinique, genétique, endocrinienne et metabolique d'une nouvelle observation familiale. *Pediatrie* 32:753, 1977.

278. ILLINGWORTH DR, CONNOR WE, BUIST NRM, JHAVERI BM, LIN DS, MCMURRY MP: Sterol balance in abetalipoproteinemia: Studies in a patient with homozygous familial hypobetalipoproteinemia. *Metabolism* 28:1152, 1979.

279. TAMIR I, LEVTOW O, LOTON D, LEQUIN C, HENDENBERG D, WERBIN B: Further observations on familial hypobetalipoproteinemia. *Clin Genet* 9:149, 1976.

280. BERGER GMB, BROWN G, HENDERSON HE, BONNICI F: Apolipoprotein B detected in the plasma of a patient with homozygous hypobetalipoproteinemia: Implications for aetiology. *J Med Genet* 20:189, 1983.

281. VEGA GL, VON BERGMANN K, GRUNDY SM, BELTZ W, JAHN C, EAST C: Increased catabolism of VLDL-apolipoprotein B and synthesis of bile acids in a case of hypobetalipoproteinemia. *Metabolism* 36:262, 1987.

282. FORTE TM: Unpublished results.

283. SCOTT BB, MILLER JP, LOSOWSKY MS: Hypobetalipoproteinaemia—A variant of the Bassen-Kornzweig syndrome. *Gut* 20:163, 1979.

284. SIGURDSSON G, NICOLL A, LEWIS B: Turnover of apolipoprotein B in two subjects with familial hypobetalipoproteinemia. *Metabolism* 26:25, 1977.

284a. YOUNG SG, NORTHEY ST, MCCARTHY BJ: Low plasma cholesterol levels caused by a short deletion in the apo B gene. *Science* 241:591, 1988.

284b. COLLINS DR, KNOTT TJ, PEASE RJ, POWELL LM, WALLIS SC, ROBERTSON S, PULLINGER CR, MILNE RW, MARCEL YL, HUMPHRIES SE, TALMUD PJ, LLOYD JK, MILLER NE, MULLER D, SCOTT J: Truncated variants of apolipoprotein B cause hypobetalipoproteinemia. *Nucleic Acids Res* 16:8361, 1988.

284c. ROSS RS, GREGG RE, LAW SW, MONGE JC, GRANT SM, HIGUCHI K, TRICHE TJ, JEFFERSON J, BREWER HB JR: Homozygous hypobetalipoproteinemia: A disease distinct from abetalipoproteinemia at the molecular level. *J Clin Invest* 81:590, 1988.

285. FREDRICKSON DS, GOTTO AM, LEVY RI: Familial lipoprotein deficiency, in Stanbury JB, Wyngaarden JB, Fredrickson DS (eds): *The Metabolic Basis of Inherited Disease,* 3d ed. New York, McGraw-Hill, 1972, p 493.

286. YEE RD, HERBERT PN, BERGSMA DR, BIEMER JJ: Atypical retinitis pigmentosa in familial hypobetalipoproteinemia. *Am J Ophthalmol* 82:64, 1976.

287. HARDMAN DA, FROUSSARD P, PROTTER A, KANE JP, MALLOY MJ: Unpublished observations.

288. TAKASHIMA Y, KODAMA T, IIDA H, KAWAMURA M, ABURATANI H, ITAKURA H, AKANUMA Y, TAKAKU F, KAWADE M: Normotriglyceridemic abetalipoproteinemia in infancy: An isolated B-100 deficiency. *Pediatrics* 75:541, 1985.

289. HERBERT PN, HYAMS JS, BERNIER DN, BERMAN MM, SARITELLI AL, LYNCH KM, NICHOLS AV, FORTE TM: Apolipoprotein B-100 deficiency. *J Clin Invest* 76:403, 1985.

290. STEINBERG D, GRUNDY SM, MOK HI, TURNER JD, WEINSTEIN DB, BROWN WV, ALBERS JJ: Metabolic studies in an unusual case of asymptomatic familial hypobetalipoproteinemia with hypoalphalipoproteinemia and fasting chylomicronemia. *J Clin Invest* 64:292, 1979.

290a. YOUNG SG, PERALTA FP, DUBOIS BW, CURTISS LK, BOYLES JK, WITZTUM JL: Lipoprotein B37, a naturally occurring lipoprotein containing the amino-terminal portion of apolipoprotein B-100, does not bind to the apolipoprotein B,E (low density lipoprotein) receptor. *J Biol Chem* 262:16604, 1987.

291. YOUNG SG, BERTICS SJ, CURTISS LK, DUBOIS BW, WITZTUM JL: Genetic analysis of a kindred with familial hypobetalipoproteinemia—Evidence for two separate gene defects: One associated with an abnormal apolipoprotein B species, apo B-37, and a second associated with low plasma concentrations of apo B-100. *J Clin Invest* 79:1842, 1987.

292. ANDERSON CM, TOWNLEY RRW, FREEMAN JP: Unusual causes of steatorrhea in infancy and childhood. *Med J Aust* 11:617, 1961.

293. LAMY M, FREZAL J, REY J, JOS J, NEZELOT C, HERRAULT A, COHEN-SOLAL J: Diarrhée chronique par trouble du transport intracellulaire des lipides. *Arch Fr Pediatr* 24:1079, 1967.

294. PARTIN JC, SCHUBERT WK: Jejunal mucosa biopsy studies in two new types of hypobetalipoproteinemias: Light, electron microscopical and biochemical analysis. *Gastroenterology* 58:1022, 1970.

295. POLONOVSKI C, NAVARRO J, FONTAINE JL, DE GOUYON F, SAUDUBRAY JM, CATHELINEAU L: Maladie d'Anderson. *Ann Pediatr (Paris)* 17:342, 1970.

296. BOUMA M-E, BEUCLER I, AGGERBECK L-P, INFANTE R, SCHMITZ J: Hypobetalipoproteinemia with accumulation of an apoprotein B-like protein in intestinal cells. *J Clin Invest* 78:398, 1986.

297. ROY CC, LEVY E, GREEN PHR, SNIDERMAN A, LETARTE J, BUTS JP, ORGUIN J, BROCHU P, WEBER AM, MORIN CL, MARCEL Y, DECKELBAUM RJ: Malabsorption, hypocholesterolemia, fat-filled enterocytes with increased intestinal apoprotein B: Chylomicron retention disease. *Gastroenterology* 92:390, 1987.

298. LEVY E, MARCEL Y, DECKELBAUM RJ, MILNE R, LEPAGE G, SEIDMAN E, BENDAYAN M, ROY CC: Intestinal apo B synthesis, lipids and lipoproteins in chylomicron retention disease. *J Lipid Res* 28:1263, 1987.

299. GOLDSTEIN JL, SCHROTT HG, HAZZARD WR, BIERMAN EL, MOTULSKY AG: Hyperlipidemia in coronary artery disease. II: Genetic analysis of lipid levels in 176 families and delineation of a new inherited disorder, combined hyperlipidemia. *J Clin Invest* 52:1544, 1973.

300. HAZZARD WR, GOLDSTEIN JL, SCHROTT HG, MOTULSKY AG, BIERMAN EL: Evaluation of lipoprotein phenotypes of 156 genetically defined survivors of myocardial infarction. *J Clin Invest* 52:1569, 1973.

301. BRUNZELL JD, ALBERS JJ, CHAIT A, GRUNDY SM, GROSZEK E, MCDONALD GB: Plasma lipoproteins in familial combined hyperlipidemia and monogenic familial hypertriglyceridemia. *J Lipid Res* 24:147, 1983.

302. NIKKILA EA, ARO A: Family study of serum lipids and lipoproteins in coronary heart disease. *Arteriosclerosis* 1:82, 1981.

303. ROSE HG, KRANZ P, WEINSTOCK M, JULIANO J, HAFT JI: Inheritance of combined hyperlipoproteinemia: Evidence for a new lipoprotein phenotype. *Am J Med* 54:148, 1973.

304. CHAIT A, BRUNZELL JD: Severe hypertriglyceridemia: Role of familial and acquired disorders. *Metabolism* 32:209, 1983.

305. KRAUSS RN, ALBERS JJ, BRUNZELL JD: An apolipoprotein B-enriched low density lipoprotein subspecies in familial combined hyperlipidemia. *Clin Res* 31:503a, 1983.

306. KWITEROVICH PO, WHITE S, FORTE T, BACHORIK PS, SMITH H, SNIDERMAN A: Hyperapobetalipoproteinemia in a kindred with familial combined hyperlipidemia and familial hypercholesterolemia *Arteriosclerosis* 7:211, 1987.

307. CHAIT A, ALBERS JJ, BRUNZELL JD: Very low density lipoprotein overproduction in genetic forms of hypertriglyceridemia. *Eur J Clin Invest* 10:17, 1980.

308. CHAIT A, FOSTER D, ALBERS JJ, BRUNZELL JD: Familial hypercholesterolemia vs. familial combined hyperlipidemia: Low density lipoprotein apolipoprotein-B kinetics. *Arteriosclerosis* 1:82, 1981.

309. JANUS ED, NICOLL AM, TURNER PR, MAGILL P, LEWIS B: Kinetic bases of the primary hyperlipidemias: Studies of apolipoprotein B turnover in genetically defined subjects. *Eur J Clin Invest* 10:161, 1980.

310. KISSEBAH AH, ALFARSI S, EVANS DJ: Low density lipoprotein metabolism in familial combined hyperlipidemia: Mechanisms of the multiple lipoprotein phenotype expression. *Arteriosclerosis* 4:614, 1984.

311. BEIL V, GRUNDY SM, CROUSE JR, ZECH L: Triglyceride and cholesterol metabolism in primary hypertriglyceridemia. *Arteriosclerosis* 2:44, 1982.

312. CHAIT A, FOSTER DM, ALBERS JJ, FAILOR A, BRUNZELL JD: Low density lipoprotein metabolism in familial combined hyperlipidemia and familial hypercholesterolemia: Kinetic analysis using an integrated model. *Metabolism* 35:697, 1986.

313. BRUNZELL JD, CHAIT A, ALBERS JJ, FOSTER DM, FAILOR A, BIERMAN EL: Metabolic consequences of genetic heterogeneity of lipoprotein composition (lipoprotein heterogeneity). *Am Heart J* 113A:583, 1987.

314. GOLDSTEIN JL, DANA SE, BRUNSCHEDE GY, BROWN MS: Genetic hetero-

geneity in familial hypercholesterolemia: Evidence for two different mutations affecting function of low-density lipoprotein receptor. *Proc Natl Acad Sci USA* 72:1092, 1975.

315. KESANIEMI YA, GRUNDY SM: Overproduction of low density lipoproteins associated with coronary heart disease. *Arteriosclerosis* 3:40, 1983.

316. TENG B, THOMPSON GR, SNIDERMAN AD, FORTE TM, KRAUSS RM, KWITEROVICH PO: Composition and distribution of low density lipoprotein fractions in hyperapobetalipoproteinemia, normolipidemia and familial hypercholesterolemia. *Proc Natl Acad Sci USA* 80:6662, 1983.

317. BRUNZELL JD, SCHROTT HG, MOTULSKY AG, BIERMAN EL: Myocardial infarction in the familial forms of hypertriglyceridemia. *Metabolism* 25:313, 1976.

318. BERG K: A new serum type system in man—The Lp system. *Acta Pathol Microbiol Scand* 59:369, 1963.

319. ALBERS JJ, ADOLPHSON JL, HAZZARD WR: Radioimmunoassay of human plasma Lp(a) lipoprotein. *J Lipid Res* 18:331, 1977.

320. GROENER JEM, KOSTNER GM: Lipid tranfer protein-catalyzed exchange of cholesteryl ester between high density protein and apo B-containing lipoproteins. *J Lipid Res* 28:1053, 1987.

321. RIDER AK, LEVY RI, FREDRICKSON DS: "Sinking prebeta" lipoprotein and the Lp antigen. *Circulation* [*Suppl*] 42:10, 1970.

322. SCHRIEWER H, ASSMANN G, SANDKAMP M: The relationship of lipoprotein(a) (Lp(a)) to risk factors of coronary disease. *J Clin Chem Clin Biochem* 22:591, 1984.

323. GUYTON JR, DAHLÉN GH, PATSCH W, KAUTZ JA, GOTTO AM JR: Relationship of plasma lipoprotein Lp(a) levels to race and to apolipoprotein B. *Arteriosclerosis* 5:644, 1985.

324. MURAI A, MIYAHARA T, FUJIMOTO N, MATSUDA M, KANEYAMA M: Lp(a) are a risk factor for coronary heart disease and cerebral infarction. *Atherosclerosis* 59:199, 1986.

325. DAHLÉN GH, GUYTON JR, ATTAR M, FARMER JA, KAUTZ JA, GOTTO AM JR: Association of levels of lipoprotein Lp(a), plasma lipids, and other lipoproteins with coronary artery disease documented by angiography. *Circulation* 74:758, 1986.

326. DAHLÉN G, BERG K, GILLNAS T, ERICSON C: Lp(a) lipoprotein prebeta$_1$-lipoprotein in Swedish middle-aged males and in patients with coronary heart disease. *Clin Genet* 7:334, 1974.

327. FRICK MH, DAHLÉN G, BERG K, VALLE M, HEKALI P: Serum lipids in angiographically assessed coronary atherosclerosis. *Chest* 73:62, 1978.

328. BERG K, DAHLÉN G, BORRESON AL: Lp(a) phenotypes, other lipoprotein parameters and a family history of coronary heart disease in middle-aged males. *Clin Genet* 16:347, 1979.

329. PAPADOPOULOS NM, BEDYNEK JL: Serum lipoprotein patterns in patients with coronary atherosclerosis. *Clin Chim Acta* 44:153, 1973.

330. INSULL W, NAJMI M, VLOEDMAN DA: Plasma pre-beta subfractions in diagnosis of coronary artery disease. *Circulation* [*Suppl*] 45:170, 1972.

331. BERG K, DAHLÉN G, FRICK MH: Lp(a) lipoprotein and pre-β_1 lipoprotein in patients with coronary disease. *Clin Genet* 6:230, 1974.

332. RENNINGER WG, WENDT G, NAWROCKI P, WIEGAND H: Beitrag zur Problematik des Lp-systems. *Humangenetik* 1:658, 1965.

333. DAHLÉN G, ERICSON C, FURBERG C, LUNDQVIST L, SVARDSUDD K: Studies on an extra pre-beta lipoprotein fraction. *Acta Med Scand* [*Suppl*] 531:1, 1972.

334. SCHULTZ JS, SHREFFLER DC, SING CF, HARVIE NR: The genetics of the Lp antigen—Its quantitation and distribution in a sample population. *Ann Hum Genet* 38:39, 1974.

335. HEIBERG A, BERG K: On the relationship between Lp(a) lipoprotein, "sinking prebeta lipoprotein" and inherited hyperbetalipoproteinemia. *Clin Genet* 5:144, 1974.

336. RHOADS GG, MORTON NE, GULBRANDSEN CL, KAGAN A: Sinking pre-beta lipoprotein and coronary heart disease in Japanese-American men in Hawaii. *Am J Epidemiol* 108:350, 1978.

337. KOSTNER GM, AVOGARO P, CAZZOLATO G, MARTH E, BITTOLO-BON G, QUNICI GB: Lipoprotein Lp(a) and the risk for myocardial infarction. *Atherosclerosis* 38:51, 1981.

338. RHOADS GC, DAHLÉN G, BERG K, MORTON NE, DANNENBERG AL: Lp(a) lipoprotein as a risk factor for myocardial infarction. *JAMA* 256:2450, 1986.

339. ARMSTRONG VW, CREMER P, EBERLE E, MANKE A, SCHULZE F, WIELAND H, KRENZER H, SEIDEL D: The association between Lp(a) concentrations and angiographically assessed coronary atherosclerosis: Dependence on LDL levels. *Atherosclerosis* 62:249, 1986.

340. UTERMANN G, WEBER W: Protein composition of Lp(a) lipoprotein from human plasma. *FEBS Lett* 154:357, 1983.

341. ENHOLM C, GAROFF J, RENKONEN O, SIMONS K: Protein and carbohydrate composition of Lp(a) lipoprotein from human plasma. *Biochemistry* 11:3229, 1972.

342. HARVIE NR, SCHULTZ JS: Studies on the heterogeneity of human serum Lp lipoproteins and on the occurrence of double Lp lipoprotein variants. *Biochem Genet* 9:235, 1973.

343. FLESS GM, ROLIH CA, SCANU AM: Heterogeneity of human plasma lipoprotein (a): Isolation and characterization of the lipoprotein subspecies and their apoproteins. *J Biol Chem* 259:11470, 1984.

344. NOTHIG-LASLO V, JURGENS G: How does limited trypsinization influence the surface structure and binding of calcium to lipoprotein (a): A spin-labeling study. *Arch Biochem Biophys* 215:329, 1982.

345. UTERMANN G, MENZEL H-J, KRAFT HG, DUBA HC, KEMMLER HG, SEUTZ C: Lp(a) glycoprotein phenotypes: Inheritance and relation to Lp(a) lipoprotein concentrations in plasma. *J Clin Invest* 80:458, 1987.

346. ARMSTRONG VW, WALLI AK, SEIDEL DJ: Isolation, characterization, and uptake in human fibroblasts of an apo (a)-free lipoprotein obtained on reduction of lipoprotein. *J Lipid Res* 26:1314, 1985.

347. FLESS GM, ZUM MALLEN M, SCANU AM: Physicochemical properties of apolipoprotein (a) and lipoprotein (a−) derived from the dissociation of human plasma lipoprotein (a). *J Biol Chem* 261:8712, 1986.

348. MCLEAN JW, TOMLINSON JE, KUANG W-J, EATON DL, CHEN EY, FLESS GM, SCANU AM, LAWN RM: cDNA sequence of human apolipoprotein (a) is homologous to plasminogen. *Nature* 330:132, 1987.

349. EATON DL, FLESS GM, KOHR WJ, MCLEAN JW, XU Q-T, MILLER CG, LAWN RM, SCANU AM: Partial amino acid sequence of apolipoprotein (a) shows that it is homologous to plasminogen. *Proc Natl Acad Sci USA* 84:3224, 1987.

350. BERSOT TP, INNERARITY TL, PITAS RE, RALL SC, WEISGRABER KH, MAHLEY RW: Fat feeding in humans induces lipoproteins of density less than 1.006 that are enriched in apolipoprotein (a) and that cause lipid accumulation in macrophases. *J Clin Invest* 77:622, 1986.

351. KREMPLER F, KOSTNER G, BOLZANO K, SANDHOFER F: Lipoprotein (a) is not a metabolic product of other lipoproteins containing apolipoprotein B. *Biochim Biophys Acta* 575:63, 1979.

352. BILHEIMER DW, HARDMAN DA, MALLOY MJ, KANE JP: Unpublished observations.

353. KREMPLER F, KOSTNER GM, BOLZANO K, SANHOFER F: Turnover of lipoprotein (a) in man. *J Clin Invest* 65:1483, 1980.

354. FLOREN C-H, ALBERS JJ, BIERMAN EL: Uptake of Lp(a) lipoprotein by cultured fibroblasts. *Biochem Biophys Res Commun* 102:636, 1981.

355. HAVEKES L, VERNEER BJ, BRUGMAN T, EMEIS J: Binding of Lp(a) to the low density lipoprotein receptor of human fibroblasts. *FEBS Lett* 132:169, 1981.

356. HARDMAN DA, FIELDING PE, KANE JP: Unpublished observations.

357. KREMPLER F, KOSTNER GM, ROSCHER A, HASLAUER F, BOLZANO K, SANDHOFER F: Studies on the role of specific cell surface receptors in the removal of lipoprotein (a) in man. *J Clin Invest* 71:1431, 1983.

358. MAARTMANN-MOE K, BERG K: Lp(a) lipoprotein enters cultured fibroblasts independently of the plasma membrane low density lipoprotein receptor. *Clin Genet* 20:352, 1981.

359. ISELIUS L, DAHLÉN G, DE FAIRE U, LUNDMAN T: Complex segregation analysis of the Lp(a)/pre-lipoprotein trait. *Clin Genet* 20:147, 1981.

360. SCHULTZ JS, SHREFFLER DC, SING CF, HARVIE NR: The genetics of the Lp antigen I: Its quantitation and distribution in a sample population. *Ann Hum Genet* 38:39, 1974.

361. SING CF, SCHULTZ JS, SHREFFLER DC: The genetics of the Lp antigen II: A family study and proposed models of genetic control. *Ann Hum Genet* 38:47, 1974.

362. ALBERS JJ, WAHL P, HAZZARD WR: Quantitative genetic studies of the human plasma Lp(a) lipoprotein. *Biochem Genet* 11:475, 1974.

363. HEWITT D, MILNER J, OWEN ARG, BRECKENRIDGE WC, MACGUIRE GF, JONES GJL, LITTLE JA: The inheritance of sinking-pre-beta lipoprotein and its relation to the Lp(a) antigen. *Clin Genet* 21:301, 1982.

364. HASSTEDT SJ, WILSON DE, EDWARDS CQ, CANNON WN, CARMELLI D, WILLIAMS RD: The genetics of quantitative plasma Lp(a): Analysis of a large pedigree. *Am J Med Genet* 16:179, 1983.

365. LUC G, CHAPMAN MJ, DE GENNES J-L, TURPIN G: A study of the structural heterogeneity of low-density lipoproteins in two patients homozygous for familial hypercholesterolaemia, one of phenotype E2/2. *Eur J Clin Invest* 16:329, 1986.

366. VESSBY B, KOSTNER G, LITHELL H, THOMIS J: Diverging effects of cholestyramine on apolipoprotein B and lipoprotein Lp(a): A dose-response study of the effects of cholestyramine in hypercholesterolemia. *Atherosclerosis* 44:61, 1982.

367. GURAKAR A, HOEG JM, KOSTNER G, PAPADOPOULOS NM, BREWER HB JR: Levels of lipoprotein Lp(a) decline with neomycin and niacin treatment. *Atherosclerosis* 57:293, 1985.

368. ROSS RS, GREGG RE, LAW SW, MONGE JC, GRANT SM, HIGUCHI K, TRICHE TJ, JEFFERSON J, BREUER HB JR: Homozygous hypobetalipoproteinemia: A disease distinct from abetalipoproteinemia at the molecular level. *J Clin Invest* 81:590, 1988.

CHAPTER **45**

FAMILIAL LIPOPROTEIN LIPASE DEFICIENCY AND OTHER CAUSES OF THE CHYLOMICRONEMIA SYNDROME

JOHN D. BRUNZELL

1. *This chapter discusses three inherited disorders in which chylomicrons accumulate in plasma: familial lipoprotein lipase deficiency, familial apolipoprotein C-II deficiency, and familial inhibitor to lipoprotein lipase. Chylomicronemia can also occur in individuals with common familial forms of hypertriglyceridemia who also have an acquired cause of hypertriglyceridemia such as diabetes mellitus, estrogen or antihypertensive drug therapy, or alcohol use.*
2. *Familial lipoprotein lipase deficiency is a rare autosomal recessive disorder characterized by a massive accumulation of chylomicrons in plasma and a corresponding increase of plasma triglyceride concentration. The concentration of very low density lipoprotein (VLDL) is fairly normal. The disease is usually detected in childhood on the basis of repeated episodes of abdominal pain, recurrent attacks of pancreatitis, eruptive cutaneous xanthomatosis, and hepatosplenomegaly. The severity of symptoms is proportional to the degree of chylomicronemia, which in turn is dependent on dietary fat intake. The disorder is heterogeneous and caused by a deficiency of lipoprotein lipase, a lipolytic enzyme that is present on vascular endothelial cells of extrahepatic tissues. This enzyme is normally responsible for hydrolysis and removal of chylomicron and VLDL triglycerides. The enzyme is released into the blood by heparin and can be assayed in postheparin plasma or directly in biopsies of adipose tissue. Diagnosis is based on low or absent enzyme activity in an assay system that excludes other lipolytic enzymes and contains normal plasma or apoprotein C-II, a necessary cofactor of the enzyme. Heterozygotes exhibit a 50 percent decrease of lipoprotein lipase in postheparin plasma but have normal or only slightly elevated plasma lipid levels. The disorder is not associated with atherosclerotic vascular disease, but recurrent pancreatitis may threaten the patient's life. Restriction of dietary fat to 20 g/day or less is usually sufficient to reduce plasma triglyceride levels and keep the patient free of symptoms. Available lipid-lowering drugs are not effective.*
3. *Familial apolipoprotein C-II deficiency is a rare autosomal recessive disorder in which the clearance of chylomicrons from the blood is greatly impaired, and triglyceride levels accumulate in plasma. VLDL may also be elevated. The disorder is diagnosed in children or adults on the basis of recurrent attacks of pancreatitis or by milky fasting plasma detected by chance. The underlying biochemical defect is a deficiency of apolipoprotein C-II, a cofactor for lipoprotein lipase. Absence of this peptide creates a functional enzyme deficiency with accumulation of the substrate lipoproteins in the blood. The diagnosis is based on assay of lipoprotein lipase activity in postheparin plasma and on gel electrophoresis of VLDL apolipoproteins. Transfusion of normal plasma into the patient is followed by a dramatic fall of plasma triglyceride level. Most heterozygotes have a 50 percent reduction in apo C-II levels. Treatment involves use of a moderately fat restricted diet throughout life. In case of severe pancreatitis, transfusion of normal plasma may be helpful.*
4. *Familial lipoprotein lipase inhibitor has been described as an autosomal dominant disorder in one family. Chylomicrons and VLDL accumulate owing to defective lipoprotein lipase-mediated triglyceride hydrolysis. Pancreatitis and eruptive xanthomatosis are noted during adolescence. The diagnosis is dependent on demonstrating an inhibitor to lipoprotein lipase in plasma. Treatment requires moderate dietary fat restriction to prevent pancreatitis.*
5. *Chylomicronemia is seen in other hypertriglyceridemic states in the absence of abnormalities in the lipoprotein lipase system. This hypertriglyceridemia is clinically important because plasma triglyceride levels above 2000 mg/dl predispose to pancreatitis. The simultaneous occurrence of a common familial form and a common acquired cause for hypertriglyceridemia such as diabetes mellitus, certain drug therapy, or alcohol use can lead to this degree of hypertriglyceridemia. Treatment should be directed at both the familial and the acquired disorder. Other familial causes of chylomicronemia with normal lipoprotein lipase are known but poorly characterized.*

Historical Aspects

Milky (lipemic) plasma was noted in 1799,[1] and eruptive xanthomas were described as early as 1851.[2] The eruptive xanthomas were called *xanthomata diabeticorum* owing to their occurrence in diabetic patients[3] with the presence of lipemic plasma. The lipemic serum which occasionally occurred in the untreated diabetic patient cleared with successful therapy for the hyperglycemia.[4] Now it is realized that the untreated diabetic state is accompanied by lipemic plasma with signs and symptoms of the chylomicronemia syndrome only when an independent familial form of hypertriglyceridemia also is present.[5]

In 1921 patients were noted who had eruptive xanthomata and did not have diabetes,[6] and in 1932 the first patient with a familial form of chylomicronemia was described.[7] He was a young boy with extensive eruptive xanthomas, hepatosplenomegaly, and milky plasma. The lipemia and all symptoms cleared after switching to a fat-free diet. The familial nature of the disorder was suggested since the parents were cousins. These patients were included in a group with what was then entitled *idiopathic familial lipemia,* [8,9] later called *essential hyperlipemia,*[10] *fat-induced lipemia,*[11] and finally *type I hyperlipo-*

Nonstandard abbreviations used in this chapter are: apo = apolipoprotein; HDL = high density lipoprotein; HL = hepatic triglyceride lipase; LPL = lipoprotein lipase; VLDL = very low density lipoprotein.

proteinemia.[12] In 1960 lipoprotein lipase deficiency[13] was noted as a cause of familial chylomicronemia in children with this syndrome, and in 1978 the case of a patient with functional deficiency of apolipoprotein C-II (apo C-II), which is required for activation of lipoprotein lipase, was reported, pointing to apo C-II deficiency being another cause of familial chylomicronemia.[14]

The Structure and Function of Lipoprotein Lipase and Apo C-II

Lipoprotein lipase (LPL) is a glycoprotein located on the luminal surface of capillary endothelial cells. The active enzyme is a noncovalent homodimer.[15] The enzyme has an apparent monomeric molecular weight of 60,000 on sodium dodecyl sulfate polyacrylamide gel electrophoresis (SDS PAGE) and between 41,700[16] and 48,400[15] by sedimentation equilibrium ultracentrifugation. A complementary DNA for human lipoprotein lipase that codes for a mature protein of 448 amino acids with a molecular weight of 50,394 has been cloned and sequenced.[17] A cDNA for bovine mammary LPL predicts a protein of 450 amino acids and a molecular weight of 50,548.[18] Since bovine LPL is about 8 percent carbohydrate,[15] the molecular weight of the glycosylated monomeric subunit would be approximately 54,500.

Lipoprotein lipase has putative binding sites for heparin, lipid, and apo C-II in addition to a separate catalytic site for triglyceride hydrolysis. LPL binds to heparan sulfate[19,20] on the surface of endothelial cells via the heparin binding site (Fig. 45-1), which allows the LPL to be extended into the plasma.[21] By administration of intravenous heparin, LPL can be displaced from the endothelial surface into plasma where enzyme activity can be measured.

Lipoprotein lipase is a member of a family of related enzymes which are serine esterases. A high degree of homology exists between the catalytic site of LPL, and of hepatic lipase, pancreatic lipase, lingual lipase, and lecithin:cholesterol acyltransferase.[17,22] Triglyceride and monoglyceride are preferred substrates for LPL, while lecithin is hydrolyzed at a slower rate. LPL preferentially hydrolyzes the 1- and 3-ester bonds in triglyceride-generating 2-monoglyceride, which is converted to 1-monoglyceride by isomerization for further hydrolysis.

Fig. 45-1 A schematic model of the action of lipoprotein lipase at the capillary endothelium. Heparan sulfate proteoglycans are intercalated onto the surface of the endothelial cell. LPL (small spheres) bound to heparan sulfate is extended into the lumen where chylomicrons and VLDL can be bound. (*Modified from Olivecrona and Bengtsson-Olivecrona.*[46] *Used by permission.*)

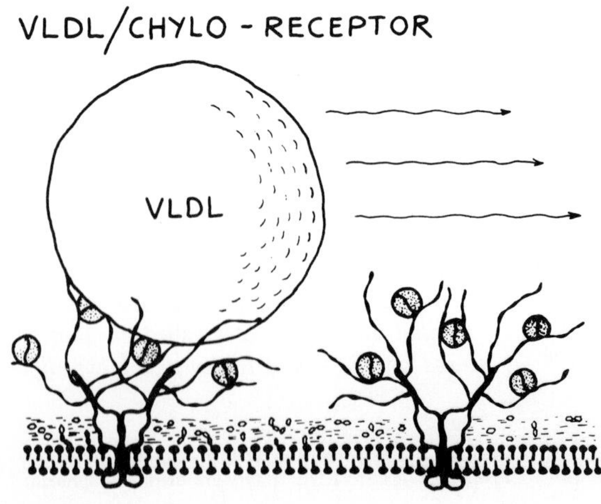

The specific activity of lipoprotein lipase from various tissues depends on the assay conditions.[22] Optimized assays reveal similar specific activities of purifed enzyme ranging from rat adipose tissue: 15,000 μmol/h per milligram[24]; bovine milk: 21,000 to 42,000[15,25,26]; guinea pig milk: 34,200[27]; to human postheparin plasma: 50,000.[28] Studies of the molecular size of LPL in various tissues of the guinea pig suggest that a similar or identical enzyme is present in adipose tissue, heart, skeletal muscle, lung, and lactating mammary gland.[29] The active enzyme bound to heparan sulfate on the capillary endothelium is predominantly in the dimeric form. The dimeric enzyme is less susceptible to degradation than the monomeric enzyme.[30] Apparently the active monomeric enzyme is in equilibrium with the dimeric form, with heparin[31] and heparan sulfate helping to maintain the enzyme as a dimer. The monomeric enzyme loses activity irreversibly to an inactive monomeric enzyme that is ultimately degraded by the liver.[32,33] LPL is secreted from the adipocyte and transported[34] in an unknown fashion to heparan sulfate on the luminal surface of the capillary endothelium.[32] At this site it has several functions in the processing of triglyceride-rich lipoproteins. The enzyme is also synthesized in a number of other cells including cardiac and skeletal muscle cells, monocyte-derived macrophages, and Kupffer cells.

The details of lipoprotein lipase synthesis and secretion (Fig. 45-2) have been demonstrated in studies of isolated and cultured adipocytes[35–37] and cultured heart cells.[38] An inactive proenzyme is synthesized in the endoplasmic reticulum and is transported to the Golgi apparatus. A multiple-step glycosylation process is associated with activation of the enzyme. Secretory vesicles and the microtubular system are involved in the secretion of the active enzyme from the cell, a process which is enhanced by heparin in cultured cell systems. The active enzyme may also be degraded by lysosomes intracellularly. An inactive form of the enzyme, presumably one which has not undergone all steps of glycosylation, can also be secreted from the cell. Immunoreactive enzyme can be demonstrated in adipocytes, connective tissue cells, and endothelial cells of capillaries and larger vessels.[39]

The synthesis, processing, and secretion of LPL from various cell types seems to be under hormonal control.[35,37] In rats, feeding leads to a marked increase in LPL activity in adipose tissue and to a reciprocal decrease in activity in heart and skeletal muscle. Although addition of insulin to rat adipose tissue in vitro is associated with an increase in LPL activity,[35,37] the role of insulin as a primary regulator of LPL synthesis and secretion is not clear. In humans, adipose tissue LPL activity does not vary much when meals of normal composition are consumed,[40] but when high carbohydrate meals are ingested, an increase in LPL activity is seen after 3 to 6 h. A similar increase is seen when insulin and glucose are given intravenously to humans.[41–43] However, it has been difficult to demonstrate a primary regulatory role of insulin for adipose tissue LPL in humans.[44] At a minimum, insulin may be permissive for the synthesis of LPL in many tissues, as might thyroxine and glucocorticoid hormones.[35] An alternative method of feedback regulation of adipose and muscle LPL might be via the β-adrenegic system, which is activated with feeding. β-Adrenegic stimulation decreases LPL activity in adipose tissue[35,45] and increases LPL in muscle cells in culture.[38]

LPL activity increases markedly in the lactating breast, pre-

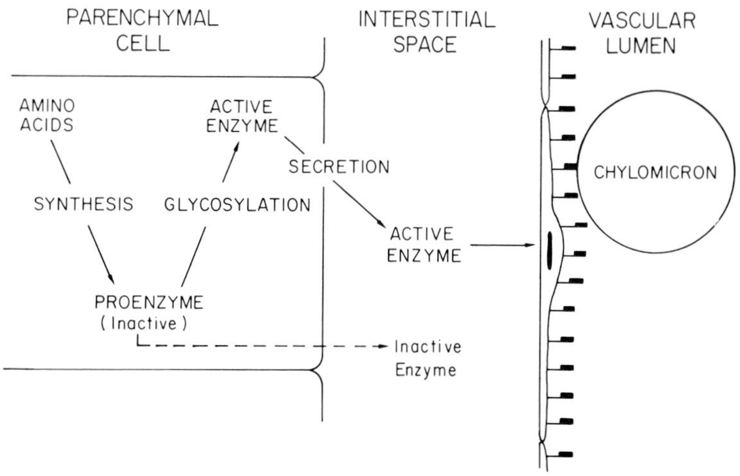

PARENCHYMAL CELL
INTERSTITIAL SPACE
VASCULAR LUMEN
AMINO ACIDS
ACTIVE ENZYME
SECRETION
SYNTHESIS
GLYCOSYLATION
ACTIVE ENZYME
CHYLOMICRON
PROENZYME (Inactive)
Inactive Enzyme

Fig. 45-2 Posttranslational processing and extracellular transit of LPL. LPL is synthesized in parenchymal cells in inactive form. Activation of the enzyme occurs in the Golgi apparatus. The active enzyme is released from the cell and bound to the endothelial cell surface. Inactive enzyme can also be released from the cell. *(From Garfinkel and Schotz.[37] Used by permission.)*

sumably to allow for hydrolysis of plasma lipoprotein triglyceride for the formation of milk,[46,47] and seems to be regulated by prolactin levels.[47] In response to endotoxin, macrophages secrete a protein, termed *cachectin,* or *tumor necrosis factor,* which decreases LPL synthesis in adipose tissue.[48,49] The role this system has in regulating adipose tissue mass in animals and humans is not well understood.

Apolipoprotein C-II is synthesized in the liver and secreted into plasma. It binds to lipids via amphipathic helices on the amino terminal end of the protein.[50] Apo C-II recycles between HDL and the triglyceride-rich lipoproteins, chylomicrons, and VLDL.[51] The carboxyterminal portion of apo C-II binds to a specific site on LPL leading to enzyme activation. Apo C-II is present in excess in plasma; it has been estimated that only 10 percent of normal values are needed for maximal activity.[52] Apo C-III has been suggested to be an inhibitor of activation of LPL by apo C-II; however, a marked excess of apo C-III above physiological levels would be required.[53]

LPL bound to the endothelial cell, in conjunction with apo C-II contained in chylomicrons and very low density lipoproteins, is a major focal point in the processing of lipoproteins. The hydrolysis of triglycerides in the core of these lipoproteins provides free fatty acids to be utilized as energy by muscle and other tissues or to be stored in adipose tissue. The enzyme seems to play a gatekeeper role for energy storage,[54] since fat cell size is proportional to enzyme activity in adipose tissue.[40,55] With reduction of body fat content and fat cell size by dieting, adipose tissue LPL measured after an overnight fast is increased in males[56] but not in females.[55] However, in weight-reduced obese women, adipose tissue LPL is increased in the fed state.[57,58] This paradoxical increase in LPL activity in the reduced obese state has been suggested to be a feedback mechanism for maintenance of body weight or fat cell size.[56]

The role of LPL in clearing plasma triglyceride can be demonstrated in both the fasted and fed state. The fractional clearance of triglyceride-rich lipoproteins from plasma is correlated with adipose tissue[59,60,61] and postheparin plasma LPL activity[60] in the fasting state. The decrease in plasma triglyceride levels following high carbohydrate meals is correlated with changes in adipose tissue LPL activity in this carbohydrate fed state[44,61] when one would expect adipose tissue to predominate. The capacity for LPL to hydrolyze triglyceride seems limited, since triglyceride-rich lipoprotein removal is a kinetically saturable process.[62]

The lipoprotein core remnants remaining after hydrolysis of the triglyceride in chylomicrons and VLDL are further processed in the liver (see Chap. 44a). The chylomicron remnant is completely degraded, while some of the very low density lipoprotein remnant is processed to form low density lipoproteins. A small portion of the core triglyceride from chylomicrons and VLDL can be transferred to the high density lipoproteins (HDL). However, more important contributors to the HDL are the surface remnants of the triglyceride-rich lipoproteins that occur as a result of hydrolysis of core triglycerides. A relationship between LPL activity and HDL cholesterol has been noted in many clinical situations by Nikkilä and his coworkers.[63] The transfer of the lipoprotein surface containing unesterified cholesterol and phospholipid prolongs the residence time of these apolipoprotein A-I- and A-II-containing particles accentuating the increase in HDL cholesterol[59] (Fig. 45-3). Thus, LPL functions at an important junction in lipoprotein metabolism, regulating the distribution of energy in the form of free fatty acids and the distribution of cholesterol to LDL and HDL.

Normal Genes for LPL and Apo C-II

The locus for human LPL has been mapped to chromosome 8.[64] Two messenger RNAs have been identified in human adipose tissue of about 3350 and 3750 nucleotides[17] that arise from alternative sites of 3′ terminal polyadenylation. The mRNA has a short 5′ untranslated region and a long 3′ untranslated region. The message predicts a 475-residue protein of which the amino terminal 27 amino acid prepeptide is re-

Fig. 45-3 Interrelations among adipose tissue LPL activity, VLDL catabolism (apo B fractional catabolic rate), and plasma HDL apoprotein catabolism in humans. The VLDL apo B fractional catabolic rate (fcr) was determined by measurement of disappearance from plasma of autologous radiolabeled apo B in VLDL. HDL cholesterol and A-II residence times (1/fcr) were determined in a similar fashion. *(From Brunzell et al.[96] Used by permission.)*

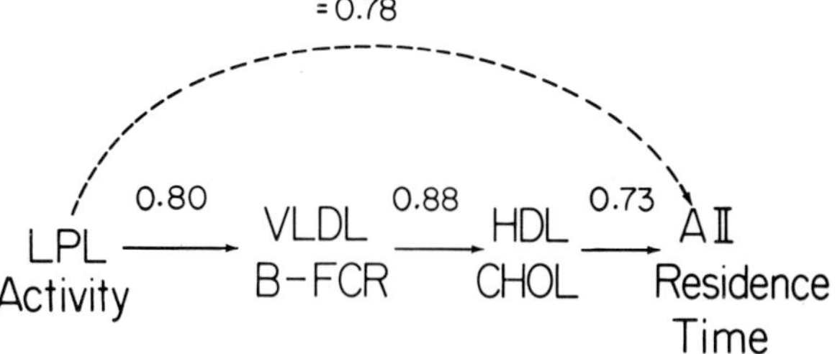

moved to form the mature LPL of 448 residues. The predicted translated molecular weight for the unglycosylated protein is 50,394. The message has been found in human adipose tissue, and also in adrenal, kidney, and intestinal, but not the liver tissue. The mRNA for LPL in humans is highly homologous with that of the mouse, rat, and cow.[17,18] It also has 46 percent homology with the mRNA for hepatic triglyceride lipase (HL). This homology between LPL and HL might represent similar catalytic, heparin, and lipid binding sites, while the apo C-II binding site of LPL might represent an area of difference. The cDNA isolated from lactating bovine mammary gland[18] predicts an enzyme with 450 residues and an unglycosylated molecular weight of 50,548, which is slightly larger than human LPL.

In studies of normal twins, a highly significant intrapair resemblance was noted for adipose tissue LPL activity in monozygotic male twins before and during short-term overfeeding.[65] In a comparison between monozygotic and dizygotic risk male twins, a high pairwise correlation for postheparin plasma hepatic lipase was found for monozygotic twins, but the intrapair correlation for postheparin plasma LPL in monozygotic twins was low.[66] The high degree of heritability for adipose tissue LPL but not postheparin LPL may reflect the multiple tissue sites which contribute to postheparin plasma LPL, several of which may be under opposite physiological regulation.[67,68]

Apolipoprotein C-II is one of a family of apolipoproteins in which the gene has four exons and three introns.[69–71] The gene for apo C-II is on chromosome 19[72] and is closely linked to the genes for apo E and apo C-I. The gene for the LDL receptor is also on chromosome 19, but it is not linked to the genes for these apolipoproteins. The similarity of gene structure for apo A-I, apo C-III, and apo A-IV, which are present on chromosome 11, with the apolipoprotein genes on chromosome 19 suggests a common ancestry for these apolipoproteins. The entire gene for apo C-II spans 3320 nucleotides,[69–71] while the mRNA deduced from complementary DNA is 494 nucleotides in length. Messenger RNA for apo C-II is found in the liver and intestine in humans and nonhuman primates and is also found in Hep-G2 cells, a liver cell line. Preproapo C-II contains 101 amino acids, and undergoes intracellular removal of 22 amino acids, leaving the remaining 79 amino acid proapo C-II. The proapo C-II undergoes further posttranslational processing, deglycosylation, and further proteolysis to remove six amino acids to become the mature apo C-II of 73 amino acids.[73] The apo C-II is present on HDL and is transferred to nascent chylomicrons and VLDL to act as an activator for lipoprotein lipase, as noted above. Carboxy terminal amino acids 55 to 73 contain the activator site, while the amino terminal two-thirds of the apolipoprotein contains the lipoprotein binding site(s), but both ends are needed for full activity.

Clinical Manifestations of the Chylomicronemia Syndrome

Chylomicronemia is defined as the presence in plasma of large macromolecular lipoprotein complexes that originate from dietary fat. Chylomicrons appear in the circulation shortly after the ingestion of meals containing fat by normal individuals. However, these particles are cleared rapidly from plasma and are not normally present after an overnight fast. In individuals with moderate endogenous hypertriglyceridemia, a postprandial state of 10 to 12 h is also long enough to clear chylomicrons from plasma. Moderately hypertriglyceridemic individuals without chylomicrons in the fasting state have been arbitrarily divided into subgroups type IIB and type IV hyperlipoproteinemia, depending on the presence or absence of elevated levels of low density lipoprotein cholesterol.[74] Individuals with dysbetalipoproteinemia, or type III hyperlipoproteinemia (see Chap. 47), also may have no chylomicrons in their plasma in the postabsorptive state; however, some of these individuals do have detectable chylomicrons 10 to 12 h after their last meal. Subjects with fasting chylomicronemia have been arbitrarily divided into subgroups (types I and V hyperlipoproteinemia), depending on the level of very low density lipoproteins[74]; however, this distinction appears to have had little clinical or genetic utility. A more helpful clinical measure is the absolute level of plasma triglyceride.

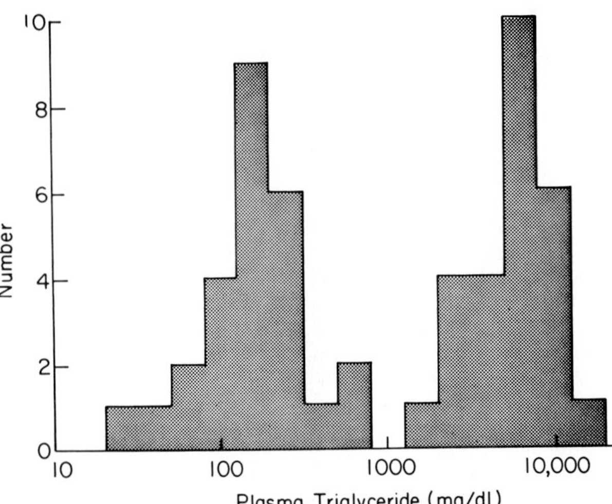

Fig. 45-4 Frequency distribution of plasma triglyceride levels in patients with possible pancreatitis at the University of Washington Hospital. Note bimodal distribution of triglyceride levels; highest triglyceride level in lower mode was 759 mg/dl; lowest in higher mode was 1925 mg/dl. *(From Brunzell and Bierman.[75] Used by permission.)*

Although fasting chylomicronemia often occurs at plasma triglyceride levels between 500 and 2000 mg/dl, the symptoms and signs associated with the chylomicronemia syndrome almost always occur at higher triglyceride levels (Fig. 45-4). We define the chylomicronemia syndrome as the presence of one or more of a set of symptoms or signs occurring in a patient with a plasma triglyceride level of 2000 mg/dl or higher. For unexplained reasons, some individuals with massive hypertriglyceridemia, up to triglyceride levels of 29,000 mg/dl, have no symptoms or signs at all. More commonly, eruptive xanthomata, lipemia retinalis, and pancreatitis occur together (Table 45-1).

For many years the clinical sequelae of chylomicronemia have been known to occur in individuals with classic lipoprotein lipase deficiency.[12] The association of abdominal pain and pancreatitis with hypertriglyceridemia in other situations also has long been appreciated; however, it was once thought that the pancreatitis caused the hypertriglyceridemia. The opposite now appears to be the case.[76–78] Marked hypertriglyceridemia has been reported in from 12 to 22 percent of patients admitted to a hospital for acute pancreatitis.[77–79] The pancreatitis is usually of acute onset and often is recurrent, occasionally leading to total pancreatic necrosis and death. Mild fat malabsorption can occur, but apparently pancreatic calcification does

Table 45-1 Manifestations of Chylomicronemia Syndrome

Manifestation	*Prevalence,* %
Recent memory loss	85
Abdominal pain and/or pancreatitis (documented pancreatitis, 28%)	63
Objective dyspnea	46
Eruptive xanthomata	40
Flushing with alcohol	25
Lipemia retinalis	23

not. The abdominal pain of the chylomicronemia syndrome is usually midepigastric and migrates through to the back, but it can also be present in the right or left upper abdominal quadrants or even the mid-anterior chest. The pain can range across a wide spectrum, from a mild, bothersome ache to one that causes severe incapacitation. It has been difficult to determine if the pain reported in the chylomicronemia syndrome always reflects classic pancreatitis since both serum and urinary amylase levels are frequently normal. Indeed, amylase levels have been found to be normal in some patients with pancreatitis documented at laparotomy.[76,77,80] However, many patients with *severe* pancreatitis due to the chylomicronemia syndrome will have elevated serum or urine amylase levels. Normal amylase levels in the presence of marked hypertriglyceridemia might be due to the interference of the plasma lipids with the assay[81] or due to an inhibitor of the assay present in the plasma and urine.[82,83] The recognition and treatment of the abdominal pain as part of the chylomicronemia syndrome in a patient with marked hypertriglyceridemia leads to reduced morbidity and mortality if plasma triglyceride levels are maintained at levels somewhat lower than 2000 mg/dl.[76] The recognition of the etiology of the marked hypertriglyceridemia and the lack of recurrent pain with maintenance of low triglyceride levels has led to the conclusion that the pain is due to the hyperchylomicronemia and that pancreatitis does not cause significant hypertriglyceridemia. Hepatomegaly is commonly found with chronic chylomicronemia[12] as well as with many milder forms of hypertriglyceridemia. Splenomegaly is less commonly present, but the spleen can be rock hard. The enlarged spleen can return to normal size within 1 week of lowering of triglyceride levels in patients with lipoprotein lipase deficiency who are placed on a very low fat diet.

Eruptive xanthomas are deposits of lipid in the skin (Fig. 45-5), which result from the phagocytosis of chylomicrons by macrophages in the skin.[84] These lesions represent recent, chronic chylomicronemia. The xanthomas are localized over the buttocks, knees, and extensor surfaces of the arms, and they may become generalized. They are small, yellow, papular, cutaneous lesions. As a single lesion, they may be several millimeters in diameter; when they coalesce they form plaques but retain their individual papular component. These lesions are usually not tender unless they occur at a site susceptible to repeated trauma. The xanthomas initially are composed of chylomicrons leading to triglyceride enrichment of lipid-laden foam cells. With lowering of plasma triglyceride levels, the xanthomas clear over the course of weeks to several months. Recurrent or persistent eruptive xanthomas are indications of inadequate triglyceride-lowering therapy. As they regress, the triglyceride is mobilized, leaving transient, erythematous lesions that are rich in cholesteryl ester.[84]

With triglyceride levels above 4000 mg/dl, "lipemia retinalis" can be detected by examination of the fundus of the eye. The retinal arterioles and venules, and often the fundus itself, develop a pale pink color. This change is due to the light scattering of the large chylomicrons and is reversible. Vision is not affected, and there appear to be no clinical sequelae of lipemia retinalis. Neuropsychiatric findings, including dementia, depression, and memory loss, also have been reported with chylomicronemia.[85]

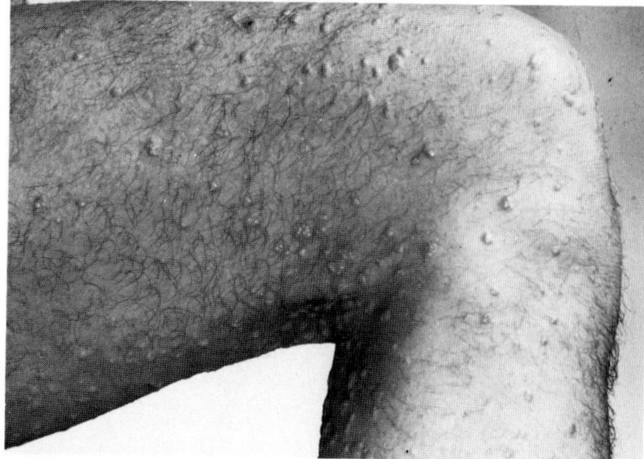

Fig. 45-5 Eruptive xanthomas of the skin in patient with chronic chylomicronemia. *(From Brunzell and Bierman.[75] Used by permission.)*

Both objective and subjective dyspnea have been noted in patients with chylomicronemia,[16] and symptoms resolve with lowering of triglyceride levels. The observed relationship between hyperlipidemia and angina led to the hypothesis that hypertriglyceridemia might impair both oxygen uptake from the lungs and oxygen delivery to tissues.[86] Subsequent studies on oxygenation in hyperlipemia focused on the finding of arterial hypoxemia[87] and an increased affinity of hemoglobin for oxygen associated with normal 2,3-diphosphoglycerate (DPG) levels.[88] It now appears that these abnormalities were artifactual, related to the interference by lipemic plasma with the blood O_2 electrode[89] and with the measurement of hemoglobin levels.[90] Thus, the explanation for the dyspnea of the chylomicronemia remains unknown. Other laboratory tests can also be misleading in the presence of marked hypertriglyceridemia. Chylomicrons may interfere directly with measurement of amylase and hemoglobin levels, as noted earlier. Bilirubin levels also are artifactually elevated in chylomicronemic plasma; this may be a partial explanation for the hyperbilirubinemia seen in Zieve syndrome. Chylomicrons also replace water volume which leads to artifactual decreases in plasma components by dilution. For example, serum sodium levels are decreased from 2 to 4 meq for each 1000 mg/dl of plasma triglyceride.[91,92] Thus, a variety of clinical and biochemical findings have been reported with the chylomicronemia syndrome, although some are artifacts. The spectrum of acute and chronic symptoms and signs may be quite puzzling.

Several methods have been described for the detection of chylomicrons in plasma in the postabsorptive state. The simplest test is the development of a layer of chylomicrons at the top of a tube of plasma placed overnight at 4°C in a refrigerator. During refrigeration chylomicrons usually will float to the top of the sample, where they can be seen as a discrete milky layer separate from the remaining plasma. Chylomicrons remain at the origin during electrophoresis of plasma on paper or agarose, while other lipoproteins migrate away from the site

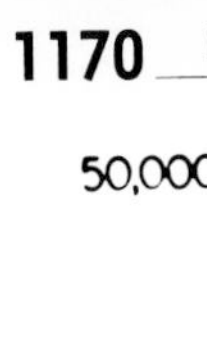

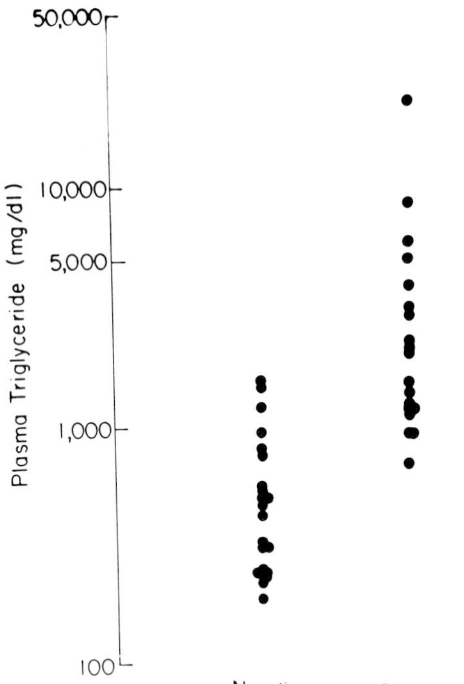

Fig. 45-6 Presence or absence of chylomicrons in fasting plasma as a function of plasma triblyceride concentration. *(From Brunzell and Bierman.[75] Used by permission.)*

of application of plasma. Incubation of plasma in tubes containing 3 percent polyvinylpyrrolidone will effectively separate chylomicrons of dietary origin from other lipoproteins.[93] The refrigeration test, although simplest, is often falsely negative in the presence of massive hypertriglyceridemia. Agarose electrophoresis, which can produce variable results, also can be falsely negative.

For clinical purposes, two practical approaches for the detection and evaluation of chylomicronemia can be used. First, the presence of chylomicrons in plasma after an overnight fast is usually related to the absolute plasma triglyceride level (Fig. 45-6). Fasting plasma with triglyceride levels below 1000 mg/dl usually does not contain chylomicrons, whereas plasma with triglyceride concentrations above 1500 mg/dl almost always does contain them. Second, since the large fat particles scatter light and cause turbidity *(lactescence,* or *lipemia),* visual inspection of serum or plasma can often lead to a fairly accurate estimation of plasma triglyceride levels in the presence of chylomicrons. Plasma with the appearance of 4 percent whole milk will have a triglyceride level about equal to that of whole milk, i.e., 4000 mg/dl; 2 percent milk, about 2500 mg/dl; 1 percent milk, about 1500 mg/dl; and nonfat skim milk, about 1000 mg/dl.

LIPOPROTEIN LIPASE DEFICIENCY

History

The clinical syndrome associated with lactescent plasma in childhood was first described in 1932 by Bürger and Grütz in a young male offspring of a consanguineous marriage.[7] In 1960 Havel and Gordon[13] demonstrated defective clearance of triglyceride-rich lipoproteins in this disorder related to diminished lipolytic activity in plasma after intravenous heparin. Harlan et al.[94] found decreased LPL activity in adipose tissue to be associated with the decrease in postheparin plasma lipolytic activity in two patients. In 1974 Krauss et al.[95] separated the postheparin plasma activities into LPL and hepatic lipase and noticed very low levels of LPL with normal levels of hepatic lipase in this disease. Recently, many of these patients have been noted to have a defective enzyme protein.[96]

Clinical Phenotype

Familial LPL deficiency is a rare disease,[97] estimated to occur less frequently than once per million population.[98] This estimate is based on the number of patients and families described, assuming that early, complete detection of patients with this defect is possible. The disease is usually manifested in childhood. Of 43 cases in one review,[99] 13 were detected in the first year of life, another 22 before the age of 10, and eight at a later age. Although the age of detection may be related to the ability of the patient to avoid dietary fat intake,[98] it is possible that patients with deficiency of LPL activity in all tissues become symptomatic earlier in life than those with variant forms of LPL deficiency (see "Variants" below). Some adult patients present during pregnancy or following a period of dietary excess. The disease has been described among whites, blacks, and Asians, and it affects both sexes equally.[99]

The disease often presents in infancy with colicky pain, failure to thrive, and the other symptoms and signs of the chylomicronemia syndrome. At all ages the most common clinical manifestation is episodic abdominal pain. The pain may be epigastric with radiation to the back or may be diffuse with the appearance of an emergent acute abdomen. This has often led to surgery where either no abnormality or pancreatitis was noted. Young patients learn to prevent the abdominal pain by avoiding food high in fat content. It is unusual for these patients to develop diabetes, steatorrhea, or pancreatic calcification, even after recurrent bouts of acute pancreatitis. Hepatomegaly is very common in LPL deficiency, and splenomegaly is often present during periods when plasma triglyceride levels are markedly increased. The organomegaly occurs as a result of triglyceride uptake by macrophages, which become foam cells and may rapidly regress with a decrease in dietary fat intake.

About half of the patients with LPL deficiency have been noted to have eruptive xanthomas of the skin. These are the only xanthomas that occur in LPL deficiency. They are not specific for this disorder but reflect the presence, or recent presence, of chylomicronemia. These xanthomas can appear rapidly with plasma triglyceride levels over 2000 mg/dl, and can clear over several weeks after plasma triglyceride levels have been lowered.

Patients with LPL deficiency do not seem to be predisposed to atherosclerosis. In the past many patients died at an early age of pancreatitis. With the recognition of the disease, the avoidance of unnecessary abdominal surgery, and the maintenance of a low fat diet, these patients can lead a fairly normal life.

Mutant Gene and Genetics

The nature of the lesion at the level of the gene has not been examined in a patient with lipoprotein lipase deficiency. Since many patients appear to synthesize immunoreactive LPL, which has no catalytic activity,[96] it would be expected that some of these patients might have minor gene nucleotide changes. With the recent development of cDNA probes for LPL, descriptions of specific gene defects are soon expected.

Consanguinity is common in LPL deficiency,[96–98] suggesting that the abnormal allelles for the defective LPL activity are very rare. Multiple affected siblings, the lack of parent-to-child transmission, and equal involvement of both sexes are observations consistent with an autosomal recessive pattern of inheritance. The obligate heterozygote parents and other family members have been noted to have normal LPL activity[100,101] or decreased LPL activity[102,103] in postheparin plasma. With the development of an enzyme-linked immunosorbent assay (ELISA) to measure LPL immunoreactivity in plasma, it has been possible to demonstrate that the postheparin plasma activity and mass in heterozygotes is intermediate between that of normal controls and LPL-deficient probands.[104] Mild hyperlipidemia and variable lipid phenotype (similar to familial combined hyperlipidemia) have been observed in parents and relatives in some families of probands with LPL deficiency,[96,100–102,105] while the families of other probands are normolipidemic.[96,100,101,103]

Pathophysiology

Classical Form. Over 50 patients have been described who have a familial abnormality in LPL activity.[97–99,106,107] Most of these patients can be characterized by a familial syndrome of chylomicronemia with clinical onset in childhood, which will here be termed *classical lipoprotein lipase deficiency*. Variations of this syndrome are considered below.

The lactescent or lipemic plasma seen in LPL deficiency is due to the accumulation of dietary fat in plasma as triglyceride-rich chylomicrons. The severity of the hypertriglyceridemia is related to the amount of ingested long chain fatty acids; thus the terms *fat-induced,* or *exogenous, hypertriglyceridemia.*[11] Although it is difficult to separate endogenous, triglyceride-rich VLDL from chylomicrons (particularly when the latter are markedly elevated), VLDL are usually not elevated in children and young adults with LPL deficiency. However, compelling data exist which indicate that VLDL triglyceride is nonetheless catabolized abnormally in LPL deficiency,[108] and therefore factors in addition to LPL deficiency must exist for the presence (phenotype V) or absence (phenotype I) of VLDL. Low density and high density lipoproteins have altered composition and are decreased in amount.[97]

LPL activity in plasma is low or absent in these patients following a bolus of heparin[95,97] (Fig. 45-7) and is not responsive to higher doses or prolonged infusions of heparin.[109] In contrast, postheparin plasma HL activity is present in low or normal amounts.[95,97] Adipose tissue LPL activity is very low[94] or undetectable.[109] LPL activity was also not detected in cultured monocyte-derived macrophages from a subject with the classic form of LPL deficiency.[110] Thus, the patient with the classical form of LPL deficiency presents in childhood with chylomicronemia, has low to absent levels of LPL activity in all tissues, and has normal HL activity.

Immunoreactive LPL mass has been detected in the postheparin plasma of some of the patients with LPL deficiency studied.[96,104] However, the enzyme protein in these patients has no detectable catalytic activity for triglyceride-phospholipid emulsions in the presence of apo C-II. The lack of catalytic activity might reflect a subtle change in the catalytic site

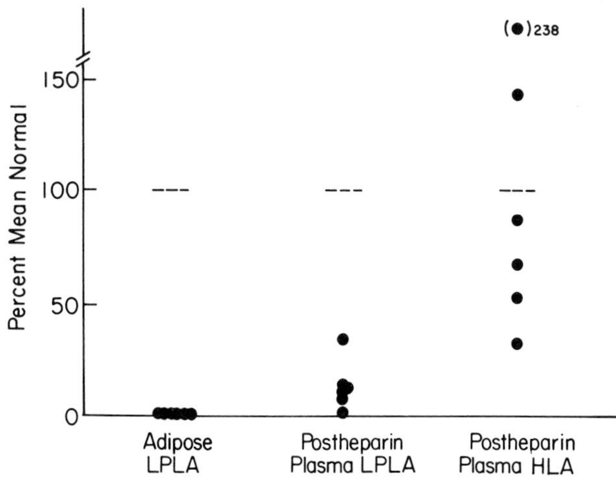

Fig. 45-7 Various lipase activities plotted as percent of mean normal values (---) in subjects with classic LPL deficiency. *(From Brunzell et al.[96] Used by permission.)*

of the enzyme or in the apo C-II binding site. The enzyme appears to have maintained the dimeric structure since it is be detected by an ELISA, which only detects the dimeric form of the enzyme. The immunoreactive enzyme in some patients binds to heparin-Sepharose, while in others it does not, reflecting a probable defect in the heparin-binding region of the protein. Thus there appear to be several defects in LPL structure that can lead to classical LPL deficiency.

Variants. In addition to the individuals with the classical forms of LPL deficiency, there are unusual patients with different and unique variations in the syndrome.

SITE-SPECIFIC LIPOPROTEIN LIPASE DEFICIENCY. While most LPL-deficient patients probably have decreased LPL activity in all tissues, two subjects have been noted who may have a tissue site-specific abnormality in the enzyme.[109] One of these patients, at age 28,[111] was found to have less than 10 percent of normal LPL activity in plasma shortly after the injection of heparin (60 units/kg). However, she had normal levels of LPL activity in adipose tissue and in plasma during the last two hours of a 6-h, high dose heparin infusion.[109] The abnormal fatty acid composition of this patient's breast milk (following a successful pregnancy) suggests the defect also included the mammary gland LPL.[111] From observations made in this patient, it has been postulated that the LPL appearing in plasma during the late phase of the heparin infusion arises from adipose tissue, while the LPL released into plasma during the early phase of the heparin infusion comes from other tissue sources (Fig. 45-8). The enzyme bound to capillary endothelium would not appear to greatly contribute to the total activity of LPL in plasma after a heparin bolus.

In support of this possibility, a second patient has been described with very low adipose tissue LPL activity and low activity during the late phase of the heparin infusion; however, the LPL activity released early during the infusion was normal.[109] The patient presented at the age of 20 years with mild abdominal discomfort and lipemic plasma. He had been investigated 10 to 15 years earlier at the University of California at San Francisco, but he had remained almost symptom-free without overt dietary modification. A second patient, seemingly similar to this, has been described by Burton and Nadler.[112] Since these patients were able to eat essentially normal diets and did not become symptomatic until young adult life,

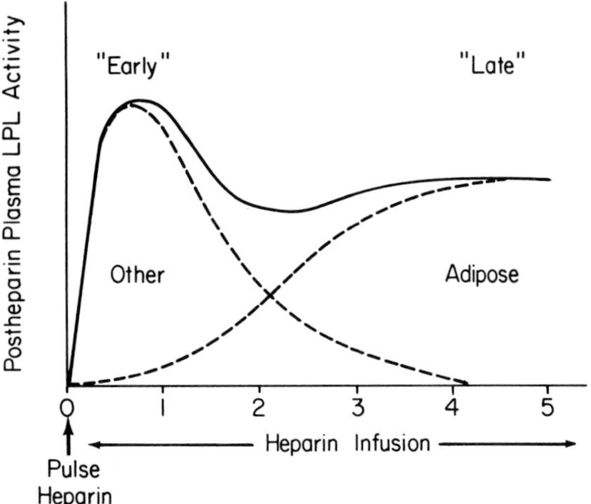

Fig. 45-8 Model of tissue site contribution of lipoprotein lipase to postheparin plasma LPL activity during a heparin infusion. *(From Brunzell et al.[96] Used by permission.)*

they appear to have less severe problems than most patients with classic LPL deficiency. The individuals with tissue site-specific LPL deficiency may have mutations at sites involved in the regulation of LPL rather than in regions encoding structural domains of the enzyme protein. Consistent with this, the enzymes in adipose tissue and in muscle are regulated in opposite ways during fasting and feeding, although the mechanisms to account for this regulation are not understood.

TRANSIENT LIPOPROTEIN LIPASE DEFICIENCY. Very low levels of LPL activity in postheparin plasma were found in a 9-year-old boy several weeks after recovering from an episode of pancreatitis associated with lactescent plasma.[113] His triglyceride level was 7280 mg/dl and his postheparin plasma hepatic lipase activity was normal. Following institution of moderately severe dietary fat restriction, his LPL activity returned to normal and his triglyceride fell to 57 mg/dl. Both parents had borderline hyperlipidemia. A similar problem has been reported in an adult.[96] The improvement in LPL activity might be secondary to the marked decrease in plasma triglyceride levels. Perhaps triglyceride-rich lipoproteins were competing for the enzyme loosely bound to the endothelial surface. Infusion of lipid emulsions into rodents[114] and into humans[115] has been associated with decreases in lipolytic activity in plasma.

OTHER UNUSUAL PATIENTS. One patient has been noted with very low levels of postheparin lipolytic activity after moderate doses of intravenous heparin but normal lipolytic activity after high doses of heparin.[116] Another unusual patient was not diagnosed to have LPL deficiency until the age of 75 years.[117]

Diagnosis and Treatment

Familial LPL deficiency is suspect in anyone with the chylomicronemia syndrome. This is particularly true if a simultaneous increase in VLDL is not present. An estimation of VLDL levels can be made by refrigerating plasma for several days; chylomicrons will float to the top leaving a clear infranate if no increase in VLDL is present. The absence of secondary causes of hypertriglyceridemia (diabetes, alcohol, estrogen therapy, certain antihypertensive agents, and paraproteinemic disorders) increases the possibility of LPL deficiency. A presumptive diagnosis can be made if a marked decrease in plasma triglyceride occurs after a week on a severely restricted low fat diet. In this instance apo C-II deficiency also has to be considered.

The definitive diagnosis of LPL deficiency requires the specific assay of LPL activity in postheparin plasma or adipose tissue.[118,119] Since it contains no hepatic lipase activity as seen in plasma, measurement of adipose tissue enzyme has an advantage over postheparin plasma. Adipose tissue for the measurement of LPL activity should be obtained immediately before assay for best results, which limits its routine use. Plasma LPL activity obtained 10 to 15 min after the intravenous injection of 60 to 100 units/kg body weight is stable if immediately refrigerated and quickly frozen. LPL activity has to be differentiated from the hepatic triglyceride lipase activity since both are released simultaneously with heparin. These enzymatic activities can be separated in several ways. Hepatic lipase can be removed by specific antibodies to the enzyme, the residual activity is LPL. Alternatively, the activity removed as LPL can be estimated by three methods: (1) an antibody to LPL can be added, (2) protamine sulfate which inhibits LPL can be included, or (3) the assay can be performed with high ionic strength to inhibit LPL activity. A more laborious, but precise, technique involves the separation of postheparin plasma hepatic lipase and LPL by heparin-Sepharose chromatography.[119] Once decreased LPL activity has been demonstrated, one has to distinguish between absent catalytic activity due to enzyme defects, absent apo C-II activating capacity, and the presence of an inhibitor to LPL (see "Familial Lipoprotein Lipase Inhibitor" below).

Treatment of familial LPL deficiency is predominantly by dietary fat restriction. The aim of therapy is to reduce the chylomicronemia to a level associated with clearance of symptoms and signs of the chylomicronemia syndrome. Success depends on the patient's acceptance of a diet extremely low in dietary fat. It is critical for the patient and family to realize that unsaturated as well as saturated fat must be restricted. Often dietary restriction of fat to 15 percent of calories will be adequate to maintain plasma triglyceride levels consistently below 1000 to 2000 mg/dl and to control symptoms. Medium chain triglycerides can be used for cooking since they are absorbed into the portal vein without becoming incorporated into chylomicron triglyceride. Additional measures in the prevention of excessive hypertriglyceridemia are avoidance of agents which are known to increase endogenous triglyceride levels, such as alcohol, estrogens, diuretics, and β-adrenergic blocking agents. During pregnancy extreme dietary fat restriction with close monitoring of triglyceride levels has resulted in normal term delivery.[111] When VLDL levels are increased in a patient with LPL deficiency, such as might occur in adults, fibric acid derivatives such as clofibrate or gemfibrosil may lower triglyceride levels slightly, especially when the patient is on a low fat, high carbohydrate diet.[120]

APOLIPOPROTEIN C-II DEFICIENCY

History

In 1978 Breckenridge et al.[14] reported a 59-year-old male with gross hypertriglyceridemia and absent postheparin lipolytic activity. He had recurrent abdominal pain since the age of 18 and developed diabetes mellitus and steatorrhea. In spite of insulin therapy, he remained markedly hypertriglyceridemic. On a low fat diet his triglyceride levels dropped from about 4000 to below 1000 mg/dl. Following a transfusion for anemia, he had a marked decrease in triglyceride levels into the normal range, suggesting that a plasma component for which he was deficient was supplied by the transfusion. These workers demonstrated that he had no normal apolipoprotein C-II, and that the addition of normal apo C-II to his plasma corrected his postheparin lipolytic activity. Other individuals in his family have been found with functional apo C-II deficiency. The relatives heterozygous for the defect have half of the levels of normal apo C-II in plasma, thus establishing the familial nature of this disorder.

Clinical Phenotype

Since apo C-II deficiency results in the functional deficiency of lipoprotein lipase, it is not surprising that the clinical manifestations are similar to those in primary lipoprotein lipase deficiency. However, some interesting differences have been found between apo C-II deficiency and the classical form of LPL deficiency. These patients have a milder, later onset of the chylomicronemia syndrome, similar to that seen in the variant LPL-deficient syndromes. Compared to the patients with familial LPL deficiency, the homozygous apo C-II-deficient subject generally has been detected at a later age ranging from 13 to 60 years of age. Even so, the symptoms often can be traced to earlier childhood or adolescence. The symptoms have not been as severe as in LPL deficiency, and these patients usually have been able to tolerate a higher dietary fat content.

The predominant symptom reported in the apo C-II-deficient patients has been recurrent abdominal pain, apparently caused by repeated attacks of pancreatitis. The prevalence of pancreatitis in the Toronto kindred was found to be 64 percent among 14 affected individuals, which is higher than that reported for the pancreatitis in familial lipoprotein lipase deficiency.[14,106] It is possible that the patients with lipoprotein lipase deficiency learn to avoid dietary fat early in life, while those with apo C-II deficiency, even as adults, consume more dietary fat and subsequently suffer more frequent episodes of pancreatitis. The index patient in the Toronto family had repeated attacks of pancreatitis, which resulted in chronic pancreatic insufficiency with steatorrhea and insulin dependent diabetes. It has been suggested that the apo C-II-deficient patients do not have eruptive xanthomas or hepatosplenomegaly as often as those with LPL deficiency. In the Toronto pedigree, anemia was reported in 8 of the 14 patients, although the characteristics of this anemia have not been described in detail. As in lipoprotein lipase deficiency, there is no evidence for premature atherosclerosis in individuals with apo C-II deficiency.

The delay in onset of symptoms and the higher dietary fat tolerance in apo C-II deficiency might be related to a less severe defect in the clearance of chylomicrons and VLDL, since some residual lipoprotein lipase activity might exist. The homozygous apo C-II-deficient patients have markedly elevated fasting plasma triglyceride levels ranging from 500 to 10,000 mg/dl. Most of this triglyceride is in the form of chylomicrons, but there is also an increase in VLDL triglyceride. The VLDL cholesterol levels are elevated above the normal range, while the levels of low density lipoproteins and high density lipoproteins are very low, similar to that seen in familial lipoprotein lipase deficiency. Immunoassays have revealed low plasma levels of apolipoprotein A-I, A-II, and B, and high concentrations of apolipoproteins C-III and E in these patients. Activation of lipoprotein lipase in the homozygote by the intravenous infusion of plasma rapidly reduces the concentrations of chylomicrons and very low density lipoproteins. These changes were associated with reciprocal increases in low density lipoproteins, high density lipoproteins, and the plasma levels of apo A-I and apo B.

Mutant Gene and Genetics

Apolipoprotein C-II deficiency is an autosomal recessive disorder described in at least 11 families involving at least 33 individuals, with 15 homozygotes in the Toronto kindred (see Table 45-2,[121]). The Toronto family[14,122] was of British origin via the Caribbean. Although four of the other families have Italian ancestry, families have been reported from Japan,[123,124] Puerto Rico,[132] England,[128] France,[135] and Germany,[121] suggesting worldwide ethnic distribution. Consanguinity has been reported in at least four families, including the Toronto family in whom the parents were first cousins.

Although one heterozygote relative has been reported to have hypertriglyceridemia in the Toronto family, no vertical transmission of apo C-II deficiency has been documented. The heterozygous state is relatively easy to detect in most families since these individuals have one-half the normal amount of functional apo C-II. The heterozygotes for apo C-II deficiency usually have normal plasma lipid and lipoprotein levels.[14,128] Thus, it appears that the level of apo C-II in plasma in heterozygotes and in normal subjects is not limiting for the clearance of chylomicron and VLDL triglyceride. In the heterozygous relatives of probands with lipoprotein lipase deficiency, the lipid phenotype often has been reported to be similar to that of familial combined hyperlipidemia (see Chap. 44B and "Mutant Gene and Genetics" under "Lipoprotein Lipase Deficiency," above). No such variable hyperlipidemia is seen in the heterozygous relatives of individuals with homozygous apo C-II deficiency. Again, the reason for these differences is unknown.

The gene for apo C-II has been studied in 6 of the 11 families. Using a group of restriction enzymes (*Bam*HI, *Bgl*I, *Eco*RI, *Hind*III, and *Sst*I), the gene appeared grossly normal in two families.[133] A *Taq*I polymorphism (3.5 and 3.8 kb) exists in the vicinity of this gene. The mutant alleles in two of these families were associated with the 3.5-kb fragment, while in three other families the 3.8-kb fragment was found (Table 45-2). In one family recently reported from West Germany, a single base substitution of the first nucleotide for the highly conserved consensus sequence of the donor splice site of intron 2 was seen.[121] Although homozygosity for the defect is likely in most of the families in whom consanguinity has been reported, the patients in families without consanguinity may often be compound heterozygotes for the apo C-II mutation.

Apo C-II has been detected by immunoblot or radioimmunoassay in about one-half of the families with apo C-II deficiency. This disorder appears to be very heterogenous (Table 45-2). In the Toronto kindred, the apo C-II that is present has an abnormal migration on two-dimensional gel electrophoresis.[122] Amino acids 1 to 68 are apparently intact, but amino acids 69 to 73 on the carboxyl-terminal end, the region of the proposed activation of LPL, are missing. The protein in the family from Padova appears to be present but has an abnormal isoelectric point and is decreased in molecular weight. The

Table 45-2 Apo C-II Deficient Families

Number	*Ref.*	*Site*	*Year*	*Number affected*	*Consanguinity*	*Gene*†	*Protein present*‡	
1	14,122	Toronto	1978	15	+		+	Deletion of AA 69–73
2	123,124	Japan	1979	2	+		—	
3	102,125–127	Padova*	1980	2		3.8,NL	+	↓M_r + ΔpI
4	128-129	London	1981	1	—	NL§	—	
5	130	Holland	1981	4	—	3.5,NL	+	NL pI
6	131	Milan*	1983	1	—		—	
7	132	Cincinnati	1984	1	—	3.8,NL	—	
8	133	Bethesda*	1984	1	—	3.4,NL	+	ΔpI
9	134	Vancouver*	1986	2	+	3.8,NL	—	
10	121,135,136	France	1987	>1	—	3.8,NL	—	
11	121	W. Germany	1988	3	+	3.8,NL	+	

*Italian descent, one parent only in family number 8.
†NL: Gene grossly normal by restriction enzyme fragment analysis. The lengths of the DNA fragments which contain the gene for apo C-II are indicated as 3.8, 3.5, or 3.4 kb.
‡Some apo C-IIs have normal pI on two-dimensional gel electrophoresis; some are changed [Δ]. Patient 11 has a C for G substitution at donor splice site of intron 2.
§P. Bell and J. Brunzell, unpublished observation.

family from Bethesda also has a detectable protein with an abnormal pI, but this defect is different from the defect seen in the family from Padova. Of note, the mother of the family from Bethesda also is of Italian ancestry. The Dutch family has very low levels of apo C-II, which appears to be normal on two-dimensional gels. Five of the families appear to have no detectable apo C-II by immunoblot and/or radioimmunoassay. The decrease in lipoprotein lipase activity in the postheparin plasma of patients with apo C-II deficiency is corrected by the addition of normal apo C-II in vitro or by the intravenous infusion of apo C-II in all the families in which it has been reported, with the notable exception of the Dutch family. In the Dutch family, a concomitant decrease in lipoprotein lipase activity in postheparin plasma has also been reported.[130] This decrease in lipolytic activity did not correct with the addition of apo C-II from normal plasma. Whether this decrease in lipoprotein lipase activity is due to the presence of an abnormal apo C-II not yet detected or to some other abnormality in lipoprotein lipase has not yet been determined. It is of interest that adipose tissue lipoprotein lipase activities were markedly increased in the patient from London,[129] suggesting that lipoprotein lipase in adipose tissue is under feedback control, and this increase in adipose tissue LPL reflects an attempt to overcome the defect in apo C-II deficiency. The postheparin plasma LPL was also increased in this patient. Adipose tissue LPL was mildly increased in the patient from Vancouver (Brunzell, unpublished observation), and postheparin plasma LPL may have been mildly increased in the families from Toronto and Japan but was not increased in the family from Milan. For reasons that are unknown, moderate decreases in hepatic lipase activity have been reported in at least three of the probands with the apo C-II deficiency.

Pathophysiology

When apo C-II is absent or nonfunctional, the function of lipoprotein lipase is severely impaired, with a marked increase in the K_m of lipoprotein lipase for the hydrolysis of triglyceride-rich lipoproteins. It may be that minimal lipoprotein lipase activity still is present, allowing hydrolysis of some of the triglyceride contained in these lipoproteins. As a result of apo C-II deficiency, triglyceride, predominantly in the form of chylomicrons and endogenously synthesized VLDL, accumulates in plasma. There is no difficulty with the accumulation of triglyceride in fat cells, suggesting pathways for energy uptake by fat cells through mechanisms other than the lipoprotein lipase/apo C-II system. There is a decrease in low density lipoproteins and high density lipoproteins, in part due to a decrease in input of core and surface components from the triglyceride-rich lipoprotein remants normally produced during triglyeride hydrolysis.

Diagnosis and Treatment

The deficiency of apo C-II manifests itself as diminished postheparin plasma lipoprotein lipase activity when assayed in the absence of apo C-II. With the addition of normal apo C-II to the assay, the decrease in postheparin plasma lipolytic activity corrects to normal. One can also use a source of lipoprotein lipase, such as bovine milk lipoprotein lipase or guinea pig postheparin plasma, which is free of apo C-II, to evaluate the plasma of a patient with potential apo C-II deficiency. One can then titrate the amount of apo C-II needed to correct the LPL activity. Deficiency of apo C-II can be verified by electrophoresis of the apolipoproteins contained in VLDL and chylomicrons on two-dimensional gels. The treatment of apo C-II deficiency is the same as that outlined above for LPL deficiency.

FAMILIAL LIPOPROTEIN LIPASE INHIBITOR

A mother and son have been reported[129] who have the chylomicronemia syndrome and very low levels of postheparin plasma lipolytic activity. They differ from subjects with lipoprotein lipase deficiency in that adipose tissue lipoprotein lipase activity is elevated above normal. Unlike apo C-II deficient patients, these subjects have normal to elevated levels of apo C-II.[129]

The proband was a 47-year-old female who was found to have a plasma triglyceride of 3865 mg/dl after developing eruptive xanthomas on her feet. She had had recurrent ab-

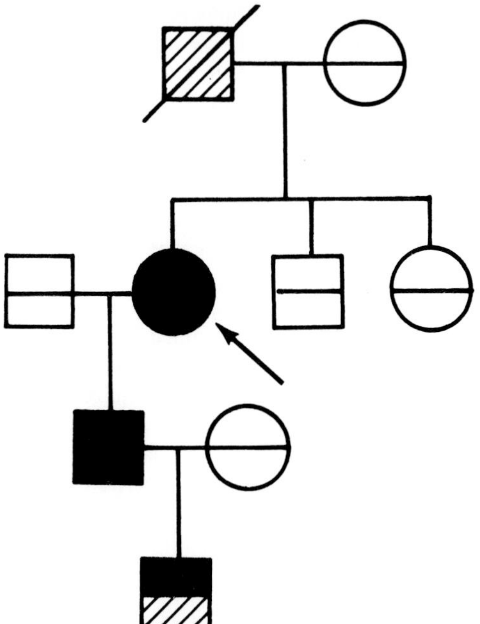

Fig. 45-9 Family with lipoprotein lipase inhibitor in plasma. ⬓ or ◒, = chylomicronemia; ⬒ or ◓, = LPL inhibitor in plasma; ▨; = presumed affected relatives. *(From Brunzell et al.[129] Used by permission.)*

dominal pain since the age of 16 years. On an unrestricted diet her lipoproteins were similar to those seen in lipoprotein lipase deficiency and apo C-II deficiency. She responded to severe dietary fat restriction by an 80 percent reduction in plasma triglyceride.

Her father died at 39 years of age after abdominal surgery for acute abdominal pain. Her son also had marked hypertriglyceridemia (3596 mg/dl) at age 21 years, as did his son (2400 mg/dl) at age 4 months (Fig. 45-9). The son was able to tolerate this level of plasma triglyceride without symptoms while consuming a normal dietary fat intake. The patient's mother, two siblings, husband, and daughter-in-law had normal lipid levels. It is possible the patient's father had chylomicron-induced pancreatitis. The presence of chylomicronemia in three generations is consistent with autosomal dominant transmission. This pattern of inheritance is very different from that seen in lipoprotein lipase or apo C-II deficiency.

Both the patient and her son appeared to have an inhibitor of lipoprotein lipase activity in their whole plasma that was found to inhibit the lipoprotein lipase activity in adipose tissue and postheparin plasma of normal subjects. The inhibitor was nondialyzable, heat stable, and sensitive to repeated freezing and thawing, and it appeared to be present in the nonlipoprotein fraction of plasma.

The presence of a plasma inhibitor to lipoprotein lipase can be verified by the addition of the suspected plasma to a source of active lipoprotein lipase with resultant inhibition of activity. These patients have elevated adipose tissue lipoprotein lipase activity as opposed to the lipoprotein lipase-deficient subjects, and normal apo C-II does not correct their defect in postheparin plasma.

Moderate dietary fat restriction is indicated to prevent the recurrent attacks of pancreatitis and other signs and symptoms of the chylomicronemia syndrome. These patients appeared to be able to tolerate more dietary fat intake than the patients with classic lipoprotein lipase deficiency.

CHYLOMICRONEMIA OF RELATED DISORDERS

History

Fredrickson and Lees[12] first separated patients with fasting chylomicronemia into those who had elevated levels of VLDL, the type V lipoprotein pattern, and those who did not, the type I lipoprotein pattern. Type I hyperlipoproteinemia was subsequently modified to include the absence of postheparin plasma LPL activity.[74] Type V hyperlipoproteinemia is a highly diverse group of primary and secondary disorders with moderate to severe hypertriglyceridemia. Many individuals with monogenic familial hypertriglyceridemia have moderate hypertriglyceridemia with chylomicrons present in plasma after an overnight fast on many occasions (type V) but not on others (type IV).

The families of probands with chylomicronemia often contain hypertriglyceridemic relatives.[137,138] Often the proband has a secondary cause for hypertriglyceridemia, such as alcohol intake, estrogen treatment, or diabetes,[137] which increases the difficulty in determining the specific metabolic defect in the family. It has been demonstrated that the majority of probands with plasma triglyceride levels above 2000 mg/dl have both a common familial form of hypertriglyceridemia and a common secondary cause,[76] which would account for the lesser degree of hypertriglyceridemia seen in the affected relatives who do not have the secondary cause for the increase in plasma triglyceride. When probands with a type V pattern with secondary causes of hypertriglyceridemia were excluded,[138] hypertriglyceridemia was found in 61 of 181 first-degree relatives, of whom 29 had fasting chylomicronemia. Since the median plasma triglyceride level was 770 mg/dl in the male probands, it is difficult to assess how many of these families represented monogenic familial hypertriglyceridemia. In the study of Greenberg et al.[138] and in a study of the relatives of families with familial hypertriglyceridema,[139] no increase in atherosclerosis was seen.

Clinical Phenotype and Pathophysiology

All of the primary familial disorders with plasma triglyceride levels over 2000 mg/dl with chylomicronemia as causes of the chylomicronemia syndrome are relatively rare, but they may account for up to 10 percent of individuals referred to a lipid clinic. The vast majority of patients with chylomicronemia and plasma triglyceride levels above 2000 mg/dl do not have one of these rare genetic disorders. Rather, they appear to have one of the more common genetic disorders of triglyceride metabolism occurring simultaneously with, and independent of, a common, acquired, secondary form of hypertriglyceridemia.[75] The combination of the primary familial and the secondary acquired abnormality, each alone capable of causing mild to moderate hypertriglyceridemia, seems to lead to massive hypertriglyceridemia (Table 45-3) and the chylomicronemia syndrome.

Two genetic disorders, familial combined hyperlipidemia and monogenic familial hypertriglyceridemia, are commonly seen in the chylomicronemia syndrome; dysbetalipoproteinemia is also occasionally seen. The most prevalent acquired form of hypertriglyceridemia associated with these genetic dis-

Table 45-3 Etiology of Chylomicronemia Syndrome

Disease no. 1	*Disease no. 2*
1. Familial lipoprotein lipase deficiency (gene no. 1)	Familial lipoprotein lipase deficiency (gene no. 2)
2. Familial apoprotein C-II deficiency (gene no. 1)	Familial apoprotein C-II deficiency (gene no. 2)
3. Familial form of hypertriglyceridemia (gene no. 1)	Familial form of hypertriglyceridemia (gene no. 2)
4. Familial form of hypertriglyceridemia	Secondary form of hypertriglyceridemia *a.* Untreated diabetes *b.* Estrogen therapy *c.* Alcohol *d.* Others

orders is related to the mild to moderate defect in lipoprotein lipase documented in untreated or recently treated diabetes mellitus.[5,140] The increase in triglyceride synthesis in familial hypertriglyceridemia and the increase in VLDL apo B synthesis seen in familial combined hyperlipidemia appear to interact with the lipoprotein lipase-related removal defect of the diabetic state to cause chylomicronemia. Such massive elevations in plasma triglyceride levels are rare, with other acquired abnormalities of adipose tissue lipoprotein lipase, such as in hypothyroidism or uremia, occurring concomitantly with one of the common familial forms of hypertriglyceridemia.[141]

Obesity seems to be associated with elevated VLDL triglyceride synthesis and leads to further increased triglyceride levels in familial hypertriglyceridemia, but not to the levels seen in the chylomicronemia syndrome. Other acquired forms of hypertriglyceridemia related to drugs or hormones that appear to be associated with increased VLDL triglyceride synthesis, such as estrogen therapy, the third trimester of pregnancy, glucocorticoid therapy and alcohol use, may in themselves be associated with mild to moderate hypertriglyceridemia but not with chylomicronemia. However, we commonly see plasma triglyceride levels above 2000 mg/dl in individuals with one of these drug- or hormone-related causes of increased VLDL triglyceride production who also have familial hypertriglyceridemia.

Whether massive hypertriglyceridemia can occur as the result of two separate but concurrent acquired causes of hypertriglyceridemia is unknown. Massive hypertriglyceridemia has been reported[97] with multiple myeloma, systemic lupus erythematosus, and lymphomatous disease, which reversed with therapy aimed at the acquired disease and may have been due to the one acquired disease alone. Diuretics and β-adrenergic blocking agents, which mildly increase triglyceride levels in normolipidemic subjects with hypertension, may be found to play a significant role in the chylomicronemia syndrome when these drugs are given to patients with familial forms of hypertriglyceridemia.

Of the 123 patients with marked hypertriglyceridemia studied in our laboratory,[140] all but 13 have a known acquired cause of hypertriglyceridemia. Five of these were found to have a genetic abnormality in LPL activity. Five other individuals had a genetic form of hypertriglyceridemia in the families of *both* parents. These individuals could quite possibly be homozygous for a common familial form of hypertriglyceridemia or a mixed heterozygous combination of two common familial disorders. In the remaining three individuals, the cause of the marked hypertriglyceridemia remains unknown.

There is no doubt that families exist in which marked hypertriglyceridemia exists among multiple relatives[60,137,138,141] who do not have defect in lipoprotein lipase, but the nature of the disorder(s) remains obscure. Fallat and Glueck[137] and Greenberg et al.[138] have studied individuals with marked hypertriglyceridemia, many with plasma triglyceride levels above 2000 mg/dl. They have noted a high prevalence of acquired forms of hypertriglyceridemia among these individuals. Because these subjects have hypertriglyceridemic relatives, their disorder has been characterized as "familial type V." It appears that they were studying the same phenomenon reported here, i.e., chylomicronemia syndrome in the index patients caused by an interaction of a common familial disorder with an acquired form of hyperlipidemia. Triglyceride levels in their relative rarely exceeded 2000 mg/dl, and acquired disorders among relatives were less common, suggesting that many of the index patients with familial type V in fact come from families with one of the common genetic hypertriglyceridemias.

Prevalence

It is difficult to measure directly the prevalence of plasma triglyceride levels over 2000 mg/dl. In the Lipid Research Clinics' Prevalence Study, seven individuals with this degree of hypertriglyceridemia were found among a population of 39,090 randomly chosen adult whites. This is 1.8 such individuals per 10,000 population, or about 20,000 such individuals in the adult white population in the United States. Although no data are available, it would appear that the prevalence and incidence of massive hypertriglyceridemia is more common in diabetes clinics and in hospitals established for the care of alcoholism. Based on the conservative estimated prevalence of familial hypertriglyceridemia of 0.2 percent and of familial combined hyperlipidemia of 0.3 percent, one might expect that at least 0.5 percent of untreated symptomatic diabetic patients could have massive hypertriglyceridemia.

Treatment

All the clinical manifestations of the chylomicronemia syndrome are reversible with the reduction of plasma triglyceride levels. Thus, therapy is directed toward elimination of the causes of the hypertriglyceridemia. As in individuals with the rare genetic defects in lipoprotein lipase, most of those who appear to have inherited a common familial form of hypertriglyceridemia from each parent (homozygotes or mixed heterozygotes) will require a low-fat diet. Such individuals usually learn to avoid certain fat-containing foods, such as milk, on their own. To be pain-free, however, they often need to severely restrict dietary fat intake. These patients with hypertriglyceridemia inherited from each parent may respond dramatically to therapy with nicotinic acid alone or in combination with other drugs.

Treatment of the hypertriglyceridemia in the more common patients, with concomitant familial and acquired disorders, should be directed first toward the acquired disorder. With symptomatic, untreated diabetes, insulin or oral sulfonylurea therapy is almost always required. Younger, thin individuals with insulin dependent diabetes mellitus, with or without ketosis, may require no therapy other than insulin to keep triglyceride levels lowered. Many with insulin dependent diabetes will have mild residual elevations in plasma triglyceride or cholesterol levels. Patients with non-insulin dependent diabetes and marked hypertriglyceridemia are often more difficult to treat than those with insulin independent diabetes. This difficulty might be related to the often associated obesity and its resultant potential for hypertriglyceridemia and the use of other drugs that might affect triglyceride metabolism. Some individuals with non-insulin dependent diabetes respond to insulin therapy alone, while others require clofibrate, in addition to significantly lower triglyceride levels. Occasionally a patient with non-insulin dependent diabetes will have lower triglyceride levels when taking clofibrate and an oral sulfonylurea than when given insulin with clofibrate. Rarely, a patient with non-insulin dependent diabetes will require still further therapy in addition to the oral sulfonylurea and clofibrate. Chronic nicotinic acid therapy should be used with great caution in the presence of diabetes because of its hyperglycemic effect. We believe that weight loss is contraindicated in the small subset of obese patients with non-insulin dependent diabetes and the chylomicronemia syndrome. Although weight loss and maintenance of the weight loss are extremely effective forms of therapy, the maintenance of reduced weight is unusual; with the often inevitable weight regain, extreme hypertriglyceridemia and, frequently, pancreatitis can occur.

The marked hypertriglyceridemia that occurs in individuals with a familial form of hypertriglyeridemia treated with estrogens, glucocorticoids, or alcohol will almost always respond to the discontinuation of the drug or alcohol, with no further antihyperlipidemic therapy required. In general, marked hypertriglyceridemia that is unresponsive to a low fat diet and/or treatment of the acquired disease is a definite indication for the addition of clofibrate to the therapeutic program.

Most of the minor symptoms of the chylomicronemia syndrome do not require urgent therapy. However, in the presence of moderate to severe abdominal pain or pancreatitis, immediate therapy is indicated. Pancreatitis associated with the chylomicronemia syndrome is treated in the same way as are the usual forms of pancreatitis. The discontinuation of oral intake will stop chylomicron triglyceride formation, and replacement with hypocaloric parenteral nutrition will decrease VLDL triglyceride production. The administration of excess calories, as in hyperalimentation, is contraindicated in the acute state, and the intravenous administration of lipid emulsions may lead to persistent or recurrent pancreatitis. With this regimen subjects with alcohol-induced hypertriglyceridemia will respond rapidly; those with estrogen- or glucocorticoid-induced hypertriglyceridemia will respond less quickly. The non-insulin dependent diabetic, however, presents a special situation. Although triglyceride levels will fall with hypocaloric intravenous fat-free fluids in combination with antihyperglycemic drugs and clofibrate, the defect in LPL does not correct rapidly with treatment of the diabetes and the patient may need to be watched closely for 2 to 3 months on a low fat diet.

REFERENCES

1. THANNHAUSER SJ: *Lipidoses. Diseases of the Intracellular Lipid Metabolism*, 3d ed. New York, Grune & Stratton, 1985, p 296.
2. ADDISON T, GULL W: On a certain affection of the skin, vitiligoidea (a) plana, (b) tuberosa, with remarks. *Guy's Hosp Rep* 7:265, 1851.
3. JENSEN J: The story of xanthomatosis in England prior to the first world war. *Clio Med* 2:289, 1967.
4. JOSLIN EP: *The Treatment of Diabetes Mellitus*. Philadelphia, Lea and Febiger, 1916, frontispiece.
5. BRUNZELL JD, HAZZARD WR, MOTULSKY AG, BIERMAN EL: Evidence for diabetes mellitus and genetic forms at hypertriglyceridemia as independent entities. *Metabolism* 24:1115, 1975.
6. SIEMANS HW: Zur kenntnis der xanthoma. *Arch Dermatol Syph* 136:159, 1921.
7. BÜRGER M, GRÜTZ O: Úber hepatosplenomegale lipoidose mit xanthomatosen veränderungen in haut und schleimhaut. *Arch Dermatol Syph* 166:542, 1932.
8. HOLT LE Jr, AYLWARD FX, TIMBRES HG: Idiopathic familial lipemia. *Bull Johns Hopkins Hosp* 64:279, 1939.
9. POULSEN HM: Familial lipemia, a new form of lipoidosis showing increase in neutral fats combined with attacks of acute pancreatitis. *Acta Med Scand* 138:413, 1950.
10. MALMROS H, SWAHN B, TRUEDSSON E: Essential hyperlipidaemia. *Acta Med Scand* 149:91, 1954.
11. AHRENS EH Jr, HIRSCH J, OETTE K, FARQUHAR JW, STEIN Z: Carbohydrate-induced and fat-induced lipemia. *Trans Assoc Am Physicians* 74:134, 1961.
12. FREDRICKSON DS, LEES RS: Familial hyperlipoproteinemia, in Stanbury JB, Wyngaarden JB, Fredricksen DS (eds): *The Metabolic Basis of Inherited Disease*, 2d ed. New York, McGraw-Hill, 1966, p 429.
13. HAVEL R, GORDON RS Jr: Idiopathic hyperlipemia: Metabolic studies in an affected family. *J Clin Invest* 39:1777, 1960.
14. BRECKENRIDGE WC, LITTLE JA, STEINER G, CHOW A, POAPST M: Hypertriglyceridemia associated with deficiency of apolipoprotein C-II. *N Engl J Med* 298:1265, 1978.
15. IVERIUS P-H, OSTLUND-LINDQVIST A-M: Lipoprotein lipase from bovine milk: Isolation procedure, chemical characterization, and molecular weight analysis. *J Biol Chem* 251:7791, 1976.
16. OLIVECRONA T, BENGTSSON G, OSBORNE JC Jr: Molecular properties of lipoprotein lipase: Effects of limited trypsin digestion on molecular weight and secondary structure. *Eur J Biochem* 124:629, 1982.
17. WION KL, KIRCHGESSNER TG, LUSIS AJ, SCHOTZ MC, LAWN RM: Human lipoprotein lipase complementary DNA sequence. *Science* 235:1638, 1987.
18. SENDA M, OKA K, BROWN WV, QASBA PK, FURUICHI Y: Molecular cloning and sequence of a cDNA coding for bovine lipoprotein lipase. *Proc Natl Acad Sci USA* 84:4369, 1987.
19. CLARKE AR, LUSCOMBE M, HOLBROOK JJ: The effect of chain length of heparin units interaction with lipoprotein lipase. *Biochim Biophys Acta* 747:130, 1983.
20. KLINGER MM, MARGOLIS RU, MARGOLIS RK: Isolation and characterization of heparan sulfate proteoglycans of brain: Use of affinity chromatography on lipoprotein lipase-agarose. *J Biol Chem* 260:4082, 1985.
21. PEDERSEN ME, COHEN M, SCHOTZ MC: Immunocytochemical localization of the functional fraction of lipoprotein lipase in the perfused heart. *J Lipid Res* 24:512, 1983.
22. BEN-AVRAM CM, BEN-ZEEV O, LEE TD, HAAGA K, SHIVELY JE, GOERS J, PEDERSEN ME, REEVE JR Jr, SCHOTZ MC: Homology of lipoprotein lipase to pancreatic lipase. *Proc Natl Acad Sci USA* 83:4185, 1986.
23. CRYER A: Comparative biochemistry and physiology of lipoprotein lipase, in Borensztajn J (ed): *Lipoprotein Lipase*. Chicago, Evener Publishers, 1987, p 277.
24. PARKIN SM, SPEAKE BK, ROBINSON DS: Homology of lipoprotein lipase to pancreatic lipase. *Biochem J* 207:485, 1982.
25. BENGTSSON G, OLIVECRONA T: Interaction of lipoprotein lipase with Heparin-Sepharose. *Biochem J* 167:109, 1977.
26. KINNUNEN PKJ, HUFFUNEN JK, EHNHOLM C: Properties of purified bovine milk lipoprotein lipase. *Biochim Biophys Acta* 450:342, 1976.
27. WALLINDER LA, BENGTSSON G, OLIVECRONA T: Purification and properties of lipoprotein lipase in guinea pig milk. *Biochim Biophys Acta* 711:107, 1982.
28. SCHEIBEL MS, IVERIUS P-H, BRUNZELL JD, AUWERX JH, FUJIMOTO WY: An enzyme linked immunosorbent assay for nondenatured human lipoprotein lipase. Submitted.
29. SEMB H, OLIVECRONA T: Lipoprotein lipase in guinea pig tissues. *Biochim Biophys Acta* 878:330, 1986.
30. OLIVECRONA T, BENGTSSON-OLIVECRONA G, OSBORNE JC Jr, KEMPNER ES: Molecular size of bovine lipoprotein lipase as determined by radiation inactivation. *J Biol Chem* 260:6888, 1985.
31. CUPP M, BENSADOUN A, MELFORD K: Heparin decreases the degradation rate of lipoprotein lipase in adipocytes. *J Biol Chem* 262:6383, 1987.
32. CHENG C-F, OOSTA GM, BENSADOUN A, ROSENBERG RD: Binding of lipoprotein lipase to endothelial cells in culture. *J Biol Chem* 256:12893, 1981.
33. WALLINDER L, PETERSON J, OLIVECRONA T, BENGTSSON-OLIVECRONA G: Hepatic and extrahepatic uptake of intravenously injected lipoprotein lipase. *Biochim Biophys Acta* 795:513, 1984.

34. SCOW RO, DESNUELLE P, VERGER R: Lipolysis and lipid movement in a membrane model: Action of lipoprotein lipase. *J Biol Chem* 254:6456, 1979.
35. ROBINSON DS, PARKIN SM, SPEAKE BK, LITTLE JA: Hormonal control of rat adipose tissue lipoprotein lipase activity, in Angel A, Hollenberg CH, Roncari DAK (eds): *The Adipocyte and Obesity: Cellular and Molecular Mechanisms*. New York, Raven, 1983, p 127–136.
36. AILHAUD G, EZ-ZOUBIR A, ETIENNE J, NEGREL R, VANNIER C: Development and maturation of lipoprotein lipase in cultured adipose cells, in Freysz L, Dreyfus H, Massarelli R, Gatt S (eds): *Enzymes of Lipid Metabolism II*. New York, Plenum, 1986, p 485.
37. GARFINKEL AS, SCHOTZ MC: Lipoprotein lipase, in Gotto AM Jr (ed): *Plasma Lipoproteins*. Amsterdam, Elsevier, 1987, p 335.
38. STEIN O, STEIN Y, FRIEDMAN G, CHAKEKK-SHAUL T: Lipoprotein lipase, synthesis and regulation, in Schlierf G, Morl H (eds): *Expanding Horizons in Atherosclerosis Research*. Berlin, Springer-Verlag, 1987, p 204.
39. JONASSON L, HANSSON GK, BONDJERS G, BENGTSSON G, OLIVECRONA T: Immunohistochemical localization of lipoprotein lipase in human adipose tissue. *Atherosclerosis* 51:313, 1984.
40. PYKALISTO OJ, SMITH PH, BRUNZELL JD: Determinants of human adipose tissue lipoprotein lipase: Effects of diabetes and obesity on basal and diet induced activity. *J Clin Invest* 56:1108, 1975.
41. TASKINEN M-R, NIKKILA EA: Lipoprotein lipase of adipose tissue and skeletal muscle in human obesity: Response to glucose and to semistarvation. *Metabolism* 30:810, 1981.
42. SADUR CN, ECKEL RH: Insulin stimulation of adipose tissue lipoprotein lipase: Use of the euglycemic clamp technique. *J Clin Invest* 69:1119, 1982.
43. YKI-JARVINEN H, TASKINEN M-R, KOIVISTO VA, NIKKILA EA: Response of adipose tissue lipoprotein lipase activity and serum lipoproteins to acute hyperinsulinemia in man. *Diabetologia* 27:364, 1984.
44. BRUNZELL JD, SCHWARTZ RS, ECKEL RH, GOLDBERG AP: Insulin and adipose tissue lipoprotein lipase in humans. *Int J Obes* 5:685, 1981.
45. SPEAKE BK, PARKIN SM, ROBINSON DS: Degradation of lipoprotein lipase in rat adipose tissue. *Biochim Biophys Acta* 840:419, 1985.
46. OLIVECRONA T, BENGTSSON-OLIVECRONA G: Lipoprotein lipase from milk—the model enzyme in lipoprotein lipase research, in Borensztajn J (ed): *Lipoprotein Lipase*. Chicago, Evener Publishers, 1987, p 15.
47. SCOW RO, CHERNICK SS: Role of lipoprotein lipase during lactation, in Borensztajn J (ed): *Lipoprotein Lipase*. Chicago, Evener Publishers, 1987, pp 149–185.
48. KAWAKAMI M, PEKALA PH, LANE MD, CERAMI A: Lipoprotein lipase suppression in 3T3-L1 cells by an endotoxin-induced mediator from exudate cell. *Proc Natl Acad Sci USA* 79:912, 1982.
49. SEMB H, PETERSON J, TAVERNIER J, OLIVECRONA T: Multiple effects of tumor necrosis factor on lipoprotein lipase *in vivo*. *J Biol Chem* 262:8390, 1987.
50. HOSPATTANKAR AV, FAIRWELL T, RONAN R, BREWER HB Jr: Amino acid sequence of human plasma apolipoprotein C-II from normal and hyperlipoproteinemic subjects. *J Biol Chem* 259:318, 1984.
51. HAVEL RJ, KANE JP, KASHYAP ML: Interchange of apolipoproteins between chylomicrons and high density lipoproteins during alimentary lipemia in man. *J Clin Invest* 52:32, 1973.
52. JACKSON RL, TAJIMA S, YAMAMURA T, YOKOYAMA S, YAMAMOTO A: Comparison of apolipoprotein C-II deficient triacylglycerol-rich lipoproteins and trioleoylglycerol/phosphatidylcholine-stabilized particles as substrates for lipoprotein lipase. *Biochim Biophys Acta* 857:211, 1986.
53. CARDIN AD, JACKSON RL, JOHNSON JD: 5-dimethylaminonaphthalene-1-sulfonyl 3-aminotryosyl apolipoprotein C-III, preparation, characterization, and interaction with phospholipid vesicles. *J Biol Chem* 257:4987, 1982.
54. GREENWOOD MRC: The relationship of enzyme activity to feeding behavior in rats: Lipoprotein lipase as the metabolic gatekeeper. *Int J Obes* 9 (*suppl* 1):67, 1985.
55. ECKEL RH: Adipose tissue lipoprotein lipase, in Borensztajn J (ed): *Lipoprotein Lipase*. Chicago, Evener Publishers, 1987, p 79.
56. SCHWARTZ RS, BRUNZELL JD: Increase of adipose tissue lipoprotein lipase activity with weight loss. *J Clin Invest* 67:1425, 1981.
57. TASKINEN MR, NIKKILÄ EA: Basal and postprandial lipoprotein lipase activitiy in adipose tissue during caloric restriction and refeeding. *Metabolism* 36:625, 1987.
58. ECKEL RH, JOST TJ: Weight reduction increases adipose tissue lipoprotein lipase responsiveness in obese women. *J Clin Invest* 80:992, 1987.
59. MAGILL P, RAO SN, MILLER NE, NICOLL A, BRUNZELL J, ST. HILAIRE J, LEWIS B: Relationships between the metabolism of high density and very-low density lipoproteins in man: Studies of apolipoprotein kinetics and adipose tissue lipoprotein lipase activity. *Eur J Clin Invest* 12:113, 1982.
60. TASKINEN M-R: Lipoprotein lipase in hypertriglyceridemias, in Borensztajn J (ed): *Lipoprotein Lipase*. Chicago, Evener Publishers, 1987, p 201.
61. PAGANO MIRANI-OOSTDIJK C, HAVEKES L, TERPSTRA J, FRÖLICH M, VAN GENT CM, JANSEN H: Diurnal changes in serum triglycerides as related to changes in lipolytic enzymes, apolipoproteins and hormones in normal subjects on a carbohydrate-rich diet. *Eur J Clin Invest* 13:301, 1983.
62. BRUNZELL JD, HAZZARD WR, PORTE D Jr, BIERMAN EL: Evidence for a common saturable triglyceride removal mechanism for chylomicrons and very low density lipoproteins in man. *J Clin Invest* 52:1578, 1978.
63. NIKKILÄ EA, TASKINEN MR, KEKKI M: Relation of plasma high density lipoprotein cholesterol to lipoprotein-lipase activity in adipose tissue and skeletal muscle of man. *Atherosclerosis* 29:497, 1978.
64. SPARKS RS, ZOLLNER S, KLISAK I, KIRCHGESSNER TG, KOMAROMY MC, MOHANDAS T, SCHOTZ MC, LUSIS AJ: Human genes involved in lipolysis of plasma lipoproteins: Mapping of loci for lipoprotein lipase to 8p22 and hepatic lipase to 15q21. *Genomics* 1:138, 1987.
65. POEHLMAN ET, DESPRES J-P, MARCOTTE M, TREMBLAY A, THERIAULT G, BOUCHARD C: Genotype dependency of adaptation in adipose tissue metabolism after short-term overfeeding. *Am J Physiol* 250:E480, 1986.
66. KUUSI T, KESANIEMI YA, VUORISTO M, MIETTINEN TA, KOSKENVUO M: Inheritance of high density lipoprotein and lipoprotein lipase and hepatic lipase activity. *Atherosclerosis* 7:421, 1987.
67. BORENSZTAJN J: Heart and skeletal muscle lipoprotein lipase, in Borensztajn J (ed): *Lipoprotein Lipase*, Chicago, Evener Publishers, 1987, p 133.
68. BEN-ZEEV O, LUSIS AJ, LeBOEUF RC, NIKAZY J, SCHOTZ MC: Evidence for independent genetic regulation of heart and adipose lipoprotein lipase activity. *J Biol Chem* 258:13632, 1983.
69. FOJO SS, LAW SW, BREWER HB Jr: The human apoprotein C-II gene: Complete nucleic acid sequence and genomic organization. *Proc Natl Acad Sci (USA)* 213:221, 1987.
70. DAS HK, JACKSON CL, MILLER DA, LEFF T, BRESLOW JL: The human apolipoprotein C-II gene sequence contains a novel chromosome 19-specific minisatellite in its third intron. *J Biol Chem* 262:4787, 1987.
71. WEI C-F, TSAO Y-K, ROBBERSON DL, GOTTO AM Jr, BROWN K, CHAN L: The structure of the human apolipoprotein C-II gene: Electron microscopic analysis of RNA:DNA hybrids, complete nucleotide sequence, and identification of 5′ homologous sequences among apolipoprotein genes. *J Biol Chem* 260:15211, 1985.
72. HUMPHRIES SE, BERG K, GILL L, CUMMING AM, ROBERTSON FW, STALENHOEF AFH, WILLIAMSON R, BORRESEN A-L: The gene for apolipoprotein C-II is closely linked to the gene for apolipoprotein E on chromosome 19. *Clin Genet* 26:389, 1984.
73. FOJO SS, TAAM L, FAIRWELL T, RONAN R, BISHOP C, MENG MS, HOEG JM, SPRECHER DL, BREWER HB Jr: Human preproapolipoprotein C-II: Analysis of major plasma isoforms. *J Biol Chem* 261:9591, 1986.
74. BEAUMONT JL, CARLSON LA, COOPER GR, FEJFAR Z, FREDRICKSON DS, STRASSER T: Classification of hyperlipidemias and hyperlipoproteinemias. *Bull WHO* 43:891, 1971.
75. BRUNZELL JD, BIERMAN EL: Chylomicronemia syndrome: Interaction of genetic and acquired hypertriglyceridemia. *Med Clin North Am* 66:455, 1982.
76. BRUNZELL JD, SCHROTT HG: The interaction of familial and secondary causes of hypertriglyceridemia: Role in pancreatitis. *Trans Assoc Am Physicians* 86:245, 1973.
77. CAMERON JL, CAPUZZI DM, ZUIDEMA GD, MARGOLIS S: Acute pancreatitis with hyperlipidemia: The incidence of lipid abnormalities in acute pancreatitis. *Ann Surg* 177:483, 1973.
78. FARMER RG, WINKELMAN EI, BROWN HB, LEWIS LA: Hyperlipoproteinemia and pancreatitis. *Am J Med* 54:161, 1973.
79. GREENBERGER NJ, HATCH FT, DRUMMEY GD, ISSELBACHER KJ: Pancreatitis and hyperlipemia: A study of serum lipid alterations in 25 patients with acute pancreatitis. *Medicine (Baltimore)* 45:161, 1966.
80. HOWARD JM, EHRLICH E, SPITZER JJ, SINGH LM: Hyperlipemia in patients with acute pancreatitis. *Ann Surg* 160:210, 1964.
81. FALLAT RW, VESTOR JW, GLUECK CJ: Suppression of amylase activity by hypertriglyceridemia. *JAMA* 225:1331, 1973.
82. LESSER PB, WARSHAW AL: Diagnosis of pancreatitis masked by hyperlipemia. *Ann Intern Med* 82:795, 1975.
83. WARSHAW AL, BELLINI CA, LESSER PB: Inhibition of serum and urine amylase activity in pancreatitis with hyperlipemia. *Ann Surg* 182:72, 1975.
84. PARKER F, BAGDADE JD, ODLAND GF, BIERMAN EL: Evidence for the chylomicron origin of lipids accumulating in diabetic eruptive xanthomas: A correlative lipid biochemical, histochemical and electron microscopic study. *J Clin Invest* 49:2172, 1970.
85. CHAIT A, ROBERTSON HT, BRUNZELL JD: Chylomicronemia syndrome in diabetes mellitus. *Diabetes Care* 4:343, 1981.
86. KUO PT, WHEREAT AF, HOROWITZ O: The effect of lipemia upon coronary

and peripheral arterial circulation in patients with essential hyperlipemia. *Am J Med* 26:68, 1959.

87. TALBOT GD, FRAYSER R: Hyperlipidaemia: A cause of decreased oxygen saturation. *Nature* 200:684, 1963.

88. DITZEL J, DYERBERG J: Hyperlipoproteinemia, diabetes, and oxygen affinity of hemoglobin. *Metabolism* 26:141, 1977.

89. ROBERTSON HT, CHAIT A, HLASTALA MP, BRUNZELL JD: Red cell oxygen affinity in severe hypertriglyceridemia. *Proc Soc Exp Biol Med* 159:437, 1978.

90. SHAH PC, PATEL AR, RAO KRP: Hyperlipemia and spuriously elevated hemoglobin levels. *Ann Intern Med* 82:382, 1975.

91. SIMONS LA, WILLIAMS PF, TURTLE JR: Type V hyperlipoproteinemia revisited: Findings in a Sydney population. *Aust NZ J Med* 5:210, 1975.

92. STEFFES MW, FREIER EF: A simple and precise method of determining true sodium, potassium and chloride concentrations in hyperlipemia. *J Lab Clin Med* 88:683, 1976.

93. O'HARA DD, PORTE D Jr, WILLIAMS RH: Use of constant composition of polyvinylpyrrolidone columns to study the interaction of fat particles with plasma. *J Lipid Res* 7:264, 1966.

94. HARLAN WR JR, WINESETT PS, WASSERMAN AJ: Tissue lipoprotein lipase in normal individuals and in individuals with exogenous hypertriglyceridemia and the relationship of this enzyme to assimilation of fat. *J Clin Invest* 46:239, 1967.

95. KRAUSS RM, LEVY RI, FREDRICKSON DS: Selective measurement of two lipase activities in postheparin plasma from normal subjects and patients with hyperlipoproteinemia. *J Clin Invest* 54:1107, 1974.

96. BRUNZELL JD, IVERIUS PH, SCHEIBEL MS, FUJIMOTO WY, HAYDEN MR, McLEOD R, FRÖHLICH J: Primary lipoprotein lipase deficiency, in Angel A, Fröhlich J (eds): *Lipoprotein Deficiency Syndromes*. New York, Plenum, 1986, p 227.

97. NIKKILÄ EA: Familial lipoprotein lipase deficiency and related disorders of chylomicron metabolism, in Stanbury JB, Wyngaarden JB, Fredrickson DS, Goldstein JL, Brown MS (eds): *The Metabolic Basis of Inherited Disease*, 5th ed. New York, McGraw-Hill, 1983, p 622.

98. FREDRICKSON DS, GOLDSTEIN JL, BROWN MS: The familial hyperlipoproteinemias, in Stanbury JB, Wyngaarden JB, Fredrickson DS (eds): *The Metabolic Basis of Inherited Disease*, 4th ed. New York, McGraw-Hill, 1978, p 604.

99. LEES RS, WILSON DE, SCHOENFELD G, FLEET S: The familial dyslipoproteinemias. *Prog Med Genet* 9:237, 1973.

100. GAGNE C, BRUN D, MOORJANI S, LUPIEN P-J: Hyperchylomicronémie familiale: Étude de l'ractivité lipolytique dans une famille. *Union Med Can* 106:333, 1977.

101. WILSON DE, EDWARD CQ, CHAN I-F: Phenotypic heterogeneity in the extended pedigree of a proband with lipoprotein lipase deficiency. *Metabolism* 32:1107, 1983.

102. FELLIN R, BAGGIO G, POLI A, AUGUSTIN J, BAIOCCHI R, BALDO G, SINIGAGLIA M, GRETEN H, CREPALDI G: Familial lipoprotein lipase and apolipoprotein C-II deficiency: Lipoprotein and apoprotein analysis, adipose tissue and hepatic lipoprotein lipase levels in seven patients and their first degree relatives. *Atherosclerosis* 49:55, 1983.

103. KONDO Y, KUROBANE I, OMURA K, SANO R, ABE R, CHIDA N, TADA K: Postheparin plasma lipoprotein lipase activity in heterozygotes of familial lipoprotein lipase deficiency. *Tohuku J Exp Med* 145:1, 1985.

104. BABIRAK SP, FUJIMOTO WY, BRUNZELL JD: Is the heterozygote state for LPL deficiency a subset of familial combined hyperlipidemia? *Atherosclerosis* 7:538a, 1987.

105. POTTER JM, MACDONALD WB: Primary type I hyperlipoproteinaemia: A metabolic and family study. *Aust NZ J Med* 9:688, 1979.

106. LEVY RI, FREDRICKSON DS: Familial hyperlipoproteinemia, in Stanbury JB, Wyngaarden JB, Fredrickson DS (eds): *The Metabolic Basis of Inherited Disease*, 3d ed. New York, McGraw-Hill, 1972, p 545.

107. BROWN WV, BAGINSKY ML, EHNHOLM C: Primary type I and type V hyperlipoproteinemia, in Rifkind BM, Levy RI (eds): *Hyperlipidemia: Diagnosis and Therapy*. New York, Grune & Stratton, 1977, p 93.

108. CHAIT A, BRUNZELL J: Very low density lipoprotein kinetics in familial forms of hypertriglyceridemia, in Berman M, Grundy S, Howard B (eds): *Lipoprotein Kinetics and Modeling*. New York, Academic Press, 1982, p 69.

109. BRUNZELL JD, CHAIT A, NIKKILÄ EA, EHNHOLM C, HUTTUNEN JK, STEINER G: Heterogeneity of primary lipoprotein lipase deficiency. *Metabolism* 29:624, 1980.

110. CHAIT A, IVERIUS P-H, BRUNZELL J: Lipoprotein lipase secretion by human monocyte-derived macrophages. *J Clin Invest* 69:490, 1982.

111. STEINER G, MYHER JJ, KUKSIS A: Milk and plasma lipid composition in a lactating patient with type I hyperlipoproteinemia. *Am J Clin Nutr* 41:121, 1985.

112. BURTON BK, NADLER HL: Primary type I hyperlipoproteinemia with normal lipoprotein lipase activity. *J Pediatr* 90:777, 1977.

113. GOLDBERG IJ, PATERNITI JR Jr, FRANKLIN BH, GINSBERG HN, GINSBERG-FELLNER F, BROWN WV: Case report: Transient lipoprotein lipase deficiency with hyperchylomicronemia. *Am J Med Sci* 286:28, 1983.

114. SHAFRIR E, BIALE Y: Effect of experimental hypertriglyceridemia on tissue and serum lipoprotein lipase activity. *Eur J Clin Invest* 1:19, 1970.

115. KISSEBAH AH, ADAMS PW, WYNN V: Plasma free fatty acid and triglyceride transport kinetics in man. *Clin Sci Mol Med* 47:259, 1974.

116. HORST A, PALUSZAK J, ZAWILSKA K, SOBISZ S: Three variants of postheparin lipoprotein lipase activity in idiopathic hyperlipoproteinemia. *Bull Acad Pol Sci* 21:199, 1973.

117. HOEG JM, OSBORNE JC JR, GREGG RE, BREWER HB JR: Initial diagnosis of lipoprotein lipase deficiency in a 75-year-old man. *Am J Med* 75:889, 1983.

118. NILSSON-EHLE P: Measurements of lipoprotein lipase activity, in Borensztajn J (ed): *Lipoprotein Lipase*. Chicago, Evener Publishers, 1987, p 59.

119. IVERIUS P-H, OSTLUND-LINDQVIST A-M: Preparation, characterization, and measurement of lipoprotein lipase. *Methods Enzymol* 129:691, 1986.

120. BIERMAN EL, BRUNZELL JD, BAGDADE JD, LERNER RL, HAZZARD WR, PORTE D Jr: On the mechanism of action of Atromid-S on triglyceride transport in man. *Trans Assoc Am Physicians* 83:211, 1970.

121. FOJO SS, BREWER HB Jr: Personal communication.

122. CONNELLY PW, MAGUIRE GF, HOFMANN T, LITTLE JA: Structure of apolipoprotein C-II Toronto, a nonfunctional human apolipoprotein. *Proc Natl Acad Sci USA* 84:270, 1987.

123. YAMAMURA T, SUDO H, ISHIKAWA K, YAMAMOTO A: Familial type I hyperlipoproteinemia caused by apolipoprotein C-II deficiency. *Atherosclerosis* 34:53, 1979.

124. MATSUOKA N, SHIRAI K, JOHNSON JD, KASHYAP ML, SRIVASTAVA LS, YAMAMURA T, YAMAMOTO A, SAITO Y, KUMAGAI A, JACKSON RL: Effects of apolipoprotein C-II (apo C-II) on the lipolysis of very low density lipoproteins from apo C-II deficient patients. *Metabolism* 30:818, 1981.

125. CREPALDI G, FELLIN R, BAGGIO G, AUGUSTIN J, GRETEN H: Lipoprotein and apoprotein, adipose tissue and hepatic lipoprotein lipase levels in patients with familial chylomicronemia and their immediate family members, in Gotto AM Jr, Smith LC, Allen B (eds): *Atherosclerosis V*. Berlin, Springer-Verlag, 1980, p 250.

126. MANZATO E, MARIN R, GASPAROTTO A, BAGGIO G, FELLIN R, CREPALDI G: The plasma lipoproteins in familial chylomicronemia: Analysis by zonal ultracentrifugation. *J Lab Clin Med* 104:778, 1984.

127. BAGGIO G, MANZATO E, GABELLI C, FELLIN R, MARTINI S, ENZI GB, VERLATO F, BAIOCCHI MR, SPRECHEAR DL, KASHYAP ML, BREWER HB Jr, CREPALDI G: Apolipoprotein C-II deficiency syndrome: Clinical features, lipoprotein characterization, lipase activity, and correction of hypertriglyceridemia after apo lipoprotein C-II administration in two affected patients. *J Clin Invest* 77:520, 1986.

128. MILLER NE, RAO SN, ALAUPOVIC P, NOBLE N, SLACK J, BRUNZELL JD, LEWIS B: Familial apolipoprotein C-II deficiency: Plasma lipoproteins and apolipoproteins in heterozygous and homozygous subjects and the effects of plasma infusion. *Eur J Clin Invest* 11:69, 1981.

129. BRUNZELL JD, MILLER NE, ALAUPOVIC P, ST. HILAIRE RJ, WANG CS, SARSON DL, BLOOM SR, LEWIS B: Familial chylomicronemia due to a circulating inhibitor of lipoprotein lipase activity. *J Lipid Res* 24:12, 1983.

130. STALENHOEF AFH, CASPARIE AF, DEMACKER PNM, STOUTEN JTJ, LUTTERMAN JA, VAN'T LAAR A: Combined deficiency of apolipoprotein C-II and lipoprotein lipase in familial hyperchylomicronemia. *Metabolism* 30:919, 1981.

131. CATAPANO AL, MILLS GL, ROMA P, LA ROSA M, CAPURSO A: Plasma lipids, lipoproteins and apoproteins in a case of apo C-II deficiency. *Clin Chim Acta* 130:317, 1983.

132. SAKU K, CEDRES C, McDONALD B, HYND BA, LIU BW, SRIVASTAVA LS, KASHYAP ML: C-II anapolipoproteinemia and severe hypertriglyceridemia: Report of a rare case with absence of C-II apolipoprotein isoforms and review of the literature. *Am J Med* 77:457, 1984.

133. FOJO SS, LAW SW, SPRECHER DL, GREGG RE, BAGGIO G, BREWER HB JR: Analysis of the apo C-II gene in apo C-II deficient patients. *Biochem Biophys Res Commun* 124:308, 1984.

134. HAYDEN MR, VERGANI C, HUMPHRIES SE, KIRBY L, SHUKIN R, McLEOD R: The genetics and molecular biology of apolipoprotein C-II, in Angel A, Fröhlich J (eds): *Lipoprotein Deficiency Syndromes*. New York, Plenum, 1986, p 241.

135. FOJO SS, RYU YN, DE GENNES JL, LAW SW, BREWER HB JR: Molecular heterogeneity in the defect of a patient with apo C-II deficiency. *Arteriosclerosis* 7:519a, 1987.

136. DE GENNES JL, DAIROU F, GARDETTE J, TRUFFERT J, BEUCLER I, PIGIER

AM, AGHELI N: Type I hypertriglyceridemia by apo C-II deficiency, a report of a case. In press.

137. FALLAT RW, GLUECK CJ: Familial and acquired type V hyperlipoproteinemia. *Atherosclerosis* 23:41, 1976.

138. GREENBERG BH, BLACKWELDER WC, LEVY RI: Primary type V hyperlipoproteinemia. A descriptive study in 32 families. *Ann Intern Med* 87:526, 1977.

139. BRUNZELL JD, SCHROTT HG, MOTULSKY AG, BIERMAN EL: Myocardial infarction in the familial forms of hypertriglyceridemia. *Metabolism* 25:313, 1976.

140. CHAIT A, ROBERTSON HT, BRUNZELL JD: Chylomicronemia syndrome in diabetes mellitus. *Diabetes Care* 4:343, 1981.

141. CHAIT A, BRUNZELL JD: Severe hypertriglyceridemia: Role of familial and acquired disorders. *Metabolism* 32:209, 1983.

CHAPTER **46**

FAMILIAL LECITHIN:CHOLESTEROL ACYLTRANSFERASE DEFICIENCY, INCLUDING FISH EYE DISEASE

KAARE R. NORUM
EGIL GJONE
JOHN A. GLOMSET

1. *Familial lecithin:cholesterol acyltransferase (LCAT) deficiency is characterized by a combination of clinical, tissue, and plasma lipoprotein abnormalities that result from a failure of LCAT to esterify cholesterol in the plasma.*
2. *The clinical abnormalities include corneal opacities, anemia, and frequently, though not invariably, proteinuria. Renal failure can be a life-threatening complication.*
3. *The disease is inherited as an autosomal recessive trait. A total of 51 patients from 27 families have been described. The defect has been localized to chromosome 16.*
4. *The tissue abnormalities include foam cells in the bone marrow and glomerular tufts, lamellar inclusions in cells of the spleen, and target-shaped erythrocytes that contain abnormally high amounts of unesterified cholesterol and phosphatidylcholine.*
5. *The plasma lipoprotein abnormalities involve all lipoprotein classes and affect composition, shape, distribution, and concentration. Unusual particles, rich in unesterified cholesterol and phosphatidylcholine, are particularly striking in some patients.*
6. *Active LCAT is absent or nearly absent from the plasma, and little or no esterification of cholesterol occurs when the plasma is incubated in vitro. However, immunochemical techniques revealed LCAT protein in the plasma of several patients. Apparently, mutation of the LCAT gene on chromosome 16 can lead to synthesis and secretion of an inactive enzyme. As a result, unesterified cholesterol and phosphatidylcholine accumulate in the plasma, and there is a plasma cholesteryl ester deficit. Unesterified cholesterol and phosphatidylcholine accumulate in tissues as well, and this may ultimately give rise to tissue dysfunction.*
7. *Fish eye disease is characterized by corneal opacities and plasma lipoprotein abnormalities, including increased amounts of triglyceride in whole plasma, in VLDL, and in LDL. HDL concentration is only about 10 percent of normal. Upon incubation of whole plasma and mixtures of plasma lipoprotein fractions, VLDL and LDL cholesterols, but not HDL cholesterol, are esterified.*
8. *The LCAT gene has been cloned. Studies on DNA samples from several unrelated patients with familial LCAT deficiency and two related patients with fish eye disease revealed no large deletions or rearrangements of the LCAT gene sequences.*

HISTORY

In 1966, a 33-year-old woman (patient A. R.) from western Norway was admitted to Rikshospitalet, the National Hospital of Norway, in Oslo. She had diffuse grayish corneal opacities, anemia, proteinuria, and hyperlipemia, and was presumed to have chronic nephritis. Renal function proved to be normal, and the serum albumin level was only slightly reduced. Both plasma triglyceride and cholesterol levels were increased, but most of the cholesterol was unesterified. Plasma phosphatidylcholine, or lecithin, level was increased, but the level of plasma lysolecithin was decreased and no pre-β- or α-lipoproteins could be detected on electrophoresis. A kidney biopsy was not unusual in that it showed foam cells in the glomerular tufts. Subsequently, the same clinical features and the same relative abnormalities in plasma cholesterol and phospholipid were found in two of the patient's sisters, and further studies of all three sibs disclosed the absence of lecithin:cholesterol acyltransferase (LCAT) activity in plasma (Fig. 46-1). Because all three were afflicted and because none had a history of liver or kidney disease that could account for the abnormalities, it appeared that they suffered from a previously undiscovered inborn error of metabolism.[1–3]

In 1969, a Swedish family with this condition was described.[4] A 47-year-old woman had corneal opacities, anemia, proteinuria, hyperlipemia, and the same plasma lipid and lipoprotein abnormalities as the three Norwegian sisters. The level of plasma LCAT activity was very low. The patient's brother had developed the same symptoms and died of uremia at age 40 years. Three additional Norwegian families have been found since 1970.[5–8] They live in the same general area of Norway as the first family. As of January 1981, 26 patients from 12 different families were known (see Table 31-1 in the fifth edition of this text).[9] These patients had been discovered in Norway, Sweden, Germany, the United Kingdom, France, Canada, and Japan. Since then another 15 families with 25 patients have been discovered. These new patients come from Japan, the United States, France, Italy, Canada, Germany, and Bulgaria.[10–17]

Nonstandard abbreviations used in this chapter are: LCAT = lecithin:cholesterol acyltransferase; VLDL = very low density lipoprotein; LDL = low density lipoprotein; IDL = intermediate density lipoprotein; HDL = high density lipoprotein; apo (as in apo C-II, apo C-III, etc.) = apolipoprotein.

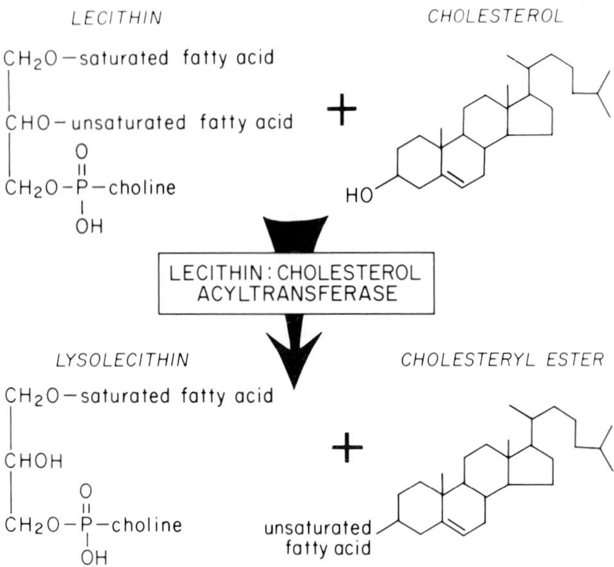

Fig. 46-1 Principal lipid reactants in the plasma lecithin:cholesterol acyltransferase (EC 2.3. 1.43) reaction.

CHARACTERISTICS

Present information about familial LCAT deficiency is derived from studies of many different patients. The Norwegian patients have been studied intensively. The patients show significant heterogeneity, even within families.

Clinical and Tissue Abnormalities

Ocular Features. Corneal opacities are present in all patients from early childhood and are easily detectable. They consist of numerous minute, grayish dots in the entire corneal stroma that give the cornea a cloudy to misty appearance (Fig. 46-2). Near the limbal area the dots increase in number, forming a grayish, circular band resembling an arcus lipoides senilis.[18] The material in the dots has not yet been identified, but ultrastructural examination of sections obtained by superficial keratectomy[19,20] has revealed the presence of numerous vacuoles, many of which contain electron-dense, or "membranous," deposits. These vacuoles occur in both Bowman layer and the anterior stroma.

Fundus changes have been observed in two patients. Angioid streaks were found in one, whereas the other developed papilledema and impaired ocular blood supply with functional loss, presumably caused by arterial obstruction and leakage of lipid material into the nervous tissue of the optic disk.[18] Although the presence of excess lipids has not been verified chemically or morphologically, crystals that may be cholesterol have been seen by polarized light in both the cornea and the fundus. The cornea of a patient who received a cornea transplant contained excess unesterified cholesterol and phospholipid.[21]

It is interesting that similar corneal findings have been noted in other genetic diseases affecting HDL metabolism. Thus, corneal opacities are found in several patients with Tangier disease,[22] in patients with combined apo A-I/apo C-III deficiency,[23] and in patients with fish eye disease.[24] If these opacities consist of cholesterol deposits, they may provide direct visual evidence of the role of apo A-I and LCAT in the transport of cholesterol from peripheral tissue. The arcus presenilis observed in patients with familial hypercholesterolemia is quite different from the findings in familial LCAT deficiency and never affects the pupillary zone of the cornea.

Hematologic Features. Anemia with a hemoglobin concentration of about 10 g/dl is seen in most patients and is of the normochromic type.[25] Hematologic data (see Table 31-2 in the previous edition of this text[9]) and bone marrow studies suggest that the anemia is due to moderate hemolysis combined with reduced compensatory erythropoiesis. Radioisotope studies of the erythrocyte life span have shown half-lives of 16 to 17 days in two patients (normal half-life, 23 to 35 days). The patients' spleens have not been particularly active in erythrocyte destruction.

The erythrocytes show abnormalities in appearance and lipid composition.[26] Target cells are found in increased numbers in dry smears of both peripheral blood and bone marrow. Measurements of whole erythrocytes from Scandinavian patients revealed up to twice the normal amount of unesterified cholesterol and phosphatidylcholine but decreased amounts of sphingomyelin and phosphatidylethanolamine and normal amounts of total phospholipid. Measurements of erythrocyte membrane preparations from Canadian patients[27] revealed similar abnormalities in content of unesterified cholesterol, phosphatidylcholine, and phosphatidylethanolamine, although the content of sphingomyelin was normal. The increased amount of unesterified cholesterol in the red cell membrane should lead to decreased membrane fluidity. The effect of increased unesterified cholesterol appeared to be counteracted by changed phospholipid composition, especially by shorter chain length and more unsaturated bonds.[28]

The red cells in LCAT deficiency have markedly decreased sodium influx and decreased activity of acetylcholinesterase. Both of these functions are markers of the outer leaflet of the red cell membrane.[29] It is not yet clear whether other blood cells show related abnormalities, but platelet function and lipid composition are normal.[30]

Foam cells have been found in the bone marrow of several patients. Giemsa stain has revealed sea-blue histiocytes (Fig. 46-3) in both bone marrow and spleen of all patients studied,[31]

Fig. 46-2 Corneal infiltrate in patient A. R. It is localized to the parenchyma, is composed of numerous minute dots, and is most prominent in the periphery, where it resembles a corneal arcus. *(From Gjone and Bergaust.[18] Used by permission.)*

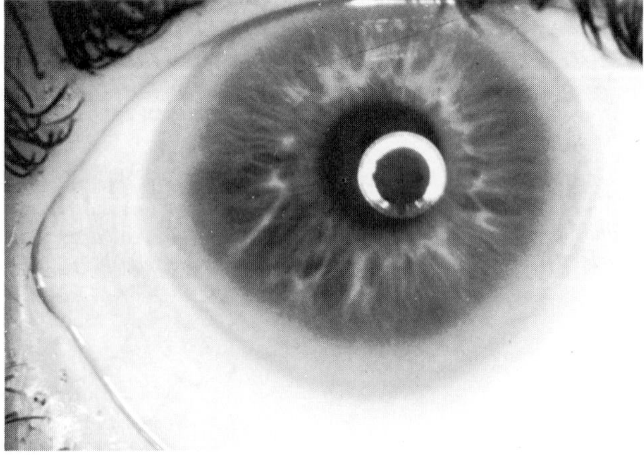

and ultrastructural studies[32] have shown that the histiocyte granules are composed of membranes in a lamellar arrangement (Fig. 46-4). These membranes presumably contain unesterified cholesterol and phosphatidylcholine since both lipids are present in increased amounts in the spleen as well as in the liver.[33]

Renal Manifestations. In most patients the urine contains protein, erythrocytes, and hyaline casts. Most of the urinary protein migrates in the position of albumin on electrophoresis; α_1- and α_2-migrating proteins are also present. Proteinuria is usually detected early in life and remains moderate (about 0.5 to 1.5 mg protein per milliliter of urine) for many years, but it increases with the onset of renal insufficiency. In many patients, proteinuria increased markedly in the fourth and fifth decades of life as renal function deteriorated. A few patients had never had proteinuria.

The concentration of albumin in the serum is usually only slightly reduced, but it decreases considerably in association with the increased proteinuria that accompanies renal failure. Serum creatinine and urea concentrations, as well as clearance of creatinine, inulin, and para-aminohippuric acid, remain normal for many years, as does the blood pressure. Renal insufficiency and hypertension may develop rapidly and without warning.[25]

Light-microscopic examination of renal biopsies has revealed foam cells in the glomerular tufts in most of the patients examined so far. Arterioles have thickened intimas and narrow lumens. Subendothelial deposits of lipid material have been found in the renal arteries and arterioles. Lipid analysis of isolated glomeruli has shown that the amounts of unesterified cholesterol and phospholipid are markedly higher than normal (Table 46-1).[33] Electron-microscopic studies[32,34,25] have demonstrated capillary lumens that are partly filled with a meshwork of membranes and particles with an amorphous mottled structure. The capillary walls appear to be abnormal. Endothelial cells are frequently absent, the basal lamina is of irregular thickness, endothelial foot processes are fused, and membrane-surrounded particles are present in both the subendothelial and subepithelial regions. "Moth-eaten" holes were found in the periphery of mesangial deposits, and most of the holes contained osmiophilic lamellar bodies. Immunofluorescence identified complement (C3) deposits in the mesangium.[36]

Table 46-1 Lipid Concentrations in Kidneys, Liver, and Spleen of LCAT-Deficient Patient A. R.

	Concentration, nmol lipid/mg protein				
Organ	*TC†*	*UC*	*PL*	*TG*	*UC/PL*
Kidneys					
Cortex, A. R., Jan. 1973		170	257	9	0.7
Cortex, A. R., July 1973*		80	207	12	0.4
Cortex, control		50	109	4	0.5
Glomeruli, A. R., Jan. 1973		416	455	9	0.9
Glomeruli, A. R., July 1973*		153	229	21	0.7
Glomeruli, control		57	103	14	0.6
Liver					
A. R., Jan. 1973	90	83	273	21	0.3
Control	20	18	185	9	0.1
Spleen					
A. R., Jan. 1973	284	268	372	12	0.7
Control	3	3	—	14	—

*In kidney from normal donor transplanted 6 months earlier.
†TC = total cholesterol; UC = unesterified cholesterol; PL = total phospholipids; TG = triglyceride; — = not determined.
SOURCE: From Stokke et al.[33]

Atherosclerosis. Early atherosclerosis has developed in many patients with familial LCAT deficiency, and tendon and planar xanthomas have been noted in a few patients. Calcification in the aorta has been demonstrated before the age of 40, and postmortem examinations have revealed atherosclerosis of the aorta and large arteries.[25,33] Renal arteries and arterioles also show early atherosclerotic changes. Histologic examination shows fibrosis and hyalinization of renal arterial walls, with marked narrowing of the vessel lumens.[32]

Electron-microscopic studies of sections from renal and iliac arteries and from the aorta have revealed accumulation of lipidlike material of the same type observed in the other organs. This material is present in the different layers of the vessel wall. Foam cells are present as well, and there is sometimes smooth-muscle cell proliferation in the intimal layer.[33]

Lipid analysis of an atheroma from a renal artery revealed that only 35 percent of total cholesterol was esterified (Table 46-2). This contrasts with findings of about 75 percent choles-

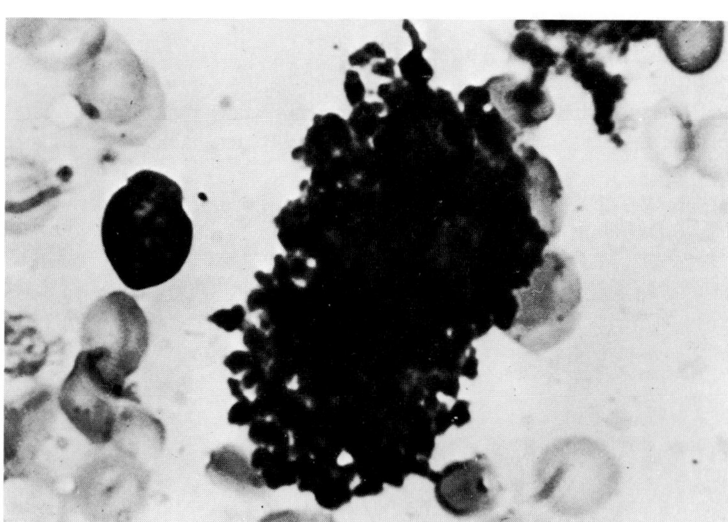

Fig. 46-3 Sea-blue histiocyte in a spleen aspirate from a patient with LCAT deficiency.

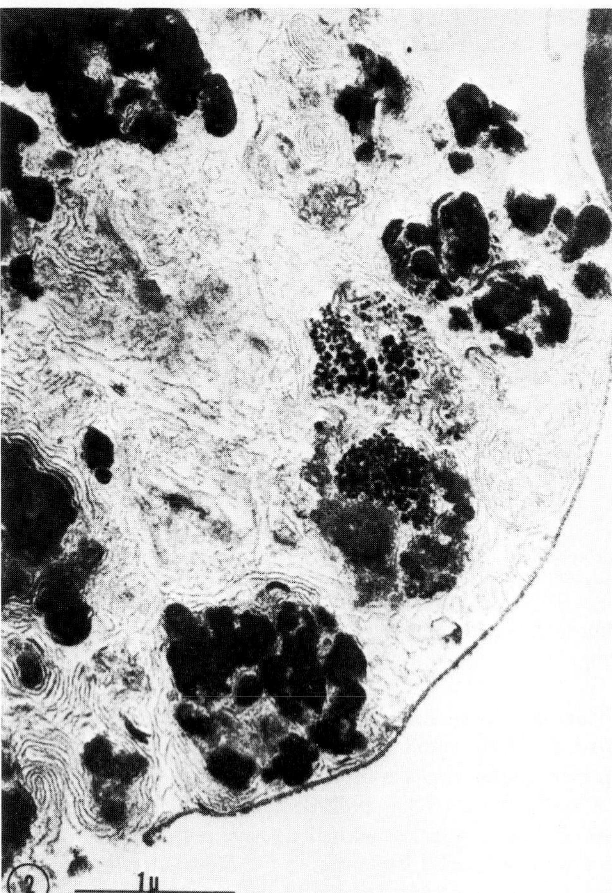

Fig. 46-4 Sea-blue histiocyte from spleen with inclusions and cytoplasmic membranes. Note the plasma membrane, which is about three times thicker than normal. *(From Jacobsen et al.*[31] *Used by permission.)*

teryl ester in the atheromas of patients dying with other diseases.[37] The fatty acid pattern of atheroma cholesteryl ester was distinctly different from that usually seen in atherosclerotic lesions. The ratio of oleic to linoleic acid was about 4:1, whereas this ratio in plaques usually varies between 2:1 and 1:1. Thus, fatty acid composition of cholesteryl ester in the atheroma resembles the abnormal pattern found in plasma (see below) and is similar to the intracellular pattern normally formed by acyl coenzyme A:cholesterol acyltransferase.

Plasma Lipoprotein Abnormalities

Patients who have familial LCAT deficiency show multiple plasma lipoprotein abnormalities, some readily detectable by analysis of the whole plasma. All patients have high concentrations of plasma unesterified cholesterol and phosphatidylcholine, and all have low concentrations of plasma cholesteryl ester and lysolecithin.[38] The cholesteryl esters contain abnormally high proportions of palmitic and oleic acids and an abnormally low proportion of linoleic acid. Upon electrophoresis of the plasma on paper or agarose gel, no pre-β-lipoprotein band is seen, although hypertriglyceridemia may be present, and an α_1-lipoprotein band, if visible, is very faint.

Many additional abnormalities become apparent when the plasma lipoproteins are isolated and examined by special techniques such as ultracentrifugation, gel filtration, electron microscopy, and apolipoprotein analysis.[39,40] Very low density lipoproteins (VLDL), i.e., lipoproteins of $d < 1.006$ g/ml, show abnormal β mobility on electrophoresis and are frequently elevated in concentration. Whether elevated or not, they contain high amounts of unesterified cholesterol compared with phosphatidylcholine, low amounts of total protein, and particularly low amounts of apolipoproteins C-II and C-III (apo C-II, apo C-III).[41] Since these apolipoproteins are normally the most electronegative components of VLDL, their low content in the patients' VLDL probably accounts for the unusually slow electrophoretic mobility of these lipoproteins.

When patient VLDL of different sizes are examined by gel filtration and electron microscopy, those that are 60 nm in diameter or larger can be seen to include notched particles. The same size VLDL contain an unusually high proportion of surface components (Table 46-3), high amounts of cholesterol ester and apolipoproteins C-I and E (apo C-I, apo E), and two major tetramethylurea-insoluble proteins. One of the proteins insoluble in tetramethylurea is similar in size to apolipoprotein B_{100} (apo B_{100}); the other appears to be somewhat smaller, probably apo B_{48}. It has been suggested that the notched particles are chylomicron remnants.[39] When the concentration of plasma triglyceride is high, the lipoproteins of $d < 1.006$ g/ml include a high proportion of particles that are greater than 90 nm in diameter. These particles are present in the plasma of patients who have fasted overnight, but disappear or decrease markedly in concentration when the patients consume fat-free diets for several days[40]; hence they are believed to be chylomicrons.

VLDLs that are 40 nm in diameter or smaller are probably of hepatic origin. They contain low amounts of cholesterol ester, normal amounts of apo C-I and apo E, and a single protein insoluble in tetramethylurea that cannot be distinguished from apo B_{100}.

Less is known about the patients' intermediate density lipoproteins (IDL, LDL_1), i.e., lipoproteins of density 1.006 to 1.019 g/ml. These include both normal size and unusually large particles, as demonstrated by gel filtration on 2% agarose.[41] The composition of the large and normal size particles is intermediate between that of corresponding size VLDL and low density lipoproteins of density 1.019 to 1.063 g/ml (LDL_2).

LDL_2 also frequently includes unusually large particles. After filtration through 2% agarose, LDL_2 usually yields three relatively well defined subfractions, whereas normal LDL_2 yields only one (Fig. 46-5). These three fractions of LDL_2 are believed to be formed from the action of lipoprotein lipase on triglyceride-rich lipoproteins (Fig. 46-6). One of the LDL_2 subfractions not found in normal plasma emerges in the void volume of the 2% agarose column (Fig. 46-5). It comprises particles 90 nm in diameter that have a multilamellar structure and that contain unesterified cholesterol and phosphatidylcho-

Table 46-2 Lipid Concentrations in an Atheroma of LCAT-Deficient Patient A. R.

	Concentration, nmol lipid/mg protein					
	TC†	*UC*	*PL*	*TG*	*UC/PL*	*CE/TC*
Atheroma, A. R., Jan. 1973	749	485	371	21	1.31	0.35
Plaque material from controls*					1.12	0.75

*Smith.[37]
†TC = total cholesterol; UC = unesterified cholesterol; PL = total phospholipids; TG = triglyceride; CE = cholesteryl esters.
SOURCE: From Stokke et al.[33]

Table 46-3 Comparison of Patient and Control VLDL of Two Different Diameters*

	40-nm Particles		*60-nm Particles*	
	Patients	*Controls*	*Patients*	*Controls*
Total protein, gram × 10^{-19}/particle	30†	52	55†	93
Apoprotein, molecules/particle				
E	6.0	7.4	25.5†	9.4
C-I	9.5	6.4	21.7‡	13.1
C-II	6.1†	12.2	13.3†	37.4
$C\text{-}III_1$	12.4†	49.4	25.1†	124.0
$C\text{-}III_2$	14.9†	42.5	33.4†	110.0
Lipids, 10^3 molecules/particle				
PL	4.9	4.7	15.8†	12.0
UC	4.4†	2.7	15.5†	6.3
CE	0.9†	2.3	4.6§	2.8
TG	13.8‡	12.2	47.1†	53.0

*Values for patient and control lipoproteins predicted from analyses of subfractions obtained by gel filtration.
†$p < 0.001$.
‡$p < 0.05$.
§$p < 0.01$.
SOURCE: From Glomset et al.[39]

line in the unusually high molar ratio of 2:1 (Table 46-4). The two types of "surface" lipid no doubt account for the lamellar structure of the particles, since the width of the lamella, measured by electron microscopy, is identical with that of unesterified cholesterol/phosphatidylcholine bilayers formed in vitro. The very small amount of protein present in the particles is largely albumin. The total concentration of these particles in the plasma of different patients varies from 0 to 48 mg cholesterol per deciliter plasma, and appears to be roughly proportional to the concentration of chylomicrons. Moreover, the concentrations of the large LDLs and of chylomicrons both decrease when the patients consume fat-free diets.[40]

Fig. 46-5 Subfractions of LDL of density 1.019 to 1.063 g/ml from patients M. R. and L. G., obtained by filtration through 2% agarose columns. L, I, and S = subfractions comprising of large, intermediate, and small particles, respectively. Normal LDL will emerge from the columns where the S subfraction emerges. *(From Glomset et al.[41] Used by permission.)*

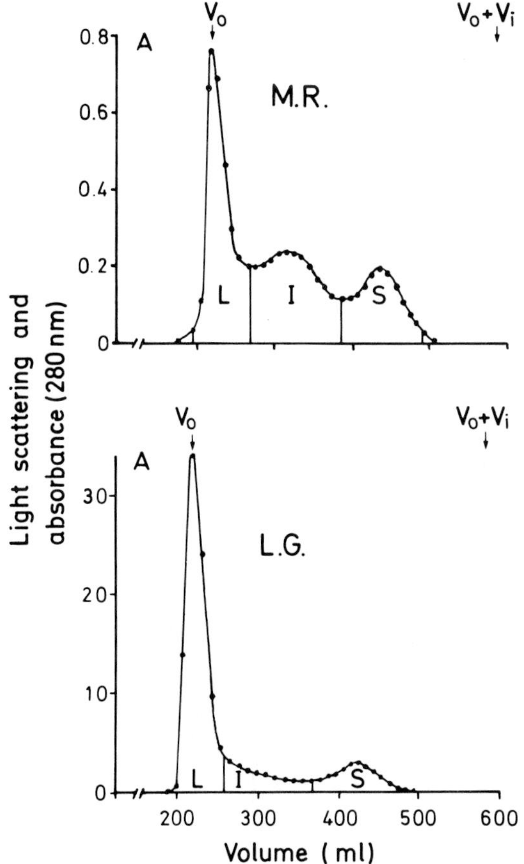

A second subfraction of patient LDL_2 is made up of particles 30 to 80 nm in diameter that emerge just after the void volume. These particles also have no obvious counterparts in normal plasma, although similar particles (Lp X) are found in cholestasis.[42] The particles have a disk-shaped appearance when examined by electron microscopy and often form stacks (Fig. 46-6). They largely contain unesterified cholesterol, phosphatidylcholine, and apo C. The relative content of apo C-I is very high. The total concentration of LP X–like particles in patient plasma has been estimated after isolation of the LP X by an electrophoretic technique.[43] It ranges from about 10 to 60 mg cholesterol per deciliter plasma.

Table 46-4 Lipid/Lipoprotein Ratios of Normal LDL and Large, Intermediate, and Small LDL. Particles from Two Patients with Familial LCAT Deficiency*

	Lipid/lipoprotein ratios, μmol lipid/mg protein			
	PC‡	*UC*	*CE*	*TG*
Normal† LDL	0.48	1.4	1.8	0.11
Large LDL_2				
Patient L. G.	21.5	39.8	0.40	1.72
Patient M. R.	12.0	20.9	0.50	1.23
Intermediate LDL_2				
Patient L. G.	5.05	8.64	0.19	0.95
Patient M. R.	5.54	8.24	0.32	0.58
Small LDL_2				
Patient L. G.	1.01	1.0	0.19	1.53
Patient M. R.	0.78	0.83	0.47	0.95

*The subfractions correspond to those shown in Fig. 46-5.
†The mean from six normal females.
‡PC = phosphatidylcholine; UC = unesterified cholesterol; CE = cholesterol ester; TG = triglyceride.
SOURCE: From Glomset et al.[41]

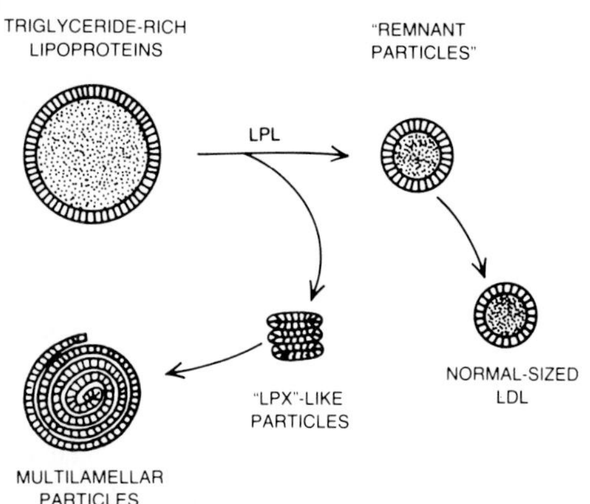

Fig. 46-6 Proposed mechanism of formation of patient large-, intermediate-, and small-molecular-weight LDL_2 by action of lipoprotein lipase (LPL) on triglyceride-rich lipoproteins. LPL produces two direct products: "remnant particles" that contain both core and surface material, and which float in the VLDL and IDL range; and Lp X-like particles that contain surface materials and float in the LDL_2 range. The remnant particles give rise to normal size LDL_2. The Lp X-like particles, which are equivalent ot the intermediate size LPL_2 (Fig. 46-5), are converted to multilamellar particles, which are equivalent to the large size LDL_2 (Fig. 46-5).

Other LDL_2s in the second subfraction that emerges from 2% agarose are spherical and resemble normal remnants of chylomicrons and VLDL metabolism (Fig. 46-6). They can be separated from the Lp X–like particles by adsorption on heparin-agarose and appear to contain triglyceride, cholesterol ester, and both apo B and apo E.

A third subfraction of patient LDL_2 contains spherical particles that, like normal LDL_2, are 20 to 22 nm in diameter (Fig. 46-6). Unlike normal LDL_2, the spherical particles of patient LDL_2 contain large amounts of triglyceride, but the content of cholesterol ester is correspondingly reduced; thus both the content of total "core" lipid and the proportion of core lipid to surface lipid and protein are normal.[38,41] Furthermore, the protein is apo B_{100}, as in normal LDL_2. The concentration of the normal sized LDL_2 appears to be quite low, however, since the concentration of total apo B in patient plasma is only one-half to one-third that in normal persons.[38]

HDL from these patients also includes particles of unusual shape and composition.[44–48] Some of the particles are disk-shaped, while others are spherical, as in normal HDL, but unusually small. The disk-shaped particles mainly contain unesterified cholesterol, phosphatidylcholine, and apo E or apolipoprotein A-I and A-II (apo A-I, apo A-II).[49] Patient disk-shaped HDLs that contain apo E have been isolated and characterized sufficiently to allow calculation of their composition and structure[50] (Table 46-5). The particles show many similarities to disk-shaped "nascent HDLs" that have been isolated from rat liver perfusates[51,52] and from intestinal rat lymph.[53] A notable feature is that the disk thickness corresponds to that of a phospholipid bilayer, while just enough apolipoprotein is present to form a three-tiered rim of amphipathic helix that defines the disk perimeter (Fig. 46-7). Perhaps for this reason the linkage of apo E to the particle is unusually stable.[51]

The disk-shaped HDL particles that contain apo A-I are similar in shape and lipid composition to the disk-shaped HDLs that contain apo E. Several types of these apo A-I-rich particles can be separated by gradient gel electrophoresis, but pure particles rich in apo A-I have not yet been characterized sufficiently to permit calculation of their structure. Characterization of the particles may never be complete because the linkage of apo A-I to the particles is unusually labile and much of the apo A-I appears to dissociate from the HDL during ultracentrifugation. This may partially explain the low content of protein in the HDL fraction and the high content of apo A-I in the protein fraction of $d > 1.25$ g/ml.[54,55] Even so, the total concentration of apo A-I in patient plasma is only about one-third of normal.[38]

The spherical HDLs are only about 6 nm in diameter. They contain unesterified cholesterol, phosphatidylcholine, a small amount of core lipid, and apo A-I. Calculations suggest that there may be two molecules of apo A-I per 94,600-dalton particle.[56]

The concentration of the small HDL particles varies somewhat with the diet. It increases in most patients on a high-fat diet, and decreases on a low-fat diet.[40]

It is conceivable that the small HDLs, which contain apo A-I as the only protein,[49] are derived from chylomicrons. Thus Green et al.[57] found that some of the phospholipids and

Table 46-5 Comparison of Patient Apolipoprotein E–Rich HDL with "Nascent HDL" from Rat Liver Perfusates*

	Patient HDL	*Nascent HDL†*
Dimensions, nm		
Diameter	19.5	19.1
Thickness	4.4	4.5
ΔR‡	1.5	1.5
Particle weight, daltons	892,000	843,000
Apolipoproteins, molecules/particle		
Apo E	7.4	9.0
Apo A-I	0.6	1.0
Lipids, molecules/particle		
Phospholipid	569	401
Unesterified cholesterol	441	261
Cholesteryl ester	n.d.§	55
Triglyceride	n.d.	52

*Values predicted from a disk-shaped model.
†Data from Hamilton et al.[51]
‡ΔR is protein rim width chosen to approximate diameter of amphipathic helix (d = 1.5 nm).
§n.d. = not detected.
SOURCE: From Mitchell et al.[50]

Fig. 46-7 *Model of patient disk-shaped apo E-rich HDL. (Based on data from Mitchell et al.[50] Used by permission.)*

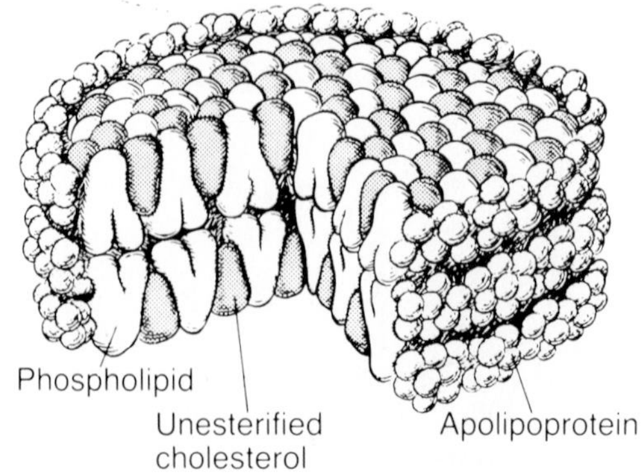

a large fraction of apo A-I are lost from human chylomicrons to HDL. Furthermore, Erkelens et al.[58] have studied the interaction between apo A-I and apo C and triglyceride-rich particles. They found that binding of apolipoproteins to the triglyceride-rich particles was accompanied by a particle disruption. The new lipoprotein particles, containing apo A-I, had a density range of HDL_3.

However, the small HDL particles may also originate in the liver. Thus, Hoffman and Benditt[59] have found that such particles are secreted from a primary, serum-free culture of mouse hepatocytes.

The small HDL particles are very good substrate for LCAT. When the small particles are incubated with partially purified LCAT and an extra source of cholesterol, the esterification of cholesterol proceeds at a higher rate and for a much longer time than when the disk-shaped HDL particles are incubated under similar conditions.[45] Furthermore, upon incubation with LCAT and erythrocyte membranes, the small HDL resulted in much more cholesteryl ester formation than the disk-shaped HDL. This may suggest that the small HDL particles are active acceptors of unesterified cholesterol from cellular plasma membranes, whereas the disk-shaped large HDL particles preferentially use their own cholesterol for esterification.

In other words, small HDL particles in normal plasma may be active in the reversed transport of cholesterol from peripheral cells to the liver. These particles may constitute the minor lipoprotein fraction proposed by Fielding and Fielding,[60] containing apo A-I unassociated with other apolipoproteins. This lipoprotein fraction probably catalyzes sterol efflux from cultured fibroblast to human plasma medium, and this appears to be the first step of LCAT-linked sterol transport from cells.

Lecithin:Cholesterol Acyltransferase (LCAT)

The enzyme LCAT is a glycoprotein of about 63,000 daltons that has been purified to apparent homogeneity from human blood plasma.[61–63] By cDNA and genomic cloning, the mRNA and amino acid sequence of human LCAT have been determined. The mature protein contains 416 amino acid residues and is distinguished by a number of extended sequences of hydrophobic amino acids, one of which is similar to sequences in both pancreatic and lingual lipase.[64] Blot hybridization data suggest that there is only one LCAT gene in humans.[65]

LCAT is formed in the liver, and probably only in the liver.[65] It circulates in blood plasma as a complex with components of HDL and cholesteryl ester transfer protein.[66–69] It is activated by apolipoprotein A-I[70] and catalyzes the reaction shown in Fig. 46-1.

However, the first step in the LCAT reaction is a phospholipase A_2 reaction,[71,72] leading to lysolecithin and an acylated enzyme, and the second step is the transfer of the acyl group[73] to cholesterol, other sterols,[74] water,[72] or lysolecithin.[75]

The LCAT activity in plasma can be demonstrated by incubating plasma at 37°C and measuring the decrease in concentration of plasma unesterified cholesterol. Alternatively, radioactive unesterified cholesterol, introduced either in plasma lipoproteins[76] or by using the radioactive substrate in liposomes or micelles,[77] may be incubated with plasma or plasma fractions, and the amount of radioactive cholesterol ester formed can be determined. Little or no activity is demonstrable in patient plasma by either method.[1]

In vivo studies have yielded results that are consistent with the in vitro data.[1] The plasma unesterified cholesterol of patient I. S. rapidly became labeled when she was injected with radioactive mevalonate, whereas no label appeared in the plasma cholesterol ester. Plasma unesterified cholesterol and cholesteryl ester both are labeled when normal subjects are treated similarly.

Absence of LCAT activity is not due to the presence of inhibitors, since addition of patient plasma to normal plasma does not inhibit LCAT activity.[1] Moreover, incubation of patient plasma with LCAT that has been purified from normal plasma leads to formation of substantial amounts of cholesteryl ester.[77]

Measurements of the mass of LCAT protein present in patient plasma by immunochemical techniques[78,79] have shown that some plasma samples contain reduced or no LCAT protein, whereas samples from other patients contain small amounts of an apparently inactive enzyme (see "Genetics," below).

Other Findings. The lipoprotein lipase level was low in several of the Norwegian patients, whereas the hepatic lipase level was normal.[80]

Serum uric acid concentrations were elevated in some of the hyperlipidemic patients, and one of the patients has developed gout. Slightly elevated serum acid phosphatase levels also have been observed.

Usually, the liver and spleen are not enlarged, and there is no evidence of generalized hepatic dysfunction. No symptoms suggestive of central nervous system dysfunction are found.

Xanthomatous deposits of the skin are observed in a few patients. Lymph nodes and tonsils are not enlarged, and the tonsils are normal in color.

PATHOPHYSIOLOGY

A simple working hypothesis concerning familial LCAT deficiency is that primary failure to synthesize or secrete active LCAT into the plasma causes abnormalities in the structure and function of HDL and that these abnormalities give rise to other lipoprotein and tissue abnormalities that ultimately lead to clinical complications. This hypothesis is largely based on results of in vitro and in vivo experiments with patient lipoproteins and erythrocytes.

There are several reasons for believing that the abnormalities in patient HDL depend on the LCAT deficiency. First, incubation experiments with mixtures of normal LCAT and patient lipoproteins have shown that the enzyme reacts directly with patient HDL, but minimally if at all with other patient lipoproteins.[45] Second, early studies showed that incubation with LCAT converts the disk-shaped HDL into spherical particles that resemble normal HDL.[38] Furthermore, kinetic studies have shown that the HDLs are initially converted into particles that are similar in size to normal HDL_2 and HDL_3.[77] Thus, when a plasma fraction with density > 1.063 g/ml containing the whole population of HDL from a patient with LCAT deficiency (both the small, globular and the large, disk-shaped particles) was incubated with LCAT, two subpopulations of HDL were formed.[77] They corresponded in size to normal HDL_2 and HDL_3. Maximal expression of these subfractions was seen after 4 h, and the time course of the reaction suggested that the patient's small HDL was converted into HDL_3 and the disks into HDL_2. In other words, based on these incubation experiments, it is more likely that HDL_3 and HDL_2 originate from different parent or nascent particles, and that the role of LCAT is not just a conversion of HDL_3 to HDL_2.

The conversion of disk-shaped HDL into spherical particles is probably a direct effect of the conversion of HDL unesterified cholesterol and phosphatidylcholine to cholesteryl ester. The latter are thought to penetrate between the surface layers of the disk-shaped HDL to form a spherical interior core. The LCAT reaction presumably continues until just enough surface lipid remains to form a tightly packed monolayer surrounding the newly formed cholesteryl ester core.[81] This disk-to-sphere transition is not yet completely understood. The kinetic studies mentioned above showed that formation of HDL_2 and HDL_3 size particles continues for some time after HDL cholesteryl esters have ceased to accumulate, which suggests that extensive particle rearrangements are taking place.

Reaction of patient HDL with LCAT alters not only the shape, distribution, and lipid composition of the HDL, but also the content of apo E, apo A-I, and apo C. The content of apo E decreases whether the HDLs are incubated in the absence or presence of other lipoproteins.[51] As mentioned earlier, the linkage of apo E to the patients' disk-shaped HDL appears to be unusually stable. However, apo E dissociates readily from patient HDLs that have been incubated with LCAT, as it does from normal HDL. This effect may depend directly on the disk-to-sphere transition. If three tiers of apo E amphipathic helix form a rim that defines the perimeter of patient disk-shaped HDL (Fig. 46-7), then hydrophobic interactions between the helices and phospholipid acyl chains, coupled with electrostatic interactions among the helices, might account for the unusual stability of the apo E-disk linkage. The LCAT-dependent conversion of the disks to spheres might then substantially weaken the apo E-HDL linkage by changing the orientation of the acyl chains.

Incubation of patient HDL with LCAT promotes the binding of apo A-I. The mechanism that underlies this normalizing effect is not clear, but it must be very different from that affecting the binding of apo E. Binding of apo A-I to cholesteryl ester may be involved since the conformation of apo A-I appears to be affected by cholesteryl ester.[45,58]

Incubation of patient HDL with LCAT also appears to promote the binding of apo C. Thus, when patient HDL is incubated with patient VLDL in the presence of LCAT, transfer of apo C occurs from the VLDL to the HDL, while transfer of apo E occurs in the opposite direction.[77] Additional studies will be required to determine whether the change in apo C also tends to normalize the apolipoprotein content of patient HDL.

To summarize, reaction of patient HDL with LCAT alters their shape, distribution, and lipid and apolipoprotein composition. This strongly suggests that the native HDL from patients is not abnormal in the strict sense, but consists of nascent particles that have been secreted by the liver[51] or intestine[53] or formed by interaction of apo A-I with triglyceride-rich lipoproteins.[56,58] In other words, patient HDL may be unusual only because it has not reacted with LCAT. Even the abnormally low content of apo A-I in patient plasma may depend directly on the LCAT deficiency if apo A-I dissociates from patient HDL as readily in vivo as it does in vitro, and if free apo A-I is rapidly removed from the circulation. The study of apo A-I isoproteins in patients with familial LCAT deficiency suggests that, as in Tangier disease, there is a rapid catabolism of HDL in LCAT deficiency.[55]

If incubation studies with LCAT and patient HDL support the idea that absence of LCAT from the plasma leads directly to the HDL abnormalities that characterize familial LCAT deficiency, what evidence is there that the HDL abnormalities affect other plasma lipoproteins? Evidence derived from in vitro studies indicates that action of LCAT on patient HDL indirectly affects both LDL and VLDL.[54] Most of the unesterified cholesterol and phosphatidylcholine consumed when patient whole plasma is incubated with LCAT is in fact contributed by LDL and VLDL, and most of the cholesteryl ester produced is recovered in these lipoproteins. The unesterified cholesterol and phosphatidylcholine are mainly derived from the large and intermediate size LDL (Fig. 46-6) and from the large VLDL, whereas the cholesteryl esters are recovered in normal size particles. Thus, it appears that unesterified esters and phosphatidylcholine, associated with the large LDL and VLDL, either transfer to or are converted to HDL, that the latter subsequently react with LCAT, and that the cholesteryl ester formed is subsequently transferred to normal size LDL and VLDL by the plasma cholesteryl ester transfer protein.[82–84] The combined effect of these transfer reactions is to normalize the LDL, since the concentrations of the large and intermediate size LDLs decrease and the content of cholesteryl ester in the normal size LDL increases by as much as fivefold. The transfer reactions also appear to have a normalizing effect on the VLDL since, as mentioned earlier, VLDLs that are 60 nm in diameter or larger contain excess surface lipid, whereas those that are 40 nm in diameter or smaller contain abnormally low amounts of cholesteryl ester. The transfer of apo E from HDL to VLDL and the transfer of apo C from VLDL to LDL (see above) exaggerate rather than ameliorate abnormalities in the native VLDL. Both these abnormalities and the abnormalities in concentration of the VLDL and LDL thus remain to be explained.

In vivo studies of patient lipoproteins have provided insight into the origin of the large and the intermediate size LDL_2. When patients consumed fat-free diets for several days, the concentrations of both the large VLDL, i.e., the putative chylomicrons, and the large and intermediate size LDL_2 decreased markedly.[40] In one case, the concentration of the small spherical HDL decreased as well. In contrast, changing the intake of dietary cholesterol influenced only the content of cholesteryl ester in the VLDL, and substitution of a medium chain triglyceride diet for a fat-free diet had no effect. This suggests that the large and intermediate size LDL_2, and possibly the small spherical HDL, may be derived from chylomicrons. In vitro studies by Deckelbaum et al.[85] support the possibility that unusual particles, rich in unesterified cholesterol and phosphatidylcholine, are formed when triglyceride-rich lipoproteins are attacked by lipoprotein lipase. Furthermore, the possibility that action in vivo of lipoprotein lipase on patient chylomicrons might have a similar effect is consistent with the suggestion of Schumaker and Adams[86] that LCAT normally plays a role in the catabolism of triglyceride-rich lipoproteins. These authors pointed out that an excess of surface lipid would be expected to develop as the triglyceride-rich interior of chylomicrons or VLDL is removed by the hydrolytic action of lipoprotein lipase. They suggested that the role of the LCAT reaction might be to correct the resulting imbalance between surface lipid and core lipid by converting surface unesterified cholesterol and phosphatidylcholine to cholesteryl ester. Although they envisaged that LCAT might act directly on remnants of chylomicrons and VLDL, present evidence favors the possibility that segments of the remnant surface pinch off to form particles that float in the density range of LDL_2 and that these particles subsequently contribute lipid substrates for the LCAT reaction, as mentioned earlier. The cholesteryl ester formed might then be transferred to lipoproteins such as VLDL, IDL, or LDL that have a core of nonpolar lipid that can act as an acceptor.

Thus, studies of familial LCAT deficiency support the possibility that two types of remnant particles are formed from triglyceride-rich lipoproteins (Fig. 46-6). One type has flotation properties similar to VLDL. It contains residual core lipid, i.e., triglyceride and cholesteryl ester, and is spherical, though notched. The cholesteryl ester is probably derived from the intestinal mucosa. As mentioned previously, it increases in concentration following ingestion of cholesterol-rich diets. It has a fatty acid composition similar to that of normal human thoracic duct lipoproteins, and it becomes labeled following the ingestion of radioactive cholesterol, but not following the injection of radioactive mevalonate.[1]

The second type of remnant particle has a density similar to LDL_2, contains surface lipid, i.e., unesterified cholesterol and phosphatidylcholine, but no core lipid, and has a bilayered or lamellar character. This type of surface remnant may give rise to the large and intermediate size LDL_2 observed in patient plasma. Why core remnants accumulate in patient plasma is not yet known, but surface remnants presumably accumulate because the unesterified cholesterol and phosphatidylcholine are not converted to cholesteryl ester in the absence of LCAT. Formation of HDL cholesteryl ester from surface remnant unesterified cholesterol and phosphatidylcholine would normally prevent accumulation of the particles. The cholesteryl ester would be transferred to VLDL, IDL, and LDL, and then be removed from the plasma by receptor-dependent mechanisms.

A question of considerable interest is whether the accumulation of putative surface remnants in patient plasma ultimately causes tissue abnormalities. For example, removal of the large LDL_2 by reticuloendothelial cells may account for the lamellar inclusions observed in sea-blue histiocytes in the spleen. Moreover, the unusually high content of unesterified cholesterol in the large LDL_2 may tend to increase the content of unesterified cholesterol in erythrocytes and other cells.

Results of incubation studies with patient erythrocytes clearly indicate that the abnormally high content of unesterified cholesterol in the erythrocyte membranes is related to the high content of this lipid in patient plasma. Patient erythrocytes lose unesterified cholesterol when incubated in normal plasma, whereas normal erythrocytes gain unesterified cholesterol when exposed to patient plasma.[87] Similar effects can be anticipated in relation to erythrocyte phosphatidylcholine, although this phospholipid is thought to exchange only slowly with plasma phospholipids.

A question not yet answered is whether the abnormal lipid composition of patient erythrocytes and the high content of lipid in the spleen and bone marrow account for the anemia that accompanies familial LCAT deficiency. Anemia is seen in other conditions associated with high relative contents of unesterified cholesterol in the plasma,[38] but the basis for the anemia is not yet clear. The basis for the corneal and renal abnormalities also remains to be established.

Gjone et al.[7] have proposed that the high-molecular-weight LDL found in all but one of the Norwegian patients is related to the kidney failure. Thus, a patient without the high-molecular-weight LDL had no proteinuria and normal kidney function. The hypothesis has been challenged by Borysiewicz et al.,[88] who described three patients with familial LCAT deficiency. All three had the typical lipid abnormalities, including the high-molecular-weight LDL particles. However, only one patient had proteinuria and renal failure, and that patient had the lowest concentration of the large abnormal LDL particles of the three patients. Borysiewicz et al.[88] noted that LCAT deficiency causes widespread accumulation of lipids in reticuloendothelial cells and general abnormalities in plasma membranes that could predispose to the development of glomerulonephritis, which has been reported in several patients with familial LCAT deficiency.

GENETICS

Knowledge of the genetics of familial LCAT deficiency was initially derived from studies of five Scandinavian families, four Norwegian and one Swedish.[9] The Norwegian families come from the same geographically isolated area of Norway. The cluster of cases in Norway is interesting. The epidemiology of the disease indicates that the genetic basis of the Norwegian form of LCAT deficiency is one mutational event. The family studies show that this must have occurred before approximately the year 1700. Because of inbreeding and chance, the defective gene has acquired a surprisingly high frequency in the part of Norway where these families live. From the number of patients and the population size, a gene frequency of about 2 percent can be estimated in this region of the country. This gives a frequency of heterozygous carriers of approximately 4 percent.

At present, at least 51 patients from 27 families with the disease are known. They come from all over the world. The genetic patterns in the families, with horizontal distribution and both sexes afflicted, strongly indicate an autosomal recessive inherited disease (Fig. 46-8). The heterozygotes are clini-

Fig. 46-8 Haptoglobin (Hp) subtypes in the members of three families where LCAT deficiency has been found. Hp types marked with an X have been deduced from the types of the other family members. Filled symbols: patients with LCAT deficiency. Open symbols: family members with no signs of disease. *(From Teisberg et al.[95] Used by permission.)*

Fam. 1:

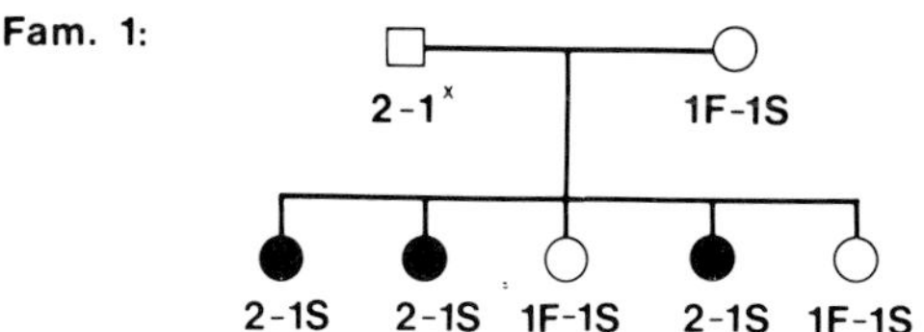

Fam. 2:

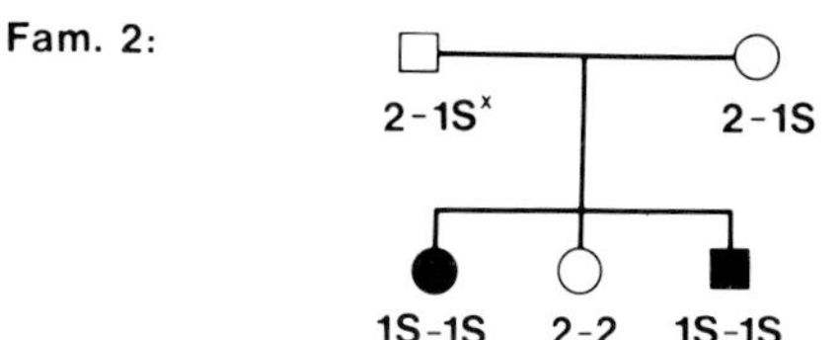

Fam. 3:

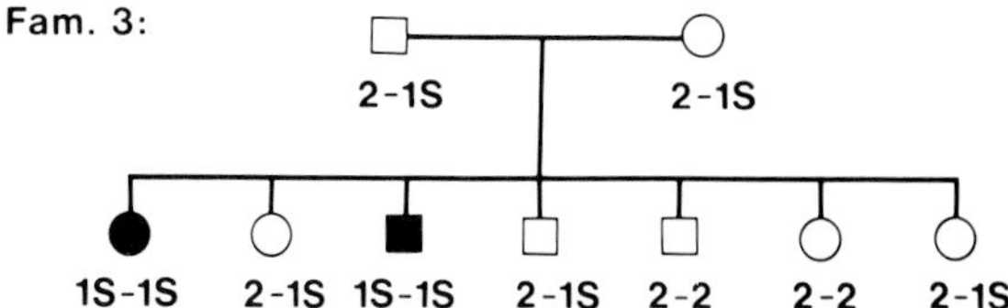

cally healthy, but both the activity of LCAT and the mass of enzyme are clearly affected. Frohlich et al.[89] have developed a method based on "rocket" immunoelectrophoresis using specific anti-LCAT antiserum, and they found no immunoreactive protein in two patients with familial LCAT deficiency, whereas heterozygotes had half-normal values. Albers et al. have developed a sensitive and specific radioimmunoassay for LCAT and tested most of the known families with LCAT deficiency.[90–94] Based on their findings, Albers and coworkers suggest that the heterogeneity of familial LCAT deficiency can be divided into three classes: the disease is due either to (1) the presence of a functionally defective enzyme; (2) very low levels of enzyme; or (3) complete absence of enzyme.[93] Table 46-6 gives data on LCAT activity and mass determination in some families as examples of the classification proposed by Albers.

In an attempt to characterize further the genetic defect operating in familial LCAT deficiency, Teisberg and Gjone[95] carried out linkage studies to several known genetic marker systems. Based on studies in Norwegian families, they found linkage to serum haptoglobin types and concluded that the LCAT gene is located in close proximity to the α-Hp locus, which is situated between the middle and the telomere of the long arm of chromosome 16. Genetic studies in other families with LCAT deficiency have confirmed the linkage to the Hp locus.[96]

The human LCAT gene has recently been sequenced. The gene is divided into six exons, one of which codes for amino acids homologous to the active sites of several lipases, and also codes for an amphipathic α helix resembling the carboxy terminus of apo E. Southern blot hybridization data suggest that there is only one LCAT gene in humans.[65]

Humphries et al.[97] have recently used polyclonal antibodies and a cDNA clone for human LCAT to study the LCAT protein and the structure of the LCAT gene, respectively, in patients with familial LCAT deficiency from Norway, Ireland, Germany, and Italy. Enzymic disgestion of DNA samples from the patients produced LCAT gene fragments which were indistinguishable from those found in normal individuals. Rogne et al.[98] have used another cDNA clone; they investigated Norwegian patients with LCAT deficiency and found no difference in the normal and LCAT-deficient gene.

The observed heterogeneity in patients with familial LCAT deficiency is not surprising. Model studies, especially of the hemoglobins, indicate that such heterogeneity is the rule rather than the exception in genetic disease. Each mutation may be expected to produce its own biochemical pattern with regard to amount and functional activity of the protein produced.

The patients show marked differences in the concentrations of plasma TG and large and intermediate size LDL_2. Furthermore, patients of Sardinian origin, studied in Germany,[9] show other differences. Their plasma may lack disk-shaped HDLs, which are rich in apolipoprotein E. No LCAT-dependent changes in distribution of this apolipoprotein have been observed in incubation studies.[99]

TREATMENT

Blood Transfusion

Since at present it is not possible to treat the disease by intravenous LCAT replacement, whole plasma or blood transfusions have been employed. In one instance, patient A. R. was given 450 ml blood and 500 ml plasma in a single transfusion.[100] This caused an immediate rise in plasma cholesteryl ester, followed by a slower increase to a peak level at 6 days. The peak level considerably exceeded that attributable to cholesteryl ester of the transfused plasma, the plasma cholesteryl ester composition shifted toward that of normal plasma, and the plasma lysolecithin increased. Therefore, the changes in cholesteryl ester were probably caused by the transfused LCAT. The plasma cholesteryl ester had again diminished to the pretreatment level 2 weeks later. This diminution probably reflected the half-life of the transfused LCAT, which was 4.6 days on another occasion.

In another instance the same patient was treated with several successive plasma transfusions.[9] The plasma cholesteryl ester increased from 35 to 310 mg/dl, while the unesterified cholesterol concentration decreased moderately. The lesser change in unesterified cholesterol may have been due to an influx from plasma membranes, because erythrocyte choles-

Table 46-6 Genetic Heterogeneity in Familial LCAT Deficiency The Values in the Table Show the Percent of Normal Values Found When the Laboratories Assayed the LCAT Mass and the LCAT Activity

	Functionally defective enzyme			*Low level of enzyme, Sardinian family§*	*Absence of enzyme, Canadian family¶*
	*Norwegian families**	*Japanese*			
		k family†	*y family‡*		
LCAT mass**					
Patients	20	43	35	5.4	<2
Heterozygotes	68	78	80	44	55
LCAT activity††					
Patients	0	8.7	<0.1	<2	<1
Heteroygotes	53	57	50	51	51

*From Albers et al.[92]
†From Albers et al.[93]
‡From Albers et al.[110]
§From Albers and Uterman.[79]
¶From Albers et al.[90] and Frohlich et al.[111]
**Determined with immunologic technique.
††Determined with an assay using a surplus of exogenous substrate.

terol (all unesterified) decreased from 1.8 to 1.3 mg per 10^{10} cells. The relative concentration of plasma phosphatidylcholine increased from 1.8 to 3.4 percent. No other changes in plasma phospholipid pattern were observed, nor did α_1-lipoproteins appear. Furthermore, the plasma triglyceride concentration did not change significantly, although some lipoproteins of pre-β mobility appeared. The edema cleared, but there was no apparent change in the anemia or proteinuria. Effects of transfusion obtained in the Norwegian patients and in Japanese patients[101] have suggested that treatment will have to be continued for much longer periods if plasma lipoprotein and plasma membrane defects are to be corrected.

Dietary Treatment

Dietary treatment has been tried, with particular interest focused on the large LDL_2 particles and their possible association with the kidney damage. Since the large LDL may be diminished by dietary change, we advise patients with LCAT deficiency to restrict the intake of fat. Whether this can delay or prevent the serious kidney complications is so far unknown.

Kidney Transplantation

Kidney transplants have been performed in several patients. Transplantation does not reverse the lipid or lipoprotein abnormalities in plasma or increase the LCAT activity, but the concentration of triglycerides in the plasma of patient A. R. was much lower after transplantation than before, when she had a nephrotic syndrome.

There is evidence that early deposition of lipid occurs in the transplanted kidneys. The renal graft of patient A. R. showed morphologic changes 6 months after transplantation consistent with lipid deposition both in the mesangium and in the basement membrane. Similar changes were found after 14 months in the renal graft of another Norwegian patient.

Nevertheless, the clinical course after renal transplantation has generally been successful, and good renal function has been maintained.[102,103]

Cornea Transplantation

In one patient with corneal opacities to the extent that vision was heavily disturbed, a cornea graft was successfully transplanted.[21]

FAMILIAL PARTIAL LCAT DEFICIENCY—FISH EYE DISEASE

In 1975 a 61-year-old woman was referred to Professor Lars A. Carlson in Stockholm because of hypertriglyceridemia. The patient had pronounced corneal opacities and mentioned that her father and two older sisters had the same. People said that their eyes looked like those of boiled fish, and the disease was named fish eye disease. Three patients from two families in Sweden and one patient from Canada have been described.[24,104,105]

The only clinical sign is the corneal opacities, which are very pronounced and in mature age require corneal transplantation. The patients have dyslipoproteinemia with an increased amount of triglyceride in whole plasma, in the VLDL and in the LDL fractions. HDL concentration is reduced to about 10 percent of normal, and the HDL particle appears as a homogeneous population of abnormally small size, 115 kd, on polyacrylamide gradient gel electrophoresis.[24,106] The major HDL species was a small spherical particle with a diameter of 7.6 nm. Diskoidal particles were also present, and these had a tendency to form disks when examined by electron microscopy.[106] No qualitative abnormalities have been found in apolipoproteins from patients with fish eye disease. When the rate of plasma cholesterol esterification was tested with the Stokke-Norum method,[76] a normal rate was found. However, when the enzyme activity of LCAT was tested with several different methods, the activity was found to be markedly reduced. Since the relative amounts of esterified cholesterol were normal in VLDL and in LDL, but very low in the HDL, Carlson and Holmquist noted that there was a "paradoxical esterification" of plasma cholesterol in patients with fish eye disease.[107] Experiments with mixtures of isolated lipoprotein and plasma fractions from the patients and normal lipoprotein and plasma fractions have led Carlson and Holmquist to suggest that two LCAT activities exist in plasma.[108,108a] One putative activity mainly esterifies cholesterol on HDL, and one on LDL and VLDL. According to Carlson and Holmquist, patients with fish eye disease have a deficiency in the LCAT that esterifies HDL, while the other activity is normal. Although this is a possible explanation for the abnormal findings in the patients and the data from the incubation experiments, other possibilities must be taken into account. The data can also be explained by an LCAT enzyme which has lost the ability to bind to HDL, or by abnormalities involving cholesteryl ester transfer, although lipoprotein-free plasma from patients with fish eye disease normally facilitates transfer of cholesteryl ester and triglycerides from HDL to LDL.[109] Additional evidence that net lipid transfer processes between the different lipoproteins in fish eye disease plasma are normal was obtained from incubation experiments with native fish eye disease plasma supplemented with normal purified HDL_2 and HDL_3 fractions.[109a] More recently it was demonstrated that addition of a subnormal amount of highly purified normal LCAT to native fish eye disease plasma completely normalized both its HDL cholesteryl ester content and particle size.[109b] This suggests that the presence or lack of inhibitors or activators, respectively, of the enzyme are not important factors for the development of the typical dyslipoproteinemia of fish eye disease. Further speculations may have to await results from studies on the LCAT gene in the patients with fish eye disease. So far no abnormalities in the LCAT gene from fish eye disease have been found,[98] and studies on the LCAT gene in normals suggest that only one LCAT gene exists in humans.[65]

The studies described in this chapter were partially supported by the Howard Hughes Medical Institute, U.S. Public Health Service grant RR00166, The R. J. Reynolds Industries, Inc., Anders Jahre Foundation, and the Norwegian Medical Research Council.

REFERENCES

1. NORUM KR, GJONE E: Familial plasma lecithin:cholesterol acyltransferase deficiency. Biochemical study of a new inborn error of metabolism. *Scand J Clin Lab Invest* 20:231, 1967.
2. GJONE E, NORUM KR: Familial serum-cholesterol ester deficiency: Clinical study of a patient with a new syndrome. *Acta Med Scand* 183:107, 1968.

3. TORSVIK H, GJONE E, NORUM KR: Familial plasma cholesteryl ester deficiency: Clinical studies in a family. *Acta Med Scand* 183:387, 1968.

4. HAMNSTRØM B, GJONE E, NORUM KR: Familial plasma lecithin:cholesterol acyltransferase deficiency: Report of a Swedish family. *Br Med J* 2:283, 1979.

5. NORUM KR, BØRSTING S, GRUNDT I: Familial lecithin:cholesterol acyltransferase deficiency. *Acta Med Scand* 188:323, 1970.

6. GJONE E, SKARBØVIK AJ, BLOMHOFF JP, TEISBERG P: Familial lecithin:cholesterol acyltransferase deficiency: Report of a third Norwegian family with two afflicted members. *Scand J Clin Lab Invest* 33:*suppl* 137, 101, 1974.

7. GJONE E, BLOMHOFF JP, SKARBØVIK AJ: Possible association between an abnormal low density lipoprotein and nephropathy in lecithin:cholesterol acyltransferase deficiency. *Clin Chim Acta* 54:11, 1974.

8. GJONE E, BLOMHOFF JP, HOLME R, HOVIG T, OLAISEN B, SKARBØVIK AJ, TEISBERG P: Familial LCAT deficiency: Report of a fourth family from Northwestern Norway. *Acta Med Scand* 210:3, 1981.

9. STANBURY JB, WYNGAARDEN JB, FREDRICKSON DS, GOLDSTEIN JL, BROWN MS(eds): *Metabolic Basis of Inherited Disease*. 5th ed. New York, McGraw-Hill, 1983, chap 31.

10. SAKUMA M, AKANUMAA Y, KODOMA T, YAMADA N, MURATA S, MURASA T, ITAKURA H, KOSAKA K: Familial plasma lecithin:cholesterol acyltransferase deficiency: A new family with partial LCAT activity. *Acta Med Scand* 212:225, 1982.

11. KATO K, MURAYAMA N, FUJITA T, ASANO Y, HOSADA S: Familial LCAT deficiency: Report of a third Japanese family with two afflicted members. *J Jpn Soc Intern Med* 72:1774, 1983.

12. OHTA Y, YAMAMOTO S, TSUCHIDA H, MURANO S, SAITOH Y, TOHJO S, OKADA M: Nephropathy of familial lecithin:cholesterol acyltransferase deficiency: Report of a case. *Am J Kidney Dis* VII:41, 1986.

13. HESTERBERG RC, TREDICI TJ: Corneal opacification and LCAT deficiency: A case report. *Ann Ophthalmol* 16:616, 1984.

14. BORIES P, ADOUE D, SOLERA ML, DE GRAEVE J, LEBOT M, SEGONDS A, BEC P, SUC JM: Nouveau case français de nephropathie par deficit familial LCAT. *Nephrologie* 2:197, 1981.

15. VERGANI C, ALBERICO LC, ROMA P, GIUDICI G: A new case of familial LCAT deficiency. *Acta Med Scand* 214:173, 1983.

16. SHOJANIA AM, JAIN SK, SHOHET SB: Hereditary lecithin:cholesterol acyltransferase deficiency: Report of 2 new cases and review of the literature. *Clin Invest Med* 6:49, 1983.

17. WEBER P, OWEN JS, DESAI K, CLEMENS MR: Hereditary lecithin:cholesterol acyltransferase deficiency: Case of a German patient. *Am J Clin Pathol* 88:510, 1987.

18. GJONE E, BERGAUST B: Corneal opacity in familial plasma cholesterol ester deficiency. *Acta Ophthalmol* 47:222, 1969.

19. BRON AJ, LLOYD JK, FOSBROOKE AS, WINDER AF, TRIPATHI RC: Primary lecithin:cholesterol acyltransferase deficiency disease. *Lancet* 1:928, 1975.

20. BETHELL W, MCCULLOCH C, GHOSH M: Lecithin:cholesterol acyltransferase deficiency. Light and electron microscopic findings from two corneas. *Can J Ophthalmol* 10:494, 1975.

21. WINDER AF, BRON AJ: Lecithin:cholesterol acyltransferase deficiency presenting as visual impairment, with hypocholesterolaemia and normal renal function. *Scand J Clin Lab Invest* 38:*suppl* 150,151,78.

22. CHU FC, KUWABARA T, COGAN DG, SCHAEFER EJ, BREWSTER B Jr: Ocular manifestations of familial high-density lipoprotein deficiency (Tangier disease). *Arch Ophthalmol* 97:1926, 1979.

23. NORUM RA, LAKIER JB, GOLDSTEIN S, ANGEL A, GOLDBERG RB, BLOCK WD, NOFFZE DK, DOLPHIN PJ, EDELGLASS J, BOGORAD DD, ALAUPOVIC P: Familial deficiency of apolipoproteins A-I and C-III and precocious coronary-artery disease. *N Engl J Med* 306:1513, 1982.

24. CARLSON LA: Fish eye disease: A new familial condition with massive corneal opacities and dyslipoproteinaemia. Clinical and laboratory studies in two afflicted families. *Eur J Clin Invest* 12:41, 1982.

25. GJONE E: Familial lecithin:cholesterol acyltransferase deficiency: A clinical survey. *Scand J Clin Lab Invest* 33:*suppl* 137, 73, 1974.

26. GJONE E, TORSVIK H, NORUM KR: Familial plasma cholesterol ester deficiency: A study of the erythrocytes. *Scand J Clin Lab Invest* 21:237, 1968.

27. GODIN DV, GRAY GR, FROHLICH J: Erythrocyte membrane alterations in lecithin:cholesterol acyltransferase deficiency. *Scand J Clin Lab Invest* 38:*suppl* 150, 162, 1978.

28. YAWATA Y, MIYASHIMA K, SUGIHARA T, MURAYAMA N, HOSODA S, NAKASHIMA S, IIDA H, NOZAWA Y: Self-adaptive modification of red-cell membrane lipids in lecithin:cholesterol acyltransferase deficiency. *Biochim Biophys Acta* 769:440, 1984.

29. MURAYAMA N, ASANO Y, HOSODA S, MAESAWA M, SAITO M, TAKAKU F, SUGIHARA T, MIYASHIMA K, YAWATA Y: Decreased sodium influx and abnormal red cell membrane lipids in a patient with familial plasma lecithin:cholesterol acyltransferase deficiency. *Am J Hematol* 16:129, 1984.

30. NORDØY A, GJONE E: Familial plasma lecithin:cholesterol acyltransferase deficiency: A study of the platelets. *Scand J Clin Lab Invest* 27:263, 1965.

31. JACOBSEN CD, GJONE E, HOVIG T: Sea-blue histiocytes in familial lecithin:cholesterol acyltransferase deficiency. *Scand J Haematol* 9:106, 1972.

32. HOVIG T, GJONE E: Familial lecithin:cholesterol acyltransferase deficiency: Ultrastructural aspects of a new syndrome with particular reference to lesions in the kidneys and the spleen. *Acta Pathol Microbiol Scand* 81:681, 1973.

33. STOKKE KT, BJERVE KS, BLOMHOFF JP, ØYSTESE B, FLATMARK A, NORUM KR, GJONE E: Familial lecithin:cholesterol acyltransferase deficiency: Studies on lipid composition and morphology of tissues. *Scand J Clin Lab Invest* 33:*suppl* 137,93, 1973.

34. HOVIG T, GJONE E: Familial lecithin:cholesterol acyltransferase deficiency: Ultrastructural studies on lipid deposition and tissue reactions. *Scand J Clin Lab Invest* 33:*suppl* 137,135, 1974.

35. MAGIL A, CHAGE W, FROLICH J: Unusual renal biopsy findings in a patient with familial lecithin:cholesterol acyltransferase deficiency. *Hum Pathol* 13:183, 1982.

36. INBASCIATI E, PATIES C, SCARPIONI L, MIHATSCH MJ: Renal lesions in familial lecithin-cholesterol acyltransferase deficiency. *Am J Nephrol* 6:66, 1986.

37. SMITH EB: The influence of age and atherosclerosis on the chemistry of aortic intima. *J Atheroscler Res* 5:224, 1965.

38. GLOMSET JA, NORUM KR: The metabolic role of lecithin:cholesterol acyltransferase: Perspectives from pathology. *Adv Lipid Res* 2:1, 1973.

39. GLOMSET JA, APPLEGATE K, FORTE T, KING WC, MITCHELL CD, NORUM KR, GJONE E: Abnormalities in lipoproteins of d = 1.006 g/ml in familial lecithin:cholesterol acyltransferase deficiency. *J Lipid Res* 21:1116, 1980.

40. GLOMSET JA, NORUM KR, NICHOLS AV, KING WC, MITCHELL CD, APPLEGATE KR, GONG EL, GJONE E: Plasma lipoproteins in familial lecithin:cholesterol acyltransferase deficiency: Effects of dietary manipulation. *Scand J Clin Lab Invest* 35:*suppl* 142,3, 1975.

41. GLOMSET JA, NICHOLS AV, NORUM KR, KING W, FORTE T: Plasma lipoproteins in familial lecithin:cholesterol acyltransferase deficiency: Further studies of very low and low density lipoprotein abnormalities. *J Clin Invest* 52:1078, 1973.

42. HAMILTON RL, HAVEL RJ, KANE JP, BLAUROCK AE, SATA T: Cholestasis: Lamellar structure of the abnormal human serum lipoprotein. *Science* 172:475, 1971.

43. RITLAND S, GJONE E: Quantitative studies of LP-X in familial lecithin:cholesterol acyltransferase deficiency and during cholesterol esterification. *Clin Chim Acta* 59:109, 1975.

44. TORSVIK H: Presence of $alpha_1$-lipoprotein in patients with familial plasma lecithin:cholesterol acyltransferase deficiency. *Scand J Clin Lab Invest* 24:187, 1969.

45. GLOMSET JA, NORUM KR, KING W: Plasma lipoproteins in familial lecithin:cholesterol acyltransferase deficiency; lipid composition and reactivity in vitro. *J Clin Invest* 49:1827, 1970.

46. NORUM KR, GLOMSET JA, NICHOLS AV, FORTE T: Plasma lipoproteins in familial lecithin:cholesterol acyltransferase deficiency: Physical and chemical studies of low and high density lipoproteins. *J Clin Invest* 50:1131, 1971.

47. TORSVIK H, SOLAAS MH, GJONE E: Serum lipoproteins in plasma lecithin:cholesterol acyltransferase deficiency studied by electron microscopy. *Clin Genet* 1:139, 1970.

48. FORTE T, NORUM KR, GLOMSET JA, NICHOLS AV: Plasma lipoproteins in familial lecithin:cholesterol acyltransferase deficiency: Structure of low and high density lipoproteins as revealed by electron microscopy. *J Clin Invest* 50:1141, 1971.

49. TORSVIK H: Studies on the protein moiety of serum high density lipoprotein from patients with familial lecithin:cholesterol acyltransferase deficiency. *Clin Genet* 3:188, 1972.

50. MITCHELL CD, KING WC, APPLEGATE KR, FORTE T, GLOMSET JA, NORUM KR, GJONE E: Characterization of apolipoprotein E-rich high density lipoproteins in familial lecithin:cholesterol acyltransferase deficiency. *J Lipid Res* 21:625, 1980.

51. HAMILTON RL, WILLIAMS MC, FIELDING CJ, HAVEL RJ: Discoidal bilayer structure of nascent high density lipoproteins from perfused rat livers. *J Clin Invest* 58:667, 1976.

52. FELKER TE, FAINARU M, HAMILTON RL, HAVEL RJ: Secretion of the arginine-rich and A-I apolipoproteins by the isolated perfused rat liver. *J Lipid Res* 18:465, 1977.

53. GREEN PHR, TALL AR, GLICKMAN RM: Rat intestine secretes discoid high density lipoprotein. *J Clin Invest* 61:528, 1978.

54. NORUM KR, GLOMSET JA, NICHOLS AV, FORTE T, ALBERS JJ, KING WC, MITCHELL CD, APPLEGATE KR, GONG EL, CABANA V, GJONE E: Plasma li-

poproteins in familial lecithin:cholesterol acyltransferase deficiency. Effects of incubation with lecithin:cholesterol acyltransferase in vitro. *Scand J Clin Lab Invest* 35:*suppl* 142,31, 1975.

55. TERAMOTO T, KATO H, HASHIMOTO Y, KINOSHITA M, OKA H, NAITO C: The basic apolipoprotein A-I in the patients with familial lecithin:cholesterol acyltransferase deficiency. *Scand J Clin Invest* 46:297, 1986.

56. CHEN C, APPLEGATE K, KING WC, GLOMSET JA, NORUM KR, GJONE E: A study of the small spherical high density lipoproteins of patients afflicted with familial lecithin:cholesterol acyltransferase deficiency. *J Lipid Res* 25:269, 1984.

57. GREEN PH, GLICKMAN RM, SANDEK CD, BLUM CB, TALL AR: Human intestinal lipoproteins: Studies in chyluric subjects. *J Clin Invest* 64:233, 1979.

58. ERKELENS DW, CHEN C, MITCHELL CD, GLOMSET JA: Studies of the interaction between apolipoproteins A and C and triacylglycerol-rich particles. *Biochim Biophys Acta* 665:221, 1981.

59. HOFFMAN JS, BENDITT EP: Secretion of serum amyloid protein and assembly of serum amyloid protein-rich high density lipoprotein in primary mouse hepatocyte culture. *J Biol Chem* 257:10518, 1982.

60. FIELDING CJ, FIELDING PE: Evidence for a lipoprotein carrier in human plasma catalyzing sterol efflux from cultured fibroblasts and its relationship to lecithin:cholesterol acyltransferase. *Proc Natl Acad Sci USA* 78:3911, 1981.

61. ALBERS JJ, CABANA VG, STAHL YDB: Purification and characterization of human plasma lecithin:cholesterol acyltransferase. *Biochemistry* 15:1084, 1976.

62. ARON L, JONES S, FIELDING CJ: Human plasma lecithin:cholesterol phospholipase activity. *J Biol Chem* 253:7220, 1978.

63. CHUNG J, ABANO DA, FLESS GM, SCANU AM: Isolation, properties, and mechanism of in vitro action of lecithin:cholesterol acyltransferase from human plasma. *J Biol Chem* 254:7459, 1979.

64. MCLEAN J, FIELDING C, DRAYNA D, DIEPLINGER H, BAER B, KOHR W, HENZEL W, LAWN R: Cloning and expression of human lecithin-cholesterol acyltransferase cDNA. *Proc Natl Acad Sci USA* 83:2335, 1986.

65. MCLEAN J, WION K, DRAYNA D, FIELDING C, LAWN R: Human lecithin-cholesterol acyltransferase gene: Complete gene sequence and sites of expression. *Nucl Acids Res* 14:9397, 1986.

66. GLOMSET JA: The plasma lecithin:cholesterol acyltransferase reaction. *J Lipid Res* 9:155, 1968.

67. FIELDING PE, FIELDING CJ: A cholesteryl ester transfer complex in human plasma. *Proc Natl Acad Sci USA* 77:3327, 1980.

68. FIELDING CJ, FIELDING PE: Cholesterol transport between cells and body fluids. Role of plasma lipoproteins and the plasma cholesterol esterification system. *Med Clin North Am* 66:363, 1982.

69. CHEUNG MC, WOLF AC, LUM KD, TOLLEFSON JH, ALBERS JJ: Distribution and localization of lecithin:cholesterol acyltransferase and cholesteryl ester transfer activity in A-I-containing lipoproteins. *J Lipid Res* 27:1135, 1986.

70. FIELDING CJ, SHORE VG, FIELDING PE: A protein cofactor of lecithin:cholesterol acyltransferase. *Biochem Biophys Res Commun* 46:1493, 1972.

71. ARON L, JONES S, FIELDING CJ: Human plasma lecithin:cholesterol acyltransferase: Characterization of cofactor-dependent phospholipase activity. *J Biol Chem* 253:7220, 1978.

72. YOKOYAMA S, FUKUSHIMA D, KUPFERBERG JP, KEZDY FJ, KAISER ET: The mechanism of activation of lecithin:cholesterol acyltransferase by lipoprotein A-I and an amphilic peptide. *J Biol Chem* 255:7333, 1980.

73. JAUHIAINEN M, DOLPHIN PJ: Human plasma lecithin-cholesterol acyltransferase. *J Biol Chem* 261:7032, 1986.

74. NORDBY G, NORUM KR: Substrate specificity of lecithin:cholesterol acyltransferase. Esterification of desmosterol, betha-sitosterol, and cholecalciferol in human plasma. *Scand J Clin Lab Invest* 35:677, 1975.

75. SUBBAIAH PV, ALBERS JJ, CHEN CH, BAGDADE JD: Low density lipoprotein-activated lysolecithin acylation by human plasma lecithin-cholesterol acyltransferase. Identity of lysolecithin acyltransferase and lecithin-cholesterol acyltransferase. *J Biol Chem* 255:9275, 1980.

76. STOKKE KT, NORUM KR: Determination of lecithin:cholesterol acyltransfer in human blood plasma. *Scand J Clin Lab Invest* 27:21, 1971.

77. GLOMSET JA, MITCHELL CD, KING WC, APPLEGATE KR, FORTE T, NORUM KR, GJONE E: In vitro effects of lecithin:cholesterol acyltransferase on apolipoprotein distribution in familial lecithin:cholesterol acyltransferase deficiency. *Ann NY Acad Sci* 348:224, 1980.

78. ALBERS JJ, ADOLPHSON JL, CHEN CH: Radioimmunoassay of human plasma lecithin:cholesterol acyltransferase. *J Clin Invest* 67:141, 1981.

79. ALBERS JJ, UTERMANN G: Genetic control of lecithin:cholesterol acyltransferase: Measurement of LCAT mass in a large kindred with LCAT deficiency. *Am J Hum Genet* 33:702, 1981.

80. BLOMHOFF JP, HOLME R, SAUAR J, GJONE E: Familial lecithin:cholesterol acyltransferase deficiency. Further studies on plasma lipoproteins and plasma postheparin lipase activity of a patient with normal renal function. *Scand J Clin Lab Invest* 38:*suppl* 150,177, 1978.

81. NICHOLS AV, GONG EL, BLANCHE PJ, FORTE TM, SHORE VG: Pathways in the formation of human plasma high density lipoprotein subpopulations containing apolipoprotein A-I without apolipoprotein A-II. *J Lipid Res* 28:719, 1987.

82. PATTNAIK NM, ZILVERSMIT DB: Interaction of cholesteryl ester exchange protein with human plasma lipoproteins and phospholipid vesicles. *J Biol Chem* 254:2782, 1979.

83. CHAJEK T, FIELDING CJ: Isolation and characterization of human serum cholesteryl ester transfer protein. *Proc Natl Acad Sci USA* 75:2445, 1978.

84. ALBERS JJ, CHEUNG MC, EWENS SL, TOLLEFSON JH: Characterization and immunoassay of apolipoprotein D. *Atherosclerosis* 39:395, 1981.

85. DECKELBAUM RJ, EISENBERG S, FAINARU M, BARENHOLZ Y, OLIVECRONA T: In vitro production of human plasma low density lipoprotein-like particles. A model for very low density lipoprotein catabolism. *J Biol Chem* 254:6079, 1979.

86. SCHUMAKER VN, ADAMS GH: Very low density lipoproteins: Surface-volume changes during metabolism. *J Theor Biol* 26:89, 1970.

87. NORUM KR, GJONE E: The influence of plasma from patients with familial plasma lecithin:cholesterol acyltransferase deficiency on the lipid pattern of erythrocytes. *Scand J Clin Lab Invest* 22:94, 1968.

88. BORYSIEWICZ LK, SOUTAR AK, EVANS DJ, THOMPSON GR, REES AJ: Renal failure in familial lecithin:cholesterol acyltransferase deficiency. *QJ Med New Series* LI204:411, 1982.

89. FROHLICH J, MCLEOD R, HON K: Lecithin:cholesterol acyltransferase (LCAT). *Clin Biochem* 156:269, 1982.

90. ALBERS JJ, CHEN CH, ADOLPHSON JL: Familial lecithin-cholesterol acyltransferase: Identification of heterozygotes with half-normal enzyme activity and mass. *Hum Genet* 58:306, 1981.

91. ALBERS JJ, CHEN CH, ADOLPHSON JL: Lecithin:cholesterol acyltransferase (LCAT) mass; its relationship to LCAT activity and cholesterol esterification rate. *J Lipid Res* 22:1206, 1981.

92. ALBERS JJ, GJONE E, ADOLPHSON JL, CHEN CH, TEISBERG P, TORSVIK H: Familial lecithin-cholesterol acyltransferase deficiency in four Norwegian families. *Acta Med Scand* 210:455, 1981.

93. ALBERS JJ, CHEN CH, ADOLPHSON J, SAKUMA M, KODAMA T, AKANUMA Y: Familial lecithin-cholesterol acyltransferase deficiency in a Japanese family: Evidence for functionally defective enzyme in homozygotes and obligate heterozygotes. *Hum Genet* 62:82, 1982.

94. ALBERS JJ, UTERMANN G: Genetic control of lecithin:cholesterol acyltransferase: Measurement of LCAT mass in a large kindred with LCAT deficiency. *Am J Hum Genet* 33:702, 1981.

95. TEISBERG P, GJONE E: The lecithin:cholesterol acyltransferase deficiency locus in man: Probable linkage to the alpha-haptoglobin locus on chromosome no. 16. *Nature* 149:550, 1974.

96. SAKUMA M, AKANUMA Y, KODAMA T, YAMADA N, MURATA S, MURASE T, ITAKURA H, KOSAKA K: Familial plasma lecithin:cholesterol acyltransferase deficiency. A new family with partial LCAT activity. *Acta Med Scand* 212,225, 1982.

97. HUMPHRIES SE, CHAVES ME, TATA F, LIMA VLM, OWEN JS, BORYSIEWICZ LK, CATAPANO A, VERGANI C, GJONE E, CLEMENS MR, WILLIAMSON R, MCINTYRE N: A study of the structure of the gene for lecithin:cholesterol acyl transferase (LCAT) in four unrelated individuals with familial LCAT deficiency. *Clin Sci* 74:91, 1988.

98. ROGNE S, SKRETTING G, LARSEN F, MYKLEBOST O, MEVÅG B, CARLSON LA, HOLMQUIST L, GJONE E, PRYDZ H: The isolation and characterisation of a cDNA clone for human lecithin:cholesterol acyl transferase and its use to analyse the genes in patients with LCAT deficiency and fish eye disease. *Biochem Biophys Res Commu* 148:161, 1987.

99. UTERMANN G, MENZEL HJ, ADLER G, DIEKER P, WEBER W: Substitution in vitro of lecithin:cholesterol acyltransferase, analysis of changes in plasma lipoproteins. *Eur J Biochem* 107:225, 1980.

100. NORUM KR, GJONE E: The effect of plasma transfusion on the plasma cholesteryl esters in patients with familial plasma lecithin:cholesterol acyltransferase deficiency. *Scand J Clin Lab Invest* 22:339, 1968.

101. MURAYAMA N, ASANO Y, KATO K, SAKAMOTO Y, HOSODA S, YAMADA N, KODAMA T, ØMURASE T, AKANUMA Y: Effects of plasma infusion on plasma lipids, apoproteins and plasma enzyme activities in familial lecithin:cholesterol acyltransferase deficiency. *Eur J Clin Invest* 14:122, 1984.

102. FLATMARK AL, HOVIG T, MYHRE E, GJONE E: Renal transplantation in patients with familial lecithin:cholesterol acyltransferase deficiency. *Transplant Proc* 9:1665, 1977.

103. MYHRE E, GJONE E, FLATMARK A, HOVIG T: Renal failure in familial lecithin-cholesterol acyltransferase deficiency. *Nephron* 18:239, 1977.

104. CARLSON LA, PHILIPSON B: Fish-eye disease. A new familial condition

with massive corneal opacities and dyslipoproteinemia. *Lancet* 8149:921, 1979.

105. FROHLICH J, HOAG G, MCLEOD R, HAYDEN M, GODIN DV, WADSWORTH LD, CRITCHLEY JD, PRITCHARD PH: Hypoalphalipoproteinemia resembling fish eye disease. *Acta Med Scand* 221:291, 1987.

106. FORTE TM, CARLSON LA: Electron microscopic structure of serum lipoproteins from patients with fish eye disease. *Arteriosclerosis* 4:130, 1984.

107. CARLSON LA, HOLMQUIST L: Paradoxical esterification of plasma cholesterol in fish eye disease. *Acta Med Scand* 217:491, 1985.

108. CARLSON LA, HOLMQUIST L: Evidence for deficiency of high density lipoprotein lecithin:cholesterol acyltransferase activity (alpha-LCAT) in fish eye disease. *Acta Med Scand* 218:189, 1985.

108a. CARLSON LA, HOLMQUIST L: Evidence for the presence in human plasma of lecithin:cholesterol acyltransferase activity (β-LCAT) specifically esterifying free cholesterol of combined pre-β - and β-lipoproteins. Studies of Fish Eye Disease patients and control subjects. *Acta Med Scand* 218:197–205, 1985.

109. CALVERT GD, CARLSON LA: Plasma lipid transfer in fish-eye disease. *Acta Med Scand* 213:253, 1983.

109a. HOLMQUIST L, CARLSON LA: Net lipid transfer between lipoproteins in Fish-Eye Disease plasma supplemented with normal high density lipoproteins. *Lipids* 22:305–311, 1987.

109b. HOLMQUIST L, CARLSON LA: In vitro normalization of cholesteryl ester content and size of high density lipoprotein particles in Fish Eye Disease plasma by purified normal human lecithin:cholesterol acyltransferase. *Lipids* 1988, in press.

110. ALBERS JJ, ADOLPHSON J, CHENCH, MURAYAMA N, HONMA S, AKANUMA Y: Defective enzyme causes lecithin-cholesterol acyltransferase deficiency in a Japanese kindred. *Biochim Biophys Acta* 835:253, 1985.

111. FROHLICH J, HON K, MCLEOD R: Detection of heterozygotes for familial lecithin:cholesterol acyltransferase (LCAT) deficiency. *Am J Hum Genet* 34:65, 1982.

CHAPTER 47

TYPE III HYPERLIPOPROTEINEMIA (Dysbetalipoproteinemia): The Role of Apolipoprotein E in Normal and Abnormal Lipoprotein Metabolism

ROBERT W. MAHLEY
STANLEY C. RALL, JR.

1. *Patients with type III hyperlipoproteinemia have elevated concentrations of both plasma cholesterol and triglyceride. A biochemical characteristic of the disorder is the occurrence of β-migrating very low density lipoproteins (β-VLDL), which are cholesterol-enriched remnants of both intestinal and hepatic origin. The β-VLDL are enriched in apolipoprotein (apo) E, which in type III hyperlipoproteinemic subjects is a dysfunctional mutant.*
2. *Clinical features of the disorder are varied. Many type III subjects have cutaneous xanthomas, particularly of two types: tuberoeruptive or tuberous xanthomas and xanthomas of the palmar creases (xanthoma striata palmaris); the latter has not been described in any other disorder. There is a high incidence of premature coronary and (especially) peripheral atherosclerosis in these subjects. Overt hyperlipidemia is only rarely manifested before adulthood, and type III subjects frequently have other types of disorders that exacerbate the hyperlipoproteinemia.*
3. *The primary molecular defect in type III hyperlipoproteinemia is the presence of a mutant form of apo E (apo E-2) that differs from normal apo E (apo E-3) by only a single amino acid substitution (cysteine for arginine at residue 158). Apolipoprotein E is a polymorphic protein that results from the existence of multiple alleles at a single gene locus and from posttranslational sialylation. The genetically determined polymorphism of apo E has a significant impact on normal variations in lipid, lipoprotein, and apolipoprotein levels in the human population. The mutant form of apo E found in type III hyperlipoproteinemic subjects does not bind normally to lipoprotein receptors.*
4. *The normal catabolism of remnant lipoprotein particles, which is directed by apo E, is altered in type III hyperlipoproteinemia. The presence of the defective apo E (apo E-2) results in the accumulation in plasma of chylomicron and VLDL remnants (β-VLDL), which in turn have a propensity for uptake by macrophages in peripheral tissues. As a result of massive cholesterol deposition, these macrophages become foam cells that may be the progenitors of cholesterol-laden cells in the atherosclerotic lesion. In almost all cases, the development of overt hyperlipidemia in type III hyperlipoproteinemia requires inheritance of two alleles for the mutant apo E-2 (phenotype E-2/2). This is a necessary but not usually sufficient requirement, however, as most E-2/2 subjects are either normolipidemic or even hypolipidemic. Thus, type III hyperlipoproteinemia appears to be a multifactorial disorder involving other genetic, hormonal, or environmental influences that alter the expression of the hyperlipidemia.*
5. *Diagnosis of type III hyperlipoproteinemia is indicated by increased plasma cholesterol and triglyceride, the presence of β-VLDL, xanthomas (especially palmar xanthomas), premature vascular disease (especially of the peripheral arteries), and apo E phenotype E-2/2. While few type III subjects can be expected to have all these clinical features, the diagnostic hallmark of this disorder is the presence of apo E that is defective in binding to lipoprotein receptors.*
6. *Type III hyperlipoproteinemia is usually very responsive to therapy. Dietary control is the preferred form of treatment, but a drug regimen may also be required to lower lipid levels. Useful drugs for treatment of type III hyperlipoproteinemia include nicotinic acid, clofibrate, gemfibrozil, and perhaps mevinolin.*

HISTORY AND OVERVIEW

The lipoprotein disorder now known as type III hyperlipoproteinemia was first described by Gofman et al.[1,2] in the 1950s and was originally termed *xanthoma tuberosum,* based on the occurrence of xanthomatous lesions of the skin over extensor tendons and planar xanthomas of the volar surfaces of the hands. Affected patients had a distinctively abnormal lipoprotein profile as determined by analytical ultracentrifugation, characterized by an increase in the concentration of lipoproteins with flotation rates of S_f = 12 to 20 [small very low density lipoproteins (VLDL) and intermediate density lipoproteins (IDL)] and S_f = 20 to 400 (larger VLDL), but a decrease in lipoproteins of S_f = 0 to 12 [especially low density lipoproteins (LDL)].[1,2] Gofman and coworkers also recognized the probable familial nature of this disorder.

It was later appreciated that xanthoma tuberosum was identical with one of the distinct classes of familial hyperlipoproteinemias (type III hyperlipoproteinemia) established by Fredrickson et al.[3] in 1967. Classifying hyperlipidemic subjects by using a combination of ultracentrifugation and paper electrophoresis, they found that one group had a VLDL fraction with β, rather than the normal pre-β, electrophoretic mobility. These lipoproteins, referred to as β-VLDL,[4] were enriched in cholesterol. These observations were confirmed by others, and the association with accelerated or premature atherosclerosis became well established.[5–7] Through the years, other designations have been used for this disorder, most notably *broad-beta disease,*[3] based on the peculiar migration pattern of the abnormal β-VLDL on paper electrophoresis, and *dysbetalipoproteinemia*,[8] used to denote the unusual chemical and physical properties of the VLDL. More recently, the β-VLDL have been shown to represent two different lipoproteins that accumulate in the plasma—chylomicron remnants of intestinal origin and VLDL remnants of hepatic origin.[9,10] In fact, the disorder has also been referred to as *remnant removal disease*.[11]

The abnormal cholesterol-enriched β-VLDL were the hallmark diagnostic feature of type III hyperlipoproteinemia for some years, until an apolipoprotein abnormality came to light. In 1973, Havel and Kane[12] showed that type III subjects had an absolute increase in the plasma levels of apolipoprotein (apo) E, or *arginine-rich apoprotein*. Apolipoprotein E is one of several protein components that occur normally on VLDL, chylomicrons, and certain subclasses of high density lipoproteins (HDL) (for review, see Ref. 13). Later, in a pioneering series of studies, Utermann and associates[14–18] demonstrated, by isoelectric focusing, that a particular isoform of apo E was invariably absent in type III subjects. These observations suggested that the primary genetic defect in type III hyperlipoproteinemia was homozygosity for a mutant isoform of apo E (referred to as apo E-2 to distinguish it from the normal apo E-3). The genetics and mode of inheritance of apo E, as first described by Utermann et al. and later refined by Zannis and Breslow,[19,20] were pivotal in understanding the basis of apo E polymorphism and in establishing the association of the mutant apo E with type III hyperlipoproteinemia.

Studies by Mahley and coworkers established the amino acid structural differences among the various apo E isoforms[21–23] and defined, at a molecular level, the role of the mutant apo E in the development of type III hyperlipoproteinemia (for review, see Refs. 13 and 24 to 26). The discovery that apo E was a major ligand for the LDL receptor[27–29] and was the apolipoprotein responsible for mediating the cellular uptake of chylomicron remnants and VLDL remnants (the lipoproteins referred to collectively as β-VLDL that accumulate in the plasma in type III hyperlipoproteinemia)[30–33] focused attention on the role of this apolipoprotein in the regulation of the plasma levels of these lipoproteins. These data, in association with the observation that the mutant apo E did not bind normally to the lipoprotein receptors,[30,34,35] suggested that the primary defect in type III hyperlipoproteinemia was the defective interaction of mutant apo E with the lipoprotein receptors, which led to the accumulation of β-VLDL in the plasma. However, as will be discussed below ("Genetic and Environmental Factors Influencing the Expression of Type III Hyperlipoproteinemia"), the overt expression of hyperlipidemia in subjects with the mutant apo E is modulated by other genetic and environmental factors.

BIOCHEMICAL FEATURES OF THE DISORDER

Blood Lipids, Lipoproteins, and Apolipoproteins

There is a wide range in the lipid, lipoprotein, and apolipoprotein values of subjects who demonstrate the hallmark biochemical defects, i.e., β-VLDL and the mutant apo E. The most dramatic demonstration of the abnormalities is found in untreated patients who express the most overt hyperlipidemia (Table 47-1). In severely affected patients, plasma cholesterol levels are usually greater than 300 mg/dl and may approach 1000 mg/dl.[5] Plasma triglyceride concentrations are in the same range and tend to be about equal to or exceed those of cholesterol in any given subject. The diagnosis of type III hyperlipoproteinemia should be considered in hyperlipidemic individuals when the cholesterol and triglyceride levels are both elevated and approximately equal.

As determined by ultracentrifugal analysis and paper or agarose electrophoresis, there is a prominent β band (β-VLDL) in the $d < 1.006$-g/ml fraction (Fig. 47-1) and a dramatic absolute increase (compared with normal) in the β-migrating lipoproteins found in this fraction (as assessed by cholesterol determinations). Pre-β-VLDL are also present in the $d < 1.006$-g/ml fraction and can occur as a single or double electrophoretic band in non-type III subjects.[36] The double pre-β band can sometimes lead to a misinterpretation regarding the presence of β-VLDL. In type III subjects, there is also a modest increase in the $d = 1.006$- to 1.019-g/ml fraction (IDL). In contrast, the $d = 1.02$- to 1.063-g/ml lipoproteins (LDL) are almost always significantly reduced.[17] If the ultracentrifugal fractionation is performed so as to include the IDL and LDL ($d = 1.006$ to 1.063 g/ml) within the same fraction, the cholesterol may or may not show a decrease, because of the compensating effects of increased IDL and decreased LDL. The concentration of cholesterol in the $d = 1.063$- to 1.21-g/ml fraction (HDL) is usually also modestly reduced in type III hyperlipoproteinemic subjects. With treatment of the hyperlipidemia, the HDL cholesterol concentration frequently

Table 47-1 Plasma Lipoprotein Concentrations in Subjects with Untreated Type III Hyperlipoproteinemia*

				Cholesterol content, mg/dl		
Subjects	*Number*	*Cholesterol, mg/dl*	*Triglycerides, mg/dl*	*VLDL*	*LDL + IDL*	*HDL*
Type III hyperlipoproteinemia						
All subjects	47	453 ± 21	699 ± 77	287 ± 25	121 ± 8	38 ± 3
Men, mean age 40	27	440 ± 25	694 ± 104	268 ± 32	131 ± 14	37 ± 3
Women, mean age 49	20	470 ± 36	705 ± 117	307 ± 39	131 ± 9	39 ± 5
Control						
Men, ages 30–39	50	210 ± 5	78 ± 6	21 ± 2	143 ± 4	48 ± 2
Women, ages 40–49	44	217 ± 5	80 ± 6	14 ± 1	130 ± 4	62 ± 2

*Values cited are mean ± SEM; control values are derived from Fredrickson, Levy, and Lindgren.[4]
SOURCE: Adapted from Morganroth, Levy, and Fredrickson.[5]

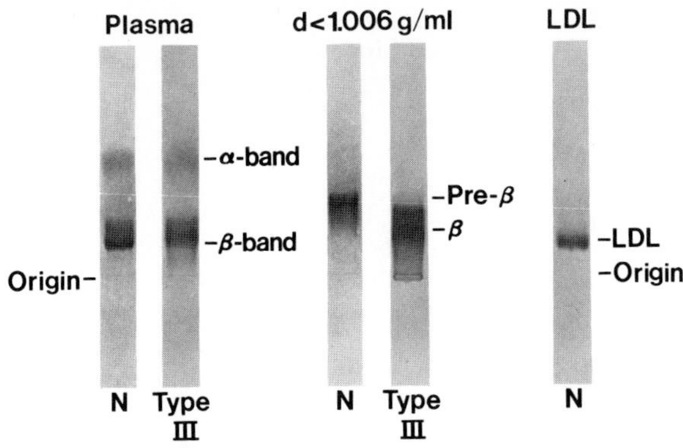

Fig. 47-1 Agarose gel electrophoretic pattern of plasma lipoproteins. Identification of the lanes, from left to right: total plasma lipoproteins from a normal subject; total plasma lipoproteins from a type III hyperlipoproteinemic subject; VLDL ($d < 1.006$ g/ml) from a normal subject; VLDL ($d < 1.006$ g/ml) from a type III hyperlipoproteinemic subject; LDL ($d = 1.02$ to 1.063 g/ml) from a normal subject. *(Courtesy of Dr. David A. Chappell.)*

increases, whereas the concentration of the LDL cholesterol may remain low.[5] See Table 47-1 for an illustration of the changes in lipoprotein concentrations seen in type III patients.

Abnormal Lipoproteins

The major abnormal lipoprotein in type III hyperlipoproteinemia is β-VLDL. These particles are remnant lipoproteins that derive from both chylomicrons secreted by the intestine and VLDL secreted by the liver.[9,10] That β-VLDL represent both intestinal and hepatic remnants has been amply demonstrated by the presence of the two forms of apo B. One form, apo B-100, is synthesized in the liver and is secreted as a constituent of VLDL.[37] The other form, apo B-48, is synthesized exclusively in the intestine and is secreted as a constituent of chylomicrons.[37,38] The complete primary structure of apo B-100 ($M_r \simeq 550{,}000$) has been determined,[39–42] and it is now known that apo B-48 ($M_r \simeq 264{,}000$) represents approximately the amino-terminal half of apo B-100.[42–45] Both forms of apo B can be found in β-VLDL, and the two types of remnants can be separated from one another by biochemical or immunologic techniques.[9,10,46]

Normally, chylomicrons synthesized by the intestine enter the blood and are acted upon by lipoprotein lipase, which catalyzes the hydrolysis of the triglyceride, resulting in the formation of chylomicron remnants (cholesterol-rich particles devoid of much of their triglyceride). The chylomicron remnants are rapidly and efficiently cleared from the circulation via the liver.[8] Likewise, the normal pre-β-VLDL are processed through a lipolytic cascade, resulting in progressively smaller and more cholesterol-rich lipoproteins as the VLDL remnants become IDL and finally LDL.[8] A certain portion of these hepatic VLDL remnants is also removed from the circulation via the liver before reaching the final stage in the cascade, i.e., the formation of LDL.

In type III hyperlipoproteinemia, the remnants accumulate in the plasma. The intestinal β-VLDL appear to be derived directly from chylomicrons. However, the hepatic β-VLDL may represent VLDL that are synthesized by the liver and have an increased content of cholesterol or, more likely, may represent a cholesterol-enriched intermediate derived from the hepatic pre-β-VLDL.[47] Both forms of β-VLDL may be normal intermediates of chylomicron and pre-β-VLDL catabolism that accumulate in the plasma in type III hyperlipoproteinemia to abnormally high levels secondary to impaired catabolism of these lipoproteins. This will be more thoroughly discussed in "Pathogenesis of Type III Hyperlipoproteinemia," below.

The physical and chemical characteristics of β-VLDL found in type III hyperlipoproteinemia are quite distinct from those of normal pre-β-VLDL (Table 47-2). Although hepatic β-VLDL tend to be only slightly smaller in particle diameter than normal pre-β-VLDL, the chemical compositions of these lipoproteins are strikingly dissimilar. The β-VLDL are considerably more cholesterol-enriched (mostly as cholesteryl esters) and are relatively depleted in triglycerides.[46–49] In addition, the complement of apolipoproteins is both quantitatively and qualitatively different.[12,46,50] Whereas β-VLDL and VLDL have a roughly similar total protein content, β-VLDL have much less of the C apolipoproteins. In contrast, there is a relative and absolute increase in apo E on β-VLDL.[12,46] In addition, the mutant apo E of type III individuals is dysfunctional in terms of its ability to bind to specific cell-surface receptors (see "Pathogenesis of Type III Hyperlipoproteinemia," below).

The IDL fraction in the plasma of type III individuals is also abnormal in that it is increased and contains some apo B-48, indicating the presence of some intestinal remnants. The IDL in type III individuals, therefore, probably represents the lower end of the spectrum of particle sizes of β-VLDL, as well as normal IDL, although this conclusion can be disputed.[51]

Other lipoproteins in patients with type III hyperlipoproteinemia do not appear to be noticeably abnormal in size, shape, or chemical composition.[52] This applies to HDL, LDL ($d = 1.02$ to 1.063 g/ml), and probably to pre-β-VLDL, although pre-β-VLDL have not been extensively characterized in type III subjects.

Table 47-2 Chemical Composition of β-Very Low Density Lipoproteins from Type III Hyperlipoproteinemic Individuals and Pre-β-Very Low Density Lipoproteins from Normal Individuals

Lipoprotein	*Mean particle diameter, nm*	*Composition, % mass**					*Apolipoproteins*
		CE	*FC*	*TG*	*PL*	*Protein*	
Intestinal β-VLDL	82	32	7	43	14	4	B(35%) > E > C
Hepatic β-VLDL	38	26	7	39	19	9	B(55%) > E > C
Hepatic pre-β-VLDL	44	12	5	59	16	8	B(45%) > C > E

*CE = cholesteryl ester; FC = free cholesterol; TG = triglyceride; PL = phospholipid.
SOURCE: Average of mean values from various sources, including Refs. 5, 9, 10, and 46 to 49.

CLINICAL EXPRESSION AND MANIFESTATION OF THE DISORDER

Approximately 1 percent of the North American and Northern European populations is homozygous for the mutant form of apo E (phenotype E-2/2; see "Apolipoprotein E Genetics and Structure-Function Correlates," below) that is associated with type III hyperlipoproteinemia. All individuals with this apo E phenotype have detectable β-VLDL in their plasma, reflecting the presence of the variant apo E. However, most of these individuals do not have overt hyperlipoproteinemia; in fact, many are normolipidemic or even hypolipidemic.[15,17,53] It is reasonable to classify these individuals as having *dysbetalipoproteinemia* because they do have β-VLDL in their plamsa (although not in sufficient quantities to result in elevated plasma lipid levels) and because they have the genetic predisposition, i.e., the presence of the abnormal apo E variant, to develop hyperlipidemia. Overt hyperlipoproteinemia, characterized by elevated concentrations of plasma cholesterol and triglyceride, occurs rather rarely, with a frequency of about 1 to 5 per 5000 in the general population.[53] Individuals with overt hyperlipoproteinemia should be classified as having *type III hyperlipoproteinemia* (to distinguish them from those with normal lipid levels but with plasma β-VLDL, i.e., with dysbetalipoproteinemia). The apparent discrepancy between the occurrence of the mutant form of apo E and the expression of overt hyperlipoproteinemia indicates that the disorder is modulated by other genetic and environmental factors that affect the absolute levels of plasma lipids, which range from hypolipidemic to hyperlipidemic. However, it is important to emphasize that an absolute requirement for expression of the disorder is the occurrence of the mutant form of apo E that is defective in binding to the lipoprotein receptors (see "Pathogenesis of Type III Hyperlipoproteinemia," below).

Age at Onset

Type III hyperlipoproteinemia rarely manifests itself before adulthood[5,50,54–59]; there are only a few reports of its occurrence in teenagers.[16,54,56,60,61] The disease is much more prevalent in men than in women (Table 47-3), and it tends to occur earlier in men.[5] Women usually do not express the disorder until after menopause. There seems to be some correlation between obesity and age at onset, and the presence of other clinical disorders, such as diabetes mellitus or hypothyroidism, also may result in an earlier onset.

Xanthomas

The most striking clinical feature of type III hyperlipoproteinemia is the occurrence of xanthomas (Fig. 47-2), one type of which has not been described in any other disorder and is therefore essentially pathognomonic for type III hyperlipoproteinemia (for review, see Refs. 62 and 63). These particular xanthomas, termed *xanthoma striata palmaris,*[64] occur as yellowish lipid deposits in the palmar creases and also have been called *planar xanthomas* or *palmar xanthomas.*[3] Roughly half of untreated patients have this particular lesion (Table 47-3). Other types of palmar xanthomas (but never in the palmar creases) have been described in individuals with familial hypercholesterolemia.

Table 47-3 Clinical Data on 185 Patients with Type III Hyperlipoproteinemia

No. of patients	185
Male/female	131/54
Age range, years	16 to 95
Mean cholesterol, mg/dl	450
Mean triglyceride, mg/dl	570
Clinical finding	*Percent of patients*
Xanthomas	
Striata palmaris	55
Tendon	13
Tuberous and tuberoeruptive	64
Xanthelasma	7
Corneal arcus	11
Coronary heart disease	28
Peripheral vascular disease	21
Cerebrovascular disease	4
Gout	4
Diabetes mellitus (clinical)	4
Hypothyroidism	4

SOURCE: Pooled data from Refs. 5, 54 to 56, 58, and 59.

In addition, individuals with type III hyperlipoproteinemia have other types of xanthomas, especially tuberous and tuberoeruptive xanthomas, but these lesions are not unique to type III hyperlipoproteinemia. The tuberous xanthomas appear most frequently on the elbows, knees, buttocks, and knuckles (Fig. 47-2). Xanthelasmas and tendinous xanthomas (particularly in the Achilles tendon) are also sometimes seen, but these occur more frequently in familial hypercholesterolemia. See Table 47-3 for a summary of results concerning xanthomas in 185 patients. Xanthomas in type III patients usually disappear rather rapidly once treatment is initiated.

Premature Atherosclerosis

Premature or accelerated atherosclerosis does occur in individuals with type III hyperlipoproteinemia (Table 47-3). The vascular disease in type III hyperlipoproteinemia, which occurs in one-third to more than one-half of affected subjects,[5,54–56,58,59] has an unusual distribution. Peripheral vascular disease involving the lower extremities is almost as common as coronary artery disease. This is strikingly different from the distribution of vascular disease seen in familial hypercholesterolemia, in which there is less involvement of the lower extremities. Although the mechanism underlying the predisposition for atherosclerosis of peripheral vessels in type III hyperlipoproteinemia is unknown, it is noteworthy that certain cholesterol-fed animals that have high levels of β-VLDL also have much more peripheral vascular disease than coronary atherosclerosis.[24,65,66]

Morganroth et al.[5] reported that 43 percent of 47 type III patients had vascular disease, and about one-third had definite coronary artery disease. In a study of 39 patients, Stuyt and Van't Laar[58] described the occurrence of atherosclerotic vascular disease in 22 type III patients (56 percent): 15 had coronary artery disease and 18 had definite peripheral vascular disease. Vascular disease generally becomes symptomatic earlier in men (mean age, about 40 years) than in women (mean age, about 50 years).[5] Less than 1 percent of all myocardial infarction survivors were found to have type III hyperlipoproteinemia[67]; however, overt hyperlipoproteinemia imposes a high risk for premature vascular disease.

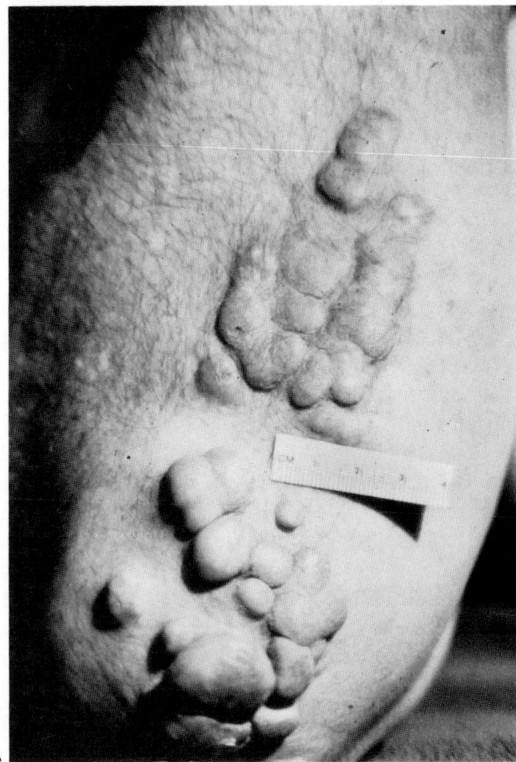

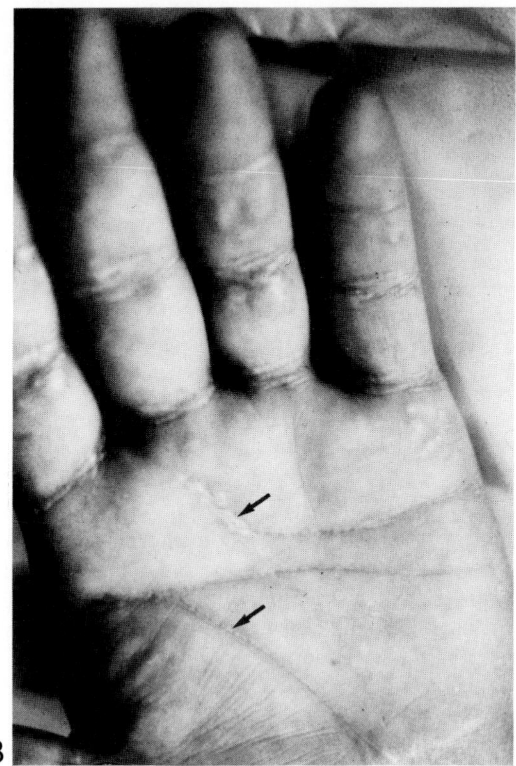

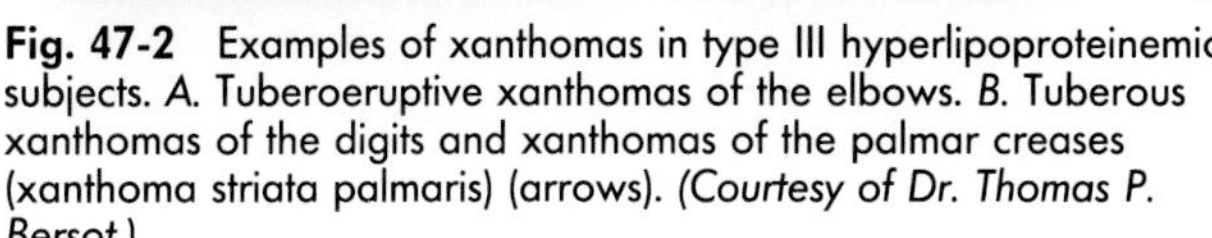

Fig. 47-2 Examples of xanthomas in type III hyperlipoproteinemic subjects. *A.* Tuberoeruptive xanthomas of the elbows. *B.* Tuberous xanthomas of the digits and xanthomas of the palmar creases (xanthoma striata palmaris) (arrows). *(Courtesy of Dr. Thomas P. Bersot.)*

Associated Disorders

Other types of disorders are also frequently associated with type III hyperlipoproteinemia, which suggests that their presence may exacerbate the hyperlipidemia. Asymptomatic hyperuricemia is present in up to half of the subjects, but only about 4 percent have clinical gout[5] (Table 47-3). Glucose intolerance is also common in type III subjects, but again only a small percentage (about 4 percent) have clinical diabetes. Obesity is common in type III hyperlipoproteinemia,[3] and this may be associated with the high level of glucose intolerance. Hypothyroidism markedly exacerbates the lipid and lipoprotein abnormalities in type III hyperlipoproteinemia[5,68]; in contrast, hyperthyroidism can essentially eliminate overt hyperlipidemia.

PATHOLOGIC FINDINGS IN TYPE III HYPERLIPOPROTEINEMIA

Necropsy reports on 10 patients with type III hyperlipoproteinemia have appeared in the literature.[69–75] The first report, by Roberts et al.,[69] described findings from a 57-year-old woman with severe coronary artery atherosclerosis. The lumen of all three major coronary arteries was severely narrowed by deposits of lipid-laden foam cells rather than the more typical complicated plaques. The entire aorta and iliac arteries contained numerous foam cell lesions, and plaques also narrowed the small arteries of the kidney, adrenals, and pancreas. Lipid deposits were also seen in the mural endocardium of the left atrium and in the mitral valve leaflets. Foam cells, presumably macrophages, also characterized the atheroma of a 64-year-old woman with diffuse coronary and peripheral artery atherosclerosis.[72] In the same study, foam cells were seen in the endocardium of the left atrium and ventricle, in the spleen, and in the mesangium of the renal glomeruli. However, other reports describe the atherosclerosis as being more typical, characterized by extensive fibrotic, complicated lesions.[70,73,74]

More recently, Cabin et al.[74] and Schwartz[75] reviewed the anatomic data on six patients with type III hyperlipoproteinemia at the National Institutes of Health. Four of the six were women, and death occurred between ages 50 and 74 years. All the patients had ischemic heart disease, and four had intermittent claudication. One of the six was described in the original report.[69] All six patients had severe coronary, aortic, and common iliac atherosclerosis. There was a strikingly high incidence of left main coronary artery narrowing; however, the atherosclerosis involved the coronary arteries diffusely. Almost half of the patients had coronary artery narrowing of greater than 76 percent. Only one of the six patients (presumably the one from the original report) had foam cell atherosclerosis. Lesions from the other patients were more fibrous and complicated and resembled atherosclerosis seen in patients with other types of hyperlipidemia.

It is likely that the morphologic appearance of the atherosclerotic lesions changes with time and the extent of the disease process. Currently, it is thought that many (and possibly most) atherosclerotic lesions begin with an abundance of foam cells, i.e., lipid-laden macrophages,[76] which evolve into more complicated plaques. However, there is also reason to believe that macrophage foam cells may play a unique role in the development of lipid-laden lesions in type III hyperlipoproteinemia. The β-VLDL from patients with type III hyperlipoproteinemia and from animals fed high levels of fat and cholesterol are uniquely capable of causing cholesterol accumulation in macrophages in cell culture (see also "Pathogenesis of

Type III Hyperlipoproteinemia," below).[77,78] Laboratory studies have demonstrated that β-VLDL are the only naturally occurring lipoproteins that cause a 100- to 200-fold increase in cholesterol content in mouse peritoneal macrophages. Macrophages are known to be major progenitors of atherosclerotic and xanthomatous foam cells. The β-VLDL appear to represent the atherogenic lipoproteins in these patients and in animals fed diets high in fat and cholesterol.[24,25,66]

APOLIPOPROTEIN E GENETICS AND STRUCTURE-FUNCTION CORRELATES

The Molecular Basis for Apolipoprotein E Polymorphism

Because the development of type III hyperlipoproteinemia is dependent on the inheritance of an abnormal form of apo E, an understanding of the genetics, structure, and function of apo E is crucial in the consideration of the disease (for review, see Refs. 13, 29, and 79). The polymorphic nature of apo E was first appreciated in the studies of Utermann and associates,[14–18] who used isoelectric focusing to demonstrate the polymorphism. These studies clearly established the familial nature of the polymorphism and also demonstrated that one of the isoforms of apo E was invariably deficient or absent in subjects with type III hyperlipoproteinemia. Their studies suggested that this missing isoform was the normal apo E and that type III hyperlipoproteinemia resulted from the inheritance of two abnormal apo E alleles.

Subsequently, Zannis and Breslow[19,20] using a two-dimensional electrophoretic technique, made two important observations that helped to clarify the polymorphism of apo E. They found that there were actually two types of apo E polymorphism, one genetically determined and one not. The latter polymorphism was shown to be the result of posttranslational sialylation of the apo E polypeptide, giving rise to one or several more acidic isoforms.[19] These minor isoforms could be readily distinguished in the second dimension of the gel analysis by their slightly higher apparent molecular weight, caused by the addition of sialic acids. When the apo E was treated with neuraminidase (an enzyme that cleaves sialic acid residues), these higher-molecular-weight forms disappeared and comigrated with the major, genetically determined apo E isoforms. The appreciation of this complexity of apo E isoform patterns allowed a more thorough understanding of the genetically determined polymorphism.

The second contribution of the Zannis and Breslow studies was the determination that the three major isoforms of apo E were all products of the same gene and that apo E genetics could be explained by the existence of three alleles at a single gene locus.[20] As a result, six phenotypes are possible, three homozygous and three heterozygous, with the heterozygous phenotypes arising from the inheritance of any two different alleles. The occurrence of these six common phenotypes and their pattern of inheritance has been amply confirmed in a large number of family studies by many investigators (see "Population Studies of Apolipoprotein E Polymorphism," below).

A unifying system of nomenclature for apo E genetics and polymorphism that blended the original findings and nomenclature of Utermann with those of Zannis and Breslow was established in 1982.[80] In this system, the three genetically determined isoforms are termed E-4, E-3, and E-2, with E-4 being the most basic ($pI \approx 6$) and E-2 the most acidic ($pI \approx 5.7$). The corresponding alleles for these three gene products are termed $\epsilon 4$, $\epsilon 3$, and $\epsilon 2$. The six common phenotypes are then E-4/4, E-3/3, or E-2/2 (homozygous) and E-4/3, E-3/2, or E-4/2 (heterozygous). The minor sialylated isoforms are designated with a subscript *s*, e.g., E-4$_s$, E-3$_s$, depending on the isoform that has been modified. It is the apo E phenotype E-2/2 that is associated with type III hyperlipoproteinemia.

The molecular basis for apo E polymorphism has been established by Mahley and coworkers.[21–25] They determined the primary structure of apo E and found that the isoforms E-4, E-3, and E-2 differed from one another by single amino acid substitutions at two sites in the protein (Fig. 47-3). The existence of the single amino acid substitutions confirmed that E-4, E-3, and E-2 arose from separate alleles at a single gene locus, as proposed by Zannis and Breslow. These substitutions also explain the single unit charge differences among the three isoforms, since they involve the substitution of the basic amino acid arginine by the neutral amino acid cysteine. The molecular basis for the second type of apo E polymorphism, i.e., that conferred by posttranslational glycosylation, has also been determined. The glycosylated (sialylated) isoforms apparent in plasma apo E are due to the attachment of carbohydrate to a single site in apo E at threonine residue 194.[81]

Population Studies of Apolipoprotein E Polymorphism

Stimulated by the findings of Utermann et al. and Zannis and Breslow, several laboratories have undertaken major investigations of apo E phenotype frequencies in both normal and other populations.[53,82–88] Screening of primarily Caucasian populations in several countries has established that the relative frequencies of the six apo E phenotypes are, with the pos-

Fig. 47-3 Isoelectric focusing of apo-VLDL demonstrating the three homozygous apo E phenotypes. The amino acid substitutions that account for the charge differences among the isoforms are shown. The minor, more acidic apo E isoforms in each case represent sialylated isoforms. The E-2/2 phenotype is from a type III hyperlipoproteinemic subject. *(From Mahley and Angelin.[24] Used by permission of* Advances in Internal Medicine.*)*

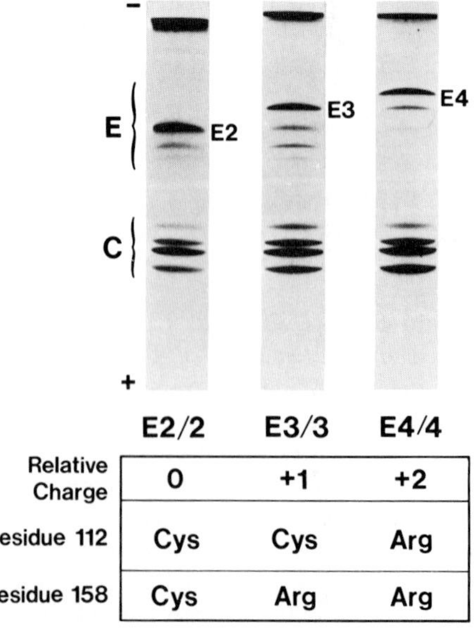

	E2/2	E3/3	E4/4
Relative Charge	0	+1	+2
Residue 112	Cys	Cys	Arg
Residue 158	Cys	Arg	Arg

sible exception of Finland, similar from one country to another (Table 47-4). These studies clearly show that the E-3/3 phenotype is by far the most common and that the corresponding ε3 allele makes up a large majority of the apo E gene pool. Therefore, apo E-3 is considered to be the parent form of apo E, and apo E-2 and apo E-4 are considered variants. The less frequently occurring ε4 and ε2 alleles nonetheless contribute significantly to the gene pool. In fact, the existence of this relatively stable gene and protein polymorphism at such a high frequency is of major interest for the field of population genetics. As a result of the lower frequencies of the ε4 and ε2 alleles, the phenotypes E-4/4, E-4/2, and E-2/2 are relatively rare (Table 47-4).

The impact of apo E phenotypes on normal variations of lipids, lipoproteins, and apolipoproteins has also been investigated. Sing and Davignon[89] found that alleles ε4 and ε2 had significant effects on various parameters (Fig. 47-4) compared with the population mean. While the ε3 allele (coding for the apo E-3 gene product) showed no deviations from the population mean, the ε4 allele was associated with lower plasma triglycerides but higher plasma cholesterol, mostly because of higher LDL cholesterol. In contrast, the ε2 allele was associated with higher plasma triglycerides but very significantly lower plasma cholesterol, mostly because of lower LDL cholesterol. The association of lower LDL levels in subjects having one or two ε2 alleles for the E-2 protein had been made some years earlier by Utermann et al.[17] Utermann has subsequently shown[53] that one or two doses of ε2 (i.e., E-3/2 or E-2/2 phenotypes) correlates with increased plasma apo E and decreased apo B, while ε4 (E-4/3 and E-4/4 phenotypes) has just the opposite effect (Fig. 47-5). Some of these phenomena may be accounted for by the differences in functional properties of the E-4, E-3, and E-2 isoforms that are imparted to them by their structural differences. Gregg and coworkers have shown that apo E-2 is catabolized in vivo more slowly than apo E-3,[90] which has important implications in type III hyperlipoproteinemia (see "Pathogenesis of Type III Hyperlipoproteinemia," below). In contrast, apo E-4 is catabolized in vivo faster than apo E-3.[91] Apolipoprotein E-4 also differs from apo E-3 in its lipoprotein distribution: apo E-4 is predominantly associated with VLDL, while apo E-3 is predominantly associated with HDL.[91] All these results imply that

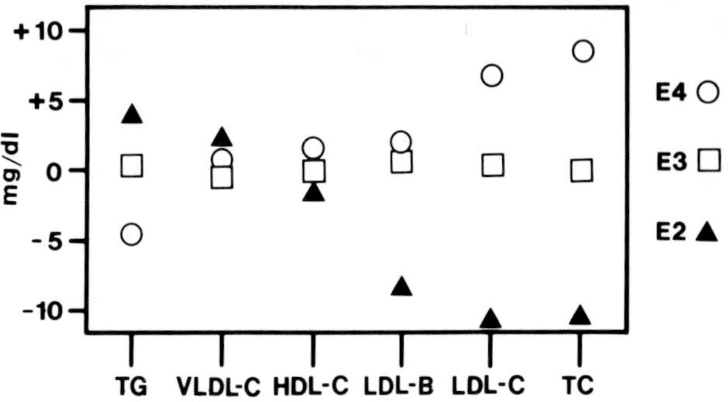

Fig. 47-4 The effects of apo E alleles on various lipoprotein parameters. TG = total plasma triglyceride; VLDL-C = VLDL cholesterol; HDL-C = HDL cholesterol; LDL-B = LDL apo B; LDL-C = LDL cholesterol; TC = total plasma cholesterol. *(Adapted from Sing and Davignon.[89] Used by permission of the American Journal of Human Genetics.)*

some major differences in the regulation of lipoprotein metabolism are associated with apo E polymorphism.

The study of apo E phenotypes in hyperlipidemic and heart disease populations has also been revealing. Utermann et al.[92] have found that apo E-2 is found significantly more frequently in hypertriglyceridemic subjects, while apo E-4 is observed significantly more frequently in hypercholesterolemic subjects. Both apo E-2 and apo E-4 occur more frequently in mixed hyperlipidemias. Studies of patients with coronary artery disease and myocardial infarction have yielded conflicting information on whether the presence of apo E-4 may impose some risk for developing cardiovascular disease.[93,94] In contrast, it seems clear that the presence of apo E-2 correlates with reduced risk, but only in non-type III subjects, who do not express overt hyperlipidemia.[84,93,94]

Apolipoprotein E Gene Structure and Mapping

The apo E gene is 3.7 kb in length and contains four exons.[95,96] Comparison of the apo E gene structure with the structure of six other apolipoproteins (apo A-I, apo A-II, apo A-IV, apo C-I, apo C-II, and apo C-III) reveals a strikingly similar location of the introns and suggests a common ances-

Table 47-4 Apolipoprotein E Phenotypes and Gene Frequencies in Normolipidemic Populations

Year *Country* *No. of subjects*	*1982* *Germany* *1031*	*1982* *New Zealand* *426*	*1983* *Germany* *1000*	*1984* *Scotland* *400*	*1984* *Canada* *102*	*1985* *U.S.A.* *152*	*1986* *Finland* *615*
Phenotype				%			
E4/4	2.8	0.9	2.3	1.0	3.9	3.0	6.3
E4/3	22.9	25.1	20.2	24.8	20.6	14.0	31.9
E3/3	59.8	51.4	62.7	58.3	61.8	58.0	54.0
E3/2	12.0	20.0	11.0	12.8	9.8	22.0	6.7
E2/2	1.0	1.4	0.8	0.5	2.0	1.3	0.3
E4/2	1.5	1.2	3.0	2.8	2.0	2.0	0.8
Allele				%			
ε4	15.0	14.1	13.9	15	15.2	11	22.7
ε3	77.3	73.9	78.3	77	77.0	76	73.3
ε2	7.7	12.0	7.8	8	7.8	13	4.1
Reference	82	83	84	85	86	87	88

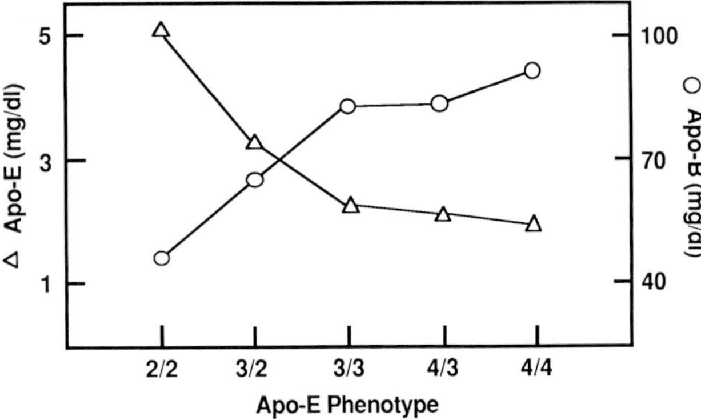

Fig. 47-5 Plasma concentrations of apo E (△) and apo B (○) in relation to apo E phenotypes. *(From Utermann.[53] Used by permission of Elsevier Science Publishers.)*

tral origin for this family of genes.[97,98] The apo E gene codes for an mRNA of 1163 base pairs.[99,100] The primary translation product is composed of 317 amino acids, with the amino-terminal 18 amino acids serving as a signal peptide. Thus, the mature apo E is secreted as a 299-amino acid protein. The apo E gene occurs on chromosome 19[95,101] and is closely linked to apo C-I and an apo C-I pseudogene.[102] In addition, apo C-II[103] and the LDL receptor[104] have been mapped to chromosome 19, but they do not appear to be closely linked to apo E.

Apolipoprotein E Structure-Function Correlates

Apolipoprotein E-containing lipoproteins, including chylomicron and VLDL remnants (the two lipoproteins of β-VLDL) and a subclass of HDL, participate in the transport of lipids among various cells and tissues. The cellular uptake of apo E-containing lipoproteins is mediated by lipoprotein receptors, and it is now possible to describe in some detail the chemical nature of the interaction of apo E with the LDL receptor (for review, see Refs. 13, 29, and 79). As will be discussed later, both apo E and apo B are ligands for the LDL receptor, and LDL uptake is mediated by apo B (see "Pathogenesis of Type III Hyperlipoproteinemia," below).

The receptor binding domain of the apo E molecule has been mapped by using several complementary techniques. Initially, selective chemical modification of various amino acids established that a limited number of arginine and lysine residues within apo E are critical in mediating its binding to the LDL receptor.[105,106] Furthermore, chemical modification of these amino acid residues interfered with the normal plasma clearance of apo E-containing lipoproteins,[107–109] which established that arginine and lysine residues of apo E are also important in vivo.

The receptor binding domain of apo E was subsequently localized to the middle of the apo E molecule in the vicinity of residues 140 to 160.[13,29,79] This region is enriched in basic amino acid residues (arginine, lysine, and histidine). The apo E mutations associated with type III hyperlipoproteinemia are single amino acid substitutions in this region of the molecule. Most type III patients have a mutant form of apo E, apo E-2(Arg_{158}→Cys), in which cysteine has been substituted for the normally occurring arginine at residue 158. This mutant form of apo E binds very poorly to lipoprotein receptors. The several other rare variants of apo E that are associated with type III hyperlipoproteinemia have also been found to be defective in binding to the lipoprotein receptors. This usually has been determined in in vitro assays using apo E that is combined with phospholipid (see "Pathogenesis of Type III Hyperlipoproteinemia," below). Table 47-5 summarizes the nature of the mutations and their effect on receptor binding activity. The mutations involve single amino acid substitutions, in which neutral amino acids are substituted for basic residues, and the substitutions occur in the vicinity of residues 140 to 160. The amino acid sequence of this region of apo E is shown in Fig. 47-6.

Other approaches have also implicated the midportion of apo E in mediating receptor binding, including studying the receptor binding activity of fragments of the apo E molecule,[115] mapping the epitope of an apo E monoclonal antibody that blocked binding of apo E to the receptor,[116] and producing site-directed mutant forms of apo E in *Escherichia coli* by using recombinant DNA technology.[112,117] It has been postulated that apo E binds to the LDL receptor through an ionic interaction between these key basic amino acid residues of the ligand and acidic amino acid residues of the LDL receptor. The LDL receptor has been shown to possess seven repeated segments near its amino terminus that are enriched in the acidic amino acids aspartate and glutamate.[118,119]

Apolipoprotein E Sites of Synthesis

Apolipoprotein E has been shown to be produced in many organs throughout the body (for review, see Ref. 13). Significant quantities of apo E mRNA are detected in the liver, brain, spleen, lung, adrenal, ovary, kidney, and muscle in several different species.[120–122] Apolipoprotein E mRNA has not been found in the epithelium of the intestine, in spite of the fact that the intestine is a major site for lipoprotein biosynthesis. The largest quantity of apo E mRNA is found in the liver, which is the major source for plasma apo E. The second largest quantity of apo E mRNA is found in the brain. Apolipoprotein E production in the liver occurs primarily in the parenchymal cells. In several other organs, macrophages are likely to account for the apo E production. Macrophages in culture and *in situ* can produce large quantities of this protein and release it into the medium or interstitial fluid in high concentrations.[123,124] In the brain, apo E is produced almost entirely by astrocytes.[125] Another cell type capable of apo E production is the smooth-muscle cell.[126,127]

Therefore, apo E is present in substantial concentrations in the plasma and interstitial fluid and is available to associate with various lipoproteins. Apolipoprotein E plays a major role in redistributing cholesterol from cells containing excess cholesterol to cells requiring cholesterol for metabolic processes, including new membrane biosynthesis for cell proliferation or repair (for review, see Ref. 13). The apo E·lipid complexes are taken up via the LDL receptors expressed on the cholesterol-

Table 47-5 Apolipoprotein E Variants Associated with Type III Hyperlipoproteinemia

Isoelectric focusing position	*Amino acid substitution(s)*	*Receptor binding activity, %*	*Reference(s)*
E2	Arg_{158}→Cys	<2	22, 35
E2	Arg_{145}→Cys	45	23
E2	Lys_{146}→Gln	40	110
E2	Arg_{136}→Ser	40	111, 112
E3	Cys_{112}→Arg, Arg_{142}→Cys	<4	113, 114

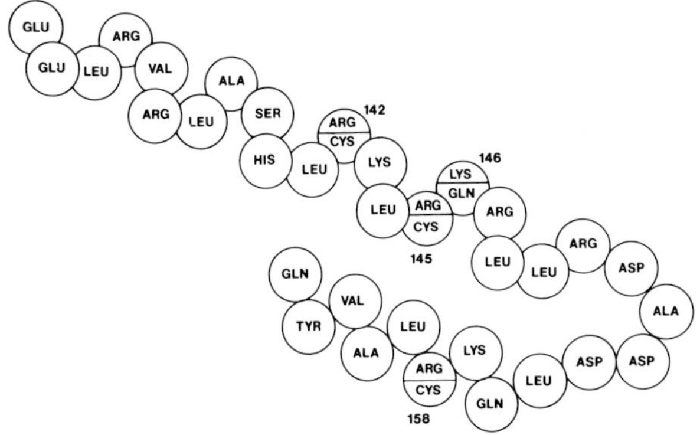

Fig. 47-6 Amino acid sequence of apo E in a region critical for receptor binding. Sites where neutral amino acids substitute for basic amino acids in receptor binding-defective apo E from type III hyperlipoproteinemic subjects are indicated. *(Adapted from Mahley and Innerarity.[29] Used by permission of* Biochimica et Biophysica Acta.*)*

deficient cells. This function appears to occur during tissue injury and repair; e.g., apo E may play a key role in peripheral nerve regeneration.[128–130]

PATHOGENESIS OF TYPE III HYPERLIPOPROTEINEMIA

Role of Apolipoprotein E in Normal Remnant Metabolism

Remnants of triglyceride-rich intestinal lipoproteins (chylomicrons) and hepatic lipoproteins (VLDL) are removed from the circulation primarily through receptor-mediated processes.[8] The LDL receptor, originally described by Brown and Goldstein (for review, see Chap. 48 and Refs. 131 and 132) in extrahepatic cells, was subsequently demonstrated to exist in hepatic tissue as well.[133–137] The existence of a second hepatic lipoprotein receptor, the *chylomicron remnant* or *apo E receptor,* has also been postulated to be involved in hepatic removal of lipoproteins.[138,139] However, the presence of several apo E-binding proteins in the liver has made it difficult to isolate a specific chylomicron remnant (apo E) receptor.[140,141]

There are two ligands responsible for the uptake of lipoproteins by the LDL receptor (for review, see Refs. 29 and 79). Apolipoprotein B-100, which is the only protein constituent of LDL, has been shown to be responsible for the binding and uptake of LDL by the LDL receptor. In addition, apo E has been shown to mediate the uptake of other lipoproteins via interaction with the LDL receptor. Originally, the interaction of apo E with the LDL receptor was demonstrated with the lipoprotein HDL_c,[27–29,142] a cholesterol-induced HDL species that contains apo E as its primary or, in certain instances, exclusive protein component. Because this lipoprotein lacks apo B, it was suggested that apo E also served as a ligand for the LDL receptor. This was also proven in studies using phospholipid recombinants of apo E.[143,144] Furthermore, apo E HDL_c and apo E phospholipid recombinants both demonstrate a twentyfold higher affinity for the LDL receptor than do LDL.[28,145] Because of the demonstration of the two apolipoprotein ligands, the LDL receptor is also referred to as the apo B,E(LDL) receptor.

As discussed earlier, the major site of synthesis of apo E is the liver; there is little or none by the intestine. Nevertheless, apo E is a prominent component of intestinally derived chylomicron remnants and directs their catabolism by interaction with hepatic lipoprotein receptors.[31,33] Chylomicrons acquire apo E almost certainly by exchange from other apo E-containing lipoproteins. Chylomicrons, as they emerge from the intestine, undergo substantial changes before they are cleared from the circulation. The exceedingly triglyceride-rich core of these particles is lipolyzed by lipoprotein lipase on the luminal surface of endothelial cells in the capillary beds, resulting in a dramatic reduction in the size of the particle.[8] As a consequence, the surface of the particle is also reorganized. Some of the apolipoprotein constitutents of newly secreted chylomicrons are lost, in particular apo A-I and apo A-IV. It is during these changes that apo E is acquired, resulting in a remnant that is relatively depleted in triglyceride and whose protein components are apo B-48, apo E, and the apo C proteins. The apo B-48 component of these remnants does not appear to participate in their receptor-mediated catabolism; instead, apo E serves this function.[146]

The hepatic-derived VLDL undergo lipolytic processing similar to that of chylomicrons, generating smaller particles with a more cholesterol-enriched core (primarily cholesteryl esters) (for review, see Refs. 8 and 132). Eventually this cascade leads to the production of IDL and LDL in a classic precursor-product manner. Unlike chylomicrons, VLDL contain apo E as they are synthesized of the liver, but during lipolysis their remnants become relatively depleted of all protein components except apo B-100. When further processing converts IDL to LDL, apo E is lost, leaving apo B-100 as the only protein component of LDL. The catabolism of particles along this pathway is complex: a portion of the particles in the lipolytic cascade can be removed from circulation by receptor-mediated processes, whereas others proceed completely through this metabolic process to become LDL. Apolipoprotein E serves as the ligand for the removal of these remnants. Farther along the pathway, as more lipolysis occurs and as apo E is lost, apo B-100 becomes the ligand for receptor-mediated catabolism of LDL.

Apolipoprotein E-2 and Impaired Remnant Catabolism

Given the importance of apo E in determining the fate of remnants, it is not surprising that a mutant form of apo E, i.e., apo E-2, which does not bind normally to hepatic receptors, could lead to the accumulation of remnants in the plasma of type III patients. The first evidence that the different apo E isoforms had different abilities to mediate hepatic uptake of lipoproteins came from the studies of Havel and coworkers,[30] who used liver perfusion of estradiol-treated rats as the experimental model. Estradiol causes the expression of hepatic LDL receptors to be increased ten- to twentyfold. These investigators found that phospholipid vesicles in which normal apo E had been incorporated were efficiently taken up by the treated rat livers, whereas vesicles containing apo E-2 from a type III patient were taken up poorly, suggesting defective receptor recognition of apo E-2.

This phenomenon was subsequently studied directly by investigating the comparative binding of apo E isoforms from various subjects to the LDL receptor. Schneider et al.[34] showed that apo E-2 bound poorly in these assays compared with apo E-3. In a similar study, Weisgraber et al.[35] showed that apo E-2 from a type III patient had a binding affinity that

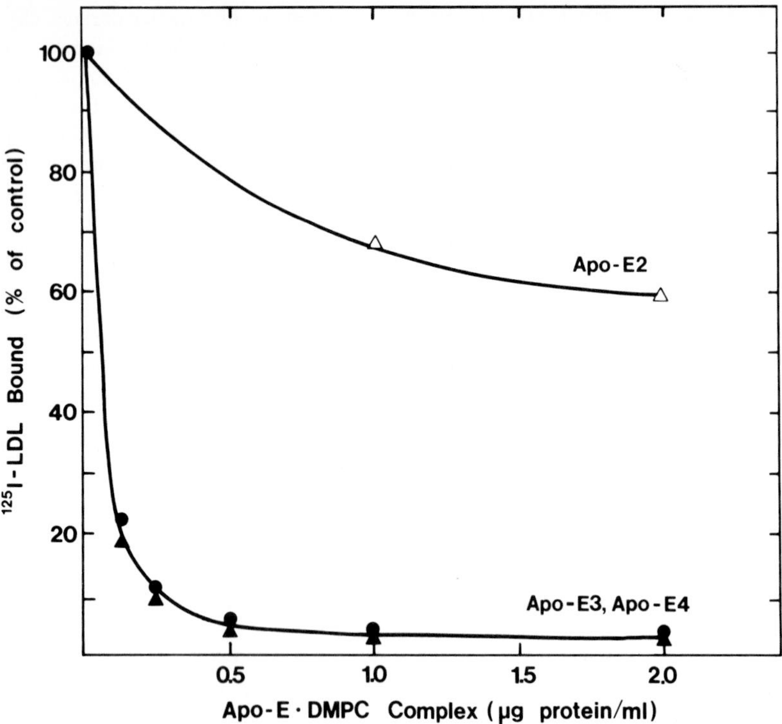

Fig. 47-7 Receptor binding activity of apo E-2 (△), apo E-3 (▲), and apo E-4 (●) as assessed in an in vitro competition assay. Human ^{125}I-LDL was used as the competitor for the binding of apo E·DMPC complexes to normal human fibroblasts. The apo E-2 is from a type III hyperlipoproteinemic subject. *(From Weisgraber, Innerarity, and Mahley.[35] Used by permission of* The Journal of Biological Chemistry.*)*

was only 1 to 2 percent that of apo E-3 (Fig. 47-7). In contrast, apo E-4, the other genetically determined polymorphic form of apo E, had a binding capacity identical with that of apo E-3 (Fig. 47-7). It was also demonstrated by Gregg et al.[90] that radiolabeled apo E-2 and E-3 were cleared from plasma differently in both normal and type III individuals (Fig. 47-8). In both cases, apo E-2 clearance was significantly retarded, suggesting that the clearance impairment was due to a defective ligand rather than defective receptors.

The aforementioned studies directly implicate apo E-2 in the accumulation of the abnormal lipoproteins β-VLDL in type III hyperlipoproteinemia. Less readily explained, however, is why type III individuals, and E-2/2 homozygotes in general, have significantly lower concentrations of LDL in their plasma compared with the population mean. One could argue that the receptor binding-defective apo E-2 might actually reduce the percentage of hepatic VLDL remnants (but not intestinal remnants) that are cleared as VLDL particles, resulting in a higher rate of conversion of these particles to LDL. Thus, one might expect LDL concentrations to increase as a consequence of an enhanced LDL "rate of synthesis." However, the finding that LDL concentrations in apo E-2/2 individuals are actually decreased suggests that apo E may have a role in lipolytic processing. In fact, Ehnholm and associates[147] have presented data that this may be the case. They found that the hepatic β-VLDL, but not the intestinal β-VLDL, of type III subjects could be converted to LDL by the addition of normal apo E-3, but not by the addition of the abnormal apo E-2, to these lipoproteins. These data suggest a role for apo E in remodeling the particles during lipolytic processing of normal VLDL to LDL and suggest that this complex process is impaired by the presence of apo E-2.

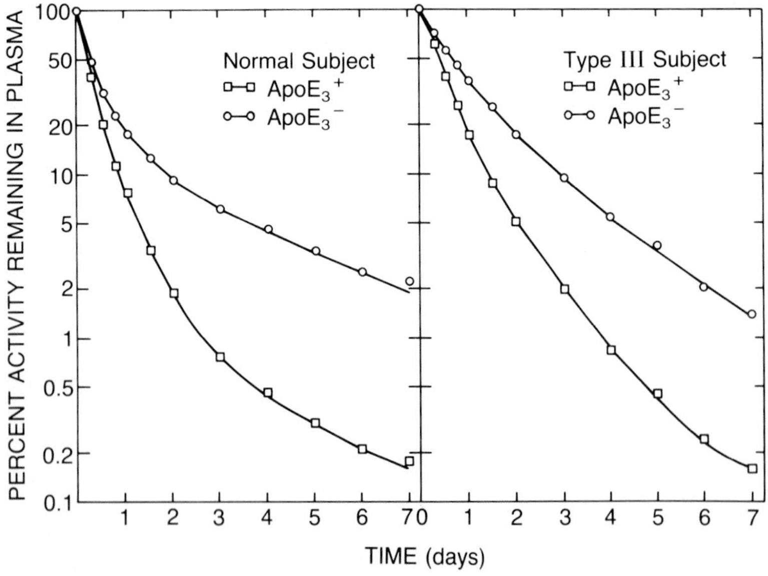

Fig. 47-8 Clearance of simultaneously injected apo E-3 (E_3^+) and apo E-2 (E_3^-) from the plasma of a normal subject *(left)* and a type III hyperlipoproteinemic subject *(right)*. *(From Gregg et al.[90] Used by permission of* Science.*)*

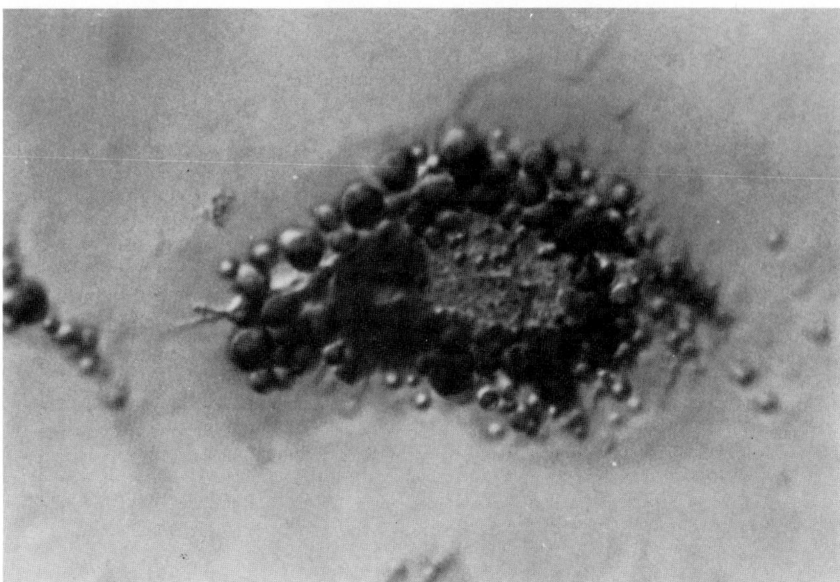

Fig. 47-9 A cultured mouse peritoneal macrophage after incubation with canine β-VLDL. The large droplets are cholesteryl esters. *(Courtesy of Dr. Robert E. Pitas.)*

Deposition of β-VLDL in Macrophages

The β-VLDL have an unusual propensity for being taken up by macrophages (Fig. 47-9) and for causing a massive accumulation of cholesterol (as cholesteryl esters) in these cells (for review, see Refs. 25, 29, 79, and 148 to 151). This was first demonstrated in mouse peritoneal macrophages, but it has also been shown to occur in human monocyte-macrophages.[77,78] The foam cells in xanthomas and early atherosclerotic lesions derive, at least in part, from macrophages. The avid uptake of β-VLDL (and especially the intestinal β-VLDL) by macrophages may partially explain the tendency of type III patients to develop xanthomas and premature atherosclerosis.[9] Thus, the atherogenic nature of β-VLDL probably derives primarily from their uptake by macrophages (for review, see Refs. 25, 150, and 151).

The uptake of β-VLDL by macrophages is a receptor-mediated event, and early studies suggested that there was a specific β-VLDL receptor in these cells.[77,78,152] However, it has been demonstrated in mouse macrophages that it is the LDL receptor (albeit possibly a "modified" LDL receptor) that is responsible for the uptake of β-VLDL.[153] Furthermore, the LDL receptor is responsible for remnant uptake in human monocyte-macrophages.[154,155] The ligand for the macrophage uptake of β-VLDL is apo E,[156] as demonstrated in animals that had been fed a cholesterol-enriched diet. The β-VLDL induced by the cholesterol feeding have physical and chemical properties similar to those of β-VLDL of human type III patients, except that the animal β-VLDL do not contain a genetically abnormal form of apo E. Human β-VLDL, despite the presence of receptor binding-defective apo E-2, are also taken up by macrophages via apo E-directed binding.[156] At first glance this would seem to be a paradox. However, human β-VLDL from type III individuals are generally less efficient than animal β-VLDL in stimulating cholesterol deposition in macrophages, and human β-VLDL uptake by macrophages can be enhanced by the incorporation of normal apo E-3 into these particles. Therefore, it is probable that the deposition of β-VLDL cholesterol in macrophages is not due to any special property of apo E itself, but instead is a reflection of the general overloading of these particles in the circulation accompanied by a breakdown in the capacity of the system to remove cholesterol from macrophages.

Apolipoprotein E almost certainly has a role in the mobilization of cholesterol from peripheral cells, including macrophages.[157,158] It has been shown that cholesterol accumulation in macrophages stimulates production and secretion of apo E.[123,124] The apo E secreted from these cells forms apo E·lipid complexes or is incorporated into HDL particles. These complexes or particles can acquire cholesterol from cholesterol-loaded cells and redistribute it to cells requiring cholesterol. Apolipoprotein E-enriched HDL (HDL_c) are present in high concentrations in the plasma of cholesterol-fed animals.[29,65,150,159] HDL_c of cholesterol-fed animals and HDL-with apo E (the comparable particles in humans) have been postulated to remove cholesterol from peripheral cells (including but not restricted to macrophages) and transport it to other cells requiring cholesterol or to the liver, where cholesterol can be excreted from the body in the bile as bile salts or free cholesterol (for review, see Refs. 13, 25, 29, and 150). The uptake of these particles occurs via a receptor-mediated process in which apo E serves as the ligand. This process of redistributing cholesterol is sometimes referred to as reverse cholesterol transport.[160] It is likely that in type III individuals with high levels of β-VLDL the reverse cholesterol transport system is taxed beyond its ability to achieve a normal balance in cholesterol flux.

Mode of Inheritance of Type III Hyperlipoproteinemia

With rare exceptions, individuals with type III hyperlipoproteinemia have inherited two ε2 alleles for the defective apo E-2; i.e., they are of the E-2/2 phenotype. Without exception, type III subjects display the abnormal lipoprotein β-VLDL; i.e., they all have primary dysbetalipoproteinemia. However, type III hyperlipoproteinemia is not a typical example of a recessive disease because, as mentioned earlier, only a small percentage of all E-2/2 homozygotes actually ever develop overt hyperlipidemia. In addition, as initially observed by Utermann and as amply confirmed subsequently, most E-2/2 sub-

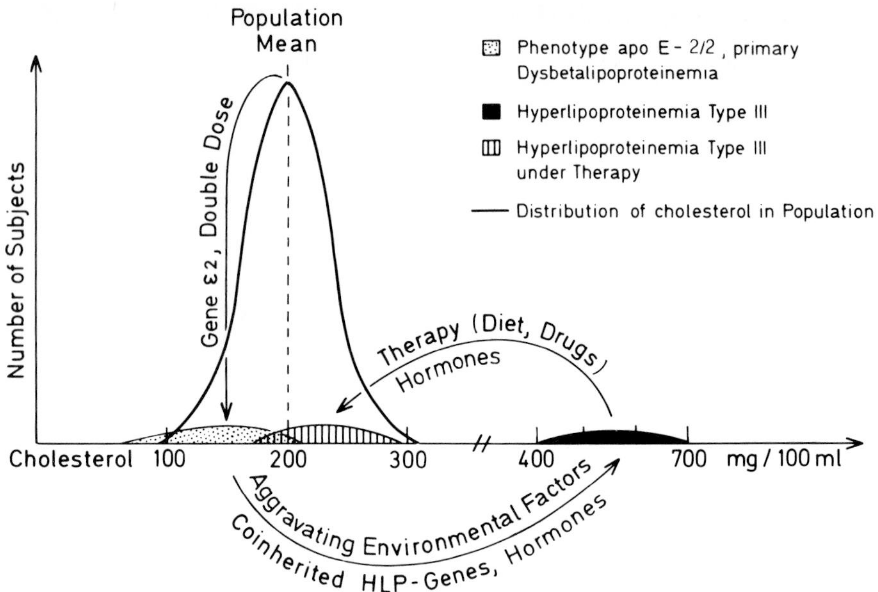

Fig. 47-10 Type III hyperlipoproteinemia as a multifactorial disorder. Factors involved in the pathogenesis and modulation of the expression of type III hyperlipoproteinemia are indicated. HLP = hyperlipoproteinemia. *(From Utermann.[53] Used by permission of Elsevier Science Publishers.)*

jects are actually hypocholesterolemic, owing to reduced levels of LDL.[18,53,161] Thus, the development of type III hyperlipoproteinemia seemingly requires the coexistence of another factor, either genetic or environmental, in addition to the inheritance of two alleles for the abnormal apo E.

Individuals with the E-3/2 phenotype usually display none of the clinical features of type III hyperlipoproteinemia[17] and only rarely demonstrate dysbetalipoproteinemia, i.e., detectable β-VLDL. Thus, dysbetalipoproteinemia is fundamentally a recessive characteristic. A single ε2 allele does have an impact on lipoprotein levels in E-3/2 subjects, however. These subjects have somewhat increased levels of triglyceride, VLDL cholesterol, and apo E, and a reduced level of LDL cholesterol, findings suggestive of some accumulation of remnantlike lipoproteins (see also "Population Studies of Apolipoprotein E Polymorphism," above, and Figs. 47-4 and 47-5). On rare occasions, apo E-3/2 individuals do develop overt type III hyperlipoproteinemia.[17,110,162]

The complexity of the genetics of type III hyperlipoproteinemia is further apparent in the rare occurrence of type III disease in individuals with other apo E phenotypes.[113,163–165] In at least two of these kindreds,[113,165] the mode of inheritance seems consistent with a dominant expression caused by a single dose of an allele for rare mutant apo E proteins that do not fit into the isoform classifications of Fig. 47-3. Type III hyperlipoproteinemia has also been noted in a kindred with apo E deficiency.[166,167] These subjects have no or barely detectable plasma apo E but have all the clinical and biochemical features of the type III disorder. The molecular defect in these apo E-deficient subjects has been identified as a mutation in the acceptor splice site of the third intron of the apo E gene; the mutation leads to the production of unstable apo E mRNA that does not result in protein synthesis.[168] These studies support the concept of the key role of apo E in normal lipoprotein metabolism and emphasize the impact that the abnormal apo E-2 has in the usual forms of type III hyperlipoproteinemia.

In spite of this complexity, the clinical, genetic, and biochemical studies make it clear that type III hyperlipoproteinemia is a multifactorial disorder requiring, in many cases, the involvement of other genetic or environmental influences, or both, for overt expression (Fig. 47-10). The simultaneous inheritance of two alleles for the abnormal apo E-2 is thus a necessary (in almost all cases) but not sufficient requirement. Nevertheless, the primary molecular defect in type III hyperlipoproteinemia is a structurally and functionally abnormal apo E, i.e., apo E that does not bind normally to lipoprotein receptors (see also Table 47-5).

Genetic and Environmental Factors Influencing the Expression of Type III Hyperlipoproteinemia

Based on his clinical genetic studies,[15–18] Utermann hypothesized that the development of type III hyperlipoproteinemia also required the simultaneous but independent inheritance of other genetic defects that produce hyperlipidemia, especially the gene for familial combined hyperlipidemia. In a study of 19 kindreds, it was found that those E-2/2 subjects who expressed type III hyperlipoproteinemia had relatives with other genetic defects that led to other hyperlipidemias, whereas E-2/2 subjects who did not have type III hyperlipoproteinemia had relatives who had no other hyperlipidemias.[16] One of the best examples of this two-gene hypothesis comes from a thorough study of a large family from Seattle.[169] In this case, the genes for dysbetalipoproteinemia (i.e., the E-2/2 phenotype) and for familial combined hyperlipidemia were shown to segregate independently. The simultaneous occurrence of the gene for familial combined hyperlipidemia and the E-2/2 phenotype resulted in the clinical expression of type III, while only other lipoprotein phenotypes (types IIa, IIb, or IV) were associated with other apo E phenotypes. The Utermann hypothesis remains the most satisfactory explanation of separate genetic influences in the expression of type III disease.

It is also likely that the separate genetic factors may include polygenic abnormalities, not just the monogenic forms of hyperlipidemia. For example, certain genetically determined disturbances in hormonal regulation could influence the development of type III hyperlipoproteinemia. On the other hand, hormonal disturbances need not be strictly genetically driven, but may also arise from environmental influences. The complex relationship of genetic and environmental factors is also exemplified by the frequent association of disorders such as hypothyroidism[170] and diabetes (glucose intolerance)[5] with type III hyperlipoproteinemia. Other endogenous and exoge-

Table 47-6 Metabolic Defects Associated with the Development of Type III Hyperlipoproteinemia

Metabolic defect(s)	*Possible mechanism(s) responsible*
Accumulation of chylomicron remnants (intestinal β-VLDL)	Defective lipoprotein receptor-mediated uptake due to abnormal apo E binding; Down-regulation in expression of LDL receptors (decrease induced by diet, hormones, etc.)
Accumulation of cholesterol-rich hepatic β-VLDL	Defective lipoprotein receptor-mediated uptake Down-regulation in expression of LDL receptors Overproduction of hepatic VLDL and/or cholesterol Impaired conversion of hepatic β-VLDL to LDL (impaired interaction of β-VLDL with lipase, or impaired lipase activity secondary to presence of abnormal apoE)
Low levels of LDL	Impaired conversion of VLDL and hepatic β-VLDL to LDL Accelerated catabolism of LDL (up-regulation of LDL receptors due to impaired remnant catabolism)
Accelerated vascular disease and tissue macrophage lipid loading	Enhanced uptake of intestinal and hepatic β-VLDL by macrophages

SOURCE: Modified from Mahley and Angelin.[24]

nous factors such as age, sex, nutrition, and alcohol consumption can also be aggravating factors. Of the environmental factors, one that seems to be prevalent is obesity. The correspondence between the presentation of type III clinical expression and weight has been noted. Furthermore, the usually prompt response of type III hyperlipoproteinemia to diet control emphasizes the impact of caloric intake (see "Diagnosis and Treatment," below).

The exacerbating influence of all these genetic and environmental factors suggests that biochemical mechanisms may be involved in the expression of type III hyperlipoproteinemia (for review, see Refs. 24, 25, and 151). Some of these factors are summarized in Fig. 47-11 and Table 47-6. Clearly, the presence of an apo E defective in receptor binding activity could account for the accumulation of both intestinal and hepatic lipoprotein remnants, but in many E-2/2 subjects the accumulation of β-VLDL is not pronounced. This suggests that there are situations in which an adequate metabolic compensation is made for this binding defect. One possibility is that the estimation of the severity of the apo E-2 receptor binding defect, which is generally determined in vitro, may not always reflect the magnitude of the defect on native particles in vivo. Also, certain of the other rare mutants of apo E known to be associated with type III hyperlipoproteinemia do not have a particularly severe binding defect, as assessed in vitro (see Table 47-5). Therefore, the pronounced accumulation of β-VLDL in type III hyperlipoproteinemia cannot be explained solely on the basis of a defective receptor-ligand interaction (although in any individual case it may be sufficient).

Fig. 47-11 Events in lipoprotein metabolism that may interact to cause the spectrum of lipoprotein changes seen in homozygous E-2 subjects. (1) Removal of chylomicron and VLDL remnants from the plasma, which is carried out by the liver, could be disrupted by the presence of abnormal apo E. (2) Expression of hepatic lipoprotein receptors in the uptake of chylomicron and VLDL remnants by the liver. (3) Increased synthesis of hepatic cholesterol or VLDL. (4) Impaired conversion of VLDL or IDL to LDL, resulting in low levels of LDL in the plasma. Apo-B,E receptors = LDL receptors.

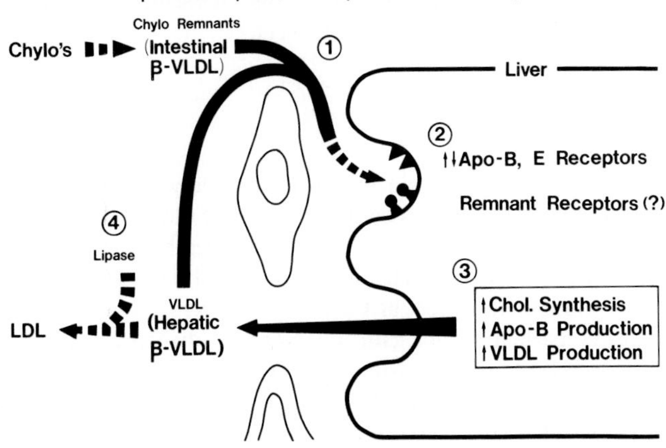

One factor that could have a profound modulating effect on hepatic remnant uptake is the absolute level of hepatic lipoprotein receptors. The expression of hepatic LDL receptors is particularly sensitive to regulation.[171] The expression of this receptor is rapidly regulated by diet, drugs, and hormones,[171] and is age-dependent, at least in certain animals.[139] It is possible that the clinical expression of type III hyperlipoproteinemia is influenced by the level of hepatic LDL receptors. First, there is a reduction in receptor number with age, and type III hyperlipoproteinemia usually manifests itself during adulthood. Second, the fact that type III hyperlipoproteinemia is more prevalent in men than in women and that women who develop type III hyperlipoproteinemia are primarily postmenopausal suggests that estrogen balance may be an important factor in type III expression. In support of this concept, it has been demonstrated in several cases that estrogen treatment can reverse the hyperlipidemia in type III subjects.[172,173] Furthermore, estrogens can profoundly increase the level of hepatic LDL receptors in animals,[133–135] although this requires pharmacologic doses. Nevertheless, the actual changes in hepatic receptor expression needed to reverse or prevent hyperlipidemia may be very slight. Third, the exacerbation of type III hyperlipoproteinemia by hypothyroidism[170] may be related to the decreased receptor-mediated uptake of lipoproteins,[174] which may come about by suppression of hepatic LDL receptor expression. Fourth, the influence of diet on the development of type III hyperlipoproteinemia may also be related to receptor expression. Increased dietary cholesterol and plasma lipoproteins are known to down-regulate LDL receptor expression.[171] Thus, the level of LDL receptor expression in the liver may be crucial in regulating intestinal chylomicron and hepatic VLDL remnant accumulation in the circulation (Fig. 47-11 and Table 47-6).

Yet another mechanism that may contribute to remnant accumulation is overproduction of lipoproteins. Two factors that may be major contributors to this phenomenon are diet and separate genes for hyperlipidemia. Increased caloric intake would certainly be expected to stimulate intestinal lipoprotein production, and probably hepatic VLDL as well, since cholesterol of dietary origin carried in chylomicron remnants is presumed to be a regulator of hepatic cholesterol synthesis.[175–177] Although the mechanisms of other genetically determined hyperlipidemias are not well understood, at least some involve hepatic overproduction of VLDL.[178]

The occurrence of hepatic β-VLDL may be secondary to an increased conversion of pre-β-VLDL to these remnant particles. Chappell has demonstrated that pre-β-VLDL from type III hyperlipoproteinemic patients bind less well to apo B,E(LDL) receptors than do pre-β-VLDL isolated from normal subjects.[47] The poor receptor binding of the pre-β-VLDL would increase the amount of VLDL available for conversion to VLDL remnants, and, in combination with one of the several possible mechanisms responsible for the hyperlipoproteinemia, the hepatic β-VLDL could accumulate to abnormally high levels.

The low levels of LDL observed in type III subjects and E-2/2 homozygotes in general may be due to a combination of factors (Fig. 47-11 and Table 47-6). One of these is likely to be LDL receptor expression in the liver. In conditions of impaired remnant clearance, the liver may "sense" a deficiency in cholesterol delivery and stimulate expression of more hepatic LDL receptors. The increased level of receptors would then allow for a more accelerated uptake of LDL, which in type III individuals do not appear to deviate from normal LDL in composition or other respects. Increased catabolism of LDL would lead to low plasma LDL levels, but so would impaired conversion of VLDL remnants to LDL. The possible involvement of apo E in this latter process has been noted earlier.[147] Furthermore, the hepatic β-VLDL have an abnormal lipid composition compared with normal VLDL and IDL, and so they may prevent or reduce the capacity for lipase action.[179]

DIAGNOSIS AND TREATMENT

Diagnosis

A single simple diagnostic test for type III hyperlipoproteinemia is not available, but there are some diagnostic markers. Individuals who have both elevated plasma cholesterol and triglyceride concentrations at nearly the same level ($\approx$ 400 mg/dl) should be suspected of having type III hyperlipoproteinemia. However, the cholesterol and triglyceride levels tend to vary greatly among type III individuals. Determination of the ratio of the concentration of VLDL cholesterol to the concentration of plasma triglyceride is very useful. In general, a ratio of $\geqslant$0.3 reflects the presence of cholesterol-rich β-VLDL and is indicative of type III hyperlipoproteinemia, but this can be misleading in some cases. Demonstration of the broad β band on agarose electrophoresis of whole plasma can also be unreliable. However, when used in combination with ultracentrifugally separated lipoproteins, electrophoretic demonstration of β-migrating particles in the $d<$ 1.006-g/ml fraction is predictive of type III hyperlipoproteinemia. It should be noted that dysbetalipoproteinemia, i.e., the presence of β-VLDL in the plasma, persists regardless of whether the subject is overtly hyperlipidemic and therefore can almost always be detected.

The most diagnostic of the clinical features are the xanthomas, but these do not occur in all individuals with type III hyperlipoproteinemia. The planar xanthomas in the palmar creases appear to be uniquely associated with type III hyperlipoproteinemia, so their presence indicates a near certainty for the type III disorder. Xanthomas of the tuberous variety, while frequent in type III hyperlipoproteinemia, also occur in other disorders, especially familial hypercholesterolemia (type IIa). The coexistence of premature vascular disease and hyperlipidemia is cause for suspecting type III hyperlipoproteinemia, particularly if peripheral vascular disease is present.

The most reliable biochemical marker diagnostic of type III hyperlipoproteinemia is the apo E phenotype. The concurrence of phenotype E-2/2 with any of the other characteristics noted above is virtually diagnostic of type III hyperlipoproteinemia. The vast majority of all type III subjects will have the E-2/2 phenotype, which can be determined by isoelectric focusing of the $d<$ 1.006- or $d <$ 1.02-g/ml fraction of a small volume of fresh plasma. Phenotyping can also be performed directly on plasma.[180] In general, one-dimensional isoelectric focusing is sufficient for accurate phenotyping,[82] but in some cases, such as when excess sialylated isoforms are present, the two-dimensional technique may be required for unambiguous assignment.[80] The apo E phenotype will obviously persist regardless of other factors or conditions.

Because of the familial nature of type III hyperlipoproteinemia and the predisposition of type III patients for accelerated cardiovascular disease, family members of the affected patients should be screened for hyperlipidemia and should be phenotyped. Since apo E-2/2 predisposes individuals to the development of overt hyperlipoproteinemia, family counseling should stress the elimination of factors known to exacerbate the expression of type III hyperlipoproteinemia (obesity, excessive alcohol consumption, hypothyroidism, glucose intolerance). Particular attention should be given to adolescents and postmenopausal women since the expression of hyperlipidemia frequently begins in these settings. In the absence of factors known to influence the expression of type III hyperlipoproteinemia, the E-2/2 phenotype poses little risk for the development of premature vascular disease, and probably even affords some protection, owing to the characteristically low levels of plasma LDL in these subjects.

Treatment

Type III hyperlipoproteinemia is usually very responsive to therapy.[181–188] In most cases dietary therapy alone or in combination with treatment of a preexisting metabolic condition will normalize lipid levels. Metabolic conditions that commonly unmask the effect of the E-2/2 phenotype are hypothyroidism, marked weight gain, uncontrolled diabetes mellitus, and excessive alcohol consumption. Treatment of the thyroid deficiency, normalization of weight, control of diabetes, and cessation of alcohol consumption usually promptly reduce lipid levels. However, even after triglyceride and cholesterol levels are corrected, small quantities of β-VLDL will persist in the plasma, secondary to the presence of the abnormal apo E-2.

Dietary modification should always be the first form of treatment of patients with hyperlipidemia.[181–183,186,189] The basic approach to diet therapy is to restrict caloric intake in patients who are overweight and to reduce saturated fat and cholesterol in the diet. A progressive approach to diet has been recommended by the American Heart Association.[190] The goal of the first phase is to reduce total fat in the diet to approximately 30 percent of total calories (from the ≈40 percent in the current U.S. diet) and to decrease saturated fat to 10 percent or less of total calories. It is recommended that cholesterol content of the diet be reduced to 250 to 300 mg/day.

Drugs are sometimes required to normalize the triglyceride and cholesterol levels; however, drug therapy should only be instituted after an adequate attempt to control lipid levels by diet modification. Useful drugs for type III hyperlipoproteinemia include nicotinic acid (niacin), clofibrate, and gemfibrozil.

Nicotinic acid may well be the drug of choice in treating type III hyperlipoproteinemia.[181–183,188] It usually reduces plasma triglyceride and VLDL cholesterol levels by 40 percent, while LDL cholesterol decreases 20 percent and HDL cholesterol increases 20 percent. The Coronary Drug Project Research Group used nicotinic acid in a large prospective study and found that the rate of recurrent myocardial infarction in men treated with this drug was significantly lower than in placebo-treated subjects.[191] The drug decreases VLDL triglyceride synthesis and increases the VLDL catabolic rate.[192] Therapy should be initiated at a dose of 100 mg taken orally three times per day. This can be increased to an average dose of 1 g three times per day. Liver enzymes, uric acid, and glucose levels in the serum should be monitored periodically. Side effects of nicotinic acid are flushing, pruritus, and gastrointestinal distress. These side effects can be minimized by taking an aspirin tablet about 30 min before the nicotinic acid and by taking the drug with meals.

Clofibrate has been used widely for treating type III hyperlipoproteinemia because it lowers triglyceride and cholesterol levels and is convenient to administer.[181–183,186–188] Typically, a dose of 1 g twice a day will lower triglyceride and VLDL cholesterol approximately 30 percent and LDL cholesterol slightly. A major effect of the drug is a reduction in hepatic cholesterol synthesis and an increase in lipolytic activity.[193–197] Clofibrate was used in the large World Health Organization trial to determine its effect on primary prevention of coronary heart disease.[198] The drug did reduce the rate of coronary disease; however, there was no improvement in overall mortality, and there were more noncoronary deaths. There was also an increase in gastrointestinal diseases. Furthermore, results of the Coronary Drug Project indicated a twofold increase in cholelithiasis.[191] Care should be exercised in the chronic use of this drug. In addition, clofibrate potentiates the action of warfarin. Gemfibrozil is structurally similar to clofibrate.[181–183,188] A dose of 600 mg twice a day usually dramatically reduces triglyceride and VLDL cholesterol levels.

A competitive inhibitor of HMG-CoA reductase [mevinolin (Lovastatin)] has recently been approved as a drug to reduce cholesterol. In addition to inhibiting cholesterol biosynthesis within the liver by serving as a competition inhibitor of HMG-CoA reductase, this drug has been shown to increase LDL receptors in the liver.[137,199–201] It can be envisioned that some type III hyperlipoproteinemic patients may benefit from treatment with this drug. Although experience with mevinolin in type III patients is limited, it may have a positive effect.[202]

The decline in lipid levels with diet or drug therapy correlates with a decrease in the size of xanthomas or a complete disappearance of these lipid deposits.[62,63] Improved blood flow using plethysmographic measurements was obtained in type III patients after several months of therapy.[203] In addition, some diminution in symptoms of intermittent claudication and angina pectoris has been reported.[186]

REFERENCES

1. MCGINLEY J, JONES H, GOFMAN J: Lipoproteins and xanthomatous diseases. *J Invest Dermatol* 19:71, 1952.
2. GOFMAN JW, DELALLA O, GLAZIER F, FREEMAN NK, LINDGREN FT, NICHOLS AV, STRISOWER B, TAMPLIN AR: The serum lipoprotein transport system in health, metabolic disorders, atherosclerosis and coronary heart disease. *Plasma* 2:413, 1954.
3. FREDRICKSON DS, LEVY RI, LEES RS: Fat transport in lipoproteins—An integrated approach to mechanisms and disorders. *N Engl J Med* 276:34, 94, 148, 215, 273, 1967.
4. FREDRICKSON DS, LEVY RI, LINDGREN FT: A comparison of heritable abnormal lipoprotein patterns as defined by two different techniques. *J Clin Invest* 47:2446, 1968.
5. MORGANROTH J, LEVY RI, FREDRICKSON DS: The biochemical, clinical, and genetic features of type III hyperlipoproteinemia. *Ann Intern Med* 82:158, 1975.
6. HAZZARD WR, O'DONNELL TF, LEE YL: Broad-β disease (type III hyperlipoproteinemia) in a large kindred. Evidence for a monogenic mechanism. *Ann Intern Med* 82:141, 1975.
7. MISHKEL MA, NAZIR DJ, CROWTHER S: A longitudinal assessment of lipid ratios in the diagnosis of type III hyperlipoproteinaemia. *Clin Chim Acta* 58:121, 1975.
8. HAVEL RJ, GOLDSTEIN JL, BROWN MS: Lipoproteins and lipid transport, in Bondy PK, Rosenberg LE (eds): *Metabolic Control and Disease,* 8th ed. Philadelphia, Saunders, 1980, p 393.
9. FAINARU M, MAHLEY RW, HAMILTON RL, INNERARITY TL: Structural and metabolic heterogeneity of β-very low density lipoproteins from cholesterol-fed dogs and from humans with Type III hyperlipoproteinemia. *J Lipid Res* 23:702, 1982.
10. KANE JP, CHEN GC, HAMILTON RL, HARDMAN DA, MALLOY MJ, HAVEL RJ: Remnants of lipoproteins of intestinal and hepatic origin in familial dysbetalipoproteinemia. *Arteriosclerosis* 3:47, 1983.
11. CHAIT A, BRUNZELL JD, ALBERS JJ, HAZZARD WR: Type-III hyperlipoproteinaemia ("remnant removal disease"). Insight into the pathogenetic mechanism. *Lancet* 1:1176, 1977.
12. HAVEL RJ, KANE JP: Primary dysbetalipoproteinemia: Predominance of a specific apoprotein species in triglyceride-rich lipoproteins. *Proc Natl Acad Sci USA* 70:2015, 1973.
13. MAHLEY RW: Plasma apolipoprotein E: Cholesterol transport protein with expanding role in cell biology. *Science* 240:622, 1988.
14. UTERMANN G, JAESCHKE M, MENZEL J: Familial hyperlipoproteinemia type III: Deficiency of a specific apolipoprotein (apo E-III) in the very-low-density lipoproteins. *FEBS Lett* 56:352, 1975.
15. UTERMANN G, HEES M, STEINMETZ A: Polymorphism of apolipoprotein E and occurrence of dysbetalipoproteinaemia in man. *Nature* 269:604, 1977.
16. UTERMANN G, VOGELBERG KH, STEINMETZ A, SCHOENBORN W, PRUIN N, JAESCHKE M, HEES M, CANZLER H: Polymorphism of apolipoprotein E. II. Genetics of hyperlipoproteinemia type III. *Clin Genet* 15:37, 1979.
17. UTERMANN G, PRUIN N, STEINMETZ A: Polymorphism of apolipoprotein E. III. Effect of a single polymorphic gene locus on plasma lipid levels in man. *Clin Genet* 15:63, 1979.
18. UTERMANN G, LANGENBECK U, BEISIEGEL U, WEBER W: Genetics of the apolipoprotein E system in man. *Am J Hum Genet* 32:339, 1980.
19. ZANNIS VI, BRESLOW JL: Human very low density lipoprotein apolipoprotein E isoprotein polymorphism is explained by genetic variation and posttranslational modification. *Biochemistry* 20:1033, 1981.
20. ZANNIS VI, JUST PW, BRESLOW JL: Human apolipoprotein E isoprotein subclasses are genetically determined. *Am J Hum Genet* 33:11, 1981.
21. WEISGRABER KH, RALL SC JR, MAHLEY RW: Human E apoprotein heterogeneity. Cysteine-arginine interchanges in the amino acid sequence of the apo-E isoforms. *J Biol Chem* 256:9077, 1981.
22. RALL SC JR, WEISGRABER KH, MAHLEY RW: Human apolipoprotein E. The complete amino acid sequence. *J Biol Chem* 257:4171, 1982.

23. RALL SC JR, WEISGRABER KH, INNERARITY TL, MAHLEY RW: Structural basis for receptor binding heterogeneity of apolipoprotein E from type III hyperlipoproteinemic subjects. *Proc Natl Acad Sci USA* 79:4696, 1982.
24. MAHLEY RW, ANGELIN B: Type III hyperlipoproteinemia: Recent insights into the genetic defect of familial dysbetalipoproteinemia. *Adv Intern Med* 29:385, 1984.
25. MAHLEY RW: Atherogenic lipoproteins and coronary artery disease: Concepts derived from recent advances in cellular and molecular biology. *Circulation* 72:943, 1985.
26. HAVEL RJ: Familial dysbetalipoproteinemia. New aspects of pathogenesis and diagnosis. *Med Clin North Am* 66:441, 1982.
27. BERSOT TP, MAHLEY RW, BROWN MS, GOLDSTEIN JL: Interaction of swine lipoproteins with the low density lipoprotein receptor in human fibroblasts. *J Biol Chem* 251:2395, 1976.
28. INNERARITY TL, MAHLEY RW: Enhanced binding by cultured human fibroblasts of apo-E-containing lipoproteins as compared with low density lipoproteins. *Biochemistry* 17:1440, 1978
29. MAHLEY RW, INNERARITY TL: Lipoprotein receptors and cholesterol homeostasis. *Biochim Biophys Acta* 737:197, 1983.
30. HAVEL RJ, CHAO Y-S, WINDLER EE, KOTITE L, GUO LSS: Isoprotein specificity in the hepatic uptake of apolipoprotein E and the pathogenesis of familial dysbetalipoproteinemia. *Proc Natl Acad Sci USA* 77:4349, 1980.
31. SHERRILL BC, INNERARITY TL, MAHLEY RW: Rapid hepatic clearance of the canine lipoproteins containing only the E apoprotein by a high affinity receptor. Identity with the chylomicron remnant transport process. *J Biol Chem* 255:1804, 1980.
32. SHELBURNE F, HANKS J, MEYERS W, QUARFORDT S: Effect of apoproteins on hepatic uptake of triglyceride emulsions in the rat. *J Clin Invest* 65:652, 1980.
33. WINDLER E, CHAO YS, HAVEL RJ: Determinants of hepatic uptake of triglyceride-rich lipoproteins and their remnants in the rat. *J Biol Chem* 255:5475, 1980.
34. SCHNEIDER WJ, KOVANEN PT, BROWN MS, GOLDSTEIN JL, UTERMANN G, WEBER W, HAVEL RJ, KOTITE L, KANE JP, INNERARITY TL, MAHLEY RW: Familial dysbetalipoproteinemia. Abnormal binding of mutant apoprotein E to low density lipoprotein receptors of human fibroblasts and membranes from liver and adrenal of rats, rabbits, and cows. *J Clin Invest* 68:1075, 1981.
35. WEISGRABER KH, INNERARITY TL, MAHLEY RW: Abnormal lipoprotein receptor-binding activity of the human E apoprotein due to cysteine-arginine interchange at a single site. *J Biol Chem* 257:2518, 1982.
36. PAGNAN A, HAVEL RJ, KANE JP, KOTITE L: Characterization of human very low density lipoproteins containing two electrophoretic populations: Double pre-beta lipoproteinemia and primary dysbetalipoproteinemia. *J Lipid Res* 18:613, 1977.
37. KANE JP: Apolipoprotein B: Structural and metabolic heterogeneity. *Annu Rev Physiol* 45:637, 1983.
38. KANE JP, HARDMAN DA, PAULUS HE: Heterogeneity of apolipoprotein B: Isolation of a new species from human chylomicrons. *Proc Natl Acad Sci USA* 77:2465, 1980.
39. KNOTT TJ, PEASE RJ, POWELL LM, WALLIS SC, RALL SC JR, INNERARITY TL, BLACKHART B, TAYLOR WH, MARCEL Y, MILNE R, JOHNSON D, FULLER M, LUSIS AJ, MCCARTHY BJ, MAHLEY RW, LEVY-WILSON B, SCOTT J: Complete protein sequence and identification of structural domains of human apolipoprotein B. *Nature* 323:734, 1986.
40. YANG C-Y, CHEN S-H, GIANTURCO SH, BRADLEY WA, SPARROW JT, TANIMURA M, LI W-H, SPARROW DA, DELOOF H, ROSSENEU M, LEE F-S, GU Z-W, GOTTO AM JR, CHAN L: Sequence, structure, receptor-binding domains and internal repeats of human apolipoprotein B-100. *Nature* 323:738, 1986.
41. LAW SW, GRANT SM, HIGUCHI K, HOSPATTANKAR A, LACKNER K, LEE N, BREWER HB JR: Human liver apolipoprotein B-100 cDNA: Complete nucleic acid and derived amino acid sequence. *Proc Natl Acad Sci USA* 83:8142, 1986.
42. CLADARAS C, HADZOPOULOU-CLADARAS M, NOLTE RT, ATKINSON D, ZANNIS VI: The complete sequence and structural analysis of human apolipoprotein B-100: Relationship between apoB-100 and apoB-48 forms. *EMBO J* 5:3495, 1986.
43. POWELL LM, WALLIS SC, PEASE RJ, EDWARDS YH, KNOTT TJ, SCOTT J: A novel form of tissue-specific RNA processing produces apolipoprotein-B48 in intestine. *Cell* 50:831, 1987.
44. INNERARITY TL, YOUNG SG, POKSAY KS, MAHLEY RW, SMITH RS, MILNE RW, MARCEL YL, WEISGRABER KH: Structural relationship of human apolipoprotein B48 to apolipoprotein B100. *J Clin Invest* 80:1794, 1987.
45. CHEN S-H, HABIB G, YANG C-Y, GU Z-W, LEE BR, WENG S-A, SILBERMAN SR, CAI S-J, DESLYPERE JP, ROSSENEU M, GOTTO AM JR, LI W-H, CHAN L: Apolipoprotein B-48 is the product of a messenger RNA with an organ-specific in-frame stop codon. *Science* 238:363, 1987.
46. MILNE RW, WEECH PK, BLANCHETTE L, DAVIGNON J, ALAUPOVIC P, MARCEL YL: Isolation and characterization of apolipoprotein B-48 and B-100 very low density lipoproteins from type III hyperlipoproteinemic subjects. *J Clin Invest* 73:816, 1984.
47. CHAPPELL DA: Pre-β-very low density lipoproteins as precursors of β-very low density lipoproteins: A model for the pathogenesis of familial dysbetalipoproteinemia (type III hyperlipoproteinemia). *J Clin Invest*, in press.
48. SATA T, HAVEL RJ, JONES AL: Characterization of subfractions of triglyceride-rich lipoproteins separated by gel chromatography from blood plasma of normolipemic and hyperlipemic humans. *J Lipid Res* 13:757, 1972.
49. HAZZARD WR, BIERMAN EL: Broad-β disease versus endogenous hypertriglyceridemia: Levels and lipid composition of chylomicrons and very low density lipoproteins during fat-free feeding and alimentary lipemia. *Metabolism* 24:817, 1975.
50. HAVEL RJ, KOTITE L, VIGNE J-L, KANE JP, TUN P, PHILLIPS N, CHEN GC: Radioimmunoassay of human arginine-rich apolipoprotein, apoprotein E. Concentration in blood plasma and lipoproteins as affected by apoprotein E-3 deficiency. *J Clin Invest* 66:1351, 1980.
51. PATSCH JR, SAILER S, BRAUNSTEINER H: Lipoprotein of the density 1.006-1.020 in the plasma of patients with type III hyperlipoproteinaemia in the postabsorptive state. *Eur J Clin Invest* 5:45, 1975.
52. QUARFORDT S, LEVY RI, FREDRICKSON DS: On the lipoprotein abnormality in type III hyperlipoproteinemia. *J Clin Invest* 50:754, 1971.
53. UTERMANN G: Genetic polymorphism of apolipoprotein E—Impact on plasma lipoprotein metabolism, in Crepaldi G, Tiengo A, Baggio G (eds): *Diabetes, Obesity and Hyperlipidemias-III*. Amsterdam, Elsevier, 1985, p 1.
54. HAZZARD WR: Primary type III hyperlipoproteinemia, in Rifkind BM, Levy RI (eds): *Hyperlipidemia. Diagnosis and Therapy*. New York, Grune & Stratton, 1977, p 137.
55. BORRIE P: Type III hyperlipoproteinaemia. *Br Med J* 2:665, 1969.
56. MISHKEL MA: Type III hyperlipoproteinaemia with xanthomatosis, in Peeters H (ed): *Protides of the Biological Fluids*. Oxford, Pergamon, 1972, p 283.
57. VESSBY B, HEDSTRAND H, LUNDIN L-G, OLSSON U: Inheritance of type-III hyperlipoproteinemia. Lipoprotein patterns in first-degree relatives. *Metabolism* 26:225, 1977.
58. STUYT PMJ, VAN'T LAAR A: Clinical features of type III hyperlipoproteinaemia. *Neth J Med* 26:104, 1983.
59. VERMEER BJ, VAN GENT CM, GOSLINGS B, POLANO MK: Xanthomatosis and other clinical findings in patients with elevated levels of very low density lipoproteins. *Br J Dermatol* 100:657, 1979.
60. GLUECK CJ, FALLAT RW, MELLIES MJ, STEINER PM: Pediatric familial type III hyperlipoproteinemia. *Metabolism* 25:1269, 1976.
61. GODOLPHIN WJ, CONRADI G, CAMPBELL DJ: Type-III hyperlipoproteinaemia in a child. *Lancet* 1:209, 1972.
62. PARKER F: Xanthomas and hyperlipidemias. *J Am Acad Dermatol* 13:1, 1985.
63. HABER C, KWITEROVICH PO JR: Dyslipoproteinemia and xanthomatosis. *Pediatr Dermatol* 1:261, 1984.
64. POLANO MK: Xanthomatosis and hyperlipoproteinemia. A review. *Dermatologica* 149:1, 1974.
65. MAHLEY RW, INNERARITY TL, WEISGRABER KH, FRY DL: Canine hyperlipoproteinemia and atherosclerosis: Accumulation of lipid by aortic medial cells *in vivo* and *in vitro*. *Am J Pathol* 87:205, 1977.
66. MAHLEY RW: Dietary fat, cholesterol, and accelerated atherosclerosis, in Paoletti R, Gotto AM Jr (eds): *Atherosclerosis Reviews*. New York, Raven, 1979, vol 5, p 1.
67. HAZZARD WR, GOLDSTEIN JL, SCHROTT HG, MOTULSKY AG, BIERMAN EL: Hyperlipidemia in coronary heart disease. III. Evaluation of lipoprotein phenotypes of 156 genetically defined survivors of myocardial infarction. *J Clin Invest* 52:1569, 1973.
68. DYERBERG J: Type III hyperlipoproteinemia with low plasma thyroxine binding globulin. *Metabolism* 18:50, 1969.
69. ROBERTS WC, LEVY RI, FREDRICKSON DS: Hyperlipoproteinemia. A review of the five types with first report of necropsy findings in type 3. *Arch Pathol* 90:46, 1970.
70. HOLIMON JL, WASSERMAN AJ: Autopsy findings in type 3 hyperlipoproteinemia. *Arch Pathol* 92:415, 1971.
71. ROBERTS WC, FERRANS VJ, LEVY RI, FREDRICKSON DS: Cardiovascular pathology in hyperlipoproteinemia. Anatomic observations in 42 necropsy patients with normal or abnormal serum lipoprotein patterns. *Am J Cardiol* 31:557, 1973.
72. AMATRUDA JM, MARGOLIS S, HUTCHINS GM: Type III hyperlipoproteinemia with mesangial foam cells in renal glomeruli. *Arch Pathol* 98:51, 1974.

73. GOWN AM, HAZZARD WR, BENDITT EP: Type III hyperlipoproteinemia and atherosclerosis: A case report and re-evaluation. *Hum Pathol* 13:506, 1982.
74. CABIN HS, SCHWARTZ DE, VIRMANI R, BREWER HB JR, ROBERTS WC: Type III hyperlipoproteinemia: Quantification, distribution, and nature of atherosclerotic coronary arterial narrowing in five necropsy patients. *Am Heart J* 102:830, 1981.
75. SCHWARTZ D (discussant): Pathology, in Type III hyperlipoproteinemia: Diagnosis, molecular defects, pathology, and treatment, HB Brewer Jr (moderator). *Ann Intern Med* 98 (part 1):632, 1983.
76. ROSS R: The pathogenesis of atherosclerosis—An update. *N Engl J Med* 314:488, 1986.
77. GOLDSTEIN JL, HO YK, BROWN MS, INNERARITY TL, MAHLEY RW: Cholesteryl ester accumulation in macrophages resulting from receptor-mediated uptake and degradation of hypercholesterolemic canine β-very low density lipoproteins. *J Biol Chem* 255:1839, 1980.
78. MAHLEY RW, INNERARITY TL, BROWN MS, HO YK, GOLDSTEIN JL: Cholesteryl ester synthesis in macrophages: Stimulation by β-very low density lipoproteins from cholesterol-fed animals of several species. *J Lipid Res* 21:970, 1980.
79. MAHLEY RW, INNERARITY TL, RALL SC JR, WEISGRABER KH: Plasma lipoproteins: Apolipoprotein structure and function. *J Lipid Res* 25:1277, 1984.
80. ZANNIS VI, BRESLOW JL, UTERMANN G, MAHLEY RW, WEISGRABER KH, HAVEL RJ, GOLDSTEIN JL, BROWN MS, SCHONFELD G, HAZZARD WR, BLUM C: Proposed nomenclature of apoE isoproteins, apoE genotypes, and phenotypes. *J Lipid Res* 23:911, 1982.
81. RALL SC, WEISGRABER KH, INNERARITY TL, MAHLEY RW: The carbohydrate moiety of human plasma apolipoprotein E. *Circulation* 72:III-143, 1985.
82. UTERMANN G, STEINMETZ A, WEBER W: Genetic control of human apolipoprotein E polymorphism: Comparison of one- and two-dimensional techniques of isoprotein analysis. *Hum Genet* 60:344, 1982.
83. WARDELL MR, SUCKLING PA, JANUS ED: Genetic variation in human apolipoprotein E. *J Lipid Res* 23:1174, 1982.
84. MENZEL H-J, KLADETZKY R-G, ASSMANN G: Apolipoprotein E polymorphism and coronary artery disease. *Arteriosclerosis* 3:310, 1983.
85. CUMMING AM, ROBERTSON FW: Polymorphism at the apoprotein-E locus in relation to risk of coronary disease. *Clin Genet* 25:310, 1984.
86. DAVIGNON J, SING CF, LUSSIER-CACAN S, BOUTHILLIER D: Xanthelasma, latent dyslipoproteinemia and atherosclerosis: Contribution of apo E polymorphism, in de Gennes JL, Polonovski J, Paoletti R (eds): *Latent Dyslipoproteinemias and Atherosclerosis*. New York, Raven, 1984, p 213.
87. BRESLOW JL: Genetics of the human apolipoproteins, in Scanu AM, Spector AA (eds): *Biochemistry and Biology of Plasma Lipoproteins*. New York, Marcel Dekker, 1986, p 85.
88. EHNHOLM C, LUKKA M, KUUSI T, NIKKILÄ E, UTERMANN G: Apolipoprotein E polymorphism in the Finnish population: Gene frequencies and relation to lipoprotein concentrations. *J Lipid Res* 27:227, 1986.
89. SING CF, DAVIGNON J: Role of the apolipoprotein E polymorphism in determining normal plasma lipid and lipoprotein variation. *Am J Hum Genet* 37:268, 1985.
90. GREGG RE, ZECH LA, SCHAEFER EJ, BREWER HB JR: Type III hyperlipoproteinemia: Defective metabolism of an abnormal apolipoprotein E. *Science* 211:584, 1981.
91. GREGG RE, ZECH LA, SCHAEFER EJ, STARK D, WILSON D, BREWER HB JR: Abnormal in vivo metabolism of apolipoprotein E_4 in humans. *J Clin Invest* 78:815, 1986.
92. UTERMANN G, KINDERMANN I, KAFFARNIK H, STEINMETZ A: Apolipoprotein E phenotypes and hyperlipidemia. *Hum Genet* 65:232, 1984.
93. UTERMANN G, HARDEWIG A, ZIMMER F: Apolipoprotein E phenotypes in patients with myocardial infarction. *Hum Genet* 65:237, 1984.
94. LENZEN HJ, ASSMANN G, BUCHWALSKY R, SCHULTE H: Association of apolipoprotein E polymorphism, low-density lipoprotein cholesterol, and coronary artery disease. *Clin Chem* 32:778, 1986.
95. DAS HK, MCPHERSON J, BRUNS GAP, KARATHANASIS SK, BRESLOW JL: Isolation, characterization, and mapping to chromosome 19 of the human apolipoprotein E gene. *J Biol Chem* 260:6240, 1985.
96. PAIK Y-K, CHANG DJ, REARDON CA, DAVIES GE, MAHLEY RW, TAYLOR JM: Nucleotide sequence and structure of the human apolipoprotein E gene. *Proc Natl Acad Sci USA* 82:3445, 1985.
97. LUO C-C, LI W-H, MOORE MN, CHAN L: Structure and evolution of the apolipoprotein multigene family. *J Mol Biol* 187:325, 1986.
98. ELSHOURBAGY NA, WALKER DW, PAIK Y-K, BOGUSKI MS, FREEMAN M, GORDON JI, TAYLOR JM: Structure and expression of the human apolipoprotein A-IV gene. *J Biol Chem* 262:7973, 1987.
99. ZANNIS VI, MCPHERSON J, GOLDBERGER G, KARATHANASIS SK, BRESLOW JL: Synthesis, intracellular processing, and signal peptide of human apolipoprotein E. *J Biol Chem* 259:5495, 1984.
100. MCLEAN JW, ELSHOURBAGY NA, CHANG DJ, MAHLEY RW, TAYLOR JM: Human apolipoprotein E mRNA. cDNA cloning and nucleotide sequencing of a new variant. *J Biol Chem* 259:6498, 1984.
101. OLAISEN B, TEISBERG P, GEDDE-DAHL T JR: The locus for apolipoprotein E (apoE) is linked to the complement component C3 (C3) locus on chromosome 19 in man. *Hum Genet* 62:233, 1982.
102. LAUER SJ, WALKER D, ELSHOURBAGY NA, REARDON CA, LEVY-WILSON B, TAYLOR JM: Two copies of the human apolipoprotein C-I gene are linked closely to the apolipoprotein E gene. *J Biol Chem* 263:7277, 1988.
103. JACKSON CL, BRUNS GAP, BRESLOW JL: Isolation and sequence of a human apolipoprotein CII cDNA clone and its use to isolate and map to human chromosome 19 the gene for apolipoprotein CII. *Proc Natl Acad Sci USA* 81:2945, 1984.
104. FRANCKE U, BROWN MS, GOLDSTEIN JL: Assignment of the human gene for the low density lipoprotein receptor to chromosome 19: Synteny of a receptor, a ligand, and a genetic disease. *Proc Natl Acad Sci USA* 81:2826, 1984.
105. MAHLEY RW, INNERARITY TL, PITAS RE, WEISGRABER KH, BROWN JH, GROSS E: Inhibition of lipoprotein binding to cell surface receptors of fibroblasts following selective modification of arginyl residues in arginine-rich and B apoproteins. *J Biol Chem* 252:7279, 1977.
106. WEISGRABER KH, INNERARITY TL, MAHLEY RW: Role of the lysine residues of plasma lipoproteins in high affinity binding to cell surface receptors on human fibroblasts. *J Biol Chem* 253:9053, 1978.
107. MAHLEY RW, INNERARITY TL, WEISGRABER KH, OH SY: Altered metabolism (in vivo and in vitro) of plasma lipoproteins after selective chemical modification of lysine residues of the apoproteins. *J Clin Invest* 64:743, 1979.
108. MAHLEY RW, INNERARITY TL, WEISGRABER KH: Alterations in metabolic activity of plasma lipoproteins following selective chemical modification of the apoproteins. *Ann NY Acad Sci* 348:265, 1980.
109. MAHLEY RW, WEISGRABER KH, MELCHIOR GW, INNERARITY TL, HOLCOMBE KS: Inhibition of receptor-mediated clearance of lysine and arginine-modified lipoproteins from the plasma of rats and monkeys. *Proc Natl Acad Sci USA* 77:225, 1980.
110. RALL SC JR, WEISGRABER KH, INNERARITY TL, BERSOT TP, MAHLEY RW, BLUM CB: Identification of a new structural variant of human apolipoprotein E, E2(Lys_{146}→Gln), in a type III hyperlipoproteinemic subject with the E3/2 phenotype. *J Clin Invest* 72:1288, 1983.
111. WARDELL MR, BRENNAN SO, JANUS ED, FRASER R, CARRELL RW: Apolipoprotein E2-Christchurch (136 Arg→Ser). New variant of human apolipoprotein E in a patient with type III hyperlipoproteinemia. *J Clin Invest* 80:483, 1987.
112. LALAZAR A, WEISGRABER KH, RALL SC JR, GILADI H, INNERARITY TL, LEVANON AZ, BOYLES JK, AMIT B, GORECKI M, MAHLEY RW, VOGEL T: Site-specific mutagenesis of human apolipoprotein E. Receptor binding activity of variants with single amino acid substitutions *J Biol Chem* 263:3542, 1988.
113. HAVEL RJ, KOTITE L, KANE JP, TUN P, BERSOT T: Atypical familial dysbetalipoproteinemia associated with apolipoprotein phenotype E3/3. *J Clin Invest* 72:379, 1983.
114. RALL SC JR, WEISGRABER KH, CLARKE HRG, NEWHOUSE YM, MCCARTHY BJ, MAHLEY RW, BERSOT TP: Type III hyperlipoproteinemia associated with apolipoprotein phenotype E3/3: Structure and genetics of a rare apolipoprotein E3 variant. In preparation.
115. INNERARITY TL, FRIEDLANDER EJ, RALL SC JR, WEISGRABER KH, MAHLEY RW: The receptor-binding domain of human apolipoprotein E. Binding of apolipoprotein E fragments. *J Biol Chem* 258:12341, 1983.
116. WEISGRABER KH, INNERARITY TL, HARDER KJ, MAHLEY RW, MILNE RW, MARCEL YL, SPARROW JT: The receptor-binding domain of human apolipoprotein E. Monoclonal antibody inhibition of binding. *J Biol Chem* 258:12348, 1983.
117. VOGEL T, WEISGRABER KH, ZEEVI MI, BEN-ARTZI H, LEVANON AZ, RALL SC JR, INNERARITY TL, HUI DY, TAYLOR JM, KANNER D, YAVIN Z, AMIT B, AVIV H, GORECKI M, MAHLEY RW: Human apolipoprotein E expression in *Escherichia coli:* Structural and functional identity of the bacterially produced protein with plasma apolipoprotein E. *Proc Natl Acad Sci USA* 82:8696, 1985.
118. YAMAMOTO T, DAVIS CG, BROWN MS, SCHNEIDER WJ, CASEY ML, GOLDSTEIN JL, RUSSELL DW: The human LDL receptor: A cysteine-rich protein with multiple Alu sequences in its mRNA. *Cell* 39:27, 1984.
119. SUDHOF TC, GOLDSTEIN JL, BROWN MS, RUSSELL DW: The LDL receptor gene: A mosaic of exons shared with different proteins. *Science* 228:815, 1985.
120. BLUE M-L, WILLIAMS DL, ZUCKER S, KHAN SA, BLUM CB: Apolipoprotein

E synthesis in human kidney, adrenal gland, and liver. *Proc Natl Acad Sci USA* 80:283, 1983.

121. ELSHOURBAGY NA, LIAO WS, MAHLEY RW, TAYLOR JM: Apolipoprotein E mRNA is abundant in the brain and adrenals, as well as in the liver, and is present in other peripheral tissues of rats and marmosets. *Proc Natl Acad Sci USA* 82:203, 1985.

122. LIN C-T, XU Y, WU J-Y, CHAN L: Immunoreactive apolipoprotein E is a widely distributed cellular protein. Immunohistochemical localization of apolipoprotein E in baboon tissues. *J Clin Invest* 78:947, 1986.

123. BASU SK, BROWN MS, HO YK, HAVEL RJ, GOLDSTEIN JL: Mouse macrophages synthesize and secrete a protein resembling apolipoprotein E. *Proc Natl Acad Sci USA* 78:7545, 1981.

124. BASU SK, HO YK, BROWN MS, BILHEIMER DW, ANDERSON RGW, GOLDSTEIN JL: Biochemical and genetic studies of the apoprotein E secreted by mouse macrophages and human monocytes. *J Biol Chem* 257:9788, 1982.

125. BOYLES J, PITAS RE, WILSON E, MAHLEY RW, TAYLOR JM: Apolipoprotein E associated with astrocytic glia of the central nervous system and with nonmyelinating glia of the peripheral nervous system. *J Clin Invest* 76:1501, 1985.

126. DRISCOLL DM, GETZ GS: Extrahepatic synthesis of apolipoprotein E. *J Lipid Res* 25:1368, 1984.

127. MAJACK RA, CASTLE CK, WEISGRABER KH, MAHLEY RW, SHOOTER EM, GEBICKE-HAERTER PJ: Regulation of expression of apolipoprotein E by cultured vascular smooth muscle cells. *J Cell Biol*, in press.

128. IGNATIUS MJ, GEBICKE-HARTER PJ, SKENE JHP, SCHILLING JW, WEISGRABER KH, MAHLEY RW, SHOOTER EM: Expression of apolipoprotein E during nerve degeneration and regeneration. *Proc Natl Acad Sci USA* 83:1125, 1986.

129. BOYLES JK, WEISGRABER KH, MAHLEY RW, IGNATIUS MJ, GEBICKE-HARTER P, SCHILLING J, SHOOTER EM: Apolipoprotein E production at the site of neural tract injury. *J Cell Biol* 101:125a, 1985.

130. SNIPES GJ, MCGUIRE CB, NORDEN JJ, FREEMAN JA: Nerve injury stimulates the secretion of apolipoprotein E by nonneuronal cells. *Proc Natl Acad Sci USA* 83:1130, 1986.

131. BROWN MS, GOLDSTEIN JL: A receptor-mediated pathway for cholesterol homeostasis. *Science* 232:34, 1986.

132. BROWN MS, GOLDSTEIN JL: Lipoprotein receptors in the liver. Control signals for plasma cholesterol traffic. *J Clin Invest* 72:743, 1983.

133. KOVANEN PT, BROWN MS, GOLDSTEIN JL: Increased binding of low density lipoprotein to liver membranes from rats treated with 17α-ethinyl estradiol. *J Biol Chem* 254:11367, 1979.

134. CHAO Y-S, WINDLER EE, CHEN GC, HAVEL RJ: Hepatic catabolism of rat and human lipoproteins in rats treated with 17α-ethinyl estradiol. *J Biol Chem* 254:11360, 1979.

135. WINDLER EET, KOVANEN PT, CHAO Y-S, BROWN MS, HAVEL RJ, GOLDSTEIN JL: The estradiol-stimulated lipoprotein receptor of rat liver. A binding site that mediates the uptake of rat lipoproteins containing apoproteins B and E. *J Biol Chem* 255:10464, 1980.

136. KOVANEN PT, BROWN MS, BASU SK, BILHEIMER DW, GOLDSTEIN JL: Saturation and suppression of hepatic lipoprotein receptors: A mechanism for the hypercholesterolemia of cholesterol-fed rabbits. *Proc Natl Acad Sci USA* 78:1396, 1981.

137. KOVANEN PT, BILHEIMER DW, GOLDSTEIN JL, JARAMILLO JJ, BROWN MS: Regulatory role for hepatic low density lipoprotein receptors *in vivo* in the dog. *Proc Natl Acad Sci USA* 78:1194, 1981.

138. HUI DY, INNERARITY TL, MAHLEY RW: Lipoprotein binding to canine hepatic membranes. Metabolically distinct apo-E and apo-B,E receptors. *J Biol Chem* 256:5646, 1981.

139. MAHLEY RW, HUI DY, INNERARITY TL, WEISGRABER KH: Two independent lipoprotein receptors on hepatic membranes of dog, swine, and man. Apo-B,E and apo-E receptors. *J Clin Invest* 68:1197, 1981.

140. BEISIEGEL U, WEBER W, HAVINGA JR, IHRKE G, HUI DY, WERNETTE-HAMMOND ME, TURCK CW, INNERARITY TL, MAHLEY RW: Apolipoprotein E-binding proteins isolated from dog and human liver. *Arteriosclerosis* 8:288, 1988.

141. MAHLEY RW, HUI DY, INNERARITY TL, BEISIEGEL U: Chylomicron remnant metabolism: The role of hepatic lipoprotein receptors in mediating uptake. *Arteriosclerosis*, in press.

142. ASSMANN G, BROWN BG, MAHLEY RW: Regulation of 3-hydroxy-3-methylglutaryl coenzyme A reductase activity in cultured swine aortic smooth muscle cells by plasma lipoproteins. *Biochemistry* 14:3996, 1975.

143. INNERARITY TL, PITAS RE, MAHLEY RW: Binding of arginine-rich (E) apoprotein after recombination with phospholipid vesicles to the low density lipoprotein receptors of fibroblasts. *J Biol Chem* 254:4186, 1979.

144. PITAS RE, INNERARITY TL, MAHLEY RW: Cell surface receptor binding of phospholipid·protein complexes containing different ratios of receptor-active and -inactive E apoprotein. *J Biol Chem* 255:5454, 1980.

145. PITAS RE, INNERARITY TL, ARNOLD KS, MAHLEY RW: Rate and equilibrium constants for binding of apo-E HDL_c (a cholesterol-induced lipoprotein) and low density lipoproteins to human fibroblasts: Evidence for multiple receptor binding of apo-E HDL_c. *Proc Natl Acad Sci USA* 76:2311, 1979.

146. HUI DY, INNERARITY TL, MILNE RW, MARCEL YL, MAHLEY RW: Binding of chylomicron remnants and β-very low density lipoproteins to hepatic and extrahepatic lipoprotein receptors. A process independent of apolipoprotein B48. *J Biol Chem* 259:15060, 1984.

147. EHNHOLM C, MAHLEY RW, CHAPPELL DA, WEISGRABER KH, LUDWIG E, WITZTUM JL: Role of apolipoprotein E in the lipolytic conversion of β-very low density lipoproteins to low density lipoproteins in type III hyperlipoproteinemia. *Proc Natl Acad Sci USA* 81:5566, 1984.

148. BROWN MS, GOLDSTEIN JL: Lipoprotein metabolism in the macrophage: Implications for cholesterol deposition in atherosclerosis. *Annu Rev Biochem* 52:223, 1983.

149. BROWN MS, GOLDSTEIN JL: How LDL receptors influence cholesterol and atherosclerosis. *Sci Am* 251:58, 1984.

150. MAHLEY RW: Development of accelerated atherosclerosis. Concepts derived from cell biology and animal model studies. *Arch Pathol Lab Med* 107:393, 1983.

151. MAHLEY RW, INNERARITY TL, RALL SC JR, WEISGRABER KH: Lipoproteins of special significance in atherosclerosis: Insights provided by studies of type III hyperlipoproteinemia. *Ann NY Acad Sci* 454:209, 1985.

152. VAN LENTEN BJ, FOGELMAN AM, HOKOM MM, BENSON L, HABERLAND ME, EDWARDS PA: Regulation of the uptake and degradation of β-very low density lipoprotein in human monocyte macrophages. *J Biol Chem* 258:5151, 1983.

153. KOO C, WERNETTE-HAMMOND ME, INNERARITY TL: Uptake of canine β-very low density lipoproteins by mouse peritoneal macrophages is mediated by a low density lipoprotein receptor. *J Biol Chem* 261:11194, 1986.

154. KOO C, WERNETTE-HAMMOND ME, GARCIA Z, MALLOY MJ, UAUY R, EAST C, BILHEIMER DW, MAHLEY RW, INNERARITY TL: Uptake of cholesterol-rich remnant lipoproteins by human monocyte-derived macrophages is mediated by low density lipoprotein receptors. *J Clin Invest* 81:1332, 1988.

155. ELLSWORTH JL, KRAEMER FB, COOPER AD: Transport of β-very low density lipoproteins and chylomicron remnants by macrophages is mediated by the low density lipoprotein receptor pathway. *J Biol Chem* 262:2316, 1987.

156. INNERARITY TL, ARNOLD KS, WEISGRABER KH, MAHLEY RW: Apolipoprotein E is the determinant that mediates the receptor uptake of β-very low density lipoproteins by mouse macrophages. *Arteriosclerosis* 6:114, 1986.

157. GORDON V, INNERARITY TL, MAHLEY RW: Formation of cholesterol- and apoprotein E-enriched high density lipoproteins *in vitro*. *J Biol Chem* 258:6202, 1983.

158. KOO C, INNERARITY TL, MAHLEY RW: Obligatory role of cholesterol and apolipoprotein E in the formation of large cholesterol-enriched and receptor-active high density lipoproteins. *J Biol Chem* 260:11934, 1985.

159. MAHLEY RW, WEISGRABER KH, INNERARITY T: Canine lipoproteins and atherosclerosis. II. Characterization of the plasma lipoproteins associated with atherogenic and nonatherogenic hyperlipidemia. *Circ Res* 35:722, 1974.

160. GLOMSET JA: The plasma lecithin:cholesterol acyltransferase reaction. *J Lipid Res* 9:155, 1968.

161. RALL SC JR, WEISGRABER KH, INNERARITY TL, MAHLEY RW, ASSMANN G: Identical structural and receptor binding defects in apolipoprotein E2 in hypo-, normo-, and hypercholesterolemic dysbetalipoproteinemia. *J Clin Invest* 71:1023, 1983.

162. JANUS ED, GRANT S, LINTOTT CJ, WARDELL MR: Apolipoprotein E phenotypes in hyperlipidaemic patients and their implications for treatment. *Atherosclerosis* 57:249, 1985.

163. BRESLOW JL, ZANNIS VI, SANGIACOMO TR, THIRD JLHC, TRACY T, GLUECK CJ: Studies of familial type III hyperlipoproteinemia using as a genetic marker the apoE phenotype E2/2. *J Lipid Res* 23:1224, 1982.

164. BERSOT TP, INNERARITY TL, MAHLEY RW, HAVEL RJ: Cholesteryl ester accumulation in mouse peritoneal macrophages induced by β-migrating very low density lipoproteins from patients with atypical dysbetalipoproteinemia. *J Clin Invest* 72:1024, 1983.

165. HAVEKES L, DE WIT E, GEVERS LEUVEN J, KLASEN E, UTERMANN G, WEBER W, BEISIEGEL U: Apolipoprotein E3-Leiden. A new variant of human apolipoprotein E associated with familial type III hyperlipoproteinemia. *Hum Genet* 73:157, 1986.

166. GHISELLI G, SCHAEFER EJ, GASCON P, BREWER HB JR: Type III hyperlipoproteinemia associated with apolipoprotein E deficiency. *Science* 214:1239, 1981.

167. SCHAEFER EJ, GREGG RE, GHISELLI G, FORTE TM, ORDOVAS JM, ZECH LA,

BREWER HB JR: Familial apolipoprotein E deficiency. *J Clin Invest* 78:1206, 1986.

168. CLADARAS C, HADZOPOULOU-CLADARAS M, FELBER BK, PAVLAKIS G, ZANNIS VI: The molecular basis of a familial apoE deficiency. An acceptor splice site mutation in the third intron of the deficient apoE gene. *J Biol Chem* 262:2310, 1987.

169. HAZZARD WR, WARNICK GR, UTERMANN G, ALBERS JJ: Genetic transmission of isoapolipoprotein E phenotypes in a large kindred: Relationship to dysbetalipoproteinemia and hyperlipidemia. *Metabolism* 30:79, 1981.

170. HAZZARD WR, BIERMAN EL: Aggravation of broad-β disease (type 3 hyperlipoproteinemia) by hypothyroidism. *Arch Intern Med* 130:822, 1972.

171. ANGELIN B, RAVIOLA CA, INNERARITY TL, MAHLEY RW: Regulation of hepatic lipoprotein receptors in the dog. Rapid regulation of apolipoprotein B,E receptors, but not of apolipoprotein E receptors, by intestinal lipoproteins and bile acids. *J Clin Invest* 71:816, 1983.

172. KUSHWAHA RS, HAZZARD WR, GAGNE C, CHAIT A, ALBERS JJ: Type III hyperlipoproteinemia: Paradoxical hypolipidemic response to estrogen. *Ann Intern Med* 87:517, 1977.

173. FALKO JM, SCHONFELD G, WITZTUM JL, KOLAR J, WEIDMAN SW: Effects of estrogen therapy on apolipoprotein E in type III hyperlipoproteinemia. *Metabolism* 28:1171, 1979.

174. THOMPSON GR, SOUTAR AK, SPENGEL FA, JADHAV A, GAVIGAN SJP, MYANT NB: Defects of receptor-mediated low density lipoprotein catabolism in homozygous familial hypercholesterolemia and hypothyroidism *in vivo*. *Proc Natl Acad Sci USA* 78:2591, 1981.

175. GRUNDY SM: Cholesterol metabolism in man. *West J Med* 128:13, 1978.

176. MYANT NB: *The Biology of Cholesterol and Related Steroids*. London, William Heinemann, 1981.

177. ANGELIN B, EINARSSON K: Regulation of HMG-CoA reductase in human liver, in Preiss B (ed): *Regulation of HMG-CoA Reductase*. Orlando, FL, Academic, 1985, p 281.

178. CHAIT A, ALBERS JJ, BRUNZELL JD: Very low density lipoprotein overproduction in genetic forms of hypertriglyceridaemia. *Eur J Clin Invest* 10:17, 1980.

179. CHUNG BH, SEGREST JP: Resistance of a very low density lipoprotein subpopulation from familial dysbetalipoproteinemia to in vitro lipolytic conversion to the low density lipoprotein density fraction. *J Lipid Res* 24:1148, 1983.

180. MENZEL H-J, UTERMANN G: Apolipoprotein E phenotyping from serum by Western blotting. *Electrophoresis* 7:492, 1986.

181. SCHAEFER EJ, LEVY RI: Pathogenesis and management of lipoprotein disorders. *N Engl J Med* 316:1300, 1985.

182. GOTTO AM JR, JONES PH, SCOTT LW: The diagnosis and management of hyperlipidemia. *DM* 32:245, 1986.

183. SCHAEFER EJ (discussant): Dietary and drug treatment, in Type III hyperlipoproteinemia: Diagnosis, molecular defects, pathology, and treatment, HB Brewer Jr (moderator). *Ann Intern Med* 98 (part 1):633, 1983.

184. GRUNDY SM: Hypertriglyceridemia: Mechanisms, clinical significance, and treatment. *Med Clin North Am* 66:519, 1982.

185. LEVY RI, FREDRICKSON DS, SHULMAN R, BILHEIMER DW, BRESLOW JL, STONE NJ, LUX SE, SLOAN HR, KRAUSS RM, HERBERT PN: Dietary and drug treatment of primary hyperlipoproteinemia (symposium). *Ann Intern Med* 77:267, 1972.

186. FALKO JM, WITZTUM JL, SCHONFELD G, WEIDMAN SW, KOLAR JB: Type III hyperlipoproteinemia. Rise in high-density lipoprotein levels in response to therapy. *Am J Med* 66:303, 1979.

187. HOOGWERF BJ, PETERS JR, FRANTZ ID JR, HUNNINGHAKE DB: Effect of clofibrate and colestipol singly and in combination on plasma lipids and lipoproteins in type III hyperlipoproteinemia. *Metabolism* 34:978, 1985.

188. HOOGWERF BJ, BANTLE JP, KUBA K, FRANTZ ID JR, HUNNINGHAKE DB: Treatment of type III hyperlipoproteinemia with four different treatment regimens. *Atherosclerosis* 51:251, 1984.

189. CONNOR WE, CONNOR SL: The dietary treatment of hyperlipidemia. Rationale, technique, and efficacy. *Med Clin North Am* 66:485, 1982.

190. AMERICAN HEART ASSOCIATION: *Counseling the Patient with Hyperlipidemia*, No. 70-061-A. Dallas, American Heart Association, 1984.

191. THE CORONARY DRUG PROJECT RESEARCH GROUP: Clofibrate and niacin in coronary heart disease. *JAMA* 231:360, 1975.

192. GRUNDY SM, MOK HYI, ZECH L, BERMAN M: Influence of nicotinic acid on metabolism of cholesterol and triglycerides in man. *J Lipid Res* 22:24, 1981.

193. KUDCHODKAR BJ, SODHI HS, HORLICK L, MASON DT: Effects of clofibrate on cholesterol metabolism. *Clin Pharmacol Ther* 22:154, 1977.

194. GRUNDY SM, AHRENS EH JR, SALEN G, QUINTAO E: Mode of action of Atromid-S on cholesterol metabolism in man. *J Clin Invest* 48:33a, 1969.

195. SCOTT PJ, HURLEY PJ: Effect of clofibrate on low-density lipoprotein turnover in essential hypercholesterolaemia. *J Atheroscler Res* 9:25, 1969.

196. SEGAL P, ROHEIM PS, EDER HA: Effect of clofibrate on lipoprotein metabolism in hyperlipidemic rats. *J Clin Invest* 51:1632, 1972.

197. BOBERG J, BOBERG M, GROSS R, GRUNDY S, AUGUSTIN J, BROWN V: The effect of treatment with clofibrate on hepatic triglyceride and lipoprotein lipase activities of post heparin plasma in male patients with hyperlipoproteinemia. *Atherosclerosis* 27:499, 1977.

198. COMMITTEE OF PRINCIPAL INVESTIGATORS: WHO cooperative trial on primary prevention of ischaemic heart disease using clofibrate to lower serum cholesterol: Mortality follow-up. *Lancet* 2:379, 1980.

199. ENDO A, KURODA M, TSUJITA Y: ML-236A, ML-236B, and ML-236C, new inhibitors of cholesterogenesis produced by *Penicillium citrinum*. *J Antibiot (Tokyo)* 29:1346, 1976.

200. BILHEIMER DW, GRUNDY SM, BROWN MS, GOLDSTEIN JL: Mevinolin and colestipol stimulate receptor-mediated clearance of low density lipoprotein from plasma in familial hypercholesterolemia heterozygotes. *Proc Natl Acad Sci USA* 80:4124, 1983.

201. ILLINGWORTH DR, SEXTON GJ: Hypocholesterolemic effects of mevinolin in patients with heterozygous familial hypercholesterolemia. *J Clin Invest* 74:1972, 1984.

202. EAST CA, GRUNDY SM, BILHEIMER DW: Preliminary Report: Treatment of type 3 hyperlipoproteinemia with mevinolin. *Metabolism* 35:97, 1986.

203. ZELIS R, MASON DT, BRAUNWALD E, LEVY RI: Effects of hyperlipoproteinemias and their treatment on the peripheral circulation. *J Clin Invest* 49:1007, 1970.

CHAPTER 48

FAMILIAL HYPERCHOLESTEROLEMIA

JOSEPH L. GOLDSTEIN
MICHAEL S. BROWN

1. *Familial hypercholesterolemia (FH) is characterized clinically by: (1) an elevated concentration of low density lipoprotein (LDL), the major cholesterol-transport lipoprotein in human plasma; (2) deposition of LDL-derived cholesterol in tendons and skin (xanthomas) and in arteries (atheromas); and (3) inheritance as an autosomal dominant trait with a gene dosage effect; i.e., homozygotes are more severely affected than are heterozygotes.*
2. *Heterozygotes number about 1 in 500 persons, placing FH among the most common inborn errors of metabolism. Heterozygotes have twofold elevations in plasma cholesterol (350 to 550 mg/dl) from birth. Tendon xanthomas and coronary atherosclerosis develop after age 20.*
3. *Homozygotes number 1 in 1 million persons. They have severe hypercholesterolemia (650 to 1000 mg/dl). Cutaneous xanthomas appear within the first 4 years of life. Coronary heart disease begins in childhood and frequently causes death before age 20.*
4. *The primary defect in FH is a mutation in the gene specifying the receptor for plasma LDL. Located in coated pits on the surfaces of cells in the liver and other organs, the LDL receptor binds LDL and facilitates its uptake by receptor-mediated endocytosis. The LDL is degraded in lysosomes, and its cholesterol is released for metabolic use. When LDL receptors are deficient, the rate of removal of LDL from plasma declines, and the level of LDL rises in inverse proportion to the receptor number. The excess plasma LDL is deposited in connective tissues and in scavenger cells, producing xanthomas and atheromas.*
5. *The LDL receptor gene is on the short arm of chromosome 19. It comprises 18 exons that span 45 kb. The gene encodes a single-chain glycoprotein that contains 839 amino acids in its mature form. Four classes of mutations at the LDL receptor locus have been identified on the basis of phenotypic behavior of the mutant proteins. Each class has been subdivided into multiple alleles through molecular characterization of the mutant genes. Class 1 alleles, the most common, fail to produce an immunoprecipitable protein (null alleles). Class 2 alleles encode proteins blocked in intracellular transport between the endoplasmic reticulum and the Golgi complex. Class 3 alleles encode proteins that are synthesized and tranported to the cell surface but fail to bind LDL normally. Class 4 alleles, the rarest, encode proteins that reach the cell surface and bind LDL normally but fail to cluster in coated pits and hence do not internalize bound LDL.*
6. *FH heterozygotes have one normal allele and one mutant allele at the LDL receptor locus, and hence their cells are able to bind and take up LDL at approximately half the normal rate. Phenotypic homozygotes possess two mutant alleles at the LDL receptor locus, and hence their cells show a total or near-total inability to bind or take up LDL. Some phenotypic homozygotes inherit two identical alleles, whereas others inherit two different mutant alleles and are thus compound heterozygotes. Prenatal diagnosis of receptor-negative homozygotes has been performed by quantitative assays of LDL receptor activity in cultured amniotic fluid cells.*
7. *Treatment for heterozygotes and homozygotes is directed at lowering the plasma level of LDL. In heterozygotes the most effective therapy is the administration of drugs that stimulate the single normal gene to produce additional messenger RNA for the LDL receptor. This can be achieved through the combined administration of a bile acid-binding resin (which removes sterol from the body) and an inhibitor of 3-hydroxy-3-methylglutaryl CoA reductase (which decreases hepatic cholesterol synthesis). These drugs enhance LDL receptor activity in the liver and lower LDL production. Homozygotes with two nonfunctional genes are resistant to drugs that work by stimulating LDL receptors. Their plasma LDL levels can be lowered only by physical or surgical means. Homozygotes with one or more partially functional genes often respond to treatment with a combination of receptor-stimulating drugs.*

Familial hypercholesterolemia (FH) results from a mutation affecting the structure and function of a cell surface receptor that normally removes low density lipoprotein (LDL) from plasma. The disorder is characterized clinically by a lifelong elevation in the concentration of LDL-bound cholesterol in blood; pathologically by cholesterol deposits that form xanthomas, arcus corneae, and premature coronary heart disease; and genetically by autosomal dominant inheritance. FH was the first genetic disorder recognized to cause myocardial infarction.[1,2] To this day, it remains the most cogent illustration of the causal relation between high blood cholesterol levels and coronary atherosclerosis. But above and beyond its traditional place among diseases of lipid metabolism, FH has recently acquired importance as a prototype for a class of diseases caused by defects in receptor molecules.[3]

Patients with FH manifest two distinct syndromes, depending on whether the mutant gene is present in the heterozygous or homozygous form. Heterozygotes occur in the population at a frequency of about 1 in 500, placing FH among the most common single gene-determined diseases in human beings. As expected, homozygotes, who inherit two mutant genes at the LDL receptor locus, are much less numerous, occurring with a prevalence of 1 in 1 million. Homozygotes exhibit a syndrome that is more severe than the disease seen in heterozygotes.

Because of the high frequency of LDL receptor mutations, FH homozygotes can inherit two identical mutant genes or two different mutant genes. In the latter case, the individual is a compound heterozygote rather than a true homozygote. In this chapter, we retain the term FH homozygotes to refer to individuals who have two mutant genes at the LDL receptor locus, whether they are identical or not.

In considering FH, note that this disease is only one of several disorders that are included in the designation familial type 2 hyperlipoproteinemia. The simple finding of an elevated LDL cholesterol level does not mean that a patient has FH. Confirmation of the diagnosis requires either the demonstration of a decrease in LDL receptors, the documentation of a mutation in the LDL receptor gene, or the presence of ancillary clinical findings such as tendon xanthomas, autosomal dominant transmission, and expression in childhood.

HISTORICAL ASPECTS

The association of xanthomas in tendons and atheromas in arteries was repeatedly described before 1900.[4–7] In the 1930s Muller[1,2] and Thannhauser et al.[8,9] recognized the familial clustering of patients exhibiting xanthomas, premature coronary artery disease, and hypercholesterolemia. Their suggestions of a genetic basis for hypercholesterolemia were substantiated in the 1940s and 1950s by the family studies of Wilkinson et al.,[10,11] Adlersberg et al.,[12–14] and others.[15–20] Understanding of the genetics was greatly advanced by the extensive observations of Khachadurian, whose studies in Lebanon in the early 1960s delineated the differences between heterozygotes and homozygotes,[21] thereby providing the first unequivocal evidence for the single gene inheritance of this disorder.

Using analytical ultracentrifugation, Gofman and coworkers in the mid-1950s showed that the hypercholesterolemia in FH was due to a selective increase in the plasma concentration of one lipoprotein, now designated LDL.[22,23] Fredrickson, Levy, and coworkers in the 1960s developed the concept that FH is a disorder involving the metabolism of both the apoprotein and cholesterol components of LDL.[24] The most recent developments relate to the use of cultured fibroblasts from homozygotes to define the basic biochemical defect. The studies of Brown and Goldstein in the 1970s and 1980s disclosed the existence of the cell surface LDL receptor and demonstrated that FH is caused by mutations in the gene specifying this receptor.[3,25]

CLINICAL FEATURES

Data on the natural history of heterozygous FH have been derived from measurements of the frequency of clinical findings in affected relatives of different ages from the same large family[17,18,26,27] (see Fig. 48-1). The earliest manifestation is hypercholesterolemia, which is present at birth in virtually all affected subjects[28] and remains the only clinical finding throughout the first decade.[29] Arcus corneae and tendon xanthomas appear at the end of the second decade, and by the third decade each is present in about half of all heterozygotes. By the time of death, 80 percent of heterozygotes have xanthomas.[27] Clinical symptoms of coronary heart disease appear in the fourth decade.

The clinical picture in homozygotes is remarkably uniform and distinctly different from that in heterozygotes.[21,30–32] Marked hypercholesterolemia, present at birth, persists throughout life. Unique yellow-orange cutaneous xanthomas, frequently present at birth, develop in all homozygotes by age 4.[30–32] Homozygotes inevitably develop tendon xanthomas, ar-

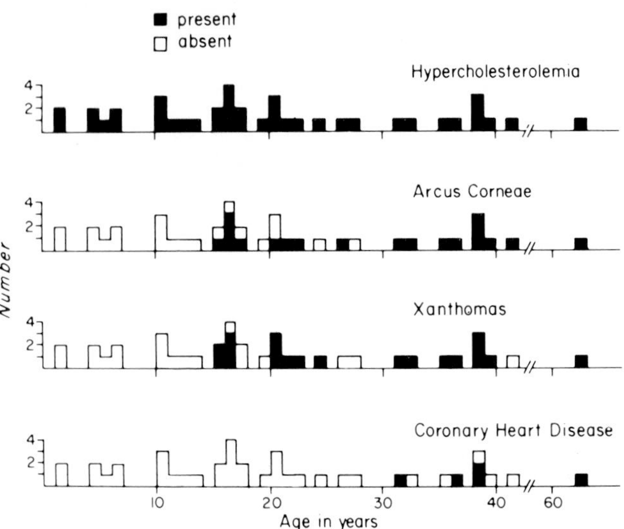

Fig. 48-1 Prevalence of clinical manifestations at different ages in the affected heterozygotes from a single large family with FH. (*Data redrawn from Scrott et al.,*[27] *by permission of* Annals of Internal Medicine.)

cus corneae, and generalized atherosclerosis in childhood. Death from myocardial infarction typically occurs before age 30.[30–32] In addition to atherosclerosis of the coronary, cerebral, and peripheral vessels, homozygotes also develop xanthomatous infiltration of the aortic valve, which produces a picture that is hemodynamically indistinguishable from rheumatic or calcific aortic stenosis.[21,33,34]

Blood Lipids and Lipoproteins

The mean plasma cholesterol level in large groups of FH heterozygotes is remarkably constant. For example, plasma cholesterol levels averaged 340 mg/dl in 56 obligate Lebanese heterozygotes,[30] 350 mg/dl in 36 affected members of a large Aleutian kindred[27]; 341 mg/dl in 73 affected first-degree relatives in 55 English families[35]; 366 mg/dl in 262 U.S. white heterozygotes[31]; and 358 mg/dl in 40 Japanese heterozygotes.[36] Despite this uniformity among populations, the cholesterol levels in individual patients, even within the same family, may vary as much as twofold (i.e., from about 270 to 550 mg/dl). In homozygotes the plasma cholesterol concentration is uniformly higher than in heterozygotes, ranging from 600 to 1200 mg/dl.[30–32]

Cholesteryl esters, which normally make up 70 to 75 percent of the total plasma cholesterol, form a similar porportion in both heterozygotes and homozygotes. Total plasma phospholipids are elevated slightly in heterozygotes and more strikingly in homozygotes.[37] Although some heterozygotes have a slight elevation of the plasma triglyceride concentration, the mean value is not significantly different from that of the general population (Table 48-1).[27,29,31] In homozygotes the level of plasma triglycerides is slightly elevated, but many patients have values in the normal range.[30–32] Occasionally a heterozygote or a homozygote with documented FH will have a plasma triglyceride level of more than 250 mg/dl. The reason for this infrequent occurrence is unknown, but it may relate to the function of the LDL receptor in removing remnants of triglyceride-carrying very low density lipoproteins (VLDL) and intermediate density lipoproteins (IDL) from the circulation.

The excess cholesterol in the plasma of heterozygotes and homozygotes is found entirely in the lipoprotein fraction of

Table 48-1 Plasma Lipids and Lipoproteins in Familial Hypercholesterolemia

Genotype	Age, years	Number of patients	Plasma cholesterol, mg/dl				Plasma triglyceride, mg/dl
			Total	VLDL	LDL	HDL	
Normal	1–19	128	175 ± 28	13 ± 8	110 ± 25	53 ± 13	60 ± 25
Heterozygotes	1–19	105	299 ± 63	15 ± 11	241 ± 60	43 ± 12	82 ± 51
Homozygotes	1–19	10	678 ± 170	19 ± 8	625 ± 160	34 ± 10	101 ± 51
Normal	≥ 20	76	194 ± 34	16 ± 10	123 ± 31	53 ± 16	83 ± 31
Heterozygotes	≥ 20	88	368 ± 78	27 ± 17	298 ± 78	44 ± 13	148 ± 75

NOTE: Mean ± 1 SD.
SOURCE: From Kwiterovich et al.,[29] by permission of *The Journal of Clinical Investigations.*

density 1.006 to 1.063 g/ml, i.e., LDL.[22,23,31] The mean LDL cholesterol concentration in heterozygotes at all ages is two to three times the mean of normal subjects of similar age. The mean LDL cholesterol concentration in homozygotes is about two to three times that of heterozygotes and about six times that of normal subjects (Table 48-1). LDL particles are increased in number in the plasma of patients with FH. Most of the particles have normal lipid and protein content, amino acid composition, density, and immunochemical reactivity.[38–40] Some LDL particles show a small decrease in triglyceride content,[37,41] a small difference in hydrated density,[42] and a slight increase in the ratio of cholesterol to phospholipid.[40] It is likely that these slight changes represent minor secondary alterations that result from excessively prolonged circulation of the lipoprotein due to the LDL receptor defect.[40] The minor structural changes do not affect the metabolism of the LDL particles. Thus, when LDL from an FH homozygote was injected into the circulation of a normal subject, the LDL was metabolized normally.[43] Moreover, LDL from homozygotes binds to LDL receptors[44] and suppresses 3-hydroxy-3-methylglutaryl coenzyme A reductase activity[45] in normal fibroblasts in the same manner as LDL from normal subjects.

The HDL cholesterol levels in FH patients are slightly lower, on average, than those in normal subjects.[29,46,47] This decrease is seen in heterozygotes as well as in homozygotes at all ages (Table 48-1). The mechanism of this reduction in HDL is not known.

Xanthomas

LDL-derived cholesterol deposits in several tissues of FH patients, especially in skin and tendons (xanthomas) and in arterial plaques (atheromas). The rate of deposition is proportional to the severity and duration of the elevation in LDL, but local trauma and unknown factors also play a role.[21,31] The types of xanthomas seen in FH are illustrated in Figs. 48-2*A* to *K* and 48-3*A* to *H*. Homozygotes and heterozygotes both may have tendon xanthomas (especially in the Achilles tendons and in the extensor tendons of the hand) (Fig. 48-2*F* to *H*), subcutaneous tuberous xanthomas (especially over the elbows), and subperiosteal xanthomas (commonly below the knee and over the olecranon process) (Fig. 48-2*D* and *E*). Palpebral xanthomas (xanthelasma) occur commonly in heterozygotes (Fig. 48-2*A* and *B*) but are rare in homozygotes. Unlike tendon xanthomas, which are virtually specific for FH, xanthelasma can occur in subjects with normal lipid levels[22,23] and may be transmitted as a genetic trait in the absence of hypercholesterolemia. Elevated orange-yellow planar cutaneous xanthomas lying superficially over the extremities, buttocks, and hands (especially in the interdigital web between the first and second fingers) (Fig. 48-3*B*,*C*,*E*,*F*) are unique to homozygotes.[30–32] Xanthomas of the tongue and the buccal mucosa occur occasionally in homozygotes.

The frequency of xanthomas in heterozygotes as a function of age is shown in Table 48-2. These data illustrate the long lag period in heterozygotes before xanthomas appear.

Patients with cerebrotendinous xanthomatosis, an extremely rare autosomal recessive disorder (Chap. 51), may develop tendon xanthomas that are indistinguishable from those in FH.[48,49] Other clinical features such as cataracts, mental deterioration, and normal plasma LDL cholesterol levels are sufficient to distinguish these patients from FH heterozygotes (see Chap. 51).

Arcus Corneae

Arcus corneae (Fig. 48-2*B*) appears in about 10 percent of heterozygotes before 30 years of age and is present in about 50 percent of heterozygotes above age 30.[31] It usually occurs before age 10 in homozygotes (Fig. 48-3*A*). Like xanthelasma, arcus corneae can also be observed in patients with normal lipid levels[22,23] and may be familial. It is frequently seen in healthy black subjects.[50]

Premature Atherosclerosis

In homozygotes cardiac atherosclerosis is rapidly progressive. Homozygotes usually display angina pectoris, myocardial infarction, or sudden death between the ages of 5 and 30.[30–32,52,53] One homozygote experienced an acute myocardial infarction at age 18 months,[31] and another died of an acute myocardial infarction at 3 years.[51] Severe atherosclerosis also occurs in the thoracic and abdominal aorta and in the major pulmonary arteries.[21,52,53] Few homozygotes survive past age 30.[32,47,53]

The prevalence of coronary heart disease among homozygotes varies inversely with the number of LDL receptors as

Table 48-2 Frequency of Xanthomas as a Function of Age in Heterozygotes with Familial Hypercholesterolemia

Age, years	Number of heterozygotes	Percentage with xanthomas
1–9	38	2.6
10–19	32	12.5
20-29	13	69.2
30–39	30	90.0
40–59	29	70.3

SOURCE: From Kwiterovich et al.,[29] by permission of *The Journal of Clinical Investigations.*

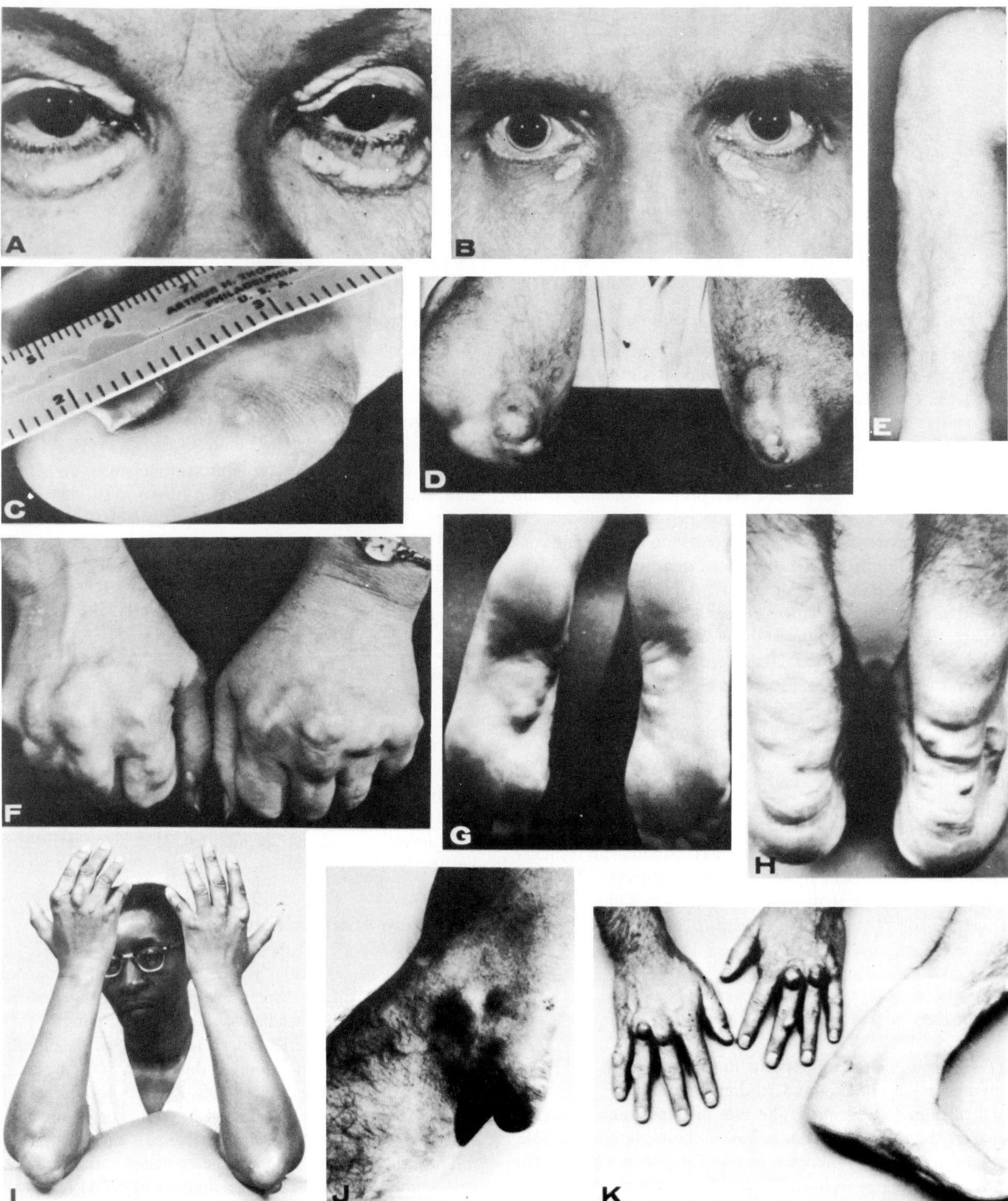

Fig. 48-2 Forms of xanthomas and other lipid deposits frequently seen in FH heterozygotes. *A.* Xanthelasma. *B.* Arcus corneae and xanthelasma *E.* Subperiosteal xanthoma over tibial tuberosity. Others in *C, D,* and *F* to *K* are either tendon xanthomas or a combination of tendon and tuberous xanthomas.

measured in cultured fibroblasts (Fig. 48-4 and Table 48-3). Homozygotes can be divided into two broad groups, according to whether or not their cells exhibit any detectable LDL receptor activity. Clinical signs of coronary heart disease occurred earlier, and coronary deaths were more frequent in homozygotes in whom receptor activity was less than 2 percent of normal as compared with those in whom receptor activity was 2 to 30 percent of normal. The level of plasma LDL also seems to be higher in the subjects whose cells produce no detectable LDL receptors. Sprecher et al. related the levels of LDL receptor activity in fibroblasts to the pretreatment levels of plasma LDL cholesterol in 13 FH homozygotes.[54] Receptor activity ranged from 2 to 29 percent of normal with LDL cholesterol ranging from 304 to 874 mg/dl. The two parameters were inversely correlated with an r value of -0.89.[54]

In some FH homozygotes xanthomas form on the endocardial surfaces of the mitral valve.[34,52,53] These may produce findings of mitral regurgitation and mitral stenosis.[9,52,55] Since the homozygote may have painful joints,[56] a persistently elevated sedimentation rate,[57] and cardiac murmurs, a misdiagnosis of acute rheumatic fever may be made.[56]

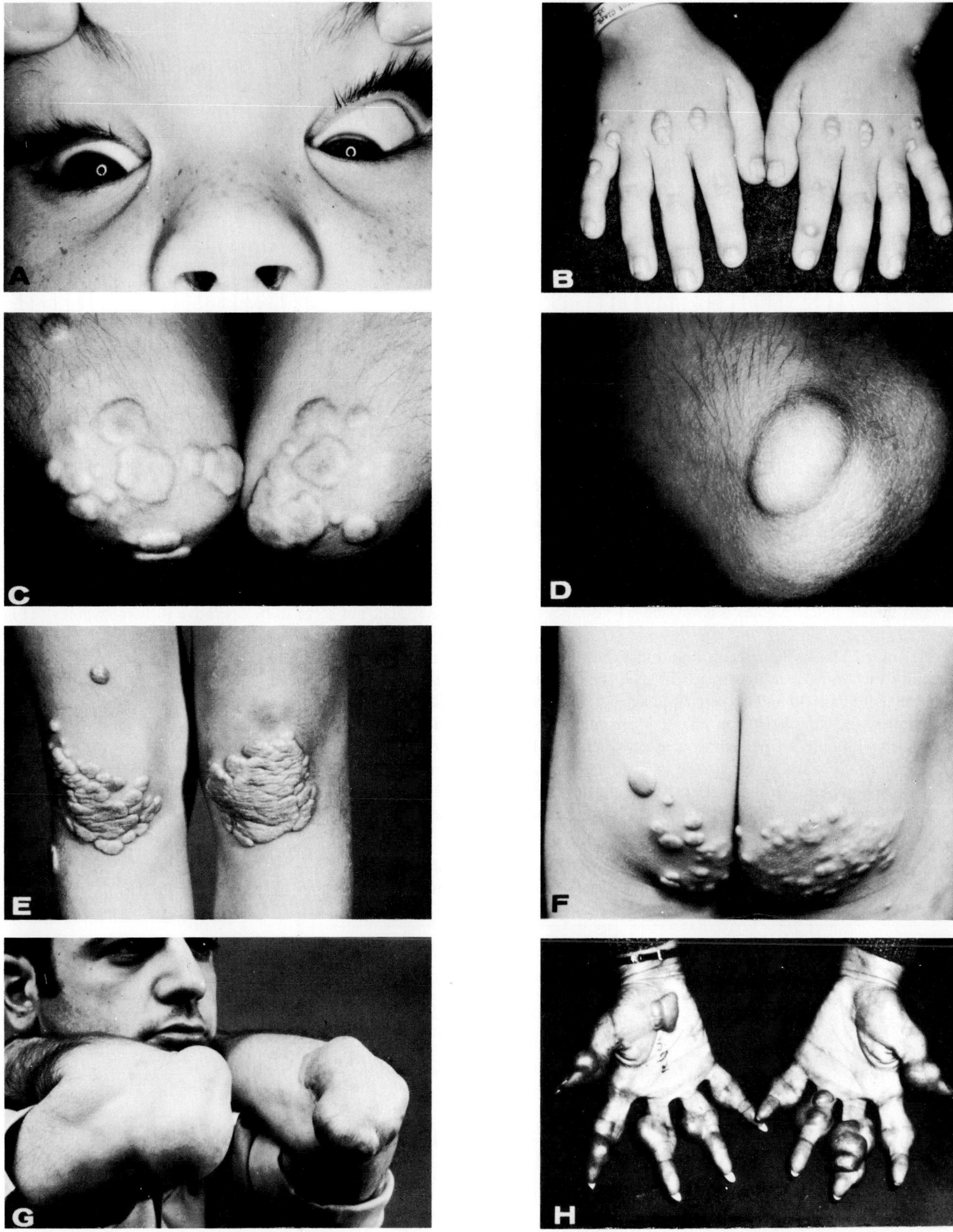

Fig. 48-3 Forms of xanthomas and other lipid deposits frequently seen in FH homozygotes. *A.* Arcus cornea. *B, C, E,* and *F.* Cutaneous planar xanthomas, usually having a bright orange hue. *C* and *D.* Tuberous xanthomas on the elbows. *H.* Tendon and tuberous xanthomas. (H *reproduced through the courtesy of Dr. A. Khachadurian.)*

The pattern of cardiac disease in the heterozygote is much more variable than in the homozygote. Affected women seem to suffer clinical coronary artery disease somewhat later than affected men. Thus, in England, Slack found that the mean age of onset of coronary artery disease was 43 years for men and 53 years for women.[58] Among heterozygous men, the risk of a myocardial infarction was 5 percent by age 30, 51 percent by age 50, and 85 percent by age 60. For women the risks at comparable ages were 0, 12, and 58 percent. In Denmark, the prevalence of coronary heart disease among heterozygotes with

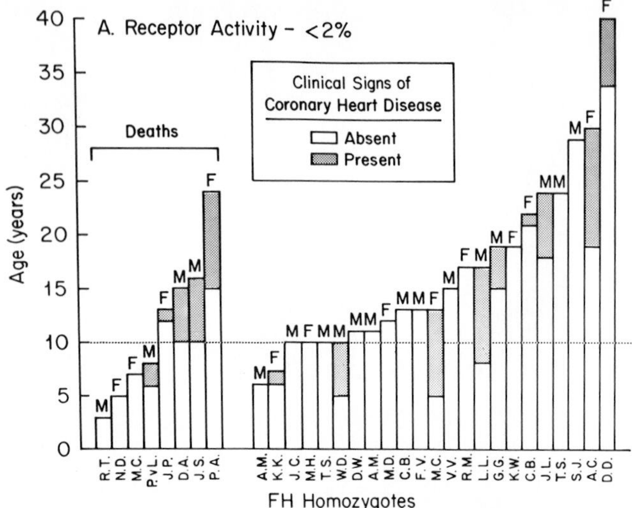

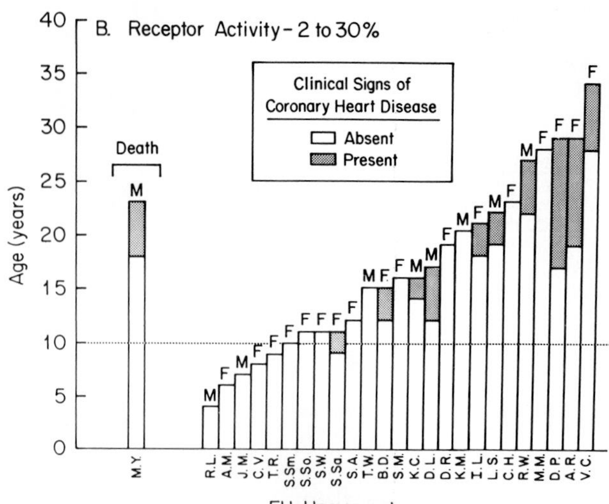

Fig. 48-4 Prevalence of clinical signs of coronary heart disease at different ages in FH homozygotes with LDL receptor activity of less than 2 percent of normal *(A)* and those with receptor activity of 2 to 30 percent of normal *(B)*. See Table 48-3 for additional information on these patients. The initials of each patient are shown at the bottom of each bar; the sex of the patient (M = male, F = female) is shown at the top of the bar. The cause of death in the deceased homozygotes was as follows: *Panel A:* R.T., sudden death due to myocardial infarction; N.D., myocardial infarction; M.C., myocardial infarction; P.V.L., sudden death due to myocardial infarction; J.P., sudden death; D.A., myocardial infarction; J.S. sudden death; P.A., ruptured spleen due to surgical complications. *Panel B:* M.Y., acute aortic insufficiency. *(J. L. Goldstein, M. S. Brown, Med Clin N Amer, 66:335, 1982. Used by permission.)*

FH (32 percent) was 25 times greater than among unaffected relatives (1.3 percent).[59] In Norway, the mean age at death for male and female heterozygotes was 55 and 64 years, respectively.[60]

In the United States, Stone et al. found that the cumulative probability of coronary heart disease in male heterozygotes was 16 percent at age 40 and 52 percent at age 60.[61] In female heterozygotes, the cumulative risk was 32.8 percent by age 60 as compared with only 9.1 percent in unaffected females. Earlier death from coronary artery disease in male heterozygotes (54 years) as compared with female heterozygotes (68 years) was reported in Japan by Mabuchi et al.[62] It is interesting to note that this sex difference, which is also a characteristic feature of the usual form of normolipidemic atherosclerotic heart disease, does not seem to be operative in homozygotes[52] (Fig. 48-4).

Table 48-4 shows the percentage of heterozygotes who exhibit symptoms of coronary artery disease or death from myocardial infarction at different ages. These values were compiled from five large studies involving more than 1000 heterozygotes.[58–61,63]

An increased frequency of hypertension and of premature cerebrovascular disease is not observed in heterozygotes.[31] Peripheral vascular disease probably does occur at a slightly in-

Table 48-3 Coronary Heart Disease (CHD) in Homozygotes Subdivided According to the Amount of Functional LDL Receptor Activity Expressed in Cultured Fibroblasts

	<2% normal receptor activity			*2–30% normal receptor activity*		
	Males	*Females*	*Total*	*Males*	*Females*	*Total*
Number of patients	18	13	31	9	17	26
Mean age, years	15	17	16	17	17	17
Prevalence of CHD*						
Age, 0–10 years	3/6	3/4	6/10 (60%)	0/2	0/4	0/6 (0%)
Age, 10–20 years	4/9	3/6	7/16 (44%)	2/4	2/7	4/11 (36%)
Age, >20 years	1/3	3/3	4/6 (67%)	3/3	4/6	7/9 (78%)
All ages	8/18	8/13	16/31 (52%)	5/9	6/17	11/26 (42%)
Deaths from CHD†	4/18	4/13	8/31 (26%)	1/9	0/17	1/26 (4%)
Mean age at death, years	10	12	11	23	—	23

NOTE: The data in this table and in Fig. 48-4 were obtained from clinical summaries of 57 homozygotes whose cultured skin fibroblasts were analyzed for LDL receptor activity.

*CHD, coronary heart disease. Clinical signs of coronary heart disease were considered to be present if the patient had any one of the following: classic angina pectoris, evidence of atherosclerosis on coronary arteriography, myocardial infarction, or sudden death.

†Deaths occurring during the follow-up period after the diagnostic skin biopsy was obtained. The mean duration of follow-up was 3.9 years and 3.7 years for the patients with < 2 percent and 2-30 percent normal receptor activity.

SOURCE: J. L. Goldstein, M. S. Brown, *Med Clin N Amer*, 66:335, 1982. Used by permission.

Table 48-4 Estimated Risk, in Percents, of Heterozygotes Having Symptoms of Coronary Heart Disease and Dying of Myocardial Infarction at Different Ages

	Male heterozygotes		*Female heterozygotes*	
Age	*Coronary symptoms*	*Coronary death*	*Coronary symptoms*	*Coronary death*
40 years	20	—	3	0
50 years	45	25	20	2
60 years	75	50	45	15
70 years	—	80	75	30

NOTE: These estimates were compiled from the data of Slack,[58] Jensen et al.,[59] Heiberg,[60] Stone et al.,[61] and Beaumont et al.[63]

creased frequency in FH,[31] although it is considerably less prevalent than coronary heart disease. Symptomatic atherosclerosis of peripheral vessels appears to be much more common in patients with familial type 3 hyperlipoproteinemia (dysbetalipoproteinemia) than in heterozygotes with FH (Chap. 47).

Polyarthritis and Tendonitis

Heterozygotes or homozygotes with FH may have recurrent attacks of polyarthritis and tenosynovitis, especially in the ankles, knees, wrists, and proximal interphalangeal joints.[56,64,65] In one study 40 percent of adult heterozygotes had at least one episode of articular pain.[64] Achilles pain or tendonitis occurred in 29 percent, oligoarticular arthritis in 7 percent, and polyarticular or rheumatic fever-like arthritis in 4 percent.[64]

Although the joints may be painful and inflamed, fever, leukocytosis, and elevated sedimentation rate occur infrequently. The typical attack beings quickly, with joint symptoms becoming maximal within 24 h of onset. Back pain is not a feature. The signs and symptoms usually persist for 3 to 12 days, after which a complete resolution occurs. Anti-inflammatory drugs do not seem to influence the course of these attacks.[65] In heterozygotes the joint attacks do not progress to articular damage or deformity. However, one homozygote had flexor contractures of the fingers due to tendon and joint xanthomas and required hand surgery for correction.[66]

The sedimentation rate may be elevated about fourfold above normal in the plasma of homozygotes, even in the absence of joint symptoms.[57] Plasma fibrinogen levels may also show a twofold elevation.[57] These elevations are presumably related to the high plasma LDL levels.

Fig. 48-5 Comparison of the distribution of age- and sex-adjusted total plasma cholesterol levels in control subjects (upper histogram) and in members of a single large family with FH. *(From Scott et al.,[27] by permission of* Annals of Internal Medicine.)

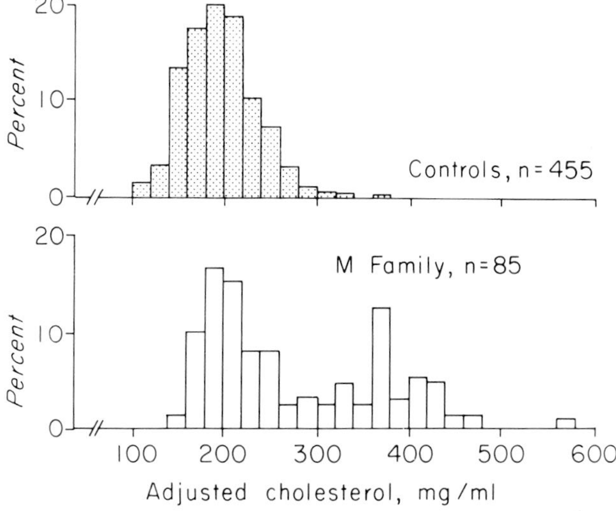

Diabetes Mellitus and Obesity

The frequency of diabetes mellitus is not increased in FH. Khachadurian et al. found that the mean fasting plasma glucose level in 49 homozygotes was 81 mg/dl, and none of these subjects had an elevated value.[32] In contrast to most of the other forms of hyperlipidemia associated with coronary heart disease, FH is not related to obesity.[67] A slender body habitus is the rule in heterozygotes and homozygotes.

GENETIC ASPECTS

Mode of Inheritance

FH is transmitted as a simple autosomal dominant trait.[68] In two large, well-studied families the clear-cut bimodality in the distribution of plasma cholesterol allowed unbiased classification of family members into affected and unaffected groups.[26,27] The distribution of plasma cholesterol values in one of these families, the Aleutian family reported by Scott et al., is shown in Fig. 48-5. The pedigree is shown in Fig. 48-6. Segregation analysis was consistent with transmission of a Mendelian autosomal dominant gene.[27] Similar conclusions were reached in studies in which data from a large number of small families were pooled.[29,31,35]

The first proof that severely affected young individuals are homozygotes rather than severely affected heterozygotes came from the studies of Khachadurian in Lebanon.[21,32] He studied 49 young individuals with juvenile xanthomatosis and rapidly developing atherosclerosis. Three lines of evidence suggested that they were homozygous for the FH gene:

1. Their mean cholesterol level (740 mg/dl) was approximately twice that of their parents, which in turn was twofold greater than that of normal Lebanese control subjects. These cholesterol values could be segregated into three discrete groups (Fig. 48-7), strongly suggesting that the children possessed two abnormal alleles and that each parent possessed one abnormal allele.

2. The frequency of consanguinity among the parents of these homozygotes (58 percent) was much higher than the frequency of consanguinity in the general Lebanese population (10 percent). This finding was consistent with inheritance of the same mutant allele from each parent, thus suggesting true homozygosity rather than a compound heterozygous state.

3. Sibship analysis using the Leng-Hogben formula yielded the number of homozygotes, heterozygotes, and normals expected for a single gene-determined trait.

In addition to the 49 Lebanese homozygotes, more than 150 other homozygotes from at least 75 families throughout the world have been reported[47,52,53,68–70] (see Fig. 48-4 and Table 48-3). In virtually all cases, these children have resulted from the marriage of two clinically identifiable heterozygotes.

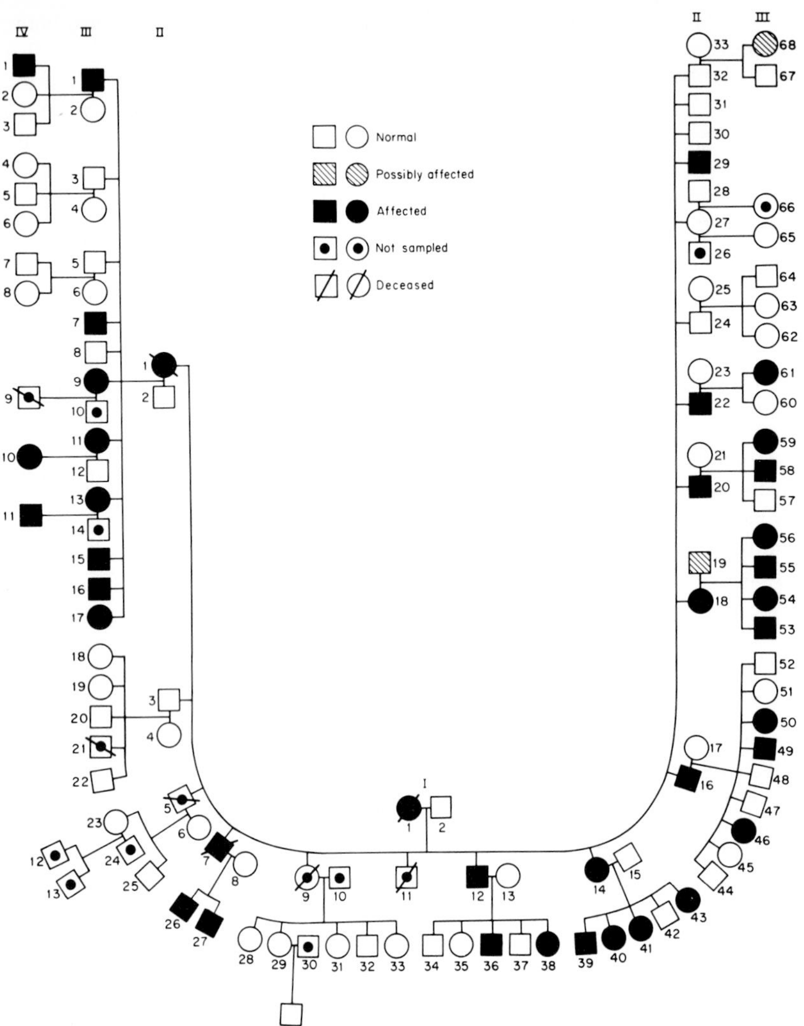

Fig. 48-6 Pedigree of a family with FH. All affected persons are heterozygotes. I-1, II-1, and II-7 each had hypercholesterolemia and tendon xanthomas and died as a result of coronary heart disease. *(From Scrott et al.,[27] by permission of Annals of Internal Medicine.)*

Clinical Expression of the FH Gene

When either the plasma total cholesterol or LDL cholesterol level is used as a genetic marker, the FH gene is highly penetrant (90 percent) at all ages. Thus, 90 percent of persons carrying the gene have a plasma cholesterol value greater than the 95th percentile value of the population. The LDL cholesterol level appears to be a slightly better marker for the gene than is the total plasma cholesterol level.[29] As discussed below, neither of these elevations is specific for FH.

Inasmuch as symptoms of heterozygous FH do not usually appear until after the childbearing years, the gene does not reduce reproductive fitness.[68] However, the rare homozygotes almost never reproduce, although one 28-year-old homozygote was reported to undergo a normal pregnancy and delivery.[71] Skin fibroblasts of this patient showed 10 to 15 percent of normal LDL receptor activity.[72] The longest-lived homozygote reported to date is a 56-year-old Japanese man who fathered one son.[73] His skin fibroblasts showed normal receptor binding of LDL but no internalization of the lipoprotein.[73]

Pedigree studies showed that the gene for FH is linked to the gene specifying the third component of complement (C3), which is known to be located on chromosome 19.[74–76] The recombination fraction was about 0.25. As expected, somatic cell genetic studies confirmed that the gene for the LDL receptor *(LDLR)* is also located on chromosome 19,[77] and in situ

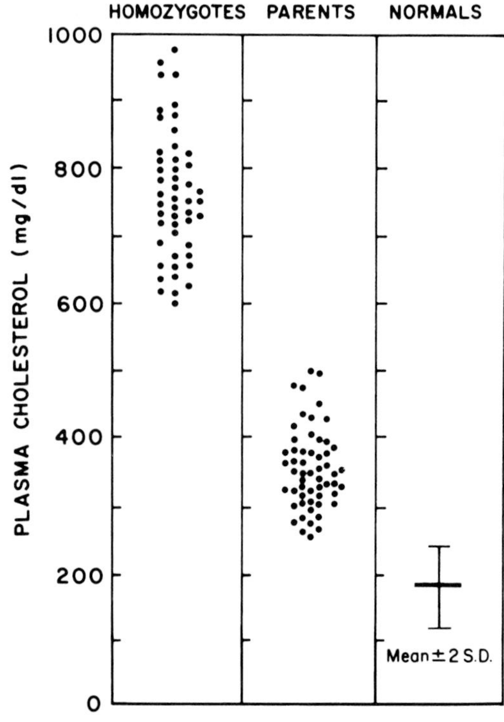

Fig. 48-7 Distribution of total plasma cholesterol levels in 49 FH homozygotes, their parents (obligate heterozygotes), and normal controls. *(Data redrawn from Khachadurian et al.[30,32])*

hybridization with a radiolabled LDL receptor cDNA probe regionally mapped the *LDLR* locus to the short arm of chromosome 19 in bands p13.1 to p13.3.[78]

Population Prevalence

The prevalence of heterozygotes with FH among patients with coronary heart disease was determined by family analysis of hyperlipidemic survivors of myocardial infarction. The data, collected by three groups of investigators, yielded remarkably similar estimates. Three percent of 193 survivors in London,[79] 4 percent of 366 survivors in Seattle,[80] and 6 percent of 101 survivors in Helsinki[81] appeared to have the heterozygous form of FH.

Among the general population, Goldstein et al. estimated a minimal heterozygote frequency among whites of 1 in 500 with a range of 1 in 200 to 1 in 1000.[80] This figure is in reasonably close agreement with the estimate of Carter, Slack, and Myant, who used the prevalence of homozygotes in London (about 10 in 10 million persons) to derive a heterozygote frequency of about 1 in 200 persons.[82] A revised estimate by Slack, which was based on the Hardy-Weinberg equation and on the identification of seven living homozygotes in England and Wales, suggests a heterozygote frequency of 1 in 500.[83] This estimate agrees with the observations of Leonard et al., who found three asymptomatic heterozygotes among 1391 children admitted to a London hospital.[84] Similar population frequencies for heterozygotes have been reported from Norway,[85] Denmark,[86] and Japan.[69,87]

A remarkably high prevalence of FH has been noted in two areas of the world. In Lebanon, the estimated prevalence of homozygotes and heterozygotes is 1 in 10,000 and 1 in 171, respectively.[83] The high gene frequency appears traceable to a founder effect, and the number of homozygotes is further increased by a high incidence of consanguinity.

A high frequency of FH occurs among Afrikaaners in Johannesburg, South Africa.[47,88] The prevalence of homozygotes and heterozygotes is 1 in 30,000 and in 1 in 100, respectively,[47] again owing to a founder effect. The current Afrikaaner population of 2.7 million stems from a few Dutch, German, and French founder families (about 1000 individuals) who settled in the Cape during the latter part of the seventeenth century.[47] If more than two of the original 1000 founders possessed the FH gene, this could explain the present high frequency.

Families with FH have been reported from most countries throughout the world. If the disorder is as frequent in other regions as it appears to be in North America, Europe, and Japan, it is probably the most common disease caused by a single gene mutation in humans.

PATHOLOGIC ASPECTS

Buja and his colleagues performed extensive pathologic studies of an aborted 20-week-old fetus and three children with homozygous FH and reviewed the pathologic findings in 21 other homozygotes.[70] These data are summarized in Table 33-5 of the previous edition of this text.[89] Additional pathologic findings in four FH homozygotes have been reported by investigators at the National Institutes of Health.[53] Only limited pathologic data are available for heterozygotes.[90]

Initial Pathologic Manifestations: Autopsy Findings in a Homozygous Fetus

Cultured amniotic fluid cells from a woman bearing a fetus at risk for homozygous FH were shown to lack LDL receptors.[91] An autopsy was performed after therapeutic abortion at 20 weeks of gestation.[70] One small focus of intimal lipid accumulation was found in the aorta and coronary arteries (Fig. 48-8*A*). Multifocal lipid deposition of a mild degree was observed in stromal macrophages in the thymus, spleen (Fig. 48-8*B* and *C*), skin, and other organs and in stromal and parenchymal cells of the kidneys. The lipid deposits were oil red O-positive, and some showed marked birefringence, indicating a high cholesteryl ester content. By electron microscopy the lipid deposits in the cytoplasm of stromal cells were round, moderately electron dense, and nonmembrane-bound. Similar lipid deposits in stromal cells were not observed in three control fetuses. Although the hepatocytes of the homozygote fetus showed prominent lipid accumulation, the control fetuses also had hepatic lipid deposits, suggesting that the hepatocellular lipid accumulation in the homozygote fetus may have represented a nonspecific fatty metamorphosis, possibly induced by intrauterine hypoxia.[70]

Cord-blood cholesterol in the homozygote fetus was 279 mg/dl, as compared with an average of 31 mg/dl in control fetuses of similar gestational age.[91] The esterified cholesterol content of the thymus was four times that of one control fetus (0.51 mg sterol per gram of tissue versus 0.12 mg sterol per gram), and the esterified cholesterol content of most other tissues was 1.5 times above normal.

Atherosclerosis of Aorta and Coronary Arteries

Homozygous children exhibit severe atherosclerosis of the aorta and coronary arteries, ischemic myocardial damage, sclerosis, and lipid deposition in aortic and mitral valves.[52,70] Lipid deposition in stromal macrophages of lymph nodes, spleen, and other organs has been reported in a few homozygotes.[70] However, the degree to which lipid is deposited in extravascular sites other than in xanthomas is not well defined since most reports have emphasized examination of the cardiovascular system.

In young FH homozygotes the atherosclerotic process appears to involve major arteries selectively and to spare veins in

Fig. 48-8 Histologic findings in a 20-week-old fetus with homozygous FH. *A*, Coronary artery is normal; *B*, thymocytes contain oil-red O-positive (dark) lipid droplets; *C*, oil-red O-positive lipid deposits are also present in the splenic capsule. *(Courtesy of Dr. L. Maximilian Buja.)*

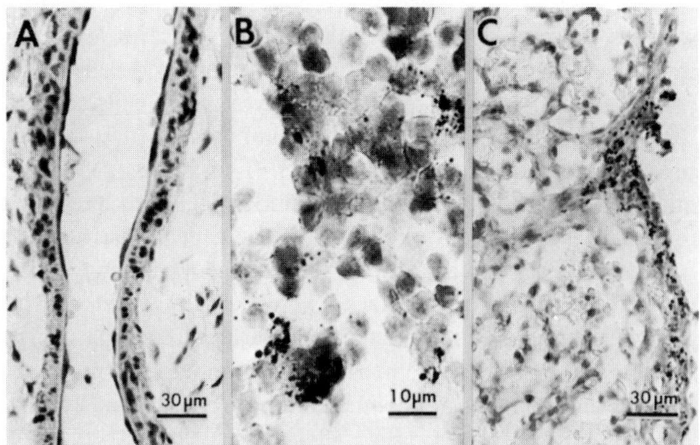

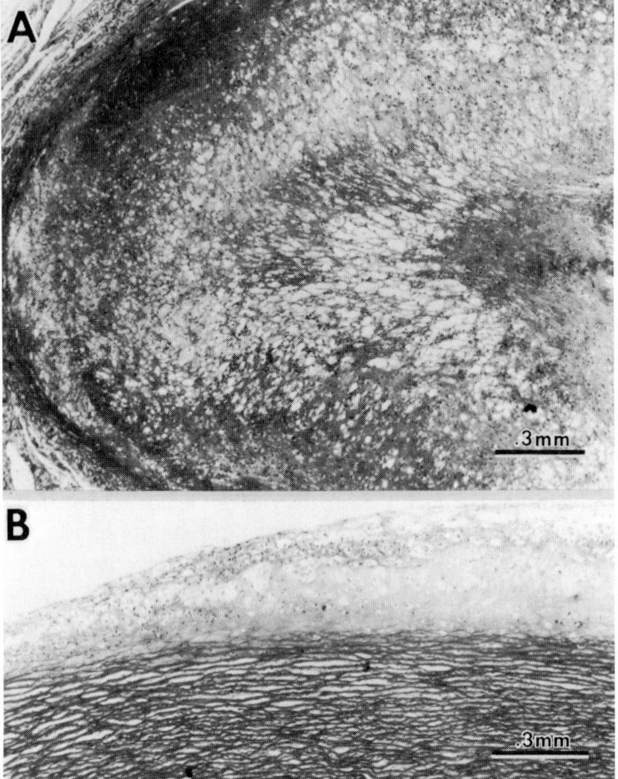

Fig. 48-9 Coronary artery *(A)* and aorta *(B)* from a 4-year-old boy with homozygous FH reported by T. Watanabe, K. Tanake, and N. Yanai *(Acta Path Jap,* 18:319, 1968*)*. These photomicrographs were made by Dr. L. Maximilian Buja from histologic sections submitted by Dr. Kenzo Tanaka of Kyushu University, Fukuoka, Japan. *A.* The lumen of the coronary artery is markedly narrowed by an atherosclerotic plaque containing numerous foam cells. (The lipid has been removed in the preparation of the paraffin sections.) *B.* The aortic intima is thickened by an atherosclerotic plaque. *(Courtesy of Dr. L. Maximilian Buja.)*

spite of severe hypercholesterolemia (Fig. 48-9). Atherosclerosis of the aorta is typically generalized, but it frequently shows a distinctive, unusually severe predilection for the thoracic aorta, particularly the ascending portion with extension into the coronary ostia.[70] Severe atherosclerosis also occurs in the abdominal aorta and in the major pulmonary arteries.[52]

Figures 48-10 and 48-11 illustrate the features of aortic atherosclerosis in a 9-year-old homozygote. The ascending aorta from this patient showed: (1) foam cell transformation of many medial smooth-muscle cells, (2) abnormal vascularization of the inner media and intima, and (3) intimal involvement by a typical atherosclerotic plaque with fibrous capsule and central atheromatous core. Cells of the plaque capsule close to the luminal surface were devoid of lipid deposits, whereas oil red O-positive cellular lipid deposits were present in the deeper portions of the plaque in elongated cells of the plaque capsule and in elongated and ovoid foam cells adjacent to the plaque core. This core was composed of lipid-rich debris and numerous cholesterol clefts. The fibrous cap of the atherosclerotic plaque contained abundant collagen but only a few small elastic fibers. The cells of the capsule had features previously described as those of altered smooth-muscle cells or myointimal cells (Fig. 48-11*A*). These features included a thin elongated shape, a prominent rough-surfaced endoplasmic reticulum, a basement membrane, and numerous pinocytotic vesicles and cytoplasmic filaments. The foam cells adjacent to the core of the plaque (Fig. 48-11*B*) usually had an ovoid shape, lacked basement membranes, had relatively sparse cytoplasmic filaments, generally lacked identifiable features of smooth-muscle cells, and actually resembled histiocytic foam cells found in the cardiac valves and xanthomas. Cellular lipid deposits in plaque cells (Fig. 48-11), medial smooth-muscle cells, and xanthomas occurred predominantly in the form of round, neutral, lipid droplets which showed variable electron density and were not membrane-bound. Some lipid deposits were located in bodies that were lined by trilaminar membranes resembling lysosomes. The membrane-bound lipid included round droplets as well as elongated acicular forms with the appearance of free cholesterol crystals.[70]

The pathologic findings suggest that plaque cells may originate from multiple sources, including smooth-muscle cells, endothelial cells, intimal histiocytes, and circulating monocytes. Recent studies indicate that a significant proportion of cells in human and experimental atherosclerotic plaques have functional characteristics of macrophages.[92] Since lipid-laden foam cells have not been identified in the blood of homozygotes or patients with other conditions predisposing to severe atherosclerosis, it seems likely that macrophages acquire their lipids after the cells have entered the atherosclerotic lesions.

Fig. 48-10 Ascending aorta with atherosclerotic plaque from a 9-year-old girl with homozygous FH. Light micrographs of thin sections from epoxy-embedded tissue *(A* to *C)* and of a frozen section stained with oil-red O *(D)*. *A.* The plaque core adjacent to the media contains abundant extracellular lipid deposits (clear spaces due to lipid extraction during tissue processing). *B.* Some elongated cells of the fibrous capsule of the plaque contain lipid deposits. *C.* Ovoid foam cells adjacent to the plaque core contain numerous lipid vacuoles. *D.* Frozen section stained with oil-red O confirms the presence of neutral lipid in the foam cells. *(Courtesy of Dr. L. Maximilian Buja.)*

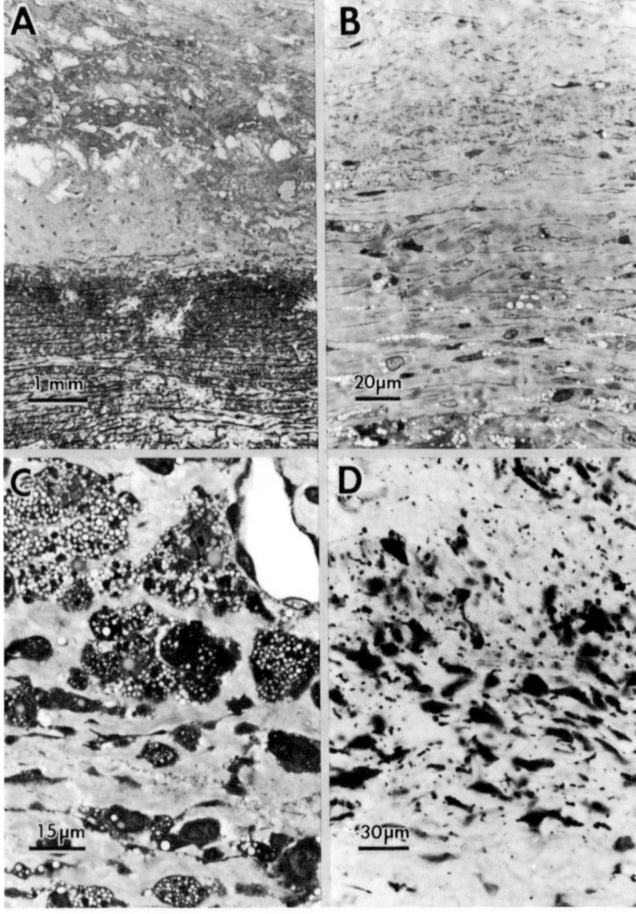

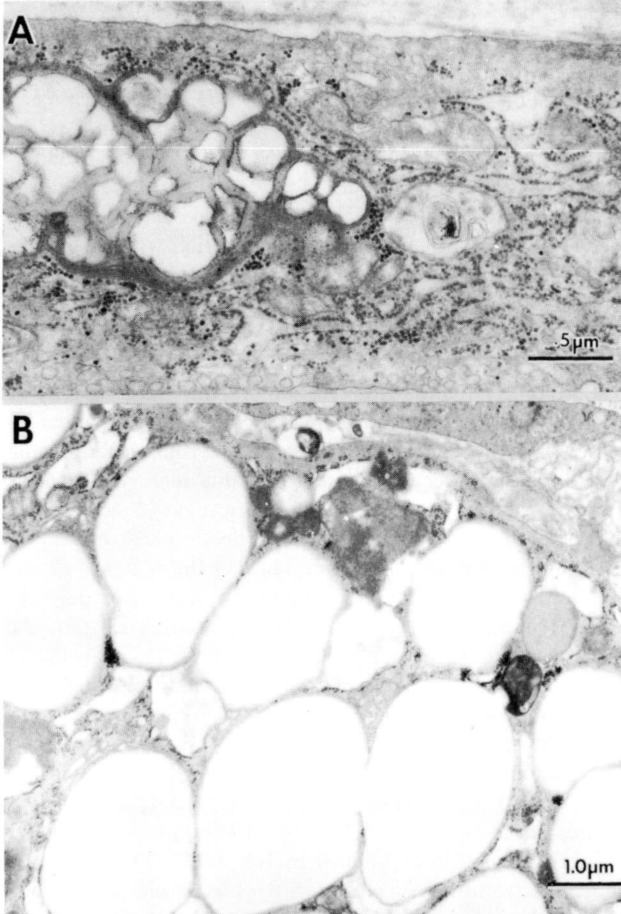

Fig. 48-11 Atherosclerotic plaque from a 9-year-old girl with homozygous FH. *A.* Elongated cell of the plaque capsule exhibits a basement membrane, pinocytotic vesicles, cytoplasmic filaments, rough-surfaced endoplasmic reticulum, and a large inclusion. *B.* Ovoid foam cell contains numerous non-membrane-bound lipid deposits. *(Courtesy of Dr. L. Maximilian Buja.)*

Aortic and Mitral Valve Involvement

Atheromatous involvement of the aortic valve leads to significant aortic stenosis more frequently than aortic regurgitation in FH homozygotes.[52] Significant aortic stenosis was reported in 12 (55 percent) of 21 homozygotes and mitral insufficiency in 2 (9.5 percent).[70] Several homozygotes have undergone successful surgical correction of a severely deformed and atherosclerotic aortic valve,[33,55] and one 7-year-old homozygote had successful replacement of both the aortic and mitral valves.[70] FH homozygotes may also have supravalvular left ventricular outflow tract obstruction, owing to bulky atherosclerotic plaques in the ascending aorta.[70]

Cutaneous and Tendon Xanthomas

Cutaneous xanthomas in FH homozygotes are composed of large numbers of histiocytic foam cells in a fibrovascular stroma (Fig. 48-12). It is noteworthy that endothelial cells of small blood vessels in the lesions are devoid of lipid deposits, suggesting selective lipid accumulation in tissue histiocytes of the xanthomas.[70,93]

Cellular lipid accumulation in homozygotes occurs predominantly in the form of cytoplasmic neutral lipid droplets that lack discrete trilaminar membranes. These findings suggest that the cytoplasm is the major site of intracellular lipid storage in this disease. The production of foam cells in homozygotes has been postulated to result from excessive endocytosis of LDL by an LDL receptor-independent pathway in response to chronic hypercholesterolemia, with subsequent lysosomal processing of the LDL and cytoplasmic reesterification of cholesterol.[94,95]

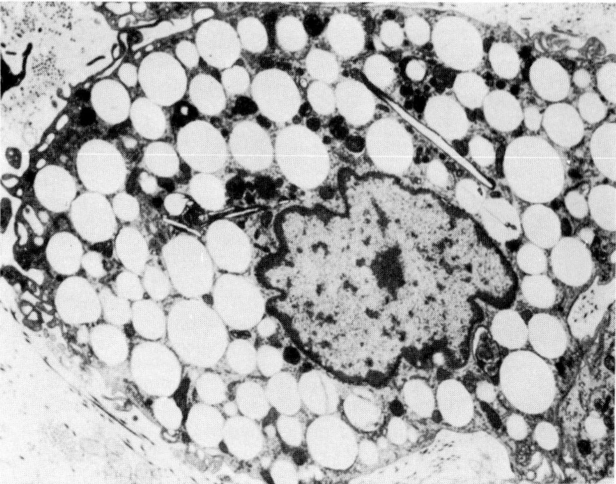

Fig. 48-12 Electron micrograph showing a typical foam cell (scavenger cell) filled with numerous lipid droplets. This mature histiocytic foam cell was observed in a tuberous xanthoma excised from a 17-year-old girl with homozygous FH. *(From Bulkley et al.,[93] by permission of* Archives of Pathology.*)*

The pattern of intracellular lipid deposition in FH patients is distinctly different from that seen in Wolman's disease and cholesteryl ester storage disease. In these two disorders, which are caused by a deficiency in lysosomal cholesteryl ester hydrolase, cholesterol deposits are found within lysosomes of stromal histiocytes as well as parenchymal cells (see Chap. 64).

PATHOGENESIS AT THE CELLULAR LEVEL

LDL Receptor Pathway in Cultured Cells

The genetic defect in FH was unraveled through studies of cholesterol metabolism in human fibroblasts in tissue culture.[3,96] Mammalian cells in tissue culture cannot survive unless they acquire cholesterol, either from a usable exogenous source or as a result of de novo synthesis.[96] The cholesterol is required as a structural component of the plasma membrane of the cell, where it modulates the fluidity of the phospholipid bilayer. Any cholesterol that accumulates within the cell above the amount that can be inserted into the plasma membrane is esterified with a long-chain fatty acid and stored within the cytoplasm as cholesteryl ester droplets.[96]

Sequential Biochemical Steps and Their Ultrastructural Counterparts

When mammalian cells are grown in the presence of animal or human serum, they produce little cholesterol, and preferentially utilize the cholesterol of the LDL that is present in the serum of the culture medium.[96] The key to the uptake process is a cell surface receptor that binds LDL by interacting with

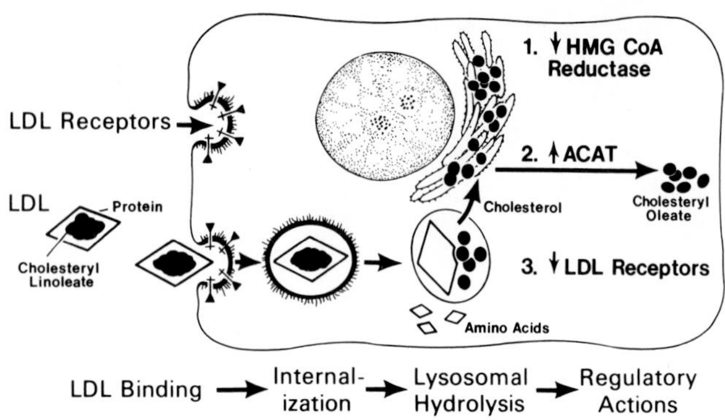

Fig. 48-13 Sequential steps in the LDL receptor pathway in cultured mammalian cells. LDL = low density lipoprotein; HMG CoA reductase = 3-hydroxy-3-methylglutaryl CoA reductase; ACAT = acyl CoA:cholesterol acyltransferase. *(M. S. Brown and J. L. Goldstein,* Proc Natl Acad Sci USA *76:3330, 1979. Used by permission.)*

its apoprotein B-100 component[97] (Fig. 48-13). Human fibroblasts produce a maximum of about 20,000 to 50,000 LDL receptors per cell,[98] the number varying according to cellular cholesterol requirements.[99]

The human LDL receptor is a cell surface glycoprotein of 839 amino acids that contains approximately two asparagine-linked (*N*-linked) oligosaccharide chains of the complex type and approximately 18 serine/threonine-linked (*O*-linked) oligosaccharide chains.[100,101] Two-thirds of the *O*-linked sugars are clustered in one region of the molecule.[102] The LDL receptor binds two proteins: (1) apo B-100, the 514,000-dalton glycoprotein that is the sole protein of LDL[97]; and (2) apo E, a 34,000-dalton protein that is normally found in multiple copies in very low density lipoproteins (VLDL), intermediate density lipoproteins (IDL), and a subclass of HDL.[103,104] Innerarity and Mahley[104] demonstrated that lipoproteins that contain multiple copies of apo E bind to LDL receptors with up to twentyfold higher affinity than LDL, which contains only one copy of apo B-100. The abilities of LDL and apo E-containing lipoproteins to bind to the LDL receptor are abolished when the lysine residues of the lipoproteins are modified by reaction with acetic anhydride[105] or diketene,[106] or when the arginine residues are blocked by reaction with cyclohexanedione.[107] These observations have provided a powerful tool by which to quantify receptor-mediated removal of LDL from human plasma in vivo.

Figure 48-14 illustrates the circuitous itinerary that the LDL receptor follows from its site of synthesis to its site of internalization in coated pits and its site of recycling in endosomes. The receptor is synthesized in the rough endoplasmic reticulum as a precursor[108] that contains high mannose *N*-linked carbohydrate chains and the core sugar (*N*-acetylgalactosamine) of the *O*-linked chains.[101] The *O*-linked core sugars are added before the mannose residues of the *N*-linked chains are trimmed, i.e., while the receptor is still in the endoglycosidase H-sensitive stage. Thus, the *O*-linked sugars must be added either in the endoplasmic reticulum or in a transitional zone between the endoplasmic reticulum and the Golgi complex. The receptor precursor migrates on sodium dodecyl sulfate (SDS) polyacrylamide gel electrophoresis as a single band corresponding to an apparent molecular weight of 120,000.[108]

Within 30 min after its synthesis, the LDL receptor decreases in mobility on SDS gels. The apparent molecular weight increases from 120,000 to 160,000.[108] This change is coincident with the conversion of the high-mannose *N*-linked oligosaccharide chains to the complex endoglycosidase H-resistant form.[101] At the same time, each *O*-linked chain is elon-

Fig. 48-14 Itinerary of the LDL receptor in mammalian cells. The receptor begins life in the endoplasmic reticulum from which it travels to the Golgi complex, cell surface, coated pit, endosome, and back to the surface. HMG CoA reductase = 3-hydroxy-3-methylglutaryl CoA reductase; ACAT = acyl CoA: cholesterol acyltransferase. Vertical arrows indicate the direction of regulatory effects. *(M. S. Brown and J. L. Goldstein,* Curr Top Cell Reg *27:3, 1985. Used by permission.)*

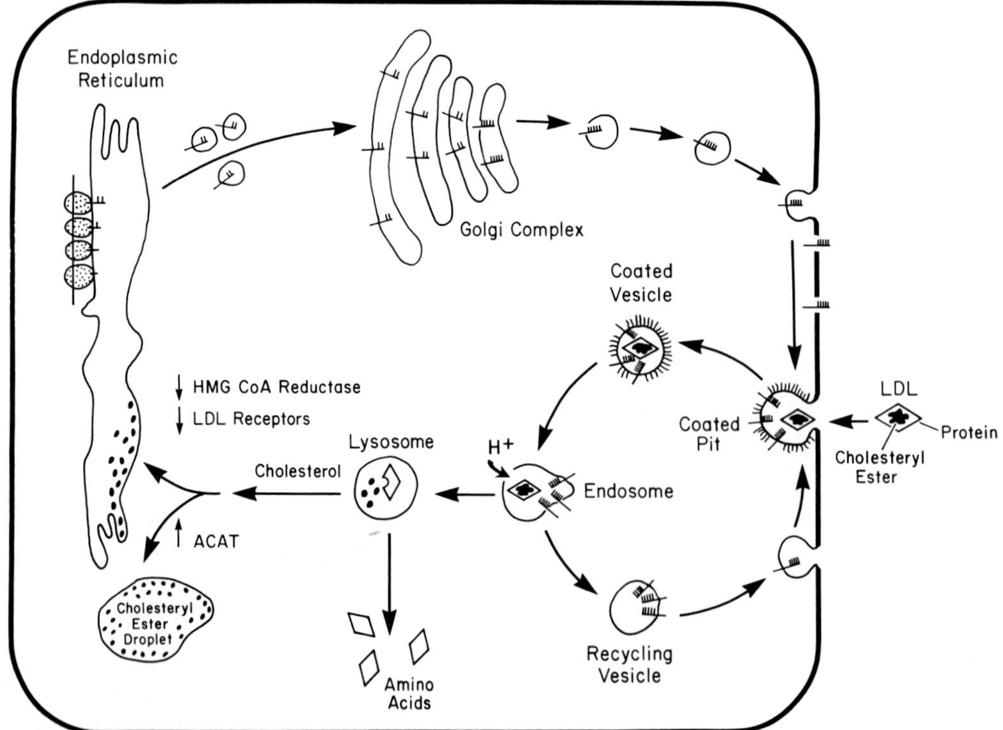

gated by the addition of one galactose and one or two sialic acid residues.[101] The amount of carbohydrate is not sufficient to account for an increase in molecular mass of 40,000 daltons. Rather, the decrease in electrophoretic mobility is primarily caused by a change in conformation of the protein that results from the elongation of the clustered *O*-linked sugars.[101,102]

About 45 min after synthesis, LDL receptors appear on the cell surface, where they gather in coated pits, which are specialized regions of the plasma membrane that are lined on the cytoplasmic surface by a protein called clathrin.[3,109] Within 3 to 5 min of their formation, the coated pits invaginate to form coated endocytic vesicles. Very quickly, the clathrin coat dissociates. Multiple endocytic vesicles then fuse to create larger sacs of irregular contour called endosomes, or receptosomes.[110] The pH of the endosomes falls below 6.5, owing to the operation of ATP-driven proton pumps in the membrane.[111] At this acid pH, the LDL dissociates from the receptor. The latter returns to the surface, apparently by clustering with other receptors in a segment of the endosomal membrane that pinches off to form a recycling vesicle. Once it reaches the surface, the receptor binds another lipoprotein particle and initiates another cycle of endocytosis.[110] Each LDL receptor makes one round-trip every 10 min in continuous fashion whether or not it is occupied with LDL.[112] The LDL that dissociates from the receptor is delivered to a lysosome when the membranes of the endosome and lysosome fuse.

Within the lysosomes the LDL is degraded by acid hydrolytic enzymes. The apoprotein of LDL is hydrolyzed by proteases to amino acids,[25] and the cholesteryl esters are hydrolyzed by a lysosomal acid lipase.[113] The resulting unesterified cholesterol crosses the lysosomal membrane and enters the cellular compartment, where it is used for membrane synthesis and as a regulator of intracellular cholesterol homeostasis[114] (see below).

The localization of LDL receptors in coated pits on the surface of human fibroblasts was demonstrated originally by thin-section electron microscopy with the use of LDL coupled to the iron-containing, electron-dense protein ferritin[115,116] and subsequently by ^{125}I-labeled LDL autoradiography.[117] Figure 48-15 shows the visual sequence of events by which LDL-ferritin is bound, internalized, and delivered to lysosomes in human fibroblasts. The technique of freeze-etching and rotary shadowing has allowed the visualization of native LDL bound to the LDL receptor on the true surface of human fibroblasts. In the freeze-etch micrograph shown in Fig. 48-16, numerous particles of LDL are seen entering the cell through coated pits.

Fig. 48-15 Electron micrographs showing representative stages in the receptor-mediated endocytosis of LDL-ferritin and its subsequent delivery to lysosomes. Normal human fibroblasts were incubated with 47.5 μg protein per milliliter of LDL-ferritin for 2 h at 4°C, washed extensively, and then warmed to 37°C for various times. Scale bar = 1000 Å. *A.* A typical coated pit (time at 37°C, 1 min). × 67,900. *B.* A coated pit being transformed into an endocytic vesicle with LDL-ferritin included (time at 37° C, 1 min). ×56,700. *C.* formation of a coated vesicle. As the plasma membrane begins to fuse to form the vesicle, some of the LDL-ferritin is excluded from the interior and is left on the surface of the cell (arrow) (time at 37°C, 1 min). ×38,150. *D.* a fully formed coated vesicle that appears to be losing its cytoplasmic coat on the right side (time at 37°C, 2 min). ×52,500. *E.* An endocytic vesicle that has completely lost its cytoplasmic coat. Note the irregular shape of this vesicle (time at 37°C, 2 min). ×52,500. *F.* An irregularly shaped endocytic vesicle that contains more LDL-ferritin than a typical coated vesicle and also has a region of increased electron density within the lumen (time at 37°C, 6 min). ×52,500. *G.* An endocytic vesicle similar to *F* with more electron-dense material in the lumen (time at 37°C, 6 min). ×48,300. *H.* A secondary lysosome that contains LDL-ferritin (time at 37°, 8 min). ×52,500 *(From Anderson et al.,[116] by permission of* Cell.*)*

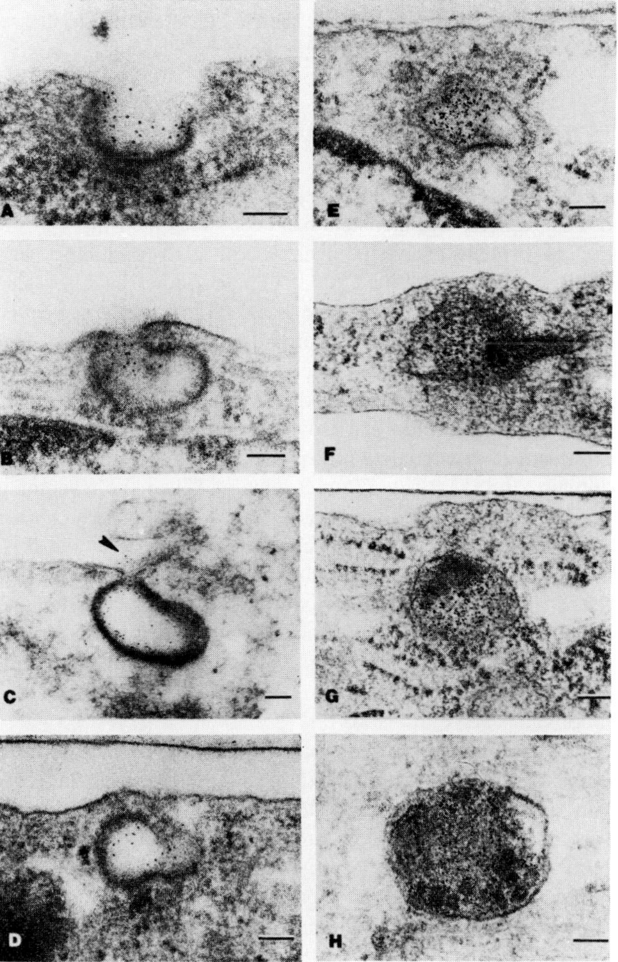

Fig. 48-16 Visualization of LDL bound to receptors on the surface of human fibroblasts. Normal human fibroblasts were incubated with 15 μg protein per milliliter of native LDL at 4°C for 2 h, after which the cells were washed extensively, warmed to 37°C for 3 min, and then fixed with glutaraldehyde. The cells were then processed by the rapid-freezing, replica technique of Heuser (*J Cell Biol* 84:560, 1980). This picture shows the appearance of native LDL bound to LDL receptors that are clustered around coated pits. The arrows point to typical LDL particles. × 112,000. *(Courtesy of Dr. Richard G. W. Anderson.)*

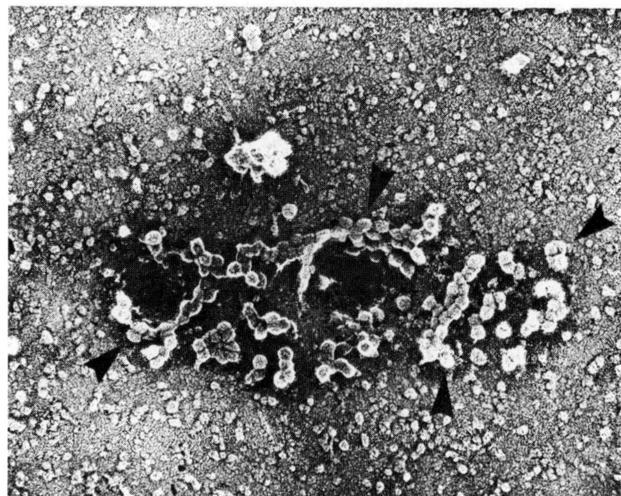

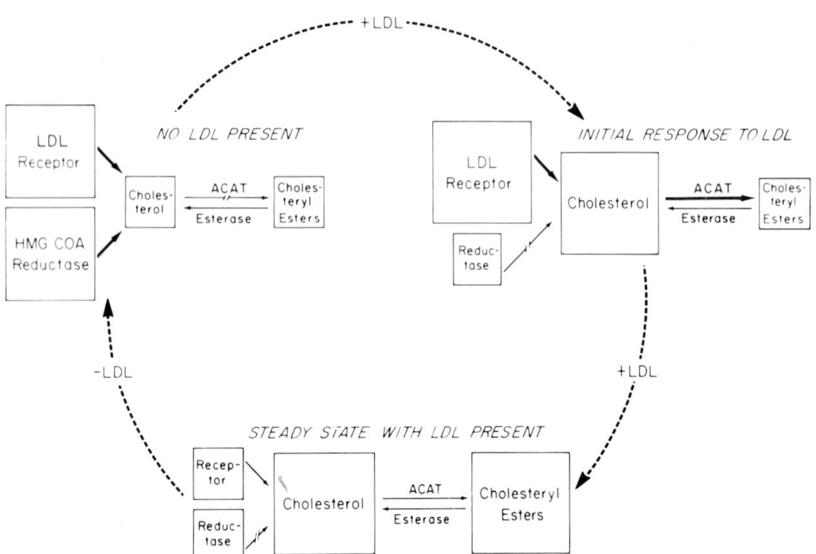

Fig. 48-17 Cyclic changes in cholesterol metabolism that occur in cultured human fibroblasts when LDL is removed from the culture medium (−LDL) and is subsequently returned to the medium (+LDL). The relative level of each constituent is indicated by the size of the square. HMG CoA reductase = 3-hydroxy-3-methylglutaryl coenzyme A reductase; ACAT = acyl CoA:cholesterol acyltransferase. *(M. S. Brown and J. L. Goldstein, Science 191:150, 1976. Used by permission.)*

Regulatory Actions of LDL-Derived Cholesterol

The cholesterol derived from the lysosomal hydrolysis of LDL's cholesteryl esters mediates a sophisticated system of feedback control that stabilizes the intracellular cholesterol concentration.[96] First, this cholesterol suppresses the activity of 3-hydroxy-3-methylglutaryl CoA reductase (HMG-CoA reductase), the rate-controlling enzyme in cholesterol biosynthesis, thereby turning off cholesterol synthesis in the cell.[118] Second, the cholesterol activates a cholesterol-esterifying enzyme called acyl CoA:cholesterol acyltransferase (ACAT) so that excess cholesterol can be stored as cholesteryl esters.[119] Third, the cholesterol turns off the synthesis of the LDL receptor, preventing further entry of LDL and thereby protecting cells against an overaccumulation of cholesterol[99] (Fig. 48-13).

The overall effect of this regulatory system is to coordinate the intracellular and extracellular sources of cholesterol so as to maintain a constant level of cholesterol within the cell in the face of fluctuations in the supply of lipoproteins. Human fibroblasts and other mammalian cells grow in the absence of lipoproteins because they can synthesize cholesterol from acetyl CoA. When LDL is available, cells preferentially use the receptor to take up LDL and keep their own cholesterol synthesis suppressed.[96,99]

Figure 48-17 summarizes the pattern of regulation of the LDL pathway in cultured human fibroblasts. When the cells are grown in the presence of normal plasma containing LDL, they establish a steady state in which HMG-CoA reductase activity (and hence cholesterol synthesis) is low and the cells derive the small amounts of cholesterol that they need by means of a small number of LDL receptors. Under these conditions, the activity of ACAT is held at an intermediate level so that the rate of synthesis of cholesteryl esters equals their rate of hydrolysis (Fig. 48-17, "steady state with LDL present"). The delicate balance inherent in this regulated steady state is disclosed when LDL is removed from the culture medium (Fig. 48-17, "no LDL present"). Under these conditions, the number of LDL receptors and the activity of HMG-CoA reductase greatly increase, while cholesterol esterifying activity declines. Since LDL is absent from the culture medium, the LDL receptors are not able to supply the cell with cholesterol and hence the cholesterol required for membrane formation is derived both from accelerated *de novo* synthesis and from a net hydrolysis of cholesteryl esters stored within the cell. When LDL is added back to the culture medium (Fig. 48-17, "initial response to LDL"), the lipoprotein is bound at the receptor site, internalized, and degraded to yield free cholesterol. The liberated sterol, in turn, suppresses *de novo* cholesterol synthesis and stimulates the esterifying system so that excess cholesterol can be reesterified and stored as cholesteryl esters. When sufficient cellular cholesterol has accumulated, the number of LDL receptors becomes suppressed and the cells return to their original steady state (Fig. 48-17, "steady state with LDL present"), thus completing a metabolic cycle. This "steady state with LDL present" duplicates the condition of most cells in the body.[3,120,121]

LDL Receptor Protein

The structure of the LDL receptor from four species (human, bovine, rabbit, and hamster) has been elucidated through the use of protein chemistry techniques, cDNA cloning, and DNA sequence analysis.[100,122–124] These studies have revealed that the mature LDL receptor is an evolutionarily conserved integral membrane protein consisting of five domains (Fig. 48-18). In order of appearance from the NH_2 terminus these domains are: (1) a ligand binding domain, (2) a domain homologous to the epidermal growth factor (EGF) precursor, (3) a domain of clustered *O*-linked sugars, (4) a transmembrane domain, and (5) a cytoplasmic domain. When the receptor is initially synthesized, it contains a sixth domain, which consists of a hydrophobic 21 amino acid signal sequence at the NH_2 terminus. This domain is removed proteolytically during synthesis in the endoplasmic reticulum. Functional roles for several of the receptor domains have been assigned by comparing the structure of the LDL receptor to other membrane proteins and by the analysis of natural and artificially constructed mutations.[124]

The *first domain* of the mature receptor, the ligand binding domain, mediates the interaction with lipoproteins that contain apo B-100 or apo E. We have postulated that the binding function is subserved by a stretch of 292 amino acids at the NH_2 terminus of the mature protein. This domain is composed of seven repeats of approximately 40 amino acids that are arranged in a head-to-tail array.[123] Each repeat contains six cysteine residues that are postulated to form three intrarepeat

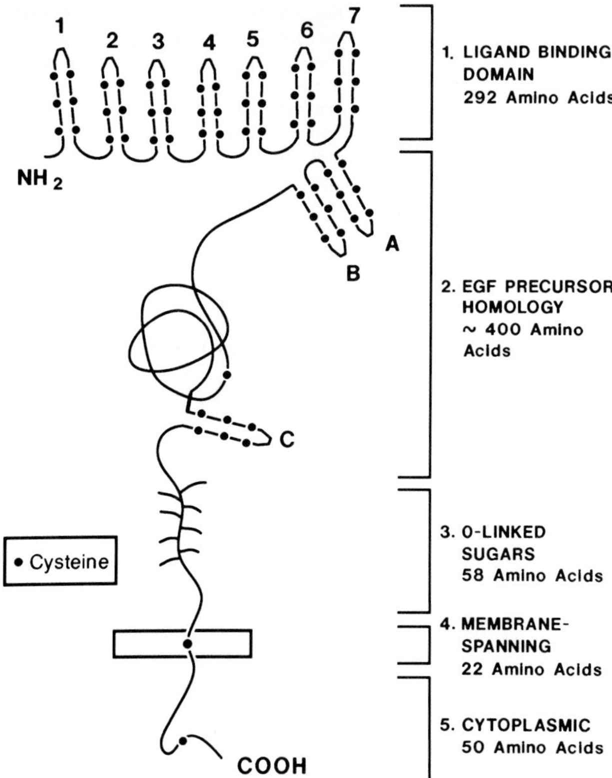

Fig. 48-18 The mature human LDL receptor: a single protein with five domains. The structure and function of each domain is discussed in the text.

disulfide bonds. Each repeat contains a cluster of negatively charged amino acids at the COOH terminal end. The center of each repeat is relatively hydrophobic, and it seems likely that many of the disulfide-bonded cysteines are buried in these hydrophobic pockets, which are flanked by polar residues. Such a conformation presumably allows the negatively charged residues to appear at the surface of the receptor where they bind to a cluster of positively charged amino acids on apo E[125] or apo B-100.[126]

The *second domain* of the LDL receptor consists of a stretch of approximately 400 amino acids whose most striking feature is a strong degree of sequence identity to the EGF precursor.[127,128] In this homologous region, approximately 35 percent of the amino acids are held in common by the two proteins. This domain is required for the acid-dependent dissociation of receptor from ligand that occurs in the endosome during receptor recycling.[128a] It also serves to position the ligand binding domain in such a way that it can bind LDL on the cell surface. This domain is not required for the binding of apo E-containing lipoproteins, such as β-VLDL.[128a]

The *third domain* consists of a sequence of 58 amino acids that is enriched in serine and threonine residues. This domain contains clustered O-linked sugar chains that retard the movement of the LDL receptor upon SDS polyacrylamide gel electrophoresis.[102,127] The function of these *O*-linked sugars is at present not known. This region of the protein can be deleted without adverse effects on receptor function in cultured fibroblasts.[102] In addition to the clustered *O*-linked sugars, the LDL receptor contains a few scattered *O*-linked sugar chains that are located in different parts of the molecule. Their precise location in the molecule is as yet unknown, but they may play a role in stabilizing the receptor.[102,128b]

The *fourth domain* of the LDL receptor consists of 22 to 25 hydrophobic amino acids that span the membrane, thus anchoring the protein. The deletion of this region in certain naturally occurring mutations results in the secretion of LDL receptors from the cell.[129] A comparison of membrane-spanning domains from LDL receptors of four different species reveals the maintenance of a hydrophobic character, but little actual sequence conservation.[124,130] Thus, it is unlikely that the transmembrane segment has a specific function, such as transducing a signal across the plasma membrane (after ligand binding) or serving as an ion channel. These conclusions are consistent with the finding that the LDL receptor recycles constitutively in the absence of ligand[110] and thus does not require that a signal be transduced to the cytoplasmic domain in order for internalization to occur.

The *fifth domain* of the LDL receptor is found at the extreme COOH terminus of the molecule and consists of 50 amino acids that are located on the cytoplasmic side of the plasma membrane.[122,127] The analysis of naturally occurring and artificial mutations has revealed that this domain targets the LDL receptor to coated pits in the plasma membrane.[131–133]

Human LDL Receptor Gene

The human LDL receptor locus spans approximately 45 kb of DNA[123] on the distal short arm (bands p13.1 to p13.3) of chromosome 19.[78] The gene is divided into 18 exons and 17 introns[123] (Fig. 48-19). There is a strong correlation between structural domains in the protein and exon sequences in the gene. The signal sequence is precisely encoded by the first exon, and most of the repeat units in the ligand binding domain are encoded by discrete exons. The EGF precursor domain is specified by eight exons that are distributed similarly in the LDL receptor and the EGF precursor genes.[128] The *O*-linked sugar domain is encoded by a discrete exon, and the membrane-spanning and cytoplasmic domains are each encoded by two exons. The most 3′ exon encodes the 12 amino acids at the COOH-terminus plus a long 3′ untranslated re-

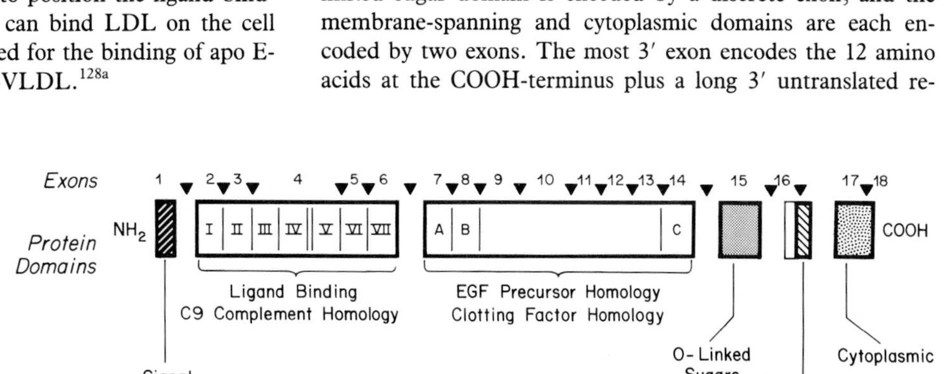

Fig. 48-19 Correlation of exons in the LDL receptor gene and domains in the protein. The five domains of the mature LDL receptor plus the signal sequence are drawn to scale. The positions at which introns interrupt the coding sequences of the LDL receptor gene are indicated by the arrowheads. Exons are numbered above the drawing. Regions of the protein that are homologous with other proteins are indicated. *(From Südhof et al.,[123] by permission of* Science.*)*

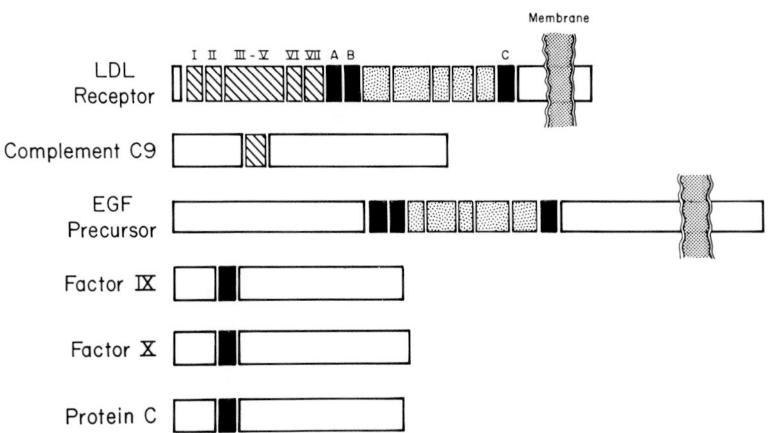

Fig. 48-20 Exon shuffling in the LDL receptor. The human LDL receptor is shown at the top. Exons that encode sequences shared with other proteins are indicated by the small blocks. Roman numerals I through VII indicate the seven repeats in the ligand binding domain. Hatched blocks represent exons encoding these repeats, one of which is found in complement component C9. Capital letters (A to C) and black boxes indicate three repeats encoded by discrete exons in the EGF precursor homology domain. One or more copies of these repeats are found in the EGF precursor, factor IX, factor X, and protein C genes. The speckled boxes indicate exons that are shared only by the LDL receptor and the EGF precursor genes. The positions of the membrane-spanning regions of the LDL receptor and EGF precursor are shown. The other proteins are secreted and have no membranous component. *(From Russell et al.,[144] by permission of* The Cold Spring Harbor Symposium on Quantitative Biology.*)*

gion (2.5 kb) that includes several repetitive *Alu* elements.[122]

The LDL receptor gene is a mosaic of coding sequences shared with several other proteins (Fig. 48-20). Parts of the EGF homology region are also found in three plasma proteases involved in blood clotting (factor IX, factor X, and protein C). The 40-amino acid cysteine-rich repeat unit of the LDL binding domain is found in complement component C9.[123,134] In each of these proteins, the shared sequences are encoded by discrete exons (Fig. 48-20). These findings support the exon shuffling hypothesis of Gilbert[135] and indicate that the LDL receptor is a member of at least two supergene families, one containing the segments encoding the EGF precursor region and the other containing the segment shared with complement component C9.[123,136]

BIOCHEMICAL GENETICS OF LDL RECEPTOR MUTATIONS

One Locus with Multiple Mutant Alleles

Fibroblasts from 128 patients with the classic clinical syndrome of homozygous FH have been studied in our laboratory. Each shows evidence of two mutant alleles at the LDL receptor locus, but not all defects are the same. There are at least 18 different mutations (Table 48-5) that fall into four broad classes (Fig. 48-21). Many of the apparent FH homozygotes are actually compound heterozygotes who inherit a different mutant receptor allele from each parent.

Class 1 mutations, the most prevalent class, fail to produce immunoprecipitable proteins (null alleles). More than half of the 128 fibroblast strains examined harbor at least one null allele. *Class 2 mutations* encode proteins blocked in transport between the endoplasmic reticulum and the Golgi complex. About one-half of the 128 fibroblast strains harbor at least one allele specifying a transport-deficient LDL receptor. *Class 3 mutations* encode proteins that are synthesized and transported to the cell surface but fail to bind LDL normally. This is an extremely heterogeneous group; affected individuals from different families show widely varying levels of LDL binding activity that range from 2 to 30 percent of normal. *Class 4 mutations,* although the rarest, have been most revealing with respect to the mechanisms of receptor-mediated endocytosis.

Fig. 48-21 Four classes of mutations at the LDL receptor locus. These mutations disrupt synthesis, transport, binding, and clustering of the LDL receptor. See text for a detailed description of specific mutant alleles in each class. *(J. L. Goldstein and M. S. Brown,* J Lipid Res *25:1450, 1984.* Used by permission.*)*

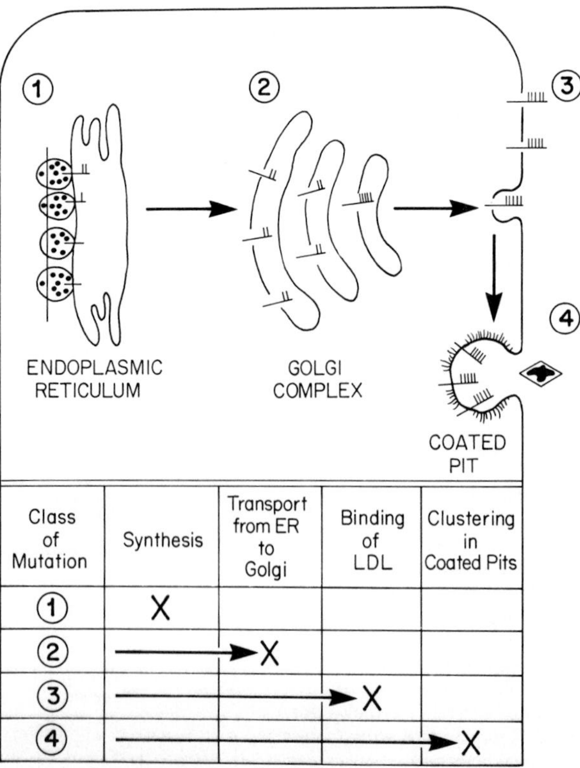

Class of Mutation	Synthesis	Transport from ER to Golgi	Binding of LDL	Clustering in Coated Pits
1	X			
2	——→	X		
3	———	——→	X	
4	———	———	——→	X

Table 48-5 Mutations at the LDL Receptor Locus that Produce FH

	Apparent M_r of receptor on SDS gels, kDa		Location of receptor					Known molecular lesion			
				Plasma membrane							
Class of mutation	*Precursor*	*Mature*	*Intra-cellular*	*Coated pits*	*Noncoated regions*	*Extra-cellular*	*LDL binding to intact cells*	*Type*	*Size*	*Location*	*Frequency among FH patients*
Class 1	None	None					None	Deletion	>10 kb*	5′ UT–intron 1*	Common in French-Canadians
Null alleles	None	None					None	Deletion	5 kb	Exon 13–intron 15	Rare
	None	None					None	Nondeletion	‡	‡	Common
Class 2	100	100	+				None	Nonsense	1 bp*	Exon 14	Common in Lebanese
Transport-defective	120	120	+				None	‡	‡	‡	Common
alleles	135	135	+				None	‡	‡	‡	Rare
	120	(160)†	+	(+)†			Reduced	Deletion	3 bp	Exon 4	Rare
	120	(160)	+	(+)			Reduced	Deletion	12 bp	Exon 4	WHHL rabbits
	120	(160)	+	(+)			Reduced	‡	‡	‡	Common in Afrikaaners
Class 3	100	140		+			None	Deletion	0.8 kb	Exon 5	Rare
Binding-defective	100	140		+			None	Deletion	4 kb	Intron 6–intron 8	Rare
alleles	120	160		+			Reduced	‡	‡	‡	Common
	170	210		+			Reduced	Duplication	14 kb	Intron 1–intron 8	Rare
Class 4	110	150			(+)†	+		Deletion	5.5 kb	Intron 15–exon 18	Rare
Internalization-	110	150			(+)	+	Normal	Deletion	7.8 kb	Intron 15–exon 18	Rare
defective alleles	120	160			+		binding;	Nonsense	1 bp	Exon 17	Rare
	120	160			+		defective	Insertion	4 bp	Exon 17	Rare
	120	160			+		internaliza-tion	Missense	1 bp	Exon 17	Rare

*kb = kilobases; bp = base pairs; 5′ UT = 5′ untranslated region.
†Symbols in parentheses refer to minor populations of receptor.
‡Details of molecular lesion not known.

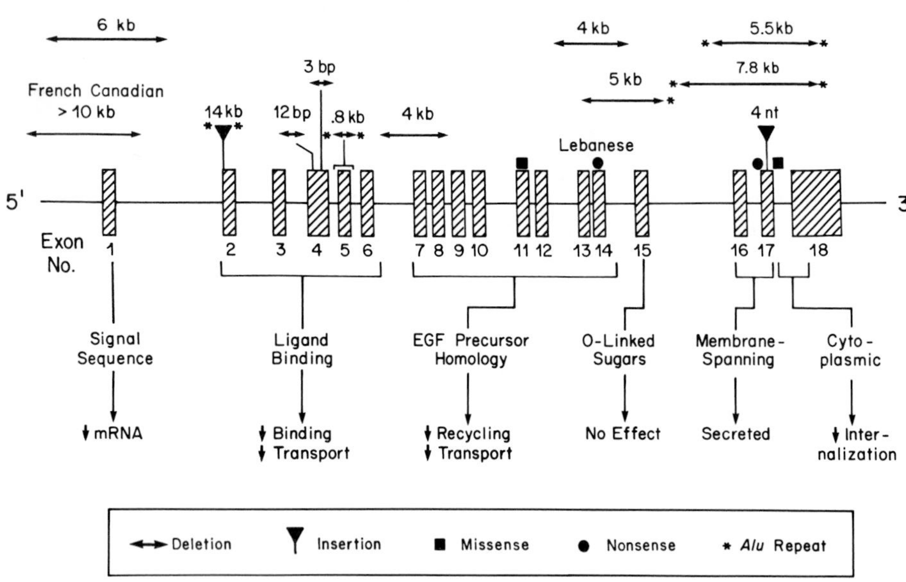

Fig. 48-22 Mutations in the LDL receptor gene. Exons, shown as hatched boxes, are separated by introns, which are drawn to approximate scale. Mutations that have been mapped or cloned are indicated above and below the gene. The mutations are: deletion of >10 kb (French-Canadian allele in FH 49, 549, 808, 859), deletion of 6 kb (FH 26), 14 kb duplication (insertion) in intron 1 (FH 295), 12-bp deletion in exon 4 (WHHL rabbit), 3-bp deletion in exon 4 (FH 563), missense mutation in exon 11 (FH 429), nonsense mutation in exon 14 (Lebanese allele in FH 264, 550, 786, 793), nonsense mutation in exon 17 (FH 683), 4-bp insertion in exon 17 (FH 763), missense mutation in exon 17 (FH 380), deletion of 0.8 kb (FH 626), deletion of 4 kb involving exons 7 and 8 (FH 359 and FH 454), deletion of 4 kb involving exons 13 and 14 (FH 651), deletion of 5 kb (FH 381), deletion of 7.8 kb (FH 781), and deletion of 5.5 kb (FH 274). See text for further details and references.

These alleles encode proteins that are efficiently synthesized and transported to the cell surface. These receptors bind LDL normally, but their ability to cluster in coated pits is deficient and thus they do not internalize bound LDL.

At least one mutant gene from each of the four classes has been characterized at the molecular level. The defects include insertion, deletion, nonsense, and missense mutations (Fig. 48-22).

Class 1 Mutations: Null Alleles. Of the 132 FH homozygotes whose fibroblasts have been studied (264 alleles), 16 (12 percent) have no immunoprecipitable LDL receptor and thus have two null alleles.[137] Twelve of the thirty-two null alleles are large deletions as determined from genomic Southern blots. Ten of these twelve deletions occur in homozygous form in five patients from different families, one Italian and four French-Canadian. The four French-Canadian FH homozygotes all have the same deletion (>10 kb) that removes the promoter and first exon of the receptor gene (Fig. 48-22). The high frequency of this null allele in French-Canadians is most likely explained by a founder effect.[137a]

Another null allele results from a 5-kb deletion that removes exons 13 through 15 (Fig. 48-22).[138] This mutation, FH 381, arose from recombination between a repetitive *Alu* sequence and a coding sequence in an exon that by chance is complementary to the *Alu* sequence (Fig. 48-23). This allele produces a truncated mRNA, but no immunoprecipitable protein can be detected. This mutation therefore represents an example of a null allele in which mRNA is produced.

Other individuals with the null phenotype do not have a gross deletion in the receptor gene. In some cases they produce nearly normal amounts of a normal-size mRNA, but no immunoprecipitable receptor is produced. These null alleles may represent nonsense mutations or other more complex abnormalities.

Fibroblasts from FH homozygotes who inherit two copies of a class 1 mutation exhibit less than 2 percent of the normal amount of high affinity ^{125}I-LDL binding, which is the lowest

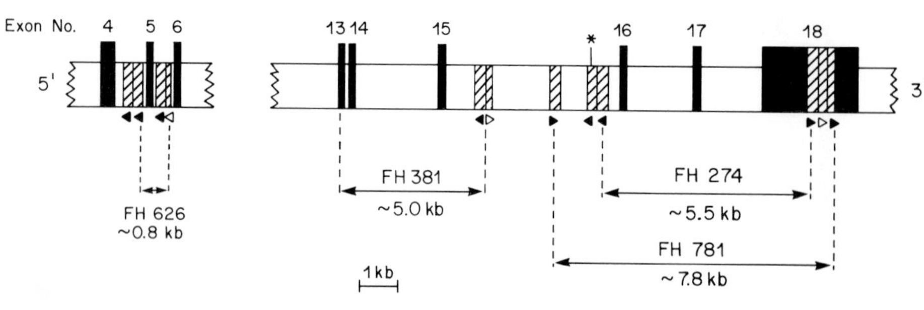

Fig. 48-23 Deletions in the LDL receptor gene that involve *Alu* repeats. Exons 4 to 6 and 13 to 18 are indicated by raised black boxes, separated by introns. Known *Alu* sequences are indicated by the hatched regions. The orientation of a given *Alu* repeat is indicated by the arrowhead below the gene map. Closed arrowheads indicate complete *Alu* elements (≈ 300 bp); open arrowheads indicate incomplete *Alu* sequences. The *Alu* sequence marked with an asterisk above the map contains a frequent PvuII polymorphism. The extent and location of deletions discussed in the text are indicated below the gene. *(From Lehrman et al.,[149] by permission of The Journal of Biological Chemistry.)*

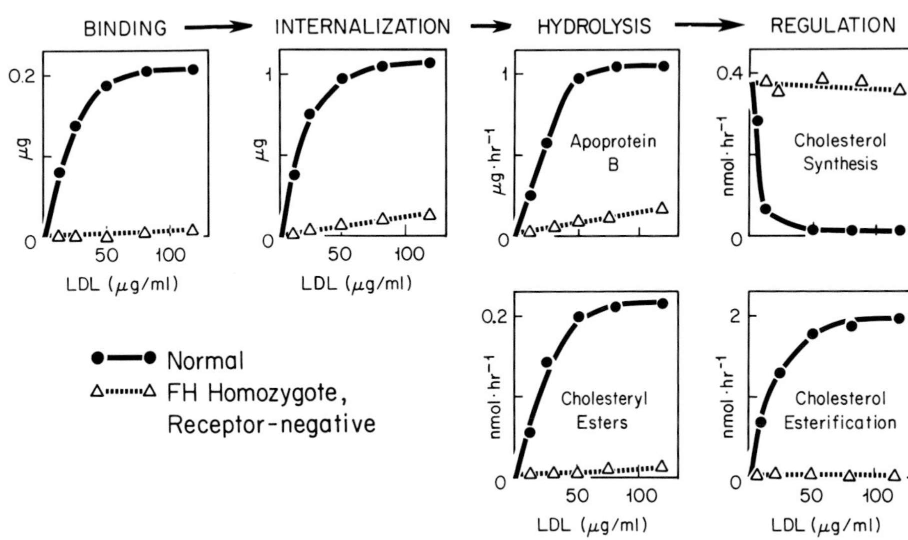

Fig. 48-24 Actions attributable to the LDL receptor in fibroblasts from a normal subject (●) and from a homozygote with the receptor-negative form of FH (Δ) incubated with varying concentrations of ^{125}I-LDL or unlabeled LDL at 37°C for 5 h. Assays were performed in growing cells in monolayers.[182] All data are normalized to 1 mg of total cell protein. The units for each assay are as follows: *binding*, μg of ^{125}I-LDL bound to cell surface; *internalization*, μg of ^{125}I-LDL contained within the cell; *hydrolysis of apoprotein B-100*, μg of ^{125}I-LDL degraded to ^{125}I-monoiodotyrosine per h; *hydrolysis of cholesteryl esters*, nmol of [^{3}H]cholesterol formed per h from the hydrolysis of LDL labeled with [^{3}H]cholesteryl linoleate; *cholesterol synthesis*, nmol of [^{14}C]acetate incorporated into [^{14}C]cholesterol per h by intact cells; *cholesterol esterification*, nmol of [^{14}C]oleate incorporated into cholesteryl [^{14}C]oleate per h by intact cells. *(M. S. Brown and J. L. Goldstein, Proc Natl Acad Sci USA 76:3330, 1979. Used by permission.)*

amount that can be reliably detected. In these cells LDL does not suppress HMG CoA reductase activity or cholesterol synthesis, nor does it activate cholesteryl ester formation.[3] Figure 48-24 shows the striking biochemical differences in these LDL-mediated processes in fibroblasts derived from a normal subject and from a homozygote with two null alleles. Ultrastructural studies using ferritin-labeled LDL have confirmed the absence of LDL receptors in these receptor-negative cells.[115]

Class 2 Mutations: Transport-Deficient Alleles. The molecular basis of three mutations that encode LDL receptors that accumulate in the endoplasmic reticulum have been described.[130,139] Two of the mutations[130] consist of small in-frame deletions (12 bp and 3 bp) in exon 4, which encodes three repeats of the ligand binding domain (Fig. 48-22). One of these was identified in the Watanabe heritable hyperlipidemic (WHHL) rabbit, an animal model of FH. The mutation removes four amino acids (Asp-Gly-Ser-Asp) from the third repeat in the binding domain. Another class 2 mutation was characterized initially by S1 nuclease mapping of the LDL receptor mRNA in fibroblasts from an FH patient (FH 563).[130] More recent studies by DNA sequence analysis show a deletion of 3 bp (and hence 1 amino acid) in the fifth binding repeat.

A third class 2 mutation, termed the Lebanese allele, was found in four unrelated Arab patients, three from Lebanon and one from Syria.[139] This mutation produces a truncated receptor lacking the last three domains: the region of clustered *O*-linked carbohydrates, the membrane-spanning region, and the cytoplasmic tail. The molecular defect results from a single nucleotide substitution that creates a premature termination codon at amino acid position 660, eliminating 180 residues from the mature protein. The truncated protein retains only two domains: a complete ligand binding region (residues 1 to 292) and a partial EGF precursor homology region (residues 293 to 659). The termination codon occurs in the middle of a cysteine-rich sequence that is part of the EGF precursor homology domain. Despite relatively large amounts of mRNA in affected fibroblasts the mutant protein is markedly reduced in amount, suggesting impaired translation. After synthesis, the receptors remain within the endoplasmic reticulum for several hours. The receptor does not move to the cell surface, and it is eventually degraded.

The Lebanese mutation creates a new restriction site for the enzyme *HinfI*, thus permitting diagnosis by Southern blotting of genomic DNA.[139] Two copies of this mutant gene were present in each of four unrelated Arab FH homozygotes.[139] Homozygosity for this allele has subsequently been detected in one more Lebanese homozygote, and the allele is present in two Lebanese heterozygotes living in the United States.[72] We believe that the Lebanese allele is responsible for the extraordinarily high incidence of FH in Lebanon.[21,83]

How do the alterations brought about by the above class 2 mutations disrupt the transport of the LDL receptor to the cell surface? All three mutations would be expected to distort the receptor in such a way that some of the cysteines can no longer form disulfide bonds, precluding proper folding of the protein. Animal cells seem to have a mechanism that prevents improperly folded proteins from reaching the cell surface. Such an improperly folded protein might bind to a hypothetical "gatekeeper" protein whose function is to prevent the transport of improperly folded proteins to the cell surface.[130,139,140]

Class 3 Mutations: Binding-Deficient Alleles. Three mutations of this class have been analyzed at the molecular level. One mutation, FH 626, was brought about by unequal crossings over between repetitive *Alu* sequences in introns 4 and 5, which deleted a segment of 0.8 kb that includes exon 5 (Figs. 43-22 and 43-23).[141] In the resultant mRNA, exon 4 is spliced to exon 6, preserving the reading frame. This mRNA produces a shortened protein that lacks the sixth repeat in the ligand binding domain. The receptor reaches the cell surface and reacts with antireceptor antibodies[142] but does not bind LDL, which contains apo B-100 as its major protein component.[141] Surprisingly, the deleted protein retains the ability to bind and internalize another lipoprotein called β-migrating very low density lipoprotein (β-VLDL).[141] This lipoprotein binds to the LDL receptor with higher affinity than LDL because it contains multiple copies of apo E, a high affinity ligand for the receptor.[143] The loss of LDL binding in this mutant is consistent with the hypothesis that the seven repeated sequences constitute the LDL binding domain. The data further indicate that the sixth repeat is required for binding of LDL, but not β-VLDL, and that deletion of a single cysteine-rich repeat can alter the binding specificity of the receptor.

A similar phenotype is manifest in two siblings with homozygous FH (FH 359 and FH 454) in which a deletion of 4 kb removed exons 7 and 8 from the LDL receptor gene (Fig. 43-22).[144] Exons 7 and 8 normally encode the cysteine-rich A and B repeats of the EGF precursor homology domain (Fig. 48-19). In the FH 359 and FH 454 mRNA, exon 6 is apparently spliced directly to exon 9, again preserving the reading frame. The resulting truncated protein is transported to the cell surface normally but does not bind LDL. It does, however, retain the ability to bind β-VLDL. These data suggest that the A and B repeats of the EGF precursor region play some role in the binding of LDL, as discussed earlier.[128a]

Although the FH 626, FH 359, and FH 454 receptors have deletions that involve cysteine-rich domains, they are not blocked in transport to the cell surface. This is in contrast to the WHHL rabbit, FH 563, and patients with the Lebanese mutation in which removal of part of a cysteine-rich repeat blocks transport. These data suggest that each cysteine-rich repeat folds independently. When one entire repeat is deleted as in class 3 mutations, there are no unpaired cysteines. When part of a repeat is deleted as in class 2 mutations, the remaining portion of the repeat contains improperly folded regions with unpaired cysteines and this accounts for the block in transport.

A third class 3 mutation was characterized in a FH homozygote (FH 295) whose fibroblasts produce a receptor precursor that is 50,000 daltons larger than normal (apparent M_r 170,000 versus 120,000).[108] The elongated protein resulted from a 14-kb duplication that encompasses exons 2 through 8 (Fig. 48-25).[145] The duplication arose from an unequal crossing-over between homologous repetitive elements (*Alu* sequences) in intron 1 and intron 8. The mutant receptor has 18 contiguous cysteine-rich repeat sequences instead of the normal nine. Seven of these duplicated repeats are derived from the ligand binding domain, and two repeats are part of the EGF precursor homology region (repeats A and B) (Fig. 48-19). The elongated receptor undergoes normal carbohydrate processing, its apparent molecular weight increases to 210,000, and the receptor reaches the cell surface where it binds reduced amounts of LDL but undergoes efficient internalization and recycling.[108,145]

Class 4 Mutations: Internalization-Defective Alleles. The discovery of an internalization-defective allele in 1976 led to the hypothesis that a defect in the (then hypothetical) cytoplasmic domain of the receptor might impair targeting of the receptor to the coated pit.[146–148] To date, we have cloned and sequenced five different internalization-defective alleles at the LDL receptor locus, and all these have alterations that affect the cytoplasmic domain.[129,131–133,149]

The molecular analysis of the internalization defects has resulted in a subclassification of internalization-defective mutations. The first subclass includes three mutations that alter only the cytoplasmic domain (Figs. 48-22 and 48-26). One of these (FH 683) is a truncation of the cytoplasmic domain

Fig. 48-25 Unequal crossing-over between two repetitive *Alu* elements in an LDL receptor gene from an FH homozygote. Two copies of the normal receptor gene, one with exons indicated by bold rectangles and the other with exons indicated by light circles, are aligned to illustrate the point of unequal crossing-over in FH 295. The crossing-over involved *Alu* elements in both genes that paired with each other. The recombination event is predicted to yield one gene with two copies of exons 2 to 8 and a hypothetical gene in which exons 2 to 8 are deleted. The exons are denoted by numbered boxes; exons and introns are not drawn to scale. (*Redrawn from Lehrman et al.,[145] by permission of* Cell.)

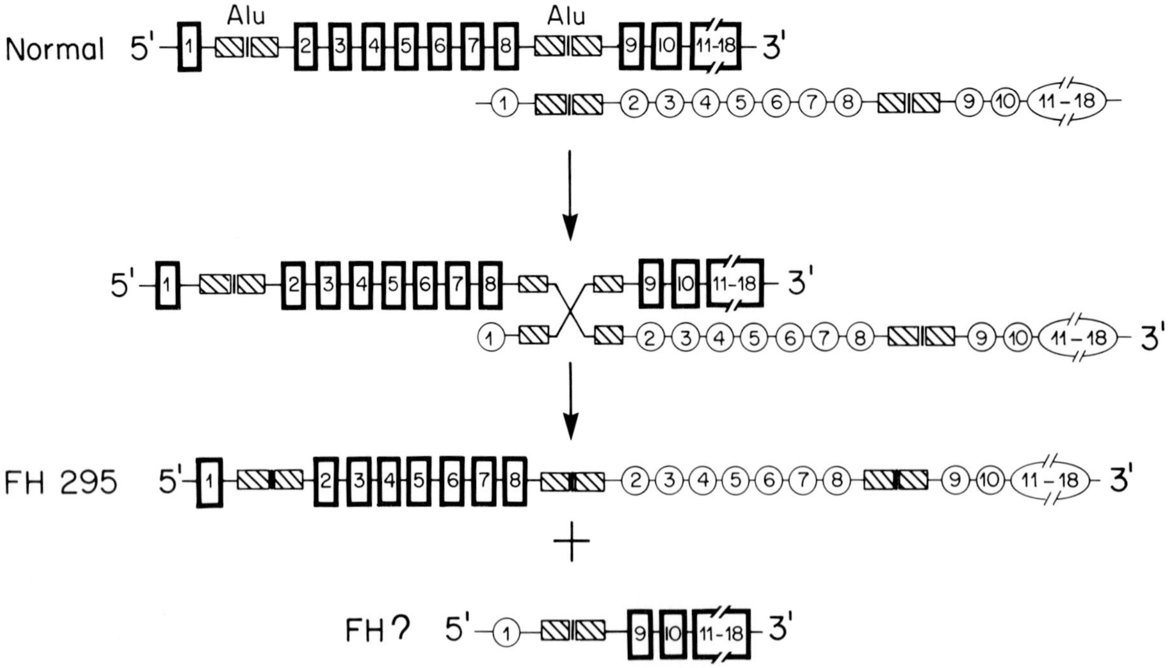

Alu Alu
Normal 5' 1 2 3 4 5 6 7 8 9 10 11-18 3'
1 2 3 4 5 6 7 8 9 10 11-18

5' 1 2 3 4 5 6 7 8 9 10 11-18 3'
1 2 3 4 5 6 7 8 9 10 11-18 3'

FH 295 5' 1 2 3 4 5 6 7 8 2 3 4 5 6 7 8 9 10 11-18 3'
+
FH? 5' 1 9 10 11-18 3'

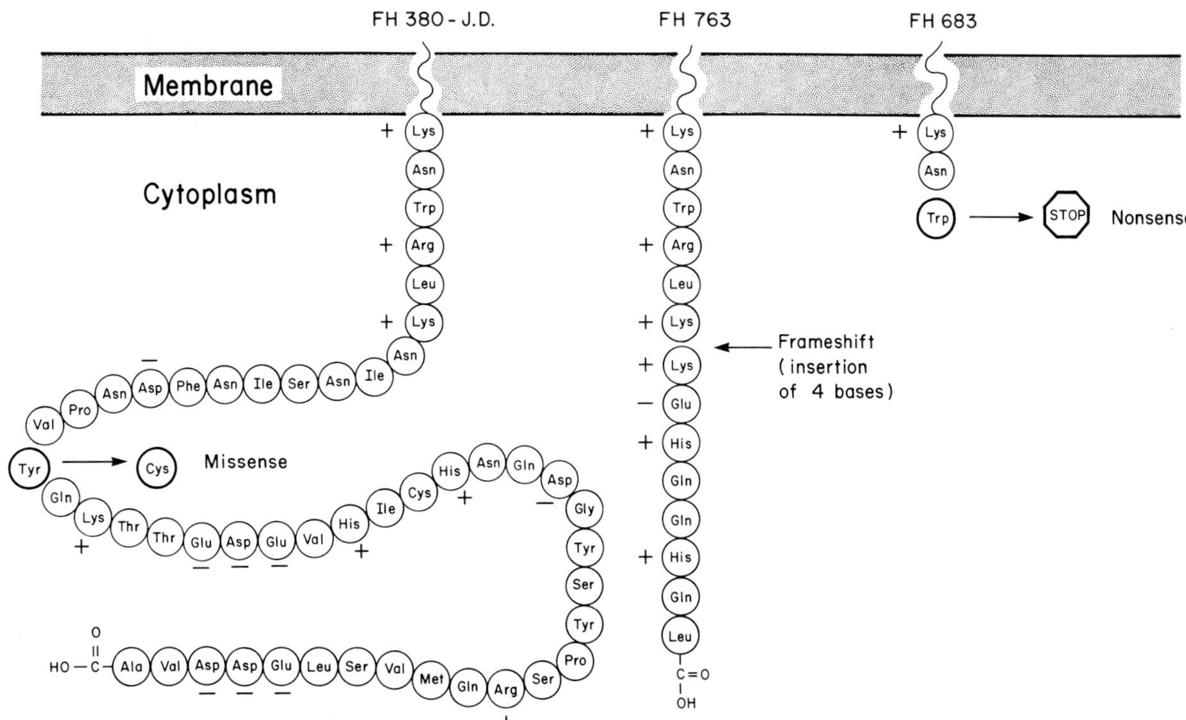

Fig. 48-26 Mutations affecting the cytoplasmic domain of the LDL receptor in three FH homozygotes with the internalization-defective form of FH. *(From Brown and Goldstein,[3] by permission of Science.)*

caused by a nonsense mutation at amino acid 792, thus leaving only two of the normal 50 amino acids in the cytoplasmic domain (Fig. 48-26). This mutation results in an almost complete block in the internalization of receptor-bound LDL.[131–133] A second mutation (FH 763) results from a duplication of four base pairs in exon 17 (Fig. 48-26). This insertion shifts the reading frame of the mRNA and results in the synthesis of an LDL receptor with six of the normal 50 amino acids and eight novel amino acids in the cytoplasmic domain.[131] A third and most revealing internalization-defective allele is found in FH 380, also referred to as J.D. (Fig. 48-26). Here, a single-base pair change results in the substitution of a cysteine residue for a tyrosine residue at position 807.[132,133] We have hypothesized that this substitution alters the structure of the cytoplasmic domain so that it can no longer bind properly to a protein that normally mediates its incorporation into coated pits.

The second subclass of internalization-defective alleles includes two examples, FH 274 and FH 781 (Figs. 48-22 and 48-23). Here, deletions of different size have resulted from recombination between repetitive *Alu* elements in intron 15 and in the untranslated region of exon 18. Both of these deletions remove the coding portions of exons 16 to 18, which encode the membrane-spanning domain as well as the cytoplasmic domain.[129,149] Genomic cloning, DNA sequencing, and S1 nuclease mapping studies indicate that exons 1 through 15 of the gene are present in the mRNA and specify the synthesis of a truncated receptor containing the normal NH_2-terminal 750 amino acids.[149] Translation continues into intron 15 before a termination is reached. This read-through produces a receptor with 55 novel amino acids at its COOH terminus. Inspection of this sequence reveals a stretch of 14 amino acids with a hydrophobic nature that could encode a pseudotransmembrane domain.[149] About 90 percent of these truncated receptors are secreted into the culture medium.[129,149] It is possible that the pseudotransmembrane domain might function inefficiently, thus retaining 10 percent of the LDL receptors within the cell while allowing the other 90 percent to be secreted.

Gene Rearrangements Caused by Recombination between Repetitive *Alu* Elements

Three of the four deletion mutations in the LDL receptor gene whose deletion joints have been cloned and sequenced (FH 274, FH 626, FH 781) involve homologous recombinations between two repetitive *Alu* sequences (Fig. 48-23).[129,141,149] The fourth (FH 381) is a recombination between one *Alu* sequence and a sequence in an exon that by chance is homologous to the *Alu* sequence[138] (Fig. 48-23). In two of the recombinations (FH 274 and FH 381), the complementary elements were oriented in opposite directions. In both cases it was possible to draw a double stem-loop (clover leaf) structure between these complementary sequences. These findings suggest that complex stem-loop structures may predispose to large deletions in the human genome.[138]

Recombination between *Alu* sequences in the same orientation caused the deletions found in FH 626 and FH 781[142,149] (Fig. 48-23). The simplest mechanism is one of homologous recombination in which unequal crossing over follows mispairing of chromatids. These unequal crossing-over events should also produce genes with duplications of the regions that are deleted from the FH 626 and FH 781 alleles. These particular duplications have not yet been found among FH genes.

The 14-kb duplication in the LDL receptor gene discussed above (FH 295) arose through homologous recombination between two *Alu* sequences. The likely mechanism for such recombination is the unequal crossing over shown in Fig. 48-25. This mechanism predicts the existence of the reciprocal product, i.e., a gene in which exons 2 through 8 have been deleted. Thus far, no evidence of such a reciprocal product has been found in any of the FH genes analyzed to date.

The data reviewed above indicate that a total of nine *Alu* sequences have been observed to be involved in mutations in the LDL receptor gene. Four *Alu* sequences have been reported to be involved in mutations in globin genes.[145,149] These data suggest that recombination involving *Alu* sequences may be a frequent cause of deletions and duplications in the human genome. Remarkably, the break points are not located at random throughout the *Alu* sequences. Rather, they are clustered as shown in Fig. 48-27.[145] Ten of the thirteen break points map within a 36-bp sequence in the left arm of the *Alu* repeat. These sequences fall between the A and B blocks that constitute the bipartite RNA polymerase III promoter in the *Alu* element.[145] It is tempting to speculate that the interaction of a transcription factor with the A and B sequences might lead to an increased susceptibility of this region to enzymes of DNA recombination.

Production of Half-normal Amounts of LDL Receptors in Heterozygotes

In normal fibroblasts, the synthesis of the LDL receptor is regulated by feedback suppression. The number of receptors declines by about tenfold when cellular cholesterol stores are increased by prolonged incubation of cells with a usable exogenous source of cholesterol, such as LDL or cholesterol dissolved in ethanol.[99] The number of receptors increases again when the exogenous cholesterol is removed and cellular cholesterol levels fall. In the steady state, the number of receptors is adjusted to allow just enough LDL uptake to provide sufficient cholesterol for cell growth and to balance cholesterol losses.[96,99]

Under growth conditions that induce a maximal rate of receptor synthesis (i.e., growth in the absence of an exogenous source of cholesterol), FH heterozygote cells produce about one-half as many functional receptors as do normal cells.[150] More important, when grown in the presence of increasing amounts of exogenous cholesterol, the heterozygote and normal cells suppress their LDL receptor activities in parallel. Over a ten- to twentyfold range of LDL receptor activities, at any given level of cellular cholesterol the heterozygote cells express about one-half as many receptors as do normal cells.[150] This relationship is evident even in the range of LDL receptor levels in which the heterozygote cells clearly had the capacity to produce as many active LDL receptors as did the normal cells, i.e., when the appropriate number of receptors was less than half the maximal number.[150] These findings indicate that in the heterozygote cells the regulatory mechanism dictates that the normal allele produces only the amount of gene product that it would normally produce at a given level of cellular cholesterol. The failure of the regulatory mechanism to stimulate the normal allele at the LDL receptor locus to produce twice its normal amount of gene product leaves the heterozygote cells with a persistent 50 percent deficiency in LDL receptors under all conditions of cell growth.

PATHOGENESIS AT THE WHOLE BODY LEVEL

The demonstration of the LDL receptor pathway in cultured human fibroblasts was followed by its demonstration in virtually all animal cells that grow in culture.[96] These cells have been obtained from humans (smooth-muscle cells, endothelial cells, lymphocytes, Burkitt lymphoma (Raji) cells, acute myelogenous leukemia cells, HeLa cells, SV40 transformed fibroblasts), mice (teratocarcinoma cells, adrenal Y-1 cells, L cells, L 1210 leukemia cells), cows (adult adrenocrotical cells, endothelial cells), dogs (fibroblasts, smooth-muscle cells), rabbits (fibroblasts), hamsters (fibroblasts), and swine (fibroblasts, smooth-muscle cells). In each of these cell types, LDL cholesterol is used for membrane synthesis and for the regulation of cholesterol homeostasis. In cultured mouse and bovine adrenal cells, the LDL serves an additional function: Its cholesterol is a precursor for steroid hormone formation.[151,152]

LDL Receptor Expression in Vivo

The first cells that were demonstrated to have LDL receptor activity in vivo were circulating blood lymphocytes. When incubated for 67 h in vitro in the absence of exogenous cho-

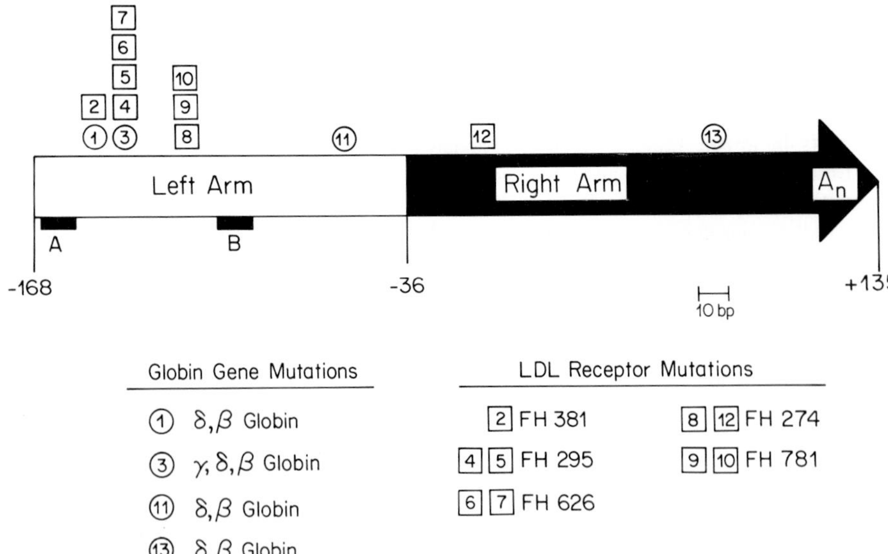

Fig. 48-27 Sites of recombinations within *Alu* repeats in human mutant genes. A consensus *Alu* repeat with left and right internal repeats (arms) is shown. The A and B boxes of the putative RNA polymerase III promoter within the left arm are denoted by the horizontal bars. The apparent break points in the globin genes (circled numbers) and in the LDL receptor gene (boxed numbers) are indicated; break points that occur within 10 bp of each other are indicated by vertical stacking. References for the globin mutations and the LDL receptor mutations are given in Ref. 145. (From *Lehrman et al.,*[145] *by permission of* Cell.)

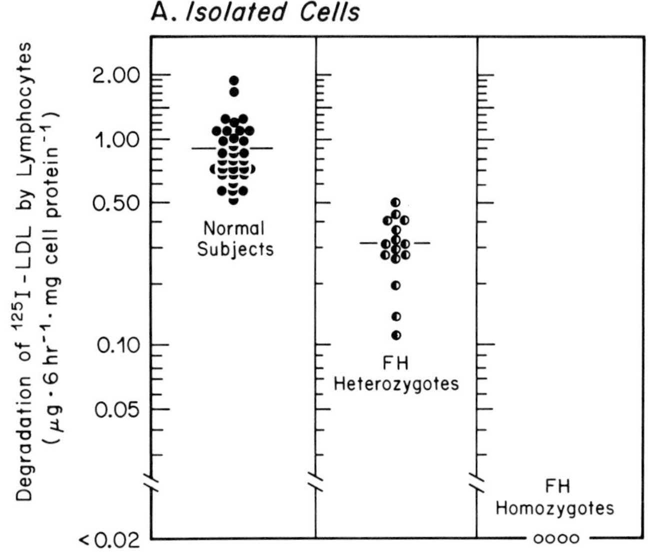

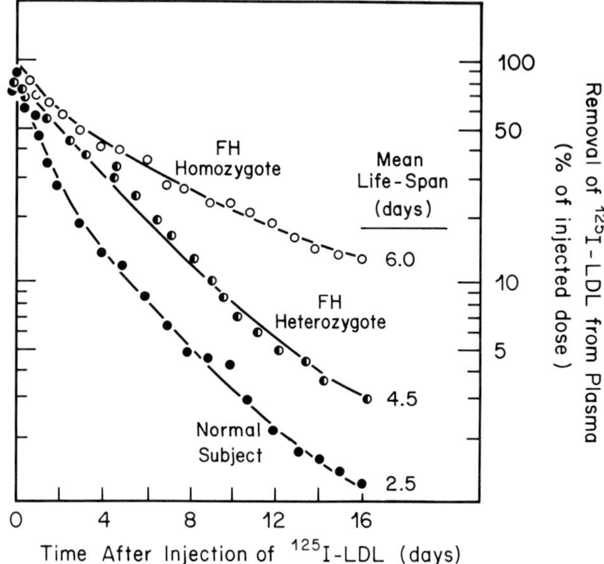

Fig. 48-28 Measurement of the number of LDL receptors in blood lymphocytes *(A)* and in living subjects *(B)*. *A*. Lymphocytes were isolated from venous blood of 32 normal subjects, 15 FH heterozygotes, and 4 FH homozygotes as indicated. After incubation for 67 h at 37°C in medium containing 10 percent lipoprotein-deficient serum, LDL receptor activity was assessed by measurement of the high affinity degradation of ^{125}I-LDL at 37°C. *B*. In the whole-body assay, a tracer amount of ^{125}I-LDL was injected intravenously, and the radioactivity remaining in the circulation over the next 16 days was measured in samples of venous blood. The higher the number of LDL receptors on body cells *(A)*, the faster the removal of ^{125}I-LDL from the blood *(B)*. *(Data in A replotted from Bilheimer et al.*[154]*; data in B replotted from Bilheimer et al.*[156]*)*

lesterol so as to derepress receptor synthesis, lymphocytes expressed abundant LDL receptors as determined by measurements of the high affinity uptake and degradation of ^{125}I-LDL (Fig. 48-28).[153,154] Lymphocytes from FH homozygotes did not express detectable LDL receptor activity, and lymphocytes from FH heterozygotes had an intermediate level consistent with the presence of only a single functional gene.[153,154] LDL receptors were also detectable on lymphocytes immediately after their isolation from the bloodstream, although the level of activity was lower than it was after derepression for 67 h.[154]

Another early clue to the function of LDL receptors in vivo came from studies of the rate of disappearance of intravenously injected ^{125}I-LDL from plasma (Fig. 48-28*B*). Such LDL is removed from the circulation more slowly in FH heterozygotes than it is in normal individuals.[155,156] In FH homozygotes the removal defect is even more profound.[156–158] The sluggishness of LDL catabolism in vivo correlates with the relative deficiency of LDL receptors as determined in isolated lymphocytes (Fig. 48-28).

More detailed demonstrations of LDL receptor function in vivo have been obtained in experimental animals. Using an assay for the binding of ^{125}I-LDL to membranes from homogenates of cultured ceils and various tissues of the cow and other animals, we found that most tissues of the cow had detectable high affinity ^{125}I-LDL binding; the adrenal gland and ovarian corpus luteum had the highest activity on a per gram basis.[159] When the weight of the organ was taken into consideration, the liver was found to produce by far the largest number of LDL receptors. Similar results were obtained in studies of human fetal tissues.[160] It was also shown that ^{125}I-LDL was taken up by perfused rat livers by a high affinity receptor-mediated process that could be markedly accelerated by administration of the estrogenic hormone, 17α-ethinyl estradiol.[161]

High levels of hepatic LDL receptors were observed when radiolabeled LDL was injected into the circulation of experimental animals and its uptake into various tissues was compared.[162] Steinberg and coworkers[163] and Dietschy and coworkers[164] showed that approximately 70 percent of the total-body uptake of radiolabeled LDL took place in the liver by LDL receptor-dependent pathways, but that the highest rates of uptake on a weight basis were seen in the adrenal gland. Various other tissues also showed receptor-mediated uptake of LDL in excess of that seen with nonspecific bulk phase markers such as radiolabeled albumin.

Measurements of receptor-mediated LDL uptake by tissues of animals were made more practical as a result of two developments: (1) Steinberg developed a method to label LDL with radioactive sucrose and later with tyramine-cellobiose.[165] In contrast to ^{125}I labeling of tyrosines, these methods produce a radioactive marker that remains trapped in lysosomes after uptake and degradation, thus allowing slow rates of uptake to be quantified cumulatively over long periods. (2) Shepherd and Packard showed that LDL whose arginine residues were modified by reaction with cyclohexanedione was cleared from the human circulation much more slowly than was native LDL, thus providing an in vivo method for quantifying the fraction of LDL clearance that is attributable to LDL receptors.[166] The rationale for these latter studies lay in previous work that showed that modification of arginine or lysine residues on LDL abolished its ability to bind to the LDL receptor.[105,106]

Although Shepherd and Packard's original studies used cyclohexanedione-LDL, more recent studies have demonstrated that this form of modified LDL underestimates the amount of clearance by the receptor pathway, because blockage of receptor binding is incomplete and because some of the cyclohexanedione comes off the particle in the circulation.[167,168] Better methods for blocking receptor binding in vivo involve methylation or glycosylation of the lysine residues of LDL[97] (Table 48-6). In healthy young humans glycosylated LDL is removed from the circulation only one-fifth as rapidly as native LDL,

Table 48-6 Receptor-Mediated Clearance of Plasma LDL in Vivo

Species	*Modified LDL used to measure receptor-independent degradation*	*LDL degraded by receptors, %*
Rat	Methyl-LDL	50–75
Guinea pig	Methyl-LDL	78
	Glucosylated LDL	78
Hamster	Methyl-LDL	72
Rabbit	Methyl-LDL	67
	Glucosylated LDL	62-75
Rhesus monkey	Methyl-LDL	50
Human	Glucosylated LDL	80

NOTE: Modification of the lysine residues on LDL by either methylation or glucosylation abolishes its ability to bind to LDL receptors. Such modified LDL is cleared from the circulation of humans and animals much more slowly than is native LDL, thus providing an in vivo method for quantifying the fraction of LDL clearance attributable to LDL receptors. The original studies from which the data in the table are derived are cited in the reference listed below.

SOURCE: From Brown and Goldstein,[97] by permission of *The Journal of Clinical Investigators*.

indicating that four-fifths of the clearance of LDL is mediated by the receptor pathway (Fig. 48-29).[168,169]

In early studies of the LDL receptor, we estimated the fraction of total LDL clearance that was receptor-dependent by comparing the rate of catabolism of intravenously injected ^{125}I-LDL in normal individuals and in FH homozygotes.[94] The fractional catabolic rate for LDL, i.e., the fraction of the total plasma pool of LDL removed per unit time, was threefold higher in normal subjects than in FH homozygotes (Fig. 48-30). From this observation we reasoned that approximately two-thirds of LDL clearance is normally mediated through the LDL receptor and the remaining one-third is mediated through a receptor-independent pathway.[94] As mentioned above, this conclusion has been borne out by a number of studies comparing the degradation rates for native versus lysine-modified LDL both in normal human subjects and in a wide variety of experimental animals (Table 48-6).

Fig. 48-29 Plasma die-away curves after the intravenous injection of native ^{125}I-LDL (●) and glucosylated ^{125}I-LDL (○) in a normal subject. FCR = the fractional catabolic rate for LDL. *(From Bilheimer et al.,[169] by permission of* Transactions of the Association of American Physicians.*)*

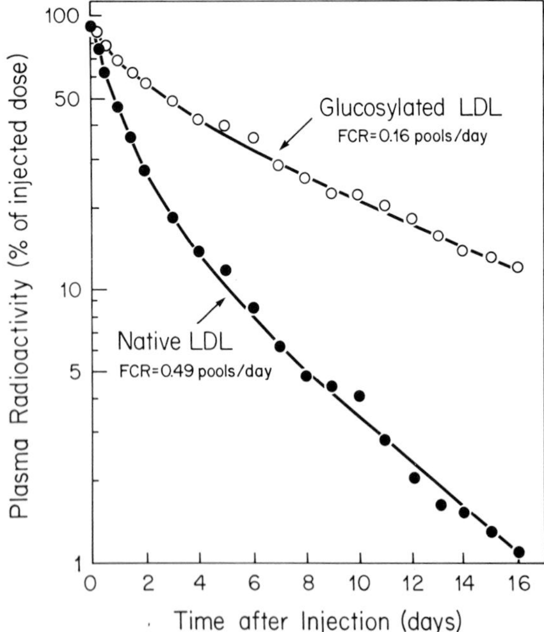

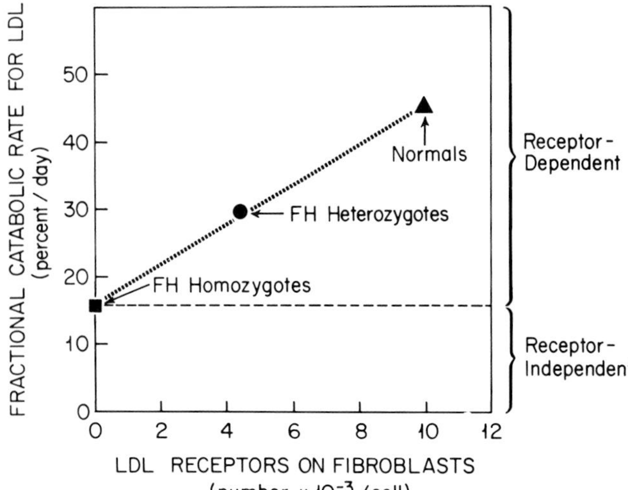

Fig. 48-30 Relation between the fractional catabolic rate (FCR) for plasma LDL and the number of LDL receptors on fibroblasts in patients with FH. The values for the fractional catabolic rate were derived from studies of the turnover of ^{125}I-apo-LDL in the plasma of six normal subjects, six FH heterozygotes, and 11 FH homozygotes. These turnover studies were performed by Bilheimer et al.[156] and by Myant and coworkers.[157,175] The number of LDL receptors per cell was calculated from experiments in which maximal ^{125}I-LDL binding was measured at 4°C in actively growing fibroblasts that were deprived of LDL for 48 h.

WHHL Rabbit: Role of LDL Receptor in Removal of IDL

One of the most important functions of LDL receptors in vivo was appreciated only in the past few years as a result of studies performed in Watanabe heritable hyperlipidemic rabbits. This strain of mutant rabbits was discovered in the late

Fig. 48-31 Photograph of Dr. Yoshio Watanabe, Kobe University, Japan, together with one of his WHHL rabbits. *(Courtesy of Dr. Toru Kita.)*

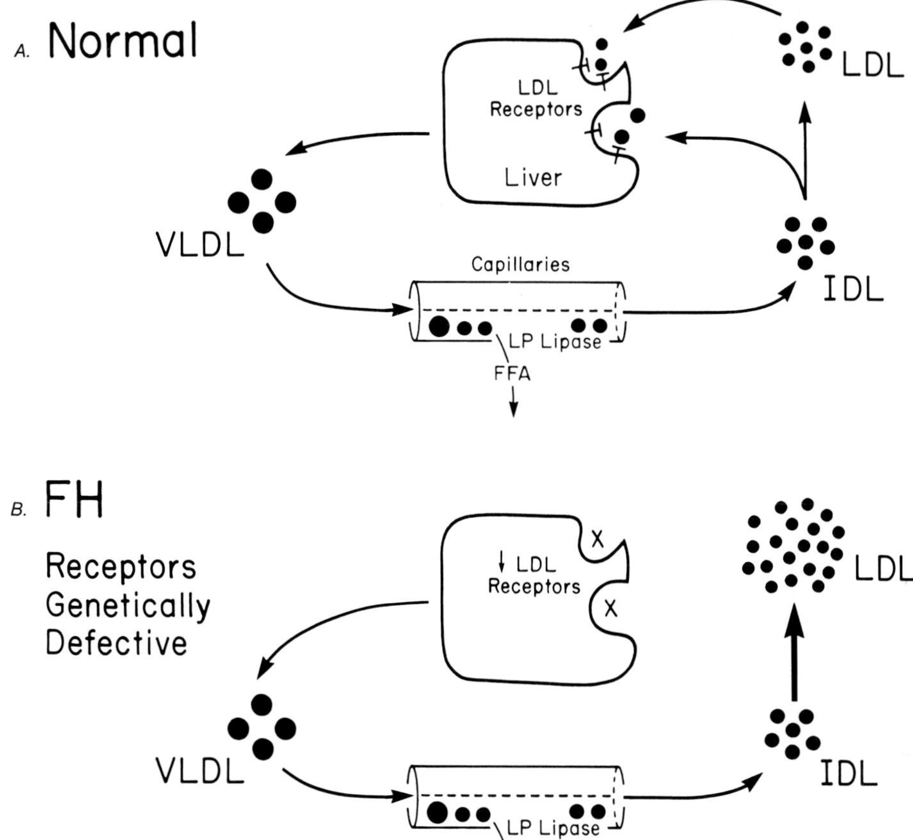

Fig. 48-32 Schematic model of the mechanism by which LDL receptors in the liver control both the production and catabolism of plasma LDL in normal human subjects *(A)* and in individuals with FH *(B)*. VLDL denotes very low density lipoprotein; IDL denotes intermediate density lipoprotein. *(From Brown and Goldstein,[3] by permission of* Science.*)*

1970s by Yosio Watanabe, a veterinarian in Kobe, Japan[170] (Fig. 48-31). These rabbits have a mutation in the LDL receptor gene that is similar to the class 2 mutations in human FH.[130,171,172] When present in the homozygous form, this mutation gives rise to extremely high LDL cholesterol levels, and the rabbits develop atherosclerosis early in life.[170,173,174]

The WHHL rabbits proved invaluable in explaining a previously puzzling feature of homozygous FH. Kinetic studies of ^{125}I-LDL metabolism by Soutar et al.[175] and by Bilheimer et al.[156] indicated that FH subjects have a dual defect. In addition to degrading LDL more slowly, FH homozygotes and heterozygotes also appeared to overproduce LDL. How does a genetic defect in the LDL receptor lead simultaneously to overproduction and reduced degradation of LDL? The answer lies in the complex biosynthetic pathway for LDL.

Early studies by Gitlin et al.[176] and later those by Bilheimer et al.[177] suggested that LDL is not secreted directly from the liver, but rather it is produced in the circulation from a blood-borne precursor, very low density lipoprotein (Fig. 48-32*A*). VLDL is a large, triglyceride-rich lipoprotein that is secreted by the liver; it transports triglyceride to adipose tissue and muscle. The triglycerides in VLDL are removed in capillaries by the enzyme lipoprotein lipase, and the VLDL returns to the circulation as a smaller particle with a new name, intermediate density lipoprotein.[121] The IDL particles have lost most of their triglyceride, but they retain cholesteryl esters. Some of the IDL particles are rapidly taken up by the liver; others remain in the circulation where they undergo further triglyceride hydrolysis and are converted to LDL. A distinguishing feature of the IDL particles is their content of multiple copies of apo E in addition to a single copy of apo B-100. The multiple copies of apo E allow IDL to bind to the LDL receptor with very high affinity. When IDL is converted to LDL, the apo E leaves the particle and only apo B-100 remains. Thereafter, the affinity for the LDL receptor is much reduced.[174]

The apparent overproduction of LDL in WHHL rabbits is due to the failure of IDL to be removed from the plasma[174,178,179] (Fig. 48-32*B*). Thus, when ^{125}I-VLDL was administered to WHHL rabbits, the resultant IDL was not taken up by the liver, as it was in normal rabbits.[178,179] Rather it remained in the circulation and was converted in increased amounts to LDL. These findings strongly suggest that IDL is normally cleared from plasma by binding to LDL receptors in the liver. Although experiments of similar detail cannot be carried out in humans, the observations of Soutar et al.[175] are consistent with the notion that enhanced conversion of IDL to LDL also occurs in FH homozygotes, thus accounting for much of the apparent overproduction of LDL.

Mechanism for Elevated Plasma LDL in FH

Figure 48-32*A* illustrates the dual role of the LDL receptor in LDL metabolism as determined from the studies of WHHL rabbits. First, the receptor limits LDL production by enhancing the removal of the precursor, IDL, from the circulation. Second, it enhances LDL degradation by mediating cellular uptake of LDL. A deficiency of LDL receptors in FH causes LDL to accumulate as a result both of overproduction and of delayed removal (Fig. 48-32*B*). By this quirk of dual functionality, LDL receptors become crucially important modulators of plasma LDL levels in humans and animals.

Receptor-Independent Removal of LDL

As discussed above and as illustrated in Fig. 48-30, the proportion of LDL cleared from the plasma each day by the receptor-independent pathway in FH homozygotes and heterozygotes is inversely related to the number of functional LDL receptors. In homozygotes with no receptors, all the plasma LDL is degraded by receptor-independent pathways. In heterozygotes with 50 percent of the normal receptor number, about one-half of plasma LDL is degraded by receptor-independent pathways, whereas in normal subjects only one-third is degraded by this route (Fig. 48-30). Kinetic studies of ^{125}I-LDL turnover in vivo have demonstrated that the receptor-independent removal pathway is considerably less efficient than the receptor-dependent pathway.[156] For example, in FH homozygotes in whom all LDL removal is by receptor-independent pathways, each LDL particle circulates with a life span of 6 days compared with a life span of 2.5 days in normal subjects.

Despite the potential importance of the receptor-independent pathway in FH patients, virtually nothing is known about the responsible cellular and biochemical mechanisms. Studies in WHHL rabbits have suggested that the receptor-independent removal of LDL is divided about equally between the liver and the extrahepatic tissues.[163,180]

Some of the receptor-independent clearance of LDL occurs in macrophages and histiocytes of the reticuloendothelials system, which are referred to collectively as "scavenger cells."[94,181,182] These cells were implicated in the receptor-independent LDL clearance for two reasons: (1) the generally accepted notion that macrophages participate in the clearance of proteins from plasma; and (2) the observation that homozygotes, in whom the largest amounts of LDL are removed by receptor-independent pathways, accumulate considerable cholesterol in splenic macrophages, hepatic Kupffer cells, bone marrow histiocytes, and similar scavenger cells in many organs. Thus, these cells have the ability to take up and degrade considerable amounts of LDL in vivo.[70,181] LDL also appears to be taken up with low efficiency by hepatic parenchymal cells and other cells in the absence of LDL receptors.

Stimulated by the hypothesis that macrophages may participate in the receptor-independent removal of LDL,[181,182] numerous investigators have begun to explore the mechanisms by which scavenger cells degrade LDL.[95] The most informative model system has been one that uses monolayers of freshly isolated macrophages obtained from the peritoneal cavity of mice.[182] In brief, these studies have shown that, although macrophages express few receptors for normal plasma LDL, they exhibit abundant receptors for LDL that has been altered by chemical derivitization, by oxidation, or by complexing with other molecules.[95] In addition, these cells have receptors for at least one type of pathologic lipoprotein (β-VLDL) that accumulates in plasma in hyperlipidemic states.[95]

No matter which receptor is involved, the uptake of cholesterol-bound lipoproteins by macrophages always seems to occur through receptor-mediated endocytosis.[95] The cholesterol liberated from the lysosomal hydrolysis of the lipoprotein enters the cytoplasm where it is reesterified and stored as cholesteryl ester droplets, resulting in the appearance of a typical foam cell as seen in vivo in xanthomas and atherosclerotic plaques.[95]

At the present time, the relevance of the in vitro macrophage studies to the accumulation of cholesteryl esters in scavenger cells of patients with FH is not yet established. A more detailed discussion of the LDL metabolism in macrophage foam cell formation is presented in Ref. 95. Finally, it must be realized that the pathogenesis of FH will not be fully understood until insight is gained into the cellular and biochemical mechanisms to which the elevated LDL level leads to accelerated atherosclerosis.

Cholesterol Synthetic Rates in Heterozygotes and Homozygotes

In cultured fibroblasts from FH patients, the deficiency of LDL receptors creates a situation in which the rate of cholesterol synthesis is higher in cells from heterozygotes and homozygotes than in cells from normal subjects when all are exposed to the same level of LDL in the incubation medium.[45,118] It has been pointed out, however, that these in vitro findings do not imply that the total-body cholesterol synthetic rate would be elevated in these patients[158] because in vivo the FH patients do not have normal levels of LDL cholesterol. Heterozygotes, for example, maintain a two- to threefold elevation of plasma LDL levels. In tissue culture, such an increase is sufficient to reduce cholesterol synthesis to the same levels that are seen in cells from normal subjects.[150] This type of compensation also seems to take place in vivo. Total-body sterol synthetic rates have been measured in heterozygotes using the sterol balance technique. These studies have shown normal rates of total-body cholesterol synthesis.[156,158,183,184]

It is not clear whether this type of LDL-related compensation can occur in homozygotes. In actively growing fibroblasts from receptor-negative homozygotes, cholesterol synthesis cannot be fully suppressed, even when very high levels of LDL are present in the culture medium.[45,118] However, when fibroblasts become confluent and cease to grow, the rate of cholesterol synthesis falls in homozygote cells as well as in normal cells.[118] Thus, in vivo cholesterol synthesis might be higher than normal in rapidly growing cells and perhaps in cells that use LDL for the production of steroid hormones. Whether this increase would be sufficient to produce a detectable increase in overall total-body cholesterol synthesis is not known.

Studies of cholesterol synthetic rates in homozygotes with the use of sterol balance[156,158,183–187] or isotopic turnover[188] techniques have shown an interesting dichotomy of results. Younger subjects in general appear to have total-body rates of cholesterol synthesis that are two- to threefold above normal, as reflected by an enhanced excretion of cholesterol from the body compared with that of normal subjects of the same age. However, in homozygotes who have been studied after the age of 10, the cholesterol synthetic rates are generally at the upper limits of normal. The one exception is a 24-year-old homozygote whose total cholesterol synthetic rate was 34.2 mg/kg per day compared with a mean normal value of 9.6 mg/kg per day.[185] Bile acid synthetic rates are generally normal in homozygotes. Although the number of subjects studied by these techniques is small, the results suggest that young FH homozygotes may have a total-body overproduction of cholesterol, whereas older homozygotes may not show such overproduction. The tissues in which such overproduction occurs are not known.

DIAGNOSIS

Clinical Diagnosis: Differentiation from Other Disorders Producing Type 2 Hyperlipoproteinemia

Homozygotes. The clinical diagnosis of FH in the homozygote usually causes no difficulty. Not only is the clinical picture of cutaneous xanthomas and juvenile atherosclerosis distinct, but the finding of a plasma cholesterol level exceeding 650 mg/dl in a nonjaundiced child is virtually pathognomonic.

The one disorder that may occasionally be confused clinically with homozygous FH is the even less frequent entity called *pseudohomozygous type 2 hypercholesterolemia*. This disorder was first described in 1974,[189] and to date at least seven affected individuals from seven unrelated families have been identified.[189–192] The clinical picture is that of a child with the following abnormalities: (1) severe hypercholesterolemia (total plasma cholesterol level 350 to 600 mg/dl) due to a selective elevation in LDL; (2) a normal triglyceride level; (3) cutaneous planar xanthomas of the type seen in homozygous FH; (4) normal plasma cholesterol levels in both parents; and (5) a striking response to dietary restriction of cholesterol, with plasma cholesterol levels falling as much as 40 percent, accompanied by regression of the xanthomas.

Pseudohomozygous type 2 hypercholesterolemia can be distinguished clinically from homozygous FH by the following features: (1) the absence of heterozygous FH in parents and other first-degree relatives; (2) the apparent absence of juvenile atherosclerosis, at least in the few cases so far described; and (3) the remarkable sensitivity to dietary manipulation. The combination of a low cholesterol diet ($<$200 mg/day) and oral cholestyramine (12 g/day) lowers plasma LDL cholesterol levels well into the normal range,[189–191] a completely different result from that obtained with homozygous FH.

Studies of the cultured fibroblasts of one of the two originally described parents with pseudohomozygous type 2 hypercholesterolemia (case 2, B.H.) and two other patients showed no abnormality in any of the steps in the LDL receptor pathway.[72,191] This finding suggests that the elevation in LDL cholesterol levels is not caused by an abnormality in the receptor-mediated catabolism of LDL. In addition, LDL isolated from the plasma of affected patients was taken up, degraded, and metabolized normally by normal human fibroblasts.[72] Studies of total-body cholesterol and bile acid production and of ^{125}I-labeled LDL turnover in plasma performed while the patients are ingesting low and high amounts of dietary cholesterol should be especially informative in identifying the biochemical lesion in this disorder.

The clinical features of pseudohomozygous type 2 hypercholesterolemia are virtually identical to those seen in the autosomal recessive syndrome of sitosterolemia and xanthomatosis (Chap. 51). Many, if not all, of the seven children diagnosed as having pseudohomozygous type 2 may actually have sitosterolemia and xanthomatosis. All patients considered to have pseudohomozygous type 2 should have measurements taken of plant sterols as well as cholesterol in their plasma (Chap. 51).

Heterozygotes. In order to diagnose the heterozygote with FH, it is first necessary to document an elevation in the plasma level of LDL. In most cases the finding of hypercholesterolemia is sufficient to establish that the LDL cholesterol level is elevated. In the absence of extreme elevation of VLDL (as indicated by a plasma triglyceride level greater than 600 mg/dl), the total plasma cholesterol level directly reflects the LDL cholesterol concentration in nearly all individuals.[121] In some cases when the total cholesterol level is at the upper limits of normal (i.e., at or near the 90th percentile cutoff), the measurement of LDL cholesterol by ultracentrifugation may help to clarify whether the concentration of LDL is elevated.[29,121]

Having documented the presence of hypercholesterolemia due to an elevated LDL level, the physician must then determine whether the cause of the elevation is the heterozygous form of FH. This distinction is of crucial importance because most patients with an elevation in total plasma cholesterol or LDL cholesterol (i.e., a type 2a or type 2b lipoprotein pattern) do *not* have FH.[80] It has been estimated that probably no more than 1 in 20 individuals in the general population with hypercholesterolemia and a type 2 lipoprotein pattern has this genetic defect.[80] Most persons with a type 2 lipoprotein pattern appear to have a form of hypercholesterolemia that is multifactorial in origin and probably derives from a combination of environmental and poorly understood polygenic factors.[80] Moreover, in addition to FH, there is at least one other monogenic cause of type 2 hyperlipoproteinemia, familial combined hyperlipidemia.[80,81,193,194] Thus, the term FH should not be considered synonymous with the term familial type 2 hyperlipoproteinemia.

The diagnosis of FH can be made on clinical grounds if the hypercholesterolemic patient has tendon xanthomas or a pedigree in which one of the parents and about one-half of the first-degree relatives have hypercholesterolemia in association with tendon xanthomas. However, many heterozygotes, including most below age 20 and approximately 25 percent of those above age 20, lack tendon xanthomas. Without family analysis, FH in these latter subjects is especially difficult to separate on clinical grounds from other causes of an elevated plasma level of LDL cholesterol.

In individual patients with a primary type 2 lipoprotein pattern and no tendon xanthomas, there are several clinical clues to help distinguish between FH and the other monogenic causes of high LDL levels. These are:

1. Heterozygotes with FH tend to have, on the average, higher cholesterol levels. The finding of a total plasma cholesterol level above 400 mg/dl is highly suggestive of this diagnosis.
2. Heterozygotes with FH do not usually have relatives with lipoprotein abnormalities of multiple types (i.e., types 2a, 2b, 4, and 5), but this is characteristic of familial combined hyperlipidemia.
3. Hypercholesterolemic individuals with familial combined hyperlipidemia rarely, if ever, have tendon xanthomas.
4. Hypercholesterolemia does not appear to express itself in children with familial combined hyperlipidemia as it does in those with FH; hence the finding of a hypercholesterolemic child in the family is strongly suggestive of FH.

A variety of nongenetic disturbances can also cause the plasma LDL cholesterol level to be elevated. For example, a type 2a lipoprotein pattern may be observed in patients with hypothyroidism, nephrotic syndrome, hepatoma, Cushing syndrome, acute intermittent porphyria, anorexia nervosa, and Werner's syndrome.[121] Patients with primary biliary cirrhosis and other forms of obstructive jaundice may also manifest a type 2a lipoprotein pattern, but their plasma will also contain elevated amounts of an unusual lipoprotein called lipoprotein X.[121]

Laboratory Diagnosis: Measurements of LDL Receptors

LDL receptor function can be measured in cultured skin fibroblasts to confirm directly a 50 percent deficiency of LDL receptors in a heterozygote and a complete or near-complete deficiency of LDL receptor activity in homozygotes.[68,195] Four tests are available for quantitation of LDL receptor function in monolayers of fibroblasts cultured from the skin of patients: (1) measurement of the cell surface binding and intracellular uptake of ^{125}I-labeled LDL; (2) measurement of the rate of proteolytic degradation of ^{125}I-labeled LDL; (3) measurement of LDL-mediated suppression of the synthesis of [^{14}C]cholesterol from [^{14}C]acetate in intact cells or of HMG-CoA reductase activity as assayed in cell-free extracts; and (4) measurement of LDL-mediated stimulation of the incorporation of [^{14}C]oleate into cellular cholesteryl [^{14}C]oleate.[195] In addition, the number of LDL receptors can be quantified by immunoblotting techniques or immunoprecipitation of ^{35}S-labeled receptors after growth of cells in [^{35}S]methionine.[142,195a]

The LDL receptor defect in FH can also be demonstrated in circulating blood lymphocytes, thus obviating the necessity for long-term culture. The lymphocyte assay is based on the observation that proliferating cells must obtain cholesterol from one of two sources, either by receptor-mediated uptake of LDL or by endogenous sterol synthesis.[196] Thus, when freshly isolated lymphocytes are cultured in lipoprotein-deficient medium and endogenous cholesterol synthesis is inhibited with an HMG CoA reductase inhibitor such as lovastatin (mevinolin), mitogen-stimulated proliferation of lymphocytes becomes dependent on the receptor-mediated uptake of LDL cholesterol.[197] Lymphocytes from normal subjects with two functional LDL receptor genes require a small concentration of LDL cholesterol (3 to 4 μg/ml) to permit maximal proliferation, as measured by [^{3}H]thymidine incorporation. In contrast, lymphocytes from homozygotes with no functional LDL receptors show no proliferative response even at LDL cholesterol levels as high as 50 μg/ml. Lymphocytes from FH heterozygotes show the same maximal proliferative response as normal cells, but they require an LDL cholesterol concentration that is two- to threefold higher than that required by normal cells.[197]

The mitogen-stimulated lymphocyte proliferation assay has yet not been tested for diagnostic utility in the general population. In one study seven unaffected subjects, six FH heterozygotes, and 12 individuals with hyperlipidemia not due to FH could easily be distinguished.[197] Further studies will be needed to determine whether this promising result can be confirmed in a large unselected sample of individuals. Since unaffected subjects outnumber FH heterozygotes by 500 to 1 in the general population, an individual with a borderline low LDL receptor activity is more likely to represent a normal individual who happens to fall in the heterozygote range rather than a true heterozygote. Repeated testing may be necessary.

Prenatal Diagnosis of Receptor-Negative Homozygotes

The development of assay methods for the quantitative assessment of LDL receptor activity in cultured cells permitted a prenatal diagnosis of homozygous FH, which was first carried out in 1978.[91] At the time of this writing, our laboratory has analyzed the amniotic cells from a total of seven at-risk pregnancies. In six cases the cells arrived in a healthy state. The predicted diagnosis (one homozygote, four heterozygotes, one normal) agreed with the clinical diagnosis at birth (four heterozygotes and one normal) or at postmortem after abortion (one homozygote) in all six cases.[51,72,91] In the seventh case, the amniotic cultures were contaminated with fungi, thus precluding a full analysis for receptor activity. In view of this complication the referring physicians in Paris obtained a fetal blood sample at the 24th week of gestation through use of a needle guided by ultrasound.[198] The total cholesterol level was 543 mg/dl as compared to the mean value of 66 mg/dl in 48 control fetuses. The diagnosis of homozygous FH was confirmed in skin fibroblasts obtained at the time of therapeutic abortion.[198]

From the above experience it would appear that the feasibility of making the prenatal diagnosis of receptor-negative homozygous FH has been established. It has not yet been established that the diagnosis can be reliably made in those FH homozygotes who have some detectable receptor activity (5 to 30 percent of normal). It is unlikely that such homozygotes can be distinguished from heterozygotes with sufficient certainty to justify the performance of a therapeutic abortion. This question may be rendered moot by recent data suggesting that the clinical sequelae of FH are less severe in the receptor-defective homozygotes than in receptor-negative ones (see Table 48-3 and Fig. 48-4). Because of their severe symptoms, the receptor-negative homozygotes may be the only ones for whom therapeutic abortion should be considered.

As more experience is obtained with gene probes for the LDL receptor and as more restriction fragment length polymorphisms are discovered in or near the LDL receptor gene, future diagnosis should be obtained with genomic Southern blotting techniques.

Neonatal Diagnosis of Heterozygotes

By measuring the level of LDL cholesterol in the cord blood of babies born to a parent who is already known to carry the FH gene, it is possible to diagnose heterozygotes at the time of birth.[28] Neonatal cord blood screening is not a reliable means for identification of heterozygotes in the general population, because, just as with adults, the vast majority of newborns with elevations of LDL cholesterol do not have FH.[199,200] The earliest age at which heterozygotes can be accurately identified in the general population is probably 1 year, and even then a family analysis is required to confirm that the elevated LDL cholesterol level is due to FH.

TREATMENT

Heterozygotes

The ideal cholesterol-lowering agent would be one that caused an enhanced production of LDL receptors in the liver, which normally uses this receptor to take up and degrade LDL and to excrete cholesterol from the body. Inasmuch as heterozygotes have one normal LDL receptor gene that is known to be under feedback regulation,[150] it may be possible to induce body cells to produce an increased number of receptors by stimulating the transcription and translation of their normal gene. One way to do this has been suggested from results in cultured cells. When the demand for cholesterol is elevated, cells produce an increased number of LDL receptors as a result of enhanced transcription of the LDL receptor gene.[201] This increase is even more pronounced when intracellular cholesterol synthesis is inhibited, thus forcing cells to rely entirely on LDL cholesterol.[195,201]

One class of drugs that act by stimulating the production of LDL receptors is made up of the bile acid-binding resins, cholestyramine and colestipol. These agents have been used extensively for two decades in the treatment of heterozygous FH and other hypercholesterolemic states.[202–205] In general, they produce a 15 to 20 percent lowering of LDL cholesterol levels.

Cholestyramine and colestipol are nonabsorbable, anion-exchange resins that bind bile acids in the intestinal lumen and thus prevent their absorption from the ileum.[204] This leads to increased fecal excretion of bile acids, which elicits an increased conversion of cholesterol to bile acids in the liver. The mechanism by which the enhanced bile acid synthesis leads to a specific lowering of plasma LDL cholesterol levels has recently been disclosed by studies of the turnover of doubly labeled LDL in human beings. Treatment of heterozygotes with cholestyramine led to an enhanced fractional catabolic rate (FCR) for ^{125}I-labeled LDL but not ^{131}I-labeled cyclohexanedione-treated LDL, which cannot bind to the LDL receptor.[206] This important finding suggests that the liver can be made to produce a larger number of LDL receptors if its demand for cholesterol is enhanced. This suggestion has been supported by two studies in animals. When rabbits were given cholestyramine, the uptake of intravenously administered ^{125}I-labeled LDL by the liver was enhanced several-fold, whereas the hepatic uptake of ^{131}I-labeled cyclohexanedione-LDL was not increased.[207] Similarly, in dogs treated with colestipol the number of LDL receptors in liver membranes increased and the FCR for intravenously administered ^{125}I-labeled LDL increased proprotionately.[208] Thus, in the dog, as well as in humans, the bile acid sequestrants lower plasma LDL levels by enhancing the efficiency of receptor-mediated removal of LDL from plasma (Fig. 48-33, *left*).

The effectiveness of bile acid sequestrants has long been known to be blunted because the liver attempts to compensate for the cholesterol deficiency by developing an enhanced rate of cholesterol synthesis (Fig. 48-33, *middle*).[183,209] By replacing the drained intracellular cholesterol pool, the increased hepatic cholesterol synthesis blunts the rise in hepatic LDL receptors. Therefore, on theoretical grounds, it would be expected that an inhibitor of cholesterol synthesis should act synergistically with a bile acid sequestrant to lower plasma LDL levels[3] (Fig. 48-33, *right*).

Fig. 48-33 Rationale for the use of a bile acid binding resin and an inhibitor of 3-hydroxy-3-methylglutaryl CoA reductase in the treatment of FH heterozygotes. A detailed discussion of this figure is presented in the text. *(From Brown and Goldstein,[3] by permission of Science.)*

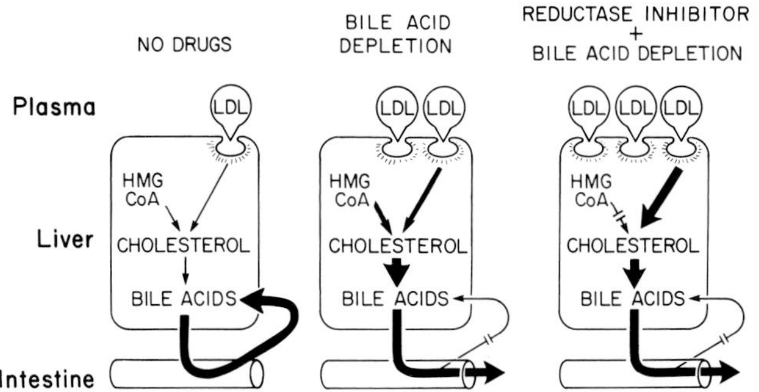

The recent development of a new class of cholesterol synthesis inhibitors has allowed this hypothesis to be confirmed in animals and in human beings. The prototype for this class of drug is compactin (ML-236B), a fungal metabolite that was isolated from *Penicillium citrinum* in 1976 by Endo and associates at the Sankyo Drug Company in Japan.[210] Compactin is a bicyclic diene with a side chain that contains a β-hydroxy-δ-lactone. Compactin is a potent reversible inhibitor of HMG CoA reductase that acts competitively with HMG CoA.[210,211] The K_m for compactin is on the order of 1 n*M*, which is 10,000-fold lower than the K_m for the natural substrate HMG CoA (about 10 μ*M*). A similar compound, mevinolin or lovastatin, was discovered in a strain of *Aspergillus*.[212] Lovastatin consists of compactin plus an additional methyl group. It is even more potent than compactin in inhibiting HMG CoA reductase.

When given to experimental animals and humans, lovastatin initially inhibits cholesterol synthesis in the liver, and this triggers a complex regulatory mechanism that lowers the plasma LDL cholesterol level. The inhibition of cholesterol synthesis elicits a complex compensatory response: (1) hepatocytes synthesize increased amounts of HMG CoA reductase; (2) they increase the number of LDL receptors; and (3) they may also decrease the amount of cholesterol incorporated into VLDL.[208,213,214] When a new steady state is attained, the increase in HMG CoA reductase is almost sufficient to overcome the inhibitory effects of compactin. Total body cholesterol synthesis is only slightly reduced.[215] Meanwhile, the plasma LDL level has fallen as a result of the increase in LDL receptors and possibly as a result of a decrease in incorporation of cholesterol into VLDL. The fall in plasma LDL levels is balanced by the increase in LDL receptors, and so the absolute amount of cholesterol entering the liver through the receptor pathway is the same as it was earlier. The difference, however, is that this delivery is now occurring at a lower plasma LDL level.

When given as a single agent to FH heterozygotes, lovastatin routinely produces a 30 percent fall in plasma LDL cholesterol levels. When given together with cholestyramine, lovastatin blocks the compensatory increase in cholesterol synthesis, and the increase in LDL receptors is even more profound (Fig. 48-33, *right*). Plasma LDL cholesterol levels fall by 50 to 60 percent.[213,216–219]

The important principle to emerge from these studies is that stimulation of LDL receptor activity lowers the plasma LDL cholesterol level without grossly distorting cholesterol transport. At present lovastatin and related compounds are in the early stages of clinical testing. Their efficacy in lowering plasma LDL cholesterol levels has been well established, but there is no information regarding long-term toxicity in humans. If these drugs turn out to be nontoxic, they will have an important role in the therapy of FH heterozygotes and other hypercholesterolemic individuals.[3]

Among the more established forms of therapy, impressive results in heterozygotes have been achieved with the use of a combination of a bile acid sequestrant and nicotinic acid.[220] Although its mechanism of action has not been definitively established, nicotinic acid probably acts by reducing hepatic secretion of VLDL, which in turn reduces LDL production.[204] When 22 severely affected FH heterozygotes were treated with nicotinic acid in combination with a bile acid sequestrant (colestipol) plus an HMG CoA reductase inhibitor (lovastatin), plasma cholesterol levels were lowered from 420 ± 53 to 184 ± 22 mg/dl and LDL cholesterol levels were lowered from 329 ± 56 to 107 ± 20.[220a]

A surgically created partial ileal bypass prevents bile salt reabsorption and produces the same therapeutic effect in heterozygotes as does cholestyramine.[221–223]

Dietary discretion is generally recommended for every person with hypercholesterolemia, including those with FH. In general, the total cholesterol intake should be limited to no more than 300 mg/day for adults (roughly equivalent to the cholesterol content of one egg yolk) and no more than 150 mg/day for children. In addition, the intake of saturated fat should be reduced and the intake of polyunsaturated fat increased.

Although drug therapy for children with heterozygous FH is beyond the scope of this chapter, this subject is discussed in several recent articles.[224,225] Another article, in *Goodman and Gilman's The Pharmacological Basis of Therapeutics*, 7th ed., reviews the doses and side effects of the various drugs used for the treatment of heterozygotes.[204]

Homozygotes

Diet, Drugs, and Partial Ileal Bypass Surgery. Homozygotes are generally resistant to the treatments that are effective in heterozygotes. As discussed above, these treatments rely on the stimulation of the normal LDL receptor gene, and FH homozygotes have few to no normal receptor genes to stimulate. Receptor-negative homozygotes show little response in plasma cholesterol levels to dietary changes, bile acid binding resins, ileal bypass, or HMG CoA reductase inhibitors.[205,226–228] FH homozygotes who have some functional LDL receptors may show some response to these agents. The resistance of FH homozygotes to therapy has been demonstrated clearly in two studies. In one of these, four Japanese FH homozygotes responded negligibly to doses of compactin that were five- to eightfold higher than that required to achieve a 33 percent reduction in cholesterol levels in heterozygotes.[227] In the other study, a bile fistula was created in an FH homozygote so that all biliary cholesterol and bile acids were drained to the exterior for 1 year. Although many grams of cholesterol were directly removed from the body by this route, there was no significant change in the plasma LDL cholesterol level.[229]

FH homozygotes whose cultured cells express 2 to 30 percent of functional LDL receptor activity should be vigorously treated with triple therapy, i.e., a combination of a bile acid binding agent, an HMG CoA reductase inhibitor, and nicotinic acid. When one FH homozygote with 25 percent of functional receptor activity was treated with triple therapy, the plasma cholesterol level was reduced from 958 to 389 mg/dl and the LDL cholesterol level was reduced from 809 to 338 mg/dl.[220a] Another drug that has been used in this context is probucol, a new agent whose mechanism of action is not understood.[204] Probucol is a lipophilic molecule that distributes into adipose tissue, and its effect is thus extremely persistent after treatment is discontinued. Because of this characteristic and the observation that probucol causes a significant reduction in plasma HDL levels, the drug is not recommended for treatment of heterozygotes. Its use should be restricted to those homozygotes with functional receptor activity in whom a 20 percent or greater lowering of LDL can be achieved.[230,231]

Portacaval Anastomosis. Several new approaches to therapy for homozygotes have recently been introduced, each of which is partially successful and all of which open up new avenues for investigation into the mechanism underlying the hypercholesterolemia in this disorder. First, Starzl and coworkers observed that intravenous hyperalimentation caused a profound reduction in the plasma cholesterol level of one homozygote.[232] Similar results were subsequently obtained in other homozygotes.[185,233] The mechanism for this effect is unknown. As a second therapeutic approach, Starzl and coworkers also observed that following the performance of an end-to-side portacaval anastomosis in a homozygote patient, the plasma cholesterol level declined from 772 to 240 mg/dl.[232] Associated with this reduction was a disappearance of angina pectoris and an improvement in the patency of the coronary arteries as determined by angiography. This improvement notwithstanding, the patient died suddenly of an apparent cardiac arrhythmia about 18 months following the operation.[234,235]

More than 30 homozygotes have now been reported to have undergone portacaval shunt surgery, and in most of them the plasma cholesterol level was reduced about 50 percent.[158,235–238] Detailed metabolic studies in one of these homozygotes showed that the portacaval anastomosis reduced total-body cholesterol synthesis by 62 percent and lowered the synthetic rate for plasma LDL by 48 percent. The plasma LDL level in this patient was reduced by 39 percent, despite a 17 percent reduction in the fractional catabolic rate for the lipoprotein.[158] In another homozygote, the procedure not only lowered total-body cholesterol and bile acid synthesis but it also elicited a net efflux of accumulated tissue cholesterol, as measured by isotopic techniques demonstrating a reduction in the body's rapidly exchangeable and total exchangeable mass of LDL cholesterol.[238] Patients generally tolerate this procedure well. Plasma albumin levels have remained unaltered and no significant changes in other liver functions have been observed.[158,235,238]

Removal of LDL by Plasma Exchange. Perhaps the most successful and widely applicable therapeutic approach for homozygotes, as well as for certain severely affected heterozygotes, involves removal of LDL from plasma by use of a continuous-flow blood cell separator to perform repeated plasma exchange. This technique was first described by Thompson et al. in 1975.[239] More than 35 FH patients, most of whom are homozygotes, have now been treated in several medical centers by this procedure.[240] If the procedure is repeated at intervals of 1 to 2 weeks and combined with oral nicotinic acid in a dose of 3 to 5 g daily, the average level of plasma cholesterol can be reduced by about 50 percent on a long-term basis.[240] The procedure is generally tolerated well, but it may be difficult to continue for periods of many years, as is required in FH homozygotes.

Several recent reports have appeared documenting an amelioration of atherosclerosis in FH homozygotes treated long-term by repeated plasma exchange. Keller and coworkers documented regression of valvular aortic stenosis by echocardiography and cardiac catheterization in a patient treated every 2 weeks for 4 years.[241] Stein et al. performed coronary angiography on a homozygote treated repeatedly for 31 months and found nonprogression of atherosclerosis in the main left coronary artery in which 30 percent narrowing was originally seen.[242] Similarly, Myant observed no progression of the atherosclerosis in the supravalvular portion of the aorta and of the coronary vessels in two homozygotes after 3 years of plasma exchange.[243] Thompson et al. reported a decreased risk of premature death in five homozygotes who were treated every 2 weeks for an average of 8.4 years.[244] These patients had survived an average of 5.5 years longer than their five respective homozygous sibs, each of whom presumably had an identical genetic defect but who died without benefit of plasma exchange.

The most recent advance in plasma exchange therapy relates to the selective removal of plasma LDL by continuous passage of the plasma extracorporeally over columns that remove apo B-100-containing lipoproteins (VLDL, IDL, and LDL) to a greater degree than HDL and other plasma proteins. These columns employ either heparin agarose,[245] anti-LDL antibody-agarose,[246] or dextran sulfate-cellulose.[247,248] Another approach, called double-filtration plasma exchange, utilizes two hollow-fiber filters with different pore sizes. The first filter (average pore diameter of 0.2 μm) works as a plasma separator, while the second filter (average pore diameter of 0.03 μm) selectively traps VLDL, IDL, and LDL preferentially relative to HDL and other plasma constituents.[249]

Liver Transplantation. A direct approach to overcoming the receptor defect in homozygous FH was recently carried out in a 6-year-old patient, whose initials are S.J. This little girl had a total cholesterol level over 1000 mg/dl and had sustained repeated episodes of myocardial infarction. After she failed to respond to two coronary bypass procedures plus a mitral valve replacement, she was subjected to combined heart-liver transplantation by a team of surgeons led by Thomas E. Starzl at the University of Pittsburgh.[250,251] The liver transplant was designed to provide a source of LDL receptors. The heart transplantation was necessitated because of the poor condition of her own heart as a result of the atherosclerotic process.

Immediately after the operation, S.J.'s total plasma cholesterol level fell from 1100 mg/dl to the range of 200 to 300 mg/dl, and it remained in that range for the succeeding 13 months (Fig. 48-34). Thereafter she was started on the HMG CoA reductase inhibitor lovastatin (mevinolin), and her cholesterol fell further to the range of 150 to 200 mg/dl.[251,252] Liver transplantation not only lowered the plasma cholesterol level but it also restored responsiveness to lovastatin, which requires a normal LDL receptor gene in order to act. Lipoprotein turnover studies performed 6 months after surgery confirmed that the new LDL receptors furnished by the transplanted liver were responsible for the dramatic drop in plasma cholesterol level.[251] S.J. remains asymptomatic at the time of this writing (4.5 years after transplantation), and her cutaneous xanthomas have resolved. However, she requires continuous therapy with cyclosporin to prevent rejection of the transplanted organs, and her long-term prognosis is uncertain.

The response to liver transplantation in S.J. underscores the importance of hepatic LDL receptors in vivo and raises the possibility that other FH homozygotes may respond to similar transplantation procedures. In appropriate cases liver transplantation should be performed before heart transplantation becomes necessary.

Fig. 48-34 Plasma total cholesterol levels in S. J., a patient with homozygous FH, before and after liver-heart transplantation. The patient was started on lovastatin, an LDL-lowering drug, at the indicated time after transplantation.

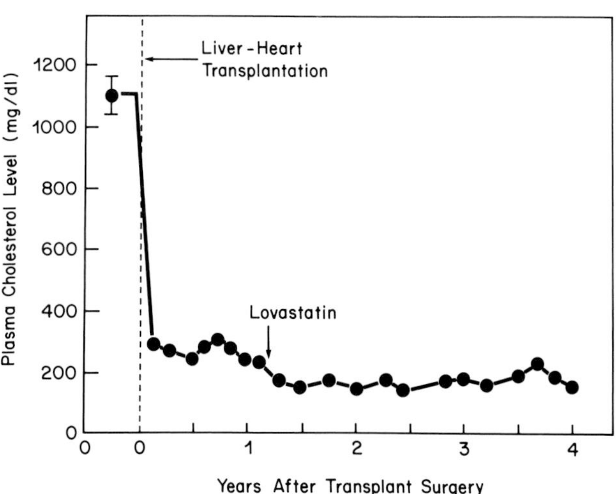

REFERENCES

1. MULLER C: Xanthomata, hypercholesterolemia, angina pectoris. *Acta Med Scand Suppl* 89:75, 1938.
2. MULLER C: Angina pectoris in hereditary xanthomatosis. *Arch Intern Med* 64:675, 1939.
3. BROWN MS, GOLDSTEIN JL: A receptor-mediated pathway for cholesterol homeostasis. *Science* 232:34, 1986.
4. FOGGE CH: General xanthelasma or vitilogoidea. *Trans Pathol Soc London* 24:242, 1872.
5. FOX TC: A case of xanthelasma multiplex. *Lancet* 2:688, 1879.
6. POENSGEN A: Mittheilung eines seltenen Falles von Xanthelasma multiplex. *Arch Pathol Anat Physiol* 91:350, 1883.
7. LEHZEN G, KNAUSS K: Über Xanthoma multiplex planum, tuberosum, mollusciforme. *Arch Pathol Anat Physiol* 116:85, 1889.
8. THANNHAUSER SJ, MAGENDANTZ H: The different clinical groups of xanthomatous diseases: A clinical physiological study of 22 cases. *Ann Intern Med* 11:1662, 1938.
9. THANNHAUSER SJ: *Lipiodoses*. New York, Oxford, 1950.
10. WILKINSON CF, HAND EA, FLIEGELMAN MT: Essential familial hypercholesterolemia. *Ann Intern Med* 29:671, 1948.
11. WILKINSON CF: Essential familial hypercholesterolemia: Cutaneous metabolic and hereditary aspects. *Bull NY Acad Med* 26:670, 1950.
12. ADLERSBERG D, PARETS AD, BOAS EP: Genetics of atherosclerosis. Studies of families with xanthoma and unselected patients with coronary artery disease under the age of fifty years. *JAMA* 141:246, 1949.
13. ADLERSBERG D: Hypercholesterolemia with predisposition to atherosclerosis: An inborn error of lipid metabolism. *Am J Med* 11:600, 1951.
14. ADLERSBERG D: Inborn errors of lipid metabolism. *Arch Pathol* 60:481, 1955.
15. BLOOM D, KAUFMAN SR, STEVENS RA: Hereditary xanthomatosis: Familial incidence of xanthoma tuberosum associated with hypercholesterolemia and cardiovascular involvement with report of several cases of sudden death. *Arch Dermatol Syph* 45:1, 1942.
16. ALVORD RM: Coronary heart disease and xanthoma tuberosum associated with hereditary hyperlipidemia. *Arch Intern Med* 84:1002, 1949.
17. PIPER J, ORRILD L: Essential familial hypercholesterolemia and xanthomatosis. *Am J Med* 21:34, 1956.
18. EPSTEIN FH, BLOCK WD, HAND EA, FRANCIS T Jr: Familial hypercholesterolemia, xanthomatosis and coronary heart disease. *Am J Med* 26:39, 1959.
19. HIRSCHHORN K, WILKINSON CF: The mode of inheritance in essential familial hypercholestrolemia. *Am J Med* 26:60, 1959.
20. GURAVICH JL: Familial hypercholesterolemic xanthomatosis: A preliminary report. *Am J Med* 24:8, 1959.
21. KHACHADURIAN AK: The inheritance of essential familial hypercholesterolemia. *Am J Med* 37:402, 1964.
22. GOFMAN JW, deLALLA O, GLAZIER F, FREEMAN NK, LINDGREN FT, NICHOLAS AV, STRISHOWER EH, TAMPLIN AR: The serum lipoprotein transport system in health metabolic disorders, atherosclerosis and coronary artery disease. *Plasma* 2:413, 1954.

23. GOFMAN JW, RUBIN L, MCGINLEY JP, JONES HB: Hyperlipoproteinemia. *Am J Med* 17:514, 1954.
24. FREDRICKSON DS, LEVY RI, LEES RS: Fat transport in lipoproteins—An integrated approach to mechanisms and disorders. *N Engl J Med* 276:32, 94, 148, 215, 273, 1967.
25. GOLDSTEIN JL, BROWN MS: Binding and degradation of low density lipoproteins by cultured human fibroblasts: Comparison of cells from a normal subject and from a patient with homozygous familial hypercholesterolemia. *J Biol Chem* 249:5153, 1974.
26. HARLAN WR JR, GRAHAM JB, ESTES EH: Familial hypercholesterolemia: A genetic and metabolic study. *Medicine* 45:77, 1966.
27. SCROTT HG, GOLDSTEIN JL, HAZZARD WR, MCGOODWIN MM, MOTULSKY AG: Familial hypercholesterolemia in a large kindred. Evidence for a monogenic mechanism. *Ann Intern Med* 76:711, 1972.
28. KWITEROVICH PO JR, LEVY RI, FREDRICKSON DS: Neonatal diagnosis of familial type II hyperlipoproteinaemia. *Lancet* 1:118, 1973.
29. KWITEROVICH PO JR, FREDRICKSON DS, LEVY RI: Familial hypercholesterolemia (one form of familial type II hyperlipoproteinemia). A study of its biochemical, genetic, and clinical presentation in childhood. *J Clin Invest* 53:1237, 1974.
30. KHACHADURIAN AK: A general view of clinical and laboratory features of familial hypercholesterolemia (type II hyperbetalipoproteinemia). *Protides Biol Fluids* 19:315, 1971.
31. FREDRICKSON DS, LEVY RI: Familial hyperlipoproteinemia, in Stanbury JB, Wyngaarden JB, Fredrickson DS (eds): *The Metabolic Basis of Inherited Disease,* 3d ed. New York, McGraw-Hill, 1972, p 545.
32. KHACHADURIAN AK, UTHMAN SM: Experiences with the homozygous cases of familial hypercholesterolemia. A report of 52 patients. *Nutr Metab* 15:132, 1973.
33. STANLEY P, CHARTRAND C, D'AVIGNON A: Acquired aortic stenosis in a twelve-year-old girl with xanthomatosis. *N Engl J Med* 273:1378, 1965.
34. BEPPU S, MINURA Y, SAKAKIBARA H, NEGATA S, PARK Y-D, NAMBU S, YAMAMOTO A: Supravalvular aortic stenosis and coronary ostial stenosis in familial hypercholesterolemia: Two-dimensional echocardiographic assessment. *Circulation* 67:878, 1983.
35. NEVIN NC, SLACK J: Hyperlipidaemic xanthomatosis. II. Mode of inheritance in 55 families with essential hyperlipidaemia and xanthomatosis. *J Med Genet* 5:9, 1968.
36. HABH T, MABUCHI H, YOSHIMURA A, WATANABE A, WAKASUGI T, TATAMI T, UEDA K, UEDA R, KAMETANI T, KOIZUMI J, MIYAMOTO S, TAKEDA R, TAKESHITA H: Effects of ML-236B (compactin) on sterol synthesis and low density lipoprotein receptor activities in fibroblasts of patients with homozygous familial hypercholesterolemia. *J Clin Invest* 67:1532, 1981.
37. SLACK J, MILLS GL: Anomalous low density lipoproteins in familial hyperbetalipoproteinaemia. *Clin Chim Acta* 29:15, 1970.
38. GOTTO AM, BROWN WV, LEVY RI, BIRNBAUMER ME, FREDRICKSON DS: Evidence for the identity of the major apoprotein in low density and very low density lipoprotein in normal subjects and patients with familial hyperlipoproteinemia. *J Clin Invest* 51:1486, 1972.
39. FISHER WR, HAMMOND MG, WARMKE GL: Measurements of the molecular weight variability of plasma low density lipoproteins among normals and subjects with hyper-β-lipoproteinemia. Demonstration of macromolecular heterogeneity. *Biochemistry* 11:519, 1972.
40. JADHAV AV, THOMPSON GR: Reversible abnormalities of low density lipoprotein composition in familial hypercholesterolaemia. *Eur J Clin Invest* 9:63, 1979.
41. BAGNALL TF, LLOYD JK: Composition of low-density lipoprotein in children with hyperlipoproteinaemia. *Clin Chim Acta* 59:271, 1975.
42. GRANT EH, SHEPPARD RJ, MILLS GL, SLACK J: A dielectric investigation of the water of hydration of low-density lipoproteins in familial hyperbetalipoproteinaemia. *Lancet* 1:1159, 1972.
43. REICHL D, SIMONS LA, MYANT NB: The metabolism of low-density lipoprotein in a patient with familial hyperbetalipoproteinaemia. *Clin Sci Mol Med* 47:635, 1974.
44. PATSCH W, WITZTUM JL, OSTLUND R, SCHONFELD G: Structure, immunology, and cell reactivity of low density lipoprotein from umbilical vein of a newborn type II homozygote. *J Clin Invest* 66:123, 1980.
45. GOLDSTEIN JL, BROWN MS: Familial hypercholesterolemia: Identification of a defect in the regulation of 3-hydroxy-3-methylglutaryl coenzyme A reductase activity associated with overproduction of cholesterol. *Proc Natl Acad Sci USA* 70:2804, 1973.
46. STREJA D, STEINER G, KWITEROVICH PO Jr: Plasma high-density lipoproteins and ischemic heart disease: Studies in a large kindred with familial hypercholesterolemia. *Ann Intern Med* 89:871, 1978.
47. SEFTEL HC, BAKER SG, SANDLER MP, FORMAN MB, JOFFE BI, MENDELSOHN D, JENKINS T, MEINY CJ: A host of hypercholesterolaemic homozygotes in South Africa. *Brit Med J* 281:633, 1980.
48. MENKES JK, SCHIMSCHOCK JR, SWANSON PD: Cerebrotendinous xanthomatosis. *Arch Neurol* 19:47, 1968.
49. PHILIPPART M, van BOGAERT L: Cholestanolosis (cerebrotendinous xanthomatosis). *Arch Neurol* 21:603, 1969.
50. MACARAEG PVJ JR, LASAGNA L, SNYDER B: Arcus not so senilis. *Ann Intern Med* 68:345, 1968.
51. ROSE V, WILSON G, STEINER G: Familial hypercholesterolemia: Report of coronary death at age 3 in a homozygous child and prenatal diagnosis in a heterozygous sibling. *J Pediatr* 100:757, 1982.
52. GOLDSTEIN JL: The cardiac manifestations of homozygous and heterozygous forms of familial type II hyperbetalipoproteinemia. *Birth Defects* 8:202, 1972.
53. SPRECHER DL, SCHAEFER EJ, KENT KM, GREGG RE, ZECH LA, HOEG JM, MCMANUS B, ROBERTS WC, BREWER HB JR: Cardiovascular features of homozygous familial hypercholesterolemia: Analysis of 16 patients. *Am J Cardiol* 54:20, 1984.
54. SPRECHER DL, HOEG JM, SCHAEFER EJ, ZECH LA, GREGG RE, LAKATOS E, BREWER HB JR: The association of LDL receptor activity, LDL cholesterol level, and clinical course in homozygous familial hypercholesterolemia. *Metabolism* 34:294, 1985.
55. HENDRY WD, SEED M: Homozygous familial hypercholesterolaemia with supravalvar aortic stenosis treated by surgery. *J R Soc Med* 78:334, 1985.
56. KHACHADURIAN AK: Migatory polyarthritis in familial hypercholesterolemia (type II hyperlipoproteinemia). *Arthritis Rheum* 11:385, 1968.
57. KHACHADURIAN AK: Persistent elevation of the erythrocyte sedimentation rate (ESR) in familial hypercholesterolemia. *J Med Liban* 20:31, 1967.
58. SLACK J: Risks of ischaemic heart-disease in familial hyperlipoproteinaemic states. *Lancet* 2:1380, 1969.
59. JENSEN J, BLANKENHORN DH, KORNERUP V: Coronary disease in familial hypercholesterolemia. *Circulation* 36:77, 1967.
60. HEIBERG A: The risk of atherosclerotic vascular disease in subjects with xanthomatosis. *Acta Med Scand* 198:249, 1975.
61. STONE NJ, LEVY RI, FREDRICKSON DS, VERTER J: Coronary artery disease in 116 kindred with familial type II hyperlipoproteinemia. *Circulation* 49:476, 1974.
62. MABUCHI H, MIYAMOTO S, UEDA K, OOTA M, TAKEGOSHI T, WAKASUGI T, TAKEDA R: Causes of death in patients with familial hypercholesterolemia. *Atherosclerosis* 61:1, 1986.
63. BEAUMONT V, JACOTOT B, BEAUMONT JL: Ischaemic disease in men and women with familial hypercholesterolaemia and xanthomatosis. A comparative study of genetic and environmental factors in 274 heterozygous cases. *Atherosclerosis* 24:441, 1976.
64. MATHON G, GAGNE C, BRUN D, LUPIEN P-J, MOORJANI S: Articular manifestations of familial hypercholesterolaemia. *Ann Rheum Dis* 44:599, 1985.
65. ROONEY PJ, THIRD J, MADKOUR MM, SPENCER D, DICK WC: Transient polyarthritis associated with familial hyperbetalipoproteinaemia. *Q J Med* 47:249, 1978.
66. GUNTHER SF, GUNTHER AG, HOEG JM, KRUTH HS: Multiple flexor tendon xanthomas and contractures in the hands of a child with familial hypercholesterolemia. *J Hand Surg* 11A:588, 1986.
67. MIETTINEN TA, ARO A: Comparison of clinical findings in patients with hyperglyceridaemia and familial hypercholesterolaemia. *Ann Clin Res* 5:1, 1973.
68. GOLDSTEIN JL, BROWN MS: The LDL receptor locus and the genetics of familial hypercholesterolemia. *Annu Rev Genet* 13:259, 1979.
69. MABUCHI H, TATAMI R, HABA T, UEDA K, UEDA R, KAMETANI T, ITOH S, KOIZUMI J, OOTA M, MIYAMOTO S, TAKEDA R, TAKESHITA H: Homozygous familial hypercholesterolemia in Japan. *Am J Med* 65:290, 1978.
70. BUJA LM, KOVANEN PT, BILHEIMER DW: Cellular pathology of homozygous familial hypercholesterolemia. *Am J Pathol* 97:327, 1979.
71. TSANG RC, GLUECK CJ, MCLAIN C, RUSSELL P, JOYCE T, BOVE K, MELLIES M, STEINER PM: Pregnancy, parturition, and lactation in familial homozygous hypercholesterolemia. *Metabolism* 27:823, 1978.
72. GOLDSTEIN JL, BROWN MS: Unpublished observations.
73. KOMURO I, KATO H, NAKAGAWA T, TAKAHASHI K, MINORI A, TAKEUCHI F, NISHIDA Y, MIYAMOTO T: The longest-lived homozygous familial hypercholesterolemia mutant with a defect in internalization. Personal communication, 1985.
74. OTT J, SCHROTT HG, GOLDSTEIN JL, HAZZARD WR, ALLEN FH JR, FALK CT, MOTULSKY AG: Linkage studies in a large kindred with familial hypercholesterolemia. *Am J Hum Genet* 26:598, 1974.
75. BERG K, HEIBERG A: Linkage studies on familial hyperlipoproteinemia with xanthomatosis: Normal lipoprotein markers and the C3 polymorphism. *Cytogenet Cell Genet* 16:266, 1976.
76. WHITEHEAD, ET AL: Assignment of the structural gene for the third component of human complement to chromosome 19. *Proc Natl Acad Sci USA* 79:5021, 1982.

77. FRANCKE U, BROWN MS, GOLDSTEIN JL: Assignment of the human gene for the low density lipoprotein receptor to chromosome 19: Synteny of a receptor, a ligand, and a genetic disease. *Proc Natl Acad Sci USA* 81:2826, 1984.

78. LINDGREN V, LUSKEY KL, RUSSELL DW, FRANCKE U: Human genes involved in cholesterol metabolism: Chromosomal mapping of the loci for the low density lipoprotein receptor and 3-hydroxy-3-methylglutaryl-coenzyme A reductase with cDNA probes. *Proc Natl Acad Sci USA* 82:8567, 1985.

79. PATTERSON D, SLACK J: Lipid abnormalities in male and female survivors of myocardial infarction and their first-degree relatives. *Lancet* 1:393, 1972.

80. GOLDSTEIN JL, SCHROTT HG, HAZZARD WR, BIERMAN EL, MOTULSKY AG: Hyperlipidemia in coronary heart disease. II. Genetic analysis of lipid levels in 176 families and delineation of a new inherited disorder, combined hyperlipidemia. *J Clin Invest* 52:1544, 1973.

81. NIKKILA EA, ARO A: Family study of serum lipids and lipoproteins in coronary heart disease. *Lancet* 1:954, 1973.

82. CARTER CO, SLACK J, MYANT NB: Genetics of hyperlipoproteinaemias. *Lancet* 1:400, 1971.

83. SLACK J: Inheritance of familial hypercholesterolemia. *Atherosclerosis Rev* 5:35, 1979.

84. LEONARD JV, FOSBROOKE AS, LLOYD JK, WOLFF OH: Screening for familial hyper-β-lipoproteinaemia in children in hospital. *Arch Dis Child* 51:842, 1976.

85. HEIBERG A, BERG K: The inheritance of hyperlipoproteinaemia with xanthomatosis. *Clin Genet* 9:203, 1976.

86. ANDERSON GE, LOUS P, FRIIS-HANSEN B: Screening for hyperlipoproteinemia in 10,000 Danish newborns. Follow-up studies in 522 children with elevated cord serum VLDL-LDL-cholesterol. *Acta Paediatr Scand* 68:541, 1979.

87. MABUCHI H, TATAMI R, UEDA K, UEDA R, HABA T, KAMETANI T, WATANABE A, WAKASUGI T, ITO S, KOIZUMI J, OHTA M, MIYAMOTO S, TAKEDA R: Serum lipid and liporotein levels in Japanese patients with familial hypercholesterolemia. *Atherosclerosis* 32:435, 1979.

88. JENKINS T, NICHOLLS E, GORDON E, MENDELSOHN D, SEFTEL HC, ANDREW MJA: Familial hypercholesterolaemia—A common genetic disorder in the Afrikaans population. *S Afr Med J* 57:943, 1980.

89. GOLDSTEIN JL, BROWN MS: Familial hypercholesterolemia, in Stanbury JB, Wyngaarden JB, Fredrickson DS, Goldstein JL, Brown MS (eds): *The Metabolic Basis of Inherited Disease*, 5th ed. New York, McGraw-Hill, 1983, chap 33, pp 672–712.

90. ROBERTS WC, FERRANS VJ, LEVY RI, FREDRICKSON DS: Cardiovascular pathology in hyperlipoproteinemia. Anatomic observations in 42 necropsy patients with normal or abnormal serum lipoprotein patterns. *Am J Cardiol* 31:557, 1973.

91. BROWN MS, KOVANEN PT, GOLDSTEIN JL, EECKELS R, VANDENBERGHE K, BERGHE HVD, FRYNS JP, CASSIMAN JJ: Prenatal diagnosis of homozygous familial hypercholesterolaemia: Expression of a genetic receptor disease in utero. *Lancet* 1:526, 1978.

92. ROSS R: The pathogenesis of atherosclerosis—An update. *N Engl J Med* 314:488, 1986.

93. BULKLEY BH, BUJA LM, FERRANS VJ, BULKLEY GB, ROBERTS WC: Tuberous xanthoma in homozygous type II hyperlipoproteinemia. *Arch Pathol* 99:293, 1975.

94. GOLDSTEIN JL, BROWN MS: Atherosclerosis: The low-density lipoprotein receptor hypothesis. *Metabolism* 26:1257, 1977.

95. BROWN MS, GOLDSTEIN JL: Lipoprotein metabolism in the macrophage: Implications for cholesterol deposition in atherosclerosis. *Annu Rev Biochem* 52:223, 1983.

96. GOLDSTEIN JL, BROWN MS: The low-density lipoprotein pathway and its relation to atherosclerosis. *Annu Rev Biochem* 46:897, 1977.

97. BROWN MS, GOLDSTEIN JL: Lipoprotein receptors in the liver: Control signals for plasma cholesterol traffic. *J Clin Invest* 72:743, 1983.

98. GOLDSTEIN JL, BASU SK, BRUNSCHEDE GY, BROWN MS: Release of low density lipoprotein from its cell surface receptor by sulfated glycosaminoglycans. *Cell* 7:85, 1976.

99. BROWN MS, GOLDSTEIN JL: Regulation of the activity of the low density lipoprotein receptor in human fibroblasts. *Cell* 6:307, 1975.

100. SCHNEIDER WJ, BEISIEGEL U, GOLDSTEIN JL, BROWN MS: Purification of the low density lipoprotein receptor, an acidic glycoprotein of 164,000 molecular weight. *J Biol Chem* 257:2664, 1982.

101. CUMMINGS RD, KORNFELD S, SCHNEIDER WJ, HOBGOOD KK, TOLLESHAUG T, BROWN MS, GOLDSTEIN JL: Biosynthesis of the N- and O-linked oligosaccharides of the low density lipoprotein receptor. *J Biol Chem* 258:15261, 1983.

102. DAVIS CG, ELHAMMER A, RUSSELL DW, SCHNEIDER WJ, KORNFELD S, BROWN MS, GOLDSTEIN JL: Deletion of clustered O-linked carbohydrates does not impair function of low density lipoprotein receptor in transfected fibroblasts. *J Biol Chem* 261:2828, 1986.

103. BERSOT TP, MAHLEY RW, BROWN MS, GOLDSTEIN JL: Interaction of swine lipoproteins with the low density lipoprotein receptor in human fibroblasts. *J Biol Chem* 251:2395, 1976.

104. INNERARITY TL, MAHLEY RW: Enhanced binding by cultured human fibroblasts of apo-E-containing lipoproteins as compared with low density lipoproteins. *Biochemistry* 17:1440, 1978.

105. BASU SK, GOLDSTEIN JL, ANDERSON RGW, BROWN MS: Degradation of cationized low density lipoprotein and regulation of cholesterol metabolism in homozygous familial hypercholesterolemia fibroblasts. *Proc Natl Acad Sci USA* 73:3178, 1976.

106. WEISGRABER KH, INNERARITY TL, MAHLEY RW: Role of the lysine residues of plasma lipoproteins in high affinity binding to cell surface receptors on human fibroblasts. *J Biol Chem* 253:9053, 1978.

107. MAHLEY RW, INNERARITY TL, PITAS RE, WEISGRABER KH, BROWN JH, GROSS E: Inhibition of lipoprotein binding to cell surface receptors of fibroblasts following selective modification of arginyl residues in arginine-rich and B-apoproteins. *J Biol Chem* 252:7279, 1977.

108. TOLLESHAUG H, GOLDSTEIN JL, SCHNEIDER WJ, BROWN MS: Posttranslational processing of the LDL receptor and its genetic disruption in familial hypercholesterolemia. *Cell* 30:715, 1982.

109. GOLDSTEIN JL, ANDERSON RGW, BROWN MS: Coated pits, coated vesicles, and receptor-mediated endocytosis. *Nature* 279:679, 1979.

110. BROWM MS, ANDERSON RGW, GOLDSTEIN JL: Recycling receptors: The round-trip itinerary of migrant membrane proteins. *Cell* 32:663, 1983.

111. HELENIUS A, MELLMAN I, WALL D, HUBBARD A: Endosomes. *Trends Biochem Sci* 8:245, 1983.

112. BASU SK, GOLDSTEIN JL, ANDERSON RGW, BROWN MS: Monensin interrupts the recycling of low density lipoprotein receptors in human fibroblasts. *Cell* 24:493, 1981.

113. GOLDSTEIN JL, DANA SE, FAUST JR, BEAUDET AL, BROWN MS: Role of lysosomal acid lipase in the metabolism of plasma low density lipoprotein: Observations in cultured fibroblasts from a patient with cholesteryl ester storage disease. *J Biol Chem* 250:8487, 1975.

114. BROWN MS, FAUST JR, GOLDSTEIN JL: Role of the low density lipoprotein receptor in regulating the content of free and esterified cholesterol in human fibroblasts. *J Clin Invest* 55:783, 1975.

115. ANDERSON RGW, GOLDSTEIN JL, BROWN MS: Localization of low density lipoprotein receptors on plasma membrane of normal human fibroblasts and their absence in cells from a familial hypercholesterolemia homozygote. *Proc Natl Acad Sci USA* 73:2434, 1976.

116. ANDERSON RGW, BROWN MS, GOLDSTEIN JL: Role of the coated endocytic vesicle in the uptake of receptor-bound low density lipoprotein in human fibroblasts. *Cell* 10:351, 1977.

117. CARPENTIER J-L, GORDON P, GOLDSTEIN JL, ANDERSON RGW, BROWN MS, ORCI L: Binding and internalization of ^{125}I-LDL in normal and mutant human fibroblasts: A quantitative autoradiographic study. *Exp Cell Res* 121:135, 1979.

118. BROWN MS, DANA SE, GOLDSTEIN JL: Regulation of 3-hydroxy-3-methylglutaryl coenzyme A reductase activity in cultured human fibroblasts: Comparison of cells from a normal subject and from a patient with homozygous familial hypercholesterolemia. *J Biol Chem* 249:789, 1974.

119. GOLDSTEIN JL, DANA SE, BROWN MS: Esterification of low density lipoprotein cholesterol in human fibroblasts and its absence in homozygous familial hypercholesterolemia. *Proc Natl Acad Sci USA* 71:4288, 1974.

120. DIETSCHY JM, WILSON JD: Regulation of cholesterol metabolism. *N Engl J Med* 282:1128, 1970.

121. HAVEL RJ, GOLDSTEIN JL, BROWN MS: Lipoproteins and lipid transport, in Bondy PK, Rosenberg LE (eds): *Metabolic Control and Disease*, 8th ed. Philadelphia, WB Saunders, 1980, p 393.

122. YAMAMOTO T, DAVIS CG, BROWN MS, SCHNEIDER WJ, CASEY ML, GOLDSTEIN JL, RUSSELL DW: The human LDL receptor: A cysteine-rich protein with multiple Alu sequences in its mRNA. *Cell* 39:27, 1984.

123. SUDHOF TC, GOLDSTEIN JL, BROWN MS, RUSSELL DW: The LDL receptor gene: A mosaic of exons shared with different proteins. *Science* 228:815, 1985.

124. GOLDSTEIN JL, BROWN MS, ANDERSON RGW, RUSSELL DW, SCHNEIDER WJ: Receptor-mediated endocytosis: Concepts emerging from the LDL receptor system. *Annu Rev Cell Biol* 1:1, 1985.

125. INNERARITY TL, WEISGRABER KH, ARNOLD KS, RALL SC JR, MAHLEY RW: Normalization of receptor binding of apolipoprotein E2: Evidence for modulation of the binding site conformation. *J Biol Chem* 259:7261, 1984.

126. KNOTT TJ, RALL SC JR, INNERARITY TL, JACOBSON SF, URDEA MS, LEVY-WILSON B, POWELL LM, PEASE RJ, EDDY R, NAKAI H, BYERS M, PRIESTLEY LM, ROBERTSON E, RALL LB, BETSCHOLTZ C, SHOWS TB, MAHLEY RW, SCOTT J: Human apolipoprotein B: Structure of carboxyl-terminal do-

mains, sites of gene expression, and chromosomal localization. *Science* 230:37, 1985.

127. RUSSELL DW, SCHNEIDER WJ, YAMAMOTO T, LUSKEY KL, BROWN MS, GOLDSTEIN JL: Domain map of the LDL receptor: Sequence homology with the epidermal growth factor precursor. *Cell* 37:577, 1984.

128. SUDHOF TC, RUSSELL DW, GOLDSTEIN JL, BROWN MS, SANCHEZ-PESCADOR R, BELL GI: Cassette of eight exons shared by genes for LDL receptor and EGF precursor. *Science* 228:893, 1985.

128a. DAVIS CG, GOLDSTEIN JL, SUDHOF TC, ANDERSON RGW, RUSSELL DW, BROWN MS: Growth factor homology region in LDL receptor mediates acid-dependent dissociation and receptor recycling. *Nature* 326:760, 1987.

128b. KINGSLEY DM, KOZARSKY KF, HOBBIE L, KRIEGER M: Reversible defects in O-linked glycosylation and LDL receptor expression in a UDP-Gal/UDP-GalNAc 4-epimerase deficient mutant. *Cell* 44:749, 1986.

129. LEHRMAN MA, SCHNEIDER WJ, SUDHOF TC, BROWN MS, GOLDSTEIN JL, RUSSELL DW: Mutation in LDL receptor: Alu-Alu recombination deletes exons encoding transmembrane and cytoplasmic domains. *Science* 227:140, 1985.

130. YAMAMOTO T, BISHOP RW, BROWN MS, GOLDSTEIN JL, RUSSELL DW: Deletion in cysteine-rich region of LDL receptor impedes transport to cell surface in WHHL rabbit. *Science* 232:1230, 1986.

131. LEHRMAN MA, GOLDSTEIN JL, BROWN MS, RUSSELL DW, SCHNEIDER WJ: Internalization-defective LDL receptors produced by genes with nonsense and frameshift mutations that truncate the cytoplasmic domain. *Cell* 41:735, 1985.

132. DAVIS CG, LEHRMAN MA, RUSSELL DW, ANDERSON RGW, BROWN MS, GOLDSTEIN JL: The J.D. mutation in familial hypercholesterolemia: Substitution of cysteine for tyrosine in cytoplasmic domain impedes internalization of LDL receptors. *Cell* 45:15, 1986.

133. DAVIS CG, VAN DRIEL IR, RUSSELL DW, BROWN MS, GOLDSTEIN JL: The LDL receptor: Identification of amino acids in cytoplasmic domain required for rapid endocytosis. *J Biol Chem* 262:4075, 1987.

134. STANLEY KK, KOCHER H-P, LUZIO JP, JACKSON P, TSCHOPP J: The sequence and topology of human complement component C9. *EMBO J* 4:375, 1985.

135. GILBERT W: Genes-in-pieces revisited. *Science* 228:823, 1985.

136. DOOLITTLE RF: The genealogy of some recently evolved vertebrate proteins. *Trends Biochem Sci* 10:233, 1985.

137. HOBBS HH, LEITERSDORF E, GOLDSTEIN JL, BROWN MS, RUSSELL DW: Multiple crm$^-$ mutations in familial hypercholesterolemia: Evidence for 13 alleles, including four deletions. *J Clin Invest* 81:909, 1988.

137a. HOBBS HH, BROWN MS, RUSSELL DW, DAVIGNON J, GOLDSTEIN JL: Deletion in the gene for the LDL receptor in majority of French Canadians with familial hypercholesterolemia. *N Engl J Med* 317:734, 1987.

138. LEHRMAN MA, RUSSELL DW, GOLDSTEIN JL, BROWN MS: Exon-Alu recombination deletes 5 kilobases from low density lipoprotein receptor gene, producing null phenotype in familial hypercholesterolemia. *Proc Natl Acad Sci USA* 83:3679, 1986.

139. LEHRMAN MA, SCHNEIDER WJ, BROWN MS, DAVIS CG, ELHAMMER A, RUSSELL DW, GOLDSTEIN JL: The Lebanese allele at the LDL receptor locus: Nonsense mutation produces truncated receptor that is retained in endoplasmic reticulum. *J Biol Chem* 262:401, 1987.

140. GETHING M-J, MCCAMMON K, SAMBROOK J: Expression of wild-type and mutant forms of influenza hemagglutinin: The role of folding in intracellular transport. *Cell* 46:939, 1986.

141. HOBBS HH, BROWN MS, GOLDSTEIN JL, RUSSELL DW: Deletion of exon encoding cysteine-rich repeat of LDL receptor alters its binding specificity in a subject with familial hypercholesterolemia. *J Biol Chem* 261:13114, 1986.

142. TOLLESHAUG H, HOBGOOD KK, BROWN MS, GOLDSTEIN JL: The LDL receptor locus in familial hypercholesterolemia: Multiple mutations disrupting the transport and processing of a membrane receptor. *Cell* 32:941, 1983.

143. MAHLEY RW, INNERARITY TL: Lipoprotein receptors and cholesterol homeostasis. *Biochim Biophys Acta* 737:197, 1983.

144. RUSSELL DW, LEHRMAN MA, SUDHOF TC, YAMAMOTO T, DAVIS CG, HOBBS HH, BROWN MS, GOLDSTEIN JL: The LDL receptor in familial hypercholesterolemia: Use of human mutations to dissect a membrane protein. *Cold Spring Harbor Symp Quant Biol* 51:811, 1987.

145. LEHRMAN MA, GOLDSTEIN JL, RUSSELL DW, BROWN MS: Duplication of seven exons in LDL receptor gene caused by Alu-Alu recombination in a subject with familial hypercholesterolemia. *Cell* 48:827, 1987.

146. BROWN MS, GOLDSTEIN JL: Analysis of mutation strain of human fibroblasts with a defect in the internalization of receptor-bound low density lipoprotein. *Cell* 9:663, 1976.

147. GOLDSTEIN JL, BROWN MS, STONE NJ: Genetics of the LDL receptor: Evidence that the mutations affecting binding and internalization are allelic. *Cell* 12:629, 1977.

148. ANDERSON RGW, GOLDSTEIN JL, BROWN MS: A mutation that impairs the ability of lipoprotein receptors to localize in coated pits on the cell surface of human fibroblasts. *Nature* 270:659, 1977.

149. LEHRMAN MA, RUSSELL DW, GOLDSTEIN JL, BROWN MS: Alu-Alu recombination deletes splice acceptor sites and produces secreted LDL receptor in a subject with familial hypercholesterolemia. *J Biol Chem* 262:3354, 1987.

150. GOLDSTEIN JL, SOBHANI MK, FAUST JR, BROWN MS: Heterozygous familial hypercholesterolemia: Failure of normal allele to compensate for mutant allele at a regulated genetic locus. *Cell* 9:195, 1976.

151. FAUST JR, GOLDSTEIN JL, BROWN MS: Receptor-mediated uptake of low density lipoprotein and utilization of its cholesterol for steroid synthesis in cultured mouse adrenal cells. *J Biol Chem* 252:4861, 1977.

152. KOVANEN PT, FAUST JR, BROWN MS, GOLDSTEIN JL: Low density lipoprotein receptors in bovine adrenal cortex. I. Receptor-mediated uptake of low density lipoprotein and utilization of its cholesterol for steroid synthesis in cultured adrenocortical cells. *Endocrinology* 104:599, 1979.

153. HO YK, BROWN MS, BILHEIMER DW, GOLDSTEIN JL: Regulation of low density lipoprotein receptor activity in freshly isolated human lymphocytes. *J Clin Invest* 58:1465, 1976.

154. BILHEIMER DW, HO YK, BROWN MS, ANDERSON RGW, GOLDSTEIN JL: Genetics of the low density lipoprotein receptor: Diminished receptor activity in lymphocytes from heterozygotes with familial hypercholesterolemia. *J Clin Invest* 61:678, 1978.

155. LANGER T, STROBER W, LEVY RI: The metabolism of low density lipoprotein in familial type II hyperlipoproteinemia. *J Clin Invest* 51:1528, 1972.

156. BILHEIMER DW, STONE NJ, GRUNDY SM: Metabolic studies in familial hypercholesterolemia: Evidence for a gene-dosage effect *in vivo*. *J Clin Invest* 64:524, 1979.

157. SIMONS LA, REICHL D, MYANT NB, MANCINI M: The metabolism of the apoprotein of plasma low density lipoprotein in familial hyperbetalipoproteinaemia in the homozygous form. *Atherosclerosis* 21:283, 1975.

158. BILHEIMER DW, GOLDSTEIN JL, GRUNDY SM, BROWN MS: Reduction in cholesterol and low density lipoprotein synthesis after portacaval shunt surgery in a patient with homozygous familial hypercholesterolemia. *J Clin Invest* 56:1420, 1975.

159. KOVANEN PT, BASU SK, GOLDSTEIN JL, BROWN MS: Low density lipoprotein receptors in bovine adrenal cortex. II. Low density lipoprotein binding to membranes prepared from fresh tissue. *Endocrinology* 104:610, 1979.

160. BROWN MS, KOVANEN PT, GOLDSTEIN JL: Receptor-mediated uptake of lipoprotein-cholesterol and its utilization for steroid synthesis in the adrenal cortex. *Recent Prog Horm Res* 35:215, 1979.

161. WINDLER EET, KOVANEN PT, CHAO Y-S, BROWN MS, HAVEL RJ, GOLDSTEIN JL: The estradiol-stimulated lipoprotein receptor of rat liver: A binding site that mediates the uptake of rat lipoproteins containing apoproteins B and E. *J Biol Chem* 255:10464, 1980.

162. BROWN MS, KOVANEN PT, GOLDSTEIN JL: Evolution of the LDL receptor concept—from cultured cells to intact animals. *Ann NY Acad Sci* 348:48, 1980.

163. PITTMAN RC, CAREW TE, ATTIE AD, WITZTUM JL, WATANABE Y, STEINBERG D: Receptor-dependent and receptor-independent degradation of low density lipoprotein in normal rabbits and in receptor-deficient mutant rabbits. *J Biol Chem* 257:7994, 1982.

164. SPADY DK, BILHEIMER DW, DIETSCHY JM: Rates of receptor dependent and independent low density lipoprotein uptake in the hamster. *Proc Natl Acad Sci USA* 80:3499, 1983.

165. STEINBERG D: Lipoproteins and atherosclerosis: A look back and a look ahead. *Arteriosclerosis* 3:283, 1983.

166. SHEPHERD J, BICKER S, LORIMER AR, PACKARD CJ: Receptor mediated low density lipoprotein catabolism in man. *J Lipid Res* 20:999, 1979.

167. MAHLEY RW, WEISGRABER KH, MELCHIOR GW, INNERARITY TL, HOLCOMBE KS: Inhibition of receptor-mediated clearance of lysine- and arginine-modified lipoproteins from the plasma of rats and monkeys. *Proc Natl Acad Sci USA* 77:225, 1980.

168. STEINBRECHER UP, WITZTUM JL, KESANIEMI YA, ELAM RL: Comparison of glucosylated low density lipoprotein with methylated or cyclohexanedione-treated low density lipoprotein in the measurement of receptor-independent low density lipoprotein catabolism. *J Clin Invest* 71:960, 1983.

169. BILHEIMER DW, GRUNDY SM, BROWN MS, GOLDSTEIN JL: Mevinolin stimulates receptor-mediated clearance of low density lipoprotein from plasma in familial hypercholesterolemia heterozygotes. *Trans Assoc Am Physicians* 96:1, 1983.

170. WATANABE Y: Serial inbreeding of rabbits with hereditary hyperlipidemia (WHHL-rabbit). Incidence and development of atherosclerosis and xanthoma. *Atherosclerosis* 36:261, 1980.

171. KITA T, BROWN MS, WATANABE Y, GOLDSTEIN JL: Deficiency of LDL re-

ceptors in liver and adrenal gland of the WHHL rabbit, an animal model of familial hypercholesterolemia. *Proc Natl Acad Sci USA* 78:2268, 1981.

172. SCHNEIDER WJ, BROWN MS, GOLDSTEIN JL: Kinetic defects in the processing of the LDL receptor in fibroblasts from WHHL rabbits and a family with familial hypercholesterolemia. *Mol Biol Med* 1:353, 1983.

173. BUJA LM, KITA T, GOLDSTEIN JL, WATANABE Y, BROWN MS: Cellular pathology of progressive atherosclerosis in the WHHL rabbit, an animal model of familial hypercholesterolemia. *Arteriosclerosis* 3:87, 1983.

174. GOLDSTEIN JL, KITA T, BROWN MS: Defective lipoprotein receptors and atherosclerosis: Lessons from an animal counterpart of familial hypercholesterolemia. *N Engl J Med* 309:288, 1983.

175. SOUTAR AK, MYANT NB, THOMPSON GR: Simultaneous measurement of apolipoprotein B turnover in very-low- and low-density lipoproteins in familial hypercholesterolaemia. *Atherosclerosis* 28:247, 1977.

176. GITLIN D, CORNWELL DG, NAKASATO D, ONCLEY JL, HUGHES WL JR, JANEWAY CA: Studies on the metabolism of plasma proteins in the nephrotic syndrome. II. The lipoproteins. *J Clin Invest* 37:172, 1958.

177. BILHEIMER DW, EISENBERG S, LEVY RI: The metabolism of very low density lipoprotein proteins. I. Preliminary *in vitro* and *in vivo* observations. *Biochim Biophys Acta* 260:212, 1972.

178. KITA T, BROWN MS, BILHEIMER DW, GOLDSTEIN JL: Delayed clearance of very low density and intermediate density lipoproteins with enhanced conversion to low density lipoprotein in WHHL rabbits. *Proc Natl Acad Sci USA* 79:5693, 1982.

179. YAMADA N, SHAMES DM, HAVEL RJ: Effect of LDL receptor deficiency on the metabolism of apo B-100 in blood plasma: Kinetic studies in normal and Watanabe heritable hyperlipidemic (WHHL) rabbits. *J Clin Invest* 80:507, 1987.

180. SPADY DK, HUETTINGER M, BILHEIMER DW, DIETSCHY JM: Role of receptor-independent low density lipoprotein transport in the maintenance of tissue cholesterol balance in the normal and WHHL rabbit. *J Lipid Res* 28:32, 1987.

181. GOLDSTEIN JL, BROWN MS: Familial hypercholesterolemia: Pathogenesis of a receptor disease. *Johns Hopkins Med J* 143:8, 1978.

182. GOLDSTEIN JL, HO YK, BASU SK, BROWN MS: Binding site on macrophages that mediates uptake and degradation of acetylated low density lipoprotein, producing massive cholesterol deposition. *Proc Natl Acad Sci USA* 76:333, 1979.

183. GRUNDY SM, AHRENS EH JR, SALEN G: Interruption of the enterohepatic circulation of bile acids in man: Comparative effects of cholestyramine and ileal exclusion on cholesterol metabolism. *J Lab Clin Med* 78:94, 1971.

184. MIETTINEN TA: Cholesterol and bile acid synthesis in two families with homozygous and heterozygous hypercholesterolemia. *Arteriosclerosis* 4:383, 1984.

185. STACPOOLE PW, GRUNDY SM, SWIFT LL, GREENE HL, SLONIM AE, BURR IM: Elevated cholesterol and bile acid synthesis in an adult patient with homozygous familial hypercholesterolemia. *J Clin Invest* 68:1166, 1981.

186. LEWIS B, MYANT NB: Studies in the metabolism of cholesterol in subjects with normal plasma cholesterol levels and in patients with essential hypercholesterolaemia. *Clin Sci* 32:201, 1967.

187. SCHWARTZ KB, WITZTUM J, SCHONFELD G, GRUNDY SM, CONNOR WE: Elevated cholesterol and bile acid synthesis in a young patient with homozygous familial hypercholesterolemia. *J Clin Invest* 64:756, 1979.

188. SAMUEL P, PERL W, HOLTZMAN CM, ROCHMAN ND, LIEBERMAN S: Long-term kinetics of serum and xanthoma cholesterol radioactivity in patients with hypercholesterolemia. *J Clin Invest* 51:266, 1972.

189. MORGANROTH J, LEVY RI, MCMAHON AE, GOTTO AM JR: Pseudohomozygous type II hyperlipoproteinemia. *J Pediatr* 85:639, 1974.

190. MISHKEL MA: Pseudohomozygous and pseudoheterozygous type II hyperlipoproteinemia. *Am J Dis Child* 130:991, 1976.

191. HAMADA K, TANAKA T, YOSHII O, SAITO S, HAYAKAWA K, KIDA N, OHTAKI S, SAKAI Y, MABUCHI H: Pseudohomozygous type II hyperlipoproteinemia. *Jpn J Hum Genet* 27:259, 1982.

192. BRESLOW JL, KAYDEN HJ: Personal communications, 1977.

193. ROSE HG, KRANZ P, WEINSTOCK M, JULIANO J, HAFT JI: Inheritance of combined hyperlipoproteinemia: Evidence for a new lipoprotein phenotype. *Am J Med* 148:160, 1973.

194. BRUNZELL JD, ALBERS JJ, CHAIT A, GRUNDY SM, BROSZEK E, MCDONALD GB: Plasma lipoproteins in familial combined hyperlipidemia and monogenic familial hypertriglyceridemia. *J Lipid Res* 24:147, 1983.

195. GOLDSTEIN JL, BASU SK, BROWN MS: Receptor-mediated endocytosis of LDL in cultured cells. *Methods Enzymol* 98:241, 1983.

195a. DANIEL TO, SCHNEIDER WJ, GOLDSTEIN JL, BROWN MS: Visualization of lipoprotein receptors by ligand blotting. *J Biol Chem* 258:4606, 1983.

196. GOLDSTEIN JL, HELGESON JAS, BROWN MS: Inhibition of cholesterol synthesis with compactin renders growth of cultured cells dependent on the low density lipoprotein receptor. *J Biol Chem* 254:5403, 1979.

197. CUTHBERT JA, EAST CA, BILHEIMER DW, LIPSKY PE: Detection of familial hypercholesterolemia by assaying functional low-density-lipoprotein receptors on lymphocytes. *N Engl J Med* 314:879, 1986.

198. DE GENNES JL, DAFFOS F, DAIROU F, FORESTIER F, CAPELLA-PAVLOSKY M, TRUFFERT J, GASCHARD JC, DARBOIS Y: Direct fetal blood examination for prenatal diagnosis of homozygous familial hypercholesterolemia. *Arteriosclerosis* 5:440, 1985.

199. GOLDSTEIN JL, ALBERS JJ, SCHROTT HG, HAZARD WR, BIERMAN EL, MOTULSKY AR: Plasmid lipid levels and coronary heart disease in adult relatives of newborns with normal and elevated cord blood lipids. *Am J Hum Genet* 26:727, 1974.

200. DARMADY JM, FOSBROOKE AS, LLOYD JK: Prospective study of serum cholesterol levels during first year of life. *Br Med J* 2:685, 1972.

201. SUDHOF TC, RUSSELL DW, BROWN MS, GOLDSTEIN JL: 42-bp element from LDL receptor gene confers end-product repression by sterols when inserted into viral TK promoter. *Cell* 48:1061, 1987.

202. HASHIM SA, VAN ITALLIE TB: Cholestyramine resin therapy for hypercholesterolemia. *JAMA* 192:289, 1965.

203. GRUNDY SM: Treatment of hypercholesterolemia by interference with bile acid metabolism. *Arch Intern Med* 130:638, 1972.

204. BROWN MS, GOLDSTEIN JL: Drugs used in the treatment of hyperlipoproteinemias, in Gilman AG, Goodman LS, Rall TW, Murad F (eds): *Goodman and Gilman's The Pharmacological Basis of Therapeutics*, 7th ed. New York, Macmillan, 1985, chap 34, p 827.

205. LEVY RI, FREDRICKSON DS, STONE NG, BILHEIMER DW, BROWN WV, GLUECK CJ, GOTTO AM, HERBERT PN, KWITEROVICH PO, LANGER T, LAROSA J, LUX SE, RIDER AK, SHILMAN RS, SLOAN HR: Cholestyramine in type II hyperlipoproteinemia. A double-blind trial. *Ann Intern Med* 79:51, 1973.

206. SHEPHERD J, PACKARD CJ, BICKER S, LAWRIE TDV, MORGAN HG: Cholestyramine promotes receptor-mediated low-density-lipoprotein catabolism. *N Engl J Med* 302:1219, 1980.

207. SLATER HR, PACKARD CJ, BICKER S, SHEPHERD J: Effects of cholestyramine on receptor mediated plasma clearance and tissue uptake of human low density lipoproteins in the rabbit. *J Biol Chem* 255:10210, 1980.

208. KOVANEN PT, BILHEIMER DW, GOLDSTEIN JL, JARAMILLO J, BROWN MS: A regulatory role for hepatic low density lipoprotein receptors *in vivo* in the dog. *Proc Natl Acad Sci USA* 78:1194, 1981.

209. MOUTAFIS CD, SIMONS LA, MYANT NB, ADAMS PW, WYNN V: The effect of cholestyramine on the faecal excretion of bile acids and neutral steroids in familial hypercholesterolaemia. *Atherosclerosis* 26:329, 1977.

210. ENDO A, KURODA M, TANZAWA K: Competitive inhibition of 3-hydroxy-3-methylglutaryl coenzyme A reductase by ML-236A and ML-236B fungal metabolites, having hypocholesterolemic activity. *FEBS Lett* 72:323, 1976.

211. BROWN MS, FAUST JR, GOLDSTEIN JL, KANEKO I, ENDO A: Induction of 3-hydroxy-3-methylglutaryl coenzyme A reductase activity in human fibroblasts incubated with compactin (ML-236B), a competitive inhibitor of the reductase. *J Biol Chem* 253:1121, 1978.

212. ALBERTS AW, CHEN J, KURON G, HUNT V, HUFF J, HOFFMAN C, ROTHROCK J, LOPEZ M, JOSHUA H, HARRIS E, PATCHETT A, MONAGHAN R, CURRIE S, STAPLEY E, ALBERS-SCHONBERG G, HENSENS O, HIRSCHFIELD J, HOOGSTEEN K, LIESCH J, SPRINGER J: Mevinolin, a highly potent competitive inhibitor of HMG-CoA reductase and cholesterol lowering agent. *Proc Natl Acad Sci USA* 77:3957, 1980.

213. BILHEIMER DW, GRUNDY SM, BROWN MS, GOLDSTEIN JL: Mevinolin stimulates receptor-mediated clearance of low density lipoprotein from plasma in familial hypercholesterolemia heterozygotes. *Proc Natl Acad Sci USA* 80:4124, 1983.

214. GRUNDY SM, VEGA GL: Influence of mevinolin on metabolism of low density lipoproteins in primary moderate hypercholesterolemia. *J Lipid Res* 26:1464, 1985.

215. GRUNDY SM, BILHEIMER DW: Inhibition of 3-hydroxy-3-methylglutaryl-CoA reductase by mevinolin in familial hypercholesterolemia heterozygotes: Effects on cholesterol balance. *Proc Natl Acad Sci USA* 81:2538, 1984.

216. MABUCHI H, SAKAI T, SAKAI Y, YOSHIMURA A, WATANABE A, WAKASUGI T, KOIZUMI J, TAKEDA R: Reduction of serum cholesterol in heterozygous patients with familial hypercholesteroliemia: Additive effects of compactin and cholestyramine. *N Engl J Med* 308:609, 1983.

217. ILLINGWORTH DR: Mevinolin plus colestipol in therapy for severe heterozygous familial hypercholesterolemia. *Ann Intern Med* 101:598, 1984.

218. HOEG JM, MAHER MB, ZECH LA, BAILEY KR, GREGG RE, LACKNER KJ, FOJO SS, ANCHORS MA, BOJANOVSKI M, SPRECHER DL, BREWER HB JR: Effectiveness of mevinolin on plasma lipoprotein concentrations in type II hyperlipoproteinemia. *Am J Cardiol* 57:933, 1986.

219. TOBERT JA, BELL GD, BIRTWELL J, JAMES I, KUKOVETZ WR, PRYOR JS, BUNTINX A, HOLMES IB, CHAO Y-S, BOLOGNESE JA: Cholesterol-lowering

effect of mevinolin, an inhibitor of 3-hydroxy-3-methylglutaryl-coenzyme A reductase, in healthy volunteers. *J Clin Invest* 69:913, 1982.

220. KANE JP, MALLOY MJ, TUN P, PHILLIPS NR, FREEDMAN DD, WILLIAMS ML, ROWE JS, HAVEL RJ: Normalization of low-density-lipoprotein levels in heterozygous familial hypercholesterolemia with a combined drug regimen. *N Engl J Med* 304:251, 1981.

220a. MALLOY MJ, KANE JP, KUNITAKE ST, TUN P: Complementary of colestipol, niacin, and lovastatin in treatment of severe familial hypercholesterolemia. *Ann Intern Med* 107:616, 1987.

221. BUCHWALD H, MOORE RB, VARCO RL: Ten years' clinical experience with partial ileal bypass in management of the hyperlipidemias. *Ann Surg* 180:384, 1974.

222. KOIVISTO P, MIETTINEN TA: Long-term effects of ileal bypass on lipoproteins in patients with familial hypercholesterolemia. *Circulation* 70:290, 1984.

223. SCHOUTEN JA, BEYNEN AC: Partial ileal bypass surgery in the treatment of heterozygous familial hypercholesterolemia: A review. *Artery* 13:240, 1986.

224. FARAH JR, KWITEROVICH PO JR, NEILL CA: Dose-effect relation of cholestyramine in children and young adults with familial hypercholesterolaemia. *Lancet* 1:59, 1977.

225. GLUECK CJ, MELLIES MJ, DINE M, PERRY T, LASKARZEWSKI P: Safety and efficacy of long-term diet and diet plus bile acid-binding resin cholesterol-lowering therapy in 73 children heterozygous for familial hypercholesterolemia. *Pediatrics* 78:338, 1986.

226. KHACHADURIAN AK: Cholestyramine therapy in patients homozygous for familial hypercholesterolemia (familial hypercholesterolemic xanthomatosis). *J Atheroscler Res* 8:177, 1968.

227. YAMAMOTO A, YAMAMURA T, YOKOYAMA S, SUDO H, MATSUZAWA Y: Combined drug therapy—cholestyramine and compactin—for familial hypercholesterolemia. *Int J Clin Pharmacol Ther Toxicol* 22:493, 1984.

228. THOMPSON GR, GOTTO AM JR: Ileal bypass in the treatment of hyperlipoproteinaemia. *Lancet* 2:35, 1973.

229. DECKELBAUM RJ, LEES RS, SMALL DM, HEDBERG SE, GRUNDY SM: Failure of complete bile diversion and oral bile acid therapy in the treatment of homozygous familial hypercholesterolemia. *N Engl J Med* 296:465, 1977.

230. BAKER SG, JOFFE BI, MENDELSOHN D, SEFTEL HC: Treatment of homozygous familial hypercholesterolaemia with probucol. *S Afr Med J* 62:7, 1982.

231. YAMAMOTO A, MATSUZAWA Y, KISHINO B-I, HAYASHI R, HIROBE K, KIKKAWA T: Effects of probucol on homozygous cases of familial hypercholesterolemia. *Atherosclerosis* 48:157, 1983.

232. STARZL TE, PUTNAM CW, CHASE HP, PORTER KA: Portacaval shunt in hyperlipoproteinaemia. *Lancet* 2:94, 1973.

233. TORSVIK H, FISCHER JE, FELDMAN HA, LEES RS: Effects of intravenous hyperalimentation on plasma-lipoproteins in severe familial hypercholesterolaemia. *Lancet* 1:601, 1975.

234. STARZL TE, CHASE HP, PUTNAM CW, NORA JJ: Follow-up of patient with portacaval shunt for the treatment of hyperlipidaemia. *Lancet* 2:714, 1974.

235. STARZL TE, PUTNAM CW, KOEP LJ: Portacaval shunt and hyperlipidemia. *Arch Surg* 113:71, 1978.

236. STEIN EA, MIENY C, SPITZ L, SAARON I, PETTIFOR J, HEIMANN KW, BERSOHN I, DINNER M: Portacaval shunt in four patients with homozygous hypercholesterolaemia. *Lancet* 1:832, 1975.

237. FORMAN MB, BAKER SG, MIENY CJ, JOFFE BI, SANDLER MP, MENDELSOHN D, SEFTEL HC: Treatment of homozygous familial hypercholesterolaemia with portacaval shunt. *Atherosclerosis* 41:349, 1982.

238. MCNAMARA DJ, AHRENS EH JR, KOLB R, BROWN CD, PARKER TS, DAVIDSON NO, SAMUEL P, MCVIE RM: Treatment of familial hypercholesterolemia by portacaval anastomosis: Effect on cholesterol metabolism and pool sizes. *Proc Natl Acad Sci USA* 80:564, 1983.

239. THOMPSON GR, LOWENTHAL R, MYANT NB: Plasma exchange in the management of homozygous familial hypercholesterolaemia. *Lancet* 1:1208, 1975.

240. POSTIGLIONE A, THOMPSON GR: Experience with plasma-exchange in homozygous familial hypercholesterolaemia. *Prog Clin Biol Res* 188:213, 1985.

241. KELLER C, SCHMITZ H, THEISEN K, ZOLLNER N: Regression of valvular aortic stenosis due to homozygous familial hypercholesterolemia following plasmapheresis. *Klin Wochenschr* 64:338, 1986.

242. STEIN EA, ADOLPH R, RICE V, GLUECK CJ, SPITZ HB: Nonprogression of coronary artery atherosclerosis in homozygous familial hypercholesterolemia after 31 months of repeitive plasma exchange. *Clin Cardiol* 9:115, 1986.

243. MYANT NB: Regression of cornary atherosclerosis in man. *Adv Exp Med Biol* 168:139, 1984.

244. THOMPSON GR, MILLER JP, BRESLOW JL: Improved survival of patients with homozygous familial hypercholesterolaemia treated with plasma exchange. *Br Med J* 291:1671, 1985.

245. LUPIEN P-J, MOORJANI S, GAGNE C, BRUN L-D, LOU M, DAGENAIS G: Long term treatment of two familial hypercholesterolemic heterozygote patients with batch affinity chromatography (BAC). *Artery* 10:286, 1982.

246. STOFFEL W, DEMANT T: Selective removal of apolipoprotein B-containing serum lipoproteins from blood plasma. *Proc Natl Acad Sci USA* 78:611, 1981.

247. YOKOYAMA S, HAYASHI R, SANTANI M, YAMAMOTO A: Selective removal of low density lipoprotein by plasmapheresis in familial hypercholesterolemia. *Arteriosclerosis* 5:613, 1985.

248. HOMMA Y, MIKAMI Y, TAMACHI H, NAKAYA N, NAKAMURA H, ARAKI G, GOTO Y: Comparison of selectivity of LDL removal by double filtration and dextran-sulfate cellulose column plasmapheresis. *Atherosclerosis* 60:23, 1986.

249. MABUCHI H, MICHISHITA I, SAKAI T, SAKAI Y, WATANABE A, WAKASUGI T, TAKEDA R: Treatment of homozygous patients with familial hypercholesterolemia by double-filtration plasmapheresis. *Atherosclerosis* 61:135, 1986.

250. STARZL TE, BILHEIMER DW, BAHNSON HT, SHAW BW JR, HARDESTY RL, GRIFFITH BP, IWATSUKI S, ZITELLI BJ, GARTNER JC JR, MALATACK JJ, URBACH AH: Heart-liver transplantation in a patient with familial hypercholesterolaemia. *Lancet* i:1382, 1984.

251. BILHEIMER DW, GOLDSTEIN JL, GRUNDY SC, STARZL TE, BROWN MS: Liver transplantation provides low density lipoprotein receptors and lowers plasma cholesterol in a child with homozygous familial hypercholesterolemia. *N Engl J Med* 311:1658, 1984.

252. EAST C, GRUNDY SM, BILHEIMER DW: Normal cholesterol levels with lovastatin (mevinolin) therapy in a child with homozygous familial hypercholesterolemia following liver transplantation. *JAMA* 256:2843, 1986.

CHAPTER **49**

FAMILIAL DISORDERS OF HIGH DENSITY LIPOPROTEIN METABOLISM

JAN L. BRESLOW

1. *A low HDL cholesterol level is a risk factor for coronary heart disease in Westernized societies. HDLs are formed in plasma and are a reservoir for lipids and apolipoproteins. HDL metabolism is complex and determined by its interactions with other lipoproteins, cell membranes, and processing proteins.*
2. *Rare inborn errors of metabolism have been described that affect HDL levels. These can be understood in the terms of where they act in the HDL metabolism pathway. They include apo A-I synthetic and structural defects, defects in lipoprotein lipase or its cofactor apo C-II, hepatic triglyceride lipase deficiency, partial or complete lecithin:cholesterol acyltransferase deficiency, and deficient activity of the cholesteryl ester transfer protein. Although apo A-I deficiency is associated with a marked increase in the risk for atherosclerosis, not all the defects that result in low HDL levels also increase atherosclerosis susceptibility. This may mean that it is not the low HDL cholesterol level itself that is atherogenic but rather that susceptibility to coronary heart disease results from a metabolic derangement associated with only some types of low HDL. The inborn errors explain only a small fraction of the variability in HDL cholesterol levels in the population.*
3. *General population studies indicate that half of the HDL cholesterol variability is genetic and the other half environmental. The genetic component appears to be principally polygenic and may be due to genetic variation at a few candidate gene loci that control HDL metabolism. Association studies indicate that one candidate is the apolipoprotein gene locus on chromosome 11, which includes the apo A-I, apo C-III, and apo A-IV genes. The common causative mutations affecting HDL cholesterol levels have not yet been identified at this or any other gene locus.*

HDL—GENERAL CONSIDERATIONS

Although a low level of high density lipoprotein (HDL) cholesterol is a major risk factor for coronary heart disease in many societies today, relatively little is known about the genetic control of HDL cholesterol levels. It is the purpose of this chapter to review this subject critically. First, it is necessary to review the structure and composition of HDL, the evidence that a reduced level of HDL is a risk factor for coronary heart disease, and aspects of HDL metabolism. Several comprehensive reviews have appeared recently on these subjects.[1–4]

HDL—Structure and Composition

HDLs are macromolecular complexes of protein and lipid that range in diameter from 70 to 100 Å and in mass from 200,000 to 400,000 daltons. They sediment in the density region 1.063 to 1.21 g/ml. Analytic ultracentrifugation reveals lighter and heavier particles in this region, called HDL_2 and HDL_3, respectively. The former are defined as those in the density region 1.063 to 1.12 g/ml, whereas the latter are those in the density region 1.12 to 1.21 g/ml. HDLs contain, on the average, 50% lipid and 50% protein. The lipid is 32% cholesteryl ester, 5% free cholesterol, 55% phospholipid, and 8% triglyceride. The protein consists principally of apo A-I (70%) and apo A-II (20%). HDL_2 is relatively lipid rich and protein poor compared with HDL_3. HDL heterogeneity in apolipoprotein composition has also been demonstrated by immunoaffinity chromatography. Three types of particles have been demonstrated: apo A-I-only, apo A-I and apo A-II, and apo E-rich. The apo A-I-only particles contain four apo A-I polypeptides and float principally in the HDL_2 region. The apo A-I and apo A-II particles contain two of each of these polypeptides and are principally in the HDL_3 region. The apo E-rich HDL particles contain apo E as their principal apolipoprotein. These particles have a density distribution that is lighter than HDL_2. Although they may be quite important metabolically, apo E-rich HDLs are not included in the clinical assays quantitating HDL cholesterol levels.[1]

HDL—Risk Factor for Coronary Heart Disease

The distribution of HDL cholesterol levels in the population was determined by the Lipid Research Clinic Prevalence Study (Table 49-1).[5] For men ages 45 to 49 years, the average HDL cholesterol level is 45 mg/dl, with the bottom decile below 33 mg/dl and the top decile above 60 mg/dl. In women, these values are 56, 39, and 78 mg/dl, respectively. From a clinical perspective, the principal interest in HDL stems from the association of low HDL cholesterol levels with an in-

Nonstandard abbreviations used in this chapter are: apo = apolipoprotein; HDL = high density lipoprotein; LDL = low density lipoprotein; IDL = intermediate density lipoprotein; VLDL = very low density lipoprotein; LCAT = lecithin:cholesterol acyltransferase; CETP = cholesteryl ester transfer protein; LPL = lipoprotein lipase; HTGL = hepatic triglyceride lipase; CAD = coronary artery disease; CHD = coronary heart disease; GGE = gradient gel electrophoresis; FCR = fractional catabolic rate; DMPC = dimyristoyl phosphatidyl choline; MZ = monozygotic; DZ = dizygotic; RFLP = restriction fragment length polymorphism; TG = triglyceride.

creased incidence of coronary heart disease.[2] This association was noted over 30 years ago.[6] However, perhaps because HDL cholesterol is normally a minor (20 to 25 percent) fraction of the circulating cholesterol, the importance of HDL levels in predicting atherosclerosis risk was largely ignored. Attention was focused on this subject in 1975. Dozens of studies have since verified the inverse association of coronary heart disease risk and HDL cholesterol levels in Westernized societies.[2,7] Recently, the Framingham Study reported a highly significant inverse relationship between coronary heart disease incidence and HDL cholesterol levels based on a 12-year follow-up.[8] The relationship held after multivariate adjustment for total cholesterol, systolic blood pressure, cigarette smoking, and body mass index. It was also found that HDL cholesterol showed a strong inverse relationship with coronary heart disease risk at low (<200 mg/dl), medium, and high (>260 mg/dl) total cholesterol levels. In another recent analysis, the Lipid Research Clinics Primary Prevention Trial reported that HDL cholesterol was a strong inverse predictor of coronary heart disease incidence in study subjects over the 7- to 10-year follow-up period.[9] Subjects with HDL cholesterol levels under 40 mg/dl had twice the incidence of coronary heart disease as those with levels over 50 mg/dl. In this study, cholestyramine and placebo treated subjects were followed. Although the major finding was that coronary heart disease incidence was lowest among men with the greatest reductions in plasma low density lipoprotein (LDL) cholesterol levels, it was also found that disease incidence decreased with HDL cholesterol increments from baseline and increased with HDL cholesterol decrements.

In cross-sectional studies, HDL cholesterol levels are inversely related to triglyceride levels.[4] However, covariate analysis in case-control studies indicates that low HDL levels are independently associated with coronary heart disease risk.[10–13] Finally, HDL cholesterol levels are not correlated with LDL cholesterol levels, which are the other major quantitative lipoprotein predictor of coronary heart disease risk. The ratio of LDL to HDL cholesterol is a better predictor of atherosclerosis susceptibility than either one alone.[14]

Because HDLs are heterogeneous, recent studies have attempted to correlate the levels of the HDL subfractions and/or the principal HDL apolipoprotein levels with coronary heart disease risk.[2] It has been suggested that HDL_2 cholesterol levels may be better predictors of risk.[15–17] Compatible with this notion is the observation that women, who are at less risk for coronary heart disease than men, have higher HDL_2 cholesterol levels.[18] In addition, exercise, which has a beneficial effect on coronary heart disease risk, increases HDL_2 levels,[19] and obesity,[20] which is detrimental, decreases them. A recent review summarized 37 completed studies covering over 9000 subjects.[2] Prospective and case-control epidemiologic studies show HDL_2 and HDL_3 cholesterol levels both diminished in coronary heart disease victims. Low HDL_2 cholesterol levels were a better discriminator of risk than low HDL_3.[2] However, HDL_2 cholesterol levels appeared not to be a better discriminator of risk than total HDL cholesterol. Epidemiologic studies have also shown low apo A-I and in most studies low apo A-II levels in coronary heart disease cases compared to controls.[2] With regard to the discriminating power of HDL cholesterol versus apolipoprotein levels in predicting coronary heart disease susceptibility, the literature is evenly divided. One cannot conclude that one is better than the other.[2]

HDL—Metabolism

To define and understand clinically significant inborn errors of HDL metabolism requires a detailed knowledge of how HDL particles are synthesized, interconverted, and catabolized. The current scheme for HDL metabolism has been extensively summarized by Eisenberg in a recent review[1] and is outlined in Fig. 49-1.

Current evidence indicates that what is measured in plasma as HDL is not secreted as such by any organ. HDL is assembled in plasma, and its major protein building blocks are apo A-I and, to a lesser extent, apo A-II. Apo A-I synthesis in the body occurs to a significant extent, and roughly equally, in intestine and liver, whereas apo A-II is made principally in the liver. Apo A-I is secreted from liver complexed with phospholipid in disklike structures, called *nascent HDL*. The major source of intestinally derived HDL apolipoproteins is thought to be the newly secreted chylomicron, where apo A-I is a major surface constituent. When lipoprotein lipase (LPL) in the

Table 49-1 Plasma High Density Lipoprotein Cholesterol Concentration*

	Normal values, mg/dl														
	Males, percentile							*Females, percentile*							
Age, yr	*5*	*10*	*25*	*50*	*75*	*90*	*95*	*5*	*10*	*25*	*50*	*75*	*90*	*95*
5–9	38	42	49	54	63	70	74	36	38	47	52	61	67	73
10–14	37	40	46	55	61	71	74	37	40	45	52	58	64	70
15–19	30	34	39	46	52	59	63	35	38	43	51	61	68	73
20–24	30	32	38	45	51	57	63	—†	37	43	50	60	68	—†
25–29	31	32	37	44	50	58	63	37	40	47	55	64	73	81
30–34	28	32	38	45	52	59	63	38	40	46	55	64	71	75
35–39	29	31	36	43	49	58	62	34	38	44	52	63	74	82
40–44	27	31	36	43	51	60	67	33	39	48	55	64	78	87
45–49	30	33	38	45	52	60	64	33	39	46	56	66	78	86
50–54	28	31	36	44	51	58	63	37	40	49	59	70	77	89
55–59	28	31	38	46	55	64	71	36	39	47	58	68	82	86
60–64	30	34	41	49	61	69	74	36	43	49	60	73	85	91
65–69	30	33	39	49	62	74	78	34	38	46	60	71	79	89
70+	31	33	40	48	56	70	75	33	37	48	60	69	82	91

*Values are based on Lipid Research Clinics population studies in the U.S. and Canada. The data include 3524 white males and 2545 white females (not using sex hormones) as derived from NIH Publication 80-1527, 1980. All subjects were sampled in the fasting state.
†No data because there were fewer than 100 cases in the cell.

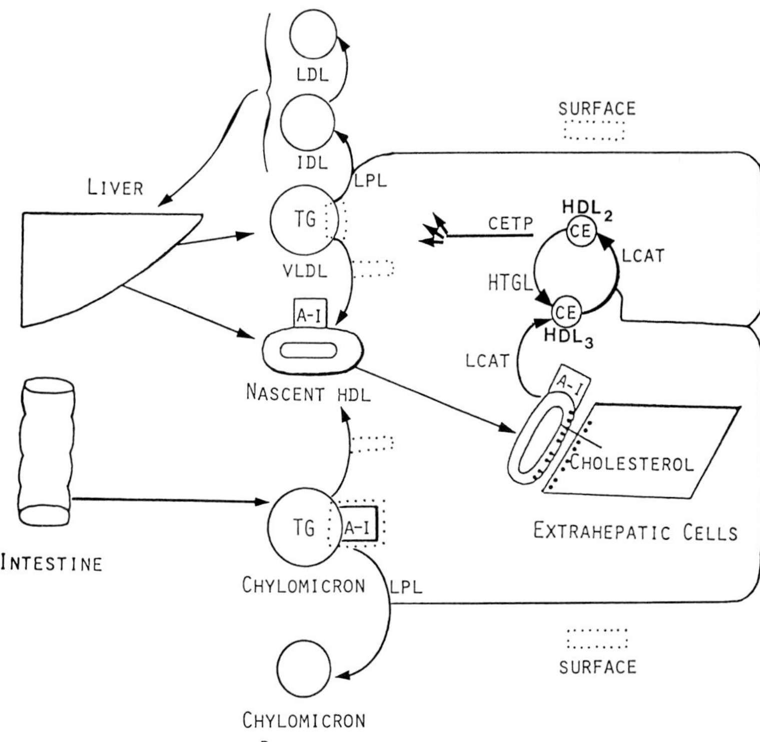

Fig. 49-1 HDL metabolism. A scheme for the formation of HDL in plasma is indicated. Details are provided in the text. The dotted lines surround bits of surface material of triglyceride-rich lipoproteins transferred to nascent HDL or HDL_3. Abbreviations: CE = cholesteryl ester; TG = triglyceride; LPL = lipoprotein lipase; CETP = cholesteryl ester transfer protein; HTGL = hepatic triglyceride lipase; LCAT = lecithin:cholesterol acyltransferase.

vascular compartment hydrolyzes the fatty acids of chylomicrons and liver-derived very low density lipoproteins (VLDL), (see Chap. 45), redundant surface material becomes available and contributes to the nascent HDL pool. These HDL precursors physically attract free cholesterol from cell membranes and/or other lipoproteins resulting in the formation of disklike structures containing apo A-I, phospholipid, and free cholesterol. Such particles are substrates for the plasma enzyme lecithin:cholesterol acyltransferase (LCAT) (see Chap. 46), which, activated by its cofactor apo A-I, esterifies free cholesterol to cholesteryl ester. The latter is more hydrophobic than free cholesterol and moves to the inside of the nascent HDL disks and transforms them into spherical particles. These particles are much more stable than the disklike particles and accumulate in plasma. Newly formed spherical HDLs are small HDLs in the HDL_3 density range. HDL_3 particles have a low molar ratio of free cholesterol to phospholipid. This makes them able to attract free cholesterol from cell membranes or from the excess surface of chylomicrons and VLDL formed during triglyceride hydrolysis by LPL. The LCAT enzyme also esterifies this free cholesterol. This increases the core cholesteryl ester content of HDL_3, resulting in the formation of larger HDL, in the HDL_2 density range.

There is also evidence that large HDL, HDL_2, can be converted to small HDL, HDL_3. Two processing reactions are involved. In the first, the cholesteryl ester transfer protein (CETP) exchanges HDL_2 core cholesteryl ester for triglyceride in VLDL, IDL, and/or LDL. In the second, hepatic triglyceride lipase (HTGL), which also possesses phospholipase activity, hydrolyzes both the core triglycerides and the surface phospholipids. This, along with the displacement of surface apolipoproteins, results in the formation of HDL_3. The CETP-mediated process provides a means by which excess cholesterol in peripheral tissues can be transferred to lipoproteins such as IDL or LDL and cleared from plasma by liver LDL receptors to be excreted either directly or as bile acids. This is the probable mechanism of transfer of peripheral cholesterol to the liver for excretion, the so-called reverse cholesterol transport pathway.

Relative plasma levels of HDL_2 and HDL_3 represent a balance between forces that drive in the directions of larger and smaller HDL particles. For example, HDL_2 levels correlate directly with LPL and inversely with HTGL activity. Normally, about 60% of HDL cholesterol is found in the HDL_3 fraction, and most of the variation of HDL cholesterol levels in the population is in the HDL_2 fraction.

HDL particles do not appear to be removed intact from plasma, but rather by complex processes that vary from tissue to tissue. The cholesteryl ester portion is removed in preference to the apolipoproteins by the liver- and steroid-hormone-producing tissues, such as adrenal and ovary. In the kidney, apolipoprotein removal is in preference to cholesteryl ester. This may represent filtration and degradation of apo A-I that has become dissociated from lipid.

In summary, HDLs are formed in plasma and serve as a reservoir for lipids and apolipoproteins. HDL metabolism is quite complex and determined by its interactions with other lipoproteins, cell membranes of various tissues, and plasma processing proteins such as LCAT, LPL, HTGL, and CETP. In addition to apolipoprotein synthesis and degradation, it is these interactions that determine the level and density distribution of plasma HDL cholesterol.

INBORN ERRORS OF METABOLISM AFFECTING HDL LEVELS

Several rare inborn errors of metabolism have been described that affect plasma HDL levels (for recent reviews see Refs. 21 to 27 and Chaps. 45 and 46). These can be understood in terms of where they act in the scheme of HDL metabolism just presented. In addition, the metabolic consequences of these inborn errors lend validity to the proposed pathway.

This section describes these disorders emphasizing their effects on HDL metabolism. Several disorders which are presented in other chapters are described only briefly here.

Apo A-I Deficiency

Patients have been described with apo A-I deficiency and very low HDL cholesterol levels. There are sufficient similarities to discuss these patients as a group but sufficient differences to designate three types. The salient features of patients with apo A-I deficiency are summarized in Table 49-2.

Clinical Features

TYPE I (APO A-I/APO C-III DEFICIENCY). Norum described two sisters with apo A-I deficiency and very low HDL cholesterol levels.[28] Both patients had planar xanthomas which began in childhood. These were on the neck, arms, trunk, and eyelids. There were no xanthomas in the finger webs, and one of the patients had a single tendon xanthoma. The tonsils were atrophic and normal in color. Xanthomatous skin was biopsied and examined by both light and electron microscopy. Aggregates of histiocytes containing lipid-laden vacuoles were seen. At ages 29 and 31, both subjects also showed mild diffuse corneal clouding bilaterally. Symptoms of heart failure developed in one patient at age 31 and in the other during delivery at age 25. In both sisters, echocardiography showed normal heart valves but an enlarged left ventricle with poor contraction. Coronary angiography demonstrated extensive obstruction in all three major vessels.

TYPE II. Another apo A-I-deficient patient with very low HDL cholesterol levels was described by Schaefer.[29,30] This woman had no xanthomas and normal tonsils. Corneal clouding was noted when the patient was 42 years old. Heart failure developed at age 45, and angiography showed obstructions in all three major vessels. At that time the patient underwent coronary artery bypass surgery and expired 1 week after the procedure. Autopsy revealed atherosclerotic lesions in the descending aorta and carotid, pulmonary, and coronary arteries. There was a lack of lipid deposition in the reticuloendothelial cells of the liver, spleen, and bone marrow. Diffuse extracellular deposition was observed in the corneal stroma.

TYPE III. Gustafson described another apo A-I-deficient patient with very low HDL levels.[31,32] This woman had planar xanthomas and corneal clouding. She had normal tonsils, but hepatosplenomegaly was present. At age 48 she suffered from angina pectoris.

A comparison of the clinical features of the three types of apo A-I-deficient patients indicates they all manifested corneal clouding and premature coronary artery disease (CAD) and none showed the tonsillar abnormalities which are the hallmark of Tangier disease. Patients with types I and III apo A-I deficiency had planar xanthomas, whereas these were lacking in type II. Finally, hepatosplenomegaly was present only in type III.

Biochemical Abnormalities. Quantitative and qualitative measurements of lipoproteins and apolipoproteins have been reported in patients with type I apo A-I deficiency.[28,33,34] They had very low HDL cholesterol levels, between 0 and 7 mg/dl. LDL cholesterol levels were approximately at the 75th percentile for age. Age-adjusted triglyceride levels were between the 5th and 25th percentile. Apolipoprotein measurement by immunoassay showed undetectable apo A-I and apo C-III. Apo A-II, apo A-IV, apo B, apo C-I, apo C-II, and apo E levels were 51, 57, 111, 39, 11 and 58 percent of normal, respectively.

Lipoproteins from the type I patients were studied by several physical methods.[33] HDLs were not detected by analytical ultracentrifugation. HDLs could be concentrated by preparative ultracentrifugation and analyzed by electron microscopy. This showed them to be spherical and slightly larger than normal. Gradient gel electrophoretic (GGE) analysis revealed an HDL particle distribution skewed toward larger particle sizes. The HDL apolipoprotein composition was principally apo A-II and apo E/apo A-II dimer. Analytical ultracentrifugation showed the patients had low levels of VLDL (20 to 400 S) and IDL (12 to 20 S). The levels and peak flotation rate of LDL (0 to 12 S) were normal. This was confirmed by electron microscopy and GGE, which showed normal LDL particle diameter.

In vivo studies of lipoprotein metabolism have also been carried out in patients with type I apo A-I deficiency.[34] After injection of autologous [^{125}I]VLDL, there was a very rapid decay of radioactivity in VLDL followed by a rapid conversion of labeled apo B in VLDL to IDL and LDL. The fractional catabolic rate (FCR) of VLDL apo B was approximately 46 pools per day compared with 6 pools per day in normal subjects. The turnover of VLDL triglycerides, determined after the injection of [2-^{3}H]glycerol, was also greatly accelerated. The FCR of VLDL triglycerides was three to nine times

Table 49-2 Lipid, Lipoprotein, and Apolipoprotein Levels* in Apo A-I Deficiency

Type		*Total chol*	*TG*	*LDL chol*	*HDL chol*	*A-I*	*A-II*	*A-IV*	*B*	*C-I*	*C-II*	*C-III*	*E*	*Planar xanthomas*	*Corneal clouding*	*Hepato-spleno-megaly*	*Age of onset coronary artery disease symptoms*
I	Patient 1	130	31	124	0	0	18	26	106	2.5	0.6	0	1.9	+	+	−	31
	Patient 2	122	51	112	0	0	20	16	111	2.8	0.2	0	2.6	+	+	−	25
	Normal†	179	86	111	56	121	37	37	98	7.0	3.7	13	4.0				
		±31	±50	±27	±13	±24	±9	±4	±20	±2.0	±2.0	±5	±0.3				
II	Patient 1	111	62	106	1	0	3	—	105	—	0.8	0	—	−	+	−	45
III	Patient 1	260	290	134	3	2	15	—	125	—	—	19	—	+	+	+	48

*Values given are means ± S/D in mg/dl.
†Lipid and lipoprotein normal levels are taken from the Lipid Research Clinics data for women of the same age. Apolipoprotein normal levels are those given by Norum et al.[28]

higher than that in controls. In contrast to enhanced rates of VLDL catabolism, the FCR for LDL apo B was normal. Previous in vitro studies have suggested that apo C-III might delay catabolism of triglyceride-rich lipoproteins. The metabolic studies in patients with type I apo A-I deficiency, who are also apo C-III deficient, suggest a role for the latter in VLDL clearance in vivo.

The proband with type II apo A-I deficiency had an HDL cholesterol level of 1 mg/dl.[29,30] The LDL cholesterol level was at the 25th percentile for age, as was the triglyceride level. Apolipoprotein measurements by immunoassay showed normal apo B levels and very low levels of apo A-II and apo C-II, while the level of apo C-III was unmeasurable. It was suggested that this patient also had apo A-I/apo C-III deficiency, but as she was deceased, this could not be verified. The exact molecular lesion in the type II patient is different from the type I patient (see "Basic Genetic Defects," below). Relatives of the proband were studied, and 17 were identified with HDL levels less than the fifth percentile for age and sex.[30] In these individuals, HDL cholesterol and apo A-I and apo C-III levels were found to be approximately 60 percent of those in relatives with normal HDL cholesterol levels.

The biochemical characteristics of the proband with type III apo A-I deficiency were the same with regard to HDL.[32] However, cholesterol, triglyceride, and LDL cholesterol levels were elevated. Apolipoprotein immunoassay detected the presence of small amounts of apo A-I, and the level of apo C-III was slightly higher than that found in normal subjects.

Basic Genetic Defect. The molecular genetic defect has been defined in type I apo A-I deficiency (apo A-I/apo C-III deficiency). The wild-type apo A-I gene has been isolated, characterized, and mapped to chromosome 11q23. In addition, the apo C-III gene was found to be 3′ to the apo A-I gene but in the opposite orientation. These genes are convergently transcribed from opposite DNA strands. Both genes have a 4 exon, 3 intron structure. The apo A-I gene is 1.9 kb and the apo C-III gene is 3.1 kb in length, and they are separated by an intergenic region of 2.5 kb (for review see Refs. 22 and 23).

Utilizing an apo A-I gene probe, Southern blotting analysis showed that the probands with type I apo A-I deficiency had a 6.5-kb fragment after *Eco*RI digestion (Fig. 49-2).[35] Wild-type DNA from normal individuals shows a 13-kb fragment under the same conditions. DNA from first-degree relatives of the probands, including both the mother and the father, showed both the 13- and the 6.5-kb fragments. This strongly suggests that the probands are homozygous for a rare mutation affecting this genetic locus. The parents were not known to be related but were from a similar ethnic background. Their ancestors were of Scottish-Irish descent and had settled in an isolated village in the Appalachian region of the United States.

Southern blotting of the probands' DNA digested with other restriction enzymes besides *Eco*RI revealed bands different from wild type.[36] This indicated that the mutation was not due to a single base pair alteration. Utilizing other probes from the apo A-I/apo C-III genomic region, it was possible to show that the apo A-I gene was interrupted in its fourth exon at approximately the codon specifying residue 80 of the mature 243 amino acid protein. DNA from the region was cloned, sequenced, and found to correspond to apo C-III gene DNA sequences.[37,38] Thus, these probands had an inversion of approximately 5.5 kb of DNA containing portions of the apo A-I and apo C-III genes. The inversion prevents both genes from coding for complete polypeptides and effectively inactivates them. This is undoubtedly the molecular basis of type I apo A-I deficiency (apo A-I/apo C-III deficiency).

The genomic architecture in the region of the apo A-I and apo C-III genes is normal by Southern blotting analysis in type II apo A-I deficiency.[30] Although the mutation in type I apo A-I deficiency is rare, it establishes the principle that apo A-I gene lesions can cause low HDL levels and susceptibility to atherosclerosis. It remains to be determined how common apo A-I gene lesions are as a cause of low HDL levels in the population.

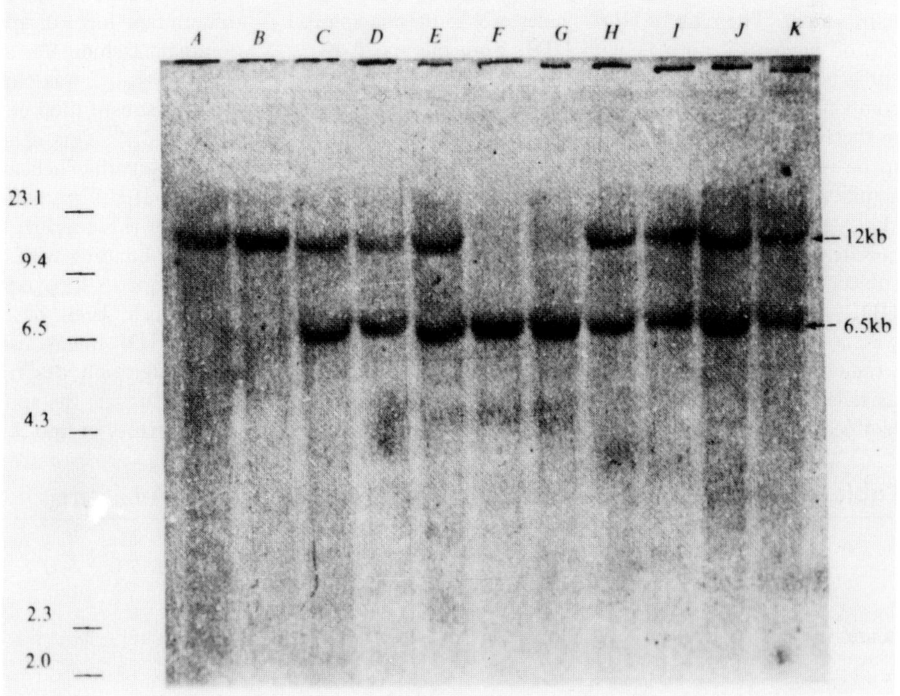

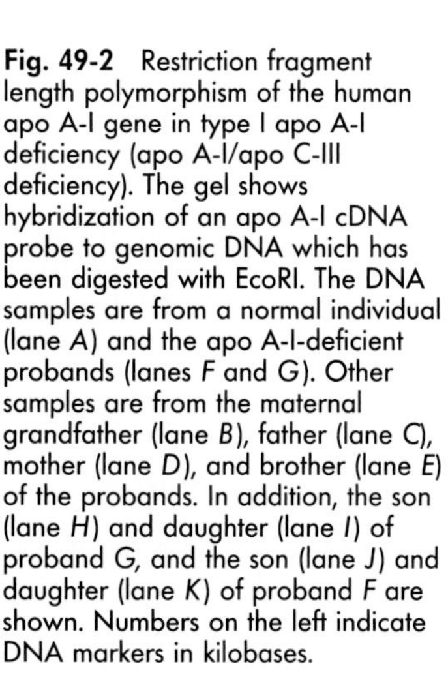

Fig. 49-2 Restriction fragment length polymorphism of the human apo A-I gene in type I apo A-I deficiency (apo A-I/apo C-III deficiency). The gel shows hybridization of an apo A-I cDNA probe to genomic DNA which has been digested with EcoRI. The DNA samples are from a normal individual (lane *A*) and the apo A-I-deficient probands (lanes *F* and *G*). Other samples are from the maternal grandfather (lane *B*), father (lane *C*), mother (lane *D*), and brother (lane *E*) of the probands. In addition, the son (lane *H*) and daughter (lane *I*) of proband *G*, and the son (lane *J*) and daughter (lane *K*) of proband *F* are shown. Numbers on the left indicate DNA markers in kilobases.

Apo A-I Structural Variants

An extensive Italian kindred from the village of Limone sul Garda has been described with many members having low HDL cholesterol levels associated with an electrophoretic variant of apo A-I. This variant has been called apo $A\text{-}I_{Milano}$.[39]

Clinical Features. In spite of low HDL cholesterol levels, individuals in this kindred with apo $A\text{-}I_{Milano}$ have no symptomatology.[39,40] In particular, they show no increased incidence of atherosclerotic disease, when compared with close relatives without the apo A-I variant. By examining the pedigree and designating probable carriers based on the segregation of the trait and the familial composition, it appears that apo $A\text{-}I_{Milano}$ may actually be associated with less fatal coronary heart disease than expected.[40]

Biochemical Abnormalities. Plasma lipid, lipoprotein, and apolipoprotein levels were compared between individuals with the apo $A\text{-}I_{Milano}$ variant and age- and sex-matched nonaffected subjects of the same kindred (Table 49-3).[39–43] The variant was associated with 33 percent of normal HDL cholesterol levels and approximately 60 percent of normal apo A-I and apo A-II levels. The group with the variant had a 75 percent increase in triglyceride and VLDL cholesterol levels. An increase in triglycerides above the 90th percentile for age and sex of the local population was found in 12 of 29 individuals with the variant but in only 4 of 29 without the variant. Levels of LDL cholesterol, apo B, apo C-II, apo C-III, and apo E were similar in affected and unaffected relatives.

Several studies of the lipoprotein abnormality in subjects with the apo $A\text{-}I_{Milano}$ variant have been undertaken.[43–45] The mass of VLDL and LDL was normal, whereas HDL mass was reduced 50 percent. VLDL composition was normal, but LDL was reduced in cholesteryl esters and enriched in triglycerides. This was true both for the hypertriglyceridemic and normotriglyceridemic apo $A\text{-}I_{Milano}$ subjects. The composition of HDL was markedly abnormal with decreased cholesteryl ester and increased triglyceride, phospholipid, and protein content. The ratio of HDL cholesterol to plasma apo A-I was 60 percent of normal, with HDL from the apo $A\text{-}I_{Milano}$ subjects having approximately a 20 percent increase in surface components. Affected subjects also had a 20 percent decrease in the ratio of apo A-I to apo A-II. LCAT activity was found to be reduced 25 percent in apo $A\text{-}I_{Milano}$ individuals with a significant increase in the ratio of plasma free cholesterol to cholesteryl ester.

Rate zonal ultracentrifugation indicated that HDL from subjects with apo $A\text{-}I_{Milano}$ contained 60 percent of normal HDL_3 mass and 35 percent of normal HDL_2 mass.[45] There was no distinct peak observed in the HDL_2 density region. Gradient gel electrophoresis revealed HDL primarily of HDL_3 particle size. The major components were normal in size and had peaks within the HDL_{3a} and HDL_{3b} intervals on gradient electrophoresis. The amount of the smaller HDL_{3b} correlated with the degree of decrease in HDL cholesterol levels as is seen in other populations. The HDL_3 from apo $A\text{-}I_{Milano}$ subjects was prepared by preparative ultracentrifugation and subfractions isolated by agarose-gel filtration. Apolipoprotein analysis indicated that the smaller particles were enriched in apo $A\text{-}I_{Milano}$ monomers, whereas the larger particles contained apo $A\text{-}I_{Milano}$/apo A-II complexes and apo $A\text{-}I_{Milano}$ dimers.[44]

The possible physiological consequences of the apo $A\text{-}I_{Milano}$ variant have been studied both in vitro and in vivo. Apo $A\text{-}I_{Milano}$ was able to incorporate normally into stable complexes with dimyristoyl phosphatidyl choline (DMPC).[46] The liposomes formed were stable and, after isolation by gel filtration, had normal dimensions and stoichiometry. Apo $A\text{-}I_{Milano}$ had a greater than normal association rate with DMPC. Using guanidine hydrochloride, apo $A\text{-}I_{Milano}$ was also more easily displaced than normal apo A-I from the DMPC-apolipoprotein complex. Physical methods indicated that apo $A\text{-}I_{Milano}$ had a diminished α-helical content. These findings suggest that disruption of the apo A-I α-helix may expose hydrophobic residues, causing faster association with phospholipids, while at the same time destabilizing the lipid protein association of the amphipathic α-helical region of apo A-I.

Apo $A\text{-}I_{Milano}$ metabolism was also studied in vivo.[47] The iodinated apolipoprotein had a mean residence time within HDL of 2.77 ± 1.21 days compared with a normal of 4.10 ± 1.5 days. In vitro the iodinated apo $A\text{-}I_{Milano}$ was taken up at a greater than normal rate by freshly isolated rat liver hepatocytes. These studies suggest that, perhaps due to altered lipid association, apo $A\text{-}I_{Milano}$ is hypercatabolized. This observation may explain the diminished HDL cholesterol and apo A-I levels in affected individuals.

Basic Genetic Defect. The basic defect in apo $A\text{-}I_{Milano}$ has been determined.[48,49] Isoelectric focusing of plasma from affected subjects indicates the normal apo A-I isoforms and a set of isoforms that are one charge unit more acidic than normal. Such individuals appear to be heterozygotes for a normal apo A-I and a mutant apo A-I. The family pedigree indicates that this mutant form of apo A-I is inherited in an autosomal codominant fashion.[40]

Apo $A\text{-}I_{Milano}$ was purified, and partial sequence analysis revealed a substitution of cysteine for arginine at amino acid 173 (Fig. 49-3.)[49] This changes the physical properties of one of the amphipathic helical regions of apo A-I involved in lipid binding. It also introduces a cysteine into a protein previously devoid of this residue. This allows apo $A\text{-}I_{Milano}$ to enter into disulfide bonding with other proteins. Apo $A\text{-}I_{Milano}$ dimers as well as apo $A\text{-}I_{Milano}$/apo A-II and apo $A\text{-}I_{Milano}$/apo E complexes have been observed. These also could significantly change HDL metabolism.

Although only described in individuals from a small Italian village thus far, the apo $A\text{-}I_{Milano}$ variant teaches us that structural variants of apo A-I can be a cause of low HDL levels.

Table 49-3 Lipid, Lipoprotein, and Apolipoprotein Levels* in Apo $A\text{-}I_{Milano}$†

	Total chol	*TG*	*VLDL chol*	*LDL chol*	*HDL chol*	*A-I*	*A-II*	*B*	*C-II*	*C-III*	*E*
$A\text{-}I_{Milano}$+	182 ± 45	188 ± 79	27 ± 14	137 ± 36	18 ± 8	74 ± 20	24 ± 5	86 ± 25	4.8 ± .7	13 ± 2	6 ± 2
Controls	216 ± 52	107 ± 52	16 ± 14	141 ± 49	54 ± 12	129 ± 18	38 ± 8	81 ± 24	4.7 ± .6	13 ± 2	7 ± 2

*Values given are means ± SD in mg/dl.

†A comparison is made between 29 apo $A\text{-}I_{Milano}$ patients and the same number of age and sex matched controls who did not have the apo A-I variant. Each group comprised 17 males and 12 females.

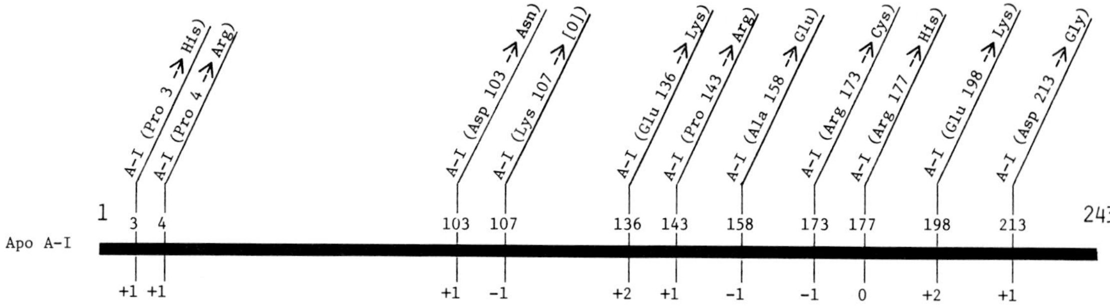

Fig. 49-3 Apo A-I structural variants. The solid bar represents the 243 amino acid long mature apo A-I polypeptide. The location and nature of the known variants are indicated. The alteration of net charge for the variant compared to wild type is indicated as +2, +1, 0, or −1. A-I (Lys 107 → [0]) indicates a three-base deletion of this codon.

This variant also raises some disquieting thoughts about our notions of the role of HDL in atherosclerosis susceptibility. Affected subjects, despite very low HDL levels and a lack of HDL_2, have no increase in cardiovascular disease. It might be that the low HDL is not itself atherogenic. HDL metabolism is complex, and low HDL can be caused by many factors. Some of these processes may be atherogenic, and others, such as the apo A-I structural defect in apo A-I_{Milano}, are not (Table 49-4).

The increased incidence of hypertriglyceridemia in apo A-I_{Milano} subjects may also be instructive, assuming there is a significant relationship. The inheritance of hypertriglyceridemia is only rarely monogenic. Most often, it is probably due to the inheritance of two or more of a number of contributory genes. The apo A-I structural defect in apo A-I_{Milano} subjects causes a quantitative and qualitative HDL abnormality. This may result in the lack of acceptors for excess surface remnants of triglyceride-rich lipoproteins formed during lipolysis. This along with other factors could contribute to the development of hypertriglyceridemia.

Population screening for apo A-I structural variants, principally by isoelectric focusing, has revealed 10 other variants.[50–54] The underlying amino acid alterations for these variants are summarized in Fig. 49-3. In contrast to apo A-I_{Milano}, none of these variants has been consistently associated with low HDL levels. The codon deletion mutation apo A-I (Lys 107 → 0) and the apo A-I (Pro 143 → Arg) have both been associated with reduced LCAT activation but not with reduced HDL cholesterol levels or clinical consequences.[55,56]

Deficiency in Lipoprotein Processing Reactions Affecting HDL Levels

As described in the section on HDL metabolism, several lipoprotein processing reactions affect HDL formation, particle size distribution, and catabolism. Rare inborn errors of metabolism characterized by deficiencies of each of these have been described, and their effects on plasma lipid and lipoprotein levels are summarized in Table 49-5. There are three post-heparin lipolytic activity deficiencies: LPL deficiency, apo C-II deficiency, and HTGL deficiency. There is a deficiency in the LCAT enzyme and a partial deficiency called fish eye disease. Finally, a deficiency in the CETP has been reported.

Table 49-4 Inborn Errors of Metabolism Altering HDL Cholesterol Levels and Their Effect on Coronary Heart Disease Susceptibility

	HDL chol	*CHD susceptibility*
Apo A-I deficiency	↓↓↓	↑↑↑
Apo A-I_{Milano}	↓↓	N, ↓
LPL deficiency	↓↓↓	N
Apo C-II deficiency	↓↓↓	N
HTGL deficiency	N, ↑, ↑↑	N, ↑
LCAT deficiency	↓↓↓	↑
Fish eye disease	↓↓↓	N, ↑
CETP deficiency	↑↑↑	N
Tangier disease	↓↓↓	N, ↑

LPL Deficiency. LPL deficiency is a recessive genetic disorder characterized by massive chylomicronemia, repeated attacks of abdominal pain and/or pancreatitis, eruptive xanthomas, and hepatosplenomegaly (for review see Refs. 24 to 26 and Chap. 45). The disorder does not appear to cause increased susceptibility to atherosclerosis. Symptoms are related to the degree of chylomicronemia, which is dependent on the dietary fat intake. Patients have very low or absent LPL. Plasma triglycerides are typically between 1500 and 4500 mg/dl (normal < 250 mg/dl), but values as high as 25,000 mg/dl have been documented. Cholesterol levels are either normal or moderately elevated, with values typically between 150 and 400 mg/dl. Lipoprotein analysis reveals excessive chylomicrons in fasting plasma with normal to slightly elevated VLDL

Table 49-5 Lipid and Lipoprotein Levels in Disorders of Lipoprotein Processing

	Chol	*TG*	*CHYLO*	*VLDL*	*LDL*	*HDL*	*HDL_2*	*HDL_3*
LPL deficiency	N, ↑	↑↑↑↑	↑↑↑↑	N, ↑	↓↓↓	↓↓↓	↓↓↓	↓
Apo C-II deficiency	N, ↑	↑↑↑	↑↑↑	↑	↓↓↓	↓↓↓	↓↓↓	↓
HTGL deficiency	↑, ↑↑	↑, ↑↑	0	↑, ↑↑	N, ↑	N, ↑, ↑↑	↑, ↑↑	N, ↑
LCAT deficiency*	↓, N, ↑	N, ↑	↑	N, ↑	↓, N, ↑	↓↓↓	↓↓↓	↓
Fish eye disease	N, ↑	↑, ↑↑	0	↑, ↑↑	N, ↑	↓↓↓	↓↓↓	↓
CETP deficiency	↑, ↑↑	N, ↑↑	↑	↓, ↑	↓, N	↑↑↑	↑↑↑	N, ↑

NOTE: The number of arrows indicates the magnitude of the increase or decrease. N indicates levels in the normal range. A zero indicates an absence of fasting chylomicronemia.

*In LCAT deficiency, all lipoprotein classes contain abnormal particles, as explained in the text.

cholesterol levels. Both LDL and HDL cholesterol levels are markedly depressed. Affected patients have virtually no HDL_2 and reduced levels of HDL_3. As already discussed, a major portion of HDL, particularly its surface components of apolipoproteins, free cholesterol, and phospholipid, originate from chylomicrons and VLDL during the lipolytic process. Therefore, the concentration of HDL, especially HDL_2, is to a large extent controlled by the activity of LPL and is markedly reduced in LPL deficiency.

Apo C-II Deficiency. Apo C-II is the physiological activator of LPL, and apo C-II deficiency results in a functional deficiency of this enzyme (for review see Refs. 24 to 26 and Chap. 45). Apo C-II deficiency appears to be a recessive genetic disorder with obligate heterozygotes having half-normal apo C-II levels but normal triglyceride concentrations. Linkage analysis has shown that the disorder is linked to the apo C-II gene locus on chromosome 19.[57] Recently, several probands with apo C-II deficiency have been found to have a small amount of a mutant form of the protein in their plasma.[58,59] This suggests that the defect in the apo C-II gene in these individuals results in the production of an unstable nonfunctional protein. In the original family reported with apo C-II deficiency, it was recently found that the mutation is a four-base insertion into the apo C-II gene which changes amino acids 69 to 74 and then introduces a stop codon.[60] Since apo C-II amino acids 77 to 79 are necessary to activate LPL, this mutation explains the physiological defect in this kindred.

Clinically apo C-II deficiency shares many of the features of LPL deficiency, including fasting chylomicronemia and repeated attacks of abdominal pain and/or pancreatitis. Patients deficient in apo C-II do not show xanthomas or hepatomegaly. Only a few show splenomegaly. Affected individuals have not usually been diagnosed until adulthood, but symptoms are present in childhood. Plasma triglycerides are quite elevated but not usually as high as in LPL deficiency. Patients usually have elevated VLDL but markedly depressed LDL and HDL cholesterol levels. The lipoprotein abnormality appears slightly less severe in apo C-II compared with that in LPL deficiency, but nevertheless it has a profound effect on HDL cholesterol levels, undoubtedly by the same mechanism.

HTGL Deficiency. Hepatic triglyceride lipase deficiency has been reported in only three families.[61–63] In the Toronto family, two brothers were reported with less than 2 percent of normal HTGL activity.[61] One of them developed angina pectoris at age 43 and had eruptive and palmar xanthomas. His cholesterol varied from 260 to 1495 mg/dl and triglycerides from 395 to 8200 mg/dl, depending in part on dietary adherence. On a strict metabolic ward diet (1200 calories, 30 percent fat, polyunsaturated fatty acids:saturated fatty acids (P:S) = 1.0, cholesterol 166 mg/dl) for 2 weeks, his cholesterol was 261 mg/dl and triglycerides 546 mg/dl. HDL cholesterol was in the normal range, whereas LDL cholesterol varied from 70 to 218 mg/dl. Lipoproteins of $d < 1.006$ had β mobility on electrophoresis, suggesting a type III hyperlipoproteinemia pattern, but the ratio of VLDL cholesterol to total triglyceride was normal. The patient did not have the apo E phenotype characteristic of type III hyperlipoproteinemia. The brother, in his 40s, had no angina or xanthomas but maximum cholesterol and triglyceride levels of 441 and 990 mg/dl, respectively, with average levels of 285 and 445 mg/dl, respectively. On two occasions, HDL cholesterol was 37 and 55 mg/dl and LDL cholesterol was 179 and 154 mg/dl. There was evidence of β-migrating VLDL, but a normal ratio of VLDL cholesterol to total triglyceride and no evidence of an apo E abnormality. Both brothers had an increase in the mass of VLDL, IDL, LDL, and HDL_2. The content of triglycerides in LDL and HDL_2 was increased four- to fivefold above normal on a weight basis.

Two Swedish brothers have also been reported with HTGL deficiency with levels measured at less than 2 percent of normal.[62] The proband was healthy at age 49 with moderate hypertriglyceridemia on routine screening. Neither he nor his brother had evidence of xanthomas or atherosclerotic disease. On two different occasions, the proband had cholesterol levels of 239 and 254 mg/dl and triglyceride levels of 380 and 495 mg/dl. Levels of VLDL cholesterol were 48 and 105 mg/dl, LDL cholesterol 115 and 71 mg/dl, and HDL cholesterol 82 and 76 mg/dl. The triglyceride contents of LDL and HDL were both seven- and eightfold elevated. His sib had a cholesterol level of 345 mg/dl and a triglyceride level of 250 mg/dl. VLDL, LDL, and HDL cholesterol levels were 23, 171, and 133 mg/dl, respectively, with LDL and HDL having very increased triglyceride content. In both brothers, VLDL exhibited β mobility despite neither having the apo E phenotype associated with type III hyperlipoproteinemia. HDL particle size was analyzed by gradient gel electrophoresis and found to be in the HDL_2 size range. Measurement of lecithin:cholesterol acyltransferase and cholesteryl ester transfer protein were found to be normal.

A Japanese family with three-generation transmission of HTGL deficiency has been briefly reported.[63] The proband was a 72-year-old female with myocardial and cerebral infarction with cholesterol, triglyceride, and HDL cholesterol levels of 261, 77, and 152 mg/dl, respectively. There was an increase in HDL_2. Postheparin plasma HTGL activity was 18 percent of normal. The proband's daughter was 52 years old with ischemic heart disease, elevated HDL_2 levels, and HTGL activity 12.5 percent of normal. The proband's granddaughter, at age 29, had high HDL_2 and HTGL activity 25 percent of normal.

Although few cases have been reported, HTGL deficiency appears to be a genetic condition affecting HDL metabolism. HDL is greatly enriched in triglyceride, and HDL cholesterol levels may be normal to greatly increased. HDL appears to be largely in the HDL_2 size range, and HDL_3 is normal or diminished. These cases lend credence to the role of HTGL in converting HDL_2 to HDL_3. It is also of interest that, in spite of a tendency toward elevated HDL_2 levels, affected individuals appear to have an increased susceptibility to atherosclerotic disease.

LCAT Deficiency. Patients have been described with LCAT deficiency (for review see Ref. 27 and Chap. 46). This is an autosomal recessive disease, which maps to chromosome 16.[64] Clinical symptoms include corneal opacities, anemia, and frequently proteinuria. In some patients, proteinuria increases markedly in the fourth and fifth decades of life, and renal insufficiency accompanied by hypertension can develop. Premature atherosclerosis occurs in LCAT deficiency. Plasma lipid levels can be quite variable in affected subjects. A consistent finding is an increased ratio of plasma free cholesterol to cholesteryl ester. Heterogeneity of particle size and shape has been documented in each lipoprotein class indicating a fundamental derangement in lipoprotein metabolism. Large spherical VLDLs (760 nm diameter) are present and include some notched particles. These VLDLs contain a high proportion of surface components. They are present in fasting plasma, but they decrease markedly when the patients consume a fat-free diet for several days. On this basis, they are believed to be chylomicrons. There are also smaller VLDL (<40 nm diameter) believed to be of hepatic origin. Three types of LDL have been identified. There are large particles, >90 nm in diameter, which have a multilamellar structure, consisting mostly of free cholesterol, phospholipid, and little protein, which is mostly albumin. Another unusual LDL is 30 to 80 nm in diameter and disk-shaped in appearanee. These contain free cholesterol, phospholipid, and apo C protein. A third particle is spherical and 20 to 22 nm in diameter. This particle resembles normal LDL but contains large amounts of triglyceride and correspondingly reduced cholesteryl esters. HDLs include disk-shaped particles and unusually small spherical particles. These are similar to newly secreted HDL, which is compatible with the notion that LCAT is necessary to transform precursors into the type of HDL normally present in plasma.

Fish Eye Disease. Severe corneal opacities in association with very low HDL levels have been reported in two unrelated families and called *fish eye disease* (see Chap. 46).[65,66] The first family was from a small village in northern Sweden. By appearance, a father and three daughters were said to have the same eye disease. The father, without previous cardiovascular symptoms, died at age 76 from myocardial infarction, and one of the sisters, who was healthy except for corneal opacities, died at age 37 of an accident. The two living sisters were studied in the seventh and eighth decades of their lives. One had an EKG compatible with coronary insufficiency at age 63, and the other had a myocardial infarction at age 77. A 70-year-old Swedish woman from an unrelated family was also reported with severe corneal opacities and low HDL levels but no clinical coronary heart disease and only a slight ST segment depression on resting EKG. In all affected individuals, the corneal opacities were first noticed in the second and third decades of life. Plasma lipid analyses of the three living subjects indicated cholesterol and triglyceride levels between 249 and 312, and 341 and 538 mg/dl, respectively. VLDL levels were elevated with a normal ratio of triglyceride to cholesterol. LDL cholesterol levels were between the 75th and 90th percentiles for age, and LDL composition was quite abnormal with a fivefold increase in the ratio of triglyceride to cholesterol. HDL cholesterol levels were extremely low, averaging 6 mg/dl or about 10 percent of normal levels. Apolipoprotein A-I and A-II levels were 22 and 11 percent of normal, respectively. Ultracentrifugation indicated the HDL was almost all in the HDL_3 density fraction. HDL unesterified cholesterol was increased relative to cholesteryl ester. Electron microscopy showed that HDL particles were morphologically heterogeneous.[67] The major species was a small spherical particle, but discoidal particles together with large vesicles were also seen.

The presence of fish eye disease in four members of the same family indicates that this is a genetic condition.[65,66] However, the mode of inheritance is uncertain. Two sibs in the first family not affected with fish eye disease had low HDL cholesterol, and the father and daughter of the proband in the second family also had low HDL cholesterol. These individuals had levels 52 to 62 percent of normal compared with 10 percent in fish eye disease. These findings suggest that first-degree relatives are heterozygous for an abnormality affecting HDL cholesterol levels, which when present in the homozygous state cause fish eye disease.

It was recently shown that serum of patients with fish eye disease fails to esterify free cholesterol in HDL, whereas total LCAT activity is essentially normal.[68,69] This implies that there are two different LCAT activities in normal plasma. One is specific for HDL and the other for VLDL-LDL. LCAT-deficient patients are missing both activities and patients with fish eye disease just the former. The size, shape, composition, and concentration of HDL in fish eye disease could be explained by such a defect.

CETP Deficiency. Cholesteryl ester transfer protein deficiency has been reported in two families from Japan.[70,71] Affected individuals were identified because of very high HDL cholesterol levels, and these people were found to have reduced CETP activity upon further analysis. In the first family, a 58-year-old male proband with an HDL cholesterol of 301 mg/dl and his 55-year-old sister with a level of 174 mg/dl were identified.[70] Both subjects were asymptomatic without clinical signs of atherosclerosis, nor was there significant cardiovascular disease in the family. The proband's brother and another sister had HDL cholesterol levels of 63 and 55 mg/dl, respectively, and three female and a male offspring ages 23 to 30 years had levels of 57, 67, 83, and 54, respectively. LDL cholesterol and triglyceride levels were quite low in the proband and his sister. Agarose column chromatography indicated their HDL was large in size, more like HDL_2. LCAT activity was found to be normal, as was the apo A-I isoelectric focusing pattern. Both subjects' sera failed to transfer [^{3}H]cholesteryl ester from HDL to VLDL plus LDL and on this basis were said to be deficient in the CETP. The presence of these findings in sibs suggests genetic transmission, but the exact mode cannot be determined with certainty from the data provided.

Another Japanese male 35 years of age was evaluated for hypercholesterolemia, hypertriglyceridemia, and high HDL cholesterol levels.[71] There was no indication of atherosclerotic disease or xanthomatous accumulation. The total cholesterol, triglyceride, HDL cholesterol, and LDL cholesterol levels were 421, 609, 205, and 125 mg/dl, respectively. Chylomicrons were present in fasting plasma, and VLDL levels were increased. Postheparin lipolytic activities and LCAT were normal. HDLs were found to be large on HPLC analysis. The subject's serum supported a very low rate of cholesterol transfer between LDL and HDL. Compatible with the concept that the CETP exchanges cholesteryl ester in HDL for triglyceride in LDL or VLDL, the subject had a lower triglyceride content in HDL when compared with that of either normal subjects or others with hypertriglyceridemia. The described cases of CETP deficiency support the role of this protein in determining HDL concentration and composition.

GENETIC REGULATION OF HDL LEVELS IN THE GENERAL POPULATION

As discussed previously, HDL cholesterol levels are negatively correlated with the incidence of coronary heart disease in the general population.[2] Environmental factors can affect HDL cholesterol levels. Dietary saturated fat, alcohol, and exercise raise HDL cholesterol levels, whereas weight gain and cigarette smoking lower levels.[19,20,72,73] In addition, hormones influence HDL cholesterol levels.[18] Exogenous hormonal preparations, such as birth control pills, with a high ratio of estrogen to progesterone raise cholesterol levels. Those with a low ratio diminish HDL cholesterol levels. Exogenous androgens also lower HDL cholesterol levels. HDL cholesterol levels are also sex-influenced.[5] In adults, men have almost 20 percent lower HDL cholesterol levels than women. Prior to puberty, boys and girls have equal HDL cholesterol levels, which are comparable to those in adult females. At puberty in males, it is the increase in endogenous androgens that decreases HDL cholesterol levels. The impressive and well documented effects of environment and hormones on HDL cholesterol levels presumably account for a significant fraction of the HDL cholesterol level variation that occurs in the general population. Current research is directed at the question of whether there are significant genetic influences on HDL cholesterol levels in the general population. If such exist, it will also need to be determined which genes are involved, the nature of the causative mutations, and what fraction of the HDL cholesterol level variation in the population can be accounted for by these mutations. Unfortunately, none of these questions can be answered satisfactorily at this time. It is clear that the rare group of inborn errors that alter HDL cholesterol levels does not explain a significant fraction of the low and high HDL cholesterol levels in the population. However, several types of investigations suggest that genetic factors do influence HDL levels.

Familial Aggregation of HDL Cholesterol Levels

HDL levels have been measured in unselected nuclear families, and correlations have been sought between family members.[74–81] In general, these have shown little to no correlation between the HDL cholesterol levels of the spouses, but significant correlations between sib-sib and parent-child values were detected. The sib-sib HDL cholesterol levels correlated with an r of 0.2 to 0.3 and parent-child levels with an r of 0.1 to 0.3. In several studies, the mother-child correlations were stronger than the father-child.[78,80,81] Such studies suggest a genetic component in determining HDL cholesterol levels, but it cannot be assumed that heredity is the basis of the sib-sib and parent-child correlations. Environmental and behavioral influences on lipid levels may be more alike between child and parent than between mother and father, particularly if a component of adult HDL cholesterol levels is determined in childhood.

A second type of study has analyzed HDL cholesterol levels in twin pairs. These studies have shown much greater correlations between HDL cholesterol levels of monozygotic (MZ) than between dizygotic (DZ) twins. Three large studies involving many sets of twins have been reported. In the Swedish; the National Heart, Lung and Blood Institute; and the Kaiser Permanente twin studies, MZ twins' HDL cholesterol correlated with an r of 0.74, 0.68, and 0.68, respectively, whereas DZ twins correlated with an r of 0.38, 0.46, and 0.34, respectively.[82–84] These types of twin studies are much more suggestive of genetic influences on HDL cholesterol levels than the studies in nuclear families. However, it is still possible that MZ twins share a more similar environment than DZ twins.

A further refinement, called *path analysis*, has been used to analyze HDL cholesterol levels in families.[82,85] Measurements are usually made in sibs in the parental generation, their spouses, and their children. Models that consider the distinct familial relationships within such a family are used to resolve genetic and environmental sources of phenotypic variation. Analysis of a family study of Swedish twins indicated heritability of HDL cholesterol levels of 0.55.[82] This could be divided into a genetic heritability component of 0.363 and a cultural heritability component of 0.187. The proportion of phenotypic variance due to residual environmental affects was 0.45. Another study of families of Swedish males who survived myocardial infarction below age 45 and families of males matched for age and residential area was analyzed by the same method.[85] The results indicated heritability of HDL cholesterol levels of 0.51 with a genetic heritability component of 0.42 and cultural heritability of 0.09. Taken together, these studies of familial aggregation of HDL cholesterol levels all suggest a large genetic component in the determination of HDL cholesterol levels.

Familial Hypo- and Hyperalphalipoproteinemias

Other evidence suggesting genetic influences on HDL cholesterol levels is the demonstration of families with clusters of individuals who have HDL cholesterol levels in either the lowest or highest deciles.[86–93] This has been called *familial hypo-* or *hyperalphalipoproteinemia*, respectively. In the Princeton School District Family Study, 272 probands, 125 randomly selected and 147 selected for hypercholesterolemia, and their relatives were assessed with regard to hypo- and hyperalphalipoproteinemias.[86] From the randomly selected group there were 5 probands with bottom decile HDL cholesterol. From the hyperlipidemic group there were 18 probands with bottom decile HDL cholesterol, and 16 out of 92 first-degree relatives also had this phenotype. Nine kindreds had no lowest decile HDL cholesterol first-degree relatives. Seven had one, one had four, and one had five. Thus by the criterion of a proband and at least two first-degree relatives with bottom decile HDL cholesterol, two families were said to have familial hypoalphalipoproteinemia. With regard to hyperalphalipoproteinemia, from the randomly selected group there were 13 probands with top decile HDL cholesterol, and 10 of their 46 first-degree relatives also had top decile HDL cholesterol. Five kindred had no top decile HDL cholesterol first-degree relatives, six had one, and two had two. From the hyperlipidemic group, there were 10 probands with top decile HDL cholesterol, and nine of 42 first-degree relatives also had this phenotype. Six kindred had no top decile HDL cholesterol first-degree relatives, four had seven, one had two, and one had three. Thus by the criterion of a proband and at least two affected first-degree relatives, four families were said to have familial hyperalphalipoproteinemia. Overall, 16 percent of first-degree relatives of bottom decile HDL cholesterol probands had the same phenotype, whereas 22 percent of such relatives of top decile HDL cholesterol had the same phenotype.

In another study of 16 probands with bottom decile HDL cholesterol referred to the Cincinnati Lipid Research Clinic, 60 of 72 living first-degree relatives were studied, and 27 (45 percent) were found to have bottom decile HDL cholesterol.[87] In two kindreds there was a three-generation transmission of bottom decile HDL cholesterol but it was accompanied by top decile triglycerides in one or more family members. Eight kindreds had two-generation vertical transmission of bottom decile HDL cholesterol, and in three there was no vertical transmission. After excluding probands, in this study there were 11 matings of people with bottom decile HDL cholesterol with normal individuals, and 13 of 30 living offspring had bottom decile HDL cholesterol. The ratio of affected to nonaffected offspring was not significantly different from 1. It was suggested that this was an autosomal dominant genetic influence on bottom decile HDL cholesterol levels.

The same clinic also studied the kindred of 18 probands with top decile HDL cholesterol.[88] They sampled 100 of 127 living first-degree relatives and found four kindreds with three-generation vertical transmission, 11 with two-generation vertical transmission, one proband with multiple affected sibs, and two probands with no affected relatives. In these families there were 22 matings of people with top decile HDL cholesterol with normal individuals, and 37 of 84 offspring had top decile HDL cholesterol. The ratio of affected to nonaffected offspring was close to 1, and it was also suggested that there was an autosomal dominant genetic influence on top decile HDL cholesterol levels.

A family from Milan has also been reported with what appears to be familial hypoalphalipoproteinemia.[92] Two brothers and a cousin all survived myocardial infarction below 50 years of age and were found to have bottom decile HDL cholesterol levels. Although the parental generation was deceased from premature myocardial infarction, two-generation transmission was documented.

Finally, a Japanese family has been described with three-generation transmission of high HDL cholesterol levels.[93] This kindred includes two sibs with HDL cholesterol levels approximately twice that of the other hyperalphalipoproteinemia family members. It was suggested that these individuals are homozygotes for familial hyperalphalipoproteinemia.

Major Locus Effects on HDL Cholesterol Levels Inferred by Complex Segregation Analysis

In family studies, a clear-cut bimodal distribution of HDL cholesterol levels would be evidence for a major locus effect. However, in the studies reviewed above, this was not the case. Rather, abnormal HDL cholesterol levels were defined arbitrarily as below or above the 10th or 90th percentile, with those in between considered normal. Probands were selected in this manner, and these criteria were also used to determine normalcy of relatives. This is not the best way to look for a major gene effect for the following reason. Families selected because of probands with low or high HDL cholesterol levels will contain a larger than average number of people with values near the cutoff points. Abnormality is then an arbitrary function of this level and ignores the effects of polygenic variation and/or environment, which could place a family member's HDL cholesterol level in one category or another. This unfairly influences the ratio of affected to unaffected in a family and can lead to the specious suggestion of the presence of dominant genes that cause familial hypo- or hyperalphalipoproteinemia.

A fairer assessment of major locus effects on HDL cholesterol levels can be derived by complex segregation analysis.[94–106] In this method, the HDL cholesterol level is treated as a continuous trait, without an arbitrary designation of abnormality and normality. HDL cholesterol levels are considered to be a function of the effect of a major biallelic locus plus a polygenic component due to an infinitely large number of additive genetic factors, plus an environmental contribution. The general model is based on several parameters including V, variance of the quantitative trait; U, mean of the quantitative trait; H, heritability or the fraction of the phenotype variation due to the polygenic component; B, sibling environmental correlation; q, gene frequency of the major locus; d, degree of dominance at major locus or the position of the heterozygous mean relative to the means of the two homozygotes; and t, displacement due to a major locus measured in standard deviation units, V, of the quantitative trait. For the general model, these seven parameters can be inferred by a computer program based on the likelihood of sibships given the phenotypes of their parents. Alternative hypotheses such as no major locus ($q = t = d = 0$), no heritability ($H = 0$), no common sib environment ($B = 0$), a major locus with dominance ($d = 1$), additivity ($d = 0.5$), or recessiveness ($d = 0$) can be tested by altering the parameters of the general model. The likelihood of these models can then be calculated and likelihood ratios used to select the model most compatible with the data.

In a study of 500 Hawaiian families of Japanese ancestry using complex segregation analysis, no major locus effect on HDL cholesterol levels was found, but polygenic inheritance was estimated to be 0.385.[96] In an analysis of the 18 kindred studied by the Cincinnati Lipid Research Clinic and identified by probands with top decile HDL cholesterol, evidence for a recessive major gene was found, but this was due entirely to three families.[99] When these were excluded from the analysis, there was no evidence for a major locus in the other 15 families, but polygenic inheritance was estimated to be 0.603. An analysis of families ascertained through 23 probands with bottom decile HDL cholesterol levels at the Cincinnati Lipid Research Clinic provided evidence for a recessive major gene for depressed levels.[101] The allele frequency was $q = 0.116$ and, in addition, polygenic inheritance was estimated to be 0.572. A recent reanalysis of the subset of these families ascertained through normotriglyceridemic probands provided evidence for a major gene effect but could not distinguish between the models of dominance, additivity, or recessiveness.[102] In addition, the polygenic component was only between 0.148 and 0.217. Complex segregation analysis in 3074 nuclear families in Jerusalem indicated a recessive major locus for low HDL cholesterol levels with an allele frequency of $q = 0.06$.[103,105] In addition, polygenic inheritance was estimated to be 0.45. Similar analysis of 55 Utah pedigrees including 2170 persons revealed a major dominant locus for low HDL cholesterol levels with an allele frequency of $q = 0.0025$.[104] Polygenic inheritance was estimated to be 0.561. The dominant locus was due to only 2 of the 55 families studied. In the others, there was no evidence of a major gene effect.

Complex segregation analysis was also performed on the data gathered as part of the Lipid Research Clinics Program Family Study.[106] Three populations were sampled including 1146 families with 4279 members in the random sample, 483 families with 1807 members in the high cholesterol sample, and 177 families with 735 members in the low HDL cholesterol sample. In all three samples, there was evidence of transmission of a major factor for low HDL cholesterol. Two major HDL cholesterol clusters with means separated by approximately three standard deviations were observed. However, the major factor for low HDL cholesterol was not transmitted in conformity with Mendelian segregation expectations. Maximum likelihood for the Mendelian mixed model, although rejected, resulted in calculated recessive allele frequencies in the three populations studied of 0.086, 0.063, and 0.028, respectively, with polygenic inheritance estimated to be 0.496, 0.569, and 0.302, respectively.

In summary, complex segregation analysis indicates no major gene for hyperalphalipoproteinemia and probably relatively rare recessive gene(s) for hypoalphalipoproteinemia varying in frequency between 0.028 and 0.116. Thus, homozygosity for the minor allele required to affect phenotype would exist in 1 percent or less of individuals. This would not explain a significant fraction of the phenotypic variation in HDL cholesterol levels in the population. However, one must be careful not to conclude that major gene effects on HDL cholesterol levels do not exist. Complex segregation analysis indicates very significant genetic variation included under polygenic inheritance. This does not have to be the result of a large number of small genetic factors, but could result from the effects of common genetic variation at only a few, perhaps two to four, loci. This has yet to be resolved.

Apo A-I and Apo A-II Gene RFLPs Associated with Altered Lipoprotein Levels and/or Coronary Heart Disease

Candidate genes that may play a role in the genetic regulation of HDL levels have been isolated. Probes have been derived from these genes and used to identify common sites of DNA variation in the population in or near these genes (for review see Refs. 22, 23, and 107). These are called *restriction fragment length polymorphisms* (RFLPs). RFLPs can be used to define alleles for a particular genetic locus. Alleles are defined either by a single RFLP or an array of RFLPs, called a *haplotype*. In one type of clinical study, called an *association study*, the allele frequency of a candidate gene, defined by RFLP analysis, is compared between cases with a given phenotype and controls without the phenotype. A significant difference in allele frequency implies that a mutation causing dysfunction has arisen on the allele associated with disease. Another way of stating this is that there is linkage disequilibrium between a causative mutation in the candidate gene and the RFLPs that specify the allele in the population under study. Cases and controls should be carefully matched with regard to their racial background. In different racial groups the same or a similar causative mutation in the candidate gene may have arisen on a different allele, which is specified by a new set of RFLPs. Association studies suggest, but do not prove, that a causative mutation resides in the candidate gene.[108]

Apo A-I and apo A-II are two candidate genes for playing a role in determining HDL level variation in the general population. These genes have been isolated, and RFLPs have been identified in or near both of them.[107] The apo A-I gene locus at chromosome 11q23, with its neighboring apo C-III and apo A-IV genes, is the most studied to date. Ten RFLPs have been identified and mapped at this locus, and their locations are indicated in Fig. 49-4. Several of these RFLPs have been used in association studies.

The first RFLP to be studied extensively was the *Sac*I (*Sst*I) RFLP.[109–124] The variant site is 2.7 kb downstream from the apo A-I gene. The minor allele is due to the presence of a *Sac*I site caused by a C-versus-G difference in the 3′ untranslated region of the apo C-III gene, which is probably of no functional significance.[110,111] Utilizing an apo A-I probe, Southern blotting of genomic DNA after *Sac*I digestion reveals either a 4.2- or a 3.2-kb band for the major and minor alleles, respectively. In their original study, Galton and colleagues found the minor allele (3.2-kb band) present in 12 of 28 patients with type IV/type V hypertriglyceridemia, in only 3 of 37 clinic controls, in none of 36 normolipidemic controls, and in none of seven patients with type IIb hyperlipoproteinemia.[109] Most of the subjects in this study were London based Caucasians, but a few were Asian. Another study by the same group found that 10 of 48 (21 percent) Caucasian post myocardial infarction patients had the minor allele compared with only 2 of 47 controls.[114] In the same study, taking hypertriglyceridemic subjects from both the patient and control groups, 6 of 25 (24 percent) had at least one minor allele. In a third study, this group found the minor allele present in 18 percent of 167 Caucasians with suspected coronary artery disease whose angiograms were positive versus only 6 percent of those whose test was negative.[113] In view of the inverse correlation of triglyceride and HDL cholesterol levels, one might assume that the *Sac*I minor allele would have also been associated with low HDL cholesterol levels had this been specifically looked for in these studies.

The importance of defining and matching the racial background of cases and controls is underscored by the finding of the variation in frequency of the *Sac*I minor allele between racial groups. In one study, this has been found to be 0 to 0.06 in normolipidemic Caucasians, 0.15 in African blacks, 0.18 in Asian Indians, 0.38 in North American Indians, and 0.48 in Chinese.[116] In addition, as already mentioned, the allele associated with a phenotype may be different in another racial group. For example, in 35 normolipidemic Japanese, the minor *Sac*I allele had a frequency of 0.33 in normolipidemic subjects, and another RFLP detected with the *Msp*I enzyme had a minor allele frequency of 0.45.[117] In 40 hypertriglyceridemic Japanese, an apo A-I gene allele haplotype specified by the *Sac*I major allele and the *Msp*I minor allele was present in 32 percent of hypertriglyceridemics and 11 percent of controls. Thus, in Japanese, there was also an association between hypertriglyceridemia and genotypes at the apo A-I locus. However, the association was with a different haplotype from that in Caucasians.

The association of the *Sac*I minor allele in Caucasians with hypertriglyceridemia and/or diminished HDL cholesterol levels and/or coronary heart disease has also received support from other investigators. Kessling found the minor allele in 5

Fig. 49-4 Restriction endonuclease sites giving rise to RFLPs at the apo A-I/C-III/A-IV gene cluster on chromosome 11. Enzymes detecting sites are indicated with capital letters: A = *Apa*I; ID = insertion/deletion; Xm = *Xmn*I; M = *Msp*I; Ps = *Pst*I; S = *Sac*I (*Sst*I); Pv = *Pvu*II; Xb = *Xba*I (two sites); and D = *Dra*I. Asterisks indicate polymorphic sites associated with clinical phenotypes.

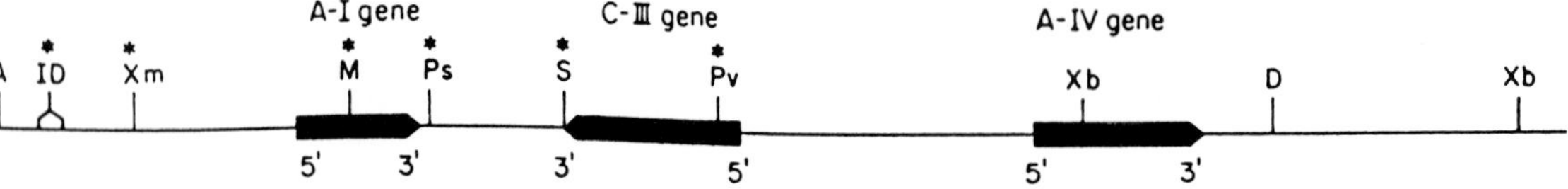

of 11 London Caucasians with type V hypertriglyceridemia and only 9 of 73 normolipidemic controls.[119] Anderson found the minor allele in Iowa Caucasians recruited from a population based survey of lipoprotein levels in 6 of 22 (27 percent) of those with lowest decile HDL cholesterol levels and in none of 20 with highest decile HDL cholesterol.[121] The *Sac*I minor allele was also associated with higher triglyceride levels. Henderson found the minor allele in 9 of 21 of those with hypertriglyceridemia in a racially mixed South African clinic compared with 22 of 160 normolipidemic controls.[122] This difference was significant for "colored" and non-Afrikaans-speaking Caucasians. Hayden showed the minor allele in 6 of 24 patients with familial combined hyperlipidemia compared with 5 of 38 controls in a clinic in Vancouver.[123] Lastly, Aalto-Setala studying Finnish subjects found the *Sac*I minor allele in 16 of 26 (62 percent) patients with hypertriglyceridemia and 10 of 61 (16 percent) controls.[124]

Association studies have been reported using other RFLPs (Fig. 49-4) at the chromosome 11 gene locus. A variant *Xmn*I site is located 2.5 kb upstream of the apo A-I gene, and Southern blotting reveals either an 8.3- or a 6.6-kb band for the major and minor alleles, respectively. The *Xmn*I RFLP minor allele (6.6-kb band) was decreased in frequency in myocardial infarction victims in both Boston and German studies of Caucasians.[125,126] A variant *Msp*I site is located within the third intron of the apo A-I gene, and Southern blotting reveals either a 1.0- or a 1.7-kb band for the major and minor alleles, respectively. The *Msp*I RFLP minor allele (1.7-kb band) was increased in frequency in myocardial infarction victims in a London study of Caucasians but not in a Boston or German study.[118,125,126] A variant *Pst*I site is located 300 bp 3′ to the apo A-I gene, and Southern blotting reveals either a 2.2- or 3.3-kb band for the major and minor alleles, respectively. The *Pst*I RFLP minor allele (3.3-kb band) in one study was associated with low HDL cholesterol levels and premature coronary artery disease.[127] The minor allele was present in 5 of 123 (4.1 percent) random controls and 1 of 30 with no angiographic evidence of coronary artery disease. This allele was present in 28 of 88 (32 percent) patients with severe coronary artery disease on angiography. It was also present in 8 of 12 index cases of kindreds with familial hypoalphalipoproteinemia. In a German study, subjects with angiographically proven coronary artery disease had an increased frequency of the *Pst*I RFLP minor allele when compared with normal controls (odds ratio 1.8).[125] In a Boston based study of Caucasians, cases of myocardial infarction showed no difference in the *Pst*I RFLP minor allele frequency when compared with controls (0.04 versus 0.04).[126] However, when these patients were segregated according to age greater or less than 60 years and compared with their controls, the minor allele frequency was significantly decreased in cases of myocardial infarction older than 60 years (0.03 versus 0.21) and was increased (although not significantly) in cases of myocardial infarction younger than 60 years (0.10 versus 0.02). A variant *Pvu*II site is located in the first intron of the apo C-III gene, and, with an apo C-III cDNA probe, Southern blotting reveals either a 3.6- or a 4.3-kb band for the major and minor alleles, respectively. The *Pvu*II RFLP minor allele (4.3-kb band) was increased in frequency in a German study of subjects with angiographically proven coronary artery disease.[125]

At the apo A-II gene locus on chromosome 1, an RFLP has been reported using the enzyme *Msp*I. This is due to a variant site located in an Alu element 200 bp 3′ to the gene. Southern blotting with an apo A-II cDNA probe reveals either a 3.0- or a 3.7-kb band for the major and minor alleles, respectively. In one study of London Caucasian men, homozygosity for the minor allele (3.7-kb band) was associated with higher plasma levels of apo A-II.[128] In another study of London Caucasians, subjects with hypertriglyceridemia had a decreased frequency of the minor allele compared with normal controls.[129] This was not found in a Boston study of Caucasians with myocardial infarction[126] or in a German study of subjects with angiographically proven coronary artery disease.[130]

The weight of the evidence is highly suggestive that a mutation or mutations at the apolipoprotein gene locus on chromosome 11 is involved in causing a high triglyceride, low HDL condition that may be associated with coronary heart disease. The exact nature of this mutation or these mutations is not yet known.

Dr. Breslow's research is supported in part by grants from the National Insitutes of Health (HL33714, HD32435, HL36461, AGO4727, CA29502), RJR-Nabisco, Inc., and a General Clinical Research Center grant (RR00102), as well as general support from the Pew Trusts. Breslow is an Established Investigator of the American Heart Association and Frederick H. Leonhardt Professor at the Rockefeller University. Grateful thanks is given to Mrs. Lori Cersosimo and Ms. Lorraine Duda for their help in preparing the manuscript.

REFERENCES

1. EISENBERG S: High density lipoprotein metabolism. *J Lipid Res* 25:1017, 1984.
2. MILLER NE: Associations of high-density lipoprotein subclasses and apolipoproteins with ischemic heart disease and coronary atherosclerosis. *Am Heart J* 113:589, 1987.
3. NESTEL PJ: High-density lipoprotein turnover. *Am Heart J* 113:518, 1987.
4. NIKKILA EA, TASKINEN MR, SANE T: Plasma high-density lipoprotein concentration and subfraction distribution in relation to triglyceride metabolism. *Am Heart J* 113:543, 1987.
5. LIPID RESEARCH CLINICS PROGRAM: The prevalence study, *Population Studies Data Book I*. U.S. Department of Health and Human Services, National Institutes of Health, Publication 80-1527, Bethesda, 1980.
6. GOFMAN JW, DE LALLA O, GLAZIER F, FREEMAN NK, LINDGREN FT, NICHOLS AV, STRISOWER EH, TAMPLIN AR: The serum lipoprotein transport system in health, metabolic disorders, atherosclerosis and coronary artery disease. *Plasma* 2:413, 1954.
7. MILLER GJ, MILLER NE: Plasma-high-density-lipoprotein concentration and development of ischaemic heart-disease. *Lancet* 1:16, 1975.
8. CASTELLI WP, GARRISION RJ, WILSON PWF, ABBOTT RF, KALOUSDIAN S, KANNEL WB: Incidence of coronary heart disease and lipoprotein cholesterol levels. The Framingham study. *JAMA* 256:2835, 1986.
9. GORDON DJ, KNOKE J, PROBSTFIELD JL, SUPERKO R, TYROLER HA: High-density lipoprotein cholesterol and coronary heart disease in hypercholesterolemic men: The lipid research clinics coronary primary prevention trial. *Circulation* 74:1217, 1986.
10. CASTELLI WP, DOYLE JT, GORDON T, HAMES CG, HJORTLAND MC, HULLEY SB, KAGAN A, ZUKEL WJ: HDL cholesterol and other lipids in coronary heart disease. The cooperative lipoprotein phenotyping study. *Circulation* 55:767, 1977.
11. WALLENTIN L, SUNDIN B: HDL_2 and HDL_3 lipid levels in coronary artery disease. *Atherosclerosis* 59:131, 1985.
12. LAAKSO M, VOUTILAINEN E, PYORALA K, SARLUND H: Association of low HDL and HDL_2 cholesterol with coronary heart disease in non-insulin-dependent diabetics. *Arteriosclerosis* 5:653, 1985.
13. HAMSTEN A, WALLDIUS G, DAHLEN G, JOHANSSON B, DE FAIRE U: Serum lipoproteins and apolipoproteins in young male survivors of myocardial infarction. *Atherosclerosis* 59:223, 1986.
14. CASTELLI WP, ABBOTT RF, MCNAMARA PM: Summary estimates of cholesterol used to predict coronary heart disease. *Circulation* 67:730, 1983.
15. GOFMAN JW, YOUNG W, TANDY R: Ishemic heart disease, atherosclerosis and longevity. *Circulation* 34:667, 1966.
16. MILLER NE, HAMMETT F, SALTISSI S, ET AL: Relation of angiographically

defined coronary artery disease to plasma lipoprotein subfractions and apolipoproteins. *Br Med J* 282:1741, 1981.

17. BALLANTYNE FC, CLARK RS, SIMPSON HS, BALLANTYNE D: High density and low density lipoprotein subfractions in survivors of myocardial infarction and in control subjects. *Metabolism* 31:433, 1982.

18. KRAUSS RM: Regulation of high density lipoprotein levels. *Med Clin North Am* 66:403, 1982.

19. WOOD PD, WILLIAMS PT, HASKELL WL: Physical activity and high-density lipoproteins, in Miller NE, Miller GJ (eds): *Clinical and Metabolic Aspects of High-Density Lipoproteins*. Amsterdam, Elsevier, 1984, p 133.

20. PIETINEN P, HUTTUNEN JK: Dietary determinants of plasma high-density lipoprotein cholesterol. *Am Heart J* 113:620, 1987.

21. SCHAEFER EJ: Clinical, biochemical and genetic features in familial disorders of high density lipoprotein deficiency. *Arteriosclerosis* 4:303, 1984.

22. BRESLOW JL: Human apolipoprotein molecular biology and genetic variation. *Annu Rev Biochem* 54:669, 1985.

23. BRESLOW JL: Apolipoprotein genetic variation and human disease. *Phys Rev* 68:85, 1988.

24. NIKKILA ES: Familial lipoprotein lipase deficiency and related disorders of chylomicron metabolism, in Stanbury JB, Wyngaarden JB, Fredrickson DS, Goldstein JL, Brown MS (eds): *The Metabolic Basis of Inherited Disease*, 5th ed. New York, McGraw-Hill, 1983, p 622.

25. TASKINEN M-R: Lipoprotein lipase in hypertriglyceridemias, in Borensztajn J (ed): *Lipoprotein Lipase*. Chicago, Evener Publishers, 1987, p 201.

26. BRECKENRIDGE WC: Deficiencies of plasma lipolytic activities. *Am Heart J* 113:567, 1987.

27. GLOMSET JA, NORUM KR, GJONE E: Familial lecithin: Cholesterol acyltransferase deficiency, in Stanbury JB, Wyngaarden JB, Fredrickson DS, Goldstein JL, Brown MS (eds): *The Metabolic Basis of Inherited Disease*, 5th ed. New York, McGraw-Hill, 1983, p 643.

28. NORUM RA, LAKIER JB, GOLDSTEIN S, ANGEL A, GOLDBERG RB, BLOCK WD, NOFFZE DK, DOLPHIN PJ, EDELGLASS J, BOGORAD DD, ALAUPOVIC P: Familial deficiency of apolipoproteins A-I and C-III and precocious coronary-artery disease. *N Engl J Med* 306:1513, 1982.

29. SCHAEFER EJ, HEATON WH, WETZEL MG, BREWER HB JR: Plasma apolipoprotein A-I absence associated with a marked reduction of high density lipoproteins and premature coronary artery disease. *Arteriosclerosis* 2:16, 1982.

30. SCHAEFER EJ, ORDOVAS JM, LAW SW, GHISELLI G, KASHYAP ML, SRIVASTAVA LS, HEATON WH, ALBERS JJ, CONNOR WE, LINDGREN FT, LEMESHEV Y, SEGREST JP, BREWER HB JR: Familial apolipoprotein A-I and C-III deficiency, variant II[1]. *J Lipid Res* 26:1089, 1985.

31. LINDESKOG GR, GUSTAFSON A: Serum lipoprotein deficiency in diffuse "normolipemic" plane xanthoma. *Arch Dermatol* 106:529, 1972.

32. GUSTAFSON A, MCCONATHY WJ, ALAUPOVIC P, CURRY MD, PERSSON B: Identification of lipoprotein families in a variant of human plasma apolipoprotein A deficiency. *Scand J Clin Lab Invest* 39:377, 1979.

33. FORTE TM, NICHOLS AV, KRAUSS RM, NORUM RA: Familial apolipoprotein AI and apolipoprotein CIII deficiency. *J Clin Invest* 74:1601, 1984.

34. GINSBERG HN, LE N-A, GOLDBERG IJ, GIBSON JC, RUBINSTEIN A, WANG-IVERSON P, NORUM R, BROWN WV: Apolipoprotein B metabolism in subjects with deficiency of apolipoproteins CIII and AI. *J Clin Invest* 78:1287, 1986.

35. KARATHANASIS SK, NORUM RA, ZANNIS VI, BRESLOW JL: An inherited polymorphism in the human apolipoprotein A-I gene locus related to the development of atherosclerosis. *Nature* 301:718, 1983.

36. KARATHANASIS SK, ZANNIS VI, BRESLOW JL: A DNA insertion in the apolipoprotein A-I gene of patients with premature atherosclerosis. *Nature* 305:823, 1983.

37. KARATHANASIS SK, FRAZER C, ZANNIS VI, BRESLOW JL: Apo CIII gene defect in patients with combined apo A-I-CIII deficiency and premature atherosclerosis. *Arteriosclerosis* 4:562a, 1984.

38. KARATHANASIS SK: DNA inversion inactivates both the apo AI and apo CIII genes in patients with combined apo AI-apo CIII deficiency and premature coronary artery disease. *Circulation* 74(*suppl 2*):157, 1986.

39. FRANCESCHINI G, SIRTORI CR, CAPURSO A, WEISGRABER KH, MAHLEY RW: AI_{Milano} apoprotein. Decreased high density lipoprotein cholesterol levels with significant lipoprotein modifications and without clinical atherosclerosis in an Italian family. *J Clin Invest* 66:892, 1980.

40. GUALANDRI V, FRANCESCHINI G, SIRTORI CR, GIANFRANCESCHI G, ORSINI GB, CERRONE A, MENOTTI A: AI_{Milano} apoprotein identification of the complete kindred and evidence of a dominant genetic transmission. *Am J Hum Genet* 37:1083, 1985.

41. FRANCESCHINI G, SIRTORI M, GIANFRANCESCHI G, SIRTORI CR: Relation between the HDL apoproteins and AI isoproteins in subjects with the AI_{Milano} abnormality. *Metabolism* 30:502, 1981.

42. GUALANDRI V, ORSINI GB, CERRONE A, FRANCESCHINI G, SIRTORI CR: Familial associations of lipids and lipoproteins in a highly consanguineous population: The Limone sul Garda study. *Metabolism* 34:212, 1984.

43. FRANCESCHINI G, SIRTORI CR, BOSISIO E, GUALANDRI V, ORSINI GB, MOGAVERO AM, CAPURSO A: Relationship of the phenotypic expression of the AI_{Milano} apoprotein with plasma lipid and lipoprotein patterns. *Atherosclerosis* 58:159, 1985.

44. FRANCESCHINI G, FROSI TG, MANZONI C, GIANFRANCESCHI G, SIRTORI CR: High density lipoprotein-3 heterogeneity in subjects with the apo-AI_{Milano} variant. *J Biol Chem* 257:9926, 1982.

45. FRANCESCHINI G, CALABRESI L, TOSI C, SIRTORI CR, FRAGIACOMO C, NOSEDA G, GONG E, BLANCHE P, NICHOLS AV: Apolipoprotein A-I_{Milano}. Correlation between high density lipoprotein subclass distribution and triglyceridemia. *Arteriosclerosis* 7:426, 1987.

46. FRANCESCHINI G, VECCHIO G, GIANFRANCESCHI G, MAGANI D, SIRTORI CR: Apolipoprotein AI_{Milano}. Accelerated binding and dissociation from lipids of a human apolipoprotein variant. *J Biol Chem* 260:16321, 1985.

47. GHISELLI G, SUMMERFIELD JA, SCHAEFER EJ, SIRTORI C, JONES EA, BREWER HB JR: Abnormal catabolism of apolipoprotein A-I_{Milano}, a cause of high density lipoprotein deficiency. *J Clin Res* 30:393a, 1982.

48. WEISGRABER KH, BERSOT TP, MAHLEY RW: A-I_{Milano} apoprotein. Isolation and characterization of a cysteine-containing variant of the A-I apoprotein from human high density lipoproteins. *J Clin Invest* 66:901, 1980.

49. WEISGRABER KH, RALL SC JR, BERSOT TP, MAHLEY RW: Apolipoprotein A-I_{Milano}. Detection of normal A-I in affected subjects and evidence for a cysteine for arginine substitution in the variant A-I. *J Biol Chem* 258:2508, 1983.

50. UTERMANN GG, FEUSSNER G, FRANCESCHINI G, HAAS J, STEINMETZ A: Genetic variants of group A apolipoproteins. *J Biol Chem* 257:501, 1982.

51. UTERMANN G, STEINMETZ A, PAETZOLD R, WILK J, FUESSNER G, KAFFARNIK H, MUELLER-ECKHARDT C, SEIDEL D, VOGELBERG KH, ZIMMER F: Apolipoprotein $AI_{Marburg}$: Studies on two kindreds with a mutant of human apolipoprotein AI. *Hum Genet* 61:329, 1982.

52. MENZEL HJ, KLADETZKY L, ASSMANN G: One-step screening method for the polymorphism of apolipoproteins A-I, A-II, and A-IV. *J Lipid Res* 23:915, 1982.

53. WEISGRABER KH, RALL SC JR, MAHLEY RW, OGAWA Y, FIELDING CJ, UTERMANN G, HAAS J, STEINMETZ A, MENZEL HJ, ASSMANN G: Human apolipoprotein A-I variants, in Nestel PJ (ed): *Proceedings of the 7th International Symposium on Atherosclerosis*. Melbourne, International Atherosclerosis Society, 1985, p 113.

54. JABS H-U, ASSMANN G, GREIFENDORF D, BENNINGHOVEN A: High performance liquid chromatography and time-of-flight secondary ion mass spectrometry: A new dimension in structural analysis of apolipoproteins. *J Lipid Res* 27:613, 1986.

55. RALL SC JR, WEISGRABER KH, MAHLEY RW, OGAWA Y, FIELDING CJ, UTERMANN G, HAAS J, STEINMETZ A, MENZEL HJ, ASSMANN G: Abnormal lecithin: Cholesterol acyltransferase activation by a human apolipoprotein A-I variant in which a single lysine residue is deleted. *J Biol Chem* 259:10063, 1984.

56. UTERMANN G, HAAS J, STEINMETZ A, PAETZOLD R, RALL SC JR, WEISGRABER KH, MAHLEY RW: Apolipoprotein A-$I_{Giessen}$ (Pro $^{143}\rightarrow$Arg). A mutant that is defective in activating lecithin:cholesterol acyltransferase. *Eur J Biochem* 144:325, 1984.

57. HUMPHRIES SE, WILLIAMS L, MYKLEBOST O, STALENHOEF AFH, DEMACKER PNM, BAGGIO G, CREPALDI G, GALTON DJ, WILLIAMSON R: Familial apolipoprotein CII deficiency: A preliminary analysis of the gene defect in two independent families. *Hum Genet* 67:151, 1984.

58. MAGUIRE GF, LITTLE JA, KAKIS G, BRECKENRIDGE WC: Apolipoprotein C-II deficiency associated with nonfunctional mutant forms of apolipoprotein C-II. *Can J Biochem Cell Biol* 62:847, 1984.

59. BAGGIO G, MANZATO E, GABELLI C, FELLIN R, MARTINI S, BALDO ENZI G, VERLATO F, BAIOCCHI MR, SPRECHER DL, KASHYAP ML, BREWER HB JR, CREPALDI G: Apolipoprotein C-II deficiency syndrome. Clinical features, lipoprotein characterization, lipase activity and correction of hypertriglyceridemia after apolipoprotein C-II administration in two affected patients. *J Clin Invest* 77:520, 1986.

60. CONNELLY PW, MAGUIRE GF, HOFMANN T, LITTLE JA: Structure of apolipoprotein C-$II_{Toronto}$, a nonfunctional human apolipoprotein. *Proc Natl Acad Sci USA* 84:270, 1987.

61. BRECKENRIDGE WC, LITTLE JA, ALAUPOVIC P, WANG CS, KUKSIS A, KAKIS G, LINDGREN F, GARDINER G: Lipoprotein abnormalities associated with a familial deficiency of hepatic lipase. *Atherosclerosis* 45:161, 1982.

62. CARLSON LA, HOLMQUIST L, NILSSON-EHLE P: Deficiency of hepatic lipase activity in post-heparin plasma in familial hyper-α-triglyceridemia. *Acta Med Scand* 219:435, 1986.

63. ITAKURA H, ITOH H, KODAMA T, SATO T, AKANUMA Y, MIYASHITA H: Familial hyper-alpha lipoproteinemia with atherosclerosis and decreased

hepatic triglyceride lipase activity, in Nestel PJ (ed): *Proceedings of Poster Communications, 7th International Symposium on Atherosclerosis*. Melbourne, International Atherosclerosis Society, 1985, p 226.

64. TEISBERG P, GJONE E, OLAISEN B: Genetics of LCAT (lecithin:cholesterol acyltransferase) deficiency. *Ann Hum Genet* 38:327, 1975.

65. CARLSON LA, PHILIPSON B: Fish-eye disease. A new familial condition with massive corneal opacities and dyslipoproteinaemia. *Lancet* 2:921, 1979.

66. CARLSON LA: Fish eye disease: A new familial condition with massive corneal opacities and dyslipoproteinaemia. Clinical and laboratory studies in two afflicted families. *Eur J Clin Invest* 12:41, 1982.

67. FORTE TM, CARLSON LA: Electron microscopic structure of serum lipoproteins from patients with fish eye disease. *Arteriosclerosis* 4:130, 1984.

68. CARLSON LA, HOLMQUIST L: Evidence for deficiency of high density lipoprotein lecithin:cholesterol acyltransferase activity (α-LCAT) in fish eye disease. *Acta Med Scand* 218:189, 1985.

69. CARLSON LA, HOLMQUIST L: Evidence for the presence in human plasma of lecithin:cholesterol acyltransferase activity (β-LCAT) specifically esterifying free cholesterol of combined pre-β- and β-lipoproteins. Studies of fish eye disease patients and control subjects. *Acta Med Scand* 218:197, 1985.

70. KOIZUMI J, MABUCHI H, YOSHIMURA A, MICHISHITA I, TAKEDA M, ITOH H, SAKAI Y, SAKAI T, UEDA K, TAKEDA R: Deficiency of serum cholesteryl-ester transfer activity in patients with familial hyperalphalipoproteinaemia. *Atherosclerosis* 58:175, 1985.

71. KURASAWA T, YOKOYAMA S, MIYAKE Y, YAMAMURA T, YAMAMOTO A: Rate of cholesteryl ester transfer between high and low density lipoproteins in human serum and a case with decreased transfer rate in association with hyperalphalipoproteinemia. *J Biochem* 98:1499, 1985.

72. CRIQUI MH, WALLACE RB, HEISS G, MISKEL M, SCHOENFELD G, JONES GTL: Cigarette smoking and plasma high density lipoprotein cholesterol: The Lipid Research Clinics Program prevalence study. *Circulation* 62(*Suppl* 4):70, 1980.

73. HAFFNER SM, APPLEBAUM-BOWDEN D, WAHL PW, HOOVER JJ, WARNICK GR, ALBERS JJ, HAZZARD WR: Epidemiological correlates of high density lipoprotein subfractions, apolipoproteins A-I, A-II, and D, and lecithin cholesterol acyltransferase. Effects of smoking, alcohol, and adiposity. *Arteriosclerosis* 5:169, 1985.

74. WEINBERG R, AVET LM, GARDNER MJ: Estimator of the heritability of serum lipoprotein and lipid concentrations. *Clin Genet* 9:588, 1976.

75. MJOS OD, THELLE DS, FORDE OH, VIK-MO H: Family study of high density lipoprotein cholesterol and the relation to age and sex. *Acta Med Scand* 201:323, 1977.

76. ELLEFSON RD, ELVEBACK LR, HODGSON PA, WEIDMAN WH: Cholesterol and triglyceride in serum lipoproteins in young persons in Rochester, Minnesota. *Mayo Clin Proc* 53:307, 1978.

77. SHEAR CL, FRERICHS RR, WEINBERG R, BERENSON GS: Childhood sibling aggregation of coronary artery disease risk factor variables in a biracial community. *Am J Epidemiol* 107:522, 1978.

78. GARRISON RJ, CASTELLI WP, FEINLEIB M, ET AL: The association of total cholesterol, triglycerides, and plasma lipoprotein cholesterol levels in first-degree relatives and spouse pairs. *Am J Epidemiol* 110:313, 1979.

79. RAO DC, MORTON NE, GULBRANDSEN CL, RHOADS GG, KAGAN A, YEE S: Cultural and biological determinants of lipoprotein concentrations. *Ann Hum Genet* 42:467, 1979.

80. SOSENKO JM, BRESLOW JL, ELLISON RC, MIETTINEN OS: Familial aggregation of total cholesterol, high density lipoprotein cholesterol, and total triglyceride levels in plasma. *Am J Epidemiol* 112:656, 1980.

81. NAMBOODIRI KK, GREEN PP, KAPLAN EB, TYROLER HA, MORRISON JA, CHASE GA, ELSTON RC, RIFKIND BM, GLUECK CJ: Family aggregation of high density ipoprotein cholesterol. Collaborative Lipid Research Clinics Program family study. *Arteriosclerosis* 3:616, 1983.

82. MCGUE M, RAO DC, ISELIUS L, RUSSELL JM: Resolution of genetic and cultural inheritance in twin families by path analysis: Application to HDL-cholesterol. *Am J Hum Genet* 37:998, 1985.

83. FEINLEIB M, GARRISON RJ, FABSITZ R, CHRISTIAN JC, HRUBEC Z, BORHANI NO, KANNEL WB, ROSENMAN R, SCHWARTZ JT, WAGNER JO: The NHLBI twin study of cardiovascular disease risk factors: Methodology and summary of results. *Am J Epidemiol* 106:284, 1977.

84. AUSTIN MA, KING M-C, BAWOL RD, HULLEY SB, FRIEDMAN GD: Risk factors for coronary heart disease in adult female twins: Genetic heritability and shared environmental influences. *Am J Epidemiol* 125:308, 1987.

85. HAMSTEN A, ISELIUS L, DAHLEN G, DE FAIRE U: Genetic and cultural inheritance of serum lipids. Low and high density lipoprotein cholesterol and serum apolipoproteins A-I, A-II and B. *Atherosclerosis* 60:199, 1986.

86. LASKARZEWSKI PM, KHOURY P, MORRISON JA, KELLY K, MELLIES MJ, GLUECK CJ: Prevalence of familial hyper- and hypolipoproteinemias: The Princeton school district family study. *Metabolism* 31:558, 1982.

87. THIRD JLHC, MONTAG J, FLYNN M, FREIDEL J, LASKARZEWSKI P, GLUECK CJ: Primary and familial hypoalphalipoproteinemia. *Metabolism* 33:136, 1984.

88. GLUECK CJ, FALLAT RW, MILLETT F, GARTSIDE P, ELSTON RC, GO RCP: Familial hyper-alpha-lipoproteinemia: Studies in eighteen kindreds. *Metabolism* 24:1243, 1975.

89. GLUECK CJ, FALLAT RW, MILLETT F, STEINER PM: Familial hyperalphalipoproteinemia. *Arch Intern Med* 135:1025, 1975.

90. AVOGARO P, CAZZOLATO G: Familial hyper-HDL-(α)-cholesterolemia. *Atherosclerosis* 22:63, 1975.

91. AVOGARO P, CAZZOLATO G, KOSTNER G, HOLASEK DRA: Familial hyper-alpha-lipoproteinaemia. Further studies on serum lipoproteins and some serum enzymes. *Clin Chim Acta* 77:139, 1977.

92. VERGANI C, BETTALE G: Familial hypo-alpha-lipoproteinemia. *Clin Chim Acta* 114:45, 1981.

93. SAITO F: A pedigree of homozygous familial hyperalphalipoproteinemia. *Metabolism* 33:629, 1984.

94. MORTON NE, MacLEAN CJ: Analysis of family resemblance. III. Complex segregation of quantitative traits. *Am J Hum Genet* 26:489, 1974.

95. MacLEAN CJ, MORTON NE, LEW R: Analysis of family resemblance. IV. Operational characteristics of segregation analysis. *Am J Hum Genet* 27:365, 1975.

96. MORTON NE, GULBRANDSEN CL, RHOADS GG, KAGAN A, LEW R: Major loci for lipoprotein concentrations. *Am J Hum Genet* 30:583, 1978.

97. SIERVOGEL RM, MORRISON JA, KELLY K, MELLIES M, GARTSIDE P, GLUECK CJSD: Familial hyper-alpha-lipoproteinemia in 26 kindreds. *Clin Genet* 17:13, 1980.

98. LALOUEL JM, MORTON NE: Complex segregation analysis with pointers. *Hum Hered* 31:312, 1981.

99. ISELIUS L, LALOUEL JM: Complex segregation analysis of hyperalphalipoproteinemia. *Metabolism* 31:521, 1982.

100. RAO DC, LALOUEL JM, SUAREZ BK, SCHOENFELD G, GLUECK CJ, SIERVOGEL RM: A genetic study of hyper-alpha-lipoproteinemia. *Am J Med Genet* 15:195, 1983.

101. BYARD PJ, BORECKI IB, GLUECK CJ, LASKARZEWSKI PM, THIRD JLHC, RAO DC: A genetic study of hypoalphalipoproteinemia. *Genet Epidemiol* 1:43, 1984.

102. BORECKI IB, RAO DC, THIRD JLHC, LASKARZEWSKI PM, GLUECK CJ: A major gene for primary hypoalphalipoproteinemia. *Am J Hum Genet* 38:373, 1986.

103. FRIEDLANDER Y, KARK JD, STEIN Y: Complex segregation analysis of low levels of plasma high-density lipoprotein cholesterol in a sample of nuclear families in Jerusalem. *Genet Epidemiol* 3:285, 1986.

104. HASSTEDT SJ, ASH KO, WILLIAMS RR: A re-examination of major locus hypothesis for high density lipoprotein cholesterol level using 2,170 persons screened in 55 Utah pedigrees. *Am J Med Genet* 24:57, 1986.

105. FRIEDLANDER Y, KARK JD: Complex segregation analysis of plasma lipid and lipoprotein variables in a Jerusalem sample of nuclear families. *Hum Hered* 37:7, 1987.

106. BUCHER KD, KAPLAN EB, NAMBOODIRI KK, GLUECK CJ, LASKARZEWSKI P, RIFKIND BM: Segregation analysis of low levels of high-density lipoprotein cholesterol in the collaborative Lipid Research Clinics Program family study. *Am J Hum Genet* 40:489, 1987.

107. HEGELE RA, BRESLOW JL: Apolipoprotein genetic variation in the assessment of atherosclerosis susceptibility. *Genet Epidemiol* 4:163, 1987.

108. BRESLOW JL: Apolipoprotein B-gene polymorphism and myocardial infarction. *N Engl J Med* 317:53, 1987.

109. REES A, SHOULDERS CC, STOCKS J, GALTON DJ, BARALLE FE. DNA polymorphism adjacent to the human apoprotein A-I gene: Relation to hypertriglyceridaemia. *Lancet* 1:444, 1983.

110. KARATHANASIS SK, MCPHERSON J, ZANNIS VI, BRESLOW JL: Linkage of human apolipoprotein A-I and C-III genes. *Nature* 304:371, 1983.

111. KARATHANASIS SK, ZANNIS VI, BRESLOW JL: Isolation and characterization of cDNA clones corresponding to two different human apo CIII alleles. *J Lipid Res* 26:451, 1985.

112. JOWETT NI, REES A, WILLIAMS LG, STOCKS J, VELLA MA, HITMAN GA, KATZ J, GALTON DJ: Insulin and apolipoprotein A-1/C-III gene polymorphisms relating to hypertriglyceridaemia and diabetes mellitus. *Diabetologia* 27:180, 1984.

113. REES A, STOCKS J, WILLIAMS LG, CAPLIN JL, JOWETT NI, CAMM AJ, GALTON DJ: DNA polymorphisms in the apolipoprotein C-III and insulin genes and atherosclerosis. *Atherosclerosis* 58:269, 1985.

114. FERNS GAA, STOCKS J, RITCHIE C, GALTON DJ: Genetic polymorphisms of apolipoprotein C-III and insulin in survivors of myocardial infarction. *Lancet* 1:300, 1985.

115. VELLA M, KESSLING A, JOWETT N, REES A, STOCKS J, WALLIS S, GALTON

D: DNA polymorphisms flanking the apo A-1 and insulin genes and type III hyperlipidaemia. *Hum Genet* 69:275, 1985.

116. REES A, STOCKS J, SHARPE CR, VELLA MA, SHOULDERS CC, KATZ J, JOWETT NI, BARALLE FE, GALTON DJ: Deoxyribonucleic acid polymorphism in the apolipoprotein A-I-CIII gene cluster. *J Clin Invest* 76:1090, 1985.

117. REES A, STOCKS J, PAUL H, OHUCHI Y, GALTON D: Haplotypes identified by DNA polymorphisms at the apolipoprotein A-1 and C-III loci and hypertriglyceridaemia. A study in a Japanese population. *Hum Genet* 72:168, 1986.

118. FERNS GAA, GALTON DJ: Haplotypes of the human apoprotein AI-CIII-AIV gene cluster in coronary atherosclerosis. *Hum Genet* 73:245, 1986.

119. KESSLING AM, HORSTHEMKE B, HUMPHRIES SE: A study of DNA polymorphisms around the human apolipoprotein AI gene in hyperlipidaemic and normal individuals. *Clin Genet* 28:296, 1985.

120. KESSLING AM, BERG K, MOCKELBY E, HUMPHRIES SE: DNA polymorphisms around the apo AI gene in normal and hyperlipidaemic individuals selected for a twin study. *Clin Genet* 29:485, 1986.

121. ANDERSON RA, BENDA TJ, WALLACE RB, ELIASON SL, LEE J, BURNS TL: Prevalence and associations of apolipoprotein A-I linked DNA polymorphisms: Results from a population study. *Genet Epidemiol* 3:385, 1986.

122. HENDERSON HE, LANDON SV, MICHIE J, BERGER GMB: Association of a DNA polymorphism in the apolipoprotein C-III gene with diverse hyperlipidaemic phenotypes. *Hum Genet* 75:62, 1987.

123. HAYDEN MR, KIRK H, CLARK C, FROHLICH J, RABKIN S, MCLEOD R, HEWITT J: DNA polymorphisms in and around the apo-AI-CIII genes and genetic hyperlipidemias. *Am J Hum Genet* 40:452, 1987.

124. AALTO-SETALA K, KONTULA K, SANE T, NIEMINEN M, NIKKILA E: DNA polymorphisms of apolipoprotein A-I/C-III and insulin genes in familial hypertriglyceridemia and coronary heart disease. *Atherosclerosis* 66:145, 1987.

125. FROSSARD PM, FUNKE H, COLEMAN RT, ASSMANN G: Genetic markers for coronary atherosclerosis in the human apolipoprotein AI-CIII-AIV gene complex. *Am J Hum Genet* 39(*Suppl*):589, 1986.

126. HEGELE RA, HERBERT PN, BLUM CB, BURING JE, HENNEKENS CH, BRESLOW JL: Unpublished data.

127. ORDOVAS JM, SCHAEFER EJ, SALEM D, WARD RH, GLUECK CJ, VERGANI C, WILSON PWF, KARATHANASIS SK: Apolipoprotein A-I gene polymorphism associated with premature coronary artery disease and familial hypoalphalipoproteinemia. *N Engl J Med* 314:671, 1986.

128. SCOTT J, KNOTT TL, PREISTLY LM, ROBERTSON ME, MANN DV, KOSTNER G, MILLER GJ, MILLER NE: High density lipoprotein composition is altered by a common DNA polymorphism adjacent to apoprotein A-II gene in man. *Lancet* 1:770, 1985.

129. FERNS GAA, SHELLEY CS, STOCKS J, REES A, PAUL H, BARALLE F, GALTON DJ: A DNA polymorphism of the apoprotein AII gene in hypertriglyceridemia. *Hum Genet* 74:302, 1986.

130. SCHULTE H, FUNKE H, FROSSARD PM, COLEMAN RT, ASSMANN G: The MspI RFLP 3′ to the human apolipoprotein AII gene is neutral with respect to atherosclerosis in Germans. *Am J Hum Genet* 39(*Suppl*):293, 1986.

CHAPTER 50

FAMILIAL HIGH DENSITY LIPOPROTEIN DEFICIENCY: Tangier Disease

GERD ASSMANN
GERD SCHMITZ
H. BRYAN BREWER, JR.

1. *Tangier disease is characterized by severe deficiency or absence of normal high density lipoproteins (HDL) in plasma and results in the accumulation of cholesteryl esters in many tissues throughout the body. These include the liver, spleen, lymph nodes, thymus, intestinal mucosa, skin, and probably the cornea.*
2. *The major clinical signs are hyperplastic orange tonsils, splenomegaly, and relapsing neuropathy. A combination of two features is pathognomonic: a low plasma cholesterol concentration accompanied by normal or elevated triglyceride levels, and hyperplastic orange-yellow tonsils and adenoidal tissue.*
3. *Plasma apolipoprotein A-I concentration is extremely low (<3 percent that of controls), and the small amount of HDL in Tangier plasma differs from normal HDL, particularly with respect to apolipoprotein content. The profound HDL deficiency results in the generation of abnormal chylomicron remnants.*
4. *The disorder appears to be due to a defective autosomal gene affecting HDL metabolism. Heterozygotes in families with known homozygotes can usually be identified by low HDL concentrations. Approximately 25 percent of cases have resulted from consanguineous matings.*
5. *The disease may involve a defect in the formation of circulating HDL or an enhanced catabolism. There is no specific treatment for Tangier disease.*

Tangier disease is a rare disorder named after the Chesapeake Bay island home of the first two patients recognized. It is characterized by severe deficiency or absence of normal high density lipoproteins (HDL) in plasma and by the accumulation of cholesteryl esters in many tissues throughout the body.[1,2] These include the liver, spleen, lymph nodes, thymus, intestinal mucosa, skin, and probably the cornea. A combination of two features is pathognomonic: a low plasma cholesterol concentration accompanied by normal or elevated triglyceride levels and hyperplastic orange-yellow tonsils and adenoidal tissue. Plasma apolipoprotein A-I concentration is extremely low (<3 percent that of controls), and the small amount of HDL in Tangier plasma differs from normal HDL, particularly with respect to apolipoprotein content. The disorder appears to be due to an autosomal gene affecting HDL metabolism. Heterozygotes in families with known homozygotes can usually be identified by low HDL concentrations.

HISTORY

The history of the discovery of Tangier disease has been recounted elsewhere.[3] Unusual tonsils were removed from a 5-year-old boy from Tangier Island, Virginia, and when many foam cells were observed on microscopic examination, he was referred to the National Institutes of Health with tentative diagnostic alternatives of histocytosis or a lipid-storage disease. The initial biochemical abnormality observed was a marked increase in cholesteryl esters in a cervical lymph node. Eventually it was discovered that the level of plasma HDL was very low. An exhaustive search of Tangier Island for similarly affected subjects uncovered a single additional case, the 6-year-old sister of the index patient. Two more sibs from an unrelated kindred in Missouri were soon identified,[4] and examination of these two kindreds established that the obligate heterozygotes and other putative heterozygous relatives had abnormally low serum HDL concentrations.[5]

Tangier disease has since been reported from England, New Zealand, Australia, Switzerland, Germany, Poland, Pakistan, Japan, Denmark, Italy, Canada, and France, for a total of 37 patients. One-third of the patients were identified because of large, yellow-orange tonsils, and another third because of symptoms of neuropathy. Identification in the remaining cases was related to splenomegaly, hypocholesterolemia, ocular abnormalities or family screening in relatives of affected subjects. The incidental finding at autopsy of abnormal tonsils prompted the diagnosis in one subject.[6]

PLASMA LIPOPROTEINS AND APOLIPOPROTEINS

Plasma Lipids

The combinations of very low plasma cholesterol and elevated triglycerides is unique, and provides a diagnostic lipoprotein profile for homozygotes with Tangier disease. In Tangier homozygotes ($n = 27$) and heterozygotes ($n = 22$) the total plasma cholesterol was 69 ± 14 mg/dl and 160 ± 34 mg/dl, respectively.[7] The average percentage of plasma cholesterol esterified was 75 percent. The low plasma cholesterol levels in Tangier disease are similar to those observed in patients with abetalipoproteinemia and hypobetalipoproteinemia, but the presence of normal to elevated triglyceride levels in Tangier disease readily differentiates the two classes of dyslipoproteinemias.[1,2,8,9]

The plasma triglyceride levels vary considerably in Tangier disease depending on the diet, and values in the 300 to 400 mg/dl range are not unusual.[7,8] Plasma phospholipid concen-

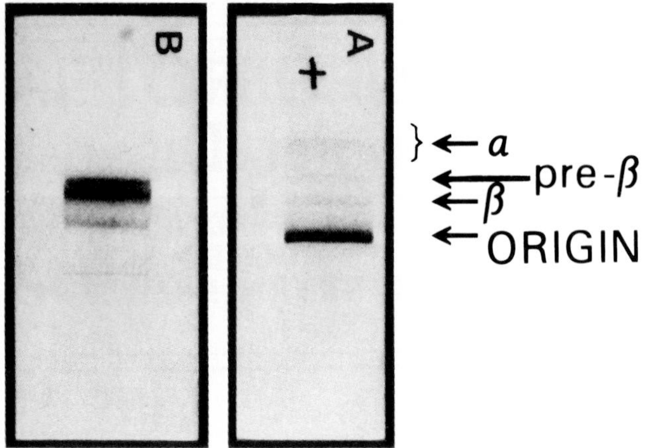

Fig. 50-1 Lipoprotein electrophoresis of plasma from a Tangier patient (A) and a normal subject (B).

trations in Tangier disease are 30 to 50 percent of normal values.[8,9]

Plasma Lipoproteins

The electrophoretic pattern of plasma lipoproteins in Tangier disease is distinctive (Fig. 50-1).[10] No α-migrating lipoproteins are present, and analytical ultracentrifugation confirms the virtual absence of HDL, the hallmark of Tangier disease.[3,4] On electrophoresis a distinct pre-β band is rarely visualized and frequently a diffuse β-preβ band is the only lipoprotein band observed.

Chylomicrons. Fasting chylomicronemia is often observed in homozygotes for Tangier disease following a 12- to 14-h fast.[3,4] Bizarre chylomicron remnants were observed in a Tangier patient following splenectomy.[11] The gross lipid and lipoprotein compositions of the chylomicrons are normal.

VLDL. Tangier VLDL migrate more slowly than normal VLDL on lipoprotein electrophoresis. VLDL morphology, gross chemical composition, and qualitative apolipoprotein content are similar to those of normal VLDL.[12] The C apolipoprotein content in the lipoproteins of density <1.006 g/ml is elevated, presumably reflecting the absence of the complement of C apolipoproteins normally associated with HDL.[12] The cholesteryl ester content of VLDL from Tangier patients was reduced by approximately 30 percent in one series,[12] reflecting the fact that these lipoproteins normally derive a significant fraction of their cholesteryl esters by exchange from HDL.[13]

HDL. The concentration of HDL in Tangier homozygotes is reduced to virtually zero. Lipoprotein electrophoresis and electron-microscopic morphology of Tangier HDL reveals striking heterogeneity in the small number of lipoprotein particles present. Particles of diameter 5.5 to 7.5 nm, 20 to 25 nm, and greater than 100 nm have been observed.[14,15] The very low concentration of HDL has precluded a detailed analysis. However, a subpopulation of these particles appears to contain only apo A-II without apo A-I.[15] HDL of normal morphology, apolipoprotein, and lipid composition has not been isolated from patients with Tangier disease.

PLASMA APOLIPOPROTEINS

Apolipoproteins A-I and A-II in Normal Subjects

Human apo A-I is a 267 amino acid apolipoprotein that is synthesized as a preproapolipoprotein (preproapo A-I) containing an 18 amino acid prepeptide, and a 6 amino acid propeptide (Fig. 50-2).[16–21] The prepeptide is cotranslationally cleaved intracellularly, and proapo A-I is secreted into lymph and plasma by the intestine and liver, respectively.[18,22,23] Plasma proapo A-I undergoes intravascular posttranslational cleavage to the 243-amino acid mature apo A-I.[23] In lymph there is a relative increase in proapo A-I (apo $A\text{-}I_{+2}$ isoform, Fig. 50-3), while the major apo A-I isoprotein in plasma in normal indi-

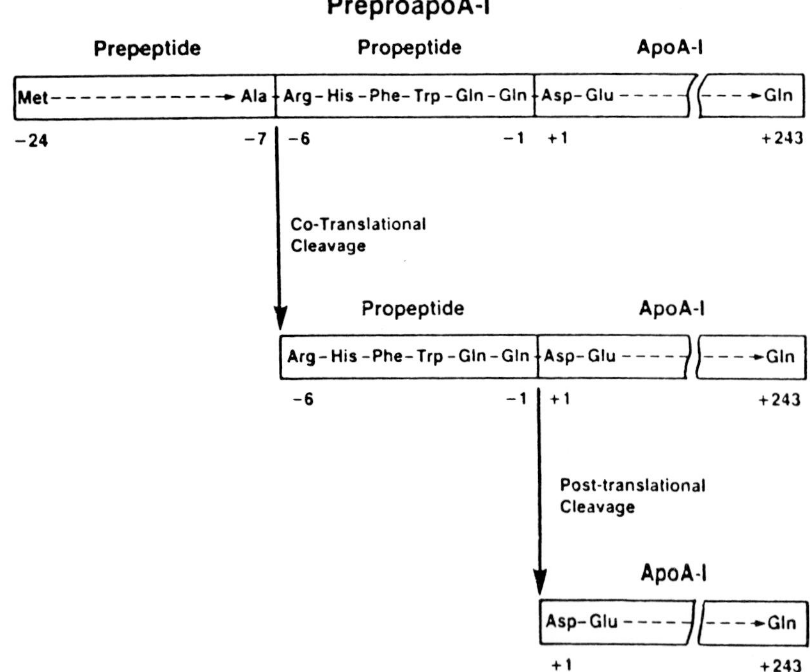

Fig. 50-2 Schematic overview of the intracellular-extracellular processing of human preproapo A-I.

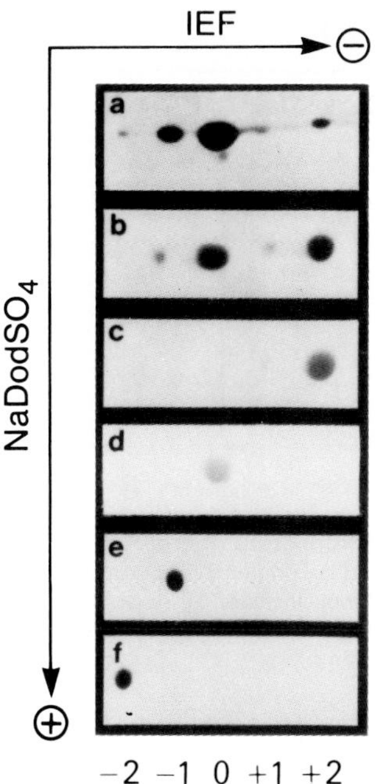

Fig. 50-3 Two-dimensional gel electrophoretogram of normal apo A-I isoforms in plasma and lymph and isolated apo A-I isoforms. Panels include: *(A)* plasma; *(B)* lymph chylomicrons; *(C)* apo A-I_{+2}, proapo A-I; *(D)* mature apo A-I_0 isoform; *(E)* mature apo A-I_{-1} isoform; and *(F)* mature apo A-I_{-2} isoform.

viduals is mature apo A-I (apo A-$I_{0,\ -1,\ -2}$ isoforms, Fig. 50-3). Intracellular apo A-I has been recently shown to undergo posttranslational acylation[24] and phosphorylation.[25] Acylation and phosphorylation may play important roles in the intracellular trafficking of the apolipoproteins. Proapo A-I in lymph has been shown to increase following diets enriched in fat, but not carbohydrate or protein, suggesting that the secretion of proapo A-I is under physiological control.[26]

Apo A-II is a glycoprotein synthesized as a 100 amino acid preproapolipoprotein (preproapo A-II) containing an 18 amino acid prepeptide and a 5-amino acid propeptide (Fig. 50-4).[27–30] The amino terminal prepeptide is cotranslationally cleaved and the 5 amino acid propeptide is cleaved posttranslationally.[31] In contrast to proapo A-I, the major apo A-II isoprotein secreted from the cell is mature apo A-II (apo A-II_0 isoform, Fig. 50-5).[30] The sequence of apo A-I amino-terminal to the cleavage site in proapo A-I contains two neutral residues (Gln-Gln), whereas proapo A-II contains two basic residues (Arg-Arg), indicating that the posttranslational cleavage of the two proapolipoproteins is very likely to be by separate enzyme systems (Figs. 50-2 and 50-4). Within plasma, apo A-II circulates as a 154 amino acid dimeric apolipoprotein composed of two identical chains of 77 amino acids linked by a single disulfide bridge at position 6 in the sequence.[32]

Apolipoprotein A-I and A-II in Tangier Disease

Tangier homozgotes have a reduction of plasma apo A-I to approximately 1 to 3 percent of normal, while the plasma level of apo A-I in heterozygotes is approximately 50 percent of normal.[33,34] Two-dimensional gel electrophoresis of apo A-I in Tangier homozygotes reveals a relative increase of proapo A-I over mature apo A-I (Fig. 50-6).[35] The relative increase in proapo A-I in Tangier disease is virtually pathognomonic and may be used in the diagnosis of Tangier disease. Detailed in vitro studies have established that there is no defect in the structure of the propeptide or the converting peptidase, and that the rate of conversion of proapo A-I to mature apo-A-I in Tangier disease was similar to that of control subjects.[35,36]

The covalent structure of apo A-I from Tangier subjects has been directly addressed. The cDNA and derived amino acid sequence of preproapo A-I was determined by cloning apo A-I cDNA prepared from the mRNA of a liver biopsy from a patient with Tangier disease. The covalent structure of preproapo A-I from the Tangier patient was identical to the sequence of normal apo A-I except for a single isosteric substitution of an Asp for a Glu at position 120.[37] These studies indicated that the covalent structure of apo A-I is normal in Tangier disease.

Apo A-II from Tangier patients was identical to normal apo

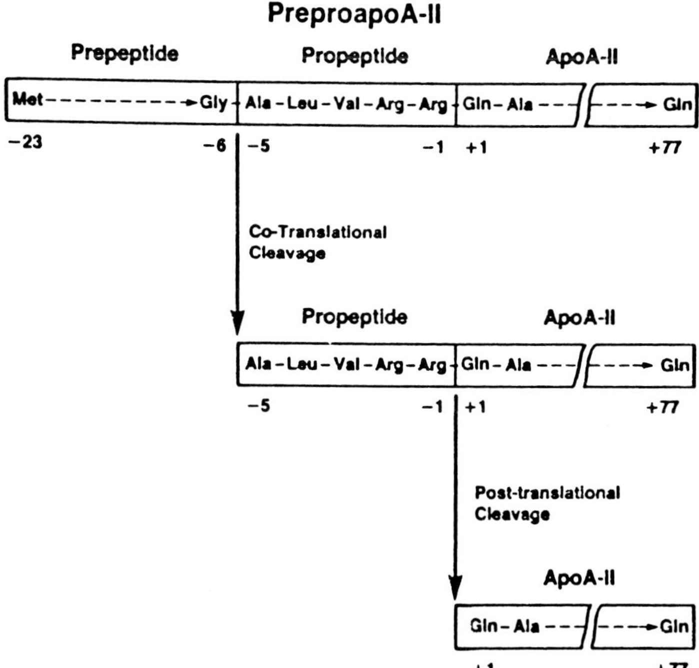

Fig. 50-4 Schematic overview of the intracellular processing of human preproapo A-II.

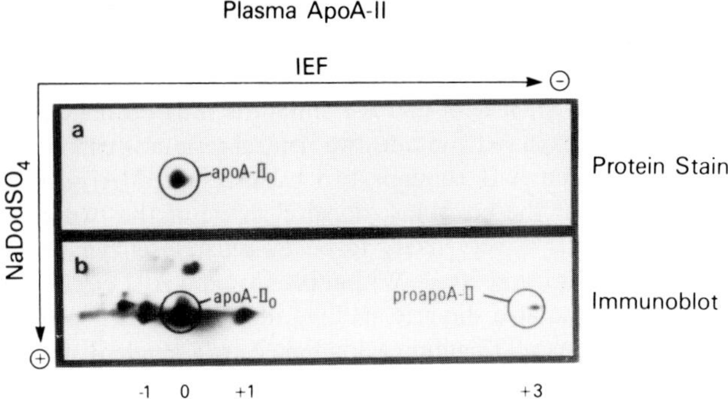

Fig. 50-5 Two-dimensional gel electrophoretogram of apo A-II isoforms of plasma HDL. *Panel A* contains Coomassie-stained electrophoretogram, and *panel B* illustrates a corresponding immunoblot utlizing a polyclonal anti-apo A-II antibody.

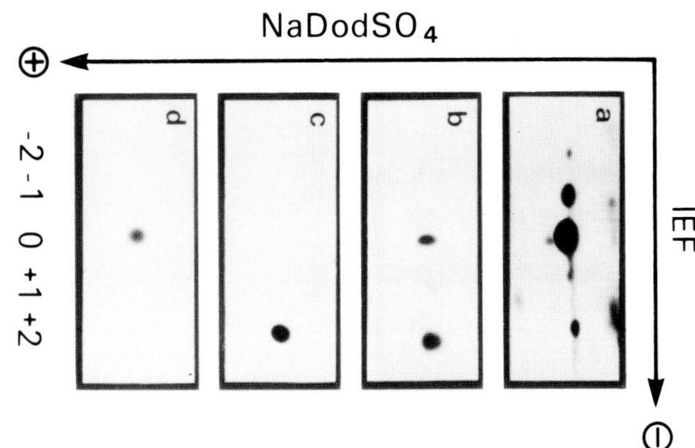

Fig. 50-6 Two-dimensional gel electrophoresis of apo A-I isoproteins in plasma of a normal and a Tangier subject as well as isolated Tangier apo A-I isoforms. Panels include: *(A)* normal apo A-I, *(B)* Tangier apo A-I, *(C)* Tangier apo A-I_{+2}, proapo A-I, and *(D)* Tangier mature apo A-I_o isoform.

A-II in amino acid composition, electrophoretic mobility, and rate of catabolism.[15,37–39] Thus, the structure of both apo A-I and apo A-II are normal in Tangier disease.

Other Plasma Apolipoproteins in Tangier Disease

No consistent changes in the plasma levels of any of the other plasma apolipoproteins have been detected in patients with Tangier disease (Table 50-1).[40] In addition, the amino acid composition and immunochemical properties of apo B in Tangier lipoproteins are identical to those of normal lipoproteins.[12] The apo E is identical in amino acid composition to normal apo E, but apo E is more sialylated in Tangier patients.[12,41]

LIPOPROTEIN METABOLISM

Apolipoprotein A-I and A-II Metabolism in Normal Subjects

The metabolism of apo A-I has been extensively studied using kinetic analysis of radiolabeled apo A-I isoproteins.[23,42,43] The individual plasma proapo A-I and mature apo A-I isoforms were purified to homogeneity from lymph VLDL and plasma HDL, respectively (Fig. 50-3). Proapo A-I (apo A-I_{+2} isoform) and the individual isoforms of mature apo A-I (apo A-$I_{0,-1,-2}$) were radiolabeled and injected into normal volunteers to determine the rate of conversion and catabolism of each apo A-I isoform.[23] The combined results from these studies established that proapo A-I was the predominate apo A-I isoprotein secreted into the plasma. Proapo A-I had a residence time of 4 to 6 h and was rapidly converted to mature apo A-I (apo A-I_0 isoform). The major mature apo A-I isoform (apo A-I_0) was slowly converted to the more basic apo A-I_{-1} and apo A-I_{-2} isoforms. The residence time of all three mature apo A-I isoforms (apo A-$I_{0,-1,-2}$) was approximately 5 days in normal human beings.[23] In fasting plasma of normal subjects approximately 4 to 5 percent of apo A-I is present as the proapo A-I isoprotein (Fig. 50-7).

The metabolism of apo A-II has also been determined by analysis of radiolabeled mature apo A-II. In contrast to apo A-I, there is not sufficient proapo A-II in lymph or plasma for isolation and kinetic analysis of the proapo A-II isoprotein.[30] Kinetic analysis of radiolabeled mature apo A-II revealed that apo A-II is catabolized at a slightly faster rate (residence time one-half as long) when compared to normal apo A-I in the same subject.[42,43] Kinetic models of apo A-I and apo A-II metabolism suggest that apo A-I and apo A-II catabolism are linked, presumably due to the presence of both apo A-I and apo A-II on the same lipoprotein particle (Lp A-I, A-II). There was also evidence for a second compartment containing only apo A-I (Lp A-I) without apo A-II, and this apo A-I particle had a shorter residence time (3.8 days) when compared to the residence time of 5 to 6 days for the Lp A-I, A-II-containing lipoprotein particle.[43]

Apolipoprotein A-I and A-II Metabolism in Tangier Disease

Initial studies on the synthesis of apo A-I and apo A-II in Tangier disease established by immunocytochemistry that both apo A-I and apo A-II were present in intestinal mucosa of Tangier homozygotes.[44,45] An increase in plasma apo A-I levels after fat ingestion in Tangier homozygotes has also been reported.[45]

Table 50-1 Plasma Apolipoprotein Concentration in Normals and Tangier Patients, mg/dl

Case	*Apo B*	*Apo C-I*	*Apo C-II*	*Apo C-III*	*Apo D*	*Apo E*
Normals (n = 50)	98.0 ± 20	7.0 ± 2	3.7 ± 2	13.0 ± 5	10.0 ± 4	10.0 ± 4
Proband 1	69.0	4.9	2.9	11.0	2.3	11.0
Proband 2	65.0	6.8	3.0	9.1	1.4	8.0
Proband 3	100.0	4.3	3.5	11.0	—	6.2
Proband 4	94.0	2.2	2.1	2.6	—	3.0
Proband 5	108.0	3.9	2.0	3.3	—	3.4

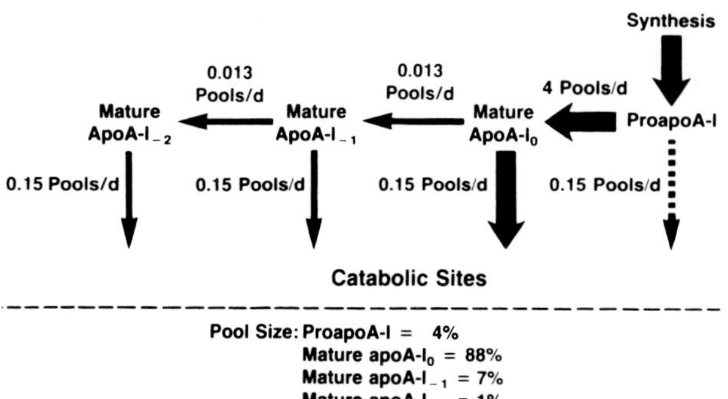

Fig. 50-7 Schematic overview of apo A-I isoprotein metabolism in human beings. Apo A-I is secreted as proapo A-I from the liver and intestine and is rapidly converted quantitatively to mature apo A-I (apo A-I_0 isoform). Mature apo A-I (apo A-I_0 isoform) is slowly converted to the more acidic apo A-I_{-1} and apo A-I_{-2} isoforms. Proapo A-I is converted to mature apo A-I (apo A-I_0 isoform) at a rate of 4 pools per day, the mature apo A-I_0 isoform is converted to the more acidic isoforms at 0.013 pools per day, and all mature apo A-I isoforms are catabolized at 0.15 pools per day.[23] The rate constants in the schematic representation which were derived from the experimental results predict the isoform distribution of the apo A-I isoform which was observed on two-dimensional gel electrophoresis.

Initial kinetic studies utilizing radiolabeled normal HDL in Tangier patients revealed an increased catabolism of apo A-I, apo A-II, and HDL in Tangier heterozygotes, and a marked increase in catabolism in homozygous Tangier patients (Fig. 50-8).[34] This increased catabolism persisted even after increasing the pool size of HDL by infusion of normal HDL into Tangier patients.[46,47] These initial studies established that the metabolic defect in Tangier disease was a rapid catabolism of apo A-I and HDL, rather than a defect in biosynthesis.

Fig. 50-8 Plasma decay curves of radiolabeled high density lipoproteins in normal subjects (○●) as well as homozygotes (□■) and heterozygotes (△▲) for Tangier disease.

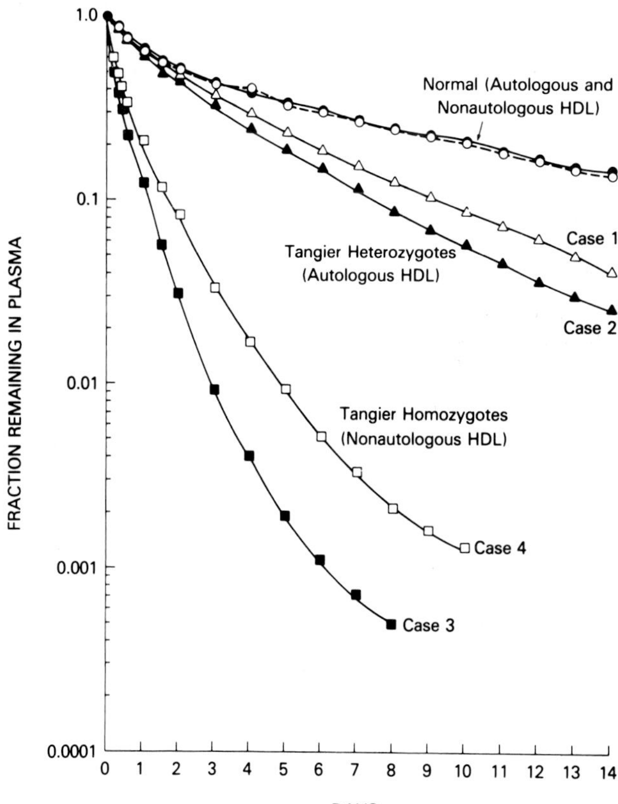

To further elucidate the metabolic defect in Tangier disease, mature apo A-I and apo A-II were isolated from Tangier and normal subjects, and the kinetics of radiolabeled apo A-I and apo A-II were analyzed in both normal subjects and patients with Tangier disease.[38,48] The catabolism of radiolabeled mature Tangier and normal apo A-I in a normal and Tangier subject is shown in Fig. 50-9*A*. Fig. 50-9*B* illustrates the catabolism of radiolabeled Tangier and normal apo A-II in a Tangier patient and normal volunteer. Both normal and Tangier A-I and A-II apolipoproteins were rapidly catabolized in the Tangier patient as compared to normals, indicating that the increased catabolism in Tangier patients occurred with both normal as well as Tangier apo A-I and apo A-II (Fig. 50-9*A*, and *B*).

To further elucidate the reason for the relative increase in proportion of proapo A-I in Tangier disease, proapo A-I and mature apo A-I were isolated from the plasma of a Tangier patient (Fig. 50-6). Kinetic analysis of radiolabeled Tangier proapo A-I (apo A-I_{+2} isoform) and mature apo A-I injected into a Tangier patient established that the rate of synthesis of apo A-I was normal and the fractional rate of conversion of proapo A-I to mature apo A-I in Tangier disease was similar to that of normal subjects.[48] The relative increase in proapo A-I compared to mature apo A-I was secondary to the rapid catabolism of both proapo A-I and mature apo A-I, resulting in a decreased *percent* conversion of proapo A-I to mature apo A-I (Fig. 50-10). In summary, the kinetic analysis of radiolabeled apo A-I and apo A-II isolated from both normal and Tangier subjects in Tangier patients has definitively established that the increased catabolism of HDL in Tangier disease is not a defect in either the A-I or A-II apolipoprotein, but a defect in the catabolism of HDL within the Tangier patient.[48]

Lipolytic Enzymes

It might be anticipated that the absence of normal HDL and the profound deficiency of apo A-I in Tangier disease would be associated with an impairment of lecithin:cholesterol acyltransferase (LCAT) activity, since LCAT is transported on HDL and apo A-I is a cofactor for the LCAT enzyme. Nevertheless, quantitation of LCAT activity in Tangier plasma has established that significant cholesterol esterification occurs[49–56] and that the fractional rate of cholesterol esterification equals that in control plasma. The ratio of cholesterol to cholesteryl esters in the plasma of Tangier patients is approximately normal, and linoleic acid is the predominant fatty acid constituent of plasma cholesteryl esters.[57] The molar rate of cholesterol esterification [nmol/(ml.h)] in normal plasma is significantly correlated with the concentration of free cholesterol. Therefore, low molar esterification rates in Tangier plasma as measured in vitro[54,55,58] presumably reflect the low cholesterol concentrations rather than a deficiency or diminished activity of the LCAT enzyme itself. However, in one patient, LCAT activity was diminished due to a decrease in LCAT mass. Addition of pure apo A-I activator to the plasma of this patient did not restore that activity to normal.[59] From studies of fish eye disease (Chap. 46) it was recently suggested that there are two separate LCAT activities with different substrate specificities in human plasma, one of which esterifies the

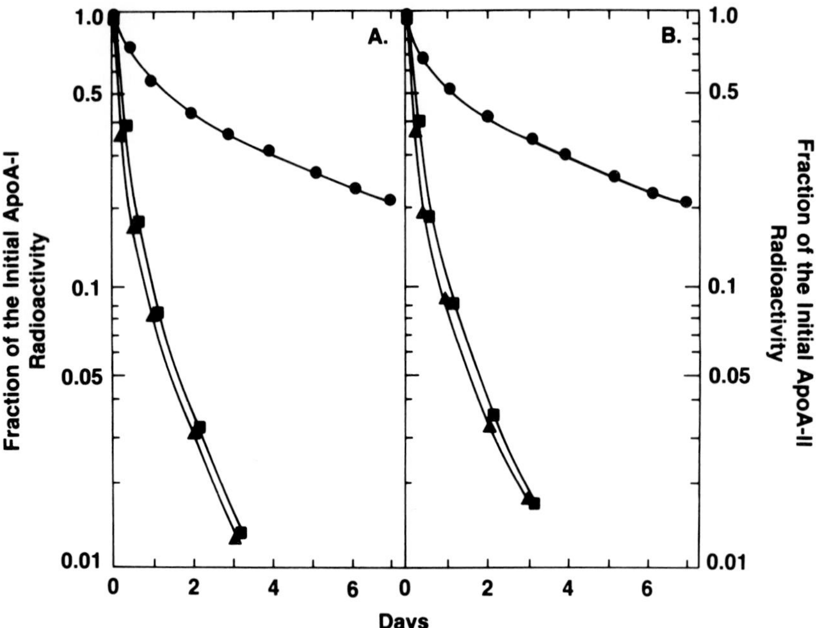

Fig. 50-9 Plasma decay curves of radiolabeled normal and Tangier apo A-I and apo A-II in a normal subject and in a patient with Tangier disease. *A.* Radiolabeled normal apo A-I (●) in a normal subject; normal apo A-I (▲) and Tangier apo A-I (■) in a Tangier patient. *B.* Radiolabeled normal apo A-II (●) in a normal subject; normal apo A-II (▲) and Tangier apo A-II (■) in a patient with Tangier disease.

free cholesterol of HDL (α-LCAT), and another esterifying the cholesterol of VLDL-LDL (β-LCAT). In fish eye disease, a specific lack of α-LCAT has been reported, while both α- and β-LCAT activities function normally in Tangier disease.[60–63] However, it should be noticed that LCAT gene analysis has failed to demonstrate the presence of two separate genes accounting for different LCAT activities (see Chap. 46).

The levels of lipoprotein lipase activity in several Tangier patients were significantly lower than in controls, which may be a reflection of the abnormal apolipoprotein composition of the triglyceride-rich lipoproteins.[64] In contrast, the levels of hepatic triacylglycerol lipase were either elevated[64] or normal.[59] In other patients, no deficiency in activity of lipoprotein lipase has been detected.[49] Whether the low activity of lipoprotein lipase, combined with compositional anomalies of triglyceride-rich lipoproteins, explains the hypertriglyceridemia in Tangier patients awaits further investigation.

Fig. 50-10 Apo A-I metabolism in a subject with Tangier disease. The width of the arrows is proportional to the flux of apo A-I through that pathway. The fractional metabolic rates are derived from experimental results,[48] and the pool estimates at the bottom of the figure are calculated from the model using the pathways and fractional metabolic rates included in the figure (see Fig. 50-7 for comparison of apo A-I metabolism in a normal subject).

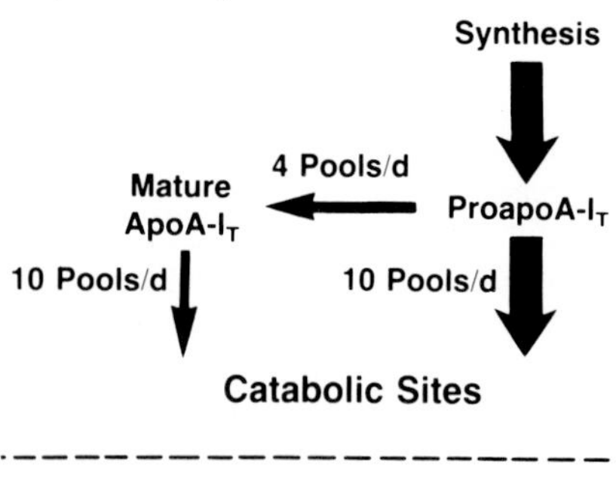

CLINICAL AND PATHOPHYSIOLOGICAL CORRELATES

Cholesteryl ester accumulation in histiocytes of many organs is the dominant pathologic finding in Tangier homozygotes. Lipid deposition also occurs in other tissues including the cornea, Schwann cells, and nonvascular smooth-muscle cells (Table 50-2).[65–71] Involvement of histiocytes regularly causes distinctive tonsillar hyperplasia, splenomegaly, and sometimes mild lymphadenopathy. Mild to moderate hepatomegaly and hypersplenism are much less common.

Corneal infiltrates do not impair vision, but Schwann cell

Table 50-2 Cholesteryl Ester Storage in Tangier Disease

Affected cell types
Histiocytes: bone marrow, thymus, spleen, mucosa of the rectum and large and small intestine, pulmonary artery, renal pelvis and ureters, mitral and tricuspid valves, skin; with inflammation in gallbladder and bile ducts, uterine cervical mucosa, and blood vessel adventitia
Schwann cells: nerves of skin and colon submucosa
Nevus cells: pigmented nevi
Neurons: Spinal ganglion, sacral spinal cord
Smooth-muscle cells: muscularis mucosa, peritoneal soft tissue (inguinal hernia)
Mast cells: colonic mucosa
Fibroblasts: subepidermis, gingiva, cornea, colonic mucosa
Unaffected cell types
Endothelial cells: arteries and veins
Smooth-muscle cells: arteries and veins, myoepithelial cells of apocrine and exocrine glands
Fibroblasts: adventitia of arteries and veins
White blood cells
Epidermal cells: keratinocytes, squamous epithelial cells
Bone marrow mesenchymal (reticulum) cells
Peritoneal mesothelial cells
Parenchymal cells: hepatocytes, intestinal mucosa, bile duct epithelium

involvement appears to underlie the peripheral neuropathy which may be asymptomatic; however, when present, it is frequently relapsing, and occasionally devastating. The functional significance, if any, of lipid deposits in nonvascular smooth-muscle cells is not known. Quite obviously, the mechanisms by which cholesteryl ester accumulates in these various tissues must be intimately related to physiological roles of HDL in reverse cholesterol transport. Therein lies the great interest in this rare mutant.

Clinical Findings

The unique appearance of the tonsils makes it possible to diagnose the disorder through examination of the oropharynx. The tonsils are large and lobulated and have a distinctive orange or yellowish-gray overlay of coloration on the normal red mucosa. When the tonsils have been removed, small plaques or tags of mucosa having the same appearance will usually reveal the diagnosis if one examines carefully. Several patients have had a history of recurrent "tonsillitis" or symptoms of obstruction which have led to tonsillectomy.

Splenomegaly is accompanied by mild thrombocytopenia and reticulocytosis in many patients. Splenectomy was deemed necessary in one patient because of progressive anemia and thrombocytopenia. The cells of the excised spleen were filled with intracytoplasmic lipid droplets and scattered clusters of cholesterol crystals.[4]

Physical examination does not usually reveal striking lymphadenopathy, but normal-sized or enlarged lymph nodes have exhibited bright-yellow streaks and morphologic characteristics like those present in the tonsils,[3,6,8,9,73] and the cholesteryl ester content has been more than 100-fold greater in them than in control lymph nodes.[8,9] Lipid deposition in the thymus has been the most extensive,[3,8,9,11] with almost complete replacement of the lobulated cortex by large, pale macrophages.

Enlargement of the liver has been noted in approximately one-third of the patients, but it may be a transient finding. Lipid infiltration of hepatic parenchymal cells has not been observed, and liver function tests are usually normal.[4,73] In one homozygous Tangier patient, reduced cholesterol concentration in bile was reported, but the pattern of glyco- and tauro-conjugated bile acids was normal.[52] Histologic examination of the liver has revealed only occasional clusters of intralobular foam cells,[3,4,73] identified as histiocytes. Moderate numbers of foam cells have also been identified in the gallbladder mucosa.[73]

The gross appearance of the rectal mucosa has been abnormal in every case examined and may be the most reliable physical finding when palatine and pharyngeal tonsils have been previously completely removed. Proctoscopy demonstrates a mucosa studded with 1 to 2 mm discrete orange-brown spots. Biopsy shows foamy histiocytes throughout the mucosa and submucosa. The ileum and colon also have numerous mucosal elevations, but the jejunum has been grossly normal.[3] The jejunal mucosal villi were free of foam cells,[66] the latter being found only below the musucularis mucosa. Bowel habits and food tolerance are usually normal in Tangier disease, although complaints of frequent stools and intermittent diarrhea and abdominal pain have received comment.[3,74] One patient had severe ulcerative colitis and underwent colectomy.[75] Radiologic examination of the gastrointestinal tract does not reveal any diagnostic features, although mild uniform thickening of the mucosal folds has been observed throughout the jejunum. The pattern was not unlike that found in amyloidosis, giardiasis, and intestinal lymphangiectasia.

Focal collections of foamy histiocytes have been reported in otherwise normal skin,[3,66,67,72,73,76] ureters, renal pelvises, tunica albuginea of testicles, mitral and tricuspid valves,[3] and the pulmonary artery.[9] Foam cells in the bone marrow have been found in 9 of 13 patients examined.[66] Ocular abnormalities were reported in 14 patients.[71,77] Corneal infiltration, evident only on slit-lamp examination, has been present in nine patients, ectropion in three patients, retinal pigment mottling in the macula and/or periphery in two patients, and diplopia on lateral gaze on one patient. Corneal infiltration, either diffuse or dotlike, may be caused by an increase of free cholesterol deposition in the corneal stroma over time. Diffuse corneal opacification has also been observed in probands with apolipoprotein A-I and C-III deficiency, high density lipoprotein deficiency with planar xanthomas, and fish eye disease[72] (Chap. 46).

Pathology and Pathophysiology

The histiocytic foam cells contain sudanophilic lipid droplets and occasionally crystalline material. The major part of the droplets within the cytoplasm is not bound by membranes and consists of deposits of cholesteryl esters (mostly cholesteryl oleate). Contrasting with similar storage phenomena in primary lysosomal enzyme deficiency states, the lipids in Tangier disease accumulate largely outside of lysosomes.

The involvement of the lipid-storing histiocytes within different organs may reflect the source of the accumulated lipid material. Histiocytes occur in all tissues which are engaged in the breakdown of cells under physiological or pathologic conditions. Lipid-laden macrophages in the bone marrow and in spleen are known to degrade phagocytized red blood cells and senescent granulocytes. A similar process of phagocytosis occurs in chronically inflamed areas. It is likely, therefore, that at least part of the histiocytic lipid content derives from phagocytosis of cell debris. Alternatively, tissues rich in histiocytes may also take up lipoprotein remnants. In Tangier plasma, grossly abnormal lipoproteins are present which may represent chylomicron surface remnants that are targets for phagocytosis.[11] Similarly, sequestration of structurally normal or abnormal HDL might account for tissue cholesterosis.

Ultrastructural data are consistent with the concept that abnormal products of chylomicron catabolism are components of the lipid deposits in various cells, particularly histiocytes in Tangier disease. In the spleen, gray-appearing, membrane-surrounded, lipid-containing organelles that fuse with lysosomal granules can be visualized by electron microscopy.[1] Their size is compatible with that of chylomicrons, and their content is osmiophilic, indicative of the presence of polyunsaturated fatty acids. By contrast, cholesteryl oleate, which is a product of cellular cholesterol reesterification, has a low binding capacity for osmium tetroxide and is extracted by solvents applied in the procedure for tissue embedding.

It is likely that removal of ingested cholesterol from histiocytes requires the presence of extracellular HDL[78,79] and that the depletion of HDL from the plasma of Tangier patients and cellular cholesterol storage share a common biochemical defect. Recently, the interaction of various Tangier lipoproteins isolated from fasting and postprandial plasma with cholesteryl ester–laden mouse peritoneal macrophages has been extensively studied.[79,80] It was concluded from these in vitro experiments that postprandial Tangier plasma contains highly abnormal triglyceride-rich lipoproteins and that cholesteryl ester storage in Tangier macrophages results from an imbalance of cholesterol influx and efflux. This then may ultimately lead to macrophage cholesteryl ester accumulation.

Neuropathology

The neurologic abnormalities in Tangier disease were discussed in detail in a previous edition of this book.[2] The neuropathy may present as a relapsing polyneuropathy, or as a syringomyelia-like syndrome with dissociated sensory loss and faciobrachial muscle weakness and wasting. The clinical manifestations may be subtle or overt; sensory, motor, or mixed; and transient or permanent. Most, if not all, patients eventually have some degree of neuromuscular dysfunction, but careful examination may be necessary to demonstrate the abnormalities. Symptoms have included weakness, paresthesias, dysesthesias, increased sweating, and diplopia. Reduced strength, ptosis, ocular muscle palsies, diminished or absent deep-tendon reflexes, muscle atrophy, and loss of pain and temperature sensation may be found. Abnormalities of proprioception are not common. Progressive debilitating neuropathy has characterized the clinical course of several patients.[9,72,76,81–86]

Based upon the variable clinical expression in this disorder, the following subtypes of neuropathy have been observed[76]: (1) transient or relapsing, often asymmetrical syndromes (including isolated cranial nerve deficits), mainly with normal nerve conduction velocities, but occasionally with isolated prolonged distal latencies; (2) slowly progressing, basically symmetrical peripheral polyneuropathy most marked in the lower extremities, with normal nerve conduction velocities; (3) slowly progressing, symmetrical polyneuropathy with a syringomyelia-like syndrome. Accentuation of atrophy and paresis in the distal parts of the upper extremities, accompanied by early loss of pain and thermal sensation, especially in the arms, are observed. In the later stages the neurologic findings may progress to global anesthesia, while the muscle stretch reflexes are fairly well preserved for a long time. Nerve conduction velocities are moderately or markedly reduced. The existence of different types of neuropathy in Tangier disease and the obvious lack of peripheral nerve involvement in other well-documented cases may ultimately be explained by genetic heterogeneity.[83]

Biopsy of the sural nerve characteristically shows an abundance of abnormal non-membrane-bound vacuoles in Schwann cells, mostly of the unmyelinated type, and some endoneurial fibroblasts, macrophages, and perineurial cells. The mononeuropathic form is characterized by de- and remyelination, whereas in the syringomyelia-like syndrome axonal degeneration of small myelinated and unmyelinated fibers prevails.[84] In a Tangier patient affected by progressive syringomyelia-like neuropathy, a spinal ganglion and the sacral spinal cord were investigated at autopsy. Numerous neurons, but not glial cells, contained membrane-bound lipid inclusions presumably representing secondary lysosomes or residual bodies. The authors suggested that the syringomyelia-like neuropathy in Tangier disease may represent a lysosomal storage disorder preferentially affecting small dorsal root ganglion cells.[84] Lipid storage was not found in neurons or macrophages of the central nervous system of an additional necropsied patient.[6]

An interesting unresolved question is the relationship of the HDL deficiency to lipid storage in Schwann cells, nevus cells, and neurons. Apo A-I, apo E, and apo B,E(LDL) receptors have been proposed to play a major role in cholesterol homeostasis in the central nervous system and during nerve degeneration and remyelination.[87–91] Within the central nervous system, all astrocytes contain appreciable concentrations of apolipoprotein E. In the peripheral nervous system, apolipoprotein E was identified in satellite cells of the superior cervical sympathetic ganglion and dorsal root ganglion, enteric glia, and a subset of nonmyelinating Schwann cells (but not in myelinating Schwann cells). It has been proposed that within the brain, apolipoprotein E is secreted by astrocytes and transports and redistributes cholesterol via brain interstitial fluid to cells that require cholesterol and express the apo B,E(LDL) receptor. Excess cholesterol might be transferred on apo E– and apo A-I–containing lipoproteins and removed from the brain into the plasma via the bulk flow of the CSF. Recent studies have further demonstrated that apo E is produced and secreted by macrophages that accumulate in nerve after injury. These macrophages store large amounts of cholesterol derived from degenerating myelin. Apo E– and Apo A-I–containing lipoproteins can deliver this cholesterol to Schwann cells that express apo B,E(LDL) receptors at the time of rapid remyelinization of regenerated axons. It is possible, therefore, that the presence of normal levels of apo A-I is a prerequisite for the effective cholesterol transfer between macrophages and Schwann cells and normal myelin production. In Tangier disease, the low plasma concentrations of apo A-I and the absence of normal HDL might impair the unloading of cholesterol stores from macrophages and Schwann cells as normally required during nerve degeneration and remyelination.

BIOCHEMICAL DEFECT

Over the last decades, several hypotheses have been formulated to explain the as yet unknown molecular defect in Tangier disease. These include (1) abnormal structure of apo A-I,[14,92] (2) impaired interconversion of proapo A-I to mature apo A-I,[14,93,94] (3) a failure of proapo A-I to associate with HDL,[95,96] (4) accelerated catabolism of HDL despite normal rates of apo A-I synthesis,[29,36,40,44,97] and (5) abnormal intracellular transport of HDL-containing organelles whereby HDL are diverted to the lysosome and degraded instead of being secreted through their regular transcellular route.[98] Recent research has provided data on several of the proposed defects in Tangier disease. As reviewed above, the structure of the apo A-I gene is normal.[37,99] The lipid-binding properties of proapo A-I are normal, and there is no in vivo defect in the conversion of proapo A-I to mature apo A-I.[48] Kinetic analyses of radiolabeled apo A-I and apo A-II in HDL have definitively established that the primary metabolic abnormality in Tangier disease involves increased catabolism rather than decreased synthesis of the HDL protein constitutents.[47,48] The hypercatabolism of HDL may be best explained by a defect in the interaction of HDL (or its precursors) with cells critically dependent upon HDL-mediated cholesterol efflux.

Macrophage storage of cholesteryl esters is the characteristic pathologic feature of Tangier disease. Therefore, the detailed understanding of cholesterol metabolism of macrophages and

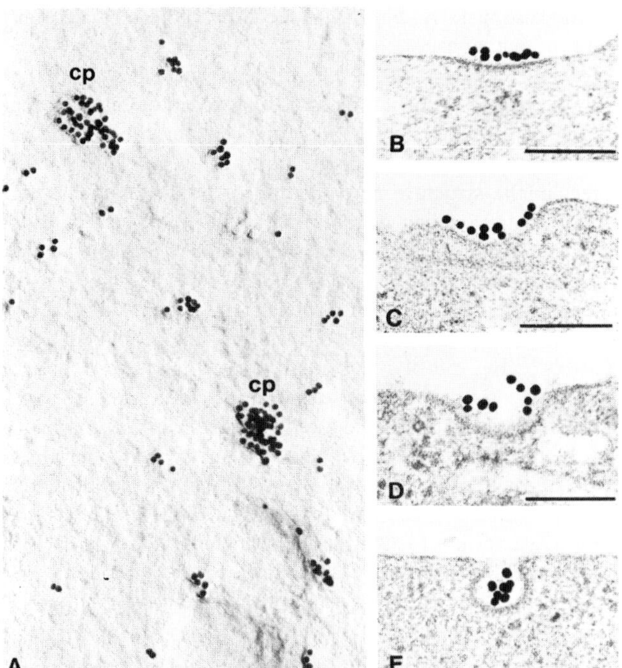

Fig. 50-11 Binding and localization of HDL receptors at the plasma membrane surface of cultured normal human monocyte-derived macrophages, as revealed after treatment (1 h at 4°C) with HDL conjugated to colloidal gold. A. Distribution of HDL receptors in a surface replica. HDL receptors are randomly distributed and are present in clusters overlaying coated pit (cp) areas. *B–E.* Thin section macrophages depicting the progressive concentration of HDL receptors in coated pits and subsequent internalization as coated vesicles. Bars = 0.2 μm. *(Micrographs used by permission of Drs. S.H. Robenek and G. Schmitz.)*

the interaction of HDL with these cells is of fundamental importance. Macrophages take up cholesterol either by phagocytosis of whole cells or of fragments of cell membranes containing cholesterol or by receptor-mediated endocytosis of cholesterol-containing lipoproteins.[79,100–109] It has been demonstrated that chemically modified LDL, oxidized LDL, Lp(a), and β-VLDL are ingested by macrophages and catavbolized in lysosomes.[100,101,110–113] When macrophages take up more cholesterol than is secreted, they are transformed into foam cells by storage of surplus cholesterol in endosomes or lysosomes or as cytoplasmic cholesteryl ester droplets. Accumulation of cytoplasmic cholesteryl esters in vitro can be prevented by the extracellular presence of HDL.[103] It has been proposed that macrophages express HDL receptors which are increased in number by cholesteryl ester loading of cells. HDL particles that bind to the receptor are internalized to a nonlysosomal, cytoplasmic compartment and then released from the cell as native lipoproteins[114–117] (Figs. 50-11 to 50-13). It appears that within the HDL density fraction those lipoprotein particles containing predominantly apo A-I exhibit the highest affinity to the HDL receptor.[118]

Numerous biochemical processes within the cell are changed when macrophages or other cells are loaded with cholesterol. These include increased HDL binding, decreased LDL binding, a reduced rate of cholesterol synthesis, and an enhanced rate of cholesteryl ester formation (see Chap. 48). The rate of cholesteryl ester formation is modulated by the microsomal enzyme acyl-CoA:cholesterol acyltransferase (ACAT). ACAT activity is normally up-regulated during the ingestion of cholesterol into the cell, leading to storage of esterified cholesterol in the form of cytoplasmic lipid droplets. Inhibitors of ACAT enhance HDL binding and promote HDL-mediated cholesterol efflux from macrophages.[115,116] Macrophages can also secrete cholesterol independent of HDL. In this pathway, cholesterol is diverted from its lysosomal route to the cellular surface, a process which can be stimulated by Ca^{2+} channel antagonists of the dihydropyridine type.[116,117]

In addition to ACAT, neutral cholesteryl ester hydrolase is involved in cytoplasmic cholesterol metabolism. The concerted action of both enzymes determines the concentrations of free cholesterol at the surface of cytoplasmic lipid droplets. Their enzymatic activities are enhanced by phosphorylation via cAMP-dependent protein kinases.[119–123] Neutral cholesteryl ester hydrolase and ACAT, however, differ considerably in their enzyme kinetics. ACAT primarily affects the ratio of free cholesterol to cholesteryl esters of cytoplasmic lipid droplets.[123] As a consequence down-regulation of ACAT is more effective than up-regulation of neutral cholesteryl ester hydro-

Fig. 50-12 Internalization of HDL into cultured normal human monocyte-derived macrophages, as revealed after treatment with HDL conjugated to colloidal gold at 4°C for 1 h and subsequent warming of cells to 37°C for 10, 20, and 30 min. *A.* Surface-bound HDL-gold conjugates are rapidly internalized after warming the cells from 4 to 37°C. After 10 min of incubation, the HDL-gold particles are located mainly in structures that belong to the peripheral cytoplasm, e.g., uncoated vesicles, small endosomes, and pleiomorphic tubular structures delineated by smooth membranes. *B.* After 20 min of incubation the vast majority of HDL-gold particles are present in large smooth-surfaced electron-lucent vesicles resembling endosomes (E). The endosomes vary greatly in appearance. Most exhibit a thin peripheral rim of gold-bound particles. Others are partly or entirely filled with a dense accumulation of randomly distributed gold-bound particles. The HDL-gold particles apparently enter the endosomes as these fuse with small smooth membrane vesicles or tubules. The latter organelles are frequently observed in the vicinity of larger endosomes. *C.* After 30 min of incubation, the gold marker is detectable in electron-lucent vesicles in the Golgi area indicating that the Golgi apparatus (G) probably plays a decisive role in the intracellular processing and resecretion of the HDL particles. N = nucleus. Bars = 0.5 μm. *(Micrographs by Drs. H. Robenek and G. Schmitz. Used by permission.)*

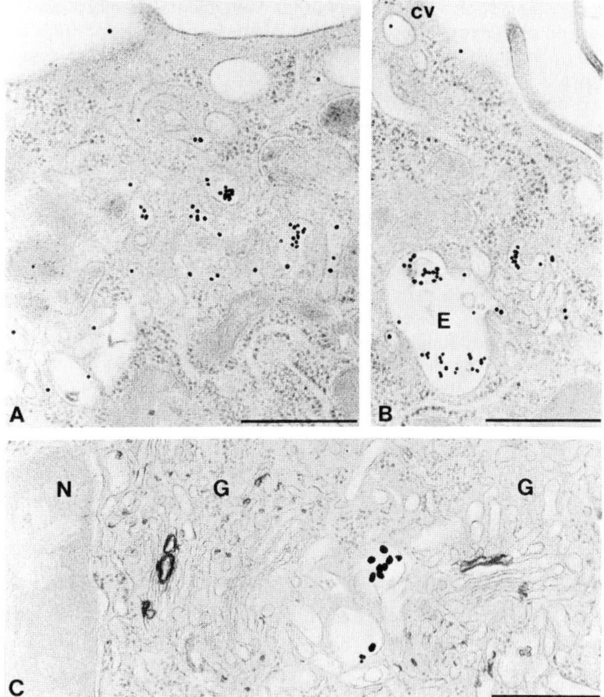

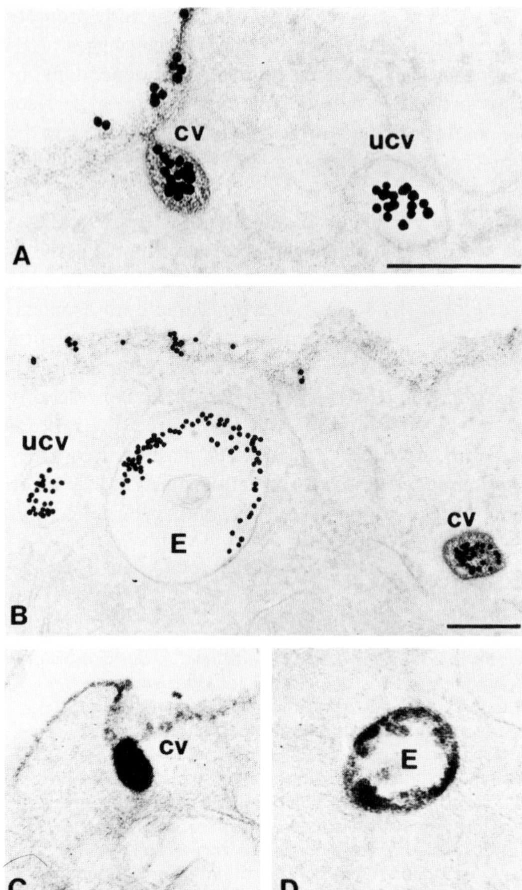

Fig. 50-13 Staining of the plasma membrane surface of cultured normal human monocyte-derived macrophages with ruthenium red (*A, B*) and localization of HDL by the immunoperoxidase technique (*C, D*). *A, B.* Staining of macrophages with ruthenium red after exposure to HDL-gold conjugates for 1 h at 4°C and subsequent warming of cells for 5 min (*A*) or 20 min (*B*) at 37°C. Ruthenium red is a polycationic dye that binds specifically with cell surface acid polysaccharides and can be visualized in thin sections as an electron-dense layer on the plasma membrane surface and in intracellular space. Therefore ruthenium red staining of cells can be used to distinguish surface membranes from internal membranes. Staining of macrophages with ruthenium red was employed here to confirm the intracellular location of HDL-gold conjugates. The cells shown in A and B both contain coated vesicles (cv) filled with HDL-gold particles and stained with ruthenium red (indicating that these organelles are in contact with the extracellular space) and uncoated vesicles (ucv) as well as endosomes (E) filled with HDL-gold particles but devoid of ruthenium red (indicating that the contents of the endosomes are free vesicles in the cytoplasm and thus confirming that the HDL-gold particles were internalized via receptor-mediated endocytosis). *C,D.* Indirect immunoperoxidase technique to demonstrate the localization of HDL on the surface and inside of the cells. Monocyte-derived macrophages [first incubated with native HDL at 4°C (*C*) and then at 37°C (*D*)] were treated with the primary antibody anti-apo A-I for 2 h followed by peroxidase-conjugated goat-anti-rabbit IgG (K+L)-Fab_2 for 1 h. At 4°C, electron-dense peroxidase reaction products are concentrated in coated vesicles (*C*) and are subseqently located in endosomes (*D*). cv = coated vesicles, E = endosome. Bars = 0.2 μm. *(Micrographs by Drs. H. Robenek and G. Schmitz. Used by permission.)*

lase in generating free cholesterol. Recent observations suggest that Ca^{2+} antagonists stimulate the activity of neutral cholesteryl ester hydrolase via cAMP-dependent protein kinase–catalyzed phosphorylation reactions and simultaneously abolish the increase in HDL binding induced by cholesterol accumulation in macrophages.[116]

It would appear that the two different mechanisms of cholesterol efflux, HDL binding to cellular receptors and the regulation of intracellular enzymes important in cholesterol metabolism, are under coordinate control. A single metabolic defect in the structure or regulation of intracellular enzymes related to the loading of HDL with cholesterol might cause the disturbance of cellular cholesterol balance that is typical in Tangier disease.

The interaction of normal human HDL with isolated human monocytes has been studied in Tangier patients and controls[98] (Fig. 50-14). It was observed that normal human monocytes, similar to mouse peritoneal macrophages, bind apo A-I–containing HDL to a cell surface receptor, internalize the bound HDL particles, and transport the internalized HDL through the cytoplasmic compartment without significant lysosomal degradation. Ultimately, HDL are resecreted from these cells. Incubation of Tangier monocyte-derived macrophages with normal HDL, however, resulted in a slight increase in HDL binding, a failure of resecretion of internal-

Fig. 50-14 Cultured normal human monocytes (*A,B*) and monocytes isolated from Tangier patients (*C,D*) preincubated with unlabeled acetyl-LDL for 3 h at 37°C. This preincubation leads to similar morphologic events in control and Tangier cells as demonstrated by the number of secondary lysosomes (L) as well as the number and size of cytoplasmic lipid droplets (Li, A, and C). The cholesteryl ester–laden cells are then chased with gold-labeled HDL for 2 h at 37°C. Thin sections of monocytes from controls (*A,B*) and Tangier patients (*C,D*) exhibit significant differences in the amount and in the intracellular distribution of the gold marker. In control monocytes only a few intracellular gold particles could be observed (*A*, arrowheads) and these particles were almost exclusively located in nonlysosomal endosomes and in probably Golgi-derived vesicles (*B*, arrowheads). By contrast, in Tangier monocytes the intracellular gold particles were significantly increased in number (*C*, arrowheads) and predominantly located in secondary lysosomes (*C,D*). G = Golgi apparatus. Bars = 1 μm (*A,C*) and 0.5 μm (*B,D*). *(Micrographs from G. Schmitz et al.[99])*

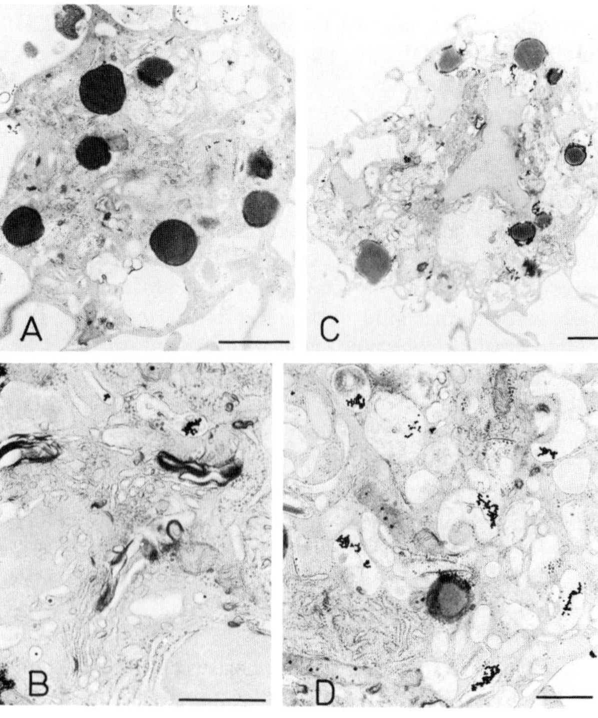

ized HDL, and a trapping of these lipoproteins in the lysosomal compartment. It was concluded from these experiments that the molecular defect in Tangier disease may lie in intracellular events involved in the assembly of cellular cholesterol with the internalized HDL and its transport back to the cellular surface. Such transcellular channeling might be disturbed in Tangier disease because of functional abnormalities in the HDL receptor, alterations in endosomal traffic normally preventing degradation of HDL by lysosomes, or a defect in an intracellular processing mechanism affecting assembly of cholesterol with HDL or its subsequent resecretion. It is not yet established whether these in vitro observations can be extended to the in vivo catabolism of HDL in other monocyte-derived cells, such as tissue macrophages or Kupffer cells. If so, they could provide an explanation for both the hypercatabolism of HDL and the tissue cholesteryl ester storage that occurs in Tangier disease.

There are other potential localizations for the primary defect in Tangier disease other than anomalies in receptor-mediated endocytosis and subsequent resecretion of HDL. The mechanism of transfer of free cholesterol from cells to HDL is not completely understood, and abnormalities in this process could result in intracellular lipid accumulation in Tangier disease. Studies have been interpreted as indicative that HDL binds to cellular receptors without subsequent internalization of the HDL particles.[124–130] Other investigators have proposed that the removal of cellular cholesterol does not require ligand-receptor interaction, and potential defects in the egress of cholesterol via this mechanism could also result in the intracellular accumulation of cholesterol in Tangier disease.[131] In summary, a considerable body of data now suggests that high affinity HDL binding to cultured cells (fibroblasts, arterial smooth-muscle cells, endothelial cells, macrophages, leukocytes, kidney cells, adipocytes, hepatoma cells, adrenocortical membranes) is a key mechanism whereby cells unload or take up cholesterol and maintain a precise intracellular cholesterol equilibrium.[131–143]

Finally, it is not yet excluded that hypercatabolism of HDL in Tangier disease may result from enhanced and irreversible uptake of HDL apoproteins into hepatocytes. Figure 50-15 illustrates four major pathways for reverse cholesterol transport, i.e., the transport of cholesterol and cholesteryl esters from peripheral cells to the liver.[144–149] The quantitative role of each pathway in cholesterol transport and the detailed role of hepatocytes versus Kupffer cells in the removal of cholesterol from peripheral tissue is currently unknown. Detailed investigation of these metabolic routes in Tangier disease is needed.

HDL, ATHEROSCLEROSIS, AND TANGIER DISEASE

The extent of clinically evident vascular disease in homozygous Tangier patients is not striking.[7] No evidence of coronary heart disease or vascular disease has been reported in homozygotes of age 40 years or less. Documented evidence of coronary heart disease exists in several older patients. One man developed significant chest pain on exertion at age 59; coronary angiography at ages 60 and 61 revealed total occlusion of the left circumflex artery beyond its origin.[7] His affected brother had the onset of moderate angina pectoris at age 43 years. An electrocardiogram at 48 years of age showed nonspecific repolarization abnormalities. He was hypertensive, obese, and also a heavy cigarette smoker. He died suddenly outside the hospital, and no autopsy was performed. Another hypertensive homozygote had characteristic angina pectoris by age 43. Cerebrovascular disease resulted in a stroke and the eventual death of a 69-year-old woman with Tangier disease.[85] Aortic valve replacement became necessary in one female homozygous patient at age 60; she died at age 61 from cardiac failure.[84] Cardiac valvular involvement was reported in two additional homozygous patients, 62 and 65 years of age, respectively.[51,150] In vivo kinetics of cholesteryl esters within the aortic wall were assessed in a Tangier homozygote in conjunction with a surgical aortic valve replacement.[151] It was demonstrated that the rate of cholesteryl ester hydroly-

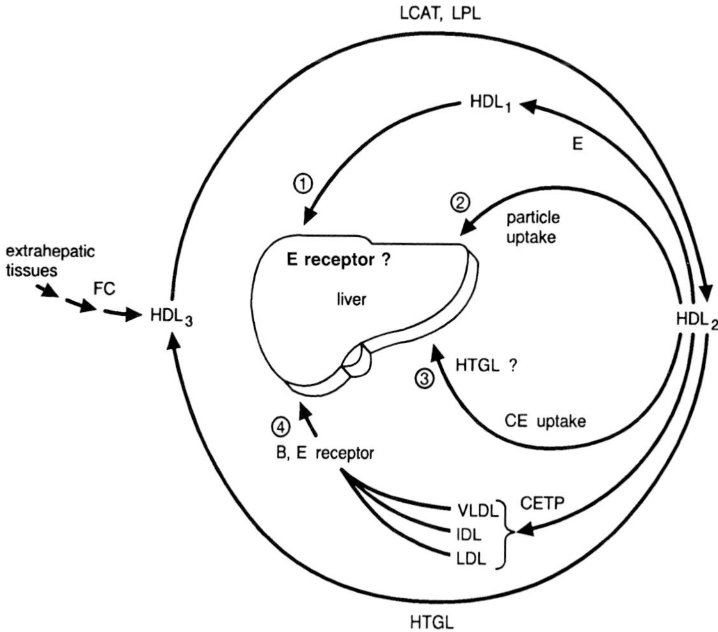

Fig. 50-15 Major pathways by which HDL may mediate reverse cholesterol transport. (1) Uptake of apo E–rich HDL_1 formed from HDL_3 and HDL_2 by the postulated apo E receptor. (2) Uptake of apo A-I–containing HDL particles. (3) Selective uptake of HDL_2 cholesteryl esters involving hepatic triglyceride lipases. (4) CETP-mediated transfer of cholesteryl esters from HDL_2 to apo B,E–containing lipoproteins leading to an LDL-receptor-mediated uptake of cholesterol. Abbreviations: LCAT = lecithin-cholesterol acyltransferase; LPL = lipoprotein lipase; CETP = cholesteryl ester transfer protein; HTGL = hepatic triglyceride lipase; CE = cholesteryl esters.

sis by the aortic wall was lower than in control subjects.

The above findings in homozygotes are not necessarily at variance with compelling epidemiologic evidence relating low HDL levels to the risk for atherosclerosis in the general population. Tangier homozygotes typically have quite low serum cholesterol concentrations. Hypocholesterolemia is related not only to the absence of HDL but to reduced LDL concentrations and substitution of triglycerides for cholesteryl esters as the major LDL neutral lipid. Thus, the normal role of HDL to inhibit uptake or promote efflux of cholesterol from the arterial wall may not be as important in Tangier homozygotes. It has also been postulated that the thrombocytopenia typical of this disorder and hyporeactivity and storage pool deficiency of platelets might diminish susceptibility to premature atherosclerosis.[151–154] Finally, it must be emphasized that the very small number of patients and the paucity of objective data obviate any generalizations regarding atherosclerosis in Tangier disease.

FINDINGS IN HETEROZYGOTES

No consistent pattern of clinical abnormalities has emerged from extended observations of obligate heterozygotes and other presumably heterozygous first-degree relatives. Neither abnormal tonsils nor neuropathic changes have been observed. The lipid content of the tonsils of one heterozygote has been determined and the tissue subjected to histochemical analysis. There was no evidence of cholesteryl ester storage.[72] Foam cells were present in the bone marrow of three of six obligate heterozygotes. Lipid-laden histiocytes have also been identified in rectal biopsies of several heterozygous patients.[155]

Since the biochemical defect in Tangier disease has not been precisely defined, heterozygotes in an unselected population cannot be identified with certainty. HDL concentrations in obligate heterozygous patients are usually below the normal range.[5] The concentrations of HDL cholesterol, apo A-I, and apo A-II in obligate heterozygotes, while quite variable among individuals, were decreased by approximately 50 percent.[34,155] The molar ratio of apo A-I to apo A-II contained in HDL was not significantly different from that of normal subjects, and the morphologic appearance of HDL, as ascertained by electron microscopy, was similar to that of control preparations.[155] Other investigators have reported that apo A-I levels were decreased to 50 percent or less of the control values, even when estimates of HDL cholesterol concentrations were normal.[156] Symptoms or signs of atherosclerosis have not been observed in heterozygotes before 40 years of age. Approximately half of the known obligate heterozygotes older than 45 years were reported to have symptoms of coronary heart disease,[7] but there have been no deaths before age 60.

GENETICS

Several families with Tangier disease have been investigated extensively to determine the mode of inheritance.[4,5,139,155] These studies indicated that the full expression of Tangier disease occurs in subjects homozygous for a mutant autosomal allele. The phenotypic expression of the defect in heterozygotes who have reduced levels of HDL cholesterol, apo A-I, and apo A-II is very mild. The limited number of recently identified cases, in spite of the enormous popularity of HDL cholesterol measurements, appears to attest to the rarity of this mutant.

OTHER FAMILIAL HDL DEFICIENCIES

The major clinical dyslipoproteinemias characterized by a deficiency of HDL are reviewed in Chap. 49 (see also Ref. 72). A virtual absence of HDL characteristic of Tangier homozygotes has also been reported in patients with apo A-I and C-III deficiency[157–159] and fish eye disease.[60–62] Apo A-I– and C-III–deficient subjects can be readily distinguished from Tangier patients due to the total absence of plasma apo A-I and apo C-III, normal plasma triglycerides and LDL, as well as the absence of orange tonsils, cholesteryl ester accumulation in the reticuloendothelial system, and premature cardiovascular disease.[157–159] Patients with fish eye disease have levels of HDL, apo A-I, and apo A-II approximately 10 percent of normal, but have elevated plasma triglycerides and near-normal plasma cholesterol levels.[60–62] The electrophoretic pattern of fish eye apo A-I and apo A-II is identical to normal A-I and A-II apolipoproteins, and there is no increase in proapo A-I as is characteristic of Tangier disease. Fish eye disease subjects also differ clinically in that they do not have orange tonsils, cholesteryl ester accumulation in the reticuloendothelial system, or premature cardiovascular disease.

Heterozygotes for Tangier disease are difficult to distinguish from other patients with reduced levels of plasma HDL. Decreased HDL levels are present in patients with heterozygous apo A-I and C-III deficiency,[157–159] familial hypoalphalipoproteinemia,[160] and hypertriglyceridemia.[161] The incidence of premature cardiovascular disease in these patients is variable and undoubtly reflects the underlying heterogeneity in the molecular defect in these diseases. Of particular importance in determining the clinical significance of reduced levels of HDL in a particular kindred may be the metabolic mechanism responsible for the reduction in HDL. Increased catabolism of HDL apolipoproteins, as is observed in Tangier patients, may not be associated with the same degree of risk for premature cardiovascular disease as is present in patients with reduced HDL apolipoprotein biosynthesis, e.g., apo A-I and C-III deficiency. The ultimate elucidation of the specific molecular defects in patients with reduced HDL levels will permit the development of more effective diagnostic tests as well as treatment of the hypoalphalipoproteinemic patient at risk for the development of premature heart disease.

DIAGNOSIS

In any patient with unexplained hepatic or splenic enlargement, corneal deposits, or neuropathy, a close examination of the oropharynx and rectal mucosa and a plasma cholesterol determination are indicated. A cholesterol level below 125 mg/dl should lead directly to triglyceride and lipoprotein cholesterol determinations. Triglyceride levels are high or normal in Tangier disease and low in the LDL deficiency states. Lipoprotein electrophoresis, irrespective of the supporting media employed, should demonstrate no trace of lipoproteins of α_1 mobility. The HDL cholesterol concentration, as routinely determined using precipitation techniques, should be below 5 mg/dl. Analysis of the apo A-I isoproteins by isoelectric focusing will reveal the increase in proapo A-I that is virtually pathognomonic for Tangier disease.

Other diseases that should be considered in the differential diagnosis of Tangier disease include:

1. Other familial HDL deficiency states (Chap. 46).

2. Obstructive liver disease, in which the plasma HDL and A apoliproproteins may be reduced to levels as low as those present in Tangier disease though the cholesterol level is not low, but high, and most of the cholesterol is not esterified.

3. Severe malnutrition.

4. Hepatic parenchymal disease. Transient infections of presumed viral origin and hepatic infiltration by lymphoma have produced plasma lipoprotein patterns indistinguishable from that in Tangier disease.

5. Acquired HDL deficiency due to dysglobulinemia. This cause may be associated with development of antibodies to HDL.[162]

6. Other storage diseases asssociated with foam cells and hepatosplenomegaly. In these conditions HDL levels are higher than those seen in Tangier disease, and typical tonsillar abnormalities are absent.

TREATMENT

There is no specific treatment for Tangier disease. Consideration may be given to reducing the fat content of the diet, since remnants of triglyceride-rich lipoproteins appear to accumulate in the plasma in association with fat intake. However, lack of certainty that blood vessel or other tissue changes are a function of abnormal chylomicrons, VLDL, or LDL generates little enthusiasm for the endorsement of radical dietary changes.

The critical advice of Dr. Donald S. Fredrickson in the preparation of this manuscript is gratefully acknowledged.

REFERENCES

1. HERBERT PN, ASSMANN G, GOTTO AM, FREDRICKSON DS: Familial lipoprotein deficiency: Abetalipoproteinemia, hypobetalipoproteinemia, and Tangier disease, in Stanbury JB, Wyngaarden JB, Fredrickson DS, Goldstein JL, Brown MS (eds): *The Metabolic Basis of Inherited Disease,* 5th ed. New York, McGraw-Hill, 1983, chap 29, p 589.
2. HERBERT PN, ASSMANN G, GOTTO AM, FREDRICKSON DS: Familial lipoprotein deficiency (abetalipoproteinemia, hypobetalipoproteinemia and Tangier disease), in Stanbury JB, Wyngaarden JB, Fredrickson DS (eds): *The Metabolic Basis of Inherited Disease,* 4th ed. New York, McGraw-Hill, 1978, chap 28, p 554.
3. FREDRICKSON DS, ALTROCCHI PH, AVIOLI LV, GOODMAN DS, GOODMAN HC: Tangier disease—Combined clinical staff conference at the National Institutes of Health. *Ann Intern Med* 55:1016, 1961.
4. HOFFMAN HN, FREDRICKSON DS: Tangier disease (familial high density lipoprotein deficiency): Clinical and genetic features in two adults. *Am J Med* 39:582, 1965.
5. FREDRICKSON DS: The inheritance of high density lipoprotein deficiency (Tangier disease). *J Clin Invest* 43:228, 1964.
6. BALE PM, CLIFTON-BLIGH P, BENJAMIN BN, WHYTE HM: Pathology of Tangier disease. *J Clin Pathol* 24:609, 1971.
7. SCHAEFER EJ, ZECH LA, SCHWARTZ DE, BREWER HB JR: Coronary heart disease prevalence and other clinical features in familial high-density lipoprotein deficiency (Tangier disease). *Ann Intern Med* 93:261, 1980.
8. FREDRICKSON DS, GOTTO AM, LEVY RI: Familial lipoprotein deficiency, in Stanbury JB, Wyngaarden JB, Fredrickson DS (eds): *The Metabolic Basis of Inherited Disease,* 3d ed. New York, McGraw-Hill, 1972, p 493.
9. FREDRICKSON DS: Familial high density lipoprotein deficiency: Tangier disease, in Stanbury JB, Wyngaarden JB, Fredrickson DS (eds): *The Metabolic Basis of Inherited Disease,* 2d ed. New York, McGraw-Hill, 1966, p 486.
10. PAPADOPOULOS NM: Detection of lipoprotein abnormalities by a sensitive electrophoretic test system for the prevention of cardiovascular disease. *Intern Angiology* 4:249, 1985.
11. HERBERT PN, FORTE T, HEINEN RJ, FREDRICKSON DS: Tangier disease. One explanation for lipid storage. *N Engl J Med* 299:519, 1978.
12. HEINEN RS, HERBERT P, FREDRICKSON DS, FORTE T, LINDGREN FT: Properties of the plasma very low and low density lipoproteins in Tangier disease. *J Clin Invest* 61:120, 1978.
13. TALL AR: Plasma lipid transfer proteins. *J Lipid Res* 27:361, 1986.
14. LUX SE, LEVY RI, GOTTO AM, FREDRICKSON DS: Studies on the protein defect in Tangier disease: Isolation and characterization of an abnormal high density lipoprotein. *J Clin Invest* 51:2505, 1972.
15. ASSMANN G, HERBERT PN, FREDRICKSON DS, FORTE T: Isolation and characterization of an abnormal high density lipoprotein in Tangier disease. *J Clin Invest* 60:242, 1977.
16. LAW SW, GRAY G, BREWER HB JR: cDNA cloning of human apoA-I: Amino acid sequence of preproapoA-I. *Biochem Biophys Res Commun* 112:257, 1983.
17. CHEUNG P, CHAN L: Nucleotide sequence of cloned cDNA of human apolipoprotein A-I. *Nucleic Acids Res* 11:3703, 1983.
18. GORDON JI, SIMS HF, LENTZ SR, EDELSTEIN C, SCANU AM, STRAUSS AW: Proteolytic processing of human preproapolipoprotein A-I: A proposed defect in the conversion of proA-I to A-I in Tangier disease. *J Biol Chem* 258:4037, 1983.
19. KARATHANASIS SK, ZANNIS VI, BRESLOW JL: Isolation and characterization of the human apolipoprotein A-I gene. *Proc Natl Acad Sci USA* 80:6147, 1983.
20. SHOULDERS CC, KORNBLIHTT AR, MUNRO BS, BARALLE FE: Gene structure of human apolipoprotein A-I. *Nucleic Acids Res* 11:2877, 1983.
21. LAW SW, BREWER HB JR: Nucleotide sequence and the encoded amino acids of human apoA-I mRNA. *Proc Natl Acad Sci USA* 81:66, 1984.
22. EDELSTEIN C, GORDON JI, TOSCAS K, SIMS HF, STRAUSS AW: In vitro conversion of proapoprotein A-I to apoprotein A-I: Partial characterization of an extracellular enzyme activity, *J Biol Chem* 258:11430, 1983.
23. BOJANOVSKI D, GREGG RE, GHISELLI G, SCHAEFER EJ, LIGHT JA, BREWER HB JR: Human apolipoprotein A-I isoprotein metabolism: ProapoA-I conversion to mature apoA-I. *J Lipid Res* 26:185, 1985.
24. HOEG JM, MENG MS, RONAN R, FAIRWELL T, BREWER HB JR: Human apolipoprotein A-I: Posttranslational modification by fatty acid acylation. *J Biol Chem* 261:3911, 1986.
25. BEG ZH, STONIK JM, HOEG JM, DEMOSKY SJ JR, BREWER HB JR: Phosphorylation of human apolipoprotein A-I. *Circulation (suppl)* 76:467, 1987.
26. GHISELLI G, SCHAEFER EJ, LIGHT JA, BREWER HB JR: Apolipoprotein A-I isoforms in human thoracic duct lymph: Effect of fat absorption. *J Lipid Res* 24:731, 1983.
27. LACKNER K, LAW S, BREWER HB JR: Human apolipoprotein A-II: Complete nucleic acid sequence of preapoA-II. *FEBS Lett* 175:159, 1984.
28. KNOTT TJ, PRIESTLEY LM, URLEA M, SCOTT J: Isolation and characterization of a cDNA encoding the precursor for human apolipoprotein A-II. *Biochem Biophys Res Commun* 120:734, 1984.
29. LACKNER KJ, LAW SW, BREWER HB JR: The human apolipoprotein A-II gene: Complete nucleic acid sequence and genomic organization. *Nucleic Acids Res* 13:4597, 1985.
30. LACKNER KJ, EDGE SB, GREGG RE, HOEG JM, BREWER HB JR: Isoforms of apolipoprotein A-II in human plasma and thoracic duct lymph. *J Biol Chem* 260:703, 1985.
31. GORDON JI, BRIDELIER KA, SIMS HF, EDELSTEIN C, SCANU AM, STRAUSS AW: Biosynthesis of human preapolipoprotein A-II. *J Biol Chem* 258:14054, 1983.
32. BREWER HB JR, LUX SE, RONAN R, JOHN KM: Amino acid sequence of human apoLp-Gln-II (apoA-II): An apolipoprotein isolated from the high density lipoprotein complex. *Proc Natl Acad Sci USA* 69:1304, 1972.
33. ASSMANN G, SMOOTZ E, ADLER K, CAPRUSO A, OETTE K: The lipoprotein abnormality in Tangier disease. Quantitation of A apoproteins. *J Clin Invest* 59:565, 1977.
34. SCHAEFFER EJ, BLUM CB, LEVY RI, JENKINS LL, ALAUPOVIC P, FOSTER DM, BREWER BH JR: Metabolism of high density apolipoproteins in Tangier disease. *N Engl J Med* 299:905, 1978.
35. BREWER HB JR, FAIRWELL T, MENG MS, KAY L, RONAN R: Human proapoA-$I_{Tangier}$: Isolation of proapoA-$I_{Tangier}$ and amino acid sequence of the peptide. *Biochem Biophys Res Commun* 113:934, 1983.
36. BOJANOVSKI D, GREGG RE, BREWER HB JR: Tangier disease: In vitro con-

version of proapoA-$I_{Tangier}$ to mature apoA-$I_{Tangier}$. *J Biol Chem* 259:6049, 1984.

37. LAW SW, BREWER HB JR: Tangier disease: The complete mRNA sequence encoding for preproapoA-I. *J Biol Chem* 260:12810, 1985.

38. SCHAEFER EJ, KAY LL, ZECK LA, LINDGREN FT, BREWER HB JR: Tangier disease: High density lipoprotein deficiency due to defective metabolism of an abnormal apolipoprotein apoA-I (apoA-$I_{Tangier}$). *J Clin Invest* 70:934, 1982.

39. SCHMITZ G, ILSEMANN K, MELNIK B, ASSMANN G: Isoproteins of human apolipoprotein A-II: Isolation and characterization. *J Lipid Res* 24:1021, 1983.

40. ALAUPOVIC P, SCHAEFER EJ, MCCONATHY WJ, FESMIRE JD, BREWER HB JR: Plasma apolipoprotein concentrations in familial apolipoprotein A-I and A-II deficiency (Tangier disease). *Metabolism* 30:813, 1980.

41. ZANNIS VI, LEES AM, LEES RS, BRESLOW JL: Abnormal apoprotein A-I isoprotein composition in patients with Tangier disease. *J Biol Chem* 257:4978, 1982.

42. SCHAEFER EJ, ZECH LA, JENKINS LL, BRONZERT TJ, RUBALCABA EA, LINDGREN FT, ANMODT RL, BREWER HB JR: Human apolipoprotein A-I and A-II metabolism. *J Lipid Res* 23:850, 1982.

43. ZECH LS, SCHAEFER EJ, BRONZERT TJ, AAMODT RL, BREWER HB JR: Metabolism of human apolipoproteins A-I and A-II. Compartmental models. *J Lipid Res* 24:60, 1983.

44. ASSMANN G, CAPURSO A, SMOOTZ E, WELLNER U: Apoprotein A metabolism in Tangier disease. *Atherosclerosis* 30:321, 1978.

45. GLICKMAN RM, GREEN PHR, LEES RS, TALL A: Apoprotein A-I synthesis in normal and intestinal mucosa and in Tangier disease. *N Engl J Med* 299:1424, 1978.

46. ASSMANN G, SMOOTZ E: High density lipoprotein infusion and partial plasma exchange in Tangier disease. *Eur J Clin Invest* 8:131, 1978.

47. SCHAEFER EJ, ANDERSON DW, ZECH LA, LINDGREN FT, BRONZERT TB, RUBALCABA EA, BREWER HB JR: Metabolism of high density lipoprotein subfractions and constituents in Tangier disease following the infusion of high density lipoproteins. *J Lipid Res* 22:217, 1981.

48. BOJANOVSKI D, GREGG RE, ZECH LA, MENG MS, BISHOP C, RONAN R, BREWER HB JR: In vivo metabolism of proapolipoprotein A-I in Tangier disease. *J Clin Invest* 80:1742, 1987.

49. GRETEN H, HANNEMANN T, GUSEK W, VIVELL O: Lipoproteins and lipolytic plasma enzymes in a case of Tangier. *N Engl J Med* 291:548, 1974.

50. ASSMANN G, SCHMITZ G, HECKERS H: Lecithin-cholesterol acyltransferase in Tangier disease. *Scand J Clin Lab Invest (suppl)* 38:98, 1978.

51. ASSMANN G: Structure-function relationship of lipoproteins in Tangier disease, in Greten H (ed): *Lipoprotein Metabolism*. Berlin, Springer-Verlag, 1976, p 106.

52. VERGANI C, PLANCHER AC, ZUIN M, CATTANEO M, TRAMALONI C, MACCARI S, ROMA P, CATAPANO AL: Bile lipid composition and haemostatic variables in a case of high density lipoprotein deficiency (Tangier disease). *Eur J Clin Invest* 14:49, 1983.

53. OHTAKI S, NAKAGAWA H, KIDA N, NAKAMURA H, TSUDA K, YOKOYAMA S, YAMAMURA T, TAJIMA S, YAMAMOTO A: A Japanese family with high density lipoprotein deficiency. *Atherosclerosis* 49:70, 1983.

54. CLIFTON-BLIGH P, NESTEL PJ, WHYTE HM: Tangier disease: Report of a case and studies of lipid metabolism. *N Engl J Med* 286:567, 1972.

55. SCHERER R, RUHENSTROTH-BAUER G: Untersuchung der Lecithin-Cholesterin Acyltransferase-Aktivität im Serum von drei Patienten mit Tangier-Krankheit (Hyp-alpha-liproteinämie). *Klin Wochenschr* 51:1059, 1973.

56. PRITCHARD PH, FRÖHLICH J: Apoprotein A-I and lecithin: Cholesterol acyltransferase metabolism in a patient with Tangier disease, in Angel A, Fröhlich J (eds): *Lipoprotein Deficiency Syndromes*. New York, Plenum, 1986, p 181.

57. YAO JK, DYCK PJ: In vitro cholesterol esterification in human serum. *Clin Chem* 23:447, 1977.

58. UTERMANN G, MENZEL HJ, SCHOENBORN W: Plasma lipoprotein abnormalities in a case of primary high density lipoprotein (HDL) deficiency. *Clin Genet* 8:258, 1975.

59. PRITCHARD PH, FRÖLICH J: Apoprotein A-I and lecithin: Cholesterol acyltransferase in a patient with Tangier disease. *Adv Exp Med Biol* 201:105, 1987.

60. CARLSON LA: Fish eye disease: A new familial condition with massive corneal opacities and dyslipoproteinaemia. *Eur J Clin Invest* 12:41, 1982.

61. CARLSON LA, HOLMQUIST L: Evidence for deficiency of high density lipoprotein lecithin: Cholesterol acyltransferase activity (α-LCAT) in fish eye disease. *Acta Med Scand* 218:189, 1985.

62. CARLSON LA, HOLMQUIST L: Evidence for the presence in human plasma of lecithin: Cholesterol acyltransferase activity (β-LCAT) specifically esterifying free cholesterol of combined pre-β and β-lipoproteins. Studies on fish eye disease patients and control subjects. *Acta Med Scand* 218:197, 1985.

63. CARLSON LA, HOLMQUIST L, ASSMANN G: Different substrate specifities of plasma lecithin: Cholesterol acyl transferase in fish eye disease and Tangier disease. *Acta Med Scand* 222:345, 1987.

64. WANG C-S, ALAUPOVIC P, GREGG RE, BREWER HB JR: Studies on the mechanism of hypertriglyceridemia in Tangier disease. Determination of plasma lipolytic activities, k_1 values and apolipoprotein composition of the major lipoprotein density classes. *Biochim Biophys Acta* 920:9, 1987.

65. SCHAEFER HE, ASSMANN G: Morphological findings in Tangier disease. In preparation.

66. FERRANS VJ, FREDRICKSON DS: The pathology of Tangier disease: A light and electron microscopic study. *Am J Pathol* 78:101, 1975.

67. WALDORF DS, LEVY RI, FREDRICKSON DS: Cutaneous cholesterol ester deposition in Tangier disease. *Arch Dermatol* 95:161, 1967.

68. DYCK PM, ELLEFSON RD, YAO JK, HERBERT PN: Adult-onset Tangier disease. I. Morphometric and pathologic studies suggesting delayed degradation of neutral lipids after fiber degeneration. *J Neuropathol Exp Neurol* 37:119, 1978.

69. ASSMANN G, SCHAEFER HE: Possible mechanisms of lipid storage in Tangier disease, in Gotto AM Jr, Smith LC, Allen B (eds): *Atherosclerosis V*, New York, Springer-Verlag, 1980, p 666.

70. ASSMANN G, SCHAEFER HE: High density lipoprotein deficiency and lipid deposition in Tangier disease, in Carlson LA, et al (eds): *International Conference on Atherosclerosis*. New York, Raven, 1978, p 97.

71. CHU FC, KUWABARA T, COGAN DG, SCHAEFER EJ, BREWER HB JR: Ocular manifestations of familial high-density lipoprotein deficiency (Tangier disease). *Arch Ophthalmol* 97:1926, 1979.

72. SCHAEFER EJ: Clinical, biochemical, and genetic features in familial disorders of high density lipoprotein deficiency. *Arteriosclerosis* 4:303, 1984.

73. KUMMER H, LAISSUR J, SPIESS H, PFLUGSHAUPT R, BUCHER U: Familiäre Analphalipoproteinämie (Tangier-krankheit). *Schweiz Med Wochenschr* 98:406, 1968.

74. HAAS LF, AUSTAD WI, BERGIN JD: Tangier disease. *Brain* 97:351, 1974.

75. ENGEL WK, DORMAN JD, LEVY RI, FREDRICKSON DS: Neuropathy in Tangier disease: α-Lipoprotein deficiency manifesting as familial recurrent neuropathy and intestinal lipid storage. *Arch Neurol* 17:1, 1967.

76. GIBBELS E, SCHAEFER HE, RUNNE U, SCHRÖDER JM, HAUPT WF, ASSMANN G: Severe polyneuropathy in Tangier disease mimicking syringomyelia or leprosy. Clinical, biochemical, electrophysiological, and morphological evaluation, including electron microscopy of nerve, muscle, and skin biopsies. *J Neurol* 232:283, 1985.

77. PRESSLY, TA, SCOTT WJ, IDE CH, WINKLER A, REAMS GP: Ocular complications of Tangier disease. *Am J Med* 83:991, 1987.

78. BROWN MS, HO YK, GOLDSTEIN JL: The cholesteryl ester cycle in macrophage foam cells. *J Biol Chem* 255:9344, 1980.

79. SCHMITZ G, ASSMANN G, BRENNHAUSEN B, SCHAEFER H-J: Interaction of Tangier lipoproteins with cholesteryl ester-laden mouse peritoneal macrophages. *J Lipid Res* 28:222, 1987.

80. KOCEN RS, LLOYD JK, LASCELLES PT, FOSBROOKE AS, WILLIAMS D: Familial α-lipoprotein deficiency (Tangier disease) with neurological abnormalities. *Lancet* 1:1341, 1967.

81. HAAS LF, BERGIN JD: Alpha lipoprotein deficiency with neurological features. *Aust Ann Med* 19:76, 1970.

82. YAO JK, HERBERT PN, FREDRICKSON DS, ELLEFSON RD, HEINEN RJ, FORTE T, DYCK PJ: Biochemical studies in a patient with a Tangier syndrome. *J Neuropathol Exp Neurol* 37:138, 1978.

83. POLLOCK M, NUKADA H, FRITH RW, SIMCOCK, ALLPRESS S: Peripheral neuropathy in Tangier disease. *Brain* 106:911, 1983.

84. SCHMALBRUCH H, STENDER S, BOYSEN G: Abnormalities in spinal neurons and dorsal root ganglion cells in Tangier disease presenting with a syringomyelia-like syndrome. *J Neuropathol Exp Neurol* 46:533, 1987.

85. PIETRINI V, RIZZUTO N, VERGANI C, ZEN F, MILONE FF: Neuropathy in Tangier disease: A clinicopathologic study and a review of the literature. *Acta Neurol Scand* 72:495, 1985.

86. HAGER H, ZIMMERMANN P: Licht- und elektronenmikroskopische sowie cytometrische Untersuchungen an peripheren Nerven bei Morbus Tangier. *Acta Neuropathol (Berl)* 45:53, 1979.

87. PITAS RE, BOYLES JK, LEE SH, FOSS D, MAHLEY RW: Astrocytes synthesize apolipoprotein E and metabolize apolipoprotein E-containing lipoproteins. *Biochim Biophys Acta* 917:148, 1987.

88. PITAS RE, BOYLES JK, LEE SH, HUI D, WEISGRABER KH: Lipoproteins and their receptors in the central nervous system: Characterization of the lipoproteins in cerebrospinal fluid and identification of apolipoprotein B,E(LDL) receptors in the brain. *J Biol Chem* 262:14352, 1987.

89. MÜLLER HW, GEBICKE-HÄRTER PJ, HANGEN DH, SHOOTER: A specific 37,000-Dalton protein that accumulates in regenerating but not in nonregenerating mammalian nerves. *Science* 228:499, 1985.

90. STOLL G, MÜLLER HW: Macrophages in the peripheral nervous system and astrologia in the central nervous system of rat commonly express apo-

lipoprotein E during development but differ in their response to injury. *Neuro Sci Lett* 72:233, 1986.

91. BOYLES JK, WEISGRABER KH, HUI DY, MAHLEY RW, PITAS RE, GEBICKE-HAERTER PJ, IGNATIUS MJ, SHOOTER EM: A role for apolipoproteins E and A-I in cholesterol transport during nerve degeneration and remyelinization. *J Clin Invest,* in press, 1988.

92. KAY L, DONAN R, SCHAEFER EJ, BREWER HB JR: Tangier disease: A structural defect in apolipoprotein A-I (apo A-$I_{Tangier}$). *Proc Natl Acad Sci USA* 79:2485, 1982.

93. ZANNIS VI, KARATHANASIS SK, KEUTMANN HT, GOLDBERGER G, BRESLOW JL: Intracellular and extracellular processing of human apolipoprotein A-I: Secreted apolipoprotein A-I isoprotein 2 is a propeptide. *Proc Natl Acad Sci USA* 80:2574, 1983.

94. EDELSTEIN C, GORDON JI, VERGANI CA, CATAPANO AL, PIETRINI V, SCANU AM: Comparative in vitro study of the pro-apolipoprotein A-I to apolipoprotein A-I converting activity between normal and Tangier plasma. *J Clin Invest* 74:1098, 1984.

95. SCHMITZ G, ASSMANN G, RALL SC JR, MAHLEY RW: Tangier disease: Defective recombination of a specific Tangier apolipoprotein A-I (pro-ApoA-I) with high density lipoproteins. *Proc Natl Acad Sci USA* 80:6081, 1983.

96. ROSSENEU M, ASSMANN G, TAVEIRNE MJ, SCHMITZ G: Lipid binding properties of the Tangier apolipoprotein A-I and its isoproteins. *J Lipid Res* 25:111, 1984.

97. ZANNIS VI, BRESLOW JL, KATZ AJ: Isoproteins of human apolipoprotein A-I, demonstrated in plasma and intestinal organ culture. *J Biol Chem* 255:8612, 1980.

98. SCHMITZ G, ASSMANN G, ROBENEK H, BRENNHAUSEN B: Tangier disease: A disorder of intracellular membrane traffic. *Proc Natl Acad Sci USA* 82:6305, 1985.

99. FUNKE H, ASSMANN G: The defect in Tangier disease is not related to apolipoprotein A-I. In preparation.

100. BROWN MS, GOLDSTEIN JL, KRIEGER M, HO JK, ANDERSON RWG: Reversible accumulation of cholesteryl esters in macrophages incubated with acetylated lipoproteins. *J Cell Biol* 82:597, 1979.

101. BROWN MS, GOLDSTEIN JL: Lipoprotein metabolism in the macrophage: Implications for cholesterol deposition in atherosclerosis. *Annu Rev Biochem* 52:223, 1983.

102. WERB Z, COHN ZA: Cholesterol metabolism in the macrophage. III. Ingestion and intracellular fate of cholesterol and cholesterol esters. *J Exp Med* 135:21, 1972.

103. HO YK, BROWN MS, GOLDSTEIN JL: Hydrolysis and excretion of cytoplasmic cholesteryl esters by macrophages: Stimulation by high density lipoprotein and other agents. *J Lipid Res* 21:391, 1980.

104. GOLDSTEIN JL, HO YK, BASU SK, BROWN MS: Binding site on macrophages that mediates uptake and degradation of acetylated low density lipoproteins, producing massive cholesterol deposition. *Proc Natl Acad Sci USA* 76:333, 1979.

105. FOGELMAN AM, SCHECHTER I, SEAGER J, HOKOM M, CHILD JS, EDWARDS PA: Malondialdehyde alteration of low density lipoproteins leads to cholesteryl ester accumulation in human monocyte macrophages. *Proc Natl Acad Sci USA* 77:2214, 1980.

106. HENRIKSEN T, MAHONEY EM, STEINBERG D: Enhanced macrophage degradation of biologically modified low density lipoprotein. *Arteriosclerosis* 3:149, 1983.

107. STEINBRECHER UP, PARTHASARATHY S, LEAKE DS, WITZTUM JL, STEINBERG D: Modification of low density lipoprotein by endothelial cells involves lipid peroxidation and degradation of low density lipoprotein phospholipids. *Proc Natl Acad Sci USA* 81:3883, 1984.

108. ROBENEK H, SCHMITZ G, ASSMANN G: Topography and dynamics of receptors for acetylated and malondialdehyde-modified low density lipoproteins in the plasma membrane of mouse peritoneal macrophages as visualized by colloidal gold in conjunction with surface replicas. *J Histochem Cytochem* 32:1017, 1984.

109. MCGOOKEY DJ, ANDERSON RGW: Morphological characterization of the cholesteryl ester cycle in cultured mouse macrophage foam cells. *J Cell Biol* 97:1156, 1983.

110. MAHLEY RW, INNERARITY TL: Lipoprotein receptors and cholesterol homeostasis. *Biochim Biophys Acta* 737:197, 1983.

111. STEINBRECHER UP: Oxidation of human low density lipoprotein results in derivatization of lysine residues of apolipoprotein B by lipid peroxide decomposition products. *J Biol Chem* 262:3603, 1987.

112. WALTON KW, HITCHENS J, MAGNANI N, KHAN M: A study of study methods of identification and estimation of Lp(a) lipoprotein and of its significance in health. *Atherosclerosis* 20:323, 1974.

113. KREMPLER F, KOSTNER GM, ROCHER A, BOLRANO K, SENDHOFER S: The interaction of human apoB containing lipoproteins with mouse peritoneal macrophages: A comparison of Lp(a) with LDL. *J Lipid Res* 25:283, 1984.

114. SCHMITZ G, ROBENEK H, ASSMANN G: Role of the high-density lipoprotein receptor cycle in macrophage cholesterol metabolism, in Catapano AL, Salvioli G, Vergani C (eds): High-density lipoproteins: Physiopathological aspects and clinical significance. New York, Raven, 1987, p 95.

115. SCHMITZ G, NIEMANN R, BRENNHAUSEN B, KRAUSE R, ASSMANN G: Regulation of high density lipoprotein receptors in cultured macrophages: Role of acyl-CoA:cholesterol acyltransferase. *EMBO J* 4:2773, 1985.

116. SCHMITZ G, ROBENEK H, BEUCK M, KRAUSE R, SCHUREK A, NIEMANN R: Ca^{++}-antagonists and ACAT-inhibitors promote cholesterol efflux from macrophages by different mechanisms. I. Characterization of cellular lipid metabolism. *Arteriosclerosis* 8:46, 1988.

117. ROBENEK H, SCHMITZ G: Ca^{++}-antagonists and ACAT-inhibitors promote cholesterol efflux from macrophages by different mechanisms. II. Characterization of intracellular morphological changes. *Arteriosclerosis* 8:57, 1988.

118. BARBARAS R, PUCHOIS P, FRUCHARD J-C, AILHAUD G: Cholesterol efflux from cultured adipose cells is mediated by LpA_I particles but not by LpA_I:LpA_{II} particles. *Biochem Biophys Acta* 142:63, 1987.

119. HAJJAR DP: Regulation of neutral cholesteryl esterase in arterial smooth muscle cells: Stimulation by antagonists of adenylate cyclase and cyclic AMP-dependent protein kinase. *Arch Biochem Biophys* 247:49, 1986.

120. KHOO JC, MAHONEY EM, STEINBERG DS: Neutral cholesterol esterase activity in macrophages and its enhancement by cyclic AMP-dependent protein kinase. *J Biol Chem* 256:12659, 1981.

121. YATSU FM, ALAM R, ALAM SS: Enhancement of cholesteryl ester metabolism in cultured human monocyte-derived macrophages by verapamil. *Biochim Biophys Acta* 847:77, 1985.

122. HAJJAR DP, WEKSLER BB, FALCONE DJ, HEFTON JM, TACK-GOLDMANN K, MINICK CR: Prostacyclin modulates cholesteryl ester hydrolytic activity by its effect on cyclic adenosine monophosphate in rabbit aortic smooth muscle cells. *J Clin Invest* 70:479, 1982.

123. SUCKLING KE, STANGE EF: Role of acyl-CoA: cholesterol acyltransferase in cellular cholesterol metabolism. *J Lipid Res* 26:647, 1985.

124. ORAM JF, JOHNSON CJ, BROWN TA: Interaction of high density lipoprotein with its receptor on cultured fibroblasts and macrophages. *J Biol Chem* 262:2405, 1987.

125. BIERMAN EL, ORAM JF: The interaction of high-density lipoproteins with extrahepatic cells. *Am Heart J* 113:549, 1987.

126. BRINTON EA, ORAM JF, CHEN CH, ALBERS JJ, BIERMAN EL: Binding of high density lipoprotein to cultured fibroblasts after chemical alteration of apoprotein amino acid residues. *J Biol Chem* 261:495, 1986.

127. BRINTON EA, ORAM JF, BIERMAN EL: The effect of variations in lipid composition of high-density lipoprotein on its interaction with receptors on human fibroblasts. *Biochim Biophys Acta* 920:68, 1987.

128. GRAHAM LD, ORAM JF: Identification of the high density lipoprotein receptor in cultured cells by ligand blotting. *Arteriosclerosis* 6:537a, 1986.

129. SLOTTE JP, ORAM JF, BIERMAN EL: Binding of high density lipoproteins to cell receptors promotes translocation of cholesterol from intracellular membranes to the cell surface. *J Biol Chem* 262:12904, 1987.

130. KARLIN JB, JOHNSON WJ, BENEDICT CR, CHACKO GK, PHILIPS MC, ROTHBLAT GH: Cholesterol flux between cells and high density lipoprotein. Lack of relationship of specific binding of the lipoprotein to the cell surface. *J Biol Chem* 262:12557, 1987.

131. SCHMITZ G, WULF G, BRÜNING T, ASSMANN G: Flow-cytometric determination of HDL binding on human white blood cells by flow cytometry. *Clin Chem* 33:2195, 1987.

132. BIESBROECK R, ORAM JF, ALBERS JJ, BIERMAN EL: Specific high affinity binding of high density lipoprotein in cultured human skin fibroblasts and arterial smooth muscle cells. *J Clin Invest* 71:525, 1983.

133. TABAS I, TALL AR: Endothelial cells bind ^{125}I-HDL_3 to a higher degree than either smooth muscle cells or fibroblasts. *J Biol Chem* 259:13897, 1984.

134. BARBARAS R, GRIMALDI P, NEGREL R, AILHAUD G: Characterization of high density lipoprotein binding and cholesterol efflux in cultured mouse adipose cells. *Biochim Biophys Acta* 888:143, 1986.

135. FIDGE NH: Partial purification of a high density lipoprotein-binding protein from rat liver and kidney membranes. *FEBS Lett* 199:265, 1986.

136. FIDGE N, KAGAMI A, O'CONNOR M: Identification of a high density lipoprotein binding protein from adrenocortical membranes. *Biochem Biophys Res Commun* 129:759, 1985.

137. FONG BS, PEDRO O, ANGEL R, ANGEL A: Enhanced binding of low and high density lipoproteins to human adipocyte plasma membranes: Effects of temperature and proteases. *Biochem Cell Biol* 64:1378, 1987.

138. FONG BS, SALTER AM, JIMENEZ J, ANGEL A: The role of apolipoprotein A-I and apolipoprotein A-II in high-density lipoprotein binding to human adipocyte plasma membranes. *Biochim Biophys Acta* 920:105, 1987.

139. FRÖHLICH J, FONG B, JULIEN P, DESPRES JP, ANGEL A, HAYDEN M, MCLEOD R, CHOW C, DAVISON RH, PRITCHARD H: Interaction of high density

lipoprotein with adipocytes in a new patient with Tangier disease. *Clin Invest Med* 10:377, 1987.

140. GOTTLIEB BA, MARSH JB: High density lipoprotein binding by rat Fu5AH hepatoma cells is not related to cholesterol content. *Atherosclerosis* 67:251, 1987.

141. OPPENHEIMER MJ, ORAM JF, BIERMAN EL: Down regulation of high density lipoprotein receptor activity of cultured fibroblasts by platelet-derived growth factor. *Arteriosclerosis* 7:325, 1987.

142. ORAM JF: Receptor mediated transport of cholesterol between cultured cells and high density lipoprotein. *Methods Enzymol* 129:645, 1986.

143. ORAM JF, BRINTON E, BIERMAN EL: Regulation of high density lipoprotein receptor activity in cultured human skin fibroblasts and human arterial smooth muscle cells. *J Clin Invest* 72:1611, 1983.

144. MILLER NE, LAVILLE A, CROCK D: Direct evidence that reverse cholesterol transport is mediated by high-density lipoprotein in rabbit. *Nature* 314:109, 1985.

145. PITTMAN RC, KNECHT TP, ROSENBAUM MS, TAYLOR CA JR: A nonendocytotic mechanism for the selective uptake of high density lipoprotein-associated cholesterol esters. J Biol Chem 262:2443, 1987.

146. RINNINGER F, PITTMAN RC: Regulation of the selective uptake of high density lipoprotein-associated cholesteryl esters. *J Lipid Res* 28:1313, 1987.

147. GRANOT E, TABAS I, TALL AR: Human plasma cholesteryl ester transfer protein enhances the transfer of cholesteryl ester from high density lipoproteins into cultured HepG2 cells. *J Biol Chem* 262:3482, 1987.

148. PITTMAN RC, GLASS CK, ATKINSON D, SMALL DM: Synthetic high density lipoprotein particles. Application to studies of the apolipoprotein specificity for selective uptake of cholesterol esters. *J Biol Chem* 262:2435, 1987.

149. EISENBERG S: High density lipoprotein metabolism. *J Lipid Res* 25:1017, 1984.

150. PRESSLEY TA, FRANKLIN JO, ALPERT MA, REAMS GP, TAYLOR LM: Cardiac valvular involvement in Tangier disease. *Am Heart J* 113:200, 1987.

151. STENDER S, HJELMS E, BOYSEN G: In vivo transfer of free and esterified cholesterol from plasma into the ascending aorta of a patient with Tangier disease. *Atherosclerosis* 7:395, 1986.

152. SHASTRI K, CARVALHO ACA, LEES RS: Platelet function and platelet lipid composition in the dyslipoproteinemias. *J Lipid Res* 21:47, 1980.

153. ROSS R, GLOMSET JA: Atherosclerosis and the arterial smooth muscle cell. *Science* 180:1332, 1973.

154. ROSS R, GLOMSET JA, KARIYA B, HARKER L: A platelet-dependent serum factor that stimulates the proliferation of arterial smooth muscle cells in vitro. *Proc Natl Acad Sci USA* 71:1207, 1974.

155. ASSMANN G, SIMANTKE O, SCHAEFER HE, SMOOTZ E: Characterization of high density lipoproteins in patients heterozygous for Tangier disease. *J Clin Invest* 60:1025, 1977.

156. HENDERSON LO, HERBERT PN, FREDRICKSON DS, HEINEN RJ, EASTERLING JC: Abnormal concentration and anomalous distribution of apolipoprotein A-I in Tangier disease. *Metabolism* 27:165, 1978.

157. KARATHANASIS SK, ZANNIS VI, BRESLOW JL: A DNA insertion in the apolipoprotein A-I gene of patients with premature atherosclerosis. *Nature* 305:823, 1983.

158. KARATHANASIS SK: DNA inversion inactivates both the apoA-I and C-III genes in patients with combined apoA-I apoC-III deficiency and premature coronary artery disease. *Circulation* 74 SII:157, 1986.

159. SCHAEFER EJ, ORDOVAS JM, LAW SW, GHISELLI G, KASHYAP ML, SRIVASTAVA LS, HEATON WH, ALBERS JJ, CONNOR WE, LINDGREN FT, LEMESHEU Y, SEGREST JP, BREWER HB JR: Familial apolipoprotein A-I and C-III deficiency variant II. *J Lipid Res* 26:1089, 1985.

160. THIRD JLHC, MONTAG J, FLYNN M, FREIDEL J, LASKARZEWSKI P, GLUECK CJ: Primary and familial hypoalphalipoproteinemia. *Metabolism* 33:136, 1984.

161. NIKKILA ES: Familial lipoprotein lipase deficiency and related disorders of chylomicron metabolism, in Stanbury JB, Wyngaarden JB, Fredrickson DS, Goldstein JL, Brown MS (eds): *The Metabolic Basis of Inherited Disease*, 5th ed. New York, McGraw-Hill, 1983, p 622.

162. NOSEDA G, RIESEN W, MORELL A, SCHLUMPF E: Hyperkatabole Hypo-β-lipoproteinämie infolge Autoantikörper. *Kongr Inn Med* 78:1313, 1972.

CHAPTER **51**

FAMILIAL DISEASES WITH STORAGE OF STEROLS OTHER THAN CHOLESTEROL: Cerebrotendinous Xanthomatosis and Phytosterolemia

INGEMAR BJÖRKHEM
SVERRE SKREDE*

1. *Cerebrotendinous xanthomatosis (CTX) is a rare familial sterol storage disease with accumulation of cholestanol and cholesterol in most tissues and in particular in xanthomas, bile, and brain. Clinically this disorder is characterized by dementia, spinal cord paresis, cerebellar ataxia, tuberous and tendon xanthomas, early atherosclerosis, and cataracts. Between 100 and 150 patients with this syndrome have been reported.*
2. *CTX is inherited as an autosomal recessive trait. The underlying biochemical defect is a lack of the hepatic mitochondrial 26-hydroxylase involved in the normal biosynthesis of bile acids. This leads to a block in bile acid biosynthesis, resulting in reduced biosynthesis of cholic acid and, in particular, of chenodeoxycholic acid. The reduced feedback inhibition of the rate limiting enzyme cholesterol 7α-hydroxylase in bile acid biosynthesis leads to increased formation of intermediates in bile acid biosynthesis. Metabolites of these intermediates, such as 5β-cholestane-3α,7α,12α,23-tetrol, 5β-cholestane-3α,7α,12α, 25-tetrol, and 5β-cholestane-3α,7α,12α,24,25-pentol, are excreted in great amounts in bile, feces, and urine. At least part of the excess cholestanol in patients with CTX is formed from accumulated 7α-hydroxylated intermediates in bile acid biosynthesis. The reason for the accumulation of cholesterol is not known with certainty. In general, patients with CTX have normal levels of cholesterol in serum, whereas the levels of cholestanol are markedly increased.*
3. *Patients with CTX should be treated with chenodeoxycholic acid, which reduces the 7α-hydroxylation of cholesterol, and thereby also reduces the formation of cholestanol and the excretion of bile alcohols in feces and urine.*
4. *Phytosterolemia (sitosterolemia) is a rare, inherited sterol storage disease characterized by tendon and tuberous xanthomas and by a strong predisposition to premature coronary atherosclerosis. Some patients have developed hemolytic syndromes. Increased amounts of phytosterols (plant sterols) such as sitosterol and campesterol and their 5α-stanols are found in blood plasma, erythrocytes, and different tissues, and particularly in the xanthomas and arteries of affected subjects. Increased serum cholesterol and cholestanol have also been found in many patients. Twenty-two cases have been described so far.*
5. *Studies of affected families support the concept that phytosterolemia is inherited as an autosomal recessive trait. The basic biochemical defect has not been identified. Increased intestinal absorption of phytosterols and shellfish sterols has been observed in some cases. Evidence has also been presented for decreased biliary and fecal excretion of cholesterol, phytosterols, and shellfish sterols.*
6. *Patients with phytosterolemia should be treated with diets low in plant and shellfish sterols. In addition, they should be given cholestyramine, which causes increased excretion and lowered plasma levels of phytosterols.*

CEREBROTENDINOUS XANTHOMATOSIS (CTX)

This rare disease was first reported by van Bogaert, Scherer, and Epstein in 1937.[1] The patient they described suffered from dementia, ataxia, cataracts, and xanthomas in the tendons and nervous system. It was later reported by the same group that a relative of this patient had the same symptoms.[2,3] Patients with this "van Bogaert's disease" were subsequently also described by Epstein and Lorenz[4] and Epstein and Kreitner.[5] In 1968, Menkes, Schimshock, and Swanson reported that the central nervous sytems of two patients with CTX contained increased levels of cholestanol.[6] It was later shown that blood, xanthomas, and bile from these patients also contained elevated levels of cholestanol.[7–16] These patients' levels of cholesterol were found to be elevated in tissues but not in blood. Salen reported in 1971 that the composition of bile from CTX patients was abnormal, with very low concentrations of chenodeoxycholic acid.[8] In 1974, Setoguchi et al. made the key discovery that these patients had a defect in bile acid biosynthesis with incomplete oxidation of the C_{27} steroid side chain, leading to excretion of great amounts of C_{27} bile alcohols in bile, feces, and urine.[17] In 1980, Oftebro et al. reported that a liver biopsy from a patient with CTX had an almost complete lack of the mitochondrial 26-hydroxylase involved in the normal biosynthesis of bile acids.[18] The same group of authors also reported that the hepatic levels of different substrates for the 26-hydroxylase were increased in patients with CTX.[19] The results of different in vivo studies with labeled intermediates in bile acid biosynthesis were also in accord with the contention that the hepatic 26-hydroxylase is missing.[20] More recent studies have shown that at least part of the excessive cholestanol formed in patients with CTX is formed from accumulated 7α-hydroxylated intermediates in bile acid biosynthesis.[21] In 1975, Salen and collaborators showed that replacement therapy with chenodeoxycholic acid had an inhibiting effect on cholesterol and cholestanol synthesis in patients with CTX,[22] and this has been the therapy of choice ever since.

*Professor Skrede died on March 10, 1987.

Clinical Phenotype

Between 100 and 150 patients with this disease have been reported. Most come from Japan (44 patients),[14,15,24] the United States (26 patients),[6,8,9,23,23a] The Netherlands (24 patients),[12] Israel (18 patients)[24a] but cases are also known in Norway,[25] Great Britain,[26] and Iran.[10]

In the previous edition of this text, Salen et al. gave a detailed review of the clinical symptoms of the first 53 patients reported to have CTX.[23] Table 51-1 summarizes the major clinical findings in these patients. These include Achilles tendon xanthomas (Fig. 51-1*A*), tuberous xanthomas (Fig. 51-1*B*), neurologic dysfunction, low intelligence, and cataracts. In addition some patients have respiratory insufficiency and cardiovascular disease. A few patients have been reported to have endocrinologic disturbances.

The development of the symptoms in patients with CTX is extremely variable. Some patients are already mentally retarded in childhood, whereas others have normal intelligence even in the sixth decade of life.[23] Tendon xanthomas are most often developed in the third or fourth decade but may occur as early as age 15.[27,28] The Achilles tendon is the most common site, but xanthoma may also occur on the tibial tuberosities, on the extensor tendons of the fingers, and in the triceps (for a more detailed review, see Ref. 23). The xanthomas are histologically similar to those developed in familial hypercholesterolemia and other types of hyperlipoproteinemia (Chap. 48). A chemical analysis for cholestanol content must be performed in order to separate the two types.

Spasticity, often associated with ataxia, most often develops during the second and third decades of life and becomes more severe with increasing age. During the fourth or fifth decade, the patient may become incapacitated.[1,5,23]

In the final stage of CTX, spasticity, tremor, and ataxia increase in parallel with the enlargement of the xanthomas. Patients may develop bladder and bowel incontinence. In addition, they can lose pain and vibratory sensation and may have difficulty in swallowing. Death usually occurs between the fourth and sixth decades from myocardial infarction or progressive neurologic deterioration, including pseudobulbar paralysis.[23] In the previous edition of this text,[23] three patients between ages 44 and 46 were reported to have tendon xanthomas and spastic gaits but were otherwise functioning normally. We have studied one patient who at age 59 had large xanthomas but no neurologic symptoms except a mild distal peripheral neuropathy.[29] This patient, however, had symptoms of angina pectoris since age 53 (two-vessel coronary artery disease).

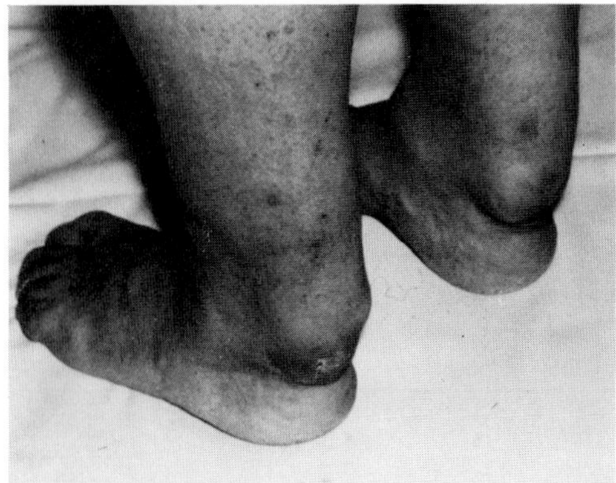

A.

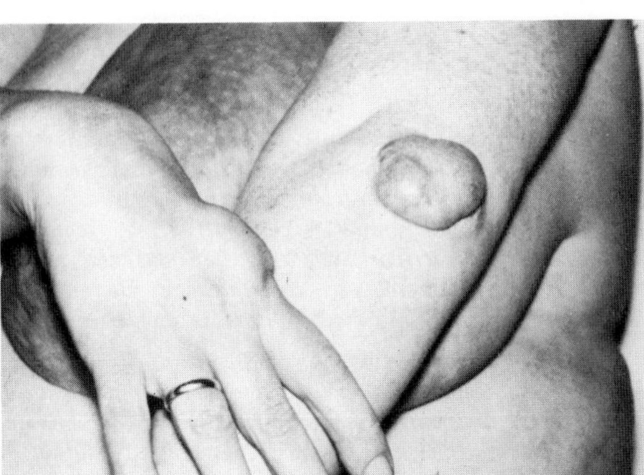

B.

Fig. 51-1 Achilles tendon xanthomas *(A)* and tuberous xanthomas *(B)* in CTX from one of the patients referred to in Ref. 25.

Table 51-1 Clinical Findings in 53 Patients with CTX

	No. of patients		
	Documented	*Absent*	*Not mentioned*
Tendon xanthomas			
Achilles	49	4	—
Other	16	33	4
Xanthelasma	6	15	32
Neurologic dysfunction			
Motor paresis	34	8	11
Ataxia	34	8	11
Speech	15	8	30
Cataracts	35	7	11
Low intelligence	38	5	10
Cardiovascular disease	4	21	28
Respiratory insufficiency	4	18	31
Endocrine abnormalities	3	2	49

SOURCE: Data from Ref. 23.

Pathologic Findings

Nervous System. Van Bogaert et al. gave a detailed description of the central nervous system in CTX.[1-3,7] The most prominent changes occur in the cerebellum, where yellow xanthomas sometimes replace most of the white matter. The adjacent folia may be atrophic, and there is demyelination of specific parts of the white matter.[1,30] In these areas of demyelination there can be cystic spaces and needle-shaped clefts.[23] The cysts and clefts contain large mononuclear cells with foamy, vacuolated cytoplasm. Multinucleated giant cells may also surround the clefts and cysts.[1,30] In general there is a loss of Purkinje cells and granule cells in the demyelinated zones. In addition, there may be degeneration of the olivocerebellar fibers.[1,2,30]

Despite the dementia and mental retardation in many patients, the cerebral cortex seems to be almost free of morphologic and histologic changes. The forebrain, however, may contain xanthomas in the cerebral peduncles and globus pallidus.[1,2] Mononuclear cells with foamy cytoplasm are also found in the caudate nucleus, the basal ganglia, thalamus, and the white matter adjacent to the lateral ventricles.[1,2,7] Demyelination has been reported in the cerebral peduncles, in the fibers of ansa lenticularis,[1,7,30] and in parts of the globus pallidus and corona radiata.[7] The optic pathway is often atrophic.[1] Lesions have also been reported in the midbrain and the brain stem[1,2,7] as well as in the spinal cord.[1,30] In a recent study of nerve biopsies from patients with CTX, demyelination and remyelination were reported as well as production of onion bulbs.[5]

In the report by Menkes et al.[6] referred to above, up to 25 percent of the total free sterol fraction from affected parts of the cerebellum was cholestanol. In morphologically and histologically normal parts of the gray and white matter of the cerebrum, the corresponding cholestanol content was 20 percent. The total esterified sterol fraction from affected parts of cerebellum contained 49 percent cholestanol ester. Similar findings in brain as well as in peripheral nerves[9] have also been reported from other groups.[7,9] Increased content of cholesteryl esters has been found both in normal and abnormal brain tissue from patients with CTX.[8,31]

Tendons. Light microscopy of the tendon xanthomas shows birefringent crystalline clefts surrounded by multinucleated giant cells with foamy cytoplasm.[1,4,23]

Philippart and van Bogaert were the first to demonstrate accumulation of cholestanol in tendon xanthoma.[7] Salen et al. reported that cholestanol accounted for 11 percent of the total sterols in an Achilles tendon xanthoma and 7.3 percent of the sterols in a tuberous xanthoma.[23] The tendon xanthoma from one of our patients contained 17 percent cholestanol in the sterol fraction.[18] Similar findings were reported by Bhattacharyya and Connors.[9] It was recently reported that one CTX patient with hyperapobetalipoproteinemia had a marked accumulation of apolipoprotein B in a xanthoma.[31a] Such accumulation is not seen in xanthomas from patients with familial hypercholesterolemia.

Cardiovascular System. Premature atherosclerosis seems to be a characteristic feature in CTX. In the previous edition of this text, four patients were reported to have died after myocardial infarction.[23] The aorta and the atheromatous plaque obtained at autopsy of one patient contained cholestanol corresponding to 2 and 2.8 percent respectively, of the total sterols.

Lens. Cataract is common in CTX.[1,7,23] Electron microscopy revealed electron-lucent areas in the anterior cortex and vacuoles in the epithelial cells of the lens in one of our patients.[32]

Liver. It has been reported[33] that hepatocytes from two patients with CTX contained a light golden pigment which at high magnification appeared in two forms: either as diffuse, amorphous electron-dense material enveloped by the smooth endoplasmic reticulum or as free-floating bodies in the cytosol. The cytosol also contained free rhomboid-shaped crystals.

Lung and Skeleton. Granulomatous lesions containing multinucleated giant cells and large foam cells have been seen in the lung[1,30] in the femur,[1,2] and in the bodies of the lumbar vertebrae.[1]

Plasma. In most cases, plasma cholesterol levels are normal (115 to 220 mg/dl). Elevated levels (up to 400 mg/dl) have been reported in a few patients.[1,4,23] With few exceptions,[34,35] plasma triglyceride levels are also normal. Plasma cholestanol levels are, however, always elevated in untreated CTX patients. The values range from 1.3 to 15 mg/dl and are in general between 3 and 15 times higher than mean values in normal plasma (0.1 to 0.6 mg/dl).[23] One case has been reported with a very moderate increase in the ratio between cholestanol and cholesterol.[36] According to a recent study by Kasama et al.,[24] the ratio between cholestanol and cholesterol gives a better discrimination than the concentration of cholestanol alone. The serum levels of some accumulated bile acid intermediates such as 7α-hydroxy-4-cholesten-3-one and a potential cholestanol precursor, cholesta-4, 6-dien-3-one, are also increased in untreated patients with CTX.[29] As a consequence of the high activity of the rate limiting enzyme in bile acid biosynthesis, the cholesterol 7α-hydroxylase,[48] the level of 7α-hydroxycholesterol in serum is also increased.[37] As could be expected from the decreased pool of bile acids, the levels of bile acids in serum are low.[37a] It was recently shown that patients with CTX have increased plasma levels of bile alcohol glucuronides.[37b]

Shore et al.[35] have reported decreased mean levels of HDL cholesterol in eight CTX subjects (14.5 ± 3.2 mg/dl versus normally 48.0 ± 9.0 mg/dl). The ratio between apoprotein and total cholesterol in the HDL of these patients was also two to three times greater than normal. The above abnormalities have not been confirmed by other groups, however, and cannot be easily explained by the basic metabolic defect.[18] Two Norwegian patients studied by one of us (S.S.) had normal levels of HDL cholesterol. One of them had slightly increased levels of VLDL, but the other lipoprotein fractions as isolated by ultracentrifugation did not deviate from the normal pattern. A normal pattern of lipoproteins has been documented in at least one additional patient.[29]

Cerebrospinal Fluid. Salen et al. have reported that mean cholesterol and cholestanol levels in cerebrospinal fluid from CTX patients are about 1.5 and 20 times higher, respectively, than normal.[38] Drastic changes in the protein pattern were observed. The concentration of apolipoprotein B was increased about 100-fold and the level of albumin about three- to fourfold compared with normal.[38]

Bile. In patients with CTX, considerable amounts of cholestanol are excreted in bile, and cholestanol constitutes from 4 to 11 percent of total biliary neutral sterols.[8,23] In normal bile, the corresponding figure is less than 1 percent. Bile from patients with CTX also contains excessive amounts of some cholesterol precursors such as lanosterol and 7-cholesten-3β-ol.[8]

The composition of bile acids in bile is also abnormal in CTX. Cholic acid constitutes about 80 percent and the content of chenodeoxycholic acid is very low, only a few percent of the total bile acids.[8] There is almost no deoxycholic acid. Normally there are about equal amounts of cholic acid and chenodeoxycholic acid in bile. The low content of chenodeoxycholic acid is a direct consequence of the metabolic block.[18] The low content of deoxycholic acid may be due to an inhibitory effect of bile alcohols on the microbial 7α-dehydroxylation of cholic acid.[38a] It has been reported that about 2 percent of the total bile acids in CTX consist of allocholic acid.[8,9] Allocholic acid is a 5α-bile acid derived from cholestanol and is present only in trace amounts in normal bile.[39]

The unique finding in bile from subjects with CTX is the high concentration of different 25-hydroxylated C_{27} bile alcohols containing four or five hydroxyl groups.[17,40–43] 5β-Cholestane-3α,7α,12α,23-tetrol, 5β-cholestane-3α,7α,12α,25-tetrol, and 5β-cholestane-3α,7α,12α,24(*R*),25-pentol are the dominant bile alcohols (Fig. 51-2). These steroids are excreted in the bile mainly as conjugates of glucuronic acid.[44] In feces, however, they are found in deconjugated form.

Urine. Patients with CTX excrete considerable amounts of glucuronidated bile alcohols in urine.[44a,45,46] In contrast to bile, where the predominant bile alcohol is 5β-cholestane-3α,7α,12α,25-tetrol, 5β-cholestane-pentols dominate in urine. The pentols have hydroxyl groups at C-22, C-23, or C-25 in addition to hydroxyl groups at C-3, C-7, and C-12. There is probably also some urinary excretion of C_{27}hexols and heptols[45] (Sjövall et al., unpublished observation). Batta et al.[46] reported 5β-cholestane-3α,7α,12α,23,25-pentol to be the dominant urinary bile alcohol (56 percent). 5β-Cholestane-3α,7α,12α,24(*S*),25-pentol was not detected in bile but was isolated from urine in all the patients studied. In addition to these unusual alcohols, abnormal bile acids such as 23-hydroxycholic acid and 23-norcholic acid can also be found in urine of patients with CTX.[36,46] Koopman et al. have recently reported that CTX patients treated with chenodeoxycholic acid excrete significant amounts of 23-hydroxychenodeoxycholic acid.[47] Treatment with ursodeoxycholic acid leads to excretion of 23-hydroxyursodeoxycholic acid and 23-norursodeoxycholic acid.[47] These findings seem to reflect increased 23-hydroxylase activity.

Normal Biosynthesis of Bile Acids

According to current concepts, the sequence of reactions in the normal biosynthesis of bile acids is that shown in Fig. 51-3 (for a detailed review, see Ref. 48). The first reaction that is rate limiting is the 7α-hydroxylation of cholesterol. The microsomal hydroxylase responsible for this reaction is subjected to a negative feedback regulation by bile acids reabsorbed from the intestine and transported to the liver via the portal vein. The detailed mechanism of this regulation is not known. The 7α-hydroxycholesterol is oxidized by a microsomal Δ^5-3β-hydroxysteroid dehydrogenase to 7α-hydroxy-4-cholesten-3-one. 7α-Hydroxy-4-cholesten-3-one may be 12α-hydroxylated by the microsomal 12α-hydroxylase to 7α,12α-dihydroxy-4-cholesten-3-one. The last compound is a precursor to cholic acid. In an alternative pathway, 7α-hydroxy-4-cholesten-3-one may instead be 26-hydroxylated by the mitochondrial 26-hydroxylase. The product in this reaction, 7α,26-dihydroxy-4-cholesten-3-one is a precursor for chenodeoxycholic acid. Alternatively, the double bond of 7α-hydroxy-4-cholesten-3-one could be saturated and the 3-oxo group reduced by soluble enzymes prior to 12α-hydroxylation and/or 26-hydroxylation.

According to newer terminology based on stereochemical investigations, the mitochondrial enzyme should be denoted 27-hydroxylase.[48] In this review, however, we prefer to use the more conventional term 26-hydroxylase.

It was recently shown that the final steps in bile acid biosynthesis after the mitochondrial 26-hydroxylation, involving β-oxidation of the steroid side chain to a C_{24}-carboxylic acid, occur in the peroxisomes (for a review, see Ref. 49 and Chap. 57).

Shefer and collaborators[50,51] have described an alternative pathway for oxidation of the steroid side chain (Fig. 51-4). This pathway can be utilized only for biosynthesis of cholic acid. 5β-Cholestane-3α,7α,12α-triol may be 25-hydroxylated by a microsomal 25-hydroxylase, yielding 5β-cholestane-3α,7α,12α,25-tetrol. As discussed above, this steroid is excreted in great amounts in bile and feces of CTX patients. 5β-Cholestane-3α,7α,12α,25-tetrol is then subjected to 24(*S*)-hydroxylation by a microsomal enzyme, yielding 5β-cholestane-3α,7α,12α,24(*S*),25-pentol. The latter steroid can be further oxidized into cholic acid by soluble cleavage enzyme.[50] It should be pointed out that it is the 24(*R*)-isomer of 5β-cholestane-3α,7α,12α,-24,25-pentol that is excreted in feces of CTX subjects.[41,42]

The contention that the major pathway for cholic acid biosynthesis involves 26-hydroxylated intermediates and the minor pathway involves 25-hydroxylated intermediates is based on the findings that 26-oxidized intermediates are converted into cholic acid considerably more efficiently than 25-oxidized

Fig. 51-2 Structures of bile alcohols excreted in bile and feces of CTX subjects.[17]

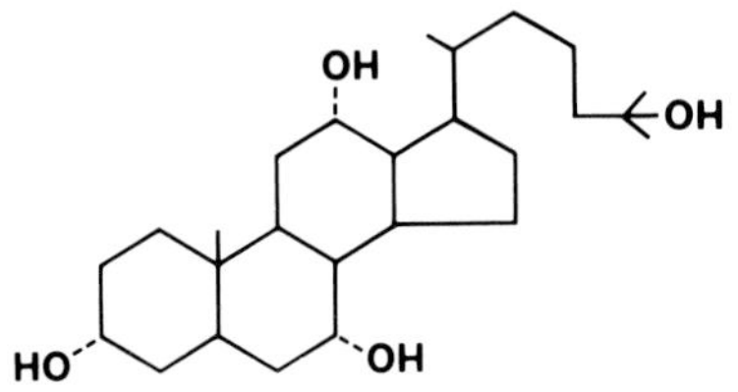

OH
OH
HO
OH

5β-Cholestane-3α,7α,12α,25-tetrol

OH
OH
OH
HO
OH

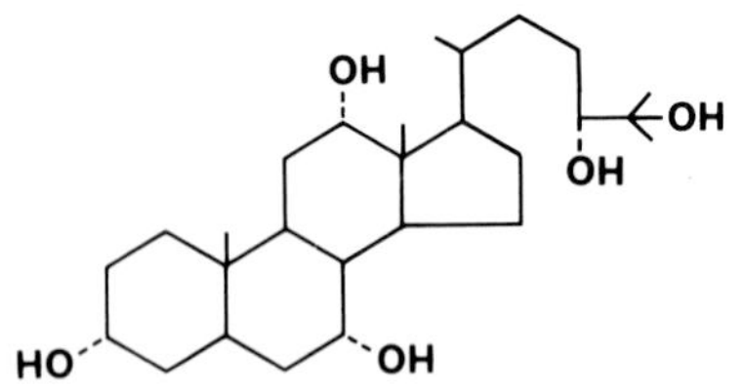

5β-Cholestane-3α,7α,12α,24R,25-pentol

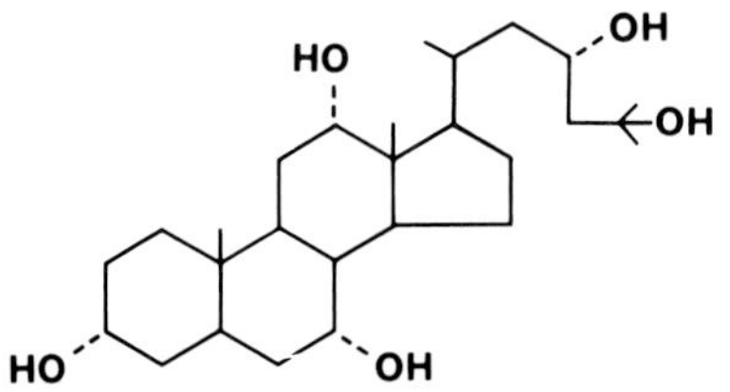

HO
OH
OH
HO
OH

5β-Cholestane-3α,7α,12α,23R,25-pentol

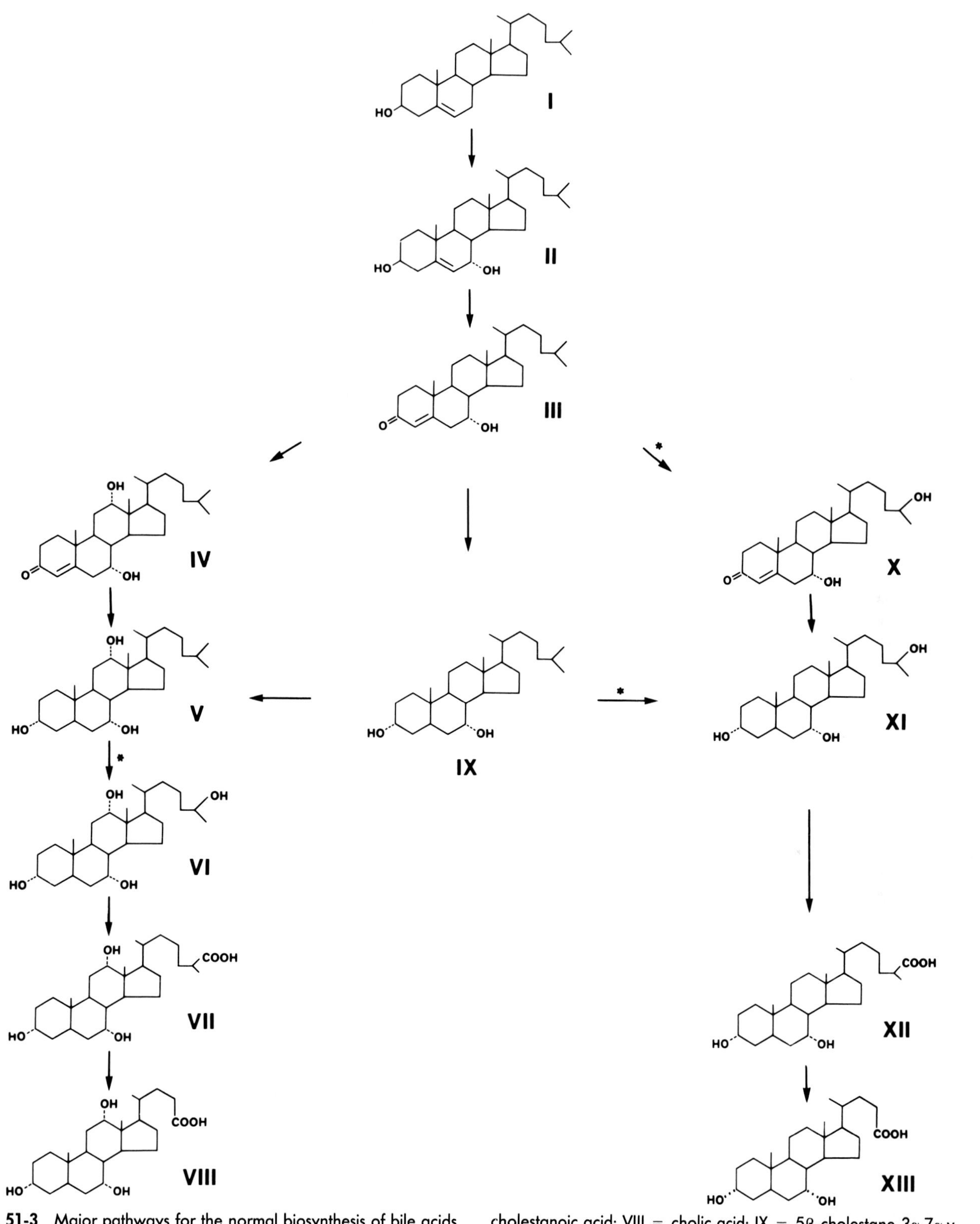

Fig. 51-3 Major pathways for the normal biosynthesis of bile acids from cholesterol.[48] I = cholesterol; II = 7α-hydroxycholesterol; III = 7α-hydroxy-4-cholesten-3-one; IV = 7α,12α-dihydroxy-4-cholesten-3-one; V = 5β-cholestane-3α,7α,12α-triol; VI = 5β-cholestane-3α,7α,12α,26-tetrol; VII = 3α,7α,12α-trihydroxy-5β-cholestanoic acid; VIII = cholic acid; IX = 5β-cholestane-3α,7α,v-diol; X = 7α,26-dihydroxy-4-cholesten-3-one; XI = 5β-cholestane-3α,7α,26-triol; XII = 3α,7α-dihydroxy-5β-cholestanoic acid; XIII = chenodeoxycholic acid. Those reactions affected in CTX are denoted with an asterisk.

intermediates in rats and humans.[52,53] In addition, two inborn errors which affect enzyme in the 26-hydroxylase pathway are known—CTX and Zellweger disease (Chap. 57). In both these diseases there are accumulations of bile acid intermediates and their metabolites at a stage prior to the metabolic block. Such accumulation would not be expected if the 26-hydroxylase pathway had been a minor one. The minor 25-hydroxylase pathway may, however, be utilized under conditions when the major 26-hydroxylase pathway is blocked as is the case in CTX.[18] Thus, most of the cholic acid formed in this disease is probably a product of the 25-hydroxylase pathway. The accumulation of 5β-cholestane-3α,7α,12α,25-tetrol in CTX may be

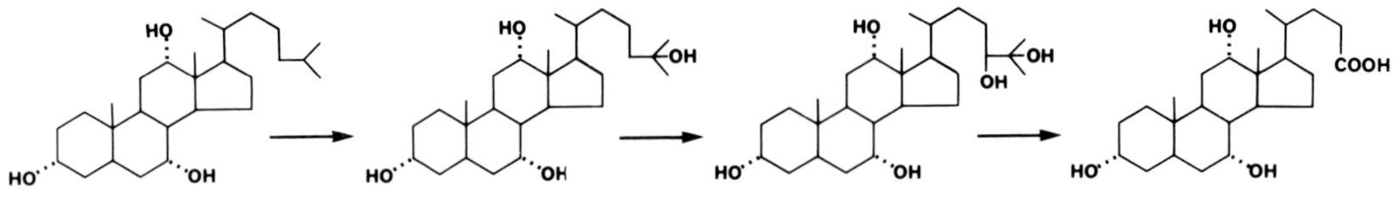

Fig. 51-4 Formation of cholic acid from 5β-cholestane-3α,7α,12α-triol by the 25-hydroxylase pathway described by Salen et al.[50] I = 5β-cholestane-3α,7α,12α-triol; II = 5β-cholestane-3α,7α,12α,25-tetrol; III = 5β-cholestane-3α,7α,12α,24(S),25-pentol; IV = cholic acid.

due to a relatively low capacity of the 24(*S*)-hydroxylase. The very small formation of chenodeoxycholic acid in patients with CTX is probably due to the fact that the 25-hydroxylase pathway cannot be utilized for biosynthesis of chenodeoxycholic acid. Thus 5β-cholestane-3α,7α-diol is not a substrate for the microsomal 25-hydroxylase.[54]

Normal Biosynthesis and Metabolism of Cholestanol

Small amounts of cholestanol accompany cholesterol in most or all mammalian tissues. Cholesterol is the precursor of cholestanol in experimental animals, in healthy subjects, and in subjects with CTX.[55] It is generally believed that the major pathway in the normal biosynthesis of cholestanol involves a rate limiting oxidation of cholesterol into 4-cholesten-3-one by a microsomal NAD-dependent 3β-hydroxy-Δ^5-dehydrogenase[56] (Fig. 51-5). This enzyme has a very low capacity and is difficult to assay. 4-Cholesten-3-one is then converted into cholestanol by a microsomal Δ^4-3-oxosteroid 5α-reductase and a 3β-hydroxysteroid dehydrogenase.[57–59] This reaction sequence from cholesterol to cholestanol does not share any intermediates with the pathways for biosynthesis of cholesterol and bile acids. The possibility has been discussed, however, that the microsomal, NAD-dependent, 3β-hydroxy-Δ^5-dehydrogenase involved in cholestanol synthesis is the same as that involved in bile acid biosynthesis.[60]

We have recently described a normally minor pathway for formation of cholestanol; it involves intermediates in bile acid biosynthesis as precursors.[21,61–64] After oral administration of [4-^{14}C]7α-hydroxy-4-cholesten-3-one to rabbits (see Fig. 51-3), labeled cholesta-4,6-dien-3-one, 4-cholesten-3-one, and cholestanol could be isolated.[64] Also 7α-hydroxycholesterol, the immediate precursor to 7α-hydroxy-4-cholesten-3-one, was converted into cholestanol when administered orally to rabbits or intravenously to a CTX patient.[21,63] The possibility has been excluded that the conversion of 7α-hydroxycholesterol into cholestanol involves cholesterol as an intermediate.[63] The entire sequence of reactions from 7α-hydroxycholesterol to cholestanol is shown in Fig. 51-6. Intestinal microorganisms are not necessary for the conversion since the overall conversion occurred also in germ-free rats.[64] Using bile-fistula rats it was shown that the 7α-dehydroxylation step occurs mainly in the liver. Microsomal fractions from rat or human liver were found to be able to catalyze a slow removal of the 7α-hydroxyl group from 7α-hydroxy-4-cholesten-3-one.[62] This enzyme is not active toward 7α-hydroxycholesterol or 5α-cholestane-3β,7α-diol.[62]

The quantitative significance of early 7α-hydroxylated bile acid intermediates as precursors of cholestanol was studied with use of cholesterol specifically ^{3}H-labeled in the 7α position. In experimental animals, a mixture of [7α-^{3}H]cholesterol and [4-^{14}C]cholesterol was administered.[21] Since 7α hydroxylation occurs with a stereospecific replacement of hydrogen, cholestanol synthesized from 7α-^{3}H-labeled intermediates would be expected to be devoid of ^{3}H. By the direct route from cholesterol via 4-cholesten-3-one, on the other hand, 7α-^{3}H would be retained. Figure 51-7 shows that in rats, as well as in rabbits, cholestanol could be isolated which had a ^{3}H/^{14}C ratio about 20 percent lower than that in reisolated cholesterol.[21] We concluded that there is a pathway to cholestanol involving 7α-hydroxylated intermediates. Under normal circumstances, this pathway is of minor significance and is re-

Fig. 51-5 Major pathway for the normal biosynthesis of cholestanol from cholesterol. I = cholesterol; II = 4-cholesten-3-one; III = 5α-cholestane-3-one; IV = cholestanol.

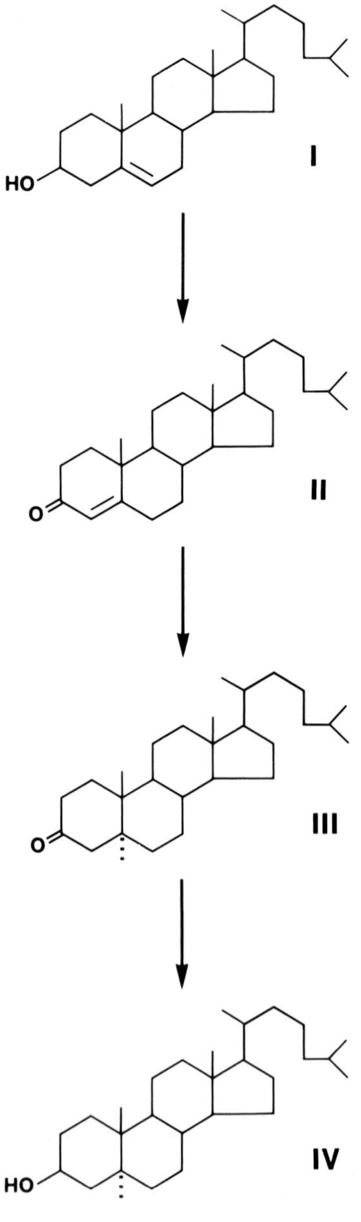

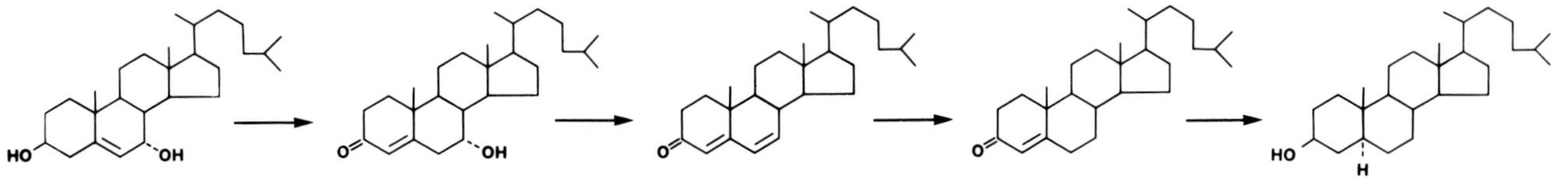

Fig. 51-6 Mechanism of biosynthesis of cholestanol from 7α-hydroxycholesterol.[62] I = 7α-hydroxycholesterol; II = 7α-hydroxy-4-cholesten-3-one; III = cholesta-4,6-dien-3-one; IV = 4-cholesten-3-one; V = cholestanol.

sponsible for at most 20 percent of the cholestanol formed in these species. In a similar experiment with a healthy male volunteer, the reduction of $^3H/^{14}C$ value in the isolated cholestanol was about 28 percent, indicating that this pathway is present also in humans (Fig. 51-7).

There is evidence that at least part of the cholestanol accumulating in patients with CTX is formed by the pathway involving bile acid intermediates as precursors.[21] Like cholesterol, cholestanol is transported mainly in the LDL fraction,[65] and part of the cholestanol in plasma is esterified. LCAT (plasma lecithin:cholesterol acyltransferase) is the enzyme responsible for esterification of cholestanol. LCAT activity is normal in CTX.[25] Cholestanol is degraded to 5α-bile acids (allocholic acid and allochenodeoxycholic acid) by the same or similar enzymes as those involved in the biosynthesis of the normal 5α-bile acids.[39,66]

Metabolic Defect in CTX: Lack of the Mitochondrial 26-Hydroxylase

The major symptoms in CTX are due to the generalized accumulation of cholestanol and cholesterol in almost every tissue, including the central nervous system. This accumulation may be due to increased synthesis and/or increased influx of the two sterols from the circulation. Another alternative is a reduced rate of efflux from the tissues and/or reduced degradation. Salen and collaborators have shown convincingly that both cholesterol and cholestanol synthesis are increased in the livers of patients with CTX.[22,23,65] This group of authors have also reported that, when grown in a cholesterol-free medium, fibroblasts from CTX patients synthesize cholesterol but not cholestanol.[67] In addition the fibroblasts did respond normally to LDL with a supression of the rate limiting enzyme in cholesterol biosynthesis, the HMG-CoA reductase.[67] In view of this it seems most probable that cholestanol or a precursor of cholestanol is transported to the different tissues after synthesis elsewhere. The most likely hypothesis is that the accumulation of cholesterol and cholestanol in the tissues of CTX patients is secondary to increased synthesis of cholesterol and cholestanol in the liver.[23] The increased synthesis of cholesterol may be due to a decreased feedback inhibition of the hepatic HMG-CoA reductase by bile acids, particularly chenodeoxycholic acid. The possible importance of such a feedback regulation by bile acids is, however, a matter of controversy.[48] The increased synthesis of cholestanol may be secondary to the increased synthesis of cholesterol or due to the accumulation of some bile acid intermediates in bile acid biosynthesis.[21] In any case there is general agreement that the primary defect in patients with CTX is localized to bile acid biosynthesis and that the accumulation of neutral sterols is secondary to such a mechanism. The possibility that the rate of transport of cholesterol and cholestanol from the tissues may be abnormal in CTX also has to be considered.

Recently Barron reported that skin fibroblasts cultured from patients with CTX and passaged four times had markedly increased levels of cholestanol compared to skin fibroblasts cultured from healthy controls.[68] On the basis of this finding, it was suggested that the primary defect in CTX is the increased production of cholestanol and that the disorder in bile acid

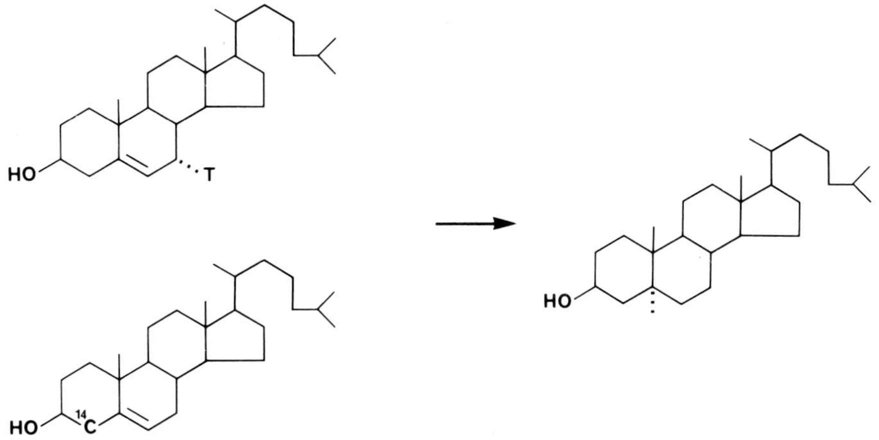

Rat	$T/^{14}C = 1.25$	$T/^{14}C = 1.02$
Healthy man	$T/^{14}C = 1.74$	$T/^{14}C = 1.25$
CTX-patient	$T/^{14}C = 1.54$	$T/^{14}C = 0.35$

Fig. 51-7 Biosynthesis of cholestanol from cholesterol involving 7α-hydroxylated intermediates.[21]

biosynthesis is secondary. One of us (S.S.) recently repeated Barron's experiment. After 10 passages, however, the concentration of cholestanol was about the same in the fibroblasts from three CTX patients as in those from 17 control subjects. At present there is overwhelming evidence that the primary defect in CTX is localized to the biosynthesis of bile acids and that the accumulation of cholestanol is secondary to this.

A liver biopsy from one or our Norwegian patients was found to be completely devoid of mitochondrial 26-hydroxylase activity toward different 7α-hydroxylated intermediates in bile acid biosynthesis.[18] The lack of the 26-hydroxylase activity was not due to a general inactivation of the mitochondrial fraction, since another mixed function oxidase located at the inner mitochondrial membrane, the vitamin D_3 25-hydroxylase, was found to be active. A defect in the mitochondrial 26-hydroxylation led to accumulation of substrates for the enzyme. Using isotope dilution mass spectrometry, we could demonstrate very high levels of 5β-cholestane-3α,7α,12α-triol and 7α,12α-dihydroxy-4-cholesten-3-one in the liver of the CTX-patient.[19] The accumulation of the latter steroid may be secondary to accumulation of 7α-hydroxy-4-cholesten-3-one, which is efficiently 12α-hydroxylated. These findings are in accord with the contention that activity of 26-hydroxylase is deficient.

Results of different in vivo experiments also indicate that 26-hydroxylase activity is deficient in patients with CTX.[20] One patient with CTX and two control subjects received intravenously a mixture of [4-^{14}C]7α-hydroxy-4-cholesten-3-one and [6β-^{3}H]7α, 26-dihydroxy-4-cholesten-3-one. The ratio between ^{14}C and ^{3}H in cholic acid and chenodeoxycholic acid isolated from bile of the CTX patient was less than 3 percent of those of the control subjects, indicating a very low degree of conversion of the steroid lacking a 26-hydroxyl group (Fig. 51-8). A similar experiment with similar result was also performed with [4-^{14}C]5β-cholestane-3α,7α-diol and [1,2-^{3}H]5β-cholestane-3α,7α,26-triol.

Using isotope dilution mass spectrometry Javitt et al. were able to demonstrate the presence of 26-hydroxycholesterol in human serum from healthy subjects.[69] As could be expected in 26-hydroxylase deficiency, the serum levels of 26-hydroxycholesterol were much lower in patients with CTX than in healthy control subjects.[69]

The mitochondrial 26-hydroxylase is a species of cytochrome P_{450}, which requires ferredoxin and ferredoxin reductase for the transport of electrons from HADPH to the substrate. Reconstituted systems containing ferredoxin, ferredoxin reductase, and partially purified cytochrome P_{450} have been characterized in detail.[70] The cytochrome P_{450} component was recently purified to homogeneity.[71] The enzyme was previously believed to be located exclusively in the liver, but we have been able to show that cultured fibroblasts contain 26-hydroxylase activity and that the substrate specificity is similar to that in the liver.[72] Fibroblasts from patients with CTX had only traces of 26-hydroxylase activity. This study also showed that the deficient activity of the 26-hydroxylase was not due to inhibition of the enzyme activity by accumulated intermediates. As could be expected for a recessive disease, fibroblasts from heterozygotes had activities about 50 percent of normal.[73]

Attempts have been made to quantitate the components of the 26-hydroxylase system in liver of control patients and patients with CTX. Using antibodies against adrenodoxin, adrenodoxin reductase, and adrenal cytochrome P_{450} active against cholesterol, Miki et al. found that the concentrations of ferredoxin in the patients were not different from those of controls, but the level of ferredoxin reductase was increased three times compared to the control.[74] With the antibodies used, no mitochondrial cytochrome P_{450} was detected in the patients, but it was present in the control liver.

The lack of the mitochondrial 26-hydroxylase in patients with CTX explains most of the biochemical abnormalities in this disease. The accumulation of one of the major substrates for the 26-hydroxylase, 5β-cholestane-3α,7α,12α-triol, in the liver of CTX subjects leads to exposure of this substrate to the normally less active microsomal 23-, 24-, and 25-hydroxylases. One of the products of these "abnormal" hydroxylations, 5β-cholestane-3α,7α,12α,25-tetrol, may be converted into cholic acid via the minor alternative pathway described by Shefer et al.[50] Since this alternative pathway cannot produce chenodeoxycholic acid, only cholic acid is formed. The reduced synthesis

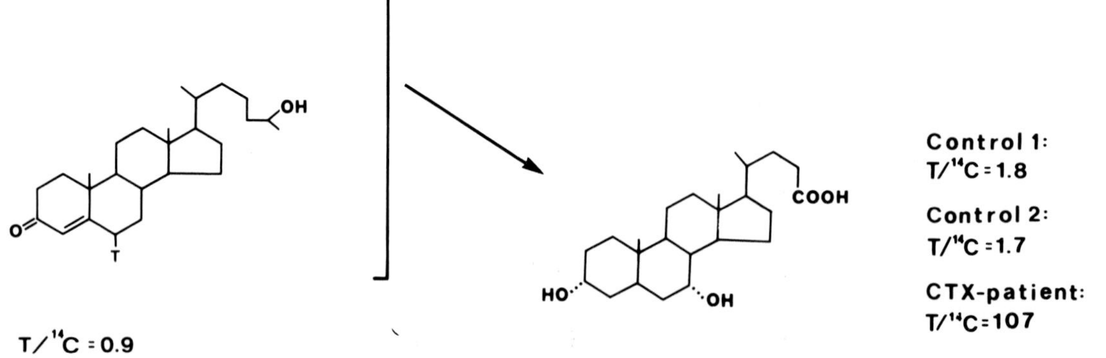

Fig. 51-8 In vivo conversion of different labeled precursors into cholic acid and chenodeoxycholic acid in control subjects and subjects with CTX.[20]

Control 1: T/^{14}C = 0.5
Control 2: T/^{14}C = 0.5
CTX-patient: T/^{14}C = 21

Control 1: T/^{14}C = 1.8
Control 2: T/^{14}C = 1.7
CTX-patient: T/^{14}C = 107

T/^{14}C = 0.9

of the primary bile acids leads to a reduced feedback inhibition of the rate limiting enzyme in bile acid biosynthesis, the cholesterol 7α-hydroxylase.[48]

In spite of the increased activity of the cholesterol 7α-hydroxylase, the total biosynthesis of bile acids in CTX subjects has been reported to be only 100 to 150 mg/day,[65] which is about 50 percent of the normal value. The total excretion of 7α-hydroxylated bile alcohols, however, may be up to about 2 g/day,[65a] indicating that most of the 7α-hydroxycholesterol formed is shunted into a pathway with bile alcohols as end products.

Salen et al. have reported that the activity of the microsomal 12α-hydroxylase is increased about threefold in liver biopsies of CTX patients.[23,75] In the liver biopsy we studied, an apparent 12α-hydroxylase activity was also found in the mitochondrial fraction of the liver homogenate.[76] In normal human liver, the 12α-hydroxylase involved in bile acid biosynthesis is strictly microsomal. Very recently, however, it was reported that fetal human liver contains some mitochondrial 12α-hydroxylase activity.[77] The increased 12α-hydroxylase activity in patients with CTX may contribute to the very high proportion of cholic acid formed in relation to chenodeoxycholic acid. The induction of the 12α-hydroxylase activity is probably secondary to the accumulation of substrate.

Considerable amounts of 23-hydroxylated bile alcohols are excreted in feces and urine of CTX patients. Abnormal 23-hydroxylated bile acids are also excreted in urine.[47] It seems probable that the hepatic 23-hydroxylase is increased in patients with CTX, probably due to induction by the accumulated substrate. It has been suggested that the biochemical defect in CTX may be a relative deficiency of the microsomal 24S-hydroxylase active on 5β-cholestane-3α,7α,12α,25-tetrol.[78] The rate of formation of 5β-cholestane-3α,7α,12α,24(*S*),25-pentol from radioactive 5β-cholestane-3α,7α,12α,25-tetrol by CTX hepatic microsomes was found to be 25 percent of the corresponding activity in control microsomes. A reduced 24(*S*)-hydroxylation of 5β-cholestane-3α,7α,12α,25-tetrol would affect overall biosynthesis of bile acids only if the 25-hydroxylase pathway (Fig. 51-4) is of major importance for side-cleavage. As discussed above, however, several findings indicate that the 25-hydroxylase pathway is of minor importance under normal conditions.

From a theoretical point of view, accumulation of intermediates in bile acid biosynthesis is expected only if the activity of the affected enzyme is reduced to a level below that of the rate limiting enzyme in the biosynthesis of bile acids, the cholesterol 7α-hydroxylase. The activity of the latter enzyme as measured in vitro has been reported to be about 5 to 20 pmol/min per milligram in the normal state.[79,80] We have found the activity of the human hepatic mitochondrial 26-hydroxylase to be less than 2 pmol/min per milligram in CTX patients using 5β-cholestane-3α,7α,12α,-triol as substrate. The activity of 5β-cholestane-3α,7α,12α,25-tetrol-24(S)-hydroxylase was reported to be about 150 pmol/min per milligram in two patients with CTX.[78] These findings are also in accord with the contention that the important defect in CTX is the deficient 26-hydroxylation.

Mechanisms Behind the Increased Synthesis of Cholestanol

Increased biosynthesis of cholestanol may not be unique to patients with CTX. Increased levels of cholestanol have also recently been reported in some hepatic disorders, in particular in primary biliary cirrhosis.[81]

There are three hypotheses for the mechanism behind the increased synthesis of cholestanol in patients with CTX:

1. The activity of the rate limiting enzyme in the normal biosynthesis of cholestanol, the microsomal Δ^5-3β-hydroxysteroid dehydrogenase active on cholesterol, may be increased in patients with CTX.
2. The increased biosynthesis of cholestanol may be secondary to the increased biosynthesis of cholesterol.
3. The increased biosynthesis of cholestanol may be due to increased utilization of bile acid intermediates as precursors for cholestanol.[21] As a consequence of the metabolic block, considerable amounts of such intermediates accumulate in CTX.[19]

The first hypothesis has been put forward by Salen et al.[60] They showed that the apparent formation of 4-cholesten-3-one from cholesterol by hepatic microsomes from one subject with CTX was about threefold higher than that obtained with control microsomes. In view of the great difficulty of assaying this low activity (see Ref. 56), the result may be difficult to evaluate. In contrast, we have not found any significant difference between the activity of the Δ^5-3β-hydroxysteroid dehydrogenase in liver biopsies from control subjects and that from patients with CTX.[82] In our experiments we used 7α-hydroxycholesterol as substrate since we were unable to accurately measure the low conversion obtained with cholesterol as substrate. From a theoretical standpoint, it is difficult to understand why the Δ^5-3β-hydroxysteroid dehydrogenase activity should increase as a consequence of an increased rate of 7α-hydroxylation and/or lack of the 26-hydroxylase.

The second hypothesis is also not well supported by what is known concerning cholesterol and cholestanol metabolism. If an increased rate of cholesterol synthesis increases the rate of cholestanol synthesis, other conditions with increased cholesterol biosynthesis would also be expected to yield increased amounts of cholestanol. It was recently reported that treatment of a patient with CTX with mevinolin, an inhibitor of cholesterol synthesis, caused a considerable reduction in the level of cholestanol in plasma.[26] On the other hand, mevinolin may also have some effects on bile acid biosynthesis,[83] and the possibility that the effect on cholestanol was secondary to the effect on bile acid biosynthesis cannot be excluded.

According to the third hypothesis, the bile acid intermediates accumulating in patients with CTX due to the lack of the 26-hydroxylase may be shunted into the cholestanol pathway (Fig. 51-9). In accordance with this hypothesis, we observed that cholestanol isolated from serum, bile, and feces from a CTX patient treated with a mixture of [4-^{14}C]cholesterol and [7α-^{3}H]cholesterol had lost about 75 percent of the ^{3}H label (Fig. 51-7). This indicates that about 75 percent of the cholestanol had been formed by a pathway involving 7α-hydroxylation and 7α-dehydroxylation. In addition, there was a significant conversion of intravenously administered 7α-[7β-^{3}H]hydroxycholesterol into cholestanol in a patient with CTX.[21,63] 7α-Hydroxy-4-cholesten-3-one would normally be expected to be an intermediate in the conversion of 7α-hydroxycholesterol into cholestanol. When labeled 7α-hydroxy-4-cholesten-3-one was administered to a CTX patient, however, little or no conversion into cholestanol could be demonstrated.[20] Less than optimal amounts of labeled steroid were used in that experiment. Another explanation may be compartmentalization and dilution of the administered labeled ste-

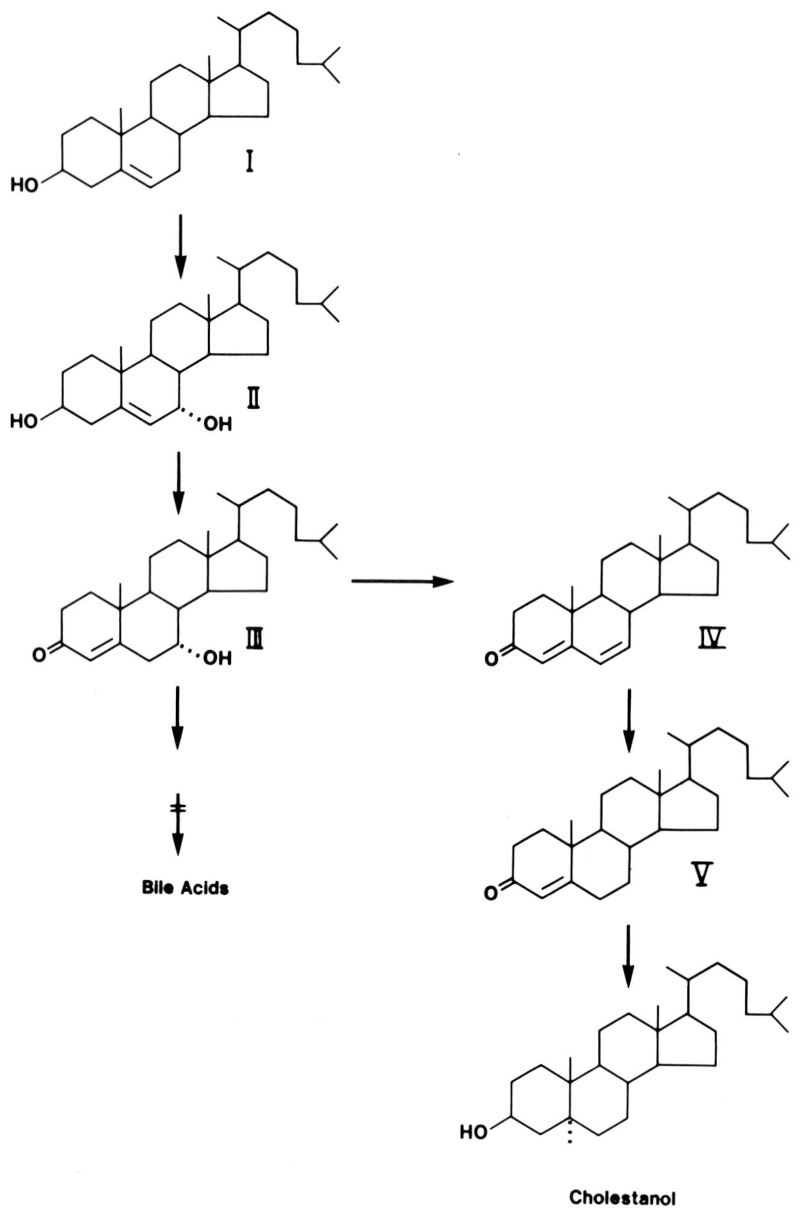

HO I

HO II OH

O III OH

Bile Acids

O IV

O V

HO

Cholestanol

Fig. 51-9 Shunting of 7α-hydroxylated intermediates into the pathway leading to cholestanol in CTX patients. I = cholesterol; II = 7α-hydroxy-cholesterol; III = 7α-hydroxy-4-cholesten-3-one; IV = cholesta-4,6-dien-3-one; V = 4-cholesten-3-one.

roid. Since plasma contains relatively high concentrations of this steroid,[29] the administered 7α-hydroxy-4-cholesten-3-one may not equilibrate with the small intrahepatic pool of this compound utilized for cholestanol biosynthesis.[29] It should be noted that only a small shunting (2 to 4 percent) of the 7α-hydroxycholesterol formed into the cholestanol pathway is required to explain the increased synthesis of cholestanol in patients with CTX (Fig. 9, Ref. 21).

At present the third hypothesis has the best experimental support, and at least part of the cholestanol is synthesized by this pathway in patients with CTX. This hypothesis can also explain the effects of different treatments on the synthesis of cholestanol. Treatment with chenodeoxycholic acid is the therapy of choice (see below) and reduces plasma levels of cholestanol dramatically in patients with CTX. By feedback inhibition, treatment with chenodeoxycholic acid inhibits the cholesterol 7α-hydroxylase, which leads to reduction in the amounts of 7α-hydroxylated precursors to cholestanol. We have recently shown that the elevated levels of 7α-hydroxy-4-cholesten-3-one and cholesta-4,6-dien-3-one in patients with CTX decrease dramatically after treatment with chenodeoxycholic acid.[29] It has been reported that treatment of CTX patients with cholestyramine leads to increased levels of cholestanol.[22] This effect can also be explained by the third hypothesis. Thus treatment with cholestyramine should lead to increased 7α-hydroxylation of cholesterol and therefore to increased levels of 7α-hydroxylated precursors for biosynthesis of cholestanol.

Mechanism(s) Behind the Increased Synthesis of Cholesterol

The reason for the increased biosynthesis of cholesterol in patients with CTX may be the reduced feedback inhibition of HMG-CoA reductase in the liver by bile acids returning to the liver in the enterohepatic circulation. The increased synthesis of cholesterol may also be secondary to the accumulation of cholestanol. Shefer et al. reported that feeding rats with 2 percent cholestanol in their diets increased the activity of the rate limiting enzyme in cholesterol biosynthesis, the HMG-CoA reductase.[84] However, it was also shown that cholestanol was less readily absorbed than cholesterol and interfered with cholesterol absorption. The observed effect of the dietary cholestanol on cholesterol synthesis may thus have been due to malabsorption of cholesterol rather than a direct derepressive effect on the HMG-CoA reductase.

Mechanism(s) for the Accumulation of Cholesterol and Cholestanol in the Brain

It is clear that explanations can be offered for the increased biosynthesis of cholesterol and cholestanol in the liver in patients with CTX. However, because of the blood-brain barrier, it is not evident that increased levels of cholesterol and cholestanol or their precursors in the circulation would lead to an accumulation in the brain. In view of this, it is interesting that Salen et al. recently reported drastically increased levels of apolipoprotein B (about 100-fold) with smaller increase in concentrations of other lipoproteins (1.5- to 3-fold) and of albumin (3- to 4-fold) in the cerebrospinal fluid of patients with CTX.[38] The concentration of cholestanol was about 20 times higher in CTX patients than in controls. Treatment of the CTX patients with chenodeoxycholic acid decreased the levels of cholestanol in cerebrospinal fluid about threefold. Thus the permeability of the blood-brain barrier seems to be affected in CTX by unknown mechanisms.

A recent study by Buchmann and Clausen[85] showed that rabbits fed diets enriched with cholestanol (3.5 g/week) for 8 weeks had cholestanol levels in the brain about twofold higher than in controls. After an additional regression period with cholestyramine for 8 weeks, the increased content of cholestanol in the brain was unchanged. It is thus clear that cholestanol can to some extent pass the blood-brain barrier in experimental animals. The possibility must also be considered that a precursor to cholestanol might pass the blood-brain barrier and be converted into cholestanol in the brain. We have recently shown that the microsomal fraction of a homogenate of rat brain is able to catalyze formation of cholestanol from cholesta-4,6-dien-3-one.[86]

Diagnosis

CTX should be suspected in all patients with tendon xanthomas and normal or only slightly elevated serum cholesterol. The diagnosis must also be considered in all cases of unexplained juvenile cataracts. These characteristic features may precede the neurologic disturbances by decades. Because of the slow progression of the disease, the diagnosis is seldom achieved before the second decade of life, except in cases where CTX is suspected from family history. The diagnosis may be confirmed by quantitation of cholestanol in serum by gas chromatography. Bile and xanthoma should also be analyzed. It may be difficult to separate cholestanol from cholesterol by a simple gas-chromatographic step, so a prepurification step may be necessary. Since the trimethylsilylether of cholestanol contains a specific ion at m/z 306 in its mass spectrum, which is not present in the mass spectrum of the corresponding derivative of cholesterol, selected ion monitoring is a suitable method for quantitation of cholestanol in serum.[86a] High-performance liquid chromatography of the benzoyl derivative of cholestanol is also a suitable method for quantitation.[24] In specialized laboratories, the diagnosis may be obtained by quantitation of 5β-cholestane-3α,7α,12α,23,25-pentol in the urine. Koopman et al. have suggested a very simple urinary screening test for CTX suitable for larger populations. In this method a simple commercial kit for assay of 7α-hydroxylated bile acids is used for detection of elevated levels of 7α-hydroxylated bile alcohols in urine.[87] In all positive cases the diagnosis must be confirmed by more specific means. It was recently reported that fast atomic bombardment mass spectrometry may be suitable for diagnosis of CTX.[87a] A definitive identification of the lack of the 26-hydroxylase can easily be done with fibroblast cultures.[72]

In principle it should also be possible to identify heterozygotes by assay of the level of 26-hydroxylase activity in cultured fibroblasts.[73] Control fibroblasts from several individuals must be used. A simpler method has been suggested by Koopman et al.[88] They showed that when carriers and noncarriers for the disease were subjected to cholestyramine treatment, by which endogenous bile acid synthesis was stimulated, the urinary excretion of 5β-cholestane-3α,7α,12α,23,25-pentol in the carrier increased considerably, but it remained essentially the same in the noncarriers. This test may be valuable for the genetic counseling of carriers for CTX and for detection of newborn infants with CTX.

Early diagnosis of CTX is very important. If the disease is detected in early childhood, treatment of the not yet affected patient with chenodeoxycholic acid therapy can prevent the occurrence of irreversible CNS damage and the other symptoms.

Treatment

Salen was the first to treat a CTX-patient with chenodeoxycholic acid.[22] He showed that the expansion of the deficient bile acid pool resulted in a marked drop in plasma cholestanol, and that cholesterol and cholestanol production rates were suppressed. In addition, HMG-CoA reductase, the rate-controlling enzyme in cholesterol synthesis, was inhibited fourfold during the therapy, and bile alcohols almost disappeared from the bile. It has been reported that a number of patients on therapy with chenodeoxycholic acid showed reversal of their neurologic disability, with clearing of the dementia, better orientation, a rise in IQ, and improved strength and independence.[23,89]

Very recently, a report appeared that treatment with mevinolin, an inhibitor of cholesterol synthesis, markedly reduced the cholestanol levels in plasma.[26] More experience is needed however, before it can be determined whether this therapy is as effective as therapy with chenodeoxycholic acid. The possibility of combining the two different therapies should also be considered.

PHYTOSTEROLEMIA (SITOSTEROLEMIA)

This rare familial disorder of sterol metabolism was first described by Bhattacharyya and Connor,[90,91] who studied two sisters with extensive tendon xanthomas but normal plasma cholesterol levels. Plant sterols constituted 15.6 and 11.3 percent of their total plasma sterols. Erythrocytes and tendon xanthomas also contained unusually high concentrations of plant sterols. Increased absorption of sitosterol in both patients (24 to 28 percent versus normally <5 percent) was suggested as a possible cause of the disease.

We have chosen to use the term *phytosterolemia* for this disease. Bhattacharyya and Connor have suggested *sitosterolemia and xanthomatosis* as an alternative. The above terms should, however, be made more precise as soon as the biochemical defect is defined.

Clinical Phenotype

Until now, 22 cases of this disease have been published.[90–102] Seven of the patients were males, and 15 were females. All patients have developed subcutaneous and tendon xanthomas during the first years of life, in one case as early as age 1½.[92] The xanthomas have in most cases been found to involve the Achilles tendon and the extensor tendons of the hands. In some patients, xanthelasmas have been present, and subcutaneous xanthomas have been noted in different regions, e.g., on the buttocks (Fig. 51-10). Arcus corneae has been observed in a couple of cases.

The xanthomatosis has in some cases been misinterpreted to indicate familial hypercholesterolemia. However, almost half of the patients have been reported to have normal serum cholesterol. In the remaining cases, only moderate hypercholesterolemia has been present, but in one case (a 12-year-old girl), serum cholesterol was as high as 750 mg/100 ml.[95] Hyperapobetalipoproteinemia was reported in several of the affected subjects.[98]

Premature atherosclerosis has been present in many cases. Three of the seven males reported to have sitosterolemia have died as a consequence of coronary atherosclerosis, at ages 13, 18, and 42 years,[97,98,101] but only one[98,101] of the 15 females has died of coronary heart disease—at the age of 39. Extensive coronary atherosclerosis has been demonstrated by coronary angiography in one additional male patient.[93] Males with this disease are predisposed to developing vascular complications at an early age.

Four patients with phytosterolemia have exhibited episodic hemolysis or chronic hemolytic anemia.[93,97,100] Hypersplenism and platelet abnormalities have also been present in these cases. One of the two sisters with sitosterolemia first described by Bhattacharyya and Connor[91] complained of pain in the knees and heels, and other patients have also had episodes of arthritis.

Table 51-2 summarizes the main clinical symptoms in the first described 16 cases of sitosterolemia given in the previous edition of this text.[23]

Pathologic Anatomy. An 18-year-old white male with phytosterolemia who died suddenly of an acute myocardial infarction was recently described in detail.[101] A postmortem examination revealed extensive coronary atherosclerosis with about 60 percent occlusion of the proximal left main and proximal right coronary arteries (Fig. 51-11). Diffuse atherosclerotic lesions were also present in the right and left anterior descending and circumflex arteries, as well as in the thoracic and abdominal aorta and the iliac vessels. Histologic evidence of acute infarction was not found, but many areas of myocardial fibrosis suggested previous infarctions, and death was attributed to cardiac arrhythmia and myocardial infarction.

In two other male patients with phytosterolemia (one now deceased), extensive coronary atherosclerosis was shown by coronary angiography.[93,97]

Normal Biochemistry of Plant Sterols (Phytosterols)

Phytosterols are found in the lipids of plants. Particularly rich sources of plant sterols are vegetable oils, nuts, avocados, and

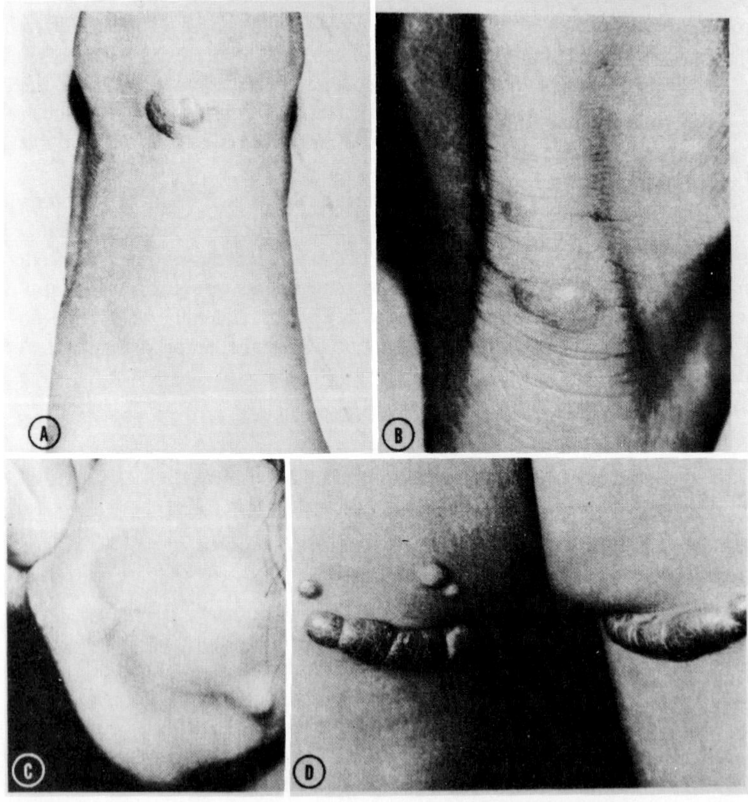

Fig. 51-10 Xanthomas in areas of the anterior ankle *(A)*, Achilles tendon *(B)*, posterior aspect of ear *(C)*, and buttocks area *(D)*. *(Figures from Ref. 102.)*

Table 51-2 Clinical Findings in 16 Patients with Phytosterolemia

	No. of patients		
	Documented	*Absent*	*Not mentioned*
Tendon xanthomas			
Achilles	16	—	—
Other	16	—	—
Xanthelasma	2	6	8
Arcus corneae	2	6	8
Atherosclerosis			
Coronary	2	7	7
Large vessel	3	8	5
Hemolysis	3	7	6
Hypersplenism	3	7	6
Platelet abnormalities	4	3	9
Arthralgia-arthritis	3	3	10
Hypercholesterolemia	9	7	—

SOURCE: Data from Ref. 23.

other fat-rich vegetables and fruits. The most commonly found plant sterols are sitosterol, campesterol (Fig. 51-12), and stigmasterol. They all have the same ring structure as cholesterol, but have a different side chain. Sitosterol and stigmasterol are C_{29} sterols, with the substitution of an ethyl group at C_{24}. Stigmasterol in addition has a double bond at C_{22}.

Fig. 51-11 Photomicrograph of anterior descending branch of left coronary artery showing almost 60 percent occlusion of the lumen by subintimal fibrosis (H&E, $\times 40$). *(Figure from Ref. 101.)*

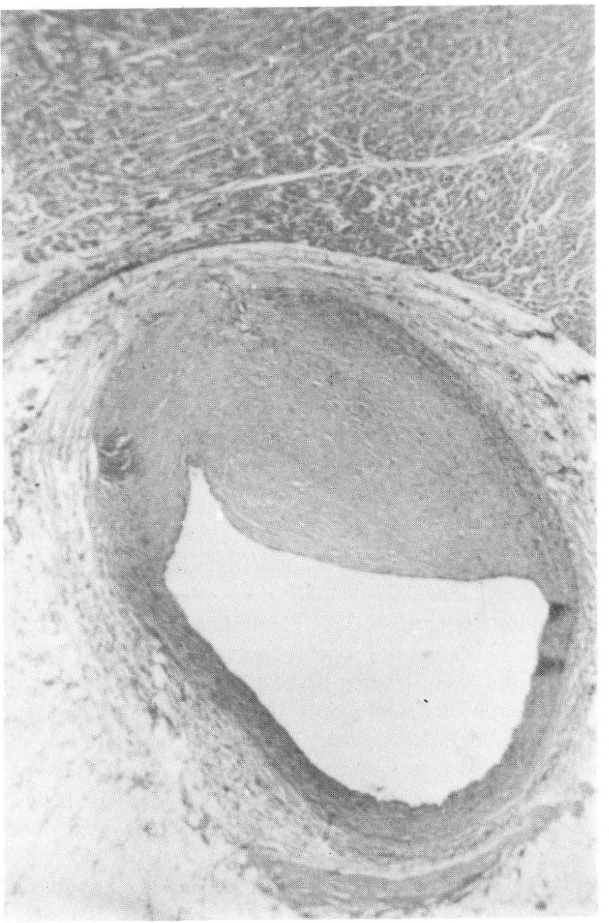

Campesterol (C_{28}) differs from cholesterol with an extra methyl group at C_{24}. The plant sterols react similarly to cholesterol in colorimetric assays and are also measured by methods based on cholesterol oxidase. They can be separated by different high performance liquid chromatography methods, or by capillary gas chromatography. Plant sterols cannot be synthesized in the mammalian organism.[103,104]

The intake of plant sterols varies widely in different geographic regions, and is high in regions where vegetable oils and fat-rich vegetables are much used. In the United States up to 250 mg may be consumed each day.[105]

Phytosterols are absorbed in the gut to a much lesser extent than cholesterol. Less than 5 percent of ingested sitosterol is absorbed in humans and other mammals (e.g., the rat).[104,106–109] Both in dogs and white Carneau pigeons, campesterol (C_{28}) is absorbed more easily than sitosterol.[110–112] Unabsorbed phytosterols are metabolized in the gut analogous to cholesterol, but to a moderately lesser extent. In about three-fourths of the North American population,[113] cholesterol is converted to coprostanol by intestinal bacteria. In the same individuals, phytosterols are metabolized in the gut to 5β-sitostanol and corresponding metabolites of other plant sterols.[112] Because of its low degree of absorption, sitosterol has been used as a marker in cholesterol balance studies.[114] The mechanisms of intestinal discrimination between animal and plant sterols are poorly understood. One possible cause may be that sitosterol is less soluble in micelles than cholesterol[115] and enters the brush border membranes less easily than cholesterol.[116] The CoA-dependent esterification rate of sitosterol in the intestinal mucosa is also very slow compared with that of cholesterol.[115] Plant sterols interfere with the absorption of cholesterol in the gut[117] and have been widely used as serum cholesterol lowering agents. 5α-Sitostanol has a higher hypocholesterolemic effect than sitosterol.[119] To decrease cholesterol absorption, the plant sterol should be taken at the same meal in quantities related to the cholesterol intake.[118,120] The luminal and/or mucosal sites at which these sterols interfere with cholesterol absorption have not been definitely localized. One possible mechanism is that plant sterols interfere with cholesterol absorption by crystallization and coprecipitation of the sterols in the intestinal lumen.[120]

After absorption, about 70 percent of the cholesterol in the thoracic lymph is esterified, compared with 25 percent of the sitosterol.[121] In blood plasma, however, sitosterol is esterified to almost the same extent as cholesterol (67 and 72 percent, respectively).[91] Lecithin: cholesterol acyltransferase (LCAT) is the most important enzyme for formation of circulating plant sterol esters.[122]

The organ distribution of plant steroids and their excretion has been studied in experimental animals after oral[123] or parenteral administration.[124,125] Plant steroids such as sitosterol,[123–125] campesterol[123] or 24-ethyl-4-cholesten-3-one[125] were enriched in the liver as compared with cholesterol. The lysosomal and microsomal fraction contained slightly more plant sterols than the other subcellular fractions,[123,125] but the subcellular distribution was quite similar to that of cholesterol. The adrenal glands and gonads contained the greatest amounts of phytosterols among the organs examined.[124,125] In the rat, plant sterols were incorporated into serum lipoproteins to a greater extent than was cholesterol.[100,125] No striking differences from cholesterol were noted with respect to the distribution among different lipoproteins. In the rats HDL contained more than 80 percent of the phytosterols.[123,125] In humans, about 70 percent of the total plasma phytosterols are

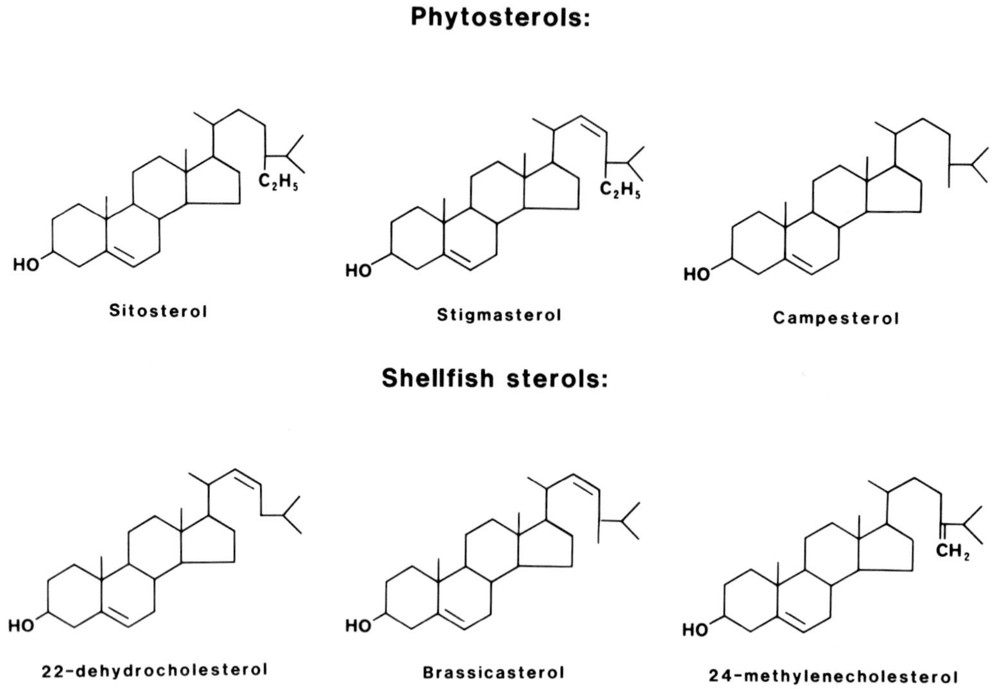

Phytosterols:

C_2H_5 HO Sitosterol

C_2H_5 HO Stigmasterol

HO Campesterol

Shellfish sterols:

HO 22-dehydrocholesterol

HO Brassicasterol

CH_2 HO 24-methylenecholesterol

Fig. 51-12 Structures of the most important phytosterols and shellfish steroids.

found in LDL.[91,93] Most of the remainder is found in HDL. VLDL contains only traces. Phytosterols are probably incorporated into lipoproteins in the liver, and they accumulate in organs rich in lipoprotein receptors (e.g., the adrenal glands).[125]

According to an early study by Werbin and coworkers,[126] dietary sitosterol may serve as precursor of cortisol. However, the rate of this conversion is slower than that from cholesterol.[127,128] Another metabolite of sitosterol is 5α-sitostanol, which is formed in the liver.[100] The most important pathway seems to involve a direct conversion of sitosterol to 24-ethyl-4-cholesten-3-one.[100] It has not been possible to demonstrate a conversion of sitosterol to cholesterol in the rat.[124]

Intake of phytosterols also affects cholesterol metabolism in organs other than the intestine. In sitosterol-fed rats, the activity of the hepatic HMG-CoA reductase was found to be increased about twofold, whereas the activity of the 7α-hydroxylase was unchanged.[129,130] Also in humans, cholesterol synthesis is increased by the intake of plant sterols.[131] This is thought to be an intestinal effect of sitosterol on the reabsorption of endogenous cholesterol excreted through the bile, causing decreased feedback of hepatic HMG-CoA reductase.

Studies of the effect of phytosterols on serum levels of cholesterol have given conflicting results. In chicks which received soy sterols orally or by subcutaneous injections,[132] serum cholesterol was lowered. In contrast, oral administration of sitosterol and campesterol was found to increase serum cholesterol in rabbits.[133,134]

Both in experimental animals and in humans, phytosterols are converted into bile acids less efficiently than cholesterol.[23,104,124,125] After intraperitoneal administration of [^{14}C]cholesterol to rats, more than 80 percent of the ^{14}C excreted in the bile was present as bile acids.[124,125] After injection of labeled sitosterol, however, the corresponding figure was only about 40 percent.[125] Salen and coworkers[104] found that only about 20 percent of absorbed dietary sitosterol was converted to bile acids and that the remainder was excreted as free sterol in the bile. It has also been reported that phytosterols may be excreted to some extent through the skin.[135]

The low rate of bile acid formation from sitosterol and other plant steroids may be due to their slow 7α-hydroxylation (less than 1 percent of that of cholesterol).[136] It has been reported that the bile acids formed from sitosterol in humans are cholic acid and chenodeoxycholic acid.[104] In contrast, no data have been obtained to indicate dealkylation of sitosterol to cholesterol in rats or formation of C_{24} bile acids from sitosterol in this species[124,137–141] or in monkeys.[142] In rat and human liver mitochondria, sitosterol and campesterol are 26- and 29-hydroxylated by a ω-hydroxylating system.[137,138] Subbiah and coworkers[139–141] have suggested that C_{26} and C_{29} bile acids are formed from sitosterol in the rat. In monkeys,[142] there is evidence for conversion of β-sitosterol into cholestanoic acids with either mono- or dihydroxy substitution, but without a dealkylated side chain.

Normal Biochemistry of Shellfish Sterols

Recently a sitosterolemic subject was reported to have an increased intestinal absorption of some shellfish sterols.[143] The shellfish steroids are found in clams, oysters, and scallops but not in shrimps, lobsters, or most species of crabs. Shellfish steroids include 22-dehydrocholesterol, brassicasterol, 22-*trans*-24-norcholesta-5,22-dien-3β-ol (C_{26} sterol) and 24-methylene cholesterol (Fig. 51-12). These unusual steroids constitute up to 50 percent of the total tissue sterols of these organisms.[143] After daily feeding of healthy human subjects with shellfish sterols for 3 to 4 weeks, the absorption of the dietary C_{26} sterol, 22-dehydrocholesterol, brassicasterol, and 24-methylene cholesterol was found to be 54, 35, 4, and 11 percent, respectively.[144] A comparison of the ratios of various shellfish sterols to cholesterol in plasma and in bile suggested selectively greater excretion of shellfish sterols relative to cholesterol.[145] Shellfish sterols do not seem to be preferentially concentrated in any lipoprotein class in plasma, and 50 to 65 percent of these sterols are found in esterified form in the circulation.[143] To what extent, if any, shellfish sterols may be degraded to bile acids is not known.

The Pathophysiology of Phytosterolemia

Blood. All reported patients with phytosterolemia[90–102] have had increased concentrations of sitosterol and campesterol in blood serum. In some cases, increased amounts of stigmasterol were detected, and in one patient,[93] avenasterol (24-ethylidinecholesterol, a fucosterol) was identified. In several patients,[94,96,97,100,146,147] but not in all,[93] 5α derivatives of sitosterol and campesterol were present, in some cases combined with increased concentrations of cholestanol.[97,147] In normal blood serum, the concentration of sitosterol is less than 1 mg/dl.[147] In untreated patients with phytosterolemia, serum sitosterol values in the range 10 to 65 mg/dl have been reported,[23,147] and the levels of campesterol are usually slightly below 50 percent of this. As much as 15 to 20 percent of the total amounts of unsaturated sterols may be plant sterols. The 5α-phytostanols are formed in the liver,[100] and their concentrations are often about 15 percent of their parent plant sterols.[147] In contrast, cholestanol constitutes only about 1.5 percent of the cholesterol in serum. The phytosterols and their 5α derivatives are mainly carried by the LDL fraction.[91,147] The plasma unsaturated phytosterols and particularly their 5α-derivatives are esterified to a lower extent than is cholesterol.[147] In two families with a total of eight cases, hyperapobetalipoproteinemia was present in all patients.[91,98] The content of phytosterols in erythrocytes is increased, and the phytosterol/cholesterol ratio in the red blood cells is about the same as in serum.[91]

In a sitosterolemic patient fed shellfish sterols, high levels were obtained in plasma (13.1 mg/dl versus 1.9 mg/dl in normal subjects).[143]

Tissues. In phytosterolemia, the plant sterols and their 5α-stanols are deposited in virtually all tissues (except brain) in the same proportion as in plasma.[91,147] In the tendon xanthomas, phytosterols account for about 15 to 20 percent of the total sterols.[91,101,147] The rest is mainly cholesterol. In one lethal case,[101] a slightly higher concentration of sitosterol (relative to cholesterol) was found in xanthomas and thoracic aorta than in other tissues. The plant sterols deposited are less esterified than cholesterol.[101] Unlike in CTX, cholestanol is not deposited in the brain.[101]

Bile. The bile has been examined in some patients with phytosterolemia, and only C_{24} bile acids (cholic acid, chenodeoxycholic, and deoxycholic acid) have been found.[9,93,97] In one case, a relative deficiency of chenodeoxycholic acid (as in CTX) was reported.[97] Miettinen[93] found that, quantitatively, bile acid synthesis was normal or even higher than in the controls and that cholic acid constituted about 60 percent of the bile acids. In this patient, the total excretion of sterols in the bile (including phytosterols) was less than 50 percent of the controls. The bile was undersaturated with respect to cholesterol, and Miettinen pointed out that decreased biliary sterol excretion may be an important pathophysiological factor.[93] The relative proportions between phytosterols and cholesterol were the same in the bile as in LDL.[9,93] In contrast, it has been reported that the biliary secretion of sitosterol is preferential to cholesterol in normal individuals.[104] The biliary phospholipid output in phytosterolemia is normal.[93]

In a sitosterolemic subject fed shellfish sterols, a relative deficiency was found with respect to the ability to concentrate the shellfish sterols in bile.[143] Whereas normal controls concentrated the shellfish sterols about sixfold relative to the plasma concentration, the study subject was only able to concentrate them about twofold.

Feces. The bile acid excretion has been reported to be normal on the solid food diet, but the fecal neutral sterols were exceptionally low.[93] Fecal cholesterol was only 10 to 15 percent of normal in Miettinen's case. Salens group has described the fecal excretion of 26-nor-5β-cholestane-3α,7α,12α,24,25-pentol, 5β-cholestane-3α,7α,12α,24-tetrol, 5β-cholestane-3α,7α,12α,25-tetrol, 5β-cholestane-3α,7α,12α,24(*R*),25-pentol, and 5β-cholestane-3α,7α,12α,25,26-pentol in one patient.[148] The total amounts of bile alcohols were 1 mg/g of feces. In another patient, where stools were collected daily over a prolonged period, fecal bile alcohols were not present in significant amounts.[149]

Urine. In the patient described by Dayal et al., small amounts (about 2 mg/liter) of the 26-norpentol and the 25,26-pentol were also excreted in the urine.[148]

The Metabolic Defect(s)

The primary metabolic defect in phytosterolemia has not been identified. In the first study of this condition Bhattacharyya and Connor[91] found that their two patients with phytosterolemia absorbed increased amounts of orally administered sitosterol (24 to 28 percent versus normally <5 percent). Miettinen[93] found that his patient absorbed 19 percent of ingested plant sterols. Increased absorption of plant sterols as well as shellfish sterols[143] is thus a well documented feature of phytosterolemia, but the mechanism has not been clarified. Hypothetical reasons for the decreased specificity of intestinal sterol absorption would be disturbances of the solubilization of phytosterols in intestinal micelles, changed uptake by the mucosal cells, decreased sterol specificity of mucosal ACAT or pathologic changes of intracellular transport processes. Miettinen also showed, however, that the biliary excretion of sterols (where phytosterols accounted for one-third) in his patient was less than 20 percent of that of healthy controls.[93] The biliary and fecal excretion of bile acids was normal.[93] The undersaturation of the bile with respect to cholesterol would decrease the dilution of intestinal plant sterols. The deficient biliary excretion of cholesterol might thus increase the micellar solubilization of phytosterols in the intestine and thereby facilitate their absorption. This can however hardly be the primary cause of phytosterolemia. Compatible with the observation of low sterol excretion in phytosterolemia, Lin et al.[150] observed prolonged half-lives of injected [^{3}H]sitosterol and [^{14}C]cholesterol in one patient. Their results were also compatible with increased absorption of sitosterol.

Salen et al.[96,101,148] have discussed the possibility that bile acid formation might be impaired in phytosterolemia, since bile alcohols were detected in feces and urine in one case. This finding is not present in all patients,[149] and it may therefore be a secondary phenomenon. The 26-nor-5β-cholestane-3α,7α,12α,24,25-pentol and the other bile alcohols reported in one case of phytosterolemia have been demonstrated in patients with cholestasis or with other types of liver disease.[151–153.]

A striking feature of phytosterolemia is the increased incidence of coronary heart disease, particularly in male subjects.[93,97,98,101] The pathogenesis of the premature atherosclerosis in phytosterolemia is unexplained, but it may be related to the increased levels of serum phytosterols that may constitute up to 30 percent of total serum sterols.[91,93,147] Also in experimental animals, C_{29} sterols are retained in the liver to a higher extent than C_{27} sterols and accumulate in serum lipoproteins and lipoprotein receptor-rich organs.[100,125] This accumulation is probably due to the fact that the C_{29} sterols are poor precursors for bile acid biosynthesis.[136] The 5α-stanols present in serum of patients with phytosterolemia[94,96,97,100,146,147] are most probably formed in the liver via a Δ^4,3-ketonic intermediate.[100] Their relation to the development of premature atherosclerosis is unknown. Not only serum 5α-phytostanols but also cholestanol may be increased in phytosterolemia.[97,147] The mechanism of the hypercholestanolemia is probably widely different in CTX and phytosterolemia. In CTX, a hyperproduction of cholestanol is at least in part caused by the drainage of a small fraction of early bile acid intermediates into a pathway involving cholesta-4,6-dien-3-one as intermediate.[21] The analogous route for synthesis of 5α-phytostanols is probably almost inactive.[100] It has been suggested that the increased cholestanol levels in phytosterolemia could result from increased absorption because of the loss of the sterol recognition capacity in the gut.[154] The different mechanism for the hypercholestanolemia in phytosterolemia and CTX is also visualized by the effect of cholestyramine, which causes a decrease of serum cholestanol in phytosterolemia[9,94] but an increase in CTX.[23]

The xanthomas in phytosterolemia resemble those which develop in familial hypercholesterolemia, both with respect to localization and histologic features.[155] It is not known whether the increased concentrations of phytosterols in plasma contribute to their formation.[155]

Bouts of hemolysis have been reported in several patients with phytosterolemia.[23,93,97,100] The erythrocytes contain increased amounts of sitosterol in the same proportion as in plasma.[91] This may be the cause of the increased fragility of the red blood cells. However, the exchange of sitosterol between plasma and the erythrocytes is slower than that of cholesterol.[116,125]

Diagnosis

Phytosterolemia should be suspected in patients who develop xanthomas in early childhood, despite normal or only moderately elevated serum cholesterol. Some of the reported cases have for a period been misinterpreted as heterozygotes for familial hypercholesterolemia.

The diagnosis can easily be established by gas chromatographic examination of the plasma sterols (Fig. 51-13). Normally, the levels of sitosterol are less than 1 mg/dl,[147] but they may increase up to 9 mg/dl in normal infants fed vegetable oil-rich formulas.[156] In phytosterolemia, levels of 10 to 65 mg/dl have been reported. Increased levels of campesterol, stigmasterol, and 5α derivatives of plant sterols and cholestanol are also regularly present.[147]

For confirmation of the diagnosis, increased proportions of phytosterols should also be demonstrated in erythrocytes, or in a xanthoma.

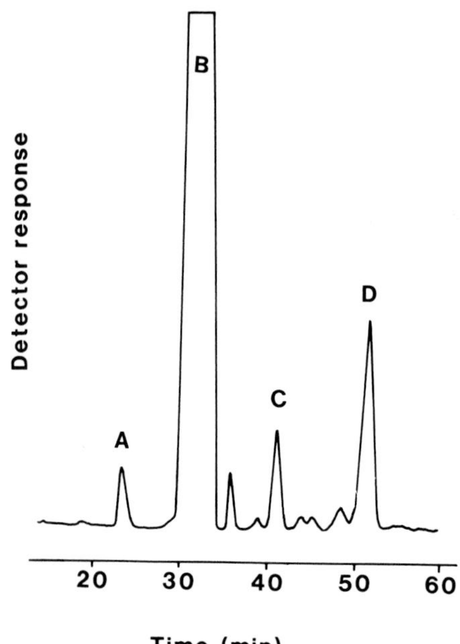

Fig. 51-13 Gas chromatogram of the plasma sterols of a subject (100) with sitosterolemia and xanthomatosis. A = epicoprostanol (internal standard); B = cholesterol; C = campesterol; D = sitosterol. The concentration of sitosterol in this sample was 9.2 mg per 100 ml (normally less than 1 mg per 100 ml).[147]

Treatment

Patients with phytosterolemia should be given a diet containing the lowest possible amount of plant sterols. When such a regimen is instituted, the plasma phytosterol levels decrease rapidly,[9,155] but full normalization is difficult to achieve.[93,100]

To compose a diet low in plant sterols, all sources of vegetable fats should be eliminated, and all plant foods with high contents of fat should be avoided. This means that the diet should not contain vegetable oils, shortening, or margarine, and that nuts, seeds, chocolate, olives, and avocados must be avoided. Only cereal products without the germ should be used. The diet may thus contain fruits and vegetables and refined cereal products (e.g., bread made without fat or with lard, rice, spaghetti, etc.). Food derived from animal sources with cholesterol as the dominating sterol is allowed, e.g., meat, butter, lard, cheese, eggs, and milk powder. Shellfish should, however, be avoided since they may contain the shellfish sterols referred to above. Compositions of suitable diets and sample menus were given in the previous edition of this text.[9]

Cholestyramine should be used in addition to diet, since this causes a significant reduction of serum phytosterols, cholesterol, and cholestanol.[94] During such treatment, bile acid biosynthesis and excretion is stimulated, and the output of fecal plant sterols increases.[93] As an alternative to cholestyramine therapy, treatment with neomycin has been suggested.[93] This drug is supposed to make the sterol balance even more negative.

Genetics

The reports of Bhattacharyya and Connor[91] and Kwiterovitch et al.[98] indicate that the disease is inherited by an autosomal recessive pattern. Kwiterovitch et al. suggested that in the homozygote state, phytosterolemia, xanthomas, and hyperbetalipoproteinemia are present.[98] In some individuals supposed to be heterozygotes there was hyperapobetalipoproteinemia without phytosterolemia, and in some family members only xanthomas were present. It has been speculated that there may be two different mutations.[98] From a detailed genetic investigation including determinations of serum phytosterols in 240 relatives to five siblings with phytosterolemia, Beaty et al. concluded that the phenotype of the disease is controlled by a rare autosomal recessive gene.[157] There was a significant familial correlation in plasma sitosterol levels that was attributed to a polygenic component under a mixed model but could also be due to shared environments such as diets.[157] More studies are needed to fully clarify the genetics of phytosterolemia.

We are most grateful to the following colleagues for unpublished material referred to in this review: Dr. B. J. Koopman, Dr. B. G. Wolthers, Dr. G. Salen, Dr. Y. Seyama, and Dr. J. Sjövall.

The cited work carried out in the author's laboratories has been supported by grants from the Swedish Medical Research Council (project 03X-3141) and from the Norwegian Council for Science and the Humanities (project 13.10.99-009).

REFERENCES

1. VAN BOGAERT L, SCHERER HJ, EPSTEIN E: *Une Forme cerebrale de la cholestérinose géneralisée.* Paris, Masson et Cie, 1937.
2. VAN BOGAERT L, SCHERER JH, FROELICH A, EPSTEIN E: Une deuxiéme observation de cholestérinose tendineuse symétrique avec symptomes cérébraux. *Ann Med* 42:69, 1937.
3. VAN BOGAERT L: Les Aspects neurologiques des cholestérinoses généralisées. *Prog Med (Paris)* 22:785, 1938.
4. EPSTEIN E, LORENZ K: Beitrag zur Pathologie und Pathochemie der cholesterinigen Lipidose vom Typus van Bogaert-Scherer. *Klin Wochenschr* 16:1320, 1937.
5. EPSTEIN E, KREITNER H: Beitrag zu einer vergleichenden Pathologie und Pathochemie der allgemeinen Cholesterinlipoidosen. *Virchows Arch (B)* 306:53, 1940.
6. MENKES J, SCHIMSHOCK JR, SWANSON PD: Cerebrotendinous xanthomatosis: The storage of cholestanol within the nervous system. *Arch Neurol* 19:47, 1968.
7. PHILIPPART M, VAN BOGAERT L: Cholestanolosis (cerebrotendinous xanthomatosis): A follow-up study on the original family. *Arch Neurol* 21:603, 1969.
8. SALEN G: Cholestanol deposition in cerebrotendinous xanthomatosis: A possible mechanism. *Ann Intern Med* 75:843, 1971.
9. BHATTACHARYYA AK, CONNOR WE: Familial diseases with storage of sterols other than cholesterol: Cerebrotendinous xanthomatosis, and β-sitosterolemia and xanthomatosis, in Stanburgy JB, Wyngaarden JB, Fredrickson DS (eds): *The Metabolic Basis of Inherited Diseases,* 3d ed. New York, McGraw-Hill, 1978, p 656.
10. FARPOUR H, MAHLOUDJI M: Familial cerebrotendinous xanthomatosis. *Arch Neurol* 32:223, 1975.
11. BERGNER V, KORCZYN AP, MAYERSDORF A: Cerebrotendinous xanthomatosis. *Harefuah* 92:537, 1977.
12. DE JONG JGY, VAN GENT CM, DELLMAN JW: Cerebrotendinous cholestanolosis in relation to other cerebral xanthomatosis. *Clin Neurol Neurosurg* 79:253, 1977.
13. BRASSEUR G, MARX P, LANGLOIS J, HOUDENT G: Cerebrotendinous xanthomatosis. *Bull Soc Ophtalmol Fr* 78:913, 1978.
14. SEYAMA Y, ICHIKAWA K, YAMAKAWA T: Quantitative determination of cholestanol in plasma with mass fragmentography. Biochemical diagnosis of cerebrotendinous xanthomatosis. *J Biochem* 80:223, 1976.
15. OHNISHI A, YAMASHITA Y, GOTO I, KUROIWA Y, MURAKAMI S, IKEDA M: De- and remyelination and onion bulb in cerebrotendinous xanthomatosis. *Acta Neuropathol* 45:43, 1979.
16. KURITZY A, BERGINER VM, KORCZYN AD: Peripheral neuropathy in cerebrotendinous xanthomatosis. *Neurology* 29:880, 1979.
17. SETOGUCHI T, SALEN G, TINT GS, MOSBACH EH: A biochemical abnormality in cerebrotendinous xanthomatosis: Impairment of bile acid biosynthesis associated with incomplete degradation of the cholesterol side chain. *J Clin Invest* 531:1395, 1974.
18. OFTEBRO H, BJÖRKHEM I, SKREDE S, SCHREINER A, PEDERSEN J: Cerebrotendinous xanthomatosis: A defect in mitochondrial 26-hydroxylase required for normal biosynthesis of cholic acid. *J Clin Invest* 65:1418, 1980.
19. BJÖRKHEM I, OFTEBRO H, SKREDE S, PEDERSEN JI: Assay of intermediates in bile acid biosynthesis using isotope dilution—mass spectrometry; hepatic levels in the normal state and in CTX. *J Lipid Res* 22:191, 1981.
20. BJÖRKHEM I, FAUSA O, HOPEN G, OFTEBRO H, PEDERSEN JI, SKREDE S: Role of the 26-hydroxylase in the biosynthesis of bile acids in the normal state and in CTX. An in vivo study. *J Clin Invest* 71:142, 1983.
21. SKREDE S, BJÖRKHEM I, BUCHMANN MS, HOPEN G, FAUSA S: A novel pathway for biosynthesis of cholestanol with 7α-hydroxysteroids as intermediates, and its importance for the accumulation of cholestanol in CTX. *J Clin Invest* 75:448, 1985.
22. SALEN G, MERIWETHER TW, NICOLAU G: Chenodeoxycholic acid inhibits increased cholesterol and cholestanol synthesis in patients with cerebrotendinous xanthomatosis. *Biochem Med* 14:57, 1975.
23. SALEN G, SHEFER S, BERGINER VM: Familial diseases with storage of sterols other than cholesterol: Cerebrotendinous xanthomatosis and sitosterolemia with xanthomatosis, in Stanbury JB, Wyngarden JB, Frederickson DS, Brown MS, Goldstein JL (eds): *The Metabolic Basis of Inherited Disease,* 5th ed. New York, McGraw-Hill, 1983, p 713.

23a. SALEN G: Personal communication, 1987.

24. KASAMA T, BYUN DS, SEYAMA Y: Quantitative analysis of sterols in serum by HPLC. Application to the biochemical analysis of CTX. *J Chromatogr* 400:241, 1987.

24a. BERGINER VM: Personal communication.

25. SKREDE S, STOKKE KT: Plasma esterification of cholestanol, normally and in CTX. *Scand J Clin Lab Invest* 33:97, 1974.
26. LEWIS B, MITCHELL WD, MARENAH CB, CORTESE C: Cerebrotendinous xanthomatosis: Biochemical response to inhibition of cholesterol synthesis. *Br Med J* 287:July 2, 21, 1983.
27. GIAMPALMO A: Über einen Fall von cholesterinlipidose vom Typus van Bogaert-Scherer. *Verh Dtsch Ges Pathol* 34:227, 1950.
28. VINDITTI D: Una rara Lipidosi di interesse ortopedico: Forma cerebrotendinea della cholesterinosi generalizzata. *Chir Organi Mov* 34:429, 1950.
29. BJÖRKHEM I, SKREDE S, BUCHMANN MS, EAST C, GRUNDY S: Accumulation of 7α-hydroxy-4-cholesten-3-one and cholesta-4,6-dien-3-one in patients with CTX. Effect of treatment with chenodeoxycholic acid. *Hepatology* 7:266, 1987.
30. SCHIMSCHOCK JR, ALVORD EC JR: Cerebrotendinous xanthomatosis: Clinical and pathological studies. *Arch Neurol* 18:688, 1968.
31. GIAMPALMO A: Les Lipoidoses cholesteriniques due système nerveaux. *Acta Neurol Belg* 54:786, 1954.

31a. LUSSIER-CACAN S, CANTIN M, ROY CC, SNIDERMANN AD, NESTRUCK AC, DAVIDNON I: Tendon xanthomas associated with cholestanolosis and hyperbetalipoproteinemia. *Clin Invest Med* 9:94, 1986.

32. SELAND JH, SLAGSVOLD JE: The ultrastructure of lens and iris in cerebrotendinous xanthomatosis. *Acta Ophthalmol* 55:201, 1977.
33. SALEN G, ZAKI FG, SABESIN S, BOEHME D, SHEFER S, MOSBACH EH: Intrahepatic pigment and crystal forms in patients with cerebrotendinous xanthomatosis (CTX). *Gastroenterology* 74:82, 1978.
34. SCHREINER A, HOPEN G, SKREDE S: Cerebrotendinous xanthomatosis (cholestanolosis): Investigations on two sisters and their family. *Acta Neurol Scand* 51:405, 1975.
35. SHORE V, SALEN G, CHENG FW, FORTE T, SHEFER S, TINT GS, LINGREN F: Abnormal high density lipoproteins in cerebrotendinous xanthomatosis. *J Clin Invest* 68:1295, 1981.
36. KOOPMAN BJ, WOLTHERS BG, MOLEN JC, NAGEL GT, WATERREUS RJ, OOSTERHUIS HJGH: Capillary gas chromatographic determinations of urinary bile acids and bile alcohols in CTX patients proving the ineffectivity of ursodeoxycholic acid treatment. *Clin Chim Acta* 142:103, 1984.
37. KOOPMAN BJ, MOLEN JC, WOLTHERS BG: Determination of some hydroxycholesterols in human serum samples. *J Chromatogr* 416, 1987.

37a. BEPPU T, SEYAMA Y, KASAMA T, SERIZAWA S, YAMAKAWA T: Serum bile acid profiles in CTX. *Clin Chim Acta* 118:167, 1982.

37b. BATTA A, SALEN B, SHEFER S, TINT S, BATTA M: Increased plasma bile alcohol glucuronides in patients with CTX: effect of chenodeoxycholic acid. *J Lipid Res,* 28:1006, 1987.

38. SALEN G, TINT S, SHEFER S: Increased cerebrospinal fluid cholestanol and apolipoprotein B concentrations in CTX: Effect of chenodeoxycholic acid. Abstract IX, International Bile Acid Meeting, Basel, 1986, p 59.

38a. LINDQVIST A, MIDTVEDT T, SKREDE S, SJÖVALL J: Effect of bile alcohols on the microbial 7α-dehydroxylation of chenodeoxycholic acid. In manuscript, 1987.

39. ELLIOT WH: Allo-bile acids, in Nair PP, Kritchevsky D (eds): *The Bile*

Acids: Chemistry, Physiology and Metabolism. New York, Plenum, 1971, p 47.

40. SHEFER S, DAYAL B, TINT GS, SALEN G, MOSBACH EH: Identification of pentahydroxy bile alcohols in cerebrotendinous xanthomatosis: Characterization of 5β-cholestane-3α,7α,12α,24,25-pentol and 5βcholestane 3α,7α,12α,23,25-pentol. *J Lipid Res* 16:280, 1975.

41. DAYAL B, SALEN G, TINT GS, TOOME V, MOSBACH EH: Absolute configuration of pentahydroxy bile alcohols excreted by patients with cerebrotendinous xanthomatosis. A circular dichroism study. *J Lipid Res* 19:187, 1978.

42. HOSHITA T, YASUHARA M, KIHIRA K, KURAMOTO T: Identification of (23S)-5β-cholestane-3α,7α,12α,23,25-pentol excreted by patients with cerebrotendinous xanthomasosis. *Steroids* 27:657, 1976.

43. DAYAL B, TINT GS, SHEFER S, SALEN G: Configurational assignment of 5β-cholestane-3α,7α,12α,23,25-pentol excreted by patients with cerebrotendinous xanthomatosis (a circular dichroism study). *Steroids* 33:327, 1979.

44. HOSHITA T, YASUHARA M, UNE M, KIBE A, ITOGA E, KITO S, KURAMOTO T: Occurrence of bile alcohol glucuronides in bile of patients with cerebrotendinous xanthomatosis. *J Lipid Res* 21:1015, 1980.

44a. KARLAGANIS G, KARLAGANIS V, SJÖVALL J: Bile alcohol glucuronides in urine: Secondary metabolites of intermediates in the formation of bile acids from cholesterol? in Paumgartner G, Stiehl A, Gerok W (eds): *Bile Acids and Cholesterol in Health and Disease*. Falk-Symposium 33, Basel, MTP Press, 1983, p 119.

45. WOLTHERS BG, VOLMER M, MOLEN J, KOOPMAN BJ, JAGER AEJ, WATTERREVS RJ: Diagnosis of CTX and effect of chenodeoxycholic acid therapy by analysis of urine using capillary gas chromatography. *Clin Chim Acta* 131:53, 1983.

46. BATTA AK, SHEFER S, BATTA M, SALEN G: Effect of chenodeoxycholic acid on biliary and urinary bile acids and bile alcohols in CTX; monitoring by high performance liquid chromatography. *J Lipid Res* 26:690, 1985.

47. KOOPMAN BJ, WOLTHERS BJ, MOLEN JC, NAGEL GT, RUTGERS H, STRIJTVEEN B, KAPTEIN B: Increased 23R-hydroxylase activity in patients suffering from CTX, resulting in 23R-hydroxylation of bile acids. *Biochim Biophys Acta* 883:585, 1986.

48. BJÖRKHEM I: Mechanism of bile acid biosynthesis in mammalian liver, in Danielsson H, Sjövall J (eds): *Comprehensive Biochemistry, Sterol and Bile Acids*. Amsterdam, Elsevier, 1985, p 217.

49. BJÖRKHEM I, KASE F, PEDERSEN JI: Role of peroxisomes in the biosynthesis of bile acids. *Scand J Clin Lab Invest* 45 (*suppl*)177:23, 1985.

50. SHEFER S, CHENG FW, DAYAL B, HAUSER S, TINT GS, SALEN G, MOSBACH EH: A 25-hydroxylation pathway of cholic acid biosynthesis in man and rat. *J Clin Invest* 57:897, 1976.

51. CHENG FW, SHEFER S, DAYAL B, TINT GS, SETOGUCHI T, SALEN G, MOSBACH EH: Cholic acid biosynthesis: Conversion of 5β-cholestane-3α,7α,12α,25-tetrol into 5β-cholestane-3α,7α,12α,24S,25-pentol by human and rat liver microsomes. *J Lipid Res* 18:6, 1977.

52. CRONHOLM T, JOHANSSON G: Oxidation of 5β-cholestane-3α,7α,12α,-triol by rat liver microsomes. *Eur J Biochem* 16:373, 1970.

53. HANSON RF, STAPLES AB, WILLIAMS GC: Metabolism of 5β-cholestane-3α,7α,12α,26-tetrol and 5β-cholestane-3α,7α,12α,25-tetrol into cholic acid in normal subjects. *J Lipid Res* 20:489, 1979.

54. BJÖRKHEM I, GUSTAFSSON J, JOHANSSON G, PERSSON B: Biosynthesis of bile acids in man: Hydroxylation of the C_{27}-steroid side chain. *J Clin Invest* 55:178, 1975.

55. SALEN G, POLITO A: Biosynthesis of 5α-cholestan-3β-ol in cerebrotendinous xanthomatosis. *J Clin Invest* 51:134, 1972.

56. BJÖRKHEM I, KARLMAR KE: Biosynthesis of cholestanol: Conversion of cholesterol into 4-cholesten-3-one by rat liver microsomes. *Biochim Biophys Acta* 337:129, 1974.

57. SHEFER S, MILCH S, MOSBACH EH: Biosynthesis of 5α-cholestan-3β-ol in the rabbit and guinea pig. *J Biol Chem* 239:1731, 1964.

58. SHEFER S, MILCH S, MOSBACH EH: Biosynthesis of 5α-cholestan-3β-ol in rat and guinea pig liver in vitro. *J Lipid Res* 6:33, 1965.

59. SHEFER S, HAUSER S, MOSBACH EH: Biosynthesis of cholestanol: 5α-cholestan-3-one reductase of rat liver. *J Lipid Res* 7:763, 1966.

60. SALEN G, SHEFER S, TINT GS: Transformation of 4-cholesten-3-one and 7α-hydroxy-4-cholesten-3-one into cholestanol and bile acids in CTX. *Gastroenterology* 87:276, 1984.

61. SKREDE S, BJÖRKHEM I: Biosynthesis of cholestanol from intestinal 7α-hydroxy-4-cholesten-3-one. *J Biol Chem* 257:8363, 1982.

62. SKREDE S, BJÖRKHEM I: A novel route for the biosynthesis of cholestanol, and its significance for the pathogenesis of CTX. *Scand J Clin Lab Invest* 45:(*suppl*)177, 1985, p 15.

63. BUCHMANN MS, BJÖRKHEM I, LUND AM, SKREDE S: On the mechanism of biosynthesis of cholestanol from 7α-hydroxycholesterol. *Scand J Clin Lab Invest* 46:(*suppl*)184, 1986, p 41.

64. SKREDE S, BJÖRKHEM I, BUCHMANN MS, MIDTVEDT T: Biosynthesis of cholestanol from bile acid intermediates in the rabbit and the rat. *J Biol Chem* 260:77, 1985.

65. SALEN G, GRUNDY SM: The metabolism of cholestanol, cholesterol, and bile acids in cerebrotendinous xanthomatosis. *J Clin Invest* 52:2822, 1973.

65a. SJÖVALL J, SETCHELL KDR, LAWSON A, KARLAGANIS G, SKREDE S: Excretion of bile alcohols in feces and urine of two patients with CTX. In manuscript, 1987.

66. BJÖRKHEM I, GUSTAFSSON J: On the conversion of cholesterol into allocholic acid in rat liver. *Eur J Biochem* 18:207, 1971.

67. TINT GS, SALEN G: Synthesis of cholesterol and its precursors but not cholestanol in cultured fibroblasts from patients with cerebrotendinous xanthomatosis. *J Lipid Res* 23:597, 1982.

68. BARRON JL: Cerebrotendinous xantomathosis. *N Engl J Med* 313:455, 1985.

69. JAVITT NB, KOK E, COHEN B, BURSTEIN S: Cerebrotendinous xanthomatosis, reduced serum 26-hydroxycholesterol. *J Lipid Res* 23:627, 1982.

70. PEDERSEN JI, BJÖRKHEM I, GUSTAFSSON J: 26-hydroxylation by soluble liver mitochondrial cytochrome P-450. *J Biol Chem* 254:6464, 1979.

71. ANDERSSON S, BOSTRÖM H, DANIELSSON H, WIKVALL K: Purification from rabbit and rat liver of cytochromes P-450 involved in bile acid biosynthesis. *Methods Enzymol* 3:364, 1985.

72. SKREDE S, BJÖRKHEM I, KVITTINGEN EA, BUCHMANN MS, LIE S, EAST C, GRUNDY S: Demonstration of 26-hydroxylation of C_{27}-steroids in human skin fibroblasts, and a deficiency of this activity in CTX. *J Clin Invest* 78:729, 1986.

73. SKREDE S, BJÖRKHEM I, KVITTINGEN EA, BUCHMANN MS, EAST C, GRUNDY S: Further evidence that the C_{27}-steroid 26-hydroxylase gene is the site of the primary defect in cerebrotendinous xanthomatosis. *Scand J Clin Lab Invest*, in press, 1988.

74. MIKI H, TAKEUCHI H, YAMADA A, NISHIOKA M, MATSUZAWA Y, HAMAMOTO I, HIWATASHI A, ICHIKAWA Y: Quantitative analysis of the mitochondrial cytochrome P-450 linked monooxygenase system: NADPH-hepatoredoxin reductase, hepatoredoxin, and cytochrome P-450_{S27} in livers of patients with CTX. *Clin Chim Acta* 160:255, 1986.

75. SALEN G, SHEFER S, TINT GS, NICOLAV G, DAYAL B, BATTA AK: Biosynthesis of bile acids in CTX. Relationship of bile acid pool sizes and synthesis rates to hydroxylations at C-12, C-25 and C-26. *J Clin Invest* 76:744, 1985.

76. OFTEBRO H, BJÖRKHEM I, STORMER FC, PEDERSEN JI: CTX: defective liver mitochondrial hydroxylation of chenodeoxycholic acid precursors. *J Lipid Res* 22:632, 1981.

77. GUSTAFSSON J: Bile acid synthesis during development. Mitochondrial 12α-hydroxylation in human fetal liver. *J Clin Invest* 75:604, 1985.

78. SALEN G, SHEFER S, CHENG FW, DAYAL B, BATTA AK, TINT GS: Cholic acid biosynthesis: The enzymatic defect in cerebrotendinous xanthomatosis. *J Clin Invest* 63:38, 1979.

79. NICOLAU G, SHEFER S, SALEN G, MOSBACH EH: Determination of hepatic cholesterol 7α-hydroxylase activity in man. *J Lipid Res* 15:146, 1974.

80. EINARSSON K, ANGELIN B, EWERTH S, NILSELL K, BJÖRKHEM I: Bile acid synthesis in man: Assay of hepatic microsomal cholesterol 7α-hydroxylase activity by isotope dilution—mass spectrometry. *J Lipid Res* 27:82, 1986.

81. KOOPMAN BJ, MOLEN JC, WOLTHERS BJ, JAGER AEJ, WATERREUS RJ, GIPS CH: Capillary gas chromatographic determination of cholestanol/cholesterol ratio in biological fluids. Its potential usefulness for the follow up of some liver diseases and its lack of specificity in diagnosing CTX. *Clin Chim Acta* 137:305, 1984.

82. SKREDE S, BJÖRKHEM I, BUCHMANN MS, FAUSA O: Studies on the mechanism of the increased biosynthesis of cholestanol in CTX: The activity of Δ^5-3β-hydroxysteroid dehydrogenase. *Scand J Gastroenterol* 20:1262, 1985.

83. BJÖRKHEM I: Effects of mevinolin in rat liver: Evidence for a lack of coupling between synthesis of hydroxymethylglutaryl-CoA reductase and cholesterol 7α-hydroxylase activity. *Biochem Biophys Acta* 877:43, 1986.

84. SHEFER S, HAUSER S, SALEN G, ZAKI FG, BULLOCK J, SALGADO E, SHEVITZ J: Comparative effects of cholestanol and cholesterol on hepatic sterol and bile acid metabolism in the rat. *J Clin Invest* 74:1773, 1984.

85. BUCHMANN MS, CLAUSEN OP: Effects of cholestanol feeding and cholestyramine treatment on the tissue sterols in the rabbit. *Lipids* 21:738, 1986.

86. BUCHMANN MS, BJÖRKHEM I, SKREDE S: Metabolism of the cholesterol precursor cholesta-4,6-dien-3-one in different tissues. *Biochim Biophys Acta* 922:111, 1987.

86a. SEYAMA Y, ICHIKAWA K, YAMAKAWA T: Quantitative determination of cholestanol in plasma with mass fragmentography. Biochemical diagnosis of CTX. *J Biochem (Tokyo)* 80:223, 1976.

87. KOOPMAN BJ, MOLEN JC, WOLTHERS BG, WATERREUS RJ: Screening for

CTX by using an enzymatic assay for 7α-hydroxylated steroids in urine. *Clin Chem* 33:142, 1987.

87a. EGESTAD B, PETTERSON P, SKREDE S: Fast atomic bombardment in the diagnosis of CTX. *Scand J Clin Lab Invest* 45:443, 1985.

88. KOOPMAN BJ, WATERREUS RJ, BREKEL HWC, WOLTHERS BG: Detection of carriers of CTX. *Clin Chim Acta* 158:179, 1986.

89. BERGINER VM, SALEN G, SHEFER S: Long-term treatment of CTX with chenodeoxycholic acid. *N Engl J Med* 26:1649, 1984.

90. BHATTACHARYYA AK, CONNOR WE: β-Sitosterolemia and xanthomatosis. A newly described lipid storage disease in two sisters. *J Clin Invest* 52:9a, 1973.

91. BHATTACHARYYA AK, CONNOR WE: β-Sitosterolemia and xanthomatosis. A newly described lipid storage disease in two sisters. *J Clin Invest* 53:1033, 1974.

92. SHULMAN RS, BHATTACHARYYA AK, CONNOR WE, FREDERICKSON DS: β-Sitosterolemia and xanthomatosis. *N Engl J Med* 294:482, 1976.

93. MIETTINEN TA: Phytosterolemia, xanthomatosis and premature atherosclerotic arterial disease: A case with high plant sterol absorption, impaired sterol elimination and low cholesterol synthesis. *Eur J Clin Invest* 10:27, 1980.

94. WHITINGTON GL, RAGLAND JB, SABESIN SM, KUIKEN LB: Neutral sterolemia and xanthoma. *Circulation* 60:(II)33, 1979.

95. KOTTKE BA, CORNICELLI JA, DIDISHEIM P, KAZMIER FJ, BARHAM SS, WEIDMAN WH: Phytosterolemia, xanthomatosis and acquired aortic valve stenosis. *Circulation* 62:(2)24, 1980.

96. KHACHADURIAN AK, SALEN G: Familial phytosterolemia: cholestanolemia and abnormal bile salt composition. *Clin Res* 28(3):397A, 1980.

97. WANG C, LIN HJ, CHAN TK, SALEN G, CHAN WC, TSE TF: A unique patient with coexisting cerebrotendinous xanthomatosis and β-sitosterolemia. *Am J Med* 71:313, 1981.

98. KWITEROVITCH PO, BACHORIK PS, SMITH HH, MCKUSICK VA, CONNOR WE, RENG B, SNIDERMAN AD: Hyperapobetalipoproteinemia in two families with xanthomas and phytosterolemia. *Lancet* 1:466, 1981.

99. MATSUO I, YOSHINO K, OZAWA A, OHKIDO M: Phytosterolemia and type IIa hyperlipoproteinemia with tuberous xanthomas. *J Am Acad Dermatol* 4:47, 1981.

100. SKREDE B, BJÖRKHEM I, BERGESEN O, KAYDEN HJ, SKREDE S: The presence of 5α-sitostanol in the serum of a patient with phytosterolemia, and its biosynthesis from plant steroids in rats with bile fistula. *Biochim Biophys Acta* 836:368, 1985.

101. SALEN G, HORAK I, ROTHKOPF M, COHEN JL, SPECK J, TINT GS, SHORE V, DAYAL B, CHEN T, SHEFER S: Lethal atherosclerosis associated with abnormal plasma and tissue sterol composition in sitosterolemia with xanthomatosis. *J Lipid Res* 26:1126, 1985.

102. MCARTHUR RG, ROUCARI DAK, LITTLE JA, KUKSIS A, MYHER JJ, MARAI L: Phytosterolemia and hypercholesterolemia in childhood. *J Pediatr* 108:254, 1986.

103. NICHOLAS JH: The biogenesis of terpenes in plants, in Bernfeld P (ed): *Biogenesis of Natural Compound,* 2d ed. New York, Pergamon, 1967, chap 14, p 829.

104. SALEN G, AHRENS EH JR, GRUNDY SM: Metabolism of β-sitosterol in man. *J Clin Invest* 49:952, 1970.

105. CONNOR WE: Dietary sterols: Their relationship to atherosclerosis. *J Am Diet Assoc* 52:202, 1968.

106. GOULD RG: Absorbability of beta-sitosterol. *Trans NY Acad Sci* 18:129, 1955.

107. GOULD RG, JONES RJ, LEROY GV, WISSLER RW, TAYLOR CB: Absorbability of β-sitosterol in humans. *Metabolism* 18:652, 1969.

108. SYLVEN C, BORGSTRÖM B: Absorption and lymphatic transport of cholesterol and sitosterol in the rat. *J Lipid Res* 10:179, 1969.

109. VAHOUNY GV, CONNOR WE, SUBRAMANIAN S, LIN DS, GALLO LL: Comparative lymphatic absorption of sitosterol, stigmasterol, and fucosterol and differential inhibition of cholesterol absorption. *Am J Clin Nutr* 37:805, 1983.

110. KUKSIS A, HUANG TC: Differential absorption of plant sterols in the dog. *Can J Biochem Physiol* 40:1493, 1962.

111. SUBIAH MTR, KOTTKE BA, CARLO IA: Experimental studies in the spontaneous-atherosclerosis-susceptible white Carneau pigeon: Nature of biliary and fecal neutral steroids. *Mayo Clin Proc* 45:729, 1970.

112. SUBBIAH MTR, KOTTKE BA, CARLO IA, NAYTON MC: Human intestinal specificity toward dietary sterols studied by balance methods. *Nutr Metabol* 18:23, 1975.

113. WILKINS TD, HACKMAN AS: Two patterns of neutral steroid conversion in the feces of normal North Americans. *Cancer Res* 34:2250, 1974.

114. GRUNDY SM, AHRENS EH, SALEN G: Dietary β-sitosterol as an internal standard to correct for cholesterol losses in sterol balance studies. *J Lipid Res* 9:374, 1968.

115. FIELD FJ, MATHUR SN: β-Sitosterol: Esterification by intestinal acylcoenzyme A: Cholesterol acyl-transferase (ACAT) and its effect on cholesterol esterification. *J Lipid Res* 24:409, 1983.

116. SLOTA T, KOZLOV NA, AMMON HV: Comparison of cholesterol and β-sitosterol: Effects on jejunal fluid secretion induced by oleate, and absorption from mixed micellar solutions. *Gut* 24:653, 1983.

117. CHILD P, KUSKIS A: Uptake of 7-dehydro derivatives of cholesterol, campesterol, and β-sitosterol by rat erythrocytes, jejunal villus cells, and brush border membrane. *J Lipid Res* 24:552, 1983.

118. BEST MM, DUNCAN CH, VAN LOON EH, WATHEN JD: The effects of sitosterol on serum lipids. *Am J med* 19:61, 1955.

119. SUGANO M, MORIOKA H, IKEDA I: A comparison of hypocholesterolemic activity of β-sitosterol and β-sitostanol in rats. *J Nutr* 107:2011, 1977.

120. MATTSON FH, GRUNDY SM, CROUSE JR: Optimizing the effect of plant sterols on cholesterol absorption in man. *Am J Clin Nutr* 35:697, 1982.

121. DUNHAM LW, FOTNER RE, MOORE RD, CULP HW, RICE CN: Comparative lymphatic absorption of β-sitosterol and cholesterol by the rat. *Arch Biochem Biophys* 82:50, 1959.

122. NORDBY G, NORUM KR: Substrate specificity of lecithin: Cholesterol acyltransferase. Esterification of desmosterol, β-sitosterol and cholecalciferol in human plasma. *Scand J Clin Lab Invest* 35:677, 1975.

123. SUGANO M, MORIOKA H, KIDA Y, IKEDA I: The distribution of dietary plant sterols in serum lipoproteins and liver subcellular fractions of rats. *Lipids* 13:427, 1978.

124. SUBBIAH MTR, KUKSIS A: Differences in metabolism of cholesterol and sitosterol following intravenous injection in rats. *Biochim Biophys Acta* 306:95, 1973.

125. BOBERG KM, SKREDE B, SKREDES S: Metabolism of 24-ethyl-4-cholesten-3-one and 24-ethyl-5-cholesten-3β-ol (sitosterol) after intraperitoneal injection in the rat. *Scand J Clin Lab Invest Suppl* 184:46, 1986.

126. WERBIN H, CHAIKOFF IL, JONES EE: The metabolism of H^3-β-sitosterol in the guinea pig: Its conversion to urinary cortisol. *J Biol Chem* 235:1629, 1960.

127. MIETTINEN TA: Cholestanol and plant sterols in the adrenal gland of the rat. *Acta Chem Scand* 21:286, 1967.

128. ARINGER L, ENEROTH P, NORDSTRÖM L: Side-chain cleavage of 4-cholesten-3-one, 5-cholesten-3α-ol, β-sitosterol, and related steroids in endocrine tissues from rat and man. *J Steroid Biochem* 11:1271, 1979.

129. FISHLER-MATES Z, BUDOWSKI P, PINSKY A: Effect of soy sterols on cholesterol synthesis in the rat. *Lipids* 8:40, 1973.

130. RAICHT RF, COHEN BI, SHEFER S, MOSBACH EH: Sterol balance studies in the rat. Effects of dietary cholesterol and β-sitosterol on sterol balance and rate-limiting enzymes of sterol metabolism. *Biochim Biophys Acta* 388:374, 1975.

131. GRUNDY SM, AHRENS EH JR, DAVIGNON J: The interaction of cholesterol absorption and cholesterol synthesis in man. *J Lipid Res* 10:304, 1969.

132. KONLANDE JE, FISHER H: Evidence for a nonabsorptive antihypercholesterolemic action of phytosterols in the chicken. *J Nutr* 98:435, 1969.

133. BHATTACHARYYA AK, LOPEZ LA: Absorbability of plant sterols and their distribution in rabbit tissues. *Biochim Biophys Acta* 574:146, 1979.

134. BOBERG KM, SKREDE S, BJÖRKHEM I: Unpublished results.

135. BHATTACHARYYA AK, CONNOR WE, LIN DS: The origin of plant sterols in the skin surface lipids in humans: From diet to plasma to skin. *J Invest Dermatol* 80:294, 1983.

136. ARINGER L, ENEROTH P: Studies on the formation of C_7-oxygenated cholesterol and β-sitosterol metabolites in cell-free preparations of rat liver. *J Lipid Res* 14:563, 1973.

137. ARINGER L: Studies on the metabolism of cholesterol, β-sitosterol, and related steroids in rat liver subcellular fractions. Thesis. Stockholm, 1975.

138. NORDSTRÖM L: Studies on mitochondrial metabolism of cholesterol and related steroids in liver and endocrine tissue in vitro. Thesis, Stockholm, 1978.

139. SUBBIAH MT, KUKSIS A: Oxidation of 4-^{14}C-β-sitosterol by mitochondria of rat liver and testes. *Fed Proc* 28:515, 1969.

140. SUBBIAH MTR, KUKSIS A, MOOKHERJEA S: Secretion of bile salts by intact and isolated rat liver. *Can J Biochem* 47:847, 1969.

141. SUBBIAH MTR, KUKSIS A: Metabolism of β-sitosterol-4-^{14}C in the rat liver. *Proc Can Fed Biol Soc* 12:69, 1969.

142. KRITCHEVSKY D, DAVIDSON LM, MOSBACH EH, COHEN BI: Identification of acidic steroids in feces of monkeys fed β-sitosterol. *Lipids* 16:77, 1981.

143. GREGG RE, CONNOR WE, LIN DS, BREWER HB: Abnormal metabolism of shellfish sterols in a patient with sitosterolemia and xanthomatosis. *J Clin Invest* 77:1864, 1986.

144. CONNOR WE, LIN DS: Absorption and transport of shellfish sterols in human subjects. *Gastroenterology* 81:276, 1981.

145. LIN DS, DONNOR WE, PHILLIPSON BE: Sterol composition of normal human bile. Effects of feeding shellfish (marine) sterols. *Gastroenterology* 86:611, 1984.

146. DAYAL B, TINT GS, BATHA AK, SPECK J, KHACHADURIAN AK, SHEFER S, SALEN G: Identification of 5α-stanols in patients with sitosterolemia and xanthomatosis: Stereochemistry of the protonolysis of steroidal organoboranes. *Steroids* 40:233, 1982.

147. SALEN G, KWITEROVITCH PO, SHEFER S, TINT GS, HORAK I, SHORE V, DAYAL B, HORAK E: Increased plasma cholestanol and 5α-saturated plant sterol derivatives in subjects with sitosterolemia and xanthomatosis. *J Lipid Res* 26:203, 1985.

148. DAYAL B, TINT GS, TOOME V, BATHA AK, SHEFER S, SALEN G: Synthesis and structure of 26- (or 27)-nor-5β-cholestane-3α,7α,12α,24S,25-pentol isolated from the urine and feces of a patient with sitosterolemia and xanthomatosis. *J Lipid Res* 26:298, 1985.

149. SETCHELL KDR, IVES JA, LAWSON AM, KAYDEN JH: Fecal bile acid and sterol excretion in a case of phytosterolemia. Falk-Symposium 42, VIII International Bile Acid Meeting, Berne, p 84.

150. LIN HJ, WANG C, SALEN G, LAN KC, CHAN TK: Sitosterol and cholesterol metabolism in a patient with sitosterolemia and xanthomatosis. *Metabolism* 32:126, 1983.

151. KARLAGANIS G, ALME B, KARLAGANIS V, SJÖVALL J: Bile alcohol glucuronides in urine. Identification of 27-nor-5β-cholestane-3α,7α,12α,24,25-pentol in man. *J Steroid Biochem* 14:341, 1981.

152. KARLAGANIS G, NEMETH A, HAMMARSKJÖLD B, STRANDVIK B, SJÖVALL J: Urinary excretion of bile alcohols in normal children and patients with α_1-antitrypsin deficiency during development of liver disease. *Eur J Clin Invest* 12:399, 1982.

153. LUDWIG-KOHN H, HEMMING HV, SZIEDAL A, MATTHAI D, SPITELLER G: The identification of urinary bile alcohols by gas chromatography–mass spectrometry in patients with liver disease and in healthy individuals. *Eur J Clin Invest* 13:91, 1983.

154. BHATTACHARYYA AK: The pathogenesis of xanthomata: The role of sterols. *Artery* 2:2, 1976.

155. MELLIES M, GLUECK CJ, SWEENEY C, FALLAT RW, TSANG RC, ISHIKAWA TT: Plasma and dietary phytosterols in children. *Pediatrics* 57:60, 1976.

156. GREGG RE, BREWER JR HB, LIN DS: β-Sitosterolemia, the loss of specificty at an important sterol recognition site. *Clin Res* 30:282A, 1982.

157. BEATY TH, KWITEROVICH PO, KHOURY MJ, WHITE S, BACHORIK PS, SMITH HH, TENG B, SNIDERMAN A: Genetic analysis of plasma sitosterol, apoprotein B, and lipoproteins in a large Amish pedigree with sitosterolemia. *Am J Hum Genet* 38:492, 1986.

PART 8

PORPHYRINS AND HEME

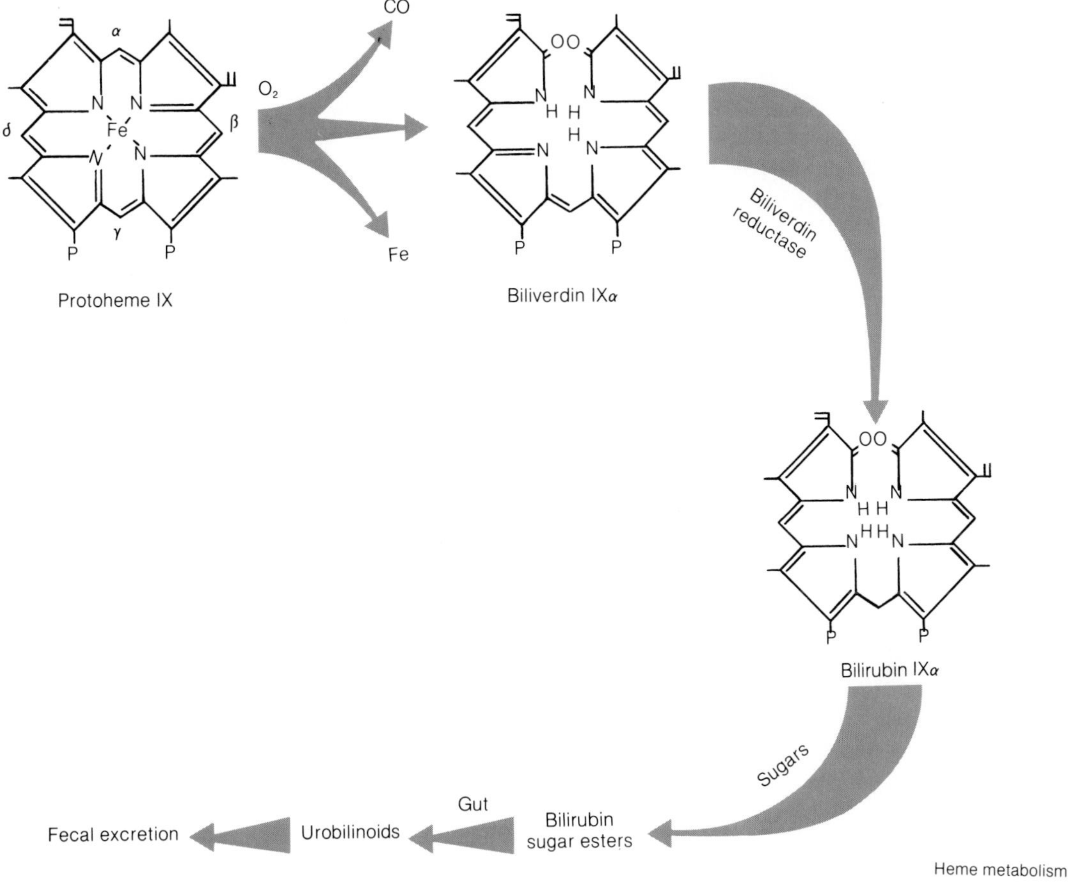

Heme metabolism

CHAPTER **52**

THE PORPHYRIAS

ATTALLAH KAPPAS
SHIGERU SASSA
RICHARD A. GALBRAITH
YVES NORDMANN

1. *The porphyrias are inherited and acquired disorders in which the activities of the enzymes of the heme biosynthetic pathway are partially deficient. Porphyrias are classified as either hepatic or erythroid, depending on the principal site of expression of the specific enzymatic defect in each disorder. There are eight enzymes involved in the synthesis of heme, and, with the exception of the first enzyme, an enzymatic defect at each step of heme synthesis accompanies each form of porphyria (Table 52-1). In this chapter, each disease is described according to the order of the enzymes in the heme biosynthetic sequence.*
2. *δ-Aminolevulinic acid dehydratase deficiency porphyria (ALADP) is inherited in an autosomal recessive fashion and is characterized by a marked deficiency of δ-aminolevulinic acid dehydratase (ALA dehydratase). It is the least frequent form of porphyria; only three cases have been reported. Symptoms are neurologic without skin photosensitivity.*
3. *Acute intermittent porphyria (AIP) is the most common autosomal dominant form of acute hepatic porphyria. Symptomatic and asymptomatic heterozygotes for this defect have 50% deficiency of porphobilinogen deaminase (PBG deaminase) activity. Approximately 90% of individuals who inherit PBG deaminase deficiency remain clinically unaffected throughout their lives. Patients with acute intermittent porphyria present with neurologic symptoms but lack cutaneous photosensitivity. Acute intermittent porphyria is latent before puberty, and symptoms are more frequent in females than in males. Hormonal, drug, and nutritional factors may aggravate the disease, probably by inducing hepatic δ-aminolevulinic acid synthase (ALA synthase). Clinical management includes a high carbohydrate intake, intravenous glucose or hematin, and prevention of exposure to harmful drugs.*
4. *Congenital erythropoietic porphyria (CEP) is inherited in an autosomal recessive fashion and is characterized by marked skin photosensitivity. The genetic defect in this disorder is a deficiency of uroporphyrinogen III cosynthase (URO cosynthase), which usually manifests at birth. Patients with congenital erythropoietic porphyria usually have hemolysis, which may serve as a further stimulus for increased porphyrin production in the bone marrow. Hemolysis may improve after splenectomy. The management of congenital erythropoietic porphyria includes avoidance of sunlight and treatment of secondary skin infections.*
5. *Porphyria cutanea tarda (PCT) is the most common form of porphyria and usually begins in middle or late adult life. A deficiency of hepatic uroporphyrinogen decarboxylase (URO decarboxylase) activity appears to characterize all forms of porphyria cutanea tarda. A subset of patients has a genetic form of the disease, and the heterozygous enzyme deficiency can be demonstrated in extrahepatic tissues as well as in the liver. Patients with porphyria cutanea tarda have mild to severe photosensitivity and often have overt liver disease. Alcohol, estrogens, and hepatic siderosis are common aggravating factors. Porphyria cutanea tarda can be successfully treated by avoidance of alcohol and estrogens and by phlebotomy, which reduces hepatic iron stores. Homozygous deficiency of uroporphyrinogen decarboxylase is known as hepatoerythropoietic porphyria (HEP) and is characterized by severe photosensitivity without frank liver involvement.*
6. *Hereditary coproporphyria (HCP) is similar to but generally milder than acute intermittent porphyria, but patients who have it may display skin photosensitivity in addition to neurologic symptoms. The underlying genetic defect in hereditary coproporphyria is the autosomal dominant inheritance of a 50 percent deficiency of coproporphyrinogen oxidase (COPRO oxidase). Clinical expression of hereditary coproporphyria is dependent on the same metabolic and chemical factors that influence expression of the gene defect in acute intermittent porphyria, and clinical management of the two conditions is identical.*
7. *Variegate porphyria (VP) has been recognized in many populations, but is most common in South African whites. The underlying defect involves a mutation resulting in a 50 percent deficiency of protoporphyrinogen oxidase (PROTO oxidase) activity. Since the disease is expressed in the heterozygote, inheritance is autosomal dominant. The clinical expression in the heterozygote, the symptoms, and the management are identical to those of acute intermittent prophyria. Additionally, photosensitivity due to the accumulation of porphyrins in the skin is more common than in hereditary coproporphyria.*

Nonstandard abbreviations used in this chapter are: AIA = 2-allyl-2-isopropylacetamide; AIP = acute intermittent porphyria; ALA = δ-aminolevulinic acid; ALAD = δ-aminolevulinic acid dehydratase; ALADP = δ-aminolevulinic acid dehydratase deficiency porphyria; AMP = adenosine monophosphate; CEP = congenital erythropoietic porphyria; COPRO = coproporphyrinogen; CPK = creatine phosphokinase; DDC = 3,5-diethoxycarbonyl-1,4-dihydrocollidine; dioxin = 2,3,7,8-tetrachlorodibenzo-*p*-dioxin; DMSO = dimethyl sulfoxide; DTT = dithiothreitol; EDTA = ethylenediaminetetraacetic acid; EPP = erythropoietic protoporphyria; GMP = guanosine monophosphate; HCP = hereditary coproporphyria; HEP = hepatoerythropoietic porphyria; HPLC = high performance liquid chromatography; LHRH = lutenizing hormone releasing hormone; MEL = murine erythroleukemia cells; PBG = porphobilinogen; PCB = polychlorinated biphenyls; PROTO = protoporphyrinogen; SDS = sodium dodecyl sulfate; URO = uroporphyrinogen; VP = variegate porphyria.

Table 52-1 Classification of the Major Human Porphyrias

Classification	Deficient enzyme	Inheritance	Principal symptomatology	Increased erythrocyte porphyrins*	Excess excretion of ALA, PBG, porphyrins*	
					Urine	Stool
Erythropoietic						
Congenital erythropoietic porphyria	Uroporphyrinogen III cosynthase	Autosomal recessive	Photosensitivity	Uroporphyrin, coproporphyrin	Uroporphyrin,‡ coproporphyrin‡	Coproporphyrin‡
Erythropoietic protoporphyria	Ferrochelatase	Autosomal dominant	Photosensitivity	Protoporphyrin	Absent	Protoporphyrin
Hepatic						
ALA dehydratase deficiency porphyria	ALA dehydratase	Autosomal recessive	Neurovisceral	Protoporphyrin	ALA	—
Acute intermittent porphyria	PBG deaminase	Autosomal dominant	Neurovisceral	Absent	ALA, PBG	—
Hereditary coproporphyria	Coproporphyrinogen oxidase	Autosomal dominant	Neurovisceral ± photosensitivity	Absent	ALA, PBG, coproporphyrin	
Variegate porphyria	Protoporphyrinogen oxidase	Autosomal dominant	Neurovisceral ± photosensitivity	Absent	ALA, PBG, coproporphyrin	coproporphyrin, protoporphyrin
Porphyria cutanea tarda	Uroporphyrinogen decarboxylase	Variable†	Photosensitivity	Absent	Uroporphyrin, 7-carboxylate porphyrin	Isocoproporphyrin
Hepatoerythropoietic porphyria	Uroporphyrinogen decarboxylase	Autosomal recessive	Photosensitivity ± neurovisceral	Protoporphyrin	Uroporphyrin, 7-carboxylate porphyrin	Isocoproporphyrin

*Only major diagnostic findings are listed.
†Autosomal dominant inheritance has been documented in some families but not in others.
‡Type I isomers.
NOTE: ALA = δ-aminolevulinic acid; PBG = porphobilinogen.

8. *Erythropoietic protoporphyria (EPP) is an autosomal dominant disease due to a 50 percent deficiency of ferrochelatase activity. The disease is characterized by mild to moderate photosensitivity. Clinical expression is highly variable. Some heterozygotes have normal red cell protoporphyrin levels and no photosensitivity. Avoidance of sunlight is important in prevention of cutaneous symptoms, and the use of a sun-protective agent is often helpful in reducing photosensitivity.*

THE HEME BIOSYNTHETIC PATHWAY

The biosynthesis of one molecule of heme* requires 8 molecules of glycine and 8 molecules of succinyl CoA. The first intermediate of this pathway is δ-aminolevulinic acid (ALA), a 5-carbon aminoketone, which is formed by the condensation of glycine and succinyl CoA. The reaction requires pyridoxal 5′-phosphate. Two molecules of ALA are combined to form porphobilinogen (PBG), which is a monopyrrole, and four molecules of PBG are then combined to form uroporphyrinogen, a cyclic tetrapyrrole. Uroporphyrinogen is converted to coproporphyrinogen and subsequently to protoporphyrin IX.† Protoporphyrin is the immediate precursor of the various hemes and chlorophylls. Cobalamins are formed from uroporphyrinogen.

**Heme* is ferroprotoporphyrin IX, i.e., the iron (Fe^{2+}) chelate of protoporphyrin IX. Heme is readily autooxidized in vitro to the ferric (Fe^{3+}) form, called ferriprotoporphyrin IX, or *hemin.* In this form, there is one residual positive charge, and the chelate is usually isolated as a halide (e.g., hemin chloride). In alkaline solution, the halide is replaced by the hydroxyl ion, forming *hematin.* The terms are used interchangeably in the text, depending on literature citations.

†Of the 15 possible protoporphyrin isomers only type IX is of physiological significance. Therefore protoporphyrin IX is referred to simply as *protoporphyrin* throughout the text.

Porphyrins and Porphyrinogens

Porphyrins and porphyrinogens are cyclic tetrapyrroles (Fig. 52-1). The immediate products formed in the heme biosynthetic pathway are the reduced forms of porphyrins, i.e., porphyrinogens. Porphyrinogens undergo rapid oxidation under air to become porphyrins, which are the usual forms of the cyclic tetrapyrroles found in biologic specimens. With the exception of protoporphyrin, which is the substrate for the terminal enzyme ferrochelatase, all other enzymatic steps require porphyrinogens as substrates.

Porphyrin nomenclature was originally developed by Hans Fischer and his school at Munich,[1] and a revised nomenclature has been recommended by the International Union of Pure and Applied Chemistry (IUPAC) and the International Union of Biochemistry (IUB).[2] The IUPAC-IBU recommendations were intended to systematize porphyrin nomenclature since a large number of trivial names are used in the Fischer system. Unfortunately, most porphyrin nomenclature which has appeared in the literature to date is still based almost exclusively on the Fischer nomenclature. Thus, in this chapter, the traditional Fischer system is used for convenience. Structures and trivial names of porphyrins are described in Table 52-2. Comparison of the Fischer system with the IUPAC-IUB system is found in Fig. 52-1 and Table 52-2.[2]

Porphyrins have unique photo-optical properties. They are readily excited by light at around 400 nm and emit intense red fluorescence. In acidic solution, porphyrins display two strong emission bands, one at 600 to 610 nm and the other at 640 to 660 nm. Spectrofluorometric methods thus provide a very sensitive means of detection of porphyrins.[3]

In contrast to porphyrins, heme, i.e., Fe-protoporphyrin, does not fluoresce. Porphyrins which are chelated to other paramagnetic metals (e.g., Mn, Co) also do not fluoresce,

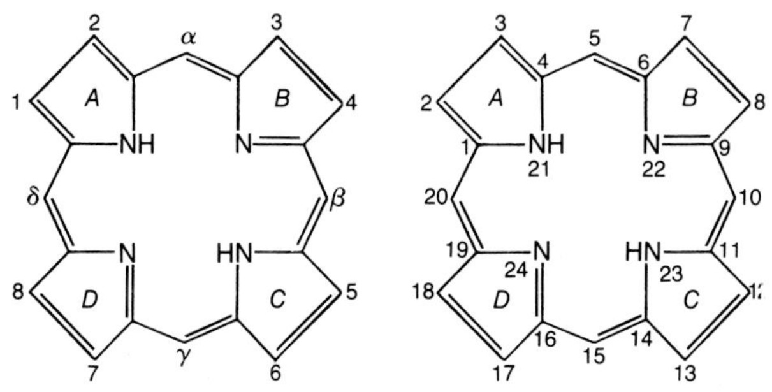

Fig. 52-1 Structure and nomenclature of the porphyrin macrocycle. *Porphin* (Fischer nomenclature) or *porphyrin* (IUPAC nomenclature) is the basic structure of biologically occurring ring tetrapyrroles. The systems differ in the numeration of the carbon and nitrogen atoms of the macrocycle.

while porphyrin chelates of diamagnetic metals (e.g., Zn, Sn, Mg) do. With the exception of heme and chlorophylls containing Mg-protoporphyrin, other metalloporphyrins are found only in small quantities in nature.

Porphyrins or metalloporphyrins which lack fluorescence can be determined using their characteristic absorbance properties. All porphyrins display an absorption spectrum consisting of a major band in the 400-nm region, called the Soret band, and four smaller absorption bands between 500 and 630 nm, with decreasing intensity toward the red (Fig. 52-2). The Soret band generally has a 10 to 15 times greater absorption (molar extinction coefficient of 2 to 5 $\times$ 10^5) than the next major band, which occurs at around 500 nm. With the formation of a porphyrin dication in aqueous HCl, or the formation of the metal complex of a porphyrin,[4,5] the four bands in the longer-wavelength region are replaced by two bands, called α and β (Fig. 52-2).

The water solubility of porphyrins decreases with reduction in the number of carboxylic acid side chains. Thus, uroporphyrin (8-carboxylic porphyrin) is most water-soluble, and protoporphyrin (2-carboxylic porphyrin) is least water-soluble. Protoporphyrin is so hydrophobic that it is excreted only into lipid-rich bile, while uroporphyrin and coproporphyrin are excreted mostly in urine.

Free porphyrins do not appear to carry out any useful biologic functions. Upon illumination at ultraviolet wavelengths and in the presence of molecular oxygen, metal-free as well as diamagnetic metalloporphyrins cause photodynamic effects on tissues, cells, subcellular elements, and biomacromolecules via singlet oxygen production.[6] Because of photosensitized injury of plasma membranes and lysosomal membranes, as well as the activation of the complement system, photodynamic activation of porphyrins may elicit significant cell damage.[6,7] Hematoporphyrin derivatives have been used to identify and treat certain tumors by virtue of their photoactive properties.[8] Animals and humans treated with porphyrins may show characteristic signs and symptoms of photosensitization such as intense itching, erythema, edema, pigmentation, ulceration, and scarring of the skin.[9]

In contrast, heme, chlorophyll, and corrins, which are Fe, Mg, and Co chelates of porphyrin (or porphyrin derivatives), respectively, carry out critically important biologic functions. For example, heme is the prosthetic group of a number of hemeproteins. Thus heme is necessary for oxygen binding and transport (as hemoglobin and myoglobin), for electron transport (as cytochromes), for mixed-function oxidation (as cytochrome P_{450}), for decomposition of hydrogen peroxide (as catalase), for activation of hydrogen peroxide (as peroxidase), and for oxidation of tryptophan (as tryptophan pyrrolase). Heme also serves as an essential cofactor in the oxidation of prostaglandins (as prostaglandin endoperoxide synthase),[10] the oxidation of indoleamine (as indoleamine 2,3-dioxygenase),[11] and the production of cyclic GMP (as guanylate cyclase).[12]

Most organisms have the ability to synthesize both heme and appropriate apoproteins for their hemeproteins. Some organisms, however, rely on an exogenous source of heme for hemeprotein synthesis, such as *Haemophilus influenzae*[13] and hemoflagellates.[14] Leghemoglobin is formed with heme, which is the product of *Rhizobium*, the bacterium residing in the plant root, and apohemoglobin, which is the plant product.[15]

Table 52-2 Structures and Trivial Names of Porphyrins

Name	*Substituent**							
IUPAC† numeration:	2	3	7	8	12	13	17	18
Fischer numeration:	1	2	3	4	5	6	7	8
Etioporphyrin I	M	E	M	E	M	E	M	E
Etioporphyrin II	M	E	E	M	M	E	E	M
Etioporphyrin III	M	E	M	E	M	E	E	M
Etioporphyrin IV	M	E	E	M	E	M	M	E
Uroporphyrin I	A	P	A	P	A	P	A	P
Uroporphyrin III	A	P	A	P	A	P	P	A
Heptacarboxylate porphyrin III	M	P	A	P	A	P	P	A
Hexacarboxylate porphyrin III	M	P	M	P	A	P	P	A
Pentacarboxylate porphyrin III	M	P	M	P	A	P	P	M
Dehydroisocoproporphyrin III	M	V	M	P	A	P	P	M
Coproporphyrin I	M	P	M	P	M	P	M	P
Coproporphyrin III	M	P	M	P	M	P	P	M
Protoporphyrin IX	M	V	M	V	M	P	P	M
Mesoporphyrin IX	M	E	M	E	M	P	P	M
Hematoporphyrin IX	M	HE	M	HE	M	P	P	M
Deuteroporphyrin IX	M	H	M	H	M	P	P	M

*Substituent abbreviations: M = $-CH_3$; E = $-C_2H_5$; A = $-CH_2COOH$;
P = $-CH_2CH_2COOH$;
V = $-CH=CH_2$; HE = $-CHOHCH_3$

†The International Union of Pure and Applied Chemistry.

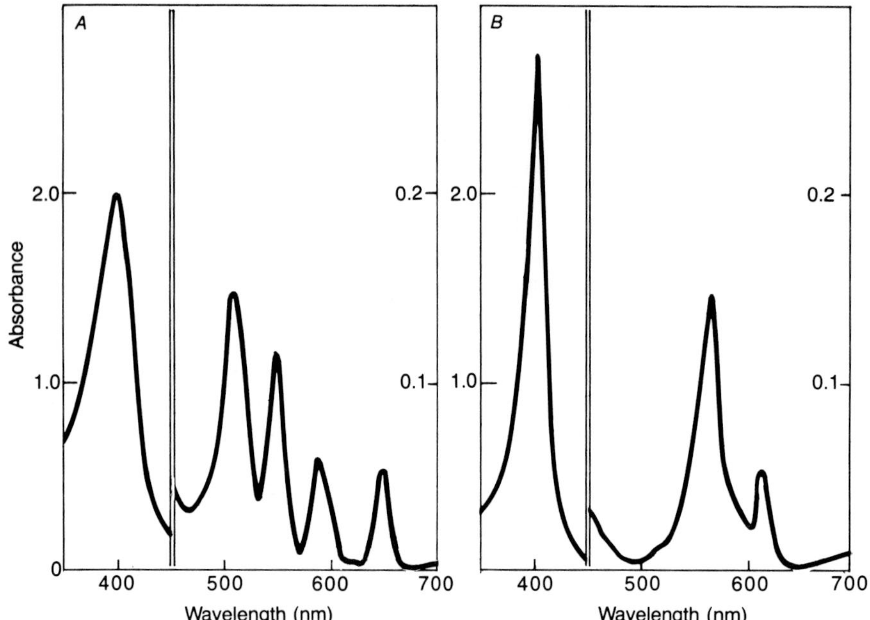

Fig. 52-2 Absorption spectra of protoporphyrin. *A.* Protoporphyrin dimethylester in $CHCl_3$. *B.* Protoporphyrin in 1 *N* HCl. The typical absorption spectrum of protoporphyrin in an organic solvent is shown in *A* and consists of an intense Soret band and four smaller absorption peaks in the longer-wavelength region of the spectrum. Formation of the porphyrin di-cation in HCl leads to the spectral changes

Exogenously administered heme can also associate with certain apohemeproteins such as apocytochrome P_{450}[16–20] and apohemoglobin.[21]

Enzymes and Chemical Intermediates of the Heme Biosynthetic Pathway

The biochemical pathway for the formation of heme is illustrated in Fig. 52-3. There are eight enzymes involved in the synthesis of heme. The first and the last three of these enzymes are localized in the mitochondria; the intermediate enzymes are localized in the cytosol. Normal values for activities of enzymes in the heme biosynthetic pathway in several human tissues are summarized in Table 52-3, and the alterations of these enzymatic activities in the various human porphyrias are summarized in Table 52-4.

δ-AMINOLEVULINIC ACID SYNTHASE (ALA SYNTHASE) AND ITS ROLE IN THE REGULATION OF HEME BIOSYNTHESIS

ALA synthase [succinyl CoA→glycine C-succinyl transferase (decarboxylating) (EC 2.3.1.37)] is the first enzyme in the heme biosynthetic pathway and condenses glycine and succinyl CoA to form ALA. In mammalian cells, the enzyme is localized in the inner membrane of mitochondria. The enzyme activity has been found in a variety of organisms including, among others, bacteria,[48] yeast,[49] insects,[50] avian[51,52] and mammalian liver cells,[53,54] erythroid cells,[55,56] kidney cells,[57] harderian gland,[58] heart,[59] and brain.[60,61]

Synthesis

In mammalian liver, ALA synthase is synthesized on cytoplasmic ribosomes and subsequently transferred into mitochondria. The enzyme is functional only in mitochondria, which provide succinyl CoA as substrate for the enzyme reaction.

Properties

Mitochondrial ALA synthase partially purified from rabbit, rat, and guinea pig liver has K_m values for glycine, succinyl CoA, and pyridoxal-5′-phosphate in the range of 5 to 19 m*M*, 60 to 200 μ*M*, and 1 to 10 μ*M*, respectively.[55,62–66] The relatively high K_m (i.e., low affinity of the enzyme) for glycine raises the possibility that the enzyme activity may be regulated by the physiological concentration of glycine.[67] In support of this idea, the administration of *p*-aminobenzoic acid or sodium benzoate, which increases glycine metabolism via other pathways, is known to suppress the increase in activity of hepatic ALA synthase caused by 3,5-diethoxycarbonyl-1,4-dihydrocollidine (DDC).[68,69] The V_{max} of the purified rat liver mitochondrial ALA synthase is 2000 nmol/h per milligram of protein,[70] while it is over 20,000 nmol/h per milligram of protein for the chick embryo liver enzyme.[66]

In vitro translation experiments suggest that ALA synthase in chick embryo liver is synthesized initially as a larger precursor of a minimum molecular weight 60,000[71,72] and is then packaged into mitochondria. In mitochondria, the enzyme exists as a dimer of molecular weight 140,000.[73] The complete nucleotide sequence of a cDNA clone coding for the precursor has been determined. The deduced amino acid sequence of the precursor protein contains 635 amino acids, and the predicted molecular mass is 70,029 daltons.[74] Electron-microscopic studies on the purified enzyme suggest that chick embryo liver ALA synthase consists of two curved and identical subunits associated in opposite polarities, each subunit having a molecular weight of ≈70,000.[75]

By providing succinyl CoA, glycine, and pyridoxal 5′-phosphate to an enzyme assay mixture, ALA synthase activity can be demonstrated in the cytosol of livers from rats treated with allylisopropylacetamide (AIA), a potent inducer of the enzyme in this organ.[62,76,77] An antibody against cytosolic ALA synthase cross-reacts with the mitochondrial enzyme.[78]

The half-life of cytosolic ALA synthase in rat liver is only 20 min, which is considerably shorter than that of the mitochondrial enzyme (≈70 min).[54,77,79] The shorter half-life of the cytosolic ALA synthase compared to that of the mitochondrial enzyme presumably reflects both enzyme degradation in the

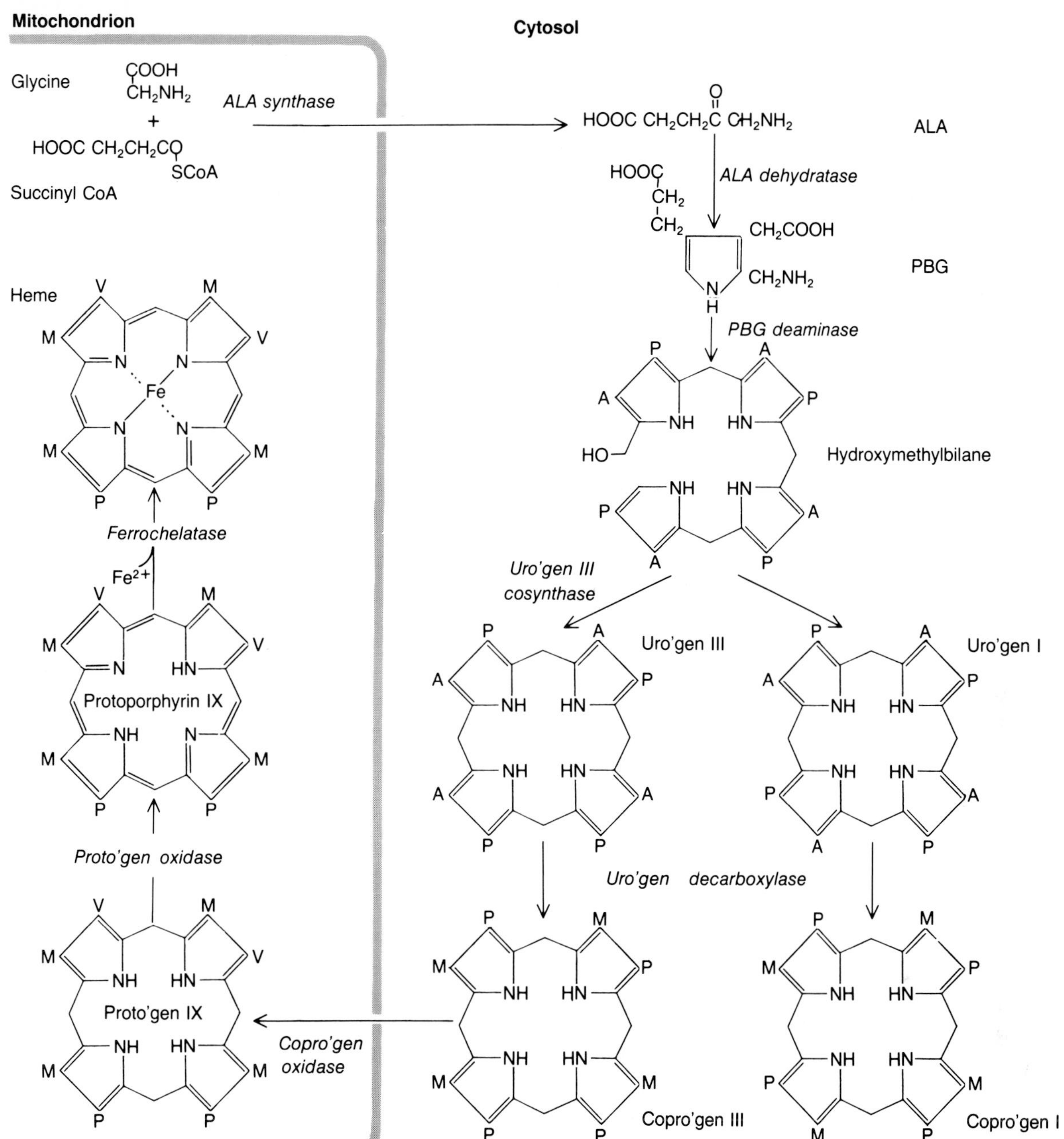

Fig. 52-3 The heme biosynthetic pathway. Subcellular distribution of enzymes and intermediates in the synthesis of heme is shown. A = —CH_2·COOH; M = —CH_3; P = —CH_2·COOH; V = —CH=CH_2.

cytosol and transport of the enzyme from cytosol into mitochondria.

The Reaction Mechanism

The elegant studies of Shemin and Rittenberg[80,81] demonstrated the arrangement in the porphyrin macrocycle of the carbon and nitrogen atoms originating from the eight glycine and succinic acid molecules that are the precursors of porphyrins. Subsequently it was shown that the α-carbon atom of glycine is utilized to label both the pyrrolic ring carbons and the methene bridge carbons,[82,83] and it was proposed that the 5-carbon aminoketone ALA is the product of the condensation of glycine and succinate.

Using ALA synthase purified from *Rhodopseudomonas spheroides*, the following reaction mechanism has been elucidated[84–86] (Fig. 52-4). (1) Glycine forms a Schiff base with pyridoxal-5′-phosphate, which is bound to the enzyme yielding a stable carbanion. (2) A proton (*R* configuration) is removed from the methylene carbon atom of glycine. (3) Succinyl CoA condenses to the carbanion to form α-amino-β-ketoadipic acid with the loss of CoA. (4) α-Amino-β-ketoadipic acid is decarboxylated to yield ALA. The proton on the methylene carbon atom of glycine which is lost at step (1) is specifically that of the *R* configuration, while the one having the *S* configuration is incorporated into ALA.[84] Succinyl CoA is not required for the proton removal reaction.[90] Heme, an allosteric effector of the enzyme activity in the bacterium, has no effect on the loss of the proton from glycine.[90] Decarboxylation of α-amino-β-ketoadipic acid to ALA occurs on the enzyme, and then ALA is released into the medium from the pyridoxal-enzyme complex.[86]

Table 52-3 Normal Values of Heme Pathway Enzymes in Human Tissues

Enzyme	*Liver*	*Erythroid cells*	*Fibroblasts*	*Lymphocytes*
ALA synthase, nmol/h of ALA per gram	24[22]	49.2[b,d,23]	5.34[a,24]	116[a,i,25]
ALA dehydratase, nmol/h of PBG per gram	1080, 1340[26]	2513[e,27]	115[a,28]	290[a,i,25]
PBG deaminase, nmol/h of uro I per gram	2.75[29]	37.7[e,30]	6.14[a,h,31]	6.05[a,i,25] 10.3[a,j,25]
Uroporphyrinogen III cosynthase, nmol/h of uro III per gram	—	6636[c,e,f,32]	8775[a,f,32]	—
Uroporphyrinogen decarboxylase, nmol/h of copro per gram	174[a,33]	717[a,n,34]	313[a,35]	480[a,k,36]
Coproporphyrinogen oxidase, nmol/h of proto per gram	224[a,37]	—	87[a,38]	73[a,k,39]
Protoporphyrinogen oxidase, nmol/h of proto per gram	—	—	300[a,40]	658[a,k,41]
Ferrochelatase, nmol/h of heme per gram	352[24]	18.4[b,d,24]	3.74[a,g,24] 6.2[g,42]	313[a,k,41] 1932[o]
Protoporphyrin formation from added ALA	—	—	4.10[a,l,31]	2.02[a,i,m,43]

NOTE: Only mean values are cited in this table. In order to make comparisons of enzymatic activities, certain assumptions were made to recalculate reported data so that they could be expressed per gram of tissue per hour of incubation.

[a]Assuming 150 mg of protein per gram of tissue.
[b]Assuming 2 × 10^8 erythroblasts per gram of bone marrow.
[c]Assuming 300 mg hemoglobin per gram of erythrocytes.
[d]Bone marrow.
[e]Erythrocytes.
[f]At 31°C.
[g]Protoporphyrin as substrate.
[h]At 60°C.
[i]Mitogen-stimulated lymphocytes.
[j]EB-virus transformed lymphocytes.
[k]Nonstimulated lymphocytes.
[l]With EDTA.
[m]Without EDTA.
[n]Assuming that uroporphyrinogen III is used as substrate (≈5 times faster than 5-carboxylate porphyrinogen I).
[o]Mesoporphyrin as substrate.

Table 52-4 Activities of Heme Pathway Enzymes in Human Porphyrias

Enzyme	*Disease displaying abnormal activity*	*Liver*	*Bone marrow*	*Erythrocyte*	*Fibroblasts*	*Lymphocytes*
ALA synthase, nmol/h of ALA per gram	AIP	171[22] ↑ 160[45] ↑ 264–455[29] ↑	— —	— —	Normal[44,24]	Normal[25]
	HCP	234[46] ↑	—	—	—	—
	VP	505[47] ↑	—	—	—	—
PBG deaminase, nmol/h of uro I per gram	AIP	<1.1[29] ↓	—	18.0[30] ↓	18.6[31] ↓	2.61[25] ↓
Uroporphyrinogen III cosynthase, nmol/h of uro III per gram	CEP	—	—	966[32] ↓	2647[32] ↓	—
Uroporphyrinogen decarboxylase, nmol/h of copro I per gram	PCT (sporadic)	81[33] ↓	—	Normal[34,35] ↓	Normal[35]	Normal[36]
	PCT (familial)					
	Patients	—	—	77[34] ↓	—	262[36] ↓
	Carriers	—	—	80[34] ↓	—	—
Coproporphyrinogen oxidase, nmol/h of proto per gram	HCP					
	Homozygote	—	—	—	4.2[38] ↓ ↓	1.2 ↓ ↓
	Heterozygote	—	—	—	31–57[38] ↓	20–32[39] ↓
Protoporphyrinogen oxidase, nmol/h of proto per gram	VP	—	—	—	135[40] ↓	361[41] ↓
Ferrochelatase, nmol/h of heme per gram	EPP	44.2[24] ↓	4.4[23] ↓	—	0.54[24] ↓	75[41] ↓
	VP (?)	—	—	—	3.6[42] ↓	—
Protoporphyrin formation from added ALA, nmol/h of proto per gram	AIP	—	—	—	1.44[31] ↓ (control 4.10)	3.75[25] ↓ (control 7.92)
	EPP	—	—	—	—	4.79[25] ↓ (control 2.02)

NOTE: ↓ ↓ Especially marked

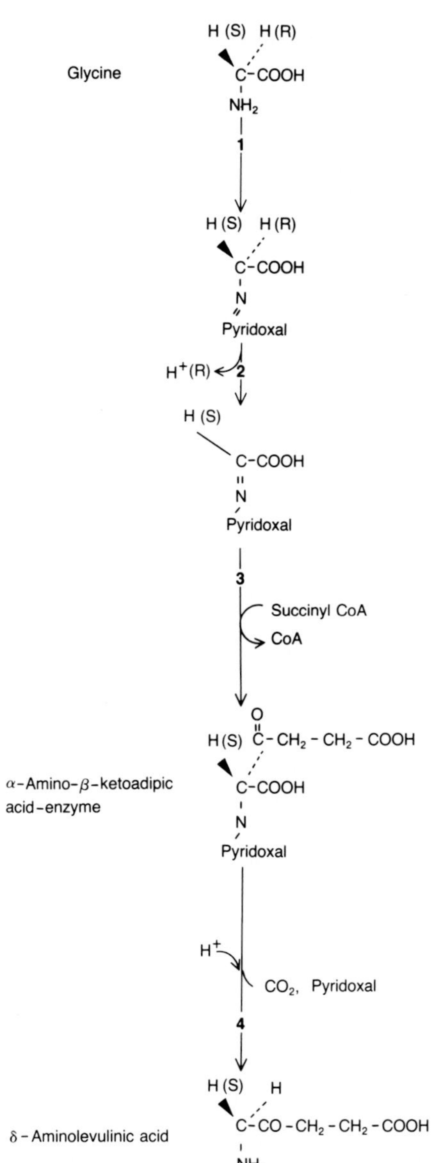

Fig. 52-4 The reaction catalyzed by ALA synthase. (1) Glycine forms a Schiff base with pyridoxal 5′-phosphate-enzyme complex. (2) A proton (*R* configuration) is removed from the methylene carbon atom of glycine. (3) The succinyl group is transferred from succinyl CoA to form α-amino-β-ketoadipic acid. (4) After decarboxylation of the intermediate, a proton is stereospecifically inserted and free ALA is released.[87–89]

Molecular Biology

Hepatic ALA synthase is encoded by a nuclear gene and is synthesized on free polyribosomes as a cytosolic precursor of molecular weight about 6 kDa greater than the mature mitochondrial form.[91] The precursor is processed to the mature form during translocation into mitochondria[91] and, by analogy with other mitochondrial precursor proteins, mature ALA synthase is presumed to be formed through the cleavage of an N-terminal precursor sequence. Heme has been shown to specifically inhibit the transfer of ALA synthase precursor into mitochondria.[91]

cDNA clones containing sequences coding for chick liver ALA synthase have been recently isolated[92]; clones were selected from a cDNA library constructed using free polysomal poly (A)-rich RNA from livers of drug-induced chick embryos; the identity of these clones has been confirmed by comparing DNA sequence data with the amino acid sequence of peptides from purified ALA synthase. The size of the mRNA for ALA synthase was estimated by Northern blot analysis to be 2800 base pairs (bp), approximately 600 bp more than that required to code for the primary translation product of a relative molecular mass of 74,000. The complete nucleotide sequence of a cDNA clone coding for the cytosolic precursor of ALA synthase was recently reported.[72] The deduced amino acid sequence shows that the precursor consists of a mature enzyme of 579 amino acids and an N-terminal extension of 56 amino acids. This presequence is highly basic in nature and in this respect resembles other mitochondrial preproteins.

cDNA clones encoding ALA synthase have also been isolated from adult hen erythrocytes[93]; the authors reported that the erythroid ALA synthase mRNA can be distinguished from its hepatic counterpart on the basis of hybridization studies, suggesting that the ALA synthase enzyme(s) are encoded by a family of genes expressed in a tissue-specific manner. These findings might explain the distinct regulatory features of ALA synthase in liver and in erythroid cells, as well as the difference in sizes between the two enzymes, either as pre- or as mature proteins.[56] However, more recent studies concerning the nucleotide sequences of cDNAs from mouse liver and anemic mouse spleen, an erythropoietic tissue,[94] showed that both sequences not only were identical but also had extensive homology to ALA synthase of chick embryonic liver. Messenger RNAs from mouse liver, spleen, and mouse erythroleukemia cells, detected by Northern blot analysis, were also shown to have the same size.

A chicken ALA synthase gene has been isolated with a liver cDNA probe and its nucleotide sequence recently described.[95] The gene spans 6.9 kb of DNA and is divided into 10 exons and split by nine introns. The exons contain 2103 nucleotides and encode an ALA synthase precursor protein of 635 amino acids. The N-terminal extension of 56 amino acids is subsequently removed during transfer of the precursor into mitochondria. A fragment with 257 bp of 5′ flanking region extending 34 bp into the first exon showed promoter activity when introduced into the nuclei of *Xenopus laevis* oocytes. An interesting feature of the gene is a CG-rich region at the 5′ end, associated with a high frequency of CG dinucleotides. Such CG clusters have been observed in the 5′ end of several genes encoding "housekeeping" proteins.[96] They are thought to be a consequence of undermethylation of the germ-line DNA[95] and may be linked to the requirement for constitutive expression of some genes. The 5′ flanking region contains a number of potential control and promoter elements including two TATA and CAAT box combinations.[95] The TATA box at −30 has been shown to direct transcription in chick embryo liver. It is not known whether the second TATA box functions in other tissues. The gene was shown to exist as a single copy in the chick genome by Southern blot analysis. If a separate gene for chick erythroid ALA synthase exists as proposed by Yamamoto et al.,[93] such a gene does not cross-hybridize with a full-length chick embryo liver cDNA probe at the same stringency as in other work.[95]

More recently, ALA synthase mRNA from chicken liver and reticulocytes has been shown to be identical by RNase mapping and primer extension studies.[74] ALA synthase protein from these tissues was the same size as judged by immunoblot analysis. In addition, a single mRNA species (2.1 kb) for ALA synthase was shown to be present in chicken liver, reticulocytes, brain, and heart, and an avian erythroblastosis virus-transformed chicken erythroblast cell line. Primer extension analysis has also established that a TATA/CAAT box combination proximal to the transcription start site is used in both liver and reticulocytes. Southern analysis showed the presence of only one gene copy for ALA synthase in the chicken haploid genome.[74] However, in vitro translation experiments suggest that ALA synthase synthesized in vitro using polysomes from chicken erythroid cells shows a subunit molecular weight of 55,000, whereas the enzyme synthesized in vitro using liver polysomes has a subunit molecular weight of 73,000.[56]

Recently, the 5′ regulatory region of the gene coding for ALA synthase of *Rhizobium meliloti* has been studied[97]; there was a distinct homology between the amino acid sequence of chicken ALA synthase beginning with exon 4 and that known for (the first 76 amino acids) *R. meliloti* ALA synthase. However, the bacterial gene does not contain a sequence corresponding to the first three exons of the chicken gene.[95] The bacterial enzyme is also smaller than the chicken ALA synthase precursor, which has a molecular weight of 70,000. The chicken enzyme is still fully active when its molecular weight is reduced by proteolysis to 50,000.[73] This might be expected if the amino acids encoded by the first three exons are lost by the proteolytic treatment. We infer that the active site of mitochondrial chicken ALA synthase is encoded by the conserved sequences in exons 4 to 10, whereas the cytosolic presequence is defined by exon 1. The yeast gene coding for ALA synthase has also been cloned by genetic complementation and restriction mapping[98,99]; the gene is contained within a 2.9-kb region.[99]

The Effect of Heme on ALA Synthase

There is a substantial body of evidence indicating that ALA synthase in the liver is regulated by the end product of the biosynthetic pathway, heme. Three possible mechanisms have been proposed for the feedback regulatory effect of heme on ALA synthase, and all may be important to some degree.

1. The activity of purified ALA synthase is inhibited (approximately 50 percent) in vitro by hemin at concentrations of 10 to 50 μM.[55,62,63,66] The enzyme activity in crude homogenates is not inhibited by hemin at these concentrations.[100]

2. The transport of cytosolic ALA synthase into mitochondria is inhibited by hemin.[101] In rats treated with AIA and hemin, a considerable increase in cytosolic ALA synthase is observed with a concomitant decrease in mitochondrial ALA synthase activity, in comparison with rats treated with AIA alone.[101] Inhibition of intracellular translocation of ALA synthase was further evidenced by a kinetic study using a combination of tracer ([^{3}H]leucine) and immunochemical methods employing a rabbit antibody specific to ALA synthase.[78,102] Hemin-mediated inhibition of enzyme translocation was also demonstrated in an in vitro system using chicken liver ALA synthase and homologous liver mitochondria.[103] In the rat liver, both the transport and the processing of the enzyme were significantly inhibited by hemin. A 50 percent inhibition of ALA synthase translocation can be achieved by intracellular heme concentrations lower than those necessary to achieve full saturation of tryptophan pyrrolase.[104]

3. Hemin represses the synthesis of ALA synthase. Hemin repression of enzyme synthesis occurs at a concentration of $0.1 \times 10^{-6}\ M$,[105] which is considerably less than the concentration required for inhibition of the enzyme activity (10 to $50 \times 10^{-6}\ M$).[55,62,63,66]

ALA Formation via a Pathway Not Involving Glycine and Succinyl CoA

ALA formation in higher plants does not involve glycine or succinyl CoA. Instead C-1 of glutamate becomes C-5 of ALA via the formation of an intermediate, γ,δ-dioxovalerate (DOVA)[106,107] (Fig. 52-5). Transamination of DOVA to ALA then occurs as has been shown in extracts of *Chlorella,*[109] bean leaves,[110] and *R. spheroides.*[111] DOVA transaminase has also been purified from *Chlorella,*[112] radish seedlings,[113] and *Clostridium,*[114] and mitochondria from rat liver[115] and bovine liver.[108]

A reaction similar to that catalyzed by DOVA transaminase has been found in mammalian cells. Varticovski et al.[108] purified DOVA transaminase from bovine liver mitochondria. The enzyme had a molecular weight of 240,000. The K_m for DOVA was $2.4 \times 10^{-4}\ M$. Pyridoxal-5′-phosphate was required as a cofactor. Total DOVA transaminase activity was found to be considerably greater than that of ALA synthase in bovine liver. The role of DOVA transaminase in the regulation of heme formation in animal tissues, however, remains to be defined. In the C-5 pathway to form ALA from glutamate, glutamate must be activated. Recently it has been shown that a tRNA participates in this reaction. This specific tRNA was purified to homogeneity, sequenced, and identified to be a chloroplast glutamate acceptor RNA.[116] This is the first demonstration that a tRNA possesses an enzymic property for activation of a carboxylic group for the purpose of reduction. It is not clear whether a similar tRNA participates in the activation of glutamate in mammalian cells.

Regulation of Heme Biosynthesis

Biosynthesis of heme in the liver is controlled largely by the rate of production of ALA synthase.[51,117] The activity of this enzyme is rate limiting, and the enzyme is feedback-regulated by the intracellular concentration of heme. In contrast to the liver, the regulation of heme synthesis in erythroid cells may not be controlled by ALA synthase alone. Although ALA synthase may be rate limiting for hemoglobin formation in avian

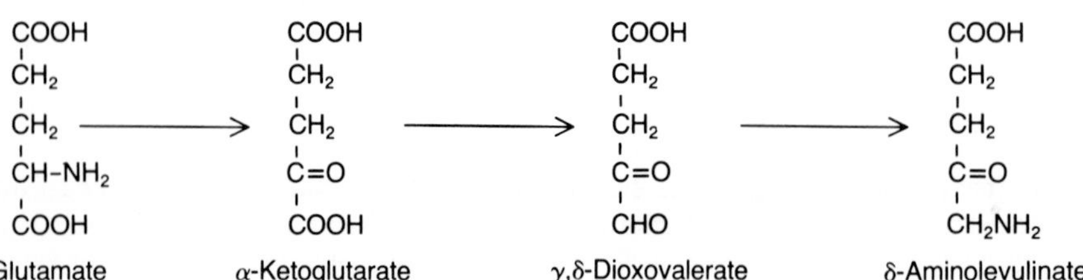

Fig. 52-5 Formation of ALA in plant cells. The formation of ALA does not involve glycine or succinyl CoA; instead C-1 of α-ketoglutarate or glutamate is incorporated into C-5 of ALA via γ,δ-dioxovalerate.[107] An enzyme which catalyzes the transamination of γ,δ-dioxovalerate to ALA has also been demonstrated in bovine liver.[108]

embryonic erythroid cells,[118] it appears not to be rate limiting for heme formation in mammalian erythroid cells.[21,68,119] It should be noted that in contrast to the liver, the erythron responds to a stimulus for heme synthesis mainly by increasing its cell number. It is perhaps appropriate, therefore, for regulatory influences on hemoglobin synthesis in the erythron to act primarily on the process of cell differentiation to meet changing requirements for heme in this tissue.

Heme Synthesis in the Liver

Of the ALA produced in rat liver, as much as 65 percent is utilized for the formation of microsomal cytochrome P_{450}, about 15 percent for the synthesis of catalase in the peroxizomes, 6 percent for the formation of mitochondrial cytochromes, and 8 percent for the formation of cytochrome b_5.[120] Total bilirubin production in normal humans has been estimated to be about 5 to 8 μmol bilirubin daily per kilogram of body weight.[121] Liver cells normally make about 15 percent of the heme that is synthesized in the body.[117] It requires approximately 54 mg of ALA per day for this amount of hepatic heme synthesis. The remainder of heme formation takes place in the bone marrow for the synthesis of hemoglobin which requires approximately 304 mg ALA/day. In AIP the liver may form as much ALA as the normal bone marrow does. This suggests that the rate of ALA synthesis is an important controlling step for heme formation in the liver.

ALA Synthase and Its Rate Limiting Nature in the Liver

There is much evidence for the rate limiting nature of ALA synthase in the liver.[51,52]

1. The activity of ALA synthase in normal liver is very low (30 to 100 nmol ALA per hour per gram of mouse liver).[122] Another enzyme in the heme synthetic pathway that is present at a similarly low level is PBG deaminase (35 to 60 nmol PBG per hour used per gram of mouse liver).[122] Thus, under conditions of increased ALA production, ALA and PBG can accumulate and be excreted in excess amounts. The third enzyme of the heme pathway which has a relatively low activity is ferrochelatase (0.4 nmol/min of heme formed per milligram of mitochondria protein in rat liver, or about 1200 nmol of heme per hour per gram of liver),[123] but its activity is normally higher than that of ALA synthase and PBG deaminase.

2. ALA synthase activity can be markedly increased by treatment of animals with a variety of chemicals which produce an accumulation of porphyrins in the liver. The increase of enzyme activity is a result of increased *de novo* synthesis of the enzyme, which can be abolished by inhibitors of RNA or protein synthesis. In the case of AIP, the level of ALA synthase in the liver is elevated several-fold as compared with the level in healthy normal humans, thus leading to an overproduction of ALA.

3. The uninduced level of ALA synthase is sufficient to make the amount of heme that is necessary for maintenance of normal levels of liver hemeproteins.

4. In contrast to the very low level of ALA synthase activity, other enzymatic activities of the heme biosynthetic pathway are usually present in excess. For example, administration of ALA to rats and mice results in the induction of heme oxygenase,[124] in an increase in bilirubin production,[125] and in repression of ALA synthase.[126,127] These findings suggest that ALA is readily converted to heme and ultimately to bilirubin. Hepatic heme can also be labeled with radioactive ALA, and, in cultured rat hepatocytes, ALA treatment has been reported to increase the level of cytochrome P_{450}.[126] These data suggest that ALA administration enhances the rate of heme synthesis in the liver, although increases in hepatic hemeprotein concentration may not always be detectable or consistent.[125]

5. The rate of turnover of ALA synthase is very rapid, a property appropriate for an enzyme catalyzing a rate limiting reaction. The half-life of mitochondrial ALA synthase in rat liver is approximately 70 min[79]; it is 3 h in mouse liver[128] and in cultured chick embryo liver cells.[129] The half-life of mitochondrial ALA synthase is among the shortest of all mitochondrial proteins, which generally turn over with a half-life of approximately 5 days.

Control by Glycine

ALA synthase has an unusually high K_m (i.e., a low affinity) for glycine. K_m's of 5 to 19 mM for mammalian mitochondrial ALA synthase have been reported. The concentration of glycine in the chick embryo liver is about 1 mM.[130] This concentration of glycine, which is tenfold greater than that in human plasma, suggests an active transport mechanism for glycine. However, this concentration of the amino acid is still only one-fifth to one-twentieth of the K_m for ALA synthase. The seemingly insufficient concentration of glycine for ALA synthase may be due to the high activity of glycine acyltransferase or the glycine cleavage system[131] in liver mitochondria.[132,133] This raises the possibility that the activity of hepatic ALA synthase in vivo may also be regulated by the glycine concentration. If ALA synthase activity follows Michaelis-Menten kinetics, an increase in the substrate concentration from the K_m value to twice the K_m value would result in a 33 percent increase in the rate of product formation, while an increase of the substrate concentration from one-tenth of the K_m, as in the case of glycine in liver, to two-tenths would yield 83 percent more product.[134] In chick embryo liver, the glycine concentration rose from 1 to 3 mM when protein synthesis was inhibited by cyclohexamide. This treatment was shown to be accompanied by a 60 percent increase in ALA synthase activity as determined without added glycine.[130] The glycine cleavage system functions in the direction of glycine synthesis in the presence of thiol compounds,[131] and this system is potentially important in the regulation of ALA synthase activity. Treatment of rats with *p*-aminobenzoic acid or sodium benzoate reverses the experimental porphyria induced by DDC.[68] Both benzoic acid derivatives require glycine conjugation, and these conjugates are readily excreted by the kidney, thereby decreasing the hepatic glycine concentration. Consistent with this hypothesis is the observation that administration of glycine prevents the reversal by *p*-aminobenzoic acid or sodium benzoate of the porphyria elicited by DDC.[68]

Control by Heme

The regulatory effects of heme on heme biosynthesis are multiple, i.e., inhibition of ALA synthase synthesis at both transcriptional and translational steps, inhibition of the enzyme transfer from cytosol into mitochondria, and inhibition of its catalytic activity. All these steps can be affected by intracellular heme or hemin administered exogenously. The intracellular heme concentration can be affected by a number of factors. Direct inhibition of ALA synthase by hemin (K_i 2 × 10^{-5} M)[55] does not appear to be a physiologically significant process, since formation of ALA synthase is suppressed at substantially lower heme concentrations. For example, repression of ALA synthase formation in cultured chick embryo liver cells maintained in a serum-free medium takes place at a hemin concentration of 10^{-7} M.[105,135] The K_r (i.e., the concentration of hemin which reduces the rate of synthesis of ALA synthase by one-half) was 1 to 2 × 10^{-8} M[136,137] under these conditions (Fig. 52-6). It was also shown that heme generated in mitochondria was not sufficient to inhibit ALA synthase activity,[139] but may be sufficient to exert end product–mediated inhibition of the synthesis of ALA synthase.

Several heme-binding proteins exist in the cytosol of liver and intestinal cells which facilitate the uptake of heme. Conversely, efflux of heme from mitochondria may be facilitated by heme-binding proteins. Efflux is also inversely related to mitochondrial energy levels.[140] In liver cell cultures treated with hemin, ALA synthase decays with a half-life of approximately 3 h, which is similar to the half-life determined by the use of inhibitors of protein synthesis.[129] Findings in cultured avian embryonic liver cells suggest that hemin either shortens the lifetime of the mRNA for ALA synthase or interferes specifically with the synthesis of ALA synthase at the posttranscriptional level[129,141] (Fig. 52-7). Recent evidence suggests that hemin may also repress the synthesis of the mRNA for ALA synthase.[142]

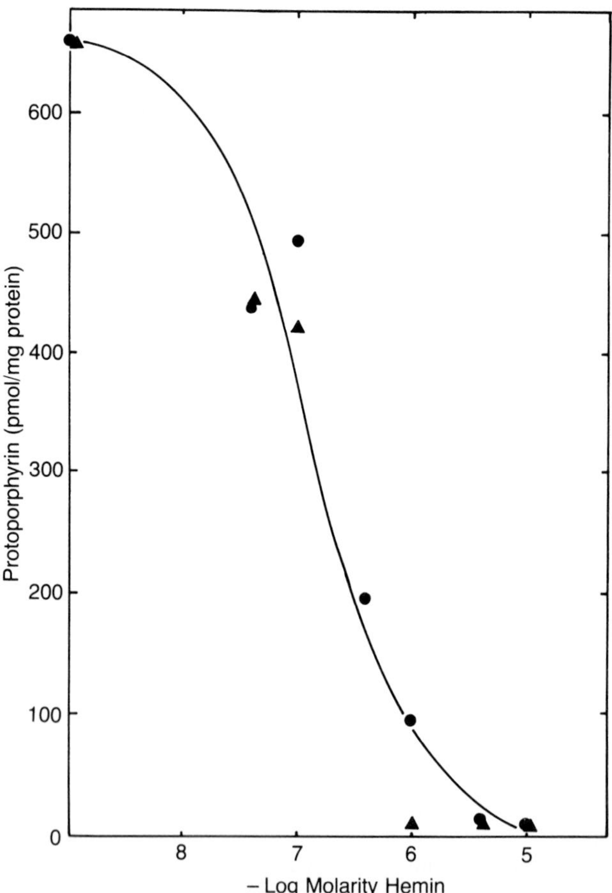

Fig. 52-6 Inhibitory effect of hemin on protoporphyrin formation induced by the 5β steroid metabolite, etiocholanolone, in cultured chick embryo liver cells. Similar inhibition by hemin is exerted against the inducing action of the barbiturate analogue AIA. (*From Sassa, Bradlow and Kappas.*[138] *Used by permission of the Journal of* Biological Chemistry.)

There is much evidence to suggest that the induction response of hepatic ALA synthase elicited by certain chemicals can be enhanced by concurrent heme depletion or inhibition of heme synthesis,[143–147] although heme depletion alone may not lead to a marked induction of ALA synthase. There are three general experimental conditions under which cellular heme balance can be affected by exogenous chemicals (Fig. 52-7).

1. Certain chemicals such as AIA[148–150] and many related unsaturated compounds[151–157] destroy cytochrome P_{450} heme, leading to an accumulation of abnormal green pigments in the liver. These green pigments show the properties of *N*-alkylated porphyrin species and can be considered products of heme degradation by allyl-containing compounds.[158] A clear correlation exists between the fall of cytochrome P_{450} and hepatic heme content caused by AIA,[148,159] but the apoprotein of cytochrome P_{450} may not necessarily be damaged by AIA, since decreased levels of cytochrome P_{450} and its associated hydroxylase activity can be partially restored by exogenous hemin.[19,20,160]

2. Compounds like DDC or griseofulvin cause a rapid inhibition of ferrochelatase,[144,145,161] thus leading to a decrease in heme formation. Animals treated with DDC[162] or griseofulvin[163] accumulate green porphyrins in the liver that are distinct from those observed after AIA treatment, and such compounds display a profound inhibitory activity toward ferrochelatase.

3. Phenobarbital and related compounds, on the other hand, probably reduce the concentration of regulatory free heme (which is in the range of 10^{-8} to 10^{-7} M) by eliciting an increased synthesis of apocytochrome P_{450}.[164,165] It has been shown, for example, that the apoprotein for cytochrome P_{450} is increased in rat liver after treatment with phenobarbital and lead.[18]

The regulatory role of heme with respect to its own biosynthesis and catabolism can be best explained by assuming the existence of one or more free heme pools, as outlined in the hypothetical scheme shown in Fig. 52-7. Free heme can be considered as heme that is either synthesized very recently and not yet bound, as the prosthetic group of specific hemeproteins, or possibly heme that has just been released from hemeproteins. Free heme pools probably exist, at least, in mitochondria, cytosol, and endoplasmic reticulum. All free heme pools are presumed to be very small and probably turn over very rapidly. Although the existence of free heme pools remains hypothetical, there is good evidence that such pools must in fact exist as functional entities in liver cells. For example, a certain fraction of heme can be quickly labeled (1 to 2 h) after a brief pulse of [^{14}C]glycine in the rat.[166] The appearance of this labeled heme is so prompt that it probably cannot be derived from hemeproteins.[117] This implies the existence of a rapidly synthesized heme fraction that can be considered to be a free heme pool. In cultured adult rat hepatocytes, 20 percent of newly formed heme is directly converted to bile pigment without being incorporated into hepatic hemeproteins.[167] As illustrated in Fig. 52-7, free heme pools may affect heme biosynthesis and catabolism in a number of ways.

1. Free heme in mitochondria may regulate the rate of syn-

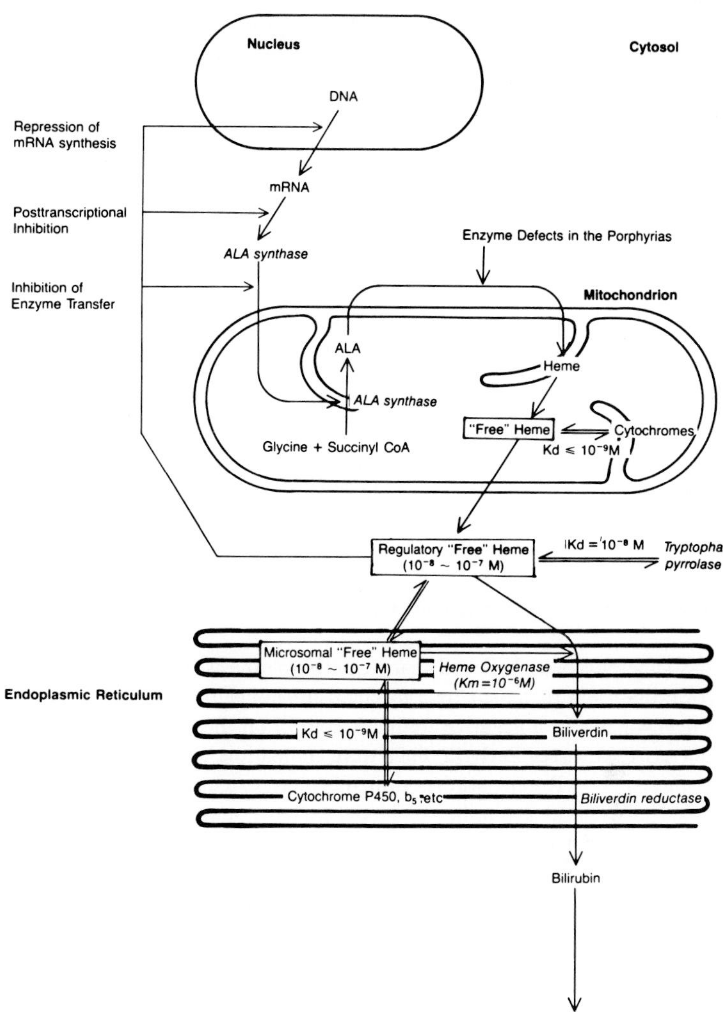

Fig. 52-7 The hypothetical role of "free" heme in cellular heme metabolism.

thesis of subunits of cytochrome oxidase that are synthesized in the mitochondrial ribosomes.

2. Cytosolic free heme may repress the rate of synthesis of ALA synthase, or induce heme oxygenase, the enzyme that degrades heme to bile pigments. This fraction plays a critically important role in the biosynthesis and catabolism of heme and thus can be considered as "regulatory" heme.

3. Microsomal free heme may regulate the activity of heme oxygenase in addition to serving as substrate for the enzyme.

It has been shown that tryptophan pyrrolase is a very sensitive marker for assessing subtle changes in the cytosolic free heme concentration. This rate limiting enzyme of tryptophan metabolism exists in two forms, heme-free apoenzyme and heme-containing holoenzyme. Inhibition of heme synthesis and increased destruction or utilization of heme decrease saturation of tryptophan pyrrolase. The degree of heme saturation of tryptophan pyrrolase increases with increasing hemin dosage, and the relative distribution of ALA synthase in the liver cytosol and the mitochondria also changes significantly, displaying a good correlation with the change in the degree of heme saturation of tryptophan pyrrolase. Based on the decrease of heme saturation of the pyrrolase produced by DDC plus phenylbutazone, it has been calculated that the largest amount of heme that can be removed from tryptophan pyrrolase is 0.093 μM.[168] This exchangeable heme in the pyrrolase is probably in equilibrium with free heme, and its concentration is very close to that which inhibits the synthesis of ALA synthase (i.e., $K_r = 0.1\ \mu M$).[105]

Compounds that destroy free heme or inhibit heme formation are usually strong inducers of ALA synthase. In particular, the most marked induction of ALA synthase occurs when animals are treated with two compounds (such as DDC and phenobarbital[161,169] or DDC and AIA[66]) that affect heme biosynthesis by different mechanisms. Potentiation of ALA synthase induction by AIA can also be produced by simultaneous treatment with desferrioxamine[146] or CaMg EDTA,[143] or a small dose of DDC.[144,145] Both desferrioxamine and CaMg EDTA, by chelating iron, and DDC, by forming *N*-methylprotoporphyrin, a potent inhibitor of ferrochelatase, inhibit ferrochelatase activity. Thus CaMg EDTA or a low dose of DDC (which can inhibit ferrochelatase without inducing ALA synthase) leads to a potentiation of ALA synthase formation caused by other inducing chemicals such as phenobarbital.

This situation is analogous to that in the human hepatic porphyrias in which a deficiency of an enzyme activity of the heme biosynthetic pathway (e.g., a 50 percent deficiency of PBG deaminase activity in AIP) reflects the primary gene defect. One-half of the normal level of enzymatic activity appears to be sufficient to maintain normal hepatic heme synthesis in porphyric subjects during remission or in clinically latent gene carriers who also carry the same enzymatic deficiency as in the clinically manifest porphyric subjects. However, when the liver has to increase its heme formation significantly in response to chemical treatment or exposure to certain steroids, other drugs, and environmental agents, particularly in circumstances in which hepatic cytochrome P_{450} formation is induced, the primary enzyme deficiency then can become rate limiting for heme formation, resulting in a decrease in the regulatory free heme concentration. The regulatory mechanism for synthesis of ALA synthase is then freed from heme repression, and the susceptibility of ALA synthase to induction then becomes increased.

A mechanism operating at the level of heme degradation, as well as one operating at the level of heme synthesis, could potentially serve to control the level of regulatory free heme, resulting in an alteration of ALA synthase formation. For example, agents (e.g., divalent metals,[170–174] endotoxins,[126] organic chemicals,[152,175]) or clinical circumstances (e.g., nutritional deprivation) that stimulate the synthesis *de novo* of heme oxygenase might be able to result in depletion of the regulatory free heme pool. For example, starvation leads to increased heme oxygenase activity and is known to precipitate acute porphyric symptoms in some patients with hereditary hepatic porphyria,[176,177] and these clinical attacks can be prevented by the feeding of a high carbohydrate diet.[178]

Heme Synthesis in Erythroid Cells

It has generally been believed that heme biosynthesis in nonhepatic tissues is regulated by a mechanism similar to that in the liver—namely, a negative feedback control on the synthesis of ALA synthase. Early findings were compatible with this hypothesis.[118,179] Recent studies utilizing more extensive and detailed analysis in a number of model systems suggest that there are distinct regulatory features of heme biosynthesis in erythroid cells.[119,180–184] For example, erythroid ALA synthase is not inducible by drugs that induce hepatic porphyria.[185]

More recent studies using murine erythroleukemia (MEL) cells, human erythroleukemia cells in culture, and normal bone marrow colonies in vitro suggest that the regulation of heme biosynthesis in erythroid cells is not exerted through a feedback control by heme on ALA synthase formation. When MEL cells are treated with dimethyl sulfoxide (DMSO) or a variety of other compounds, the cells undergo erythroid differentiation and display many characteristics of normal erythroid cells, including the formation of hemoglobin.[186] It has been shown that not only ALA synthase but also all other enzymes of the heme biosynthetic pathway are induced when MEL cells undergo erythroid differentiation.[100,180,184] A clone of Friend cells has also been isolated in which the induction of ALA synthase and the response to inducers occur normally, but the cells lack the ability to form heme for hemoglobin formation in response to inducer treatment.[182–184] Clearly there is not always a correlation between ALA synthase activity and heme content in erythroid cells. Perhaps the most important finding concerning the role of heme in hemoglobin formation in erythroid cells is the fact that treatment of a wild-type clone of MEL cells with hemin can cause not only increased synthesis of hemoglobin[187,188] but also increased levels of ALA synthase, ALA dehydratase, PBG deaminase, and ^{59}Fe incorporation into heme (21,100). Increases in ALA synthase activity in response to hemin treatment in erythroid cells are in striking contrast to the effect of hemin in the liver, where hemin suppresses the synthesis of ALA synthase. A similar finding of hemin-mediated induction of heme pathway enzymes, including ALA synthase, has been reported in human erythroleukemia cells.[119] Hemin, but not ALA, stimulates hemoglobin formation in normal mouse bone marrow cultures.[189]

These studies point to the importance of ferrochelatase, the final enzyme of heme biosynthesis, in controlling the rate of heme formation in erythroid cells. Evidence which substantiates the rate limiting role of ferrochelatase in erythroid cells follows:

1. Hemoglobin formation does not occur until ferrochelatase activity increases in MEL cells treated with DMSO, despite the fact that other enzymatic activities of the heme pathway have increased considerably earlier than the increase in ferrochelatase activity.[180,187]

2. Hemin, but not ALA, PBG, or protoporphyrin, can increase hemoglobin content in undifferentiated murine erythroleukemic (MEL) cells.[21,187,188]

3. In the mutant clone of MEL cells, which displays the normal induction responses of ALA synthase, ALA dehydratase, and PBG deaminase, but which is not able to make hemoglobin after DMSO treatment (presumably owing to an enzyme block after PBG deaminase), DMSO plus hemin can correct for the defect of hemoglobin formation.[182,183]

4. The ferrochelatase deficiency in erythropoietic protoporphyria (EPP) appears to be expressed in terms of protoporphyrin accumulation mainly in erythroid tissue, although ferrochelatase is presumably deficient in all tissue. This suggests that deficient ferrochelatase activity may become rate limiting in erythroid cells but not in nonerythroid tissues.

Concerning the effect of hemin on heme formation in erythroid cells, two lines of contrasting evidence exist. An earlier observation that the incorporation of radiolabeled glycine, but not ALA, into heme was decreased by hemin treatment[190] suggests that hemin may directly inhibit ALA synthase activity in reticulocytes. This does not establish hemin inhibition of ALA synthase activity conclusively, however, since direct measurements of the activity of ALA synthase are not affected in vitro by hemin even at concentrations as high as $10^{-4}\ M$.[100] In addition, incorporation of ^{59}Fe into heme (i.e., the ferrochelatase reaction) is strongly inhibited by hemin treatment.[21] Recent work suggests that the principal role of hemin in heme synthesis in erythroid cells is to regulate the transport of iron into reticulocytes.[191] It should also be noted that in the fetal rodent liver, which is highly erythropoietic, ALA synthase activity is constitutively high[192,193] and cannot be suppressed by hemin treatment.[194] Likewise, fetal ALA synthase is suppressed by aminotriazole treatment rather than increased as is the case with adult rat liver ALA synthase, and a reversal of the aminotriazole suppression of the fetal enzyme can be brought about by treatment with hemin.[194] Recently, it has been reported that ALA synthase from the fetal liver is similar to that of the adult erythropoietic form but can be distinguished from the adult liver form of the enzyme using an affinity column composed of AMP (6-amino) and CoA (sulfhydryl)-carboxyhexyl-Sepharose.[195] This finding substantiates the interesting possibility that ALA synthase in erythroid and liver cells may be distinct isozymes.

Heme Synthesis in Other Cell Types

Control of heme biosynthesis in cell types other than liver and erythroid cells has been little studied. It appears that the regulation of heme biosynthesis in nonhepatic tissues differs from that in the liver. Potent inducers of hepatic ALA synthase do not increase ALA synthase activity in the Harderian gland of mice[58]; heart,[196] adrenal gland,[197] testes,[198] brain,[60] or spleen[185] in the rat; or cultured human amniotic cells.[199] On the other hand, specific hormones increase the level of ALA synthase activity in nonhepatic target tissues. For example, adrenocorticotropic hormone increases ALA synthase activity in the adrenal gland,[197] human chorionic gonadotrophin increases enzyme activity in the testes,[198] and erythropoietin increases ALA synthase in the spleen.[185]

The effect of hemin on ALA synthase activity in nonhepatic tissues is also quite different from that in liver. Hemin does not suppress ALA synthase in mouse Harderian gland,[58] heart,[196] adrenal gland,[197] or testes[198] in the rat. ALA synthase in the fetal rodent liver, which is largely erythroid during the fetal period, is also refractory to inhibition by hemin.[65] Changes in ALA synthase activity in fetal guinea pig liver are correlated with the change in erythropoietic activity in this organ.[195] Thus, regulation of the enzymatic activity of fetal liver reflects, by and large, that of erythroid cells.

Nonhepatic tissues, e.g., skin fibroblasts or lymphocytes, obtained from patients with the acute hepatic porphyrias, fully express the deficiency of heme pathway enzymes relevant to their diseases in cell culture, and the enzyme deficiency in these cells is almost certainly similar to that found in the liver. However, cultured skin fibroblasts[44,200] or mitogen-stimulated lymphocytes[201] from patients with AIP do not show elevated ALA synthase activity in spite of a major deficiency of PBG deaminase. These findings suggest either that heme deficiency does not occur in isolated cultured cells to the same extent as is presumed to be the case in the liver of patients with active AIP, or that ALA synthase in cells derived from nonhepatic tissues in culture is not controlled by the cellular free heme concentration.

Watson[202] postulated that a heme deficiency involving cytochrome P_{450} may develop in central nervous system tissues, leading to a decrease in the activity of cytochrome P_{450}-associated mixed-function oxidases. Whether a deficiency of cytochrome P_{450} occurs in the central nervous system is not known, but there is evidence that central nervous system cells contain cytochrome P_{450},[203] that they can form porphyrins from ALA,[124] and that they might be capable of forming heme from appropriate precursors. For example, cultured dorsal root ganglion cells from chick embryo[204] and mouse[205] can form protoporphyrin from ALA. Thus, the heme pathway enzymes, at least from ALA dehydratase to ferrochelatase, are present in these cultured cells. This enzymatic activity is predominant in Schwann cells rather than in neuronal cells,[204] and it is subject to inhibition by potent inhibitors of heme biosynthesis such as lead.[205,206] These findings provide a potential explanation for demyelination of nerve fibers in vivo and for deterioration of neuronal functions that may be dependent on normally functioning Schwann cells.[206] Hemin treatment of dorsal root ganglion cells can limit the extent of the demyelination produced by lead.[207] It is possible, therefore, that neuronal cells may depend to some extent on the supply of heme or heme precursors, which may be provided by surrounding nonneuronal elements such as Schwann cells or other supporting cells. It may also be possible that a heme deficiency in central nervous system tissues can be corrected by exogenous hemin.

ALA DEHYDRATASE DEFICIENCY PORPHYRIA

Definition

ALA dehydratase deficiency porphyria (ALADP) is an autosomal recessive disorder resulting from a homozygous deficiency in ALA dehydratase activity (Fig. 52-8). The condition was first recognized by Doss et al.[208,209] in 1979. The symptomatology is similar to that seen in AIP, although the onset of symptoms in one patient with ALADP has been reported before puberty.

Prevalence

Three cases have been reported to date; two were the postpubertal males originally reported by Doss et al.,[208] and one was a male infant diagnosed at 2 years of age.[210]

Enzymology

ALA dehydratase [δ-aminolevulinate hydrolase (EC 4.2.1.24)] is a cytosolic enzyme which catalyzes the condensation of two molecules of ALA to form a monopyrrole, PBG, with the removal of two molecules of water (Fig. 52-8). ALA dehydratase has been isolated from animals,[211] plants,[212] and bacteria.[28] The enzyme, from bovine liver and human erythrocytes, has a molecular weight of 285,000[213] and 252,000,[214] respectively, with each having eight apparently identical subunits.[214,215] ALA dehydratase purified from mammalian erythrocytes and liver requires sulfhydryl compounds such as β-mercaptoethanol, cysteine, reduced glutathione, or dithiothreitol (DTT)[214–216] as well as Zn^{2+} for maximal activity.[214,217] The enzyme contains 1 atom of Zn per mole of subunit.[218,219] Enzyme activity is quickly lost when the sulfhydryl groups of the enzyme are inactivated by oxidation, by mercaptide formation, or if Zn^{2+} is displaced from the enzyme.[218]

One molecule of ALA forms a covalent bond to the enzyme through the formation of a Schiff base between the ε-amino group of a lysine residue and the keto group of ALA[220] (Fig. 52-9). Competitive inhibitors of the enzyme also have a keto

Fig. 52-8 The enzymatic deficiency in ALADP is an almost complete deficiency of ALA dehydratase activity. Patients with this disorder present clinical symptoms indistinguishable from those with AIP. Unlike patients with AIP who excrete excessive amounts of ALA and PBG, patients with ALADP excrete an excessive amount of ALA, but not PBG. Clinical disease does not occur in heterozygous gene carriers. ALA = δ-aminolevulinic acid; PBG = porphobilinogen; Uro'gen = uroporphyrinogen; Copro'gen = coproporphyrinogen; Proto'gen = protoporphyrinogen; Proto = protoporphyrin.

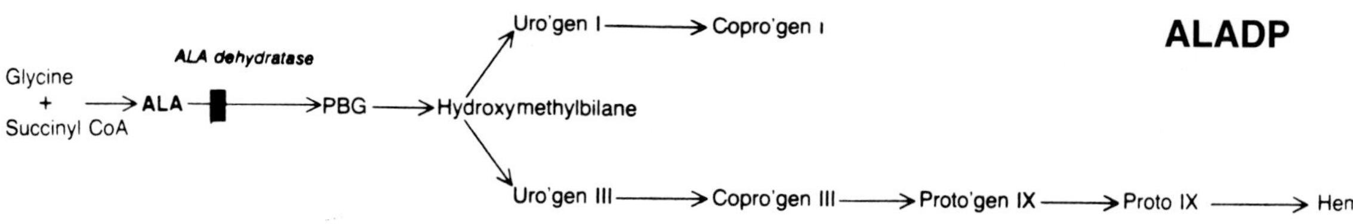

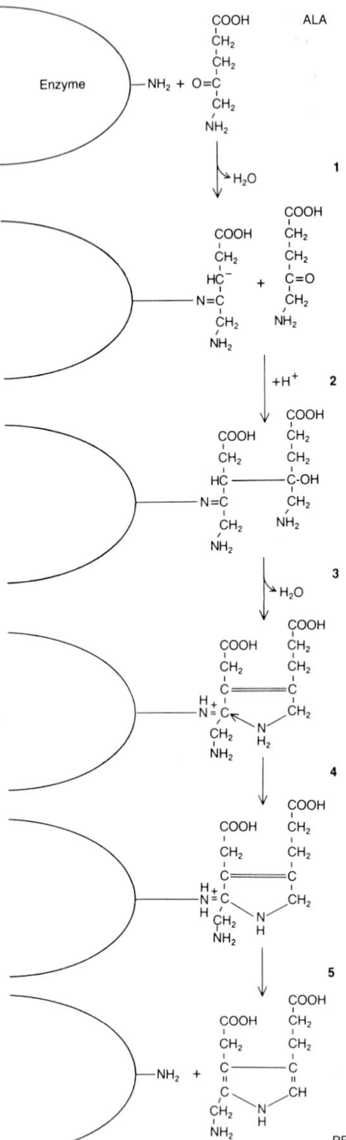

Fig. 52-9 The reaction catalyzed by ALA dehydratase. (1) The first molecule of ALA is bound covalently to the enzyme through a Schiff base between the ε-amino group of the lysine residue and the keto group of ALA. (2) This stabilized carbanion then participates in an aldol condensation with a second ALA molecule. (3) The removal of one water molecule. (4) A proton is then transferred from the amino group of the second ALA molecule to the ε-amino group of lysine. (5) The enzyme is released, and after intramolecular rearrangement a PBG molecule is formed.[220]

group gamma to the carboxyl carbon. It has been demonstrated that the ALA molecule initially bound to the enzyme is the one which contributes to the propionic acid side chain of PBG[221](Fig. 52-9). The purified enzyme obtained from bovine liver and human erythrocytes is pale yellowish in color, and spectral analysis suggests that pyridoxal-5′-phosphate may be bound to the enzyme.[214]

Electron-microscopic analysis of the bovine enzyme is compatible with a structure consisting of eight subunits.[213] ALA dehydratases purified from different mammalian tissues are remarkably similar[222]; the molecular weights are approximately 280,000; K_m values for ALA are 1 to 4 × 10^{-4} *M;* and V_{max} values are 20 to 24 μmol/h per milligram of protein at 37°C. There are no tissue-specific isozymes of ALA dehydratase or strain-specific differences in various strains of mice and rats,[223,224] although differences in the level of activity occur (see below).

ALA dehydratase activity can be inhibited by lead,[225] levulinic acid,[226] hemin,[227,228] or succinylacetone (4,6-dioxoheptanoic acid).[229,230] Lead is a potent inhibitor of erythrocyte ALA dehydratase and presumably acts by displacing zinc from the enzyme. Lead-inhibited ALA dehydratase activity can be completely reactivated by the addition of Zn^{2+} and/or DTT, both of which reduce binding of lead to the enzyme.[225] The most potent inhibitor of the enzyme is probably succinylacetone, which is found in urine and blood of patients with hereditary tyrosinemia.[229–231] As shown in Fig. 52-10, succinylacetone is a structural analogue of ALA; it is an extremely potent competitive inhibitor of purified ALA dehydratase from bovine liver or human red cells. The K_i of succinylacetone for the bovine enzyme is 5 × 10^{-8} *M*, which is about 1/10,000 of the K_m of the enzyme for ALA.[232] Although a 50 percent loss of ALA dehydratase activity in hereditary ALA dehydratase deficiency has no apparent effect on heme synthesis, an inhibition of the enzyme activity by iron or trichloroethylene has been reported to limit heme synthesis.[233,234]

ALA dehydratase activity in mice shows a threefold range of interstrain variability, which is due to differences in the rate of synthesis of the enzyme and which is determined by codominant alleles at the *Lv* locus.[227,235] The *Lv* locus is known to occur in very close vicinity to brown *b*, in linkage group VIII.[27] Thus, mouse strains homozygous for the Lv^a allele have approximately three times higher ALA dehydratase activity than strains homozygous for Lv^b alleles. The heterozygotes (Lv^a/Lv^b) show an intermediate level of the enzyme activity.[235] Erythrocyte ALA dehydratase in the human population also shows a three- to fourfold range of enzyme activity. In contrast, identical twins have very similar values of the enzyme activity.[236] This finding strongly suggests genetic control of the enzyme synthesis in humans as well as in the experimental animal.

ALA dehydratase activity of erythroid cells changes during erythroid maturation. The enzyme activity increases early and sharply during erythroid differentiation and precedes the appearance of hemoglobin.[237–239] In contrast, it falls with the maturation of reticulocytes into mature erythrocytes.[240] For example, ALA dehydratase activity in mouse reticulocytes is approximately 15 times higher than in mature erythrocytes. A

Fig. 52-10 Structures of ALA and succinylacetone. The 4-oxopentanoic acid structure shown in bold letters is common to both ALA and succinylacetone, making the latter a potent competitive inhibitor in the ALA dehydratase reaction.

δ-Aminolevulinic Acid

$$HOOC-CH_2-CH_2-\overset{\overset{\displaystyle O}{\|}}{C}-CH_2-NH_2$$

Succinylacetone

$$HOOC-CH_2-CH_2-\overset{\overset{\displaystyle O}{\|}}{C}-CH_2-\overset{\overset{\displaystyle O}{\|}}{C}-CH_3$$

similar decline in the enzyme activity with red cell age is observed in human red cells.[241]

ALA dehydratase is assayed by incubating homogenates of tissues with ALA and then determining colorimetrically the amount of PBG generated enzymatically, after reacting the latter with modified Ehrlich reagent. In order to obtain the maximal rate of reaction, it is necessary to maintain an optimum pH for the reaction (pH 6.3 to 6.7), to include sulfhydryl compounds such as DTT or reduced glutathione, and to maintain the Zn cation at the catalytic site of the enzyme.[242]

Molecular Biology

cDNA clones encoding rat liver ALA dehydratase have been recently isolated.[243] Eighty percent homology was found between the partial nucleotide sequence and the N-terminal protein sequence of the bovine enzyme.[244] Rat liver ALA dehydratase cDNA reacted with genomic DNA from several species such as humans, rabbits, and mice. Gene dose differences were found among different strains of mice, explaining the known differences in the enzymatic level among these animals.[227] cDNA clones encoding ALA dehydratase have also been obtained from human liver cDNA libraries.[245,246] Sequence determination revealed an open reading frame of 990 bp coding for a protein of molecular weight 36,274, in good agreement with experimental data on the protein. The predicted N-terminal amino acid sequence was colinear with the first 13 residues of sequenced ALA dehydratase from human erythrocytes, and extensive homologies were found not only between sequences of human protein and of bovine ALA dehydratase peptides[244] but also between the nucleotide sequences from human and rat liver cDNAs.[247] The sequences corresponding to the active lysine residue at the catalytic site[248] and the cysteine- and histidine-rich zinc binding site of the protein were identified.

Clinical Findings

The two male postpubertal cases of homozygous ALA dehydratase deficiency both presented at 16 years of age with vomiting, pain in the arms and legs, and neuropathy; the first patient also developed abdominal pain.[208,209] Later, the second patient developed paralysis of the arms, legs, and the respiratory muscles; over the next 6 years he had a variable but continuous mixed motor/sensory polyneuropathy. Both patients displayed clinical exacerbations following stress, decreased food intake, or alcohol intake. One patient responded favorably to intravenous glucose infusions.[208,209,249]

The third known case was diagnosed at age 2 but the patient had had a stormy clinical course from birth.[210] General muscle hypotonia and respiratory insufficiency necessitated ventilation for several weeks during the slow recovery of muscle tone and tendon reflexes. The EMG changes had normalized by 10 months of age, although the patient still vomited frequently. Thirteen months later decreased food intake preceded the onset of bilateral paralysis of the legs and the demonstration of abnormal porphyrin metabolism. Subsequently, his clinical course comprised a series of exacerbations and remissions leading to ankle contractures, atrophy of the calf muscles, and impaired hand movements.[210]

Biochemical Findings

Urinary ALA excretion has been markedly elevated in all cases, as would be predicted from the low activity of ALA dehydratase. In contrast, urinary PBG excretion was not increased (Fig. 52-8). Surprisingly, urinary and erythrocyte porphyrins (predominantly coproporphyrin III and protoporphyrin, respectively) have been elevated approximately 100-fold. No satisfactory explanation has yet been advanced to account for this observation. Fecal porphyrin excretion has been normal or marginally elevated.

All cases have displayed decreased activity of ALA dehydratase in erythrocytes. In two cases, bone marrow cells showed ≈2 percent of normal activity. Approximately 50 percent decreases in activity were found in the parents' red cell enzyme. No decreases in PBG deaminase activity have been reported in any case, and uroporphyrinogen decarboxylase activity was normal in both teenage patients. These two patients also had normal bone marrow morphology, iron metabolism, and hemoglobin concentrations. In contrast, the infant had a hemolytic anemia which required transfusion. It is unclear if this is another aspect of the neonatal disease or is unrelated. The mutations characterizing the ALA dehydratase deficiency state in all three cases reported have been CRM-positive.[250,251]

Diagnosis

Definitive diagnosis is dependent on the demonstration of defective ALA dehydratase activity and deficiency of enzyme protein in erythrocytes. In the three documented cases, this activity has been approximately 2 percent of normal values, consistent with a homozygous deficiency. Intermediate decreases in ALA dehydratase activity, as were seen in the patients' relatives and in the family described by Bird et al.,[252] presumably reflect the heterozygous deficiency state. Heterozygote levels have not been associated with any clinical signs and symptoms and are not compatible with the diagnosis of ALADP. Supporting evidence for the diagnosis includes massive elevations in urinary ALA, substantial elevations of porphyrins in urine and erythrocytes, and perhaps modest elevations in fecal porphyrins.

Treatment

The fact that there are only three reported cases of ALADP obviously limits the provision of definitive treatment guidelines. In the case of the two teenage males, one responded to intravenous glucose. Both experienced exacerbation following stress, fasting, or alcohol intake.[208,209,249] The third patient failed to respond to intravenous glucose (5 g/kg) or nasogastrically administered Caloreen (a high carbohydrate fluid), and displayed no obvious response to intravenous hematin (2 mg/kg) or heme arginate (3 mg/kg).[210] However, the similarities between this form of acute porphyria and AIP suggest that prudent management of ALADP should probably be directed along the same lines as the management of AIP. Thus, avoidance of known precipitating factors, maintenance of an adequate and regular carbohydrate intake, and intravenous glucose and/or hematin during exacerbations are to be recommended. There is also one report of successful administration of ALA dehydratase-loaded erythrocyte ghosts to a patient with chronic lead intoxication.[253] Whether this same approach could be used in ALADP is unknown.

ACUTE INTERMITTENT PORPHYRIA

Synonyms

Synonyms for acute intermittent porphyria (AIP) are Swedish porphyria, pyrroloporphyria, and intermittent acute porphyria.

Definition

AIP is an autosomal dominant disorder resulting from a deficiency in PBG deaminase activity (Fig. 52-11). The deficient enzyme activity is almost always 50 percent of normal, consistent with the heterozygous state of affected individuals. However, the majority (≈90 percent) of people with this genetic enzyme deficiency remain otherwise biochemically and clinically normal (i.e., latent). Clinical expression of the disease is usually linked to environmental or acquired factors (e.g., nutritional status, hormones or their metabolites, drugs), which may intermittently precipitate acute exacerbations. The cardinal pathobiology of the disease is a neurologic dysfunction of indeterminant etiology, which may affect the peripheral, autonomic, or central nervous systems; the resulting neuropathic symptoms may therefore be variable and highly diverse.

Prevalence

Lapland, Scandinavia, and the United Kingdom are generally held to have the highest incidence of AIP, although it has been reported in many population groups.[254–256] The incidence of the defective gene in the United States has been estimated at between 5 and 10 per 100,000.[257] In Sweden, the incidence of the clinical disease, which represents only a small fraction (<10%) of the gene carrier state, was estimated (based on urinary ALA and PBG determinations) to be 1.5 per 100,000.[258] Regrettably, the incidence of AIP in psychiatric populations is still considerably higher than in the normal population (0.21 percent of 3867 patients[259]). Epidemiologic data based on erythrocyte PBG deaminase measurements are not available except within individual families where relatives have been screened for carrier status. The disorder is expressed clinically almost invariably after puberty and more commonly in women than in men. AIP is probably the most common of all the genetic porphyrias.

Enzymology

Porphobilinogen (PBG) Deaminase [Porphobilinogen Ammonia-Lyase (Polymerizing) (EC 4.3.1.8)]. Uroporphyrinogen III, a key intermediate in the biosynthesis of all naturally occurring tetrapyrroles, is formed from PBG through the sequential action of two enzymes. Although chemical condensation of four molecules of PBG can yield four possible uroporphyrinogen isomers[260,261] (Fig. 52-12), enzyme-catalyzed reactions yield only the type I and III isomers of uroporphyrinogen.

Reaction Mechanism. PBG deaminase [hydroxymethylbilane synthase, or uroporphyrinogen I synthase (EC 4.3.1.8)], catalyzes the polymerization of four molecules of PBG yielding a tetrapyrrole intermediate, hydroxymethylbilane.[262,263] In this reaction four units of PBG are assembled head-to-tail by the deaminase, starting with ring A and building around to ring D to form the unrearranged bilane (Fig. 52-13). In the absence

Fig. 52-11 The enzymatic defect in AIP is a partial (≈50 percent) deficiency of PBG deaminase activity. The extent of the enzyme deficiency is the same in clinically latent *(top)* and clinically expressed AIP *(bottom)* subjects. Full clinical expression of the AIP gene defect occurs with exposure to factors such as hormones and drugs, which appear to activate the disease primarily by inducing ALA synthase (bold letters) in the liver. Activation of the disease is associated with excess production and excretion of ALA and PBG (bold letters). A similar transition from clinically latent to clinically expressed disease characterizes HCP and VP. ALA = δ-aminolevulinic acid; PBG = porphobilinogen; Uro'gen = uroporphyrinogen; COPRO'gen = corproporphyrinogen; Proto'gen = protoporphyrinogen; PROTO = protoporphyrin.

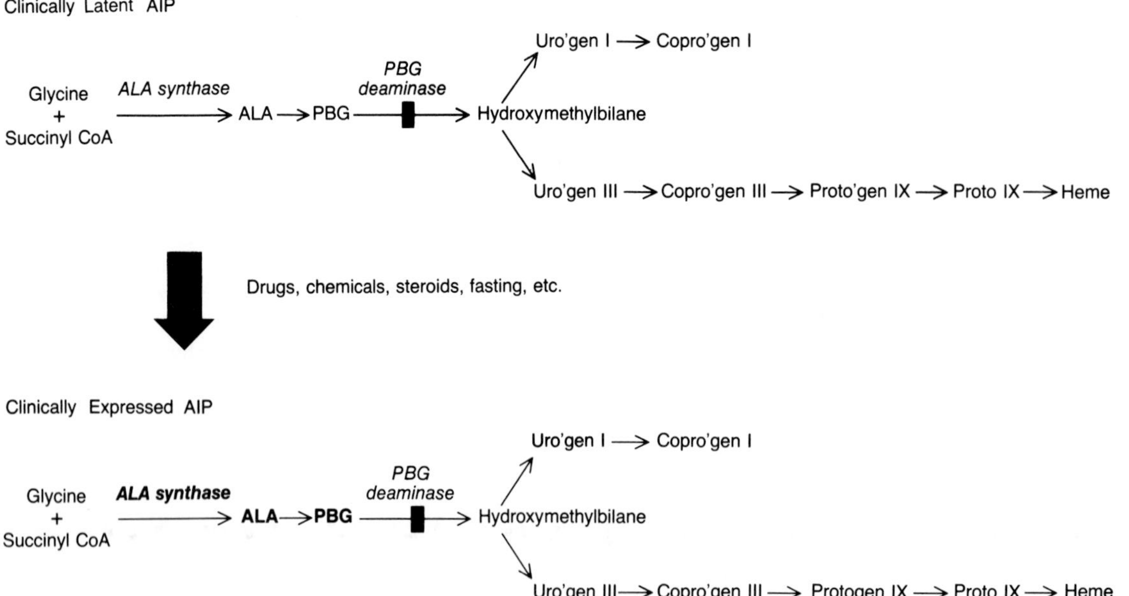

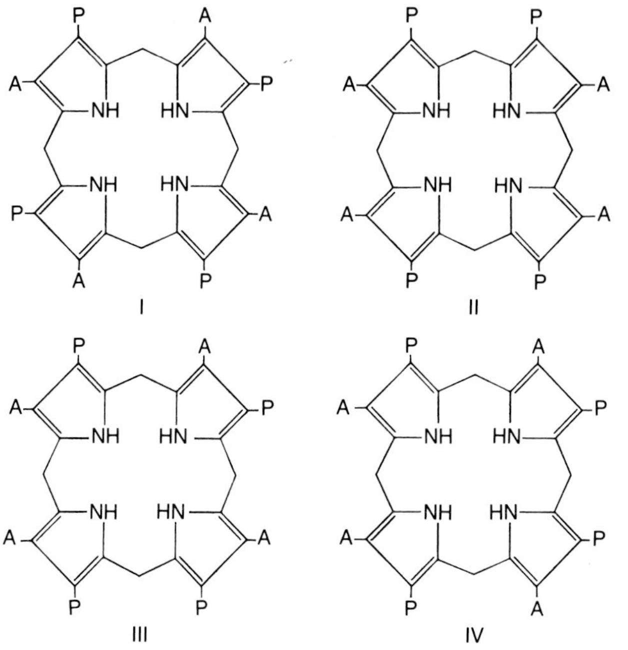

Fig. 52-12 The four isomers of uroporphyrinogen. The only isomers found in nature are types I and III, and only isomer III can proceed to the formation of heme. A = —CH_2·COOH; P = —CH_2·CH_2·COOH.

of the subsequent enzyme, uroporphyrinogen III cosynthase, the bilane is released into the medium as hydroxymethylbilane[263] (Fig. 52-13). Thus the deaminase furnishes a straight chain tetrapyrrole hydroxymethylbilane, but it is not an enzyme for ring closure.[266] Uroporphyrinogen III cosynthase then rapidly converts the intermediate into uroporphyrinogen III (Fig. 52-13). This involves an intramolecular rearrangement which affects only ring D and the atoms which become C-15 and C-20 of uroporphyrinogen III. There is also evidence suggesting an association or complex of the deaminase and cosynthase molecules which would account for the rapid enzymatic formation of uroporphyrinogen III.[267–269]

PBG deaminase purified from human erythrocytes has been shown to form stable covalent complexes bearing up to four condensed PBG units.[270] Subsequently the enzyme-substrate (ES) complexes were also identified in *R. spheroids*,[271–273] *Euglena gracilis*,[274,275,277] and rat spleen. Studies on the *R. spheroids*–ES complex[278] suggested that the substrate is covalently attached to the enzyme. However, unlike the case with the human enzyme, no complex corresponding to bound tetrapyrrole was detected in the bacterium. It was also shown that the erythrocyte-specific isozymes may be in part due to posttranslational modification by deamidation or glycosylation.[276] Genetic evidence indicates that all these isozymes are encoded by the same structural gene.[276]

Properties. PBG deaminase purified from human erythrocytes has a specific activity of ≈2300 units per milligram of protein.[270] The pH optimum of the enzyme from human erythrocytes is 8.2, and the K_m is 6 μM. Molecular weights of deaminases from human and other sources are in the range of 36,000 to 40,000.[270,279,280] PBG deaminase is apparently more stable when it is bound covalently to its substrate than when it is free.[281]

Lead has been reported to inhibit the activity of erythrocyte PBG deaminase in vitro,[282] although the concentrations required are higher than those found in lead poisoning. There is no evidence for inhibition of the enzyme activity in erythrocytes from patients with plumbism. A recent study showed that PBG deaminase from rat liver is inhibited in vitro by a wide range of divalent and trivalent metal ions.[283] Very soft ions such as Hg^{2+}, intermediate ions such as Cr^{3+}, and very hard ions such as Al^{3+} all inhibited the enzyme activity, suggesting that there may be three different types of inhibitory binding sites at or near the active site. A dialysable factor that has a protective effect on the lead-inhibited deaminase has

Fig. 52-13 Formation of uroporphyrinogen I and III from PBG. PBG deaminase catalyzes the condensation of four PBG molecules in a head-to-tail fashion to yield a linear unrearranged bilane. This is released from the enzyme as hydroxymethylbilane, which cyclizes nonenzymatically to form uroporphyrinogen I. Thus the product of the PBG deaminase catalyzed reaction is not porphyrinogen; therefore the enzyme should no longer be referred to as uroporphyrinogen I synthase. In the presence of uroporphyrinogen III cosynthase, hydroxymethylbilane is converted to uroporphyrinogen III.[264,265] E = PBG deaminase; A = —CH_2·COOH; P = —CH_2·CH_2·COOH.

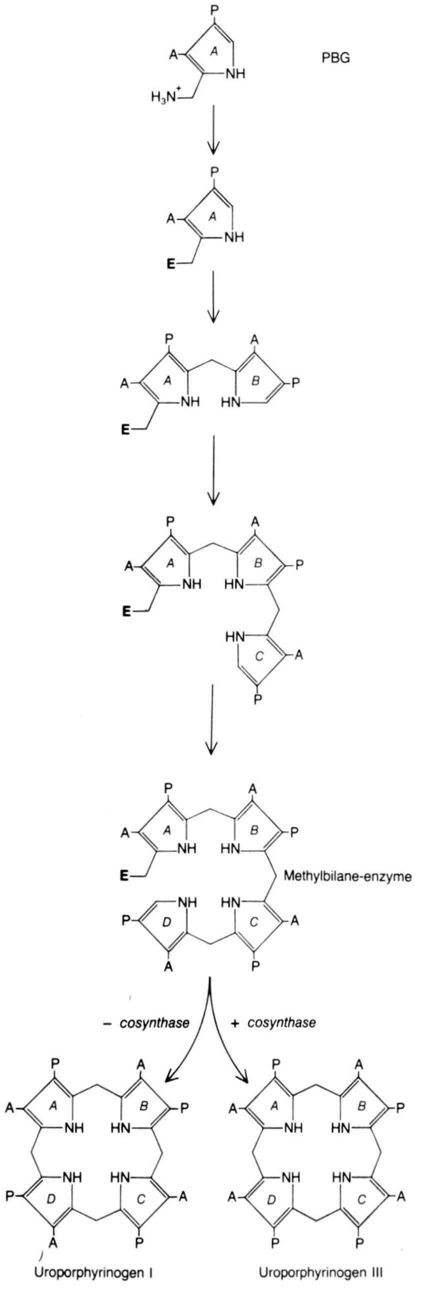

been purified from rat liver and has been determined to be a pteroylpolyglutamate derivative.[284] Folic acid, which may serve as a precursor for pteroylglutamate, has also been reported to produce both clinical and biochemical improvement in some patients with AIP.[285]

Inheritance. The human gene locus encoding PBG deaminase has been assigned to chromosome 11 by data from human × mouse somatic cell hybrids.[286] Subsequently the regional gene assignments for human PBG deaminase and esterase A_4 were made to chromosome 11q23→qter using somatic cell hybridization and immunologic, electrophoretic, and cytogenetic techniques.[287,288] Electrophoretic variants of two mouse enzymes, PBG deaminase and esterase 17, have been mapped to the proximal region of mouse chromosome 9.[289,290] Eight inbred mouse strains were found to carry the common allele at both loci, while a single strain, LP/J, had a basic variant of both enzymes, suggesting a degree of linkage disequilibrium among inbred strains.[291]

Assay. PBG deaminase activity is measured by the formation of uroporphyrin from PBG. Uroporphyrinogen, after oxidation to uroporphyrin, can be determined spectrophotometrically[279,292] or fluorometrically.[30,293] PBG consumption and tetrapyrrole formation are stoichiometric using a homogeneously purified deaminase from *Chlorella*,[294] but PBG consumption can also result in falsely higher values of the enzyme activity when crude tissues or partially purified enzyme preparations are used.[295] The discrepancy between PBG consumption and uroporphyrinogen formation can be due in part to another enzyme that metabolizes PBG, i.e., PBG oxygenase. PBG oxygenase has been found in rat liver and brain, wheat germ, spinach chloroplasts,[296,297] and human erythrocytes[298] and is inducible by phenobarbital as well as certain steroids in rat liver.[297]

Molecular Biology

A cDNA clone containing sequences complementary to the mRNA coding for anemic rat spleen PBG deaminase has been isolated.[298] Analysis of anemic human spleen RNA using the rat cDNA probe indicated that human PBG deaminase has the same length as the homologous rat sequence. Southern blot analysis of PBG deaminase sequences in rat and human DNA showed a simple restriction pattern suggesting that genomic sequences encoding PBG deaminase do not belong to a multigenic family. Subsequently, the molecular cloning and the complete primary sequence of the human cDNA were reported.[299,300] The source of RNA was an erythroid spleen removed from a thalassemic patient. The PBG deaminase mRNA expression had been found to be always higher in erythroid than in nonerythroid tissues. The largest PBG deaminase cDNA contained 1450 bp, with a single open reading frame of 1038 bp starting at position 82. It also contained a sequence of 267 bp corresponding to the mRNA 3′ noncoding regions. The sequence of the 19 amino acid residues adjacent to the N-terminal residue of PBG deaminase purified from human erythrocytes is identical with the sequence deduced from the nucleotide sequence downstream from the ATG codon (methionine) at position 82. When this initiator methionine is included, the reading frame encodes 344 amino acids and accounts for a protein having a molecular weight of 37,627. The value of 37,000 was obtained for the enzyme by SDS-polyacrylamide gel electrophoresis.[298] Southern blotting analysis of human genomic restriction fragments revealed evidence for only one gene for PBG deaminase.

The nucleotide sequence of the *hemC* locus encoding PBG deaminase of *Escherichia coli* K12 was recently described.[301] The structural gene is encoded by a 942-bp sequence. The coding region was confirmed by sequencing the N terminal of the enzyme and by comparison of the predicted molecular weight of 33,857 with that obtained using SDS-polyacrylamide gel electrophoresis or gel filtration. Similarity between the sequences of human and *E. coli* PBG deaminase was found to be around 43 percent (personal communication, P. M. Jordan). The PBG deaminase gene of yeast has also been isolated[302] by genetic complementation of a mutant strain previously shown to be defective in this enzyme.

Recently two distinct molecular forms of PBG deaminase were identified in mouse erythroleukemic cells by gel electrophoresis.[303] The heavier form (44 kDa) corresponds to a nonerythroid form of the enzyme, while the lighter form (42 kDa) represents an erythroid-specific form. Similar data were obtained in human cells.[304] Analysis of cell-free translation products directed by mRNAs from human erythropoietic spleen and from human liver showed that the two isoforms of PBG deaminase were encoded by distinct mRNAs. Comparison of the sequences from human erythropoietic mRNA[299] to nonerythropoietic (lymphoblastoid cells) mRNA[304] revealed a 1320-bp stretch of almost perfect identity; however, the two mRNA species differed at their 5′ extremity: an additional inframe AUG codon was found 52 bp upstream from the initiating codon of the nonerythropoietic cDNA (Fig. 52-14). It could be deduced that an additional peptide of 17 amino acid residues at the N-terminal of the nonerythropoietic isoform of PBG deaminase accounts for this higher molecular mass. From the different human cell type studies, it was clear that the erythropoietic type of mRNA is restricted to erythropoietic cells. The generation of alternative mRNAs from a single gene is probably linked to transcription from different promoters, although the published data cannot exclude the possibility of a single primary transcript processed differently by alternative splicing.

PBG deaminase activity is decreased in the tissues of patients with AIP. The enzyme activity is usually ≈50 percent of the enzyme activity found in normal subjects, and the deficiency is observed in erythrocytes (Fig. 52-15),[236,305–307] skin fibroblasts,[31,307–309] liver,[29,310] lymphocytes,[25] and amniotic cells.[31,307] In some families with AIP, the PBG deaminase deficiency appears to be restricted to nonerythropoietic tissues.[311] In light of the recent data describing[304] erythropoietic and nonerythropoietic isoforms of PBG deaminase specified by two mRNAs with different 5′ ends, it can be hypothesized that the molecular defect in these families lies within sequences of the PBG deaminase gene, which are specifically expressed in nonerythropoietic cells.

Clinical Findings

The clinical findings from three large series of 417 patients with AIP[312–314] are summarized in Table 52-5. Abdominal pain is almost invariably present and is often the initial symptom of an acute attack. It may be generalized or localized, and in severe cases it may mimic an acute surgical abdomen, sometimes leading to inappropriate laparotomy. Although seen less commonly today, such surgical explorations coupled with bar-

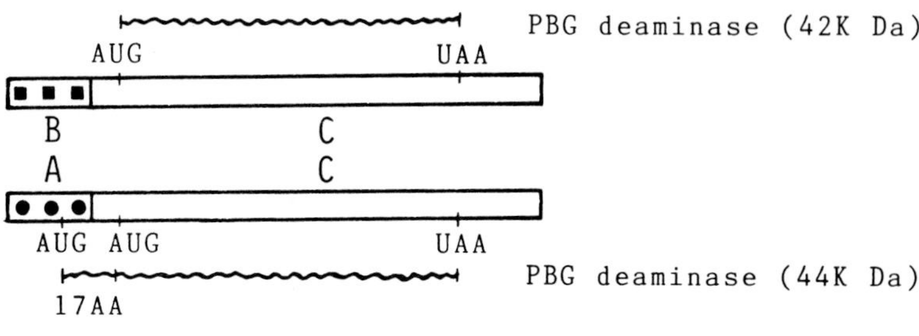

Fig. 52-14 PBG deaminase: Comparison of complete coding sequences of erythropoietic and nonerythropoietic mRNAs. There is a 1320-bp stretch of perfect identity (C) in the two RNAs whereas the 5′ end of nonerythropoietic mRNA (A) displayed no homology with the sequence of the erythropoietic mRNA (B); an additional peptide of 17 amino acids is encoded between both initiating codons (AUG), explaining the higher molecular mass of the nonerythropoietic isoform of PBG deaminase.

biturate induction of anesthesia can lead to disastrous exacerbations of an already acute attack of porphyria. Chest, back, and limb pain may also occur either in the presence or absence of abdominal pain. Characteristically, such pains are intermittent, but a subgroup of patients appears to have chronic pain of fluctuating severity which may be unrelated to the normal biochemical indices of porphyria activity. Other gastroenterologic features are common and may include nausea, vomiting, constipation, diarrhea, abdominal distension, and ileus. Urinary incontinence, dysuria, and frequency may occur, although urinary retention is probably more common; in severe cases, the urine may be of a port wine color owing to the high content of porphobilin, an autooxidized product of PBG, and some porphyrins, which are formed by nonenzymatic cyclization of PBG. Both urinary retention and constipation may be exacerbated by treatment, especially with narcotic analgesics.

Attendant increases in sympathetic outflow tract activity are often manifested as tachycardia and hypertension, and less frequently by fever, sweating, restlessness, and tremor. Catecholamine hypersecretion, when severe, has been implicated

Fig. 52-15 Erythrocyte PBG deaminase activities in normal subjects, patients with clinically expressed AIP, and individuals with clinically latent AIP. Activity of this enzyme is approximately 50 percent deficient in clinically expressed or latent AIP subjects and does not vary with disease activity. There is some overlap between the AIP and normal ranges of this enzyme activity in red cells.

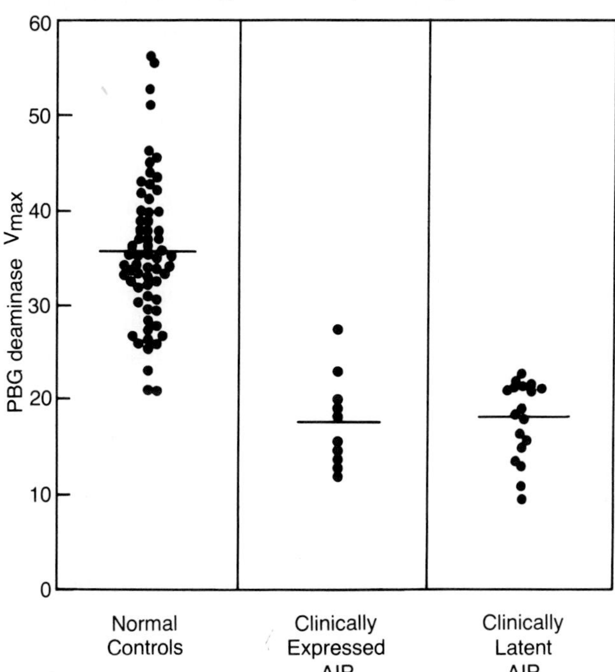

in sudden death, possibly secondary to cardiac arrhythmias.[284,315] In up to 40 percent of patients, hypertension may become sustained between acute attacks. It has been suggested that porphyria-induced hypertension may constitute a major factor in the pathogenesis of chronic renal failure which has been reported to occur in certain middle-aged AIP patients.[316] However, the pathogenesis of such renal failure may, in addition, be related to analgesic nephropathy and to nephrotoxic effects of heme pathway intermediates either passively filtered[316] or synthesized locally in the nephron.[317]

Neuropathy is a common feature of AIP. Although motor neuropathies predominate, it should be stressed that virtually any type of neuropathy may occur. Muscle weakness often begins proximally in the legs but may involve the arms or the distal extremities; involvement may be symmetric, asymmetric, or focal[318] and, in severe cases, may be associated with a decrease in or loss of tendon reflexes.[315] Motor neuropathy may also involve the cranial nerves (most commonly the VIIth and Xth) or lead to bulbar paralysis, respiratory deficiency, and death. AIP may rarely present as respiratory failure.[319] Patchy sensory neuropathy often coexists when motor neuropathy is severe and may be manifested by acute or chronic paresthesia, numbness, or dysesthesia.[320] Rarely, visual abnormalities may occur secondarily to ocular porphyrin accumulation,[321] or blindness may result from involvement of the optic nerves or the occipital lobes.[314,322,323] Autonomic neuropathy is also frequently present and may manifest as tachycardia, hypertension,[324] postural hypotension,[325] vomiting, constipation, diarrhea, sweating, and abnormal urinary bladder function. Objective signs of autonomic neuropathy such as abnormal cardiovascular reflexes have been reported in AIP patients during acute attacks but not during periods of remission or in those with latent cases of the disease.[326]

Anxiety, restlessness, insomnia, paranoia, and depression are not infrequent in acute AIP attacks. In some cases, depression and anxiety may become chronic. The differentiation between affective disorders and reactive disorders secondary to porphyria can pose a difficult diagnostic dilemma. Although it has been suggested that a specific porphyria mental syndrome may exist,[327] its definition remains elusive, especially when severe mental symptoms such as hallucinations and violent behavior may be worsened by inappropriate medications. AIP has also been incriminated as a cause of the rare Klüver-Bucy syndrome[328] which comprises oral tendencies, hypersexuality, hyperbulia, and hypermetamorphosis.

Sometimes AIP patients are labeled as hysterical.[329] The results of three studies (in 1961, 1976, and 1985) where psychiatric populations were screened for AIP have shown a significantly greater incidence than that seen in the general population.[259,330,331] It is distressing to realize that certain un-

Table 52-5 Incidence of Symptoms and Signs of Acute Intermittent Porphyria

	Percent incidence		
Symptoms & signs	*Waldenstrom, 1957*[312] *321 cases*	*Goldberg, 1959*[313] *50 cases*	*Satein & Tschudy, 1970*[314] *46 cases*
Abdominal pain	85	94	95
Vomiting	59	88	43
Constipation	48	84	48
Diarrhea	9	12	5
Limb, head, neck, or chest pain	—	52	50
Muscle weakness	42	68	60
Sensory loss	9	38	26
Convulsions	10	16	20
Respiratory paralysis	14	10	9
Mental symptoms	55	58	40
Hypertension	40	54	36
Tachycardia	28	64	80
Fever	37	14	9

fortunate individuals still languish, sometimes for years, in psychiatric institutions prior to the recognition that their correct diagnosis is porphyria.[332]

Acute attacks of AIP are fairly frequently accompanied by seizures, especially in patients with hyponatremia due to vomiting, inappropriate fluid therapy, or the syndrome of inappropriate antidiuretic hormone release. Rarely, epilepsy may be the presenting symptom in AIP.[333,334] As in the differential diagnosis of mental disturbances in porphyria mentioned above, it is often difficult to distinguish between any of the above causes of seizures and idiopathic epilepsy. An additional complication stems from the fact that many of the standard medications for the treatment of seizures are themselves porphyrinogenic and hence may lead to further exacerbation of porphyria.[335–338]

The course of an acute attack of AIP is variable both within and between patients, with attacks lasting for a few days to several months. Some patients develop a chronic, grumbling porphyria syndrome with or without acute-on-chronic exacerbations, but the majority of patients have fairly well delineated attacks with relatively asymptomatic intervening remissions. Motor or sensory neuropathies may never resolve,[320] but more typically there is a gradual return to normal functions. In some cases, however, recovery may take several years.[313]

Pathogenesis of the Clinical Findings. The symptomatology of AIP is believed to result largely from neurologic dysfunction. Evidence to support a neurologic basis for the abdominal pain, the cardinal symptom of porphyria, is provided by radiologic findings in upper GI series,[339] by the lack of significant gut pathology on laparotomy,[339] by the response to splanchnicectomy or ganglionic blockade,[340] and by postmortem findings in some cases. Histologic changes in peripheral and autonomic nerves include edema and irregularity of the myelin sheaths, thinned and irregular axons, axonal vacuolization and degeneration, and cellular infiltration.[315,341–344] Such pathologic findings correlate fairly well with results of electromyographic and nerve conduction studies, which may show muscle denervation and, in severe cases, decreased motor nerve conduction velocities.[345–347] There is also one report of delayed motor conduction in people with latent AIP.[348] A child with coexistent AIP and Hirschsprung disease prompted the interesting hypothesis that the pathogenesis of the degenerating ganglion cells typically seen in rectal biopsies in Hirschsprung disease may be related to the pathogenesis of the autonomic neural pathologies seen in AIP.[349] Central nervous system pathologies comprise chromatolysis and vacuolization of neurons, focal perivascular demyelination, reactive glial proliferation,[341] and reddish fluorescence in the white matter[315,343,350]; EEG changes have also been reported.[351] The supraoptic and paraventricular nuclei of the hypothalamus have also been reported to show neuronal loss, gliosis, and vacuolization.[284,352,353] These findings provide a pathologic basis for the clinical reports of inappropriate antidiuretic hormone syndrome in acute porphyria attacks,[354–361] and possibly of abnormal release of growth hormone[362] and ACTH.[363]

However, despite the above evidence linking the symptoms of AIP to neurologic dysfunction, the proximate pathogenesis of the various neuropathies remains obscure. An additional confounding factor is that postmortem findings have sometimes been minimal despite subjective and objective antemortem evidence of the presence of neuropathies. This observation suggests that the initial lesion is metabolic and that the emergence of frank histologic lesions is a late or secondary feature. The experimental findings and etiologic theories advanced to explain porphyria neuropathies fall into two major categories: first, a lack of heme, and second, a surfeit of heme pathway intermediates.

Heme pathway enzymes[364,365] and microsomal[366] and mitochondrial[367] cytochrome P_{450} and associated functions have been reported in rodent brain. The deficiency of PBG deaminase, which is presumed (but not proven) to affect all tissues in an individual with AIP, could therefore limit the availability of heme for its various and largely ill-defined functions as a prosthetic group in nervous tissue. However, rodent brain cytochrome P_{450} and heme biosynthetic enzymes appear (perhaps because of their relative isolation behind the blood-brain barrier) to be less inducible by stimuli known to induce these enzymes in nonneurologic sites such as the liver.[364,365,368–370] Heme might also be transported to the nervous system following synthesis in other sites, but it has been reported that [^{14}C]heme is not taken up by the brain.[371] Studies utilizing organotypic cultures of chick dorsal root ganglia have shown protection from the toxicity of lead following treatment with exogenous heme.[372] This observation, in conjunction with a series of studies of heme synthesis in the same in vitro system,[373,374] suggests that heme may be synthesized in glial cells and subsequently transferred to neurons.

The second theory concerns the toxic effects of elevated concentrations of heme pathway intermediates. Such intermediates might accumulate as a result of disordered local heme synthesis in the brain, but the relative refractoriness to induction of brain heme biosynthetic enzymes mentioned above[364,365,368–370] favors the idea of CNS uptake of intermediates from nonneurologic tissues. Brain uptake of ALA has been demonstrated in rodents,[375–377] and both ALA and PBG are found in the cerebrospinal fluid (CSF) of AIP patients in crisis.[341,378–380] It is interesting to note that hypothalamic uptake of labeled ALA is greater than that in any other area of the brain[381]; this may explain the occurrence of hypothalamic dysfunctions in AIP patients. Administration of ALA to rats has been reported to cause behavioral effects,[375] and direct installation of ALA into the brain causes both behavioral effects[381] and convulsions.[381,382] The latter effect is also seen following PBG administration into the brain.[382] AIA-induced porphyria in rats is also associated with increased excretion of ALA and PBG, somnolence,[383] hind limb weakness and ataxia,[384] and increased susceptibility to convulsions.[385]

Reports of the effects of in vitro administration of ALA abound in the literature. Effects on motor nerve conduction velocity,[386] acetylcholine release,[387] stretch receptors,[388] GABA release,[389] muscle resting membrane potential,[390] porphyrin synthesis,[391] duodenal contraction,[392] and Na^+,K^+-ATPase[393] have been reported. However, the majority of these in vitro studies have utilized concentrations of ALA in the range of 10^{-3} to 10^{-4} *M*. Although plasma concentrations of ALA may occasionally reach these levels, patients with AIP rarely, if ever, demonstrate cerebrospinal fluid concentrations in this range.[379,380] Furthermore, some investigators have concluded that their results are frankly inconsistent with a neuropharmacologic role for ALA in causing neurologic dysfunction.[380,394] This issue remains moot.

A more recent theory concerning the pathogenesis of central nervous aberrations in AIP invokes an indirect metabolic consequence of hepatic heme deficiency. Plasma concentrations largely determine brain levels of tryptophan and the subsequent synthesis of brain 5-hydroxytryptamine (5HT).[395] In turn, plasma tryptophan concentrations are largely determined by the activity of hepatic tryptophan pyrrolase (TP), a heme-dependent enzyme[396] which converts tryptophan to kynurenine. In acute attacks of AIP, deficiency of hepatic heme may lead to decreased activity of tryptophan pyrrolase, enhanced plasma levels and brain uptake of tryptophan, and ultimately increased 5HT synthesis. Experimental evidence for this sequence of events has been reported in a rodent model of porphyria (DDC-treated, phenobarbital-primed rat).[397,398] Resultant increased serotonergic tonus in the brain may account for some of the observed symptoms and signs of porphyria.[398] In support of this hypothesis are the observations that porphyria patients excrete indoles abnormally into the urine[399,400] and that normal subjects respond to tryptophan or 5-hydroxytryptamine administration with nausea, abdominal pain, dysuria, and psychomotor disturbances.[401–404] However, in another chemically induced model of porphyria (the AIA-treated rat), tryptophan pyrrolase activity was increased[384] which would predict a decrease in brain 5-hydroxytryptamine synthesis.

Pyridoxal phosphate is a coenzyme in the condensation of glycine and succinyl-CoA, which is catalyzed by ALA synthase. The similarities between the neuropathies of AIP and pyridoxal phosphate deficiency (e.g., secondary to isoniazid administration) have led to the hypothesis that overactivity of ALA synthase in AIP may lead to depletion of the coenzyme and result in neuropathy.[405] Plasma pyridoxal phosphate concentrations were found to be lower in AIP patients than in controls following a tryptophan loading test, but there was no correlation between coenzyme concentrations and clinical activity of the disease.[406] Likewise, although urinary excretion of ALA and PBG was decreased during experimental diet-induced pyridoxine deficiency in a woman with AIP, there was no worsening of her porphyria despite the development of optic neuritis.[407]

Kryptopyrrole (2,4-dimethyl-3-ethyl-pyrrole or "mauve factor") and hemopyrrole have been reported in the urine of patients with AIP and schizophrenia, and they have been implicated in the pathogenesis of porphyria.[408–414] However, one study failed to detect these pyrroles in either AIP or schizophrenic patients,[415] and no clear-cut association between their urinary concentrations and the clinical expression of porphyria has been established. Their contribution to the pathogenesis of porphyria thus appears unclear.[416]

Precipitating Factors. One of the central, unexplained mysteries in AIP has been the relatively recent understanding that up to 90 percent of people with documented deficiencies of PBG-deaminase activity remain asymptomatic throughout their lifetimes (Fig. 52-16). Such asymptomatic heterozygotes may be AIP carriers who display no abnormalities in concentrations of heme pathway intermediates or may have latent AIP characterized by increased production and excretion of heme pathway intermediates but without clinical expression of the gene defect of the disorder. Persons with both latent and clinically expressed AIP may be precipitated into an acute AIP attack by endogenous or exogenous environmental factors. Most, but not all, of such precipitating factors can be related to an associated increase in the activity of ALA synthase in liver; in one fatal case following barbiturate treatment, hepatic ALA synthase activity was found to be elevated fortyfold.[341] This phenomenon can be appreciated if one remembers that the activity of PBG deaminase is usually decreased by $\approx$50 percent in individuals with AIP. Thus, under normal conditions, the rate of flux of substrates through the heme pathway is generally below the threshold at which the affected enzyme becomes rate limiting. However, an increase in the metabolic demand for heme in the liver, regardless of the reason, may lead to an induction of ALA synthase, and the resulting accelerated flux of ALA through the pathway can render PBG deaminase rate limiting. Accumulation of intermediates (ALA and PBG) ensues, and deficiency of the final product, heme, may lead to further induction of ALA synthase and provoke an escalating metabolic chain reaction.

Endocrine factors have long been recognized to play a major role in the induction of AIP activity. Clinically expressed AIP, although reported,[417–419] is exceedingly rare before puberty and the incidence and severity of AIP decline in women after the menopause. Furthermore, the clinical disease is more common in women, especially at the time of menses.[420] In fact, a subset of female patients experiences regular cyclical perimenstrual exacerbations of their disease. Progesterone has been implicated in increased heme catabolism,[421,422] and progesterone levels are highest in the luteal phase. Synthetic estrogens[423] and progesterone[424] have been reported to induce porphyria. Naturally occurring sex steroid metabolites also induce the *de novo* synthesis of hepatic ALA synthase[425] and enhance the concentration of cytochrome P_{450} in the liver.[426]

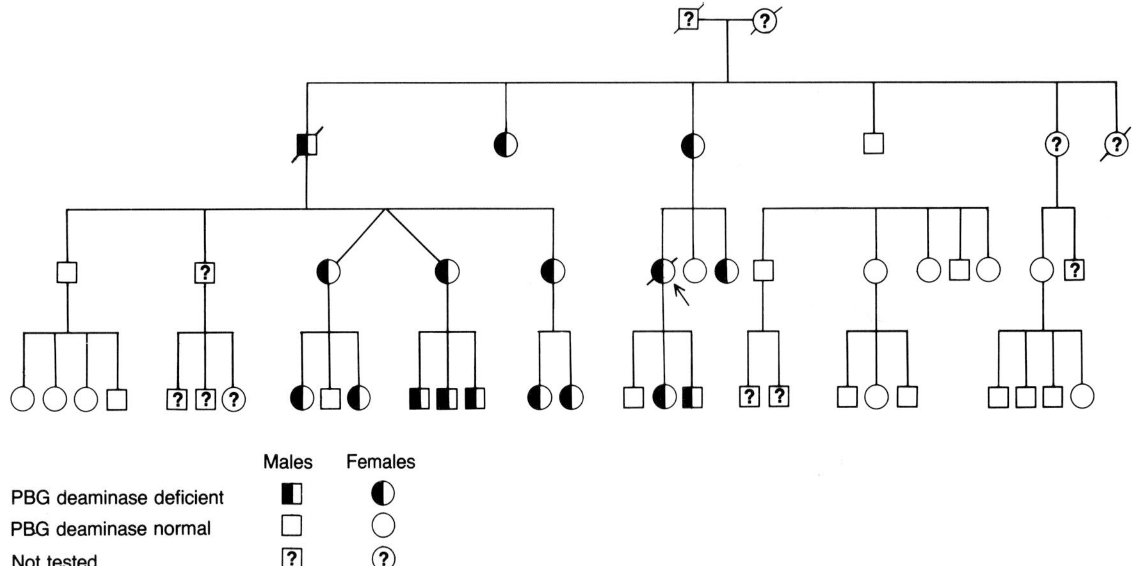

Fig. 52-16 Lineage of a patient with AIP. As shown by studies of erythrocyte PBG deaminase, the AIP gene defect was inherited from the patient's mother and transmitted to two of her three chldren. Sixteen clinically latent gene carriers of AIP were also detected in this lineage. Only two adult gene carriers had increased urinary excretion of PBG, and in the 15 years since this AIP lineage was identified only the propositus, indicated by an arrow, developed the clinical syndrome of AIP.

Despite the massive elevations in sex steroid concentrations during pregnancy,[427] women with AIP usually fare well during gestation, although their clinical condition occasionally deteriorates to the point where therapeutic abortion is indicated. In normal pregnant women, urinary excretion of ALA is increased[428] and urinary excretion of ALA, PBG, and coproporphyrin rises during the last month of gestation[429,430]; all parameters normalize within two months postpartum.[429] Progesterone metabolism during the last trimester is predominantly by 5α reduction,[431] and progesterone itself appears to increase 5α reduction of androgens.[432] A relative preponderance of 5α metabolites may decrease the porphyrinogenic potential of these steroids in contrast to that of their 5β epimers (see below).[138,433–436] Serum from pregnant women or patients receiving contraceptive steroids has been shown to induce ALA synthase in chick hepatocytes in culture,[437,438] whereas postpartum serum was inhibitory[438,439]; the factors responsible for these effects have not yet been delineated. It is also of interest that in pregnant rats, the response of ALA synthase to AIA induction is markedly abrogated,[440] and cytochrome P_{450} concentrations and functions are decreased in the liver.[441] It is not known if mechanisms similar to those mentioned above are operative in pregnant women, but if so, they would help to explain the generally favorable course of AIP during pregnancy.

In vitro studies utilizing primary cultures of chick embryo hepatocytes as well as whole avian liver have established that hepatic ALA synthase is induced by sex steroid metabolites, especially those with a 5β (A:B ring cis) configuration as noted above. AIP patients with the clinically expressed disorder have increased urinary excretion[442,443] of steroids with a predominantly 5β configuration due to impaired hepatic 5α-reductase activity[444–446]; AIP gene carriers who have remained entirely latent display no such abnormality.[447] Such alterations in 5α reduction appear confined to the liver. Shunting of precursor hormone metabolism toward the production of 5β steroid metabolites may favor induction of hepatic ALA synthase and thus act to exacerbate porphyria. Evidence from family studies suggests that the impared 5α-reductive capacity observed in clinically expressed AIP is acquired.[30,447] Further evidence to support this view is the observation that 5α-reductase deficiency is also seen following administration to humans of the porphyrinogenic drug phenobarbital.[448]

Another often underemphasized precipitating factor is inadequate nutrition. Reducing diets, especially those aimed at a sudden precipitous loss of weight, often lead to exacerbation of AIP.[449] In our experience, certain unusually sensitive patients may experience porphyria attacks after missing several meals. Urinary ALA and PBG excretion have been shown to increase in AIP patients following only a 20 percent decrease in caloric intake.[450] Conversely, additional carbohydrate-derived calories added to a preexisting adequate diet decreased PBG excretion.[450,451] The ratio of 5β:5α steroid metabolism is also considerably altered by the ratio of protein to carbohydrate in the diet.[452] This effect of the protein/carbohydrate ratio mimics that produced by phenobarbital in humans[448] and certain environmental chemicals in experimental animals.[452] Animal studies have revealed attenuated ALA synthase induction reponses to AIA in rat liver after glucose administratior both in vivo[453] and in vitro.[454] Available evidence favors the idea that this represents an effect of glucose rather than an indirect effect of insulin,[451] although the insulin/glucagon ratio may be important.[455] Despite considerable experimental study, the mechanism of this glucose effect remains unclear.

The third major category of inducers of acute attacks of AIP includes drugs and foreign chemicals. It must be stressed that the following discussion and the contents of Table 52-6 apply to all the acute "inducible" porphyrias. Barbiturates are the best known and potentially the most injurious group of drugs known to exacerbate or induce hepatic porphyria. Fortunately, the disastrous consequences of their administration are less often seen since the widespread decrease in their use as general sedatives and a greater recognition of their harmful potential in patients with porphyria. However, barbituates, especially those with a short duration of action, are still used commonly for the induction of anesthesia, and their use increases the likelihood of a severe paralytic porphyria crisis.[313] Many chemicals which exacerbate porphyria are thought to

Table 52-6 Reported Drug Experience in Acute Porphyrias

1. *Unsafe*
   - Antipyrine[456–458]
   - Amidopyrine[456–458]
   - Aminoglutethimide[459]
   - Barbiturates[314,456,460]
   - Carbamazepine[336,456]
   - Carbromal[461]
   - Chlorpropramide[459,461,462]
   - Danazol[463,464]
   - Dapsone[458,465]
   - Diclophenac[456,466]
   - Diphenylhydantoin[314,336,337,456,462,467]
   - Ergot preparations[456,462]
   - Ethclorvynol[457]
   - Ethinamate[461]
   - Glutethimide[456,459,462]
   - Griseofulvin[449,468]
   - Isopropylmeprobamate[469]
   - Mephenytoin[456,459]
   - Meprobamate[456,462,469]
   - Methylprylon[456,459,462]
   - *N*-butylscopolammonium bromide[456]
   - Novobiocin[456]
   - Phenylbutazone[456–458]
   - Primadone[456]
   - Pyrazolone preparations[456]
   - Succinimides[459,469]
   - Sulfonamide antibiotics[314,456]
   - Sulfonethylmethane[479]
   - Sulfonmethane[479]
   - Synthetic estrogens, progestins[456,462,480]
   - Tolazamide[461]
   - Tolbutamide[459,462,468]
   - Trimethadione[456,459]
   - Valproic acid[337,456,481]
2. *Potentially unsafe*
   - Alfadolone acetate[470,471]
   - Alfaxolone[470,471]
   - Alkylating agents[457]
   - 2-Allyloxy-3-methylbenzamide[472]
   - Bemegride[457]
   - Clonidine[473]
   - Chloroform[458]
   - Chloroquine[462]
   - Colistin[458]
   - Etomidate[258]
   - Erythromycin[458]
   - Fluroxene[474]
   - Food additives[457,475]
   - Heavy metals[457,462,476]
   - Hydralazine[473]
   - Ketamine[477,478]
   - Methyldopa[462]
   - Metoclopramide[458]
   - Metyrapone[459]
   - Nalidixic acid[458]
   - Nikethamide[457,459,461]
   - Nitrazepam[458]
   - Nortryptyline[483]
   - o,p′-DDD[459]
   - Pargyline[459,473]
   - Pentazocine[462]
   - Pentylenetetrazole[457,459]
   - Phenoxybenzamine[473]
   - Pyrazinamide[457,484]
   - Rifampicin[485]
   - Spironolactone[473]
   - Theophylline[457]
   - Tolazamide[449]
   - Tranylcypromine[459]
3. *Probably safe*
   - Adrenaline[458]
   - Chloramphenicol[456,459]
   - Chlordiazepoxide[456,459]
   - Colchicine[458]
   - Diazepam[456,459]
   - Dicumarol[482]
   - Digoxin[456]
   - Diphenhydramine[459]
   - Guanethidine[482]
   - Hyoscine[458]
   - Ibuprofin[458]
   - Imipramine[457]
   - Indocid[458]
   - Labetalol[458]
   - Lithium[458]
   - Mandelamine[482]
   - Mefanamic acid[458]
   - Methylphenidate[459]
   - Naproxen[458]
   - Neostigmine[482]
   - Nitrofurantoin[482]
   - Nitrous oxide[482]
   - Paracetamol[458]
   - Penicillamine[458]
   - Procaine[458]
   - Propanid[482]
   - Propoxyphene[482]
   - Prostigmin[482]
   - Rauwolfia alkaloids[482]
   - Thiouracil[458]
   - Thyroxine[458]
   - Tubocurarine[458]
   - Vitamin B[482]
   - Vitamin C[482]
4. *Safe*
   - Acetaminophen[456]
   - Amitryptyline[456]
   - Aspirin[456]
   - Atropine[456]
   - Bromides[337,467,475]
   - Chloral hydrate[313,473]
   - EDTA[457]
   - Ether[456–458]
   - Glucocorticoids[482]
   - Insulin[457]
   - Narcotic analgesics[456,473]
   - Penicillin and derivatives[482]
   - Phenothiazines[456,473]
   - Propranolol[482]
   - Streptomycin[482]
   - Succinylcholine[457,458]
   - Tetracycline[482]

have the potential to induce cytochrome P_{450}, and the resultant enhanced demand for *de novo* heme synthesis is presumed to lead to induction of hepatic ALA synthase activity. Surprisingly, evidence to support this presumed sequence of events is lacking for many drugs. In the case of the sulfonamide antibiotics, the evidence points rather to a direct inhibition of hepatic PBG deaminase, which is independent of an intermediary effect on cytochrome P_{450}.[457] As a corollary, cytochrome P_{450}-dependent drug metabolism is often abnormal in patients with clinically expressed porphyria.[486–488]

Notwithstanding the indeterminate mechanism of their action, certain drugs have been clearly shown to reproducibly aggravate porphyria; these drugs are listed in Table 52-6 as unsafe. Conversely, drugs that have consistently been without effect in porphyria are listed as safe. Drugs listed as potentially unsafe and probably safe are more problematical. Often these judgments are based on a few anecdotal reports or limited personal experiences of authorities in the field, and such reports sometimes lead to conflicting conclusions. Further complications stem from the interpretation of data from the in vitro systems frequently used to screen questionable drugs for their porphyria-inducing potential. The most commonly utilized test systems make use of primary cultures of chick embryo hepatocytes, check embryo livers in ovo, and in vivo treatment of laboratory rodents. Often cultures or animals are "primed" with chemicals to elevate basal activities of ALA synthase and porphyrin production. The problems of extrapolation from pharmacologic observations in diverse species of animals to human pathophysiology are familiar to most biologists, and the results from different test systems are often contentious. Even drugs in category 1 (unsafe) are not always deleterious. Consequently, the categories in Table 52-6 should be treated only as a guide in determining the usage of the agents listed. Ultimately, therapeutic decisions must be made, as in all cases, by balancing the relative merits and disadvantages of a given drug with respect to a particular patient. The above guidelines, in conjunction with other published reviews of the subject[456–458,482,484,489] are intended to provide information to facilitate such decisions.

Lastly, stress, as in many other diseases, may sometimes appear to exacerbate porphyria. Similarly, intercurrent illnesses, infections,[490] alcoholic excess, and surgery (including, in our experience, dental extractions under local anesthesia) may all contribute to the genesis of an acute attack of porphyria. It is also quite common for patients to present with an acute attack of porphyria in which no precipitating factor can be identified.

Biochemical Findings

Patients with clinically expressed AIP, as well as some individuals with latent AIP, excrete variably increased amounts of ALA and PBG in the urine between attacks. In the majority of cases, the onset of an acute attack is accompanied by further marked to massive increases in excretion of these precursors (ALA, 25 to 100 mg/day; PBG, 50 to 200 mg/day).[491] The "port wine" urine which is sometimes seen in severe cases is due to the presence of porphyrins in urine or reflects the conversion of urinary PBG to porphobilin. The latter reaction is accelerated by light, heat, or acid. This explains why physicians formerly placed urine from suspected porphyria patients on the windowsill to test for the appearance of a reddish color. It also underscores the need to collect urine specimens without acid and to refrigerate and protect them from light. Urinary porphyrins may form nonenzymatically from PBG or may be synthesized in extrahepatic sites,[317,492] which may explain the preponderance of porphyrins of the isomer III series seen in urine from patients with AIP. Urinary dipyrrolmethanes (brown pigments) have also been detected in the urine of AIP patients.[493] Acute attacks may also be associated with elevations in the serum concentrations of ALA, PBG, and porphyrins, which are normally undetectable. Stool porphyrins are usually normal or, at most, slightly elevated.[494]

The Watson-Schwartz test[495,496] continues to be widely used as a screening test for urinary PBG. PBG chromogens are generated with Ehrlich reagent, and contaminating chromogens (e.g., from indoles, urobilinogen) are extracted with chloroform and butanol; PBG chromogens are quantitated colorimetrically in the aqueous fraction. Variability in color interpretation between different operators and in different laboratories has led to large variations in positive results in population surveys.[327,482] Other disadvantages of the Watson-Schwartz test are (1) its relative lack of sensitivity, (2) the incidence of false positives, and (3) the fact that it is not quantitative. A modification proposed as a bedside test, the Hoesch test,[497,498] is of comparable sensitivity to the Watson-Schwartz test. Neither is as sensitive or specific as the quantitative column method of Mauzerall and Granick,[499] which should be used to verify positive results from either screening test. False positives have been reported following treatment with phenothiazines.[500] The column method also allows for sequential elution into a second column to quantitate ALA concentrations. We have recently described an improvement to the method utilizing a different chromatographic matrix for PBG determinations.[501] Plasma ALA concentrations may be determined using gas-liquid chromatography.[502] Longitudinal determinations of urinary PBG concentrations constitute the major biochemical index of porphyria activity in patients with an established diagnosis of AIP and in evaluating the biochemical response to therapy.

Nonspecific alterations in liver function tests (e.g., bromosulfophthalein excretion[503]) or high plasma bilirubin levels secondary to coexistent Gilbert syndrome,[314,503,504] a common genetically determined form of hyperbilirubinemia, are occasionally seen in AIP (see Chap. 53). Hematologic profiles are usually normal unless aberrations of salt or water balance supervene.[356] Hemoglobin synthesis and bilirubin production are normal in AIP.[356,505] Hypomagnesemia[353] and hypercalcemia after prolonged paralysis[506] have also been reported. Creatinine phosphokinase (CPK) concentrations were fivefold elevated in one AIP patient. It is interesting to note that isozyme analysis suggested that the source of the elevated CPK was the Meissner and Auerbach plexi.[507]

Hypercholesterolemia is a fairly frequent finding in patients with AIP.[353,508] Elevations in β-lipoprotein concentrations were reported in patients in the United States,[509] but patients from Finland were found to have normal β-lipoprotein concentrations and a trend toward elevated high density lipoproteins[434]; differences may, in part, be dietary. Clinically induced porphyria in animals[508,510–512] and humans[513] is associated with hyperlipidemia. Taken together, the evidence suggests a secondary effect of porphyria on lipid metabolism.

Various endocrinopathies have also been reported in AIP. The syndrome of inappropriate secretion of antidiuretic hormone has already been mentioned above.[284,352,354,357–361] Its occurrence is biochemically indistinguishable from the same syndrome due to other pathologies (e.g., serum hyponatremia and hypoosmolality, with inappropriately high urine osmolality in the absence of evidence of hypovolemia). Other reported abnormalities of hypophyseal regulation include paradoxical glucose-stimulated growth hormone release,[362] defective ACTH release,[363] and galactorrhea presumably reflecting increased prolactin secretion.[353] Abnormalities in glucose tolerance[514] and hyperinsulinemia[515] have been reported; one case of primary aldosteronism has been described with AIP.[516] AIP has also been associated with elevations of protein-bound iodine and thyroxine-binding globulin[517,518] and, more rarely, with findings consistent with frank thyrotoxicosis.[519–522] There may also be abnormalities in the heme-dependent activity of thyroid peroxidase.[523] The signs and symptoms of thyrotoxicosis and AIP can be very similar, but it is unclear whether the two pathologies are causally related.

Diagnosis

Diagnosis rests on the demonstration of reduced PBG deaminase activity in erythrocytes, while the distinction between carrier or latent status and clinically expressed AIP is dependent on the demonstration of elevated urinary excretion of PBG and ALA and on the natural history of the individual subject. The latter tests (i.e., ALA and PBG output) alone are poor criteria for the diagnosis of AIP, as patients do not necessarily always hyperexcrete PBG or ALA, and many AIP carriers or latent porphyrics will go unrecognized. Quantitative tests for ALA and PBG[499,501] are preferrable to qualitative screening tests[495,497]; positive results from the latter tests should in any case be confirmed by quantitative methods. Elevated levels of ALA and PBG may also be seen in hereditary coproporphyria (HCP) and variegate porphyria (VP); measurement of urinary and stool porphyrins will usually differentiate these conditions from AIP. The nonspecific symptoms and signs of AIP, and its rarity, dictate that the diagnostic tests for porphyria must frequently be performed based on a low index of suspicion and that most tests will be negative. Unfortunately, the diagnosis is frequently not made until recognition of the characteristic clinical and biochemical findings of a major, acute attack.

PBG deaminase is conveniently determined in erythrocytes and may be decreased in uremia[524] and increased in hemolytic diseases,[525] in hepatic diseases,[526] and in neonates.[527] Abnormal values for PBG deaminase activity in AIP will generally be approximately 50 percent of normal, but there is a wide variation in normal values. Borderline cases may be better interpreted if the erythrocyte PBG deaminase activities of other family members, especially the parents, are measured. A small subset of AIP patients has normal erythrocyte PBG deaminase activities[528]; in these cases, decreased activities may be detected in cultured fibroblasts[529] or mitogen-stimulated lymphocytes.[530] Previously used provocative tests to increase porphyrin precursor excretion[531,532] are no longer justifiable since the advent of PBG deaminase determinations which have enabled efficient detection of carriers or latent cases of AIP.

Treatment

The treatment of AIP, as well as HCP and VP, is essentially identical, and the following discussion applies to all three forms of porphyria. All such patients should be provided with medical warning bracelets. Treatment between attacks comprises adequate nutritional intake, avoidance of drugs known to exacerbate porphyria, and prompt treatment of other intercurrent diseases or infections. In some patients, the onset of an acute AIP attack can be aborted by increasing carbohydrate intake or, if nausea, anorexia, or vomiting supervene, by substitution or supplementation with Polycose (Abbott Laboratories), a high-concentration glucose polymer preparation, by mouth. Unresponsive or more severe cases should be admitted to the hospital and intravenous administration of carbohydrate initiated with 10% dextrose to provide a minimum of 300 g of carbohydrate per day. The response to carbohydrate treatment is highly variable and may improve following an increase to 500 g/day.[353] Oral sucrose, intravenous fructose (levulose[533]), oral glycerol,[451] and oral corn oil[534] have all been utilized to this end. Large volumes of intravenous fluids (often hypotonic) may favor the onset of inappropriate secretion of antidiuretic hormone, which should be treated with fluid restriction and, in severe cases, hypertonic saline. More commonly,[357] hyponatremia develops in the absence of inappropriate antidiuretic hormone secretion due to gastrointestinal or renal salt loss. Treatment in this circumstance should be directed at salt and fluid replacement.

Pain, which is invariably present and severe, should be treated with frequent doses of narcotic analgesics; nonnarcotic analgesia is usually inadequate. As attacks are generally episodic, narcotic addiction is uncommon; concerns about addiction and the minimal behavioral responses of patients chronically conditioned to pain often result in the administration of insufficient analgesia. Anxiety, nausea, or vomiting are best treated with phenothiazines. Chloral hydrate and/or diazepam are suitable to induce sedation or sleep. A few patients have reported a generalized beneficial effect or a specific analgesic effect of hypnosis or acupuncture. There is a tendency to automatically attribute any and all symptoms and signs in a sick patient to porphyria. Diligent observation for other disease processes should continue throughout hospitalization.

Tachycardia and hypertension are frequently seen in acute attacks of AIP. The hypertension is labile, and unless sustained and severe, there is no absolute indication for therapy. When indicated, β-adrenergic blockade (usually with propranolol) has proved an effective treatment for tachycardia and hypertension[535–539] and has apparently decreased porphyrin precursor excretion[535–537,540] and, on occasion, abdominal pain.[535,539]

The use of intravenous hematin has escalated over the last few years and is now generally held to be effective in reducing ALA and PBG excretion, in curtailing acute attacks, and perhaps in reducing the severity of neuropathies.[378,538,541–549] It has also been used prophylactically (200 mg weekly) to abolish cyclical perimenstrual porphyria attacks.[550] A lyophilized hematin preparation is now available from Abbott Laboratories (trademark Panhematin). Hematin is given intravenously, preferably over 30 min or more, in doses up to 4 mg/kg body weight, as frequently as every 12 h. The initial half-life is approximately 10 h,[541] but hematin may be detected in plasma for up to 5 days following intravenous administration[551] and accelerates the catabolism of hemopexin.[552] Hematin is very unstable in solution.[553,554]

Hematin therapy is frequently associated with phlebitis or thrombophlebitis,[541] which was found to occur in 50 percent of normal subjects after infusion in doses of 4 mg/kg body weight.[555] Coagulopathy[555–557] and hemolysis[558] have also been reported after hematin infusion but not in association with frank hemorrhage. One patient received an unusually large dose of hematin (1000 mg) very rapidly and had transient renal failure suggestive of acute tubular necrosis.[559] Another had transient circulatory collapse after a standard dose (4 mg/kg) was given.[560] Frequent treatments with hematin may induce heme oxygenase, thus enhancing heme degradation and possibly leading to a reduced therapeutic effect. Hematin has also been reported to be efficacious in EPP,[561,562] lead intoxication,[563] and CEP.[564]

Haem-arginate (Normosang, Medica Pharmaceutical Company Ltd., Finland) is a new compound which has been recently introduced for treatment of the acute porphyrias. Experience with its use is limited, but it appears to be effective in reducing porphyrin precursor excretion and in limiting the duration of acute attacks; additionally, its use appears not to be associated with coagulopathy or thrombophlebitis, and it is stable in solution for up to 6 years.[565,566] It is, however, an excellent substrate for heme oxygenase, which may limit its long-term efficacy.

Another promising compound which inhibits, but is not enzymatically degraded by, heme oxygenase, is the synthetic heme analogue Sn-protoporphyrin, which in large doses effectively inhibits ALA synthase induction and ALA and PBG excretion in AIA-induced porphyria in the rodent.[567] Our preliminary unpublished observations on this compound in AIP are encouraging. Hemoperfusion to remove porphyrin precursors has also been employed in AIP. Results with charcoal were disappointing,[568] but results with Amberlite resin have been encouraging.[569,570]

Another approach to the treatment of AIP has been endocrine manipulation. Women with cyclical perimenstrual acute attacks have benefited from exogenous steroids which suppress ovulation,[482,571] but steroid treatments may also aggravate porphyria symptoms.[463,464,480,572] Recently, nasal or subcutaneous administration of long-acting agonists of LHRH has been shown to inhibit ovulation and greatly reduce the incidence of perimenstrual attacks of AIP.[573,574]

Other treatments which have been proposed, often based on few observations, include the administration of zinc,[575,576] chelating agents,[577,578] pyridoxine,[406] AMP,[579] vitamin E,[580,581] folic acid,[285] and corticosteroids[582] and the use of transcutaneous nerve stimulation.[583]

CONGENITAL ERYTHROPOIETIC PORPHYRIA

Synonyms

Synonyms for congenital erythropoietic porphyria (CEP) are Günther disease, erythropoietic porphyria, congenital porphyria, congenital hematoporphyria, and erythropoietic uroporphyria.

Definition

CEP is a rare disease which is inherited in an autosomal recessive fashion. The primary abnormality in the affected homozygote is a decreased activity of URO cosynthase [hydroxymethylbilane hydrolase (cyclizing) (EC 4.2.1.75)] activity, which results in accumulation and hyperexcretion of predominantly type I porphyrins (Fig. 52-17). Clinically, this enzymatic defect is expressed in infancy and results in cutaneous photosensitivity, hemolysis, and a decreased life expectancy.

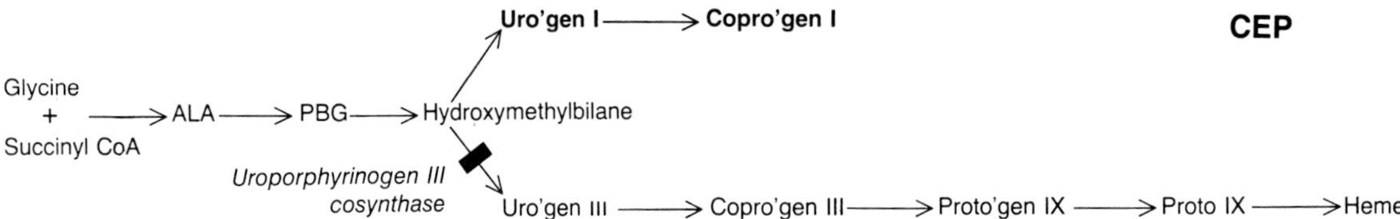

Fig. 52-17 The enzymatic defect in the heme pathway in CEP is a marked deficiency of uroporphyrinogen III cosynthase activity. The deficiency in enzyme activity is sufficiently severe in homozygotes to make inefficient the formation of uroporphyrinogen III, such that normal or increased heme synthesis in the bone marrow occurs only with an associated marked overproduction of the type I isomers of uroporphyrinogen and coproporphyrinogen, as shown in bold letters. ALA = δ-aminolevulinic acid; PBG = porphobilinogen; Uro'gen = uroporphyrinogen; Copro'gen = coproporphyrinogen; Proto'gen = protoporphyrinogen; Proto = protoporphyrin.

Prevalance

CEP is extremely rare. Only 60 cases were reported in the literature up until 1972,[584] and some of those cases may really have had porphyria cutanea tarda[585,586] or hepatoerythropoietic porphyria. At the time of writing (1987), fewer than 200 cases had been reported. No clear racial or sexual predominances have yet emerged, although 21 cases had been reported from India prior to 1971.[587]

Enzymology

URO cosynthase catalyzes the formation of uroporphyrinogen III from hydroxymethylbilane or from PBG if PBG deaminase[588,589] is also present. Normal human erythrocytes[590] and mouse spleen[591] contain an excess of the cosynthase relative to deaminase activity, which favors the predominant synthesis of type III uroporphyrinogen in these tissues. Even in tissues with cosynthase activity that is lower than in red cells and spleen, such as brain, muscle, testes, heart, kidney, liver, and lung in mice, PBG deaminase activity is much lower than that of cosynthase activity (1.6 to 5.5 units per milligram of protein).[591] PBG deaminase activity is quite low in most normal tissues and corresponds almost to the level of ALA synthase activity. In contrast, in erythrocytes from human patients or cattle with CEP, cosynthase activity is greatly reduced (40 percent of normal),[32,592] and this disease is accompanied by overproduction and excretion of uroporphyrinogen I. The fox squirrel is a species which naturally has a low cosynthase activity and excretes large amounts of uroporphyrinogen I in urine.[593]

Properties. The purified cosynthase from rat liver has a molecular weight of approximately 42,000 and can be resolved by polyacrylamide gel electrophoresis into two bands, each possessing cosynthase activity.[594] More detailed studies were made on cosynthase purified from *E. gracilis,* which is a monomer of molecular weight 38,500 by gel filtration studies and 31,000 by sodium dodecyl sulfate–polyacrylamide gel electrophoresis.[595] The pI of the bacterial enzyme is in the range 4.8 to 5.1. In contrast to the rat cosynthase, no evidence for any cofactors was found in *E. gracilis,* and folate derivatives were shown to be absent. No metal ions appeared to be present in the enzyme.[595] The K_m for hydroxymethylbilane is in the range of 12 to 40 μM, and the product, uroporphyrinogen III, is an inhibitor of the enzyme activity. Chemical modification studies suggest that arginine residues are essential, but histidine, cysteine, and tyrosine residues are not.[595]

Recently URO cosynthase has been purified to homogeneity from human erythrocytes.[596] The purified enzyme had a specific activity of over 300,000 nmol uroporphyrinogen III formed/per milligram of protein per hour, an isoelectric point of 5.5, and was thermolabile ($t_{1/2}$ at 60°C ≈ 1 min). Molecular weight studies by gel filtration (M_r = 30,000) and analytical SDS–polyacrylamide gel electrophoresis (M_r = 29,500) indicated that the enzyme was a monomer. The pH optimum was 7.4, and the K_m for hydroxymethylbilane was 5 to 20 μM. The enzyme was activated by Na^+, K^+, Mg^+, and Ca^{2+} and was inhibited by Cd^{2+}, Cu^{2+}, Hg^{2+}, and Zn^{2+}.

Assay. Since the rate of PBG consumption is principally determined by PBG deaminase, PBG loss in the reaction cannot be used as a measure of cosynthase activity. Levin[591] determined URO cosynthase activity in the presence of a partially purified deaminase by measuring the rate of disappearance of PBG and the percentage of uroporphyrinogen found as the type III isomer. Using this method, he and his associates described a deficiency of cosynthase activity in red cell hemolysates[591] and in fibroblasts from bovine[597] and human subjects with CEP.[598] Rat hepatic URO cosynthase has been shown to be thermolabile, and a time-dependent loss of enzyme activity during reaction with PBG deaminase and PBG was observed.[599] Cosynthase activity can be directly determined by the use of chemically prepared hydroxymethylbilane[595] or enzymatically synthesized preuroporphyrinogen[600,601] as substrate in the absence of PBG deaminase.

Clinical Findings

The first clue suggesting the diagnosis of CEP in infants is often pink to dark brown staining of the diapers due to large amounts of porphyrins in the urine. Early onset of cutaneous photosensitivity is characteristic and is excerbated by exposure to sunlight. Subepidermal bullous lesions progress to crusted erosions which heal with scarring and either hyperpigmentation or, more rarely, hypopigmentation. Repetitive damage from secondary infection and scarring may eventually lead to epidermal atrophy, pseudoscleroderma, resorption of the distal phalanges, contractures, and severe functional limitations. Facial mutilation (especially of the nasal and auricular cartilages), ectropion, keratoconjunctivitis, and even loss of vision may occur.[602–604] Hypertrichosis and alopecia are common, and erythrodontia (with red fluorescence under ultraviolet light) is virtually pathognomonic of CEP.

Patients may display symptoms and signs of anemia (usually hemolytic) with splenomegaly and porphyrin-rich gallstones.[605] Compensatory expansion of hyperactive bone marrow may result in pathologic fractures with vertebral compression or collapse and shortness of stature. Although the onset of symptoms of CEP is most often in early infancy, some patients present as adults.[603,606–609] The reasons for late clinical presentation and frequently milder symptoms are unknown but appear not to be related to heterozygosity of the URO cosynthase defect.[607,610]

Pathogenesis of the Clinical Findings. Autopsy findings in a 14-year-old previously splenectomized boy with CEP who died following a massive episode of hematemesis revealed orange-red fluorescence of all the viscera, skin, and bones under ultraviolet light.[611] Microscopy showed fluorescence of erythrocytes, skin, bile duct, and nephrons but not of hepatocytes. There was atrophic epidermis with thickened dermis containing periodic acid-Schiff (PAS)-positive staining vessels. Cirrhosis was absent, but tuberculoid granulomas were found in the liver and mesenteric lymph nodes. No evidence for a microbial genesis of the granulomas was found, and the hypothesis was advanced that they resulted from a reaction to the high concentration of porphyrins.[611] Another autopsy result confirmed the absence of cirrhosis and reported large accumulations of hemosiderin in the liver and other viscera.[612]

The primary site of expression of the enzymatic defect is the bone marrow wherein fluorescence secondary to porphyrin accumulation is variably distributed but invariably present. Most marrow normoblasts display fluorescence, principally localized in the nuclei of the cells.[586,613–616] Such fluorescent cells are morphologically abnormal and also display heme deposition in nuclear vacuoles, whereas nonfluorescent cells are morphologically normal.[586] Fluorescence appears to be limited to mature marrow elements such as normoblasts and reticulocytes.[586,617] It is these porphyrin-laden cells which can be detected in the peripheral blood circulation.[618,619] There is recent evidence that the characteristically massive elevations of systemic porphyrins in CEP are derived from such porphyrin-laden cells. After in vitro incubation of erythrocytes from a patient with CEP for 18 h in normal homologous plasma, porphyrins were found to have been released into the plasma (uroporphyrin > coproporphyrin > protoporphyrin) in the absence of detectable hemolysis.[610] However, there must also be a direct efflux of porphyrins from the marrow as it has been calculated that the porphyrin content of circulating erythrocytes cannot account for the rate of porphyrin excretion in CEP.[586,615,617]

Thus bone marrow-derived porphyrins become distributed throughout the body (as attested to by the autopsy report above showing widespread tissue fluorescence) and spill into the urine and feces; by virtue of their phototoxicity, this widespread distribution of porphyrins acccounts for the multiple pathologies of the integument. The spleen has been shown to be the major site for removal of damaged or hemolyzed erythrocytes.[617] The splenomegaly frequently observed in CEP is presumed to be secondary to this process. However, the pathogenesis of the hemolysis of CEP is not so easily accounted for and remains a contentious issue.

Although hemolysis is usually present, it is not always accompanied by anemia. The hypertrophied and hyperactive marrow is sometimes able to compensate for the increased rate of erythrocyte destruction. Often the degree of compensation varies over time, leading to exacerbations and remissions of hemolysis and anemia.[584,586] Evidence to support the occurrence of hemolysis is derived from morphologic abnormalities of erythrocytes, increased circulating concentrations of reticulocytes and normoblasts, elevations in serum unconjugated bilirubin and fecal urobilinogen, and undetectable levels of serum haptoglobin. All CEP patients also show increased plasma iron turnover.[603,610,617]

Extrinsic abnormalities of erythrocytes seem unlikely, as the direct Coombs' test is only occasionally positive,[617,620,621] possibly due to reticulocyte transferrin.[604] Also, the survival time of normal erythrocytes transfused into CEP patients is entirely normal.[622] Evidence to support an intrinsic abnormality of erythrocytes leading to hemolysis is derived from abnormal autohemolysis tests,[614,615,617,621,623,624] although osmotic fragility has been reported as normal.[613] Moreover, the survival time of erythrocytes from CEP patients is decreased after infusion into normal subjects.[617,621] Studies of red cell survival in CEP utilizing [^{15}N]glycine[615,624–629] or ^{51}Cr-labeled cells[603,616,617,630] appear to give conflicting results. Taken together, they suggest that survival is generally decreased or that the disappearance is initially increased and later decreased in those cases where there was evidence of hemolytic anemia at the time of the test. Where there was no demonstrable hemolytic anemia at the time of the test, there was no change in red cell survival.[630] These results also serve to emphasize that the degree of hemolysis fluctuates over time.

Hemolysis of erythrocytes may also result from photolysis as porphyrin-laden cells are exposed to light in the dermal capillaries. Wavelengths of light suitable for porphyrin photoactivation are known to penetrate the skin to a depth sufficient to produce this phenomenon,[610] and photohemolysis has been demonstrated *in vitro* although it is not quantitatively correlated with light exposure.[631] If this phenomenon were to occur in vivo, it would predominantly affect young cells which contain 50 to 100 times more uroporphyrin and coproporphyrin than old cells.[610]

Biochemical Findings

Urinary porphyrins are always elevated (from twenty- to sixtyfold) above normal levels. Uroporphyrin is increased more than coproporphyrin, and although type I isomers predominate, type III isomers are also elevated. Smaller amounts of 7-, 6-, and 5-carboxylic porphyrins are hyperexcreted.[584,617,632,633] Urinary porphyrin excretion may fluctuate with changing disease activity, and the resulting color of the urine may vary. Urinary PBG excretion is almost never increased, and ALA excretion is rarely increased. Fecal porphyrin excretion is usually increased and is predominantly type I coproporphyrin with lesser and variable elevations of uroporphyrin, or rarely protoporphyrin (also predominantly type I). Elevated type I uroporphyrin and sometimes coproporphyrin concentrations are found in plasma and in erythrocytes. Essentially similar elevations may be seen in biopsies or at autopsy in bone marrow, spleen, and less often liver. Erythrocyte protoporphyrin is usually normal or mildly elevated, although certain notable exceptions to this have been reported where protoporphyrin was the dominantly elevated porphyrin in erythrocytes.[603,607,617,621,634–637]

Fluctuating degrees of anemia may be present, and erythrocytes may exhibit polychromasia, poikilocytosis, anisocytosis, and basophilic stippling. Increased reticulocytes and normoblasts may be detected in the peripheral circulation. Occasionally anemia can be severe and require transfusion.[614,629] Rarely, thrombocytopenia or leukopenia may be seen in association with hypersplenism, and the former may predispose to clinical bleeding diatheses.[603,608,609,613,632]

Diagnosis

Pink urine, or the onset of severe cutaneous photosensitivity in infancy (or rarely in adults) should suggest the diagnosis of CEP. Demonstration of elevated urinary, fecal, and erythrocyte porphyrins should preferably be followed by analysis of porphyrin type and isomer. Elevation of both urinary and erythrocyte porphyrins is highly suggestive, as this pattern is quite specific for CEP and renders EPP, PCT, HCP, and VP unlikely. HEP may also present in childhood with photosensitivity and elevated porphyrin excretion, but such cases (in contrast to CEP) have elevated fecal levels of isocoproporphyrin and 5-carboxylic porphyrins and often excrete zinc protoporphyrin into the urine.[638,639]

Measurement of URO cosynthase activity is generally available only as a research procedure but can be performed on cultured fibroblasts[598] to confirm a diagnosis or screen for heterozygotes. This method has also been used to screen for CEP in amniotic fluid cells.[639a]

Treatment

The avoidance of sunlight, trauma to the skin, and infections forms the mainstay of preventive care in CEP. Topical sunscreens may be of some help, as may oral treatment with β-carotene.[640–644] Transfusions with packed erythrocytes transiently decrease hemolysis and its attendant drive to increased erythropoiesis, and also decrease porphyrin excretion.[634,640,645] The hazards of repeated transfusions and iron overload are a serious potential drawback of this therapeutic approach. Splenectomy has been utilized fairly frequently with short-term reductions in hemolysis, porphyrin excretion, and skin manifestations,[613,621,632] but not all cases respond and long-term improvement is probably not obtained.[604,614,621,646] Hematin infusions have been administered to a woman with CEP and were reported to reduce porphyrin output with approximately the same efficacy as packed erythrocyte transfusions, but over a shorter duration.[606] Recently, a promising new therapy was reported based on the binding of porphyrins to charcoal. Oral treatment with charcoal for 9 months lowered porphyrin levels in plasma and skin and resulted in complete clinical remission during therapy of a man with CEP.[647]

Other treatments which have been advocated include metabolic alkalinization to facilitate porphyrin excretion[648] and administration of pyridoxine, adenosine monophosphate, chloroquine, or inosine.[578,613,614,617,636] Prednisolone may improve anemia.[603,608]

PORPHYRIAS DUE TO UROPORPHYRINOGEN DECARBOXYLASE DEFICIENCY; PORPHYRIA CUTANEA TARDA AND HEPATOERYTHROPOIETIC PORPHYRIA

The last decade has seen an intensification of efforts to define and categorize the biochemical bases and inheritance of forms of porphyria associated with deficiencies of URO decarboxylase activity. It has become clear that these porphyrias, despite their clinical similarities, are manifestations of a heterogeneous group of enzymatic abnormalities. Furthermore, the etiology of such enzymopathies—and their clinical expression—may be hereditary, environmental, or mixed. Although certain details remain unclear or controversial, the available evidence seems to justify a major division of these porphyrias into PCT based on heterozygous deficiencies of URO decarboxylase and HEP based on homozygous deficiencies of URO decarboxylase. This classification is used in this section.

PORPHYRIA CUTANEA TARDA

Synonyms

Synonyms for porphyria cutanea tarda are symptomatic porphyria, porphyria cutanea symptomatica, and idiosyncratic porphyria.

Definition

PCT refers to a heterogeneous group of porphyric diseases which may be inherited (familial, or type II), or, more commonly, acquired (sporadic, or type I). Both forms of the disease display approximately 50 percent reductions in the activity of URO decarboxylase in the liver (Fig. 52–18). In the autosomal dominant inherited form, the enzyme is deficient in all tissues, whereas in the acquired form, the defect is confined to the liver. Acquired PCT typically presents in adults, either

Fig. 52-18 PCT is associated with a deficiency of uroporphyrinogen decarboxylase activity in liver, which can result in the accumulation or porphyrins corresponding to the porphyrinogen (bold letters) substrates for this enzyme. In familial PCT the enzyme deficiency is also found in erythrocytes, lymphocytes, and fibroblasts. As a result of the enzyme deficiency in liver, 7-, 6-, and 5-carboxylate porphyrinogens as well as uroporphyrinogen itself accumulate since all serve as substrates for the enzyme. ALA = δ-aminolevulinic acid; PBG = porphobilinogen; Uro'gen = uroporphyrinogen; Copro'gen = coproporphyrinogen; Proto'gen = protoporphyrinogen; Proto = protoporphyrin.

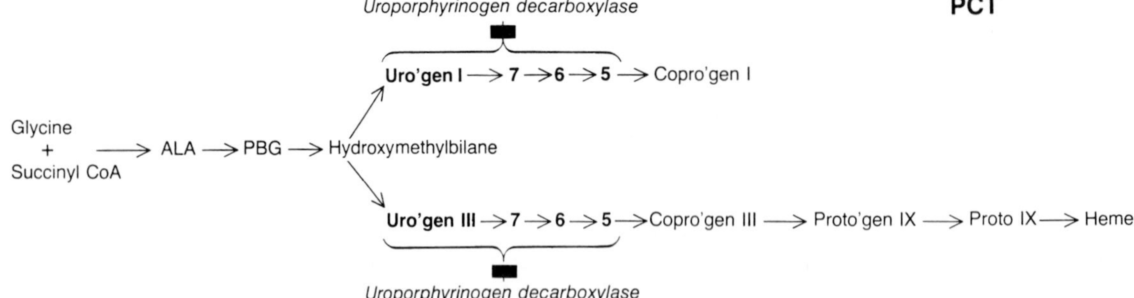

spontaneously or more commonly in conjunction with precipitating environmental factors such as alcohol, estrogen, or drug use or in association with other disorders. The hallmark of the disease is cutaneous photosensitivity due to increased production of uroporphyrin and 7-carboxylic porphyrin.

Prevalence

PCT is the most common of all the porphyrias but the least well characterized in terms of its incidence. Many thousands of cases have been recognized, including 700 from Prague alone in 1974.[649] The disease is recognized worldwide and seems to show no racial predilection except among the Bantus in South Africa,[650,651] probably secondary to their high incidence of hemosiderosis (see Chap. 55). Sporadic PCT is more common than familial PCT in Europe, South Africa, and South America,[652] although it may be less common in North America.[653] PCT was held to be more common in men than women, perhaps secondary to higher alcohol intake, but the incidence in females has increased of late, probably due to increased use of contraceptive steroids, postmenopausal estrogen therapy, and use of alcohol.[654–658]

Enzymology

A cytosolic enzyme, URO decarboxylase, catalyzes the sequential removal of the four carboxylic groups of the acetic acid side chains in uroporphyrinogen to yield coproporphyrinogen[659] (Fig. 52–19). The enzyme decarboxylates all four isomers of uroporphyrinogen, but the naturally most abundant type III isomer is decarboxylated most rapidly, followed by types IV, II, and I isomers in decreasing order.[659,661,662] There is clear evidence that only one enzyme mediates the four successive decarboxylation steps to convert the 8-carboxylate uroporphyrinogen to the 4-carboxylate coproporphyrinogen.[34,663] In fact, the reaction catalyzed by the purified URO decarboxylase yields all the subsequent intermediates from uroporphyrinogen, i.e., hepta-, hexa-, penta-, and tetracarboxylate porphyrinogens.[664,665]

Properties. URO decarboxylase is active only on porphyrinogen substrates and not on the corresponding porphyrins.[666] The enzyme from *R. spheroides*[667] seems to require a cofactor, but the enzyme from mammalian cells, including human erythrocytes,[668] does not. With uroporphyrinogen III as substrate the order of decarboxylation of acetate groups on each pyrrolic ring proceeds in a clockwise fashion starting from ring D (Fig. 52–19). Series III isomers always have a higher affinity than their corresponding series I isomers. The affinity of the enzyme for the substrate decreases with the number of carboxylic groups in the substrate, from a K_m value of 0.5×10^{-6} *M* for uroporphyrinogen to 8×10^{-6} *M* in the case of pentacarboxylate porphyrinogen.[662] Type I and type III porphyrinogens with the same number of carboxylic groups appear to be decarboxylated at the same active center, whereas decarboxylation of porphyrinogen substrates with different numbers of carboxylic groups appear to occur at four different active centers.[668] URO decarboxylase purified from human erythrocytes[664] has a molecular weight of 46,000, an isoelectric point of 4.6, and a specific activity of 9970 units per milligram of protein using uroporphyrinogen III as substrate. Enzyme

Uroporphyrinogen III

Heptacarboxylate porphyrinogen III

Hexacarboxylate porphyrinogen III

Pentacarboxylate porphyrinogen III

Coproporphyrinogen III

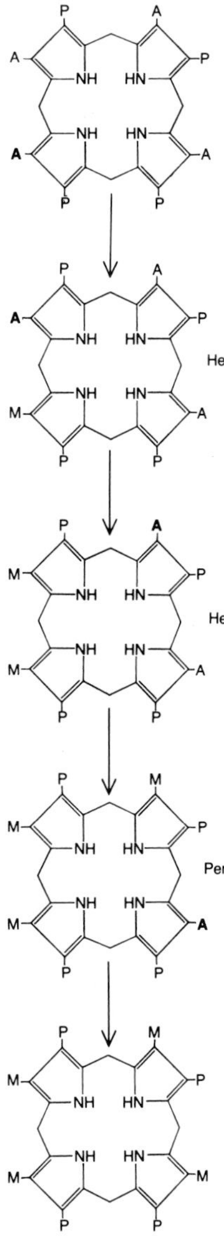

Fig. 52-19 Formation of coproporphyrinogen from uroporphyrinogen. The decarboxylation of the four acetic acid groups in uroporphyrinogen III proceeds clockwise around the macrocycle starting from ring D to yield the four methyl groups in coproporphyrinogen III.[660] The sequence of decarboxylations is indicated by bold letters. A = —$CH_2 \cdot COOH$; M = —CH_3; P = —$CH_2 \cdot CH_2 \cdot COOH$.

activity is inhibited by metals, such as Cu, Hg, and Pb, and is sensitive to sulfhydryl modification. The effect of iron on the enzyme activity remains controversial. Using purified enzyme preparations, it has been reported that the enzyme activity was either uninhibited by Fe^{2+} and Fe^{3+},[664,665] inhibited by Fe^{2+},[669] or stimulated by Fe^{2+}.[670]

The enzyme activity is decreased in the liver of all patients with PCT,[35,663] in erythrocytes[671–673] in patients with familial PCT, and in livers of rats fed hexachlorobenzene.[674–676] URO decarboxylase has an apparently long half-life. It does not show decay for at least 10 h after treatment with cycloheximide.[677] Iron removal by venesection is known to be highly beneficial in the treatment of PCT patients.[678–685] An experimental porphyria inducible with 2,3,7,8-tetrachlorodibenzo-*p*-dioxin (dioxin) in normal mice does not occur in animals made iron-deficient by phlebotomy.[686] Rats with genetic[687] or acquired[688,689] siderosis are more susceptible to hexachlorobenzene-induced porphyria than nonsiderotic rats.

Gene Locus. A gene locus encoding human URO decarboxylase was assigned to chromosome 1 using somatic cell hybrids and a quantitative immunoassay.[690] Subsequently, regional assignment of the URO decarboxylase gene was made to chromosome 1 pter → p21.[691]

Assay. The principle of the assay of URO decarboxylase activity is to determine the rate of conversion of uroporphyrinogen to coproporphyrinogen.[692] The two main difficulties in the measurement of the enzyme activity are (1) preparation of the substrate and (2) separation and measurement of the reaction product. Many methods use as the substrate uroporphyrinogen I or III, which may be prepared either by reducing the appropriate porphyrin with sodium amalgam or by enzymatic synthesis from PBG. Chemical reduction is useful to produce substrates other than uroporphyrin I and III. In most recent techniques, the reaction products and remaining substrate have been converted to the methyl ester derivatives, followed by separation by paper or thin layer chromatography or by HPLC. Since a single enzyme catalyzes all four decarboxylation reactions from uro- to coproporphyrinogen, 5-carboxylate porphyrinogen can be used as substrate to provide an assay in which there is only a single product of reaction (i.e., coproporphyrinogen).[664] This step represents the most rapid decarboxylation catalyzed by the enzyme.[668] Curiously, investigators using an enzymatic method to prepare substrate for the reaction by preincubating PBG with PBG deaminase have reported diminished URO decarboxylase activity in erythrocytes from most patients with PCT,[671-673] while those who have used chemical reduction of 5-carboxylate porphyrin or uroporphyrin to prepare the enzyme substrate have found such a decrease in the liver,[35,663] but not in erythrocytes of all patients with sporadic PCT.[34,663,665] The latter workers, however, did find decreased URO decarboxylase activity in erythrocytes in patients with familial PCT and in some patients with sporadic PCT who most likely represent familial PCT.[665] The demonstration of a 50 percent decrease of URO decarboxylase activity in hemolysates in subjects with familial PCT using 8-, 7-, 6-, or 5-carboxylate porphyrinogen as substrate supports the existence of a single decarboxylase for these successive decarboxylation reactions.[34]

Molecular Biology

The cloning of a cDNA sequence complementary to URO decarboxylase mRNA from rat has been reported.[693] This cDNA clone cross-hybridized with human URO decarboxylase mRNA and was used to isolate several human URO decarboxylase cDNA clones from mRNA from the spleen of a patient with β-thalassemia major.[694] The largest cDNA contained 1300 bp corresponding to the full-length coding sequence of URO decarboxylase mRNA; the cDNA had a single large open reading frame starting at position 19 with an ATG codon and extending to position 1120. The deduced 367 amino acid sequence is consistent with the partial amino acid sequence of cyanogen bromide peptides and the total amino acid composition of the purified enzyme. The deduced molecular weight of URO decarboxylase was 40,831 in good agreement with the value of 42,000 estimated by SDS–polyacrylamide gel electrophoresis. Southern blotting analysis of human genomic DNA showed that the URO decarboxylase gene is present as a single copy gene. Northern blotting analysis showed the presence of a single size species of mRNA in erythroid and nonerythroid tissues; the level of URO decarboxylase mRNA was higher in erythroid than nonerythoid tissues, suggesting that the enzyme expression is differentially regulated at a pretranslational level in a tissue-specific manner. Direct evaluation of the transcriptional activity of the URO decarboxylase gene in isolated nuclei showed a fourfold higher rate of transcription of the URO decarboxylase gene in K562 or HEL cell lines (human erythroleukemia cells) as compared with HL-60 (myeloid) cell lines.

Clinical Findings

Sporadic PCT usually presents in adults, often in late life. Onset in childhood is usually[695-697] though not necessarily[698,699] a manifestation of familial PCT. The dominant finding is cutaneous lesions on the light-exposed areas of the dorsum of the hands and on the arms and face. Involvement of the legs and feet is more common in women than in men. Patients frequently complain of increased skin fragility such that minor trauma results in erosions from shearing of the skin, and subsequent healing may be delayed. Sun exposure may subsequently lead to the appearance of vesicles and bullae (Fig. 52-20), up to 2 to 3 cm in diameter, which crust over and sometimes take several weeks to heal. Rarely, patients may display immediate light urticaria.[701] Healed skin may be atrophic, or scarring may occur, especially in repetitively affected areas or following secondary infections of the lesions. Occasionally, eroded areas may permit entry of organisms which cause systemic disease. One case of necrotizing fascitis has been reported.[702] Milia may develop in the dermis where bullae have healed, particularly on the face and hands. Hyperpigmentation, melanosis, and violaceous-brownish discolorations may develop, especially on the face or other light-exposed areas. In Ethiopian patients, hyperpigmentation has been reported to often precede the onset of PCT.[703] Ectropion[704] and hyperkeratoses[705] have also been found.

Facial hypertrichosis develops slowly and is most noticeable in women. Initially fine lanugo hair may coarsen and darken. Less commonly the process spreads to involve the arms or trunk. Alopecia may develop in sites of repeated trauma or bullous formation. Hypopigmented indurated plaques of skin may develop in either light-exposed or protected areas. If

Fig. 52-20 Large bullae on the dorsum of the hand of a patient with PCT. (*From Harber.*[700] *Used by permission of Harper & Row.*)

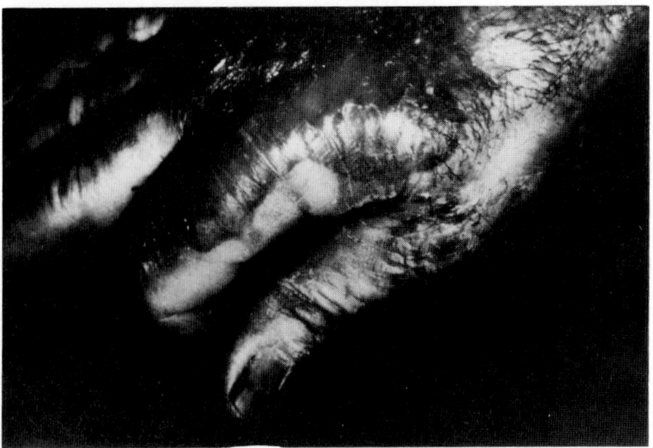

widespread, such pseudoscleroderma may suggest the diagnosis of systemic scleroderma. However, no evidence was found to suggest the development of systemic scleroderma during several years of follow-up of several such cases.[706] In severe cases, the lesions may persist and develop dystrophic calcifications and nonhealing ulcerations, especially over the preauricular region of the face. Rarely, onycholysis of the fingernails is seen.[707]

Pathogenesis of the Clinical Findings. Microscopic examination of cutaneous biopsies from PCT patients shows subepidermal bullae with dermal papillae at their bases ("festooning"), elastosis and PAS-positive vessels in the dermis, and acid mucopolysaccharides at the dermal-epidermal junction.[708,709] Immunofluorescence microscopy has revealed accumulations of IgG, IgM, or complement around the dermal vessels and dermal-epidermal junction.[708–710] Electron-microscopic studies have shown that the initial event in bullous formation is the appearance of membrane-limited vacuoles in the superficial dermis[711] and confirmed that the site of split formation is the lamina lucida.[712] Collagen fibrils in sclerodermalike lesions in PCT have been shown to be of decreased diameter[713] as in morphea (circumscribed scleroderma).

Porphyrin biosynthesis in the skin of PCT patients is increased compared with that of normal controls.[714] Thus phototoxic porphyrins in the skin may be derived both from the liver and locally in the skin. Activation of the complement system after irradiation has been demonstrated in PCT patients both in vivo[715,716] and in vitro in serum.[717,718] This is presumed to result from the generation of reactive oxygen species, most likely singlet oxygen.[719] Bullous fluid is known to contain prostaglandin E_2,[720] and photoactivation of uroporphyrin is known to damage lysosomes[721]; inflammation and autolysis may be attributable to these factors. Retinol binding protein concentration in serum from PCT patients is decreased, but the significance of this observation is unknown.[722]

Liver biopsy specimens from patients with PCT almost invariably display siderosis but of widely variable degree with fatty changes, necrosis, chronic inflammatory changes, and granuloma formation.[665,723–726] Red autofluorescence and needlelike cytoplasmic inclusion bodies have been reported frequently.[726–728] These may represent crystallized porphyrins. The reported incidence of cirrhosis is highly variable, but most cases have evidence of cirrhosis at autopsy.[655,679,726,729] Serum antibodies directed against hepatocytes from patients with PCT have been detected and were suggested to be partially a result of hepatic porphyrin content.[730] Rat models have shown that liver membrane damage results from exposure to alcohol or hexachlorobenzene and may facilitate the efflux of porphyrins from the liver.[731,732] Iron, estrogens, alcohol, and chlorinated hydrocarbons may all aggravate PCT, and all are potential hepatotoxins. The incidence of hepatitis B infection may also be higher in PCT patients.[733,734] Any or all of these factors, or porphyrins themselves, may predispose the liver of PCT patients toward neoplastic change, and the incidence of hepatocellular carcinoma in PCT is known to be greater than in the general population.[659,726,735,736] Rarely, primary hepatomas may secrete porphyrins and simulate PCT.[737]

Precipitating Factors. Sporadic PCT is often triggered by environmental agents. The most frequently incriminated agents are alcohol, estrogens, iron, and polychlorinated cyclic hydrocarbons. Alcohol has long been recognized to exacerbate PCT, and the incidence of heavy alcohol intake in different series of PCT patients has varied from 25 to 100 percent.[655,738,739] The degree of alcohol intake which exacerbates PCT may range from one or two drinks daily to frank debilitating alcoholism. Hepatic cirrhosis has been reported to develop in up to 30 to 40 percent of cases,[655,726] but only about 2 percent of alcoholics with cirrhosis develop PCT.[740] The mechanisms by which alcohol exacerbates PCT are unclear, but alcohol has been reported to increase the uptake of iron in PCT[741] and in normal subjects,[742] and increased iron may also contribute to the pathogenesis of PCT. Alcohol has also been shown to stimulate ALA synthase activity[743] and inhibit ALA dehydratase activity[744] in livers of PCT patients and to decrease URO decarboxylase activity in rat liver.[745] Additionally, alcohol is a well-known hepatotoxin and may nonspecifically impair hepatic function.

Estrogen administration to patients with prostatic carcinoma,[746–751] for postmenopausal replacement therapy,[658,752] or for contraceptive purposes[654,657,707,753] has been associated with aggravation or precipitation of PCT. The majority of such cases have been sporadic, but one[749] is known to be familial. Pregnancy, and its associated high production of estrogens, has also been reported to aggravate or precipitate PCT,[754–757] and PCT has been associated with the hyperestrogenic condition, Klinefelter syndrome.[758,759] It is also of interest that chronic alcoholics may display signs of hyperestrogenization (e.g., gynecomastia, spider naevi) which may contribute to the role of alcohol in the development of PCT. Elevated hepatic ALA synthase activity has been demonstrated in males receiving stilbestrol for carcinoma of the prostate,[760] but otherwise few clues concerning the mechanism of these estrogen effects on PCT have been garnered. As with alcohol exposure, the vast majority of patients receiving estrogens do not develop PCT.

Many observations point to a role of iron in the pathogenesis of PCT. Serum iron and ferritin concentrations are frequently elevated or in the upper range of normal in PCT patients,[655,761] and iron absorption and turnover have ranged from normal to elevated in different studies.[725,761–764] Some degree of hemosiderosis is seen in about 80 percent of liver biopsy specimens from patients with PCT,[655,725,762] and this may be more exaggerated in those with cirrhosis. Phlebotomy decreases the activity of PCT, whereas oral iron supplementation may lead to relapse or delay the induction of remission during phlebotomy therapy.[765,766] Addition of iron to in vitro systems has been reported to inhibit URO decarboxylase[767] and uroporphyrinogen III cosynthase[768] activities in porcine hepatic lysates, but activation of URO decarboxylase by iron in rat liver lysates has also been reported.[670] It has also been suggested that the K_m of URO decarboxylase is higher and the enzyme more susceptible to iron inhibition in PCT patients than in normal individuals.[769] Recently the augmentation of hexachlorobenzene-induced porphyria by iron in mice[770] and rats has been suggested to be related to the generation of toxic free radicals leading to lipid peroxidation,[771] and further evidence has been presented suggesting that such radicals may interact with URO decarboxylase or its substrates.[772] The mechanism by which iron augments PCT activity remains unsettled, but it is important to note that, as is the case with alcohol and estrogen exposure, not all patients with iron overload develop PCT. This suggests that exposure to alcohol, estrogens, or iron somehow augments or unmasks an underlying defect in hepatic URO decarboxylase and associated porphyrin metabolism. The nature of this putative defect awaits further elucidation.

Polychlorinated cyclic hydrocarbons have been associated with the development of PCT in humans and in laboratory animals. The best known example was a massive outbreak of about 4000 cases of PCT from 1956 to 1961 in Turkey following the widespread ingestion of hexachlorobenzene-contaminated wheat.[773–775] Weakness, fatigue, photosensitivity, bullae, hypertrichosis, hyperpigmentation with, curiously, painless arthritis, thyromegaly, and corneal opacification developed, most commonly in children, about 6 months after ingestion of the contaminated wheat. Breast-fed children were seen to die of "Pembe Yara" characterized by weakness, seizures, and annular erythema, possibly owing to transmission of the toxin via the mother's milk.[776,777] A recent 20-year follow-up revealed persistent scarring, hyperpigmentation, hirsutism, arthritis, and thyromegaly in 32 patients; some also retained detectable levels of hexachlorobenzene and elevated urinary porphyrins.[776] Dioxin was reported to cause PCT in 11 chemical factory workers in Czechoslovakia[512] and in a worker in Missouri who also had sarcoma,[778] and it was found to unmask symptoms in two sibs who were subsequently shown to have familial PCT.[779] Three cases of PCT were reported from a factory manufacturing the herbicides 2,4-dichloro- and trichlorophenoxyacetic acid,[780] and one woman developed PCT after accidental exposure to polychlorinated biphenyls (PCB) in a disinfectant.[781] A number of studies on the porphyrinogenic effects of dioxin, hexachlorobenzene, and PCB have been carried out in mice,[782,783] rats,[784–787] and tissue culture models.[788,789] The results suggest that metabolic activation of the compounds (probably by cytochrome P_{450}) is required to decrease URO decarboxylase activity.

Another increasingly recognized factor in the expression of PCT is hemodialysis in patients with renal failure.[790–803] Several theories to account for this have been advanced, but the mechanism remains obscure. PCT has also been observed in association with systemic lupus erythematosus (20 to 30 cases), but the basis for this association is also unknown.[804–810] Other autoimmune diseases that have been reported in association with PCT are Sjögren syndrome[811] and rheumatoid arthritis.[812] Also reported, but of unknown etiologic significance, are diabetes mellitus,[813] viral hepatitis,[814] Wilson's disease,[815] tumors and reticuloses,[816–821] thalassemia minor, hemophilia,[822,823] and four cases of AIDS.[824,825] Griseofulvin has been reported to increase fecal coproporphyrin in PCT,[826] but others failed to confirm this result.[827] Diazinon,[828] an organophosphorus insecticide, and rifampicin[829] have caused PCT in rats and humans, respectively, and nalidixic acid, tetracycline, and furosemide may cause photosensitive pseudoporphyria without disturbances in porphyrin metabolism.[830,831]

Biochemical Findings

Increased concentrations of uroporphyrin (mainly isomer I) and 7-carboxylic porphyrins (mainly isomer III) are found in the urine in PCT, with lesser increases of coproporphyrin and 5- and 6-carboxylic porphyrins.[832–836] Porphyrins can be separated by thin-layer chromatography (TLC) or HPLC.[837] Two compounds known as phyriaviolin and phyriazulin are also found in the urine in PCT, but their origins and significance are unclear.[838,839] Urinary porphyrin patterns correlate well with and are similar to serum porphyrin patterns.[840,841] Small quantities of isocoproporphyrin may be detected in serum or in urine, but in feces this is often the dominant porphyrin excreted.[697,842–844] Coproporphyrin, 7-carboxylic porphyrin, uroporphyrin, and X-porphyrin content of stool may all be increased in PCT.[845–847] Total daily fecal porphyrin excretion exceeds total urinary porphyrin excretion, and hydrophobic porphyrins account for the majority of those excreted; in contrast, hydrophilic (8- and 7-carboxylic) porphyrins appear to accumulate in the liver.[848] Skin porphyrins are increased especially in areas where photoactivation has not destroyed them.[849]

Biochemical indicators of liver disease may also be present. Elevated serum transminases and γ-glutamyltranspeptidase (especially in alcoholics) are often seen. Bromosulfophthalein excretion is often reduced but no more than seen in other nonporphyric liver diseases.[850] Serum iron and ferritin concentrations are frequently elevated. Excessive urinary excretion of pentoses is also seen.[851]

Diagnosis

The clinical picture in PCT is fairly specific but can obviously be confused with other porphyric (e.g., VP) and nonporphyric (e.g., systemic lupus erythematosus) diseases. Clinical suspicion of PCT should lead to examination of the urine for fluorescence under an ultraviolet light and to quantitation of porphyrins. Specimens should be refrigerated and protected from light during collection. Ideally, porphyrin fractionation by carboxyl number and isomer is performed. In practice, these tests are usually unavailable, and uroporphyrin (mainly 8- and 7-carboxylic) and coproporphyrin (mainly 5- and 4-carboxylic) fractions are generally measured. Uroporphyrin > coproporphyrin favors PCT; the reverse favors VP or HCP and may be associated with elevations in urinary ALA and PBG concentrations. Plasma porphyrins are invariably elevated in PCT and in other photosensitizing porphyrias. Fecal porphyrins will often be elevated; if available, laboratory testing for isocoproporphyrin (or isocoproporphyrin/coproporphyrin ratio > 0.1) is virtually diagnostic of PCT.[852] Measurement of erythrocyte URO decarboxylase is generally a research procedure and identifies only those patients with familial PCT. The pattern of porphyrin formation after addition of PBG to hemolysates has been reported to be specific in familial PCT.[853]

Treatment

The identification and avoidance of precipitating factors, as in other porphyric diseases, is the first line of treatment.[854] Patients have variable success in discontinuing their alcohol intake, and in our experience the need for abstinence may be accepted only after several cycles of remission followed by resumption of alcohol intake and relapse. The clinical response to cessation of alcohol ingestion is also highly variable,[855,856] but most authorities still recommend abstinence.

Since 1961,[857] the mainstay of treatment for PCT has been phlebotomy, which is usually effective in reducing urinary porphyrin concentrations and in induction of clinical remissions. There is strong evidence that the beneficial effects of phlebotomy result from a diminution in the stores of body iron.[678,724,858–866] Replenishment of iron after remission may accelerate the onset of subsequent relapse,[765,867,868] which, in the absence of supplemental iron administration, typically occurs from 1 to 8 years later. Phlebotomy has been reported to improve hepatic function[869] but not morphology[870] and to be associated with regression of sclerodermalike skin changes,[871] although this finding was not confirmed in another series.[706] Typically, 450 ml (≈one pint) of blood is withdrawn at each phlebotomy, and this is initially repeated one to two times weekly; intervals between treatments can be increased as patients respond. Remission is usually achieved after withdrawal of a total of about 4 to 10 liters of blood, but there is a wide variation. The best objective index of progress is probably the serum iron[706] or preferably the ferritin levels,[872] which should be reduced to the lower limit of normal. Reductions in serum γ-glutamyltranspeptidase concentrations are a good index of improved liver function.[873] Reduction of porphyrin excretion usually precedes clinical improvement which starts with an abatement of new skin lesions and may eventually progress to healing of scars and even loss of skin fragility.

Phlebotomy is sometimes ineffective or contraindicated owing to the presence of other diseases such as anemia or cardiopulmonary disorders. In such cases, low dose chloroquine therapy may be effective. Many authors have reported a favorable response to low dose chloroquine therapy (125 mg twice weekly), and some have utilized high dose therapy (500 mg daily) in refractory cases.[874–888] Both treatment regimes transiently induce increases in plasma and urinary porphyrin concentrations and in liver transaminases. High dose therapy may also lead to fever, malaise, nausea, vomiting, abdominal pain, and occasionally histologic signs of centrilobular hepatic necrosis.[877] Continued therapy eventually leads to a reduction in porphyrin excretion, and clinical improvement or remission may occur typically in 6 to 9 months. Despite this, little improvement has been noted in liver biopsies from patients with chloroquine-induced remissions of PCT.[889] Chloroquine is known to cause retinopathy but adherence to a safe low dose (≈1.0 mg/kg body weight) reduces the risk of this complication.[890] Ophthalmologic examination by slit lamp is prudent before initiating therapy and periodically thereafter during treatment.[876] Efficacy of chloroquine therapy and phlebotomy is probably similar,[891,892] and some reports suggest that a combined approach is useful and may diminish the incidence of side effects.[893,894] The mechanism of action of chloroquine therapy is thought to be related to its ability to chelate porphyrins in a water-soluble and hence more easily excretable form.[895]

Other therapies which have been advocated are plasmapheresis,[899,900] metabolic alkalinization,[896–898] adenosine-5′-monophosphoric acid,[901] desferrioxamine,[902,903] and vitamin E.[904] It is interesting to note that vitamin E is known to complex with iron and estrogens, and the putative therapeutic effect may be related to removal of these two precipitating factors.

HEPATOERYTHROPOIETIC PORPHYRIA

Definition

Hepatoerythropoietic porphyria (HEP) is a rare form of porphyria probably resulting from a homozygous defect in URO decarboxylase activity. Clinically, HEP is indistinguishable from CEP and characterized by the childhood onset of severe photosensitivity and skin fragility. HEP, like CEP, was initially described by Günther,[905] but the descriptive name of HEP was coined later and serves as a reminder that excess porphyrins are synthesized in both the liver and the bone marrow.

Incidence

HEP is extremely rare. Sixteen cases had been reported worldwide as of 1987.[906]

Clinical Findings

Clinical findings are very similar to those seen in CEP. Pink urine, severe photosensitivity leading to scarring and mutilation of sun-exposed areas of skin, sclerodermoid changes, hypertrichosis, erythrodontia, anemia (often hemolytic), and hepatosplenomegaly characterize HEP. Onset is usually in early infancy or childhood,[906–912] but adult onset has also been described.[913,914] Curiously, some of the cases with onset in childhood have experienced resolution of their photosensitivity,[909] and others have experienced relatively mild symptoms from onset despite markedly elevated porphyrin concentrations.[906] In contrast to PCT patients, serum iron concentrations have usually been normal in HEP patients. Likewise, the incidence of bone marrow and liver fluorescence and anemia and evidence of abnormal liver function and histology have been highly variable in the reported cases. Skin biopsies have shown subepidermal bullae and other findings similar to the lesions of PCT.[910] Evidence incriminating the liver as a site of excessive porphyrin production includes the excretion of uroporphyrin of both isomer types, porphyrin excretion profiles similar to those seen in PCT, and sometimes the presence of liver disease. Evidence favoring the bone marrow as a source of elevated porphyrins is the elevated erythrocyte protoporphyrin level and sometimes the detection of fluorescing normoblasts upon examination of the bone marrow.[911,912]

Molecular Biology

Recent availability of a human URO decarboxylase cDNA clone[694] allowed de Verneuil et al.[915] to investigate the mutant gene and its expression in lymphoblastoid cell lines from a family with two cases of HEP. Southern blot analysis after digestion of genomic DNA showed the same restriction fragments in DNA isolated from a normal cell line or from both patients, thus excluding large deletion or rearrangements in the mutant gene. Northern and dot blot analysis demonstrated that the concentration of mRNA was very similar in cell lines from controls, heterozygous parents, or homozygous patients. Study of in vitro translation products of URO decarboxylase mRNA showed a normal amount of immunoprecipitable URO decarboxylase in all cell lines. Size and molecular weight of the protein were identical with those of the marker enzyme. The only explanation of the very low level of URO decarboxylase protein in cells (5 percent of control value[915]) was provided by a study of the half-life of the enzyme; $t_{1/2}$ was 82 h in control cells, while it was only 7 h in the patient's cells (Fig. 52-21). Thus the enzyme defect appears to lead to rapid degradation in vivo of an unstable protein.

Cloning and sequencing of a cDNA of the mutated gene in one patient from this family[916] has revealed the nature of the mutation which consists of a G to A change at nucleotide 860 in cDNA sequence leading to a Gly (GGG) to Glu (GAG) change in the amino acid sequence at position 281. In vitro experiments revealed that the cDNA with this mutation encoded a polypeptide product that was very rapidly degraded

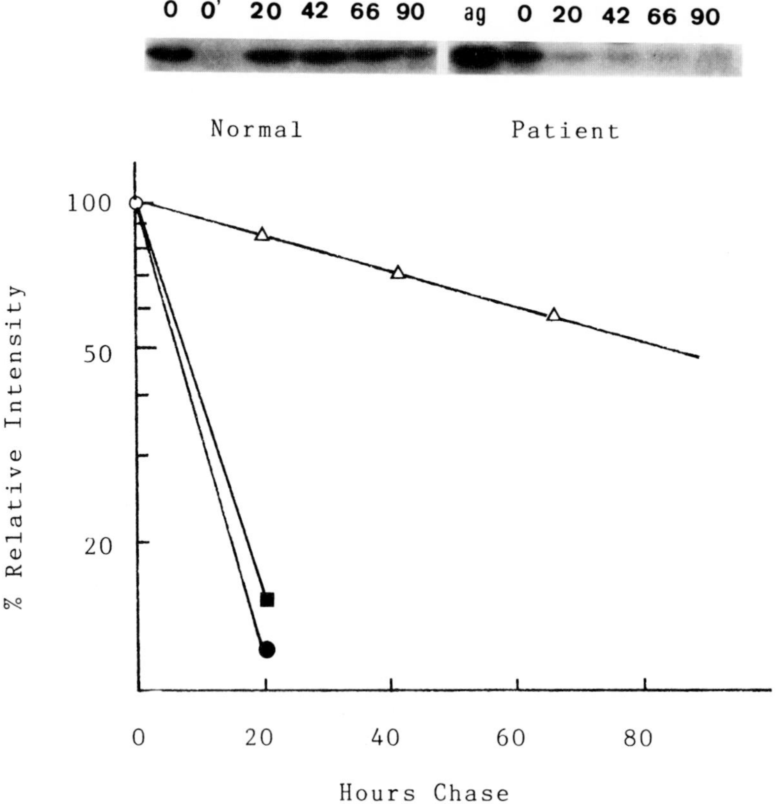

Fig. 52-21 Turnover rate of [^{35}S]methionine-labeled uroporphyrinogen decarboxylase. The upper part of the figure shows autoradiograms of uroporphyrinogen decarboxylase immunoprecipitates obtained by incubating lymphoblast cells for 0, 20, 42, 66, and 90 h (0′:0 h chase time point immunoprecipitated in the presence of 1 μg of cold antigen; ag: pure [^{14}C]uroporphyrinogen decarboxylase). The lower part shows that the half-life (7 h) of the protein from the patient was about 1/12 that of uroporphyrinogen decarboxylase in cell lines from controls (82 h).[915] ■, ● = patient cell line, △ = normal cell line. (*Used by permission of the* Journal of Clinical Investigation.)

when compared with the polypeptide encoded by the normal cDNA. This observation is consistent with decreased stability of the mutant protein in vivo. Further work will permit a determination of whether the detected mutation is common to other cases of HEP and to cases of familial PCT, or if it represents a unique URO decarboxylase defect. On the other hand, molecular heterogeneity of the URO decarboxylase deficiency has already been demonstrated at the protein level,[917] suggesting that a corresponding heterogeneity of mutations will probably be found.

Biochemical Findings

Most cases have displayed elevations in urinary porphyrins, predominantly uroporphyrin of isomer type I with lesser quantities of 7-carboxylic porphyrins, mainly type III. Isocoproporphyrin concentrations equal to or greater than coproporphyrin have also been detected in urine and feces. Elevated erythrocyte protoporphyrin (usually zinc protoporphyrin) has also been a feature of several cases of HEP. Biochemical evidence of anemia and impaired hepatic function is highly variable. Serum iron is usually normal.

Diagnosis

The diagnosis must be suspected in patients with severe photosensitivity and especially considered in the differential diagnosis of CEP. Diagnostic criteria include the elevated levels of fecal or urinary isocoproporphyrin and erythrocyte zinc protoporphyrin. Included in the differential diagnosis is EPP in which erythrocyte protoporphyrin is also elevated but, in contrast to HEP, urinary porphyrins are normal. EPP also tends to be clinically milder than HEP. Measurement of erythrocyte or fibroblast URO decarboxylase activities typically shows reductions to 2 to 10 percent of normal control values with intermediate reductions of URO decarboxylase activities in family members.[906]

Treatment

Avoidance of the sun and the use of topical sunscreens is, unfortunately, essentially all that can be offered these patients at present. Response to phlebotomy has not been observed,[906] although this is perhaps not surprising as serum iron levels, in contrast to PCT patients, are invariably normal. Charcoal therapy, which has recently been reported to be of value in CEP patients, may also prove effective in the treatment of HEP in the future.

HEREDITARY COPROPORPHYRIA

Definition

Hereditary coproporphyria (HCP) is a disease caused by a heterozygous deficiency of coproporphyrinogen oxidase (COPRO oxidase) activity (Fig. 52-22), which is inherited in an autosomal dominant manner. Clinically, the disease is similar to AIP, although it is often milder; additionally, HCP may be associated with photosensitivity. Expression of the disease is variable and influenced by the same precipitating factors responsible for the exacerbation of AIP. Very rarely, homozygous deficiency of this enzyme may occur and is associated with a more severe form of the disease.

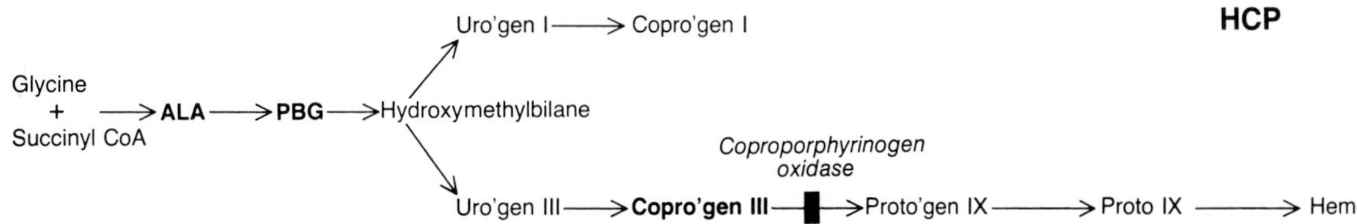

Fig. 52-22 The enzyme defect in HCP is a deficiency of coproporphyrinogen oxidase activity. This enzyme defect favors the accumulation of coproporphyrinogen III (bold letters). As in AIP, full clinical expression of the disease occurs in the presence of factors that induce ALA synthase; this and the near rate limiting activity of normal PBG deaminase cause ALA and PBG (bold letters) to accumulate during exacerbations of the disease. ALA = δ-aminolevulinic acid; PBG = porphobilinogen; Uro'gen = uroporphyrinogen; Copro'gen = corproporphyrinogen; Proto'gen = protoporphyrinogen; Proto = protoporphyrin.

Prevalence

Clinically expressed HCP is much less common than clinically expressed AIP, but, as is the case in the latter disease, latent HCP or HCP gene carriers are being recognized with greater frequency since the advent of improved laboratory techniques for their detection. Until 1968, approximately 40 cases had been reported, and about 60 percent were latent;[918] by 1977, 111 cases had been reported.[919] In Denmark, the incidence has been estimated at two per million.[920] Homozygous HCP has been reported in five cases[921,955,956] and was suspected in another.[922]

Enzymology

COPRO oxidase (EC 1.3.3.3) in mammalian cells is a mitochondrial enzyme which catalyzes the removal of the carboxyl group and the two hydrogens from the propionic groups of pyrrole rings A and B of coproporphyrinogen to form vinyl groups at these positions (Fig. 52-23). The reaction thus yields a divinyl compound, protoporphyrinogen.[923]

This mitochondrial enzyme can be readily solubilized without use of detergent[924–926] and evidently is not membrane-bound. Elder and Evans,[927] using a technique for preferentially rupturing the outer mitochondrial membrane,[928] demonstrated that COPRO oxidase is situated in the intermembrane space of rat liver mitochondria. The oxidase activity was not released as completely as adenylate cyclase or sulfide oxidase, which exemplify intermembrane space enzymes. These authors thus suggested that COPRO oxidase may be loosely bound to one of the membrane surfaces surrounding the intermembrane space.[927] These findings are consistent with the observations of Grandchamp et al.[929] that COPRO oxidase is present in the intermembrane space, with a fraction loosely bound to the inner mitochondrial membrane. The intermembrane localization of COPRO oxidase implies that either protoporphyrinogen or protoporphyrin must cross the inner membrane since heme is formed within the inner membrane.

Purified COPRO oxidase from bovine liver is a monomeric protein and has a molecular weight of 74,000 as measured by gel filtration and 71,000 as measured by SDS-polyacrylamide gel electrophoresis.[930] The purified bovine enzyme has a specific activity of 6920 units per milligram of protein and a K_m of 48 μM for coproporphyrinogen III; this is higher than that of the crude enzyme extract (20 to 30 μM). Oxygen is an absolute requirement for the enzymatic function, and other oxidants cannot replace oxygen. No metals are found in the pure enzyme. Reducing agents such as NADPH are not required for enzyme activity. Prosthetic groups such as flavin and heme are not contained in the purified enzyme. Thiol groups are not involved in the catalytic site of the enzyme. This oxidase is unusual in that it does not contain a metal and its activity is unaffected by treatment with metal chelators.[930]

The decarboxylation of coproporphyrinogen by the oxidase proceeds only at the β-carbon atom at the propionate side chains, with a stereospecific loss of one of the hydrogen atoms.[931,932] An intermediate 3-carboxylate porphyrinogen in the decarboxylation of hydroxypropionic porphyrin to protoporphyrin was also isolated by high performance liquid chromatography and characterized by field desorption mass spectrometry to be harderoporphyrinogen. The corresponding porphyrin was originally isolated from the harderian gland of rodents.[933]

In yeast, COPRO oxidase is localized in the cytosol.[934] In contrast to the mammalian enzyme, the purified yeast enzyme has a molecular weight of ≈35,000 by SDS-polyacrylamide gel electrophoresis and 70,000 by gel filtration, suggesting that it is a dimeric protein. Two iron atoms per molecule of native protein were also detected. The enzyme used molecular oxygen as electron acceptor. Although an anaerobic activity of yeast COPRO oxidase was reported when $NADP^+$, ATP, and methionine were provided in the incubation mixture,[926] a more recent study could not detect anaerobic enzyme activity.[934] Thiol-directed reagents partially inhibited the enzyme,

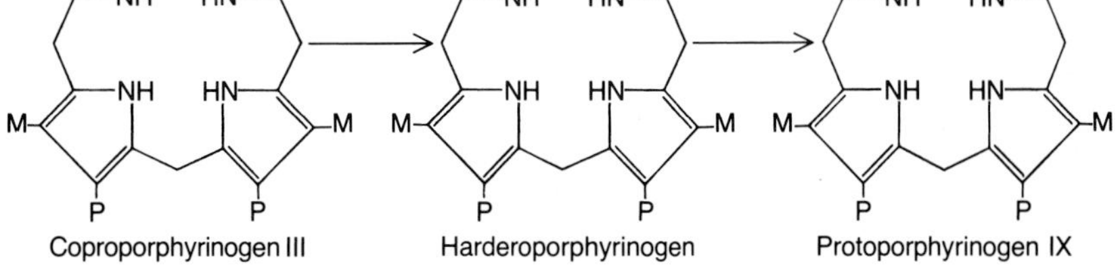

Coproporphyrinogen III → Harderoporphyrinogen → Protoporphyrinogen IX

Fig. 52-23 Formation of protoporphyrinogen from coproporphyrinogen III. The propionic acid group in ring A is first decarboxylated to a vinyl group yielding harderoporphyrinogen (a 3-carboxylate porphyrinogen); then another decarboxylation takes place on ring B of harderoporphyrinogen to yield protoporphyrinogen. The sequence of decarboxylations is indicated by bold letters. M = $—CH_3$; P = $—CH_2{\cdot}CH_2{\cdot}COOH$; V = $—CH{=}CH_2$.

indicating the involvement of a sulfhydryl group in activity.[934] Thus the bovine and the yeast COPRO oxidase differ from each other in their intracellular localization, subunit composition, and metal content.

COPRO oxidase activity has been assayed by spectrophotometric determination of the product found after oxidation of protoporphyrinogen to protoporphyrin and separation by solvent partition from the substrate.[925,926] These assays are, however, not sensitive enough to measure COPRO oxidase activity in small amounts of tissues such as human lymphocytes or cultured fibroblasts. Degradation of protoporphyrinogen or protoporphyrin during extraction presents another problem in the reproducibility of the assay. More recently a sensitive radiochemical method for the determination of COPRO oxidase activity was described by Elder and Evans.[935] The method measures the rate of production of $^{14}CO_2$ from the radiolabeled substrate, [^{14}C]coproporphyrinogen III. In this method [^{14}C]coproporphyrinogen III was labeled in the carboxyl carbon atoms of the 2- and 4-propionate groups. Grandchamp and Nordmann[39] circumvented the problem of tedious and difficult chemical synthesis of the substrate by enzymatically synthesizing [^{14}C]coproporphyrin III from [δ-4-^{14}C]ALA. Both methods appear to be very sensitive. A high specific activity of the substrate can be obtained, and the use of an internal standard of cobalt protoporphyrin allows good reproducibility of the measurement of the protoporphyrin IX formed.[936]

A fluorometric assay for COPRO oxidase has also been described.[937] In this method, COPRO oxidase activity (limiting) is measured in the presence of a large excess of protoporphyrinogen oxidase provided by yeast mitochondrial membranes isolated from commercial baker's yeast. Also a sensitive and accurate reverse phase HPLC method for COPRO oxidase assay has been reported.[938]

Clinical Findings

Neurovisceral symptomatology predominates in HCP and is essentially indistinguishable from the symptoms of AIP. Abdominal pain, vomiting, constipation, neuropathies, and psychiatric manifestations were reported to be most common in a review of 111 cases.[919] Cutaneous photosensitivity was a feature in about 30 percent of cases.[919] Although the disease is often relatively mild, tetraplegia and respiratory paralysis may occur.[939] Death from respiratory paralysis has been reported.[940,941] Involvement of the liver is unusual, but three cases have displayed recurrent attacks of jaundice with photosensitivity,[942–944] perhaps because impaired biliary excretion of porphyrins led to their accumulation in the skin. The incidence of symptomatic HCP in women is greater than in men.[919,945] Symptoms have been reported to occur in patients as young as 12 and as old as 87 years of age.[945] Attacks have been precipitated by pregnancy, the menstrual cycle, and contraceptive steroids.[943,946,947] The most common precipitating factor has been administration of drugs, most notably of barbiturates.[335,945,948–950] Neuropathies may be associated with abnormalities detected by electromyographic nerve conduction studies and tests of autonomic nervous system function.[951] Sural nerve biopsies in two patients were consistent with "dying-back" axonal degeneration.[952] Lymphocyte[919] and hepatic[46] ALA synthase activity has been demonstrated to be elevated in HCP. The liver enzyme activity has been reported to be normal during periods of clinical remission.

Homozygous HCP has been reported in one patient who was observed to have hypertrichosis and hyperpigmentation of the face and hands at age 4 and experienced two acute attacks at ages 10 and 20, the latter when she was pregnant.[921,953] COPRO oxidase activity was reduced by 98 percent in the propositus and by 50 percent in the parents.[921] In vitro studies of the patient's fibroblasts revealed increased synthesis and excretion of coproporphyrin.[954] Homozygous HCP has also been suspected in another patient.[922] Four other cases of homozygous COPRO oxidase deficiency have been reported with childhood onset of severe jaundice, hemolytic anemia, and hepatosplenomegaly.[955,956] However, in addition to elevations in urinary and fecal coproporphyrin concentrations, these patients displayed marked increases in excretion of harderoporphyrin. Lymphocyte COPRO oxidase has been shown to have abnormal kinetic properties in three of these cases,[955] and this variant of HCP has been termed *harderoporphyria*.

Biochemical Findings

The biochemical hallmark of HCP is hyperexcretion of coproporphyrin (predominantly type III) into the urine and feces. Fecal coproporphyrins may be chelated with copper,[957] and fecal protoporphyrin may be modestly elevated. Hyperexcretion of ALA, PBG, and uroporphyrin into the urine may accompany acute attacks, but in contrast to AIP, often normalizes between attacks. COPRO oxidase activity is typically reduced by about 50 percent in heterozygotes and by about 90 to 98 percent in homozygotes. The latter also show elevations in urinary ALA, PBG, and uroporphyrins. Additionally, patients with harderoporphyria have elevated erythrocyte protoporphyrin and higher total fecal porphyrins, of which about 60 percent is harderoporphyrin.

Diagnosis

The diagnosis of HCP should be suspected in patients with the signs, symptoms, and clinical course characteristic of the acute inducible porphyrias (AIP, HCP, and VP) but in whom PBG deaminase activity is normal. Urinary excretion of heme precursors is similar in HCP and VP, but fecal predominance of coproporphyrin is more suggestive of HCP than VP, in which fecal coproporphyrin and protoporphyrin concentrations are usually approximately equal. Fecal or urinary predominance of harderoporphyrin, with greatly reduced COPRO oxidase activity, indicates harderoporphyria, but both of the necessary assay methodologies are generally confined to research laboratories. In the absence of the availability of enzyme determinations, the best index for screening family members is the demonstration of elevated coproporphyrin in the urine and the stool.

Treatment

The identification and avoidance of precipitating factors are essential. Treatment of acute attacks is identical to the treatment of AIP.

VP

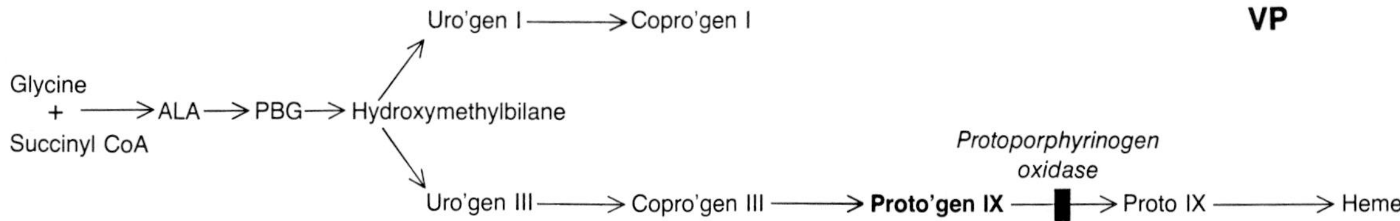

Fig. 52-24 The enzyme defect in VP is a deficiency of protoporphyrinogen oxidase activity. As in AIP, the disease becomes fully expressed in the presence of additional factors that appear to act primarily by inducing ALA synthase. During exacerbations of the disease, induction of ALA synthase coupled with the normally low levels of PBG deaminase results in ALA and PBG (bold letters). ALA = δ-aminolevulinic acid; PBG = porphobilinogen; Uro'gen = uroporphyrinogen; Copro'gen = coproporphyrinogen; Proto'gen = protoporphyrinogen; Proto = protoporphyrin.

VARIEGATE PORPHYRIA

Synonyms

Synonyms for variegate porphyria (VP) are porphyria variegata, protocoproporphyria, South African genetic porphyria, and Royal malady.

Definition

Variegate porphyria is caused by a heterozygous deficiency in protoporphyrinogen oxidase (PROTO oxidase) activity (Fig. 52-24) and is inherited in an autosomal dominant manner. The variability implicit in its name refers to the propensity of the disease to present with neurovisceral symptoms, photosensitivity, or both. Very rare forms of VP are seen with homozygous deficiencies in PROTO oxidase activity.

Prevalence

The VP incidence of 3 per 1000 in South Africa is substantially higher than elsewhere. In 1980, it was estimated that there were 10,000 affected individuals in South Africa,[958] and there is good evidence to suggest that they are all descendants of a single union between two Dutch settlers in 1680.[959] However, the disease has now been reported worldwide, and outside South Africa, there is probably no racial or geographic predilection. The incidence in Finland is reported at 1.3 per 100,000.[960] Outside South Africa, VP is probably less common than AIP.

Fig. 52-25 Formation of protoporphyrin from protoporphyrinogen. In this conversion, a hydrogen atom is removed from each of the four methene bridge carbons, and two hydrogens are removed from pyrrolic nitrogens, as indicated. M = $-CH_3$; P = $-CH_2 \cdot CH_2 \cdot COOH$; V = $-CH{=}CH_2$.

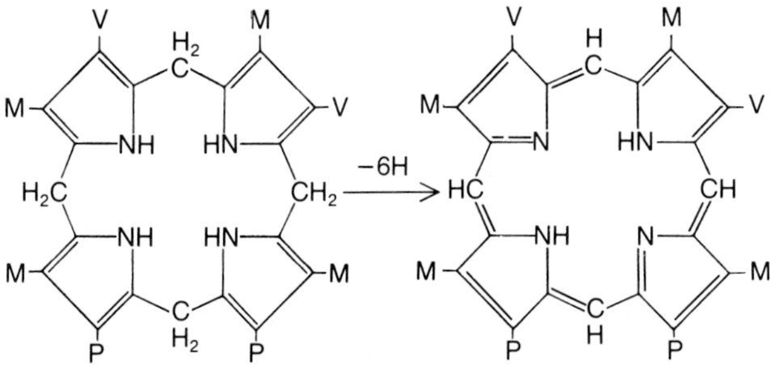

Protoporphyrinogen IX —(−6H)→ Protoporphyrin IX

Enzymology

The oxidation of protoporphyrinogen to protoporphyrin is mediated by PROTO oxidase (EC 1.3.3.4), which catalyzes the removal of six hydrogen atoms from the porphyrinogen nucleus (Fig. 52-25). This is the penultimate step in the heme biosynthetic pathway.

Properties. Since protoporphyrinogen oxidation can occur nonenzymatically at an appreciable rate, the significance of an enzyme for this step was clearly established only recently. With the advent of convenient assays for PROTO oxidase, an enzyme that catalyzes this oxidation step has clearly been identified in yeast,[961] *E. coli,*[962,963] rat liver, human fibroblasts, human erythrocytes, human leukocytes,[964] and beef liver.[924] PROTO oxidase has been purified from rat liver mitochondria and has been shown to have a molecular weight of 35,000, a K_m of 11 μM, a V_{max} of 8.7 nmol/min per milligram of protein, and an absolute requirement for oxygen. The same enzyme purified from yeast has a molecular weight of 180,000 and a K_m of 4.8 μM.[961] The enzyme acts specifically on protoporphyrinogen and does not catalyze the oxidation of coproporphyrinogen I, coproporphyrinogen III, or uroporphyrinogen I. Sulfhydryl reducing agents such as reduced glutathione at low concentrations can stimulate the enzyme activity.[964] In *E. coli,* fumarate[963] and nitrate[965] serve as alternative electron acceptors to replace oxygen in the oxidation of protoporphyrinogen under anaerobic conditions, but the nature of the primary electron acceptor in eukaryotic systems has not been elucidated. Since the enzymatic conversion of protoporphyrinogen to protoporphyrin is not inhibited by cyanide, 2,4-dinitrol phenol or azide, disulfide bonds are not essential for activity.[961] Hemin (50 μM) inhibits the enzyme activity by approximately 50 percent, and the inhibition is apparently noncompetitive and irreversible.[961] Human skin fibroblasts display PROTO oxidase activity (2 to 3 nmol of protoporphyrin formed per hour per milligram of protein[964,966]). Rat liver mitochondria are known to display enzyme activity in the range of 10 to 12 nmol protoporphyrin per hour per milligram of protein.[966] Fibroblasts from patients with VP, but not from patients with EPP, have been reported to have decreased levels of PROTO oxidase activity.[966]

Assay. Spectrophotometric and fluorometric assays for protoporphyrinogen oxidation have been described for use in rat liver mitochondria and other tissues.[967] The fluorometric assay appears more sensitive, while the spectrophotometric assay may be more useful for assaying a wider variety of tissues. In both assays, three properties of protoporphyrin are important for evaluating the validity of the assay. First, protoporphyrin, unlike uroporphyrin, has unusual solubility characteristics and has a tendency to aggregate at neutral pH in aqueous solvents. Addition of tissue or a neutral detergent is required to circumvent this problem. Second, protoporphyrinogen oxidation occurs at a significant rate and should be minimized by addition of a reducing agent such as glutathione. Third, a chelating agent must be present to prevent the spontaneous formation of certain metalloporphyrin complexes, such as zinc protoporphyrin, which have an absorption spectrum different from free protoporphyrin. Chelating agents also prevent the incorporation of iron.[967]

Clinical Findings

The neurovisceral symptomatology is indistinguishable from that observed in AIP and HCP, which has been described above. Photosensitivity is more common, and the resulting lesions tend to be more chronic in VP than in HCP. Cutaneous manifestations comprise vesicles, bullae, hyperpigmentation, milia, hypertrichosis, and increased skin fragility. Lesions are clinically and histologically indistinguishable from PCT, and in the absence of neurovisceral symptoms, the diagnosis of VP is easily overlooked.[968] Skin manifestations are less frequently observed in cold climates (e.g., 45 percent in a series from Finland[960]) than in hot climates (e.g., 85 percent in a series from South Africa[958]).

The same spectrum of factors which leads to activation of AIP and HCP also appears to induce VP. Thus, barbiturates,[969–971] dapsone,[972] lead from "moonshine" whiskey,[973] contraceptive steroids,[974–976] pregnancy,[977,978] and decreased carbohydrate intake[979,980] have all been reported to induce or exacerbate VP. Screening of drugs for porphyrinogenicity in VP is most commonly performed in the DDC-primed rat as this model most closely resembles VP.[981–984]

Hepatic involvement in VP is generally mild or absent. Liver biopsies in three patients have shown mild nonspecific inflammatory changes with normal iron stores in two of the three cases.[985,986] The demonstration of normal ferrochelatase activity and decreased PROTO oxidase activity in fibroblasts from VP patients[40] led to the suggestion that similar hepatic defects would favor the biliary excretion of protoporphyrin which, after autooxidation in the gut, would account for the increased fecal concentrations of protoporphyrin seen in VP.[40,987] This hypothesis has been contested, based on the demonstration of uroporphyrin and 7-carboxylic porphyrins, but not protoporphyrin, in liver biopsies from VP patients. An alternative hypothesis proposed that the mucosa of the small intestine and colon may synthesize the elevated amounts of protoporphyrin found in feces.[988] Renal synthesis of protoporphyrin may also be involved.[989]

Pathogenesis of the Clinical Findings. Ferrochelatase activity has been reported to be both normal[990] and abnormal[991] in VP, whereas PROTO oxidase activity has been consistently found to be decreased.[40,991,992] Additionally, erythrocyte PBG deaminase activity has been reported to be decreased[992] in VP patients and in patients with "dual porphyria" from Chester.[993,994] Dual porphyria refers to the coexistence of two forms of porphyria and has also been reported involving VP and PCT.[995,996] Further studies are clearly needed to unravel the complexities of the pathogenesis of VP.

Homozygous VP has been documented in three patients and suspected in another.[997,998] Symptoms were severe photosensitivity, growth and mental retardation, and marked neurologic abnormalities in two cases; onset was in childhood in all cases.

Biochemical Findings

The biochemical hallmark of VP is elevated fecal porphyrin excretion. Usually, but not invariably, protoporphyrin exceeds coproporphyrin (mostly isomer III). Fecal meso- and deuteroporphyrins may also be elevated. Fecal X-porphyrins (ether-acetic acid-insoluble, extracted with urea-triton), a heterogeneous group of porphyrin-peptide conjugates, are elevated in VP more than in any other type of porphyria. Fecal porphyrins often do not become elevated until after puberty.[960,999] Urinary coproporphyrin (type III), ALA, and PBG are often normal between attacks but may become markedly elevated during acute attacks. Urinary porphyrins may be elevated preferentially in attacks induced by barbiturates which induce hepatic ALA synthase. Estrogens induce attacks by reducing biliary excretion and exacerbating photosensitivity.[1000] Plasma invariably contains a porphyrin-peptide conjugate[1001,1002] and a porphyrin with a fluorescence emission that is maximal at 626 ± 1 nm and appears specific for VP.[1003,1004] X-porphyrins have also been detected in bile.[1005,1006] Pseudoporphyria with porphyrin excretion patterns suggestive of VP has been reported following excessive ingestion of porphyrin-laden yeast tablets.[1007]

Diagnosis

VP should be considered in the differential diagnosis of acute porphyria, especially if PBG deaminase activity is normal. Characteristic plasma porphyrin fluorescence is usually seen in VP.[1003,1004] The differentiation of VP from HCP is usually possible following fecal porphyrin analysis. In patients with only cutaneous manifestations, the demonstration of urinary 8- and 7-carboxylic porphyrins and isocoproporphyrin in PCT is usually sufficient for differentiation from VP. Urinary ALA and PBG concentrations are of little help diagnostically except to rule out PCT.

PROTO oxidase activity can be measured in fibroblasts or lymphocytes, but the assay is not generally available. In the absence of this determination, screening of family members is best achieved by measuring fecal porphyrin concentrations. Fecal porphyrins may, unfortunately, be little elevated in prepubertal or elderly heterozygotes.[980]

Treatment

Identification and avoidance of precipitating factors are essential. Photosensitivity can be minimized by protective clothing and a β-carotene analogue (Canthaxanthrin) may be of some help.[1008] The treatment of neurovisceral symptoms is identical to that described for AIP. Resin hemoperfusion has been reported to be ineffective in one child,[1009] but further trials may be worthwhile.

ERYTHROPOIETIC PROTOPORPHYRIA

Synonyms

Synonyms for erythropoietic protoporphyria (EPP) are protoporphyria and erythrohepatic protoporphyria.

Definition

Erythropoietic protoporphyria is a form of porphyria associated with decreased activity of ferrochelatase (Fig. 52-26) and is inherited in an autosomal dominant fashion. Biochemically, this defect results in massive accumulations of protoporphyrin in erythrocytes, plasma, and feces. Clinically, the disease is characterized by the childhood onset of cutaneous photosensitivity in light-exposed areas, but skin lesions are milder and less disfiguring than those seen in CEP. Hepatobiliary dysfunction, which may become severe, is seen in a minority of cases.

Prevalence

EPP is the most common form of erythropoietic porphyria. Three hundred cases were reported by 1976.[1010] There is no racial or sexual predilection, and onset is typically in childhood. Homozygous EPP has been reported in one case.[1010a]

Enzymology

The final step of heme biosynthesis is the insertion of iron into protoporphyrin (Fig. 52-27). This reaction is catalyzed by the enzyme ferrochelatase [heme synthase, heme synthetase, or protoheme-ferrolyase (EC 4.99.1.1)].

Properties. Ferrochelatase activity in mammalian cells is localized in the inner membrane of mitochondria. The enzyme activity is also found in plant chloroplasts and chromatophores of photosynthetic bacteria. Unlike other enzymatic steps in the heme biosynthetic pathway which utilize porphyrinogens, ferrochelatase utilizes protoporphyrin as substrate. In addition to protoporphyrin, other 2-carboxylate porphyrins, e.g., deutero- and mesoporphyrin (Table 52-2), serve as good substrates for this enzyme in vitro.[1011–1013] Only the reduced form of iron (Fe^{2+}) is incorporated into protoporphyrin by the enzyme.[1014] Co^{2+} and Zn^{2+} are more efficient enzyme substrates than Fe^{2+}.[1012] Therefore, various rates of ferrochelatase activity are obtained, depending on which metal and porphyrin substrates are used.[1012] There is also experimental evidence that suggests more than one ferrochelatase in pig liver,[1013,1014] but conclusive proof of this finding has not been obtained.

Ferrochelatase has been purified to apparent homogeneity from rat liver mitochondria.[1015,1016] The molecular weight of the purified enzyme was reported to be either 63,000[1015] or 42,000[1016] as determined by SDS-polyacrylamide gel electrophoresis. The enzyme is enriched in lysine (11 percent) and hydrophobic amino acid residues (48 percent).[1016] The purified enzyme from rat liver has a specific activity of 7 μmol heme formed per hour per milligram protein, an optimum pH of 7.8, and a K_m of 28.5 μM. These properties were determined using iron and protoporphyrin as substrates.[1016] The enzyme activity is markedly stimulated by the addition of fatty acids, while it is inhibited by metals such as Co, Zn, Pb, Cu, or Mn.[1016] Bovine ferrochelatase from liver mitochondria has been purified to homogeneity.[1017,1018] The molecular weight of the homogeneous protein was estimated to be either 42,500[1017] or 40,000[1018] by SDS-polyacrylamide gel electrophoresis,[1017] but approximately 200,000 by gel filtration. Other physicochemical properties of the bovine enzyme were similar to those of the rat enzyme. An antibody specific for purified bovine ferrochelatase inhibited the incorporation of iron, zinc, and cobalt into protoporphyrin, confirming that the synthetic activities for these metalloporphyrins are ascribable to a single enzyme protein.[1017] Human liver mitochondrial membranes were found to contain large amounts of endogenous metals, especially zinc, which act as substrates for ferrochelatase, leading to a lack of linearity of the activity as a function of protein concentration. This lack of linearity was found mainly due to a high Zn-chelatase activity with endogenous zinc.[1019] Thus, endogenous zinc content in biologic samples must be taken into account when measuring ferrochelatase activity.

Inhibitor. A powerful inhibitor of ferrochelatase identified as *N*-methylprotoporphyrin[1020] has been isolated from the livers of mice given DDC. Synthetic *N*-methylprotoporphyrin has also been shown to inhibit purified bovine ferrochelatase and activity in crude preparations from liver and microorganisms.[1018] It has been shown that *N*-alkylated dicarboxylic porphyrins compete reversibly with the protoporphyrin substrate for the enzyme and that structural and steric factors affect the inhibitory activity by modifying the affinity of the *N*-alkyl porphyrin inhibitor for the active site of the enzyme.[1021]

Abnormal Findings. Ferrochelatase deficiency has been reported in tissues from patients with EPP[23,24,1022] and from cattle with the same disorder.[1023] The disease in cattle is inherited as an autosomal recessive trait, while the human disease is inherited as an autosomal dominant trait. Ferrochelatase deficiency in EPP can be functionally demonstrated in cultured

Fig. 52-26 The enzymatic defect in the heme pathway in EPP is a partial deficiency of ferrochelatase activity. The enzyme defect results in protoporphyrin accumulation (bold letters) primarily in erythroid cells in some heterozygotes, even though hemoglobin synthesis is not impaired. ALA = δ-aminolevulinic acid; PBG = porphobiliniogen; Uro'gen = uroporphyrinogen; Copro'gen = coproporphyrinogen; Proto'gen = protoporphyrinogen; Proto = protoporphyrin.

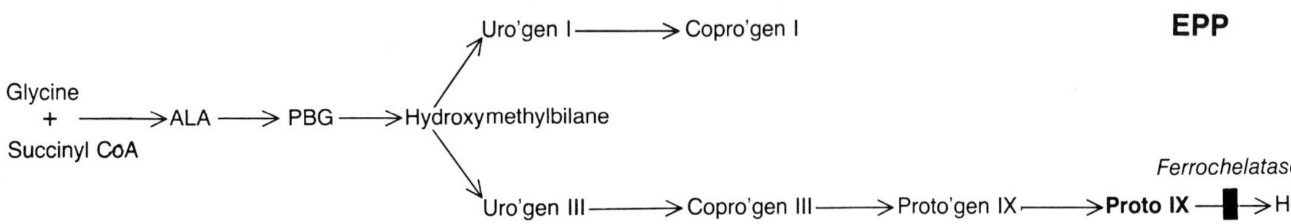

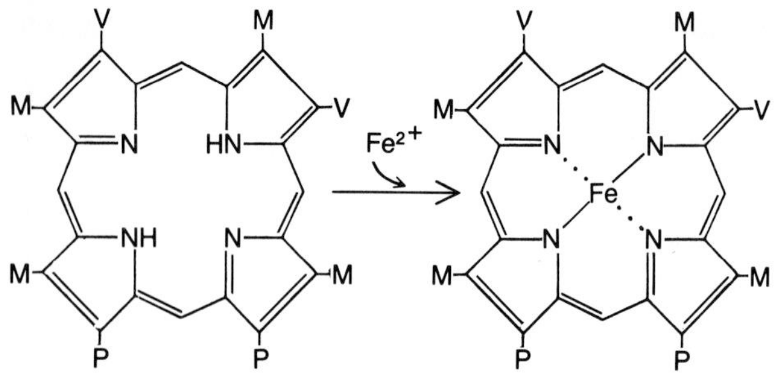

Fig. 52-27 Formation of heme from protoporphyrin and iron. M = —CH_3; P = —$CH_2 \cdot CH_2 \cdot COOH$; V = —$CH{=}CH_2$.

lymphocytes from human patients[1024] or in skin fibroblasts from affected cattle.[1025] Gene dosage-dependent protoporphyrin accumulation was demonstrated in cattle.[1025]

Assay. Ferrochelatase activity has been measured by three different methods.[1026] (1) ^{59}Fe is used as a metal substrate, and the radioactivity in the purified heme fraction is determined after the reaction. This method is the most sensitive,[1026] but is tedious, and great care must be taken to ascertain the purity and the complete recovery of the radioactive heme product. (2) Formation of heme is determined by the pyridine hemochromogen assay.[1014,1027] This method gives the most unequivocal results, but has a low sensitivity. Greater sensitivity has been reported using mesoporphyrin (Table 52-2) rather than protoporphyrin as substrate.[1028] The alkaline pyridine mesohemochromogen has an absorption peak distinct from that of the background protohemochromogen derived from preexisting tissue heme. The enzyme activity determined with one type of porphyrin or metal substrate may differ from that determined with another substrate.[1029] For example, using protoporphyrin as the porphyrin substrate, it has been shown that DDC inhibits ferrochelatase activity,[1030] but does not inhibit cobalt chelatase activity.[1031] When Co^{2+} and mesoporphyrin are used as substrates, DDC inhibits cobalt mesoheme formation.[1032] (3) Disappearance of the porphyrin substrate during the incubation is determined as a measure of ferrochelatase activity. Loss of porphyrin substrate may occur by reactions other than ferrochelatase, such as photocatalyzed oxidation. Moreover, sufficient substrate concentrations must be provided to maintain a linear rate of product formation throughout the incubation. Ideally, for product formation, greater than 90 percent of the substrate should remain at the end of incubation. This would make the porphyrin disappearance assay insensitive.

Clinical Findings

The most common symptoms in a series of 32 patients with EPP are shown in Table 52-7. Symptoms are usually worse during spring and summer and occur in light-exposed areas, especially of the face and hands. Within 1 h of exposure to the sun, stinging or painful burning sensations in the skin occur and are followed several hours later by erythema and edema. Petechiae, or more rarely, purpura, vesicles, and crusting may develop, and persist for several days after sun exposure. Some patients experience burning sensations in the absence of such objective signs of cutaneous phototoxicity. Artificial lights may also cause photosensitivity, especially theater lights.[1033] Intense and repeated exposure to the sun may result in lysis of the nails, leathery, hyperkeratotic skin over the dorsum of the hands, and mild scarring. Bullae, skin fragility, hypertrichosis, hyperpigmentation, severe scarring, and mutilation are unusual in EPP. Gallstones, sometimes presenting at an unusually early age, are fairly common, and hepatic disease, although unusual, may be severe and associated with significant morbidity. Anemia is uncommon. There are no known precipitating factors and no neurovisceral manifestations.

Pathogenesis of the Clinical Findings. Histologic examination of skin biopsies from EPP patients shows thickened dermal capillary walls surrounded by amorphous hyalinelike deposits, immunoglobins, complement, and PAS-positive mucopolysaccharides.[1034–1036] Basement membrane abnormalities are observed in EPP but are quantitatively less marked than in other forms of porphyria.[1035,1037] Thus EPP can be suggested but not positively identified from skin biopsies.

The maximal light absorption range for porphyrins, the Soret region, corresponds well to the wavelength of light (about 400 nm) known to trigger photosensitivity reactions in the skin of EPP patients.[1038] Such reactions can be prevented by short-term occlusions of arterial blood flow to the arm,[1039] and light-excited porphyrins are known to generate free radicals and singlet oxygen.[1040–1043] Thus, such radicals, notably singlet oxygen, may lead to peroxidation of lipids[1041] and cross-linking of membrane proteins,[1044,1045] which, in erythrocytes, may result in reduced deformability.[1046] Bone marrow reticulocytes may display fluorescence, but protoporphyrin content and fluorescence of circulating reticulocytes are nonuniform and decreases with age.[23,1047] In vitro studies of erythrocytes have revealed that photohemolysis is more severe when exogenous protoporphyrin is added to normal cells than that seen in endogenously protoporphyrin-loaded cells.[1048] The presence of albumin in the system decreases the extent of such photohemolysis, presumably by binding the released protoporphyrin.[1049,1050] Hydrophobic compounds are destroyed more easily by uroporphyrin, whereas lipophilic compounds are more easily damaged by protoporphyrin.[1042] Thus, the solubility and partition properties of porphyrins appear to determine their localization and hence their phototoxicity toward different target tissues.[1051,1052] Interestingly, protoporphyrin, but not Zn-protoporphyrin, is released from erythrocytes following irradiation which may explain why lead intoxication

Table 52-7 Common Clinical Features of EPP from a Series of 32 Cases[1010]

Symptoms and signs	*Percent incidence*
Burning	97
Edema	94
Itching	88
Erythema	69
Scarring	19
Vesicles	3
Anemia	27
Cholelithiasis	12
Abnormal liver function results	4

and iron deficiency, although associated with elevated erythrocyte Zn-protoporphyrin levels, are not associated with photosensitivity.[1053,1054] Forearm irradiation in EPP patients leads to complement activation and polymorphonuclear chemotaxis.[1055] Similar results have been obtained in vitro,[1056–1058] and these events may also contribute to the pathogenesis of skin lesions in EPP.

Light- and electron-microscopic examination of liver biopsies from EPP patients have revealed a wide variability in findings ranging from complete normality to periportal fibrosis and severe cirrhosis.[1059–1070] Abnormally elevated, sometimes massive, accumulations of protoporphyrin have been detected as brown pigment in hepatocytes, Kupffer cells, and biliary cannaliculae.[1071–1073] These deposits are doubly refractive under polarizing lenses. Approximately 20 cases of EPP have been reported to develop hepatic failure which resulted in death, presumably secondary to protoporphyrin damage.[1067,1074–1080] The same characteristic hepatic histopathologies were noted at autopsy. Similar liver findings are also seen in the griseofulvin-treated mouse, which accumulates protoporphyrin and represents an animal model of EPP.[1081–1083] Why some patients with EPP develop hepatic pathology while the majority do not is unknown. It has been suggested that this may relate to hepatic overproduction of porphyrins in some cases versus predominant protoporphyrin synthesis in the erythron, in which case the liver is primarily involved in clearance.[1084,1085] In this regard, rat liver mitochondria showed evidence of damage following irradiation prior to signs of lysosomal damage.[1086] The photodamage after exposure to exogenous protoporphyrin was predominantly in the plasmalemma, whereas with endogenous protoporphyrin accumulation, photodamage was primarily seen in mitochondria.[1087]

Biochemical Findings

The biochemical hallmark of EPP is excessive concentrations of protoporphyrin in erythrocytes, plasma, bile, and feces. Because of its poor solubility in water, it is not excreted in urine. Available evidence tends to favor the bone marrow and the newly released reticulocyte/erythrocyte as the major source of elevated protoporphyrin concentrations.[23,1047,1088] However, as discussed earlier, the liver may contribute in certain cases.[1089,1090] In this regard, hepatic ALA synthase activity may be increased in EPP.[1065,1091]

Plasma hemopexin levels may be decreased in EPP,[1092] and erythrocyte PBG deaminase activities can be increased.[1093] Both changes may be indicative of mild hemolysis. The decreased hemopexin may be due to increased porphyrins, while increased PBG deaminase is due to reticulocytosis. Mild anemia with hypochromia and microcytosis may occasionally be seen.[23,1010] Mild hypertriglyceridemia also occurs with increased frequency in patients with EPP.[1094]

Diagnosis

Photosensitivity should suggest the diagnosis which can be confirmed by the demonstration of elevated concentrations of free protoporphyrin in erythrocytes, plasma, and stools with normal urinary porphyrins. The presence of protoporphyrin (as evidenced by its characteristic spectrum) in both plasma and erythrocytes is a finding specific for EPP. Fluorescent reticulocytes on examination of peripheral blood smear may also suggest the diagnosis.

Treatment

Avoidance of the sun and use of topical sunscreen agents may be helpful, especially those with a high sun protection factor (SPF 26 or 34). Oral administration of β-carotene may afford systemic photoprotection resulting in improved, but highly variable, tolerance to the sun.[1095–1100] The recommended serum β-carotene level of 600 to 800 μg/dl[1010] is usually achieved with oral doses of 120 to 180 mg daily, and beneficial effects are typically seen 1 to 3 months after the onset of therapy. Mild yellow-orange discoloration of the skin may result, but is the only known side effect of β-carotene.[1101] The mechanism of sun protection probably involves quenching of activated oxygen radicals[1096]; porphyrin concentrations are unchanged.

Hypertransfusion therapy has also been advocated to suppress erythropoiesis,[1102,1103] but the potential hazards of transfusion are a significant drawback to this form of therapy. Cholestyramine has been reported to improve photosensitivity and reduce hepatic protoporphyrin content.[1070,1104] Zinc[1105] and vitamin E, inosine, adenosine monophosphate, antimalarials, and antihistamines have also been tried with little success.[1010,1106] Lastly, with the increasing realization that hepatic involvement, although uncommon, may be severe, efforts to prevent hepatotoxicity from drugs or chemicals should be made. Iron, vitamin E, and cholestyramine have been advocated to halt the progression of frank hepatocellular dysfunction.[1060,1070] Another modality which may be promising, based on findings in griseofulvin-treated mice, is the administration of cholic acid.[1083,1107]

PRENATAL DIAGNOSIS OF PORPHYRIA

The advent of methods to measure the activities of the various enzymes which are deficient in the different porphyrias has made the prenatal diagnosis of all porphyria diseases theoretically possible. However, many of these enzyme activity determinations are made only in a few specialized research laboratories. Additionally, it must be stressed that in the heterozygous porphyrias, even though prenatal diagnosis is possible, clinical expression of inherited defective enzyme activity is far from inevitable (e.g., only 1 in 10 in the case of AIP). In addition, there is potential for overlap between the normal and heterozygous ranges for enzyme activities. Consequently, the demonstration of decreased enzyme activities compatible with heterozygous forms of autosomal dominant porphyria usually is not considered an indication for termination of pregnancy. Although decreased enzyme activities consistent with homozygous porphyrias, because of their more severe clinical course, might be considered an indication for termination of pregnancy, homozygous cases are exceedingly rare. Autosomal recessive porphyria (CEP) has been diagnosed utilizing amniocentesis and excluded during the pregnancy of a mother who had previously borne a child with CEP.[639a,1108,1109]

REFERENCES

1. FISCHER H, ORTH H: *Die Chemie des Pyrrols*. New York, Johnson Reprint Co. (Leipzig, Akademische Verlags Gesellschaft, 1934), vols I, II, III, 1968.
2. IUPAC-IUB JOINT COMMISSION ON BIOCHEMICAL NOMENCLATURE (JCBN): Nomenclature of tetrapyrroles: Recommendations 1978. *Eur J Biochem* 108:1, 1980.
3. FUHRHOP JH, SMITH KM: Laboratory methods, in *Porphyrin and Metalloporphyrin Research*. Amsterdam, Elsevier, 1975, p 1.
4. FALK JE: *Porphyrins and Metalloporphyrins*. New York, Elsevier, vol 2, 1964.
5. WILLIAMS RJP: The properties of metalloporphyrins. *J Chem Soc Commun* 299, 1956.
6. SPIKES JD: Porphyrins and related compounds as photodynamic sensitizers. *Ann NY Acad Sci* 244:496, 1975.
7. LIM HW, PEREX HD, GOLDSTEIN IM, GIGLI I: Complement-derived chemotactic activity is generated in human serum containing uroporphyrin after irradiation with 405 nm light. *J Clin Invest* 67:1072, 1981.
8. DIAMOND I, GRANELLI SG, MCDONAGH AF, NIELSEN S, WILSON CB, JAENICKE R: Photodynamic therapy of malignant tumours. *Lancet* 2:1175, 1972.
9. BLUM HF: *Photodynamic Action and Diseases Caused by Light*. New York, Reinhold, 1941.
10. VAN DER OUDERAA FJ, BUYTENHEK M, SLIKKERVEER FJ, VAN DORP DA: On the haemoprotein character of prostaglandin endoperoxide synthetase. *Biochim Biophys Acta* 572:29, 1979.
11. SONO M, DAWSON JH: Extensive studies of the heme coordination structure of indoleamine 2,3-dioxygenase and of trypotophan binding with magnetic and natural circular dichroism and electron paramagnetic resonance spectroscopy. *Biochim Biophys Acta* 789:170, 1984.
12. IGNARRO LJ, WOOD KS, WOLIN MS: Regulation of purified soluble guanylate cyclase by porphyrins and metalloporphyrins: A unifying concept, in Greengard P, et al (eds): *Advances in Cyclic Nucleotide and Protein Phosphorylation Research*. New York, Raven, 1984, vol 17, p 267.
13. WHITE DC, GRANICK S: Hemin biosynthesis in Haemophilus. *J Bacteriol* 85:842, 1963.
14. CHANG KP: Cellular and molecular mechanisms of intracellular symbiosis in leishmaniasis. *Int Rev Cytol Suppl* 14:267, 1983.
15. CUTTING JA, SCHULMAN HM: The site of heme synthesis in soybean root nodules. *Biochim Biophys Acta* 192:486, 1969.
16. NEGISHI M, OMURA T: Presence of apo-cytochrome b_5 in microsomes from rat liver. *J Biochem (Tokyo)* 67:745, 1970.
17. HARA T, MINAKAMI S: Presence of apo-cytochrome b_5 in microsomes. Incorporation of radioactive heme to the cytochrome in vitro. *J Biochem (Tokyo)* 67:741, 1970.
18. CORREIA MA, MEYER UA: Apocytochrome P-450: Reconstitution of functional cytochrome with hemin in vitro. *Proc Natl Acad Sci USA* 72:400, 1975.
19. CORREIA MA, FARRELL GC, SCHMID R, ORTIZ DE MONTELLANO PR, YOST GS, MICO BA: Incorporation of exogenous heme into hepatic cytochrome P-450 in vivo. *J Biol Chem* 254:15, 1979.
20. FARRELL GC, CORREIA MA: Structural and functional reconstitution of hepatic cytochrome P-450 *in vivo*: Reversal of allylisopropylacetamide-mediated destruction of the hemoprotein by exogenous heme. *J Biol Chem* 255:10128, 1980.
21. GRANICK JL, SASSA S: Hemin control of heme biosynthesis in mouse Friend-virus transformed erythroleukemia cells in culture. *J Biol Chem* 253:5402, 1978.
22. TSCHUDY DP, PERLROTH MG, MARVER HS, COLLINS A, HUNTER G JR, RECHCIGL M JR: Acute intermittent porphyria: The first "overproduction disease" localized to a specific enzyme. *Proc Natl Acad Sci USA* 53:841, 1965.
23. BOTTOMLEY SS, TANAKA M, EVERETT MA: Diminished erythroid ferrochelatase activity in Protoporphyria. *J Lab Clin Med* 86:126, 1975.
24. BONKOWSKY HL, BLOOMER JR, EBERT PS, MAHONEY MJ: Heme synthetase deficiency in human Protoporphyria. *J Clin Invest* 56:1139, 1975.
25. SASSA S, ZALAR GL, KAPPAS A: Studies in porphyria. VII. Induction of uroporphyrinogen-I synthase and expression of the gene defect of acute intermittent porphyria in mitogen-stimulated human lymphocytes. *J Clin Invest* 61:499, 1978.
26. KAUFMAN K, MARVER HS: Biochemical defects in two types of human hepatic porphyria. *N Engl J Med* 283:954, 1970.
27. HUTTON JJ, COLEMAN D: Linkage analyses using biochemical variants in mice II. Levulinate dehydratase and autosomal glucose 6-phosphate dehydrogenase. *Biochem Genet* 3:517, 1969.
28. BURNHAM BF, LASCELLES J: Control of porphyrin biosynthesis through a negative-feedback mechanism: Studies with preparation of delta-aminolevulinate synthase and delta-aminolevulinate dehydratase from *Rhodopseudomonas spheroides*. *Biochem J* 87:462, 1963.
29. STRAND LJ, FELSHER BF, REDEKER AG, MARVER HS: Heme biosynthesis in intermittent acute porphyria: Decreased hepatic conversion of porphobilinogen to porphyrins and increased delta aminolevulinic acid synthetase activity. *Proc Natl Acad Sci USA* 67:1315, 1970.
30. SASSA S, GRANICK S, BICKERS DR, BRADLOW HL, KAPPAS A: A microassay for uroporphyrinogen I synthase, one of three abnormal enzyme activities in acute intermittent porphyria, and its application to the study of the genetics of this disease. *Proc Natl Acad Sci USA* 71:732, 1974.
31. SASSA S, SOLISH G, LEVERE RD, KAPPAS A: Studies in porphyria. IV. Expression of the gene defect of acute intermittent porphyria in cultured human skin fibroblasts and amniotic cells: Prenatal diagnosis of the porphyric trait. *J Exp Med* 142:722, 1975.
32. ROMEO G, LEVIN EY: Uroporphyrinogen III cosynthetase in human congenital erythropoietic porphyria. *Proc Natl Acad Sci USA* 63:856, 1969.
33. ELDER GH, TOVEY JA: Uroporphyrinogen decarboxylase activity of human tissues. *Biochem Soc Trans* 5:1470, 1977.
34. DE VERNEUIL H, AITKEN G, NORDMANN Y: Familial and sporadic porphyria cutanea: Two different diseases. *Hum Genet* 44:145, 1978.
35. ELDER GH, LEE GB, TOVEY JA: Decreased activity of hepatic uroporphyrinogen decarboxylase in sporadic Porphyria Cutanea Tarda. *N Engl J Med* 299:274, 1978.
36. DE VERNEUIL H, NORDMANN Y: Porphyrie cutanee symptomatique. *Nouv Presse Med* 10:3541, 1981.
37. ELDER GH, EVANS JO, THOMAS N, COX R, BRODIE MJ, MOORE MR, GOLDBERG A, NICHOLSON DC: The primary enzyme defect in hereditary coproporphyria. *Lancet* 2:1217, 1976.
38. GRANDCHAMP B, DEYBACK JC, GRELIER M, DE VERNEUIL H, NORDMANN Y: Studies of porphyrin synthesis in fibroblasts of patients with congenital erythropoietic porphyria and one patient with homozygous coproporphyria. *Biochim Biophys Acta* 629:577, 1980.
39. GRANDCHAMP B, NORDMANN Y: Decreased lymphocyte coproporphyrinogen III oxidase activity in hereditary coproporphyria. *Biochem Biophys Res Commun* 74:1089, 1977.
40. BRENNER DA, BLOOMER JR: The enzymatic defect in variegate porphyria. Studies with human cultured skin fibroblasts. *N Engl J Med* 302:765, 1980.
41. DEYBACH JC, DE VERNEUIL H, NORDMANN Y: The inherited enzymatic defect in porphyria variegata. *Hum Genet* 58:425, 1981.
42. VILJOEN DJ, CAYANIS E, BECKER DM, KRAMER S, DAWSON B, BERNSTEIN R: Reduced ferrochelatase activity in fibroblasts from patients with Porphyria Variegata. *Am J Hematol* 6:185, 1979.
43. SASSA S, ZALAR GL, POH-FITZPATRICK MB, KAPPAS A: Studies in Porphyria IX: Detection of the gene defect of Erythropoietic Protoporphyria in mitogen-stimulated human lymphocytes. *Trans Assoc Am Physicians* 92:268, 1979.
44. MEYER UA: Intermittent acute porphyria: Clinical and biochemical studies of disordered heme biosynthesis. *Enzyme* 16:334, 1973.
45. NAKAO K, WADA O, KITAMURA T, UONO K: Activity of aminolaevulinic acid synthetase in normal and porphyric human livers. *Nature* 210:838, 1966.
46. McINTYRE N, PEARSON AJG, ALLAN DJ, CRASKE S, WEST GML, MOORE MR, PAXTON J, BEATTIE AD, GOLDBERG A: Hepatic δ-aminolaevulinic acid synthetase in an attack of hereditary coproporphyria and during remission. *Lancet* 1:560, 1971.
47. DOWDLE EB, MUSTARD P, EALES L: δ-Aminolevulinic acid synthetase activity in normal and porphyric human livers. *S Afr Med J* 41:1093, 1967.
48. TAIT GH: Coproporphyrinogenase activities in extracts of *Rhodopseudomonas spheroides* and *Chromatium* strain D. *Biochem J* 128:1159, 1972.
49. PORRA RJ, BARNES R, JONES TOG: The level and sub-cellular distribution of δ-aminolaevulinate synthase activity in semi-anaerobic and aerobic yeast. *Hoppe-Seyler's Z Physiol Chem* 353:1365, 1972.
50. BRATTSTEN LB, WILKINSON CF: Properties of 5-aminolaevulinate synthetase and its relationship to microsomal mixed-function oxidation in the Southern Armyworm (*Spodoptera eridania*). *Biochem J* 150:97, 1975.
51. GRANICK S: The induction *in vitro* of the synthesis of δ-aminolevulinic acid synthetase in chemical porphyria: A response to certain drugs, sex hormones, and foreign chemicals. *J Biol Chem* 241:1359, 1966.
52. GRANICK S, URATA G: Increase in activity of δ-aminolevulinic acid synthetase in liver mitochondria induced by feeding of 3,5-dicarbethoxy-1,4-dihydrocollidine. *J Biol Chem* 238:821, 1963.
53. MARVER HS, TSCHUDY DP, PERLROTH MG, COLLINS A: δ-Aminolevulinic acid synthetase. I. Studies in liver homogenates. *J Biol Chem* 241:2803, 1966.
54. MARVER HS, COLLINS A, TSCHUDY DP, RECHCIGHL M JR: δ-Aminolevulinic acid synthetase. II. Induction in rat liver. *J Biol Chem* 241:4323, 1966.
55. AOKI Y, WADA O, URATA G, TAKAKU F, NAKAO K: Purification and some

properties of δ-aminolevulinate (ALA) synthetase in rabbit reticulocytes. *Biochem Biophys Res Commun* 42:568, 1971.

56. WATANABE N, HAYASHI N, KIKUCHI G: delta-Aminolevulinate synthase isozymes in the liver and erythroid cells of chicken. *Biochem Biophys Res Commun* 113:377, 1983.

57. SARDESAI VM, LENAGHAN R, ROSENBERG JC: Tissue delta-aminolevulinic acid synthetase activity in hemorrhagic shock. *Biochem Med* 6:366, 1972.

58. MARGOLIS FL: Regulation of porphyrin biosynthesis in the Harderian gland of inbred mouse strains. *Arch Biochem Biophys* 145:373, 1971.

59. CONDIE LW, TEPHLY TR: δ-Aminolevulinic acid synthetase. Sensitive methods in liver for hemoprotein biosynthesis, in Fleischer S, Packer L (eds): *Methods in Enzymology*. New York, Academic, 1978, vol 52 (Biomembranes), part C, p 350.

60. PATERNITI JR JR, SIMONE JJ, BEATTIE DS: Detection and regulation of δ-aminolevulinic acid synthetase activity in the rat brain. *Arch Biochem Biophys* 189:86, 1978.

61. DE MATTEIS F, ZETTERLUND P, WETTERBERG L: Brain 5-aminolevulinate synthase. Developmental aspects and evidence for regulatory role. *Biochem J* 196:811, 1981.

62. WHITING MJ, ELLIOTT WH: Purification and properties of solubilized mitochondrial δ-aminolevulinic acid synthetase and comparison with the cytosol enzyme. *J Biol Chem* 247:6818, 1972.

63. KAPLAN BH: δ-Aminolevulinic acid synthetase from the particulate fraction of liver of porphyric rats. *Biochim Biophys Acta* 235:381, 1971.

64. SCHOLNICK PL, HAMMAKER LE, MARVER HS: Soluble δ-aminolevulinic acid synthetase of rat liver. I. Some properties of the partially purified enzyme. *J Biol Chem* 247:4126, 1972.

65. WOODS JS, MURTHY VV: δ-Aminolevulinic acid synthetase from fetal rat liver: Studies on the partially purified enzyme. *Mol Pharmacol* 11:70, 1975.

66. WHITING MJ, GRANICK S: δ-Aminolevulinic acid synthase from chick embryo liver mitochondria. I. Purification and some properties. *J Biol Chem* 251:1340, 1976.

67. SINCLAIR P, GRANICK S: Two methods for determining the activity of δ-aminolevulinate synthetase within intact liver cells in culture. *Anal Biochem* 79:380, 1977.

68. PIPER WN, CONDIE LW, TEPHLY TR: The role of substrates for glycine acyl transferase in the reversal of chemically induced porphyria in the rat. *Arch Biochem Biophys* 159:671, 1973.

69. TEPHLY TR, CONDIE LW, PIPER WN: The role of substrates for glycine acyltransferase, and the role of sulfanilamide and acetate in the reversal of chemically-induced porphyria in the rat. *Enzyme* 16:187, 1973.

70. PATERNITI JR, BEATTIE DS: δ-Aminolevulinic acid synthetase from rat liver mitochondria: Purification and properties. *J Biol Chem* 254:6112, 1979.

71. ADES IZ, HARPE KG: Biogenesis of mitochondrial proteins. Identification of the mature and precursor forms of the chick subunit of 5-aminolevulinate synthase from embryonic chick liver. *J Biol Chem* 256:9329, 1981.

72. BORTHWICK IA, SRIVASTAVA G, DAY AR, PIROLA BA, SNOSWELL MA, MAY BK, ELLIOTT WH: Complete nucleotide sequence of hepatic 5-aminolaevulinate synthase precursor. *Eur J Biochem* 150:481, 1985.

73. BORTHWICK IA, SRIVASTAVA G, BROOKER JD, MAY BK, ELLIOTT WH: Purification of 5-aminolaevulinate synthase from liver mitochondria of chick embryo. *Eur J Biochem* 129:615, 1983.

74. ELFERINK CJ, SRIVASTAVA G, MAGUIRE DJ, BORTHWICK IA, MAY BK, ELLIOTT WH: A unique gene for 5-aminolevulinate synthase in chickens. Evidence for expression of an identical messenger RNA in hepatic and erythroid tissues. *J Biol Chem* 262:3988, 1987.

75. PIROLA BA, MAYER F, BORTHWICK IA, SRIVASTAVA G, MAY BK, ELLIOTT WH: Electron microscopic studies on liver 5-aminolevulinate synthase. *Eur J Biochem* 144:577, 1984.

76. PATTON GM, BEATTIE DS: Studies on hepatic δ-aminolevulinic acid synthetase. *J Biol Chem* 248:4467, 1973.

77. HAYASHI N, YODA B, KIKUCHI G: Mechanism of allylisopropylacetamide-induced increase of δ-aminolevulinate synthetase in liver mitochondria. IV. Accumulation of the enzyme in the soluble fraction of rat liver. *Arch Biochem Biophys* 131:83, 1969.

78. NAKAKUKI M, YAMAUCHI K, HAYASHI N, KIKUCHI G: Purification and some properties of δ-aminolevulinate synthase from the rat liver cytosol fraction and immunochemical identity of the cytosolic enzyme and the mitochondrial enzyme. *J Biol Chem* 255:1738, 1980.

79. TSCHUDY DP, MARVER HS, COLLINS A: A model for calculating messenger RNA half-life: Short-lived messenger RNA in the induction of mammalian δ-aminolevulinic acid synthetase. *Biochem Biophys Res Commun* 21:480, 1965.

80. SHEMIN D, RITTENBERG D: The biological utilization of glycine for the synthesis of the protoporphyrin of hemoglobin. *J Biol Chem* 166:621, 1946.

81. SHEMIN D, RITTENBERG D: The life-span of the human red blood cell. *J Biol Chem* 166:627, 1946.

82. RADIN NS, RITTENBERG D, SHEMIN D: The role of glycine in the biosynthesis of heme. *J Biol Chem* 184:745, 1950.

83. GRINSTEIN M, KAMEN MD, MOORE CV: Observation on the utilization of glycine in the biosynthesis of hemoglobin. *J Biol Chem* 174:767, 1948.

84. ZAMAN Z, JORDAN PM, AKHTAR M: Mechanism and stereochemistry of the 5-aminolaevulinate synthetase reaction. *Biochem J* 135:257, 1973.

85. AKHTAR M, ABBOUD MM, BARNARD G, JORDAN P, ZAMAN Z: Mechanism and stereochemistry of enzymic reactions involved in porphyrin biosynthesis. *Philos Trans R Soc Lond (Biol)* 273:117, 1976.

86. ABBOUD MM, JORDAN PM, AKHTAR M: Biosynthesis of 5-aminolaevulinic acid. Involvement of a retention-inversion mechanism. *J Chem Soc Chem Commun* 1974, p. 643.

87. ZAMAN Z, JORDAN PM, AKHTAR M: Mechanism and stereochemistry of the 5-aminolaevulinate synthetase reaction. *Biochem J* 135:257, 1973.

88. AKHTAR M, ABBOUD MM, BARNARD G, JORDAN P, ZAMAN Z: Mechanism and stereochemistry of enzymic reactions involved in porphyrin biosynthesis. *Philos Trans R Soc Lond (Biol)* 273:117, 1976.

89. ABBOUD MM, JORDAN PM, AKHTAR M: Biosynthesis of 5-aminolaevulinic acid. Involvement of a retention-inversion mechanism. *J Chem Soc Chem Commun* 1974, p. 643.

90. LAGHAI A, JORDAN PM: A partial reaction of δ-aminolevulinic acid synthetase from *Rhodopseudomonas spheroides*. *Biochem Soc Trans* 4:52, 1976.

91. ADES IZ: Transport of newly synthesized proteins into mitochondria—A review. *Mol Cell Biochem* 43:113, 1982.

92. BORTHWICK IA, SRIVASTAVA G, HOBBS AA, PIROLA BA, BROOKER JD, MAY BK, ELLIOTT WH: Molecular cloning of hepatic 5-aminolevulinate synthase. *Eur J Biochem* 144:95, 1984.

93. YAMAMOTO M, YEW NS, FEDERSPIEL M, DODGSON JB, HAYASHI N, ENGEL JD: Isolation of recombinant cDNAs encoding chicken erythroid delta-aminolevulinate synthase. *Proc Natl Acad Sci USA* 82:3702, 1985.

94. SCHOENHAUT DS, CURTIS PJ: Nucleotide sequence of mouse 5-aminolevulinic acid synthase cDNA and expression of its gene in hepatic and erythroid tissues. *Gene* 48:55, 1986.

95. MAGUIRE DJ, DAY AR, BORTHWICK IA, SRIVASTAVA G, WIGLEY PL, MAY BK, ELLIOTT WH: Nucleotide sequence of the chicken 5-aminolevulinate synthase gene. *Nucleic Acids Res* 14:1379, 1986.

96. TYKOCINSKI ML, MAX EE: CG dinucleotide clusters in MHC genes and 5′ demethylated genes. *Nucleic Acids Res* 12:4385, 1984.

97. LEONG SA, WILLIAMS PH, DITTA GS: Analysis of the 5′ regulatory region of the gene for delta aminolevulinic acid synthetase of *Rhizobium meliloti*. *Nucleic Acids Res* 13:5965, 1985.

98. ARRESE M, CARVAJAL E, ROBISON S, SAMBUNARIS A, PANEK A, MATTOON J: Cloning of the delta-aminolevulinic acid synthase structural gene in yeast. *Curr Genet* 7:175, 1983.

99. URBAN-GRIMAL D, RIBES V, LABBE-BOIS R: Cloning by genetic complementation and restriction mapping of the yeast HEM gene coding for 5-aminolevulinate synthase. *Curr Genet* 8:327, 1984.

100. SASSA S: Control of heme biosynthesis in erythroid cells, in Rossi GB (ed): *In Vivo and In Vitro Erythropoiesis: The Friend System*. Amsterdam, Elsevier, 1980, p 219.

101. HAYASHI N, KURASHIMA Y, KIKUCHI G: Mechanism of allylisopropylacetamide-induced increase of δ-aminolevulinate synthetase in liver mitochondria. V. Mechanism of regulation by hemin of the level of δ-aminolevulinate synthetase in rat liver mitochondria. *Arch Biochem Biophys* 148:10, 1972.

102. YAMAUCHI K, HAYASHI N, KIKUCHI G: Translocation of delta-aminolevulinate synthase from the cytosol to the mitochondria and its regulation by hemin in the rat liver. *J Biol Chem* 255:1746, 1980.

103. HAYASHI N, WATANABE N, KIKUCHI G: Inhibition by hemin of in vitro translocation of chicken liver δ-aminolevulinate synthase into mitochondria. *Biochem Biophys Res Commun* 115:700, 1983.

104. YAMAMOTO M, HAYASHI N, KIKUCHI G: Regulation of synthesis and intracellular translocation of δ-aminolevulinate synthase by heme and its relation to the heme saturation of tryptophan pyrrolase in rat liver. *Arch Biochem Biophys* 209:451, 1981.

105. GRANICK S, SINCLAIR P, SASSA S, GRIENINGER G: Effects by heme, insulin, and serum albumin on heme and protein synthesis in chick embryo liver cells cultured in a chemically defined medium, and a spectrofluorometric assay for porphyrin composition. *J Biol Chem* 250:9215, 1975.

106. BEALE SI, CASTELFRANCO PA: The biosynthesis of δ-aminolevulinic acid in higher plants. II. Formation of ^{14}C-δ-aminolevulinic acid from labeled precursors in greening plant tissues. *Plant Physiol* 53:297, 1974.

107. BEALE SI, GOUCH SP, GRANICK S: Biosynthesis of δ-aminolevulinic acid from the intact carbon skeleton of glutamic acid in greening barley. *Proc Natl Acad Sci USA* 72:2719, 1975.

108. VARTICOVSKI L, KUSHNER JP, BURNHAM BF: Biosynthesis of porphyrin

precursors: Purification and characterization of mammalian L-alanine γ-δ-dioxovaleric acid aminotransferase. *J Biol Chem* 355:3742, 1980.

109. GASSMAN M, PLUSCEC J, BOGORAD L: δ-Aminolevulinic acid transaminase in *Chlorella vulgaris*. *Plant Physiol* 43:1411, 1968.

110. GASSMAN M, PLUSCEC J, BOGORAD L: δ-Aminolevulinic acid transaminase from *Chlorella* and *Phaseolus*. *Plant Physiol* 41 (*Suppl*):xiv, 1966.

111. NEUBERGER A, TURNER JM: γ,δ-Dioxovalerate aminotransferase activity in *Rhodopseudomonas spheroides*. *Biochim Biophys Acta* 67:342, 1963.

112. SHIOI Y, NAGAMINE M, SASA T: Purification and properties of L-alanine:4,5-dioxovalaerate aminotransferase from *Chlorella regularis*. *Arch Biochem Biophys* 234:117, 1984.

113. SHIOI Y, DOI M, SASA T: Purification and characterization of L-alanine:4,5-dioxovalerate (glyoxalate) aminotransferase from radish (*Raphanus sativus L.*) seedlings. *Plant Cell Physiol* 25:1487, 1984.

114. BAJKOWSKI AS, FRIEDMANN HC: Delta-aminolevulinic acid formation. Purification and properties of alanine:4,5-dioxovalerate aminotransferase and isolation of 4,5-dioxovalerate from *Clostridium tetanomorphum*. *J Biol Chem* 257:2207, 1982.

115. SHANKER J, DATTA K: Purification and some properties of L-alanine:4,5-dioxovaleric acid transaminase from rat liver mitochondria. *Biochem Int* 7:23, 1983.

116. SCHON A, DRUPP G, GOUGH S, BERRY-LOWE S, KANNANGARA CG, SOLL D: The RNA required in the first step of chlorophyll biosynthesis is a chloroplast glutamate tRNA. *Nature* 322:281, 1986.

117. GRANICK S, SASSA S: δ-Aminolevulinic acid synthetase and the control of heme and chlorophyll synthesis, in Vogel HJ (ed): *Metabolic Regulation*. New York, Academic, 1971, p 77.

118. LEVERE RD, GRANICK S: Control of hemoglobin synthesis in the cultured chick blastoderm by δ-aminolevulinic acid synthetase: Increase in the rate of hemoglobin formation with δ-aminolevulinic acid. *Proc Natl Acad Sci USA* 54:134, 1965.

119. HOFFMAN R, IBRAHIM N, MURNANE MJ, DIAMOND A, FORGET BG, LEVERE RD: Hemin control of heme biosynthesis and catabolism in a human leukemia cell line. *Blood* 56:567, 1980.

120. SASSA S, KAPPAS A: Genetic, metabolic, and biochemical aspects of the porphyrias, in Harris H, Hirschhorn KH (eds): *Advances in Human Genetics*. New York, Plenum, 1981, vol 11, p 121.

121. BERK PD, RODKEY FL, BLASCHKE TF, COLLISON HA, WAGGONER JG: Comparison of plasma bilirubin turnover and carbon monoxide production in man. *J Lab Clin Med* 83:29, 1974.

122. HUTTON JJ, GROSS SR: Chemical induction of hepatic porphyria in inbred strains of mice. *Arch Biochem Biophys* 141:284, 1970.

123. JONES MS, JONES OTG: The structural organization of haem synthesis in rat liver mitochondria. *Biochem J* 113:507, 1969.

124. ANDERSON KE, DRUMMOND GS, FREDDARA U, SARDANA MK, SASSA S, KAPPAS A: Porphyrogenic effects and induction of heme oxygenase *in vivo* by δ-aminolevulinic acid. *Biochim Biophys Acta* 676:289, 1981.

125. SONG CS, MOSES HL, ROSENTHAL AS, GELB NA, KAPPAS A: The influence of postnatal development on drug-induced hepatic porphyria and the synthesis of cytochrome P-450. *J Exp Med* 134:1349, 1971.

126. BISSELL DM, HAMMAKER LE: Cytochrome P-450 heme and the regulation of hepatic heme oxygenase activity. *Arch Biochem Biophys* 176:91, 1976.

127. BISSELL DM, HAMMAKER LE: Cytochrome P-450 heme and the regulation of δ-aminolevulinic acid synthetase in the liver. *Arch Biochem Biophys* 176:103, 1976.

128. GAYATHRI AK, RAO MR, PADMANABAN G: Studies on the induction of δ-aminolevulinic acid synthetase in mouse liver. *Arch Biochem Biophys* 155:299, 1973.

129. SASSA S, GRANICK S: Induction of δ-aminolevulinic acid synthetase in chick embryo liver cells in culture. *Proc Natl Acad Sci USA* 67:517, 1970.

130. COWTAN ER, YODA B, ISRAELS LG: Cycloheximide enhanced porphyrin synthesis in chick embryo liver: Association with an increase in the hepatic glycine pool. *Arch Biochem Biophys* 155:194, 1973.

131. KIKUCHI G: The glycine cleavage system: Composition, reaction mechanism, and physiological significance. *Mol Cell Biochem* 1:169, 1973.

132. KIELLEY RK, SCHNEIDER WC: Synthesis of p-aminohippuric acid by mitochondria of mouse liver homogenates. *J Biol Chem* 187:869, 1950.

133. SCHACHTER D, TAGGART JV: Glycine N-acylase: Purification and properties. *J Biol Chem* 208:263, 1954.

134. GRANICK S, BEALE SI: Hemes, chlorophylls, and related compounds: Biosynthesis and metabolic regulation, in Meister A (ed): *Advanced Enzymology and Related Areas of Molecular Biology*. New York, Wiley, 1978, p 33.

135. SASSA S, BRADLOW HL, KAPPAS A: Steroid induction of δ-aminolevulinic acid synthase and porphyrins in liver: Structure-activity studies on the permissive effects of hormones on the induction process. *J Biol Chem* 254:10011, 1979.

136. SINCLAIR PR, GRANICK S: The transport of hemin and protoporphyrin across the plasma membrane of chick embryo liver cells in culture. *Ann Clin Res* 8 (*Suppl* 17):250, 1976.

137. SRIVASTAVA G, BROOKER JD, MAY BK, ELLIOTT WH: Haem control in experimental porphyria. The effect of haemin on the induction of δ-aminolaevulinate synthase in isolated chick-embryo liver cells. *Biochem J* 188:781, 1980.

138. SASSA S, BRADLOW HL, KAPPAS A: Steroid induction of δ-aminolevulinic acid synthase and porphyrins in liver: Structure-activity studies on the permissive effects of hormones on the induction process. *J Biol Chem* 254:10011, 1979.

139. WOLFSON SJ, BARTCZAK A, BLOOMER JR: Effect of endogenous heme generation on δ-aminolevulinic acid synthase activity in rat liver mitochondria. *J Biol Chem* 254:3543, 1979.

140. ROMSLO I, HUSBY P: Iron, porphyrin and heme transport in mitochondria. *Int J Biochem* 12:709, 1980.

141. TYRRELL DL, MARKS GS: Drug-induced porphyrin biosynthesis. V. Effect of protohemin on the transcriptional and post-transcriptional phases of δ-aminolevulinic acid synthetase induction. *Biochem Pharmacol* 21:2077, 1972.

142. WHITING MJ: Synthesis of δ-aminolaevulinate synthase by isolated liver polyribosomes. *Biochem J* 158:391, 1976.

143. SASSA S, KAPPAS A: Induction of δ-aminolevulinate synthase and porphyrins in cultured liver cells maintained in chemically defined medium: Permissive effects of hormones on the induction process. *J Biol Chem* 252:2428, 1977.

144. RIFKIND AB: Maintenance of microsomal hemoprotein concentrations following inhibition of ferrochelatase activity by 3,5-diethoxycarbonyl-1,4-dihydrocollidine in chick embryo liver. *J Biol Chem* 254:4636, 1979.

145. ANDERSON KE: Effects of antihypertensive drugs on hepatic heme biosynthesis, and evaluation of ferrochelatase inhibitors to simplify testing of drugs for heme pathway induction. *Biochim Biophys Acta* 543:313, 1978.

146. SINCLAIR P, GRANICK S: Heme control on the synthesis of delta-aminolevulinic acid synthetase in cultured chick embryo liver cells. *Ann NY Acad Sci* 244:509, 1975.

147. SASSA S, KAPPAS A: Hereditary tyrosinemia and the heme biosynthetic pathway. Profound inhibition of delta-aminolevulinic acid dehydratase activity by succinylacetone. *J Clin Invest* 71:625, 1983.

148. DE MATTEIS F: Loss of haem in rat liver caused by the porphyrogenic agent 2-allyl-2-isopropylacetamide. *Biochem J* 124:767, 1971.

149. DE MATTEIS F: Rapid loss of cytochrome P-450 and heme caused in the liver microsomes by the prophyrogenic agent 2-allyl-2-isopropylacetamide. *FEBS Lett* 6:343, 1970.

150. DE MATTEIS F: Loss of microsomal components in drug induced liver damage in cholestasis and after administration of chemicals which stimulate heme catabolism. *Pharmacol Ther* 2:693, 1978.

151. DE MATTEIS F: Hepatic porphyrias caused by 2-allyl-2-isopropylacetamide, 3,5-diethoxycarbonyl-1,4-dihydrocollidine, griseofulvin and related compounds, in De Matteis F, Aldridge WN (eds): *Heme and Hemoproteins. Handbook of Experimental Pharmacology*, New York, Springer-Verlag, 1978, vol 44, p 129.

152. LEVIN W, SERNATINGER E, JACOBSON M, KUNTZMAN R: Destruction of cytochrome P-450 by secobarbital and other barbiturates containing allyl groups. *Science* 176:1341, 1972.

153. IOANNIDES C, PARKE DV: The effect of allyl compounds on hepatic microsomal mixed function oxidation and porphyrogenesis. *Chem Biol Interact* 14:241, 1976.

154. ORTIZ DE MONTELLANO PR, MICO BA: Destruction of cytochrome P-450 by ethylene and other compounds. *Mol Pharmacol* 18:128, 1980.

155. ORTIZ DE MONTELLANO PR, KUNZE KL: Self-catalyzed inactivation of hepatic cytochrome P-450 by ethynyl substrates. *J Biol Chem* 255:5578, 1980.

156. WHITE INH, MULLER-EBERHARD U: Decreased liver cytochrome P-450 in rats caused by norethindrone or ethynyloestradiol. *Biochem J* 166:57, 1977.

157. WHITE INH: Metabolic activation of acetylene substituents to derivatives in the rat causing the loss of hepatic cytochrome P-450 and haem. *Biochem J* 174:853, 1978.

158. DE MATTEIS F, CANTONI J: Alteration of the porphyrin nucleus of cytochrome P-450 caused in the liver by treatment with allyl-containing drugs: Is the modified porphyrin N-substituted? *Biochem J* 183:99, 1979.

159. BRADSHAW JJ, ZIMAN MR, IVANETICH KM: The degradation of different forms of cytochrome P-450 *in vivo* by fluroxene and allylisopropylacetamide. *Biochem Biophys Res Commun* 85:859, 1978.

160. FARRELL GC, SCHMID R, KUNZE KL, ORTIZ DE MONTELLANO PR: Exogenous heme restores *in vivo* functional capacity of hepatic cytochrome P-450 destroyed by allylisopropylacetamide. *Biochem Biophys Res Commun* 89:456, 1979.

161. DE MATTEIS F, ABBRITTI G, GIBBS AH: Decreased liver activity of porphyrin-metal chelatase in hepatic porphyria caused by 3,5-diethoxycarbonyl-1,4-dihydrocollidine. Studies in rats and mice. *Biochem J* 134:717, 1973.

162. DE MATTEIS F, GIBBS AH, TEPHLY TR: Inhibition of protohaem ferrolyase in experimental porphyria: Isolation and partial characterization of a modified porphyrin inhibitor. *Biochem J* 188:145, 1980.

163. DE MATTEIS F, GIBBS AH: Drug-induced conversion of liver haem into modified porphyrins: Evidence for two classes of products. *Biochem J* 187:285, 1980.

164. BARON J, TEPHLY TR: Further studies on the relationship of the stimulatory effects of phenobarbital and 3,4-benzpyrene on hepatic heme synthesis to their effects in hepatic microsomal drug oxidations. *Arch Biochem Biophys* 139:410, 1970.

165. RAJAMANICKAM C, RAO MR, PADMANABAN G: On the sequence of reactions leading to cytochrome P-450 synthesis: Effect of drugs. *J Biol Chem* 250:2305, 1975.

166. YANNONI CZ, ROBINSON SH: Early-labeled haem in erythroid and hepatic cells. *Nature* 258:330, 1975.

167. GRANDCHAMP B, BISSELL DM, LICKO V, SCHMID R: Formation and disposition of newly synthesized heme in adult rat hepatocytes in primary culture. *J Biol Chem* 256:11677, 1981.

168. BADAWY AA: Tryptophan pyrrolase, the regulatory free haem and hepatic porphyrias: Early depletion of haem by clinical and experimental exacerbations of porphyria. *Biochem J* 172:487, 1978.

169. DE MATTEIS F, GIBBS AH: Stimulation of liver 5-aminolaevulinate synthetase by drugs and its relevance to drug-induced accumulation of cytochrome P-450. Studies with phenylbutazone and 3,5-diethoxycarbonyl-1,4-dihydrocollidine. *Biochem J* 126:1149, 1972.

170. MAINES MD, KAPPAS A: Cobalt induction of hepatic heme oxygenase with evidence that cytochrome P-450 is not essential for this enzymatic activity. *Proc Natl Acad Sci USA* 71:4293, 1974.

171. MAINES MD, KAPPAS A: Cobalt stimulation of heme degradation in the liver: Dissociation of microsomal oxidation of heme from cytochrome P-450. *J Biol Chem* 250:4171, 1975.

172. MAINES MD, KAPPAS A: Studies on the mechanism of induction of haem oxygenase by cobalt and other metal ions. *Biochem J* 154:125, 1976.

173. MAINES MD, KAPPAS A: Metals as regulators of heme catabolism. *Science* 198:1215, 1977.

174. DRUMMOND GS, KAPPAS A: Metal ion interactions in the control of haem oxygenase induction in liver and kidney. *Biochem J* 192:637, 1980.

175. ROSENBERG D, DRUMMOND GS, CORNISH HC, KAPPAS A: Prolonged induction of hepatic haem oxygenase and decreases in cytochrome P-450 content by organotin compounds. *Biochem J* 190:465, 1980.

176. WELLAND FH, HELLMAN ES, GADDIS EM, COLLINS A, HUNTER GW JR, TSCHUDY DP: Factors affecting the excretion of porphyrin precursors by patients with acute intermittent porphyria. I. The effects of diet. *Metabolism* 13:232, 1964.

177. FELSHER BF, REDEKER AG: Acute intermittent porphyria: Effect of diet and griseofulvin. *Medicine* 46:217, 1967.

178. TSCHUDY DP, WELLAND FH, COLLINS A, HUNTER G JR: The effect of carbohydrate feeding on the induction of δ-aminolevulinic acid synthetase. *Metabolism* 13:396, 1964.

179. LEVERE RD, GRANICK S: Control of hemoglobin synthesis in the cultured chick blastoderm. *J Biol Chem* 242:1903, 1967.

180. SASSA S: Sequential induction of heme pathway enzymes during erythroid differentiation of mouse Friend leukemia virus-infected cells. *J Exp Med* 143:305, 1976.

181. SASSA S, URABE A: Uroporphyrinogen I synthase induction in normal human bone marrow cultures; An early and quantitative response of erythroid differentiation. *Proc Natl Acad Sci USA* 76:5321, 1979.

182. SASSA S, GRANICK JL, EISEN H, OSTERTAG W: Regulation of heme biosynthesis in mouse Friend virus-transformed cells in culture, in Murphy MJ (ed): *In Vitro Aspects of Erythropoiesis*. New York, Springer-Verlag, 1978, p 135.

183. EISEN H, KEPPEL-BALLIVET F, GEORGOPOULOS CP, SASSA S, GRANICK J, PRAGNELL I, OSTERTAG W: Biochemical and genetic analysis of erythroid differentiation in Friend-virus-transformed murine erythroleukemia cells, in Clarkson B, Marks PA, Till JE (eds): *Differentiation of Normal and Neoplastic Hematopoietic Cells*. Cold Spring Harbor Lab, Cold Spring Harbor Conference on Cell Proliferation, 1978, vol 5, p 277.

184. RUTHERFORD T, THOMPSON GG, MOORE MR: Heme biosynthesis in Friend erythroleukemia cells: Control by ferrochelatase. *Proc Natl Acad Sci USA* 76:833, 1979.

185. WADA O, SASSA S, TAKAKU F, YANO Y, URATA G, NAKAO K: Different responses of the hepatic and erythropoietic δ-aminolevulinic acid synthetase of mice. *Biochim Biophys Acta* 148:585, 1967.

186. FRIEND C, SCHER W, HOLLAND JG, SATO T: Hemoglobin synthesis in murine virus-induced leukemic cells *in vitro*: Stimulation of erythroid differentiation by dimethylsulfoxide. *Proc Natl Acad Sci USA* 68:378, 1971.

187. ROSS J, SAUTNER D: Induction of globin mRNA accumulation by hemin in cultured erythroleukemic cells. *Cell* 8:513, 1976.

188. DABNEY BJ, BEAUDET AL: Increase in globin chains and globin mRNA in erythroleukemia cells in response to hemin. *Arch Biochem Biophys* 179:106, 1977.

189. PORTER PN, MEINTS RH, MESNER K: Enhancement of erythroid colony growth in culture by hemin. *Exp Hematol* 7:11, 1979.

190. KARIBIAN D, LONDON IM: Control of heme synthesis by feedback inhibition. *Biochem Biophys Res Commun* 18:243, 1965.

191. PONKA P, SCHULMAN HM: Regulation of heme synthesis in erythroid cells by iron delivery from transferrin, in Nordmann Y (ed): *Porphyrins and Porphyrias*. Paris, Colloque INSERM/John Libbey Eurotext, 1986, vol 134, p 55.

192. WOODS JS, DIXON RL: Perinatal differences in delta-aminolevulinic acid synthetase activity. *Life Sci* 9:711, 1970.

193. WOODS JS, DIXON RL: Studies on the perinatal differences in the activity of hepatic δ-aminolevulinic acid synthetase. *Biochem Pharmacol* 21:1735, 1972.

194. WOODS JS: Studies on the role of heme in the regulation of δ-aminolevulinic acid synthetase during fetal hepatic development. *Mol Pharmacol* 10:389, 1974.

195. BISHOP DF, KITCHEN H, WOOD WA: Evidence for erythroid and nonerythroid forms of δ-aminolevulinate synthetase. *Arch Biochem Biophys* 206:380, 1981.

196. BRIGGS DW, CONDIE LW, SEDMAN RM, TEPHLY TR: δ-Aminolevulinic acid synthetase in the heart. *J Biol Chem* 251:4996, 1976.

197. CONDIE LW, BARON J, TEPHLY TR: Studies on adrenal δ-aminolevulinic acid synthetase. *Arch Biochem Biophys* 172:123, 1976.

198. TOFILON PJ, PIPER WN: Measurement and regulation of rat testicular δ-aminolevulinic acid synthetase activity. *Arch Biochem Biophys* 201:104, 1980.

199. SASSA S, LEVERE RD, SOLISH G, KAPPAS A: Studies on the porphyrin-heme biosynthetic pathway in cultured human amniotic cells. *J Clin Invest* 53:70a, 1974.

200. BONKOWSKY HL, TSCHUDY DP, WEINBACH EC, EBERT PS, DOHERTY JM: Porphyrin synthesis and mitochondrial respiration in acute intermittent porphyria: Studies using cultured human fibroblasts. *J Lab Clin Med* 85:93, 1975.

201. SASSA S, ZALAR GL, KAPPAS A: Studies in porphyria. VII: Induction of uroporphyrinogen-1 synthase and expression of the gene defect of acute intermittent porphyria in mitogen-stimulated human lymphocytes. *J Clin Invest* 61:499, 1978.

202. WATSON CJ: Hematin and porphyria (editorial). *N Engl J Med* 293:605, 1975.

203. COHN J, ALBARES AP, KAPPAS A: On the occurrence of cytochrome P-450 and aryl hydrocarbon hydroxylase activity in rat brain. *J Exp Med* 145:1607, 1977.

204. WHETSELL WO JR, SASSA S, BICKERS D, KAPPAS A: Studies on porphyrin-heme biosynthesis in organotypic cultures of chick dorsal root ganglion. I. Observations on neuronal and non-neuronal elements. *J Neuropathol Exp Neurol* 37:497, 1978.

205. WHETSELL WO JR, SASSA S, KAPPAS A: Studies on effects of chronic lead exposure upon porphyrin biosynthesis and myelin in cultures of mouse dorsal root ganglia (DRG). *J Neuropathol Exp Neurol* 38:348, 1979.

206. SASSA S, WHETSELL WO JR, KAPPAS A: Studies on porphyrin-heme biosynthesis in organotypic cultures of chick dorsal root ganglia. II. The effect of lead. *Environ Res* 19:415, 1979.

207. WHETSELL WO JR, KAPPAS A: Protective effect of exogenous heme against lead toxicity in organotypic cultures of mouse dorsal root ganglia (DRG): Electron microscopic observations. *J Neuropathol Exp Neurol* 40:334, 1981.

208. DOSS M, VON TIEPERMANN R, SCHNEIDER J, SCHMID H: New types of hepatic porphyria with porphobilinogen synthase defect and intermittent acute clinical manifestation. *Klin Wochenschr* 57:1123, 1979.

209. DOSS M, VON TIEPERMANN R, SCHNEIDER J: Acute hepatic porphyria syndrome with porphobilinogen synthase defect. *Int J Biochem* 12:823, 1980.

210. THUNELL S, HOLMBERG L, LUNDGREN J: Aminolevulinate dehydratase porphyria in infancy. A clinical and biochemical study. *J Clin Chem Clin Biochem* 25:5, 1987.

211. GIBSON KD, NEUBERGER A, SCOTT JJ: The purification and properties of δ-aminolevulinic acid dehydrase. *Biochem J* 61:618, 1955.

212. GRANICK S: Enzymatic conversion of delta-aminolevulinic acid to porphobilinogen. *Science* 120:1105, 1954.

213. WU WH, SHEMIN D, RICHARDS KE, WILLIAMS RC: The quaternary structure of δ-aminolevulinic acid dehydratase from bovine liver. *Proc Natl Acad Sci USA* 71:1767, 1974.

214. ANDERSON PM, DESNICK RJ: Purification and properties of δ-aminolevulinate dehydratase from human erythrocytes. *J Biol Chem* 254:6924, 1979.

215. BEVAN DR, BODLAENDER P, SHEMIN D: Mechanism of porphobilinogen synthase. Requirement of Zn^{2+} for enzyme activity. *J Biol Chem* 255:2030, 1980.

216. BARNARD GF, ITOH R, HOHBERGER LH, SHEMIN D: Mechanism of porphobilinogen synthase. Possible role of essential thiol groups. *J Biol Chem* 252:8965, 1977.

217. TSUKAMOTO I, YOSHINAGA T, SANO S: Zinc and cysteine residues in the active site of bovine liver δ-aminolevulinic acid dehydratase. *Int J Biochem* 12:751, 1980.

218. TSUKAMOTO I, YOSHINAGA T, SANO S: The role of zinc with special reference to the essential thiol groups in δ-aminolevulinic acid dehydratase of bovine liver. *Biochim Biophys Acta* 570:167, 1979.

219. SOMMER R, BEYERSMANN D: Zinc and cadmium in 5-aminolevulinic acid dehydratase. Equilibrium, kinetic, and ^{113}Cd-NMR studies. *J Inorg Biochem* 20:131, 1984.

220. NANDI DL, SHEMIN D: δ-Aminolevulinic acid dehydratase of *Rhodopseudomonas spheroides*. III. Mechanism of porphobilinogen synthesis. *J Biol Chem* 234:1236, 1968.

221. JORDAN P, SEEHRA JS: Mechanism of action of δ-aminolevulinic acid dehydratase: Stepwise order of addition of the two molecules of δ-aminolevulinic acid in the enzymic synthesis of porphobilinogen. *J Chem Soc Chem Commun* 240, 1980.

222. SHEMIN D: δ-Aminolevulinic acid dehydratase, in Boyer PD (ed): *The Enzymes*, 3d ed. New York, Academic, 1972, vol VII, p 323.

223. CHANG CS, SASSA S, DOYLE D: An immunological study of δ-aminolevulinic acid dehydratase: Specificity consistent with the phylogeny of species. *Biochim Biophys Acta* 797:297, 1987.

224. YAMAMOTO M, FUJITA H, WATANABE N, HAYASHI N, KIKUCHI G: An immunochemical study of δ-aminolevulinate synthase and δ-aminolevulinate dehydratase in rat liver and erythroid cells. *Arch Biochem Biophys* 245:76, 1987.

225. GRANICK JL, SASSA S, GRANICK S, LEVERE RD, KAPPAS A: Studies in lead poisoning II. Correlation between the ratio of activated to inactivated δ-aminolevulinic acid dehydratase of whole blood and the blood lead level. *Biochem Med* 8:159, 1973.

226. BEALE SI: The biosynthesis of δ-aminolevulinic acid in *Chlorella*. *Plant Physiol* 45:505, 1970.

227. DOYLE D, SCHIMKE RT: The genetic and developmental regulation of hepatic δ-aminolevulinate dehydratase in mice. *J Biol Chem* 244:5440, 1969.

228. WEISSBERG JB, LIPSCHUTZ F, OSKI FA: δ-Aminolevulinic acid dehydratase activity in circulating blood cells. A sensitive laboratory test for the detection of childhood lead poisoning. *N Engl J Med* 284:565, 1971.

229. LINDBLAD B, LINDSTEDT S, STEEN G: On the enzymic defects in hereditary tyrosinemia. *Proc Natl Acad Sci USA* 74:4641, 1977.

230. TSCHUDY DP, HESS RA, FRYKHOLM BC: Inhibition of δ-aminolevulinic acid dehydratase by 4,6-dioxoheptanoic acid. *J Biol Chem* 256:9915, 1981.

231. STONER E, STARKMAN H, WELLNER D, WELLNER VP, SASSA A, RIFKIND AB, GRENIER A, STEINHERZ PG, MEISTER A, NEW MI, LEVINE LS: Biochemical studies of a patient with hereditary hepatorenal tyrosinemia: Evidence of glutathione deficiency. *Pediatr Res* 18:1332, 1984.

232. SASSA S, KAPPAS A: Hereditary tyrosinemia and the heme biosynthetic pathway. Profound inhibition of δ-aminolevulinic acid dehydratase activity by succinylacetone. *J Clin Invest* 71:625, 1983.

233. BONKOWSKY HL, HEALEY JF, SINCLAIR PR, SINCLAIR JF, SHEDLOFSKY SI, ELDER GH: Iron and the liver: Acute effects of iron-loading on hepatic heme synthesis of rats. Role of decreased activity of δ-aminolevulinate dehydratase. *J Clin Invest* 71:1175, 1983.

234. FUJITA H: Inhibition of δ-aminolevulinate dehydratase in trichloroethylene-exposed rats, and the effects of heme regulation. *Biochim Biophys Acta* 800:1, 1984.

235. COLEMAN DL: Purification and properties of δ-aminolevulinate dehydratase from tissues of two strains of mice. *J Biol Chem* 241:5511, 1966.

236. SASSA S, GRANICK S, BICKERS DR, LEVERE RD, KAPPAS A: Studies on the inheritance of human erythrocyte δ-aminolevulinate dehydratase and uroporphyrinogen synthetase. *Enzyme* 16:326, 1973.

237. SASSA S: Sequential induction of heme pathway enzymes during erythroid differentiation of mouse Friend leukemia virus-infected cells. *J Exp Med* 143:305, 1976.

238. SASSA S: Control of heme biosynthesis in erythroid cells, in Rossi GB (ed): *In Vivo and In Vitro Erythropoiesis: The Friend System.* Amsterdam, Elsevier, 1980, p 219.

239. HOFFMAN R, IBRAHIM N, MURNANE MJ, DIAMOND A, FORGET BG, LEVERE RD: Hemin control of heme biosynthesis and catabolism in a human leukemia cell line. *Blood* 56:567, 1980.

240. SASSA S, BERNSTEIN SE: Levels of δ-aminolevulinate dehydratase, uroporphyrinogen-I synthase, and protoporphyrin IX in erythrocytes from anemic mutant mice. *Proc Natl Acad Sci USA* 74:1181, 1977.

241. ANDERSON KE, SASSA S, PETERSON CM, KAPPAS A: Increased erythrocyte uroporphyrinogen-I-synthase, δ-aminolevulinic acid dehydratase and protoporphyrin in hemolytic anemias. *Am J Med* 63:359, 1977.

242. SASSA S: δ-Aminolevulinic acid dehydratase assay. *Enzyme* 28:133, 1982.

243. BISHOP TR, COHEN PJ, BOYER SH, NOYES AN, FRELIN LP: Isolation of a rat liver delta aminolevulinate dehydratase (ALAD) cDNA clone: Evidence for unequal ALAD gene dosage among inbred mouse strains. *Proc Natl Acad Sci USA* 83:5568, 1986.

244. LINGNER B, KLEINSCHMIDT T: N-terminal sequence of a porphobilinogen-synthase. *Z Naturforsch* 38c:1059, 1983.

245. WETMUR JG, BISHOP DF, OSTASIEWICZ L, DESNICK RJ: Molecular cloning of a cDNA for human delta aminolevulinate dehydratase. *Gene* 43:123, 1986.

246. WETMUR JG, BISHOP DF, CANTELMO C, DESNICK RJ: Human delta aminolevulinate dehydratase: Nucleotide sequence of a full-length cDNA clone. *Proc Natl Acad Sci USA* 83:7703, 1986.

247. BISHOP TR, FRELIN LP, BOYER SH: Nucleotide sequence of rat liver delta aminolevulinic acid dehydratase cDNA. *Nucleic Acids Res* 14:10115, 1986.

248. GIBBS PN, JORDAN PM: Identification of lysine at the active site of human 5-aminolaevulinate dehydratase. *Biochem J* 236:447, 1986.

249. DOSS M, SCHNEIDER J, VON TIEPERMANN R, BRANDT A: New type of acute porphyria with porphobilinogen synthase (δ-aminolevulinic acid dehydratase) defect in the homozygous state. *Clin Biochem* 15:52, 1982.

250. DE VERNEUIL H, DOSS M, BRUSCO N, BEAUMONT C, NORDMANN Y: Hereditary hepatic porphyria with delta aminolevulinate dehydratase deficiency: Immunologic characterization of the non-catalytic enzyme. *Hum Genet* 69:174, 1985.

251. FUJITA H, SASSA S, LUNDGREN J, HOLMBERG L, THUNELL S, KAPPAS A: Immunochemical studies of the enzymatic defect in a child with hereditary hepatic porphyria due to homozygous δ-aminolevulinic acid dehydratase deficiency. *Pediatrics* 80:880, 1987.

252. BIRD TD, HAMERNYIK P, NUTTER JY, LABBE RF: Inherited deficiency of delta-aminolevulinic acid dehydratase. *Am J Hum Genet* 31:662, 1979.

253. DEL BATTLE AM, BUSTOS NL, STELLA AM, WIDER EA, CONTI HA, MENDEZ A: Enzyme replacement therapy in porphyrias. IV. First successful human trial of δ-aminolevulinate dehydratase-loaded erythrocyte ghosts. *Int J Biochem* 15:1261, 1983.

254. KREIMER-BIRNBAUM M, BANNERMAN RM, EL KHATIB M, FRANCO-SAENZ R: Afro-Americans and acute intermittent porphyria (AIP). *Int J Biochem* 12:795, 1980.

255. DOENECKE AL, BUDHLALL AGD: Acute intermittent porphyria in a 15-year-old West Indian girl. *Arch Intern Med* 140:988, 1980.

256. ODONGA AM, WAMBWA JR, ORINDA DAO: Acute intermittent porphyria in an East African female. *East Afr Med J* 57:716, 1980.

257. BONKOWSKY HL: Porphyrin and heme metabolism and the porphyrias, in Zakim D, Boyer TD (eds): *Hepatology: A Textbook of Liver Disease.* Philadelphia, Saunders, 1982, pp 351–393.

258. GOLDBERG A, RIMINGTON C: *Diseases of Porphyrin Metabolism.* Springfield, IL, CC Thomas, 1962.

259. TISHLER PV, WOODWARD B, O'CONNOR J, HOLDBROOK DA, SEIDMAN LJ, HALLETT M, KNIGHTON DJ: High prevalence of intermittent acute porphyria in a psychatric patient population. *Am J Psychiatry* 142:1430, 1985.

260. COOKSON GH, RIMINGTON C: Porphobilinogen. *Biochem J* 57:476, 1954.

261. MAUZERALL D: The thermostability of porphyrinogens. *J Am Chem Soc* 82:2601, 1960.

262. BATTERSBY AR, FOOKES CJR, MATCHAM GWJ, McDONALD E, GUSTAFSON-POTTER KE: Biosynthesis of the natural porphyrins: Experiments on the ring closure steps and with the hydroxy-analogue of porphobilinogen. *J Chem Soc Chem Commun* 539, 1979.

263. BATTERSBY AR, FOOKES CJR, MATCHAM GWJ, MCDONALD E: Order of assembly of the four pyrrole rings during biosynthesis of the natural porphyrins. *J Chem Soc Chem Commun* 539, 1979.

264. BATTERSBY AR, HODGSON GL, HUNT E, MCDONALD E, SAUNDERS J: Biosynthesis of porphyrins and related macrocycles. VI. Nature of the rearrangement process leading to the natural type III porphyrins. *J Chem Soc Perkins Trans I*, 1976, p 273.

265. LEVIN EY: Uroporphyrinogen III cosynthetase in bovine erythropoietic porphyria. *Science* 161:907, 1968.

266. BATTERSBY AR, FOOKES CJR, MATCHAM GWJ, MCDONALD E: Biosynthesis of the pigments of life: Formation of the macrocycle. *Nature* 285:17, 1980.

267. FRYDMAN RB, FEINSTEIN G: Studies on porphobilinogen deaminase and

uroporphyrinogen III cosynthase from human erythrocytes. *Biochim Biophys Acta* 350:358, 1974.

268. HIGUCHI M, BOGORAD L: The purification and properties of uroporphyrinogen I synthase and uroporphyrinogen III cosynthase. Interactions between the enzymes. *Ann NY Acad Sci* 244:401, 1975.

269. ROSSETTI MV, JUKNAT DE GERALNIK AA, KOTLER M, FUMAGALLI S, BATTLE DEL C AM: Occurrence of multiple molecular forms of porphobilinogenase in diverse organisms: The minimum quaternary structure of porphobilinogenase is a promoter of one deaminase and one isomerase domain. *Int J Biochem* 12:761, 1980.

270. ANDERSON PM, DESNICK RJ: Purification and properties of uroporphyrinogen I synthase from human erythrocytes. Identification of stable enzyme-substrate intermediates. *J Biol Chem* 255:1993, 1980.

271. WITH TK, PEDERSEN JS: Uroporphyrinogen synthetase in erythrocytes. Its diagnostic value in latent acute intermittent porphyria with special regard to the gene penetrance. *Dan Med Bull* 28:27, 1981.

272. BERRY A, JORDAN PM, SEEHRA JS: The isolation and characterization of catalytically competent porphobilinogen deaminase-intermediate complexes. *FEBS Lett* 129:220, 1981.

273. BERRY A, JORDAN PM: Porphobilinogen deaminase: Involvement of stable covalent enzyme intermediate complexes in the enzyme from *Rhodopseudomonas spheroides*. *Biochem Soc Trans* 9:231, 1981.

274. BATTERSBY AR, FOOKES CJR, MATCHAM GWJ, MCDONALD E (in part), HOLLENSTEIN R: Biosynthesis of porphyrins and related macrocycles. Part 20. Purification of deaminase and studies on its mode of action. *J Chem Soc Perkin Trans I*:3031, 1983.

275. BATTERSBY AR, FOOKES CJR, HART G, MATCHAM GWJ, PANDEY PS: Biosynthesis of porphyrins and related macrocycles. Part 21. The interaction of deaminase and its product (hydroxymethylbilane) and the relationship between deaminase and cosynthetase. *J Chem Soc Perkin Trans I*:3041, 1983.

276. MEISLER MH, CARTER MLC: Rare structural variants of human and murine uroporphyrinogen I synthase. *Proc Natl Acad Sci USA* 77:2848, 1980.

277. WILLIAMS DC, MORGAN GS, McDONALD E, BATTERSBY AR: Purification of porphobilinogen deaminase from *Euglena gracilis* and studies of its kinetics. *Biochem J* 193:301, 1981.

278. JORDAN PM, BERRY A: Mechanism of action of porphobilinogen deaminase. The participation of stable enzyme substrate covalent intermediates between porphobilinogen and the porphobilinogen deaminase from *Rhodopseudomonas spheroides*. *Biochem J* 195:177, 1981.

279. JORDAN PM, SHEMIN D: Purification and properties of uroporphyrinogen I synthase from *Rhodopseudomonas spheroides*. *J Biol Chem* 248:1019, 1973.

280. MIYAGI K, KANESHIMA M, KAWAKAMI J, NAKADA F, PETRYKA ZJ, WATSON CJ: Uroporphyrinogen I synthase from human erythrocytes: Separation, purification, and properties of isoenzymes. *Proc Natl Acad Sci USA* 76:6172, 1979.

281. BEAUMONT C, GRANDCHAMP B, BOGARD M, DE VERNEUIL H, NORDMANN Y: Porphobilinogen deaminase is unstable in the absence of its substrate. *Biochim Biophys Acta* 882:384, 1986.

282. PIPER WN, TEPHLY TR: Differential inhibition of erythrocyte and hepatic uroporphyrinogen I synthase activity by lead. *Life Sci* 14:873, 1974.

283. FARMER DJ, HOLLEBONE BR: Comparative inhibition of hepatic hydroxymethylbilane synthase by both hard and soft metal cations. *Can J Biochem Cell Biol* 62:49, 1984.

284. STEIN JA, CURL FD, VALSAMIS M, TSHUDY DP: Abnormal iron and water metabolism in acute intermittent porphyria with new morphologic findings. *Am J Med* 53:784, 1972.

285. WIDER DE XIFRA EA, BATTLE DEL C AM, STELLA AM, MALAMUD S: Acute intermittent porphyria—Another approach to therapy. *Int J Biochem* 12:819, 1980.

286. MEISLER M, WANNER L, EDDY RE, SHOWS TB: The *UPS* locus encoding uroporphyrinogen I synthase is located on human chromosome II. *Biochem Biophys Res Commun* 95:170, 1980.

287. WANG AL, ARREDONDO-VEGA FX, GIAMPIETRO PF, SMITH M, ANDERSON WF, DESNICK RJ: Regional gene assignment of human porphobilinogen deaminase and esterase A_4 to chromosome 11q23-11qter. *Proc Natl Acad Sci USA* 78:5734, 1981.

288. DE VERNEUIL H, PHUNG N, NORDMANN Y, ALLARD D, LEPRINCE F, JEROME H, AURIAS A, RETHONE MO: Assignment of human uroporphyrinogen II synthase locus to region 11qter by gene dosage effect. *Hum Genet* 60:212, 1982.

289. ANTONUCCI TK, CHAPMAN VC, MEISLER MH: Linkage of the structural gene for uroporphyrinogen I synthase to markers on mouse chromosome 9 in a cross between feral and inbred mice. *Biochem Genet* 20:703, 1982.

290. OTTO P, VON DEIMLING O: Esterase-17 (ES-17): Characterization and linkage to chromosome 9 of a new bis-p-nitrophenyl phosphate resistant esterase of the house mouse (Mus musculus). *Biochem Genet* 21:37, 1983.

291. ANTONUCCI TK, VON DEIMLING OH, ROSENBLUM BB, SKOW LC, MEISLER MH: Conserved linkage within a 4-cM region of mouse chromosome 9 and human chromosome 11. *Genetics* 107:463, 1984.

292. GRANDCHAMP B, PHUNG N, GRELIER M, NORDMANN Y: The spectrophotometric determination of uroporphyrinogen I synthetase activity. *Clin Chim Acta* 70:113, 1976.

293. STRAND LJ, MEYER UA, FELSHER BF, REDEKER AG, MARVER HS: Decreased red cell uroporphyrinogen I synthetase activity in intermittent acute porphyria. *J Clin Invest* 51:2530, 1972.

294. SHIOI Y, NAGAMINE M, KUROKI M, SASA T: Purification by affinity chromatography and properties of uroporphyrinogen I synthetase from *Chlorella regularis*. *Biochim Biophys Acta* 616:300, 1980.

295. YUAN M, RUSSELL CS: Porphobilinogen derivatives as substrates for porphobilinogenase. *FEBS Lett* 46:34, 1974.

296. FRYDMAN RB, TOMARO ML, WANSCHELBAUM A, ANDERSEN EM, AWRUCH J, FRYDMAN B: Porphobilinogen oxygenase from wheat germ: Isolation, properties and products formed. *Biochemistry* 12:5253, 1973.

297. TOMARO ML, FRYDMAN RB, FRYDMAN B: Porphobilinogen oxygenase from rat liver: Induction, isolation and properties. *Biochemistry* 12:5263, 1973.

298. GRANDCHAMP B, ROMEO PH, DUBART A, RAICH N, ROSA J, NORDMANN Y, GOOSSENS M: Molecular cloning of a cDNA sequence complementary to porphobilinogen deaminase mRNA from rat. *Proc Natl Acad Sci USA* 81:5036, 1984.

299. ROMEO PH, RAICH N, DUBART A, BEAUPAIN D, MATTEI MG, GOOSSENS M: Molecular cloning and tissue-specific expression analysis of human PBG deaminase and uroporphyrinogen decarboxylase, in Nordmann Y (ed): *Porphyrins and Porphyrias*. Paris, Colloque INSERM/John Libbey Eurotext, 1986, vol 134, p 25.

300. RAICH N, ROMEO PH, DUBART A, BEAUPAIN D, COHEN-SOLAL M, GOOSSENS M: Molecular cloning and complete primary sequence of human erythrocyte porphobilinogen deaminase. *Nucleic Acids Res* 14:5955, 1986.

301. THOMAS SD, JORDAN PM: Nucleotide sequence of the *hemC* locus encoding porphobilinogen deaminase of *Escherichia coli* K12. *Nucleic Acids Res* 14:6215, 1986.

302. GELLERFORS PL, SALTZGABER-MULLER J, DOULAS MG: Selection by genetic complementation and characterization of the gene coding for the yeast porphobilinogen deaminase. *Biochem J* 240:673, 1986.

303. GRANDCHAMP B, BEAUMONT C, DE VERNEUIL H, WALTER O, NORDMANN Y: Genetic expression of PBG deaminase and uroporphyrinogen decarboxylase during the erythroid differentiation of mouse erythroleukemic cells, in Nordmann Y (ed): *Porphyrins and Porphyrias*. Paris, Colloque INSERM/John Libbey Eurotext, 1986, vol 134, p 35.

304. GRANDCHAMP B, DE VERNEUIL H, BEAUMONT C, CHRETIEN S, WALTER O, NORDMANN Y: Tissue-specific expression of porphobilinogen deaminase: Two isoenzymes from a single gene. *Eur J Biochem* 162:105, 1987.

305. MEYER UA, STRAND LJ, DOSS M, REES AC, MARVER HS: Intermittent acute porphyria—Demonstration of a genetic defect in porphobilinogen metabolism. *N Engl J Med* 286:1277, 1972.

306. STRAND LJ, MEYER UA, FELSHER BF, REDEKER AG, MARVER HS: Decreased red cell uroporphyrinogen I synthetase activity in intermittent acute porphyria. *J Clin Invest* 51:2530, 1972.

307. SASSA S, GRANICK S, KAPPAS A: Effects of lead and genetic factors on heme biosynthesis in the human red cell. *Ann NY Acad Sci* 244:419, 1975.

308. BONKOWSKY HL, TSCHUDY DP, WEINBACH EC, EBERT PS, DOHERTY JM: Porphyrin synthesis and mitochondrial respiration in acute intermittent porphyria: Studies using cultured human fibroblasts. *J Lab Clin Med* 85:93, 1975.

309. MEYER UA: Intermittent acute porphyria: Clinical and biochemical studies of disordered heme biosynthesis. *Enzyme* 16:334, 1973.

310. MIYAGI K, CARDINAL R, BOSSENMAIER I, WATSON CJ: The serum porphobilinogen and hepatic porphobilinogen deaminase in normal and porphyric individuals. *J Lab Clin Med* 78:683, 1971.

311. MUSTAJOKI P: Normal erythrocyte uroporphyrinogen I synthase in a kindred with acute intermittent porphyria. *Ann Intern Med* 95:162, 1981.

312. WALDENSTROM J: The porphyrias as inborn errors of metabolism. *Am J Med* 22:758, 1957.

313. GOLDBERG A: Acute intermittent porphyria: A study of 50 cases. *Q J Med* 28:183, 1959.

314. STEIN JA, TSCHUDY DP: Acute intermittent porphyria. A clinical and biochemical study of 46 patients. *Medicine* 49:1, 1970.

315. RIDLEY A: Porphyric neuropathy, in Dyck PJ, Thomas PK, Lambert EH (eds): *Peripheral Neuropathy*. Philadelphia, Saunders, 1975, vol 2, p 942.

316. YEUNG LAIWAH AAC, MACTIER R, McCOLL KEL, MOORE MR, GOLDBERG A: Early-onset chronic renal failure as a complication of acute intermittent porphyria. *Q J Med* 52:92, 1983.

317. DAY RS, EALES L, DISLER PB: Porphyrins and the kidney. *Nephron* 28:261, 1981.

318. POSER CM, EDWARDS K: Transient monoparesis in acute intermittent porphyria. *Arch Neurol* 35:550, 1978.

319. GREENSPAN GH, BLOCK AJ: Respiratory insufficiency associated with acute intermittent porphyria. *South Med J* 74:954, 1981.

320. SORENSEN HWS, WITH TK: Persistent pareses after porphyric attacks. *Acta Med Scand* 190:219, 1971.

321. WOLTER JR, CLARK RL, KALLET HA: Ocular involvement in acute intermittent porphyria. *Am J Ophthalmol* 74:666, 1972.

322. LAI CW, HUNG TP, LIN WSJ: Blindness of cerebral origin in acute intermittent porphyria. Report of a case and postmortem examination. *Arch Neurol* 34:310, 1977.

323. DE FRANCISCO M, SAVINO PJ, SCHATZ NJ: Optic atrophy in acute intermittent porphyria. *Am J Ophthalmol* 87:221, 1979.

324. ALLEN SC, REES GAD: A previous history of acute intermittent porphyria as a complication of obstetric anaesthesia. *Br J Anaesth* 52:835, 1980.

325. SIM M, HUDON R: Acute intermittent porphyria associated with postural hypotension. *Can Med Assoc J* 121:845, 1979.

326. YEUNG LAIWAH AC, MacPHEE GJA, BOYLE P, MOORE MR, GOLDBERG A: Autonomic neuropathy in acute intermittent porphyria. *J Neurol Neurosurg Psychiatry* 48:1025, 1985.

327. WETTERBERG L: *A Neuropsychiatric and Genetical Investigation of Acute Intermittent Porphyria*. Svenska Bokforlaget, Norstedts, Scandinavian University Books, 1967.

328. GUIDOTTI TL, CHARNESS ME, LAMON JM: Acute intermittent porphyria and the Klüver-Bucy syndrome. *Johns Hopkins Med J* 145:233, 1979.

329. WALDENSTROM J: Neurological symptoms caused by so-called acute porphyria. *Acta Psychiatr Neurol* 14:375, 1939.

330. KAEBLING R, CRAIG JP, PASAMANICK B: Urinary porphobilinogen: Results of screening 2500 psychiatric patients. *Arch Gen Psychiatry* 5:494, 1961.

331. SCHUMAKER HM, TISHLER PV, KNIGHTON DJ: A spot test for uroporphyrinogen I synthase, the enzyme that is deficient in acute intermittent porphyria. *Clin Chem* 22:1991, 1976.

332. CARTER JH: Updating acute intermittent porphyria: A case of self-mutilation. *J Natl Med Assoc* 69:51, 1977.

333. GORCHEIN A: Acute intermittent porphyria presenting as epilepsy. *Br Med J* 292:1271, 1986.

334. SCANE AC, WIGHT JP, GODWIN-AUSTEN RB: Acute intermittent porphyria presenting as epilepsy. *Br Med J* 292:946, 1986.

335. BIRCHFIELD RI, COWGER ML: Acute intermittent porphyria with seizures. Anticonvulsant medication-induced metabolic changes. *Am J Dis Child* 112:561, 1966.

336. LARSON AW, WASSERSTROM WR, FELSHER BF, SHIH JC: Posttraumatic epilepsy and acute intermittent porphyria: Effects of phenytoin, carbamazepine, and clonazepam. *Neurology* 28:824, 1978.

337. BONKOWSKY HL, SINCLAIR PR, SCOTT E, SINCLAIR JF: Seizure management in acute hepatic porphyria: Risks of valproate and clonazepam. *Neurology* 30:588, 1980.

338. YEUNG LAIWAH AAC, THOMPSON GG, PHILIP MF, BRODIE MJ, RAPEPORT WG, MacPHEE GJA, MOORE MR, GOLDBERG A: Carbamazepine-induced non-hereditary acute porphyria. *Lancet* 1(2):790, 1983.

339. OTTE RC: Gastric changes during an attack of acute intermittent porphyria. *Radiology* 93:673, 1969.

340. GIBO Y, NAGATA A, KIYOSAWA K, SODEYAMA T, WADA S, FURUTA S: Intranuclear particles in the hepatocytes of patients with non-A, non-B hepatitis and acute intermittent porphyria. *Gastroenterology* 82:818, 1982.

341. SWEENEY VP, PATHAK MA, ASBURY AK: Acute intermittent porphyria. Increased ALA-synthetase activity during an acute attack. *Brain* 93:369, 1970.

342. BEHSE F, BUCKTHAL F: Sensory action potentials and biopsy of the sural nerve in neuropathy. *Brain* 101:473, 1978.

343. GIBSON JB, GOLDBERG A: The neuropathy of acute porphyria. *J Pathol Bacteriol* 71:495, 1956.

344. DENNY-BROWN D, SCIARRA D: Changes in the nervous system in acute porphyria. *Brain* 68:1, 1945.

345. WOCHNIK-DYJAS D, NIEWIADOMSKA M, KOSTRZEWSKA E: Porphyric polyneuropathy and its pathogenesis in the light of electrophysiological investigations. *J Neurol Sci* 35:243, 1978.

346. ALBERS JW, ROBERTSON WC, DAUBE JR: Electrodiagnostic findings in acute porphyric neuropathy. *Muscle Nerve* 1:292, 1978.

347. FLUGEL KA, DRUSCHKY KF: Electromyogram and nerve conduction in patients with acute intermittent porphyria. *J Neurol* 214:267, 1977.

348. MUSTAJOKI P, SEPPALAINEN AM: Neuropathy in latent hereditary hepatic porphyria. *Br Med J* 2:310, 1975.

349. GOODALL J: Acute intermittent porphyria and Hirschsprung's disease. *Proc R Soc Med* 60:47, 1967.

350. HEILMANN E, MULLER KM, NIEDORF H, VON BASSEVITZ DB: Special clinical, light and electron microscopic aspects of acute intermittent porphyria. *Ann Clin Res* 8:213, 1976.

351. PAPY JJ, ROGER J, DANIEL F, PONCET M, GASTAUT H: EEG aspects of acute intermittent porphyria. *Electroencephalogr Clin Neurophysiol* 25:93, 1968.

352. PERLROTH MG, TSCHUDY DP, MARVER HS, BERARD CW, ZEIGEL RF, RECHCIGL M, COLLINS A: Acute intermittent porphyria. New morphologic and biochemical findings. *Am J Med* 41:149, 1966.

353. TSCHUDY DP, VALSAMIS M, MAGNUSSEN CR: Acute intermittent porphyria: Clinical and selected research aspects. *Ann Intern Med* 83:851, 1975.

354. HELLMAN ES, TSCHUDY DP, BARTTER FC: Abnormal electrolyte and water metabolism in acute intermittent porphyria. *Am J Med* 32:734, 1962.

355. NIELSEN B, THORN NA: Transient excess urinary excretion of antidiuretic material in acute intermittent porphyria with hyponatremia and hypomagnesemia. *Am J Med* 38:345, 1965.

356. BLOOMER JR, BERK PD, BONKOWSKY HL, STEIN JA, BERLIN NI, TSCHUDY DP: Blood volume and bilirubin production in acute intermittent porphyria. *N Engl J Med* 284:17, 1971.

357. EALES L, DOWDLE EB, SWEENEY GD: The acute porphyria attack 1. *S Afr J Lab Clin Med* 17:89, 1971.

358. DESAGA V, LEONHADT KF, FRAHM H, DOSS M: Clinical and experimental investigations of vasopressin secretion in acute porphyrias. *Exp Clin Endocrinol* 86:79, 1985.

359. KERR GD: Acute intermittent porphyria and inappropriate secretion of antidiuretic hormone in pregnancy. *Proc R Soc Med* 66:19, 1973.

360. LIPSCHUTZ DE, REITER JM: Acute intermittent porphyria with inappropriately elevated ADH secretion. *JAMA* 230:716, 1974.

361. FARESE RV, KARSH SJ, BIDOT-LOPEZ P: Acute intermittent porphyria associated wtih inappropriate antidiuretic hormone secretion, hypokalemic alkalosis, and secondary hyperaldosteronism. *South Med J* 72:1201, 1979.

362. PERLROTH MG, TSCHUDY DP, WAXMAN A, ODELL WD: Abnormalities of growth hormone regulation in acute intermittent porphyria. *Metabolism* 16:87, 1967.

363. WAXMAN AD, BERK PD, SCHALCH D, TSCHUDY DP: Isolated adrenocorticotrophic hormone deficiency in acute intermittent porphyria. *Ann Intern Med* 70:317, 1969.

364. GIBSON SLM, GOLDBERG A: Defects in haem synthesis in mammalian tissues in experimental lead poisoning and experimental porphyria. *Clin Sci* 38:63, 1970.

365. PERCY VA, SHANLEY BC: Studies on haem biosynthesis in rat brain. *J Neurochem* 33:1267, 1979.

366. COHN JA, ALVARES AP, KAPPAS A: On the occurrence of cytochrome P-450 and aryl hydrocarbon hydroxylase activity in rat brain. *J Exp Med* 145:1607, 1977.

367. DAS M, SETH PK, MUKHTAR H: NADH-dependent inducible aryl hydrocarbon hydroxylase activity in rat brain mitochondria. *Drug Metab Dispos* 9:69, 1981.

368. PATERNITI JR, SIMONE JJ, BEATTIE DS: Detection and regulation of δ-aminolevulinic acid synthetase activity in the rat brain. *Biochem J* 150:97, 1975.

369. FEUER G, SOSA-LUCERO JC, LUND G, MODDEL G: Failure of various drugs to induce drug-metabolizing enzymes in extrahepatic tissues of the rat. *Toxicol Appl Pharmacol* 19:579, 1971.

370. NABESHIMA T, FONTENOT J, HO JK: Effects of chronic administration of phenobarbital or morphine on the brain microsomal cytochrome P450 system. *Biochem Pharmacol* 30:1142, 1981.

371. DE MATTHEIS F, ZETTERLUND P, WETTERBERG L: Brain 5-aminolevulinate synthase. Developmental aspects and evidence for a regulatory role. *Biochem J* 196:811, 1981.

372. WHETSELL WO JR, SASSA S, KAPPAS A: Porphyrin-heme biosynthesis in organotypic cultures of mouse dorsal root ganglia. *J Clin Invest* 74:600, 1984.

373. WHETSELL WO JR, SASSA S, BICKERS D, KAPPAS A: Studies on porphyrin-heme biosynthesis in organotypic cultures of chick dorsal root ganglia. *J Neuropathol Exp Neurol* 37:497, 1978.

374. WHETSELL WO JR, SASSA S, KAPPAS A: Studies on the effects of chronic lead exposure on porphyrin biosynthesis and myelin in cultures of mouse dorsal root ganglia. *J Neuropathol Exp Neurol* 38:348, 1979.

375. MCGILLON FB, MOORE MR, GOLDBERG A: The effect of δ-aminolaevulinic acid on the spontaneous activity of mice. *Scott Med J* 18:133, 1973.

376. MCGILLON FB, THOMPSON GC, MOORE MR, GOLDBERG A: The passage of δ-aminolevulinic acid across the blood brain barrier of the rat: Effect of ethanol. *Biochem Pharmacol* 23:472, 1974.

377. MCGILLON PB, THOMPSON GC, GOLDBERG A: Tissue uptake of δ-aminolevulinic acid. *Biochem Pharmacol* 24:299, 1975.

378. BONKOWSKY HL, TSCHUDY DP, COLLINS A, DOHERTY J, BOSSENMAIER I, CARDINAL R, WATSON CJ: Repression of the overproduction of porphyrin

precursors in acute intermittent porphyria by intravenous infusions of hematin. *Proc Natl Acad Sci USA* 68:2725, 1971.

379. PERCY VA, SHANLEY RC: Porphyrin precursors in blood, urine and cerebrospinal fluid in acute porphyria. *S Afr Med J* 52:219, 1977.

380. GORCHEIN A, WEBBER R: δ-Aminolevulinic acid in plasma, cerebrospinal fluid, saliva and erythrocytes: Studies in normal, uremic and porphyric subjects. *Clin Sci* 72:103, 1987.

381. SHANLEY BC, NEATHLING AC, PERCY VA, CARSTENS M: Neurochemical aspects of porphyria: Studies on the possible neurotoxicity of delta-aminolevulinic acid. *S Afr J Lab Clin Med* 49:576, 1975.

382. PIERACH CA, EDWARDS PS: Neurotoxicity of δ-aminolevulinic acid and porphobilinogen. *Exp Neurol* 62:810, 1978.

383. BIEMPICA L, KOSOWER NS, NOVIKOFF AB: Cytochemical and ultrastructural changes in rat liver in experimental porphyria. *Lab Invest* 17:171, 1967.

384. YUWILER A, WETTERBERG L, GELLER E: Tryptophan pyrrolase, tryptophan and tyrosine transaminase changes during allylisopropylacetamide-induced porphyria in the rat. *Biochem Pharmacol* 19:189, 1970.

385. KOSOWER NS, ROCK RA: Seizures in experimental porphyria. *Nature* 217:565, 1968.

386. SIMA AAF, KENNEDY JC, BLAKESLEE D, ROBERTSON DM: Experimental porphyric neuropathy. *J Can Sci Neurol* 8:105, 1981.

387. BORNSTEIN JC, PICKETT JB, DIAMOND I: Inhibition of the evoked release of acetylcholine by the porphyrin precursor δ-aminolevulinic acid. *Neurology* 5:94, 1979.

388. DICHTER HN, TADDEINI L, LIN S, AYALA GF: Delta amino levulinic acid. Effect of a porphyrin precursor on an isolated neuronal preparation. *Brain Res* 126:189, 1977.

389. BRENNAN MJW, CANTRILL RC: δ-Aminolaevulinic acid is a potent agonist for GABA autoreceptors. *Nature* 280:514, 1979.

390. BECKER DM, GOLDSTUCK N, KRAMER S: Effect of δ-aminolevulinic acid on the resting membrane potential of frog sartorius muscle. *S Afr Med J* 49:1790, 1975.

391. DURKO I, JUHASZ A: Porphyrin synthesis in primary nervous tissue cultures from 10^{-3} M delta-aminolevulinic acid in the presence of metatonin and neuropeptides. *Neurochem Res* 11:607, 1986.

392. CULTER MG, MOORE MR, DICK JM: Effects of δ-aminolevulinic acid on contractile activity of rabbit duodenum. *Eur J Pharmacol* 64:221, 1980.

393. BECKER D, VILJOEN D, KRAMER S: The inhibition of red cell and brain ATPase by δ-aminolevulinic acid. *Biochim Biophys Acta* 225:26, 1971.

394. EDWARDS SR, SHANLEY BC, REYNOLDSON JA: Neuropharmacology of delta-aminolevulinic acid. *Neuropharmacology* 23:477, 1984.

395. GREEN H, GREENBURG SM, ERICKSON RW, SAWYER JL, ELLISON J: Effect of dietary phenylalanine and tryptophan upon rat brain anine levels. *J Pharmacol Exp Ther* 136:174, 1962.

396. KNOX WE: The regulation of tryptophan pyrrolase activity by tryptophan. *Adv Enzyme Regul* 4:287, 1966.

397. LITMAN DA, CORREIA MA: Elevated brain tryptophan and enhanced 5-hydroxytryptamine turnover in acute hepatic heme deficiency: Clinical implications. *J Pharmacol Exp Ther* 232:337, 1985.

398. LITMAN DA, CORREIA MA: L-tryptophan: A common denominator of biochemical and neurological events of acute hepatic porphyria. *Science* 222:1031, 1983.

399. PRICE JM, BROWN RR, PETERS HA: Tryptophan metabolism in porphyria, schizophrenia and a variety of neurologic and psychiatric diseases. *Neurology* 9:456, 1959.

400. LUDWIG GD, EPSTEIN IS: A genetic study of two families having the acute intermittent type of porphyria. *Ann Intern Med* 55:81, 1961.

401. HOSOBUCHI Y: Tryptophan reversal of tolerance to analgesia induced by central grey stimulation. *Lancet* 2:47, 1978.

402. THAL LJ, SHARPLESS NS, WOLFSON L, KARTZMAN R: Treatment of myoclonus with L-5-hydroxytryptophan and carbidopa: Clinical, electrophysiological and biochemical observations. *Ann Neurol* 7:570, 1979.

403. SMITH B, PROCKOP DJ: Central nervous system effects of ingestion of L-tryptophan by normal subjects. *N Engl J Med* 276:1338, 1962.

404. BAHOH RW, DIETZ J, SPOONER JW: Myoclonus and ocular oscillations induced by L-tryptophan. *Ann Neurol* 11:95, 1981.

405. CAVANAGH JB, RIDLEY AR: The nature of the neuropathy complicating acute intermittent porphyria. *Lancet* 2:1023, 1967.

406. HAMFELT A, WETTERBERG L: Pyridoxal phosphate in acute intermittent porphyria. *Ann NY Acad Sci* 166:361, 1969.

407. ELDER TD, MENGEL CE: Effect of pyridoxine deficiency on porphyria precursor excretion in acute intermittent porphyria. *Am J Med* 41:369, 1966.

408. IRVINE DG, WETTERBERG L: Kryptopyrrole-like substance in acute intermittent porphyria. *Lancet* 2:1201, 1972.

409. WETTERBERG L, FORMGREN B: Pharmacological and biochemical properties of kryptopyrrole and its oxidation products possibly related to acute intermittent porphyria. *Ann Clin Res* 8:162, 1976.

410. GRAHAM DJM, BRODIE MJ, McCOLL KEL, MOORE MR, GOLDBERG A: Quantitation of 3-ethyl-5-hydroxy-4,5-dimethyl-Δ^3-pyrrolin-2-one in the urine of patients with acute intermittent porphyria. *Eur J Clin Invest* 9:49, 1979.

411. IRVINE DG, BAYNE W, MIYASHITA H: Identifications of kryptopyrrole in human urine and its possible relation to psychosis. *Nature* 224:811, 1969.

412. IRVINE DG: Pyrroles in neuropsychiatric and porphyric disorders: Confirmation of a metabolite structure by synthesis. *Life Sci* 23:983, 1978.

413. MOORE MR, GRAHAM DJM: Monopyrroles in porphyria, psychosis and lead exposure. *Int J Biochem* 12:827, 1980.

414. GRAHAM DJM, THOMPSON GG, MOORE MR, GOLDBERG A: The effects of selected monopyrroles on various aspects of heme synthesis and degradation in the rat. *Arch Biochem Biophys* 197:132, 1979.

415. GENDER PL, DUHAN HA, RAPOPORT H: Hemopyrrole and kryptopyrrole are absent from the urine of schizophrenics and normal persons. *Clin Chem* 24:230, 1978.

416. GORCHEIN A: Urine concentration of 3-ethyl-5-hydroxy-4,5-dimethyl-Δ^3-pyrrolin-2-one ("mauve factor") is not causally related to schizophrenia or to acute intermittent porphyria. *Clin Sci* 58:469, 1980.

417. BARCLAY N: Acute intermittent porphyria in childhood. A neglected diagnosis? *Arch Dis Child* 49:404, 1974.

418. KREIMER-BIRNBAUM M, BANNERMAN RM: Acute intermittent porphyria in childhood. A neglected diagnosis? *Arch Dis Child* 50:494, 1975.

419. GREGOR A, KOSTRZEWSKA E, PROKURAT H, PUCEK Z, TORBICKA E: Increased protoporphyrin in erythrocytes in a child with acute intermittent porphyria. *Arch Dis Child* 52:947, 1977.

420. McCOLL KEL, WALLACE AM, MOORE MR, THOMPSON GG, GOLDBERG A: Alterations in haem biosynthesis during the human menstrual cycle: Studies in normal subjects and patients with latent and active acute intermittent porphyria. *Clin Sci* 62:183, 1982.

421. MERCKE C, LUNDH B: Erythrocyte filterability and heme catabolism during the menstrual cycle. *Ann Intern Med* 85:322, 1976.

422. DELIVORIA-PAPADOPOULOS M, COBURN RF, FORSTER RE: Cyclic variations of rate of carbon monoxide production in normal women. *J Appl Physiol* 36:49, 1974.

423. WELLAND FH, HELLMEN ES, COLLINS A, HUNTER GW, TSCHUDY DP: Factors affecting the excretion of porphyrin precursors by patients with acute intermittent porphyria. *Metabolism* 13:251, 1964.

424. LEVIT EJ, NODINE JH, PERLOFF WH: Progesterone-induced porphyria. *Am J Med* 22:831, 1957.

425. KAPPAS A, SONG CS, LEVERE RD, SACHSON RA, GRANICK S: The induction of δ-aminolevulinic acid synthetase *in vivo* in chick embryo liver by natural steroids. *Proc Natl Acad Sci USA* 61:509, 1968.

426. ANDERSON KE, FREDDARA U, KAPPAS A: Induction of hepatic cytochrome P-450 by natural steroids: Relationships to the induction of δ-aminolevulinate synthase and porphyrin accumulation in the avian embryo. *Arch Biochem Biophys* 217:597, 1982.

427. KAPPAS A: Estrogens and the liver. *Gastroenterology* 52:113, 1967.

428. KOSTULA P, TOIVONEN I: Urinary excretion of coproporphyrin isomers I & III and δ-aminolevulinic acid in normal pregnancy and obstetric hepatosis. *Acta Obstet Gynecol Scand* 47:292, 1968.

429. LYBERATOS C, CHALEVALAKIS G, PLATIS A, GARDIKAS C: Urinary porphyrins and their precursors in human pregnancy and after delivery. *J Obstet Gynaecol Br Commonw* 79:921, 1972.

430. DEKLERK M, WEIDMAN A, MALAN A, SHANLEY BC: Urinary porphyrins and porphyrin precursors in normal pregnancy. *S Afr Med J* 49:581, 1975.

431. LAATIKAINEN T, KARJALAINEN O: Excretion of conjugates of neutral steroids in human bile during late pregnancy. *Acta Endocrinol* 69:775, 1972.

432. ALTMAN K, GORDON GG, SOUTHREN AL, VITTEN J, WILKIR S: Induction of hepatic testosterone A-ring reductase by methoxyprogesterone acetate. *Endocrinology* 90:1252, 1972.

433. LITHNER F, WETTERBERG L: Hepatocellular carcinoma in patients with acute intermittent porphyria. *Acta Med Scand* 215:271, 1984.

434. MUSTAJOKI P, NIKKILA EA: Serum lipoproteins in asymptomatic acute prophyria: No evidence for hyperbetalipoproteinemia. *Metabolism* 33:266, 1984.

435. GRANDCHAMP B, ROMEO PH, DUBART A, RAICH N, ROSA J, NORDMANN Y, GOOSSENS M: Molecular cloning of a cDNA sequence complementary to porphobilinogen deaminase mRNA from rat. *Proc Natl Acad Sci USA* 81:5036, 1984.

436. HARDELL L, BENGTSSON NO, JONSSON U, ERIKSSON S, LARSSON LG: Aetiological aspects on primary liver cancer with special regard to alcohol, organic solvents and acute intermittent porphyria—An epidemiological investigation. *Br J Cancer* 50:389, 1984.

437. KAPPAS A, RIFKIND A: The occurrence of inducers and inhibitors of hepatic porphyrin synthesis in human plasma. *Trans Am Clin Climatol Assoc* 82:52, 1970.

438. RIFKIND AB, SASSA S, MERKATZ IR, WINCHESTER R, HARBER L, KAPPAS A: Stimulators and inhibitors of hepatic porphyrin formation in human sera. *J Clin Invest* 53:1167, 1974.

439. KAPPAS A, SONG CS, SASSA S, LEVERE RD, GRANICK S: The occurrence of substances in human plasma capable of inducing the enzyme delta-aminolevulinate synthetase in liver cells. *Proc Natl Acad Sci USA* 64:557, 1969.

440. PAUL S, BICKERS DR, LEVERE RD, KAPPAS A: Inhibited induction of hepatic δ-aminolevulinate synthetase in pregnancy. *FEBS Lett* 41:192, 1974.

441. SARDANA MK, SASSA S, KAPPAS A: Differential induction responses of δ-aminolevulinate synthetase and heme oxygenase during pregnancy. *Biochem J* 198:403, 1981.

442. GOLDBERG A, MOORE MR, BEATTIE AD, HALL PE, MCCALLUN J, GRANT JK: Excessive urinary excretion of certain porphyrinogenic steroids in human acute intermittent porphyria. *Lancet* 1:115, 1969.

443. PAXTON JW, MOORE MR, BEATTIE AD, GOLDBERG A: 17-Oxosteroid conjugates in plasma and urine of patients with acute intermittent porphyria. *Clin Sci Mol Med* 46:207, 1974.

444. KAPPAS A, BRADLOW HL, GILLETTE PN, GALLAGHER TF: Abnormal steroid hormone metabolism in the genetic liver disease acute intermittent porphyria. *Ann NY Acad Sci* 179:611, 1971.

445. KAPPAS A, BRADLOW HL, GILLETTE PN, LEVERE RD, GALLAGHER TF: A defect of steroid hormone metabolism in acute intermittent porphyria. *Fed Proc* 31:1293, 1972.

446. BRADLOW HL, GILLETTE PN, GALLAGHER TF, KAPPAS A: Studies in porphyria. II. Evidence for a deficiency of steroid Δ^4-5α-reductase activity in acute intermittent porphyria. *J Exp Med* 138:754, 1973.

447. ANDERSON KE, BRADLOW HL, SASSA S, KAPPAS A: Studies in porphyria: VIII. Relationships of the 5α-reductive metabolism of steroid hormones to clinical expression of the genetic defect in acute intermittent porphyria. *Am J Med* 66:644, 1979.

448. KAPPAS A, BRADLOW HL, BICKERS DR, ALVARES AP: Induction of a deficiency of steroid Δ^4-5α-reductase activity in liver by a porphyrinogenic drug. *J Clin Invest* 59:159, 1977.

449. FELSHER BF, REDEKER AG: Acute intermittent porphyria: Effect of diet and griseofulvin. *Medicine* 46:217, 1967.

450. WELLAND FH, HELLMAN ES, GADDIS EM, COLLINS A, HUNTER GW, TSCHUDY DP: Factors affecting the excretion of porphyrin precursors by patients with acute intermittent porphyria. I. Effects of diet. *Metabolism* 13:232, 1964.

451. BONKOWSKY HL, MAGNUSSEN CR, COLLINS AR, DOHERTY JM, HESS RA, TSCHUDY DP: Comparative effects of glycerol and dextrose on porphyrin precursor excretion in acute intermittent porphyria. *Metabolism* 25:405, 1976.

452. KAPPAS A, ANDERSON KE, CONNEY AH, PANTUCK EJ, FISHMAN J, BRADLOW HL: Nutrition-endocrine interaction: Induction of reciprocal changes in the Δ^4-5α-reduction of testosterone and the cytochrome P-450-dependent oxidation of estradiol by dietary macronutrients in man. *Proc Natl Acad Sci USA* 80:7646, 1983.

453. MARVER HS, COLLINS A, TSCHUDY DP, RECHCIGL M: δ-Aminolevulinic acid synthetase. *J Biol Chem* 241:4323, 1966.

454. CANEPA ET, LLAMBIAS EBC, GRINSTEIN M: Effect of glucose on the induction of δ-aminolevulinic acid synthase and ferrochelatase in isolated rat hepatocytes by ALA. *Biochim Biophys Acta* 804:8, 1984.

455. MARKS GS, STEPHENS JK, FISCHER PWF, MORGAN RO: Hormonal effects on the regulation of hepatic heme biosynthesis. *Mol Cell Biochem* 25:111, 1979.

456. EALES L: Porphyria and the dangerous life-threatening drugs. *S Afr Med J* 56:914, 1979.

457. RIFKIND AB: Drug induced exacerbations of porphyria. *Primary Care* 3:665, 1976.

458. MOORE MR: International review of drugs in acute porphyria. *Int J Biochem* 12:1089, 1980.

459. RIFKIND AB, GILLETTE PN, SONG CS, KAPPAS A: Drug stimulation of δ-aminolevulinic acid synthetase and cytochrome P-450 *in vivo* in chick embryo liver. *J Pharmacol Exp Ther* 185:214, 1973.

460. THOMAS SD, JORDAN PM: Nucleotide sequence of the *hemC* locus encoding porphobilinogen deaminase of *Escherichia coli* K12. *Nucleic Acids Res* 14:6215, 1986.

461. DE MATTEIS F: Drugs and porphyria. *S Afr J Med* 17:126, 1971.

462. WETTERBERG L: Internationell enkat om farliga och ufarliga lakemedel vid akut intermittent porfyri. *Lakartidningen* 73:4090, 1976.

463. LAMON JM, FRYKHOLM BC, HERRERA W, TSCHUDY DP: Danazol administration to females with menses-associated exacerbations of acute intermittent porphyria. *J Clin Endocrinol Metab* 48:123, 1979.

464. HUGHES MJ, RIFKIND AB: Danazol, a new steroidal inducer of δ-aminolevulinic acid synthetase. *J Clin Endocrinol Metab* 52:549, 1981.

465. MUSTAJOKI P, VUORISTO M, REUNALA T: Celiac disease or dermatitis herpetiformis in three patients with porphyria. *Dig Dis Sci* 26:618, 1981.

466. BLEKKENHORST GH, COOK ES, EALES L: Drug safety in porphyria. *Lancet* 1:1367, 1980.

467. MAGNUSSEN CR, DOHERTY JM, HESS RA, TSCHUDY DP: Grand mal seizures and acute intermittent porphyria. The problem of differential diagnosis and treatment. *Neurology* 25:1121, 1975.

468. GRANICK S: The induction *in vitro* of the synthesis of δ-aminolevulinic acid synthetase in chemical porphyria: A response to certain drugs, sex hormones and foreign chemicals. *J Biol Chem* 241:1359, 1966.

469. COUGER ML, LABBE RF: Contraindications of biological oxidation inhibitors in the treatment of porphyria. *Lancet* 1:88, 1965.

470. FISCHER PWF, FERIZOVIC A, NEILSON IR, MARKS GS: Porphyria-induced activity of alfaxolone and alfadolone acetate in chick embryo liver cells. *Anesthesiology* 50:350, 1979.

471. PARIKH RK, MOORE MR: Effect of certain anesthetic agents on the activity of rat hepatic δ-aminolaevulinate synthase. *Br J Anaesth* 50:1099, 1978.

472. TSCHUDY DP, BONKOWSKY HL: Experimental porphyria. *Fed Proc* 31:147, 1972.

473. ANDERSON KE: Effects of antihypertensive drugs on hepatic heme biosynthesis and evaluation of ferrochelatase inhibitors to simplify testing of drugs for heme pathway induction. *Biochim Biophys Acta* 543:313, 1978.

474. ZIMAN MR, BRADSHAW JJ, IVANETICH KM: The effect of fluroxene [(2,2,2-trifluoroethoxy)ethane] on haem biosynthesis and degradation. *Biochem J* 190:571, 1980.

475. PETERS HA, CRIPPS DJ, REESE HH: Porphyria. Theories of etiology and treatment. *Int Rev Neurobiol* 16:301, 1974.

476. EISEMAN JL, ALVARES AP: Alterations induced in heme pathway enzymes and monooxygenases by gold. *Mol Pharmacol* 14:1176, 1978.

477. KOSTRZEWSKA E, GREGOR A, LIPINSKA D: Ketamine in acute intermittent porphyria—Dangerous or safe? *Anesthesiology* 49:376, 1978.

478. HARRISON GG, MOORE MR, MEISSNER PN: Porphyrinogenicity of etomidate and ketamine as continuous infusions. Screening in the DDC-primed rat model. *Br J Anaesth* 57:420, 1985.

479. WITH TK: Toxic porphyria after treatment with sulphonal and trional. *S Afr J Lab Clin Med* 17:133, 1971.

480. RIFKIND AB, GILLETTE PN, SONG CS, KAPPAS A: Induction of hepatic δ-aminolevulinic acid synthetase by oral contraceptive steroids. *J Clin Endocrinol Metab* 30:330, 1970.

481. GARCIA-MERINO JA, LOPEZ-LOZANO JJ: Risks of valproate in porphyria. *Lancet* 2:856, 1980.

482. TSCHUDY DP, LAMON JM: Porphyrin metabolism and the porphyrias, in Bondy PK, Rosenerg LE (eds): *Duncan's Diseases of Metabolism*, 8th ed. Philadelphia, Saunders, 1980, p 939.

483. KRUMMEL SJ, WESNER RB: Exacerbation of acute intermittent porphyria by nortriptyline. *Drug Intell Clin Pharm* 20:487, 1986.

484. TREECE GL, MAGNUSSEN CR, PATTERSON JR, TSCHUDY DP: Exacerbation of porphyria during treatment of pulmonary tuberculosis. *Am Rev Respir Dis* 113:233, 1976.

485. BRODIE MJ: Drug safety in porphyria. *Lancet* 2:86, 1980.

486. SONG CS, BONKOWSKY HL, TSCHUDY DP: Salicylamide metabolism in acute intermittent porphyria. *Clin Pharmacol Ther* 15:431, 1973.

487. ANDERSON KE, ALVARES AP, SASSA S, KAPPAS A: Studies in porphyria. V. Drug oxidation rates in hereditary hepatic porphyria. *Clin Pharmacol Ther* 19:47, 1976.

488. OSTROWSKI J, KOSTRZEWSKA E, MICHALAK T, ZAWIRSKA B, MEDRZEJEWSKI W, GREGOR A: Abnormalities in liver function and morphology and impaired aminopyrine metabolism in hereditary hepatic porphyrias. *Gastroenterology* 85:1131, 1983.

489. DISLER PB, BLEKKENHORST GH, EALES L, MOORE MR, STRAUGHAN J: Guidelines for drug prescription in patients with the acute porphyrias. *S Afr Med J* 61:656, 1982.

490. DUDZINSKI B, WEINSTEIN AJ: Infectious mononucleosis presenting as acute intermittent porphyria. *South Med J* 77:523, 1984.

491. GRANICK S, VAN DEN SCHREIECK HG: Porphobilinogen and δ-aminolevulinic acid in acute porphyria. *Proc Soc Exp Biol Med* 88:270, 1955.

492. DOSS M, SCHERMULY E: Urinary porphyrin excretion pattern and isomer distribution of I and III in human porphyrin disorders, in Doss M (ed): *Porphyrias and Human Disease*. Basel, Karger, 1976, p 189.

493. SEARS WG, EALES L: Urinary dipyrrylmethenes in patients with porphyria. A preliminary study of the brown pigments in the urine of a case of acute intermittent porphyria. *Enzyme* 17:11, 1974.

494. WETTERBERG L, HAEGER-ARONSEN B, STATHERS G: Faecal porphyrins as a diagnostic index between acute intermittent porphyria and porphyria variegata. *Scand J Clin Lab Invest* 22:131, 1968.

495. WATSON CJ, SCHWARTZ S: A simple test for urinary porphobilinogen. *Proc Soc Exp Biol Med* 47:393, 1941.

496. WATSON CJ, TADDEINI L, BOSSENMAIER I: Present status of the Ehrlich aldehyde reaction for urinary porphobilinogen. *JAMA* 190:501, 1964.

497. LAMON J, WITH TK, REDEKER AG: The Hoesch test: Bedside screening for urinary porphobilinogen in patients with suspected porphyria. *Clin Chem* 11:1438, 1974.

498. LAMON J, FRYKHOLM BC, TSCHUDY DP: Screening tests in acute porphyria. *Arch Neurol* 34:709, 1977.

499. MAUZERALL D, GRANICK S: The occurrence and determination of δ-aminolevulinic acid and porphobilinogen in urine. *J Biol Chem* 219:435, 1956.

500. REIO L, WETTERBERG L: False porphobilinogen reactions in the urine of mental patients. *JAMA* 207:148, 1969.

501. GALBRAITH RA, SASSA S, KAPPAS A: A comparison of the utility of Dowex resin and polybenzimidazole Aurorez resin in the determination of urinary porphobilinogen concentrations. *Clin Chim Acta* 164:235, 1987.

502. MacGEE J, RODA SMB, ELIAS SV, LINGTON A, TABOR MW, HAMMOND PB: Determination of δ-aminolevulinic acid in blood plasma and urine by gas-liquid chromatography. *Biochem Med* 17:31, 1977.

503. STEIN JA, BLOOMER JR, BERK PD, CORCORAN PL, TSCHUDY DP: The kinetics of organic anion excretion by the liver in acute intermittent porphyria. *Clin Sci* 38:677, 1970.

504. KOBZA K, GYR K, NEUHAUS K, GUDAT F: Acute intermittent porphyria with relapsing acute pancreatitis and unconjugated hyperbilirubinemia without overt hemolysis. *Gastroenterology* 71:494, 1976.

505. JONES EA, BLOOMER JR, BERLIN NI: The measurement of the synthetic rate of bilirubin from hepatic hemes in patients with acute intermittent porphyria. *J Clin Invest* 50:2259, 1971.

506. BAROIS A, GAJDOS P, LIENHART A, GOULON M: Hypercalcemie au cours de la porphyrie aigue intermittente. *Semin Hop Paris* 53:1115, 1977.

507. MANNA R, ANNESE V: Raised creatinine phosphokinase activities in hepatic porphyria. *Br Med J* 290:518, 1985.

508. TADDEINI L, NORDSTROM KL, WATSON CJ: Hypercholesterolemia in experimental and human hepatic porphyria. *Metabolism* 13:691, 1964.

509. LEES RS, SONG CS, LEVERE RD, KAPPAS A: Hyperbeta-lipoproteinemia in acute intermittent porphyria. Preliminary report. *N Engl J Med* 282:432, 1970.

510. GOLDBERG A, RIMINGTON C, FENTON JCB: Experimentally produced porphyria in animals. *Proc R Soc Lond [Biol]* 143:257, 1955.

511. PINELLI A, FAVELLI L, FORMENTO M: Antiporphyric activity of 3,5-dimethylpyrazole in allylisopropylacetemide-treated rats. *Life Sci* 12:117, 1973.

512. BUCKBERG AM, KINNIBURGH AJ: Induction of liver apolipoprotein A-IV mRNA in porphyric mice. *Nucleic Acids Res* 13:1953, 1985.

513. PAZDEROVA-VEJLUPKOVA J, NEMCOVA N, PICKOVA J, JIRASEK L, LUKOS E: The development and prognosis of chronic intoxication by tetrachlorodibenzo-p-dioxin in man. *Arch Environ Health* 36:5, 1981.

514. WAXMAN A, SCHALACH DS, ODELL WD, TSCHUDY DP: Abnormalities of carbohydrate metabolism in acute intermittent porphyria. *J Clin Invest* 46:1129, 1967.

515. SIXEL-DIETRICH F, VERSPOHL F, DOSS M: Hyperinsulinemia in acute intermittent porphyria. *Horm Metab Res* 17:375, 1985.

516. BASILIERE J, NEWCOMER AD: Primary aldosteronism associated with acute intermittent porphyria. *N Engl J Med* 285:595, 1971.

517. HALLMAN ES, TSCHUDY DP, ROBBINS J, RALL JE: Elevation of the serum protein-bound iodine in acute intermittent porphyria. *J Clin Endocrinol Metab* 23:1185, 1963.

518. HOLLANDER CS, SCOTT RL, TSCHUDY DP, PERLROTH M, WAXMAN A, STERLING K: Increased protein-bound iodine and thyroxine-binding globulin in acute intermittent porphyria. *N Engl J Med* 277:995, 1967.

519. MANN JG, DE NARDO GL: Acute intermittent porphyria associated with hyperthyroidism. *J Clin Endocrinol Metab* 25:1151, 1965.

520. BRODIE MJ, GOLDBERG A, BEASTALL GH, YEO PPB, RATCLIFF JG: Abnormal thyroid function in symptomatic acute intermittent porphyria. *Proc Soc Endocrinol* 75:20P, 1977.

521. BRODIE MJ, GRAHAM DJM, GOLDBERG A, BEASTALL GH, RATCLIFFE WA, RATCLIFFE JG, YEO PPB: Thyroid function in acute intermittent porphyria: A neurogenic cause of hyperthyroidism? *Horm Metab Res* 10:327, 1978.

522. HAMILTON PR, BROEKHUIZEN FF: Acute intermittent porphyria and hydatid mole: Etiology of hyperthyroidism. *Am J Obstet Gynecol* 149:226, 1984.

523. HAUST HL, HEAGY FC: Abnormal perchlorate-induced radio-iodide loss from the thyroid gland in porphyrinopathies. *Int J Biochem* 12:981, 1980.

524. ANDRIOLA A, MOCELIN AJ, STELLA SR, AJZEN H, RAMOS OL: Determination of erythrocyte uroporphyrinogen I synthase activity in chronic renal failure. *Clin Chim Acta* 104:241, 1980.

525. ANDERSON KE, SASSA S, PETERSON CM, KAPPAS A: Increased erythrocyte uroporphyrinogen-I-synthetase, δ-aminolevulinic acid dehydratase and protoporphyrin in hemolytic anemias. *Am J Med* 63:359, 1977.

526. BLUM M, KOEHL C, ABECASSIS J: Variations in erythrocyte uroporphyrinogen I synthetase activity in non porphyrias. *Clin Chim Acta* 87:119, 1978.

527. HUGHES MJ, RIFKIND AB: Danazol, a new steroidal inducer of δ-aminolevulinic acid synthetase. *J Clin Endocrinol Metab* 52:549, 1981.

528. MUSTAJOKI P, TENHUNEN R: Variant of acute intermittent porphyria with normal erythrocyte uroporphyrinogen-I-synthase activity. *Eur J Clin Invest* 15:281, 1985.

529. SASSA S, SOLISH G, LEVERE RD, KAPPAS A: Studies in porphyria. IV. Expression of the gene defect of acute intermittent porphyria in cultured human skin fibroblasts and amniotic cells: Prenatal diagnosis of the porphyric trait. *J Exp Med* 142:722, 1975.

530. SASSA S, ZALAR GL, KAPPAS A: Studies in porphyria. VII. Induction of uroporphyrinogen-I synthase and expression of the gene defect of acute intermittent porphyria in mitogen-stimulated human lymphocytes. *J Clin Invest* 61:499, 1978.

531. LORIAUX DL, DELENA S, BROWN H: Glycine loading test in acute intermittent porphyria patients and their relatives. *Metabolism* 18:860, 1969.

532. WATSON CJ, RUNGE W, BOSSENMAIER I: Increased urinary porphobilinogen and uroporphyrin after administration of stilbestrol in a case of latent porphyria. *Metabolism* 11:1129, 1962.

533. BRODIE MJ, MOORE MR, THOMPSON GG, GOLDBERG A: The treatment of acute intermittent porphyria with laevulose. *Clin Sci Mol Med* 53:365, 1977.

534. TSCHUDY DP: Acute intermittent porphyria. *Semin Hematol* 5:370, 1968.

535. BEATTIE AD, MOORE MR, GOLDBERG A, WARD RL: Acute intermittent porphyria: Response of tachycardia and hypertension to propranolol. *Br Med J* 3:257, 1973.

536. MENAWAT AS, KOCHAR DK, PANWAR RB, JOSHI CK: Propranolol in acute intermittent porphyria. *Postgrad Med J* 55:546, 1979.

537. DOUER D, WEINBERGER A, PINKHAS J, ATSMON A: Treatment of acute intermittent porphyria with large doses of propranolol. *JAMA* 240:766, 1978.

538. BREZIS M, GHANEM J, WEILER-RAVELL D, EPSTEIN O, MORRIS D: Hematin and propranolol in acute intermittent porphyria. Full recovery from quadriplegic coma and respiratory failure. *Eur Neurol* 18:289, 1979.

539. ATSMON A, BLUM I, FISCHL J: Treatment of an acute attack of porphyria variegata with propanolol. *S Afr Med J* 46:311, 1972.

540. BLUM I, ATSMON A: Reduction of porphyrin excretion in porphyria variegata by propanolol. *S Afr Med J* 50:898, 1976.

541. LAMON JM, FRYKHOLM BC, HESS RA, TSCHUDY DP: Hematin therapy for acute porphyria. *Medicine* 58:252, 1979.

542. MOORE MR, MCCOLL KEL, GOLDBERG A: The activities of the enzymes of haem biosynthesis in the porphyrias and during treatment of the acute intermittent porphyrias. *Int J Biochem* 12:941, 1980.

543. PIERACH CA: Hematin therapy for the porphyria attack. *Semin Liver Dis* 2:125, 1982.

544. WATSON CJ, PIERACH CA, BOSSENMAIER I, CARDINAL R: Postulated deficiency of hepatic heme and repair by hematin infusions in the "inducible" hepatic porphyrias. *Proc Natl Acad Sci USA* 74:2118, 1977.

545. BOSCH EP, PIERACH CA, BOSSENMAIER I, CARDINAL R, THORSON M: Effect of hematin in porphyric neuropathy. *Neurology* 27:1053, 1977.

546. PETERSON A, BOSSENMAIER I, CARDINAL R, WATSON CJ: Hematin treatment of acute porphyria. Early remission of an almost fatal relapse. *JAMA* 235:520, 1976.

547. MCCOLL KEL, MOORE MR, THOMPSON GT, GOLDBERG A: Haematin therapy and leucocyte δ-aminolaevulinic-acid-synthase activity in prolonged attack of acute porphyria. *Lancet* 1:133, 1979.

548. MCCOLL KEL, MOORE MR, THOMPSON GG, GOLDBERG A: Treatment with haematin in acute hepatic porphyria. *Q J Med* 198:161, 1981.

549. DHAR GJ, BOSSENMAIER I, PETRYKA ZJ, CARDINAL R, WATSON CJ: Effects of hematin in hepatic porphyria. Further studies. *Ann Intern Med* 83:20, 1975.

550. LAMON JM, BENNET M, FRYKHOLM BC, TSCHUDY DP: Prevention of acute porphyric attacks by intravenous haematin. *Lancet* 2:492, 1978.

551. PETRYKA ZJ, DHAR GJ, BOSSENMAIER I: Hematin clearance in porphyria, in Doss M (ed): *Porphyrins in Human Disease*. Basel, Karger, 1976, p 259.

552. WOCHNER RD, SPILBERG I, LIO A, LIEM HH, MULLER-EBERHARD U: Hemopexin metabolism in sickle cell disease, porphyrias, and control subjects. Effects of heme injection. *N Engl J Med* 290:822, 1974.

553. MENDENHALL DW: Instability of hematin solutions. *N Engl J Med* 311:539, 1984.

554. GOETSCH CA, BISSEL DM: Instability of hematin used in the treatment of acute hepatic porphyria. *N Engl J Med* 315:235, 1986.

555. SIMIONATTO CS, GALBRAITH RA, JONES R, CABAL R, KAPPAS A: Hematin infusions impair hemostasis in normal subjects. *Clin Res* 34:651A, 1986.

556. MORRIS DL, DUDLEY MD, PEARSON RD: Coagulopathy associated with hematin treatment for acute intermittent porphyria. *Ann Intern Med* 95:700, 1981.

557. GLUECK R, GREEN D, COHEN I, TS'AO CH: Hematin: Unique effects on hemostasis. *Blood* 61:243, 1983.

558. PETERSEN JM, PIERACH CA: Hematin-induced hemolysis in acute porphyria. *Ann Intern Med* 101:877, 1984.

559. DHAR GJ, BOSSENMAIER I, CARDINAL R, PETRYKA ZJ, WATSON CJ: Transitory renal failure following rapid administration of a relatively large amount of hematin in a patient with acute intermittent porphyria in clinical remission. *Acta Med Scand* 203:437, 1978.

560. KHANDERIA U: Circulatory collapse associated with hemin therapy for acute intermittent porphyria. *Clin Pharm* 5:690, 1986.

561. LAMON JM, POH-FITZPATRICK MB, LAMOLA AA: Hepatic protoporphyrin production in human protoporphyria. Effects of intravenous hematin and analysis of erythrocyte protoporphyrin distribution. *Gastroenterology* 79:115, 1980.

562. BLOOMER JR, PIERACH CA: Effect of hematin administration to patients with protoporphyria and liver disease. *Hepatology* 2:817, 1982.

563. LAMON JM, FRYKHOLM BC, TSCHUDY DP: Hematin administration to an adult with lead intoxication. *Blood* 53:1007, 1979.

564. WATSON CJ, BOSSENMAIER I, CARDINAL R, PETRYKA ZJ: Repression by hematin of porphyrin biosynthesis in erythrocyte precursors in congenital erythropoietic porphyria. *Proc Natl Acad Sci USA* 71:278, 1974.

565. KORDAC V, MARTASEK P: Haem arginate in acute hepatic porphyria. *Br Med J* 293:1098, 1986.

566. MUSTAJOKI P, TENHUNEN R, TOKOLA O, GOTHONI G: Haem arginate in the treatment of acute hepatic porphyrias. *Br Med J* 293:538, 1986.

567. GALBRAITH RA, DRUMMOND GS, KAPPAS A: Sn-protoporphyrin suppresses chemically induced experimental hepatic porphyria: Potential clinical implications. *J Clin Invest* 76:2436, 1985.

568. LAIWAH ACY, JUNOR B, MacPHEE GJA, THOMPSON GG, McCOLL KEL: Charcoal haemoperfusion and haemodialysis in acute intermittent porphyria. *Br Med J* 287:1746, 1983.

569. HORAK J, MARTASEK P, KORDAC V, MERTL L, JIRSA M, TLUSTAKOVA, HOUSTKOVA H: Resin hemoperfusion in hepatic porphyrias. *Artif Organs* 9:169, 1985.

570. GRANDCHAMP B, BEAUMONT C, DE VERNEUIL H, NORDMANN Y: Accumulation of porphobilinogen deaminase, uroporphyrinogen decarboxylase, and α- and β-globin mRNAs during differentiation of mouse erythroleukemic cells. Effects of succinylacetone. *J Biol Chem* 260:9630, 1985.

571. PERLROTH MG, MARVER HS, TSCHUDY DP: Oral contraceptive agents and the management of acute intermittent porphyria. *JAMA* 194:135, 1965.

572. ZIMMERMAN TS, MCMILLIN JM, WATSON CJ: Onset of manifestations of hepatic porphyria in relation to the influence of female sex hormones. *Arch Intern Med* 118:229, 1966.

573. ANDERSON KE, SPITZ IM, SASSA S, BARDIN CW, KAPPAS A: Prevention of cyclical attacks of acute intermittent porphyria with a long-acting agonist of luteinizing hormone-releasing hormone. *N Engl J Med* 311:643, 1984.

574. SEMON C, DUPOND JL, MALLET H, GRANDMOTTET-CAMBEFORT G, HUMBERT P: Traitement d'une porphyrie aigue intermittente avec attaques cycliques par un agoniste LH-RH administre par voie nasale. *Ann Endocrinol (Paris)* 47:399, 1986.

575. OLSSON RA, TICKTIN HF: Zinc metabolism in acute intermittent porphyria. *J Lab Clin Med* 60:48, 1962.

576. ROMAN W: Zinc in porphyria. *Am J Clin Nutr* 22:1290, 1969.

577. PETERS HA, WOODS S, EICHAEN PL, REESE HH: The treatment of acute porphyria with chelating agents: A report of 21 cases. *Ann Intern Med* 47:889, 1957.

578. PETERS HA, CRIPPS DJ, REESE HH: Porphyria. Theories of etiology and treatment. *Int Rev Neurobiol* 16:301, 1974.

579. GAJDOS A, GAJDOS-TOROK M: Studies on the porphyrias in France. *S Afr J Lab Clin Med* 9:295, 1963.

580. MUSTAJOKI P: Vitamin E in porphyria. *JAMA* 221:714, 1972.

581. WATSON CJ, BOSSENMAIER I, CARDINAL R: Lack of significant effect of vitamin E on porphyrin metabolism. *Arch Intern Med* 131:698, 1973.

582. JUSIC A, SOSTARKO M, MAJIC D: Long-term ACTH and corticosteroid therapy in two siblings with polyneuropathy due to acute intermittent porphyria. *Eur Neurol* 14:294, 1976.

583. KAADA B, ROMSLO I: Use of transcutaneous nerve stimulation in the attacks of acute intermittent porphyria. *Int J Biochem* 17:235, 1985.

584. MARVER HS, SCHMID R: The porphyrias, in Stanbury JB, Wyngaarden JB, Frederickson DS (eds): *The Metabolic Basis of Inherited Disease*, 4th ed. New York, McGraw-Hill, 1972, p 1087.

585. SCHMID R, SCHWARTZ S, WATSON CJ: Porphyrin content in bone marrow and liver in the various forms of porphyria. *Arch Intern Med* 93:167, 1954.

586. SCHMID R, SCHWARTZ S, SUNDBERG RD: Erythropoietic (congenital) porphyria: A rare abnormality of normoblasts. *Blood* 10:416, 1955.

587. CHATTERJI AK, CHATTERJEA JB: Porphyria erythropoietia in India: A review report of 21 cases. *J Indian Med Assoc* 56:255, 1971.

588. FRYDMAN RB, TOMARO ML, FRYDMAN B: Porphobilinogen oxygenase from erythrocytes. *Clin Chim Acta* 97:269, 1979.

589. BOGORAD L: The enzymatic synthesis of porphyrins from porphobilinogen. II. Uroporphyrin III. *J Biol Chem* 233:510, 1958.

590. STEVENS E, FRYDMAN RB, FRYDMAN B: Separation of porphobilinogen deaminase and uroporphyrinogen III cosynthase from human erythrocytes. *Biochim Biophys Acta* 158:496, 1968.

591. LEVIN EY: Uroporphyrinogen III cosynthase in bovine erythropoietic porphyria. *Science* 161:907, 1968.

592. LEVIN EY: Uroporphyrinogen III cosynthase from mouse spleen. *Biochemistry* 7:3781, 1968.

593. LEVIN EY, FLYGER V: Erythropoietic porphyria of the fox squirrel *Sciurus niger*. *J Clin Invest* 52:96, 1973.

594. KOHASHI M, CLEMENT RP, TSE J, PIPER WN: Rat hepatic uroporphyrinogen III co-synthase. Purification and evidence for a bound folate coenzyme participating in the biosynthesis of uroporphyrinogen III. *Biochem J* 220:775, 1984.

595. HART GJ, BATTERSBY AR: Purification and properties of uroporphyrinogen III synthase (co-synthase) from *Euglena gracilis*. *Biochem J* 232:151, 1985.

596. TSAI S-F, BISHOP DF, DESNICK RJ: Purification and properties of uroporphyrinogen III synthase from human erythrocytes. *J Biol Chem* 262:1268, 1987.

597. ROMEO G, KABACK MM, LEVIN EY: Uroporphyrinogen III cosynthetase activity in fibroblasts from patients with congenital erythropoietic porphyria. *Biochem Genet* 4:659, 1970.

598. ROMEO G, GLENN BL, LEVIN EY: Uroporphyrinogen III cosynthetase in asymptomatic carriers of congenital erythropoietic porphyria. *Biochem Genet* 4:719, 1970.

599. CLEMENT RP, KOHASHI M, PIPER WN: Rat hepatic uroporphyrinogen III cosynthase: Purification, properties and inhibition by metal ions. *Arch Biochem Biophys* 214:657, 1982.

600. JORDAN PM: Uroporphyrinogen III cosynthase: A direct assay method. *Enzyme* 28:158, 1982.

601. JORDAN PM, BERRY A: Preuroporphyrinogen, a universal intermediate in the biosynthesis of uroporphyrinogen III. *FEBS Lett* 112:86, 1980.

602. POH-FITZPATRICK MB: The erythropoietic porhyrias. *Dermatol Clin* 4:291, 1986.

603. KRAMER S, VILJOEN E, MEYER AM, METZ J: The anemia of erythropoietic porphyria with the first description of the disease in an elderly patient. *Br J Haematol* 11:666, 1965.

604. KAUFMAN BM, VICKERS HR, RAYNE J, RYAN TJ: Congenital erythropoietic porphyria. Report of a case. *Br J Dermatol* 79:210, 1967.

605. FEURLE GE, HO AD, WOSIEWITZ U, ENCKE A: Cholelithiasis bei einem bisher nicht beschriebenen. Fall von Porphyria erythropoietica congenita. *Dtsch Med Wochenschr* 105:1153, 1980.

606. WATSON CJ, BOSSENMAIER I, CARDINAL R, PETRYKA ZJ: Repression by hematin of porphyrin biosynthesis in erythrocyte precursors in congenital erythropoietic porphyria. *Proc Natl Acad Sci USA* 71:278, 1974.

607. DEYBACH JC, DE VERNEUIL H, PHUNG N, NORDMANN Y, PUISSANT A, BOFFETY B: Congenital erythropoietic porphyria (Gunther's disease): Enzymatic studies on two cases of late onset. *J Lab Clin Med* 97:551, 1981.

608. PAIN RW, WELCH FW, WORDROFFE AJ, HANDLEY DA, LOCKWOOD WH: Erythropoietic uroporphyria of Gunther first presenting at 58 years with positive family studies. *Br Med J* 3:621, 1975.

609. WESTON MJ, NICHOLSON DC, LIM CK, CLARK KG, MacDONALD A, HENDERSON MA, WILLIAMS R: Congenital erythropoietic uroporphyria (Gunther's disease) presenting in a middle aged man. *Int J Biochem* 9:921, 1978.

610. NORDMANN Y, DEYBACH JC: Congential erythropoietic porphyria. *Semin Liver Dis* 2:154, 1982.

611. BHUTANI LK, SOOD SK, DAS PK, DESHPANDE SG, MULAY DN, KANDHARI KC: Congenital erythropoietic porphyria. An autopsy report. *Arch Dermatol* 110:427, 1974.

612. BORST M, KÖNIGSDORFFER H: Untersuchungen über Porphyrie, mit besonderer Berücksichtigung der Porphyria Congenita. Leipzig, S. Hirzel, 1929, p 213.

613. VARADI S: Haematological aspects in a case of erythropoietic porphyria. *Br J Haematol* 4:270, 1958.

614. GROSS S: Hematologic studies on erythropoietic porphyria: A new case with severe hemolysis, chronic thrombocytopenia and folic acid deficiency. *Blood* 23:762, 1964.

615. WATSON CJ, PERMAN V, SPURREL FA, HOYT HH, SCHWARTZ S: Some stud-

ies of the comparative biology of human and bovine porphyria erythropoietia. *Trans Assoc Am Physicians* 71:196, 1968.

616. HEILMEYER VL, CLOTTEN R, KERP L, MERKER H, PARRE CA, WETZEL HP: Porphyria erythropoietica congenita Gunther. *Dtsch Med Wochenschr* 51:2449, 1963.

617. HAINING RG, COWGER ML, SHURTLEFF DB, LABBE RF: Congenital erythropoietic porphyria. I. Case report, special studies and therapy. *Am J Med* 45:624, 1968.

618. CRIPPS DJ, PETERS HA: Fluorescing erythrocytes and porphyrin screening tests on urine, stool and blood. *Arch Dermatol* 96:712, 1967.

619. POH-FITZPATRICK MB: Laboratory testing in the porhyrias. *Int J Dermatol* 18:453, 1979.

620. CHATTERJEA JB: Correspondence: Erythropoietic porphyria. *Blood* 24:806, 1964.

621. ROSENTHALL IM, LIPTON EL, ASROW G: Effect of splenectomy on porphyria erythropoietica. *Pediatrics* 15:663, 1955.

622. MUKERJI SK, PIMSTONE NR, GANDHI SN, TAN KT: Biochemical diagnosis and monitoring therapeutic modulation of disease activity in an unusual case of congenital erythropoietic porphyria. *Clin Chem* 31:1946, 1985.

623. WATSON CJ, BOSSENMAIER I, CARDINAL R: Formation of porphyrin isomers from porphobilinogen by various hemolysates of red cells from bovine and human subjects with erythropoietic (Uro-) porphyria. *J Clin Chem Clin Biochem* 7:119, 1959.

624. ZAIL SS, KRAWITZ P, VILJOEN E, KRAMER S: The anemia of erythropoietic porphyria II. *Br J Haematol* 13:60, 1967.

625. GRAY CH: Isotope studies in porphyria. *Br Med Bull* 8:229, 1952.

626. GRAY CH, NEUBERGER A, SNEATH PHA: Studies in congenital porphyria 3. *Biochem J* 47:542, 1950.

627. GRINSTEIN M, ALDRICH RA, HAWKINSON V, WATSON CJ: An isotopic study of porphyria and hemoglobin metabolism in a case of porphyria. *J Biol Chem* 179:983, 1949.

628. LONDON IM, WEST R, SHEMIN D, RITTENBERG D: Porphyrin formation and hemoglobin metabolism in congenital porphyria. *J Biol Chem* 184:365, 1950.

629. SATO A, TAKAHASI N: A new form of congenital hematoporphyria: Oligochromenia porphyrinuria (megalosplenica congenita). *Am J Dis Child* 32:325, 1926.

630. CANIVET J, PELHARD-CONSIDERE M: Étude de l'hemolyse dans deux cas de porphyrie congenitale. *Rev Fr Etud Clin Biol* 3:27, 1958.

631. SASSA S, KAPPAS A: The porphyrias, in Harris H, Hirschhorn K (eds): *Advances in Human Genetics*. New York, Plenum Press, vol II, 1981.

632. ALDRICH RA, HAWKINSON V, GRINSTEIN M, WATSON CJ: Photosensitive or congenital porphyria with hemolytic anemia I. *Blood* 6:685, 1951.

633. TADDEINI L, WATSON CJ: The clinical porphyrias. *Semin Hematol* 5:335, 1968.

634. HAINING RG, COWGER ML, LABBE RF, FINCH CA: Congenital erythropoietic porphyria. II. The effects of induced polycythemia. *Blood* 36:297, 1970.

635. RIMINGTON C, WITH TK: Porphyrin studies in congenital erythropoietic porphyria. Studies on a sample of faeces and a sample of urine from a patient with C.E.P. and comparison with a bovine case of this disease. *Dan Med Bull* 20:5, 1973.

636. MOORE MR, THOMPSON GG, GOLDBERG A, IPPEN H, SEUBERT A, SEUBERT S: The biosynthesis of haem in congenital (erythropoietic) porphyria. *Int J Biochem* 9:933, 1978.

637. DAROCHA T: Family study in congenital erythropoietic porphyria. *S Afr J Lab Clin Med* 17:231, 1971.

638. ELDER GH, SMITH SG, HERRERO C, MASCARO JM, LECHA M, MUNIESA AM, CZARNECKI DB, BRENNAN J, POULOUS U, DE SALAMANCA RE: Hepatoerythropoietic porphyria: A new uroporphyrinogen decarboxylase defect in homozygous porphyria cutanea tarda? *Lancet* 1:916, 1981.

639. LIM HW, POH-FITZPATRICK MB: Hepatoerythropoietic porphyria: A variant of childhood-onset porphyria cutanea tarda. *J Am Acad Dermatol* 11:1103, 1984.

639a. NITOWSKY HM, SASSA S, NAKAGAWA M, JAGANI B: Prenatal diagnosis of congenital erythropoietic porphyria. *Pediatr Res* 12:455, 1978.

640. ERIKSEN L, SEIP M: The effect of various therapeutic trials on the porphyrin excretion in a case of congenital erythropoietic porphyria. *Acta Paediatr Scand* 64:287, 1975.

641. GAJDOS A, DE PAILLERETS F, BOUGYUES D: Un cas de porphyrie érythropoietique congénitale (maladie de Gunther) traité par le β-caroténe. *Nouv Presse Med* 6:2345, 1977.

642. SEIP M, THUNE PO, ERIKSEN L: Treatment of photosensitivity in congenital erythropoietic porphyria (CEP) with beta-carotene. *Acta Derm Venereol (Stockh)* 54:239, 1974.

643. SNEDDON IB, STRETCHER GS: Beta-carotene in congenital erythropoietic porphyria. *Arch Dermatol* 114:1242, 1978.

644. MATHEWS-ROTH MM: Beta carotene in congenital porphyria. *Arch Dermatol* 115:641, 1979.

645. PIOMELLI S, POH-FITZPATRICK MB, SEAMAN C, SKOLNICK LM, BERDON WE: Complete suppression of the symptoms of congenital erythropoietic porphyria by long-term treatment with high-level transfusions. *N Engl J Med* 314:1029, 1986.

646. GRAY CH, NEUBERGER A: Effect of splenectomy in a case of congenital porphyria. *Lancet* 1:851, 1952.

647. PIMSTONE NR, GANDHI SN, MUKERJI SK: Therapeutic efficacy of oral charcoal in congenital erythropoietic porphyria. *N Engl J Med* 316:390, 1987.

648. STRETCHER GS: Erythropoietic porphyria. Two cases and the results of metabolic alkalinization. *Arch Dermatol* 113:1553, 1977.

649. MALINA L, CHLUMSKY J, CHLUMSKY A: Porphyria cutanea tarda: New facts on etiology, pathogenesis, clinical manifestations and treatment. Czechoslovakia, Universita Karlova, 1974.

650. BANES HD: Porphyria in the Bantu races on the Witwatersrand. *S Afr Med J* 29:781, 1955.

651. DEAN G: *The Porphyrias. A Study of Inheritance and Environment*, 2d ed. London, Pitman Medical, 1971.

652. ELDER GH: Recent advances in the identification of enzyme deficiencies in the porphyrias. *Br J Dermatol* 108:729, 1983.

653. KUSHNER JP: The enzymatic defect in Porphyria Cutanea Tarda. *N Engl J Med* 306:799, 1982.

654. BEHM AR, UNGER WP: Oral contraceptives and Porphyria Cutanea Tarda. *Can Med Assoc J* 110:1052, 1974.

655. GROSSMAN ME, BICKERS DR, POH-FITZPATRICK MB, DeLEO VA, HARBER LC: Porphyria Cutanea Tarda. *Am J Med* 67:277, 1979.

656. SIXEL-DIETRICH F, DOSS M: Hereditary uroporphyrinogen-decarboxylase deficiency predisposing Porphyria Cutanea Tarda (chronic hepatic porphyria) in females after oral contraceptive medication. *Arch Dermatol Res* 278:13, 1985.

657. DOSS M: Hereditärer Uroporphyrinogen-Decarboxylase-Defekt bei Porphyria Cutanea Tarda durch hormonale Kontrazeptiva. *Dtsch Med Wochenschr* 108:1857, 1983.

658. DE SALAMANCA RE, MINGO D, CHINARRO S, MUNOZ JJ, PERPINA J: Patterns of porphyrin-excretion in female estrogen-induced Porphyria Cutanea Tarda. *Arch Dermatol Res* 274:179, 1982.

659. PIERACH C: Porphyria and hepatocellular carcinoma. *Br J Cancer* 55:111, 1987.

660. JACKSON AH, SANCOVICH HA, FERRAMOLA AM, EVANS N, GAMES DE, MATLIN SA, ELDER GH, SMITH SG: Macrocyclic intermediates in the biosynthesis of porphyrins. *Philos Trans R Soc Lond (Biol)* 273:119, 1975.

661. CORNFORD P: Transformation of porphobilinogen into porphyrins by preparations from human erythrocytes. *Biochem J* 91:64, 1964.

662. SMITH AG, FRANCIS JE: Decarboxylation of porphyrinogens by rat liver uroporphyrinogen decarboxylase. *Biochem J* 183:455, 1979.

663. ELDER GH, TOVEY JA: Uroporphyrinogen decarboxylase activity of human tissues. *Biochem Soc Trans* 5:1470, 1977.

664. DE VERNEUIL H, SASSA S, KAPPAS A: Purification and properties of uroporphyrinogen decarboxylase from human erythrocytes. A single enzyme catalyzing the four successive decarboxylations of uroporphyrinogen I and III. *J Biol Chem* 258:2454, 1983.

665. ZUYDERHOUDT FMJ, SINDRAM JW, MARX JJM, JORNING GGA, VAN GOOL J: The amount of ferritin and hemosiderin in the liver of patients with iron-loading diseases. *Hepatology* 3:232, 1983.

666. BATTLE DEL C AM, GRINSTEIN M: Porphyrin biosynthesis. II. Phyriaporphyrinogen III. A normal intermediate in the biosynthesis of protoporphyrin IX. *Biochim Biophys Acta* 82:13, 1962.

667. HOARE DS, HEATH H: Intermediates in the biosynthesis of porphyrins from porphobilinogen by *Rhodopseudomonas spheroides*. *Nature* 181:1592, 1958.

668. DE VERNEUIL H, GRANDCHAMP B, NORDMANN Y: Some kinetic properties of human red cell uroporphyrinogen decarboxylase. *Biochim Biophys Acta* 611:174, 1980.

669. STRAKA JG, KUSHNER JP: Purification and characterization of bovine hepatic uroporphyrinogen decarboxylase. *Biochemistry* 22:4664, 1983.

670. BLEKKENHORST GH, EALES L, PIMSTONE NR: Activation of uroporphyrinogen decarboxylase by ferrous iron in Porphyria Cutanea Tarda. *S Afr Med J* 56:918, 1979.

671. KUSHNER JP, BARBUTO AJ, LEE GR: An inherited enzymatic defect in Porphyria Cutanea Tarda. *J Clin Invest* 58:1089, 1976.

672. FELSHER BF, NORRIS ME, SHIH JC: Red-cell uroporphyrinogen decarboxylase activity in Porphyria Cutanea Tarda and in other forms of porphyria. *N Engl J Med* 299:1095, 1978.

673. TIEPERMANN VON R, DOSS M: Uroporphyrinogen-Decarboxylase in Erythrocyten: Untersuchungen zum primären genetischer Enzymdefekt der chronische hepatischer Porphyrie. *J Clin Chem Biochem* 17:513, 1978.

674. TALJAARD JJF, SHANLEY BC, JOUBERT SM: Decreased uroporphyrinogen decarboxylase activity in experimental symptomatic Porphyria. *Life Sci* 10:887, 1971.

675. TALJAARD JJF, SHANLEY BC, DEPPE WM, JOUBERT SM: Porphyrin metabolism in experimental hepatic siderosis II. Combined effect on iron overload and hexachlorobenzene. *Br J Haematol* 23:513, 1972.

676. TALJAARD JJF, SHANLEY BC, DEPPE WM, JOUBERT SM: Porphyrin metabolism in experimental hepatic siderosis in the rat. III. Effect on iron overload and hexachlorobenzene on liver haem biosynthesis. *Br J Haematol* 23:587, 1972.

677. SMITH AG, FRANCIS JE: Investigations of rat liver uroporphyrinogen decarboxylase. *Biochem J* 195:241, 1981.

678. IPPEN H: Treatment of Porphyria Cutanea Tarda by phlebotomy. *Semin Hematol* 14:253, 1977.

679. SWEENEY GD, JONES KG: Porphyria Cutanea Tarda: Clinical and laboratory features. *Can Med Assoc J* 120:803, 1979.

680. KUSHNER JP, STEINMULLER DP, LEE GR: The role of iron in the pathogenesis of porphyria cutanea tarda. II. Inhibition of uroporphyrinogen decarboxylase. *J Clin Invest* 56:661, 1975.

681. DANBY CWE, KOVAL A, WYLLIE J: Acquired porphyria cutanea tarda: Two cases treated by repeated phlebotomies. *Can Med Assoc J* 94:1358, 1966.

682. EPSTEIN JH, REDEKER AG: Porphyria cutanea tarda symptomatica (PCT-S): A study of the effect of phlebotomy therapy. *Arch Dermatol* 92:286, 1965.

683. HICKMAN R, SAUNDERS SJ, EALES L: Treatment of symptomatic porphyria by venesection. *S Afr Med J* 41:456, 1967.

684. IPPEN H: Allgemeine Symptome. Der späten Hautporphyrie (Porphyria cutanea tarda) als Hinweise für deren Behandlung. *Dtsch Med Wochenschr* 86:127, 1961.

685. SAUNDERS SJ: Iron metabolism in symptomatic porphyria. *S Afr J Lab Clin Med* 9:277, 1963.

686. SWEENEY GD, JONES KG, COLE FM, BASFORD D, KRETYNSKI F: Iron deficiency prevents liver toxicity of 2,3,7,8-tetrachlorodibenzo-p-dioxin. *Science* 204:332, 1979.

687. SMITH AG, CABRAL JRP, DE MATTEIS F: A difference between two strains of rats in their liver non-haem iron content and in their response to the porphyrogenic effect of hexachlorobenzene. *Chem Biol Interact* 27:353, 1979.

688. BLEKKENHORST GH, DAY RS, EALES L: The effect of bleeding and iron administration on the development of hexachlorobenzene-induced rat porphyria. *Int J Biochem* 12:1013, 1980.

689. LOUW M, NEETHLING AC, PERCY VA, CARSTENS M, SHANLEY BC: Effects of hexachlorobenzene feeding and iron overload on enzymes of haem biosynthesis and cytochrome P450 in rat liver. *Clin Sci Mol Med* 53:111, 1977.

690. DE VERNEUIL H, GRANDCHAMP B, FOUBERT C, WEIL D, NGUYEN VC, GROSS MS, SASSA S, NORDMANN Y: Assignment of the gene for uroporphyrinogen decarboxylase to human chromosome 1 by somatic cell hybridization and specific enzyme immunoassay. *Hum Genet* 66:202, 1984.

691. MCLELLAN T, PRYOR MA, KUSHNER JP, EDDY RL, SHOWS TB: Assignment of uroporphyrinogen decarboxylase (UROD) to the pter-p21 region of human chromosome 1. *Cytogenet Cell Genet* 39:224, 1985.

692. BOGORAD L: Porphyrin synthesis III. Uroporphyrinogen decarboxylase, in Colowick SP, Kaplan NO (eds): *Methods in Enzymology*. New York, Academic, 1962, vol V, p 893.

693. ROMEO PH, DUBART A, GRANDCHAMP B, DE VERNEUIL H, ROSA J, NORDMANN Y, GOOSSENS M: Isolation and identification of a cDNA clone coding for rat uroporphyrinogen decarboxylase. *Proc Natl Acad Sci USA* 81:3346, 1984.

694. ROMEO PH, RAICH N, DUBART A, BEAUPAIN D, PRYOR M, KUSHNER J, COHEN-SOLAL M, GOOSSENS M: Molecular cloning and nucleotide sequence of a complete human uroporphyrinogen decarboxylase cDNA. *J Biol Chem* 261:9825, 1986.

695. PRADO MJC, DE SALAMANCA RE, HERNANDO MV, PAYERO MLP, BELTRAN TC, AGUILAR AR: Two cases of infantile and familial Porphyria Cutanea Tarda. *Dermatologica* 161:205, 1980.

696. DOUTRE MS, BEYLOT C, BEYLOT J, NORDMANN Y, DE VERNEUIL H, BIOULAC P: Porphyrie Cutanée Tardive de l'enfant. Une observation avec étude enzymatique familiale. *Nouv Presse Med* 10:1502, 1981.

697. DAY RS, EALES L, PIMSTONE NR: Familial symptomatic porphyria in South Africa. *S Afr Med J* 56:909, 1979.

698. WELLAND FH, CARLSEN RA: Porphyria Cutanea Tarda in an 8-year-old boy. *Arch Dermatol* 99:451, 1969.

699. KANSKY A: Porphyria Cutanea Tarda in a 2-year-old girl. *Br J Dermatol* 90:213, 1974.

700. HARBER LC: Porphyria cutanea tarda, in Dennis J, Crounse R, Dobson R, McGuire J (eds): *Clinical Dermatology*. New York, Harper & Row, 1980, vol 2, p 2.

701. ICHIHASHI M, HASEI K, HORIKAWA T: A case of Porphyria Cutanea Tarda with experimental light urticaria. *Br J Dermatol* 113:745, 1985.

702. KRANZ KR, REED OM, GRIMWOOD RE: Necrotizing fasciitis associated with Porphyria Cutanea Tarda. *J Am Acad Dermatol* 14:361, 1986.

703. TSEGA E, DAMTEW B, LANDELLS JW, BESRAT A, SEYOUM E: Hyperpigmentation of the face and hands without blisters: Porphyria Cutanea Tarda. *Br J Dermatol* 103:187, 1980.

704. SOBER AJ, GROVE AS, MUHLBAUER JE: Cicatricial ectropion and lacrimal obstruction associated with the sclerodermoid variant of Porphyria Cutanea Tarda. *Am J Ophthalmol* 91:396, 1981.

705. MACKIE RM: Porphyria Cutanea Tarda and hyperkeratosis. *Br J Clin Pract* 26:487, 1972.

706. GROSSMAN ME, POH-FITZPATRICK MB: Porphyria Cutanea Tarda. *Med Clin North Am* 64:807, 1980.

707. BYRNE JPH, BOSS JM, DAWBER RPR: Contraceptive pill-induced Porphyria Cutanea Tarda presenting with onycholysis of the finger nails. *Postgrad Med J* 52:535, 1976.

708. CORMANE RH, SZABO E, HOO TT: Histopathology of the skin in acquired and hereditary Porphyria Cutanea Tarda. *Br J Derm* 85:531, 1971.

709. EPSTEIN JH, TUFFANELLI DL, EPSTEIN WL: Cutaneous changes in the porphyrias. *Arch Dermatol* 107:689, 1973.

710. GOGATE P, VALENZUELA R, DEODHAR SD, BERGFELD WF, YEIP M: Globular deposits of immunoglobulins and complement in the papillary dermis. *Am J Clin Pathol* 73:512, 1980.

711. CAPUTO R, BERTI E, GASPARINI G, MONTI M: The morphologic events of blister formation in Porphyria Cutanea Tarda. *Int J Dermatol* 22:467, 1983.

712. KLEIN GF, HINTNER H, SCHULER G, FRITSCH P: Junctional blisters in acquired bullous disorders of the dermal-epidermal junction zone: Role of the lamina lucida as the mechanical locus minoris resistentiae. *Br J Dermatol* 109:499, 1983.

713. PARRA CA, PIZZI DE PARRA N: Diameter of the collagen fibrils in the sclerodermatous skin of Porphyria Cutanea Tarda. *Br J Dermatol* 9:573, 1979.

714. BICKERS DR, KEOGH L, RIFKIND AB, HARBER LC, KAPPAS A: Studies in Porphyria. VI. Biosynthesis of porphyrins in mammalian skin and in the skin of porphyric patients. *J Invest Dermatol* 68:5, 1977.

715. LIM WH, POH-FITZPATRICK MB, GIGLI I: Activation of the complement system in patients with Porphyrias after irradiation in vivo. *J Clin Invest* 74:1961, 1984.

716. MEURER M, SCHULTE C, WEILER A, GOERZ G: Photodynamic action of uroporphyrin on the complement system in Porphyria Cutanea Tarda. *Arch Dermatol Res* 277:293, 1985.

717. TORINUKI W, MIURA T, TAGAMI H: Activation of complement of 405-nm light in serum from Porphyria Cutanea Tarda. *Arch Dermatol Res* 277:174, 1985.

718. PIGATTO PD, POLENGHI MM, ALTOMARE GF, GIACCHETTI A, CIRILLO R, FINZI AF: Complement cleavage products in the phototoxic reaction of Porphyria Cutanea Tarda. *Br J Dermatol* 114:567, 1986.

719. SANDBERG S, ROMSLO I: Porphyrin-induced photodamage at the cellular and the subcellular level as related to the solubility of the porphyrin. *Clin Chim Acta* 109:193, 1981.

720. STRANDBERG K, HAGERMARK O: Prostaglandin E_2 in blister fluid of bullous diseases and experimental suction blisters. *Acta Derm Venereol (Stockh)* 57:487, 1977.

721. SANDBERG S, ROMSLO I, HØVDING G, BJØRNDAL T: Porphyrin-induced photodamage as related to the subcellular localization of the porphyrins. *Acta Derm Venerol (Stockh) Suppl* 100:75, 1982.

722. BENOLDI D, MANFREDI G, PEZZAROSSA E, ALLEGRA F: Retinol binding protein in normal human skin and in cutaneous disorders. *Br J Dermatol* 105:659, 1981.

723. FELSHER BF, REDEKER AG: Acquired Porphyria Cutanea Tarda, primary refractory anemia, and hepatic siderosis. *Arch Intern Med* 118:163, 1966.

724. STRICKLAND GT JR: Porphyria Cutanea Tarda in association with hemosiderosis of the liver. *Am J Gastroenterol* 50:202, 1968.

725. LUNDVALL O, WEINFELD A, LUNDIN P: Iron storage in Porphyria Cutanea Tarda. *Acta Med Scand* 188:37, 1970.

726. CORTES JM, OLIVA H, PARADINAS FJ, HERNANDEZ-GUIO C: The pathology of the liver in Porphyria Cutanea Tarda. *Histopathology* 4:471, 1980.

727. LUNDVALL O, ENERBACK L: Hepatic fluorescence in Porphyria Cutanea Tarda studied in fine needle aspiration biopsy smears. *J Clin Pathol* 22:704, 1969.

728. JAMES KR, CORTES JM, PARADINAS FJ: Demonstration of intracytoplasmic needle-like inclusions in hepatocytes of patients with Porphyria Cutanea Tarda. *J Clin Pathol* 33:899, 1980.

729. WICKS ACB, THOMAS GE, CLAIN DJ, LOON N, SEGGIE J, BRAMSTON B: Cirrhosis of the liver in Rhodesian blacks. *S Afr Med J* 51:911, 1977.

730. BARAVALLE E, PRIETO J: Serum antibodies against porphyric hepatocytes in patients with Porphyria Cutanea Tarda and liver disease. *Gastroenterology* 84:1483, 1984.

731. KOSZO F, SIKLOSI CS, SIMON N: Liposome model experiment for the study of assumed membrane damage in Porphyria Cutanea Tarda. *Biochim Biophys Acta* 363:182, 1974.

732. KOSZO F, HORVATH LI, SIMON N, SIKLOSI C, KISS M: The role of possible membrane damage in Porphyria Cutanea Tarda: A spin label study of rat liver cell membranes. *Biochem Pharmacol* 31:11, 1982.
733. UTHEMANN H, KOTITSCHKE R, LISSNER R, GOERZ G: Serologische Hepatitis-B-marker bei Porphyria Cutanea Tarda. *Dtsch Med Wochenschr* 105:1718, 1980.
734. BEL A, GIRARD D: Porphyrie Cutanée Tardive avec antigène HBs de hépatite chronique agressive. *Nouv Presse Med* 9:2027, 1980.
735. PACKE GE, CLARKE CWF: Is Porphyria Cutanea Tarda a risk factor in the development of hepatocellular carcinoma? *Oncology* 42:44, 1985.
736. KORDAC V: Frequency of occurrence of hepatocellular carcinoma in patients with porphyria cutanea tarda in long-term followup. *Neoplasma* 19:135, 1972.
737. TIO TH, LEIJNSE B, JARRETT A, RIMINGTON C: Acquired porphyria from a liver tumor. *Clin Sci Mol Med* 16:517, 1959.
738. BRUNSTING LA: Observations on porphyria cutanea tarda. *Arch Dermatol* 70:551, 1954.
739. TSEGA E, BESRAT A, LANDELLS JW, SEYOUM E: Porphyria Cutanea Tarda in Ethiopia. *Trans R Soc Trop Med Hyg* 75:201, 1981.
740. HALTEN J, KROOK H: Follow-up studies on an unselected ten-year material of 360 patients with liver cirrhosis in one community. *Acta Med Scand* 173:479, 1963.
741. FELSHER BF, KUSHNER JP: Hepatic siderosis and Porphyria Cutanea Tarda: Relation of iron excess to the metabolic defect. *Semin Hematol* 14:243, 1977.
742. CHARLTON RU, JACOBS P, SEFTEL H: Effect of alcohol on iron absorption. *Br J Med* 2:1427, 1964.
743. SHANLEY BC, ZAIL SS, JOUBERT SM: Effect of ethanol on liver delta-aminolevulinate synthetase activity and urinary porphyrin excretion in symptomatic porphyria. *Br J Haematol* 17:389, 1969.
744. KONDO M, URATA G, SHIMIZU Y: Decreased liver δ-aminolaevulinate dehydratase activity in Porphyria Cutanea Tarda and in alcoholism. *Clin Sci* 65:423, 1983.
745. DOSS M, VON TIEPERMANN R, STUTZ G, TESCHKE R: Alcohol-induced decrease in uroporphyrinogen decarboxylase activity in rat liver and spleen. *Enzyme* 26:24, 1981.
746. VAIL JT: Porphyria Cutanea Tarda and estrogens. *JAMA* 201:101, 1967.
747. DOMONKOS AN: Porphyria Cutanea Tarda induced by estrogen therapy. *Arch Dermatol* 102:229, 1970.
748. ROENIGK HH JR, GOTTLOB ME: Estrogen-induced Porphyria Cutanea Tarda. *Arch Dermatol* 102:260, 1970.
749. MALINA L, CHLUMSKY J: Oestrogen-induced familial Porphyria Cutanea Tarda. *Br J Dermatol* 92:707, 1975.
750. WHITE MI: Porphyria Cutanea Tarda induced by oestrogen therapy. *Br J Urol* 49:468, 1977.
751. WEIMAR VM, WEIMAR GW, CEILLEY RI: Estrogen-induced Porphyria Cutanea Tarda complicating treatment of prostatic carcinoma. *J Urol* 120:643, 1978.
752. STEIN KM, RAQUE CJ, ZEIGERMAN JH, SHRAGER JD: Porphyria Cutanea Tarda induced by natural estrogens. *Obstet Gynecol* 38:755, 1971.
753. WILLERSON D, ISRAEL CW, HERNDON JH: Familial Porphyria Cutanea Tarda in a patient with retinitis pigmentosa. *Ann Ophthalmol* 11(3):409, 1979.
754. LAMON JM, FRYKHOLM BC: Pregnancy and Porphyria Cutanea Tarda. *Johns Hopkins Med J* 145:235, 1979.
755. BAXI LV, RUBEO TJ, KATZ B, HARBER LC: Porphyria Cutanea Tarda and pregnancy. *Am J Obstet Gynecol* 146:333, 1983.
756. MARKS R: Porphyria Cutanea Tarda. *Arch Dermatol* 118:452, 1982.
757. RAJKA G: Pregnancy and Porphyria Cutanea Tarda. *Acta Derm Venereol (Stockh)* 64:444, 1984.
758. SACED-UZ-ZAFAR M, GRONEWALD WR, BLUHM GB: Co-existent Klinefelter's syndrome, acquired cutaneous hepatic porphyria and systemic lupus erythematosus. *Henry Ford Hosp Med J* 18:227, 1970.
759. STERN R, FISHMAN J, BRUSMAN H, KUNKEL HG: Systemic lupus erythematosus associated with Klinefelter's syndrome. *Arthritis Rheum* 20:18, 1977.
760. LEVERE RD: Stilbestrol-induced porphyria: Increase in hepatic delta-aminolevulinic acid synthetase. *Blood* 28:569, 1966.
761. REIZENSTEIN P, HOGLUND S, LANDEGREN J, CARLMARK B, FORSBERG K: Iron metabolism in Porphyria Cutanea Tarda. *Acta Med Scand* 198:95, 1975.
762. TURNBULL A, BAKER H, VERNON-ROBERTS B, MAGNUS IA: Iron metabolism in Porphyria Cutanea Tarda and erythropoietic protoporphyria. *Q J Med* 166:341, 1973.
763. SAUNDERS SJ: Iron metabolism in symptomatic porphyria. *S Afr J Lab Clin Med* 9:277, 1963.
764. FRENCH TJ, WEIR H, DOWDLE E: Ferrokinetics in symptomatic porphyria. *S Afr J Lab Clin Med* 17:62, 1971.
765. LUNDVALL O: The effect of replenishment of iron stores after phlebotomy therapy in Porphyria Cutanea Tarda. *Acta Med Scand* 189:51, 1971.
766. FELSHER BF, JONES ML, REDEKER AG: Iron and hepatic uroporphyrin synthesis. *JAMA* 226:663, 1973.
767. KUSHNER JP, STEINMOLLER DP, LEE GR: The role of iron in the pathogenesis of porphyria cutanea tarda II. Inhibition of uroporphyrinogen decarboxylase. *J Clin Invest* 56:661, 1975.
768. KUSHNER JP, LEE GR, NACHT S: The role of iron in the pathogenesis of Porphyria Cutanea Tarda. *J Clin Invest* 51:3044, 1972.
769. MUKERJI SK, PIMSTONE NR, TAN KT: A potential biochemical explanation for the genesis of Porphyria Cutanea Tarda. *FEBS Lett* 189:217, 1985.
770. SMITH AG, FRANCIS JE: Synergism of iron and hexachlorobenzene inhibits hepatic uroporphyrinogen decarboxylase in inbred mice. *Biochem J* 214:909, 1983.
771. ALLEMAN MA, KOSTER JF, WILSON JHP, EDIXHOVEN-BOSDIJK A, SLEE RG, KROOS MJ, EIJK HGV: The involvement of iron and lipid peroxidation in the pathogenesis of HCB induced Porphyria. *Biochem Pharmacol* 34:161, 1984.
772. MUKERJI SK, PIMSTONE NR, BURNS M: Dual mechanism of inhibition of rat liver uroporphyrinogen decarboxylase activity by ferrous iron: Its potential role in the genesis of Porphyria Cutanea Tarda. *Gastroenterology* 87:1248, 1984.
773. CAM C, NIGOGOYSAN G: Acquired toxic porphyria cutanea tarda due to hexachlorobenzene. *JAMA* 183:88, 1963.
774. DOGRAMICI I: Porphyrias and porphyrin metabolism with special reference to porphyria in childhood. *Adv Pediatr* 13:11, 1964.
775. SCHMID R: Cutaneous porphyria in Turkey. *N Engl J Med* 263:397, 1960.
776. CRIPPS DJ, GOCMAN A, PETERS HA: Porphyria turcica. Twenty years after hexachlorobenzene intoxication. *Arch Dermatol* 116:46, 1980.
777. KANTAMIR I, CAM C, KAYAALP O: Investigation and observations on two diseases Kara Yara and Pembe Yara which are observed in the south-east part of Turkey. *Turk Bull Hyg Exp Biol* 20:79, 1960.
778. HOPE W, RUSSELL W, WEISS S: Porphyria Cutanea Tarda and sarcoma in a worker exposed to 2,3,7,8-tetrachlorodibenzodioxin—Missouri. *JAMA* 251:1534, 1984.
779. DOSS M, SAUER H, VON TIEPERMANN R, COLOMBI AM: Development of chronic hepatic Porphyria (Porphyria Cutanea Tarda) with inherited uroporphyrinogen decarboxylase deficiency under exposure to dioxin. *Int J Biochem* 16:369, 1984.
780. POLAND AP, SMITH D, METTER G, POSSICK P: A health survey of workers in a 2,4-D and 2,4,5-T plant. *Arch Environ Health* 22:316, 1971.
781. LYNCH RE, LEE GR, KUSHNER JP: Porphyria Cutanea Tarda associated with disinfectant misuse. *Arch Intern Med* 135:549, 1975.
782. CANTONI L, DAL FIUME D, FERRAROLI A, SALMONA M, RUGGIERI R: Different susceptibility of mouse tissue to porphyrogenic effect of 2,3,7,8-tetrachlorodibenzo-p-dioxin. *Toxicol Lett* 20:201, 1984.
783. GREIG JB, FRANCIS JE, KAY SJE, LOVELL DP, SMITH AG: Incomplete correlation of 2,3,7,8-tetrachlorodibenzo-p-dioxin hepatotoxicity with Ah phenotype in mice. *Toxicol Appl Pharmacol* 74:17, 1984.
784. ELDER GH, SHEPPARD DM: Immunoreactive uroporphyrinogen decarboxylase is unchanged in Porphyria caused by TCDD and hexachlorobenzene. *Biochem Biophys Res Commun* 109:113, 1982.
785. VAN GOERZ G, SICK N, VIZETHUM W, LISSNER R, KRIEG T: Einfluss von p-Aminobenzoesäure auf die Hexachlorbenzol-induzierte Porphyrie der Ratte. *Arzneimittelforschung* 30:817, 1980.
786. SMITH AG, FRANCIS JE, DINSDALE D, MANSON MM, CABRAL JRP: Hepatocarcinogenicity of hexachlorobenzene in rats and the sex difference in hepatic iron status and development of Porphyria. *Carcinogenesis* 6:631, 1985.
787. WAINSTOK DE CALMANOVICI R, DEL C RIOS DE MOLINA M, TAIRA DE YAMASATO MC, TOMIO JM, SAN MARTIN DE VIALE LC: Mechanism of hexachlorobenzene-induced Porphyria in rats. *Biochem J* 218:753, 1983.
788. DE VERNEUIL H, SASSA S, KAPPAS A: Effects of polychlorinated biphenyl compounds, 2,3,7,8-tetrachlorodibenzo-p-dioxin, phenobarbital and iron on hepatic uroporphyrinogen decarboxylase. *Biochem J* 214:145, 1983.
789. DEBETS FMH, REINDERS JH, DEBETS AJM, LOSSBROEK TG, STRIK JJTWA, KOSS G: Biotransformation and porphyrinogenic action of hexachlorobenzene and its metabolites in a primary liver cell culture. *Toxicology* 19:185, 1981.
790. KECZKES K, FARR M: Bullous dermatosis of chronic renal failure. *J Dermatol* 95:541, 1976.
791. GRIFFON-EUVRARD S, THIVOLET J, LAURENT G, CALEMARD E, GAILLEMIN J, PERROT H, ORTONNE JP: Recherche de la pseudo-porphyrie cutanee tardive chez 100 hemodialyses. *Dermatologica* 155:193, 1977.
792. BRIVET F, DRUEKE T, GUILLEMETTE J, ZINGRAFF J, CROSNIER J: Porphyria Cutanea Tarda-like syndrome in hemodialyzed patients. *Nephron* 20:258, 1978.

793. WILKIN JK, KAPLAN RJ, ACCHIARDO SR: Porphyria Cutanea Tarda in a chronic hemodialysis patient. *South Med J* 73:1066, 1980.

794. DAY RS, EALES L: Porphyrins in chronic renal failure. *Nephron* 26:90, 1980.

795. PARRILA JG, ORTEGA R, PENA ML, RODICIO JL, DE SALAMANCA RE, OLMOS A, ELDER GH: Porphyria Cutanea Tarda during maintenance haemodialysis. *Br Med J* 2:1358, 1980.

796. POH-FITZPATRICK MB, MASULLO AS, GROSSMAN ME: Porphyria Cutanea Tarda associated with chronic renal disease and hemodialysis. *Arch Dermatol* 116:191, 1980.

797. LICHTENSTEIN JR, BABB EJ, FELSHER BF: Porphyria Cutanea Tarda (PCT) in a patient with chronic renal failure on haemodialysis. *Br J Dermatol* 104:575, 1981.

798. TOPI GC, D'ALLESSANDRO GL, CANCARINI GC, DE COSTANZA F, GRISO D, RAVELLI M: Porphyria Cutanea Tarda in a haemodialysed patient. *Br J Dermatol* 104:579, 1981.

799. HANNO R, CALLEN JP: Porphyria Cutanea Tarda as a cause of bullous dermatosis of hemodialysis. *Cutis* 28:261, 1981.

800. HARLAN SL, WINKELMANN RK: Porphyria cutanea tarda and chronic renal failure. *Mayo Clin Proc* 58:467, 1983.

801. GOLDSMAN CI, TAYLOR JS: Porphyria Cutanea Tarda and bullous dermatoses associated with chronic renal failure: A review. *Cleve Clin Q* 50:151, 1983.

802. KING J, DAY RS, MILNE FJ, BEZWODA WR, VILJOEN JD, KRAMER S: Delayed onset of overt Porphyria Cutanea Tarda in a patient on long-term haemodialysis. *S Afr Med J* 63:743, 1983.

803. SEUBERT S, SEUBERT A, RUMPF KW, KIFFE H: A Porphyria Cutanea Tarda-like distribution pattern of porphyrins in plasma, hemodialysate, hemofiltrate, and urine of patients on chronic hemodialysis. *J Invest Dermatol* 85:107, 1985.

804. CRAM DL, EPSTEIN JH, TUFFANELLI DL: Lupus Erythematosus and Porphyria. *Arch Dermatol* 108:779, 1973.

805. HOXTELL E, MANICK KP, FISHER I: Coexistence of discoid lupus erythematosus and Porphyria Cutanea Tarda. *Cutis* 17:83, 1976.

806. CALLEN JF, ROSS L: Subacute cutaneous Lupus Erythematosus and Porphyria Cutanea Tarda. *Am Acad Dermatol* 5:269, 1981.

807. CLEMMENSEN O, THOMSEN K: Porphyria Cutanea Tarda and systemic lupus erythematosus. *Arch Dermatol* 118:160, 1982.

808. WEATHERHEAD L, ADAM J: Discoid Lupus Erythematosus. Coexistence with Porphyria Cutanea Tarda. *Int J Dermatol* 24:453, 1985.

809. ROSEMARIN JI, NIGRO EJ, LEVERE RD, MASCARENHAS BR: Systemic lupus erythematosus and acute intermittent porphyria: Coincidence or association? *Arthritis Rheum* 25:1134, 1982.

810. HARRIS MY, MILLS GC, LEVIN WC: Coexistent systemic lupus erythematosus and porphyria. *Arch Intern Med* 117:425, 1966.

811. RAMASAMY R, KUBIK MM: Porphyria Cutanea Tarda in association with Sjogren's syndrome. *Practitioner* 226:1297, 1982.

812. NYMAN CR: Porphyria Cutanea Tarda, carcinoma of the lung, rheumatoid arthritis, right hydronephrosis. *Proc R Soc Med* 65:688, 1972.

813. FRANKS AG, PULINI M, BICKERS DR, RAYFIELD EJ, HARBER LC: Carbohydrate metabolism in Porphyria Cutanea Tarda. *Am J Med Sci* 277:163, 1979.

814. COBURN PR, COLEMAN JC, CREAM JJ, HAWK JLM, LAMB SGS, MURRAY-LYON IM: Porphyria Cutanea Tarda and Porphyria Variegata unmasked by viral hepatitis. *Clin Exp Dermatol* 10:169, 1985.

815. CHESNEY TMCC, WARDLAW LL, KAPLAN RJ, CHOW JF: Porphyria Cutanea Tarda complicating Wilson's disease. *Am Acad Dermatol* 4:64, 1981.

816. DUTCHER JP, FISHER M, SPIVACK M, WIERNIK PH: Porphyria Cutanea Tarda in a patient with acute leukemia. *Am J Hematol* 23:69, 1986.

817. LAI CL, WU PC, LIN HJ, WONG KL: Case report of symptomatic Porphyria Cutanea Tarda associated with histocytic lymphoma. *Cancer* 53:573, 1984.

818. FIVENSON DP, KING AJ: Porphyria Cutanea Tarda in a patient with agnogenic myeloid metaplasia. *Arch Dermatol* 120:538, 1984.

819. MAUGHAN WZ, MULLER SA, PERRY HO: Porphyria Cutanea Tarda associated with lymphoma. *Acta Derm Venereol (Stockh)* 59:55, 1979.

820. GROSSMAN ME, BICKERS DR: Porphyria Cutanea Tarda. A rare cutaneous manifestation of hepatic tumors. *Cutis* 21:782, 1978.

821. RAYHANZADEH S, SHOSS RG, NOYES J: Porphyria Cutanea Tarda associated with lymphosarcoma. *Arch Dermatol* 111:129, 1975.

822. BURNETT JW, LAMON JM, LEVIN J: Haemophilia, hepatitis and porphyria. *Br J Dermatol* 97:453, 1977.

823. CHAPMAN RWG: Porphyria Cutanea Tarda and beta-thalassaemia minor with iron overload in mother and daughter. *Br Med J* 280(6226):1255, 1980.

824. WISSEL PS, SORDILLO P, ANDERSON K, SASSA S, SAVILLO RL, KAPPAS A: Porphyria cutanea tarda associated with the acquired immune deficiency syndrome. *Am J Hematol* 25:107, 1987.

825. LANIER C, AVENEL M, ROUSSELET MC, TUCHAIS E, VENRET JL, BOYER J: Granulomatous hepatitis induced by mycobacterium avium in one patient with Acquired Immune Deficiency revealed by porphyria cutanea tarda. *Gastroenterol Clin Biol* 11:264, 1987.

826. ZIPRKOWSKI L, SZEINBERG A, CRISPIN M, KRAKOWSKI A, ZAIDMAN J: The effect of griseofulvin in Hereditary Porphyria Cutanea Tarda. *Arch Dermatol* 93:21, 1966.

827. SPIRO JM, DEMIS DJ: The effects of griseofulvin on Porphyria Cutanea Tarda. *J Invest Dermatol* 50:202, 1968.

828. BLEAKLEY P, NICHOL AW, COLLINS AG: Diazinon and Porphyria Cutanea Tarda. *Med J Aust* 1:314, 1979.

829. MILLAR JW: Rifampicin-induced Porphyria Cutanea Tarda. *Br J Dis Chest* 74:405, 1980.

830. KEANE JT, PEARSON RW, MALKINSON FD: Nalidixic acid-induced photosensitivity in mice: A model for pseudoporphyria. *J Invest Dermatol* 82:210, 1984.

831. Pseudoporphyria from naproxen therapy. *Physicians Drug Alert* 8:73, 1986.

832. CHU TC, CHU EJ: Porphyrin patterns in different types of porphyria. *Clin Chem* 13:371, 1967.

833. NACHT S, SAN MARTIN DE VIALE LC, GRINSTEIN M: Human Porphyria Cutanea Tarda. Isolation and properties of the urinary porphyrins. *Clin Chim Acta* 27:445, 1970.

834. MAGNIN PH, WIDER DE XIFRA EA, LENCZNER M, STELLA AM, DEL C, BATTLE AM: Studies on the excretion pattern of porphyrins and its use as a tool for diagnosing both symptomatic and asymptomatic cases of Porphyria Cutanea Tarda. *J Biochem* 12:873, 1980.

835. SMITH SG, RAO KR, JACKSON AH: The porphyrins of normal human urine, with a comparison of the excretion pattern in Porphyria Cutanea Tarda. *J Biochem* 12:1081, 1980.

836. DOWDLE E, GOLDSWAIN P, SPONG N, EALES L: The pattern of porphyrin isomer accumulation and excretion in symptomatic porphyria. *Clin Sci* 39:147, 1970.

837. JOHANSSON IM, NIKLASSON FA: Determination of porphyrins in urine by direct injection on a liquid chromatographic column coated with tributylphosphate. *J Chromatogr* 275:51, 1983.

838. GRINSTEIN M, FERRAMOLA DE, SANCOVICH AM, SANCOVICH HA: The isolation of a new compound from urine of humans with Porphyria Cutanea Tarda. *Biochim Biophys Acta* 500:433, 1977.

839. GRINSTEIN M, FERRAMOLA DE, SANCOVICH AM, SANCOVICH HA: The isolation of another new compound from the urine of humans with Porphyria Cutanea Tarda. *Biochim Biophys Acta* 543:583, 1978.

840. MOORE MR, THOMPSON GG, ALLEN BR, HUNTER JAA, PARKER S: Plasma porphyrin concentrations in Porphyria Cutanea Tarda. *Clin Sci Mol Med* 45:711, 1973.

841. KALB RE, GROSSMAN ME, POH-FITZPATRICK MB: Correlation of serum and urinary porphyrin levels in Porphyria Cutanea Tarda. *Arch Dermatol* 121:1289, 1985.

842. DAY RS, PIMSTONE MR, EALES L: The diagnostic value of blood plasma porphyrin methyl ester profiles produced by quantitative TLC. *Int J Biochem* 9:897, 1978.

843. ELDER GH: The metabolism of porphyrins of the isocoporphyrin series. *Enzyme* 17:61, 1974.

844. SMITH SG: Porphyrins found in urine of patients with symptomatic porphyria. *Biochem Soc Trans* 5:1472, 1977.

845. LOCKWOOD WH, POULOS V, ROSSI E, CURNOW DH: Rapid procedure for fecal porphyrin assay. *Clin Chem* 31:1163, 1985.

846. ELDER GH, MAGNUS IA, HANDA F, DOYLE M: Faecal "X porphyrin" in the hepatic porphyrias. *Enzyme* 17:29, 1973.

847. DOSS VM, LOOK D, HENNING H, LANDERS CJ, DOLLE W, STROHMEYER G: Chronische hepatische Porphyrien. *J Clin Chem Clin Biochem* 9:471, 1971.

848. ELDER GH: Porphyrin metabolism in Porphyria Cutanea Tarda. *Semin Hematol* 14:227, 1977.

849. MALINA L, MILLER VI, MAGNUS IA: Skin porphyrin assay in Porphyria. *Clin Chim Acta* 83:55, 1978.

850. DE SALAMANCA RE, LADERO JM, CATALAN T, MAS V, RICO R, OLMOS A: Hepatic metabolism of bromosulphthalein in Porphyria Cutanea Tarda. *J Biochem* 12:855, 1980.

851. PICCARDO MG, ROSA M, RUSSO L: Mellituria screening in some metabolic diseases. *Enzyme* 29:138, 1983.

852. ELDER GH: Differentiation of Porphyria Cutanea Tarda symptomatica from other types of Porphyria by measurement of isocoproporphyrin in faeces. *J Clin Pathol* 28:601, 1975.

853. ALLEMAN MA, WILSON JHP, VAN DEN BERG JWO, EDIXHOVEN-BOSDIJK A, VAN GASTEL-QUIST LMH: Familial Porphyria Cutanea Tarda: The pattern of porphyrins formed from porphobilinogen by hemolysates. *Clin Chem* 28:1144, 1982.

854. TOPI GC, AMANTEA A, GRISO D: Recovery from Porphyria Cutanea Tarda with no specific therapy other than avoidance of hepatic toxins. *Br J Dermatol* 111:75, 1984.

855. ADDY JH: Pathogenesis and natural history of Porphyria Cutanea Tarda. *Lancet* 2:213, 1974.

856. RAMSAY CA, MAGNUS IA, TURNBULL A, BAKER H: The treatment of Porphyria Cutanea Tarda by venesection. *Q J Med* 169:1, 1974.

857. IPPEN H: Allgemeine Symptome der späten Hautporphyrie (Porphyria cutanea tarda) als Hinweise für deren Behandlung. *Dtsch Med Wochenschr* 86:127, 1961.

858. EPSTEIN JH, REDEKER AG: Porphyria Cutanea Tarda. A study of the effect of phlebotomy. *N Engl J Med* 279:1301, 1968.

859. Phlebotomy for Porphyria Cutanea Tarda (Editorial). *JAMA* 207:1142, 1969.

860. BAKER H, TURNBULL A: Porphyria Cutanea Tarda treated by repeated venesection: Clinical and biochemical response. *Proc R Soc Med* 62:590, 1969.

861. COPELAN HL: Porphyria Cutanea Tarda remission by venesection. *West J Med* 111:357, 1969.

862. KALIVAS JT, PATHAK MA, FITZPATRICK TB: Phlebotomy and iron-overload in Porphyria Cutanea Tarda. *Lancet* 1:1184, 1969.

863. LUNDVALL O: The effect of phlebotomy therapy in Porphyria Cutanea Tarda. *Acta Med Scand* 189:33, 1971.

864. ERIKSEN L, THUNE PO: Urinary excretion of porphyrins in two cases of Porphyria Cutanea Tarda during a period of various treatments. *Scand J Clin Lab Invest* 38:273, 1978.

865. DE SALAMANCA RE, RICO R, PENA ML, ROMERO F, OLMOS A, JIMENEZ J: Patterns of porphyrin excretion in Porphyria Cutanea Tarda under venesection treatment. *J Biochem* 12:861, 1980.

866. SWEENEY GD: Porphyria Cutanea Tarda, or the uroporphyrinogen decarboxylase deficiency diseases. *Clin Biochem* 19:3, 1986.

867. LUNDVALL O, WEINFELD A: Studies of the clinical and metabolic effects of phlebotomy treatment in Porphyria Cutanea Tarda. *Acta Med Scand* 184:191, 1968.

868. LUNDVALL O: Phlebotomy treatment of Porphyria Cutanea Tarda. *Acta Derm Venereol (Stockh) Suppl* 100:107, 1982.

869. MEISTER F, REICHEN J: Quantitative Leberfunctionstests bei Porphyria Cutanea Tarda: Verbesserung unter Therapie mit Phlebotomie. *Schweiz Med Wochenschr* 116:341, 1986.

870. DI PADOVA C, MARCHESI L, CAINELLI T, GORI G, PODENZANI SA, ROVAGNATI P, RIZZARDINI M, CANTONI L: Effects of phlebotomy on urinary porphyrin pattern and liver histology in patients with Porphyria Cutanea Tarda. *Am J Med* 285:2, 1983.

871. FRIEDMAN SJ, DOYLE JA: Sclerodermoid changes of Porphyria Cutanea Tarda: Possible relationship to urinary uroporphyrin levels. *J Am Acad Dermatol* 13:70, 1985.

872. ROCCHI E, GIBERTINI P, CASSANELLI M, PIETRANGELO A, BORGHI A, VENTURA E: Serum ferritin in the assessment of liver iron overload and iron removal therapy in Porphyria Cutanea Tarda. *J Lab Clin Med* 107:36, 1986.

873. ADJAROV D, IVANOV E: Clinical value of serum γ-glutamyl transferase estimation in Porphyria Cutanea Tarda. *Br J Dermatol* 102:541, 1980.

874. FINNERTY EF: Management of Porphyria Cutanea Tarda. *Cutis* 20:133, 1977.

875. WISE RD, MALKINSON FD: Ferrous iron and Porphyria Cutanea Tarda. *Acta Dermatol* 113:850, 1977.

876. PERCIVAL SPB: Ophthalmological safety of chloroquine. *Br J Ophthalmol* 53:101, 1969.

877. FELSHER BF, REDEKER AG: Effect of chloroquine on hepatic uroporphyrin metabolism in patients with Porphyria Cutanea Tarda. *Medicine* 45:575, 1966.

878. BLOOM M: Porphyria Cutanea Tarda treated with chloroquine phosphate. *Arch Dermatol* 100:375, 1969.

879. VOGLER WR, GALAMBOS JT, OLANSKY S: Biochemical effects of chloroquine therapy in Porphyria Cutanea Tarda. *Am J Med* 49:316, 1970.

880. KOWERTZ MJ: The therapeutic effect of chloroquine. *JAMA* 223:515, 1973.

881. TALJAARD JJF, SHANLEY BC, JOUBERT SM, DEPPE WM: Incorporation of [4-^{14}C]δ-aminolaevulinate into urinary porphyrins in Porphyria Cutanea Tarda: Effect of chloroquine therapy. *Clin Sci* 44:571, 1973.

882. KORDAC V, SEMRADOVA M: Treatment of Porphyria Cutanea Tarda with chloroquine. *Br J Dermatol* 90:95, 1974.

883. KOWERTZ MJ: Retreatment with chloroquine in Porphyria Cutanea Tarda. *JAMA* 233:22, 1975.

884. KORDAC V, PAPEZOVA R, SEMRADOVA M: Chloroquine in the treatment of Porphyria Cutanea Tarda. *N Engl J Med* 296:949, 1977.

885. GOULD P: Photosensitivity after treatment of Porphyria Cutanea Tarda with low dose chloroquine. *Br J Dermatol* 98:225, 1978.

886. MALKINSON FD, LEVITT L: Hydroxychloroquine treatment of Porphyria Cutanea Tarda. *Arch Dermatol* 116:1147, 1980.

887. TSEGA E, BESRAT A, DAMTEW B, SEYOUM E, LANDELLS JW: Chloroquine in the treatment of Porphyria Cutanea Tarda. 75:401, 1981.

888. ASHTON RE, HAWK JL, MAGNUS IA: Low-dose oral chloroquine in the treatment of Porphyria Cutanea Tarda. *Br J Dermatol* 111:609, 1984.

889. CHLUMSKA A, CHLUMSKY J, MALINA L: Liver changes in Porphyria Cutanea Tarda patients treated with chloroquine. *Br J Dermatol* 102:261, 1980.

890. KORANDA FC: Antimalarials. *Am Acad Dermatol* 4:650, 1981.

891. MALINA L, CHLUMSKY J: A comparative study of the results of phlebotomy therapy and low-dose chloroquine treatment in Porphyria Cutanea Tarda. *Acta Derm Venereol (Stockh)* 61:346, 1981.

892. CAINELLI T, DI PADOVA C, MARCHESI L, GORI G, ROVAGNATI P, PODENZANI SA, BESSONE E, CANTONI L: Hydroxychloroquine versus phlebotomy in the treatment of Porphyria Cutanea Tarda. *Br J Dermatol* 108:593, 1983.

893. SWANBECK G, WENNERSTEN G: Treatment of Porphyria Cutanea Tarda with chloroquine and phlebotomy. *Br J Dermatol* 97:77, 1977.

894. WENNERSTEN G, ROS AM: Chloroquine in treatment of Porphyria Cutanea Tarda. *Acta Derm Venerol (Stockh) Suppl* 100:119, 1982.

895. SCHOLNICK PL, EPSTEIN J, MARVER HS: The molecular basis of the action of chloroquine in Porphyria Cutanea Tarda. *J Invest Dermatol* 61:226, 1973.

896. WIEGAND SE, MONCKTON COPEMAN PW, PERRY HO: Metabolic alkalinization in Porphyria Cutanea Tarda. *Arch Dermatol* 100:544, 1969.

897. BURROWS D: Porphyria Cutanea Tarda treated with sodium bicarbonate. *Irish Dermatolog Soc Proc*, 6:200,1970.

898. PERRY HO, MULLANAX MG, WIEGAND SE: Metabolic alkalinization therapy in Porphyria Cutanea Tarda. *Arch Dermatol* 102:359, 1970.

899. MIYAUCHI S, SHIRAISHI S, MIKI Y: Small volume plasmapheresis in the management of Porphyria Cutanea Tarda. *Arch Dermatol* 119:752, 1983.

900. DISLER P, DAY R, BURMAN N, BLEKKENHORST G, EALES L: Treatment of hemodialysis-related Porphyria Cutanea Tarda with plasma exchange. *Am J Med* 72:989, 1982.

901. GAJDOS A: A.M.P. in Porphyria Cutanea Tarda. *Lancet* 1:163, 1974.

902. ROCCHI E, GIBERTINI P, CASSANELLI M, PIETRANGELO A, BORGHI A, PANTALEONI M, JENSEN J, VENTURA E: Iron removal therapy in Porphyria Cutanea Tarda: Phlebotomy versus slow subcutaneous desferrioxamine infusion. *Br J Dermatol* 114:621, 1986.

903. PRAGA M, DE SALAMANCA RE, ANDRES A, NICHO J, OLIET A, PERPIN J, MORALES JM: Treatment of hemodialysis-related porphyria cutanea tarda with deferroxamine. *N Engl J Med* 316:547, 1987.

904. AYRES S, MIHAN R: Porphyria Cutanea Tarda: Response to vitamin E. *Cutis* 22:50, 1978.

905. GÜNTHER WW: The porphyrias and erythropoietic protoporphyria: An unusual case. *Australas J Dermatol* 9:23, 1967.

906. TOBACK AC, SASSA S, POH-FITZPATRICK MB, SCHACTER J, ZAIDER E, HARBER LC, KAPPAS A: Hepatoerythropoietic porphyria: Clinical, biochemical and enzymatic studies in a three-generation family lineage. *N Engl J Med* 316:645, 1987.

907. DE VERNEUIL H, BEAUMONT C, DEYBACK JC, NORDMANN Y, SFAR Z, KASTALLY R: Enzymatic and immunological studies of uroporphyrinogen decarboxylase in familial Porphyria Cutanea Tarda and Hepatoerythropoietic Porphyria. *Am J Hum Genet* 36:613, 1984.

908. LAZARO P, DE SALAMANCA RE, ELDER GH, VILLASECA ML, CHINARRO S, JAQUETI G: Is Hepatoerythropoietic Porphyria a homozygous form of Porphyria Cutanea Tarda? Inheritance of uroporphyrinogen decarboxylase deficiency in a Spanish family. *Br J Dermatol* 110:613, 1984.

909. CZARNECKI DB: Hepatoerythropoietic Porphyria. *Arch Dermatol* 116:307, 1980.

910. LIM HW, POH-FITZPATRICK MB: Hepatoerythropoietic Porphyria: A variant of childhood-onset Porphyria Cutanea Tarda. *J Am Acad Dermatol* 11:1103, 1984.

911. PINOL-AGUADE J, HERRERO C, ALMEIDA J, CASTELLS A, FERRANDO J, DEASPRER J, PALON A, GIMENEZ A: Porphyrie hepatoerythrocytaire. Une nouvelle forme de porphyrie. *Ann Dermatol Syphiligr* 102:129, 1975.

912. HOFSTAD F, SEIP M, ERIKSEN L: Congenital erythropoietic porphyria with a hitherto undescribed porphyrin pattern. *Acta Paediatr Scand* 62:380, 1973.

913. SIMON N, BERKO GY, SCHNEIDER I: Hepatoerythropoietic porphyria presenting as scleroderma and acrosclerosis in a sibling pair. *Br J Dermatol* 96:663, 1977.

914. PINOL-AGUADE J, CASTELLS A, INACOCHEA A, RODES J: A case of biochemically unclassifiable hepatic porphyria. *Br J Dermatol* 81:270, 1969.

915. DE VERNEUIL H, GRANDCHAMP B, ROMEO PH, RAICH N, BEAUMONT C, GOOSSENS M, NICOLAS H, NORDMANN Y: Molecular analysis of uropor-

phyrinogen decarboxylase deficiency in a family with two cases of Hepatoerythropoietic Porphyria. *J Clin Invest* 77:431, 1986.

916. DE VERNEUIL H, GRANDCHAMP B, BEAUMONT C, PICAT C, NORDMANN Y: Uroporphyrinogen decarboxylase structural mutant (Gly281→Glu) in a case of porphyria. *Science* 234:732, 1986.

917. DE VERNEUIL H, BEAUMONT C, GRANDCHAMP B, PHUNG LN, NORDMANN Y: Molecular heterogeneity of uroporphyrinogen decarboxylase deficiency in hepatoerythropoietic porphyria, in Nordmann Y (ed): *Porphyrins and Porphyrias*. Paris, Colloque INSERM/John Libbey Eurotext, 1986, vol 134, p 201.

918. HAEGER-ARONSEN B, STATHERS G, SWAHN G: Hereditary coproporphyria. Study of a Swedish family. *Ann Intern Med* 69:221, 1968.

919. BRODIE MJ, THOMPSON GG, MOORE MR, BEATTIE AD, GOLDBERG A: Hereditary coproporphyria. Demonstration of the abnormalities in haem biosynthesis in peripheral blood. *Q J Med* 46:299, 1977.

920. WITH TK: Hereditary coproporphyria and variegate porphyria in Denmark. *Dan Med Bull* 30:106, 1983.

921. GRANDCHAMP B, PHUNG N, NORDMANN Y: Homozygous case of hereditary coproporphyria. *Lancet* 2(2):1348, December 24, 31, 1977.

922. BERGER H, GOLDBERG A: Hereditary coproporphyria. *Br Med J* 2:85, 1955.

923. GRANICK S, MAUZERALL D: Enzymes of porphyrin synthesis in red blood cells. *Ann NY Acad Sci* 75:115, 1958.

924. SANO S, GRANICK S: Mitochondrial coproporphyrinogen oxidase and protoporphyrin formation. *J Biol Chem* 236:1173, 1961.

925. BATTLE DEL C AM, BENSON A, RIMINGTON C: Purification and properties of coproporphyrinogenase. *Biochem J* 97:731, 1965.

926. POULSON R, POLGLASE WJ: Aerobic and anaerobic coproporphyrinogenase activities in extracts from *Saccharomyces cerevisiae*. Purification and characterization. *J Biol Chem* 249:6367, 1974.

927. ELDER GH, EVANS JO: Evidence that the coproporphyrinogen oxidase activity of rat liver is situated in the intermembrane space of mitochondria. *Biochem J* 172:345, 1978.

928. GREENAWALT JW: The isolation of outer and inner mitochondrial membranes. *Methods Enzymol* 31:310, 1974.

929. GRANDCHAMP B, PHUNG N, NORDMANN Y: The mitochondrial localization of coproporphyrinogen III oxidase. *Biochem J* 176:97, 1978.

930. YOSHINAGA T, SANO S: Corporphyrinogen oxidase. 1. Purification, properties and activation by phospholipids. *J Biol Chem* 255:4722, 1980.

931. ZAMAN Z, ABBOUD MM, AKHTAR M: Mechanism and stereochemistry of vinyl group formation in heme biosynthesis. *J Chem Soc Chem Commun* 1263, 1972.

932. BATTERSBY AR, BALDAS J, COLLINS J, GRAYSON DH, JAMES KJ, MCDONALD E: Mechanism of biosynthesis of the vinyl groups of protoporphyrin IX. *J Chem Soc Chem Commun* 1265, 1972.

933. JACKSON AH, JONES DM, PHILIP G, LASH TD, BATTLE DEL C AM, SMITH SG: Synthetic and biosynthetic studies of porphyrins. IV. Further studies of the conversion of coproporphyrinogen III to protoporphyrin IX: Mass spectrometric investigation of the incubation of specifically deuteriated coproporphyrinogen III with chicken red cell haemolysates. *Int J Biochem* 12:681, 1980.

934. CAMADRO JM, CHAMBON H, JOLLES J, LABBE P: Purification and properties of coproporphyrinogen oxidase from the yeast Saccaromyces cervisiae. *Eur J Biochem* 256:579, 1986.

935. ELDER GH, EVANS JO: A radiochemical method for the measurement of coproporphyrinogen oxidase and utilization of substrates other than coproporphyrinogen III by the enzyme from rat liver. *Biochem J* 169:205, 1978.

936. GRANDCHAMP B, NORDMANN Y: Coproporphyrinogen oxidase assay. *Enzyme* 28:196, 1982.

937. LABBE P, CAMADRO JM, CHAMBON H: Fluorometric assays for coproporphyrinogen oxidase and protoporphyrinogen oxidase. *Anal Biochem* 149:248, 1985.

938. LI F, LIM CK, PETERS TJ: A high performance liquid chromatographic method for the assay of coproporphyrinogen oxidase activity in rat liver. *Biochem J* 239:481, 1986.

939. PFLÜGER KH, DOSS M: Hereditäre Koproporphyrie. Klinische Fehldiagnosen bei akuter hepatischer Porphyrie über ein Dezennium. *Dtsch Med Wochenschr* 107:777, 1982.

940. DEAN G, KRAMER S, LAMB P: Coproporphyria. *S Afr Med J* 43:138, 1969.

941. JAEGER A, TEMPE JD, CREISLER F, NORDMANN Y, MANTZ JM: La coproporphyrie hereditaire. *Nouv Presse Med* 4:2783, 1985.

942. CONNON JJ, TURKINGTON V: Hereditary coproporphyria. *Lancet* I:263, 1968.

943. ROBERTS DT, BRODIE MJ, MOORE MR, THOMPSON GG, GOLDBERG A, MACSWEEN RNM: Hereditary coprophyria presenting with photosensitivity induced by the contraceptive pill. *Br J Dermatol* 96:549, 1977.

944. HAWK LM, MAGNUS A, ELDER GH, PARKES A, DOYLE M: Deficiency of hepatic coproporphyrinogen oxidase in hereditary coproporphyria. *J R Soc Med* 71:775, 1978.

945. ANDREWS J, ERDJUMENT H, NICHOLSON DC: Hereditary coproporphyria: Incidence in a large English family. *J Med Genet* 21:341, 1984.

946. PAXTON JW, MOORE MR, BEATTIE AD, GOLDBERG A: Urinary excretion of 17-oxosteroids in hereditary coproporphyria. *Clin Sci Mol Med* 49:441, 1975.

947. HUNTER JAA, KHAN SA, HOPE E, BEATTIE AD, BEVERDGE CW, SMITH AWM, GOLDBERG A: Hereditary coproporphyria. Photosensitivity, jaundice and neuropsychiatric manifestations associated with pregnancy. *Br J Dermatol* 84:301, 1971.

948. LOMHOLT JC, WITH TK: Hereditary coproporphyria. A family with unusually few and mild symptoms. *Acta Med Scand* 186:83, 1969.

949. GOLDBERG A, RIMINGTON C, LOCHHEAD AC: Hereditary coproporphyria. *Lancet* 1:632, March 25, 1967.

950. HOUSTON AB, BRODIE MJ, MOORE MR, THOMPSON GG, STEPHENSON JBP: Hereditary coproporphyria and epilepsy. *Arch Dis Child* 52:646, 1977.

951. SCULLY RE, MARK EJ, MCNEELY BU: Case records of the Massachusetts General Hospital. Case 39-1984. *N Engl J Med* 311:839, 1984.

952. DI TRAPANI G, CASALI C, TONALI P, TOPI GC: Peripheral nerve findings in hereditary coproporphyria. Light and ultrastructural studies in two sural nerve biopsies. *Acta Neuropathol (Berl)* 63:96, 1984.

953. NORDMANN Y, GRANDCHAMP B, PHUNG N, DE VERNEUIL H, GRELIER M, NOIRE J, GAJDOS A, LAMOTTE-BARILLON S, GUERIN JM, BARRIER J, WEIL J, DELECHE H: Coproporphyrie hereditaire. Le 1[er] cas homozygote demontre. *Nouv Presse Med* 7:847, 1978.

954. GRANDCHAMP B, DEYBACH JC, GRELIER M, DE VERNEUIL H, NORDMANN Y: Studies of porphyrin synthesis in fibroblasts of patients with congenital erythropoietic porphyria and one patient with homozygous coproporphyria. *Biochim Biophys Acta* 629:577, 1980.

955. NORDMANN Y, GRANDCHAMP B, DE VERNEUIL H, PHUNG L, CARTIGNY B, FONTAINE G: Harderoporphyria: A variant hereditary coproporphyria. *J Clin Invest* 72:1139, 1983.

956. DOSS M, VON TIEPERMANN R, KOPP W: Harderoporphyrin coproporphyria. *Lancet*:292, 1984.

957. CARLSON RE, DOLPHIN D, BERNSTEIN M: Copper coproporphyrin: Excretion in familial coproporphyria. *Clin Chem* 24:2009, 1978.

958. EALES L, DAY RS, BLEKKENHORST GH: The clinical and biochemical features of variegate porphyria: An analysis of 300 cases studied at Groote Schuur Hospital, Cape Town. *Int J Biochem* 12:837, 1980.

959. DEAN G: *The Porphyrias*. London, Pitman Medical, 1971, pp 1–170.

960. MUSTAJOKI P: Variegate porphyria. Twelve years' experience in Finland. *Q J Med* 194:191, 1980.

961. POULSON R, POLGLASE WJ: The enzymic conversion of protoporphyrinogen IX to protoporphyrin IX. Protoporphyrinogen oxidase activity in mitochondrial extracts of *Saccharomyces Cerevisiae*. *J Biol Chem* 250:1269, 1975.

962. POLGLASE WJ, WHITLOW KJ, POULSON R: Regulation of porphyrin biosynthesis in *E. coli*. *Fed Proc* 34:694, 1975.

963. JACOBS NJ, JACOBS JM: Fumarate as alternate electron acceptor for the late steps of anaerobic heme synthesis in *Escherichia coli*. *Biochem Biophys Res Commun* 65:435, 1975.

964. POULSON R: The enzymic conversion of protoporphyrinogen IX to protoporphyrin IX in mammalian mitochondria. *J Biol Chem* 251:3730, 1976.

965. JACOBS NJ, JACOBS JM: Nitrate, fumarate, and oxygen as electron acceptors for a late step in microbial heme synthesis. *Biochim Biophys Acta* 449:1, 1976.

966. BRENNER DA, BLOOMER JR: A fluorometric assay for measurement of protoporphyrinogen oxidase activity in mammalian tissue. *Clin Chim Acta* 100:259, 1980.

967. JACOBS NJ, JACOBS JM: Assay for enzymatic protoporphyrinogen oxidation, a late step in heme synthesis. *Enzyme* 28:206, 1982.

968. POH-FITZPATRICK MB: The importance of correct diagnosis in variegate porphyria. *J Am Acad Dermatol* 8:115, 1983.

969. STEWART PM, HENSLEY WJ: An acute attack of variegate porphyria complicated by severe autonomic neuropathy. *Aust NZ J Med* 11:82, 1981.

970. LYBERATOS C, ARAPAKIS G, ARONIS E, GARDIKAS C: Variegate porphyria with unusual neurologic manifestations. *Am J Med Sci* 272:211, 1976.

971. MUSTAJOKI P, HEINONEN J: General anesthesia in "inducible" porphyrias. *Anesthesiology* 53:15, 1980.

972. MUSTAJOKI P, VUORISTO M, REUNALA T: Celiac disease or dermatitis herpetiformis in three patients with porphyria. *Dig Dis Sci* 26:618, 1981.

973. HUGES GS, DAVIS L: Variegate porphyria and heavy metal poisoning from ingestion of "moonshine." *South Med J* 76:1027, 1983.

974. BAXTER DL, PERMOXICZ SE: Variegate porphyria (mixed porphyria). *Arch Dermatol* 96:98, 1967.

975. FOLWER CJ, WARD JM: Porphyria variegata provoked by contraceptive pill. *Br Med J* 1:663, 1975.
976. MCKENZIE AW, ACHARYA U: The oral contraceptive and variegate porphyria. *Br J Dermatol* 86:453, 1972.
977. BRODIE MJ, MOORE MR, THOMPSON GG, GOLDBERG A, LOW RAL: Pregnancy and the acute prophyrias. *Br J Obstet Gynaecol* 84:726, 1977.
978. HANDA F, KUMAR K, KUMAR R: A case of variegate porphyria in an Indian. *Br J Dermatol* 92:347, 1975.
979. QUIROZ-KENDALL E, WILSON FA, KING LE: Acute variegate porphyria following a Scarsdale Gourmet Diet. *J Am Acad Dermatol* 8:46, 1983.
980. PERLOTH MG, TSCHUDY DP, RATNER A, SPAUR W, RADEKER A: The effect of diet in variegate porphyria. *Metabolism* 17:571, 1968.
981. DE MATTEIS F: Drug interactions in experimental hepatic porphyria: A model for the exacerbation by drugs of human variegate porphyria. *Proc Biochem Soc* 127:21P, 1972.
982. DE MATTEIS F: Drug interactions in experimental hepatic porphyria. A model for the exacerbation by drugs of human variegate porphyria. *Enzyme* 16:266, 1973.
983. BLEKKENHORST GH, HARRISON GG, COOK ES, EALES L: Screening of certain anaesthetic agents for their ability to elicit acute porphyric phases in susceptible patients. *Br J Anaesthesiol* 52:759, 1980.
984. HARRISON GG, MOORE MR, MEISSNER PN: Porphyrinogenicity of etomidate and ketamine as continuous infusions. Screening in the DDC-primed rat model. *Br J Anaesthesiol* 57:420, 1985.
985. MCGRATH H, TAAFFE JA, GILSENAN D, CUNNANE K: An Irish family with variegate porphyria. *Clin Exp Dermatol* 9:583, 1984.
986. MASCARO M, BRUGUERA M, HERRERO C, LECHA M, MUNIESA AM: Microscopic abnormalities in the liver of two patients with porphyria variegata. *J Cutan Pathol* 12:395, 1985.
987. BLOOMER JR: Enzyme defects in the porphyrias and their relevance to the biochemical abnormalities in these disorders. *J Invest Dermatol* 77:102, 1981.
988. DAY RS, BLEKKENHORST GH, EALES L: Hepatic porphyrins in variegate porphyria. *N Engl J Med* 303:1368, 1980.
989. DAY RS, EALES L: Porphyrins in renal transplantation. *Nephron* 30:22, 1982.
990. PIMSTONE NR, BLEKKENHORST G, EALES L: Enzymatic defects in hepatic porphyria. Preliminary observations in patients with porphyria cutanea tarda and variegate porphyria. *Enzyme* 16:354, 1973.
991. SIEPKER L, KRAMER S: Protoporphyrin accumulation by mitogen stimulated lymphocytes and protoporphyrinogen oxidase activity in patients with porphyria variegata and erythropoietic porphyria: Evidence for a deficiency of protoporphyrinogen oxidase and ferrochelatase in both diseases. *Br J Haematol* 60:65, 1985.
992. MEISSNER PN, DAY RS, MOORE MR, DISLER PB, HARLEY E: Protoporphyrinogen oxidase and porphobilinogen deaminase in variegate porphyria. *Eur J Clin Invest* 16:257, 1986.
993. MCCOLL KEL, THOMPSON GG, MOORE MR, GOLDBERG A, CHURCH SE, QADIRI MR, YOUNGS GR: Chester porphyria: Biochemical studies of a new form of acute porphyria. *Lancet* 2:796, 1985.
994. QADIRI MR, CHURCH SE, MCCOLL KEL, MOORE MR, YOUNGS GR: Chester porphyria: A clinical study of a new form of acute porphyria. *Br Med J* 292:455, 1986.
995. DAY RS, EALES L, MEISSNER D: Coexistent variegate porphyria and porphyria cutanea tarda. *N Engl J Med* 307:36, 1982.
996. MARTASEK P, KORDAC V, JIRSA M: Variegate porphyria and porphyria cutanea tarda. *Arch Dermatol* 119:537, 1983.
997. KORDA V, DEYBACK JC, MARTASEK P, ZEMAN J, DA SILVA V, NORDMANN Y, HOUSTKOVA H, RUBIN A, HOLUB J: Homozygous variegate porphyria. *Lancet* 1:851, 1984.
998. MURPHY GM, HAWK JLM, MAGNUS IA, BARRETT DF, ELDER GH, SMITH SG: Homozygous variegate porphyria: Two similar cases in unrelated families. *J R Soc Med* 79:361, 1986.
999. MUSTAJOKI P: Variegate porphyria. *Ann Intern Med* 89:238, 1978.
1000. RIMINGTON C: Patterns of porphyrin excretion and their interpretation. *S Afr J Lab Clin Med* 9:255, 1963.
1001. RIMINGTON C, LOCKWOOD WH, BELCHER RV: The excretion of porphyrin-peptide conjugates in porphyria variegata. *Clin Sci* 35:211, 1968.
1002. LONGAS MO, POH-FITZPATRICK MB: A tightly bound protein-prophyrin complex isolated from the plasma of a patient with variegate porphyria. *Clin Chim Acta* 118:219, 1982.
1003. POH-FITZPATRICK MB: A plasma porphyrin fluorescence marker for variegate porphyria. *Arch Dermatol* 116:543, 1980.
1004. COREY TJ, DELEO VA, CHRISTIANSON H, POH-FITZPATRICK MB: Variegate porphyria. Clinical and laboratory features. *J Am Acad Dermatol* 2:36, 1980.
1005. SMITH SG, BELCHER RV, MAHLER R, YUSKIN J: Bile and faecal porphyrins in the quiescent phase of variegate porphyria. *Proc Biochem Soc* 110:15P, 1968.
1006. SMITH SG, BELCHER RV, MAHLER R, YUDKIN J: Preliminary studies on bile porphyrins in the quiescent phase of variegate porphyria. *Clin Chim Acta* 23:241, 1969.
1007. LIM CK, RIDEOUT JM, PETERS TJ: Pseudoporphyria associated with consumption of brewers' yeast. *Br Med J* 288:1640, 1984.
1008. EALES L: The effects of canthaxanthin on the photocutaneous manifestations of porphyria. *S Afr Med J* 54:1050, 1978.
1009. HORAK J, MARTASEK P, KORDAC V, MERTL L, JIRSA M, TLUSTAKOVA M, HOUSTKOVA H: Resin hemoperfusion in hepatic porphyrias. *Artif Organs* 9:169, 1985.
1010. DELEO VA, POH-FITZPATRICK M, MATHEWS-ROTH MM, HARBER LC: Erythropoietic Protoporphyria. 10 years experience. *Am J Med* 60:8, 1976.
1010a. DEYBACH JC, DA SILVA V, PASQUIER Y, NORDMANN Y: Ferrochelatase in human erythropoietic protoporphyria: The first case of a homozygous form of the enzyme deficiency, in Nordmann Y (ed): *Porphyrins and Porphyrias*. Paris, Colloque INSERM/John Libbey Eurotext, 1986, vol 134, p 163.
1011. JONES MS, JONES OTG: The structural organization of heme synthesis in rat liver mitochondria. *Biochem J* 113:507, 1969.
1012. JOHNSON A, JONES TOG: Enzymic formation of hemes and other metalloporphyrins. *Biochim Biophys Acta* 93:171, 1964.
1013. PORRA RJ, JONES OTG: Studies on ferrochelatase. 2. An investigation of the role of ferrochelatase in the biosynthesis of various haem prosthetic groups. *Biochemistry J* 87:186, 1963.
1014. PORRA RJ, JONES OTG: Studies on ferrochelatase. 1. Assay and properties of ferrochelatase from a pig liver mitochondrial extract. *Biochemistry* 87:181, 1963.
1015. MAILER K, POULSON R, DOLPHIN D, HAMILTON AD: Ferrochelatase: Isolation and purification via affinity chromatography. *Biochem Biophys Res Commun* 96:777, 1980.
1016. TAKETANI S, TOKUNAGA R: Rat liver ferrochelatase. Purification, properties and stimulation by fatty acids. *J Biol Chem* 256:12738, 1981.
1017. TAKETANI S, TOKUNAGA R: Purification and substrate specificity of bovine liver ferrochelatase. *Eur J Biochem* 127:443, 1982.
1018. DAILY HA, FLEMING JE: Bovine ferrochelatase. Kinetic analysis of inhibition by N-methyl protoporphyrin, manganese, and heme. *J Biol Chem* 258:11453, 1983.
1019. CAMADRO JM, IBRAHAM NG, LEVERE RD: Kinetic studies of human liver ferrochelatase. Role of endogenous metals. *J Biol Chem* 259:5678, 1984.
1020. ORTIZ DE MONTELLANO PR, BEILAN HS, KUNZI KL: N-Methylprotoporphyrin IX: Chemical synthesis and identification as the green pigment produced by 3,5-diethoxycarbonyl-1,4-dihydrocollidine treatment. *Proc Natl Acad Sci USA* 78:1490, 1981.
1021. DE MATTEIS F, GIBBS AH, HARVEY C: Studies on the inhibition of ferrochelatase by N-alkylated dicarboxylic porphyrins: Steric factors involved and the evidence that inhibition is reversible. *Biochem J* 226:537, 1985.
1022. BLOOMER JR, BRENNER DA, MAHONEY MJ: Study of factors causing excess protoporphyrin accumulation in cultured skin fibroblasts from patients with Protoporphyria. *J Clin Invest* 60:1354, 1977.
1023. RUTH GR, SCHWARTZ S, STEPHENSON B: Bovine Protoporphyria: The first nonhuman model of this hereditary photosensitizing disease. *Science* 198:199, 1977.
1024. SASSA S, ZALAR MB, POH-FITZPATRICK MB, ANDERSON KE, KAPPAS A: Studies in Porphyria. Functional evidence for a partial deficiency of ferrochelatase activity in mitogen-stimulated lymphocytes from patients with Erythropoietic Protoporphyria. *J Clin Invest* 69:809, 1982.
1025. SASSA S, SCHWARTZ S, RUTH G: Accumulation of protoporphyrin IX from δ-aminolevulinic acids in bovine skin fibroblasts with Hereditary Erythropoietic Protoporphyria. A gene-dosage effect. *J Exp Med* 153:1094, 1981.
1026. BLOOMER JR, MORTON KO: A radiochemical assay for heme synthase activity. *Enzyme* 28:220, 1982.
1027. RIFKIND AB: Maintenance of microsomal hemoprotein concentrations following inhibition of ferrochelatase activity by 3,5-diethoxycarbonyl-1,4-dihydrocollidine in chick embryo liver. *J Biol Chem* 254:4636, 1979.
1028. PORRA RJ: A rapid spectrophotometric assay for ferrochelatase (E.C.4.99.1.1) in preparations containing high concentrations of haemoglobin, in Doss M (ed): *Porphyrins in Human Diseases*. Basel, Karger, 1976, p 123.
1029. TEPHLY TR: Inhibition of liver hemoprotein synthesis, in De Mattheis F, Aldridge WM (eds): *Heme and Hemoproteins—Handbook of Experimental Pharmacology*. Berlin, Springer-Verlag, 1978, vol 44, p 81.
1030. ONISAWA J, LABBE RF: Effects of diethyl-1,4-dihydro-2,4,6-trimethylpyridine 3,5-dicarboxylate on the metabolism of porphyrins and iron. *J Biol Chem* 238:724, 1963.

1031. TEPHLY TR, HASEGAWA E, BARON J: Effect of drugs on heme synthesis in the liver. *Metabolism* 20:200, 1971.

1032. DE MATTEIS F, ABBRITTI G, GIBBS AH: Decreased liver activity of porphyrin-metal chelatase in hepatic porphyria caused by 3,5-diethoxycarbonyl-1,4-dihydrocollidine. Studies in rats and mice. *Biochem J* 134:717, 1973.

1033. MOONEY B, TENNANT F: Operating theatre lights as hazard in photosensitive patients. *Br Med J* 287:1028, 1983.

1034. RYAN EA: Histochemistry of the skin in Erythropoietic Protoporphyria. *Br J Dermatol* 78:43, 1966.

1035. EPSTEIN JH, TUFFANELLI DL, EPSTEIN WL: Cutaneous changes in the porphyrias. A microscopic study. *Arch Dermatol* 107:689, 1973.

1036. RYAN EA: Histochemistry of the skin in erythropoietic protoporphyria. *Br J Dermatol* 78:501, 1971.

1037. POH-FITZPATRICK MB: The Erythropoietic Porphyrias. *Dermatol Clin* 4:291, 1986.

1038. MAGNUS IA, JARRETT A, PRANKERT TAJ, RIMINGTON C: Erythropoietic protoporphyria: A new porphyria syndrome with solar urticaria due to protoporphyrinaemia. *Lancet* 2:448, 1961.

1039. POH-FITZPATRICK MB: Erythropoietic porphyrias: Current mechanistic, diagnostic and therapeutic considerations. *Semin Hematol* 14:211, 1977.

1040. SPIKES JD: Porphyrins and related compounds as photodynamic sensitizers. *Ann NY Acad Sci* 244:496, 1975.

1041. GOLDSTEIN BD, HARBER LC: Erythropoietic Protoporphyria: Lipid peroxidation and red cell membrane damage associated with photohemolysis. *J Clin Invest* 51:892, 1972.

1042. SANDBERG S, ROMSLO I: Protoporphyrin-induced photodamage at the cellular and the subcellular level as related to the solubility of the porphyrin. *Clin Chim Acta* 109:193, 1981.

1043. BODANESS RS, CHAN DC: Singlet oxygen as a mediator in the hematoporphyrin-catalyzed photooxidation of NADPH to NADP in deuterium oxide. *J Biol Chem* 252:8554, 1977.

1044. SCHOTHORST AA, VAN STEVENINCK J, WENT LN, SUURMOND D: Photodynamic damage of the erythrocyte membrane caused by protoporphyrin in Protoporphyria and in normal red blood cells. *Clin Chim Acta* 39:161, 1972.

1045. DE GOEIJ AFPM, VAN STEVENINCK J: Photodynamic effects of protoporphyrin on cholesterol and unsaturated fatty acids in erythrocyte membranes in Protoporphyria and in normal red blood cells. *Clin Chim Acta* 68:115, 1976.

1046. DUBBELMAN TMAR, DEBRUIJNE AW, VAN STEVENICK J: Photodynamic effects of protoporphyrin on red blood cell deformability. *Biochem Biophys Res Commun* 77:811, 1977.

1047. CLARK KGA, NICHOLSON DC: Erythrocyte protoporphyrin and iron uptake in Erythropoietic Protoporphyria. *Clin Sci* 41:363, 1971.

1048. BRUN A, HØVDING G, ROMSLO I: Protoporphyrin-induced photohemolysis: Differences related to the subcellular distribution of protoporphyrin in erythropoietic Protoporphyria and when added to normal red cells. *Int J Biochem* 13:225, 1981.

1049. JOEJE H, WOUTERSEN RA, DE LA FAILLE HB: Inhibitory effect of plasma on photohaemolysis in Erythropoietic Protoporphyria. *Dermatologica* 163:285, 1981.

1050. SANDBERG S, BRUN A: Light-induced protoporphyrin release from erythrocytes in Erythropoietic Protoporphyria. *J Clin Invest* 70:693, 1982.

1051. DE PAOLIS A, CHANDRA S, CHARALAMBIDES AA, BONNETT R, MAGNUS IA: The effect on photohaemolysis of variation in the structure of the porphyrin photosensitizer. *Biochem J* 226:757, 1985.

1052. BRUN A, SANDBERG S: Photodynamic release of protoporphyrin from intact erythrocytes in Erythropoietic Protoporphyria: The effect of small repetitive light doses. *Photochem Photobiol* 41:535, 1985.

1053. SANDBERG S, TALSTAD I, HØVDING G, BEJELLAND N: Light-induced release of protoporphyrin, but not of zinc protoporphyrin, from erythrocytes in a patient with greatly elevated Erythropoietic Protoporphyria. *Blood* 62:846, 1983.

1054. SANDBERG S, BRUN A, HØVDING G, BJORDAL M, ROMSLO I: Effect of zinc on Protoporphyrin induced photohaemolysis. *Scand J Clin Lab Invest* 40:185, 1980.

1055. LIM HW, POH-FITZPATRICK MB, GIGLI I: Activation of the complement system in patients with porphyrias after irradiation in vivo. *J Clin Invest* 74:1961, 1984.

1056. GIGLI I, SCHOTHORST AA, SOTER NA, PATHAK MA: Erythropoietic Protoporphyria. Photoactivation of the complement system. *J Clin Invest* 66:517, 1980.

1057. LIM WH, PEREZ HD, POH-FITZPATRICK M, GOLDSTEIN IM, GIGLI I: Generation of chemotactic activity in serum from patients with Erythropoietic Protoporphyria and Porphyria Cutanea Tarda. *N Engl J Med* 304:212, 1981.

1058. LIM WH, GIGLI I: Role of complement in porphyrin-induced photosensitivity. *J Invest Dermatol* 76:4, 1981.

1059. BONKOVSKY HL, SCHNED AR: Fatal liver failure in Protoporphyria. Synergism between ethanol excess and the genetic defect. *Gastroenterology* 90:191, 1986.

1060. GORDEUK VR, BRITTENHAM GM, HAWKINS CW, MUKHTAR H, BICKERS DR: Iron therapy for hepatic dysfunction in Erythropoietic Protoporphyria. *Ann Intern Med* 105:27, 1986.

1061. POH-FITZPATRICK MB, WHITLOCK RT, LEFTKOWITCH JH: Changes in protoporphyrin distribution dynamics during liver failure and recovery in a patient with Protoporphyria and Epstein-Barr Viral Hepatitis. *Am J Med* 80:943, 1986.

1062. MacDONALD DM, GERMAIN D, PERROT H: The histopathology and ultrastructure of liver disease in Erythropoietic Protoporphyria. *Br J Dermatol* 104:7, 1981.

1063. EALES L: Liver involvement in Erythropoietic Protoporphyria (EP). *Int J Biochem* 12:915, 1980.

1064. CONLEY CL, CHISHOLM JJ: Recovery from hepatic decompensation in Protoporphyria. *Johns Hopkins Med J* 145:237, 1979.

1065. PIMSTONE NR, WEBBER BL, BLEKKENHORST GH, EALES L: The hepatic lesion in Protoporphyria (PP): Preliminary studies of haem metabolism, liver structure and ultrastructure. *Ann Clin Res* 8:122, 1976.

1066. BRUGUERA L, ESQUERDA JE, MASCARO JM, PINOL J: Erythropoietic Protoporphyria. A light, electron, and polarization microscopical study of the liver in three patients. *Arch Pathol Lab Med* 100:587, 1976.

1067. EALES L, DAY RS, PIMSTONE NR: Protoporphyrin (proto)-determined hepatopathy of a South African Jewish family. *Ann Clin Res* 10:205, 1978.

1068. CRIPPS DJ, GOLDFARB SS: Erythropoietic Protoporphyria: Hepatic cirrhosis. *Br J Dermatol* 98:349, 1978.

1069. ROMSLO I, HØVDING G, HAMRE E, LAERUM OD: Porphyrin production and liver involvement in a patient with Erythropoietic Protoporphyria. *Scand J Clin Lab Invest* 38:529, 1978.

1070. BLOOMER JR: Pathogenesis and therapy of liver disease in Protoporphyria. *Yale J Biol Med* 52:39, 1979.

1071. KLATSKIN G, BLOOMER JR: Birefringence of hepatic pigment deposits in Erythropoietic Protoporphyria. *Gastroenterology* 67:294, 1974.

1072. WOLFF K, WOLFF-SCHREINER E, GSCHNAIT F: Liver inclusions in Erythropoietic Protoporphyria. *Eur J Clin Invest* 5:21, 1975.

1073. BLOOMER JR, ENRICHEZ R: Evidence that hepatic crystalline deposits in a patient with Protoporphyria are composed of protoporphyrin. *Gastroenterology* 82:569, 1982.

1074. DONALDSON EM, MCCALL AJ, MAGNUS IA, SIMPSON JR, CALDWELL RA, HARGREAVES T: Erythropoietic Protoporphyria: Two deaths from hepatic cirrhosis. *Br J Dermatol* 84:14, 1971.

1075. THOMPSON RPH, MOLLAND EA, NICHOLSON DC, GRAY CH: "Erythropoietic" Protoporphyria and cirrhosis in sisters. *Gut* 14:934, 1973.

1076. BLOOMER JR, PHILLIPS MJ, DAVIDSON DL, KLATSKIN G: Hepatic disease in Erythropoietic Protoporphyria. *Am J Med* 58:869, 1975.

1077. CRIPPS DJ, GILBERT LA, GOLDFARB SS: Erythropoietic Protoporphyria: Juvenile protoporphyrin hepatopathy cirrhosis and death. *J Pediatr* 91:744, 1977.

1078. SINGER JA, PLAUT AG, KAPLAN MM: Hepatic failure and death from Erythropoietic Protoporphyria. *Gastroenterology* 74:588, 1978.

1079. WELLS MM, GOLITZ LE, BENDER BJ: Erythropoietic Protoporphyria with hepatic cirrhosis. *Arch Dermatol* 116:429, 1980.

1080. ROMSLO I, GADEHOLT HG, HØVDING G: Erythropoietic Protoporphyria terminating in liver failure. *Arch Dermatol* 118:668, 1982.

1081. MATILLA A, MOLLAND EA: A light and electron microscopic study of the liver in case of Erythropoietic Protoporphyria and in griseofulvin-induced porphyria in mice. *J Clin Pathol* 27:698, 1974.

1082. GESCHNAIT F, KONRAD K, HONIGSMANN H, DENK H, WOLFF F: Mouse model for Protoporphyria. I. The liver and hepatic protoporphyrin crystals. *J Invest Dermatol* 65:290, 1975.

1083. POH-FITZPATRICK MB, SKLAR JA, GOLDSMAN C, LEFKOWITCH JA: Protoporphyrin hepatopathy. Effects of cholic acid ingestion in murine griseofulvin-induced Protoporphyria. *J Clin Invest* 72:1449, 1983.

1084. LAMON JM, POH-FITZPATRICK MB, LAMOLA AA, FRYKHOLM BC, FREEMAN ML, DOLEIDEN FH: Hepatic Protoporphyria production in human Protoporphyria. *Gastroenterology* 79:115, 1980.

1085. POH-FITZPATRICK MB: Protoporphyrin metabolic balance in human Protoporphyria. *Gastroenterology* 88:1239, 1985.

1086. SANDBERG S: Protoporphyrin-induced photodamage to mitochondria and lysosomes from rat liver. *Clin Chim Acta* 111:55, 1981.

1087. SANDBERG S, ROMSLO I, HØVDING G, BJØRNDAL T: Porphyrin-induced photodamage as related to the subcellular localization of the porphyrins. *Acta Derm Venereol (Stockh) Suppl* 100:75, 1982.

1088. PORTER S: Congenital erythropoietic protoporphyria II. *Blood* 22:532, 1963.

1089. SCHOLNICK P, MARVER HS, SCHMID R: 1350rythropoietic Protoporphyria: Evidence for multiple sites of excess protoporphyrin formation. *J Clin Invest* 50:203, 1971.

1090. NICHOLSON DC, COWGER ML, KALIVAS J, THOMPSON RPH, GRAY CH: Isotopic studies of the erythropoietic and hepatic components of congenital Porphyria and "Erythropoietic" Protoporphyria. *Clin Sci* 44:135, 1973.

1091. CRIPPS DJ, MacEACHERN WN: Hepatic and Erythropoietic Protoporphyria. *Arch Pathol* 91:497, 1971.

1092. MULLER-EBERHARD U, LIEM HH, MATHEWS-ROTH MM, EPSTEIN JH: Plasma levels of hemopexin and albumin in disorders of porphyrin metabolism. *Proc Soc Exp Med Biol* 146:694, 1974.

1093. BRODIE MJ, MOORE MR, THOMPSON GG, GOLDBERG A, HOLTI G: Haem biosynthesis in peripheral blood in erythropoietic protoporphyria. *Clin Exp Dermatol* 2:381, 1978.

1094. POH-FITZPATRICK MB, PALMER RH: Elevated plasma triglyceride levels are associated with human Protoporphyria. *J Lab Clin Med* 104:257, 1984.

1095. MATHEWS-ROTH MM, PATHAK MA, FITZPATRICK TB, HARBER LC, KASS EH: β-Carotene as an oral photoprotective agent in Erythropoietic Protoporphyria. *JAMA* 228:1004, 1974.

1096. MATHEWS-ROTH MM, PATHAK MA, FITZPATRICK TB, HARBER LH, KASS EH: Beta carotene therapy for Erythropoietic Protoporphyria and other photosensitivity diseases. *Arch Dermatol* 113:1229, 1977.

1097. THOMSEN K, SCHMIDT H, FISHER A: Beta-carotene in Erythropoietic Protoporphyria: 5 years' experience. *Dermatologica* 159:82, 1979.

1098. HAEGER-ARONSEN B, KROOK G, ABDULLA M: Oral carotenoids for photohypersensitivity in patients with Erythropoietic Protoporphyria, polymorphous light eruptions and lupus erythematodes discoides. *Int J Dermatol* 18:73, 1979.

1099. KROOK G, HAEGER-ARONSEN B: β-Carotene in the treatment of Erythropoietic Protoporphyria. *Acta Derm Venereol (Stockh) Suppl* 100:125, 1982.

1100. MATHEWS-ROTH MM: Systemic photoprotection. *Dermatol Clin* 4:335, 1986.

1101. POH-FITZPATRICK MB, BARBERA LG: Absence of crystalline retinopathy after long-term therapy with β-carotene. *J Am Acad Dermatol* 11:111, 1984.

1102. BECHTEL MA, BERTOLONE SJ, HODGE SJ: Transfusion therapy in a patient with Erythropoietic Protoporphyria. *Arch Dermatol* 117:99, 1981.

1103. DOBOZY A, CSATO M, SIKLOSI C, SIMON N: Transfusion therapy for Erythropoietic Protoporphyria. *Br J Dermatol* 109:571, 1983.

1104. KNIFFEN JC: Protoporphyrin removal in intrahepatic porphyrastasis. *Gastroenterology* 58:1027, 1970.

1105. BRUN A, SANDBERG S, HÓVDING G, BJORDAL M, ROMSLO I: Zinc as an oral photoprotective agent in Erythropoietic Protoporphyria? *Int J Biochem* 12:931, 1980.

1106. SUURMOND D: Some aspects of erythropoietic porphyria in the Netherlands. *Dermatologica* 138:303, 1969.

1107. LEFKOWITCH JH, FENG-CHEN KC, SKLAR JA, POH-FITZPATRICK MB: Cholic acid amelioration of light and electron microscopic hepatic lesions in experimental Protoporphyria. *Hepatology* 3:399, 1983.

1108. KAISER IH: Brown amniotic fluid in congenital erythyropoietic porphyria. *Obstet Gynecol* 56:383, 1980.

1109. DEYBACH JC, GRANDCHAMP B, GRELIER M, NORDMANN Y, BOUE J, BOUE A, DE BERRANGER P: Prenatal exclusion of congenital erythropoietic porphyria (Gunther's disease). *Hum Genet* 53:217, 1980.

CHAPTER 53

HEREDITARY JAUNDICE AND DISORDERS OF BILIRUBIN METABOLISM

JAYANTA ROY CHOWDHURY
ALLAN W. WOLKOFF
IRWIN M. ARIAS

1. *Bilirubin is an orange pigment derived from the degradation of heme proteins, particularly the hemoglobin of mature circulating erythrocytes.*

2. *Bilirubin is a waste product that is normally excreted into bile by the liver. Bilirubin is usually rendered harmless by binding to serum albumin. However, toxicity occurs in patients, particularly neonates, with profound unconjugated hyperbilirubinemia, who are at risk for bilirubin encephalopathy (kernicterus). Accumulation of bilirubin in plasma and tissues results in jaundice, which has attracted the attention of patients and clinicians since antiquity.*

3. *Following formation in the reticuloendothelial system, bilirubin is released into the circulation where it avidly binds to serum albumin and is rapidly cleared by the liver. Extraction of bilirubin from the circulation under physiological conditions appears to be a specific hepatic function and has carrier-mediated kinetics. Within the liver cell, bilirubin binds to cytosolic proteins, the most abundant of which is ligandin. The water-insoluble bilirubin molecule is transformed into water-soluble bilirubin mono- and diglucuronides, which are excreted into the bile canaliculus.*

4. *Heritable disorders of bilirubin metabolism result in hyperbilirubinemia. Their study provides much of our understanding of normal hepatic bilirubin transport and metabolism. These disorders include those resulting in predominantly unconjugated hyperbilirubinemia (Gilbert syndrome; Crigler-Najjar syndrome, types I and II) and those resulting in predominantly conjugated hyperbilirubinemia (Dubin-Johnson syndrome, Rotor syndrome, benign recurrent intrahepatic cholestasis). Deficient activity of bilirubin UDP-glucuronyltransferase has been described in each of the three unconjugated hyperbilirubinemias (absence in Crigler-Najjar syndrome, type I; partial deficiency in Crigler-Najjar syndrome, type II, and Gilbert syndrome). An additional uptake defect for bilirubin has been observed in some patients with Gilbert syndrome. The pathogenesis of the conjugated hyperbilirubinemias is less well understood. The Dubin-Johnson syndrome is associated with a characteristic abnormality of porphyrin metabolism in which over 80 percent of urinary coproporphyrin is coproporphyrin I, compared with less than 35 percent in normal individuals. Although phenotypically similar to Dubin-Johnson syndrome, Rotor syndrome differs with respect to urinary coproporphyrin excretion and hepatic metabolism of bromosulfphthalein (BSP).*

5. *Family studies reveal that Crigler-Najjar syndrome, type I, has an autosomal recessive pattern of inheritance. Inheritance patterns of Crigler-Najjar syndrome, type II, and Gilbert syndrome are unclear, although there is evidence for an autosomal recessive pattern in some families with Crigler-Najjar syndrome, type II, and evidence for dominant inheritance in some families with Gilbert syndrome. These two syndromes may differ only by degree. Studies of urinary coproporphyrin excretion reveal autosomal recessive patterns of inheritance for Dubin-Johnson and Rotor syndromes.*

6. *Several animal models of heritable disorders of bilirubin metabolism are important in understanding the pathophysiology of their human counterparts. These models include the Gunn rat (Crigler-Najjar syndrome, type I), Bolivian squirrel monkeys (Gilbert syndrome), mutant Southdown sheep (Gilbert syndrome), and mutant albino rats with organic anion excretion defect and mutant Corriedale sheep (Dubin-Johnson syndrome).*

Bilirubin is an orange pigment derived from the degradation of heme proteins, particularly the hemoglobin of mature circulating erythrocytes. Bilirubin is a potentially toxic waste product that is generally harmless because of binding to serum albumin. However, patients with profound unconjugated hyperbilirubinemia are at risk for bilirubin encephalopathy (kernicterus). Studies of bilirubin chemistry, synthesis, transport, metabolism, distribution, and excretion have attracted the attention of generations of chemists, biologists, and clinical investigators. Because bilirubin is an organic anion of limited aqueous solubility, it has proved to be a model for the study of the transport, metabolism, and excretion of other biologically important organic anions.

Defects in bilirubin formation or disposal are usually manifested by hyperbilirubinemia and jaundice. A number of inherited disorders affecting these pathways have been described in both humans and animals. Study of these disorders has provided important information regarding normal and abnormal metabolic pathways. Specific forms of treatment have been discovered for a few of the inherited disorders; others remain a therapeutic challenge and continue to stimulate research.

BILIRUBIN

Formation of Bilirubin

Bilirubin is exclusively derived from heme. In humans, 250 to 400 mg of bilirubin is formed daily by breakdown of hemoglobin, other hemoproteins, and free heme. Approximately 80 percent is derived from the hemoglobin of senescent erythrocytes.[1] After injection of radiolabeled porphyrin precursors,

Nonstandard abbreviations used in this chapter are: BSP = bromosulphthalein; DBSP = dibromosulphthalein; GSH = reduced glutathione; HPLC = high performance liquid chromatography.

glycine, or δ-aminolevulinic acid in humans or rats, radioactivity is incorporated into bile pigments in two peaks[2-5] (Fig. 53-1). The first peak (*early-labeled peak of bilirubin,* or ELB) appears within 3 days and contains an initial component and a slow later phase. The initial component constitutes two-thirds of the ELB in humans and is largely derived from hepatic hemoproteins such as cytochromes, catalase, peroxidase, and tryptophan pyrrolase.[4,6] The labeled bilirubin that appears in bile within 15 min after administration of the precursor may be derived from a rapidly turning over pool of free heme in the cytosol of hepatocytes.[7] Approximately 20 percent of this free heme pool is degraded without incorporation into heme proteins.[8] Myoglobin has a relatively long half-life and is an unlikely source. Induction of hepatic cytochrome P_{450} enhances the ELB. The slower phase of the ELB is derived from erythroid and nonerythroid sources and is enhanced in conditions associated with "ineffective erythropoiesis" such as congenital dyserythropoietic anemias, megaloblastic anemias, iron-deficiency anemia, and lead poisoning.[6] The ELB is also increased in erythropoietic porphyria[5] but not in porphyria cutanea tarda[10] or acute intermittent porphyria.[11] The erythroid phase is increased in accelerated erythropoiesis, probably due to intramedullary destruction of normoblasts, destruction of reticulocytes in the peripheral circulation,[12,13] and injury to reticulocytes during maturation.[14] δ-Aminolevulinic acid is preferentially incorporated into hepatic hemoproteins. When labeled δ-aminolevulinic acid is used as a precursor, the slow component of the early labeled peak of bilirubin does not include radioactivity.[4] A late-labeled peak appears approximately at 50 days in rats and by 110 days in humans and is derived from the hemoglobin of senescent erythrocytes.[4]

In the liver, heme derived from exogenously administered hemoglobin is quantitatively converted to bilirubin.[15] A portion of heme associated with hepatic hemoproteins may not be converted to bilirubin.[16] This suggests that exogenous heme and hepatocellular heme may be processed differently by the liver.

Mechanism of Opening of the Heme Ring. Ferroprotoporphyrin IX is the heme prosthetic group (Fig. 53-2) in mammalian hemoproteins. The porphyrin ring is selectively cleaved at the α-methene bridge. The first step is catalyzed by

Fig. 53-1 Labeling of plasma bilirubin in UDP-glucuronosyltransferase-deficient rats (Gunn strain) after the injection of [2-^{14}C]glycine. The early (0 to 3 days) peak has an initial "sharp" and a slower component (see text for details). *(Reprinted from S. H. Robinson,* Hemopoetic Cellular Proliferation, *F. Stohlman Jr., ed., Grune and Stratton, New York, 1970, p. 180.)*

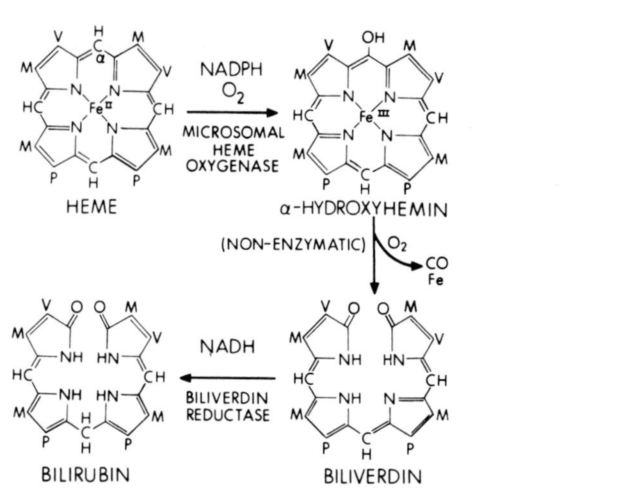

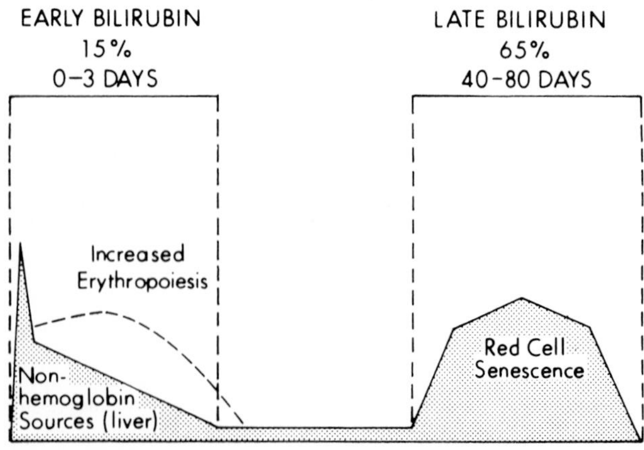

Fig. 53-2 Mechanism of heme ring opening and subsequent reduction of biliverdin to bilirubin.

microsomal heme oxygenase and requires an electrophilic attack at Fe(II) by a reducing agent, such as NADPH and oxygen. This reaction results in formation of α-oxyheme (Fig. 53-2).[17] Heme oxygenase activity is highest in the spleen, which is involved in sequestration of senescent erythrocytes, and is enhanced in hemolytic states.[18] The enzyme activity is also detectable in liver and kidney. Within the liver, hepatocytes and Kupffer cells have heme oxygenase activity. In Kupffer cells, the enzyme activity is comparable to that in the spleen.[19] Induction of heme oxygenase activity results in enhanced degradation of heme in various tissues,[20] and heme stimulates synthesis of heme oxygenase by enhancing transcription of specific mRNA.[21] These findings suggest that heme oxygenase is rate limiting in heme oxidation and in the formation of bilirubin.[20] However, this has not been directly confirmed, and evidence has been presented supporting a contrasting view that heme oxygenase is present in excess compared to its substrate.[22] Heme oxygenase has been purified from microsomal fractions of porcine spleen,[23] bovine spleen,[24] and rat liver.[25] The binding of purified heme oxygenase to heme requires heme iron and the propionic acid substituents in the C-6 and C-7 positions. Protoporphyrins which contain other metals, such as tin, bind with even greater affinity.[24] Oxygen binds to ferrous heme and undergoes reductive activation. Tin-protoporphyrin does not activate O_2 and is, therefore, not degraded by heme oxygenase, and competitively inhibits heme degradation.[24]

The second step in opening the heme ring involves oxidation by molecular oxygen and probably occurs nonenzymatically.[26,27] Carbons at the angular positions of the porphyrin ring neighboring the α-methene bridge are oxidized, and carbon monoxide is eliminated. This step is linked to addition of two additional oxygen atoms that are derived from two different oxygen molecules.[28,29] These oxygen atoms appear as the lactam oxygens of biliverdin and bilirubin. The open tetrapyrrole still contains iron and is protein-bound. Release of iron occurs after addition of electrons, suggesting that conversion of ferric to ferrous iron is required.[30] The resulting green pigment is biliverdin.

Conversion of Biliverdin to Bilirubin. Biliverdin is readily excreted by the liver and is the major bile pigment in many amphibian, avian, and fish species. However, in most mammals, biliverdin is converted to bilirubin prior to biliary excretion. Since bilirubin requires conjugation for biliary excretion, the physiological benefit of conversion of biliverdin to bilirubin is not clear. Bilirubin is less polar than is biliverdin and crosses the placental membranes more readily than does biliverdin.[31] However, this cannot be a complete explanation for conversion of biliverdin to bilirubin because some placentate animals, such as nutria and rabbits, excrete biliverdin as the main bile pigment.[32] Moreover, formation of bilirubin is not limited to placentate animals. Many species of fish excrete predominantly bilirubin in bile.[33,34]

Conversion of biliverdin to bilirubin is catalyzed by a cytosolic enzyme, biliverdin reductase, which requires NADH or NADPH for activity.[35,36] Guinea pig liver biliverdin reductase is a 70,000-dalton protein.[37] Three interconvertible molecular forms of biliverdin reductase have been described in rat liver.[38] Rat liver biliverdin reductase has a broad substrate specificity. Substrate activity is not restricted to bilitrienes with nonpolar substituents.[39]

The most abundant product of these reactions is bilirubin IXα; in addition, small amounts of non-α isomers (Fig. 53-3) have been detected in human and animal bile.[40–43] Bilirubin IXβ is the predominant isomer in the bile of fetal primates.[44] The mechanism of formation of non-α bilirubins is not known.

Quantitation of Bilirubin Production

Since bilirubin production reflects turnover of biologically important hemoproteins, quantitation is important in physiological investigation. Since bilirubin is almost quantitatively excreted in bile, bilirubin production can be quantitated as biliary excretion in animals, but this is not practical in humans. Bilirubin is converted to urobilinogen by bacteria in the gastrointestinal tract, (see "Fate of Bilirubin in the Gastrointestinal Tract," below), and fecal urobilinogen excretion approximates daily bilirubin production.[45–47]

In humans, bilirubin production is conveniently quantitated from the turnover of radioisotopically labeled bilirubin. Radiolabeled bilirubin bound to albumin is injected intravenously, blood samples are collected at frequent intervals, and plasma bilirubin concentration and radioactivity are measured.[48] Plasma bilirubin clearance (the fraction of plasma from which bilirubin is irreversibly extracted) is proportional to the reciprocal of the area under the radiobilirubin disappearance curve.[49] Bilirubin removal is quantitated as the product of plasma bilirubin concentration and clearance. When plasma bilirubin concentrations remain constant, removal of bilirubin equals the amount of newly synthesized bilirubin entering the plasma pool. This method does not take into account a small portion of bilirubin which is produced in the liver and excreted directly into bile without appearing in the circulation and, therefore, slightly underestimates bilirubin production.

Bilirubin formation can also be quantitated from carbon monoxide production. The subject is placed in a closed rebreathing system to prevent carbon monoxide (CO) excretion. Carbon monoxide production is calculated from the CO concentration in the breathing chamber or from an increment in blood carboxyhemoglobin saturation.[50–53] This method assumes that body CO stores rapidly equilibrate, blood carboxyhemoglobin reflects total body CO, and metabolism of CO is insignificant compared to its rate of production. Under certain circumstances, such as anoxia, assumption of a steady equilibrium of body stores of CO with blood carboxyhemoglobin may not be correct.[54] Carbon monoxide production exceeds plasma bilirubin turnover by 12 to 18 percent. This discrepancy is partly due to a small portion of bilirubin which is produced in the liver and excreted into bile without appearing in serum. A portion of carbon monoxide in expired air may be produced from nonheme sources, such as halogenated methane[55] and polyphenolic compounds, including catecholamines.[56] A small fraction of the carbon monoxide may be formed by intestinal bacteria.[57]

Fig. 53-3 Nonenzymatic cleavage of heme in vitro results in formation of four isomeric forms of biliverdin owing to nonequivalence of the four methene bridge positions (α, β, γ, and δ). P = CH_2CH_2COOH.

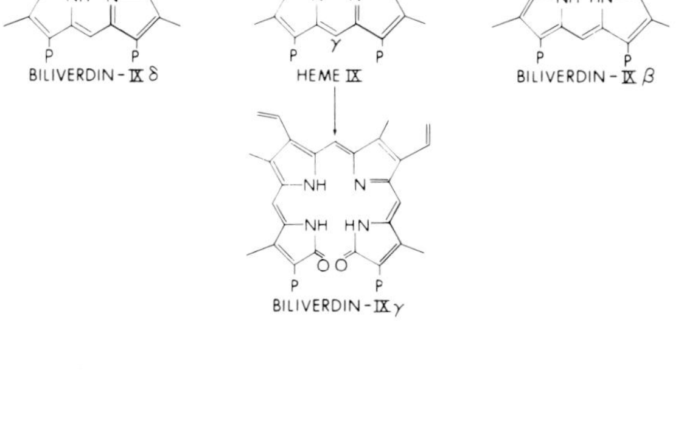

BILIVERDIN-IX α

BILIVERDIN-IX δ

HEME IX

BILIVERDIN-IX β

BILIVERDIN-IX γ

Pharmacologic Inhibition of Bilirubin Production. Administration of a nonmetabolized inhibitor of heme oxygenase, such as tin-protoporphyrin, results in marked inhibition of the enzyme activity in various organs.[24] A single dose of tin-protoporphyrin immediately after birth suppresses neonatal hyperbilirubinemia in rats[58] and rhesus monkey.[59] A rapid increase in heme saturation of hepatic tryptophan pyrrolase occurs after tin-protoporphyrin administration, indicating increased functional heme content of the liver.[60] Tin-protoporphyrin is excreted in bile.[61] Biliary excretion of heme also increases after tin-protoporphyrin administration.[61] However, inhibition of hepatic and splenic heme oxygenase activity in newborn rats by tin-protoporphyrin may not be accompanied by a reduction in endogenous carbon monoxide production.[62,63] This observation suggests that heme oxygenase may not be rate limiting in bilirubin production. Further studies are needed before tin-protoporphyrin is used in the hyperbilirubinemia in human infants.

Chemistry of Bilirubin

The systemic name given bilirubin IXα is 1′8′-dioxo-1,3,6,7-tetramethyl-2,8-divinylbiladiene-*a*,*c*-dipropionic acid(4,5).[64] The gross chemical structure (Fig. 53-3) assigned to bilirubin by Fischer and Plieninger[65] has been confirmed by analysis of x-ray diffraction data (Fig. 53-4).[66] The bonds between pyrrolenone rings A and B (C_4 and C_5) and C and D (C_{15} to C_{16}) are in the *Z* or trans configuration. The oxygen attached to

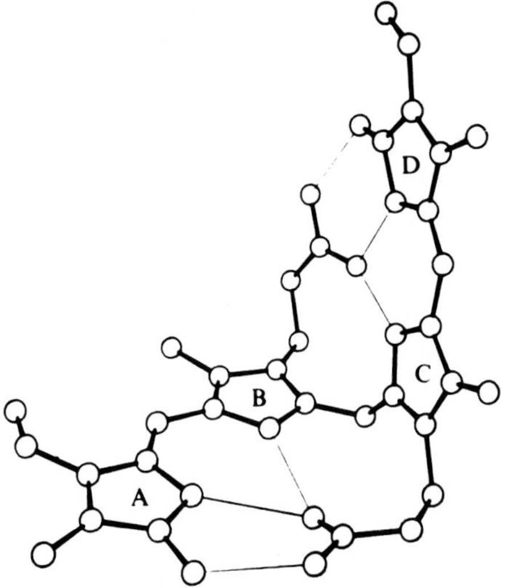

Fig. 53-4 X-ray crystallographic structure of bilirubin showing a ridge-tile configuration caused by internal hydrogen bonding of the propionic acid carboxyls to the amino groups and the lactam oxygen of the pyrrolenone rings of the opposite half of the molecule. The bonds between the pyrrolenone rings A and B and C and D are in the Z (trans) configuration.

the outer pyrrolenone ring is in a lactam rather than lactim configuration. Titration of bilirubin in aqueous solutions suggests a pK value of 7 to 8.[67,68] Since bilirubin tends to form insoluble aggregates below pH 8.0, determination of pK by titration of aqueous solutions of bilirubin is misleading.[69] Studies utilizing ^{13}C nuclear magnetic resonance (nmr) spectra and potentiometric and spectrophotometric titrations in aqueous solutions indicate that bilirubin has four acidic groups. The pK value of the two carboxyl groups is 4.4, and that of the two lactam groups is 13.0.[69]

Physical Conformation and Solubility of Bilirubin IXα. Accurate measurement of the solubility of bilirubin IXα at physiological pH is difficult because the pigment is unstable in aqueous solutions and tends to form colloids or surface films.[69] Crystallized bilirubin IXα-*Z,Z* with two protonated carboxyl groups is virtually insoluble in water. At acidic, neutral, or mildly alkaline pH, bilirubin partitions from aqueous solutions to water-immiscible solvents such as chloroform, ethyl acetate, or methylethyl ketone. After intravenous injection, bilirubin stains adipose tissues. These observations have given rise to the misleading impression that bilirubin is lipophilic. However, determination of solubility in progressively nonpolar solvents indicates that bilirubin is readily soluble in polar solvents, provided the intramolecular hydrogen bonds can be interrupted.[70] Bilirubin, which is apparently deposited in adipose tissues or brain, is mainly in aggregates on the surface of polar phospholipid membranes, and very little is dissolved in fat. Bilirubin shares a binding site in a polar region of albumin[69] with other polar substances, such as sulfonamides.[71] Thus, despite its insolubility in water at physiological pH, bilirubin should be considered as a relatively polar substance. The mechanism of injury by toxins which are truly lipid-soluble, such as DDT, may differ from that of bilirubin, which forms solid aggregates on the surface of relatively polar lipoid membranes.[71]

Although both bilirubin and biliverdin have two propionic acid side chains, bilirubin IXα is less polar than is biliverdin IXα at physiological pH[48,72] (Fig. 53-2). A possible explanation for this apparent inconsistency was suggested by Fog and Jellum[73] and Kuenzle et al.,[74,75] who proposed that bilirubin IXα may be internally stabilized by hydrogen bonding between the carboxyl and the two external pyrrolenone rings (Fig. 53-5). X-ray diffraction studies of crystalline bilirubin confirm hydrogen bonding between each propionic acid side chain and the pyrrolic and lactam sites in the opposite half of the molecule.[66] The molecule takes the form of a "ride tile" in which the two dipyrrolic halves of the molecule lie in two different planes with an interplanar angle of 98° (Fig. 53-4). The integrity of the hydrogen bonded structure requires the interpyrrolic bridges at the 5 and 15 positions of bilirubin to be in trans, or *Z*, configuration. In nonpolar solvents, the structure of unconjugated bilirubin oscillates between that shown in Fig. 53-3 and its mirror image.[76] A similar conformation has been proposed for bilirubin dianions in aqueous solutions (Fig. 53-4).[77] The preferred conformation of bilirubin in body fluids is uncertain. The hydrogen bonded structure may explain many of its physicochemical properties. Both carboxylic groups, all amino groups, and the two lactam oxygens are involved in hydrogen bonding and make the molecule insoluble in water. Addition of methanol, ethanol, or 6 *M* urea interferes with the hydrogen bonded structure and makes bilirubin more labile,[74,75] water-soluble, and reactive with diazo reagents. Bilirubin IXβ, IXγ, and IXδ lack the internally hydrogen bonded structure and are more polar than is bilirubin

Fig. 53-5 Ionic species of bilirubin. *A*, Internally hydrogen bonded form; *B*, bilirubin acid with hydrogen bonds disrupted; *C*, bilirubin dianion.

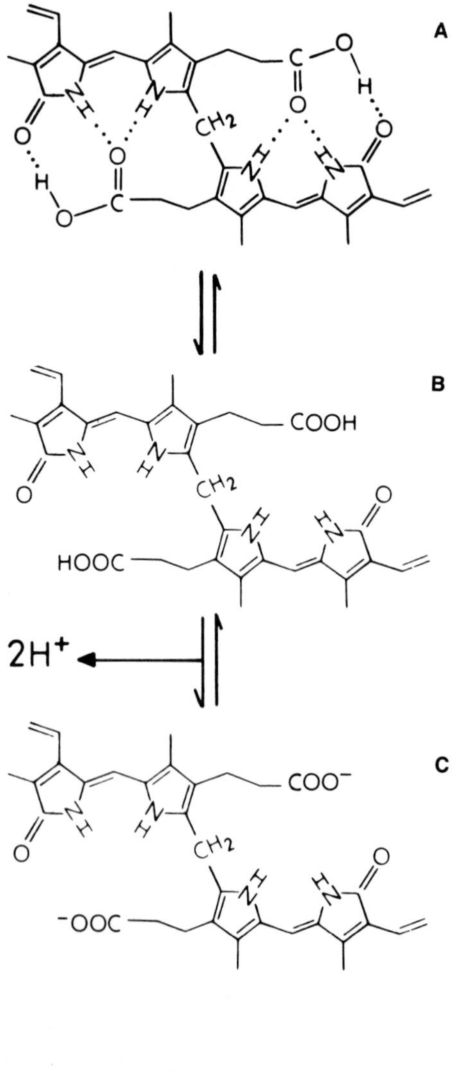

IXα. Following injection in rats, these unnatural isomers were readily excreted in bile in unconjugated form.[78] In contrast, bilirubin IXα requires conversion to a polar molecule before excretion in bile.

Ultraviolet/Visible Absorption Spectra. The position of the main absorption band (λ_{max}) of bilirubin depends on the bile pigment and the solvent. Bilirubin isomers (IIIα, IXα, and XIIIα) form strong internal hydrogen bonds and have absorption maxima which lie within a narrow range in most organic solvents. In contrast, the spectrum of bilirubin IXα dimethylester, in which the hydrogen bond-forming propionic acid carboxyl groups are blocked, is sensitive to change in solvents.[79] Unconjugated bilirubin IXα has a λ_{max} of 450 to 474 nm in most organic solvents and an extinction coefficient (OD_{1cm}^{max} or E_{max}) of 48.0 to 63.4 nM^{-1}. In alkaline aqueous solutions, there is a 10- to 30-nm shift of the λ_{max} toward shorter wavelengths and a weaker absorption band at 280 to 300 nm.

Dimerization and Aggregation of Bilirubin. The λ_{max} of bilirubin in dilute alkaline aqueous solution is 440 nm. With increasing concentration, a shoulder appears around 520 nm due to dimerization of bilirubin. Dimer formation is rapid, reversible, and independent of pH in the range of 7.5 to 9.0.[80] The equilibrium is shifted toward dissociation with increasing temperature and toward dimerization at high salt concentrations. In contrast, at near neutral pH, when the bilirubin concentration exceeds the limit of solubility, there is a slow decrease in absorbance and gradual appearance of a shoulder at 490 nm, followed by abrupt increase in light scattering caused by the self-aggregation of bilirubin. The temporary stability of the colloid solution may be explained by persistence of a negative charge at the surface of the aggregated particles.[69] A single crystal may initiate crystallization, which proceeds until equilibrium is reached between aggregation and dissolution. Lee and Gartner propose that bilirubin toxicity may result from interaction of the colloidal sol of bilirubin with the surface of cells.[81]

Effect of Light on Bilirubin. The effects of light are: (1) *Fluorescence.* Pure bilirubin does not fluoresce. When it is dissolved in detergent, albumin solution, or alkaline methanol, an intense fluorescence is observed at 510 to 530 nm.[82–84] Determination of fluorescence of bilirubin can be used for rapid quantitation of both blood bilirubin concentration and the unsaturated bilirubin binding capacity of albumin. (2) *Geometric isomerization and cyclization.* As mentioned earlier (Fig. 53-4), the 5 and 15 bridges of bilirubin are in a trans, or *Z*, configuration. Exposure of circulating bilirubin to light changes the configuration of one or both of the interpyrrolic bridges at 5 and 15 positions to *E*, or cis, configuration. The resulting *ZE*, *EZ*, or *EE* isomers lack one or more internal hydrogen bonds, are more polar than is bilirubin IXα-*ZZ*, and can be excreted in bile without conjugation.[85–87] The vinyl substituent in the endovinyl half of bilirubin IXα-*EZ* may be subsequently cyclized with the methyl substituent on the internal pyrrole ring forming the structural isomer, *E*-cyclobilirubin.[88] Although cyclization of bilirubin occurs at a slower rate than formation of configurational isomers, because of the relative stability of cyclobilirubin, this form may be quantitatively more important in phototherapy of neonatal jaundice.[88] (3) *Photooxidation and degradation.* Whether in aqueous solution, bound to protein or bound to lipid, bilirubin undergoes gradual bleaching in light and oxygen.[89] Bleaching results in formation of colorless fragments, chiefly maleimides and propentdyopent adducts, due to a self-sensitized reaction involving singlet oxygen. A small amount of biliverdin is also formed by mechanisms that are not established.[89] (4) *Dipyrrolic scrambling.* When bilirubin IXα is irradiated in deoxygenated aqueous solution, free radical disproportionation results in formation of bilirubin IIIα and bilirubin XIIIα (Fig. 53-6), which are nonphysiological symmetric isomers of bilirubin.[90] The reaction is faster in the presence of oxygen and is catalyzed by acid[91] and inhibited by ascorbic acid.

Toxicity of Bilirubin

Toxic effect of bilirubin on the brain of neonates has been known for at least five centuries.[92] Kernicterus, or degenerative changes associated with yellow discoloration of brain, was described in 1949.[93]

Biochemical Mechanism of Bilirubin Toxicity

Bilirubin inhibits RNA synthesis, protein synthesis, and carbohydrate metabolism in brain[94,95] and impairs protein synthesis in liver.[96] Bilirubin inhibited DNA synthesis in a mouse neuroblastoma cell line.[97] Bilirubin also may uncouple oxidative phosphorylation and inhibit ATPase activity of brain mitochondria.[98] Studies in vitro reveal that bilirubin inhibits hydrolytic enzymes,[99] dehydrogenases,[100] and enzymes involved in electron transport.[101] In mutant rats (Gunn strain) with congenital nonhemolytic hyperbilirubinemia (see "Gunn Rat," below), bilirubin inhibited RNA synthesis, protein synethesis, and carbohydrate metabolism in brain and inhibited protein synthesis in liver.[102–106] Bilirubin also decreased respiration of isolated brain mitochondria, uncoupled oxidative phosphorylation, inhibited ATPase activity, and induced swelling in the brain.[106–110] Bilirubin released glyceraldehyde-3-phosphate dehydrogenase from erythrocyte membranes, eventually resulting in hemolysis.[111,112] Bilirubin damages several tissues in vivo and in culture by inhibition of protein synthesis and tissue respiration.[113–117] In vitro, bilirubin inhibits many enzymes, including hydrolytic enzymes,[118] dehydrogenases,[119–121] and enzymes involved in the electron transport system.[120,122] The toxic effects of bilirubin are reduced or reversed by albumin in vivo and in vitro. Increased plasma concentrations of bilirubin increase the risk of bilirubin encephalopathy in newborn babies. A serum concentration of 20 mg/dl is generally accepted as the highest limit of safety,[123] although kernicterus can occur at lower serum bilirubin concentration.[124] Serum albumin concentrations, pH, and substances which compete for albumin binding are important in the pathogenesis of bilirubin encephalopathy.[125] Recently, bilirubin has been shown to inhibit protein kinase–mediated phosphorylation of neural proteins.[126,127] In a cell-free system, bilirubin irreversibly inhibited Ca^{2+}-activated, phospholipid-dependent protein kinase (protein kinase C) activity and cAMP-dependent protein kinase activity.[128]

Clinical Features of Bilirubin Encephalopathy. Kernicterus occurs in infants with severe unconjugated bilirubinemia and in young adults with high serum unconjugated bilirubin levels due to severe inherited deficiency of bilirubin-UDP-glucuronosyltransferase activity (see "Crigler - Najjar Syndrome, Type I," below). Kernicterus usually presents between the third

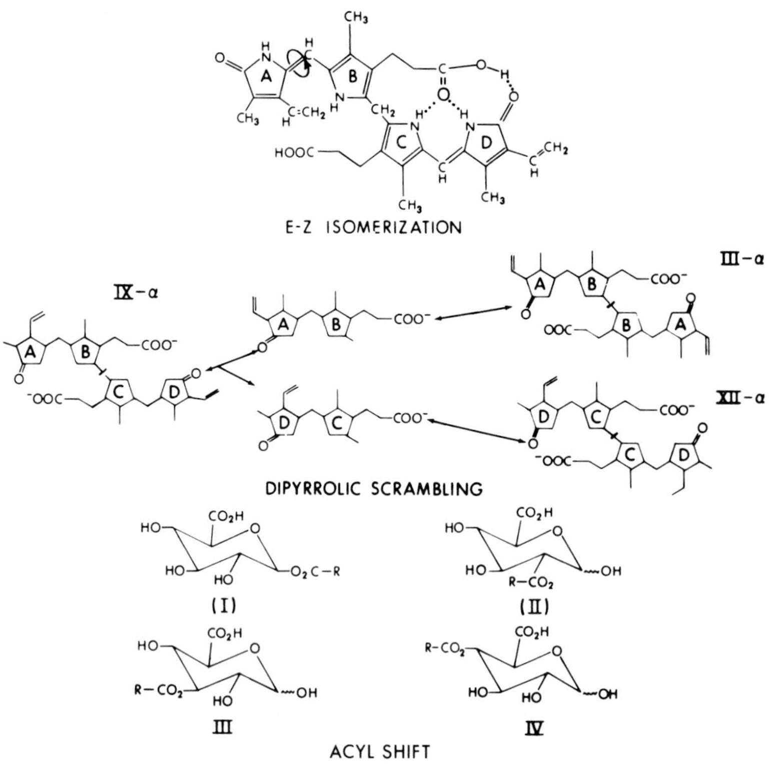

E-Z ISOMERIZATION

DIPYRROLIC SCRAMBLING

ACYL SHIFT

Fig. 53-6 Isomerization of unconjugated and conjugated bilirubin. *Upper panel:* Geometric isomerization: The bond between the pyrrolenone rings A and B or C and D can change into an *E* (cis) configuration, as shown here on the left half of the bilirubin molecule, resulting in the *EZ, ZE,* or *EE* isomers. *E* configuration of the bond between the pyrrolenone rings interferes with hydrogen bonding and renders the molecule relatively polar. *Middle panel:* Nonenzymatic dipyrrolic scrambling involves formation of dipyrrolic free radicals and their random reassembly into asymmetric (bilirubin IXα) and symmetric (bilirubin IIIα and XIIIα) tetrapyrroles. *Lower panel:* Acyl shifting of bilirubin glucuronides occurs on nonenzymatic incubation, resulting in conversion of the normal 1-O-acylglucuronide to 2-, 3-, or 4-O-acyl forms (see text). R = propionyl side chain of bilirubin.

and sixth days of life associated with hypotonia, hyporeflexia, athetoid movements, and reflex opisthotonus in response to a startling stimulus. This may progress to lethargy, atonia, and death. Long-term sequelae including hearing loss, cranial nerve palsy, athetosis, and mental retardation. Moderately high serum unconjugated bilirubin levels may result in a higher incidence of impaired neurologic or intellectual performance in later life.[129]

Bilirubin staining of the hippocampus, basal ganglia, and nuclei of the cerebellum and brain stem is observed in infants who die of acute kernicterus.[130] In infants dying within 72 h of the onset of kernicterus, there may be no cellular damage of the brain seen by light microscopy. Early histologic changes occur after this period and include cytoplasmic degeneration, loss of Nissl substance, and fine vacuolation and swelling of nuclear chromatin.[131] Evidence of cell death may be present. In children dying in the chronic stage of the disorder, bilirubin staining is not found in the brain,[130] but focal necrosis of neurons and glia are found. Gliosis of the affected areas occurs in later cases.[131] Since histologic lesions are not present in the early stages of kernicterus, these probably are not primary pathophysiological events in bilirubin encephalopathy. Localized bilirubin staining of the brain may occur in other forms of brain injury. Therefore, confirmation of the diagnosis of classic kernicterus requires the demonstration of neuronal degenerative changes.[132]

Role of the Blood-Brain Barrier. Tight junctions between capillary endothelial cells and foot processes of astroglial cells restrict the exchange of water-soluble substances and proteins between blood and brain.[133] In addition, specific transport processes for ions, water, and nutrients from plasma to brain may provide a functional blood-brain barrier. Conventionally, the immaturity of the blood-brain barrier in neonates has been thought to contribute to kernicterus. However, a more rapid passage of labeled markers[134] or lipophilic substances[135] into the immature brain has been difficult to confirm, and there is little evidence to support the concept of immaturity of the blood-brain barrier in the neonate. Rather, a special proclivity of the neonatal brain cells to bind bilirubin may facilitate the retention of bilirubin in the brain of newborns with severe unconjugated hyperbilirubinemia.

Hyperosmolarity-associated shrinkage of capillary endothelial cells results in temporary and reversible opening of the tight junctions. When the blood-brain barrier is opened in newborn rats by infusion of hypertonic urea[136] or arabinose,[133] an intravenously administered complex of albumin-bilirubin rapidly enters the brain. Following reversal of opening of the blood-brain barrier, bilirubin is rapidly cleared from the brain in parallel with clearance from the serum, suggesting that bilirubin is cleared by diffusion or transport back into the general circulation.[137] However, damaged and edematous brain may bind bilirubin,[138] be unable to clear it rapidly, and be more vulnerable to bilirubin toxicity for that reason.

Binding of Bilirubin to Albumin

In the circulation, bilirubin is tightly but reversibly bound to albumin. The physiological importance of albumin binding was emphasized by Benhold in 1929.[139] Albumin protects against otherwise lethal effects of unconjugated bilirubin following intravenous injection in puppies.[140] Toxicity of bilirubin on isolated brain mitochondria is abolished by an equimolar amount of albumin.[141] Administration of sulfonamides in newborn babies enhances bilirubin encephalopathy,[142] probably as a result of dissociation of bilirubin by sulfonamide from its binding to albumin.[143] Infusion of albumin increases the plasma bilirubin concentration because of transfer of bilirubin from tissues to plasma.[144–146]

When bilirubin binds to albumin, two complexes may form: (1) In normal plasma, bilirubin is bound almost exclusively as the dianion to a primary bonding site on albumin; smaller amounts are located at one or two secondary sites.[69] The reaction is fast and reversible. The binding affinity is high, and equilibrium is independent of pH. (2) The second type of binding occurs slowly at pH 7.4 or below, involves aggregation of albumin molecules with nonionized bilirubin acid,[147] and depends critically on a low pH. In hyperbilirubinemic states combined with acidosis, the plasma is supersaturated with respect to bilirubin, and there is a tendency to form bilirubin acid–albumin aggregates.[69] Binding isotherms indicate that there are primary and secondary binding sites on albumin for bilirubin.[148,149] Spectrophotometric studies provide evidence for a third binding site. When delipidated albumin is used, a fourth binding site becomes apparent.[150]

The binding of bilirubin to albumin has been evaluated by separating bound from free bilirubin by ultrafiltration, ultracentrifugation, gel chromatography, affinity chromatography on albumin agarose polymers, dialysis, and electrophoresis. Unbound bilirubin is rapidly destroyed by treatment with H_2O_2 and horseradish peroxidase, as compared with bound bilirubin. Binding of bilirubin to albumin induces bilirubin fluorescence, circular dichroism, quenching of protein fluorescence, and a shift in the absorbance spectra. Each effect that has been used to quantitate the binding of bilirubin to the primary site has been investigated (see Table 53-1 for results). In most studies, the primary binding constant at physiological pH and temperature is slightly below $10^8\ M^{-1}$. The binding constant for the secondary site is believed to be 10 times less.[69]

Peptides derived by enzymatic hydrolysis or cyanogen bromide cleavage of albumin have also been studied. Fragments containing amino acid residues 186 to 248,[151] 1 to 386, 49 to 307,[152] and 182 to 585[153] bind bilirubin. Affinity labeling studies indicate that bilirubin is primarily bound to a fragment containing residues 124 to 297 and, to a lesser extent, to residues 446 to 547.[154] Enzymatic hydrolysis and analysis of albumin covalently bound to bilirubin indicate that bilirubin binds to lysine 240 in human albumin and to lysine 238 in bovine serum albumin.[155]

Binding of other ligands to albumin plays a major role in determining bilirubin binding capacity. The other ligand may bind at the same site as does bilirubin, resulting in competitive displacement or noncompetitive displacement at a different site. Noncompetitive binding may not affect bilirubin binding or may produce conformational changes which enhance (cooperative binding) or decrease (anticooperative) bilirubin binding. Sulfonamides, anti-inflammatory drugs, and contrast media used for cholangiography displace bilirubin competitively from albumin and increase the risk of kernicterus in jaundiced newborn babies.[156] Some benzodiazepine drugs and long-chain fatty acids in low concentrations bind to human albumin without affecting bilirubin binding.[157–159] Albumin binding of medium-chain fatty acids, such as laurate and myristate, increases the binding constant for bilirubin.[160] Short-chain fatty acids bind to albumin anticooperatively with bilirubin.[161] When large amounts of fatty acid bind to albumin, major conformational changes occur which generally decrease the binding of other ligands, including bilirubin. Acidosis increases the risk of brain damage in neonatal jaundice[162,163] but does not influence bilirubin binding to the primary site of albumin. The increased risk of kernicterus may result from increased transport of bilirubin from plasma to selected areas of the central nervous system.[69]

Because of the influence of many metabolites and drugs on albumin binding of bilirubin and its transfer from plasma to the central nervous system, measurement of plasma bilirubin concentration does not accurately estimate the risk of brain damage from unconjugated bilirubin. It is generally believed, although not experimentally verified, that unbound bilirubin is transferred from plasma to the central nervous system.[143] Efforts have been made to quantitate unbound bilirubin in serum by gel chromatography,[164] peroxidase treatment,[165] electrophoresis on cellulose acetate,[166] and fluorimetry of serum with or without detergent treatment.[167] Free bilirubin concentration is determined from the equilibrium equation

$$[F] = [B]([RA]\cdot K)$$

where [F] is the free bilirubin concentration, [B] is albumin-bound bilirubin concentration, [RA] is the concentration of reserve bilirubin binding sites on albumin, and K is the association constant for bilirubin. Equilibrium between free and bound bilirubin is assumed, and the binding of bilirubin to tissues and secondary binding sites on albumin is ignored. The numerical values for binding constants, as determined from experiments with pure albumin and bilirubin, are assumed to be valid in serum. These assumptions may not be valid with icteric serum, and, therefore, it is not possible to calculate reliably the concentration of unbound bilirubin.[69] The alternative approach is to determine the amount of unoccupied bilirubin binding sites on albumin. Titration of serum with bilirubin or a dye which binds to albumin has been used to estimate unoccupied bilirubin binding sites. Binding to secondary binding sites occurs before primary sites are saturated, and some dyes bind at sites other than the bilirubin site. Binding of bilirubin to erythrocytes depends on the albumin/bilirubin ratio in serum and indirectly reflects reserve bilirubin binding sites on albumin.[168] Competitive binding by a ^{14}C-labeled ligand (monoacetyl-4,4′-diaminodiphenyl sulfone)[169] or a spin-labeled ligand [1-*N*-(2,2,6,6-tetramethyl-1-oxyl-4-piperidinyl)5-*N*-(1-aspartate)-2,4-dinitrobenzene][170] has been used to determine reserve binding capacity. A fluorimetric method for determination of bound albumin and reserve bilirubin binding capacity[167] in small quantities of whole blood is simple and useful. Despite inaccuracies, several empirical tests for determination of reserve bilirubin binding capacity of serum albumin correlate clinically with brain damage[171] and may be useful in assessing the risk of bilirubin toxicity. The newer methods are more accurate and theoretically sound, but more clinical experience is needed for their evaluation.

Uptake of Bilirubin by the Liver

Although tightly bound to albumin, bilirubin is rapidly removed from the circulation by the liver (Fig. 53-7). Extraction of bilirubin from the circulation under physiological conditions appears to be a specific hepatic function.[172,173] Kinetic studies of bilirubin uptake in isolated perfused liver of dog[174] and rat[175,176] and in rats in vivo[172] reveal that the process is saturable. A preloading effect on transport of bilirubin in rat liver has been described[172] (i.e., following an intravenous loading dose of bilirubin, the plasma disappearance of a subsequent tracer dose of [^{3}H]bilirubin is enhanced). Countertransport of bilirubin (i.e., efflux of radiolabeled ligand from liver after subsequent infusion with unlabeled ligand) has been claimed,[172] but the data may represent efflux of ligand from intracellular binding sites. Mutual competition for hepatic uptake in vivo has been described with respect to bilirubin and

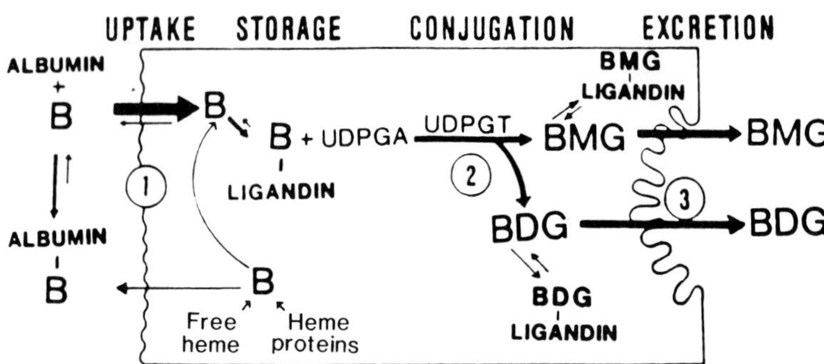

Fig. 53-7 Summary of hepatic metabolism of bilirubin (B). Bilirubin is strongly bound to albumin in the circulation. This complex dissociates, and bilirubin enters hepatocytes by a specific uptake mechanism (1). A fraction of the bilirubin is also derived from catabolism of hepatocellular heme proteins. Within the hepatocyte, bilirubin binds to a group of cytosolic proteins, termed ligandins; this inhibits the efflux of bilirubin from the cell. UDP-glucuronosyltransferase (UDPGT) (2), an endoplasmic reticulum enzyme, catalyzes the transfer of glucuronic acid from UDP-glucuronate (UDPGA) to bilirubin, forming bilirubin monoglucuronide (BMG) and diglucuronide (BDG). Both conjugates may bind to ligandins in the cytosol. Normally, conjugation is obligatory for biliary excretion (3) of bilirubin; only small amounts of unconjugated bilirubin are found in bile. Canalicular excretion is thought to be an energy-dependent process that is normally rate limiting and may be shared by other organic anions, except bile salts.

other organic anions, such as indocyanine green (ICG),[172,177] bromosulphthalein (BSP),[172,177] and conjugated bilirubin.[178] Bile acids do not compete with these compounds for hepatic uptake.[172,175,178]

Bilirubin is extracted from albumin before entering the liver cell. Albumin does not accompany bilirubin into the hepatocyte. Five minutes after intravenous injection of a mixture of [^{3}H]bilirubin and ^{131}I-labeled albumin into rats, approximately 60 percent of injected bilirubin is in the liver, whereas only 10 percent of injected albumin is in the liver, probably in the vascular space.[126] In isolated, perfused rat and dog liver, simultaneous injection of ^{125}I-albumin and [^{3}H]bilirubin discloses rapid bilirubin uptake, with no removal of albumin from the perfusate.[174,175,179,180] Similar results have been described in rat liver tissue slices[181] and in humans.[145]

The potential role of the albumin-bilirubin complex in hepatic uptake of bilirubin is controversial. It is not clear whether free or albumin-bound bilirubin interacts with the hepatocyte. Early studies suggested that the equilibrium-free fraction of ligand is taken up by the hepatocyte.[181a] This view was challenged by investigators, who found that uptake of albumin-bound ligands by the perfused rat liver correlated poorly with the free concentration.[182–188] For example, increasing the albumin concentration tenfold from 0.5 to 5 g/dl reduced the concentration of free taurocholate by a factor of 5, but reduced uptake by only 50 percent.[185] Similar results were found for uptake of fatty acids, bilirubin, and BSP.[182,184,188] In addition, uptake of a 1:1 complex of one of these ligands with albumin was saturable and competitively inhibited by albumin.[182] It was suggested that albumin mediated hepatic uptake of these ligands,[185] and a receptor for albumin on the liver cell surface was postulated.[182]

The existence of and possible physiological role for a liver cell albumin receptor remain conjectural. Much of the evidence for hepatocyte-mediated facilitation of albumin-ligand dissociation was obtained from mathematical models of kinetic studies.[182,189–191] Several findings, however, do not support a classic receptor-ligand system. Organic anions are readily taken up by hepatocytes in the absence of albumin.[192–195] In the isolated perfused rat liver, bilirubin which was taken up in the absence of albumin was as readily conjugated and excreted into bile as was bilirubin which had been presented as a complex with albumin.[193] Thus, albumin does not appear to direct the ligand to a particular transport system or intracellular compartment. There is no specificity for albumin in the uptake of organic anions. Several studies have demonstrated rapid and efficient bilirubin transport despite presentation as a complex with ligandin, which is a high affinity binding protein normally found in liver cell cytosol.[193,195] Although albumins from different species are immunologically distinct proteins and have varied affinities for organic anions, there is no apparent species specificity for interaction with the putative albumin receptor. Binding of tracer quantities of radiolabeled albumin to hepatocytes has been described.[182] However, binding is of relatively low affinity and high capacity, which may have little relevance to normal physiology.[196] In studies performed in the isolated rat liver perfused with protein-free medium, there was no delay in transit of tracer ^{125}I-albumin as compared with [^{14}C]sucrose.[193] This suggests that the off rate of albumin from a putative hepatocyte receptor would have to be very rapid, which is unusual for high affinity receptor-ligand interaction. Affinity chromatography studies of solubilized liver membrane proteins over albumin-agarose gel failed to provide evidence for a membrane protein with a high affinity for albumin.[196]

An alternative hypothesis to explain albumin receptorlike kinetics has recently been formulated by Weisiger and colleagues.[197,198] They suggest that the unbound ligand interacts with the liver cell plasma membrane, but the rate of dissociation of ligand from albumin may limit uptake. This new model of dissociation-limited uptake of albumin is compatible with the albumin receptor model and adequately describes BSP uptake in perfused elasmobranch liver.[197] In further support of this hypothesis is a study by Van der Sluijs et al.[199] In this study, uptake of dibromosulphthalein (DBSP) was quantitated in rat liver perfused with either 1% (150 μM) bovine serum albumin or 1% (150 μM) lactosylated bovine serum albumin. This modification of the protein converts it into a substrate for the liver cell receptor for asialoglycoproteins (galactose-terminating glycoproteins). However, a concentration of 150 μM is far above the maximal capacity of the liver to bind and endocytose asialoglycoproteins,[199a] and little change in the circulating level of protein would be expected. This modification of albumin resulted in a small increase in affinity for dibromosulphthalein but a 50 percent reduction in the off rate of bound DBSP. Presentation to the liver of DBSP bound to lactosylated albumin resulted in reduced initial uptake and biliary excretion of the ligand as compared with DBSP which was presented as a complex with native albumin. Initial clearance and extraction of ligand were reduced by approximately 50 percent in the presence of lactosylated albumin. These results do not depend on assumptions of sinusoidal ligand distribution and are essentially model-independent. Data were also fit to a two-compartment model, and unidirectional rate constants for influx, efflux, and biliary excretion were derived. Only influx was altered and was reduced by approximately 50 percent in lactosylated albumin studies, which is consistent with the model-independent findings. Further studies utilizing modified albumins may help to clarify the role in hepatic uptake of protein binding and interaction of ligand with specific liver cell membrane transporters.

To evaluate the role of albumin binding on solute distribution within the zones of the hepatic acinus, Gumucio et al. studied BSP transport in isolated rat liver perfused with 0.01 to 1.0 m*M* BSP with or without albumin.[200] When steady-state conditions of BSP excretion were established, the liver was frozen and relative BSP concentrations in various zones of the liver acinus were estimated. Without albumin, there was 95 percent extraction of BSP in a single pass; a decreasing concentration gradient from zone 1 (periportal) to zone 3 (pericentral) was observed. Inclusion of 4.5% or 1% albumin in the perfusate resulted in single pass extraction of only 8 to 22 percent of BSP, and the zonal gradient of BSP content was abolished. The results demonstrate that albumin binding produces more homogeneous distribution of organic anions within the liver acinus. When the liver was perfused retrogradely (through the hepatic vein) in the absence of albumin, BSP was taken up predominantly by hepatocytes of zone 3, and a decreasing gradient from zone 3 to zone 1 was produced. BSP conjugated with glutathione (GSH) appeared in bile during antegrade and retrograde perfusion, indicating that hepatocytes of both zones have the ability to conjugate and excrete BSP.

To elucidate the mechanism and driving forces responsible for hepatic organic anion uptake, many studies have been performed on isolated rat hepatocytes.[201–204] These experiments, conducted in the absence of albumin, suggested temperature-dependent sodium-independent uptake. However, due to rapid binding of a significant proportion of ligand to the cell surface, quantitation of ligand transported into cells was difficult. More recent studies of [^{35}S]BSP uptake in short-term cultured rat hepatocytes were performed in the presence of a molar excess of bovine albumin[205] and reveal linear uptake of BSP over at least 15 min with little formation of its GSH conjugate over this time. That [^{35}S]BSP entered cells and was not on the surface was suggested by inability to remove cell-associated ligand with repeated washing or by displacement with unlabeled BSP. These procedures rapidly remove ligand bound to liver cell plasma membrane preparations.[206] BSP uptake into these cultured hepatocytes was highly temperature-dependent. Energy dependence of the uptake process was suggested by finding that reduction of cellular ATP levels by preincubation in a mixture of sodium azide and 2-deoxyglucose reduced initial uptake of BSP by 70 percent. The site at which BSP transport may be coupled to energy utilization is not known. Previous studies[207] revealed that uptake of GSH-BSP by isolated rat hepatocytes and perfused liver was not accompanied by increased oxygen consumption. However, the high background level of oxygen consumption in hepatocytes may preclude accurate quantitation of changes produced by transport of this compound. An energy requirement for BSP uptake was observed in some investigations[202] but not others.[201] This apparent discrepancy may be due to differences in metabolic inhibitors, as has been described in studies of GSH-BSP uptake by isolated rat hepatocytes.[204] Initial uptake of [^{35}S]BSP was also depressed by isosmotic substitution of NaCl by sucrose. This finding does not represent nonspecific toxicity of modified media on cultured hepatocytes as was demonstrated in previous studies of asialoglycoprotein endocytosis.[208] A specific cation requirement for BSP uptake is unlikely, as uptake was unaffected by substitution of NaCl by KCl or LiCl. However, substitution of Cl^- by HCO_3^- or gluconate markedly inhibited BSP uptake. Replacement of Cl^- by the more permeant anion NO_3^- enhanced uptake.

Studies in rat liver perfused with NaCl or Na gluconate-substituted media reveal similar inhibition of bilirubin influx.[205] The obligate role of Cl^- or NO_3^- for BSP transport may be similar to that for organic anion transport by renal tubules, in which several studies have revealed evidence for Cl^-/organic anion exchange.[209–211] An anion exchanger with affinity for *p*-aminohippurate, OH^-, and Cl^- has been described in dog and rat microvillus membrane vesicles.[209,210] In rat basolateral vesicles, an anion exchanger with affinity for urate and Cl^-, but not *p*-aminohippurate, has been described.[211] Recent studies in rat intestinal basolateral membrane vesicles also reveal evidence for inorganic anion/bile acid exchange.[212]

Several abundant liver cell cytosolic proteins that bind bilirubin have been described, and their role in hepatic uptake has been examined. The possible role of ligandin was studied in isolated perfused liver from normal or thyroidectomized rats before and after treatment with phenobarbital.[213] Because ligandin is induced after phenobarbital administration and stabilized in the absence of thyroid hormone, these treatments increase liver ligandin levels two- to threefold.[213,214] There was no positive correlation between hepatic ligandin concentration and the influx rate of bilirubin; however, the efflux rate of bilirubin from liver back to plasma varied inversely with hepatic ligandin concentration.[213,215] Thus, intracellular protein binding of bilirubin appears to play no role in its extraction from serum albumin and subsequent transport into the hepatocyte; however, binding to ligandin influences the net uptake of bilirubin by regulating efflux. A similar study was performed in isolated perfused liver from rats treated with clofibrate. This drug induces *Z* protein (see below) but not ligandin. Despite a 147 percent induction of *Z* protein in treated animals, there was no effect on influx or efflux of tracer BSP or bilirubin,[216] suggesting that *Z* protein plays no role in transport under normal physiological conditions.

In the transfer of organic anions from the space of Disse to the hepatocyte, the liver cell plasma membrane is the first barrier to entry into the cell and presumably is the site of interaction with organic anions, which results in carrier-mediated uptake kinetics. Several studies of organic anion interaction with liver plasma membrane preparations have been performed in an attempt to describe the nature of the putative carrier. Early studies demonstrated saturable binding of BSP to membrane; bilirubin had no effect on BSP binding.[217] In other studies, high affinity binding of BSP to liver plasma membranes was reduced by preincubation of plasma membrane with trypsin and phospholipases.[218] These investigators subsequently isolated a 55,000-dalton bilirubin and BSP binding protein from rat liver cell plasma membrane.[218,219] Other investigators described high affinity BSP binding to rat liver cell plasma membrane[220,221] and isolated a 170,000-dalton protein (bilitranslocase) composed of 37,000- and 35,000-dalton subunits.[222] Bilitranslocase has been reported to reconstitute BSP transport in liposomes, but a nonspecific effect on permeabilizing liposomes to BSP has not been ruled out.[223] Studies by Wolkoff et al.[206] revealed high affinity, saturable binding of [^{35}S]BSP, which was eliminated after preincubation of liver cell plasma membrane with trypsin. To identify specific membrane binding proteins, a photoaffinity probe was devised in which [^{35}S]BSP was covalently bound to liver cell plasma membrane after exposure to uv light. Subsequent SDS-polyacrylamide gel electrophoresis and fluorography revealed radioactivity predominantly associated with a single 55,000-dalton protein. This organic anion binding protein (OABP) was purified from deoxycholate-solubilized liver cell plasma membrane after affinity chromatography on GSH-BSP-agarose gel.[206] The OABP is immunologically distinct from rat albumin and ligandin. It contains sialic acid.[206] The relationship of the OABP to bilitranslocase is unknown. The OABP appears to be closely related biochemically and immunologically to the liver cell membrane protein isolated by Berk and colleagues,[218,219] who reported that antibody to this protein selectively inhibits uptake of bilirubin and BSP by isolated hepatocytes.[224]

A liver cell membrane protein of 54,000 daltons that binds bile acids with high affinity and mediates bile acid transport has been described.[225–227] Although it has been suggested that the organic anion and bile acid binding proteins may be related,[228] there is no direct evidence for this hypothesis. Recent observations indicate that the 54,000-dalton protein also mediates hepatocyte uptake of phalloidin and antaminide but not BSP.[229,230]

Several studies performed in regenerating rat liver reveal modulation of organic anion uptake. The normal rat hepatocyte divides approximately once per year.[231] Following two-thirds hepatectomy, rapid cellular replication occurs throughout the liver remnant and is associated with expression of oncofetal antigens.[232–234] These findings suggest that hepatic regeneration is accompanied by transient "retrodifferentiation" of hepatocytes.[235] Using a multiple indicator dilution technique, single-pass transport of [^{3}H]bilirubin was determined in isolated perfused rat liver from 6 h to 6 days after two-thirds hepatectomy or sham surgery.[233] In this procedure, influx of bilirubin is independent of liver mass. Within 6 h of two-thirds hepatectomy, influx of bilirubin decreased by 50 percent compared with that in sham-operated controls and returned to normal 4 days later. The fact that influx of bilirubin and asialoorosomucoid reached a nadir at the time of greatest cellular proliferation and subsequently returned to normal suggests "maturation" of liver cell function for restoration of specific hepatocyte function.

Previous studies suggested a role for the cytoskeleton in modulation of cell surface proteins during liver regeneration.[236] To determine whether the hepatic cytoskeleton plays such a role, normal unoperated rats or rats following two-thirds hepatectomy or sham surgery were injected with colchicine, lumicolchicine, or saline.[237] Colchicine, compared with lumicolchicine, pretreatment reduced apparent influx of bilirubin and asialoorosomucoid in isolated perfused regenerating liver by 50 percent but had no effect in liver from normal or sham-operated rats. Analysis of indicator dilution curves revealed that reduced influx in colchicine-treated liver was attributable to an increased vascular volume of distribution. These results suggest that microtubules may play a role in maintenance of normal hepatic vascular architecture during regeneration. Lack of effect of colchicine on modulation of bilirubin and asialoorosomucoid uptake during regeneration suggests that other, as yet unknown, factors result in down-regulation of the specific hepatocellular transport systems for these two ligands. To determine whether depressed transport in liver regeneration occurs in other states of hepatocellular proliferation, rats were pretreated with nafenopin, a drug that causes rapid hepatocellular proliferation similar to that seen in regeneration.[238] One day after nafenopin treatment, liver weight increased by 40 percent. There was no change in transport parameters for bilirubin and asialoorosomucoid, but approximately 50 percent reduction in influx of BSP and conjugated bilirubin in perfused liver from nafenopin-pretreated rats. These studies suggest that hepatocellular proliferation is not solely responsible for transport alterations during liver regeneration. Nafenopin effectively unmasks differences in uptake of bilirubin and other more soluble organic anions, such as BSP and conjugated bilirubin, suggesting that their uptake mechanisms are partially independent.

Intrahepatocellular Storage of Bilirubin

Fifteen minutes following intravenous injection of [^{3}H]bilirubin into rats, over 90 percent disappeared from plasma, and 25 to 30 percent of the injected dose remained in liver.[239–241] Radioactivity does not appear in bile until 3 to 4 min after injection and subsequently appears at a rate of approximately 3 percent of the injected dose per minute.[239] Thus, from the time bilirubin is cleared from plasma and subsequently excreted into bile, it is stored within hepatocytes.

At all times after intravenous injection, a large proportion of [^{3}H]bilirubin is associated with the 100,000 × g cytosol of liver homogenates.[239–241] Bilirubin is only slightly soluble in aqueous solutions at physiological pH and is presumably bound to protein in cytosol. Gel filtration of cytosol containing [^{3}H]bilirubin or [^{35}S]BSP reveals that radioactivity is associated with two protein peaks, termed Y and Z (Fig. 53-8).[242] These proteins differ from albumin and each other with respect to biochemical and immunologic characteristics.[243] When a tracer quantity of radiolabeled anion is added to liver homogenate, binding is almost exclusively to the Y protein. With larger amounts, binding to Z protein becomes more apparent.[242] This suggests that, under physiological conditions, Y

Fig. 53-8 Binding of bilirubin to cytosolic proteins. Sephadex G75 gel chromatography of 110,000 × g rat liver supernatant to which [^{14}C]bilirubin has been added reveals association of radioactivity with two protein peaks, Y and Z. Y protein was determined to be quantitatively more important in organic anion binding and has subsequently been named ligandin.

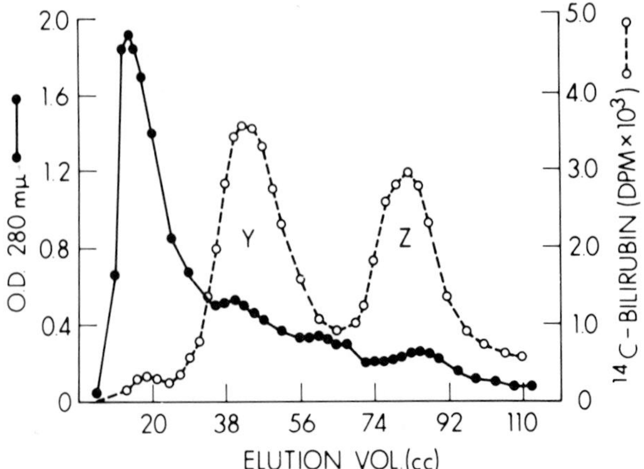

protein is the principal cytoplasmic protein to which organic anions bind.

Y protein was purified to homogeneity,[243] and further study revealed that it avidly binds many compounds, including various drugs, hormones, and organic anions.[242,244–247] Similar proteins have been identified by other investigators. Morey and Litwack[248] identified a protein by its ability to bind a cortisol metabolite, while Ketterer et al.[249] identified a protein that bound an axo-dye carcinogen. These three proteins proved to be identical by structural and immunologic techniques, and were termed ligandin.[250] Ligandin accounts for approximately 5 percent of liver cytosol protein[243,251] and is identical to GSH-transferase B, the major member of a class of six distinct basic GSH transferases which were purified from rat liver cytosol.[252–255] Five GSH transferases have been isolated from human liver, but unlike the comparable rat proteins, the human proteins have identical amino acid composition and cross-react immunologically.[256] Each of the rat and human GSH transferases avidly binds bilirubin and other organic anions as nonsubstrate ligands.[239,245,256–259]

The high affinity of these proteins for organic anions suggested that they may play a role in transport by the liver.[260–261a] Circumstantial evidence for this hypothesis was provided by studies of ontogeny and phylogeny. Addition of BSP to liver cytosol followed by Sephadex G75 chromatography revealed that in elasmobranchs, teleosts, and the gill-breathing amphibia, there was no detectable Y peak; the Z peak was either undetectable or present in trace amounts. Prominent Y and Z peaks were found in lung-breathing amphibians, reptiles, birds, and mammals.[262]

An ontogenic study to determine the developmental pattern of the soluble organic anion binding proteins in three species of frog during metamorphosis failed to reveal Y and Z peaks in the youngest forms. After partial development, a prominent Z peak was seen, and both Y and Z peaks were present in adults.[262] Similar results were obtained in guinea pigs[263] and monkeys[264]; "maturation" of ligandin coincided with normalization of hepatic organic anion transport. Additional studies of organic anion transport in elasmobranchs revealed that the relationship of ligandin and other GSH transferases to hepatic organic anion transport may be complex.[265,266] These animals have low but detectable levels of GSH transferase activity in liver, but 75 to 85 percent of [^{35}S]BSP was recovered in bile and liver 24 h after injection.[267]

Although many organic anions bind to ligandin following their uptake by the liver, the ability to bind to ligandin does not imply that a given compound will be removed from the circulation by the liver. An example is Evans blue dye, which is slowly excreted by the liver in vivo. After intravenous injection of Evans blue dye into a rat, no binding to the Y and Z fractions of rat liver cytosol occurs. Addition of the dye to liver cytosol in vitro reveals binding to the Y peak to a similar degree as with BSP or indocyanine green.[242]

Although bilirubin and other organic anions are stored in the liver primarily bound to ligandin, the selectivity of organic anion uptake by the liver cell is probably a function of the plasma membrane (see preceding section). Studies showing that serum albumin has a greater affinity for bilirubin than does ligandin challenged its transport role.[268] One suggestion is that affinity of ligandin for bilirubin decreases during purification.[269] That this view is incorrect was demonstrated in a circular dichroism study of bilirubin-ligandin interactions in rat liver cytosol and in fractions obtained at various stages during purification of ligandin.[270] Ligandin retained its capacity to bind bilirubin in the presence of components of liver supernatant, but albumin lost the capacity to bind bilirubin in liver supernatant. In their respective physiological milieus, albumin and ligandin are structurally adapted to bind ligands: albumin in serum and ligandin in the cytosol of the liver cell. With respect to organic anion transport, ligandin may function within the hepatocyte much as albumin does in the circulation, binding bilirubin and preventing efflux from the hepatocyte back into the circulation[162] and avoiding nonspecific diffusion of bilirubin into compartments of the hepatocyte in which it may do harm. This hypothesis is supported by the finding that bilirubin inhibits mitochondrial respiration in vitro, an effect that is prevented by ligandin.[271] The precise relationship of ligandin binding of bilirubin and its conjugates to conjugation and biliary excretion is not known.

Conjugation of Bilirubin

Efficient excretion of bilirubin across the bile canaliculus requires its conversion to polar conjugates by esterification of the propionic acid carboxyl groups. Esterification of one or both propionic acid side chains forms mono- or diconjugates, respectively. Glucuronic acid is, by far, the major conjugating group in normal mammalian bile pigments.[272] In addition, human T-tube bile[273,274] and bile from dogs,[275–277] alligators, cats, chickens, horses, opossums, rabbits, and snakes[278] contain xylosyl and glucosyl conjugates. Although the existence of bilirubin monoglucuronide as a chemical entity was questioned in earlier studies,[279,280] bilirubin glucuronides are now known to be present as mono- and diconjugates (Fig. 53-9).[281,282] Bilirubin IXα is an asymmetric molecule, and therefore, bilirubin IXα monoglucuronide exists as two isomers, depending on where the glucoronyl group is attached. The two isomers have been separated by thin-layer chromatography, high performance liquid chromatography (HPLC) after substitution of the conjugating group by NH_2[283] or CH_3[284] groups, or HPLC of underivatized bile pigments.[285–288] Bilirubin diglucuronide is the major pigment in human, dog, and rat bile.[289–291]

UDP-Glucuronosyltransferase-Mediated Conjugation of Bilirubin. Conjugation of bilirubin with glucuronic acid is catalyzed by the microsomal enzyme uridine diphosphoglucuronate β-D-glucuronosyltransferase (UDP-glucuronosyltransferase, EC 2.4.1.17), which catalyzes transfer of the glucuronyl moiety of UDP-glucuronate to a variety of aglycones forming ether, ester, thiol, and *N*-glucuronides.[292] UDP-glucuronosyltransferase is present in the endoplasmic reticulum and nuclear envelope of hepatocytes and various other epithelial cells. It is an integral membrane protein and requires membrane lipids for its function. Delipidation results in loss of enzyme activity, which is restored upon addition of phospholipid micelles.[293,294] UDP-glucuronosyltransferase activity in microsomal vesicles is partially latent. Membrane perturbation by detergent treatment,[295] sonication,[296] storage at 0°C in potassium chloride solution,[297] or brief incubation with phospholipase A[298] removes the latency, and full activity of the enzyme is expressed. UDP-glucuronosyltransferase activity in native microsomes is also enhanced by low concentrations of UDP-*N*-acetylglucosamine, which has been postulated to be a physiological activator of the transferase. Two mechanisms have been proposed to explain this activation. In the compartmental model, microsomal lipid membranes are thought to pose a

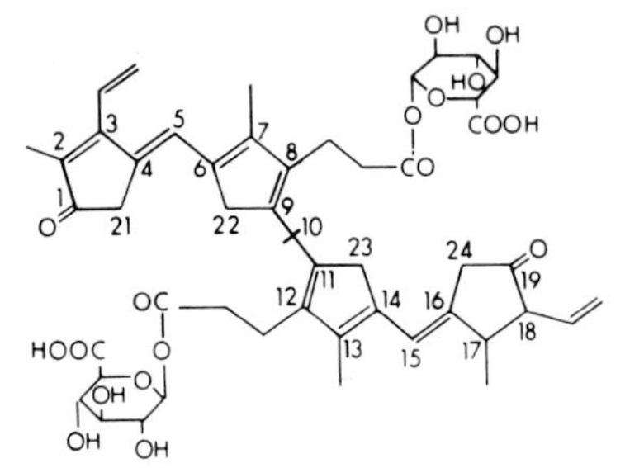

1. BILIRUBIN DIGLUCURONIDE

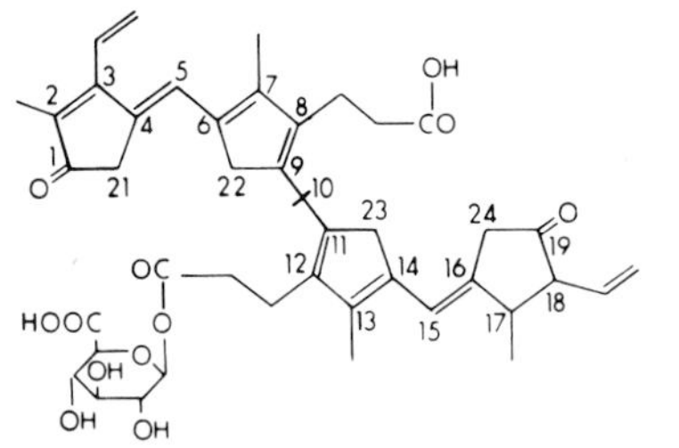

2. BILIRUBIN MONOGLUCURONIDE (C-12)

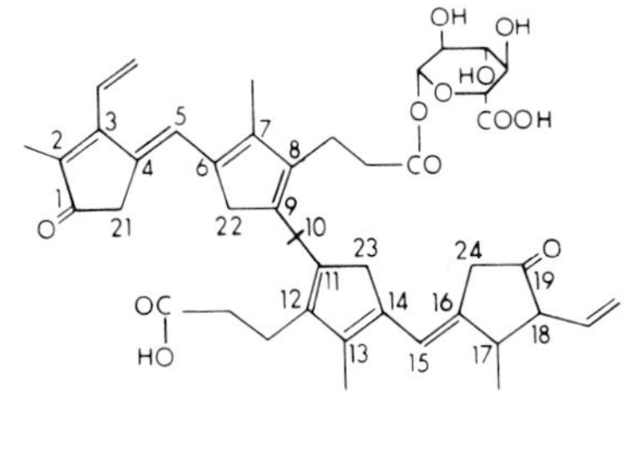

3. BILIRUBIN MONOGLUCURONIDE (C-8)

Fig. 53-9 Bilirubin glucuronides. Both propionic acid side chains are glucuronidated in bilirubin diglucuronide. Bilirubin monoglucuronide can exist as two molecular species, depending on whether the C_{12} or C_8 propionic acid is conjugated.

partial barrier between the catalytic site of the enzyme and UDP-glucuronic acid. This model also postulates the presence of a "permease" in the microsomal membranes which facilitates access of UDP-glucuronic acid to the catalytic site of the transferase. UDP-*N*-acetylglucosamine is envisioned as an activator of the permease. Membrane perturbation is thought to enhance enzyme activity in vitro by increasing the permeability of the lipid membranes to UDP-glucuronic acid.[299] In the allosteric model, enzyme activity is constrained by the membrane. Activating agents release the enzyme from constraint and increase enzyme activity.[300]

UDP-glucuronosyltransferase consists of a family of functionally heterogeneous forms. Thus, transferase activities toward various substrates differ in the time of appearance during ontogenic development, degree of induction by specific enzyme inducing agents, and extent of defect in mutant humans and animals. UDP-glucuronosyltransferase activity develops perinatally in rats. Enzyme activity toward 4-nitrophenol and other simple phenolic substrates develops in late fetal life, whereas activity toward bilirubin and steroid substrates develops after birth.[301] Treatment of pregnant rats with glucocorticoids results in precocious development of fetal UDP-glucuronosyltransferase activity toward phenolic substrates. Treatment of adult rats with 3-methylcholanthrene induces UDP-glucuronosyltransferase activity toward the "late fetal" substrates.[302] In contrast, UDP-glucuronosyltransferase activity toward bilirubin is specifically induced by clofibrate.[303] Treatment of rats with tri-iodothyronine results in a threefold increase in transferase activity toward 4-nitrophenol, whereas activity toward bilirubin is decreased by 80 percent.[304] Homozygous Gunn rats lack UDP-glucuronosyltransferase activity toward bilirubin but form acyl- and *N*-glucuronides and glucuronides of several phenolic substrates, such as thyroxine and tetrahydrocortisol.[305] Glucuronidating activity toward *o*-aminophenol is deficient in vitro but is restored to normal by pretreatment of microsomes with diethylnitrosamine. Diethylnitrosamine does not restore the transferase activity for bilirubin.[306]

Biochemical separation and purification of multiple forms of UDP-glucuronosyltransferase have provided firm evidence for heterogeneity of the enzyme. Several groups of investigators have chromatographically separated and purified two or more forms of UDP-glucuronosyltransferase from detergent-solubilized liver microsomal fractions.[307–313] Recently, by the combination of chromatofocusing, affinity chromatography, and high pressure gel permeation chromatography, multiple forms of rat liver UDP-glucuronosyltransferase have been isolated.[314] Substrate specificity and analysis of peptides produced by proteolytic digestion indicate the presence of at least four, and probably seven, different forms of UDP-glucuronosyltransferase in rat liver. Two isoforms are active toward bilirubin; one appears to have bilirubin as its only natural aglycone substrate.[314] The purified bilirubin-UDP-glucuronosyltransferase isoform also catalyzes formation of bilirubin glucoside and bilirubin xyloside with UDP-glucose and UDP-xylose as respective cosubstrates.[315–317] These studies indicate that UDP-glucuronic acid may not be the only sugar donor substrate for UDP-glucuronosyltransferase. The purified bilirubin-UDP-glucuronosyltransferase also uses bilirubin monoglucuronide as a substrate. On incubation of bilirubin monoglucuronide and UDP-glucuronic acid with this isoform, bilirubin diglucuronide is formed.[317] In the presence of UDP-glucose, purified bilirubin-UDP-glucuronosyltransferase catalyzes the formation of bilirubin glucuronide-glucoside mixed conjugates.[317] Thus, activity of this UDP-glucuronosyltransferase isoform may account for all major bilirubin conjugates in mammalian bile. A functional defect in this isoform occurs in Gunn rats, and a similar defect is found in a corresponding human form(s) in patients with Crigler-Najjar syndrome, type I, which may explain the virtual absence of all sugar conjugates of bilirubin in the bile of these mutants. The transferase reaction is reversible. Incubation of bilirubin monoglucuronide with UDP results in formation of bilirubin and UDP-glucuronic acid. However, the pH optimum for the reverse reaction is 5.5,[317] which may not be physiologically relevant.

Although bilirubin is bound to ligandins within the liver cell, it is not clear whether it interacts with UDP-glucuronosyltransferase in a free or bound state. It has been proposed that bilirubin is taken into the endoplasmic reticulum before enzyme-catalyzed glucuronidation occurs.[318]

Bilirubin monoglucuronide is the major product of bilirubin-UDP-glucuronosyltransferase-mediated conjugation of bilirubin in vitro.[319] Conversion of bilirubin monoglucuronide to diglucuronide can be catalyzed by UDP-glucuronosyltransferase in microsomal fractions from cat,[320] rat,[321] and human[322] liver, and by purified rat liver bilirubin-UDP-glucuronosyltransferase.[317] A UDP-glucuronic acid-independent mechanism of bilirubin diglucuronide formation has been described whereby dismutation of 2 mol of bilirubin monoglucuronide catalyzed by rat liver plasma membranes results in equimolar amounts of bilirubin diglucuronide and unconjugated bilirubin.[323–325] However, bilirubin diglucuronide can also be formed nonenzymatically by scrambling the two dipyrrolic halves of bilirubin monoglucuronide.[326,327] Dipyrrolic scrambling results in formation of symmetric and asymmetric isomers of bilirubin; this reaction does not occur in vivo. Dipyrrolic scrambling of bilirubin monoglucuronide is inhibited by ascorbic acid, which also inhibits formation of bilirubin diglucuronide by dismutation. Thus, dismutation of bilirubin monoglucuronide may not be enzyme-catalyzed and may not occur in vivo.[327]

cDNA clones for multiple rat UDP-glucuronosyltransferases have recently been isolated. One clone corresponds to the transferase isoform which has activity for androsterone.[328] Two other clones correspond to 3-methylcholanthrene[329] and phenobarbital inducible forms,[330] respectively. Nucleotide sequences of these forms show that the various UDP-glucuronosyltransferase isoforms differ in primary structure.[328–330]

The apparent molecular weights of purified UDP-glucuronosyltransferase isoforms, as determined by SDS-polyacrylamide gel electrophoresis, range from 50,000 to 58,000 daltons. These sizes may not represent the configuration of the transferases in the endoplasmic reticulum. The molecular size of UDP-glucuronosyltransferases, estimated by radiation inactivation studies in microsomal preparations, suggests that the UDP-glucuronosyltransferase isoform which catalyzes the formation of bilirubin monoglucuronide from bilirubin exists in microsomal membranes in a molecular size which is close to the size of the purified isoform.[331] However, the data also suggest that other transferase isoforms may exist as oligomers. Functional significance of this finding is not known.

Quantitation of Bilirubin and its Conjugates

Bile pigments are quantitated as native or derivatized tetrapyrroles or are measured after conversion to azoderivatives.

Quantitation of Bilirubin by Diazo Methods. Reaction of bilirubin with diazo reagents begins with electrophilic attack by a diazonium ion at the 9 and 11 positions of bilirubin[332] and converts the tetrapyrrole to diazotized azodipyrroles and formaldehyde (Fig. 53-10). The azoderivatives are more stable than is bilirubin and its conjugates and can be quantitated colorimetrically. Unconjugated bilirubin is converted to two unconjugated dipyrroles; bilirubin diconjugates form two conjugated azodipyrroles, and bilirubin monoconjugates form one conjugated and one unconjugated azodipyrrole. In 1916, van den Bergh and Muller[333] showed that, on the basis of diazo reaction, serum bile pigments can be classified into a "direct" and an "indirect" reacting species. The direct reaction occurs within minutes, and the indirect reaction occurs rapidly only in the presence of accelerator substances, such as methanol or caffeine.[333] Subsequently, the direct and indirect reacting components were identified as conjugated and unconjugated bilirubin, respectively.[334] Various modifications of the van den Bergh reaction are commonly used for clinical determination of bilirubin conjugates. More recently, diazotized ethylanthranilate and *p*-iodoaniline were used in place of sulfanilic acid diazo reagent. These methods are more sensitive, accurate, and selective. The azodipyrroles formed can be extracted and analyzed by thin-layer[335] and high performance liquid chromatography (Fig. 53-11). The conjugated azodipyrrole formed by reaction of bilirubin conjugates with diazotized ethylanthranilate has been characterized as the 1-*O*-acylglucopyranuric acid glycoside.[337] When bile flow is impeded, bilirubin IXα-1-*O*-acyl glucuronides rearrange with formation of 2-, 3-, and 4-acyl glucuronides.[337] This sequential migration of the bilirubin *O*-acyl group from position 1 to positions 2, 3, and 4 of glucuronic acid is nonenzymatic and base catalyzed and occurs on incubation of bile or isolated bilirubin IXα glucuronides at 37°C.[338]

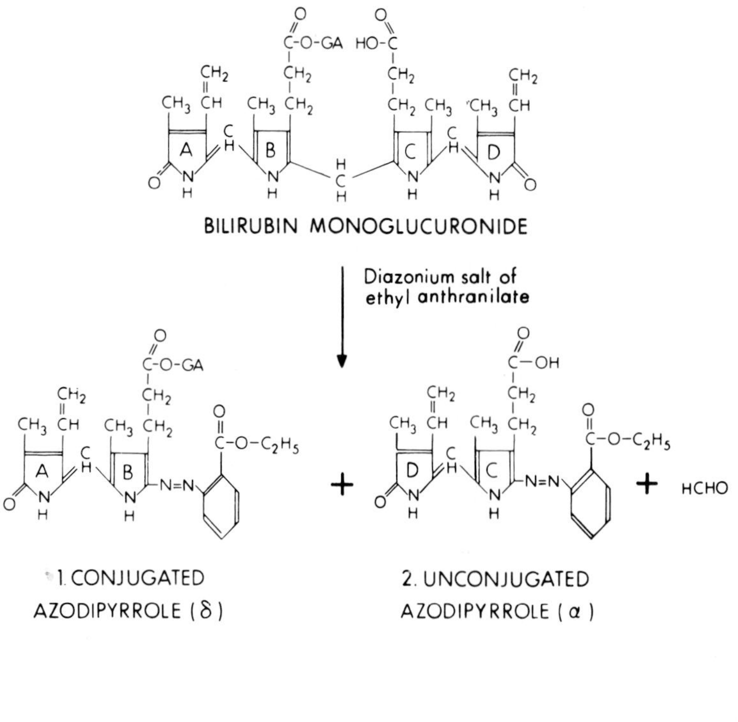

BILIRUBIN MONOGLUCURONIDE

Diazonium salt of ethyl anthranilate

1. CONJUGATED AZODIPYRROLE (δ)

2. UNCONJUGATED AZODIPYRROLE (α)

+ HCHO

Fig. 53-10 Reaction of bilirubin tetrapyrrole with the diazonium salt of ethylanthranilate results in the formation of equimolar amounts of two azodipyrroles. The central methenyl bridge is converted to formaldehyde. GA = glucuronic acid.

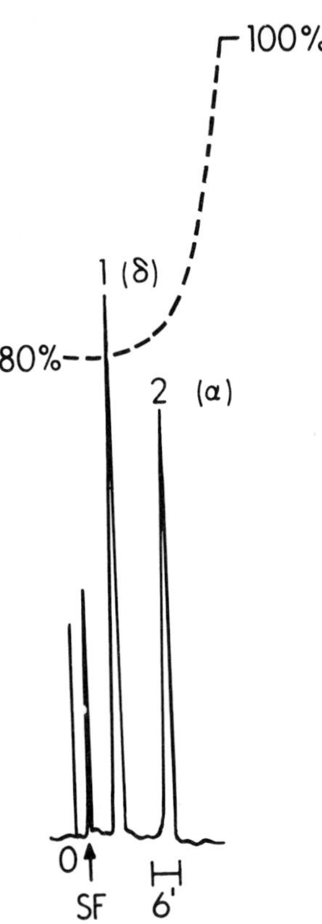

Fig. 53-11 Separation of ethylanthranilate azodipyrroles by HPLC. Wistar rat bile was diazotized with ethylanthranilate diazo reagent, azodipyrroles were extracted,[277] organic solvents were eliminated in reduced pressure, and the pigments were dissolved in methanol and separated by reverse phase HPLC (μ-Bondapak C-18 column, Waters) using a concave gradient (interrupted line) of methanol (80 to 100 percent) in sodium acetate (0.1 M, pH 4.0) containing 5 mM 1-heptane sulfonic acid for 30 min, at 1 ml/min. SF = solvent front. Peak 1 (OD, 530 nm) represents glucuronidated azodipyrrole, which was designated δ by Heirwegh and his associates[277] and peak 2 represents the unconjugated azodipyrrole, designated α[277] (see Fig. 53-10).

Diazo methods for bilirubin quantitation are routinely used in clinical laboratories. However, since 10 to 15 percent of unconjugated bilirubin may be direct reacting, the direct diazo reaction overestimates the levels of conjugated bilirubin. Although a direct-reacting bilirubin concentration of less than 15 percent of total is considered normal in most clinical laboratories, analysis of intact tetrapyrroles detects hardly any conjugated bilirubin in normal serum. In addition, the irreversibly albumin-bound fraction of serum bilirubin, which is formed in conjugated hyperbilirubinemia, exhibits a direct diazo reaction[339] resulting in an overestimation of conjugated bilirubin. Since the irreversibly protein-bound bilirubin is cleared slowly, it remains in serum for a relatively long period after reversal of biliary obstruction. Finding of direct reacting bilirubin during this period may give a false impression of continued biliary obstruction. In renal failure, indican accumulates in serum and may interfere with the diazo reaction of bilirubin.[340] Finally, the diazo method cannot be applied to separately quantitate bilirubin mono- and diconjugates when they are present in a complex mixture. The latter requires analysis of intact bilirubin tetrapyrroles.

Separation and Quantitation of Intact Bilirubin Tetrapyrroles. In 1954, Cole et al. separated serum bile pigment into unconjugated bilirubin and two direct reacting components, pigment I and pigment II, by column chromatography.[341] Pigment II was characterized as bilirubin diglucuronide. The exact nature of pigment I, which yielded equimolar amounts of conjugated and unconjugated azodipyrroles on diazo reaction, remained controversial. Subsequently, Heirwegh and associates[342] developed highly resolving thin-layer chromatographic systems for separation of bilirubin and its conjugates. Analysis of azoderivatives of each tetrapyrrole revealed predominantly bilirubin IXα conjugates in the bile of various species. In addition, small amounts of bilirubin IXβ, IXγ, and IXδ occur in dog bile.[42,342] Small amounts of sulfate, phosphate, and taurine conjugates of bilirubin have also been described in bile.[72,343–346] Although separation of intact bilirubin tetrapyrroles by thin-layer chromatography has led to better understanding of bilirubin conjugates, the methods are tedious and quantitative pigment recovery after thin-layer chromatography is not possible. HPLC offers high resolution and quantitative recovery of bile pigments. Methyl esters formed by alkaline methanolysis of bilirubin mono- and diconjugates have been separated and quantitated by HPLC.[347] The methyl derivatives can readily be extracted and quantitated. However, because the conjugating sugars are replaced by methyl groups, the pigments cannot be separated on the basis of their conjugating moieties. Methods for separation and quantitation of intact bilirubin tetrapyrrole conjugates by HPLC have recently been developed[348–351] and offer accurate and sensitive means to identify and quantitate bilirubin conjugates in body fluids and in vitro (Fig. 53-12).

Methods for bilirubin quantitation that require extraction of serum bile pigments in organic solvents underestimate serum bilirubin because the irreversibly protein-bound fraction is lost. Recently, reverse-phase HPLC of incompletely deproteinated serum[339] was used to quantitate irreversibly protein-bound and other bilirubin fractions simulataneously. These studies indicate that the irreversibly protein-bound serum bilirubin fraction is present in conditions associated with conjugated hyperbilirubinemia. After successful surgical correction of biliary obstruction, the reversibly protein-bound fraction of serum bilirubin is rapidly excreted in bile; this results in an increase in the proportion of the irreversibly protein-bound fraction of serum bilirubin. If biliary obstruction persists, both reversibly protein-bound and irreversibly protein-bound fractions are retained and no increase in the proportion of the latter is observed.

Slide Tests. Two slide tests have been introduced for determination of conjugated, unconjugated, and irreversibly protein-bound bilirubin. One slide (Ektachem "TIBL") is used for quantitation of total bilirubin by a diazo technique.[352] The other slide has a special coating that allows only the free and reversibly protein-bound bilirubins to come in contact with the diazo reagent; conjugated and unconjugated bilirubin are separately quantitated by reflectometric measurements at two wavelengths.[353] The difference between total bilirubin and the sum of conjugated and unconjugated bilirubin gives the value for irreversibly protein-bound bilirubin. These results have been verified by HPLC and indicate that the results obtained by the Ektachem slide tests are consistent and reliable.[352,353]

Fluorimetric Analysis. Fluorescence characteristics of bilirubin have been utilized in the development of a method for determination of total and albumin-bound bilirubin and reserve bilirubin-binding capacity from as little as 0.1 ml of whole blood. Bilirubin bound to the high affinity site of albu-

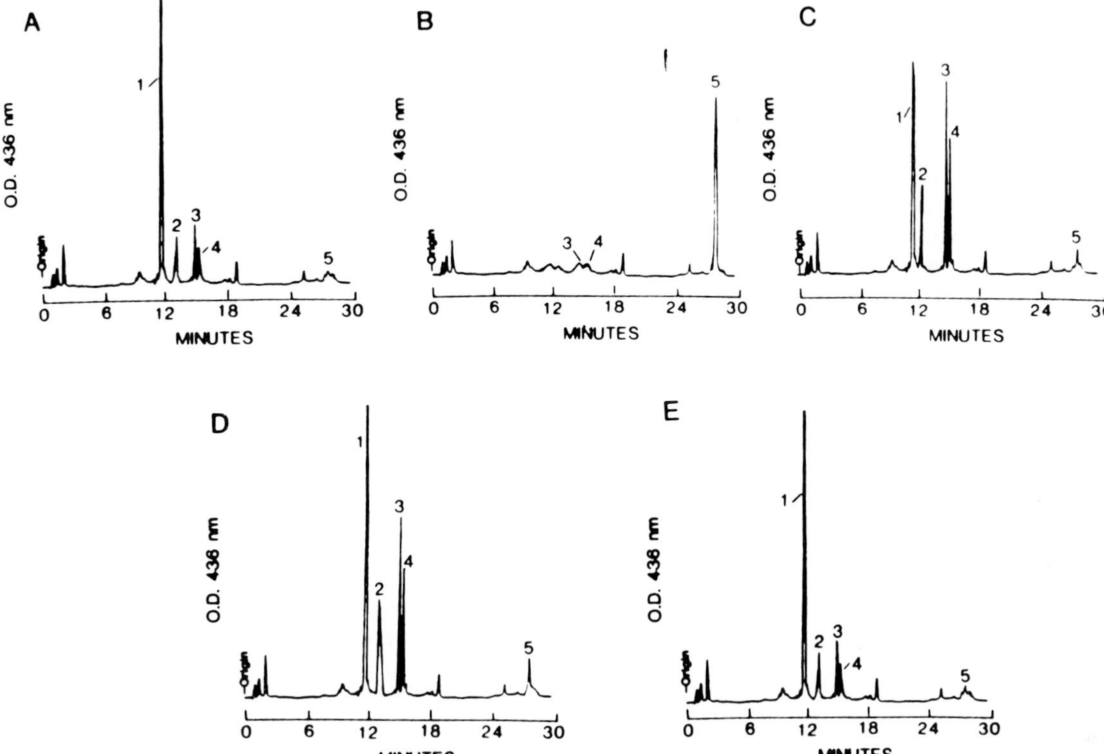

Fig. 53-12 High pressure liquid chromatography of intact underivatized bilirubin tetrapyrroles in human bile from a normal individual *(A)* and from patients with Crigler-Najjar syndrome, type I *(B)*; Crigler-Najjar syndrome, type II (Arias syndrome) *(C)*; Gilbert syndrome *(D)*; and Dubin-Johnson syndrome *(E)*. Bile pigments were separated by reverse-phase chromatography. Absorbance at 436 nm (ordinate) and retention time (abscissa) are shown. Peaks are as follows: 1 = bilirubin diglucuronide; 2 = bilirubin glucoside-glucuronide mixed conjugate; 3 and 4 = C-8 and C-12 isomers of bilirubin monoglucuronide; 5 = unconjugated bilirubin.

min has a fluorescence peak at 520 nm when excited at 430 nm. Unbound bilirubin and bilirubin bound to other proteins have negligible fluorescence. Addition of a saturating amount of bilirubin to blood results in maximum fluorescence allowing determination of total bilirubin-binding capacity. Addition of a detergent, dodecylmethylamine oxide, to whole blood results in hemolysis and quantitative incorporation of bilirubin into the detergent micelles. Fluorescence of detergent-bound bilirubin is used for quantitation of total bilirubin. These parameters can be readily determined using a digital hematofluorometer. Since fluorescence also depends on hemoglobin concentration, hemoglobin values are independently determined by the hematofluorometer and taken into account in calculation of displayed values for total and albumin-bound bilirubin and reserve bilirubin binding capacity.[354]

Biliary Excretion of Bilirubin

Canalicular excretion of bilirubin is thought to be an energy-dependent process which transports the pigment against a concentration gradient. In fish, unconjugated bilirubin can be excreted in bile. In mammals, conjugation is essential in bilirubin excretion. For example, Gunn rats and patients with the Crigler-Najjar syndrome, type I, lack UDP-glucuronyltransferase activity and manifest lifelong unconjugated hyperbilirubinemia. Accumulation of conjugated bilirubin in serum following intravenous infusion of unconjugated bilirubin at a rate exceeding the maximal excretory capacity of bilirubin suggests that canalicular transport, rather than conjugation, is rate limiting in bilirubin excretion.[355,356] When UDP-glucuronyltransferase activity is partially or totally deficient, conjugation may be rate limiting in bilirubin excretion.[357]

Patients with the Dubin-Johnson syndrome and mutant Corriedale sheep with an analogous hepatic defect have reduced capacity to transport conjugated bilirubin, bromosulphthalein, indocyanine green, iopanoic acid, phylloerythrin, and metanephrine glucuronide into the bile. Affected patients and sheep have normal transport maximum for infused taurocholate.[358–361] A dissociation between bilirubin and bile salt excretory capacity also occurs in the primate fetus.[362] These observations indicate that there are at least two mechanisms for organic anion excretion by the liver, one for bile salts and another for other organic anions.

Maximal bilirubin excretory capacity (T_{max}) depends on bile flow. Flow is increased by infusion of bile salts[363] or by phenobarbital treatment, which enhances bile flow rate by a nonbile salt-dependent mechanism.[364] The T_{max} of bilirubin is enhanced in both cases. Several other bile salt-independent choleretics increase bile flow, but not the T_{max} for organic anions.[365]

It has been proposed that incorporation of bilirubin conjugates into bile salt mixed micelles in bile reduces the concentration of bilirubin in bile and results in canalicular excretion of bilirubin down a gradient into a "micellar sink."[366] Infusion of bile salts that will not form micelles also enhances bilirubin excretory capacity.[367] The relationship of bile salt excretion, bile flow, and bilirubin excretion has been studied in patients with gallstones.[368] Approximately one-third of bilirubin excretion was calculated to be bile salt-independent. This suggests that bile salt micelles are not essential for canalicular transport of conjugated bilirubin in humans. Excretion of unconjugated bilirubin, which constitutes about 3 percent of bilirubin excreted in humans, may depend on interaction with mixed micelles.[369] Kinetic studies of taurocholate and BSP excretion suggest that there may be an interaction of bile salt receptors and receptors for other organic anions at the level of canalicular excretion.[370] Self-aggregation and incorporation of bilirubin in mixed micelles[366] may occur in bile and decrease the bilirubin concentration in the aqueous phase; the functional significance of this phenomenon is uncertain.[6]

Bilirubin, BSP, and indocyanine green apparently compete for biliary excretion. Since these anions compete for hepatic uptake and share intracellular binding proteins, it cannot be assumed that they share a common receptor in the bile canaliculus. Combined bilirubin and BSP infusion studies in rats indicate that BSP is excreted by two canalicular pathways. Bilirubin competes for only one of these.[369]

Recent studies have identified and purified a 100,000-dalton bile acid binding protein in rat liver cell canalicular membrane fractions.[371–373] This protein was absent from sinusoidal membrane fractions. Antibodies to this protein inhibited taurocholate transport in canalicular membrane vesicles. A similar protein was described in rat ileum and kidney. The relationship of this protein to pathophysiology of liver cell canalicular organic anion excretion remains to be established.

Fate of Bilirubin in the Gastrointestinal Tract. Bilirubin reaches the intestinal tract mainly conjugated and is not substantially absorbed.[374] In some circumstances, there may be enhanced excretion of unconjugated bilirubin into the intestine. Absorption of unconjugated bilirubin from the intestine may contribute to neonatal hyperbilirubinemia.[375] Absorption of bilirubin from the gallbladder occurs in animals.[376]

Bilirubin is degraded by intestinal bacteria into a series of urobilinogens and related products.[377,378] The specific products may relate to strains of bacteria present in the intestine.[379] Urobilinogens are present in deconjugated states. It is not known whether deconjugation precedes or follows bilirubin degradation, but bacterial β-glucuronidase plays a role in the deconjugation.[375,380] Most of the urobilinogen reabsorbed from the intestine is reexcreted in the bile. A small fraction is excreted by the kidney. Enhanced tubular absorption and instability of the pigment in acid urine make urobilinogen excretion in urine an unreliable indicator of the status of bilirubin metabolism. Absence of urobilinogen in stool and urine indicates complete obstruction of the bile duct. In liver disease and states of increased bilirubin production, urinary urobilinogen excretion is increased. Urobilinogen is colorless. Oxidation leads to formation of urobilin, which contributes to the color of normal urine and stool.

Alternate Pathways of Bilirubin Elimination. After injection of labeled unconjugated bilirubin, only 3 percent of radioactivity is normally excreted by the kidney in humans.[381] Even in the presence of marked hyperbilirubinemia, bile remains the main route of bilirubin excretion.[6]

In patients with Crigler-Najjar syndrome and in Gunn rats, a small amount of unconjugated bilirubin is secreted in bile. Additional unconjugated bilirubin may reach the intestinal lumen by passage across the intestinal wall or by desquamation of intestinal epithelial cells.[382] Ambient light or phototherapy forms geometric isomers of bilirubin (*EE*, *EZ*, or *ZE* forms), which are excreted in unconjugated forms and converted to bilirubin IXα-*ZZ* in the bile.[85,383,384] Considerable bilirubin is degraded to polar diazo-negative compounds which are excreted in both bile and urine.[382] A fraction of pigment is converted to tetrapyrrole dihydroxyl derivatives and dipyrroles.[385,386] Bilirubin catabolism in the liver is enhanced by induction of mixed function oxidases.[387]

In intrahepatic or extrahepatic cholestasis, the concentration of conjugated bilirubin in the plasma increases. After injection of radiolabeled bilirubin in animals with experimentally ligated bile ducts[388] and in children with biliary atresia,[389] 50 to 90 percent of injected radioactivity is excreted in urine. In total biliary obstruction, urinary excretion becomes the major pathway of bilirubin excretion.[390] Renal excretion of conjugated bilirubin depends on glomerular filtration of a small protein-free fraction of conjugated bilirubin.[390,391] There is evidence for tubular reabsorption but not for tubular secretion of bilirubin.[391]

DISORDERS OF BILIRUBIN METABOLISM

The hepatic transport of bilirubin involves four distinct but probably interrelated stages: (1) uptake from the circulation; (2) intracellular binding or storage; (3) conjugation, largely with glucuronic acid; and (4) biliary excretion. Abnormalities in any of these processes may result in hyperbilirubinemia. Complex clinical disorders, such as hepatitis or cirrhosis, may affect multiple processes. In several genetic disorders, the transfer of bilirubin from blood to bile is disrupted at a specific step. Study of these disorders has permitted better understanding of bilirubin metabolism in health and disease. Each disorder is characterized by varied degrees of hyperbilirubinemia of the unconjugated or conjugated type.

Disorders of Bilirubin Metabolism Resulting in Predominantly Unconjugated Hyperbilirubinemia

Neonatal Hyperbilirubinemia. By adult standards, every newborn has hyperbilirubinemia, and about half of all neonates become clinically jaundiced during the first 5 days of life. Serum bilirubin is predominantly unconjugated. Exaggeration of this "physiological jaundice" can result in marked hyperbilirubinemia with an attendant risk of kernicterus (see "Bilirubin Toxicity," above). In 4000 consecutive infants, 16 percent had maximal serum bilirubin concentrations of 10 mg/dl or above, and in 5 percent bilirubin concentrations exceeded 15 mg/dl.[392] In the normal, full-term human neonate, the serum bilirubin concentration increases rapidly from 1 to 2 to 5 to 6 mg/dl in approximately 72 h and subsequently decreases until normal levels are attained in 7 to 10 days.[393] Physiological jaundice of the newborn appears to result from a combination of increased bilirubin production and delayed maturation in the capability of the liver to dispose of bilirubin. Severe neonatal unconjugated hyperbilirubinemia results from exaggeration in one or more of the regularly occurring developmental restrictions which are characteristic of the newborn period or superimposition of additional mechanisms.

BILIRUBIN PRODUCTION. Increased bilirubin production in the newborn period is evidenced by increased endogenous carbon monoxide production,[394] increased early labeled peak from erythroid and nonerythroid sources,[392] and decreased erythrocyte half-life.[395,396] Meconium contains unconjugated bilirubin, which is primarily derived from hydrolysis of conjugated bilirubin by intestinal β-glucuronidase.[397] Compared to adults, newborns lack intestinal bacteria which degrade bilirubin to urobilinogen and have a greater surface-to-volume ratio of the bowel. As a result, intestinal absorption of unconjugated bilirubin in neonates may be increased.[397,398] Hemolytic diseases of the fetus increase bilirubin production and may lead to severe neonatal unconjugated hyperbilirubinemia. Rh incompatibility between mother and fetus used to be a common cause of severe neonatal unconjugated hyperbilirubinemia and kernicterus ("erythroblastosis fetalis"). This disease can be prevented by treatment of the mother with anti-Rh immunoglobulins.[399,400] Major blood group (ABO) incompatibility remains a common cause of exaggerated neonatal hyperbilirubinemia, which often requires treatment.[401,402]

HEPATIC BILIRUBIN UPTAKE. Cumulative hepatic bilirubin uptake capacity is reduced during the first 25 h of life in the rhesus monkey. Relative hepatic uptake deficiency extends beyond the second day of life and correlates with maturation of hepatic ligandin,[403–405] which influences the "net" hepatic uptake of bilirubin (see "Bilirubin Uptake," above). Delayed closure of the ductus venosus may permit portal blood, which is enriched in unconjugated bilirubin from the intestine, to bypass the liver.[406] Reduced caloric intake, which reduces hepatic bilirubin clearance in adults (see "Gilbert Syndrome," below), may have a similar effect in neonates.

HEPATIC BILIRUBIN CONJUGATION. In many mammals, including humans, UDP-glucuronyltransferase activity toward bilirubin is deficient in fetal liver and rapidly develops to adult levels during the first few days of life.[407,408] In fetal dog liver, UDP-glucuronyltransferase activity toward bilirubin is relatively mature, and newborn puppies do not have unconjugated hyperbilirubinemia.[409] Deficiency in bilirubin conjugation is not the only defect in the newborn; BSP clearance[406] and T_{max} for conjugated bilirubin[410] are also reduced. Deficiency of UDP-glucuronyltransferase activity may be prolonged and exaggerated in some genetic disorders due to inhibitory factor(s) in maternal milk or serum (see "Transient Familial Neonatal Hyperbilirubinemia," below).

CANALICULAR EXCRETION OF BILIRUBIN. During the late newborn period, hepatic bilirubin uptake, conjugation, and canalicular excretion attain adult levels, even though the bilirubin load remains increased. In this period of life, as in adults, canalicular excretion appears to be rate limiting in the hepatic disposition of bilirubin. Consequently, when the bilirubin load is further increased, conjugated bilirubin accumulates in serum.[411]

Transient Nonhemolytic Unconjugated Hyperbilirubinemia Associated with Breast-feeding. Plasma bilirubin concentrations tend to be higher in breast-fed infants compared with those in formula-fed babies,[412] and they occasionally rise to maximum concentrations of 15 to 24 mg/dl within 10 to 19 days of life.[410] Discontinuation of breast-feeding promptly ameliorates jaundice, which otherwise disappears within 1 month. No infant with this syndrome has developed kernicterus.[413]

Neonatal unconjugated hyperbilirubinemia related to breast-feeding is associated with an inhibitor of UDP-glucuronyltransferase activity in maternal milk but not maternal serum.[413–415] A progestational steroid, 3α,20β-pregnanediol, was isolated from the milk of mothers of infants who had the syndrome. The steroid inhibited *o*-aminophenol glucuronidation by guinea pig liver microsomes[413] and bilirubin glucuronidation by rat and rabbit liver,[413,414] but not by human liver.[415] Experimental feeding of the steroid to healthy infants yielded contradictory results.[416,417] Women whose infants have prolonged jaundice associated with breast-feeding have increased amounts of 3α,20β-pregnanediol in their urine.[418]

The free fatty acid concentration in maternal milk correlates positively with its inhibitory effect on human hepatic glucuronyltransferase activity,[416] and free fatty acids inhibit UDP-glucuronyltransferase activity in vitro in proportion to the number of double bonds in unsaturated fatty acids and in inverse proportion to the chain lengths of saturated fatty acids (C_{10} to C_{18}).[419] Foliot and associates postulate[419] that a lipolytic enzyme, which is present in some maternal milk samples, may be responsible for the increased concentration of free fatty acids in the milk. The inhibitory effect of maternal milk on UDP-glucuronyltransferase increases on storage and is destroyed by heating at 56°C.[419] Prolonged neonatal jaundice in breast-fed infants appears to result from multiple causes.

Transient Familial Neonatal Hyperbilirubinemia. In this syndrome, which was described by Lucey, Arias, and their associates in 1963,[420,421] jaundice occurs within the first 4 days of life. In 24 infants,[421] peak serum bilirubin concentrations of 8.9 to 65 mg/dl were reached within 7 days. An unidentified inhibitor of UDP-glucuronyltransferase was found in the serum of mothers of these infants. One died at age 36 h. This condition is clinically distinguished from jaundice associated with digestion of maternal milk by earlier onset of severe hyperbilirubinemia and occasional kernicterus.

Management of Neonatal Unconjugated Hyperbilirubinemia. Although a plasma bilirubin concentration of 20 mg/dl is usually considered dangerous, kernicterus occurs at lower concentrations of bilirubin (see "Toxicity of Bilirubin," above). The goal of treatment is to decrease serum bilirubin concentrations to an acceptable level until the capacity of the liver to dispose of bilirubin matures. Exchange transfusion and phototherapy are commonly used modes of management (see "Treatment of Crigler-Najjar Syndrome, Type I," below). Although phototherapy is useful and safe, concern persists about its potential side effects. Ingestion of agar to bind unconjugated bilirubin in the intestine also decreases serum bilirubin concentrations,[398] but the efficacy of this treatment is not certain.[397]

Increased Bilirubin Production. Hyperbilirubinemia in the presence of normal liver function often occurs in disorders associated with increased bilirubin production. The serum bilirubin is unconjugated and rarely exceeds 3 to 4 mg/dl. Higher levels usually indicate hepatobiliary dysfunction in addition to bilirubin overproduction.[6,422] The most common cause of increased bilirubin production is hemolysis such as occurs in sickle-cell anemia, hereditary spherocytosis, and toxic or idiosyncratic drug reactions in susceptible individuals. These disorders are associated with premature destruction of erythrocytes; red cell morphology and life span are often abnormal. In acute massive hemolysis, the rate of bilirubin production may transiently exceed the excretory transport maximum for biliary excretion of conjugated bilirubin, and conjugated hyperbilirubinemia may result.[423,424] Ineffective erythropoiesis occurs in thalassemia and other hematologic disorders and is often associated with hyperbilirubinemia.[425] Congenital dyserythropoietic anemias are a group of rare hereditary anemias characterized by ineffective erythropoiesis, intramedullary normoblastic hyperplasia, secondary hemochromatosis, and unconjugated hyperbilirubinemia.[426–429]

Crigler-Najjar Syndrome, Type I

CLINICAL FINDINGS. Crigler-Najjar syndrome, type I, is a rare disorder in which hepatic bilirubin UDP-glucuronyltransferase activity is absent (Table 53-1). The syndrome was described by Crigler and Najjar in 1952 in six infants in three related families.[430] All infants manifested severe nonhemolytic icterus within the first few days of life. Jaundice was characterized by increased plasma concentration of indirect-reacting bilirubin and was lifelong. Five of the six infants died of kernicterus by the age of 15 months. Although icteric, the single surviving infant was free of neurologic disease until age 15 years, when he suddenly developed kernicterus and died 6 months later.[421,432] A female cousin also had Crigler-Najjar syndrome with neurologic symptoms developing at 18 years of age. She died at the age of 24.[6,433,434] This family has increased consanguinity and several other recessively inherited traits, such as Morquio syndrome, homocystinuria, metachromatic leukodystrophy, and bird-headed dwarfism.[435]

Since 1952, over 70 other patients with Crigler-Najjar syndrome, type I, have been described, almost all of whom died with kernicterus during the neonatal period.[6,436,437] Survival past the neonatal period is uncommon, but several individuals have survived only to succumb to kernicterus later in life.[428,430,431,434–436] With the advent of better treatment of neonatal hyperbilirubinemia, individuals with this disorder survive into childhood. The syndrome occurs in all races, is transmitted as an autosomal recessive trait (Fig. 53-13),[432,439–441] and is often associated with consanguinity.

LABORATORY EXAMINATION. Laboratory test results in Crigler-Najjar syndrome, type 1, are normal except for the serum bilirubin level, which is usually 20 to 25 mg/dl but may be as high as 50 mg/dl.[430–434,436–438,440,441] Virtually all the serum bilirubin is unconjugated, and no serum conjugated bilirubin has been found. There is no bilirubinuria, but the urine may be yellow due to a chloroform-soluble pigment of unknown structure.[442] The level of icterus in a given patient varies and is lower in summer and on exposure to sun, and is higher during intercurrent illness.[382,433,437,443] The bile may be pale.[441] Stool color is normal, and fecal urobilinogen excretion is reduced.[430,441,444] Bilirubin production,[382,433,444] hematocrit, bone marrow morphology, and red cell survival[433,441,443] are normal. Results of routine liver function tests are normal, including studies of plasma disappearance of bromosulphthalein[430,433] and indocyanine green[433] and radiologic visualization of the biliary tree by cholecystographic agents. The patients have normal physical examinations, apart from jaundice and neurologic impairment, and lack hepatosplenomegaly. Liver biopsy reveals normal histology. In several patients, canalicular and bile ductular cholestasis were described (Fig. 53-14).[430,433,437] This probably results from biliary excretion of unconjugated bilirubin as an effect of phototherapy, with subsequent precipitation of bilirubin in the bile canaliculi. Electron microscopy of the liver reveals no specific pathologic change.[445–449]

Gunn Rat. The description by Gunn in 1938 of mutant Wistar rats with nonhemolytic unconjugated hyperbilirubinemia[450] and the wisdom of the late Professor William E. Castle, emeritus professor of genetics at Berkeley, who maintained the mutants for over 15 years, have resulted in major advances in understanding bilirubin metabolism, transport, and encephalopathy. Jaundice in these animals is inherited as an autosomal recessive trait.[450] Heterozygotes are anicteric. Homozygous rats have bilirubin levels that range from 3 to 20 mg/dl, depending on the rat strain.[451] All serum bilirubin is unconjugated,[452] there is no bilirubinuria, and bile is virtually colorless, although small amounts of nonglucuronide and

Table 53-1 Principal Differential Characteristics of Chronic Unconjugated Hyperbilirubinemias

	Crigler-Najjar syndrome, type I	*Crigler-Najjar syndrome, type II*	*Gilbert syndrome*
Histology of liver	Normal	Normal	Normal
Serum bilirubin concentration	20–50 mg/dl	<20 mg/dl	Usually <3 mg/dl
Routine liver function test results	Normal	Normal	Normal
45-min plasma BSP retention	Normal	Normal	Usually normal, may be elevated in some patients
Bile	Usually pale; contains trace of unconjugated bilirubin and monoconjugates	Increased proportion of bilirubin monoglucuronide	Increased proportion of bilirubin monoglucuronide
Hepatic bilirubin UDP-glucuronyltransferase activity	Absent	Reduced	Reduced
Effect of phenobarbital on serum bilirubin concentration	None	Reduction	Reduction
Mode of inheritance	Autosomal recessive	?Autosomal recessive	?Autosomal dominant
Prevalence	Rare	Uncommon	Common (≤5% of the population)
Prognosis	Kernicterus	Usually benign	Benign
Animal model	Homozygous Gunn rat	Heterozygous Gunn rat?	Mutant Southdown sheep?

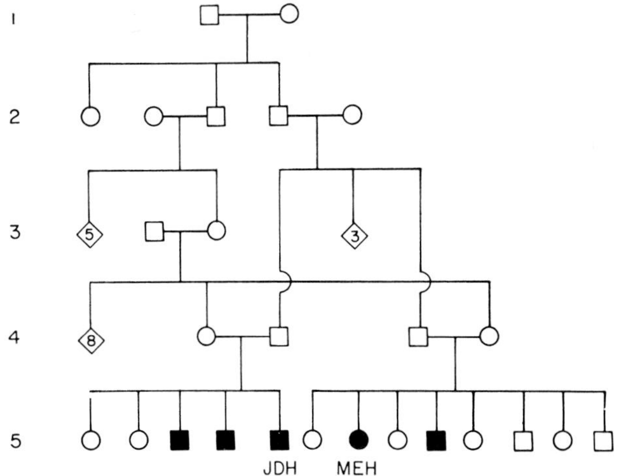

Fig. 53-13 Inheritance of Crigler-Najjar syndrome, type I. This family, originally described by Crigler and Najjar in 1962, is unique in that two cousins, JDH and MEH, escapted kernicterus in infancy only to die at ages 16 and 24, respectively. *(From Blaschke et al.*[433] *Used by permission.)*

glucuronide conjugates of bilirubin have been detected.[386] Liver histology is normal by light microscopy[452] and shows minor nonspecific structural modifications of the endoplasmic reticulum on electron microscopy.[446]

Homozygous Gunn rats are prototypes of Crigler-Najjar syndrome, type I, and frequently develop kernicterus.[437,452,453] Before studies in the Gunn rat, investigation of the pathogenesis of bilirubin encephalopathy was hampered by lack of a good experimental model.[437] Regional staining of the brain and selective necrosis of gray matter nuclei could not be produced in experimental animals by infusion of bilirubin, unless there was superimposed asphyxia. The Gunn rat is the only experimental model in which endogenously produced bilirubin results in neuropathologic lesions and neurologic deficits. These rats develop cytoplasmic neuronal changes on the third day of life, and, by 2 weeks, degeneration of Purkinje cells and other neurons occurs. The degenerative changes begin by enlargement of mitochondria and formation of membranous cytoplasmic bodies. By age 8 days, many mitochondria contain glycogen.[454,455] Although all Gunn rats have degenerative lesions of the brain, only half have gross disturbances of gait.[437] When a clinically healthy Gunn rat is killed and rapidly perfused with saline or formalin, the brain does not show yellow staining. Administration of sulfadimethoxine, a drug that competes with bilirubin for binding to albumin, to 14-day-old animals results in neurologic deterioration and yellow staining in the brain.[456] The basis of selectivity of bilirubin for certain types of neurons is unknown.[162] Whether these neurons specifically bind bilirubin or depend on metabolic processes that are specifically inhibited by bilirubin cannot be answered at the present time.[141,457]

Fig. 53-14 High power view (hematoxylin and eosin; magnification × 650) of a liver biopsy obtained from a patient with Crigler-Najjar syndrome, type I, during phototherapy. A portal area is shown with portal vein (PV) and a bile ductule B containing amorphous material, which appeared to be bilirubin. *(From Wolkoff et al.*[437] *Used by permission.)*

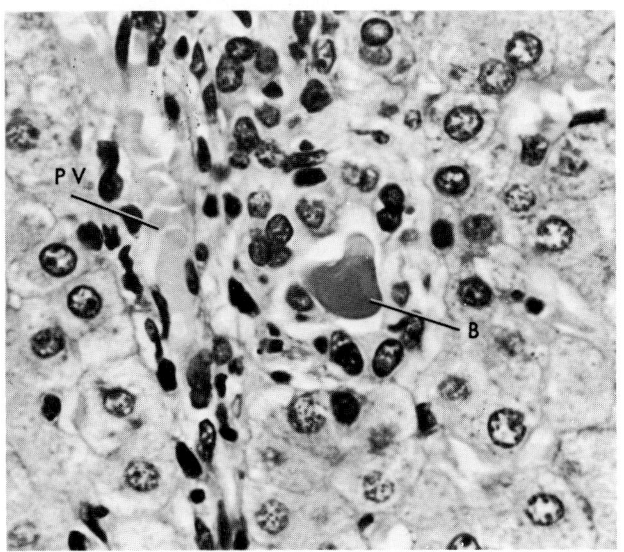

Gunn rats cannot concentrate their urine and do not tolerate water deprivation.[458,459] The renal medullary bilirubin concentration is high and interferes with sodium and water transport.[458–460] Occasionally, renal papillary necrosis occurs.[460] Treatment of rats with agents designed to lower serum bilirubin, such as cholestyramine, agar, or phototherapy, may ameliorate the renal lesion.[459,461,462] Similar concentrating problems have not been described in patients with Crigler-Najjar syndrome, type I, although bilirubin is deposited in the kidney.[180,462] Hereditary hydronephrosis and renal cysts occur in some Gunn rat colonies but are unrelated to the disorder in bilirubin metabolism and reflect a concomitant genetic abnormality.[463]

BIOCHEMICAL DEFECT. Similar to patients with Crigler-Najjar syndrome, type I, Gunn rats have virtually no bilirubin conjugates in bile.[382,386,452] Although they can excrete many organic anions, including BSP,[386] phenol red,[464] and conjugated bilirubin,[178,259] little if any exogenously administered unconjugated bilirubin is excreted in bile.[78,360,452] Although Gunn rats lack UDP-glucuronosyltransferase activity toward bilirubin, transferase activity for aniline,[465] steroid substrates,[305] and thyroid hormone[466] is normal. The transferase activity toward 4-nitrophenol is present at a lower level but is restored to normal upon addition of diethylnitrosamine in vitro.[306] A defective form of UDP-glucuronosyltransferase, which exhibits transferase activity toward 4-nitrophenol only in the presence of diethylnitrosamine, has been isolated.[467] Recently, five UDP-glucuronosyltransferase isoforms were purified from Gunn rat liver by chromatofocusing, affinity chromatography, and hydrophobic interaction chromatography.[468] The isoform that is normally active toward bilirubin is present in an immunoreactive form but is enzymatically inactive in Gunn rats. Another isoform that normally catalyzes glucuronidation of 4-nitrophenol and methylumbeliferone has a greatly reduced level of activity, but activity is restored to near normal levels by diethylnitrosamine. Three other isoforms, which are normally active toward steroid substrates, have normal transferase activity in Gunn rats.

TREATMENT OF CRIGLER-NAJJAR SYNDROME, TYPE I. Unconjugated hyperbilirubinemia in Crigler-Najjar syndrome, type I, is usually associated with bilirubin encephalopathy (kernicterus). Treatment is designed to reduce serum bilirubin levels and is often ineffective or impractical on a long-term basis. Unlike results in patients with Crigler-Najjar syndrome, type II, and Gilbert syndrome, the serum bilirubin level and hepatic bilirubin glucuronidation activity do not respond to phenobarbital administration.[433,441,443,469,470] Plasmapheresis is the most efficient means for reducing serum bilirubin concentration acutely (Fig. 53-15).[433,434,437] This procedure takes advantage of the fact that bilirubin is tightly bound to serum albumin and may be quantitatively removed from the body by removal of albumin. Phototherapy has received widespread acceptance and is the major treatment for icteric newborns whose serum bilirubin concentrations place them at risk for kernicterus.[383,433,434,437,469–472] Experience with phototherapy in older children and adults is limited to patients with Crigler-Najjar syndrome, type I. After children reach 3 or 4 years of age, phototherapy becomes relatively less effective due to thickening of the skin, increased skin pigmentation, and decreased surface area in relation to body mass.[437] The mechanisms whereby phototherapy reduces serum bilirubin concentrations are complex and are described in "Chemistry of Bilirubin," above.

Chronic phlebotomy in Crigler-Najjar syndrome, type I, was used in one patient to reduce the average age of circulating erythrocytes and hence reduce bilirubin production.[473] As expected, bilirubin production fell significantly but was accompanied by unexpected reduction in plasma bilirubin clearance. The plasma bilirubin level remained unaffected. Affinity chromatography of bilirubin-containing blood on albumin-conjugated agarose gel has also been suggested as treatment for this disorder.[434,474,475] Although effective in reducing hyperbilirubinemia in Gunn rats, difficulties due to removal of formed elements are encountered with simian or human blood.[476,477]

Crigler-Najjar syndrome, type I, is a single enzyme deficiency disease, and UDP-glucuronosyltransferase replacement is a possible future treatment. Transplantation of a normal Wistar rat kidney, which contains bilirubin UDP-glucuronosyltransferase activity, into homozygous Gunn rats results in a rapid decrease in serum bilirubin concentration and in excretion of bilirubin glucuronides in bile.[325] However, since enzyme activity is undetectable in human kidney, renal transplantation cannot be recommended for the treatment of Crigler-Najjar syndrome, type I.

Subcutaneous transplantation of rat hepatoma cells[478] and portal venous infusion of hepatocytes[479] isolated from heterozygous Gunn rats resulted in transient biliary excretion of bilirubin glucuronides in homozygous Gunn rats and in reduction of plasma bilirubin concentration. Transplantation of small pieces of normal rat liver into homozygous Gunn rats was also reported to reduce serum bilirubin concentration[480]; however, attempts at confirmation of these results were unsuccessful.[481]

Intraperitoneal injection of isolated liver cells bound to collagen-coated dextran microcarriers has been successfully used to provide bilirubin UDP-glucuronosyltransferase activity to Gunn rats.[482–484] The injected microcarriers with attached hepatocytes rapidly form conglomerates on the anterior surface of the pancreas and develop their own blood supply.[483] When normal rat hepatocytes were transplanted into congeneic recipients, conjugated bilirubin was present in bile for at least 6 weeks, and serum bilirubin progressively decreased to near normal levels over the course of 4 weeks.[482–484]

Because, at present, there is no other effective long-term treatment for patients with this condition, liver transplantation has been proposed as definitive therapy.[485] Although this procedure is not without risk in these individuals, there has been a recent report of successful orthotopic liver transplantation in a 3-year-old girl with Crigler-Najjer syndrome, type I.[486] Serum bilirubin rapidly declined to normal levels after transplantation.

Fig. 53-15 Summary of the hospital course of a 19-year-old patient with Crigler-Najjar syndrome, type I, who was admitted with acute bilirubin encephalopathy. Before hospitalization, the patient's serum bilirubin ranged between 35 and 45 mg/dl. After an initial course of plasmapheresis and maintenance phototherapy, serum bilirubin was maintained between 10 and 15 mg/dl. *(From Wolkoff et al.[437] Used by permission.)*

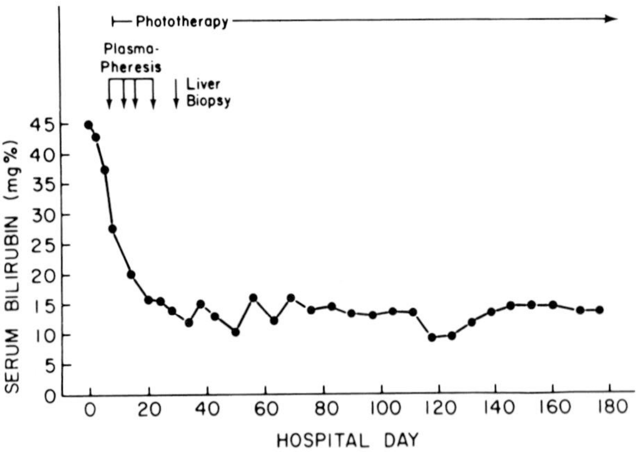

Crigler-Najjar Syndrome, Type II

CLINICAL FINDINGS. Crigler-Najjar syndrome, type II, is phenotypically similar to Crigler-Najjar syndrome, type I, except that it is almost always clinically benign and the serum bilirubin concentration is usually below 20 mg/dl (Table 53-1).[422] This disorder was first described in 1962[438] in a study of chronic unconjugated hyberilirubinemia in 8 patients between 14 and 52 years of age. Although half the patients were icteric before the age of 1 year, one patient was 30 years old before jaundice was noted. In these patients, serum bilirubin concentration ranged from 8 to 18 mg/dl. Each had reduced hepatic glucuronyltransferase activities using bilirubin, *o*-aminophenol, or 4-methylumbelliferone as glucuronide acceptor. Survival of ^{51}Cr red cells was normal. All patients were clinically normal, apart from icterus, except for a 43-year-old female with a neurologic syndrome resembling kernicterus. The patient died at the age of 44. Autopsy revealed a histologically normal liver. The brain was small and lacked bilirubin staining but demonstrated the typical histology of kernicterus.

Several other cases of neurologic abnormality in Crigler-Najjar syndrome, type II, have been described subsequently. Three brothers had Crigler-Najjar syndrome, type II, for over 50 years.[487] Two were neurologically normal. The third had a slight bilateral intention tremor and nonspecific abnormalities on electroencephalogram. These nonspecific neurologic changes had not been noted previously. The third patient was a 15-year-old male who was icteric from the second day of life.[488] Total serum bilirubin was 24 mg/dl at 10 months and averaged approximately 15 mg/dl thereafer. Development was normal, although psychological testing revealed a perceptual deficit and slightly subnormal intelligence. At age 13, following surgery for acute appendicitis, the serum bilirubin rose to 40 mg/dl, and the patient developed diplopia, generalized seizures, confusion, and an abnormal electroencephalogram. He was treated for hyperbilirubinemia and, after recovering from surgery, resumed a bilirubin level of 15 mg/dl. His neurologic status returned to baseline, and he has remained well.

LABORATORY EXAMINATION. As in Crigler-Najjar syndrome, type I, laboratory examination is normal except for elevated serum bilirubin, which is usually less than 20 mg/dl but may be as high as 40 mg/dl during fasting[487] or intercurrent illness.[488] Serum bilirubin is unconjugated, and there is no bilirubinuria. The bile is pigmented, although less than 50 percent of estimated daily bilirubin production is excreted into bile.[441,488] Although over 90 percent of conjugated bilirubin in normal bile is bilirubin diglucuronide, the major pigment in this syndrome is bilirubin monoglucuronide.[438,485] The biochemical reason for this change in biliary conjugates is not known. The liver has virtually no bilirubin UDP-glucuronyltransferase activity.[488,489]

EFFECT OF PHENOBARBITAL. The reduced levels of hepatic bilirubin UDP-glucuronyltransferase activity in Crigler-Najjar syndrome, type II, suggested that an inducer of microsomal enzymes could ameliorate the hyperbilirubinemia.[490–491] Subsequent study revealed that hyperbilirubinemia is reduced following treatment with phenobarbital.[441] Similar results were obtained with other liver microsomal enzyme inducers.[492–497] The response to phenobarbital treatment differentiates Crigler-Najjar syndrome, type I, in which there is no response, from Crigler-Najjar syndrome, type II (Fig. 53-16).[441] Although phenobarbital may act by inducing bilirubin UDP-glucuronyltransferase activity, increased enzyme activity has only rarely been demonstrated (Fig. 53-17).[487,496] Assay of the enzyme is relatively insensitive, and a small increase in activity could ameliorate hyperbilirubinemia. Occasional patients have been described in whom differentiation of these two types of Crigler-Najjar syndrome is difficult.[497]

INHERITANCE. Crigler-Najjar syndrome, type II, commonly occurs in families.[438,441] There is neither sex predilection nor evidence of consanguinity. The pattern of inheritance is not certain. Both autosomal dominant transmission with incomplete penetrance[438,441] and autosomal recessive transmission[497,498] have been suggested. The data suggest that individuals with substantial elevations of bilirubin are homozygotes or compound heterozygotes at this locus, while some heterozygous family members have more subtle biochemical abnormalities. In one study of three families, parents and sibs of affected individuals had mild unconjugated hyperbilirubinemia consistent with Gilbert syndrome,[497,498] and it was suggested that Crigler-Najjar syndrome, type II, might represent a homozygous form of Gilbert syndrome.[499] This would not appear to provide a complete explanation, since the majority of parents of Crigler-Najjar patients do not have the Gilbert syndrome. More detailed biochemical analysis of bilirubin conjugates in patients and their families may clarify the inheritance of these disorders.[488,489] The availability of cloned DNAs for UDP-glucuronyltransferase may determine the extent to which these disorders represent allelic conditions with a range of symptoms in homozygotes, compound heterozygotes, and heterozygotes for various alleles.

Gilbert Syndrome

CLINICAL FINDINGS. This syndrome, described by Gilbert in 1901, has also been called constitutional hepatic dysfunction and familial nonhemolytic jaundice.[500,501] It is characterized by mild, chronic, unconjugated hyperbilirubinemia (Table 53-1). Familial occurrence is common,[502] and a dominant mode of inheritance has been suggested,[503] although most patients present as isolated cases.

Typically, Gilbert syndrome is diagnosed in young adults who present with mild, predominantly unconjugated hyperbilirubinemia.[504] Serum bilirubin levels are usually less than 3 mg/dl, fluctuate with time, and rise to higher levels during intercurrent illness. Aside from icterus, physical examination is normal. Some patients complain of vague constitutional symptoms, including fatigue and abdominal discomfort.[504] These patients usually have seen many physicians and have undergone many diagnostic tests. Their symptoms are probably manifestations of anxiety. Newly presenting patients are rarely symptomatic. Results of routine laboratory tests in Gilbert syndrome are normal except for elevated serum bilirubin concentrations. There is no elevation of serum alkaline phosphatase or aminotransferase activities. Oral cholecystography allows visualization of the gallbladder. Although percutaneous liver biopsy is not routinely indicated in patients with Gilbert syndrome, liver histology is normal. Often a nonspecific ac-

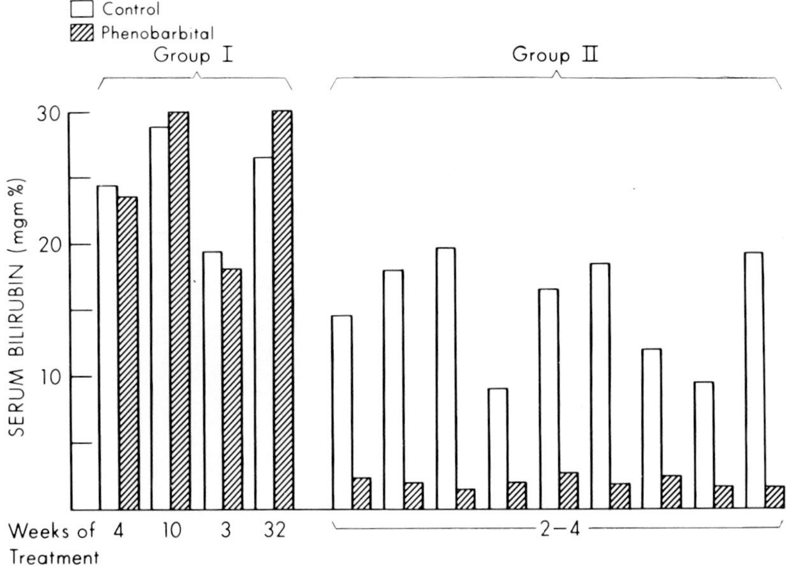

Fig. 53-16 Differentiation of types I and II Crigler-Najjar syndrome on the basis of response to phenobarbital. All patients had chronic unconjugated hyperbilirubinemia and were treated for at least several weeks with phenobarbital. *(From Arias et al.[441] Used by permission.)*

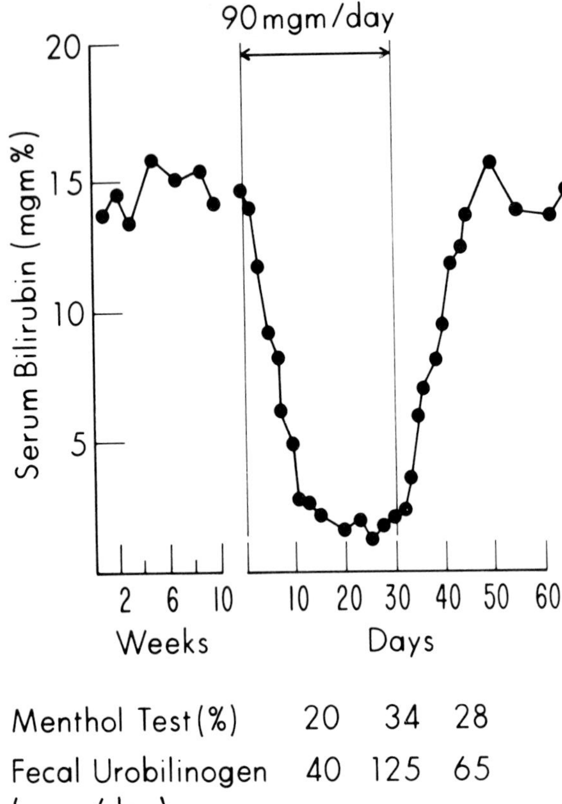

Fig. 53-17 The effect of phenobarbital administration on serum bilirubin concentration, menthol tolerance test, and fecal urobilinogen excretion in a patient with Crigler-Najjar syndrome, type II. *(From Arias et al.[441] Used by permission.)*

cumulation of lipofuscin pigment is seen in the centrilobular zones.[445,505] Electron-microscope studies have not revealed consistent ultrastructural alterations.[506–508]

ORGANIC ANION TRANSPORT. The pathogenesis of unconjugated hyperbilirubinemia in Gilbert syndrome is not known. Several studies of the disappearance of plasma bilirubin after intravenous injection into patients with Gilbert syndrome have demonstrated reduced clearance (Fig. 53-18.)[496,509–516] Multicompartmental analysis suggests that reduced plasma clearance results from reduction in hepatic bilirubin uptake as well as bilirubin conjugation.[509,510,512,513] Because the hepatic uptake of bilirubin is independent of intracellular events, such as protein binding,[180] the presence of defects in uptake and conjugation in Gilbert syndrome suggests coexistence of two seemingly unrelated biochemical abnormalities. Goresky et al.[515] determined the initial plasma disappearance of radiolabeled bilirubin and then determined an initial space of distribution by dividing the injected dose by the plasma volume as determined after radiolabeled albumin injection. The initial plasma disappearance of bilirubin was as rapid in patients with Gilbert syndrome as in normal subjects. These results suggest that uptake of bilirubin is normal in Gilbert syndrome.[515,516] Reduced activity of hepatic bilirubin UDP-glucuronyltransferase has been described in Gilbert syndrome (Fig. 53-19).[438,441,494,517–520] Its relationship to hyperbilirubinemia is not clear, since the remaining enzyme activity exceeds by tenfold that which is necessary to conjugate normal daily bilirubin production. Because of low intrinsic activity, this membrane-bound enzyme is assayed after activation with detergents.[517] Consequently the measured enzyme activity may not truly reflect that which is physiologically available. Administration of phenobarbital or other microsomal enzyme inducers reduces the hyperbilirubinemia in Gilbert syndrome and increases the plasma clearance of bilirubin.[494,497,521,522] Hepatic bilirubin UDP-glucuronyltransferase activity does not increase in these patients.[434,496,519,523]

It is likely that Gilbert syndrome represents a heterogeneous group of disorders, some of which have an anion uptake defect. Although plasma disappearance of organic anions other than bilirubin is usually normal in Gilbert syndrome (Fig. 53-20), two subsets were described in which plasma disappearance of bromosulphthalein[524–526] and indocyanine green[527] was abnormal (Fig. 53-21). In one group, reduced disappearance of BSP and indocyanine green from the plasma suggested reduced hepatic uptake. In the second group, compartmental analysis revealed a defect in BSP transport at a later stage in the transport process. BSP is conjugated in the liver with glutathione, whereas indocyanine green is excreted into bile intact. Excretion of neither of these compounds depends on bilirubin UDP-glucuronyltransferase activity, since their plasma

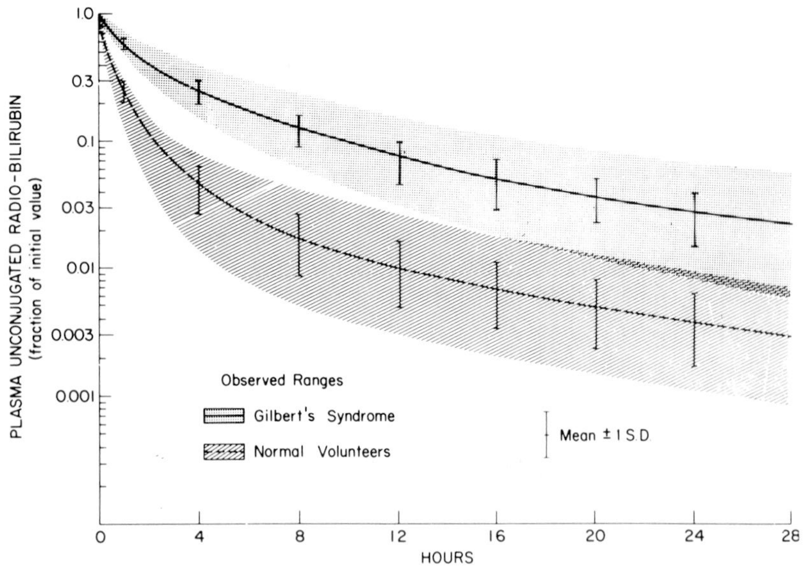

Fig. 53-18 Plasma disappearance of a tracer dose of [^{3}H]bilirubin after intravenous administration to patients with Gilbert syndrome and to normal volunteers. There is no overlap between the two groups for the first 16 h after injection. *(From Berk et al.[510] Used by permission.)*

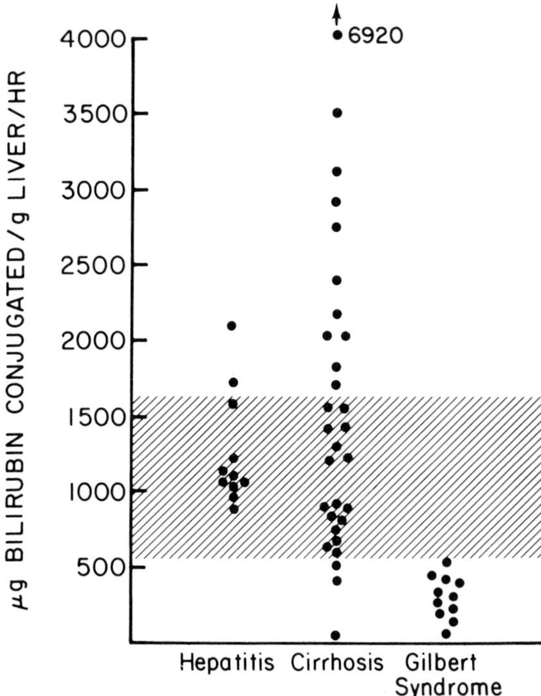

Fig. 53-19 Hepatic bilirubin UDP-glucuronyltransferase activity in patients with hepatitis, cirrhosis, and Gilbert syndrome. The hatched area indicates the normal range. *(From Black and Billing.*[517] *Used by permission.)*

disappearance is normal in Crigler-Najjar syndrome, type I, and in Gunn rats.

The serum bilirubin level in a patient with Gilbert syndrome fluctuates for unknown reasons.[504] Factors such as intercurrent illness, physical exertion, and stress have been implicated, and a relationship to the menstrual cycle has been

Fig. 53-20 Plasma concentration of BSP 45 min after intravenous administration of 5 mg/kg to normal individuals and patients with Gilbert syndrome. There is a subset of patients in whom BSP retention is elevated. *(From Berk et al.*[524] *Used by permission.)*

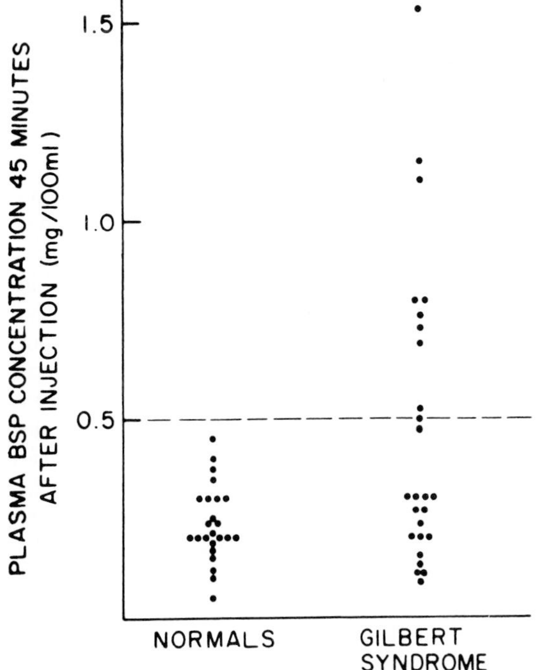

reported in two women.[528] A 48-h fast exaggerates the unconjugated hyperbilirubinemia of Gilbert syndrome.[514,523,529–535] Serum bilirubin levels in normal individuals[523,529–535] and in individuals with other hepatobiliary disorders also rise with fasting.[523,531] Although serum bilirubin response following a 48-h fast has been claimed to be diagnostic of Gilbert syndrome, this is controversial. The fasting test appears to be of limited use in the differential diagnosis of Gilbert syndrome.

The mechanism of fasting-induced hyperbilirubinemia is not understood. It results from reduced hepatic clearance of bilirubin from plasma rather than increased production of bilirubin.[496,522,535] Studies in normal rats revealed no change in hepatic bilirubin UDP-glucuronyltransferase activity during fasting,[536] although there was reduced activity of UDP-glucose dehydrogenase resulting in reduced hepatic content of UDP-glucuronate.[537] Fasting must also affect hepatic disposition of bilirubin at a step other than conjugation, because fasting exacerbates hyperbilirubinemia in homozygous Gunn rats.[535,536,538,539] It may be a result of several factors, and roles for increased serum nonesterified fatty acids[540] and reduced hepatic content of the cytosolic ligandin and *Z* protein[541] have been suggested.

Intravenous nicotinic acid administration has also been proposed as a provocative test for the diagnosis of Gilbert syndrome.[542,543] Like that for fasting, its diagnostic value is controversial, and it does not clearly separate patients with Gilbert syndrome from normal subjects or those with hepatobiliary disease.[543,544] Unconjugated hyperbilirubinemia following nicotinic acid administration does not occur after splenectomy,[542] and nicotinic acid-induced unconjugated hyperbilirubinemia is probably the result of increased erythrocyte fragility, increased splenic heme oxygenase activity, and increased splenic bilirubin formation.[545]

The diagnosis of Gilbert syndrome has conventionally been applied to individuals with mild unconjugated hyperbilirubinemia without evidence of hemolysis or structural liver disease. By determining plasma clearance of radiolabeled bilirubin in hyperbilirubinemic patients with hemolysis, individuals with reduced clearance, as is characteristic in Gilbert syndrome, may be more frequently seen in chronic hemolysis,[546] because the combination of both factors results in higher, more clinically apparent bilirubin levels than in individuals with either abnormality alone. In a recent investigation, radiolabeled bilirubin clearance studies were performed in patients with chronic hemolysis due to hereditary spherocytosis.[547] Following elective splenectomy, which normalized the hemolytic state, the studies were repeated. In seven patients, initially normal values for bilirubin clearance were unaltered by surgery. In another seven patients, low preoperative bilirubin clearance values uniformly improved following splenectomy and became normal in five patients. Family studies and reduced activity of hepatic bilirubin UDP-glucuronyltransferase supported the initial diagnosis of Gilbert syndrome. These patients may represent a latent form of Gilbert syndrome which is unmasked by increased bilirubin production during hemolysis.

The relative content of bilirubin mono- and diglucuronide in bile is of potential use in the diagnosis of Gilbert syndrome. Similar to findings in patients with Crigler-Najjar syndrome, type II, and heterozygous Gunn rats, bile from patients with Gilbert syndrome has an increased proportion of bilirubin monoglucuronide (Table 53-2).[478,479,515,548] The relationship of reduced hepatic bilirubin UDP-glucuronyltransferase activity to this abnormal pattern of biliary bilirubin conjugates is not

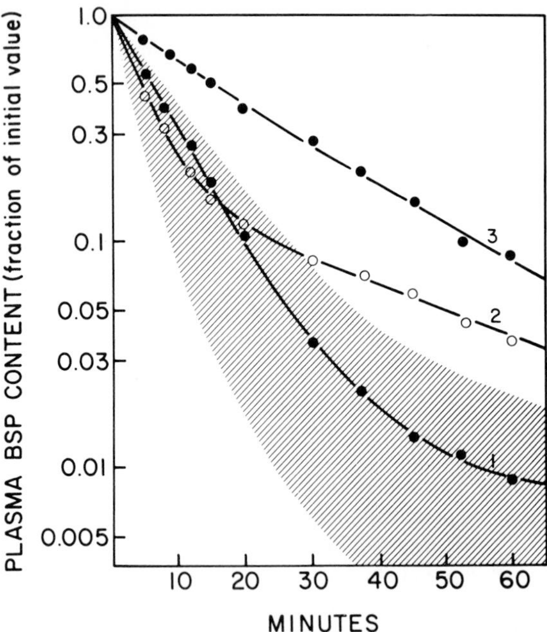

Fig. 53-21 Plasma BSP disappearance curves in three patients with Gilbert syndrome. The shaded area indicates the normal range. Curve 1 is indistinguishable from normal. Curves 2 and 3 are representative of the two subtypes of abnormal BSP disappearance seen in some patients with otherwise typical Gilbert syndrome. *(From Berk et al.*[524] *Used by permission.)*

known. The findings suggest that Crigler-Najjar syndrome, type II, may represent a more pronounced phenotypic expression than does Gilbert syndrome of a common biochemical defect. Although the specificity of elevated bilirubin monoglucuronide in bile for these two syndromes is not known, it may serve as a useful marker for diagnosis and for studies of inheritance.

INHERITANCE. Although it is a relatively common disorder, the incidence of Gilbert syndrome is not known, primarily because a uniform definition for diagnosis has not been established. It is commonly accepted that the sine qua non of Gilbert syndrome is unconjugated hyperbilirubinemia without overt hemolysis. The normal upper limit of serum bilirubin is not always apparent in a given laboratory, and serum bilirubin levels in the general population have been described as following a skewed[549–552] rather than a Gaussian distribution. Others suggest a bimodal distribution.[503,553] Serum bilirubin levels in males are significantly higher than in females,[553–555] which may account, in part, for the reported higher incidence of Gilbert syndrome in males.[503,504] Because of these difficulties in diagnosis, mild Gilbert syndrome may go unrecognized. A clinically inapparent latent form of the disorder has been described.[547] In contrast, unconjugated hyperbilirubinemia to levels of 5 to 8 mg/dl occurs in Gilbert syndrome and in patients with Crigler-Najjar syndrome, type II. Differentiation of these disorders based upon serum bilirubin levels, hepatic bilirubin UDP-glucuronyltransferase activity, and bilirubin monoglucuronide content of bile may be arbitrary.

That Gilbert syndrome is a genetic disorder, although often difficult to diagnose, is clear.[501–503,551,556–559] Whether Gilbert syndrome and Crigler-Najjar syndrome, type II, represent distinct pathophysiological disorders, or a spectrum of a single disorder, is not clear. Although an autosomal dominant inheritance has been suggested for Gilbert syndrome,[503,551,556] the difficulties inherent in diagnosing the disorder make this conclusion tenuous. Additional family studies using markers such as bilirubin monoglucuronide content of bile may provide more conclusive information as to inheritance.

The genetics of Crigler-Najjar syndrome, type II, and Gilbert syndrome remains unclear. Many of these patients could be affected with homozygous or compound heterozygous genotypes which leave residual enzyme activity. Transmission from generation to generation might be related to pseudodominance, since mutant genes for the Gilbert phenotype may be very common. Alternatively, dominant negative mutations (see Chap. 1) might account for the generation-to-generation transmission with the abnormal gene product impairing the function of the normal gene product. Crigler-Najjar syndrome, types I and II, and Gilbert syndrome all could be explained by different mutations at a single locus, or multiple loci might be involved. The availability of cloned DNAs for UDP-glucuronyltransferase may help to resolve these questions soon.

Table 53-2 Distribution of Bile Pigments in Biliary Aspirates from Normal Control Subjects and Patients with Gilbert Syndrome

	Relative content, %, mean ± SD	
Bilirubin tetrapyrrole	*Normal subjects,* n = *13*	*Patients with syndrome,* n = *16*
Bilirubin diglucuronide	87.6 ± 4.3	67.8 ± 9.3*
Bilirubin monoglucoside monoglucuronide diester	2.2 ± 3.7	3.6 ± 3.4
Bilirubin monoglucuronide	6.8 ± 4.7	23.4 ± 9.4*
Bilirubin	4.4 ± 3.5	5.0 ± 2.7

*$p < 0.001$.
SOURCE: From Goresky et al.[515] Used by permission.

Mutant Southdown Sheep. Congenital photosensitivity in Southdown sheep was first observed in New Zealand in 1942.[560] It is inherited as an autosomal recessive trait[561] and is characterized by unconjugated hyperbilirubinemia and photodermatitis resulting from retention of phylloerythrin, the end product of chlorophyll metabolism that is normally excreted by the liver into bile.[562] The original mutant line of sheep was lost but similar photosensitive mutants were later found in California.[563] These sheep have reduced plasma disappearance of intravenously administered bilirubin, BSP, cholate, indocyanine green, and ^{131}I-labeled rose bengal[560] and reduced BSP transport maximum (T_m) and relative storage capacity (S).[563,564] It has been suggested that mutant sheep have increased bilirubin production from nonerythroid sources, and overproduction of bilirubin from hepatic heme has been postulated.[565] Plasma disappearance of intravenously administered [^{14}C]bilirubin has been studied, and it was suggested on the basis of compartmental analysis that the results resembled those obtained during similar studies in patients with Gilbert syndrome,[566] but there was a similarity only in reduced hepatic influx of bilirubin. As distinct from patients with Gilbert syndrome, mutant sheep had significantly increased efflux from liver to plasma and normal hepatic sequestration rates. Bilirubin UDP-glucuronyltransferase activity is normal in mutant sheep.[479] The mechanism of unconjugated hyperbilirubinemia in these animals most likely differs from that in patients with Gilbert syndrome. In addition to hyperbilirubinemia, mutant sheep demonstrate chronic interstitial nephritis manifested by polyuria, increased sodium excretion, and reduced renal plasma flow, glomerular filtration rate, and urea clearance.[567,568] The relationship of these findings to the hyperbilirubinemia is unknown.

Bolivian Squirrel Monkey. Bolivian squirrel monkeys have higher postcibal serum unconjugated bilirubin concentration and a greater degree of fasting hyperbilirubinemia than does a closely related Brazilian population.[569] Compared to the Brazilian population, Bolivian monkeys have slower plasma clearance of intravenously administered bilirubin, a lower level of hepatic bilirubin UDP-glucuronosyltransferase activity, and a higher bilirubin monoglucuronide to diglucuronide ratio in bile.[569] The two populations of squirrel monkeys have comparable erythrocyte life span and hepatic glutathione-*S*-transferase activity.[569] In these respects, the Bolivian squirrel monkeys are a model of human Gilbert syndrome. Fasting hyperbilirubinemia is rapidly reversed by oral or intravenous administration of carbohydrates, but not by lipid administration.[570]

Disorders of Bilirubin Metabolism Resulting in Predominantly Conjugated Hyperbilirubinemia

Dubin-Johnson Syndrome

CLINICAL FINDINGS. In 1954, Dubin and Johnson[571] and Sprinz and Nelson[572] described patients with chronic nonhemolytic jaundice. The liver was grossly black, but the histology was normal except for an unidentified pigment in hepatocytes. Subsequently this disorder has been described in both sexes in virtually all nationalities and races.[436,573–584] Dubin-Johnson syndrome occurs frequently (1:1300) in Persian Jews[585] in whom it is associated with deficiency of clotting factor VII[586–588] (Chap. 85).

The syndrome is clinically characterized by mild, predominantly conjugated hyperbilirubinemia (Table 53-3). Except for jaundice, physical examination is normal. An occasional patient may have hepatosplenomegaly. Mild constitutional complaints such as vague abdominal pains and weakness occur, but for the most part patients are asymptomatic.[573,585] Pruritus is absent in Dubin-Johnson syndrome, and serum bile acid levels are normal.[583,589] The degree of icterus is increased by intercurrent illness, oral contraceptives, and pregnancy (Fig. 53-22).[583] The Dubin-Johnson syndrome is rarely detected before puberty, although cases have been reported in neonates.[590–592] Often the disorder is not noted until a woman becomes pregnant or receives oral contraceptives which convert mild chemical hyperbilirubinemia into overt jaundice.[583]

LABORATORY EXAMINATION. Routine laboratory examination[573,575,580,583–585] reveals normal complete blood count, serum albumin, cholesterol, transaminases, alkaline phosphatase, and prothrombin time. Serum bilirubin is usually between 2 and 5 mg/dl but can be as high as 20 to 25 mg/dl. Bilirubinuria is frequent, and 50 percent or more of total serum bilirubin is conjugated. The serum bilirubin level fluctuates, and frequently individual determinations may be normal. Oral cholecystography, even using a "double dose" of contrast material, usually does not visualize the gallbladder, although visualization may occur 4 to 6 h after intravenous injection of iodipamide.[593–595] On direct inspection, the liver is black. Light microscopy reveals normal histology except for accumulation of a dense pigment, which on electron microscopy appears to be contained within lysosomes.[596,597]

Several investigators have suggested that these pigment granules are composed primarily of poorly defined lipofuscins.[598–600] On the basis of histochemical staining characteristics and physichochemical properties of extracted pigment, other investigators suggested that the Dubin-Johnson pigment resembled melanin.[601–604] The mutant Corriedale sheep is an animal model of Dubin-Johnson syndrome (see "Mutant Corriedale Sheep," below) in which the hepatic pigment has also

Table 53-3 Principal Differential Characteristics of Chronic Conjugated Hyperbilirubinemias

	Dubin-Johnson syndrome	*Rotor syndrome*
Appearance of liver	Grossly black	Normal
Histology of liver	Dark pigment; predominantly in centrilobular areas; otherwise normal	Normal; no increase in pigmentation
Serum bilirubin	Usually elevated, occasionally as high as 20 mg/dl; predominantly direct reacting	Usually elevated, occasionally as high as 20 mg/dl; predominantly direct reacting
Routine liver function tests	Normal except for bilirubin	Normal except for bilirubin
45-min plasma BSP retention	Normal or elevated; secondary rise at 90 min	Elevated; no secondary rise at 90 min
BSP infusion studies	T_m virtually 0; S normal	T_m and S both reduced
Oral cholecystogram	Usually does not visualize the gallbladder	Usually visualizes the gallbladder
Urinary coproporphyrin	Normal total; >80% as coproporphyrin I	Elevated total; elevated proportion of coproporphyrin I but <80%
Mode of inheritance	Autosomal recessive	Autosomal recessive
Prevalence	Uncommon (1:1300 in Persian Jews)	Rare
Prognosis	Benign	Benign
Animal model	Mutant Corriedale sheep Mutant rat	None

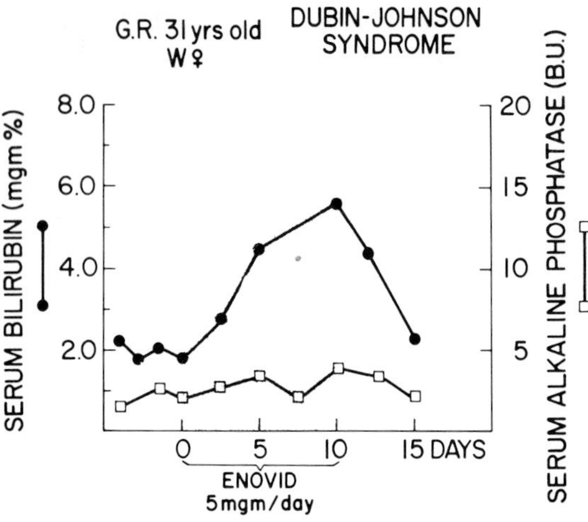

Fig. 53-22 Exacerbation of conjugated hyperbilirubinemia by oral contraceptive administration in a patient with Dubin-Johnson syndrome. Similar findings may be seen in pregnancy.

been shown to resemble melanin histochemically.[605] Studies performed in mutant Corriedale sheep infused with [^{3}H]epinephrine revealed reduced biliary excretion of radioactivity and demonstrated incorporation of the isotope into the hepatic pigment,[606–608] which is consistent with the pigment being a melaninlike derivative. A study of Dubin-Johnson pigment by electron spin resonance (esr) spectroscopy suggests differences from authentic melanin.[609] The nature of the pigment was not defined, and the study was consistent with the pigment being composed of polymers of epinephrine metabolites.[610,611] A recent study of computerized tomography of the liver revealed that attenuation values were significantly higher in patients with Dubin-Johnson syndrome as compared with normal controls, although there was considerable overlap between the two groups.[612] The possible relationship of the liver cell pigment to this finding is not known. The degree of hepatic pigmentation may be variable in individuals with the Dubin-Johnson syndrome.[575,577] Some variability in pigmentation may be due to occurrence of coincidental disease such as acute viral hepatitis, in which the pigment is cleared from the liver only to accumulate slowly after recovery.[613–617]

ORGANIC ANION TRANSPORT. In the Dubin-Johnson syndrome, initial plasma disappearances of bilirubin,[509,618] bromosulphthalein (BSP),[583–585,618–620] dibromosulphthalein (DBSP),[620] indocyanine green,[618,620] and ^{125}I-labeled rose bengal[620] following intravenous administration are usually normal, although plasma BSP concentration at 45 min may be normal or may show mild retention.[583–585,618] Of diagnostic significance is that in approximately 90 percent of patients, the plasma BSP concentration is higher 90 min after intravenous administration than at 45 min (Fig. 53-23).[583–585,593,621] This is due to reflux of conjugated BSP from the liver cell into the circulation.[593,621] This secondary rise is not seen following intravenous administration of other organic anions such as DBSP,^{125}I-labeled rose bengal, and indocyanine green, which are not conjugated prior to excretion by the hepatocyte.[618,620] A similar secondary rise has been described following intravenous administration of unconjugated bilirubin.[609,618] Administration of glutathione-conjugated BSP (GSH-BSP) to two patients with Dubin-Johnson syndrome resulted in markedly delayed plasma disappearance without the appearance of a secondary rise.[619] Although the secondary rise of plasma BSP is characteristic of Dubin-Johnson syndrome, it is not diagnostic and occurs in other hepatobiliary disorders.[622]

Studies of BSP transport during constant intravenous infusion reveal that T_m is reduced to only 10 percent of normal, and the relative hepatic storage capacity is normal.[358,583,623] This finding was also demonstrated directly in a patient with Dubin-Johnson syndrome who had a biliary fistula.[359] In this patient, dehydrocholate choleresis did not augment biliary BSP excretion. Similar studies of BSP transport have been performed in phenotypically normal parents and children (i.e., carriers) of Dubin-Johnson syndrome patients and were normal.[358,583]

INHERITANCE AND URINARY COPROPORPHYRIN EXCRETION. The familial nature of Dubin-Johnson syndrome was noted in its initial descriptions, but its mode of inheritance was unclear. The available data did not fit an autosomal dominant pattern, and investigators were unable to detect carriers for the syndrome, even with constant infusion studies of BSP transport.[358,583] In 1967, Koskelo et al. observed that urinary coproporphyrin I excretion is increased in patients with Dubin-Johnson syndrome to a greater degree than in patients with other hepatobiliary disorders.[624] These results were confirmed in Israel,[625] the United States,[626] and Japan.[627] Coproporphyrin exists in two isomeric forms, coproporphyrin I and coproporphyrin III. Isomer III prophyrins are precursors of heme, whereas isomer I porphyrins are metabolic byproducts without known junction and are excreted into urine and bile.[628]

Coproporphyrin isomers I and III are normally found in urine, where approximately 75 percent of total urinary coproporphyrin is coproporphyrin III. In Dubin-Johnson syndrome, total urinary coproporphyrin excretion is normal, but over 80 percent is coproporphyrin I.[625–627] Urinary coproporphyrin excretion has been determined in phenotypically normal relatives of patients with Dubin-Johnson syndrome (Fig. 53-24).[626,627,629] In obligate heterozygotes (i.e., unaffected parents and children of patients with Dubin-Johnson syndrome) total urinary coproporphyrin excretion was reduced by 40 percent as compared with that in normal control subjects.[626,627,629]

Fig. 53-23 Typical BSP plasma disappearance curve in a patient with Dubin-Johnson syndrome. A secondary rise occurs 45 min after the intravenous injection of the dye. *(From Erlinger et al.[620] Used by permission.)*

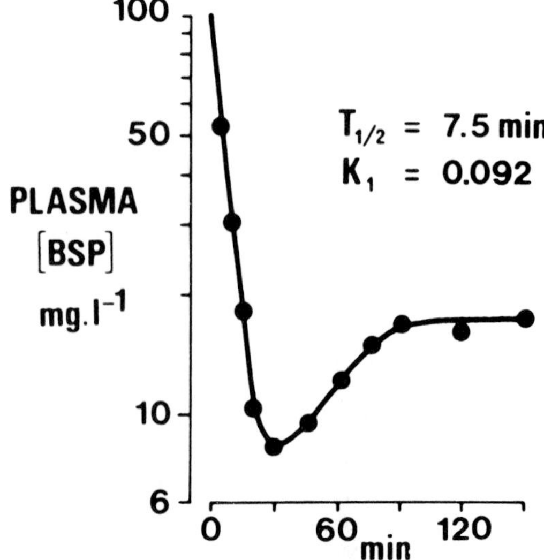

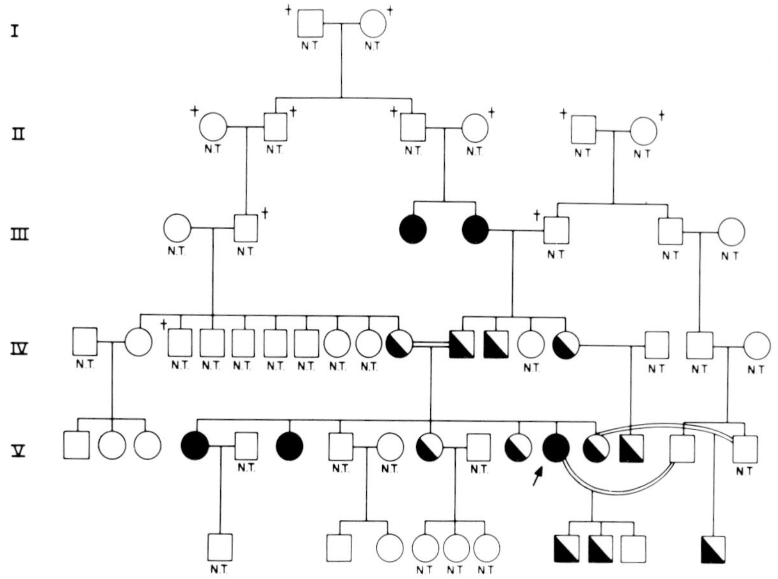

Fig. 53-24 Pedigree of a family in which consanguinity resulted in three children with Dubin-Johnson syndrome (generation V). Solid symbols indicate individuals with Dubin-Johnson syndrome. Partial symbols indicate phenotypically normal individuals with urinary coproporphyrin excretion in the heterozygous range. Clear symbols represent phenotypically normal individuals with normal urinary coproporphyrin excretion. NT indicates those individuals who were not tested. In this family, the defect was detected in four generations. *(From Wolkoff et al.[626] Used by permission.)*

This was due to a 50 percent reduction in coproporphyrin III excretion. The proportion of coproporphyrin I in urine was intermediate between results in controls and in patients with Dubin-Johnson syndrome. Analysis of data from studies revealed that with respect to urinary coproporphyrin excretion Dubin-Johnson syndrome is inherited as an autosomal recessive characteristic (Fig. 53-24). A similar mode of inheritance was determined in a study of BSP and bilirubin metabolism in 173 sibs of 44 patients with Dubin-Johnson syndrome.[630] No other hepatobiliary disorder or porphyria has been described in which total urinary coproporphyrin excretion is normal, with over 80 percent of the total as coproporphyrin I. In the presence of a consistent history and physical examination, urinary coproporphyrin excretion appears to be diagnostic of this disorder.

The overlap of results in carriers with those in controls[626,627,629] makes determination of urinary coproporphyrin excretion less useful in deciding whether an individual carries the gene for the syndrome, although this disorder is benign and genetic counseling is rarely required. Urinary coproporphyrin excretion proved useful in diagnosing Dubin-Johnson syndrome in two neonates.[590,592] Although neonates normally have elevated urinary content of coproporphyrin I as compared with that in adults, levels are not as high as seen in Dubin-Johnson syndrome.[631]

The pathogenesis of the abnormal urinary coproporphyrin excretion in this syndrome is unknown, as is its relationship to conjugated hyperbilirubinemia. In addition to being present in urine, coproporphyrins are also found in bile, where isomer I constitutes approximately 65 percent of the total.[628] Normally, total daily biliary coproporphyrin excretion is approximately three times that of total daily urinary excretion. In most hepatobiliary disorders, including cholestasis, coproporphyrin levels are increased in urine.[625,632] In these disorders, total urinary coproporphyrin excretion is elevated and the proportion of isomer I in urine is usually less than 65 percent. Dubin-Johnson syndrome is unique in that total urinary coproporphyrin is normal, but the proportion of isomer I is over 80 percent. It seems unlikely that the abnormal pattern of coproporphyrin isomers seen in the Dubin-Johnson syndrome results simply from reduced biliary excretion, and an alteration in hepatic porphyrin biosynthesis has been postulated (Fig. 53-25).[626,631] Reduced coproporphyrin III formation could result from decreased activity of hepatic uroporphyrin III cosynthetase.[626] Enzyme activity as determined in blood cells and liver from four patients did not differ from normal.[633] Following an intravenous load of δ-aminolevulinic acid, coproporphyrin III content of urine and bile changed very little in patients with Dubin-Johnson syndrome, as compared with results in normal control subjects.[634,635] Further study of porphyrin biosynthesis is required to elucidate the mechanism of abnormal coproporphyrin excretion and the relationship of the porphyrin abnormality to the conjugated hyperbilirubinemia which characterizes the syndrome.

Mutant Corriedale Sheep. In 1965, Cornelius et al. described a mutant strain of Corriedale sheep showing photosensitivity, mild conjugated hyperbilirubinemia, hepatic pigmentation, and reduced biliary excretion of conjugated bilirubin, BSP, indocyanine green, phylloerythrin, iodopanoic acid, and ^{125}I-labeled rose bengal.[564,605–608,636–638] Taurocholate excretion is normal, and infusion of taurocholate does not increase biliary excretion of BSP.[361,608] Biliary excretion of the organic cation procainamide ethobromide is normal in mutant sheep, as is

Fig. 53-25 Pathway of porphyrin biosynthesis. δ-Aminolevulinic acid (δ-ALA) condenses to form porphobilinogen (PBG). In the presence of uroporphyrinogen synthetase, PBG forms the isomer I porphyrins, which are excretory products without known function. On addition of uroporphyrinogen cosynthetase, PBG forms the isomer III porphyrins which are precursors of heme. *(From Wolkoff et al.[626] Used by permission.)*

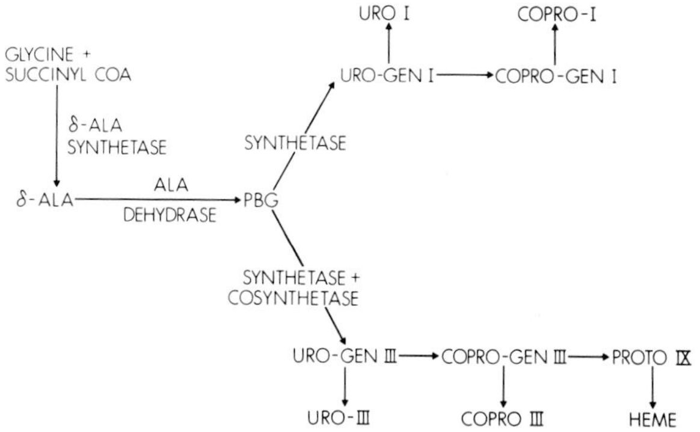

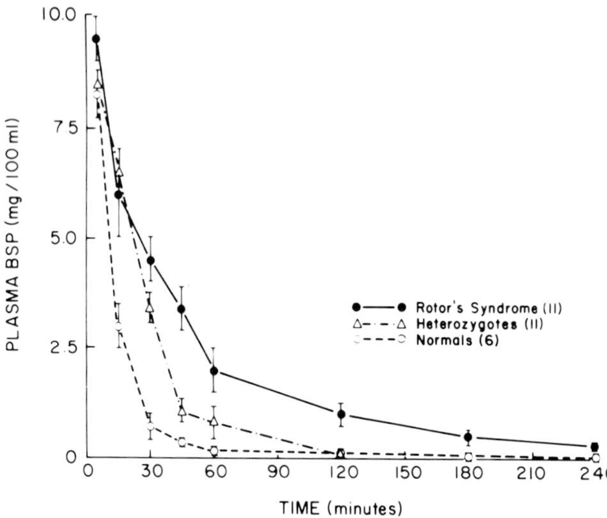

Fig. 53-26 Plasma disappearance of BSP after intravenous injection of a 5 mg/kg dose into 11 patients with Rotor syndrome, 11 phenotypically normal first-degree relatives defined as heterozygotes for the syndrome on the basis of urinary coproporphyrin administration, and six normal controls. There is no secondary rise of plasma BSP, and conjugated BSP is not found in plasma. *(From Wolpert et al.*[645] *Used by permission.)*

renal excretion of *p*-aminohippurate.[361] Studies suggesting that the hepatic pigment granules are related to melanin have been discussed under "Dubin-Johnson Syndrome," above. The photosensitivity manifested by the sheep results from retention of phylloerythrin.[360,637] The disorder is transmitted as an autosomal recessive trait, and the organic anion excretory defect in the mutant sheep is indistinguishable morphologically and functionally from Dubin-Johnson syndrome in humans. Whether these two disorders represent similar metabolic defects remains to be determined.

Hereditary Chronic Conjugated Hyperbilirubinemia in Mutant Rats. Jansen and colleagues have described a mutant strain of rats with autosomal recessive conjugated hyperbilirubinemia.[639] Serum bilirubin levels are elevated to 5 to 10 mg/dl with over 90 percent bilirubin glucuronides. Serum γ-glutamyltransferase, alkaline phosphatase, aminotransaminase, cholesterol, and phospholipid levels are normal.

In these rats, dibromosulphthalein and ouabain clearances are reduced to 7 and 37 percent of normal, respectively, owing to severely impaired excretion from liver to bile. Initial uptake of these compounds is normal. In the isolated perfused liver, dibromosulphthalein is retained within liver and perfusion medium, and the 60-min recovery in bile is reduced to 1.5 versus 75 percent in normal controls. Biliary excretion of cholate, taurocholate, and the quaternary ammonium cation, tributylmethyl ammonium, is not impaired.

Liver histology is also normal. Several features differentiate this hepatobiliary disorder from the Dubin-Johnson syndrome in humans. Although plasma BSP disappearance is delayed, there is no secondary plasma rise of refluxed dye. Serum bile acids are elevated approximately fivefold, and urinary coproporphyrin I, although elevated, represents only 20 percent of the total. Normal rats have only 5 percent of urinary coproporphyrin as isomer I, so that the elevation seen in mutant rats may be comparable to that seen in patients with the Dubin-Johnson syndrome. The pathophysiology of the organic anion transport defect in these rats and its relationship to that in Dubin-Johnson and Rotor syndromes in humans remain to be established.

Rotor Syndrome

CLINICAL FINDINGS. In 1948, Rotor, Manahan, and Florentin described several individuals from two families in whom there was chronic predominantly conjugated hyperbilirubinemia.[640] Serum alkaline phosphatase and cholesterol values were normal. Plasma disappearance of BSP was greatly delayed. Liver histology was normal. For many years, Rotor and Dubin-Johnson syndromes were considered to be variants of a single pathophysiological disorder.[577,641–643] Recently, it has become evident that these disorders differ (Table 53-3).[644,645] Rotor syndrome is benign and is characterized by chronic predominantly conjugated hyperbilirubinemia without evidence of hemolysis.[640–650] The liver is normal on histologic examination and does not have excess pigmentation. Although it has been described in several nationalities and races, Rotor syndrome is rare.

ORGANIC ANION EXCRETION. Oral cholecystographic agents usually do not visualize the gallbladder in the Dubin-Johnson syndrome, whereas roentgenologic visualization usually is possible in Rotor syndrome.[642,643] In Dubin-Johnson syndrome, plasma retention of BSP 45 min after the intravenous injection of a 5 mg/kg dose is inconstant and rarely exceeds 15 percent, whereas in Rotor syndrome dye retention is a regular occurrence and invariably exceeds 25 percent.[641–643,645,651,652] In Dubin-Johnson syndrome, the plasma BSP level is higher 90 min after BSP injection than at 45 min owing to reflux of conjugated BSP from the liver (Fig. 53-23). This secondary rise of BSP does not occur in Rotor syndrome, and conjugated BSP is not found in plasma (Fig. 53-26).[619,645,651] Following their intravenous administration, there is also marked plasma retention of unconjugated bilirubin[646,651] and indocyanine green.[651] Phenotypically normal obligate heterozygotes for Rotor syndrome have mildly abnormal BSP retention at 45 min, which is intermediate between results in affected patients and normal controls.[645]

With the use of a constant infusion technique, BSP T_m and relative hepatic storage capacity S have been determined in patients with Rotor syndrome (Fig. 53-27).[645,651] In Dubin-Johnson syndrome, the I_m is virtually zero, while S is normal. In Rotor syndrome, S was reduced by 75 to 90 percent, and T_m was reduced by 50 percent.[645,651] Determination of T_m and S in phenotypically normal obligate heterozygotes revealed re-

Fig. 53-27 Hepatic relative storage capacity (*S*) and transport maximum (T_m) for BSP in six patients with Rotor syndrome, five phenotypically normal heterozygotes, and six normal controls. *(From Wolpert et al.*[645] *Used by permission.)*

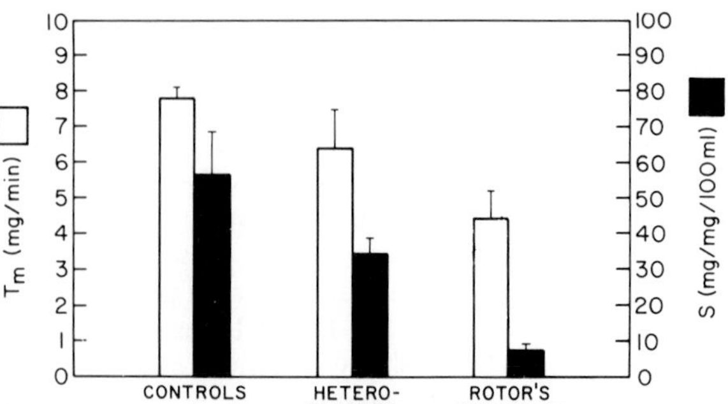

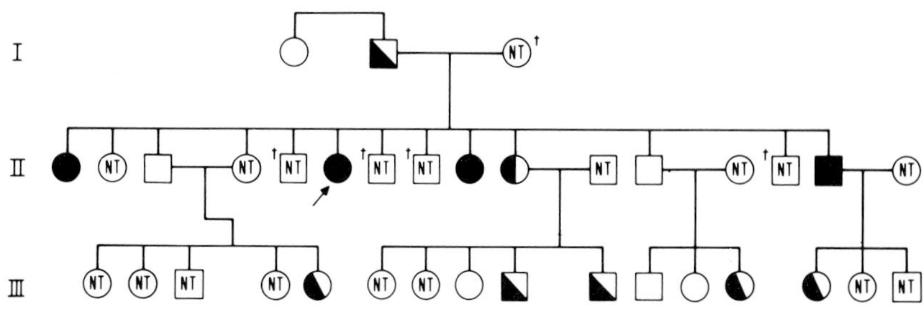

Fig. 53-28 Pedigree of a Philippine family originally described by Rotor in 1948. Solid symbols indicate individuals with Rotor syndrome. Partial symbols indicate phenotypically normal individuals with urinary coproporphyrin excretion in the heterozygous range. Clear symbols represent phenotypically normal individuals with normal urinary coproporphyrin excretion. NT indicates those individuals who were not tested. *(From Wolkoff et al.[644] Used by permission.)*

sults intermediate between those in patients with Rotor syndrome and controls.[645] The modest reduction in T_m accompanied by a larger reduction in S is similar to observations in hepatic storage disease, a familial disorder manifested by predominantly conjugated hyperbilirubinemia and normal liver histology.[653,654] Since there is little to differentiate Rotor syndrome from hepatic storage disease, they may represent a single pathophysiological entity.

URINARY COPROPORPHYRIN EXCRETION. As occurred in Dubin-Johnson syndrome, the familial nature of Rotor syndrome was initially recognized, but the mode of inheritance remained unclear. The finding of abnormal BSP transport in obligate heterozygotes suggested an autosomal recessive pattern of inheritance.[645] A more complete genetic analysis was performed following determination of urinary coproporphyrin excretion in patients with Rotor syndrome and phenotypically normal relatives (Fig. 53-28).[644,652] Unlike results for Dubin-Johnson syndrome, total urinary coproporphyrin is increased by 250 to 500 percent as compared to control subjects, and the proportion of coproporphyrin I in urine is approximately 65 percent of total.[644,652] In a recent report, however, two brothers with clinical Rotor syndrome had over 80 percent of urinary coproporphyrins as isomer I.[655] These results are similar to those seen in many other hepatobiliary disorders.[624,625,632,656–658] Phenotypically normal obligate heterozygotes have a coproporphyrin excretory pattern which is intermediate between that of control subjects and patients with Rotor syndrome. Statistical analysis reveals that, with respect to urinary coproporphyrin excretion, Rotor syndrome is inherited as an autosomal recessive characteristic and is distinct from Dubin-Johnson syndrome (Fig. 53-29).[644,652] The urinary coproporphyrin abnormality in Rotor syndrome, unlike that in Dubin-Johnson syndrome, is most likely caused by a reduced biliary excretion of coproporphyrins, with concomitant increased filtration and excretion by the kidney. The nature of the organic anion transport defect in Rotor syndrome is unknown.

Benign Recurrent Intrahepatic Cholestasis

CLINICAL FINDINGS. Benign recurrent intrahepatic cholestasis is a rare disorder first described in 1959 by Summerskill and Walshe.[659] The disorder is characterized by recurrent attacks of cholestasis. Generally, there is a preicteric phase lasting 2 to 4 weeks in which patients experience malaise, anorexia, and pruritus.[660–663] Subsequently, patients become iceteric and may have an enlarged tender liver. There is no splenomegaly, and patients are afebrile.[659–669] The clinical presentation may suggest biliary obstruction, and in the past many of these patients underwent one or more exploratory laparotomies. The onset of symptoms is usually in adolescence or early adulthood,[663] although this disorder has been described as presenting in infancy[662–664,668] as well as in middle age.[667] Typically, episodes of cholestasis last from a few weeks to several months,[663] and intervals between attacks may range from several months to years. In a given patient, recurrent attacks resemble each other as to symptoms and duration. Because of the prolonged cholestasis, patients may develop malabsorption characterized by steatorrhea and weight loss, and may require parenteral administration of fat-soluble vitamins. Between episodes of cholestasis, patients are clinically normal. The disorder is termed benign because no negative influence on longevity has been noted. The familial nature of this disorder has been clearly documented, but the mode of inheritance is not known.[663]

LABORATORY FINDINGS. Early in the course of cholestatic episodes, serum bile acids rise to abnormal levels.[661,669–672] This is accompanied by elevated serum alkaline phosphatase activ-

Fig. 53-29 Urinary coproporphyrin excretion in Dubin-Johnson and Rotor syndromes. The shaded bars represent the percentage of total urinary coproporphyrin excreted as coproporphyrin I. The open bars represent total urinary coproporphyrin excretion. Vertical bars represent 1 SEM. Total urinary coproporphyrin excretion is normal in the Dubin-Johnson syndrome (DJS) with a markedly elevated proportion of coproporphyrin I (>80 percent). Both variables are elevated in Rotor syndome, and, with respect to urinary coproporphyrin excretion, the two disorders are distinct. Results in obligate heterozygotes for each of these disorders (DJS hetero, rotor hetero) lie intermediate between results in normal individuals and in individuals manifesting the respective disorder. *(From Berk et al.[422] Used by permission.)*

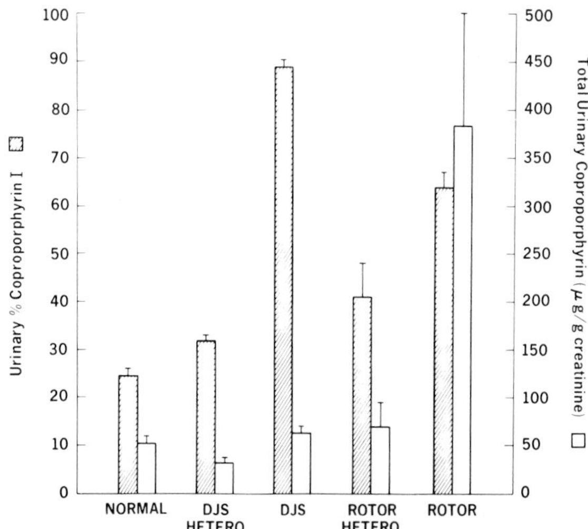

ity and conjugated hyperbilirubinemia. Serum transaminases may be mildly elevated, and the prothrombin time may be elevated because of malabsorption of vitamin K. During the cholestatic episode, plasma disappearance of unconjugated bilirubin is normal, but conjugated bilirubin rises in serum as it refluxes from liver.[660,673–675] Light-microscopic examination of the liver during episodes reveals typical features of intrahepatic cholestasis.[659–670,675–678] Electron-microscopic examination reveals markedly altered bile canaliculi with distorted and reduced microvilli, almost complete disappearance of nucleoside phosphatase activity, and reduction in the number of acid phosphatase-rich lysosomes.[662,670,678] These changes are not specific for this disorder and may be seen nonspecifically in cholestasis. Between attacks biochemical studies are normal in these patients, and histology of the liver is normal by both light microscopy and electron microscopy.[662,670,678] The pathogenesis of this rare disorder is unknown. There is no specific treatment to prevent or shorten the occurrence of cholestatic episodes.

REFERENCES

1. BERK PD, HOWE RB, BLOOMER JR, BERLIN NI: Studies on bilirubin kinetics in normal adults. *J Clin Invest* 48:2176, 1979.
2. LONDON IM, WEST R, SHEMIN D, RITTENBERG D: On the origin of bile pigment in normal man. *J Biol Chem* 184:351, 1950.
3. GRAY CH, NEUBERGER A, SNEATH PHA: Studies in congenital porphyria. 2. Incorporation of ^{15}N in the stercobilin in the normal and in the prophyric. *Biochem J* 47:87, 1950.
4. ROBINSON SH: Origins of the early-labeled peak, in Berk PD, Berlin NI (eds): *Bile Pigments: Chemistry and Physiology*. Washington, DHEW, NIH, 1977, p 175.
5. SCHWARTZ S, JOHNSON JA, STEPHENSON BD, ANDERSON AS, EDMONDSON PR, FUSARO RM: Erythropoietic defects in protoporphyria: A study of factors involved in labelling of porphyrins and bile pigments from ALA^3–H and glycine-^{14}C. *J Lab Clin Med* 78:411, 1971.
6. BERK PD, JONES EA, HOWE RB, BERLIN NI: Disorders of bilirubin metabolism, in Bondy PK, Rosenberg LE (eds): *Metabolic Control and Disease*, 8th ed. Philadelphia, Saunders, 1980, p 1009.
7. YANNONI CZ, ROBINSON SH: Early-labelled heme synthesis in normal rats and rats with iron deficiency anemia. *Biochim Biophys Acta* 428:533, 1976.
8. GRANDCHAMP B, BISSEL DM, LICKO V, SCHMID R: Formation and disposition of newly synthesized heme in adult rat hepatocytes in primary cultures. *J Biol Chem* 256:11677, 1981.
9. LEVITT M, SCHACTER BA, ZIPURSKY A, ISRAELS LG: The nonerythropoietic component of early bilirubin. *J Clin Invest* 47:1281, 1968.
10. GRAY CH, SCOTT JJ: The effect of haemorrhage on the incorporation of [^{14}C]glycine into stercobilin. *Biochem J* 71:38, 1959.
11. DOWDLE E, MUSTARD P, SPONG N, EALES L: The metabolism of [5-^{14}C]δ-aminolaevulic acid in normal and porphyric human subjects. *Clin Sci* 34:233, 1968.
12. HAMER JW, FITZGERALD PH: Disturbed marrow cell proliferation in primary shunt hyperbilirubinemia. *Blood* 41:38, 1973.
13. ROBINSON SH, TSONG M: Hemolysis of "stress" reticulocytes: A source of erythropoietic bilirubin formation. *J Clin Invest* 49:1025, 1970.
14. COME SE, SHOHET SB, ROBINSON SH: Surface remodeling vs. whole-cell hemolysis of reticulocytes produced with erythroid stimulation or iron deficiency anemia. *Blood* 44:817, 1974.
15. LANDAW SA: Quantitative recovery of ^{14}C-labeled carbon monoxide (^{14}CO) from viable heme-labeled red blood cells in the rat. *Blood* 40:257, 1972.
16. BISSEL DM, GUZELIAN PS: Degradation of endogenous hepatic heme by pathways not yielding carbon monoxide: Studies in normal rat liver and primary hepatocyte culture. *J Clin Invest* 65:1135, 1980.
17. TENHUNEN R, MARVER HS, SCHMID R: Microsomal heme oxygenase: Characterization of the enzyme. *J Biol Chem* 244:6388, 1969.
18. TENHUNEN R, MARVER HS, SCHMID R: The enzymatic catabolism of hemoglobin: Stimulation of microsomal heme oxygenase by hemin. *J Lab Clin Med* 75:410, 1970.
19. BISSEL DM, HAMMAKER L, SCHMID R: Liver sinusoidal cells. Identification of a subpopulation for erythrocyte catabolism. *J Cell Biol* 54:107, 1972.
20. SASSA S, KAPPAS A, BERNSTEIN SE, ALVARES AP: Heme biosynthesis and drug metabolism in mice with hereditary hemolytic anemia. *J Biol Chem* 254:729, 1979.
21. ISHIZAWA S, YOSHIDA T, KIKUCHI G: Induction of heme oxygenase in rat liver. *J Biol Chem* 258:4220, 1983.
22. POSSELT AM, COWAN BE, KWONG LK, VREMAN HJ, STEVENSON DK: Effect of tin protoporphyrin on the excretion rate of carbon monoxide in newborn rats after hematoma formation. *J Pediatr Gastroenterol Nutr* 4:650, 1985.
23. YOSHIDA T, KIKUCHI G: Heme oxygenase purified to apparent homogeneity from pig spleen microsomes. *J Biochem* 81:265, 1977.
24. YOSINGA T, SASSA S, KAPPAS A: The occurrence of molecular interactions among NADPH-cytochrome C reductase, heme oxygenase and biliverdin reductase in heme degradation. *J Biol Chem* 257:7778, 1982.
25. MAINES MD, IBRAHIM NG, KAPPAS A: Solubilization and partial purification of heme oxygenase from rat liver. *J Biol Chem* 252:5900, 1977.
26. JACKSON AH, KENNER W: Recent developments in porphyrin chemistry, in Goodwin TW (ed): *Porphyrins and Related Compounds*. London and New York, Academic, 1968, p 5.
27. LEMBERG R: The chemical mechanism of bile pigment formation. *Rev Pure Appl Chem* 6:1, 1956.
28. BROWN SB, KING RFGJ: An ^{18}O double-labeling study of hemoglobin catabolism in the rat. *Biochem J* 150:565, 1975.
29. BROWN SB, KING RFGJ: The mechanism of heme catabolism: Bilirubin formation in living rats by [^{18}O]oxygen labeling. *Biochem J* 170:297, 1978.
30. YOSHIDA T, KIKUCHI G: Features of the reaction of heme degradation catalyzed by the reconstituted microsomal hemeoxygenase system. *J Biol Chem* 253:4230, 1978.
31. CORNELIUS CE: Comparative bile pigment metabolism in vertebrates, in Ostrow JD (ed): *Bile Pigments and Jaundice*. New York, Marcel Dekker, 1986, p 601.
32. McDONAGH AF, PALMA LA, SCHMID R: Reduction of biliverdin and placental transfer of bilirubin and biliverdin in the pregnant guinea pig. *Biochem J* 194:273, 1981.
33. BRUSS ML, CORNELIUS CE, HIMES JA: Effect of bilirubin infusion on excretion of bilirubin and biliverdin in rabbits. *Comp Biochem Physiol* 76a:339, 1983.
34. ROY CHOWDHURY J, ROY CHOWDHURY N, ARIAS IM: Bilirubin conjugates in the spiny dogfish, *Squalus acanthias*, the small skate, *Raja erinacea* and the winter flounder *Pseudopleuronectes americanas*. *Comp Biochem Physiol* 66b:523, 1980.
35. COLLERAN E, O'CARRA P: Enzymology and comparative physiology of biliverdin reduction, in Berk PD, Berlin NI (eds): *Bile Pigments: Chemistry and Physiology*. Washington, DHEW, NIH, 1977, p 69.
36. TENHUNEN R, ROSS ME, MARVER HS, SCHMID R: Reduced nicotinamide–adenine dinucleotide phosphate dependent biliverdin reductase: Partial purification and characterization. *Biochemistry* 9:298, 1970.
37. COLLERAN E, O'CARRA P: Enzymology and comparative physiology of biliverdin reduction, in Berk PD, Berlin NI (eds): *Bile Pigments: Chemistry and Physiology*. Washington, DHEW, NIH, 1977, p 69.
38. FRYDMAN RB, TOMARO ML, AWRUCH J, FRYDMAN B: Interconversion of the molecular forms of biliverdin reductase from rat liver. *Biochim Biophys Acta* 759:257, 1983.
39. TOMARO ML, FRYDMAN RB, AWRUCH J, VALASINAS A, FRYDMAN B, PANDEY RK, SMITH K: The specificity of biliverdin reductase: A study with different biliverdin types. *Biochim Biophys Acta* 791:350, 1984.
40. BLUMENTHAL SG, TAGGART DB, IDEDA RM, RUEBNER B, BERGSTROM DE: Conjugated and unconjugated bilirubins in bile of humans and rhesus monkeys. Structure of adult human and rhesus-monkey bilirubins compared with dog bilirubin. *Biochem J* 167:535, 1977.
41. HEIRWEGH KPM, BLANCKAERT N, COMPERNOLLE F, FEVERY J, ZAMAN Z: Detection and properties of the non-α-isomers of bilirubin-IX. *Biochem Soc Trans* 5:316, 1977.
42. BLANCKAERT N, FEVERY J, COMPERNOLLE F, HEIRWEGH KPM: Presence of bilirubin IXβ, γ and δ in bile of man and various animals. *Gastroenterology* 69:810, 1975.
43. BLANCKAERT N, HEIRWEGH KPM, COMPERNOLLE F: Synthesis and separation by thin-layer chromatography of bilirubin-IX isomers. Their identification as tetrapyrroles and dipyrrol anthranilate azo derivatives. *Biochem J* 155:405, 1976.
44. BLUMENTHAL SG, STUCKER T, RASMUSSEN RD, IKEDA RM, RUEBNER BH, BERGSTROM DE, HANSON FW: Changes in bilirubin in human prenatal development. *Biochem J* 186:693, 1980.
45. HOWE RB, BERLIN NI, BERK PD: Estimation of bilirubin production in man, in Berk PD, Berlin NI (eds): *Bile Pigments: Chemistry and Physiology*. Washington, DHEW, NIH, 1977, p 105.

46. DHAR GJ: Enterohepatic circulation and plasma transport of urobilinogen, in Berk PD, Berlin NI (eds): *Bile Pigments: Chemistry and Physiology*. Washington, DHEW, NIH, 1977, p 526.

47. BLOOMER JR, BERK PD, HOWE RB, WAGGONER JG, BERLIN NI: Comparison of fecal urobilinogen excretion with bilirubin production in normal volunteers and patients with increased bilirubin production. *Clin Chim Acta* 29:463, 1970.

48. JONES EA, SHRAGER R, BLOOMER JR, BERK PD, HOWE RB, BERLIN NI: Quantitative studies of the delivery of hepatic synthesized bilirubin to plasma utilizing δ-aminolevulinic acid-4-^{14}C and bilirubin-^{3}H in man. *J Clin Invest* 51:2450, 1972.

49. JONES EA, BLOOMER JR, BERK PD, CARSON ER, OWENS D, BERLIN NI: Quantitation of hepatic hibirubin synthesis in man, in Berk PD, Berlin NI (eds): *Bile Pigments: Chemistry and Physiology*. Washington, USDHEW, NIH, 1977, p 189.

50. COBURN RF, BLAKEMORE WS, FORSTER RE: Endogenous carbon monoxide production in man. *J Clin Invest* 42:1172, 1963.

51. BERK PD, RODKEY FL, BLASCHKE, COLLISON HA, WAGGONER JG: Comparison of plasma bilirubin turnover and carbon monoxide production in man. *J Lab Clin Med* 83:29, 1974.

52. BENSINGER TA, MAISELS MJ, MAHMOOD L, McCURDY PR, CONRAD MD: Effect of intravenous urea in invert sugar on heme catabolism in sickle cell anemia. *N Engl J Med* 285:995, 1971.

53. LYNCH SR, MOEDE AL: Variation in the rate of endogenous carbon monoxide production in normal human beings. *J Lab Clin Med* 79:85, 1972.

54. COBURN RF, GONDRIE P, ABBOUD F, PLOEGMAKERS E: Myocardial myoglobin oxygen tension. *Am J Physiol* 224:870, 1973.

55. STEWART RD, FISHER TN, HOSKO MJ, PETERSON JE, BARETTA ED, DODD HC: Carboxyhemoglobin elevation after exposure to dichloromethane. *Science* 176:295, 1972.

56. ENGEL RR: Alternative sources of carbon monoxide, in Berk PD, Berlin NI (eds): *Bile Pigments: Chemistry and Physiology*. Washington, DHEW, NIH, 1977, p 148.

57. WESTLAKE DWS, ROXBURGH JM, TALBOT G: Microbial production of carbon monoxide from flavinoids. *Nature* 189:510, 1961.

58. DRUMMOND GS, KAPPAS A: Chemoprevention of neonatal jaundice, potency of tin-protoporphyrin in an animal model. *Science* 217:6466, 1982.

59. CORNELIUS CS, RODGERS PA: Prevention of neonatal hyperbilirubinemia in rhesus monkey by tin-protoporphyrin. *Pediatr Res* 18:728, 1984.

60. KAPPAS A, DRUMMOND GS, SARDANA MK: Sn-protoporphyrin rapidly and markedly enhances the heme saturation of hepatic tryptophan pyrrolase. Evidence that this synthetic metalloporphyrin increases the functional content of heme in the liver. *J Clin Invest* 75:302, 1985.

61. KAPPAS A, SIMONATTO CS, DRUMMOND GS, SASSA S: The liver excretes large amounts of heme into bile when heme oxygenase is inhibited competitively by Sn-protoporphyrin. *Proc Natl Acad Sci USA* 82:896, 1985.

62. POSSELT AM, COWAN BE, KWONG LK, VREMAN HJ, STEVENSON DK: Effect of tin-protoporphyrin on the excretion rate of carbon monoxide in newborn rats after hematoma formation. *J Pediatr Gastroenterol Nutr* 4:650, 1985.

63. STEVENSON DK, OSTRANDER CA, JOHNSON JD: Effect of erythrocyte destruction on the pulmonary excretion rate of carbon monoxide in adult male Wistar rats. *J Lab Clin Med* 94:649, 1979.

64. RUDIZER W: In Herz W, Grischback H, Kirby GW (eds): *Progress in the Chemistry of Organic Natural Compounds*. Wien, New York, Springer-Verlag, 1972, vol 29.

65. FISCHER H, PLIENINGER H: Synthese des biliverdins (uteroverdins) und bilirubins der biliverdine XIII, und III, sowie der Vinulneoxanthosaure. *Hoppe-Seyler's Z Physiol Chem* 274:231, 1942.

66. BONNET RJ, DAVIS E, HURSTHOUSE MB: Structure of bilirubin. *Nature* 262:326, 1976.

67. GRAY CH, KULCZYCKA A, NICHOLSON DC: The chemistry of bile pigments, IV. Spectrophotometric titration of the bile pigments. *J Chem Soc* 442:2276, 1961.

68. KRASNER J, YAFFE SJ: The automatic titration of bilirubin. *Biochem Med* 7:128, 1973.

69. BRODERSON R: Binding of bilirubin to albumin. *CRC Crit Rev Clin Lab Sci* 11:305, 1980.

70. BRODERSEN R: Aqueous solubility, albumin binding and tissue distribution of bilirubin, in Ostrow JD (ed): *Bile Pigments and Jaundice*. New York, Marcel Dekker, 1986, p 157.

71. BRODERSEN R: Free bilirubin in the blood plasma of the newborn. Effects of albumin, fatty acids, pH, displacing drugs and phototherapy. Appendix A: Provisional survey of the bilirubin displacing effect of 150 drugs, in Stern L (ed): *Intensive Care of the Newborn*. New York, Masson, 1978, vol 2, p 331.

72. BRODERSEN R: Physical chemistry of bilirubin: Binding to macromolecules and membranes, in Heirwegh KPM, Brown SB (eds): *Bilirubin*. Boca Raton, FL, CRC Press, 1982, vol I, p 75.

73. FOG J, JELLUM E: Structure of bilirubin. *Nature* 198:88, 1963.

74. KUENZLE CC, WEIBEL MH, PELLONI RR: A proposed novel structure for the metal chelates of bilirubin. *Biochem J* 130:1147, 1973.

75. KUENZLE CC, WEIBEL MN, PELLONI RR: The reaction of bilirubin with diazomethane. *Biochem J* 133:357, 1973.

76. MANITTO P, MONTI D: Free energy barrier of conformational inversion in bilirubin. *J Chem Soc Chem Commun* 122, 1976.

77. KNELL AJ, HANCOCK F, HUTCHINSON DW: In Bakken AF, Fog J (eds): *Bilirubin and Related Tetrapyrroles*. Oslo, Norway, Pediatric Research Institute, Rikshospitalet, 1975, p 234.

78. BLANCKAERT N, HEIRWEGH KPM, ZAMAN Z: Comparison of the biliary excretion of the four isomers of bilirubin-IX in Wistar and homozygous Gunn rats. *Biochem J* 164:229, 1977.

79. McDONAGH AF: Bilitrienes and 5,15 biladines, in Dolphin D (ed): *The Porphyrins, Bile Pigments*. New York, Academic, 1979, vol XI, p 293.

80. BRODERSEN R: Dimerization of bilirubin anion in aqueous solution. *Acta Chem Scand* 20:2895, 1966.

81. LEE KS, GARTNER LM: Spectrophotometric characteristics of bilirubin. *Pediatr Res* 10:782, 1976.

82. CU A, BELLAH GF, LIGHTNER DA: On the fluorescence of bilirubin. *J Am Chem Soc* 97:2579, 1975.

83. KRASNER J, YAFFE SJ: Fluorescent properties of the bilirubin-albumin complex. *Birth Defects* 12(2):168, 1976.

84. MCDONAGH AF, PALMA LA: Mechanism of bilirubin photodegradation: Role of singlet oxygen, in Berlin NI, Berk PD, Watson CJ (eds): *Bile Pigments: Chemistry and Physiology*. Washington, DHEW, NIH, 1977, p 81.

85. LIGHTNER DA, WOLLRIDGE TA, MCDONAGH AF: Photobilirubin. An early bilirubin photoproduct detected by absorbance difference spectroscopy. *Proc Natl Acad Sci USA* 76:29, 1979.

86. STOLL MS: Phototherapy of jaundice, in Ostrow JD (ed): *Bile Pigments and Jaundice*. New York, Marcel Dekker, 1986, p 551.

87. MCDONAGH AF, PALMA LA, LIGHTNER DA: Phototherapy for neonatal jaundice. Stereospecific and regiospecific photoisomerization of bilirubin bound to human serum albumin and NMR characterization of intramolecularly cyclized photoproducts. *J Am Chem Soc* 104:6867, 1982.

88. ITHO S, ONISHI S: Kinetic study of the photochemical changes of (ZZ)-bilirubin IX bound to human serum albumin. Demonstration of (EZ)-bilirubin IX as an intermediate in photochemical changes from (ZZ)-bilirubin IX to (EZ)-cyclobilirubin IX. *Biochem J* 226:251, 1985.

89. LIGHTNER DA: Products of bilirubin photodegradation, in Berlin NI, Berk PD, Watson CJ (eds): *Bile Pigments: Chemistry and Physiology*. Washington, DHEW, NIH, 1977, p 93.

90. MCDONAGH AF: Thermal and photochemical reactions of bilirubin IX. *Ann NY Acad Sci* 244:553, 1975.

91. MANITO P, MONTI D: Photochemistry of bilirubin in the absence of oxygen, in Bakken AF, For J (eds): *Metabolism and Chemistry of Bilirubin and Related Tetrapyrrols*. Oslo, Norway, Pediatric Research Institute, Rikshospitalet, 1975, p 191.

92. SCHENKER S, HOYUMPA AM, MCCANDLESS DW: Bilirubin toxicity to the brain (kernicterus) and other tissues, in Ostrous JD (ed): *Bile Pigments and Jaundice*. New York, Marcel Dekker, 1986, p 395.

93. MOLLISON PL, CUTBUSH M: Hemolytic disease of the newborn: criteria of severity. *Br Med J* 1:123, 1949.

94. NANDI MAJUMDAR AP: Bilirubin encephalopathy. Effect on RNA polymerase activity and chromatin template activity in the brain of the Gunn rat. *Neurobiology* 4:425, 1974.

95. KATOH R, KASHIWAMATA S, NIWA F: Studies on cellular toxicity of bilirubin. Effect on the carbohydrate metabolism in the young rat brain. *Brain Res* 83:81, 1975.

96. NANDI MAJUMDAR AP, GREENFIELD S: Evidence of defective protein synthesis in liver in rats with congenital hyperbilirubinemia. *Biochim Biophys Acta* 335:250, 1974.

97. SCHIFF D, CHAN G, POZNASKY MJ: Bilirubin toxicity in neural cell lines N115 and NBR10A. *Pediatr Res* 19:908, 1985.

98. MUSTAFA MG, COWGER ML, KING TE: Effects of bilirubin on mitochondrial reactions. *J Biol Chem* 244:6403, 1969.

99. STRUMIA E: Effect of bilirubin on some hydrolases. *Boll Soc Ital Biol Sper* 35:2160, 1959.

100. FLITMAN R, WORTH NH: Inhibition of hepatic alcohol dehydrogenase by bilirubin. *J Biol Chem* 251:669, 1966.

101. COWGER ML, IGO RP, LABBE RF: The mechanism of bilirubin toxicity studied with purified respiratory enzyme and tissue culture systems. *Biochemistry* 4:2763, 1965.

102. KATOH R, KASHIWAMATA S, NIWA F: Studies on cellular toxicity of bili-

rubin. Effect on the carbohydrate metabolism in the young rat brain. *Brain Res* 83:81, 1975.

103. GREENFIELD S, NANDI MAJUMDAR AP: Bilirubin encephalopathy. Effect on protein synthesis in the brain of the Gunn rat. *J Neurol Sci* 22:83, 1974.

104. NANDI MAJUMDAR AP: Bilirubin encephalopathy. Effect on RNA polymerase activity and chromatin template activity in the brain of the Gunn rat. *Neurobiology* 4:425, 1974.

105. NANDI MAJUMDAR AP, GREENFIELD S: Evidence of defective protein synthesis in liver in rats with congenital hyperbilirubinemia. *Biochim Biophys Acta* 335:260, 1974.

106. MUSTAFA MG, COWGER ML, KING TE: Effects of bilirubin on mitochondrial reactions. *J Biol Chem* 244:6403, 1969.

107. DIAMOND I, SCHMID R: Oxidative phosphorylation in experimental bilirubin encephalopathy. *Science* 155:1288, 1967.

108. MENKEN M, WAGGONER JG, BERLIN NI: The influence of bilirubin on oxidative phosphorylation and related reactions in brain and liver mitochondria. Effects of protein binding. *J Neurochem* 13:1241, 1966.

109. VOGT MT, BASFORD RE: The effect of bilirubin on the energy metabolism of brain mitochondria. *J Neurochem* 15:1313, 1968.

110. ZETTERSTROM R, ERNSTER L: Bilirubin, an uncoupler of oxidative phosphorylation in isolated mitochondria. *Nature* 178:1335, 1956.

111. KAPOOR CL, KRISHNA MURTI CR, BAJPAI PC: Toxic effect of bilirubin on human red blood cells and its reversal by RBC liquids. *Indian J Med Res* 60:918, 1972.

112. GIROTTI AW: Glyceraldehyde-3-phosphate dehydrogenase in the isolated human erythrocyte membrane. Selective displacement by bilirubin. *Arch Biochem Biophys* 173:210, 1976.

113. COWGER ML, IGO P, LABBE RF: The mechanism of bilirubin toxicity studied with purified respiratory enzyme and tissue culture systems. *Biochemistry* 4:2763, 1965.

114. DAY R: In Sass-Kortsak A (ed): *Kernicterus*. Toronto, University of Toronto Press, 1959, p 167.

115. KIKICHI K: Effects of bilirubin on the multiplication of animal cells in tissue culture. *Jpn J Exp Med* 31:71, 1961.

116. RASMUSSEN LF, WENNBERG RP: Pharmacologic modification of bilirubin toxicity in tissue culture cells. *Res Commun Pathol Pharmacol* 3:567, 1972.

117. PARADISI F, GRAZIANO L, DE RITIS F: The action of unconjugated bilirubin on some enzyme activities of in vitro cultured cells. *Res Exp Med* 161:224, 1973.

118. STRUMIA E: Effect of bilirubin on some hydrolases. *Boll Soc Ital Biol Sper* 35:2160, 1959.

119. FLITMAN R, WORTH NH: Inhibition of hepatic alcohol dehydrogenase by bilirubin. *J Biol Chem* 241:669, 1966.

120. NOIR BA, BOVERIS A, GARASO PEREIPA AM, and STOPPANI AOM: Bilirubin: A multi-site inhibitor of mitochondrial respiration. *FEBS Lett* 27:270, 1972.

121. OGASAWARE N, WATANABE T, GOTO H: Bilirubin: A potent inhibitor of NAD^+ linked isocitrate dehydrogenase. *Biochim Biophys Acta* 327:233, 1973.

122. HADDOCK JH, NADLER HL: Bilirubin toxicity in human cultivated fibroblasts and its modification by light treatment. *Proc Soc Exp Biol Med* 134:45, 1970.

123. HSIA DY-Y, ALLEN FH, GELLIS SS, DIAMOND LK: Erythroblastosis fetalis. VII. Studies on serum bilirubin in relation to kernicterus. *N Engl J Med* 247:668, 1970.

124. ODELL GB: Influence of binding on the toxicity of bilirubin. *Ann NY Acad Sci* 226:225, 1973.

125. LEE KS, GARTNER LM, EIDELMAN AI, EZHUTHACHAN S: Unconjugated hyperbilirubinemia in very low birth weight infants. *Clin Perinatol* 4:305, 1977.

126. CONSTANTOPOULOS A, MATSANIOTIS N. Bilirubin inhibition of protein kinase: its prevention by cyclic AMP. *Cytobios* 17:17, 1976.

127. MORPHIS I, CONSTANTOPOULOS A, MATSANIOTIS N, PAPAPHILIS A: Bilirubin-induced modulation of cerebral protein phosphorylation in neonate rabbits in vivo. *Science* 218:156, 1982.

128. SANO K, NAKAMURA H, TAMOTSU M: Mode of inhibitory action of bilirubin on protein kinase C. *Pediatr Res* 19:587, 1985.

129. NAEYE RL: Amniotic fluid infections, neonatal hyperbilirubinemia and psychomotor impairment. *Pediatrics* 62:497, 1978.

130. ZUELZER WW, MUDGETT RT: Kernicterus. Etiologic study based on an analysis of 55 cases. *Pediatrics* 6:452, 1950.

131. VAUGHAN VC, ALLEN FC, DIAMOND LK: Erythroblastosis fetalis. IV. Further observations on kernicterus. *Pediatrics* 6:706, 1950.

132. TURKEL SB, MILLER CA, GUTTENBERG ME, MOYNES DR, HODGMAN JE: A clinical pathologic reappraisal of kernicterus. *Pediatrics* 69:267, 1982.

133. RAPPAPORT SI: *Blood-Brain Barrier in Physiology and Medicine*. New York, Raven, 1976.

134. PURPURA DP, CARMICHAEL MW: Characteristics of blood-brain barrier to gamma-aminobutyric acid in neonatal cat. *Science* 131:410, 1960.

135. CORNFORD EM, BRAUN LD, OLDENDORP WH, HILL MA: Comparison of lipid-mediated blood-brain barrier penetrability in neonates and adults. *Am J Physiol* 243:C161, 1982.

136. LAAS R, HELMKE K: Regional cerebral blood flow following unilateral blood-brain barrier alteration induced by hyperosmolar perfusion in the albino rat, in Cervos-Navarro J, Fritschka E (eds): *Cerebral Circulation and Metabolism*. New York, Raven, 1981, p 317.

137. LEVINE RL, FREDERICKS WR, RAPPAPORT SI: Clearance of bilirubin from rat brain after reversible osmotic opening of the blood-brain barrier. *Pediatr Res* 19:1040, 1985.

138. LEE K-S, GARTNER LM: Management of unconjugated hyperbilirubinemia in the newborn. *Semin Liver Dis* 3:52, 1983.

139. BENHOLD H: The transport of bilirubin in the circulating blood and its pathogenic importance. *Acta Med Scand Suppl* 445:223, 1966.

140. BOWEN WR, PORTER E, WATERS WF: The protective action of albumin in bilirubin toxicity in new born puppies. *Am J Dis Child* 98:568, 1959.

141. MUSTAFA MG, COWGER ML, KING TE: Effects of bilirubin on mitochondrial reactions. *J Biol Chem* 244:6403, 1969.

142. SILVERMANN WA, ANDERSEN DH, BLAND WA, CROZIER DN: A difference in mortality rate and incidence of kernicterus among premature infants allotted to prophylactic antibacterial regimens. *Pediatrics* 18:614, 1956.

143. ODELL GB: The dissociation of bilirubin from albumin and its clinical implications. *J Pediatr* 55:268, 1959.

144. SCHMID R, DIAMOND I, HAMMAKER I, GUNDERSEN CB: Interaction of bilirubin with albumin. *Nature* 204:1041, 1965.

145. BLOOMER JR, BERK PD, VERGALLA J, BERLIN NI: Influence of albumin on the extravascular distribution of unconjugated bilirubin. *Clin Sci Mol Med* 45:517, 1973.

146. ODELL GB, COHEN SN, GORDES EH: Administration of albumin in the management of hyperbilirubinemia by exchange transfusion. *Pediatrics* 30:613, 1962.

147. BRODERSEN R, FUNDING L, PEDERSON AO, ROJGAARD-PETERSEN H: Binding of bilirubin to low-affinity sites of human serum albumin in vitro followed by co-crystalization. *Scand J Clin Lab Invest* 29:433, 1972.

148. JACOBSEN J: Binding of bilirubin to human serum albumin. Determination of the dissociation constants. *FEBS Lett* 5:112, 1969.

149. BRODERSEN R: Bilirubin solubility and interaction with albumin and phospholipid. *J Biol Chem* 254:2364, 1979.

150. BERDE CB, HUDSON BS, SIMONI RD, SKLAR LA: Human serum albumin: Spectroscopic studies of binding and proximity relationships for fatty acid and bilirubin. *J Biol Chem* 254:391, 1979.

151. REED RG, FELDHOFF RC, CLUTE OL, PETERS T: Fragments of bovine serum albumin produced by limited proteolysis. Conformation and ligand binding. *Biochemistry* 14:4578, 1975.

152. GEISOW MG, BEAVEN GH: Large fragments of human serum albumin. *Biochem J* 161:619, 1977.

153. SJODIN T, HANSSON R, SJOHOLM I: Isolation and identification of a trypsin-resistant fragment of human serum albumin with bilirubin and drug-binding properties. *Biochim Biophys Acta* 494:61, 1977.

154. GITZELMANN-CUMARASAMY N, KUENZLE CC, WILSON KJ: Mapping of the primary bilirubin binding site of human serum albumin. *Experientia* 32:768, 1976.

155. JACOBSEN C: Lysine residue 240 of human serum albumin is involved in high-affinity binding of bilirubin. *Biochem J* 171:453, 1978.

156. BRODERSEN R: Free bilirubin in blood plasma of the newborn. Effects of albumin, fatty acids, pH, displacing drugs and phototherapy. Appendix: A provisional survey of the bilirubin-displacing effect of 150 drugs, in Stern L (ed): *Intensive Care in the Newborn*. New York, Masson, 1978, vol 2, p 331.

157. BRODERSEN R, SJODIN T, SJOHOLM I: Independent binding of benzodiazepines and bilirubin to human serum albumin. *J Biol Chem* 252:5067, 1977.

158. ODELL GB: The distribution of bilirubin between albumin and mitochondria. *J Pediatr* 68:164, 1966.

159. WOOLLEY PW, HUNTER M: Binding and circular dichroism data on bilirubin-albumin in the presence of oleate and salicylate. *Arch Biochem Biophys* 140:197, 1970.

160. BRODERSEN R: Binding of bilirubin and other ligands of human serum albumin, in Peters T, Sjoholm I (eds): *Albumin, Structure, Biosynthesis, Function*. FEBS 11th Meeting, Copenhagen, 1977. Oxford, Pergamon, 1978, p 61.

161. RUDMAN D, BIXLER TJ, DEL RIO AE: Effect of free fatty acid on binding

of drugs by bovine serum albumin, by human serum albumin and by rabbit serum. *J Pharmacol Exp Ther* 176:261, 1971.

162. DIAMOND I, SCHMID R: Experimental bilirubin encephalopathy. The mode of entry of bilirubin-^{14}C into the central nervous system. *J Clin Invest* 45:678, 1966.

163. STERN L, DENTON RL: Kernicterus in small premature infants. *Pediatrics* 35:483, 1965.

164. KAPITULNIK J, VALAES T, KAUFMANN NA, BLONDHEIM SH: Clinical evaluation of Sephadex gel filtration of bilirubin binding in serum in neonatal jaundice. *Arch Dis Child* 49:886, 1974.

165. BRODERSEN R, CASHORE W, WENNBERG RP, AHLFORS CE, RASSMUSSEN LF, SHUSTERMAN D: Kinetics of bilirubin oxidation with peroxidase, as applied to studies of bilirubin-albumin binding. *Scand J Clin Lab Invest* 39:143, 1979.

166. ATHANASSIADIS S, CHOPRA DR, FISHER M, MCKENNA J: An electrophoretic method for detection of unbound bilirubin and reserve bilirubin binding capacity in serum of newborns. *J Lab Clin Med* 83:968, 1974.

167. LAMOLLA AA, EISINGER J, BLUMBERG WE, PALET SC, FLORES J: Fluorometric study of the partition of bilirubin among blood components: Basis for rapid microassays of bilirubin and bilirubin binding capacity in whole blood. *Anal Biochem* 15:25, 1979.

168. BRATLID D: Reserve albumin binding capacity salicylate saturation index, and red cell binding of bilirubin in neonatal jaundice. *Arch Dis Child* 48:393, 1973.

169. BRODERSEN R: Determination of the vacant amount of high affinity bilirubin binding site on serum albumin. *Acta Pharmacol Toxicol* 42:153, 1978.

170. HSIA JC, KWAN NH, ER SS, WOOD DJ, CHANCE GW: Development of a spin assay for reserve bilirubin loading capacity of human serum. *Proc Natl Acad Sci USA* 75:1542, 1978.

171. PORTER EG, WATERS WJ: A rapid micromethod for measuring the reserve albumin binding capacity in serum for newborn infants with hyperbilirubinemia. *J Lab Clin Med* 67:660, 1966.

172. SCHARSCHMIDT BF, WAGGONER JG, BERK PD: Hepatic organic anion uptake in the rat. *J Clin Invest* 56:1280, 1975.

173. BROWN WR, GRODSKY GM, CARBONE JV: Intracellular distribution of tritiated bilirubin during hepatic uptake and excretion. *Am J Physiol* 207:1237, 1964.

174. GORESKY CA: The hepatic uptake process: Its implications for bilirubin transport, in Goresky CA, Fisher MM (eds): *Jaundice*. New York, Plenum, 1975, p 159.

175. BAUMGARTNER G, REICHEN J: Kinetics of hepatic uptake of unconjugated bilirubin. *Clin Sci Mol Med* 51:169, 1976.

176. BLOOMER JR, ZACCARIA J: Effect of graded bilirubin loads on bilirubin transport by perfused rat liver. *Am J Physiol* 203:736, 1976.

177. HUNTON DB, BOLLMAN JL, HOFFMAN HN II: The plasma removal of indocyanine green and sulfobromophthalein: Effect of dosage and blocking agents. *J Clin Invest* 40:1648, 1961.

178. SHUPECK M, WOLKOFF AW, SCHARSCHMIDT BF, WAGGONER JG, BERK PD: Studies of the kinetics of purified conjugated bilirubin-3H in the rat. *Am J Gastroenterol* 70:259, 1978.

179. GORESKY CA: The hepatic uptake and excretion of sulfobromophthalein and bilirubin. *Can Med Assoc J* 92:851, 1965.

180. WOLKOFF AW, GORESKY CA, SELLIN J, GATMAITAN Z, ARIAS IM: Role of ligandin in transfer of bilirubin from plasma into liver. *Am J Physiol* 236:E638, 1979.

181. BLOOMER JR, BERK PD, BERGALLA J, BERLIN NI: Influence of albumin on the hepatic uptake of unconjugated bilirubin. *Clin Sci Mol Med* 45:505, 1973.

181a. BARNHART JL, CLARENBURG R: Factors determining clearance of bilirubin in perfused rat liver. *Am J Physiol* 225:497, 1973.

182. WEISIGER RA, GOLLAN JL, OCKNER RK: Receptor for albumin on the liver cell surface may mediate uptake of fatty acids and other albumin-bound substances. *Science* 211:1048, 1981.

183. WEISIGER RA, GOLLAN JL, OCKNER RK: The role of albumin in hepatic uptake processes. *Prog Liver Dis* 7:71, 1982.

184. OCKNER RK, WEISIGER RA, GOLLAN JL: Hepatic uptake of albumin-bound substance: Albumin receptor concept. *Am J Physiol* 245:G13, 1983.

185. FORKER EL, LUXON BA: Albumin helps mediate removal of taurocholate by rat liver. *J Clin Invest* 67:1517, 1981.

186. FORKER EL, LUXON BA, SNELL M, SHURMANTINE WO: Effect of albumin binding on the hepatic transport of rose bengal: Surface-mediated dissociation of limited capacity. *J Pharmacol Exp Ther* 223:342, 1982.

187. FORKER EL, LUXON BA, SHARMA VS: Hepatic transport and binding of rose bengal in the presence of albumin and gamma globulin. *Am J Physiol* 248:G702, 1985.

188. FLEISCHER AB, SHURMANTINE WO, LUXON BA, FORKER EL: Palmitate uptake by hepatocyte monolayers. Effect of albumin binding. *J Clin Invest* 77:964, 1986.

189. FORKER EL, LUXON BA: Effects of unstirred Disse fluid, nonequilibrium binding, and surface-mediated dissociation on hepatic removal of albumin-bound organic anions. *Am J Physiol* 248:G702, 1985.

190. MORGAN DJ, JONES DB, SMALLWOOD RA: Modeling of substrate elimination by the liver: Has the albumin receptor model superseded the well-stirred model? *Hepatology* 5:1231, 1985.

191. FORKER EL, LUXON BA: Lumpers vs. distributors. *Hepatology* 5:1236, 1985.

192. GRAUSZ H, SCHMID R: Reciprocal relation between plasma albumin level and hepatic sulfobromophthalein removal. *N Engl J Med* 284:1403, 1971.

193. STOLLMAN YR, GARTNER U, THEILMANN L, OHMI N, WOLKOFF AW: Hepatic bilirubin uptake in the isolated perfused rat liver is not facilitated by albumin binding. *J Clin Invest* 72:718, 1983.

194. INOUE M, OKAJIMA K, NAGASE S, MORINO Y: Plasma clearance of sulfobromophthalein and its interaction with hepatic binding proteins in normal and analbuminemic rats: Is plasma albumin essential for vectorial transport of organic anions in the liver? *Proc Natl Acad Sci USA* 80:7654, 1983.

195. INOUE M, HIRATA E, MORINO Y, NAGASE S, ROY CHOWDHURY J, ROY CHOWDHURY N, ARIAS IM: The role of albumin in the hepatic transport of bilirubin: Studies in mutant analbuminemic rats. *J Biochem* 97:737, 1985.

196. STREMMEL W, POTTER BJ, BERK PD: Studies of albumin binding to rat liver plasma membranes. Implications for the albumin receptor hypotheses. *Biochim Biophys Acta* 746:20, 1983.

197. WEISIGER RA, ZACKS CM, SMITH ND, et al: Effect of albumin binding on extraction of sulfobromophthalein by perfused elasmobranch liver: Evidence for dissociation-limited uptake. *Hepatology* 4:492, 1984.

198. WEISIGER RA: Dissociation from albumin: A potential rate-limiting step in the clearance of substances by the liver. *Proc Natl Acad Sci USA* 82:1563, 1985.

199. VAN DER SLUIJS P, POSTEMA B, MEIJER DKF: Lactosylation of albumin reduces uptake rate of dibromosulphthalein in perfused rat liver, and dissociation rate from albumin *in vitro*. *Hepatology* 7:688, 1987.

199a. REGOECZI E, DEBANNE MT, HATTON MWC, KOJ A: Elimination of asialofetiun and asialoorosomucoid by the intact rat. Quantitative aspects of the hepatic clearance mechanism. *Biochim Biophys Acta* 541:372, 1978.

200. GUMUCIO DL, GUMUCIO JJ, WILSON JAP: Albumin influences sulfobromophthalein transport by hepatocytes of each acinar zone. *Am J Physiol* 246:G86, 1984.

201. SCHWENK M, BURR R, SCHWARZ L, PFAFF E: Uptake of bromosulfophthalein by isolated liver cells. *Eur J Biochem* 64:189, 1976.

202. VAN BEZOOIJEN CF, GRELL T, KNOOK DL: Bromosulfophthalein uptake by isolated liver parenchymal cells. *Biochem Biophys Res Commun* 69:354, 1976.

203. APERCHE T, PREAUX AM, BERTHELOT P: Two systems are involved in the sulfobromophthalein uptake by rat liver cells: One is shared with bile salts. *Biochem Pharmacol* 30:1333, 1982.

204. SCHWARZ LR, GOTZ R, KLASSEN CD: Uptake of sulphobromophthalein gluthathione conjugates by isolated hepatocytes. *Am J Physiol* 239:C118, 1980.

205. WOLKOFF AW, SAMUELSON SC, JOHANSEN KL, NAKATA R, WITHERS D, SOSIAK S: Influence of Cl^- on organic anion transport in short-term cultured rat hepatocytes and isolated perfused rat liver. *J Clin Invest* 79:1259, 1987.

206. WOLKOFF AW, CHUNG CT: Identification, purification and partial characterization of an organic anion binding protein from rat liver cell plasma membrane. *J Clin Invest* 65:1152, 1980.

207. VAN DYKE RW, GOLLAN JL, SCHARSCHMIDT BF: Oxygen consumption by rat liver: Effects of taurocholate and sulfobromophthalein transport, glucagon and cation substitution. *Am J Physiol* 244:G523, 1983.

208. WOLKOFF AW, KLAUSNER RD, ASHWELL G, HARFORD J: Intracellular segregation of asialoglycoproteins and their receptor: A prelysosomal event subsequent to the dissociation of the ligand-receptor complex. *J Cell Biol* 98:375, 1984.

209. KAHN AM, ARONSON PS: Urate transport via anion exchange in dog renal microvillous membrane vesicles. *Am J Physiol* 244:F56, 1983.

210. KAHN AM, HARNATH S, WEINMAN EJ: Urate and p-aminohippurate transport in rat renal basolateral vesicles. *Am J Physiol* 244:F56, 1983.

211. KAHN AM, BRANHAM S, WEINMAN EJ: Mechanism of urate and p-aminohippurate transport in rat renal microvillous membrane vesicles. *Am J Physiol* 245:F151, 1983.

212. WEINBERG SL, BURCKHARDT G, WILSON FA: Taurocholate transport by rat intestinal basolateral membrane vesicles: Evidence for the presence of an anion exchange transport system. *J Clin Invest* 78:44, 1986.

213. WOLKOFF AW, GORESKY CA, SELLIN J, GATMAITAN Z, ARIAS IM: Role of ligandin in transfer of bilirubin from plasma into liver. *Am J Physiol* 286:E638, 1979.

214. REYES H, LEVI AJ, GATMAITAN Z, ARIAS IM: Studies of Y and Z, two hepatic cytoplasmic anion-binding proteins: Effect of drugs, chemicals, hormones and cholestasis. *J Clin Invest* 50:2242, 1971.

215. WOLKOFF AW: The gluthathione S-transferases: Their role in the transport of organic anions from blood to bile, in Javitt NB (ed): *Liver and Biliary Tract Physiology I*. Baltimore, University Park Press, 1980, p 151.

216. THEILMAN L, STOLLMAN YR, ARIAS IM, WOLKOFF AW: Does Z-protein have a role in transport of bilirubin and bromosulfophthalein by isolated perfused rat liver? *Hepatology* 4:923, 1984.

217. REICHEN J, BLITZER BL, BERK PD: Binding of unconjugated and conjugated sulfobromophthalein to rat liver plasma membrane fractions *in vitro*. *Biochim Biophys Acta* 640:298, 1981.

218. REICHEN J, BERK PD: Isolation of an organic anion binding protein from rat liver plasma membrane fractions by affinity chromatography. *Biochem Biophys Res Commun* 91:484, 1979.

219. STREMMEL W, GARBER MA, GLAZEROV V, THUNG SN, KOCHWA S, BERK PD: Physiochemical and immunohistological studies of a sulphobromophthalein and bilirubin-binding protein from rat liver plasma membrane. *J Clin Invest* 71:1796, 1983.

20. TIRIBELLI C, PANFILI E, SANDRI G, FREZZA M, SOTTOCASA GL: Liver bromosulphophthalein transport as a carrier mediated process, in Leevy CM (ed): *Diseases of the Liver and Biliary Tract*. Basal, Karger, 1976, p 55.

221. TIRIBELLI C, LUNAZZI G, LUCIANI GL, PANFILI E, GAZZIN B, LIUT G, SANDRI G, SOTTOCASA G: Isolation of a sulfobromophthalein-binding protein from hepatocyte plasma membrane. *Biochim Biophys Acta* 532:105, 1978.

222. LUNAZZI G, TIRIBELLI C, GAZZIN B, SOTTOCASA G: Further studies on bilitranslocase, a plasma membrane protein involved in hepatic organic anion uptake. *Biochim Biophys Acta* 685:177, 1982.

223. SOTTOCASA GL, BALDINI G, SANDRI G, LUNAZZI G, TIRIBELLI C: Reconstitution *in vitro* of sulfobromophthalein transport by bilitranslocase. *Biochim Biophys Acta* 685:123, 1982.

224. STREMMEL W, BERK PD: Hepatocellular uptake of sulfobromophthalein and bilirubin is selectively inhibited by an antibody to the liver plasma membrane sulfobromophthalein/bilirubin binding protein. *J Clin Invest* 78:822, 1986.

225. VON DIPPE P, LEVY DS: Characterization of the bile acid transport system in normal and transformed hepatocytes. *J Biol Chem* 258:8896, 1983.

226. LEVY DS, VON DIPPE P: Reconstitution of the bile acid transport system derived from hepatocyte sinusoidal membranes. *Hepatology* 3:839, 1983.

227. VON DIPPE P, ANANTHANARAYANAN M, DRAIN P, LEVY D: Purification and reconstitution of the bile acid transport system from hepatocyte sinusoidal plasma membranes. *Biochim Biophys Acta* 862:352, 1986.

228. FRIMMER M, PETZINGER E, ZIEGLER K: Protective effects of anionic cholecystographic agents against phalloidin on isolated hepatocytes by competitive inhibition of the phallotoxin uptake. *Naunyn Schmiedebergs Arch Pharmacol* 313:85, 1980.

229. PETZINGER E, JOPPEN C, FRIMMER M: Common properties of hepatocellular uptake of cholate, iodipamide, and antamanide, as distinct from the uptake of bromosulfophthalein. *Naunyn Schmiedebergs Arch Pharmacol* 322:174, 1983.

230. WEILAND T, NASSAL M, KRAMER W, FRICKER G, BICKEL U, KURZ G: Identity of membrane transport systems for bile salts, phalloidin, and antamanide by photoaffinity labeling. *Proc Natl Acad Sci USA* 81:5232, 1984.

231. STEINER JW, PERZ ZM, TAICHMAN LB: Cell population dynamics in the liver. A review of quantitative morphological techniques applied to the study of physiological growth. *Exp Mol Pathol* 5:146, 1966.

232. BUCHLER NL, MALT PR: *Regeneration of Liver and Kidney*. Boston, Little, Brown, 1971.

233. GARTNER U, STOCKERT RJ, MORELL AG, WOLKOFF AW: Modulation of the transport of bilirubin and asialoorosomucoid during liver regeneration. *Hepatology* 1:99, 1981.

234. BONNEY RJ, WALKER PR, POTER VR: Isoenzyme patterns in parenchymal and non-parenchymal cells isolated from regenerating and regenerated rat liver. *Biochem J* 136:947, 1973.

235. URIEL J: Cancer, retrodifferentiation, and the myth of Faust. *Cancer Res* 36:4269, 1976.

236. WALKER PR, WHITFIELD JF: Inhibition by colchicine of changes in amino acid transport and initiation of DNA synthesis in regenerating rat liver. *Proc Natl Acad Sci USA* 75:1394, 1978.

237. STOLLMAN YR, THEILMAN L, STOCKERT RJ, WOLKOFF AW: Reduced transport of bilirubin and asialoorosomucoid in regenerating rat liver is a microtubule-independent event. *Hepatology* 5:798, 1985.

238. GARTNER U, STOCKERT RJ, LEVINE WJ, WOLKOFF AW. Effect of nafenopin on the uptake of bilirubin and sulfobromophthalein by isolated perfused rat liver. *Gastroenterology* 83:1163, 1982.

239. WOLKOFF AW, KETLEY JN, WAGGONER JG, BERK PD, JAKOBY W: Hepatic accumulation and intracellular binding of conjugated bilirubin. *J Clin Invest* 61:142, 1978.

240. BERNSTEIN LH, BEN-EZZAR JB, GARTNER L, ARIAS IM: Hepatic intracellular distribution of tritium-labeled unconjugated and conjugated bilirubin in normal and Gunn rats. *J Clin Invest* 45:1194, 1966.

241. BROWN WR, GRODSKY GM, CARBONE JV: Intracellular distribution of tritiated bilirubin during hepatic uptake and excretion. *Am J Physiol* 207:1237, 1964.

242. LEVI AJ, GATMAITAN Z, ARIAS IM: Two hepatic cytoplasmic protein fractions, Y and Z, and their possible role in the hepatic uptake of bilirubin, sulfobromophthalein and other anions. *J Clin Invest* 48:2156, 1969.

243. FLEISCHNER G, ROBBINS J, ARIAS IM: Immunological studies of Y protein: A major cytoplasmic organic anion binding protein in rat liver. *J Clin Invest* 51:677, 1972.

244. LICHTER M, FLEISCHNER G, KIRSCH R, LEVI AJ, KAMISAKA K, ARIAS IM: Ligandin and Z protein in binding of thyroid hormones by the liver. *Am J Physiol* 230:1113, 1976.

245. KAMISAKA K, LISTOWSKY I, GATMAITAN Z, ARIAS IM: Interactions of bilirubin and other ligands with ligandin. *Biochemistry* 14:2175, 1975.

246. KIRSCH R, KAMISAKA K, FLEISCHNER G, ARIAS IM: Structural and functional studies of ligandin, a major renal organic anion binding protein. *J Clin Invest* 55:1009, 1975.

247. GOLDSTEIN EJ, ARIAS IM: Interaction of ligandin with radiographic contrast media. *Invest Radiol* 11:594, 1976.

248. MOREY KS, LITWACK G: Isolation and properties of cortisol metabolite binding proteins of rat liver cytosol. *Biochemistry* 8:4813, 1969.

249. KETTERER B, ROSS-MANSELL P, WHITEHEAD JK: The isolation of carcinogen-binding protein from livers of rats given 4-dimethylaminoazobenzene. *Biochem J* 103:316, 1967.

250. LITWACK G, KETTERER B, ARIAS IM: An abundant liver protein which binds steroids, bilirubin, carcinogens and a number of exogenous anions. *Nature* 234:466, 1971.

251. FLEISHNER GM, ROBBINS JB, ARIAS IM: Cellular localization of ligandin in rat, hamster, and man. *Biochem Biophys Res Commun* 74:992, 1977.

252. HABIG WH, PABST MJ, JAKOBY WB: Glutathione S-transferases. The first enzymatic step in mercapturic acid formation. *J Biol Chem* 249:7130, 1974.

253. HABIG WH, PABST MJ, FLEISCHNER G, GATMAITAN Z, ARIAS IM, JAKOBY WB: The identity of gluthathione S-transferase B with ligandin, a major binding protein of liver. *Proc Natl Acad Sci USA* 10:3879, 1974.

254. HABIG WH, PABST MJ, JAKOBY WB: Gluthathione S-transferase AA from rat liver. *Arch Biochem Biophys* 175:710, 1976.

255. PABST MJ, HABIG WH, JAKOBY WB: Glutathione S-transferase A: A novel kinetic mechanism in which the major reaction pathway depends on substrate concentration. *J Biol Chem* 249:7140, 1974.

256. KAMISAKA K, HABIG WH, KETLEY JN, ARIAS IM, JAKOBY WB: Multiple forms of human glutathione S-transferase and their affinity for bilirubin. *Eur J Biochem* 60:153, 1975.

257. KETLEY JN, HABIG WH, JAKOBY WB: Binding of non-substrate ligands to the gluthathione transferases. *J Biol Chem* 250:8670, 1975.

258. BHARGAVA MM, LISTOWSKY I, ARIAS IM: Ligandin: Bilirubin binding and gluthathione S-transferase activity are independent processes. *J Biol Chem* 253:4112, 1978.

259. BHARGAVA MM, OHMI N, LISTOWSKY I, ARIAS IM: Structural, catalytic, binding, and immunological properties associated with each of the two subunits of rat liver ligandin. *J Biol Chem* 255:718, 1980.

260. JAKOBY WB: The gluthathione S-transferases: A group of multifunctional detoxification proteins, in Meister A (ed): *Advances in Enzymology and Related Areas of Molecular Biology*. New York, Wiley, 1978, p 383.

261. WOLKOFF AW, WEISIGER RA, JAKOBY WB: The multiple roles of the gluthathione transferases (Ligandins), in Popper H, Schaffner F (eds): *Progress in Liver Diseases*. New York, Grune & Stratton, 1979, vol 6, p 213.

261a. ARIAS IM: Ligandin: A review and update of a multifunctional protein. *Med Biol* 57:328, 1979.

262. LEVINE RI, REYES H, LEVI AJ, GATMAITAN Z, ARIAS IM: Phylogenetic study of organic anion transfer from plasma into the liver. *Nature* 231:277, 1971.

263. LEVI AJ, GATMAITAN Z, ARIAS IM: Deficiency of hepatic organic anion-binding protein as a possible cause of nonhaemolytic unconjugated hyperbilirubinemia in the newborn. *Lancet* 2:139, 1969.

264. LEVI AJ, GATMAITAN Z, ARIAS IM: Deficiency of hepatic organic anion-binding protein, impaired organic anion uptake by liver and "physiologic" jaundice in newborn monkeys. *N Engl J Med* 283:1136, 1970.

265. BOYER JL, SCHWARZ J, SMITH N: Biliary secretion in elasmobranchs. I. Bile collection and composition. *Am J Physiol* 230:970, 1976.

266. BOYER JL, SCHWARZ J, SMITH N: Biliary secretion in elasmobranchs. II.

Hepatic uptake and biliary excretion of organic anions. *Am J Physiol* 230:974, 1976.

267. BEND JR, FOUTS JR: Gluthathione S-transferase: Distribution in several marine species and partial characterization in hepatic soluble fractions from little skate, Raja erinaces, liver. *Bull Mt Desert Isl Biol Lab* 13:4, 1973.

268. KAMISAKA K, LISTOWSKY I, FLEISCHNER G, GATMAITAN Z, ARIAS IM: The binding of bilirubin and other organic anions to serum albumin and ligandin (Y protein), in *Bilirubin Metabolism in the Newborn* (II). Excerpta Medica International Congress Series No. 380, Amsterdam, Excerpta Medica, 1976, p 156.

269. KETTERER B, TIPPING E, BEALE D, MEUWISSEN JATP: Ligandin, glutathione transferase, and carcinogen binding, in Arias IM, Jakoby WB (eds): *Gluthathione: Metabolism and Function.* New York, Raven, 1976, p 243.

270. LISTOWSKY I, GATMAITAN Z, ARIAS IM: Ligandin retains and albumin loses bilirubin binding capacity in liver cytosol. *Proc Natl Acad Sci USA* 75:1214, 1978.

271. KAMISAKA K, GATMAITAN Z, MOORE CL, ARIAS IM: Ligandin reverses bilirubin inhibition of liver mitochondrial respiration in vitro. *Pediatr Res* 9:903, 1975.

272. GORDON ER, GORESKY CA, CHAN TH, PERLIN AS: The isolation and characterization of bilirubin diglucuronide, the major bilirubin conjugate in dog and human bile. *Biochem J* 155:477, 1976.

273. HEIRWEGH KPM, VAN HEES GP, LEROY P, VAN ROY FP, JANSEN FH: Heterogeneity of bile pigment conjugates as revealed by chromatography of their ethyl anthranilate axopigments. *Biochem J* 120:877, 1979.

274. KUENZLE CC: Bilirubin conjugates in human bile. *Biochem J* 119:411, 1970.

275. BLANCKAERT N, COMPERNOLLE F, LEROY P, VAN HOUTTE R, FEVERY J, HEIRWEGH KPM: The fate of bilirubin IXα glucuronide in cholestasis and during storage in vitro. *Biochem J* 171:203, 1978.

276. COMPERNOLLE F, VAN HEES GP, FEVERY J, HEIRWEGH KPM: Mass-spectrometric structure elucidation of dog bile azopigments as the acyl glycosides of glucopyranose and xylopyranose. *Biochem J* 125:811, 1971.

277. FEVERY J, VAN HEES GP, LEROY P, COMPERNOLLE F, HEIRWEGH KPM: Excretion in dog bile of glucose and xylose conjugates of bilirubin. *Biochem J* 125:803, 1971.

278. CORNELIUS CE, KELLY KC, HIMES JA: Heterogeneity of bilirubin conjugates in several animal species. *Cornell Vet* 65:90, 1975.

279. WEBER A, SCHALM L, WITMANS J: Bilirubin monoglucuronide (pigment I): A complex. *Acta Med Scand* 173:19, 1963.

280. NOSSLIN B: The direct diazo reaction of bile pigments in serum. Experimental and clinical studies. *Scand J Clin Lab Invest [Suppl]* 12:1, 1960.

281. OSTROW JD, MURPHY NH: Isolation and properties of conjugated bilirubin and bile. *Biochem J* 120:311, 1970.

282. JANSEN FH, BILLING BH: Separation and structural analysis of vinyl and isovinyl azobilirubin derivatives. *Biochem J* 125:585, 1971.

283. JANSEN FH, BILLING BH: The identification of mono-conjugates of bilirubin in bile as amide derivatives. *Biochemistry* 125:917, 1971.

284. BLANCKAERT N: Analysis of bilirubin and bilirubin mono and diconjugates. Determination of their relative amounts in biological fluids. *Biochem J* 185:115, 1980.

285. ONISHI S, ITHO S, KAWADE N, ISOBE K, SUGIYAMA S: An accurate and sensitive analysis by high pressure liquid chromatography of conjugated and unconjugated bilirubin IXα in various biological fluids. *Biochem J* 185:281, 1980.

286. SPIVAK W, CAREY MC: Reverse-phase h.p.l.c. separation, quantification and preparation of bilirubin and its conjugates from native bile. *Biochem J* 225:787, 1985.

287. ROY CHOWDHURY J, ROY CHOWDHURY N: Quantitation of bilirubin and its conjugates by high pressure liquid chromatography. *Falk Hepatology* 11:1649, 1982.

288. ROY CHOWDHURY J, ARIAS IM: Disorders of bilirubin conjugation, in Ostrow JD (ed): *Bile Pigments and Jaundice.* New York, Marcel Dekker, 1986, p 317.

289. FEVERY JB, VAN DAMME R, MICHIELS R, DE GROOTE J, HEIRWEGH KPM: Bilirubin conjugates in bile of man and rat in the normal state and in liver disease. *J Clin Invest* 51:2482, 1972.

290. GORDON ER, DADOUN M, GORESKY CA, CHAN TH, PERLIN AS: The isolation of an axobilirubin-D monoglucoside from dog gall bladder bile. *Biochem J* 143:97, 1974.

291. BILLING BH, COLE PG, LATHE GH: The excretion of bilirubin as a diglucuronide giving the direct Van den Bergh reaction. *Biochem J* 65:774, 1957.

292. DUTTON GJ, BURCHELL B: Newer aspects of glucuronidation. *Prog Drug Metab* 2:1, 1977.

293. GRAHAM AB, PECHEY DT, TOOGOOD KC, THOMAS SB, WOOD GC: The phospholipid dependence of uridine diphosphate glucuronyl transferase. *Biochem J* 163:117, 1977.

294. JANSEN PLM, ARIAS IM: Delipidation and reactivation of UDP glucuronosyl transferase from rat liver. *Biochim Biophys Acta* 391:28, 1975.

295. JANSEN PLM: Studies on UDP glucuronyl transferase. Doctoral dissertation, University of Nijimegen, The Netherlands, 1972.

296. HENDERSON P: Activation *in vitro* of rat hepatic UDP glucuronyl transferase by ultrasound. *Life Sci* 9(II):511, 1970.

297. GRAHAM AD, WOOD GC: Factors affecting the response of microsomal UDP-glucuronyltransferase to membrane perturbants. *Biochim Biophys Acta* 311:45, 1973.

298. VASSEY DA, ZAKIM D: Regulations of microsomal enzymes by phospholipids. *J Biol Chem* 246:4649, 1971.

299. HEIRWEGH KPM, CAMPBELL M, MEUWISSEN JATP: Compartmentation of membrane bound enzymes. Some basic concepts and consequences for kinetic studies, in Aitio A (ed): *Conjugation Reactions in Drug Biotransformation.* Amsterdam, Elsevier, 1978, p 191.

300. HALLINAN T: Comparison of compartmented and of conformational phospholipid-constraint models for the intramembranous arrangement of UDP-glucuronyltransferase, in Aitio A (ed): *Conjugation Reactions in Drug Biotransformation.* Amsterdam, Elsevier, 1978, p 257.

301. WISHART GF: Functional heterogeneity of UDP glucuronosyl transferase as indicated by its differential development and inducibility by glucocorticoids. *Biochem J* 174:485, 1978.

302. BOCK KW, FROHLING W, REMMER H, REXER B: Effects of phenobarbital and 3-methyl cholanthrene on substrate specificity of rat liver microsomal UDP glucuronyl transferase. *Biochim Biophys Acta* 327:46, 1973.

303. LILLIENBLUM W, WALLI AK, BOCK KW: Differential induction of rat liver microsomal UDP-glucuronosyltransferase activities by various inducing agents. *Biochem Pharmacol* 31:907, 1982.

304. ROY CHOWDHURY J, ROY CHOWDHURY N, MOSCIONI AD, TUKEY R, TEPHLEY TR, ARIAS IM: Differential regulation by triiodothyronine of substrate-specific uridinediphosphoglucuronate glucuronyl transferases in rat liver. *Biochim Biophys Acta* 761:58, 1983.

305. DRUCKER WD: Glucuronic acid conjugation of tetrahydrocortisone p-nitrophenol in the homozygous Gunn rats. *Proc Soc Exp Biol Med* 129:303, 1968.

306. MOWAT AP, ARIAS IM: Observations of the effect of diethyl nitrosamine on glucuronide formation. *Biochim Biophys Acta* 212:175, 1970.

307. GORSKI JP, KASPER CB: Purification and properties of microsomal UDP glucuronyl transferase from rat liver. *J Biol Chem* 252:1336, 1977.

308. BURCHELL B: Purification of UDP glucuronyl transferase from untreated rat liver. *FEBS Lett* 78:101, 1977.

309. BOCK KW, JOSLING D, LILENBLUM WM, PFEIL H: Purification of rat liver glucuronyl transferase—separation of two enzyme forms inducible by 3-methyl-cholanthrene or phenobarbital. *Eur J Biochem* 98:19, 1977.

310. BOCK KW, KITTEL J, JOSTING G: Purification of rat liver UDP glucuronyl transferase: Separation of two enzyme forms with different substrate specificity and differential inducibility, in Aitio A (ed): *Conjugation Reactions in Drug Biotransformation.* Amsterdam, Elsevier, 1978. p 357.

311. BURCHELL B: Identification and purification of multiple forms of UDP-glucuronosyltransferase. *Rev Biochem Toxicol* 3:1, 1981.

312. FALANY CN, ROY CHOWDHURY J, ROY CHOWDHURY N, TEPHLY TW: Steroid 3- and 17-OH-UDPglucuronosyltransferase activities in rat and rabbit liver microsomes. *Drug Metab Dispos* 11:426, 1983.

313. FALANY CN, TEPHLY TR: Separation, purification and characterization of three isozymes of UDP-glucuronyl transferase from rat liver microsomes. *Arch Biochem Biophys* 227:248, 1983.

314. ROY CHOWDHURY J, ROY CHOWDHURY N, FALANY CN, TEPHLY TW, ARIAS IM: Isolation and characterization of multiple forms of rat liver UDP-glucuronoate glucuronosyltransferase. *Biochem J* 233:827, 1986.

315. BURCHELL B, BLANCKAERT N: Bilirubin mono- and diglucuronide formation by purified rat liver microsomal bilirubin-UDP-glucuronyl transferase. *Biochem J* 223:461, 1984.

316. ROY CHOWDHURY J, ROY CHOWDHURY N, ARIAS IM: UDP-glucuronosyl transferase deficiency in man and animals. *Biochem Soc Trans* 12:81, 1984.

317. ROY CHOWDHURY N, ARIAS IM, LEDERSTEIN M, ROY CHOWDHURY J: Substrates and products of purified rat liver bilirubin-UDP-glucuronosyltransferase. *Hepatology* 6:123, 1986.

318. WHITMER DL, RUSSEL PE, ZIURYS JC, GOLLAN JL: Hepatic microsomal glucuronidation of bilirubin is modulated by the lipid microenvironment of membrane-bound substrate. *J Biol Chem* 261:7170, 1986.

319. HEIRWEGH KPM, van de VIJVER M, FEVERY J: Assay and properties of digitonin-activated bilirubin uridine diphosphate glucuronyl transferase from rat liver. *Biochem J* 129:605, 1972.

320. JANSEN PLM: Mono and diglucuronidation of bilirubin. *Folia Med Neurol* 15:205, 1972.

321. BLANCKAERT N, GOLLAN J, SCHMID R: Bilirubin diglucuronide synthesis by a UDP glucuronide acid dependent enzyme system in rat liver microsomes. *Proc Natl Acad Sci USA* 76:2037, 1979.

322. ROY CHOWDHURY J, ROY CHOWDHURY N, WU G, SHOUVAL R, ARIAS IM: Bilirubin monoglucuronide and diglucuronide formation by human liver *in vitro:* Assay by high pressure liquid chromatography. *Hepatology* 1:622, 1981.

323. JANSEN PLM, ROY CHOWDHURY J, FISCHBERG EB, ARIAS IM: Enzymatic conversion of bilirubin monoglucuronide to diglucuronide by rat liver plasma membranes. *J Biol Chem* 252:2710, 1977.

324. ROY CHOWDHURY J, ROY CHOWDHURY N, BHARGAVA M, ARIAS IM: Purification and partial characterization of rat liver bilirubin glucuronoside glucuronosyl transferase. *J Biol Chem* 254:8336, 1979.

325. ROY CHOWDHURY J, FISCHBERG EB, DANILLER A, JANSEN PLM, ARIAS IM: Hepatic conversion of bilirubin monoglucuronide to bilirubin diglucuronide in uridine diphosphate glucuronyl transferase deficient man and rat by bilirubin glucuronoside glucuronosyl transferase. *J Clin Invest* 21:191, 1978.

326. JANSEN PLM: The isomerization of bilirubin monoglucuronide. *Clin Chim Acta* 49:233, 1973.

327. SIEG A, van HEES GP, HEIRWEGH KPM: Uridine diphosphate-glucuronic acid-independent conversion of bilirubin monoglucuronide to diglucuronide in presence of plasma membranes from rat liver is non-enzymatic. *J Clin Invest* 69:347, 1982.

328. JACKSON MR, BURCHELL B: The full length coding sequence of rat liver androsterone UDP-glucuronyltransferase cDNA and comparison with other members of the gene family. *Nucleic Acids Res* 14:779, 1986.

329. IYANAGI T, HANIU M, SOGAWA K, FUJII-KURIYAMA Y, WATANABE S, SHIVELY J, ANAN K: Cloning and characterization of cDNA encoding 3-methyl-cholanthrene-inducible rat mRNA for UDP-glucuronosyltransferase. *J Biol Chem* 261:15607, 1986.

330. MacKENZIE PI: Rat liver UDP-glucuronosyltransferase: Sequence and expression of a cDNA encoding a phenobarbital-inducible form. *J Biol Chem* 261:6119, 1986.

331. PETERS WKM, JANSEN PLM, NAUTA H: Molecular weights of UDP-glucuronoyltransferase determined by radiation inactivation analysis. *J Biol Chem* 259:11701, 1983.

332. HUTCHINSON DW, JOHNSON B, KNELL AJ: The reaction between bilirubin and aromatic diazo compounds. *Biochem J* 27:907, 1972.

333. van den BERGH AAH, MULLER P: Ueber eine direkte und eine indirekte Diazoreaktion auf Bilirubin. *Biochem Z* 77:90, 1916.

334. TALAFANT E: Properties and composition of bile pigment giving direct diazo reaction. *Nature* 178:312, 1956.

335. HEIRWEGH KPM, FEVERY JB, MEUWISSEN JATP, de GROOTE J, COMPERNOLLE F, DESMET V, van ROY FP: Recent advances in the separation and analysis of diazo-positive bile pigments. *Methods Biochem Anal* 22:205, 1974.

336. TROTMAN BW, ROY CHOWDHURY J, WIRT GD, BERNSTEIN SE: Azodipyrrole analysis of unconjugated and conjugated bilirubin using diazotized ethyl-anthranilate in dimethylsulfoxide. *Anal Biochem* 121:175, 1982.

337. COMPERNOLLE F, VAN HEES GP, BLANCKAERT N, HEIRWEGH KPM: Glucuronic acid conjugates of bilirubin IXα glucuronide in cholestasis and during storage *in vitro*. *Biochem J* 171:203, 1978.

338. BLANCKAERT N, COMPERNOLLE F, LEROY P, van HOURTEE R, FEVERY J, HEIRWEGH KPM: The fate of bilirubin IXα glucuronide in cholestasis and during storage *in vitro*. *Biochem J* 171:203, 1978.

339. LAUFF JJ, KASPER ME, AMBROS RT: Quantitative liquid chromatographic estimation of bilirubin species in pathological serum. *Clin Chem* 29:800, 1983.

340. POON R, HINBERG IH: Indican interference with six commercial procedures for measuring total bilirubin. *Clin Chem* 31:92, 1985.

341. COLE PG, LATHE GH, BILLING BH: Separation of the bile pigments of serum, bile and urine. *Biochem J* 57:514, 1954.

342. HEIRWEGH KPM, FEVERY J, MICHIELS R, VAN HEES GP, COMPERNOLLE F: Separation by thin layer chromatography and structure elucidation of bilirubin conjugates isolated from dog bile. *Biochem J* 145:185, 1975.

343. ISSELBACHER KG, MCCARTHY EA: Studies on bilirubin sulfate and other nonglucuronide conjugates. *J Clin Invest* 38:645, 1959.

344. NOIR BA, DE WALZ AT, RODRIGUEZ G: Studies on the bilirubin sulfate conjugate excreted in human bile. *Biochim Biophys Acta* 222:15, 1970.

345. TENHUNEN R: Studies on bilirubin and its metabolism. *Ann Med Exp Biol Fenn Suppl* 6:1, 1965.

346. ETTER-KJELSAAS H, KUENZLE CC: A polypeptide conjugate of bilirubin from human bile. *Biochim Biophys Acta* 400:83, 1975.

347. BLANCKAERT N, KABRA PM, FARINA FA, STAFFORD BE, MARTON LJ, SCHMIDT R: Measurement of bilirubin and its mono- and diconjugates in human serum by alkaline methanolysis and high performance liquid chromatography. *J Lab Clin Med* 96:198, 1980.

348. ONISHI S, ITHO S, KAWADE N, ISOBE K, SUGIYAMA S: An accurate and sensitive analysis by high pressure liquid chromatography of conjugated and unconjugated bilirubin IXα in various biological fluids. *Biochem J* 185:281, 1980.

349. JANSEN PLM: β-Glucuronidase resistant bilirubin glucuronide isomers in cholestatic liver disease—Determination of bilirubin metabolites in serum by means of high-pressure liquid chromatography. *Clin Chim Acta* 110:309, 1981.

350. JANSEN PLM, TANGERMAN A: Separation and characterization of bilirubin conjugates by high performance liquid chromatography. *J Chromatogr* 182:100, 1980.

351. ROY CHOWDHURY J, ARIAS IM: Dismutation of bilirubin. *Methods Enzymol* 77:192, 1981.

352. DAPPEN GM, SUNDBERG MW, WU TW, BABB BE, SCHAEFFER JR: A diazo-based dry film for determination of total bilirubin in serum. *Clin Chem* 29:37, 1983.

353. KUBASIK NP, MAYER TK, BASKAR AG, SINE HE, D'SOUZA JP: The measurement of fractionated bilirubin by Ektachem Film Slides. Method validation and comparison of conjugated bilirubin measurements with direct bilirubin in obstructive and hepatocellular jaundice. *Am J Clin Pathol* 84:518, 1985.

354. BROWN AK, EISINGER J, BLUMBERG WE, FLORES J, BOYLE G, LAMOLA AA: A rapid fluorometric method for determining bilirubin levels and binding in the blood of neonates: Comparison with other methods. *Pediatrics* 65:767, 1980.

355. JANSEN PLM, ROY CHOWDHURY J, FISCHBERG EB, ARIAS IM: Enzymatic conversion of bilirubin monoglucuronide to diglucuronide by rat liver plasma membranes. *J Biol Chem* 252:2710, 1977.

356. ARIAS IM, JOHNSON L, WOLFSON S: Biliary excretion on injected conjugated and unconjugated bilirubin by normal and Gunn rats. *Am J Physiol* 200:1091, 1961.

357. ROBINSON SH, YANNONI C, NAGASAWA S: Bilirubin excretion in rats with normal and impaired bilirubin conjugation. Effect of phenobarbital. *J Clin Invest* 50:2606, 1971.

358. SHANI M, GILON E, BEN-EZZER J, SHEBA C: Sulfobromophthalein tolerance test in patients with the Dubin-Johnson syndrome and their relatives. *Gastroenterology* 59:842, 1970.

359. GUTSTEIN S, ALPERT S, ARIAS IM: Studies of hepatic excretory function. IV. Biliary excretion of sulfobromophthalein in a patient with Dubin-Johnson syndrome and a biliary fistula. *Isr J Med Sci* 4:46, 1968.

360. CORNELIUS CE: Organic anion transport in mutant sheep with congenital hyperbilirubinemia. *Arch Environ Health* 19:852, 1969.

361. ALPERT S, MOSHER M, SHANSKE A, ARIAS IM: Multiplicity of hepatic excretory mechanism for organic anions. *J Gen Physiol* 53:238, 1969.

362. BERNSTEIN RB, NOVY MJ, PIASECKI GJ, LESTER R, JACKSON BT: Bilirubin metabolism in the fetus. *J Clin Invest* 48:1678, 1969.

363. UPSON DW, GRONWALL RR, CORNELIUS CE: Maximal hepatic excretion of bilirubin in sheep. *Proc Soc Exp Biol Med* 134:9, 1970.

364. KLAASSEN CD, PLAA GL: Studies on the mechanism of phenobarbital-enhanced sulfobromophthalein disappearance. *J Pharmacol Exp Ther* 161:361, 1968.

365. BARNHART J, RITT S, WARE A , COOMBES B: A comparison of the effects of taurocholate and theophylline on BSP excretion in dogs, in Paumgartner G, Preisig R (eds): *The Liver: Quantitative Aspects of Structure and Function*. Basel, Karger, 1973, p 315.

366. SCHARSCHMIDT BF, SCHMID R: The "micellar sink." *J Clin Invest* 62:1122, 1978.

367. BINET S, DELAGE Y, ERLINGER S: Influence of taurocholate, taurochenodeoxycholate and taurodehydrocholate on sulfobromophthalein transport into bile. *Am J Physiol* 236:E10, 1979.

368. SHULL SD, WAGNER CI, TROTMAN BW, SOLOWAY RD: Factors affecting bilirubin excretion in patients with cholesterol or pigment gallstones. *Gastroenterology* 72:625, 1977.

369. CLARENBURG R, KAO CC: Shared and separate pathways for biliary excretion of bilirubin and BSP in rats. *Am J Physiol* 225:192, 1973.

370. FORKER EL: Canalicular anion transport. Effect of bile acid-independent choleretics, in Berk PD, Berlin NI (eds): *Bile Pigments: Chemistry and Physiology*. Washington, DHEW, NIH, 1977, chap 38, p 383.

371. MEIER PG, RUETZ ST, HUGENTOBLER G, FRICKER G, KURTZ G: Identification and isolation of the putative canalicular bile acid carrier from rat liver. *Hepatology* 5:958, 1985.

372. MEIER PJ, RUETZ ST, FRICKER G, LANDMANN L: Identical bile acid transport systems are present in apical membranes of liver, ileum and kidney epithelial cells. *Hepatology* 6:1134, 1986.

373. BUSCHER HP, FRICKER G, GEROK W, KRAMER W, KURTZ G, MULLER M,

SCHNEIDER S: Membrane transport of amphiphilic compounds by hepatocytes, in Gretin H, Windler E, Beisiegel U (eds): *Receptor-Mediated Uptake in the Liver*. New York, Springer-Verlag, 1986, p 189.

374. LESTER R, SCHMID R: Intestinal absorption of bile pigments. II. Bilirubin absorption in man. *N Engl J Med* 269:178, 1963.

375. BRODERSON R, HERMAN LS: Intestinal reabsorption of unconjugated bilirubin: A possible contributing factor in neonatal jaundice. *Lancet* 1:1242, 1963.

376. OSTROW JD: Absorption of bile pigments by the gall bladder. *J Clin Invest* 46:2035, 1967.

377. WATSON CJ: The urobilinoids: Milestones in their history and some recent developments, in Berk PD, Berlin NI (eds): *Bile Pigments: Chemistry and Physiology*. Washington, DHEW, NIH, 1977, p 469.

378. STOLL MS, LIM CK, GRAY CH: Chemical variants of the urobilins, in Berk PD, Berlin NI (eds): *Bile Pigments: Chemistry and Physiology*. Washington, DHEW, NIH, 1977, p 483.

379. MOSCOWITZ A, WEINER M, LIGHTNER DA, PETRYKA ZJ, DAVIS H, WATSON CJ: The *in vitro* conversion of bile pigments to the urobilinoids by a rat clostridia species as compared with the human fecal flora. III. Natural d-urobilin, synthetic l-urobilin, and synthetic l-urobilinogen. *Biochem Med* 4:149, 1970.

380. ELDER G, GRAY CH, NICHOLSON DG: Bile pigment fate in gastrointestinal tract. *Semin Hematol* 9:71, 1972.

381. BERK PD: Personal communication.

382. SCHMID R, HAMMAKER L: Metabolism and disposition of C^{14}-bilirubin in congenital nonhemolytic jaundice. *J Clin Invest* 42:1720, 1963.

383. LUND HT, JACOBSEN J: Influence of phototherapy on the biliary bilirubin excretion patterns in newborn infants with hyperbilirubinemia. *J Pediatr* 85:262, 1974.

384. OSTROW JD: Photocatabolism of labeled bilirubin in the congenitally jaundiced (Gunn) rat. *J Clin Invest* 50:707, 1971.

385. BERRY CS, ZAREMBO JE, OSTROW JD: Evidence for conversion of bilirubin to dihydroxyl derivatives in the Gunn rat. *Biochem Biophys Res Commun* 49:1366, 1972.

386. BLANCKAERT N, FEVERY J, HEIRWEGH KPN, COMPERNOLLE F: Characterization of the major diazopositive pigments in bile of homozygous Gunn rats. *Biochem J* 164:237, 1977.

387. KAPITULNIK J, OSTROW JD: Stimulation of bilirubin catabolism in jaundiced Gunn rats by an inducer of microsomal mixed function monooxygenases. *Proc Natl Acad Sci USA* 75:682, 1978.

388. CAMERON JL, PULASKI EJ, ABEL T, IBER FL: Metabolism and excretion of bilirubin ^{14}C in experimental obstructive jaundice. *Ann Surg* 163:330, 1966.

389. CAMERON JL, FILLER RM, IBER FL, ABEL T, RANDOLPH JG: Metabolism and excretion of ^{14}C labeled bilirubin in children with biliary atresia. *N Engl J Med* 274:231, 1966.

390. FULOP M, SANDSON J, BRAZEAU P: Dialyzability, protein binding, and renal excretion of plasma conjugated bilirubin. *J Clin Invest* 44:666, 1965.

391. GOLLAN JL, DALLINGER KJC, BILLING BH: Excretion of conjugated bilirubin in the isolated perfused rat kidney. *Clin Sci Mol Med* 54:381, 1978.

392. HARDY JB, PEEPLES MO: Serum bilirubin levels in new born infants. Distributions and associations with neurological abnormalities during the first year of life. *Johns Hopkins Med J* 128:265, 1971.

393. GARTNER LM, LEE K, VAISMAN S, LANE D, ZARAFU I: Development of bilirubin transport and metabolism in the newborn Rhesus monkey. *J Pediatr* 90:513, 1977.

394. MAISELS MJ, PATHAK A, NELSON NM, NATHAN DG, SMITH CA: Endogenous production of carbon monoxide in normal and erythroblastic newborn infants. *J Clin Invest* 50:1, 1971.

395. VEST M, STREBEL L, HAUENSTEIN D: The extent of "shunt" bilirubin and erythrocyte survival in the newborn infant measured by the administration of (^{15}N) glycine. *Biochem J* 95:11c, 1965.

396. PEARSON HA: Life-span of the fetal red blood cell. *J Pediatr* 70:166, 1967.

397. BRODERSEN R, HEWAN LS: Intestinal reabsorption of unconjugated bilirubin: A possible contributing factor in neonatal jaundice. *Lancet* 1, 1242, 1963.

398. POLAND RL, ODELL GB: Physiologic jaundice: The enterohepatic circulation of bilirubin. *N Engl J Med* 284:1, 1971.

399. FREDA VJ, GORMAN JG, POLLACK W: Successful prevention of experimental Rh sensitization in man with an anti Rh gamma 2 globulin antibody preparation. *Transfusion* 4:26, 1964.

400. CLARKE CA, DONOHOE WTA, FINN R, LEHANE D, MCCONNELL RB, SHEPPARD PM, TOWERS SH, WOODROW JC, BOWLEY CC, TOVEY LAD, BIAS WB, KREVANS JR: Combined study: Prevention of Rh hemolytic disease: Final results of the "high risk" clinical trial. A combined study from centers in England and Baltimore. *Br Med J* 2:607, 1971.

401. HABERMAN S, KRAFT EJ, LEUCKE PE, PEACH RO: ABO isoimmunization: The use of the specific Coombs and best elution tests in the detection of hemolytic disease. *J Pediatr* 56:471, 1960.

402. HSIA D Y-Y, GELLIS SS: Studies on erythroblastosis fetalis due to ABO incompatibility. *Pediatrics* 13:503, 1954.

403. LEVI AJ, GATMAITAN Z, ARIAS IM: Deficiency of hepatic organic anion-binding protein as a possible causes of nonhaemolytic unconjugated hyperbilirubinemia in the new born. *Lancet* 2:139, 1969.

404. GRODSKY GM, KOLB HJ, FANSKA RE, NEMECHEK C: Effect of age of rat on development of hepatic carriers for bilirubin: A possible explanation for physiologic jaundice and hyperbilirubinemia in the newborn. *Metabolism* 3:246, 1970.

405. LEVI AJ, GATMAITAN Z, ARIAS IM: Deficiency of hepatic organic anion-binding protein, impaired organic anion uptake by liver and "physiologic" jaundice in newborn monkeys. *N Engl J Med* 283:1136, 1970.

406. ODELL GB: "Physiologic" hyperbilirubinemia in the neonatal period. *N Engl J Med* 277:193, 1967.

407. BROWN AK, ZUELZER WW: Studies on the neonatal development of the glucuronide conjugating system. *J Clin Invest* 37:332, 1958.

408. BERNSTEIN RB, NOVY MJ, PLASECKI GJ, LESTER R, JACKSON BT: Bilirubin metabolism in the fetus. *J Clin Invest* 48:1678, 1969.

409. MARTIUS G, HUBER W: Bromosulphthalein clearance and bilirubin levels in the newborn. *Ger Med Mon* 10:192, 1965.

410. GARTNER LM, ARIAS IM: The transfer of bilirubin from blood to bile in the neonatal guinea pig. *Pediatr Res* 3:171, 1969.

411. HSIA DY-Y, PATTERSON P, ALLEN FH, DIAMOND LK, GELLIS SS: Prolonged obstructive jaundice in infancy: General survey of 156 cases. *Pediatrics* 10:243, 1952.

412. ARTHUR LJH, BEVAN BR, HOLTON JB: Neonatal hyperbilirubinemia and breast feeding. *Dev Med Child Neurol* 8:279, 1966.

413. ARIAS IM, GARTNER LM, SEIFTER S, FURMAN M: Prolonged neonatal unconjugated hyperbilirubinemia associated with breast feeding and a steroid, pregnane-3(alpha), 20(beta)-diol, in maternal milk that inhibits glucuronide formation in vitro. *J Clin Invest* 43:2037, 1964.

414. HARGREAVES T, PIPER RF: Breast milk jaundice: Effect of inhibitory breast milk and $3\alpha,20\beta$-pregnanediol on glucuronyl transferase. *Arch Dis Child* 46:195, 1971.

415. HOLTON JB, LATHE GH: Inhibitors of bilirubin conjugation in newborn infant serum and male urine. *Clin Sci* 25:499, 1963.

416. ARIAS IM, GARTNER LM: Production of unconjugated hyperbilirubinemia in full-term newborn infants following administration of pregnane-3(alpha),20(beta)-diol. *Nature* 203:1292, 1964.

417. RAMOS A, SILBERBERG M, STERN I: Pregnanediols and neonatal hyperbilirubinemia. *Am J Dis Child* 111:353, 1966.

418. JOHNSON JD: Neonatal nonhemolytic jaundice. *N Engl J Med* 292:194, 1975.

419. FOLIOT A, PLOUSSARD JP, HOUSETT E, CHRISTOFOROV B, LUZEAN R, ODIEVRE M: Breast milk jaundice: In vitro inhibition of rat liver bilirubin-uridine diphosphate glucuronyl transferase activity and Z protein-bromosulfophthalein binding by human breast milk. *Pediatr Res* 10:594, 1976.

420. LUCEY JF, DRISCOL JJ: Physiological jaundice re-examined, in Sass-Kortsak A (ed): *Kernicterus*. Toronto, University of Toronto Press, 1961, p 29.

421. ARIAS IM, WOLFSON S, LUCEY JF, MCKAY RJ Jr: Transient familial neonatal hyperbilirubinemia. *J Clin Invest* 44:1442, 1965.

422. BERK PD, WOLKOFF AW, BERLIN NI: Inborn errors of bilirubin metabolism. *Med Clin North Am* 59:803, 1975.

423. SCHALM L, WEBER AP: Jaundice with conjugated bilirubin in hyperhaemolysis. *Acta Med Scand* 176:549, 1964.

424. SNYDER AL, SATTERLEE W, ROBINSON SH, SCHMID R: Conjugated plasma bilirubin in jaundice caused by pigment overload. *Nature* 213:93, 1967.

425. ROBINSON S, VANIER T, DESFORGES JF, SCHMID R: Jaundice in thalassemia minor: A consequence of "ineffective erythropoiesis." *N Engl J Med* 267:512, 1962.

426. ISRAELS LG, ZIPURSKY A: Primary shunt hyperbilirubinemia due to an alternate path of bilirubin production. *Am J Med* 27:693, 1959.

427. BERENDSOHN S, LOWMAN J, SUNDBERG D, WATSON CJ: Idiopathic dyserythropoietic jaundice. *Blood* 24:1, 1964.

428. VERWILGHEN R, VERHAEGEN H, WAUMANNS P, BEERT J: Ineffective erythropoiesis with morphologically abnormal erythroblasts and unconjugated hyperbilirubinemia. *Br J Haematol* 17:27, 1969.

429. VERWILGHEN R, LEWIS S, DACIE J, CROOKSTON J, CROOKSTON M: Hempas: Congenital dyserythropoietic anaemia (type II). *Q J Med* 42:257, 1973.

430. CRIGLER JF, NAJJAR VA: Congenital familial non-hemolytic jaundice with kernicterus. *Pediatrics* 10:169, 1952.

431. CHILDS B, NAJJAR VA: Familial nonhemolytic jaundice with kernicterus: A report of two cases without neurological damage. *Pediatrics* 18:369, 1956.

432. CHILDS B, SIDBURY JB, MIGEON CJ: Glucuronic acid conjugation by patients with familial non-hemolytic jaundice and their relatives. *Pediatrics* 23:903, 1959.

433. BLASCHKE TF, BERK PD, SCHARSCHMIDT BF, GUYTHER JR, VERGALLA J, WAGGONER JG: Crigler-Najjar syndrome: An unusual course with development of neurologic damage at age eighteen. *Pediatr Res* 8:573, 1974.

434. BERK PD, MARTIN JF, BLASCHKE TF, SCHARSCHMIDT BF, PLOTZ PH: Unconjugated hyperbilirubinemia: Physiological evaluation and experimental approaches to therapy. *Ann Intern Med* 82:552, 1975.

435. SLEISENGER MH, KAHN I, BARNIVILLE H, RUBIN W, BEN EZZER J, ARIAS IM: Nonhemolytic unconjugated hyperbilirubinemia with hepatic glucuronyl transferase deficiency: A genetic study in four generations. *Trans Assoc Am Physicians* 80:259, 1967.

436. SCHMID R: Hyperbilirubinemia, in Stanbury JB, Wyngaarden JB, Frederickson DS (eds): *The Metabolic Basis of Inherited Disease*, 3d ed. New York, McGraw-Hill, 1972, p 1141.

437. WOLKOFF AW, ROY CHOWDHURY J, GARTNER LA, ROSE AL, BIEMPICA L, GIBLIN DR, FINK D, ARIAS IM: Crigler-Najjar syndrome (Type I) in an adult male. *Gastroenterology* 76:3380, 1979.

438. ARIAS IM: Chronic unconjugated hyperbilirubinemia without overt signs of hemolysis in adolescents and adults. *J Clin Invest* 41:2233, 1962.

439. JARVIS GA: Constitutional nonhemolytic hyperbilirubinemia with findings resembling kernicterus. *Arch Neurol Psychiatr* 81:55, 1959.

440. SZABO L, EBREY P: Studies on the inheritance of Crigler-Najjar syndrome by the menthol test. *Acta Paediatr Hung* 4:153, 1963.

441. ARIAS IM, GARTNER LM, COHEN M, BEN EZZER J, LEVI AJ: Chronic nonhemolytic unconjugated hyperbilirubinemia with glucuronyl transferase deficiency: Clinical, biochemical, pharmacologic, and genetic evidence for heterogeneity. *Am J Med* 47:395, 1969.

442. KAPITULNIK J, KAUFMANN NA, GOITEIN K, CIVIDALLI G, BLONDHEIM SH: A pigment found in the Crigler-Najjar syndrome and its similarity to an ultrafilterable photo-derivative of bilirubin. *Clin Chim Acta* 57:231, 1974.

443. BLOOMER JR, BERK PD, HOWE RB, BERLIN NI: Bilirubin metabolism in congenital nonhemolytic jaundice. *Pediatr Res* 5:256, 1971.

444. BILLING GH, GRAY CH, KULCYCKA A, MANFIELD P, NICHOLSON DC: The metabolism of ^{14}C-bilirubin in congenital nonhaemolytic hyperbilirubinaemia. *Clin Sci* 27:163, 1964.

445. NOVIKOFF AB, ESSNER E: The liver cell. *Am J Med* 19:102, 1960.

446. DE BRITO T, BORGES MA, DASILVA LC: Electron microscopy of the liver in nonhemolytic acholuric jaundice with kernicterus (Crigler-Najjar) and in idiopathic conjugated hyperbilirubinemia (Rotor). *Gastroenterologia* 106:325, 1966.

447. MINIOPALUELLO, GAUTIER A, MAGNENAT P: L'ultrastructure du foie humain dans un cas de Crigler-Najjar. *Acta Hepatosplenol* 15:65, 1968.

448. HUANG PWH, ROZDILSKY B, GERRARD JW, GOLUBOFF N, HOLMANNCH: Crigler-Najjar syndrome in four of five siblings with post-mortem findings in one. *Arch Pathol* 90:536, 1970.

449. ROTHMALER G, LOWE H: Elektronenoptische untersuchungen der lever bei einem fall von kongenitalem nichtamolytischen ikterus (morbus Crigler-Najjar). *Paediatr Radiol* 7:135, 1970.

450. GUNN CH: Hereditary acholuric jaundice in a new mutant strain of rats. *J Hered* 29:137, 1938.

451. JOHNSON L, SARMIENTO F, BLANC WA, DAY R: Kernicterus in rats with an inherited deficiency of glucuronyl transferase. *Am J Dis Child* 97:591, 1959.

452. SCHMID R, AXELROD J, HAMMAKER L, SWARN RL: Congenital jaundice in rats due to a defective glucuronide formation. *J Clin Invest* 37:1123, 1958.

453. BLANC WA, JOHNSON L: Studies on kernicterus. *J Neuropathol Exp Neurol* 18:165, 1959.

454. SCHUTTA HS, JOHNSON L: Bilirubin encephalopathy in the Gunn rat: A fine structure study of the cerebellar cortex. *J Neuropathol Exp Neurol* 26:377, 1967.

455. ROSE AL, JOHNSON A: Bilirubin encephalopathy: Neuropathological and histochemical studies in the Gunn rat model. *Neurology* 22:420, 1972.

456. SCHUTTA HS, JOHNSON L: Clinical signs and morphologic abnormalities in Gunn rats treated with sulfadiethoxine. *J Pediatr* 75:1070, 1969.

457. COWGER ML: Bilirubin encephalopathy, in Gaull G (ed): *Biology of Brain Dysfunction*. New York, Plenum, 1973, vol 2, p 265.

458. ODELL GB, NATZSCHKA JC, STOREY G: Bilirubin nephropathy in the Gunn strain of rat. *Am J Physiol* 212:931, 1967.

459. CALL NB, TISHER CC: The urinary concentrating defect in the Gunn strain of rat. Role of bilirubin. *J Clin Invest* 55:319, 1975.

460. AXELSEN RA: Spontaneous renal papillary necrosis in the Gunn rat. *Pathology* 5:43, 1973.

461. ODELL GB, BOLEN JL, POLAND RL, SEUNGDAMBONG S, CUKIER JD: Protection from bilirubin nephropathy in jaundiced Gunn rats. *Gastroenterology* 66:1218, 1974.

462. GARDNER WA, KONIGSMARK B: Familial nonhemolytic jaundice: Bilirubinosis and encephalopathy. *Pediatrics* 43:365, 1969.

463. LOZZIO BB, CHERNOFF AL, MACHEDO ER, LOZZIO SH: Hereditary renal disease in a mutant strain of rats. *Science* 156:1742, 1967.

464. HOWAN ER, GUARINO AM: Biliary excretion of phenol red by Wistar and Gunn rats. *Proc Soc Exp Biol Med* 146:46, 1974.

465. ARIAS IM: Ethereal and N-linked glucuronide formation by normal and Gunn rats *in vitro* and *in vivo*. *Biochem Biophys Res Commun* 6:81, 1961.

466. FLOCK EV, BOLLMAN JL, OWEN CA, ZOLLMAN PE: Conjugation of thyroid hormones and analogues by the Gunn rat. *Endocrinology* 77:303, 1965.

467. WEATHERILL PJ, BURCHELL B: Reactivation of a pure defective UDP-glucuronosyltransferase from homozygous Gunn rat liver. *FEBS Lett* 87:207, 1978.

468. ROY CHOWDHURY N, GROSS F, MOSCIONI AD, KRAM M, ARIAS IM, ROY CHOWDHURY J: Isolation and purification of multiple normal and functionally defective forms of UDP-glucuronosyltransferase from livers of inbred Gunn rats. *J Clin Invest* 79:327, 1987.

469. GORODISCHER R, LEVY G, KRASNER J, YAFFE SJ: Congenital nonobstructive, nonhemolytic jaundice: Effect of phototherapy. *N Engl J Med* 282:375, 1970.

470. KARON M, IMACH D, SCHWARTZ A: Effective phototherapy in congenital nonobstructive, nonhemolytic jaundice. *N Engl J Med* 282:377, 1970.

471. BEHRMAN RE, BROWN AK, CURRIE MR, HARBER LC, HASTINGS JW, ODELL GB, SCHAFFER R, SETLOW RB, VOGL TP, WURTMAN RJ: Committee on phototherapy in the newborn. Final report of the committee. Division of Medical Sciences, Assembly of Life Sciences, Washington, DC, National Research Council, National Academy of Sciences, 1974.

472. CALLAHAN EW, THALER M, KARON M, BAUER K, SCHMID R: Phototherapy of severe unconjugated hyperbilirubinemia: Formation and removal of labeled bilirubin derivatives. *Pediatrics* 46:841, 1970.

473. BERK PD, SCHARSCHMIDT BF, WAGGONER JG, WHITE SC: The effect of repeated phlebotomy on bilirubin turnover, bilirubin clearance and unconjugated hyperbilirubinaemia in the Crigler-Najjar syndrome and the jaundiced Gunn rat: Application of computers to experimental design. *Clin Sci Mol Med* 50:333, 1976.

474. PLOTZ PH, BERK PD, SCHARSCHMIDT BF, GORDON JK, VERGALLA J: Removing substances from blood by affinity chromatography. I. Removing bilirubin and other albumin-bound substances from plasma and blood with albumin-conjugated agarose beads. *J Clin Invest* 53:778, 1974.

475. SCHARSCHMIDT BF, PLOTZ PH, BERK PD, WAGGONER JG, VERGALLA J: Removing substances from blood by affinity chromatography. II. Removing bilirubin from the blood of jaundiced rats by hemoperfusion over albumin-conjugated agarose beads. *J Clin Invest* 53:786, 1974.

476. SCHARSCHMIDT BF, MARTIN JF, SHAPIRO LJ, PLOTZ PH, BERK PD: Hemoperfusion through albumin-conjugated agarose gel for the treatment of neonatal jaundice in Rhesus monkeys. *J Lab Clin Med* 89:101, 1977.

477. SCHARSCHMIDT BF, MARTIN JF, SHAPIRO LJ, PLOTZ PH, BERK PD: The use of calcium chelating agents and prostaglandin E1 to eliminate platelet and white blood cell losses resulting from hemoperfusion through uncoated charcoal, albumin-agarose gel, and neutral and cation exchange resin. *J Lab Clin Med* 90:110, 1977.

478. RUGSTAD HE, ROBINSON SM, YANNONI C, TASJIA AH: Transfer of bilirubin uridine diphosphate glucuronyl transferase to enzyme deficient rats. *Science* 170:553, 1970.

479. SEBROW O, GATMAITAN Z, ORLANDI F, ROY CHOWDHURY J, ARIAS IM: Replacement of hepatic UDP glucuronyl transferase activity in homozygous Gunn rats. *Gastroenterology* 78:1332, 1980.

480. MUKHERJEE AB, KRASNER J: Induction of an enzyme in genetically deficient rats after grafting of normal liver. *Science* 183:68, 1973.

481. van HOUWELINGEN CAJ, ARIAS IM: Attempts to induce hepatic uridine diphosphate glucuronyl transferase in genetically deficient Gunn rats by grafting of normal liver tissue. *Pediatr Res* 10:830, 1976.

482. DEMETRIOU AA, LEVENSON SM, WHITING J, FELDMAN D, MOSCIONI AD, KRAM M, ROY CHOWDHURY N, ROY CHOWDHURY J: Replacement of hepatic functions in rats by transplantation of microcarrier-attached hepatocytes. *Science* 233:1190, 1986.

483. DEMETRIOU AA, LEVENSON SW, WHITING J, FELDMAN D, NOVIKOFF PM, NOVIKOFF AB, ROY CHOWDHURY N, ROY CHOWDHURY J: Organization, morphology and function of microcarrier-attached transplanted hepatocytes in rats. *Proc Natl Acad Sci USA* 83:7475, 1986.

484. DEMETRIOU AA, WHITING J, LEVENSON SM, ROY CHOWDHURY N, SCHECHNER R, MICHALSKI S, FELDMAN D, ROY CHOWDHURY J: New method of

hepatocyte transplantation and extracorporeal liver support. *Ann Surg* 204:259, 1986.

485. Liver Transplantation—Consensus Conference. *JAMA* 250:2961, 1983.

486. KAUFMAN SS, WOOD RP, SHAW BW, MARKIN RS, ROSENTHAL P, GRIDELLI B, VANDERHOOD JA: Orthotopic liver transplantation for type I Crigler-Najjar syndrome. *Hepatology* 6:1259, 1986.

487. GOLLAN JL, HUANG SM, BILLING B, SHERLOCK S: Prolonged survival in three brothers with severe type II Crigler-Najjar syndrome. Ultrastructural and metabolic studies. *Gastroenterology* 68:1543, 1975.

488. GORDON ER, SHAFFER EA, SASS-KORTSAK A: Bilirubin secretion and conjugation in the Crigler-Najjar syndrome type II. *Gastroenterology* 70:761, 1976.

489. FEVERY J, BLANCKAERT N, HEIRWEGH KPM, PREAUX A-M, BERTHELOT P: Unconjugated bilirubin and an increased proportion of bilirubin monoconjugates in the bile of patients with Gilbert's syndrome and Crigler-Najjar syndrome. *J Clin Invest* 60:970, 1977.

490. ARIAS IM, GARTNER L, FURNAM, WOLFSON S: Studies of the effect of several drugs on hepatic glucuronide formation in newborn rats and humans. *Ann NY Acad Sci* 111:274, 1963.

491. CATZ C, YAFFE SJ: Pharmacological modification of bilirubin conjugation in the newborn. *Am J Dis Child* 104:516, 1962.

492. YAFFE SJ, LEVY G, MATZUSAWA T, BALIAH T: Enhancement of glucuronide-conjugating capacity in a hyperbilirubinemic infant due to apparent enzyme induction by phenobarbital. *N Engl J Med* 275:1461, 1966.

493. THOMPSON RPH, PILCHER CWT, ROBINSON J, STRATHERS GM, MCLEAN AEM, WILLIAMS R: Treatment of unconjugated jaundice with dicophane. *Lancet* 2:4, 1969.

494. HUNTER J, THOMPSON RPH, RAKE MO, WILLIAMS R: Controlled trial of phetharbital, a non-hypnotic barbiturate, in unconjugated hyperbilirubinaemia. *Br Med J* 2:497, 1971.

495. ORME MLE: Increased glucuronidation of bilirubin in men and rat by administration of antipyrine (phenazone). *Clin Sci Mol Med* 46:511, 1974.

496. BLACK M, FEVERY J, PARKER D, JACOBSEN J, BILLING BH, CARSON ER: Effect of phenobarbitone on plasma (^{14}C) bilirubin clearance in patients with unconjugated hyperbilirubinaemia. *Clin Sci Mol Med* 46:1, 1974.

497. BLASCHKE TF, BERK PD, RODKEY FL, SCHARSCHMIDT BF, COLLISON HA, WAGGONER JG: Effects of glutethimide and phenobarbital on hepatic bilirubin clearance, plasma bilirubin turnover, and carbon monoxide production in man. *Biochem Pharmacol* 23:2795, 1974.

498. HUNTER JO, THOMPSON RPH, DUNN PM, WILLIAMS R: Inheritance of type II Crigler-Najjar hyperbilirubinemia. *Gut* 14:46, 1973.

499. SMITH PM, MIDDLETON JE, WILLIAMS R: Studies on the familial incidence and clinical history of patients with chronic unconjugated hyperbilirubinemia. *Gut* 8:449, 1967.

500. GILBERT A, LEREBOULLET P: La cholamae simple familiale. *Sem Med* 21:241, 1901.

501. GILBERT A, LEREBOULLET P, HERSCHER M: Les trois cholemies congenitales. *Bull Mem Soc Med Hop Paris* 24:1203, 1907.

502. THOMPSON RPH: Genetic transmission of Gilbert's syndrome, in Okolicsanyi L (ed): *Familial Hyperbilirubinemia*. New York, Wiley, 1981, p 91.

503. POWELL LW, HEMINGWAY E, BILLING BH, SHERLOCK S: Idiopathic unconjugated hyperbilirubinemia (Gilbert's syndrome): A study of 42 families. *N Engl J Med* 277:1108, 1967.

504. FOULK WT, BUTT HR, OWEN CA, WHITCOMB FF: Constitutional hepatic dysfunction (Gilbert's disease): Its natural history and related syndrome. *Medicine (Baltimore)* 38:25, 1959.

505. SAGILD U, DALGARD OZ, TYGSTRUP N: Constitutional hepatic dysfunction (Gilbert's disease): Its natural history and related syndrome. *Medicine (Baltimore)* 38:25, 1959.

506. SIMON G, VAVONIER HS: Étude au microscope electronique du foie de deux cas d'ictere non-hemolytique congenital de type Gilbert. *Schweiz Med Wochenschr* 93:459, 1963.

507. FELDMAN G, ONDEA P, DOMARTONDES MC, MOLAS G, FAUVERT R: L'ultrastructure hepatique au cours de la maladie de Gilbert. *Pathol Biol (Paris)* 16:943, 1968.

508. MCGEE JOD, ALLAN JG, RUNEL RL, PATRICK RS: Liver ultrastructure in Gilbert's syndrome. *Gut* 16:220, 1975.

509. BILLING BH, WILLIAMS R, RICHARDS TG: Defects in hepatic transport of bilirubin in congenital hyperbilirubinaemia. An analysis of plasma bilirubin disappearance curves. *Clin Sci* 27:245, 1964.

510. BERK PD, BLOOMER JR, HOWE RB, BERLIN NI: Constitutional hepatic dysfunction (Gilbert's syndrome): A new definition based on kinetic studies with unconjugated radiobilirubin. *Am J Med* 49:296, 1970.

511. FREZZA M, PERONA G, CORROCHER R, CELLERING R, BASSETTO MA, DESANDRE G: Bilirubin ^{3}H kinetic studies: Pattern of normals, Gilbert's syndrome and hemolytic state. *Acta Hepatogastroenterol (Stuttgart)* 20:363, 1973.

512. COBELLI C: Modeling, identification and parameter estimation of bilirubin kinetics in normal, hemolytic and Gilbert's states. *Comput Biomed Res* 8:522, 1975.

513. OKOLICSANYI L, GHIDINI O, ORLANDO R, CORTELLAZZO S, BENEDETTI G, NACCARATO R, MANITTO P: An evaluation of bilirubin kinetics with respect to the diagnosis of Gilbert's syndrome. *Clin Sci Mol Med* 54:535, 1978.

514. OKOLICSANYI L, ORLANDO R, VENUTI M, DALBRUN G, CORBELLI C, RUGGERI A, SALVAT A: A modeling study of the effect of fasting on bilirubin in Gilbert's syndrome. *Am J Physiol* 240:266, 1981.

515. GORESKY CA, GORDON ER, SHAFFER EA, PARIE P, CARASSAVAS D, ARONOFF A: Definition of a conjugation dysfunction in Gilbert's syndrome: Studies of the handling of bilirubin loads and of the pattern of bilirubin conjugates secreted in bile. *Clin Sci Mol Med* 1:63, 1978.

516. SCHARSCHMIDT BF: Bilirubin kinetics in Gilbert's syndrome: Clinical applications and pathophysiological implications, in Okolicsanyi L (ed): *Familial Hyperbilirubinemia*. New York, Wiley, 1978, p 99.

517. BLACK M, BILLING BH: Hepatic bilirubin UDP glucuronyltransferase activity in liver disease and Gilbert's syndrome. *N Engl J Med* 280:1266, 1969.

518. AUCLAIR C, HAKIM J, BOIVIN P, TROUBE H, BOUCHERROT J: Bilirubin and paranitrophenol glucuronyl transferase activity of the liver in patients with Gilbert's syndrome. *Enzyme* 21:97, 1976.

519. FELSHER BF, CRAIG JR, CARPIO N: Hepatic bilirubin glucuronidation in Gilbert's syndrome. *J Lab Clin Med* 81:829, 1973.

520. BELLET H, RAYNANA A: An assay of bilirubin UDP glucuronyl transferase on needle biopsies applied to Gilbert's syndrome. *Clin Chim Acta* 53:51, 1974.

521. BLACK M, SHERLOCK S: Treatment of Gilbert's syndrome with phenobarbitone. *Lancet* 1:1359, 1970.

522. KIRSHENBAUM G, SHAMES DM, SCHMID R: An expanded model of bilirubin kinetics: Effect of feeding, fasting and phenobarbital in Gilbert's syndrome. *J Pharmacokinet Biopharm* 2:115, 1976.

523. FELSHER BR, CARPIO NM: Caloric intake and unconjugated hyperbilirubinemia. *Gastroenterology* 69:42, 1975.

524. BERK PD, BLASCHKE TF, WAGGONER JG: Defective BSP clearance in patients with constitutional hepatic dysfunction (Gilbert's syndrome). *Gastroenterology* 63:472, 1972.

525. CARTEL GVM, CHISESI T, CAZZAVILLIAN M, BARBUI T, BATTISTA R, DINI E: Bromsulphthalein-Ausscheidung und Hyperbilirubinaemia beim Gilbert Syndrom. *Dtsch Z Verdau Stoffwechselkr* 35:169, 1975.

526. COBELLI C, RUGGERI A, TOFFOLO G, OKOLICSANYI L, VENUTI M, ORLANDO R: BSP vs bilirubin kinetics in Gilbert's syndrome, in Okolicsanyi L (ed): *Familial Hyperbilirubinemia*. New York, Wiley, 1981, p 121.

527. MARTIN JF, VIERLING JM, WOLKOFF AW, SCHARSCHMIDT BF, VERGALLA J, WAGGONER JF: Abnormal hepatic transport of indocyanine green in Gilbert's syndrome. *Gastroenterology* 70:385, 1976.

528. YAMAGUCHI K, OKUDA Y, YANEMITSU H, TSUKADA Y, SHIGATA H: Cyclic premenstrual unconjugated hyperbilirubinemia. Report of two cases. *Ann Intern Med* 83:514, 1975.

529. FELSHER BF, RICKARD D, REDEKER AG: The reciprocal relation between caloric intake and the degree of hyperbilirubinemia in Gilbert's syndrome. *N Engl J Med* 283:170, 1970.

530. BARRETT PVD: The effect of diet and fasting on the serum bilirubin concentration in the rat. *Gastroenterology* 4:572, 1971.

531. OWENS D, SHERLOCK S: Diagnosis of Gilbert's syndrome: Role of reduced caloric intake test. *Br Med J* 3:559, 1973.

532. BENSINGER TA, MAISELS MJ, MARLSON DE, CONRAD ME: Effect of low caloric diet on endogenous carbon monoxide production: Normal adults and Gilbert's syndrome. *Proc Soc Exp Biol Med* 144:417, 1973.

533. GOLLAN JL, BATEMAN C, BILLING BH: Effect of dietary composition on the unconjugated hyperbilirubinemia of Gilbert's syndrome. *Gut* 5:335, 1976.

534. FELSHER BJ: Effect of changes in dietary components on the serum bilirubin in Gilbert's syndrome. *Am J Clin Nutr* 7:705, 1976.

535. BLOOMER JR, BARRETT PV, RODKEY FL, BERLIN NI: Studies on the mechanisms of fasting hyperbilirubinemia. *Gastroenterology* 61:479, 1971.

536. BARRETT PVD: Hyperbilirubinemia of fasting. *JAMA* 217:1349, 1971.

537. FELSHER BF, CARPIO NM, VAN COUVERING K: Effect of fasting and phenobarbital on hepatic UDP-glucuronic acid formation in the rat. *J Lab Clin Med* 93:414, 1979.

538. GOLLAN JL, HATT KJ, BILLING BH: The influence of diet on unconjugated hyperbilirubinemia in the Gunn rat. *Clin Sci Mol Med* 49:229, 1975.

539. GOLLAN JL, HOLE DR, BILLING BH: The role of dietary lipid in the regulation of unconjugated hyperbilirubinemia in Gunn rats. *Clin Sci* 57:327, 1979.

540. COWAN RE, THOMPSON RPH, KAYE JP, CLARK GM: The association between fasting hyperbilirubinaemia and serum non-esterified fatty acids in man. *Clin Sci Mol Med* 53:155, 1977.

541. STEIN LB, MISHKIN S, FLEISCHNER G, GATMAITAN Z, ARIAS IM: Effect of fasting on hepatic ligandin, Z protein, and organic anion transfer from plasma in rats. *Am J Physiol* 231:1371, 1976.
542. FROMKE VL, MILLER D: Constitutional hepatic dysfunction (CHD: Gilbert's disease): A review with special reference to a characteristic increase and prolongation of the hyperbilirubinemic response to nicotinic acid. *Medicine (Baltimore)* 51:451, 1972.
543. DAVIDSON AR, ROJAS-BUENO A, THOMPSON RPH, WILLIAMS R: Reduced caloric intake and nicotinic acid provocation tests in diagnosis of Gilbert's syndrome. *Br Med J* 2:480, 1975.
544. FEVERY J, VERWILGHEN R, TAN TG, DEGROOTE J: Glucuronidation of bilirubin and the occurrence of pigment gallstones in patients with chronic haemolytic diseases. *Eur J Clin Invest* 10:219, 1980.
545. OHKUBO H, MUSHA H, OKUDA K: Studies on nicotinic acid interaction with bilirubin metabolism. *Dig Dis Sci* 24:700, 1979.
546. POWELL LW, BILLING BH, WILLIAMS HS: An assessment of red cell survival in idiopathic unconjugated hyperbilirubinemia (Gilbert's syndrome) by the use of radioactive diisopropyl-fluorophosphate and chromium. *Aust Ann Med* 16:221, 1967.
547. BERK PD, BERMAN MD, BLITZER BL, CHRETIEN P, MARTIN JF, SCHARSCHMIDT BF, VIERLING J, WOLKOFF AW, VERGALLA J, WAGGONER JG: Effect of splenectomy on hepatic bilirubin clearance in patients with hereditary spherocytosis: Implications for the diagnosis of Gilbert's syndrome. *J Lab Clin Med* 98:37, 1981.
548. VAN STEENBERGEN W, KUTZ K, FEVERY J: Effects of conjugation, bile flow and bile acid load on the apparent maximal excretion of bilirubin ("Tm"), in Preisig R, Paumgartner G (eds): *The Liver. Proceedings of the 3rd Gstaad Symposium.* Aulendorf, Editio Cantor, 1979, p 208.
549. VAUGHAN JM, HASLEWOOD GAD: The normal level of plasma bilirubin. *Lancet* 1:133, 1938.
550. ALWALL N, LAURELL CB, NILSBY I: Studies on heredity in cases of "Non-hemolytic hyperbilirubinemia without direct van den Bergh reaction" (hereditary, non-hemolytic bilirubinemia). *Acta Med Scand* 124:114, 1946.
551. O'HAGEN JE, HAMILTON T, DE BRETON EG, SHAW AE: Human serum bilirubin. *Clin Chem* 3:609, 1957.
552. BAILEY A, ROBINSON D, DAWSON AM: Does Gilbert's disease exist? *Lancet* 1:931, 1977.
553. OWENS D, EVANS J: Population studies on Gilbert's syndrome. *J Med Genet* 12:152, 1975.
554. WERNER M, TOLLS RE, HULTIN JV, MELLECKER J: Influence of sex and age on the normal range of eleven serum constituents. *Z Klin Chem Klin Biochem* 8:105, 1970.
555. WILDING P, ROLLASEN JG, ROBINSON D: Patterns of change for various biochemical constituents detected in well population screening. *Clin Chim Acta* 41:375, 1972.
556. DAMASHEK W, SINGER K: Familial nonhemolytic jaundice. Constitutional hepatic dysfunction with indirect van den Bergh reaction. *AMA Arch Intern Med* 67:259, 1941.
557. ALWALL N: On hereditary non-hemolytic bilirubinemia. *Acta Med Scand* 123:560, 1946.
558. MEULENGRACHT E: A review of chronic intermittent juvenile jaundice. *Q J Med* 16:83, 1947.
559. BAROODY WG, SHUGART RT: Familial nonhemolytic icterus. *Am J Med* 20:314, 1956.
560. CUNNINGHAM IJ, HOPKIRK CSM, FILMER JF: Photosensitivity diseases in New Zealand. I. Facial eczema: Its clinical pathological and biochemical characteristics. *NZ J Sci Tech* 24A:185, 1942.
561. HANCOCK J: Congenital photosensitivity in Southdown sheep. A new sublethal factor in sheep. *NZ J Sci Tech* 32A:16, 1950.
562. CLARE NT: Photosensitivity diseases in New Zealand. IV. Photosensitizing agent in Southdown photosensitivity. *NZ J Sci Tech* 27A:23, 1945.
563. CORNELIUS CE, GRONWALL RR: Congenital photosensitivity and hyperbilirubinemia in Southdown sheep in the United States. *Am J Vet Res* 29:291, 1968.
564. GRONWALL R: Sulfobromophthalein sodium excretion and hepatic storage in Corriedale and Southdown sheep with inherited hepatic dysfunction. *Am J Vet Res* 31:2131, 1970.
565. MIA AS, CORNELIUS CE, GRONWALL RR: Increased bilirubin production from sources other than circulating erythrocytes in mutant Southdown sheep. *Proc Soc Exp Biol Med* 136:227, 1971.
566. MIA AS, GRONWALL RR, CORNELIUS CE: Bilirubin ^{14}C turnover in normal and mutant Southdown sheep with congenital hyperbilirubinemia. *Proc Soc Exp Biol Med* 133:955, 1970.
567. MIA AS, GRONWALL RR, MCGAVIN MD, CORNELIUS CE: Renal function defect in mutant Southdown sheep with congenital hyperbilirubinemia. *Proc Soc Exp Biol Med* 137:1237, 1971.
568. MCGAVIN MD, GRONWALL RR, CORNELIUS CE, MIA AS: Renal radial fibrosis in mutant southdown sheep with congenital hyperbilirubinemia. *Am J Pathol* 67:601, 1972.
569. PORTMAN OW, ROY CHOWDHURY J, ROY CHOWDHURY N, ALEXANDER M, CORNELIUS CE, ARIAS IM: A non-human primate model for Gilbert's syndrome. *Hepatology* 4:175, 1984.
570. PORTMAN OW, ALEXANDER M, ROY CHOWDHURY J, ROY CHOWDHURY N, CORNELIUS CE, ARIAS IM: Effects of nutrition on hyperbilirubinemia in Bolivian squirrel monkeys. *Hepatology* 4:454, 1984.
571. DUBIN IN, JOHNSON FB: Chronic idiopathic jaundice with unidentified pigment in liver cells: A new clinocopathologic entity with a report of 12 cases. *Medicine (Baltimore)* 33:155, 1954.
572. SPRINZ H, NELSON RS: Persistent nonhemolytic hyperbilirubinemia associated with lipochrome-like pigment in liver cells: Report of four cases. *Ann Intern Med* 41:952, 1954.
573. DUBIN IN: Chronic idiopathic jaundice: A review of fifty cases. *Am J Med* 23:268, 1958.
574. BEKER S, READ AE: Familial Dubin-Johnson syndrome. *Gastroenterology* 35:387, 1958.
575. WOLF RL, PIZETTE M, RICHMAN A, DREILING DA, JACOBS W, FERNANDEZ O, POPPER H: Chronic idiopathic jaundice: A study of two afflicted families. *Am J Med* 28:32, 1950.
576. BERKOWITZ D, ENTINE J, CHUNN L: Dubin-Johnson syndrome: Report of a case occurring in a Negro male. *N Engl J Med* 2:1028, 1960.
577. ARIAS IM: Studies of chronic familial non-hemolytic jaundice with conjugated bilirubin in the serum with and without an unidentified pigment in the liver cells. *Am J Med* 31:510, 1961.
578. HISLOP DMC: A case of Dubin-Johnson syndrome in a North American Cree Indian with suggestive evidence of familial occurrence. *Can Serv Med J* 10:61, 1964.
579. BURNSCOX CJ: The Dubin-Johnson syndrome in a Timorese. *Med J Malaya* 19:311, 1965.
580. BUTT HR, ANDERSON VE, FOULK WT, BAGGENSTOSS AH, SCHOENFIELD LJ, DICKSON ER: Studies of chronic idiopathic jaundice (Dubin-Johnson syndrome). II. Evaluation of a large family with the trait. *Gastroenterology* 51:619, 1966.
581. BANERJEE AK: Dubin-Johnson syndrome: A family study. *Med J Malaya* 25:21, 1970.
582. VAUGHAN JP, MARUBBIO AT, MADDOCKS I, COOKE RA: Chronic idiopathic jaundice in Papua and New Guinea: A report of nine patients with Dubin-Johnson's syndrome or Rotor's syndrome. *Trans R Soc Trop Med Hyg* 64:287, 1970.
583. COHEN L, LEWIS C, ARIAS IM: Pregnancy, oral contraceptives, and chronic familial jaundice with predominantly conjugated hyperbilirubinemia (Dubin-Johnson syndrome). *Gastroenterology* 62:1182, 1972.
584. KONDO T, KUCHIBA K, OHTSUKA Y, YANAGISAWA W, SHIOMURA T, TAMINATO T: Clinical and genetic studies on Dubin-Johnson syndrome in a cluster area in Japan. *Jpn J Human Genet* 18:378, 1974.
585. SHANI M, SELIGSOHN U, GILON E, SHEBA C, ADAM A: Dubin-Johnson syndrome in Israel. I. Clinical laboratory, and genetic aspects of 101 cases. *West J Med* 39:549, 1970.
586. SELIGSOHN U, SHANI M, RAMOT B, ADAM A, SHEBA C: Hereditary deficiency of blood clotting factor VII and Dubin-Johnson syndrome in an Israeli family. *Isr J Med Sci* 5:1060, 1969.
587. SELIGSOHN U, SHANI M, RAMOT B, ADAM A, SHEBA C: Dubin-Johnson Syndrome in Israel. II. Association with factor-VII deficiency. *Q J Med* 39:569, 1970.
588. LEVANON M, RIMON S, SHANI M, RAMOT B, GOLDBERG E: Active and inactive factor-VII in Dubin-Johnson syndrome with factor-VII deficiency, hereditary factor-VII deficiency and on coumadin administration. *Br J Haematol* 23:669, 1972.
589. JAVITT NB, KONDO T, KUCHIBA K: Bile acid excretion in Dubin-Johnson syndrome. *Gastroenterology* 75:931, 1978.
590. KONDO T, YAGI R, KUCHIBA K: Dubin-Johnson syndrome in a neonate. *N Engl J Med* 292:1028, 1975.
591. IVICIC L, SOSOVEC V: Vrodena benigni konjugovena hyperbilirubinemia S pigmentom peceni (Dubin-Johnson syndrom) u novorodenca. *Cesk Pediatr* 30:287, 1975.
592. NAKATA F, OYANAGI K, FUJIWARA M, SOGAWA H, MINAIN R, HORINO K, NAKAO T, KONDO T: Dubin-Johnson syndrome in a neonate. *Eur J Pediatr* 132:299, 1979.
593. MANDEMA E, DE FRAITURE WH, NIEWEG HO, ARENDS A: Familial chronic idiopathic jaundice (Dubin-Sprinz disease), with a note on bromsulphalein metabolism in this disease. *Am J Med* 28:42, 1960.
594. DITTRICH H, SEIFERT E: Über das verhalten des pigmentes sowie der biligrafin ausscheidung bei einem patienten mit Dubin-Johnson syndrom. *Acta Hepatosplenol* 9:45, 1962.

595. MORITA M, KIHAVA T: Intravenous cholecystography and metabolism of meglumine iodipamide (biligrafin) in Dubin-Johnson syndrome. *Radiology* 99:57, 1971.

596. ESSNER E, NOVIKOFF AB: Human hepatocellular pigments and lysosomes. *J Ultrastruct Res* 3:3764, 1960.

597. MUSCATELLO U, MUSSINI L, AGNOLUCCI MT: The Dubin-Johnson syndrome: An electronmicroscopic study of the liver cell. *Acta Hepatosplenol* 14:162, 1967.

598. OPPERMANN A, CARBILLET J-P, GISSELBRECHT H, PAGEANT G, CLEMENT D: Syndrome de Dubin-Johnson: Donnees ultrastructurales. *Sem Hop Paris* 47:2721, 1971.

599. CALLARD P, GANTER P, KALIFAT SR, DUPUY-COIN AM, DELARUE J: Étude cytochimique et ultrastructurale de pigment d'un cas de maladie de Dubin-Johnson. *Virchows Arch (B)* 7:63, 1971.

600. KERMAREC J, DUPLAY H, DANIEL R: Étude histochimique et ultrastructurale comparative des pigments de la melanose colique et du syndrome de Dubin-Johnson. *Ann Biol Clin* 30:567, 1972.

601. EHRLICH JC, NOVIKOFF AB, PLATT R, ESSNER E: Hepatocellular lipofuscin and the pigment of chronic idiopathic jaundice. *Bull NY Acad Med* 36:488, 1960.

602. WEGMANN R, RANGIER M, ETEVE J, CHARBONNIER A, CAROLI J: Melanose hepatosplenique avec ictere chronique a bilirubine directe: Maladie de Dubin-Johnson? Étude clinique et biologique de la maladie. Étude histochimique, chimique et spectographique de pigment anormal. *Sem Hop Paris* 26:1761, 1960.

603. DE SARAM WG, GALLAGHER CH, GOODRICH BS: Melanosis of sheep liver. I. Chemistry of the pigment. *Aust Vet J* 45:105, 1969.

604. SOSNNET J, STEICHEN-DE FALQUE M, BRISBOIS P: Isolement et proprietes d'une melanine obtenue a partir de melanogenes urinaires dans un cas de maladie de Dubin-Johnson. *Clin Chim Acta* 24:325, 1969.

605. ARIAS IM, BERNSTEIN L, TOFFLER R, CORNELIUS C, NOVIKOFF AB, ESSNER E: Black liver disease in Corriedale sheep: A new mutation affecting hepatic excretory function. *J Clin Invest* 43:1249, 1964.

606. ARIAS IM, BERNSTEIN L, ROFFLER R, BEN EZZER J: Biliary and urinary excretion of metabolites of 7-H^3-epinephrine in mutant Corriedale sheep with hepatic pigmentation. *Gastroenterology* 48:495, 1965.

607. ARIAS IM, BERNSTEIN L, ROFFLER R, BEN EZZER J: Black liver diseases in Corriedale sheep: Metabolism of tritiated epinephrine and incorporation of isotope into the hepatic pigment *in vivo*. *J Clin Invest* 44:1026, 1965.

608. ARIAS IM: Chronic idiopathic jaundice, in Bock K (ed): *Ikterus*. Stuttgart, FK Schattauer Verlag, 1968, p 65.

609. SWARTZ HM, SARNA T, VARMA RR: On the nature and excretion of the hepatic pigment in the Dubin-Johnson syndrome. *Gastroenterology* 76:958, 1979.

610. ARIAS IM, BLUMBERG W: The pigment in Dubin-Johnson syndrome. *Gastroenterology* 77:820, 1979.

611. SWARTZ HM, SARNAT T, VARMA RR: The pigment in Dubin-Johnson syndrome. *Gastroenterology* 77:821, 1979.

612. RUBINSTEIN ZJ, SELIGSON U, MODAN M, SHANI M: Hepatic computerized tomography in the Dubin-Johnson syndrome: Increased liver density as a diagnostic aid. *Comput Radiol* 9:315, 1985.

613. HUNTER FM, SPARKS RD, FLINNER RL: Hepatitis with resulting mobilization of hepatic pigment in a patient with Dubin-Johnson syndrome. *Gastroenterology* 47:631, 1964.

614. MASUDA M: On the relation between Dubin-Johnson syndrome and Rotor type; A case of Dubin-Johnson syndrome complicated with serum hepatitis. *Rev Intern Hepatol* 15:1227, 1965.

615. VARMA RR, GRAINGER JM, SCHEUER PJ: A case of the Dubin-Johnson syndrome complicated by acute hepatitis. *Gut* 11:817, 1970.

616. WARE AJ, EIGENBRODT EH, SHOEY J, COMBES B: Viral hepatitis complicating the Dubin-Johnson syndrome. *Gastroenterology* 63:331, 1972.

617. WARE A, EIGENBRODT E, NAFTALIS J, COMBES B: Dubin-Johnson syndrome and viral hepatitis. *Gastroenterology* 67:560, 1974.

618. SCHOENFIELD LJ, MCGILL DB, HUNTON DB, FOULK MT, BUTT HR: Studies of chronic idiopathic jaundice (Dubin-Johnson syndrome). I. Demonstration of hepatic excretory defect. *Gastroenterolgy* 44:101, 1963.

619. ABE H, OKUDA K: Biliary excretion of conjugated sulfobromophthalein (BSP) in constitutional conjugated hyperbilirubinemias. *Digestion* 13:373, 1975.

620. ERLINGER S, DHUMEAUX D, DESJEUX JF, BENHAMOU JP: Hepatic handling of unconjugated dyes in the Dubin-Johnson syndrome. *Gastroenterology* 64:106, 1973.

621. CHARBONNIER A, BRISBOIS P: Étude chromatographique de la BSP au cours de l'epreuve clinique d'epuration plasmatique de ce colorant. *Rev Intern Hepatol* 10:1163, 1960.

622. RODES J, ZUBIZARRETA A, BRUGUERA M: Metabolism of the bromsulphalein in Dubin-Johnson syndrome. Diagnostic value of the paradoxical in plasma levels of BSP. *Dig Dis* 17:545, 1972.

623. WHEELER HO, MELTZER JI, BRADLEY SE: Biliary transport and hepatic storage of sulfobromophthalein sodium in the unanesthetized dog, in normal man, and in patients with hepatic disease. *J Clin Invest* 39:1131, 1960.

624. KOSKELO P, TOIVONEN I, ADLERCREUTZ H: Urinary coproporphyrin isomer distribution in Dubin-Johnson syndrome. *Clin Chem* 13:1006, 1967.

625. BEN-EZZER J, RIMINGTON C, SHANI M, SELIGSOHN U, SHEBA C, SZEINBERG A: Abnormal excretion of the isomers of urinary coproporphyrin by patients with Dubin-Johnson syndrome in Israel. *Clin Sci* 40:17, 1971.

626. WOLKOFF AW, COHEN LE, ARIAS IM: Inheritance of the Dubin-Johnson syndrome. *N Engl J Med* 288:113, 1973.

627. KONDO T, KUCHIBA K, SHIMIZU Y: Coproporphyrin isomers in Dubin-Johnson syndrome. *Gastroenterology* 70:1117, 1976.

628. KAPLOWITZ N, JAVITT N, KAPPAS A: Coproporphyrin I and III excretion in bile and urine. *J Clin Invest* 51:2895, 1972.

629. BEN-EZZER J, BLONDER J, SHANI M, SELIGSOHN U, POST CA, ADAM A, SZEINBERG A: Dubin-Johnson syndrome. Abnormal excretion of the isomers or urinary coproporphyrin by clinically unaffected family members. *Isr J Med Sci* 9:1431, 1973.

630. EDWARDS RH: Inheritance of the Dubin-Johnson-Sprinz syndrome. *Gastroenterology* 68:734, 1975.

631. WOLKOFF AW, ARIAS IM: Coproporphyrin excretion in amniotic fluid and urine from premature infants: A possible maturation defect. *Pediatr Res* 8:591, 1974.

632. AZIZ MA, SCHWARZ S, WATSON CJ: Studies of coproporphyrin. VIII. Reinvestigation of the isomer distribution in jaundice and liver diseases. *J Lab Clin Med* 63:596, 1964.

633. SHIMIZU Y, KONDO T, KUCHIBA K, URATA G: Uroporphyrin III cosynthetase in liver and blood in the Dubin-Johnson syndrome. *J Lab Clin Med* 89:517, 1977.

634. SHIMIZU Y, IDA S, NARUTO H, URATA G: Excretion of porphyrins in urine and bile after the administration of delta-aminolevulinic acid. *J Lab Clin Med* 92:795, 1978.

635. KONDO T, KUCHIBA K, SHIMIZU Y: Metabolic fate of exogenous delta-aminolevulinic acid in Dubin-Johnson syndrome. *J Lab Clin Med* 94:421, 1979.

636. CORNELIUS CE, ARIAS IM, OSBURN BI: Hepatic pigmentation with photosensitivity: A syndrome in Corriedale sheep resembling Dubin-Johnson syndrome in man. *J Am Vet Med Assoc* 146:709, 1965.

637. CORNELIUS CE, OSBURN BI, GRONWALL RR, CARDINET GH: Dubin-Johnson syndrome in immature sheep. *Am J Dig Dis* 13:1072, 1968.

638. MIA AS, GRONWALL RR, CORNELIUS CE: Unconjugated bilirubin transport in normal and mutant Corriedale sheep with Dubin-Johnson syndrome. *Proc Soc Exp Biol Med* 135:33, 1970.

639. JANSEN PLM, PETERS WH, LAMERS WH: Hereditary chronic conjugated hyperbilirubinemia in mutant rats caused by defective hepatic anion transport. *Hepatology* 5:573, 1985.

640. ROTOR AB, MANAHAN L, FLORENTIN A: Familial nonhemolytic jaundice with direct van den Bergh reaction. *Acta Med Phil* 5:37, 1948.

641. PECK OC, REY DF, SNELL AM: Familial jaundice with free and conjugated bilirubin in the serum and without liver pigmentation. *Gastroenterology* 39:625, 1969.

642. PORUSH JG, DELMAN AJ, FEUER MM: Chronic idiopathic jaundice with normal liver histology. *Arch Intern Med* 109:102, 1962.

643. PEREIRA-LIMA JE, UTZ E, ROSENBERG I: Hereditary nonhemolytic conjugated hyperbilirubinemia without abnormal liver cell pigmentation. A family study. *Am J Med* 40:628, 1966.

644. WOLKOFF AW, WOLPERT E, PASCASIO FM, ARIAS IM: Rotor's syndrome: A distinct inheritable pathophysiologic entity. *Am J Med* 60:173, 1976.

645. WOLPERT E, PASCASIO FM, WOLKOFF AW, ARIAS IM: Abnormal sulfobromophthalein metabolism in Rotor's syndrome and obligate heterozygotes. *N Engl J Med* 296:1099, 1977.

646. SCHIFF L, BILLING BH, OIKAWA Y: Familial nonhemolytic jaundice with conjugated bilirubin in the serum. *N Engl J Med* 260:1315, 1959.

647. HAVERBACK BJ, WIRTSCHAFTER SK: Familial nonhemolytic jaundice with normal liver histology and conjugated bilirubin. *N Engl J Med* 262:113, 1960.

648. POBLETE PF, REYES M, MANAHAN L, DALMACIO-CRUZ A: Rotor's syndrome: A family study. *Acta Med Phil* 4:64, 1967.

649. PASCASIO FM, DE LA FUENTE D: Rotor-Manahan-Florentin syndrome: Clinical and genetic studies. *Phil J Med* 7:151, 1969.

650. PASCASIO FM, DE LA FUENTE D: Rotor-Manahan-Florentin syndrome: The mode of inheritance of a family included in the report of Rotor et al. *Acta Med Phil* 5:127, 1969.

651. KAWASAKI H, KINWA N, IRISA T, HIRAYAMA C: Dye clearance studies in Rotor's syndrome. *Am J Gastroenterol* 71:380, 1979.

652. SHIMIZU Y, NARUTO H, IDA S, KOHAKURA M: Urinary coproporphyrin isomers in Rotor's syndrome. A study in eight families. *Hepatology* 1:173, 1981.

653. HADCHOUEL P, CHARBONNIER A, LAGERON A, LEMONNIER F, RAUTUREAU M, SCOTTO J, CAROL J: A propos d'une nouvelle forme d'ictere chronique idiopathique. Hypothese physio-pathologique. *Rev Med Chir Mal Foie* 146:61, 1971.

654. DHUMEAUX D, BERTHELOT P: Chronic hyperbilirubinemia associated with hepatic uptake and storage impairment: A new syndrome resembling that of the mutant Southdown sheep. *Gastroenterology* 69:988, 1975.

655. RAPACINI GL, TOPI GC, ANTI M, D'ALLASANDRO GL, GRISO D, AMANTEA A, DEVITIS I, FEDELI G: Porphyrins in Rotor syndrome: A study on an Italian family. *Hepatogastroenterology* 33:11, 1986.

656. LOCALIO SA, SCHWARTZ MS, GANNON CF: The urinary/fecal coproporphyrin ratio in liver disease. *J Clin Invest* 20:7, 1941.

657. KOSKELO P, EISALA A, TOIVONEN I: Urinary excretion of porphyrin precursors and coproporphyrin in healthy females on oral contraceptives. *Br Med J* 1:652, 1966.

658. KOSKELO P, TOIVONEN I: Urinary excretion of coproporphyrin isomers I and III and aminolaevulinic acid in normal pregnancy and obstetric hepatosis. *Acta Obstet Gynecol Scand* 47:292, 1968.

659. SUMMERSKILL WHJ, WALSHE JM: Benign recurrent intrahepatic obstructive jaundice. *Lancet* 2:686, 1959.

660. WILLIAMS R, CARTTER MA, SHERLOCK S, SCHEUER PG, HILL KR: Idiopathic recurrent cholestasis: A study of the functional and pathological lesions in four cases. *Q J Med* 33:387, 1964.

661. SPIEGEL EL, SCHUBERT W, PERRIN E, SCHIFF L: Benign recurrent intrahepatic cholestasis with response to cholestyramine. *Am J Med* 39:682, 1965.

662. RUYMANN FB, TAKEUCHI A, BOYCE HW: Idiopathic, recurrent cholestasis. *Pediatrics* 45:812, 1970.

663. DE PAGTER AGF, VAN BERGE HENEGOUWEN GP, BOKKEL-HUINNUK JA, BRANDT K-H: Familial benign recurrent intrahepatic cholestasis. *Gastroenterology* 71:202, 1976.

664. TYGSTRUP N: Intermittent possibly familial intrahepatic cholestatic jaundice. *Lancet* 1:1171, 1960.

665. KUHN HA: Intrahepatic cholestasis in two brothers. *Ger Med Mon* 8:185, 1963.

666. SCHAPIRO RH, ISSELBACHER KJ: Benign recurrent intrahepatic cholestasis. *N Engl J Med* 268:708, 1963.

667. SUMMERSKILL WHJ: The syndrome of benign recurrent cholestasis. *Am J Med* 38:298, 1965.

668. TYGSTRUP N, JENSEN B: Intermittent intrahepatic cholestasis of unknown etiology in five young males from the Faroe Islands. *Acta Med Scand* 185:523, 1969.

669. SCHUBERT WK, GARANCIS J, PERRIN E: Idiopathic benign recurrent cholestasis: Biochemical and histologic changes induced by cholestyramine therapy. *Clin Res* 13:409, 1965.

670. BIEMPICA L, GUTSTEIN S, ARIAS IM: Morphological and biochemical studies of benign recurrent cholestasis. *Gastroenterology* 52:521, 1967.

671. VAN BERGE HENEGOUWEN GP, BRANDT K-H, DE PAGTER AGF: Is an acute disturbance in hepatic transport of bile acids the primary cause of cholestasis in benign recurrent intrahepatic cholestasis? *Lancet* 1:1249, 1974.

672. ENDO T, UCHIDA K, AMURO Y, HIGASHINO K, YAMAMURA Y: Bile acid metabolism in benign recurrent intrahepatic cholestasis. Comparative studies on the icteric and anicteric phases of a single case. *Gastroenterology* 76:1002, 1979.

673. BLOOMER JR, BERK PD, HOWE RB: Hepatic clearance of unconjugated bilirubin in colestatic liver diseases. *Am J Dig Dis* 19:9, 1974.

674. BRODERSEN R, TYGSTRUP N: Serum bilirubin studies in patients with intermittent intrahepatic cholestasis. *Gut* 8:46, 1967.

675. SUMMERFIELD JA, SCOTT J, BERMAN M, GHENT C, BLOOMER JR, BERK PD, SHERLOCK S: Benign recurrent intrahepatic cholestasis: Studies of bilirubin kinetics, bile acids, and cholangiography. *Gut* 21:154, 1980.

676. DICKSON ER, FLEISCHER J, SUMMERSKILL WHJ: Ultrastructural changes of the liver in benign recurrent cholestasis. *Proc Mayo Clin* 40:288, 1965.

677. LESSER PB: Benign familial recurrent intrahepatic cholestasis. *Am J Dig Dis* 18:259, 1973.

678. BEUDOIN M, FELDMANN G, ERLINGER S, BENHAMOU J-P: Benign recurrent cholestasis. *Digestion* 9:49, 1973.

PART 9

METALS

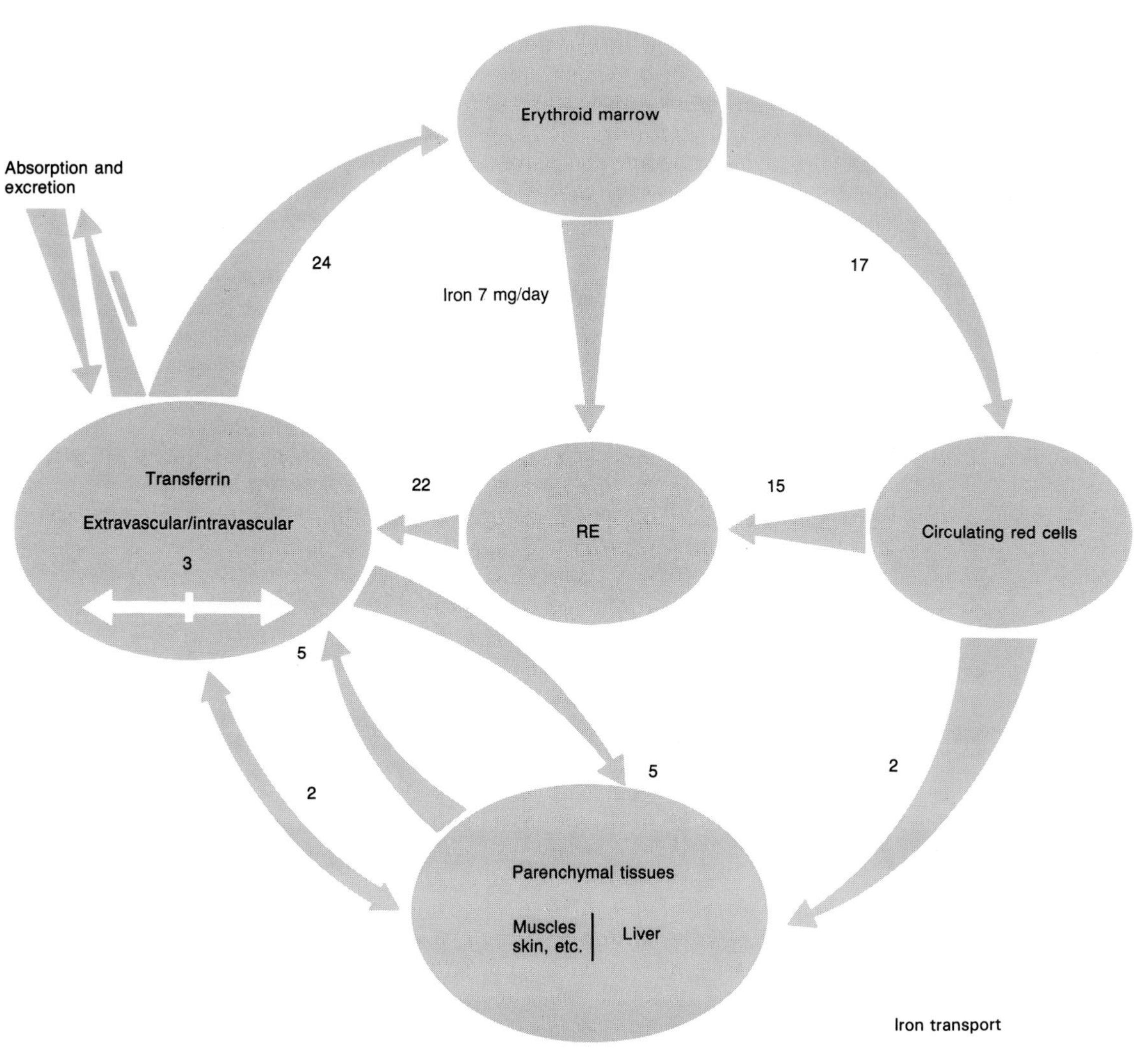

Iron transport

CHAPTER **54**

DISORDERS OF COPPER TRANSPORT

DAVID M. DANKS

1. *Three diseases are known to be caused by genetic defects in copper transport. Defective biliary excretion of copper is seen in the autosomal recessive Wilson's disease with toxic effects due to copper accumulation in the liver and brain causing liver disease from late childhood onward or neurologic symptoms in mid-adult life. Menkes disease and the occipital horn syndrome are both X-linked recessive, and both involve deficient supply of copper to copper enzymes, with neurologic and connective tissue consequences in the former but predominantly connective tissue effects in the latter.*
2. *Because a number of essential enzymes have it as an integral component, copper has been determined to be essential for human health. It is also a very toxic ion. Consequently, a complex series of copper transport processes must exist to deliver copper to the sites of enzyme synthesis. The details of these processes are not known.*
3. *Copper homeostasis depends on a balance between intestinal copper absorption and biliary excretion of copper in an unabsorbable form. Separate processes may be involved in the liver for storage, biliary excretion, and ceruloplasmin production. It is not certain whether ceruloplasmin has a function in copper transport or whether it is merely a copper enzyme present in serum serving ferroxidase and other functions.*
4. *In Wilson's disease, biliary excretion of copper and incorporation into ceruloplasmin are both severely impaired. The defective biliary excretion leads to accumulation of copper in the liver with progressive liver damage and subsequent overflow to brain causing loss of coordination plus involuntary movements. Deposition in the cornea produces Kayser-Fleischer rings, and accumulation in other sites may cause renal tubular damage, osteoporosis, arthropathy, cardiomyopathy, and hypoparathyroidism.*
5. *Symptoms of liver disease may occur in children over 8 years or in young adults, but acute onset is surprisingly frequent, and hemolysis is often pronounced. Neurologic effects are more frequent in adults up to middle age or even older. It is important to remember this treatable disease in all patients with chronic liver disease and in all adults with neurologic symptoms referable to the basal ganglia.*
6. *The classic diagnostic features of Kayser-Fleischer rings, low ceruloplasmin concentration, increased nonceruloplasmin copper, and increased urinary copper are found in all neurologic cases but in only 70 to 90 percent of hepatic cases. Increased liver copper (>300 μg/g dry weight) is a reliable finding, and lack of incorporation of* ^{64}*Cu or* ^{67}*Cu into ceruloplasmin over 48 h is the most definitive test available.*
7. *Inheritance is autosomal recessive. The incidence is of the order of 1 in 100,000 live births. The gene concerned is near 13q14, closely linked to the esterase D locus. Sibs must be carefully investigated. Heterozygote detection by isotope studies is only 80 to 90 percent reliable and therefore of little practical use.*
8. *Treatment with penicillamine is very effective, and long-term results are excellent, but the 3- to 6-month lag before improvement occurs may be too long in patients presenting in acute liver failure. Side effects are less frequent than generally thought, and dangers of the use of penicillamine in pregnancy do not appear great. Trientene or orally administered zinc salts provide alternatives available for patients unable to use penicillamine. Liver transplantation has a place in cases with irreversible liver damage.*
9. *In Menkes disease, defective intestinal absorption leads to copper deficiency. The same defect which prevents copper absorption and causes copper to accumulate in mucosal cells is present in most other body cells including cultured fibroblasts, and it prevents even copper given parenterally from fully correcting the deficient synthesis of copper enzymes.*
10. *Defective synthesis of copper enzymes explains most features of the disease, which include abnormal and depigmented (steely) hair, a characteristic facies, hypothermia, arterial degeneration due to defective elastin synthesis, neuronal degeneration especially in the cerebellum, osteoporosis, metaphyseal fractures, and urinary tract diverticulae. Death usually occurs before 2 years. Treatment has not yet been found to alter the course of the disease significantly.*
11. *Inheritance is X-chromosomal. Location at Xp13 is likely. The brindled mutant in the mouse appears to be homologous, and its study is contributing greatly to progress in understanding the disease. Prenatal diagnosis is well established in a few laboratories using the altered copper metabolism observed in cultured cells or the high levels of copper present in chorionic villi. Heterozygote detection is made difficult by mosaic X-chromosome inactivation, but it can usually be achieved by taking multiple skin biopsies or by cloning cells.*
12. *Two patients with a mild form of Menkes disease are known who have less severe neurologic effects plus connective tissue effects of different degrees in each patient. The copper phenotype in cultured cells is indistinguishable from that in cells from typical cases.*
13. *The occipital horn syndrome may be an even more mild form of the same defect. The phenotype in cultured cells is indistinguishable from that seen in the two forms of Menkes disease. Clinically, connective tissue features (lax skin, loose joints, hernias, bladder diverticulae, abnormally shaped bones) predominate, but intelligence is less than average. Survival into adult life is usual. Lysyl oxidase is reduced in tissues and in cultured cells. Homology to the blotchy mutant mouse seems likely.*
14. *Typical Menkes disease, mild Menkes disease, and the occipital horn syndrome may be the result of allelic mutations, as may the brindled and blotchy mice. Alternatively, there may be two or more linked loci concerned with copper transport on the human and mouse X chromosomes.*

15. *Further genetic defects of copper metabolism must be expected and may be sought among patients with liver diseases, those with defects of connective tissue or keratin formation, and those with neurologic diseases. Several forms of liver disease show consistent severe copper accumulation (primary biliary cirrhosis and Indian childhood cirrhosis). These may be primary or secondary.*

Three genetic diseases caused by defects of copper transport are now known. None of them can yet be described in precise molecular terms. The first discovered, Wilson's disease, shows autosomal recessive inheritance and appears to involve a defect in hepatic copper metabolism. Menkes disease was the second recognized, is X-linked in inheritance, and involves a widespread disturbance of the cellular transport of copper. The third condition, the occipital horn syndrome, is also X-linked and may prove to be a very mild form of Menkes disease or a defect in a closely linked gene. Since normal copper transport undoubtedly involves more than three active processes, further genetic defects must be anticipated. Some forms of liver diseases which show marked copper retention may be candidates, as may disorders of collagen and elastin and certain types of neurologic disease. Study of animal mutants with effects similar to human diseases is proving valuable.

Certain aspects of the normal transport and functions of copper are reviewed as a background to discussion of these diseases. The original evidence for statements not specifically referenced will be found in major reviews of copper metabolism.[1–7] The same approach is adopted with the diseases, especially with Wilson's disease, which has been reviewed frequently and exhaustively.

NORMAL COPPER METABOLISM AND HOMEOSTASIS

Copper is an essential micronutrient for humans and animals, being an integral component of a number of important enzymes[1] (Table 54-1). Copper has been identified in some other enzymes, but further evidence is required before accepting them as true copper enzymes. Copper is also a very toxic ion. Consequently, efficient methods must exist for transporting copper to the sites where it is required without allowing toxic accumulation of the free ions. Harmful effects of both deficiency and excess are well documented in humans and in animals.[1–7]

Copper Homeostasis

The normal adult human body contains 70 to 100 mg of copper. Homeostasis depends on a balance between intestinal absorption and biliary excretion, other means of intake and loss being insignificant (Table 54-2). Absorption and excretion are normally in the range of 1 to 5 mg daily. Copper can be absorbed through the skin if applied in solution, and small amounts are even absorbed from metallic copper in prolonged contact with the skin and from copper-containing intrauterine contraceptive devices. Very little copper is excreted in the urine. Some copper is lost in the sweat.

Intestinal Absorption. Direct evidence regarding the site and mechanism of absorption is lacking in humans. Absorption from the upper small intestine has been demonstrated in chickens and in rats.[8] Both species show two processes—a rapid transport system of low capacity, which is inhibited by anoxia or by dinitrophenol, and a slower process, which is less readily inhibited and has a greater capacity. In the rat and mouse, an additional absorptive process of pinocytosis exists transiently in neonatal animals. This is probably peculiar to rodents, but human neonates have not been studied. The malabsorption of copper in babies with Menkes disease indicates that absorption is an active process in humans. The similarity of the disturbance of absorption in Menkes disease and in the mottled mutants in mice suggests similarity in the normal process of humans and mice.

The role of metallothionein in the intestinal absorption of copper is not clear.[8] In rats, zinc diminishes copper absorption by inducing increased production of metallothionein in mucosal cells which then binds copper preferentially.[9] Most of the bound copper is then lost when the cells are shed from the villi. Since excessive zinc administration has been shown to induce copper deficiency in humans[10] and to reduce copper accumulation in patients with Wilson's disease,[11,12] similar mechanisms may operate. Evidence that the metallothionein content of intestinal cells changes with the copper content of the diet is not impressive.[8]

Table 54-1 Copper Enzymes in Humans

Common name	*Functional role*	*Known or expected consequence of deficiency*
Cytochrome oxidase	Electron transport chain	Muscle weakness; neurologic effects; hypothermia
Superoxide dismutase	Free radical detoxification	Uncertain
Tyrosinase	Melanin production	Failure of pigmentation
Dopamine β-hydroxylase	Catecholamine production	Neurologic effects; possible hypothermia
Lysyl oxidase	Cross-linking of collagen and elastin	Arterial abnormalities; bladder diverticulae; loose skin and joints
Ceruloplasmin	Ferroxidase; ? copper transport	Anemia; ? secondary copper deficiency
Enzyme not known	Cross-linking of keratin (disulfide bonds)	Pili torti

Table 54-2 Copper Homeostasis in Humans—Normal and Abnormal*

	Normal, mg	*Wilson's disease, mg*	*Menkes disease, mg*
Intestinal absorption	2	2	0.1–0.2
Biliary excretion	2	0.2–0.4	Not known
Urinary excretion	0.04	1	Increased
Net balance	0	Positive	Negative

*Approximate figures based on assumed normal dietary copper intake of 4 mg daily.

The overall efficiency of absorption of copper isotopes has been estimated to be 40 to 70 percent.[13] Copper isotopes become detectable in the blood very quickly after oral administration, and the peak level of radioactivity occurs after 90 to 150 min. This suggests a site of absorption high in the intestine.

Copper in the Plasma. Most of the copper absorbed from the intestine is found to be attached to albumin in the early hours after administration. A small amount is attached to amino acids or small peptides. Copper isotope is cleared from the plasma rapidly, reaching 10 percent of the initial level after intravenous administration in 20 to 25 min.[14,15] External counting shows preferential uptake by the liver[13] but some uptake by all tissues. Difficulty of allowing for the blood present in each tissue complicates these assessments.

Albumin binds copper at a specific site involving the aminoterminal tripeptide (Asp-Ala-His in humans) with the histidine residue having special significance.[16] Bovine, rat, and human albumins differ in residues 1 and 2, yet they bind copper well. Dog albumin has tyrosine at position 3 and binds copper poorly. A susceptibility of dogs to copper poisoning has been attributed to this, but the matter has not been adequately investigated. Pig albumin has a similar deficiency in copper binding, but pigs are very tolerant of copper excess. No comments have been made on copper metabolism in the various reports of humans and rats with analbuminemia. More copper can be dialyzed from dog plasma than from other species. This suggests that free amino acids take over the copper transport role. Proalbumin has six additional amino acids on the amino terminal end[16] and does not bind copper. This may prevent copper from leaving the liver as albumin is exported.

Copper which reaches the liver attached to albumin is transferred to amino acids, principally to histidine, and then absorbed as a copper-histidine complex by a mechanism separate from that involved with the uptake of histidine alone.[17–19] Thus, albumin may serve as a "reservoir" for copper, limiting the rate of uptake into the liver.

Over 90 percent of the copper in human plasma is present in ceruloplasmin, a blue α_2-globulin glycoprotein whose function is still poorly defined after 30 years of intense interest.[5,20,21] Radioactive copper starts to appear in ceruloplasmin within a few hours of intravenous administration and rises in linear fashion over at least 7 days, reaching 5 to 6 percent of the dose administered by that time.[15] Computer analysis suggests a rapid phase and a slower phase involving hepatic storage. Both processes are defective in Wilson's disease, whereas only the rapid phase is reduced in primary biliary cirrhosis.[15]

Ceruloplasmin, and therefore serum copper, levels are increased by a variety of factors including pregnancy, oral contraceptives, and acute inflammation (Table 54-3). Genetic factors also influence the levels seen in different normal individuals,[22] and a dominantly inherited symptomless condition of hypoceruloplasminemia has been described.[23] For all these reasons, a single measurement of serum copper is not a good indicator of nutritional copper status.[24] Severe copper deficiency can be recognized by a single measurement, but two measurements separated by a few days during which copper replacement therapy is given may be more useful in diagnosing less severe copper deficiency.[25]

The nonceruloplasmin component of serum copper is not easily measured with accuracy, but it can be estimated by calculation and appears to vary little in healthy persons or in most diseases. This component is increased in Wilson's disease, but is not changed greatly in Menkes disease or in copper deficiency, persisting even when no ceruloplasmin can be detected. Massive increase is seen in acute copper poisoning and in acute hemolytic crises in Wilson's disease.

A small amount of copper is present in plasma bound to metallothionein in rats,[26] and the same will probably be found in humans when specific antibodies become available. Since the turnover of this component is rapid, it may contribute significantly to the transport of copper via the plasma.

Recently, another copper-binding protein, named *transcuprein,* has been described in human and rat plasma.[27] A role in transport of copper to the liver has been claimed. More work is required to determine the nature and function of this protein.

It is generally assumed that copper in the liver acts as a store available to other tissues in circumstances of copper deficiency. This role has been claimed particularly in sheep[28] and in human babies who are born with very high liver copper levels. It was argued that babies were born with this store because human milk has a low copper content. However, this copper is in an easily absorbable form, and young babies actually absorb an adequate amount of copper. The high levels of copper in the neonatal liver may merely reflect the late development of biliary copper excretion.

The method by which copper is transferred from the liver to other tissues is not known. Some have assumed that ceruloplasmin must play a role in transport just because there is so much present. Opinions remain sharply divided.[4] The little evidence that does exist suggests a role of ceruloplasmin in delivery of copper to cytochrome C oxidase[29] and to superoxide dismutase.[29a] Studies of the exchange of copper with ceruloplasmin suggest that the protein may need to be degraded to release copper. Some workers have described receptors for ceruloplasmin on aortic[30] and hepatic[31] endothelial cells and on red cells. We have been unable to find receptors on fibroblasts

Table 54-3 Change in Ceruloplasmin Levels, in Milligrams per Liter, with Age and Status—Range of Levels

Cord blood	20–130
6 months	200–400
2 years	300–500
Adult males	200–400
Adult females	200–400
Effect of	
Acute infection	+50%
Oral contraceptive	+100%
Pregnancy (3d trimester)	+100%

or evidence of uptake of copper into fibroblasts from ceruloplasmin (H. McArdle, personal communication).

The Role of the Liver. The liver plays a central role in copper homeostasis, being the principal recipient of recently absorbed copper, the organ with the highest (and most variable) copper content, and the principal organ of excretion. Some major species differences are apparent, especially between sheep and other species.

Kinetic analyses using computer curve fitting models have been used in rats,[32] in sheep,[28] and in humans.[15,33,34] In the rat, the simplest model involves three interconnected functional compartments in the liver related to storage, to biliary excretion, and to ceruloplasmin production.[32] Many have argued that the disturbance of both ceruloplasmin production and biliary excretion in Wilson's disease implies a common mode of access to these two compartments. It is interesting that these same two processes are greatly reduced in efficiency in the sheep in which a simpler two-compartment model suffices to explain the kinetic findings.[28]

In rats, and probably in humans, biliary excretion varies in response to liver copper load[4,5] and therefore indirectly in response to copper intake. This tends to prevent chronic copper accumulation. In sheep, biliary excretion is much less responsive to intake and hardly affected by liver copper levels. This allows accumulation of very high levels if intake is excessive,[28] allowing sheep to cope with "feast or famine" circumstances of copper supply but leaving them susceptible to copper poisoning when pasture deficiencies are replaced too enthusiastically. Symptomless accumulation of copper may occur for long periods followed by abrupt hemolytic crises—a sequence similar to that seen in Wilson's disease.[1,35] Humans and rats are both quite resistant to chronic copper toxicity.[1]

Most of the copper found in bile is in a form (or forms) which cannot be reabsorbed. There is no effective enterohepatic circulation of copper.[4,5] No consensus has yet been reached about the molecular form (forms) of copper complexes in bile. Reabsorption also occurs by pinocytosis in young rodents and has been suggested in young babies on very low copper intakes.[4]

The form in which copper is stored in the liver has also been investigated extensively without complete resolution.[5] Much of the copper is found in the supernatant fraction attached to metallothionein. Copper bound to a polymerized form of metallothionein is found attached to heavy lysosomes which were initially confused with mitochondria in differential centrifugation experiments leading to terms like *mitochondriocuprein*. It is uncertain whether copper bound to metallothionein can be released without degradation of the protein, which has a half-life of about 20 h.

Other Tissues. The role of the kidney in copper homeostasis is usually dismissed with a brief statement about the small amount of copper excreted in the urine. However, it seems likely that copper bound to amino acids is filtered through the glomerulus and reabsorbed in the tubules along with these amino acids. Intravenous loading with histidine leads to a considerable increase in urinary copper excretion in humans (and to massive excretion of zinc).[36] In Menkes disease and mottled mice, renal copper levels are increased greatly and urinary losses are high considering the low levels of copper in the serum. Other forms of renal tubular damage may be associated with loss of copper.

Most other tissues act merely as recipients of the copper required to form their copper enzyme. Several of the enzymes are ubiquitous (Table 54-1).

The distribution of copper in the normal brain corresponds approximately to the distribution of catecholamine neurones as might be expected considering that dopamine β-hydroxylase is a copper enzyme. Presumably all parts of the brain contain copper in cytochrome C oxidase and superoxide dismutase.

The Copper Enzymes. The copper enzymes listed in Table 54-1 all require incorporation of copper during their synthesis.[4] The effect of copper on apoenzyme production has been studied for several enzymes. In these, copper is required for apoenzyme production, but excess copper does not superinduce enzyme production. The detailed mechanisms by which copper is made available to the sites of enzyme synthesis are unknown, but they appear to differ from one enzyme to another and from one tissue to another, at least in the rat. For example, copper deficiency reduced superoxide dismutase levels more than cytochrome C oxidase in liver, but the reverse pattern was seen in heart and muscle.[37]

CERULOPLASMIN. This is the best known but least understood copper protein. Indeed, it is only recently that there has been conclusive evidence that this 132,000 molecular weight glycoprotein has just one polypeptide chain.[20] Previous claims of multiple subunits have been resolved by showing several sites which are very susceptible to proteolytic cleavage. Recent cloning by two groups[38,39] of a cDNA which corresponds to the full length protein confirmed these findings.

The protein contains six atoms of copper per molecule. Ceruloplasmin can oxidize Fe(II) to Fe(III) thereby allowing release from ferritin and attachment to transferrin. However, patients with Wilson's disease or Menkes disease who have no detectable ceruloplasmin do not usually develop anemia.[40–42] It can oxidize a number of biogenic amines in vitro but is not proved to play this role in vivo. It also inhibits lipid peroxidation. It responds as an acute phase reactant, but no function in inflammation has been found. Its role in copper transport is debated.[4] The fact that failure of other copper enzymes is not seen in patients with Wilson's disease who have no ceruloplasmin indicates that any role in copper transport is not indispensable.

The human ceruloplasmin gene has been assigned to chromosome 3.[38] The rat ceruloplasmin gene has been shown to respond strongly to inflammation with a fivefold increase in RNA.[43] Expression has proved to be strongest in the choroid plexus, yolk sac, liver, and testis, in that order.[43] Studies of the function in these extrahepatic tissues will be of great interest.

The other copper enzymes listed in Table 54-1 showed less marked reduction in copper deficiency, yet effects due to their inadequate function make up the syndrome of copper deficiency.[42]

METALLOTHIONEIN. This is the other major enigma among the copper proteins.[5,8,44,45] The ease of oxidation of its many cysteine residues had made it a very difficult protein to analyze. However, cloning of metallothionein cDNAs from several species has allowed detailed analysis of the genes concerned and of the factors which control expression of the genes.[44,45] In just a few years, it has become one of the best studied models of gene expression. The control sequences have been studied in intact rats and mice, in cultured cells, and in transgenic mice.[44,45] Responses to metals (zinc, cadmium, mercury, and, to a lesser degree, copper), to corticosteroids, to α-interferon, and to interleukin 2 have been demonstrated, and the 5′-DNA sequences involved in these responses have been identified.

Rats and mice each have just two closely linked metallothionein genes (MT-I and MT-II). The mouse genes are on chromosome 8.[46] Humans and sheep have more complex families of MT genes. Some of the 10+ genes of the human have been studied—a cluster of genes including two functional MT-I genes and one functional MT-II gene on chromosome 16.[47] The remaining sequences, which include at least one pseudogene, are dispersed on at least four autosomes, but none could be found on the X chromosome. The sheep has one cluster of three MT-I genes, one MT-II gene, and a pseudogene plus at least four other sequences which have not yet been located.[48]

Despite all this knowledge, the function of the metallothioneins is still uncertain. I agree with Hamer[44] that the best present hypothesis would involve a key role for metallothionein in the homeostasis and availability of zinc within cells and a secondary role in "mopping-up" excess copper or toxic nonessential metals like cadmium and mercury.

It is very unlikely that any of the three genetic defects in human copper metabolism can be explained by mutations of metallothionein genes. Secondary induction of metallothionein synthesis occurs in all three and contributes to the pathophysiology and to the laboratory findings. Abnormal responsiveness to zinc induction of metallothionein synthesis may underly the deviant (relative to other species) metabolism of copper in the liver of sheep (J. Mercer, personal communication).

Copper Deficiency

The effects of nutritional copper deficiency have been reviewed[42,49] and are mostly those which might be predicted from the known functions of copper enzymes (Tables 54-1 and 54-4). Interesting differences in the effects are seen in different species. For instance, sheep are very resistant to the vascular effects but sensitive to neurologic consequences, whereas vascular lesions predominate in pigs and poultry. Anemia, neutropenia, and osteoporosis have been the main features observed in human nutritional copper deficiency, but in Menkes disease, damage to brain and arteries is predominant with no anemia or neutropenia. The former may reflect more severe and prolonged deficiency, but the absence of hematologic effects is difficult to explain.

Human copper deficiency has been described as part of a general nutritional deficiency in Peruvian children; in young babies and in adults receiving parenteral alimentation with copper-deficient solutions, especially when these are used after extensive gut resection; in children receiving continuous ambulatory peritoneal dialysis; and in adults treated with large doses of zinc for defective wound healing or for sickle cell disease. Chronic low grade deficiency may become a problem in western countries because removal of copper is important in achieving a long shelf life for prepared foods.[42]

Table 54-4 Effects Seen in Nutritional Copper Deficiency in Human Beings, Sheep, Rats, Pigs, and Menkes Disease

Effect	*Human beings*	*Sheep*	*Rats*	*Pigs*	*Menkes disease*
Anemia	+	+	+	+	–
Neutropenia	+	+	+	+	–
Abnormal hair structure	±	++	+	+	++
Depigmentation	±	+	+	+	+
Arterial rupture	?	–	+	++	++
Myocardial fibrosis	?	–	+	+	–
Osteoporosis	+	+	+	++	+
Emphysema	?	–	+	–	+
Cerebellar ataxia	–	+*	+*	+*	+
Other brain damage	–	+*	+*	+	++

*Seen only after fetal copper deficiency.

Copper Poisoning

Acute copper poisoning is seen frequently in India, where it is a popular method of suicide.[2] Accidental poisoning is occasionally seen in young children in western cities.[50] Acute irritation and damage to the intestine causes vomiting and diarrhea with bleeding. Circulatory collapse may occur at an early stage. Over the next 2 or 3 days, acute liver failure, acute renal failure, and severe hemolysis may occur. Nonceruloplasmin copper levels are very greatly increased. Chronic copper poisoning is very rare in patients without preexisting liver disease, but it has been described in some industrial situations.[2] The normal human liver has a great excretory capacity. Moderately excessive intake may cause copper overload in patients with chronic liver disease. Recirculating copper-lined water systems may produce water with a remarkably high copper content if the water is soft.

Animal Models (Tables 54-5 and 54-6)

Discovery and study of animals with defects identical with those in human genetic diseases allows studies which are impossible in patients.[6,51] Even if animal mutants do not prove homologous to human genetic diseases, their study may help by giving more understanding of the processes of copper transport.

The mottled mutants in mice[6,51–53] bear a very close similarity to Menkes disease and the occipital horn syndrome. They were recognized first in the 1950s as X-linked mutants giving patchy deficiency of pigment in the coats of females with lethal effects in males, survivors having a uniform lack of pigment. It has been usual to regard the six mutants, mottled (Mo), dappled (Mo^{db}), tortoiseshell (Mo^{to}), brindled (Mo^{br}), viable-brindled (Mo^{vbr}), and blotchy (Mo^{blo}), as allelic. The last four have been shown to affect copper transport in a manner almost identical with the effect in the human mutants, but mottled and dappled have not been evaluated in this way. The X linkage in both species supports the hypothesis of homology.[53] The resemblance between brindled mutants and Menkes diseases is sufficient to suggest homology as is that between blotchy mutants and the occipital horn syndrome. Yet there are qualitative, rather than quantitative, differences between these two pairs of conditions sufficient to make one wonder whether two closely linked loci might be involved in each species rather than one allelic series at one locus in each. Infor-

Table 54-5 Comparison of Wilson's Disease with Copper Storage in Toxic Milk Mice, in Bedlington Terriers, and in Sheep

	Wilson's disease	*Toxic milk mice*	*Bedlington terriers*	*Normal sheep*	*Copper-loaded sheep*
Hepatic copper accumulation, µg/g dry weight	+ + (200–3000)	+ + (300–400)	+ + + (2000–12000)	+ (300–600)	+ + + (2000–8000)
Reduced biliary excretion of copper	+ +	NK*	+	+	+
Reduced ^{67}Cu incorporated into ceruloplasmin	+ + +	+ +	+ +	+	+
Liability to hemolytic crisis	+	+	+ +	−	+ +
Chronic liver cell damage	+ +	+ +	+/−	−	+/−
Overflow to other tissues	+ +	+/−	+/−	−	+/−

*NK = not known.

mation gleaned from study of the mice is used freely in discussion of the human diseases.

The toxic milk (tx) mutation in mice has many features in common with Wilson's disease.[54,55] Copper accumulates to abnormal levels in the liver with progressive histologic changes leading to multimodular cirrhosis but no neurologic effects. These mice were first recognized as having an autosomal recessive trait lethal to the pups of affected females because the milk is copper-deficient.[54] It is unfortunate that these mice, known since before 1977, have never been released for assessment by other research groups.

Many (perhaps most) Bedlington terriers suffer an autosomal recessive hepatic copper toxicosis which resembles Wilson's disease in many ways.[56–58] Acute hemolytic crises occur after massive hepatic copper accumulation. As with the toxic milk mice, cerebral effects are lacking.

Normal sheep have many features in common with Wilson's disease patients, toxic milk mice, and Bedlington terriers with copper toxicosis.

Suggestions that crinkled (cr) mice have a defect in copper transport[59] were not confirmed.[60] A claim of amelioration of the quaking (qk) mutation by copper supplementation[59] has not been confirmed.

Table 54-6 Comparison of Menkes Disease and Occipital Horn Syndrome with Mouse Mutants Suggested as Models

	Menkes disease	*Brindled ($Mo^{br/y}$) mice*	*Blotchy ($Mo^{blo/y}$) mice*	*Occipital horn syndrome*
Inheritance	XL	XL	XL	XL
Hair deformity	+ +	+	+	NK*
Hair keratin disulfide deficiency	+	+	+	+/−
Arterial abnormality	+ +	+/−	+	+
Lysyl oxidase deficiency (skin)	+	+	+	+
Life expectancy	1–2 years	13–15 days	6–18 months	NK
Liver copper reduced	+	+	+	NK
Kidney and intestinal copper increased	+	+	+	NK

*NK = not known.

WILSON'S DISEASE (HEPATOLENTICULAR DEGENERATION)

Readers are referred to the fourth edition of this text[3] for references to early publications and to recent monographs[61,62] for support of unreferenced statements. Facts established since publication of the more recent of these monographs[62] are referenced, as are a few other key facts. Generally only most recent papers are given.

Described as a clinical entity by Kinnear-Wilson in 1912, the disease was related to copper accumulation in liver and brain in the 1940s. Little progress has been made in understanding the defect in copper transport in over 40 years. Despite this, effective treatment has been available since 1956 when Walshe introduced penicillamine.

Basic Defect and Pathogenesis

Although the basic defect is still not known, enough is understood about the pathogenesis to provide a logical basis for diagnosis and treatment. A statement made in many genetics and medical texts must be refuted; Wilson's disease is *not* caused by a molecular defect in ceruloplasmin. The gene coding for ceruloplasmin is on chromosome 3,[38] and that concerned in Wilson's disease is on chromosome 13.[63]

The two most fundamental disturbances of copper metabolism in Wilson's disease are a reduction in the rate of incorporation of copper into ceruloplasmin and reduction in biliary excretion of copper.[64] Kinetic models of hepatic copper metabolism in the rat have indicated separate functional pools of copper for ceruloplasmin production and for biliary excretion.[32] Interference with both processes by one mutation suggests some preceding common pathway of entry to both these pools in humans.

Indirect estimation of biliary excretion indicated reduction to 20 and 40 percent of normal.[33] Direct measurement in two patients showed an even greater reduction.[64] Since intestinal absorption is normal in Wilson's disease, there is a substantial positive net copper balance (Table 54-2). Increased renal losses do very little to redress this situation.

The first effect is progressive accumulation of copper in the liver. In some patients, this process may continue for many years with only minor effect on the liver cells. In other patients, the accumulation of copper leads to severe liver damage and death due to liver failure by the age of 8 to 10 years. Later, the level of nonceruloplasmin copper in the plasma increases, leading to increased renal excretion of copper and to deposition of copper in various extrahepatic tissues: cornea (Kayser-Fleischer rings); brain, especially basal ganglia (lenticular degeneration); kidney (renal tubular damage); skeletal and heart muscle; bones; and joints. "Overflow" from the liver to these tissues seems the most probable sequence, but it has not been proved. Deposition in all tissues from the beginning is also possible, though less likely. Kayser-Fleischer rings are frequently absent in asymptomatic homozygotes, quite often lacking in childhood cases with hepatic symptoms, but almost always present in adults with brain symptoms. Development of corneal deposits has been observed in untreated asymptomatic siblings. These facts and the rarity of neurologic presentation before 10 to 12 years are all in keeping with the sequence of events suggested. Development of neurologic symptoms due to lenticular copper deposition in a 5-year-old girl who accumulated massive amounts of copper secondary to the recessively inherited cholestatic syndrome of Aagenes also provides further circumstantial support for the concept of overflow from the liver,[65] as does the development of Kayser-Fleischer rings in patients with copper overload in other types of liver disease.[66,67]

The distribution and form of copper observed within liver cells in Wilson's disease and in other situations involving hepatic copper accumulation has attracted great interest.[62] Young patients with Wilson's disease tend to show copper spread diffusely in the cytoplasm, whereas the increased copper in the liver in normal neonates and in primary biliary cirrhosis tends to be in lysosomes. Cytoplasmic copper is generally attached to monomeric metallothionein, and lysosomal copper is found in polymeric complexes of metallothionein. In older patients with Wilson's disease and well compensated liver disease, the copper is mainly lysosomal.

Why should liver damage develop rapidly in some patients and not in others? Allelic (or even nonallelic) differences in the mutant gene might be responsible. While there is some tendency to see similar presenting features in siblings, there are many reports of childhood hepatic symptoms in one sibling and adult neurologic presentation in another. The variability observed within a large inbred Japanese kindred also showed that allelic heterogeneity is not the whole explanation.[68] Variation in dietary copper intake may be important. The ages of onset of both hepatic and neurologic cases are earlier in Japanese reports than in western countries[68]; perhaps high intake from copper cooking vessels is important. However, this is not true in Taiwan.[69] Finally, intercurrent hepatic viral infections may be important. The number of patients presenting with acute onset of hepatic symptoms or with multiple acute episodes is too high to ignore. In an unpublished study of 52 cases of childhood cirrhosis in London in 1961, I found only three children with a really impressive history suggesting posthepatitic cirrhosis; all three had Wilson's disease. In childhood liver disease, one commonly finds multiple causative factors in those patients who develop cirrhosis, and a number of viruses other than the named hepatitis viruses are probably capable of damaging a liver already suffering from chemical injury.

The disturbance of ceruloplasmin production in Wilson's disease has been studied by many groups, but little has been added to the original observations of the early 1950s. Use of ^{67}Cu has allowed measurements to continue as long as 7 days, and even at this stage no definite incorporation of isotope (administered intravenously) into ceruloplasmin could be detected.[15,62] Others have observed low levels of incorporation.[34] It is hard to match these findings with the existence of affected homozygotes who have low normal levels of ceruloplasmin. None of these particular patients appears to have been studied with ^{67}Cu. Dilution of isotope in a large intrahepatic pool may be a factor, but hepatic storage of a similar degree in primary biliary cirrhosis and other liver diseases causes only a mild reduction (or no change) in isotope incorporation. It seems that the ceruloplasmin present in these cases of Wilson's disease must be drawing copper from a pool into which the administered isotope is not entering.[15,34]

Many theories have been proposed to explain cell damage in copper accumulation[62]: oxidation of lipids in membranes, binding to proteins and to nucleic acids, free-radical generation, and many others. Certainly cell necrosis seems to be the final result in each of the affected organs.

The hemolytic crises seen in some patients are accompanied by very high levels of nonceruloplasmin copper comparable to those seen in acute copper poisoning, and, indeed, the symptoms of hemolysis, acute tubular damage, and acute hepatic necrosis are similar. Sudden massive release of copper from the liver seems likely. In some cases, this is caused by infarction of a large regenerative nodule in a cirrhotic liver. Acute viral infection with widespread liver cell damage and release of copper may be involved in other patients. Similarly, in sheep, acute hemolytic crises occur in chronic copper overdosage after large amounts of copper have accumulated in the liver.[1,35,70]

The most surprising result of research in recent years has been the observation of increased levels of copper in cultured fibroblasts from patients with Wilson's disease—an observation made independently in three different laboratories, each experienced with copper studies in cell culture through work on Menkes disease.[71–73] This result is surprising because the defect in copper transport seemed likely to be confined to the liver with its specialized mechanism for copper excretion and therefore not likely to be manifest in cultured fibroblasts. This is important because the basic defect should now be more accessible to study.

The demonstration of a defect in hepatic copper metabolism occurring as a common autosomal recessive trait in Bedlington terriers[32,56–58] provided an animal model (Table 54-5). The condition differs from Wilson's disease in that effects on organs other than the liver are minimal. The resemblance to copper toxicosis in sheep is particularly close. A primary defect in metallothionien has been excluded in the dogs by analysis of mRNA levels,[74] and is unlikely in Wilson's disease because the main cluster of human metallothionein genes is located on chromosome 16,[47] whereas Wilson's disease has been mapped to chromosome 13.[63] However, some other genes coding for metallothionein have yet to be located. Increased sensitivity of the metallothionein gene to induction by zinc may be involved in producing the copper-accumulating phenotype in sheep (J. Mercer, personal communication). Little is known about the basic lesion in toxic milk mice.

Clinical Features

Patients with Wilson's disease most often present with liver disease or with neurologic symptoms. A substantial number have symptoms of both types. Series from general hospitals show about equal numbers of cases in each of these three categories.[68,69,75–77] Children, adolescents, or young adults with Wilson's disease may present and die without a correct diagnosis from acute liver failure in centers not keenly interested in the disease.[78–81] The large classic series almost certainly underestimate the frequency of liver disease as the presenting feature. These patients quite often lack some of the classic signs and laboratory findings, and some clinicians have been slow to accept them as true cases of Wilson's disease. We have recently seen four adults aged 32 to 59 years presenting with liver disease without neurological features or Kayser-Fleischer rings.

Other presenting symptoms include acute hemolytic crisis, joint symptoms, renal stones, renal tubular acidosis, pancreatic disease, cardiomyopathy, and hypoparathyroidism. Wilson's disease is *not* a cause of mental retardation despite its presence on lists of biochemical causes of retardation in some texts and reviews.

Although the liver disease may cause symptoms at any age beyond about 6 years, this form of presentation is most frequent between 8 and 16 years. Females are a little more likely to present in this way, and males more often present with neurologic features.[75] Neurologic symptoms are very unusual before the age of 12 years, if we exclude hepatic coma from consideration, and can develop as late as 60 years of age.[82,83]

Almost any symptom of liver disease may occur. Acute episodes of jaundice, vomiting, and malaise are quite frequent. They may resolve spontaneously and may recur. All young patients with chronic or recurrent liver disease should be investigated for Wilson's disease (see "Laboratory Findings" and "Diagnosis"). Acute hemolysis occurs in acute hepatic episodes and may appear without obvious features of liver disease. Investigation reveals the underlying liver abnormalities.

Dysarthria and deterioration of coordination of voluntary movements are the most frequent neurologic symptoms. These are often accompanied by involuntary movements and by disorders of posture and tone. Onset of pseudobulbar palsy may develop quite early in the illness in some patients and is the mode of death in many untreated cases. Deterioration in intellectual function and disturbances of behavior are infrequent in the early stages but are usual later. It is unwise to make or dismiss the diagnosis on clinical signs alone. All patients in whom any of the neurologic features develop after age 8 years should be investigated for Wilson's disease.

Evidence of bone and joint disorders can be found in many patients with Wilson's disease.[62,77,84] The most frequent findings are osteoporosis, osteomalacia, reduction in the joint spaces in limbs and spine, osteophytes around large joints, and ligamentous laxity. Most of these changes are asymptomatic, back or joint pain or stiffness occurring in less than 20 percent of older patients. Penicillamine therapy seems not to prevent (or to cause) these effects. Acute arthritis may occur as a complication of penicillamine therapy.[84]

Renal stones have been described in 7 of 45 patients with Wilson's disease[85] being present at the time of diagnosis in four. Inadequate acidification of urine because of renal tubular malfunction was blamed along with hypercalciuria. Most patients with Wilson's disease show some elements of renal tubular malfunction, and some have the full picture of the Fanconi syndrome including aminoaciduria, glucosuria, alkaline urine, and rickets. Poor growth and acidosis due to the renal lesion may be the presenting features. Hypoparathyroidism can occur and causes confusion when present along with renal tubular defects.[86]

The Kayser-Fleischer ring is the most important sign of Wilson's disease. It is a yellow-brown (dull copper colored) granular deposit on the Descemet membrane at the limbus of the cornea usually seen earliest and most densely at the upper and lower poles.[62] When fully developed, the rings are easily seen with the naked eye or ophthalmoscope, but at early stages a slit lamp is required, especially when the irides are green-brown. Most series show the rings present in 100 percent of patients with neurologic presentation and about 95 percent of all patients. Our experience in a pediatric hospital shows that absence of Kayser-Fleischer rings is considerably more frequent (over 30 percent) among children presenting with relatively acute liver disease. Certainly, absence of the rings does not exclude Wilson's disease as a cause of hepatic symptoms. The rings are often (usually) absent in asymptomatically affected sibs of clinical patients. Sunflower cataracts occur in a smaller proportion of patients (15 to 20 percent). Both these ocular signs improve with effective penicillamine chelation.

Kayser-Fleischer rings have been described in a small number of patients with massive hepatic copper accumulation in primary biliary cirrhosis[66,67] and other liver diseases.[67,87]

Laboratory Findings

Typically, serum ceruloplasmin is greatly reduced, and the nonceruloplasmin copper is increased, giving a net reduction in serum copper. Urinary copper excretion is increased, and this increase is greatly augmented by penicillamine administration. Liver copper is greatly increased. Typical figures are quoted in Table 54-7.

Each of these test results may give misleading results on occasion. First of all, it is essential to check that the serum copper and ceruloplasmin results are compatible with one another. Multiplying the ceruloplasmin result in milligrams per liter by 3.0 gives its contribution to serum copper in micrograms per liter (division by 63.6 gives micromoles per liter). In normal people, this figure is 90 to 95 percent of total serum copper. If it is double the serum copper reported, then the laboratory has made an error in one or the other measurement. In Wilson's disease nonceruloplasmin copper may be as high as 200 to 300 μg/liter (3 to 5 μmol/liter), but higher levels are seen only in episodes of acute liver failure and/or acute hemolysis (also acute in copper poisoning). Copper-contaminated tubes or bottles may be responsible for overestimation of serum or urine copper.

Apart from these technical problems, ceruloplasmin may

Table 54-7 Typical Copper Measurements in Wilson's Disease

	Wilson's disease	*Normal (adults)*
Serum ceruloplasmin		
OD units per ml	0–0.25	0.25–0.49
mg/liter	0–200	200–400
Serum copper, μmol/liter	3–10	11–24
Urinary copper, μg/24 h	100–1000	40
Untreated		
On penicillamine, 250 mg every 6 h	1500–3000	100–600
Liver copper (μg/g dry weight)	200–3000	20–50

fall during acute liver failure in patients who do not have Wilson's disease or rise to normal at such times in patients who do. Considerable numbers of cases with normal ceruloplasmin levels have been reported, especially in younger patients with liver disease, but also in adults.

Urinary copper is very variable in normal persons. Some authors have therefore suggested measuring urine excretion after penicillamine. Various regimes of dosage and collection period have been used, but none has been standardized enough to be very reliable.

Liver biopsy with assay of copper content by graphite furnace atomic absorption spectrometry (or neutron activation) is by far the most reliable test.[80,81] The technique of collection of the biopsy and of assay must be meticulous in avoiding contamination. Uneven distribution of copper in the liver may give spurious results in either direction if too small a sample is assayed. Samples above 5 mg (5 to 10 mm of needle biopsy core) should give reliable results, provided the tissue is parenchymal and not just fibrous tissue from a cirrhotic liver.

The ultimate test for Wilson's disease currently available is demonstration of negligible incorporation of copper isotope into ceruloplasmin.[62] Simple counting of total plasma radioactivity for 48 h after giving the radiolabeled copper is required. Intravenous administration is recommended to avoid the compounding influence of variable rates of absorption. ^{67}Cu would be ideal for this test, but is not yet generally available. Using ^{64}Cu, a dose of 500 μCi is required in an adult, and blood should be drawn at 5 to 10 min, 1, 2, 4, 24, and 48 h. The first four samples should be counted soon after the 4-h sample is taken and the other two samples soon after taking. This is because the 12.8-h half-life of ^{64}Cu can cause very low count rates in the 2-, 4-, and 24-h samples if they are held back for counting when all samples have been taken. Normal subjects show a steady secondary rise in corrected counts in the plasma from 2 to 48 h as the ^{64}Cu appears in newly synthesized ceruloplasmin. In Wilson's disease, corrected counts fall progressively (Fig. 54-1). Intermediate results (i.e., smaller secondary rise) are seen in some heterozygotes and in patients with copper retention in other forms of liver disease.

Other tests show the effects of damage to various organs. Liver function test abnormalities show no specific pattern although the elevation of liver enzyme levels in serum in fulminant cases is often less than in severe viral hepatitis. Aminoaciduria, glucosuria, and defective urinary acidification occur in many diseases affecting renal tubules. Anemia (normochronic) is not frequent except when there is hemolysis, but thrombocytopenia (50 percent of cases) and neutropenia (30 percent of cases) are more frequent.[40]

The pathology of the liver in Wilson's disease has been studied intensively, and a thorough review has been published recently.[62] Although there are some remarkable microscopic and ultrastructural features, many of these can also occur in other liver diseases (e.g., chronic active hepatitis), and it would be unwise to rely on these methods alone for diagnosis. Much has been written about histochemical identification of copper in liver sections.[62] The differences in staining of copper attached to different ligands are interesting, and these methods show very nicely the uneven distribution of the copper in Wilson's disease. No method is sufficiently reliable to replace copper assay in diagnosis. The ultrastructural changes in liver mitochondria may be unique.[62]

EEG changes are rarely helpful in diagnosis of neurologic cases. CT or nmr scans may reveal radiolucency of the basal

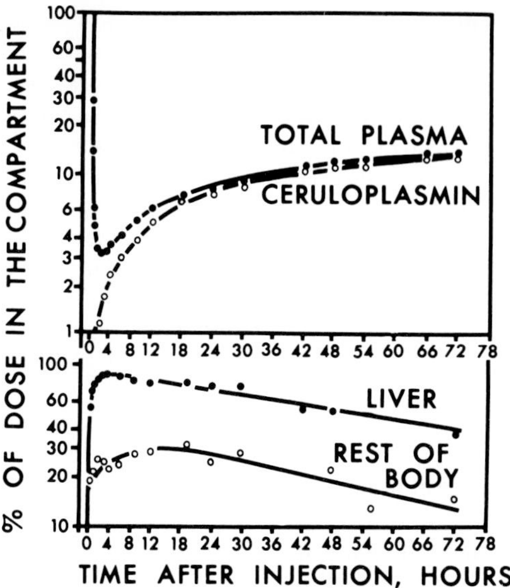

Fig. 54-1 Changes in radioactivity in plasma and ceruloplasmin and in liver and other body tissues after intravenous administration of ^{67}Cu. *(Courtesy of Dr. A. Sass Kortsak.)*

ganglia, but they have proved positive in only a minority of neurologic cases.[88,89]

The accumulation of copper in cultured fibroblastic cells is not yet sufficiently established as a diagnostic test and remains a research procedure at present.

Diagnosis

The essential first step is to remember Wilson's disease as a possible diagnosis in all patients with chronic liver disease and in all patients over age 12 years with relevant neurologic symptoms and signs.[62,90] Chronic liver disease in children or young adults is Wilson's disease until proved otherwise, but it may be necessary to depart from this dictum a little in conditions like alcoholic cirrhosis in adults. It is probably the most frequent cause of chronic liver disease in childhood and certainly the most frequent treatable cause. Patients with Wilson's disease can develop liver symptoms even in late middle age.[83,91]

In children and young adults a clinician should seriously consider Wilson's disease in acute hepatitis if the course is unusual in any way, e.g., severe, prolonged, or recurrent, or associated with hemolysis.

The most reliable method of ensuring that the diagnosis of Wilson's disease is not missed is to measure the copper content of the initial liver biopsy in every patient with chronic liver disease.[80,81]

One may go through the standard system of slit-lamp examination of the eyes and measurement of serum copper, ceruloplasmin, and urine copper, but negative results to all these tests do not provide the 100 percent exclusion of Wilson's disease that each patient deserves.

Not all patients with high levels of liver copper (over 300 μg/g dry weight) have Wilson's disease. Some have copper accumulation secondary to other liver diseases. ^{64}Cu administration is then used to resolve this point. When copper retention occurs in other liver diseases, chelation treatment may be beneficial (see "Copper Retention in Other Forms of Liver Disease").

In patients with neurologic symptoms, there may be no other reason to do a liver biopsy, and the classic signs and tests are much more reliable. Slit-lamp examination and measurement of serum copper, ceruloplasmin, and urine copper do constitute sufficient investigation. Further tests should be entertained only if negative results conflict with particularly characteristic clinical features. Of course, liver biopsy is generally necessary to assess the condition of the liver after Wilson's disease has been diagnosed, and the opportunity to measure the copper content should be taken.

A diagnosis of Wilson's disease should always lead to examination and investigation of siblings (see "Genetic Counseling").

Treatment and Prognosis

The management of Wilson's disease was revolutionized by Walshe's introduction of penicillamine in 1956.[62,92] In the early years, a mixture of D and L isomers was used, and toxic reactions, especially nephrotic syndrome and pyridoxine deficiency, were frequent. The concern generated has persisted inappropriately into the era of pure D-penicillamine usage. Undesirable side effects do occur in 5 to 10 percent of patients, but D-penicillamine remains the standard treatment for the disease.

Adults require at least 1 g daily divided into two doses. Some patients require a larger dose—up to 3 g daily can be given safely in adults. Childhood dosage is not well defined, but 500 mg daily is probably reasonable for those under 10 years and 1 g in older children. In all patients, 24-h urinary copper excretion should be monitored with adjustment of dose to achieve losses of over 2 mg/day in the early stages of treatment. After a year or two, the amount of copper available to mobilize decreases, and excretion of over 1 g per day is satisfactory.

Several other effective treatments are available. These are generally reserved for patients who have experienced serious side effects of penicillamine. Proponents of these regimes are arguing that experience with them will soon be sufficient to put them forward as alternative initial treatments.

Triethylene tetramine (Trientine) was also introduced by Walshe and appears as effective as penicillamine.[93] Commercial availability of the substance is a major problem. It is given in doses of 400 to 800 mg three times daily before meals. No toxic effects have been described with 20 patients using the drug for up to 13 years. Urinary copper excretion can be used to monitor treatment, as with penicillamine.

Zinc salts can block copper absorption, and a net negative copper balance can be achieved. This is certainly sufficient for maintenance of patients already decoppered by penicillamine. Two groups have claimed that this method can reduce body load of copper satisfactorily when used from the time of diagnosis in patients without immediately life-threatening disease.[11,12] The zinc induces high levels of metallothionein in intestinal mucosal cells, and this binds copper preferentially, preventing its passage to the bloodstream.[9] Monitoring of treatment is more difficult than with chelators. Repeated measurement of liver copper is the ultimate indicator of success. Progressive reduction in urinary copper excretion or in penicillamine-induced urinary excretion can give indirect evidence of reduced copper burden. Oral ^{64}Cu administration can demonstrate that intestinal absorption has been diminished.[94] Although the regimes used vary, most groups recommend 100 to 150 mg of zinc per day as acetate or sulfate, given in three or four doses at least 1 h before meals. Zinc acetate apparently causes less gastric irritation than zinc sulfate.[94]

Beneficial clinical effects of any of these treatments take some time—weeks for neurologic improvement and months for improvement in liver function. Consequently, it is very difficult to save patients who are diagnosed only in an advanced stage of liver failure or in an acute fulminant hepatic episode.[62,82,95] One must somehow keep the patient alive for 3 to 6 months until improvement occurs. The levels of nonceruloplasmin plasma copper may be extraordinarily high during acute episodes (up to 30 μmol/liter), and these levels undoubtedly set up a vicious cycle of cell damage and copper release. As much as 600 μmol of copper can be released per day (personal observations). Some method of removing large amounts of copper rapidly is needed. Peritoneal dialysis and plasmapheresis are the most effective of the established measures in my experience. Addition of albumin to the peritoneal dialysate and maintenance of plasma albumin levels by infusion assist in binding the copper. Hemodialysis is a poor substitute for peritoneal dialysis in removing copper. Intravenous administration of tetrathiomolybdate, which has proved valuable in copper toxicosis in sheep,[96] can bind all nonceruloplasmin copper within minutes. We have used it in three cases after the other measures described have failed, but it has not rescued any of these desperate cases. Earlier administration might be more effective.

Liver transplantation has been used in a number of patients with very advanced liver disease.[97] The correction achieved in all features of the disease speaks in favor of the "liver overflow" hypothesis of pathogenesis. However, exchange of the prognosis of treated Wilson's disease for that of liver transplantation is clearly a bad bargain, except when liver disease is irreversible. The procedure has a place in acute fulminant cases and in other advanced cases.[97]

L-Dopa may be useful in the control of neurologic symptoms which are not reversed by penicillamine or while awaiting a response.

The outcome with modern treatment is mainly determined by the amount of damage which has occurred before treatment is started. A normal life span with normal health seems likely for patients diagnosed before cirrhosis or severe neurologic effects have developed. Treatment stops active liver damage, and the degree of fibrosis may diminish quite remarkably. Even patients with ascites and other features of chronic hepatic decompensation may return to good health. Many of the neurologic effects may also be reversible. It is difficult to predict how much improvement will occur in an individual patient; one must wait to see the response. Some patients may become so complacent about their good health that they cease treatment. Serious symptoms recur within 2 or 3 years, sometimes with rapidly fatal outcomes.[98]

Skin rashes, thrombocytopenia, nephrotic symptoms, and acute arthritis are the most frequent side effects of D-penicillamine.[62,84] Cessation of therapy generally leads to resolution, and slow reintroduction is often tolerated without recurrence. A short course of corticosteroids may help prevent these hypersensitivity effects. Bone marrow aplasia or persistent nephrotic syndrome may prevent continuation of penicillamine. Elastosis perforans is a more persistent and often irreversible complication.[62]

The use of penicillamine in pregnancy has aroused considerable debate. Over 50 pregnancies have been reported in patients in good clinical health on penicillamine treatment without serious symptoms during pregnancy and with normal babies.[62,99] Two reports have described babies with unusual connective tissue changes born to women on penicillamine therapy for cystinuria and rheumatoid arthritis, respectively.[100,101] Interference with collagen cross-linking by penicillamine was blamed. None of 11 babies born to mothers taking trientine has had any relevant abnormality.[102] Animal studies have shown that the teratogenic effects of penicillamine and of trientine can be prevented by copper supplementation.[103] These findings may explain the human experience in different diseases treated with penicillamine. Patients with excessive copper stores seem protected from effects on the fetus. For the present, it seems reasonable to continue penicillamine during pregnancy if the maternal disease has been treated for a relatively short time. In long-treated patients, no clinical effects are seen during rests from therapy for 6 or 9 months, and cessation or reduction of dosage during pregnancy might be considered.

Genetics

Autosomal recessive inheritance is well documented in studies in many countries[62,68,69,76,104–106] by the frequency of the disease in sibs and by parental consanguinity in some families. The incidence of the disease is not known accurately. Experience in Melbourne suggests a figure in the range 1 in 50,000 to 1 in 100,000 livebirths. A figure of 1 in 35,000 has been found in Sardinia.[76]

Linkage to esterase D,[63] to the "retinoblastoma locus," and to the polymorphic DNA marker, D13 S10 on chromosome 13 in the region 13q14, has been demonstrated in five large Middle Eastern kindreds (one Israeli-Arab, two Druze, one Iraqi-Jewish, and one Iranian-Jewish). Linkage to esterase D is closest ($\theta = 0.03$, lod score = 5.20), and the order centromere-D13S10-esterase D-Wilson's disease is proposed.[107]

Heterogeneity (allelic and nonallelic) is the rule in genetic diseases and must be anticipated in Wilson's disease. The variability of disease effects and of age of onset is all in keeping with such heterogeneity, but environmental variables such as copper intake and virus infections may also be important. One large kindred described from an isolated Japanese island with a population of only 300 contained patients presenting at ages ranging from 6 to 25 years, some with hepatic and some with neurologic symptoms,[68] yet all the patients must have been homozygous for the same allele. Caution is necessary in attempting to define genetic heterogeneity by crude clinical criteria. This kindred and many smaller families show that hepatic and neurologic cases may occur in sibs. The mild neurologic symptoms described in New York in middle-age Jewish immigrants from Eastern Europe may indicate one genetic variant,[104] and differences between Jewish and Arab patients in Israel seem rather striking.[106] Linkage studies have not, so far, shown evidence of multiple loci, but few families provide enough data to test this point.

Heterozygotes do not have any clinical manifestations. Approximately 20 percent have lowered levels of ceruloplasmin (and serum copper).[62,108] A reduced secondary rise in plasma radioactivity after ^{64}Cu or ^{67}Cu is seen in heterozygotes as a group but cannot identify all heterozygotes. Another approach, measuring urinary excretion of copper and copper isotope after intravenous administration of isotope, has been described.[109] In suitable families, linkage analysis can now be used.

Genetic Counseling

Sibs of a patient with Wilson's disease have a 1 in 4 risk of developing the disease. These sibs should be examined for liver or neurologic disease and for Kayser-Fleischer rings and by measuring serum copper, serum ceruloplasmin, and urinary copper. Patients older than the index case may be assumed to be unaffected if no abnormalities are detected. Younger sibs should be investigated more fully using liver biopsy or ^{64}Cu studies if initial tests are normal. In suitable families, linkage analysis may be helpful. The risk of affected children is very low.

Investigation of potential heterozygotes has little value because available tests are not better than 80 to 90 percent reliable and cannot therefore be interpreted when applied to individuals with low a priori risks of being heterozygotes (e.g., spouses of relatives who may be heterozygotes). Linkage tests will not help in resolving this problem.

Prenatal Diagnosis/Presymptomatic Diagnosis

Prenatal diagnosis has not been possible, but linkage tests now raise this possibility. Some would doubt the place of prenatal diagnosis in a disease of late onset for which effective treatment is available.

Mass screening of newborn babies has been suggested, and simple methods of measuring serum ceruloplasmin do exist. However, the very low levels of ceruloplasmin seen in normal newborn babies (Table 54-3) make recognition at this age very difficult. Early symptomatic diagnosis of cases through constant awareness should be sufficient.

Copper Retention in Other Forms of Liver Disease

Copper retention occurs in forms of liver disease other than Wilson's disease; some of these diseases may prove to be caused by genetic defects of copper metabolism and may gain places of their own in future editions of this text (Table 54-8). Some of the conditions may cause diagnostic confusion. Copper chelation may be beneficial in some patients.

Copper retention would be expected in any form of chronic liver disease which interferes with biliary excretion. Prolonged mechanical obstruction of the bile ducts, as in extrahepatic biliary atresia, does cause a progressive rise in liver copper, but variation is considerable.[110] In other forms of liver disease, copper accumulation is even more variable but sometimes very severe.[66,87,110–112] A few forms of liver disease are more consistently associated with copper retention.

Table 54-8 Liver Copper (Micrograms per Gram of Dry Weight) in Various Liver Diseases Associated with Copper Retention

Normal	20–50
Wilson's disease	200–3000
Primary biliary cirrhosis	100–2000
Indian childhood cirrhosis	1000–5000[114]
Extrahepatic biliary atresia	30–500[110,111]
Åagenes syndrome (1 case)	1195[65]
Arteriodoctular hypoplasia (7 cases)	71, 243, 288, 327, 1440, 1545, 2119*

*A. L. Smith, J. Deutsch, D. M. Danks, unpublished data. Other figures not referenced are composite data from numerous articles.

Primary Biliary Cirrhosis. This disease shows a consistent and gross hepatic copper retention.[62] Promising responses to penicillamine therapy were described,[113] but prolonged treatment has met with only modest success. Detailed isotope studies indicate a disturbance of the initial rapid phase of incorporation of freshly injected copper into ceruloplasmin.[15] This may be a rather specific secondary effect in this disease, which is not usually familial and may have an autoimmune basis.

Indian Childhood Cirrhosis. This is a familial and probably genetically determined disease. An extreme degree of hepatic copper accumulation has been found[114] which is probably the result of excessive ingestion of copper during early infancy.[114a] Penicillamine has been found beneficial.[114a,b] Copper metabolism in cultured fibroblasts from four cases has been investigated with negative results (J. Camakaris, unpublished results).

Åagenes Syndrome. This syndrome (lymphedema and cholestasis from birth)[115] was accompanied by progressive and rapid copper accumulation in one patient, who developed lenticular degeneration terminally and copper deposition in the brain at age 5 years.[65] Other patients with this recessive disorder should be studied.

The Arterioductular Hypoplasia Syndrome. This dominantly inherited syndrome of bile duct hypoplasia, pulmonary arterial stenoses, and characteristic facies[116] is frequently associated with copper retention which may be secondary to the abnormalities of small bile ducts in this autosomal dominant condition.

Copper retention has been described in a variety of other cases of neonatal cholestatic liver disease.[87,112]

MENKES (STEELY HAIR) DISEASE AND THE OCCIPITAL HORN SYNDROME

These two conditions are discussed together because they are closely related. It is not yet clear whether they are allelic mutants or mutants at different X-chromosomal loci which are closely linked. Recently, an international committee considering the nosology of connective tissue disorders recommended linking them together and discarding the previous names used for the occipital horn syndrome. Statements made in this section apply to both conditions unless specifically stated.

Citation of references is restricted to those essential to establish facts, generally choosing the most recent article rather than the first. General reviews[6,7,51,53] are not as numerous as for Wilson's disease.

The clinical features, neuropathology, and X-linked inheritance of Menkes disease were clearly described in 1962.[117] Over the next decade, a small number of case reports added to the range of features and confirmed the pattern of inheritance. Discovery of a defect in copper metabolism in 1972[41,118] explained the pleiotropic features and triggered a new burst of interest in the disease. The combination of brain changes, like those of copper-deficient sheep, with arterial abnormalities like those seen in copper-deficient pigs had suggested copper deficiency.

At first, a simple defect in intestinal absorption seemed possible, but disturbances of copper transport in many tissues became apparent to the great frustration of those endeavoring to treat the disease with parenteral copper therapy.

A number of names have been used for this disease. Menkes steely hair disease acknowledges the role of the discoverer and the similarity of the hair changes to the abnormalities of wool seen in copper-deficient sheep (known as *steely wool* for many years) and describes the hair quite accurately. The hair is not "kinky" like the hair of Negroid races and the wool of normal sheep. Trichopoliodystrophy, X-linked copper malabsorption, and X-linked copper deficiency are other terms which have been used.

The occipital horn syndrome has also been described under several different names—X-linked cutis laxa, X-linked Ehlers-Danlos syndrome, and Ehlers-Danlos syndrome type IX. It differs from the X-linked Ehlers-Danlos type V.[119] Originally emphasis was placed on the deficiency of lysyl oxidase without full appreciation of the significance of the low levels of serum copper observed in the patients.[120]

Basic Defect and Pathogenesis

To discuss the present understanding of the basic defects in these diseases and their pathogenesis, we have to draw upon research conducted on patients, on cells from patients (fibroblastic and continuous lymphoid cell cultures), on mottled mouse mutants, and on their cells in culture. The relationship between the human and mouse mutants is close.[6,51,53] Most of the work done in cultured cells has used human cells, and most studies of copper distribution in tissues and of copper enzymes in tissues have used mice, for obvious reasons. Sufficient work of each type has been done in the other species to support the application of the findings to both species. Menkes disease and brindled mice have been studied most extensively (Fig. 54-2). They show similarities close enough to suggest homology.[6,51,53] Both are lethal at an early age because of neurologic effects. The occipital horn syndrome and blotchy mice are similar in showing predominantly the connective tissue consequences of copper deficiency and long survival. It is not clear whether the differential involvement of copper enzymes reflects a different severity of the same underlying defect in copper transport or whether different steps in a chain of copper transport processes are affected.[51,121]

At a cellular level, the mutations cause excessive accumulation of copper accompanied by deficient activity of copper enzymes.[71,122–124] The initial uptake of copper into the cells is normal.[125] The copper which accumulates in excess is bound to metallothionein, which is present in increased amounts. In normal cells grown in medium with a low copper content, very little copper is bound to metallothionein. However, if excess copper is added to the medium, most of it becomes attached to metallothionein, just as it is in mutant cells grown in low-copper media[126] (S. Herd, J. Camakaris, personal communication). Measurement of metallothionein mRNA confirms that these findings reflect increased induction of gene expression by increasing levels of copper, not preexisting overexpression of the genes (S. Herd, T. Stevenson, J. Camakaris, J. Mercer, personal communication).

The simplest explanation of these findings postulates an intracellular copper transport protein which normally carries copper to the intracellular sites of copper enzyme assembly. When normal cells are grown in high-copper media, the uptake of copper overloads this carrier, and the resulting "free" copper induces metallothionein synthesis. Mutant cells lack this carrier function, and "free" copper capable of inducing

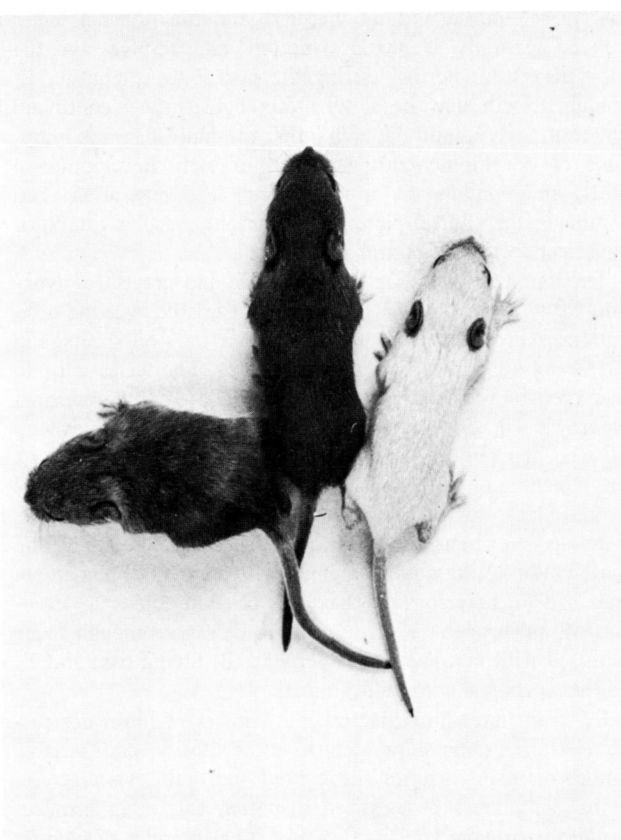

Fig. 54-2 Brindled mutant mice—affected male ($Mo^{br/y}$) showing depigmentation and growth failure, heterozygote ($Mo^{br/+}$); littermate is of normal size but shows the brindled coat.

metallothionein synthesis accumulates even in low-copper media. There could be one carrier serving all copper enzymes, or there could be a series of carriers for different groups of enzymes, defects of which would have similar effects on metallothionein induction but different effects on copper enzyme levels (e.g., in Menkes disease/brindled mouse compared with occipital horn syndrome/blotchy mouse).[51]

Other explanations are possible. The defect could be in processes of extrusion of copper from the cells, but evidence argues against this.[125] More complex possibilities remain.[127]

Earlier hypotheses included a mutation of metallothionein causing irreversible binding of copper or constitutive overproduction of metallothionein. The former was eliminated when the cloned metallothionein genes were shown to be on chromosomes other than X, chromosome 8 in mice,[46] and chromosome 16 in humans.[47] The latter was excluded by showing dose-related induction of metallothionein mRNA in cells from patients with Menkes disease and in tissues of mutant mice (T. Stevenson, J. Camakaris, J. Mercer, personal communication).

The mutation appears to affect all tissues except the liver. This may reflect the specialized role of the liver in copper homeostasis and, in some ways, makes these mutants the antithesis of Wilson's disease. Interpretation is difficult if we look only at findings in patients with Menkes disease at the time of diagnosis or at postmortem. Copper levels are low in most tissues except kidney and intestinal mucosa, with levels in liver remarkably lowered[118,128] (Table 54-9). In affected fetuses (20 weeks), all tissues except liver show increased copper content.[129] Placental transport of copper is only moderately reduced in mutant mice.[130] Intestinal absorption of copper is grossly diminished.[52,118] Putting these facts together, we conclude that all tissues except liver accumulate copper in excess (express the mutant phenotype) when sufficient copper is available; postnatally, malabsorption of copper reduces the amount available so that only those tissues with special access to copper (intestinal mucosa, renal tubules) manifest the phenotype. Injection of ^{64}Cu into mutant mice confirms that the tendency of all tissues except liver to accumulate copper in excess persists postnatally.[131]

In studies of this type, blotchy mice show a similar pattern of copper accumulation or deficiency in tissues to brindled mice, but the changes are all less severe.[132]

Several copper enzymes have been studied in tissues or cells of the mutant mice—lysyl oxidase (LO),[133,134] cytochrome C oxidase (CO),[135] superoxide dismutase (SOD),[135] dopamine β-hydroxylase (DBH) (M. Phillips, personal communication), and tyrosinase.[136] Two points of particular interest emerge. Despite the very low levels of copper present in the liver, enzyme activities are maintained at normal levels,[135] supporting the view that this organ is spared the direct effects of the mutation and shows only the effects of malabsorption of copper. The levels of CO and SOD are generally closer to normal in blotchy mutants than in brindled mice,[135] as would be expected from the tissue copper results. Conversely, blotchy mice have lower levels of LO in skin than brindled mice,[134] a finding of considerable interest given the predominance of connective tissue effects in the blotchy mutants. It is this departure from what one might expect if blotchy were merely a

Table 54-9 Copper Levels in Serum and Tissues in Menkes Disease and in Brindled mice

	Normal baby (6–12 mo)	*Typical Menkes disease*	*Normal fetus (20 wk)*[129]	*Menkes disease (20 wk)*[129]	*Normal mice (11 days)*[128]	*$Mo^{br/y}$ mice (11 days)*[128]	*$Mo^{br/+}$ mice (11 days)*[128]
Serum, μmol/liter	11–24	2–6	NK*	NK	76	24	58
Liver, μg/g dry weight	50–120	10–20	36†	12†	169	13	25
Brain, μg/g dry weight	20–30	1–7	0.4†	1.0†	12	3	8
Kidney, μg/g dry weight	10–20	240	0.8†	17.0†	16	50	112
Duodenal mucosa, μg/g dry weight	7–29	50–90	NK	NK	16	41	44

*NK = not known.
†μg/g wet weight.
NOTE: Results for typical Menkes disease represent range of personal experience and published cases. Figures for mice are presented as means only—more detailed figures are in original report.[128]

less severe mutant at the same locus as brindled which raises the possibility of linked loci governing sequential carrier proteins within cells.[51] The effects of copper therapy upon enzyme activity range from negligible effect on LO[133,134] to complete restoration of activity of tryosinase.[136]

In humans LO deficiency has been demonstrated in tissues and cultured cells from patients with Menkes disease[133,138] and the occipital bony syndrome.[120,121,137,138] The levels of residual activity and of residual LO protein are comparable in cells cultured from patients with both diseases,[138] and addition of copper did not alter protein levels[138] or activity.[133,138] Unfortunately, no detailed comparison of clinical features of the two diseases by clinicians with personal experience of both has yet appeared. Although the emphasis has been on urinary tract abnormalities and abnormal bone configuration in the occipital horn syndrome, it is clear that arterial abnormalities and osteoporosis are seen and that mental development is not entirely normal.[139] Conversely, urinary tract abnormalities are prominent in longer-lived patients with Menkes disease; descriptions of the radiologic features of bones, including skull, of these older patients are lacking.

In considering the possibilities of allelism or linked loci, the situation is further complicated by two patients with a mild form of Menkes disease (see "Mild Menkes Disease"). They exhibit different degrees of involvement of brain and connective tissue relative to one another and to patients with the occipital horn syndrome.

The phenotype of abnormal copper accumulation and excessive induction of metallothionein genes is the same in cells cultured from brindled and blotchy mice and in cells of typical cases or mild cases of Menkes disease as in those of patients with the occipital horn syndrome. No difference in degree of alteration of copper transport in cells has been reported.

Despite all these uncertainties about the basic defect(s) and about the precise relationships between the various mutants, there is no doubt that the clinical phenotypes of the two human diseases are explicable by deficient function of copper enzymes. The structural changes in the hair are due to defective disulfide bonding in keratin[41,118] as seen in copper-deficient sheep. Depigmentation is due to tyrosinase deficiency.[136] The arterial disease is principally the result of defective cross-linking of elastin and collagen secondary to lysyl oxidase deficiency.[133,138] The collagen abnormality presumably underlies the osteoporosis. The relative roles of catecholamine deficiency secondary to DBH deficiency, of CO deficiency, and of SOD deficiency in the neurologic and thermostability disturbances have not been determined. It is tempting to attribute a major role to DBH. Brindled mice show reduced catecholamine levels and have brain disease; blotchy mice have normal catecholamine levels and no neurologic features.[140,141] However, primary DBH deficiency seems to cause a remarkably mild neurologic disease in humans.[142]

Clinical Features

Classic Menkes Disease. The key components of the clinical syndrome are abnormal hair, abnormal facies, progressive cerebral degeneration, hypopigmentation, bone changes, arterial rupture and thrombosis, and hypothermia.[41,53,143]

Premature delivery is very frequent, as are neonatal hypothermia and hyperbilirubinemia. Hypothermia may also occur in older babies. In the neonatal period, the child's appearance is usually normal with fine normal hair, but some have trichorrhexis nodosa and monilethrix, and the unusual facies may be apparent. Neonatal symptoms may resolve, and the baby may seem normal during the next 2 or 3 months, although growth may be slow. Other babies show continued symptoms. By about age 3 months, the more flagrant symptoms of developmental delay, loss of early developmental skills, and convulsions appear. Cerebral degeneration then dominates the clinical picture with various vascular complications, particularly subdural hematoma.

The hair becomes tangled, lusterless, and grayish or ivory colored with a stubble of broken hairs palpable over the occiput and temporal regions where the hair rubs on sheets. Pili torti is found microscopically (Fig. 54-3). The facies is quite characteristic with pudgy cheeks, sagging jowls, and abnormal eyebrows (Fig. 54-4*A*) and is recognizable even in babies who have no hair (Fig. 54-4*B*). Skeletal x-rays show osteoporosis and widening of the flared metaphyses with spiky protrusions at the edges, which may fracture.[41,144,145] Rib fractures are common. Wormian bones are usually seen in the skull. The combination of these bony changes with a subdural hematoma may lead to the erroneous diagnosis of child abuse.[146] Osteoporosis and proneness to fracture can be severe enough to be confused with osteogenesis imperfecta (B. Steinmman and E. Gautier, personal communication).

CT scan may show macroscopic patches of brain destruction. Arteriograms show elongation, tortuosity, and variable caliber of major arteries throughout the brain, viscera, and limbs, with areas of localized dilatation and other areas of marked narrowing[41,144,146] (Fig. 54-5). Diverticulae of bladder or ureters may rupture or predispose to recurring infection.[147] These complications pose major problems in some patients, especially those who survive longer. Emphysema, retinal degeneration, and iris cysts[148] have been described.

In most cases, death occurs at ages between 3 months and 3 years, most often about 12 months. Several patients have lived on in a decerebrate state for longer periods, even up to 12 years[149] (R. R. Howell, personal communication).

Mild Menkes Disease. I am aware of two patients with mild forms of Menkes disease. They must be distinguished from a small group of patients who ran the typical course of brain degeneration over the first year of life but survived for many years profoundly impaired[149] (R. Howell, personal communication); they must also be distinguished from two patients who have been treated from infancy and are surviving with rela-

Fig. 54-3 Pili torti.

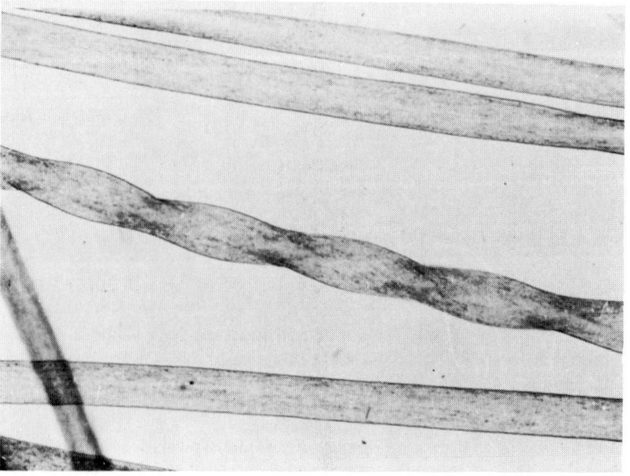

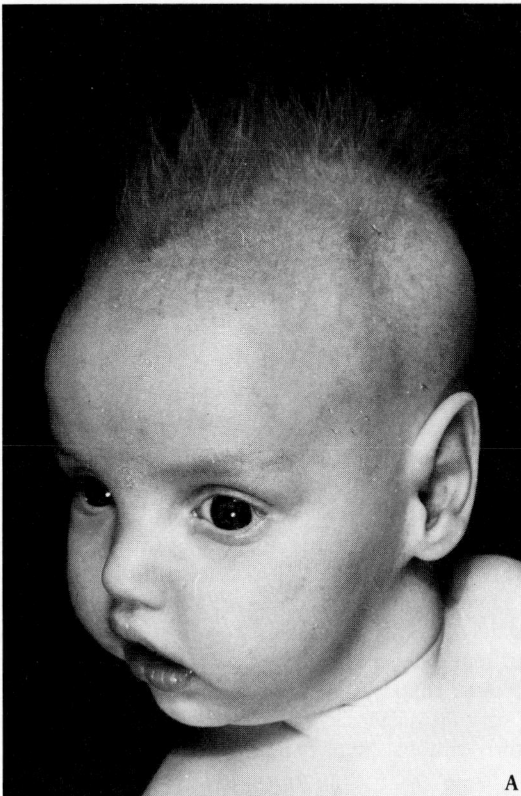

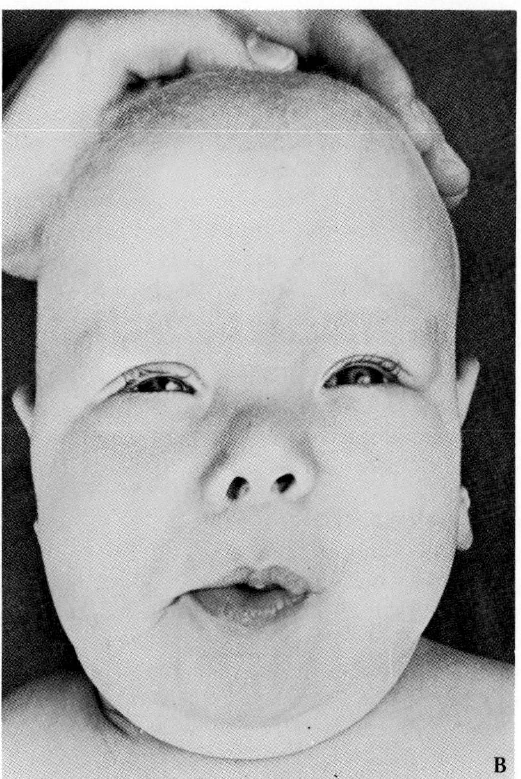

Fig. 54-4 Typical facies of Menkes disease in two unrelated cases, with (A) and without (B) visible hair.

tively mild disabilities (see "Treatment" below) and from those with the occipital horn syndrome.

One of these patients presented at 2 years with mild developmental delay in nonmotor skills and marked cerebellar ataxia.[150] Pili torti was obvious and led to detailed investigation despite serum copper levels at the lower limit of normal. Mild bone changes were present, and arteriography showed generalized elongation and uniform dilatation of arteries. CT scan was normal. Liver copper levels were low, and intestinal mucosal levels were increased. We have treated him for 7 years with daily injections of copper (1 mg) as copper histidinate. This dose has maintained normal serum and liver copper levels. His progress at school is average for age despite his severe ataxia, which persists unaltered. Ultrasound examination shows no bladder or ureteric diverticulae. Joint and skin laxity are minimal. Pili torti persists to a mild degree. It is impossible to determine whether copper therapy has altered the course of his disease.

The second patient was seen in 1985 through the courtesy of Drs. Grant Morrow, Charles Swisher, and Gene Pergament. He was 7 years of age, had obvious pili torti, diminished pigmentation, typical facies, sagging jowls, loose skin, lax joints, mild ataxia, and mild intellectual delay. Urinary tract diverticulae had caused recurrent infections. Arteriography was performed later and showed only mild uniform dilatation. He had never received copper therapy. Serum copper levels had been diagnostically reduced.

The Occipital Horn Syndrome. Patients with this condition have presented with inguinal hernias, complications of bladder or ureteric diverticulae, or skin and joint laxity.[120,121,137,139] Chronic diarrhea has been described in some cases.[139] Facial appearance has been described as unusual but has generally

Fig. 54-5 Aortogram showing tortuosity, elongation, patchy dilatation, and areas of stenosis of many arteries.

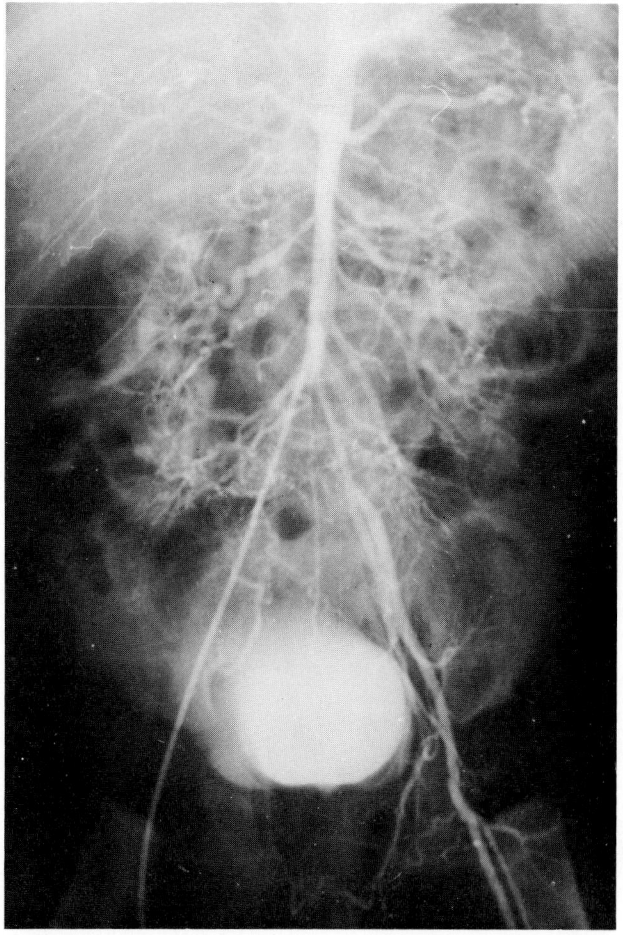

not attracted comment. Radiologic changes have been remarkable and diagnostic.[139] They include the ossified occipital horn (which is also palpable), a "hammerlike" expansion of the lateral end of the clavicles and a wavy outline of the cortex of most long bones. Arterial tortuosity, elongation, and stenoses have been described.[139] Lysyl oxidase levels in skin and cultured cells are low.[120,121,134,138] Serum copper is generally reduced to a mild extent. Definitive diagnosis may depend on analysis of copper transport in cultured fibroblastic cells, which yield results indistinguishable from Menkes disease.[121,137,138] To date only a few families have been described, and details of hair structure, skin pigmentation, and tissue copper levels (especially liver and intestinal mucosa) for comparison with Menkes disease are lacking. Intellect seems to be in the low normal to mildly retarded range[139] (I. Kaitila, personal communication).

Laboratory and Cell Culture Findings

In classic Menkes disease, serum copper and ceruloplasmin levels are very low (Table 54-10). Interpretation is difficult in the first 2 or 3 weeks of life when the ceruloplasmin and serum copper levels are very low in normal babies (Table 54-3). Cord blood levels in affected babies fall within the normal range.[143] The distinction from normal is clear by 2 weeks when normal levels have risen several-fold, but levels in affected males have fallen further.

The liver content of copper is grossly reduced, and duodenal or jejunal biopsy shows greatly increased copper content (normal 10 to 30 μg/g dry weight) (Table 54-10). Oral ^{64}Cu is poorly absorbed; ^{64}Cu given intravenously is cleared from plasma and incorporated into ceruloplasmin quite normally.[41,151,152,153]

The disturbances of copper handling in cultured cells (Table 54-11) provide the most definitive test for the disease.[122–124,152] Copper content is increased, ^{64}Cu accumulation over 24 hours is increased, and release of ^{64}Cu during further culture in isotope-free medium is reduced. Cells are also hypersensitive to copper toxicity. Fibroblastic, amniotic, chorionic, and lymphoid cells all show these changes, although the exact figures differ a little in the four cell types. The influence of the phase of cell growth at the time of testing is troublesome with fibroblastic and amniotic cells. Use of confluent cultures which have been held in a nondividing state by reducing the fetal calf serum in the medium gives most reproducible results in our experience,[125] especially if tested in low copper media. Special care is needed in prenatal diagnosis using amniotic cells.

Table 54-10 Typical Copper Measurements in Menkes Disease at Usual Age of Diagnosis

	Menkes disease (3–12 mo)	*Mild Menkes disease (2 yr)*[150]	*Normal (3–12 mo)*
Serum ceruloplasmin,			
OD units/ml	<0.08	0.20	>0.25
mg/liter	<50	160	>200
Serum copper, μmol/liter	<6	9.5	>12
Liver copper, μg/g dry weight	10–20	18	140–70*
Duodenal copper, μg/g dry weight	50–80	98	7–29

*Higher levels observed in younger babies.

Table 54-11 Findings of Menkes Disease in Cultured Fibroblastic Cells in Our Laboratory[122]

	Normal cells	*Menkes cells*
Copper content, μg per 10^6 cells, in normal medium	0.023 ± 0.013*	0.282 ± 0.091
^{64}Cu content after 24 h, μg ^{64}Cu per 10^6 cells	0.004 ± 0.001*	0.060 ± 0.019*
^{64}Cu efflux over subsequent 24 h in culture, percentage of content at 24 h	70 – 90%	0 – 5%

*Standard deviation.

Reduced levels of various copper enzyme activities have been demonstrated but are of little diagnostic assistance. Noradrenaline is decreased and dopamine increased in cerebrospinal fluid as expected in dopamine β-hydroxylase deficiency.[154] Hair keratin analysis shows defective disulfide bonding.[118]

In mild Menkes disease, serum copper and ceruloplasmin reductions may be too slight to be diagnostic. Demonstration of reduced hepatic copper content by liver biopsy or of increased copper content of the intestinal mucosa by biopsy can prove the diagnosis, as can analysis of copper transport in cultured fibroblastic or lymphoid cells.

In the occipital horn syndrome, serum copper and ceruloplasmin levels may or may not be reduced.[120,137] Hepatic and intestinal mucosal copper levels might be diagnostic but have not been reported. Altered copper transport can be demonstrated in cultured cells.[121,137,138]

Pathology

Gross and microscopic pathology is abundant in this disease. Arteries show the most remarkable and precocious degenerative changes with elongation, aneurysmal dilatations, rupture, stenoses, and areas of intimal proliferation and of thrombosis. Microscopically, the fragmentation, disruption, and reduplication of the internal elastic lamina are quite extreme, especially in large arteries[41] (Fig. 54-6). Intimal changes are also visible. Ultrastructural changes suggest defective formation of elastin rather than disruption of elastic fibers.[155] Abnormalities of collagen and elastin have been described in skin[155] and cartilage.[147]

Neuronal destruction is widespread in the cerebral cortex and in the cerebellum, and there is associated gliosis.[117,156–158] The changes in the cerebellum are particularly severe with neuronal loss in the internal granule cell layer and molecular layer. Many Purkinje cells are lost, and the remaining cells show an unusual elaboration of dendritic sprouts from the cell body and grotesque proliferation of the dendritic tree which has been considered unique to this disease.[156–158] Similar changes found in brindled mice have been studied in detail.[159,160] The pronounced involvement of the cerebellum fits in well with the marked cerebellar ataxia seen in the mildly affected boy described above.[150]

Naturally, myelin is deficient in such a damaged brain, but all the findings could be secondary to neuronal loss. Chemical markers of myelin destruction are found. In the late stages of the disease, brain infarction and hemorrhage secondary to arterial disease are seen.

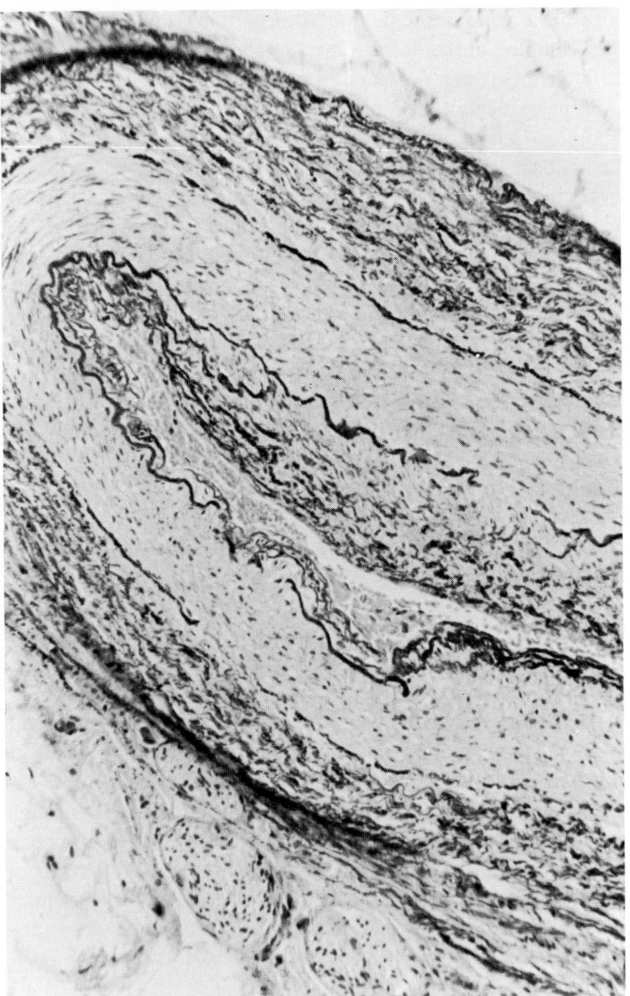

Fig. 54-6 Section of larger artery showing fragmentation and reduplication of the internal elastic lamina and intimal thickening.

Changes in skeletal muscle (glycogen accumulation, mitochondrial disorganization)[156,159] and in the iris and retina[148] have been described.

Diagnosis

The diagnosis can be made with great confidence by the clinical and radiologic features once one or two cases have been seen. Microscopic examination of the hair is very helpful, even in a mild case.[161] Low levels of serum copper and ceruloplasmin will usually clinch the diagnosis. If doubt still exists, assay of copper in gut mucosal or liver biopsies, or studies of cell cultures may be used, which constitute the ultimate test, showing marked abnormality even when the reduction of ceruloplasmin and serum copper is too slight to be diagnostic.

Treatment

No form of treatment has yet been proven to be truly effective. Copper has been administered parenterally in a number of different forms—copper sulfate, copper chloride, copper EDTA, copper glycinate, copper histidinate, and copper albumin complex. Copper nitriloacetate is the only form of copper which has proved to be absorbed from the intestine.[162] All these forms of treatment have corrected the hepatic copper deficiency and restored normal levels of serum copper. Some improvement in physical condition has resulted, but in most cases, there has been continuing cerebral degeneration. Restoration of normal brain copper levels has not been described.[143,162] One patient is making encouraging progress at 10 years. His development is only mildly delayed, but he has marked laxity of skin and joints. Treatment with copper histidinate (600 mg copper per day) started in the second month, before symptoms developed (A. Sass-Kortsak, G. Sherwood, personal communication).

It is probable that many of the effects of the disease are already established *in utero* and that postnatal treatment cannot be fully effective. Nevertheless, the search should be continued for some chemical form of copper which can bypass the disturbance in copper transport and deliver the copper to the copper enzymes which require it, especially in the brain. The sensitivity of affected cells in culture to toxic effects of excess copper[122] may indicate that delivery of too much copper may also prove injurious.

Since some of the more serious effects of the disease may be the result of defective catecholamine synthesis, trials of monoamine oxidase inhibitors seemed warranted. I used transcyclypramine sulfate in two children without benefit.

Treatment of the brindled mice has proved surprisingly simple and effective. A single dose of 50 mg copper (best as Cu^+) given on day 7 restores normal growth and allows survival to at least 1 year (middle age for mice).[163] Treatment at 10 days has been unsuccessful.[164] These results suggest a critical stage in brain development at which copper is vital.[164] Mice are immature at birth relative to humans, 7 days postnatal being equivalent to mid-third trimester for humans in many aspects of brain development. This led to an idea of treating affected fetuses *in utero* or of using premature delivery to make babies available for early treatment. We are currently treating in this way the son of a woman who did not wish to terminate the pregnancy after the disease was diagnosed by amniocentesis and requested experimental treatment. The baby was delivered at 35 weeks and has received copper histidinate by daily injection since day 2, monitored by repeated serum and liver copper assays. Development at 18 months approximates that expected at 12 to 15 months. He has mild ataxia.

Genetics and Genetic Heterogeneity

Numerous pedigrees show X-linked recessive inheritance of classic Menkes disease. This is further supported by the mosaic skin depigmentation seen in a Negro heterozygous female[165] and the pili torti seen in some heterozygotes.[161] Patchy suntanning can occur in white heterozygotes. Full manifestation of the disease has been described in three girls. One was a Japanese girl, the sister of a severely affected male.[166] The second girl has been described only in an abstract[167]; karyotype was stated to be normal 46XX. The third affected girl is of special interest because she carried a 2/X balanced translocation with the break point at Xp13, strongly suggesting localization of the Menkes disease gene at this site.[168] Other studies in cell hybrids and using X-chromosomal DNA markers had provided some evidence of a locus in the proximal part of Xp.[169]

Experience in Melbourne in 1966 to 1971 suggested an incidence of 1 in 35,000,[41] a figure distorted by a chance cluster of cases. Extension of the period of collection of cases to 1986 has modified this figure to 1 in 90,000. The true figure is presumably in the range 1 in 50,000 to 1 in 100,000.

Heterozygotes may show abnormalities in cultured cells similar to those seen in affected males, but X-chromosome inactivation confounds the situation. In fact, only about half of obligate heterozygotes are identified by studies on a single skin biopsy.[122,170] Exhaustive examination of hair for pili torti identifies a similar proportion.[161] Use of two or three biopsies from separate sites improves the diagnostic ability, as does cloning of the fibroblastic cells grown from a biopsy.[171] Development of a test using hair roots or cloned lymphocytes seems desirable. The presence of pili torti, of mosaic skin pigmentation, or of abnormal cell culture results demonstrates heterozygosity in a female relative, but we cannot exclude heterozygosity with certainty. Measurement of placental copper levels seems to be a particularly good method of diagnosing heterozygotes when new females are born into affected families.[172]

The mild form of Menkes disease has been identified in only two boys, each the only affected person in his family. Our observation of elevated copper levels in the placenta of a sister born into the first family supports X-linked inheritance.

X-linked inheritance of the occipital horn syndrome is well established by examination of pedigrees. The limited experience available with fibroblastic cell cultures from obligate heterozygotes is similar to that described in classic Menkes disease. Nothing is known about the location of this gene or the X chromosome except by analogy with studies in mice.

The mottled locus was mapped to a region of the X chromosome close to the tabby locus by classic breeding experiments using the original mottled (mo) mutant, but more extensive studies of brindled (Mo^{br}) and blotchy (Mo^{blo}) mutants mapped both 4 cM from tabby. Later work placed these mutants just 1 cM from the phosphoglucomutase (PGM) locus. The allelism of the mutants seems to have been accepted without much question, but this is, in fact, not easily established. Although doubly heterozygous ($Mo^{br/blo}$) females are quite severely affected, they are not identical with $Mo^{br/br}$ or $Mo^{blo/blo}$ homozygotes (M. Phillips, personal communication). Ultimate proof will require complementation studies in tetraploid male cells expressing two X chromosomes or gene cloning. The near recessive behavior of the Mo^{br} mutant should make complementation studies possible.[173]

Prenatal Diagnosis

Any or all of the disturbances of copper metabolism in cultured cells can be used for prenatal diagnosis on cultured amniotic cells or cultured chorion villus (CVS) samples. Experience in Melbourne indicates a need for great care in standardizing the cell culture conditions. Unhealthy cells show abnormalities similar to those seen in Menkes disease. The batch of cells tested should include fibroblastic cells from an affected relative, normal amniotic cells, and amniotic cells from an affected male. ^{64}Cu retention after 24 h alone has been used successfully in 42 pregnancies,[172] but in the Melbourne experience it has proved particularly susceptible to alteration according to the phase of cell culture and to the copper content of the medium. Release of ^{64}Cu during a subsequent 24-h growth in media without isotope is less affected by culture variables and is the most reliable single test. It is best to use both these measurements and also the total copper content of the cells. Use of media with low copper content maximizes the difference between normal and mutant cells.

Prenatal diagnosis should probably be concentrated in a few laboratories heavily involved with research on cellular copper metabolism until more experience has accumulated. The high levels of copper found in the placenta allow confirmation of diagnosis in terminated male pregnancies and appear to be useful in heterozygote diagnosis.[172] This characteristic of the disease suggested that the copper content of uncultured CVS might be useful for prenatal diagnosis. Danish experience has confirmed this prediction.[174] Great care is necessary to ensure that all instruments and solutions used at each step of the procedure are free of copper contamination, which can exceed the original copper content of the sample if these precautions are not taken.

Other Patients (Families) with Possible Copper Deficiency

Willemse et al.[175] described a boy with an X-linked clinical disease indistinguishable from Menkes disease with similar pathologic changes and copper results in blood, urine, and tissues. He differed in showing near-normal intestinal absorption of copper and much less copper bound to metallothionein in cultured cells than is usually found in Menkes disease.

Haas et al.[176] described two male cousins related through their mothers who suffered mental retardation with progressive decerebrate posturing and athetosis. Oral absorption of copper was grossly diminished although intravenous doses were incorporated into ceruloplasmin normally. A gross disparity in the liver copper results reported in the two boys is disturbing.

Mehes and Petrovicz[177] reported benign copper deficiency with X-linked or autosomal dominant inheritance. Fair hair, widened metaphyses, mild anaemia, and seizures which responded to oral copper therapy were features in the index case. A disparity between serum copper and ceruloplasmin levels was hard to explain in this report.

Work reported in this chapter was supported by a Program Grant from the National Health and Medical Research Council and by the Scobie and Claire Mackinnon Trust.

REFERENCES

1. UNDERWOOD EJ: *Trace Elements in Human and Animal Nutrition,* 4th ed. New York, Academic, 1977.
2. MASON KE: A conspectus of research on copper metabolism and requirements in man. *J Nutr* 109:1979, 1979.
3. SASS-KORTSAK A, BEARN AG: Hereditary disorders of copper metabolism—Wilson's disease (hepatolenticular degeneration) and Menkes' disease (kinky-hair or steely-hair syndrome), in Stanbury JB, Wyngaarden JB, Fredrickson DS (eds): *The Metabolic Basis of Inherited Disease,* 4th ed. New York, McGraw-Hill, 1978.
4. CIBA FOUNDATION SYMPOSIUM 79: *Biological Roles of Copper.* Amsterdam, Excerpta Medica, 1980.
5. COUSINS RJ: Absorption, transport, and hepatic metabolism of copper and zinc: Special reference to metallothionein and ceruloplasmin. *Physiol Rev* 65:238, 1985.
6. CAMAKARIS J, DANKS DM: Mutations affecting trace elements, in Harris H, Hirshhorn K (eds): *Advances in Human Genetics.* New York, Plenum, 1983, vol 13, p 149.
7. HOWELL JMCC, GAWTHORNE JM (eds): *Copper in Man and Animals.* Boca Raton, CRC Press Inc, 1987.

8. BREMNER I: Absorption, transport and distribution of copper, in *CIBA Foundation Symposium 79: Biological Roles of Copper*. Amsterdam, Excerpta Medica, 1980, p 23.

9. HALL AC, YOUNG BW, BREMNER I: Intestinal metallothionein and the mutual antagonism between copper and zinc in the rat. *J Inorg Biochem* 11:57, 1979.

10. PRASAD AG, BREWER GJ, SCHOOMAKER EB, RABBONI P: Hypocupremia induced by zinc therapy in adults. *JAMA* 240:2166, 1978.

11. HILL GM, BREWER GJ, PRASAD AS, HYDRICK CR, HARTMANN DE: Treatment of Wilson's disease with zinc: I. Oral zinc therapy regimens. *Hepatology* 7:822, 1987.

12. HOOGENRAAD TU, VAN DEN HAMER CJA: Three years of continuous oral zinc therapy in 4 patients with Wilson's disease. *Acta Neurol Scand* 67:356, 1983.

13. STRICKLAND GT, BECKNER WM, LEU M-L: Absorption of copper in homozygotes and heterozygotes for Wilson's disease and controls: Isotope tracer studies with ^{67}Cu and ^{64}Cu. *Clin Sci* 43:617, 1972.

14. SMALLWOOD RA, MCILVEEN B, ROSENOER VM, SHERLOCK S: Copper kinetics in liver disease. *Gut* 12:139, 1971.

15. VIERLING JM, SHRAGER MA, RUMBLE WF, AAMODT R, BERMAN MD, JONES EA: Incorporation of radiocopper into ceruloplasmin in normal subjects and in patients with primary biliary cirrhosis and Wilson's disease. *Gastroenterology* 74:652, 1978.

16. PETERS T JR: Serum albumin: Recent progress in the understanding of its structure and biosynthesis. *Clin Chem* 23:5, 1977.

17. HARRIS DIM, SASS-KORTSAK A: The influence of amino acids on copper uptake by rat liver slices. *J Clin Invest* 46:659, 1967.

18. DARWISH HM, HOKE JE, ETTINGER MJ: Kinetics of Cu(II) transport and accumulation by hepatocytes from copper-deficient mice and the brindled mouse model of Menkes disease. *J Biol Chem* 258:13621, 1983.

19. MCARDLE HJ, GROSS SM, DANKS DM: The uptake of copper by mouse hepatocytes. *J Cell Physiol*, 1988, in press.

20. FRIEDEN E: Ceruloplasmin: A multi-functional metalloprotein of vertebrate plasma, in *CIBA Foundation Symposium 79: Biological Roles of Copper*. Amsterdam, Excerpta Medica, 1980, p 93.

21. GUTTERIDGE JMC, STOCKS J: Caeruloplasmin: Physiological and pathological perspectives. *Clin Lab Sci* 14:257, 1981.

22. COX DW: Factors influencing serum ceruloplasmin levels in normal individuals. *J Lab Clin Med* 68:893, 1966.

23. EDWARDS CQ, WILLIAMS DM, CARTWRIGHT GE: Hereditary hypoceruloplasminemia. *Clin Genet* 15:311, 1979.

24. SOLOMONS NW: On the assessment of zinc and copper nutriture in man. *Am J Clin Nutr* 32:856, 1979.

25. DANKS DM: Diagnosis of trace metal deficiency—With emphasis on copper and zinc. *Am J Clin Nutr* 34:278, 1981.

26. MEHRA RK, BREMNER I: Species differences in the occurrence of copper-metallothionein in the particulate fractions of the liver of copper-loaded animals. *Biochem J* 219:539, 1984.

27. WEISS KC, LINDER MC: Copper transport in rats involving a new plasma protein. *Am J Physiol* 249:E77, 1985.

28. WEBER KM, BOSTON RC, LEAVER DD: A kinetic model of copper metabolism in sheep. *Aust J Agric Res* 31:773, 1980.

29. LINDER MC, MOOR JR: Plasma ceruloplasmin: Evidence for its presence in and uptake by heart and other organs of the rat. *Biochem Biophys Acta* 499:329, 1977.

29a. DAMERON CT, HARRIS ED: Regulation of aortic CuZn-superoxide dismutase with copper: Effects in vivo. *Biochem J* 248:663, 1987.

30. STEVENS MD, DISILVESTRO RA, HARRIS ED: Specific receptor for ceruloplasmin in membrane fragments from aortic and heart tissues. *Biochemistry* 23:261, 1984.

31. KATAOKA M, TAVASSOLI M: Ceruloplasmin receptors in liver cell suspensions are limited to the endothelium. *Exp Cell Res* 155:232, 1984.

32. OWEN CA JR: Copper and hepatic function, in *CIBA Foundation Symposium 79: Biological Roles of Copper*. Amsterdam, Excerpta Medica 1980, p 267.

33. STRICKLAND GT, BECKNER WM, LEU M-L, O'REILLY S: Turnover studies of copper in homozygotes and heterozygotes for Wilson's disease and controls: Isotope tracer studies with ^{67}Cu. *Clin Sci* 43:605, 1972.

34. GIBBS K, WALSHE JM: Studies with radioactive copper (^{64}Cu and ^{67}Cu): The incorporation of radioactive copper into ceruloplasmin in Wilson's disease and in primary biliary cirrhosis. *Clin Sci* 41:189, 1971.

35. HOWELL JMCC: The pathology of chronic copper poisoning in sheep, in Kirchgessner M (ed): *Proceedings of 3rd International Symposium on Trace Element Metabolism in Man and Animals*, Friesing-Weihenstephan, Arbeitskreis für Tierernährungs Forschung, 1978, p 536.

36. HENKIN RI: Metal-albumin-amino acid interactions: Chemical and physiological interrelationships, in Friedman M (ed): *Protein-Metal Interactions*. New York, Plenum, 1974, p 15.

37. PAYNTER DI, MOIR RJ, UNDERWOOD EJ: Changes in activity of the Cu-Zn superoxide dismutase enzyme in tissues of the rat with changes in dietary copper. *J Nutr* 109:1570, 1979.

38. YANG F, NAYLOR SL, LUM JB, CUTSHAW S, MCCOMBS JL, NABERHAUS KH, MCGILL JR, ADRIAN GS, MOORE CM, BARNETT DR, BOWMAN BH: Characterization, mapping, and expression of the human ceruloplasmin gene. *Proc Natl Acad Sci USA* 83:3257, 1986.

39. MERCER JFB, GRIMES A: Isolation of a cDNA clone for human caeruloplasmin that includes the complete N-terminus. *FEBS Lett* 203:185, 1986.

40. HOAGLAND HC, GOLDSTEIN NP: Hematologic (cytopenic) manifestations of Wilson's disease (hepatolenticular degeneration). *Mayo Clin Proc* 53:498, 1978.

41. DANKS DM, CAMPBELL PE, STEVENS BJ, MAYNE V, CARTWRIGHT E: Menkes' kinky hair syndrome: An inherited defect in copper absorption with widespread effects. *Pediatrics* 50:188, 1972.

42. DANKS DM: Copper deficiency in humans, in *CIBA Foundation Symposium 79: Biological Roles of Copper*. Amsterdam, Excerpta Medica, 1980, p 209.

43. ALDRED AR, GRIMES A, SCHREIBER GA, MERCER JFB: Rat ceruloplasmin. Molecular cloning and gene expression in liver, choroid plexus, yolk sac, placenta and testis. *J Biol Chem* 262:2875, 1987.

44. HAMER DH: Metallothionein. *Annu Rev Biochem* 55:913, 1986.

45. KARIN M: Metallothioneins: Proteins in search of function. *Cell* 41:9, 1985.

46. COX DR, PALMITER RD: The metallothionein-I gene maps to mouse chromosome 8: Implications for human Menkes' disease. *Hum Genet* 64:61, 1983.

47. SCHMIDT CJ, HAMER DH, MCBRIDE OW: Chromosomal location of human metallothionein genes: Implications for Menkes disease. Chromosome 16. *Science* 224:1104, 1984.

48. PETERSON MG, HANNAN F, MERCER JFB: The sheep metallothionein family—Structure, sequence and evolutionary relationship of five linked genes. *Eur J Biochem*, 1988, in press.

49. HAMBIDGE KM: Trace elements in pediatric nutrition. *Adv Pediatr* 24:191, 1978.

50. WALSH FM, CROSSON FJ, BAYLEY M, MCREYNOLDS J, PEARSON BJ: Acute copper intoxication: Pathophysiology and therapy with a case report. *Am J Dis Child* 131:149, 1977.

51. DANKS DM: Of mice and men, metals and mutations. *J Med Genet* 23:99, 1986.

52. HUNT DM: Primary defect in copper transport underlies mottled mutants in the mouse. *Nature* 249:852, 1974.

53. DANKS DM: Copper transport and utilisation in Menkes' syndrome and in mottled mice. *Inorg Perspect Biol Med* 1:73, 1977.

54. RAUCH H: Toxic milk, a new mutation affecting copper metabolism in the mouse. *J Hered* 74:141, 1983.

55. RAUCH H, DUPUY D, STOCKERT RJ, STERNLIEB I: Hepatic copper and superoxide dismutase activity in toxic milk mutant mice, in Rotilio G (ed): *Superoxide and Superoxide Dismutase in Chemistry, Biology, and Medicine*. Amsterdam, Elsevier, 1986.

56. TWEDT DC, STERNLIEB I, GILBERTSON SR: Clinical morphologic and chemical studies on copper toxicosis of Bedlington terriers. *J Am Vet Assoc* 175:269, 1979.

57. SU LC, RAVANSHAD S, OWEN CA JR, MCCALL JT, ZOLLMAN PE, HARDY RM: A comparison of copper-loading disease in Bedlington terriers and Wilson's disease in humans. *Am J Physiol* 243:G226, 1982.

58. SU LC, OWEN CA JR, ZOLLMAN PE, HARDY RM: A defect of biliary excretion of copper in copper-laden Bedlington terriers. *Am J Physiol* 243:G231, 1982.

59. HURLEY LS, KEEN CL, LONNERDAL B: Copper in fetal and neonatal development, in *CIBA Foundation Symposium 79: Biological Roles of Copper*. Amsterdam, Excerpta Medica, 1980, p 227.

60. MANN JR, CAMAKARIS J, GILLESPIE M, KOELLREUTER B, MATTHIEU JM, ROYCE PM, DANKS DM: Failure to confirm abnormal copper utilization in crinkled (*cr*) mice. *Biol Trace Element Res* 3:117, 1981.

61. OWEN CA JR: *Wilson's Disease*. Park Ridge, NJ, Noyes Publications, 1981.

62. SCHEINBERG IH, STERNLIEB I: *Wilson's Disease*. Philadelphia, Saunders, 1984.

63. BONNÉ-TAMIR B, FARRER LA, FRYDMAN M, KANAANEH H: Evidence for linkage between Wilson disease and esterase D in three kindreds: Detection of linkage for an autosomal recessive disorder by the family study method. *Genet Epidemiol* 3:201, 1986.

64. GIBBS K, WALSHE JM: Biliary excretion of copper in Wilson's disease. *Lancet* 2:538, 1980.

65. SMITH AL, DANKS DM: Secondary copper accumulation with neurological damage in children with chronic liver disease. *Br Med J* 2:1400, 1978.

66. FLEMING CR, DICKSON ER, WAHNER HW, HOLLENHORST RW, MCCALL JT:

Pigmented corneal rings in non-Wilsonian liver disease. *Ann Intern Med* 86:285, 1977.

67. FROMMER D, MORRIS J, SHERLOCK S, ABRAMS J, NEWMAN S: Kayser-Fleischer-like rings in patients without Wilson's disease. *Gastroenterology* 72:1331, 1977.
68. ARIMA M, SANO I: Genetic studies of Wilson's disease in Japan. *Birth Defects* 4(2):54, 1968.
69. STRICKLAND GT, FROMMER D, LEU M-L, POLLARD R, SHERLOCK S, CUMMINGS JN: Wilson's disease in the United Kingdom and Taiwan. *Q J Med* 42:619, 1973.
70. HOWELL JMCC, GOONERATNE SR, GAWTHORNE JM: Copper poisoning in sheep: Wilson's disease. *Comp Pathol Bull* 16:3, 1984.
71. GOKA TJ, STEVENSON RE, HEFFERAN PM, HOWELL RR: Menkes' disease: A biochemical abnormality in cultured human fibroblasts. *Proc Natl Acad Sci USA* 73:604, 1976.
72. CHAN WY, CUSHING W, COFEMAN MA, RENNERT OM: Genetic expression of Wilson's disease in cell culture: A diagnostic marker. *Science* 208:299, 1980.
73. CAMAKARIS J, ACKLAND L, DANKS DM: Phenotype expression of Wilson's disease in cultured fibroblasts. *J Inherited Metab Dis* 3:155, 1980.
74. HUNT DM, WAKE SA, MERCER JFB, DANKS DM: A study of the role of metallothionein in the inherited copper toxicosis of dogs. *Biochem J* 236:409, 1986.
75. STRICKLAND GT, LEU M-L: Wilson's disease: Clinical and laboratory manifestations in 40 patients. *Medicine* 54:113, 1975.
76. GIAGHEDDU A, DEMELIA L, PUGGIONI G, NURCHI AM, CONTU L, PIRARI G, DEPLANO A, RACHELE MG: Epidemiologic study of hepatolenticular degeneration (Wilson's disease) in Sardinia (1902–1983). *Acta Neurol Scand* 72:43, 1985.
77. DOBYNS WB, GOLDSTEIN NP, GORDON H: Clinical spectrum of Wilson's disease (hepatolenticular degeneration). *Mayo Clin Proc* 54:35, 1979.
78. SASS-KORTSAK A: Wilson's disease: A treatable cause of liver disease in children. *Pediatr Clin North Am* 22:963, 1975.
79. ODIEVRE M, VEDRENNE J, LANDRIEU P, ALAGILLE D: Les formes hepatiques "pures" de la maladie de Wilson chez l'enfant: A propos de dix observations. *Arch Fr Pediatr* 31:215, 1974.
80. DANKS DM, STEVENS BJ: Diagnosis of Wilson's disease in children with liver disease: A report of two families. *Lancet* 1:22, 1969.
81. PERMAN JA, WERLIN SL, GRAND RJ, WATKINS JB: Laboratory measures of copper metabolism in the differentiation of chronic active hepatitis and Wilson's disease in children. *J Pediatr* 94:564, 1979.
82. MCCULLOUGH AJ, FLEMING CR, THISTLE JL, BALDUS WP, LUDWIG J, MCCALL JT, DICKSON ER: Diagnosis of Wilson's disease presenting as fulminant hepatic failure. *Gastroenterology* 84:161, 1983.
83. MADDEN JW, IRONSIDE JW, TRIGER DR, BRADSHAW JPP: An unusual case of Wilson's disease. *Q J Med* 55:63, 1985.
84. GOLDING DN, WALSHE JM: Arthropathy of Wilson's disease: Study of clinical and radiological features in 32 cases. *Ann Rheum Dis* 36:99, 1977.
85. WIEBERS DO, WILSON DM, MCLEOD RA, GOLDSTEIN NP: Renal stones in Wilson's disease. *Am J Med* 67:249, 1979.
86. CARPENTER TO, CARNES DL JR, ANAST CS: Hypoparathyroidism in Wilson's disease. *N Engl J Med* 309:873, 1983.
87. KAPLINSKY C, STERNLEIB I, JAVITT N, ROTEM Y: Familial cholestatic cirrhosis associated with Kayser-Fleischer rings. *Pediatrics* 65:782, 1980.
88. WILLIAMS FJB, WALSHE JM: Wilson's disease. An analysis of the cranial computerized tomographic appearances found in patients and the changes in response to treatment with chelating agents. *Brain* 104:735, 1981.
89. DETTORI P, RACHELE MG, DEMELIA L, PELAGHI AE, NURCHI AM, AROMANDO P, GIAGHEDDU M: Computerized cranial tomography in presymptomatic and hepatic form of Wilson's disease. *Eur Neurol* 23:56, 1984.
90. CARTWRIGHT GE: Diagnosis of treatable Wilson's disease. *N Engl J Med* 298:1347, 1978.
91. FITZGERALD MA, GROSS JB, GOLDSTEIN NP, WAHNER HW, MCCALL JT: Wilson's disease (hepatolenticular degeneration) of late adult onset. *Mayo Clin Proc* 50:438, 1975.
92. WALSHE JM: Copper chelation in patients with Wilson's disease. *Q J Med* 42:441, 1973.
93. WALSHE JM: Treatment of Wilson's disease with trientine (triethylene tetramine) dihydrochloride. *Lancet* 1:643, 1982.
94. HILL GM, BREWER GJ, JUNI JE, PRASAD AS, DICK RD: Treatment of Wilson's disease with zinc. II. Validation of oral ^{64}Copper with copper balance. *Am J Med Sci* 29:344, 1986.
95. HAMLYN AN, GOLLAN JL, DOUGLAS AP, SHERLOCK S: Fulminant Wilson's disease with hemolysis and renal failure: Copper studies and assessment of dialysis regimes. *Br Med J* 2:660, 1977.
96. GOONERATNE SR, HOWELL JMCC, GAWTHORNE JM: Intravenous administration of thiomolybdate for the prevention and treatment of chronic copper poisoning in sheep. *Br J Nutr* 46:457, 1981.
97. EDE RJ, NAZER H, MOWAT AP, WILLIAMS R: Wilson's disease: Clinical presentation and use of prognostic index. *Gut* 27:1377, 1986.
98. WALSHE JM, DIXON AK: Dangers of non-compliance in Wilson's disease. *Lancet* 1:845, 1986.
99. WALSHE JM: Pregnancy in Wilson's disease. *Q J Med* 46:73, 1977.
100. MJOLNEROD OK, RASMUSSEN K, DOMMERUD SA, GJERULDSEN ST: Congenital connective-tissue defect probably due to D-penicillamine treatment in pregnancy. *Lancet* 1:673, 1971.
101. LINARES A, ZARRANZ JJ, RODRIGUEZ-ALARCON J, DIAZ-PEREZ JL: Reversible cutis laxa due to maternal D-penicillamine treatment. *Lancet* 2:43, 1979.
102. WALSHE JM: The management of pregnancy in Wilson's disease treated with trientine. *Q J Med* 58:81, 1986.
103. KEEN CL, COHEN NL, LONNERDAL B, HURLEY LS: Teratogenesis and low copper status resulting from triethylenetetramine in rats (41693). *Proc Soc Exp Biol Med* 173:598, 1983.
104. BEARN AG: Genetic analysis of Wilson's disease. *Ann Hum Genet* 24:33, 1960.
105. SAITO T: Evaluation of segregation ratio in Wilson's disease. *J Med Genet* 20:271, 1983.
106. PASSWELL J, ADAM A, GARFINKEL D, STREIFFLER M, COHEN BE: Heterogeneity of Wilson's disease in Israel. *Isr J Med Sci* 13:15, 1977.
107. BOWCOCK AM, FARRER LA, CAVALLI-SFORZA LL, HEBERT JM, KIDD KK, FRYDMAN M, BONNE-TAMIR B: Mapping the Wilson disease locus to a cluster of linked polymorphic markers on chromosome 13. *Am J Hum Genet* 41:27, 1987.
108. GIBBS K, WALSHE JM: A study of the ceruloplasmin concentrations found in 75 patients with Wilson's disease, their kinships and various control groups. *Q J Med* 48:1, 1979.
109. GIBBS K, HANKA R, WALSHE JM: The urinary excretion of radiocopper in presymptomatic and symptomatic Wilson's disease, heterozygotes and controls: Its significance in diagnosis and management. *Q J Med* 47:349, 1978.
110. REED GB, BUTT EM, LANDING BH: Copper in childhood liver disease: A histologic, histochemical and chemical survey. *Arch Pathol* 93:249, 1972.
111. SMALLWOOD RA, WILLIAMS HA, ROSENOER VM, SHERLOCK S: Liver copper levels in liver disease: Studies using neutron activation analysis. *Lancet* 2:1310, 1968.
112. EVANS J, NEWMAN S, SHERLOCK S: Liver copper levels in intrahepatic cholestasis of childhood. *Gastroenterology* 75:875, 1978.
113. DEERING TB, DICKSON ER, FLEMING CR, GEALL MG, MCCALL JT, BAGGENSTOSS AH: Effects of D-penicillamine on copper retention in patients with primary biliary cirrhosis. *Gastroenterology* 72:1208, 1977.
114. TANNER MS, PORTMANN B: Indian childhood cirrhosis. *Arch Dis Child* 56:4, 1981.
114a. TANNER MS: Indian childhood cirrhosis: Copper ingestion, penicillamine treatment, and prevention. *Ind J Pediatr* 54:467, 1987.
114b. BARROW L, TANNER MS: Penicillamine in Indian childhood cirrhosis. *Lancet* 2:513, 1987.
115. ÅAGENES O: Hereditary recurrent cholestasis with lymphoedema: Two new families. *Acta Paediatr Scand* 63:465, 1974.
116. ALAGILLE D, ESTRADA A, HAOCHOUEL M, GAUTIER M, ODIEVRE M, DOMMERGUES JP: Syndrome paucity of interlobular bile ducts (Alagille syndrome or arteriohepatic dysplasia)—Review of 80 cases. *J Pediatr* 110:195, 1987.
117. MENKES JH, ALTER M, STEIGLEDER GK, WEAKLEY DR, SUNG JH: A sex-linked recessive disorder with retardation of growth, peculiar hair and focal cerebral and cerebellar degeneration. *Pediatrics* 29:764, 1962.
118. DANKS DM, STEVENS BJ, CAMPBELL PE, GILLESPIE JM, WALKER-SMITH J, BLOMFIELD J, TURNER B: Menkes' kinky-hair syndrome. *Lancet* 1:110, 1972.
119. BEIGHTON B, CURTIS D: X-linked Ehlers-Danlos syndrome type V; the next generation. *Clin Genet* 27:472, 1985.
120. BYERS PH, SIEGEL RC, HOLBROOK KA, NARAYANAN AS, BORNSTEIN P, HALL JG: X-linked cutis laxa: Defective cross-link formation in collagen due to decreased lysyl oxidase activity. *N Engl J Med* 303:61, 1980.
121. PELTONEN L, KUIVANIEM H, PALOTIE A, HORN N, KAITILA I, KIVIRIKKO KL: Alterations of copper and collagen metabolism in the Menkes syndrome and a new subtype of Ehlers-Danlos Syndrome. *Biochemistry* 22:6156, 1983.
122. CAMAKARIS J, DANKS DM, ACKLAND L, CARTWRIGHT E, BORGER P, COTTON RGH: Altered copper metabolism in cultured cells from human Menkes' syndrome and mottled mouse mutants. *Biochem Genet* 18:117, 1980.
123. CHAN W-Y, GARNICA AD, RENNERT OM: Cell culture studies of Menkes kinky hair syndrome. *Clin Chim Acta* 88:495, 1978.
124. BERATIS NG, PRICE P, LaBADIE G, HIRSCHORN K: ^{64}Cu metabolism in Menkes' and normal cultured skin fibroblasts. *Pediatr Res* 12:699, 1978.

125. HERD SM, CAMAKARIS J, CHRISTOFFERSON R, WOOKEY P, DANKS DM: Uptake and efflux of copper-64 in Menkes' disease and normal continuous lymphoid cell lives. *Biochem J* 247:341, 1987.

126. LEONE A, PAVLAKIS GN, HAMER DH: Menkes disease: Abnormal metallothionein gene regulation in response to copper. *Cell* 40:301, 1985.

127. CAMAKARIS J: Copper absorption, transport and storage, in Howell JMcC, Gawthorne JM (eds): *Copper in Man and Animals*. Boca Raton, FL, CRC Press, 1987.

128. CAMAKARIS J, MANN JR, DANKS DM: Copper metabolism in mottled mouse mutants: Copper concentrations in tissues during development. *Biochem J* 180:597, 1979.

129. HEYDORN K, DAMSGAARD E, HORN N, MIKKELSEN M, TYGSTRUP I, VESTERMARK S, WEBER J: Extra-hepatic storage of copper. A male foetus suspected of Menkes' disease. *Humangenetik* 29:171, 1975.

130. MANN JR, CAMAKARIS J, DANKS DM: Copper metabolism in mottled mouse mutants: Defective placental transfer of ^{64}Cu to foetal brindled (Mo^{br}) mice. *Biochem J* 186:692, 1980.

131. MANN JR, CAMAKARIS J, DANKS DM: Copper metabolism in mouse mutants: Distribution of ^{64}Cu in brindled (Mo^{br}) mice. *Biochem J* 180:613, 1979.

132. MANN JR, CAMAKARIS J, FRANCIS N, DANKS DM: Copper metabolism in mottled mouse *(Mus musculus)* mutants. Studies of blotchy (Mo^{blo}) mice and a comparison with brindled (Mo^{br}) mice. *Biochem J* 196:81, 1981.

133. ROYCE PM, CAMAKARIS J, DANKS DM: Reduced lysyl oxidase activity in skin fibroblasts from patients with Menkes' syndrome. *Biochem J* 192:579, 1980.

134. ROYCE PM, CAMAKARIS J, MANN JR, DANKS DM: Copper metabolism in mottled mouse mutants. The effect of copper therapy on lysyl oxidase activity in brindled (Mo^{br}) mice. *Biochem J* 202:369, 1982.

135. PHILLIPS M, CAMAKARIS J, DANKS DM: Comparisons of copper deficiency states in the murine mutants blotchy and brindled. Changes in copper-dependent enzyme activity in 13-day-old mice. *Biochem J* 238:177, 1986.

136. HOLSTEIN TJ, FUNG RQ, QUEVEDO WC, BIENIEKI TC: Effect of altered copper metabolism induced by mottled alleles and diet on mouse tyrosinase. *Proc Soc Exp Biol Med* 162:264, 1979.

137. KUIVANIEMI H, PELTONEN L, PALOTIE A, KAITILA I, KIVIRIKKO KI: Abnormal copper metabolism and deficient lysyl oxidase activity in a heritable connective tissue disorder. *J Clin Invest* 69:730, 1982.

138. KUIVANIEMI H, PELTONEN L, KIVIRIKKO KI: Type IX Ehlers-Danlos syndrome and Menkes syndrome: The decrease in lysyl oxidase activity is associated with a corresponding deficiency in the enzyme protein. *Am J Hum Genet* 37:798, 1985.

139. SARTORIS DJ, LUZZATTI L, WEAVER DD, MacFARLANE JD, HOLLISTER DW, PARKER BR: Type IX Ehlers-Danlos syndrome: A new variant with pathognomonic radiographic features. *Radiology* 152:665, 1984.

140. HUNT DM: Catecholamine biosynthesis and the activity of a number of copper-dependent enzymes in the copper-deficient mottled mouse mutants. *Comp Biochem Physiol* 57:79, 1977.

141. HUNT DM: Copper and neurological function, in *CIBA Foundation Symposium 79: Biological Roles of Copper*. Amsterdam, Excerpta Medica, 1980.

142. VELD AJM, MOLEMAN P, BOOMSMA F, SCHALEKAMP MADH: Congenital dopamine-beta-hydroxylase deficiency. *Lancet* 1:183, 1987.

143. GROVER WD, JOHNSON WC, HENKIN RI: Clinical and biochemical aspects of trichopoliodystrophy. *Ann Neurol* 5:65, 1979.

144. WESENBERG RL, GWINN JL, BARNES GR: Radiological findings in the kinky-hair syndrome. *Radiology* 92:500, 1969.

145. KOZLOWSKI K, MCCROSSIN R: Early osseous abnormalities in Menkes' kinky-hair syndrome. *Pediatr Radiol* 8:191, 1979.

146. ADAMS PC, STRAND RD, BRESNAN MJ, LUCKY AW: Kinky hair syndrome: Serial study of radiological findings with emphasis on similarity to the battered child syndrome. *Radiology* 112:401, 1974.

147. HARA K, OOHIRA A, NOGAMI H, WATANABE K, MIYAZAKI S: Kinky hair disease: Biochemical, histochemical, and ultrastructural studies. *Pediatr Res* 13:1222, 1979.

148. SEELENFREUND MH, GARTNER S, VINGER PF: The ocular pathology of Menkes' disease. *Arch Ophthalmol* 80:718, 1968.

149. BAERLOCHER KE, STEINMANN B, RAO VH, GITZELMANN R, HORN N: Menkes' disease: Clinical, therapeutic and biochemical studies. *J Inherited Metab Dis* 6 (*Suppl* 2):87, 1983.

150. PROCOPIS P, CAMAKARIS J, DANKS DM: A mild form of Menkes' syndrome. *J Pediatr* 98:97, 1981.

151. LUCKY AW, HSIA YE: Distribution of ingested and injected radiocopper in two patients with Menkes' kinky-hair disease. *Pediatr Res* 13:1280, 1980.

152. DEKABAN AS, AAMODT R, RUMBLE WF, JOHNSTON GS, O'REILLY S: Kinky hair disease. Study of copper metabolism with use of ^{64}Cu. *Arch Neurol* 32:672, 1975.

153. PRINS HW, VAN DEN HAMER CJA: Primary biochemical defect in copper metabolism in mice with a recessive X-linked mutation analogous to Menkes' disease in man. *Inorg Biochem* 10:19, 1979.

154. GROVER WD, HENKIN RI, SCHWARTZ M, BRODSKY N, HOBDELL E, STOLK JM: A defect in catecholamine metabolism in kinky-hair disease. *Ann Neurol* 12:263, 1982.

155. OAKES BW, DANKS DM, CAMPBELL PE: Human copper deficiency: Ultrastructural studies of the aorta and skin in a child with Menkes' syndrome. *Exp Mol Pathol* 25:82, 1976.

156. GHATAK NR, HIRANO A, POON TP, FRENCH JH: Trichopoliodystrophy. II. Pathological changes in skeletal muscle and nervous system. *Arch Neurol* 26:60, 1972.

157. HIRANO A, LLENA JF, FRENCH JH, GHATAK NR: Fine structure of the cerebellar cortex in Menkes' kinky-hair disease: X-chromosome-linked copper malabsorption. *Arch Neurol* 34:52, 1977.

158. VUIA O, HEYE D: Neuropathologic aspects in Menkes' kinky hair disease (trichopoliodystrophy). *Neuropaediatrie* 5:329, 1974.

159. YAMANO T, PALDINO AM, SUZUKI K: Ultrastructural and morphometric studies of Purkinje cells of brindled mouse after administration of cupric chloride. *J Neuropathol Exp Neurol* 44:97, 1985.

160. YAMANO T, SUZUKI K: Abnormalities of Purkinje cell arborization in brindled mouse cerebellum. A Golgi study. *J Neuropathol Exp Neurol* 44:85, 1985.

161. MOORE CM, HOWELL RR: Ectodermal manifestations in Menkes disease. *Clin Genet* 28:532, 1985.

162. GROVER WD, SCRUTTON MC: Copper therapy in trichopoliodystrophy. *J Pediatr* 86:216, 1975.

163. MANN JR, CAMAKARIS J, DANKS DM, WALLICZEK EG: Copper metabolism in mottled mouse mutants: Copper therapy of brindled (Mo^{br}) mice. *Biochem J* 180:605, 1979.

164. WENK G, SUZUKI K: The effect of copper supplementation on the concentration of copper in the brain of the brindled mouse. *Biochem J* 205:485, 1982.

165. VOLPINTESTA EJ: Menkes' kinky hair syndrome in a black infant. *Am J Dis Child* 128:244, 1974.

166. IWAKAWA Y, NIWA T, TOMITA M: Menkes' kinky hair syndrome: Report on an autopsy case and his female sibling with similar clinical manifestations. *Brain Dev* 11:260, 1979.

167. BARTON NW, DAMBROSIA JM, BARRANGER JA, BETHESDA MD: Menkes kinky-hair syndrome: Report of a case in a female infant. *Neurology* 33 (*Suppl* 2):154, 1983.

168. KAPUR S, HIGGINS JV, DELP K, ROGERS B: Menkes syndrome in a girl with X-autosome translocation. *Am J Med Genet* 26:503, 1987.

169. HORN N, STENE J, MOLLEKAER MA, FRIEDRICH U: Linkage studies in Menkes disease. The Xg blood group system and C-banding of the X chromosome. *Ann Hum Genet* 48:161, 1984.

170. HORN N: Menkes' X-linked disease: Heterozygous phenotypic uncloned fibroblast cultures. *J Med Genet* 17:257, 1980.

171. HORN N, MOOY P, MCGUIRE VM: Menkes X-linked disease: Two clonal cell populations in heterozygotes. *J Med Genet* 17:262, 1980.

172. HORN N: Menkes' X-linked disease: Prenatal diagnosis of hemizygous males and heterozygous female. *Prenat Diagn* 1:107, 1981.

173. BROWN RM, CAMAKARIS J, DANKS DM: Observations on the Menkes and brindled mouse phenotypes in cell hybrids. *Somatic Cell Mol Genet* 10:321, 1984.

174. TØNNESEN T, HORN N, SØNDERGAARD F, MIKKELSEN M, BOUØE J, DAMSGAARD E, HEYDORN K: Measurement of copper in chorionic villi for first-trimester diagnosis of Menkes disease. *Lancet* 1:1038, 1985.

175. WILLEMSE J, VAN DEN HAMER DJA, PRINS HW, JONKER PL: Menkes' kinky hair disease. I. Comparison of classical and unusual clinical and biochemical features in two patients. *Brain Dev* 4:105, 1982.

176. HAAS RH, ROBINSON A, EVANS K, LASCELLES PT, DUBOWITZ V: An X-linked disease of the nervous system with disordered copper metabolism and features differing from Menkes' disease. *Neurology (Minneap)* 31:852, 1981.

177. MEHES K, PETROVICZ E: Familial benign copper deficiency. *Arch Dis Child* 57:716, 1982.

CHAPTER **55**

HEMOCHROMATOSIS

THOMAS H. BOTHWELL
ROBERT W. CHARLTON
ARNO G. MOTULSKY

1. Hemochromatosis *is the term applied when organ structure and function are impaired by the presence of excessive quantities of iron in the parenchymal cells. The iron is stored predominantly as hemosiderin, and at least 15 g is found at the time of clinical presentation. The liver, heart, pancreas, endocrine organs, skin, and joints are principally affected. Cirrhosis, cardiomyopathy, diabetes mellitus, hypogonadism, pigmentation and arthritis are the usual manifestations.*
2. *The iron enters the body either via the gastrointestinal tract, as a consequence of a failure of the mechanism controlling the absorption of dietary iron, or in the hemoglobin of transfused blood. Hereditary hemochromatosis is the result of an inborn error of metabolism which leads to enhanced absorption. In thalassemia major and other refractory anemias characterized by a hyperplastic marrow with a large degree of ineffective erythropoiesis, absorption is also enhanced, and the iron overload is usually compounded by multiple transfusions. Acquired hemochromatosis is rare. In refractory hypoplastic anemias requiring multiple transfusions, the iron is located initially in reticuloendothelial cells where it is relatively innocuous, although with time parenchymal cell loading can occur. Iron overload due to exposure to a diet containing large quantities of bioavailable iron affects hepatocytes as well as the reticuloendothelial system, but accumulation of the amounts necessary to affect organ structure or function is rare.*
3. *The nature of the metabolic defect responsible for the excessive absorption of iron in hereditary hemochromatosis has not been elucidated. The reticuloendothelial cells as well as the upper intestinal mucosal cells release more iron to the plasma than is needed. As a result they contain very little of the superfluous iron, and the binding capacity of the specialized transport protein in the plasma, transferrin, is saturated. The reason iron absorption is enhanced in those hyperplastic anemias, both genetic and acquired, in which erythropoiesis is largely ineffective, is also not known.*
4. *Hereditary hemochromatosis is transmitted by autosomal recessive inheritance of the mutant gene, which is situated close to the HLA-A locus on the short arm of chromosome 6. Current evidence suggests that the gene is present in about 10 percent of most Caucasoid populations, with approximately 3 in 1000 of the population being homozygous. Phenotypic expression in homozygotes is dependent on the presence of sufficient quantities of absorbable iron in the diet. The average American diet permits a maximal positive daily balance of 2 to 4 mg in males, and the age of clinical presentation is thus usually 40 years or older. In women, menstruation and the smaller dietary intake diminish the positive balance so that full phenotypic expression occurs at a later age and 10 times less often than in men. In countries such as India, where the bioavailable iron content of the average diet is low, clinically manifest hemochromatosis has not been reported. In Australia, the large meat consumption contributes to the high prevalence there. Alcohol plays a part in many patients, contributing to the organ damage and the iron loading.*
5. *The diagnosis of fully developed hereditary hemochromatosis is made by establishing the presence of massive iron overload with a parenchymal distribution and normal erythropoiesis. The finding of a raised transferrin saturation and a markedly raised plasma ferritin concentration should lead to needle biopsy of the liver, which provides a specimen for both chemical analysis and histologic examination. Homozygotes among the sibs of such individuals can usually be identified by HLA typing.*
6. *Once clinical manifestations have appeared, iron overload is eventually fatal unless the iron can be removed. The common causes of death are cardiac failure, arrhythmia, hepatic failure, hepatoma, or the complications of diabetes. Removal of the iron in hereditary hemochromatosis is most conveniently achieved by weekly venesections of 500 to 600 ml blood. These must be continued for up to 3 years, depending on the amount of iron in the body. Thereafter a venesection every 3 to 4 months is sufficient to prevent reaccumulation of the iron. Removal of the iron prolongs survival, cures the cardiomyopathy and the skin pigmentation, and arrests the liver damage. Diabetes may improve, but hypogonadism and arthropathy do not, and hepatoma may develop even years later.*
7. *The incomplete reversal of the effects of iron overload by removal of iron, and in particular the high incidence of hepatoma, oblige the physician who discovers a patient with hereditary hemochromatosis to identify all homozygotes among blood relatives, especially sibs. If venesections can be instituted before organ damage has occurred, the consequences of phenotypic expression of the disease can be avoided.*
8. *Hemochromatosis secondary to refractory anemia must be treated with iron chelators. The best of these is the iron-specific deferoxamine, but it must be given parenterally. In thalassemia major, nightly subcutaneous infusions over 10 to 12 h out of every 24 have been shown to limit storage iron accumulation to about 4 to 5 g.*

Although iron is the second most abundant metal in the earth's crust, it exists almost exclusively in the ferric [Fe(III)] state, which greatly reduces its accessibility. As a result, humans have difficulty in acquiring enough iron from the environment for their needs, and iron deficiency is a worldwide problem. In contrast, iron overload is uncommon and arises only in very special circumstances. The occasional association of cirrhosis with heavy hepatic deposits of the iron-containing compound hemosiderin was first recognized toward the end of the last century and the name *hemochromatosis* was given to the condition. Hereditary hemochromatosis is now known to be the result of an inherited metabolic defect or defects, in which excessive quantities of iron are absorbed from the diet. At the same time it has become apparent that iron overload can arise in other ways and that it may give rise to similar metabolic, pathologic, and clinical consequences. Iron absorption inappropriate to body needs occurs in a number of refractory anemias caused by genetic defects, such as thalassemia major. An additional factor in such subjects is repeated blood transfusions, the hemoglobin iron thus bypassing the mechanism which controls iron absorption. Multiple transfusions may also give rise to iron overload in refractory anemias in which absorption is not enhanced, such as in aplastic anemia. Finally, iron overload occurs in many Southern African blacks who have no genetic defect but who absorb more iron than they require from alcoholic beverages brewed in iron drums. In order to understand iron overload and its metabolic consequences, it is essential to have a background knowledge of the normal content and distribution of iron in the body and of the processes involved in the maintenance of iron balance.

The body of a healthy adult male contains between 3 and 4 g iron.[1] The major portion is in the iron porphyrin complexes hemoglobin, myoglobin, and a variety of heme-containing enzymes (Table 55-1). There are also many nonheme enzymes which either contain iron or require it as a cofactor. The remaining iron in the body is stored as ferritin and hemosiderin, in which forms it is relatively nonreactive. The size of this reserve of iron depends on the previous iron nutrition of the individual, and it normally varies between 0 and 1000 mg. The subsequent discussion is centered on the storage complexes, since in iron overload the superfluous iron is present in these forms. In addition, consideration is given to the iron transport protein transferrin, which plays a key part in the distribution of iron within the body.

THE METABOLISM OF IRON

Storage Iron

The diffuse, soluble, mobile fraction of storage iron is called *ferritin*, and the insoluble, aggregated deposits are known as *hemosiderin*.[1] Most of the storage iron in the body is normally in the form of ferritin, but with increasing degrees of iron overload the proportion of hemosiderin rises progressively. Ferritin consists of a protein shell surrounding an iron core, while hemosiderin results from the breakdown of ferritin in secondary lysosomes.[2,3] Ferritin appears to represent the end point of the intracellular storage iron pathway.[4] The apoprotein shell of ferritin (M_r = 480,000), which is made up of 24 subunits, encloses a core of iron in the form of ferric hydroxyphosphate[5,6] (Fig. 55-1). The core may contain up to 4500 atoms of iron. The inner cavity of the ferritin molecule communicates with the exterior via six channels which decrease in diameter from 1.7 nm at the inner surface to 0.9 to 1.3 nm at the outer.[7] It is through these channels that iron enters and leaves the molecule. Although ferritins are very similar in all species, preparations of ferritin from various tissues exhibit a good deal of heterogeneity even within the same subject. These differences are due to the presence of differing proportions of two subunits, the one (H) with M_r = 21,000 and the other (L) with M_r = 19,000.[8] The H subunit predominates in the more acidic ferritins present in the heart and the L subunit in the more basic ferritins of liver and spleen. There is only 55 percent homology between the two subunits.[9] Data obtained with cDNA clones suggest that a multigene family codes for the H and L subunits.[10,11] While the functional H and L subunits are coded for by genes on chromosomes 11 and 19, respectively,[12,13] multiple gene copies of H sequences have been detected.[9,14] H genes have been found on at least seven different chromosomes,[15,16] while L genes and related sequences are on at least three different chromosomes.[16] Presumably some of these sequences will be found to be pseudogenes.[17] However, others may be expressed in a tissue-specific or developmental manner. It is of interest that some H ferritin sequences have been localized to 3q21, the site of both the transferrin and the transferrin receptor genes, and others to 6p12—not far from the gene for hereditary hemochromatosis (see "Nature of the Metabolic Abnormality," below). Whether isoferritins have different physiological roles is not known.[18] While they are all able to store iron reversibly, acidic isoferritins contain a higher proportion of iron-rich molecules than do basic ones.[19] Iron loading of tissues is associated with an increase in the synthesis of the more basic ferritins.[19,20]

Table 55-1 Iron-Containing Compounds in Humans

	mg in a 75 kg male (approximate)	*mg/kg (approximate)*
Functional compounds		
Hemoglobin	2300	31
Myoglobin	320	4
Heme enzymes	80	1
Nonheme enzymes	100	1
	2800	
Storage complexes		
Ferritin	700	9
Hemosiderin	300	4
	1000	13
Total	3800	50

Uptake and Release of Iron by Ferritin. When iron enters tissues, their ferritin content rises. This is due not only to the incorporation of iron into preexisting apoferritin but also to the specific stimulation of apoferritin synthesis.[21] Regulation

Fig. 55-1 A model for ferritin iron uptake and release. *A.* Fe(II) enters the shell through channels and is bound at sites favoring oxidation (arrows). *B.* An Fe(III)OOH iron-core nucleus forms on the bound Fe(III). *C* and *D.* The microcrystal builds up by oxidation of further Fe(II) at its surface. The available surface for iron deposition (thick line) first increases and then decreases as the molecule fills. Iron is lost from the microcrystal surface, so that the last added iron is released first. *(From Harrison et al.[6] Used by permission.)*

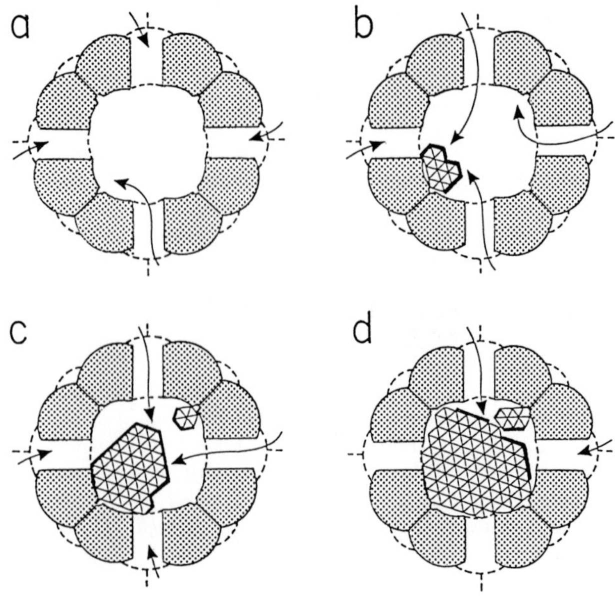

of ferritin synthesis appears to be controlled at both the transcriptional[22] and translational levels.[23,24] Ferritin mRNA is abundant in polyribosomes[25] in a form which is readily available for translation when iron is present in excess.[26] While apoferritin synthesis occurs mostly on free polyribosomes, as much as 20 percent may be made on membrane-bound polyribosomes.[27] In vitro observations suggest that iron deposition in ferritin involves the oxidation of Fe(II), catalyzed by the protein,[28] with molecular oxygen as electron acceptor.[29] This is followed by hydrolysis and deposition of the ferric oxyhydroxide in the interior of the protein shell. Iron may then be progressively deposited in the iron core particles until saturation is approached.[30] Iron stored as ferritin is readily available for deployment in functional compounds when required. Rat liver ferritin has a half-life of about 50 to 70 h,[31] and there is morphologic evidence that lysosomes are involved in its breakdown.[32] The iron so released may be converted to hemosiderin, or solubilized and stored again in fresh ferritin molecules, or incorporated into functional compounds. Iron can also be mobilized from ferritin without disruption of the molecule. In vitro this has been achieved using either Fe(III) chelators or reducing agents such as cysteine, glutathione, and ascorbic acid. However, the rates at which iron is mobilized by such means is slower than occurs physiologically. Of the biologic reductants that have been tested, by far the most rapid are the reduced riboflavins,[33] but their physiological role has not yet been defined.

Although ascorbic acid does not seem to be involved directly in the normal release of iron from ferritin, there is evidence that iron release from reticuloendothelial stores is impaired when there is a deficiency of the vitamin.[34–36] This may be due to the accelerated degradation of the protein shell of ferritin,[37] which leads to an increased hemosiderin/ferritin ratio[34] and a reduction in the intracellular pool of chelatable iron.[37]

Sites of Iron Storage. In normal subjects most of the body's iron reserve is present in roughly equal proportions in the liver, bone marrow, and skeletal muscles.[1] In the liver, 95 percent of the ferritin is in hepatocytes,[38] while most of the hemosiderin, which becomes visible at concentrations of iron greater than 0.1 percent dry weight, is present in Kupffer cells,[39] perhaps because there is less space available for storage in Kupffer cells, which are less than one-tenth the size of hepatocytes.[40] Storage iron in the bone marrow and spleen is confined to reticuloendothelial cells, and this may also be true for skeletal muscles.[41] The iron stored in hepatocytes is derived from the plasma transferrin[42] and to a lesser extent from hemoglobin-haptoglobin and heme-hemopexin complexes,[43] while reticuloendothelial cells derive their iron from broken down red cells.

Plasma Ferritin as a Measure of Storage Iron. Minute amounts of ferritin normally circulate in the plasma.[44] This ferritin is of low iron content[45,46] and probably has the same molecular weight as spleen ferritin.[45] While its origin is speculative, there is some evidence that plasma ferritin arises from reticuloendothelial cells.[47] The fact that a large proportion of the protein is glycosylated is in keeping with the concept that it is a secretory protein, arising in membrane-bound polyribosomes.[48,49] Tissue ferritin has a half-life in the plasma of only about 10 min,[50] while the sialated form, which is secreted by cells, has a longer half-life of about 50 h.[51] Ferritin is almost completely taken up by hepatocytes, which have been shown to have receptors for the molecule on their membranes.[52]

In normal subjects there is a close correlation between the plasma ferritin concentration and the size of the body iron stores, with each microgram per liter of ferritin being equivalent to about 8 mg storage iron.[53,54] The geometric mean value for normal adult males has been found to be approximately 100 μg/liter, and for premenopausal females about one-third of this.[55] The quite marked variations that have been noted to occur at different ages in the two sexes reflect the changes in iron nutritional status with development (Fig. 55-2).[56] In males consuming Western-type diets there is a steady rise in the plasma ferritin concentration throughout adult life, while a similar trend occurs in females after the menopause. These changes presumably reflect, at least in part, a slight positive iron balance with a slow buildup in iron stores. Plasma ferritin concentrations are relatively stable in healthy individuals.[44]

In iron deficiency the plasma ferritin concentration is always below 12 μg/liter,[57,58] while in iron overload it is greatly elevated. With increasing degrees of overload, the relationship between the plasma ferritin concentration and the size of the body iron stores becomes less precise. There are three possible reasons for this. First, the tissue damage associated with severe iron overload may lead to the release of ferritin especially from hepatocytes.[49,59] Second, there is some evidence that the secretion of glycosylated ferritin from reticuloendothelial cells

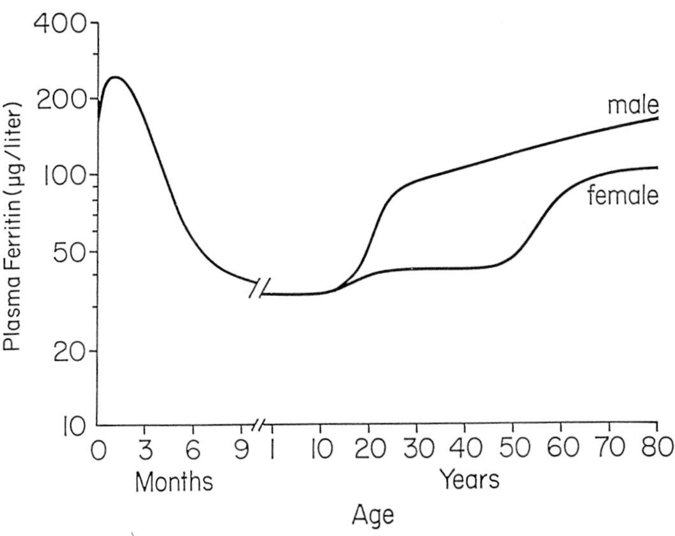

Fig. 55-2 The mean plasma ferritin concentration in American males and females at different ages. *(From Dallman et al.[56] Used by permission.)*

eventually reaches a plateau, perhaps reflecting a maximum rate of synthesis.[49] Third, ascorbic acid deficiency has been shown in guinea pigs to produce falsely low plasma ferritin concentrations,[60] and iron overload predisposes to ascorbic acid deficiency (see "Relationship between Iron Overload and Tissue Damage," below). A simple relationship between the plasma ferritin concentration and the size of the iron stores should therefore not be assumed with ferritin values above 4000 μg/liter or in patients who have received more than 100 units of transfused blood.[49]

There are several situations in which the plasma ferritin concentration may be inappropriately high for the size of the body iron stores. The first, hepatic damage, has already been mentioned. Particularly high values have been noted with viral and drug-induced liver disease.[58,59,61,62] Raised ferritin concentrations are also a feature of infection[58] and are due, at least in part, to the impaired reticuloendothelial iron release and consequential increase in iron stores. Other types of inflammatory reactions, such as those produced by endotoxin, surgical procedures,[63] and rheumatoid arthritis,[64] have also been shown to be associated with high plasma ferritin concentrations. The same is true of a number of neoplasms.[44,48,65,66] It is not clear whether the raised concentrations in neoplastic diseases are due to the production of specific carcinofetal ferritins, to liver damage, or to disturbances in iron metabolism induced by the tumor.[44,48,66]

Transferrin

Proteins specialized for the transport of iron (transferrins) have evolved in parallel with dependence on hemoglobin for oxygen transport, and they appear to be essential for the efficient distribution of iron.[1] Transferrin in the plasma picks up iron from donor cells, binds it very tightly, and delivers it to specific receptors on recipient cells. Only with such a system can the iron requirements of the erythroid marrow and the placenta, which are as much as a hundredfold greater than those of other tissues, be met. Plasma transferrin is also present in extracellular fluids, including lymph, cerebrospinal fluid, and edema fluid; as much as 50 to 60 percent of the total amount is extravascular. There is some evidence that transferrins are involved in intracellular as well as extracellular iron transport, e.g., in the transfer of iron across the intestinal mucous membrane during absorption,[67–69] but this is not generally accepted.[70–72]

Transferrin is a single chain polypeptide of 77,000 daltons[73] with two iron-binding sites, each residing in a similar domain.[74–76] Two identical doubly branched carbohydrate chains terminating in sialic acid are attached to asparaginyl residues.[77,78] Some 21 genetic variants have been identified by electrophoresis.[79,80] They probably represent single amino acid substitutions, since no differences in molecular weight, carbohydrate content, or iron distribution have been established. Although a number of tissues can synthesize transferrin, the origin of most of the plasma transferrin is the liver.[81] The human transferrin gene has been identified, characterized, and localized to band q21-25 on chromosome 3.[82]

The half-life of transferrin in the plasma is about 8 days. In normal subjects it is present in amounts capable of binding about 330 μg iron per deciliter of plasma. The concentration rises in iron deficiency and falls in iron overload; there is thus an inverse relationship with the plasma ferritin concentration.[58] The plasma transferrin concentration is also low in the nephrotic syndrome and in protein-losing enteropathies, protein malnutrition, hemolysis, and inflammation of various etiologies including infections, rheumatoid arthritis, myocardial infarction, and malignant neoplasms.[1] An increased transferrin concentration is found also in pregnancy, even when there is no iron deficiency, and in women taking estrogen-containing contraceptives,[1] because of a direct effect of estrogen on mRNA transcription.[83]

The iron-binding capacity of transferrin is normally only about one-third saturated, and the plasma iron concentration is of the order of 120 μg/dl. There is a considerable circadian variation in plasma iron concentration, with a morning peak and an evening trough, due principally to variation in the donation of iron to transferrin by the cells of the reticuloendothelial system.[84,85] There are also sizable day-to-day variations. Differences in the quantity of iron stored in the body have little effect on plasma iron concentration until the iron reserve has been exhausted, when the concentration falls. In iron deficiency anemia, this drop combines with the increased transferrin concentration to lower the transferrin saturation. Inflammation, whether of infective, traumatic, neoplastic, or other origin also lowers the plasma iron concentration by inhibiting reticuloendothelial iron release, but the concomitant fall in transferrin concentration results in the transferrin saturation being not as low as it is in iron deficiency.

The Binding and Release of Transferrin Iron. Transferrin binds iron at either or both of its binding sites, so that diferric and two monoferric transferrin species coexist with apotransferrin in the plasma, the proportions varying according to the percentage saturation. Differential loading and release can be achieved in vitro,[86,87] and there is experimental evidence that binding at one of the sites leads to preferential distribution of the iron to certain tissues.[88,89] However, loading of the two sites is random in vivo,[90] and there is no evidence of a differential tissue distribution.[76] Tissue uptake is a function of transferrin saturation, being considerably greater from diferric molecules,[91,92] and of the number of receptors for transferrin.

The receptor for transferrin is a glycoprotein that has been isolated, purified, and characterized.[93–96] Its gene has been cloned and sequenced[97–99] and mapped on chromosome 3q21-25.[82,100,101] Thus, the gene for transferrin and its receptor are located close to each other on the same chromosome. The receptor is a dimer with a single disulfide link, each component capable of binding a diferric transferrin molecule at the pH of the plasma[102,103] (Fig 55-3). During internalization of the complex, the receptor is phosphorylated via a calcium-calmodulin-protein kinase C-dependent mechanism.[104–106] The resultant endocytic vesicle is transported by saltatory motion along microtubular and microfilamentary tracts to the site of iron delivery.[107] There the pH is lowered by energy-dependent protonation,[108] which releases the iron. However, the apotransferrin remains bound to the receptor, preventing its transfer to the lysosome.[109–111] After the return of the vesicle to the exterior of the cell, the rise in pH releases the apotransferrin so that the receptor can bind with another diferric molecule. While this is the most efficient and quantitatively the most important mechanism for iron uptake from transferrin,[73,107,108,112,113] other receptor-mediated pathways have also been studied, mostly in hepatocytes.[114–120] Of these, the asialoglycoprotein receptor pathway is of particular interest since significant amounts of desialated transferrin circulate in subjects who abuse alcohol, and uptake of the desialated material by this receptor may play a part in alcoholic hepatic siderosis.[121]

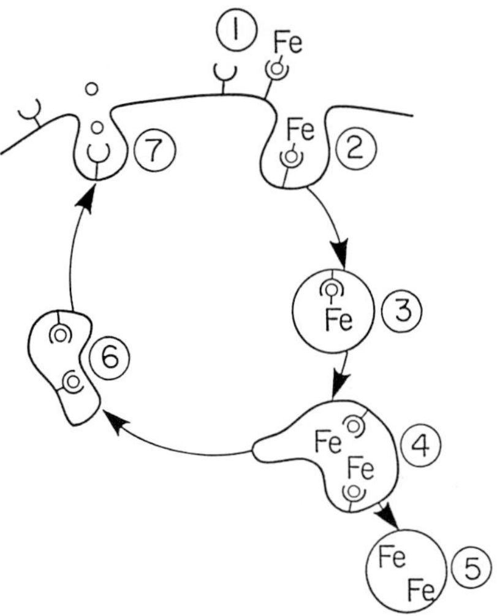

Fig. 55-3 The receptor-mediated endocytic pathway for transferrin. Specific binding of diferric transferrin to the transferrin receptor (1) results in the formation of an endocytic vesicle (2 and 3). The vesicle becomes protonated, which results in the uncoupling of the receptor and its ligand (4). In this acidic environment (4), iron is detached from transferrin (5). The apotransferrin so released has a high affinity for the transferrin receptor at the acidic pH within the endocytic vesicle and thus escapes digestion (6). The vesicle is then exteriorized (6 and 7). On exposure to the physiological pH (7), the apotransferrin loses its affinity for the transferrin receptor and is released into the plasma.

Internal Iron Exchange

Over the last several years a good measure of agreement has been obtained on quantitative aspects of internal iron exchange in health and disease.[122,123] These concepts have largely been developed from studies in which transferrin has been labeled with radioiron. Two approaches have been used. In one, the exchange of iron between plasma transferrin and individual tissues was studied in vivo and in vitro. In the other, attempts were made to characterize all internal iron exchange, and in particular the transport of iron by the erythroid marrow, by detailed analysis of the patterns of disappearance of transferrin-bound radioiron from the circulation and by its subsequent reappearance in erythrocytes.

Plasma iron follows three main pathways (Fig. 55-4). By far the largest fraction goes to the erythron, virtually all to be incorporated into hemoglobin. Radioiron appears within circulating erythrocytes after an interval during which cell maturation takes place within the marrow. There is a small "wastage" component due to intramedullary death of some red cells. Either these cells are phagocytosed in the reticuloendothelial system, or they release their hemoglobin to be bound to haptoglobin and transported to hepatocytes.[43] The second plasma iron pathway is to parenchymal cells, particularly those of the liver. The quantity normally is small, but if the erythroid marrow uptake is inhibited, virtually all the plasma iron can be deposited in the liver parenchyma.[42] The third pathway is to extravascular fluids.

Fig. 55-4 The approximate amounts of iron (milligrams per day) exchanging between different body compartments in a 70-kg subject. These data are largely based on ferrokinetic analyses. *(From Bothwell et al.[1] Used by permission.)*

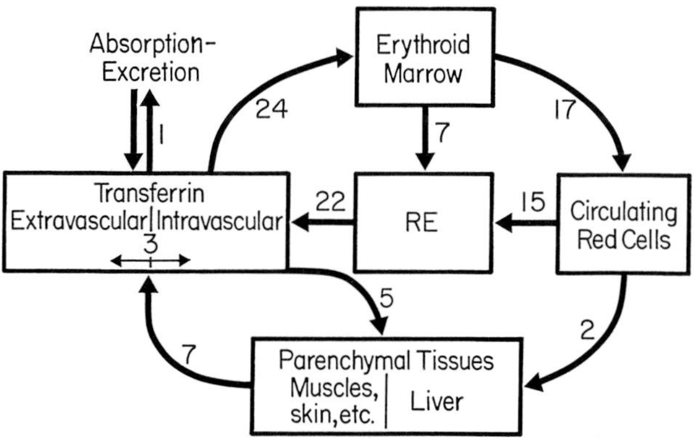

Most of the iron entering the plasma is contributed by the cells of the reticuloendothelial system. This iron is derived mainly from hemoglobin catabolism, but there is also a contribution from storage compounds. A much smaller fraction originates from stores in other tissues. About 3 percent of the plasma iron turnover is normally iron absorbed from the diet by the mucosal cells of the upper small intestine. Unless the body iron stores are exhausted, the supply of iron to the plasma iron pool is capable of adjustment within wide limits to match changing demands. The requirement for transferrin iron is determined by the major recipient, the erythroid marrow. In chronic hemolytic states, the quantity of iron passing through the plasma can increase six- to eightfold. This flux diminishes to one-third of normal on descending from high altitudes when erythropoiesis virtually ceases.[42] The regulation of release of iron from reticuloendothelial stores is rapid so that there are only transient changes in the plasma iron concentration. Little is known of how this homeostasis is achieved. Erythropoietic demand is reflected by the numbers of transferrin receptors, but except for the placenta in pregnancy, the number of receptors for transferrin is not known to vary among parenchymal cells. Parenchymal uptake of transferrin iron nevertheless does increase with the amount of transferrin iron in the plasma.[122]

External Iron Exchange

For adequate iron nutrition a positive iron balance is necessary during childhood and adolescence. In this way the growing demand of the body for functional iron is satisfied and storage depots are gradually built up. Thereafter, the amounts absorbed from the diet must at least match the average daily losses from the body. Additional amounts must be absorbed to meet the requirements of pregnancy and to replace any abnormal losses through blood donation or hemorrhage.

Iron Excretion. Iron is lost from the body physiologically by desquamation of surface cells from the skin and gastrointestinal and urinary tracts and from the minimal gastrointestinal blood loss which occurs even in healthy individuals. There are also very low concentrations of extracellular iron in the sweat, bile, and urine. In women the losses incurred through menstruation and pregnancy must be added. Using a variety of chemical and radioisotopic techniques, it has been possible to define these losses in moderately precise terms. Total daily iron losses in adult males amount to between 0.9 and 1 mg (12 to 14 μg/kg per day).[124] Most of this is from the gastrointestinal tract, with 0.45 mg due to blood loss and 0.15 mg from bile and desquamated cells.[124] A further 0.2 to 0.3 mg is shed from the skin, while daily urinary iron losses amount to 0.1 mg. It should be noted that skin losses are not increased significantly by the excessive sweating that occurs in hot, humid climates. Basal iron losses are affected by the iron content of the body, but to a limited degree. They are reduced to about half in iron deficiency[125] and may be increased up to twice normal in states of iron overload.[124]

Because of their smaller surface areas, basal daily losses in women would be expected to be correspondingly less, about 0.7 to 0.8 mg. The mean normal menstrual losses when expressed in terms of daily iron balance are approxiamtely 0.5 mg, but there is considerable variation, and it has been calculated that in 5 percent of normal women the figure is greater than 1.4 mg.[126] During pregnancy the requirement in women is even greater, since an expanding maternal red cell mass and a growing fetus and placenta must be supplied. It has been calculated that about 1 g of iron is needed for each pregnancy.[1] This is equivalent to an average daily requirement of between 5 and 6 mg throughout the last two trimesters. Not all this iron is lost to the body, since that present in the expanded maternal red cell mass is returned to stores at the end of pregnancy.

Iron Absorption. The amount of iron absorbed from the diet at any one time is dependent on three factors—the quantity of iron, the composition of the diet, and the behavior of the mucosa of the upper small bowel.

DIETARY IRON CONTENT. Typical Western diets usually contain about 6 mg iron per 1000 kcal, with surprisingly little variation from meal to meal.[127] In certain circumstances the iron content is appreciably increased by extrinsic iron, either in the form of dirt or from the surface of containers or cooking vessels. The former is usually of very low bioavailability,[128,129] but iron derived from pans or containers can add significantly to the absorbable iron intake, especially when the pH of the food being prepared in them is low.[130,131] This is strikingly illustrated by the traditional alcoholic beverages brewed in iron containers by Southern African blacks, whose daily iron intake may be increased from about 15 mg to as much as 100 mg as a result.[132]

BIOAVAILABILITY OF IRON. Variations in the bioavailiability of food iron are of greater importance for iron nutrition than is the amount of iron in the diet. Heme iron is easily absorbed whatever the dietary composition, whereas nonheme iron, usually of low bioavailability, is markedly influenced by other ingredients in the diet.[133,134] Heme iron is taken up by mucosal cells as such, and the iron within it is therefore not exposed to the effects of the many ligands in the diet which inhibit nonheme iron absorption.[135,136] In addition to containing heme, meat promotes the absorption of the various forms of nonheme iron present in a mixed diet,[137] possibly due to the release during digestion of amino acids which form stable complexes with iron.[138,139] The other single most important promoter of the absorption of nonheme iron is ascorbic acid,[140,141] which not only is a powerful reductant but also binds iron equimolarly. Its action is dose-dependent, and it is effective in a number of dietary settings.[142–144]

A number of inhibitors of iron absorption have been recognized.[145] These include bran,[146] the tannates in Indian tea,[147] the polyphenols in vegetables,[143] the phosphoprotein in egg yolk,[148] and a factor in soy protein.[149] The importance of phytates and some components of dietary fiber[143,150] is still unclear.[134,151–153]

To the effects of exogenous dietary ligands on nonheme iron absorption must be added those of the secretions of the upper intestinal tract. During peptic digestion a proportion of the nonheme iron in food is rendered ionizable[154] while heme is split from its globin bond.[155] Gastric hydrochloric acid plays a key role in this regard and has been shown to be necessary for the adequate absorption of ferric iron salts[156,157] and of nonheme food iron.[158] This is presumably because polymeric iron complexes are less likely to form at low pH. While other components of the gastrointestinal secretions must be relevant to iron absorption in that they promote digestion with release of iron from food, they do not contain a specific carrier.[1,158]

MUCOSAL BEHAVIOR. The most active site of iron absorption is the duodenum and upper jejunum.[159,160] There are two components to the absorptive mechanism, uptake from the lumen of the gut into the intestinal epithelial cells and transfer into the body. In animal studies it has been shown that the uptake of iron is linear over a wide range (0.1 to 5.0 m*M*),[161] but the slope varies depending on the recent dietary intake of iron[162] and on the amount of iron present in the body.[163] A proportion of the iron entering the mucosal cell is transferred to the portal circulation within minutes. Transfer continues at a much slower rate for 12 to 24 h, but some of the iron is stored as ferritin and is eventually discarded when the mucosal cells exfoliate.[164,165] The relative proportions following these alternative pathways depend on the requirement for iron, transfer being enhanced when iron deficiency is present and ferritin formation being maximal when the body is replete with iron.[166] The protein carrier which transports iron rapidly through mucosal cells may be transferrin. It has been suggested that transferrin secreted in the bile picks up dietary iron in the lumen of the gut and then transports it into mucosal cells,[167] but iron bound to transferrin is no better absorbed than is ferric chloride,[71] and it has not been possible to demonstrate transferrin receptors on the luminal borders of the mucosal cells.[160]

The amount of iron absorbed at any one time is markedly influenced by the body iron content (Fig. 55-5). Absorption is therefore inversely related to the plasma ferritin concentration, which reflects the body iron reserve.[55,168–171] In early animal

Fig. 55-5 The inverse relationship between the percentage absorption of a 3-mg dose of ferrous iron and the nonheme marrow iron concentration in a group of 50 subjects. *(From Bezwoda et al.[171] Used by permission.)*

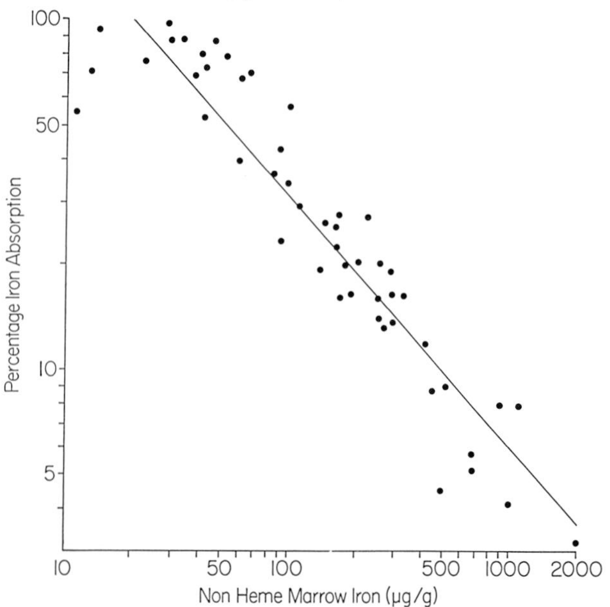

experiments a direct relationship was also noted between iron absorption and the rate of erythropoiesis,[172] but in humans the situation is more complicated. Absorption is not enhanced in chronic hemolytic states such as hereditary spherocytosis,[173] but it is increased in conditions such as thalassemia major which are characterized by markedly increased but ineffective erythropoietic activity. The tendency to absorb excessive iron is probably secondary to an inability of the iron stores to supply the markedly increased needs of the large but ineffective erythroid marrow.[174] While it has been suggested that there may be a separate genetic defect in thalassemia which is responsible for the increased absorption of iron,[175] this seems unlikely, since the absorption rate falls when erythropoiesis is depressed by raising the hemoglobin concentration.[176] The reason iron overload is not usually a feature of many other hemolytic syndromes is not clear, but it may be because the rate of erythropoiesis is usually less.[177] At the same time, there are several reports of significant iron overload in subjects with idiopathic refractory sideroblastic anemia[178] and hereditary spherocytosis.[179] Family studies suggested that the affected individuals were also heterozygous for the HLA-linked iron-loading gene.[178,179] However, these associations may have occurred by chance, since the HLA haplotype associated with iron loading was not found to occur with increased frequency in a group of subjects with idiopathic refractory sideroblastic anemia.[180]

The actual mechanisms involved in the control of iron absorption have not been elucidated. It has been suggested that the regulation is a local one, perhaps mediated by changes in the luminal secretions, the brush border receptors for iron, the intracellular transport protein, or the cells' ability to sequester ferritin,[181–184] but no definitive evidence favors any of these possibilities.[1] Attempts to demonstrate that the plasma iron transport system regulates iron absorption have been equally unsuccessful,[185,186] as have those involving a search for some humoral controlling mechanism.[187] Perhaps the most plausible of current hypotheses is that the iron content of individual tissues is itself a regulating factor.[188] A labile pool of iron available to transferrin is assumed to be present in all body tissues, the size of the pool in each tissue being proportional to that tissue's iron stores. Iron uptake from transferrin is determined by the requirements of the erythroid marrow, and each tissue supplies iron to transferrin in proportion to its iron pool (Fig. 55-6).[189] Thus, a decrease in tissue iron content results in an increased entrance of iron from the gut, while a rise in plasma iron turnover due to enhanced erythropoietic activity also results in increased iron absorption. Some experimental evidence supporting the hypothesis has been obtained in rats,[187,190] but the exact nature of the mechanism by which the output of iron by donor tissues is regulated to match requirements still eludes explanation.

Quantitative Aspects of Iron Absorption. Although the daily intake of dietary iron normally varies between 10 and 20 mg, the amount absorbed is much less than this.[136] In the adult iron-replete male consuming a mixed Western type diet, the amount of iron absorbed each day matches the obligatory basal losses of about 1.0 mg. Absorption is somewhat greater in the female during her reproductive years, since menstruation increases physiological losses to the equivalent of about 1.4 mg daily.[126] The absorptive behavior of the intestinal mucosa changes in an attempt to maintain the body iron content at optimal levels, but the amount of dietary iron that can be absorbed is limited because of its restricted bioavailability. Absorption thus rises to only 3 to 4 mg daily when the body is depleted of iron and falls to less than 0.5 mg daily when iron overload is present (Fig.55-7). These figures underline how small daily external iron exchange is in relation to the total body iron content.

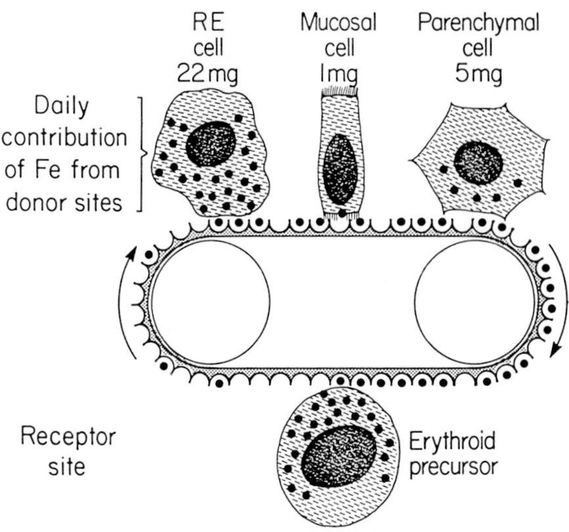

Fig. 55-6 The regulation of internal iron exchange. The plasma iron turnover is visualized as a conveyer belt driven by the uptake of transferrin iron by erythroid precursors. The amount of iron released at any one time from donor sites onto transferrin is dependent on the amounts of iron being removed by the erythroid precursors. *(From Hershko.[189] Used by permission.)*

One final point merits comment. In countries such as India, in which the population subsists on cereal diets containing little meat or ascorbic acid, the iron is even less bioavailable, and the body's ability to step up absorption is therefore even more restricted.

HEREDITARY HEMOCHROMATOSIS

An inherited metabolic abnormality, the nature of which has still to be established, leads to the absorption of more iron than is required, and massive quantities may eventually be present in the body in a proportion of affected individuals.[1] The process extends over many years. When the diagnosis is

Fig. 55-7 A diagrammatic representation of the average amounts of iron absorbed and excreted daily by normal, iron-deficient, and iron-loaded subjects consuming a Western-type diet.

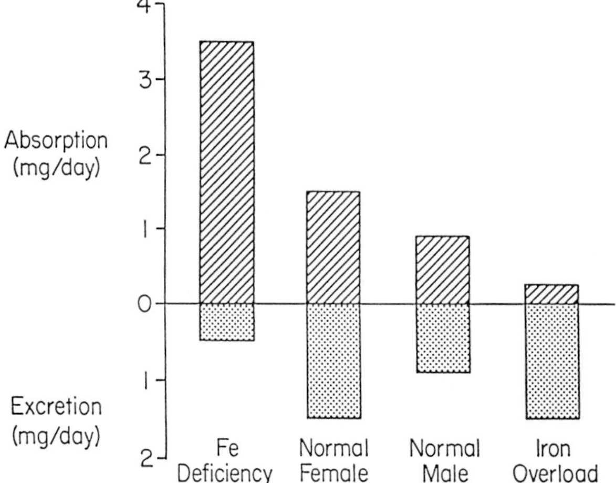

made clinically, cirrhosis and skin pigmentation are often present and may be accompanied by diabetes mellitus, hypogonadism, arthritis, or cardiac failure. Even in the asymptomatic stages, the plasma iron concentration and the plasma transferrin saturation may be high. Deposits of hemosiderin in the liver and other organs become more prominent as the years pass. Organ damage occurs only after markedly increased concentrations of storage iron have accumulated.

Genetics of Hereditary Hemochromatosis

Mode of Inheritance. Hereditary hemochromatosis is an inherited disease since abnormalities in iron metabolism can consistently be demonstrated among some relatives of affected patients.[191] This is not the case in families of patients with alcoholic cirrhosis who exhibit increased liver iron.[192] For many years the finding of detectable abnormalities in iron metabolism among offspring or parents of patients suggested autosomal dominant inheritance of the disease. More detailed studies of many families, however, have established that overt clinical hemochromatosis is less common than minor abnormalities in iron metabolism among children and parents. Full-blown clinical hemochromatosis is most frequently seen in the adult male sib.[191] Genetic analysis of such data led to the hypothesis that hereditary hemochromatosis was an autosomal recessive condition with expression of the full clinical disease largely limited to adult males, while the minor abnormalities in iron metabolism apparent in other family members were manifestations of the heterozygous state.[193,194] However, the problems of delayed clinical expression and the low manifestation rate in females made interpretation difficult, and no consensus regarding the mode of inheritance existed.

HLA Studies Clarify Autosomal Recessive Transmission. A fortuitous observation that HLA-A3 was frequently found among patients with hemochromatosis[195] was confirmed in many series of patients of European origin[196–205] and clarified the mode of inheritance.[191] While HLA-A3 occurs in no more than 30 percent of persons of European origin, it was present in 73 percent of 384 hemochromatotic patients in a collective series.[191] HLA-B14 was also found more frequently than among controls.[191] In contrast, the frequencies of HLA-A3 and HLA-B14 in patients with alcoholic cirrhosis and increased liver iron did not differ from those in controls.[206] Many different diseases have been observed to be associated with one or several HLA alleles. While the pathogenetic explanation of such associations often remains less than clear, the possibility of genetic linkage (i.e., the physical proximity of the HLA locus to a disease-producing gene) must always be considered, particularly when the HLA "association" occurs with a monogenic disease such as hereditary hemochromatosis.[207] Family investigations have indicated that the gene for hereditary hemochromatosis is in fact located in close proximity to the HLA complex, which includes the loci for HLA-A, -B, -DR, -DP, -DQ, and others on the short arm of chromosome 6, since it is usually transmitted together with the HLA haplotype.[208–210] Sibs with overt hemochromatosis in a given family usually share both their HLA haplotypes, i.e., have identical HLA alleles on both maternal and paternal chromosomes. Thus, a chromosomal segment comprising a gene for hereditary hemochromatosis and a linked group of HLA genes is contributed by *both* father and mother of each affected offspring (Fig. 55-8). These data establish homozygosity, or autosomal recessive inheritance for the disease. The genetic locus for hemochromatosis is clearly distinct from any of the HLA loci, since different HLA-A alleles—not only HLA-A3—may be found in various hemochromatosis kindreds. The A3-B7 and A3-B14 haplotypes are the most common.[205,211] Recombination between the hemochromatosis gene and the HLA gene is rare.[211] A recombination fraction of 1 percent has been calculated.[211] The gene for hereditary hemochromatosis appears to be located closer to the HLA-A locus than to the other HLA loci, and a location between the HLA-A and B loci closer to HLA-A has been suggested.[205,211] The use of DNA probes for this chromosomal region has been initiated[212] and promises to elucidate the nature of the hemochromatosis gene. As has already happened for other genetic diseases, the basic lesion of hemochromatosis may be clarified by "reverse genetics" (see Chap. 2). This means that the gene for hereditary hemochromatosis may be identified before an understanding of the underlying basic defect at the pathophysiological level has been accomplished.

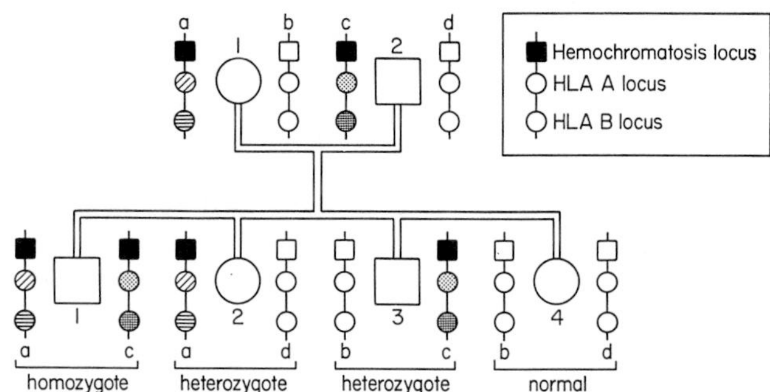

Fig. 55-8 Hypothetical distribution of iron-loading alleles, each designated by an HLA haplotype, among family members of a patient with fully developed hereditary hemochromatosis. The topographic relationships between the gene and the HLA loci are diagrammatic approximations. *(From Beaumont et al.[422] Used by permission.)*

Prevalence and Genetic Frequencies. Fully developed hereditary hemochromatosis is uncommon but not rare. By 1935, 350 well documented cases had been reported,[213] and during the next 20 years there were another 800.[214] Since 1955 many further reports have appeared.[215] Phenotypic expression of the gene obviously depends not only on the gene frequency in the population, but also on the amount of iron which can be absorbed from the average diet. Because this is limited, as has already been discussed, iron overload of any etiology occurs infrequently in most communities. In a study in which the storage iron concentrations in almost 4000 liver specimens from 18 countries were measured, only three were found to be more than five times normal, and none of these was anywhere near the hemochromatotic range of 20 to 50 times normal.[216] In addition, none of more than 3000 apparently normal individuals in the Seattle, Washington, area had a plasma ferritin concentration approaching that found in hereditary hemochromatosis.[217] In one comprehensive review, the prevalence of clinically or pathologically identifiable hereditary hemochromatosis was estimated to be 1 in 20,000 hospital admissions and 1 in 7000 deaths.[214] The prevalence in Olmstead County, Minnesota, was calculated to be 4 per 100,000,[215] but in Glasgow, Scotland, it was as high as 1 in 556 male necropsies or about 1 in 2500 male deaths.[218] In Malmo, Sweden, eight cases of hereditary hemochromatosis were detected in a carefully studied autopsy series of 8834 men for a frequency of 0.1 percent.[219]

Data from Utah and Brittany indicate that the gene does indeed occur a good deal more commonly than its clinical expression suggests.[208,220] As many as 8.4 percent and 10.5 percent, respectively, of the two populations were considered to be heterozygotes, yielding calculated homozygote frequencies of 1 in 319 and 1 in 400.

Several epidemiologic studies based solely on indices of iron metabolism (percent iron saturation, serum ferritin) also indicated a high percentage of the homozygous state. The resultant homozygote "disease" frequencies were: Canada, 0.27 percent;[221] Sweden (2 different studies), 0.5[222] and 0.24 percent;[223] United Kingdom, 0.3 percent;[224] South Africa (white Afrikaners), 1.3 percent.[225] Differentiation from heterozygosity for hemochromatosis was often difficult in these studies, and the results highlight the need for an unequivocal test for the disease that can be used in epidemiologic studies. The data suggest that the gene is one of the most common abnormal genes in populations of European origin.

With relatively rare recessive genes, one expects a higher frequency of consanguinity among parents of affected patients. This finding would be less likely with more common genes such as this one. The increased frequency of consanguinity in one of the early French studies is therefore hard to interpret.[194,226] It is necessary to hypothesize that there is a series of rare hemochromatosis alleles (h^1, h^2, h^3, etc.) which in the homozygous state (i.e., h^1h^1, h^2h^2, h^3h^3, etc.) but *not* in the compound heterozygous state (i.e., h^1h^2, h^2h^3, h^1h^3, etc.) are capable of producing the clinical picture of hereditary hemochromatosis. Mutational heterogeneity at the genetic locus for hereditary hemochromatosis remains a possibility; it is the rule in many genetic diseases.

If the hereditary hemochromatosis gene is common, matings between homozygous individuals and heterozygotes would not be infrequent. With a homozygote frequency of 1/500 (q^2), 8.5 percent of the population would be heterozygotes (2pq), and therefore 8.5 percent of all matings by homozygotes would be with a heterozygote. Since 50 percent of the children of homozygote × heterozygote matings would be homozygotes, the explanation for the observed "vertical" pedigree pattern mimicking autosomal dominant inheritance (i.e., psueododominance) is apparent.

Origin of the Gene. The reason for the high frequency of the HLA-linked iron-loading gene is unknown. It is possible that in the past heterozygotes had a selective advantage if they absorbed more dietary iron and were therefore relatively protected against developing iron deficiency with its deleterious effects.[227] It is conceivable that the accumulation of larger body iron reserves improved survival during infancy, childhood, and pregnancy in comparison with the rest of the population. As a result, there would have been a gradual increase in the frequency of the gene. Selection against subjects homozygous for hereditary hemochromatosis is minimal, since the disease usually exerts its harmful effects only after the reproductive period is over, at a time when such patients have transmitted their abnormal gene to their offspring. Alternatively, it is possible that the gene reached a high frequency because of "hitchhiking" with the closely linked HLA complex. According to this hypothesis, positive selection of an unknown nature would have resulted from possession not of the iron-loading gene, but of some other gene or genes in the HLA cluster.

The reason for the high frequency of HLA-A3 in affected individuals could mean that all iron-loading genes tagged with that HLA marker had a common origin. A mutation leading to increased iron absorption might have arisen on a chromosome carrying the HLA-A3 allele. Because of tight linkage, recombination would not have separated these genes over the generations, so that all current HLA-A3 alleles in hereditary hemochromatosis might be derived from a common ancestor in whom the mutation first occurred. Current data show an excess of HLA-A3 genes in patients from Germany, France, Belgium, England, Scotland, and Ireland, as well as from Australia and the United States. A Celtic origin with spread of the gene by migration has been postulated to account for these findings.[191] The hypothesis of a rare if not unique mutational origin of this gene with subsequent modification of HLA haplotypes by migration and by recombination at the HLA locus has been recently restated in a French study.[205] Alternatively, multiple mutations might have occurred and selective factors of an unknown nature preserved the linkage over many generations. This hypothesis would require a special selective advantage for the HLA-A3 gene (or a closely linked gene) over other HLA-A alleles. In this connection, examination of HLA types in populations other than those of European origin will be of interest. Were the HLA-A3 linkage with the iron-loading gene to be found also in non-European patients, then a common origin would be unlikely, and some selective advantage seems a more probable explanation.

In a study of the HLA haplotypes of hemochromatosis among South Africans of Afrikaans origin—a population that started with few founders, the expected "founder" effect in the form of a single haplotype was *not* detected.[205] Instead, among 10 hemochromatotic chromosomes carried by five randomly ascertained homozygous hemochromatosis patients, eight different HLA haplotypes were found.[225] These data suggest that the hemochromatosis gene attained its high frequency among European populations before 1652—the year of the European settlement of the South African Cape of Good Hope. The hemochromatosis gene was then introduced into the South African population by several persons with different haplotypes.

Nature of the Metabolic Abnormality

The nature of the metabolic abnormality responsible for the accumulation of unneeded iron awaits definition. From a theoretical standpoint, it could be due to a defect or defects at a number of sites. These include the lumen of the gut, the mucosal cells of the upper small intestine, the transferrin of plasma, the liver, and the reticuloendothelial system.

Initial claims that gastric secretions contain a glycoprotein, "gastroferrin," which normally inhibits iron absorption, and that this protein is absent in hereditary hemochromatosis[228] have not been confirmed in subsequent studies.[229,230] Of more potential interest has been the observation that there is less ferritin than would be expected in the mucosal cells of the upper gut,[181] although this, too, was not confirmed in a subsequent study.[231] A larger proportion than normal of the iron taken up by mucosal cells is transferred into the body,[166,232,233] and in vitro studies demonstrated increased uptake of iron by the mucosal cells of the duodenum.[234] The nature of this defect has not, however, been defined. The possibility that the increased absorption of iron might be secondary to an abnormality in the transferrin of plasma has been investigated, but with negative results. Transferrin from subjects with hereditary hemochromatosis takes up and releases iron normally.[235,236] Furthermore, studies in families whose members exhibit transferrin variants have shown that there is no correlation between the inheritance of transferrin and the HLA locus;[237] the genes coding for transferrin and its receptor are situated on chromosome 3,[82,101,238] whereas the hemochromatosis gene is on chromosome 6. A claim based on kinetic studies that the liver has an abnormal affinity for iron in the condition[239] does not seem tenable, since iron stored in the hemochromatotic liver is readily mobilized in response to venesection.[1] In addition, disturbances in the hepatic uptake of transferrin iron that have been described in hereditary hemochromatosis[240] are very similar to those found in alcoholic siderosis.[241] The suggestion that a deficiency of xanthine oxidase might be responsible[242] is no longer acceptable, since it is now known that the enzyme is not involved in the mobilization of iron from ferritin, and thus does not affect iron transport.[243,244] The hepatic isoferritin pattern is abnormal in patients with fully developed hereditary hemochromatosis,[245] but similar changes are found in other varieties of iron overload,[46,246] and revert to normal after removal of the excess iron.[247] All the current evidence indicates that ferritin is biochemically normal in the disease,[248] and its synthesis appears to be normal in a variety of tissues.[249–251] Finally, there is recent evidence that the functional H and L subunits of the protein are coded for on chromosomes 11 and 19, respectively,[12,13] and not chromosome 6. However, other ferritin gene sequences of yet unknown functional significance are located on 10 different chromosomes. Thus, a gene for the H subunit of ferritin could be assigned to chromosome 6p12—a site not far away from the HLA complex at 6p21 where the gene for hereditary hemochromatosis is located.[16] While this location is probably fortuitous and unrelated to the pathogenesis of hereditary hemochromatosis, the possibility of this ferritin gene somehow being involved in the disease needs to be kept in mind.

Further insight into the possible site or sites of the metabolic defect is provided by the distribution of the excess iron in those individuals who have developed the clinical disease. In every other variety of iron overload, large amounts are present in the reticuloendothelial cells, particularly of the spleen, bone marrow, and liver, with variable involvement of the parenchymal cells of the liver and other organs.[1] In hereditary hemochromatosis the parenchymal cells contain virtually all the hemosiderin deposits, and the reticuloendothelial system very little.[252] On the basis of these findings, it has been suggested that intestinal and reticuloendothelial cells have a common defect leading to reduced iron storage and the delivery of increased amounts of iron via the plasma to hepatocytes and other parenchymal cells.[1] Some support for this contention has been obtained in kinetic studies involving reticuloendothelial function in hereditary hemochromatosis.[85] A defect in storing iron, which is common to the two cell types, is certainly compatible with a number of observations in the condition including the paucity of iron present in these cells, the increased iron absorption, and the high percentage iron saturation of circulating transferrin, which is noted long before the accumulation of large amounts of iron. The deposition of iron in hepatocytes and other parenchymal tissues would then be expected to occur as a passive consequence of the saturated transferrin.[253] Current information on reticuloendothelial function in the disease is conflicting. In one series of studies, iron uptake by cultured monocytes from venesected subjects with the disease was found to be normal[254] as was ferritin synthesis,[251] while in another investigation increased transferrin receptor expression was demonstrated.[255]

Environmental Factors

Environmental factors play an important part in the phenotypic expression. It is obvious that surplus iron cannot be accumulated unless the diet permits the absorption of more iron than is required. Iron overload sufficient to produce organ damage and clinical manifestations can develop only very rarely in a country such as India, where the bioavailability of the dietary iron is poor, iron deficiency is rife, and storage iron concentrations in the liver are low. Indeed, it does not appear to have been reported. On the other hand, the heavy per capita consumption of meat, which contains bioavailable iron in the form of heme and promotes the absorption of the nonheme iron in the diet, must contribute to the high prevalence and relatively early age of presentation of fully developed hemochromatosis in Australia.[166,256]

Individuals who increase their iron intake by using iron cooking utensils or by consuming iron-containing medicinal preparations accelerate the appearance of the clinical phase of the disease. On the negative side of the iron balance equation, hookworm infestation could cause the elimination through intestinal blood loss of any superfluous iron absorbed, and regular blood donation would have a similar effect.

Alcohol and Iron Overload. The place of alcohol deserves special mention. In most published series a high proportion of patients with fully developed hereditary hemochromatosis have been more than moderate users of alcohol.[1] This was largely responsible for the former view that hemochromatosis was not a genetic disorder, but merely alcoholic or nutritional cirrhosis in subjects whose dietary intake of iron was high.[257] Certainly, the association of alcoholic cirrhosis with increased quantities of hepatic hemosiderin has been observed frequently. In Southern African blacks the severity of the unique variety of iron overload still commonly encountered there is closely related to the quantity of home-brewed alcohol consumed by the affected individual. There appear to be several reasons for these associations.[258]

The most obvious is the iron present in some varieties of alcoholic beverages. The beers indigenous to Southern Africa are based on millet and maize and are often brewed in pots or drums made of iron. During fermentation the iron content rises as the pH falls. The final mean concentration in one study was 40 mg/liter[259] and in another 15 mg/liter.[260] The alcohol content is low, and large quantities are regularly consumed by many adult males, so that an additional 50 to 100 mg of iron in a highly bioavailable form is ingested each day. This is several times more than the normal total dietary iron intake. The high bioavailability of the iron, equivalent to that of an inorganic ferric salt,[259] must be ascribed to the fermentation process, since equivalent amounts of iron added to porridge prepared from the ingredients before fermentation are very poorly absorbed.[261] Several factors contribute to the increase in bioavailability. These are the removal by filtration through cloth of most of the grits, which inhibit iron absorption; perhaps the alcohol itself, by potentiating the absorption of ferric iron; and probably certain small molecular fermentation products which serve as solubilizing ligands.[261] Alcoholic beverages in other parts of the world, notably certain red wines, have also been found to contain significant amounts of iron. While concentrations of up to 90 mg/liter have been reported,[262] values greater than 15 mg/liter are uncommon,[257,263] and the average for Italian wines was found to be only 6 mg/liter for the reds and about half this for the whites.[264] However, the bioavailability of this iron would be expected to be low, since the tannins which are present in red wines inhibit absorption. In one study only 6.8 percent of the iron in a Swiss red wine was absorbed by fasting normal subjects,[265] while in another the figure was 4.4 percent.[266]

While the dietary iron intake can thus be increased by certain alcoholic beverages, most varieties do not contain significant quantities. Distilled spirits in particular contain virtually none. Additional reasons must therefore be sought for the association between alcohol and iron overload. The enhancement of the absorption of ferric iron by alcohol mentioned above was demonstrated with a solution of ferric chloride in the fasting state, and appears to be ascribable to the stimulation of HCl secretion.[267] However, ethanol had no effect on the absorption of nonheme iron from a standard meal in another study.[268] Another possibility is that absorption is enhanced by an indirect mechanism, such as the ineffective erythropoiesis and increased plasma iron turnover resulting from the disordered folate metabolism which alcohol induces.[258,268] Alternatively, organ damage produced by alcohol may lead to increased iron absorption. The pancreas has been implicated,[269] but later work has not substantiated this.[270–272] The evidence indicating that liver disease might be responsible is weightier, since a number of workers observed enhanced iron absorption in some patients with cirrhosis.[273–277] Portacaval anastomosis seems to lead to an increase in the density of hemosiderin deposition in the liver cells,[278] but whether the body's store of iron is really increased or merely redistributed is less certain.[1] Absorption was not found to be increased on direct measurement.[279]

The position is thus far from clear. Alcohol abuse is certainly not always associated with an increase in the body iron content; in two carefully documented Swedish studies the iron stores were found to be within the normal range,[280,281] and in a group of distilled liquor drinkers the stores were actually lower than normal. Only 7 percent of 157 alcoholics with liver disease studied in London had significant hepatic siderosis,[282] while iron stores were only mildly raised in another group of alcoholics with liver disease of varying severity.[241] Why only a minority of alcoholics should exhibit siderosis is not known. In some instances it may reflect only a redistribution of body iron, but in others the amounts can be explained only by excessive iron absorption. The question has been raised as to whether alcoholics with siderosis may be homozygous or heterozygous for the hereditary hemochromatosis gene, but the results of several studies indicate that those with mild siderosis do not have an increased frequency of the HLA antigens associated with hereditary hemochromatosis.[208]

Despite the evidence that alcohol itself seldom, if ever, leads to severe iron overload, there is no doubting the validity of an association between an increased alcohol intake and the development of the clinical manifestations of hereditary hemochromatosis. Alcohol must contribute to the organ damage associated with iron overload, and therefore accelerate the onset of the clinical phase of the condition. This cannot be the only reason, however, since in one study the iron load of those subjects with hereditary hemochromatosis who had an alcoholic history was only slightly less than that of the nondrinkers[283] while in another it was actually 50 percent higher.[284]

A final syndrome in which iron overload and alcohol are associated deserves brief consideration, namely *porphyria cutanea tarda* (see Chap. 52). In sporadic porphyria cutanea tarda there is a reduction in hepatic heme synthesis due to decreased hepatic uroporphyrinogen decarboxylase activity, while in the familial variety both liver and erythrocyte uroporphyrinogen decarboxylase activity are decreased.[285] Molecular analysis in the hepatoerythropoietic variety using uroporphyrin decarboxylase cDNA has shown that the enzyme defect is due to rapid degradation of the protein.[286] Genetic studies suggest an autosomal dominant pattern of inheritance in the familial disease,[287] while there is some evidence that sporadic porphyria cutanea tarda is inherited as an autosomal recessive trait[285,288]; further confirmation is required.[289]

The urinary excretion of uroporphyrin, and usually also of coproporphyrin, is increased. Cutaneous lesions are found predominantly in sun-exposed areas and consist of increased skin fragility, milia, vesicles, bullae, and increased pigmentation.[287] The majority of patients give a history of prolonged consumption of excessive quantities of alcohol and on liver biopsy usually show some degree of siderosis, although it is typically only mild to moderate.[290,291] While it has been suggested that heterozygosity for the hereditary hemochromatosis gene is responsible for the hepatic siderosis in sporadic porphyria cutanea tarda,[288] there is no general agreement that this is so.[292] At the same time there is good evidence that the siderosis, irrespective of its cause, plays a part in the production of the clinical manifestations, since there are reports of clinical and biochemical remission following the removal of the iron either via phlebotomy[287,293,294] or deferoxamine.[295] The beneficial effects of removing iron are not surprising, since ferrous iron has been shown to inhibit uroporphyrinogen decarboxylase by direct competitive inhibition and by the generation of free radicals.[296] Furthermore, oxidation of the accumulating uroporphyrinogen to uroporphyrin may be potentiated by iron-enhanced lipid peroxidation.[297] Iron's role in the genesis of porphyria cutanea tarda may therefore be to accentuate the genetically determined enzyme deficiency. Iron overload is, however, not invariably present, and clinical and biochemical improvement may occur in siderotic individuals before significant amounts of iron have been removed by phlebotomy.[298] The association with alcoholism may be a direct one or may merely reflect the association between iron overload and the consumption of alcohol. It nevertheless seems clear that both the hereditary enzyme deficiency and some acquired factor must be present, and that the latter is frequently iron overload, with or without alcohol. In this context, it is of interest that the relative importance of different exogenous factors may be changing, and that estrogen-containing oral contraceptives now represent a significant exacerbating factor.[299]

Factors Influencing the Distribution of Iron in Iron Overload

The pattern of iron distribution in fully developed hereditary hemochromatosis is unique since most of the iron is confined to parenchymal cells throughout the body. Factors that appear to influence the distribution of iron in other forms or iron overload include the route of entry of the iron, the rate of red cell production, and the degree of ineffective erythropoiesis, the duration of the disease, the ascorbic acid nutrition, and the transferrin saturation.

In aplastic anemias, erythropoiesis is by definition inhibited, and the superfluous iron enters in the form of hemoglobin in the transfused blood. As the cells reach the end of their life span, they are engulfed by reticuloendothelial cells and the iron is deposited there. With time, though, some distribution to parenchymal tissues does occur, and indeed in pure red cell aplasia of childhood, marked parenchymal involvement may eventually develop.[300] On the other hand, in those anemias where much of the erythropoiesis in the hypercellular marrow is ineffective, the location of the iron is mostly parenchymal.[170] There appear to be several reasons for this. The plasma iron turnover is increased to several times normal, and the transferrin saturation is raised. In some of these conditions, notably β-thalassemia major, the transferrin is fully saturated, and there is iron present in the plasma that is not bound by transferrin;[301,302] such iron is deposited in parenchymal tissues.[1,303] Dietary iron absorption is enhanced[304] in addition to the iron loading via transfusion, any iron entering the portal venous system is removed by hepatocytes, if the binding capacity of transferrin is exceeded.[305] The extra hemoglobin released into the plasma by the disintegration of the faulty erythrocytes, which are produced in great numbers by the marrow, is also taken up by the hepatocytes.[43]

It might be anticipated that the distribution of orally derived iron would be predominantly parenchymal, but, except for hereditary hemochromatosis, this is not so. If experimental animals are given large amounts of oral iron, the deposits are almost entirely reticuloendothelial.[1] In Southern African blacks, dietary iron overload of hemochromatotic proportions is seen mainly in adult males with 20 or so years of regular beer drinking.[306] Reticuloendothelial siderosis is always very marked, particularly in the spleen, the bone marrow, and the Kupffer cells, but the hepatocytes contain equally heavy deposits of hemosiderin. Other parenchymal cells are not involved. The condition can therefore be distinguished from hereditary hemochromatosis by histologic examination of the liver.[307] Since the excess iron enters the portal system from the intestine, hepatocyte involvement is hardly surprising, but the reason for the reticuloendothelial localization of the remainder of the iron is not quite so obvious. In many of these subjects, ascorbic acid deficiency probably contributes to the retention of the iron by the reticuloendothelial cells. With the superimposition of the inadequate dietary intake of ascorbic acid which is common among urban black South Africans, the deficiency is frequently severe and even leads to frank clinical scurvy. In scorbutic guinea pigs, disordered release of iron to the plasma by the reticuloendothelial cells has been demonstrated, and they accumulate hemosiderin as a result.[34] In iron overloaded Southern African blacks, the injection of ascorbic acid produces an immediate rise in the plasma iron concentration, suggesting that reticuloendothelial iron release may be defective in them also. However, the predominantly reticuloendothelial localization of the iron in experimental oral iron overload is seen even when species not susceptible to scurvy are used, and this indicates that ascorbic acid deficiency cannot be solely responsible for the reticuloendothelial predominance. The main factor may simply be that much of the absorbed iron becomes incorporated into hemoglobin in the marrow. As a consequence, there is a concomitant reduction in the supply of iron from reticuloendothelial stores.[308] The same argument could obviously be applied to hereditary hemochromatosis, and the need to postulate an additional factor in the genetic disease is therefore apparent.

It is worth noting that the presence of micronodular cirrhosis in black Southern Africans with iron overload is associated with an increased deposition of hemosiderin in parenchymal cells, particularly in the heart; pituitary, thyroid, and adrenal glands; and pancreas.[309] Although micronodular cirrhosis is found much more commonly in subjects with severe iron overload than in those with little or no iron,[309,310] the parenchymal cell deposits in the cirrhotic individuals cannot be ascribed simply to the large quantity of iron in the body, since they are not seen in noncirrhotic subjects with equally heavy iron overload. The reason probably lies in the transferrin saturation, which is higher in the cirrhotic group,[1] and this leads to increased uptake of plasma iron by parenchymal cells, but why cirrhosis should be associated with a rise in the transferrin saturation is not known. Whatever the explanation, cirrhosis cannot be invoked as the reason for the parenchymal distribution of the iron in hereditary hemochromatosis, since it is seen before cirrhosis develops, and indeed very severe parenchymal loading with cardiac failure and hypogonadism has been observed in the absence of cirrhosis[311] and even in the absence of hepatic fibrosis.[284]

Pathogenesis of Symptomatic Hereditary Hemochromatosis

The clinical manifestations of hereditary hemochromatosis appear in those subjects homozygous for the gene whose diets have permitted the accumulation of toxic quantities of iron. In such individuals the body iron content is between 15 and 40 g, 5 to 10 times the normal quantity,[312] but all the additional iron is in storage compounds which are increased 20 to 50 times.[1,213,214,313,314] Since the positive iron balance is limited to a few milligrams per day, it is obvious that the accumulation of 20 to 40 g surplus iron takes many years. Most subjects are, therefore, ages 40 to 60 years at the time of diagnosis, although a number of younger patients have been described, including some in early adulthood[311] and even children.[315] The clinical manifestations of the disease are encountered approximately 10 times more frequently in males than in females because of the differences in iron uptake and iron losses. Also, the age of onset of clinical manifestations tends to be younger in males than in females.[214] In many affected females there is a history of scanty menstruation for several years preceding the onset of symptoms.[214]

At the time of diagnosis the absorption of iron may be increased,[316] but it is usually within the normal range.[1,215] A normal absorption rate in the presence of the grossly enlarged iron stores is actually inappropriately high.[53,317] During venesection therapy absorption rises to high levels, and it may remain above normal for years after phlebotomies have been discontinued.[230,279,318,319] These observations suggest that iron absorption is subject to the usual influences in each individual, but the setting of the control mechanism is higher than normal.

Pathologic and Clinical Findings in the Full-Blown Disease

The frequencies of clinical features are summarized in Fig. 55-9.[320] The storage iron concentration in the liver and pan-

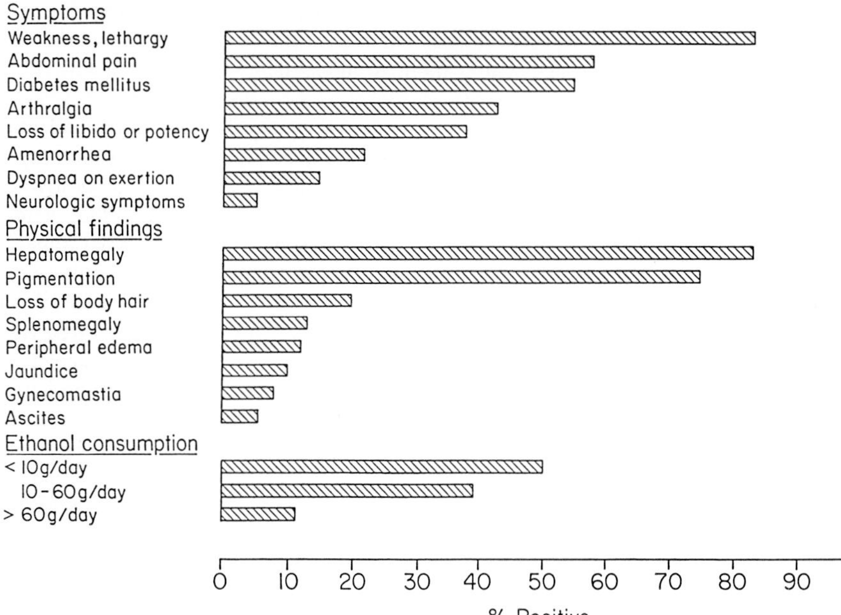

Fig. 55-9 Frequency of clinical features at the time of diagnosis in 163 patients with hereditary hemochromatosis. *(From Niederau et al.[320] Used by permission.)*

creas reaches 50 to 100 times the normal figures, in the thyroid about 25 times, in the heart and adrenal gland 10 to 15 times, and in the skin, spleen, kidney, and stomach about 5 times normal. The surplus iron is predominantly in the form of hemosiderin and is visible on histologic examination, particularly after staining with potassium ferrocyanide.

Skin. Pigmentation is virtually always present, although it may have developed so insidiously as not to have attracted the patient's notice. It is particularly prominent in exposed areas and old scars. It involves the conjunctiva and lid margin in about 30 percent of patients and the oral mucosa in 10 to 15 percent.[321] The pigmentation is due to melanin in the deeper layers of the epidermis, associated with increased amounts of hemosiderin in only about half of the cases. When present, it is most obvious in the sweat glands, but deposits can also be seen in vascular endothelium and in the connective tissue of the corium. The characteristic skin color is bronze, except in those individuals in whom iron deposits are present in addition to the melanin, where the color is slate gray. The skin is typically fine with soft and scanty facial, pubic, and axillary hair. Xerosis ranging in severity up to generalized ichthyosis has been reported in almost half the patients in a recent series, together with atrophy of both epidermis and dermis.[321]

Liver. The liver is usually considerably enlarged, the average weight being 2400 g, and is rusty red in color. A fine monolobular cirrhosis is almost invariably present, the lobules being typically separated by wide bands of fibrous tissue. A characteristic pattern of fibrosis and lobular disruption has been recognized in nonalcoholic subjects.[322] In young subjects, a lesser degree of fibrosis may occur,[311] and it may rarely be absent despite massive iron overload and damage to their tissues.[284] The striking feature in every case is the heavy deposition of hemosiderin granules in the hepatocytes. These deposits are scattered throughout the lobules, but a centripetal predominance can be discerned. The degree of hemosiderosis may vary from zone to zone and from lobule to lobule, tending to be less in areas of regeneration.[1] The bile duct epithelium also invariably contains heavy deposits of hemosiderin, but the amounts in Kupffer cells and in the fibrous connective tissue are far less than in some other forms of iron overload. The hepatocytes are mostly normal in size and staining quality, but may be larger at the edge of the lobules, with more prominent nucleoli and chromatin[323] especially in subjects with a history of excessive alcohol intake, in whom fatty change may also be present. As the cells degenerate, their nuclei become pyknotic and they release their iron to fibroblasts at the lobular periphery and in the portal spaces.

Severe portal hypertension is much less common than with Laennec's cirrhosis, and esophageal varices are seen less frequently. Clinical evidence of ascites is also not common, and in a recent series was associated with cardiac failure.[284] Palmar erythema and spider angiomas may be present, but gynecomastia is unusual. Hepatic function is typically not seriously deranged provided the individual does not drink alcohol excessively,[214,284] but episodes of acute hepatic failure may occur, often provoked by blood loss or surgical procedures. The serum albumin concentration is frequently within the normal range.[284] In half or more of the patients the plasma glutamic oxalacetic transaminase, alkaline phosphatase, and bilirubin concentrations are not elevated, and the prothrombin time is not prolonged. Minor changes in protein patterns have been recorded, and reflect impaired liver function or diabetes.

Hepatoma is an important late complication, and the frequency is about 200 times that in the general population.[320,324] It is always associated with cirrhosis,[320] and in one series developed in 13 of 112 patients with hemochromatotic cirrhosis. In the majority of these 13 patients, hepatomas developed after the successful removal of iron.[320] Malignant change is suggested by the onset of unexplained weight loss, fever, nodular enlargement of the liver, ascites, jaundice, abdominal pain, anemia, or insulin insensitivity.[214]

A picture of the evolution of hepatic pathology has been built up from the liver biopsies that have been performed on asymptomatic homozygous relatives of patients.[325] In the early stages discrete granules of hemosiderin can be seen in the hepatocytes, either finely dispersed throughout the liver lobules or in the focal scattered areas, especially peripherally. When greater quantities are present, it is aggregated into coarser masses and is more uniformly distributed. Marked hemosiderosis, equivalent to a storage iron concentration of at least 2.2 percent dry weight,[325] is associated with a slight to moderate increase in portal tract fibrosis.

Diabetes. Symptoms ascribable to the onset of diabetes, including weight loss, lassitude, and weakness, are frequently present at the time of diagnosis, and diminished glucose tolerance can be demonstrated in most subjects. In the past it was assumed that the diabetes of hemochromatosis is due to damage to the islets of Langerhans, and low levels of circulating insulin have indeed been demonstrated in some patients.[326] Extensive hemosiderin deposits are present in the pancreas, although they are more prominent in the exocrine than in the endocrine cells, and fibrosis is almost invariably present. However, it is now apparent that other factors play a greater part in the pathogenesis of the diabetes. The importance of heredity is revealed by the much greater prevalence of diabetes with high levels of circulating insulin among first-degree relatives of diabetic patients with hereditary hemochromatosis than among the first-degree relatives of nondiabetic hemochromatotics.[326–328] Hepatic damage may play a part, since cirrhosis is associated with both insulin resistance[329] and hyperglucagonemia.[330] Insulin resistance has also been demonstrated in noncirrhotic hemochromatosis patients whose glucose tolerance was normal[331]; it is suggested that this is caused by the iron in the hepatocytes. In summary, the diabetes that occurs in hemochromatosis may sometimes be ascribable to damage to the pancreas by iron, but it is usually due to a combination of iron overload, with or without cirrhosis, and genetic predisposition.

Although it has been stated that the vascular complications of diabetes occur uncommonly in hemochromatosis,[213] nephropathy, neuropathy, retinopathy, and peripheral vascular disease, either singly or together, have been reported in a significant percentage of patients.[1,326] The prevalence of retinopathy among subjects who have been diabetic for 10 or more years appears to be similar to that in nonhemochromatotic diabetics,[332] although it may possibly be not as severe.[333]

Hypogonadism. Diminished sexual function is a relatively frequent finding and is almost invariable in young subjects. Loss of libido, testicular atrophy, impotence, amenorrhea, and sparse body hair are common. The body hair may be scanty for many years before other manifestations of the disease appear. These are typical features of cirrhosis, but in hemochromatosis may be present before liver function is significantly impaired. Moreover, although testosterone levels are low in both conditions, the gynecomastia which is characteristic of other varieties of cirrhosis is uncommon in hemochromatosis. In contrast to alcoholic cirrhosis, plasma estrogen concentrations are not raised[334] and luteinizing hormone concentrations are low.[335] The hypogonadism is due to gonadotrophin deficiency, and the low responses to gonadotrophin releasing hormone suggest that the lesion is at the pituitary level.[336–338] A decrease in prolactin reserve has also been demonstrated.[338,339] In contrast, the secretion of other trophic pituitary hormones is not impaired.

Heart. Cardiac manifestations are the presenting feature in only 15 percent, but arrhythmias or cardiac failure eventually develop in more than one-third of untreated cases, the average age of onset being 56 years.[284] Ischemic heart disease may play a part in some of these individuals. In young subjects cardiac complications are more frequently the presenting feature and almost always the cause of death, which follows within a year of diagnosis unless the excess iron is removed.[1]

The onset may be acute with cardiac failure developing over a few days, and the pulmonary congestion and peripheral edema may be very severe. Clinically the picture is usually that of a congestive cardiomyopathy with bilateral ventricular dilatation. On radiographic investigation the cardiac profile has a globular appearance with a decrease in the amplitude of the cardiac pulsations. However, restrictive features have also been described.[1,340] On pathologic examination the weight of the heart is often two or three times normal. The ventricular walls are thickened, and iron pigment is visible in the myocardial fibers, especially in the perinuclear region. Degeneration, fragmentation, and necrosis of myocardial cells with fibrosis and interstitial edema have been described.[1,341]

Arrhythmias indicate a poor prognosis. Ventricular ectopic beats are the most common manifestation, but supraventricular and ventricular tachycardias, ventricular fibrillation, and varying degrees of heart block may also occur.[1] Other rather nonspecific EKG changes such as low voltage, left axis deviation, and flattening or inversion of T waves may be noted.

Joints. Arthropathy is present in 40 to 75 percent of subjects[320,342,343] and may be the presenting feature.[343–345] Chondrocalcinosis, due to the deposition of calcium pyrophosphate dihydrate crystals, can be demonstrated radiologically in one or more joints, most often the knees and the wrists. The incidence and severity increase as the years pass in spite of the removal of the iron by venesection therapy.[342] The chondrocalcinosis is typically asymptomatic, but in some subjects attacks of acute inflammatory synovitis occur (pseudogout). Similar findings in other forms of iron overload[346] suggest that the iron is directly responsible; it has been reported to inhibit pyrophosphatase activity and thus to interfere with the hydrolysis of pyrophosphate to soluble orthophosphate. Iron is present in the chondrocytes, but there is no constant relationship with the pyrophosphate crystals.[347] The synovial lining cells are heavily laden with hemosiderin; in contrast to rheumatoid arthritis the type B cells are more affected than the type A.[348]

Arthritis with loss of joint space, cysts, and destruction of articular surfaces also occurs. This manifestation is found mainly in the hands, primarily the second and third metacarpophalangeal joints. These features distinguish hemochromatotic chondrocalcinosis from the idiopathic variety.[349] Clinically there is bony swelling, deformity, and limitation of movement, usually without serious disablement.

Abdominal Pain and Infections. Abdominal pain occurs quite frequently and may be the presenting symptom. In such subjects, cirrhosis is usually demonstrable.[320] An aching sensation in the epigastrium or right hypochondrium, which may persist for long periods, is the commonest complaint. It may have a variety of causes, including peptic ulceration, hepatoma, variceal bleeding, ascites, cholecystitis, and nephrolithiasis.[284] The acute onset of severe pain, often associated with shock,[350] may be due to gram-negative peritonitis[350] and *Yersinia enterocolitica* has been particularly incriminated.[351–353] Unlike most microorganisms, this bacterium does not possess a high affinity iron chelating system and seldom causes systemic infections because it is unable to obtain sufficient iron from the internal environment of the body. However, it is able to proliferate in hereditary hemochromatosis and other varieties of iron overload where the transferrin is saturated and non-transferrin-bound iron may be present. *Pasteurella pseudotuberculosis*[354] and *Escherichia coli*[350] septicemias have also been described, and there is experimental and clinical evidence that iron loading enhances the susceptibility to a variety of other microorganisms.[1,355] In addition to making iron more easily available to the parasites, the iron overload was found to inhibit the phagocytic activity of the monocytes of a hemochromatotic patient with *Listeria monocytogenes* meningitis.[356] A similar inhibition of the neutrophil function was noted in frequently transfused patients on hemodialysis, who had more infectious episodes than others who were not iron-overloaded.[357] However, there is not a great deal of clinical evidence of increased susceptibility to infection in hereditary hemochromatosis.

Hematology. The rates of red cell production and destruction are normal, and erythropoiesis is effective.[42] Mild macrocytosis consistent with the liver disease may occur,[214] as may mild leukopenia and thrombocytopenia, presumably the result of hypersplenism. In about half the subjects iron-containing macrophages can be demonstrated in buffy coat preparations of venous blood.[358] An unexplained rise in the leukocyte count, uncontrolled diabetes, or cardiac failure should suggest the emergence of a hepatoma.[1] Blood coagulation studies are usually normal except for the hypoprothrombinemia that may accompany the liver disease.

The average weight of the spleen is about 400 g, somewhat above normal. Congestive changes secondary to portal hypertension may be present.[213] Hemosiderin deposits are not prominent, and they are usually confined to the capsule, blood vessel walls, and trabeculae. The iron concentrations in the spleen and bone marrow are low compared with other varieties of iron overload,[252,311] in keeping with the minimal reticuloendothelial involvement in the disease, although lymph nodes, especially those draining markedly siderotic organs, may contain hemosiderin.

Relationship Between Iron Overload and Tissue Damage

Parenchymal tissues are damaged by high concentrations of iron, whereas the effects on reticuloendothelial cells are minimal. Features common to severe parenchymal overload of whatever etiology are hepatic portal fibrosis and cirrhosis, cardiopathy, hypogonadism, and diabetes mellitus. Removal of the iron prevents the organ damage or arrests its progression (see "Prognosis," below).

Mechanisms of Chronic Iron Toxicity. In the presence of iron overload, *lipid peroxidation* can be demonstrated both in vivo[359–361] and in vitro.[362,363] The rate of peroxidation is a function of the iron concentration, and it is inhibited by the iron chelator deferoxamine as well as by antioxidants such as α-tocopherol. It has been suggested that the iron catalyzes the formation of oxygen free radicals which lead to lipid peroxidation,[364–366] but there is evidence suggesting that peroxidation may be initiated by a ferrous-dioxygen-ferric chelate complex rather than by free radicals.[367] However mediated, it is postulated that the lipid peroxidation involves intracellular organelle membranes and thus compromises cell function. Evidence of damage to lysosomes, mitochondria, and microsomes has been obtained. Excess iron accumulates in hepatocyte lysosomes, and their fragility increases in proportion to the hemosiderin content, suggesting that hydrolytic enzymes may be released intracellularly.[364,368–371] Both lipid peroxidation and inhibited oxidative metabolism have been demonstrated in mitochondria from iron-loaded hepatocytes,[372] together with a net efflux of potassium ions.[373] At higher iron concentrations microsomal lipid peroxidation has also been observed.[360]

Fibrosis is a feature of most organs containing excessive amounts of storage iron, even when there is little or no evidence of parenchymal cell damage. In the liver it appears when concentrations above 2.2 percent dry weight are reached,[325] and the evidence indicates that collagen synthesis is directly stimulated.[374–376] In rat experiments the activity of a key enzyme in the biosynthetic pathway, prolyl hydroxylase, is increased, the hydroxyproline content rises, and before collagen is visible by light microscopy, electron microscopy reveals collagen fibrils adjacent to the hepatocytes although no fibroblasts, inflammatory cells, or damage to hepatocyte organelles are visible.[377]

A third consequence of iron overload is *ascorbic acid depletion*. A proportion of the available dietary ascorbic acid is irreversibly oxidized. Administration of large amounts of ascorbic acid to normal subjects soon leads to the excretion of most of the dose unchanged in the urine, but if iron overload is present, there is instead an increase in the excretion of the oxidation product oxalic acid.[378] With physiological amounts of ascorbic acid, the major oxidation product is carbon dioxide.[379] Since ferric iron catalyzes the first step in the oxidation sequence in vitro, the accumulation of ferric iron in the tissues is presumably responsible. The severity of the resultant ascorbic acid deficiency is determined by the dietary intake of ascorbic acid; clinical scurvy is seen in siderotic Southern African blacks mainly in late winter and early spring, when the dietary ascorbic acid content is at its lowest. Even in well nourished subjects, however, mild to moderate ascorbic acid deficiency is frequently demonstrable, for example, by measuring the leukocyte ascorbic acid concentration, and this is so in hereditary hemochromatosis and iron-loading anemias as well as in dietary iron overload.[380–383]

Chronic low grade ascorbic acid deficiency may have metabolic consequences even if it does not reach scorbutic proportions. Tryptophan metabolism has been reported to be adversely affected.[384] Of possibly greater significance is the circumstantial evidence that chronic ascorbic acid deficiency can lead to osteoporosis. Osteoporosis of the spine[385,386] and the femoral head[387] is frequently present in middle-aged Southern African black males with iron overload, but not in the absence of siderosis, and osteoporosis is not common in elderly women in this population. The mineral density of the iliac crest bone has been shown to be inversely correlated with the concentration of storage iron in the liver.[386] The ascorbic acid nutrition of these subjects is also inversely related to the severity of the iron overload.[386] In experimental animals and in children, scurvy causes osteoporosis,[1] presumably because ascorbic acid is needed for osteogenesis, for the synthesis of bone collagen, for the formation of osteoid, and for osteoblast maturation. The expected reduction in bone formation surface was found when semiquantitative microradiography was applied to the osteoporotic bones of guinea pigs deficient in ascorbic acid, but there was, in addition, an increase in bone resorption surface.[380] In iron-overloaded blacks with osteoporosis, the bone resorption surface was also increased.[380] Experiments with radiocalcium suggested that these subjects had both reduced bone formation and enhanced bone resorption, and when ascorbic acid was administered, the urinary calcium excretion fell.[388] It has been postulated that the iron overload leads to chronic ascorbic acid deficiency and that this, in turn, produces osteoporosis. Support for the hypothesis was provided by an experiment with guinea pigs.[380] On a diet which kept the control animals healthy, the group overloaded with iron by repeated injections of iron dextran had very low hepatic ascorbic acid concentrations and diminished bone mineral density after several months. These changes were prevented by administering large parenteral ascorbic acid supplements to a third group. It should be noted, however, that iron-loaded pigs (a species which does not require dietary ascorbic acid) showed no decrease in serum ascorbic acid levels, although bone formation was inhibited.[389]

Osteoporosis has been described in fully developed hereditary hemochromatosis.[390,391] The prevalence has not been established, but it may be influenced by the amount of ascorbic acid in the habitual diet.

Diagnosis of Hereditary Hemochromatosis

The diagnosis of symptomatic hereditary hemochromatosis should be suspected from the history and the characteristic physical findings and confirmed by demonstrating the presence of grossly increased iron stores in parenchymal tissues through laboratory investigations. It is essential to cultivate a high index of suspicion. Recognition of the classic triad of cirrhosis, diabetes, and hyperpigmentation is relatively easy, but many cases will be missed unless hemochromatosis is thought of whenever these findings are encountered individually, and also as a possible cause of cardiopathy, arthritis, impotence or sterility, abdominal pain, weakness, tiredness, asymptomatic hepatomegaly, or unexplained elevation of serum transaminases, alone or in combination. Findings compatible with hemochromatosis should trigger further investigation even when the patient's complaints do not appear to be related to iron overload; as many as half the subjects identified in a recent study[392] fell into this category. Even if asymptomatic, the first-degree relatives of probands should be screened. Vigilance and diligence are mandatory because removal of the iron before organ damage has occurred converts a life-threatening disease into one which is associated with a normal life expectancy.

In addition to establishing the presence of hemochromatosis, the presence and extent of associated organ damage should be established, but a detailed discussion of the special tests used for the assessment of hepatic, cardiac, endocrine, or pancreatic function is beyond the scope of this chapter.

The plasma iron concentration, the transferrin saturation, and the plasma ferritin concentration should first be estimated. The *plasma iron concentration* is typically over 200 μg/dl if the iron overload is severe, and it may be high even before the body iron content is significantly increased.[393,394] In as many as one-third of young asymptomatic homozygotes, however, it may be less than two standard deviations above the mean.[394] Furthermore, a high plasma iron concentration, especially on a single measurement, may be due to causes other than iron overload, e.g., iron medication.

More useful diagnostically than the plasma iron concentration is the *transferrin saturation*. Values greater than 90 percent are typical of fully developed hereditary hemochromatosis; in most such subjects the transferrin is actually fully saturated, but methodological deficiencies make it appear as if there is up to 40 μg/dl unsaturated iron-binding capacity.[395] Intercurrent infection or hepatoma may lower the transferrin saturation. For identifying the homozygous relatives of hemochromatotic probands, the transferrin saturation is valuable: a figure of 70 percent or more is virtually diagnostic, and values rising from 50 to 70 percent indicate homozygosity with increasing probability.[392,394,396] However, in as many as 16 percent of young homozygous relatives identified by HLA typing, the transferrin saturation was less than 50 percent on initial examination.[394] Conversely, a significant number of relatives with transferrin saturations greater than 50 percent are heterozygotes or noncarriers.[392] These studies have made it clear that while heterozygotes may exhibit abnormalities in iron transport, they do not develop significant iron overload.

The *plasma ferritin concentration* provides a useful estimate of the quantity of iron in the body. In untreated fully developed hereditary hemochromatosis, the values are typically several thousand micrograms per liter, and although the amount of storage iron cannot be calculated with absolute precision (see "Plasma Ferritin as a Measure of Storage Iron," above), the progress of venesection therapy can be monitored by following the decrease in the ferritin concentration.[284,397] Valuable though this test has proved to be, it is not infallible. Both false positive and false negative results occur. Causes of an elevated plasma ferritin concentration other than enlarged iron stores have been considered in a previous section. Falsely low concentrations may be due to laboratory error. In addition, three families have been described in which the asymptomatic relatives of patients with full-blown hereditary hemochromatosis had normal plasma ferritin concentrations in spite of considerably increased iron stores.[398,399] Whether this represents a different variety of hemochromatosis, an impairment in the production of plasma ferritin, or an antigenic variation resulting in falsely low estimates, is not yet clear.

The plasma ferritin concentration will not be elevated in homozygotes with hereditary hemochromatosis who have not accumulated excess storage iron. Fifteen percent of the young homozygous relatives of subjects with hereditary hemochromatosis had plasma ferritin concentrations within the normal range.[394] However, only two (a 17-year-old girl and a 15-year-old boy) of 34 such individuals had normal values for all three of the screening tests, namely, the plasma iron concentration, transferrin saturation, and plasma ferritin concentration. Two years later, the results for these two individuals also were abnormal. The value of this combination of three tests as a screen for homozygosity is therefore high.[394]

Clinical suspicion reinforced by positive results usually justifies proceeding immediately to *needle biopsy of the liver*, but there are exceptions. If there is a reasonable possibility that the high plasma ferritin concentration may reflect inflammation or neoplasm rather than iron overload, other tests should first be performed to clarify the position. On the other hand, young asymptomatic relatives of hemochromatotic patients shown to be homozygous by HLA typing, but whose plasma ferritin concentrations are less than 70 μg/dl, need not be subjected to liver biopsy since hepatic fibrosis or cirrhosis does not occur until the accumulation of storage iron has proceeded well beyond the quantity reflected by this figure.[394] Under all other circumstances, however, a biopsy should be taken for histologic and chemical examination. On light microscopy the predominantly parenchymal localization of the hemosiderin, which helps to distinguish hereditary hemochromatosis from other forms of iron overload,[307] can be observed, as well as the presence or absence of cirrhosis, which has great prognostic significance as discussed in a later section. The iron concentration may be measured by either a chemical technique[400] or atomic absorption spectrophotometry.[401]

If further evidence of iron overload is needed, several noninvasive methods are available. The *quantity of iron excreted in the urine after injecting a chelator* correlates with the amount of mobilizable storage iron, particularly in parenchymal tissues.[284] A convenient method is to inject 10 mg deferoxamine per kilogram body weight intramuscularly and measure the iron content of the urine passed during the following 24 h.[280] Various elaborations of this test have been described,[402] but they are unnecessary for the diagnosis of iron overload.[1]

Several newer noninvasive techniques for estimating the degree of iron overload have been developed. *Computed tomography* can be used to measure the iron content of the liver; the liver attenuation coefficient has been shown to correlate with both the hepatic iron concentration and the amount of storage iron subsequently removed by repeated phlebotomies.[403] Falsely low values may be obtained if significant fatty infiltration is present. The paramagnetic properties of hemosiderin and ferritin permit the use of a superconducting quantum-interference device to measure the *hepatic magnetic susceptibility,* which is very closely correlated with the hepatic iron concentration.[404] *Nuclear magnetic resonance* techniques promise to prove useful,[405] as does the measurement of *nuclear resonance scattering* of γ rays.[406]

The total amount of storage iron in the body can also be estimated retrospectively by performing *weekly phlebotomies.* Iron is mobilized from the tissue deposits to replace that in the blood removed by venesection, and the hemoglobin concentration is maintained until the stored iron is exhausted. In normal subjects this occurs between the third and fourth weeks, after the removal of about 1 g iron as hemoglobin. In full-blown hereditary hemochromatosis, the phlebotomies can be continued for many months before the hemoglobin falls. The quantity of iron removed before this occurs reflects the amount of storage iron originally present and can be calculated from the hemoglobin content of blood removed.[214]

Radioiron absorption studies have no place in the diagnosis of fully developed hemochromatosis since values within the normal range are found in most cases.[215] On the other hand, the measurement of radioiron absorption may be helpful in uncovering affected relatives, if the storage iron status of the individual is taken into account.[317] A test relating the plasma ferritin concentration to the postprandial plasma iron concentration has been described for this purpose.[319]

Several methods of diagnosis used in the past have fallen into disfavor because they are not quantitative and are unreliable. They include the demonstration of hemosiderin in the urine, in the skin, in the stomach mucosa, and in the reticuloendothelial cells of the bone marrow.[1] Claims that ferrokinetic measurements can be used to distinguish between cirrhosis with hyperferremia and hereditary hemochromatosis are no longer accepted, the earlier finding of greater nonerythroid iron turnover possibly being ascribable to incomplete transferrin binding of the injected radioiron.[42]

Differential Diagnosis

The differential diagnosis of fully developed hereditary hemochromatosis poses only two real problems. The first is solved by excluding the presence of thalassemia or one of the other chronic iron-loading anemias. This is usually simple, although in thalassemia intermedia and refractory sideroblastic anemia a hemoglobin concentration closer to the normal can lead to diagnostic error. The second diagnostic differentiation, the separation of alcoholic cirrhosis with significant hemosiderin deposits in the liver from hereditary hemochromatosis in subjects who abuse alcohol, poses a greater challenge. It cannot be too strongly stated that the key to this conundrum is the quantity of hepatic iron, and this should be established by chemical analysis rather than by relying on histologic grading. The cellular localization of the hemosiderin does provide a useful clue, however. If there is little Kupffer cell involvement, hereditary hemochromatosis is probable.[307] But it is the concentration of storage iron which is critical, and, by using HLA typing to identify homozygotes, it has been firmly established that figures in the hemochromatotic range (about 2% dry weight, equivalent to about 5.0 mg per 100 mg wet weight in units used below) are not found in alcoholic cirrhosis.[206,407] In most alcoholic cirrhotic patients the hepatic iron concentration is not more than twice the upper limit of normal.[394,407] The dietary siderosis of Southern Africa represents a special situation not encountered elsewhere.

In a prospective study[283] of 61 subjects selected solely on the basis of heavy hepatic hemosiderin deposits with fibrosis or cirrhosis, there were no significant differences between those with and those without a history of excessive alcohol consumption with respect to affected relatives and the prevalence of HLA antigens associated with hereditary hemochromatosis. It was concluded that they were all homozygous for hereditary hemochromatosis and that alcoholism in subjects who have not inherited a double dose of the hereditary hemochromatosis genes does not lead to siderosis of hemochromatotic proportions.

Treatment

Diabetes, hepatic failure, and cardiac failure should be managed along conventional lines. Loss of libido and secondary sexual characteristics are often benefited by the administration of androgens.[1] In addition to this supportive treatment, it is essential to undertake definitive therapy in the form of the *removal of the excess iron.* The method of choice is repeated venesection.[1] The quantity of iron removed with each 500 ml of blood depends on the hemoglobin concentration but is usually about 200 to 250 mg. The erythroid marrow responds to the induced anemia by stepping up the rate of erythropoiesis, and iron is mobilized from the tissues to replace that which has been removed. Most patients tolerate the removal of 500 ml of blood every week for prolonged periods, and even more frequent venesections may be possible.[408] Before initiating the venesection program, it is important to assess the degree of cardiac involvement, clinically and by special investigations including radiography, electrocardiography, and echocardiography.[409] Since myocardial irritability with attendant arrhythmias may be aggravated by the mobilization of free iron, continuous infusions of deferoxamine (see "Hemochromatosis in Refractory Anemias," below) may have to be administered while the initial venesections are cautiously performed. β-Adrenergic blocking agents have proved to be valuable for controlling supraventricular tachycardias.

The hemoglobin concentration initially falls somewhat, but the hematocrit soon returns to within 10 percent of its initial level (Fig. 55-10). It should be measured before each weekly phlebotomy, and the plasma iron and ferritin concentration should be estimated each month, so that progress with the

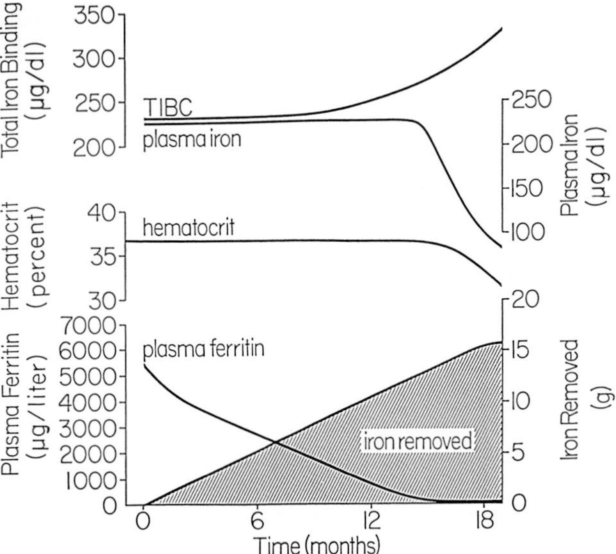

Fig. 55-10 Serial changes in the hematocrit, plasma iron concentration, total iron-binding capacity, and plasma ferritin concentration in a subject with hereditary hemochromatosis on repeated venesection therapy. *(From Bothwell et al.*[1] *Used by permission.)*

elimination of the excess iron can be monitored. Two to three years of venesection therapy are usually required to remove the iron, but in some patients less is present and the treatment is correspondingly shorter.[410] After the excess has been eliminated, reaccumulaiton can be prevented by venesection every 2 to 3 months. Typically the plasma iron concentration remains high until tissue iron stores are almost exhausted, but occasionally a pseudo-iron-deficient state may occur while abundant iron is still present in the tissues. This may be due to the development of a hepatoma, or else to ascorbic acid deficiency, which inhibits the mobilization of storage iron.[34] If the venesection rate is reduced for a period, a satisfactory response usually returns. Ascorbic acid supplements can be administered, but this should be done cautiously since there is some evidence that the repair of the ascorbic acid deficiency may result in parenchymal cell damage, notably to the myocardium,[411] perhaps by facilitating lipid peroxidation.[412] The ascorbic acid deficiency, which is a consequence of iron overload (see "Relationship between Iron Overload and Tissue Damage," above), may actually be protective.

The plasma albumin concentration is usually well maintained during the venesection program, although it is reasonable to prescribe a moderately high protein diet. In alcoholic subjects the liver damage may lead to hypoproteinemia, and plasma may have to be replaced. If the restrictive form of cardiomyopathy is present, it may be necessary to infuse plasma while the venesection is being performed in order to prevent hypovolemic shock.[1] It is not worth attempting to restrict the dietary intake of iron, since the amount absorbed is small in relation to the quantities being removed.

Chelating agents, of which the iron-specific deferoxamine is the best, can be used to remove excess iron from the body. Indeed, it is the only treatment available for the iron overload secondary to refractory anemias. However, the rate of removal of iron is slower than with venesection unless continuous daily infusion techniques are used.[413–415] Deferoxamine is expensive and the parenteral route of administration inconvenient; the search for orally effective agents continues.[416]

Prognosis

If the iron is not removed, the 5-year survival after diagnosis is 18 percent, and the 10-year survival, 6 percent.[417] Removing the iron improves the prognosis dramatically. In a large long-term study,[320] the life expectancy in those patients in whom cirrhosis was not present when phlebotomies were initiated reverted to normal. Even in those with cirrhosis, the 10-year survival was over 75 percent, better than that in other forms of cirrhosis (Fig. 55-11). However, the prognosis in subjects with the clinical and biochemical features of markedly disordered liver function and portal hypertension was grave: of 10 such patients, seven died before all the iron could be removed. Not surprisingly, the survival of subjects with diabetes was significantly shorter than that of the nondiabetic individuals. Heavy iron loading also carried a worse prognosis, even for those who were successfully depleted of iron, presumably because of the greater organ damage; cirrhosis does not develop in nonalcoholic subjects at liver iron concentrations less than 2.2 percent dry weight.[325] The 13 patients who died from hepatoma (8 percent of the 163 subjects in this series)[320] had the

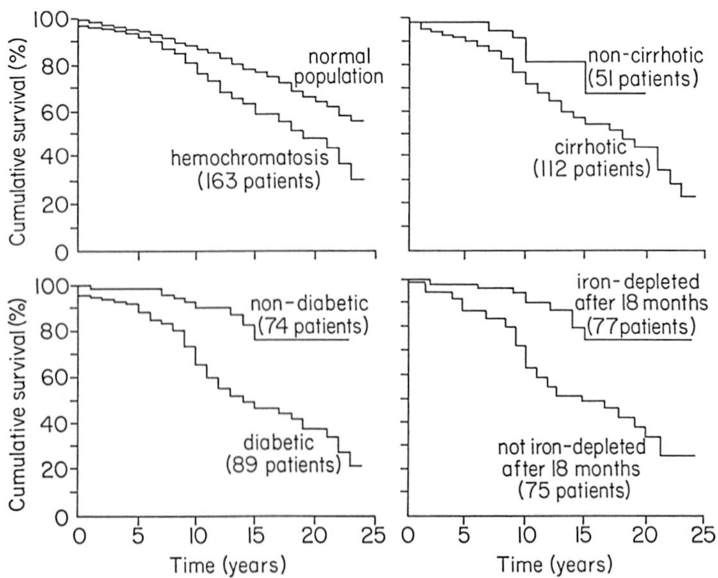

Fig. 55-11 Cumulative survival in 163 patients with hereditary hemochromatosis. Survival was significantly reduced in comparison with the normal population. Results in various subgroups indicated that diabetes, cirrhosis, and inadequate venesection therapy adversely affected prognosis. The survival rate in the 51 noncirrhotic patients was not significantly different from that in normal subjects. *(From Niederau et al.*[320] *Used by permission.)*

highest pretreatment iron loads, and in 11 of them, the iron had been removed 3 to 19 years previously (mean 9.1 years). In an earlier study as many as 29 percent of treated subjects eventually died of hepatoma.[417] Hepatoma has not been observed in subjects who have been relieved of the iron overload before the development of cirrhosis.[320] Alcoholism is a further adverse factor; 17 of 18 subjects whose consumption was more than 60 g/day had cirrhosis,[320] and more alcoholics than nonalcoholics died before the iron could be removed.[319]

After elimination of the iron, the cardiopathy usually regresses,[1,418] the pigmentation disappears, and hepatic funciton improves in 50 to 70 percent of subjects.[320,417] While some reduction in hepatic fibrosis may occur, cirrhosis and portal hypertension are not reversed and the risk of hepatoma is not diminished. In about half the insulin-dependent diabetics, the dose can be reduced. Arthralgia improves in about one-third, although it may also worsen.[342] The chance of improved sexual function is slight.[320]

Detection of Affected Family Members

Since hereditary hemochromatosis is a treatable genetic disease, every effort must be made to detect homozygous subjects. The combination of HLA typing and the studies of iron status allows for the identification of such subjects among the relatives of patients with the clinically manifested disease long before clinical manifestations have occurred. Once a diagnosis of hereditary hemochromatosis is made in any patient, all sibs past age 10 years should be tested for HLA type and iron status. The studies should include plasma iron concentration, transferrin saturation, and plasma ferritin concentration. Since HLA typing is expensive and its interpretation may be difficult, some observers have questioned its utility in family testing for hemochromatosis, suggesting that studies of iron status alone will give all the necessary information. Unlike the study of iron parameters, however, HLA testing needs to be done only once to ascertain whether a sib has both, one, or none of the HLA haplotypes of the index patient. If all four HLA parental haplotypes (two for each parent) are different, the interpretation is clear-cut. Sibs who have both haplotypes of the affected patient are homozygous abnormal and require assessment of their iron status. If such tests suggest significant iron loading, a liver biopsy to assess the extent of iron storage is indicated. Those who share one haplotype are at least heterozygous, and those who share none do not carry any of the hemochromatosis genes present in the affected sib. However, studies of iron status are also required in sibs who share only one HLA haplotype with the index case, since one of the parents may have been an undetected homozygote, i.e., he or she may have carried a double dose of the hemochromatosis gene, each associated with a different HLA haplotype. Homozygosity for hemochromatosis in a sib could therefore result from such a parental heterozygote × abnormal homozygote mating so that two sibs with hemochromatosis have only one haplotype in common. All children of homozygotes for hemochromatosis will be at least heterozygotes and have a 50 percent chance of being homozygotes if the other parent is a heterozygote for the gene.

Periodic venesections should be instituted in those with raised iron stores. If this is done before organ damage has occurred, the clinical disease, including liver tumors, can be prevented. Haplotype-identical sibs who do not show evidence of a significant iron load should be restudied every 2 to 3 years in order to detect the earliest manifestations of iron accumulation. The initial investigation of female sibs can perhaps be deferred until after age 20 years, since the rate of iron loading is less rapid, and clinical manifestations occur in consequence much less frequently and at a later age. Since certain HLA haplotypes have a much higher probability of carrying the hemochromatosis gene, this knowledge can be incorporated in family studies when assessing whether obligatory heterozygotes of hemochromatosis have inherited a second hemochromatosis gene on their other chromosome. As an example, if an obligatory heterozygote for hemochromatosis is found to carry an additional A3-B14 haplotype, the probability that such a person will actually be a homozygote and not a heterozygote for the hemochromatosis gene is high.[418,419] This inference is based on the fact that the frequency of the A3-B14 haplotype in the general population is low (0.3 percent), while it is much higher in a population of hemochromatosis patients (14 percent).

Identification of affected individuals in the preclinical phase of the disorder and of carriers should make it possible to study the cellular dynamics of iron metabolism in homozygotes and heterozygotes in much more detail. If it is possible to identify the basic defect in hereditary hemochromatosis, tests can be developed to detect both heterozygotes and homozygotes in the population at large and not just in the families of homozygotes who have already accumulated significant amounts of iron.

The Widening Clinical Spectrum of Hereditary Hemochromatosis

The availability of the HLA system as a linked marker for the iron-loading gene has made it possible to define the distinction between homozygotes and heterozygotes among the relatives of patients with fully developed hereditary hemochromatosis. The ability to detect a genetic disease prior to the development of clinical signs and symptoms usually changes our understanding of its symptomatology, and it becomes apparent that the pattern of clinical manifestations among many "affected" persons is often considerably less severe than was suggested earlier. This has proved to be the case with hereditary hemochromatosis. It is now known that many homozygous individuals are asymptomatic,[220] and the classic triad of hepatomegaly, skin pigmentation, and diabetes mellitus is uncommon.[393] These facts explain the discrepancy between the high frequencies of abnormal homozygotes revealed by genetic surveys and the lower frequencies of hemochromatosis in clinical and autopsy studies. More and more cases are now being detected by finding abnormal tests of iron status in patients with nonspecific complaints such as weakness and abdominal pain. In a study of 35 homozygotes, 14 of whom were probands, only half the subjects had hepatomegaly, cirrhosis, and skin pigmentation, while diabetes was present in fewer than 10 percent and cardiac failure in none.[420] The plasma ferritin concentration was actually found to be normal in a small proportion of male homozygotes, although the hepatic iron concentration was always raised (Fig. 55-12).[393] Complete saturation of transferrin and increased liver iron was the rule only after the age of 20 years, and clinical manifestations were seen only in adults.[220,392] With advancing age, iron loading increased, reaching a peak in the fifth decade (Fig. 55-13),[220] and it is obvious that the risk of developing the clinical disease increased in parallel. The "textbook" description of clinical and pathologic hereditary hemo-

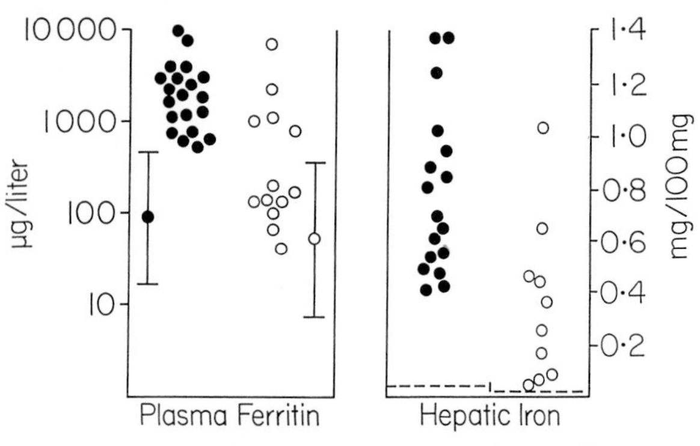

Fig. 55-12 Plasma ferritin (micrograms per liter) and hepatic iron concentrations (milligrams per 100 mg wet liver) in male (•) and female (○) subjects homozygous for the hereditary hemochromatosis gene. The normal mean value (± SD) for serum ferritin is shown, as is the upper limit of normal (broken lines) for hepatic iron concentrations. *(From Edwards et al.[393] Used by permission.)*

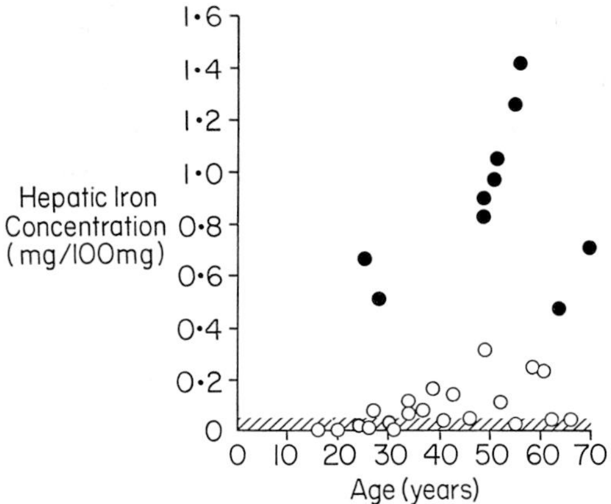

Fig. 55-13 Hepatic iron concentrations (milligrams per 100 mg wet liver) as a function of age in males homozygous (•) and heterozygous (○) for the hereditary hemochromatosis gene. The normal range is indicated by the cross-hatched area. *(From Cartwright et al.[220] Used by permission.)*

chromatosis therefore represents only the most severe end of the spectrum. A recent study in Sweden suggests that adults, and especially males, with unexplained elevation of the serum transaminases ("transaminitis") should be investigated for iron overload.[421] Various studies have confirmed that female homozygotes are much less frequently affected clinically, the main reason being that they lose a significant amount of iron with each menstrual period.

Heterozygotes. Carriers are always much more numerous than affected homozygotes. With the high homozygote frequencies found in European populations, there are 30 to 50 times as many carriers as homozygotes.

At present heterozygotes can be identified with relative certainty only by inference from HLA testing among relatives of iron-loaded homozygous individuals. Occasionally, heterozygote status may be suspected when serum ferritin and transferrin saturation are equivocal. There is no definitive test, including HLA testing, that will detect heterozygote carriers in the general population. The mean values for the various laboratory tests of iron metabolism (plasma iron concentration, transferrin saturation, plasma ferritin concentration, liver iron concentration) have been found to be somewhat higher in such heterozygotes than in normal subjects, but in general they were closer to the normal values than to those found in abnormal homozygotes (Table 55-2).[220,422] However, the liver iron concentration did gradually increase with age, with the result that by middle age 20 to 30 percent of heterozygotes had accumulated sufficient iron to qualify as a minor iron load (defined as more than 50 percent transferrin saturation and/or a hepatic iron load of more than 0.03 mg per 100 mg of wet liver in men and more than 0.02 mg per 100 mg of wet liver in women) (Fig 55-13).[220,422] No heterozygotes had any *clinical* manifestation of iron overload. No further changes were observed after 45 years of age. It is conceivable that factors such as alcoholism, excess iron intake, porphyria cutanea tarda, or accelerated erythropoiesis might lead to the occasional clinical expression of overt iron storage disease among heterozygotes. Idiopathic refractory sideroblastic anemia may sometimes be associated with a single allele for hereditary hemochromatosis, since there is a higher frequency for HLA-A3 in such patients.[178] Similarly, myopathy associated with iron overload may develop in some patients on maintenance hemodialysis because they carry a single hereditary hemochromatosis gene.[423] Heterozygosity for this gene may therefore be the reason only certain patients develop iron overload under a variety of circumstances.

It has been suggested that the level of iron fortification of flour in the United States should be increased in order to reduce the prevalence of iron deficiency.[424] While there is little doubt that the resulting increase in the amount of absorbable iron in the average diet would cause clinical manifestations of iron overload to occur more frequently and at a younger age in affected homozygotes, it remains conjectural as to whether it would have any deleterious effects on the great majority of heterozygotes.[425] From what is commonly known of iron balance, it would be expected that there would be an increase in

Table 55-2 Iron Status of Male Subjects with the Hereditary Hemochromatosis Gene in Utah*

	Normal subjects			*Heterozygotes*			*Homozygotes*†		
	No.	*Mean*	*95% limit*	*No.*	*Mean*	*95% limit*	*No.*	*Mean*	*95% limit*
Age, years	44	33	0–77	67	33	0–75	13	48	25–70
Serum iron, µg/dl	44	106	50–162	67	135	62–208	13	244	173–307
Transferrin saturation, %	44	32	14–50	67	44	19–69	13	95	80–100
Serum ferritin, µg/liter‡	41	93	16–542	64	96	15–617	12	2099	565–11560
Urinary iron, mg/24 h§	19	1.3	0.4–2.2	38	1.6	0.2–3.0	12	11.2	4.4–26.5
Parenchymal stainable cell iron, grade	22	0.2	0–1	22	1.1	0–3	12	3.9	3.4
Hepatic iron, mg/100 mg	22	0.012	0–0.029	22	0.096	0–0.282	10	0.877	0.486–1.417

*Data rearranged from Cartwright and coworkers.[220]
†Majority identified because of signs and symptoms of fully developed hereditary hemochromatosis.
‡Geometric mean.
§After deferoxamine 15 µg per kilogram of body weight intramuscularly.

the iron stores in such individuals, but not to levels that would be potentially harmful. In fact, Sweden's program of iron fortification has been in operation for a number of years, and there is as yet no evidence that heterozygotes have been adversely affected. At the same time it is imperative that the situation in Sweden be carefully and repeatedly monitored.

HEMOCHROMATOSIS IN HEREDITARY ANEMIAS

Clinical and pathologic features similar to those found in hereditary hemochromatosis have been reported in patients suffering from a variety of chronic anemias.[1] These fall into two distinct groups on the basis of the degree of erythropoietic activity in the bone marrow. Those with hypoplastic anemia who are maintained on repeated blood transfusions over many years tend to exhibit milder overt pathologic and metabolic consequences because of the initial predominantly reticuloendothelial localization of the iron. When reports of 20 such individuals were analyzed, only one had developed cirrhosis of the liver, although four had impaired glucose tolerance and five had overt diabetes.[426] The finding of disturbed glucose tolerance and endocrine function in several such subjects[427] indicates that there may be enough redistribution of iron from reticuloendothelial into parenchymal tissues for disorders of cellular function to occur. In the chronic hyperplastic anemias in which erythropoiesis is largely ineffective, there is heavy hepatocyte loading and parenchymal deposits in other tissues, and the full hemochromatosis syndrome is typically seen.[1] This group comprises thalassemia major and sometimes thalassemia intermedia, hereditary and acquired sideroblastic anemias, pyridoxine-responsive anemias, and a variety of other anemias associated with blocks in the incorporation of iron into hemoglobin.[1] By far the most common of these conditions are the thalassemic syndromes (see Chap. 93).

Subjects heterozygous for any of the thalassemic genes do not accumulate excessive amounts of iron,[174,176,428] but iron overload is a feature of patients carrying two different abnormal genes (e.g., thalassemia-hemoglobin E disease). In general, the most severe degrees of iron overload are encountered in patients with β-thalassemia major.

Pathologic and Clinical Features

The iron load in frequently transfused patients with thalassemia major is about 20 g by the age of 10 years.[429] This figure is equivalent to the average amount found at the time clinical manifestations occur in hereditary hemochromatosis. In individuals who survive for 20 years it is as much as 80 to 100 g. The clinical and pathologic features of the hemochromatosis of thalassemia are similar to those seen in young and very severely affected patients with hereditary hemochromatosis.

In a recent analysis of 57 deaths from thalassemia in Britain, 21 occurred at an early age from anemia or hypersplenism.[174] Infections caused death at all ages. The ages at death in the 25 who succumbed to iron overload ranged from 11 to 24 years, and the terminal event in every case was *cardiac failure.* The cardiac manifestations are essentially those of a cardiomyopathy,[174,176,429] with arrhythmias being a frequent cause of death.[430] The cardiac iron is stored in distinct particles, possibly lysosomes, which accumulate in the perinuclear space and down the core of the cardiac muscle fibers. If the teens are reached, *endocrine failure* becomes prominent.[431,432] Failure or severe retardation of puberty is the most common manifestation and is associated with absence or retardation of the adolescent growth spurt. While maintaining the hemoglobin concentration at higher levels does improve the early growth rate, severe growth retardation nevertheless becomes obvious between 11 and 12 years.[174,176,429,433,434] It is not due to growth hormone deficiency,[428] although the hepatic response to the hormone may be impaired as a result of somatomedin deficiency.[435] In most subjects there is laboratory evidence of prediabetes. Insulin dependence is relatively uncommon, although its frequency will probably increase as patients live longer.[174] *Liver disease* is a constant feature. In the first decade, hepatomegaly with cirrhosis is usually well established, and it is uniformly found in heavily transfused patients.[174] In a series of 32 liver biopsies, a good correlation was found between the severity of the fibrosis and both the age and the liver iron concentration.[436] At iron concentrations of less than 0.6 mg/100 mg, progression was relatively slow, but thereafter it accelerated. At all stages the iron is located in the cytoplasm and in lysosomes[437] of both reticuloendothelial cells and hepatocytes. Parenchymal deposition was increased when the liver iron concentration was greater than 0.75 mg per 100 mg.[436] The iron deposition is accompanied by collagen deposition and later by fibrosis. Splenectomy has been reported to promote parenchymal loading in the liver and to accelerate the development of cirrhosis.[438–440] However, the role of the spleen as a major iron depository has been disputed,[441] and splenectomy should be performed if hypersplenism is leading to increased blood requirements.[174,442] A final factor aggravating liver damage in thalassemia major may be serum hepatitis.[443,444]

Management

The management of thalassemia major changed in 1964 following the demonstration that children transfused frequently were healthier and lived just as long as undertransfused patients.[445] High transfusion programs in which the mean hemoglobin concentration is held at 12 g/dl appear to be the most desirable, both in the short and long term.[174] The blood requirements are not increased,[446] there is a delay in the development of hypersplenism, and gastrointestinal iron absorption is decreased. As a result, the rate of iron loading is no greater than in patients transfused less often. Growth is normal until about age 11 years on such therapy, but then the complications resulting from the iron overload appear. It is obviously desirable to remove as much iron as possible, and deferoxamine has been increasingly used for this purpose in recent years. Continuous intravenous infusion mobilizes more iron than intramuscular injections, but this is obviously not feasible for long-term daily treatment. Continuous subcutaneous infusion has been shown to be almost as effective, and the development of small infusion pumps has made the method a practical one for home use (Fig. 55-14).[413,415,447] It is now usually given only overnight since urinary iron losses are almost as great as when it is continued around the clock.[413–415,448–450] Iron excretion in the stool adds at least 30 percent to the urinary elimination.[451] A dose of 25 to 45 mg/kg per day is usual. On such therapy it is now possible to induce a negative iron balance in heavily transfused patients,[411,413,415,449,450] with demonstrable improvement in mor-

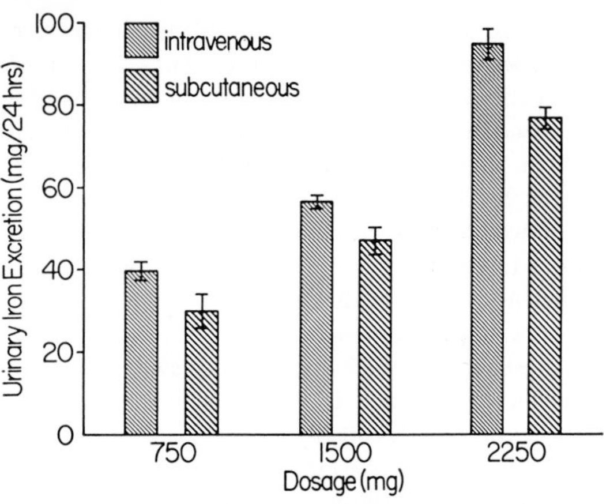

Fig. 55-14 A comparison of the effects on urinary iron excretion of intermittent intramuscular injections of deferoxamine with those of continuous subcutaneous and continuous intravenous administration. Mean values (± 1 SE) are given at three different dosage levels in patients with iron overload secondary to multiple transfusions. *(After Propper et al.[413] Used by permission.)*

bidity and mortality.[174] Subcutaneous deferoxamine treatment has been associated with the arrest of hepatic fibrosis,[452] diminished cardiotoxicity,[453–455] and prolonged survival.[456] On standard treatment with doses less than 50 mg/kg, deferoxamine toxicity is not normally a problem. However, in a recent careful study of 89 patients receiving subcutaneous deferoxamine (34 to 150 mg/kg per day), 13 exhibited auditory and/or visual defects.[457] The defects occurred particularly in those who had small iron burdens and were receiving large doses of the chelator.

As was mentioned above ("Relationship between Iron Overload and Tissue Damage"), ascorbic acid deficiency may occur in thalassemia major.[458,459] Correction of the deficiency causes a mean increase of twofold in deferoxamine-induced urinary iron excretion, and ascorbic acid has therefore been widely used.[174,429] However, the demonstration by Nienhuis[411,459] that it might be hazardous has provoked the formulation of guidelines for its use. Ascorbic acid should not be given to iron-loaded patients who are not receiving regular chelation therapy or to massively iron-loaded patients just starting on deferoxamine therapy.[174] The oral dose of ascorbic acid should be the smallest necessary to achieve augmented iron excretion and no more than 200 mg daily.[411] Two recent studies showed an improvement in heart function on such a regimen.[454,455] The transfusion of young red cells (neocytes) has been advocated,[460] but it is technically difficult and preliminary results have not shown any significant decrease in transfusion requirements.[452,461] Another therapeutic strategy that has been suggested has been the drinking of tea with meals so that the tannins will reduce the bioavailability of the food iron.[462]

While current results using deferoxamine are promising, such treatment is both expensive and complicated; it is therefore unsuitable for application in many areas where thalassemia major is common. We hope that in the future there will be combinations of effective and cheap chelators with differing and complementary modes of action, which can be given in depot form or, preferably, orally.[416,463,464] Further therapeutic options which are being explored include bone marrow transplantation,[465] manipulation of fetal globin genes using 5-azacytidine,[466] and gene therapy using recombinant DNA methodology. Currently, such techniques are experimental, and their application is limited to highly specialized centers.

REFERENCES

1. BOTHWELL TH, CHARLTON RW, COOK JD, FINCH CA: *Iron Metabolism in Man*. Oxford, Blackwell, 1979.
2. BELL SH, WEIR MP, DICKSON DP, GIBSON JF, SHARP GA, PETERS TJ: Mossbäuer spectroscopic studies of human haemosiderin and ferritin. *Biochim Biophys Acta* 787:227, 1984.
3. WEIR MP, GIBSON JF, PETERS TJ: Biochemical studies on the isolation and characterization of human spleen haemosiderin. *Biochem J* 223:31, 1984.
4. COOK JD, SKIKNE BS: Serum ferritin: A possible model for the assessment of nutrient stores. *Am J Clin Nutr* 35:1180, 1982.
5. HARRISON PM: Ferritin: An iron-storage molecule. *Semin Hematol* 14:55, 1977.
6. HARRISON PM, CLEGG GA, MAY K: Ferritin structure and function, in Jacobs A, Worwood M (eds): *Iron in Biochemistry and Medicine II*. London, New York, Academic, 1980, p 131.
7. HARRISON PM: The structure and function of ferritin. *Ciba Found Symp* 51:19, 1977.
8. DRYSDALE JW: Ferritin phenotypes: Structure and metabolism, *Ciba Found Symp* 51:41, 1977.
9. CONSTANZO F, SANTORO C, COLANTUONI Y, BENSI G, RANGEI G, ROMANO V, CORTESE R: Cloning and sequencing of a full length cDNA coding for a human apoferritin H chain: Evidence for a multigene family. *EMBO J* 3:23, 1984.
10. BOYD D, VECOLI C, BELCHER DM, JAIN SK, DRYSDALE JW: Structural and functional relationships of human ferritin H and L chains deduced from cDNA clones. *J Biol Chem* 260:11755, 1985.
11. JAIN SK, BARRETT KJ, BOYD D, FAVREAU MF, CRAMPTON J, DRYSDALE JW: Ferritin H and L chains are derived from different multigene families. *J Biol Chem* 260:11762, 1985.
12. CASKEY J, JONES C, MILLER YE, SELIGMAN PA: Ferritin gene is assigned to chromosome 19. *Proc Natl Acad Sci USA* 80:482, 1983.
13. WORWOOD M, BROOK JD, CRAGG SJ, HELLKUHL B, JONES BM, PERERA P, ROBERTS SH, SHAW DJ: Assignment of human ferritin genes to chromosomes 11 and 19q 13.3—19 q ter. *Hum Genet* 69:371, 1985.
14. BOYD D, JAIN SK, CRAMPTON J, BARRETT KH, DRYSDALE J: Isolation and characterization of cDNA clone for human ferritin heavy chain. *Proc Natl Acad Sci USA* 81:4651, 1984.
15. CRAGG SJ, DRYSDALE J, WORWOOD M: Genes for the "H" subunit of human ferritin are present on a number of human chromosomes. *Hum Genet* 71:108, 1985.
16. MCGILL JR, NAYLOR SL, SAKAGUSHI QY, MOORE CM, BOYD D, BARRETT KJ, SHOWS TB, DRYSDALE JW: Human ferritin H and L sequences lie on ten different chromosomes. *Hum Genet* 76:66, 1987.
17. WORWOOD M: Serum ferritin. *Clin Sci* 70:215, 1986.
18. WAGSTAFF M, WORWOOD M, JACOBS A: Properties of human tissue isoferritins. *Biochem J* 173:969, 1978.
19. TREFFREY A, LEE PJ, HARRISON PM: Functional studies on rat liver isoferritins. *Biochim Biophys Acta* 785:22, 1984.
20. BOMFORD A, CONLAN-HOLLINGSHEAD C, MUNRO HH: Adaptive responses of rat tissue isoferritins to iron administration. Changes in sub-unit synthesis, isoferritin abundance and capacity for iron storage. *J Biol Chem* 256:948, 1981.
21. DOOLITTLE RL, RICHTER GW: Isoferritins in rat Kupffer cells, hepatocytes and extrahepatic macrophages. Biosynthesis in cell suspensions and cultures in response to iron. *J Lab Invest* 45:567, 1981.
22. CAIRO G, BARDELLA L, SCHIAFFONATI L, AROSIO P, LEVI S, BERNELLI-ZAZZERA A: Multiple mechanisms of iron-induced ferritin synthesis in HeLa cells. *Biochem Biophys Res Commun* 133:314, 1985.
23. SHULL GE, THEIL EC: Translational control of ferritin synthesis by iron in embryonic reticulocytes of the bull frog. *J Biol Chem* 257:14187, 1982.
24. AZIZ N, MUNRO HN: Both subunits of rat liver ferritin are regulated at a translational level by iron induction. *Nucleic Acids Res* 14:915, 1986.
25. WATANABE N, DRYSDALE J: Studies on heterogeneity in ferritin subunits. *Biochim Biophys Acta* 743:98, 1983.
26. SHULL GE, THEIL EC: Regulation of ferritin mRNA. A possible gene sparing phenomenon. Induction of ferritin synthesis by iron in liver as well as red cells, combines high translational efficiency with increased utilization of preformed ferritin mRNA. *J Biol Chem* 258:7921, 1983.
27. KONIJN AM, BALIGA BS, MUNRO HN: Synthesis of liver ferritin on free and membrane-bound polyribosomes of different sizes. *FEBS Lett* 37:249, 1973.
28. CHASTEEN ND, THEIL EC: Iron binding by horse spleen apoferritin. A Vanadyl (IV) EPR skin probe study. *J Biol Chem* 257:7672, 1982.
29. CRICHTON RR: Interactions between iron metabolism and oxygen activation. *Ciba Found Symp* 65:57, 1979.

30. TREFFREY A, HARRISON PM: Now random distributing of iron entering rat liver ferritin *in vivo*. *Biochem J* 220:857, 1984.

31. DRYSDALE JW, MUNRO HN: Regulation of synthesis and turnover of ferritin in rat liver. *J Biol Chem* 241:3630, 1966.

32. LINDER MC, MUNRO HN: Metabolic and chemical feature of ferritins, a series of iron inducible tissue proteins. *Am J Pathol* 72:263, 1973.

33. SIRIVECH S, FRIEDEN E, OSAKI S: The release of iron from horse spleen ferritin by reduced flavins. *Biochem J* 143:311, 1974.

34. LIPSCHITZ DA, BOTHWELL TH, SEFTEL HC, WAPNICK AA, CHARLTON RW: The role of ascorbic acid in the metabolism of storage iron. *Br J Haematol* 20:155, 1971.

35. HILTON JW, CHO CY, SLINGER SJ: Effect of graded levels of supplementa' ascorbic acid in practical diets fed to Rainbow Trout (Salmo gairdneri). *J Fish Res Board Can* 35:431, 1978.

36. ROESER HP: The role of ascorbic acid in the turnover of storage iron. *Semin Hematol* 20:91, 1982.

37. BRIDGES KR, HOFFMAN KE: The effects of ascorbic acid on the intracellular metabolism of iron and ferritin. *J Biol Chem* 261, 14273, 1986.

38. COOK JD, HERSHKO C, FINCH CA: Storage iron kinetics. I. Measurements of the cellular distribution of ^{59}Fe in rat liver. *J Lab Clin Med* 80:613, 1972.

39. CHARLTON RW, BOTHWELL TH: Hemochromatosis: Dietary and genetic aspects. *Prog Hematol* 5:298, 1966.

40. WEIBEL ER, STAUBLI W, GNAGI HR, HESS FA: Correlated morphometric and biochemical studies on the liver cell. I. Morphometric model, stereologic methods, and normal morphometric data for rat liver. *J Cell Biol* 42:68, 1969.

41. TORRANCE JD, CHARLTON RW, SCHMAMAN A, LYNCH SR, BOTHWELL TH: Storage iron in "muscle." *J Clin Path* 21:495, 1968.

42. FINCH CA, DEUBELBEISS K, COOK JD, ESCHBACH JW, HARKER LA, FUNK DD, MARSAGLIA G, HILLMAN RS, SLICHTER S, ADAMSON JW, GANZONI A, GIBLETT ER: Ferrokinetics in man. *Medicine (Baltimore)* 49:17, 1970.

43. HERSHKO C, COOK JD, FINCH CA: Storage iron kinetics. II. The uptake of hemoglobin iron by hepatic parenchymal cells. *J Lab Clin Med* 80:624, 1972.

44. JACOBS A: Ferritin. An interim review. *Curr Top Hematol* 5:25, 1985.

45. WORWOOD M, DAWKINS S, WAGSTAFF M, JACOBS A: Purification and properties of ferritin from human serum. *Biochem J* 157:97, 1976.

46. AROSIO P, YOKOTA M, DRYSDALE JW: Characterization of serum ferritin in iron overload: Possible identity to natural apoferritin. *Br J Haematol* 36:199, 1977.

47. SIIMES MA, DALLMAN PR: New kinetic role for serum ferritin in iron metabolism. *Br J Haematol* 28:1, 1974.

48. WORWOOD M: Serum ferritin. *CRC Crit Rev Clin Lab Sci* 10:171, 1979.

49. WORWOOD M, CRAGG SJ, JACOBS A, MCLAREN C, RICKETTS C, ECONOMIDOU J: Binding of serum ferritin to concanavalin A: Patients with homozygous β thalassaemia and transfusional iron overload. *Br J Haematol* 46:409, 1980.

50. CRAGG SJ, COVELL AM, BURCH A, OWEN GM, JACOBS A, WORWOOD M: Turnover of ^{131}I-human spleen ferritin in plasma. *Br J Haematol* 55:83, 1983.

51. WORWOOD M, CRAGG SJ, WILLIAMS AM, WAGSTAFF M, JACOBS A: The clearance of ^{131}I-human plasma ferritin in man. *Blood* 60:827, 1982.

52. MACK U, POWELL LW, HALLIDAY JW: A receptor for ferritin on hepatocytes. *J Biol Chem* 258:4672, 1983.

53. WALTERS GO, MILLER FM, WORWOOD M: Serum ferritin concentration and iron stores in normal subjects. *J Clin Pathol* 26:770, 1973.

54. BEZWODA WR, BOTHWELL TH, TORRANCE JD, MacPHAIL AP, CHARLTON RW, KAY G, LEVIN J: The relationship between marrow iron stores, plasma ferritin concentrations and iron absorption. *Scand J Haematol* 22:113, 1979.

55. COOK JD, LIPSCHITZ DA, MILES LEM, FINCH CA: Serum ferritin as a measure of iron stores in normal subjects. *Am J Clin Nutr* 27:681, 1974.

56. DALLMAN PR, SIIMES MA, STEKEL A: Iron deficiency in infancy and childhood. *Am J Clin Nutr* 33:86, 1974.

57. JACOBS A, MILLER E, WORWOOD M, BEAMISH MR, WARDROP CA: Ferritin in the serum of normal subjects and patients with iron deficiency and iron overload. *Br Med J* 4:206, 1972.

58. LIPSCHITZ DA, COOK JD, FINCH DA: A clinical evaluation of serum ferritin. *N Engl J Med* 290:1213, 1974.

59. PRIETO J, BARRY M, SHERLOCK S: Serum ferritin in patients with iron overload and with acute and chronic liver disease. *Gastroenterology* 68:525, 1975.

60. ROESER HP, HALLIDAY JW, SIZEMORE DJ, NIKLES A, WILLGOSS D: Serum ferritin in ascorbic acid deficiency. *Br J Haematol* 45:457, 1980.

61. ZUYDERHOUDT FMJ, JOMING GGA, DE HAAN JG, SAMSON G, VAN GOOL J: Rat liver storage iron and plasma ferritin during D-galactosamine-HCl-induced hepatitis. *Clin Sci* 58:321, 1980.

62. HENGEVELD P, ZUYDERHOUDT FMJ, JOBSIS AC, VAN GOOL J: Some aspects of iron metabolism during acute viral hepatitis. *Hepatogastroenterology* 29:138, 1982.

63. ELIN RJ, WOLFF SM, FINCH CA: Effect of induced fever on serum iron and ferritin concentrations in man. *Blood* 49:147, 1977.

64. SMITH RJ, DAVIS P, THOMSON AB, WADSWORTH LD, FACKRE P: Serum ferritin levels in anemia of rheumatoid arthritis. *J Rheumatol* 4:389, 1977.

65. SIIMES MA, WANG WC, DALLMAN PR: Elevated serum ferritin in children with malignancies. *Scand J Haematol* 19:153, 1977.

66. JACOBS A: Serum ferritin in malignant tumours. *Med Oncol Tumor Pharmacother* 1:149, 1984.

67. POLLACK S, LASKY FD: A new iron-binding protein isolated from intestinal mucosa. *J Lab Clin Med* 87:670, 1976.

68. HUEBERS H, HUEBERS E, RUMMEL W, CRICHTON RR: Isolation and characterization of iron-binding proteins from rat intestinal mucosa. *Eur J Biochem* 66:447, 1976.

69. HUEBERS H, HUEBERS E, CSIBA E, RUMMEL W, FINCH CA: The significance of transferrin for intestinal iron absorption. *Blood* 61:283, 1983.

70. PARMLEY RT, BARTON JC, CONRAD ME: Ultrastructural localization of transferrin, transferrin receptor and iron binding sites on human placental and duodenal micro villi. *Br J Haematol* 60:81, 1985.

71. BEZWODA WR, MacPHAIL AP, BOTHWELL TH, BAYNES RD, DERMAN DP, TORRANCE JD: Failure of transferrin to enhance iron absorption in achlorhydric human subjects. *Br J Haematol* 63:749, 1986.

72. BANERJEE D, FLANGAN PR, CLUETT J, VALBERG LS: Transferrin receptors in the human gastrointestinal tract. Relationship to body iron stores. *Gastroenterology* 91:861, 1986.

73. MORGAN EH: Transferrin, biochemistry, physiology and clinical significance. *Mol Aspects Med* 4:1, 1981.

74. MacGILLIVRAY RTA, MENDEZ E, BREW K: Structure and evolution of serum transferrin, in Brown EB, Aisen P, Fielding J, Crichton RR (eds): *Proteins of Iron Metabolism*. New York, Grune & Stratton, 1977, p 133.

75. EVANS RW, WILLIAMS J: Studies on the binding of different iron donors to human serum transferrin and isolation of iron-binding fragments from the N- and C-terminal regions of the protein. *Biochem J* 173:543, 1978.

76. HUEBERS HA, FINCH CA: Transferrin: Physiologic behaviour and clinical implications. *Blood* 64:763, 1984.

77. JAMIESON GA, JETT M, DE BARNARDO SL: The carbohydrate sequence of the glyco-peptide chains of human transferrin. *J Biol Chem* 246:3686, 1971.

78. SPIK G, BAYARD B, FOURNET B, STRECKER G, BOUQUELET S, MONTREUIL J: Studies on glycoconjugates. LXIV. Complete structure of two carbohydrate units of human serotransferrin. *FEBS Lett* 50:296, 1975.

79. GIBLETT ER: Transferrin, in *Physiological Pharmacology*. New York, Academic, 1974, vol V, p 555.

80. PUTMAN FW: Transferrin, in *The Plasma Proteins,* 2d ed. New York, Academic, 1975, p 266.

81. LANE RS: Transferrin, in Allison AL (ed): *Structure and Function of Plasma Proteins*. New York, Plenum, 1976, vol 2, p 53.

82. YANG F, LUM JB, MCGILL JR, MOORE CM, NAYLOR SL, BAN BRAGT PH, BALDWIN WD, BOWMAN BH: Human transferrin: cDNA characterization and chromosomal localization. *Proc Natl Acad Sci USA* 81:2752, 1984.

83. MCKNIGHT GS, LEE DC, PALMITER RD: Transferrin gene expression. Regulation of mRNA transcription in chicken liver by steroid hormones and iron deficiency. *J Biol Chem* 255:148, 1980.

84. LYNCH SR, SIMON M, BOTHWELL TH, CHARLTON RW: Circadian variation in plasma iron concentration and reticuloendothelial iron release in the rat. *Clin Sci Mol Med* 45:331, 1973.

85. FILLET G, MARSAGLIA G: Idiopathic hemochromatosis (IH). Abnormality in RBC transport of iron by the reticuloendothelial system (RES). *Proceedings of the XVIIIth Meeting of the American Society of Hematology,* 1975, p 53.

86. DONOVAN JW, BEARDSLEE RA, ROSS KD: Formation of monoferric ovotransferrins in the presence of chelates. *Biochem J* 153:631, 1976.

87. HARRIS DC: Functional equivalence of iron bound to human transferrin at low pH or high pH. *Biochim Biophys Acta* 496:563, 1977.

88. FLETCHER J, HUEHNS ER: Function of transferrin. *Nature* 218:1211, 1968.

89. ZAK O, AISEN P: Non-random distribution of iron in circulating transferrin. *Blood* 68:157, 1986.

90. HUEBERS HA, JOSEPHSON B, HUEBERS E, CSIBA E, FINCH CA: Occupancy of the iron binding sites by human transferrin. *Proc Natl Acad Sci USA* 81:4326, 1984.

91. HUEBERS HA, CSIBA E, HUEBERS E, FINCH CA: Competitive advantage of diferric transferrin in delivering iron to reticulocytes. *Proc Natl Acad Sci USA* 80:300, 1983.

92. HUEBERS H, CSIBA E, HUEBERS E, FINCH CA: Molecular advantage of differic transferrin in delivering iron to reticulocytes. A comparative study. *Proc Soc Exp Biol Med* 179:222, 1985.

93. WITT DP, WOODWORTH RC: Identification of the transferrin receptor of the rabbit reticulocyte. *Biochemistry* 17:3913, 1978.

94. VAN BOCKXMEER FM, MORGAN EH: Transferrin receptors during rabbit reticulocyte maturation. *Biochim Biophys Acta* 584:76, 1979.

95. SELIGMAN PA, SCHLEICHER RB, ALLEN RH: Isolation and characterization of the transferrin receptor from human placenta. *J Biol Chem* 254:9943, 1979.

96. LOH TT, HIGUCHI DA, VAN BOCKXMEER FM, SMITH CH, BROWN EB: Transferrin receptors on the human placental microvillous membrane. *J Clin Invest* 65:1182, 1980.

97. MCCLELLAND A, KUHN LC, RUDDLE F: The human transferrin receptor gene: Genomic organization and the complete primary structure of the receptor deduced from cDNA sequence. *Cell* 39:267, 1984.

98. SCHNEIDER C, OWEN MJ, BANVILLE D, WILLIAMS JG: Primary structure of human transferrin receptor deduced from the mRNA sequence. *Nature* 311:675, 1984.

99. KUHN LC, MCCLELLAND A, RUDDLE FH: Gene transfer, expression and molecular cloning of the human transferrin receptor gene. *Cell* 37:95, 1984.

100. MILLER YE, JONES C, SLOGGIN C, MORSE H, SELIGMAN P: Chromosome 3q (22-ter) encodes the human transferrin receptor. *Am J Hum Genet* 35:573, 1983.

101. RABIN M, MCCLELLAND A, KÜHN L, RUDDLE FH: Regional localization of the human transferrin receptor gene to 3q 26.2 – q-ter. *Am J Hum Genet* 37:1112, 1985.

102. ERNS CA, SUSSMAN HH: Physical characterization of the transferrin receptor in human placenta. *J Biol Chem* 256:9820, 1981.

103. SELIGMAN PA: Structure and function of the transferrin receptor. *Prog Hematol* 13:131, 1983.

104. MAY WS, JACOBS S, CUATRECASAS P: Association of phorbol ester induces hyperphosphorylation and reversible regulation of transferrin membrane receptors in HL 60 cells. *Proc Natl Acad Sci USA* 81:2016, 1984.

105. MAY WS, SAHYOUN N, JACOBS S, WOLF M, CUATRECASAS P: Mechanism of phorbol-diester-induced regulation of surface transferrin receptor involves the action of activated protein kinase C and an intact cytoskeleton. *J Biol Chem* 260:9419, 1985.

106. HUBERT D, MORGAN EH: Calmodulin antagonists inhibit and phorbol esters enhance transferrin endocytosis and iron uptake by immature erythroid cells. *Blood* 65:758, 1985.

107. MAY WS, CUATRECASAS P: Transferrin receptor: Its biological significance. *J Membr Biol* 88:205, 1985.

108. WILEMAN T, HARDING C, STAHL P: Receptor mediated endocytosis. *Biochem J* 232:1, 1985.

109. DAUTRY-VARSAT A, CIEHANOVER A, LODISH HF: pH and the recycling of transferrin during receptor mediated endocytosis. *Proc Natl Acad Sci USA* 80:2258, 1983.

110. MORGAN EH: Effect of pH and iron content of transferrin on its binding to reticulocyte receptors. *Biochim Biophys Acta* 762:498, 1983.

111. KLAUSNER RD, ASHWELL G, VAN RENSWOUDE J, HARFORD J, BRIDGES KR: Binding of apotransferrin to K562 cells: Explanation of the transferrin cycle. *Proc Natl Acad Sci USA* 80:2263, 1983.

112. BOMFORD AB, MUNRO HN: Transferrin and its receptor: Their roles in cell function. *Hepatology* 5:870, 1985.

113. STAHL P, SCHWARTZ AL: Receptor mediated endocytosis. *J Clin Invest* 77:657, 1986.

114. YOUNG SP, BOMFORD A, WILLIAMS R: Dual pathways for the uptake of rat asialotransferrin by rat hepatocytes. *J Biol Chem* 258:4972, 1983.

115. PAGE MA, BAKER E, MORGAN EH: Transferrin and iron uptake by rat hepatocytes in culture. *Am J Physiol* 246:G26, 1984.

116. SODA R, TAVASSOLI M: Liver endothelium and not hepatocytes or Küpffer cells have transferrin receptors. *Blood* 63:270, 1984.

117. DEKKER CJ, KROOS MJ, VAN DER HUEL C, VAN EIJK HG: Uptake of sialo and asialo transferrins by isolated rat hepatocytes: Comparison of a heterozygous and a homologous system. *Int J Biochem* 17:701, 1985.

118. REGOECZI E, KOJ A: Diacytosis of human asialotransferrin type 3 in the rat liver is due to the sequential engagement of two receptors. *Exp Cell Res* 160:1, 1985.

119. RUDOLPH JR, REGOECZI E, CHINDEMI PA, DEBANNE MT: Preferential hepatic uptake of iron from rat asialotransferrin: possible engagement of two receptors. *Am J Physiol* 251:G398, 1986.

120. TAVASSOLI M, KISHIMOTO T, SODA R, KATAOKA M, HARJES K: Liver endothelium mediates the uptake of iron-transferrin complex by hepatocytes. *Exp Cell Res* 165:369, 1986.

121. REGOECZI E, CHINDEMI PA, DEBANNE MT: Transferrin glycans: A possible link between alcoholism and hepatic siderosis. *Clin Exp Res* 8:287, 1984.

122. COOK JD, MARSAGLIA G, ESCHBACH JW, FUNK DD, FINCH CA: Ferrokinetics: A biologic model for plasma iron exchange in man. *J Clin Invest* 49:197, 1970.

123. RICKETTS C, JACOBS A, CAVILL I: Ferrokinetics and erythropoiesis in man: The measurement of effective erythropoiesis, ineffective erythropoiesis and red cell life span using ^{59}Fe. *Br J Haematol* 31:65, 1975.

124. GREEN R, CHARLTON RW, SEFTEL H, BOTHWELL T, MAYET F, ADAMS B, FINCH C, LAYRISSE M: Body iron excretion in man. A collaborative study. *Am J Med* 45:336, 1968.

125. DUBACH R, MOORE CV, CALLENDER S: Studies in iron transportation and metabolism. IX. The excretion of iron as measured by the isotope technique. *J Lab Clin Med* 45:599, 1955.

126. HALLBERG L, HOGDAHL A-M, NILSSON L, RYBO G: Menstrual blood loss—A population study. Variation at different ages and attempts to define normality. *Acta Obstet Gynecol Scand* 45:320, 1966.

127. HALLBERG L, BJÖRN-RASMUSSEN E: Measurement of iron absorption from meals contaminated with iron. *Am J Clin Nutr* 34:2808, 1981.

128. DERMAN D, SAYERS M, LYNCH SR, CHARLTON RW, BOTHWELL TH, MAYET F: Iron absorption from a cereal diet containing cane sugar fortified with ascorbic acid. *Br J Nutr* 38:261, 1977.

129. HALLBERG L, BJÖRN-RASMUSSEN E, ROSSANDER L, SUWANIK R, PLEEHACHINDA R, TUNTAWIROON M: Iron absorption from some Asian meals containing contamination iron. *Am J Clin Nutr* 32:272, 1983.

130. MOORE CV: Iron nutrition and requirement. *Scand J Haematol* 6:1, 1965.

131. DERMAN DP, BOTHWELL TH, MacPHAIL AP, TORRANCE JD, BEZWODA WR, CHARLTON RW, MAYET FGH: Importance of ascorbic acid in the absorption of iron from foods. *Scand J Haematol* 25:193, 1980.

132. CHARLTON RW, BOTHWELL TH, SEFTEL HC: Dietary iron overload. *Clin Haematol* 2:383, 1973.

133. HUNGERFORD DM, LINDER MC: Interactions of pH and ascorbate in intestinal iron absorption. *J Nutr* 113:2615, 1983.

134. CLYDESDALE FM: Biochemical determinants of iron bioavailability. *Food Technol* October:133, 1983.

135. HALLBERG L: Bioavailability of dietary iron in man. *Annu Rev Nutr* 1:123, 1981.

136. BOTHWELL TH, CHARLTON RW: A general approach to the problem of iron deficiency and iron overload in the population at large. *Semin Hematol* 19:54, 1982.

137. LAYRISSE M, MARTINEZ-TORRES C, COOK JD, WALKER R, FINCH CA: Iron fortification of food: Its measurement by the extrinsic tag method. *Blood* 41:333, 1973.

138. HALLBERG L, BJÖRN-RASMUSSEN E, HOWARD L, ROSSANDER L: Dietary heme iron absorption. *Scand J Gastroenterol* 14:769, 1979.

139. LAYRISSE M, MARTINEZ-TORRES C, LEETS I, TAYLOR P, RAMIREZ J: Effect of histidine, glutathione or beef on iron absorption in humans. *J Nutr* 114:217, 1984.

140. SAYERS MH, LYNCH SR, JACOBS P, CHARLTON RW, BOTHWELL TH, WALKER RB, MAYET F: The effects of ascorbic acid supplementation on the absorption of iron in maize, wheat and soya. *Br J Haematol* 24:209, 1973.

141. BJÖRN-RASMUSSEN E, HALLBERG L: Iron absorption from maize. Effect of ascorbic acid on iron absorption from maize supplemented with ferrous sulphate. *Nutr Metab* 16:94, 1974.

142. DERMAN DP, BOTHWELL TH, MacPHAIL AP, TORRANCE JD, BEZWODA WR, CHARLTON RW, MAYET FGH: Importance of ascorbic acid in the absorption of iron from infant foods. *Scand J Haematol* 25:193, 1980.

143. GILLOOLY M, BOTHWELL TH, TORRANCE JD, MacPHAIL AP, DERMAN DP, BEZWODA WR, MILLS M, CHARLTON RW, MAYET F: The effects of organic acids, phytates and polyphenols on the absorption of iron from vegetables. *Br J Nutr* 49:331, 1983.

144. GILLOOLY M, BOTHWELL TH, CHARLTON RW, TORRANCE JD, BEZWODA WR, MacPHAIL AP, DERMAN DP, NOVELLI L, MORALL P, MAYET F: Factors affecting the absorption of iron from cereals. *Br J Nutr* 51:37, 1984.

145. FORTH W, RUMMEL W: Iron absorption. *Physiol Rev* 53:724, 1973.

146. BJÖRN-RASMUSSEN E: Iron absorption from wheat bread influence of various amounts of bran. *Nutr Metab* 16:101, 1974.

147. DISLER PB, LYNCH SR, CHARLTON RW, TORRANCE JD, BOTHWELL TH: The effect of tea on iron absorption. *Gut* 16:193, 1975.

148. HALKETT JAE, PETERS T, ROSS JF: Studies on the deposition and nature of egg yolk iron. *J Biol Chem* 231:187, 1958.

149. COOK JD, MORCK TA, LYNCH SR: The inhibitory effect of soy products on non-heme iron absorption. *Am J Clin Nutr* 34:2622, 1981.

150. OLSSEN E, ISAKSSON B, NORRBY A, SOLVELL L: Food iron absorption in iron deficiency. *Am J Clin Nutr* 31:106, 1978.

151. REINHOLD JG, GARCIA JS, GARZON P: Binding of iron by fiber on wheat and maize. *Am J Clin Nutr* 34:1384, 1981.

152. SIMPSON KM, MORRIS ER, COOK JD: The inhibitory effect of bran on iron absorption in man. *Am J Clin Nutr* 34:1469, 1981.

153. MORRIS ER, ELLIS R: Phytate, wheat bran and bioavailability of dietary iron, in Kies C (ed): *Nutritional Bioavailability of Iron*. Washington, DC, American Chemical Society, 1982, p 121.

154. JACOBS A, GREENMAN DA: Availability of food iron. *Br Med J* 1:673, 1969.

155. CONRAD ME, BENJAMIN BI, WILLIAMS HL, FOY AL: Human absorption of hemoglobin iron. *Gastroenterology* 53:5, 1967.

156. JACOBS P, BOTHWELL TH, CHARLTON RW: Role of hydrochloric acid in iron absorption. *J Appl Physiol* 19:187, 1964.

157. SKIKNE BS, LYNCH SR, COOK JD: Role of gastric acid in food iron absorption. *Gastroenterology* 81:1068, 1981.

158. BEZWODA WR, CHARLTON RW, BOTHWELL TH, TORRANCE JD, MAYET F: Gastric hydrochloric acid and iron absorption. *J Lab Clin Med* 92:108, 1978.

159. RICHTER GW, LEE YH: Absorption of iron from gut into blood; sex- and time-related studies in rats. *Experientia* 38:583, 1982.

160. PARMLEY RT, BARTON JC, CONRAD ME: Ultrastructural localization of transferrin, transferrin receptor and iron binding sites on human placental and duodenal microvilli. *Br J Haematol* 60:81, 1985.

161. THOMSON ABR, VALBERG LS: Kinetics of intestinal iron absorption in the rat: Effect of cobalt. *Am J Physiol* 220:1080, 1971.

162. FAIRWEATHER-TAIT SJ, WRIGHT AJA: The influence of previous iron intake on the estimation of bioavailability of iron from a test meal given to rats. *Br J Nutr* 51:185, 1984.

163. COX TM, PETERS TJ: *In vitro* studies of duodenal iron uptake in patients with primary and secondary iron storage disease. *Q J Med* 49:249, 1980.

164. CONRAD ME Jr, CROSBY WH: Intestinal mucosal mechanisms controlling iron absorption. *Blood* 22:406, 1963.

165. CHARLTON RW, JACOBS P, TORRANCE JD, BOTHWELL TH: The role of ferritin in iron absorption. *Lancet* 2:762, 1963.

166. POWELL LW, CAMPBELL CB, WILSON E: Intestinal mucosal uptake of iron and iron retention in idiopathic haemochromatosis as evidence for a mucosal abnormality. *Gut* 11:727, 1970.

167. IDZERDA RL, HUEBERS H, FINCH CA, MCNIGHT GS: Rat transferrin gene expression: Tissue-specific regulation by iron deficiency. *Biochemistry* 83:3723, 1986.

168. WALTERS GO, JACOBS A, WORWOOD M, TREVETT D: Iron absorption in normal subjects and patients with idiopathic hemochromatosis: Relationship with serum ferritin concentration. *Gut* 16:188, 1975.

169. CHARLTON RW, DERMAN D, SKIKNE B, LYNCH SR, SAYERS MH, TORRANCE JD, BOTHWELL TH: Iron stores, serum ferritin and iron absorption, in Brown EB, Aisen P, Fielding J, Crichton RR (eds): *Proteins of Iron Metabolism*. New York, Grune & Stratton, 1977, p 387.

170. HEINRICH HC, BENDER-GOTZE CH, GABBE EE, BARTELS H, OPPITZ KH: Absorption of inorganic iron ($^{59}Fe^{2+}$) in relation to iron stores in pancreatic exocrine insufficiency due to cystic fibrosis. *Klin Wochenschr* 55:587, 1977.

171. BEZWODA WR, BOTHWELL TH, TORRANCE JD, MacPHAIL AP, CHARLTON RW, KAY G, LEVIN J: The relationship between marrow iron stores, plasma ferritin concentrations and iron absorption. *Scand J Haematol* 22:113, 1979.

172. BOTHWELL TH, PRIBILLA WF, MEBUST W, FINCH CA: Iron metabolism in the pregnant rabbit. Iron transport across the placenta. *Am J Physiol* 193:615, 1958.

173. BENDER-GOTZE C, HEINRICH HC, GABBE EE, OPPITZ KH, SCHAFER KH, SCHROTER W, WHANG DH: Intestinal iron absorption under the influence of available storage iron and erythroblastic hyperplasia. *Z Kinderheilk* 118:283, 1975.

174. MODELL B, BERDOUKAS V: *The Clinical Approach to Thalassaemia*. London, New York, Grune & Stratton, 1984.

175. CROSBY WH: Hemochromatosis and hemolytic disease. *Arch Intern Med* 140:894, 1980.

176. MODELL CB: Transfusional haemochromatosis, in Kief H (ed): *Iron Metabolism and Its Disorders*. Amsterdam, Excerpta Medica, 1975, p 230.

177. HUEBERS HA, FINCH CA: Transferrin: Physiologic behaviour and clinical implications. *Blood* 64:763, 1984.

178. CARTWRIGHT GE, EDWARDS CO, SKOLNICK EMH, FLMOS DB: Association of HLA-linked hemochromatosis with idiopathic refractory sideroblastic anemia. *J Clin Invest* 65:989, 1980.

179. MOHLER DN, WHEBY MS: Hemochromatosis heterozygotes may have significant iron overload when they also have hereditary spherocytosis. *Am J Med Sci* 292:320, 1986.

180. SIMON M, BEAUMONT C, BRIERE J, BRISSOT P, DEUGNIER Y, EDAN G, FAUCHET R, GARO G, CHANDOUR C, GROLLEAU J, GROSBOIS B, KEMP FM, LEBLAY R, LE MIGNON L, LE PRISE PY: Is the HLA-linked haemochromatosis allele implicated in idiopathic sideroblastic anaemia? *Br J Haematol* 60:75, 1985.

181. CROSBY WH: Editorial review. The control of iron balance by the intestinal mucosa. *Blood* 22:44, 1963.

182. CHARLTON RW, JACOBS P, TORRANCE JD, BOTHWELL TH: The role of the intestinal mucosa in iron absorption. *J Clin Invest* 44:543, 1965.

183. HUEBERS H, HUEBERS E, CRICHTON RR: Isolation and characterization of rat mucosal ferritin. *FEBS Lett.* 44:302, 1974.

184. HUEBERS H, HUEBERS E, FORTH W, RUMMEL W: Iron absorption and iron-binding proteins in intestinal mucosa of mice with sex-linked anaemia. *Hoppe-Seylers Z Physiol Chem* 355:1159, 1974.

185. SCHADE SG, FELSHER BF, CONRAD ME: An effect of intestinal motility on iron absorption. *Proc Soc Exp Biol Med* 130:757, 1969.

186. LEVINE PH, LEVINE AJ, WEINTRAUB L: The role of transferrin in the control of iron absorption studies on a cellular level. *J Lab Clin Med* 80:333, 1972.

187. ROSENMUND A, GERBER S, HUEBERS H, FINCH C: Regulation of iron absorption and storage iron turnover. *Blood* 56:30, 1980.

188. CAVILL I, WORWOOD M, JACOBS A: Internal regulation of iron absorption. *Nature* 256:328, 1975.

189. HERSHKO C: Storage iron regulation, in Brown EB (ed): *Progress in Hematology*. New York, Grune & Stratton, 1977, p 105.

190. FINCH CA, HUEBERS H, ENG M, MILLER L: Effect of transfused reticulocytes on iron exchange. *Blood* 59:364, 1982.

191. SIMON M, ALEXANDRE J-L, RAUCHET R, GENETET B, BOUREL M: The genetics of hemochromatosis. *Prog Med Genet* 4:135, 1980.

192. POWELL LW: Iron storage in relatives of patients with haemochromatosis and in relatives of patients with alcoholic cirrhosis and haemosiderosis. A comparative study of 27 families. *Q J Med* 34:427, 1965.

193. SCHEINBERG IH: The genetics of hemochromatosis. *Arch Intern Med* 132:126, 1973.

194. SADDI R, FEINGOLD J: Idiopathic haemochromatosis: An autosomal recessive disease. *Clin Genet* 5:234, 1974.

195. SIMON M, PAWLOTSKY Y, BOUREL M, FAUCHET R, GENETET B: Hemochromatose idiopathique: Maladie associée a l'antigene tissulaire HL-A3? *Nouv Presse Med* 4:1432, 1975.

196. WALTERS JM, WATT PW, STEVEN FM, et al: HLA antigens in haemochromatosis. *Br Med J* 4:520, 1975.

197. SHEWAN WG, MOUAT SA, LLAN TM: HLA antigens in haemochromatosis. *Br Med J* 1:281, 1976.

198. BOMFORD A, EDDLESTON ALWF, KENNEDY LA, BATCHELOR LH, WILLIAMS R: Histo-compatibility antigens as marker of abdominal iron metabolism in patients with idiopathic haemochromatosis and their relatives. *Lancet* 1:327, 1977.

199. MORRIS PJ, VAUGHAN H, TAIT BD, MacKAY R: Histo-compatibility antigens (HLA): Association with immunopathic diseases and with response to microbial antigens. *Aust NZ J Med* 7:616, 1977.

200. HENKE J, UNGAR W: HLA-antigens in idiopathic haemochromatosis (I.H.) preliminary report. *Z Immunitaetsforsch Immunobiol* 154:41, 1978.

201. LAWKENS P, VERSIECK J, DE POTTER E, BARBIER F: Association of HLA antigens with idiopathic hemochromatosis. *Gastroenterology* 75:1351, 1978.

202. SIMON M, BOUREL M, GENETET B, FAUCHET R, EDAN G, BRISSOT P: Association of HLA antigens with idiopathic hemochromatosis. *Gastroenterology* 75:3151, 1978.

203. LIPINSKI M, HORS J, SALAEUN JP, SADDI R, PASSA P, LAFAURIE S, FEINGOLD N, DAUSSET J: Idiopathic hemochromatosis: Linkage with HLA. *Tissue Antigens* 11:471, 1978.

204. DYRSZKA H, EBERHARDT G, ECKERT G: HL-phenotype and hemochromatosis in Germany. *Gastroenterology* 75:555, 1978.

205. SIMON M, LE MIGNON L, FAUCHET R, YAOUANQ J, DAVID V, EDAN G, BOUREL M: A study of 609 HLA haplotypes marking for the hemochromatosis gene: (1) Mapping of the gene near the HLA-A locus and characters required to define a heterozygous population and (2) hypothesis concerning the underlying cause of hemochromatosis-HLA association. *Am J Hum Genet* 41:89, 1987.

206. SIMON M, BOUREL M, GENETET B, FAUCHET R, EDAN G, BRISSOT P: Idiopathic hemochromatosis and iron overload in alcoholic liver disease: Differentiation by HLA phenotypes. *Gastroenterology* 73:655, 1977.

207. KIDD KK: Genetic linkage and hemochromatosis. *N Engl J Med* 301:209, 1979.

208. SIMON M, BOUREL M, GENETET B, FAUCHET R: Idiopathic hemochromatosis. Demonstration of recessive transmission and early detection by family HLA typing. *N Engl J Med* 297:1017, 1977.

209. KRAVITZ K, SKOLNICK M, CANNINGS C, CARMELLI D, BATY B, AMOS B, JOHNSON A, MENDEL N, EDWARDS C, CARTWRIGHT G: Genetic linkage between hereditary hemochromatosis and HLA. *Am J Hum Genet* 31:601, 1979.

210. LALOUEL JM, LE MIGNON L, SIMON M, FAUCHET R, BOUREL M, RAO DC, MORTON NE: Genetic analysis of idiopathic hemochromatosis using both

qualitative (disease status) and quantitative (serum iron) information. *Am J Hum Genet* 37:300, 1985.

211. EDWARDS CQ, GRIFFEN LM, DADONE MM, SKOLNICK MH, KUSHNER JP: Mapping the locus for hereditary hemochromatosis: Localization between HLA-B and HLA-A. *Am J Hum Genet* 38:805, 1986.

212. DAVID V, PAUL P, SIMON M, LE GALL J-Y, FAUCHET R, GICQUEL I, DUGAST I, LE MIGNON L, YAOUANQ J, COHEN D, BOUREL M: DNA polymorphism related to the idiopathic hemochromatosis gene: Evidence in recombinant family. *Hum Genet* 74:113, 1986.

213. SHELDON JH: *Haemochromatosis.* London, Oxford University Press, 1935.

214. FINCH SC, FINCH CA: Idiopathic hemochromatosis, an iron storage disease. A. Iron metabolism in hemochromatosis. *Medicine (Baltimore),* 34:381, 1955.

215. FAIRBANKS VF, FAHEY JL, BUETLER E: In *Clinical Disorders of Iron Metabolism.* New York and London, Grune & Stratton, 1971.

216. CHARLTON RW, HAWKINS DM, MAVOR MO, BOTHWELL TH: Hepatic storage iron concentrations in different population groups. *Am J Clin Nutr* 23:358, 1970.

217. COOK JD, FINCH CA, SMITH N: Evaluation of the iron status of a population. *Blood* 48:449, 1976.

218. MacSWEEN RNM, SCOTT AR: Hepatic cirrhosis: A clinico-pathological review of 520 cases. *J Clin Pathol* 26:936, 1972.

219. LINDMARK B, ERIKSSON S: Regional differences in the idiopathic hemochromatosis gene frequency in Sweden. *Acta Med Scand* 218:299, 1985.

220. CARTWRIGHT GE, EDWARDS CQ, KRAVITZ K, SKOLNICK M, AMOS DB, JOHNSON A, BUSKJAER L: Hereditary hemochromatosis. Phenotypic expression of the disease. *N Engl J Med* 301:175, 1979.

221. VALBERG LS, SORBIE J, LUDWIG J, PELLETIER O: Serum ferritin and the iron status of Canadians. *Can Med Assoc J* 114:471, 1976.

222. OLSSON KS, RITTER B, ROSEN U, HEEDMAN PA, STAUGARD F: Prevalence of iron overload in central Sweden. *Acta Med Scand* 213:145, 1983.

223. OLSSON KS, ERIKSSON K, RITTER B, HEEDMAN PA: Screening for iron overload using transferrin saturation. *Acta Med Scand* 215:105, 1984.

224. TANNER AR, DESAI S, LU W, WRIGHT R: Screening for haemochromatosis in the UK: Preliminary results. *Gut* 26:1139, 1985.

225. MEYER TE, BALLOT D, BOTHWELL TH, GREEN A, DERMAN DP, BAYNES RD, JENKINS T, JOOSTE PL, DU TOIT ED, JACOBS P: The HLA linked iron loading gene in an Afrikaner population. *J Med Genet* 24:348, 1987.

226. DEBRE R, DREYFUS J-C, FREZAL J, LABIE D, LAMY M, MAROTEAUX P, SCHAPIRA F, SCHAPIRA G: Genetics of haemochromatosis. *Ann Hum Genet* 23:16, 1958.

227. MOTULSKY AG: Genetics of hemochromatosis. *N Engl J Med* 301:1291, 1979.

228. LUKE CG, DAVIS PS, DELLER DJ: Gastric iron binding in haemochromatosis, secondary iron overload, cirrhosis and diabetes. *Lancet* 2:844, 1968.

229. WYNTER CVA, WILLIAMS R: Iron-binding properties of gastric juice in idiopathic haemochromatosis. *Lancet* 2:534, 1968.

230. BEZWODA WR, DISLER PB, LYNCH SR, CHARLTON RW, TORRANCE JD, DERMAN DP, BOTHWELL TH, WALKER RB, MAYET F: Patterns of food iron absorption in iron-deficient white and Indian subjects and in venesected haemochromatotic patients. *Br J Haematol* 33:265, 1976.

231. HALLIDAY JW, MACK U, POWELL LW: Duodenal ferritin content and structure. *Arch Intern Med* 138:1109, 1978.

232. BOENDER CA, VERLOOP MC: Iron absorption, iron loss and iron retention in man: Studies after oral administration of a tracer dose of $^{59}FeSO_4$ and $^{131}BaSO_4$. *Br J Haematol* 17:45, 1969.

233. MARX JJM:: Mucosal uptake, mucosal transfer and retention of iron, measured by whole body counting. *Scand J Haematol* 23:293, 1979.

234. COX TM, PETERS TJ: In vitro studies of duodenal iron uptake in patients with primary and secondary iron storage disease. *Q J Med* 49:249, 1980.

235. BOTHWELL TH, JACOBS P, TORRANCE JD: Studies on the behaviour of transferrin in idiopathic haemochromatosis. *S Afr J Med Sci* 27:35, 1962.

236. WHEBY MS, BALCERZAK SP, ANDERSON P, CROSBY WH: Brief report: Clearance of iron from hemochromatosis and normal transferrin in vivo. *Blood* 24:765, 1964.

237. JENKINS T, BOTHWELL TH, MAIER C, AVRIL LAIDIER: Is transferrin normal in idiopathic haemochromatosis? *Br J Haematol* 52:4933, 1982.

238. MILLER YE, JONES C, SCOGGIN C, MORSE H, SELIGMAN P: Chromosome 3q (22-ter) encodes the human transferrin receptor. *Am J Hum Genet* 35:573, 1983.

239. POLLYCOVE M: Hemochromatosis, in Stanbury JB, Wyngaarden JB, Fredrickson DS (eds): *The Metabolic Basis of Inherited Disease,* 4th ed. New York, McGraw-Hill, 1978, p 1128.

240. BATEY RG, PETTIT JE, NICHOLAS AW, SHERLOCK S, HOFFBRAND AV: Hepatic iron clearance from serum in treated hemochromatosis. *Arch Dermatol* 113:161, 1977.

241. CHAPMAN RW, MORGAN MY, BELL R, SHERLOCK S: Hepatic iron uptake in alcoholic liver disease. *Gastroenterology* 84:143, 1983.

242. MAZUR A, SACKLER M: Haemochromatosis and hepatic xanthine oxidase. *Lancet* 1:254, 1967.

243. AWAI M, BROWN EB: Examination of the role of xanthine oxidase in iron absorption by the rat. *J Lab Clin Med* 733:366, 1969.

244. GREEN R, LEVIN NW, SAMASSA D, CHARLTON RW, BOTHWELL TH: The effect of allopurinol on iron metabolism. *S Afr Med J* 42:776, 1968.

245. POWELL LW, ALPERT E, ISSELBACHER KJ, DRYSDALE JW: Abnormality in tissue isoferritin distribution in idiopathic haemochromatosis. *Nature* 250:333, 1974.

246. POWELL LW, HALLIDAY JW, MCKEERING LV, TWEEDALE R: Alterations in serum and tissue isoferritins in disease states. II. Hemochromatosis and malignant disease, in Brown EB, Aisen P, Fielding J (eds): *Proteins of Iron Metabolism.* New York, San Francisco, London, Grune & Stratton, 1977, p 61.

247. HALLIDAY JW, MCKEERING LV, TWEEDAL R, POWELL LW: Serum ferritin in haemochromatosis: Changes in the isoferritin composition during venesection therapy. *Br J Haematol* 36:395, 1977.

248. WAGSTAFF M, WORWOOD M, JACOBS A: Properties of human tissue isoferritins. *Biochem J* 173:969, 1978.

249. BEAUMONT C, SIMON M, SMITH PM, WORWOOD M: Hepatic serum ferritin concentrations in patients with idiopathic haemochromatosis. *Gastroenterology* 79:877, 1980.

250. JACOBS A, SUMMERS MR: Iron uptake and ferritin synthesis by peripheral blood leukocytes in patients with primary idiopathic haemochromatosis. *Br J Haematol* 49:649, 1981.

251. BASSETT ML, DOVAN TJ, HALLIDAY JW: Ferritin synthesis in peripheral blood monocytes in idiopathic haemochromatosis. *J Lab Clin Med* 100:137, 1982.

252. BRINK B, DISLER P, LYNCH S, JACOBS P, CHARLTON R, BOTHWELL TH: Patterns of iron storage in dietary iron overload and idiopathic hemochromatosis. *J Lab Clin Med* 88:725, 1977.

253. COOK JD, BARRY WE, HERSHKO C, FILLET G, FINCH GA: Iron kinetics with emphasis on iron overload. *Am J Pathol* 72:337, 1973.

254. SIZEMORE DJ, BASSET ML: Monocyte transferrin-iron uptake in hereditary haemochromatosis. *Am J Hematol* 16:347, 1984.

255. BJÖRN-RASMUSSEN E, HAGEMAN J, VAN DER DUNGEN P: Transferrin receptors on circulating monocytes in hereditary haemochromatosis. *Scand J Hematol* 34:308, 1985.

256. SAINT EG: Hemochromatosis. *Med J Aust* 50:137, 1963.

257. MacDONALD RA: In *Hemochromatosis and Hemosiderosis.* Springfield, CC Thomas, 1964.

258. CONRAD ME, BARTON JC: Anemia and iron kinetics in alcoholism. *Semin Hematol* 17:149, 1980.

259. BOTHWELL TH, SEFTEL H, JACOBS P, TORRANCE JD, BAUMSLAG N: Iron overload in Bantu subjects. Studies on the availability of iron in Bantu beer. *Am J Clin Nutr* 14:47, 1964.

260. GORDEUK VR, BOYD RD, BRITTENHAM GM: Dietary iron overload persists in rural sub-Saharan Africa. *Lancet* 1:1310, 1986.

261. DERMAN DP, BOTHWELL TH, TORRANCE JD, BEZWODA WR, MacPHAIL AP, KEW MC, SAYERS MH, DISLER PB, CHARLTON RW: Iron absorption from maize (Zea mays) and sorghum (Sorghum vulgare) beer. *Br J Nutr* 43:271, 1980.

262. PERMAN G: Hemochromatosis and red wine. *Acta Med Scand* 182:281, 1967.

263. BARRY M: Iron overload: Clinical aspects, evaluation and treatment. *Clin Haematol* 2:405, 1973.

264. ANGUISSOLA AB: The nutritional value of wine as regards its iron content, in Harwerth HG, Vannotti A (eds): *Iron Deficiency, Pathogenesis, Clinical Aspects Therapy.* New York, Academic, 1970, p 71.

265. CELADA A, RUDOLF H, DONATH A: Effect of a single ingestion of alcohol on iron absorption. *Am J Hematol* 5:225, 1978.

266. BEZWODA WR, TORRANCE JD, BOTHWELL TH, MacPHAIL AP, GRAHAM B, MILLS W: Iron absorption from red and white wines. *Scand J Haematol* 34:121, 1985.

267. CHARLTON RW, JACOBS P, SEFTEL H, BOTHWELL TH: Effect of alcohol on iron absorption. *Br Med J* 2:1427, 1964.

268. CELADA A, RUDOLF H, DONATH A: Effect of experimental chronic alcohol ingestion and folic acid deficiency on iron absorption. *Blood* 54:906, 1979.

269. DAVIS AE, BADENOCH J: Iron absorption in pancreatic disease. *Lancet* 2:6, 1962.

270. MURRAY MJ, STEIN N: Does the pancreas influence iron absorption? A critical review of information to date. *Gastroenterology* 51:694, 1966.

271. BALCERZAK SP, PETERNEI WW, HEINLE EW: Iron absorption in chronic pancreatitis. *Gastroenterology* 53:257, 1967.

272. KAVIN H, CHARLTON RW, JACOBS P, BOTHWELL TH: Effect of the exocrine pancreatic secretions on iron absorption. *Gut* 8:556, 1967.

273. CALLENDER ST, MALPAS JS: Absorption of iron in cirrhosis of liver. *Br Med J* 2:1516, 1963.

274. GREENBERG MS, STROHMEYER G, HINE GJ, KEENE WR, CURTIS G, CHALMERS TC: Studies in iron absorption. III. Body radioactivity measurements of patients with liver disease. *Gastroenterology* 46:651, 1964.
275. FRIEDMAN BI, SCHAEFER JW, SCHIFF L: Increased iron-59 absorption in patients with hepatic cirrhosis. *J Nucl Med* 7:594, 1966.
276. BOTHWELL TH: Total iron loss and relative importance of different sources, in Hallberg L, Harwerth HG, Vannotti A (eds): *Iron Deficiency Pathogenesis Clinical Aspects Therapy*. London, New York, Academic, 1970, p 151.
277. AUZEPY P, VALETTE H, ALBESSARD F, DEPARIS M: Cardiomyopathie alcoholique avec hypersideremie par absorption digestive exageree du fer. *Ann Med Interne (Paris)* 125:923, 1974.
278. CONN HO: Portacaval anastomosis and hepatic haemosiderin deposition: A prospective, controlled investigation. *Gastroenterology* 62:61, 1972.
279. WILLIAMS R, WILLIAMS HS, SCHEUER PJ, PITCHER CS, LOIZEAN E, SHERLOCK S: Iron absorption and siderosis in chronic liver disease. *Q J Med* 36:151, 1967.
280. LUNDVALL O, WEINFELD A, LUNDIN P: Iron stores in alcohol abusers. I. Liver iron. *Acta Med Scand* 185:259, 1969.
281. LUNDVALL O, WEINFELD A: Iron stores in alcohol abusers. II. As measured with the desferrioxamine test. *Acta Med Scand* 185:271, 1969.
282. JAKOBOVITZ AW, MORGAN MY, SHERLOCK S: Hepatic siderosis in alcoholics. *Am J Digest Dis* 24:305, 1979.
283. LESAGE GD, BALDUS WP, FAIRBANKS VF, BAGGENSTOSS AH, MCCALL JT, MOORE SB, TASWELL HF, GORDON H: Hemochromatosis: Genetic or alcohol-induced? *Gastroenterology* 84:1471, 1983.
284. MILDER MS, COOK JD, STRAY S, FINCH C: Idiopathic hemochromatosis, an interim report. *Medicine (Baltimore)* 59:34, 1980.
285. ELDER GH, SHEPPARD DM, DE SALAMANCA RE, OLMOS A: Identification of two types of porphyria cutanea tarda by measurements of erythrocyte uroporphyrinogen decarboxylase. *Clin Sci* 58:477, 1980.
286. DE VERNEUIL H, GRANDCHAMP B, ROMEO PH, RAICH N, BEAUMONT C, GOOSEN M, NICHOLAS H, NORDMANN Y: Molecular analysis of uroporphyrinogen decarboxylase deficiency in a family with two cases of hepatoerythropoietic porphyria. *J Clin Invest* 77:431, 1986.
287. PIMSTONE NZ: Porphyria cutanea tarda. *Semin Liver Dis* 2:132, 1982.
288. KUSHNER JP, EDWARDS CQ, DADONE MN, SKOLNICK MH: Heterozygosity for HLA-linked hemochromatosis as a likely cause of the hepatic siderosis associated with sporadic porphyria cutanea tarda. *Gastroenterology* 88:1232, 1985.
289. ELDER GH: Porphyria cutanea tarda and HLA linked hemochromatosis. *Gastroenterology* 88:1276, 1985.
290. HINES JD: Effects of alcohol on inborn errors of metabolism: Porphyria cutanea tarda and hemochromatosis. *Semin Hematol* 17:113, 1980.
291. LEFKOWITCH JH, GROSSMAN ME: Hepatic pathology in porphyria cutanea tarda. *Liver* 3:19, 1983.
292. BEAUMONT C, NORDMANN Y, FAUCHET R: (Correspondence) *Gastroenterology* 90:800, 1986.
293. EPSTEIN JH, REDEKER AG: *N Engl J Med* 279:1301, 1968.
294. TURNBULL A, BAKER H, VERNON-ROBERTS B, MAGNUS IA: Iron metabolism in porphyria cutanea tarda and in erythropoietic protoporphyria. *Q J Med* 42:341, 1973.
295. GIBERTINI P, ROCCHI E, CASSAHELLI M, PIETRANGELO A, VENTURA E: Advances in the treatment of porphyria cutanea tarda. Effectiveness of slow subcutaneous desferrioxamine infusion. *Liver* 4:280, 1984.
296. MUKERJI SK, PIMSTONE NR, BURNS M: Dual mechanism of inhibition of rat liver uroporphyrinogen decarboxylase activity by ferrous iron: Its potential role in the genesis of porphyria cutanea tarda. *Gastroenterology* 87:1248, 1984.
297. MUKERJI SK, PIMSTONE NR: Dual effects of hepatic iron in the biochemical expression of the metabolic defect for porphyria cutanea tarda. *Gastroenterology* 84:1387, 1983.
298. KALIVAS JT, PATHAK MA, FITZPATRICK TB: Phlebotomy and iron overload in porphyria cutanea tarda. *Lancet* 1:1184, 1969.
299. GROSSMAN MF, BICKERS DR, POH-FITZPATRICK MG, DELEO VA, HARBER LC: Porphyria cutanea tarda. Clinical features and laboratory findings in 40 patients. *Am J Med* 67:277, 1979.
300. DIAMOND LK, ALLEN DM, MAGILL FB: Congenital (erythroid) hypoplastic anemia. A 25 year study. *Am J Dis Child* 102:403, 1961.
301. HERSHKO C, GRAHAM G, BATES GW, RACHMILEWITZ EA: Non-specific serum iron in thalassemia—Abnormal serum iron fraction of potential toxicity. *Br J Haematol* 40:255, 1978.
302. GRAHAM G, BATES GW, RACHMILEWITZ EZ, HERSHKO C: Non-specific serum iron in thalassemia: Quantitation and chemical reactivity. *Am J Hematol* 6:207, 1979.
303. BRISSOT P, WRIGHT TL, MA W-L, WEISIGER RA: Efficient clearance of non-transferrin-bound iron by rat liver: Implications for hepatic loading in iron overload states. *J Clin Invest* 76:1463, 1985.
304. HEINRICH HC, GABBE EE, OPPITZ KH, WHANG DH, GOTZE CH B, SCHAFER KH, SCHROTER W, PFAU AA: Absorption of inorganic and food iron in children with heterozygous and homozygous β-thalassemia. *Z Kinderheilk* 115:1, 1973.
305. WHEBY MS, UMPIERRE G: Effect of transferrin saturation on iron absorption in man. *N Engl J Med* 271:1391, 1964.
306. MACPHAIL AP, SIMON MO, TORRANCE JD, CHARLTON RW, BOTHWELL TH, ISAACSON C: Changing patterns of dietary iron overload in black South Africans. *Am J Clin Nutr* 32:1272, 1979.
307. BOTHWELL TH, ABRAHAMS C, BRADLOW BA, CHARLTON RW: Idiopathic and Bantu hemochromatosis. Comparative histological study. *Arch Pathol* 79:163, 1965.
308. BOTHWELL TH, BRADLOW BA: Siderosis in the Bantu. A combined histopathological and chemical study. *Arch Pathol* 70:279, 1960.
309. ISAACSON C, SEFTEL H, KEELEY KJ, BOTHWELL TH: Siderosis in the Bantu. The relationship between iron overload and cirrhosis. *J Lab Clin Med* 58:845, 1961.
310. BRADLOW B, DUNN J, HIGGISON J: The effect of cirrhosis on iron storage. *Am J Pathol* 3:221, 1961.
311. CHARLTON RW, ABRAHAMS C, BOTHWELL TH: Idiopathic hemochromatosis and chemical findings in four patients. *Arch Pathol* 83:132, 1967.
312. LYNCH SR, LIPSCHITZ DA, BOTHWELL TH, CHARLTON RW: Iron and the reticuloendothelial system, in Jacobs A, Worwood M (eds): *Biochemistry and Medicine*. New York, Academic, 1974, p 563.
313. MURRAY MJ, STEIN N: Does the pancreas influence iron absorption? A critical review of information to date. *Gastroenterology* 51:694, 1966.
314. GRACE NA, POWELL LW: Iron storage disorders of the liver. *Gastroenterology* 64:1257, 1974.
315. PERKINS KW, MCINNES IWS, BLACKBURN CRB, BEAL RW: Idiopathic haemochromatosis in children. Report of a family. *Am J Med* 39:118, 1965.
316. LOSOWSKY MS, WILSON AR: Whole-body counting of the absorption and distribution of iron in haemochromatosis. *Clin Sci* 32:151, 1967.
317. VALBERG LS, GHENT CN, LLOYD DA, FREI JV, CHAMBERLAIN MJ: Iron absorption in idiopathic hemochromatosis: Relationship to serum ferritin concentration in asymptomatic relatives. *Clin Invest Med* 2:17, 1979.
318. SARGENT T, SAITO H, WINCHELL HS: Iron absorption in hemochromatosis before and after phlebotomy therapy. *J Nucl Med* 12:660, 1971.
319. MILDER MS, COOK JD, FINCH CA: The influence of food iron absorption on the plasma iron level in idiopathic hemochromatosis. *Acta Haematol (Basel)* 60:65, 1978.
320. NIEDERAU C, FISCHER R, SONNENBERG A, STREMMEL W, TRAMPISCH HJ, STROHMEYER G: Survival and causes of death in cirrhotic and in noncirrhotic patients with primary hemochromatosis. *N Engl J Med* 313:1256, 1985.
321. CHEVRANT-BRETON J, SIMON M, BOUREL M, FERRAND B: Cutaneous manifestations of idiopathic hemochromatosis. *Arch Dermatol* 113:161, 1977.
322. POWELL LW, KERR JFR: The pathology of the liver in hemochromatosis, in Ioachim HL (ed): *Pathobiology Annual*. New York, Appleton-Century-Crofts, 1975, p 317.
323. BLOCK M, MOORE G, WASI P, HAIBY G: Histogenesis of the hepatic lesion in primary hemochromatosis: With consideration of the pseudo-iron deficient state produced by phlebotomies. *Am J Pathol* 47:89, 1965.
324. BRADBEAR RA, BAIN C, SISKIND V, SCHOFIELD FD, WEBB S, AXELSEN EM, HALLIDAY JM, BASSETT ML, POWELL LW: Cohort study of internal malignancy in genetic hemochromatosis and other chronic nonalcoholic liver diseases. *J Natl Cancer Inst* 75:81, 1985.
325. BASSETT M, HALLIDAY JW, POWELL LW: Value of hepatic iron measurements in early hemochromatosis and determination of the critical iron level associated with fibrosis. *Hepatology* 6:24, 1986.
326. DYMOCK IW, CASSAR J, PYKE DA, OAKLEY WG, WILLIAMS R: Observations on the pathogenesis, complications and treatment of diabetes in 115 cases of haemochromatosis. *Am J Med* 52:203, 1972.
327. BALCERZAK SP, MINTZ DH, WESTERMAN MP: Diabetes mellitus and idiopathic hemochromatosis. *Am J Med Sci* 255:53, 1968.
328. POZZA G, GHINDONI A: Studies on the diabetic syndrome of idiopathic haemochromatosis. *Diabetologia* 4:83, 1968.
329. MEGYESI C, SAMOLS E, MARKS V: Glucose tolerance and diabetes in chronic liver disease. *Lancet* 2:1051, 1967.
330. SHERWIN R, JOSHI P, HENDLER R, FELIG P, CONN HO: Hyperglucagonemia in Laennec's cirrhosis. *N Engl J Med* 290:239, 1974.
331. NIEDERAU C, BERGER M, STREMMEL W, STARKE A, STROHMEYER G, EBERT R, SIEGEL E, CREUTZFELDT W: Hyperinsulinaemia in noncirrhotic haemochromatosis: Impaired hepatic insulin degradation. *Diabetologia* 26:441, 1984.
332. GRIFFITHS JD, DYMOCK IW, DAVIES EWG, HILL DW, WILLIAMS R: Occurrence and prevalence of diabetic retinopathy in hemochromatosis. *Diabetes* 20:766, 1971.
333. PASSA P, ROUSSELIE F, GAUVILLE C, CANIVET J: Retinopathy and plasma

growth hormone levels in idiopathic hemochromatosis with diabetes. *Diabetes* 26:113, 1977.

334. KLEY HK, NIEDERAU C, STREMMEL W, LAX R, STROHMEYER G, KRÜSKEMPER HL: Conversion of androgens to estrogens in idiopathic hemochromatosis: Comparison with alcoholic liver cirrhosis. *J Clin Endocrinol Metab* 61:1, 1985.

335. STOCKS AE, POWELL LW: Pituitary function in idiopathic haemochromatosis and cirrhosis of the liver. *Lancet* 2:298, 1972.

336. BEZWODA WR, BOTHWELL TH, VAN DER WALT LA, KRONHEIN S, PIMSTONE BL: An investigation into gonadal dysfunction in patients with idiopathic hemochromatosis. *Clin Endocrinol* 6:377, 1977.

337. CHARBONNEL B, CHUPIN M, LE GRAND A, GUILLON J: Pituitary function in idiopathic hemochromatosis: Hormonal study in 36 male patients. *Acta Endocrinol* 98:178, 1981.

338. WALTIM C, KELLY WF, LAING I, BU'LOCK DE: Endocrine abnormalities in idiopathic hemochromatosis. *Q J Med* 205:99, 1983.

339. LEVY CL, CHARLTON HE: Decreased prolactin reserve in hemochromatosis. *J Clin Endocrinol Metab* 47:444, 1978.

340. CUTLER DJ, ISNER JM, BRACEY AW, HUFNAGEL CA, CONRAD PW, ROBERTS WC, KERWIN DM, WEINTRAUB AM: Hemochromatosis heart disease: An unemphasized cause of potentially reversible restrictive cardiomyopathy. *Am J Med* 69:923, 1980.

341. BUJA LM, ROBERTS WC: Iron in the heart. Etiology and clinical significance. *Am J Med* 51:209, 1971.

342. HAMILTON FBD, BOMFORD AB, LAWS JW, WILLIAMS R: The natural history of arthritis in idiopathic haemochromatosis: Progression of the clinical and radiological features over ten years. *Q J Med* 199:321, 1981.

343. SCHATTENKIRCHNER M, FISCHBACHER L, GIEBNER-FISCHBACHER U, ALBERT ED: Arthropathic bei der idiopathischen Hämochromatose. *Klin Wochenschr* 61:119, 1983.

344. M'SEFFAR A, FORNASIER VL, FOX IH: Arthropathy as the major clinical indicator of occult iron storage disease. *JAMA* 238:1825, 1977.

345. ASKARI AD, MUIR WA, ROSNER IA, MOSKOWITZ RW, MCLAREN GD, BRAUN WE: Arthritis of hemochromatosis: Clinical spectrum, relation to histocompatibility antigens, and effectiveness of early phlebotomy. *Am J Med* 75:957, 1983.

346. ABBOTT DF, GRESHAM GA: Arthropathy in transfusional siderosis. *Br Med J* 1:418, 1972.

347. SCHUMACHER HR: Articular cartilage in the degenerative arthropathy of hemochromatosis. *Arthritis Rheum* 25:1460, 1982.

348. ATKINS CJ, MCIVOR J, SMITH PM, HAMILTON E, WILLIAMS R: Chondrocalcinosis and arthropathy: Studies in haemochromatosis and in idiopathic chondrocalcinosis. *Q J Med* 39:71, 1970.

349. ADAMSON TC, RESNIK CS, GUERRA J, VINT VC, WEISMAN MH, RESNICK D: Hand and wrist arthropathies of hemochromatosis and calcium pyrophosphate deposition disease: Distinct radiographic features. *Radiology* 147:377, 1983.

350. MACSWEEN RNM: Acute abdominal crises, circulatory collapse and sudden death in haemochromatosis. *Q J Med* 35:589, 1966.

351. ROBINS-BROWNE RM, RABSON AR, KOORNHOF HJ: Generalized infection with *Yersinia enterocolitica* and the role of iron. *Contrib Microbiol Immunol* 5:277, 1979.

352. CAPRON J-P, CAPRON-CHIVRAC D, TOSSOU H, DELAMARRE J, EF F: Spontaneous *Yersinia enterocolitica* peritonitis in idiopathic hemochromatosis. *Gastroenterology* 87:1372, 1984.

353. ROBINS-BROWNE RM, PRPIC JK: Effects of iron and desferrioxamine on infections with *Yersinia enterocolitica*. *Infect Immun* 47:774, 1985.

354. YAMASHIRO KM: Pasteurella pseudotuberculosis. Acute sepsis with survival. *Arch Intern Med* 128:605, 1971.

355. WEINBERG LR, GORAL A, GRASSO J, FRANZBLAU C, SULLIVAN A, SULLIVAN S: Pathogenesis of hepatic fibrosis in experimental iron overload. *Br J Haematol* 59:321, 1985.

356. VAN ASBECK BS, VERBRUGH HA, VAN OOST BA, MARX JJM, IMHOF HW, VERHOEF J: Listeria monocytogenes meningitis and decreased phagocytosis associated with iron overload. *Br Med J* 284:542, 1982.

357. WATERLOT Y, CANTINIEAUX B, HARIGA-MULLER C, DE MAERTELAERE-LAURENT E, VAN HERWEGHEM JL, FONDU P: Impaired phagocytic activity of neutrophils in patients receiving haemodialysis: The critical role of iron overload. *Br Med J* 291:501, 1985.

358. YAM LT, FINKEL HE, WEINTRAUB LR, CROSBY WH: Circulating iron-containing macrophages in hemochromatosis. *N Engl J Med* 279:512, 1968.

359. GOLDBERG L, MARTI LE, BATCHELOR A: Biochemical changes in the tissues of animals injected with iron. 3. Lipid peroxidation. *Biochem J* 83:291, 1962.

360. BACON BR, TAVILL AS, BRITTENHAM GM, PARK CH, RECKNAGEL RO: Hepatic lipid peroxidation *in vivo* in rats with chronic iron overload. *J Clin Invest* 71:429, 1983.

361. BACON BR, BRITTENHAM GM, TAVILL AS, MCLAREN CE, PARK CH, RECKNAGEL RO: Hepatic lipid peroxidation *in vivo* in rats with chronic dietary iron overload is dependent on hepatic iron concentration. *Trans Assoc Am Physicians* 96:146, 1983.

362. O'CONNELL MJ, WARD RJ, BAUM H, PETERS TJ: The role of iron in ferritin- and haemosiderin-mediated lipid peroxidation in liposomes. *Biochem J* 229:135, 1985.

363. LINK G, PINSON A, HERSHKO C: Heart cells in culture: A model of myocardial iron overload and chelation. *J Lab Clin Med* 106:147, 1985.

364. PETERS TJ, SEYMOUR CA: Acid hydrolase activities and lysosomal integrity in liver biopsies from patients with iron overload. *Clin Sci Molec Med* 50:75, 1976.

365. PETERS TJ, SELDEN C, SEYMOUR CA: Lysosomal disruption in the pathogenesis of hepatic damage in primary and secondary haemochromatosis. *Ciba Found Symp* 51:317, 1977.

366. FLOYD RA: Direct demonstration that ferrous iron complexes of di- and triphosphate nucleotides catalyze hydroxyl free radical formation from hydrogen peroxide. *Arch Biochem Biophys* 225:263, 1983.

367. BUCHER JR, TIEN M, AUST SD: The requirement for ferric iron in the initiation of lipid peroxidation by chelated ferrous iron. *Biochem Biophys Res Commun* 111:777, 1983.

368. RICHTER GW: The iron-loaded cell—The cytopathology of iron storage. *Am J Pathol* 91:363, 1978.

369. SEYMOUR CA, PETERS TJ: Organelle pathology in primary and secondary haemochromatosis with special reference to lysosomal changes. *Br J Haematol* 40:239, 1978.

370. SELDEN C, OWEN M, HOPKINS JMP, PETERS TJ: Studies on the concentration and intracellular localization of iron proteins in liver biopsy specimens from patients with iron overload with special reference to their role in lysosomal disruption. *Br J Haematol* 44:593, 1980.

371. MAK IT, WEGLICKI WB: Characterization of iron-mediated peroxidative injury in isolated hepatic lysomes. *J Clin Invest* 75:58, 1985.

372. BACON BR, PARK CH, BRITTENHAM GM, O'NEILL R, TAVILL AS: Hepatic mitochondrial oxidative metabolism in rats with chronic dietary iron overload. *Hepatology* 5:789, 1985.

373. MASINI A, TRENTI T, VENTURA E, CECCARELLI-STANZANI D, MUSCATELLO V: Functional efficiency of mitochondrial membrane of rats with hepatic chronic iron overload. *Biochem Biophys Res Commun* 124:462, 1984.

374. IANCU TL, NEUSTEIN HB, LANDING BH: The liver in thalassemia major: Ultrastructural observations. *Ciba Found Symp* 51:293, 1977.

375. HUNT J, RICHARDS RJ, HARWOOD RJ, JACOBS A: The effect of desferrioxamine on fibroblasts and collagen formation in cell cultures. *Br J Haematol* 41:69, 1979.

376. ROJKING M, DUNN MA: Hepatic fibrosis. *Gastroenterology* 76:849, 1979.

377. WEINTRAUB LR, GORAL A, GRASSO J, FRANZBLAU C, SULLIVAN S: Pathogenesis of hepatic fibrosis in experimental iron overload. *Br J Haematol* 59:321, 1985.

378. LYNCH SR, SEFTEL HC, TORRANCE JD, CHARLTON RW, BOTHWELL TH: Accelerated oxidative catabolism of ascorbic acid in siderotic Bantu. *Am J Clin Nutr* 20:641, 1967.

379. HANKES LV, JANSEN CR, SCHMAELER M: Ascorbic acid catabolism in Bantu with hemosiderosis (scurvy). *Biochem Med* 9:244, 1974.

380. WAPNICK AA, LYNCH SR, KRAWITZ P, SEFTEL HC, CHARLTON RW, BOTHWELL TH: Effects of iron overload on ascorbic acid metabolism. *Br Med J* 3:704, 1968.

381. MODELL CB, BECK J: Long-term desferrioxamine therapy in thalassemia. *Ann NY Acad Sci* 232:201, 1974.

382. O'BRIEN RT: Ascorbic enhancement of desferrioxamine-induced urinary iron excretion in thalassemia major. *Ann NY Acad Sci* 232:221, 1974.

383. BRISSOT P, DEUGNIER Y, LeTREUT A, REGNOUARD F, SIMON M, BOUREL M: Ascorbic acid status in idiopathic hemochromatosis. *Digestion* 17:479, 1978.

384. HAWKES LV: Influence of iron and ascorbic acid on tryptophan metabolism in man. *Acta Vitaminol Enzymol* 29:174, 1975.

385. SEFTEL HC, MALKIN C, SCHAMAN A, ABRAHAMS C, LYNCH SR, CHARLTON RW, BOTHWELL TH: Osteoporosis, scurvy and siderosis in Johannesburg Bantu. *Br Med J* 1:642, 1966.

386. LYNCH SR, BERELOWITZ I, SEFTEL HC, MILLER GB, KRAWITZ P, CHARLTON RW, BOTHWELL TH: Osteoporosis in Johannesburg Bantu Males. Its relationship to siderosis and ascorbic acid deficiency. *Am J Clin Nutr* 20:799, 1967.

387. SOLOMON L, BEIGHTON P: Rheumatic disorders in the South African negro. Part III. Idiopathic necrosis of the femoral head. *S Afr Med J* 49:1825, 1975.

388. LYNCH SR, SEFTEL HC, WAPNICK AA, CHARLTON RW, BOTHWELL TH: Some aspects of calcium metabolism in normal and osteoporotic Bantu subjects with special reference to the effects of iron overload and ascorbic acid depletion. *S Afr J Med* 35:45, 1970.

389. DE VERNEJOUL MC, POINTILLART A, CYWINER GOLENZER C, MORIEUX C,

BIELAKOFF J, MODROWSKI D, MIRAVET L: Effects of iron overload on bone remodelling in pigs. *Am J Pathol* 116:377, 1984.

390. DELBARRE F: L'osteoporose des hemochromatoses. *Semin Hop* 36:3279, 1960.

391. DU LAC T, DELOUX G, DENIL R: Arthropathies et chondrocalcinoses au cours des hemochromatoses. *Rev Rheum* 34:758, 1967.

392. BORWEIN S, GHENT CN, VALBERG LS: Diagnostic efficacy of screening tests for hereditary hemochromatosis. *Can Med Assoc J* 131:895, 1984.

393. EDWARDS CO, CARTWRIGHT GE, SKOLNICK MH, AMOS DB: Homozygosity for hemochromatosis: Clinical manifestations. *Ann Intern Med* 93:519, 1980.

394. BASSETT ML, HALLIDAY JW, POWELL LW: Genetic hemochromatosis. *Semin Liver Dis* 4:217, 1984.

395. COOK JD: Methods to determine plasma iron and total iron-binding capacity, in Hallberg L, Harwerth HG, Vannotti A (eds): *Iron Deficiency, Pathogenesis, Clinical Aspects, Therapy*. London, New York, Academic, 1969 p 397.

396. DADONE MM, KUSHNER JP, EDWARDS CQ, BISHOP DT, SKOLNICK MH: Hereditary hemochromatosis. Analysis of laboratory expression of the disease by genotype in 18 pedigrees. *Am J Clin Pathol* 78:196, 1982.

397. VAN OOST BA, VAN DEN BELF B, VAN ASBECK S, MARX JJM: Monitoring of intensive phlebotomy therapy in iron overload by serum ferritin assay. *Am J Hematol* 18:7, 1985.

398. WANDS JR, ROWE JA, MEZEY SE, WATERBURY LA, WRIGHT JR, HALLIDAY JW, ISSELBACHER KJ, POWELL LW: Normal serum ferritin concentrations in precirrhotic hemochromatosis. *N Engl J Med* 294:302, 1976.

399. ROWE JW, WANDS JR, MEZEY E, WATERBURY LA, WRIGHT JR, TOBIN J, ANDRES R: Familial hemochromatosis: Characteristics of the precirrhotic stage in a large kindred. *Medicine* 56:197, 1977.

400. TORRANCE JD, BOTHWELL TH: Tissue iron stores, in Cook JD (ed): *Methods in Hematology*. New York, Churchill Livingstone, 1980, p 90.

401. BARRY M, SHERLOCK S: Measurement of liver-iron concentration in needle biopsy specimens. *Lancet* 1:100, 1971.

402. FIELDING J: Desferrioxamine chelatable body iron. *J Clin Pathol* 20:668, 1967.

403. ROUDOT-THORAVAL F, HALPHEN M, LARDE D, GALLIOT M, RYMER J-C, GALACTEROS F, DHUMEAUX D: Evaluation of liver iron content by computed tomography: Its value in the follow-up of treatment in patients with idiopathic hemochromatosis. *Hepatology* 3:974, 1983.

404. BRITTENHAM GM, FARRELL DE, HARRIS JW, FELDMAN ES, DANISH EH, MUIR WA, TRIPP JH, BELLON EM: Magnetic-susceptibility measurement of human iron stores. *N Engl J Med* 3307:1671, 1982.

405. STARK DD, MOSELEY ME, BACON BR, MOSS AA, GOLDBERG HI, BASS NM, JAMES TL: Magnetic resonance imaging and spectroscopy of hepatic iron overload. *Radiology* 154:137, 1985.

406. WIELOPOLSKI L, ANCONA RC, MOSSEY RT, VASWANI AN, COHN SH: Nuclear resonance scattering measurement of human iron stores. *Med Phys* 12:401, 1985.

407. CHAPMAN RW, MORGAN MY, LAULICHT M, HOFFBRAND AV, SHERLOCK S: Hepatic iron stores and markers of iron overload in alcoholics and patients with idiopathic hemochromatosis. *Dig Dis Sci* 27:909, 1982.

408. CROSBY WH: Treatment of haemochromatosis by energetic phlebotomy. One patient's response to the letting of 55 litres of blood in 11 months. *Br J Haematol* 4:82, 1958.

409. HENRY WL, NIENHUIS AW, WIENER M, MILLER DR, CANALE VC, PIOMELLI S: Echo-cardiographic abnormalities in patients with transfusion-dependent anemia and secondary myocardial iron deposition. *Am J Med* 64:547, 1978.

410. WILLIAMS R, SMITH PM, SPICER EJF, BARRY M, SHERLOCK S: Venesection therapy in idiopathic haemochromatosis: An analysis of 40 treated and 18 untreated patients. *Q J Med* 38:1, 1969.

411. NIENHUIS AW, BENZ EJ, PROPPER R, CORASH L, ANDERSON F, BORER J: Thalassemia major: Molecular and clinical aspects. *Ann Intern Med* 91:883, 1979.

412. GRAZIANO JH: Potential usefulness of fine radical scavengers in iron overload, in Bergsma D, Cerami A, Peterson CM, Graziano JH (eds): *Iron Metabolism and Thalassemia*. New York, AR Liss, 1976, p 135.

413. PROPPER RD, COOPER B, RAFO RR, NIENHUIS AW, ANDERSON WF, BUNN HF, ROSENTHAL A, NATHAN DG: Continuous subcutaneous administration of deferoxamine in patients with iron overload. *N Engl J Med* 297:418, 1977.

414. HUSSAIN MAM, FLYNN DM, GREEN N, HOFFBRAND AV: Effect of dose, time and ascorbate on iron excretion after subcutaneous desferrioxamine. *Lancet* 1:977, 1977.

415. PIPPARD MJ, CALLENDER ST, WEATHERALL DJ: Intensive iron-chelation therapy with desferrioxamine in iron-loading anaemias. *Clin Sci Mol Med* 54:99, 1978.

416. CERAMI A, GRADY RW, PETERSON CM, BHARGAVA KK: The status of new iron chelators. *Ann NY Acad Sci* 344:425, 1980.

417. BOMFORD A, WILLIAMS R: Long term results of venesection therapy in idiopathic haemochromatosis. *Q J Med* (New Series) 45:611, 1976.

418. CONTE WJ, ROTTER JI: The use of association data to identify family members at high risk for marker-linked diseases. *Am J Hum Genet* 36:152, 1984.

419. LIN HJ, CONTE WJ, ROTTER JI: Disease risk estimates from marker association data. Application to individuals at risk for hemochromatosis. *Clin Genet* 27:127, 1985.

420. MONSEN ER, HALLBERG L, LAYRISSE M, HEGSTED DM, COOK JD, MERTZ W, FINCH CA: Estimation of available dietary iron. *Am J Clin Nutr* 31:134, 1978.

421. OLSSON KS, RITTER B, LUNDIN PM: Liver affection in iron overload studied with serum ferritin and serum aminotransferases. *Acta Med Scand* 8:58, 1984.

422. BEAUMONT CM, SIMON M, FAUCHET R, HESPEL JP, BRISSOT P, BENETET B, BOUREL M: Serum ferritin as a possible marker of the hemochromatosis allele. *N Engl J Med* 301:169, 1979.

423. BREGMAN H, GELFAND MC, WINCHESTER JF, MANZ HJ, KNEPSHIELD JK, SCHRINER GE: Iron-overload-associated myopathy in patients on maintenance haemodialysis: A histocompatibility-linked disorder. *Lancet* 2:882, 1980.

424. WADDELL J, SASSOON HG, FISHER JD, CARR CJ: A review of the significance of dietary iron on iron storage phenomena. *Life Sci Res Off*, Federation of American Societies for Experimental Biology, Maryland, 1972

425. BOTHWELL TH, DERMAN D, BEZWODA WR, TORRANCE JD, CHARLTON RW: Can iron fortification of flour cause damage to genetic susceptibles (idiopathic haemochromatosis and β-thalassaemia major)? *Hum Genet Suppl* 1:131, 1978.

426. BOTHWELL TH, FINCH CA: *Iron Metabolism*. Boston, Little, Brown, 1962.

427. SCHAFER AI, CHERON RG, DLUHY R, COOPER B, GLEASON RE, SOELDNER JS, BUNN HF: Clinical consequences of acquired transfusional iron overload in adults. *N Engl J Med* 304:319, 1981.

428. MODELL CB, MATTHEWS R: Thalassemia in Britain and Australia, in Bergsma D, Cerami A, Peterson CM, Graziano JH (eds): *Iron Metabolism and Thalassemia*. New York, AR Liss, 1976, p 13.

429. MODELL CB: Total management of thalassemia major. *Arch Dis Child* 52:489, 1977.

430. NIENHUIS AW: Evaluation of cardiac function in patients with thalassemia major. *Ann NY Acad Sci* 344:384, 1980.

431. BARRY M, FLYNN DM, LETSKY EA, RISDON RA: Long term chelation therapy in thalassemia major: Effect on liver iron concentration, liver histology and clinical progress. *Br Med J* 2:16, 1974.

432. MCINTOSH N: Endocrinopathy in thalassemia major. *Arch Dis Child* 51:195, 1976.

433. JOHNSON FE, KROGMAN WM: Patterns of growth in children with thalassemia major. *Ann NY Acad Sci* 232:667, 1974.

434. NECHELES TF, CHUNG S, SABBAH R, WHITTEN D: Intensive transfusion therapy in thalassemia major: An eight-year follow-up. *Ann NY Acad Sci* 232:179, 1974.

435. HERINGTON AC: Studies on the possible mechanism for deficiency of non-suppressible insulin-like activity in thalassemia major. *J Clin Endocrinol Metabol* 52:393, 1981.

436. RISDON RA, BARRY M, FLYNN DM: Transfusional iron overload: The relationship between tissue iron concentration and hepatic fibrosis in thalassaemia. *J Pathol* 116:83, 1975.

437. IANCU TC: Iron overload. *Mol Aspects Med* 6:1, 1982.

438. WITZLEBEN CL, WYATT JP: The effect of long survival on the pathology of thalassaemia major. *J Pathol Bacteriol* 82:1, 1961.

439. BERRY CL, MARSHALL WC: Iron distribution in the liver of patients with thalassemia major. *Lancet* 1:103, 1967.

440. OKON E, LEVU IS, RACHMILEWITZ EA: Splenectomy, iron overload and liver cirrhosis in β-thalassemia major. *Acta Haematol* 56:142, 1976.

441. BORNA-PIGNATTI C, DE STEFANO P, BONGO IG, AVATO F, CAZZOLA M: Spleen iron content is low in thalassaemia. *Am J Pediatr Hematol Oncol* 6:3340, 1984.

442. GRAZIANO HJ, PIOMELLI S, HILGARTNER M, GIARDINA P, KARPATKIN M, ANDREW M, LOIACONO N, SEAMAN C: Chelation therapy in beta-thalassaemia major III. The role of splenectomy in achieving iron balance. *J Pediatr* 99:695, 1981.

443. O'BRIEN RT: Iron overload: Clinical and pathologic aspects in pediatrics. *Semin Hematol* 14:115, 1977.

444. AL DOURI M, WONKE B, FLYNN D, HOFFBRAND V, SCHEUER P, KIBBLER C, BROWN D, THOMAS H: Effects of eight year subcutaneous desferrioxamine on hepatitis status in thalassaemia major, in *Book of Abstracts*. XXI Congress of the International Society of Haematology, 1986.

445. WOLMAN IJ: Transfusion therapy in Cooley's anemia: Growth and health

as related to long-range hemoglobin levels, a progress report. *Ann NY Acad Sci* 119:736, 1964.

446. MASERA G, TERZOLI S, AVANZINI A, FONTANELLI G, MAURI RA, PIACENTINI G, FERRARI M: Evaluation of the supertransfusion regimen in homozygous beta-thalassaemia children. *Br J Haematol* 52:111, 1982.

447. GRAZIANO JH, MARKENSON A, MILLER DR, CHANG H, BESTAK M, MEYERS P, PISCIOTTO P, RIFKIND A: Chelation therapy in beta thalassaemia major. I. Intravenous and subcutaneous deferoxamine. *J Pediatr Surg* 13:25, 1978.

448. COOPER B, BUNN HF, PROPPER RD, NATHAN DG, ROSENTHAL DS, MOLONEY WC: Treatment of iron overload in adults with continuous parenteral deferrioxamine. *Am J Med* 63:958, 1977.

449. COHEN A, SCHWARTZ E: Decreasing iron stores during intensive chelation therapy. *Ann NY Acad Sci* 344:405, 1980.

450. PIOMELLI S, GRAZIANO J, KARPATKIN M, DUDELL GG, HART D, HILGARTNER M, KUSUM K, VALDES-CRUZ M, VORA S: Chelation therapy, transfusion requirement, and iron balance in young thalassemic patients. *Ann NY Acad Sci* 344:409, 1980.

451. PIPPARD MJ, CALLENDER ST, FINCH CA: Ferrioxamine excretion in iron-loaded man. *Blood* 60:288, 1982.

452. COHEN A, SCHMIDT JM, MARTIN MB, BARNSLEY W, SCHWARTZ E: A clinical trial of young red cell transfusions. *J Pediatr* 104:865, 1984.

453. FREEMAN AP, GILES RW, BERDOUKAS VA, WALSH WF, CHOY D, MURRAY PO: Early left ventricular dysfunction and chelation therapy in thalassemia major. *Ann Intern Med* 99:450, 1983.

454. MARCUS RE, DAVIES SC, BANTOCK HM, UNDERWOOD SR, WALTON S, HUEHNS ER: Desferrioxamine to improve cardiac function in iron-overloaded patients with thalassaemia major. *Lancet* 1:392, 1984.

455. WOLFE L, OLIVIERI N, SALLAN D, COLAN S, ROSE V, PROPPER R, FREEDMAN MH, NATHAN DG: Prevention of cardiac disease by subcutaneous deferoxamine in patients with thalassemia major. *N Engl J Med* 312:1600, 1985.

456. MODELL B, LETSKY EA, FLYNN DM, PETO R, WEATHERALL DJ: Survival and desferrioxamine in thalassaemia major. *Br Med J* 284:1081, 1982.

457. OLIVIERI NF, BUNCIC JR, CHEW E, GALLANT T, HARRISON RV, KEENAN N, LOGAN W, MITCHELL P, RICI G, STRAF B, TAYLOR M, FREEDMAN MH: Visual and auditory neurotoxicity in patients receiving subcutaneous deferoxamine infusion. *N Engl J Med* 314:869, 1986.

458. CHARLTON RW, BOTHWELL TH: Iron, ascorbic acid and thalassemia, in Bergsma D, Cerami A, Peterson CM, Graziano JH (eds): *Iron Metabolism in Thalassemia*. New York, AR Liss, 1976, p 63.

459. NIENHUIS AW, DELEA C, AAMODT R, BARTTER F, ANDERSON WF: Evaluation of desferrioxamine and ascorbic acid for the treatment of chronic iron overload, in Bergsma D, Cerami A, Peterson CM, Graziano JH (eds): *Iron Metabolism in Thalassemia*. New York, AR Liss, 1976, p 177.

460. PROPPER RD, BUTTON LN, NATHAN DG: New approaches to the transfusion management of thalassemia. *Blood* 55:55, 1980.

461. MARCUS RE, WONKE B, BANTOCK HM, THOMAS MJG, PARRY ES, TAITE H, HUEHNS ER: A prospective trial of young red cells in 48 patients with transfusion-dependent thalassaemia. *Br J Haematol* 60:153, 1985.

462. DE ALARCON PA, DONOVAN M-E, FORBES GB, LANDAW SA, STOCKONAN JA: Iron absorption in the thalassemia syndromes and its inhibition by tea. *N Engl J Med* 300:5, 1979.

463. GRADY RW: The development of new drugs for use in iron chelation therapy, in Bergsma D, Cerami A, Peterson CM, Graziano JH (eds): *Iron Metabolism in Thalassemia*. New York, AR Liss, 1976, p 161.

464. PITT CG, GUPTA G, ESTES WE, ROSENKRANTZ H, METTERVILLE AL, CRUMBLESS AL, PALMER RA, NORDQUEST KW, SPRINKEL HARDY KA, WHITCOMB DR, BYERS BR, ARCENEUX JEL, GAINES CG, SCIORTINO CV: The selection and evaluation of new chelating agents for the treatment of iron overload. *J Pharmacol Exp Ther* 208:12, 1979.

465. LUCARELLI G, GALIMBERTI M, DELFINI C, AGOSTINELLI F, GIORGI C, GIARDINI C, POLCHI P, IZZI T, MANNA M, BARONCIANI D, ANGELUCCI E, POLITI P: Marrow transplantation for thalassaemia following busulphan and cyclophosphamide. *Lancet* 1:1355, 1985.

466. NIENHUIS AW, ANAGNON NP, LEY TJ: Advances in thalassemia research. *Blood* 63:738, 1984.

CHAPTER **56**

MOLYBDENUM COFACTOR DEFICIENCY

JEAN L. JOHNSON
SYBE K. WADMAN

1. *The molybdenum cofactor is a low molecular weight prosthetic group in which the metal is complexed to a unique pterin species termed molybdopterin. The cofactor is essential for the function of the human enzymes sulfite oxidase, xanthine dehydrogenase, and aldehyde oxidase. Molybdenum cofactor deficiency has been described in 15 patients. Affected individuals exhibit a combined deficiency of sulfite oxidase and xanthine dehydrogenase with symptoms which include severe neurologic abnormalities, dislocated ocular lenses, mental retardation, and xanthinuria. They excrete elevated levels of sulfite, thiosulfate, S-sulfocysteine, taurine, xanthine, and hypoxanthine and very low amounts of sulfate and uric acid.*
2. *The disease is inherited as an autosomal recessive trait with obligate heterozygotes displaying no symptoms. At least two genetic complementation groups have been identified. Patients belong to a variety of ethnic groups and are found among the populations of Central and Southern Europe, Northern Africa, Turkey, and Asia.*
3. *Pathologic studies in three cases have revealed a severe encephalopathy with marked neuronal loss and demyelination in the white matter accompanied by gliosis and diffuse spongiosis. The similarity of these lesions to those described in a case of isolated sulfite oxidase deficiency suggests that the pathophysiology of the combined deficiency is largely attributable to the absence of sulfite oxidase activity. Brain damage might occur as a result of accumulation of toxic levels of sulfite, as a result of a deficiency of sulfate in tissues dependent on sulfite oxidase for its production, or both.*
4. *Prenatal diagnosis is accomplished by assay of sulfite oxidase activity in cultured amniotic cells or in chorionic villi. Of value also is the analysis of S-sulfocysteine in amniotic fluid.*
5. *Molybdenum cofactor deficiency is a fatal disease for which no effective therapy is currently available. Administration of diets low in sulfur-containing amino acids and supplementation with sulfate and molybdate have been undertaken and resulted in positive biochemical response but no clinical improvement. Due to the extreme instability of the isolated molybdenum cofactor, therapy based on cofactor replacement must await further characterization of the pathways of biosynthesis and metabolism of this molecule in human tissues.*
6. *Three cases of sulfite oxidase deficiency have been described where molybdenum cofactor and xanthine dehydrogenase functions are unaffected.*

A combined deficiency of sulfite oxidase and xanthine dehydrogenase was described for the first time in 1978.[1] The patient presented in the neonatal period with feeding difficulties, severe neurologic abnormalities, dislocated ocular lenses, and dysmorphic features of the head. Chemical screening revealed xanthinuria as well as the metabolic characteristics of sulfite oxidase deficiency. The occurrence of two rare inherited defects in a single individual was thought to be highly improbable. However, because molybdenum is an essential component of both xanthine dehydrogenase and sulfite oxidase, a defect in molybdenum metabolism or transport was suspected. Molybdenum deficiency of dietary origin could be excluded, although it was later shown by Abumrad et al.[2] that a dietary deficiency of the metal in a patient receiving total parenteral nutrition led to a similar depressed functioning of both enzymes. The underlying primary defect in the index case of the heritable form of combined deficiency of sulfite oxidase and xanthine dehydrogenase was established[3] as a deficiency of the molybdenum cofactor, the low molecular weight prosthetic group of molybdoenzymes in which the metal is complexed to a unique pterin species termed *molybdopterin*. Evidence was also presented indicating that a third molybdenum cofactor-dependent enzyme, aldehyde oxidase, was deficient in this patient.[3] Soon after the description of the first patient, other cases with similar clinical and chemical hallmarks were diagnosed.[4,5] Direct evidence for genetic inheritance was provided by the occurrence of two cases in a single family.[6]

A key to the diagnosis of molybdenum cofactor deficiency was the description, several years earlier, of a patient with an isolated case of sulfite oxidase deficiency.[7,8] This patient was subsequently shown to have normal xanthine dehydrogenase and molybdenum cofactor function.[9] The clinical and biochemical features which were identified in this case, and two that followed,[10] laid the groundwork for characterization of the combined deficiency disease. After the description of these original cases of sulfite oxidase deficiency, no additional patients have been reported; thus, the isolated deficiency remains an extremely rare disease. In contrast, the number of cases of the combined deficiency is steadily growing, suggesting that it is most probably the more common variant of sulfite oxidase deficiency. The emphasis in the sections that follow is on inherited molybdenum cofactor deficiency; however, information on the isolated deficiency of sulfite oxidase is summarized and included as well.

THE MOLYBDENUM COFACTOR

Chemistry of the Molybdenum Cofactor

Sulfite oxidase, xanthine dehydrogenase, and aldehyde oxidase, the three known molybdoenzymes present in human tissues, each contain the metal as a part of a molybdenum cofac-

Nonstandard abbreviations used in this chapter are: CRM = cross reacting material; HPLC = high pressure liquid chromatography; PKU = phenylketonuria.

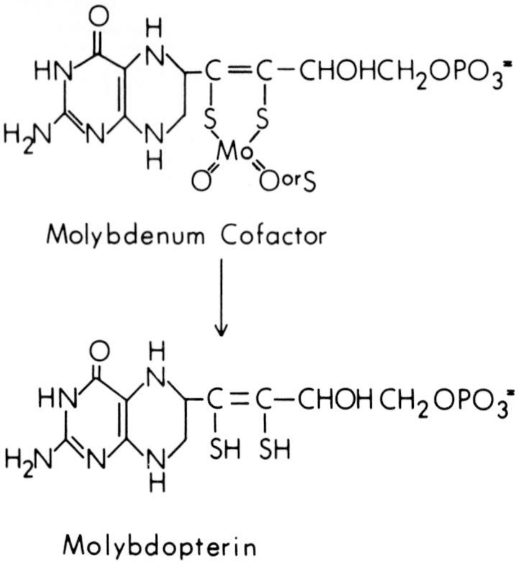

Fig. 56-1 Chemical structures of the molybdenum cofactor and molybdopterin.

tor in which the metal is complexed to a unique organic moiety termed *molybdopterin.*[11–14] The structures of the molybdenum cofactor and molybdopterin are shown in Fig. 56-1. The molybdenum cofactor within the protective environment of an enzyme is quite stable and very tightly bound to the protein. In each enzyme the metal appears to be coordinated by ligands provided by the protein as well as those supplied by molybdopterin. Extraction of the cofactor from the protein requires denaturing conditions, disrupts the molybdenum ligand field, and yields an unstable molybdenum-molybdopterin complex. Dissociation of the metal from the free complex, which occurs quite readily, leaves a species with two highly reactive vicinal sulfhydryl groups which can decay into a multitude of products. For these reasons, reversible resolution and reconstitution of the cofactor from molybdoenzymes has not been accomplished. The instability of the side chain and reduced pterin ring in the released complex has made chemical characterization of the active species particularly difficult and will have important implications in terms of design of potential therapeutic agents to correct molybdenum cofactor deficiency.

Chemical characterization of the molybdenum cofactor was accomplished by analyzing a number of stable degradation products, two of which are formed in vitro,[13] one which is produced metabolically and excreted in the urine,[12] and a fourth which was generated by specific chemical modification based on the predicted structure.[14] The structures of these derivatives are shown in Fig. 56-2.

The form A and form B derivatives form spontaneously when an enzyme containing the molybdenum cofactor is denatured by boiling at acid pH in the presence or absence of iodine, respectively. In form A, the linear nature of the 6-alkyl side chain is retained, but an oxidative elimination of both sulfur atoms has occurred. In the form B derivative, one sulfur is retained as a result of the side chain cyclizing to form a thiophene ring. Rigorous structural characterization of these derivatives[13] established with certainty that the molybdenum cofactor is a pterin with a 4-carbon side chain bearing at least one sulfur atom. The presence of a terminal glycol function masked by a phosphate ester was also demonstrated.

In the course of investigations into the structure of the form A and form B derivatives, certain chemical similarities were noted between the form B derivative and another pterin which had been described in the literature many years earlier. The thienopterin urothione had been identified in 1940[15] and structurally characterized in 1969[16] as a minor constituent of unknown function present in human urine. The metabolic relationship between the molybdenum cofactor and urothione was established by the discovery that patients with molybdenum cofactor deficiency excrete no detectable urothione.[12,17] The presence of sulfur atoms on adjacent carbon atoms in urothione suggested that the active molybdenum cofactor might also have two sulfurs. These would be located, in an open-chain configuration, in an optimal position to serve as ligands to the molybdenum, and their presence would offer a very reasonable explanation for cofactor instability, even under anaerobic conditions where pterin ring oxidation could be prevented. A logical series of steps to convert molybdenum cofactor to urothione for excretion would include methylation of the sulfur on carbon 1, oxidation of the pterin ring, cyclization to the thienopterin, and dephosphorylation.

To test the validity of these hypotheses, the molybdenum cofactor was specifically derivatized using the sulfhydryl reagent iodoacetamide.[14] Chemical, mass spectral, and nmr analyses of the resulting derivative indeed confirmed the presence of an alkyl side chain in the 6 position bearing two carboxymethylated sulfhydryl groups. The presence of the side-chain double bond was also verified by these analyses.

Two areas of active investigation remain in the structural characterization of the molybdenum cofactor. The cofactor

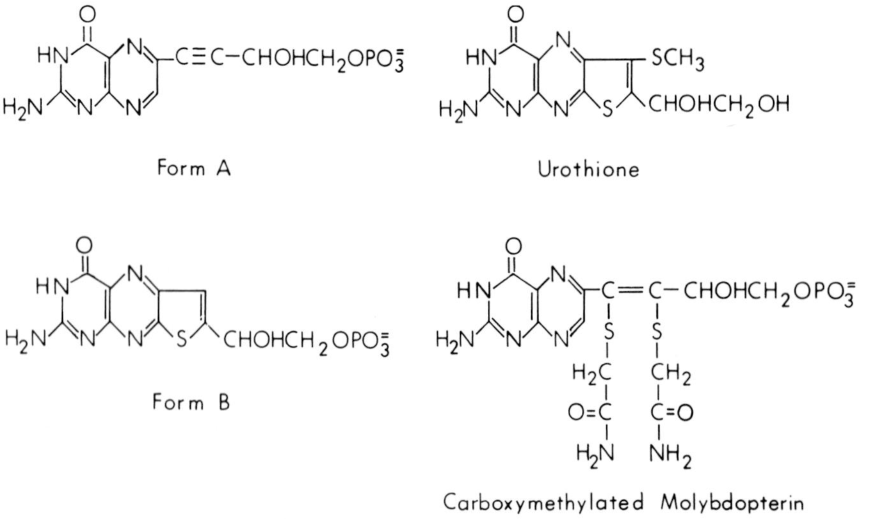

Fig. 56-2 Chemical structures of four derivatives of the molybdenum cofactor.

pterin is known to be present in a reduced state, illustrated in Fig. 56-1 at the tetrahydro level. However, the pterin ring can also exist in a number of dihydro configurations. Recent findings[18] suggest that the level of reduction and precise ring configuration of molybdopterin vary with the particular enzyme in which the cofactor resides and in fact may even change as a function of catalysis. These results will also be of critical importance in any anticipated cofactor replacement therapy attempts. Ultimately, proof of the proposed cofactor structure will depend on characterization of a functional derivative and chemical synthesis of such a species. The carboxymethylated derivative most probably retains all elements essential for biologic activity but of course is irreversibly modified in a manner which precludes metal ligation. Work with various reversible protecting agents may eventually allow characterization of an active species.

Metabolic Origins of the Molybdenum Cofactor

The pathway of biosynthesis of the molybdenum cofactor has not yet been elucidated. Of the other complex pterins present in human tissues, tetrahydrobiopterin, the cofactor for phenylalanine hydroxylase and related enzymes, is synthesized *de novo* from guanosine triphosphate (GTP), while folic acid is dietarily derived (Fig. 56-3). From studies of cultured cells of animal origin, it has become clear that tetrahydrobiopterin and the molybdenum cofactor do not share a common biosynthetic pathway.[19] A number of cell lines have been identified which fail to express GTP cyclohydrolase I, the first enzyme in the pathway of tetrahydrobiopterin biosynthesis, and are consequently devoid of tetrahydrobiopterin, yet do contain significant levels of active sulfite oxidase. Similarly, patients with atypical phenylketonuria (PKU) resulting from abnormal biopterin cofactor biosynthesis have been identified (see Chap. 15), but none of these individuals appear to be afflicted with a simultaneous molybdenum cofactor deficiency. These clinical findings are suggestive of separate biosynthetic pathways for the two cofactors, but not definitive, since defects in the PKU patients could be in genes coding for enzymes required after a branch point in a pathway with shared early steps. However, the identification of a patient with a specific defect in GTP cyclohydrolase I and apparently normal molybdenum metabolism[20] gives further support to a molybdenum cofactor biosynthetic pathway separate from that of tetrahydrobiopterin.

The possibility that the molybdenum cofactor is partially or totally derived from the diet is worthy of consideration. The cofactor is present in a variety of molybdoenzymes of bacterial, fungal, plant, and animal origin and as such could be supplied in the diet. However, the observed lability of the free cofactor would suggest that a stabilizing molecule of some sort would be required for assimilation of dietary molybdenum cofactor. Similarly, carrier proteins and receptors thereof might be involved in transport and cellular uptake and provide bases for the inborn, heritable nature of molybdenum cofactor deficiency. A case study by Abumrad et al.,[2] however, would suggest that at least a part of the molybdenum cofactor require-

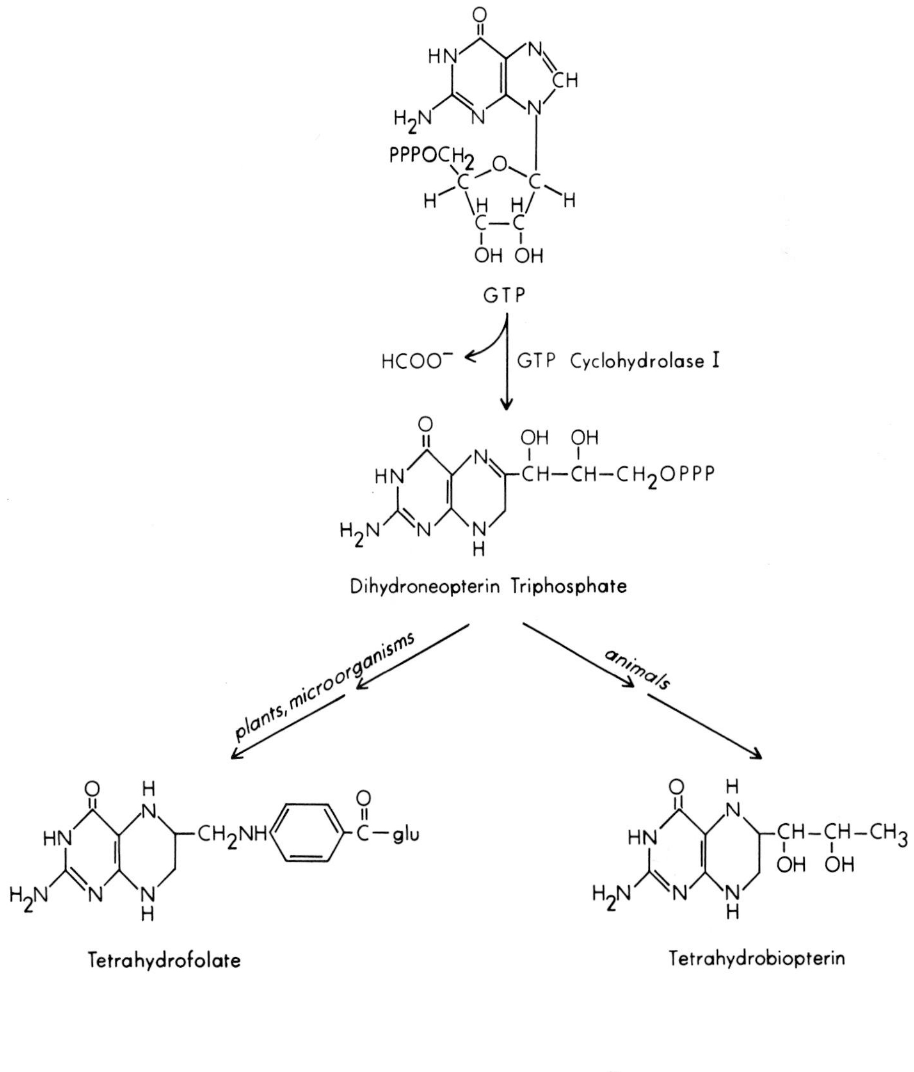

GTP

$HCOO^-$ — GTP Cyclohydrolase I

Dihydroneopterin Triphosphate

plants, microorganisms — animals

Tetrahydrofolate

Tetrahydrobiopterin

Fig. 56-3 Biosynthesis of tetrahydrofolate and tetrahydrobiopterin.

ment is met by endogenous biosynthesis of the pterin component. The patient described developed symptoms of molybdoenzyme deficiency after an 18-month course of total parenteral nutrition. The biochemical parameters and some of the clinical symptoms indicative of the deficiency state were reversed by administration of ammonium molybdate at 330 μg/day. The chemically defined nature of the nutrient solution supplied to the patient and its apparent lack of molybdenum and molybdenum cofactor would indicate that the metal administered as a corrective measure was able to combine with endogenous pterin to yield functional molybdenum cofactor.

The possibility that the molybdenum cofactor might be derived from the pterin portion of folic acid does not appear to be likely.[19] Preliminary studies have established that animal cells cultured under conditions of folate deficiency express normal levels of sulfite oxidase activity.

The expression of molybdenum cofactor in bacteria and fungi[21–23] is under the control of a number of genes, several of which are thought to be directly involved in biosynthesis. A similar complex pathway in humans would raise the possibility of multiple genetic variants of molybdenum cofactor deficiency. Indeed, preliminary evidence that this is the case has been presented.[24] When fibroblasts from either of two cofactor-deficient sibs were cocultured with cells from any of four other unrelated molybdenum cofactor-deficient patients (or with those from a patient with isolated sulfite oxidase deficiency), sulfite oxidase activity was expressed. Complementation occurred without heterokaryon formation, suggesting that the corrective factor may be a diffusible precursor of the molybdenum cofactor. From these results it would appear that cofactor-deficient patients can be grouped into at least two complementation classes. As more patients are identified, it should be possible to further define the molecular genetics of the deficiency disease.

Enzymes and Metabolic Pathways Dependent on the Molybdenum Cofactor

Xanthine dehydrogenase (EC 1.2.1.37) catalyzes the hydroxylation of hypoxanthine and xanthine to produce uric acid as the final product. The enzyme is also active, to varying degrees, with a variety of other heterocyclic substrates.[25] The reaction mechanism[26] involves abstraction of a hydride ion from the substrate and replacement with a hydroxyl ion ultimately derived from water. Substrate binding and hydroxylation occur at the molybdenum center with concomitant reduction of Mo(VI) to Mo(IV). The molybdenum is reoxidized as electrons are passed on through an enzyme-bound electron transport chain consisting of flavin adenine dinucleotide (FAD) and two 2Fe/2S centers. The physiological oxidizing substrate for the reaction is NAD^+, although under certain conditions the enzyme is converted to a form which reduces molecular oxygen.[27,28] It is this form of the enzyme which is referred to by the more familiar name, *xanthine oxidase*.

The role of the enzyme in metbolism is in the pathway of purine degradation for excretion. Because hypoxanthine and guanine can be reclaimed to a large extent by the action of hypoxanthine-guanine phosphoribosyl transferase and because hypoxanthine and xanthine are not highly toxic compounds, deficiencies of xanthine dehydrogenase in humans are largely benign (see Chap. 42). The major clinical symptoms attributed to xanthinuria, as the isolated deficiency disease or as a result of molybdenum cofactor deficiency, relate to the limited solubility of xanthine at physiological pH and are manifest as deposits or calculi in kidney, muscle (Chap. 42), and possibly brain tissue.[17]

Xanthine dehydrogenase is a soluble enzyme present in liver and intestine and, at lower levels, in kidney, lung, spleen, skeletal and heart muscle, and brain.[29] It is also a normal constituent of milk; the enzyme from bovine milk is one of the most studied enzymes to date. The function of the enzyme in milk is unknown, although the possibility that it may serve as a source of molybdenum or molybdenum cofactor for the suckling newborn must be considered. If such is the case, some concern must be given to the findings of greatly diminished levels of the enzyme in colostrum and milk of xanthinuric individuals[30] as well as in colostrum from an obligate heterozygous carrier of molybdenum cofactor deficiency.[31] Xanthine dehydrogenase activity is not expressed in cultured human cell lines.[32]

Sulfite oxidase (EC 1.8.2.1) functions as the terminal enzyme in the pathway of degradation of sulfur amino acids (see Fig. 56-4). Besides functioning to eliminate endogenously produced sulfite, the enzyme fills and important role in detoxifying exogenously supplied sulfite and sulfur dioxide.[33] Rats which have been made deficient in sulfite oxidase have been shown to be more sensitive to the deleterious effects of these agents. Thus, a potential concern is that humans with even a partial deficiency of sulfite oxidase could have adverse reactions if exposed to sulfite as a preservative solution in foods or drugs or to elevated levels of sulfur dioxide.

Sulfite oxidase exists as a soluble protein compartmentalized in the intermembrane space of the mitochondrion (Fig. 56-5). In this location, it has ready access to its reducing substrate, sulfite, which can diffuse across the mitochondrial membranes, and to its physiological electron acceptor, cytochrome

Fig. 56-4 Major pathway of cysteine catabolism: direct oxidation.

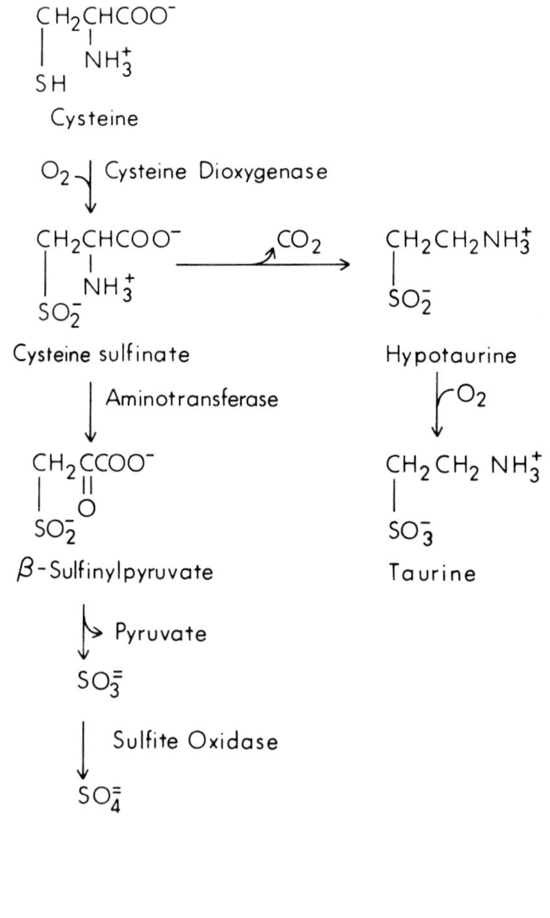

$$\underset{\text{Cysteine}}{HS{-}CH_2CH(NH_3^+)COO^-} \xrightarrow[\text{Cysteine Dioxygenase}]{O_2} \underset{\text{Cysteine sulfinate}}{^-O_2S{-}CH_2CH(NH_3^+)COO^-}$$

$$\text{Cysteine sulfinate} \xrightarrow{\text{Aminotransferase}} \underset{\beta\text{-Sulfinylpyruvate}}{^-O_2S{-}CH_2C(=O)COO^-} \xrightarrow{\text{Pyruvate}} SO_3^= \xrightarrow{\text{Sulfite Oxidase}} SO_4^=$$

$$\text{Cysteine sulfinate} \xrightarrow{-CO_2} \underset{\text{Hypotaurine}}{^-O_2S{-}CH_2CH_2NH_3^+} \xrightarrow{O_2} \underset{\text{Taurine}}{^-O_3S{-}CH_2CH_2NH_3^+}$$

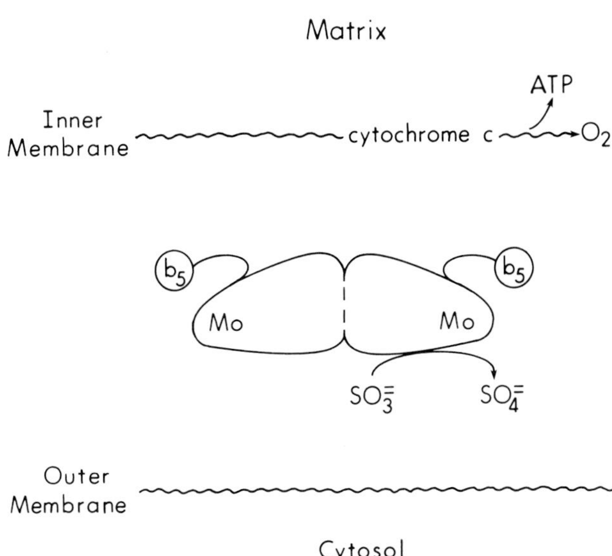

Fig. 56-5 Schematic representation of sulfite oxidase in the mitochondrial intermembrane space. *(From JL Johnson and KV Rajagopalan, Sulphur in Biology, Ciba Foundation Symposium 72, 1980. Used by permission.)*

c.[34] Oxidation of sulfite occurs at the molybdenum center with reduction of the metal from Mo(VI) to Mo(IV). The electrons are then transferred one at a time through the b_5 heme of the enzyme and from there to cytochrome c. The enzyme exists as a dimer of identical subunits; each monomer contains a larger molybdenum domain and a smaller heme domain.[35] The heme domain possesses a strong antigenic determinant. Polyclonal antibodies generated against the sulfite oxidase protein are directed primarily to this antigenic region and strongly inhibit enzyme activity.[9,36] The enzyme is found in many tissues with highest levels in liver, kidney, lung, and heart. No detectable activity was found in blood or skeletal muscle.[37] The enzyme is expressed in fibroblasts, cultured amniotic fluid cells, and lymphoblasts.[10,38,39]

A deficiency of sulfite oxidase can arise from a specific defect in the enzyme protein or from a lack of functional molybdenum cofactor. At present the number of cases of cofactor-based sulfite oxidase deficiency is considerably larger than that of the specific single-enzyme deficiency, but the clinical picture is very similar in the two diseases. These findings lead to the conclusion that most, if not all, of the devastating sequelae of molybdenum cofactor deficiency stem from the absence of sulfite oxidase, as is considered in more detail below.

Aldehyde oxidase (EC 1.2.3.1) shares many physicochemical properties with xanthine dehydrogenase (cofactor composition, molecular weight, and subunit structure) and shows some overlap in substrate specificity as well.[26] Aldehyde oxidase will hydroxylate hypoxanthine to yield xanthine but cannot convert the latter to uric acid.[25] The enzyme works on a wide variety of heterocyclic compounds and xenobiotics and may function as a part of the body's general detoxification system.[40] The enzyme is present in the soluble cell fraction and exists as a constitutive and irreversible oxidase, reducing oxygen to hydrogen peroxide and superoxide. Aldehyde dehydrogenases have been described in various systems, but none of these are molybdoenzymes.

An isolated deficiency of aldehyde oxidase in humans has never been reported; thus, the metabolic and clinical ramifications of a deficiency of this enzyme in cases of molybdenum cofactor deficiency are difficult to assess. Because the enzyme is unstable in samples of liver tissue which have been frozen, the absence of aldehyde oxidase activity in patients with molybdenum cofactor deficiency has not been demonstrated directly. In the first case reported, however, an in vivo test of aldehyde oxidase function, measuring the conversion of L-histidine to hydantoin-5-propionic acid, indicated a deficiency of this enzyme as well.[3]

CLINICAL ASPECTS OF MOLYBDENUM COFACTOR DEFICIENCY

The Clinical Phenotype

Molybdenum cofactor deficiency is apparently not extremely rare. Since the discovery of the disease fewer than 10 years ago, 15 patients have been identified; 11 of them have been described in the literature. Data on the affected families are summarized in Table 56-1. The disease is not confined to a single ethnic group. Patients have been identified among the populations of Central and Southern Europe, Northern Africa, Turkey, and Asia. The mode of inheritance is autosomal recessive, with nearly equal numbers of males and females affected. Obligate heterozygotes do not display any symptoms.

In addition to the 15 patients studied, there are three suspected but undiagnosed cases in two of the families, and two abortions were reported. Prenatal diagnosis has been done seven times; a positive result was obtained twice, and no false negative cases were observed. Consanguinity was registered six times; five couples were first cousins, and in one case parents were second cousins.

Table 56-2 summarizes clinical data on the known molybdenum cofactor-deficient patients. Birth was at term in 13 out of 14 pregnancies. Moderate neonatal depression (Apgar score 4 to 7 at 1 min) was mentioned in three out of nine cases. Birth weight, height, and head circumference were in the normal ranges for gestational age in most patients, except patient 11, with a weight somewhat low for gestational age. The majority of patients were reported to have a normal physical status at birth. However, patient 1, the index case, displayed dysmorphic features of the head: a large head, full cheeks, upturned nose, enophthalmus, and telecanthus. Patient 3 had a soft palate cleft and a broad nose bridge. Patient 11 was microcephalic and anorexic. Upon observation at a later age, additional physical anomalies were noted. Patient 2, at 2 months of age, had a triangular face, thick lips, and a microcephaly. Patient 9 had a large, coarse face, a broad nose bridge, large ears, loose skin, and wrinkles on the forehead.

Molybdenum cofactor deficiency is a fatal disease. Nine of the known patients died at an early age, and at least four others were severely affected children cared for in institutions. The onset of symptoms is in the first or second week after birth, perhaps as a consequence of excessive sulfite production following oral intake of protein. Feeding difficulties start soon after birth, and patients develop severe and characteristic neurologic symptoms. These and other signs and symptoms are summarized in Table 56-3. The neurologic picture includes tonic/clonic seizures observed in many patients, axial hypotonia, and peripheral hypertonicity. The seizures are refractory to anticonvulsants or difficult to suppress. Progression is variable, but brain damage appears to take place even before birth. Patients who survive the neonatal period develop lens dislocation. This has been seen in seven patients.

Table 56-1 Data on Affected Families

	Patient code						
	1 EV	*2 KZ*	*3 MV*	*4 KM*	*5 CT*	*6 SB* (*sibs*)	*7 ZB* (*sibs*)
Sex	F	F	M	M	F	M	F
Birthdate	1/11/77	1/24/79	7/2/80	7/15/79	7/11/77	1/23/79	3/31/82
Offspring number	2	1	2	1	2	1	2
Ethnic background							
Father	Dutch	Tunisian	Dutch	Pakistani	Dutch	Tunisian	Tunisian
Mother	Dutch	Tunisian	Dutch	Pakistani	Dutch	Tunisian	Tunisian
Number of children	3	2	2	1	3	2	2
Affected	1	1	1	1	1	2	2
Abortions	1	0	0	0	0		
Suspected but undiagnosed cases	0	0	0	0	2	0	0
Prenatal diagnosis	0	3	0	0	0	1	1
Positive		2				0	0
Consanguinity	No	Yes	No	Yes	No	Yes	Yes
First cousins		Yes		Yes			
Other						Second cousins	Second cousins

Three patients with an isolated deficiency of sulfite oxidase have been described in the literature.[7–10] The clinical phenotype of these individuals is quite similar to that of molybdenum cofactor deficiency even though molybdenum cofactor and xanthine dehydrogenase functions appear normal. The first patient described[7,8] was very severely affected with many neurologic abnormalities including severe mental retardation, seizures, and opisthotonos. Lens dislocation was found at age 2, and the patient died at age 2½. The second patient[10] was somewhat less severely affected with normal growth and development up to age 17 months. At that time there was a sudden onset of hemiplegia and progressive development of choreoathetoid movements and seizures. Dislocated lenses were seen at age 4 years. The patient is still living at age 16 and exhibits only mild to moderate mental and physical impairment. Very little information is available on the third patient[10]; however, the clinical features parallelled quite closely those of the second case.

Table 56-2 Clinical Data

	Patient code						
	1 EV	*2 KZ*	*3 MV*	*4 KM*	*5 CT*	*6 SB* (*sibs*)	*7 ZB* (*sibs*)
Birth information							
Pregnancy	40 wk	Full term	Full term	Full term	Full term	Full term	Full term
Apgar scores							
1 min	?	10	?	5	4	?	8
5 min				10			9
Weight, kg	P_{10}	3.54	4.2	2.52	2.80	3.80	3.80
Height, cm	P_{10}	50	53	49	?	?	51
Head circumference, cm	P_{50}	35.5	35	32.6	?	?	33
Physical status:							
Normal	No	Yes	No	No	Yes	Yes	Yes
Current status							
Age, if living	10 yr				9 4/12 yr		?
Age at expiration		2 1/12 yr	8 days	8 mo		3 yr	
Onset of symptoms	9 days	15 days	4 days	1 day	2 days	2 days	10 days
Initial mode of feeding	?	Breast-fed	Formula-fed	Breast-fed	Formula-fed	Breast-fed	Breast-fed
Special treatments		No	No				
Low sulfur diet	Yes			Yes		Yes	Yes
Allopurinol	Yes				Yes		
Sodium sulfate	Yes					Yes	Yes
Ammonium molybdate	Yes					Yes	Yes
Response							
To special treatments:							
Change in $SO_3^{=}$, $S_2O_3^{=}$, etc.	↓			↓		↓	↓
To anticonvulsants		No	No	Yes	Yes		
Clinical improvement	No			No		No	No
References	1, 3, 4	4, 5	4	4	4	6	6

*No follow up.

8 DG	*9 FM*	*10 KD*	*11 FA*	*12 LB*	*13 TR*	*14 JW*	*15 CK*
M	M	F	F	F	M	M	M
8/19/83	11/8/83	5/3/85	11/20/85	12/1/85	12/3/85	3/20/83	1981
1	2	5	1	1	2	1	?
French	Spanish	Turkish	Algerian	Caucasian	Portuguese	Caucasian	?
French	Spanish	Turkish	Algerian	Caucasian	Portuguese	Caucasian	?
1	2	5	1	1	2	1	?
1	1	1	1	1	1	1	?
0	0	0	0	1	0	0	?
0	0	1	0	0	0	0	?
1	0	0	0	1	0	0	?
(0)				0			
No	No	Yes	Yes	No	Yes	No	?
		Yes	Yes		Yes		

Pathology

Results of pathologic investigations are available from three patients with molybdenum cofactor deficiency. The most detailed are from patient 2[43] and are summarized first. Macroscopic study revealed severe cerebral atrophy and extreme microgyria with fine vermiform, tortuous convolutions separated by wide and deep sulci, a feature which was less marked in the gyri hippocampi. No necrosis, softening, hemorrhage, or tumors were noted. There was bilateral ventricular enlargement, with enlargement of the fourth ventricle and multicystic subcortical and juxtacortical focal lesions in the white matter. Microscopic examination revealed lesions in the frontal, temporal, and occipital cortex characterized by a marked loss of neurons. These were replaced by an astrocytic gliosis and accumulation of microgliocytic granular bodies. In the deeper layers the cortical lesions were accompanied by microcavitations and spongiosis with an essentially astrocytic granulosis

8 DG	*9 FM*	*10 KD*	*11 FA*	*12 LB*	*13 TR*	*14 JW*	*15 CK*
39 wk	41 wk	35 wk	38 wk	Full term	38.5 wk	Full term	?
10	8	9	?	9	4	7	?
10	10			10	7	8	
?	3.47	2.54	2.00	3.23	3.25	3.5	?
?	50	47	− 3 SD	56	51.5	?	?
?	35	33.5	−4 SD	34	35.5	?	?
Yes	No (probably)	Yes	No (probably)	Yes	No	Yes	?
		1 yr*		13 mo			?
9 days	1 1/12 yr		2 mo		8 days	1 9/12 yr	?
3 days	5 days	4 days	1 day	4 days	1 day	1 day	?
Formula-fed	Breast-fed	?	Breast-fed	Formula-fed	?	Formula-fed	?
No		No	No	No	No	No	?
	Yes						
	Yes						
	Yes						
	↓						
	?						
41		42				17	

Table 56-3 Symptoms and Signs*

	Patient code						
	1 EV	*2 KZ*	*3 MV*	*4 KM*	*5 CT*	*6 SB* (*sibs*)	*7 ZB* (*sibs*)
Feeding difficulties	D 9	D 15	D 5	D 1	D 2	D 2	+
Vomiting	D 9			–	D 2	–	–
Seizures, tonic/clonic	D 9	M 2	D 5	D 1	D 3	D 2	D 12
Hypotonia	–	+	+	–	M 2	M 1	M 2
Hypertonicity	+	+	+	W 8	–	+	D 22
Myoclonia	+	+		–	–	+	D 15
Pyramidal syndrome	–	+		+	Y 2(±)	+	
Spastic tetraplegia	–	+	+	+	Y 2(±)		
Opisthotonus	–	–	+	–	M 2		
Dilatated ventricles	–	M 2		+	M 2	+	D 15
Hydrocephalus		M 2		–	M 6		D 22
Brain hypodensity	–	M 2			M 2		D 13
Brain atrophy	M 2	+		W 9	M 2		W 4
Bilateral ectopic lenses	M 3	M 18		–	Y 4	Y1	–
Enophthalmus	+	–		–	–		
Nystagmus	–	M 18	?	–	–	–	
Ring of Brushfield spots	+	–	–	–			–
Unresponsiveness to light	+	M 18	+	+			W 3
Psychomotor retardation	+	M 2	?	+	M 2	W 1	W 2

*When known, the age when symptom was first noted is indicated as day (D), week (W), month (M), or year (Y).

and microgliocytic granular bodies. In the white matter, demyelination was noted, combined with a very marked axonal loss. In the cerebellum, granular and Purkinje cells were scarce, but no other noteworthy lesions were seen.

Pathologic studies in patient 3[44] revealed brain shrinkage and severe loss of neurons, particularly in all layers of the isocortex, thalamus, and basal ganglia, Paucity of myelin in the long tracts was noticed along with isomorphic gliosis. There was a diffuse spongiosis, affecting both the neuropil and white matter structures.

In patient 14,[17] the right side of the brain was considerably smaller than the left. The left side contained mostly gray matter with only small amounts of white, the right side more white than gray. There was considerable gliosis on the right side and multiple dark purplish deposits. The right cerebellar hemisphere was also atrophic and showed extensive gliosis. The highly asymmetric effects seen in this patient point to a more complex etiology of disease than simply a uniform exposure to a toxic metabolite.

Pathologic studies of a patient with isolated sulfite oxidase deficiency were described by Rosenblum.[45] The brain of this patient also displayed a massive loss of neurons and their axons with intense demyelination and glial proliferation consisting of multiple discrete cavitary formations in the deep cerebral white matter. Cystic and gliotic lesions were also found in basal ganglia, thalamus, and cerebellum. These lesions were considered not to result from ischemia or anoxia, nor to correspond with those seen in cystic encephalomalacia of infancy, in leukodystrophies, or in Schilder diffuse sclerosis. The similarities between the lesions in the molybdenum cofactor deficiencies (patients 2 and 3) and those observed in Rosenblum's patient[45] suggest that the cerebral lesions are due to the consequences of sulfite oxidase deficiency. Xanthine dehydrogenase deficiency does not result in encephalopathy, and while no isolated deficiency of aldehyde oxidase has been described, the absence of this enzyme in molybdenum cofactor deficiency does not lead to a marked overflow of any known metabolites under basal conditions. Thus, the encephalopathy described appears to be characteristic of sulfite oxidase deficiency, be it the isolated form or the consequence of molybdenum cofactor deficiency.

Biochemical Hallmarks and Clinical Diagnosis

Abnormal Metabolites and Metabolic Screening Procedures. In sulfite oxidase deficiency, sulfite accumulates and sulfate production is decreased. Sulfite overflow is apparently moderated to some extent by an enhanced degradation of cysteine sulfinate to taurine (see Fig. 56-4). The presence of elevated levels of sulfite leads to accumulation of *S*-sulfocysteine formed by direct reaction of sulfite with cysteine. Increased levels of thiosulfate are also characteristic of the sulfite oxidase deficiency as a consequence of elevated sulfite. Catabolism of cysteine by transamination produces mercaptopyruvate (see Fig. 56-6). Transsulfuration of mercaptopyruvate provides a source of reduced sulfur which combines with sulfite to yield thiosulfate. Elevated urinary mercaptolactate-cysteine disulfide is not a hallmark of sulfite oxidase deficiency. Xanthine dehydrogenase deficiency presents with markedly elevated urinary xanthine and moderately increased hypoxanthine. Uric acid is low, both in urine and plasma.

A metabolic consequence of molybdenum cofactor deficiency which is not seen in isolated deficiencies of sulfite oxidase or xanthine dehydrogenase is an absence of urinary urothione, believed to be the excreted degradation product of molybdopterin.[12]

All patients with molybdenum cofactor deficiency displayed a similar metabolic profile characteristic of an absence of functional sulfite oxidase and xanthine dehydrogenase (see Table 56-4), although excretory levels of the various metabolites varied substantially due to differences in protein intake, catabolism, and creatinine production. For diagnosis of molybdenum cofactor deficiency, urinary sulfite is easily detected with a strip test (Merkoquant 10013 Sulfit Test or Macherey-Nagel Quantofix $SO_3^{=}$), but fresh urine must be used since sulfite is

8 DG	*9 FM*	*10 KD*	*11 FA*	*12 LB*	*13 TR*	*14 JW*	*15 CK*
D 1	D 5	–	+	D 4	D 1	D 1	
D 2	–		–	–	–	D 1	
D 3	D 7	D 4	M 1	W 5	D 1	D 1	+ (t/c?)
D 1	–	D 4	M 2	W 6		–	
D 3	W 1	+	M 1	M 3	W 1	D 2	
D 3	–		–	W 4			
–	W 1	M 11	M 1	–		–	
–	W 1			M 3		M 3	+
–	W 4	–	M 1	–	–	D 1	
–	M 3	M 11	M 2	W 6	–	D 3	
–	M 3		M 1	–	–	–	
D 4	W 4	M 11	M 2	W 6		–	
–	W 4	M 11	M 2	–	–	D 3	
	M 8	M 11	–	–	–	–	+
–	W 1	M 11	–	–	–	–	
–	W 1	–	–	M 3(±)		W 2	
	–	–	–	–		–	
	M 3	M 11		M 3		+	+
	+	M 1	M 1	W 5		M 1	

rapidly destroyed by oxidation at room temperature.[46] The Macherey-Nagel strips are currently distributed in the United States by Gallard-Schlesinger. Test strips should be used as a screening procedure only, however, since false positive reactions are sometimes seen. The mucolytic drug 2-mercaptoethanesulfonate, for instance, produces a positive test.[47] Quantitative determinations of sulfite, thiosulfate, and sulfate are best performed with anion column chromatography.[46,48] *S*-sulfocysteine can be identified by high voltage electrophoresis and quantitated by amino acid analysis.[3] Numerous procedures are available for quantitation of urinary and plasma oxypurines; the high pressure liquid chromatography (HPLC) assay described by Crawhall et al.[49] is very effective. Urothione may be measured by the HPLC assay described by Johnson and Rajagopalan.[12]

Enzyme and Molybdenum Cofactor Assays. When appropriate tissue samples are available, the absence of sulfite oxidase and xanthine dehydrogenase activities can be verified directly. Such assays have been carried out on tissues from many of the molybdenum cofactor-deficient patients, as indicated in Table 56-4. In tissues from several patients, a study has been made of the content of autigenically cross-reacting material (CRM) representing the nonfunctional proteins of xanthine dehydrogenase and sulfite oxidase.[3,4] CRM for xanthine dehydrogenase was found to be present and immunologically identical with the native enzyme. A variety of assays failed to detect any CRM for sulfite oxidase, but all assays relied upon a polyclonal antibody preparation with a high avidity for a determinant on the heme domain of the enzyme. Minor conformational differences in a protein lacking the molybdenum cofactor or the absence of the b_5 prosthetic group may in fact have been responsible for the apparent absence of sulfite oxidase CRM.

Fig. 56-6 Minor pathway of cysteine catabolism: transamination and transsulfuration.

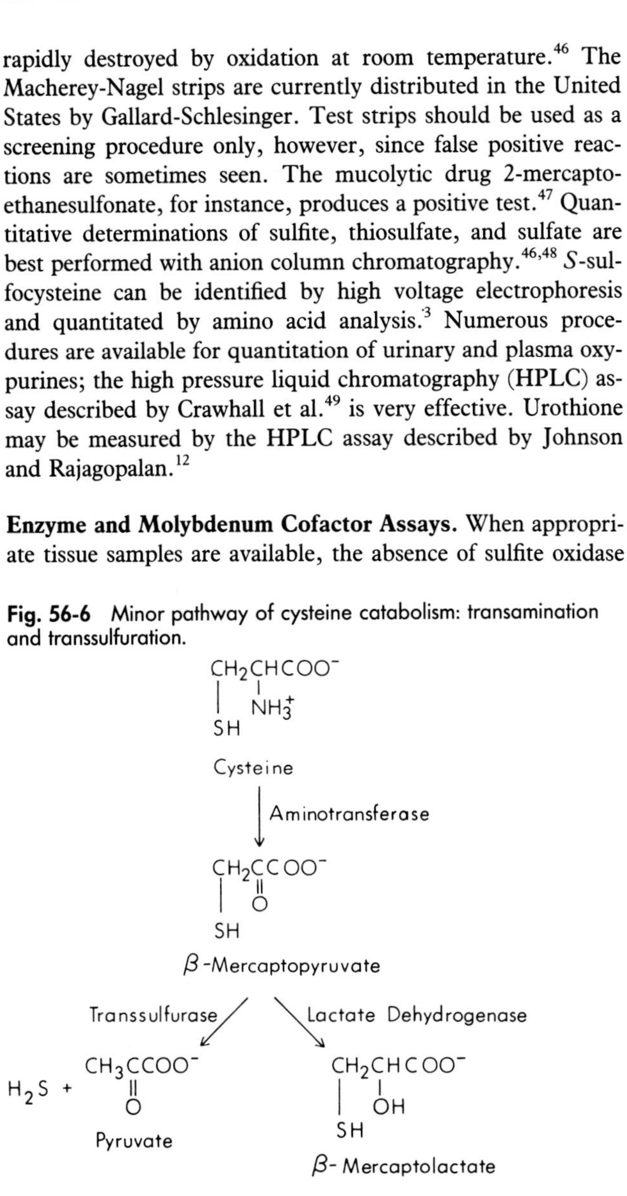

CH_2CHCOO^- (SH, NH_3^+)

Cysteine

↓ Aminotransferase

CH_2CCOO^- (SH, =O)

β-Mercaptopyruvate

Transsulfurase ↙ ↘ Lactate Dehydrogenase

H_2S + CH_3CCOO^- (=O)

Pyruvate

CH_2CHCOO^- (SH, OH)

β-Mercaptolactate

Liver samples from three patients have been tested for the presence of active molybdenum cofactor using a preparation of rat liver demolybdo sulfite oxidase as the acceptor molecule.[50,51] While liver tissue from control individuals contained cofactor which could reconstitute sulfite oxidase activity, samples from the patients failed to do so.[3] Similarly, when liver tissue from these patients was treated to convert molybdopterin to the form A derivative, the results of HPLC quantitation of the form A produced were indicative of a deficiency of molybdopterin as well.[31]

All molybdenum cofactor deficient patients tested to date have shown normal levels of plasma molybdenum. However, in the two patients where it has been measured, hepatic molybdenum has been found to be severely decreased.[3,17] This finding suggests that virtually all hepatic molybdenum is present in cofactor form and that, in the absence of functional cofactor to bind the metal, any molybdenum taken up by the cells is rapidly exported.

The three patients with an isolated deficiency of sulfite oxidase[7,10] each displayed the characteristic pattern of excreted sulfur metabolites which has been described for cases of molybdenum cofactor deficiency. The second and third patients excreted approximately 50 percent of total sulfur as inorganic sulfate, in contrast to the first where sulfate accounted

Table 56-4 Chemical Data

	Patient code						
	1 EV	*2 KZ*	*3 MV*	*4 KM*	*5 CT*	*6 SB* (sibs)	*7 ZB* (sibs)
Urinary metabolites, mmol/g creatinine							
Sulfite	0.8–12.3	6.3–15.6	0.7–3.0	2.5	8.9	↑	2.6
Thiosulfate	1.1–3.6	1.3–2.9	1.8–3.0	4.2	0.6	0.5	2.6
Sulfate	1.9–13.7	2.2–4.2	1.2–2.5	20.8	4.2	↓	
S-sulfocysteine	2.3–2.6	1.4–7.2	1.3–1.9	3.0	3.3	↑	↑
Taurine	1.9–7.6	8.7–13.8	5.6–8.3	0.6	4.6	8.0	1.6
Uric acid	0–0.3	0–0.4	0.05–0.2	0.1	0.1	↓	↓
Xanthine	3.7–7.6	1.1–5.6	7.7–10.1	14.2	4.0		
Hypoxanthine	0.1–1.1	0.1–0.7	0.7–2.2	0.8	3.8		
Plasma metabolites, mmol/liter							
S-sulfocysteine		0.031				0.057	0.057
Taurine		0.085				0.123	0.158
Cystine		0.012				0.012	0.013
Uric acid	0.01–0.07	0.020	0.05			0.015	0.015
Sulfite oxidase, units/g protein							
Fibroblasts	↓ <0.8	↓ <0.8	↓ <0.8	↓ <0.8	0.37	↓	↓
Liver	↓ <0.1	↓ <0.1	↓ <0.1				
Xanthine dehydrogenase, units/g protein							
Liver	↓ <0.05	↓ <0.05	↓ <0.05				
Intestine	↓						
References	4	4	4	4		6	6

for less than 5 percent of total sulfur. Sulfite oxidase deficiency in the first patient was established by direct assay of tissues post mortem.[8] In the second case, the deficiency was demonstrated in cultured fibroblasts[10]; the finding of reduced levels of sulfite oxidase activity in fibroblasts from both parents was compatible with autosomal recessive inheritance.

Prenatal Diagnosis. Sulfite oxidase is expressed in amniotic cells, and assay of this activity in cultured cells has been used successfully several times[38,41] for prenatal diagnosis of molybdenum cofactor deficiency. Activities are quite low, however, even in normal cells, such that several million cells are required for each assay. Recently sulfite oxidase was found to be present in chorionic villi at levels approaching those found in liver (about 20 times that which is measured in amniotic cells).[52] Xanthine dehydrogenase activity is also detected in chorionic villi, but the level is very low. The use of chorionic villi obtained at the ninth week of amenorrhea makes very early antenatal diagnosis possible. Of value also is the analysis of *S*-sulfocysteine in amniotic fluid, which can be accomplished very rapidly.[38] Free sulfite has not been detected in amniotic fluid samples.

Pathogenesis

There is as yet no documented evidence which defines the biochemical basis of the pathology associated with molybdenum cofactor deficiency. We have concluded that the severe neurologic abnormalities are a consequence of the absence of sulfite oxidase activity, but it is not clear whether the brain damage occurs as a result of accumulation of a toxic metabolite or perhaps because of a deficit in the reaction product (sulfate). If the damage arises from a toxic metabolite, a possible candidate is sulfite itself. Exogenous sulfite is classified as a slightly toxic compound[33] which is readily oxidized to sulfate in the intestine, lung, and liver. In patients with sulfite oxidase deficiency, however, there is accumulation of endogenously formed sulfite, sometimes added to by an exogenous burden as well, which overflows into the body fluids. It is not known whether plasma sulfite can pass the blood-brain barrier; however, sulfite oxidase is present in the human brain,[8] suggesting that the sulfinate pathway is operative and cerebral sulfite production occurs. Even before birth, accumulation of sulfite takes place in affected fetuses as evidenced by the demonstration of *S*-sulfocysteine in amniotic fluid. The toxicity of sulfite at the biochemical level has been discussed extensively.[53] The compound readily attacks disulfide bonds according to the reaction $RSSR' + HSO_3^- \longrightarrow RSSO_3^- + R'SH$; reaction with free SH groups can occur as well. Sulfite may destroy thiamine,[54] which could lead to disturbed pyruvate metabolism in cell compartments of the central nervous system. Unsaturated fatty acids are susceptible to attack by sulfite with possible compromise of membrane integrity.[55] Also, reactions of sulfite with nucleic acids have been considered, but no direct evidence for mutagenic defects in humans have been shown to date.[53]

The mode of interference of sulfite with processes at the molecular level in sulfite oxidase deficiency is completely unknown. The reaction of sulfite with disulfide bonds or with sulfhydryl groups is a general process which would be expected to occur in all organs and not particularly in certain areas of the brain. However, the central nervous system may be especially sensitive to sulfite with certain parts more affected than others. This could occur either because of local differences in sulfite production or supply of the precursor of cysteine or as the result of disturbance of a delicate chemical process such as neurotransmitter function, perhaps unique to specific areas of the brain. Ocular lens subluxation, a common feature of sulfite oxidase deficiency, might also arise as a con-

8 DG	*9 FM*	*10 KD*	*11 FA*	*12 LB*	*13 TR*	*14 JW*	*15 CK*
↑	17.9	↑	↑	4.4		↑	↑
↑	4.6		2.3			2.5	↑
	5.4		(0.5)				
	2.8	0.22	2.9	↑	1.3		↑
	12.6	10.5	1.2		4.5		
↓	0.27	↓	↓	0.26		↓	
↑	6.9	↑	0.16	0.16?		2.7	
↑				0.65			
0.06		0.035	0.040		0.034		
0.108	0.135–0.297	0.134	0.058	0.064	0.125		
0.001	0	trace	trace	0	trace		
0.04	<0.05	0	0.012	0.023	0.015	0.012	↓
↓ 0	↓ <0.01	↓ 0		↓ 0		↓ 0	
↓ 0	↓ <0.01		↓ 0			↓ 0	
	↓ <0.001		↓ 0			↓ 0	
↓ 0.03							
41		42				17	

sequence of disruption of cystine cross-linking by excess sulfite.[7]

Other metabolites which accumulate as a result of sulfite oxidase deficiency appear to be less toxic than sulfite. Thiosulfate and *S*-sulfocysteine might be considered in a sense as detoxification products. Both are excreted by the healthy blotched Kenya genet[56,57] and are without harmful effects on the central nervous system in this animal. It has been noted by Olney et al.,[58] however, that the injection of *S*-sulfocysteine into rat brain induced neuronal degeneration and swelling of dendritic processes. Thus potential toxic effects from this compound in humans cannot be ruled out. Taurine is a normal metabolite of cysteine oxidation (Fig. 56-4); its concentration is also high in the urine of the genet.

Finally, the possibility that brain damage in sulfite oxidase deficiency occurs as a result of sulfate deficiency must be considered. Even though sulfate is a normal dietary constituent, the extent to which it is made available to a developing fetus or to specific tissues (especially brain) before and after birth is not clear. Sulfite oxidase may in fact be an important source of the sulfate required for formation of the sulfatides of neural tissue. Percy et al.[59] examined the composition and quantities of sulfate esters in brain and kidney tissue of a patient with isolated sulfite oxidase deficiency and also measured excretion of indoxyl-3-sulfate and tyrosine-*O*-sulfate. In the tissues, sulfatides were present in normal concentrations and were of normal composition (i.e., substitution of sulfite for sulfate in the esterified products was ruled out); however, because the brain weight was severely below normal, the total brain content of sulfatides was also severely depressed. Excretion of sulfate esters was in the normal range. Thus, it appears that even though enough sulfate was available to support some brain sulfatide synthesis and myelin production, the diffuse deficiencies of myelin in this and other sulfite oxidase-deficient patients may be at least in part attributable to a lack of sufficient sulfate.

Therapy

Thus far no therapeutic attempts have successfully reversed the clinical symptoms of molybdenum cofactor deficiency. However, certain measures have been implemented which may be of some benefit to individual patients. The first measure is to diminish sulfite production by restriction of the intake of the precursor sulfur-containing amino acids. When designing diets to accomplish this, however, the possibility of inducing molybdenum deficiency as a consequence of long-term administration of a synthetic diet devoid of this trace element should be kept in mind. The administration of sulfite-binding substances such as penicillamine or mercaptoethanesulfonate could also be considered. Extra thiamine may be given to protect against a possible deficiency of this vitamin. In view of the potential ramifications of sulfate deficiency, as have been discussed, it may be beneficial to supplement the diet with inorganic sulfate.

The administration of ammonium molybdate could be useful in cases where deficiency of molybdenum cofactor is the consequence of a defect in metal transport or uptake. Thus far, no patients have been identified with such a defect; however, the isolation of bacterial mutants with pleiotropic loss of several molybdoenzymes which is corrected by growth on high molybdate[60] raises the possibility that a similar defect may arise in the human population. We hope that, as the pathways of molybdenum cofactor biosynthesis and metabolism are elucidated and the defects in human molybdenum cofactor deficiency are defined at the molecular level, the possibility of effective therapy based on administration of stabilized cofactor derivatives or precursors will come closer to being a reality.

We are grateful to the following colleagues for providing information on the patients described in this chapter: Dr. F. A. Beemer, University Children's Hospital, Het Wilhelmina Kinderzieken-

huis, Utrecht; Professor J. M. Saudubray, Hôpital des Enfants Malades, Paris; Dr. G. P. A. Smit, State University, Groningen; Dr. P. Divry and Dr. P. Baltassat, Hôpital Debrousse, Lyon; Professor W. T. Endres, Kinderspital der Universität, München; Dr. M. J. Bennet, Children's Hospital, Sheffield; Dr. R. A. Roesel, Medical College of Georgia, Augusta; Dr. F. Bowyer, Medical Center of Central Georgia, Macon; and Dr. V. E. Shih, Massachusetts General Hospital, Boston. We also thank Dr. K. V. Rajagopalan, Duke University, for his many useful comments and suggestions. This work was supported in part by grant AM35029 from the National Institutes of Health.

REFERENCES

1. DURAN M, BEEMER FA, VAN DER HEIDEN C, KORTELAND J, DE BREE PK, BRINK M, WADMAN SK: Combined deficiency of xanthine oxidase and sulphite oxidase: A defect of molybdenum metabolism or transport? *J Inherited Metab Dis* 1:175, 1978.
2. ABUMRAD NN, SCHNEIDER AJ, STEEL D, ROGERS LS: Amino acid intolerance during prolonged total parenteral nutrition reversed by molybdate therapy. *Am J Clin Nutr* 34:2551, 1981.
3. JOHNSON JL, WAUD WR, RAJAGOPALAN KV, DURAN M, BEEMER FA, WADMAN SK: Inborn errors of molybdenum metabolism: Combined deficiencies of sulfite oxidase and xanthine dehydrogenase in a patient lacking the molybdenum cofactor. *Proc Natl Acad Sci USA* 77:3715, 1980.
4. WADMAN SK, DURAN M, BEEMER FA, CATS BP, JOHNSON JL, RAJAGOPALAN KV, SAUDUBRAY JM, OGIER H, CHARPENTIER C, BERGER R, SMIT GPA, WILSON J, KRYWAWYCH S: Absence of hepatic molybdenum cofactor: An inborn error of metabolism leading to a combined deficiency of sulphite oxidase and xanthine dehydrogenase. *J Inherited Metab Dis* 6, *Suppl* 1:78, 1983.
5. OGIER H, SAUDUBRAY JM, CHARPENTIER C, MUNNICH A, PERIGNON JL, KESSELER A, FREZAL J: Double déficit en sulfite et xanthine oxydase, cause d'encéphalopathie due à une anomalie héréditaire du métabolisme du molybdène. *Ann Med Interne (Paris)* 133:594, 1982.
6. MUNNICH A, SAUDUBRAY JM, CHARPENTIER C, OGIER H, COUDE FX, FREZAL J, YACOUB L, HARBI A, SNOUSSI S: Multiple molybdoenzyme deficiencies due to an inborn error of molybdenum cofactor metabolism: Two additional cases in a new family. *J Inherited Metab Dis* 6, *Suppl* 2:95, 1983.
7. IRREVERRE F, MUDD SH, HEIZER WD, LASTER L: Sulfite oxidase deficiency: Studies of a patient with mental retardation, dislocated ocular lenses, and abnormal urinary excretion of S-sulfo-L-cysteine, sulfite, and thiosulfate. *Biochem Med* 1:187, 1967.
8. MUDD SH, IRREVERRE F, LASTER L: Sulfite oxidase deficiency in man: Demonstration of the enzymatic defect. *Science* 156:1599, 1967.
9. JOHNSON JL, RAJAGOPALAN KV: Human sulfite oxidase deficiency. Characterization of the molecular defect in a multicomponent system. *J Clin Invest* 58:551, 1976.
10. SHIH VE, ABROMS IF, JOHNSON JL, CARNEY M, MANDELL R, ROBB R, CLOHERTY JP, RAJAGOPALAN KV: Sulfite oxidase deficiency. Biochemical and clinical investigations of a hereditary metabolic disorder in sulfur metabolism. *N Engl J Med* 297:1022, 1977.
11. JOHNSON JL, HAINLINE BE, RAJAGOPALAN KV: Characterization of the molybdenum cofactor of sulfite oxidase, xanthine oxidase, and nitrate reductase. Identification of a pteridine as a structural component. *J Biol Chem* 255:1783, 1980.
12. JOHNSON JL, RAJAGOPALAN KV: Structural and metabolic relationship between the molybdenum cofactor and urothione. *Proc Natl Acad Sci USA* 79:6856, 1982.
13. JOHNSON JL, HAINLINE BE, RAJAGOPALAN KV, ARISON BH: The pterin component of the molybdenum cofactor. Structural characterization of two fluorescent derivatives. *J Biol Chem* 259:5414, 1984.
14. KRAMER SP, JOHNSON JL, RIBEIRO AA, MILLINGTON DS, RAJAGOPALAN KV: The structure of the molybdenum cofactor. Characterization of di-(carboxamidomethyl) molybdopterin from sulfite oxidase and xanthine oxidase. *J Biol Chem* 262:16357, 1987.
15. KOSCHARA W: Urothion, ein gelber, schwefelreicher farbstoff aus menschenharn. *Hoppe-Seyler's Z Physiol Chem* 263:78, 1940.
16. GOTO M, SAKURAI A, OHTA K, YAMAKAMI H: Die struktur des urothions. *J Biochem* 65:611, 1969.
17. ROESEL RA, BOWYER F, BLANKENSHIP PR, HOMMES FA: Combined xanthine and sulphite oxidase defect due to a deficiency of molybdenum cofactor. *J Inherited Metab Dis* 9:343, 1986.
18. GARDLIK S, RAJAGOPALAN KV: The state of reduction of molybdopterin. *Fed Proc* 46:1978, 1987.
19. JOHNSON JL, RAJAGOPALAN KV, DUCH DS, NICHOL CA: Metabolic origins of the molybdenum cofactor in animal cells. *Abstracts, 13th International Congress of Biochem* 63:1985.
20. NIEDERWIESER A, BLAU N, WANG M, JOLLER P, ATARES M, CARDESA-GARCIA J: GTP cyclohydrolase I deficiency, a new enzyme defect causing hyperphenylalaninemia with neopterin, biopterin, dopamine, and serotonin deficiencies and muscular hypotonia. *Eur J Pediatr* 141:208, 1984.
21. SCAZZOCCHIO C: The genetics of the molybdenum-containing enzymes, in Coughlan MP (ed): *Molybdenum and Molybdenum-Containing Enzymes*. Oxford, Pergamon Press, 1980, p 487.
22. REISS J, KLEINHOFS A, KLINGMULLER W: Cloning of seven differently complementing DNA fragments with *chl* functions from *Escherichia coli* K12. *Mol Gen Genet* 206:352, 1987.
23. JOHNSON ME, RAJAGOPALAN KV: Involvement of *chlA*, *E*, *M*, and *N* loci in *Escherichia coli* molybdopterin biosynthesis. *J Bacteriol* 169:117, 1987.
24. SHIH VE, MANDELL R, JOHNSON JL: Complementation in variants of sulfite oxidase deficiency. *Ped Res* 18:226A, 1984.
25. KRENITSKY TA, SHANNON MN, ELION GB, HITCHINGS GH: A comparison of the specificities of xanthine oxidase and aldehyde oxidase. *Arch Biochem Biophys* 150:585, 1972.
26. COUGHLAN MP: Aldehyde oxidase, xanthine oxidase and xanthine dehydrogenase: Hydroxylases containing molybdenum, iron-sulphur and flavin, in Coughlan MP (ed): *Molybdenum and Molybdenum-Containing Enzymes*. Oxford, Pergamon Press, 1980, p 119.
27. STIRPE F, DELLA CORTE E: The regulation of rat liver xanthine oxidase: Conversion *(in vitro)* of the enzyme activity from dehydrogenase (type D) to oxidase (type O). *J Biol Chem* 244:3855, 1969.
28. WAUD WR, RAJAGOPALAN KV: The mechanism of conversion of rat liver xanthine dehydrogenase from an NAD^+-dependent form (type D) to an O_2-dependent form (type O). *Arch Biochem Biophys* 172:365, 1976.
29. JOHNSON JL, RAJAGOPALAN KV, COHEN HJ: Molecular basis of the biological function of molybdenum. Effect of tungsten on xanthine oxidase and sulfite oxidase in the rat. *J Biol Chem* 249:859, 1974.
30. OLIVER I, SPERLING O, LIBERMAN U, FRANK M, DE VRIES A: Deficiency of xanthine oxidase activity in colostrum of a xanthinuric female. *Biochem Med* 5:279, 1971.
31. JOHNSON JL: Unpublished observation.
32. BRUNSCHEDE H, KROOTH RS: Studies on the xanthine oxidase activity of mammalian cells. *Biochem Genet* 8:341, 1973.
33. COHEN HJ, DREW RT, JOHNSON JL, RAJAGOPALAN KV: Molecular basis of the biological function of molybdenum. The relationship between sulfite oxidase and the acute toxicity of bisulfite and SO_2. *Proc Natl Acad Sci USA* 70:3655, 1973.
34. RAJAGOPALAN KV: Sulphite oxidase, in Coughlan MP (ed): *Molybdenum and Molybdenum Containing Enzymes*. Oxford, Pergamon Press, 1980, p 241.
35. JOHNSON JL, RAJAGOPALAN KV: Tryptic cleavage of rat liver sulfite oxidase. Isolation and characterization of molybdenum and heme domains. *J Biol Chem* 252:2017, 1977.
36. JOHNSON JL, RAJAGOPALAN KV: Purification and properties of sulfite oxidase from human liver. *J Clin Invest* 58:543, 1976.
37. KESSLER DL, JOHNSON JL, COHEN HJ, RAJAGOPALAN KV: Visualization of hepatic sulfite oxidase in crude tissue preparations by electron paramagnetic resonance spectroscopy. *Biochim Biophys Acta* 334:86, 1974.
38. OGIER H, WADMAN SK, JOHNSON JL, SAUDUBRAY JM, DURAN M, BOUE J, MUNNICH A, CHARPENTIER C: Antenatal diagnosis of combined xanthine and sulphite oxidase deficiencies. *Lancet* 2:1363, 1983.
39. SHIH VE, JOHNSON JL: Unpublished observations.
40. RAJAGOPALAN KV: Xanthine oxidase and aldehyde oxidase, in Jacoby WB (ed): *Enzymatic Basis of Detoxification*. New York, Academic, 1980, p 295.
41. DESJACQUES P, MOUSSON B, VIANEY-LIAUD C, BOULIEU R, BORY C, BALTASSAT P, DIVRY P, ZABOT MT, COTTE J, LAGIER P, PHILIP N: Combined deficiency of xanthine oxidase and sulphite oxidase. Diagnosis of a new case followed by an antenatal diagnosis. *J Inherited Metab Dis* 8, *Suppl* 2:117, 1985.
42. HERVE F, BERGER JP, SOULIER J: Le déficit en sulfite- et xanthine-oxydase: un diagnostic reposant sur deux examens simples. *Ann Pediatr (Paris)* 33:857, 1986.
43. ROTH A, NOGUES C, MONNET JP, OGIER H, SAUDUBRAY JM: Anatomopathological findings in a case of combined deficiency of sulphite oxidase and xanthine oxidase with a defect of molybdenum cofactor. *Virchows Arch (A)* 405:379, 1985.
44. BARTH PG, BEEMER FA, CATS BP, DURAN M, WADMAN SK: Neuropathological findings in a case of combined deficiency of sulphite oxidase and xanthine dehydrogenase. *Virchows Arch (A)* 408:105, 1985.

45. ROSENBLUM J: Neuropathologic changes in a case of sulfite oxidase deficiency. *Neurology* 18:1187, 1968.

46. WADMAN SK, CATS BP, DE BREE PK: Sulfite oxidase deficiency and the detection of urinary sulfite. *Eur J Pediatr* 141:62, 1983.

47. DURAN M, AARSEN G, FOKKENS RH, NIBBERING NMM, CATS BP, DE BREE PK, WADMAN SK: 2-Mercaptoethanesulfonate-cysteine disulfide excretion following the administration of 2-mercaptoethanesulfonate—A pitfall in the diagnosis of sulfite oxidase deficiency. *Clin Chim Acta* 111:47, 1981.

48. COLE DEC, SCRIVER CR: Microassay of inorganic sulfate in biological fluids by controlled flow anion chromatography. *J Chromatogr* 225:359, 1981.

49. CRAWHALL JC, ITIABA K, KATZ S: Separation and quantitation of oxypurines by isocratic high-pressure liquid chromatography: Application to xanthinuria and the Lesch-Nyhan syndrome. *Biochem Med* 30:261, 1983.

50. JOHNSON JL, COHEN HJ, RAJAGOPALAN KV: Molecular basis of the biological function of molybdenum. Molybdenum-free sulfite oxidase from livers of tungsten-treated rats. *J Biol Chem* 249:5046, 1974.

51. JOHNSON JL, JONES HP, RAJAGOPALAN KV: *In vitro* reconstitution of demolybdosulfite oxidase by a molybdenum cofactor from rat liver and other sources. *J Biol Chem* 252:4994, 1977.

52. DESJACQUES P, BALTASSAT P, SAUDUBRAY JM: Use of chorionic villi for the antenatal diagnosis of xanthine oxidase and sulphite oxidase combined deficiency. *J Inherited Metab Dis,* in press.

53. SHAPIRO R: Genetic effects of bisulfite (sulfur dioxide). *Mutat Res* 39:149, 1977.

54. TIL HP, FERON VJ, DE GROOT AP: The toxicity of sulphite I. Long-term feeding and multigeneration studies in rats. *Food Cosmet Toxicol* 10:291, 1972.

55. SOUTHERLAND WM, AKOGYERAM CO, TOGHROL F, SLOAN L, SCHERRER R: Interaction of bisulfite with unsaturated fatty acids. *J Toxicol Environ Heatlh* 10:479, 1982.

56. CRAWHALL JC, SEGAL S: Sulphocysteine in the urine of the blotched Kenya genet. *Nature* 208:1320, 1967.

57. DURAN M, KORTELAND J, BEEMER FA, VANDERHEIDEN C, DE BREE PK, BRINK M, WADMAN SK: Variability of sulfituria: Combined deficiency of sulfite oxidase and xanthine oxidase, in Hommes FA (ed): *Models for the Study of Inborn Errors of Metabolism.* Amsterdam, Elsevier, 1979, p 103.

58. OLNEY JW, MISRA CH, DE GUBAREFF T: Cysteine-S-sulfate: Brain damaging metabolite in sulfite oxidase deficiency. *J Neuropathol Exp Neurol* 34:167, 1975.

59. PERCY AK, MUDD SH, IRREVERRE F, LASTER L: Sulfite oxidase deficiency: Sulfate esters in tissues and urine. *Biochem Med* 2:198, 1968.

60. JOHNSON JL: The molybdenum cofactor common to nitrate reductase, xanthine dehydrogenase and sulfite oxidase, in Coughlan MP (ed): *Molybdenum and Molybdenum-Containing Enzymes.* Oxford, Pergamon Press, 1980, p 345.

INDEX

INDEX

Page references in *italic* indicate tables; page references in **boldface** indicate illustrations.

NOTES

NOTES

NOTES

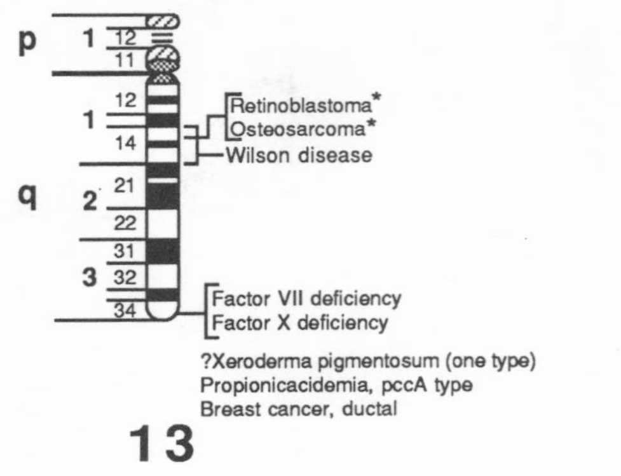

13

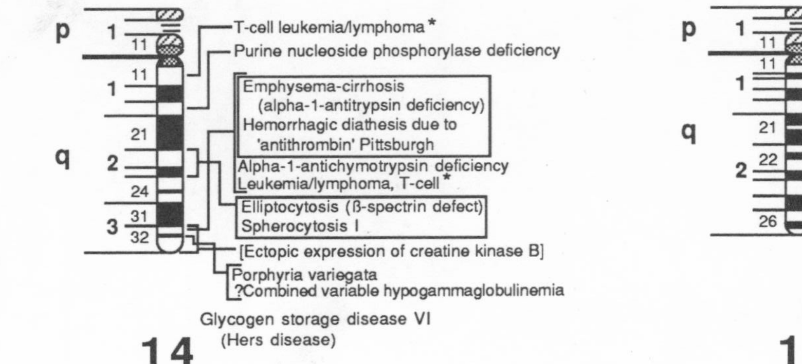

14

p
q
1
11
21
2
22
26
Dyslexia-1
Prader-Willi syndrome•
Isovalericacidemia
?Gynecomastia, familial
Hepatic lipase deficiency
Hemodialysis-related amyloidosis
Tay-Sachs disease
GM2-gangliosidosis, juvenile, adult
[HexA pseudodeficiency]
Glutaricaciduria, type II
Tyrosinase I
Lipoid adrenal hyperplasia, congenital
Xeroderma pigmentosum, group F

15

p
q
13
1
12
11
11
12
2
23
24
Alpha-Heinz body anemias
Alpha-thalassemias
Alpha-erythremias
Alpha-methemoglobinemias
[Glyoxalase II deficiency]
Polycystic kidney disease
Hb H mental retardation syndrome
Cataract, Marner type
Batten disease
Norum disease
Tyrosinemia II
?Aldolase A deficiency
Urolithiasis, 2.8-dihydroxyadenine
[Cystathioninuria]

16

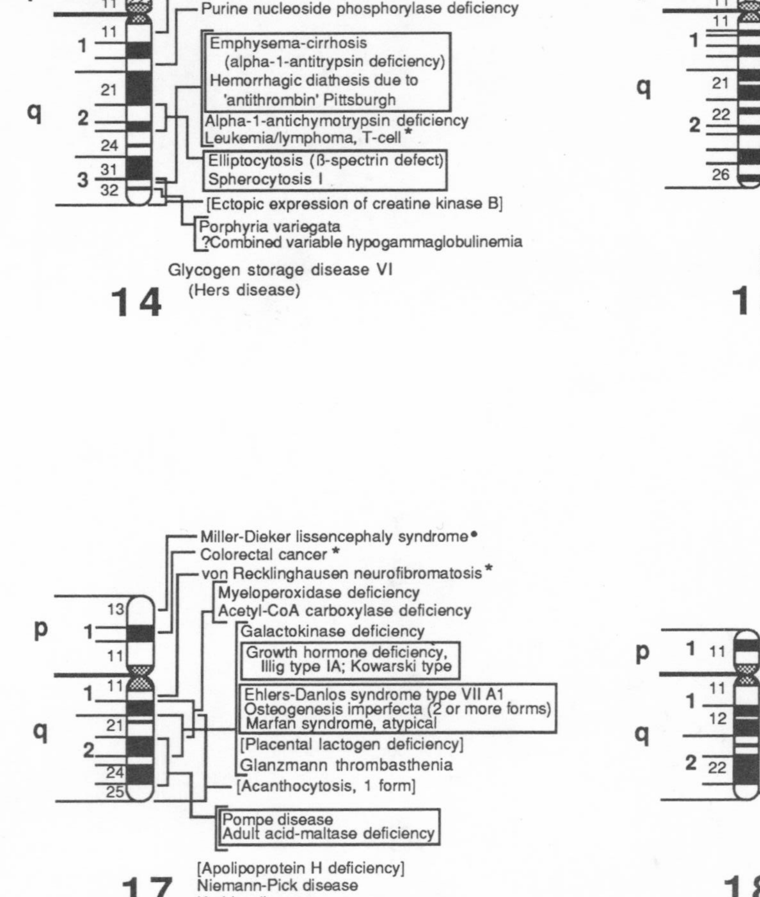

17

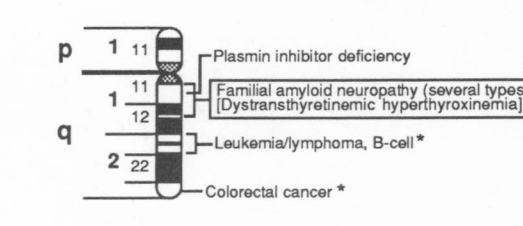

p
q
1
11
11
12
2
22
Plasmin inhibitor deficiency
Familial amyloid neuropathy (several types)
[Dystransthyretinemic hyperthyroxinemia]
Leukemia/lymphoma, B-cell*
Colorectal cancer*

18

(Continued)